GENERAL INFORMATION

How to Use the Engine Performance Section
Engine Performance Safety Precautions
Diagnostic Routine Outline
Service Reminder Indicators
Using Mitchell's Wiring Diagrams
Trouble Shooting
Engine Overhaul Procedures

General Cooling System Servicing
Gear Tooth Contact Patterns
Drive Axle Noise Diagnosis
Anti-Lock Brake Safety Precautions
Wheel Alignment Theory & Operation
Commonly Used Abbreviations
English-Metric Conversion Chart

ACURA

CHRYSLER/MITSUBISHI

FORD MOTOR CO.

GEO

HONDA

HYUNDAI

LATEST CHANGES & CORRECTIONS

NOTE: For Eagle Summit information, see Chrysler/Mitsubishi Contents page.

Asian Volume 2:	Asian Volume 3:	European Volume 4:	Asian & European Vol. 5:
INFINITI	*NISSAN*	*AUDI*	*1994 ASIAN &*
ISUZU	*SUBARU*	*BMW*	*EUROPEAN*
KIA	*SUZUKI*	*JAGUAR*	*ACCESSORIES*
LEXUS	*TOYOTA*	*MERCEDES-BENZ*	*& EQUIPMENT*
MAZDA		*PORSCHE*	*WIRING DIAGRAMS*
		SAAB	
		VOLKSWAGEN	
		VOLVO	

REFERENCE

1994 MITCHELL® IMPORTED CARS, LIGHT TRUCKS & VANS SERVICE & REPAIR

Mitchell®

The Leader in Professional Estimating and Repair Information.

Mitchell International

ACKNOWLEDGMENT

Mitchell International thanks the domestic and import automobile and light truck manufacturers, distributors, and dealers for their generous cooperation and assistance which make this manual possible.

MARKETING

Senior Vice President
David Peterson

Product Managers
Catherine Smith
Daniel D. Fleming

EDITORIAL

Vice President
Thomas Garrett

Manager, Annual Data Editorial
Thomas L. Landis

Manager, Special Product Editorial
Ronald E. Garrett

Administrative Services
Becky Gwyn

Senior Editors
Chuck Vedra
Ramiro Gutierrez
John M. Fisher
Tom L. Hall
James A. Hawes
Serge G. Pirino

Technical Editors
Scott A. Olsen
Bob Reel
David W. Himes
Alex A. Solis
Donald T. Pellettera
Lori Sullivan
Michael C. May
Scott A. Tiner
James R. Warren
James D. Boxberger
Bobby R. Gifford
Linda M. Murphy
Tim P. Lockwood
Dave L. Skora
Donald Lawler
Wayne D. Charbonneau
Sal Caloca
Charles "Bud" Gardner
Dan Hankins
Robert L. Eller
Nick DiVerde
Trang Nguyen
Julia A. Gillis

WIRING DIAGRAMS

Manager
Matthew M. Krimple

TECHNICAL LIBRARIAN

Charlotte Norris

PRODUCT SUPPORT

Manager
Eddie Santangelo

Senior Product Specialist
Robert L. Rothgery

Product Specialists
James A. Wafford
Stephen Hill
Jeffrey H. Lenzkes

GRAPHICS

Manager
Judie LaPierre
Supervisor
Ann Klimetz

Published By

MITCHELL INTERNATIONAL
9889 Willow Creek Road
P.O. Box 26260
San Diego, CA 92196-0260

ISBN 0-8470-1489-4

© 1995 Mitchell International
All Rights Reserved

Printed in U.S.A.

Customer Service Numbers:
Subscription/Billing Information:
1-800-648-8010 or 619-578-6550, Ext. 8907
Technical Information:
1-800-342-4705 or 619-578-6550, Ext. 6112
Or Write: P.O. Box 26260, San Diego, CA 92196-0260

1994 GENERAL INFORMATION
Contents

ALL MODELS   **Page**

We have designed Mitchell® manuals to make them easy to use by organizing service and repair information by manufacturer. Below is a brief description of how to use ENGINE PERFORMANCE section.

INTRODUCTION

Here you will find out how to identify an engine by its Vehicle Identification Number (VIN). The manufacturer's MODEL COVERAGE chart lists each model and its engine option, fuel system, ignition system and engine code. Engine serial number locations are also shown here.

SERVICE & ADJUSTMENT SPECIFICATIONS

Here you will find easy-to-use tables covering *important* specifications. You can find valuable information like spark plug wire resistance, valve clearance, firing orders, etc.

EMISSION APPLICATIONS

Here you will find a chart listing emission control devices used on each model. These are helpful when performing government-required emissions inspections.

ON-VEHICLE ADJUSTMENTS

Here you will find adjustment procedures for checking/adjusting valves, base ignition timing and idle speed. Use this section when performing routine maintenance.

THEORY & OPERATION

Here you will find information on how various engine system and components work. Before diagnosing a vehicle or system with which you are not completely familiar, read this section.

BASIC DIAGNOSTIC PROCEDURES

This is the *first step* in diagnosing any driveability problem. These procedures can help you avoid skipping a simple step early, like checking base timing, which could be costly in both time and money later. Once all systems are "GO" here, proceed to SELF-DIAGNOSTICS or TROUBLE SHOOTING – NO CODES.

SELF-DIAGNOSTICS

Use this information to retrieve and interpret trouble codes accessed from the vehicle's self-diagnostic system. Once information is retrieved, diagnostic procedures are given to help pinpoint and repair computer system/component faults. Also included are steps for clearing trouble codes, once these faults are repaired. If there is a problem not indicated by trouble codes, proceed to TROUBLE SHOOTING – NO CODES.

TROUBLE SHOOTING – NO CODES

This is where to go when you have a problem that does not have a trouble code or when working on a non-computer controlled vehicle. It can help with symptoms and intermittent testing procedures. Procedures in this information should lead you to a specific component or system test.

SYSTEM & COMPONENT TESTING

Here you will find various tests for engine performance systems and their components, such as air induction (turbochargers and superchargers), fuel control, ignition control and emission systems.

PIN VOLTAGE CHARTS

These are supplied (when available) to quicken the diagnostic process. By checking pin voltages at the electronic control unit, you can determine if the control unit is receiving and/or transmitting proper voltage signals.

SENSOR OPERATING RANGE CHARTS

These are supplied (when available) to determine if a sensor is out of calibration. An out-of-calibration sensor may not set a trouble code, but it will cause driveability problems.

WIRING DIAGRAMS

Here you can identify and trace component circuits or locate shorts and opens in circuits. They can also help you understand how individual circuits function within a system.

VACUUM DIAGRAMS

Here we give you underhood views of vacuum-hose routing which can help you find incorrectly routed hoses. Remember, a vacuum leak on computer-controlled vehicle can cause many driveability problems.

REMOVAL, OVERHAUL & INSTALLATION

After you've diagnosed the problem, this is where to go for the nuts-and-bolts of the job. Here you'll find procedures and specifications for removing, overhauling (if available) and installing components.

1994 GENERAL INFORMATION
Engine Performance Diagnostic Routine Outline

WHERE TO BEGIN DIAGNOSING A DRIVEABILITY PROBLEM

STEP 1 – PERFORM BASIC INSPECTION

a) Verify Customer Complaint
b) Perform Visual Inspection
   (See *BASIC DIAGNOSTIC PROCEDURES*)
c) Test Engine Sub-Systems
   (See *BASIC DIAGNOSTIC PROCEDURES*)
   • Mechanical Condition (Compression)
   • Ignition Output
   • Fuel Delivery
d) Check Air Induction System For Leaks
e) Check & Adjust Basic Engine Settings
   (See *ON-VEHICLE ADJUSTMENTS*)
   • Ignition Timing
   • Idle Speed

STEP 2 – CHECK FOR TROUBLE CODES

a) If equipped with self-diagnostics, check for
   trouble codes. (See *SELF-DIAGNOSTICS*)
b) Repair cause of trouble codes.
c) Clear control unit memory.

STEP 3 – DIAGNOSE SYMPTOM

a) If self-diagnostics and trouble codes
   are not available, identify complaint
   by symptom.
b) See trouble shooting procedure to
   identify problem.
   (See *TROUBLE SHOOTING – NO CODES*)

STEP 4 – TEST & REPAIR SYSTEM

a) Perform required tests.
   (See *SYSTEM & COMPONENT TESTING*)
b) Verify complaint is repaired.

- Always refer to Engine Tune-Up Decal in engine compartment before performing tune-up. If manual and decal differ, always use decal specifications.
- Do not allow or create a condition of misfire in more than one cylinder for an extended period of time. Damage to converter may occur due to loading converter with unburned air/fuel mixture.
- Always turn ignition off and disconnect negative battery cable BEFORE disconnecting or connecting computer or other electrical components.
- DO NOT drop or shock electrical components such as computer, airflow meter, etc.
- DO NOT use fuel system cleaning compounds that are not recommended by the manufacturer. Damage to gaskets, diaphragm materials and catalytic converter may result.
- Before performing a compression test or cranking engine using a remote starter switch, disconnect coil wire from distributor and secure it to a good engine ground, or disable ignition.
- Before disconnecting any fuel system component, ensure fuel system pressure is released.
- Use a shop towel to absorb any spilled fuel to prevent fire.
- DO NOT create sparks or have an open flame near battery.
- If any EFI components such as hoses or clamps are replaced, ensure they are replaced with components designed for EFI use.
- Always reassemble throttle body components with new gaskets, "O" rings and seals.
- If equipped with an inertia switch, DO NOT reset switch until fuel system has been inspected for leaks.
- Wear safety goggles when drilling or grinding.
- Wear proper clothing which protects against chemicals and other hazards.

GENERAL INFORMATION
Service Reminder Indicators
1980-94 Asian Cars & Trucks

NOTE: Some 1988-94 vehicles are equipped with a computer malfunction indicator light. If light comes on and remains on while driving, the vehicle requires service. After repairing fault(s) and clearing fault code(s), the malfunction indicator light should go out. Some models may use a dual-function indicator light, which is also used to indicate emission component service is due. After performing required service, reset indicator light.

ACURA

SCHEDULED SERVICE DUE LIGHT

1988-90 Legend – 1) Every 7500 miles, a SCHEDULED SERVICE DUE warning light will come on as a reminder to change oil and oil filter. After servicing is completed, reset warning light.

2) To reset warning light, locate SERVICE RESET button. *See Fig. 1.* With ignition switch in the ON position, press SERVICE RESET button for 3 seconds. To verify reset, turn ignition switch off and on. Light should not come on.

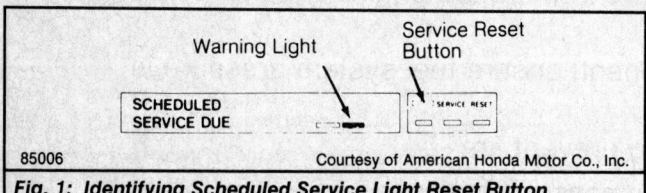

85006   Courtesy of American Honda Motor Co., Inc.

Fig. 1: Identifying Scheduled Service Light Reset Button (1988-90 Acura Legend)

MAINTENANCE REQUIRED LIGHT

1994 Integra, 1991-94 Legend, 1987-94 Legend Coupe & 1992-94 Vigor – 1) At each 7500 mile service interval, the MAINTENANCE REQUIRED light will change from Green to Yellow. If service is not performed (and light is not reset), the MAINTENANCE REQUIRED light will change from Yellow to Red.

2) On Integra, when service has been completed, reset MAINTENANCE REQUIRED reminder light. To reset reminder light, push button located under dash to the right of steering column, and hold for 3 seconds.

3) On all others, when service has been completed, reset MAINTENANCE REQUIRED reminder light. To reset reminder light, turn ignition off. Insert ignition key in slot provided below tachometer. *See Fig. 2.*

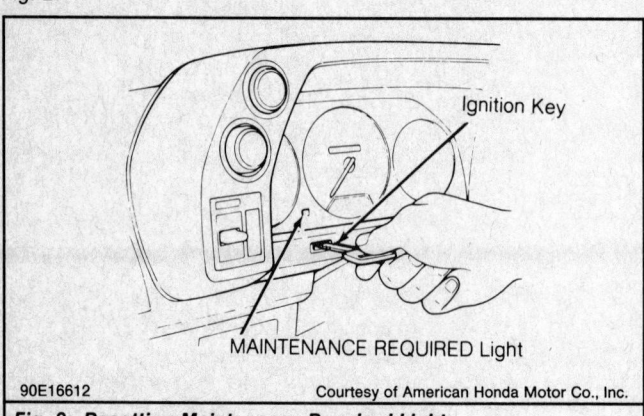

90E16612   Courtesy of American Honda Motor Co., Inc.

Fig. 2: Resetting Maintenance Required Light (Acura & Honda)

CHRYSLER CORP. & MITSUBISHI

EGR/MAINTENANCE REQUIRED WARNING LIGHT

1) On some models, an EGR or MAINTENANCE REQUIRED warning light in dash will come on as a reminder to have EGR system serviced (each 50,000 miles), oxygen sensor replaced (each 80,000 miles), or evaporative carbon canister replaced (100,000 miles).

2) After servicing or replacing components, reset mileage counter. On all models except 1987-94 Pickup and Ram-50, reset switch is located on back of instrument cluster. *See Figs. 3, 4, 6, 7 and 8.*

3) On 1987-94 Pickup and Ram-50, reset switch is on lower right corner of instrument cluster, behind cluster face trim. *See Fig. 5.* Slide switch to opposite side to reset indicator light.

4) Remove warning light bulb after 150,000 mile service on Colt Vista and Colt Wagon. Remove light bulb after 100,000 mile service on Montero. Remove light bulb after 120,000 mile service on Pickup, Ram-50, Van and Wagon.

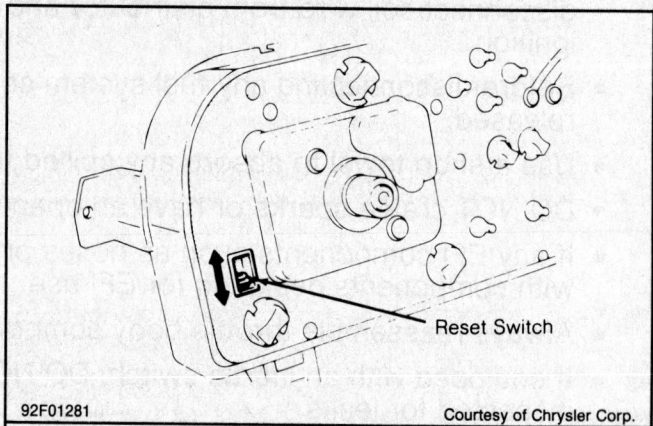

92F01281   Courtesy of Chrysler Corp.

Fig. 3: Locating Warning Light Reset Switch (Colt Vista; Colt Wagon Is Similar)

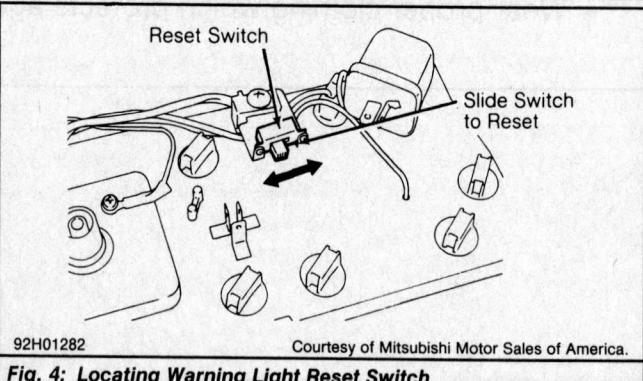

92H01282   Courtesy of Mitsubishi Motor Sales of America.

Fig. 4: Locating Warning Light Reset Switch (1985-86 Pickup & Ram-50)

GENERAL INFORMATION
Service Reminder Indicators
1980-94 Asian Cars & Trucks (Cont.)

GENERAL INFO.
5

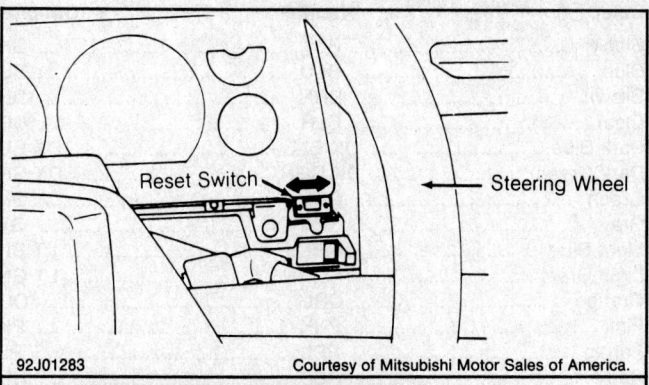

Fig. 5: Locating Warning Light Reset Switch (1987-94 Pickup & Ram-50)

92J01283   Courtesy of Mitsubishi Motor Sales of America.

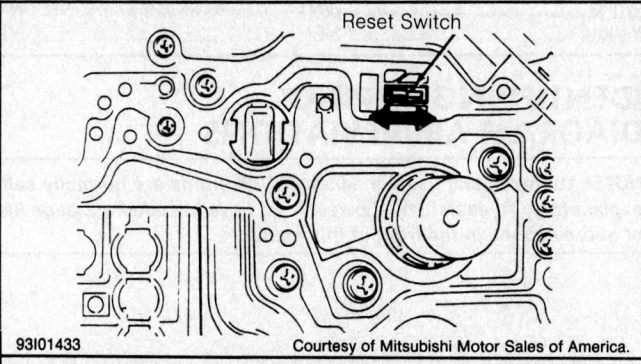

Fig. 6: Locating Warning Light Reset Switch (1983-93 Montero)

93I01433   Courtesy of Mitsubishi Motor Sales of America.

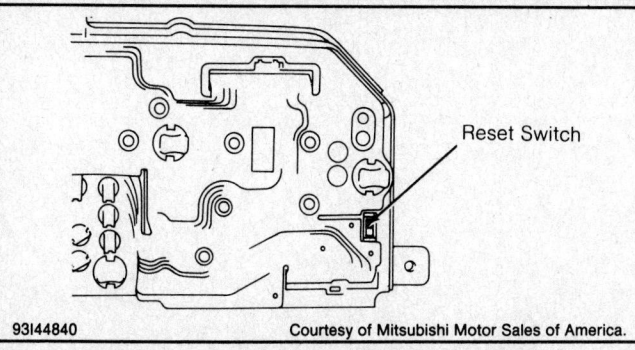

Fig. 7: Locating Warning Light Reset Switch (1994 Montero)

93I44840   Courtesy of Mitsubishi Motor Sales of America.

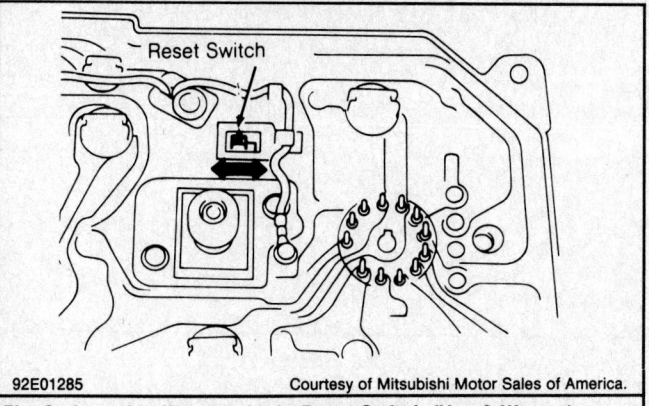

Fig. 8: Locating Warning Light Reset Switch (Van & Wagon)

92E01285   Courtesy of Mitsubishi Motor Sales of America.

DAIHATSU

OXYGEN SENSOR WARNING LIGHT

Rocky – 1) O2S warning light will come on at 80,000 miles to indicate oxygen sensor needs replacement. Warning light cannot be reset. Bulb must be removed to disable warning light after replacing oxygen sensor. To remove bulb, disconnect negative battery cable.

2) Remove steering wheel and instrument panel lower cover. Remove instrument cluster upper trim panel. Remove 4 instrument cluster mounting screws. Disconnect rear window defogger switch and hazard warning switch.

3) Pull gauge assembly outward from instrument panel. Disconnect electrical connectors and speedometer cable. Remove gauge assembly. Remove bulb from O2S light. Reverse removal instructions to install gauge assembly.

DATSUN

See NISSAN.

GENERAL MOTORS

OXYGEN SENSOR WARNING LIGHT

1984-86 Sprint – At 30,000 mile intervals, a SENSOR light in dash will start flashing, indicating oxygen sensor needs replacement. To reset mileage counter (after sensor replacement), locate SENSOR light cancel switch on right side of fuse box. Return cancel switch to OFF position. Start engine to ensure light remains off.

GEO

CHECK ENGINE LIGHT

1989-90 Tracker (Federal) – 1) CHECK ENGINE light functions as a service reminder indicator and emission system service. CHECK ENGINE light will come on each 50,000 miles (PCV and EGR), each 80,000 miles (oxygen sensor) and each 100,000 miles (charcoal canister) to indicate needed emission system service.

2) After servicing and/or replacing components, reset CHECK ENGINE light by sliding cancel switch to its opposite position. The 3-wire cancel switch is located on main wiring harness, behind access panel in instrument panel, below steering column.

HONDA

SERVICE INTERVAL REMINDER

1982-85 Accord – Oil, filter and service interval indicator flags/lights activate every 7500 miles. To reset indicators, insert ignition key into appropriate slot below glowing indicator flags/lights at lower right corner of instrument cluster. Push key in until reminder window changes from Red to Green.

MAINTENANCE REQUIRED REMINDER LIGHT

1991-94 Accord – 1) At each 7500-mile service interval, the MAINTENANCE REQUIRED light will change from Green to Yellow. If service is not performed (and light is not reset), the MAINTENANCE REQUIRED light will change from Yellow to Red.

2) When service has been completed, reset MAINTENANCE REQUIRED reminder light. To reset reminder light, turn ignition off. Insert ignition key in slot provided to the right of tachometer. *See Fig. 2.*

1994 GENERAL INFORMATION
Using Mitchell's Wiring Diagrams

INTRODUCTION

Mitchell® obtains wiring diagrams and technical service bulletins, containing wiring diagram changes, from the domestic and import manufacturers. These are checked for accuracy and are all redrawn into a consistent format for easy use.

In the past, when cars were simpler, diagrams were simpler. All components were connected by wires, and diagrams seldom exceeded 4 pages in length. Today, some wiring diagrams require more than 16 pages. It would be impractical to expect a service technician to trace a wire from page 1 across every page to page 16.

Removing some of the wiring maze reduces eyestrain and time wasted searching across several pages. Today, the majority of Mitchell® diagrams follow a much improved format, which permits space for internal switch details.

Today, the wiring diagram necessary to support a given repair procedure is included within that article. For example, the wiring diagram for an EEC-IV system is included in ENGINE PERFORMANCE for Ford Motor Co., the wiring diagram for cruise control system is included in ACCESSORIES & EQUIPMENT for the specific vehicle manufacturer, and the wiring diagram for the anti-lock brake system is included in BRAKES section for the specific manufacturer.

POWER & GROUND DISTRIBUTION in this manual now contains 3 specific types of wiring diagrams: Data Link Connectors, Ground Distribution and Power Distribution. The Data Link Connectors wiring diagrams show the circuits by which the various on-board computers exchange information, and the diagnostic connectors used for diagnosis and their location. The Ground Distribution wiring diagrams show all vehicle ground points, their location, and the components common to those ground points. The Power Distribution wiring diagrams show the power feed circuits and their source of power.

Wiring diagrams used to support the information in ACCESSORIES & EQUIPMENT are drawn in a "top-down" format. The diagrams are drawn with the power source at the top of the diagram and the ground point at the bottom of the diagram. Component locations are identified on the wiring diagrams. Any wires that don't connect directly to a component are identified on the diagram to indicate where they go.

COLOR ABBREVIATIONS

Color	Normal	Optional
Black	BLK	BK
Blue	BLU	BU
Brown	BRN	BN
Clear	CLR	CR
Dark Blue	DK BLU	DK BU
Dark Green	DK GRN	DK GN
Green	GRN	GN
Gray	GRY	GY
Light Blue	LT BLU	LT BU
Light Green	LT GRN	LT GN
Orange	ORG	OG
Pink	PNK	PK
Purple	PPL	PL
Red	RED	RD
Tan	TAN	TN
Violet	VIO	VI
White	WHT	WT
Yellow	YEL	YL

IDENTIFYING WIRING DIAGRAM ABBREVIATIONS

NOTE: Abbreviations used on Mitchell® diagrams are normally self-explanatory. To assist you, however, we have included a 2-page list of abbreviations in the front of this manual.

IDENTIFYING WIRING DIAGRAM SYMBOLS

NOTE: Standard wiring symbols are used on Mitchell® diagrams. The list below will help clarify any symbols that are not easily understood at a glance. Most components are labeled "Motor", "Switch" or "Relay" in addition to being drawn with the standard symbol.

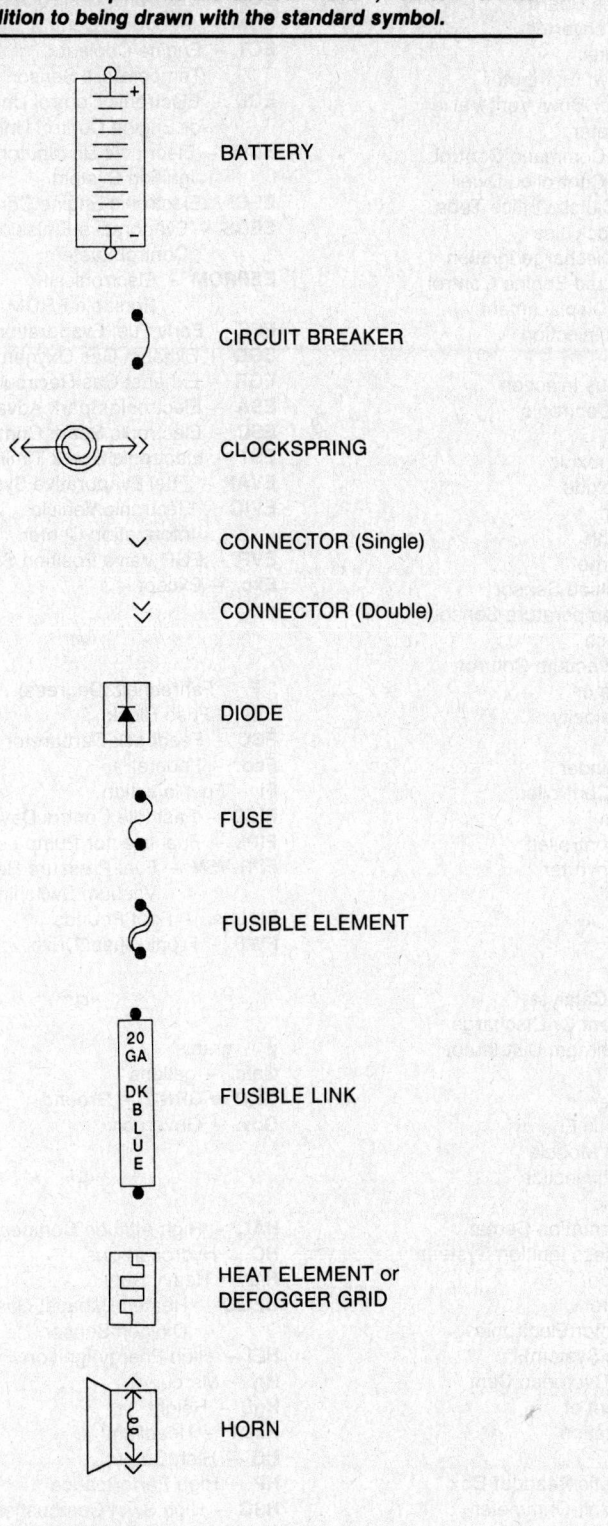

BATTERY

CIRCUIT BREAKER

CLOCKSPRING

CONNECTOR (Single)

CONNECTOR (Double)

DIODE

FUSE

FUSIBLE ELEMENT

20 GA DK BLUE — FUSIBLE LINK

HEAT ELEMENT or DEFOGGER GRID

HORN

KNOCK SENSOR

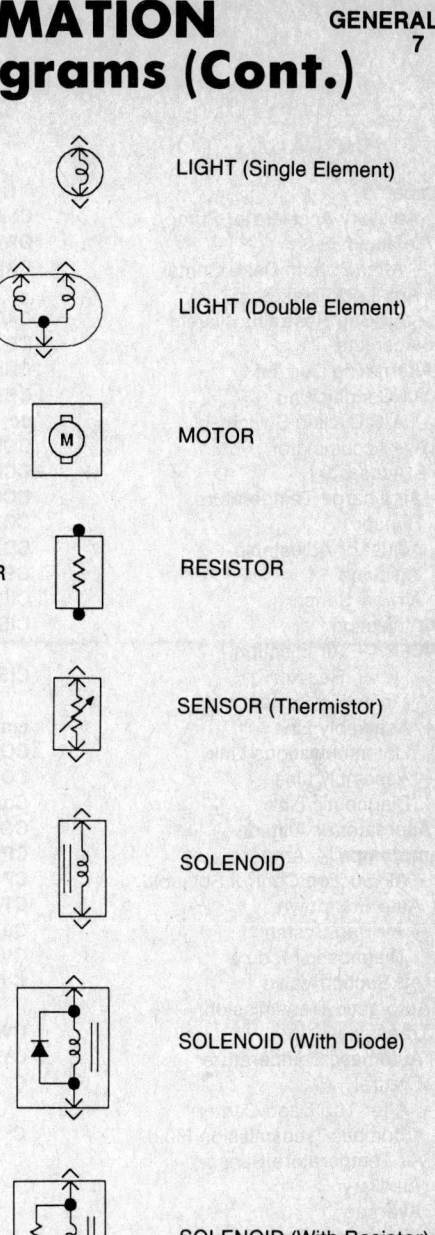

LIGHT (Single Element)

LIGHT (Double Element)

MOTOR

RESISTOR

SENSOR (Thermistor)

SOLENOID

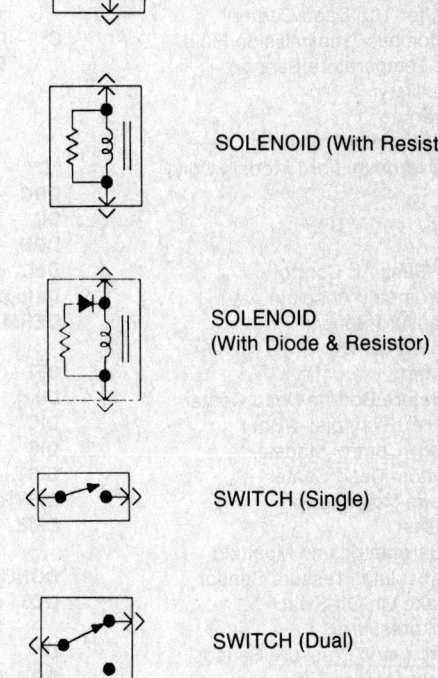

SOLENOID (With Diode)

SOLENOID (With Resistor)

SOLENOID (With Diode & Resistor)

SWITCH (Single)

SWITCH (Dual)

1994 GENERAL INFORMATION
Commonly Used Abbreviations

"A"

A – Amperes
AAP – Auxiliary Accelerator Pump
AB – Air Bleed
ABDC – After Bottom Dead Center
ABS – Anti-Lock Brakes
ABRS – Air Bag Restraint System
Abs. – Absolute
AC – Alternating Current
A/C – Air Conditioning
ACCS – A/C Cycling Switch
ACCUM – Accumulator
ACCY – Accessory
ACT – Air Charge Temperature
    Sensor
ADJ – Adjust or Adjustable
ADV – Advance
AFS – Airflow Sensor
AI – Air Injection
AIR or A.I.R. – Air Injection
    Reactor
AIS – Air Injection System
ALCL – Assembly Line
    Communications Link
ALDL – Assembly Line
    Diagnostic Link
Alt. – Alternator or Altitude
Amp./amp/amps – Ampere
ASCS – Air Suction Control Solenoid
ASD – Auto Shutdown
ASDM – Air Bag System
    Diagnostic Module
ASV – Air Suction Valve
A/T – Automatic Transmission/
    Transaxle
ATC – Automatic Temperature
    Control
ATDC – After Top Dead Center
ATF – Automatic Transmission Fluid
ATS – Air Temperature Sensor
Aux. – Auxiliary
Avg. – Average
AXOD – Automatic Transaxle
    Overdrive (Ford Models Only)

"B"

BAC – By-Pass Air Control
BAP – Barometric Absolute
    Pressure Sensor
BARO – Barometric
Batt. – Battery
BBDC – Before Bottom Dead Center
Bbl. – Barrel (Example: 4-Bbl.)
BCM – Body Control Module
BDC – Bottom Dead Center
BHP – Brake Horsepower
Blst. – Ballast
BMAP – Barometric and Manifold
    Absolute Pressure Sensor
BOO – Brake On-Off Switch
B/P – Backpressure
BPS – Barometric Pressure Sensor
BPT – Backpressure Transducer
BTDC – Before Top Dead Center
BTU – British Thermal Unit
BVSV – Bimetallic Vacuum
    Switching Valve

"C"

° C – Celsius (Degrees)
Calif. – California
CANP – Canister Purge
CARB – California Air
    Resources Board
CAT – Catalytic Converter
CB – Circuit Breaker
CBD – Closed Bowl Distributor
CBVV – Carburetor Bowl Vent Valve
cc – cubic centimeter
CCC – Computer Command Control
CCD – Computer Controlled Dwell
CCOT – Cycling Clutch Orifice Tube
CCW – Counterclockwise
CDI – Capacitor Discharge Ignition
CEC – Computerized Engine Control
CID – Cubic Inch Displacement
CIS – Continuous Injection
    System
CIS-E – Continuous Injection
    System-Electronic
cm – Centimeter
CO – Carbon Monoxide
CO_2 – Carbon Dioxide
Cont. – Continued
CONV – Convertible
CP – Canister Purge
CPS – Crank Position Sensor
CTS – Coolant Temperature Sensor
Cu. In. – Cubic Inch
CVC – Constant Vacuum Control
CV – Check Valve or
    Constant Velocity
CW – Clockwise
CYL or Cyl. – Cylinder
$C^3 I$ – Computer Controlled
    Coil Ignition
C^4 – Computer Controlled
    Catalytic Converter

"D"

"D" – Drive
DBC – Dual Bed Catalyst
DC – Direct Current Or Discharge
DDD – Dual Diaphragm Distributor
Def. – Defrost
Defog. – Defogger
DERM – Diagnostic Energy
    Reserve Module
DFI – Digital Fuel Injection
Diag. – Diagnostic
DIC – Driver Information Center
DIS – Distributorless Ignition System
DIST – Distribution
DISTR – Distributor
DME – Digital Motor Electronics
    (Motronic System)
DOHC – Double Overhead Cam
DOT – Department of
    Transportation
DP – Dashpot
DRB-II – Diagnostic Readout Box
DVOM – Digital Volt-Ohmmeter

"E"

EAC – Electric Assist Choke
EACV – Electric Air Control Valve
EBCM – Electronic Brake
    Control Module
ECA – Electronic Control Assembly
ECM – Electronic Control Module
ECT – Engine Coolant
    Temperature Sensor
ECU – Electronic Control Unit
    or Engine Control Unit
EDIS – Electronic Distributorless
    Ignition System
EEC – Electronic Engine Control
EECS – Evaporative Emission
    Control System
EEPROM – Electronically
    Erasable PROM
EFE – Early Fuel Evaporation
EGO – Exhaust Gas Oxygen Sensor
EGR – Exhaust Gas Recirculation
ESA – Electronic Spark Advance
ESC – Electronic Spark Control
EST – Electronic Spark Timing
EVAP – Fuel Evaporative System
EVIC – Electronic Vehicle
    Information Center
EVP – EGR Valve Position Sensor
Exc. – Except

"F"

° F – Fahrenheit (Degrees)
F/B – Fuse Block
FBC – Feedback Carburetor
Fed. – Federal
FI – Fuel Injection
FICD – Fast Idle Control Device
FIPL – Fuel Injector Pump Lever
FPR-VSV – Fuel Pressure Regulator
    Vacuum Switching Valve
Ft. Lbs. – Foot Pounds
FWD – Front Wheel Drive

"G"

g – grams
Gals. – gallons
GND or GRND – Ground
Gov. – Governor

"H"

HAC – High Altitude Compensation
HC – Hydrocarbons
H/D – Heavy Duty
HEGO – Heated Exhaust Gas
    Oxygen Sensor
HEI – High Energy Ignition
Hg – Mercury
Hgt. – Height
HLDT – Headlight
HO – High Output
HP – High Performance
HSC – High Swirl Combustion
HSO – High Specific Output
HTR – Heater
Hz – Hertz (Cycles Per Second)

"I"

IAC – Idle Air Control
IACV – Idle Air Control Valve
IC – Integrated Circuit
ID – Identification
I.D. – Inside Diameter
Ign. – Ignition
In. – Inches
INCH Lbs. – Inch Pounds
in. Hg – Inches of Mercury
Inj. – Injector
IP – Instrument Panel
IPC – Instrument Panel Cluster
ISC – Idle Speed Control
IVSV – Idle Vacuum Switching Valve

"J"

J/B – Junction Block

"K"

KAPWR – Keep Alive Power
k/ohms – kilo-ohms
    (1000 ohms)
kg – Kilograms (weight)
kg/cm² – Kilograms Per
    Square Centimeter
KM/H – Kilometers Per Hour
KOEO – Key On, Engine Off
KOER – Key On, Engine Running
KS – Knock Sensor
kW – Kilowatt
kV – Kilovolt

"L"

L – Liter
lbs. (Lbs. when used in table) – Pounds
LCD – Liquid Crystal Display
L/D – Light Duty
LED – Light Emitting Diode
LH – Left Hand

"M"

mA – Milliamps
MA or MAF – Mass Airflow
MAFS – Mass Airflow Sensor
MAP – Manifold Absolute Pressure
MAT – Manifold Air Temperature
MCU – Microprocessor Control Unit
MCV – Mixture Control Valve
Mem. – Memory
MEM-CAL – Memory Calibration
    Chip
mfd. – Microfarads
MFI – Multiport Fuel Injection
MIL – Malfunction Indicator Light
MPI – Multi-Point (Fuel) Injection
mm – Millimeters
MPH – Miles Per Hour
mV – Millivolts

"N"

NA – Not Available
N.m – Newton Meter
No. – Number
Nos. – Numbers
NOx – Oxides of Nitrogen

"O"

O_2 – Oxygen
OC – Oxidation Catalyst
OD – Overdrive
O.D. – Outside Diameter
ODO – Odometer
OHC – Overhead Camshaft
O/S – Oversize
oz. – Ounce
ozs. – Ounces

"P"

"P" – Park
PAV – Pulse Air Valve
P/C – Printed Circuit
PCM – PowerTrain Control Module
PCS – Purge Control Solenoid
PC-SOL – Purge Control Solenoid
PCV – Positive Crankcase
    Ventilation
P⁻ Port Fuel Injection
F A-CARB – Programmed
    Carburetor
PGM-FI – Programmed
    Fuel Injection
PIP – Profile Ignition Pick-up
P/N – Park/Neutral
PRNDL – Park Reverse Neutral
    Drive Low
PROM – Programmable
    Read-Only Memory
psi – Pounds Per Square Inch
P/S – Power Steering
PSPS – Power Steering
    Pressure Switch
PTC – Positive Temperature
    Coefficient
PTO – Power Take-Off
Pts. – Pints
Pwr. – Power

"Q"

Qts. – Quarts

"R"

RABS – Rear Anti-Lock Brake
    System
RECIRC – Recirculation
RH – Right Hand
RPM – Revolutions Per Minute
RWAL – Rear Wheel
    Anti-Lock Brake
RWD – Rear Wheel Drive

"S"

SBC – Single Bed Converter
SBEC – Single Board
    Engine Controller
SEN – Sensor
SES – Service Engine Soon
SFI – Sequential (Port) Fuel Injection
SIL – Shift Indicator Light
SIR – Supplemental Inflatable Restraint
SOHC – Single Overhead Cam
SOL or Sol. – Solenoid
SPFI – Sequential Port
    Fuel Injection
SPK – Spark Control
SPOUT – Spark Output
SRS – Supplemental
    Restraint System (Air Bag)
SSI – Solid State Ignition
STAR – Self-Test Automatic
    Readout
STO – Self-Test Output
SUB-O_2 – Sub Oxygen Sensor
Sw. – Switch
Sys. – System

"T"

TAB – Thermactor Air By-Pass
TAC – Thermostatic Air Cleaner
TAD – Thermactor Air Diverter
TBI – Throttle Body Injection
TCC – Torque Converter Clutch
TCCS – Toyota Computer
    Control System
TDC – Top Dead Center
Temp. – Temperature
TFI – Thick Film Ignition
THERMAC – Thermostatic Air
    Cleaner
TPS – Throttle Position
    Sensor/Switch
TS – Temperature Sensor
TV – Thermovalve
T.V. – Throttle Valve
TWC – Three-Way Catalyst

"V"

V – Valve
Vac. – Vacuum
VAF – Vane Airflow
VAPS – Variable Assist
    Power Steering
VCC – Viscous Converter Clutch
VIN – Vehicle Identification Number
VM – Vacuum Modulator
Volt. – Voltage
VOM – Volt-Ohmmeter (Analog)
VRV – Vacuum Regulator Valve
VSS – Vehicle Speed Sensor
VSV – Vacuum Switching Valve

"W"

W/ – With
W/O – Without
WAC – Wide Open Throttle
    A/C Switch
WOT – Wide Open Throttle

CHARGING SYSTEM
CHARGING SYSTEM TROUBLE SHOOTING

PROBLEM
Possible Cause   **Action**

NO START CONDITION
Dead Battery .... Check/Replace Battery
Bad Cable Connections .... Clean/Replace Cables
Ignition Switch/Circuit Fault .... Check Switch/Circuit

CHARGING SYSTEM WARNING LIGHT STAYS ON
Loose/Worn Alternator Belt .... Tighten/Replace Belt
Loose Alternator Connections .... Check/Repair Connections
Warning Light Wiring .... Check/Repair Wiring
Faulty Stator/Diodes .... Test/Repair Alternator
Faulty Voltage Regulator .... Test/Repair Regulator

WARNING LIGHT OFF WITH IGNITION SWITCH ON
Blown Fuse .... Check/Replace Fuse
Faulty Alternator .... Test Alternator
Bad Warning Light Bulb .... Test/Replace Bulb

WARNING LIGHT ON WITH IGNITION SWITCH OFF
Alternator Wiring Short .... Check/Repair Wiring
Faulty Rectifier Bridge .... Test/Repair Alternator

AMMETER INDICATES DISCHARGE
Loose/Worn Alternator Belt .... Tighten/Replace Belt
Loose Alternator Connections .... Check/Repair Connections
Faulty Ammeter .... Test/Replace Ammeter

NOISY ALTERNATOR
Loose Drive Pulley .... Check/Tighten Pulley Nut
Loose Mounting Bolts .... Tighten Mounting Bolts
Worn/Dirty Alternator
  Bearings .... Clean/Replace Alternator Bearings
Faulty Diodes/Stator .... Replace Diodes/Stator

BATTERY WON'T STAY CHARGED
Defective Battery .... Replace Battery
Accessories Left ON .... Ensure Accessories Are OFF
Loose/Worn Alternator Belt .... Tighten/Replace Belt
Loose Alternator Connections .... Check/Repair Connections
Defective Alternator .... Test/Repair Alternator
Short In System .... Check/Repair Short

BATTERY OVERCHARGED
Defective Battery .... Replace Battery
Defective Alternator .... Test/Repair Alternator
Defective Regulator .... Test/Repair Regulator

STARTING SYSTEM
STARTING SYSTEM TROUBLE SHOOTING

PROBLEM
Possible Cause   **Action**

STARTER FAILS TO OPERATE
Dead Battery .... Check/Replace Battery
Bad Connections/Wiring .... Repair Connections/Wiring
Faulty Ignition Switch .... Check Switch Circuit
Faulty Solenoid/Relay .... Replace Solenoid/Relay
Faulty Ground .... Check/Repair Ground

STARTER FAILS TO OPERATE – LIGHTS DIM
Faulty Battery .... Replace Battery
Bad Cable Connections .... Check/Repair Connections
Grounded Starter Windings .... Test/Repair Starter
Faulty Bearing/Bushing .... Replace Bearing/Bushing
Faulty Ground .... Check/Repair Ground
Corroded Terminals .... Clean Terminals

STARTER TURNS – ENGINE DOES NOT
Faulty Starter Drive .... Replace Starter Drive
Broken Drive Housing .... Replace Drive Housing
Faulty Pinion Shaft .... Clean/Repair Shaft
Faulty Flywheel .... Check Flywheel/Starter

STARTING SYSTEM (Cont.)
STARTING SYSTEM TROUBLE SHOOTING (Cont.)

PROBLEM
Possible Cause   **Action**

STARTER DOES NOT CRANK ENGINE
Faulty Starter Drive .... Replace Starter Drive
Broken Drive Housing .... Replace Drive Housing
Missing Flywheel Teeth .... Replace Flywheel
Faulty Ground .... Check/Repair Ground
Frozen Engine .... Check Engine
Liquid-Locked Engine .... Pressure Test Cooling System

STARTER ROTATES ENGINE SLOWLY
Faulty Battery .... Replace Battery
Bad Connections/Wiring .... Repair Connections/Wiring
Grounded Starter Windings .... Test/Repair Starter
Faulty Starter Bearings .... Replace Bearings
Faulty Ground .... Check/Repair Ground
Engine Overheated .... Check Cooling System
Broken Drive Housing .... Replace Drive Housing
Weak Starter Solenoid .... Replace Starter Solenoid

STARTER DRIVE DOES NOT ENGAGE
Bad Solenoid Contacts .... Replace Solenoid
Bad Solenoid Ground .... Test Solenoid Ground

SOLENOID/RELAY DOES NOT CLOSE
Faulty Battery .... Replace Battery
Bad Connections/Wiring .... Repair Connections/Wiring
Faulty Safety Switch .... Replace Safety Switch
Faulty Solenoid/Relay .... Replace Solenoid/Relay

STARTER DRIVE WILL NOT DISENGAGE
Loose Starter Bolts .... Tighten Starter Bolts
Worn Drive End
  Bushing .... Replace Drive End Bushing
Missing Flywheel Teeth .... Check Flywheel/Drive
Faulty Ignition Switch .... Replace Ignition Switch

SOLENOID CLICKS
Weak Battery .... Charge/Replace Battery
Bad Solenoid Contacts .... Replace Solenoid
Bad Connections/Wiring .... Repair Connections/Wiring
Faulty Solenoid .... Replace Solenoid

HIGH CURRENT DRAW
Dragging Armature .... Replace Starter Bushings
Shorted Armature Windings .... Repair Starter

LOW CURRENT DRAW
Worn Starter Brushes .... Replace Brushes
Weak Brush Springs .... Replace Brush Springs
Faulty Engine Ground .... Check Ground Cable
High Resistance In Positive
  Battery Cable .... Replace Cable

STARTER WHINES DURING CRANKING
Starter Alignment .... Check Starter Alignment
Too Much Distance Between
  Starter Drive & Flywheel .... Ensure Flywheel is Okay
       Ensure Starter is Correct

STARTER WHINES AFTER STARTING
Starter Alignment .... Check Starter Alignment
Too Little Distance Between
  Starter Drive & Flywheel .... Ensure Flywheel is Okay
       Ensure Starter is Correct

GAS ENGINE
GAS ENGINE TROUBLE SHOOTING

PROBLEM
Possible Cause   **Action**

ENGINE LOPES AT IDLE
Leaky Intake Gasket	Replace Intake Gasket
Blown Head Gasket	Replace Head Gasket
	Pressure Test Cooling System
Worn Timing Chain/Gears	Replace Timing Chain/Gears
Worn Timing Belt	Inspect/Replace Belt
Worn Cam	Inspect Valve Train
Overheated Engine	Check Cooling System
Clogged PCV System	Check/Clear PCV System
Leaking EGR Valve	Check/Replace EGR Valve
Faulty Fuel Pump	Replace Fuel Pump

ENGINE LACKS POWER
Low Fuel Pressure	Replace Fuel Pump
Leaky Fuel Pump	Replace Fuel Pump
Sticky Valves	Inspect Valve Train
Worn Timing Chain/Gears	Replace Timing Chain/Gears
Worn Piston Rings	Check Compression
Weak Valve Springs	Inspect Valve Train
Worn Cam	Inspect Cam (Lifters)
Blown Head Gasket	Replace Head Gasket
	Check Cooling System
Clutch Slipping	Adjust/Replace Clutch
Overheated Engine	Check Cooling System
A/T Slipping	Inspect/Repair A/T
Vacuum Leaks	Repair Vacuum Leaks
Restricted Exhaust	Clear Restriction

FAULTY HIGH SPEED OPERATION
Low Fuel Pressure	Replace Fuel Pump
Leaky Fuel Pump	Replace Fuel Pump
Sticky Valves	Inspect Valve Train
Incorrect Valve Timing	Inspect Valve Train
Intake Manifold Restricted	Clear Restriction
Worn Distributor Shaft	Replace Distributor

POOR ACCELERATION
Incorrect Ignition Timing	Reset Timing
Leaky Valves	Check Compression
Weak Fuel Pump	Test/Replace Fuel Pump
Clogged Injectors	Clean/Replace Injectors
Excessive Intake Valve Deposits	Clean Valve Deposits

BACKFIRE IN INTAKE MANIFOLD
Improper Ignition Timing	Adjust Timing
Improper Valve Timing	Inspect Valve Train
Crossed Plug Wires	Correct Wire Routing
Carbon Tracking/Crossfire	Inspect Cap/Rotor/Plug Wires
Faulty Plug Wires	Replace Plug Wires
Defective EGR Valve	Replace EGR Valve
Lean Fuel Mixture	Check/Adjust Mixture
Gas in Engine Oil	Check Fuel System
Sticky Intake Valve	Check Valve Train
Vacuum Leaks	Check for Vacuum Leaks

BACKFIRE IN EXHAUST
Vacuum Leak	Repair Vacuum Leak
Faulty Diverter Valve	Replace Diverter Valve
Faulty Choke Operation	Adjust Choke
Exhaust System Leak	Repair Exhaust Leak
Carbon Tracking/Crossfire	Inspect Cap/Rotor/Plug Wires

ENGINE DETONATION/PRE-IGNITION
Too Much Timing Advance	Reset Timing
Faulty Ignition System	Check Ignition System
Faulty Spark Plugs	Replace Spark Plugs
Lean Fuel Mixture	Check Fuel System
Carbon Deposit Build-Up	Remove Carbon
Low Octane Fuel	Try Different Fuel
Compression Too High	Check Compression

GAS ENGINE (Cont.)
GAS ENGINE TROUBLE SHOOTING (Cont.)

PROBLEM
Possible Cause   **Action**

EXCESSIVE OIL CONSUMPTION
Worn Valve Guides/Stems	Inspect Valve Train
Worn Piston Rings	Inspect Engine Block
Worn Cylinder Walls	Inspect Engine Block
Intake Manifold Leak	Replace Gasket
Excessive Bearing Clearance	Inspect Bearings/Crankshaft

NO OIL PRESSURE
Low Oil Level	Add Oil/Check for Leaks
Faulty Oil Pump	Replace Oil Pump
Oil Pick-Up Screen Blocked	Clear Blockage
Loose Oil Pick-Up Tube	Check "O" Ring
Blocked Oil Passages	Inspect Engine Block
Faulty Pressure Relief Valve	Replace Relief Valve
Faulty Oil Light/Gauge	Check Light/Gauge
Worn Engine Bearings	Check/Replace Bearings

LOW OIL PRESSURE
Low Oil Level	Fill to Proper Level
Faulty Oil Pump	Replace Oil Pump
Oil Pick-Up Screen Blocked	Clear Blockage
Loose Oil Pick-Up Tube	Check "O" Ring
Blocked Oil Passages	Inspect Engine Block
Faulty Pressure Relief Valve	Replace Relief Valve
Faulty Oil Light/Gauge	Check Light/Gauge
Worn Engine Bearings	Check/Replace Bearings
Faulty Cooling System	Test Cooling System

HIGH OIL PRESSURE
Faulty Pressure Relief Valve	Replace Relief Valve
Improper Grade of Oil	Change Oil/Grade
Faulty Oil Light/Gauge	Check Light/Gauge

NOISY MAIN BEARINGS
Low Oil Level	Check Oil Level
Low Oil Pressure	Check Oil Pressure
Worn Main Bearings	Inspect Engine Block
Excessive Crankshaft End Play	Check Main Bearings
	Check Thrust Washer
Loose Flywheel/Torque Converter	Check Flywheel/Converter
Worn Vibration Damper	Replace Vibration Damper
Worn Crankshaft	Replace Crankshaft/Bearings
Excessive Belt Tension	Check/Loosen Belts

NOISY CONNECTING RODS
Low Oil Level	Check/Fill Oil Level
Low Oil Pressure	Check Oil Pressure
Worn Rod Bearings	Inspect/Replace Bearings
Worn Crankshaft	Check/Replace Crankshaft/Bearings
Misaligned Rod/Cap	Check Rod/Cap
Excessive Belt Tension	Check/Loosen Belts

NOISY VALVE TRAIN
Low Oil Pressure	Check Oil Level/Pressure
Improper Valve Lash	Check Valve Lash
Loose/Worn Timing Belt/Chain/Gears	Check Belt/Chain/Gears
Worn/Bent Push Rods	Check/Replace Push Rods
Worn Rocker Arms	Check/Replace Rocker Arms
Bent Valve	Check Valve Train/Head
Worn Camshaft	Check Camshaft/Bearings
Broken Valve Spring	Replace Valve Spring
Faulty Valve Lifters	Check Lifters/Camshaft
Worn Valve Guides	Check Valve Train
Missing Valve Keeper	Replace Valve Keeper
Loose Rocker Arm Studs	Replace Studs

DIESEL ENGINE
DIESEL ENGINE TROUBLE SHOOTING

PROBLEM
Possible Cause   Action

ENGINE WON'T CRANK
Bad Batteries .... Test/Replace Batteries
Bad Cable Connections .... Clean/Replace Cables
Bad Starter .... Test/Repair/Replace Starter
Bad Neutral Safety Switch .... Replace Neutral Safety Switch

ENGINE CRANKS SLOWLY
Bad Batteries .... Test/Replace Batteries
Bad Cable Connections .... Clean/Replace Cables
Bad Starter .... Test/Repair/Replace Starter

ENGINE CRANKS NORMALLY, WON'T START
Faulty Glow Plugs .... Test/Replace Glow Plugs
Faulty Glow Plug Controller .... Test/Replace Controller
No Fuel To Cylinders .... Test/Replace Injectors
No Fuel To Injector Pump .... Check Fuel Delivery System
Plugged Air Filter .... Replace Air Filter
Plugged Fuel Filter .... Replace Fuel Filter
Plugged Fuel Tank Filter .... Replace Tank Filter
Faulty Fuel Pump .... Test/Replace Fuel Pump
Fuel Return System Blocked .... Clear Restriction
No Voltage To Fuel Solenoid ...... Check Fuel Solenoid Wiring
Manual Shut-Off Lever Engaged .... Disengage Shut-Off Lever
Incorrect/Contaminated Fuel .... Flush/Refill Tank
Incorrect Inj. Pump Timing .... Reset Inj. Pump Timing
Low Compression .... Check Engine Condition
Faulty Injection Pump .... Test/Replace Injection Pump
Fuel Solenoid Closed
   In RUN Position .... Test/Replace Fuel Solenoid

ENGINE STARTS, WON'T IDLE
Incorrect Slow Idle Setting .... Adjust Slow Idle Setting
Plugged Air Filter .... Replace Air Filter
Faulty Fast Idle Solenoid .... Test/Replace Fast Idle Solenoid
Air In Fuel System .... Bleed Air From System
Fuel Return System Blocked .... Clear Restriction
Glow Plugs Off Too Soon .... Test Glow Plugs
Incorrect Inj. Pump Timing .... Reset Inj. Pump Timing
No Fuel To Injector Pump .... Check Fuel Delivery System
Incorrect/Contaminated Fuel .... Flush/Refill Tank
Low Compression .... Check Engine Condition
Faulty Injection Pump .... Test/Replace Injection Pump

ENGINE STARTS, IDLES ROUGH
Incorrect Slow Idle Setting .... Adjust Slow Idle Setting
Plugged Air Filter .... Replace Air Filter
Fuel Leak at Injection Line .... Repair Fuel Leak
Fuel Return System Blocked .... Clear Restriction
Air In Fuel System .... Bleed Air From System
Incorrect/Contaminated Fuel .... Flush/Refill Tank
Faulty Injector Nozzle .... Test/Replace Injector Nozzle
Low Compression .... Check Engine Condition

ENGINE SMOKES, CLEARS AFTER WARM-UP
Incorrect Inj. Pump Timing .... Reset Inj. Pump Timing
Low Compression .... Check Engine Condition
Faulty Injector Nozzle .... Test/Replace Injector Nozzle
Air In Fuel System .... Bleed Air From System

ENGINE MISFIRES ABOVE IDLE
Plugged Fuel Filter .... Replace Fuel Filter
Incorrect Inj. Pump Timing .... Reset Inj. Pump Timing
Incorrect/Contaminated Fuel .... Flush/Refill Tank

ENGINE WON'T RETURN TO IDLE
Incorrect Fast Idle Setting .... Adjust Fast Idle Setting
Faulty Injection Pump .... Test/Replace Injection Pump
External Linkage Binding .... Check/Repair Linkage
Air In Fuel System .... Repair/Bleed Air From System

DIESEL ENGINE (Cont.)
DIESEL ENGINE TROUBLE SHOOTING (Cont.)

PROBLEM
Possible Cause   Action

ENGINE LACKS POWER
Restricted Air Intake .... Clear Restriction
Faulty EGR Valve .... Replace EGR Valve
Restricted Exhaust System .... Repair Exhaust System
Blocked Fuel Cap Vent .... Replace Fuel Cap
Restricted Fuel Supply
   From Tank to Injection Pump .... Clear Restriction
Incorrect/Contaminated Fuel .... Flush/Refill Tank
Faulty Injector Nozzle .... Test/Replace Injector Nozzle
Low Compression .... Check Engine Condition
Improper Throttle Linkage Adjustment ...... Adjust Throttle Linkage

CYLINDER KNOCKING NOISE
Injector Nozzles Stuck Open .... Test/Replace Injectors
Low Injector Nozzle Pressure .... Test/Replace Injectors
Loose Wrist Pin .... Disassemble Engine
Piston Slap .... Disassemble Engine

ENGINE OVERHEATING
Cooling System Leaks .... Repair Cooling System
Loose/Damaged Belt .... Tighten/Replace Belt
Plugged Radiator .... Rod/Replace Radiator
Defective Fan .... Replace Fan
Restricted Airflow
   Across Radiator .... Clear Restriction
Thermostat Stuck Closed .... Replace Thermostat
Leaking Head Gasket .... Replace Head Gasket
                                 Test/Repair Cooling System

ENGINE WON'T SHUT OFF
Injector Pump Fuel Solenoid
   Does Not Shut Off Fuel Valve .... Test/Repair Fuel Solenoid

VACUUM PUMP TROUBLE SHOOTING

PROBLEM
Possible Cause   Action

EXCESSIVE NOISE
Loose Pump Mounting .... Tighten Pump Mounting
Loose Pump Tube .... Tighten Pump Tube
Faulty Pump Valves .... Replace Pump Valves

OIL LEAKAGE
Loose End Plug .... Tighten End Plug
Bad Seal Crimp .... Remove/Recrimp Seal

COOLING SYSTEM
COOLING SYSTEM TROUBLE SHOOTING

PROBLEM
Possible Cause   Action

OVERHEATING
Insufficient Coolant .... Fill/Pressure Test System
Coolant Leak .... Fill/Pressure Test System
Radiator Fins Clogged .... Remove/Clean Radiator
Cooling Fan Malfunction .... Test Cooling Fan/Circuit
Thermostat Stuck Closed .... Replace Thermostat
Clogged Cooling System
   Passages .... Clean/Flush Cooling System
Water Pump Malfunction .... Replace Water Pump
Fan Clutch Malfunction .... Replace Fan Clutch
Cooling Fan Motor Malfunction .... Test Fan Motor
Cooling Fan Relay Malfunction .... Test Fan Relay
Faulty Ignition Advance .... Check/Replace Advance
Faulty Radiator Cap .... Replace Radiator Cap
Broken/Slipping Fan Belt .... Replace Fan Belt
Restricted Exhaust .... Repair Exhaust System

CORROSION
Impurities in Coolant .... Clean/Flush System

COOLING SYSTEM (Cont.)

COOLING SYSTEM TROUBLE SHOOTING (Cont.)

PROBLEM
Possible Cause   **Action**

COOLANT LEAKAGE

Cause	Action
Damaged Hose	Replace Hose
Leaky Water Pump Seal	Replace Water Pump
Damaged Radiator Seam	Replace/Repair Radiator
Leaky Thermostat Cover	Replace Thermostat Cover
Cylinder Head Problem	Check Head/Head Gasket
Cylinder Block Problem	Check Cylinder Block
Air in Cooling System	Bleed Cooling System
Leaky Freeze Plugs	Replace Freeze Plugs

RECOVERY SYSTEM INOPERATIVE

Cause	Action
Loose/Defective Radiator Cap	Replace Radiator Cap
Overflow Tube Clogged/Leaking	Repair Tube
Recovery Bottle Vent Restricted	Clean Vent

NO HEATER CORE FLOW

Cause	Action
Collapsed Heater Hose	Replace Heater Hose
Plugged Heater Core	Clean/Replace Heater Core
Faulty Heater Valve	Replace Heater Valve

CLUTCH

CLUTCH TROUBLE SHOOTING

PROBLEM
Possible Cause   **Action**

CLUTCH CHATTERS/GRABS

Cause	Action
Incorrect Pedal Adjustment	Adjust Free Play
Worn Input Shaft Spline	Replace Input Shaft
Binding Pressure Plate	Replace Pressure Plate
Binding Throw-Out Lever	Check Throw-Out Lever
	Check Throw-Out Bearing
	Check Bearing Retainer
Uneven Pressure Plate Contact With Flywheel	Align/Replace Worn Parts
Transmission Misaligned	Align Transmission
Worn Pressure Plate	Replace Clutch Assembly
Oil-Saturated Disc	Replace Clutch Assembly
	Repair Oil Leak
Loose Engine Mounts	Replace Engine Mounts

CLUTCH PEDAL STICKS DOWN

Cause	Action
Clutch Cable Binding	Replace Clutch Cable
Weak Pressure Plate Springs	Replace Clutch Assembly
Binding Clutch Linkage	Lubricate Linkage
Broken Clutch Pedal Return Spring	Replace Return Spring

CLUTCH WILL NOT RELEASE

Cause	Action
Oil-Saturated Disc	Replace Clutch Assembly
	Repair Oil Leak
Defective Disc Face	Replace Clutch Assembly
Disc Sticking on Input Shaft Splines	Replace Disc/Input Shaft
Binding Pilot Bearing	Replace Pilot Bearing
Faulty Clutch Master Cylinder	Replace Master Cylinder
Faulty Clutch Slave Cylinder	Replace Slave Cylinder
Blown Clutch Flex Hose	Replace Flexhose
Sticky Throw-Out Bearing Sleeve	Clean/Lube Sleeve
Clutch Cable Binding	Replace Clutch Cable
Broken/Loose Bellhousing	Check Bellhousing

RATTLING/SQUEAKING

Cause	Action
Broken Throw-Out Lever Return Spring	Replace Return Spring
Faulty Throw-Out Bearing	Replace Throw-Out Bearing
Faulty Clutch Disc	Replace Clutch Disc
Faulty Pilot Bearing	Replace Pilot Bearing
Worn Throw-Out Bearing	Replace Throw-Out Bearing
Dry Bearing Retainer Slide For Throw-Out Bearing Sleeve	Lubricate Slide

CLUTCH TROUBLE SHOOTING (Cont.)

PROBLEM
Possible Cause   **Action**

SLIPPING

Cause	Action
Faulty Pressure Plate	Replace Clutch Assembly
Worn Clutch Disc	Replace Clutch Assembly
Incorrect Alignment	Realign Clutch Assembly
Faulty Clutch Slave Cylinder	Replace Slave Cylinder

NO PEDAL PRESSURE

Cause	Action
Leaky Hydraulic System	Check Clutch Master Cylinder
	Check Clutch Slave Cylinder
	Check Clutch Flexhose
Broken Clutch Cable	Replace Clutch Cable
Faulty Throw-Out Lever	Replace Throw-Out Lever
Broken Clutch Linkage	Repair Clutch Linkage

NOISY CLUTCH PEDAL

Cause	Action
Faulty Safety Switch	Check/Replace Switch
Noisy Self-Adj. Ratchet	Replace Ratchet
Dry Throw-Out Bearing	Replace Throw-Out Bearing
Dry Pilot Bearing	Replace Pilot Bearing
Worn Input Shaft	Replace Input Shaft

DRIVE AXLE (RWD)

DRIVE AXLE (RWD) TROUBLE SHOOTING

PROBLEM
Possible Cause   **Action**

KNOCKING OR CLUNKING

Cause	Action
Differential Side Gear Clearance	Check Clearance
Worn Pinion Shaft	Replace Pinion Shaft
Axle Shaft End Play	Check End Play
Missing Gear Teeth	Check Diff./Replace Gear
Wrong Axle Backlash	Check Backlash
Misaligned Driveline	Realign Driveline

CLUNKING DURING ENGAGEMENT

Cause	Action
Side Gear Clearance	Check Side Gear Clearance
Ring and Pinion Backlash	Check Backlash
Worn/Loose Pinion Shaft	Replace Shaft/Bearing
Bad "U" Joint	Replace "U" Joint
Sticking Slip Yoke	Lube Slip Yoke
Broken Rear Axle Mount	Replace Mount
Loose Drive Shaft Flange	Check Flange

CLICK/CHATTER ON TURNS

Cause	Action
Differential Side Gear Clearance	Check Clearance
Worn Clutch Plates [1]	Replace Clutch Plates
Wrong Diff. Lubricant [1]	Change Lubricant

RHYTHMIC KNOCK OR CLICK

Cause	Action
Flat Spot on Rear Wheel Bearing	Replace Wheel Bearing

HUM/LOW VIBRATION AT ALL SPEEDS

Cause	Action
Faulty Wheel Bearings	Replace Bearings
Faulty "U" Joint	Replace "U" Joint
Faulty Drive Shaft	Balance Drive Shaft
Faulty Companion Flange	Replace Flange
Faulty Slip Yoke Flange	Replace Flange

[1] – Limited slip differential only.

1994 GENERAL INFORMATION
Trouble Shooting (Cont.)

WHEEL ALIGNMENT (Cont.)
WHEEL ALIGNMENT TROUBLE SHOOTING (Cont.)

PROBLEM
Possible Cause   Action

FRONT END SHIMMY
Tires Out of Balance	Balance Tires
Radial Belt Separation	Replace Tires
Excessive Wheel Runout	Repair/Replace Wheel
Alignment Out	Check Alignment
Worn Rack Bushings	Replace Bushings
Worn Front Suspension	Check Suspension
Loose/Worn Wheel Bearings	Replace Bearings
Dry/Worn CV Joints	Lube/Replace CV Joints

SUSPENSION
SUSPENSION TROUBLE SHOOTING

PROBLEM
Possible Cause   Action

FRONT END NOISE
Loose/Worn Wheel Bearings	Replace Bearings
Worn Shocks/Struts	Replace Shocks/Struts
Worn Strut Mountings	Replace Mountings
Loose Steering Gear-to-Frame Mounting Bolts	Check Mounting
Worn Control Arm Bushings	Replace Bushings
Dry Ball Joints	Lubricate Ball Joints

FRONT END SHIMMY
Tires Out of Balance	Balance Tires
Excessive Wheel Runout	Repair/Replace Wheel
Alignment Out	Check Alignment
Worn Rack Bushings	Replace Bushings
Worn Front Suspension	Check Suspension
Loose/Worn Wheel Bearings	Replace Bearings
Dry/Worn CV Joints	Lube/Replace CV Joints

PULLS TO ONE SIDE
Incorrect Tire Pressure	Check Pressure
Brake Drag	Inspect Brakes
Mismatched Tires	New Tires
Alignment Out	Check Alignment
Frame Bent	Check Frame Damage
Worn Front Suspension	Check Suspension
Worn Steering Linkage	Check/Replace Linkage
Uneven/Worn Springs	Replace Springs
Loose/Worn Wheel Bearings	Replace Bearings
Power Steering Unbalance	Check Power Steering

SPRING NOISES
Loose "U" Bolts	Check "U" Bolts
Loose/Worn Bushings	Replace Bushings
Worn/Missing Leaf Spacers	Replace Spacers

CAR LEANS/SWAYS ON CORNERS
Loose Stabilizer Bar	Replace Bushings
Worn Shocks/Struts	Replace Shocks/Struts
Worn Spring/Shock	Replace Spring/Shock

STEERING COLUMN
STEERING COLUMN TROUBLE SHOOTING

PROBLEM
Possible Cause   Action

NOISE IN COLUMN
Coupling Pulled Apart	Check Coupling
Column Incorrectly Aligned	Align Column
Broken Lower Joint	Replace Joint
Dry Horn Contact Ring	Lube Contact Ring
Dry Column Bearings	Lube/Replace Bearings
Shaft Snap Ring Loose	Seat Snap Ring
Shroud Hits Wheel	Realign Shroud
Lock Plate Ring Loose	Seat Ring
Tight "U" Joint	Replace "U" Joint

STEERING SHAFT BINDS
Column Misaligned	Align Column
Shroud Misaligned	Align Shroud
Faulty Column Bearings	Replace Bearings
Tight "U" Joint	Replace "U" Joint

SHIFT LEVER BINDS
Column Misaligned	Align Column
Shroud Misaligned	Align Shroud
Faulty Column Bearings	Replace Bearings
Misadjusted Shifter	Adjust Shifter
Damaged Shift Tube	Replace Tube

EXCESS PLAY IN COLUMN
Mounting Bracket Loose	Check Bolts
Broken Weld on Jacket	Repair/Replace Column

IGNITION SWITCH STICKS
Poorly Installed Switch	Check Switch Installation
Worn Key Switch	Replace Key Switch

TILT STEERING COLUMN
TILT STEERING COLUMN TROUBLE SHOOTING

PROBLEM
Possible Cause   Action

STEERING WHEEL LOOSE
Housing/Pivot Pin Loose	Check Clearance
Faulty Anti-Lash Springs	Replace Springs
Upper Bearing Loose	Seat Upper Bearing
Misadjusted Tilt Lock	Adjust Tilt Lock
Loose Support Screws	Tighten Screws
Missing/Broken Bearing Preload Spring	Replace Spring
Housing Jacket Loose	Tighten Screws

PLAY IN COLUMN MOUNT
Loose Support Screws	Tighten Screws/Bracket
Loose Housing Shoes	Check Housing Shoes
Loose Tilt Pivot Pins	Check Pivot Pins
Loose Shoe Lock Pin	Check Shoe Lock

HOUSING SCRAPES ON BOWL
Damaged Bowl	Replace Bowl

WHEEL DOES NOT LOCK
Shoe Seized on Pivot Pin	Check Shoe
Dirty/Damaged Shoe	Clean/Replace Shoe
Faulty Shoe Lock Spring	Replace Spring

WHEEL DOES NOT RETURN
Bound Pivot Pins	Clean/Replace Pins
Damaged Tilt Spring	Replace Tilt Spring
Turn Signal Switch Wires Too Tight	Reset Wires

NOISE WHEN TILTING
Worn Upper Tilt Bumpers	Replace Bumpers
Tilt Spring Rubs Housing	Adjust Springs

DRIVE AXLE (FWD)
DRIVE AXLE (FWD) TROUBLE SHOOTING

PROBLEM Possible Cause	Action
GREASE LEAKING	
Ripped CV Boot	Replace Boot
CLICKING NOISE WHILE CORNERING	
Dry/Worn CV Joints	Replace Outer CV Joints
CLUNK ON ACCELERATION	
Dry/Worn CV Joints	Replace Inner CV Joints
Worn Trans. Gears/Bearings	Inspect Trans.
VIBRATION/SHUDDER ON ACCELERATION	
Dry/Worn CV Joints	Replace CV Joints
Alignment Out	Check Alignment
Incorrect Spring Height	Check Spring Height
SQUEALING OR HUMMING	
Dry/Worn CV Joints	Lube/Replace CV Joints
Faulty Wheel Bearing	Replace Wheel Bearing

BRAKE
BRAKE TROUBLE SHOOTING

PROBLEM Possible Cause	Action
CAR PULLS WHILE BRAKING	
Faulty Caliper	Rebuild/Replace Caliper
Restricted Brake Hose	Replace Hose
Faulty Rear Brakes	Inspect Rear Brakes
Worn Front Suspension	Check Suspension
Alignment Out	Check Alignment
Incorrect Tire Pressure	Check Pressure
Mismatched Tires	New Tires
HIGH-PITCHED SQUEAL (BRAKES OFF)	
Wear Indicators Rubbing	Replace Disc Pads
Faulty Wheel Bearing	Replace Bearing
HIGH-PITCHED SQUEAL (BRAKES ON)	
Worn Brake Pads	Replace Disc Pads
Glazed Rotors	Replace Pads/Resurface Rotor
CHATTERING/PULSATING	
Faulty Rotors/Drums	Check Runout/Parallelism
Loose Wheel Bearings	Check Bearings
Poorly Installed Pads	Correct Installation
EXCESSIVE PEDAL EFFORT	
Faulty Master Cylinder	Rebuild/Replace Cylinder
Faulty Power Booster	Repair/Replace Booster
Worn or Glazed Pads/Shoes	Replace Pads/Shoes
Frozen Caliper Piston	Replace Caliper
Poor Brake Adjustment	Adjust Brakes
Low Fluid Level	Fill Fluid/Inspect System
Air in Lines	Inspect/Bleed System
Heat Boiling Brake Fluid	Reroute Brake Lines
EXCESSIVE PEDAL TRAVEL	
Brake Adjustment	Adjust Brakes
Low Fluid Level	Fill Fluid/Inspect System
Air in Lines	Inspect/Bleed System
Faulty Master Cylinder	Rebuild/Replace Cylinder
Faulty Brake Booster	Repair/Replace Booster
Worn or Glazed Pads/Shoes	Replace Pads/Shoes
Frozen Caliper Piston	Replace Caliper
Booster Actuator Rod Adjustment	Adjust Rod Clearance
Contaminated Fluid	Flush/Bleed System

BRAKE (Cont.)
BRAKE TROUBLE SHOOTING (Cont.)

PROBLEM Possible Cause	Action
BRAKES DRAG	
Faulty Master Cylinder	Rebuild/Replace Cylinder
Restricted Brake Lines	Clear Restrictions
Frozen Parking Brake Cables	Replace Cables
Gear Oil-Soaked Pads/Shoes	Repair Oil Leak Replace Pads/Shoes
Brake Fluid-Soaked Pads/Shoes	Repair Fluid Leak Replace Pads/Shoes
Oil Accidentally Mixed With Brake Fluid	Check/Replace All Cylinders/Calipers/Hoses Flush/Bleed System
BRAKES GRAB/UNEVEN ACTION	
Faulty Combination Valve	Replace Combination Valve
Faulty Power Booster	Repair/Replace Booster
Binding Brake Pedal	Check Pedal

WHEEL ALIGNMENT
WHEEL ALIGNMENT TROUBLE SHOOTING

PROBLEM Possible Cause	Action
PREMATURE TIRE WEAR	
Incorrect Tire Pressure	Check Pressure
Alignment Out	Check Alignment
Worn Front Suspension	Check Suspension
Tires Out of Balance	Balance Tires
Worn Steering Linkage	Check/Replace Linkage
Improper Riding Height	Check/Adjust Riding Height
Uneven/Worn Springs	Replace Springs
Loose/Worn Wheel Bearings	Replace Bearings
Bent Wheel/Rim	Replace Wheel/Rim
Worn/Defective Shocks	Replace Shocks
PULLS TO ONE SIDE	
Incorrect Tire Pressure	Check Pressure
Brake Drag	Inspect Brakes
Mismatched Tires	New Tires
Radial Belt Separation	Replace Tires
Alignment Out	Check Alignment
Frame Bent	Check Frame Damage
Worn Front Suspension	Check Suspension
Worn Steering Linkage	Check/Replace Linkage
Uneven/Worn Springs	Replace Springs
Loose/Worn Wheel Bearings	Replace Bearings
STEERING TOO HARD	
Tight Idler Arm Bushing	Retorque Idler Arm
Tight Ball Joint	Replace Ball Joint
Alignment Out	Check Alignment
Power Steering Fluid Low	Fill/Check Leaks
Power Steering Belt Loose	Tighten Belt
Power Steering Pump Faulty	Repair/Replace Pump
Faulty Steering Gear	Repair/Replace Gear
Faulty Steering Knuckle	Replace Steering Knuckle
Worn Front Suspension	Check Suspension
Incorrect Tire Pressure	Check Pressure
VEHICLE WANDERS	
Incorrect Tire Pressure	Check Pressure
Loose/Worn Wheel Bearings	Replace Bearings
Alignment Out	Check Alignment
Loose Strut Rod (Bushings)	Repair Strut Rod
Faulty Stabilizer Bar	Repair Stabilizer Bar
Worn Spring/Shock	Replace Spring/Shock
Worn Front Suspension	Check Suspension

FUEL INJECTION
FUEL INJECTION TROUBLE SHOOTING

PROBLEM
Possible Cause   **Action**

ENGINE WON'T START

Cold Start Valve Inoperative	Test Cold Start Valve
Poor Vacuum/Electrical Connection	Repair Connections
Contaminated Fuel	Test Fuel for Water/Alcohol
Bad Fuel Pump Relay/Circuit	Test Relay/Wiring
Battery Voltage Low	Charge/Test Battery
Low Fuel Pressure	Test Press. Regulator/Pump
No Distributor Reference Pulse	Repair Ignition System
Coolant Temp. Sensor Defective	Test Temp. Sensor/Circuit
Shorted WOT Switch	Check/Replace WOT Switch
Defective ECM	Replace ECM
No Power To Injectors	Check Injector Fuse/Relay

HARD STARTING

Defective Idle Air Control (IAC)	Test IAC and Circuit
EGR Valve Open	Test EGR Valve/Control Circuit
Stalls With A/C On	Check A/C "On" Signal to ECM
Restricted Fuel Lines	Inspect/Replace Fuel Lines
Poor MAP Sensor Signal	Test MAP Sensor/Circuit
Engine Stalls During Parking Maneuver	Check P.S. Press. Switch

ROUGH IDLE

Poor MAP Sensor Signal	Test MAP Sensor/Circuit
Intermittent Fuel Injector Operation	Check Harness Connectors
Erratic Vehicle Speed Sensor Inputs	Harness Too Close to Plug Wires
Poor O$_2$ Sensor Signal	Test O$_2$ Sensor/Circuit
Faulty PCV System	Check PCV Valve and Hoses

POOR HIGH SPEED OPERATION

Low Fuel Pump Volume	Faulty Fuel Pump/Filter
Poor MAP Sensor Signal	Test Speed Sensor/Circuit

ACCELERATION PING/KNOCK

Poor Knock Sensor Signal	Test Knock Sensor/Circuit
Poor Baro Sensor Signal	Test Baro Sensor/Circuit
Improper Ignition Timing	Adjust Timing
Engine Overheating	Check Cooling System
Poor Quality Fuel	Use Different Fuel
Carbon Build-Up	Decarbon Engine

TURBOCHARGER
TURBOCHARGER TROUBLE SHOOTING

PROBLEM
Possible Cause   **Action**

Faulty Spark Advance System	Check Distributor/Ignition
Defective EGR Operation	Check EGR System
Air Inlet Restriction	Clear Restriction
Excessive Boost	Check/Adjust Boost Pressure
Fuel System Fault	Check Fuel System
Internal Turbo Defect	Repair/Replace Turbo

LOW ENGINE POWER

Faulty Spark Advance System	Check Distributor/Ignition
Defective EGR Operation	Check EGR System
Loose Turbo Bolts	Check/Tighten Bolts

BLUE EXHAUST SMOKE

Oil Inlet Leak	Check/Repair Fittings
Oil Drain Leak/Plugged	Check/Repair Fittings
Turbo Seal Leak	Check/Replace Seal

MANUAL STEERING GEAR
MANUAL STEERING GEAR TROUBLE SHOOTING

PROBLEM
Possible Cause   **Action**

EXCESSIVE STEERING PLAY
Wheel Bearing Misadjusted .... Check Wheel Bearing
Worn/Loose Linkage .... Check Linkage
Worn/Loose Ball Joints .... Check Ball Joints
Loose Pitman Arm .... Check Arm/Gear Splines
Loose Pitman Shaft .... Check Gear
Loose Gear Mount .... Check Gear Mount
Loose Rack Mount .... Check Rack Mount

WHEEL CENTERS POORLY
Steering Gear Adjusted
  Too Tightly .... Check Gear Free Play
Dry Steering Linkage .... Lubricate/Replace Linkage
Dry Ball Joints Bind .... Lubricate/Replace Joints
Binding Rack Slide .... Inspect Rack
Shaft Contacts Seals .... Check Shaft/Replace Seal

POWER STEERING
POWER STEERING TROUBLE SHOOTING

PROBLEM
Possible Cause   **Action**

POWER STEERING PUMP GROWLS/GROANS
Air In System .... Bleed/Check System
Low Fluid Level .... Check Fluid/Leaks
High Pressure in Hoses .... Clear Restriction
Scored Pump Plates .... Check Pump Plates
Worn Cam Ring .... Replace Cam Ring

POWER STEERING PUMP RATTLES
Rotor Slot Vanes Sticking .... Clean/Replace Vanes

POWER STEERING PUMP SWISHES
Faulty Flow Control Valve .... Replace Valve

POWER STEERING PUMP SQUAWKS DURING TURN
Spool Valve "O" Ring Cut .... Replace "O" Ring

POWER STEERING PUMP MOANS/WHINES
Pump Shaft Bearing Scored .... Inspect Bearing
Air In Fluid .... Fill/Bleed System
Low Fluid Level .... Fill/Bleed System
Poor Bracket Alignment .... Correct Alignment

POWER STEERING PUMP HISSES DURING TURN
Internal Leakage in
  Steering Gear .... Check Steering Gear

POWER STEERING PUMP CHIRPS
Loose Power Steering Belt .... Tighten/Replace Belt

POWER STEERING PUMP BUZZES
Bearing Loose on Shaft .... Replace Bearing

POWER STEERING PUMP CLICKS
Broken Vane Springs .... Replace Springs
Worn/Nicked Rotors .... Replace Rotors

FLUID FOAMY/MILKY
Internal Pump Leakage .... Reseal Pump
Power Steering Belt Slipping .... Tighten/Replace Belt
Pump Output Low .... Check Pressure
Faulty Steering Gear .... Check Gear

WHEEL SURGES/JERKS
Low Fluid Level .... Check/Fill Fluid
Power Steering Belt Slipping .... Tighten/Replace Belt
Pump Output Low .... Check Pressure

TUNE-UP
TUNE-UP TROUBLE SHOOTING

PROBLEM
Possible Cause   **Action**

CARBON FOULED PLUGS
Clogged Air Filter .... Replace Air Filter
Incorrect Idle Speed .... Reset Idle Speed
Faulty Ignition Wiring .... Replace Ignition Wiring
Sticky Valves/Worn Valve Seal .... Check Valve Train
Fuel Injection Operation .... Check Fuel Injection

WET/OIL FOULED PLUGS
Worn Rings/Pistons .... Check Block Condition
Excessive Cylinder Wear .... Rebore/Replace Block

PLUG GAP BRIDGED
Combustion Chamber
  Carbon Deposits .... Clean Combustion Chamber

BLISTERED ELECTRODE
Engine Overheating .... Check Cooling System
Loose Spark Plugs .... Clean/Torque Plugs
Over-Advanced Timing .... Reset Timing
Wrong Plug Heat Range .... Install Correct Plug

MELTED ELECTRODES
Incorrect Timing .... Reset Timing
Burned Valves .... Replace Valves
Engine Overheating .... Check Cooling System
Wrong Plug Heat Range .... Install Correct Plug

ENGINE WON'T START
Loose Connections .... Check Connections
No Power .... Check Fuses/Battery

ENGINE RUNS ROUGH
Leaky/Clogged Fuel Lines .... Repair Fuel Lines
Incorrect Timing .... Reset Timing/Check Advance
Faulty Plugs/Wires .... Replace Plugs/Wires

COMPONENT FAILURE
Spark Arcing .... Replace Faulty Part
Defective Pick-Up Coil .... Replace Pick-Up Coil
Defective Ignition Coil .... Replace Ignition Coil
Defective Control Unit .... Replace Control Unit

IGNITION DIAGNOSIS BY SCOPE PATTERN

ALL FIRING LINES ABNORMALLY HIGH
Retarded Ignition Timing .... Reset Ignition Timing
Lean Air/Fuel Mixture .... Adjust Fuel Mixture
High Secondary Resistance .... Repair Secondary Ignition

ALL FIRING LINES ABNORMALLY LOW
Rich Air/Fuel Mixture .... Adjust Air/Fuel Mixture
Arcing Coil Wire .... Replace Coil Wire
Cracked Coil Arcing .... Replace Coil
Low Coil Output .... Replace Coil
Low Compression .... Check/Repair Engine

SEVERAL HIGH FIRING LINES
Fuel Mixture Unbalanced .... Adjust Fuel Mixture
EGR Valve Stuck Open .... Clean/Replace EGR Valve
High Plug Wire Resistance .... Replace Plug Wire
Cracked/Broken Plugs .... Replace Plugs
Intake Vacuum Leak .... Repair Leak

SEVERAL LOW FIRING LINES
Fuel Mixture Unbalanced .... Adjust Fuel Mixture
Plug Wires Arcing .... Replace Plug Wires
Cracked Coil Arcing .... Replace Coil
Low Compression .... Check/Repair Engine
Faulty Spark Plugs .... Replace Plugs

CYLINDERS NOT FIRING
Cracked Distributor Cap .... Replace Cap
Shorted Plug Wires .... Replace Plug Wires
Mechanical Engine Fault .... Check/Repair Engine
Spark Plugs Fouled .... Replace Plugs
Carbon Track in Distributor Cap .... Replace Cap

HARD STARTING
Defective Ignition Coil(s) .... Replace Coil(s)
Fouled Spark Plugs .... Replace Plugs
Incorrect Timing .... Reset Ignition Timing

1994 GENERAL INFORMATION
Engine Overhaul Procedures

DESCRIPTION

Examples used in this article are general in nature and do not necessarily relate to a specific engine or system. Illustrations and procedures have been chosen to guide mechanic through engine overhaul process. Descriptions of cleaning, inspection, and assembly processes are included.

ENGINE IDENTIFICATION

Engine may be identified from Vehicle Identification Number (VIN) stamped on a metal tab. Metal tab may be located in different locations depending on manufacturer. Engine identification number or serial number is located on cylinder block. Location varies with each manufacturer.

INSPECTION PROCEDURES

Engine components must be inspected to meet manufacturer's specifications and tolerances during overhaul. Proper dimensions and tolerances must be met to obtain proper performance and maximum engine life.

Micrometers, depth gauges and dial indicator are used for checking tolerances during engine overhaul. Magnaflux, Magnaglo, dye-check, ultrasonic and x-ray inspection procedures are used for parts inspection.

MAGNETIC PARTICLE INSPECTION

Magnaflux & Magnaglo – Magnaflux is an inspection technique used to locate material flaws and stress cracks. Component is subjected to a strong magnetic field. Entire component or a localized area can be magnetized. Component is coated with either a wet or dry material that contains fine magnetic particles.

Cracks which are outlined by the particles cause an interruption of magnetic field. Dry powder method of Magnaflux can be used in normal lighting and crack appears as a bright line.

Fluorescent liquid is used along with a Black light in the Magnaglo Magnaflux system. Darkened room is required for this procedure. The crack will appear as a glowing line. Complete demagnetizing of component upon completion is required on both procedures. Magnetic particle inspection applies to ferrous materials only.

PENETRANT INSPECTION

Zyglo – The Zyglo process coats material with a fluorescent dye penetrant. Component is often warmed to expand cracks that will be penetrated by the dye. Using darkened room and Black light, component is inspected for cracks. Crack will glow brightly.

Developing solution is often used to enhance results. Parts made of any material, such as aluminum cylinder heads or plastics, may be tested using this process.

Dye Check – Penetrating dye is sprayed on the previously cleaned component. Dye is left on component for 5-45 minutes, depending upon material density. Component is then wiped clean and sprayed with a developing solution. Surface cracks will show up as a bright line.

ULTRASONIC INSPECTION

If an expensive part is suspected of internal cracking, ultrasonic testing is used. Sound waves are used for component inspection.

X-RAY INSPECTION

This form of inspection is used on highly stressed components. X-ray inspection may be used to detect internal and external flaws in any material.

PRESSURE TESTING

Cylinder heads can be tested for cracks using a pressure tester. Pressure testing is performed by plugging all but one of the holes of cylinder head and injecting air or water into the open passage.

Leaks are indicated by the appearance of wet or damp areas when using water. When air is used, it is necessary to spray the head surface with a soap solution. Bubbles will indicate a leak. Cylinder head may also be submerged in water heated to specified temperature to check for cracks created during heat expansion.

CLEANING PROCEDURES

All components of an engine do not have the same cleaning requirements. Physical methods include bead blasting and manual removal. Chemical methods include solvent blast, solvent tank, hot tank, cold tank and steam cleaning of components.

BEAD BLASTING

Manual removal of deposits may be required prior to bead blasting, followed by some other cleaning method. Carbon, paint and rust may be removed using bead blasting method. Components must be free of oil and grease prior to bead blasting. Beads will stick to grease or oil soaked areas causing area not to be cleaned.

Use air pressure to remove all trapped residual beads from component after cleaning. After cleaning internal engine parts made of aluminum, wash thoroughly with hot soapy water. Component must be thoroughly cleaned as glass beads will enter engine oil resulting in bearing damage.

CHEMICAL CLEANING

Solvent tank is used for cleaning oily residue from components. Solvent blasting sprays solvent through a siphon gun using compressed air.

The hot tank, using heated caustic solvents, is used for cleaning ferrous materials only. DO NOT clean aluminum parts such as cylinder heads, bearings or other soft metals using the hot tank. After cleaning, flush parts with hot water.

A non-ferrous part will be ruined and caustic solution will be diluted if placed in the hot tank. Always use eye protection and gloves when using the hot tank.

Use of a cold tank is for cleaning aluminum cylinder heads, carburetors and other soft metals. A less caustic and unheated solution is used. Parts may be left in the tank for several hours without damage. After cleaning, flush parts with hot water.

Steam cleaning, with boiling hot water sprayed at high pressure, is recommended as the final cleaning process when using either hot or cold tank cleaning.

COMPONENT CLEANING

SHEET METAL PARTS

Examples of sheet metal parts are rocker covers, front and side covers, oil pan and bellhousing dust cover. Glass bead blasting or hot tank may be used for cleaning.

Ensure all mating surfaces are flat. Deformed surfaces should be straightened. Check all sheet metal parts for cracks and dents.

INTAKE & EXHAUST MANIFOLDS

Using solvent cleaning or bead blasting, clean manifolds for inspection. If intake manifold has an exhaust crossover, all carbon deposits must be removed. Inspect manifolds for cracks, burned or eroded areas, corrosion and damage to fasteners.

Exhaust heat and products of combustion cause threads of fasteners to corrode. Replace studs and bolts as necessary. On "V" type intake manifolds, sheet metal oil shield must be removed for proper cleaning and inspection. Ensure all manifold parting surfaces are flat and free of burrs.

CYLINDER HEAD REPLACEMENT

REMOVAL

Remove intake and exhaust manifolds and valve cover. Cylinder head and camshaft carrier bolts (if equipped) should be removed only when engine is cold. On many aluminum cylinder heads, removal while hot will cause cylinder head warpage. Mark rocker arm or overhead cam components for location.

Remove rocker arm components or overhead cam components. Components must be installed in original location. Individual design rocker arms may utilize shafts, ball-type pedestal mounts or no rocker arms. For all design types, wire components together and identify according to corresponding valve. Remove cylinder head bolts. Note length and location. Some applications require cylinder head bolts be removed in proper sequence to prevent cylinder head damage. See Fig. 1. Remove cylinder head.

INSTALLATION

Ensure all surfaces and head bolts are clean. Check that head bolt holes of cylinder block are clean and dry to prevent block damage when bolts are tightened. Clean threads with tap to ensure accurate bolt torque.

Install head gasket on cylinder block. Some manufacturers may recommend sealant be applied to head gasket prior to installation. Note that all holes are aligned. Some gasket applications may be marked so that certain area faces upward. Install cylinder head using care not to damage head gasket. Ensure cylinder head is fully seated on cylinder block.

Some applications require head bolts be coated with sealant prior to installation. This is done if head bolts are exposed to coolant passages. Some applications require head bolts be coated with light coat of engine oil.

Install head bolts. Head bolts should be tightened in proper steps and sequence to specification. See Fig. 1. Install remaining components. Tighten all bolts to specification. Adjust valves if required. See VALVE ADJUSTMENT in this article.

NOTE: *Some manufacturers require that head bolts be retightened after specified amount of operation. This must be done to prevent head gasket failure.*

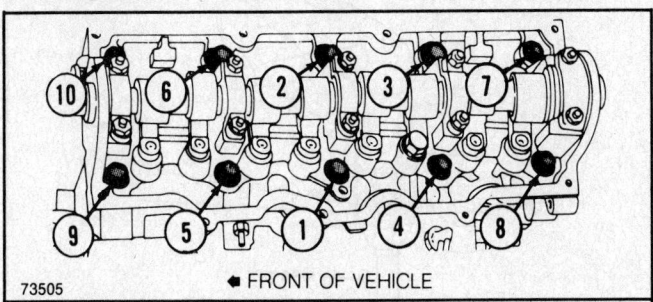

Fig. 1: *Typical Cylinder Head Tightening or Loosening Sequence*

VALVE ADJUSTMENT

Engine specifications will indicate valve train clearance and temperature at which adjustment is to be made on most models. In most cases, adjustment will be made with a cold engine. In some cases, both a cold and a hot clearance will be given for maintenance convenience.

On some models, adjustment is not required. Rocker arms are tightened to specification and valve lash is automatically set. On some models with push rod actuated valve train, adjustment is made at push rod end of rocker arm while other models do not require adjustment.

Clearance will be checked between tip of rocker arm and tip of valve stem in proper sequence using a feeler gauge. Adjustment is made by rotating adjusting screw until proper clearance is obtained. Lock nut is then tightened. Engine will be rotated to obtain all valve adjustments to manufacturer's specifications.

Some models require hydraulic lifter to be bled down and clearance measured. Push rods of different length can be used to obtain proper clearance. Clearance will be checked between tip of rocker arm and tip of valve stem in proper sequence using a feeler gauge.

Overhead cam engines designed without rocker arms actuate valves directly on a cam follower. A hardened, removable disc is installed between the cam lobe and lifter. Clearance will be checked between cam heel and adjusting disc in proper sequence using a feeler gauge. Engine will be rotated to obtain all valve adjustments.

On overhead cam engines designed with rocker arms, adjustment is made at valve end of rocker arm. Ensure valve to be adjusted is riding on heel of cam on all engines. Clearance will be checked between tip of rocker arm and tip of valve stem in proper sequence using a feeler gauge. Adjustment is made by rotating adjusting screw until proper clearance is obtained. Lock nut is then tightened. Engine will be rotated to obtain all valve adjustments to manufacturer's specifications.

CYLINDER HEAD OVERHAUL

CYLINDER HEAD DISASSEMBLY

Mark valves for location. Using valve spring compressor, compress valve springs. Remove valve locks. Carefully release spring compressor. Remove retainer or rotator, valve spring, spring seat and valve. See Fig. 2.

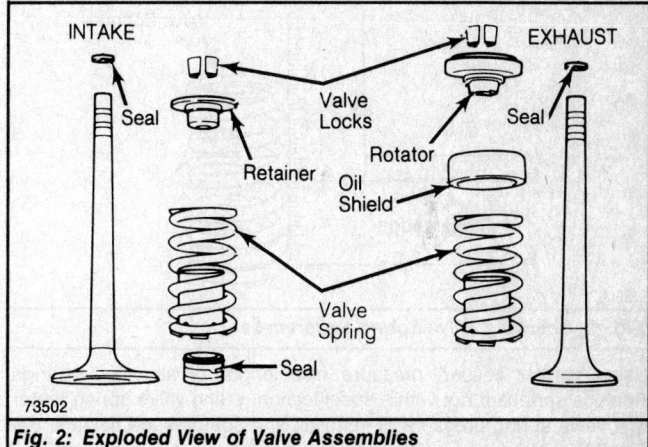

Fig. 2: *Exploded View of Valve Assemblies*

CYLINDER HEAD CLEANING & INSPECTION

Clean cylinder head and valve components using approved cleaning methods. Inspect cylinder head for cracks, damage or warped gasket surface. Place straightedge across gasket surface. Determine clearance at center of straightedge. Measure across both diagonals, longitudinal center line and across cylinder head at several points. See Fig. 3.

On cast iron cylinder heads, if warpage exceeds .003" (.08 mm) in a 6" span, or .006" (.15 mm) over total length, cylinder head must be resurfaced. On most aluminum cylinder heads, if warpage exceeds .002" (.05 mm) in any area, cylinder head must be resurfaced. Warpage specification may vary by manufacturer. If warpage exceeds specification on some cylinder heads, cylinder head must be replaced.

Cylinder head thickness should be measured to determine amount of material which can be removed before replacement is required. Cylinder head thickness must not be less than the manufacturer's specification.

If cylinder head required resurfacing, it may not align properly with intake manifold. On "V" type engines, misalignment is corrected by machining intake manifold surface that contacts cylinder head. Cylinder head may be machined on surface that contacts intake manifold. Using oil stone, remove burrs or scratches from all sealing surfaces.

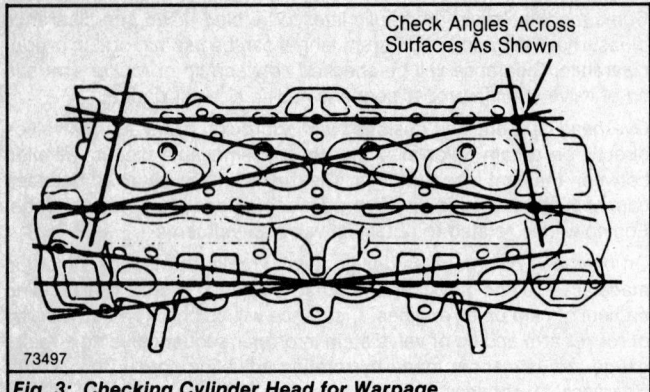

73497
Fig. 3: Checking Cylinder Head for Warpage

VALVE SPRINGS

Inspect valve springs for corroded or pitted valve spring surfaces which may lead to breakage. Polished spring ends caused by a rotating spring indicate that spring surge has occurred. Replace springs showing evidence of these conditions.

Inspect valve springs for squareness using a 90 degree straightedge. See Fig. 4. Replace valve spring if out-of-square exceeds manufacturer's specification.

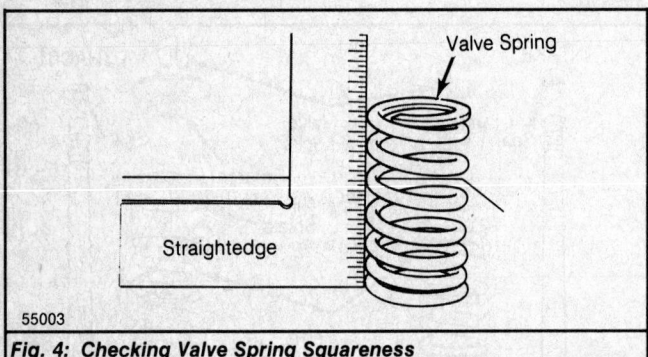

55003
Fig. 4: Checking Valve Spring Squareness

Using vernier caliper, measure free length of all valve springs. Replace springs if not within specification. Using valve spring tester, test valve spring pressure at installed and compressed heights. See Fig. 5.

Usually compressed height is installed height minus valve lift. Replace valve spring if not within specification. It is recommended to replace all valve springs when overhauling cylinder head. Valve springs may need to be installed with color coded end or small coils at specified area according to manufacturer.

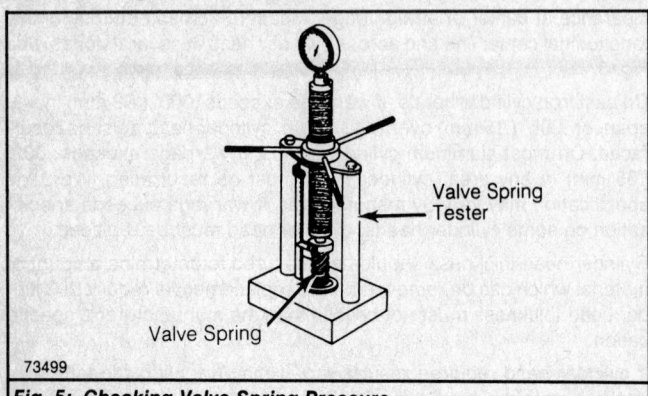

73499
Fig. 5: Checking Valve Spring Pressure

VALVE GUIDE

Measuring Valve Guide Clearance – Check valve stem-to-guide clearance. Ensure valve stem diameter is within specification. Install valve in valve guide. Install dial indicator assembly on cylinder head with tip resting against valve stem just above valve guide. See Fig. 6.

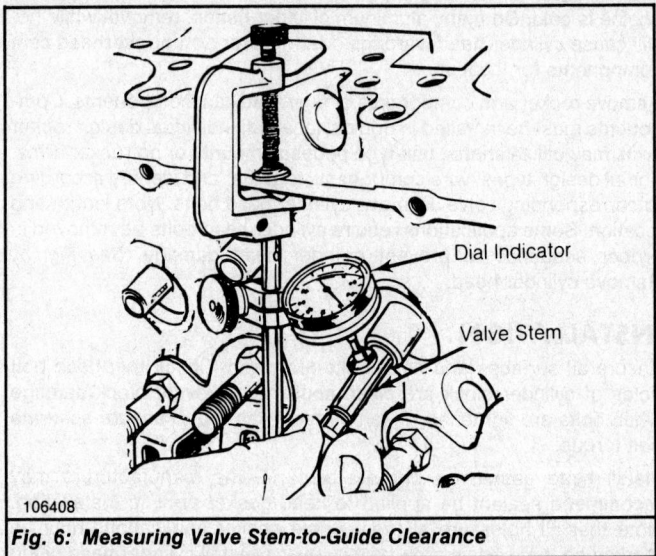

106408
Fig. 6: Measuring Valve Stem-to-Guide Clearance

Lower valve approximately 1/16" below valve seat. Push valve stem against valve guide as far as possible. Adjust dial indicator to zero. Push valve stem in opposite direction and note reading. Clearance must be within specification.

If valve guide clearance exceeds specification, valves with oversize stems may be used and valve guides are reamed to larger size or valve guide must be replaced. On some applications, a false guide is installed, then reamed to proper specification. Valve guide reamer set is used to ream valve guide to obtain proper clearance for new valve.

Reaming Valve Guide – Select proper reamer for size of valve stem. Reamer must be of proper length to provide clean cut through entire length of valve guide. Install reamer in valve guide and rotate to cut valve guide. See Fig. 7.

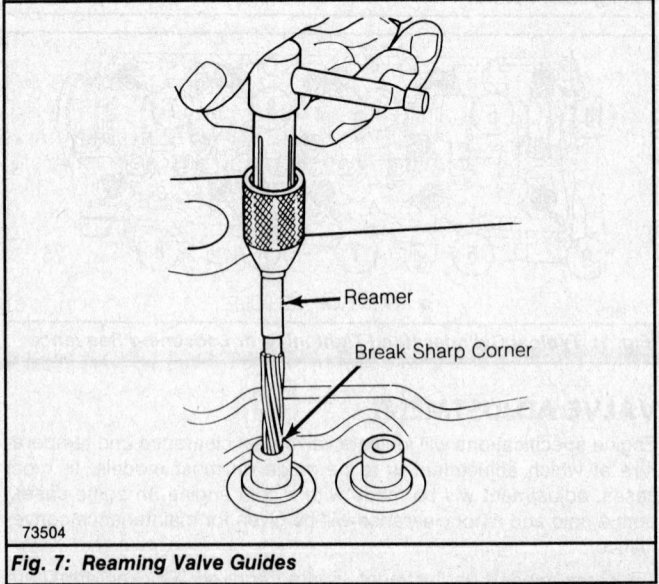

73504
Fig. 7: Reaming Valve Guides

Replacing Valve Guide – Replace valve guide if clearance exceeds specification. Valve guides are either pressed, hammered or shrunk in place, depending upon cylinder head design and type of metal used.

Remove valve guide from cylinder head by pressing or tapping on a stepped drift. See Fig. 8. Once valve guide is installed, distance from cylinder head to top of valve guide must be checked. This distance must be within specification.

Aluminum heads are often heated before installing valve guide. Valve guide is sometimes cooled in dry ice prior to installation. Combination of a heated cylinder head and cooled valve guide ensures a tight guide fit upon assembly. The new guide must be reamed to specification.

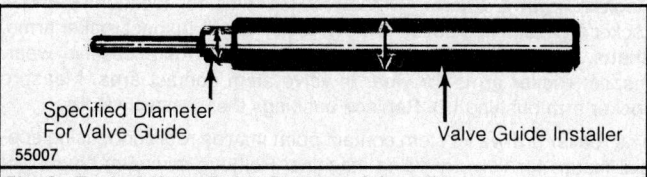

Specified Diameter
For Valve Guide

Valve Guide Installer

55007

Fig. 8: Typical Valve Guide Remover & Installer

VALVES & VALVE SEATS

Valve Grinding – Valve stem O.D. should be measured in several areas to indicate amount of wear. Replace valve if not within specification. Valve margin area should be measured to ensure that valve can be ground. See Fig. 9.

If valve margin is less than specification, the valves will be burned. Valve must be replaced. Due to minimum margin dimensions during manufacture, some new type valves cannot be reground. Some manufacturers use stellite coated valves that must NOT be machined. Valves can only be lapped into valve seat.

CAUTION: Some valves are sodium filled. Extreme care must be used when disposing of damaged or worn sodium-filled valves.

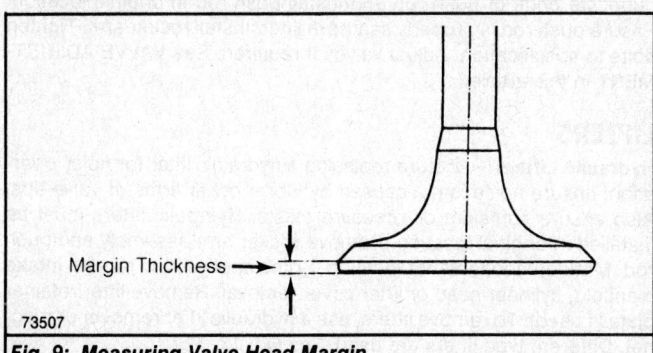

Margin Thickness →

73507

Fig. 9: Measuring Valve Head Margin

Resurface valve to proper angle specification using valve grinding machine. Follow manufacturer's instructions for valve grinding machine. Specifications may indicate a different valve face angle than seat angle.

Measure valve margin after grinding. Replace valve if not within specification. Valve stem tip can be refinished using valve grinding machine.

Valve Lapping – During valve lapping of recently designed valves, be sure to follow manufacturer's recommendations. Surface hardening and materials used with some valves do not permit lapping. Lapping process will remove excessive amounts of the hardened surface.

Valve lapping is done to ensure adequate sealing between valve face and seat. Use either a hand drill or lapping stick with suction cup attached.

Moisten and attach suction cup to valve. Lubricate valve stem and guide. Apply a thin coat of fine valve grinding compound between valve and seat. Rotate lapping tool between the palms or with hand drill.

Lift valve upward off the seat and change position often. This is done to prevent grooving of valve seat. Lap valve until a smooth polished seat is obtained. Thoroughly clean grinding compound from components. Valve-to-valve seat concentricity should be checked. See VALVE SEAT CONCENTRICITY.

CAUTION: Valve guides must be in good condition and free of carbon deposits prior to valve seat grinding. Some engines contain an induction hardened valve seat. Excessive material removal will damage valve seats.

Valve Seat Grinding – Select coarse stone of correct size and angle for seat to be ground. Ensure stone is true and has a smooth surface. Select correct size pilot for valve guide dimension. Install pilot in valve guide. Lightly lubricate pilot shaft. Install stone on pilot. Move stone off and on the seat approximately 2 times per second during grinding operation.

Select a fine stone to finish grinding operation. Various angle grinding stones are used to center and narrow the valve seat as required. See Fig. 10.

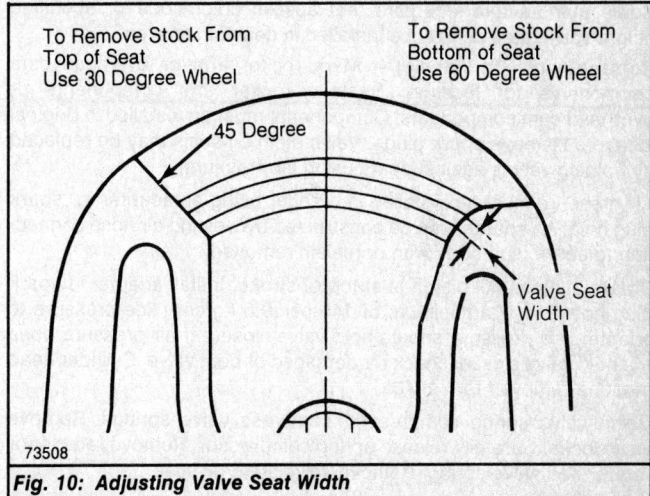

To Remove Stock From
Top of Seat
Use 30 Degree Wheel

To Remove Stock From
Bottom of Seat
Use 60 Degree Wheel

45 Degree

Valve Seat
Width

73508

Fig. 10: Adjusting Valve Seat Width

Valve Seat Replacement – Replacement of valve seat inserts is done by cutting out the old insert and machining an oversize insert bore. Replacement oversize insert is usually cooled and the cylinder head is sometimes warmed. Valve seat is pressed into the head. This operation requires specialized machine shop equipment.

Valve Seat Concentricity – Using dial gauge, install gauge pilot in valve guide. Position gauge arm on the valve seat. Adjust dial indicator to zero. Rotate arm 360 degrees and note reading. Runout should not exceed specification.

To check valve-to-valve seat concentricity, coat valve face lightly with Prussian Blue dye. Install valve and rotate it on valve seat. If pattern is even and entire seat is coated at valve contact point, valve is concentric with the valve seat.

CYLINDER HEAD REASSEMBLY

Valve Stem Installed Height – Valve stem installed height must be checked when new valves are installed or when valves or valve seats have been ground. Install valve in valve guide. Measure distance from tip of valve stem to spring seat. See Fig. 11. Distance must be within specification to allow sufficient clearance for valve operation.

Remove valve and grind valve stem tip if height exceeds specification. Valve tips are surface hardened. DO NOT remove more than .010" (.25 mm) from tip. Chamfer sharp edge of reground valve tip. Recheck valve stem installed height.

VALVE STEM OIL SEALS

Valve stem oil seals must be installed on valve stem. See Fig. 2. Seals are needed due to pressure differential at the ends of valve guides. Atmospheric pressure above intake guide, combined with manifold vacuum below guide, causes oil to be drawn into the cylinder.

Exhaust guides also have pressure differential created by exhaust gas flowing past the guide, creating a low pressure area. This low pressure area draws oil into the exhaust system.

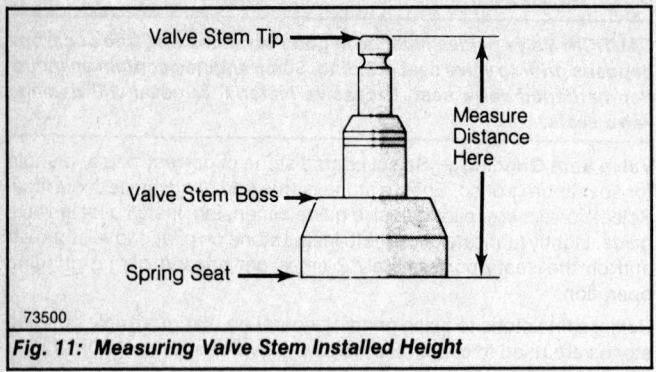

Fig. 11: Measuring Valve Stem Installed Height

Some manufacturers require that special color code or specified height valve stem oil seal be installed in designated area.

Replacement (On-Vehicle) – Mark rocker arm or overhead cam components for location. Remove rocker arm components or overhead cam components. Components must be installed in original location. Remove spark plugs. Valve stem oil seals may be replaced by holding valves against seats using air pressure.

Air pressure must be installed in cylinder using an adapter for spark plug hole. An adapter can be constructed by welding air hose connection to spark plug body with porcelain removed.

Rotate engine until piston is at top of stroke. Install adapter in spark plug hole. Apply a minimum of 140 psi (9.8 kg/cm²) line pressure to adapter. Air pressure should hold valve closed. If air pressure does not hold valve closed, check for damaged or bent valve. Cylinder head must be removed for service.

Using valve spring compressor, compress valve springs. Remove valve locks. Carefully release spring compressor. Remove retainer or rotator and valve spring. Remove valve stem oil seal.

If oversize valves have been installed, oversize oil seals must be used. Coat valve stem with engine oil. Install protective sleeve over end of valve stem. Install new oil seal over valve stem and seat on valve guide. Remove protective sleeve. Install spring seat, valve spring and retainer or rotator. Compress spring and install valve locks. Remove spring compressor. Ensure valve locks are fully seated.

Install rocker arms or overhead cam components. Tighten all bolts to specification. Adjust valves if required. Remove adapter. Install spark plugs, valve cover and gasket.

VALVE SPRING INSTALLED HEIGHT

Valve spring installed height should be checked during reassembly. Measure height from lower edge of valve spring to the upper edge. DO NOT include valve spring seat or retainer. Distance must be within specification. If valves and/or seats have been ground, a valve spring shim may be required to correct spring height. See Fig. 12.

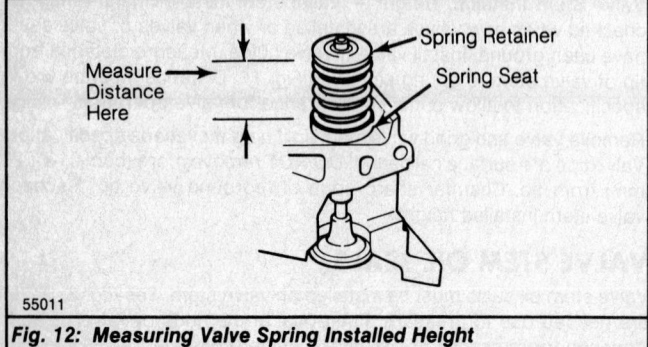

Fig. 12: Measuring Valve Spring Installed Height

ROCKER ARMS & ASSEMBLIES

Rocker Studs – Rocker studs are either threaded or pressed in place. Threaded studs are removed by locking 2 nuts on the stud.

Unscrew the stud by turning the jam nut. Coat new stud threads with Loctite and install. Tighten to specification.

Pressed-in stud can be removed using a stud puller. Ream stud bore to proper specification and press in a new oversize stud. Pressed-in studs are often replaced by cutting threads in the stud bore to accept a threaded stud.

Rocker Arms & Shafts – Mark rocker arms for location. Remove rocker arm retaining bolts. Remove rocker arms. Inspect rocker arms, shafts, bushings and pivot balls (if equipped) for excessive wear. Inspect rocker arms for wear in valve stem contact area. Measure rocker arm bushing I.D. Replace bushings if excessively worn.

The rocker arm valve stem contact point may be reground, using special fixture for valve grinding machine. Remove minimum amount of material as possible. Ensure all oil passages are clear. Install rocker arm components in original location. Ensure rocker arm is properly seated in push rod. Tighten bolts to specification. Adjust valves if required. See VALVE ADJUSTMENT in this article.

PUSH RODS

Remove rocker arms. Mark push rods for location. Remove push rods. Push rods can be steel or aluminum, solid or hollow. Hollow push rods must be internally cleaned to ensure oil passage to rocker arms is cleaned. Check push rods for damage, such as loose ends on steel tipped aluminum types.

Check push rod for straightness. Roll push rod on a flat surface. Using feeler gauge, check clearance at center. Replace push rod if bent. The push rod can also be supported at each end and rotated. A dial indicator is used to detect a bent area in the push rod.

Lubricate ends of push rod and install push rod in original location. Ensure push rod is properly seated in lifter. Install rocker arm. Tighten bolts to specification. Adjust valves if required. See VALVE ADJUSTMENT in this article.

LIFTERS

Hydraulic Lifters – Before replacing a hydraulic lifter for noisy operation, ensure noise is not caused by worn rocker arms or valve tips. Also ensure sufficient oil pressure exists. Hydraulic lifters must be installed in original location. Remove rocker arm assembly and push rod. Mark components for location. Some applications require intake manifold, cylinder head or lifter cover removal. Remove lifter retainer plate (if used). To remove lifters, use a hydraulic lifter remover or magnet. Different type lifters are used. See Fig. 13.

On sticking lifters, disassemble and clean lifter. DO NOT mix lifter components or positions. Parts are select-fitted and are not interchangeable. Inspect all components for wear. Note amount of wear in lifter body-to-camshaft contact area. Surface must have smooth and convex contact face. If wear is apparent, carefully inspect cam lobe.

Inspect push rod contact area and lifter body for scoring or signs of wear. If body is scored, inspect lifter bore for damage and lack of lubrication. On roller type lifters, inspect roller for flaking, pitting, loss of needle bearings and roughness during rotation.

Measure lifter body O.D. in several areas. Measure lifter bore I.D. Ensure components or oil clearance is within specification. Some models offer oversize lifters. Replace lifter if damaged.

If lifter check valve is not operating, obstructions may be preventing it from closing or valve spring may be broken. Clean or replace components as necessary.

Check plunger operation. Plunger should drop to bottom of the body by its own weight when assembled dry. If plunger is not free, soak lifter in solvent to dissolve deposits.

Lifter leak-down test can be performed on lifter. Lifter must be filled with special test oil. New lifters contain special test oil. Using lifter leak-down tester, perform leak-down test following manufacturer's instructions. If leak-down time is not within specifications, replace lifter assembly.

Lifters should be soaked in clean engine oil several hours prior to installation. Coat lifter base, roller (if equipped) and lifter body with ample amount of Molykote or camshaft lubricant. *See Fig. 13.* Install lifter in original location. Install remaining components. Valve lash adjustment is not required on most hydraulic lifters. Preload of hydraulic lifter is automatic. Some models may require adjustment.

NOTE: Some manufacturers require that a crankcase conditioner be added to engine oil and engine operated for specified amount of time to aid in lifter break-in procedure if new lifters or camshaft are installed.

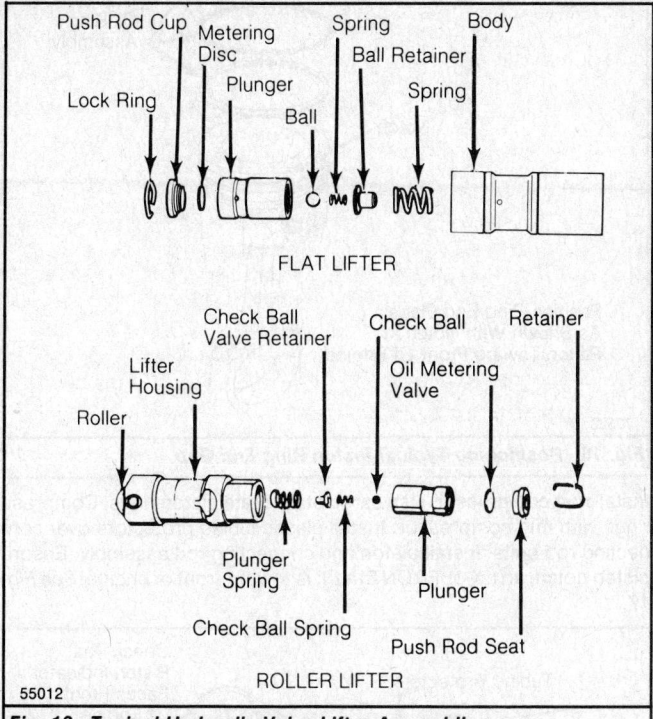

FLAT LIFTER

ROLLER LIFTER

Fig. 13: Typical Hydraulic Valve Lifter Assemblies

Mechanical Lifters – Lifter assemblies must be installed in original locations. Remove rocker arm assembly and push rod. Mark components for location. Some applications require intake manifold or lifter cover removal. Remove lifter retainer plate (if used). To remove lifters, use lifter remover or magnet.

Inspect push rod contact area and lifter body for scoring or signs of wear. If body is scored, inspect lifter bore for damage and lack of lubrication. Note amount of wear in lifter body-to-camshaft contact area. Surface must have smooth and convex contact face. If wear is apparent, carefully inspect cam lobe.

Coat lifter base, roller (if equipped) and lifter body with ample amount of Molykote or camshaft lubricant. Install lifter in original location. Install remaining components. Tighten bolts to specification. Adjust valves. See VALVE ADJUSTMENT in this article.

PISTONS, CONNECTING RODS & BEARINGS

RIDGE REMOVAL

Ridge in cylinder wall must be removed prior to piston removal. Failure to remove ridge prior to removing pistons will cause piston damage in piston ring lands or grooves.

With piston at bottom dead center, place rag in bore to trap metal chips. Install ridge reamer in cylinder bore. Adjust ridge reamer using manufacturer's instructions. Remove ridge using ridge reamer. DO NOT remove an excessive amount of material. Ensure ridge is completely removed.

PISTON & CONNECTING ROD REMOVAL

Note top of piston. Some pistons may contain a notch, arrow or be marked FRONT. Piston must be installed in proper direction to prevent damage with valve operation.

Check that connecting rod and cap are numbered for cylinder location and which side of cylinder block the number faces. Proper cap and connecting rod must be installed together. Connecting rod cap must be installed on connecting rod in proper direction to ensure bearing lock procedure. Mark connecting rod and cap if necessary. Pistons must be installed in original location.

Remove cap retaining nuts or bolts. Remove bearing cap. Install tubing protectors on connecting rod bolts. This protects cylinder walls from scoring during removal. Ensure proper removal of ridge. Push piston and connecting rod from cylinder. Connecting rod boss can be tapped with a wooden dowel or hammer handle to aid in removal.

PISTON & CONNECTING ROD

Disassembly – Using ring expander, remove piston rings. Remove piston pin retaining rings (if equipped). Note direction of piston installation on connecting rod. On pressed type piston pins, special fixtures and procedures according to manufacturer must be used to remove piston pins. Follow manufacturer's recommendations to avoid piston distortion or breakage.

Cleaning – Remove all carbon and varnish from piston. Pistons and connecting rods may be cleaned in cold type chemical tank. Using ring groove cleaner, clean all deposits from ring grooves. Ensure all deposits are cleaned from ring grooves to prevent ring breakage or sticking. DO NOT attempt to clean pistons with wire brush.

Inspection – Inspect pistons for nicks, scoring, cracks or damage in ring areas. Connecting rod should be checked for cracks using Magnaflux procedure. Piston diameter must be measured in manufacturer's specified area.

Using telescopic gauge and micrometer, measure piston pin bore of piston in 2 areas, 90 degrees apart. This is done to check diameter and out-of-round.

Install proper bearing cap on connecting rod. Ensure bearing cap is installed in proper location. Tighten bolts or nuts to specification. Using inside micrometer, measure inside diameter in 2 areas, 90 degrees apart.

Connecting rod I.D. and out-of-round must be within specification. Measure piston pin bore I.D. and piston pin O.D. All components must be within specification. Subtract piston pin diameter from piston pin bore in piston and connecting rod to determine proper fit.

Connecting rod length must be measured from center of crankshaft journal inside diameter to center of piston pin bushing using proper caliper. Connecting rods must be the same length. Connecting rods should be checked on an alignment fixture for bent or twisted condition. Replace all components which are damaged or not within specification.

PISTON & CYLINDER BORE FIT

Ensure cylinder is checked for taper, out-of-round and properly honed prior to checking piston and cylinder bore fit. See CYLINDER BLOCK in this article. Using dial bore gauge, measure cylinder bore.

Measure piston skirt diameter at 90 degree angle to piston pin at specified area by manufacturer. Subtract piston diameter from cylinder bore diameter to determine piston-to-cylinder clearance. Clearance must be within specification. Mark piston for proper cylinder location.

ASSEMBLING PISTON & CONNECTING ROD

Install piston on connecting rod for corresponding cylinder. Ensure reference marking on top of piston corresponds with connecting rod and cap number. *See Fig. 14.*

Lubricate piston pin and install in connecting rod. Ensure piston pin retainers are fully seated (if equipped). On pressed type piston pins, follow manufacturer's recommended procedure to avoid distortion or breakage.

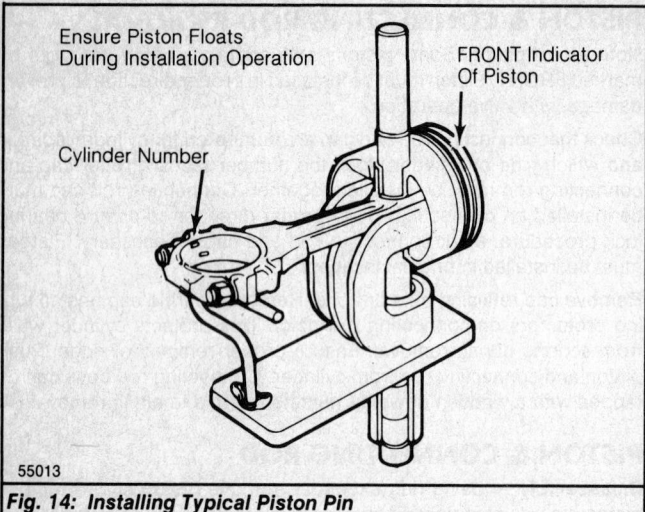

Fig. 14: Installing Typical Piston Pin

CHECKING PISTON RING CLEARANCES

Piston rings must be checked for side clearance and end gap. To check end gap, install piston ring in cylinder in which it is to be installed. Using an inverted piston, push ring to bottom of cylinder in smallest cylinder diameter.

Using feeler gauge, check ring end gap. See Fig. 15. Piston ring end gap must be within specification. Ring breakage will occur if insufficient ring end gap exists.

Some manufacturers permit correcting insufficient ring end gap by using a fine file while other manufacturers recommend using another ring set. Mark rings for proper cylinder installation after checking end gap.

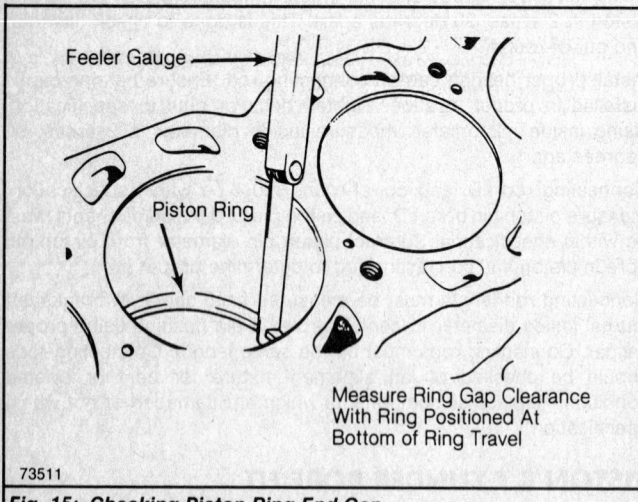

Fig. 15: Checking Piston Ring End Gap

For checking side clearance, install rings on piston. Using feeler gauge, measure clearance between piston ring and piston ring land. Check side clearance in several areas around piston. Side clearance must be within specification.

If side clearance is excessive, piston ring grooves can be machined to accept oversize piston rings (if available). Normal practice is to replace piston.

PISTON & CONNECTING ROD INSTALLATION

Cylinders must be honed prior to piston installation. See CYLINDER HONING under CYLINDER BLOCK in this article.

Install upper connecting rod bearings. Lubricate upper bearings with engine oil. Install lower bearings in rod caps. Ensure bearing tabs are

properly seated. Position piston ring gaps according to manufacturer's recommendations. See Fig. 16. Lubricate pistons, rings and cylinder walls.

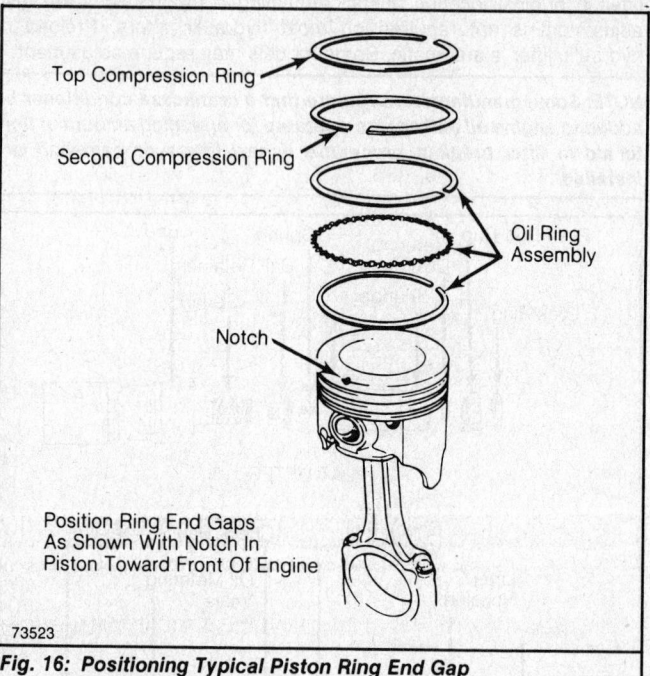

Fig. 16: Positioning Typical Piston Ring End Gap

Install ring compressor. Use care not to rotate piston rings. Compress rings with ring compressor. Install plastic tubing protectors over connecting rod bolts. Install piston and connecting rod assembly. Ensure piston notch, arrow or FRONT mark is toward front of engine. See Fig. 17.

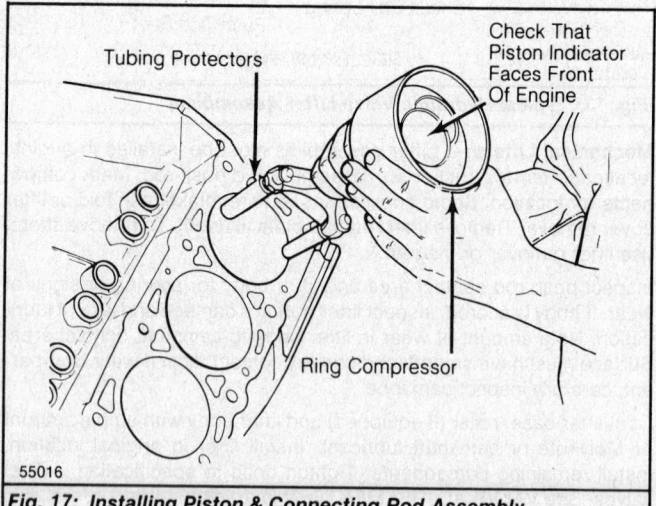

Fig. 17: Installing Piston & Connecting Rod Assembly

Carefully tap piston into cylinder until rod bearing is seated on crankshaft journal. Remove protectors. Install rod cap and bearing. Lightly tighten connecting rod bolts. Repeat procedure for remaining cylinders. Check bearing clearance. See MAIN & CONNECTING ROD BEARING CLEARANCE in this article.

Once clearance is checked, lubricate journals and bearings. Install bearing caps. Ensure marks are aligned on connecting rod and cap. Tighten rod nuts or bolts to specification. Ensure rod moves freely on crankshaft. Check connecting rod side clearance. See CONNECTING ROD SIDE CLEARANCE in this article.

CONNECTING ROD SIDE CLEARANCE

Position connecting rod toward one side of crankshaft as far as possible. Using feeler gauge, measure clearance between side of connecting rod and crankshaft. *See Fig. 18.* Clearance must be within specification.

Check for improper bearing installation, wrong bearing cap or insufficient bearing clearance if side clearance is insufficient. Connecting rod may require machining to obtain proper clearance. Excessive clearance usually indicates excessive wear at crankshaft. Crankshaft must be repaired or replaced.

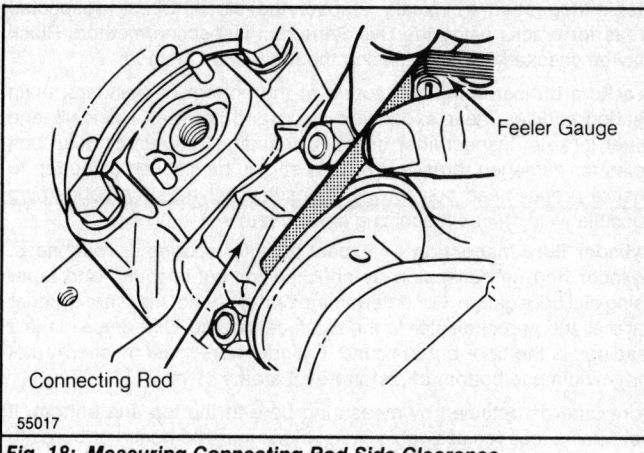

Fig. 18: Measuring Connecting Rod Side Clearance

MAIN & CONNECTING ROD BEARING CLEARANCE

Plastigage Method – Plastigage method may be used to determine bearing clearance. Plastigage can be used with an engine in service or during reassembly. Plastigage material is oil soluble.

Ensure journals and bearings are free of oil or solvent. Oil or solvent will dissolve material and false reading will be obtained. Install small piece of Plastigage along full length of bearing journal. Install bearing cap in original location. Tighten bolts to specification.

CAUTION: DO NOT rotate crankshaft while Plastigage is installed. Bearing clearance will not be obtained if crankshaft is rotated.

Remove bearing cap. Compare Plastigage width with scale on Plastigage container to determine bearing clearance. *See Fig. 19.* Rotate crankshaft 90 degrees. Repeat procedure. This is done to check journal eccentricity. This procedure can be used to check oil clearance on both connecting rod and main bearings.

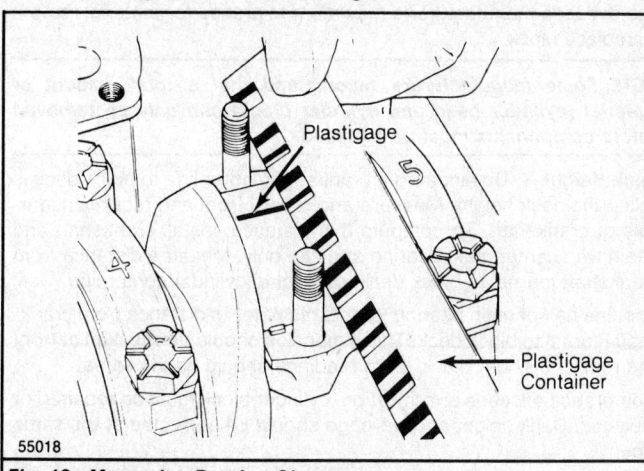

Fig. 19: Measuring Bearing Clearance

Micrometer & Telescopic Gauge Method – A micrometer is used to determine journal diameter, taper and out-of-round dimensions of the crankshaft. See CLEANING & INSPECTION under CRANKSHAFT & MAIN BEARINGS in this article.

With crankshaft removed, install bearings and caps in original location on cylinder block. Tighten bolts to specification. On connecting rods, install bearings and caps on connecting rods. Install proper connecting rod cap on corresponding rod. Ensure bearing cap is installed in original location. Tighten bolts to specification.

Using a telescopic gauge and micrometer or inside micrometer, measure inside diameter of connecting rod and main bearings bores. Subtract each crankshaft journal diameter from the corresponding inside bearing bore diameter. This is the bearing clearance.

CRANKSHAFT & MAIN BEARINGS

REMOVAL

Ensure all main bearing caps are marked for location on cylinder block. Some main bearing caps have an arrow stamped on them. The arrow must face timing belt or timing chain end of engine. Remove main bearing cap bolts. Remove main bearing caps. Carefully remove crankshaft. Use care not to bind crankshaft in cylinder block during removal.

CLEANING & INSPECTION

Thoroughly clean crankshaft using solvent. Dry with compressed air. Ensure all oil passages are clear and free of sludge, rust, dirt, and metal chips.

Inspect crankshaft for scoring and nicks. Inspect crankshaft for cracks using Magnaflux procedure. Inspect rear seal area for grooving or damage. Inspect bolt hole threads for damage. If pilot bearing or bushing is used, check pilot bearing or bushing fit in crankshaft. Inspect crankshaft gear for damaged or cracked teeth. Replace gear if damaged. Check that oil passage plugs are tight (if equipped).

Using micrometer, measure all journals in 4 areas to determine journal taper, out-of-round and undersize. *See Fig. 20.* Some crankshafts can be reground to the next largest undersize, depending on the amount of wear or damage. Crankshafts with rolled fillet cannot be reground and must be replaced.

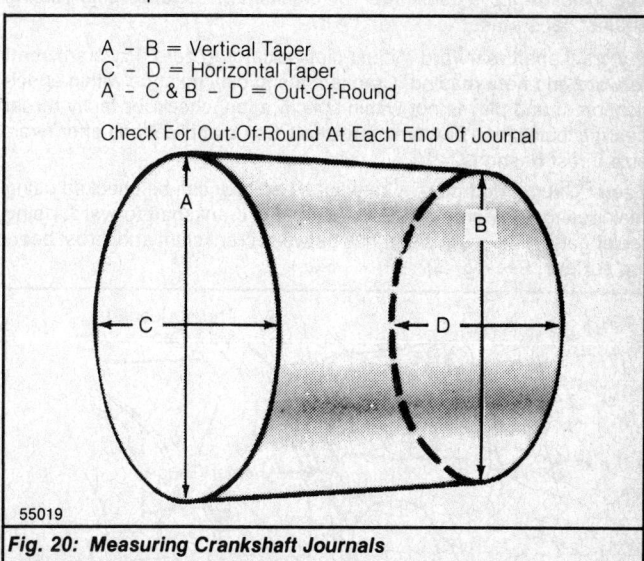

A – B = Vertical Taper
C – D = Horizontal Taper
A – C & B – D = Out-Of-Round

Check For Out-Of-Round At Each End Of Journal

Fig. 20: Measuring Crankshaft Journals

Crankshaft journal runout should be checked. Install crankshaft in "V" blocks or bench center. Position dial indicator with tip resting on the main bearing journal area. *See Fig. 21.* Rotate crankshaft and note reading. Journal runout must not exceed specification. Repeat procedure on all main bearing journals. Crankshaft must be replaced if runout exceeds specification.

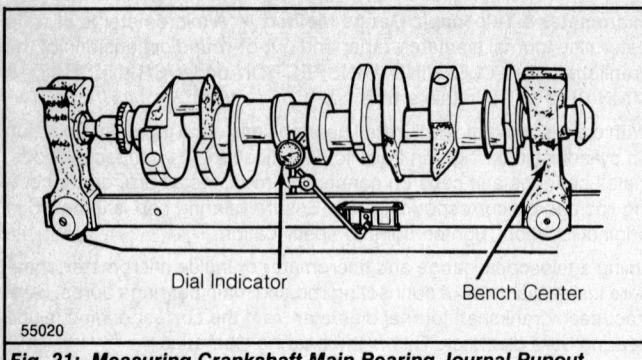

Dial Indicator   Bench Center

55020

Fig. 21: Measuring Crankshaft Main Bearing Journal Runout

INSTALLATION

Install upper main bearing in cylinder block. Ensure lock tab is properly located in cylinder block. Install bearings in main bearing caps. Ensure all oil passages are aligned. Install rear seal (if removed).

Ensure crankshaft journals are clean. Lubricate upper main bearings with clean engine oil. Carefully install crankshaft. Check each main bearing clearance using Plastigage method. See MAIN & CONNECTING ROD BEARING CLEARANCE in this article.

Once clearance is checked, lubricate lower main bearing and journals. Install main bearing caps in original location. Install rear seal in rear main bearing cap (if removed). Some rear main bearing caps require sealant to be applied in corners to prevent oil leakage.

Install and tighten all bolts except thrust bearing cap to specification. Tighten thrust bearing cap bolts finger tight only. Some models require that thrust bearing must be aligned. On most applications, crankshaft must be moved rearward then forward. Procedure may vary with manufacturer. Thrust bearing cap is then tightened to specification. Ensure crankshaft rotates freely. Crankshaft end play should be checked. See CRANKSHAFT END PLAY in this article.

CRANKSHAFT END PLAY

Dial Indicator Method – Crankshaft end play can be checked using dial indicator. Mount dial indicator on rear of cylinder block. Position dial indicator tip against rear of crankshaft. Ensure tip is resting against flat surface.

Pry crankshaft rearward. Adjust dial indicator to zero. Pry crankshaft forward and note reading. Crankshaft end play must be within specification. If end play is not within specification, check for faulty thrust bearing installation or worn crankshaft. Some applications offer oversize thrust bearings.

Feeler Gauge Method – Crankshaft end play can be checked using feeler gauge. Pry crankshaft rearward. Pry crankshaft forward. Using feeler gauge, measure clearance between crankshaft and thrust bearing surface. See Fig. 22.

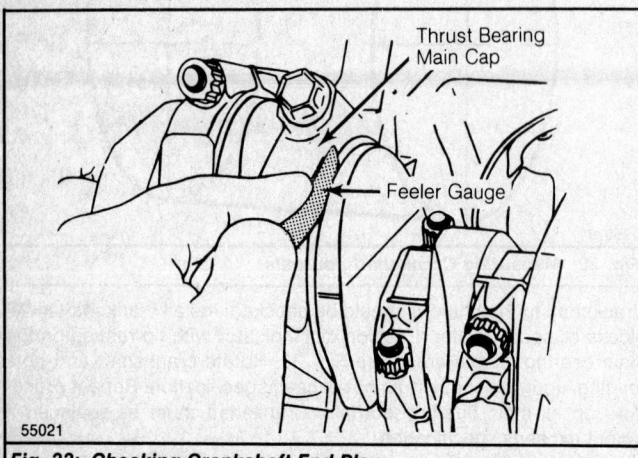

Thrust Bearing
Main Cap

Feeler Gauge

55021

Fig. 22: Checking Crankshaft End Play

Crankshaft end play must be within specification. If end play is not within specification, check for faulty thrust bearing installation or worn crankshaft. Some applications offer oversize thrust bearings.

CYLINDER BLOCK

Block Cleaning – Only cast cylinder blocks should be hot tank cleaned. Aluminum cylinder blocks should be cleaned using cold tank method. Cylinder block is cleaned in order to remove carbon deposits, gasket residue and water jacket scale. Remove oil gallery plugs, freeze plugs and cam bearings prior to block cleaning.

Block Inspection – Visually inspect the block. Check suspected areas for cracks using the Dye Penetrant inspection method. Block may be checked for cracks using the Magnaflux method.

Cracks are most commonly found at the bottom of cylinders, main bearing saddles, near expansion plugs and between cylinders and water jackets. Inspect lifter bores for damage. Inspect all head bolt holes for damaged threads. Threads should be cleaned using tap to ensure proper head bolt torque. Consult machine shop concerning possible welding and machining (if required).

Cylinder Bore Inspection – Inspect bore for scoring or roughness. Cylinder bore is dimensionally checked for out-of-round and taper using dial bore gauge. For determining out-of-round, measure cylinder parallel and perpendicular to the block center line. Difference in the 2 readings is the bore out-of-round. Cylinder bore must be checked at top, middle and bottom of piston travel area.

Bore taper is obtained by measuring bore at the top and bottom. If wear has exceeded allowable limits, block must be honed or bored to next available oversize piston dimension.

Cylinder Honing – Cylinder must be properly honed to allow new piston rings to properly seat. Cross-hatching at correct angle and depth is critical to lubrication of cylinder walls and pistons.

A flexible drive hone and power drill are commonly used. Drive hone must be lubricated during operation. Mix equal parts of kerosene and SAE 20W engine oil for lubrication.

Apply lubrication to cylinder wall. Operate cylinder hone from top to bottom of cylinder using even strokes to produce 45 degree cross-hatch pattern on the cylinder wall. DO NOT allow cylinder hone to extend below cylinder during operation.

Recheck bore dimension after final honing. Wash cylinder wall with hot soapy water to remove abrasive particles. Blow dry with compressed air. Coat cleaned cylinder walls with lubricating oil.

Deck Warpage – Check deck for damage or warped gasket surface. Place a straightedge across gasket surface of the deck. Using feeler gauge, measure clearance at center of straightedge. Measure across width and length of cylinder block at several points.

If warpage exceeds specifications, deck must be resurfaced. If warpage exceeds manufacturer's maximum tolerance for material removal, replace block.

NOTE: *Some manufacturers recommend that a total amount of material (cylinder head and cylinder block) can only be removed before components must be replaced.*

Deck Height – Distance from crankshaft center line to block deck is called the deck height. Measure and record front and rear main journals of crankshaft. To compute this distance, install crankshaft and retain with center main bearing and cap only. Measure distance from crankshaft journal to block deck, parallel to cylinder center line.

Add one half of main bearing journal diameter to distance from crankshaft journal to block deck. This dimension should be checked at front and rear of cylinder block. Both readings should be the same.

If difference exceeds specification, cylinder block must be repaired or replaced. Deck height and warpage should be corrected at the same time.

Main Bearing Bore & Alignment – For checking main bearing bore, remove all bearings from cylinder block and main bearing caps. Install main bearing caps in original location. Tighten bolts to specification.

Using inside micrometer, measure main bearing bore in 2 areas 90 degrees apart. Determine bore size and out-of-round. If diameter is not within specification, block must be align-bored.

For checking alignment, place a straightedge along center line of main bearing saddles. Check for clearance between straightedge and main bearing saddles. Block must be align-bored if clearance exists.

Expansion Plug Removal – Drill hole in center of expansion plug. Remove with screwdriver or punch. Use care not to damage sealing surface.

Expansion Plug Installation – Ensure sealing surface is free of burrs. Coat expansion plug with sealer. Using wooden dowel or pipe of slightly smaller diameter, install expansion plug. Ensure expansion plug is evenly located.

Oil Gallery Plug Removal – Remove threaded oil gallery plugs using appropriate wrench. Soft press-in plugs are removed by drilling into plug and installing a sheet metal screw. Remove plug with slide hammer or pliers.

Oil Gallery Plug Installation – Ensure threads or sealing surface is clean. Coat threaded oil gallery plugs with sealer and install. Replacement soft press-in plugs are installed with a hammer and drift.

CAMSHAFT

CLEANING & INSPECTION

Clean camshaft with solvent. Ensure all oil passages are clear. Inspect cam lobes and bearing journals for pitting, flaking or scoring. Using micrometer, measure bearing journal O.D.

Support camshaft at each end with "V" blocks. Position dial indicator with tip resting on center bearing journal. Rotate camshaft and note camshaft runout reading. If reading exceeds specification, replace camshaft.

Check cam lobe lift by measuring base circle of camshaft using micrometer. Measure again at 90 degree angle to tip of cam lobe. Cam lift can be determined by subtracting base circle diameter from tip of cam lobe measurement.

Different lift dimensions are given for intake and exhaust cam lobes. Reading must be within specification. Replace camshaft if cam lobes or bearing journals are not within specification.

Inspect camshaft gear for chipped, eroded or damaged teeth. Replace gear if damaged. On camshafts using thrust plate, measure distance between thrust plate and camshaft shoulder. Replace thrust plate if not within specification.

CAMSHAFT BEARINGS

Removal & Installation – Remove camshaft rear plug. Camshaft bearing remover is assembled with shoulder resting against bearing to be removed according to manufacturer's instructions. Tighten puller nut until bearing is removed. Remove remaining bearings, leaving front and rear bearings until last. These bearings act as a guide for camshaft bearing remover.

To install new bearings, puller is rearranged to pull bearings toward the center of block. Ensure all lubrication passages of bearing are aligned with cylinder block. Coat new camshaft rear plug with sealant. Install camshaft rear plug. Ensure plug is even in cylinder block.

CAMSHAFT INSTALLATION

Lubricate bearing surfaces and cam lobes with ample amount of Molykote or camshaft lubricant. Carefully install camshaft. Use care not to damage bearing journals during installation. Install thrust plate retaining bolts (if equipped). Tighten bolts to specification. On overhead camshafts, install bearing caps in original location. Tighten bolts to specification. On all applications, check camshaft end play.

CAMSHAFT END PLAY

Using dial indicator, check camshaft end play. Position dial indicator on front of engine block or cylinder head. Position indicator tip against camshaft. Push camshaft toward rear of cylinder head or engine and adjust indicator to zero.

Move camshaft forward and note reading. Camshaft end play must be within specification. End play may be adjusted by relocating gear, shimming thrust plate or replacing thrust plate depending on each manufacturer.

TIMING CHAINS & BELTS

TIMING CHAINS

Timing chains will stretch during operation. Limits are placed upon amount of stretch before replacement is required. Timing chain stretch will alter ignition timing and valve timing.

To check timing chain stretch, rotate crankshaft to eliminate slack from one side of timing chain. Mark reference point on cylinder block. Rotate crankshaft in opposite direction to eliminate slack from remaining side of timing chain. Force other side of chain outward and measure distance between reference point and timing chain. *See Fig. 23.* Replace timing chain and gears if not within specification.

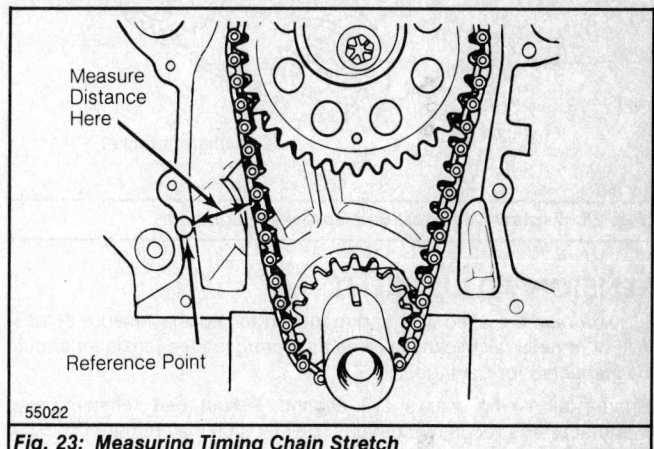

55022
Fig. 23: Measuring Timing Chain Stretch

Timing chains must be installed so timing marks on camshaft gear and crankshaft gear are aligned according to manufacturer. *See Fig. 24.*

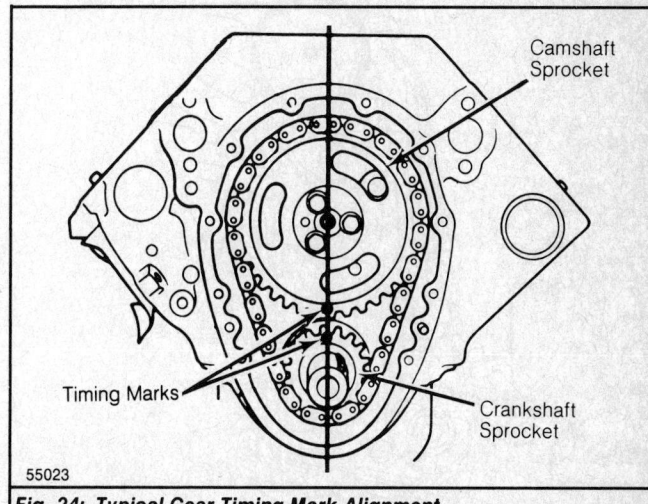

55023
Fig. 24: Typical Gear Timing Mark Alignment

TIMING BELTS

Cogged tooth belts are commonly used on overhead cam engines. Inspect belt teeth for rounded corners or cracking. Replace belt if it is cracked, damaged, missing teeth, or oil soaked.

Used timing belt must be installed in original direction of rotation. Inspect all sprocket teeth for wear. Replace all worn sprockets.

Sprockets are marked for timing purposes. Engine is positioned so that crankshaft sprocket mark will be upward. Camshaft sprocket is aligned with reference mark on cylinder head or timing belt cover and then timing belt can be installed. See Fig. 25.

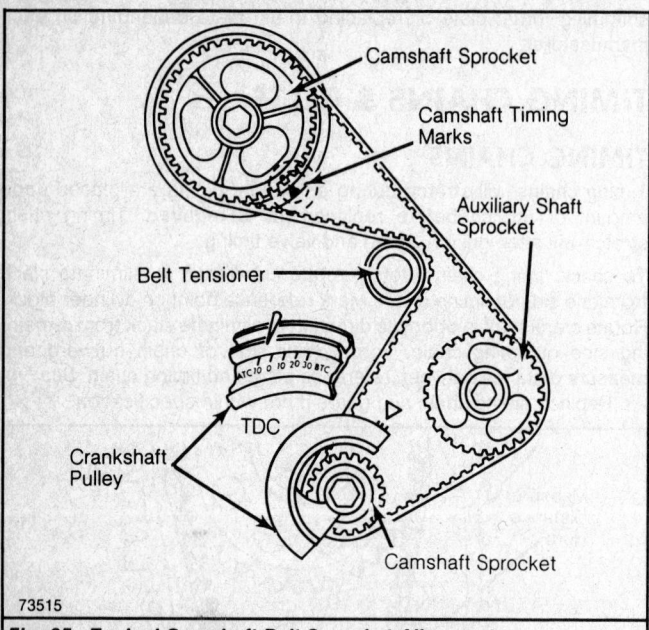

Fig. 25: Typical Camshaft Belt Sprocket Alignment

TENSION ADJUSTMENT

If guide rails are used with spring loaded tensioners, ensure at least half of original rail thickness remains. Spring loaded tensioner should be inspected for damage.

Ensure all timing marks are aligned. Adjust belt tension using manufacturer's recommendations. Belt tension may require checking using tension gauge. See Fig. 26.

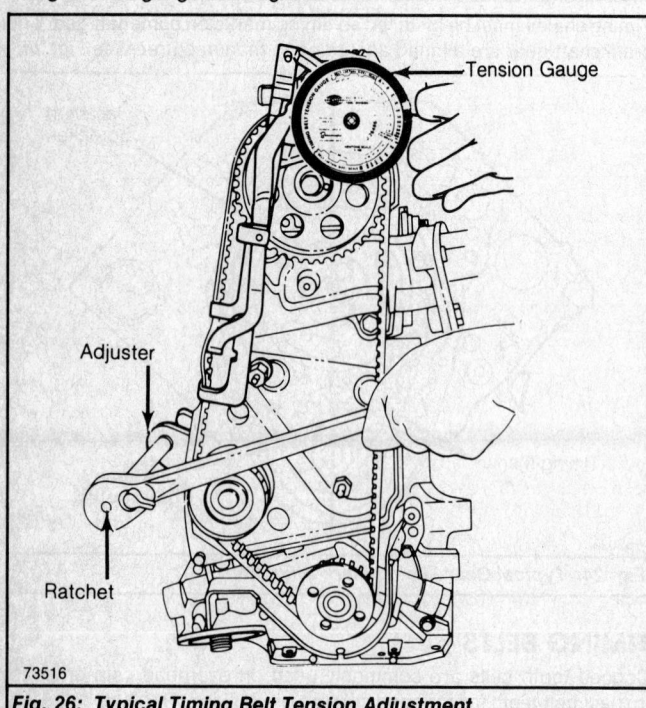

Fig. 26: Typical Timing Belt Tension Adjustment

TIMING GEARS

TIMING GEAR BACKLASH & RUNOUT

On engines where camshaft gear operates directly on crankshaft gear, gear backlash and runout must be checked. To check backlash, install dial indicator with tip resting on tooth of camshaft gear. Rotate camshaft gear as far as possible. Adjust indicator to zero. Rotate camshaft gear in opposite direction as far as possible and note reading.

To determine timing gear runout, mount dial indicator with tip resting on face edge of camshaft gear. Adjust indicator to zero. Rotate camshaft gear 360 degrees and note reading. If backlash or runout exceeds specification, replace camshaft and/or crankshaft gear.

REAR MAIN OIL SEAL INSTALLATION

One-Piece Type Seal – For one-piece type oil seal installation, coat block contact surface of seal with sealer if seal is not factory coated. Ensure seal surface is free of burrs. Lubricate seal lip with engine oil and press seal into place using proper oil seal installer. See Fig. 27.

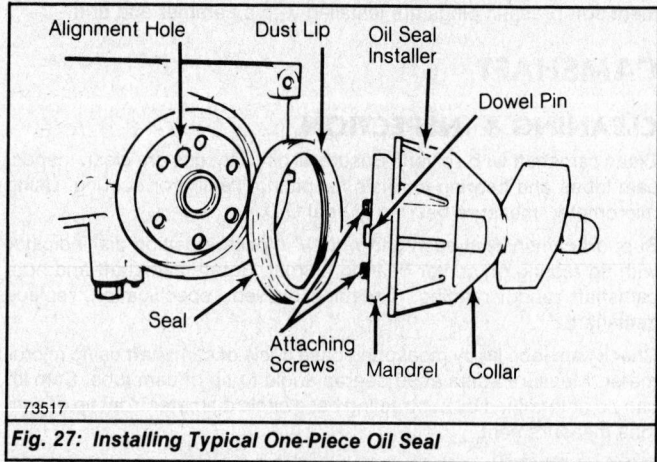

Fig. 27: Installing Typical One-Piece Oil Seal

Rope Type Seal – For rope type rear main oil seal installation, press seal lightly into seat area. Using seal installer, fully seat seal in bearing cap or cylinder block.

Trim seal ends even with cylinder block parting surface. Some applications require sealer to be applied on main bearing cap prior to installation. See Fig. 28.

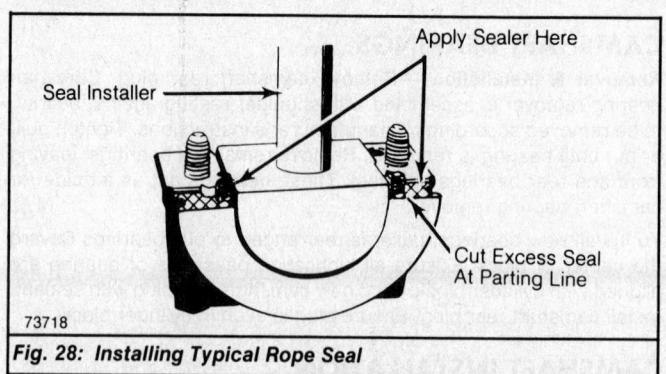

Fig. 28: Installing Typical Rope Seal

Split-Rubber Type Seal – Follow manufacturer's procedures when installing split-rubber type rear main oil seals. Installation procedures vary with manufacturer and engine type. See Fig. 29.

OIL PUMP

ROTOR TYPE

Mark oil pump rotor locations prior to removal. See Fig. 30. Remove outer rotor and measure thickness and diameter. Measure inner rotor

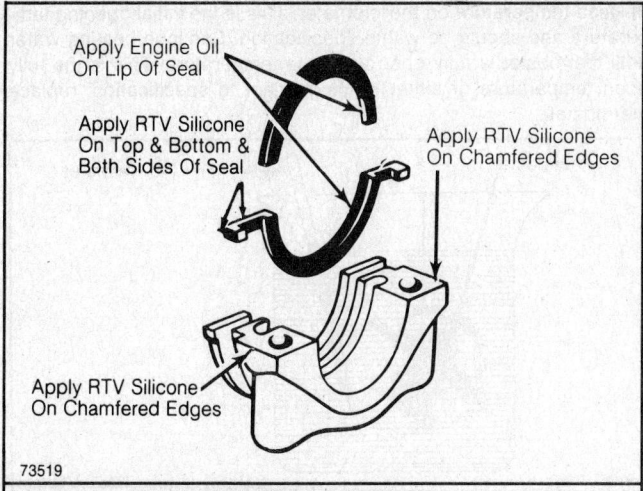

Fig. 29: Installing Typical Split-Rubber Seal

thickness. Inspect shaft for scoring or wear. Inspect rotors for pitting or damage. Inspect cover for grooving or wear. Replace worn or damaged components.

Measure outer rotor-to-body clearance. Replace pump assembly if clearance exceeds specification. Measure clearance between rotors. *See Fig. 31.* Replace shaft and both rotors if clearance exceeds specification.

Install rotors in pump body. Position straightedge across pump body. Using feeler gauge, measure clearance between rotors and straightedge. Pump cover wear is measured using a straightedge and feeler gauge. Replace pump if clearance exceeds specification.

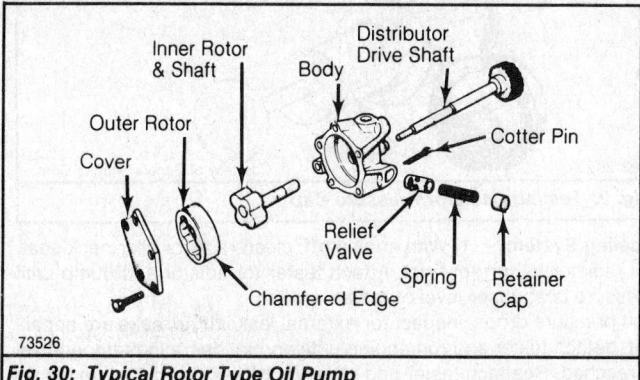

Fig. 30: Typical Rotor Type Oil Pump

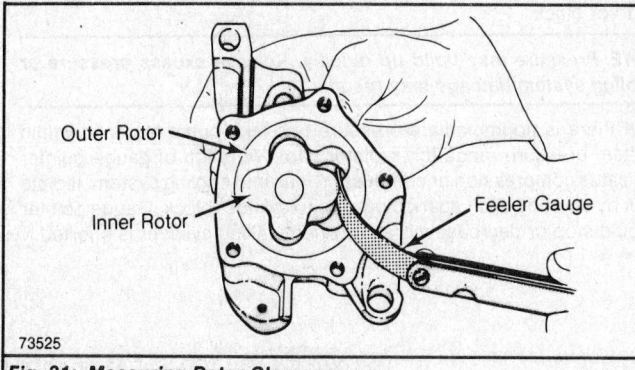

Fig. 31: Measuring Rotor Clearance

GEAR TYPE

Mark oil pump gear location prior to removal. *See Fig. 32.* Remove gears from pump body. Inspect gears for pitting or damage. Inspect cover for grooving or wear. Measure gear diameter and length. Measure gear housing cavity depth and diameter. *See Fig. 33.* Replace worn or damaged components.

Measure pump cover wear using a straightedge and feeler gauge. Replace pump or components if warpage/wear exceeds specification. Check pump mating surface for scratches or grooves.

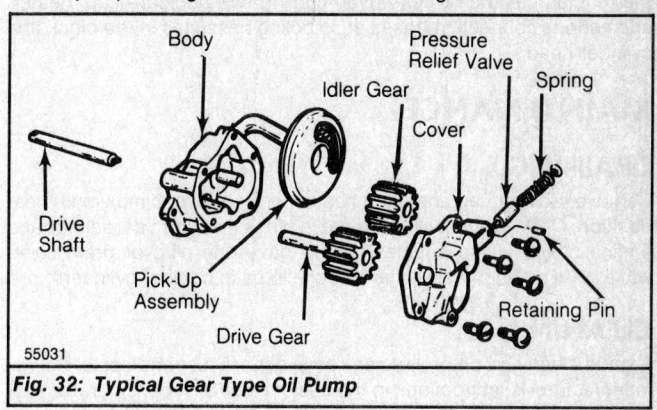

Fig. 32: Typical Gear Type Oil Pump

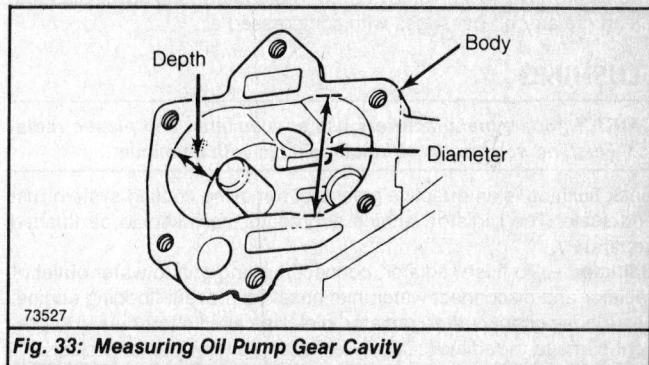

Fig. 33: Measuring Oil Pump Gear Cavity

BREAK-IN PROCEDURE

ENGINE PRE-OILING

Pre-oil engine prior to operation to prevent engine damage. A lightly oiled oil pump will cavitate unless oil pump cavities are filled with engine oil or petroleum jelly.

Engine pre-oiling can be done using pressure oiler (if available). Connect pressure oiler to oil pressure sending unit hole. Operate pressure oiler until oil fills crankcase. Check oil level while pre-oiling.

If pressure oiler is not available, disconnect ignition system. Remove oil pressure sending unit and install oil pressure test gauge. Using starter motor, rotate engine starter until gauge shows normal oil pressure for several seconds. DO NOT crank engine for more than 30 seconds to avoid starter motor damage. Ensure oil pressure has reached the furthest point from oil pump.

NOTE: If installing new lifters and camshaft, some manufacturers recommend adding a "crankcase conditioner" to engine oil.

INITIAL START-UP

Start engine and run at low RPM. Check for coolant, fuel and oil leaks. Stop engine. Recheck coolant and oil level. Fill if necessary.

CAMSHAFT

Break-in procedure is required when new or reground camshaft has been installed. Operate and maintain engine speed between 1500-2500 RPM for approximately 30 minutes.

PISTON RINGS

Piston rings require a break-in procedure to ensure seating of rings to cylinder walls. Follow piston ring manufacturer's recommended break-in procedure.

1994 GENERAL INFORMATION
General Cooling System Servicing

DESCRIPTION

The basic liquid cooling system consists of a radiator, water pump, thermostat, electric or belt-driven cooling fan, pressure cap, heater, and various connecting hoses and cooling passages in the block and cylinder head.

MAINTENANCE

DRAINING

Remove radiator cap and open heater control valve to maximum heat position. Open drain cocks or remove plugs in bottom of radiator and engine block. In-line engines usually have one plug or drain cock, while "V" type engines will have 2, one in each bank of cylinders.

CLEANING

A good cleaning compound can remove most rust and scale. Follow manufacturer's instructions in the use of cleaner. If considerable rust and scale have to be removed, cooling system should be flushed. Clean radiator air passages with compressed air.

FLUSHING

CAUTION: Some manufacturers use an aluminum and plastic radiator. Flushing solution must be compatible with aluminum.

Back flushing is an effective means of removing cooling system rust and scale. The radiator, engine and heater core should be flushed separately.
Radiator – To flush radiator, connect flushing gun to water outlet of radiator and disconnect water inlet hose. To prevent flooding engine, use a hose connected to radiator inlet. Use air in short bursts to prevent damage to radiator. Continue flushing until water runs clear.
Engine – To flush engine, remove thermostat and replace housing. Connect flushing gun to water outlet of engine. Flush using short air bursts until water runs clean.
Heater Core – Flush heater core as described for radiator. Ensure heater control valve is set to maximum heat position before flushing heater.

REFILLING

NOTE: When refilling cooling system, ensure air bleed(s) are opened as necessary (if equipped).

To prevent air from being trapped in engine block, engine should be running when refilling cooling system. After system is full, continue running engine until thermostat is open, then recheck fill level. Do not overfill system.

TESTING

THERMOSTAT

1) Remove and visually inspect thermostat for corrosion and proper sealing of valve and seat. If okay, suspend thermostat and thermometer in a 50/50 mixture of coolant and water. See Fig. 1. DO NOT allow thermostat or thermometer to touch bottom of container. Heat water until thermostat begins to open.

2) Read temperature on thermometer. This is the initial opening temperature and should be within specification. Continue heating water until thermostat is fully open and note temperature. This is the fully open temperature. If either reading is not to specification, replace thermostat.

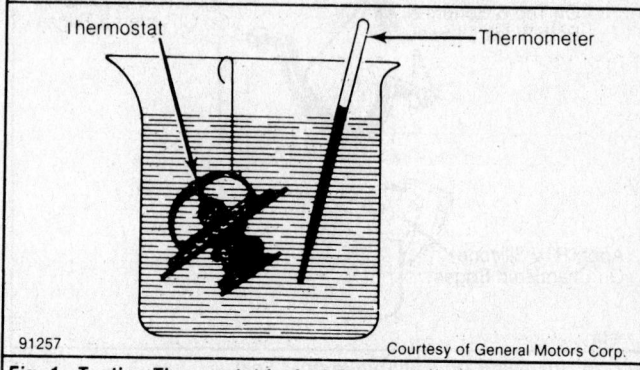
Fig. 1: Testing Thermostat in Anti-Freeze/Water Solution

PRESSURE TESTING

A pressure tester is used to check both radiator cap and complete cooling system. Follow pressure tester manufacturer's instructions and test components as follows:
Radiator Cap – Visually inspect radiator cap, then dip cap into water and connect to tester. Pump tester to bring pressure to upper limit of cap specification. See Fig. 2. If cap fails to hold pressure or releases at higher pressure than specification, replace cap.

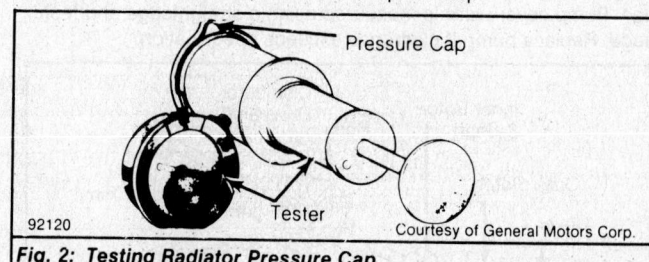
Fig. 2: Testing Radiator Pressure Cap

Cooling System – 1) With engine off, clean radiator filler neck seat. Fill radiator to correct level. Attach tester to radiator and pump until pressure is at upper level of radiator rating.
2) If pressure drops, inspect for external leaks. If no leaks are apparent, detach tester and run engine until normal operating temperature is reached. Reattach tester and observe. If pressure builds up immediately, a possible leak exists from a faulty head gasket or crack in head or block.

NOTE: Pressure may build up quickly. Release excess pressure or cooling system damage may result.

3) If there is no immediate pressure build up, pump tester to within system pressure range (on radiator cap). Vibration of gauge pointer indicates compression or combustion leak into cooling system. Isolate leak by shorting each spark plug wire to cylinder block. Gauge pointer should stop or decrease vibration when leaking cylinder is shorted.

INSPECTION

Clean lubricant from internal parts, then rotate gears and inspect for wear or damage. Mount a dial indicator to housing and check backlash at several points around ring gear. Backlash must be within specifications at all points. If no defects are found, check gear tooth contact pattern.

GEAR TOOTH CONTACT PATTERN

NOTE: Drive pattern should be well centered on ring gear teeth. Coast pattern should be centered but may be slightly toward toe of ring gear teeth.

1) Paint ring gear teeth with a marking compound. Apply some form of load to differential case to resist rotation. Rotate pinion gear until ring gear has made one full revolution .

2) Rotate pinion gear in opposite direction to complete one full revolution of ring gear. Examine ring gear teeth for contact pattern. Correct as necessary by moving appropriate shims. Backlash between drive gear and pinion must be maintained within specified limits until correct tooth pattern is obtained.

ADJUSTMENTS

GEAR BACKLASH & PINION SHIM CHANGES

NOTE: Change in tooth pattern is directly related to change in shim and/or backlash adjustment.

1) With no change in backlash, moving pinion further from ring gear moves drive pattern toward heel and top of tooth, and moves coast pattern toward toe and top of tooth.

2) With no change in backlash, moving pinion closer to ring gear moves drive pattern toward toe and bottom of tooth, and moves coast pattern toward heel and bottom of tooth.

3) With no change in pinion shim thickness, an increase in backlash moves ring gear further from pinion. Drive pattern moves toward heel and top of tooth, and coast pattern moves toward heel and top of tooth.

4) With no change in pinion shim thickness, a decrease in backlash moves ring gear closer to pinion gear. Drive pattern moves toward toe and bottom of tooth, and coast pattern moves toward toe and bottom of tooth.

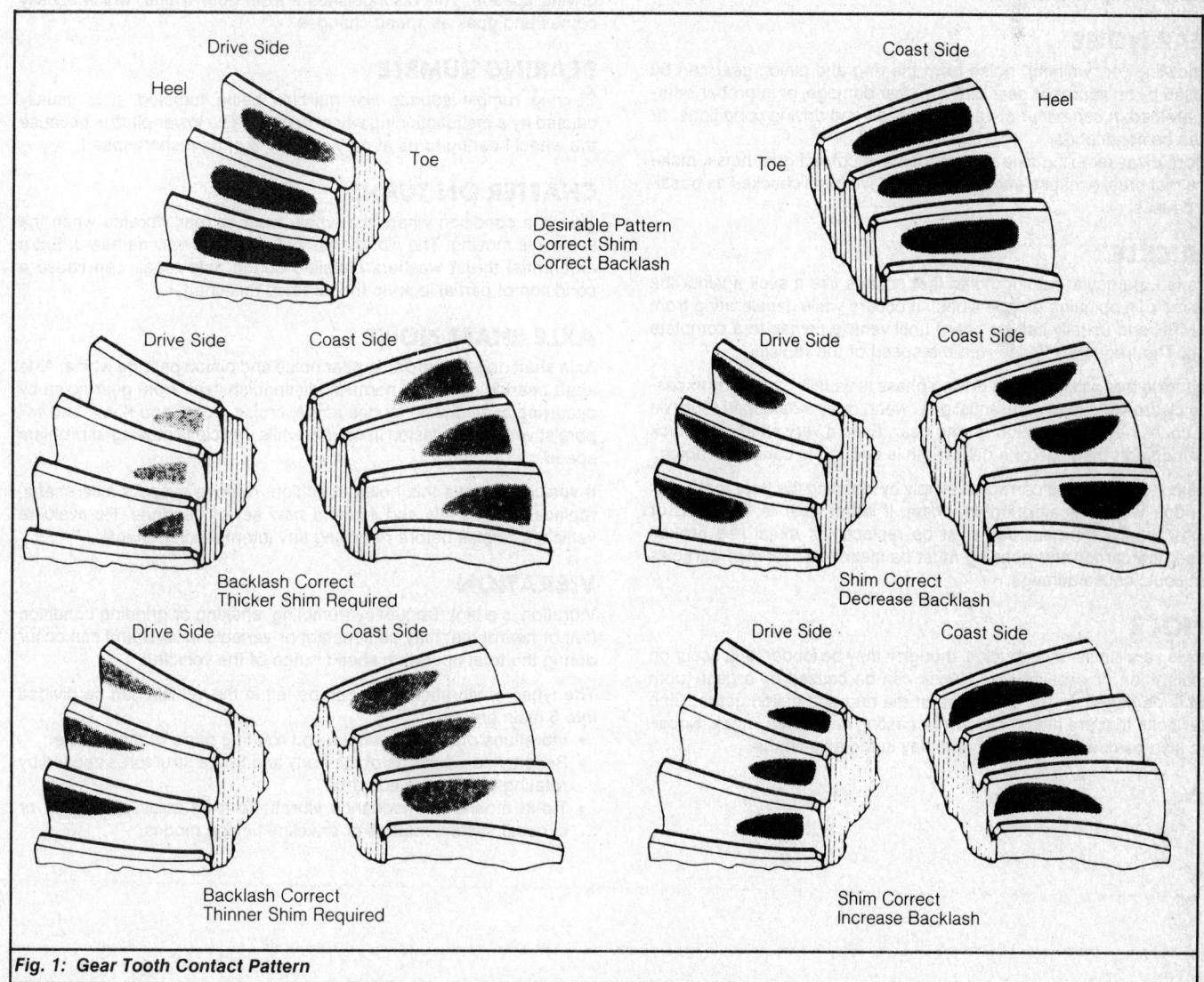

Fig. 1: Gear Tooth Contact Pattern

1994 GENERAL INFORMATION
Drive Axle Noise Diagnosis

UNRELATED NOISES

Some driveline trouble symptoms are also common to the engine, transmission, wheel bearings, tires, and other parts of the vehicle. Make sure that cause of trouble actually is in the drive axle before adjusting, repairing, or replacing any of its parts.

NON-DRIVE AXLE NOISES

A few conditions can sound just like drive axle noise and have to be considered in pre-diagnosis. The 4 most common noises are exhaust, tires, CV/universal joints and trim moldings.

In certain conditions, the pitch of the exhaust gases may sound like gear whine. At other times, it may be mistaken for a wheel bearing rumble.

Tires, especially radial and snow tires, can have a high-pitched tread whine or roar, similar to gear noise. Also, some non-standard tires with an unusual tread construction may emit a roar or whine.

Defective CV/universal joints may cause clicking noises or excessive driveline play that can be improperly diagnosed as drive axle problems.

Trim and moldings also can cause a whistling or whining noise. Ensure that none of these components are causing the noise before disassembling the drive axle.

GEAR NOISE

A "howling" or "whining" noise from the ring and pinion gear can be caused by an improper gear pattern, gear damage, or improper bearing preload. It can occur at various speeds and driving conditions, or it can be continuous.

Before disassembling axle to diagnose and correct gear noise, make sure that tires, exhaust, and vehicle trim have been checked as possible causes.

CHUCKLE

This is a particular rattling noise that sounds like a stick against the spokes of a spinning bicycle wheel. It occurs while decelerating from 40 MPH and usually can be heard until vehicle comes to a complete stop. The frequency varies with the speed of the vehicle.

A chuckle that occurs on the driving phase is usually caused by excessive clearance due to differential gear wear, or by a damaged tooth on the coast side of the pinion or ring gear. Even a very small tooth nick or a ridge on the edge of a gear tooth is enough to cause the noise.

This condition can be corrected simply by cleaning the gear tooth nick or ridge with a small grinding wheel. If either gear is damaged or scored badly, the gear set must be replaced. If metal has broken loose, the carrier and housing must be cleaned to remove particles that could cause damage.

KNOCK

This is very similar to a chuckle, though it may be louder, and occur on acceleration or deceleration. Knock can be caused by a gear tooth that is damaged on the drive side of the ring and pinion gears. Ring gear bolts that are hitting the carrier casting can cause knock. Knock can also be due to excessive end play in the axle shafts.

CLUNK

Clunk is a metallic noise heard when an automatic transmission is engaged in Reverse or Drive, or when throttle is applied or released. It is caused by backlash somewhere in the driveline, but not necessarily in the axle. To determine whether driveline clunk is caused by the axle, check the total axle backlash as follows:

1) Raise vehicle on a frame or twinpost hoist so that drive wheels are free. Clamp a bar between axle companion flange and a part of the frame or body so that flange cannot move.

2) On conventional drive axles, lock the left wheel to keep it from turning. On all models, turn the right wheel slowly until it is felt to be in drive condition. Hold a chalk marker on side of tire about 12" from center of wheel. Turn wheel in the opposite direction until it is again felt to be in drive condition.

3) Measure the length of the chalk mark, which is the total axle backlash. If backlash is one inch or less, clunk will not be eliminated by overhauling drive axle.

BEARING WHINE

Bearing whine is a high-pitched sound similar to a whistle. It is usually caused by malfunctioning pinion bearings. Pinion bearings operate at driveshaft speed. Roller wheel bearings may whine in a similar manner if they run completely dry of lubricant. Bearing noise will occur at all driving speeds. This distinguishes it from gear whine, which usually comes and goes as speed changes.

BEARING RUMBLE

Bearing rumble sounds like marbles being tumbled. It is usually caused by a malfunctioning wheel bearing. The lower pitch is because the wheel bearing turns at only about 1/3 of driveshaft speed.

CHATTER ON TURNS

This is a condition where the whole front or rear vibrates when the vehicle is moving. The vibration is plainly felt as well as heard. Extra differential thrust washers installed during axle repair can cause a condition of partial lock-up that creates this chatter.

AXLE SHAFT NOISE

Axle shaft noise is similar to gear noise and pinion bearing whine. Axle shaft bearing noise will normally distinguish itself from gear noise by occurring in all driving modes (drive, cruise, coast and float), and will persist with transmission in neutral while vehicle is moving at problem speed.

If vehicle displays this noise condition, remove suspect axle shafts, replace wheel seals and install a new set of bearings. Re-evaluate vehicle for noise before removing any internal components.

VIBRATION

Vibration is a high-frequency trembling, shaking or grinding condition (felt or heard) that may be constant or variable in level and can occur during the total operating speed range of the vehicle.

The types of vibrations that can be felt in the vehicle can be divided into 3 main groups:
- Vibrations of various unbalanced rotating parts of the vehicle.
- Resonance vibrations of the body and frame structures caused by rotating of unbalanced parts.
- Tip-in moans of resonance vibrations from stressed engine or exhaust system mounts or driveline flexing modes.

NOTE: *Refer to appropriate Anti-Lock Brake System (ABS) article for description, operation, depressurizing, testing, system bleeding, trouble shooting and servicing of specific system. Failure to depressurize ABS could lead to physical injury.*

- NEVER open a bleeder valve or loosen a hydraulic line while ABS is pressurized.

- NEVER disconnect or reconnect any electrical connectors while ignition is on. Damage to ABS control unit may result.

- DO NOT attempt to bleed hydraulic system without first referring to the appropriate article in your Mitchell service and repair manual.

- ONLY use specially designed brake hoses/lines on ABS equipped vehicles.

- DO NOT tap on speed sensor components (sensor, sensor rings). Speed rings must be pressed into hubs, NOT hammered into hubs. Striking these components can cause demagnetization or a loss of polarization, affecting the accuracy of the speed signal returning to the ABS control unit.

- DO NOT mix tire sizes. Increasing the width, as long as tires remain close to the original diameter, is acceptable. Rolling diameter must be identical for all 4 tires. Some manufacturers recommend tires of the same brand, style and type. Failure to follow this precaution may cause inaccurate wheel speed readings.

- DO NOT contaminate speed sensor components with grease. Only use recommended coating, when system calls for an anti-corrosion coating.

- When speed sensor components have been removed, ALWAYS check sensor-to-ring air gaps when applicable. These specifications can be found in each appropriate article.

- ONLY use recommended brake fluids. DO NOT use silicone brake fluids in an ABS equipped vehicle.

- When installing transmitting devices (CB's, telephones, etc.) on ABS equipped vehicles, DO NOT locate the antenna near the ABS control unit (or any control unit).

- Disconnect all on-board computers, when using electric welding equipment.

- DO NOT expose the ABS control unit to prolonged periods of high heat (185°F/85°C for 2 hours is generally considered a maximum limit).

1994 GENERAL INFORMATION
Wheel Alignment Theory & Operation

PRE-ALIGNMENT INSTRUCTIONS

Before adjusting wheel alignment, check the following:

- Ensure each axle uses tires of same construction and tread style, equal in tread wear and overall diameter. Using a dial indicator, verify that radial and axial runout of tires is not excessive. Inflation should be at manufacturer's specifications. *See Fig. 1.*
- Ensure steering linkage and suspension does not have excessive play. Check for wear in tie rod ends and ball joints. Springs must not be sagging. Check that control arm and strut rod bushings do not have excessive play.
- Vehicle must be on level floor with full fuel tank, no passenger load, spare tire in place and no load in trunk. Bounce front and rear end of vehicle several times. Confirm vehicle is at normal riding height.
- Ensure steering wheel is centered with wheels in straight ahead position. If required, shorten one tie rod adjusting sleeve and lengthen opposite sleeve (equal amount of turns). *See Fig. 2.*
- Ensure that wheel bearings have correct preload and that lug nuts are tightened to manufacturer's specifications. Adjust camber, caster and toe-in using this sequence. Follow instructions of the alignment equipment manufacturer.

CAUTION: DO NOT attempt to correct alignment by straightening parts. Damaged parts must be replaced.

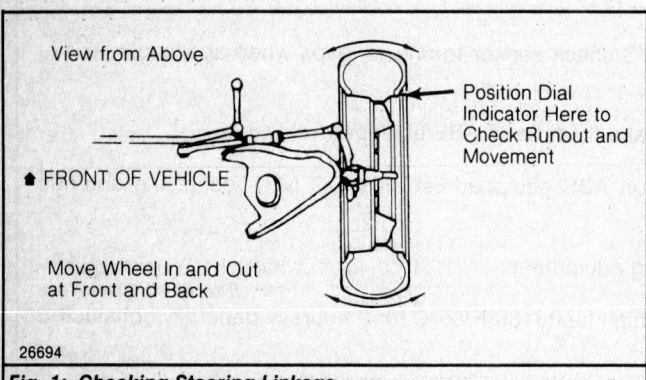

26694

Fig. 1: Checking Steering Linkage

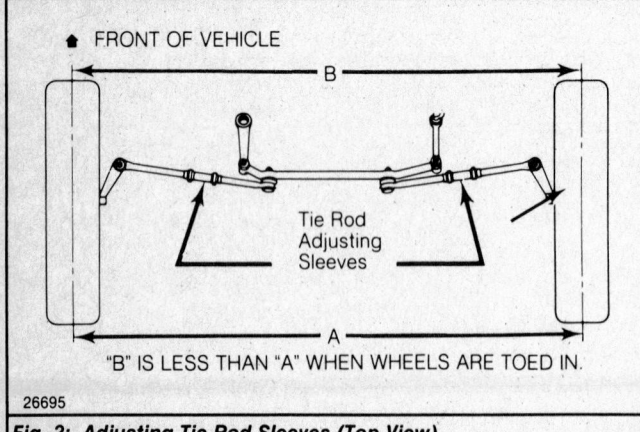

26695

Fig. 2: Adjusting Tie Rod Sleeves (Top View)

CAMBER

1) Camber is the tilting of the wheel, outward at either top or bottom, as viewed from front of vehicle. *See Fig. 3.*
2) When wheels tilt outward at the top (from centerline of vehicle), camber is positive. When wheels tilt inward at top, camber is negative. Amount of tilt is measured in degrees from vertical.

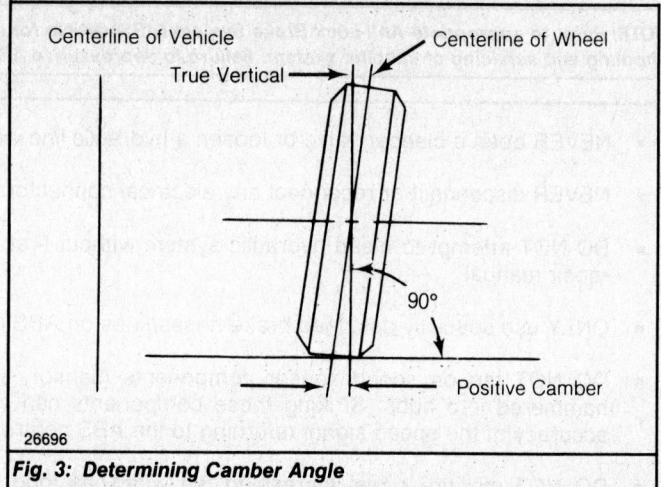

26696

Fig. 3: Determining Camber Angle

CASTER

1) Caster is tilting of front steering axis either forward or backward from vertical, as viewed from side of vehicle. *See Fig. 4.*
2) When axis is tilted backward from vertical, caster is positive. This creates a trailing action on front wheels. When axis is tilted forward, caster is negative, causing a leading action on front wheels.

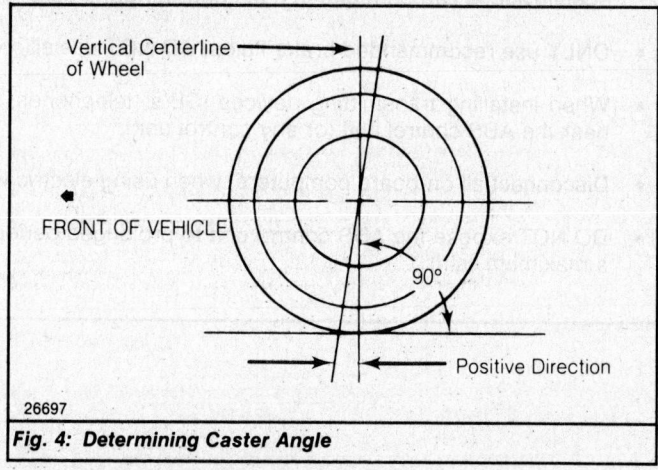

26697

Fig. 4: Determining Caster Angle

TOE-IN ADJUSTMENT

Toe-in is the width measured at the rear of the tires subtracted by the width measured at the front of the tires at about spindle height. *See Fig. 5.* Toe-in specification is Dimension A less Dimension B. A positive figure would indicate toe-in and a negative figure would indicate toe-out. If the distance between the front and rear of the tires is the same, toe measurement would be zero. Use the following procedures to adjust toe-in:

1) Measure toe-in with front wheels in straight ahead position and steering wheel centered. To adjust toe-in, loosen clamps and turn adjusting sleeve or adjustable end on right and left tie rods. *See Figs. 2 and 5.*
2) Turn equally and in opposite directions to maintain steering wheel in centered position. Face of tie rod end must be parallel with machined surface of steering rod end to prevent binding.
3) When tightening clamps, make certain that clamp bolts are positioned so there will be no interference with other parts throughout the entire travel of the steering linkage.

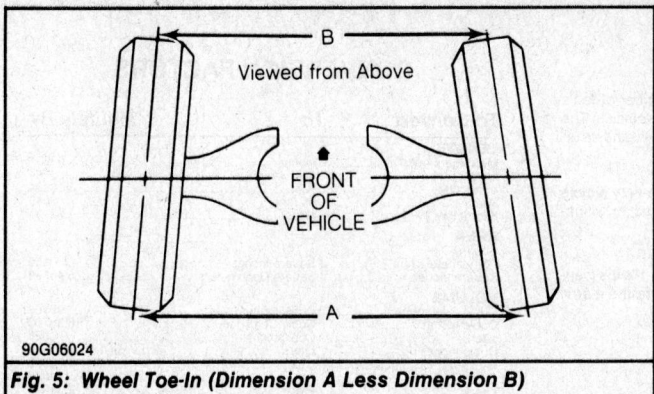

Fig. 5: Wheel Toe-In (Dimension A Less Dimension B)

TOE-OUT ON TURNS

1) Toe-out on turns (turning radius) is a check for bent or damaged parts, and not a service adjustment. With caster, camber, and toe-in properly adjusted, check toe-out with weight of vehicle on wheels.

2) Use a full floating turntable under each wheel, repeating test with each wheel positioned for right and left turns. Incorrect toe-out generally indicates a bent steering arm. Replace steering arm, if necessary, and recheck wheel alignment.

STEERING AXIS INCLINATION

1) Steering axis inclination is a check for bent or damaged parts, and not a service adjustment. Vehicle must be level and camber should be properly adjusted. *See Fig. 6.*

2) If camber cannot be brought within limits and steering axis inclination is correct, steering knuckle is bent. If camber and steering axis inclination are both incorrect by approximately the same amount, the upper and lower control arms are bent.

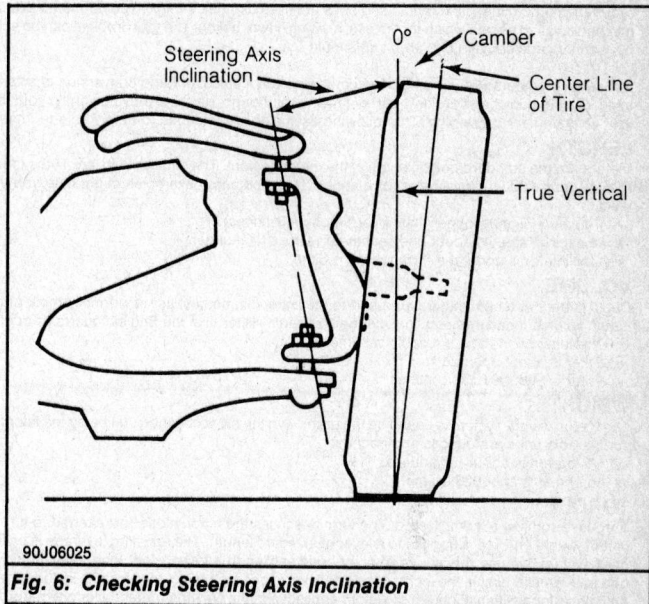

Fig. 6: Checking Steering Axis Inclination

1994 GENERAL INFORMATION
English-Metric Conversion Chart

METRIC CONVERSIONS

Metric conversions are making life more difficult for the mechanic. In addition to doubling the number of tools required, metric-dimensioned nuts and bolts are used alongside English components in many new vehicles. The mechanic has to decide which tool to use, slowing down the job. The tool problem can be solved by trial and error, but some metric conversions aren't so simple.

Converting temperature, lengths or volumes requires a calculator and conversion charts, or else a very nimble mind. Conversion charts are only part of the answer though, because they don't help you "think" metric, or "visualize" what you are converting. The following examples are intended to help you "see" metric sizes:

LENGTH

Meters are the standard unit of length in the metric system. The smaller units are 10ths (decimeter), 100ths (centimeter), and 1000ths (millimeter) of a meter. These common examples might help you to visualize the metric units:

- A meter is slightly longer than a yard (about 40 inches).
- An aspirin tablet is about one centimeter across (.4 inches).
- A millimeter is about the thickness of a dime.

VOLUME

Cubic meters and centimeters are used to measure volume, just as we normally think of cubic feet and inches. Liquid volume measurements include the liter and milliliter, like the English quarts or ounces.

- One teaspoon is about 4 cubic centimeters.
- A liter is about one quart.
- A liter is about 61 cubic inches.

WEIGHT

The metric weight system is based on the gram, with the most common unit being the kilogram (1000 grams). Our comparable units are ounces and pounds:

- A kilogram is about 2.2 pounds.
- An ounce is about 28 grams.

TORQUE

Torque is somewhat complicated. The term describes the amount of effort exerted to turn something. A chosen unit of weight or force is applied to a lever of standard length. The resulting leverage is called torque. In our standard system, we use the weight of one pound applied to a lever a foot long, resulting in the unit called a foot-pound. A smaller unit is the inch-pound (the lever is one inch long). Metric units include the meter kilogram (lever one meter long with a kilogram of weight applied) and the Newton-meter (lever one meter long with force of one Newton applied). Some conversions are:

- A meter kilogram is about 7.2 foot pounds.
- A foot pound is about 1.4 Newton-meters.
- A centimeter kilogram (cmkg) is equal to .9 inch pounds.

PRESSURE

Pressure is another complicated measurement. Pressure is described as a force or weight applied to a given area. Our common unit is pounds per square inch. Metric units can be expressed in several ways. One is the kilogram per square centimeter (kg/cm²). Another unit of pressure is the Pascal (force of one Newton on an area of one square meter), which equals about 4 ounces on a square yard. Since this is a very small amount of pressure, we usually see the kiloPascal, or kPa (1000 Pascals). Another common automotive term for pressure is the bar (used by German manufacturers), which equals 10 Pascals. Thoroughly confused? Try the examples below:

- Atmospheric pressure at sea level is about 14.7 psi.
- Atmospheric pressure at sea level is about 1 bar.
- Atomspheric pressure at sea level is about 1 kg/cm².
- One pound per square inch is about 7 kPa.

WE ENCOURAGE
PROFESSIONALISM

ASE CERTIFIED

THROUGH TECHNICIAN
CERTIFICATION

CONVERSION FACTORS

To Convert	To	Multiply By
LENGTH		
Millimeters (mm)	Inches	.03937
Inches	Millimeters	25.4
Meters (M)	Feet	3.28084
Feet	Meters	.3048
Kilometers (Km)	Miles	.62137
AREA		
Square Centimeters (cm²)	Square Inches	.155
Square Inches	Square Centimeters	6.45159
VOLUME		
Cubic Centimeters	Cubic Inches	.06103
Cubic Inches	Cubic Centimeters	16.38703
Liters	Cubic Inches	61.025
Cubic Inches	Liters	.01639
Liters	Quarts	1.05672
Quarts	Liters	.94633
Liters	Pints	2.11344
Pints	Liters	.47317
Liters	Ounces	33.81497
Ounces	Liters	.02957
WEIGHT		
Grams	Ounces	.03527
Ounces	Grams	28.34953
Kilograms	Pounds	2.20462
Pounds	Kilograms	.45359
WORK		
Centimeter Kilograms	Inch Pounds	.8676
Pounds/Sq. Inch	Kilograms/Sq. Centimeter	.07031
Bar	Pounds/Sq. Inch	14.504
Pounds/Sq. Inch	Bar	.06895
Atmosphere	Pounds/Sq. Inch	14.696
Pounds/Sq. Inch	Atmosphere	.06805
TEMPERATURE		
Centigrade Degrees	Fahrenheit Degrees	$(C° \times \%) + 32$
Fahrenheit Degrees	Centigrade Degrees	$(F° - 32) \times \%$

Inches	Decimals	mm
1/64	.016	.397
1/32	.031	.794
3/64	.047	1.191
1/16	.063	1.588
5/64	.078	1.984
3/32	.094	2.381
7/64	.109	2.778
1/8	.125	3.175
9/64	.141	3.572
5/32	.156	3.969
11/64	.172	4.366
3/16	.188	4.763
13/64	.203	5.159
7/32	.219	5.556
15/64	.234	5.953
1/4	.250	6.350
17/64	.266	6.747
9/32	.281	7.144
19/64	.297	7.541
5/16	.313	7.938
21/64	.328	8.334
11/32	.344	8.731
23/64	.359	9.128
3/8	.375	9.525
25/64	.391	9.992
13/32	.406	10.319
27/64	.422	10.716
7/16	.438	11.113
29/64	.453	11.509
15/32	.469	11.906
31/64	.484	12.303
1/2	.500	12.700
33/64	.516	13.097
17/32	.531	13.494
35/64	.547	13.891
9/16	.563	14.288
37/64	.578	14.684
19/32	.594	15.081
39/64	.609	15.478
5/8	.625	15.875
41/64	.641	16.272
21/32	.656	16.669
43/64	.672	17.066
11/16	.687	17.463
45/64	.703	17.859
23/32	.719	18.256
47/64	.734	18.653
3/4	.750	19.050
49/64	.766	19.447
25/32	.781	19.844
51/64	.797	20.241
13/16	.813	20.638
53/64	.828	21.034
27/32	.844	21.431
55/64	.859	21.828
7/8	.875	22.225
57/64	.891	22.622
29/32	.906	23.019
59/64	.922	23.416
15/16	.938	23.813
61/64	.953	24.209
31/32	.969	24.606
63/64	.984	25.003
1	1.000	25.400

MITCHELL INTERNATIONAL
9889 Willow Creek Road
P.O. Box 26260
San Diego, CA 92196-0260

1994 ACURA CONTENTS

STEERING

TRANSMISSION SERVICING

1994 MODEL COVERAGE

MODEL	BODY CODE	ENGINE	ENGINE ID	FUEL SYSTEM	IGNITION SYSTEM [1]
Integra	[2]	1.8L (B18B1)	[3]	PGM-FI	Magnetic
Integra GS-R	[4]	1.8L (B18C1)	[3]	PGM-FI	Magnetic
Legend	[5]	3.2L (C32A1)	[3]	PGM-FI	DIS
Vigor	CC2	2.5L (G25A1)	[3]	PGM-FI	Magnetic

[1] – Timing is computer controlled.
[2] – DC4-Hatchback; DB7-Sedan.
[3] – Engine and body code are identified by the fourth, fifth and sixth characters of the VIN.
[4] – DC2-Hatchback; DB8-Sedan.
[5] – KA8-Coupe; KA7-Sedan.

VIN DEFINITION

J H 4 K A 5 5 4 X P C 0 0 0 0 0 1
① ② ③ ④ ⑤ ⑥ ⑦ ⑧ ⑨ ⑩ ⑪ ⑫ ⑬ ⑭ ⑮ ⑯ ⑰

①Indicates Nation of Origin.
②Indicates Manufacturer.
③Indicates Model.
④⑤⑥**Indicates Engine/Body Code.**
⑦Indicates Body & Transmission Type.
⑧Indicates Model Series.
⑨Indicates Check Digit.
⑩**Indicates Model Year.**
⑪Indicates Assembly Plant.
⑫⑬⑭⑮⑯⑰Indicates Production Sequence.

MODEL YEAR VIN CODE APPLICATION

VIN Code	Model Year
N	1992
P	1993
R	1994

ENGINE CODE LOCATION

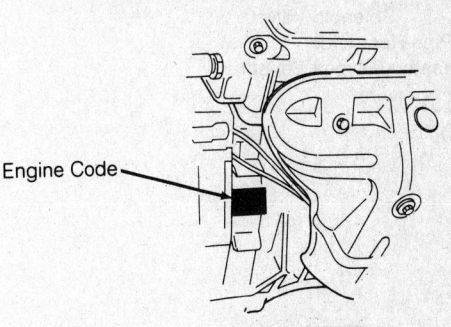

Engine Code

4-CYLINDER

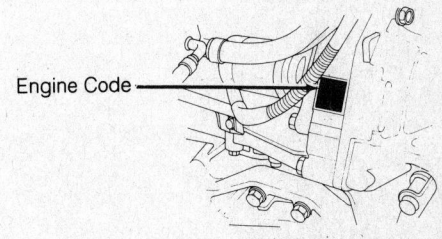

Engine Code

5-CYLINDER

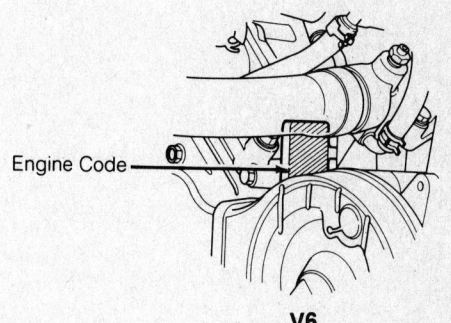

Engine Code

V6

92J26186

Courtesy of American Honda Motor Co., Inc.

1994 ENGINE PERFORMANCE
Emission Applications

1994 ACURA

Model, Engine & Fuel System	Emission Control Systems & Devices
Integra	
1.8L 4-Cyl. SFI	**PCV, EVAP, TWC, FR, SPK, HO2S, CEC, MIL,** EVAP-PCSV
Legend	
3.2L V6 SFI	**PCV, EVAP, TWC, FR, EGR, SPK,** [1] **PAIR, HO2S, CEC, MIL,** [1] PAIR-ASVL, [1] PAIR-ASCS, EGR-CVCV, EGR-SOL, EGR-PS, EVAP-PCSV
Vigor	
2.5L 5-Cyl. SFI	**PCV, EVAP, TWC, FR, EGR, SPK, HO2S, CEC, MIL,** EGR-CVCV, EGR-SOL, EGR-PS, EVAP-PCSV

[1] – Used on L and LS sedan models only.

NOTE: For quick reference, major emission control systems and devices are listed in bold type; components and other related devices are listed in light type.

CEC – Computerized Engine Controls
EGR – Exhaust Gas Recirculation
EGR-CVCV – EGR Constant Vacuum Control Valve
EGR-PS – EGR Position Sensor
EGR-SOL – EGR Solenoid
EVAP – Fuel Evaporative System
EVAP-PCSV – EVAP Purge Cut-Off
        Solenoid Valve
FR – Fill Pipe Restrictor
HO2S – Heated Oxygen Sensor

MIL – Malfunction Indicator Light
PAIR – Pulsed Secondary Air Injection
PAIR-ASCS – Air Suction Control Solenoid
PAIR-ASVL – Air Suction Valve
PCV – Positive Crankcase Ventilation
SFI – Sequential Fuel Injection
SPK – Spark Controls
TWC – Three-Way Catalyst

Integra, Legend, Vigor

INTRODUCTION

Use this article to quickly find specifications related to servicing and on-vehicle adjustments. This is a quick-reference article to use when you are familiar with an adjustment procedure and only need a specification.

CAPACITIES

BATTERY SPECIFICATIONS

Application	Amp Hr. Rating
Integra	36
Legend	
Coupe	61
Sedan	72
Vigor	54

FLUID CAPACITIES

Application	Quantity
Auto. Transaxle (Dexron-II)	
Integra	
Fluid Change	2.9 Qts. (2.7L)
Overhaul	6.2 Qts. (5.9L)
Legend	
Fluid Change	3.5 Qts. (3.3L)
Overhaul	9.2 Qts. (8.7L)
Vigor	
Fluid Change	2.6 Qts. (2.5L)
Overhaul	7.6 Qts. (7.2L)
Cooling System (Includes Heater)	
Integra	5.3 Qts. (5.0L)
Legend	9.2 Qts. (8.7L)
Vigor	6.3 Qts. (6.0L)
Crankcase (Includes Filter)	
Integra	
1.8L GS-R	4.2 Qts. (4.0L)
1.8L Except GS-R	4.0 Qts. (3.8L)
Legend	5.0 Qts. (4.7L)
Vigor	4.5 Qts. (4.3L)
Differential (SAE 90 GL4 or 5)	[1] 1.1 Qts. (1.0L)
Man. Transaxle (SAE 10W-40 API SE or SF)	
Integra	2.3 Qts. (2.2L)
Legend	2.4 Qts. (2.3L)
Vigor	1.9 Qts. (1.8L)

[1] – Except Integra, which has an integral transaxle/differential.

QUICK-SERVICE

SERVICE INTERVALS & SPECIFICATIONS

REPLACEMENT INTERVALS

Component	Miles
Air Filter	30,000
Anti-Lock Brake System High Pressure Hose	60,000
Automatic Transmission Fluid	30,000
Brake Fluid	30,000
Cam Timing Belt	90,000
Coolant	45,000
Differential	30,000
Engine Oil & Filter	7500
Fuel Filter	60,000
Manual Transmission Oil	30,000
Spark Plugs	
Integra (Except GS-R) & Vigor	30,000
Integra GS-R & Legend	60,000
Valve Clearance	15,000

BELT ADJUSTMENT

Application	[1] Deflection – In. (mm)
A/C Compressor	
Integra	9/32-11/32 (7-9)
Legend	5/16-13/32 (8-10.5)
Vigor	1/4-11/32 (6-9)
Alternator	
Integra	9/32-13/32 (7-10.5)
Legend	3/8-29/64 (9.5-11.5)
Vigor	19/64-3/8 (7.5-9.5)
Power Steering	
Integra	5/16-13/32 (8.0-10.5)
Legend	29/64-17/32 (11.5-13.5)
Vigor	1/4-11/32 (6.5-9)

[1] – Deflection is with 22 lbs. (10 kg) pressure applied midway on longest belt run.

MECHANICAL CHECKS

ENGINE COMPRESSION

ENGINE COMPRESSION [1]

Application	Specification
Integra	
Compression Ratio	
GS-R	10.0:1
Except GS-R	9.2:1
Compression Pressure at 250 RPM	
Standard	
GS-R	270 psi (19.0 kg/cm²)
Except GS-R	200 psi (14.0 kg/cm²)
Minimum	135 psi (9.5 kg/cm²)
Legend	
Compression Ratio	9.6:1
Compression Pressure at 200 RPM	
Standard	200 psi (14.0 kg/cm²)
Minimum	142 psi (10.0 kg/cm²)
Vigor	
Compression Ratio	9.0:1
Compression Pressure at 250 RPM	
Standard	206 psi (14.5 kg/cm²)
Minimum	135 psi (9.5 kg/cm²)

[1] – Maximum variation between cylinders is 28 psi (2 kg/cm²).

VALVE CLEARANCE

NOTE: Legend models are equipped with hydraulic lifters. No adjustments are required.

VALVE CLEARANCE ADJUSTMENT [1]

Application	In. (mm)
Integra	
1.8L (GS-R)	
Intake	.006-.007 (.15-.18)
Exhaust	.007-.008 (.18-.20)
1.8L (Except GS-R)	
Intake	.003-.005 (.08-.13)
Exhaust	.006-.008 (.15-.20)
Vigor	
Intake	.009-.011 (.24-.28)
Exhaust	.011-.013 (.28-.32)

[1] – Adjust valves when engine is cold.

IGNITION SYSTEM

IGNITION COIL

IGNITION COIL RESISTANCE – Ohms @ 77°F (25°C)

Application	Primary	Secondary
Integra	.6-.8	12,800-19,200
Legend	.9-1.1	[1]
Vigor	.03-.05	10,800-16,200

[1] – Information is not available from manufacturer.

1994 ENGINE PERFORMANCE
Service & Adjustment Specifications (Cont.)

DISTRIBUTOR SENSORS
DISTRIBUTOR SENSOR RESISTANCE

Application	Ohms
Integra	
CRANK Sensor	350-700
CYL Sensor	350-700
TDC Sensor	350-700
Legend	
CRANK Sensor	650-900
CYL Sensor	650-900
Vigor	
CRANK Sensor	650-850
CYL Sensor	650-850
TDC Sensor	650-850

HIGH TENSION WIRE RESISTANCE
HIGH TENSION WIRE RESISTANCE

Application	Ohms
All Models	25,000 Maximum

SPARK PLUGS
SPARK PLUG TYPE

Application	NGK	Nippondenso
Integra		
GS-R		
Normal Driving	PFR6G-13	PK20PR-L13
Except GS-R		
Normal Driving	ZFR5F-11	KJ16CR-L11
Hot Climates	ZRF6F-11	KJ20CR-L11
Legend Coupe		
& GS Sedan		
Normal Driving	[1] PFR6G-11	[1] PK20PR-L11
Hot Climates	PFR7G-11	PK22PR-L11
Cold Climates	PFR5G-11	PK16PR-L11
Legend L & LS		
Normal Driving	PFR6G-11	PK20PR-L11
Hot Climates	PFR7G-11	PK22PR-L11
Cold Climates	PFR5G-11	PK16PR-L11
Vigor		
Normal Driving	BKR5E-N11	K16PR-L11
Hot Climates	BKR6E-N11	K20PR-L11

[1] – May also use NGK PFR6F-11 or Nippondenso PKJ20CR-L11.

SPARK PLUG SPECIFICATIONS

Application	Gap In. (mm)	Torque Ft. Lbs. (N.m)
All Models [1]	.043 (1.1)	13 (18)

[1] – On Integra GS-R models, do not regap. Replace spark plug is gap exceeds .043" (1.1 mm).

FIRING ORDER & TIMING MARKS

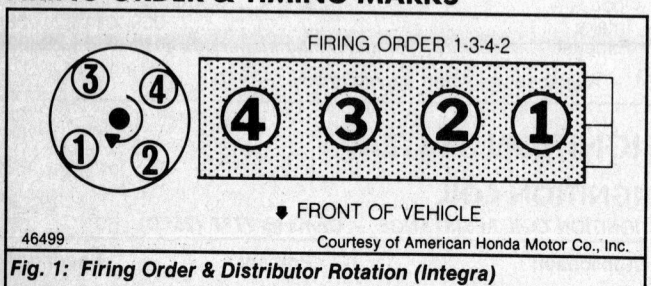

FIRING ORDER 1-3-4-2

➜ FRONT OF VEHICLE

46499
Courtesy of American Honda Motor Co., Inc.

Fig. 1: Firing Order & Distributor Rotation (Integra)

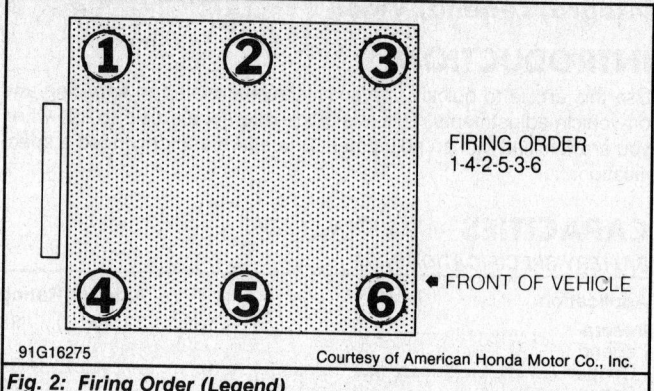

FIRING ORDER
1-4-2-5-3-6

◄ FRONT OF VEHICLE

91G16275
Courtesy of American Honda Motor Co., Inc.

Fig. 2: Firing Order (Legend)

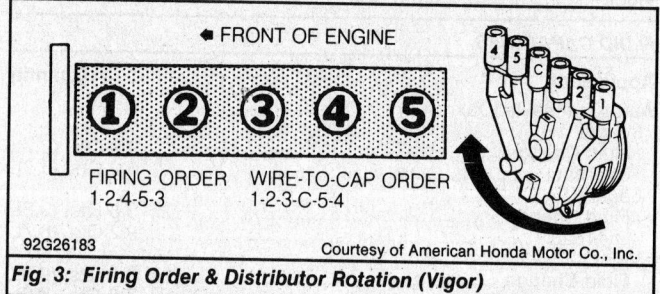

◄ FRONT OF ENGINE

FIRING ORDER
1-2-4-5-3

WIRE-TO-CAP ORDER
1-2-3-C-5-4

92G26183
Courtesy of American Honda Motor Co., Inc.

Fig. 3: Firing Order & Distributor Rotation (Vigor)

IGNITION TIMING
IGNITION TIMING (Degrees BTDC @ RPM)

Application	[1] Man. Trans.	[2] Auto. Trans.
Integra	14-18 @ 700-800	14-18 @ 700-800
Legend		
Coupe & GS Sedan	13-17 @ 630-730	13-17 @ 580-680
Sedan L & LS	13-17 @ 600-700	13-17 @ 550-650
Vigor	13-17 @ 650-750	13-17 @ 650-750

[1] – Manual transmission in Neutral.
[2] – Automatic transmission in Neutral or Park.

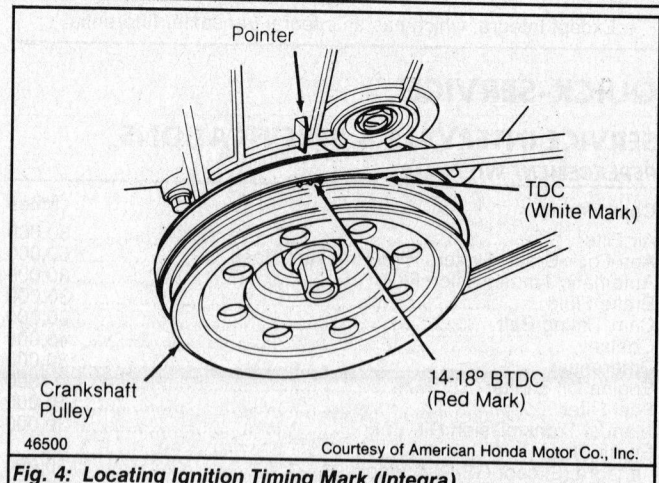

Pointer

TDC
(White Mark)

14-18° BTDC
(Red Mark)

Crankshaft
Pulley

46500
Courtesy of American Honda Motor Co., Inc.

Fig. 4: Locating Ignition Timing Mark (Integra)

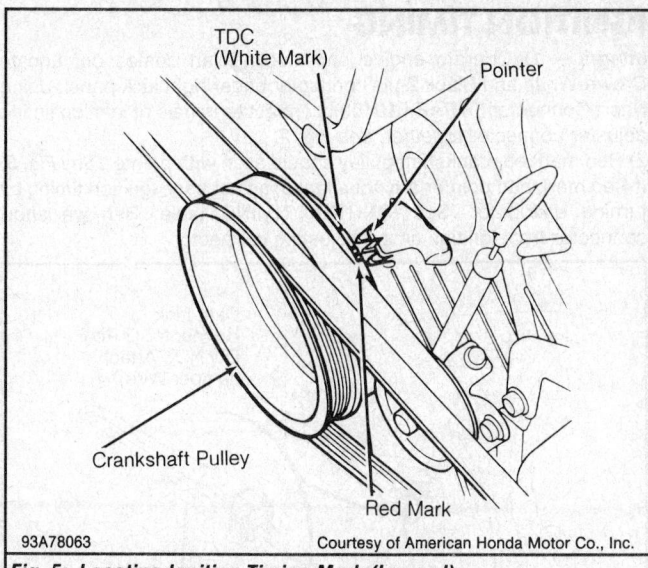

93A78063   Courtesy of American Honda Motor Co., Inc.

Fig. 5: Locating Ignition Timing Mark (Legend)

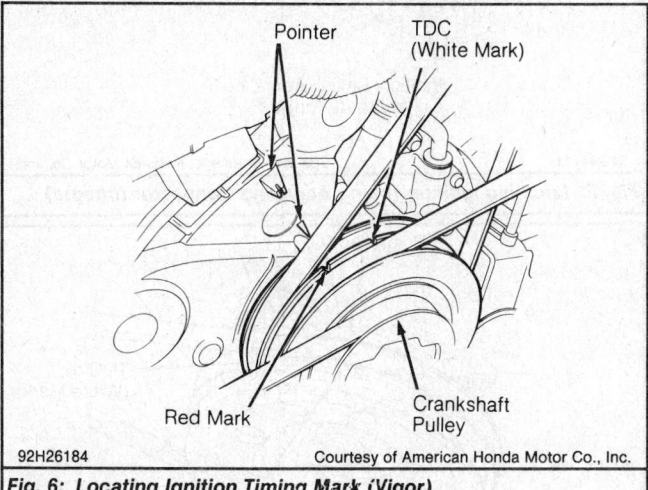

92H26184   Courtesy of American Honda Motor Co., Inc.

Fig. 6: Locating Ignition Timing Mark (Vigor)

FUEL SYSTEM

FUEL PUMP

NOTE: *Fuel pump performance is a measurement of fuel pressure and volume availability, not regulated fuel pressure.*

FUEL PUMP PERFORMANCE

Application	Pressure psi (kg/cm²)	Min. Vol. In 10 Sec. Pts. (L)
Integra		
1.8L GS-R	[1] 40 (2.8)	.41 (.22)
1.8L Except GS-R	[1] 35 (2.5)	.34 (.20)
Legend		
Coupe & GS Sedan	[1] 40 (2.8)	.63 (.30)
Sedan L & LS	[1] 33 (2.3)	.48 (.23)
Vigor	[1] 35 (2.5)	.48 (.23)

[1] – Approximate. See REGULATED FUEL PRESSURE table.

REGULATED FUEL PRESSURE

Application	At Idle W/O Vacuum psi (kg/cm²)	At Idle W/ Vacuum psi (kg/cm²)
Integra		
1.8L GS-R	48-56 (3.4-3.9)	39-46 (2.8-3.3)
1.8L Except GS-R	41-48 (2.9-3.4)	33-39 (2.3-2.8)
Legend		
Coupe & GS Sedan	44-51 (3.1-3.6)	36-43 (2.5-3.0)
Sedan L & LS	35-41 (2.5-2.9)	29-35 (2.1-2.4)
Vigor	43-50 (3.0-3.5)	33-41 (2.3-2.9)

INJECTOR RESISTANCE

INJECTOR RESISTANCE SPECIFICATIONS

Application	Ohms
Integra	10-13
Legend & Vigor	1.5-2.5

IDLE SPEED & MIXTURE

IDLE SPEED SPECIFICATIONS

Application	RPM
Integra	[1] 700-800
Legend	
Coupe & GS Sedan	
Automatic Trans.	[1] 580-680
Manual Trans.	630-730
Sedan L & LS	
Automatic Trans.	[1] 550-650
Manual Trans.	600-700
Vigor	[1] 650-750

[1] – Automatic transmission in Neutral or Park.

IDLE CO LEVEL

Application	CO Level
All Models	0.1%

FAST IDLE SPEED

FAST IDLE SPEED SPECIFICATIONS

Application	RPM
Integra	1400-1800
Legend	1300-1700
Vigor	1400

THROTTLE ANGLE SENSOR

NOTE: *Throttle angle sensor is not adjustable. For testing procedures, refer to SELF-DIAGNOSTICS or SYSTEM & COMPONENT TESTING article.*

1994 ENGINE PERFORMANCE
On-Vehicle Adjustments

Integra, Legend, Vigor

ENGINE MECHANICAL

Before performing any on-vehicle adjustments to fuel or ignition system, ensure engine mechanical condition is okay.

VALVE CLEARANCE

NOTE: Legend is equipped with hydraulic lifters. Adjustments are not required.

Integra – 1) Cylinder head temperature must be less than 100°F (38°C). Remove valve cover, timing belt covers and distributor cap.
2) Align pointer on timing belt lower cover with TDC (White mark). UP marks on both camshaft sprockets should be at top of cam gears. Distributor rotor should point to No. 1 spark plug wire on cap. Adjust valves on cylinder No. 1.
3) Rotate crankshaft counterclockwise 180 degrees to bring No. 3 piston to TDC on compression stroke. Adjust valves on cylinder No. 3.
4) Rotate crankshaft counterclockwise 180 degrees to bring No. 4 piston to TDC on compression stroke. Adjust valves on cylinder No. 4.
5) Rotate crankshaft counterclockwise 180 degrees to bring No. 2 piston to TDC on compression stroke. Adjust valves on cylinder No. 2.

VALVE CLEARANCE ADJUSTMENT (INTEGRA)

Application [1]	In. (mm)
1.8L (GS-R)	
Intake	.006-.007 (.15-.19)
Exhaust	.007-.008 (.17-.21)
1.8L (Except GS-R)	
Intake	.003-.005 (.08-.12)
Exhaust	.006-.008 (.16-.20)

[1] – Adjust valves when engine is cold.

Vigor – 1) Engine temperature must be less than 100°F (38°C). Remove cylinder head cover. Align No. 1 mark on camshaft sprocket with mark on cam holder. *See Fig. 1.*
2) Loosen adjustment screw lock nut. Adjust valves on cylinder No. 1. Tighten lock nut. Recheck clearance. Repeat procedure if clearance changes.
3) Rotate crankshaft 144 degrees. Align No. 2 mark on camshaft sprocket with mark on cam holder. Repeat adjustment procedure on cylinder No. 2. Tighten lock nut. Recheck clearance. Repeat procedure on cylinders No. 4, 5 and 3 in this order.

VALVE CLEARANCE ADJUSTMENT (VIGOR)

Application [1]	In. (mm)
Intake	.009-.011 (.24-.28)
Exhaust	.011-.013 (.28-.32)

[1] – Adjust valves when engine is cold.

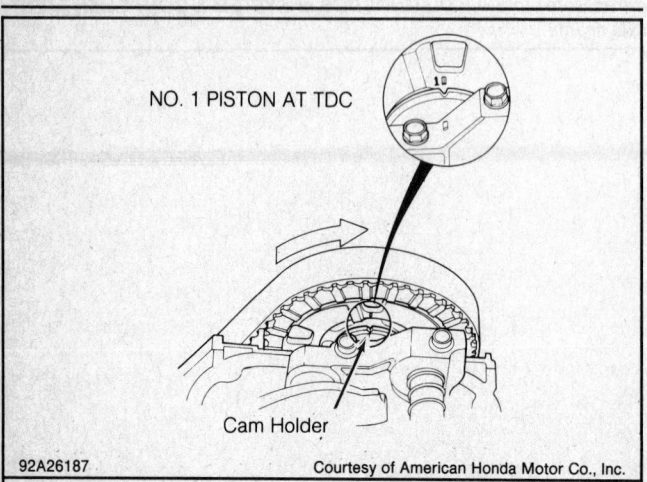

NO. 1 PISTON AT TDC

Cam Holder

92A26187   Courtesy of American Honda Motor Co., Inc.

Fig. 1: Identifying No. "1" Mark On Camshaft Sprocket (Vigor – No. "2" Through "5" Marks Are Similar)

IGNITION TIMING

Integra – 1) Operate engine until cooling fan comes on. Locate Brown/White and Black 2-pin connector under right kick panel. Using Short Connector (07PAZ-010100), connect terminals of ignition timing adjuster connector together. *See Fig. 2.*
2) Red mark on crankshaft pulley should align with pointer. *See Fig. 3.* If Red mark and pointer are not aligned, adjust base ignition timing by turning distributor. See IGNITION TIMING table. Remove short connector from ignition timing adjusting connector.

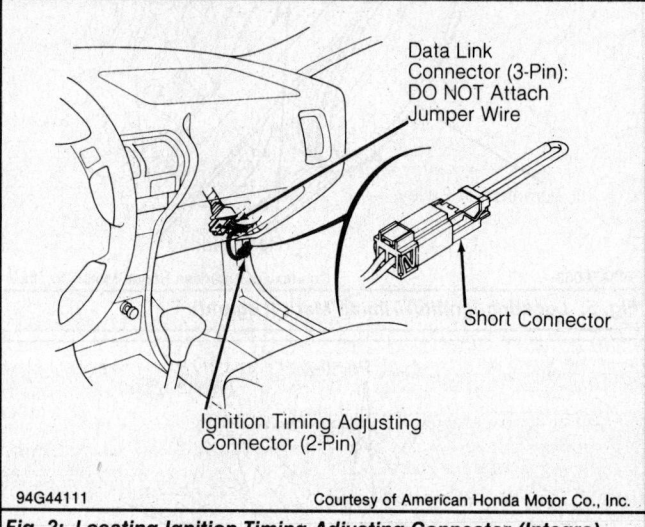

Data Link Connector (3-Pin): DO NOT Attach Jumper Wire

Short Connector

Ignition Timing Adjusting Connector (2-Pin)

94G44111   Courtesy of American Honda Motor Co., Inc.

Fig. 2: Locating Ignition Timing Adjusting Connector (Integra)

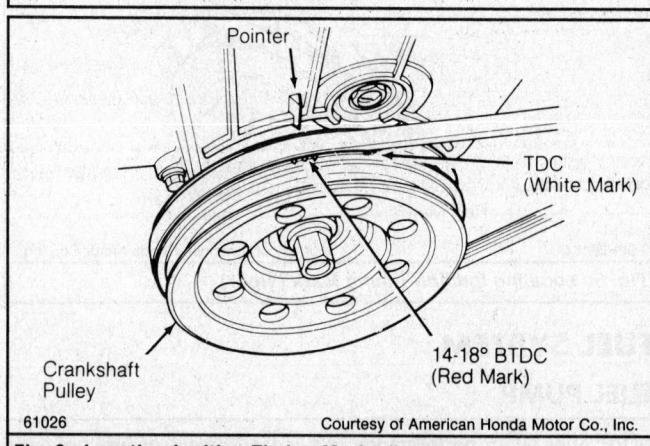

Pointer

TDC (White Mark)

14-18° BTDC (Red Mark)

Crankshaft Pulley

61026   Courtesy of American Honda Motor Co., Inc.

Fig. 3: Locating Ignition Timing Marks (Integra)

IGNITION TIMING (Degrees BTDC @ RPM)

Application	[1] M/T	[2] A/T
Integra	14-18 @ 700-800	14-18 @ 700-800
Legend		
Coupe & GS Sedan	13-17 @ 630-730	13-17 @ 580-680
Sedan "L" & LS	13-17 @ 600-700	13-17 @ 550-650
Vigor	13-17 @ 650-750	13-17 @ 650-750

[1] – Manual transmission in Neutral.
[2] – Automatic transmission in Neutral or Park.

Legend & Vigor – 1) Operate engine until cooling fan comes on. Locate ignition timing adjusting connector under right side of dash or at center console. Connect terminals of connector using a jumper wire. *See Fig. 4.*
2) Connect timing light. With engine at idle, Red mark on crankshaft pulley should align with pointer. *See Fig. 5.* If Red mark and pointer are not aligned, adjust timing. See IGNITION TIMING table.
3) Adjust ignition timing by turning adjusting screw on ignition timing adjuster. *See Fig. 6.* Remove control box cover. Using a 3/16" drill bit, drill out 2 rivets from adjuster. Remove cover.

4) Turn adjusting screw counterclockwise to retard timing or clockwise to advance timing. After adjustment, install cover to ignition timing adjuster using new rivets. Remove jumper wire from ignition timing adjusting connector.

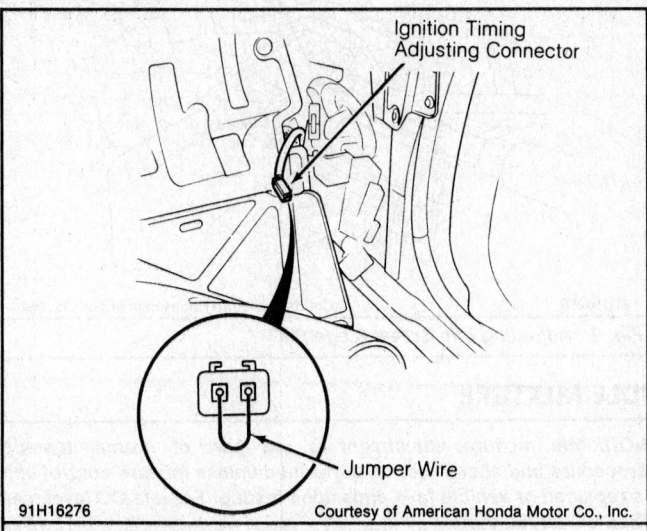

Fig. 4: Locating Ignition Timing Adjusting Connector (Legend Shown; Vigor Is Similar)

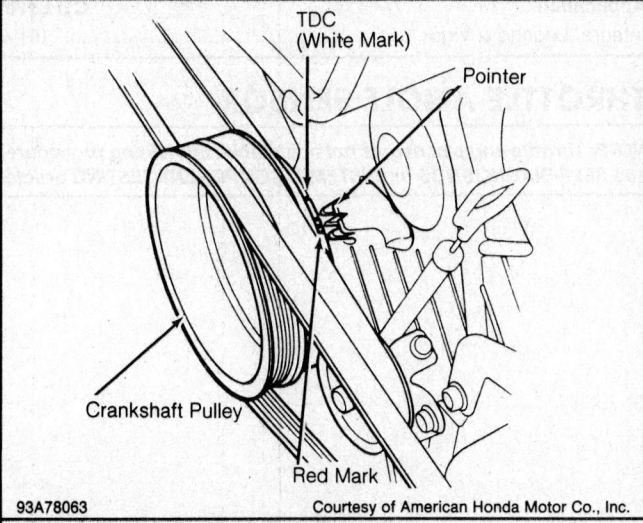

Fig. 5: Locating Ignition Timing Marks (Legend Shown; Vigor Is Similar)

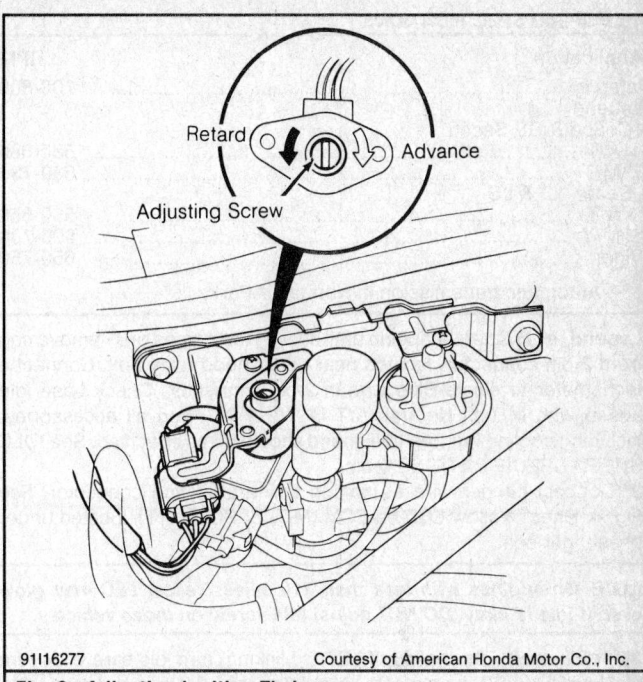

Fig. 6: Adjusting Ignition Timing (Legend Shown; Vigor Is Similar)

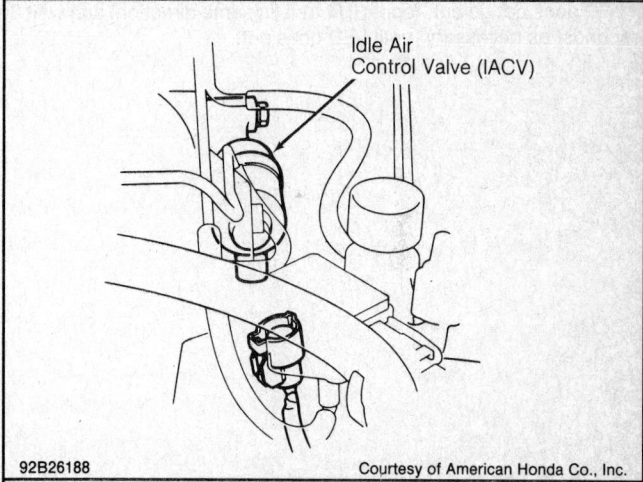

Fig. 7: Disconnecting IACV (Integra Shown; Vigor Is Similar)

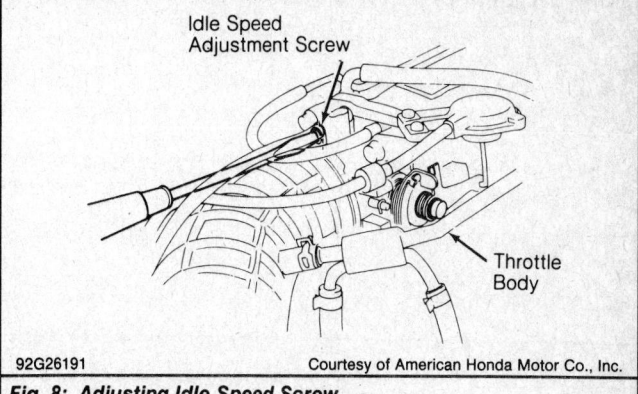

Fig. 8: Adjusting Idle Speed Screw (Integra Shown; Vigor Is Similar)

IDLE SPEED & MIXTURE

IDLE SPEED

Integra & Vigor – **1)** Operate engine until cooling fan comes on. Turn engine off. Connect tachometer. Disconnect 2-wire connector from Idle Air Control Valve (IACV). *See Fig. 7.*

2) Restart engine and hold at 1000 RPM momentarily. Let engine return to idle. Check base idle speed with M/T in Neutral (A/T in "N" or "P") and all accessories, including cooling fan, off. Base idle speed should be 430-530 RPM for Integra and 500-600 RPM for Vigor. If necessary, turn screw to adjust base idle speed. *See Fig. 8.*

3) Turn ignition off. Reconnect 2-wire IACV connector. Remove BACK-UP fuse (7.5-amp on Integra; 10-amp on Vigor) in main underhood fuse box for 10 seconds to reset ECU. Start engine and allow to idle for one minute. Check idle speed. Idle speed should be as specified. See IDLE SPEED SPECIFICATIONS table.

IDLE SPEED SPECIFICATIONS

Application	RPM
Integra	[1] 700-800
Legend	
Coupe & GS Sedan	
A/T	[1] 580-680
M/T	630-730
Sedan "L" & LS	
A/T	[1] 550-650
M/T	600-700
Vigor	[1] 650-750

[1] – Automatic transmission in Neutral or Park.

Legend – 1) Operate engine until cooling fan comes on. Remove cap from 2-pin connector, located near under-hood relay box. Connect a tachometer to single-Blue wire in 2-pin connector. Check base idle speed with M/T in Neutral (A/T in "N" or "P") and all accessories, including cooling fan, off. Idle speed should be as specified. See IDLE SPEED SPECIFICATIONS table.

2) Connect jumper wire at ignition timing adjusting connector. *See Fig. 4.* Check Yellow LED on ECM (M/T) or PCM (A/T), located under passenger seat.

NOTE: On engines with less than 310 miles, Yellow LED may glow even if idle is okay. DO NOT adjust idle screw on these vehicles.

3) If LED is off, idle is okay. If LED is blinking, turn idle screw 1/4 turn clockwise. If LED is on steady, turn idle screw 1/4 turn counterclockwise. *See Fig. 9.*

4) After turning idle screw 1/4 turn, wait 30 seconds for LED to go out. If LED does not go out, repeat 1/4 turn (in same direction) and wait 30 seconds, as necessary, until LED goes out.

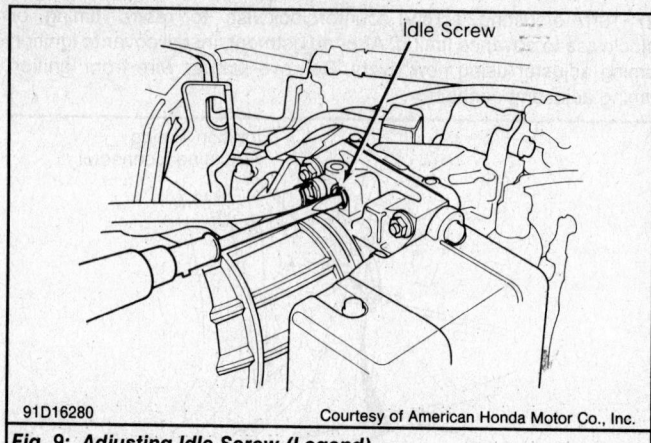

91D16280   Courtesy of American Honda Motor Co., Inc.

Fig. 9: Adjusting Idle Screw (Legend)

IDLE MIXTURE

NOTE: Idle mixture adjustment is not part of normal tune-up procedure and should not be performed unless mixture control unit is replaced or vehicle fails emissions testing. For idle CO level, see IDLE CO LEVEL table.

IDLE CO LEVEL

Application	CO Level
Integra, Legend & Vigor	0.1%

THROTTLE ANGLE SENSOR

NOTE: Throttle angle sensor is not adjustable. For testing procedure, see SELF-DIAGNOSTICS or SYSTEM & COMPONENT TESTING article.

Integra, Legend, Vigor

INTRODUCTION

This article covers basic description and operation of engine performance-related systems and components. Read this article before diagnosing vehicles or systems with which you are not completely familiar.

AIR INDUCTION SYSTEM

BY-PASS CONTROL SYSTEM (INTEGRA 1.8L GS-R & VIGOR)

Intake manifold has 2 air intake paths: long and short. Increased engine torque over a broad range is achieved by switching paths. High torque at low RPM is achieved by using the long intake path only. High torque at higher RPM is achieved by using both intake paths.

By-Pass Control Solenoid Valve – When engine RPM is less than 5750 RPM, signal from PCM activates by-pass control solenoid valve and intake air goes through long intake path. When engine speed is more than 5750 RPM, by-pass solenoid valve is shut off and intake air goes through both intake paths.

BY-PASS CONTROL SYSTEM (LEGEND)

Intake manifold has 3 air intake paths: short, medium and long. Increased engine torque over a broad range is achieved by switching paths. High torque at less than 3100 RPM (3300 RPM on Coupe and Sedan GS) is achieved by using a single long intake path. High torque at higher RPM is achieved by using both medium and long intake paths. Maximum horsepower is achieved by using all 3 intake paths.

By-Pass Low & High Control Solenoid Valves – When engine RPM is less than about 3200 RPM, signal from PCM activates by-pass low and high control solenoid valves to prevent opening of additional intake paths. Intake air goes through the single long intake path. When engine speed is about 3600 RPM, by-pass low solenoid valve is shut off, allowing intake air to go through both long and medium intake paths. At engine speeds greater than 3900 RPM (4300 RPM on Coupe and Sedan GS), PCM switches off both solenoid valves and intake air goes through all intake paths.

VARIABLE VALVE TIMING

VARIABLE VALVE TIMING & LIFT ELECTRONIC CONTROL SYSTEM (VTEC)

Integra 1.8L GS-R – VTEC uses 3 different intake cam lobes and rocker arms, synchronizer pistons, and a spool valve. See Fig. 1. Low lift cam lobes operate primary and secondary (outer) rocker arms. High lift cam lobe operates connecting (middle) rocker arm. PCM controls spool valve and synchronizer pistons.

At low speed, primary and secondary rocker arms control intake valve timing, lift and duration. Connecting rocker arm remains disengaged and has no effect on engine operation. At high RPM with heavy engine load, PCM activates spool valve and oil pressure is applied to

synchronizer pistons located in primary and secondary rocker arms. This locks primary, connecting and secondary rocker arms together so they are driven as a single unit by high lift cam lobe.

COMPUTERIZED ENGINE CONTROLS

POWERTRAIN CONTROL MODULE (PCM)

PCM contains memories for fuel injection timing and duration, idle speed control, ignition timing control, PCM back-up functions, and other control functions. The PCM is located under the carpet, in passenger-side footwell.

NOTE: Components are grouped into 2 categories. The first category is INPUT DEVICES, which are components that control or produce voltage signals monitored by the PCM. The second category is OUTPUT SIGNALS, which are components controlled by the PCM.

INPUT DEVICES

Vehicles are equipped with different combinations of input devices. Not all devices are used on all models. To determine the input device usage on a specific model, see WIRING DIAGRAMS article. The available input signals include:

A/C Switch Signal – Signals PCM when A/C is turned on. PCM uses this input to change engine RPM to compensate for extra engine load.

A/T Shift Position Signal – Informs PCM when automatic transmission is in Neutral or Park.

Alternator FR Signal – Sends signals to inform PCM that alternator is charging.

Barometric Pressure Sensor (Legend & Vigor) – Converts atmospheric pressure into electrical signals. Barometric pressure sensor is inside PCM.

Battery Voltage (IGN 1) – When ignition switch is ON position, a battery voltage signal (ignition circuit) is sent to PCM.

Brake Switch Signal – Signals PCM that brake pedal has been depressed. PCM uses this input signal to control idle speed.

Coolant Temperature Sensor – Coolant temperature sensor is a thermistor. The resistance of thermistor decreases as coolant temperature increases. PCM uses input to determine air/fuel mixture, timing and idle speed.

Clutch Switch – Signals PCM that clutch is engaged.

Crank Sensor – See IGNITION TIMING CONTROL under IGNITION SYSTEM.

Cylinder (CYL) Sensor – See IGNITION TIMING CONTROL under IGNITION SYSTEM.

EGR Position Sensor – See EGR POSITION SENSOR under EMISSION SYSTEMS.

Heated Oxygen Sensor (HO2S) – Detects oxygen content in exhaust gas and sends this information to PCM. PCM uses input from sensor to vary duration of fuel injection. Legend has 2 HO2S sensors. See OXYGEN SENSOR HEATER under EMISSION SYSTEMS.

Intake Air Temperature (TA) Sensor – TA sensor is a thermistor. Resistance of thermistor decreases as intake air temperature increases. PCM uses input from sensor to determine air/fuel mixture.

Ignition Output – Detects ignition signal. PCM will set a trouble code if PCM does not receive an ignition signal.

Knock Sensor(s) – If knock sensor detects detonation, ignition timing is retarded.

MAP Sensor – Converts manifold absolute pressure into electrical signals and sends this information to PCM. PCM uses input to determine air/fuel mixture.

Power Steering Pressure Signal – Signals PCM of high power steering load. PCM increases idle speed through Idle Air Control Valve (IACV).

Starter Signal – Signals PCM of engine start-up (cranking). PCM uses this to control IACV to promote easy starting.

TDC Sensor (Integra & Vigor) – See IGNITION TIMING CONTROL under IGNITION SYSTEM.

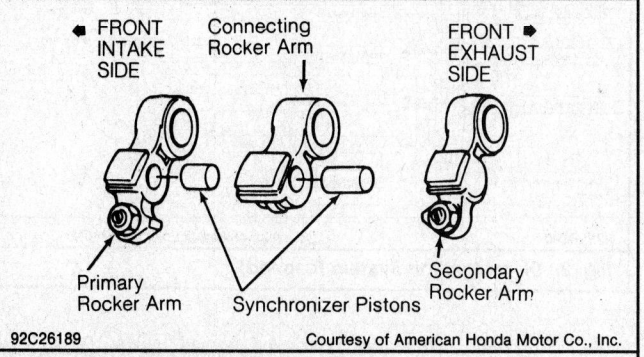

FRONT INTAKE SIDE ◄   Connecting Rocker Arm   FRONT EXHAUST SIDE ►

Primary Rocker Arm   Synchronizer Pistons   Secondary Rocker Arm

92C26189   Courtesy of American Honda Motor Co., Inc.

Fig. 1: Identifying VTEC Rocker Arms & Synchronizer Piston Assembly (Integra 1.8L GS-R)

Throttle Position Sensor – Throttle position sensor is a potentiometer connected to throttle valve shaft. As throttle opening changes, sensor varies voltage signal to PCM. PCM uses signal to determine fuel injection duration.

Vehicle Speed Sensor (VSS) – Sensor monitors vehicle speed and generates signal to PCM. Signal produces 4 pulses (switch closures to ground) per revolution of speedometer cable. PCM uses input from sensor to determine timing and fuel injection.

Variable Valve Timing & Lift Electronic Control System (VTEC) Pressure Switch Signal – Signals PCM to indicate oil pressure in VTEC. PCM uses information to determine activation of VTEC synchronizer pistons through solenoid. If failure occurs, PCM will set a trouble code.

OUTPUT SIGNALS

Vehicles are equipped with different combinations of computer-controlled components. Not all components listed below are used on every vehicle. For theory and operation of each output component, refer to indicated system.

A/C Compressor Clutch Relay Signal – See IDLE SPEED under FUEL SYSTEM.

By-Pass Control Solenoid Valve(s) – See appropriate BY-PASS CONTROL SYSTEM under AIR INDUCTION SYSTEM.

Malfunction Indicator Light (MIL) – See SELF-DIAGNOSTIC SYSTEM.

EGR Control Solenoid – See EMISSION SYSTEMS.

EVAP Purge Cut-Off Solenoid Valve – See EMISSION SYSTEMS.

Fuel Injectors – See FUEL CONTROL under FUEL SYSTEM.

Fuel Pressure Regulator Cut-Off Solenoid Valve – See FUEL DELIVERY under FUEL SYSTEM.

Fuel Pump Main Relay – See FUEL DELIVERY under FUEL SYSTEM.

Idle Air Control Valve – See IDLE SPEED under FUEL SYSTEM.

Ignitor Unit – See IGNITION SYSTEM.

Oxygen Sensor Heater – See EMISSION SYSTEMS.

PAIR Air Suction Control Solenoid Valve (Legend L & LS Sedan) – See EMISSION SYSTEMS.

FUEL SYSTEM

FUEL DELIVERY

Fuel Pump – Fuel pump is located inside fuel tank. When engine is started, main relay operates fuel pump. The pump has a relief valve to prevent excess pressure build-up. If discharge side is blocked, relief valve opens to by-pass fuel from discharge side to inlet side. When engine is turned off, the pump stops. A check valve in the fuel pump maintains fuel pressure in fuel line.

Fuel Pump Main Relay – Main relay is located on left side of firewall or left kick panel. Main relay contains 2 individual relays. First relay operates with ignition on and supplies battery voltage to PCM, injectors and second relay (fuel pump power). PCM controls second relay for 2 seconds after ignition is turned on and whenever engine is running.

Fuel Pressure Regulator – Fuel pressure regulator maintains constant fuel pressure to injectors. When the difference between fuel pressure and manifold pressure exceeds 36-50 psi (2.6-3.5 kg/cm²), the diaphragm is pushed upward and excess fuel is fed back into fuel tank. A vacuum-operated diaphragm inside regulator maintains fuel pressure at a specific range, allowing for changes in engine load.

At idle, intake manifold vacuum is high, causing diaphragm to be pulled up, thus reducing fuel pressure. When throttle is depressed, intake manifold vacuum decreases and regulator spring overcomes manifold vacuum. This causes fuel pressure to increase.

Fuel Pressure Regulator Cut-Off Solenoid Valve (Legend) – When coolant temperature exceeds 221°F (105°C) or intake air temperature exceeds 176°F (80°C), pressure regulator cut-off solenoid valve cuts vacuum to pressure regulator. This ensures high fuel pressure to injectors and prevents vapor lock.

Injector Resistor – Resistor reduces current supplied to injectors to prevent damage to injector coils.

FUEL CONTROL

Fuel Injectors – When current is applied to solenoid coil, valve lifts up and pressurized fuel is injected close to intake valve. PCM controls injector timing and length of time injector is opened. Injector is sealed by an "O" ring and a seal ring at each injector end (top and bottom).

Fuel Cut-Off – During deceleration, with the throttle valve closed and engine speed more than 1000 RPM, current to the fuel injectors is stopped. Current is also stopped when engine speed exceeds 8100 RPM on 1.8L GS-R, 7000 RPM on 1.8L except GS-R, 7100 RPM on 2.5L and 6500 RPM on L and LS Sedan (6900 RPM on Coupe and GS Sedan) 3.2L.

Throttle Body – The throttle body is a single-barrel side-draft type. The lower portion of the throttle valve is heated by engine coolant. The idle adjusting screw (preset at factory) increases or decreases by-pass air. Canister/purge port is located on top of throttle body.

IDLE SPEED

NOTE: For other input components in idle speed circuit, see INPUT DEVICES under COMPUTERIZED ENGINE CONTROLS.

Idle speed is controlled by Idle Air Control Valve (IACV) and fast idle control valve. IACV varies amount of air by-passing into intake manifold according to input signals received from PCM. When IACV is activated, valve operates to maintain proper idle speed.

A/C Compressor Clutch Relay – Relay signals PCM when A/C circuit is operating. PCM then sends signal to IACV to maintain proper idle speed.

Air Boost Valve (Legend) – Additional air enters intake manifold during engine cranking, helping engine start easier.

Electronic Idle Air Control Valve (IACV) – To maintain proper idle speed, IACV varies amount of air by-passing throttle body according to signals received from PCM.

Fast Idle Control Valve – Thermowax plunger controls valve. When engine is cold, thermowax contracts plunger, allowing additional air to be by-passed into intake manifold and increase engine speed. Valve closes when engine reaches operating temperature.

Power Steering Pressure Switch – Switch signals PCM to increase engine idle speed when power steering load is high.

IGNITION SYSTEM

IGNITOR UNIT

Battery voltage is supplied through ignition switch to ignition coil(s) and ignitor unit. The PGM-FI control unit uses input signals from TDC/crank (or crank/CYL) sensor, throttle position sensor, coolant sensor and MAP sensor to directly activate the ignitor. When activated, ignitor triggers ignition coil(s). On Integra and Vigor, induced voltage from ignition coil is then distributed to each spark plug by the distributor.

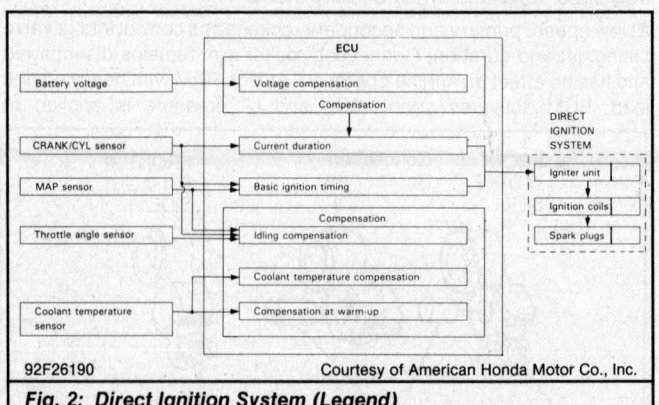

92F26190   Courtesy of American Honda Motor Co., Inc.

Fig. 2: Direct Ignition System (Legend)

DIRECT IGNITION SYSTEM (DIS)

Battery voltage is supplied through ignition switch to PCM (ECU), ignitor unit, ignition coils and spark plugs. *See Fig. 2.* PCM triggers ignitor unit based upon signals from CRANK/CYL and other sensors. Each spark plug is fired directly by one of 6 coils. Ignitor controls each coil.

IGNITION TIMING CONTROL

NOTE: For other inputs, see INPUT DEVICES under COMPUTERIZED ENGINE CONTROLS.

A microcomputer in the PCM controls the ignition timing according to engine speed and vacuum pressure in the intake manifold. Engine speed and vacuum pressure are transmitted to PCM by signals from crank sensor, cylinder (CYL) sensor, TDC sensor (Integra and Vigor), throttle position sensor, coolant temperature sensor, knock sensor(s), and MAP sensor.

The PCM contains memory for ignition timing at various engine speeds, manifold pressure and coolant temperature. When these conditions have been processed, PCM sends signals to ignitor unit to control ignition timing.

Crank Sensor – Determines timing for fuel injection and ignition of each cylinder. It also detects engine RPM.

Cylinder (CYL) Sensor – Detects position of No. 1 cylinder for sequential fuel injection to each cylinder.

Knock Sensor(s) – Detects detonation. When detonation is detected, ignition timing is retarded.

TDC Sensor (Integra & Vigor) – Determines ignition timing at start-up (cranking) and when crank position signal is abnormal.

EMISSION SYSTEMS

EGR System (Legend & Vigor) – The EGR system reduces oxides of nitrogen (NOx) emissions by recirculating exhaust manifold gas to intake manifold and into the combustion chambers. System is composed of EGR valve, Constant Vacuum Control Valve (CVCV), EGR position sensor and EGR control solenoid valve.

EGR Position Sensor (Legend & Vigor) – PCM contains data for ideal EGR valve lifts for varying operating conditions. The EGR position sensor detects amount of EGR valve lift and sends the information to PCM. PCM compares this information (actual EGR valve lift) with ideal EGR valve lift. If the 2 signals differ, PCM closes EGR control solenoid valve to reduce vacuum applied to EGR valve.

EVAP – This system prevents fuel tank vapors from escaping into the atmosphere.

EVAP Purge Cut-Off Solenoid Valve – When coolant temperature is less than 140-158°F (60-70°C), PCM supplies voltage to the purge cut-off solenoid valve to cut vacuum to purge control valve.

Oxygen Sensor Heater – Oxygen sensor heater stabilizes sensor operation, allowing more accurate determination of exhaust oxygen content. PCM uses this information to determine injector pulse duration.

Positive Crankcase Ventilation (PCV) – PCV system prevents crankcase blow-by gas from escaping into the atmosphere. The plunger in the PCV valve is lifted in proportion to the intake manifold vacuum, drawing the blow-by gases into the intake manifold.

Pulse Secondary Air (PAIR) Injection System (Legend L & LS Sedan) – System uses an vacuum operated air suction valve. When the air suction valve is activated, manifold vacuum lifts the diaphragm off the air valve. Exhaust gas pulsations draw fresh air from air cleaner into exhaust manifold through the air suction valve.

PAIR Air Suction Control Solenoid Valve (Legend L & LS Sedan) – The PAIR Air Suction Control Solenoid Valve (PAIR-ASCSV) supplies vacuum to the suction valve when engine speed is greater than 1500 RPM and vehicle speed is greater than 9 MPH. PCM delays activation of PAIR-ASCSV until engine is warm.

SELF-DIAGNOSTIC SYSTEM

MALFUNCTION INDICATOR LIGHT & LED INDICATOR

PCM supplies ground for the Malfunction Indicator Light (MIL) for about 2 seconds when ignition is turned on. When a defect is detected in signal from a sensor, PCM activates the MIL and stores fault code in memory. On Legend, LED indicator light is on PCM and is used in idle adjustment procedure.

MISCELLANEOUS CONTROLS

NOTE: Although not true engine performance-related systems, some controlled devices may affect driveability if they malfunction.

TRANSMISSION CONTROL

NOTE: For other input components, see INPUT DEVICES under COMPUTERIZED ENGINE CONTROLS.

A/T Control Solenoid Valves – On Legend, various engine sensor inputs to the PCM are used to control the A/T shift control and torque converter lock-up control solenoid valves. This provides precise timing for the gear shifts and torque converter lock-up system. On Integra and Vigor, Transmission Control Module (TCM) controls shift solenoids and torque converter lock-up solenoids.

Integra, Legend, Vigor

INTRODUCTION

The following diagnostic steps will help prevent overlooking a simple problem. This is also where to begin diagnosis for a no-start condition.

The first step in diagnosing any driveability problem is verifying the customer's complaint with a test drive under the conditions the problem reportedly occurred.

Before entering self-diagnostics, perform a careful and complete visual inspection. Most engine control problems result from mechanical breakdowns, poor electrical connections or damaged/misrouted vacuum hoses. Before condemning the computerized system, perform each test listed in this article.

NOTE: *Perform all voltage tests with a Digital Volt-Ohmmeter (DVOM) with a minimum 10-megohm input impedance, unless stated otherwise in test procedure.*

PRELIMINARY INSPECTION & ADJUSTMENTS

VISUAL INSPECTION

Visually inspect all electrical wiring, looking for chafed, stretched, cut or pinched wiring. Ensure electrical connectors fit tightly and are not corroded. Ensure vacuum hoses are properly routed and are not pinched or cut. See VACUUM DIAGRAMS article to verify routing and connections (if necessary). Inspect air induction system for possible vacuum leaks.

MECHANICAL INSPECTION

Compression – Check engine mechanical condition with a compression gauge, vacuum gauge, or an engine analyzer. See engine analyzer manual for specific instructions.

WARNING: *DO NOT use ignition switch during compression tests on fuel injected vehicles. Use a remote starter to crank engine. Fuel injectors on many models are triggered by ignition switch during cranking mode, which can create a fire hazard or contaminate the engine's oiling system.*

ENGINE COMPRESSION [1]

Application	Specification
Integra	
Compression Ratio	
GS-R	10.0:1
Except GS-R	9.2:1
Compression Pressure at 250 RPM	
Standard	
GS-R	270 psi (19.0 kg/cm²)
Except GS-R	200 psi (14.0 kg/cm²)
Minimum	135 psi (9.5 kg/cm²)
Legend	
Compression Ratio	9.6:1
Compression Pressure at 200 RPM	
Standard	200 psi (14.0 kg/cm²)
Minimum	142 psi (10.0 kg/cm²)
Vigor	
Compression Ratio	9.0:1
Compression Pressure at 250 RPM	
Standard	206 psi (14.5 kg/cm²)
Minimum	135 psi (9.5 kg/cm²)

[1] – Maximum variation between cylinders is 28 psi (2 kg/cm²).

Exhaust System Backpressure – The exhaust system can be checked with a vacuum or pressure gauge. If using a pressure gauge, remove HO2S sensor or air injection check valve (if equipped). Connect a 0-5 psi pressure gauge and run engine at 2500 RPM. If exhaust system backpressure is greater than 1 3/4 - 2 psi, exhaust system or catalytic converter is plugged.

If using a vacuum gauge, connect vacuum gauge hose to intake manifold vacuum port and start engine. Observe vacuum gauge. Open throttle part way and hold steady. If vacuum gauge reading slowly drops after stabilizing, check exhaust system for restriction.

FUEL SYSTEM

WARNING: *ALWAYS relieve fuel pressure before disconnecting any fuel injection-related component. DO NOT allow fuel to contact engine or electrical components.*

FUEL PRESSURE

Basic diagnosis of fuel system should begin with determining fuel system pressure.

NOTE: *Before disconnecting battery, obtain activation code to reset anti-theft stereo (if equipped).*

Relieving Fuel Pressure – Remove negative battery cable. Loosen fuel tank filler cap. Place clean shop rag around fuel filter. Slowly loosen 6-mm service bolt on top of fuel filter one complete turn to relieve system pressure. Always replace washer under 6-mm bolt after loosening.

Pressure Testing – **1)** After relieving fuel pressure, connect Fuel Pressure Gauge (07406-0040001) at 6-mm service bolt location. Reconnect negative battery cable. Start engine and note fuel pressure on gauge. See REGULATED FUEL PRESSURE table. If vehicle will not start, but has spark and no fuel pressure, inspect fuel pump relay. See appropriate FUEL PUMP RELAY procedure.

2) Disconnect vacuum hose from pressure regulator (fuel pressure gauge should rise), and check for manifold vacuum. If vacuum is not present, check for restriction in vacuum port or hose. Plug vacuum hose, and note fuel pressure on gauge. See REGULATED FUEL PRESSURE table.

3) If pressure is higher than specified, check for pinched or clogged fuel return line between fuel rail and fuel tank. If no problem is found in fuel line, replace pressure regulator.

4) If pressure is lower than specified, check for plugged fuel filter. If filter is not plugged, lightly pinch off fuel return line. If fuel pressure does not rise, replace fuel pump. If fuel pressure rises, replace pressure regulator.

REGULATED FUEL PRESSURE

Application	At Idle W/O Vacuum psi (kg/cm²)	At Idle W/ Vacuum psi (kg/cm²)
Integra		
1.8L GS-R	48-56 (3.4-3.9)	39-46 (2.8-3.3)
1.8L Except GS-R	41-48 (2.9-3.4)	33-39 (2.3-2.8)
Legend		
Coupe & GS Sedan	44-51 (3.1-3.6)	36-43 (2.5-3.0)
Sedan L & LS	35-41 (2.5-2.9)	29-35 (2.1-2.4)
Vigor	43-50 (3.0-3.5)	33-41 (2.3-2.9)

Fuel Pump Relay (Integra) – **1)** Remove fuel pump relay, located under left side of dash. Connect battery voltage to terminal No. 2, and ground terminal No. 1 of relay. See Fig. 1.

2) Check continuity between relay terminals No. 5 and 4. If continuity exists, go to next step. If continuity does not exist, replace relay.

3) Connect battery positive to relay terminal No. 5, and ground terminal No. 3. Check continuity between relay terminals No. 7 and 6. If continuity exists, go to next step. If continuity does not exist, replace relay.

4) Connect battery positive to relay terminal No. 6, and ground terminal No. 1. Check continuity between relay terminals No. 5 and 4. If continuity exists, relay is okay. If continuity is not present, replace relay.

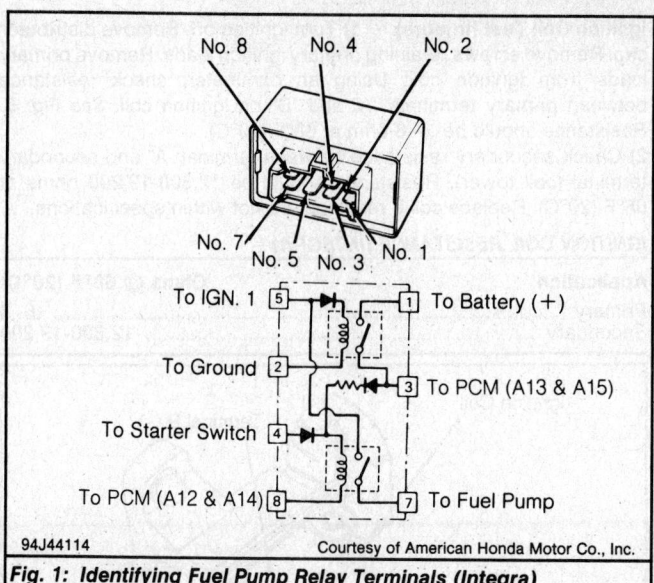

Fig. 1: Identifying Fuel Pump Relay Terminals (Integra)

Fuel Pump Relay (Legend) – 1) Remove fuel pump main relay located under left side of dash. Connect battery voltage to terminal No. 4, and ground terminal No. 8 of relay. *See Fig. 2.*

2) Check continuity between relay terminals No. 5 and 7. If continuity exists, go to next step. If continuity does not exist, replace relay.

3) Connect battery positive to relay terminal No. 6, and ground terminal No. 2. Check continuity between relay terminals No. 1 and 3. If continuity exists, go to next step. If continuity does not exist, replace relay.

4) Connect battery positive to relay terminal No. 3, and ground terminal No. 8. Check continuity between relay terminals No. 5 and 7. Continuity should exist. If continuity does not exist, replace relay.

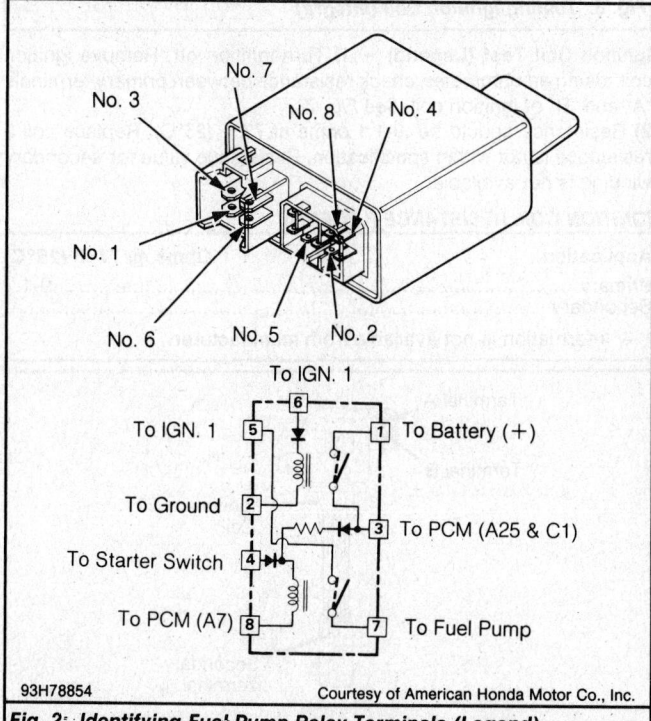

Fig. 2: Identifying Fuel Pump Relay Terminals (Legend)

Fuel Pump Relay (Vigor) – 1) Remove fuel pump main relay located under left side of dash. Connect battery voltage to terminal No. 6, and ground terminal No. 8 of relay. *See Fig. 3.*

2) Check continuity between relay terminals No. 5 and 7. If continuity exists, go to next step. If continuity does not exist, replace relay.

3) Connect battery voltage to relay terminal No. 5, and ground terminal No. 2. Check continuity between relay terminals No. 1 and 3. If continuity exists, go to next step. If continuity does not exist, replace relay.

4) Connect battery voltage to relay terminal No. 3, and ground terminal No. 8. Check continuity between relay terminals No. 5 and 7. If continuity exists, relay is okay. If continuity does not exist, replace relay.

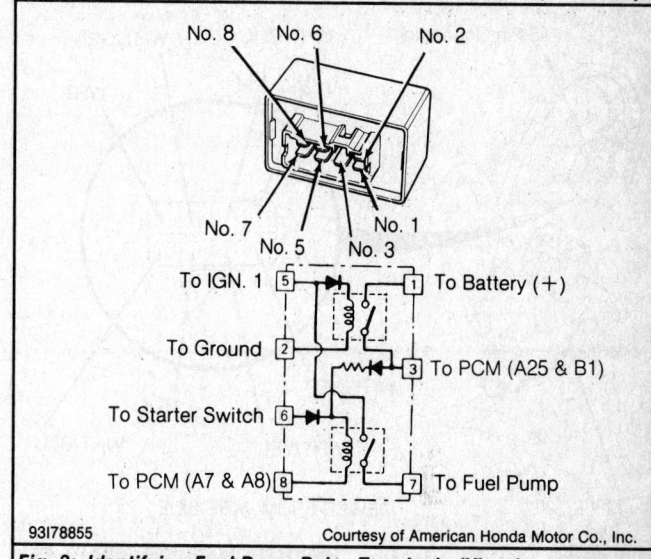

Fig. 3: Identifying Fuel Pump Relay Terminals (Vigor)

IGNITION CHECKS

ELECTRONIC IGNITION SYSTEM

Spark (Integra & Vigor) – 1) Crank engine. Using a high output spark tester, ensure strong Blue spark is present at each secondary ignition plug wire. If spark is not as described, go to step **2)**.

2) Ensure resistance of each spark plug wire is not more than 25,000 ohms. Disconnect and inspect all related ignition system connectors and harness. Clean or repair as necessary, and recheck spark. If strong Blue spark is still not present, go to IGNITION COIL POWER SOURCE procedure.

Ignition Coil Power Source – 1) On Integra and Vigor, remove distributor cap. On all models, disconnect ignition coil primary leads. Turn ignition on. Using voltmeter, check voltage between ground and Black/Yellow wire (terminal "A") of ignition coil(s) wiring harness. *See Fig. 6, 7 or 8.*

2) Ensure battery voltage exists. If battery voltage does not exist, check for open in Black/Yellow wire between ignition coil and ignition switch. If wire is okay, go to appropriate IGNITOR INPUT TEST procedure.

Ignitor Input Test (Integra) – 1) Turn ignition off. Remove distributor cap and rotor. Disconnect Black/Yellow, White/Blue, Yellow/Green, and Blue wires from ignitor. Turn ignition on. Using voltmeter, check for battery voltage between Black/Yellow wire of harness and body ground.

2) If voltage is not present, check for open in Black/Yellow wire between ignition switch and ignitor wiring harness connector. If voltage is present, check for voltage between White/Blue wire and body ground. If voltage is not present, check White/Blue wire and ignition coil for open circuit. If voltage is present, go to step **3)**.

3) Disconnect PCM wiring harness connector. Check Yellow/Green wire for continuity between PCM wiring harness connector and ignitor. Check Blue wire for continuity between ignitor and tachometer. Repair or replace wiring as necessary. If wiring is okay, replace ignitor.

Ignitor Input Test (Legend) – 1) Turn ignition off. Disconnect wiring harness from ignitor. Using ohmmeter, ensure continuity exists between Black wires and ground. If continuity does not exist, check for open wire or bad ground connection.

2) Turn ignition on. Using voltmeter, check for battery voltage between ground and each White wire of harness (including White wires with tracer color). *See Fig. 4.* If voltage is not present, check for blown fuse No. 25 (30-amp) or open circuit in White wire. If circuits and fuse are okay, replace ignition coil.

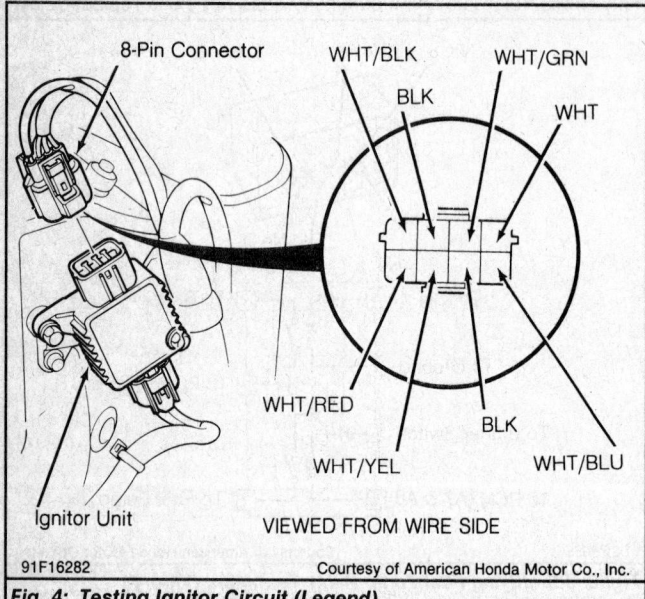

91F16282   Courtesy of American Honda Motor Co., Inc.

Fig. 4: Testing Ignitor Circuit (Legend)

Ignitor Input Test (Vigor) – **1)** Turn ignition off. Disconnect 4-pin connector from ignitor. Using ohmmeter, check for continuity between Black wire and body ground. *See Fig. 5.* If continuity does not exist, check for open wire or bad ground connection. If continuity is present, go to step **2)**.

2) Turn ignition on. Using voltmeter, check for battery voltage between Black/Yellow wire and Black wire of harness. If voltage is present, go to next step. If voltage is not present, check for open in Black/Yellow wire or wiring harness connector. If wire and connector are okay, go to appropriate IGNITION COIL TEST procedure.

3) With ignition on, ensure battery voltage exists between Blue wire and Black wire at ignitor wiring harness connector. If voltage is not present, check for open circuit in Blue wire. If circuit is okay, go to appropriate IGNITION COIL TEST procedure.

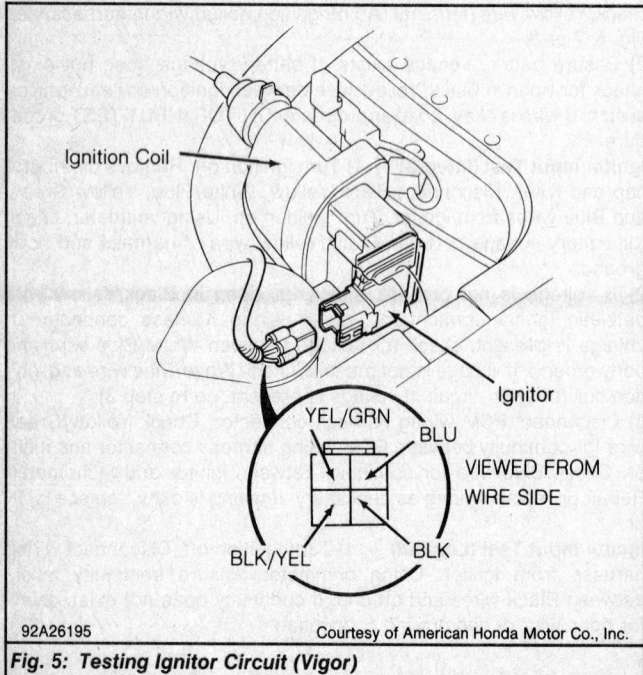

92A26195   Courtesy of American Honda Motor Co., Inc.

Fig. 5: Testing Ignitor Circuit (Vigor)

Ignition Coil Test (Integra) – **1)** Turn ignition off. Remove distributor cap. Remove screws retaining primary ignition leads. Remove primary leads from ignition coil. Using an ohmmeter, check resistance between primary terminals "A" and "B" on ignition coil. *See Fig. 6.* Resistance should be .6-.8 ohm at 68°F (20°C).

2) Check secondary resistance between terminal "A" and secondary terminal (coil tower). Resistance should be 12,800-19,200 ohms at 68°F (20°C). Replace coil if readings are not within specifications.

IGNITION COIL RESISTANCE (INTEGRA)

Application	Ohms @ 68°F (20°C)
Primary	.6-.8
Secondary	12,800-19,200

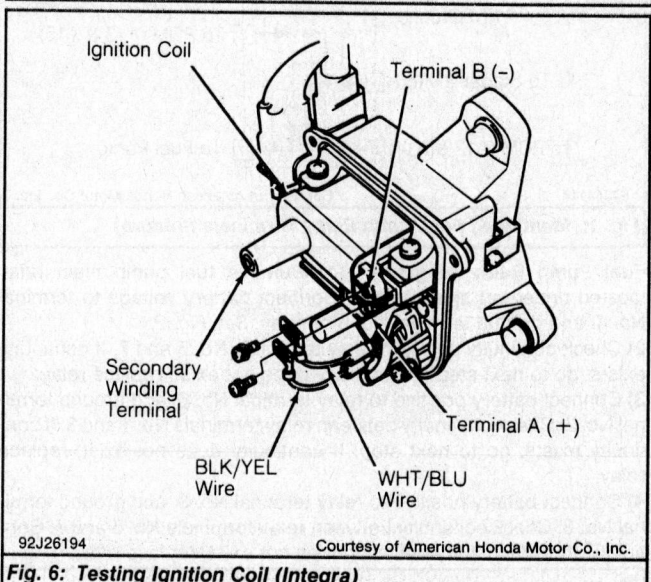

92J26194   Courtesy of American Honda Motor Co., Inc.

Fig. 6: Testing Ignition Coil (Integra)

Ignition Coil Test (Legend) – **1)** Turn ignition off. Remove ignition coil. Using an ohmmeter, check resistance between primary terminals "A" and "B" of ignition coil. *See Fig. 7.*

2) Resistance should be .9-1.1 ohms at 77°F (25°C). Replace coil if resistance is not within specification. Resistance value for secondary winding is not available.

IGNITION COIL RESISTANCE (LEGEND)

Application	Ohms @ 77°F (25°C)
Primary	.9-1.1
Secondary	1

1 – Information is not available from manufacturer.

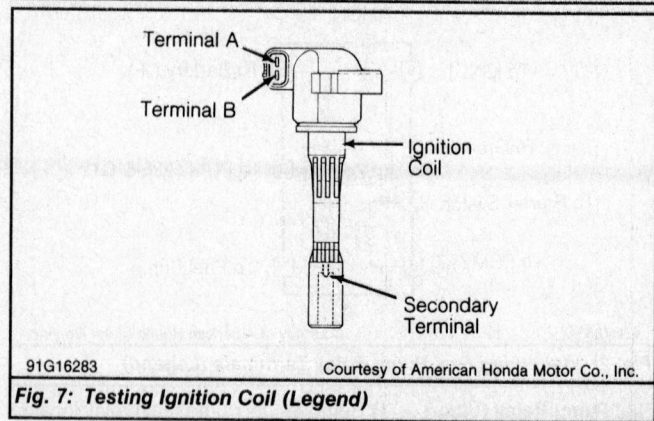

91G16283   Courtesy of American Honda Motor Co., Inc.

Fig. 7: Testing Ignition Coil (Legend)

Ignition Coil Test (Vigor) – Turn ignition off. Disconnect ignition coil connector. *See Fig. 8.* Using an ohmmeter, check resistance between indicated terminals. See IGNITION COIL RESISTANCE (VIGOR) table. Replace coil if readings are not within specifications.

IGNITION COIL RESISTANCE (VIGOR)

Application	Ohms @ 68°F (20°C)
Terminals A & D (Primary)	.3-.5
Terminals B & D	2000-2300
Terminal A & Secondary Terminal	10,800-16,200

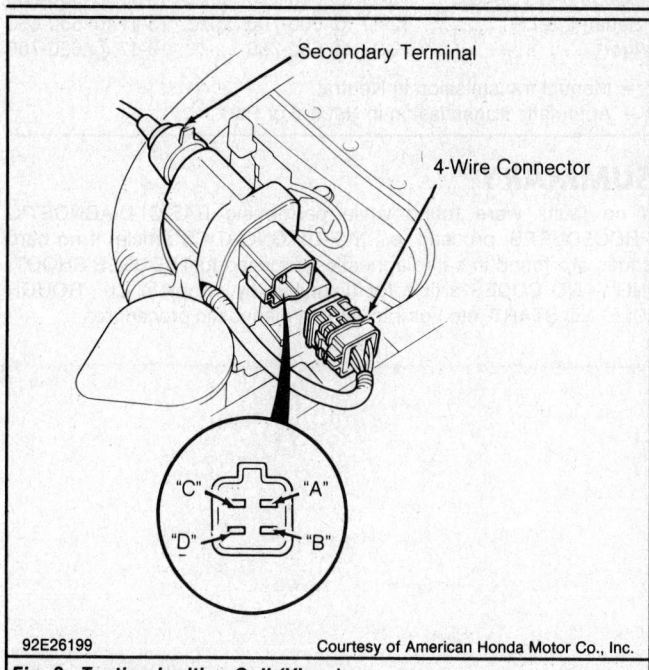

Fig. 8: Testing Ignition Coil (Vigor)

PCM Input Signals – 1) Timing control and triggering of fuel injectors are based on input signals from TDC/CRANK/CYL sensors. These sensors are Permanent Magnet (PM) generator pick-up coils.
2) Using a DVOM (preferably with bar-graph function) on low-volt scale, check each sensor for pulse voltage signal at indicated PCM harness terminals with engine cranking. See PCM INPUT SIGNAL & RESISTANCE TEST TERMINALS table. If pulse signal is present, sensor is okay. If pulse signal is not present, go to step **3)**.
3) Turn ignition off. Disconnect PCM connector. Check wiring harness and connectors. Check resistance of each sensor at indicated PCM harness terminals. See PCM INPUT SIGNAL & RESISTANCE TEST TERMINALS table. If resistance is within specification, go to step **4)**. If resistance is not within specification, go to step **5)**.

PCM INPUT SIGNAL & RESISTANCE TEST TERMINALS

Application	PCM Terminals [1]	Ohms
Integra		
CRANK	B15 & B16	350-700 Ohms
CYL	B11 & B12	350-700 Ohms
TDC	B13 & B14	350-700 Ohms
Legend		
CRANK No. 1	B15 & B16	650-900 Ohms
CRANK No. 2	B14 & B13	650-900 Ohms
CYL No. 1	B12 & B11	650-900 Ohms
CYL No. 2	B9 & B10	650-900 Ohms
Vigor		
CRANK	B15 & B16	650-850 Ohms
CYL	B11 & B12	650-850 Ohms
TDC	B13 & B14	650-850 Ohms

[1] – See Fig. 9.

4) Check continuity to ground on each terminal. If continuity exists, disconnect sensor connector, and recheck appropriate PCM terminal for continuity to ground. If continuity still exists, repair short to ground in harness. If continuity does not exist, replace sensor assembly.

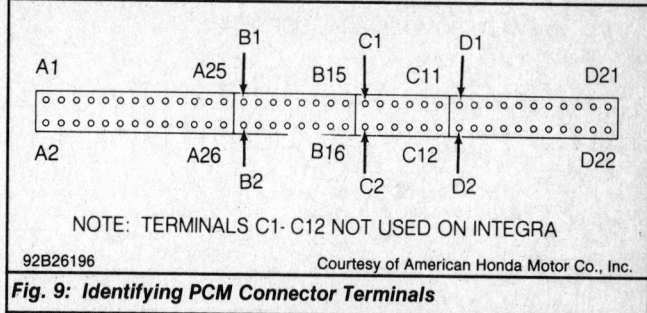

Fig. 9: Identifying PCM Connector Terminals

5) Disconnect sensor connector. Check resistance of sensor. *See Fig. 10, 11 or 12.* If resistance is within specification, repair open, short or corrosion in sensor harness between PCM and sensor. See PCM INPUT SIGNAL & RESISTANCE TEST TERMINALS table. If sensor resistance is not within specification, replace sensor assembly.

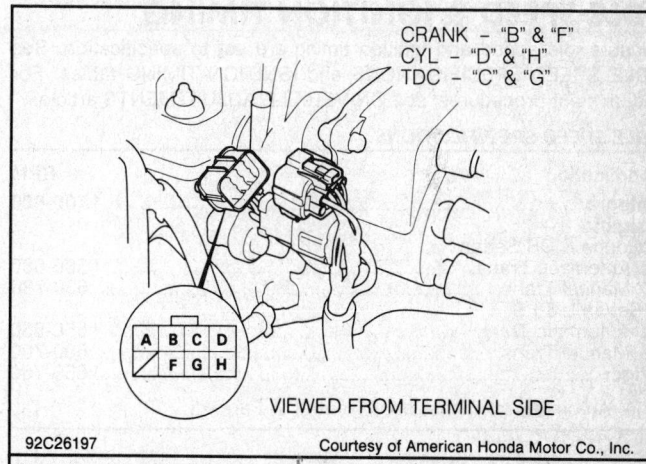

Fig. 10: Identifying Sensor Connector Terminals (Integra)

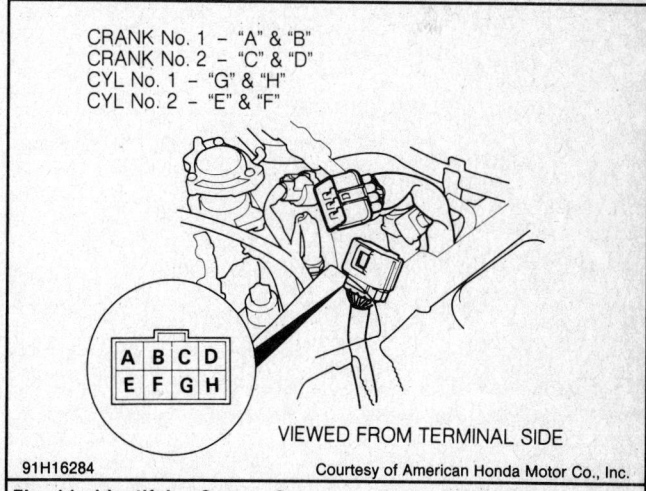

Fig. 11: Identifying Sensor Connector Terminals (Legend)

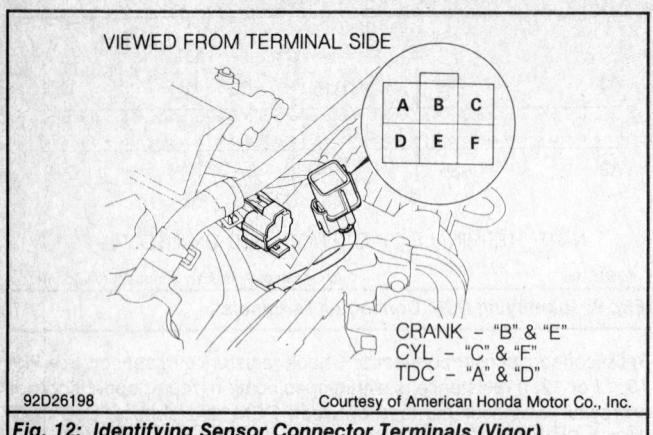

```
VIEWED FROM TERMINAL SIDE

        A  B  C
        D  E  F

CRANK – "B" & "E"
CYL – "C" & "F"
TDC – "A" & "D"
```

92D26198   Courtesy of American Honda Motor Co., Inc.

Fig. 12: Identifying Sensor Connector Terminals (Vigor)

IDLE SPEED & IGNITION TIMING

Ensure idle speed and ignition timing are set to specification. See IDLE SPEED SPECIFICATIONS and IGNITION TIMING tables. For adjustment procedures, see ON-VEHICLE ADJUSTMENTS article.

IDLE SPEED SPECIFICATIONS

Application	RPM
Integra	[1] 700-800
Legend	
Coupe & GS Sedan	
Automatic Trans.	[1] 580-680
Manual Trans.	630-730
Sedan L & LS	
Automatic Trans.	[1] 550-650
Manual Trans.	600-700
Vigor	[1] 650-750

[1] – Automatic transmission in Neutral or Park.

IGNITION TIMING (Degrees BTDC @ RPM)

Application	[1] Man. Trans.	[2] Auto. Trans.
Integra	14-18 @ 700-800	14-18 @ 700-800
Legend		
Coupe & GS Sedan ...	13-17 @ 630-730	13-17 @ 580-680
Sedan L & LS	13-17 @ 600-700	13-17 @ 550-650
Vigor	13-17 @ 650-750	13-17 @ 650-750

[1] – Manual transmission in Neutral.
[2] – Automatic transmission in Neutral or Park.

SUMMARY

If no faults were found while performing BASIC DIAGNOSTIC PROCEDURES, proceed to SELF-DIAGNOSTICS article. If no hard codes are found in self-diagnostics, proceed to TROUBLE SHOOTING – NO CODES article for diagnosis by symptom (i.e., ROUGH IDLE, NO START, etc.) or intermittent diagnostic procedures.

Integra, Legend, Vigor

INTRODUCTION

If no faults were found while performing BASIC DIAGNOSTIC PROCEDURES, proceed with self-diagnostics. If no fault codes or only pass codes are present after entering self-diagnostics, proceed to TROUBLE SHOOTING – NO CODES article for diagnosis by symptom (i.e., ROUGH IDLE, NO START, etc.).

SELF-DIAGNOSTIC SYSTEM

MALFUNCTION INDICATOR LIGHT (MIL)

All models have a Malfunction Indicator Light (MIL). As a bulb check, light will glow when ignition is on and engine is not running. MIL will also glow when a system failure is detected; a corresponding trouble code will set in Engine Control Module (ECM) memory.

Hard Failures – Hard failures cause malfunction indicator light to glow and remain on until problem is repaired. If light comes on and remains on (light may flash) during vehicle operation, determine cause of malfunction using appropriate TROUBLE CODES procedures. If a sensor fails, ECM will use a substitute value in its calculations to continue engine operation. In this condition, known as limp-in mode, vehicle runs but driveability will not be optimum.

Intermittent Failures – Intermittent failures may cause MIL to flicker or glow and go out after intermittent fault goes away. However, corresponding trouble code will be retained in ECM memory. If related fault does not reoccur within a certain time frame, related trouble code will be erased from ECM memory. Intermittent failures may be caused by sensor, connector or wiring related problems. See INTERMITTENTS in TROUBLE SHOOTING – NO CODES article.

RETRIEVING CODES

NOTE: *Before starting tests, ensure engine is in good mechanical condition and adjusted to specifications.*

NOTE: *For wiring diagrams, see WIRING DIAGRAMS article. For vacuum diagrams, see VACUUM DIAGRAMS article.*

MIL may come on indicating a hard or intermittent failure. Locate 2-pin self-diagnostic connector behind glove box. *See Fig. 1, 2 or 3.* Connect diagnostic connector terminals using Short Connector (07 PAZ-0010100) on Integra or jumper wire on Legend and Vigor. Turn ignition on. Observe MIL. Light indicates a system trouble code by number of blinks.

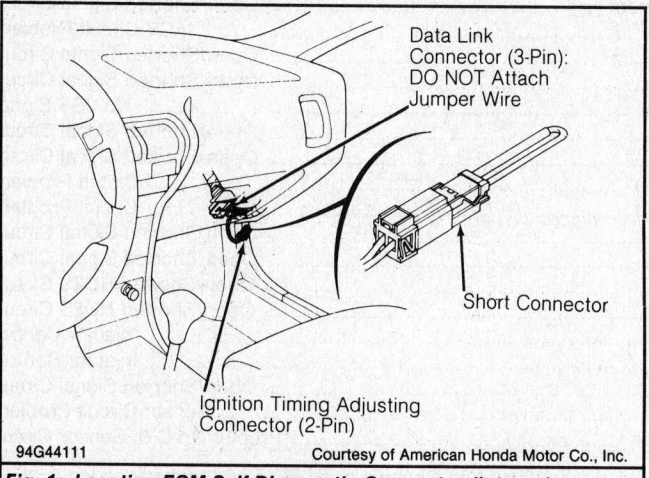

Fig. 1: *Locating ECM Self-Diagnostic Connector (Integra)*

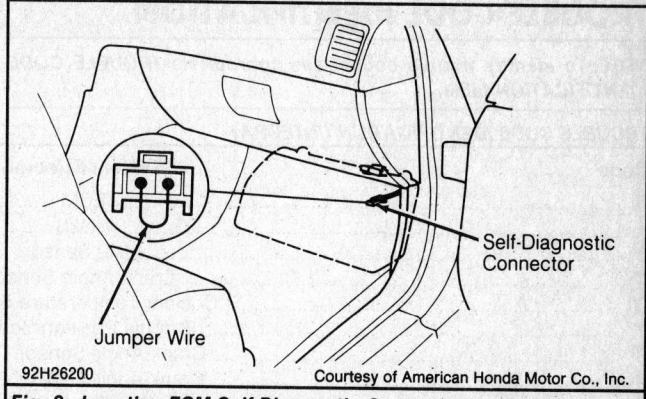

Fig. 2: *Locating ECM Self-Diagnostic Connector (Legend)*

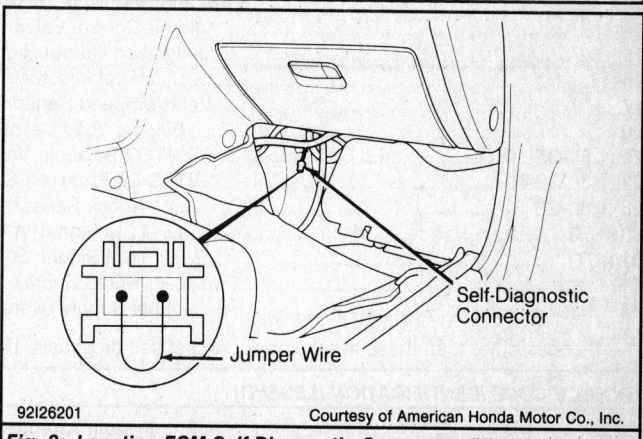

Fig. 3: *Locating ECM Self-Diagnostic Connector (Vigor)*

Single-digit trouble codes (1-9) are indicated by individual short blinks. Double-digit trouble codes (10-59) are indicated by a series of long and short blinks: number of long blinks equal first digit; number of short blinks equal second digit. See TROUBLE CODE IDENTIFICATION. If codes other than those listed are indicated, substitute a known good ECM and recheck.

CLEARING CODES

NOTE: *Before disconnecting battery, obtain anti-theft code for radio. After battery is reconnected, CODE will appear on radio display. Enter 5-digit code using select buttons and radio will begin working. If code is entered wrong 3 times, leave radio on at least one hour and enter code correctly. Any time radio power is lost, preselected radio stations will have to be set. For more information, see owners manual.*

Ensure ignition is off. To reset ECM on Integra and Vigor, remove BACK-UP fuse (7.5-amp on Integra; 10-amp on Vigor) from underhood fuse/relay box for 10 seconds. On Legend, remove ACG fuse (No. 15, 7.5-amp) from left underdash fuse box for 10 seconds.

ECM LOCATION

ECM is located on right side of vehicle, in footwell, under carpet.

SUMMARY

If no hard fault codes (or only pass codes) are present, driveability symptoms exist, or intermittent codes exist, proceed to TROUBLE SHOOTING – NO CODES article for diagnosis by symptom (i.e., ROUGH IDLE, NO START, etc.) or intermittent diagnostic procedures.

1994 ENGINE PERFORMANCE
Self-Diagnostics (Cont.)

TROUBLE CODE IDENTIFICATION

NOTE: To identify trouble codes, see appropriate TROUBLE CODE IDENTIFICATION table.

TROUBLE CODE IDENTIFICATION (INTEGRA)

Code [1]	System Affected	Probable Cause
0	ECM	No Signal To ECM
1	HO2S	HO2S Circuit Problem
3	MAP Sensor	MAP Sensor Problem
4	Crank Angle Sensor	Open/Shorted Signal Circuit
6	Coolant Temperature Sensor	Open/Shorted Signal Circuit
7	Throttle Position Sensor	Open/Shorted Signal Circuit
8	Crank Angle Sensor (TDC)	Open/Shorted Signal Circuit
9	Crank Angle Sensor (CYL)	Open/Shorted Signal Circuit
10	Intake Air Temperature (TA) Sensor	Problem With Sensor
13	Barometric Pressure (BARO) Sensor	BARO Circuit Problem
14	Idle Air Control Valve (IACV)	Open/Shorted Signal Circuit
15	Ignition Output Signal	Open/Shorted Signal Circuit
16	Fuel Injector	Open/Shorted Signal Circuit
17	Vehicle Speed Sensor (VSS)	Open/Shorted Signal Circuit
20	Electric Load Detector	Open/Shorted Signal Circuit
21 (1.8L GS-R)	VTEC Solenoid Valve	Open/Shorted Signal Circuit
22 (1.8L GS-R)	VTEC Oil Pressure Switch	Open/Shorted Signal Circuit
23 (1.8L GS-R)	Knock Sensor	Open/Shorted Signal Circuit
30 (A/T)	TCM Signal "A"	Open/Shorted Signal Circuit
31 (A/T)	TCM Signal "B"	Open/Shorted Signal Circuit
41	HO2S Heater	Open/Shorted Signal Circuit
43	Fuel Supply System	Open/Shorted HO2S Circuit

[1] – If codes other than these are indicated, repeat self-diagnosis. If codes reappear, substitute a known good ECM and recheck codes.

TROUBLE CODE IDENTIFICATION (LEGEND)

Code [1]	System Affected	Probable Cause
0	ECM	No Signal To ECM
1	Left HO2S Sensor	Open/Shorted Signal Circuit
2	Right HO2S Sensor	Open/Shorted Signal Circuit
3 [2]	MAP Sensor	MAP Sensor Electrical Problem
4	Crank Angle Sensor No. 1	Sensor Circuit Problem
5 [2]	MAP Sensor	MAP Sensor Mechanical Problem
6 [2][3]	Coolant Temperature Sensor	Open/Shorted Signal Circuit
7 [3]	Throttle Position Sensor	Open/Shorted Signal Circuit
9	Cylinder Position Sensor No. 1	Problem In CYL Sensor Circuit
10	Intake Air Temperature (TA) Sensor	Open/Shorted Signal Circuit
12	EGR System	No EGR Action
13	Barometric Pressure (BARO) Sensor	Open/Shorted Signal Circuit
14	Idle Air Control Valve (IACV)	IACV Circuit Problem
15 [2]	Ignition Output Signal	Open/Shorted Signal Circuit
16 [2]	Fuel Injector	Open/Shorted Signal Circuit
17 [2][3]	Vehicle Speed Sensor (VSS)	No VSS Signal
18	Ignition Timing Adjuster	Open/Shorted Signal Circuit
23	Left Knock Sensor	Open/Shorted Signal Circuit
35 [2][3]	Traction Control System (TCS)	Circuit Problem
36 [2][3]	Traction Control System (TCS)	Circuit Problem
41	Left HO2S Heater	Open/Shorted Signal Circuit
42	Right HO2S Heater	Open/Shorted Signal Circuit
43	Left Fuel Supply System	Open/Shorted HO2S Circuit
44	Right Fuel Supply System	Open/Shorted HO2S Circuit
45	Left Fuel Metering	Injector Control
46	Right Fuel Metering	Injector Control
53	Right Knock Sensor	Open/Shorted Signal Circuit
54	Crank Angle Sensor No. 2	Sensor Circuit Problem
59	Cylinder Position No. 2 Sensor	Problem In CYL Sensor Circuit

[1] – If codes other than these are indicated, repeat self-diagnosis. If codes reappear, substitute a known good ECM and recheck codes.

[2] – If TCS indicator light also blinks, TCS control unit may require diagnosis.

[3] – If D$_4$ on automatic transaxle indicator panel also blinks, A/T control unit may require diagnosis.

TROUBLE CODE IDENTIFICATION (VIGOR)

Code [1]	System Affected	Probable Cause
0	ECM	No Signal To ECM
1	HO2S	HO2S Circuit Problem
3	MAP Sensor	MAP Sensor Problem
4	Crank Angle	Open/Shorted Signal Circuit
5	MAP Sensor	Open/Shorted Signal Circuit
6 [2]	Coolant Temperature Sensor	Open/Shorted Signal Circuit
7 [2]	Throttle Position Sensor	Open/Shorted Signal Circuit
8	Crank Angle Sensor (TDC)	Open/Shorted Signal Circuit
9	Crank Angle Sensor (CYL)	Open/Shorted Signal Circuit
10	Intake Air Temperature (TA) Sensor	Sensor Problem
12	EGR System	Faulty EGR Valve (A/T)
13	Barometric Pressure (BARO) Sensor	BARO Circuit Problem
14	Idle Air Control Valve (IACV)	Open/Shorted Signal Circuit
15	Ignition Output Signal	Open/Shorted Signal Circuit
16	Fuel Injector	Open/Shorted Signal Circuit
17 [2]	Vehicle Speed Sensor (VSS)	Open/Shorted Signal Circuit
18	Ignition Timing Adjuster	Open/Shorted Signal Circuit
20 [3]	Electrical Load Detector (ELD)	Open/Shorted Signal Circuit
23	Knock Sensor No. 1	Open/Shorted Signal Circuit
30 Or 31 [3]	A/T FI Signal	Open/Shorted Signal Circuit
41	HO2S Heater	Open/Shorted Signal Circuit
43	Fuel Supply System	Open/Shorted HO2S Circuit
45	Fuel Metering	Incorrect Fuel Metering
53	Knock Sensor No. 2	Open/Shorted Signal Circuit

[1] – If codes other than these are indicated, repeat self-diagnosis. If codes reappear, substitute a known good ECM and recheck codes.

[2] – If S4 on automatic transaxle indicator panel also blinks, A/T control unit may require diagnosis.

[3] – MIL will not come on if malfunction is in A/T FI or Electrical Load Detector circuit. Fault code will, however, be stored in ECM memory.

TROUBLE CODES (INTEGRA)

CODE 0 OR NO CODES

No MIL – 1) Turn ignition on. If oil pressure light is on, go to next step. If light is off, inspect fuse No. 15. If fuse No. 15 is okay, repair open circuit in Yellow wire between fuse and instrument cluster. If fuse is blown, repair short in Yellow wire between fuse No. 15 and gauge assembly.

2) If oil pressure light is on, turn ignition off. Connect ECM test harness connector between ECM and ECM connectors. Jumper ECM terminal A13 to body ground. See Fig. 4. Turn ignition on. If MIL is now on, go to next step. If light is off, replace MIL bulb or repair open in Green/Orange wire between ECM terminal A13 and instrument cluster.

3) On all except 1.8L GS-R, go to next step. On 1.8L GS-R, measure voltage individually between ground and ECM terminals A23 and A24. If more than one volt is present on either terminal, repair open in that wire between ECM and ground terminal G101, located at thermostat housing. See Fig. 5. If less than one volt is present on each terminal, go to next step.

4) On all models, replace ECM and retest. If symptom goes away, replace ECM.

MIL Stays On – 1) Check ECM for fault codes. See RETRIEVING CODES under SELF-DIAGNOSTIC SYSTEMS. Service codes as necessary. If no codes are present, remove jumper from service connector and start engine. If engine starts, go to step **2)**. If engine does not start, inspect ECM fuse in underhood fuse/relay box. If fuse is okay, go to step **4)**.

2) Turn ignition off. Connect ECM Test Harness (07LAJ-PT3010A) between ECM and ECM connectors. See Fig. 4. Turn ignition on. Measure voltage between terminals D4 (+) and D22 (–). If voltage is not 5 volts, repair short to body ground between ECM terminal D4 and self-diagnostic connector. If 5 volts are present, connect jumper wire between self-diagnostic connector terminals. Measure voltage between terminals D4 and D22. If 5 volts are present, repair open circuit D4 (Brown/White wire) between ECM and self-diagnostic connector. If voltage is not 5 volts, go to step **3)**.

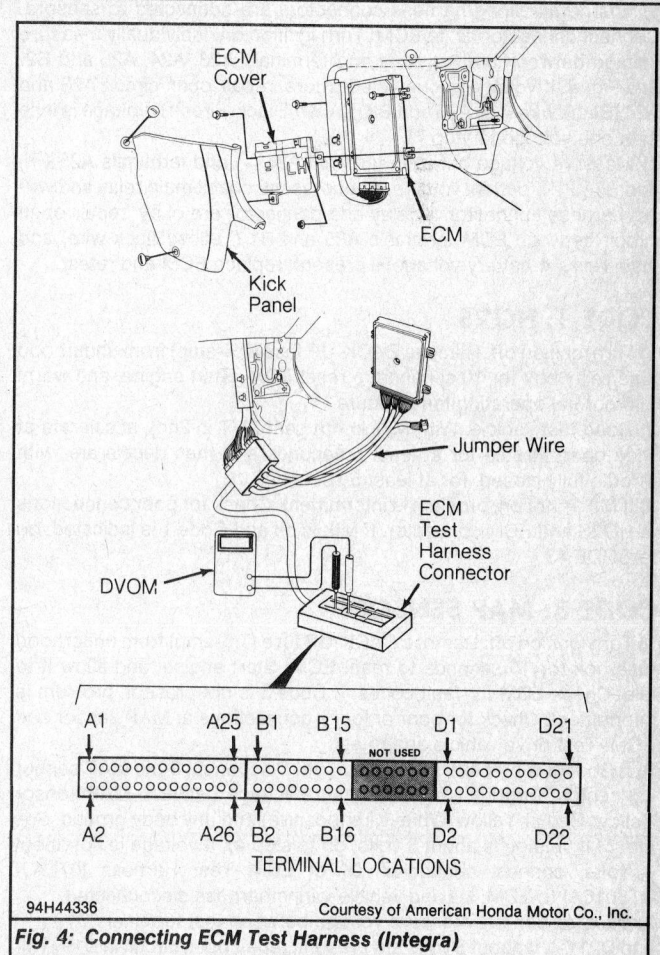

94H44336

Courtesy of American Honda Motor Co., Inc.

Fig. 4: Connecting ECM Test Harness (Integra)

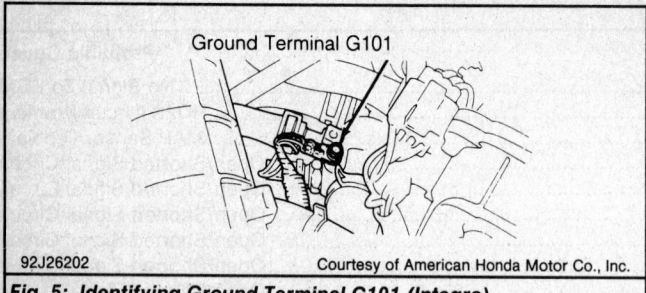

92J26202   Courtesy of American Honda Motor Co., Inc.

Fig. 5: Identifying Ground Terminal G101 (Integra)

3) Ensure jumper wire is removed from self-diagnostic connector. Turn ignition off. Disconnect connector "A" from ECM. Turn ignition on. If MIL stays on, repair short circuit in Green/Orange wire between ECM terminal A13 and MIL. If MIL goes out, replace ECM and retest.

4) Ensure jumper wire is removed from self-diagnostic connector. Inspect fuse No. 24 in underdash fuse/relay box. Replace fuse if necessary. If fuse is okay, turn ignition on. Disconnect 3-pin connectors from MAP sensor and throttle position sensor. If MIL goes out, replace sensor that caused light to go out. If MIL stays on, go to step **5)**.

5) Turn ignition off. Connect ECM Test Harness (07LAJ-PT3010A) between ECM and ECM connectors. See Fig. 4. Leave connector "D" disconnected from ECM. Using an ohmmeter, check for continuity between terminals D19 and D20. If continuity is not present, go to next step. If continuity is present, check for short to body ground in following circuits:

- D19 (Yellow/Red wire) between ECM and MAP sensor.
- D20 (Yellow/White wire) between ECM and throttle position sensor.

6) Ensure all wiring harness connectors are connected to sensors. Connect connector "D" to ECM. Turn ignition on. Individually measure voltage between body ground and terminals A23, A24, A26 and B2. See Fig. 4. If voltage is one volt or more, repair open circuit A23 and A24 (Black wires) or A26 and B2 (Brown/Black wires). If voltage is less than one volt, go to step **7)**.

7) Measure voltage between terminal A26 (–) and terminals A25 (+) and B1 (+). If battery voltage is not present, check main relay and wiring harness connector. If relay and connector are okay, repair open circuit between ECM terminals A25 and B1 (Yellow/Black wire) and main relay. If battery voltage is present, replace ECM and retest.

CODE 1: HO2S

1) Turn ignition off. Remove BACK-UP fuse (7.5-amp) from underhood fuse/relay box for 10 seconds to reset ECM. Start engine, and warm it to normal operating temperature.

2) Road test vehicle. With M/T in 4th gear (A/T in 2nd), accelerate at wide open throttle for at least 5 seconds and then decelerate, with throttle fully closed, for at least 5 seconds.

3) If MIL is not on, problem is intermittent. Check for poor connections at HO2S and ECM connector. If MIL is on and Code 1 is indicated, go to CODE 43.

CODE 3: MAP SENSOR

1) Turn ignition off. Remove BACK-UP fuse (7.5-amp) from underhood fuse box for 10 seconds to reset ECM. Start engine, and allow it to idle. Check ECM for fault codes. If Code 3 is not present, problem is intermittent. Check for poor or loose connections at MAP sensor and ECM. Test drive vehicle and retest.

2) If Code 3 is present, turn ignition off. Disconnect 3-pin MAP sensor connector. Turn ignition on. Measure voltage between MAP sensor Yellow/Red or Yellow/White wire (positive) and any body ground. See Fig. 6. If voltage is about 5 volts, go to step **4)**. If voltage is not about 5 volts, connect connector "D" of ECM Test Harness (07LAJ-PT3010A) to ECM, leaving vehicle wiring harness disconnected.

3) Turn ignition on. Measure voltage between test terminals D19 (+) and D21 (–). If about 5 volts are present, repair open circuit in D19 (Yellow/Red or Yellow/White wire) between ECM connector and MAP sensor. If voltage is not about 5 volts, replace ECM and retest.

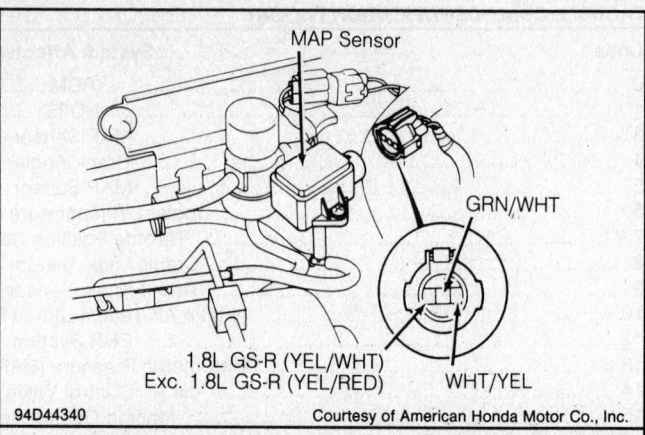

94D44340   Courtesy of American Honda Motor Co., Inc.

Fig. 6: Locating MAP Sensor & Identifying Connector Terminals (Integra)

4) If voltage was about 5 volts in step **2)**, measure voltage between Yellow/Red or Yellow/White (+) and Green/White (–) wires at MAP sensor. If voltage is not about 5 volts, repair open in Green/White wire between ECM terminal D21 and MAP sensor. If voltage is about 5 volts, check voltage between White/Yellow (+) and Green/White (–) wire terminals at MAP sensor.

5) If voltage is about 5 volts, go to step **6)**. If voltage is not about 5 volts, measure voltage between test harness terminals D17 and D21. See Fig. 4. If about 5 volts are present, repair open or short in circuit D17 (White/Yellow wire) between ECM connector and MAP sensor. If voltage is not about 5 volts, substitute a known good ECM and recheck. If voltage is about 5 volts, replace original ECM and retest. If voltage is not about 5 volts, replace MAP sensor.

6) Turn ignition off. Reconnect 3-pin MAP sensor connector. Connect ECM Test Harness (07LAJ-PT3010A) between ECM and ECM connectors. See Fig. 4. Turn ignition on. Measure voltage between test terminals D17 and D21. If voltage is not about 3 volts, replace MAP sensor. If about 3 volts are present, replace ECM and retest.

CODE 4, 8 OR 9: TDC/CRANK/CYL SENSOR

1) Turn ignition off. Remove BACK-UP (7.5-amp) fuse from underhood fuse/relay box for 10 seconds to reset ECM. Check ECM for fault codes. If Code 4, 8 or 9 is not present, problem is intermittent. Check for poor connections at ECM and distributor. Test drive vehicle and retest.

2) If MIL is on and indicates Code 4, 8 or 9, turn ignition off. Disconnect 8-pin connector from TDC/CRANK/CYL sensor connector at distributor. Check resistance between terminals of each sensor. See Fig. 7. See INPUT SIGNAL & RESISTANCE TEST TERMINALS table. If resistance is not 350-700 ohms, replace distributor sub-assembly. If resistance is 350-700 ohms, go to step **3)**.

INPUT SIGNAL & RESISTANCE TEST TERMINALS

Sensor	Code	ECM Terminal	Sensor Terminal
CRANK	4	B15	B
CRANK	4	B16	F
CYL	9	B11	D
CYL	9	B12	H
TDC	8	B13	C
TDC	8	B14	G

3) Check continuity to body ground on each terminal. If continuity exists, replace distributor sub-assembly. If continuity does not exist, reconnect 8-pin connector. Leaving ECM disconnected, connect ECM Test Harness (07LAJ-PT3010A) to ECM harness connectors. Check resistance between ECM test harness terminals. See INPUT SIGNAL & RESISTANCE TEST TERMINALS table.

4) If resistance is not 350-700 ohms, repair open in faulty circuit. If resistance is 350-700 ohms, check for continuity to body ground on test terminals B11, B13 and B15. If continuity exists on any terminal, repair short circuit. If continuity does not exist, replace ECM and retest.

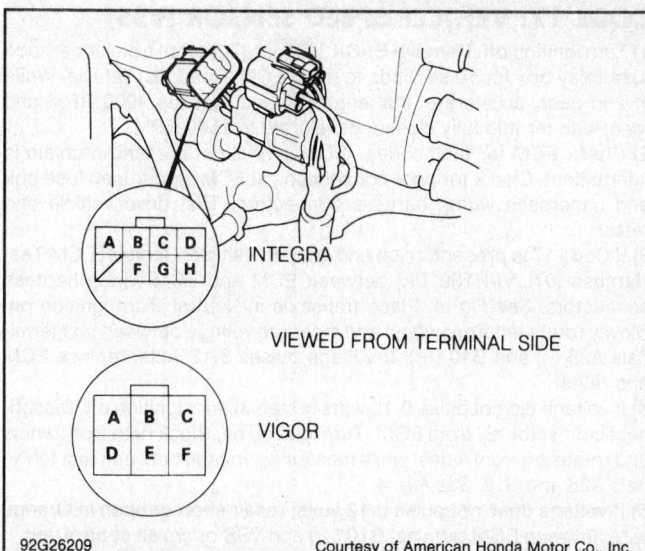

INTEGRA

VIEWED FROM TERMINAL SIDE

VIGOR

92G26209 — Courtesy of American Honda Motor Co., Inc.

Fig. 7: Identifying TDC/CRANK/CYL Sensor Connector Terminals (Integra & Vigor)

CODE 6: COOLANT SENSOR

1) Turn ignition off. Remove BACK-UP (7.5-amp) fuse from underhood fuse/relay box for 10 seconds to reset ECM. Start engine and observe MIL. If light is off, problem is intermittent. Check for poor and loose connections at coolant sensor, shock tower connectors, ECM and Transmission Control Module (TCM), if equipped. Test drive vehicle and retest.

2) If MIL is on and indicates Code 6, operate engine until cooling fan comes on. Turn engine off. Disconnect connector from coolant sensor. Measure resistance between sensor terminals. If resistance is not 200-400 ohms, replace coolant sensor.

3) If resistance is 200-400 ohms, turn ignition on. Measure voltage between Red/White wire terminal (+) and body ground. If about 5 volts are present, go to step **6)**. If voltage is not about 5 volts, go to step **4)**.

4) On A/T models, disconnect 22-pin connector from TCM. Turn ignition on. Recheck voltage at Red/White wire terminal. If voltage is about 5 volts, replace TCM. If voltage is not about 5 volts, turn ignition off and reconnect TCM. On all models, connect connector "D" of ECM Test Harness (07LAJ-PT3010A) to ECM, leaving vehicle wiring harness disconnected. Turn ignition on. Measure voltage between test terminals D13 (+) and D22 (−).

5) If voltage is about 5 volts, repair open or short in Red/White wire between ECM terminal D13 and coolant sensor. If voltage is not about 5 volts, replace ECM and retest.

6) If voltage was about 5 volts in step **3)**, measure voltage between Red/White (+) and Green/Blue (−) wire terminals. If voltage is not about 5 volts, repair open in Green/Blue wire between ECM connector terminal D22 and coolant sensor. If about 5 volts are present, replace ECM and retest.

CODE 7: THROTTLE POSITION SENSOR

1) Turn ignition off. Remove BACK-UP fuse (7.5-amp) from underhood fuse/relay box for 10 seconds to reset ECM. Check ECM for fault codes. If Code 7 is not present, problem is intermittent. Check for poor or loose connections at throttle position sensor, TCM (if equipped), left and right shock towers, and ECM connectors. Test drive vehicle and retest.

2) If MIL is on and indicates Code 7, turn ignition off. Disconnect 3-pin connector from throttle position sensor. Turn ignition on. Measure voltage between Yellow/Blue (+) and Green/Blue (−) wire terminals. If voltage is not about 5 volts, go to step **6)**. If about 5 volts are present, turn ignition off. Reconnect sensor connector. Connect ECM Test Harness (07LAJ-PT3010A) between ECM and ECM connectors. See Fig. 4.

3) Turn ignition on. Measure voltage between test terminals D11 (+) and D22 (−). Voltage should be about 0.5 volt at closed throttle and about 4.5 volts at wide open throttle. Transition from 0.5 to 4.5 volts (as throttle is opened) should be smooth. If voltage and operation is correct, replace ECM and retest.

4) If sensor voltages are not correct on M/T models, go to next step. If sensor voltages are not correct on A/T models, disconnect 22-pin connector from Transmission Control Module (TCM). Recheck voltages. If voltages and operation are correct, replace TCM. If voltages and operation are not correct, go to next step.

5) On all models, replace throttle position sensor or repair open or short in Red/Blue wire between ECM terminal D11, TCM (if equipped) and throttle position sensor.

6) If voltage between Yellow/Blue (+) and Green/Blue (−) wire terminals in step **2)** was not about 5 volts, measure voltage between Yellow/Blue wire terminal (+) and body ground. If about 5 volts are present, repair open in Green/Blue wire between ECM terminal D22 and throttle position sensor.

7) If voltage is not about 5 volts, turn ignition off. Connect ECM Test Harness (07LAJ-PT3010A) between ECM and ECM connectors. See Fig. 4. Turn ignition on. Measure voltage between test terminals D20 (+) and D22 (−). If about 5 volts are present, repair open in Yellow/White wire terminal between ECM connector terminal D20 and throttle position sensor. If voltage is not about 5 volts, repair short in Yellow/Blue wire or replace ECM and retest.

CODE 10: AIR TEMPERATURE (TA) SENSOR

1) Turn ignition off. Remove BACK-UP fuse (7.5-amp) from underhood fuse/relay box for 10 seconds to reset ECM. Check ECM for fault codes. If Code 10 is not present, problem is intermittent. Check for poor connections at ECM, air temperature sensor and wiring harness connectors.

2) Test drive vehicle and retest. If Code 10 is present, turn ignition off. Disconnect 2-pin connector from sensor connector. Using ohmmeter, measure resistance at sensor terminals. If resistance is not 400-4000 ohms, replace air temperature sensor. If resistance is 400-4000 ohms, turn ignition on. Measure voltage between Red/Yellow wire terminal and body ground.

3) If voltage is not about 5 volts, go to step **4)**. If about 5 volts are present, measure voltage between Red/Yellow (+) and Green/Blue (−) wire terminals at sensor. If voltage is not about 5 volts, repair open in Green/White wire between ECM terminal D22 and air temperature sensor. If about 5 volts are present, replace ECM and retest.

4) Turn ignition off. Connect ECM Test Harness (07LAJ-PT3010A) connector "D" to ECM, leaving wiring harness disconnected. See Fig. 4. Turn ignition on. Measure voltage between test terminals D15 (+) and D22 (−). If about 5 volts are present, repair open or short in Red/Yellow wire between ECM connector terminal D15 and air temperature sensor. If voltage is not about 5 volts, replace ECM and retest.

CODE 13: BAROMETRIC (BARO) SENSOR

NOTE: Barometric sensor is built into ECM. Circuit testing is not required.

1) Turn ignition off. Remove BACK-UP fuse (7.5-amp) from underhood fuse/relay box for 10 seconds to reset ECM.

2) Check ECM for fault codes. If Code 13 is not present, problem is intermittent. Check for poor connections at ECM connector and Transmission Control Module (TCM) connector (if equipped). Test drive vehicle and check again. If Code 13 is present, replace ECM and retest.

CODE 14: IDLE AIR CONTROL VALVE (IACV)

1) Turn ignition off. Remove BACK-UP fuse (7.5-amp) from underhood fuse/relay box for 10 seconds to reset ECM. Check ECM for fault codes. If Code 14 is not present, start engine and allow it to idle. Disconnect 2-pin connector from IACV. If engine speed is not reduced, replace IACV. If engine speed is reduced, problem is intermittent.

Check for poor connections at ECM, IACV and wiring harness. Test drive vehicle and retest.

2) If Code 14 is present, disconnect 2-pin connector from IACV. Turn ignition on. Measure voltage between Yellow/Black wire and body ground. If battery voltage is not present, repair open in Yellow/Black wire between IACV and main relay. If battery voltage is present, turn ignition off. Reconnect 2-pin connector.

3) Attach connector "A" of ECM Test Harness (07LAJ-PT3010A) to ECM wiring harness, leaving ECM disconnected. See Fig. 4. Turn ignition on. Using a jumper wire, touch test terminal A9 to test terminal A23 several times. If IACV does not click, repair open or short circuit in Blue/Yellow wire between IACV and terminal A9 of ECM connector. If IACV clicks, replace ECM and retest.

CODE 15: IGNITION OUTPUT SIGNAL

1) Turn ignition off. Remove BACK-UP fuse (7.5-amp) from underhood fuse/relay box for 10 seconds to reset ECM. Check ECM for fault codes. If Code 15 is not present, problem is intermittent. Check for poor connections at ECM, ignitor unit and wiring harness connections. Test drive vehicle and retest.

2) If Code 15 is present, turn ignition off. Disconnect 2-pin connector from distributor. Turn ignition on. Measure voltage between Black/Yellow wire and body ground. If battery voltage is not present, repair open in Black/Yellow wire between ignition switch and distributor 2-pin connector. If battery voltage is present, go to step **3)**.

3) Turn ignition off. Reconnect 2-pin connector to distributor. Connect ECM Test Harness (07LAJ-PT3010A) between ECM and ECM connectors. See Fig. 4. Turn ignition on. Measure voltage between test terminal A26 (–) and test terminal A21 (+).

NOTE: A short in Yellow/Green wire between ignitor unit and ECM may damage ignitor unit. Recheck ignitor unit.

4) If voltage is not about 10 volts, check for open or short in Yellow/Green wire between ignitor unit and ECM terminal A21. If wire is okay, replace ignitor. If about 10 volts are present, replace ECM and retest.

CODE 16: FUEL INJECTOR CIRCUIT

NOTE: If engine will not start, crank engine for 10 seconds or more, if necessary, to set code.

1) Turn ignition off. Remove BACK-UP fuse (7.5-amp) from underhood fuse/relay box for 10 seconds to reset ECM. Check ECM for fault codes. If Code 16 is not present, problem is intermittent. Check for poor connections at ECM, fuel injector and wiring harness connectors. Test drive vehicle and retest.

2) If Code 16 is present, start engine. Using a stethoscope, check for clicking sound at each injector. If injector does not click, turn ignition off. Disconnect 2-pin injector connector from affected injector. Measure resistance between injector terminals. Resistance should be 10-13 ohms. If resistance is not 10-13 ohms, replace injector. If resistance is okay, go to step **3)**.

3) Turn ignition on. Measure voltage between fuel injector harness Yellow/Black wire and body ground. If battery voltage is not present, repair open in Yellow/Black wire between fuel injector and main relay. If battery voltage is present, turn ignition off. Reconnect fuel injector connector.

4) Connect ECM Test Harness (07LAJ-PT3010A) between ECM and ECM harness connectors. See Fig. 4. Turn ignition on. Check voltage between A23 (–) and following test terminals.
- Injector No. 1: A1 (+)
- Injector No. 2: A3 (+)
- Injector No. 3: A5 (+)
- Injector No. 4: A2 (+)

If battery voltage is not present, repair open in wire between injector and affected ECM connector terminal (A1, A2, A3 or A5). If battery voltage is present, replace ECM and retest.

CODE 17: VEHICLE SPEED SENSOR (VSS)

1) Turn ignition off. Remove BACK-UP fuse (7.5-amp) from underhood fuse/relay box for 10 seconds to reset ECM. Road test vehicle. While in 2nd gear, accelerate until engine speed reaches 4000 RPM and then, with throttle fully closed, decelerate to 1500 RPM.

2) Check ECM for fault codes. If Code 17 is not present, problem is intermittent. Check for poor connections at ECM, underdash fuse box and underdash wiring harness connectors. Test drive vehicle and retest.

3) If Code 17 is present, raise and support vehicle. Connect ECM Test Harness (07LAJ-PT3010A) between ECM and ECM wiring harness connectors. See Fig. 4. Place transaxle in Neutral. Turn ignition on. Slowly rotate left front wheel and measure voltage between test terminals A26 (–) and B10 (+). If voltage pulses 0-12 volts, replace ECM and retest.

4) If voltage did not pulse 0-12 volts in step **3)**, turn ignition off. Disconnect connector "B" from ECM. Turn ignition on. Block right front wheel and rotate left front wheel while measuring voltage between test terminals A26 and B10. See Fig. 4.

5) If voltage does not pulse 0-12 volts, repair short or open in Orange wire between ECM terminal B10 (+) and VSS or cruise control unit. If wire is okay, replace VSS. If voltage pulses 0-12 volts, replace ECM and retest.

CODE 20: ELECTRIC LOAD DETECTOR

1) Turn ignition off. Remove BACK-UP fuse (7.5-amp) from underhood fuse box for 10 seconds to reset ECM. Start engine, and allow it to idle. Check ECM for fault codes. If Code 20 is not present, problem is intermittent. Check for poor or loose connections at MAP sensor and Electric Load Detector (ELD). Test drive vehicle and retest.

2) If Code 20 is present, turn ignition off. Remove underhood fuse/relay box and remove lower cover. Disconnect 3-pin ELD connector. Turn ignition on. Measure voltage between ELD Black/Yellow wire (positive) and Black wire (negative). See Fig. 8. If voltage is about 12 volts, go to step **4)**. If voltage is not about 12 volts, go to next step.

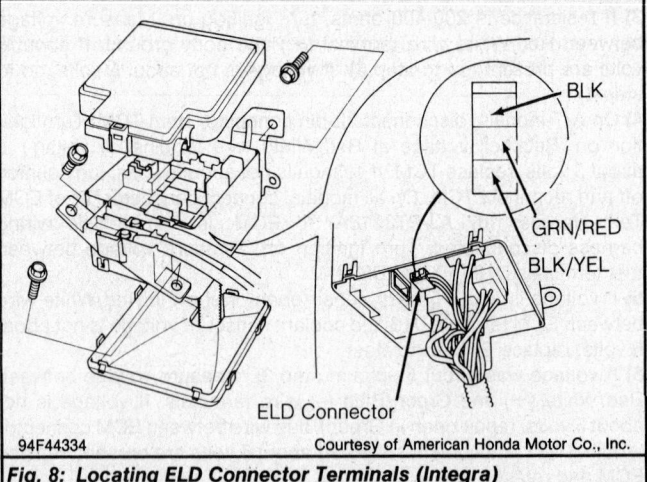

94F44334   Courtesy of American Honda Motor Co., Inc.

Fig. 8: Locating ELD Connector Terminals (Integra)

3) Measure voltage between ELD Black/Yellow wire (+) and body ground. If about 12 volts are present, repair open circuit in Black wire between 3-pin ELD connector and ground (right side of engine compartment). If voltage is not about 12 volts, repair open Black/Yellow wire between ELD connector and ACG fuse No. 24.

4) If voltage was about 12 volts in step **2)**, measure voltage between ELD Green/Red wire (+) and body ground (–). If voltage is not about 5 volts, repair open in Green/Red wire between ECM terminal D10 and ELD. If voltage is about 5 volts, go to next step.

5) If voltage is about 5 volts, turn ignition off. Reconnect 3-pin ELD connector. Connect ECM Test Harness (07LAJ-PT3010A) between ECM and ECM connectors. See Fig. 4. Turn ignition on. Measure voltage between test terminals D10 (+) and D26 (–). If voltage does not drop when headlights are turned on, replace ELD. If voltage does drop when headlights are turned on, replace ECM and retest.

CODE 21: VTEC SOLENOID VALVE (1.8L GS-R)

1) Turn ignition off. Remove BACK-UP fuse (7.5-amp) from underhood fuse/relay box for 10 seconds to reset ECM. Warm engine until cooling fan comes on. Road test vehicle. While in 1st gear, accelerate until engine speed reaches 6000 RPM and hold for at least 2 seconds. Repeat procedure 3 times. Check ECM for fault codes. If Code 21 is not present, problem is intermittent. Check for poor connections at Variable Valve Timing and Lift Electronic Control System (VTEC) solenoid valve and ECM connector.

2) If Code 21 is present, turn ignition off. Disconnect VTEC solenoid valve 1-pin connector. Check resistance between connector terminal and body ground. If resistance is not 14-30 ohms, replace VTEC solenoid valve. If 14-30 ohms are present, connect ECM Test Harness (07LAJ-PT3010A) between ECM and ECM connectors. *See Fig. 4.*

3) Check for continuity between VTEC solenoid valve connector and test terminal A4. If continuity is not present, repair open in wire between VTEC solenoid valve and ECM connector. If continuity is present, check for continuity between VTEC solenoid valve connector terminal and body ground.

4) If continuity is present, repair short in wire between VTEC solenoid valve and ECM connector. If continuity is not present, replace ECM and retest.

CODE 22: VTEC PRESSURE SWITCH (1.8L GS-R)

1) Turn ignition off. Remove BACK-UP fuse (7.5-amp) from underhood fuse/relay box for 10 seconds to reset ECM. Warm engine until cooling fan comes on. Road test vehicle. While in 1st gear, accelerate until engine speed reaches 6000 RPM and hold for at least 2 seconds. Repeat procedure 3 times. Check ECM for fault codes. If Code 22 is not present, problem is intermittent. Check for poor connections at Variable Valve Timing and Lift Electronic Control System (VTEC) pressure switch and ECM connector.

2) If Code 22 is present, turn ignition off. Disconnect switch 2-pin connector. Check for continuity between Black wire terminal and body ground. If continuity is not present, repair open in Black wire between switch connector and body ground. If continuity is present, connect ECM Test Harness (07LAJ-PT3010A) between ECM and ECM connectors. *See Fig. 4.*

3) Check for continuity between test terminal D6 and Blue/Black wire terminal. If continuity is not present, repair open in Blue/Black wire between VTEC pressure switch connector and ECM. If continuity is present, check for continuity between test terminal D6 and body ground. If continuity is present, repair short in Blue/Black wire between VTEC presure switch connector and ECM. *See Fig. 4.* If continuity is not present, go to step **4)**.

4) Remove 10-mm plug and attach oil pressure gauge. With engine at normal operating temperature, check oil pressure at 1000, 3000 and 5000 RPM. If pressure is below 7 psi (0.5 kg/cm²), replace VTEC solenoid valve. If pressure is 7 psi (0.5 kg/cm²) or more, check for continuity between switch terminals.

5) If continuity is not present, replace VTEC pressure switch. If continuity is present, remove VTEC solenoid valve connector. Connect battery voltage to VTEC solenoid valve connector terminal. Start engine. Check oil pressure at 5000 RPM.

6) If oil pressure is less than 57 psi (4 kg/cm²), replace VTEC solenoid valve. If oil pressure is 57 psi (4 kg/cm²) or more, check continuity between VTEC pressure switch terminals at 5000 RPM. If continuity is present, replace VTEC pressure switch. If continuity is not present, replace ECM and retest.

CODE 23: KNOCK SENSOR (1.8L GS-R)

NOTE: Repair any engine knocking sounds before performing test.

1) Turn ignition off. Remove BACK-UP fuse (7.5-amp) from underhood fuse/relay box for 10 seconds to reset ECM. Warm engine until cooling fan comes on. Set engine speed at 3000-4000 RPM for 10 seconds. Check ECM for fault codes. If Code 23 is not present, problem is intermittent. Check for poor connections at ECM, knock sensor and wiring harness connectors.

2) Test drive vehicle and retest. If Code 23 is present, turn ignition off. Connect ECM Test Harness (07LAJ-PT3010A) to ECM connectors, leaving ECM disconnected. *See Fig. 4.* Disconnect knock sensor connector. Check for continuity between test terminal D3 and body ground. If continuity is present, repair short in Red/Blue wire between ECM terminal D3 and knock sensor.

3) If continuity is not present, check for continuity between test terminal D3 and knock sensor connector Red/Blue wire terminal. If continuity is not present, repair open in Red/Blue wire between ECM connector terminal D3 and knock sensor.

4) If continuity is present, reconnect knock sensor. Replace knock sensor with a known good unit. Warm engine to normal operating temperature. Set engine speed at 3000-4000 RPM for 10 seconds. Check ECM for fault codes. If Code 23 is not present, replace original knock sensor. If Code 23 is present, replace ECM and retest.

CODE 30 OR 31: TCM SIGNAL "A" OR "B"

1) Turn ignition off. Remove BACK-UP fuse (7.5-amp) from underhood fuse/relay box for 10 seconds to reset ECM. Test drive vehicle for several miles (stop and go type driving). Check ECM for fault codes.

2) If Code 30 or 31 is not present, problem is intermittent. Check for poor connections at ECM, Transmission Control Module (TCM) and wiring harness connectors.

3) If Code 30 or 31 is present, turn ignition off. Connect ECM Test Harness (07LAJ-PT3010A) to ECM connectors, leaving ECM disconnected. *See Fig. 4.* Disconnect 22-pin TCM connector. Check for continuity between test terminals B3 and body ground, and between terminals B4 and body ground. If continuity is present, repair short in Green/Blue (B3) wire or Gray (B4) wire between ECM B3 or B4 terminal and 22-pin TCM connector.

4) If continuity is not present, check for continuity between Green/Blue (B3) wire or Gray (B4) wire between ECM B3 or B4 terminal and 22-pin TCM connector. If continuity is not present, repair open in Green/Blue (B3) or Gray (B4) wire between ECM and TCM. If continuity is present, replace ECM and retest.

CODE 41: HO2S HEATER

1) Turn ignition off. Remove BACK-UP fuse (7.5-amp) from underhood fuse/relay box for 10 seconds to reset ECM. Check ECM for fault codes. If Code 41 is not present, problem is intermittent. Check for poor connections at ECM, HO2S and wiring harness connectors.

2) Test drive vehicle and retest. If Code 41 is present, turn ignition off. Disconnect 4-pin HO2S connector. Measure resistance between HO2S terminals "C" and "D". *See Fig. 9.* If resistance is not 10-40 ohms, replace sensor. If resistance is 10-40 ohms, go to step **3)**.

3) Check for continuity between body ground and HO2S terminals "C" and "D". If continuity is present, replace sensor. If continuity is not present, check for continuity between terminal "D" and terminals "A" and "B". If continuity is present, replace sensor.

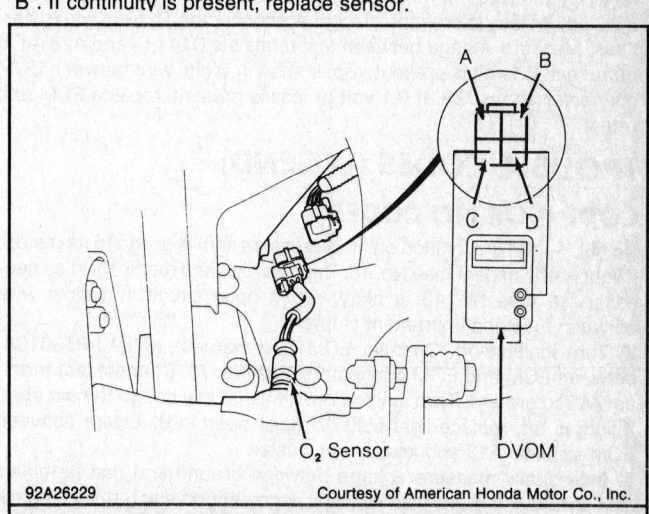

92A26229   Courtesy of American Honda Motor Co., Inc.

Fig. 9: Identifying HO2S Connector Terminals (Integra)

4) If continuity is not present, turn ignition on. Measure voltage between Yellow/Black (+) and Orange/Black (–) wire terminals at HO2S wiring harness connector. *See Fig. 9*. If battery voltage is not present, go to step **7)**. If battery voltage is present, disconnect connector "A" from ECM. Measure voltage between Yellow/Black (+) and Orange/Black (–) wires at HO2S wiring harness connector.

5) If battery voltage is present, repair short circuit in Orange/Black wire between ECM connector terminal A6 and HO2S. If battery voltage is not present, reconnect HO2S. Connect connector "A" of ECM Test Harness (07LAJ-PT3010A) to vehicle wiring harness, leaving ECM disconnected.

6) Connect ammeter between test terminals A6 (+) and A23 (–). Monitor ammeter for 5 minutes. If current is less than 0.1 amp, replace HO2S. If current is not less than 0.1 amp, replace ECM and retest.

7) If battery voltage did not exist in step **4)**, measure voltage between Yellow/Black wire terminal (+) at HO2S wiring harness connector and body ground. If battery voltage does not exist, repair open in Yellow/Black wire between HO2S and main relay. If battery voltage exists, turn ignition off. Reconnect HO2S wiring harness connector.

8) Connect connector "A" of ECM Test Harness (07LAJ-PT3010A) to ECM wiring harness, leaving ECM disconnected. Turn ignition on. Measure voltage between test terminals A6 (+) and A23 (–). If battery voltage does not exist, repair open in Orange/Black wire between ECM connector terminal A6 and HO2S. If battery voltage exists, replace ECM and retest.

CODE 43: FUEL SUPPLY SYSTEM

1) If referred here from CODE 1, go to step **2)**. If Code 43 exists, turn ignition off. Remove BACK-UP fuse (7.5-amp) from underhood fuse/relay box for 10 seconds to reset ECM. Warm engine until cooling fan comes on. With transmission in Neutral, raise engine speed to 3000 RPM and hold for 2 minutes. Check ECM for fault codes. If Code 43 does not exist, problem is intermittent. Check for poor connections at ECM, HO2S and wiring harness connectors.

2) If Code 43 is present, turn ignition off. Connect ECM Test Harness (07LAJ-PT3010A) between ECM and ECM connectors. *See Fig. 4*. Wait 2 minutes. Install jumper wire between test terminals A6 and A26. Turn ignition on while measuring voltage between terminals D14 (+) and A26 (–).

3) If 0.1 volt or less is present as ignition is turned on, go to step **5)**. If more than 0.1 volt is present as ignition is turned on, disconnect HO2S connector. Measure voltage between HO2S wiring harness connector Green/Blue and White/Red wire terminals.

4) If more than 0.1 volt is present, replace HO2S. If 0.1 volt or less is present, repair open circuit in Green/Blue or White/Red wire between HO2S and ECM connector.

5) If 0.1 volt or less was present as ignition was turned on in step **3)**, disconnect HO2S connector. Measure voltage between test terminals D14 (+) and A26 (–). If more than 0.1 volt is present, replace HO2S. If 0.1 volt or less is present, disconnect connector "D" from wiring harness. Measure voltage between test terminals D14 (+) and A26 (–). If more than 0.1 volt is present, repair short in White wire between ECM connector and HO2S. If 0.1 volt or less is present, replace ECM and retest.

TROUBLE CODES (LEGEND)

CODE 0 OR NO CODES

No MIL – **1)** Turn ignition on. If oil pressure light is on, go to next step. If light is off, inspect fuse No. 13. Replace fuse and repair short as necessary. If fuse No. 13 is okay, repair open circuit in Yellow wire between fuse and instrument cluster.

2) Turn ignition off. Connect ECM Test Harness (07LAJ-PT3010A) between ECM and ECM connectors. *See Fig. 10*. Connect test terminal A13 to ground. Turn ignition on. If MIL is now on, go to next step. If light is off, replace light bulb or repair open in Blue wire between ECM terminal A13 and instrument cluster.

3) Individually measure voltage between ground and test terminals A23 and A24. If more than one volt is present on any terminal, check open in wire between ECM and ground terminal G101 (at intake man-

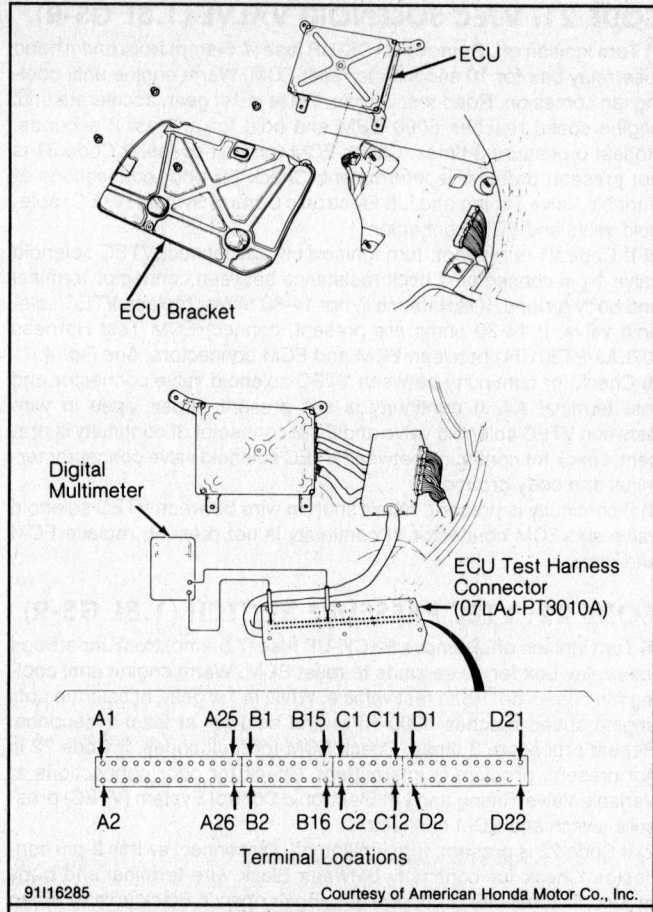

Fig. 10: Connecting ECM Test Harness (Legend & Vigor)

A1 A25 B1 B15 C1 C11 D1 D21
A2 A26 B2 B16 C2 C12 D2 D22
Terminal Locations

91116285 — Courtesy of American Honda Motor Co., Inc.

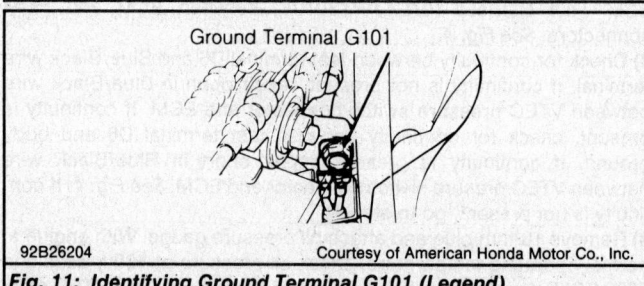

Ground Terminal G101

92B26204 — Courtesy of American Honda Motor Co., Inc.

Fig. 11: Identifying Ground Terminal G101 (Legend)

ifold). *See Fig. 11*. If less than one volt is present on each terminal, replace ECM and retest.

MIL Stays On – **1)** Check ECM for fault codes. See RETRIEVING CODES under SELF-DIAGNOSTIC SYSTEM. Service codes. If no codes are present, remove jumper wire from self-diagnostic connector. Start engine. If engine does not start, go to step **6)**. If engine starts, turn ignition off. Connect ECM Test Harness (07LAJ-PT3010A) between ECM and ECM connectors. *See Fig. 10*.

2) Turn ignition on. Measure voltage between terminals C9 (+) and A26 (–) of ECM connectors. If about 5 volts are present, go to next step. If voltage is not about 5 volts, repair short to body ground in White wire between ECM terminal C9 and self-diagnostic connector.

3) Connect jumper wire to self-diagnostic connector. If about 5 volts are now present, check for open in White wire between self-diagnostic connector and ECM. Check for open in Black wire between self-diagnostic connector and ground.

4) If about 5 volts are not present, remove jumper wire from self-diagnostic connector. Turn ignition off. Disconnect connector "A" of ECM. Turn ignition on. If MIL is on, repair short to ground in Blue wire between terminal A13 and instrument cluster. *See Fig. 10*.

5) If MIL is not on, replace ECM and retest.

6) If engine did not start, check fuses No. 5 (20-amp) and IG COIL (30-amp) in underdash fuse box. Replace bad fuses. Turn ignition on. Install jumper wire between self-diagnostic connector terminals. Individually disconnect 3-pin connectors on MAP, EGR valve lift sensors and Traction Control System (TCS), if equipped.

7) If MIL goes out, replace sensor causing MIL to go out. If MIL is on, connect jumper wire to self-diagnostic connector. Disconnect throttle position sensor or ignition timing adjuster connector. Check to see if ECM flashes Code 7 or 18. If Code 7 is indicated, replace throttle position sensor. If Code 18 is indicated, replace ignition timing adjuster.

8) If Code 7 or 18 is not indicated, turn ignition off. Remove jumper wire. Connect ECM Test Harness (07LAJ-PT3010A) between ECM and ECM connectors. See Fig. 10. Disconnect connector "D" from ECM side only. Individually check for continuity between body ground and terminals D19 and D20.

9) If continuity exists, repair short to ground in Yellow/White wire between ECM terminal D19 or D20 and MAP sensor, ignition timing adjuster, throttle position sensor or EGR valve lift sensor.

10) If continuity does not exist, reconnect connector "D". Reconnect all sensor connectors. Turn ignition on. Individually measure voltage between ECM body ground and terminals A26 and B2. See Fig. 10. If voltage is more than one volt, repair open in Brown/Black wire (A26) or Brown/Black wire (B2) between affected terminal and ground G101 at intake manifold. See Fig. 11.

11) If voltage was less than one volt, individually measure voltage between ECM terminal A26 (–) and terminals C1 (+) and A25 (+). See Fig. 11. If battery voltage is present, turn ignition off, replace ECM and retest. If battery voltage is not present, repair open in Yellow/Black wire circuit between main relay and ECM terminals A25 and C1. If circuit is okay, check main relay and connector.

CODE 1 OR 2: HO2S

1) Turn ignition off. Remove ACG fuse (No. 15, 7.5-amp) from underdash fuse box for 10 seconds to reset ECM. Start engine, and warm it until cooling fan comes on.

2) Road test vehicle. Place M/T in 4th gear (A/T in 2nd). With engine speed at 1200 RPM, accelerate at wide open throttle for at least 5 seconds and then decelerate with throttle fully closed for at least 5 seconds.

3) Check ECM for fault codes. If no codes are present, problem is intermittent. Check for poor connections at HO2S and ECM connector. If Code 1 or 2 is present, go to CODE 43 OR 44.

CODE 3: MAP SENSOR

1) Turn ignition off. Remove ACG fuse (No. 15, 7.5-amp) from underdash fuse box for 10 seconds to reset ECM. Start engine. Connect jumper wire to self-diagnostic connector. Observe MIL. If Code 3 is not present, problem is intermittent. Check for poor or loose connection at MAP sensor and ECM connector. Test drive vehicle and retest.

2) If Code 3 is present, turn ignition off. Disconnect 3-pin connector at MAP sensor. Turn ignition on. Measure voltage between Yellow/White wire terminal (+) and body ground. See Fig. 12. If about 5 volts is present, go to step **4)**. If voltage is not about 5 volts, turn ignition off. Connect connector "D" of ECM Test Harness (07LAJ-PT3010A) to ECM, leaving vehicle wiring harness disconnected.

3) Turn ignition on. Measure voltage between test terminals D17 (+) and D21 (–). If voltage is about 5 volts, repair open in Yellow/White wire between ECM terminal D19 and MAP sensor. If voltage is not about 5 volts, turn ignition off, replace ECM and retest.

4) If voltage was about 5 volts in step **2)**, measure voltage between Yellow/White and Green/White wires at MAP sensor. See Fig. 12. If voltage is not about 5 volts, repair open in Green/White wire between ECM connector terminal D21 and MAP sensor. If voltage is about 5 volts, measure voltage between Red (+) and Green/White (–) wire terminals at MAP sensor.

5) If voltage is not about 5 volts, go to step **7)**. If about 5 volts are present, turn ignition off. Reconnect MAP sensor. Install ECM Test Harness (07LAJ-PT3010A) to ECM and vehicle wiring harness. See Fig. 10. Turn ignition on.

6) Measure voltage between test terminals D17 (+) and D21 (–). If voltage is not about 3 volts, replace MAP sensor. If about 3 volts are present, replace ECM and retest.

7) If voltage was not about 5 volts in step **5)**, turn ignition off. Connect connector "D" of ECM Test Harness (07LAJ-PT3010A) to ECM, leaving vehicle wiring harness disconnected.

8) Turn ignition on. Measure voltage between test terminals D17 (+) and D21 (–). If voltage is about 5 volts, repair open or short in circuit D17 (Red wire) between ECM connector and MAP sensor. If voltage is not about 5 volts, replace ECM and retest.

CODE 4, 9, 54 OR 59: CRANK/CYL SENSOR

1) Turn ignition off. Remove ACG fuse (No. 15, 7.5-amp) in underdash fuse box for 10 seconds to reset ECM. Start engine. Connect jumper wire to self-diagnostic connector. Observe MIL. If Code 4, 9, 54 or 59 is not present, problem is intermittent. Check for poor and loose connections at CRANK/CYL sensor assembly connector and ECM connector. Test drive vehicle and retest.

2) If Code 4, 9, 54 or 59 is present, turn ignition off. Disconnect 8-pin connector from CRANK/CYL sensor. Check wiring harness and terminals. Check resistance of each sensor at indicated terminals. See INPUT SIGNAL & RESISTANCE TEST TERMINALS table. See Fig. 13. If resistance is not 650-900 ohms, replace CRANK/CYL sensor assembly. If resistance is 650-900 ohms, go to step **3)**.

INPUT SIGNAL & RESISTANCE TEST TERMINALS

Sensor	Code	ECM Terminal	Sensor Terminal
CRANK 1	4	B15	A
		B16	B
CRANK 2	54	B14	C
		B13	D
CYL 1	9	B12	G
		B11	H
CYL 2	59	B9	E
		B10	F

3) Check continuity to body ground on each terminal. If continuity exists, replace CRANK/CYL sensor assembly. If continuity does not exist, reconnect 8-pin connector. Connect ECM Test Harness (07LAJ-PT3010A) to ECM harness connectors, leaving ECM disconnected. Check resistance between ECM test harness terminals. See INPUT SIGNAL & RESISTANCE TEST TERMINALS table.

4) If resistance is not 650-900 ohms, repair open in faulty circuit. If resistance is 650-900 ohms, check for continuity to body ground on terminals B9, B11, B13 and B15. If continuity exists on any terminal, repair short circuit. If continuity does not exist, replace ECM and retest.

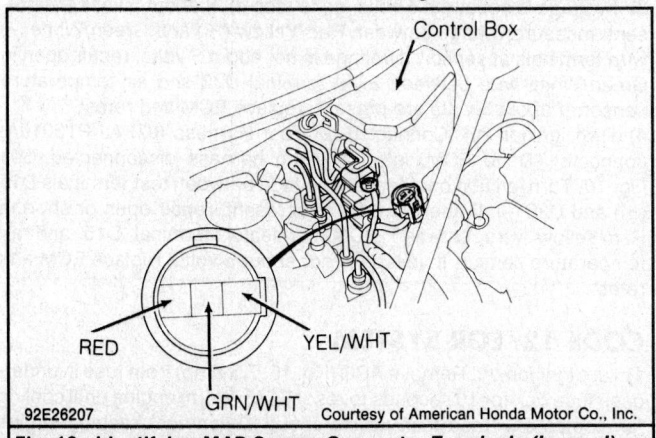

Control Box

RED YEL/WHT

GRN/WHT

92E26207   Courtesy of American Honda Motor Co., Inc.

Fig. 12: Identifying MAP Sensor Connector Terminals (Legend)

1994 ENGINE PERFORMANCE
Self-Diagnostics (Cont.)

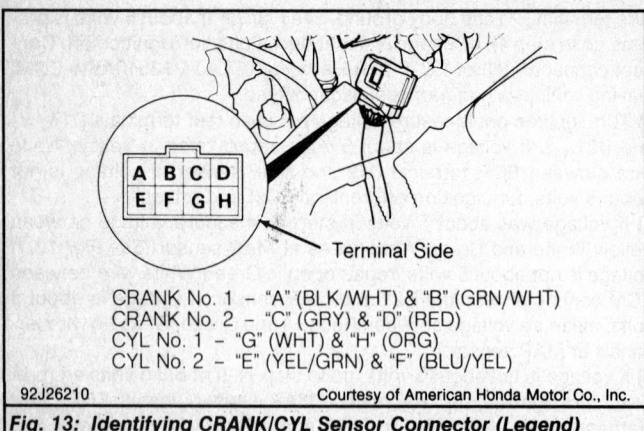

CRANK No. 1 – "A" (BLK/WHT) & "B" (GRN/WHT)
CRANK No. 2 – "C" (GRY) & "D" (RED)
CYL No. 1 – "G" (WHT) & "H" (ORG)
CYL No. 2 – "E" (YEL/GRN) & "F" (BLU/YEL)

92J26210   Courtesy of American Honda Motor Co., Inc.

Fig. 13: Identifying CRANK/CYL Sensor Connector (Legend)

CODE 5: MAP SENSOR

1) Turn ignition off. Remove ACG (No. 15, 7.5-amp) from underdash fuse box for 10 seconds to reset ECM. Start engine. Connect jumper wire to self-diagnostic connector. Observe MIL. If light is off, problem is intermittent. Check all electrical connections and vacuum hoses. Test drive vehicle and retest.
2) If MIL is on and indicates Code 5, turn ignition off. Remove MAP hose at throttle body base. Connect a hand-held vacuum pump to MAP sensor, and apply vacuum. If vacuum does not hold, replace MAP sensor. If vacuum holds, connect vacuum hose and go to step **3)**.
3) Connect "T" fitting in vacuum hose between MAP sensor and throttle body base. See Fig. 14. Start engine. If vacuum is not present, remove restriction from throttle body. If vacuum is present, turn ignition off. Connect ECM Test Harness (07LAJ-PT3010A) between ECM and ECM connectors. See Fig. 10. Turn ignition on. Measure voltage between test terminals D17 (+) and D21 (−).
4) If voltage is not about 3 volts, replace MAP sensor. If voltage is about 3 volts, start engine and allow it to idle. Recheck voltage between terminals D17 and D21. If voltage is not about one volt at idle, replace MAP sensor. If voltage is about one volt, replace ECM and retest.

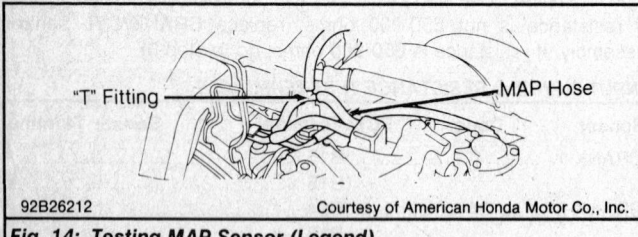

"T" Fitting   MAP Hose

92B26212   Courtesy of American Honda Motor Co., Inc.

Fig. 14: Testing MAP Sensor (Legend)

CODE 6: COOLANT SENSOR

1) Turn ignition off. Remove ACG fuse (No. 15, 7.5-amp) from underdash fuse box for 10 seconds to reset ECM. If light is off, problem is intermittent. Check for poor and loose connections at coolant sensor, ECM and right shock tower. Test drive vehicle and retest.
2) If MIL is on and indicates Code 6, operate engine until cooling fan comes on. Turn engine off. Disconnect connector from coolant sensor. Measure resistance between sensor terminals. If resistance is not 200-400 ohms, replace coolant sensor.
3) If resistance is 200-400 ohms, turn ignition on. Measure voltage between Red/White wire terminal (+) and body ground. If voltage is about 5 volts, go to step **5)**. If voltage is not about 5 volts, connect connector "D" of ECM Test Harness (07LAJ-PT3010A) to ECM, leaving vehicle wiring harness disconnected. Turn ignition on. Measure voltage between test terminals D13 (+) and D22 (−). See Fig. 10.
4) If voltage is about 5 volts, repair open or short in Red/White wire between ECM terminal D13 and coolant sensor. If voltage is not about 5 volts, replace ECM and retest.

5) If voltage was about 5 volts in step **3)**, measure voltage between Red/White (+) and Green/White (−) wire terminals. If voltage is not about 5 volts, repair open in Green/White wire between ECM connector terminal D22 and coolant sensor. If about 5 volts are present, replace ECM and retest.

CODE 7: THROTTLE POSITION SENSOR

1) Turn ignition off. Remove ACG fuse (No. 15, 7.5-amp) from underdash fuse box for 10 seconds to reset ECM. Check ECM for fault codes. If Code 7 is not present, problem is intermittent. Check for poor and loose connections at throttle position sensor, right shock tower harness connector and ECM connectors. Test drive vehicle and retest.
2) If Code 7 is present, turn ignition off. Disconnect 3-pin connector from throttle position sensor. Turn ignition on. Measure voltage between Yellow/White (+) and Green/White (−) wire terminals. If voltage is not about 5 volts, go to step **5)**. If about 5 volts are present, turn ignition off. Reconnect sensor connector. Connect ECM Test Harness (07LAJ-PT3010A) between ECM and ECM connectors. See Fig. 10.
3) Turn ignition on. Measure voltage between test terminals D11 (+) and D22 (−). Voltage should be about 0.5 volt at closed throttle and about 4.5 volts at wide open throttle. Transition from 0.5 to 4.5 volts (as throttle is opened) should be smooth.
4) If voltage is correct, replace ECM and retest. On models with TCS, disconnect 16-pin connector from TCS. Repeat step **3)**. If voltages are now correct, replace TCS control unit. On all models if voltages are not correct, replace throttle position sensor or repair open or short in Red/Blue wire between ECM terminal D11 and throttle position sensor.
5) If voltage between Yellow/White (+) and Green/White (−) wire terminals in step **2)** was not about 5 volts, measure voltage between Yellow/White (+) wire terminal and body ground. If voltage is about 5 volts, repair open in Green/White wire between ECM terminal D22 and throttle position sensor. If voltage is not about 5 volts, turn ignition off.
6) Connect ECM Test Harness (07LAJ-PT3010A) between ECM and ECM connectors. See Fig. 10. Turn ignition on. Measure voltage between test terminals D20 (+) and D22 (−). If voltage is about 5 volts, repair open in Yellow/White wire terminal between ECM connector terminal D20 and throttle position sensor. If voltage is not about 5 volts, replace ECM and retest.

CODE 10: AIR TEMPERATURE (TA) SENSOR

1) Turn ignition off. Remove ACG fuse (No. 15, 7.5-amp) from underdash fuse box for 10 seconds to reset ECM. Check ECM for fault codes. If Code 10 is not present, problem is intermittent. Check for poor and loose connections at air temperature sensor, wiring harness and ECM connectors. Test drive vehicle and retest.
2) If Code 10 is present, turn ignition off. Disconnect 2-pin connector from sensor connector. Using an ohmmeter, measure resistance at sensor terminals. If resistance is not 400-4000 ohms, replace air temperature sensor. If resistance is 400-4000 ohms, turn ignition on. Measure voltage between Red/Yellow wire terminal and body ground.
3) If voltage is not about 5 volts, go to step **4)**. If about 5 volts are present, measure voltage between Red/Yellow (+) and Green/White (−) wire terminals at sensor. If voltage is not about 5 volts, repair open in Green/White wire between ECM terminal D22 and air temperature sensor. If about 5 volts are present, replace ECM and retest.
4) Turn ignition off. Connect ECM Test Harness (07LAJ-PT3010A) connector "D" to ECM, leaving wiring harness disconnected. See Fig. 10. Turn ignition on. Measure voltage between test terminals D15 (+) and D22 (−). If about 5 volts are present, repair open or short in Red/Yellow wire between ECM connector terminal D15 and air temperature sensor. If voltage is not about 5 volts, replace ECM and retest.

CODE 12: EGR SYSTEM

1) Turn ignition off. Remove ACG (No. 15, 7.5-amp) from fuse in underdash fuse box for 10 seconds to reset ECM. Warm engine until cooling fan comes on. Road test vehicle about 10 minutes, keeping engine speed about 1700-2500 RPM. Check for fault codes. If Code 12 is not present, problem is intermittent. Check for poor connections at ECM, EGR valve, control box and shock tower wiring harness connectors.

2) Test drive vehicle and retest. If Code 12 is present, start engine. Disconnect No. 11 hose from EGR valve. *See Fig. 15.* Start engine. Check for vacuum at hose. If no vacuum is present, go to step **4)**. If vacuum is present, disconnect 4-pin connector from control box, located on right side of firewall. Check vacuum again on No. 11 hose. If vacuum is present, check vacuum hose routing. If routing is okay, replace EGR control solenoid valve.

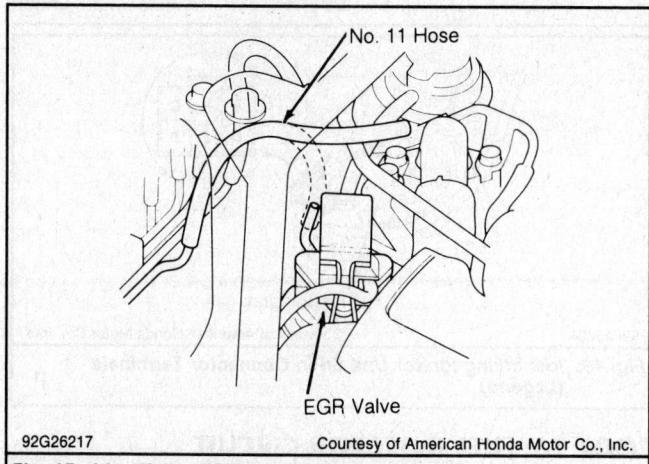

Fig. 15: Identifying EGR No. 11 Hose (Legend)

3) If vacuum is not present, turn ignition off. Remove connector "A" from ECM. Check for continuity between White wire terminal of 4-pin connector and ground. If continuity is present, repair short in White wire between EGR control solenoid valve and ECM connector terminal A11. If continuity is not present, replace ECM and retest.

4) If vacuum was not present during first vacuum test in step **2)**, install vacuum pump on EGR valve. With engine idling, apply 8 in. Hg to EGR valve. If engine does not stall or run rough or EGR valve does not hold vacuum, replace EGR valve.

5) If engine stalls or runs rough and EGR valve holds vacuum, disconnect 4-pin connector from control box. Measure voltage between Black/Yellow wire terminal and body ground. If battery voltage is not present, repair open in Black/Yellow wire between solenoid valve and FUEL PUMP fuse (No. 22, 20-amp) in underdash fuse box.

6) If battery voltage is present, install "T" fitting into No. 11 hose. Attach vacuum gauge to "T" fitting. Start engine, and allow it to idle. Connect battery voltage to terminal "A" of control box connector. *See Fig. 16.* While observing vacuum gauge, connect terminal "B" to negative battery terminal.

7) If gauge reads 6 in. Hg within one second, go to step **9)**. If gauge does not read 6 in. Hg within one second, turn ignition off. Inspect hoses for leaks, restrictions and misrouting. Repair as necessary. If hoses are okay, disconnect lower hose on EGR control solenoid valve.

8) Connect vacuum gauge to hose. *See Fig. 17.* Start engine, and allow it to idle. If 4.8-6.8 in. Hg is not present, replace Constant Vacuum Control (CVC) valve. *See Fig. 17.* If 4.8-6.8 in. Hg is present, replace EGR control solenoid valve. *See Fig. 17.*

9) If gauge read 6 in. Hg in step **7)**, turn ignition off. Reconnect 4-pin connector at control box. Disconnect EGR valve position sensor. Turn ignition on. Measure voltage between Yellow/White (+) and Green/White (–) wires. If about 5 volts are present, go to step **12)**.

10) If voltage is not about 5 volts, measure voltage between Yellow/White wire (+) and body ground. If about 5 volts are present, repair open in Green/White wire between EGR valve lift sensor and ECM connector D22. If voltage is not about 5 volts, turn ignition off.

11) Connect ECM Test Harness (07LAJ-PT3010A) connector "D" to ECM, leaving vehicle wiring harness disconnected. Turn ignition on. Measure voltage between test terminals D20 (+) and D22 (–). *See Fig. 10.* If voltage is about 5 volts, repair open in Yellow/White wire between ECM connector terminal D20 and EGR valve lift sensor. If voltage is not about 5 volts, replace ECM and retest.

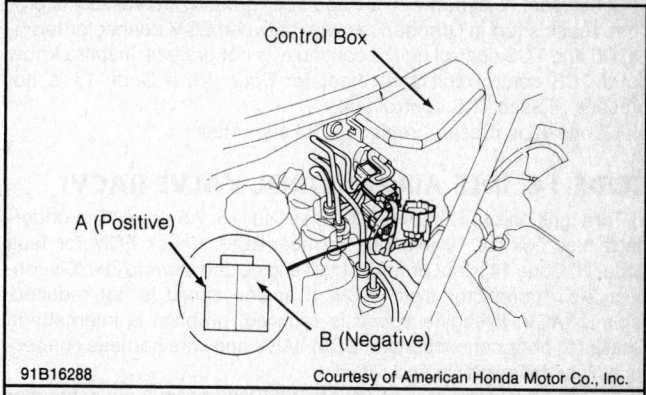

Fig. 16: Identifying Control Box Connector Terminals (Legend)

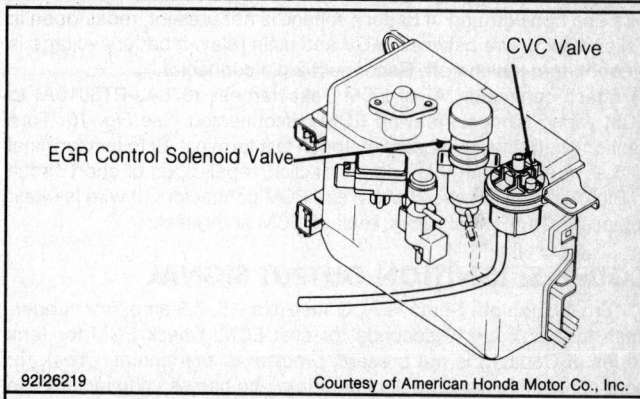

Fig. 17: Locating EGR Control Solenoid Valve & Constant Vacuum Control Valve (Legend)

12) If voltage was about 5 volts in step **9)**, turn ignition off and reconnect 3-pin connector at EGR valve lift sensor. Connect ECM Test Harness (07LAJ-PT3010A) between ECM and ECM connectors. *See Fig. 10.* Turn ignition on. Measure voltage between test terminals D12 (+) and D22 (–). Voltage should be 1.2 volts with no vacuum and 4.3 volts with 6 in. Hg vacuum applied to EGR valve. If voltage is not as specified, repair open or short in Black/White wire between EGR valve lift sensor and ECM connector terminal D12.

13) If voltage is as specified, check if it consistently increases and decreases as vacuum increases and decreases. If vacuum does not consistently increase and decrease as vacuum increases and decreases, replace EGR valve. If voltage increases and decreases with vacuum, reconnect No. 11 hose. Start engine. Allow it to idle. Connect jumper wire between test terminals A11 and A26. *See Fig. 10.*

14) If engine does not stall or run rough, repair open in White wire between ECM connector terminal A11 and EGR control solenoid valve. If engine stalls or runs rough, replace ECM and retest.

CODE 13: BAROMETRIC (BARO) SENSOR

NOTE: Barometric sensor is built into ECM. Circuit testing is not required.

1) Turn ignition off. Remove ACG fuse (No. 15, 7.5-amp) from underdash fuse box for 10 seconds to reset ECM. Check ECM for fault codes. If Code 13 is not present, problem is intermittent. Check for poor connections at ECM connector. Test drive vehicle and check again.

2) On models without TCS, go to step **4)**. On models with TCS, if Code 13 is still on, turn ignition off. Attach ECM Test Harness (07LAJ-PT3010A) to main wiring harness, leaving ECM disconnected. *See Fig. 10.* Disconnect 26-pin connector from the TCS control unit.

3) Check continuity between D5 and body ground. If continuity is present, repair short in Orange/Red wire between ECM connector terminal D5 and TCS control unit. If continuity is not present, install a know good TCS control unit and retest for Code 13. If Code 13 is not present, replace TCS control unit.

4) If Code 13 is present, replace ECM and retest.

CODE 14: IDLE AIR CONTROL VALVE (IACV)

1) Turn ignition off. Remove ACG fuse (No. 15, 7.5-amp) from underdash fuse box for 10 seconds to reset ECM. Check ECM for fault codes. If Code 14 is not present, start engine and allow to idle. Disconnect 2-pin connector from IACV. If engine speed is not reduced, replace IACV. If engine speed is reduced, problem is intermittent. Check for poor connections at ECM, IACV and wire harness connectors. Test drive vehicle and retest.

2) If Code 14 is present, turn ignition off. Disconnect 2-pin connector from IACV. Turn ignition on. Measure voltage between Yellow/Black wire and body ground. If battery voltage is not present, repair open in Yellow/Black wire between IACV and main relay. If battery voltage is present, turn ignition off. Reconnect 2-pin connector.

3) Attach connector "A" of ECM Test Harness (07LAJ-PT3010A) to ECM wiring harness, leaving ECM disconnected. *See Fig. 10*. Turn ignition on. Using a jumper wire, touch test terminal A9 to test terminal A23 several times. If IACV does not click, repair open or short circuit in Blue/Red wire between IACV and ECM connectors. If wire is okay, replace IACV. If IACV clicks, replace ECM and retest.

CODE 15: IGNITION OUTPUT SIGNAL

1) Turn ignition off. Remove ACG fuse (No. 15, 7.5-amp) from underdash fuse box for 10 seconds to reset ECM. Check ECM for fault codes. If Code 15 is not present, problem is intermittent. Check for poor connections at ECM, ignitor unit, wiring harness connectors and G102 ground terminal (located at valve cover). Test drive vehicle and retest.

2) If Code 15 is present, turn ignition off. Disconnect 8-pin connector from ignitor unit. Check for continuity between terminals "C" and "F". *See Fig. 18*. If continuity is not present, repair open in Black wire between ground terminal G102 and 8-pin connector.

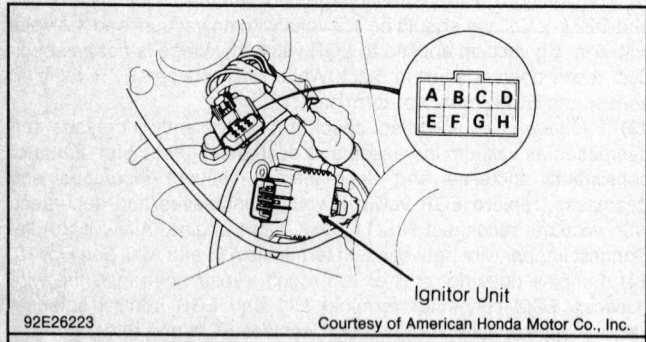

Ignitor Unit

92E26223   Courtesy of American Honda Motor Co., Inc.

Fig. 18: Identifying Ignitor Unit 8-Pin Connector Terminals (Legend)

3) If continuity is present, disconnect 6-pin connector from ignitor unit. *See Fig. 19*. Connect ECM Test Harness (07LAJ-PT3010A) to ECM wiring harness connectors, leaving ECM disconnected. *See Fig. 10*. Check for continuity between body ground and test terminals A21, A22, B3, B4, B6 and B8. If continuity is present at any terminal, repair short circuit.

4) If continuity is not present, check for continuity between ignitor unit 6-pin connector terminal and corresponding terminal at ECM connectors. See ECM/IGNITOR UNIT CONNECTOR TERMINAL IDENTIFICATION table. If continuity is not present, repair open circuit. If continuity is present, substitute a known good ignitor. If symptom/condition goes away, replace original ignitor. If symptom/condition does not go away, replace ECM and retest.

ECM/IGNITOR UNIT CONNECTOR TERMINAL IDENTIFICATION

Ignitor Unit Connector Terminals	ECM Connector Terminals	Wire Color
A	B8	Blue
B	A22	Brown
C	A21	Pink
D	B3	Red
E	B4	Gray
F	B6	Green

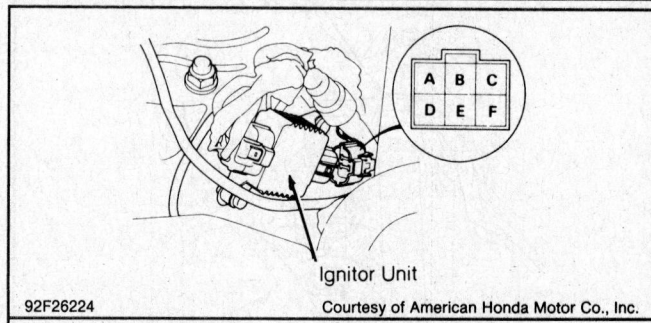

Ignitor Unit

92F26224   Courtesy of American Honda Motor Co., Inc.

Fig. 19: Identifying Ignitor Unit 6-Pin Connector Terminals (Legend)

CODE 16: FUEL INJECTOR CIRCUIT

1) Turn ignition off. Remove ACG fuse (No. 15, 7.5-amp) fuse from underdash fuse box for 10 seconds to reset ECM. Check ECM for fault codes. If Code 16 is not present, problem is intermittent. Check for poor connections at ECM, fuel injectors, fuel injector resistor and wiring harness connectors. Test drive vehicle and retest.

2) If Code 16 is present, start engine. Using a stethoscope, check for clicking sound at each injector. If injector does not click, turn ignition off. Disconnect 2-pin injector connector from affected injector. Measure resistance between injector terminals. If resistance is not 1.5-2.5 ohms, replace injector. If resistance is 1.5-2.5 ohms, go to next step.

3) Turn ignition on. Measure voltage between fuel injector wiring harness connector Red/Black wire and body ground. If battery voltage is present, go to step **6)**. If battery voltage is not present, turn ignition off.

4) Disconnect 8-pin connector at injector resistor. Turn ignition on. Measure voltage between Yellow/Black wire terminal (+) and body ground. If battery voltage is not present, repair open in Yellow/Black wire between injector resistor and main relay. If battery voltage is present, disconnect injector resistor connector.

5) Measure resistance between terminal "E" and all other terminals. *See Fig. 20*. If resistance is not 5-7 ohms, replace injector resistor. If resistance is 5-7 ohms, repair open in Red/Black wire between 2-pin connector and injector resistor.

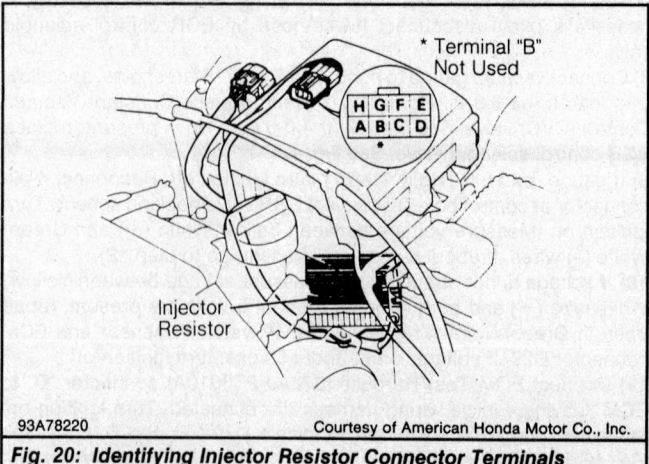

* Terminal "B" Not Used

Injector Resistor

93A78220   Courtesy of American Honda Motor Co., Inc.

Fig. 20: Identifying Injector Resistor Connector Terminals (Legend)

6) If battery voltage was present in step **3)**, turn ignition off. Reconnect fuel injector connector. Connect ECM Test Harness (07LAJ-PT3010A) between ECM and ECM connectors. *See Fig. 10*. Turn ignition on. Check voltage between A23 (–) and following test terminals.

- Injector No. 1: A1 (+)
- Injector No. 2: A3 (+)
- Injector No. 3: A5 (+)
- Injector No. 4: A2 (+)
- Injector No. 5: A4 (+)
- Injector No. 6: A6 (+)

If battery voltage is not present, repair open in wire between injector and ECM connector terminal A1, A2, A3, A4, A5 or A6. If battery voltage is present, replace ECM and retest.

CODE 17: VEHICLE SPEED SENSOR (VSS)

1) Turn ignition off. Remove ACG fuse (No. 15, 7.5-amp) from under-dash fuse box for 10 seconds to reset ECM. Road test vehicle. While in 2nd gear, accelerate until engine speed reaches 4000 RPM and then, with throttle fully closed, decelerate to 1500 RPM.

2) Check ECM for fault codes. If Code 17 is not present, problem is intermittent. Check for poor connections at ECM, VSS and wiring harness connectors. Test drive vehicle and retest.

3) If Code 17 is present, raise and support vehicle. Connect ECM Test Harness (07LAJ-PT3010A) between ECM and ECM wiring harness connectors. *See Fig. 10*. Place transaxle in Neutral. Turn ignition on. Block right front wheel and slowly rotate left front wheel. Measure voltage between test terminals A26 (–) and C2 (+). If voltage pulses 0-5 volts, replace ECM and retest.

4) If voltage does not pulse 0-5 volts, turn ignition off and disconnect connector "C" from ECM. Turn ignition on. Rotate left front wheel. If voltage does not pulse 0-5 volts, repair short or open in Yellow/Red wire between ECM terminal C2 (+) and VSS. If wire is okay, replace VSS. If voltage pulses 0-5 volts, replace ECM and retest.

CODE 18: IGNITION TIMING ADJUSTER

1) Turn ignition off. Remove ACG fuse (No. 15, 7.5-amp) from under-dash fuse box for 10 seconds to reset ECM. Check ECM for fault codes. If Code 18 is not present, problem is intermittent. Check for poor connections at ECM connector and ignition timing adjuster connector. Test drive vehicle and retest.

2) If Code 18 is present, turn ignition off. Disconnect ignition timing adjuster 3-pin connector from control box. *See Fig. 21*. Measure resistance between terminals "A" and "C" of ignition timing adjuster.

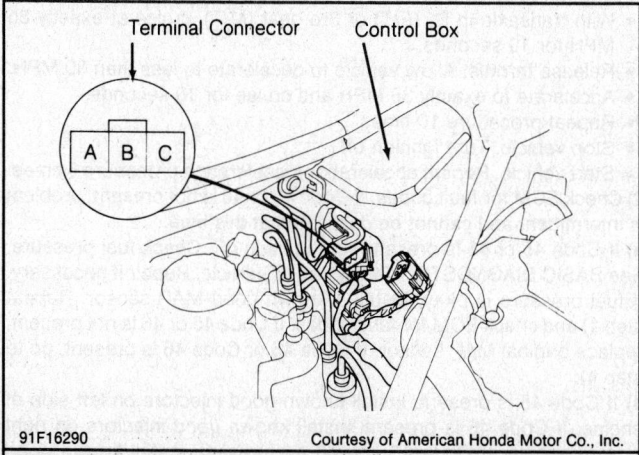

Terminal Connector   Control Box

A B C

91F16290   Courtesy of American Honda Motor Co., Inc.
Fig. 21: Locating Ignition Timing Adjuster Connector (Legend)

3) Resistance should be 3500-6500 ohms. If resistance is as specified, go to step **4)**. If resistance is not 3500-6500 ohms, replace ignition timing adjuster.

4) Measure and record resistance between terminals "A" and "B" on timing adjuster side of harness connector. Measure and record resistance between terminals "B" and "C" on same side of connector. Add both resistance values together.

5) If total resistance value is not 3500-6500 ohms, replace ignition timing adjuster. If resistance is 3500-6500 ohms, turn ignition on. Measure voltage between Yellow/White (+) and Green/White (–) wire terminals on wiring harness side of connector. If voltage is about 5 volts, go to step **8)**.

6) If voltage is not about 5 volts, measure voltage between ground and Yellow/White wire terminal. If voltage is about 5 volts, repair open in Green/White wire between ECM terminal D22 and ignition timing adjuster connector.

7) If voltage is not about 5 volts, turn ignition off. Connect ECM Test Harness (07LAJ-PT3010A) between ECM and ECM connectors. *See Fig. 10*. Turn ignition on. Measure voltage between test terminals D20 (+) and D22 (–). If about 5 volts are present, repair open in Yellow/White wire between ECM terminal D20 and ignition timing adjuster. If voltage is not about 5 volts, replace ECM and retest.

8) If voltage between Yellow/White and Green/White wire terminals in step **5)** was about 5 volts, turn ignition off. Reconnect ignition timing adjuster connector. Connect ECM Test Harness (07LAJ-PT3010A) between ECM and ECM connectors. *See Fig. 10*.

9) Turn ignition on. Measure voltage between ECM terminals D8 (+) and D22 (–). If voltage is not 0.5-4.5 volts, repair open or short in Blue/Yellow wire between ECM connector terminal D8 and ignition timing adjuster. If voltage is 0.5-4.5 volts, replace ECM and retest.

CODE 23 OR 53: KNOCK SENSOR

NOTE: Repair any engine knocking sounds before performing test.

1) Turn ignition off. Remove ACG fuse (No. 15, 7.5-amp) from under-dash fuse box for 10 seconds to reset ECM. Warm engine until cooling fan comes on. With transmission in Neutral, hold engine speed at 3000-4000 RPM for 10 seconds. Check for fault codes. If Code 23 or 53 is not present, problem is intermittent. Check for poor connections at ECM, knock sensor and wiring harness connectors. Test drive vehicle and retest.

2) If Code 23 or 53 is present, turn ignition off. Connect ECM Test Harness (07LAJ-PT3010A) to ECM harness connectors, leaving ECM disconnected. *See Fig. 10*.

3) Disconnect knock sensor connector. Check for continuity between test terminal D3 (right sensor) or D4 (left sensor) and body ground. If continuity is not present, go to step **4)**. If continuity is present, repair short in Red/Blue wire between ECM connector terminal D4 and left knock sensor or short in White wire between ECM connector terminal D3 and right knock sensor. *See Fig. 22*.

4) Check continuity between test terminal D4 and Red/Blue wire terminal at left knock sensor connector or between test terminal D3 and White wire terminal at right knock sensor connector. If continuity is not present, repair open in wire between ECM terminal D3 or D4 and knock sensor.

5) If continuity is present, reconnect knock sensors. Replace ECM with a known good unit. Warm engine until cooling fan comes on. With transmission in Neutral, hold engine speed at 3000-4000 RPM for 10 seconds. Check ECM for fault codes. If Code 23 or 53 is present, replace knock sensor. If Code 23 or 53 is not present, replace ECM.

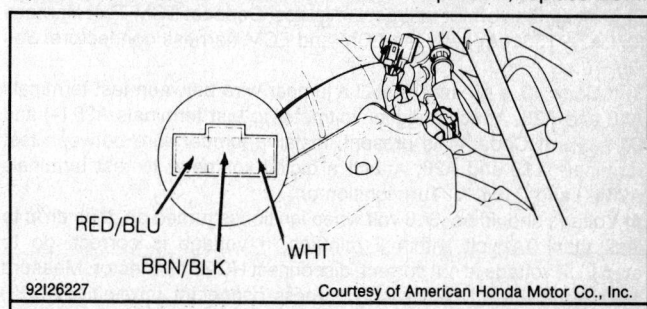

RED/BLU   WHT
BRN/BLK

92I26227   Courtesy of American Honda Motor Co., Inc.
Fig. 22: Identifying Knock Sensor Connector Terminals (Legend)

CODE 41 OR 42: HO2S HEATER

1) Turn ignition off. Remove ACG fuse (No. 15, 7.5-amp) from underdash fuse box for 10 seconds to reset ECM. Check ECM for fault codes. If Code 41 or 42 is not present, problem is intermittent. Check connections at ECM, HO2S and wiring harness connectors. Test drive vehicle and retest.

2) If Code 41 or 42 is present, turn ignition off. Disconnect 4-pin HO2S connector. Measure resistance between HO2S terminals "C" and "D". *See Fig. 23*. If resistance is not 10-20 ohms, replace sensor. If resistance is 10-20 ohms, go to next step.

3) Check continuity between body ground and all HO2S terminals. If continuity is present between any sensor terminal and ground, replace HO2S. If continuity is not present between sensor terminals and ground, check for continuity between terminal "A" and terminals "C" and "D". *See Fig. 23*. If continuity is present, replace HO2S.

4) If continuity is not present, turn ignition on. Measure voltage between HO2S wiring harness connector Black/Yellow wire and Green/Blue wire (left sensor) or Green/Red wire (right sensor). If battery voltage is present, go to step **7)**. If battery voltage is not present, measure voltage between Black/Yellow terminal and body ground. If battery voltage is present, go to step **5)**. If battery voltage is not present, check FUEL PUMP fuse (No. 22, 20-amp). If fuse is okay, repair open in Black/Yellow wire between HO2S and FUEL PUMP fuse.

5) Turn ignition off. Connect HO2S connector. Connect connector "A" of ECM Test Harness (07LAJ-PT3010A) to vehicle wiring harness, leaving ECM disconnected. Turn ignition on. Measure voltage between test terminal A23 (–) and test terminal A10 (+) for left HO2S or test terminal A12 (+) for right HO2S. *See Fig. 10*.

6) If battery voltage exists, replace ECM and retest. If battery voltage is not present, repair open in Green/Blue wire (left sensor) or Green/Red wire (right sensor) between ECM connector and HO2S.

7) If battery voltage was present in step **4)**, turn ignition off. Disconnect connector "A" from ECM. Turn ignition on. Measure voltage between HO2S wiring harness connector Black/Yellow wire and Green/Blue wire (left sensor) or Green/Red wire (right sensor). If battery voltage is present, repair short in Green/Blue or Green/Red wire between ECM connector and HO2S. If battery voltage exists, replace ECM and retest.

CODE 43 OR 44: FUEL SUPPLY SYSTEM

1) If referred here from CODE 1, go to step **2)**. Turn ignition off. Remove ACG fuse (No. 15, 7.5-amp) from underdash fuse box for 10 seconds to reset ECM. Warm engine until cooling fan comes on. With transmission in Neutral, hold engine speed at 3000 RPM for 2 minutes. Check ECM for fault codes. If Code 43 or 44 is present, go to next step. If Code 43 or 44 is not present, problem is intermittent. Check for poor connections at ECM, HO2S and wiring harness connectors. Test drive vehicle and retest.

NOTE: If driveability problems are present, test fuel-related components. See SYSTEM & COMPONENT TESTING article.

2) Turn ignition off for at least 2 minutes. Connect ECM Test Harness (07LAJ-PT3010A) between ECM and ECM harness connectors. *See Fig. 10*.

3) If Code 43 is present, install a jumper wire between test terminals A10 and A26. Attach a digital voltmeter to test terminals A26 (–) and D14 (+). If Code 44 is present, install a jumper wire between test terminals A12 and A26. Attach a digital voltmeter to test terminals A26 (–) and D16 (+). Turn ignition on.

4) Voltage should be .6-.8 volt when ignition is turned on, then drop to less than 0.1 volt within 2 minutes. If voltage is correct, go to step **6)**. If voltage is not correct, disconnect HO2S connector. Measure voltage between HO2S wiring harness connector terminals "A" (+) and "B" (–). *See Fig. 23*.

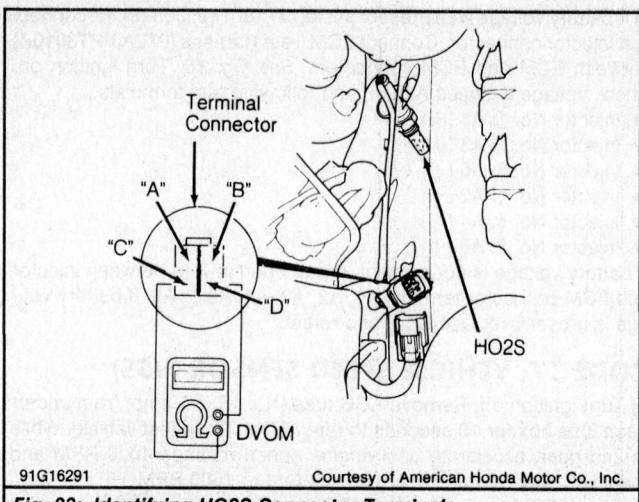

91G16291   Courtesy of American Honda Motor Co., Inc.

Fig. 23: Identifying HO2S Connector Terminals (Legend Shown; Vigor Is Similar)

5) If more than 0.1 volt is present, reconnect HO2S electrical connector. Warm engine until cooling fan comes on. With transmission in Neutral, raise engine speed to 3000 RPM and hold for 2 minutes. Measure voltage between test harness terminals D14 (+) or D16 (+) and A26 (–). Voltage should be more than 0.5 volt at wide open throttle and less than 0.5 volt when throttle is quickly released. If voltage is as specified, test fuel-related components. See SYSTEM & COMPONENT TESTING article. If voltage is not as specified, replace HO2S.

6) If voltage was correct in step **4)**, disconnect HO2S connector. Measure voltage between test terminal D14 (left sensor) or D16 (right sensor) and A26. If more than 0.1 volt is present, replace HO2S. If voltage is 0.1 volt or less, disconnect connector "D" from vehicle wiring harness.

7) Measure voltage between test terminals D14 (+) or D16 (+) and A26 (–). If more than one volt is present, repair short in Red/Blue wire (right sensor) or White wire (left sensor) between HO2S and ECM connector. If voltage is one volt or less, replace ECM and retest.

CODE 45 OR 46: FUEL METERING SYSTEM

1) Turn ignition off. Remove ACG fuse (No. 15, 7.5-amp) from underdash fuse box for 10 seconds to reset ECM. Start engine, and allow cooling fan to come on. Road test using following procedure:

- With transaxle in D_3 (A/T) or 3rd gear (M/T), cruise at exactly 35 MPH for 10 seconds.
- Release throttle. Allow vehicle to decelerate to less than 30 MPH.
- Accelerate to exactly 35 MPH and cruise for 10 seconds.
- Repeat procedure 10 times.
- Stop vehicle. Turn ignition off.
- Start vehicle. Repeat acceleration/deceleration procedure 5 times.

2) Check ECM for fault codes. If Code 45 or 46 is not present, problem is intermittent and cannot be duplicated at this time.

3) If Code 45 or 46 is present, turn ignition off. Check fuel pressure. See BASIC DIAGNOSTIC PROCEDURES article. Repair if necessary. If fuel pressure is okay, install a known good MAP sensor. Repeat step **1)** and check ECM for fault codes. If Code 45 or 46 is not present, replace original MAP sensor. If Code 45 or Code 46 is present, go to step **4)**.

4) If Code 45 is present, install known good injectors on left side of engine. If Code 46 is present, install known good injectors on right side of engine. If Code 45 and 46 are present, install known good injectors on both sides of engine.

5) Repeat step **1)** and check ECM for fault codes. If codes are not present, replace original fuel injectors. If code is present, inspect fuel line between fuel injectors and fuel filter. If restriction is found, replace or repair as necessary. If restriction is not found, replace ECM and retest.

TROUBLE CODES (VIGOR)

CODE 0 OR NO CODES

No MIL – **1)** Turn ignition on. If oil pressure light is on, go to next step. If light is off, inspect BACK-UP fuse (10-amp) located in underdash fuse box. Replace fuse and repair short as necessary. If BACK-UP fuse is okay, repair open circuit in Yellow wire between fuse and instrument cluster.

2) Turn ignition off. Connect ECM Test Harness (07LAJ-PT3010A) between ECM and ECM connectors. See Fig. 10. Connect test terminal A13 to ground. Turn ignition on. If MIL is now on, go to next step. If light is off, replace light bulb or repair open in Green/Red wire between ECM terminal A13 and instrument cluster. See Fig. 10.

3) Individually measure voltage between body ground and test terminals A23 and A24. If more than one volt is present on either terminal, repair open in wire between ECM and ground terminal G101 (located on left side of engine). See Fig. 24. If less than one volt is present on each terminal, replace ECM and retest.

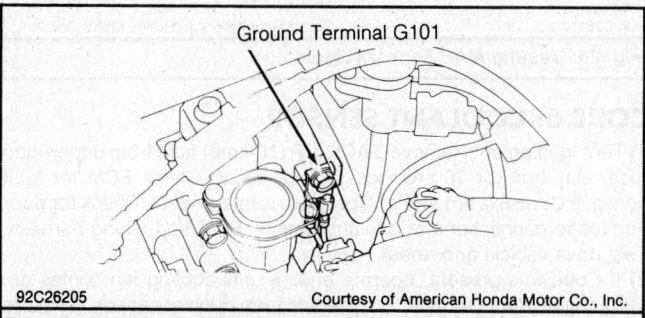

92C26205   Courtesy of American Honda Motor Co., Inc.

Fig. 24: Identifying Ground Terminal G101 (Vigor)

MIL Stays On – **1)** Check ECM for fault codes. See RETRIEVING CODES under SELF-DIAGNOSTIC SYSTEM. Service codes. If codes are not present, remove jumper wire from self-diagnostic connector. Start engine. If engine does not start, go to step **6)**. If engine starts, turn ignition off. Connect ECM Test Harness (07LAJ-PT3010A) between ECM and ECM connectors. See Fig. 10.

2) Turn ignition on. Measure voltage between test terminals D4 (+) and D22 (–). If about 5 volts (M/T models) or 11 volts (A/T models) are present, go to step **3)**. If voltage is not about 5 volts (11 volts on A/T models), repair short to body ground in Brown wire between ECM connector terminal D4, Transmission Control Module (TCM), ABS control unit and self-diagnostic connector. See Fig. 10.

3) Connect jumper wire to self-diagnostic connector. Measure voltage between test terminals D4 and D22. If about 5 volts (11 volts on A/T models) are present, check for open in Brown or Green/White wire between self-diagnostic connector and ECM.

4) If voltage is not about 5 volts (11 volts on A/T models), remove jumper wire from self-diagnostic connector. Turn ignition off. Disconnect connector "A" of ECM. Turn ignition on.

5) If MIL is on, repair short to ground in Green/Red wire between terminal A13 and MIL. If MIL is not on, replace ECM and retest.

6) If engine did not start in step **1)**, check ECM fuse (10-amp) in underhood fuse/relay box and ECM fuse (15-amp) in underdash fuse box. Replace fuses if necessary. Turn ignition on. Individually disconnect 3-pin connectors on EGR valve lift sensor, MAP sensor and throttle position sensor.

7) If MIL goes out, replace sensor causing MIL to go out. If MIL is on, connect jumper wire between self-diagnostic connector terminals. Disconnect ignition timing adjuster connector. Check if ECM flashes Code 18. If Code 18 is indicated, replace ignition timing adjuster.

8) If Code 18 is not indicated, turn ignition off. Remove jumper wire. Connect ECM Test Harness (07LAJ-PT3010A) between ECM and ECM connectors. See Fig. 10. Disconnect connector "D" from ECM side only. Individually check for continuity between body ground and terminals D19 and D20.

9) If continuity exists, repair short to body ground in Yellow/White wire between ECM terminal D19 or D20 and MAP sensor, ignition timing

adjuster, throttle position sensor or EGR position sensor. If continuity does not exist, reconnect connector "D" and all sensor connectors.

10) Turn ignition on. Individually measure voltage between ECM terminal A26 (–) and terminals B1 (+) and A25 (+). If battery voltage is not present, repair open in Yellow/Black wire circuit between main relay and ECM terminals A25 and B1. If circuit is okay, check main relay and connector. If battery voltage is present, turn ignition off, replace ECM and retest.

CODE 1: HO2S

1) Turn ignition off. Remove BACK-UP fuse (10-amp) from underhood fuse/relay box for 10 seconds to reset ECM. Start engine, and warm it to normal operating temperature.

2) Road test vehicle. With transmission in 4th gear (A/T in 2nd), accelerate at wide open throttle for at least 5 seconds and then decelerate, with throttle fully closed, for at least 5 seconds.

3) Check ECM for fault codes. If Code 1 is not present, problem is intermittent. Check for poor connections at ECM connector and HO2S. If Code 1 is present, go to CODE 43.

CODE 3: MAP SENSOR

1) Turn ignition off. Remove BACK-UP fuse (10-amp) from underhood fuse/relay box for 10 seconds to reset ECM. Start engine, and let it idle. Check ECM for fault codes. If Code 3 is not present, problem is intermittent. Check for poor or loose connections at MAP sensor and ECM connectors. Test drive vehicle and retest.

2) If Code 3 is present, turn ignition off. Disconnect 3-pin MAP sensor connector. Turn ignition on. Measure voltage between MAP sensor Yellow/White wire (+) and body ground. See Fig. 25. If voltage is about 5 volts, go to step **4)**. If voltage is not about 5 volts, connect connector "D" of ECM Test Harness (07LAJ-PT3010A) to ECM, leaving vehicle wiring harness disconnected.

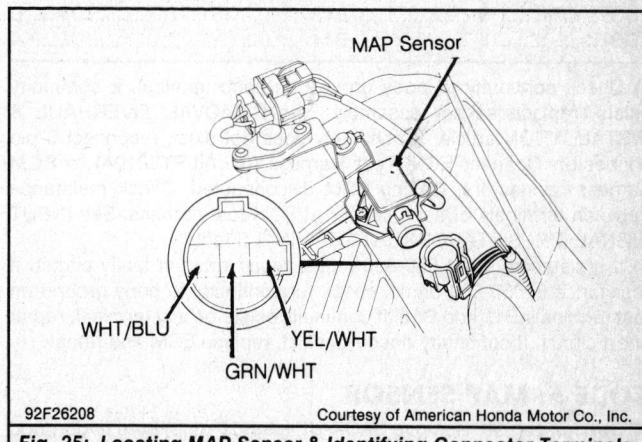

92F26208   Courtesy of American Honda Motor Co., Inc.

Fig. 25: Locating MAP Sensor & Identifying Connector Terminals (Vigor)

3) Turn ignition on. Measure voltage between test terminals D19 (+) and D21 (–). If about 5 volts are present, repair open circuit in D19 (Yellow/White wire) between ECM connector and MAP sensor. If voltage is not about 5 volts, replace ECM and retest.

4) If voltage is about 5 volts in step **2)**, measure voltage between Yellow/White (+) and Green/White (–) wires at MAP sensor. If voltage is not about 5 volts, repair open in Green/White wire between ECM terminal D21 and MAP sensor. If voltage is about 5 volts, measure voltage between White/Blue (+) and Green/White (–) wire terminals at MAP sensor.

5) If voltage is about 5 volts, go to step **7)**. If voltage is not about 5 volts, turn ignition off. On A/T models, disconnect Transmission Control Module (TCM) 22-pin connector. Turn ignition on. If about 5 volts are now present, replace TCM. If about 5 volts are still not present, turn ignition off. Go to next step.

6) On all models, connect ECM Test Harness (07LAJ-PT3010A) connector "D" only to ECM, leaving vehicle wiring harness disconnected. Measure voltage between test harness terminals D17 and D21. If about 5 volts are present, repair open or short in circuit D17 (White/Blue wire) between TCM (A/T), ECM and MAP sensor. If voltage is not about 5 volts, replace ECM and retest.

7) Turn ignition off. Reconnect 3-pin MAP sensor connector. Connect ECM Test Harness (07LAJ-PT3010A) between ECM and ECM connectors. *See Fig. 10.* Turn ignition on. Measure voltage between test terminals D17 and D21. If voltage is not about 3 volts, replace MAP sensor. If about 3 volts are present, replace ECM and retest.

CODE 4, 8, OR 9: TDC/CRANK/CYL SENSOR

1) Turn ignition off. Remove BACK-UP fuse (10-amp) from underhood fuse/relay box for 10 seconds to reset ECM. Check ECM for fault codes. If Code 4, 8 or 9 is not present, problem is intermittent. Check for poor connections at ECM, distributor and connector C308 at left shock tower. Test drive vehicle and retest.

2) If MIL is on and indicates Code 4, 8 or 9, turn ignition off. Disconnect 6-pin connector from TDC/CRANK/CYL sensor connector at cylinder head. Check resistance between terminals of each sensor. *See Fig. 7.* See INPUT SIGNAL & RESISTANCE TEST TERMINALS table. If resistance is not 650-850 ohms, replace sensor assembly. See REMOVAL, OVERHAUL & INSTALLATION article. If resistance is 650-850 ohms, go to step **3)**.

INPUT SIGNAL & RESISTANCE TEST TERMINALS

Sensor	Code	ECM Terminal	Sensor Terminal
CRANK	4	B15	E
CRANK	4	B16	B
CYL	9	B11	F
CYL	9	B12	C
TDC	8	B13	D
TDC	8	B14	A

3) Check continuity to body ground on each terminal. If continuity exists, replace sensor assembly. See REMOVAL, OVERHAUL & INSTALLATION article. If continuity does not exist, reconnect 6-pin connector. Connect ECM Test Harness (07LAJ-PT3010A) to ECM harness connectors, leaving ECM disconnected. Check resistance between terminals of each sensor at ECM test harness. See INPUT SIGNAL & RESISTANCE TEST TERMINALS table.

4) If resistance is not 650-850 ohms, repair open in faulty circuit. If resistance is 650-850 ohms, check for continuity to body ground on test terminals B11 and B13. If continuity exists on any terminal, repair short circuit. If continuity does not exist, replace ECM and retest.

CODE 5: MAP SENSOR

1) Turn ignition off. Remove BACK-UP fuse (10-amp) from underhood fuse/relay box for 10 seconds to reset ECM. Check ECM for fault codes. If Code 5 is not present, problem is intermittent. Check all vacuum hoses and connections. Test drive vehicle and retest.

2) If Code 5 is present, turn ignition off. Connect hand-held vacuum pump to MAP hose at throttle body. *See Fig. 26.* Apply vacuum. If vacuum holds, go to step **3)**. If vacuum does not hold, attach vacuum pump to MAP sensor. Apply vacuum. If vacuum does not hold, replace MAP sensor. If vacuum holds, check MAP hose for cracks, splits and looseness. Repair as necessary.

3) Connect "T" fitting in vacuum hose between MAP sensor and throttle body. Start engine. If vacuum is not present, remove restriction from throttle body. If vacuum is present, turn ignition off. Connect ECM Test Harness (07LAJ-PT3010A) between ECM and ECM connectors. *See Fig. 10.* Turn ignition on. Measure voltage between test terminals D17 (+) and D21 (-).

4) If voltage is not about 3 volts, replace MAP sensor. If voltage is about 3 volts, start engine and allow it to idle. Recheck voltage between test terminals D17 and D21. If voltage is not about one volt at idle, replace MAP sensor. If voltage is about one volt, replace ECM and retest.

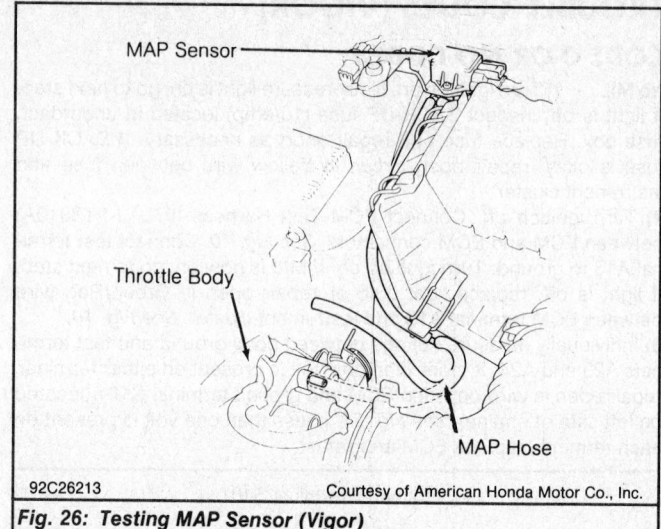

Courtesy of American Honda Motor Co., Inc.

Fig. 26: Testing MAP Sensor (Vigor)

CODE 6: COOLANT SENSOR

1) Turn ignition off. Remove BACK-UP (10-amp) fuse from underhood fuse/relay box for 10 seconds to reset ECM. Check ECM for fault codes. If Code 6 is not present, problem is intermittent. Check for poor and loose connections at coolant sensor, ECM and wiring harness. Test drive vehicle and retest.

2) If Code 6 is present, operate engine until cooling fan comes on. Turn engine off. Disconnect connector from coolant sensor. Measure resistance between sensor terminals. If resistance is not 200-400 ohms, replace coolant sensor.

3) If resistance is 200-400 ohms, turn ignition on. Measure voltage between sensor Yellow/Green wire terminal (+) and body ground. If about 5 volts are present, go to step **6)**. If voltage is not about 5 volts, go to step **4)**.

4) On A/T models, disconnect 22-pin connector from Transmission Control Module (TCM). Turn ignition on. Recheck voltage at Yellow/Green wire terminal. If voltage is about 5 volts, replace TCM. If voltage is not about 5 volts, turn ignition off and reconnect TCM. On all models, connect connector "D" of ECM Test Harness (07LAJ-PT3010A) to ECM, leaving vehicle wiring harness disconnected. Turn ignition on. Measure voltage between terminals D13 (+) and D22 (-). *See Fig. 10.*

5) If about 5 volts are present, repair open or short in Yellow/Green wire between ECM terminal D13, TCM (if equipped) and coolant sensor. If voltage is not about 5 volts, replace ECM and retest.

6) If voltage was about 5 volts in step **3)**, measure voltage between sensor Yellow/Green and Green/White wires. If voltage is not about 5 volts, repair open in Green/White wire between ECM connector terminal D22 and coolant sensor. If about 5 volts are present, replace ECM and retest.

CODE 7: THROTTLE POSITION SENSOR

1) Turn ignition off. Remove BACK-UP fuse (10-amp) from underhood fuse/relay box for 10 seconds to reset ECM. Check ECM for fault codes. If Code 7 is not present, problem is intermittent. Check for poor and loose connections at throttle position sensor, wiring harness connectors and ECM connector. Test drive vehicle and check again.

2) If Code 7 is present, turn ignition off. Disconnect 3-pin connector from throttle position sensor. Turn ignition on. Measure voltage between Yellow/White (+) and Green/White (-) wire terminals. If voltage is not about 5 volts, go to step **6)**. If about 5 volts are present, turn ignition off. Reconnect sensor connector. Connect ECM Test Harness (07LAJ-PT3010A) between ECM and ECM connectors. *See Fig. 10.*

3) Turn ignition on. Measure voltage between test terminals D11 (+) and D22 (-). Voltage should be about 0.5 volt at closed throttle and about 4.5 volts at wide open throttle. Transition from 0.5 to 4.5 volts (as throttle is opened) should be smooth. If sensor voltages are not correct, go to next step. If voltage is correct, replace ECM and retest.

4) On A/T models, disconnect 22-pin connector from Transmission Control Module (TCM). Recheck voltages. If voltages are correct, replace TCM. If sensor voltages are not correct, go to next step.

5) On all models, replace throttle position sensor or repair open or short in Red/Yellow wire between ECM terminal D11, TCM (if equipped) and throttle position sensor.

6) If voltage between Yellow/White (+) and Green/White (–) wire terminals in step **2)** was not about 5 volts, measure voltage between Yellow/White wire terminal (+) and body ground. If voltage is about 5 volts, repair open in Green/White wire between ECM terminal D22 and throttle position sensor. If voltage is not about 5 volts, turn ignition off.

7) Connect ECM Test Harness (07LAJ-PT3010A) between ECM and ECM connectors. See Fig. 10. Turn ignition on. Measure voltage between test terminals D20 (+) and D22 (–). If voltage is about 5 volts, repair open in Yellow/White wire terminal between ECM connector terminal D20 and throttle position sensor. If voltage is not about 5 volts, replace ECM and retest.

CODE 10: AIR TEMPERATURE (TA) SENSOR

1) Turn ignition off. Remove BACK-UP fuse (10-amp) from underhood fuse/relay box for 10 seconds to reset ECM. Check ECM for fault codes. If Code 10 is not present, problem is intermittent. Check for poor connections at ECM connector, air temperature sensor and wiring harness. Test drive vehicle and retest.

2) If Code 10 is present, turn ignition off. Disconnect 2-pin connector from sensor connector. Using an ohmmeter, measure resistance at sensor terminals. If resistance is not 400-4000 ohms, replace air temperature sensor. If resistance is 400-4000 ohms, turn ignition on. Measure voltage between White/Yellow wire terminal and body ground.

3) If voltage is not about 5 volts, go to next step. If voltage is about 5 volts, measure voltage between White/Yellow (+) and Green/White (–) wire terminals at sensor. If voltage is not about 5 volts, repair open in Green/White wire between ECM connector terminal D22 and air temperature sensor. If voltage is about 5 volts, replace ECM and retest.

4) Turn ignition off. Connect ECM Test Harness (07LAJ-PT3010A) connector "D" to ECM, leaving wiring harness disconnected. See Fig. 10. Turn ignition on. Measure voltage between test terminals D15 (+) and D22 (–). If voltage is about 5 volts, repair open or short in White/Yellow wire between ECM connector terminal D15 and air temperature sensor. If voltage is not about 5 volts, replace ECM and retest.

CODE 12: EGR SYSTEM

1) Turn ignition off. Remove BACK-UP fuse (10-amp) from underhood fuse/relay box for 10 seconds to reset ECM. Warm engine until cooling fan comes on. Road test vehicle for about 10 minutes, keeping engine speed about 1700-2500 RPM. Check ECM for fault codes. If Code 12 is not present, problem is intermittent. Check for poor connections at ECM, control box, EGR valve position sensor and wire harness connectors. Test drive vehicle and retest.

2) If Code 12 is present, start engine. Disconnect No. 1 hose from EGR valve. See Fig. 27. Connect vacuum gauge to hose. If no vacuum is present, go to step **4)**. If vacuum is present, disconnect 4-pin connector from control box. Check vacuum again on No. 1 hose. If vacuum is present, check vacuum hose routing. If routing is okay, replace EGR control solenoid valve.

3) If vacuum is not present, turn ignition off. Remove connector "A" from ECM. Check for continuity between Red wire terminal of control box connector and ground. If continuity is present, repair short in Red wire between EGR control solenoid valve and ECM connector terminal A11. If continuity is not present, replace ECM and retest.

4) If vacuum was not present during first vacuum test in step **2)**, install vacuum pump on EGR valve vacuum port. With engine idling, apply 6 in. Hg to EGR valve. If engine does not stall or run rough or EGR valve does not hold vacuum, replace EGR valve.

5) If engine stalls or runs rough and EGR valve holds vacuum, turn ignition off and disconnect 4-pin connector from control box, located on firewall, behind intake manifold. Turn ignition on. Measure voltage

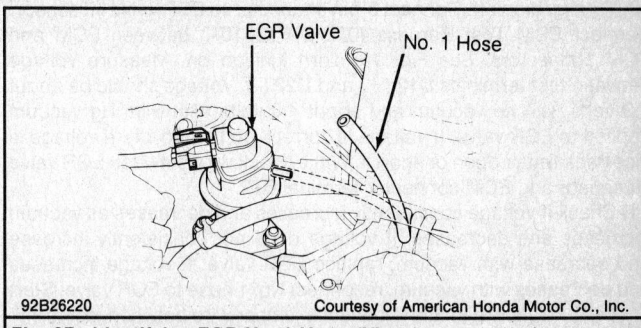

Fig. 27: Identifying EGR No. 1 Hose (Vigor)

between Black/Yellow wire terminal and body ground. If battery voltage is not present, repair open in Black/Yellow wire between solenoid valve and ECM fuse (No. 2, 15-amp) located in underdash fuse box. If battery voltage is present, install "T" fitting into No. 1 hose.

6) Attach vacuum gauge to "T" fitting. Start engine, and allow it to idle. Connect battery voltage to terminal "B" of 4-pin connector. See Fig. 28. While observing vacuum gauge, connect terminal "D" to negative battery terminal.

7) If gauge reads 6 in. Hg within one second, go to step **9)**. If gauge does not read 6 in. Hg within one second, turn ignition off. Inspect EGR hoses for leaks, restrictions and misrouting. Repair as necessary. If hoses are okay, disconnect lower hose on EGR control solenoid valve.

8) Connect vacuum gauge to disconnected hose. Start engine, and allow it to idle. If about 6 in. Hg is not present, replace Constant Vacuum Control (CVC) valve. See Fig. 29. If about 6 in. Hg is present, replace EGR control solenoid valve. See Fig. 29.

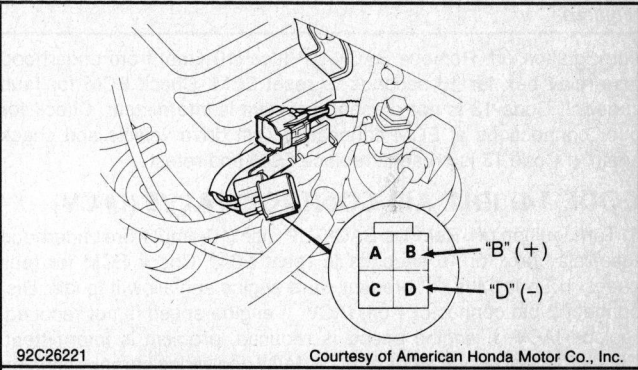

Fig. 28: Identifying Control Box Connector Terminals (Vigor)

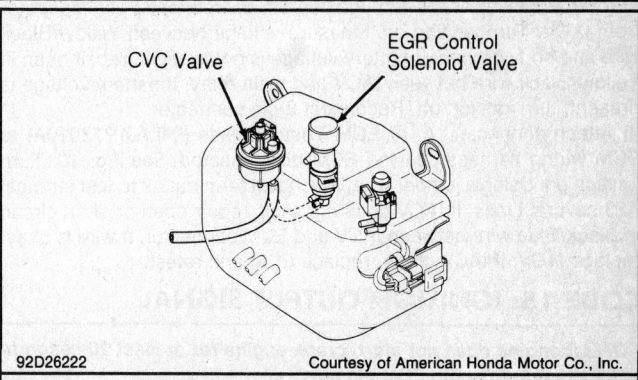

Fig. 29: Locating EGR Control Solenoid Valve & Constant Vacuum Control Valve (Vigor)

9) If gauge read 6 in. Hg in step **7)**, turn ignition off. Reconnect 4-pin connector to control box. Disconnect 3-pin connector to EGR valve lift sensor. Turn ignition on. Measure voltage between Yellow/White (+) and Green/White (–) wire terminals. If voltage is not 5 volts, go to step **12)**. If voltage is about 5 volts, go to step **10)**.

10) Turn ignition off. Connect 3-pin connector to EGR valve lift sensor. Connect ECM Test Harness (07LAJ-PT3010A) between ECM and ECM connectors. See Fig. 10. Turn ignition on. Measure voltage between test terminals D12 (+) and D22 (–). Voltage should be about 1.2 volts with no vacuum and about 4.3 volts with 6 in. Hg vacuum applied to EGR valve. If voltage is correct, go to step **11)**. If voltage is incorrect, repair open or short in White/Black wire between EGR valve lift sensor and ECM connector terminal D12.

11) Check if voltage consistently increases and decreases as vacuum increases and decreases. If voltage does not consistently increase and decrease with vacuum, replace EGR valve. If voltage increases and decreases with vacuum, reconnect No. 1 hose to EGR valve. Start engine, and allow it to idle. Connect a jumper wire between test terminals A11 and A26. See Fig. 10. If engine does not stall or run rough, repair open in Red wire between ECM connector terminal A11 and EGR control solenoid valve. If engine stalls or runs rough, replace ECM and retest.

12) If about 5 volts were not present in step **9)**, measure voltage between Yellow/White wire terminal of EGR valve position sensor 3-pin connector and body ground. If about 5 volts are present, repair open in Green/White wire between EGR valve lift sensor and ECM connector terminal D22. If voltage is not about 5 volts, connect connector "D" of ECM Test Harness (07LAJ-PT3010A) to ECM, leaving vehicle wiring harness disconnected.

13) Turn ignition on. Measure voltage between test terminals D20 (+) and D22 (–). If about 5 volts are present, repair open in Yellow/White wire between EGR valve and ECM connector terminal No. D20. If voltage is not about 5 volts, replace ECM and retest.

CODE 13: BAROMETRIC (BARO) SENSOR

NOTE: Barometric sensor is built into ECM. Circuit testing is not required.

Turn ignition off. Remove BACK-UP fuse (10-amp) from underhood fuse/relay box for 10 seconds to reset ECM. Check ECM for fault codes. If Code 13 is not present, problem is intermittent. Check for poor connections at ECM connector. Test drive vehicle and check again. If Code 13 is present, replace ECM and retest.

CODE 14: IDLE AIR CONTROL VALVE (IACV)

1) Turn ignition off. Remove BACK-UP fuse (10-amp) from underhood fuse/relay box for 10 seconds to reset ECM. Check ECM for fault codes. If Code 14 is not present, start engine and allow it to idle. Disconnect 2-pin connector from IACV. If engine speed is not reduced, replace IACV. If engine speed is reduced, problem is intermittent. Check for poor connections at ECM, IACV and wiring harness connectors. Test drive vehicle and retest.

2) If Code 14 is present, turn ignition off. Disconnect 2-pin connector from IACV. Turn ignition on. Measure voltage between Yellow/Black wire and body ground. If battery voltage is not present, repair open in Yellow/Black wire between IACV and main relay. If battery voltage is present, turn ignition off. Reconnect 2-pin connector.

3) Attach connector "A" of ECM Test Harness (07LAJ-PT3010A) to ECM wiring harness, leaving ECM disconnected. See Fig. 10. Turn ignition on. Using a jumper wire, touch test terminal A9 to test terminal A23 several times. If IACV does not click, repair open or short circuit in Black/Blue wire between IACV and ECM connector. If wire is okay, replace IACV. If IACV clicks, replace ECM and retest.

CODE 15: IGNITION OUTPUT SIGNAL

NOTE: If engine does not start, crank engine for at least 20 seconds to allow code to set in ECM memory.

1) Turn ignition off. Remove BACK-UP fuse (10-amp) from underhood fuse/relay box for 10 seconds to reset ECM. Check ECM for fault codes. If Code 15 is not present, problem is intermittent. Check for poor connections at ECM and ignitor unit. Test drive vehicle and check again.

2) If Code 15 is present, turn ignition off. Disconnect 4-pin connector from ignitor unit, located next to ignition coil. Turn ignition on. Measure voltage between Black/Yellow wire and body ground. If battery voltage is not present, repair open in Black/Yellow wire between ignition coil and ignition switch. If battery voltage is present, measure voltage between Black/Yellow wire and Black wire terminal at ignitor unit connector.

3) If battery voltage does not exist, repair open in Black wire between ignitor unit and ground terminal G101, located on left side of engine. See Fig. 24. If battery voltage exists, turn ignition off. Reconnect 4-pin connector to ignitor. Connect ECM Test Harness (07LAJ-PT3010A) between ECM and ECM wiring harness connectors.

4) Turn ignition on. Measure voltage between test terminal A26 (–) and test terminals A21 (+) and A22 (+). If voltage is not about 10 volts, check for open or short in Yellow/Green wire between ignitor unit and ECM terminals A21 or A22. If wire is shorted, ignitor may also be damaged. If wire is okay, replace ignitor. If about 10 volts are present, replace ECM and retest.

CODE 16: FUEL INJECTOR CIRCUIT

NOTE: If engine does not start, crank engine for at least 10 seconds to allow code to set in ECM memory.

1) Turn ignition off. Remove BACK-UP fuse (10-amp) from underhood fuse/relay box for 10 seconds to reset ECM. Check ECM for fault codes. If Code 16 is not present, problem is intermittent. Check for poor connections at ECM, fuel injectors, fuel injector resistor and wiring harness connectors. Test drive vehicle and retest.

2) If Code 16 is present, start engine. Using a stethoscope, check for clicking sound at each injector. If injector does not click, turn ignition off. Disconnect 2-pin injector connector from affected injector. Measure resistance between injector terminals. If resistance is not 1.5-2.5 ohms, replace injector. If resistance is 1.5-2.5 ohms, go to next step.

3) Turn ignition on. Measure voltage between fuel injector wiring harness connector Red/Black wire and body ground. If battery voltage is present, go to step **6)**. If battery voltage is not present, turn ignition off. Disconnect 8-pin connector at injector resistor.

4) Turn ignition on. Measure voltage between Yellow/Black wire terminal (+) and body ground. If battery voltage is not present, repair open in Yellow/Black wire between injector resistor and main relay. If battery voltage is present, disconnect injector resistor connector.

5) Measure resistance between terminal "A" and all other terminals. See Fig. 30. If resistance is not 5-7 ohms, replace injector resistor. If resistance is 5-7 ohms, repair open in Red/Black wire between 2-pin connector and injector resistor.

92H26226   Courtesy of American Honda Motor Co., Inc.

Fig. 30: Identifying Injector Resistor Connector Terminals (Vigor)

6) If battery voltage was present in step **3)**, turn ignition off. Reconnect fuel injector connector. Connect ECM Test Harness (07LAJ-PT3010A) between ECM and ECM wiring harness connectors. See Fig. 10. Turn ignition on. Check voltage between A23 (–) and following test terminals.

- Injector No. 1: A1 (+)
- Injector No. 2: A3 (+)
- Injector No. 3: A5 (+)
- Injector No. 4: A2 (+)
- Injector No. 5: A4 (+)

If battery voltage is not present, repair open in wire between injector and ECM connector terminal A1, A2, A3, A4 or A5 . If battery voltage is present, replace ECM and retest.

CODE 17: VEHICLE SPEED SENSOR (VSS)

1) Turn ignition off. Remove BACK-UP fuse (10-amp) from underhood fuse/relay box for 10 seconds to reset ECM. Road test vehicle. While in 2nd gear, accelerate until engine speed reaches 4000 RPM and then, with throttle fully closed, decelerate to 1500 RPM.
2) Check ECM for fault codes. If Code 17 is not present, problem is intermittent. Check for poor connections at ECM, VSS and wiring harness connectors. Test drive vehicle and retest.
3) If Code 17 is present, raise and support vehicle. Connect ECM Test Harness (07LAJ-PT3010A) between ECM and ECM connectors. *See Fig. 10.* Turn ignition on. Block right front wheel. Slowly rotate left front wheel. Measure voltage between test terminals A26 (–) and B10 (+). If voltage pulses between 0-12 volts, replace ECM and retest.
4) If voltage does not pulse 0-12 volts, turn ignition off. Disconnect test harness "B" connector from ECM, leaving wiring harness connected. Turn ignition on. Slowly rotate left front wheel while measuring voltage between test terminals A26 and B10.
5) If voltage does not pulse 0-12 volts, repair open or short in Orange wire between ECM connector terminal B10 (+) and VSS or cruise control unit. If wire is okay, replace VSS. If voltage pulses 0-12 volts, replace ECM and retest.

CODE 18: IGNITION TIMING ADJUSTER

1) Turn ignition off. Remove BACK-UP fuse (10-amp) from underhood fuse/relay box for 10 seconds to reset ECM. Check ECM for fault codes. If Code 18 is not present, problem is intermittent. Check for poor connections at ECM connector and ignition timing adjuster connector. Test drive vehicle and retest.
2) If Code 18 is present, turn ignition off. Disconnect ignition timing adjuster 3-pin connector from control box. *See Fig. 31.* Measure resistance between terminals "A" and "C" of ignition timing adjuster.

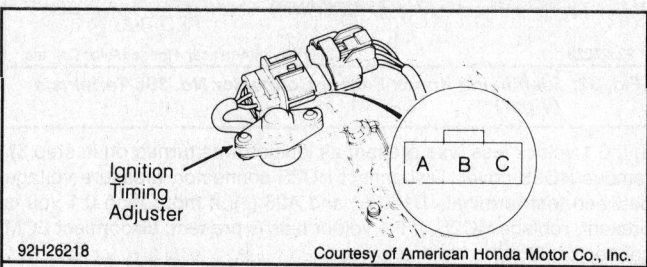

92H26218   Courtesy of American Honda Motor Co., Inc.

Fig. 31: Identifying Ignition Timing Adjuster Connector Terminals (Vigor)

3) If resistance is 3500-6500 ohms, go to step **4)**. If resistance is not 3500-6500 ohms, replace ignition timing adjuster.
4) Measure and record resistance between terminals "A" and "B" on timing adjuster side of harness connector. Measure and record resistance between terminals "B" and "C" on same side of connector. Add both resistance values together. If total resistance is not 3500-6500 ohms, replace ignition timing adjuster.
5) If resistance is 3500-6500 ohms, turn ignition on. Measure voltage between Yellow/White (+) and Green/White (–) wire terminals on harness side of connector. If voltage is not about 5 volts, go to step **8)**.
6) If voltage is about 5 volts, measure voltage between body ground and Yellow/White wire terminal. If voltage is about 5 volts, repair open in Green/White wire between ECM terminal D22 and ignition timing adjuster connector.
7) If voltage is not 5 volts, turn ignition off. Connect ECM Test Harness (07LAJ-PT3010A) between ECM and ECM connectors. *See Fig. 10.* Turn ignition on. Measure voltage between ECM terminals D20 (+) and D22 (–). If voltage is about 5 volts, repair open in Yellow/White wire between ECM connector terminal D20 and ignition timing adjuster. If voltage is not about 5 volts, replace ECM and retest.
8) If voltage in step **5)** was not about 5 volts, turn ignition off. Reconnect ignition timing adjuster 3-pin connector. Connect ECM Test Harness (07LAJ-PT3010A) between ECM and ECM connectors. *See Fig. 10.*
9) Turn ignition on. Measure voltage between ECM terminals D8 (+) and D22 (–). If voltage is not 0.5-4.5 volts, repair open or short in

Brown wire between ECM connector terminal D8 and ignition timing adjuster. If voltage is 0.5-4.5 volts, replace ECM and retest.

CODE 20: ELECTRIC LOAD DETECTOR (ELD)

1) Turn ignition off. Remove BACK-UP fuse (10-amp) from underhood fuse/relay box for 10 seconds to reset ECM. Start engine, and allow it to idle. Turn headlights on. Check ECM for fault codes. If Code 20 is not present, problem is intermittent. Check for poor connections at ECM connector and ELD connector. Test drive vehicle and retest.
2) If Code 20 is present, turn ignition off. Disconnect ELD 3-pin connector, located in underhood fuse/relay box. Turn ignition on. Measure voltage between connector Black/Yellow and Black wire terminals. If battery voltage is present, go to step **4)**. If battery voltage is not present, go to step **3)**.
3) Measure voltage between Black/Yellow wire terminal and body ground. If battery voltage is present, repair open in Black wire between 3-pin connector and ground. If battery voltage is not present, repair open in Black/Yellow wire between 3-pin connector and ECM fuse (No. 2, 15-amp).
4) If battery voltage was present in step **2)**, measure voltage between ELD connector Green/Red wire terminal and body ground. If voltage is not 4.5-5.0 volts, repair open or short in Green/Red wire between ECM terminal D10 and ELD. If 4.5-5.0 volts are present, turn ignition off. Reconnect 3-pin connector to ELD. Connect ECM Test Harness (07LAJ-PT3010A) between ECM and ECM connectors. *See Fig. 10.* Turn ignition on.
5) Measure voltage between test terminals A26 and D10 as follows:
• With headlight switch in first position, 1.8-2.8 volts should exist.
• With headlight switch in second position, 0.8-1.8 volts should exist.
If voltage is not as specified, replace ELD. If voltage is as specified, replace ECM and retest.

CODE 23 OR 53: KNOCK SENSOR

NOTE: Repair any engine knocking sounds before performing test.

1) Turn ignition off. Remove BACK-UP fuse (10-amp) from underhood fuse/relay box for 10 seconds to reset ECM. Warm engine until cooling fan comes on. With transmission in Neutral, hold engine speed at 3000-4000 RPM for 10 seconds. Check for fault codes. If Code 23 or 53 is not present, problem is intermittent. Check for poor connections at ECM, knock sensor and wiring harness connectors. Test drive vehicle and retest.
2) If Code 23 (knock sensor No. 1) or Code 53 (knock sensor No. 2) exists, turn ignition off. Connect ECM Test Harness (07LAJ-PT3010A) to ECM wiring harness connectors, leaving ECM disconnected. *See Fig. 10.* Disconnect knock sensor connector No. 308, located on left shock tower.
3) Check for continuity between test terminal C1 (sensor No. 2) or C3 (sensor No. 1) and body ground. If continuity is not present, go to next step. If continuity is present, repair short in Red/Blue wire (knock sensor No. 1) or Orange/White wire (knock sensor No. 2) between ECM connector and knock sensor. *See Fig. 32.*
4) Disconnect knock sensor connector No. 308. *See Fig. 32.* Check continuity between test terminal C3 and Red/Blue wire terminal at knock sensor connector No. 308 (knock sensor No. 1) or between test terminal C1 and Orange/White wire terminal at knock sensor connector No. 308. If continuity is not present, repair open in wire between ECM connector and knock sensor.
5) If continuity is present, replace ECM with a known good unit. Warm engine until cooling fan comes on. With transmission in Neutral, hold engine speed at 3000-4000 RPM for 10 seconds. Check ECM for fault codes. If Code 23 or 53 is present, replace appropriate knock sensor. If Code 23 or 53 is not present, replace original ECM.

CODE 30 OR 31: A/T FI SIGNAL

1) Turn ignition off. Remove BACK-UP fuse (10-amp) from underhood fuse/relay box for 10 seconds to reset ECM. Test drive vehicle for at least 5 miles, allowing transaxle to upshift and downshift. Check ECM for fault codes. If Code 30 or 31 is not present, problem is intermittent. Check for poor connections at Transmission Control Module (TCM) or ECM connectors. Test drive vehicle and retest.

2) If Code 30 or 31 is present, turn ignition off. Connect ECM Test Harness (07LAJ-PT3010A) to ECM wiring harness connectors, leaving ECM disconnected. *See Fig. 10*. Disconnect 22-pin connector from TCM. Check for continuity between body ground and test terminal B3 (Code 30) or B4 (Code 31).

3) If continuity is present, repair short in White/Green (Code 30) or White/Red (Code 31) wire between ECM connector and TCM. If continuity is not present, check White/Green wire or White/Red wire continuity between ECM and TCM wiring harness connectors. Repair wire if continuity is not present. If continuity is present, replace ECM and retest.

CODE 41: HO2S HEATER

1) Turn ignition off. Remove BACK-UP fuse (10-amp) from underhood fuse/relay box for 10 seconds to reset ECM. Check ECM for fault codes. If Code 41 is not present, problem is intermittent. Check for poor connections at ECM connector and HO2S. Test drive vehicle and retest.

2) If Code 41 is present, turn ignition off. Remove HO2S covers. Disconnect 4-pin HO2S connector. Measure resistance between HO2S terminals "C" and "D". *See Fig. 23*. If resistance is not 10-40 ohms, replace sensor. If resistance is 10-40 ohms, go to step **3)**.

3) Check continuity between body ground and HO2S terminals "C" and "D". If continuity is present, replace sensor. If continuity is not present, check for continuity between terminal "D" and terminals "A" and "B". *See Fig. 32*. If continuity is present, replace sensor. If continuity is not present, go to step **4)**.

4) Turn ignition on. Measure voltage between Yellow/Black (+) and Pink/White (–) wire terminals at HO2S wiring harness connector. If battery voltage is not present, go to step **7)**. If battery voltage is present, disconnect connector "A" from ECM. Measure voltage between Yellow/Black and Pink/White wire terminals at HO2S wiring harness connector.

5) If battery voltage is present, repair short circuit in Pink/White wire between ECM connector terminal A6 and HO2S. If battery voltage is not present, turn ignition off. Reconnect HO2S. Connect connector "A" of ECM Test Harness (07LAJ-PT3010A) to vehicle wiring harness, leaving ECM disconnected.

6) Connect ammeter between test terminals A6 (+) and A23 (–). Turn ignition on. Monitor ammeter for 5 minutes. If current is less than 0.1 amp, replace HO2S. If current is not less than 0.1 amp, replace ECM and retest.

7) If battery voltage was not present in step **4)**, measure voltage between Yellow/Black wire terminal at HO2S wiring harness connector and body ground. If battery voltage is not present, repair open in Yellow/Black wire between HO2S and main relay. If battery voltage is present, turn ignition off. Reconnect HO2S wiring harness connector.

8) Connect connector "A" of ECM Test Harness (07LAJ-PT3010A) to ECM wiring harness, leaving ECM disconnected. Turn ignition on. Measure voltage between test terminals A6 (+) and A23 (–). If battery voltage is not present, repair open in Pink/White wire between ECM connector terminal A6 and HO2S. If battery voltage is present, replace ECM and retest.

CODE 43: FUEL SUPPLY SYSTEM

NOTE: If driveability problems are present, test fuel-related components. See SYSTEM & COMPONENT TESTING article.

1) If referred here from CODE 1, go to next step. Turn ignition off. Remove BACK-UP fuse (10-amp) from underhood fuse/relay box for 10 seconds to reset ECM. Warm engine until cooling fan comes on. With transmission in Neutral, raise engine speed to 3000 RPM and hold for 2 minutes. Check ECM for fault codes. If Code 43 is present, go to next step. If Code 43 is not present, problem is intermittent. Check for poor connections at ECM and HO2S connectors. Test drive vehicle and retest.

2) Turn ignition off. Connect ECM Test Harness (07LAJ-PT3010A) between ECM and ECM harness connectors. *See Fig. 10*. Wait 2 minutes. Install jumper wire between test terminals A6 and A26. Turn igni-

tion on while measuring voltage between test terminals D14 (+) and A26 (–).

3) If 0.1 volt or less is present as ignition is turned on, go to step **5)**. If more than 0.1 volt is present as ignition is turned on, remove HO2S cover. Disconnect HO2S connector. Measure voltage between HO2S wiring harness connector terminals "A" and "B". *See Fig. 23*.

4) If 0.1 volt or less is present, repair open circuit in White wire between HO2S and ECM connector. If more than 0.1 volt is present, reconnect HO2S electrical connector. Warm engine until cooling fan comes on. With transmission in Neutral, raise engine speed to 3000 RPM and hold for 2 minutes. Measure voltage between test harness terminals D14(+) and A26(–). Voltage should be more than 0.5 volt at wide open throttle and less than 0.5 volt when throttle is quickly released. If voltage is as specified, test fuel-related components. See SYSTEM & COMPONENT TESTING article. If voltage is not as specified, replace HO2S.

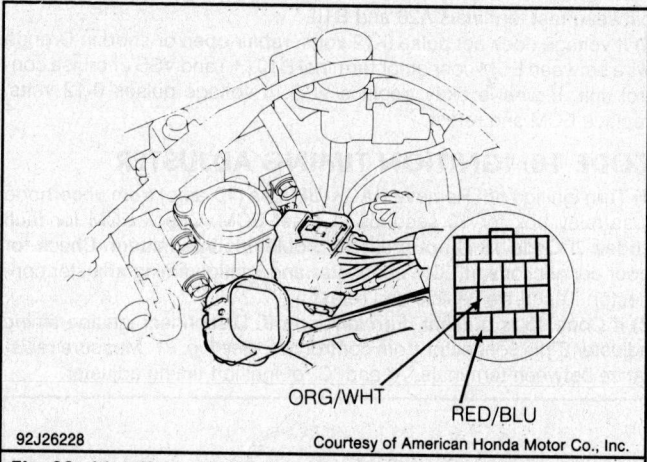

ORG/WHT   RED/BLU

92J26228   Courtesy of American Honda Motor Co., Inc.

Fig. 32: Identifying Knock Sensor Connector No. 308 Terminals (Vigor)

5) If 0.1 volt or less was present as ignition was turned on in step **3)**, remove HO2S cover. Disconnect HO2S connector. Measure voltage between test terminals D14 (+) and A26 (–). If more than 0.1 volt is present, replace HO2S. If 0.1 volt or less is present, disconnect ECM connector "D" from wiring harness.

6) Measure voltage between test terminals D14 (+) and A26 (–). If more than 0.1 volt is present, repair short in White wire between ECM connector and HO2S. If 0.1 volt or less is present, replace ECM and retest.

CODE 45: FUEL METERING SYSTEM

1) Turn ignition off. Remove BACK-UP fuse (10-amp) from underhood fuse/relay box for 10 seconds to reset ECM. Start engine, and allow cooling fan to come on. Road test using following procedure:
- With transaxle in D₃ (A/T) or 3rd gear (M/T), cruise at exactly 35 MPH for 10 seconds.
- Release throttle, Allow vehicle to decelerate to less than 30 MPH.
- Accelerate to exactly 35 MPH and cruise for 10 seconds.
- Repeat procedure 10 times.
- Stop vehicle. Turn ignition off.
- Start vehicle. Repeat acceleration/deceleration procedure 5 times.

2) Check ECM for fault codes. If Code 45 is not present, problem is intermittent and cannot be duplicated at this time.

3) If Code 45 is present, turn ignition off. Check fuel pressure. See BASIC DIAGNOSTIC PROCEDURES article. Repair if necessary. If fuel pressure is okay, install known good MAP sensor. Repeat step **1)**. Check ECM for fault codes. If Code 45 is not present, replace original MAP sensor. If Code 45 is present, go to step **4)**.

4) Install known good fuel injectors. Repeat steps **1)** and **2)**. If Code 45 is not present, replace original fuel injectors. If Code 45 is still present, inspect fuel line between fuel injectors and fuel filter. If restriction is found, replace or repair as necessary. If no restriction is found, replace ECM and retest.

Integra, Legend, Vigor

INTRODUCTION

Before diagnosing symptoms or intermittent faults, perform steps in BASIC DIAGNOSTIC PROCEDURES and SELF-DIAGNOSTICS articles. Use this article to diagnose driveability problems existing when a hard fault code is not present.

NOTE: Some driveability problems may have been corrected by manufacturer with a revised computer calibration chip or computer control unit. Check with manufacturer for latest chip or computer application.

Symptom checks can direct technician to malfunctioning component(s) for further diagnosis. A symptom should lead to a specific component, system test or adjustment.

Use intermittent test procedures to locate driveability problems that do not occur when vehicle is being tested. These test procedures should also be used if a soft (intermittent) trouble code was present but no problem was found during self-diagnostic testing.

NOTE: For specific testing procedures, see SYSTEM & COMPONENT TESTING article. For specifications, see ON-VEHICLE ADJUSTMENTS or SERVICE & ADJUSTMENT SPECIFICATIONS article.

SYMPTOMS

SYMPTOM DIAGNOSIS

Symptom checks cannot be used properly unless problem occurs while vehicle is being tested. To reduce diagnostic time, ensure steps in BASIC DIAGNOSTIC PROCEDURES and SELF-DIAGNOSTICS articles were performed before diagnosing a symptom. Recommended system and component checks may not apply to all vehicles. Symptoms available for diagnosis include following.

- Engine Will Not Start
- Difficult Cold Start
- Fast Idle Out Of Specification
- Rough Idle When Warm
- Idle RPM High When Warm
- Idle RPM Low When Warm
- Stalling During Warm-Up
- Stalling After Warm-Up
- Misfire Or Rough Operation
- Emission Test Failure
- Lack Of Power

ENGINE WILL NOT START

Ensure steps for spark and fuel testing in BASIC DIAGNOSTIC PROCEDURES article have been performed. Test ECU power and ground circuits. On Legend, also check air starting valve.

DIFFICULT COLD START

Check coolant temperature, MAP and CRANK/CYL (Legend) or TDC/CRANK/CYL (Integra and Vigor) sensors. Check ECU, injectors and idle control system components. Check air starting valve (Legend).

FAST IDLE OUT OF SPECIFICATION

Check idle control system components and fuel supply system. Check coolant temperature and throttle angle sensors.

ROUGH IDLE WHEN WARM

Check EACV operation, injectors, EGR system and other emission components. Check MAP, O_2, CRANK/CYL (Legend) or TDC/CRANK/CYL (Integra and Vigor), throttle angle and intake air temperature sensors.

IDLE RPM HIGH WHEN WARM

Check EACV and idle control system components. Check MAP sensor, air intake system and emission systems.

IDLE RPM LOW WHEN WARM

Check EACV, air intake system, MAP sensor, injectors, EGR system and idle control system components.

STALLING DURING WARM-UP

Check EACV, air intake system, idle control system components, fuel supply system and EGR system. Check MAP, CRANK/CYL (Legend) or TDC/CRANK/CYL (Integra and Vigor), coolant temperature and throttle angle sensors.

STALLING AFTER WARM-UP

Check EGR system, EACV, air intake system and fuel supply system. Check MAP, throttle angle, CRANK/CYL (Legend) or TDC/CRANK/CYL (Integra and Vigor), and vehicle speed sensors.

MISFIRE OR ROUGH OPERATION

Check each injector at idle. Check fuel supply, EACV, ignition output signal and EGR system. Check MAP, O_2, CRANK/CYL (Legend) or TDC/CRANK/CYL (Integra and Vigor), and throttle angle sensors.

EMISSION TEST FAILURE

Check injectors and all emission control components. Check MAP, O_2, CRANK/CYL (Legend) or TDC/CRANK/CYL (Integra and Vigor), and coolant temperature sensors.

LACK OF POWER

Check for binding brakes or plugged exhaust. Check fuel supply system, emission control components, injectors, air intake system and EGR system. Check MAP, throttle angle, coolant temperature and vehicle speed sensors. Check intake manifold air by-pass systems (if equiped). On Integra GS-R, check variable timing valve control solenoid and valve lift pressure switch.

INTERMITTENTS

INTERMITTENT PROBLEM DIAGNOSIS

Intermittent fault testing requires duplicating circuit or component failure to identify problem. These procedures may lead to computer setting a fault code (on some systems) which may help in diagnosis.

If problem vehicle does not produce fault codes, use DVOM to pinpoint faults. Monitor voltage or resistance values while attempting to reproduce conditions causing intermittent fault. A status change on DVOM indicates area of fault.

When monitoring voltage, ensure ignition switch is in ON position or engine is running. Ensure ignition switch is in OFF position or negative battery cable is disconnected when monitoring circuit resistance.

TEST PROCEDURES

Intermittent Simulation – To reproduce conditions creating intermittent fault, use following methods:
- Lightly vibrate component.
- Heat component.
- Wiggle or bend wiring harness.
- Spray component with water mist.
- Remove/apply vacuum source.

Monitor circuit/component voltage or resistance while simulating intermittent. If engine is running, monitor for self-diagnostic codes. Use test results to identify a faulty component or circuit.

1994 ENGINE PERFORMANCE
System & Component Testing

Integra, Legend, Vigor

INTRODUCTION

Before testing separate components or systems, perform procedures in BASIC DIAGNOSTIC PROCEDURES article. Since many computer-controlled and monitored components set a trouble code if they malfunction, also perform procedures in SELF-DIAGNOSTICS article.

NOTE: *Before disconnecting battery, obtain anti-theft code for radio. After battery is reconnected, CODE will appear on radio display. Enter 5-digit code using select buttons and radio will begin working. If code is entered wrong 3 times, leave radio on at least one hour and enter code correctly. Any time radio power is lost, preselected radio stations will have to be set. For more information, see owners manual.*

NOTE: *Testing individual components does not isolate shorts or opens. Perform all voltage tests with a Digital Volt-Ohmmeter (DVOM) with a minimum 10-megohm input impedance, unless stated otherwise in test procedure. Use ohmmeter to isolate wiring harness shorts or opens.*

AIR INDUCTION SYSTEMS

AIR INTAKE SYSTEM

NOTE: *Many tests can be performed only with Engine Control Module (ECM) Test Harness (07LAJ-PT3010A). Terminals on ECM test harness connectors match terminals on ECM and wire harness connectors. This allows the technician to test continuity and resistance of vehicle wire harness and devices. Sensor input values can also be monitored while engine is in operation. To identify ECM terminals, see Fig. 1. Integra does not use terminals C1- C12.*

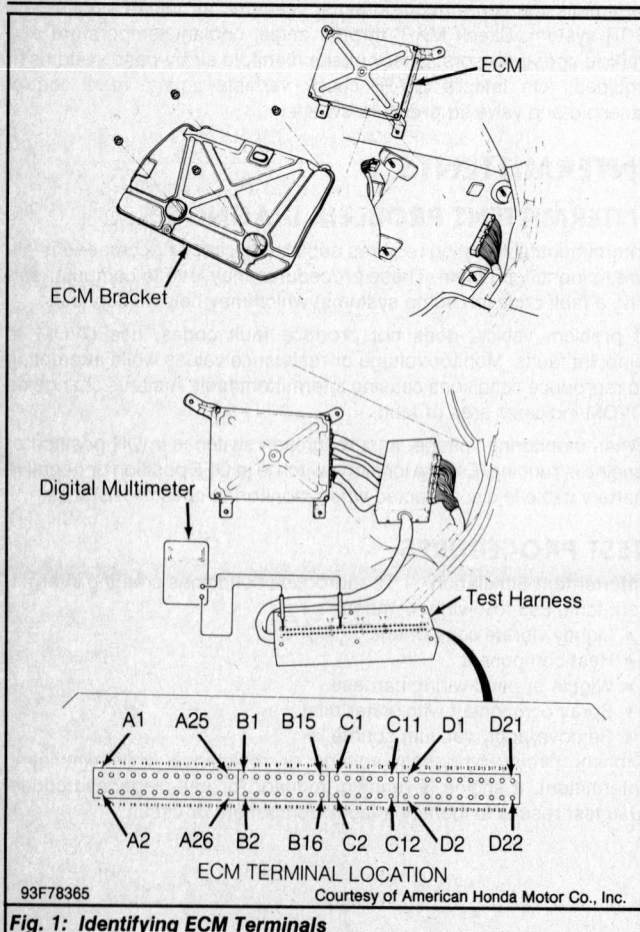

ECM

ECM Bracket

Digital Multimeter

Test Harness

A1 A25 B1 B15 C1 C11 D1 D21
A2 A26 B2 B16 C2 C12 D2 D22

ECM TERMINAL LOCATION

93F78365   Courtesy of American Honda Motor Co., Inc.

Fig. 1: Identifying ECM Terminals

Intake Air By-Pass (IAB) Control Solenoid Valves (Legend) — 1) IAB control solenoid valves are located at right front of engine compartment. Check IAB valve shaft for binding, sticking, and smooth movement. If necessary, clean linkage and shafts with carburetor cleaner. **2)** Start engine and let idle. Remove vacuum hose No. 2 from IAB low control diaphragm. See Fig. 2. Connect vacuum gauge to hose. If vacuum is not present, go to step **6)**. If vacuum is present, go to step **3)**.

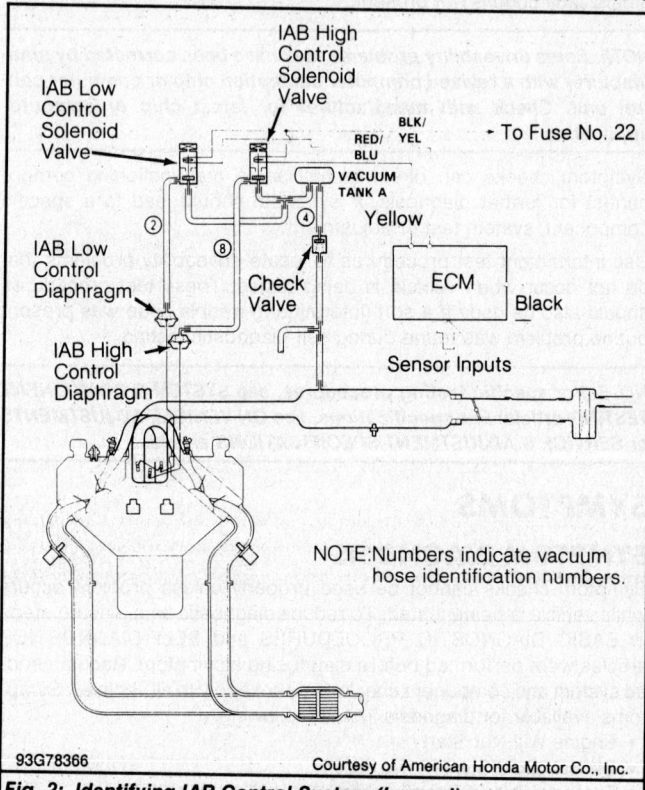

IAB High Control Solenoid Valve

IAB Low Control Solenoid Valve

RED/BLU   BLK/YEL   ← To Fuse No. 22

VACUUM TANK A

Yellow

IAB Low Control Diaphragm

Check Valve

ECM   Black

IAB High Control Diaphragm

Sensor Inputs

NOTE: Numbers indicate vacuum hose identification numbers.

93G78366   Courtesy of American Honda Motor Co., Inc.

Fig. 2: Identifying IAB Control System (Legend)

3) Disconnect vacuum hose No. 8 from IAB high control diaphragm. Connect vacuum gauge to hose. If vacuum is present, go to next step. If vacuum is not present, go to step **11**.
4) Increase engine speed to 3400 RPM. Check for vacuum at hose No. 2. If vacuum is not present, go to next step. If vacuum is present, go to step **16)**.
5) Increase engine speed to 4300 RPM. Check for vacuum at hose No. 8. If vacuum is not present, system is okay. If vacuum is present, go to step **18)**.
6) Remove vacuum hose No. 4 at IAB low control solenoid. Connect vacuum gauge to hose. If vacuum is present, go to next step. If vacuum is not present, check vacuum lines between solenoid, vacuum tank and intake manifold. See Fig. 2. Repair as necessary and recheck.
7) Turn ignition off. Unplug 6-wire connector from IAB low control solenoid. Turn ignition on. Measure voltage between Black/Yellow (positive) and Red/Blue (negative) wire terminals. If battery voltage is present, replace by-pass low control solenoid valve. If voltage is not present, go to next step.
8) Measure voltage between Black/Yellow wire terminal and body ground. If battery voltage is not present, repair open in Black/Yellow wire between solenoid 6-wire connector and fuse No. 22. If battery voltage is present, go to next step.
9) Turn ignition off. Install ECM test harness connector between ECM and ECM harness connector. Check Red/Blue wire for continuity between ECM terminal A14 and solenoid connector.
10) If continuity does not exist, repair open in Red/Blue wire. If continuity exists, substitute a known-good ECM and retest. If symptom goes away, replace ECM.
11) Remove vacuum hose No. 4 at IAB high control solenoid. Connect vacuum gauge to hose. If vacuum is present, go to next step. If vacuum is not present, check vacuum line between solenoid and intake manifold. Repair as necessary and recheck.

12) Turn ignition off. Unplug 6-wire connector from IAB high control solenoid. Turn ignition on. Measure voltage between Black/Yellow (positive) and Red/Blue (negative) wire terminals. If battery voltage is present, replace IAB high control solenoid valve. If voltage is not present, go to next step.

13) Measure voltage between Black/Yellow wire terminal and body ground. If battery voltage is not present, repair open in Black/Yellow wire between solenoid 6-wire connector and fuse No. 22. If battery voltage is present, go to next step.

14) Turn ignition off. Install ECM test harness connector between ECM and ECM harness connector. Check Yellow wire for continuity between ECM terminal A18 and solenoid connector.

15) If continuity does not exist, repair open in Yellow wire. If continuity exists, substitute a known-good ECM and retest. If symptom goes away, replace ECM.

16) Turn ignition off. Unplug 6-pin connector from IAB low control solenoid. If vacuum is present, replace IAB low control solenoid valve. If vacuum is not present, go to next step.

17) Unplug connector "A" from ECM. Check Red/Blue wire for short to ground. Repair as necessary. If Red/Blue wire is okay, substitute a known-good ECM and retest. If symptom goes away, replace ECM.

18) Unplug 6-pin connector from by-pass high control solenoid valve. If vacuum is present, replace by-pass high control solenoid valve. If vacuum is not present, go to next step.

19) Unplug connector "A" from ECM. Check Yellow wire between connector and ECM terminal A18 for short to ground. Repair as necessary. If Yellow wire is okay, substitute a known-good ECM and retest. If symptom goes away, replace ECM.

Intake Air By-Pass (IAB) Control Solenoid Valve (Integra GS-R & Vigor) – **1)** IAB control solenoid valve is located on top of intake manifold. Start and idle engine. Disconnect vacuum hose No. 13 from by-pass control diaphragm. *See Fig. 3.* Connect vacuum gauge to hose. If vacuum exists, go to step 6). If vacuum does not exist, go to next step.

2) Unplug 2-pin connector from by-pass control solenoid valve. Measure voltage between Black/Yellow and Pink/Blue wire (Blue/Red wire on Vigor) terminals of harness connector. If battery voltage exists, repair vacuum leak or blockage between intake manifold and diaphragm. If vacuum is okay, replace by-pass control solenoid valve. If battery voltage does not exist, go to next step.

3) Measure voltage between harness connector Black/Yellow wire terminal and body ground. If battery voltage does not exist, repair open in Black/Yellow wire between connector and main relay (fuse No. 2 on Vigor). If battery voltage exists, go to next step.

4) Turn ignition off. Reconnect wiring to by-pass control solenoid valve. Connect test harness to main wire harness only. DO NOT connect it to ECM.

5) Turn ignition on. Connect jumper wire between ECM terminals A17 and A26. If solenoid clicks when jumper wire is connected, substitute a known-good ECM and recheck operation. If solenoid valve does not click, repair open circuit between harness connector Pink/Blue wire (Blue/Red wire on Vigor) and ECM terminal A17.

6) Increase engine speed to 6000 RPM (4900 RPM on Vigor). Check for vacuum at hose No. 13. If there is no vacuum, system is okay. If vacuum exists, unplug 2-pin connector from by-pass control solenoid valve. If vacuum now exists, replace by-pass control solenoid valve. If vacuum does not exist, go to next step.

7) Turn ignition off. Unplug connector "A" from ECM. Check Pink/Blue wire (Blue/Red wire on Vigor) for short to ground between ECM terminal A17 and by-pass control solenoid valve connector. Repair as necessary. If Pink/Blue wire (Blue/Red wire on Vigor) is okay, substitute a known-good ECM and recheck operation. If symptom goes away, replace ECM.

COMPUTERIZED ENGINE CONTROLS

ENGINE CONTROL UNIT (ECM)

NOTE: Integra and Legend with M/T uses Engine Control Module (ECM); Integra and Legend with A/T uses Powertrain Control Module (PCM), which also controls transmission functions. When working on A/T models, all references to ECM also applies to PCM.

NOTE: On all models, ECM is located under a cover panel, in front passenger footwell.

Ground Circuits (Integra) – **1)** Measure resistance to ground on ECM terminals A23, A24, A26, and B2. Resistance should be zero ohms. If not, repair open to ground.

2) Using a DVOM, connect negative lead to a good ground. Backprobe each ground terminal. With engine running, DVOM should indicate less than one volt. If voltmeter reading is greater than one volt, check for open, corrosion, or loose connection on ground lead.

Power Circuits (Integra) – **1)** Check for battery voltage between ECM terminal D1 and ground. If battery voltage is not present, check BACK UP fuse (located in underhood fuse block). If fuse is okay, check for an open in White/Yellow wire between fuse block and control unit.

2) Turn ignition on. Check for battery voltage between ground and ECM terminals A25 and B1. If battery voltage is not present, check ECM fuse (located in underhood fuse block). If fuse is okay, check for open in Yellow/Black wire between main relay and ECM terminals A25 and B1, faulty main relay, or faulty ignition switch.

3) Connect voltmeter between ground and ECM terminal B9. Hold ignition switch in START position. Battery voltage should be present between ECM terminal B9 and ground ONLY when ignition switch is in START position.

4) If voltage is not present, check fuse No. 18 (located in underdash fuse block). If fuse is okay, check for an open in Blue/White wire between fuse No. 18 and terminal B9 of ECM, or check for a defective ignition switch.

Ground Circuits (Legend) – **1)** Using a DVOM, check for continuity to ground on ECM terminals A23, A24, A26, and B2. Resistance should be zero ohms. If not, repair open to ground.

2) Using a DVOM, connect negative lead to a good ground. Backprobe each ground terminal. With engine running, DVOM should indicate less than one volt. If DVOM reading is greater than one volt, check for open, corrosion, or loose connection on ground lead.

Power Circuits (Legend) – **1)** Check for battery voltage between ECM terminal D1 and ground. If battery voltage is not present, check fuse No. 15 (located in underdash fuse block). If fuse is okay, check for an open in Yellow/Blue wire between fuse block and ECM.

2) Turn ignition on. Check for battery voltage between ground and ECM terminals A25 and C1. If battery voltage is not present, check fuse No. 6 (located in underdash fuse block). If fuse is okay, check for an open in Yellow/Black wire between main relay and ECM terminals A25 and D1, defective main relay, or defective ignition switch.

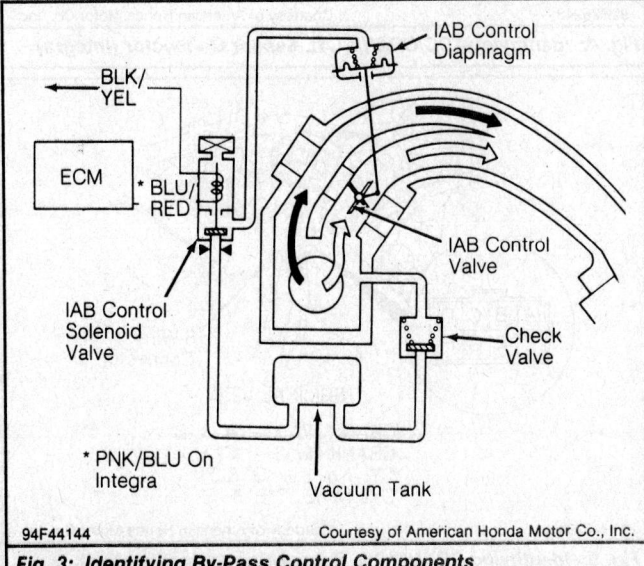

BLK/
YEL

ECM

* BLU/
RED

IAB Control
Solenoid
Valve

* PNK/BLU On
Integra

IAB Control
Diaphragm

IAB Control
Valve

Check
Valve

Vacuum Tank

94F44144

Courtesy of American Honda Motor Co., Inc.

Fig. 3: Identifying By-Pass Control Components (Integra GS-R & Vigor)

3) Connect DVOM between ECM terminal C11 and ground. Hold ignition switch in START position. Battery voltage should be present between ECM terminal C11 and ground ONLY when ignition switch is in the START position.

4) If battery voltage is not present, check fuse No. 14 (located in underdash fuse block). If fuse is okay, check for an open in Blue/White wire between fuse No. 14 and terminal C11 of ECM, or check for a defective ignition switch.

Ground Circuits (Vigor) – 1) Measure resistance to ground on ECM terminals A23, A24, A26, and B2. Resistance should be zero ohms. If resistance is not zero ohms, repair open to ground.

2) Using a DVOM, connect negative lead to a good ground. Backprobe each ground terminal. With engine running, DVOM should indicate less than one volt. If DVOM reading is greater than one volt, check for open, corrosion, or loose connection on ground lead.

Power Circuits (Vigor) – 1) Check for battery voltage between ECM terminal D1 and ground. If battery voltage is not present, check BACK UP fuse (located in underhood fuse block). If fuse is okay, check for an open in White/Green wire between fuse block and control unit.

2) Turn ignition on. Check for battery voltage between ground and ECM terminals A25 and B1. If battery voltage is not present, check ECM fuse (located in underhood fuse block). If fuse is okay, check for open in Yellow/Black wire between main relay and ECM terminals A25 and B1, defective main relay, or defective ignition switch.

3) Connect voltmeter between ground and ECM terminal B9. Hold ignition switch in START position. Battery voltage should be present between ECM terminal B9 and ground ONLY when ignition switch is in START position.

4) If battery voltage is not present, check fuse No. 18 (located in underdash fuse block). If fuse is okay, check for an open in Blue/Red wire between fuse No. 9 and terminal B9 of control unit, or check for a defective ignition switch.

ENGINE SENSORS & SWITCHES

ATMOSPHERIC PRESSURE (PA) SENSOR

Sensor is located inside ECM. Check for diagnostic trouble code stored in ECM memory. See SELF-DIAGNOSTICS article.

CLUTCH SWITCH

Legend – Turn ignition off. Unplug 2-wire connector (Pink and Black wires) from clutch switch, located on clutch pedal. With clutch pedal depressed, check continuity of switch. If no continuity exists, replace clutch switch.

COOLANT TEMPERATURE (TW) SENSOR

TW sensor is threaded into upper front side of engine on Integra, and upper right of engine on Legend and Vigor. Unplug 2-wire connector (Red/White and Green/White wires) from sensor. Resistance should be as specified in COOLANT TEMPERATURE (TW) SENSOR RESISTANCE table.

COOLANT TEMPERATURE (TW) SENSOR RESISTANCE

Temperature °F (°C)	[1] (Ohms)
–4 (–20)	15,000-18,000
68 (20)	1000-4000
176 (80)	200-400
248 (120)	50-150

[1] – Measure resistance across sensor terminals.

CRANK/CYL/TDC SENSORS

1) On Integra, CRANK/CYL/TDC sensors are located within distributor. On Legend, sensors are located under upper left timing belt cover. On Vigor, sensors are under upper timing cover. To test sensor and wiring connections, turn ignition off. Probe appropriate ECM harness terminals to check for resistance of each sensor. See CRANK/CYL/TDC SENSOR RESISTANCE table. If resistance is not as specified, go to step **3)**.

2) If resistance is as specified, check for continuity to ground at each terminal. If continuity exists, unplug sensor connector and recheck appropriate ECM terminal for continuity to ground. If continuity still exists, repair short to ground in harness. If continuity does not exist, replace sensor assembly.

3) Unplug harness connector at sensor. *See Fig. 4, 5 or 6.* Measure sensor resistance at connector. See CRANK/CYL/TDC SENSOR RESISTANCE table. If sensor resistance is as specified, repair open, short, or corrosion in sensor harness between ECM and sensor. If sensor resistance is not as specified, replace sensor assembly.

CRANK/CYL/TDC SENSOR RESISTANCE

Application	ECM Terminals	Ohms
Integra		
CRANK	B15 & B16	350-700
CYL	B11 & B12	350-700
TDC	B13 & B14	350-700
Legend		
CRANK No. 1	B15 & B16	600-950
CRANK No. 2	B14 & B13	600-950
CYL No. 1	B12 & B11	600-950
CYL No. 2	B9 & B10	600-950
Vigor		
CRANK	B15 & B16	650-850
CYL	B11 & B12	650-850
TDC	B13 & B14	650-850

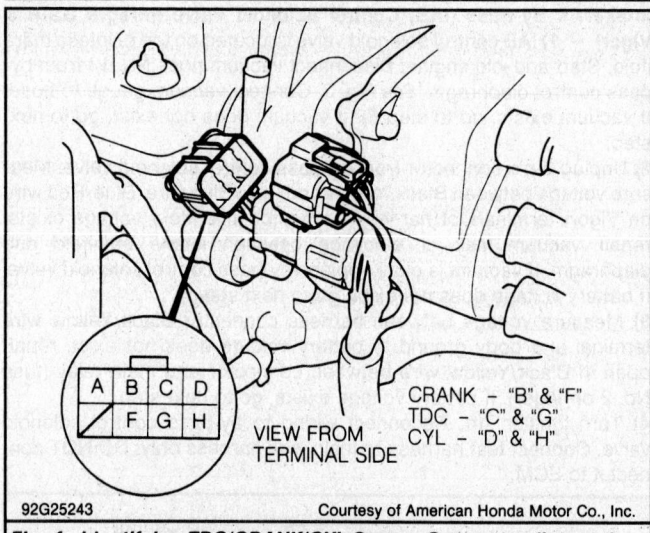

92G25243   Courtesy of American Honda Motor Co., Inc.

Fig. 4: Identifying TDC/CRANK/CYL Sensor Connector (Integra)

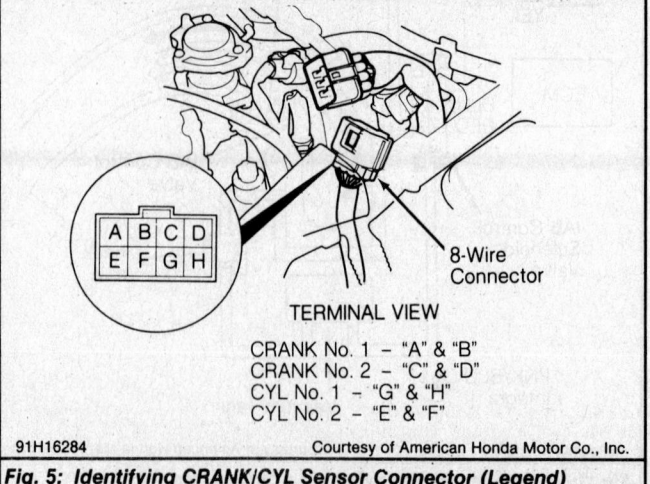

91H16284   Courtesy of American Honda Motor Co., Inc.

Fig. 5: Identifying CRANK/CYL Sensor Connector (Legend)

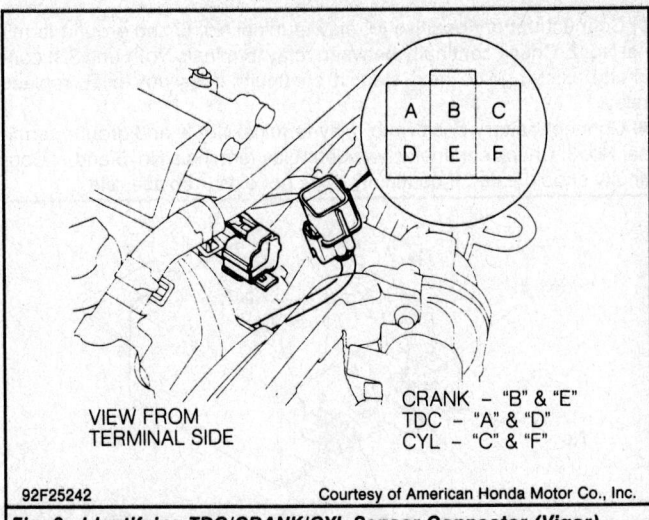

VIEW FROM
TERMINAL SIDE

CRANK – "B" & "E"
TDC – "A" & "D"
CYL – "C" & "F"

92F25242   Courtesy of American Honda Motor Co., Inc.

Fig. 6: Identifying TDC/CRANK/CYL Sensor Connector (Vigor)

EGR VALVE LIFT SENSOR

1) EGR lift sensor is part of EGR valve, located on top of engine. Turn ignition on. Measure voltage between terminals of Yellow/White wire (positive) and Green/White wire (negative) by backprobing EGR valve lift sensor connector. If voltage is not about 5 volts, repair open in Yellow/White or Green/White wire between ECM and EGR valve.

2) Measure voltage between Yellow wire (positive) and Green/White wire (negative) by backprobing EGR valve lift sensor 3-wire connector. If voltage is about 1.2 volts, slowly apply 8 in. Hg to EGR valve. Completely release and reapply vacuum several times. Voltmeter should indicate about 4 volts with vacuum applied. If voltage is not as specified, replace EGR valve.

INTAKE AIR TEMPERATURE (IAT) SENSOR

Unplug IAT sensor 2-wire connector, located on throttle body. Measure resistance between sensor terminals at specified temperatures. See INTAKE AIR TEMPERATURE (IAT) SENSOR RESISTANCE table. Replace IAT sensor if resistance is not as specified.

INTAKE AIR TEMPERATURE (IAT) SENSOR RESISTANCE [1]

Temperature F° (C°)	Ohms
–4 (–20)	15,000-18,000
68 (20)	2000-4000
176 (80)	300-400

[1] – Measure resistance between sensor terminals.

KNOCK SENSOR

Integra GS-R, Legend & Vigor – See SELF-DIAGNOSTICS article.

MAP SENSOR

1) MAP sensor is located on throttle body on Integra, inside control box on firewall (Legend) or left side of engine compartment (Vigor). Unplug connector from MAP sensor. Turn ignition on. Measure voltage between Yellow/Red and Green/White wires on Integra (except GS-R), or between Yellow/White and Green/White wires on all others. If voltmeter does not indicate about 5 volts, repair wiring between MAP sensor and ECM. If wiring is okay, replace ECM. If voltmeter indicates about 5 volts, go to next step.

2) Turn ignition off. Connect test harness between ECM and vehicle wire harness. Turn ignition on. Measure voltage between terminals D19 and D21. If voltage is not as specified in MAP SENSOR VOLTAGE table, check sensor output wire between MAP sensor and ECM. Wire is Green/White on Integra, Yellow/White on Legend and White/Blue on Vigor. If wire is okay, replace MAP sensor.

MAP SENSOR VOLTAGE

In. Hg Vacuum Applied	Volts
0	2.8-3.0
5	2.3-2.5
10	1.8-2.0
15	1.3-1.5
20	.8-1.0
25	.3-.5

OXYGEN SENSOR

Oxygen sensor(s) is threaded into exhaust manifold(s). Turn ignition off. Connect test harness between ECM and vehicle wire harness. Connect voltmeter between terminals specified in OXYGEN SENSOR TEST TERMINALS table. Turn ignition on. If voltmeter does not indicate .4 - .5 volt when ignition is first turned on, and less than .1 volt in less than 2 minutes, check wiring between ECM and oxygen sensor. If wiring is okay, replace oxygen sensor.

OXYGEN SENSOR TEST TERMINALS

Model	Terminals
Integra & Vigor	A26 & D14
Legend	
Left Oxygen Sensor	A26 & D14
Right Oxygen Sensor	A26 & D16

POWER STEERING PRESSURE (PSP) SWITCH

1) Unplug PSP switch connector, located near front of engine. Check continuity through PSP switch. With front wheels stationary, switch should be closed. Turn steering wheel left and right, and ensure switch is open. If continuity is not as specified, replace PSP switch.

2) To check wiring harness, unplug PSP switch 2-wire connector. Turn ignition on. Check for battery voltage between PSP switch terminals. If no voltage is present, repair open in wire(s). If wires are okay, substitute a known-good ECM. If problem goes away, replace ECM.

THROTTLE POSITION (TP) SENSOR

Integra – **1)** Unplug connector from TP sensor, located on throttle body. Turn ignition on. Measure voltage between Yellow/Blue (positive) and Green/Blue (negative) wire terminals. If voltage is not about 5 volts, check wiring between TP sensor and ECM. If wiring is okay, replace ECM.

2) If voltage is about 5 volts, turn ignition off. Reconnect wire harness to throttle angle sensor. Connect test harness between ECM and vehicle wire harness. Turn ignition on. Measure voltage between test harness terminals D11 and D22. Voltage should be about .5 volt with throttle valve at full-closed position, and about 4.5 volts with throttle valve at full-open position. As throttle opens, voltage should increase smoothly from .5 volt to 4.5 volts.

3) On Integra with automatic transmission, if voltage is not as specified, disconnect Transmission Control Module (TCM) and repeat step **2)**. If voltage is now as specified, replace TCM.

4) On all models, if voltage is not as specified, check for short or open in Red/Black wire between ECM and TP sensor. Repair as necessary. If wire is okay, replace TP sensor.

Vigor & Legend) – **1)** Unplug connector from TP sensor, located on throttle body. Turn ignition on. Measure voltage between Yellow/White (positive) and Green/White (negative) wire terminals. If voltage is not about 5 volts, check wiring between TP sensor and ECM. If wiring is okay, replace ECM.

2) If voltage is about 5 volts, turn ignition off. Reconnect wire harness to throttle angle sensor. Connect test harness between ECM and vehicle wire harness. Turn ignition on. Measure voltage between test harness terminals D11 and D22. Voltage should be about .5 volt with throttle valve at full-closed position, and about 4.5 volts with throttle valve at full-open position. As throttle opens, voltage should increase smoothly from .5 volt to 4.5 volts.

3) On automatic transmission models, if voltage is not as specified, disconnect Transmission Control Module (TCM) and repeat step **2)**. If voltage is now as specified, replace TCM.

4) On all models, if voltage is not as specified, check for short or open in Red/Blue wire (Legend) or Red/Yellow wire (Vigor) between ECM and TP sensor. Repair as necessary. If wire is okay, replace TP sensor.

VEHICLE SPEED SENSOR (VSS)

1) VSS is located at left front wheel. Connect test harness between ECM and VSS harness connectors. Block rear wheels. Set parking brake. Raise and support front of vehicle. Connect voltmeter between test harness terminals A26 and B10 (Integra and Vigor) or between terminals A26 and C2 (Legend).

2) Turn ignition on. Slowly rotate left front wheel. Voltage should pulsate between zero and 5 volts. If voltage pulsates as specified, go to step **3)**. If voltage does not pulsate as specified, check for open or short in Orange wire between ECM terminal B10 and speed sensor (Integra), check for open or short in Yellow/Red wire between ECM terminal C2 and speed sensor (Legend) or check for open or short in Yellow/Red wire between ECM terminal B16 and speed sensor (Vigor). If wire is okay, replace faulty VSS or ECM.

3) Substitute a known-good ECM, and retest. If problem goes away, replace ECM.

RELAYS & SOLENOIDS

RELAYS

NOTE: The fuel pump relay is an integral component of the main relay.

Fuel Pump Relay (Integra) – 1) Remove fuel pump relay, located under left side of dash. Connect battery voltage to terminal No. 2, and ground terminal No. 1 of relay. *See Fig. 7.*

2) Check continuity between relay terminals No. 5 and 4. If continuity exists, go to next step. If continuity does not exist, replace relay.

3) Connect battery positive to relay terminal No. 5, and ground terminal No. 3. Check continuity between relay terminals No. 7 and 6. If continuity exists, go to next step. If continuity does not exist, replace relay.

4) Connect battery positive to relay terminal No. 6, and ground terminal No. 1. Check continuity between relay terminals No. 5 and 4. If continuity exists, relay is okay. If continuity is not present, replace relay.

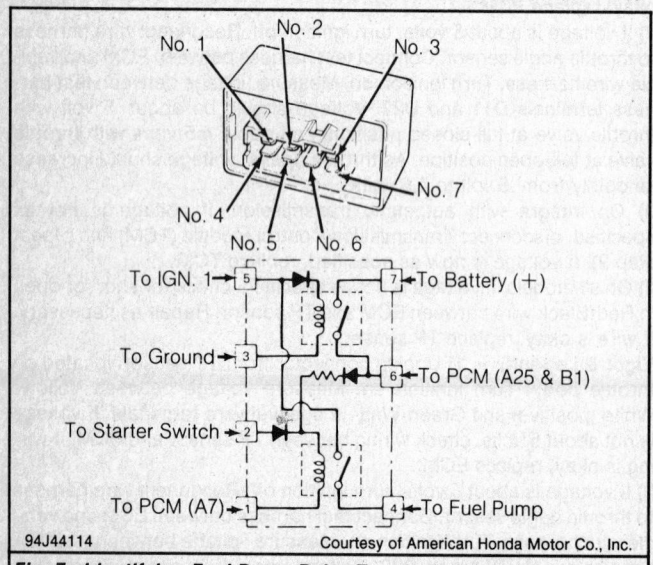

Fig. 7: Identifying Fuel Pump Relay Terminals (Integra)

Fuel Pump Relay (Legend) – 1) Remove fuel pump main relay located under left side of dash. Connect battery voltage to terminal No. 4, and ground terminal No. 8 of relay. *See Fig. 8.*

2) Check continuity between relay terminals No. 5 and 7. If continuity exists, go to next step. If continuity does not exist, replace relay.

3) Connect battery positive to relay terminal No. 6, and ground terminal No. 2. Check continuity between relay terminals No. 1 and 3. If continuity exists, go to next step. If continuity does not exist, replace relay.

4) Connect battery positive to relay terminal No. 3, and ground terminal No. 8. Check continuity between relay terminals No. 5 and 7. Continuity should exist. If continuity does not exist, replace relay.

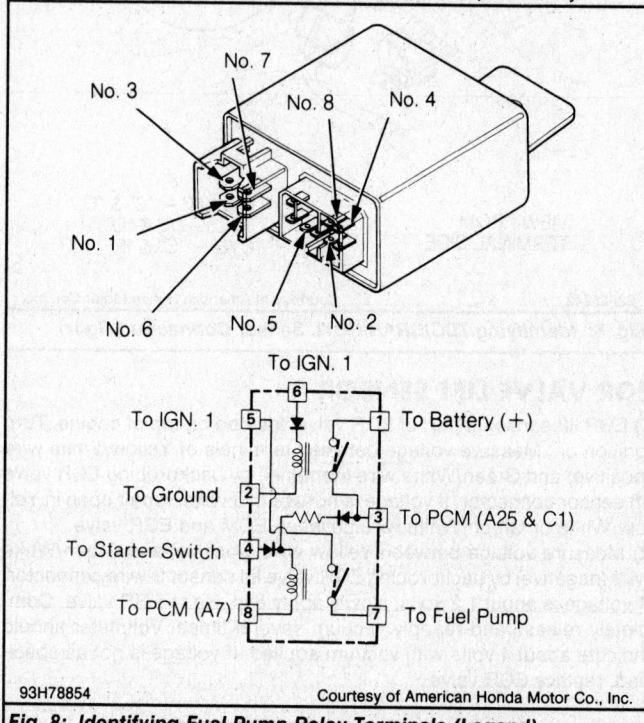

Courtesy of American Honda Motor Co., Inc.

Fig. 8: Identifying Fuel Pump Relay Terminals (Legend)

Fuel Pump Relay (Vigor) – 1) Remove fuel pump main relay located under left side of dash. Connect battery voltage to terminal No. 6, and ground terminal No. 8 of relay. *See Fig. 9.*

2) Check continuity between relay terminals No. 5 and 7. If continuity exists, go to next step. If continuity does not exist, replace relay.

3) Connect battery voltage to relay terminal No. 5, and ground terminal No. 2. Check continuity between relay terminals No. 1 and 3. If continuity exists, go to next step. If continuity does not exist, replace relay.

4) Connect battery voltage to relay terminal No. 3, and ground terminal No. 8. Check continuity between relay terminals No. 5 and 7. If continuity exists, relay is okay. If continuity does not exist, replace relay.

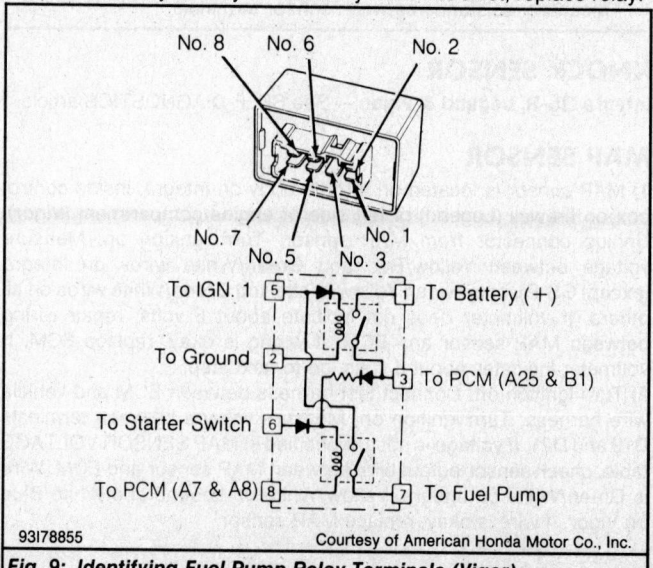

Courtesy of American Honda Motor Co., Inc.

Fig. 9: Identifying Fuel Pump Relay Terminals (Vigor)

SOLENOIDS

Air Suction Control Solenoid Valve (Legend) – See AIR INJECTION under EMISSION SYSTEMS & SUB-SYSTEMS.

By-Pass Control Solenoid Valves – See AIR INTAKE SYSTEM under AIR INDUCTION SYSTEMS.

EGR Control Solenoid Valve – See EXHAUST GAS RECIRCULATION (EGR) under EMISSION SYSTEMS & SUB-SYSTEMS.

Fuel Pressure Regulator Cut-Off Solenoid Valve (Legend) – See FUEL DELIVERY under FUEL SYSTEM.

Purge Cut-Off Solenoid Valve – See FUEL EVAPORATION under EMISSION SYSTEMS & SUB-SYSTEMS.

FUEL SYSTEM

FUEL DELIVERY

NOTE: For fuel system pressure testing, see BASIC DIAGNOSTIC PROCEDURES article.

Pressure Regulator Control Solenoid Valve (Legend) – **1)** Pressure regulator control solenoid valve is located in control box on firewall. *See Fig. 10.* Warm engine to operating temperature. Disconnect vacuum hose No. 1 from pressure regulator. Connect vacuum gauge to hose. If manifold vacuum is present, go to step **3)**. If manifold vacuum is not present, go to next step.

2) Unplug 4-pin connector from control box on firewall. *See Fig. 10.* If manifold vacuum is now present, repair shorted Light Green wire between ECM terminal A19 and control box connector. If wire is okay, substitute a known-good ECM. If vacuum is not present, check vacuum hoses No. 1 and 3 for leaks or obstructions. If hoses are okay, replace pressure regulator control solenoid valve.

3) Turn ignition off. Unplug 4-pin connector from control box. Using a fused jumper wire, connect positive battery terminal to terminal "C" (Black/Yellow wire) of cut-off solenoid valve side of connector. Connect negative battery terminal to terminal "D" (Light Green wire) of cut-off solenoid valve side of connector. Start and idle engine. If manifold vacuum is now present, replace cut-off solenoid valve.

4) If manifold vacuum is not present, measure voltage between Black/Yellow (positive) wire and ground. If battery voltage does not exist, repair open in Black/Yellow wire between fuse No. 22 and solenoid valve connector. Reconnect wire harness to solenoid valve.

5) Connect test harness between ECM and vehicle harness. Start engine. Connect jumper wire from terminal A19 to ground. If manifold vacuum is not present, cut-off solenoid valve is okay. If vacuum is present, repair open in Light Green wire between ECM and solenoid valve connector.

FUEL CONTROL

Fuel Injector – Unplug electrical connector from fuel injector. Measure resistance between fuel injector terminals. Resistance should be 10-13 ohms on Integra, or 1.5-2.5 ohms on Legend and Vigor.

Fuel Pressure Regulator – See FUEL SYSTEM in BASIC DIAGNOSTIC PROCEDURES article.

Fuel Pump – See FUEL SYSTEM in BASIC DIAGNOSTIC PROCEDURES article.

Fuel Pump Relay – See RELAYS under RELAYS & SOLENOIDS.

Injector Resistor (Legend & Vigor) – Injector resistor assembly is located on left side of engine compartment. Unplug injector resistor connector. Measure resistance between each injector resistor terminal and Yellow/Black power wire terminal. If resistance is not 5-7 ohms, replace injector resistor.

IDLE CONTROL SYSTEM

Air Conditioning Signal (Integra) – **1)** Connect ECM test harness between ECM and ECM connectors. Unplug connector "B" from main harness only. DO NOT disconnect from ECM. Turn ignition on.

2) Measure voltage between ECM terminals B5 (positive) and A26 (negative). *See Fig. 1.* If voltage is not about 5 volts, substitute a known-good ECM and recheck.

3) If voltage is about 5 volts, reconnect connector "B" to main wiring harness. Momentarily connect terminals A15 and A26 together and check for clicking of A/C clutch.

4) If A/C clutch clicks, go to next step. If A/C clutch does not click, jumper Black/Red wire of A/C clutch relay connector to ground. If A/C clutch clicks, repair open in Black/Red wire. If A/C clutch still does not click, repair A/C clutch circuit.

5) Start engine. Turn blower on. Turn A/C switch on. If A/C operates, A/C signal is okay. If A/C does not operate, measure voltage between terminals B5 (positive) and A26 (negative).

6) If voltage is more than one volt, repair open in Blue/Red wire between ECM terminal B5 and A/C pressure switch. If voltage is less than one volt, substitute a known-good ECM, and recheck voltage.

Air Conditioning Signal (Legend) – **1)** Connect ECM test harness between ECM and ECM connectors. Unplug connector "C" from main harness only. DO NOT disconnect from ECM. Turn ignition on.

2) Measure voltage between ECM terminals C3 (positive) and A26 (negative). *See Fig. 1.* If voltage is not about 10 volts, substitute a known-good ECM, and recheck voltage.

3) If voltage is about 10 volts, reconnect connector "C" to main wiring harness. Momentarily connect terminals A15 and A26 together and check for clicking of A/C clutch.

4) If A/C clutch clicks, go to next step. If A/C clutch does not click, jumper Red/Blue wire of A/C clutch relay connector to ground. If A/C clutch clicks, repair open in Red/Blue wire. If A/C clutch still does not click, repair A/C clutch circuit.

5) Start engine, and turn blower on. Turn A/C switch on. If A/C operates, A/C signal is okay. If A/C does not operate, measure voltage between terminals C3 (positive) and A26 (negative).

6) If voltage is more than one volt, repair open in Blue/Black wire between terminal C3 and cooling fan control unit. If voltage is less than one volt, substitute a known-good ECM, and recheck voltage.

Air Conditioning Signal (Vigor) – **1)** Connect ECM test harness between ECM and ECM connectors. Unplug connector "B" from main harness only. DO NOT disconnect from ECM. Turn ignition on.

2) Measure voltage between ECM terminals B5 (positive) and A26 (negative). *See Fig. 1.* If voltage is not about 10 volts, substitute a known-good ECM, and recheck voltage.

3) If voltage is about 10 volts, reconnect connector "B" to main wiring harness. Momentarily connect terminals A15 and A26 together and check for clicking of A/C clutch.

4) If A/C clutch clicks, go to next step. If A/C clutch does not click, jumper Red/Blue wire of A/C clutch relay connector to ground. If A/C clutch clicks, repair open in Red/Blue wire. If A/C clutch still does not click, repair A/C clutch circuit.

5) Start engine. Turn blower on. Turn A/C switch on. If A/C operates, A/C signal is okay. If A/C does not operate, measure voltage between terminals B5 (positive) and A26 (negative).

6) If voltage is more than one volt, repair open in Blue/Black wire between ECM terminal B5 and A/C pressure switch. If voltage is less than one volt, substitute a known-good ECM and recheck voltage.

Alternator FR Signal – **1)** Connect ECM test harness between ECM and ECM connectors. Unplug connector "D" from main wire harness only. DO NOT disconnect from ECM. Turn ignition on. Measure voltage between terminals D9 (positive) and A26 (negative). *See Fig. 1.* If voltage is not about 5 volts, substitute a known-good ECM and recheck.

2) If voltage is about 5 volts, turn ignition off. Reconnect connector "D" to main harness. Start and warm engine to operating temperature. Measure voltage between ECM terminals D9 (positive) and A26.

3) Turn headlights and rear defogger on. If voltage does not decrease, go to next step. If voltage decreases, alternator FR signal is okay. Remove alternator sensor fuse for 10 seconds to reset ECM.

4) Turn ignition off. Unplug connector "D" from ECM only. Disconnect negative battery cable. Check for continuity between ECM test harness terminal D9 and ground. If no continuity exists, go to step **6)**. If continuity exists, unplug Green connector from alternator.

5) Check again for continuity between ECM test harness terminal D9 and ground. If continuity does not exist, check alternator for possible failure. If continuity is present, repair White/Red wire between alternator and ECM terminal D9.

6) Connect White/Red wire to body ground. Check for continuity between ECM terminal D9 and ground. If continuity exist, service alternator. If continuity does not exist, repair White/Red wire between alternator and ECM terminal D9.

Automatic Transmission Shift Position Signal (Integra) – 1) While watching shift indicator, shift transmission gear lever to each position. If shift indicator lights up correctly for all positions, turn ignition off.

2) Connect ECM test harness between ECM and ECM connectors. Unplug connector "B" from main harness only. DO NOT disconnect from ECM. Turn ignition on. Measure voltage between ECM terminals B7 (positive) and A26. See Fig. 1.

3) If voltage is about 5 volts, reconnect connector "B" to main wiring harness. Go to next step. If voltage is not as specified, substitute a known-good ECM and retest.

4) Turn ignition off. Reconnect wire harness to ECM. Place transmission in Neutral. Start engine. Measure voltage between terminals B7 (positive) and A26 (negative) with transmission selector in Park and Neutral positions.

5) If voltage is more than one volt in Neutral, repair open in Light Green/Black wire between ECM terminal B7 and gauge assembly or open in Green wire between gauge asembly and automatic transmission shift position switch. If voltage is less than one volt, go to next step. If voltage is more than one volt in Park, repair open in Green/White wire between gauge assembly and automatic transmission shift position switch. If voltage is less than one volt, go to next step.

6) Set transmission selector to Drive position. Measure voltage between terminals B7 (positive) and A26 (negative). If voltage is about 10 volts, repair short circuit in Light Green/Black wire between ECM terminal B7 and gauge assembly. If voltage is as specified, shift position signal is okay.

Automatic Transmission Shift Position Signal (Legend) – 1) While watching shift indicator, shift transmission gear lever to each position. If shift indicator lights up correctly for all positions, turn ignition off.

2) Connect ECM test harness between ECM and ECM connectors. Unplug connector "B" from main harness only. DO NOT disconnect from ECM. Turn ignition on. Measure voltage between ECM terminals B7 (positive) and A26. See Fig. 1.

3) If voltage is about 10 volts, reconnect connector "B" to main wiring harness. Go to next step. If voltage is not as specified, substitute a known-good ECM and retest.

4) Turn ignition off. Reconnect wire harness to ECM. Place transmission in Neutral. Start engine. Measure voltage between terminals B7 (positive) and A26 (negative).

5) If voltage is more than one volt in Neutral, repair open in Light Green wire between ECM terminal B7 and gauge assembly or open in Green wire between gauge asembly and automatic transmission shift position switch. If voltage is less than one volt, go to next step. If voltage is more than one volt in Park, repair open in Green/White wire between gauge assembly and automatic transmission shift position switch. If voltage is less than one volt, go to next step.

6) Set transmission selector to Drive position. Measure voltage between terminals B7 (positive) and A26 (negative). If voltage is not about 10 volts, repair short circuit in Light Green wire between ECM terminal B7 and gauge assembly. If voltage is as specified, shift position signal is okay.

Automatic Transmission Shift Position Signal (Vigor) – 1) While watching shift indicator, shift transmission gear lever to each position. If shift indicator lights up correctly for all positions, turn ignition off.

2) Connect ECM test harness between ECM and ECM connectors. Unplug connector "B" from main harness only. DO NOT disconnect from ECM. Turn ignition on. Measure voltage between ECM terminals B7 (positive) and A26. See Fig. 1.

3) If voltage is about 5 volts, reconnect connector "B" to main wiring harness. Go to next step. If voltage is not as specified, substitute a known-good ECM and retest.

4) Turn ignition off. Reconnect wire harness to ECM. Place transmission in Neutral. Start engine. Measure voltage between terminals B7 (positive) and A26 (negative) with transmission selector in Park and Neutral positions. If voltage is more than one volt, repair open in Yellow/Green wire between ECM terminal B7 and gauge assembly. If voltage is less than one volt, go to next step.

5) Set transmission selector to Drive position. Measure voltage between terminals B7 (positive) and A26 (negative). If voltage is not about 10 volts, repair short circuit in Yellow/Green wire between ECM terminal B7 and combination meter. If voltage is as specified, shift position signal is okay.

Brake Switch Signal – 1) Ensure stoplights operate properly. Connect ECM Test Harness (07LAJ-PT3010A) to ECM main harness. DO NOT connect test harness to ECM. Measure voltage between test harness terminals D2 (positive) and A26 (negative). See Fig. 1.

2) Depress brake pedal. If battery voltage is present, switch is okay. If battery voltage is not present, repair open in Green/White wire and ECM terminal D2.

Clutch Signal Switch (Legend) – 1) Unplug connector at clutch switch, located on clutch pedal. Check continuity between clutch switch terminals. If continuity is not present, replace clutch switch. If continuity is present, turn ignition on and measure voltage between Pink (positive) wire terminal and ground.

2) If battery voltage is present, repair open in Black wire between clutch switch and ground connector. If battery voltage is not present, repair open in Pink wire between ECM and switch.

NOTE: Fast idle thermovalve is factory adjusted and should not be disassembled.

Fast Idle Thermovalve – 1) Fast idle thermovalve opens an air passage, which by-passes throttle plate. This allows more air for a fast idle speed. Coolant warms thermovalve and closes air passage. Ensure fast idle thermovalve is closed when engine is at operating temperature.

2) To check fast idle thermovalve, remove air hose from pipe to thermovalve. Start engine. With coolant temperature less than 86°F (30°C) and engine at idle, vacuum should be present at pipe to thermovalve. If vacuum is not present, replace fast idle thermovalve and retest.

3) Warm engine until cooling fan comes on. Check if thermovalve is completely closed. Vacuum should not be present at pipe to thermovalve. If vacuum is present, check coolant level and for air in coolant system. If coolant system is okay, replace fast idle thermovalve and retest.

Intake Air Control Valve (IACV) – 1) Turn ignition off. Unplug 2-wire connector on IACV. Turn ignition on. Measure voltage between Yellow/Black wire terminal of IACV connector and ground. If battery voltage is not present, repair open in Black/Yellow wire between IACV connector and main relay. If battery voltage is present, go to step 2).

2) Connect ECM test harness connector "A" to main wire harness only. DO NOT connect to ECM. Turn ignition on. Momentarily connect and disconnect jumper wire between terminals A9 and A23 on Integra, or between terminals A9 and A26 on Legend and Vigor. See Fig. 1. If IACV clicks, substitute a known-good IACV and recheck symptom. If IACV does not click, check Black/Blue wire (Integra and Vigor) or Blue/Red wire (Legend) between IACV and ECM terminal A9. If wire is okay, replace IACV.

Manual Transmission Neutral Switch (Legend) – 1) Connect ECM test harness between ECM and ECM connectors. Turn ignition on. Place transmission in Neutral, and measure voltage between ECM terminals B7 (positive) and A26 (negative). See Fig. 1. If voltage is not about 10 volts, go to step 4). If voltage is about 10 volts, go to next step.

2) Disconnect neutral switch 2-wire connector. Connect jumper wire between White wire terminal and Black wire terminal of neutral switch. Turn ignition on.

3) If voltage is not about 10 volts, replace neutral switch. If voltage is about 10 volts, repair open in White wire between ECM and manual transmission neutral switch or Black wire between neutral switch and ground (located at intake manifold).

4) Shift transmission into a gear. If voltage is about 10 volts, manual transmission neutral switch is okay. If voltage is not about 10 volts, turn ignition off.

5) Disconnect ECM connector "B" from ECM test harness only. DO NOT disconnect from ECM. Turn ignition on. If voltage is now approximately 10 volts, go to next step. If voltage is not approximately 10 volts, substitute a known-good ECM and recheck. If voltage is now about 10 volts, replace original ECM.

6) Reconnect vehicle harness to ECM "B" connector. Unplug neutral switch 2-wire connector, located on side of transmission. Turn ignition on. If voltage is now about 10 volts, replace neutral switch. If voltage is not about 10 volts, repair open in White wire between ECM terminal B7 and neutral switch, or Black wire between neutral switch and ground.

Power Steering Pressure (PSP) Switch Signal (Integra & Vigor) – 1) Connect ECM test harness between ECM and vehicle harness connector. Turn ignition on. Measure voltage between ECM terminals B8 (positive) and A26 (negative). *See Fig. 1.* If voltage is less than one volt, go to step **3)**.

2) If voltage is greater than one volt, unplug 2-wire connector on PSP switch located on power steering pump. Connect jumper between Green (Integra) or Red and Black wire terminals. If less than one volt is present, replace PSP switch. If voltage is greater than one volt, repair open in Green (Integra) or Red (Vigor) wire (between ECM terminal B8 and PSP switch) or Black wire and ground connection.

3) Start engine. Turn steering wheel slowly. Measure voltage between ECM terminals B8 (positive) and A26 (negative) while wheel is being turned. If battery voltage exists, PSP signal is okay. If battery voltage is not present, go to next step.

4) Turn ignition off. Unplug PSP switch connector. If voltage is present, replace PSP switch. If voltage is not present, repair short in Green (Integra) or Red (Vigor) wire between ECM terminal B8 and PSP switch.

Power Steering Pressure (PSP) Switch Signal (Legend) – 1) Connect ECM test harness between ECM and ECM connectors. Measure voltage between terminals B5 (positive) and D22 (negative). If voltage is less than one volt, go to step **3)**. If battery voltage exists, disconnect 2-wire connector on PSP switch located on power steering pump. Connect jumper between Green and Green/White wire terminals.

2) If battery voltage is present, replace PSP switch. If less than one volt is present, repair open in Green wire (between ECM terminal B5 and PSP switch) or Green/White wire leading to ECM terminal D22.

3) Start engine. Turn steering wheel slowly. Measure voltage between ECM test harness terminals B5 (positive) and D22 (negative) while wheel is being turned. If battery voltage exists, PSP signal is okay.

4) If battery voltage is not present, disconnect ECM test harness connector "B" to main wire harness only. DO NOT disconnect from ECM. Turn ignition on. If 12 volts is not present, try a known-good ECM. If problem goes away, replace ECM.

5) If battery voltage exists, reconnect connector "B" to main harness. Unplug connector from PSP switch. Check Green wire for battery voltage. If battery voltage is present, replace P/S oil pressure switch. If battery voltage is not present, repair short in Green wire between ECM terminal B5 and PSP switch.

Starter Signal (Integra) – Connect ECM test harness between ECM and harness connector. Measure voltage on ECM test harness terminals B9 (positive) and A26 (negative) with ignition switch in START position. *See Fig. 1.* If battery voltage is present, starter signal is okay. If voltage is not present, inspect fuse No. 18. If fuse is okay, repair open in Blue/White wire between ECM and fuse No. 18.

Starter Signal (Legend) – Connect ECM test harness between ECM and ECM connectors. Check voltage on ECM test harness terminals C11 (positive) and A26 (negative) with ignition switch in ON position. *See Fig. 1.* If battery voltage is present, starter signal is okay. If voltage is not present, inspect fuse No. 14. If fuse is okay, repair open in Black/White wire between ECM and fuse No. 14.

Starter Signal (Vigor) – Connect ECM test harness between ECM and harness connector. Measure voltage on ECM test harness terminals B9 (positive) and A26 (negative) with ignition switch in START position. *See Fig. 1.* If battery voltage is present, starter signal is okay. If voltage is not present, inspect fuse No. 9. If fuse is okay, repair open in Blue/Red wire between ECM and fuse No. 9.

Starting Air Valve (Legend) – Testing information is not available from the manufacturer.

IGNITION SYSTEM

NOTE: For basic ignition checks, see BASIC DIAGNOSTIC PROCEDURES article.

TIMING CONTROL SYSTEM

Ignition Timing Adjuster (Legend & Vigor) – 1) Unplug ignition timing adjuster 3-pin connector. On Legend, ignition timing adjuster is located next to control box on firewall. *See Fig. 10.* On Vigor, ignition timing adjuster is located on left side of engine compartment, outboard of fuel injector resistor. *See Fig. 10.* Measure resistance between "A" and "C" terminals of ignition timing adjuster.

2) Resistance should be 3500-6500 ohms. If resistance is as specified, go to step **3)**. If resistance is not as specified, replace ignition timing adjuster.

3) Measure and record resistance between "A" and "B" terminals on timing adjuster side of harness. Measure and record resistance between "B" and "C" terminals on same side of connector. Add resistance values together. If total of resistance values is not 3500-6500 ohms, replace ignition timing adjuster.

Knock Sensors – See SELF-DIAGNOSTICS.

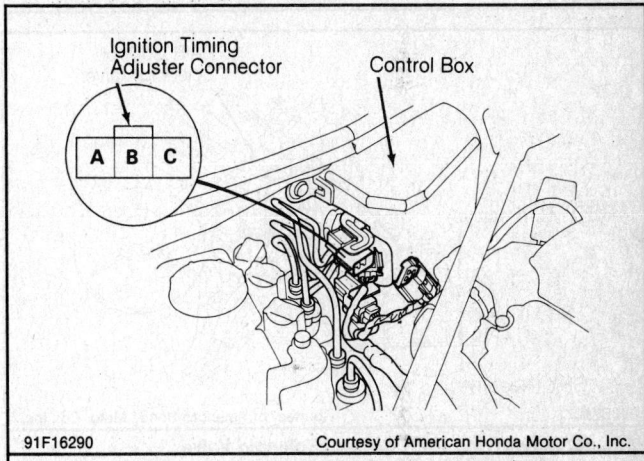

91F16290 Courtesy of American Honda Motor Co., Inc.

Fig. 10: Identifying Ignition Timing Adjuster Connector (Legend Shown; Vigor Similar)

EMISSION SYSTEMS & SUB-SYSTEMS

AIR INJECTION (LEGEND L & LS SEDAN)

Pulsed Secondary Air Injection (PAIR) System – 1) PAIR valve is located at top rear of engine. Check all vacuum hose routing. Start and warm engine until cooling fan comes on. Disconnect vacuum hose No. 7 from PAIR valve. *See Fig. 11.* Connect vacuum gauge to hose.

2) If no vacuum is present, go to step **3)**. If vacuum is present, disconnect 6-wire connector at PAIR control solenoid, located at right front of engine compartment. *See Fig. 12.* If vacuum is still present, replace PAIR control solenoid. If vacuum goes away, check for short in Gray wire between 6-pin connector and ECM terminal A17. If wire is okay, substitute a known-good ECM and retest. If problem goes away, replace ECM.

3) Block rear wheels. Raise and support front of vehicle. Start engine. Place transmission in 2nd gear (M/T) or in "2" (A/T). Check for vacuum during deceleration from greater than 9 MPH and 1500 RPM. If vacuum is present, go to step **6)**.

4) If no vacuum is present, turn ignition off. Unplug 6-wire connector at PAIR control solenoid. Start engine. Connect voltmeter to Black/Yellow (positive) and Gray (negative) wire terminals of PAIR control solenoid valve. Observe voltmeter reading during deceleration from greater than 9 MPH and 1500 RPM. If voltage is present, replace PAIR control solenoid valve. If voltage is not present, go to next step.

1994 ENGINE PERFORMANCE
System & Component Testing (Cont.)

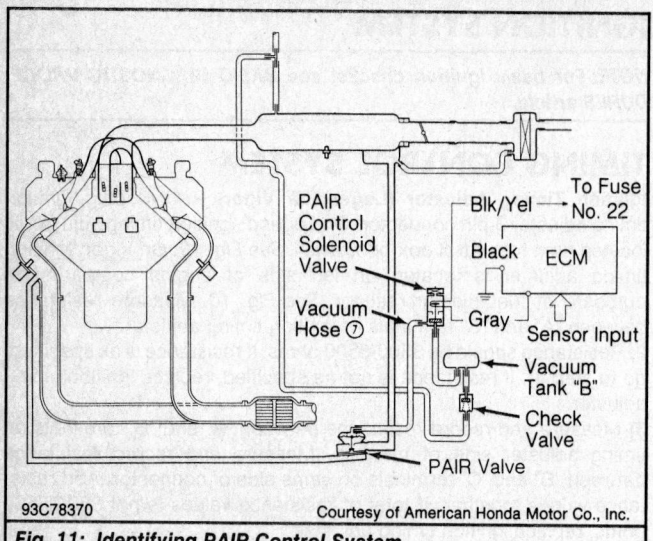

**Fig. 11: Identifying PAIR Control System
(Legend L & LS Sedan)**

93C78370   Courtesy of American Honda Motor Co., Inc.

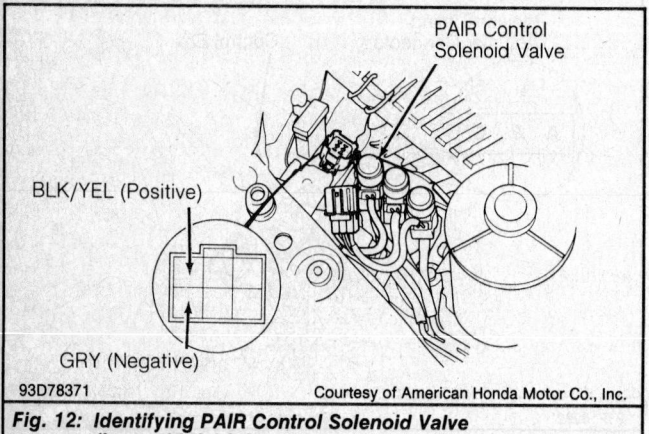

**Fig. 12: Identifying PAIR Control Solenoid Valve
(Legend L & LS Sedan)**

93D78371   Courtesy of American Honda Motor Co., Inc.

5) Check Black/Yellow wire (between connector and fuse No. 22) and Gray wire (between connector and ECM terminal A17) for opens or shorts. If no problems are found, substitute a known-good ECM and retest. If problem goes away, replace ECM.

6) Connect vacuum hose No. 7. Check for suction noise from PAIR valve during operation at speeds greater than 9 MPH and 1500 RPM. If suction noise is not present, replace PAIR valve. If suction noise is present, system is okay.

FUEL EVAPORATION

Charcoal Canister – Connect vacuum gauge to canister purge air hose located at bottom of canister. Start engine, and increase engine speed to 3500 RPM. Vacuum gauge should indicate 0-4 in. Hg within one minute. If reading is not as specified, replace charcoal canister.

Purge Control Solenoid Valve (Integra) – **1)** Purge control solenoid valve is located on left side of firewall. Ensure coolant temperature is less than 165°F (74°C). Remove vacuum hose No. 7 from purge control diaphragm valve, located on top of canister. Attach vacuum gauge to hose. Start and idle engine. If vacuum is not present, go to step **3)**. If vacuum is present, go to next step.

2) Unplug connector from purge control solenoid valve. Measure voltage between harness terminals of Black/Yellow wire (positive) and Red wire (negative). If battery voltage is present, check vacuum hose for leaks or obstruction. If hose is okay, replace purge control solenoid valve. If battery voltage is not present, check Black/Yellow wire between connector and main relay, and Red wire between ECM terminal A20 and connector. If wires are okay, substitute a known-good ECM and retest.

3) Warm engine until cooling fan comes on. Check for vacuum. If vacuum is present, go to step **5)**. If vacuum is not present, unplug connector from purge control solenoid valve. If vacuum is now present, go to next step. If vacuum is not present, check vacuum hose. If hose is okay, replace purge control solenoid valve.

4) Check Black/Yellow wire between connector and main relay, and Red wire between ECM terminal A20 and connector. If wires are okay, substitute a known-good ECM and retest.

5) Reconnect hose. Remove fuel filler cap. Connect vacuum gauge to canister purge line. Start and operate engine at 3000 RPM. If vacuum does not appear within one minute, replace canister. If vacuum appears within one minute, purge control solenoid valve is okay. Go to 2-WAY VALVE procedure.

Purge Control Solenoid Valve (Legend) – **1)** Purge control solenoid valve is located on left side of firewall. Ensure coolant temperature is less than 165°F (74°C). Remove vacuum hose No. 6 from purge control diaphragm valve, located on top of canister. Attach vacuum gauge to hose. Start and idle engine. If vacuum is not present, go to step **3)**. If vacuum is present, go to next step.

2) Unplug connector from purge control solenoid valve. Measure voltage between harness terminals of Black/Yellow wire (positive) and Light Green wire (negative). If battery voltage is present, check vacuum hose for leaks or obstruction. If hose is okay, replace purge control solenoid valve. If battery voltage is not present, check Black/Yellow wire between connector and fuel pump fuse No. 22, and Light Green wire between ECM terminal A20 and connector. If wires are okay, substitute a known-good ECM and retest.

3) Warm engine until cooling fan comes on. Check for vacuum. If vacuum is present, go to step **5)**. If vacuum is not present, unplug connector from purge control solenoid valve. If vacuum is now present, go to next step. If vacuum is not present, check vacuum hose. If hose is okay, replace purge control solenoid valve.

4) Check Black/Yellow wire between connector and fuel pump fuse No. 22, and Light Green wire between ECM terminal A20 and connector. If wires are okay, substitute a known-good ECM and retest.

5) Reconnect hose. Remove fuel filler cap. Connect vacuum gauge to canister purge line. Start and operate engine at 3500 RPM. If vacuum does not appear within one minute, replace canister. If vacuum appears within one minute, purge control solenoid valve is okay. Go to 2-WAY VALVE procedure.

Purge Control Solenoid Valve (Vigor) – **1)** Purge control solenoid valve is located on left side of firewall. Ensure coolant temperature is less than 165°F (74°C). Remove vacuum hose No. 3 from purge control diaphragm valve, located on top of canister. Attach vacuum gauge to hose. Start and idle engine. If vacuum is present, go to next step.

2) Unplug connector from purge control solenoid valve. Measure voltage between harness terminals of Black/Yellow wire (positive) and Orange wire (negative). If battery voltage is present, check vacuum hose for leaks or obstruction. If hose is okay, replace purge control solenoid valve. If battery voltage is not present, check Black/Yellow wire between connector and fuse No. 2, and Orange wire between ECM terminal A10 and connector. If wires are okay, substitute a known-good ECM and retest.

3) Warm engine until cooling fan comes on. Check for vacuum. If vacuum is present, go to step **5)**. If vacuum is not present, unplug connector from purge control solenoid valve. If vacuum is now present, go to next step. If vacuum is not present, check vacuum hose. If hose is okay, replace purge control solenoid valve.

4) Check Black/Yellow wire between connector and fuse No. 2, and Orange wire between ECM terminal A10 and connector. If wires are okay, substitute a known-good ECM and retest.

5) Reconnect hose. Remove fuel filler cap. Connect vacuum gauge to canister purge line. Start and operate engine at 3500 RPM. If vacuum does not appear within one minute, replace canister. If vacuum appears within one minute, purge control solenoid valve is okay. Go to 2-WAY VALVE procedure.

2-Way Valve – **1)** Remove fuel filler cap. See Fig. 13, 14 or 15. Remove vapor hose from fuel tank side of 2-way valve, and install "T" fitting. Connect vacuum gauge to "T" fitting and vacuum pump to hose end.

2) Slowly apply vacuum while observing vacuum gauge. Vacuum should stabilize momentarily between .2 and .6 in. Hg. If vacuum does not stabilize (valve opens) in specified range, replace 2-way valve and retest.

3) Move vacuum hose from vacuum to pressure fitting side of vacuum pump. Slowly pressurize vapor line while observing gauge. If pressure stabilizes between .4 and 1.4 in. Hg, valve is okay. If pressure does not stabilize in specified range, replace 2-way valve, and retest.

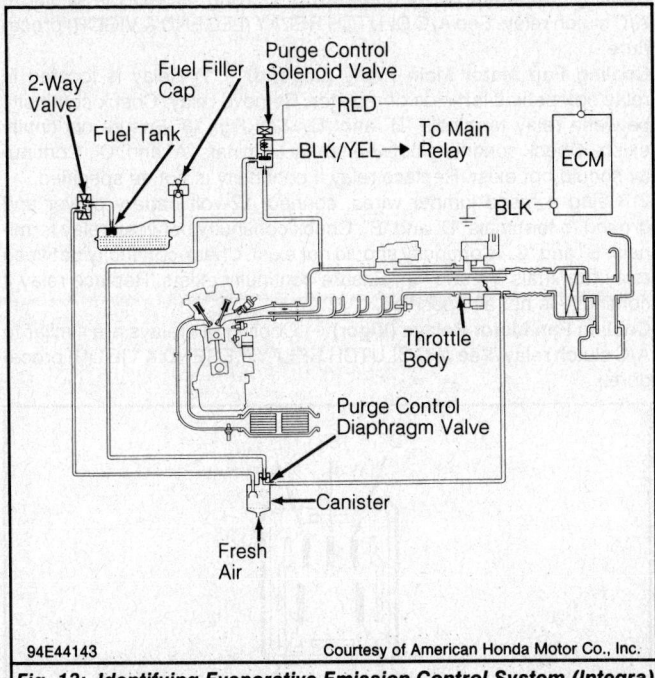

Fig. 13: Identifying Evaporative Emission Control System (Integra)

Courtesy of American Honda Motor Co., Inc.

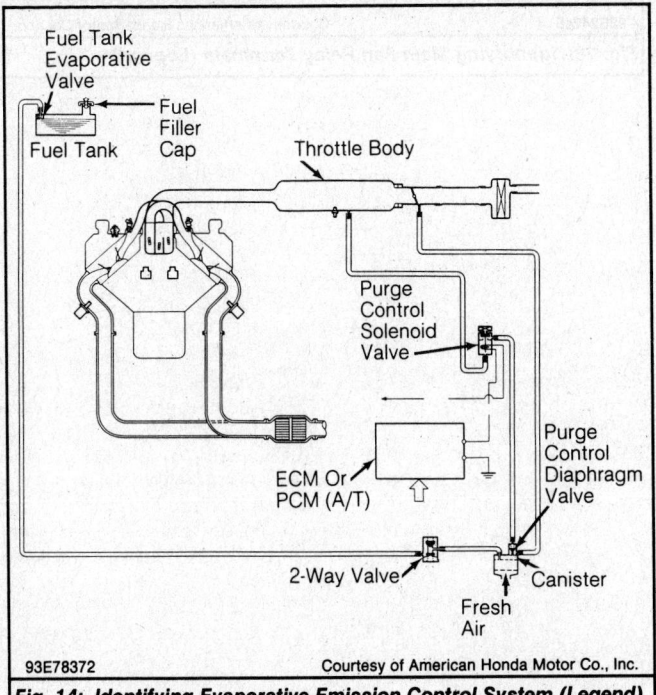

Fig. 14: Identifying Evaporative Emission Control System (Legend)

Courtesy of American Honda Motor Co., Inc.

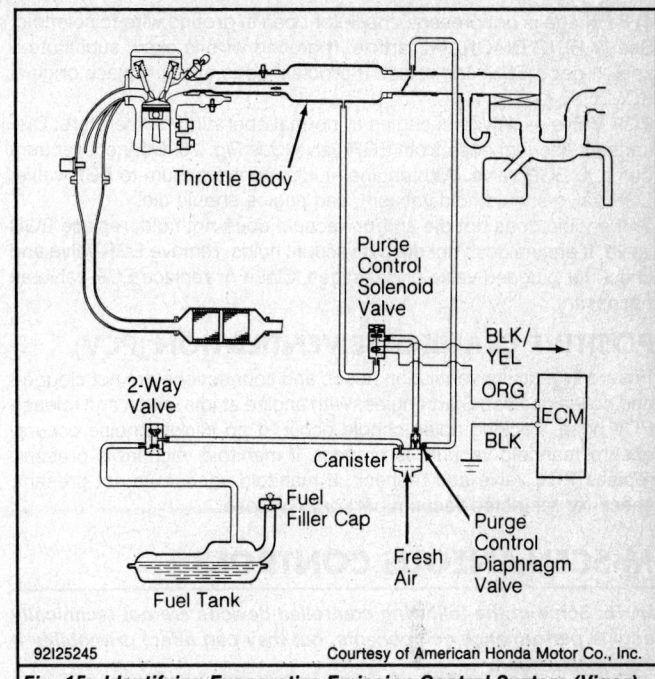

Fig. 15: Identifying Evaporative Emission Control System (Vigor)

Courtesy of American Honda Motor Co., Inc.

EXHAUST GAS RECIRCULATION (EGR)

Constant Vacuum Control (CVC) – Start engine. Verify manifold vacuum is present at CVC valve, located inside control box on firewall. Disconnect CVC vacuum hose at EGR control solenoid. Connect vacuum gauge. If vacuum is not about 8 in. Hg, replace CVC valve.

EGR Control Solenoid Valve – **1)** Disconnect vacuum hose at EGR valve. See Fig. 16. Connect vacuum gauge to hose. Warm engine until cooling fan comes on. On Legend, raise drive wheel, engage drive gear and increase engine speed to 1700-2500 RPM. On Integra and Vigor, increase engine speed to about 3000 RPM. On all models, observe vacuum gauge. If vacuum is present, solenoid is okay. If vacuum is not present, go to step **2)**.

2) Disconnect connector from EGR control solenoid valve. Turn ignition on. Connect voltmeter negative lead to ground. Backprobe Black/Yellow wire terminal at connector. If voltage is not present, check for blown fuse or open or short in EGR control solenoid Black/Yellow power supply wire.

3) If voltage is present, increase engine speed to about 3000 RPM. Check for voltage across solenoid terminals. If voltage exists but vacuum is not present, check for restricted hose. If hose is okay, replace defective solenoid.

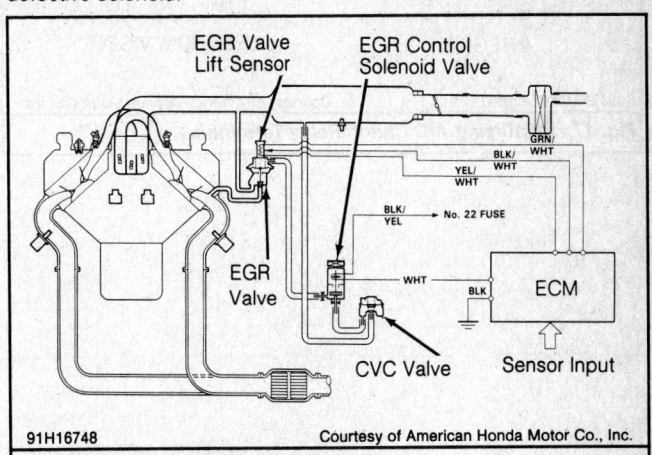

*Fig. 16: Identifying EGR System
(Legend Shown & Vigor Similar)*

Courtesy of American Honda Motor Co., Inc.

4) If voltage is not present, check for open in ground wire to solenoid. See WIRING DIAGRAMS article. If ground wire is okay, substitute a known-good ECM and retest. If problem goes away, replace original ECM.

EGR Valve – 1) Warm engine to normal operating temperature. Disconnect vacuum hose from EGR valve. *See Fig. 16*. Connect vacuum pump to EGR valve. With engine at idle, apply vacuum to EGR valve. EGR valve should hold vacuum, and engine should die.

2) If engine does not die and/or vacuum does not hold, replace EGR valve. If engine does not die but vacuum holds, remove EGR valve and check for plugged valve or passages. Clean or replace EGR valve as necessary.

POSITIVE CRANKCASE VENTILATION (PCV)

Ensure crankcase ventilation hoses and connections are not clogged and no leaks exist. Start engine. With engine at idle, pinch and release PCV hose. Clicking noise should occur. If no clicking noise occurs, ensure manifold vacuum is present. If manifold vacuum is present, replace PCV valve and recheck. If manifold vacuum is not present, check for restricted vacuum port or PCV hose.

MISCELLANEOUS CONTROLS

NOTE: Some of the following controlled devices are not technically engine performance components, but they can affect driveability if they malfunction.

A/C CLUTCH

A/C Clutch Relay (Integra) – Relay is located above compressor. Remove relay. Check continuity between terminals No. 1 and 3. *See Fig. 17*. If continuity exists, replace relay. Using jumper wires, connect 12-volt battery power and ground to terminals No. 2 and 4. Continuity should exist between terminals No. 1 and 3. If continuity is not present, replace relay.

A/C Clutch Relay (Legend & Vigor) – Relay is located in relay block, at right rear of engine compartment. Remove relay. Check continuity between terminals "A" and "B". *See Fig. 17*. If continuity exists, replace relay. Using fused jumper wires, connect 12-volt battery power and ground to terminals "C" and "D". Continuity should exist between terminals "A" and "B". If continuity is not present, replace relay.

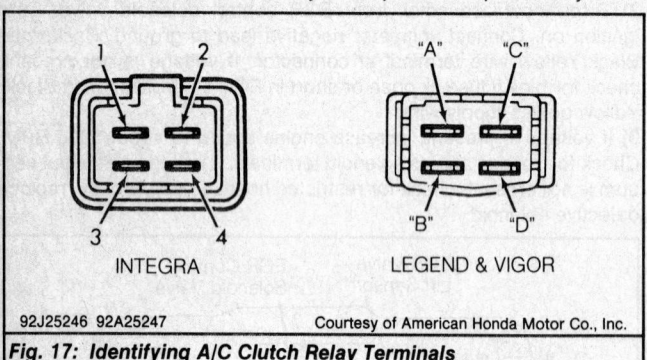

92J25246 92A25247   Courtesy of American Honda Motor Co., Inc.

Fig. 17: Identifying A/C Clutch Relay Terminals

COOLING FAN

Cooling Fan Motor – Unplug connector from fan motor. Connect Black wire terminal to body ground. Using a fused jumper wire, connect White/Blue wire terminal to positive battery terminal. Replace motor if it does not run.

Cooling Fan Motor Relay (Integra) – Cooling fan relay is similar to A/C clutch relay. See A/C CLUTCH RELAY (INTEGRA) procedure.

Cooling Fan Motor Relay (Legend) – Cooling fan relay is similar to A/C clutch relay. See A/C CLUTCH RELAY (LEGEND & VIGOR) procedure.

Cooling Fan Motor Main Relay (Legend) – 1) Relay is located in relay box behind left side of radiator. Remove relay. Check continuity between relay terminals "B" and "C". *See Fig. 18*. Ensure continuity exists. Check continuity between relay terminals "A" and "C". Continuity should not exist. Replace relay if continuity is not as specified.

2) Using a fused jumper wires, connect 12-volt battery power and ground to terminals "D" and "E". Check continuity between relay terminals "B" and "C." Continuity should not exist. Check continuity between relay terminals "A" and "C." Ensure continuity exists. Replace relay if continuity is not as specified.

Cooling Fan Motor Relays (Vigor) – Cooling fan relays are similar to A/C clutch relay. See A/C CLUTCH RELAY (LEGEND & VIGOR) procedure.

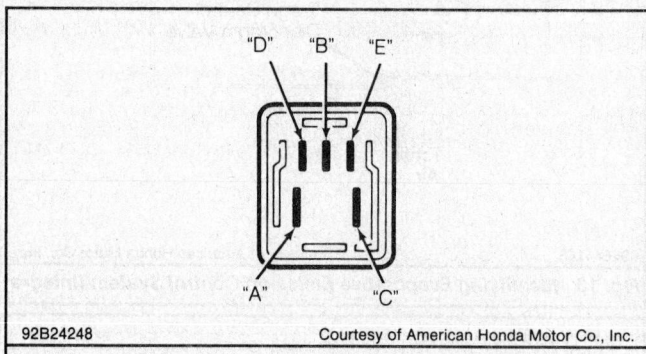

92B24248   Courtesy of American Honda Motor Co., Inc.

Fig. 18: Identifying Main Fan Relay Terminals (Legend)

Integra, Legend, Vigor

INTRODUCTION

NOTE: Unless stated otherwise in testing procedures, perform all voltage tests using a Digital Volt-Ohmmeter (DVOM) with a minimum 10-megohm input impedance. Voltage readings may vary slightly due to battery condition or charging rate.

Pin voltage charts are supplied to reduce diagnostic time. Checking pin voltages at the Programmed Fuel Injection Engine Control Module (PGM-FI ECM) determines whether it is receiving and transmitting proper voltage signals. Diagnostic charts may also help determine if ECM harness is shorted or open. *See Figs. 1-14.*

Wire Color	Terminal ID.	Function/Description	Voltage Value (DC Volts Unless Otherwise Specified)
Brown	A1	Injector No. 1	Battery Voltage With KOEO [1]
Yellow	A2	Injector No. 4	Battery Voltage With KOEO [1]
Red	A3	Injector No. 2	Battery Voltage With KOEO [1]
Green/Yellow	A4	VTEC Solenoid	N/A
Light Blue	A5	Injector No. 3	Battery Voltage With KOEO [1]
Orange/Black	A6	Oxygen Sensor Heater	Battery Voltage With KOEO [1]
Green/Blue	A7	Fuel Pump Relay	Battery Voltage For 2 Sec. After KOEO [1]
	A8	BLANK	N/A
Black/Blue	A9	Idle Air Control Valve (IACV)	N/A
	A10	BLANK	N/A
	A11	BLANK	N/A
Green	A12	Radiator Fan relay	N/A
Green/Orange	A13	MIL (CHECK ENGINE) Light	Battery Voltage With KOEO [1]
	A14	BLANK	N/A
Black/Red	A15	A/C Clutch Relay	Battery Voltage With KOEO [1]
White/Green	A16	Alternator	N/A
Pink/Blue	A17	Intake Air By-Pass Solenoid	N/A
	A18	BLANK	N/A
	A19	BLANK	N/A
Red	A20	Purge Control Solenoid Valve	Battery Voltage With KOEO [1]
Yellow/Green	A21	Ignitor	Battery Voltage With KOEO [1]
	A22	BLANK	N/A
Black	A23	Power Ground	Less Than One Volt With KOEO [1]
Black	A24	Power Ground	Less Than One Volt With KOEO [1]
Yellow/Black	A25	Fuel Pump Relay	Battery Voltage With KOEO [1]
Brown/Black	A26	Shield Ground	Less Than One Volt With KOEO [1]

[1] – KOEO – Key On, Engine Off.

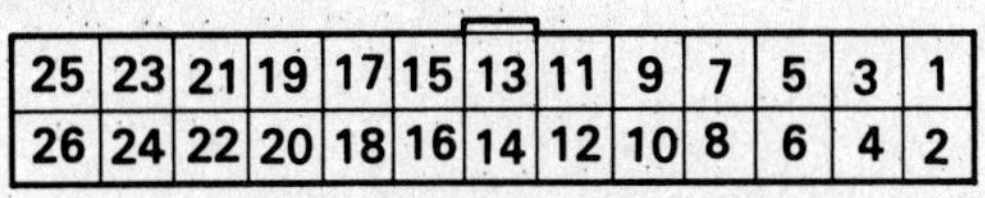

```
| 25 | 23 | 21 | 19 | 17 | 15 | 13 | 11 | 9 | 7 | 5 | 3 | 1 |
| 26 | 24 | 22 | 20 | 18 | 16 | 14 | 12 | 10 | 8 | 6 | 4 | 2 |
```

CONNECTOR "A"
VIEWED FROM HARNESS SIDE

94G44202

Courtesy of American Honda Motor Co., Inc.

Fig. 1: Identifying Connector "A" Terminals & Pin Voltage Chart (Integra 1.8L GS-R)

1994 ENGINE PERFORMANCE
Pin Voltage Charts (Cont.)

Yellow/Black

Brown/Black

Blue/Red

Green

Blue/White

Orange

Orange

White

Orange/Blue

White/Blue

Blue/Green

Blue/Yellow

Terminal ID.	Function/Description	Voltage Value (DC Volts Unless Otherwise Specified)
B1	Fuel Pump Relay	Battery Voltage With KOEO [1]
B2	Ground	Less Than One Volt [1]
B3	BLANK	N/A
B4	BLANK	N/A
B5	A/C Switch	5 Volt With KOEO [1]; .1 Volt With A/C On
B6	BLANK	N/A
B7	BLANK	N/A
B8	Oil Pressure Switch	N/A
B9	Fuel Pump Relay	Battery Voltage With Key In START
B10	Vehicle Speed Sensor	Zero & 10 Volts As Left Front Wheel Rotates
B11	CYL Sensor "P"	N/A
B12	CYL Sensor "M"	N/A
B13	TDC Sensor "P"	N/A
B14	TDC Sensor "M"	N/A
B15	CRANK Sensor "P"	N/A
B16	CRANK Sensor "M"	N/A

[1] – KOEO – Key On, Engine Off.

15	13	11	9	7	5	3	1
16	14	12	10	8	6	4	2

CONNECTOR "B"
VIEWED FROM HARNESS SIDE

94H44203

Courtesy of American Honda Motor Co., Inc.

Fig. 2: Identifying Connector "B" Terminals & Pin Voltage Chart (Integra 1.8L GS-R)

	Terminal ID.	Function/Description	Voltage Value (DC Volts Unless Otherwise Specified)
White/Blue →	D1	Vehicle Power	Battery Voltage At All Times
Green/White →	D2	Brake Signal	Battery Voltage With Brake Applied
Red/Blue →	D3	Knock Sensor	N/A
Brown/White →	D4	Service Check Connector	N/A
	D5	BLANK	N/A
Blue/Black →	D6	VTEC Pressure Switch	N/A
Light Blue →	D7	Data Link Connector	N/A
	D8	BLANK	N/A
White/Red →	D9	Alternator	Voltage Decreases When Lights Turned On
Green/Red →	D10	Electric Load Detector	Voltage Decreases When Lights Turned On
Red/Blue →	D11	Throttle Position Sensor	.5 Volt Closed; 4.5 Volts Open
Red/White →	D12	BLANK	N/A
	D13	Engine Coolant Temperature Sensor	N/A
White/Red →	D14	Oxygen Sensor	.4-.5 Volt When Ignition Is First Turned On, Decreasing To Less Than .1 Volt In Less Than 2 Minutes
Red/Yellow →	D15	Intake Air Temperature (TA) Sensor	N/A
	D16	BLANK	N/A
White/Yellow →	D17	MAP Sensor	3-5 Volts Depending On Atmospheric Pressure
	D18	BLANK	N/A
Yellow/White →	D19	MAP Sensor Reference	Approximately 5 Volts
Yellow/White →	D20	Throttle Position Sensor Reference	5 Volts
Green/White →	D21	MAP Sensor Signal Ground	Approximately Zero
Green/Blue →	D22	Signal Ground	Approximately Zero

21	19	17	15	13	11	9	7	5	3	1
22	20	18	16	14	12	10	8	6	4	2

CONNECTOR "D"
VIEWED FROM HARNESS SIDE

94I44204

Fig. 3: Identifying Connector "D" Terminals & Pin Voltage Chart (Integra 1.8L GS-R)

1994 ENGINE PERFORMANCE
Pin Voltage Charts (Cont.)

	Terminal ID.	Function/Description	Voltage Value (DC Volts Unless Otherwise Specified)
Brown →	A1	Injector No. 1	Battery Voltage With KOEO [1]
Yellow →	A2	Injector No. 4	Battery Voltage With KOEO [1]
Red →	A3	Injector No. 2	Battery Voltage With KOEO [1]
	A4	BLANK	N/A
Light Blue →	A5	Injector No. 3	Battery Voltage With KOEO [1]
Orange/Black →	A6	Oxygen Sensor Heater	Battery Voltage With KOEO [1]
Green/Black →	A7	Fuel Pump Relay	12 Volts For 2 Seconds After KOEO [1]
	A8	BLANK	N/A
Black/Blue →	A9	Idle Air Control Valve (IACV)	N/A
	A10	BLANK	N/A
	A11	BLANK	N/A
Green →	A12	Radiator Fan Relay	N/A
Green/Orange →	A13	MIL (CHECK ENGINE) Light	Battery Voltage With KOEO [1]
	A14	BLANK	N/A
Black/Red →	A15	A/C Clutch Relay	Battery Voltage With KOEO [1]
White/Green →	A16	Alternator	N/A
	A17	BLANK	N/A
	A18	BLANK	N/A
Yellow/Red →	A19	TCM	N/A
Green →	A20	Purge Control Solenoid Valve	Battery Voltage With KOEO [1]
Yellow/Green →	A21	Ignitor	Battery Voltage With KOEO [1]
	A22	BLANK	N/A
Black →	A23	Power Ground	Less Than One Volt With KOEO [1]
Black →	A24	Power Ground	Less Than One Volt With KOEO [1]
Yellow/Black →	A25	Fuel Pump Relay	Battery Voltage With KOEO [1]
Brown/Black →	A26	Shield Ground	Less Than One Volt With KOEO [1]

[1] – KOEO – Key On, Engine Off.

25	23	21	19	17	15	13	11	9	7	5	3	1
26	24	22	20	18	16	14	12	10	8	6	4	2

CONNECTOR "A"
VIEWED FROM HARNESS SIDE

94J44205

Courtesy of American Honda Motor Co., Inc.

Fig. 4: Identifying Connector "A" Terminals & Pin Voltage Chart (Integra 1.8L Except GS-R)

	Terminal ID.	Function/Description	Voltage Value (DC Volts Unless Otherwise Specified)
Yellow/Black →	B1	Fuel Pump Relay	Battery Voltage With KOEO [1]
Brown/Black →	B2	Ground	Less Than One Volt [1]
Green/Blue →	B3	A/T Signal TCM	N/A
Gray →	B4	A/T Siganl TCM	N/A
Blue/Red →	B5	A/C Switch	5 Volt KOEO [1]; .1 Volt A/C On
Green/Black →	B6	BLANK	N/A
Light Green →	B7	Park/Neutral Signal (A/T)	N/A
Blue/White →	B8	Oil Pressure Switch	N/A
Orange →	B9	Fuel Pump Relay	12 Volts With Switch In START Position
Orange →	B10	Vehicle Speed Sensor	Zero & 10 Volts As Left Front Wheel Rotates
White →	B11	CYL Sensor "P"	N/A
Orange/Blue →	B12	CYL Sensor "M"	N/A
White/Blue →	B13	TDC Sensor "P"	N/A
Blue/Green →	B14	TDC Sensor "M"	N/A
Blue/Yellow →	B15	CRANK Sensor "P"	N/A
	B16	CRANK Sensor "M"	N/A

[1] – KOEO – Key On, Engine Off.

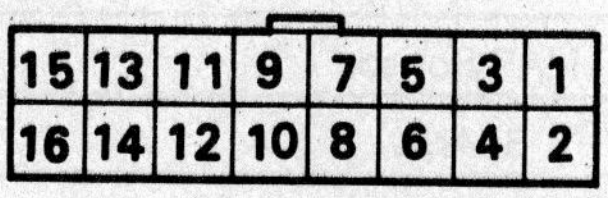

| 15 | 13 | 11 | 9 | 7 | 5 | 3 | 1 |
| 16 | 14 | 12 | 10 | 8 | 6 | 4 | 2 |

CONNECTOR "B"
VIEWED FROM HARNESS SIDE

94A44206

Courtesy of American Honda Motor Co., Inc.

Fig. 5: Identifying Connector "B" Terminals & Pin Voltage Chart (Integra 1.8L Except GS-R)

1994 ENGINE PERFORMANCE
Pin Voltage Charts (Cont.)

	Terminal ID.	Function/Description	Voltage Value (DC Volts Unless Otherwise Specified)
White/Blue →	D1	Battery Power	Battery Voltage At All Times
Green/White →	D2	Brake Signal	Battery Voltage With Brake Applied
	D3	BLANK	N/A
Brown/White →	D4	Service Check Connector	N/A
	D5	BLANK	N/A
	D6	BLANK	N/A
Light Blue →	D7	Data Link Connector	N/A
Light Green →	D8	TCM (A/T)	N/A
White/Red →	D9	Alternator	Voltage Drops When Lights Turned On
Green/Red →	D10	Electric Load Detector	Voltage Drops When Lights Turned On
Red/Blue →	D11	Throttle Position Sensor	.5 Volt Closed; 4.5 Volts Open
	D12	BLANK	N/A
Red/White →	D13	Engine Coolant Temperature Sensor	N/A
White/Red →	D14	Oxygen Sensor	.4-.5 Volt When Ignition Is First Turned On, Decreasing To Less Than .1 Volt In Less Than 2 Minutes
Red/Yellow →	D15	Intake Air Temperature (TA) Sensor	N/A
White/Black →	D16	TCM (A/T)	N/A
White/Yellow →	D17	MAP Sensor	3-5 Volts Depending On Atmospheric Pressure
	D18	BLANK	N/A
Yellow/Red →	D19	MAP Sensor Reference	Approximately 5 Volts
Yellow/Blue →	D20	Throttle Position Sensor Reference	5 Volts
Green/White →	D21	MAP Sensor Signal Ground	Approximately Zero
Green/Blue →	D22	Signal Ground	Approximately Zero

21	19	17	15	13	11	9	7	5	3	1
22	20	18	16	14	12	10	8	6	4	2

CONNECTOR "D"
VIEWED FROM HARNESS SIDE

94B44207

Courtesy of American Honda Motor Co., Inc.

Fig. 6: Identifying Connector "D" Terminals & Pin Voltage Chart (Integra 1.8L Except GS-R)

	Terminal ID.	Function/Description	Voltage Value (DC Volts Unless Otherwise Specified)
Brown	A1	Injector No. 1	Battery Voltage With KOEO [1]
White/Blue	A2	Injector No. 4	Battery Voltage With KOEO [1]
Red	A3	Injector No. 2	Battery Voltage With KOEO [1]
Black/Red	A4	Injector No. 5	Battery Voltage With KOEO [1]
Orange	A5	Injector No. 3	Battery Voltage With KOEO [1]
Yellow	A6	Injector No. 6	Battery Voltage With KOEO [1]
Green/Black	A7	Fuel Pump Relay	N/A
Red/White	A8	M/T Reverse Lock-Out Relay	N/A
Blue/Red	A9	Electronic Air Control Valve	Battery Voltage With KOEO [1]
Green/Blue	A10	Left Oxygen Sensor Heater Circuit	Battery Voltage With KOEO [1]
White	A11	EGR Control Solenoid Valve	N/A
Green/Red	A12	Right Oxygen Sensor Heater Circuit	Battery Voltage With KOEO [1]
Blue	A13	MIL (CHECK ENGINE) Light Circuit	N/A
Red/Blue	A14	By-Pass Low Control Solenoid Valve	Battery Voltage At Idle With KOER [2]
Red/Blue	A15	A/C Clutch Relay ("L" & LS Sedan)	N/A
	A16	BLANK	N/A
Gray	A17	Pulse Air Injection Control Solenoid Valve	N/A
Yellow	A18	By-Pass High Control Solenoid Valve	Battery Voltage At Idle With KOER [2]
Light Green	A19	Pressure Regulator Control Solenoid Valve	N/A
Light Green	A20	Purge Cut-Off Solenoid Valve	N/A
Pink	A21	Ignition Control Module (ICM)	N/A
Brown	A22	Ignition Control Module (ICM)	N/A
Black	A23	Ground	Less Than One Volt
Black	A24	Ground	Less Than One Volt
Yellow/Black	A25	Idle Air Control Valve (IACV)	N/A
Green/Black	A26	Knock Sensor Circuit Ground	Less Than One Volt

[1] – KOEO – Key On, Engine Off.
[2] – KOER – Key On, Engine Running.

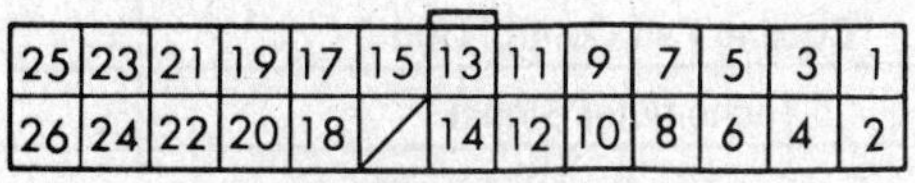

25	23	21	19	17	15	13	11	9	7	5	3	1
26	24	22	20	18	/	14	12	10	8	6	4	2

CONNECTOR "A"
VIEWED FROM HARNESS SIDE

94A44230

Courtesy of American Honda Motor Co., Inc.

Fig. 7: Identifying Connector "A" Terminals & Pin Voltage Chart (Legend)

	Terminal ID.	Function/Description	Voltage Value (DC Volts Unless Otherwise Specified)
Brown/Black	B1	BLANK	N/A
Red	B2	Ground	Less Than One Volt
Gray	B3	Ignition Control Module (ICM)	N/A
Green	B4	Ignition Control Module (ICM)	N/A
	B5	Power Steering Pressure Switch Signal	Less Than Battery Voltage With Front Wheels Straight Ahead; Battery Voltage While Slowly Turning Steering Wheel With KOER [1]
Green	B6	Ignition Control Module (ICM)	N/A
Light Green	B7	Park/Neutral Switch (A/T)	Less Than .1 Volt In "N" Or "P"
White	B7	Park/Neutral Switch (M/T)	About 10 Volts In Gear
Blue	B8	Ignition Control Module (ICM)	N/A
Blue/Green	B9	CYL Sensor No. 2 Circuit	N/A
Blue/Yellow	B10	CYL Sensor No. 2 Circuit	N/A
Orange/Blue	B11	CYL Sensor No. 1 Circuit	N/A
White/Blue	B12	CYL Sensor No. 1 Circuit	N/A
Orange	B13	CRANK Sensor No. 2 Circuit	N/A
White	B14	CRANK Sensor No. 2 Circuit	N/A
Orange/Blue	B15	CRANK Sensor No. 1 Circuit	N/A
White/Blue	B16	CRANK Sensor No. 1 Circuit	N/A

[1] – KOER – Key On, Engine Running.

```
15 13 11  9  7  5  3
16 14 12 10  8  6  4  2
```
CONNECTOR "B"
VIEWED FROM HARNESS SIDE

94B44231

Courtesy of American Honda Motor Co., Inc.

Fig. 8: Identifying Connector "B" Terminals & Pin Voltage Chart (Legend)

	Terminal ID.	Function/Description	Voltage Value (DC Volts Unless Otherwise Specified)
Yellow/Black	C1	EGR Valve Lift Sensor Signal	Varies With EGR Valve Operation
Yellow/Red	C2	Vehicle Speed Sensor	Zero & 5 Volts As Left Front Wheel Rotates
Blue/Black	C3	Cooling Fan Control Unit	Less Than .1 Volt With A/C On
Blue	C4	Tachometer Signal	N/A
Red/Blue	C5	Cooling Fan Switch Circuit	N/A
Green/Black	C6	TCM (Coupe & GS Sedan)	N/A
Pink	C7	M/T Clutch Switch	About 10 Volts With Clutch Pedal Down
Gray/Blue	C8	TCM (Coupe & GS Sedan)	N/A
White	C9	Service Check Connector	N/A
	C10	BLANK	N/A
Black/White	C11	Start Signal	Battery Voltage In START Position
Gray/Yellow	C12	TCM (Coupe & GS Sedan)	N/A

[1] – KOEO – Key On, Engine Off.

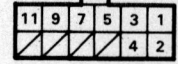

```
11  9  7  5  3  1
      4  2
```
CONNECTOR "C"
VIEWED FROM HARNESS SIDE

94C44232

Courtesy of American Honda Motor Co., Inc.

Fig. 9: Identifying Connector "C" Terminals & Pin Voltage Chart (Legend)

1994 ENGINE PERFORMANCE
Pin Voltage Charts (Cont.)

	Terminal ID.	Function/Description	Voltage Value (DC Volts Unless Otherwise Specified)
Yellow/Blue	D1	Vehicle Power From Fuse No. 15	Battery Voltage At All Times
Green/White	D2	Brake Switch Signal Input	Battery Voltage With Brake Applied KOEO [1]
White	D3	Right Knock Sensor Circuit	N/A
Red/Blue	D4	Left Knock Sensor Circuit	N/A
Orange/Red	D5	TCM (Coupe & GS Sedan)	N/A
	D6	BLANK	N/A
	D7	BLANK	N/A
Blue/Yellow	D8	Ignition Timing Adjuster Connector	.5-4.5 Volt With KOEO [1]
White/Red	D9	Alternator Charging Signal	Voltage Drops With Alt. Under Load
	D10	BLANK	N/A
Red/Blue	D11	Throttle Position Sensor Signal	About .3 Volt With KOEO [1] At Closed Throttle; About 4.5 Volts At WOT
Black/White	D12	EGR Valve Lift Sensor Signal	About 1.2 Volts At Warm Idle
Red/White	D13	Coolant Temperature Sensor Signal	0.5-4.5 Volts (Varies With Temperature)
White	D14	Left Oxygen Sensor Signal	.4-.5 Volt When Ignition Is First Turned On, Decreasing To Less Than .1 Volt In Less Than 2 Minutes
Red/Yellow	D15	Intake Air Temperature Sensor Signal	0.5-4.5 Volts (Varies With Temperature)
Red/Blue	D16	Right Oxygen Sensor Signal	.4-.5 Volt When Ignition Is First Turned On, Decreasing To Less Than .1 Volt In Less Than 2 Minutes
Red	D17	MAP Sensor Signal	3.0-4.5 Volts (Varies With Manifold Pressure)
Blue	D18	TCM (Coupe & GS Sedan)	N/A
Yellow/White	D19	MAP Sensor Power	About 5 Volts With KOEO [1]
Yellow/White	D20	Sensor Power (Except MAP Sensor)	About 5 Volts With KOEO [1]
Green/White	D21	MAP Sensor Ground	Approximately Zero
Green/White	D22	Sensor Ground (Except MAP Sensor)	Approximately Zero

[1] – KOEO – Key On, Engine Off.

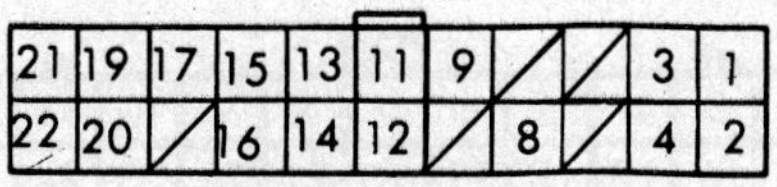
21 19 17 15 13 11 9 3 1
22 20 16 14 12 8 4 2

CONNECTOR "D"
VIEWED FROM HARNESS SIDE

94D44233

Courtesy of American Honda Motor Co., Inc.

Fig. 10: Identifying Connector "D" Terminals & Pin Voltage Chart (Legend)

	Terminal ID.	Function/Description	Voltage Value (DC Volts Unless Otherwise Specified)
Brown	A1	Injector No. 1	Battery Voltage With KOEO [1]
Yellow	A2	Injector No. 4	Battery Voltage With KOEO [1]
Red	A3	Injector No. 2	Battery Voltage With KOEO [1]
Green	A4	Injector No. 5	Battery Voltage With KOEO [1]
Blue	A5	Injector No. 3	Battery Voltage With KOEO [1]
Pink/White	A6	Oxygen Sensor Heater	N/A
Green/Black	A7	Fuel Pump Relay	12 Volts For 2 Seconds After KOEO [1]
Green/Black	A8	Fuel Pump Relay	12 Volts For 2 Seconds After KOEO [1]
Black/Blue	A9	Idle Air Control Valve (IACV)	N/A
Orange	A10	Purge Control Solenoid Valve	Battery Voltage With KOEO [1]
Red	A11	EGR Solenoid Control Valve	Battery Voltage With KOEO [1]
Lt. Green/Yellow	A12	Cooling Fan Control Unit	N/A
Green/Red	A13	MIL (CHECK ENGINE) Light	Battery Voltage With KOEO [1]
	A14	BLANK	N/A
Red/Blue	A15	A/C Clutch Relay	Battery Voltage With KOEO [1]
White/Green	A16	Alternator	N/A
Blue/Red	A17	Intake Air By-Pass Control Solenoid	N/A
Pink	A18	TCM (A/T)	N/A
	A19	BLANK	N/A
	A20	BLANK	N/A
Yellow/Green	A21	Ignition Control Module (ICM)	10 Volts With KOEO [1]
Yellow/Green	A22	Ignition Control Module (ICM)	10 Volts With KOEO [1]
Black	A23	Power Ground	Less Than One Volt With KOEO [1]
Black	A24	Power Ground	Less Than One Volt With KOEO [1]
Yellow/Black	A25	Fuel Pump Relay	Battery Voltage With KOEO [1]
Black/Red	A26	Shield Ground	Approximately Zero

[1] – KOEO – Key On, Engine Off.

CONNECTOR "A"
VIEWED FROM HARNESS SIDE

94D44191

Courtesy of American Honda Motor Co., Inc.

Fig. 11: Identifying Connector "A" Terminals & Pin Voltage Chart (Vigor)

	Terminal ID.	Function/Description	Voltage Value (DC Volts Unless Otherwise Specified)
Yellow/Black	B1	Fuel Pump Relay	Battery Voltage With KOEO [1]
Brown/Black	B2	Ground	Less Than One Volt [1]
White/Green	B3	A/T Control Unit	N/A
White/Red	B4	A/T Control Unit	N/A
Blue/Black	B5	A/C Pressure Switch	10 Volt With KOEO [1]; .1 Volt With A/C On
	B6	BLANK	N/A
Yellow/Green	B7	Park/Neutral Switch	10 Volt In "D"; .1 Volt In "N Or "P"
Red	B8	Power Steering Pressure Switch	N/A
Blue/Red	B9	Start Signal	12 Volts With Switch In START Position
Orange	B10	Vehicle Speed Sensor	Zero & 12 Volts As Left Front Wheel Rotates
Orange	B11	CYL Sensor "P"	N/A
White	B12	CYL Sensor "M"	N/A
Orange/Blue	B13	TDC Sensor "P"	N/A
White/Blue	B14	TDC Sensor "M"	N/A
Blue/Green	B15	CRANK Sensor "P"	N/A
Blue/Yellow	B16	CRANK Sensor "M"	N/A

[1] – KOEO – Key On, Engine Off.

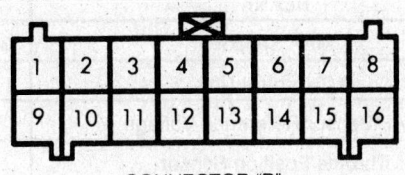

CONNECTOR "B"
VIEWED FROM HARNESS SIDE

94E44192

Courtesy of American Honda Motor Co., Inc.

Fig. 12: Identifying Connector "B" Terminals & Pin Voltage Chart (Vigor)

	Terminal ID.	Function/Description	Voltage Value (DC Volts Unless Otherwise Specified)
Orange/White	C1	Knock Sensor (Rear)	N/A
	C2	BLANK	N/A
Red/Blue	C3	Knock Sensor (Front)	N/A
	C4-C12	BLANK	N/A

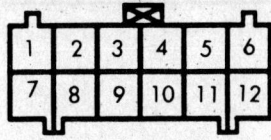

CONNECTOR "C"
VIEWED FROM HARNESS SIDE

93H78359

Courtesy of American Honda Motor Co., Inc.

Fig. 13: Identifying Connector "C" Terminals & Pin Voltage Chart (Vigor)

	Terminal ID.	Function/Description	Voltage Value (DC Volts Unless Otherwise Specified)
White/Green → Green/White →	D1	Battery Power	Battery Voltage At All Times
	D2	Brake Signal	Battery Voltage With Brake Applied
	D3	BLANK	N/A
Brown →	D4	Service Check Connector	11 Volt With A/T Or 5 Volt With M/T
	D5	BLANK	N/A
	D6	BLANK	N/A
	D7	BLANK	N/A
Brown →	D8	Ignition Timing Adjuster	N/A
White/Red →	D9	Alternator	N/A
Green/Red →	D10	Electronic Load Detector	1.3 Volt, Lights On; 5 Volt, Light Off
Red/Yellow →	D11	Throttle Position Sensor	.5 Volt Closed; 4.5 Volts Open
White/Black →	D12	EGR Valve Lift Sensor	1.0 Volt Closed; 4.5 Volts Open
Yellow/Green →	D13	Engine Coolant Temperature Sensor	N/A
White →	D14	Oxygen Sensor	.4-.5 Volt When Ignition Is First Turned On, Decreasing To Less Than .1 Volt In Less Than 2 Minutes
White/Yellow →	D15	Intake Air Temperature Sensor	N/A
	D16	BLANK	N/A
White/Blue →	D17	MAP Sensor	3-5 Volts Depending On Atmospheric Pressure
Blue/White →	D18	A/T Control Unit	N/A
Yellow/White →	D19	MAP Sensor Reference Voltage	5 Volts
Yellow/White →	D20	Throttle Position Sensor	Approximately Zero
Green/White →	D21	MAP Sensor	Approximately Zero
Green/White →	D22	Oxygen Sensor Heater	Approximately Zero

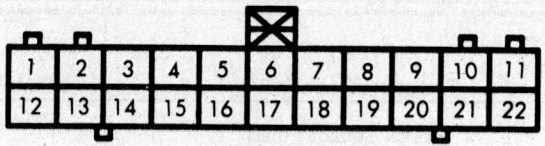

CONNECTOR "D"
VIEWED FROM HARNESS SIDE

94F44193

Courtesy of American Honda Motor Co., Inc.

Fig. 14: Identifying Connector "D" Terminals & Pin Voltage Chart (Vigor)

Integra, Legend, Vigor

INTRODUCTION

Sensor operating range information can help determine if a sensor is out of calibration. An out-of-calibration sensor may not set a trouble code, but it may cause driveability problems.

NOTE: Unless stated otherwise in test procedure, perform all voltage tests using a Digital Volt-Ohmmeter (DVOM) with a minimum 10-megohm input impedance.

COOLANT TEMPERATURE (TW) SENSOR RESISTANCE

Temperature °F (°C)	[1] (Ohms)
–4 (–20)	15,000-18,000
68 (20)	1000-4000
176 (80)	200-400
248 (120)	50-150

[1] – Measure resistance across sensor terminals.

DISTRIBUTOR SENSOR RESISTANCE [1]

Application	Ohms
Integra	
CRANK Sensor	350-700
CYL Sensor	350-700
TDC Sensor	350-700
Legend	
CRANK No. 1 Sensor	650-950
CRANK No. 2 Sensor	650-950
CYL No. 1 Sensor	650-950
CYL No. 2 Sensor	650-950
Vigor	
CRANK Sensor	650-850
CYL Sensor	650-850
TDC Sensor	650-850

[1] – See SYSTEM & COMPONENT TESTING article to identify sensor terminals.

EGR POSITION SENSOR VOLTAGE [1] (LEGEND & VIGOR ONLY)

Position	Approximate Volts
Fully Closed	1.0
Fully Open	4.5

[1] – Measure voltage between terminals D12 (positive) and D22 (negative). Voltage should increase smoothly as vacuum is applied.

INTAKE AIR TEMPERATURE (IAT) SENSOR RESISTANCE [1]

Temperature F° (C°)	Ohms
–4 (–20)	15,000-18,000
68 (20)	2000-4000
176 (80)	300-400

[1] – Measure resistance between sensor terminals.

MAP SENSOR VOLTAGE [1]

Vacuum Applied (In. Hg)	Volts
0	2.8-3.0
5	2.3-2.5
10	1.8-2.0
15	1.3-1.5
20	.8-1.0
25	.3-.5

[1] – On Integra, measure voltage between ECU terminals C11 (positive) and C12 (negative). On Legend and Vigor, measure voltage between ECU terminals D17 (positive) and D21 (negative).

OXYGEN SENSOR VOLTAGE [1]

Condition	Volts
Lean	.1
Rich	.9

[1] – Measure voltage between ground and O_2 sensor terminal using a high-impedance DVOM.

THROTTLE POSITION SENSOR VOLTAGE [1]

Position	Approximate Volts
Fully Closed	0.1-0.5
Fully Open	4.5-4.8

[1] – On Integra, measure resistance between terminals C7 (positive) and C12 (negative). On Legend, measure resistance between terminals D11 (positive) and D22 (negative). Voltage should increase smoothly as throttle is opened.

VEHICLE SPEED SENSOR VOLTAGE [1]

Model	Approximate Volts
Integra, Legend & Vigor	[2]

[1] – On Integra and Vigor, measure voltage between terminals B10 (positive) and A26 (negative). On Legend, measure voltage between terminals C2 (positive) and A26 (negative).

[2] – Rotate left front wheel slowly. On Integra and Vigor, voltage should pulse between zero and 10 volts. On Legend, voltage should pulse between zero and 5 volts.

1994 ENGINE PERFORMANCE
Vacuum Diagrams

Integra, Legend, Vigor

INTRODUCTION

This article contains underhood views or schematics of vacuum hose routing. Use these vacuum diagrams during the visual inspection in BASIC DIAGNOSTIC PROCEDURES article. This will assist in identifying improperly routed vacuum hoses, which cause driveability and/or computer-indicated malfunctions.

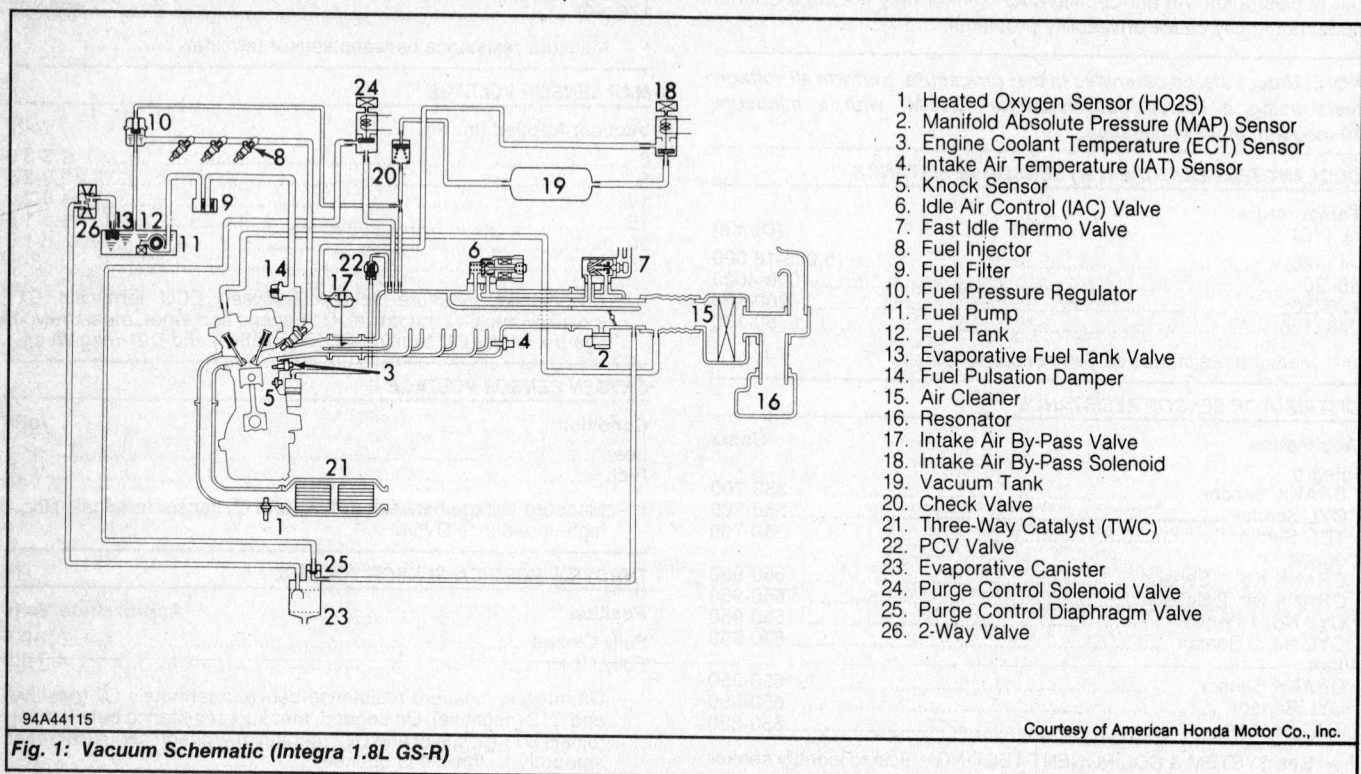

1. Heated Oxygen Sensor (HO2S)
2. Manifold Absolute Pressure (MAP) Sensor
3. Engine Coolant Temperature (ECT) Sensor
4. Intake Air Temperature (IAT) Sensor
5. Knock Sensor
6. Idle Air Control (IAC) Valve
7. Fast Idle Thermo Valve
8. Fuel Injector
9. Fuel Filter
10. Fuel Pressure Regulator
11. Fuel Pump
12. Fuel Tank
13. Evaporative Fuel Tank Valve
14. Fuel Pulsation Damper
15. Air Cleaner
16. Resonator
17. Intake Air By-Pass Valve
18. Intake Air By-Pass Solenoid
19. Vacuum Tank
20. Check Valve
21. Three-Way Catalyst (TWC)
22. PCV Valve
23. Evaporative Canister
24. Purge Control Solenoid Valve
25. Purge Control Diaphragm Valve
26. 2-Way Valve

94A44115

Courtesy of American Honda Motor Co., Inc.

Fig. 1: Vacuum Schematic (Integra 1.8L GS-R)

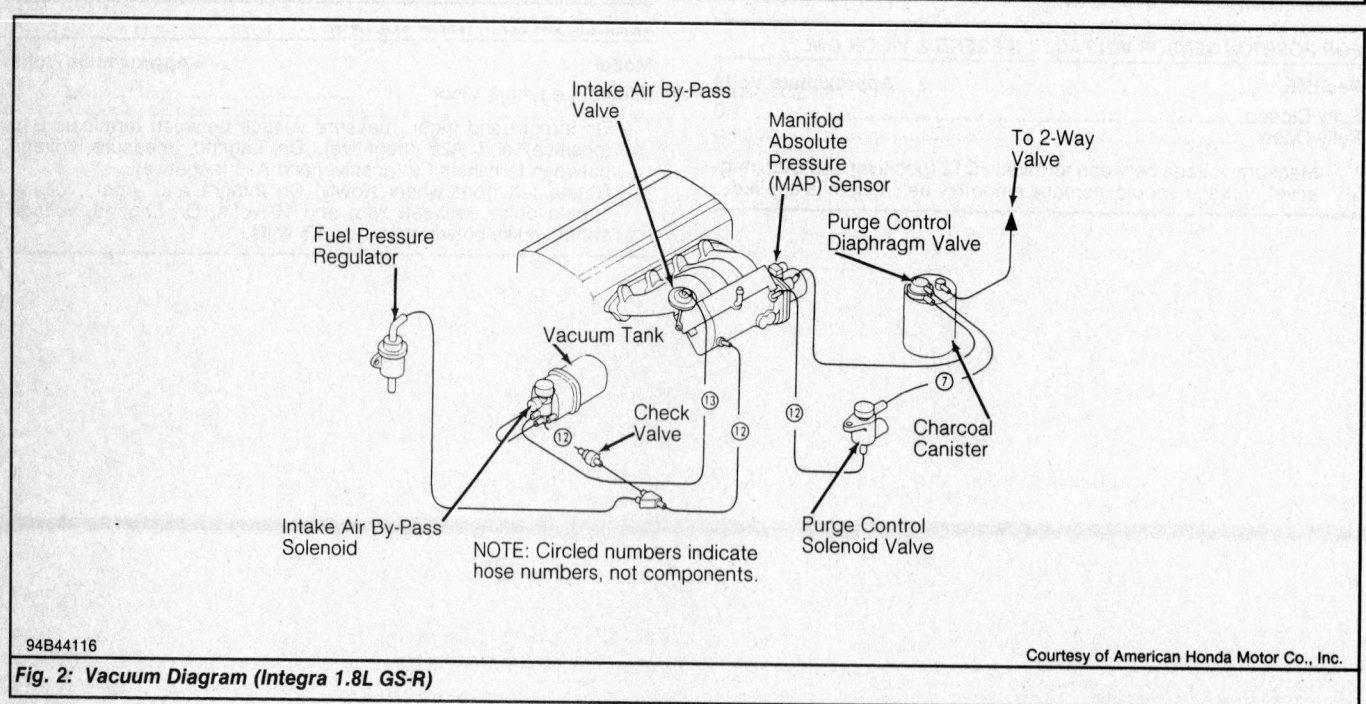

94B44116

Courtesy of American Honda Motor Co., Inc.

Fig. 2: Vacuum Diagram (Integra 1.8L GS-R)

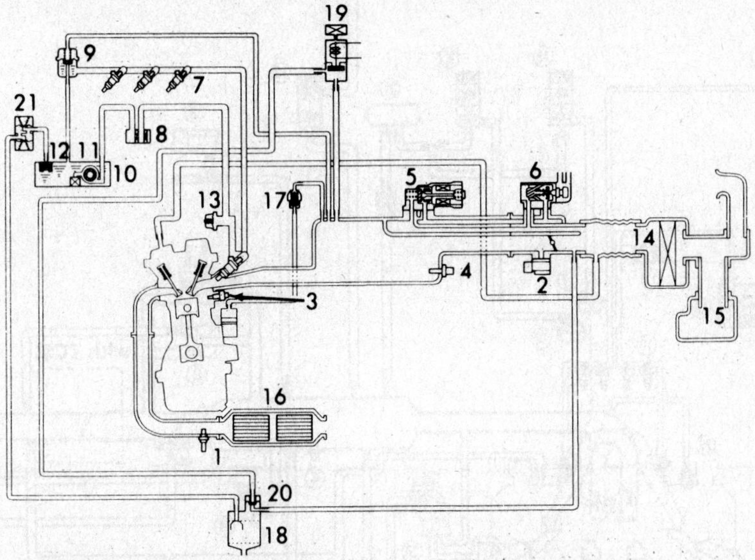

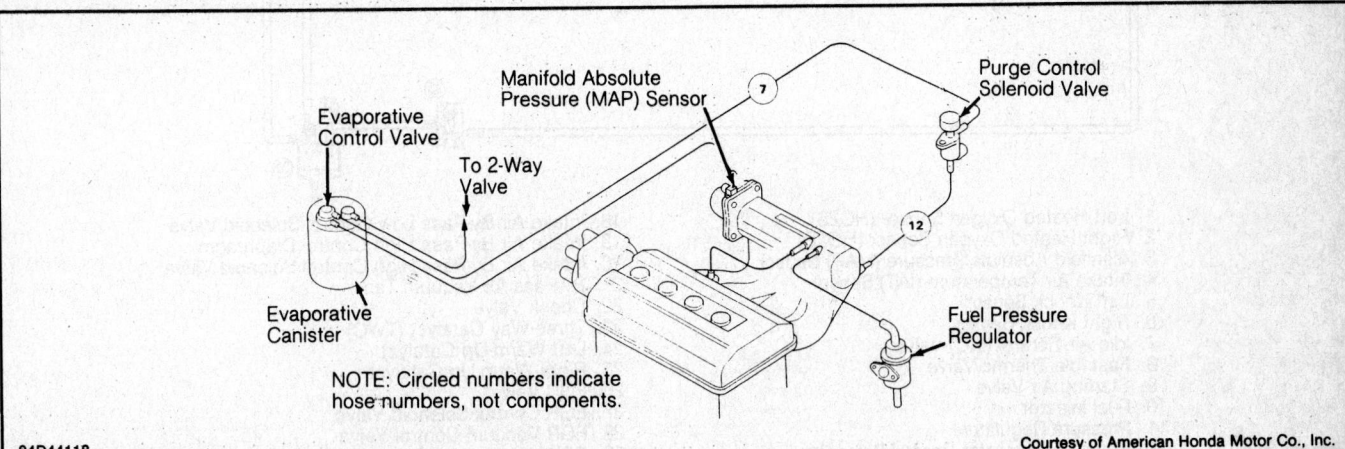

1. Heated Oxygen Sensor (HO2S)
2. Manifold Absolute Pressure (MAP) Sensor
3. Engine Coolant Temperature (ECT) Sensor
4. Intake Air Temperature (IAT) Sensor
5. Idle Air Control (IAC) Valve
6. Fast Idle Valve
7. Fuel Injector
8. Fuel Filter
9. Fuel Pressure Regulator
10. Fuel Pump
11. Fuel Tank

12. Evaporation Fuel Tank Valve
13. Pulsation Damper
14. Air Cleaner
15. Resonator
16. Three-Way Catalyst (TWC)
17. PCV Valve
18. Charcoal Canister
19. Purge Control Solenoid Valve
20. Purge Control Diaphragm Valve
21. 2-Way Valve

94C44117

Fig. 3: Vacuum Schematic (Integra 1.8L Except GS-R)

Evaporative
Control Valve

Manifold Absolute
Pressure (MAP) Sensor

Purge Control
Solenoid Valve

To 2-Way
Valve

Evaporative
Canister

Fuel Pressure
Regulator

NOTE: Circled numbers indicate
hose numbers, not components.

94D44118

Fig. 4: Vacuum Diagram (Integra 1.8L Except GS-R)

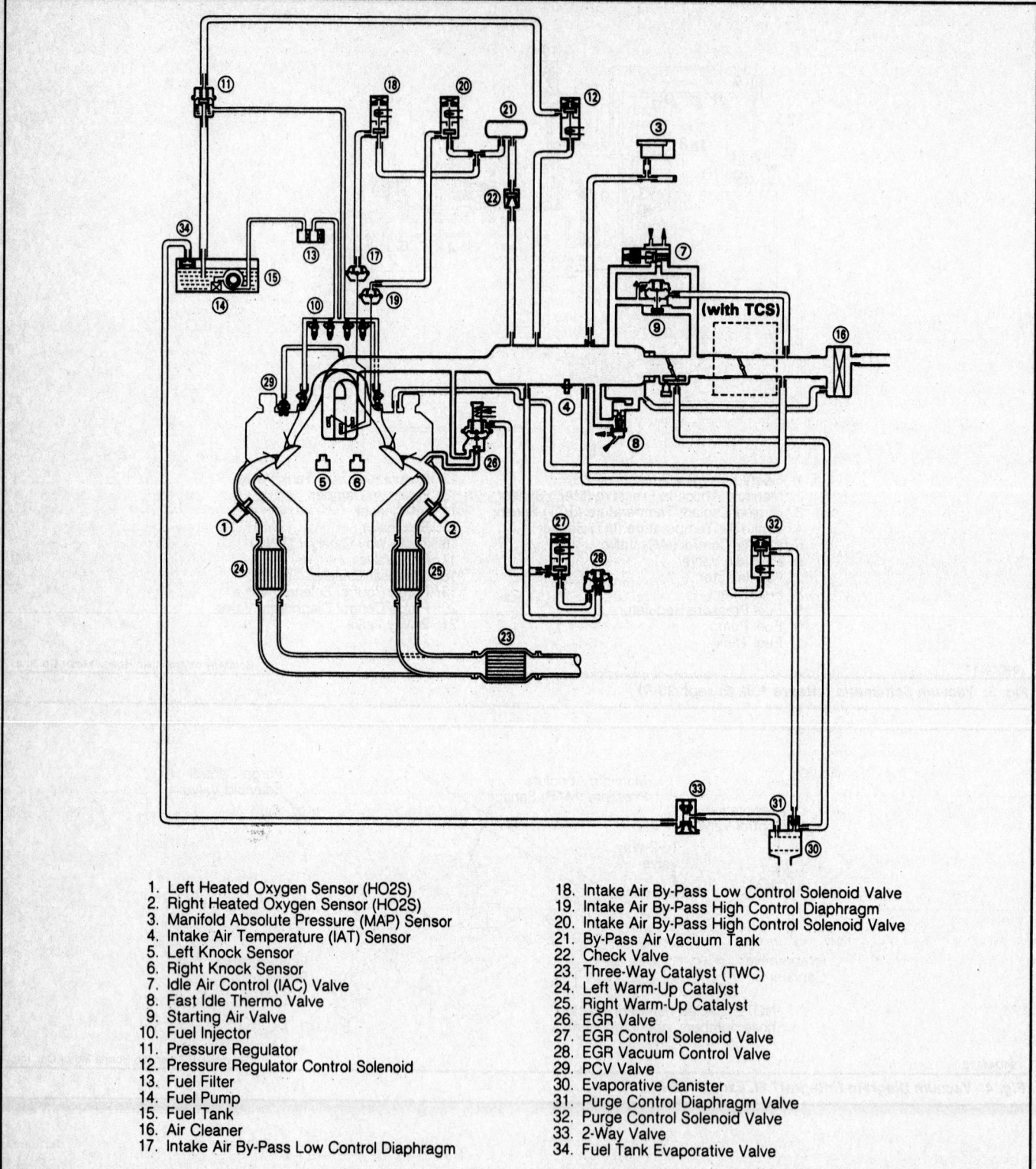

1. Left Heated Oxygen Sensor (HO2S)
2. Right Heated Oxygen Sensor (HO2S)
3. Manifold Absolute Pressure (MAP) Sensor
4. Intake Air Temperature (IAT) Sensor
5. Left Knock Sensor
6. Right Knock Sensor
7. Idle Air Control (IAC) Valve
8. Fast Idle Thermo Valve
9. Starting Air Valve
10. Fuel Injector
11. Pressure Regulator
12. Pressure Regulator Control Solenoid
13. Fuel Filter
14. Fuel Pump
15. Fuel Tank
16. Air Cleaner
17. Intake Air By-Pass Low Control Diaphragm

18. Intake Air By-Pass Low Control Solenoid Valve
19. Intake Air By-Pass High Control Diaphragm
20. Intake Air By-Pass High Control Solenoid Valve
21. By-Pass Air Vacuum Tank
22. Check Valve
23. Three-Way Catalyst (TWC)
24. Left Warm-Up Catalyst
25. Right Warm-Up Catalyst
26. EGR Valve
27. EGR Control Solenoid Valve
28. EGR Vacuum Control Valve
29. PCV Valve
30. Evaporative Canister
31. Purge Control Diaphragm Valve
32. Purge Control Solenoid Valve
33. 2-Way Valve
34. Fuel Tank Evaporative Valve

93J78111

Courtesy of American Honda Motor Co., Inc.

Fig. 5: Vacuum Schematic (Legend Coupe & GS Sedan)

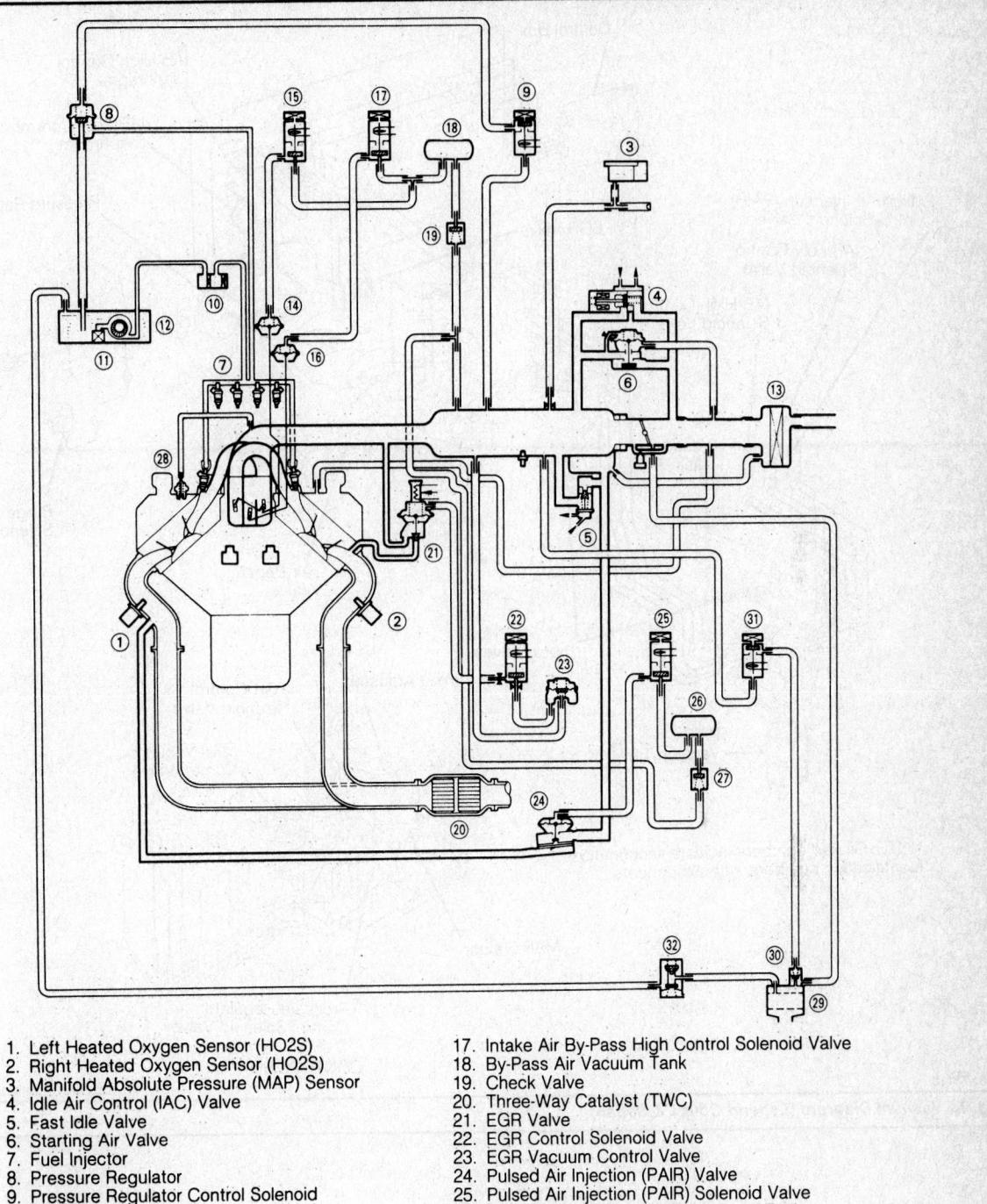

1. Left Heated Oxygen Sensor (HO2S)
2. Right Heated Oxygen Sensor (HO2S)
3. Manifold Absolute Pressure (MAP) Sensor
4. Idle Air Control (IAC) Valve
5. Fast Idle Valve
6. Starting Air Valve
7. Fuel Injector
8. Pressure Regulator
9. Pressure Regulator Control Solenoid
10. Fuel Filter
11. Fuel Pump
12. Fuel Tank
13. Air Cleaner
14. Intake Air By-Pass Low Control Diaphragm
15. Intake Air By-Pass Low Control Solenoid Valve
16. Intake Air By-Pass High Control Diaphragm

17. Intake Air By-Pass High Control Solenoid Valve
18. By-Pass Air Vacuum Tank
19. Check Valve
20. Three-Way Catalyst (TWC)
21. EGR Valve
22. EGR Control Solenoid Valve
23. EGR Vacuum Control Valve
24. Pulsed Air Injection (PAIR) Valve
25. Pulsed Air Injection (PAIR) Solenoid Valve
26. Pulsed Air Injection (PAIR) Vacuum Tank
27. Check Valve
28. PCV Valve
29. Evaporative Canister
30. Purge Control Diaphragm Valve
31. Purge Control Solenoid Valve
32. 2-Way Valve

93I78112

Courtesy of American Honda Motor Co., Inc.

Fig. 6: Vacuum Schematic (Legend "L" & LS Sedan)

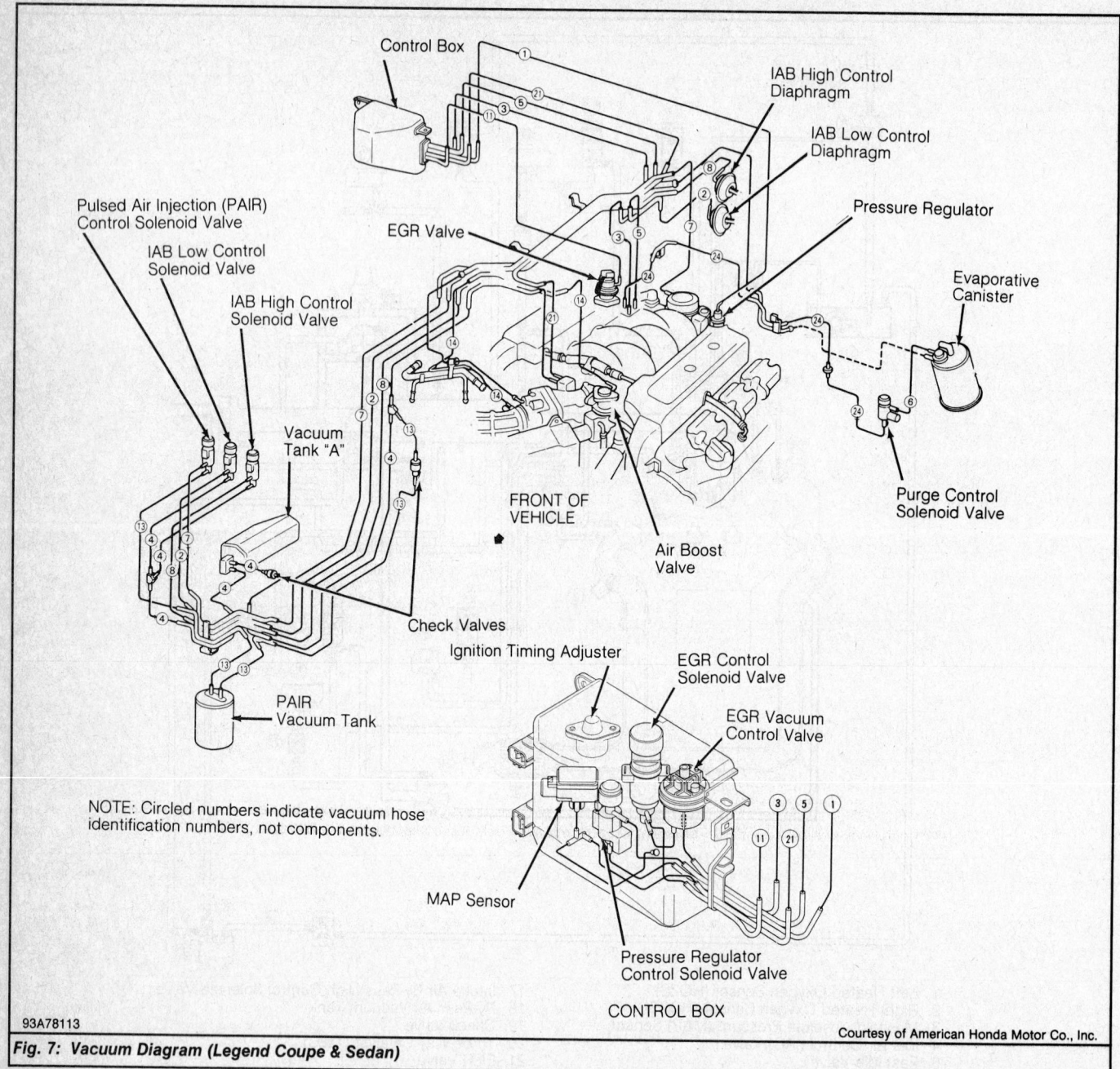

NOTE: Circled numbers indicate vacuum hose identification numbers, not components.

93A78113

Courtesy of American Honda Motor Co., Inc.

Fig. 7: Vacuum Diagram (Legend Coupe & Sedan)

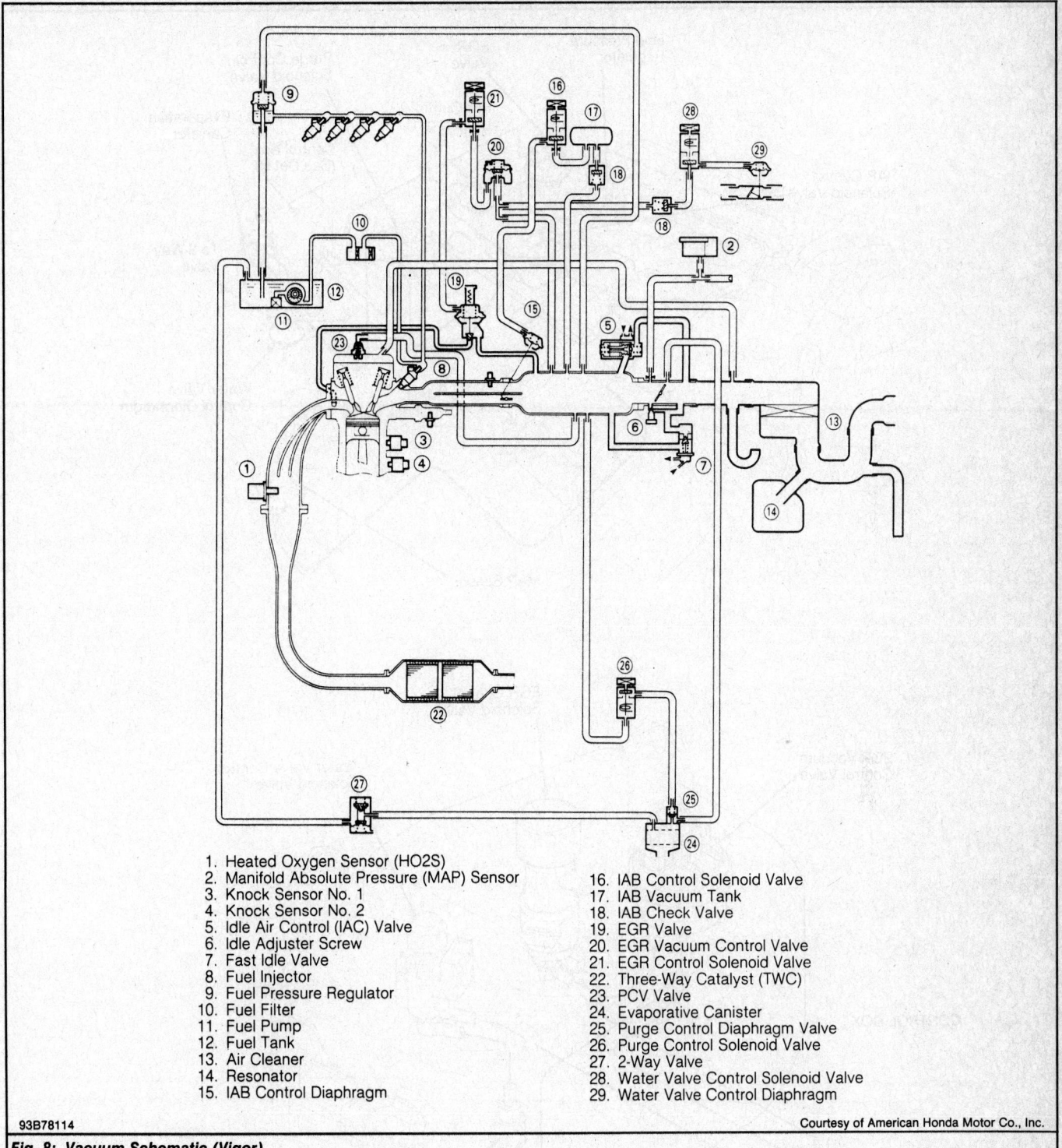

1. Heated Oxygen Sensor (HO2S)
2. Manifold Absolute Pressure (MAP) Sensor
3. Knock Sensor No. 1
4. Knock Sensor No. 2
5. Idle Air Control (IAC) Valve
6. Idle Adjuster Screw
7. Fast Idle Valve
8. Fuel Injector
9. Fuel Pressure Regulator
10. Fuel Filter
11. Fuel Pump
12. Fuel Tank
13. Air Cleaner
14. Resonator
15. IAB Control Diaphragm

16. IAB Control Solenoid Valve
17. IAB Vacuum Tank
18. IAB Check Valve
19. EGR Valve
20. EGR Vacuum Control Valve
21. EGR Control Solenoid Valve
22. Three-Way Catalyst (TWC)
23. PCV Valve
24. Evaporative Canister
25. Purge Control Diaphragm Valve
26. Purge Control Solenoid Valve
27. 2-Way Valve
28. Water Valve Control Solenoid Valve
29. Water Valve Control Diaphragm

93B78114

Courtesy of American Honda Motor Co., Inc.

Fig. 8: Vacuum Schematic (Vigor)

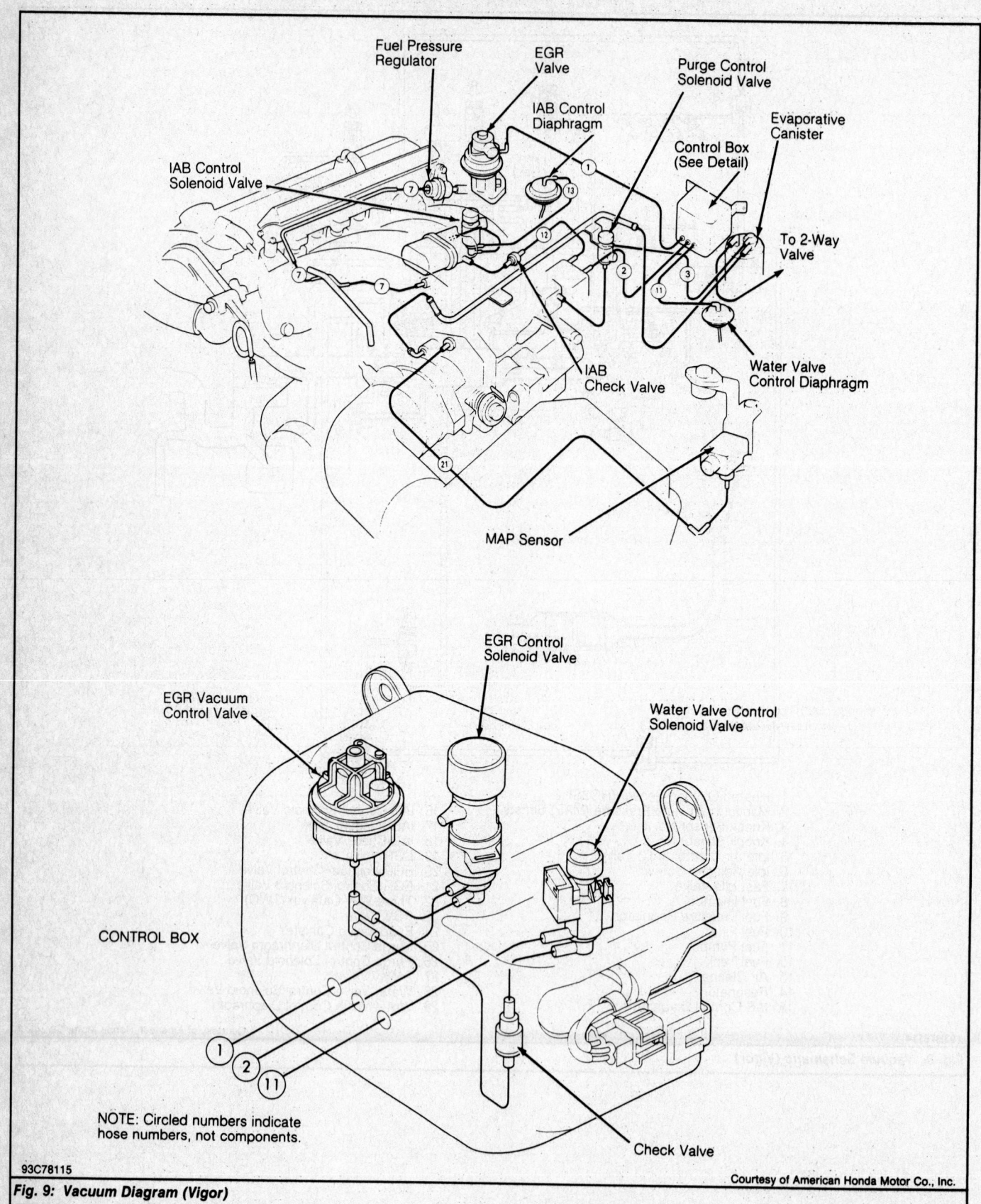

Fig. 9: Vacuum Diagram (Vigor)

93C78115

Courtesy of American Honda Motor Co., Inc.

Integra, Legend, Vigor

INTRODUCTION

Removal, overhaul and installation procedures are covered in this article. If component removal and installation is primarily an unbolt and bolt-on procedure, only a torque specification may be furnished.

IGNITION SYSTEM

DISTRIBUTOR

Removal & Installation (Integra) – **1)** Mark spark plug wires, distributor housing and cylinder head for installation reference. Unplug electrical connectors. Remove hold-down bolts and distributor.
2) Lubricate and install new "O" ring. *See Fig. 1.* Install distributor, aligning reference marks. Align distributor coupling with slot in camshaft. Connect wiring. Adjust ignition timing.

Removal & Installation (Vigor) – Note location of each spark plug wire. Disconnect wires from distributor cap. Remove hold-down bolts, distributor and seal. *See Fig. 2.* Coat new seal with engine oil. Align lugs on distributor drive with grooves in camshaft. Install hold-down bolts loosely. Connect wires. Adjust ignition timing. Tighten hold-down bolts.

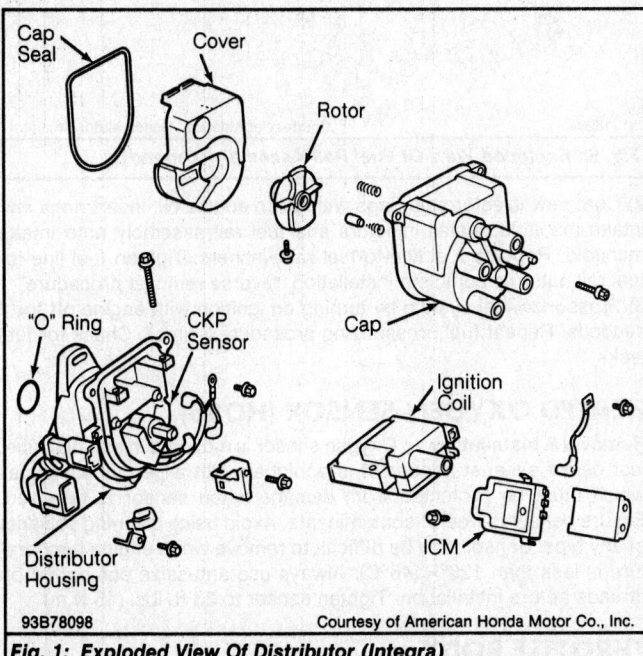

Fig. 1: Exploded View Of Distributor (Integra)

CRANKSHAFT POSITION (CKP) SENSOR

Removal & Installation (Integra) – CKP sensor is an integral component of distributor. See DISTRIBUTOR.
Removal & Installation (Legend) – Rotate engine clockwise until No. 1 piston is at top dead center. Remove upper timing belt covers. *See Fig. 3.* Remove timing belt from camshaft pulleys. Remove left camshaft pulley. Remove left backing plate. Remove CKP sensor. To install, reverse removal procedure. Check camshaft timing and ignition timing.

CRANKSHAFT POSITION (CKP) & CYLINDER POSITION (CYP) SENSORS

Removal & Installation (Vigor) – Rotate engine pulley counterclockwise until No. 1 cylinder is at top dead center. Remove upper timing belt cover. Remove timing belt from camshaft pulley. Remove CYP sensor. *See Fig. 4.* Remove camshaft pulley. Remove back cover. Remove CKP sensor. To install, reverse removal procedure. Recheck camshaft timing and ignition timing.

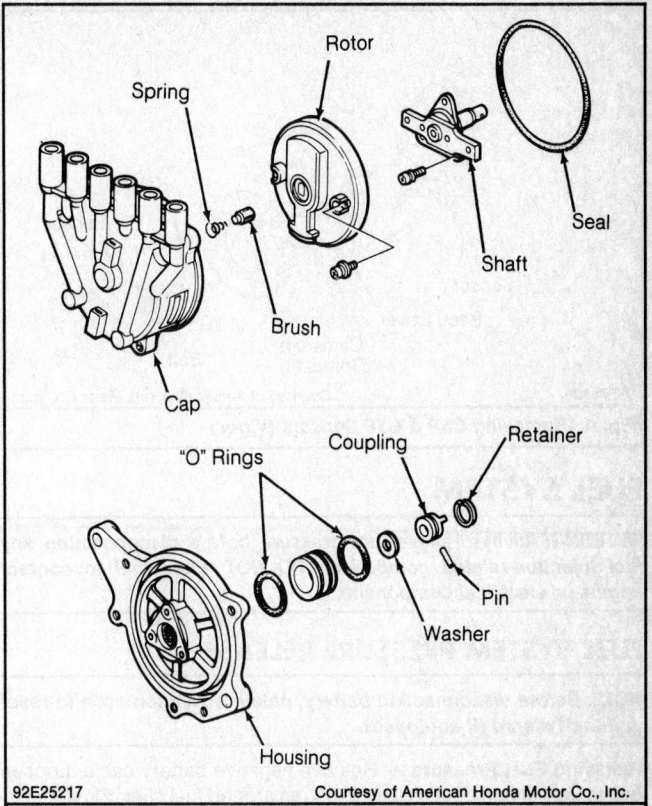

Fig. 2: Exploded View Of Distributor (Vigor)

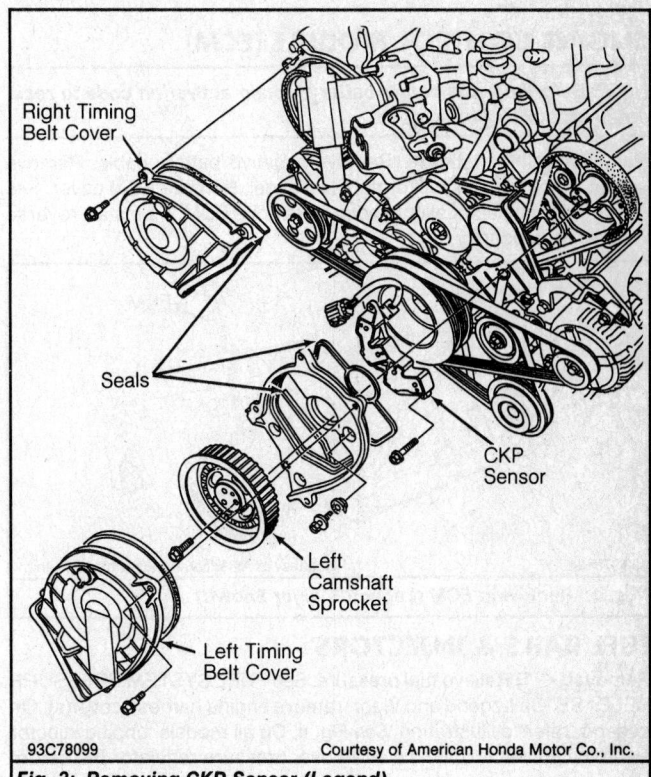

Fig. 3: Removing CKP Sensor (Legend)

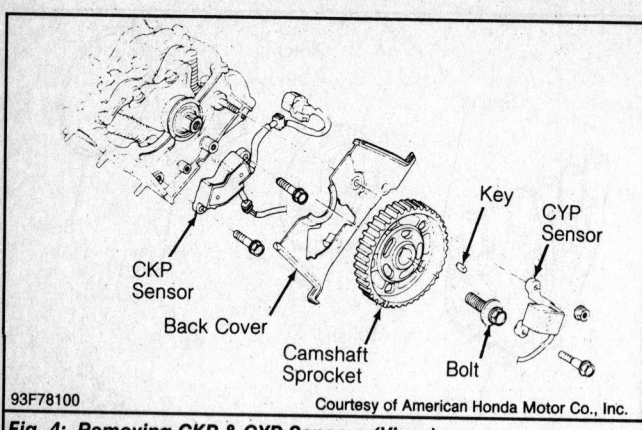

Fig. 4: Removing CKP & CYP Sensors (Vigor)

93F78100   Courtesy of American Honda Motor Co., Inc.

FUEL SYSTEM

WARNING: Always relieve fuel pressure before disconnecting any fuel injection-related component. DO NOT allow fuel to contact engine or electrical components.

FUEL SYSTEM PRESSURE RELEASE

NOTE: Before disconnecting battery, obtain activation code to reset anti-theft stereo (if equipped).

Relieving Fuel Pressure – Remove negative battery cable. Loosen fuel tank filler cap. Place clean shop rag around fuel filter. Slowly loosen 6-mm service bolt on top of fuel filter one complete turn to relieve system pressure. Always replace washer under bolt after loosening.

ENGINE CONTROL MODULE (ECM)

NOTE: Before disconnecting battery, obtain activation code to reset anti-theft stereo (if equipped).

Removal & Installation – Remove negative battery cable. Remove carpet from right footwell or right kickpanel. Remove ECM cover. See Fig. 5. Unplug electrical connectors. Remove ECM. To install, reverse removal procedure.

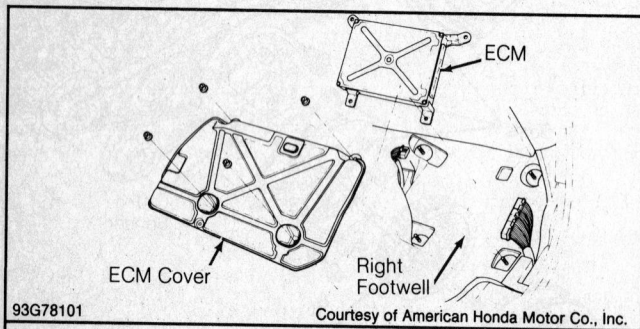

Fig. 5: Removing ECM (Legend & Vigor Shown)

93G78101   Courtesy of American Honda Motor Co., Inc.

FUEL RAILS & INJECTORS

Removal – 1) Relieve fuel pressure. See FUEL SYSTEM PRESSURE RELEASE. On Legend and Vigor, remove engine harness cover(s). On Legend, refer to illustration. See Fig. 6. On all models, unplug injector electrical connectors. Place a rag over pressure regulator fuel return hose.
2) Disconnect vacuum hose and fuel return hose from pressure regulator. Disconnect fuel line from fuel rail. Remove fuel rail retaining nuts and fuel rail. Remove injectors from intake manifold.
Installation – 1) Slide new cushion rings onto injectors. Install new "O" rings coated with clean engine oil onto injectors. Insert injectors into fuel rail. Align marks on injectors with corresponding marks on fuel rail.

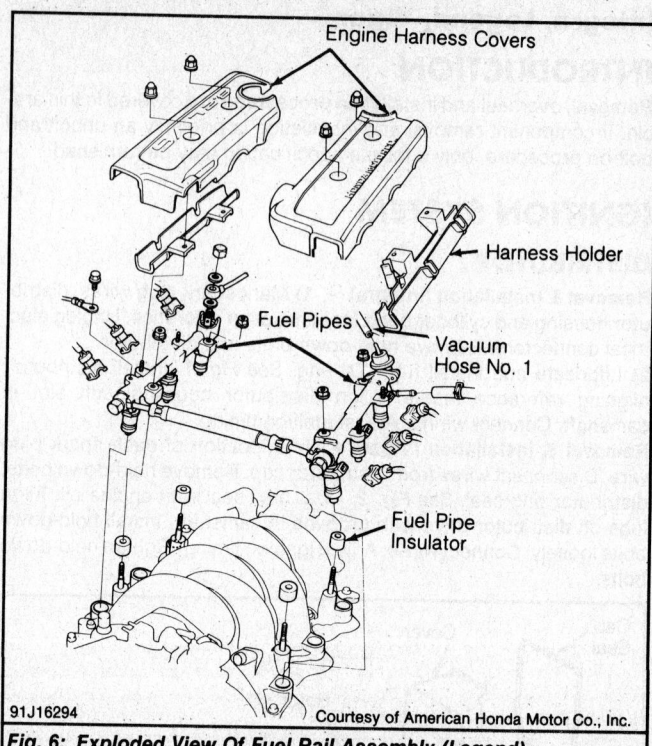

Fig. 6: Exploded View Of Fuel Rail Assembly (Legend)

91J16294   Courtesy of American Honda Motor Co., Inc.

2) Coat new injector seal rings with clean engine oil. Insert rings into intake manifold. Install injectors and fuel rail assembly onto intake manifold. Replace fuel line-to-fuel rail washers. Tighten fuel line-to-fuel rail nuts. To complete installation, reverse removal procedure.
3) Pressurize fuel system by turning on ignition with engine off for 2 seconds. Repeat fuel pressurizing procedure 3 times. Check for fuel leaks.

HEATED OXYGEN SENSOR (HO2S)

Removal & Installation – Oxygen sensor is mounted in exhaust pipe, just below exhaust header. It is equipped with a permanent pigtail which must be protected from damage when sensor is removed. Ensure sensor is free of contaminants. Avoid using cleaning solvents of any type. Sensor may be difficult to remove when engine temperature is less than 120°F (48°C). Always use anti-seize compound on threads before installation. Tighten sensor to 33 ft. lbs. (45 N.m).

THROTTLE BODY

Removal & Installation – Disconnect throttle cable at throttle body. Label and disconnect hoses and wiring from throttle body. Drain coolant. Remove retaining nuts or bolts and throttle body. To install, reverse removal procedure.

THROTTLE POSITION SENSOR

Removal & Installation – Throttle angle sensor is located on throttle body. Unplug electrical connector. Remove throttle angle sensor. To install, reverse removal procedure.

TORQUE SPECIFICATIONS
TORQUE SPECIFICATIONS

Application	Ft. Lbs. (N.m)
Distributor Hold-Down Bolts	16 (22)
Fuel Filter Service Bolt	11 (15)
Fuel Line-To-Fuel Rail Nuts	16 (22)
Oxygen Sensor	33 (45)
Throttle Body Bolts & Nuts	16 (22)
	INCH Lbs. (N.m)
CKP Sensor (Legend & Vigor)	108 (12)
CYP Sensor (Vigor)	108 (12)

Integra, Legend, Vigor

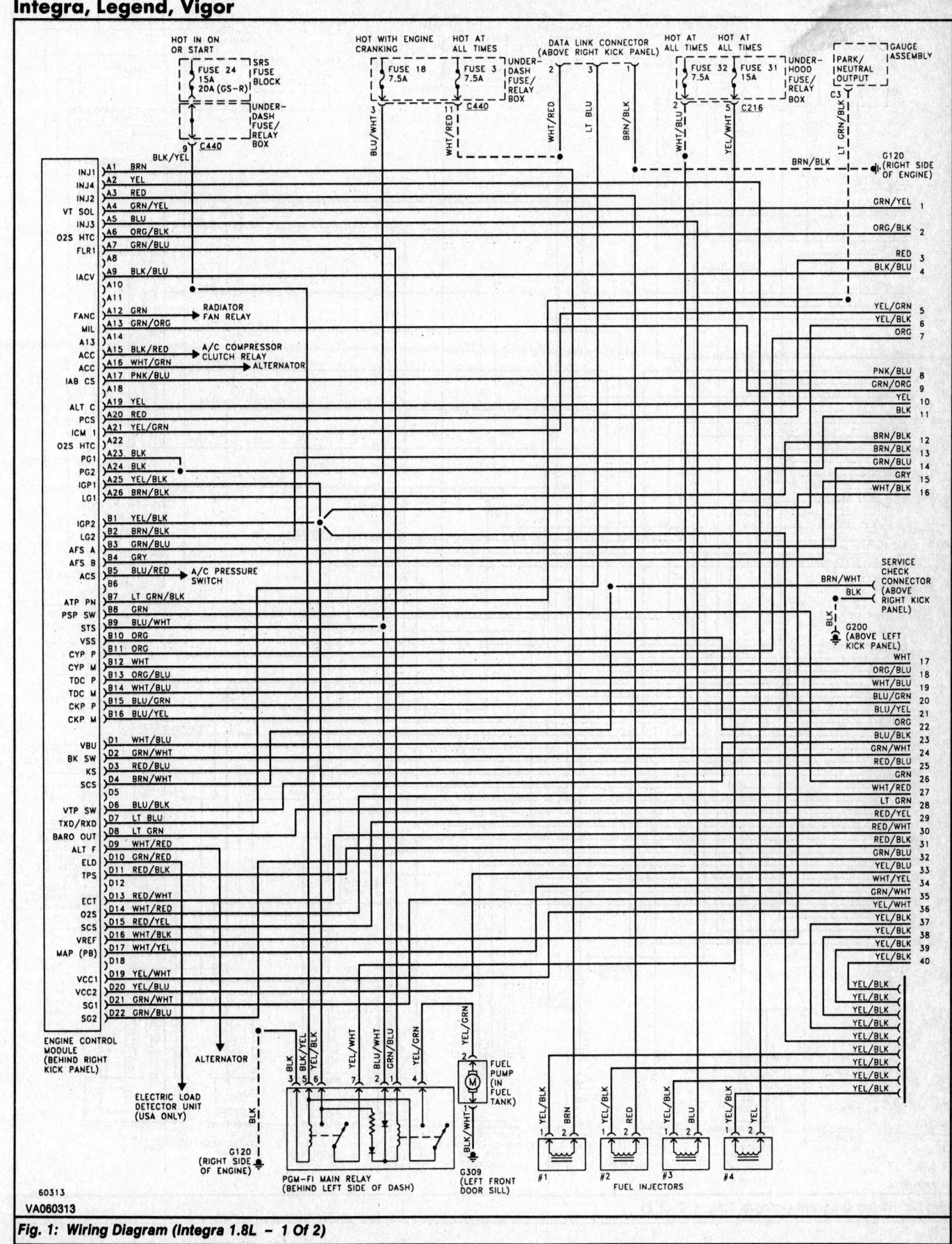

Fig. 1: Wiring Diagram (Integra 1.8L - 1 Of 2)

60313
VA060313

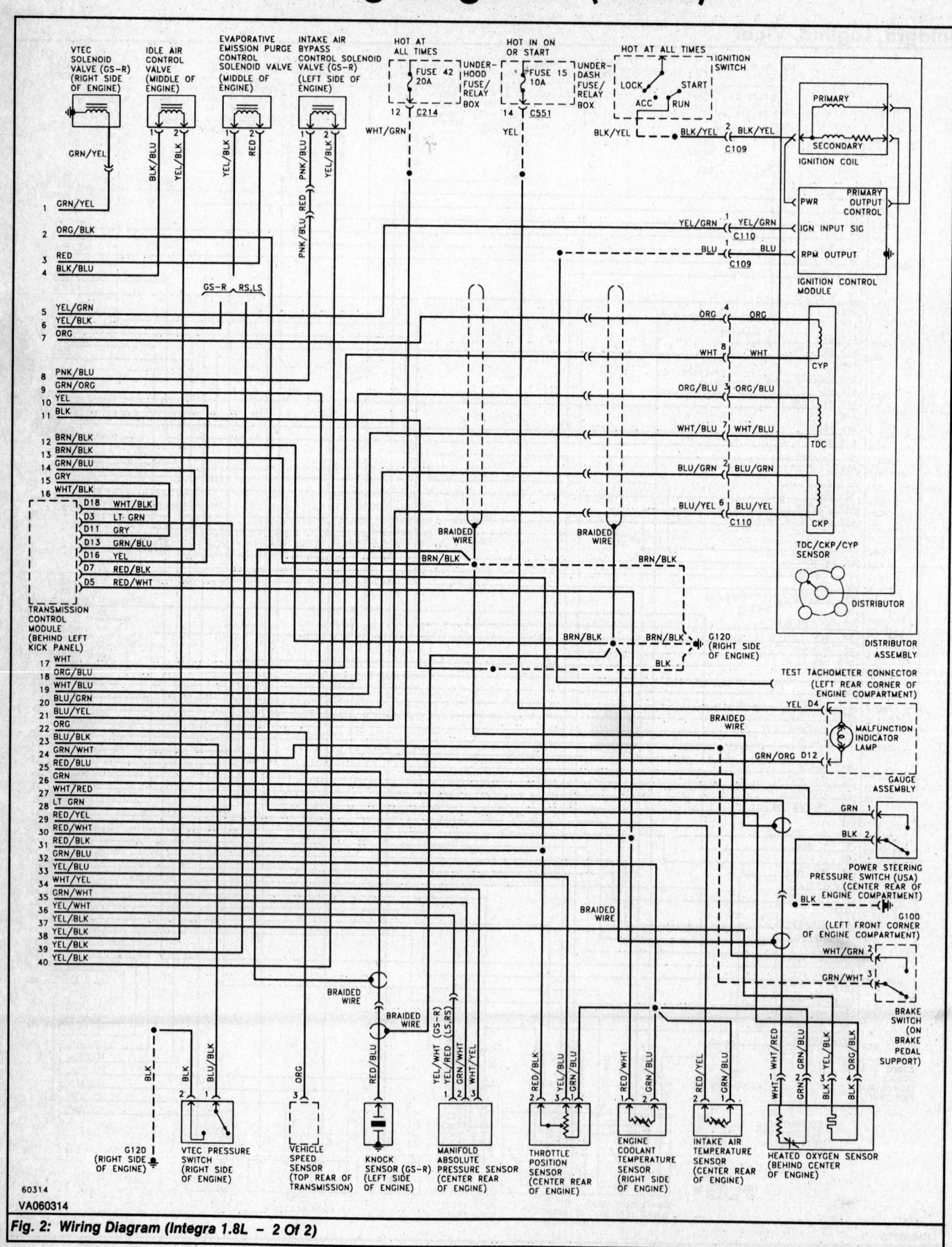

Fig. 2: Wiring Diagram (Integra 1.8L – 2 Of 2)

60314

VA060314

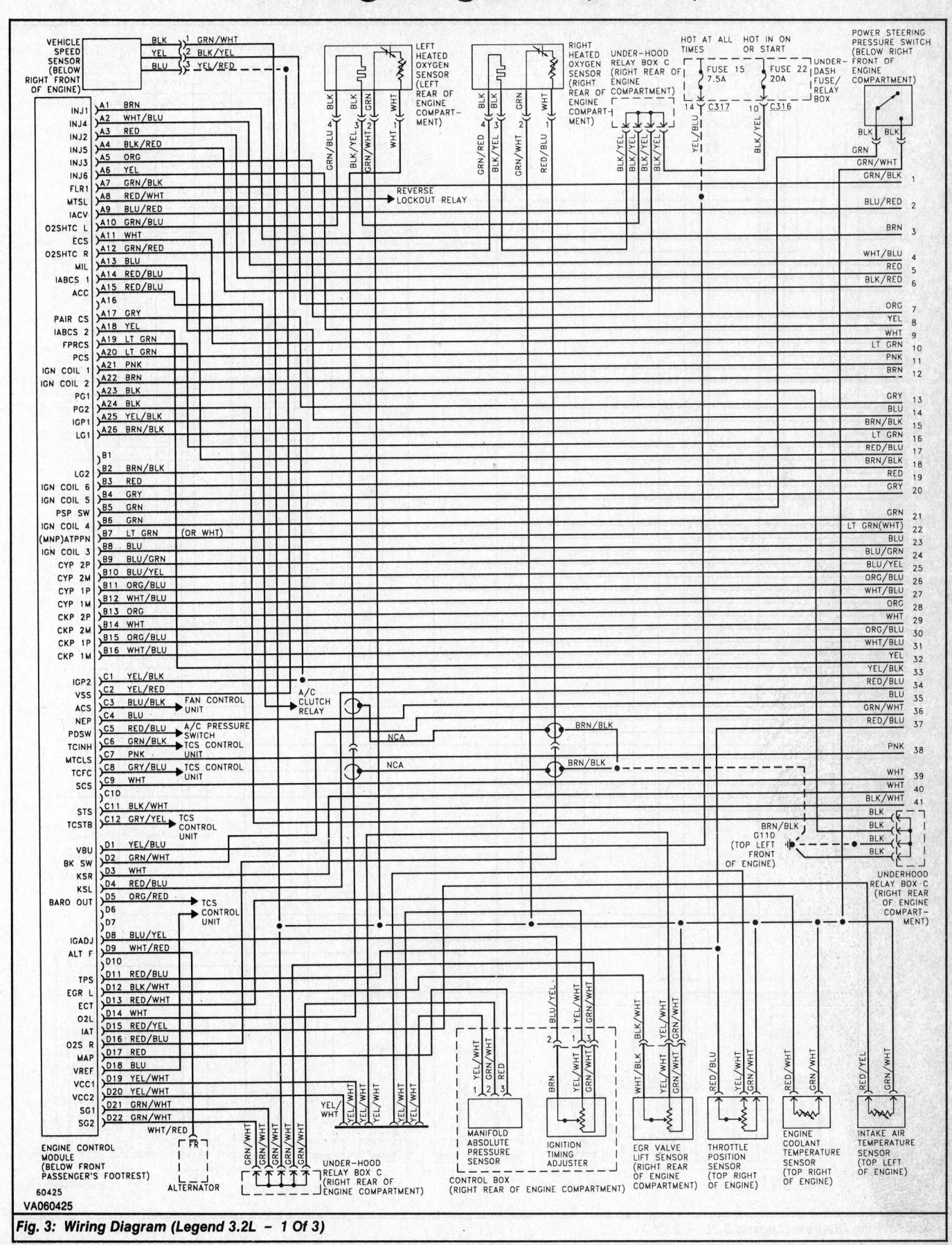

Fig. 3: Wiring Diagram (Legend 3.2L – 1 Of 3)

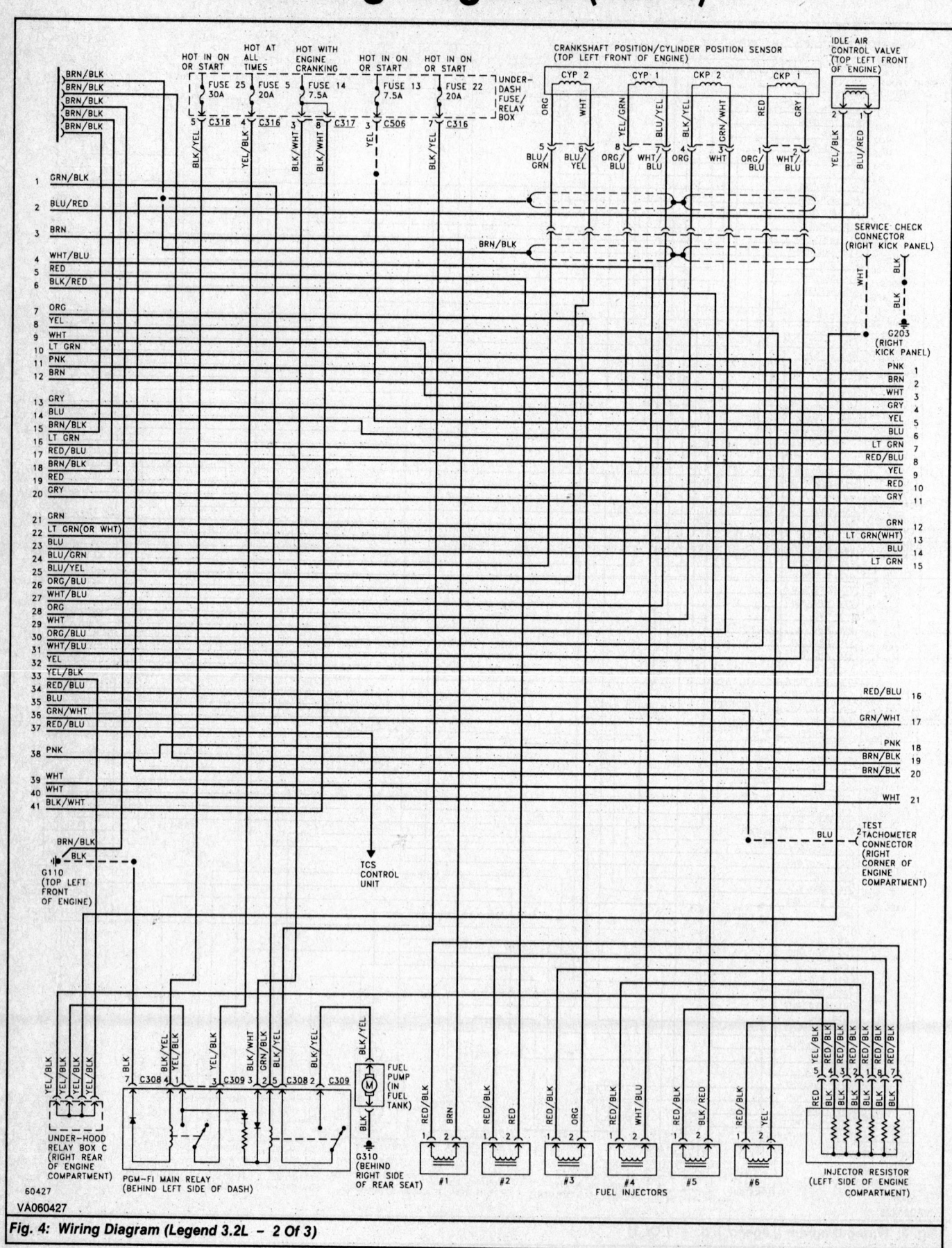

Fig. 4: Wiring Diagram (Legend 3.2L - 2 Of 3)

VA060427

60427

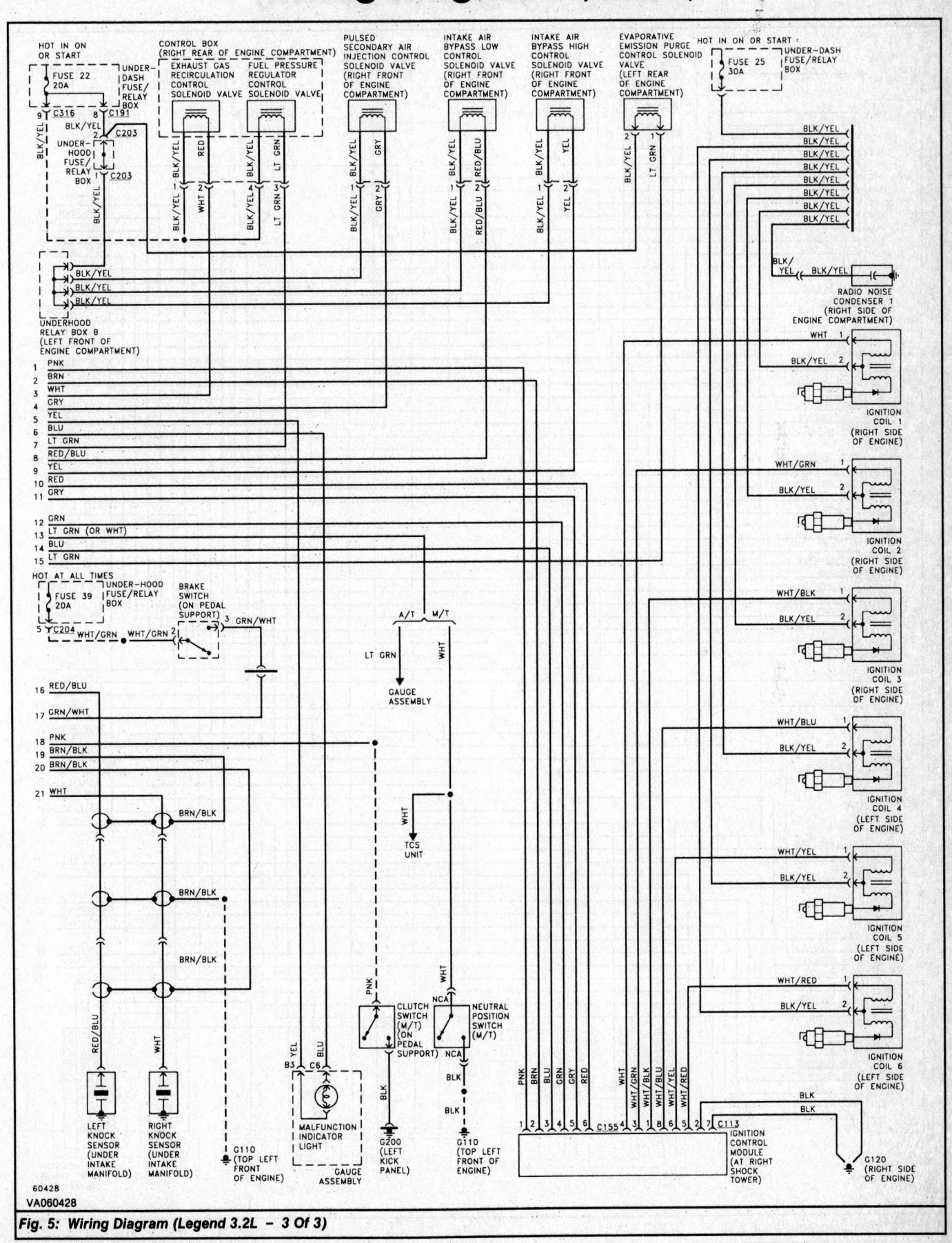

Fig. 5: Wiring Diagram (Legend 3.2L – 3 Of 3)

60428

VA060428

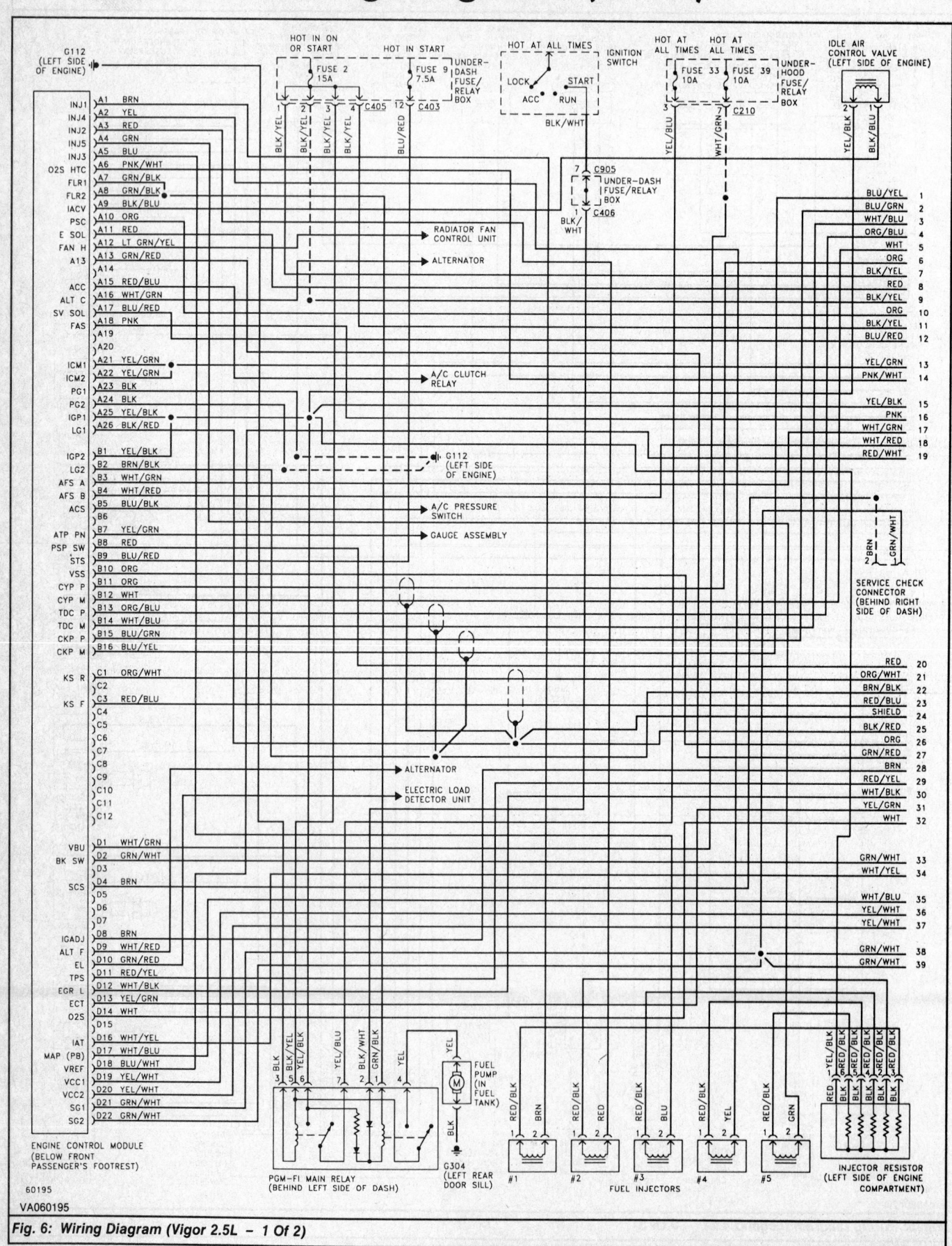

Fig. 6: Wiring Diagram (Vigor 2.5L - 1 Of 2)

60195

VA060195

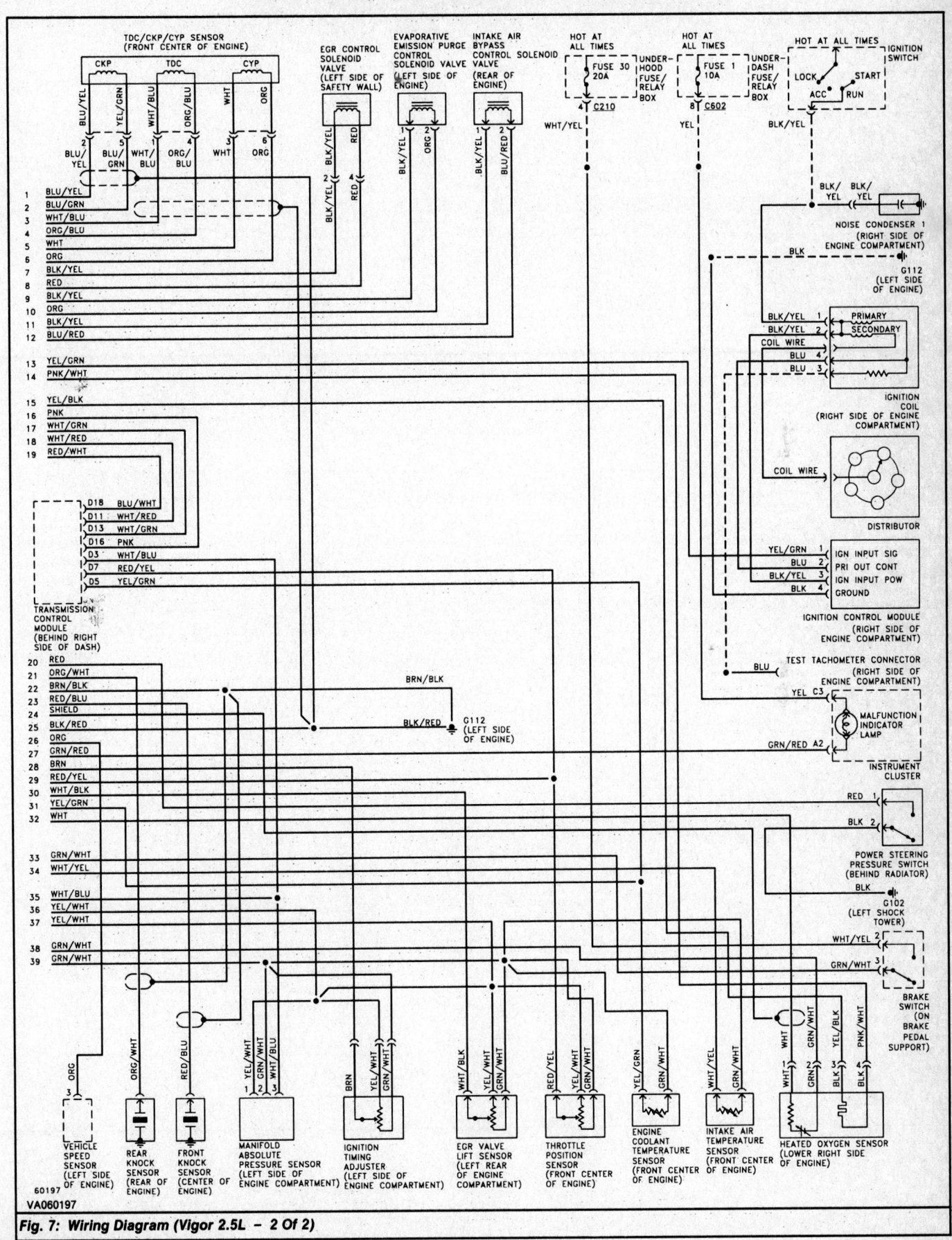

Fig. 7: Wiring Diagram (Vigor 2.5L – 2 Of 2)

VA060197

60197

Integra, Legend, Vigor

DESCRIPTION

Nippondenso 3-phase alternators use 4 positive and 4 negative diodes to rectify current. An internal Integrated Circuit (IC) voltage regulator controls charging system voltage. See WIRING DIAGRAMS.

ADJUSTMENTS

BELT ADJUSTMENT

Application	[1] Deflection – In. (mm)
A/C Compressor	
Integra	9/32-11/32 (7-9)
Legend	5/16-13/32 (8-10.5)
Vigor	1/4-11/32 (6-9)
Alternator	
Integra	9/32-13/32 (7-10.5)
Legend	3/8-29/64 (9.5-11.5)
Vigor	19/64-3/8 (7.5-9.5)
Power Steering	
Integra	5/16-13/32 (8.0-10.5)
Legend	29/64-17/32 (11.5-13.5)
Vigor	1/4-11/32 (6.5-9)

[1] – Deflection is with 22 lbs. (10 kg) pressure applied midway on longest belt run.

TROUBLE SHOOTING

NOTE: See TROUBLE SHOOTING article in GENERAL INFORMATION.

ON-VEHICLE TESTING

PRELIMINARY INSPECTION

Check alternator wiring harness connections and drive belt tension. Ensure battery is fully charged. On Integra, ensure fuse No. 24 (15-amp or 20-amp on V-TEC engine) in dash fuse box is good. On Legend, ensure fuses No. 15 (7.5-amp) and No. 22 (20-amp) in underdash fuse box are good. On Vigor, ensure fuse No. 2 (15-amp) in underdash fuse box is good.

CHARGING SYSTEM LIGHT OPERATION TEST

1) Turn ignition on. Charging system light should come on. If charging system light comes on, go to next step. If charging system light does not come on, go to step 6).

2) Start engine. Charging system light should turn off. If charging system light stays on, go to next step. If charging system light turns off, charging system light circuit is functioning properly.

3) Turn ignition off. Disconnect alternator 4-pin harness connector. Turn ignition on. If charging system light is on, turn ignition off and go to next step. If charging system light is off, go to ALTERNATOR/REGULATOR OUTPUT TEST.

4) On Integra, disconnect ABS control module 26-pin connector and integrated control module from under-dash fuse box. On Legend Coupe and GS Sedan, disconnect ABS control module 20-pin connector and disconnect integrated control module 22-pin connector. On Legend L and LS Sedan, disconnect ABS control module 18-pin connector and disconnect integrated control module 22-pin connector. On Vigor, disconnect ABS control module 18-pin connector and integrated control module 16-pin connector.

5) On all models, turn ignition on. If charging system light is on, repair short to ground in White/Blue wire. See Figs. 9, 10 or 11. After making repairs, reconnect control module connectors and reset ECM to clear and codes.

6) Turn ignition off. Check fuse No. 24 (Integra), fuse No. 22 (Legend) or fuse No. 2 (Vigor). If fuse is good, go to next step. If fuse is blown, replace fuse.

7) Disconnect alternator 4-pin harness connector. Turn ignition on. Measure voltage between ground and alternator 4-pin harness connector terminal "IG" (Black/Yellow wire). See Fig. 1. Battery voltage

should be present. If battery voltage is present, go to next step. If battery voltage is not present, repair open in Black/Yellow wire.

8) Connect a fused jumper wire between ground and alternator 4-pin harness connector terminal "L" (White/Blue wire). See Fig. 1. Charging system light should turn on. If charging system light turns on, replace voltage regulator.

9) If charging system light does not turn on, check for blown charging system light bulb and replace as necessary. If bulb is good, repair open in White/Blue wire.

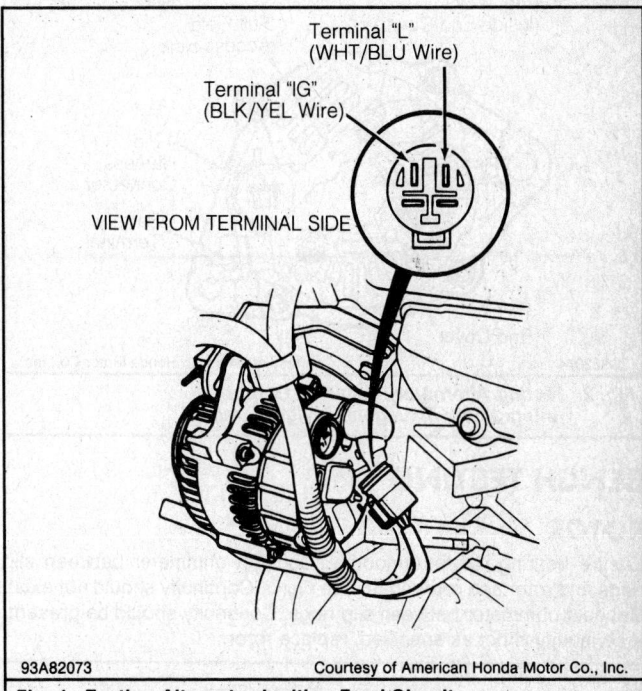

Terminal "L"
(WHT/BLU Wire)

Terminal "IG"
(BLK/YEL Wire)

VIEW FROM TERMINAL SIDE

93A82073   Courtesy of American Honda Motor Co., Inc.

Fig. 1: Testing Alternator Ignition Feed Circuit (Legend Shown; Integra & Vigor Similar)

ALTERNATOR/REGULATOR OUTPUT TEST

1) Test system using an alternator tester with integral carbon pile (to apply electrical load to system). Hook up tester according to manufacturers instructions. Turn tester selector to STARTING position. Start engine and bring to operating temperature. Raise engine speed to 2000 RPM and hold. Observe voltmeter. If voltage is greater than 15.2 volts, replace voltage regulator.

2) If voltage is less than 15.1 volts, return engine to idle. Ensure all accessories are off. Turn tester selector to CHARGING position. Remove inductive pick-up and zero ammeter. Connect inductive pick-up over alternator battery terminal (ensure arrow points away from alternator). See Fig. 2.

3) Raise engine speed to 2000 RPM and hold. Observe voltmeter. If voltage is greater than 13.9 volts, go to next step. If voltage is less than 13.9 volts, test battery condition. Recharge or replace battery as necessary.

4) While observing ammeter, apply load with alternator tester carbon pile until battery voltage drops to 12-13.5 volts. If less than 40 amps (60 amps on Integra) are present, go to next step. If more than 40 amps (60 amps on Integra) are present, charging system is functioning properly.

CAUTION: Voltage will rise rapidly during full field test. DO NOT allow voltage to exceed 18 volts. Damage to electrical system may result.

5) With engine speed still at 2000 RPM, full field alternator. Attach probe to alternator tester full field test lead. Insert probe into full field access hole located on back of alternator. See Fig. 2. Switch field selector to "A" (ground) position briefly and observe amperage reading. If more than 40 (60 amps on Integra) amps are present, go to

next step. If less than 40 amps (60 amps on Integra) are present, test and repair alternator components. See BENCH TESTING.

6) Return engine to idle and turn ignition off. Disconnect alternator 4-pin harness connector. Turn ignition on. Measure voltage between ground and alternator 4-pin harness connector terminal "IG" (Black/Yellow wire). *See Fig. 1.* If battery voltage is present, replace voltage regulator. If battery voltage is not present, repair open in Black/Yellow wire.

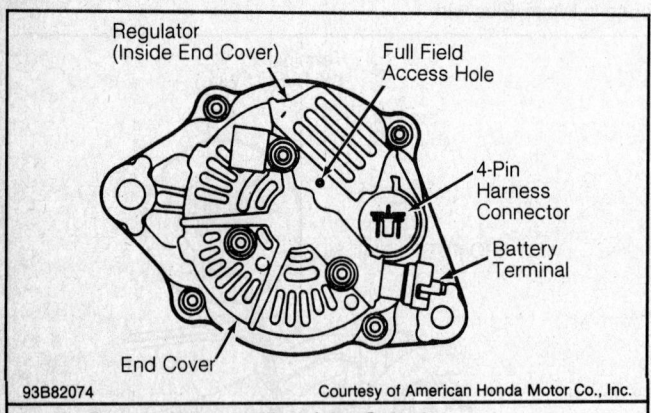

93B82074   Courtesy of American Honda Motor Co., Inc.

Fig. 2: Testing Alternator/Regulator Output (Integra Shown; Legend & Vigor Similar)

BENCH TESTING

ROTOR

Ensure bearing rotates smoothly. Connect ohmmeter between slip rings and rotor and rotor shaft. *See Fig. 3.* Continuity should not exist. Connect ohmmeter between slip rings. Continuity should be present. If continuity is not as specified, replace rotor.

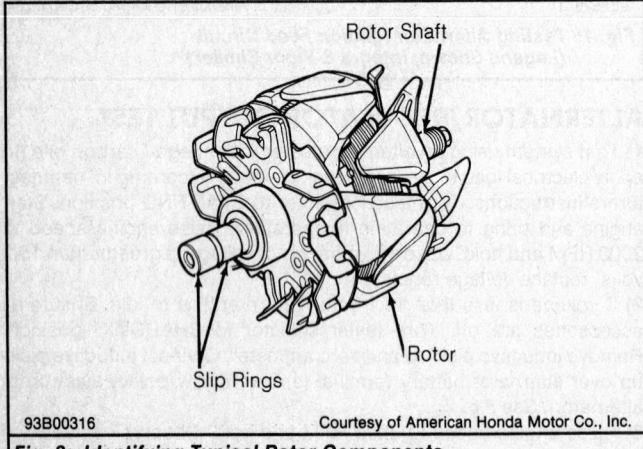

93B00316   Courtesy of American Honda Motor Co., Inc.

Fig. 3: Identifying Typical Rotor Components

STATOR

Using ohmmeter, check continuity between stator leads. *See Fig. 4.* Continuity should be present between all stator leads. Check continuity between stator leads and coil core. Continuity should not be present between stator leads and coil core. If continuity is not as specified, replace stator.

RECTIFIER DIODES

NOTE: Use an ohmmeter capable of checking diodes.

1) Check for continuity between terminal "B" and terminals P1-P5 and between terminal "E" and terminals P1-P5. *See Fig. 5.* Note ohmmeter reading.

2) Reverse leads, and repeat test. Continuity should be present in one direction and not in other. If continuity is not as specified, replace rectifier assembly.

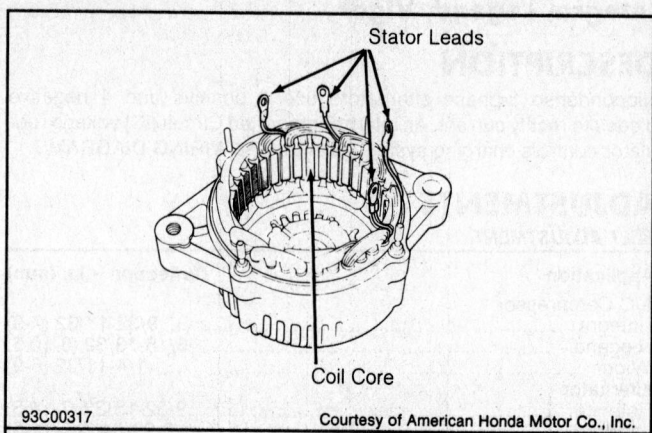

93C00317   Courtesy of American Honda Motor Co., Inc.

Fig. 4: Identifying Typical Stator Components

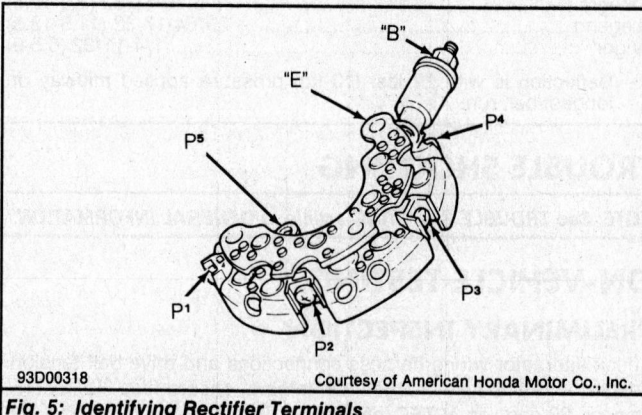

93D00318   Courtesy of American Honda Motor Co., Inc.

Fig. 5: Identifying Rectifier Terminals

COMPONENT REPLACEMENT

Brushes – Brush holder is accessed by removing end cover and removing 2 retaining screws. Ensure brushes slide smoothly in holder assembly. Check brush holder and brushes for cracks or other damage. Minimum brush length should be .06" (1.5 mm). If brushes are damaged or worn, replace brush holder assembly.

REMOVAL & INSTALLATION

CAUTION: Before disconnecting battery, obtain activation code to reset anti-theft stereo (if equipped).

ALTERNATOR

Removal & Installation (Integra) – Disconnect battery cables. Disconnect wiring harness connector and White wire from alternator. Remove upper and lower alternator mounting bolts. Remove alternator. To install, reverse removal procedure.

Removal & Installation (Legend) – Disconnect battery cables. Remove battery and battery tray. Remove lower alternator mounting bolt and adjusting rod assembly. Remove alternator from mounting bracket to access wiring on back of alternator. Disconnect wiring harness connector and Black wire from alternator. Remove alternator. To install, reverse removal procedure.

Removal & Installation (Vigor) – Disconnect battery cables. Disconnect wiring harness connector and Black wire from alternator. Remove upper and lower alternator mounting bolts. Remove alternator. To install, reverse removal procedure.

OVERHAUL

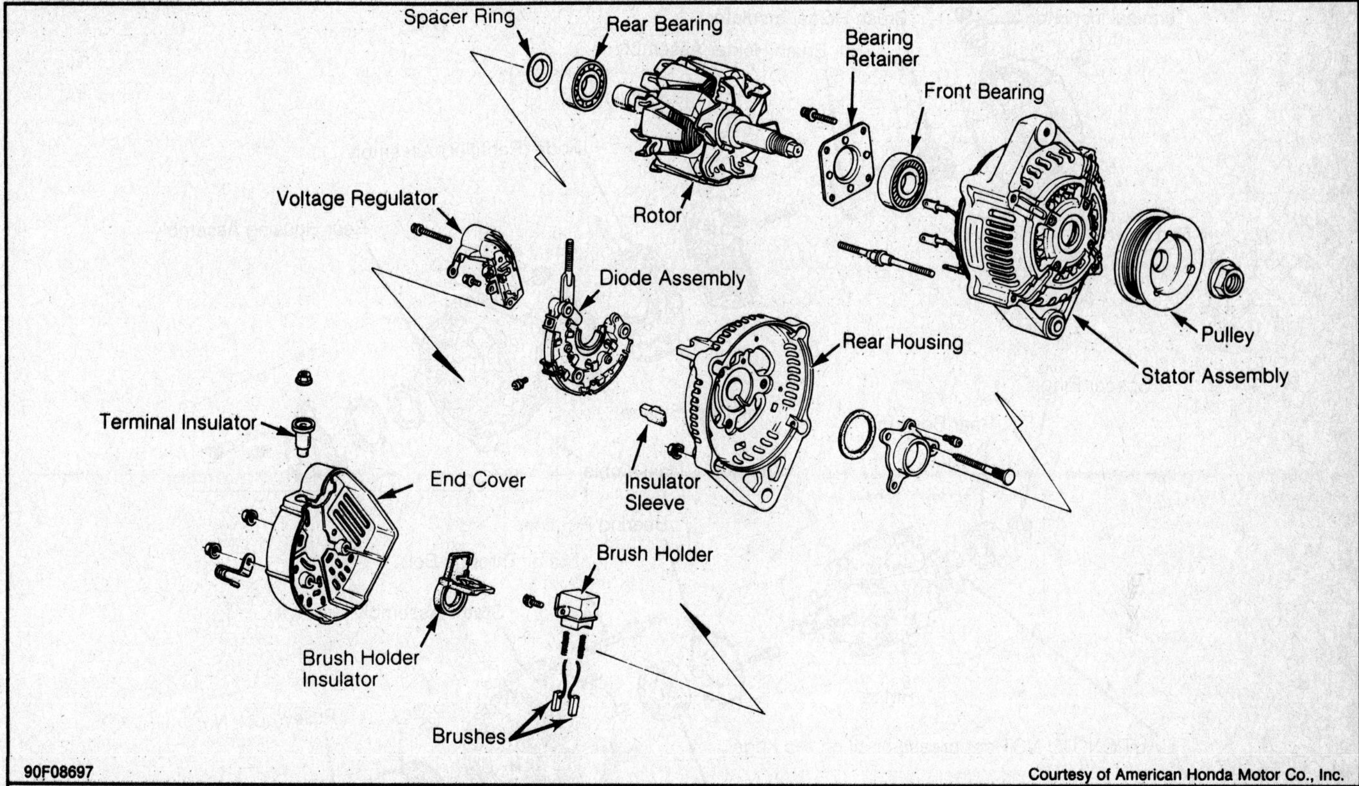

Spacer Ring
Rear Bearing
Bearing Retainer
Front Bearing
Voltage Regulator
Rotor
Diode Assembly
Rear Housing
Pulley
Stator Assembly
Terminal Insulator
End Cover
Insulator Sleeve
Brush Holder
Brush Holder Insulator
Brushes

90F08697

Courtesy of American Honda Motor Co., Inc.

Fig. 6: Exploded View Of Nippondenso Alternator (Integra)

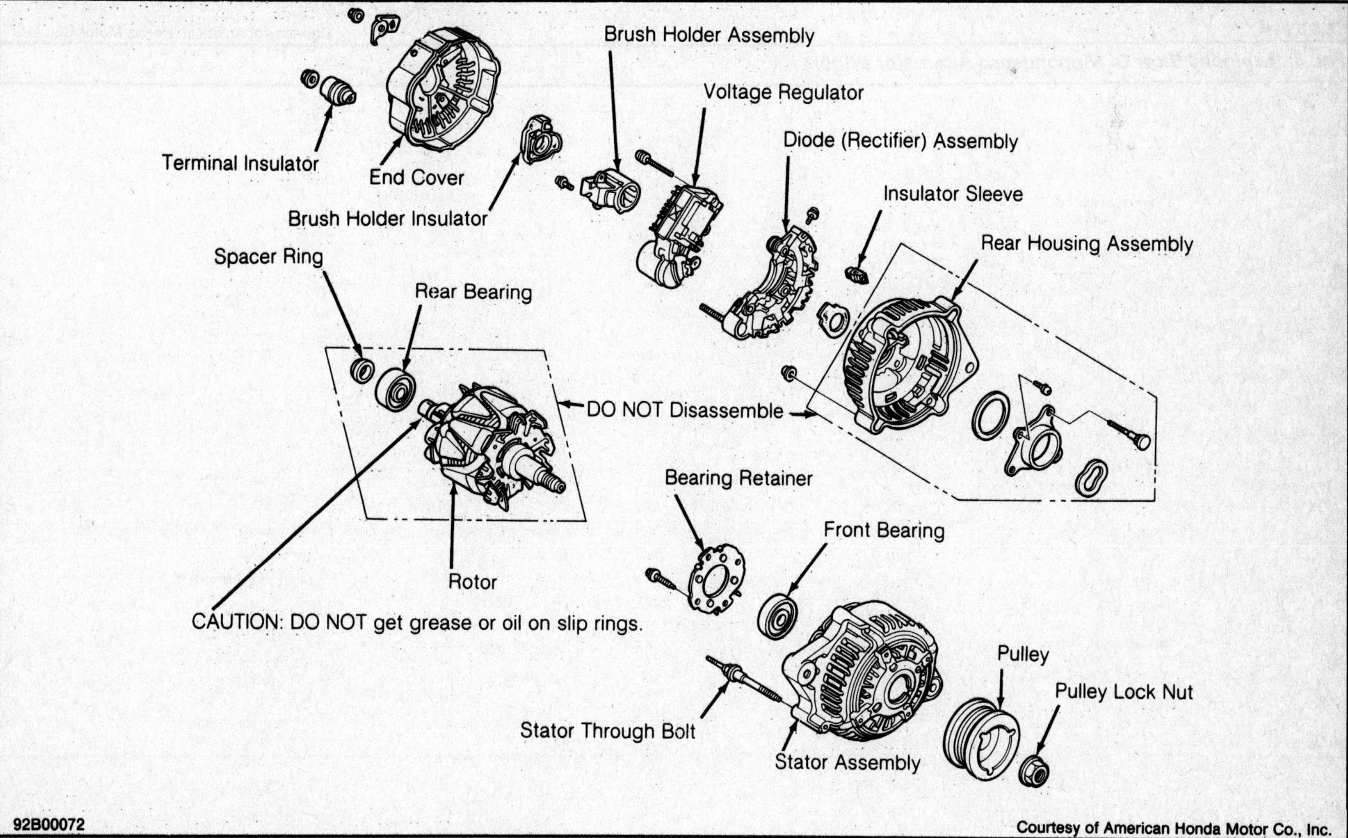

Brush Holder Assembly
Voltage Regulator
Diode (Rectifier) Assembly
Insulator Sleeve
Rear Housing Assembly
Terminal Insulator
End Cover
Brush Holder Insulator
Spacer Ring
Rear Bearing
DO NOT Disassemble
Bearing Retainer
Rotor
Front Bearing
CAUTION: DO NOT get grease or oil on slip rings.
Pulley
Pulley Lock Nut
Stator Through Bolt
Stator Assembly

92B00072

Courtesy of American Honda Motor Co., Inc.

Fig. 7: Exploded View Of Nippondenso Alternator (Legend)

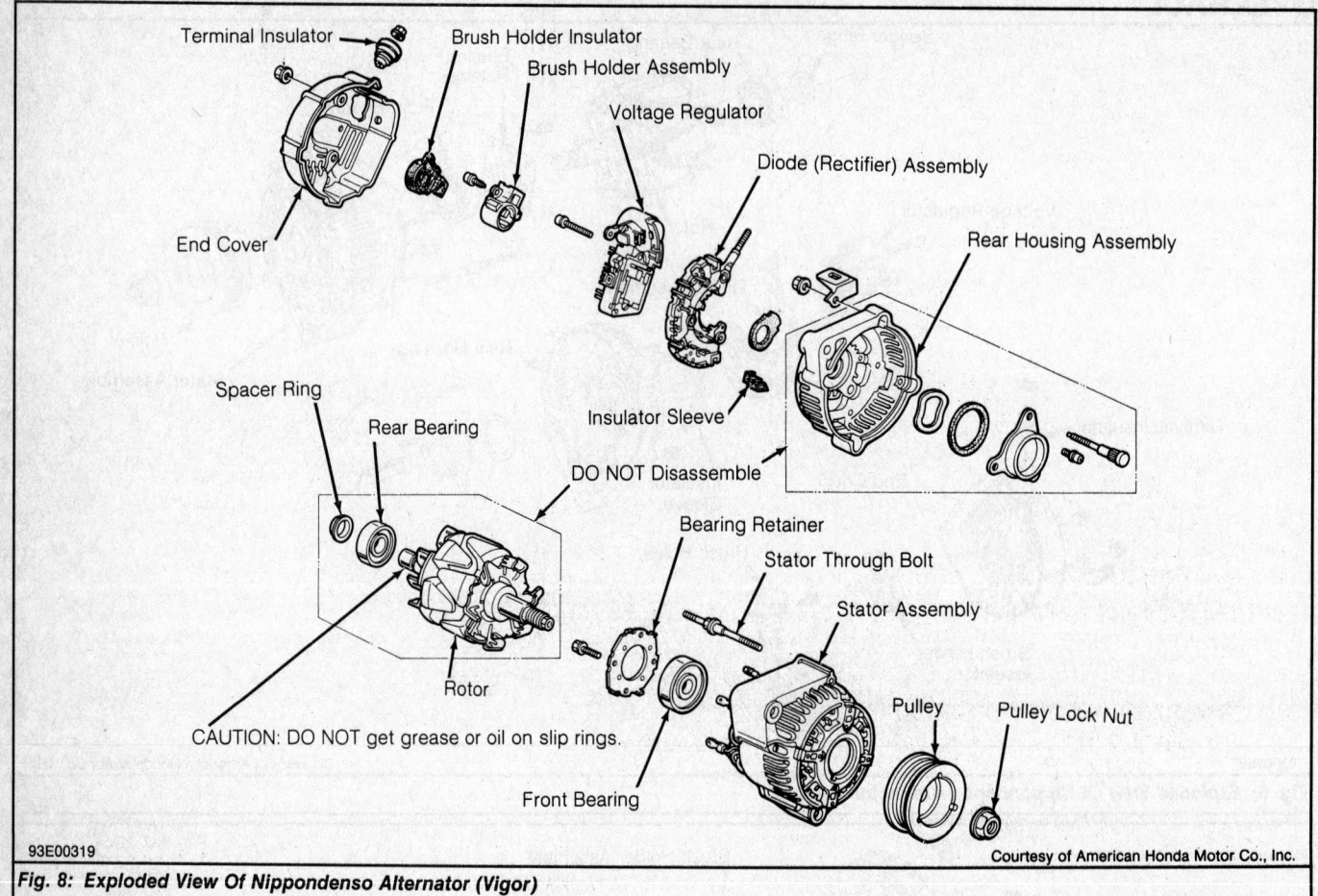

Fig. 8: Exploded View Of Nippondenso Alternator (Vigor)

93E00319

Courtesy of American Honda Motor Co., Inc.

WIRING DIAGRAMS

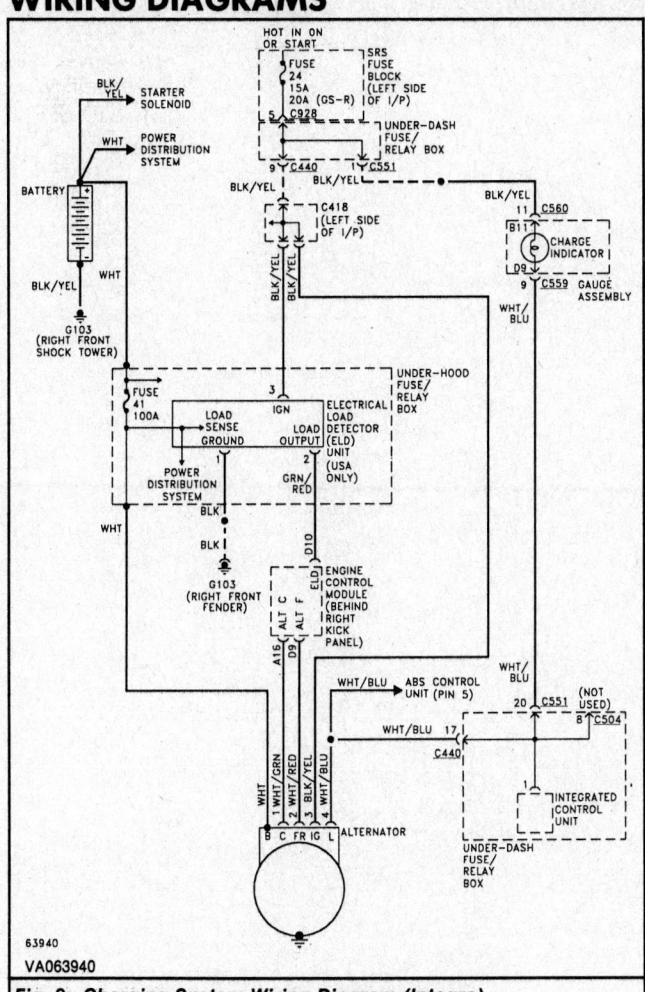

Fig. 9: Charging System Wiring Diagram (Integra)

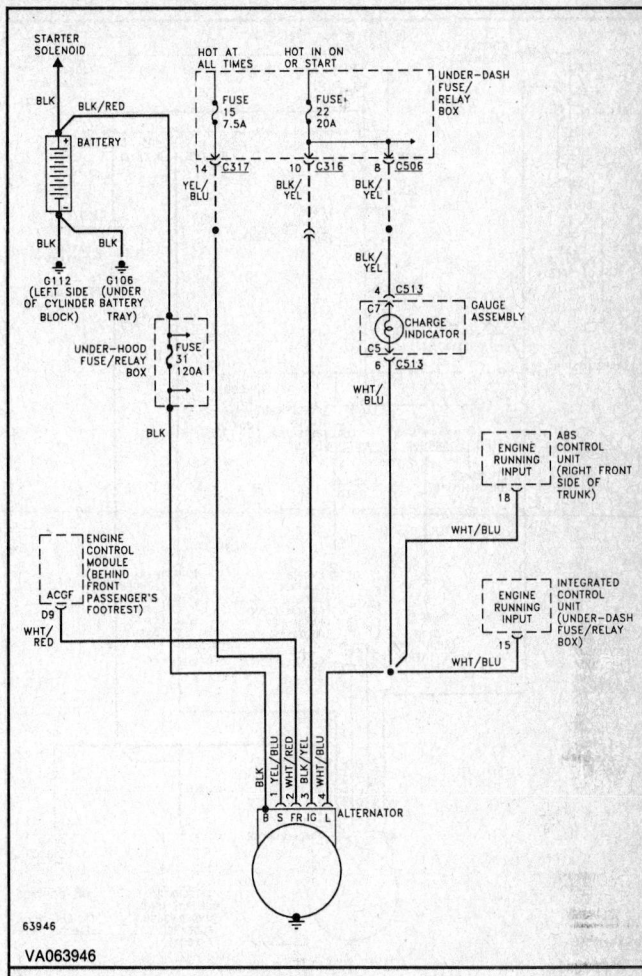

Fig. 10: Charging System Wiring Diagram (Legend)

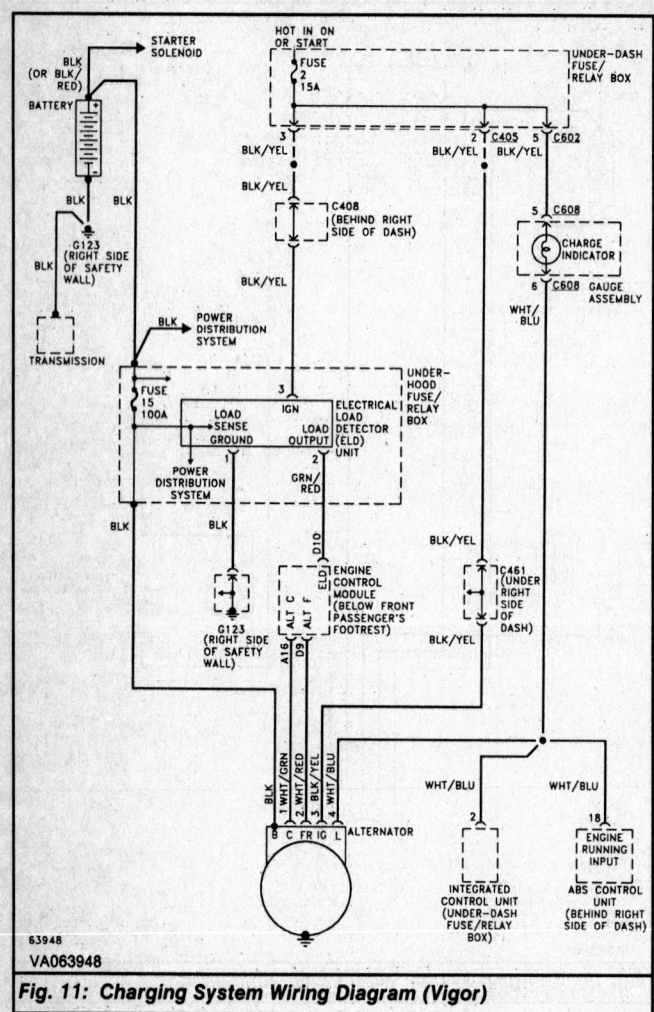

Fig. 11: Charging System Wiring Diagram (Vigor)

Integra, Legend, Vigor

DESCRIPTION & OPERATION

All starters are 4-brush, solenoid-actuated, gear-reduction type equipped with overrunning clutch. M/T models use a starter relay and a clutch interlock switch. A/T models use a starter relay and a neutral safety switch. On Integra, starter relay is mounted on the engine compartment firewall. On Legend and Vigor, starter relay is mounted on underdash fuse box.

Voltage from positive battery terminal is continuously applied to ignition switch. Starter solenoid contacts are normally open. When ignition switch is turned to the START position (clutch interlock switch or neutral safety switch closed), battery voltage is applied to the starter solenoid coils and starter engages.

TROUBLE SHOOTING

NOTE: See TROUBLE SHOOTING article in GENERAL INFORMATION.

ON-VEHICLE TESTING

STARTER FUNCTION TEST

1) Disconnect wiring harness connector from ignition coil. On M/T models, depress clutch pedal to floor. On all models, turn ignition switch to START position. Starter should crank.

NOTE: On M/T models, starter will not crank unless clutch pedal is fully depressed.

2) If starter does not crank, check battery condition. Check for loose or corroded battery cables and starter wires. Repair or replace as necessary. If starter still does not crank, unplug terminal "S" connector (Black/White wire) from starter solenoid.
3) Connect jumper wire between positive battery terminal and solenoid terminal "S". Starter should crank. If starter does not crank, remove starter and check for internal problems. If starter cranks, check Black/White wire, fuse, starter relay, ignition switch, clutch interlock switch (M/T) or neutral safety switch (A/T). Repair or replace as necessary.

CRANKING TEST

1) Connect a voltmeter and ammeter to battery. See Fig. 1. On Integra and Vigor, disconnect connector from distributor. On Legend, disconnect 8-pin and 6-pin connectors from ignition control module. Ignition control module is located on right side of engine compartment.
2) On all models, use remote starter switch to crank engine. Check cranking voltage and current draw. Ensure voltage is at least 8 volts. Current draw should be less than 350 amps. Cranking speed should be greater than 100 RPM.

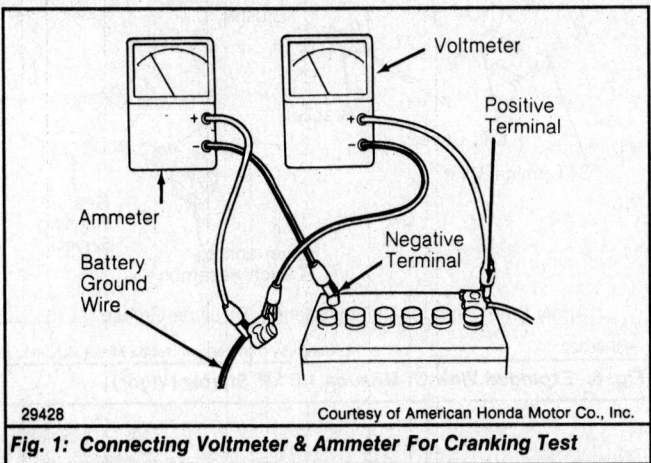

29428   Courtesy of American Honda Motor Co., Inc.

Fig. 1: Connecting Voltmeter & Ammeter For Cranking Test

BENCH TESTING

BRUSH HOLDER TEST

1) Ensure continuity does not exist between positive and negative brush holders. If continuity exists, replace brush holder assembly. Install brush into brush holder. Ensure brush contacts commutator.
2) Attach a spring scale to brush spring. Measure tension of spring as spring lifts off brush. If spring tension is not within specification, replace brush holder assembly. See STARTER SPECIFICATIONS table.

BRUSH TEST

Check brush length. If length is not within specification, replace brushes. See STARTER SPECIFICATIONS table. If brushes are replaced, wrap No. 600 sandpaper around commutator. Rotate commutator across face of brushes to seat new starter brush assemblies.

COMMUTATOR TEST

1) Check for continuity between commutator segments. If continuity is not present, replace armature. Measure commutator mica depth. See STARTER SPECIFICATIONS table. If mica depth not within specifications, replace commutator.
2) Measure commutator runout. See STARTER SPECIFICATIONS table. If runout is not within specifications, replace armature assembly. If commutator is burnt or dirty, clean using emery cloth or a lathe. Measure commutator diameter. See STARTER SPECIFICATIONS table. If diameter is less than minimum specification, replace armature assembly.

ARMATURE COIL TEST

Using an ohmmeter, check for continuity between commutator and armature coil core. Check for continuity between armature shaft and armature coil core. If continuity exists, replace armature. Using a growler, check armature for shorts. If continuity does not exist, replace armature.

FIELD COIL TEST

Integra & Vigor – Check for continuity between brushes. If continuity is not present, replace armature housing. Check for continuity between brushes and armature housing. If continuity is present, replace armature housing.

SOLENOID PLUNGER INSPECTION

Integra – Check contact points and face of starter solenoid plunger for burning and pitting. If surfaces are rough, recondition using a strip of No. 600 sandpaper.

STARTER SOLENOID TEST

Integra – Check starter solenoid for continuity between terminal "S" and armature housing (ground). See Fig. 2. Check continuity between terminals "S" and "M". Continuity should be present. If continuity is not present, replace solenoid.

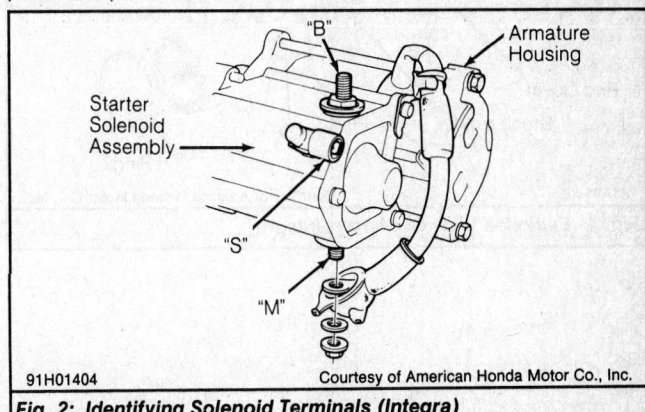

91H01404   Courtesy of American Honda Motor Co., Inc.

Fig. 2: Identifying Solenoid Terminals (Integra)

Legend & Vigor – Remove starter solenoid from starter. With starter solenoid plunger in released position, continuity should exist between terminals "M" and "S" and solenoid housing (ground). *See Fig. 3.* With starter solenoid plunger pushed in, continuity should exist between terminals "B", "M" and "S" and solenoid housing. If continuity is not present, replace solenoid.

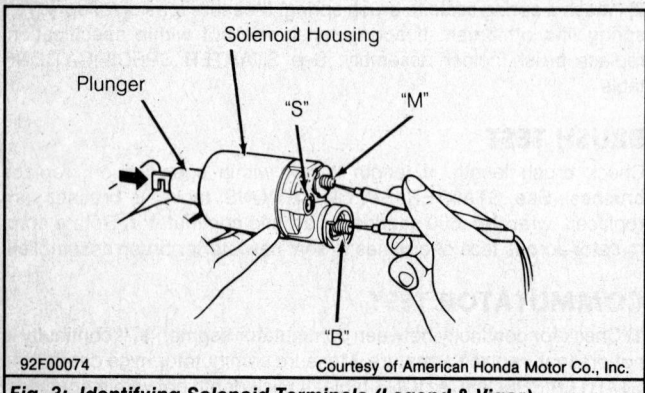

92F00074   Courtesy of American Honda Motor Co., Inc.

Fig. 3: Identifying Solenoid Terminals (Legend & Vigor)

OVERHAUL

NOTE: See exploded views of starters. See Figs. 4-8.

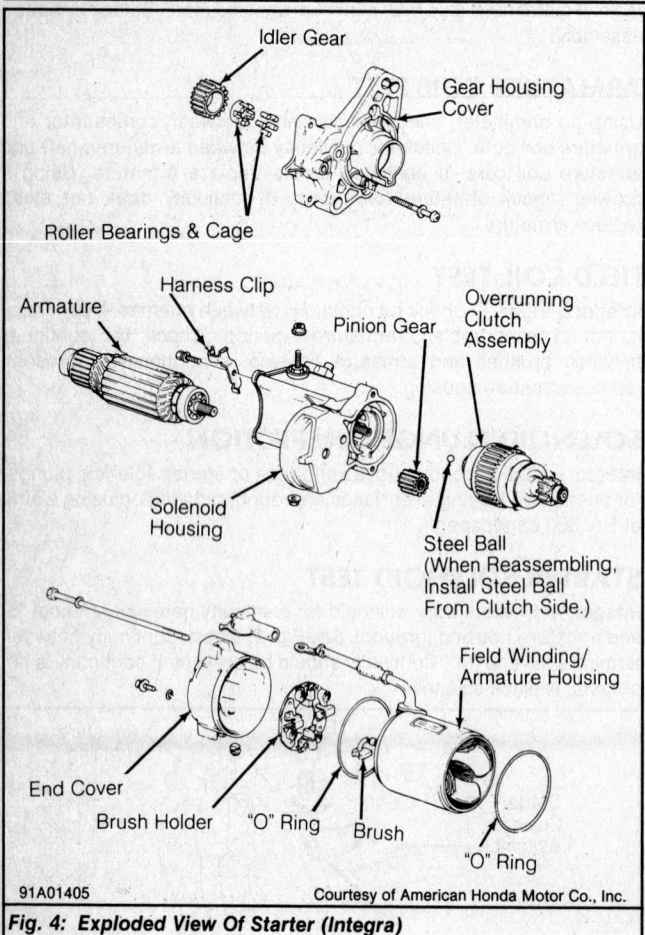

91A01405   Courtesy of American Honda Motor Co., Inc.

Fig. 4: Exploded View Of Starter (Integra)

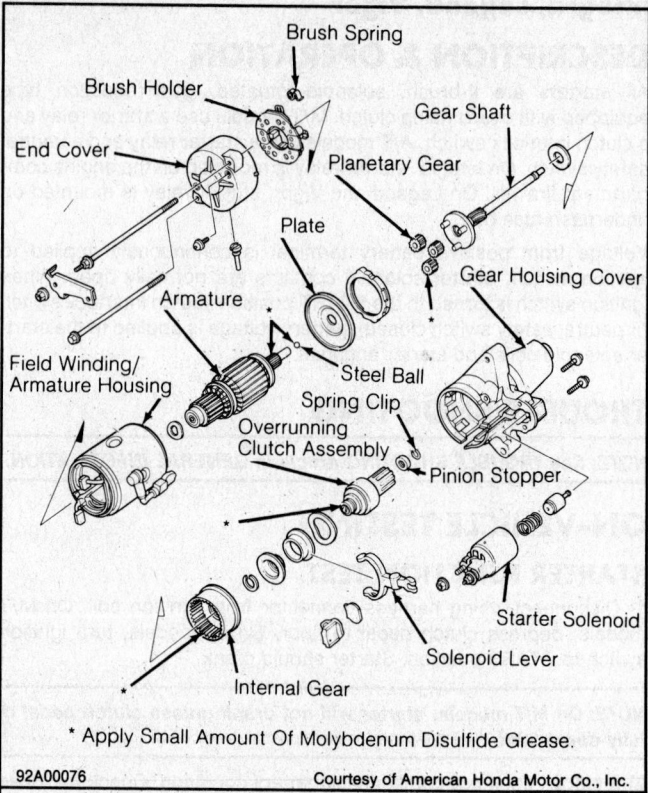

* Apply Small Amount Of Molybdenum Disulfide Grease.

92A00076   Courtesy of American Honda Motor Co., Inc.

Fig. 5: Exploded View Of Starter (Legend)

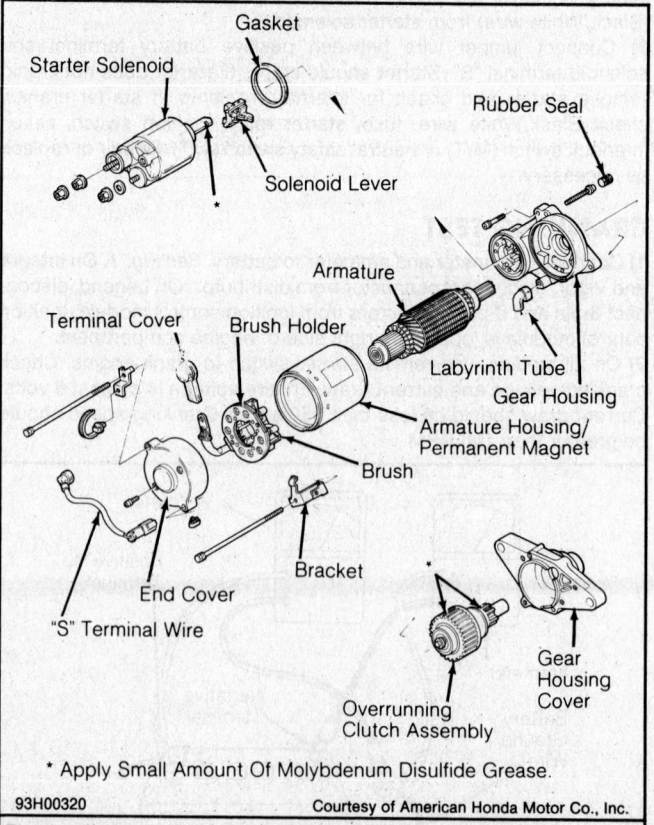

* Apply Small Amount Of Molybdenum Disulfide Grease.

93H00320   Courtesy of American Honda Motor Co., Inc.

Fig. 6: Exploded View Of Mitsuba 1.6 kW Starter (Vigor)

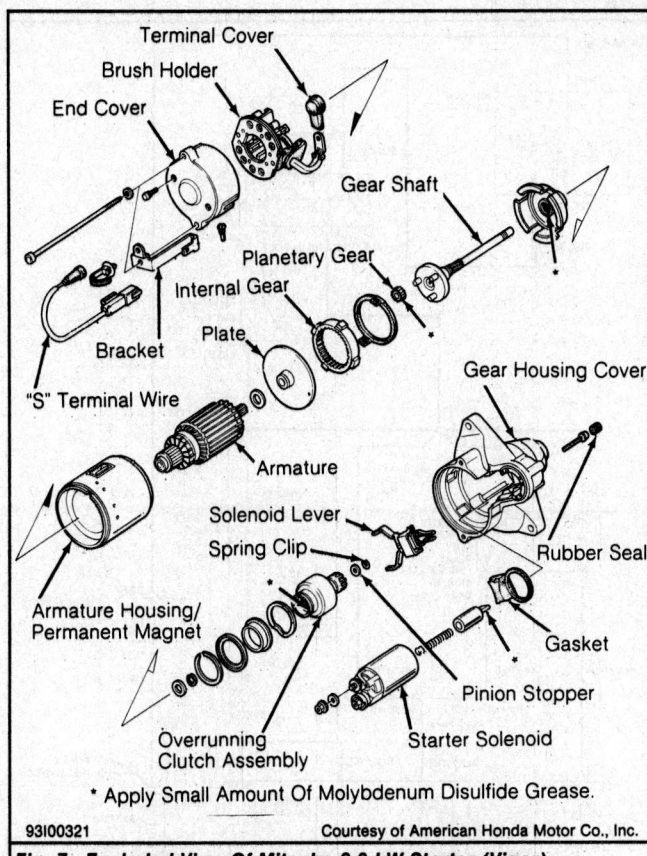

Fig. 7: Exploded View Of Mitsuba 2.0 kW Starter (Vigor)

93I00321 — Courtesy of American Honda Motor Co., Inc.

* Apply Small Amount Of Molybdenum Disulfide Grease.

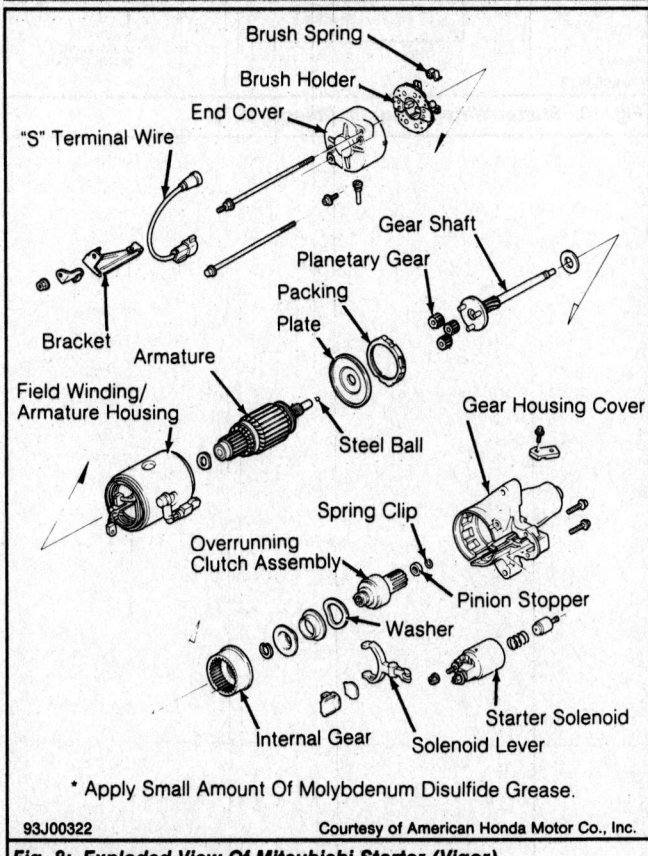

Fig. 8: Exploded View Of Mitsubishi Starter (Vigor)

93J00322 — Courtesy of American Honda Motor Co., Inc.

* Apply Small Amount Of Molybdenum Disulfide Grease.

STARTER SPECIFICATIONS

STARTER SPECIFICATIONS

Application	Specification
Carbon Brush	
Length (Standard)	
Integra	0.59-0.61" (15.0-15.5 mm)
Legend	0.71" (18.0 mm)
Vigor	
Mitsuba 1.6 KW	0.62-0.64" (15.8-16.2 mm)
Mitsuba 2.0 KW	0.66-0.68" (16.8-17.2 mm)
Mitsubishi 2.0 KW	0.71" (18.0 mm)
Length (Minimum)	
Integra	0.39" (10.0 mm)
Legend	0.43" (11.0 mm)
Vigor	
Mitsuba 1.6 KW	0.43" (11.0 mm)
Mitsuba 2.0 KW	0.43" (11.0 mm)
Mitsubishi 2.0 KW	0.43" (11.0 mm)
Spring Tension	
Integra	3.8-5.3 Lbs. (1.7-2.4 Kg)
Legend	6.55-8.00 Lbs. (2.97-3.63 Kg)
Vigor	
Mitsuba 1.6 KW	3.57-3.97 Lbs. (1.60-1.80 Kg)
Mitsuba 2.0 KW	3.75-4.19 Lbs. (1.70-1.90 Kg)
Mitsubishi 2.0 KW	6.55-8.00 Lbs. (2.97-3.63 Kg)
Commutator	
Diameter (Standard)	
Integra	1.177-1.181" (29.9-30.0 mm)
Legend	1.256-1.263" (31.9-32.1 mm)
Vigor	
Mitsuba 1.6 KW	1.102-1.106" (28.0-28.1 mm)
Mitsuba 2.0 KW	1.259-1.263" (32.0-32.1 mm)
Mitsubishi 2.0 KW	1.256-1.263" (31.9-32.1 mm)
Diameter (Minimum)	
Integra	1.14" (29.0 mm)
Legend	1.24" (31.5 mm)
Vigor	
Mitsuba 1.6 KW	1.083" (27.7 mm)
Mitsuba 2.0 KW	1.24" (31.5 mm)
Mitsubishi 2.0 KW	1.24" (31.5 mm)
Runout (Standard)	
Integra	0.001" (0.02 mm)
Legend	0.002" (0.05 mm)
Vigor	
Mitsuba 1.6 KW	0.0008" (0.02 mm)
Mitsuba 2.0 KW	0.0008" (0.02 mm)
Mitsubishi 2.0 KW	0.002" (0.05 mm)
Runout (Maximum)	
Integra	0.002" (0.05 mm)
Legend	0.004" (0.10 mm)
Vigor	
Mitsuba 1.6 KW	0.002" (0.05 mm)
Mitsuba 2.0 KW	0.002" (0.05 mm)
Mitsubishi 2.0 KW	0.004" (0.10 mm)
Mica Depth (Standard)	
Integra	0.019-0.031" (0.5-0.8 mm)
Legend	0.019-0.031" (0.5-0.8 mm)
Vigor	
Mitsuba 1.6 KW	0.016-0.020" (0.40-0.50 mm)
Mitsuba 2.0 KW	0.016-0.020" (0.40-0.50 mm)
Mitsubishi 2.0 KW	0.02-0.03" (0.5-0.8 mm)
Mica Depth (Minumum)	
Integra	0.008" (0.2 mm)
Legend	0.008" (0.2 mm)
Vigor	
Mitsuba 1.6 KW	0.006" (0.15 mm)
Mitsuba 2.0 KW	0.006" (0.15 mm)
Mitsubishi 2.0 KW	0.008" (0.02 mm)
Pinion Gap	
Integra	[1]
Legend & Vigor	0.02-0.08" (0.5-2.0 mm)
No Load At 11 Volts	
Maximum Amps	
Integra	90
Legend	140
Vigor	
Mitsuba 1.6 KW	80
Mitsuba 2.0 KW	90
Mitsubishi 2.0 KW	140

[1] – Specification is not provided by manufacturer.

STARTER SPECIFICATIONS (Cont.)

Application	Specification
Minimum RPM	
Integra	3000
Legend	3800
Vigor	
Mitsuba 1.6 KW	2600
Mitsuba 2.0 KW	2200
Mitsubishi 2.0 KW	3800

TORQUE SPECIFICATIONS
TORQUE SPECIFICATIONS

Application	Ft. Lbs. (N.m)
Starter Mounting Bolts	
Integra	33 (45)
Legend	55 (75)
Vigor	
Lower	55 (75)
Upper	33 (45)

	INCH Lbs. (N.m)
Battery Terminal Nut	
All Models	89 (10)

WIRING DIAGRAMS

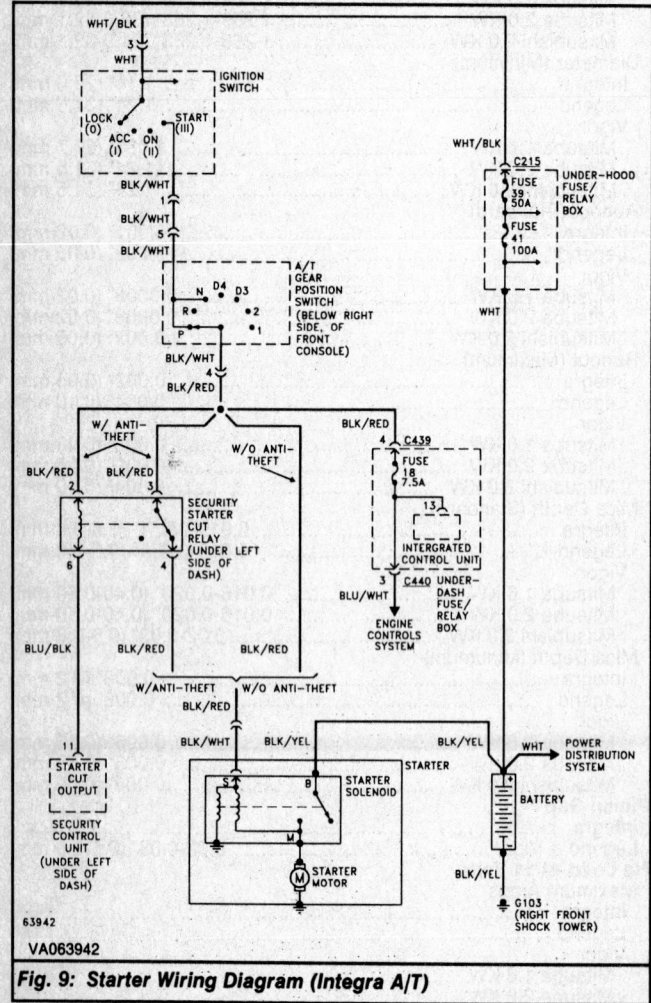

Fig. 9: Starter Wiring Diagram (Integra A/T)

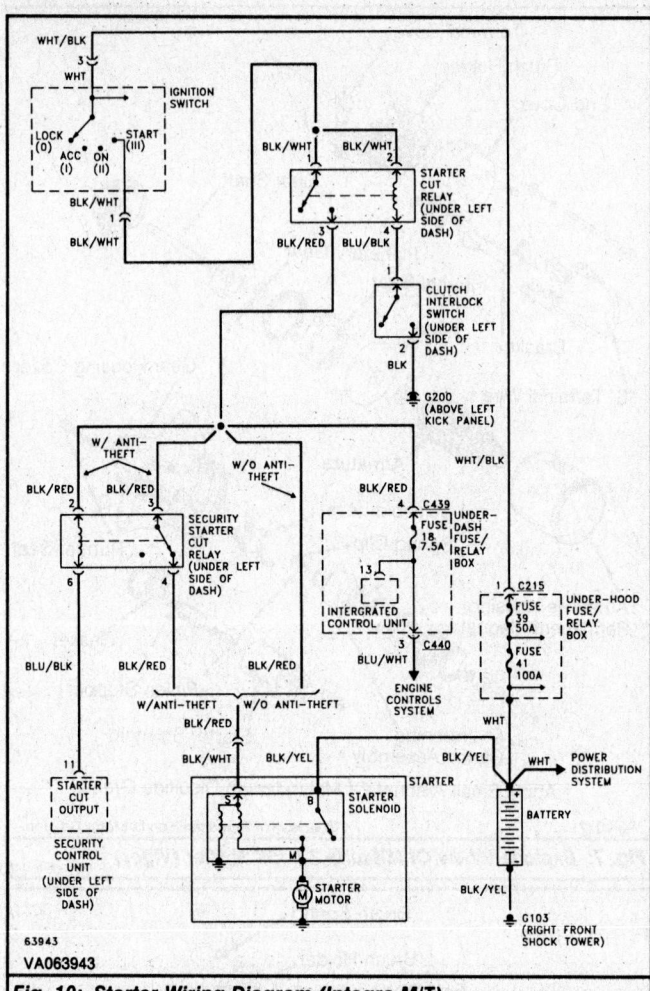

Fig. 10: Starter Wiring Diagram (Integra M/T)

1994 ELECTRICAL
Starters (Cont.)

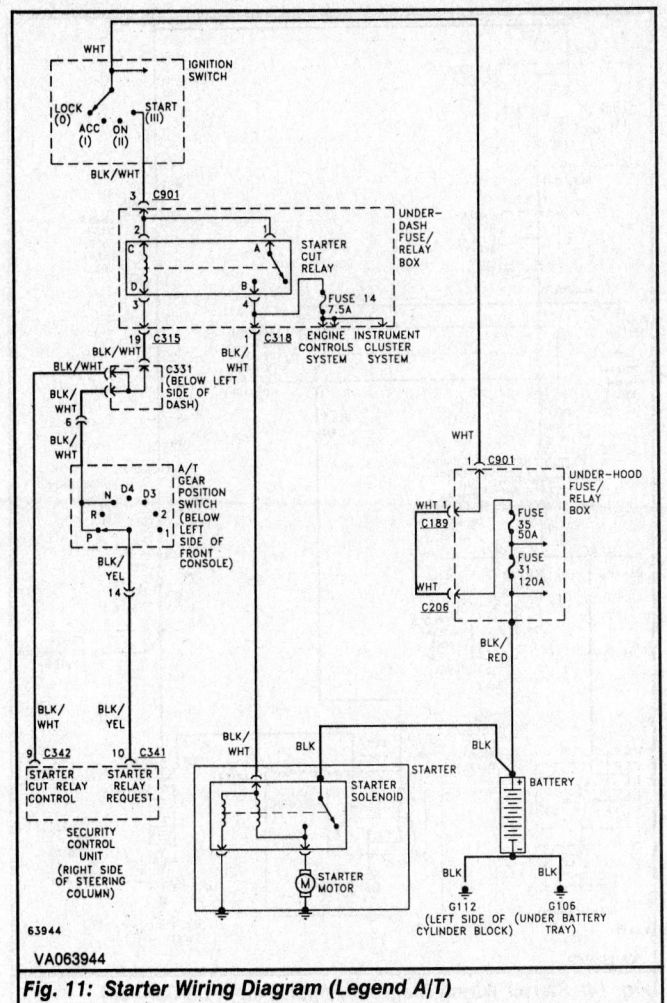

Fig. 11: Starter Wiring Diagram (Legend A/T)

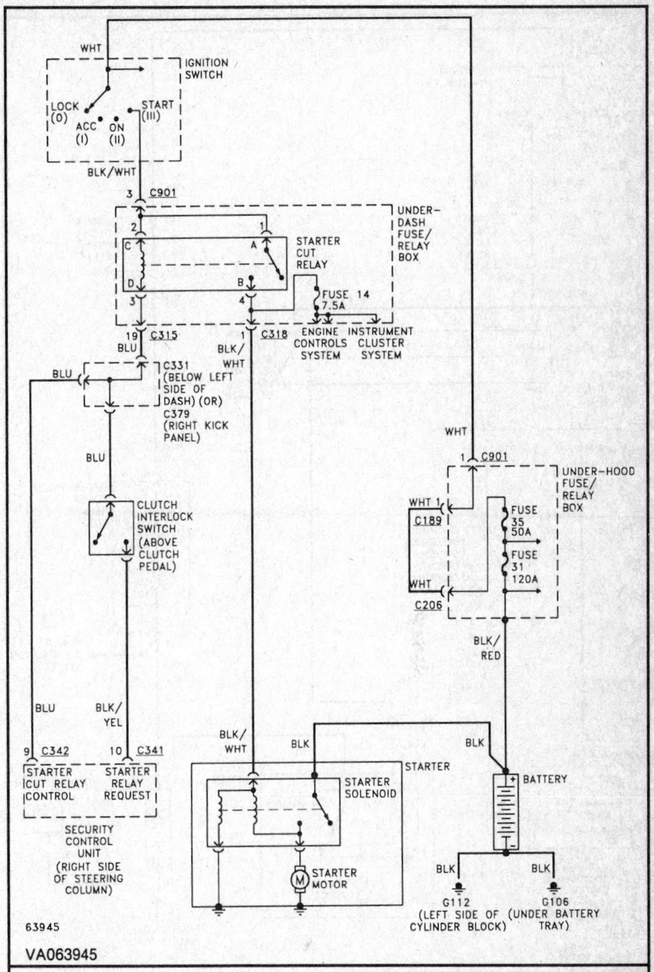

Fig. 12: Starter Wiring Diagram (Legend M/T)

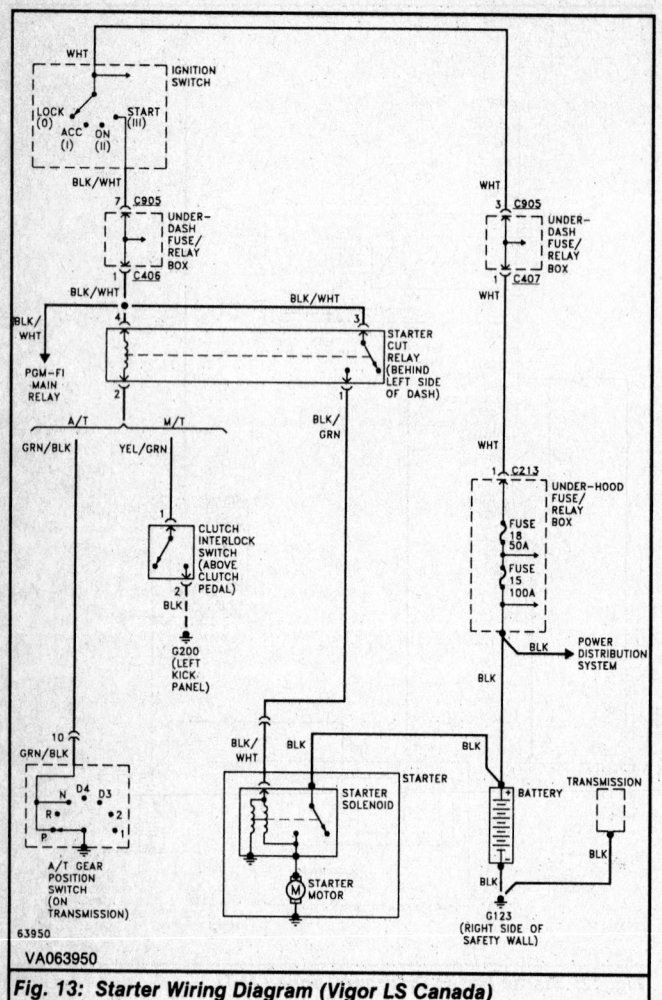

Fig. 13: Starter Wiring Diagram (Vigor LS Canada)

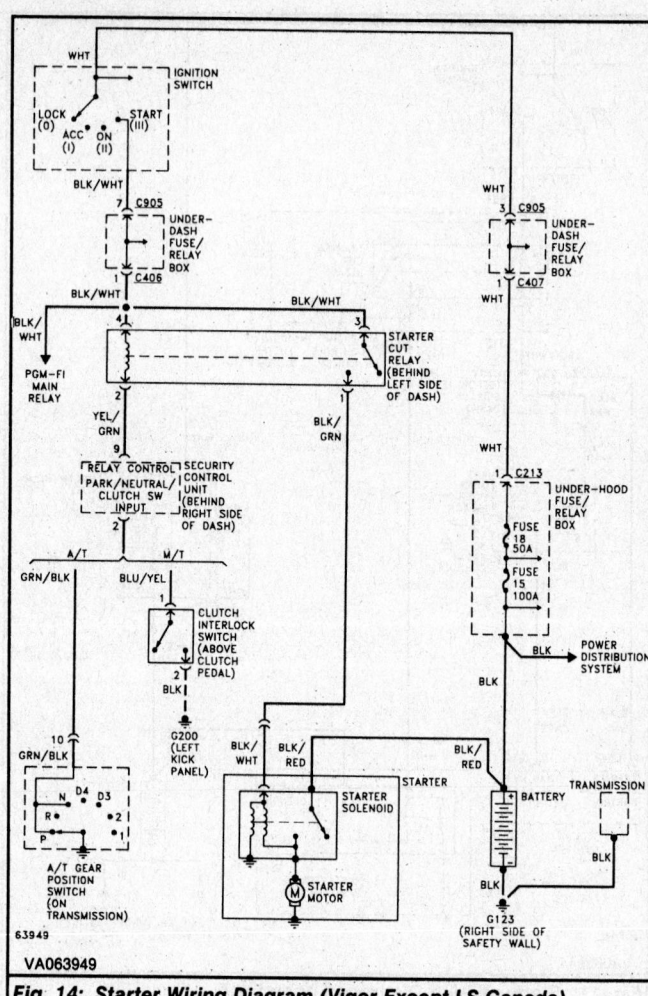

Fig. 14: Starter Wiring Diagram (Vigor Except LS Canada)

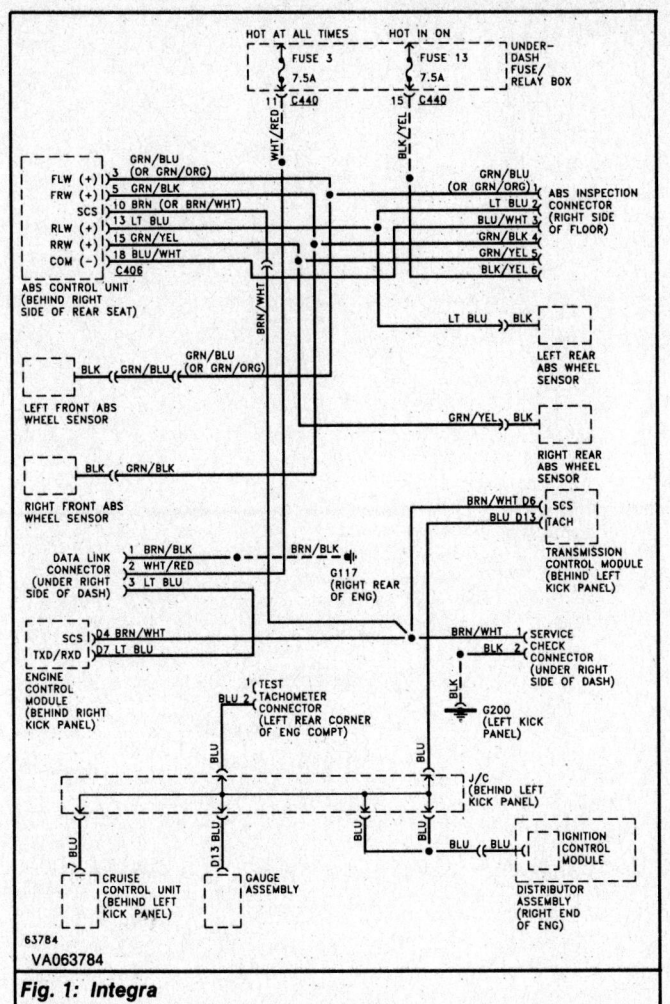

Fig. 1: Integra

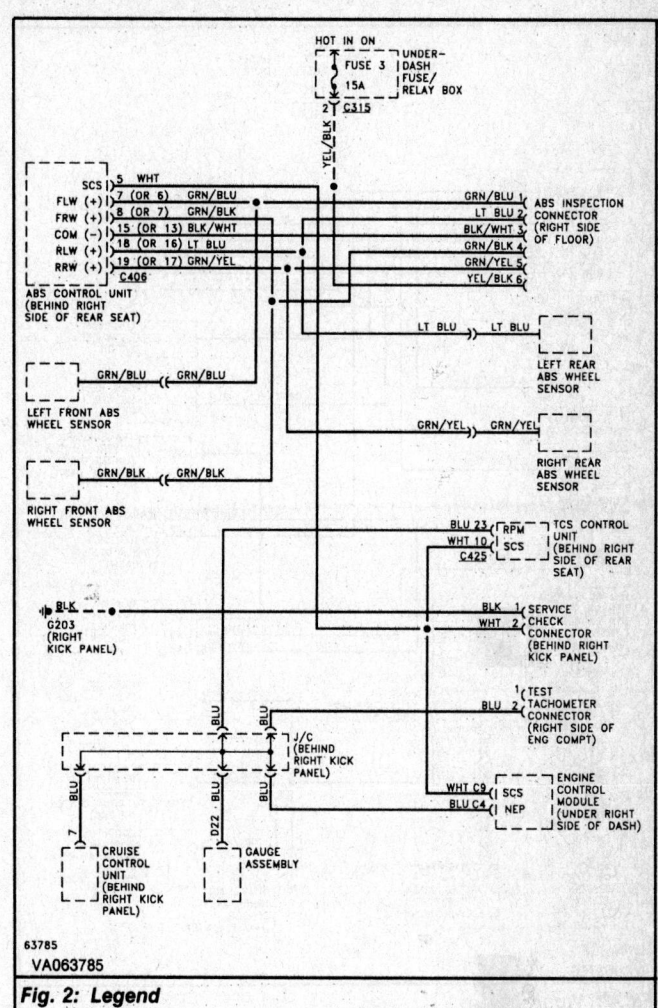

Fig. 2: Legend

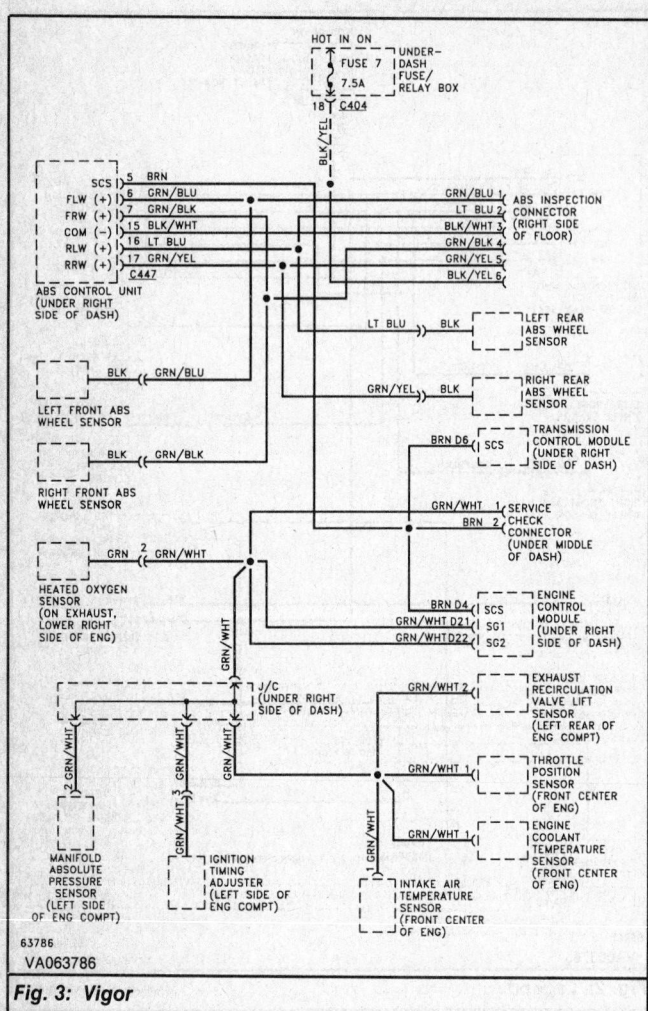

Fig. 3: Vigor

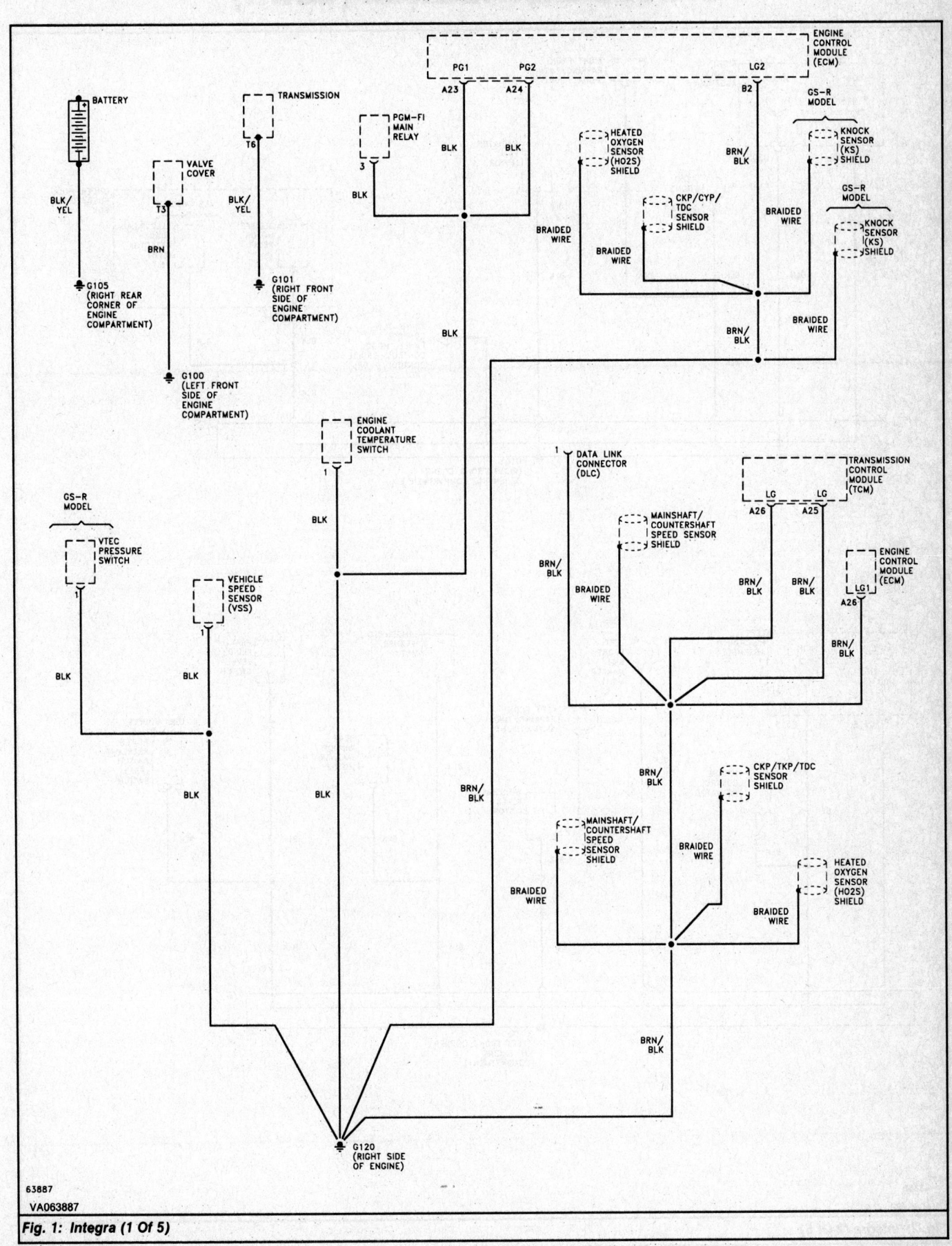

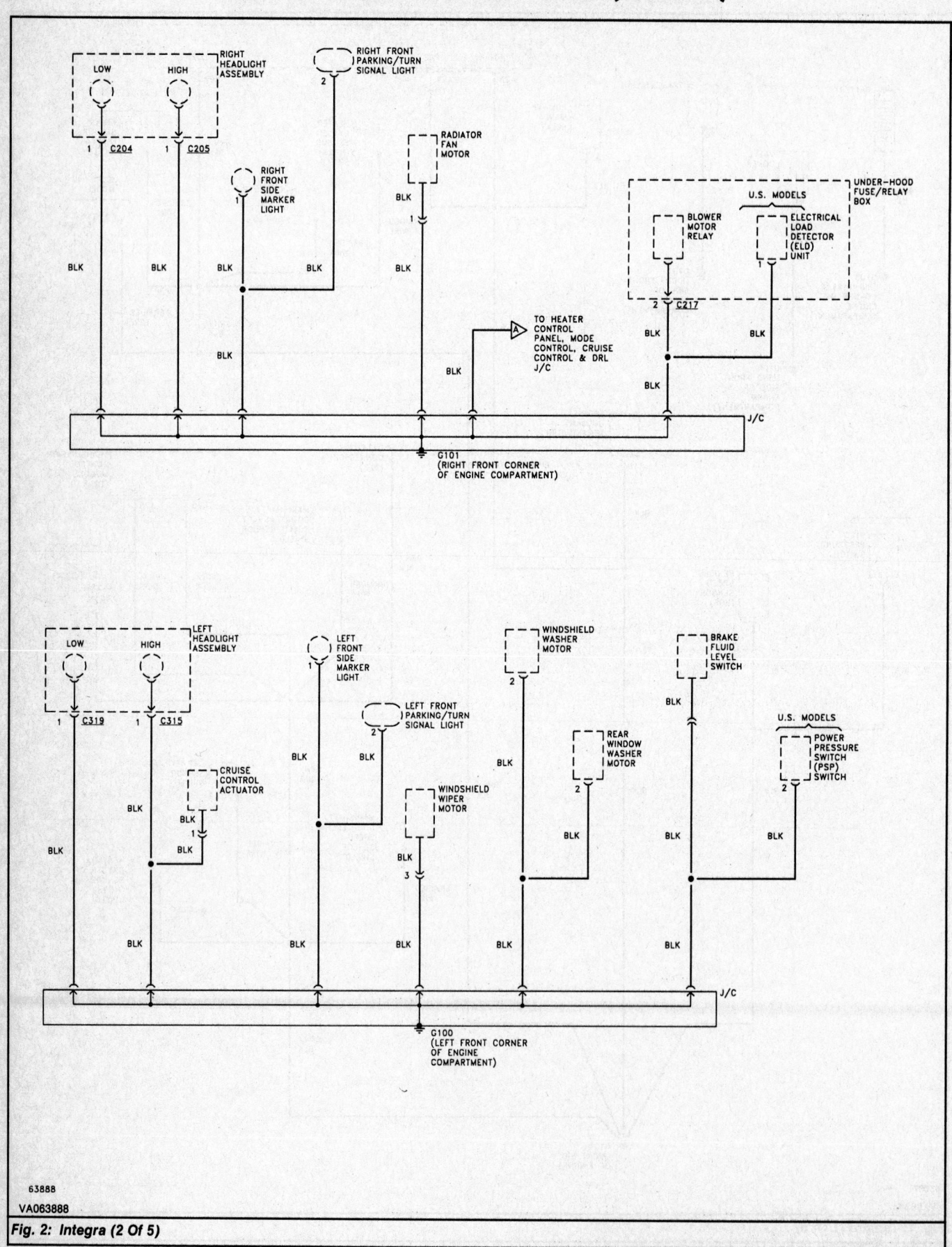

63888

VA063888

Fig. 2: Integra (2 Of 5)

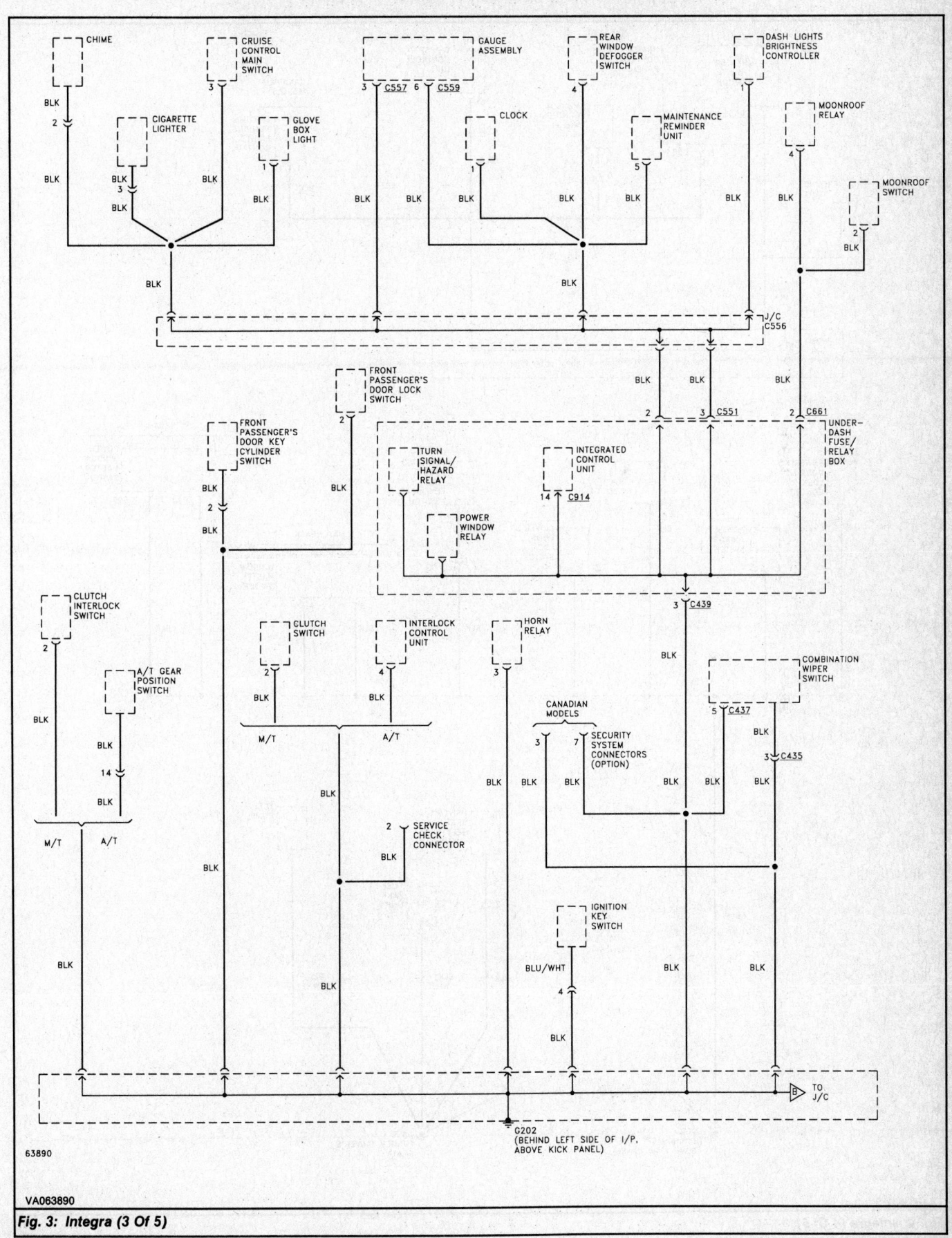

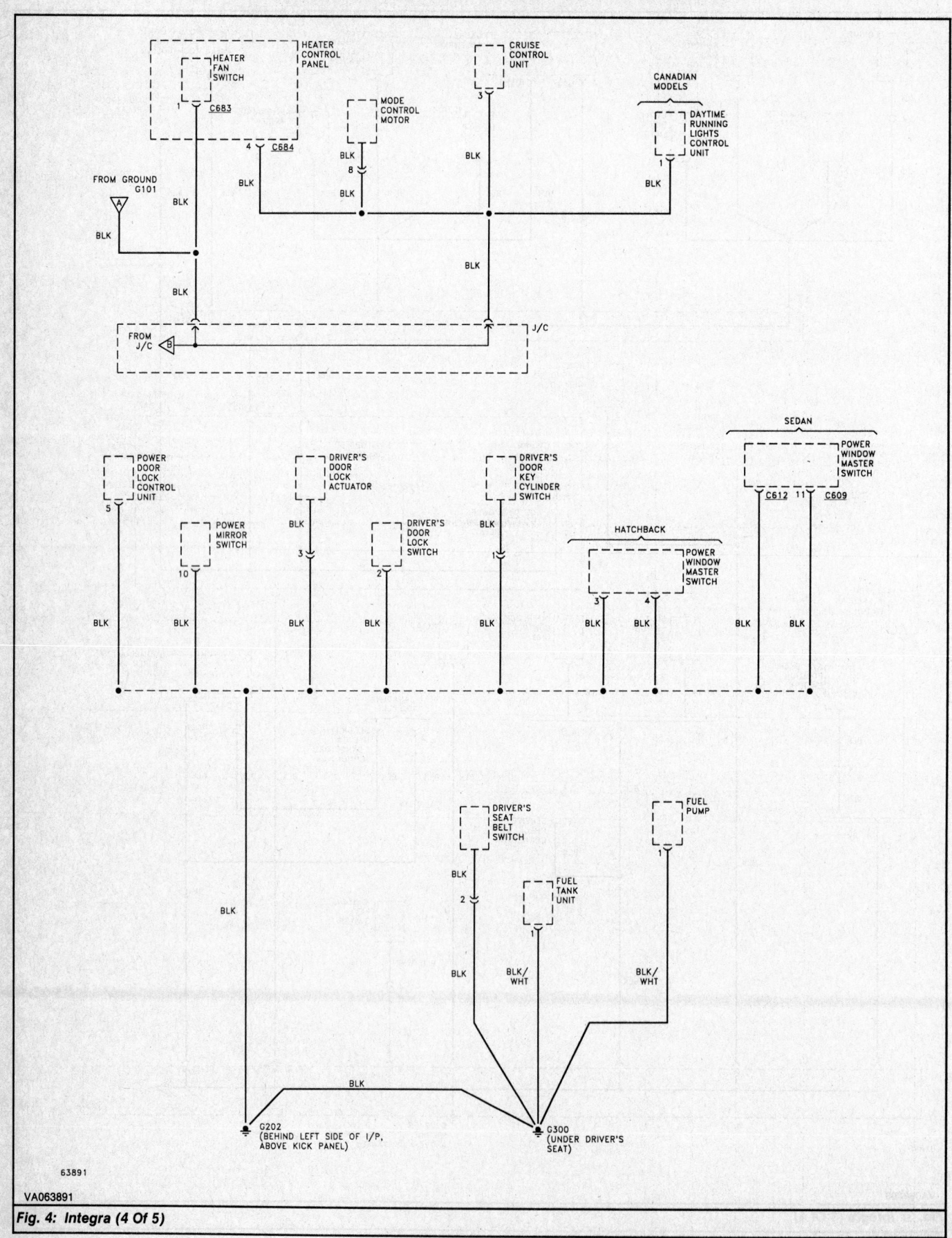

63891

VA063891

Fig. 4: Integra (4 Of 5)

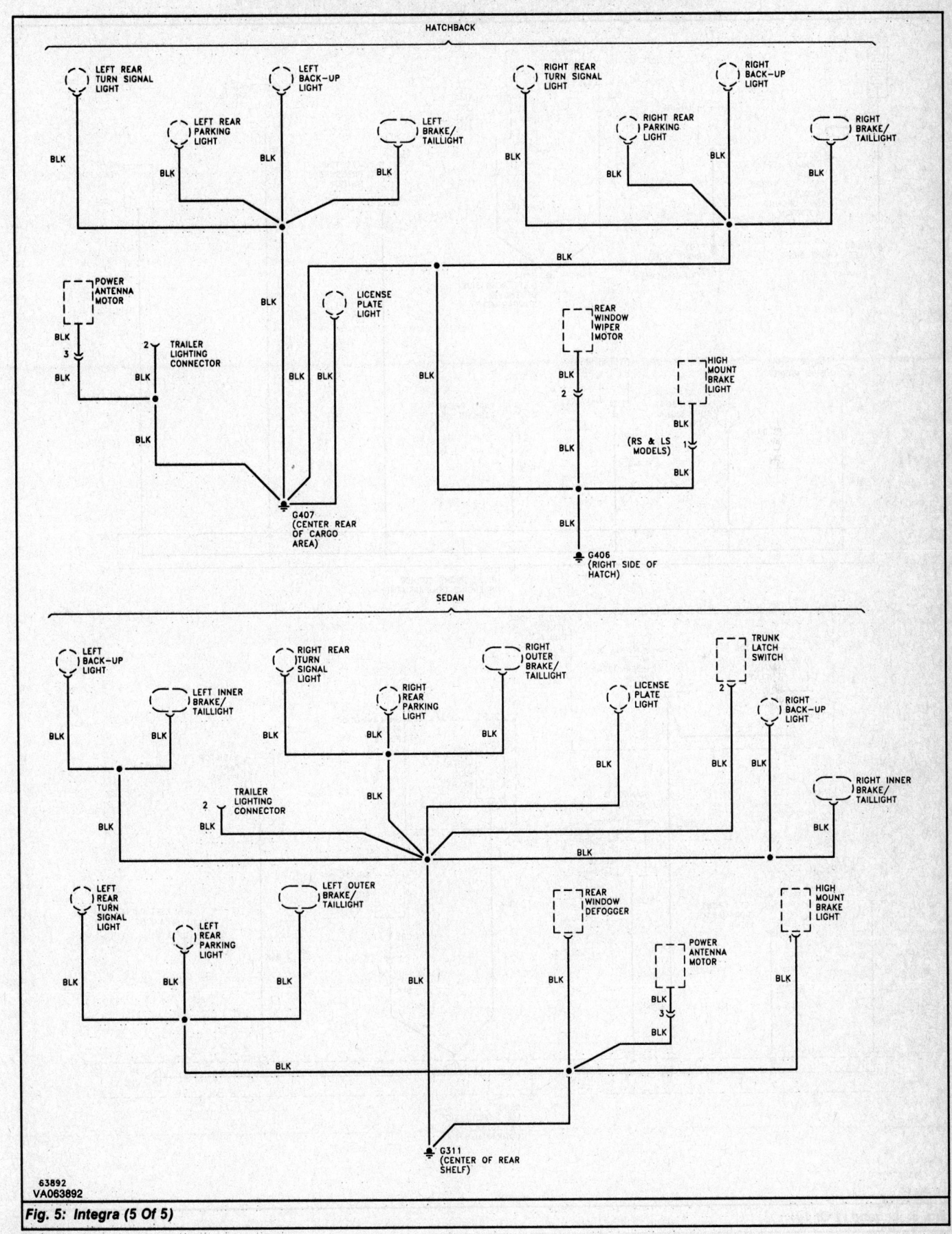

63892
VA063892

Fig. 5: Integra (5 Of 5)

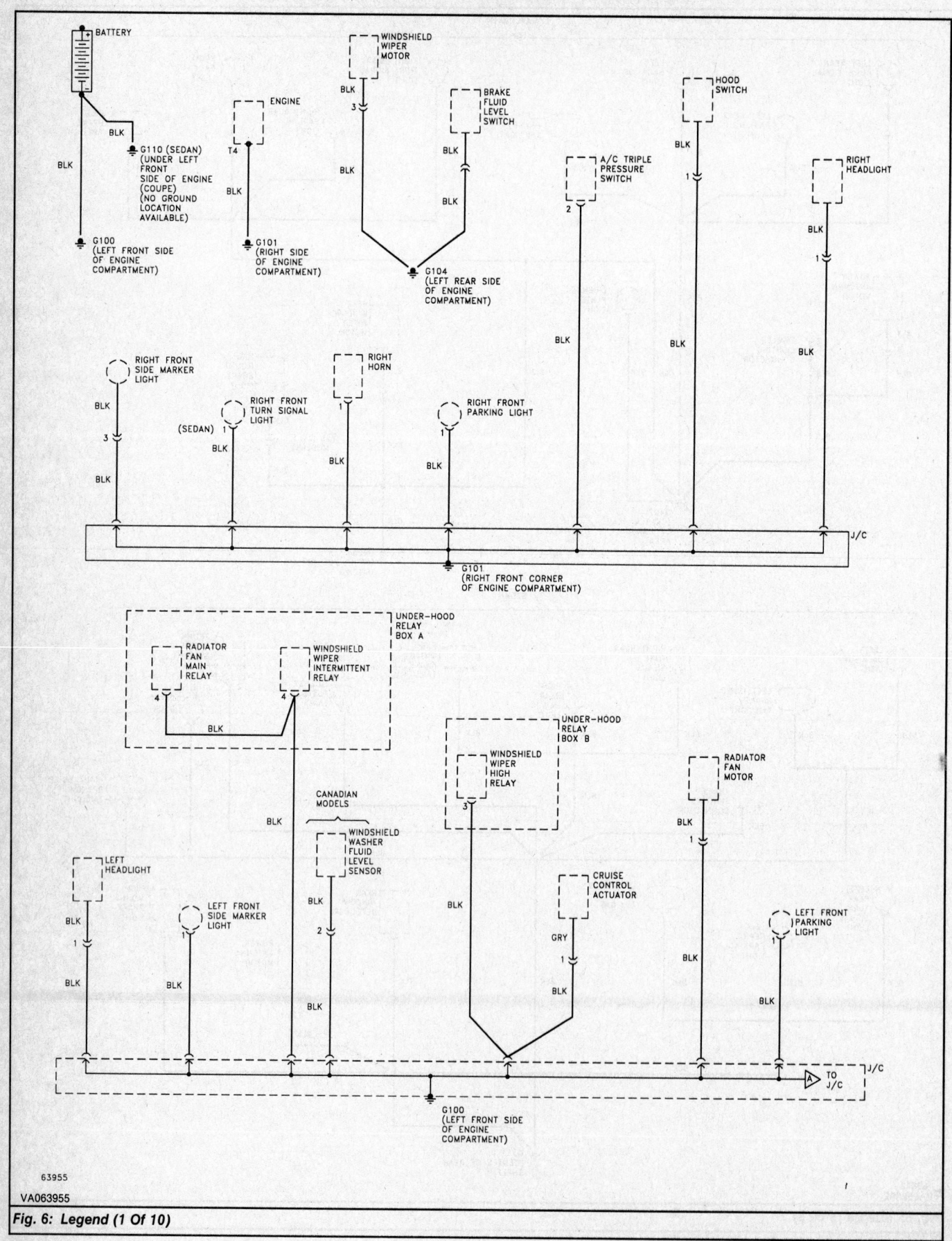

63955

VA063955

Fig. 6: Legend (1 Of 10)

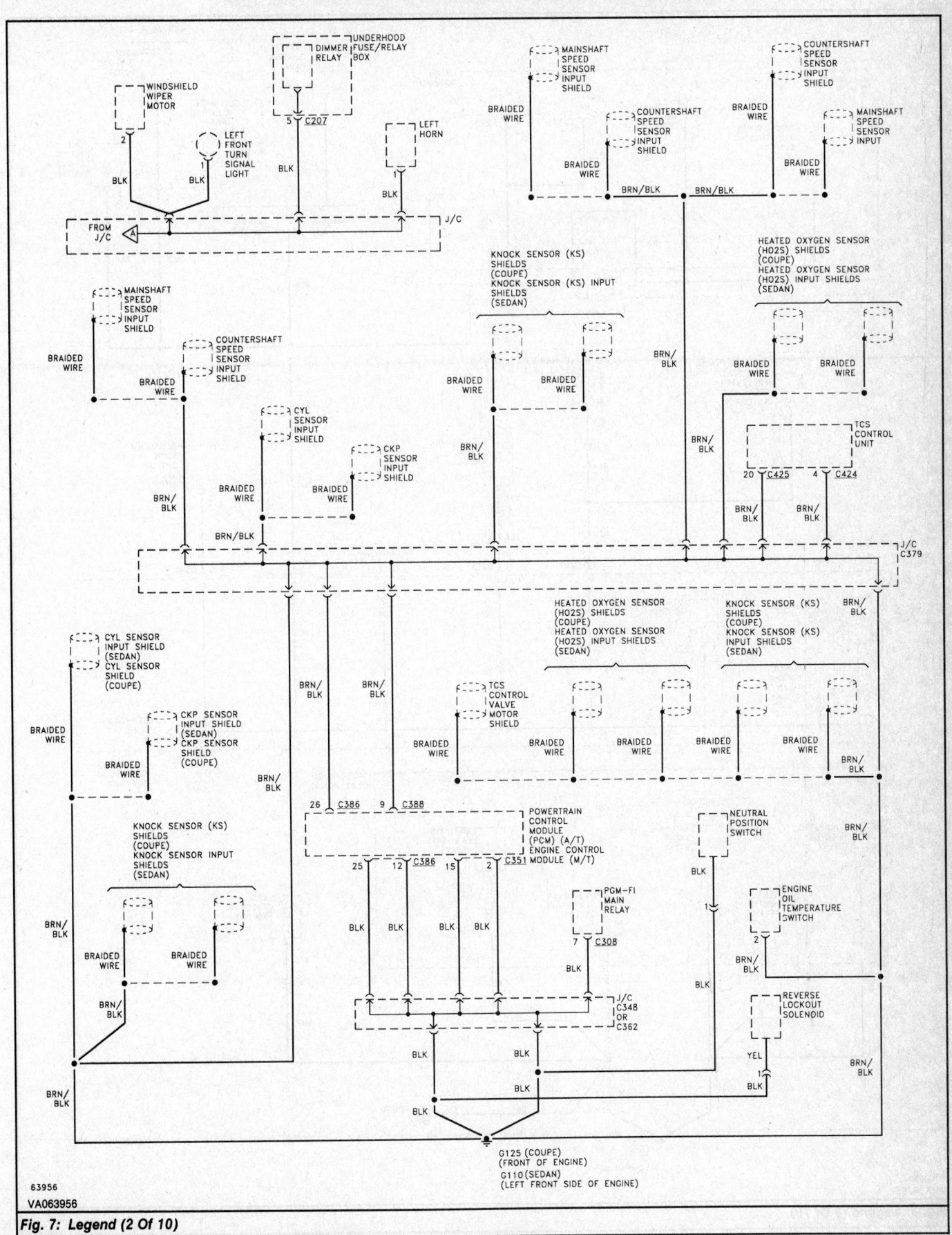

Fig. 7: Legend (2 Of 10)

63956

VA063956

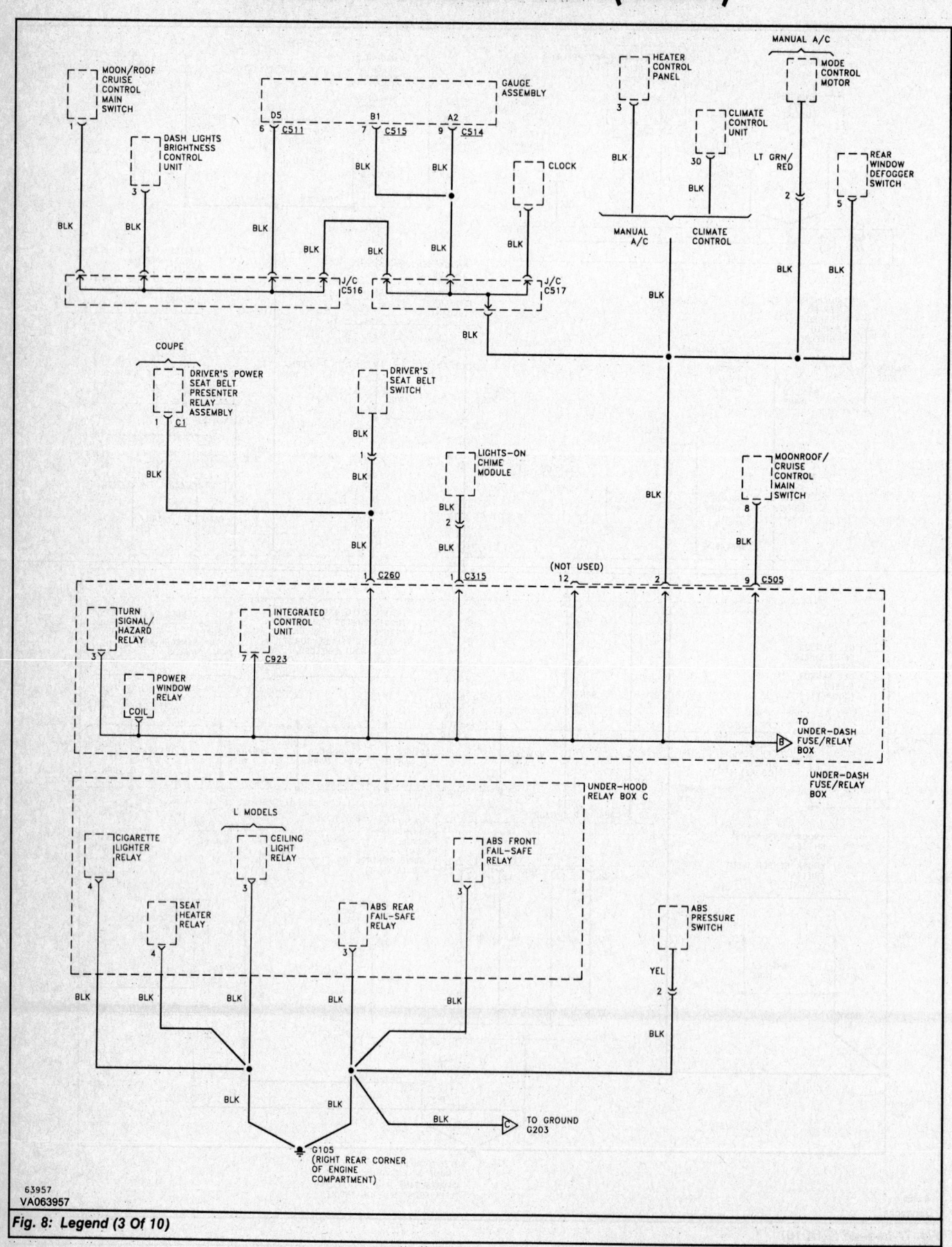

63957
VA063957

Fig. 8: Legend (3 Of 10)

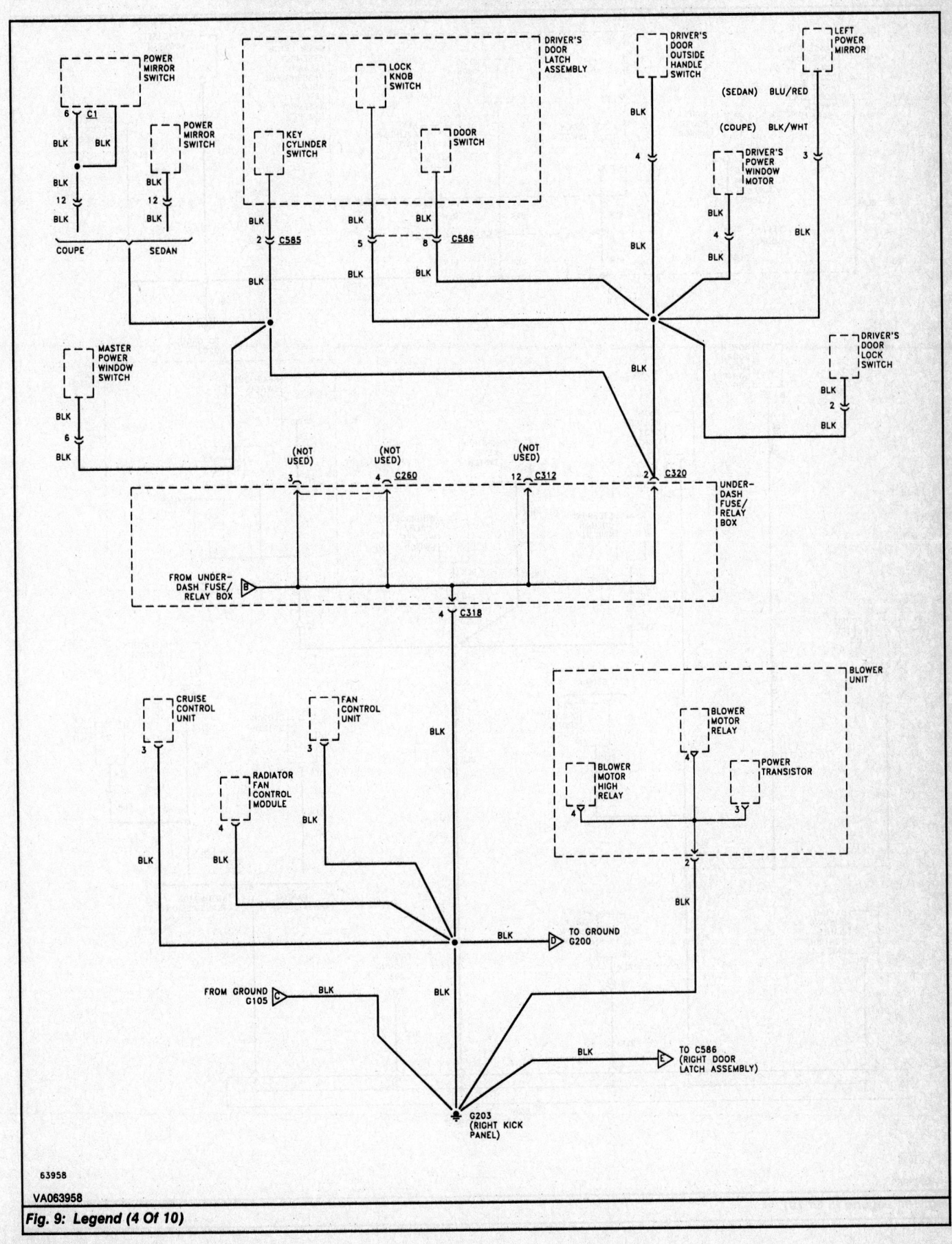

63958

VA063958

Fig. 9: Legend (4 Of 10)

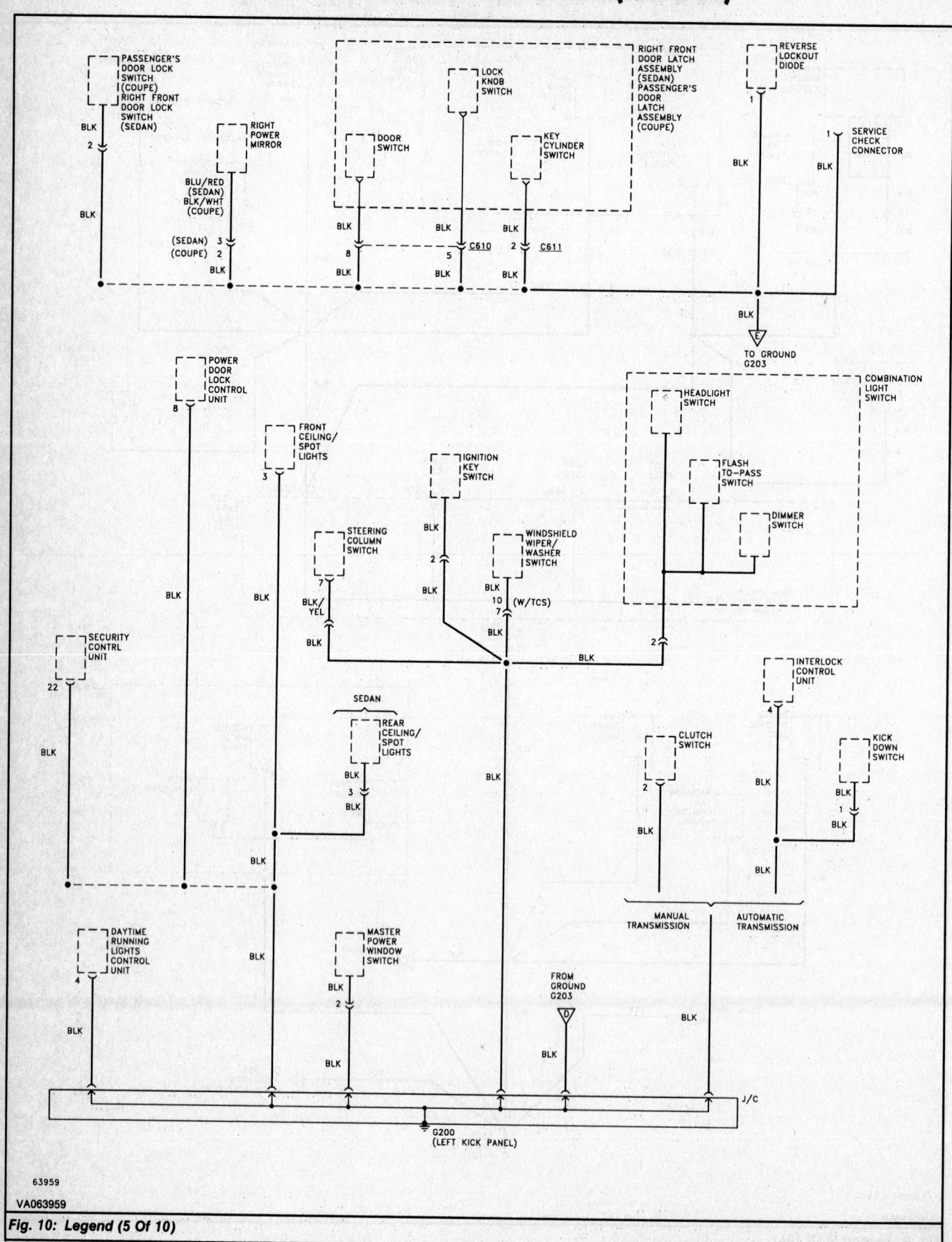

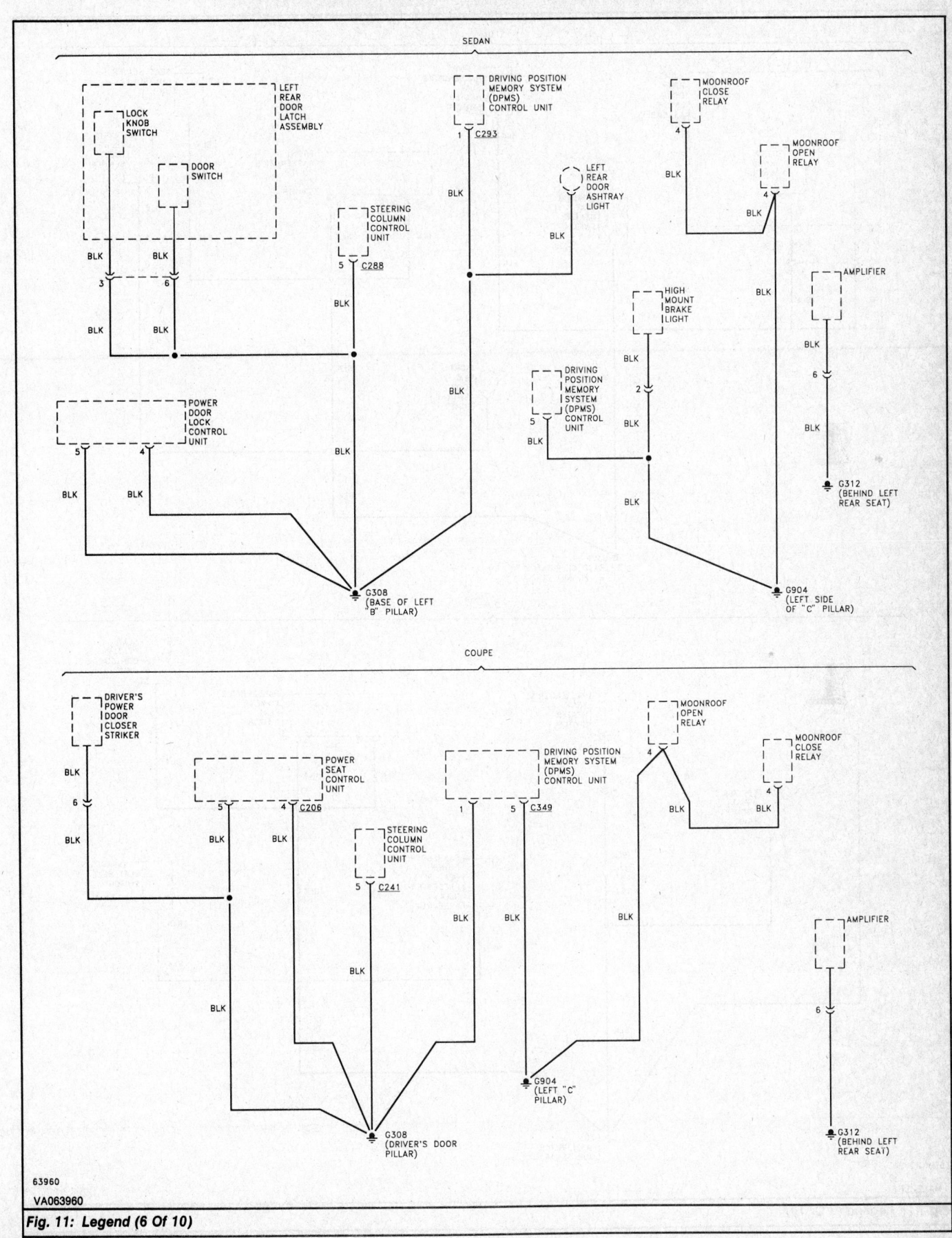

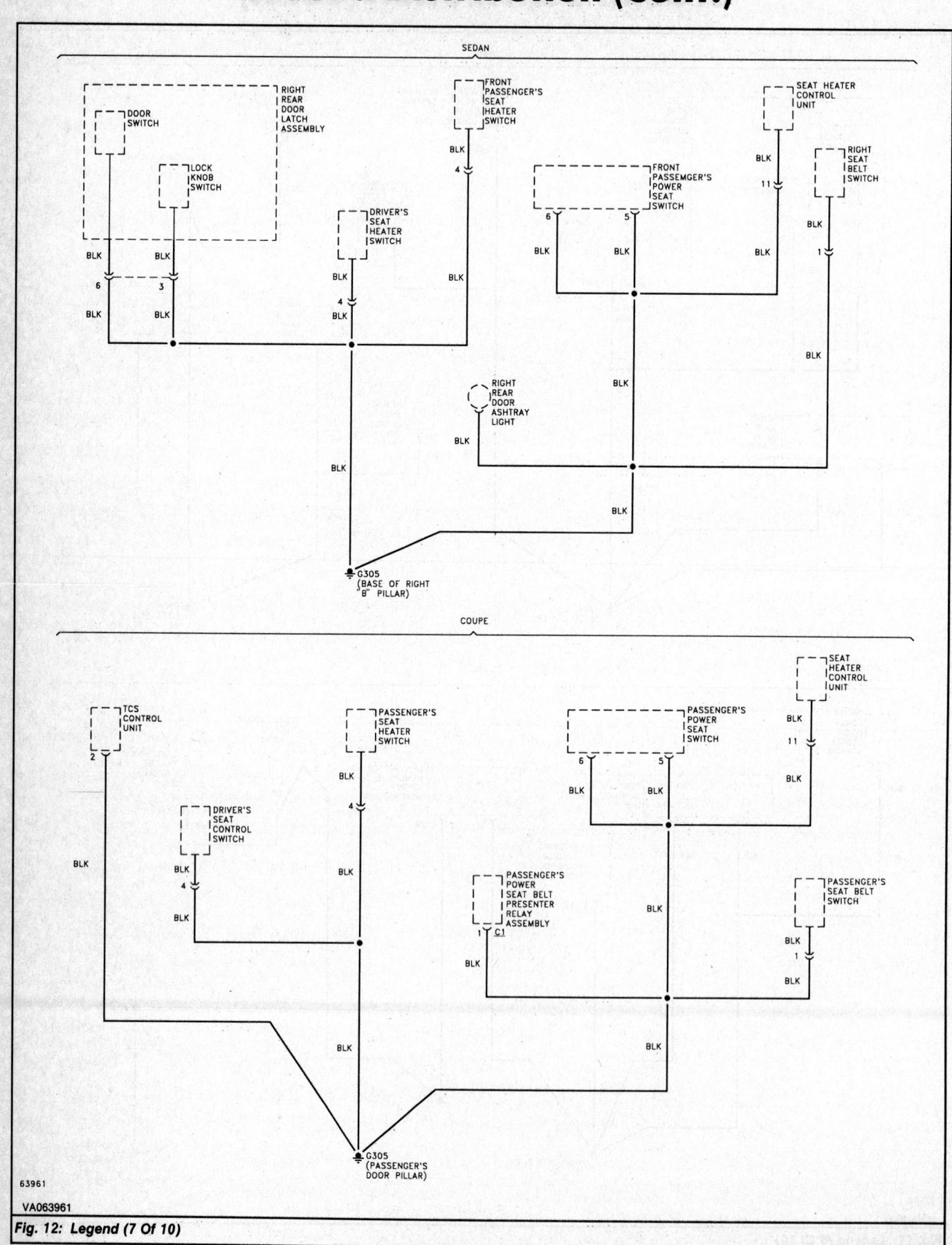

63961

VA063961

Fig. 12: Legend (7 Of 10)

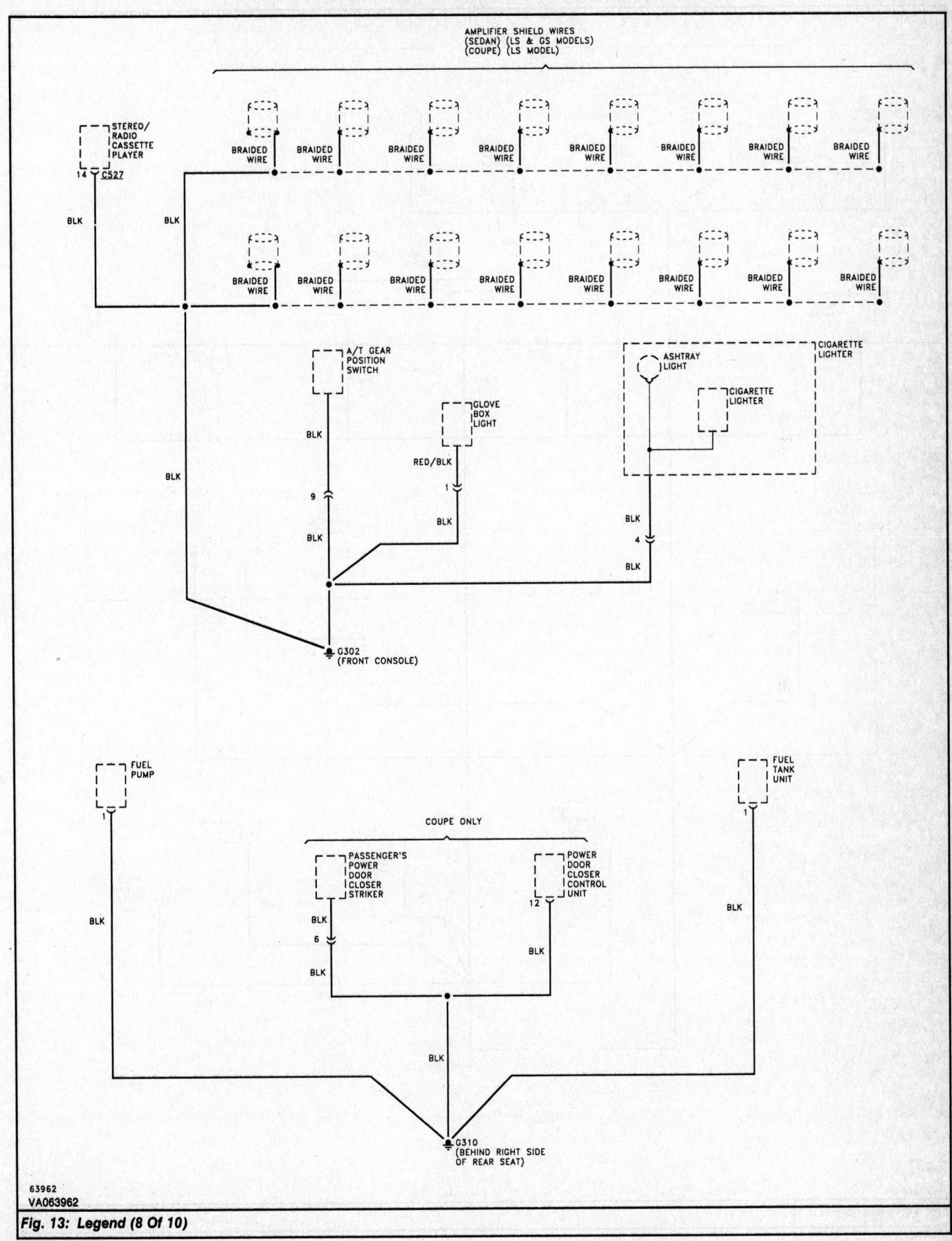

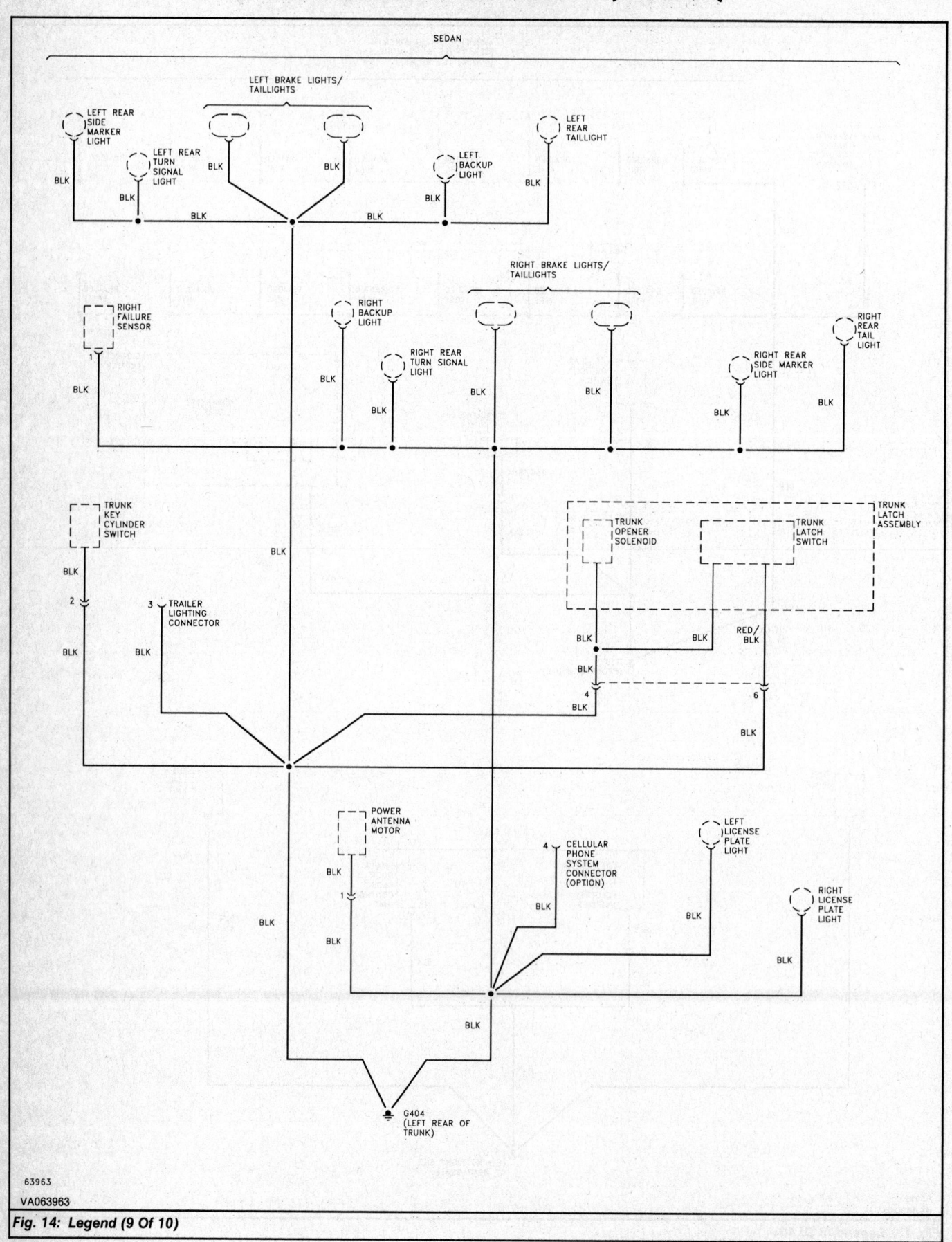

63963
VA063963

Fig. 14: Legend (9 Of 10)

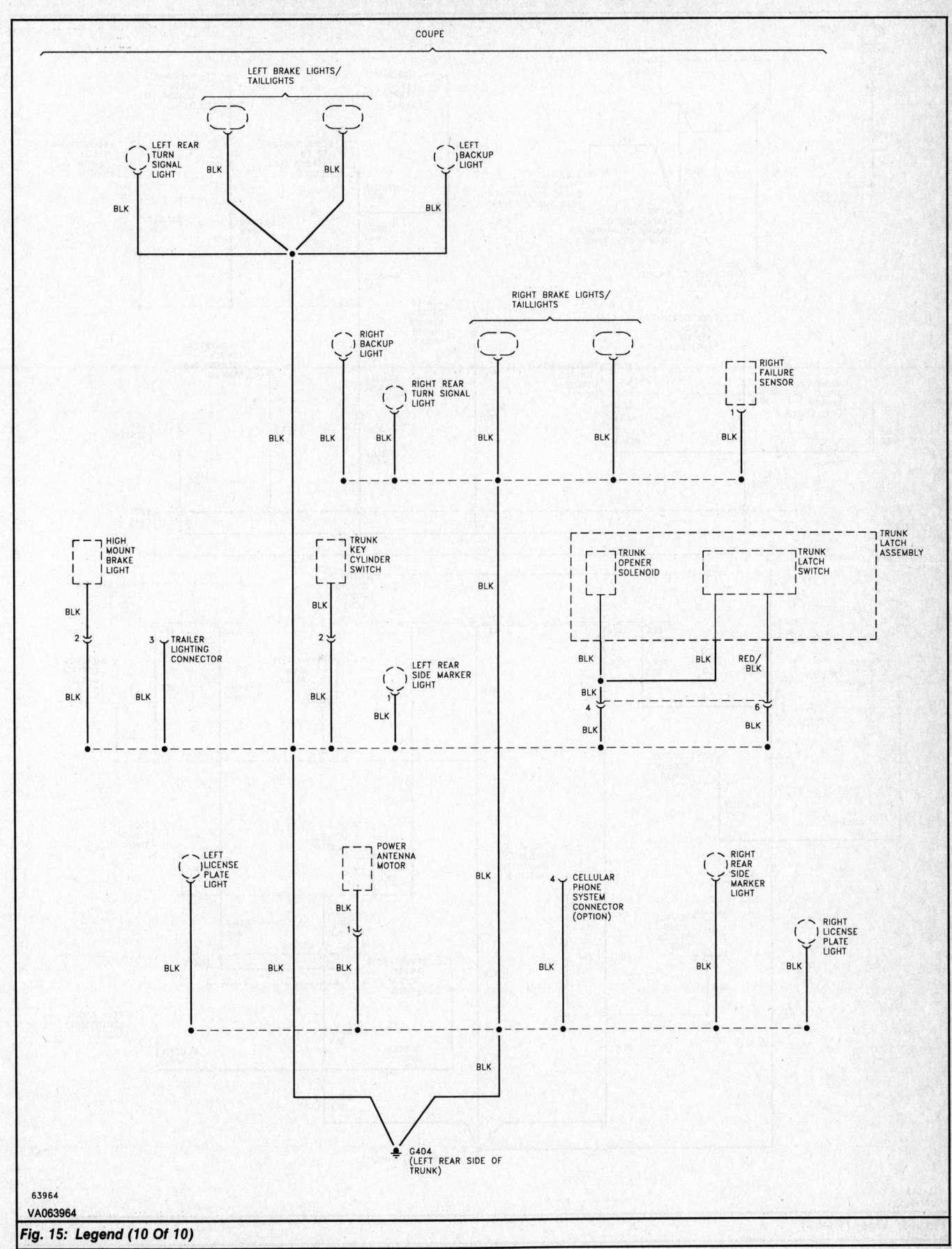

63964
VA063964

Fig. 15: Legend (10 Of 10)

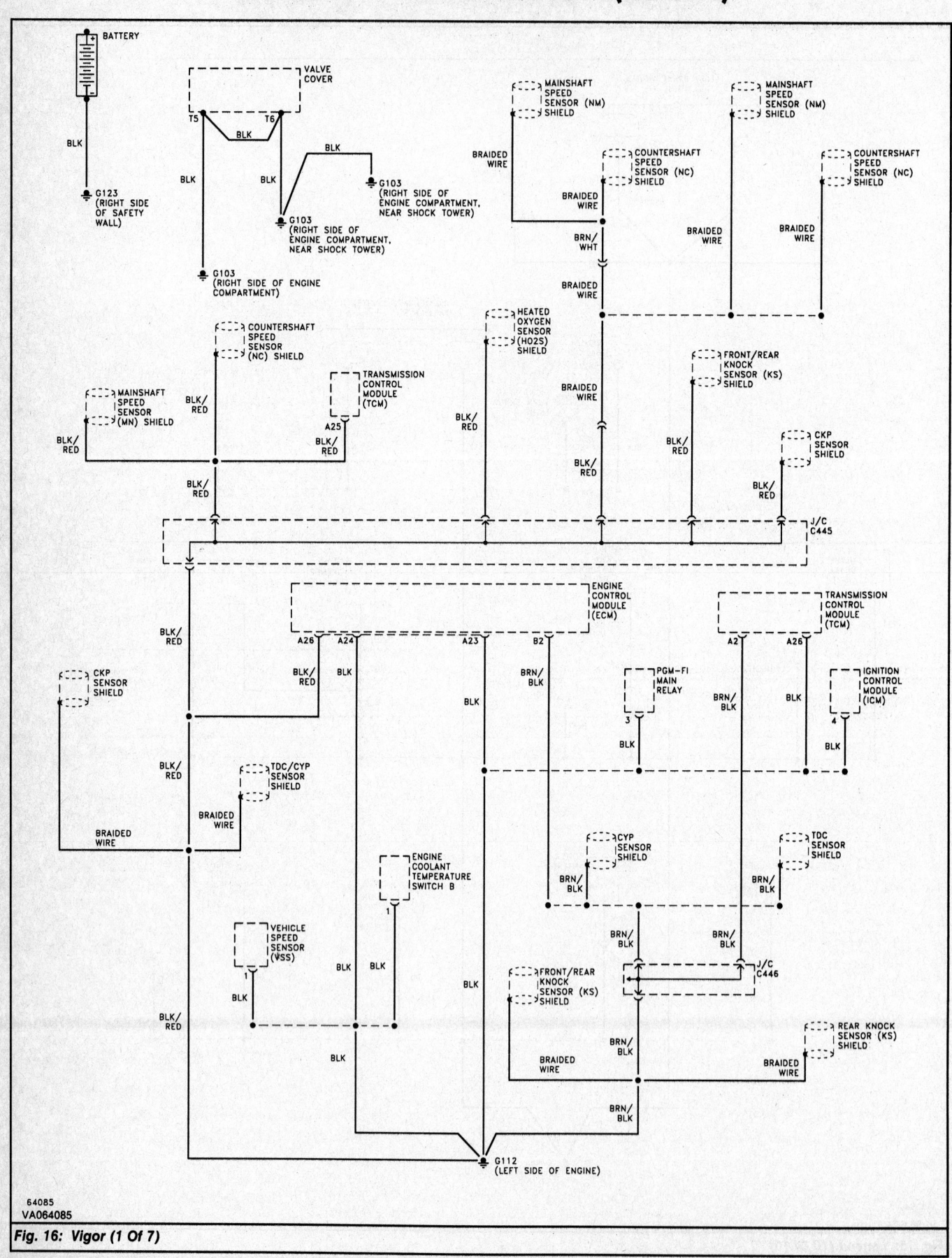

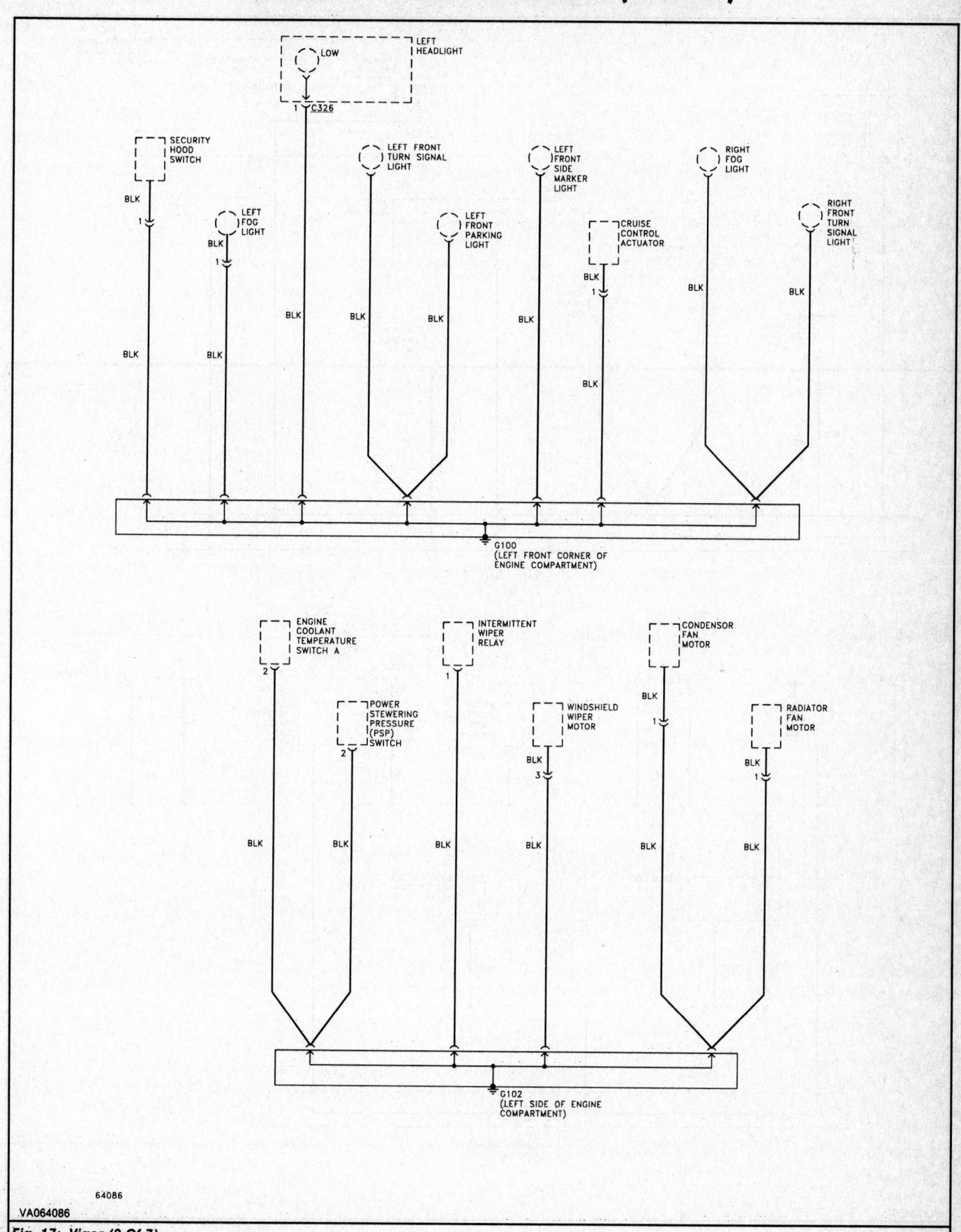

64086
VA064086

Fig. 17: Vigor (2 Of 7)

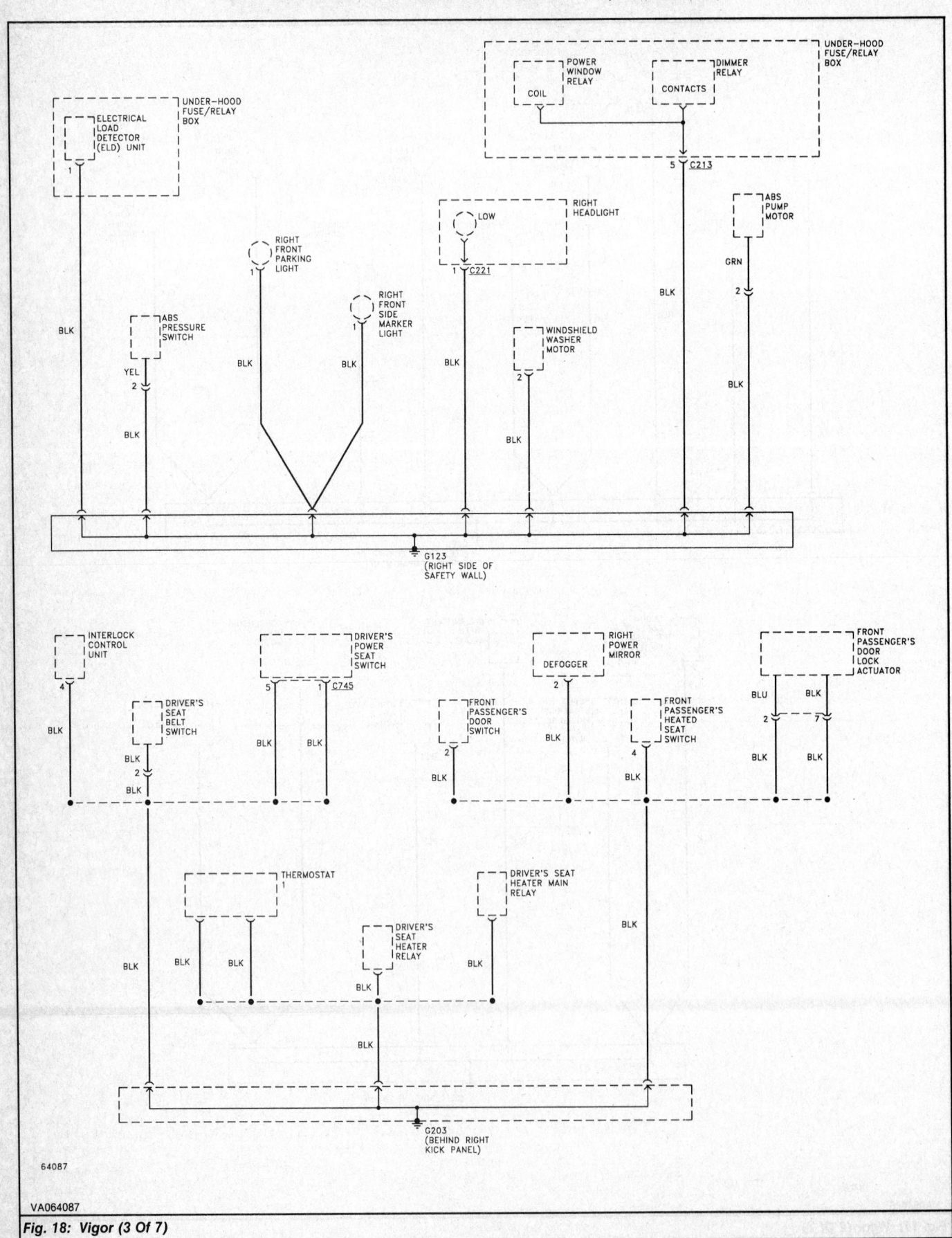

64087

VA064087

Fig. 18: Vigor (3 Of 7)

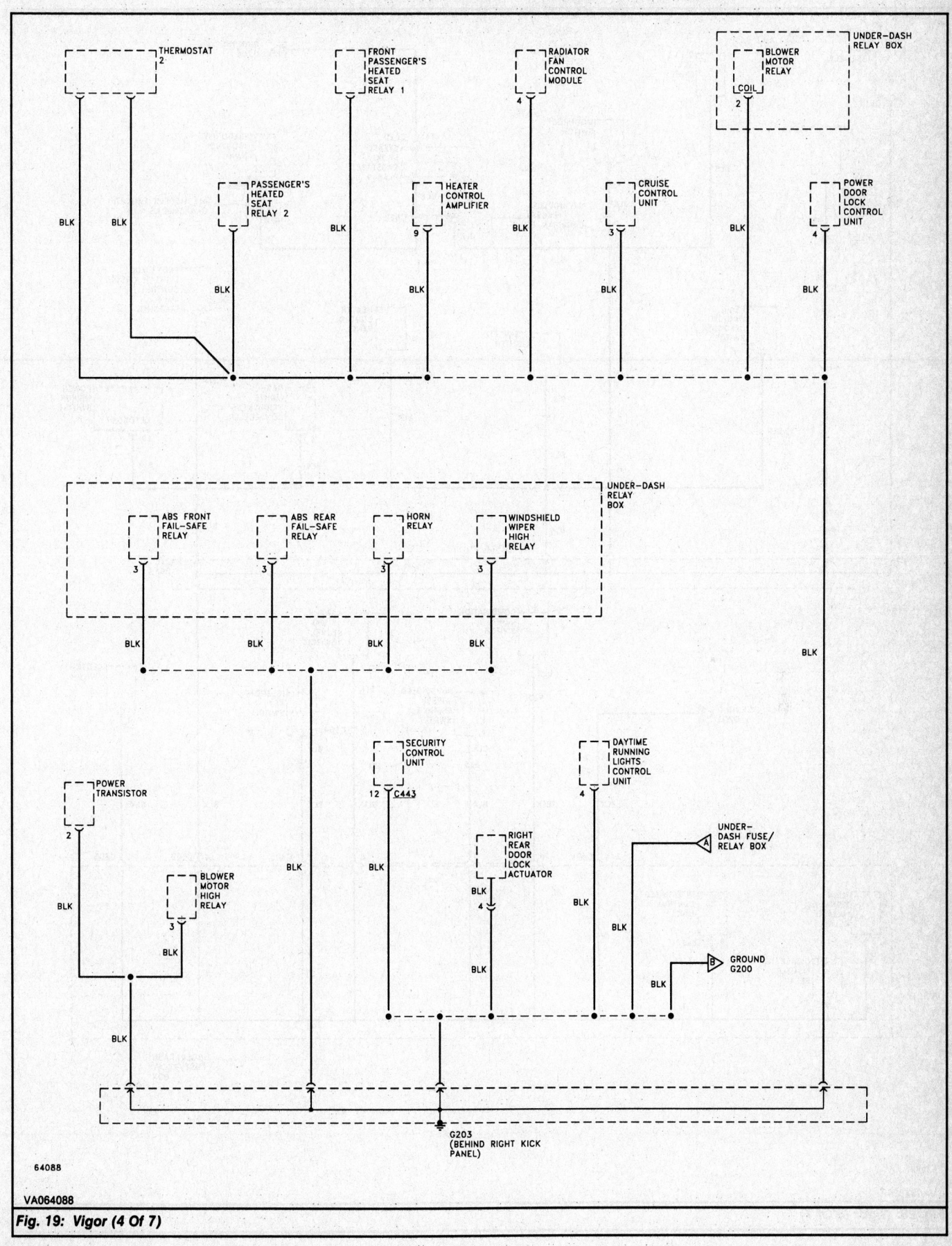

64088

VA064088

Fig. 19: Vigor (4 Of 7)

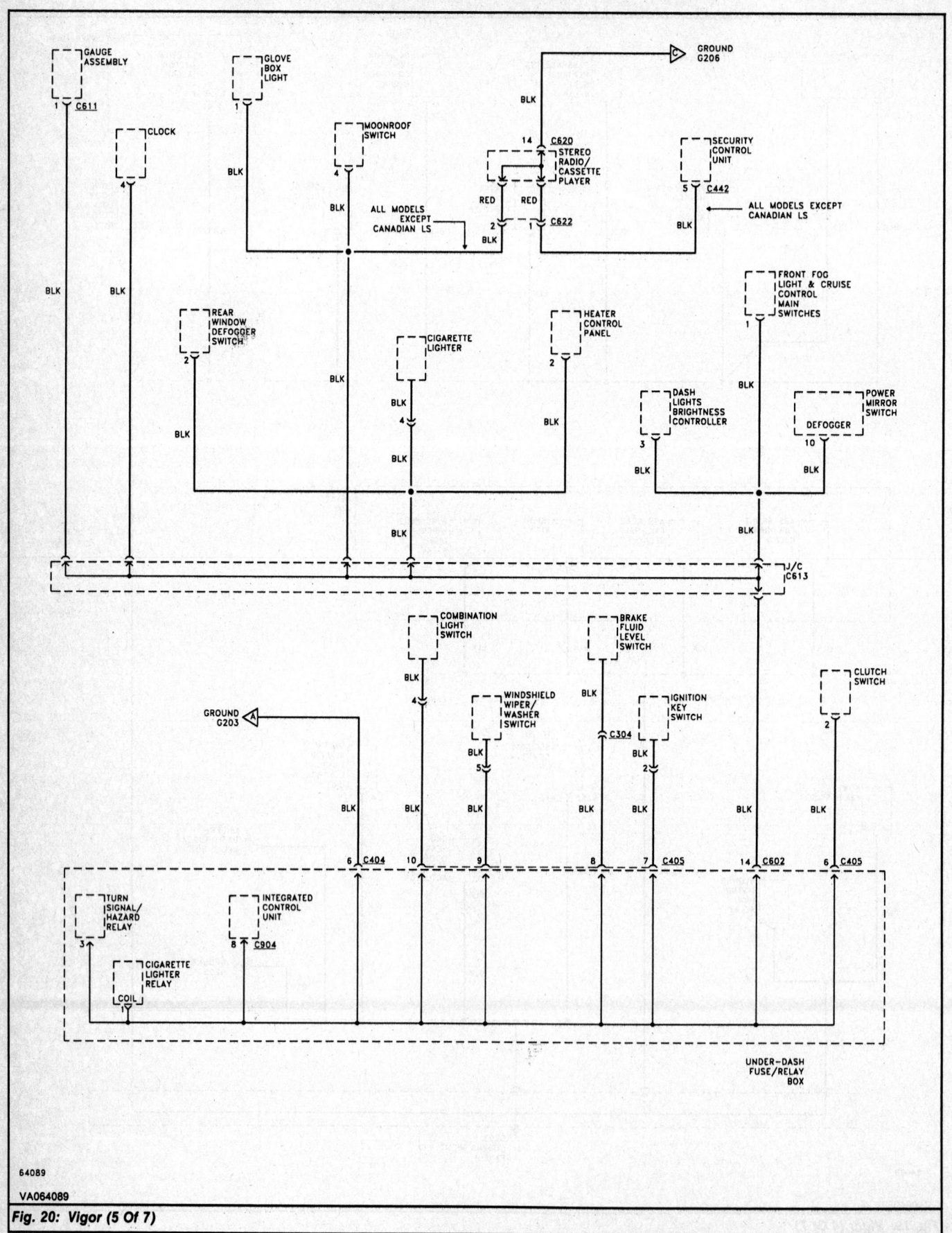

64089

VA064089

Fig. 20: Vigor (5 Of 7)

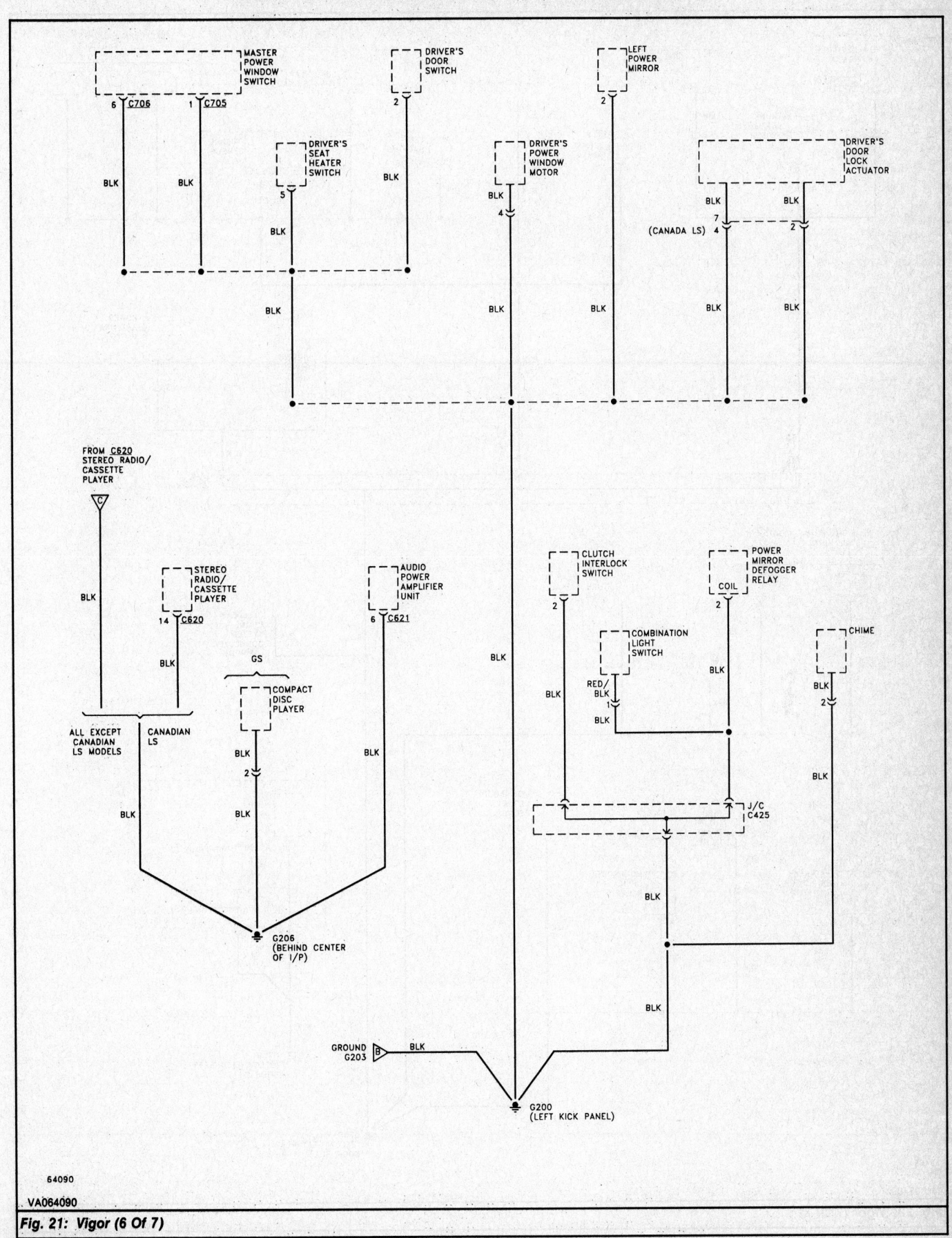

64090

VA064090

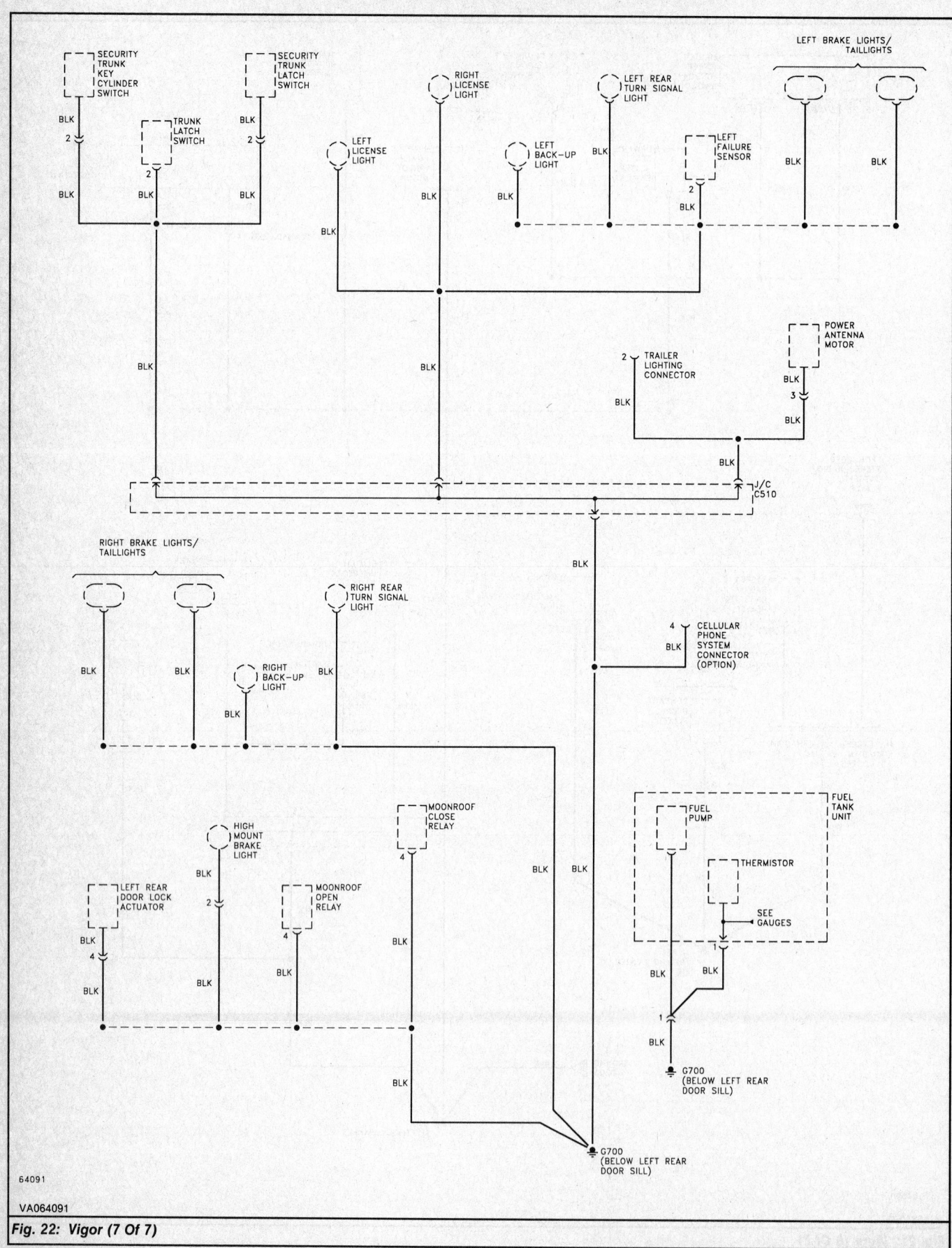

64091

VA064091

Fig. 22: Vigor (7 Of 7)

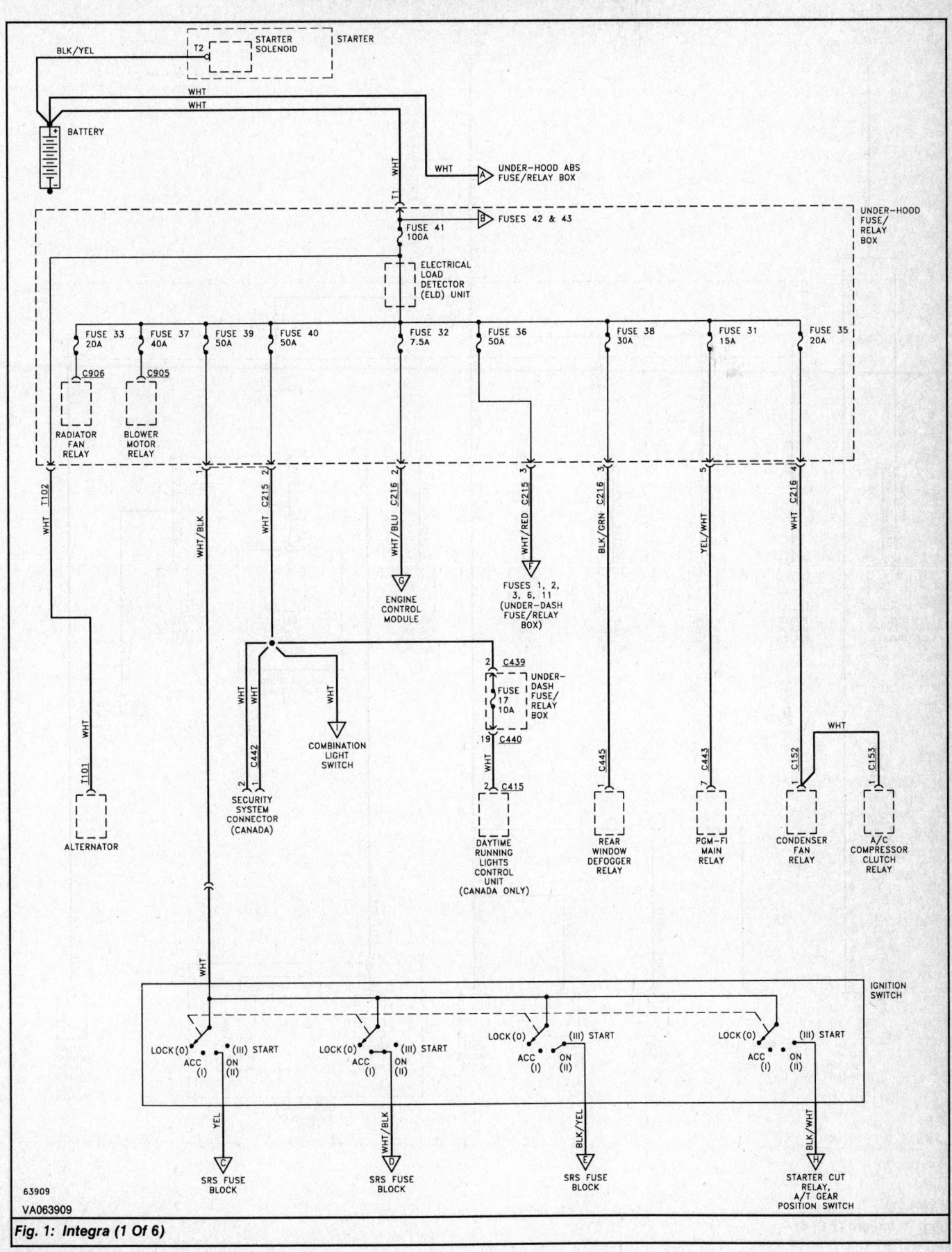

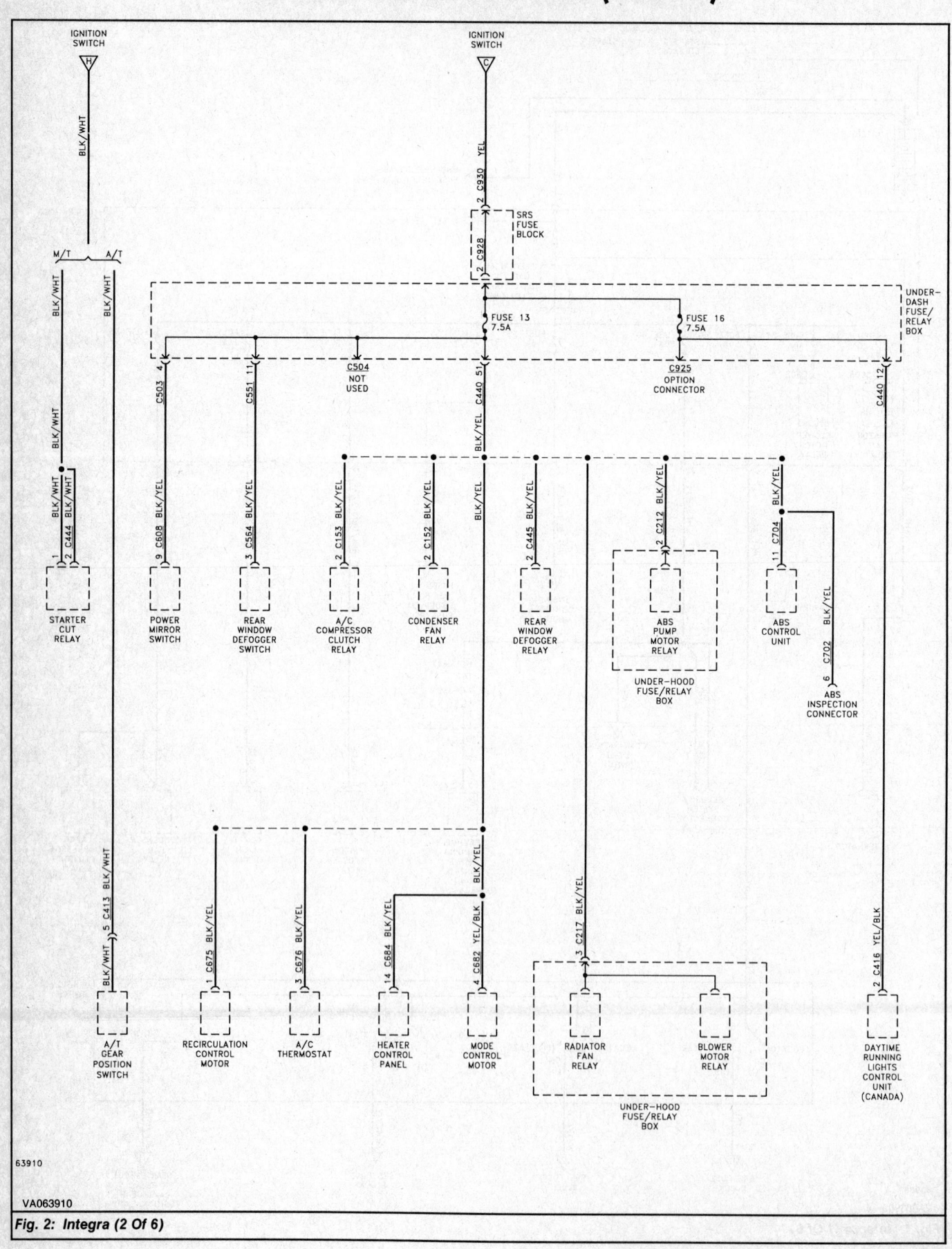

63910

VA063910

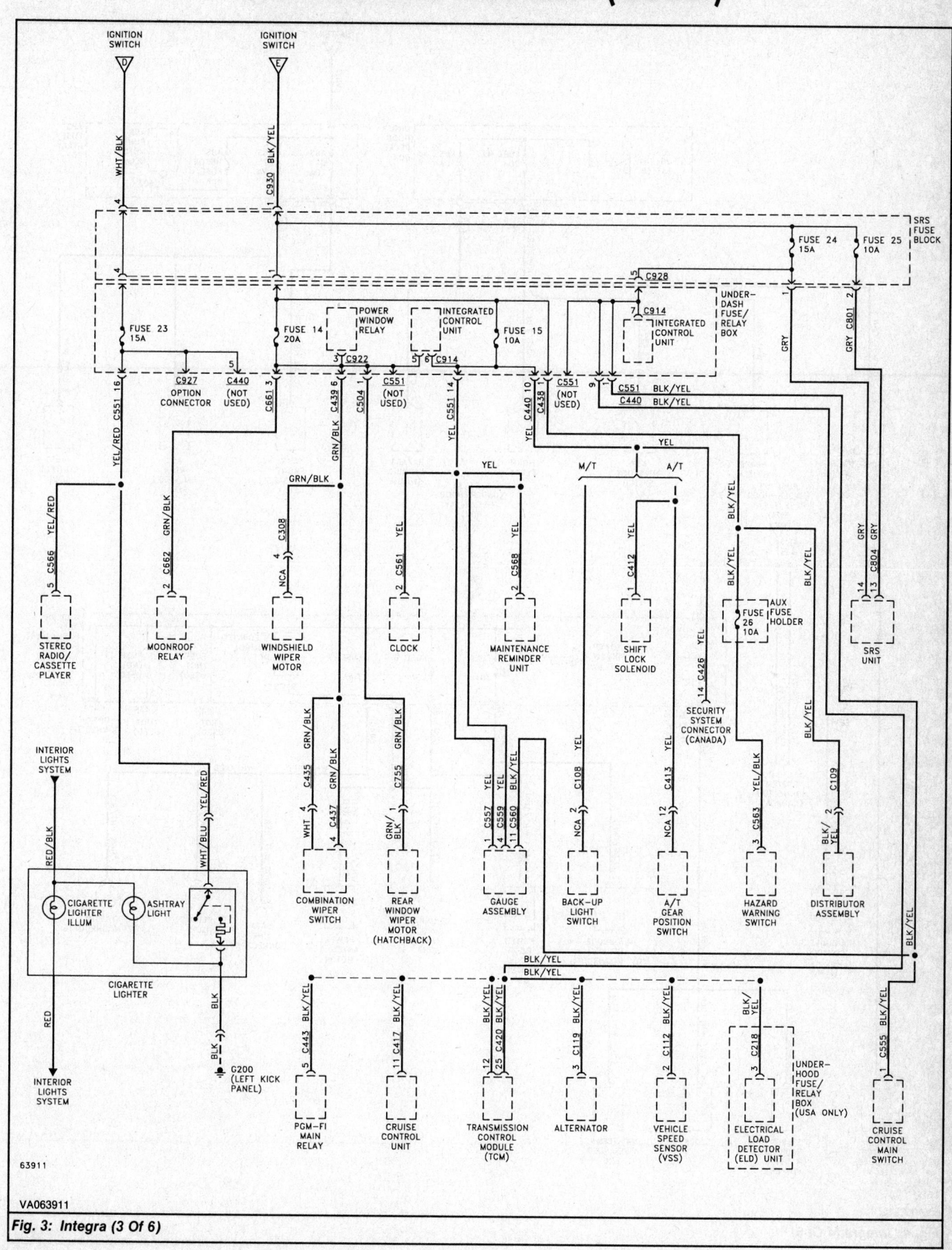

Fig. 3: Integra (3 Of 6)

63911

VA063911

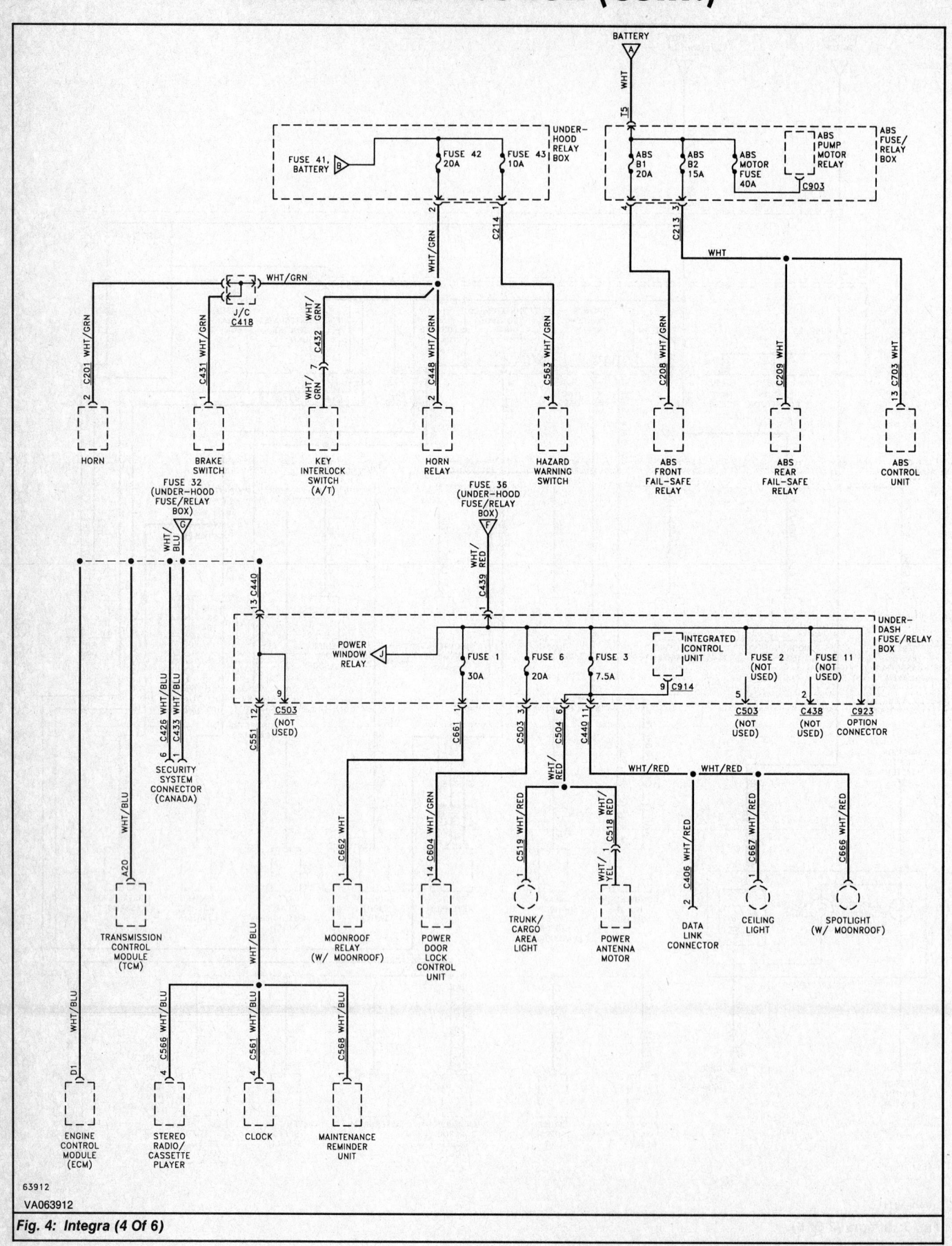

63912

VA063912

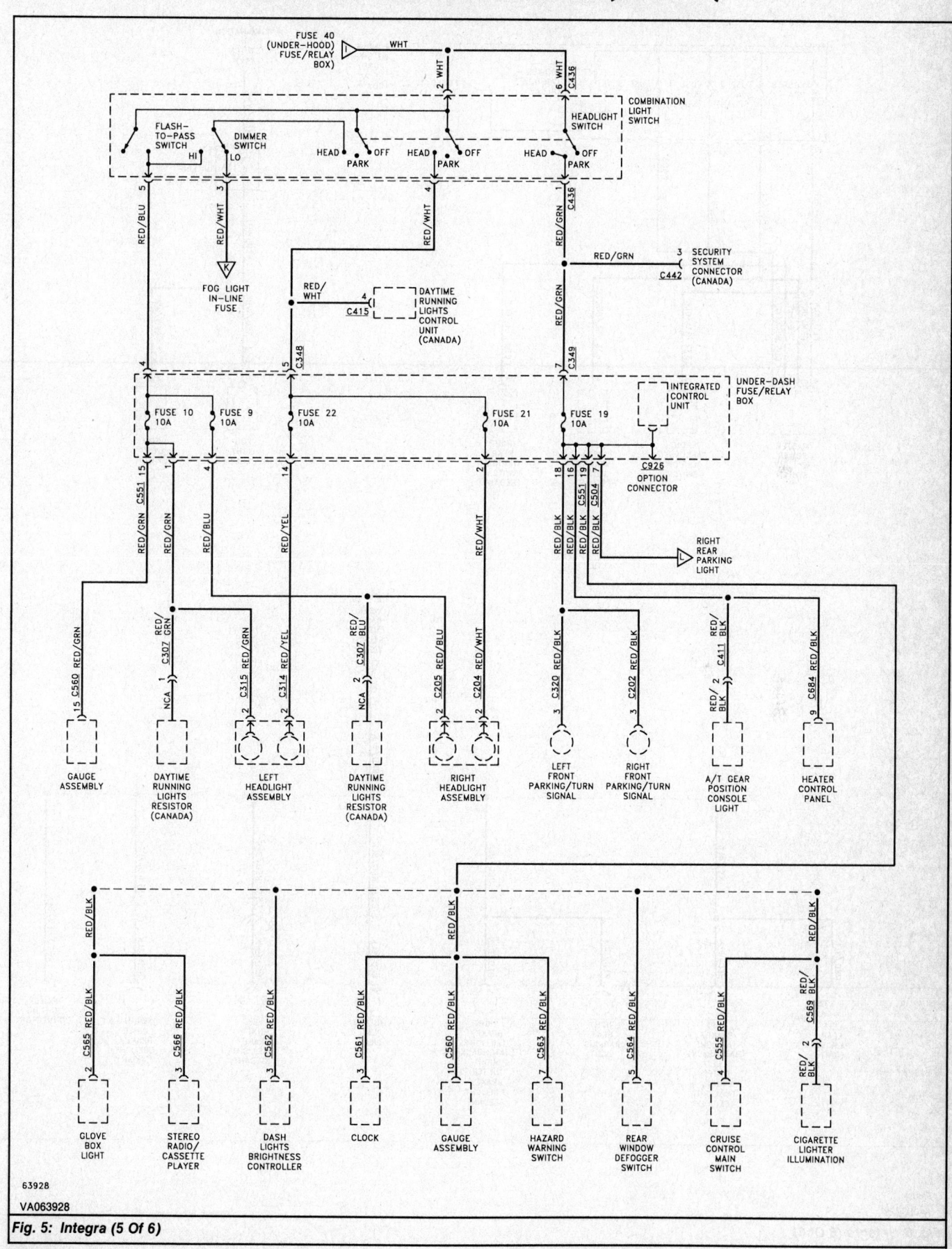

1994 WIRING DIAGRAMS
Power Distribution (Cont.)

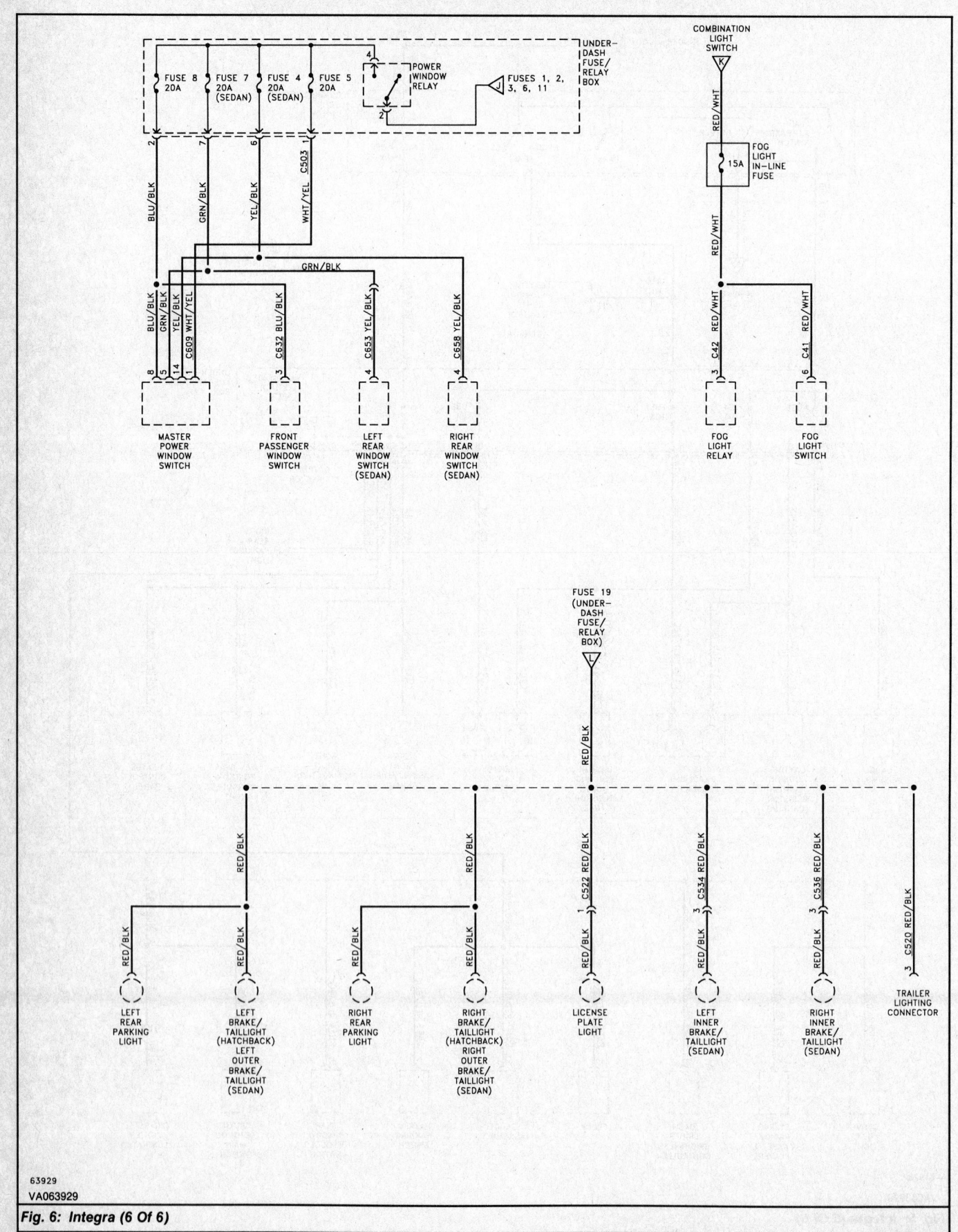

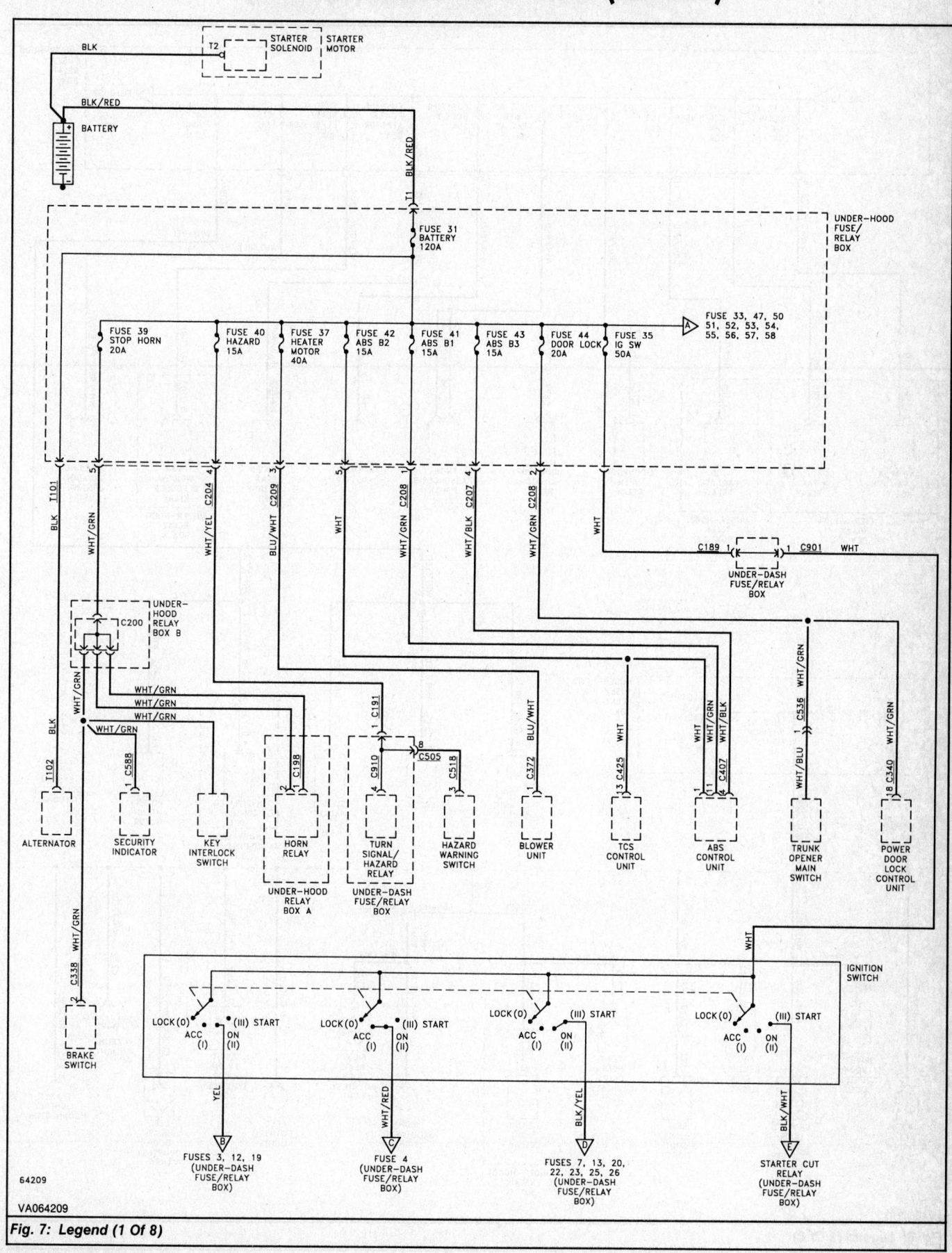

Fig. 7: Legend (1 Of 8)

64209

VA064209

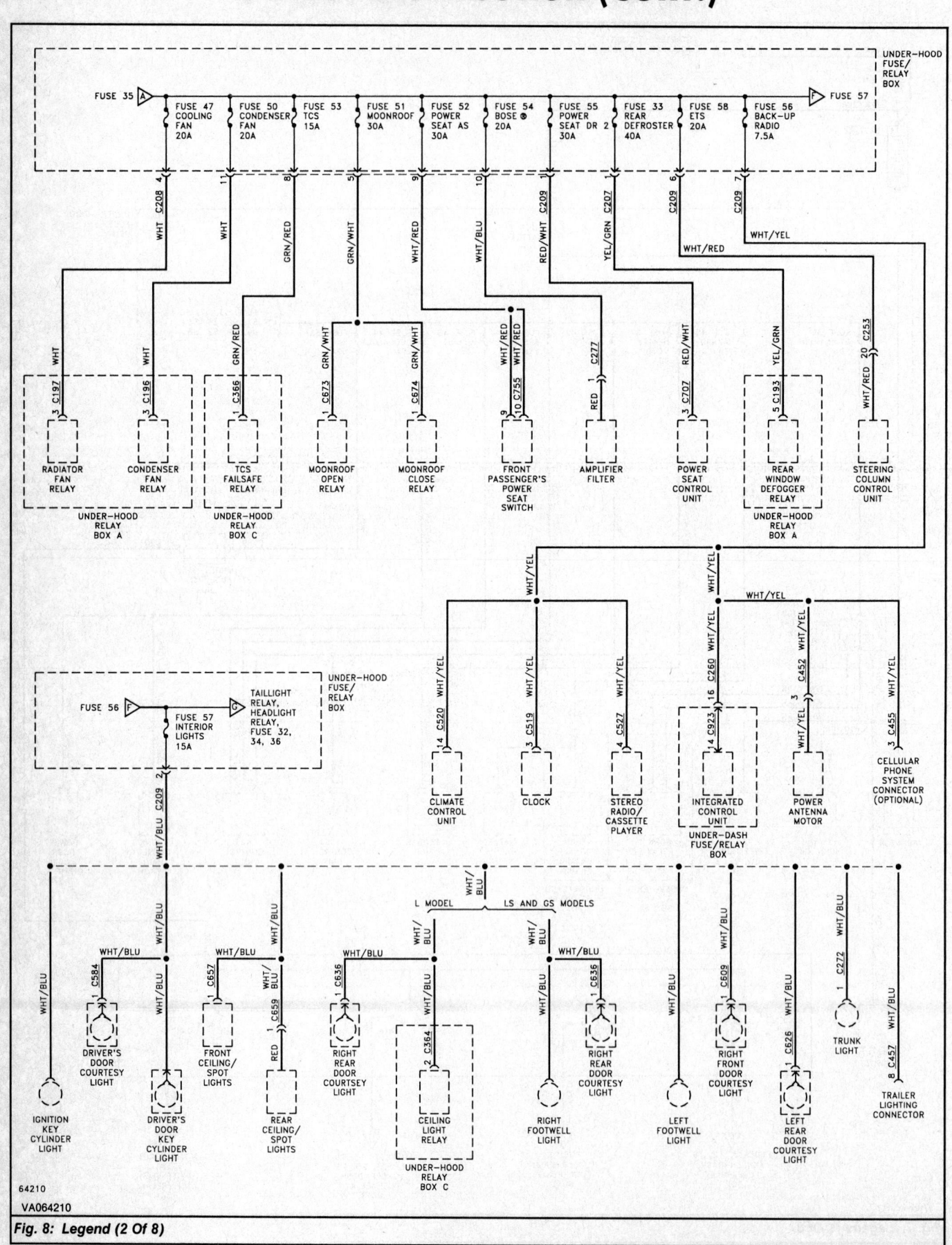

64210

VA064210

Fig. 8: Legend (2 Of 8)

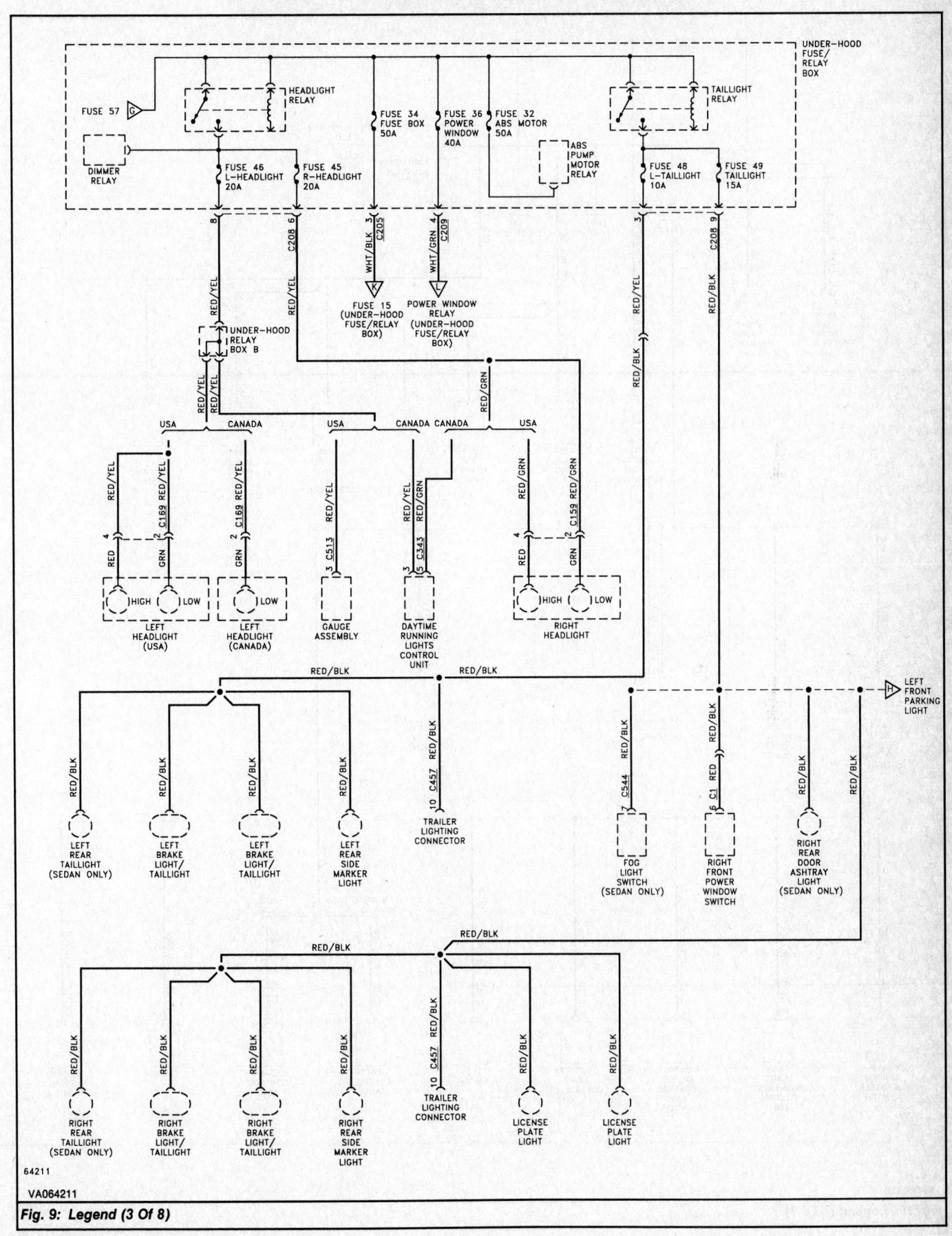

Fig. 9: Legend (3 Of 8)

64211

VA064211

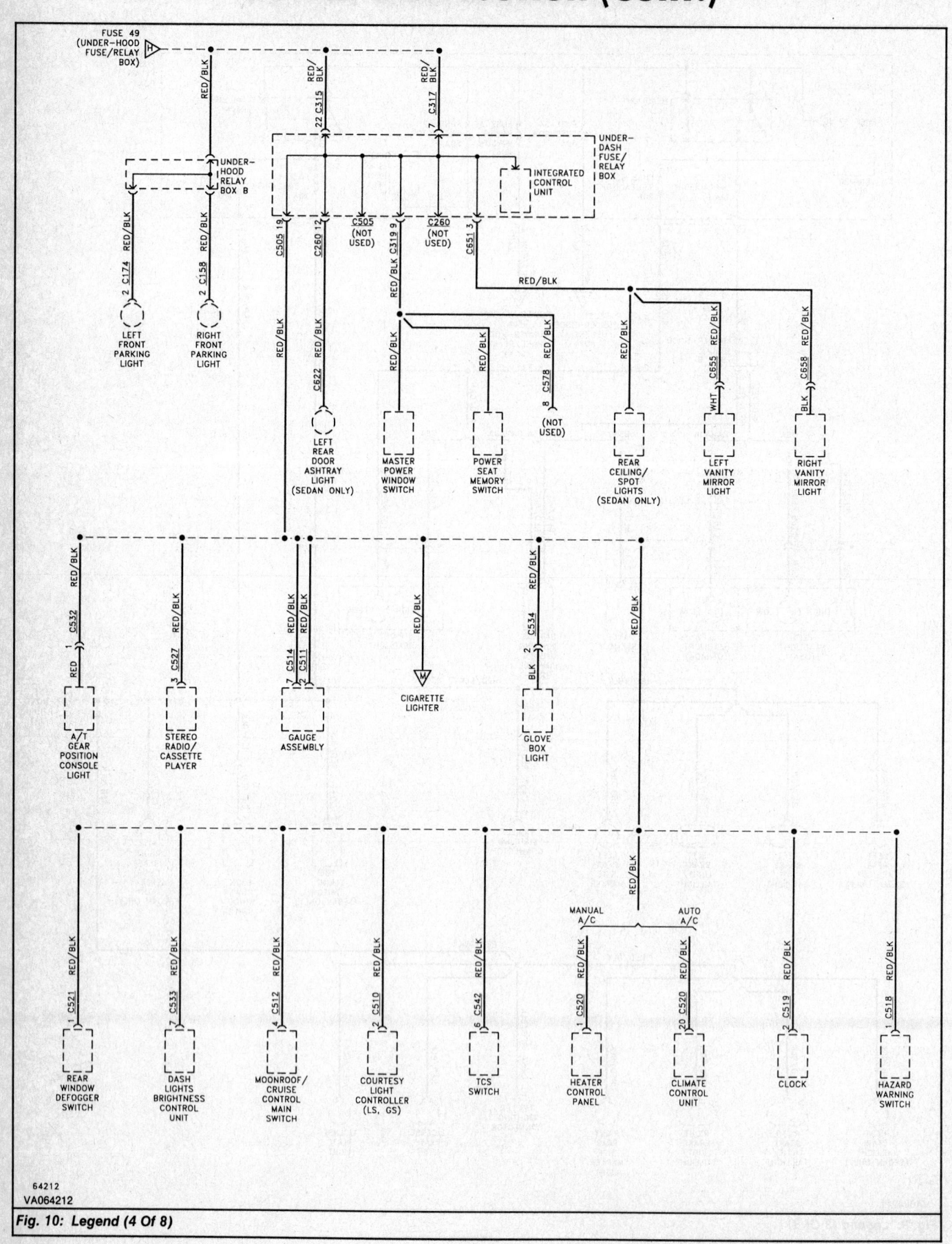

64212
VA064212

Fig. 10: Legend (4 Of 8)

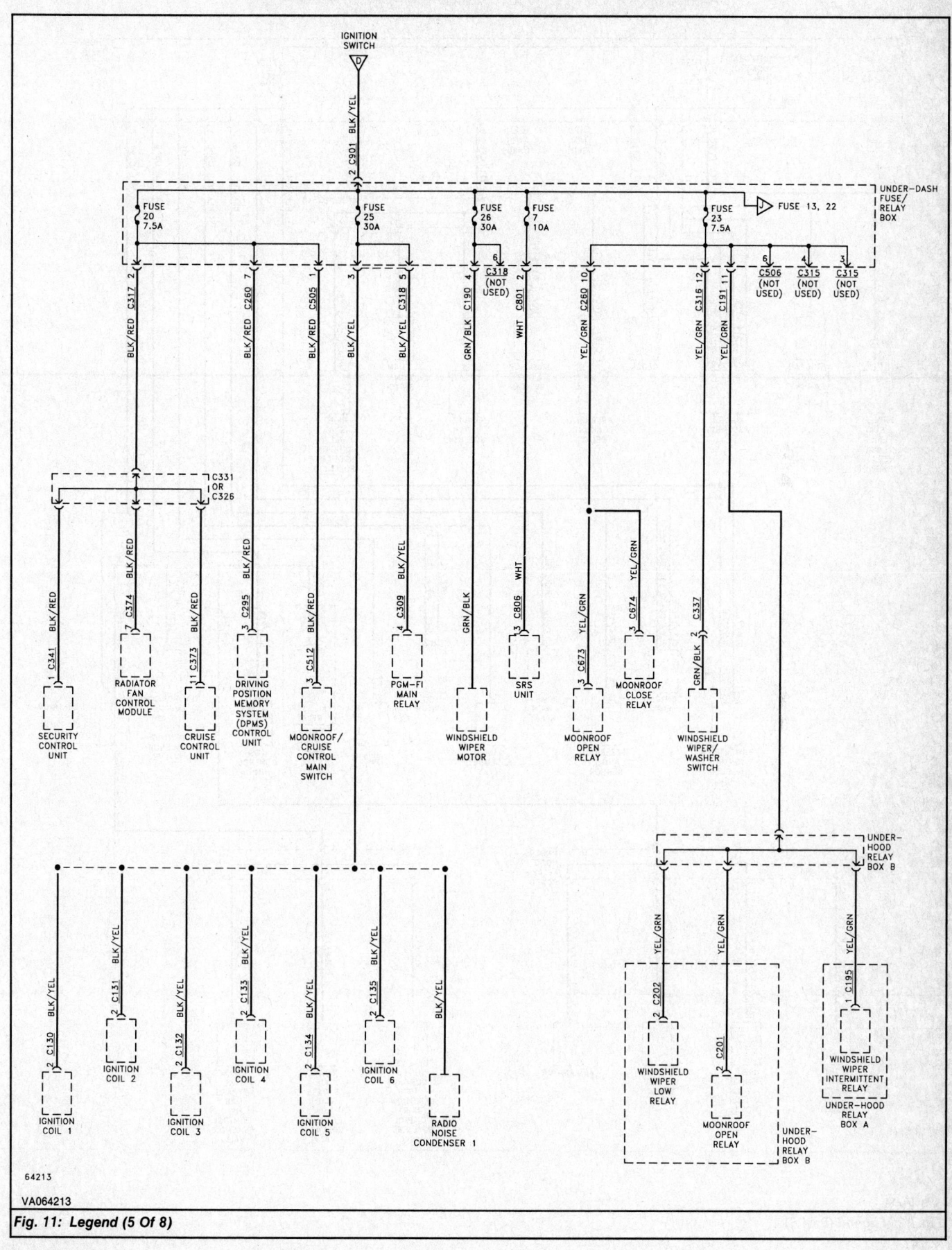

64213

VA064213

Fig. 11: Legend (5 Of 8)

1994 WIRING DIAGRAMS
Power Distribution (Cont.)

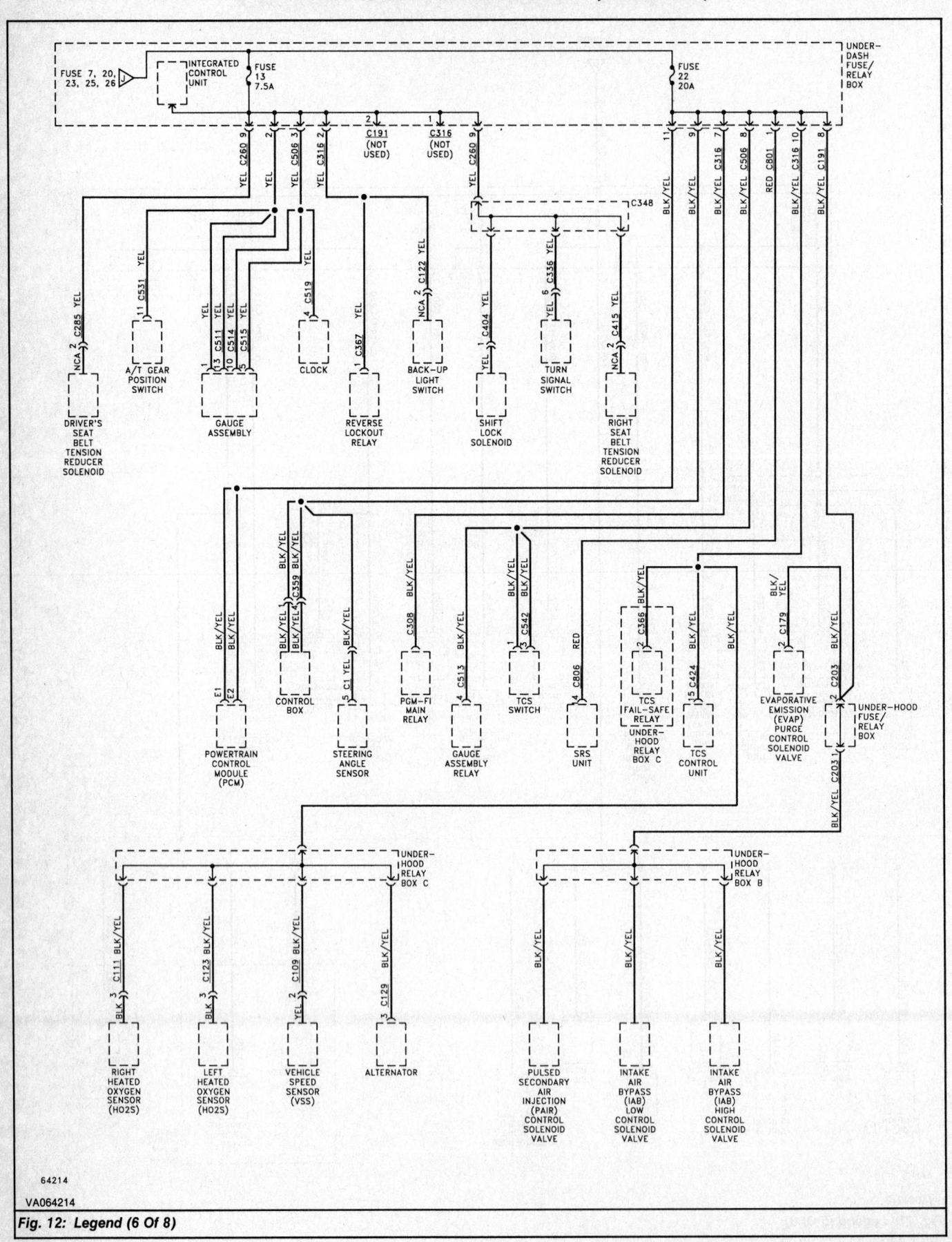

64214

VA064214

Fig. 12: Legend (6 Of 8)

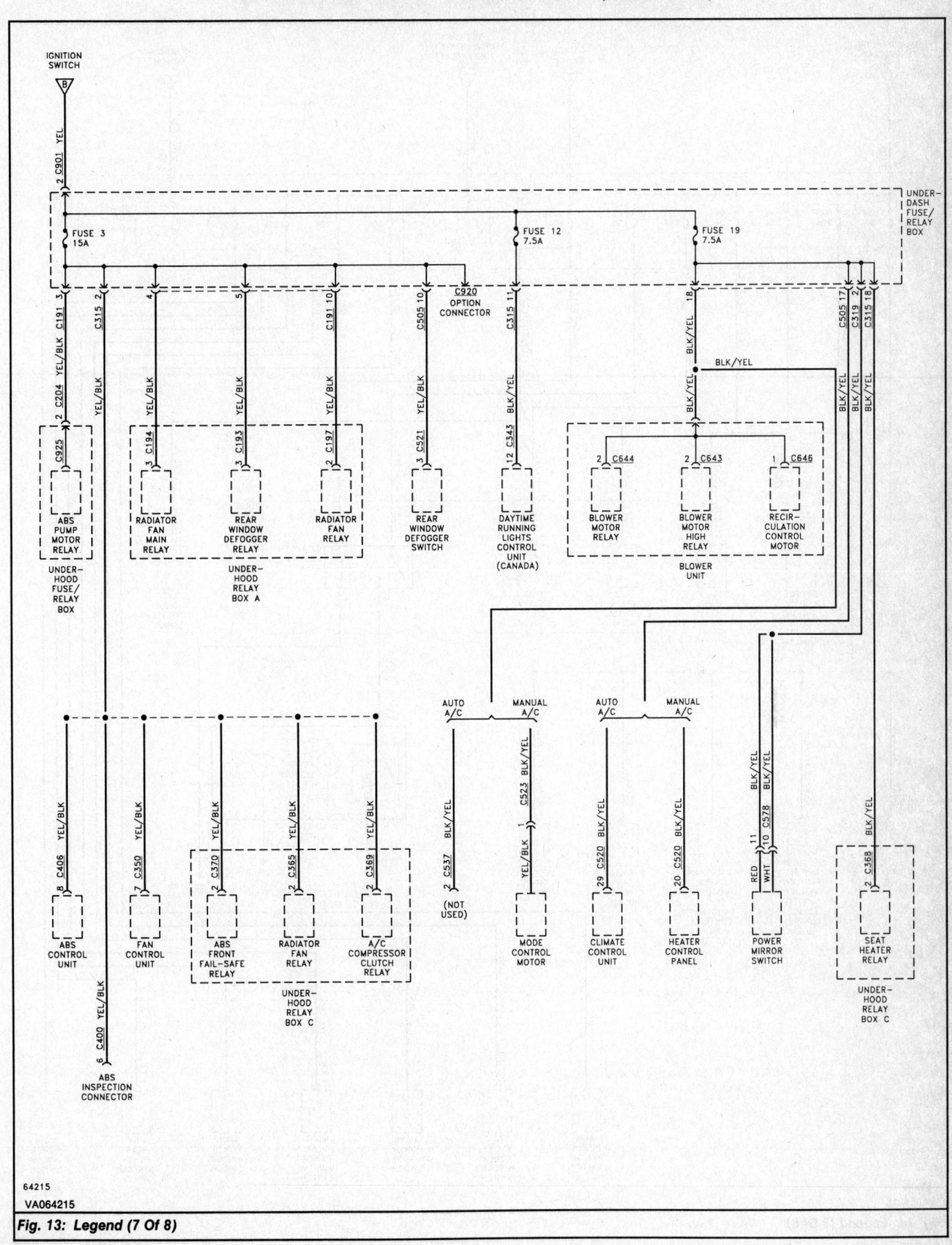

64215

VA064215

Fig. 13: Legend (7 Of 8)

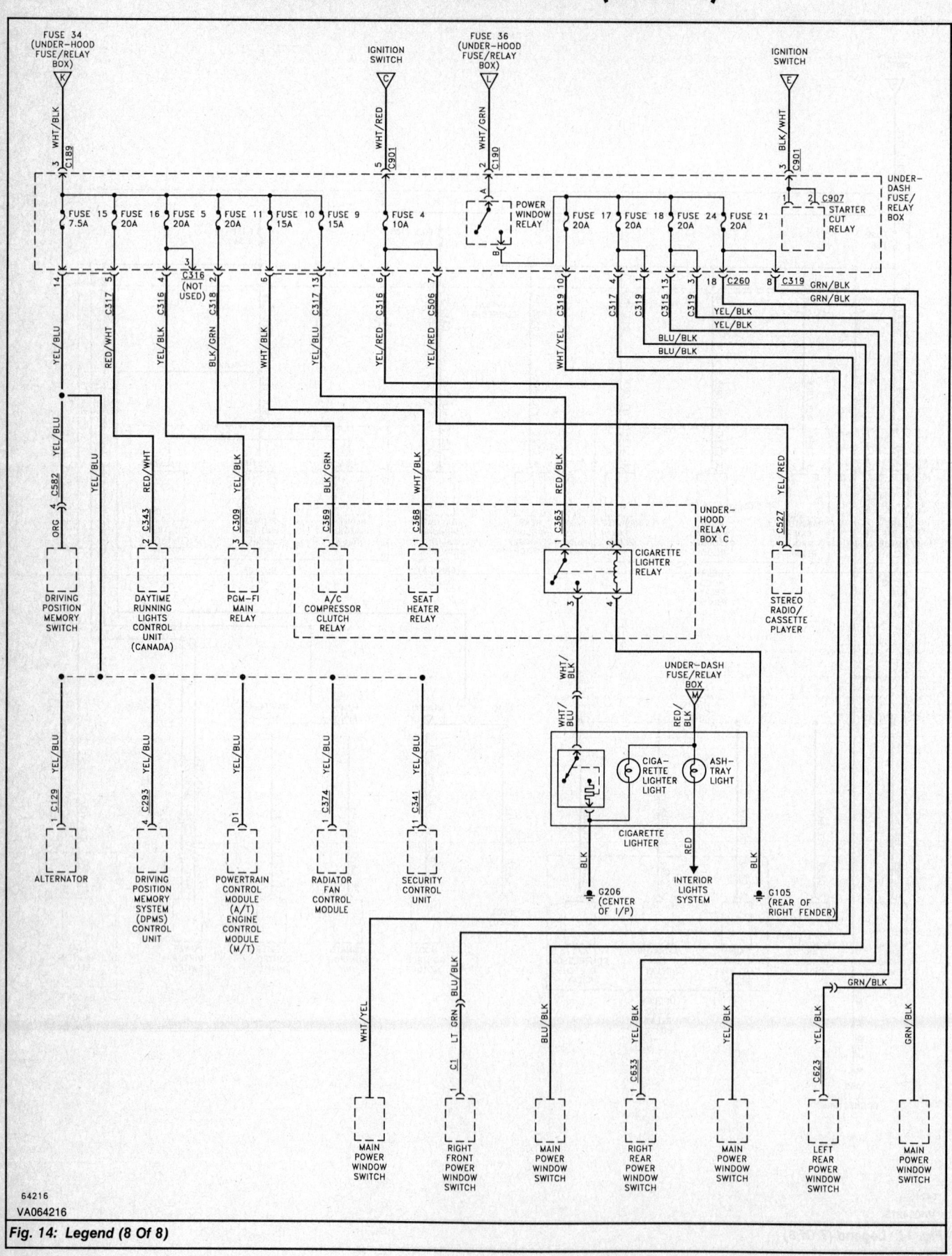

64216
VA064216

Fig. 14: Legend (8 Of 8)

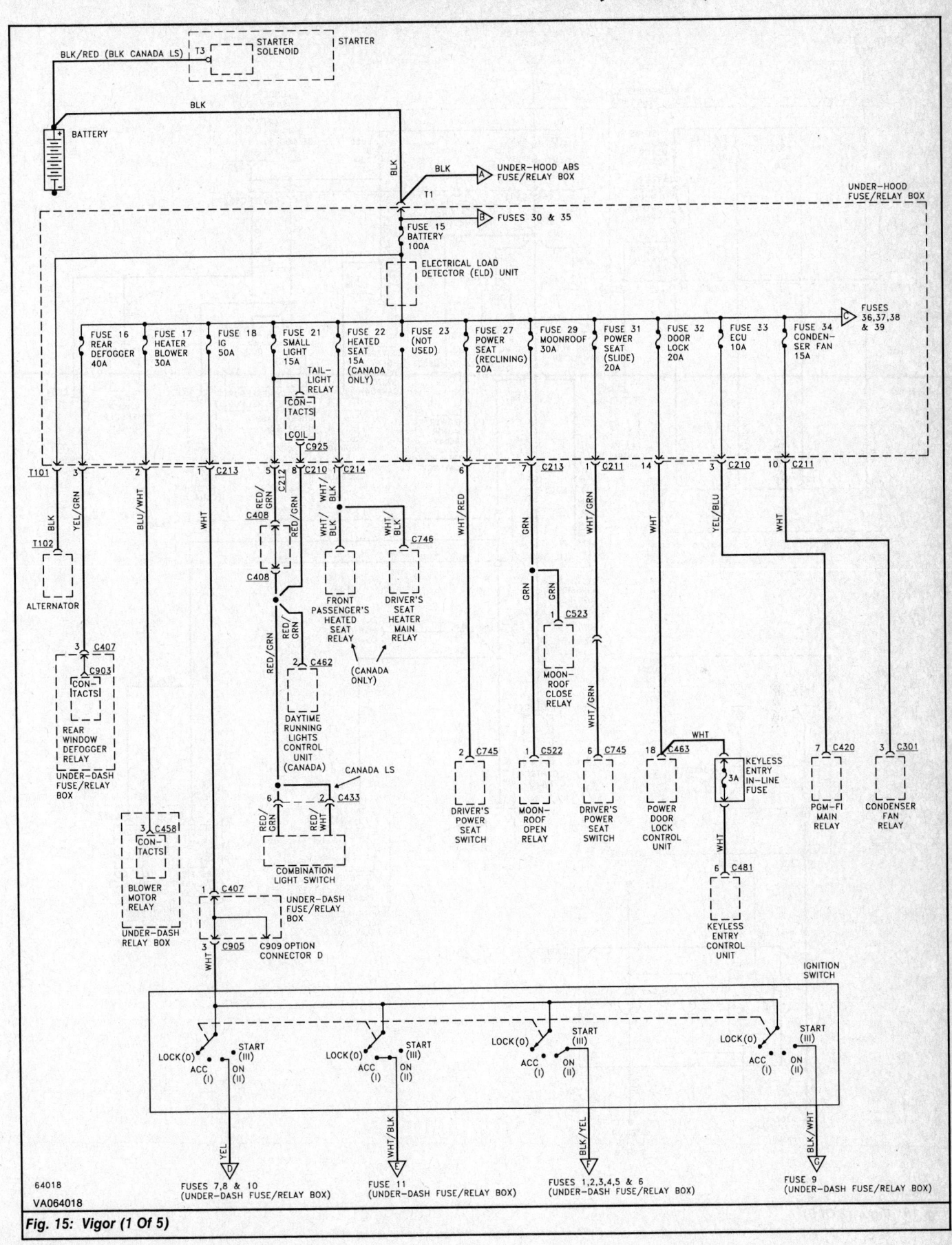

Fig. 15: Vigor (1 Of 5)

64018
VA064018

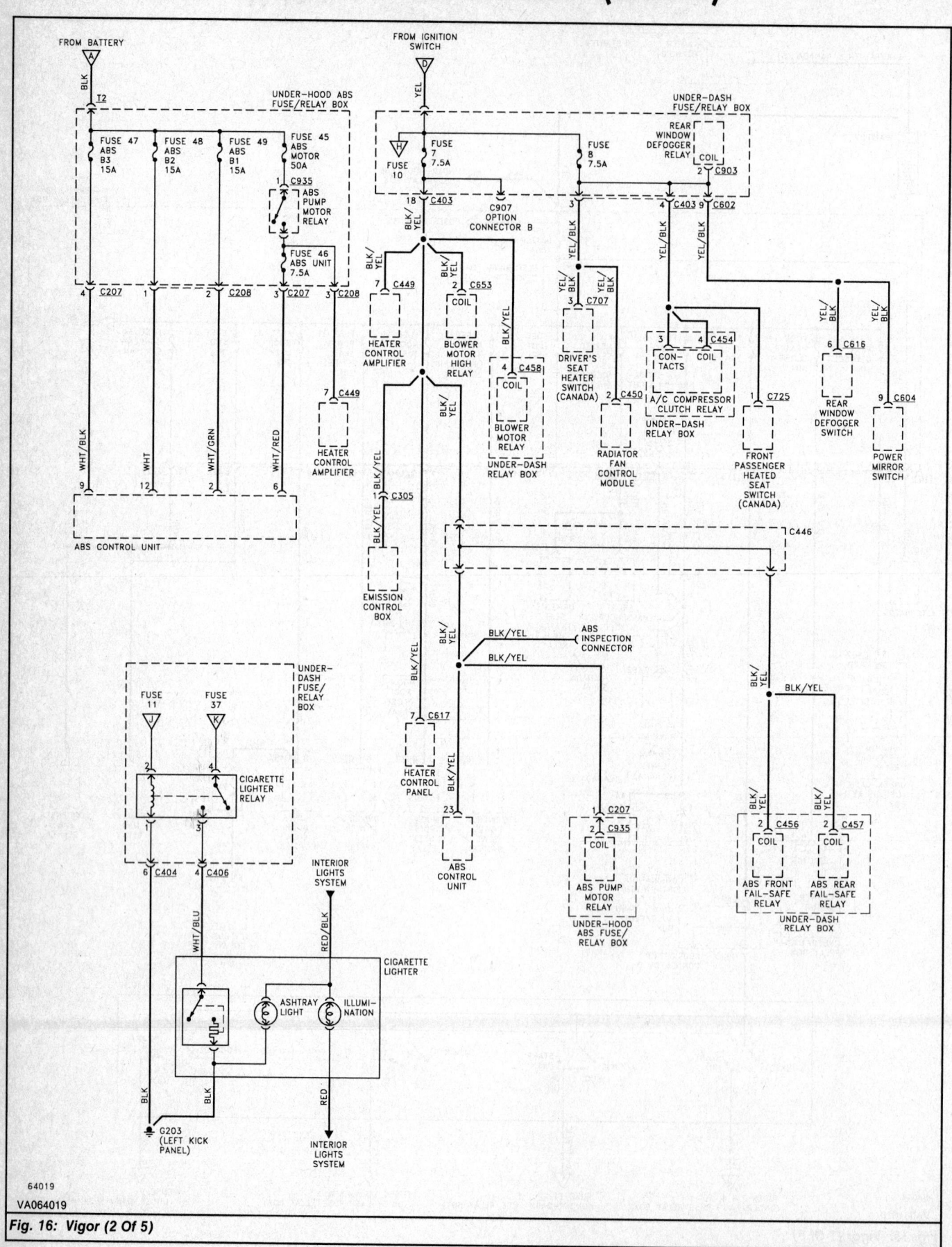

64019
VA064019

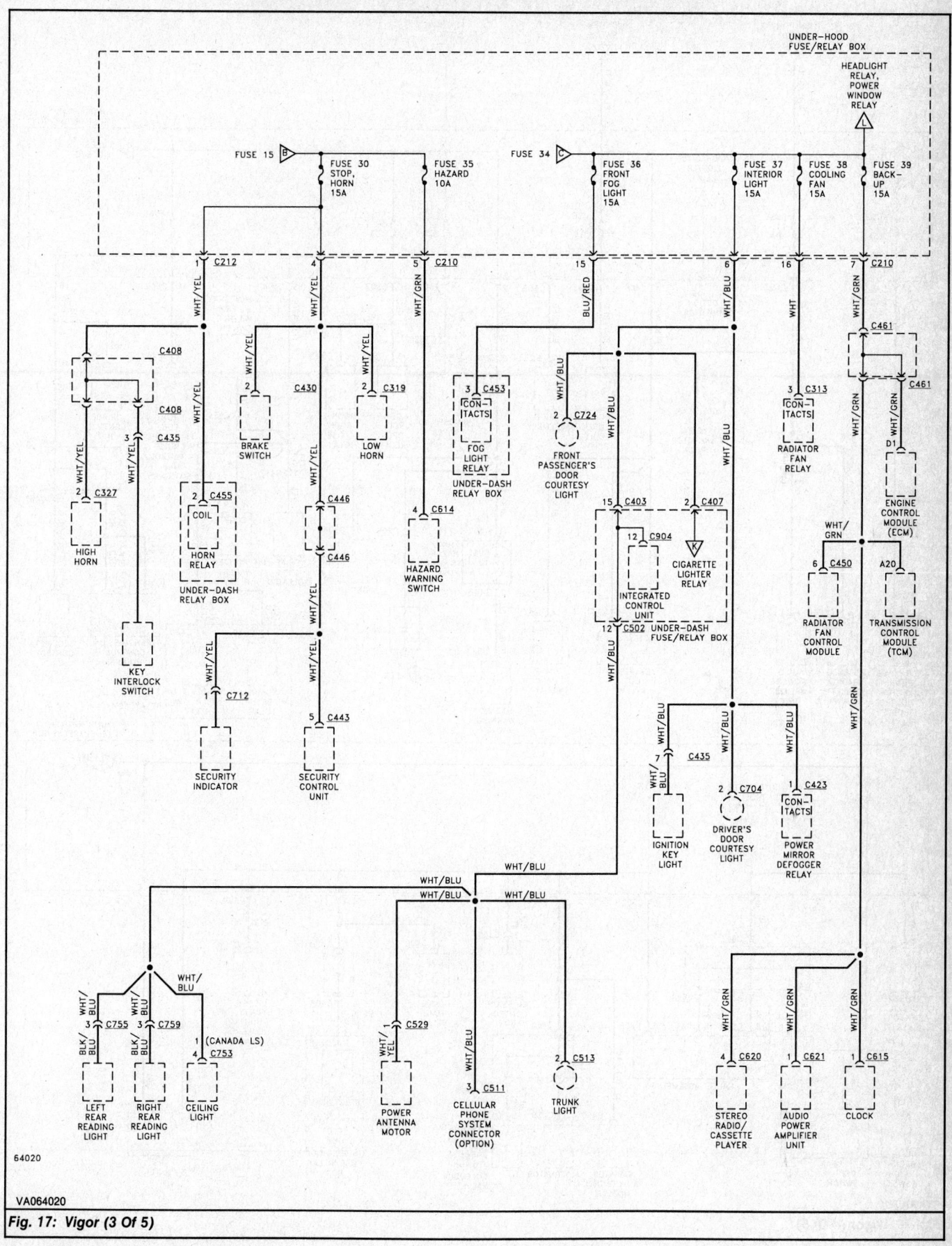

64020

VA064020

Fig. 17: Vigor (3 Of 5)

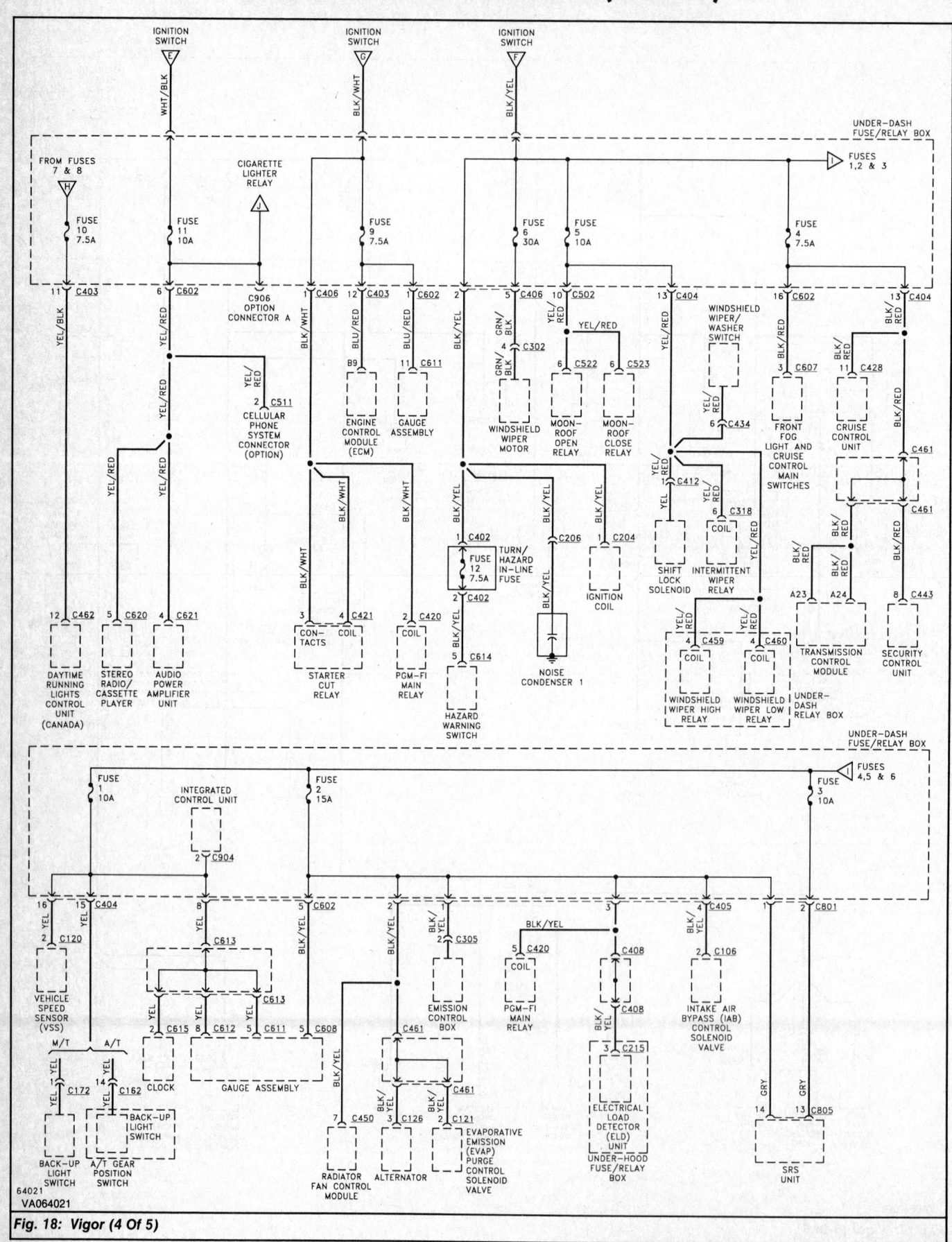

Fig. 18: Vigor (4 Of 5)

VA064021
64021

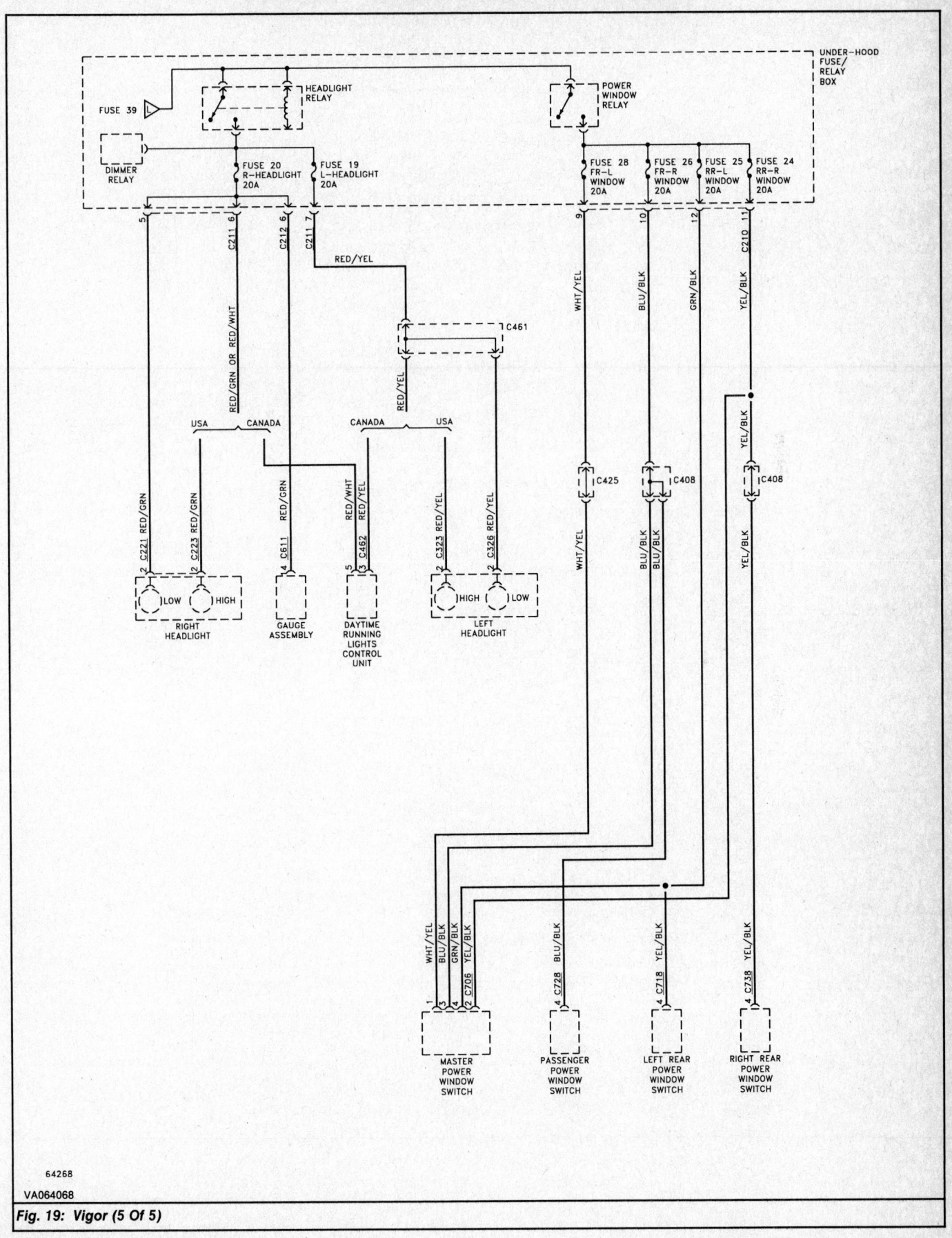

64268

VA064068

Integra, Legend, Vigor

NOTE: On all models, radio/cassette or radio/CD player contains an anti-theft protection circuit. Whenever battery is disconnected, radio will go into anti-theft mode. When battery is reconnected, radio will display CODE and will be inoperative until proper code number is entered by vehicle owner.

WARNING: To avoid injury from accidental air bag deployment, read and carefully follow all WARNINGS and SERVICE PRECAUTIONS.

NOTE: For information on air bag DIAGNOSIS & TESTING or DISPOSAL PROCEDURES, see MITCHELL® AIR BAG SERVICE & REPAIR MANUAL, DOMESTIC & IMPORTED MODELS.

DESCRIPTION & OPERATION

The Supplemental Restraint System (SRS) will activate to protect the driver and passenger when the car receives a sufficient front end impact. System includes left and right impact sensors, SRS unit with cowl sensor and driver-side and passenger-side air bags. *See Fig. 1, 2, 3 or 4.* Legend is equipped with seat belt pretensioners, which are electrically linked with the SRS air bag. In a front-end collision, pretensioner instantly retracts belt to firmly restrain occupant.

SYSTEM OPERATION CHECK

When ignition is turned on, SRS indicator light should come on and then go off after about 6 seconds. If indicator light does not come on, comes on while vehicle is driven or does not go out after about 6 seconds, inspect system as soon as possible.

SERVICE PRECAUTIONS

Observe these precautions when working with air bag systems:
- Disable SRS before servicing any SRS or steering column component. Failure to do so could result in accidental air bag deployment and possible personal injury. See DISABLING & ACTIVATING AIR BAG SYSTEM.
- Wait at least 3 minutes after deactivating air bag system. System maintains air bag system voltage for about 3 minutes after battery is disconnected. Servicing air bag system before 3 minutes may cause accidental air bag deployment and possible personal injury.
- After an accident, inspect all SRS components, including harness and brackets. Replace any damaged or bent components even if a deployment did not occur. Check steering column, knee bolster, instrument panel steering column reinforcement plate and lower brace for damage. DO NOT service any component or wiring. Replace any damaged or defective components or wiring.

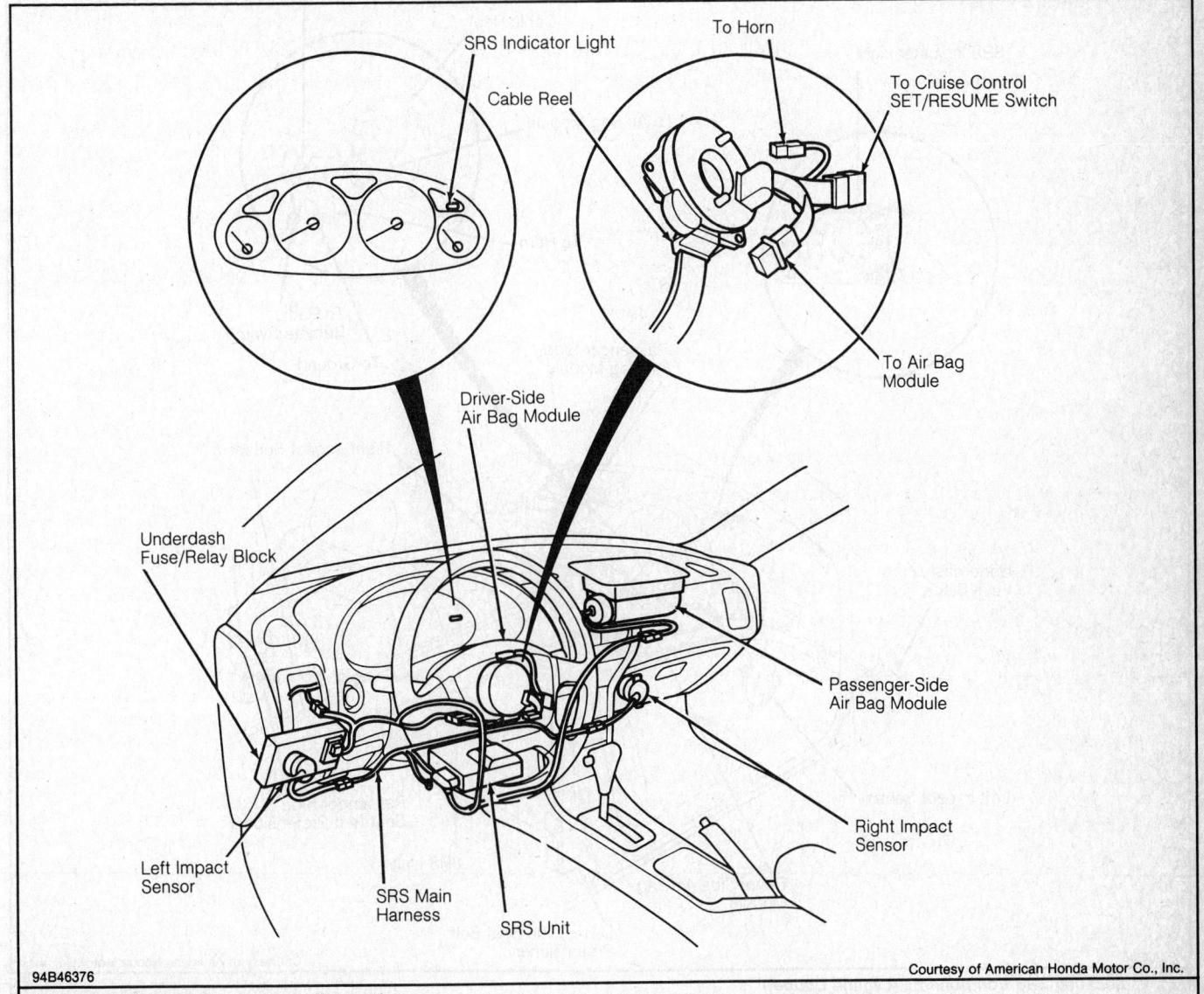

94B46376

Courtesy of American Honda Motor Co., Inc.

Fig. 1: Locating SRS Components (Integra)

- After repairs, turn ignition on from passenger side of vehicle (on single air bag models). Verify SRS indicator light works properly and no system faults are indicated. See SYSTEM OPERATION CHECK.
- Always wear safety glasses when servicing or handling an air bag.
- Air bag module must be stored in its original special container until ready for service. Store air bag module and container in a clean, dry place, away from extreme heat, sparks and sources of high electrical energy.
- When placing a live air bag module on a bench or other surface, always face air bag and trim cover up, away from surface. This will reduce motion of module if it is accidentally deployed.
- NEVER allow any electrical source near inflator on back of air bag module.
- When carrying a live air bag module, point trim cover away from your body to minimize injury in case of accidental air bag deployment.
- DO NOT probe a wire through insulator; this will damage wire and eventually cause failure due to corrosion.

- When performing electrical tests, always use test harnesses recommended by manufacturer. DO NOT use test probes directly on component connector pins or wires.
- DO NOT use electrical equipment not specified by manufacturer.
- If SRS is not fully functional for any reason, DO NOT operate vehicle until system is repaired. DO NOT remove any component or in any way disable system from operating normally. If SRS is not functional, park vehicle until repairs can be made.

DISABLING & ACTIVATING AIR BAG SYSTEM

WARNING: Wait at least 3 minutes after deactivating air bag system. System maintains voltage for about 3 minutes after battery is disconnected. Servicing air bag system before 3 minutes may cause accidental air bag deployment and possible personal injury.

DISABLING SYSTEM

Integra & Vigor – **1)** Turn ignition off. Wait at least 3 minutes to allow capacitor in back-up circuit to discharge. Disconnect battery cables.

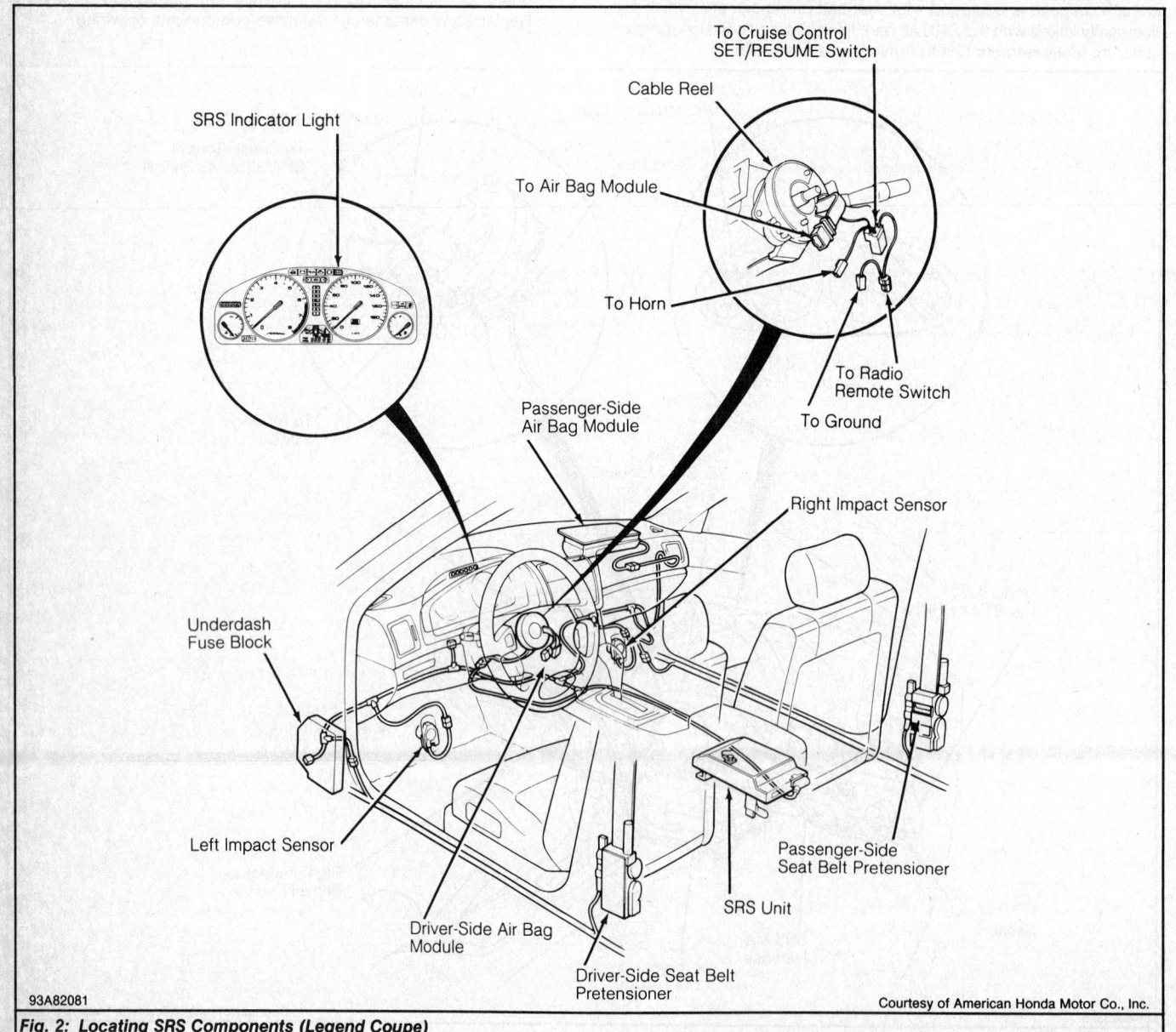

93A82081

Courtesy of American Honda Motor Co., Inc.

Fig. 2: Locating SRS Components (Legend Coupe)

Remove access panel from under air bag. *See Fig. 5.* Remove Red shorting connector. Unplug connector between air bag and cable reel. Connect Red shorting connector to air bag side of connector. On Integra, connect SRS Shorting Connector "A" (07MAZ-SP0020A) to cable reel side of connector. *See Fig. 6.*

2) For passenger-side air bag, remove glove box. Remove Red shorting connector from holder. Unplug connector between passenger-side air bag and SRS main harness. On Integra, connect Red shorting connector to air bag side of passenger-side air bag connector. *See Fig. 8.* Connect SRS Shorting Connector "A" (07MAZ-SP0020A) to cable reel side of connector. On Vigor, connect Red shorting connector to air bag side of passenger-side air bag connector. *See Fig. 10.*

Legend – 1) Turn ignition off. Wait at least 3 minutes to allow capacitor in back-up circuit to discharge. This will prevent a malfunction of seat belt pretensioner. Disconnect battery cables. Remove access panel from under driver-side air bag. *See Fig. 5.* Remove Red shorting connector.

2) Unplug 3-pin connector between air bag and cable reel. Connect Red shorting connector to air bag side of connector. Connect SRS Shorting Connector "A" (07MAZ-SP0020A) to cable reel side of connector. *See Fig. 6.*

3) For passenger-side air bag, remove glove box. Unplug connector between passenger-side air bag and SRS main harness. Connect Red shorting connector to air bag side of passenger-side air bag connector. *See Fig. 7.*

4) Connect SRS Shorting Connector "A" to SRS main harness half of 3-pin connector. *See Fig. 8.*

5) Remove quarter trim panel. Remove Red shorting connector from connector holder. Unplug seat belt pretensioner connector. Connect Red shorting connector to seat belt pretensioner half of connector. *See Fig. 9.*

ACTIVATING SYSTEM

Integra & Vigor – 1) Remove shorting connector(s) from passenger-side air bag connector. Attach shorting connector to holder. Reconnect passenger-side air bag connector to SRS main harness connector. Reinstall glove box.

2) Remove shorting connector(s) from cable reel connector from driver's side air bag. Reconnect air bag and cable reel connectors. Attach shorting connector to access panel. Reinstall access panel. Reconnect battery. Check SRS indicator light to verify system functions properly. See SYSTEM OPERATION CHECK.

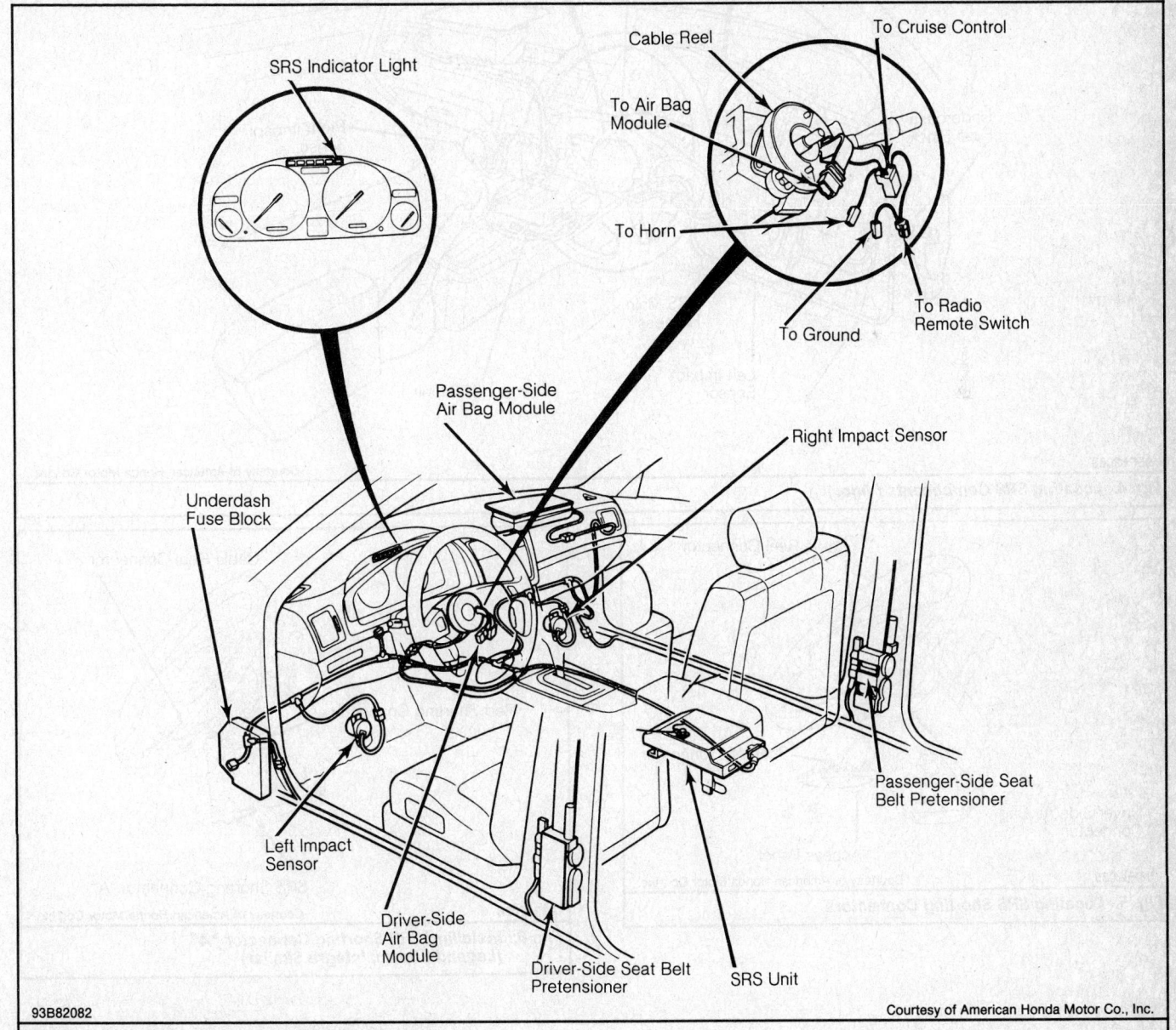

Fig. 3: Locating SRS Components (Legend Sedan)

93B82082

SRS Indicator Light

Cable Reel

To Horn

To Cruise Control

To Air Bag Module

Driver-Side Air Bag Module

Passenger-Side Air Bag Module

Right Impact Sensor

Underdash Fuse Block

SRS Main Harness

Left Impact Sensor

SRS Unit

93C82083

Courtesy of American Honda Motor Co., Inc.

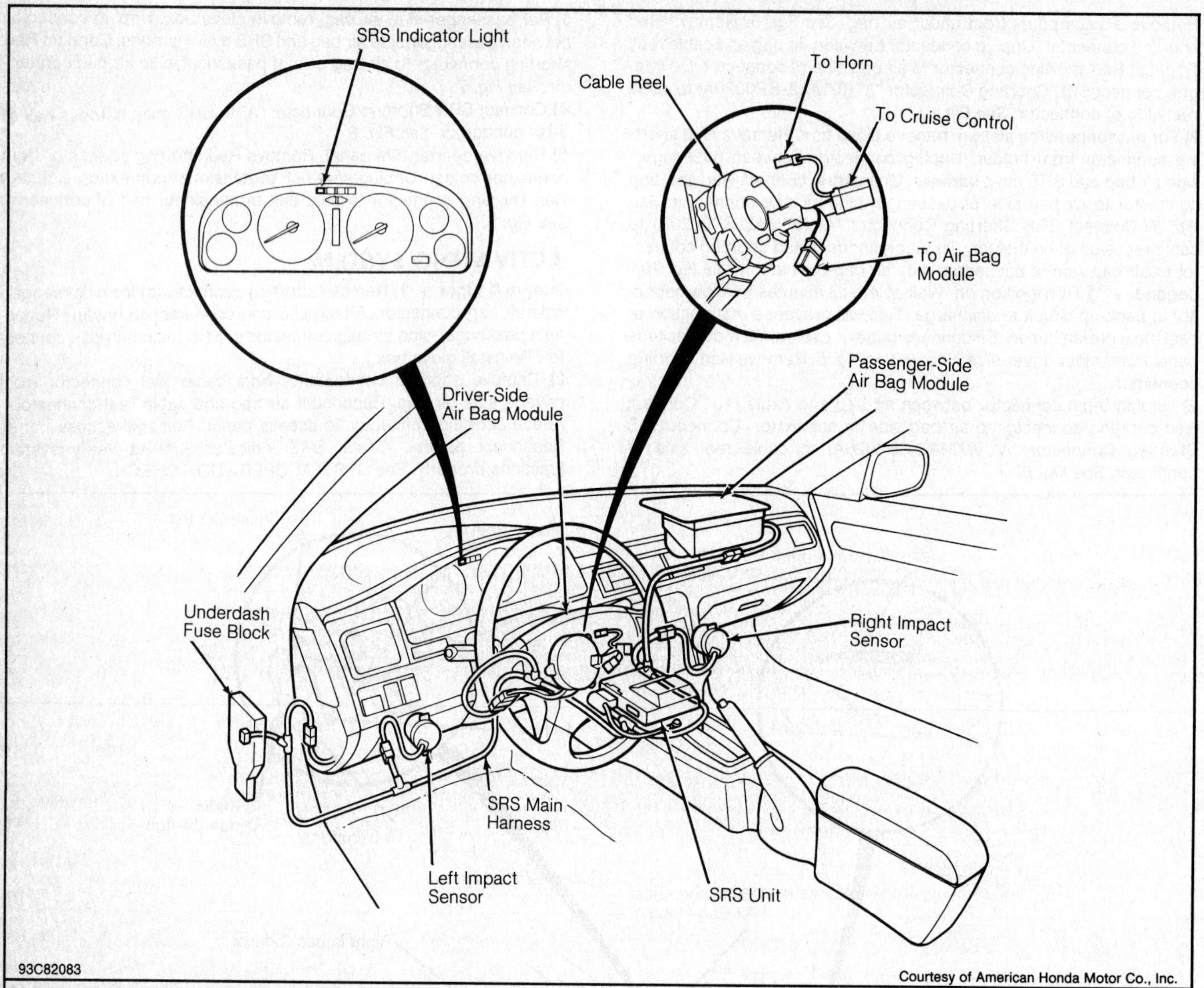

Fig. 4: Locating SRS Components (Vigor)

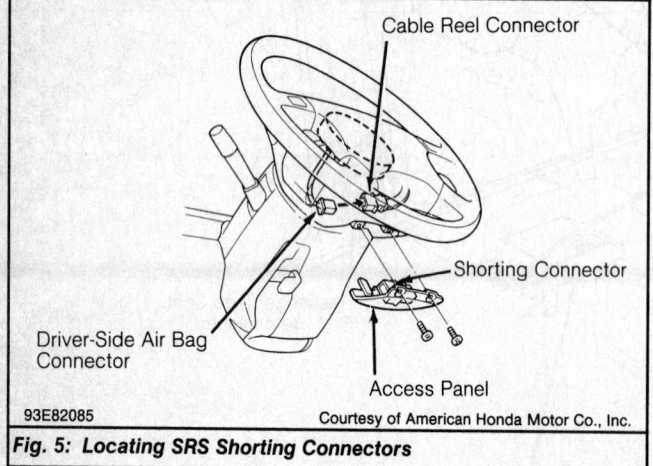

Cable Reel Connector

Shorting Connector

Driver-Side Air Bag Connector

Access Panel

93E82085

Courtesy of American Honda Motor Co., Inc.

Fig. 5: Locating SRS Shorting Connectors

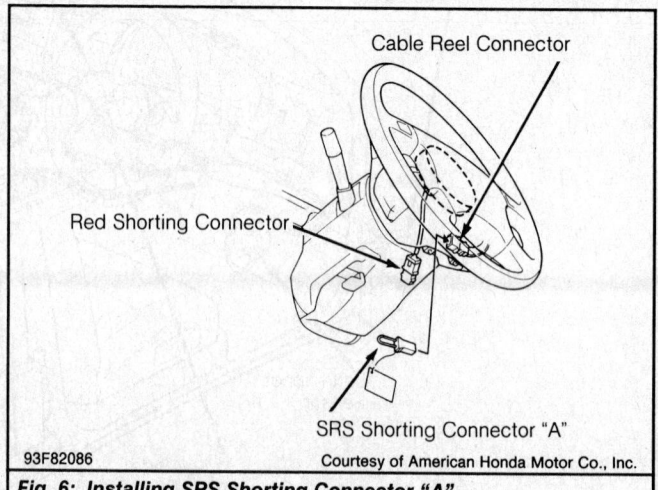

Cable Reel Connector

Red Shorting Connector

SRS Shorting Connector "A"

93F82086

Courtesy of American Honda Motor Co., Inc.

Fig. 6: Installing SRS Shorting Connector "A"
(Legend Shown; Integra Similar)

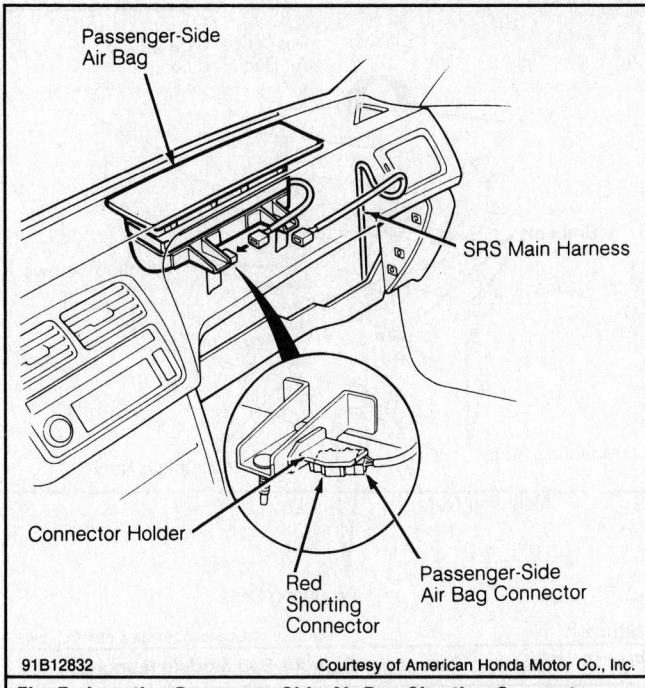

91B12832   Courtesy of American Honda Motor Co., Inc.

Fig. 7: Locating Passenger-Side Air Bag Shorting Connector (Legend)

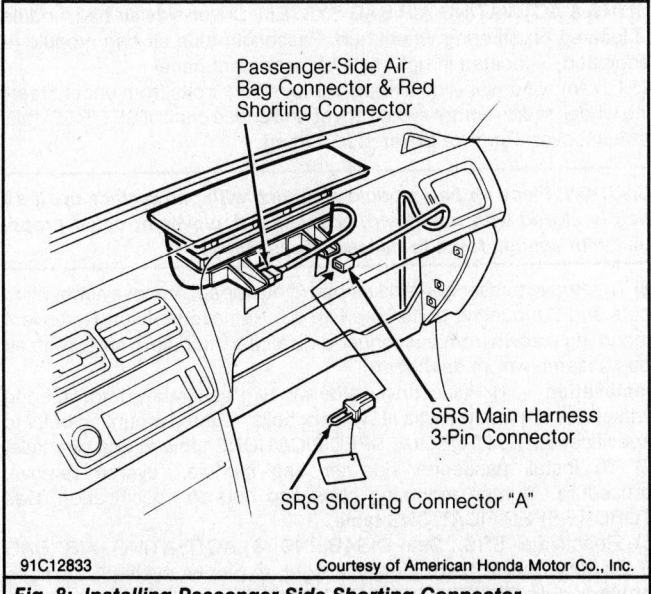

91C12833   Courtesy of American Honda Motor Co., Inc.

Fig. 8: Installing Passenger-Side Shorting Connector (Legend)

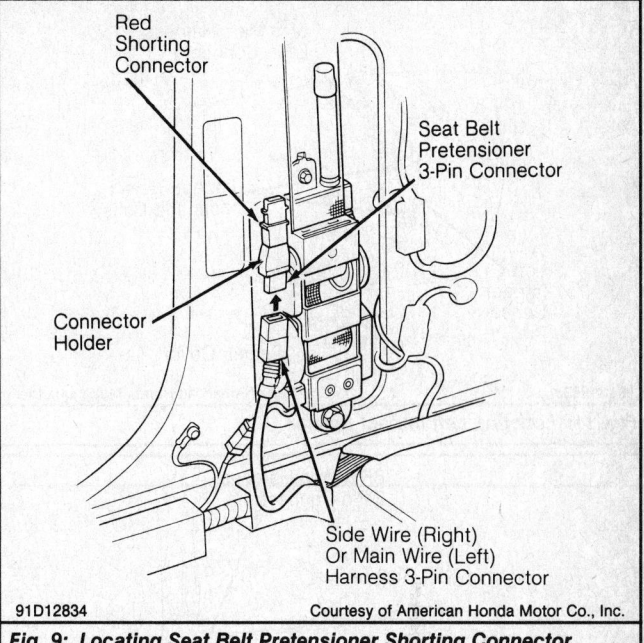

91D12834   Courtesy of American Honda Motor Co., Inc.

Fig. 9: Locating Seat Belt Pretensioner Shorting Connector (Legend)

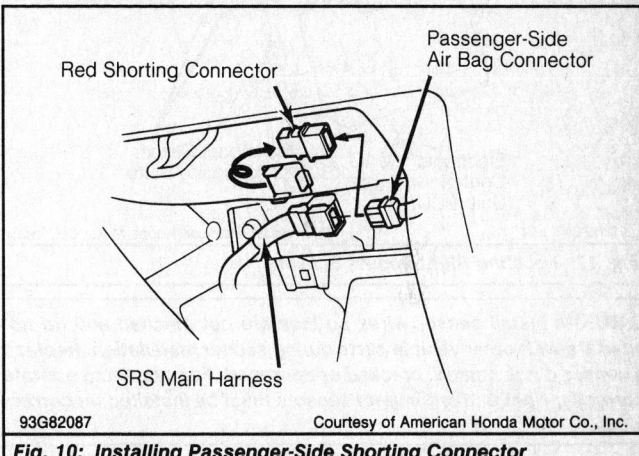

93G82087   Courtesy of American Honda Motor Co., Inc.

Fig. 10: Installing Passenger-Side Shorting Connector (Vigor)

Legend – 1) Remove shorting connectors from passenger-side air bag connector (if equipped) and SRS main harness connector. Reconnect passenger-side air bag connector (if equipped) to SRS main harness connector. Reinstall glove box.

2) Remove shorting connectors from driver-side air bag connector and from cable reel connector. Reconnect driver-side air bag connector to cable reel connector. Attach shorting connector to access panel. Reinstall access panel.

3) Remove shorting connectors from seat belt pretensioners. Attach shorting connectors to their holders. Reconnect side harness connector to right pretensioner.

4) Reconnect main wire harness to left pretensioner. Reinstall quarter trim panel. Reconnect battery. Check SRS indicator light to verify system functions properly. See SYSTEM OPERATION CHECK.

REMOVAL & INSTALLATION

WARNING: Failure to follow air bag service precautions may result in accidental deployment and personal injury. See SERVICE PRECAUTIONS. After component replacement, perform a system operation check to verify proper system operation. See SYSTEM OPERATION CHECK.

IMPACT SENSORS

Removal – 1) Before proceeding, follow air bag service precautions. See SERVICE PRECAUTIONS. Disable SRS. See DISABLING & ACTIVATING AIR BAG SYSTEM.

2) Impact sensors are located in left and right footwell areas. To remove left impact sensor, remove left footrest and left door sill molding. Pull carpet back. Remove sensor cover and sensor. See Fig. 10.

3) To remove right impact sensor, remove right door sill molding and pull back carpet. If necessary, remove Powertrain Control Module (PCM). See Fig. 11. Remove 2 mounting bolts and impact sensor.

Installation – To install, reverse removal procedure. Tighten Torx bolts to specification. See TORQUE SPECIFICATIONS. Ensure click is felt or heard when connecting SRS main harness connector. Activate air bag system. See DISABLING & ACTIVATING AIR BAG SYSTEM.

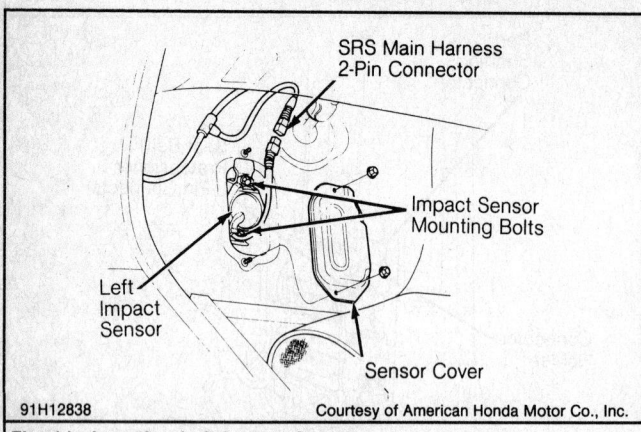

91H12838   Courtesy of American Honda Motor Co., Inc.

Fig. 11: Locating Left Impact Sensor

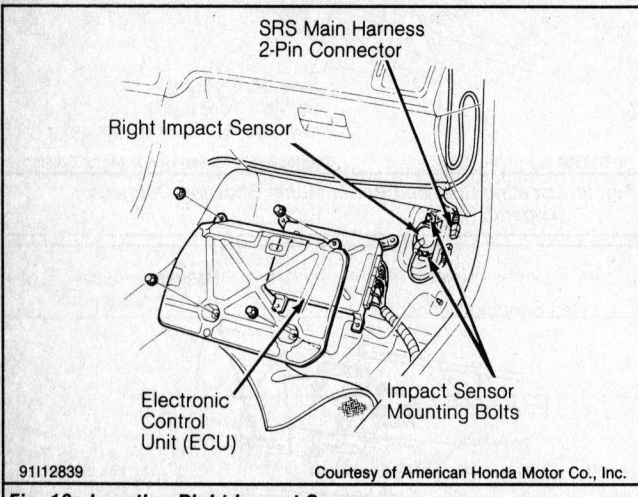

91I12839   Courtesy of American Honda Motor Co., Inc.

Fig. 12: Locating Right Impact Sensor

CAUTION: Install sensor wires so they are not pinched and do not interfere with other vehicle parts during sensor installation. Replace a sensor if it is dented, cracked or deformed. For system to operate correctly, right and left impact sensors must be installed on correct sides.

Installation – Install sensor and sensor cover. On left side, install carpet, molding and footrest. On right side, install (PCM if necessary), carpet and molding. On both sides, tighten sensor mounting bolts to specification. See TORQUE SPECIFICATIONS table at end of article. To complete installation, reverse removal procedure. Reactivate air bag system. Check SRS indicator light to verify system is functioning properly. See SYSTEM OPERATION CHECK.

AIR BAG MODULE

Removal (Integra) – 1) Before proceeding, follow air bag service precautions. See SERVICE PRECAUTIONS. Disable SRS. See DISABLING & ACTIVATING AIR BAG SYSTEM. Air bag module is located on steering wheel hub.
2) Remove access panel below air bag. Remove Red shorting connector from panel. Install shorting connector onto air bag connector. Connect SRS Shorting Connector "A" (07MAZ-SP0020A) to cable reel side of connector. Remove Torx mounting bolts and air bag module.

CAUTION: Place air bag module on bench with pad surface up. If air bag is stored with pad down, accidental deployment could propel unit with enough force to cause serious injury.

3) To remove passenger-side air bag, remove glove box. Remove 4 mounting nuts from bracket. See Fig. 14. Remove bracket and one mounting nut from passenger-side air bag module. Carefully lift air bag assembly from dashboard.

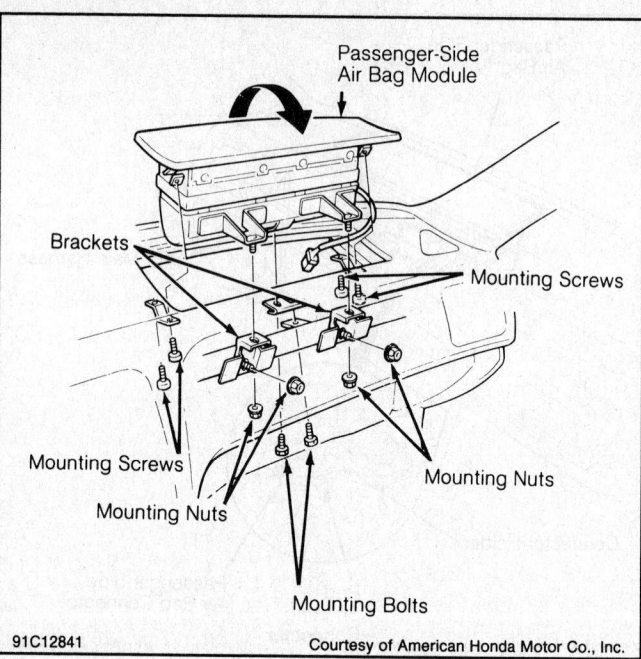

91C12841   Courtesy of American Honda Motor Co., Inc.

Fig. 13: Removing Passenger-Side Air Bag Module (Legend)

Removal (Legend) – 1) Before proceeding, follow air bag service precautions. See SERVICE PRECAUTIONS. Disable SRS. See DISABLING & ACTIVATING AIR BAG SYSTEM. Driver-side air bag module is located on steering wheel hub. Passenger-side air bag module (if equipped) is located in right side of instrument panel.
2) To remove driver-side air bag, remove Torx bolts from under steering wheel, radio remote switch cover and cruise control SET/RESUME switch cover. Remove driver-side air bag.

CAUTION: Place air bag module on bench with pad surface up. If air bag is stored with pad down, accidental deployment could propel unit with enough force to cause serious injury.

3) To remove passenger-side air bag (if equipped), remove 4 mounting nuts and 2 mounting bolts. See Fig. 13. Remove bracket. Remove 4 mounting screws from passenger-side air bag module. Carefully lift air bag assembly from dashboard.
Installation – 1) Place driver-side air bag assembly onto steering wheel. Secure module with NEW Torx bolts. Tighten mounting bolts to specification. See TORQUE SPECIFICATIONS table at end of article.
2) To install passenger-side air bag module, reverse removal procedure. Tighten mounting bolts and nuts to specification. See TORQUE SPECIFICATIONS table.
3) Reactivate SRS. See DISABLING & ACTIVATING AIR BAG SYSTEM. Check SRS indicator light to verify system functions properly. See SYSTEM OPERATION CHECK.
Removal (Vigor) – 1) Before proceeding, follow air bag service precautions. See SERVICE PRECAUTIONS. Disable SRS. See DISABLING & ACTIVATING AIR BAG SYSTEM. Air bag module is located on steering wheel hub.
2) Remove access panel below air bag. Remove Red shorting connector from panel. Install shorting connector onto air bag connector. Remove Torx mounting bolts and air bag module.

CAUTION: Place air bag module on bench with pad surface up. If air bag is stored with pad down, accidental deployment could propel unit with enough force to cause serious injury.

3) To remove passenger-side air bag, remove glove box. Remove 4 mounting nuts from bracket. See Fig. 14. Remove bracket and one mounting nut from passenger-side air bag module. Carefully lift air bag assembly from dashboard.

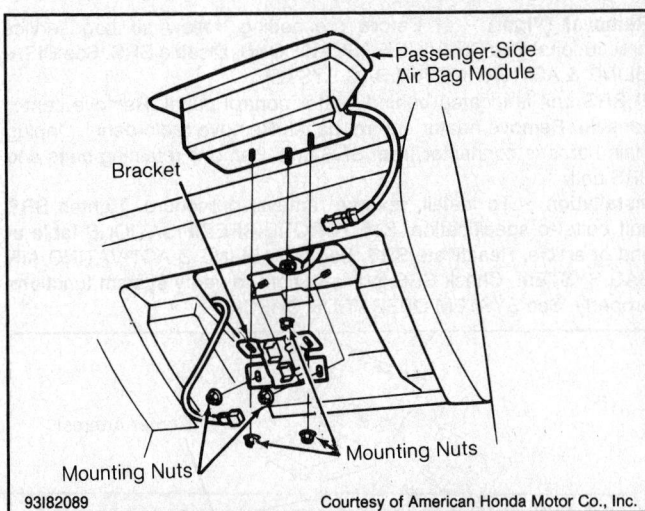

93I82089 — Courtesy of American Honda Motor Co., Inc.

Fig. 14: Removing Passenger-Side Air Bag Module (Integra & Vigor)

Installation – 1) Place air bag module onto steering wheel. Secure module with NEW Torx bolts. Tighten mounting bolts to specification. See TORQUE SPECIFICATIONS.

2) To install passenger-side air bag module, reverse removal procedure. Tighten mounting bolts and nuts to specification. See TORQUE SPECIFICATIONS table.

3) Reactivate SRS. See DISABLING & ACTIVATING AIR BAG SYSTEM. Check SRS indicator light to verify system functions properly. See SYSTEM OPERATION CHECK.

STEERING WHEEL

Removal (Integra & Vigor) – 1) Ensure front wheels are in straight-ahead position. Before proceeding, follow air bag service precautions. See SERVICE PRECAUTIONS. Disable SRS. See DISABLING & ACTIVATING AIR BAG SYSTEM. Remove air bag retaining bolt cover. Remove SET/RESUME switch cover. Remove Torx bolts and air bag module.

CAUTION: Place air bag module on bench with pad surface up. If air bag is stored with pad down, accidental deployment could propel unit with enough force to cause serious injury.

---

2) Unplug connectors from horn and SET/RESUME switches. Remove steering wheel retaining nut. Pull steadily upward while rocking steering wheel from side to side.

Installation – 1) Ensure front wheels are in straight-ahead position. Center cable reel. See CABLE REEL CENTERING under ADJUSTMENTS. Install steering wheel. Install NEW steering wheel retaining nut. Ensure steering wheel shaft engages cable reel. Install NEW Torx bolts.

2) To complete installation, reverse removal procedure. Reactivate SRS. See DISABLING & ACTIVATING AIR BAG SYSTEM. Check SRS indicator light to verify system functions properly. See SYSTEM OPERATION CHECK.

Removal (Legend) – 1) Before proceeding, follow air bag service precautions. See SERVICE PRECAUTIONS. Disable SRS. See DISABLING & ACTIVATING AIR BAG SYSTEM. Put front wheels in straight-ahead position. Remove access panel below air bag. Remove Red shorting connector from panel. Install shorting connector onto air bag connector. Remove Torx mounting bolts and air bag module.

CAUTION: Place air bag module on bench with pad surface up. If air bag is stored with pad down, accidental deployment could propel unit with enough force to cause serious injury.

---

2) Unplug connectors from horn, remote audio and SET/RESUME switches. Remove steering wheel retaining nut. Remove steering wheel by pulling steadily upward while rocking steering wheel from side to side.

Installation – 1) Ensure front wheels are in straight-ahead position. Center cable reel. See CABLE REEL CENTERING under ADJUSTMENTS. Install steering wheel. Install NEW steering wheel retaining nut. Ensure steering wheel shaft engages cable reel. Install NEW Torx bolts.

2) To complete installation, reverse removal procedure. Reactivate SRS. See DISABLING & ACTIVATING AIR BAG SYSTEM. Check SRS indicator light to verify system functions properly. See SYSTEM OPERATION CHECK. Enter anti-theft code into radio.

CABLE REEL

Removal – 1) Before proceeding, follow air bag service precautions. See SERVICE PRECAUTIONS. Disable SRS. See DISABLING & ACTIVATING AIR BAG SYSTEM. Ensure front wheels face straight ahead.

2) Cable reel is located under steering wheel, in upper steering column. See Fig. 1, 2, 3 or 4. Remove upper and lower steering column covers. Unplug connector between cable reel and SRS main harness. Remove air bag assembly from steering wheel. See AIR BAG MODULE under REMOVAL & INSTALLATION. Remove steering wheel nut.

3) Unplug connectors from horn, radio remote switch, ground and cruise control switches. Remove cable reel 3-pin connector from its clips. See Fig. 15. Remove steering wheel from column. Remove 4 bolts and cover under steering column. Remove cable reel and cancel sleeve. See Fig. 16.

Installation – 1) Align cancel sleeve grooves with projections on cable reel. See Fig. 17. Carefully install cable reel and cancel sleeve onto steering column shaft. Reinstall cover. Install steering column upper and lower covers. Center cable reel. See CABLE REEL CENTERING under ADJUSTMENTS.

2) After cable reel is centered, install steering wheel. Reattach cruise control and cable reel connectors to their clips. Connect horn connector, radio remote switch connector and ground connector.

3) Install steering wheel nut and driver-side air bag module. Tighten steering wheel nut and air bag mounting bolts to specification. See TORQUE SPECIFICATIONS table. Connect cable reel harness to SRS main harness. Attach connector holder to steering column.

4) To complete installation, reverse removal procedure. Reactivate SRS. See DISABLING & ACTIVATING AIR BAG SYSTEM. Check SRS indicator light to verify system is functioning properly. See SYSTEM OPERATION CHECK.

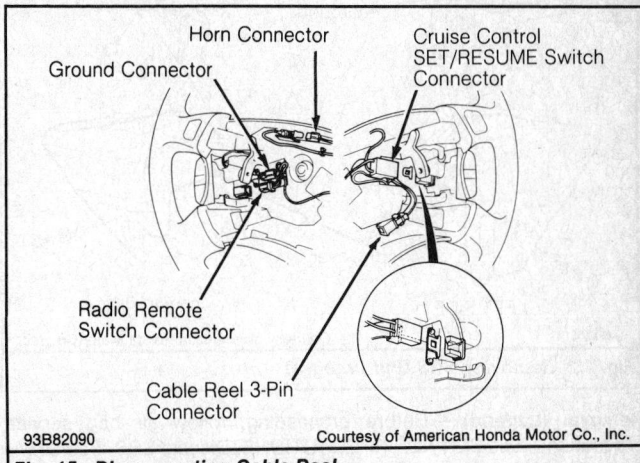

93B82090 — Courtesy of American Honda Motor Co., Inc.

Fig. 15: Disconnecting Cable Reel

SRS UNIT

Removal (Integra) – Before proceeding, read service precautions. See SERVICE PRECAUTIONS. Disable air bag system. See DISABLING & ACTIVATING AIR BAG SYSTEM. Remove cover from each side of SRS control unit. See Fig. 18. Disconnect SRS control unit wiring connector. Remove 4 Torx bolts securing SRS control unit. Remove SRS control unit from driver-side of console.

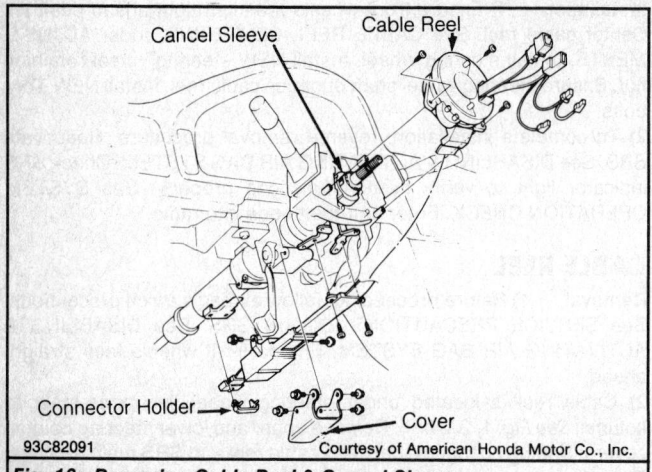

Fig. 16: Removing Cable Reel & Cancel Sleeve

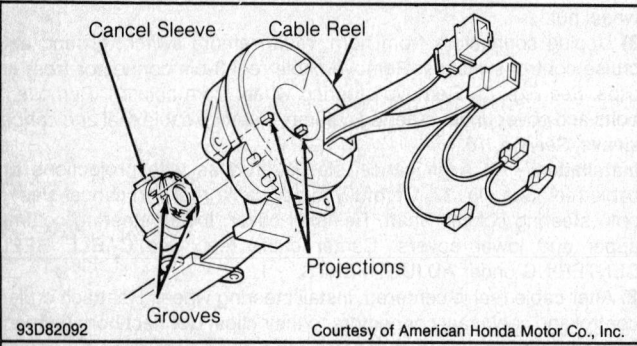

Fig. 17: Installing Cable Reel

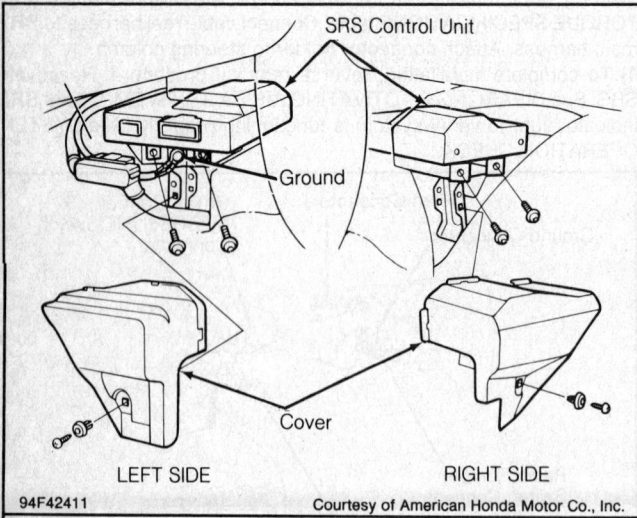

Fig. 18: Removing SRS Unit (Integra)

Removal (Legend) – Before proceeding, follow air bag service precautions. See SERVICE PRECAUTIONS. Disable SRS. See DISABLING & ACTIVATING AIR BAG SYSTEM. SRS unit is located under armrest of center console. See Fig. 19. Remove center console. Unplug SRS unit 18-pin connector. Remove 4 SRS unit mounting bolts. Remove SRS unit.

Installation – To install, reverse removal procedure. Tighten SRS unit bolts to specification. See TORQUE SPECIFICATIONS table at end of article. Reactivate SRS. See DISABLING & ACTIVATING AIR BAG SYSTEM. Check SRS indicator light to verify system is functioning properly. See SYSTEM OPERATION CHECK.

Removal (Vigor) – **1)** Before proceeding, follow air bag service precautions. See SERVICE PRECAUTIONS. Disable SRS. See DISABLING & ACTIVATING AIR BAG SYSTEM.

2) SRS unit is located behind heater control panel. Remove center console. Remove heater control panel. Remove radio panel. Unplug main harness connector from SRS unit. Remove retaining bolts and SRS unit.

Installation – To install, reverse removal procedure. Tighten SRS unit bolts to specification. See TORQUE SPECIFICATIONS table at end of article. Reactivate SRS. See DISABLING & ACTIVATING AIR BAG SYSTEM. Check SRS indicator light to verify system functions properly. See SYSTEM OPERATION CHECK.

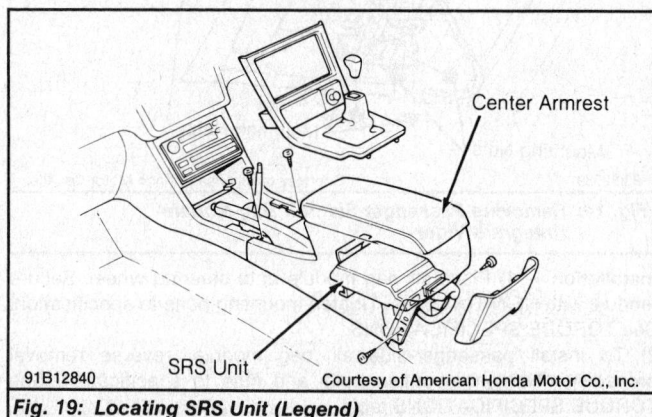

Fig. 19: Locating SRS Unit (Legend)

ADJUSTMENTS

CABLE REEL CENTERING

After installing cable reel onto steering column shaft, rotate cable reel clockwise until it stops. Rotate cable reel counterclockwise about 2 turns until Yellow gear tooth lines up with mark on cover and arrow on cable reel label points straight up. See Fig. 20. Install steering wheel. Attach cruise control and cable reel connectors to their clips.

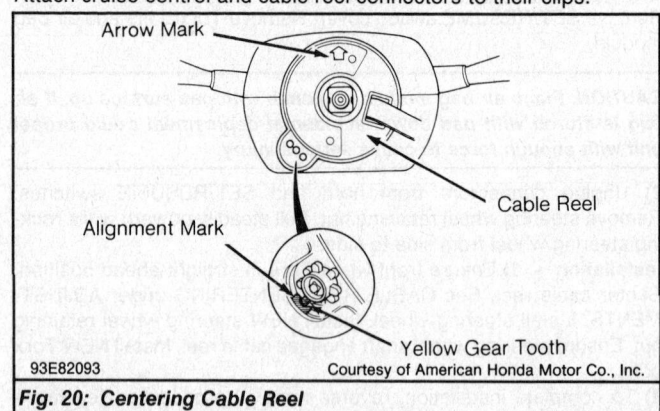

Fig. 20: Centering Cable Reel

TORQUE SPECIFICATIONS
TORQUE SPECIFICATIONS

Application	Ft. Lbs. (N.m)
Impact Sensor Mounting Bolt	16 (22)
Pretensioner Lower Mounting Bolt	24 (33)
Shoulder Harness Anchor Bolt	24 (33)
Steering Wheel Nut	36 (50)

	INCH Lbs. (N.m)
Air Bag Mounting Bolt/Nut	84 (10)
Pretensioner Upper Mounting Bolt	84 (10)
SRS Unit	84 (10)

WIRING DIAGRAMS

NOTE: See ACCESSORIES & EQUIPMENT, Volume 5.

Legend, Vigor

DESCRIPTION & OPERATION

The Acura security alarm system is activated automatically 15 seconds after everything has been closed and locked. The security alarm system indicator light, located on driver's side door, will flash after the doors are closed and properly locked. If any of the following conditions occur, the engine starter circuit will be interrupted, the horns will sound, the headlights, side marker lights, parking lights and tail lights will flash repeatedly for approximately 2 minutes, or until the system is disarmed by unlocking either door from the outside with the key.

- Door is forcibly opened.
- Trunk is opened without a key.
- Hood is opened.
- Battery terminals are removed and reconnected.
- Hood/trunk opener in vehicle is operated.
- Engine starter circuit and battery circuit are bypassed by breaking ignition switch.

TROUBLE SHOOTING

CAUTION: All models are equipped with Supplemental Restraint System (SRS). SRS wiring harness is routed close to instrument cluster, steering wheel and related components. All SRS wiring harnesses are covered by Yellow outer insulation. DO NOT use electrical test equipment on these circuits. Before working on anti-theft components, disable air bag system. See AIR BAG RESTRAINT SYSTEM article in ACCESSORIES & EQUIPMENT.

WARNING: Wait about 3 minutes after disabling air bag system. Back-up power circuit, capacitor internal to SRS module, maintains system voltage for about 3 minutes after battery is disconnected. Servicing air bag system before 3 minutes may cause accidental air bag deployment and possible personal injury.

NOTE: Radio/cassette or radio/CD player contains an anti-theft protection circuit. Whenever battery is disconnected, radio will go into anti-theft mode. When battery is reconnected, radio will display CODE and will be inoperative until proper code number is entered by vehicle owner.

NOTE: Different wires with the same color have been given a suffix number. For example, Yellow/Green[1] and Yellow/Green[2] are not the same wires. For wire and terminal identification, see appropriate WIRING DIAGRAMS.

Security Alarm Can't Be Set (Indicator Light Does Not Flash) –
1) On Legend Coupe, check for blown fuses No. 15 (7.5-amp) and No. 20 (7.5-amp) in under-hood fuse block and No. 39 (20-amp) in under-dash fuse block. Check security indicator light (LED). See SECURITY INDICATOR LIGHT (LED). Check ignition switch. See IGNITION SWITCH in STEERING COLUMN SWITCHES article. Check for poor grounds. Check for open circuit, loose or disconnected terminals on control module Yellow/Blue, Black/Red, White/Green, Red/Green[3] and Blue/White wires.
2) On Legend Sedan, check for blown fuses No. 15 (7.5-amp) and No. 20 (7.5-amp) in under-hood fuse block and No. 39 (20-amp) in under-dash fuse block. Check security indicator light (LED). See SECURITY INDICATOR LIGHT (LED). Check ignition switch. See IGNITION SWITCH in STEERING COLUMN SWITCHES article. Check for poor grounds. Check for open circuit, loose or disconnected terminals on control module Yellow/Blue, Black/Red, White/Green, Red/Green and Blue/White wires.

3) On Vigor, check for blown fuses No. 4 (7.5-amp) in under-dash fuse block and No. 30 (20-amp) in under-hood fuse block. Check security indicator light (LED). See SECURITY INDICATOR LIGHT (LED). Check ignition switch. See IGNITION SWITCH in STEERING COLUMN SWITCHES article. Check for poor ground. Check for open circuit, loose or disconnected terminals on control module White/Yellow, Black/Red, Green and Blue wires.
Security System Does Not Operate – 1) On Legend Coupe and Sedan, check Starting system. Check A/T gear position switch or M/T clutch interlock switch. Check security control module input. See SECURITY CONTROL MODULE INPUT TEST. Check for poor ground. Check for open circuit, loose or disconnected terminals on control module Black/White (A/T) or Blue (A/T), and Black/Yellow wires.
2) On Vigor, check Starting system. Check A/T gear position switch or M/T clutch interlock switch. Check security control module input. See SECURITY CONTROL MODULE INPUT TEST. Check for poor ground. Check for open circuit, loose or disconnected terminals on control module Black/White, Green/Black (A/T), Yellow/Green and Blue/Yellow (M/T) wires.
Security System Can Be Set But Horn Alarm Does Not Operate –
1) On Legend Coupe, check for blown fuse No. 39 (20-amp) in under-dash fuse block. Check horn circuit. Check security control module input. See SECURITY CONTROL MODULE INPUT TEST. Check for poor ground. Check for open circuit, loose or disconnected terminals on control module White/Green, Blue and Blue/Red[1] wires.
2) On Legend Sedan, check for blown fuse No. 39 (20-amp) in under-dash fuse block. Check horn circuit. Check security control module input. See SECURITY CONTROL MODULE INPUT TEST. Check for poor ground. Check for open circuit, loose or disconnected terminals on control module White/Green, Blue and Blue/Red wires.
3) On Vigor, check for blown fuse No. 30 (20-amp) in under-hood fuse block. Check horn circuit. Check security control module input. See SECURITY CONTROL MODULE INPUT TEST. Check for poor ground. Check for open circuit, loose or disconnected terminals on control module White/Yellow, Blue/Green[3] and Blue/Green wires.
Security System Can Be Set But Headlight Alarm Does Not Operate – 1) On Legend Coupe and Sedan, check lighting system. Check security control module input. See SECURITY CONTROL MODULE INPUT TEST. Check for open circuit, loose or disconnected terminals on control module Blue/Red[2] and Red/Green wires.
2) On Vigor, check lighting system. Check security control module input. See SECURITY CONTROL MODULE INPUT TEST. Check for poor ground. Check for open circuit, loose or disconnected terminals on control module Blue/Red[1] and Red/White wires.
Security System Can Be Set But Both Alarms Do Not Operate – On all models, check security control module input. See SECURITY CONTROL MODULE INPUT TEST.
Alarm Not Cancelled When Door Is Opened With Key – 1) On Legend Coupe, check door key cylinder switch. See DOOR KEY CYLINDER SWITCH. Check security control module input. See SECURITY CONTROL MODULE INPUT TEST. Check for poor ground. Check for open circuit, loose or disconnected terminals on control module Green/Red[2], Green/Blue[2], Green/Black and Blue/Red[3] wires.
2) On Legend Sedan, check door key cylinder switch. See DOOR KEY CYLINDER SWITCH. Check security control module input. See SECURITY CONTROL MODULE INPUT TEST. Check for poor ground. Check for open circuit, loose or disconnected terminals on control module Green/Red[2], Green/Blue[1], Green/Black and Blue/Red[3] wires.
3) On Vigor, check for blown fuse No. 4 (7.5-amp) in under-dash fuse block. Check security control module input. See SECURITY CONTROL MODULE INPUT TEST. Check for poor ground. Check for open circuit, loose or disconnected terminals on control module Blue/Red[1], Green/Yellow[2], Green/Black[2] and Blue/Red wires.

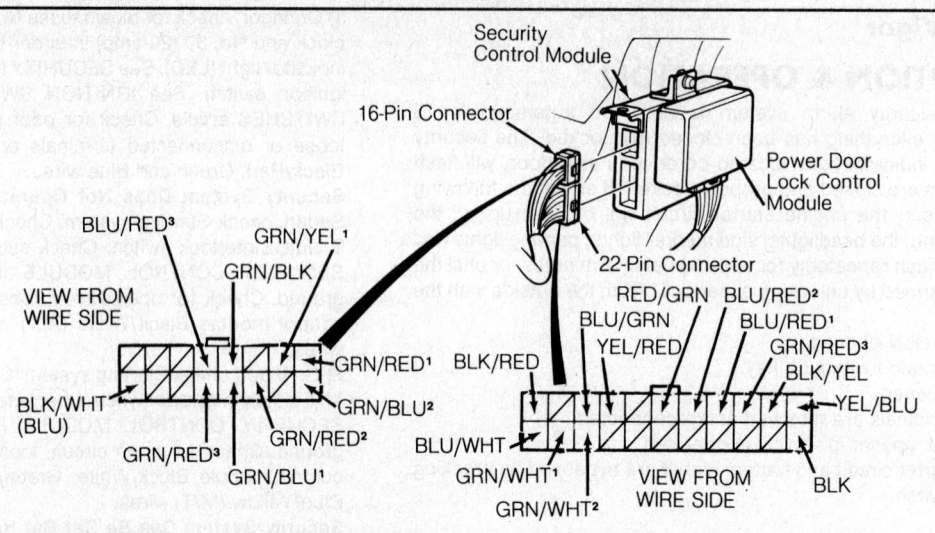

No.	Wire	Test condition	Test: Desired result	Possible cause if result is not obtained
1	BLK	Under all conditions	Check for continuity to ground: There should be continuity.	• Poor ground • An open in the wire
2	YEL/BLU	Under all conditions	Check for voltage to ground: There should be battery voltage.	• Blown No. 15 (7.5 A) fuse • An open in the wire
3	GRN/RED³	Under all conditions	Connect to ground: Security indicator should come on.	• Blown No. 39 (20 A) fuse • Faulty security indicator • An open in the wire
4	BLK/RED	Ignition switch to ON (II)	Check for voltage to ground: There should be battery voltage.	• Blown No. 20 (7.5 A) fuse • An open in the wire
5	BLK/WHT (BLU)	Ignition switch to START (III)	Check for voltage to ground: There should be battery voltage.	• Faulty starter cut relay • An open in the wire
6	BLK/YEL	Ignition switch to START (II) and: Clutch pedal pushed (M/T) Shift lever in $\boxed{P}$ (A/T)	Attach to ground: Starter should crank the engine.	• Blown No. 35 (50 A) fuse • Faulty starting system • Faulty starter cut relay • Faulty clutch interlock switch (M/T) • Faulty A/T gear position switch (A/T) • An open in the wire
7	BLU/RED¹	Under all conditions	Attach to ground: All horns should sound.	• Blown No. 39 (20 A) fuse • Faulty horn relay • Either horn faulty • Poor ground • An open in the wire
8	BLU/RED²	Under all conditions	Attach to ground: Headlights should come on.	• Faulty headlight relay • Faulty lighting system • An open in the wire
9	RED/GRN	Under all conditions	Connect to ground: Taillights should come on.	• Faulty taillight relay • Faulty taillight system • An open in the wire
10	YEL/RED	Hood open	Check for continuity to ground: There should be continuity.	• Faulty hood switch. Misadjusted hood switch • Poor ground • An open in the wire
10	YEL/RED	Hood closed	Check for continuity to ground: There should be no continuity.	• Faulty hood switch. Misadjusted hood switch • Poor ground • An open in the wire
11	BLU/GRN	Trunk lid open	Check for continuity to ground: There should be continuity.	• Faulty security trunk latch switch • Poor ground • An open in the wire
11	BLU/GRN	Trunk lid closed	Check for continuity to ground: There should be no continuity.	• Faulty security trunk latch switch • Poor ground • An open in the wire
12	GRN/BLU¹	Driver's door open	Check for continuity to ground: When the door is open, there should be continuity, and when the door is closed, there should be no continuity.	• Faulty driver's door or passenger's door switch • An open in the wire
12	GRN/BLU¹	Driver's door closed		
13	GRN/RED³	Passenger's door open		
13	GRN/RED³	Passenger's door closed		

(BLU): M/T

93I82121

Fig. 1: Security Control Module Input Test (Legend Coupe – 1 Of 2)

No.	Wire	Test condition	Test: Desired result	Possible cause if result is not obtained
14	BLU/WHT	Ignition key is inserted into the ignition switch	Check for continuity to ground: There should be continuity.	• Faulty ignition key switch • Poor ground • An open in the wire
		Ignition key is removed from the ignition switch	Check for continuity to ground: There should be continuity.	
15	GRN/WHT	Under all conditions	Check for continuity to ground: There should be continuity.	• Poor ground • An open in the wire
16	GRN/RED[1]	Trunk key in UNLOCK	Check for continuity to ground: There should be continuity.	• Faulty trunk key cylinder switch • Poor ground • An open in the wire
17	GRN/RED[2]	Driver's door key in UNLOCK	Check for continuity to ground: There should be continuity.	• Faulty driver's door or passenger's door key cylinder switch • Poor ground • An open in the wire
18	GRN/BLU[2]	Passenger's door key in UNLOCK		
19	GRN/YEL[1]	Driver's door key in LOCK	Check for continuity to ground: There should be continuity, as the door keylock is turned in LOCK.	• Faulty driver's door or passenger's door key cylinder switch • Poor ground • An open in the wire
20	GRN/WHT[2]	Right front door key in LOCK		
21	GRN/BLK	Driver's door lock knob in UNLOCK	Check for continuity to ground: There should be continuity.	• Faulty driver's door lock knob switch (Built into the actuator) • Poor ground • An open in the wire
22	BLU/RED[1]	Passenger's door lock knob in UNLOCK	Check for continuity to ground: There should be continuity.	• Faulty passenger's door lock knob switch (Built in the actuator) • Poor ground • An open in the wire

93J82122

Courtesy of American Honda Motor Co., Inc.

Fig. 2: Security Control Module Input Test (Legend Coupe – 2 Of 2)

Alarm Not Cancelled When Key Is Inserted In Ignition Switch – 1) On Legend Coupe and Sedan, check for blown fuse No. 20 (7.5-amp) in under-hood fuse block. Check ignition switch. See IGNITION SWITCH in STEERING COLUMN SWITCHES article. Check security control module input. See SECURITY CONTROL MODULE INPUT TEST. Check for open circuit, loose or disconnected terminals on control module Black/Red and Blue/White wires.

2) On Vigor, check for blown fuse No. 4 (7.5-amp) in under-dash fuse block. Check ignition switch. See IGNITION SWITCH in STEERING COLUMN SWITCHES article. Check security control module input. See SECURITY CONTROL MODULE INPUT TEST. Check for open circuit, loose or disconnected terminals on control module Blue/Red and Blue wires.

Alarm Not Cancelled When Trunk Is Opened With Key – 1) On Legend Coupe and Sedan, check trunk key cylinder switch. See TRUNK KEY CYLINDER SWITCH. Check trunk latch switch. See TRUNK LATCH SWITCH. Check security control module input. See SECURITY CONTROL MODULE INPUT TEST. Check for poor ground. Check for open circuit, loose or disconnected terminals on control module Green/Red[1] and Blue/Green wires.

2) On Vigor, check trunk key cylinder switch. See TRUNK KEY CYLINDER SWITCH. Check trunk latch switch. See TRUNK LATCH SWITCH. Check security control module input. See SECURITY CONTROL MODULE INPUT TEST. Check for poor ground. Check for open circuit, loose or disconnected terminals on control module Green/Orange and Blue/Green wires.

Alarm Does Not Operate When Hood Is Opened – On all models, check hood switch. See HOOD SWITCH. Check security control module input. See SECURITY CONTROL MODULE INPUT TEST. Check for poor ground. Check for open circuit, loose or disconnected terminals on control module Yellow/Red wire.

Alarm Does Not Operate When Door Is Opened – 1) On Legend Coupe, check door switch. See DOOR KEY SWITCH, FRONT PASSENGERS DOOR LOCK KNOB SWITCH and REAR DOOR LOCK KNOB LOCK SWITCH. Check security control module input. See SECURITY CONTROL MODULE INPUT TEST. Check for poor ground. Check for open circuit, loose or disconnected terminals on control module Green/Blue[1] and Green/Red[3] wires.

2) On Legend Sedan, check door switch. See DOOR KEY SWITCH, FRONT PASSENGERS DOOR LOCK KNOB SWITCH and REAR DOOR LOCK KNOB LOCK SWITCH. Check security control module input. See SECURITY CONTROL MODULE INPUT TEST. Check for poor ground. Check for open circuit, loose or disconnected terminals on control module Green/Blue, Green/Red[3], Green/Yellow and Green/White[1] wires.

3) On Vigor, check door switch. See DOOR KEY SWITCH, FRONT PASSENGERS DOOR LOCK KNOB SWITCH and REAR DOOR LOCK KNOB LOCK SWITCH. Check security control module input. See SECURITY CONTROL MODULE INPUT TEST. Check for poor ground. Check for open circuit, loose or disconnected terminals on control module Green/Yellow[1], Green/White, Green/Blue[2] and Green/Red wires.

TESTING

SECURITY CONTROL MODULE INPUT TEST

NOTE: Different wires with the same color have been a suffix number. For example, Yellow/Green[1] and Yellow/Green[2] are not the same wires.

Legend – Remove driver's side instrument panel lower cover. Disconnect security system control module 16-pin and 22-pin connectors. Inspect connectors to ensure terminals are making good contact. If terminals are bent, loose or corroded, repair as necessary and recheck system. If terminals are okay, use a Digital Volt/Ohmmeter to perform SECURITY CONTROL MODULE INPUT TEST. *See Figs. 1, 2, 3, and 4.* If input test is okay, replace control module.

Vigor – Remove glove box. Disconnect security system control module 12-pin and 18-pin connectors. Inspect connectors to ensure terminals are making good contact. If terminals are bent, loose or corroded, repair as necessary and recheck system. If terminals are okay, remove fuse No. 37 (15-amp) from under-hood fuse block. Using a Digital Volt/Ohmmeter, perform SECURITY CONTROL MODULE INPUT TEST. *See Figs. 5 and 6.* If input test is okay, replace control module. When test is complete, install fuse No. 37 (15-amp) in under-hood fuse block.

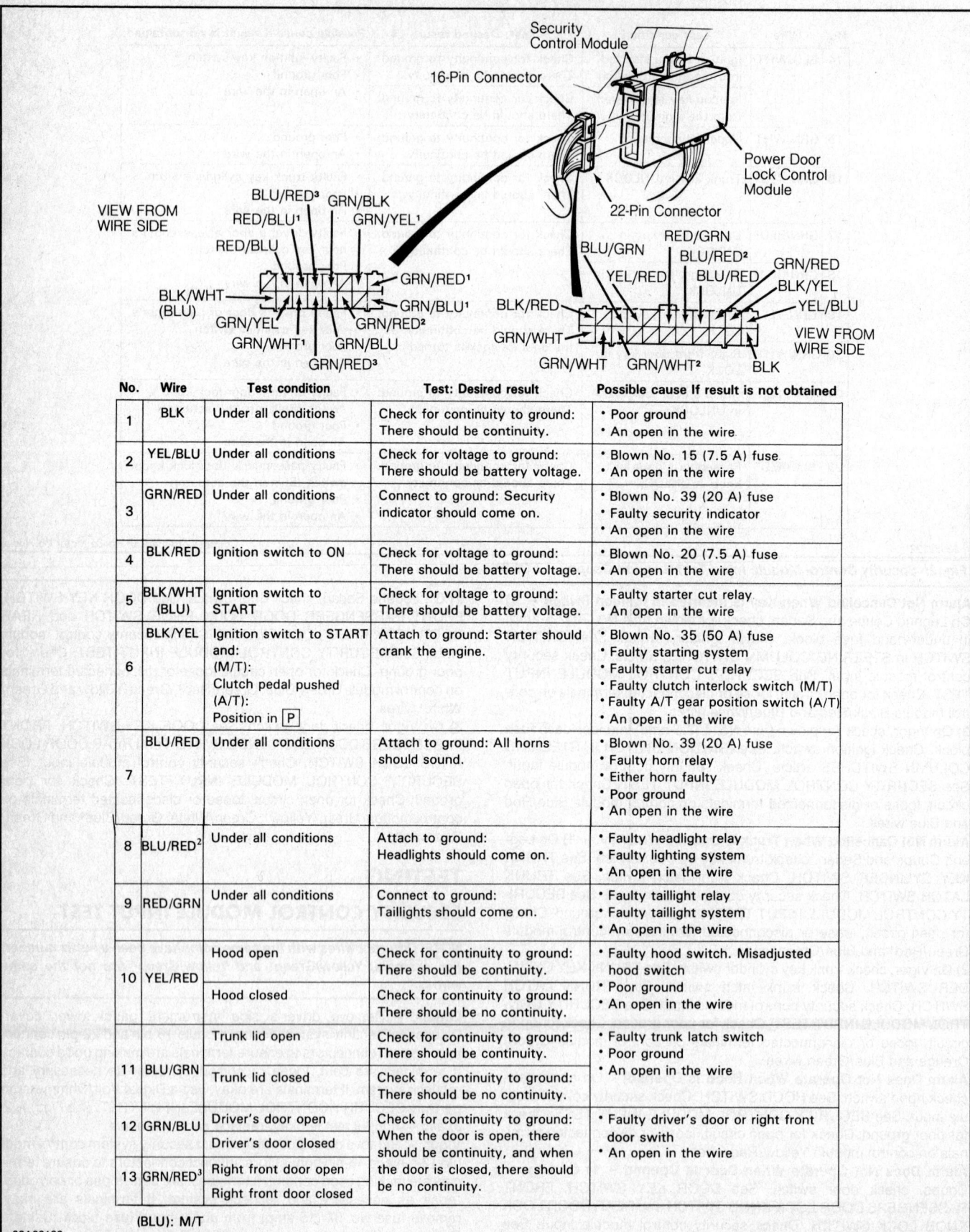

No.	Wire	Test condition	Test: Desired result	Possible cause If result is not obtained
1	BLK	Under all conditions	Check for continuity to ground: There should be continuity.	• Poor ground • An open in the wire
2	YEL/BLU	Under all conditions	Check for voltage to ground: There should be battery voltage.	• Blown No. 15 (7.5 A) fuse • An open in the wire
3	GRN/RED	Under all conditions	Connect to ground: Security indicator should come on.	• Blown No. 39 (20 A) fuse • Faulty security indicator • An open in the wire
4	BLK/RED	Ignition switch to ON	Check for voltage to ground: There should be battery voltage.	• Blown No. 20 (7.5 A) fuse • An open in the wire
5	BLK/WHT (BLU)	Ignition switch to START	Check for voltage to ground: There should be battery voltage.	• Faulty starter cut relay • An open in the wire
6	BLK/YEL	Ignition switch to START and: (M/T): Clutch pedal pushed (A/T): Position in P	Attach to ground: Starter should crank the engine.	• Blown No. 35 (50 A) fuse • Faulty starting system • Faulty starter cut relay • Faulty clutch interlock switch (M/T) • Faulty A/T gear position switch (A/T) • An open in the wire
7	BLU/RED	Under all conditions	Attach to ground: All horns should sound.	• Blown No. 39 (20 A) fuse • Faulty horn relay • Either horn faulty • Poor ground • An open in the wire
8	BLU/RED²	Under all conditions	Attach to ground: Headlights should come on.	• Faulty headlight relay • Faulty lighting system • An open in the wire
9	RED/GRN	Under all conditions	Connect to ground: Taillights should come on.	• Faulty taillight relay • Faulty taillight system • An open in the wire
10	YEL/RED	Hood open	Check for continuity to ground: There should be continuity.	• Faulty hood switch. Misadjusted hood switch • Poor ground • An open in the wire
10	YEL/RED	Hood closed	Check for continuity to ground: There should be no continuity.	• Poor ground • An open in the wire
11	BLU/GRN	Trunk lid open	Check for continuity to ground: There should be continuity.	• Faulty trunk latch switch • Poor ground • An open in the wire
11	BLU/GRN	Trunk lid closed	Check for continuity to ground: There should be no continuity.	
12	GRN/BLU	Driver's door open	Check for continuity to ground: When the door is open, there should be continuity, and when the door is closed, there should be no continuity.	• Faulty driver's door or right front door swith • An open in the wire
12	GRN/BLU	Driver's door closed		
13	GRN/RED³	Right front door open		
13	GRN/RED³	Right front door closed		

(BLU): M/T

93A82123

Fig. 3: *Security Control Module Input Test (Legend Sedan – 1 Of 2)*

No.	Wire	Test condition	Test: Desired result	Possible cause If result is not obtained
14	GRN/YEL	Left rear door open	Check for continuity to ground: When the door is open, there should be continuity, and when the door is closed, there should be no continuity.	• Faulty rear door switches • An open in the wire
		Left rear door closed		
15	GRN/WHT[1]	Right rear door open		
		Right rear door closed		
16	BLU/WHT	Ignition key is inserted into the ignition switch	Check for voltage to ground: There should be 1V or less.	• Faulty ignition key switch • Poor ground • An open in the wire
		Ignition key is removed from the igniton switch	Check for voltage to ground: There should be 1V or more.	
17	GRN/WHT or LT GRN	Under all conditions	Check for voltage to ground: There should be 1V or less.	• Poor ground • An open in the wire
18	GRN/RED[1]	Trunk key in UNLOCK	Check for voltage to ground: There should be 1V or less.	• Faulty trunk key • Poor ground • An open in the wire
19	GRN/RED[2]	Driver's door key in UNLOCK	Check for voltage to ground: There should be 1 V or less.	• Faulty driver's door or right front door key cylinder switch • Poor ground • An open in the wire
20	GRN/BLU[1]	Right front door key in UNLOCK		
21	GRN/YEL[1]	Driver's door key in LOCK	Check for voltage to ground: There should be 1 V or less, as the door keylock is turned in LOCK.	• Faulty driver's door or right front door key cylinder switch • Poor ground • An open in the wire
22	GRN/WHT[2]	Right front door key in LOCK		
23	GRN/BLK	Driver's door lock knob in UNLOCK	Check for voltage to ground: There should be 1 V or less.	• Faulty driver's door lock knob switch (built in the actuator) • Poor ground • An open in the wire
24	BLU/RED[3]	Right front door lock knob in UNLOCK	Check for voltage to ground: There should be 1 V or less.	• Faulty right front door lock knob switch (built in the actuator) • Poor ground • An open in the wire
25	RED/BLU	Left rear door lock knob in UNLOCK	Check for voltage to ground: There should be 1 V or less.	• Faulty left rear door lock knob switch (built in the actuator) • Poor ground • An open in the wire
26	RED/BLU[1]	Right rear door lock knob in UNLOCK	Check for voltage to ground: There should be 1 V or less.	• Faulty right rear door lock knob switch (built in the actuator) • Poor ground • An open in the wire

93B82124

Fig. 4: Security Control Module Input Test (Legend Sedan – 2 Of 2)

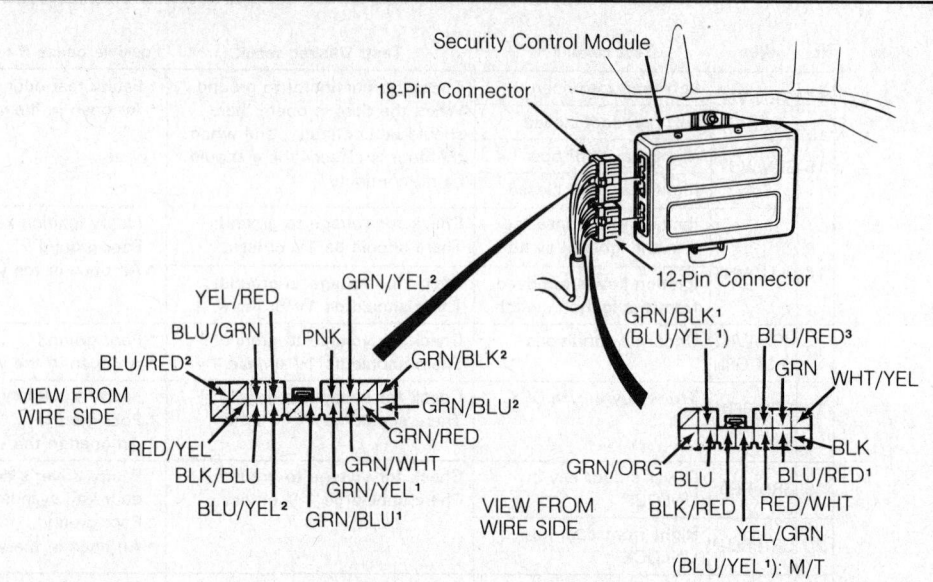

No.	Wire	Test condition	Test: Desired result	Possible cause if result is not obtained
1	BLK	Under all conditions.	Check for continuity to ground: There should have continuity.	• Poor ground • An open in the wire.
2	WHT/YEL	Under all conditions.	Check for voltage to ground: There should be battery voltage.	• Blown No. 30 (20 A) fuse (in the under-hood fuse/relay box). • An open in the wire.
3	GRN	Ignition switch ON.	Connect to ground: Security indicator should come on.	• Blown No. 30 (20 A) fuse (in the under-hood fuse/relay box). • Faulty security indicator. • An open in the wire.
4	BLK/RED	Ignition switch ON.	Check for voltage to ground: There should be battery voltage.	• Blown No.4 (7.5 A) fuse (in the under-dash fuse/relay box). • An open in the wire.
5	YEL/GRN	Ignition switch at START.	Check for voltage to ground: There should be battery voltage.	• Fualty starter cut relay. • An open in the wire.
6	BLU/RED[3]	Under all conditions.	Connect to ground: All horns should sond.	• Blown No. 30 (20 A) fuse (in the under-hood fuse/relay box). • Faulty horn relay. • Either horn faulty. • Poor ground • An open in the wire.
7	BLU/RED[1]	Under all conditions.	Connect to ground: Headlights should come on.	• Faulty headlight relay. • Faulty headlight system. • An open in the wire.
8	RED/WHT	Under all conditions.	Connect to ground: taillights shoud come on.	• Faulty taillight relay. • Faulty taillight system. • An open in the wire.
9	GRN/BLK (BLU/YEL[2])	Ignition switch On and; (M/T): clutch pedal pushed (A/T): A/T gear position P .	Check for continuity to ground: There should be continuity.	• Faulty clutch interlock switch (M/T). • Faulty A/T gear position switch (A/T). • An open in the wire.
10	YEL/RED	Hood open.	Check for continuity to ground: There should be continuity.	• Faulty hood switch (Misadjusted hood switch). • Poor ground • An open in the wire.
		Hood closed.	Check for continuity to ground: There should be no continuity.	
11	BLU	Ignition key is inserted into the ignition switch.	Check for continuity to ground: There should be continutiy.	• Faulty ignition key switch. • Poor ground • An open in the wire.
		Ignition key is removed from the ignition switch.	Check for continuity to ground: There should be no continuity.	

Fig. 5: Security Control Module Input Test (Vigor – 1 Of 2)

No.	Wire	Test condition	Test: Desired result	Possible cause if result is not obtained
12	PNK	Under all conditions.	Check for continuity to ground: There should be continuity.	• Poor ground • An open in the wire.
13	GRN/ORG	Trunk key in UNLOCK.	Check for continuity to ground: There should be continuity.	• Faulty security trunk key cylinder swtich. • Poor ground • An open in the wire.
		Trunk key in neutral position.	Check for continuity to ground: There should be no continuity.	• Faulty security trunk key cylinder switch. • Short to ground.
14	BLU/GRN	Trunk lid open.	Check for continuity to ground: There should be continuity.	• Faulty security trunk latch switch. (Misadjusted security trunk latch switch). • Poor ground • An open in the wire.
		Trunk lid closed.	Check for continuity to ground: There should be no continuity.	
15	GRN/BLU[2]	Driver's door opened.	Check for continuity to ground: When the door is opened, there should be continuity, and when the door is closed, there should be no continuity.	• Faulty driver's door or front passenger's door switches. • An open in the wire.
		Driver's door closed.		
16	GRN/RED	Front passenger's front door opened.		
		Front passenger's door closed.		
17	GRN/YEL[1]	Left rear door opened.	Check for continuity to ground: When the door is opened, there should be continuity, and when the door is closed, there should be no continuity.	• Faulty left rear door or right rear door switches. • An open in the wire.
		Left rear door closed.		
18	GRN/WHT	Right rear door opened.		
		Right rear door closed.		
19	GRN/BLK[2]	Driver's door key in UNLOCK.	Check for continuity to ground: There should be continuity.	• Faulty driver's door or front passenger's door key switches. • Poor ground • An open in the wire.
20	GRN/TEL[2]	Front passenger's front door key in UNLOCK.		
21	GRN/BLU[1]	Driver's door key in LOCK.	Check for continuity to ground: There should be continuity, as the door keylock is turned in LOCK.	• Faulty driver's door or front passenge's door key switches. • Poor ground • An open in the wire.
		Front passenger's front door key in LOCK.		
22	BLU/RED[2]	Driver's door lock knob in UNLOCK.	Check for continuity to ground: There should be continuity.	• Faulty driver's door lock knob switch (Built in the actuator). • Poor ground • An open in the wire.
23	BLU/YEL[2]	Front passenger's front door lock knob in UNLOCK.	Check for continuity to ground: There should be continuity.	• Faulty front passenger's door lock knob switch (Built in the actuator). • Poor ground • An open in the wire.
24	RED/YEL	Left rear door lock knob in UNLOCK.	Check for continuity to ground: There should be continuity.	• Faulty left rear door lock knob switch (Built in the actuator). • Poor ground • An open in the wire.
25	BLK/BLU	Right rear door lock knob in UNLOCK.	Check for continuity to ground: There should be continuity.	• Faulty right rear door lock knob switch (Built in the actuator). • Poor ground • An open in the wire.

(BLU/YEL[1]): M/T

93H82120

Fig. 6: Security Control Module Input Test (Vigor – 2 Of 2)

DOOR KEY CYLINDER SWITCH

Remove driver's door panel. Disconnect door latch assembly 8-pin connector. Check continuity between terminals listed in DOOR KEY CYLINDER SWITCH TEST table. *See Fig. 7.* If continuity is not as specified in table, replace door latch assembly.

DOOR KEY CYLINDER SWITCH TEST

Position	Terminals	Continuity
Lock	2 & 3	Yes
Unlock	1 & 2	Yes

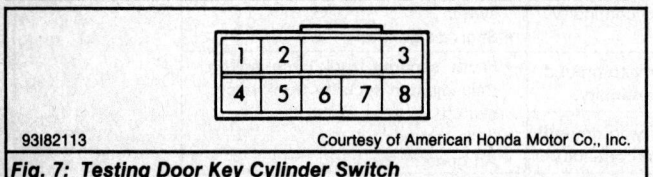

93I82113   Courtesy of American Honda Motor Co., Inc.

Fig. 7: Testing Door Key Cylinder Switch

FRONT PASSENGER'S DOOR LOCK KNOB SWITCH

Remove passenger's door panel. Disconnect door latch assembly 8-pin connector. Check continuity between terminals listed in FRONT PASSENGER'S DOOR LOCK KNOB SWITCH TEST table. *See Fig. 7.* If continuity is not as specified in table, replace door latch assembly.

FRONT PASSENGER'S DOOR LOCK KNOB SWITCH TEST

Position	Terminals	Continuity
Lock	4 & 5	No
Unlock	4 & 5	Yes

HOOD SWITCH

Open hood. Disconnect hood switch 2-pin connector. Check continuity between hood switch 2-pin connector. Continuity should exist with hood switch lever released (hood open). Continuity should not exist with hood switch lever pushed down (hood closed). If continuity is not as specified, replace hood switch assembly.

REAR DOOR LOCK KNOB SWITCH

Remove rear door panel. Disconnect door latch assembly 4-pin connector. Check continuity between terminals listed in REAR DOOR LOCK KNOB SWITCH TEST table. *See Fig. 8.* If continuity is not as specified in table, replace door latch assembly.

REAR DOOR LOCK KNOB SWITCH TEST

Position	Terminals	Continuity
Lock	1 & 2	No
Unlock	1 & 2	Yes

93A82115   Courtesy of American Honda Motor Co., Inc.

Fig. 8: Testing Rear Door Lock Knob Switch

SECURITY INDICATOR LIGHT (LED)

Remove door panel. Remove screw from security indicator light. Apply battery positive to security indicator light 2-pin connector terminal "A" and battery negative to security indicator light 2-pin connector terminal "B". *See Fig. 9.* Indicator light should turn on. If indicator light does not turn on, replace security light assembly.

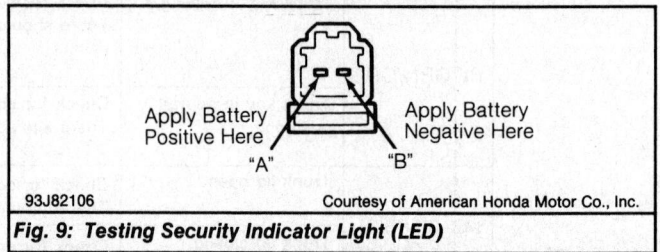

93J82106   Courtesy of American Honda Motor Co., Inc.

Fig. 9: Testing Security Indicator Light (LED)

TRUNK KEY CYLINDER SWITCH

Open trunk and remove trunk rear trim panel. Disconnect trunk key cylinder switch 2-pin connector. Check continuity between trunk key cylinder switch 2-pin connector terminals "A" and "B". *See Fig. 10.* Continuity should exist with trunk key lock is turned to UNLOCK position. Continuity should not exist when key lock is released. If switch does not operate as specified, replace trunk key cylinder switch assembly.

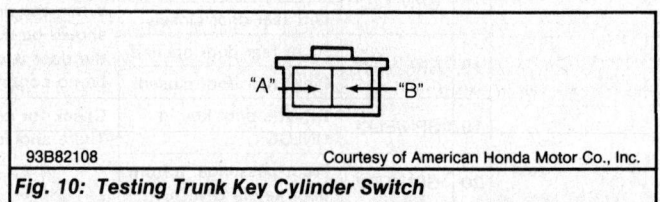

93B82108   Courtesy of American Honda Motor Co., Inc.

Fig. 10: Testing Trunk Key Cylinder Switch

TRUNK LATCH SWITCH

Open trunk and remove trunk rear trim panel. Disconnect trunk latch switch 6-pin connector. Check continuity between trunk latch switch 6-pin connector terminals "A" and "B". *See Fig. 11.* Continuity should exist with trunk lid open. Continuity should not exist with trunk latch in closed position (trunk lid closed). If switch does not operate as specified, replace trunk latch switch assembly.

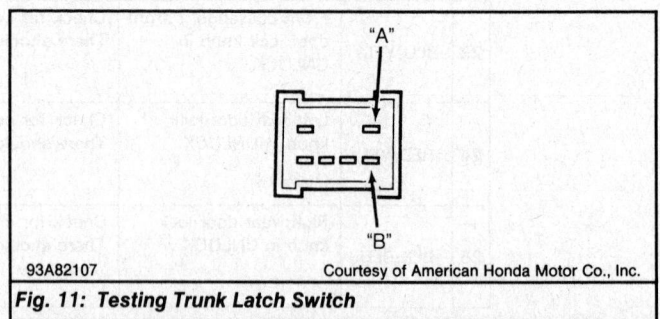

93A82107   Courtesy of American Honda Motor Co., Inc.

Fig. 11: Testing Trunk Latch Switch

Open trunk and remove trunk rear trim panel. Disconnect trunk latch switch 2-pin connector. Check continuity between trunk latch switch 2-pin connector terminals. Continuity should exist with trunk lid open. Continuity should not exist with trunk latch in closed position (trunk lid closed). If switch does not operate as specified, replace trunk latch switch assembly.

WIRING DIAGRAMS

NOTE: See ACCESSORIES & EQUIPMENT, Volume 5.

Integra, Legend, Vigor

DESCRIPTION

The cruise control unit receives command signals from cruise control main switch and cruise control SET/RESUME or SET/RESUME/CANCEL switch. It also receives operating signals from brakelight switch, Programmed Fuel Injection Electronic Control Unit (PGM-FI ECU), speed sensor, and clutch switch (M/T) or shift position switch (A/T).

The cruise control unit compares actual vehicle speed to selected speed. A signal from the brakelight switch disengages the system when the brakes are applied. The clutch switch, shift lever position switch, and cancel switch also send disengage signals to the cruise control unit.

OPERATION

The cruise control system maintains any speed greater than 30 MPH. To set, press SET switch at desired speed. Pressing main switch to off will cancel cruise control system operation and erase vehicle speed from memory.

If system is disengaged temporarily by brakelight switch, clutch switch or shift lever position switch, press RESUME switch. With RESUME switch pressed and speed memory retained, vehicle automatically returns to previous set speed. Pressing and holding RESUME switch will gradually increase vehicle speed without having to press accelerator pedal. When RESUME switch is released, system is reprogrammed for new speed.

For gradual deceleration without pressing brake pedal, press and hold SET switch until desired speed is reached. When desired speed is reached, release SET switch.

TROUBLE SHOOTING

CAUTION: All models are equipped with Supplemental Restraint System (SRS). SRS wiring harness is routed close to instrument cluster, steering wheel, and related components. All SRS wiring harnesses are covered by Yellow outer insulation. DO NOT use electrical test equipment on these circuits. Before working on steering column components, disable air bag system. See AIR BAG RESTRAINT SYSTEM article in ACCESSORIES & EQUIPMENT.

INTEGRA

Preliminary Checks – Before trouble shooting by symptom, ensure fuses No. 23 and No. 24 located in underdash fuse box are okay. Also check fuses No. 30, No. 32, and No. 37, located in underhood main fuse box. Replace fuses as necessary. Ensure horn and tachometer operate properly.

NOTE: When diagnosing vehicle by symptom, check possible failures in the order given.

Cruise Control Cannot Be Set – **1)** Check ground connection G301, located in left side of engine compartment next to windshield washer fluid reservoir. Check ground connection G201, located at right front side of engine compartment. Check ground connection G401, located behind left kick panel. Check cruise control unit inputs. See CONTROL UNIT INPUT TEST under DIAGNOSIS & TESTING. Test main switch. See MAIN SWITCH under DIAGNOSIS & TESTING.
2) Test SET/RESUME switch. See SET/RESUME SWITCH under DIAGNOSIS & TESTING. Test brakelight switch. See BRAKELIGHT SWITCH under DIAGNOSIS & TESTING. Test clutch switch on M/T vehicles. See CLUTCH SWITCH under DIAGNOSIS & TESTING. Test shift lever position switch on A/T vehicles. See SHIFT LEVER POSITION SWITCH under DIAGNOSIS & TESTING.
3) Inspect Black/Yellow wire between underdash fuse No. 24 and cruise control unit, and Light Green wire between main switch, cruise control unit, and brakelight switch. Repair wires as necessary.

Cruise Control Can Be Set, But Indicator Light Does Not Come On – **1)** Check for defective cruise control indicator bulb. Replace as necessary. Check ground connection G201, located at right front side of engine compartment. Check ground connection G401, located behind left kick panel. Repair ground connections as necessary.
2) Check cruise control unit inputs. See CONTROL UNIT INPUT TEST under DIAGNOSIS & TESTING. Check gauge dimming circuit. See DIMMER CONTROL CIRCUIT under DIAGNOSIS & TESTING. Inspect the following wires for open circuit: Yellow wire between underdash fuse No. 23 and gauge dimming circuit, and Red wire between gauge dimming circuit and cruise control unit. Repair as necessary.
Cruise Speed Noticeably Higher Or Lower Than Setting – **1)** Check vehicle speed sensor and speedometer cable. See VEHICLE SPEED SENSOR (VSS) in INSTRUMENT PANELS article. Ensure speedometer cable does not bind when rotated.
2) Test actuator assembly and cable free play. See ACTUATOR ASSEMBLY under DIAGNOSIS & TESTING and ACTUATOR CABLE under ADJUSTMENTS. Test cruise control unit inputs. See CONTROL UNIT INPUT TEST under DIAGNOSIS & TESTING.
Excessive Hunting When Trying To Achieve Set Speed – **1)** Test actuator assembly. See ACTUATOR ASSEMBLY under DIAGNOSIS & TESTING. Test vehicle speed sensor and speedometer cable. See VEHICLE SPEED SENSOR (VSS) in INSTRUMENT PANELS article.
2) Ensure speedometer cable does not bind when rotated. Test cruise control unit inputs. See CONTROL UNIT INPUT TEST under DIAGNOSIS & TESTING.
Steady Speed Not Held, Even On Flat Road – **1)** Test vehicle speed sensor and speedometer cable. See VEHICLE SPEED SENSOR (VSS) in INSTRUMENT PANELS article. Ensure speedometer cable does not bind when rotated.
2) Test actuator assembly. See ACTUATOR ASSEMBLY under DIAGNOSIS & TESTING. Test cruise control unit inputs. See CONTROL UNIT INPUT TEST under DIAGNOSIS & TESTING.
Car Does Not Decelerate Or Accelerate Accordingly When Set Or Resume Button Is Pressed – **1)** Test SET/RESUME switch. See SET/RESUME SWITCH under DIAGNOSIS & TESTING. Test cruise control unit inputs. See CONTROL UNIT INPUT TEST under DIAGNOSIS & TESTING.
2) Inspect for open circuit in Light Green/Black and Light Green/Red wires between SET/RESUME switch and cruise control unit for open. Repair wires as necessary.
Set Speed Not Canceled When Clutch Pedal Is Pressed (M/T) – Test clutch switch. See CLUTCH SWITCH under DIAGNOSIS & TESTING. Test cruise control unit inputs. See CONTROL UNIT INPUT TEST under DIAGNOSIS & TESTING.
Set Speed Not Canceled When Shift Lever Is Moved To Neutral (A/T) – Test shift lever position switch. See SHIFT LEVER POSITION SWITCH under DIAGNOSIS & TESTING. Test cruise control unit inputs. See CONTROL UNIT INPUT TEST under DIAGNOSIS & TESTING.
Set Speed Not Canceled When Brake Pedal Is Pressed – Test brakelight switch. See BRAKELIGHT SWITCH under DIAGNOSIS & TESTING. Test cruise control unit inputs. See CONTROL UNIT INPUT TEST under DIAGNOSIS & TESTING.
Set Speed Not Canceled When Main Switch Is Turned Off – Test main switch. See MAIN SWITCH under DIAGNOSIS & TESTING. Test cruise control unit inputs. See CONTROL UNIT INPUT TEST under DIAGNOSIS & TESTING.
Set Speed Not Resumed When Resume Button Is Pressed With Main Switch On, But Set Speed Temporarily Canceled – **1)** Test SET/RESUME switch. See SET/RESUME SWITCH under DIAGNOSIS & TESTING. Test cruise control unit inputs. See CONTROL UNIT INPUT TEST under DIAGNOSIS & TESTING.
2) Inspect for open circuit in Light Green/Black and Light Green/Red wires between SET/RESUME switch and cruise control unit. Repair wires as necessary.

LEGEND

Preliminary Tests – Before trouble shooting by symptom, ensure fuses No. 13 and No. 20 located in underdash fuse box are okay. Also check fuses No. 35 and No. 39, located in underhood main fuse box. Replace fuses as necessary. Ensure horn and tachometer operate properly.

Cruise Control Cannot Be Set – 1) Check ground connection G152, located at left front corner of engine compartment. Check ground connection G251, located at base of left "B" pillar. Check ground connection G301, located behind left kick panel. Check ground connection G304, located at base of right "B" pillar. Repair ground connections as necessary. Check cruise control unit inputs. See CONTROL UNIT INPUT TEST under DIAGNOSIS & TESTING. Test main switch. See MAIN SWITCH under DIAGNOSIS & TESTING.

2) Test SET/RESUME/CANCEL switch. See SET/RESUME/CANCEL SWITCH under DIAGNOSIS & TESTING. Test brakelight switch. See BRAKELIGHT SWITCH under DIAGNOSIS & TESTING. Test clutch switch on M/T vehicles. See CLUTCH SWITCH under DIAGNOSIS & TESTING. Test shift lever position switch on A/T vehicles. See SHIFT LEVER POSITION SWITCH under DIAGNOSIS & TESTING.

3) Inspect the following wires for open circuit. Repair wires as necessary.

- Blue/Red wire between horns and SET/RESUME/CANCEL switch.
- Light Green/Red wire between SET/RESUME/CANCEL switch and cruise control unit.
- Blue wire between ignition system and cruise control unit.
- Yellow wire between underdash fuse No. 13 and dimming circuit for gauges.
- Black/Red wire between underdash fuse No. 20, main switch, and cruise control unit connector.
- Light Green wire between main switch, brakelight switch, and cruise control unit.
- Gray wire between brakelight switch and cruise control unit.
- Brown wire between actuator assembly and cruise control unit.
- Brown/Black wire between actuator assembly and cruise control unit.
- Brown/White wire between actuator assembly and cruise control unit.
- Pink wire between clutch switch (M/T) or shift lever position switch (A/T) and cruise control unit.
- Yellow/Red wire between speed sensor and cruise control unit.

Cruise Control Can Be Set, But Indicator Light Does Not Come On – 1) Check for defective cruise control indicator bulb. Replace as necessary. Check ground connection G251, located at base of left "B" pillar. Check ground connection G301, located behind left kick panel. Repair ground connections as necessary.

2) Check cruise control unit inputs. See CONTROL UNIT INPUT TEST under DIAGNOSIS & TESTING. Check dimming circuit for gauges. See DIMMER CONTROL CIRCUIT under DIAGNOSIS & TESTING. Inspect the following wires for open circuit: Yellow wire between underdash fuse No. 13 and dimming circuit for gauges, and Blue/Black wire between dimming circuit for gauges and cruise control unit connector. Repair wires as necessary.

Cruise Speed Noticeably Higher Or Lower Than Setting – 1) Check for tachometer signal on cruise control unit connector (Blue wire). If tachometer signal exists, go to next step. If tachometer signal does not exist, check Blue wire for an open or short. Repair as necessary. If Blue wire is not open or shorted, check for tachometer signal. Repair as necessary.

2) Test actuator assembly. See ACTUATOR ASSEMBLY under DIAGNOSIS & TESTING. Check cruise control unit inputs. See CONTROL UNIT INPUT TEST under DIAGNOSIS & TESTING.

Excessive Hunting When Trying To Achieve Set Speed – 1) Test actuator assembly. See ACTUATOR ASSEMBLY under DIAGNOSIS & TESTING. Check for tachometer signal on cruise control unit connector (Blue wire). If tachometer signal exists, test cruise control unit inputs. See CONTROL UNIT INPUT TEST under DIAGNOSIS & TESTING.

2) If tachometer signal does not exist, check Blue wire for an open or short. Repair as necessary. If Blue wire is not open or shorted, check for ignition system failure (no tachometer signal). Repair as necessary.

Steady Speed Not Held, Even On Flat Road – 1) Check for tachometer signal on cruise control unit connector (Blue wire). If tachometer signal exists, go to next step. If tachometer signal does not exist, check Blue wire for an open or short. Repair as necessary. If Blue wire is not open or shorted, check for ignition system failure (no tachometer signal). Repair as necessary.

2) Test actuator assembly. See ACTUATOR ASSEMBLY under DIAGNOSIS & TESTING. Test cruise control unit inputs. See CONTROL UNIT INPUT TEST under DIAGNOSIS & TESTING.

Car Does Not Decelerate Or Accelerate Accordingly When Set Or Resume Button Is Pressed – 1) Test SET/RESUME/CANCEL switch. See SET/RESUME/CANCEL SWITCH under DIAGNOSIS & TESTING. Test cruise control unit inputs. See CONTROL UNIT INPUT TEST under DIAGNOSIS & TESTING.

2) Inspect the following wires for open circuit: Light Green/Black wire between SET/RESUME/CANCEL switch and cruise control unit, and Light Green/Red wire between SET/RESUME/CANCEL switch and cruise control unit. Repair wires as necessary.

Set Speed Not Canceled When Clutch Pedal Is Pressed (M/T) – Test clutch switch. See CLUTCH SWITCH under DIAGNOSIS & TESTING. Test cruise control unit inputs. See CONTROL UNIT INPUT TEST under DIAGNOSIS & TESTING.

Set Speed Not Canceled When Shift Lever Is Set To Neutral (A/T) – Test shift lever position switch. See SHIFT LEVER POSITION SWITCH under DIAGNOSIS & TESTING. Test cruise control unit inputs. See CONTROL UNIT INPUT TEST under DIAGNOSIS & TESTING.

Set Speed Not Canceled When Brake Pedal Is Pressed – Test brakelight switch. See BRAKELIGHT SWITCH under DIAGNOSIS & TESTING. Test cruise control unit inputs. See CONTROL UNIT INPUT TEST under DIAGNOSIS & TESTING.

Set Speed Not Canceled When Main Switch Is Turned Off – Test main switch. See MAIN SWITCH under DIAGNOSIS & TESTING. Test cruise control unit inputs. See CONTROL UNIT INPUT TEST under DIAGNOSIS & TESTING.

Set Speed Not Resumed When Resume Button Is Pressed, But Set Speed Temporarily Canceled – Test SET/RESUME/CANCEL switch. See SET/RESUME/CANCEL SWITCH under DIAGNOSIS & TESTING. Test cruise control unit inputs. See CONTROL UNIT INPUT TEST under DIAGNOSIS & TESTING.

VIGOR

Preliminary Tests – Before trouble shooting by symptom, ensure fuses No. 1 and No. 4 located in underdash fuse box are okay. Also check fuses No. 15, No. 18, and No. 30, located in underhood main fuse box. Replace fuses as necessary. Ensure horn and tachometer operate properly.

Cruise Control Cannot Be Set – 1) Check ground connection G401, located behind left kick panel. Check ground connection G251, located at base of left "B" pillar. Check ground connection G402, located behind right kick panel. Repair ground connections as necessary. Check cruise control unit inputs. See CONTROL UNIT INPUT TEST under DIAGNOSIS & TESTING. Test main switch. See MAIN SWITCH under DIAGNOSIS & TESTING.

2) Test SET/RESUME/CANCEL switch. See SET/RESUME/CANCEL SWITCH under DIAGNOSIS & TESTING. Test brakelight switch. See BRAKELIGHT SWITCH under DIAGNOSIS & TESTING. Test clutch switch on M/T vehicles. See CLUTCH SWITCH under DIAGNOSIS & TESTING. Test shift lever position switch on A/T vehicles. See SHIFT LEVER POSITION SWITCH under DIAGNOSIS & TESTING.

3) Inspect the following wires for open circuit. Repair wires as necessary.

- Blue/Red wire between horns and SET/RESUME/CANCEL switch.
- Light Green/Red wire between SET/RESUME/CANCEL switch and cruise control unit.
- Blue wire between ignition system and cruise control unit.
- Black/Red wire between underdash fuse No. 4 and main switch.
- Light Green wire between main switch, brakelight switch, and cruise control unit.

- Gray wire between brakelight switch and cruise control unit.
- Orange wire between vehicle speed sensor and cruise control unit.
- Brown wire between actuator assembly and cruise control unit.
- Black wire between actuator assembly and ground.
- Brown/Black wire between actuator assembly and cruise control unit.
- Brown/White wire between actuator assembly and cruise control unit.
- Pink wire between clutch switch (M/T) or shift lever position switch (A/T) and cruise control unit.

Cruise Control Can Be Set, But Indicator Light Does Not Come On –
1) Check for defective cruise control indicator bulb. Replace as necessary. Check ground connection G401, located behind left kick panel. Check ground connection G402, located behind right kick panel. Repair ground connections as necessary.

2) Check cruise control unit inputs. See CONTROL UNIT INPUT TEST under DIAGNOSIS & TESTING. Check gauge dimming circuit. See DIMMER CONTROL CIRCUIT under DIAGNOSIS & TESTING. Inspect the following wires for open circuit: Yellow wire between underdash fuse No. 1 and gauge dimming circuit, and Red wire between gauge dimming circuit for gauges and cruise control unit. Repair wires as necessary.

Cruise Speed Noticeably Higher Or Lower Than Setting – **1)** Check for signal on Orange wire from vehicle speed sensor. If signal exists, go to next step. If signal does not exist, check Orange wire for an open or short. Repair as necessary. If Orange wire is not open or shorted, check vehicle speed sensor. Repair as necessary.

2) Test actuator assembly. See ACTUATOR ASSEMBLY under DIAGNOSIS & TESTING. Check cruise control unit inputs. See CONTROL UNIT INPUT TEST under DIAGNOSIS & TESTING.

Excessive Hunting When Trying To Achieve Set Speed – **1)** Test actuator assembly. See ACTUATOR ASSEMBLY under DIAGNOSIS & TESTING. Check for signal from vehicle speed sensor (VSS) at cruise control unit connector (Orange wire). If signal exists, test cruise control unit inputs. See CONTROL UNIT INPUT TEST under DIAGNOSIS & TESTING.

2) If VSS signal does not exist, check Orange wire for an open or short. Repair as necessary. If Orange wire is not open or shorted, check VSS. See VEHICLE SPEED SENSOR (VSS) in INSTRUMENT PANELS article. Repair as necessary.

Steady Speed Not Held, Even On Flat Road – **1)** Check for signal from vehicle speed sensor (VSS) at cruise control unit (Orange wire). If signal exists, go to next step. If signal does not exist, check Orange wire for an open or short. Repair as necessary. If Orange wire is not open or shorted, check for VSS system failure. See VEHICLE SPEED SENSOR (VSS) in INSTRUMENT PANELS article. Repair as necessary.

2) Test actuator assembly. See ACTUATOR ASSEMBLY under DIAGNOSIS & TESTING. Test cruise control unit inputs. See CONTROL UNIT INPUT TEST under DIAGNOSIS & TESTING.

Car Does Not Decelerate Or Accelerate Accordingly When Set Or Resume Button Is Pressed – **1)** Test SET/RESUME/CANCEL switch. See SET/RESUME/CANCEL SWITCH under DIAGNOSIS & TESTING. Test cruise control unit inputs. See CONTROL UNIT INPUT TEST under DIAGNOSIS & TESTING.

2) Inspect the following wires for open circuit: Light Green/Black wire between SET/RESUME/CANCEL switch and cruise control unit, and Light Green/Red wire between SET/RESUME/CANCEL switch and cruise control unit.

Set Speed Not Canceled When Clutch Pedal Is Pressed (M/T) – Test clutch switch. See CLUTCH SWITCH under DIAGNOSIS & TESTING. Test cruise control unit inputs. See CONTROL UNIT INPUT TEST under DIAGNOSIS & TESTING.

Set Speed Not Canceled When Shift Lever Is Set To Neutral (A/T) – Test shift lever position switch. See SHIFT LEVER POSITION SWITCH under DIAGNOSIS & TESTING. Test cruise control unit inputs. See CONTROL UNIT INPUT TEST under DIAGNOSIS & TESTING.

Set Speed Not Canceled When Brake Pedal Is Pressed – Test brakelight switch. See BRAKELIGHT SWITCH under DIAGNOSIS &

TESTING. Test cruise control unit inputs. See CONTROL UNIT INPUT TEST under DIAGNOSIS & TESTING.

Set Speed Not Canceled When Main Switch Is Turned Off – Test main switch. See MAIN SWITCH under DIAGNOSIS & TESTING. Test cruise control unit inputs. See CONTROL UNIT INPUT TEST under DIAGNOSIS & TESTING.

Set Speed Not Resumed When Resume Button Is Pressed, But Set Speed Temporarily Canceled – Test SET/RESUME/CANCEL switch. See SET/RESUME/CANCEL SWITCH under DIAGNOSIS & TESTING. Test cruise control unit inputs. See CONTROL UNIT INPUT TEST under DIAGNOSIS & TESTING.

ADJUSTMENTS

ACTUATOR CABLE

1) Ensure actuator cable operates smoothly without binding or sticking. Start and warm engine to normal operating temperature. Measure actuator rod movement before cable pulls on accelerator lever (engine speed starts to increase). This is amount of cable free play. *See Fig. 1.* See ACTUATOR CABLE FREE PLAY SPECIFICATIONS table.

ACTUATOR CABLE FREE PLAY SPECIFICATIONS

Application	In. (mm)
Integra & Vigor	0.37-0.49 (9.5-12.5)
Legend	0.14-0.26 (3.5-6.5)

2) If free play is not as specified, loosen lock nut and turn adjusting nut as necessary. Tighten lock nut and recheck free play. Test drive vehicle and verify actual speed is within 2 MPH of set speed. If necessary, check throttle cable free play.

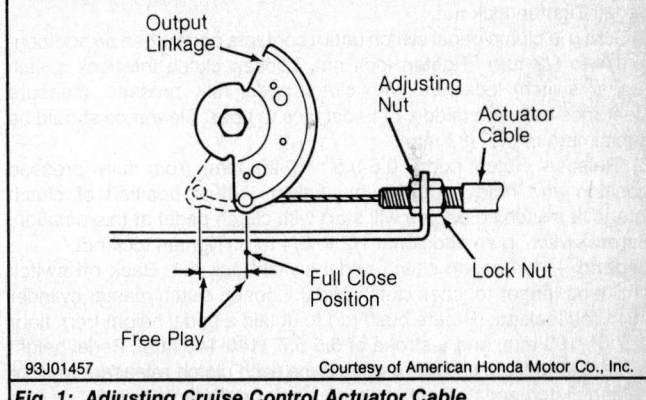

93J01457   Courtesy of American Honda Motor Co., Inc.

Fig. 1: Adjusting Cruise Control Actuator Cable

BRAKE PEDAL HEIGHT

1) Loosen brakelight switch lock nut. Back off switch until it no longer touches brake pedal. Loosen brake pedal push rod lock nut. Screw push rod in or out until pedal height from floor is to specification. See BRAKE PEDAL HEIGHT SPECIFICATIONS table. Tighten lock nut.

2) Screw in brakelight switch until plunger is fully pressed (threaded end touching pad on pedal arm). Back off switch 1/2 turn and tighten lock nut firmly. Ensure brakelights work when brake pedal is pressed.

BRAKE PEDAL HEIGHT SPECIFICATIONS

Application	In. (mm)
Integra	
A/T	6.5 (165)
M/T	6.3 (160)
Legend	8.4 (213)
Vigor	
A/T	7.6 (194)
M/T	7.8 (199)

CABLE REEL CENTERING

After installing clockspring onto steering column shaft, rotate clockspring clockwise until it stops. Rotate clockspring counterclockwise about 2 turns until Yellow gear tooth aligns with mark on cover and arrow on clockspring label points straight up. *See Fig. 2.* Install steering wheel. Attach cruise control and cable reel connectors to their clips.

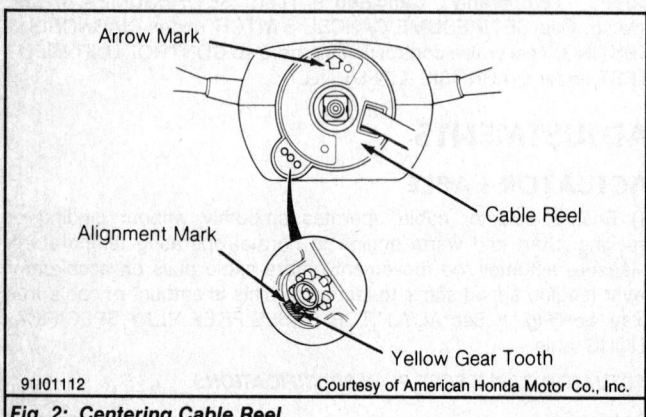

91I01112   Courtesy of American Honda Motor Co., Inc.

Fig. 2: Centering Cable Reel

CLUTCH PEDAL HEIGHT

Integra – 1) Loosen clutch pedal switch (lower switch) lock nut. Back off switch until it no longer touches clutch pedal. Loosen clutch master cylinder push rod lock nut and turn push rod to obtain a pedal height from floor of 6.5" (164 mm) and a stroke of 5.2-5.5" (130-140 mm). Pedal height is measured from middle of pedal face to floor below clutch pedal. Tighten lock nut.

2) Screw in clutch pedal switch until it contacts pedal, then an additional 1/4 to 1/2 turn. Tighten lock nut. Loosen clutch interlock switch (upper switch) lock nut. With clutch pedal fully pressed, measure clearance between middle of pedal face to floor. Clearance should be a minimum of 3.3" (83 mm).

3) Release clutch pedal 0.6-0.8" (15-20 mm) from fully pressed position and hold pedal at this height. Adjust position of clutch interlock switch so engine will start with clutch pedal at this position. Screw switch in an additional 1/2 to 3/4 turn. Tighten lock nut.

Legend – 1) Loosen clutch pedal switch lock nut. Back off switch until it no longer touches clutch pedal. Loosen clutch master cylinder push rod lock nut. Rotate push rod to obtain a pedal height from floor of 7.6" (193 mm) and a stroke of 5.5-5.7" (140-146 mm). Pedal height is measured from middle of pedal face (with clutch released) to floor behind clutch pedal. Tighten clutch master cylinder lock nut.

2) Screw in clutch pedal switch until it contacts pedal. Rotate clutch pedal switch in an additional 1/4 - 1/2 turn. Tighten clutch pedal switch lock nut. Loosen clutch interlock switch lock nut (located behind clutch master cylinder inside vehicle). With clutch pedal fully pressed, measure clearance between clutch pedal and floor. Measure from middle of pedal face to floor behind clutch pedal. Clearance should be a minimum of 3.54" (90 mm).

3) Release clutch pedal 0.6-0.8" (15-20 mm) from fully pressed position and hold pedal at this height. Adjust position of clutch interlock switch so engine will start with clutch pedal at this position. Screw switch inward an additional 1/4 to 1/2 turn. Tighten lock nut.

Vigor – 1) Loosen clutch pedal switch (lower switch) lock nut. Back off switch until it no longer touches clutch pedal. Loosen clutch master cylinder push rod lock nut and turn push rod to obtain a pedal height from floor of 8.2" (208 mm) and a stroke of 5.5-5.9" (140-150 mm). Pedal height is measured from middle of pedal face to floor below clutch pedal. Tighten lock nut.

2) Screw in clutch pedal switch until it contacts pedal, then an additional 1/4 to 1/2 turn. Tighten lock nut. Loosen clutch interlock switch (upper switch) lock nut. With clutch pedal fully pressed, measure clearance between middle of pedal face to floor. Clearance should be a minimum of 4.6" (116 mm).

3) Release clutch pedal 0.6-0.8" (15-20 mm) from fully pressed position and hold pedal at this height. Adjust position of clutch interlock switch so engine will start with clutch pedal at this position. Screw switch in an additional 1/4 to 1/2 turn. Tighten lock nut.

SHIFT LEVER POSITION SWITCH

Integra & Vigor – See SHIFT LEVER POSITION SWITCH under DIAGNOSIS AND TESTING.

Legend – 1) Remove front console. Shift lever position switch is located on left side of shift lever mechanism. Unplug shift lever position switch 14-pin connector.

2) Loosen 2 shift lever position switch mounting bolts. Slowly slide switch toward rear of vehicle while checking for continuity between shift lever position switch 14-pin connector terminals No. 9 and 12. *See Fig. 3.*

3) If continuity does not exist, go to next step. If continuity exists, shift lever position switch is okay. Tighten switch mounting bolts. Verify vehicle starts with shift lever in "P" position.

4) If continuity does not exist, check shift lever detent and bracket for damage. If no damage exists, replace shift lever position switch.

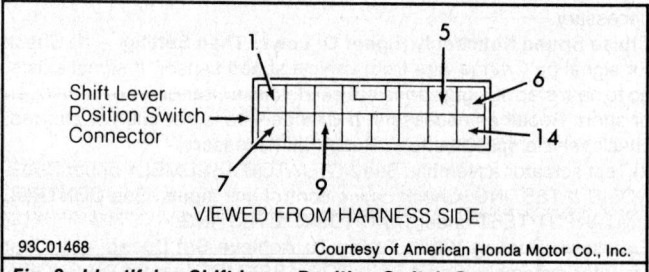

93C01468   Courtesy of American Honda Motor Co., Inc.

Fig. 3: Identifying Shift Lever Position Switch Connector Terminals (Legend)

DIAGNOSIS & TESTING

CAUTION: Legend and Vigor are equipped with Supplemental Restraint System (SRS). SRS wiring harness is routed close to instrument cluster, steering wheel, and related components. All SRS wiring harnesses are covered by Yellow outer insulation. DO NOT use electrical test equipment on these circuits. Before working on steering column components, disable air bag system. See AIR BAG RESTRAINT SYSTEM article in ACCESSORIES & EQUIPMENT.

WARNING: Wait about 3 minutes after disabling air bag system. Back-up power circuit maintains system voltage for about 3 minutes after battery is disconnected. Servicing air bag system before 3 minutes have elapsed may cause accidental air bag deployment and possible personal injury.

NOTE: Radio/cassette or radio/CD player contain an anti-theft protection circuit. Whenever battery is disconnected, radio goes into anti-theft mode. When battery is reconnected, radio displays CODE and is inoperative until proper code number is entered by vehicle owner.

ACTUATOR ASSEMBLY

1) Unplug 4-pin connector at actuator. Actuator is located on left side of engine compartment. Using jumper wires, connect terminal "D" of actuator connector to battery voltage, and terminal "A" of actuator connector to ground. *See Fig. 4.*

2) Listen for clicking sound from clutch, and locked output linkage. If actuator output linkage is not locked, replace actuator. Check actuator motor operation in each output linkage position. *See Fig. 4.* If actuator motor operates as specified, it is operating properly. Replace actuator motor if it does not operate as specified.

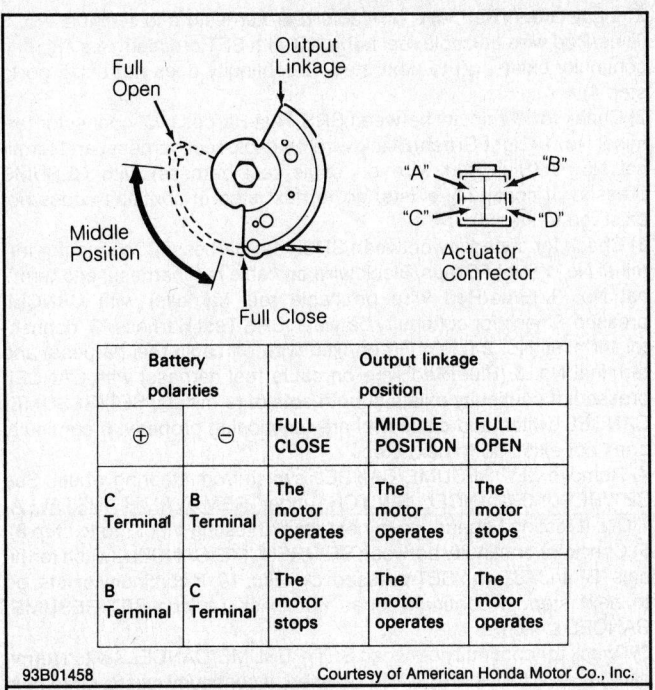

Battery polarities		Output linkage position		
⊕	⊖	FULL CLOSE	MIDDLE POSITION	FULL OPEN
C Terminal	B Terminal	The motor operates	The motor operates	The motor stops
B Terminal	C Terminal	The motor stops	The motor operates	The motor operates

93B01458   Courtesy of American Honda Motor Co., Inc.

Fig. 4: Testing Actuator Assembly

BRAKELIGHT SWITCH

1) Unplug connector from brakelight switch. Check for continuity between switch terminals "A" and "D". *See Fig. 5.* Continuity should exist. Check for continuity between switch terminals "B" and "C". Continuity should not exist.

2) Press and hold brake pedal. Check for continuity between switch terminals "A" and "D". Continuity should not exist. Check for continuity between switch terminals "B" and "C". Continuity should exist. If switch continuity is not as specified, check brake pedal height. See BRAKE PEDAL HEIGHT under ADJUSTMENTS. If brake pedal height is okay, replace brakelight switch.

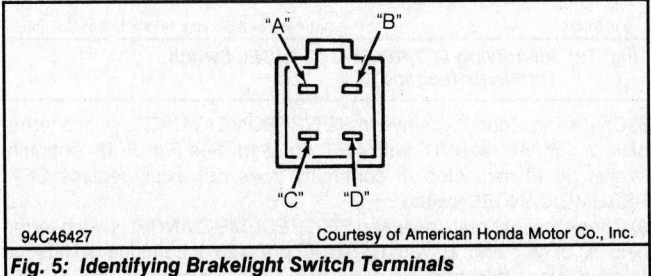

94C46427   Courtesy of American Honda Motor Co., Inc.

Fig. 5: Identifying Brakelight Switch Terminals

CABLE REEL

NOTE: Cable reel testing procedure is in SET/RESUME/CANCEL SWITCH test under DIAGNOSIS & TESTING.

CLUTCH SWITCH

Unplug connector from clutch switch. Check for continuity between clutch switch terminals. Continuity should exist. Press and hold clutch pedal. Check for continuity between clutch switch terminals. Continuity should not exist. If switch continuity is not as specified, check clutch pedal height. See CLUTCH PEDAL HEIGHT under ADJUSTMENTS. If clutch pedal height is okay, replace clutch pedal switch.

DIMMER CONTROL CIRCUIT

Integra & Vigor – 1) Turn ignition off. Remove lower dashboard cover. From behind dashboard, push out dimmer switch from dashboard. Unplug dimmer switch connector.

2) Check for continuity between dimmer switch connector Black wire and ground. Continuity should exist. If continuity exists, go to next step. If continuity does not exist, repair open in Black wire or poor ground connection G301, located at left side of engine compartment next to windshield washer fluid reservoir, or ground connection G401, located behind left kick panel.

3) With headlight switch on, check for battery voltage between dimmer switch connector Red/Black wire and ground. If battery voltage exists, go to next step. If battery voltage does not exist, replace blown fuse No. 11 or 19, replace headlight switch, or repair open circuit in Red/Black wire.

4) With headlight switch on, use a jumper wire to ground dimmer switch connector Red wire. If instrument lights come on, dimmer switch circuits are okay. Replace dimmer switch. If instrument lights do not come on, repair open circuit in Red/Black wire or Red wire from dimmer switch connector.

Legend – 1) Turn ignition off. Remove 2 screws from instrument cluster bezel. Pull out instrument cluster bezel far enough to unplug electrical connectors (one on left side and 2 on right side). Remove instrument cluster bezel.

2) Measure resistance between dimmer switch terminals "A" and "B" while rotating dimmer dial. *See Fig. 6.* Resistance should vary between zero and 20,000 ohms. If resistance is within specification, go to next step. If resistance is not within specification, replace dimmer switch.

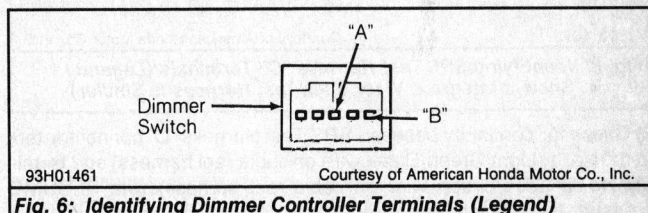

93H01461   Courtesy of American Honda Motor Co., Inc.

Fig. 6: Identifying Dimmer Controller Terminals (Legend)

3) Unplug dashlight brightness control unit 7-pin connector, located behind left side of radio. *See Fig. 7.* Check for continuity between connector Black wire and ground. If continuity exists, go to next step. If continuity does not exist, repair open in Black wire or poor ground connection G251, located at base of left "B" pillar.

4) With headlight switch on, check for battery voltage between 7-pin connector Red/Black wire and ground. If battery voltage exists, go to next step. If battery voltage does not exist, replace blown fuse No. 49, faulty taillight relay, faulty headlight switch, or open circuit in Red/Black wire.

5) With headlight switch on, use a jumper wire to ground 7-pin connector Red wire. If instrument lights come on, go to next step. If instrument lights do not come on, repair open circuit in Red/Black wire or Red wire from 7-pin connector.

6) Measure resistance between 7-pin connector Red/Green wire and Red/Blue wire. Resistance should vary between zero and 20,000 ohms when dimmer control dial is rotated. If resistance is within specification, go to next step. If resistance is not within specification, repair open circuit in Red/Green or Red/Blue wire or replace faulty dashlight brightness control unit.

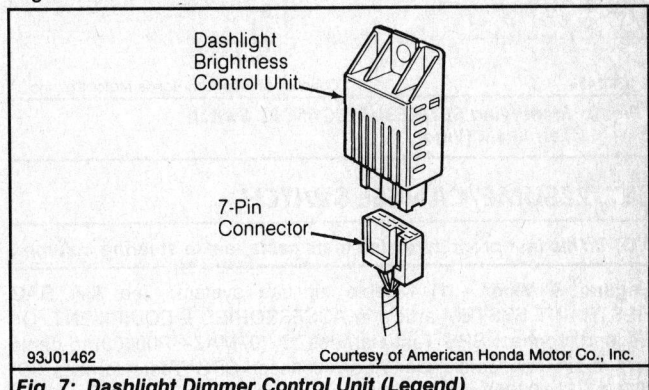

93J01462   Courtesy of American Honda Motor Co., Inc.

Fig. 7: Dashlight Dimmer Control Unit (Legend)

7) Inspect connection between 7-pin connector and dashlight brightness control unit. If connection is okay, temporarily substitute known good brightness control unit. Check operation of cruise control indicator light.

SET/RESUME SWITCH

NOTE: This test procedure also tests cable reel in steering column.

Integra – 1) Disable air bag system. See AIR BAG RESTRAINT SYSTEM article in ACCESSORIES & EQUIPMENT. Connect SRS Test Harness "C" (07LAZ-SL40300) to cable reel 6-pin connector. Check for continuity between SRS Test Harness "C" connector terminal No. 2 (Light Green/Red wire on cable reel harness) and terminal No. 3 (Blue/Green wire on cable reel harness) with SET pressed. *See Fig. 8.* If continuity exists, go to next step. If continuity does not exist, go to step **3)**.

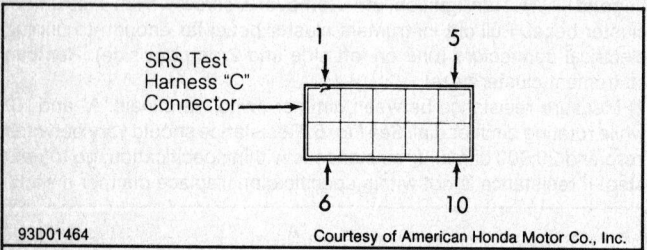

93D01464   Courtesy of American Honda Motor Co., Inc.

Fig. 8: Identifying SRS Test Harness "C" Terminals (Legend Shown; Integra & Vigor 6-Pin Test Harness Is Similar)

2) Check for continuity between SRS Test Harness "C" connector terminal No. 1 (Light Green/Black wire on cable reel harness) and terminal No. 3 (Blue/Green wire on cable reel harness) with RESUME pressed. If continuity exists, go to next step. If continuity does not exist, go to step **3)**.

3) Remove SET/RESUME switch from steering wheel. See SET/ RESUME SWITCH under REMOVAL & INSTALLATION.

4) Check for continuity between SRS Test Harness "C" connector terminals "A" or "A' " and "C" with SET pressed. *See Fig. 9.* If continuity exists, go to next step. If continuity does not exist, replace SET/ RESUME switch.

5) Check for continuity between SRS Test Harness "C" connector terminals "A" or "A' " and "C" with RESUME pressed. *See Fig. 9.* If continuity exists, go to next step. If continuity does not exist, replace SET/ RESUME switch.

6) If continuity exists in both steps **4)** and **5)**, replace cable reel. See CABLE REEL under REMOVAL & INSTALLATION. If continuity does not exist, replace SET/RESUME switch. See SET/RESUME SWITCH under REMOVAL & INSTALLATION.

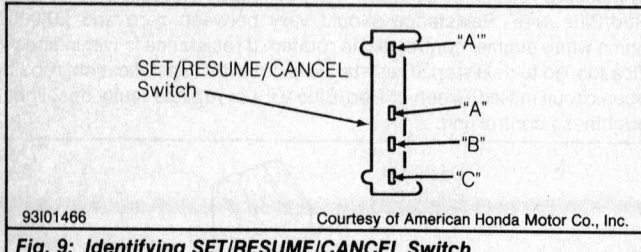

93I01466   Courtesy of American Honda Motor Co., Inc.

Fig. 9: Identifying SET/RESUME/CANCEL Switch Terminals (Vigor)

SET/RESUME/CANCEL SWITCH

NOTE: This test procedure also tests cable reel in steering column.

Legend & Vigor – 1) Disable air bag system. See AIR BAG RESTRAINT SYSTEM article in ACCESSORIES & EQUIPMENT. On Legend, connect SRS Test Harness "C" (07MAZ-SP00600) to cable reel 7-pin connector. On Vigor, connect SRS Test Harness "C" (07LAZ-SL40300) to cable reel 6-pin connector. On all models, check for continuity between SRS Test Harness "C" connector terminal No.

2 (Light Green/Red wire on cable reel harness) and terminal No. 3 (Blue/Red wire on cable reel harness) with SET pressed. *See Fig. 8.* If continuity exists, go to next step. If continuity does not exist, go to step **4)**.

2) Check for continuity between SRS Test Harness "C" connector terminal No. 1 (Light Green/Black wire on cable reel harness) and terminal No. 3 (Blue/Red wire on cable reel harness) with RESUME pressed. If continuity exists, go to next step. If continuity does not exist, go to step **4)**.

3) Check for continuity between SRS Test Harness "C" connector terminal No. 1 (Light Green/Black wire on cable reel harness) and terminal No. 3 (Blue/Red wire on cable reel harness) with CANCEL pressed. Check for continuity between SRS Test Harness "C" connector terminal No. 2 (Light Green/Red wire on cable reel harness) and terminal No. 3 (Blue/Red wire on cable reel harness) with CANCEL pressed. If continuity exists at both sets of terminals, SET/RESUME/ CANCEL switch and cable reel are functioning properly. If continuity does not exist, go to next step.

4) Remove SET/RESUME/CANCEL switch from steering wheel. See SET/RESUME/CANCEL SWITCH under REMOVAL & INSTALLATION. If testing Legend, go to next step. If testing Vigor, go to step **8)**.

5) Check for continuity between SET/RESUME/CANCEL switch terminals "B" and "C" with SET pressed. *See Fig. 10.* If continuity exists, go to next step. If continuity does not exist, replace SET/RESUME/ CANCEL switch.

6) Check for continuity between SET/RESUME/CANCEL switch terminals "A" and "C" with RESUME pressed. If continuity exists, go to next step. If continuity does not exist, replace SET/RESUME/CANCEL switch.

7) Check for continuity between SET/RESUME/CANCEL switch terminals "A" and "C" with CANCEL pressed. Check for continuity between SET/RESUME/CANCEL switch terminals "B" and "C" with CANCEL pressed. Go to step **11)** if continuity exists. If continuity does not exist, replace SET/RESUME/CANCEL switch. See SET/RESUME/CANCEL SWITCH under REMOVAL & INSTALLATION.

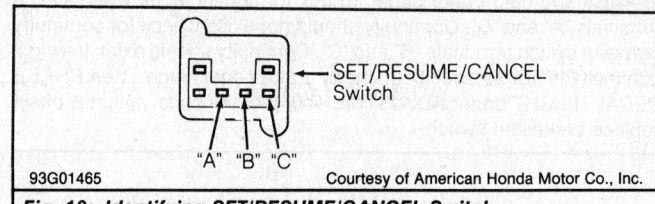

93G01465   Courtesy of American Honda Motor Co., Inc.

Fig. 10: Identifying SET/RESUME/CANCEL Switch Terminals (Legend)

8) Check for continuity between SET/RESUME/CANCEL switch terminals "A" or "A' " and "C" with SET pressed. *See Fig. 9.* If continuity exists, go to next step. If continuity does not exist, replace SET/ RESUME/CANCEL switch.

9) Check for continuity between SET/RESUME/CANCEL switch terminals "A" or "A' " and "B" with RESUME pressed. If continuity exists, go to next step. If continuity does not exist, replace SET/RESUME/ CANCEL switch.

10) Check for continuity between SET/RESUME/CANCEL switch terminals "A" or "A' " and "B" with CANCEL pressed. Check for continuity between SET/RESUME/CANCEL switch terminals "A" or "A' " and "C" with CANCEL pressed. If continuity exists at both sets of terminals, go to next step. If continuity does not exist, replace SET/RESUME/ CANCEL switch. See SET/RESUME/CANCEL SWITCH under REMOVAL & INSTALLATION.

11) Replace cable reel. See CABLE REEL under REMOVAL & INSTALLATION.

SHIFT LEVER POSITION SWITCH

NOTE: Only A/T vehicles are equipped with shift lever position switch.

Integra – 1) Shift lever position switch is located on right side of shift lever mechanism. Remove front console. Unplug shift lever position switch 14-pin connector.

2) Check for continuity between switch terminal wire color Pink and Black with shift lever in "2", "S", and "D" positions. If continuity exists in each position, shift lever position switch is okay. If continuity does not exist, replace shift lever position switch.

Legend – 1) Shift lever position switch is located on left side of shift lever mechanism. Remove front console. Unplug shift lever position switch 14-pin connector.

2) Check for continuity between switch connector terminals No. 5 and 9 with shift lever in "2", "D_3", and "D_4" positions. *See Fig. 3.* If continuity exists in each position, switch is okay. If continuity does not exist, go to next step.

3) With DVOM connected to switch connector terminals No. 5 and 9, move shift lever back and forth slightly without pressing shift lever button while in "2", "D_3", and "D_4" positions. Continuity should exist in each position.

4) If continuity exists, shift lever position switch is okay. If continuity does not exist, check shift lever position switch adjustment. See SHIFT LEVER POSITION SWITCH under ADJUSTMENTS. If adjustment is okay, replace switch and adjust as necessary. See SHIFT LEVER POSITION SWITCH under ADJUSTMENTS.

Vigor – 1) Raise and support vehicle. Remove transmission undercover. Unplug shift lever position switch 14-pin connector.

2) Check for continuity between switch connector terminal No. 11 and ground with shift lever in "2", "D_3", and "D_4" positions. *See Fig. 11.* If continuity exists in each position, switch is okay. If continuity does not exist, go to next step.

3) With DVOM connected to switch connector terminal No. 11 and ground, move shift lever back and forth slightly without pressing shift lever button while in "2", "D_3", and "D_4" positions.

4) If continuity exists in each position, switch is okay. If continuity does not exist, go to next step.

5) Loosen shift lever position switch bolts. Move switch back and forth while trying to achieve continuity readings specified in steps **2)** and **3)**. If continuity can be achieved, tighten switch bolts. If continuity cannot be achieved as specified in steps **2)** and **3)**, replace faulty shift lever position switch.

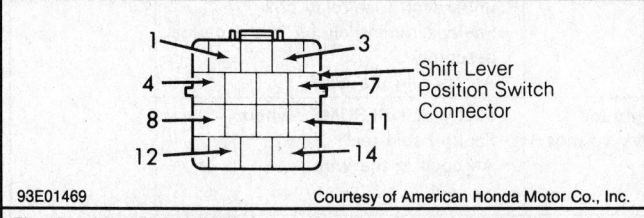

93E01469   Courtesy of American Honda Motor Co., Inc.

Fig. 11: Identifying Shift Lever Position Switch Connector Terminals (Vigor)

MAIN SWITCH

Integra – 1) Remove main switch from instrument panel. With switch off, check for continuity between switch terminals "B" and "C", and between terminals "D" and "E". *See Fig. 12.* If continuity exists, go to next step. If continuity does not exist, replace defective bulb. After replacing bulb, repeat test. If switch continuity is not as specified, replace main switch.

2) Turn switch on. Check for continuity between main switch terminals "A" and "B", "B" and "C", and "D" and "E". If continuity exists, switch is okay. If continuity does not exist between main switch terminals "A" and "B", replace switch. If continuity does not exist between main switch terminals "B" and "C" or terminals "D" and "E", go to next step.

3) Replace defective bulb inside main switch. After replacing bulb, repeat step **2)**. If continuity is not as specified, replace main switch.

Legend – 1) Turn ignition off. Remove 2 screws from instrument cluster bezel. Pull out bezel far enough to unplug connectors (one on left side and 2 on right side). Remove bezel.

2) Turn main switch off. Check for continuity between switch terminals "A" and "B", and between "D" and "E". *See Fig. 13.* If continuity exists, go to next step. If continuity does not exist, replace main switch.

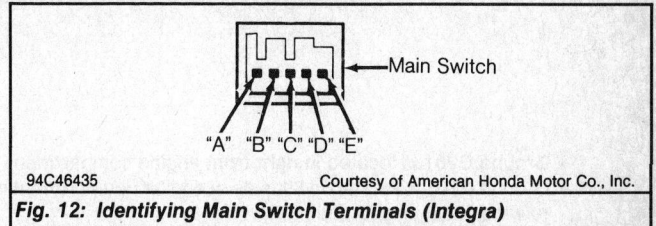

94C46435   Courtesy of American Honda Motor Co., Inc.

Fig. 12: Identifying Main Switch Terminals (Integra)

3) Turn main switch on. Check for continuity between switch terminals "A" and "B", terminals "B" and "C", and terminals "D" and "E". If continuity exists, main switch is okay. If continuity does not exist, replace switch.

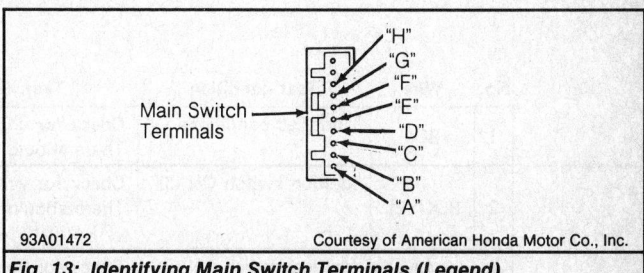

93A01472   Courtesy of American Honda Motor Co., Inc.

Fig. 13: Identifying Main Switch Terminals (Legend)

Vigor – 1) Turn ignition off. Carefully pry main switch from instrument panel. Unplug main switch connector.

2) Turn main switch off. Check for continuity between main switch terminals "A" and "B", and terminals "D" and "E". *See Fig. 14.* If continuity exists, go to next step. If continuity does not exist, replace malfunctioning main switch.

3) Turn main switch on. Check for continuity between main switch terminals "A" and "B", "B" and "C", and "D" and "E". If continuity exists for each terminal pair, switch is okay. If continuity does not exist, replace malfunctioning main switch.

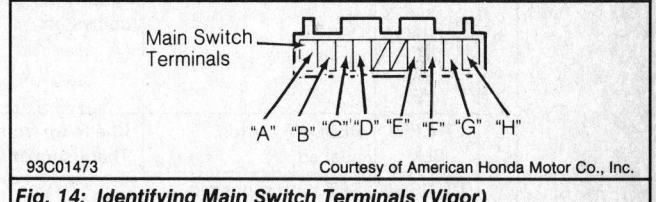

93C01473   Courtesy of American Honda Motor Co., Inc.

Fig. 14: Identifying Main Switch Terminals (Vigor)

CONTROL UNIT INPUT TEST

Integra – 1) Turn ignition off. Remove dashboard lower left cover. Remove left knee bolster. Cruise control unit is located near left kick panel. Unplug cruise control unit 14-pin connector.

2) Using a DVOM, perform cruise control unit input tests in *Fig. 15.* If all input test results are okay, inspect cruise control unit connector for damage and proper fit. If connector is okay and cruise control still malfunctions, replace cruise control unit.

Legend – 1) Cruise control unit is located near right kick panel. Turn ignition off. Remove glove box. Unplug cruise control unit 14-pin connector.

2) Using a DVOM, perform cruise control unit input tests in *Fig. 16.* If all input test results are okay, inspect cruise control unit connector for damage and proper fit. If connector is okay but cruise control still malfunctions, replace cruise control unit.

Vigor – 1) Turn ignition off. Cruise control unit is located under instrument panel above brake pedal bracket. Unplug cruise control unit 13-pin connector.

2) Using a DVOM, perform cruise control unit input tests in *Fig. 17.* If all input test results are okay, inspect cruise control unit connector for damage and proper fit. If connector is okay but cruise control still malfunctions, replace cruise control unit.

- Ground G201 is located in right front engine compartment.
- Ground G301 is located in left side of engine compartment next to windshield washer fluid reservoir.
- Ground G401 is located behind left kick panel.

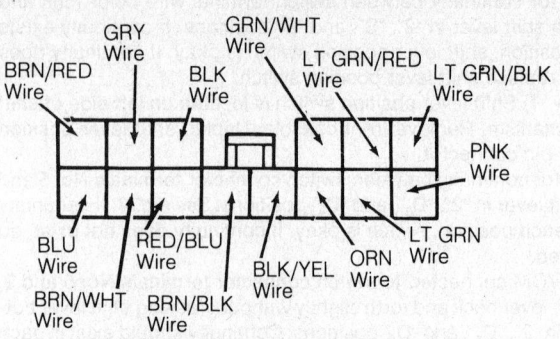

CRUISE CONTROL UNIT CONNECTOR
VIEWED FROM HARNESS SIDE

No.	Wire	Test condition	Test: Desired result	Possible cause if result is not obtained
1	BLK	Under all conditions	Check for continuity to ground: There should be continuity.	• Poor ground (G201, G401) • An open in the wire
2	BLK/YEL	Ignition switch ON (II)	Check for voltage to ground: There should be battery voltage.	• Blown No. 24 fuse in the under-dash fuse/relay box • An open in the wire
3	LT GRN	Ignition switch ON (II) and main switch ON	Check for voltage to ground: There should be battery voltage.	• Faulty main switch • An open in the wire
4	GRY	Ignition switch ON (II), main switch ON and brake pedal pushed, then released	Check for voltage to ground: There should be 0 V with the pedal pushed and battery voltage with the pedal released.	• Faulty brake switch • An open in the wire
5	GRN/WHT	Brake pedal pushed, then released	Check for voltage to ground: There should be battery voltage with the pedal pushed, and 0 V with the pedal released.	• Blown No. 42 (20 A) fuse in the underhood fuse/relay box • Faulty brake switch • An open in the wire
6	RED/BLU	Ignition switch ON (II)	Connect to ground: Indicator light in the gauge assembly comes on.	• Blown bulb • Blown No. 15 (10 A) fuse in the underdash fuse/relay box • Faulty dimming circuit in the gauge assembly • An open in the wire
7	LT GRN/ BLK	RESUME button pushed	Check for voltage to ground: There should be battery voltage.	• Faulty SET/RESUME switch • Faulty cable reel • An open in the wire
8	LT GRN/ RED	SET button pushed		
9	PNK	MT/: Clutch pedal released A/T: Shift lever in ②, ③, or ④	Check for continuity to ground: There should be continuity. NOTE: There should be no continuity when the clutch pedal is depressed or when the shift lever is in other positions.	• Faulty or misadjusted clutch switch (M/T) • Faulty A/T gear position switch (A/T) • Poor ground (G201,G401) • An open in the wire
10	BLU	Start the engine.	Check for voltage to ground: There should be battery voltage.	• Faulty ignition system or ECM • An open in the wire
11	ORN	Ignition switch ON (II) and main switch ON; raise the front of the car, rotate one wheel slowly.	Check for voltage between the ORN ⊕ and BLK ⊖ terminals: There should be 0— about 10 V—0— about 10 V repeatedly.	• Faulty vehicle speed sensor (VSS) • An open in the wire
12	BRN/WHT	Connect battery power to the BRN/WHT terminal and ground to the BRN/BLK terminal.	Check the sound of the actuator motor: You should hear the motor running smoothly.	• Faulty actuator • An open in the wire
13	BRN/BLK			
14	BRN/RED	Connect battery power to the BRN/RED terminal.	Check the operation of the magnetic clutch: Clutch should click and output link should be locked.	• Faulty actuator • An open in the wire • Poor ground (G301)

Fig. 15: Cruise Control Unit Input Test (Integra)

- Numbers 1 through 14 refer to test numbers, not terminal numbers.
- Ground G152 is located at left front corner of engine compartment.
- Ground G251 is located at base of left "B" pillar.
- Ground G301 is located behind left kick panel.
- Ground G501 is located on center floor where center console meets floor inside vehicle.

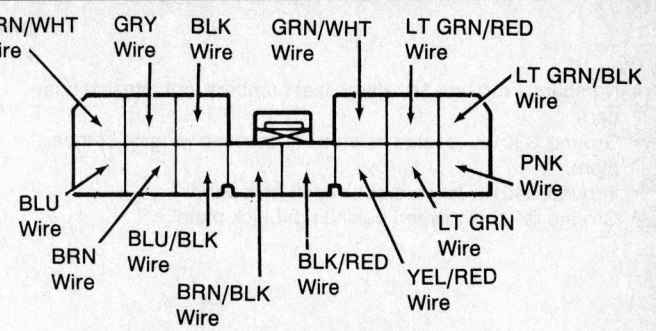

CRUISE CONTROL UNIT CONNECTOR
VIEWED FROM HARNESS SIDE

No.	Wire	Test condition	Test: Desired result	Possible cause if result is not obtained
1	BLK	Under all conditions	Check for continuity to ground: There should be continuity.	• Poor ground (G301) • An open in the wire
2	BLK/RED	Ignition switch to ON	Check for voltage to ground: There should be battery voltage.	• Blown No. 20 (7.5 A) fuse • An open in the wire
3	LT GRN	Ignition switch to ON and main switch to ON	Check for voltage to ground: There should be battery voltage.	• Blown No. 20 (7.5 A) fuse • Faulty main switch • An open in the LT GRN wire
4	LT GRN/ BLK	RESUME button pushed	Ground each terminal: Horns should sound as the switch is pushed.	• Blown No. 39 (20 A) fuse • Faulty SET/RESUME/CANCEL switch • Faulty cable reel • An open in the WHT/GRN, BLU/RED, LT GRN/BLK or GRN/RED wire
5	LT GRN/ RED	SET button pushed		
6	PNK	M/T: Clutch pedal pushed A/T: Shift lever in 2, $D3$ or $D4$	Check for continuity to ground: There should be continuity. NOTE: There should be no continuity when the clutch pedal is released or when the shift lever is in other positions.	• Faulty or misadjusted clutch switch (M/T) • Faulty A/T gear position switch • Poor ground (G301 or G501) • An open in the wire
7	BLU	Start the engine.	Check for voltage to ground: There should be battery voltage.	• Faulty ignition system or ECM (M/T) or PCM (A/T). • An open in the wire.
8	YEL/RED	Ignition switch to ON and main switch to ON Raise the front of the car and rotate one wheel slowly with the other wheel blocked.	Check for voltage between the YEL/RED ⊕ and BLK ⊖ terminals: There should be 0 – 12 – 0 – 12 V or more repeatedly.	• Faulty vehicle speed sensor (VSS) • An open in the wire • Short to ground
9	GRY	Ignition switch to ON, main switch to ON and brake pedal pushed, then released	Check for voltage to ground: There should be 0 V with the pedal pushed and battery voltage with the pedal released.	• Faulty brake switch • An open in the wire
10	GRN/WHT	Brake pedal pushed, then released	Check for voltage to ground: There should be battery voltage with the pedal pushed, and 0 V with the pedal released.	• Blown No. 39 (20 A) fuse • Faulty brake switch • An open in the wire
11	BLU/BLK	Ignition switch to ON	Attach to ground: Indicator light in the gauge assembly comes on.	• Blown bulb • Blown No. 20 (7.5 A) fuse • Faulty dimming circuit in the gauge assembly • An open in the wire
12	BRN	Connect battery power to the BRN terminal and ground to the BRN/BLK terminal.	Check the operation of the actuator motor: You should be able to hear the motor.	• Faulty actuator • An open in the wire
13	BRN/BLK			
14	BRN/WHT	Connect battery power to the BRN/WHT terminal.	Check the operation of the magnetic clutch: Clutch should click and output link should be locked.	• Faulty actuator • An open in the wire • Poor ground (G152)

Fig. 16: *Cruise Control Unit Input Test (Legend)*

- Numbers 1 through 14 refer to test numbers, not terminal numbers.
- Ground G301 is located in left front corner of engine compartment.
- Ground G401 is located behind left kick panel.
- Ground G402 is located behind right kick panel.

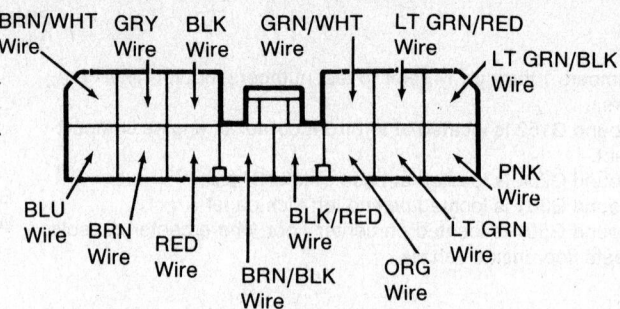

CRUISE CONTROL UNIT CONNECTOR
VIEWED FROM HARNESS SIDE

No.	Wire	Test condition	Test: Desired result	Possible cause if result is not obtained
1	BLK	Under all conditions.	Check for continuity to gound: There should be continuity.	• Poor Ground (G401, G402) • An open in the wire.
2	LT GRN	Ignition switch ON and main switch ON.	Check for voltage to ground: There should be battery voltage.	• Blown No. 4 (7.5 A) fuse (in the under-dash fuse/relay box). • Faulty main switch • An open in the wire.
3	LT GRN/BLK	RESUME button pushed.	Check for voltage to ground: There should be battery voltage.	• Blown No. 30 (20 A) fuse (in the under-hood fuse/relay box). • Faulty SET/RESUME/CANCEL switch. • Faulty horn relay. • Faulty cable reel. • An open in the wire.
4	LT GRN/RED	SET button pushed.		
5	PNK	M/T: Clutch pedal released A/T: Shift lever in ⌷2⌷, ⌷D3⌷, or ⌷D4⌷.	Check for continuity to ground: There should be continuity. NOTE: There should be no continuity when the clutch pedal is released or when the A/T shift lever is in other positions.	• Faulty or misadjusted clutch switch (M/T). • Faulty A/T gear position switch. • Poor ground (G401, G402). • An open in the wire.
6	BLU	Start the engine.	Check for voltage to ground: There should be battery voltage.	• Faulty ignition system or ECM. • An open in the wire.
7	ORN	Ignition switch ON and main switch ON. Raise the front of the car, rotate one wheel slowly.	Check for voltage between the ORN ⊕ and BLK ⊖ terminals: should be 0—5—0—5 V repeatedly.	• Faulty vehicle speed sensor (VSS) • An open in the wire. • Poor ground (G101).
8	GRY	Ignition switch ON, main switch ON and brake pedal pushed, then released.	Check for voltage to ground: There should 0 V with the pedal pushed and battery voltage with the pedal released.	• Faulty brake switch. • An open in the wire.
9	GRN/WHT	Brake pedal pushed, then released.	Check for voltage to ground: There should be battery voltage with the pedal pushed, and 0 V with the pedal released.	• Faulty brake switch. • An open in the wire.
10	RED	Ignition switch ON.	Connect to ground: Cruise indicator in the gauge assembly comes on.	• Blown bulb. • Blown No. 1 (10 A) fuse (in the under-dash fuse/relay box). • Faulty dimming circuit in the gauge assembly. • An open in the wire.
11	BRN	Connect the battery power to the BRN/WHT terminal and ground to the BRN/BLK terminal.	Check the operation of the actuator motor: You should be able to hear the motor.	• Faulty actuator. • An open in the wire.
12	BRN/BLK			
13	BRN/WHT	Connect the battery power to the BRN terminal.	Check the operation of the magnetic clutch: Clutch should click and output link should be locked.	• Faulty actuator. • Poor ground (G301). • An open in the wire.
14	BLK/RED	Ignition switch ON.	Check for voltage to ground: There should be battery voltage.	• Blown No. 4 (7.5 A) fuse (in the under-dash fuse/relay box). • An open in the wire.

93A82412

Fig. 17: Cruise Control Unit Input Test (Vigor)

REMOVAL & INSTALLATION

CAUTION: All models are equipped with Supplemental Restraint System (SRS). SRS wiring harness is routed close to instrument cluster, steering wheel, and related components. All SRS wiring harnesses are covered by Yellow outer insulation. DO NOT use electrical test equipment on these circuits. Before working on steering column components, disable air bag system. See AIR BAG RESTRAINT SYSTEM article in ACCESSORIES & EQUIPMENT.

WARNING: Wait about 3 minutes after disabling air bag system. Back-up power circuit maintains system voltage for about 3 minutes after battery is disconnected. Servicing air bag system before 3 minutes have elapsed may cause accidental air bag deployment and possible personal injury.

NOTE: Radio/cassette or radio/CD player contain an anti-theft protection circuit. Whenever battery is disconnected, radio goes into anti-theft mode. When battery is reconnected, radio displays CODE and is inoperative until proper code number is entered by vehicle owner.

CABLE REEL

Removal – **1)** Disable air bag system. See DISABLING & ACTIVATING AIR BAG SYSTEM in AIR BAG RESTRAINT SYSTEM article. Ensure front wheels are facing straight-ahead.

2) Cable reel is located under steering wheel, on upper steering column. *See Fig. 18.* Remove lower instrument panel cover below steering column. Remove upper and lower steering column covers. Unplug SRS main harness connector from cable reel connector. Remove connector holder. Remove air bag module. See AIR BAG MODULE in AIR BAG RESTRAINT SYSTEM article.

3) Remove and discard steering wheel nut. Unplug horn connector, radio remote switch connector, cruise control switch connector, and ground connector in center of steering wheel. Release cable reel harness and connectors from retaining clips. *See Figs. 18 and 19.* Pull steering wheel from shaft while guiding cable reel harness and connectors through hole in steering wheel.

4) Remove bolts retaining harness cover under steering column. Remove harness cover. Remove cable reel harness retaining screws under steering column. Remove cable reel retaining screws. Pull cable reel from steering shaft. Remove cancel sleeve.

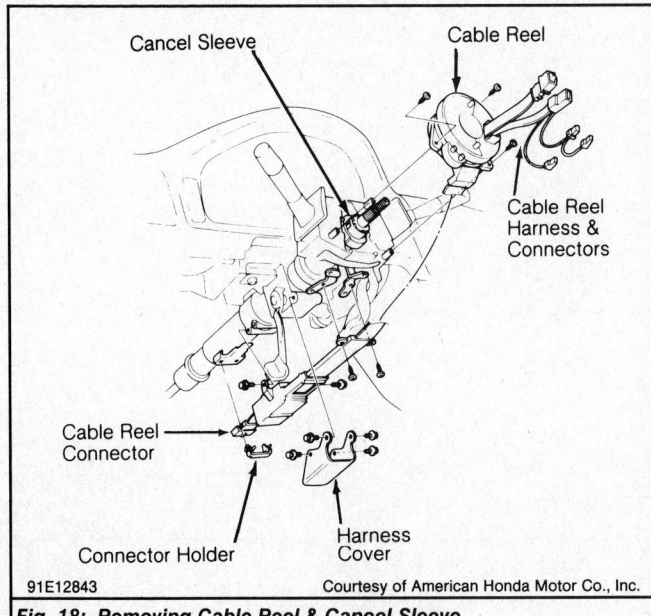

91E12843   Courtesy of American Honda Motor Co., Inc.

Fig. 18: Removing Cable Reel & Cancel Sleeve

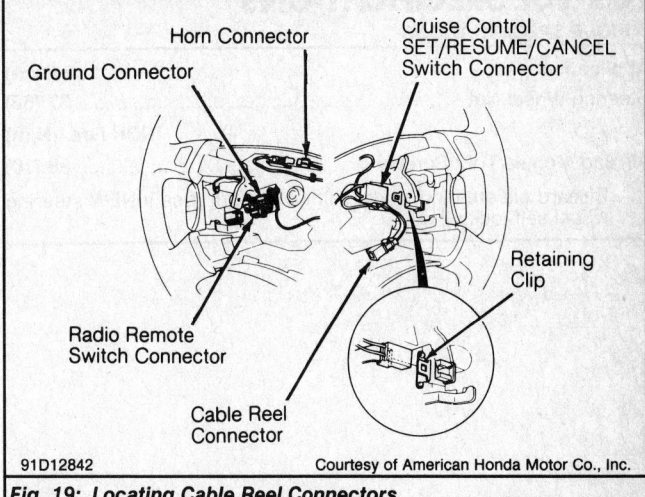

91D12842   Courtesy of American Honda Motor Co., Inc.

Fig. 19: Locating Cable Reel Connectors

Installation – **1)** Align cancel sleeve grooves with cable reel projections. *See Fig. 20.* Carefully install cancel sleeve and cable reel onto steering shaft. Install cable reel harness retaining screws. Install harness cover. Install steering column upper and lower covers. Center cable reel. See CABLE REEL CENTERING under ADJUSTMENTS.

2) Route cable reel harness and connectors through steering wheel hole. Install steering wheel. Secure each connector to respective retaining clips and connections in steering wheel.

3) Install NEW steering wheel nut, and tighten to specification. Install air bag module, and tighten mounting screws to specification. See TORQUE SPECIFICATIONS. Connect cable reel to SRS main harness under steering column. Install cable reel connector holder. Install lower instrument panel cover.

4) Activate air bag system. Check SRS indicator light to verify system is okay. See SYSTEM OPERATION CHECK in AIR BAG RESTRAINT SYSTEM article.

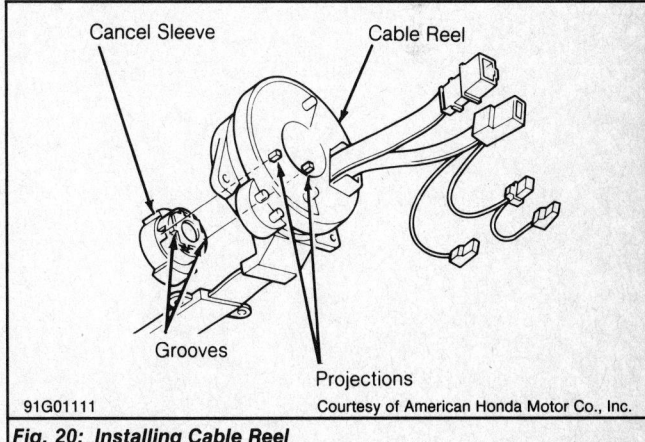

91G01111   Courtesy of American Honda Motor Co., Inc.

Fig. 20: Installing Cable Reel

SET/RESUME SWITCH

Removal & Installation (Integra) – Carefully pry cover from side of SET/RESUME switch. Remove retaining screws and SET/RESUME switch. To install, reverse removal procedure.

SET/RESUME/CANCEL SWITCH

Removal & Installation (Legend & Vigor) – Carefully pry cover from side of SET/RESUME/CANCEL switch. Remove retaining screws and SET/RESUME/CANCEL switch. To install, reverse removal procedure.

TORQUE SPECIFICATIONS

TORQUE SPECIFICATIONS

Application	Ft. Lbs (N.m)
Steering Wheel Nut [1]	37 (50)

	INCH Lbs. (N.m)
Air Bag Module Torx Screws	88 (10)

[1] – Discard old steering wheel self-locking nut. Use a NEW steering wheel self-locking nut.

WIRING DIAGRAMS

NOTE: See ACCESSORIES & EQUIPMENT, Volume 5.

Integra, Legend, Vigor

DESCRIPTION & OPERATION

Rear window defogger system consists of a heating wire grid bonded to the inside of the rear window, a dash-mounted control switch, relay, and Integrated Control Unit (ICU). ICU supplies power to grid for 25 minutes or until ignition is turned off.

TROUBLE SHOOTING

NOTE: When diagnosing problems by symptom, check for possible failures in following order.

DEFOGGER DOES NOT OPERATE

Integra – Check fuses No. 13 (7.5 amp) and No. 30 (10 amp) in dash fuse block. Check defogger timer circuit input (in ICU). ICU is located at underdash fuse panel. Check for poor connections. Check for short or open in Yellow, Black/Yellow or Black/Yellow wire.

Legend – Check fuses No. 3 (15 amp) and No. 13 (7.5 amp) in under-dash fuse block. Check defogger timer circuit input (in ICU). ICU is located at underdash fuse panel. Check for poor connections. Check for short or open in Yellow, Yellow/White, or Yellow/Black wire.

Vigor – Check fuses No. 1 (10 amp) and No. 8 (7.5 amp) in underdash fuse block. Check defogger timer circuit input (in ICU). ICU is located at underdash fuse panel. Check for poor connections. Check for short or open in Yellow, Yellow/White, or Yellow/Black wire.

INDICATOR LIGHT DOES NOT WORK

Check for burned-out bulb. On Integra, check for poor connections and open in Black/Yellow or Blue/Yellow wire. On Legend and Vigor, check for poor connections in Yellow, Yellow/White, or Yellow/Black wire.

OPERATION TIME TOO LONG OR TOO SHORT

Check defogger timer circuit input (in ICU). On Integra, check for short or open in Yellow and Black wires. On Integra, check for short or open in Yellow/Green and Black wire. On Vigor, check for short or open in Yellow/White and Black wires.

TESTING

DEFOGGER SWITCH TEST

Remove switch from instrument panel. Check for continuity with switch in each position. *See Fig. 1, 2, or 3.* If switch does not function as indicated, replace switch.

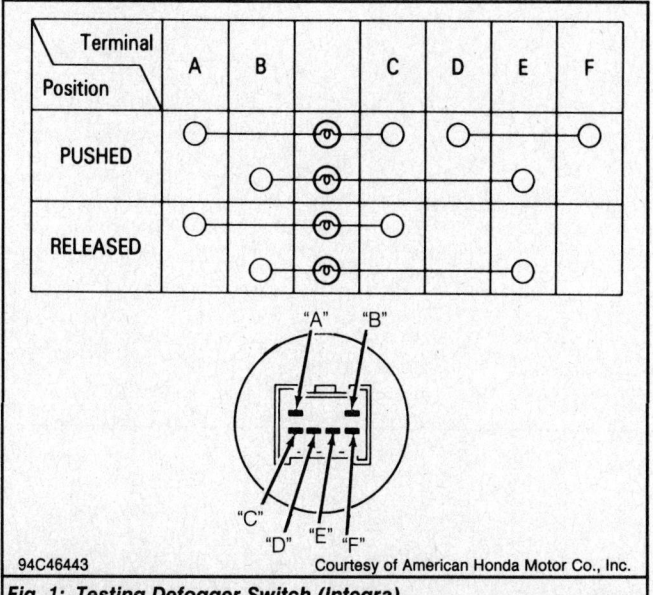

Fig. 1: Testing Defogger Switch (Integra)

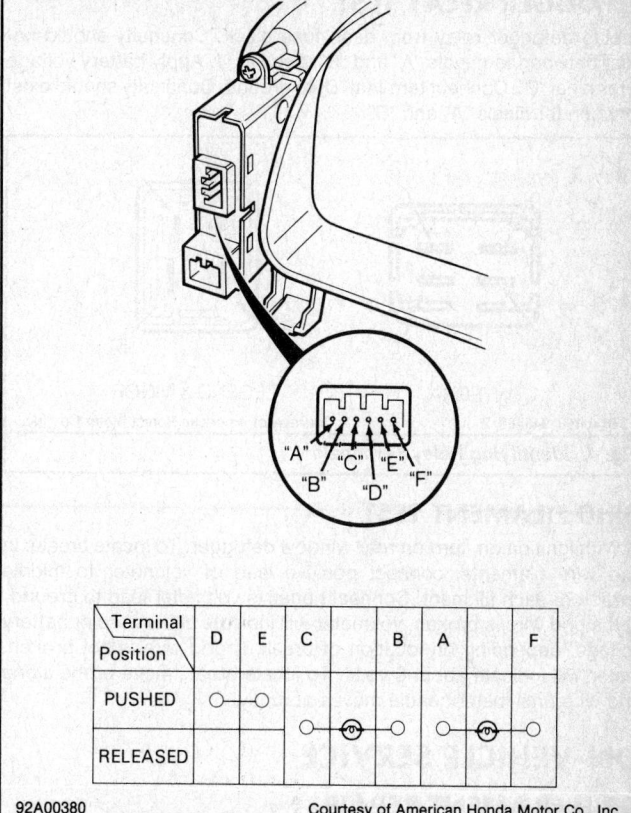

Terminal Position	D	E	C	B	A	F
PUSHED	O—O					
RELEASED			O—(⊗)—O		O—(⊗)—O	

Fig. 2: Testing Defogger Switch (Legend)

Rear Window Defogger Switch

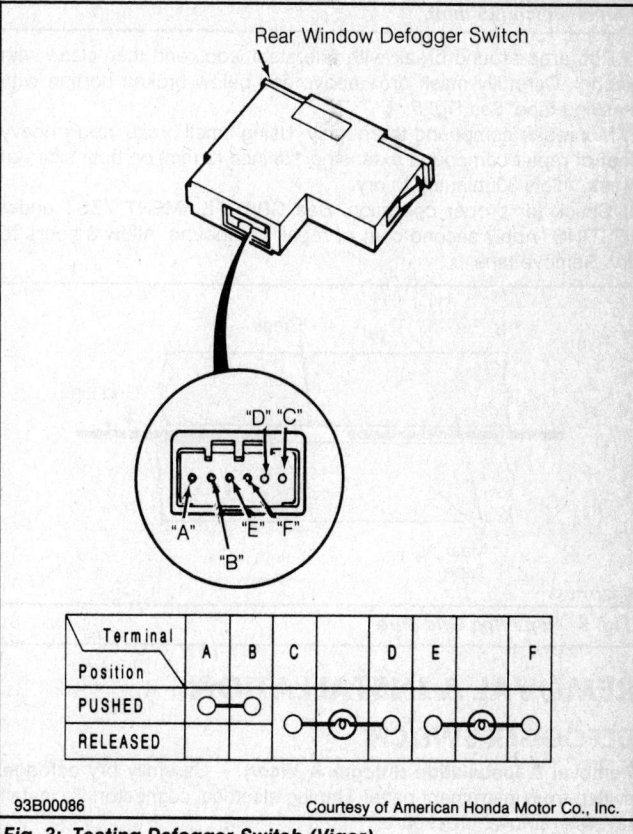

Terminal Position	A	B	C	D	E	F
PUSHED	O—O					
RELEASED			O—(⊗)—O		O—(⊗)—O	

Fig. 3: Testing Defogger Switch (Vigor)

DEFOGGER RELAY TEST

Unplug defogger relay from dash fuse block. Continuity should not exist between terminals "A" and "B". *See Fig. 4.* Apply battery voltage to terminal "C". Connect terminal "D" to ground. Continuity should exist between terminals "A" and "B".

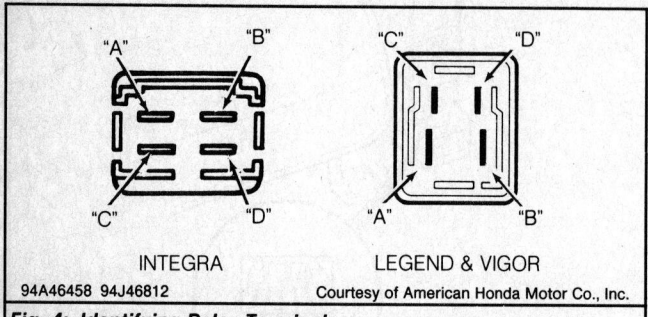

INTEGRA   LEGEND & VIGOR

94A46458 94J46812   Courtesy of American Honda Motor Co., Inc.

Fig. 4: Identifying Relay Terminals

GRID FILAMENT TEST

1) With ignition on, turn on rear window defogger. To locate breaks in grid wire filaments, connect positive lead of voltmeter to middle portion of each filament. Connect negative voltmeter lead to ground.
2) If a grid wire is broken, voltmeter will indicate either zero or battery voltage, depending on location of break. If grid wire is not broken, meter will indicate about 6 volts. To locate break, move probe along grid wire until meter needle moves abruptly.

ON-VEHICLE SERVICE

GRID FILAMENT REPAIR

NOTE: For repair to be effective, broken section must not be longer than one inch (25 mm).

1) Rub area around break with fine steel wool, and then clean with alcohol. Carefully mask area above and below broken portion with masking tape. See Fig. 5.
2) Mix repair compound thoroughly. Using small brush, apply heavy coat of repair compound extending 1/8 inch (3 mm) on both sides of break. Allow 30 minutes to dry.
3) Check for proper operation. See GRID FILAMENT TEST under TESTING. Apply second coat of repair compound. Allow 3 hours to dry. Remove tape.

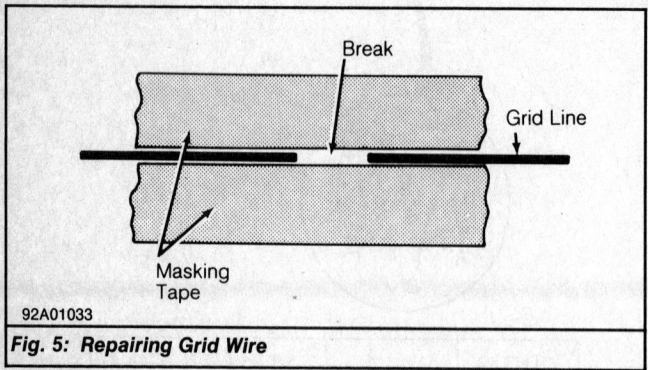

Break

Grid Line

Masking Tape

92A01033

Fig. 5: Repairing Grid Wire

REMOVAL & INSTALLATION

DEFOGGER SWITCH

Removal & Installation (Integra & Vigor) – Carefully pry defogger switch from instrument panel. Unplug electrical connector. To install, reverse removal procedure.
Removal & Installation (Legend) – Remove lower instrument panel cover. Remove 2 retaining screws and instrument trim panel. Unplug all connectors from instrument panel. Remove retaining screws and defogger switch. To install, reverse removal procedure.

DEFOGGER RELAY

Removal & Installation – Defogger relay is on underdash fuse block. Unplug relay to remove. To install, reverse removal procedure.

WIRING DIAGRAMS

NOTE: See ACCESSORIES & EQUIPMENT, Volume 5.

Integra, Legend, Vigor

DESCRIPTION & OPERATION

All models use conventional analog gauges. Instrument cluster panel includes speedometer, tachometer, fuel gauge, and temperature gauge. Instrument cluster is equipped with warning lights for charging system, low oil pressure, and Anti-Lock Brake System (ABS). Instrument cluster also includes dash light dimmer control, integrated control unit and safety indicator unit (Legend and Vigor), which control warning lights on cluster. A CHECK ENGINE light, located on instrument cluster, comes on if a computerized engine control fault occurs with engine running. Integra uses a maintenance reminder light to remind the driver of routine maintenance interval. All models are equipped with Supplemental Restraint System (SRS) warning lights.

TESTING

CAUTION: *All models are equipped with Supplemental Restraint System (SRS). SRS wiring harness is routed close to instrument cluster, steering wheel, and related components. All SRS wiring harnesses are covered by Yellow outer insulation. DO NOT use electrical test equipment on these circuits. Before working on steering column components, disable air bag system. See AIR BAG RESTRAINT SYSTEM article in ACCESSORIES & EQUIPMENT.*

DASH LIGHT DIMMER CONTROL

Integra & Vigor – 1) Turn ignition off. Remove instrument panel cover from dash. See INSTRUMENT CLUSTER under REMOVAL & INSTALLATION. Disconnect wiring from dash light dimmer control unit. Ensure Black wire has continuity to ground. See Fig. 1 or 2. If continuity does not exist, repair open in wire.

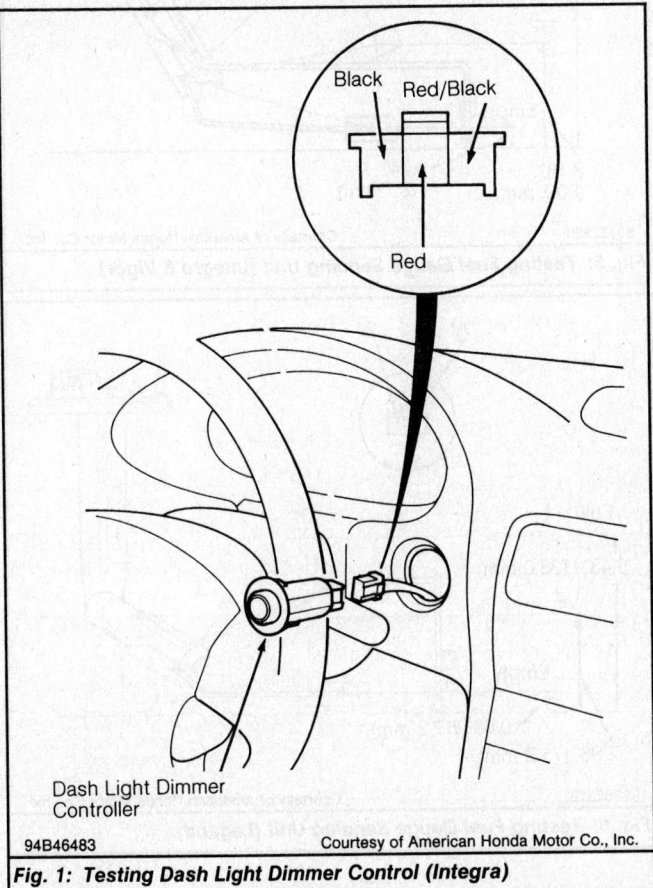

94B46483   Courtesy of American Honda Motor Co., Inc.

Fig. 1: Testing Dash Light Dimmer Control (Integra)

2) Turn headlight switch on. Check Red/Black wire for battery voltage. See Fig. 1 or 2. If battery voltage is present, go to next step. If battery voltage is not present, check fuse No. 19, combination light switch or Red/Black wire for open. Repair as necessary.

3) Ground Red wire. Dash lights should come on full bright. If lights are bright, circuits are okay. If dash lights still do not work correctly, replace dash light dimmer control unit. If lights do not go full bright, check dash bulbs condition and Red wire for open. Repair as necessary.

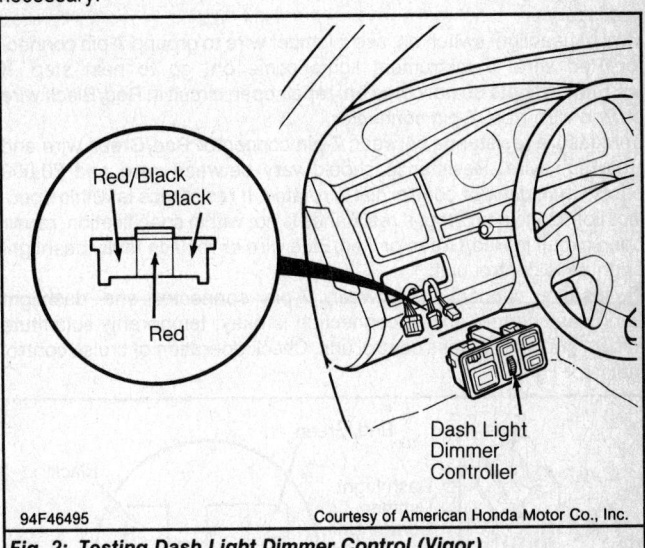

94F46495   Courtesy of American Honda Motor Co., Inc.

Fig. 2: Testing Dash Light Dimmer Control (Vigor)

Legend – 1) Turn ignition off. Remove 2 screws from instrument cluster bezel. Pull out instrument cluster bezel far enough to unplug electrical connectors (one on left side and 2 on right side). Remove instrument cluster bezel.

2) Measure resistance between dimmer switch terminals "A" and "B" while rotating dimmer dial. See Fig. 3. Resistance should vary between zero and 20,000 ohms. If resistance is within specification, go to next step. If resistance is not within specification, replace dimmer switch.

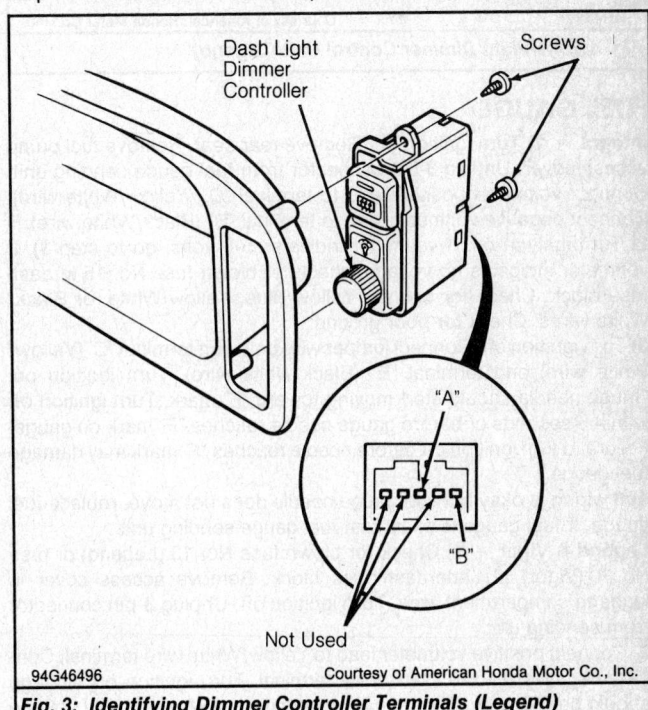

94G46496   Courtesy of American Honda Motor Co., Inc.

Fig. 3: Identifying Dimmer Controller Terminals (Legend)

3) Unplug dashlight brightness control unit 7-pin connector, located behind left side of radio. *See Fig. 4.* Check for continuity between connector Black wire and ground. If continuity exists, go to next step. If continuity does not exist, repair open in Black wire or poor ground connection G251, located at base of left "B" pillar.

4) With headlight switch on, check for battery voltage between 7-pin connector Red/Black wire and ground. If battery voltage exists, go to next step. If battery voltage does not exist, check fuse No. 49, taillight relay, headlight switch, or for open circuit in Red/Black wire. Repair as necessary.

5) With headlight switch on, use a jumper wire to ground 7-pin connector Red wire. If instrument lights come on, go to next step. If instrument lights do not come on, repair open circuit in Red/Black wire or Red wire from 7-pin connector.

6) Measure resistance between 7-pin connector Red/Green wire and Red/Blue wire. Resistance should vary between zero and 20,000 ohms when dimmer control dial is rotated. If resistance is within specification, go to next step. If resistance is not within specification, repair open circuit in Red/Green or Red/Blue wire or replace faulty dashlight brightness control unit.

7) Inspect connection between 7-pin connector and dashlight brightness control unit. If connection is okay, temporarily substitute known good brightness control unit. Check operation of cruise control indicator light.

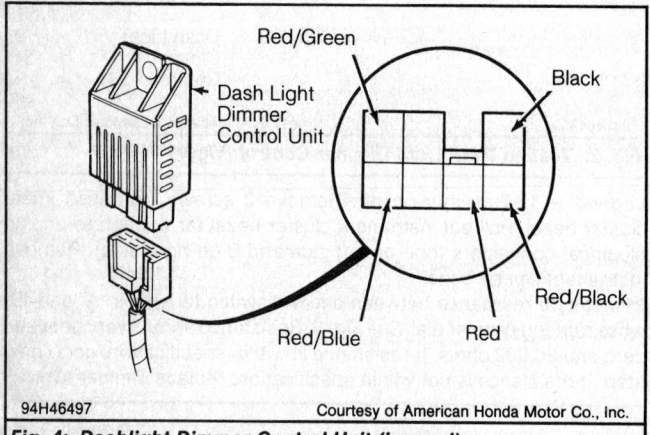

Fig. 4: Dashlight Dimmer Control Unit (Legend)

FUEL GAUGE

Integra – 1) Turn ignition off. Remove rear seat. Remove fuel pump access cover. Unplug 3-pin connector from fuel gauge sending unit. Connect voltmeter positive lead to terminal "C" (Yellow/White wire). Connect negative voltmeter lead to terminal "B" (Black/White wire).

2) Turn ignition on. If voltmeter indicates 5-8 volts, go to step **3)**. If voltmeter indicates no voltage, check for blown fuse No. 15 in dash fuse block. Check for open in Yellow/Blue, Yellow/White, or Black/White wires. Check for poor ground.

3) Turn ignition off. Connect jumper wire between terminal "C" (Yellow/White wire) and terminal "B" (Black/White wire). Turn ignition on. Gauge needle should start moving toward "F" mark. Turn ignition off within 5 seconds or before gauge needle reaches "F" mark on gauge. Failure to turn ignition off before needle reaches "F" mark may damage fuel gauge.

4) If wiring is okay but fuel gauge needle does not move, replace fuel gauge. If fuel gauge is okay, test fuel gauge sending unit.

Legend & Vigor – 1) Check for blown fuse No. 13 (Legend) or fuse No. 1 (Vigor) at underdash fuse block. Remove access cover in luggage compartment area. Turn ignition off. Unplug 3-pin connector from sending unit.

2) Connect positive voltmeter lead to Yellow/White wire terminal. Connect negative lead to Black wire terminal. Turn ignition on. Voltage should be 5-8 volts. If voltage is as specified, go to step **3)**. If voltage is not as specified, check for poor ground or open in Yellow, Yellow/White, or Black wire.

3) Turn ignition off. Connect jumper wire between Yellow/White and Black wire terminals. Turn ignition on. Fuel gauge needle should move toward "F" mark on gauge. Turn ignition off within 5 seconds or before gauge needle reaches "F" mark. Failure to turn ignition off before needle reaches "F" mark may result in damage to fuel gauge.

4) If wiring is okay but fuel gauge needle does not move, replace fuel gauge. If gauge is okay, test fuel gauge sending unit.

FUEL GAUGE SENDING UNIT

Integra & Vigor – Remove rear seat. Remove fuel pump access cover. Turn ignition off. Unplug 3-pin connector from fuel gauge sending unit. Using Fuel Sender Wrench (07GAC-SE0020A), remove sending unit. Measure resistance between sending unit terminals "B" and "C" while moving float. *See Fig. 5.* Resistance must be as specified in FUEL GAUGE SENDING UNIT RESISTANCE table.

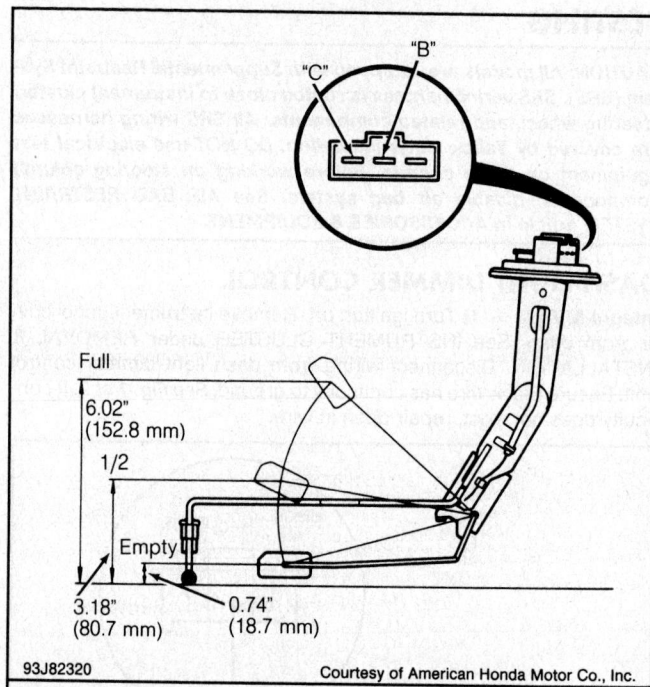

Fig. 5: Testing Fuel Gauge Sending Unit (Integra & Vigor)

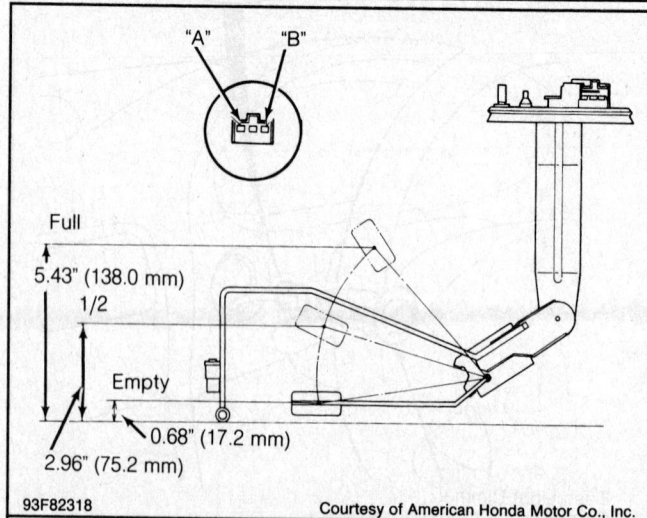

Fig. 6: Testing Fuel Gauge Sending Unit (Legend)

Legend – Remove access cover in luggage compartment area. Turn ignition off. Unplug connector at sending unit. Remove retaining nuts and sending unit. Measure resistance between sending unit terminals "A" and "B". *See Fig. 6.* Resistance must be as specified in FUEL GAUGE SENDING UNIT RESISTANCE table.

FUEL GAUGE SENDING UNIT RESISTANCE

Float Position	Ohms
Full	2-5
1/2	25-39
Empty	105-110

HAZARD WARNING SWITCH

Check for continuity between specified switch terminals with switch in ON and OFF positions. *See Fig. 7, 8, or 9.*

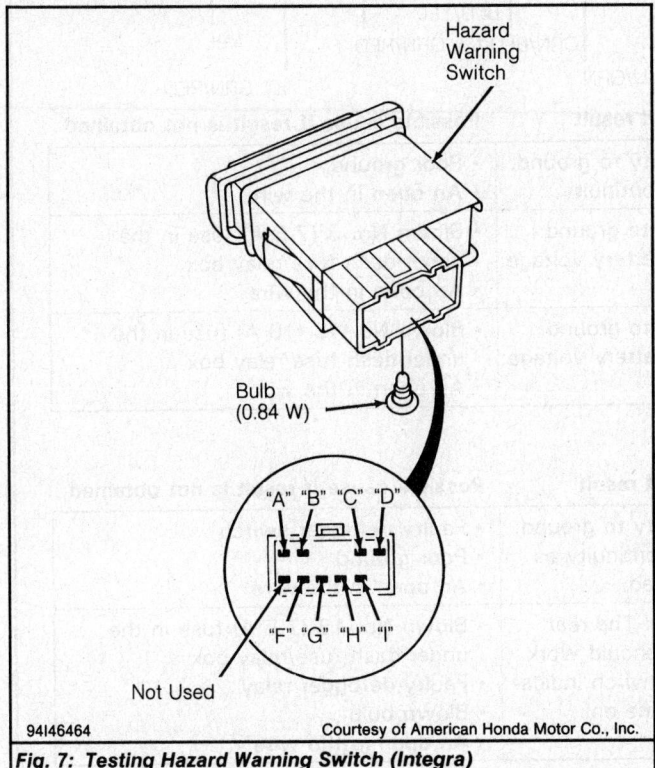

Hazard Warning Switch

Bulb (0.84 W)

"A" "B" "C" "D"

"F" "G" "H" "I"

Not Used

94146464   Courtesy of American Honda Motor Co., Inc.

Fig. 7: Testing Hazard Warning Switch (Integra)

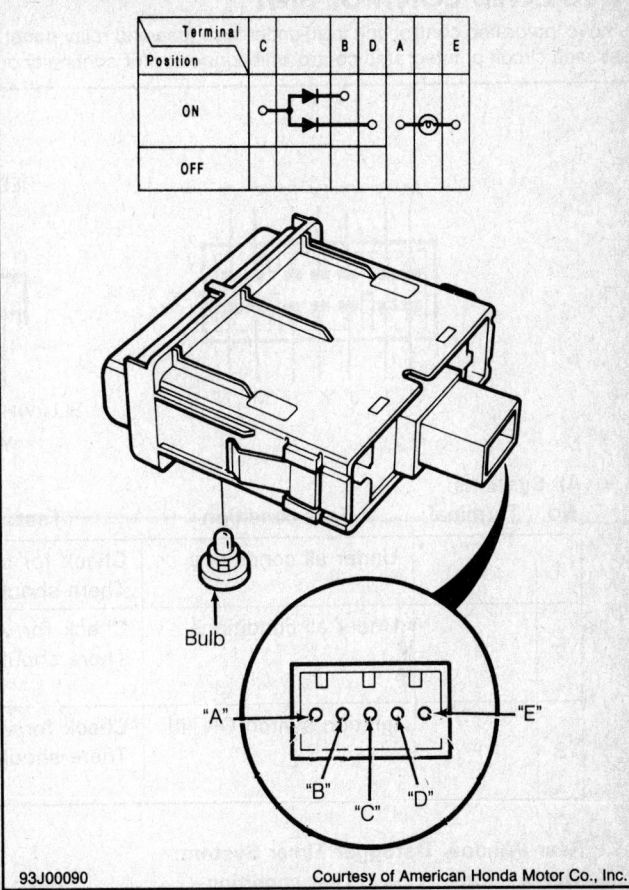

Terminal Position	C		B	D	A		E
ON							
OFF							

Bulb

"A" — — "E"

"B"   "C"   "D"

93J00090   Courtesy of American Honda Motor Co., Inc.

Fig. 8: Testing Hazard Warning Switch (Legend)

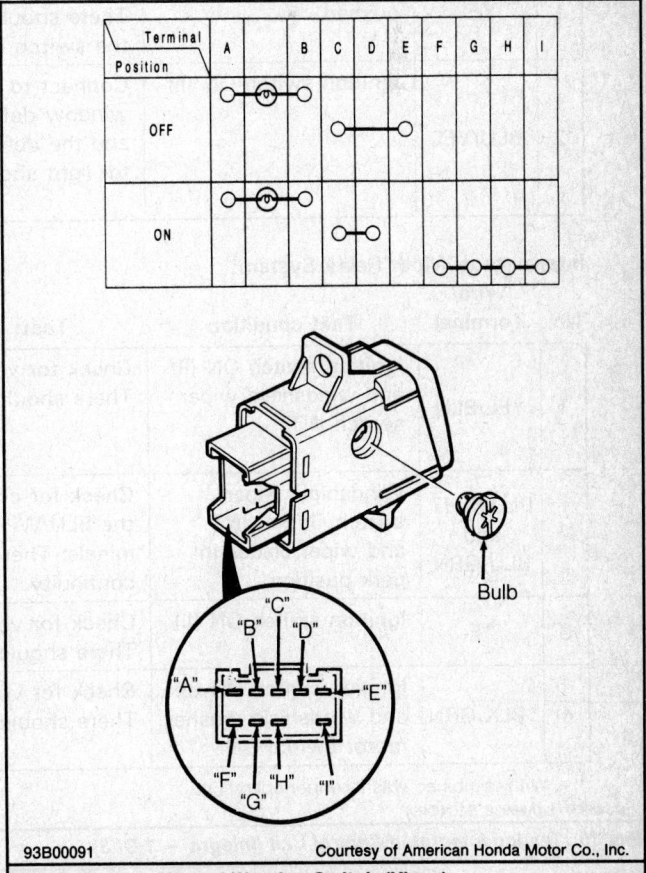

Terminal Position	A	B	C	D	E	F	G	H	I
OFF									
ON									

"C"

"B"   "D"

"A"   "E"

"F"   "H"   "I"

"G"

Bulb

93B00091   Courtesy of American Honda Motor Co., Inc.

Fig. 9: Testing Hazard Warning Switch (Vigor)

INTEGRATED CONTROL UNIT

Remove integrated control unit from underdash fuse and relay panel. Test each circuit of integrated control unit connector for continuity or voltage as indicated. *See Figs. 10-20.* Correct any problems found. If no problems are found, replace integrated control unit.

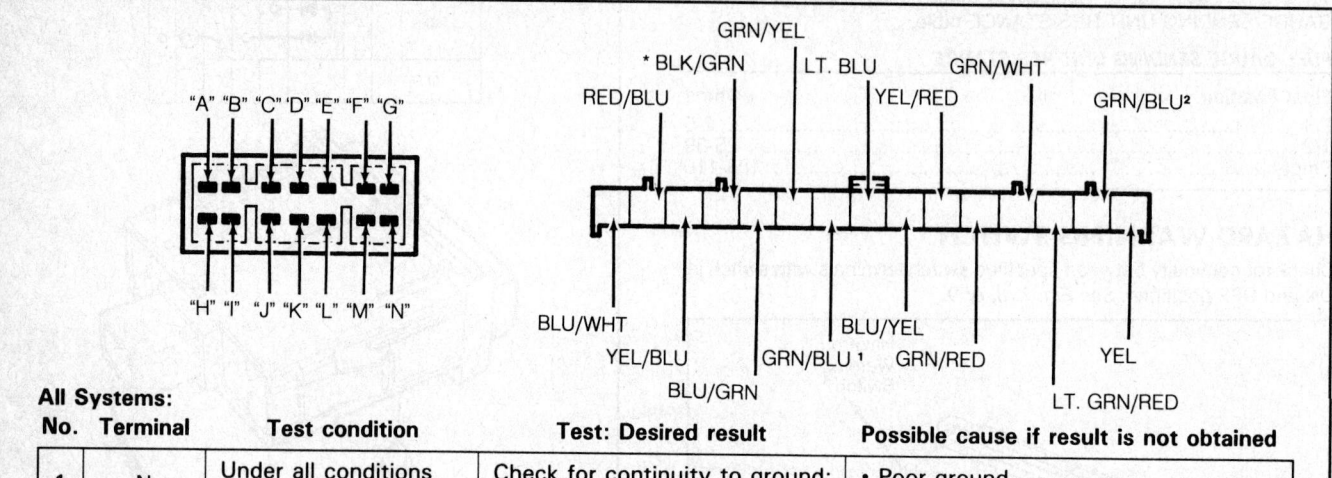

All Systems:

No.	Terminal	Test condition	Test: Desired result	Possible cause if result is not obtained
1	N	Under all conditions	Check for continuity to ground: There should be continuity.	• Poor ground • An open in the wire
2	I	Under all conditions	Check for voltage to ground: There should be battery voltage.	• Blown No. 3 (7.5 A) fuse in the under-dash fuse/relay box • An open in the wire
3	F	Ignition switch ON (II)	Check for voltage to ground: There should be battery voltage.	• Blown No. 15 (10 A) fuse in the under-dash fuse/relay box • An open in the wire

Rear Window Defogger Timer System:

No.	Wire	Test condition	Test: Desired result	Possible cause if result is not obtained
1	YEL	Defogger switch pushed	Check for continuity to ground: There should be continuity as the switch is pushed.	• Faulty defogger switch • Poor ground • An open in the wire
2	BLU/YEL	Ignition switch ON (II)	Connect to ground: The rear window defogger should work and the defogger switch indicator light should come on.	• Blown No. 13 (7.5 A) fuse in the under-dash fuse/relay box • Faulty defogger relay • Blown bulb • An open in the wire

Intermittent Wiper Relay System:

No.	Wire/ Terminal	Test condition	Test: Desired result	Possible cause if result is not obtained
1	YEL/BLU	Ignition switch ON (II) and windshield wiper switch INT	Check for voltage to ground: There should be battery voltage.	• Blown No. 14 (20 A) fuse in the under-dash fuse/relay box • Faulty windshield wiper switch • An open in the wire
2	BLU/WHT and BLU/GRN	Windshield wiper switch OFF or INT and wiper blades in park position	Check for continuity between the BLU/WHT and BLU/GRN terminals: There should be continuity.	• Faulty windshield wiper switch • Faulty windshield wiper motor • An open in the wire
3	*E	Ignition switch ON (II)	Check for voltage to ground: There should be battery voltage.	• An open in the wire
4	*BLK/GRN	Ignition switch ON (II) and windshield washer motor switch ON	Check for voltage to ground: There should be battery voltage.	• Faulty windshield washer switch • An open in the wire

* – With combined washer-wiper operation.

94J46937 94A46938 94C46484

Courtesy of American Honda Motor Co., Inc.

Fig. 10: *Testing Integrated Control Unit (Integra – 1 Of 3)*

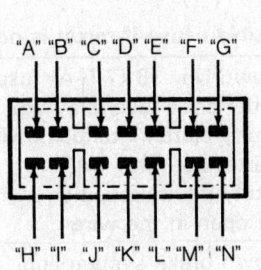

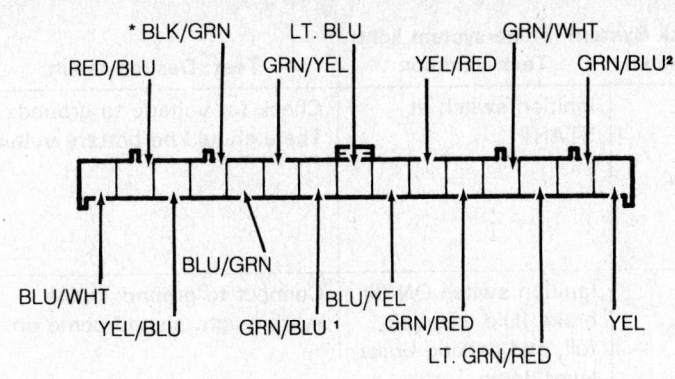

* – With combined washer-wiper operation.

Engine Oil Pressure Indicator Flasher System:

No.	Wire/ Terminal	Test condition	Test: Desired result	Possible cause if result is not obtained
1	A	Engine running	Check for voltage to ground: There should be battery voltage.	• Faulty charging system • An open in the wire
2	YEL/RED	Ignition switch OFF	Check for continuity to ground: There should be continuity.	• Faulty engine oil pressure switch • An open in the wire
		Ignition switch ON (II)	Check indicator light. If the light does not come on, attach the YEL/RED terminal to ground: The light should come on as the ignition switch is turned ON.	• Blown bulb • An open in the wire
		Start the engine.	Check for voltage to ground: There should be battery voltage.	• Insufficient oil • Improper lubrication • Faulty engine oil pressure switch

Key-in/Seat Belt Reminder System:

No.	Wire	Test condition	Test: Desired result	Possible cause if result is not obtained
1	GRN/BLU[2]	Driver's door open	Check for continuity to ground: There should be continuity.	• Faulty driver's door switch • An open in the wire
2	LT GRN/ RED	Front passenger's door switch open NOTE: Before testing, remove No. 3 (7.5 A) fuse from the under-dash fuse/relay box.	Check for continuity to ground: There should be continuity.	• Faulty front passenger's door switch • An open in the wire
3	LT BLU	Ignition key inserted into the ignition switch	Check for voltage to ground: There should be 1 V or less.	• Faulty ignition key switch • Poor ground • An open in the wire
4	RED/BLU	Ignition switch ON (II) and driver's seat belt unbuckled	Check for voltage to ground: There should be 1 V or less.	• Faulty seat belt switch • Poor ground • An open in the wire

94J46937 94A46938 94D46485

Courtesy of American Honda Motor Co., Inc.

Fig. 11: Testing Integrated Control Unit (Integra – 2 Of 3)

1994 ACCESSORIES & EQUIPMENT
Instrument Panels (Cont.)

Bulb Check System (brake system light)

No.	Terminal	Test condition	Test: Desired result	Possible cause if result is not obtained
1	M	Ignition switch at START	Check for voltage to ground: There should be battery voltage.	• Blown No. 18 (7.5 A) fuse in the under-dash fuse/relay box • Faulty clutch interlock switch or starter cut relay (M/T) • Faulty neutral position switch (A/T) • An open in the wire
2	D	Ignition switch ON (II), brake fluid reservoir full, and parking brake lever down	Connect to ground: Brake system light should come on.	• Blown brake system light • An open in the wire

Lights-on Reminder System:

No.	Wire/ Terminal	Test condition	Test: Desired result	Possible cause if result is not obtained
1	GRN/BLU[2]	Driver's door open	Check for continuity to ground: There should be continuity.	• Faulty driver's door switch • An open in the wire
2	H	Combination light switch ON.	Check for voltage to ground: There should be battery voltage.	• Blown No. 19 (10 A) fuse in the under-dash fuse/relay box • Faulty combination light switch • An open in the wire
3	J	Connect the I terminal to the J terminal.	Check chime operation: Chime should activate each time the battery is connected.	• Faulty chime • An open in the wire

Side Marker Light Flasher System:

No.	Wire/ Terminal	Test condition	Test: Desired result	Possible cause if result is not obtained
1	H	Combination light switch ON	Check for voltage to ground: There should be battery voltage.	• Blown No. 19 (10 A) fuse in the under-dash fuse/relay box • An open in the wire
2	GRN/BLU[1]	Ignition switch ON (II) and turn signal switch to "Left"	Check for voltage to ground: It should change from 0–12–0 V repeatedly.	• Blown No. 26 (10 A) fuse in the under-dash fuse/relay box • Faulty turn signal/hazard relay • An open in the wire
3	GRN/YEL	Ignition switch ON (II) and turn signal switch to "Right"		
4	GRN/WHT	Ignition switch ON (II) and turn signal switch to "Left (or Right)": Connect the H terminal to the GRN/WHT (or GRN/RED[1]) terminal.	Check the front side marker light: Left (or Right) front side marker light should come on as the battery is connected.	• Blown bulb • Poor ground • An open in the wire
5	GRN/RED[1]			

94E46486

Courtesy of American Honda Motor Co., Inc.

Fig. 12: Testing Integrated Control Unit (Integra – 3 Of 3)

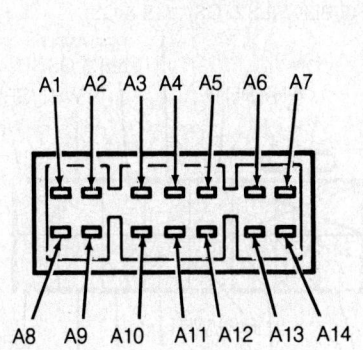

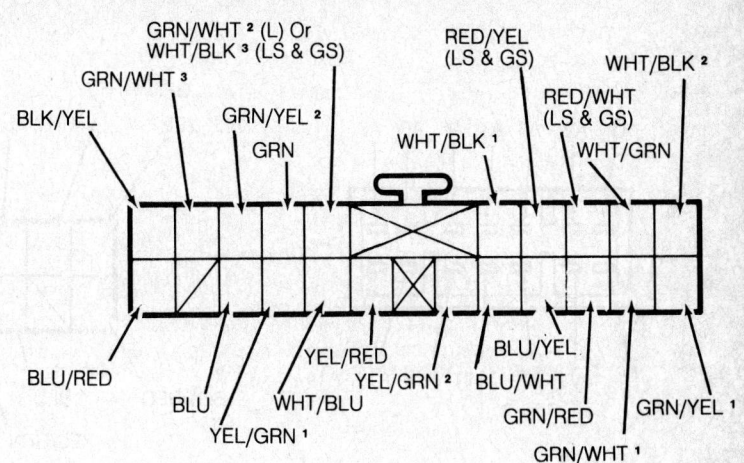

All Systems:

No.	Terminal	Test condition	Test: Desired result	Possible cause if result is not obtained
1	A7	Under all conditions	Check for continuity to ground: There should be continuity.	• Poor ground • An open in the wire
2	A14	Under all conditions	Check for voltage to ground: There should be battery voltage.	• Blown No. 56 (7.5A) fuse • An open in the wire
3	A2	Ignition switch ON (II)	Check for voltage to ground: There should be battery voltage.	• Blown bulb or No. 13 (7.5A) fuse • An open in the wire

Key-in Reminder System:

No.	Terminal/Wire	Test condition	Test: Desired result	Possible cause if result is not obtained
1	A11	Driver's door open	Check for continuity to ground: There should be continuity. NOTE: Before testing, remove No. 57 (15A) fuse.	• Faulty left front door switch • An open in the wire
2	BLU/WHT	Ignition key inserted all the way into the ignition switch.	Check for voltage to ground: There should be 1 V or less.	• Faulty ignition key switch • Poor ground • An open in the wire

Lights-on Reminder System:

No.	Terminal/Wire	Test condition	Test: Desired result	Possible cause if result is not obtained
1	A11	Driver's door open	Check for continuity to ground: There should be continuity. NOTE: Before testing, remove No. 57 (15A) fuse.	• Faulty left front door switch • An open in the wire
2	A6	Combination light switch ON (II)	Check for voltage to ground: There should be battery voltage.	• Blown No. 49 (15 A) fuse • Faulty combination light switch • Faulty taillight relay • An open in the wire
3	BLU	Connect the A14 terminal to the BLU terminal.	Check chime operation: Chime should activate each time the battery is connected.	• Faulty chime • An open in the wire

Courtesy of American Honda Motor Co., Inc.

Fig. 13: Testing Integrated Control Unit (Legend – 1 Of 4)

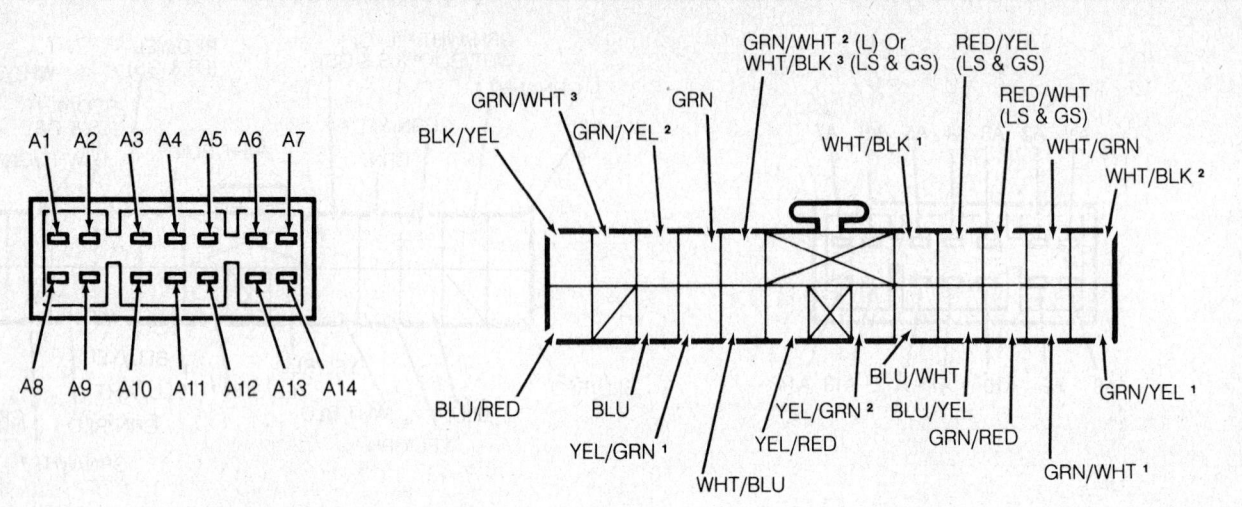

Seat Belt Reminder System:

No.	Wire	Test condition	Test: Desired result	Possible cause if result is not obtained
1	BLU/YEL	Ignition switch ON (II) and driver's seat belt not buckled	Check for voltage to ground: There should be 1 V or less.	• Faulty Driver's seat belt switch • Poor ground • An open in the wire

Rear Window Defogger Timer System:

No.	Wire/Terminal	Test condition	Test: Desired result	Possible cause if result is not obtained
1	YEL/GRN²	Defogger switch pushed	Check for continuity to ground: There should be continuity as the switch is pushed.	• Faulty defogger switch • Poor ground • An open in the wire
2	A5	Ignition switch ON (II)	Attach to ground: Rear window defogger should work and the defogger switch indicator light should come on.	• Blown No. 3 (15A) fuse • Faulty defogger relay • Blown bulb • An open in the wire

Engine Oil Pressure Indicator System:

No.	Wire	Test condition	Test: Desired result	Possible cause if result is not obtained
1	WHT/BLU	Engine running	Check for voltage to ground: There should be battery voltage.	• Faulty charging system • An open in the wire
2	YEL/RED	Ignition switch OFF	Check for continuity to ground: There should be continuity.	• Faulty engine oil pressure switch • An open in the wire
		Ignition switch ON (II)	Check indicator light operation. If the light does not come on, attach the YEL/RED terminal to ground: The light should come on as the ignition switch is turned ON (II).	• Blown bulb • An open in the wire
		Start the engine.	Check for voltage to ground: There should be battery voltage.	• Insufficient oil • Improper lubrication • Faulty engine oil pressure switch

94B46939 94E46940 94J46499

Fig. 14: *Testing Integrated Control Unit (Legend – 2 Of 4)*

Side Marker Light Flasher System:

No.	Terminal	Test condition	Test: Desired result	Possible cause if result is not obtained
1	A6	Combination light switch to ON	Check for voltage to ground: There should be battery voltage.	• Blown No. 49 (15A) fuse • Faulty combination light switch • Faulty taillight relay • An open in the wire
2	A12	Ignition switch ON (II) and turn signal switch in left position	Check for voltage to ground: If should change from 0V—12V—0V repeatedly.	• Blown No. 13 (7.5A) fuse • Faulty turn signal/hazard relay • An open in the wire
3	A13	Ignition switch ON (II) and turn signal switch in right position		
4	A1	Connect the A14 terminal to the A1 (or A8) terminal.	Check the front side marker lights: The left (or right) front side marker light should come on as power and ground are connected.	• Blown bulb • Poor ground • An open in the wire
	A8			

Power Window Key-off Timer System:

No.	Terminal/ Wire	Test condition	Test: Desired result	Possible cause if result is not obtained
1	A11	Driver's door open	Check for continuity to ground: There should be continuity. NOTE: Before testing, remove No. 57 (15A) fuse.	• Faulty door switch • An open in the wire
	GRN/RED	Right front door open		
2	A4	Connect the A14 terminal to the A4 terminal.	Check window operation: The power windows should work with key OFF.	• Faulty power window relay • Poor ground • An open in the wire

Intermittent Wiper System:

No.	Wire/ Terminal	Test condition	Test: Desired result	Possible cause if result is not obtained
1	BLU/RED	Ignition switch ON (II)	Check for voltage to ground: There should be battery voltage.	• Blown No. 23 (7.5A) fuse • Faulty wiper intermittent relay • An open in the wire
2	GRN	Ignition switch ON (II) and wiper switch at INT position	Check for voltage to ground: There should be battery voltage.	• Blown No. 23 (7.5A) fuse • Faulty wiper switch • An open in the wire
3	BLK/YEL	Ignition switch ON (II) and washer switch pushed	Check for voltage to ground: There should be battery voltage.	• Blown No. 23 (7.5A) fuse • Faulty washer switch • An open in the wire
4	GRN/YEL[2] GRN/WHT[3]	Intermittent dwell time control ring turned	Check for resistance between the terminals: It should vary from 0 Ω to 30 kΩ as the ring is turned.	• Faulty intermittent dwell time controller • An open in the wire
5	A9	Ignition switch ON (II) and wiper switch OFF	Check for voltage to ground: There should be battery voltage.	• Blown No. 26 (30 A) fuse • Faulty wiper motor (automatic-stop circuit) • An open in the wire

94C46500

Courtesy of American Honda Motor Co., Inc.

Fig. 15: Testing Integrated Control Unit (Legend – 3 Of 4)

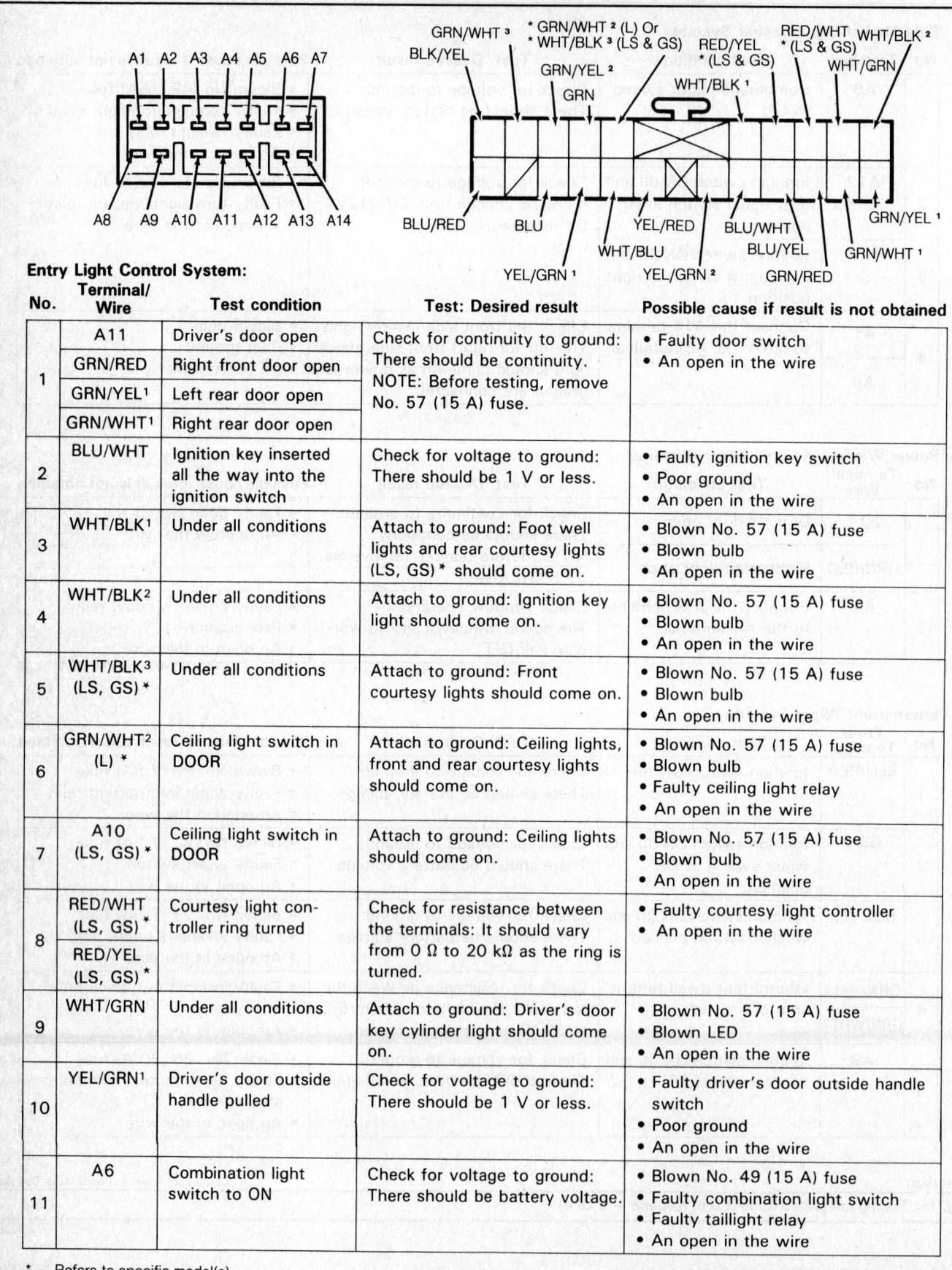

Entry Light Control System:

No.	Terminal/Wire	Test condition	Test: Desired result	Possible cause if result is not obtained
1	A11	Driver's door open	Check for continuity to ground: There should be continuity. NOTE: Before testing, remove No. 57 (15 A) fuse.	• Faulty door switch • An open in the wire
	GRN/RED	Right front door open		
	GRN/YEL[1]	Left rear door open		
	GRN/WHT[1]	Right rear door open		
2	BLU/WHT	Ignition key inserted all the way into the ignition switch	Check for voltage to ground: There should be 1 V or less.	• Faulty ignition key switch • Poor ground • An open in the wire
3	WHT/BLK[1]	Under all conditions	Attach to ground: Foot well lights and rear courtesy lights (LS, GS) * should come on.	• Blown No. 57 (15 A) fuse • Blown bulb • An open in the wire
4	WHT/BLK[2]	Under all conditions	Attach to ground: Ignition key light should come on.	• Blown No. 57 (15 A) fuse • Blown bulb • An open in the wire
5	WHT/BLK[3] (LS, GS) *	Under all conditions	Attach to ground: Front courtesy lights should come on.	• Blown No. 57 (15 A) fuse • Blown bulb • An open in the wire
6	GRN/WHT[2] (L) *	Ceiling light switch in DOOR	Attach to ground: Ceiling lights, front and rear courtesy lights should come on.	• Blown No. 57 (15 A) fuse • Blown bulb • Faulty ceiling light relay • An open in the wire
7	A10 (LS, GS) *	Ceiling light switch in DOOR	Attach to ground: Ceiling lights should come on.	• Blown No. 57 (15 A) fuse • Blown bulb • An open in the wire
8	RED/WHT (LS, GS) * RED/YEL (LS, GS) *	Courtesy light controller ring turned	Check for resistance between the terminals: It should vary from 0 Ω to 20 kΩ as the ring is turned.	• Faulty courtesy light controller • An open in the wire
9	WHT/GRN	Under all conditions	Attach to ground: Driver's door key cylinder light should come on.	• Blown No. 57 (15 A) fuse • Blown LED • An open in the wire
10	YEL/GRN[1]	Driver's door outside handle pulled	Check for voltage to ground: There should be 1 V or less.	• Faulty driver's door outside handle switch • Poor ground • An open in the wire
11	A6	Combination light switch to ON	Check for voltage to ground: There should be battery voltage.	• Blown No. 49 (15 A) fuse • Faulty combination light switch • Faulty taillight relay • An open in the wire

* – Refers to specific model(s).

94B46939 94E46940 94D46501

Fig. 16: *Testing Integrated Control Unit (Legend – 4 Of 4)*

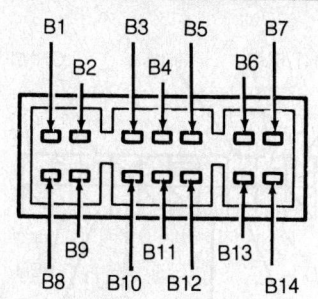

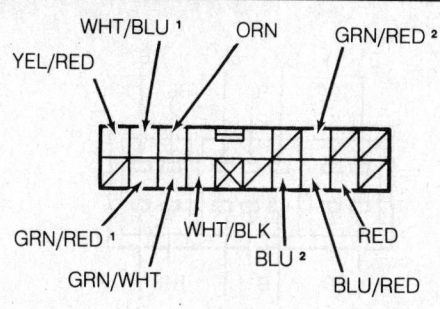

Intermittent Wiper System:

No.	Terminal	Test condition	Test: Desired result	Possible cause if result is not obtained
1	B8	Under all conditons.	Check for continuity to ground: There should be continuity.	• Poor ground • An open in the wire.
2	B9	Wiper switch at LOW.	Check for continuity to ground: There should be continuity.	• Faulty wiper switch. • An open in the wire. • Poor ground
3	B3	Ignition switch ON and wiper switch at INT.	Check for voltage to ground: There should be battery voltage.	• Blown No.1 (10 A) fuse (in the under-dash fuse/relay box). • An open in the wire
4	B4	Ignition switch ON and washer switch ON.	Check for voltage to ground: There should be battery voltage.	• Blown No.5 (10 A) fuse (in the under-dash fuse/relay box). • Faulty washer switch. • An open in the wire.
5	B10	Ignition switch ON.	Check for voltage to ground: There should be battery voltage.	• Blown No.6 (30 A) fuse (in the under-dash fuse/relay box). • An open in the wire.

Side Marker Light Flasher System:

No.	Terminal	Test condition	Test: Desired result	Possible cause if result is not obtained
1	B8	Under all conditions.	Check for continuity to ground: There should be continuity.	• Poor ground • An open in the wire.
2	B2	Ignition switch ON.	Check for voltage to ground: There should be battery voltage.	• Blown No.1 (10 A) fuse (in the under-dash fuse/relay box). • An open in the wire.
3	B13	Combination light switch ON.	Check for voltage to ground: There should be battery voltage.	• Blown No. 21 (20 A) fuse (in the under-hood fuse/relay box). • Faulty combination light switch (without security system). • Faulty taillight relay (with security system). • An open in the wire.
4	B14	Ignition switch ON and turn signal switch in left turn position.	Check for voltage to ground: There should be 0-12-0-12 repeatedly.	• Blown No. 1 (10 A) fuse (in the under-dash fuse/relay box). • Faulty turn signal system. • An open in the wire.
5	B7	Ignition switch ON and turn signal switch in right turn position.		
6	GRN/WHT	Connect the B2 terminal to the GRN/WHT (or GRN/RED1) terminal.	Check front side marker light operation: Left (or Right) front side marker light should come on as the battery is connected.	• Blown bulb • Poor ground • An open in the wire.
7	GRN/RED1			

Fig. 17: Testing Integrated Control Unit (Vigor – 1 Of 4)

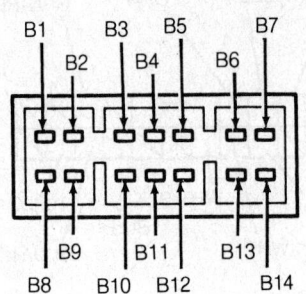

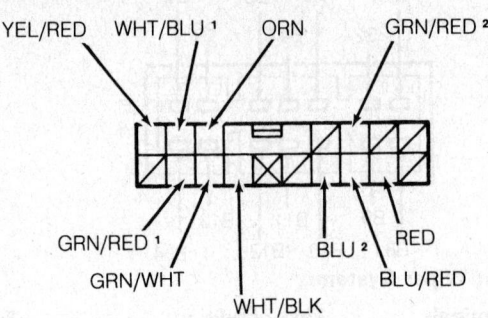

Seat Belt Reminder and Key-in Warning System:

No.	Terminal	Test condition	Test: Desired result	Possible cause if result is not obtained
1	B8	Under all conditons.	Check for continuity to ground: There should be continuity.	• Poor ground • An open in the wire.
2	B2	Ignition switch ON.	Check for voltage to ground: There should be battery voltage.	• Blown No.1 (10 A) fuse (in the under-dash fuse/relay box). • Blown bulb. • An open in the wire.
3	B1	Driver's door opened.	Check for voltage to ground: There should be 1 V or less.	• Faulty driver's door switch. • An open in the wire.
4	BLU²	Ignition key is inserted into the ignition switch.	Check for voltage to ground: There should be 1 V or less.	• Faulty ignition key switch. • An open in the wire. • Poor ground
5	BLU/RED	Driver's seat belt is not buckled.	Check for voltage to ground: There should be battery voltage.	• Faulty seat belt switch. • Poor ground • An open in the wire.

Power Window Key-off Timer System:

No.	Terminal	Test condition	Test: Desired result	Possible cause if result is not obtained
1	B8	Under all conditions.	Check for continuity to ground: There should be continuity.	• Poor ground
2	B1	Ignition switch ON and the driver's door closed.	Check for voltage to ground: There should be battery voltage.	• Blown No.1 (10 A) fuse (in the under-dash fuse/relay box). • An open in the wire.
3	B12	Under all conditions.	Check for voltage to ground: There should be battery voltage.	• Blown No.37 (15 A) fuse (in the under-hood fuse/relay box). • An open in the wire
4	GRN/RED²	Front passenger's door opened.	Check for voltage to ground: There should be 1 V or less.	• Faulty door switch. • An open in the wire.
5	RED	Connect the B12 terminal to the RED terminal.	Check window operation: Power windows should operate as the switch is turned.	• Faulty power window relay. • Poor ground • An open in the wire.

94F46941 94G46942 94A46508

Fig. 18: Testing Integrated Control Unit (Vigor – 2 Of 4)

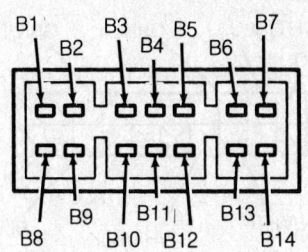
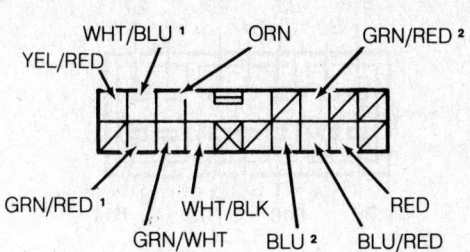

Entry Light Timer System

No.	Terminal	Test condition	Test: Desired result	Possible cause if result is not obtained
1	B8	Under all conditons.	Check for continuity to ground: There should be continuity.	• Poor ground • An open in the wire.
2	B12	Under all conditions.	Check for voltage to ground: There should be battery voltage.	• Blown No.37 (15 A) fuse (in the under-hood fuse/relay box). • An open in the wire.
3	WHT/BLK	Under all conditions.	Attach to ground: Ignition key light should come on.	• Blown bulb. • An open in the wire
4	B1	Driver's door opened.	Check for voltage to ground: There should be 1 V or less.	• Faulty driver's door switch. • An open in the wire. • Poor ground

Light-on Reminder System:

No.	Terminal	Test condition	Test: Desired result	Possible cause if result is not obtained
1	B8	Under all conditions.	Check for continuity to ground: There should be continuity.	• Poor ground • An open in the wire.
2	B13	Cabination light switch ON.	Check for voltage to ground: There should be battery voltage.	• Blown No. 21 (20 A) fuse (in the under-hood fuse/relay box). • Faulty combination light switch (Without security system). • Faulty taillight relay (With security system). • An open in the wire.
3	B2	Ignition switch ON.	Check for voltage to ground: There should be battery voltage.	• Blown No.1 (10 A) fuse (in the under-dash fuse/relay box). • An open in the wire.
4	B1	Driver's door opened.	Check for voltage to ground: There should be 1 V or less.	• Faulty driver's door switch. • An open in the wire. • Poor ground
5	ORN	Ignition switch ON and connect the B2 terminal to the ORN terminal.	Check chime operation: Chime should ring each time the battery is connected.	• Faulty chime. • An open in the wire.

94F46941 94G46942 94B46509

Fig. 19: Testing Integrated Control Unit (Vigor – 3 Of 4)

1994 ACCESSORIES & EQUIPMENT
Instrument Panels (Cont.)

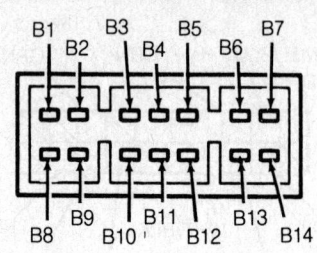

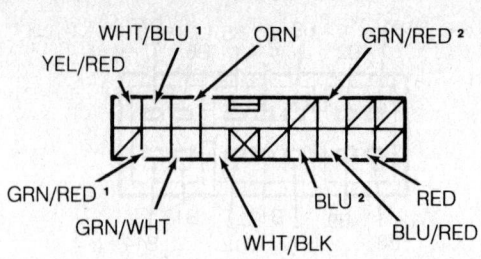

Rear Window Defogger Timer Circuit:

No.	Terminal	Test condition	Test: Desired result	Possible cause if result is not obtained
1	B8	Under all conditons.	Check for continuity to ground: There should be continuity.	• Poor ground • An open in the wire.
2	B6	Defogger switch pushed.	Check for continuity to ground: There should be continuity as the switch is pushed.	• Faulty defogger switch. • Poor ground • An open in the wire.
3	B5	Ignitioin switch ON.	Attach to ground: Rear window defogger should work and the defogger switch indicator light should come on.	• Blown No. 8 (7.5 A) fuse (in the under-dash fuse/relay box). • Faulty defogger relay. • Blown bulb. An open in the wire.
4	B2	Ignition switch ON.	Check for voltage to ground: There should be battery voltage.	• Blown No.1 (10 A) fuse (in the under-dash fuse/relay box). • An open in the wire.

Oil Pressure Indicator Flasher System:

No.	Terminal	Test condition	Test: Desired result	Possible cause if result is not obtained
1	B8	Under all conditions.	Check for continuity to ground: There should be continuity.	• Poor ground • An open in the wire.
2	B12	Ignition switch ON.	Check for voltage to ground: There should be battery voltage.	• Blown No. 1 (10 A) fuse (in the under-dash fuse/relay box). • An open in the wire.
3	WHT/BLU[1]	Engine running.	Check for voltage to ground: There should be 1 V or less	• Faulty charging system. • An open in the wire
4	YEL/RED	Ignition switch OFF.	Check for continuity to ground: There should be continuity.	• Faulty oil pressure switch. • An open in the wire.
		Ignition switch ON.	Check light operation. If the light does not come on, attach the YEL/RED terminal to ground: Light should come on as the ignition switch is turned ON.	• Blown bulb. • An open in the wire.
		Start the engine.	Check for voltage to ground: There should be battery voltage.	• Insufficient oil. • Improper lubrication. • Faulty oil pressure switch.

94F46941 94G46942 94E46510

Courtesy of American Honda Motor Co., Inc.

Fig. 20: Testing Integrated Control Unit (Vigor – 4 Of 4)

MAINTENANCE REMINDER LIGHT

Integra – 1) Turn ignition on. Maintenance reminder light should come on for 2 seconds. If light flashes or stays on, vehicle maintenance should be performed. To reset maintenance reminder unit, turn ignition on. Remove lower left dash cover. Press and hold reset button for more than 3 seconds. Install dash cover. If maintenance reminder light does not work as described, go to next step.

2) Turn ignition off. Remove lower left dash cover. Disconnect wiring from maintenance reminder unit. Ensure Black wire has continuity to ground. *See Fig. 21.* If continuity does not exist, repair open in wire.

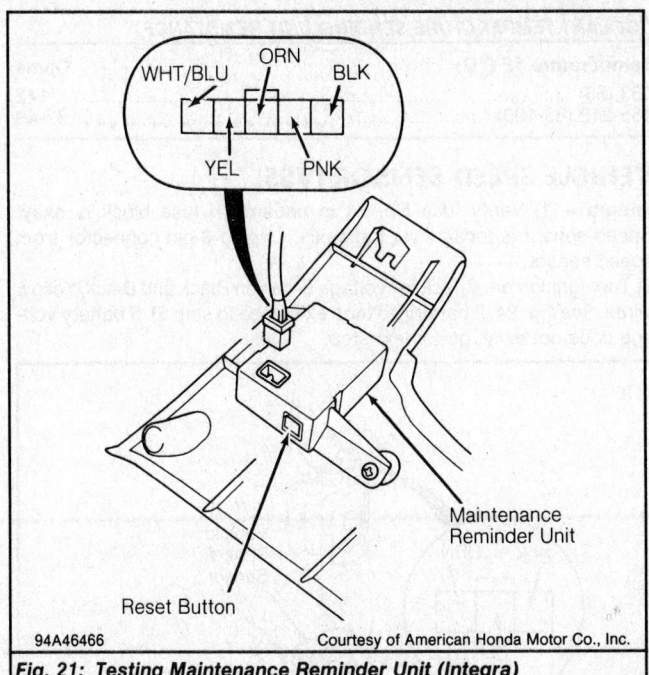

94A46466   Courtesy of American Honda Motor Co., Inc.

Fig. 21: Testing Maintenance Reminder Unit (Integra)

3) Check White/Blue wire for battery voltage. If battery voltage is present, go to next step. If battery voltage is not present, check fuse No. 32 or White/Blue wire for open. Repair as necessary.

4) Turn ignition on. Check Yellow wire for battery voltage. *See Fig. 21.* If battery voltage is present, go to next step. If battery voltage is not present, check fuse No. 15 or Yellow wire for open. Repair as necessary.

5) Ground Pink wire. Maintenance reminder light on dash should go on. If light goes on, go to next step. If light does not go on, check fuse No. 10, bulb condition and Pink wire for open. Repair as necessary.

6) Raise and support one front wheel. Check for pulsing voltage at Orange wire while rotating front wheel. If voltage pulses, circuits are okay. If maintenance reminder light still does not work correctly, replace maintenance reminder unit. If voltage does not pulse, check vehicle speed sensor or Orange wire for open. Repair as necessary.

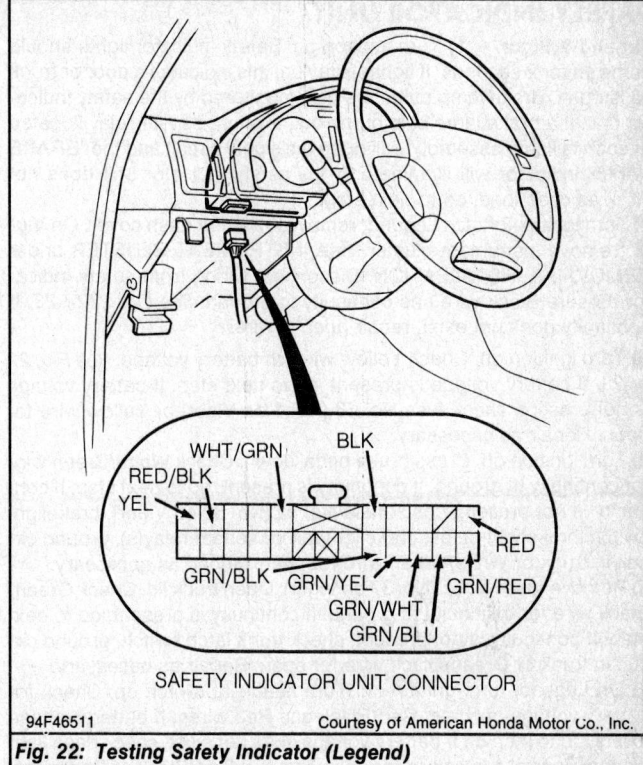

SAFETY INDICATOR UNIT CONNECTOR

94F46511   Courtesy of American Honda Motor Co., Inc.

Fig. 22: Testing Safety Indicator (Legend)

OIL PRESSURE SWITCH

Disconnect Yellow/Red wire from oil pressure switch. Switch is located at front of engine on Legend, and at base of oil filter on Integra and Vigor. With engine off, continuity should exist between oil pressure switch terminal and ground. Continuity should not exist with engine running. If switch does not function as specified but oil level and oil pressure are okay, replace oil pressure switch.

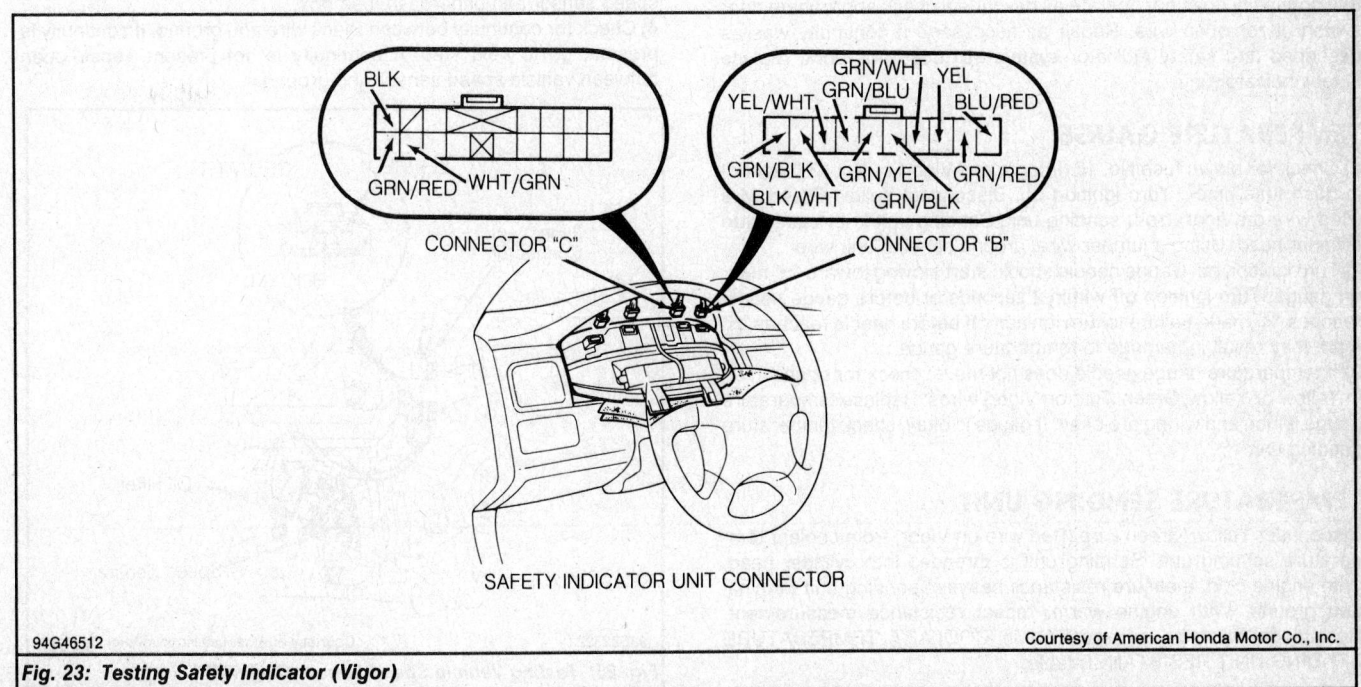

SAFETY INDICATOR UNIT CONNECTOR

94G46512   Courtesy of American Honda Motor Co., Inc.

Fig. 23: Testing Safety Indicator (Vigor)

SAFETY INDICATOR UNIT

Legend & Vigor – 1) Turn ignition on. Safety indicator lights should come on for 2 seconds. If light(s) stay on, this indicates a door or trunk lid is open. Brake lamp bulbs are also monitored by the safety indicator unit. If a brake lamp bulb burns out, a failure sensor relay (located at each taillamp assembly) will open the signal circuit and the "BRAKE LAMP" indicator will illuminate. If the safety indicator unit does not work as described, go to next step.

2) Turn ignition off. On Legend, remove lower left dash cover. On Vigor, remove instrument cluster. See INSTRUMENT CLUSTER under REMOVAL & INSTALLATION. Disconnect wiring from safety indicator. Ensure Black wire has continuity to ground. *See Fig. 22 or 23*. If continuity does not exist, repair open in wire.

3) Turn ignition on. Check Yellow wire for battery voltage. *See Fig. 22 or 23*. If battery voltage is present, go to next step. If battery voltage is not present, check fuse No. 13 (No. 1 on Vigor) or Yellow wire for open. Repair as necessary.

4) Turn ignition off. Press brake pedal down. Check White/Green wire for continuity to ground. If continuity is present, go to next step. If continuity is not present, check fuse No. 32 (No. 30 on Vigor), brakelight switch, brakelight bulbs, brakelight failure sensor relay(s), ground circuit in trunk or White/Green wire for open. Repair as necessary.

5) Remove fuse No. 57 (No. 37 on Vigor). Open trunk lid. Check Green/Black wire for continuity to ground. If continuity is present, go to next step. If continuity is not present, check trunk latch switch, ground circuit in trunk or Green/Black wire for open. Repair as necessary.

6) On Legend, turn ignition on. Turn headlight switch on. Check for battery voltage between Red/Black and Red wires. If battery voltage exists, go to step **8)**. If battery voltage does not exist, check dash light dimmer control system, or for open circuit in Red/Black or Red wires. Repair as necessary.

7) On Vigor, turn ignition on and move ceiling lamp switch to middle position. Touch Black/White wire to ground. Ceiling lamp should come on. If ceiling lamp comes on, go to next step. If ceiling lamp does not come on, check for blown fuse No. 37, faulty ceiling lamp assembly or for open in Black/White wire. Repair as necessary.

8) On all models, turn ignition off. Remove fuse No. 57 (No. 37 on Vigor). Open left front door. Green/Blue wire should have continuity to ground. Open right front door. Green/Red wire should have continuity to ground. Open left rear door. Green/Yellow wire should have continuity to ground. Open right rear door. Green/White wire should have continuity to ground.

9) If continuity does not operate as described, check appropriate door switch or for open wire. Repair as necessary. If continuity was as described and safety indicator system still does not work, replace safety indicator unit.

TEMPERATURE GAUGE

1) Check for blown fuse No. 15 (Integra and Vigor) or No. 13 (Legend) in dash fuse block. Turn ignition off. Disconnect Yellow/Green wire (Red wire on Vigor) from sending unit. Sending unit is threaded into cylinder head. Using a jumper wire, ground sending unit wire.

2) Turn ignition on. Gauge needle should start moving toward "H" mark on gauge. Turn ignition off within 2 seconds or before gauge needle reaches "H" mark. Failure to turn ignition off before needle reaches "H" mark may result in damage to temperature gauge.

3) If temperature gauge needle does not move, check for open circuit in Yellow or Yellow/Green (Red on Vigor) wires. Replace temperature gauge if fuse and wiring are okay. If gauge is okay, check temperature sending unit.

TEMPERATURE SENDING UNIT

Disconnect Yellow/Green wire (Red wire on Vigor) from coolant temperature sending unit. Sending unit is threaded into cylinder head. With engine cold, measure resistance between sending unit terminal and ground. With engine warm, repeat resistance measurement. Resistance must be as specified in COOLANT TEMPERATURE SENDING UNIT RESISTANCE table.

COOLANT TEMPERATURE SENDING UNIT RESISTANCE

Temperature °F (°C)	Ohms
133 (56)	142
185-212 (85-100)	32-49

VEHICLE SPEED SENSOR (VSS)

Integra – 1) Verify fuse No. 24 in underdash fuse block is okay. Speed sensor is located on transaxle. Unplug 3-pin connector from speed sensor.

2) Turn ignition on. Check for voltage between Black and Black/Yellow wires. *See Fig. 24*. If battery voltage exists, go to step **5)**. If battery voltage does not exist, go to next step.

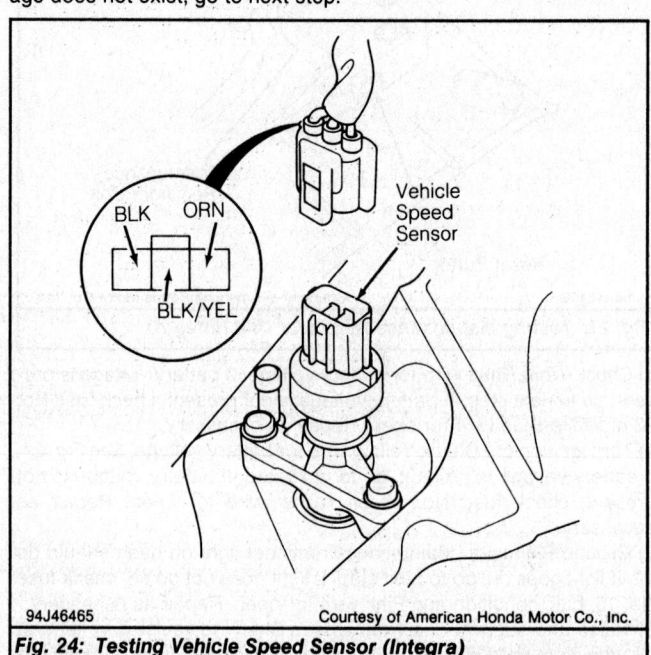

94J46465   Courtesy of American Honda Motor Co., Inc.
Fig. 24: Testing Vehicle Speed Sensor (Integra)

3) With ignition on, check for battery voltage between Black/Yellow wire and ground. If battery voltage exists, go to next step. If battery voltage does not exist, repair open in Black/Yellow wire between speed sensor and underdash fuse box.

4) Check for continuity between Black wire and ground. If continuity is present, go to next step. If continuity is not present, repair open between vehicle speed sensor and ground.

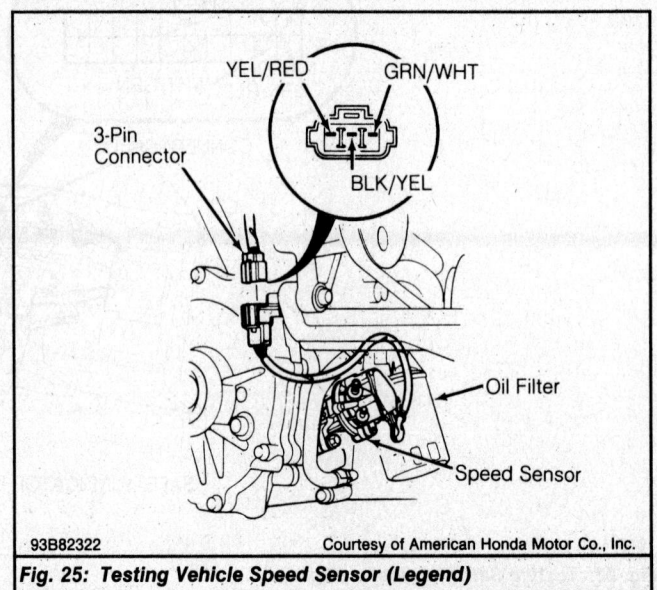

93B82322   Courtesy of American Honda Motor Co., Inc.
Fig. 25: Testing Vehicle Speed Sensor (Legend)

5) Measure voltage between Orange wire and ground. If voltage is about 5 volts, go to next step. If voltage is not about 5 volts, repair short to ground in Orange wire.

6) Reconnect wiring to speed sensor. Raise and support vehicle. Connect voltmeter between sensor connector Orange wire and ground. With ignition on and transaxle in Neutral, block one front wheel and slowly rotate other front wheel. If voltage does not pulse between zero and 10 volts, replace speed sensor.

Legend – 1) Verify fuse No. 22 in underdash fuse block is okay. Speed sensor is located next to oil filter. Unplug 3-pin connector from speed sensor.

2) Turn ignition on. Check for voltage between Green/White and Black/Yellow wires. *See Fig. 25.* If battery voltage exists, go to step **5).** If battery voltage does not exist, go to next step.

3) With ignition on, check for battery voltage between Black/Yellow wire and ground. If battery voltage exists, go to next step. If battery voltage does not exist, repair open in Black/Yellow wire between speed sensor and underdash fuse box.

4) Check for continuity between Black wire and ground. If continuity is present, go to next step. If continuity is not present, repair open between vehicle speed sensor and Powertrain Control Module (PCM) ground. PCM ground is located next to throttle body.

5) Measure voltage between Yellow/Red wire and ground. If voltage is about 5 volts, go to next step. If voltage is not about 5 volts, repair short to ground in Yellow/Red wire.

6) Reconnect wiring to speed sensor. Raise and support vehicle. Connect voltmeter between sensor connector Yellow/Red wire and ground. With ignition on and transaxle in Neutral, block one front wheel and slowly rotate other front wheel. If voltage does not pulse between zero and 5 volts, replace speed sensor.

Vigor – 1) Verify fuse No. 1 in underdash fuse block is okay. Speed sensor is located next to oil filter. Unplug 3-pin connector from speed sensor.

2) Check for continuity between Black wire and ground. If continuity exists, go to next step. If continuity does not exist, repair open between speed sensor and body ground.

3) With ignition on, measure voltage between Yellow wire and ground. If battery voltage exists, go to next step. If battery voltage does not exist, repair open in Yellow wire between speed sensor and underdash fuse block.

4) Measure voltage between Yellow/Red wire and ground. If voltage is about 5 volts, go to next step. If voltage is not about 5 volts, repair short to ground in Yellow/Red wire.

5) Reconnect wiring to speed sensor. Raise and support vehicle. Connect voltmeter between Orange wire of sensor connector and ground. With ignition on and transaxle in Neutral, block one front wheel and slowly rotate other front wheel. If voltage does not pulse between zero and 5 volts, replace speed sensor.

REMOVAL & INSTALLATION

INSTRUMENT CLUSTER

Removal & Installation (Integra) – Disconnect negative battery cable. Remove screws, instrument panel, and trim covers. Unplug switch connectors. Remove instrument cluster retaining screws. Pull instrument cluster to rear. Unplug instrument cluster connectors. Remove instrument cluster. To install, reverse removal procedure.

CAUTION: All models are equipped with Supplemental Restraint System (SRS). Disconnect negative and positive battery cables before removing instrument cluster. All SRS wiring has a Yellow cover. DO NOT use electrical test equipment on SRS circuits.

Removal & Installation (Legend & Vigor) – Disconnect battery cables. Remove lower cover. Remove upper and lower steering column covers. Remove 2 retaining screws and instrument panel trim cover. Unplug switch connectors. On Vigor, remove cruise control, foglight and rear window defogger switches. On all models, place protective cloth over combination switch. Remove 4 instrument cluster retaining screws. Pull cluster toward rear. Unplug connectors. Remove instrument cluster. To install, reverse removal procedure.

WIRING DIAGRAMS

NOTE: See ACCESSORIES & EQUIPMENT, Volume 5.

Integra, Legend, Vigor

DESCRIPTION & OPERATION

Power door locks are controlled by driver or front passenger switches which send signals to a control unit. The control unit sends appropriate signals to individual door lock actuators.

On Legend, a switch in the driver's door activates a solenoid which releases the trunk lid.

TROUBLE SHOOTING

CAUTION: All models are equipped with Supplemental Restraint System (SRS). SRS wiring harness is routed close to instrument cluster, steering wheel, and related components. All SRS wiring harnesses are covered by Yellow outer insulation. DO NOT use electrical test equipment on these circuits. Before working on steering column components, disable air bag system. See AIR BAG RESTRAINT SYSTEM article in ACCESSORIES & EQUIPMENT.

INTEGRA

System Does Not Work At All – Check fuse No. 6 in underdash fuse panel. Test control unit inputs. See CONTROL UNIT INPUTS under TESTING. Check for poor ground connections. Check White/Green wire between fuse panel and control unit.

No Passenger Door Lock Or Unlock With Driver's Switch – Test driver's door lock switch. See DOOR LOCK SWITCHES under TESTING. Test control unit inputs. See CONTROL UNIT INPUTS under TESTING. Check for poor ground connections. Check Green/Red and Green/White wires between driver's door switch and control unit. Check Blue/White wire between driver's door actuator and control unit.

One Or More Doors Does Not Lock Or Unlock With Driver's Switch – Test appropriate actuator. See ACTUATOR TEST under TESTING. Test driver's switch. Check White/Red and Yellow/Red wires between actuators and control unit.

No Door Locks Or Unlocks With Passenger's Switch – Test passenger's door switch. See DOOR LOCK SWITCHES under TESTING. Test control unit inputs. See CONTROL UNIT INPUTS under TESTING. Check for poor ground connections. Check Black/Red and Black/White wires between passenger's switch and control unit.

One or More Doors Does Not Lock Or Unlock With Passenger's Switch – Test appropriate actuator. See ACTUATOR TEST under TESTING. Check driver's door actuator and passenger's door actuator. Check White/Red and Yellow/Red wires between actuators and control unit.

No Door Locks Or Unlocks With Driver's Lock Knob – Check for problem with driver's door actuator linkage. Test driver's door switch. See DOOR LOCK SWITCHES under TESTING. Test control unit inputs. See CONTROL UNIT INPUTS under TESTING. Check for poor ground connections. Check Blue/Red and Blue/White wires between driver's door actuator and control unit.

One Or More Doors Do Not Lock Or Unlock With Driver's Lock Knob – Check driver's door actuator linkage. Test appropriate actuator. See ACTUATOR TEST under TESTING. Check actuator linkage. Test control unit inputs. See CONTROL UNIT INPUTS under TESTING. Check White/Red and Yellow/Red wires between actuators and control unit.

No Door Locks Or Unlocks With Passenger's Door Key – Test passenger's door key switch. See DOOR KEY SWITCH under TESTING. Test control unit inputs. See CONTROL UNIT INPUTS under TESTING. Check for poor ground connections. Check Light Green and Light Blue wires between passenger's door key switch and control unit.

One Or More Doors Do Not Lock Or Unlock With Passenger's Door Key – Check actuator linkage. Test appropriate actuator. See ACTUATOR TEST under TESTING. Check White/Red and Yellow/Red wires between actuators and control unit.

Driver's Door Doesn't Unlock With Driver's Door Key – Check actuator linkage. Test driver's door key switch. See DOOR KEY SWITCH under TESTING. Test driver's door lock switch. See DOOR LOCK SWITCHES under TESTING.

No Doors Unlock With Driver's Door Key – Test driver's door key switch. See DOOR KEY SWITCH under TESTING. Test control unit inputs. See CONTROL UNIT INPUTS under TESTING. Check for poor ground connections. Check Brown wire between driver's door key switch and control unit. Check White/Red and Yellow/Red wires between passenger door actuators and control unit.

LEGEND

System Does Not Work At All – Check fuse No. 44 in underhood fuse panel. Test control unit inputs. See CONTROL UNIT INPUTS under TESTING. Check for poor ground connections. Check White/Green wire between fuse panel and control unit.

No Door Locks Or Unlocks With Driver's Switch – Test driver's door lock switch. See DOOR LOCK SWITCHES under TESTING. Test control unit inputs. See CONTROL UNIT INPUTS under TESTING. Check for poor ground connections. Check Green/White and Green/Red wires between driver's door switch and control unit.

One Or More Doors Does Not Lock Or Unlock With Driver's Switch – Check appropriate actuator and linkage.

No Door Locks Or Unlocks With Passenger's Switch – Test passenger's door switch. See DOOR LOCK SWITCHES under TESTING. Test control unit inputs. See CONTROL UNIT INPUTS under TESTING. Check for poor ground connections. Check Black/Red and Black/White wires between passenger's door switch and control unit.

One or More Doors Does Not Lock Or Unlock With Passenger's Switch – Check appropriate actuator. Check White/Red and Yellow/Red wires between actuators and control unit. Test control unit inputs. See CONTROL UNIT INPUTS under TESTING.

No Door Locks Or Unlocks With Driver's Lock Knob – Test driver's door switch. See DOOR LOCK SWITCHES under TESTING. Test control unit inputs. See CONTROL UNIT INPUTS under TESTING. Check for poor ground connections. Check Green/Black and Blue/White wires between driver's door actuator and control unit.

One Or More Doors Do Not Lock Or Unlock With Driver's Lock Knob – Test appropriate actuator. See ACTUATOR TEST under TESTING. Check actuator linkage. Test control unit inputs. See CONTROL UNIT INPUTS under TESTING.

No Door Locks Or Unlocks With Passenger's Door Key – Test passenger's door key switch. See DOOR KEY SWITCH under TESTING. Test control unit inputs. See CONTROL UNIT INPUTS under TESTING. Check for poor ground connections. Check Green/Blue and Green/White wires between passenger's door key switch and control unit.

One Or More Doors Do Not Lock Or Unlock With Passenger's Door Key – Test appropriate actuator. See ACTUATOR TEST under TESTING. Check actuator linkage. Test control unit inputs. See CONTROL UNIT INPUTS under TESTING.

Driver's Door Doesn't Unlock With Driver's Door Key – Check actuator linkage.

No Doors Unlock With Driver's Door Key – Test driver's door key switch. See DOOR KEY SWITCH under TESTING. Test driver's door lock switch. See DOOR LOCK SWITCHES under TESTING. Check for poor ground connections. Check Green/Red wire between driver's door key switch and control unit. Check Green/Black wire between driver's door actuator and control unit.

Door Locks With Key Inserted And A Front Door Is Open – Check ignition switch. See STEERING COLUMN SWITCHES article. Test driver's and passenger's door switches. See DOOR LOCK SWITCHES under TESTING. Test control unit inputs. See CONTROL UNIT INPUTS under TESTING. Check for poor ground connections. Check Blue/White wire between ignition switch and control unit. Check Green/Blue wire between passenger's door key switch and control unit.

VIGOR

System Does Not Work At All – Check fuse No. 32 in underhood fuse panel. Test control unit inputs. See CONTROL UNIT INPUTS under TESTING. Check for poor ground connections. Check White wire between fuse panel and control unit.

No Doors Lock With Driver's Lock Knob – Check driver's door actuator linkage.

Passenger Doors Do Not Lock With Driver's Lock Knob – Check fuse No. 32 in underhood fuse panel. Test door lock switch in driver's door actuator. See ACTUATOR TEST under TESTING. Test control unit inputs. See CONTROL UNIT INPUTS under TESTING. Check for poor ground connections. Check Blue/White wire between driver's door actuator and control unit. Check Yellow/Red and White/Red wires between actuators and control unit.

One Or More Doors Do Not Lock With Driver's Lock Knob – Test passenger's door actuator. See ACTUATOR TEST under TESTING. Check Yellow/Red and White/Red wires between actuators and control unit.

No Doors Lock Or Unlock With Driver's Door Switch – Check fuse No. 32 in underhood fuse panel. Test driver's door lock switch. See DOOR LOCK SWITCHES under TESTING. Test control unit inputs. See CONTROL UNIT INPUTS under TESTING. Check for poor ground connections. Check Green/Red and Green/White wires between driver's door switch and control unit.

One Or More Doors Do Not Lock Or Unlock With Driver's Door Switch – Test passenger's door actuator. See ACTUATOR TEST under TESTING. Check Yellow/Red and White/Red wires between actuators and control unit.

No Doors Lock Or Unlock With Passenger's Door Switch – Check fuse No. 32 in underhood fuse panel. Test passenger's door lock switch. See DOOR LOCK SWITCHES under TESTING. Test control unit inputs. See CONTROL UNIT INPUTS under TESTING. Check for poor ground connections. Check actuator linkage. Check Black/Red and Black/White wires between driver's door switch and control unit. Check Yellow/Red and White/Red wires between actuators and control unit.

One Or More Doors Do Not Lock Or Unlock With Passenger's Door Switch – Test passenger's door actuator. See ACTUATOR TEST under TESTING. Check Yellow/Red and White/Red wires between actuators and control unit.

TESTING

CAUTION: All models are equipped with Supplemental Restraint System (SRS). SRS wiring harness is routed close to instrument cluster, steering wheel, and related components. All SRS wiring harnesses are covered by Yellow outer insulation. DO NOT use electrical test equipment on these circuits. Before working on steering column components, disable air bag system. See AIR BAG RESTRAINT SYSTEM article in ACCESSORIES & EQUIPMENT.

ACTUATOR TEST

CAUTION: To prevent damage to the actuator motor, apply power and ground only momentarily.

Integra (Driver's Door) – **1)** Remove door panel. Unplug connector. Using fused jumper wire, connect battery voltage to actuator connector terminal "D". Momentarily connect terminal "E" to ground. Actuator should move to lock position. *See Fig. 1.* Check for continuity between connector terminals "C" and "F". Continuity should exist.
2) Connect battery voltage to actuator connector terminal "E". Momentarily connect terminal "D" to ground. Actuator should move to unlock

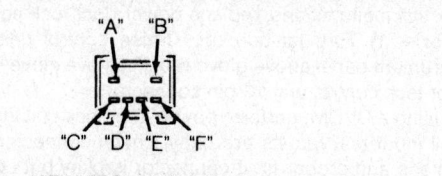

VIEW FROM WIRE SIDE

93B82462   Courtesy of American Honda Motor Co., Inc.

Fig. 1: Identifying Driver's Door Actuator Terminals (Integra)

position. Check for continuity between connector terminals "C" and "F". Continuity should not exist. Continuity should exist between terminals "B" and "C". Replace actuator if operation or continuity is not as specified.

Integra (Passenger's Door) – **1)** Remove door panel. Unplug connector. Using fused jumper wire, connect battery voltage to actuator connector terminal No. 1. Momentarily connect terminal No. 2 to ground. Actuator should move to unlock position. *See Fig. 2.*
2) Connect battery voltage to actuator connector terminal No. 2. Momentarily connect terminal No. 1 to ground. Actuator should move to lock position. Replace actuator if operation is not as specified.

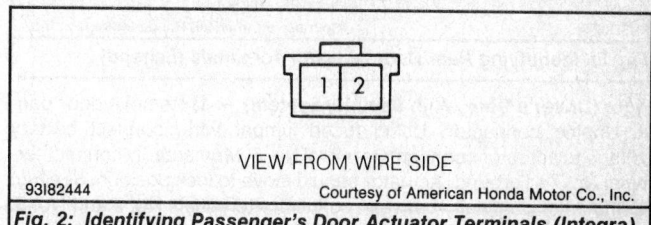

VIEW FROM WIRE SIDE

93I82444   Courtesy of American Honda Motor Co., Inc.

Fig. 2: Identifying Passenger's Door Actuator Terminals (Integra)

Legend (Driver's Door) – **1)** Remove door panel. Unplug connector. Using fused jumper wire, connect battery voltage to actuator connector terminal No. 2. Momentarily connect terminal No. 5 to ground. Actuator should move to lock position. *See Fig. 3.* Check for continuity between connector terminals No. 6 and No. 7. Continuity should exist. Check for continuity between connector terminals No. 3 and No. 6. Continuity should not exist.
2) Connect battery voltage to actuator connector terminal No. 5. Momentarily connect terminal No. 2 to ground. Actuator should move to unlock position. Check for continuity between connector terminals No. 6 and No. 7. Continuity should not exist. Check for continuity between connector terminals No. 3 and No. 6. Continuity should exist. Replace actuator if operation or continuity is not as specified.

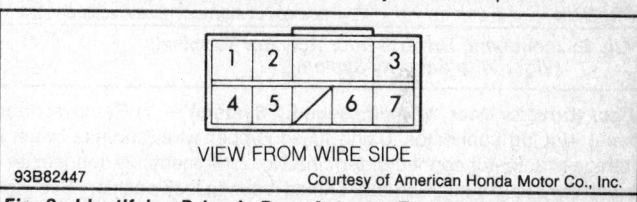

VIEW FROM WIRE SIDE

93B82447   Courtesy of American Honda Motor Co., Inc.

Fig. 3: Identifying Driver's Door Actuator Terminals (Legend)

Legend (Front Passenger's Door) – **1)** Remove door panel. Unplug connector. Using fused jumper wire, connect battery voltage to actuator connector terminal No. 2. Momentarily connect terminal No. 5 to ground. Actuator should move to lock position. *See Fig. 4.* Check for continuity between connector terminals No. 3 and No. 6. Continuity should not exist.
2) Connect battery voltage to actuator connector terminal No. 5. Momentarily connect terminal No. 2 to ground. Actuator should move to unlock position. Check for continuity between connector terminals No. 3 and No. 6. Continuity should not exist. Replace actuator if operation or continuity is not as specified.

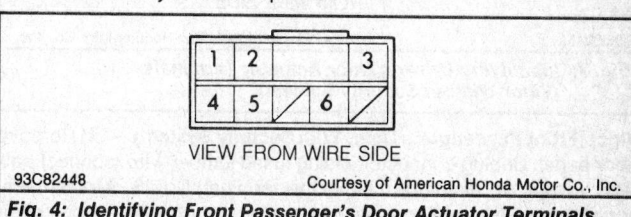

VIEW FROM WIRE SIDE

93C82448   Courtesy of American Honda Motor Co., Inc.

Fig. 4: Identifying Front Passenger's Door Actuator Terminals (Legend)

Legend (Rear Door) – **1)** Remove door panel. Unplug connector. Using fused jumper wire, connect battery voltage to actuator connector terminal No. 5. Momentarily connect terminal No. 4 to ground. Actuator should move to lock position. *See Fig. 5.* Check for continuity between connector terminals No. 2 and No. 6. Continuity should not exist.

2) Connect battery voltage to actuator connector terminal No. 4. Momentarily connect terminal No. 5 to ground. Actuator should move to unlock position. Check for continuity between connector terminals No. 2 and No. 6. Continuity should exist. Replace actuator if operation or continuity is not as specified.

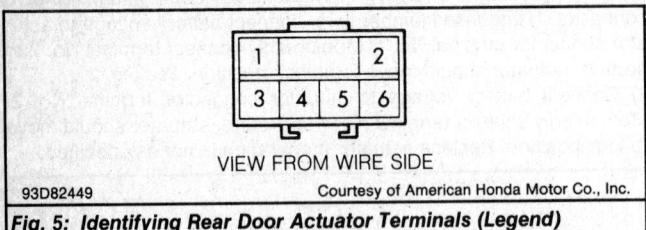

VIEW FROM WIRE SIDE

93D82449   Courtesy of American Honda Motor Co., Inc.

Fig. 5: Identifying Rear Door Actuator Terminals (Legend)

Vigor (Driver's Door, With Security System) – 1) Remove door panel. Unplug connector. Using fused jumper wire, connect battery voltage to actuator connector terminal No. 6. Momentarily connect terminal No. 7 to ground. Actuator should move to lock position. *See Fig. 6.* Check for continuity between connector terminals No. 5 and No. 8. Continuity should exist. Check for continuity between connector terminals No. 4 and No. 5. Continuity should not exist.

2) Connect battery voltage to actuator connector terminal No. 7. Momentarily connect terminal No. 6 to ground. Actuator should move to unlock position. Check for continuity between connector terminals No. 5 and No. 8. Continuity should not exist. Check for continuity between connector terminals No. 4 and No. 5. Continuity should exist. Replace actuator if operation or continuity is not as specified.

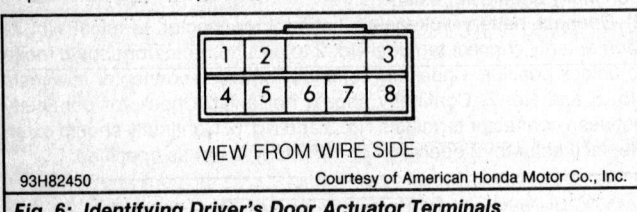

VIEW FROM WIRE SIDE

93H82450   Courtesy of American Honda Motor Co., Inc.

**Fig. 6: Identifying Driver's Door Actuator Terminals
(Vigor With Security System)**

Vigor (Driver's Door, Without Security System) – 1) Remove door panel. Unplug connector. Using fused jumper wire, connect battery voltage to actuator connector terminal No. 2. Momentarily connect terminal No. 3 to ground. Actuator should move to lock position. *See Fig. 7.* Check for continuity between connector terminals No. 1 and No. 4. Continuity should exist.

2) Connect battery voltage to actuator connector terminal No. 3. Momentarily connect terminal No. 2 to ground. Actuator should move to unlock position. Check for continuity between connector terminals No. 1 and No. 4. Continuity should not exist. Replace actuator if operation or continuity is not as specified.

VIEW FROM WIRE SIDE

93I82451   Courtesy of American Honda Motor Co., Inc.

**Fig. 7: Identifying Driver's Door Actuator Terminals
(Vigor Without Security System)**

Vigor (Front Passenger's Door, With Security System) – 1) Remove door panel. Unplug connector. Using fused jumper wire, connect battery voltage to actuator connector terminal No. 6. Momentarily connect terminal No. 7 to ground. Actuator should move to lock position. *See Fig. 8.*

2) Connect battery voltage to actuator connector terminal No. 7. Momentarily connect terminal No. 6 to ground. Actuator should move to unlock position. Replace actuator if operation is not as specified.

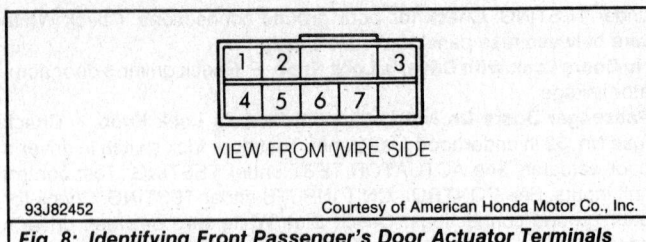

VIEW FROM WIRE SIDE

93J82452   Courtesy of American Honda Motor Co., Inc.

**Fig. 8: Identifying Front Passenger's Door Actuator Terminals
(Vigor With Security System)**

Vigor (Front Passenger's Door, Without Security System) – 1) Remove door panel. Unplug connector. Using fused jumper wire, connect battery voltage to actuator connector terminal No. 1. Momentarily connect terminal No. 2 to ground. Actuator should move to lock position. *See Fig. 9.*

2) Connect battery voltage to actuator connector terminal No. 2. Momentarily connect terminal No. 1 to ground. Actuator should move to unlock position. Replace actuator if operation is not as specified.

VIEW FROM WIRE SIDE

93A82453   Courtesy of American Honda Motor Co., Inc.

**Fig. 9: Identifying Front Passenger's Door Actuator Terminals
(Vigor Without Security System)**

Vigor (Rear Door) – 1) Remove door panel. Unplug connector. Using fused jumper wire, connect battery voltage to actuator connector terminal No. 3. Momentarily connect terminal No. 4 to ground. Actuator should move to lock position. *See Fig. 10.*

2) Connect battery voltage to actuator connector terminal No. 4. Momentarily connect terminal No. 3 to ground. Actuator should move to unlock position. Replace actuator if operation is not as specified.

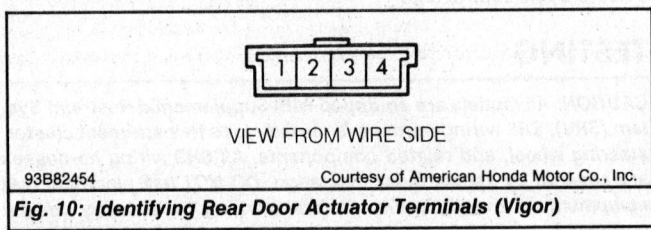

VIEW FROM WIRE SIDE

93B82454   Courtesy of American Honda Motor Co., Inc.

Fig. 10: Identifying Rear Door Actuator Terminals (Vigor)

CONTROL UNIT INPUTS

Integra – 1) Turn ignition off. Remove driver's door panel. Power door lock control unit is located in driver's door. Unplug power door lock unit 14-pin connector.

2) Using a DVOM, perform power door lock unit input tests in *Fig. 11.* If all input test results are okay, inspect connector and terminals for damage and proper fit. If connector is okay and power door lock still malfunctions, replace power door lock control unit.

Legend – 1) Power door lock control unit is located under instrument panel, to right of steering column. Turn ignition off. Remove instrument panel lower cover. Unplug control unit 18-pin connector.

2) Using a DVOM, perform power door lock control unit input tests in *Fig. 12.* If all input test results are okay, inspect connector and terminals for damage and proper fit. If connector is okay but power door lock still malfunctions, replace power door lock control unit.

Vigor – 1) Turn ignition off. Cruise control unit is located under instrument panel above glove box. Remove glove box. Unplug power door lock control unit 12-pin connector.

2) Using a DVOM, perform power door lock unit input tests in *Fig. 13.* If all input test results are okay, check connector and terminals for damage and proper fit. If connector is okay but power door lock still malfunctions, replace power door lock control unit.

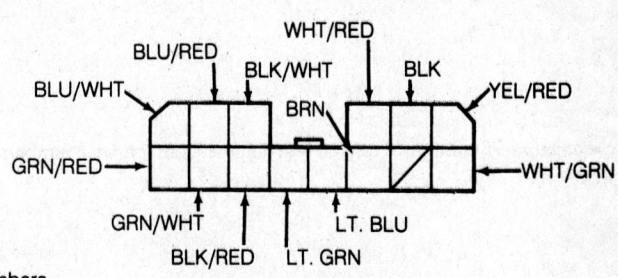

VIEW FROM WIRE SIDE

• Numbers 1 through 8 refer to test numbers, not terminal numbers.

DISCONNECT THE 14-PIN CONNECTOR FROM THE POWER DOOR LOCK CONTROL UNIT.

No.	Wire	Test condition	Test: Desired result	Possible cause if result is not obtained
1	BLK	Under all conditions	Check for continuity to ground: There should be continuity.	• Poor ground • An open in the wire
2	WHT/RED and YEL/RED	Connect the YEL/RED terminal to the WHT/GRN terminal, and the WHT/RED terminal to the BLK terminal momentarily.	Check door lock operation: All doors should unlock.	• Faulty actuator • An open in the wire • Blown No. 6 (20 A) fuse in the under-dash fuse/relay box
		Connect the WHT/RED terminal to the WHT/GRN terminal, and the YEL/RED terminal to the BLK terminal momentarily.	Check door lock operation: All doors should lock.	

RECONNECT THE 14-PIN CONNECTOR TO THE POWER DOOR LOCK CONTROL UNIT.

No.	Wire	Test condition	Test: Desired result	Possible cause if result is not obtained
3	WHT/GRN	Under all conditions	Check for voltage to ground: There should be battery voltage.	• Blown No. 6 (20 A) fuse in the under-dash fuse/relay box • An open in the wire
4	GRN/WHT	Driver's door lock switch in LOCK	Check for voltage to ground: There should be 1 V or less.	• Faulty driver's door lock switch • Poor ground • An open in the wire
	GRN/RED	Driver's door lock switch in UNLOCK		
5	BLK/WHT	Right front door lock switch in LOCK	Check for voltage to ground: There should be 1 V or less.	• Faulty front passenger's door lock switch • Poor ground • An open in the wire
	BLK/RED	Right front door lock switch in UNLOCK		
6	BLU/WHT	Driver's door lock knob in LOCK	Check for voltage to ground: There should be 1 V or less.	• Faulty driver's door lock actuator • Poor ground • An open in the wire
	BLU/RED	Driver's door lock knob in UNLOCK		
7	BRN	Driver's door key cylinder in UNLOCK	Check for voltage to ground: There should be 1 V or less as the switch is turned.	• Faulty driver's door key cylinder switch • Poor ground • An open in the wire
8	LT BLU	Front passenger's door key cylinder in LOCK	Check for voltage to ground: There should be 1 V or less as the switch is turned.	• Faulty front passenger's door cylinder switch • Poor ground • An open in the wire
	LT GRN	Front passenger's door key cylinder in UNLOCK		

Fig. 11: Power Door Locks Control Unit Input Test (Integra)

- Numbers 1 through 10 refer to test numbers, not terminal numbers.

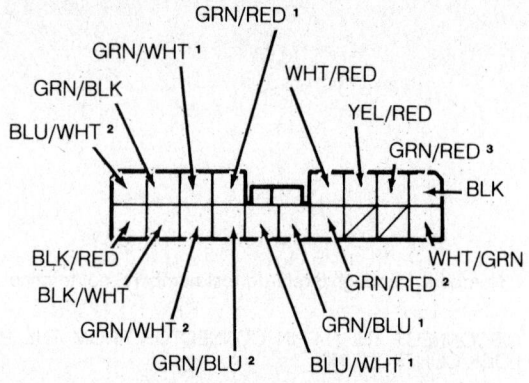

VIEW FROM WIRE SIDE

No.	Wire	Test condition	Test: Desired result	Possible cause if result is not obtained
1	BLK	Under all conditions	Check for continuity to ground: There should be continuity.	• Poor ground • An open in the wire
2	WHT/GRN	Under all conditions	Check for voltage to ground: There should be battery voltage.	• Blown No. 44 (20 A) fuse (in the under-hood fuse/relay box) • An open in the wire
3	GRN/WHT¹	Driver's door lock switch in LOCK	Check for voltage to ground: It should go from battery voltage to 1 V or less.	• Faulty driver's door lock switch • Poor ground • An open in the wire • Short to ground
	GRN/RED¹	Driver's door lock switch in UNLOCK		
4	BLK/WHT	Right front door lock switch in LOCK	Check for voltage to ground: It should go from battery voltage to 1 V or less.	• Faulty right front door lock switch • Poor ground • An open in the wire • Short to ground
	BLK/RED	Right front door lock switch in UNLOCK		
5	BLU/WHT²	Driver's door lock knob in LOCK	Check for voltage to ground: It should go from battery voltage to 1 V or less.	• Faulty driver's door lock actuator • Poor ground • An open in the wire • Short to ground
	GRN/BLK	Driver's door lock knob in UNLOCK		
6	GRN/BLU¹	Driver's door open	Check for voltage to ground: It should go from battery voltage to 1 V or less.	• Faulty door switch • Poor ground • An open in the wire
	GRN/RED²	Right front door open		
7	BLU/WHT	Ignition key inserted into the ignition switch	Check for voltage to ground: It should go from battery voltage to 1 V or less.	• Faulty ignition key switch • Poor ground • An open in the wire
8	GRN/RED³	Driver' door key cylinder in UNLOCK	Check for voltage to ground: It should go from battery voltage to 1 V or less.	• Faulty driver's door key cylinder • Poor ground • An open in the wire
9	GRN/WHT²	Right front door key cylinder in LOCK	Check for voltage to ground: It should go from battery voltage to 1 V or less.	• Faulty right fron door key cylinder • Poor ground • An open in the wire
	GRN/BLU²	Right front door key cylinder in UNLOCK		
10	WHT/RED and YEL/RED	Connect the YEL/RED terminal to the WHT/GRN terminal, and the WHT/RED terminal to the BLK terminal momentarily.	Check door lock operation: All doors should unlock as the battery is connected momentarily.	• Faulty actuator • An open in the wire
		Connect the WHT/RED terminal to the WHT/GRN terminal, and the YEL/RED terminal to the BLK terminal momentarily.	Check door lock operation: All doors should lock as the battery is connected momentarily.	

- Numbers 1 through 8 refer to test numbers, not terminal numbers.

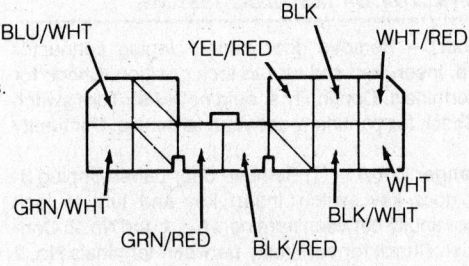

VIEW FROM WIRE SIDE

No.	Terminal	Test condition	Test: Desired result	Possible cause if result is not obtained
1	BLK	Under all conditions.	Check for continuity to ground: There should be continuity.	• Poor ground • An open in the wire.
2	WHT	Under all conditions.	Check for voltage to ground: There should be continuity.	• Blown No. 32 (20 A) fuse (in the under-hood fuse/relay box). • An open in the wire.
3	GRN/WHT	Move the driver's power door lock switch from the neutral position to LOCK.	Check for voltage to ground: There should be less than 1V.	• Faulty driver's power door lock switch. • Poor ground • An open in the wire. • Short to ground. • Faulty control unit.
4	GRN/RED	Move the driver's power door lock switch from the neutral position to UNLOCK.		
5	BLK/RED	Move the front passenger's power door lock switch from the neutral position to LOCK.	Check for voltage to ground: There should be less than 1V.	• Faulty front passenger's power door lock switch. • Poor ground • An open in the wire. • Short to ground. • Faulty control unit.
6	BLK/RED	Move the front passenger's power door lock switch from the neutral position to UNLOCK.		
7	BLU/WHT	Driver's door lock knob in LOCK.	Check for voltage to ground: There should be less than 1V.	• Faulty driver's door actuator. • Poor ground • An open in the wire.
		Driver's door lock knob in UNLOCK.	Check for voltage to ground: There should be battery voltage.	• Faulty driver's door actuator. • Short to ground. • Faulty control unit.
8	WHT/RED or YEL/RED	Connect the WHT terminal to the WHT/RED terminal, and the YEL/RED terminal to the BLK terminal momentarily.	Check door lock operation: All doors should lock as the battery is connected momentarily.	• Faulty passenger's door actuator. • Faulty driver's door actuator. • An open in the wire.
		Connect the WHT terminal to the YEL/RED terminal, and the WHT/RED terminal to the BLK terminal momentarily.	Check door unclok operation: All doors should unlock as the battery is connected memenmentarily.	

94B46582 93F82458

Fig. 13: Power Door Locks Control Unit Input Test (Vigor)

DOOR KEY SWITCH

NOTE: To test door lock key switches on other applications, see appropriate model in ACTUATOR TEST under TESTING.

Integra (Driver's Door) – Remove door panel. Unplug connector from door key switch. Insert key and turn to lock position. Check for continuity between terminals. Continuity should not exist. Turn switch to unlock position. Check for continuity between terminals. Continuity should exist.

Integra (Front Passenger Door) – 1) Remove door panel. Unplug 3-pin connector from door key switch. Insert key and turn to lock position. Check for continuity between terminals No. 1 and No. 2. Continuity should not exist. Check for continuity between terminals No. 2 and No. 3. Continuity should exist. *See Fig. 14.*

2) Turn switch to unlock position. Check for continuity between terminals No. 1 and No. 2. Continuity should exist. Check for continuity between terminals No. 2 and No. 3. Continuity should not exist.

Legend – 1) Remove door panel. Unplug 3-pin connector from actuator. Set switch to lock position. Check for continuity between terminals No. 1 and No. 2. Continuity should not exist. Check for continuity between terminals No. 2 and No. 3. Continuity should exist. *See Fig. 14.*

2) Set switch to unlock position. Check for continuity between terminals No. 1 and No. 2. Continuity should exist. Check for continuity between terminals No. 2 and No. 3. Continuity should not exist.

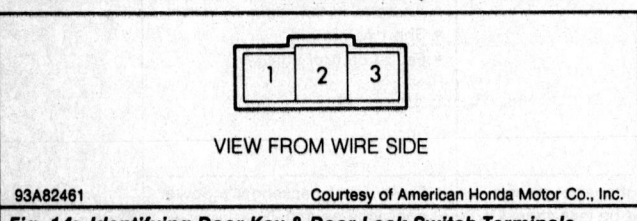

VIEW FROM WIRE SIDE

93A82461   Courtesy of American Honda Motor Co., Inc.

Fig. 14: Identifying Door Key & Door Lock Switch Terminals (Integra & Legend)

DOOR LOCK SWITCHES

Integra – 1) Remove trim plate. Unplug connector. Set switch to unlock position. Check for continuity between terminals No. 1 and 2. Continuity should not exist. Check for continuity between terminals No. 2 and No. 3. Continuity should exist. *See Fig. 14.*

2) Set switch to off position. Check for continuity between terminals No. 1 and 2. Continuity should not exist. Check for continuity between terminals No. 2 and No. 3. Continuity should not exist.

3) Set switch to lock position. Check for continuity between terminals No. 1 and 2. Continuity should exist. Check for continuity between terminals No. 2 and No. 3. Continuity should not exist. Replace switch if continuity is not as specified.

Legend – 1) Remove trim plate. Unplug connector. Set switch to unlock position. Check for continuity between terminals No. 1 and 2. Continuity should exist. Check for continuity between terminals No. 2 and No. 3. Continuity should not exist. *See Fig. 14.*

2) Set switch to off position. Check for continuity between terminals No. 1 and 2. Continuity should not exist. Check for continuity between terminals No. 2 and No. 3. Continuity should not exist.

3) Set switch to lock position. Check for continuity between terminals No. 1 and 2. Continuity should not exist. Check for continuity between terminals No. 2 and No. 3. Continuity should exist. Replace switch if continuity is not as specified.

Vigor – 1) Remove trim plate. Unplug connector. Set switch to unlock position. Check for continuity between terminals No. 1 and 2. Continuity should exist. Check for continuity between terminals No. 2 and No. 3. Continuity should not exist. *See Fig. 15.*

2) Set switch to off position. Check for continuity between terminals No. 1 and 2. Continuity should not exist. Check for continuity between terminals No. 2 and No. 3. Continuity should not exist.

3) Set switch to lock position. Check for continuity between terminals No. 1 and 2. Continuity should not exist. Check for continuity between terminals No. 2 and No. 3. Continuity should exist. Replace switch if continuity is not as specified.

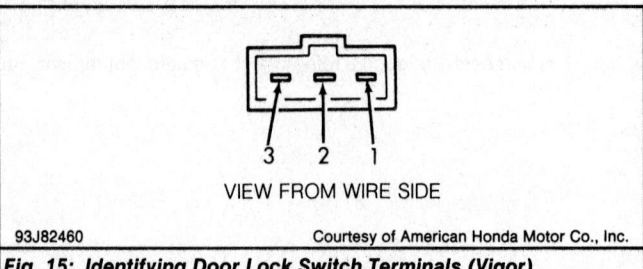

VIEW FROM WIRE SIDE

93J82460   Courtesy of American Honda Motor Co., Inc.

Fig. 15: Identifying Door Lock Switch Terminals (Vigor)

TRUNK RELEASE SOLENOID TEST

Legend – Remove trunk inner trim panel. Unplug solenoid connector. Using fused jumper wire, connect battery voltage to solenoid connector terminal "C". *See Fig. 16.* Connect terminal "D" to ground. Replace solenoid if it doesn't operate.

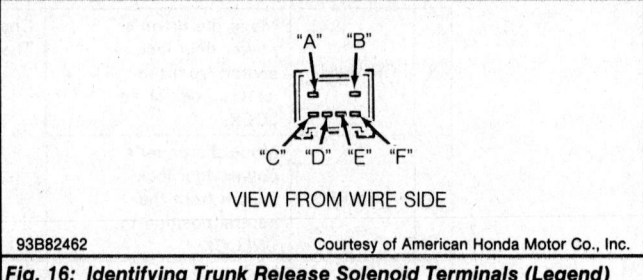

VIEW FROM WIRE SIDE

93B82462   Courtesy of American Honda Motor Co., Inc.

Fig. 16: Identifying Trunk Release Solenoid Terminals (Legend)

REMOVAL & INSTALLATION

CAUTION: When battery is disconnected, vehicle computer and memory systems may lose memory data. Driveability problems may exist until computer systems have completed a relearn cycle.

ACTUATORS

Removal & Installation – Remove inner panel. Remove plastic cover. Remove rear channel if necessary. Disconnect linkage. Unplug connector. Remove mounting screws and actuator. To install, reverse removal procedure.

CONTROL UNIT

Removal & Installation (Integra) – Power door lock control unit is located inside driver's door. Turn ignition off. Remove door panel. Unplug connector. Remove mounting screws and control unit. To install, reverse removal procedure.

Removal & Installation (Legend) – Power door lock unit is located under instrument panel, to right of steering column. Turn ignition off. Remove instrument panel lower cover. Unplug connector. Remove mounting screws and control unit. To install, reverse removal procedure.

Removal & Installation (Vigor) – Cruise control unit is located under instrument panel above glove box. Turn ignition off. Remove glove box. Unplug connector. Remove mounting screws and control unit. To install, reverse removal procedure.

DOOR LOCK SWITCHES

Removal & Installation – Remove trim plate. Unplug connector. Remove switch from trim plate. To install, reverse removal procedure.

WIRING DIAGRAMS

NOTE: See ACCESSORIES & EQUIPMENT, Volume 5.

Integra, Legend, Vigor

DESCRIPTION & OPERATION

Power mirrors are controlled by dual control switch located on driver's door panel or instrument panel. The left/right switch directs current to desired mirror. The up/down and left/right switch directs current to one of 2 motors located in the mirror/motor assembly. Mirror and motors are serviced as an assembly.

Legend and Vigor mirrors are equipped with defoggers which are controlled by a switch on the mirror control panel.

TESTING

POWER MIRROR FUNCTION TEST (INTEGRA)

Both Mirrors Inoperative – 1) Check fuse No. 13 in underdash fuse panel. Replace as necessary. Remove power mirror switch. See POWER MIRROR SWITCH under REMOVAL & INSTALLATION.

2) Turn ignition on. Check for voltage between Black/Yellow wire and ground. *See Fig. 1.* If battery voltage exists, go to next step. If battery voltage does not exist, repair open Black/Yellow wire between mirror switch and fuse box.

3) Check for continuity between Black wire and ground. If continuity does not exist, repair open circuit in Black wire or poor ground connection. If wiring is okay, substitute known good switch and retest.

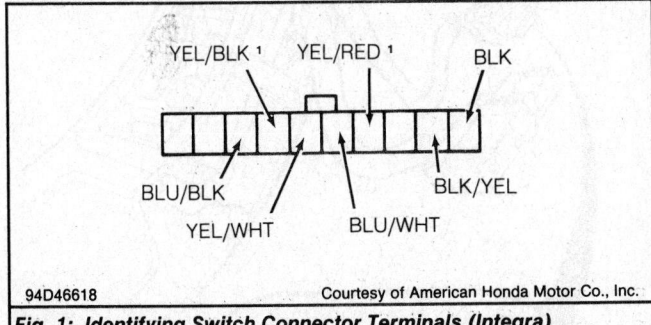

94D46618   Courtesy of American Honda Motor Co., Inc.

Fig. 1: Identifying Switch Connector Terminals (Integra)

Left Mirror Inoperative – 1) Remove power mirror switch. See POWER MIRROR SWITCH under REMOVAL & INSTALLATION. Turn ignition on. Using jumper wires, connect Black/Yellow wire to Yellow/Red wire, and either the Yellow/White or Yellow/Black wire to ground.

2) If mirror does not tilt down (or swing left), check for open in Yellow/White or Yellow/Black wire between mirror switch and mirror. If mirror doesn't move at all, check Yellow/Red wire. If wiring is okay, test mirror motor. See POWER MIRROR MOTOR TEST. If mirror operates correctly, test mirror switch. See POWER MIRROR SWITCH TEST.

Right Mirror Inoperative – 1) Remove power mirror switch. See POWER MIRROR SWITCH under REMOVAL & INSTALLATION. Turn ignition on. Using jumper wires, connect Black/Yellow wire to Blue/White wire, and either the Yellow/White or Blue/Black wire to ground.

2) If mirror does not tilt down (or swing left), check for open in Yellow/White or Blue/Black wire between mirror switch and mirror. If mirror doesn't move at all, check Blue/White wire. If wiring is okay, test mirror motor. See POWER MIRROR MOTOR TEST. If mirror operates correctly, test mirror switch. See POWER MIRROR SWITCH TEST.

POWER MIRROR FUNCTION TEST (LEGEND)

Both Mirrors Inoperative – 1) Check fuse No. 19 in underdash fuse panel. Replace as necessary. Remove power mirror switch. See POWER MIRROR SWITCH under REMOVAL & INSTALLATION.

2) Turn ignition on. Check for voltage between Black/Yellow[2] wire and ground. *See Fig. 2.* If battery voltage exists, go to next step. If battery voltage does not exist, repair open Black/Yellow[2] wire between mirror switch and fuse box.

3) Check for continuity between Black wire and ground. If continuity does not exist, repair open circuit in Black wire or poor ground connection. If wiring is okay, substitute known good switch and retest.

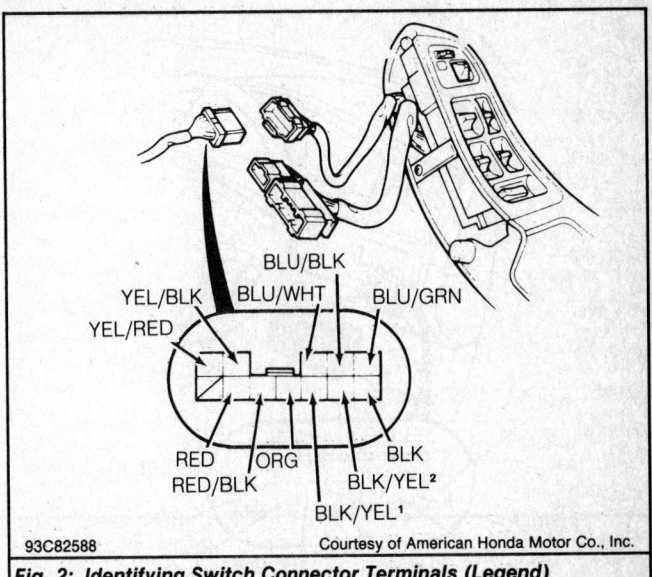

93C82588   Courtesy of American Honda Motor Co., Inc.

Fig. 2: Identifying Switch Connector Terminals (Legend)

Left Mirror Inoperative – 1) Remove power mirror switch. See POWER MIRROR SWITCH under REMOVAL & INSTALLATION. Using jumper wires, connect Black/Yellow[2] wire to Blue/Green wire, and either the Blue/White or Blue/Black wire to ground. Turn ignition on for 2 seconds, then off.

2) If mirror does not tilt down (or swing left), check for open in Blue/White or Blue/Black wire between mirror switch and mirror. If mirror doesn't move at all, check Blue/Green wire. If wiring is okay, test mirror motor. See POWER MIRROR MOTOR TEST. If mirror operates correctly, test switch. See POWER MIRROR SWITCH TEST.

Right Mirror Inoperative – 1) Remove power mirror switch. See POWER MIRROR SWITCH under REMOVAL & INSTALLATION. Using jumper wires, connect Black/Yellow[2] wire to Yellow/Red wire, and either the Blue/White or Yellow/Black wire to ground. Turn ignition on for 2 seconds, then off.

2) If mirror does not tilt down (or swing left), check for open in Blue/White or Yellow/Black wire between mirror switch and mirror. If mirror doesn't move at all, check Yellow/Red wire. If wiring is okay, test mirror motor. See POWER MIRROR MOTOR TEST. If mirror operates correctly, test switch. See POWER MIRROR SWITCH TEST.

POWER MIRROR FUNCTION TEST (VIGOR)

Both Mirrors Inoperative – 1) Check fuse No. 8 in underdash fuse panel. Replace as necessary. Remove power mirror switch. See POWER MIRROR SWITCH under REMOVAL & INSTALLATION.

2) Turn ignition on. Check for voltage between Yellow/Black[1] wire and ground. *See Fig. 3.* If battery voltage exists, go to next step. If battery voltage does not exist, repair open Yellow/Black[1] wire between mirror switch and fuse box.

3) Check for continuity between Black wire and ground. If continuity does not exist, repair open circuit in Black wire or poor ground connection. If wiring is okay, substitute known good switch and retest.

Left Mirror Inoperative – 1) Remove power mirror switch. See POWER MIRROR SWITCH under REMOVAL & INSTALLATION. Turn ignition on. Using jumper wires, connect Yellow/Black[1] wire to Yellow/Black[2] wire, and either the Blue/White or Yellow/Red wire to ground.

2) If mirror does not tilt down (or swing left), check for open in Blue/White or Yellow/Red wire between mirror switch and mirror. If mirror doesn't move at all, check Yellow/Black[2] wire. If wiring is okay, test mirror motor. See POWER MIRROR MOTOR TEST. If mirror operates correctly, test mirror switch. See POWER MIRROR SWITCH TEST.

Right Mirror Inoperative – 1) Remove power mirror switch. See POWER MIRROR SWITCH under REMOVAL & INSTALLATION. Turn ignition on. Using jumper wires, connect Yellow/Black[1] wire to Blue/Black wire, and either the Blue/White or Blue/Green wire to ground.

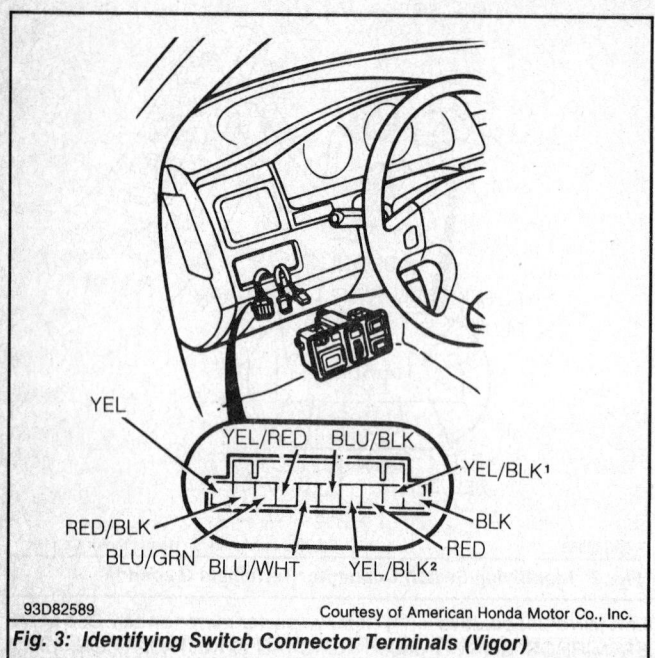

Fig. 3: Identifying Switch Connector Terminals (Vigor)

2) If mirror does not tilt down (or swing left), check for open in Blue/White or Blue/Green wire between mirror switch and mirror. If mirror doesn't move at all, check Blue/Black wire. If wiring is okay, test mirror motor. See POWER MIRROR MOTOR TEST. If mirror operates correctly, test mirror switch. See POWER MIRROR SWITCH TEST.

POWER MIRROR SWITCH TEST

Remove power mirror switch. See POWER MIRROR SWITCH under REMOVAL & INSTALLATION. Check for continuity between specified switch terminals with switch in each position. If continuity is not as specified, replace switch. See Fig. 4, 5, or 6. See appropriate POWER MIRROR SWITCH CONTINUITY TEST table.

POWER MIRROR SWITCH CONTINUITY TEST (INTEGRA)

Application	Terminal Numbers
Right Mirror	
Off	3-5-6-10
Up	3-6-10; 5-9
Down	3-6-9; 5-9
Left	3-10; 5-6-9
Right	3-9; 5-6-10
Left Mirror	
Off	4-5-7-10
Up	4-7-10; 5-9
Down	4-7-9; 5-10
Left	4-10; 5-7-9
Right	4-9; 5-7-10

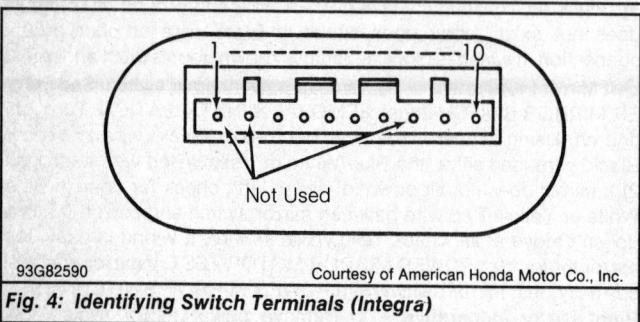

Fig. 4: Identifying Switch Terminals (Integra)

POWER MIRROR SWITCH CONTINUITY TEST (LEGEND)

Application	Terminal Number
Motor Switch	
Right Mirror	
Off	3-4-5-6
Up	3-7
Down	4-7; 5-7
Left	3-5-7
Right	4-7
Left Mirror	
Off	1-2-3-6
Up	3-7
Down	1-2-7
Left	1-3-7
Right	2-7
Defogger Switch	
On	[1] 6-8-9
Off	No Continuity

[1] – If continuity does not exist between terminals No. 6 and No. 8, replace bulb before condemning switch as defective.

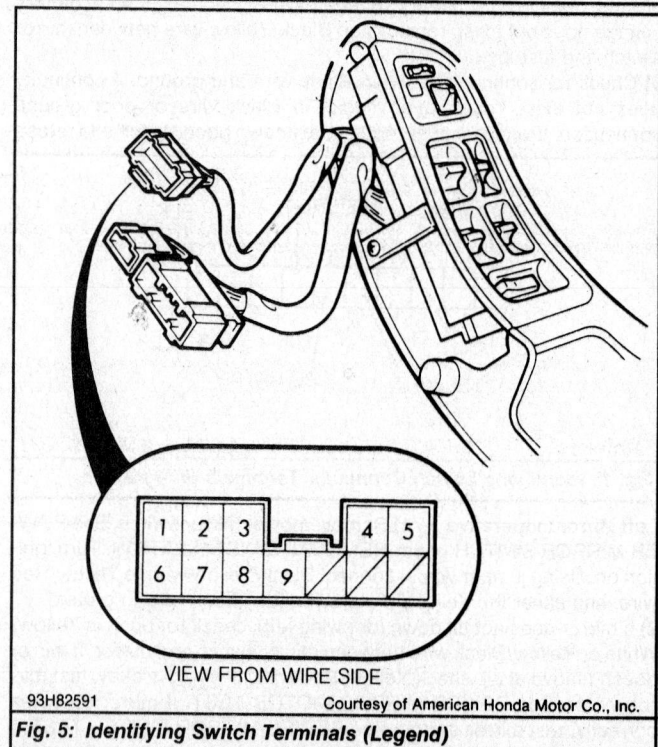

VIEW FROM WIRE SIDE

Fig. 5: Identifying Switch Terminals (Legend)

POWER MIRROR SWITCH CONTINUITY TEST (VIGOR)

Application	Terminal Numbers
Motor Switch	
Right Mirror	
Off	3-5-6-10
Up	3-6-10; 5-9
Down	3-6-9; 5-10
Left	5-6-9; 3-10
Right	3-9
Left Mirror	
Off	4-5-7-10
Up	5-9; 4-7-10
Down	4-7-9; 5-10
Left	5-7-9
Right	4-9; 5-7-10
Defogger Switch	
On	[1] 1-9-10
Off	[1] 9-10

[1] – If continuity does not exist between terminals No. 9 and No. 10, replace bulb before condemning switch as defective.

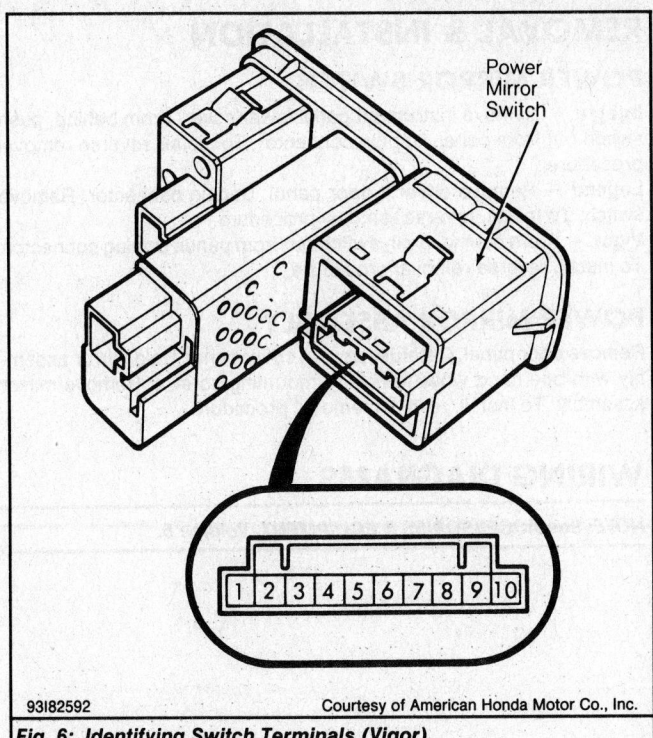

Fig. 6: Identifying Switch Terminals (Vigor)

MIRROR DEFOGGER SWITCH TEST

Legend & Vigor – See appropriate POWER MIRROR SWITCH CONTINUITY TEST table.

MIRROR DEFOGGER ELEMENT TEST

See POWER MIRROR MOTOR TEST.

POWER MIRROR MOTOR TEST

Integra – Remove door panel. Unplug connector. Using fused jumper wires, connect specified motor terminals to battery voltage and ground. *See Fig. 7.* Replace motor assembly if operation is not as specified. See POWER MIRROR MOTOR TEST (INTEGRA) table.

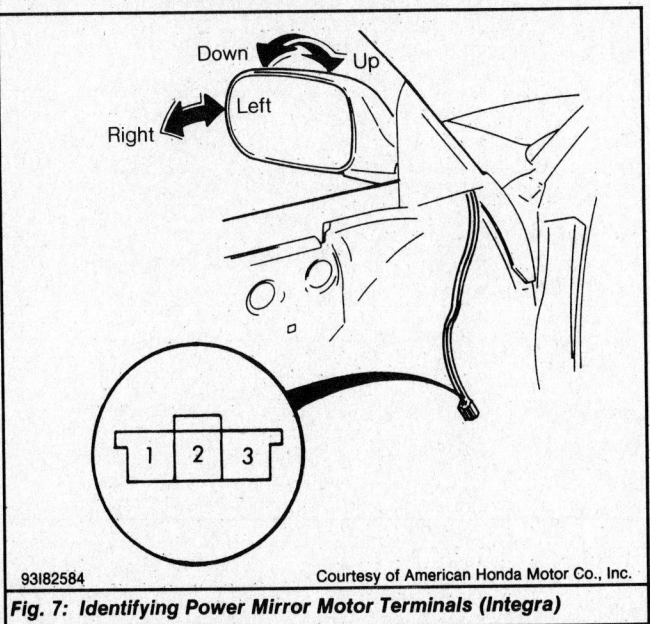

Fig. 7: Identifying Power Mirror Motor Terminals (Integra)

POWER MIRROR MOTOR TEST (INTEGRA)

Apply 12 Volts To Pin	Ground Pin	Mirror Operation
Hatchback		
3	2	Up
2	3	Down
2	1	Left
1	2	Right
Sedan		
1	2	Up
2	1	Down
2	3	Left
3	2	Right

Legend – Remove cover panel. Unplug connector. Using fused jumper wires, connect specified terminals to battery voltage and ground. *See Fig. 8 or 9.* Replace motor assembly if operation is not as specified. See POWER MIRROR MOTOR TEST (LEGEND) table.

POWER MIRROR MOTOR TEST (LEGEND)

Apply 12 Volts To Pin	Ground Pin	Mirror Operation
Coupe		
6	5	Up
5	6	Down
5	4	Left
4	5	Right
2	3	Defogger On
Sedan		
8	7	Up
7	8	Down
7	6	Left
6	7	Right
3	4	Defogger On

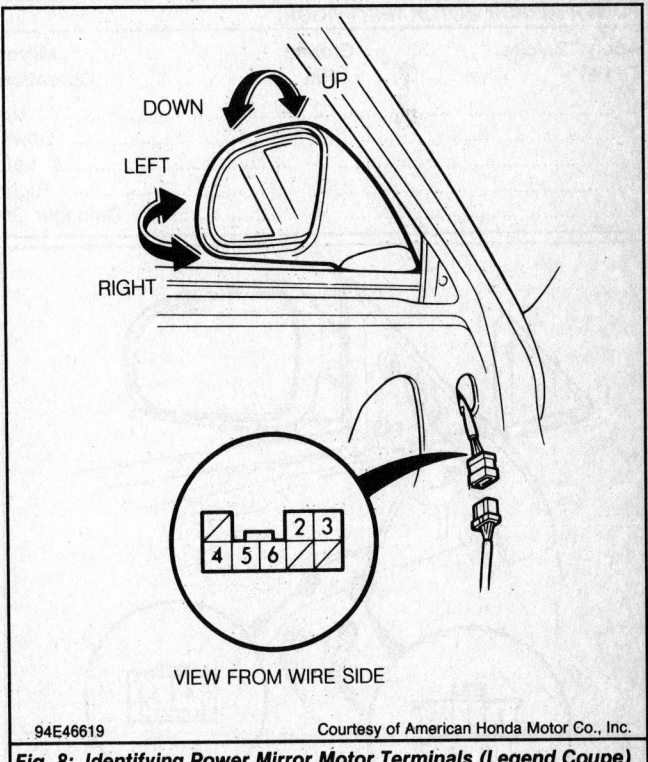

VIEW FROM WIRE SIDE

Fig. 8: Identifying Power Mirror Motor Terminals (Legend Coupe)

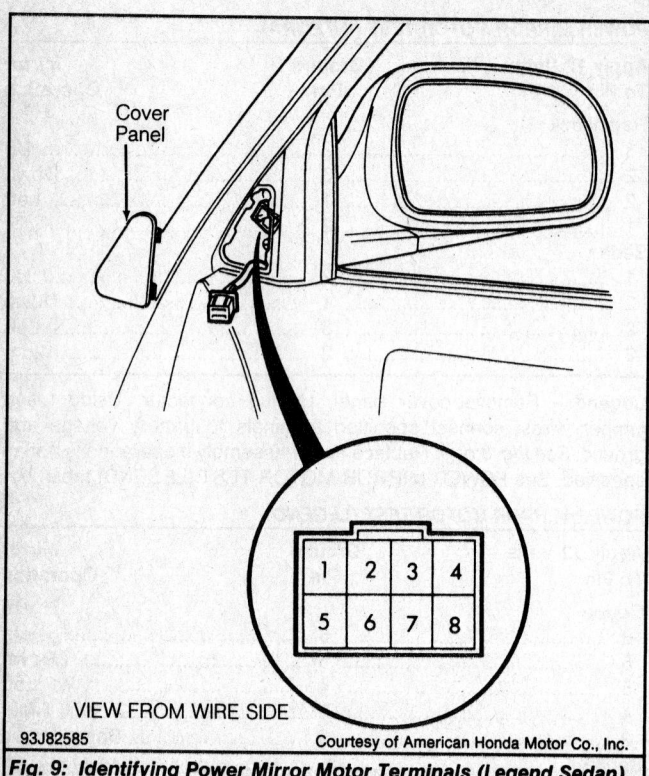

VIEW FROM WIRE SIDE

93J82585   Courtesy of American Honda Motor Co., Inc.

Fig. 9: Identifying Power Mirror Motor Terminals (Legend Sedan)

Vigor – Remove cover panel. Unplug connectors. Using fused jumper wires, connect specified terminals to battery voltage and ground. *See Fig. 10.* Replace motor assembly if operation is not as specified. See POWER MIRROR MOTOR TEST (VIGOR) table.

POWER MIRROR MOTOR TEST (VIGOR)

Apply 12 Volts To Pin	Ground Pin	Mirror Operation
1	2	Up
2	1	Down
2	3	Left
3	2	Right
5	4	Defogger On

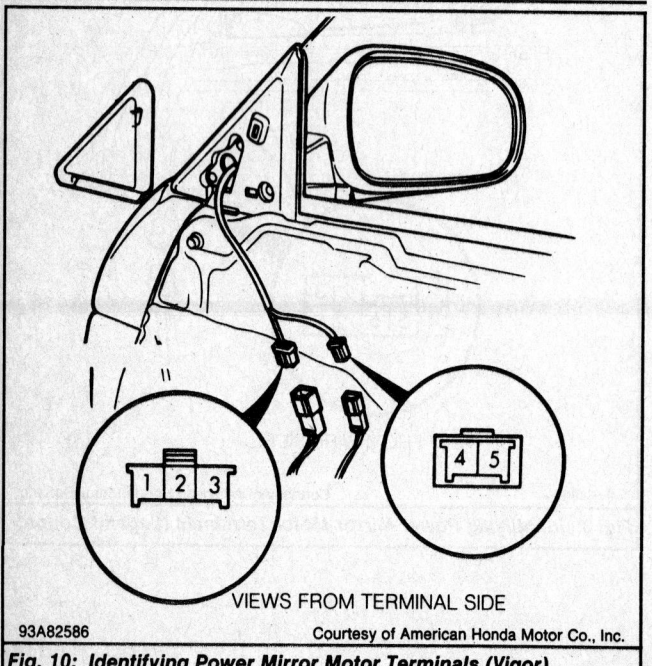

VIEWS FROM TERMINAL SIDE

93A82586   Courtesy of American Honda Motor Co., Inc.

Fig. 10: Identifying Power Mirror Motor Terminals (Vigor)

REMOVAL & INSTALLATION
POWER MIRROR SWITCH

Integra – Remove instrument panel lower cover. From behind, push switch out from panel. Unplug connector. To install, reverse removal procedure.
Legend – Remove driver's door panel. Unplug connector. Remove switch. To install, reverse removal procedure.
Vigor – From behind, push switch out from panel. Unplug connector. To install, reverse removal procedure.

POWER MIRROR ASSEMBLY

Remove door panel. Carefully pry out cover panel. Hold mirror assembly with one hand while removing mounting screws. Remove mirror assembly. To install, reverse removal procedure.

WIRING DIAGRAMS

NOTE: See ACCESSORIES & EQUIPMENT, Volume 5.

1994 ACCESSORIES & EQUIPMENT
Power Seats

Legend, Vigor

DESCRIPTION & OPERATION

On Legend, 4 motors provide for front up/down, rear up/down, forward/back, and recline adjustment. Each motor includes a reed-switch sensor, which sends a pulse signal to Driving Position Memory System (DPMS) control unit. DPMS memory feature adjusts the seat and steering wheel to either of 2 preset positions. On Vigor, 2 motors provide front/rear and tilt adjustment.

CAUTION: All models are equipped with Supplemental Restraint System (SRS). SRS wiring harness is routed close to instrument cluster, steering wheel, and related components. All SRS wiring harnesses are covered by Yellow outer insulation. DO NOT use electrical test equipment on these circuits. Before working on steering column components, disable air bag system. See AIR BAG RESTRAINT SYSTEM article in ACCESSORIES & EQUIPMENT.

TROUBLE SHOOTING (LEGEND)

Driving Position Memory System (DPMS) control unit includes self-diagnostics, which records up to 5 circuit-related problems. Diagnostic trouble codes may be retrieved from DPMS to aid in troubleshooting. Memory switch is used to display any stored trouble codes. Trouble shoot DPMS in specific order only as follows:

- Check power and ground circuits *See Figs. 1 and 2.*
- Perform automatic adjustment mode operations. See AUTOMATIC ADJUSTMENT MODE under TROUBLE SHOOTING.
- Locate appropriate flow chart based on symptom. See SYMPTOM TROUBLE SHOOTING table. See FLOW CHARTS.
- Retrieve trouble codes and perform test steps in appropriate flow chart(s). See RETRIEVING TROUBLE CODES under TROUBLE SHOOTING.
- Test components and replace as necessary. See TESTING and REMOVAL & INSTALLATION.

Disconnect the 10-P connector from the DPMS control unit, and check voltage between the YEL/BLU wire and ground.
Is there 10 – 14 V?
NO
Repair open in the YEL/BLU wire or replace blown No. 15 (7.5 A) fuse in the under-dash fuse/relay box.
YES
Check for continuity between the DPMS control unit 10-P connector BLK² wire and ground, and BLK³ wire and ground.
Is there continuity?
NO
Repair open in the BLK² or BLK³ wire, or repair poor ground
YES
Disconnect the 7-P connector A from the PS control unit, and check voltage between the RED/WHT wire and ground.
Is there 10 – 14 V?
NO
Repair open in the RED/WHT wire or replace blown No. 55 (30 A) fuse in the under-hood fuse/relay box.
YES
Disconnect the 7-P connector B from the PS control unit, and check for continuity between the two BLK⁴ wires and ground.
Is there continuity?
NO
Repair open in the BLK⁴ wires, or repair poor ground
YES
Disconnect the 7-P connector from the SC control unit, and check voltage between the WHT/RED wire and ground.
Is there 10 – 14 V?
NO
Repair open in the WHT/RED wire or replace blown No. 58 (20 A) fuse in the under-hood fuse/relay box.
YES
Check for continuity between the BLK⁵ wire of the SC control unit 7-P connector and ground.
Is there continuity?
NO
Repair open in the BLK⁵ wire, or repair poor ground
YES
Continue with the flowchart indicated by the DTC, or select a flowchart from troubleshooting

94C46658 Courtesy of American Honda Motor Co., Inc.

Fig. 1: Power & Ground Circuit Trouble Shooting Chart

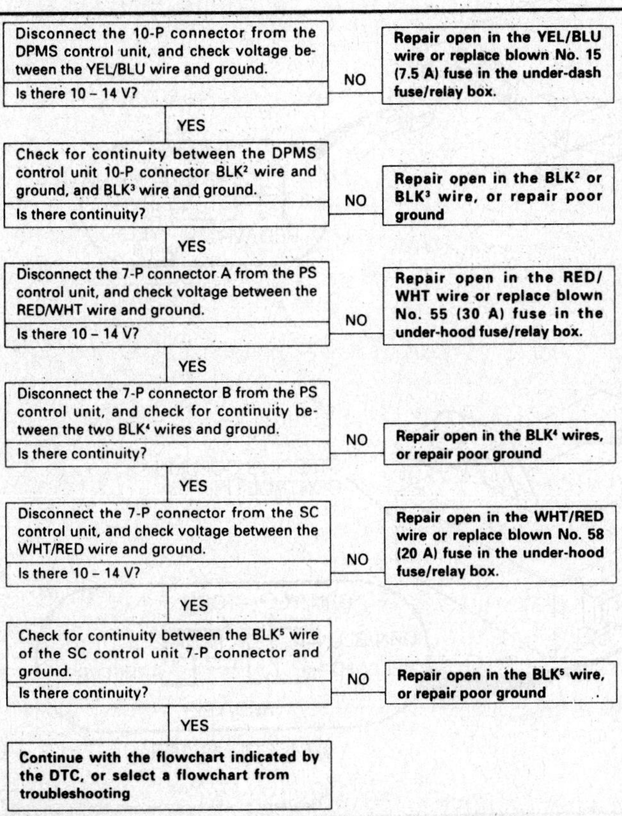

NOTE: Make all voltage checks with connectors attached. Make all continuity checks with connectors disconnected. Use care when backprobing to prevent electrical shorts or damage to insulation and terminals. All connectors are shown from the wire side. Control units use the following abbreviations. Driving Position Memory System (DPMS), Power Seat (PS) control unit and Steering Column (PS) control unit.

NOTE: This article includes some trouble codes, flow charts and illustration information related to power steering positioning. Some flow charts and test steps which only apply to power steering positioning are not included in this article.

AUTOMATIC ADJUSTMENT MODES

Perform the following mode tests. If any problems are noted, see trouble shooting symptoms and perform appropriate flow chart.

- Mode 1 – With ignition key in lock, ensure AUTO on steering column switch is on and shift lever in "P". Remove ignition key. Steering column should move to highest position and driver's seat moves to back fully.
- Mode 2 – With vehicle conditions as in Mode 1, insert ignition key without turning key. Steering column and driver's seat should move to positions before mode 1 started.
- Mode 3 – With driver's door open, insert ignition key without turning key. Using memory switch located on door panel, quickly press position button No. 1 or No. 2. Steering column and seat will move to selected positions. If ignition key is not inserted, only seat will move.
- Mode 4 – With driver's door closed, insert ignition key without turning key. Using memory switch located on door panel, quickly press position button No. 1 or No. 2. Steering column and seat will move to selected positions. If ignition key is not inserted, only seat will move.

SYMPTOM TROUBLE SHOOTING

Symptom	Flow Chart
No Automatic Adjustment Mode No. 1	1
No Automatic Adjustment Mode No. 2	2
No Automatic Adjustment Mode No. 3	3
No Automatic Adjustment Mode No. 4	4
No Automatic Seat & Steering Adjustments	5
No Automatic Seat Adjustment	6
No Automatic Steering Adjustment	7
Automatic Adjustment Mode No. 3 Works With Car Parked & Driver's Door Closed	8
Automatic Adjustment Mode No. 3 Not Working With Car Parked & Driver's Door Open	9
Automatic Adjustment Mode No. 3 Works With Car Driving & Driver's Door Open	10
Automatic Adjustment Mode No. 1 Works With "AUTO" Switch Off	11
Seat Goes Beyond Limit In Automatic Adjustment Modes No. 3 & 4	12
Automatic Adjustment Does Not Stop When Pressing Any Button	13
Automatic Adjustment Does Not Stop When Pressing Power Seat Button	14
Automatic Adjustment Does Not Stop When Pressing Steering Column Switch	15
Automatic Adjustment Does Not Stop When Pressing Any Button On Door Panel Switch	16
Steering Adjusts Automatically With Ignition Key Removed	17
Seat & Steering Do Not Adjust Manually	18
Seat Does Not Adjust Manually	19
Steering Column Does Not Adjust Manually	20
Seat Does Not Adjust With Slide Switch	21
Seat Does Not Adjust With Recline Switch	22
Seat Does Not Adjust With Front Up-Down Switch	23
Seat Does Not Adjust With Rear Up-Down Switch	24
Seat Slides For Only A Second	27
Seat Reclines For Only A Second	28
Seat Front Moves Up-Down For Only A Second	29
Seat Rear Moves Up-Down For Only A Second	30
Position Buttons Do Not Go On Or Blink	37
Position Buttons Stay On During Manual Adjustments	38
No Self-Diagnostics	39

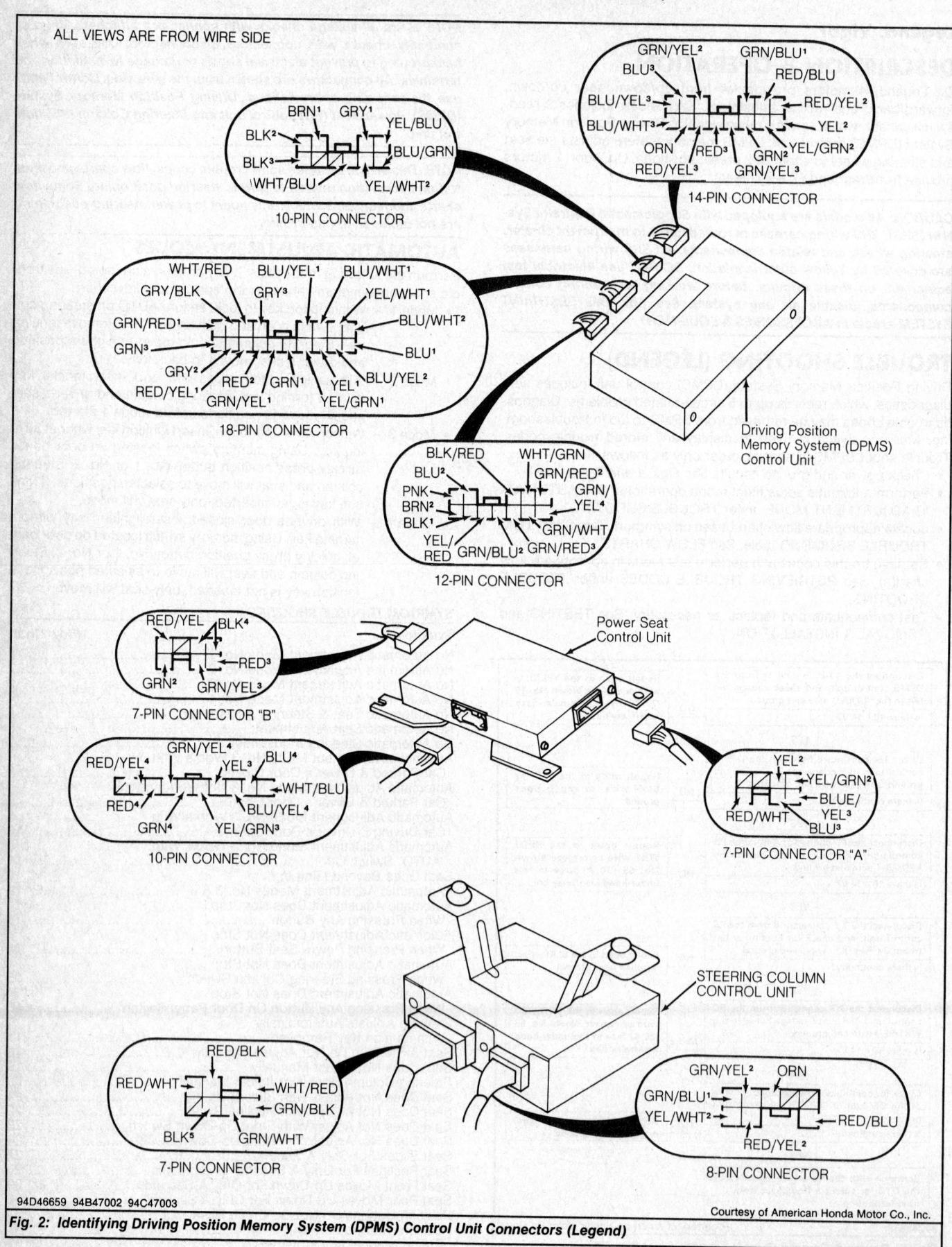

Fig. 2: Identifying Driving Position Memory System (DPMS) Control Unit Connectors (Legend)

94D46659 94B47002 94C47003

Courtesy of American Honda Motor Co., Inc.

RETRIEVING TROUBLE CODES

1) Turn ignition off. Press MEMO button and both position setting buttons on memory switch and hold then all down. Turn ignition on and wait at least one second. Release all buttons.

2) If no trouble codes are stored, position setting button LEDs will only blink one 3-second long blink. If trouble codes are stored, position setting button LEDs will blink one, two or three one-second long flashes. This is the first digit of the trouble code.

3) After the first digit is flashed, a one second pause takes place. The second digit is displayed by 1/4-second flashes of the position setting button LEDs. Each trouble code is followed by a 3 second pause before any other codes are displayed. Record all trouble codes and see appropriate flow chart to locate cause of problem. See TROUBLE CODE DEFINITIONS table.

CANCELLING TROUBLE CODE DISPLAY

To cancel trouble code display, turn ignition off or press any button on memory switch or seat control switch. To erase trouble code memory from DPMS, remove fuse No. 20 from under dash fuse/relay panel for 30 seconds.

TROUBLE CODE DEFINITIONS

Code & Cause	Flow Chart
1 – Slide Switch Circuit Causing Seat Not To Slide	21
2 – Recline Switch Circuit Causing Seat Not To Recline	22
3 – Front Up-Down Circuit Causing Seat Front Not To Move	23
4 – Rear Up-Down Circuit Causing Seat Rear Not To Move	24
5 – Tilt Switch Circuit Causing Steering Wheel Not To Tilt [1]	25
6 – Extend-Retract Switch Circuit Causing Steering Wheel Not To Move Up Or Down [1]	26
11 – Seat Slide Switch Or Relay Circuit Causing Seat Not To Slide	3, 4, 6, 21
12 – Seat Recline Switch Or Relay Circuit Causing Seat Not To Recline	3, 4, 6, 22
13 – Seat Up-Down Front Switch Or Relay Circuit Causing Seat Not To Move	3, 4, 6, 23
14 – Seat Up-Down Rear Switch Or Relay Circuit Causing Seat Not To Move	3, 4, 6, 24
15 – Tilt Switch Or Relay Circuit Causing Steering Wheel Not To Tilt [1]	3, 4, 6, 25
16 – Extend-Retract Switch Or Relay Circuit Causing Steering Wheel Not To Move Up Or Down [1]	3, 4, 6, 26
21 – MEMO Switch Circuit Causing Positions Not To Be Memorized	33
22 – Position Button No. 1 Circuit Causing Positions Not To Be Memorized	34
23 – Position Button No. 2 Circuit Causing Positions Not To Be Memorized	35
24 – Seat Slide Forward Switch Circuit Causing Seat Not To Slide	21
25 – Seat Slide Back Switch Circuit Causing Seat Not To Slide	21
26 – Seat Recline Forward Switch Circuit Causing Seat Not To Move	22
27 – Seat Recline Back Switch Circuit Causing Seat Not To Move	22
28 – Seat Front "Up" Switch Circuit Causing Seat Not To Move	23
29 – Seat Front "Down" Switch Circuit Causing Seat Not To Move	23
30 – Seat Rear "Up" Switch Circuit Causing Seat Not To Move	24
31 – Seat Rear "Down" Switch Circuit Causing Seat Not To Move	24
32-36 [1]	[2] 1, 25, 26

[1] – These trouble codes relate to power steering positioning problems.
[2] – These flow charts are not included.

FLOW CHARTS (LEGEND)

NOTE: Different wires with the same color have been given a suffix number. For example, Yellow/Green[1] and Yellow/Green[2] are not the same wires. Refer to Fig. 2 for all connector views not included in flow charts.

NOTE: Some flow charts (ie: flow charts No. 1 and 2), only apply to steering column positioning and are not included.

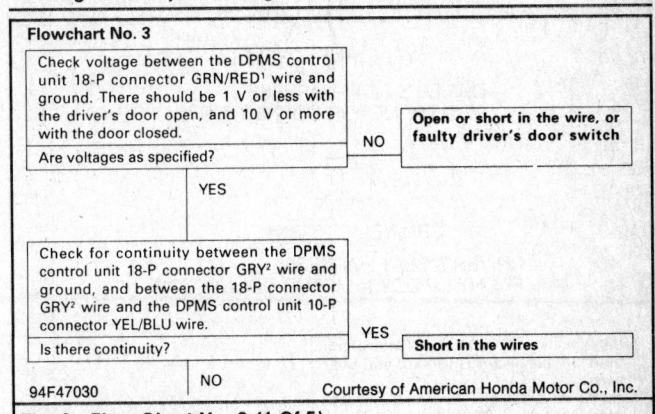

Flowchart No. 3

Check voltage between the DPMS control unit 18-P connector GRN/RED[1] wire and ground. There should be 1 V or less with the driver's door open, and 10 V or more with the door closed.
Are voltages as specified? — NO → Open or short in the wire, or faulty driver's door switch

YES

Check for continuity between the DPMS control unit 18-P connector GRY[2] wire and ground, and between the 18-P connector GRY[2] wire and the DPMS control unit 10-P connector YEL/BLU wire.
Is there continuity? — YES → Short in the wires

NO

94F47030   Courtesy of American Honda Motor Co., Inc.

Fig. 3: Flow Chart No. 3 (1 Of 5)

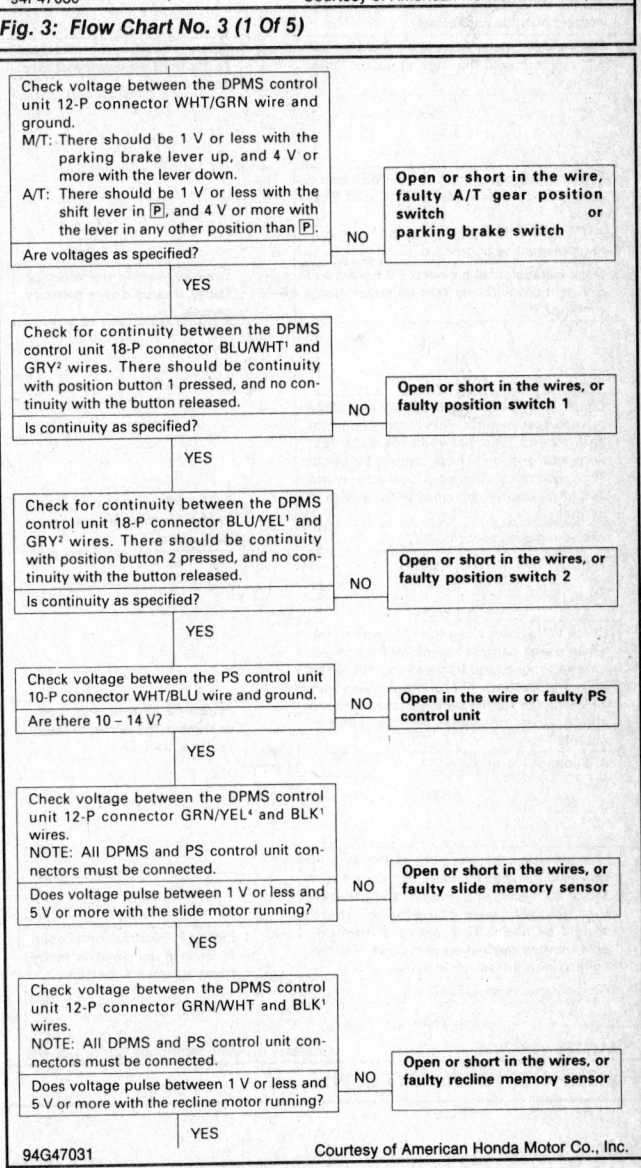

Check voltage between the DPMS control unit 12-P connector WHT/GRN wire and ground.
M/T: There should be 1 V or less with the parking brake lever up, and 4 V or more with the lever down.
A/T: There should be 1 V or less with the shift lever in P, and 4 V or more with the lever in any other position than P.
Are voltages as specified? — NO → Open or short in the wire, faulty A/T gear position switch or parking brake switch

YES

Check for continuity between the DPMS control unit 18-P connector BLU/WHT[1] and GRY[2] wires. There should be continuity with position button 1 pressed, and no continuity with the button released.
Is continuity as specified? — NO → Open or short in the wires, or faulty position switch 1

YES

Check for continuity between the DPMS control unit 18-P connector BLU/YEL[1] and GRY[2] wires. There should be continuity with position button 2 pressed, and no continuity with the button released.
Is continuity as specified? — NO → Open or short in the wires, or faulty position switch 2

YES

Check voltage between the PS control unit 10-P connector WHT/BLU wire and ground.
Are there 10 – 14 V? — NO → Open in the wire or faulty PS control unit

YES

Check voltage between the DPMS control unit 12-P connector GRN/YEL[4] and BLK[1] wires.
NOTE: All DPMS and PS control unit connectors must be connected.
Does voltage pulse between 1 V or less and 5 V or more with the slide motor running? — NO → Open or short in the wires, or faulty slide memory sensor

YES

Check voltage between the DPMS control unit 12-P connector GRN/WHT and BLK[1] wires.
NOTE: All DPMS and PS control unit connectors must be connected.
Does voltage pulse between 1 V or less and 5 V or more with the recline motor running? — NO → Open or short in the wires, or faulty recline memory sensor

YES

94G47031   Courtesy of American Honda Motor Co., Inc.

Fig. 4: Flow Chart No. 3 (2 Of 5)

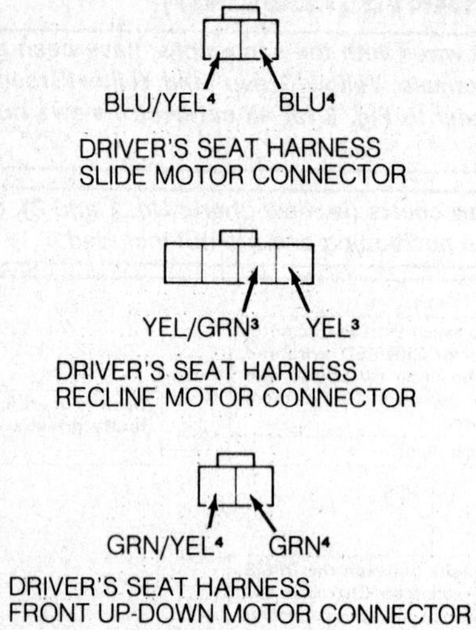

BLU/YEL⁴   BLU⁴

DRIVER'S SEAT HARNESS
SLIDE MOTOR CONNECTOR

YEL/GRN³   YEL³

DRIVER'S SEAT HARNESS
RECLINE MOTOR CONNECTOR

GRN/YEL⁴   GRN⁴

DRIVER'S SEAT HARNESS
FRONT UP-DOWN MOTOR CONNECTOR

Check voltage between the DPMS control unit 12-P connector GRN/RED³ and BLK¹ wires.
NOTE: All DPMS and PS control unit connectors must be connected.

Does voltage pulse between 1 V or less and 5 V or more with the front up-down motor running? — **NO** → Open or short in the wires, or faulty front up-down memory sensor

YES

Check voltage between the DPMS control unit 12-P connector GRN/BLU² and BLK¹ wires.
NOTE: All DPMS and PS control unit connectors must be connected.

Does voltage pulse between 1 V or less and 5 V or more with the rear up-down motor running? — **NO** → Open or short in the wires, or faulty rear up-down memory sensor

YES

Check voltage between the BLU⁴ wire of the driver's seat harness slide motor connector and ground, and between the BLU/YEL⁴ wire and ground. There should be about 12 V with the slide switch pushed forward and back, and no voltage with the switch in neutral.

Are voltages as specified? — **NO** → Faulty PS control unit, open or short in the wires, or faulty slide switch

YES

Check voltage between the YEL³ wire of the driver's seat harness recline motor connector and ground, and between the YEL/GRN³ wire and ground. There should be about 12 V with the recline switch pushed forward and back, and no voltage with the switch in neutral.

Are voltages as specified? — **NO** → Faulty PS control unit, open or short in the wires, or faulty recline switch

YES

Check voltage between the GRN⁴ wire of the driver's seat harness front up-down motor connector and ground, and between the GRN/YEL⁴ wire and ground. There should be about 12 V with the front up-down switch pushed up and down, and no voltage with the switch in neutral.

Are voltages as specified? — **NO** → Faulty PS control unit, open or short in the wires, or faulty front up-down switch

YES

94A47126 94H47032   Courtesy of American Honda Motor Co., Inc.

Fig. 5: Flow Chart No. 3 (3 Of 5)

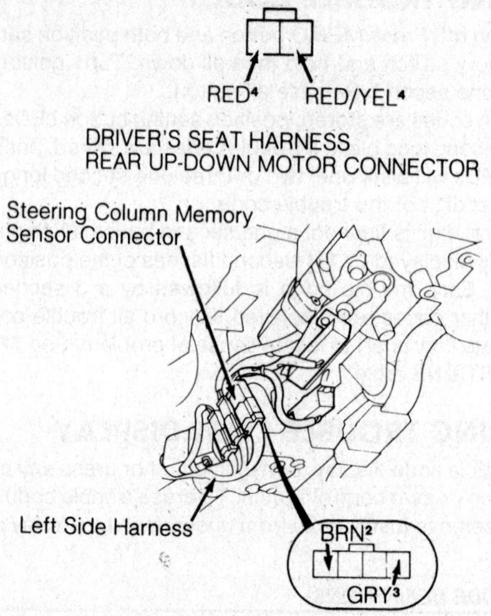

RED⁴   RED/YEL⁴

DRIVER'S SEAT HARNESS
REAR UP-DOWN MOTOR CONNECTOR

Steering Column Memory Sensor Connector

Left Side Harness

BRN²

GRY³

Check voltage between the RED⁴ wire of the driver's seat harness rear up-down motor connector and ground, and between the RED/YEL⁴ wire and ground. There should be about 12 V with the rear up-down switch pushed up and down, and no voltage with the switch in neutral.

Are voltages as specified? — **NO** → Faulty PS control unit, open or short in the wires, or faulty rear up-down switch

YES

Test the power seat slide motor

Does the motor run smoothly without noise? — **NO** → Open in the BLU⁴ or BLU/YEL⁴ motor wire, or faulty slide motor

YES

Test the power seat recline motor

Does the motor run smoothly without noise? — **NO** → Open in the YEL³ or YEL/GRN³ motor wire, or faulty recline motor

YES

Test the power seat front up-down motor

Does the motor run smoothly without noise? — **NO** → Open in the GRN⁴ or GRN/YEL⁴ motor wire, or faulty front up-down motor

YES

Test the power seat rear up-down motor

Does the motor run smoothly without noise? — **NO** → Open in the RED⁴ or RED/YEL⁴ motor wire, or faulty rear up-down motor

YES

Check voltage between the BRN² and GRY³ wires on the left side wire harness side of the steering column memory sensor connector. There should be 5 V.
NOTE: All DPMS control unit connectors must be connected.

Is there 5 V? — **NO** → Open in the wires or faulty DPMS control unit

YES

Check voltage between the SC control unit 8-P connector YEL/WHT² wire and ground.

Is there 10 – 14 V? — **NO** → Open in the wire or faulty DPMS control unit

YES

94B47127 94I47033   Courtesy of American Honda Motor Co., Inc.

Fig. 6: Flow Chart No. 3 (4 Of 5)

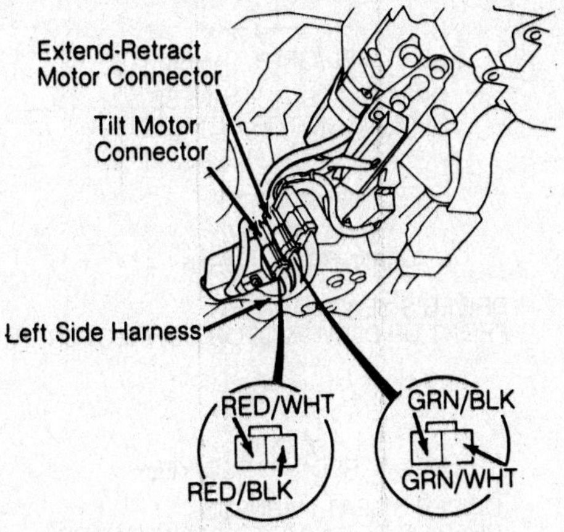

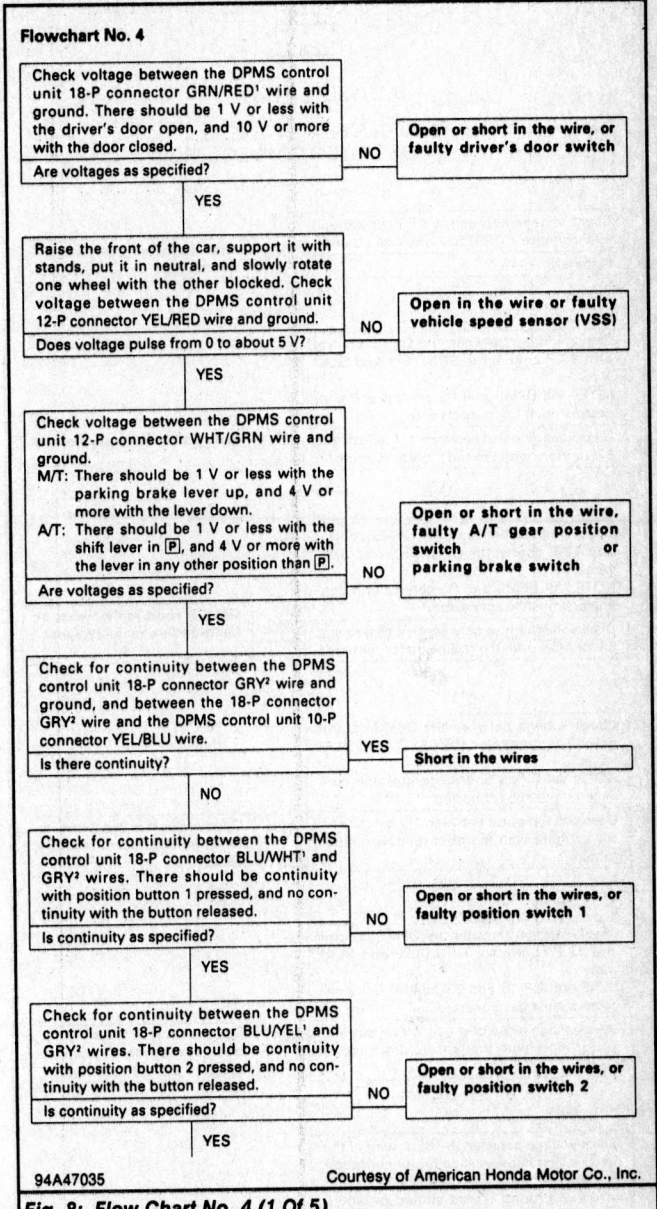

Extend-Retract
Motor Connector

Tilt Motor
Connector

Left Side Harness

RED/WHT
RED/BLK

GRN/BLK
GRN/WHT

Check voltage between the DPMS control unit 12-P connector BRN[2] and BLU[2] wires. There should be 5 V with the steering column in the fully-up position, and no voltage in the fully-down position.
NOTE: All DPMS and SC control unit connectors must be connected.

Is voltage as specified? → NO → Open or short in the wires, or faulty tilt memory sensor

YES

Check voltage between the DPMS control unit 12-P connector BRN[2] and PNK wires. There should be 5 V with the steering column in the fully-extend position, and no voltage in the fully-retract position.
NOTE: All DPMS and SC control unit connectors must be connected.

Is voltage as specified? → NO → Open or short in the wires, or faulty extend-retract memory sensor

YES

Check voltage between the RED/BLK wire on the left side wire harness side of the tilt motor connector and ground, and between the RED/WHT wire and ground. There should be 12 V with the tilt-up switch or tilt-down switch ON, and no voltage with the switches OFF.

Are voltages as specified? → NO → Open or short in the wires, or faulty SC control unit

YES

Check voltage between the GRN/BLK wire on the left side wire harness side of the extend-retract motor connector and ground, and between the GRN/WHT wire and ground. There should be 12 V with the retract or extend switch ON, and no voltage with the switches OFF.

Are voltages as specified? → NO → Open or short in the wires, or faulty SC control unit

YES

Test the steering column tilt motor

Does the motor run smoothly without noise? → NO → Open in the RED/BLK or RED/WHT motor wire, or faulty tilt motor

YES

Test the steering column extend-retract motor

Does the motor run smoothly without noise? → NO → Open in the GRN/BLK or GRN/WHT motor wire, or faulty extend-retract motor

YES

Faulty DPMS control unit

94D47129 94J47034   Courtesy of American Honda Motor Co., Inc.

Fig. 7: Flow Chart No. 3 (5 Of 5)

Flowchart No. 4

Check voltage between the DPMS control unit 18-P connector GRN/RED[1] wire and ground. There should be 1 V or less with the driver's door open, and 10 V or more with the door closed.

Are voltages as specified? → NO → Open or short in the wire, or faulty driver's door switch

YES

Raise the front of the car, support it with stands, put it in neutral, and slowly rotate one wheel with the other blocked. Check voltage between the DPMS control unit 12-P connector YEL/RED wire and ground.

Does voltage pulse from 0 to about 5 V? → NO → Open in the wire or faulty vehicle speed sensor (VSS)

YES

Check voltage between the DPMS control unit 12-P connector WHT/GRN wire and ground.
M/T: There should be 1 V or less with the parking brake lever up, and 4 V or more with the lever down.
A/T: There should be 1 V or less with the shift lever in P, and 4 V or more with the lever in any other position than P.

Are voltages as specified? → NO → Open or short in the wire, faulty A/T gear position switch or parking brake switch

YES

Check for continuity between the DPMS control unit 18-P connector GRY[2] wire and ground, and between the 18-P connector GRY[2] wire and the DPMS control unit 10-P connector YEL/BLU wire.

Is there continuity? → YES → Short in the wires

NO

Check for continuity between the DPMS control unit 18-P connector BLU/WHT[1] and GRY[2] wires. There should be continuity with position button 1 pressed, and no continuity with the button released.

Is continuity as specified? → NO → Open or short in the wires, or faulty position switch 1

YES

Check for continuity between the DPMS control unit 18-P connector BLU/YEL[1] and GRY[2] wires. There should be continuity with position button 2 pressed, and no continuity with the button released.

Is continuity as specified? → NO → Open or short in the wires, or faulty position switch 2

YES

94A47035   Courtesy of American Honda Motor Co., Inc.

Fig. 8: Flow Chart No. 4 (1 Of 5)

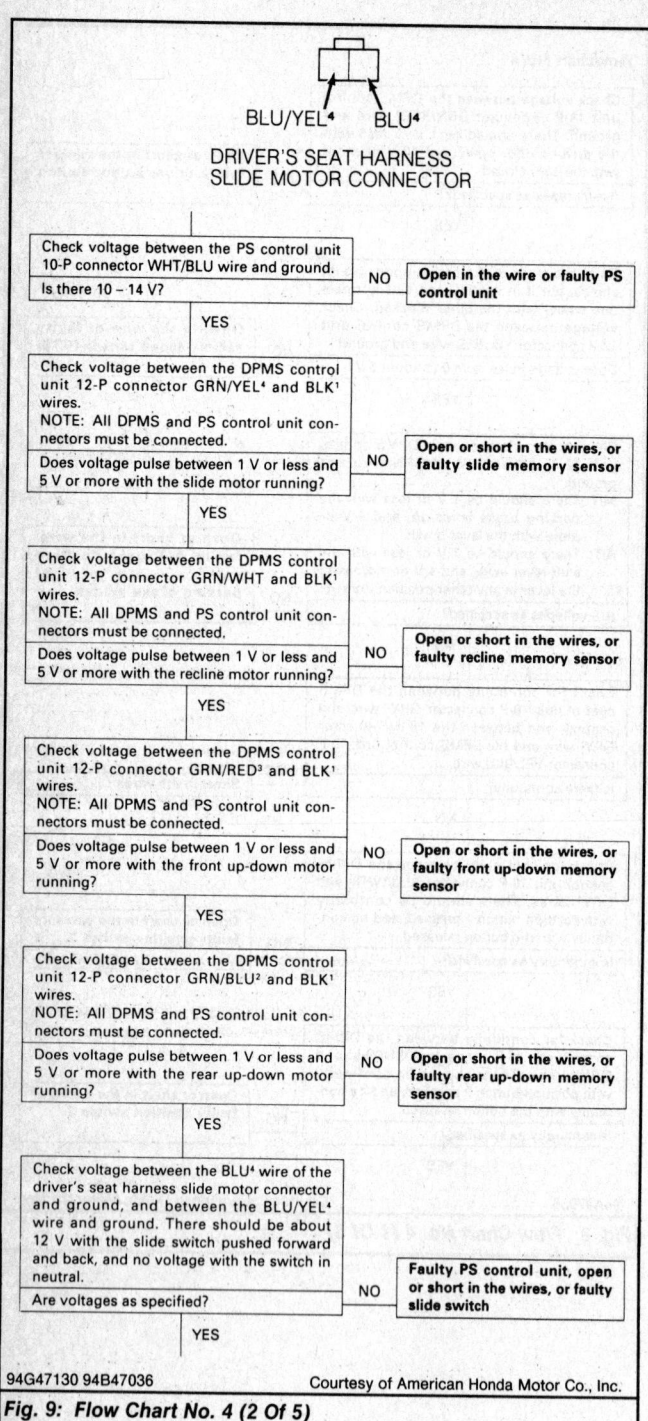

BLU/YEL[4]   **BLU[4]**

DRIVER'S SEAT HARNESS
SLIDE MOTOR CONNECTOR

Check voltage between the PS control unit 10-P connector WHT/BLU wire and ground.
Is there 10 – 14 V? — NO → Open in the wire or faulty PS control unit

YES

Check voltage between the DPMS control unit 12-P connector GRN/YEL[4] and BLK[1] wires.
NOTE: All DPMS and PS control unit connectors must be connected.
Does voltage pulse between 1 V or less and 5 V or more with the slide motor running? — NO → Open or short in the wires, or faulty slide memory sensor

YES

Check voltage between the DPMS control unit 12-P connector GRN/WHT and BLK[1] wires.
NOTE: All DPMS and PS control unit connectors must be connected.
Does voltage pulse between 1 V or less and 5 V or more with the recline motor running? — NO → Open or short in the wires, or faulty recline memory sensor

YES

Check voltage between the DPMS control unit 12-P connector GRN/RED[3] and BLK[1] wires.
NOTE: All DPMS and PS control unit connectors must be connected.
Does voltage pulse between 1 V or less and 5 V or more with the front up-down motor running? — NO → Open or short in the wires, or faulty front up-down memory sensor

YES

Check voltage between the DPMS control unit 12-P connector GRN/BLU[2] and BLK[1] wires.
NOTE: All DPMS and PS control unit connectors must be connected.
Does voltage pulse between 1 V or less and 5 V or more with the rear up-down motor running? — NO → Open or short in the wires, or faulty rear up-down memory sensor

YES

Check voltage between the BLU[4] wire of the driver's seat harness slide motor connector and ground, and between the BLU/YEL[4] wire and ground. There should be about 12 V with the slide switch pushed forward and back, and no voltage with the switch in neutral.
Are voltages as specified? — NO → Faulty PS control unit, open or short in the wires, or faulty slide switch

YES

94G47130 94B47036
Courtesy of American Honda Motor Co., Inc.

Fig. 9: Flow Chart No. 4 (2 Of 5)

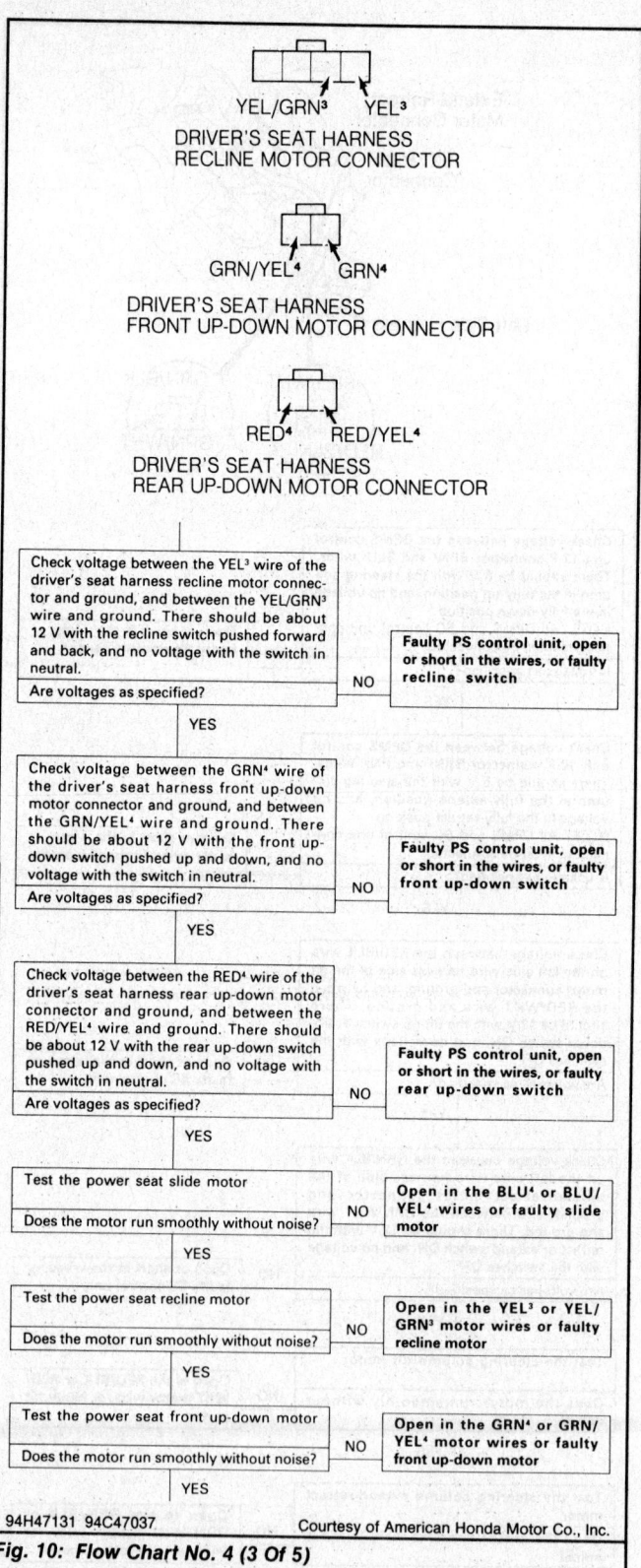

YEL/GRN[3]   **YEL[3]**

DRIVER'S SEAT HARNESS
RECLINE MOTOR CONNECTOR

GRN/YEL[4]   **GRN[4]**

DRIVER'S SEAT HARNESS
FRONT UP-DOWN MOTOR CONNECTOR

RED[4]   **RED/YEL[4]**

DRIVER'S SEAT HARNESS
REAR UP-DOWN MOTOR CONNECTOR

Check voltage between the YEL[3] wire of the driver's seat harness recline motor connector and ground, and between the YEL/GRN[3] wire and ground. There should be about 12 V with the recline switch pushed forward and back, and no voltage with the switch in neutral.
Are voltages as specified? — NO → Faulty PS control unit, open or short in the wires, or faulty recline switch

YES

Check voltage between the GRN[4] wire of the driver's seat harness front up-down motor connector and ground, and between the GRN/YEL[4] wire and ground. There should be about 12 V with the front up-down switch pushed up and down, and no voltage with the switch in neutral.
Are voltages as specified? — NO → Faulty PS control unit, open or short in the wires, or faulty front up-down switch

YES

Check voltage between the RED[4] wire of the driver's seat harness rear up-down motor connector and ground, and between the RED/YEL[4] wire and ground. There should be about 12 V with the rear up-down switch pushed up and down, and no voltage with the switch in neutral.
Are voltages as specified? — NO → Faulty PS control unit, open or short in the wires, or faulty rear up-down switch

YES

Test the power seat slide motor
Does the motor run smoothly without noise? — NO → Open in the BLU[4] or BLU/YEL[4] wires or faulty slide motor

YES

Test the power seat recline motor
Does the motor run smoothly without noise? — NO → Open in the YEL[3] or YEL/GRN[3] motor wires or faulty recline motor

YES

Test the power seat front up-down motor
Does the motor run smoothly without noise? — NO → Open in the GRN[4] or GRN/YEL[4] motor wires or faulty front up-down motor

YES

94H47131 94C47037
Courtesy of American Honda Motor Co., Inc.

Fig. 10: Flow Chart No. 4 (3 Of 5)

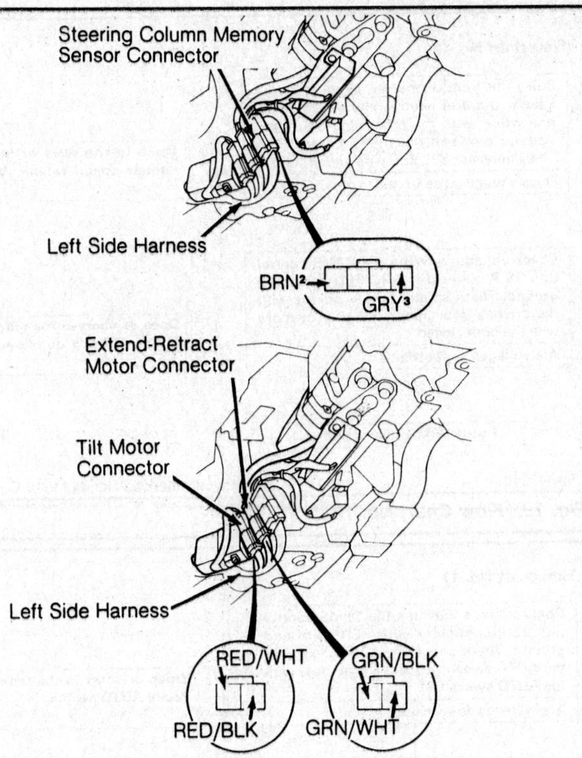

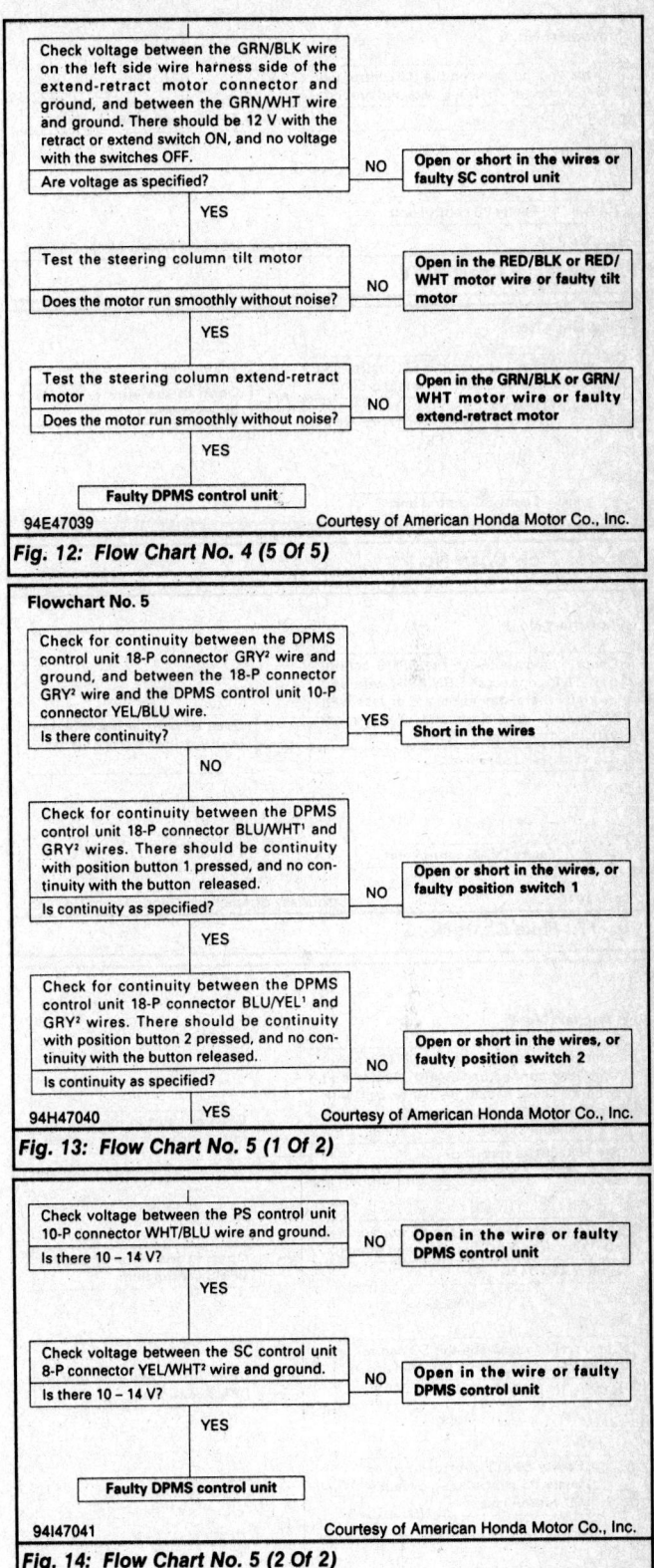

Steering Column Memory Sensor Connector

Left Side Harness

BRN² → GRY³

Extend-Retract Motor Connector

Tilt Motor Connector

Left Side Harness

RED/WHT / RED/BLK

GRN/BLK / GRN/WHT

| Test the power seat rear up-down motor | | |
| Does the motor run smoothly without noise? | NO → | Open in the RED⁴ or RED/YEL⁴ motor wires or faulty rear up-down motor |

YES ↓

| Check voltage between the BRN² and GRY³ wires on the left side wire harness side of the steering column memory sensor connector. There should be 5 V. NOTE: All DPMS control unit connectors must be connected. | | |
| Is there 5 V? | NO → | Open in the wires or faulty DPMS control unit |

YES ↓

| Check voltage between the SC control unit 8-P connector YEL/WHT² wire and ground. | | |
| Is there 10 – 14 V? | NO → | Open in the wire or faulty DPMS control unit |

YES ↓

| Check voltage between the DPMS control unit 12-P connector BRN² and BLU² wires. There should be 5 V with the steering column in the fully-up position, and no voltage in the fully-down position. NOTE: All DPMS and SC control unit connectors must be connected. | | |
| Is voltage as specified? | NO → | Open or short in the wires, or faulty tilt memory sensor |

YES ↓

| Check voltage between the DPMS control unit 12-P connector BRN² and PNK wires. There should be 5 V with the steering column in the fully-extend position, and no voltage in the fully-retract position. NOTE: All DPMS and SC control unit connectors must be connected. | | |
| Is voltage as specified? | NO → | Open or short in the wires, or faulty extend-retract memory sensor |

YES ↓

| Check voltage between the RED/BLK wire on the left side wire harness side of the tilt motor connector and ground, and between the RED/WHT wire and ground. There should be 12 V with the tilt-up switch or tilt-down switch ON, and no voltage with the switches OFF. | | |
| Are voltages as specified? | NO → | Open or short in the wires, or faulty SC control unit |

YES ↓

94J47133 94D47129 94D47038   Courtesy of American Honda Motor Co., Inc.

Fig. 11: Flow Chart No. 4 (4 Of 5)

| Check voltage between the GRN/BLK wire on the left side wire harness side of the extend-retract motor connector and ground, and between the GRN/WHT wire and ground. There should be 12 V with the retract or extend switch ON, and no voltage with the switches OFF. | | |
| Are voltage as specified? | NO → | Open or short in the wires or faulty SC control unit |

YES ↓

| Test the steering column tilt motor | | |
| Does the motor run smoothly without noise? | NO → | Open in the RED/BLK or RED/WHT motor wire or faulty tilt motor |

YES ↓

| Test the steering column extend-retract motor | | |
| Does the motor run smoothly without noise? | NO → | Open in the GRN/BLK or GRN/WHT motor wire or faulty extend-retract motor |

YES ↓

| **Faulty DPMS control unit** |

94E47039   Courtesy of American Honda Motor Co., Inc.

Fig. 12: Flow Chart No. 4 (5 Of 5)

Flowchart No. 5

| Check for continuity between the DPMS control unit 18-P connector GRY² wire and ground, and between the 18-P connector GRY² wire and the DPMS control unit 10-P connector YEL/BLU wire. | | |
| Is there continuity? | YES → | Short in the wires |

NO ↓

| Check for continuity between the DPMS control unit 18-P connector BLU/WHT¹ and GRY² wires. There should be continuity with position button 1 pressed, and no continuity with the button released. | | |
| Is continuity as specified? | NO → | Open or short in the wires, or faulty position switch 1 |

YES ↓

| Check for continuity between the DPMS control unit 18-P connector BLU/YEL¹ and GRY² wires. There should be continuity with position button 2 pressed, and no continuity with the button released. | | |
| Is continuity as specified? | NO → | Open or short in the wires, or faulty position switch 2 |

94H47040   YES   Courtesy of American Honda Motor Co., Inc.

Fig. 13: Flow Chart No. 5 (1 Of 2)

| Check voltage between the PS control unit 10-P connector WHT/BLU wire and ground. | | |
| Is there 10 – 14 V? | NO → | Open in the wire or faulty DPMS control unit |

YES ↓

| Check voltage between the SC control unit 8-P connector YEL/WHT² wire and ground. | | |
| Is there 10 – 14 V? | NO → | Open in the wire or faulty DPMS control unit |

YES ↓

| **Faulty DPMS control unit** |

94I47041   Courtesy of American Honda Motor Co., Inc.

Fig. 14: Flow Chart No. 5 (2 Of 2)

Flowchart No. 6

Check voltage between the PS control unit 10-P connector WHT/BLU wire and ground.

Is there 10 – 14 V? → NO → Open in the wire or faulty DPMS control unit

YES

Faulty PS control unit

94J47042   Courtesy of American Honda Motor Co., Inc.

Fig. 15: Flow Chart No. 6

Flowchart No. 7

Check voltage between the SC control unit 8-P connector YEL/WHT[2] wire and ground.

Is there 10 – 14 V? → NO → Open in the wire or faulty DPMS control unit

YES

Faulty SC control unit

94A47043   Courtesy of American Honda Motor Co., Inc.

Fig. 16: Flow Chart No. 7

Flowchart No. 8

Check voltage between the DPMS control unit 18-P connector GRN/RED[1] wire and ground. There should be 1 V or less with the driver's door open, and 10 V or more with the door closed.

Are voltages as specified? → NO → Open or short in the wire, or faulty driver's door switch

YES

Faulty DPMS control unit

94B47044   Courtesy of American Honda Motor Co., Inc.

Fig. 17: Flow Chart No. 8

Flowchart No. 9

Check voltage between the DPMS control unit 18-P connector GRN/RED[1] wire and ground. There should be 1 V or less with the driver's door open, and 10 V or more with the door closed.

Are voltages as specified? → NO → Open or short in the wire, or faulty driver's door switch

YES

Check voltage between the PS control unit 10-P connector WHT/BLU wire and ground.

Is there 10 – 14 V? → NO → Open in the wire or faulty DPMS control unit

YES

Check voltage between the SC control unit 8-P connector YEL/WHT[2] wire and ground.

Is there 10 – 14 V? → NO → Open in the wire or faulty DPMS control unit

YES

Faulty DPMS control unit, or faulty PS control unit, or faulty SC control unit

94C47045   Courtesy of American Honda Motor Co., Inc.

Fig. 18: Flow Chart No. 9

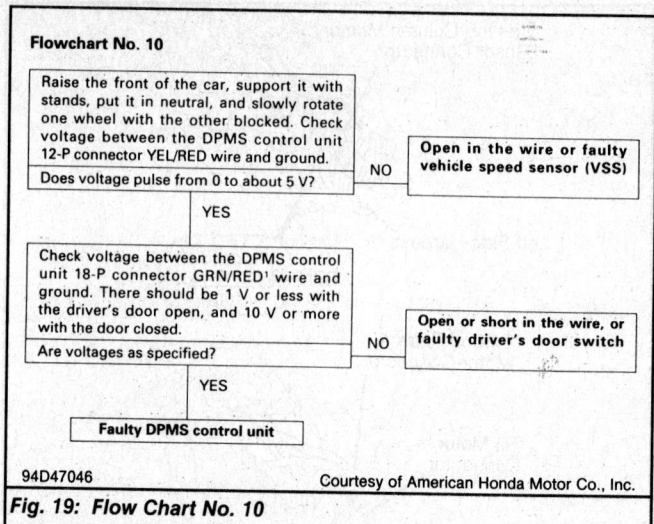

Flowchart No. 10

Raise the front of the car, support it with stands, put it in neutral, and slowly rotate one wheel with the other blocked. Check voltage between the DPMS control unit 12-P connector YEL/RED wire and ground.

Does voltage pulse from 0 to about 5 V? → NO → Open in the wire or faulty vehicle speed sensor (VSS)

YES

Check voltage between the DPMS control unit 18-P connector GRN/RED[1] wire and ground. There should be 1 V or less with the driver's door open, and 10 V or more with the door closed.

Are voltages as specified? → NO → Open or short in the wire, or faulty driver's door switch

YES

Faulty DPMS control unit

94D47046   Courtesy of American Honda Motor Co., Inc.

Fig. 19: Flow Chart No. 10

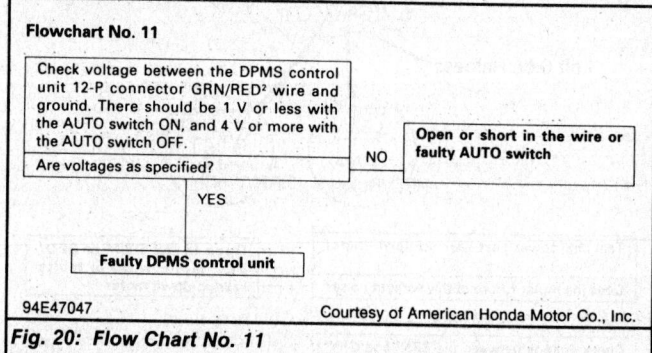

Flowchart No. 11

Check voltage between the DPMS control unit 12-P connector GRN/RED[2] wire and ground. There should be 1 V or less with the AUTO switch ON, and 4 V or more with the AUTO switch OFF.

Are voltages as specified? → NO → Open or short in the wire or faulty AUTO switch

YES

Faulty DPMS control unit

94E47047   Courtesy of American Honda Motor Co., Inc.

Fig. 20: Flow Chart No. 11

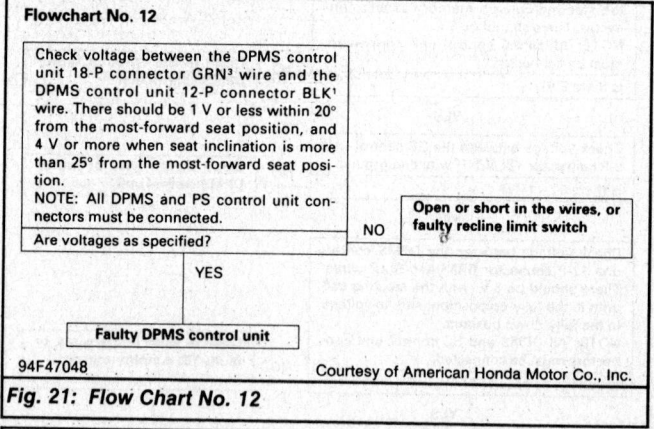

Flowchart No. 12

Check voltage between the DPMS control unit 18-P connector GRN[3] wire and the DPMS control unit 12-P connector BLK[1] wire. There should be 1 V or less within 20° from the most-forward seat position, and 4 V or more when seat inclination is more than 25° from the most-forward seat position.

NOTE: All DPMS and PS control unit connectors must be connected.

Are voltages as specified? → NO → Open or short in the wires, or faulty recline limit switch

YES

Faulty DPMS control unit

94F47048   Courtesy of American Honda Motor Co., Inc.

Fig. 21: Flow Chart No. 12

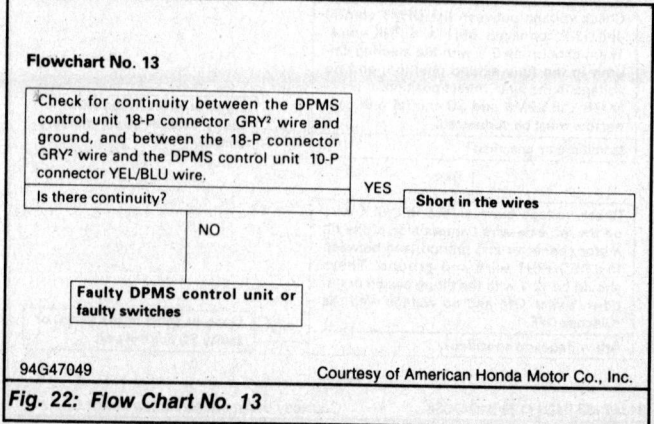

Flowchart No. 13

Check for continuity between the DPMS control unit 18-P connector GRY[2] wire and ground, and between the 18-P connector GRY[2] wire and the DPMS control unit 10-P connector YEL/BLU wire.

Is there continuity? → YES → Short in the wires

NO

Faulty DPMS control unit or faulty switches

94G47049   Courtesy of American Honda Motor Co., Inc.

Fig. 22: Flow Chart No. 13

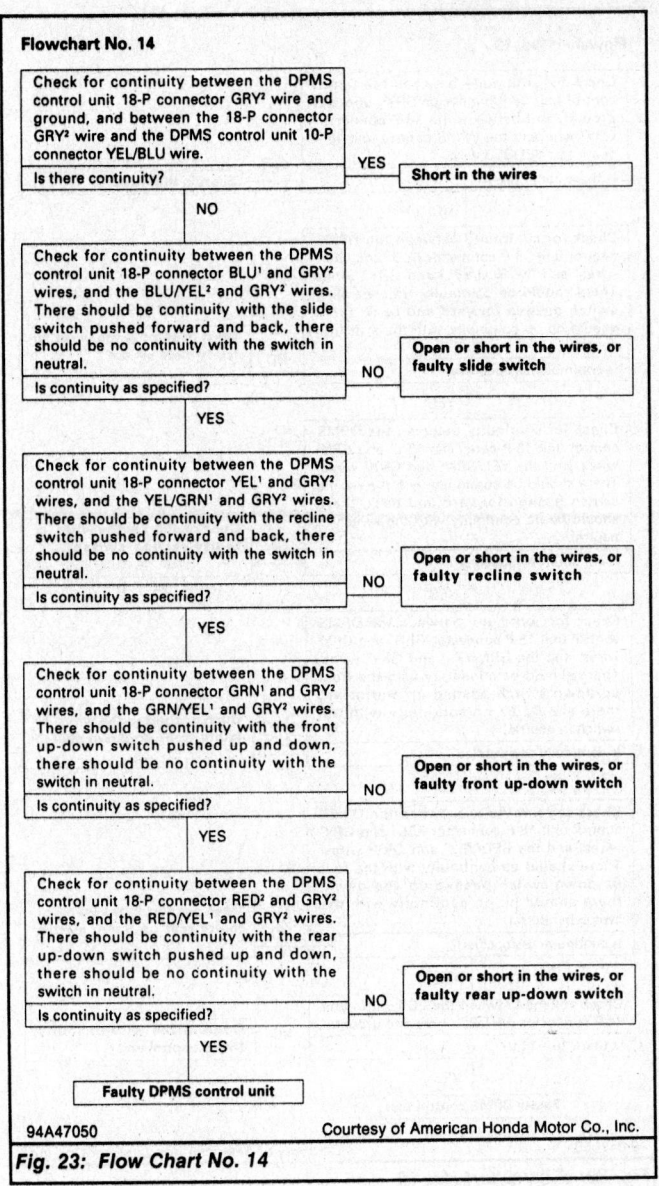

Flowchart No. 14

Check for continuity between the DPMS control unit 18-P connector GRY² wire and ground, and between the 18-P connector GRY² wire and the DPMS control unit 10-P connector YEL/BLU wire.

Is there continuity? — YES → Short in the wires

NO

Check for continuity between the DPMS control unit 18-P connector BLU¹ and GRY² wires, and the BLU/YEL² and GRY² wires. There should be continuity with the slide switch pushed forward and back, there should be no continuity with the switch in neutral.

Is continuity as specified? — NO → Open or short in the wires, or faulty slide switch

YES

Check for continuity between the DPMS control unit 18-P connector YEL¹ and GRY² wires, and the YEL/GRN¹ and GRY² wires. There should be continuity with the recline switch pushed forward and back, there should be no continuity with the switch in neutral.

Is continuity as specified? — NO → Open or short in the wires, or faulty recline switch

YES

Check for continuity between the DPMS control unit 18-P connector GRN¹ and GRY² wires, and the GRN/YEL¹ and GRY² wires. There should be continuity with the front up-down switch pushed up and down, there should be no continuity with the switch in neutral.

Is continuity as specified? — NO → Open or short in the wires, or faulty front up-down switch

YES

Check for continuity between the DPMS control unit 18-P connector RED² and GRY² wires, and the RED/YEL¹ and GRY² wires. There should be continuity with the rear up-down switch pushed up and down, there should be no continuity with the switch in neutral.

Is continuity as specified? — NO → Open or short in the wires, or faulty rear up-down switch

YES

Faulty DPMS control unit

94A47050   Courtesy of American Honda Motor Co., Inc.

Fig. 23: Flow Chart No. 14

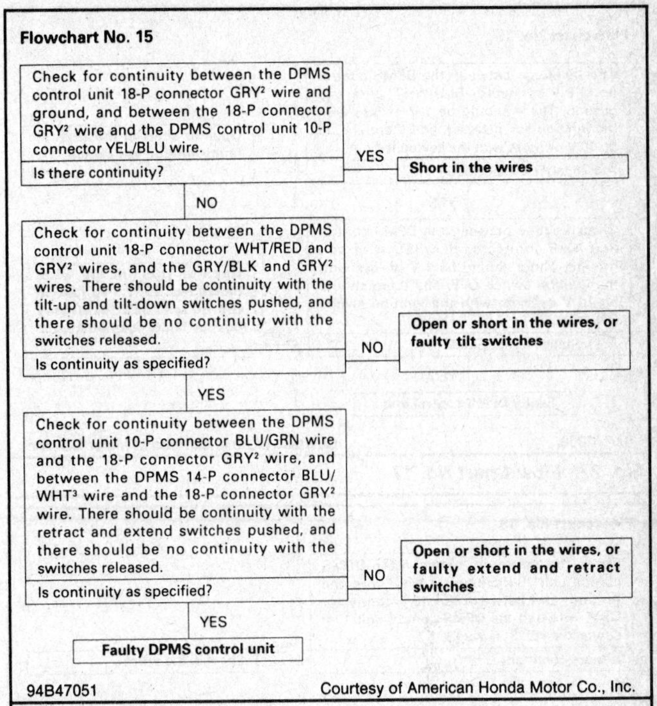

Flowchart No. 15

Check for continuity between the DPMS control unit 18-P connector GRY² wire and ground, and between the 18-P connector GRY² wire and the DPMS control unit 10-P connector YEL/BLU wire.

Is there continuity? — YES → Short in the wires

NO

Check for continuity between the DPMS control unit 18-P connector WHT/RED and GRY² wires, and the GRY/BLK and GRY² wires. There should be continuity with the tilt-up and tilt-down switches pushed, and there should be no continuity with the switches released.

Is continuity as specified? — NO → Open or short in the wires, or faulty tilt switches

YES

Check for continuity between the DPMS control unit 10-P connector BLU/GRN wire and the 18-P connector GRY² wire, and between the DPMS 14-P connector BLU/WHT³ wire and the 18-P connector GRY² wire. There should be continuity with the retract and extend switches pushed, and there should be no continuity with the switches released.

Is continuity as specified? — NO → Open or short in the wires, or faulty extend and retract switches

YES

Faulty DPMS control unit

94B47051   Courtesy of American Honda Motor Co., Inc.

Fig. 24: Flow Chart No. 15

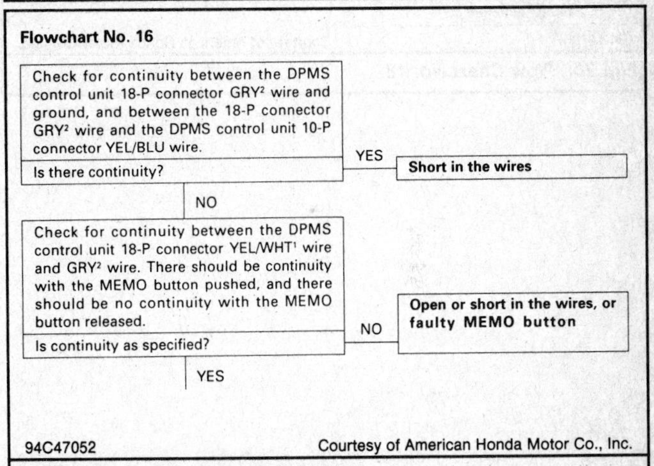

Flowchart No. 16

Check for continuity between the DPMS control unit 18-P connector GRY² wire and ground, and between the 18-P connector GRY² wire and the DPMS control unit 10-P connector YEL/BLU wire.

Is there continuity? — YES → Short in the wires

NO

Check for continuity between the DPMS control unit 18-P connector YEL/WHT¹ wire and GRY² wire. There should be continuity with the MEMO button pushed, and there should be no continuity with the MEMO button released.

Is continuity as specified? — NO → Open or short in the wires, or faulty MEMO button

YES

94C47052   Courtesy of American Honda Motor Co., Inc.

Fig. 25: Flow Chart No. 16 (1 Of 2)

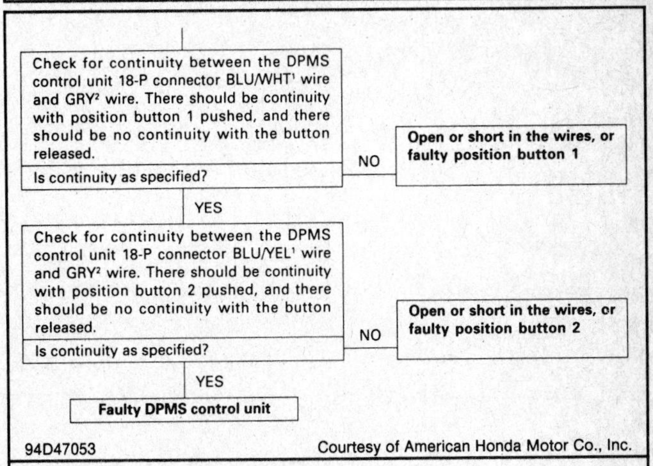

Check for continuity between the DPMS control unit 18-P connector BLU/WHT¹ wire and GRY² wire. There should be continuity with position button 1 pushed, and there should be no continuity with the button released.

Is continuity as specified? — NO → Open or short in the wires, or faulty position button 1

YES

Check for continuity between the DPMS control unit 18-P connector BLU/YEL¹ wire and GRY² wire. There should be continuity with position button 2 pushed, and there should be no continuity with the button released.

Is continuity as specified? — NO → Open or short in the wires, or faulty position button 2

YES

Faulty DPMS control unit

94D47053   Courtesy of American Honda Motor Co., Inc.

Fig. 26: Flow Chart No. 16 (2 Of 2)

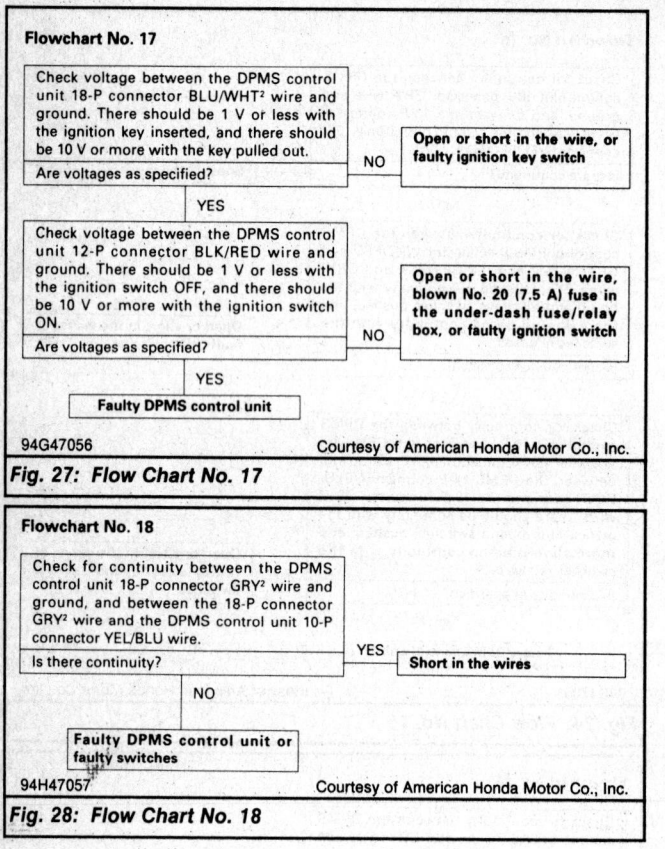

Flowchart No. 17

Check voltage between the DPMS control unit 18-P connector BLU/WHT² wire and ground. There should be 1 V or less with the ignition key inserted, and there should be 10 V or more with the key pulled out.

Are voltages as specified?

NO → **Open or short in the wire, or faulty ignition key switch**

YES ↓

Check voltage between the DPMS control unit 12-P connector BLK/RED wire and ground. There should be 1 V or less with the ignition switch OFF, and there should be 10 V or more with the ignition switch ON.

Are voltages as specified?

NO → **Open or short in the wire, blown No. 20 (7.5 A) fuse in the under-dash fuse/relay box, or faulty ignition switch**

YES ↓

Faulty DPMS control unit

94G47056   Courtesy of American Honda Motor Co., Inc.

Fig. 27: Flow Chart No. 17

Flowchart No. 18

Check for continuity between the DPMS control unit 18-P connector GRY² wire and ground, and between the 18-P connector GRY² wire and the DPMS control unit 10-P connector YEL/BLU wire.

Is there continuity?

YES → **Short in the wires**

NO ↓

Faulty DPMS control unit or faulty switches

94H47057   Courtesy of American Honda Motor Co., Inc.

Fig. 28: Flow Chart No. 18

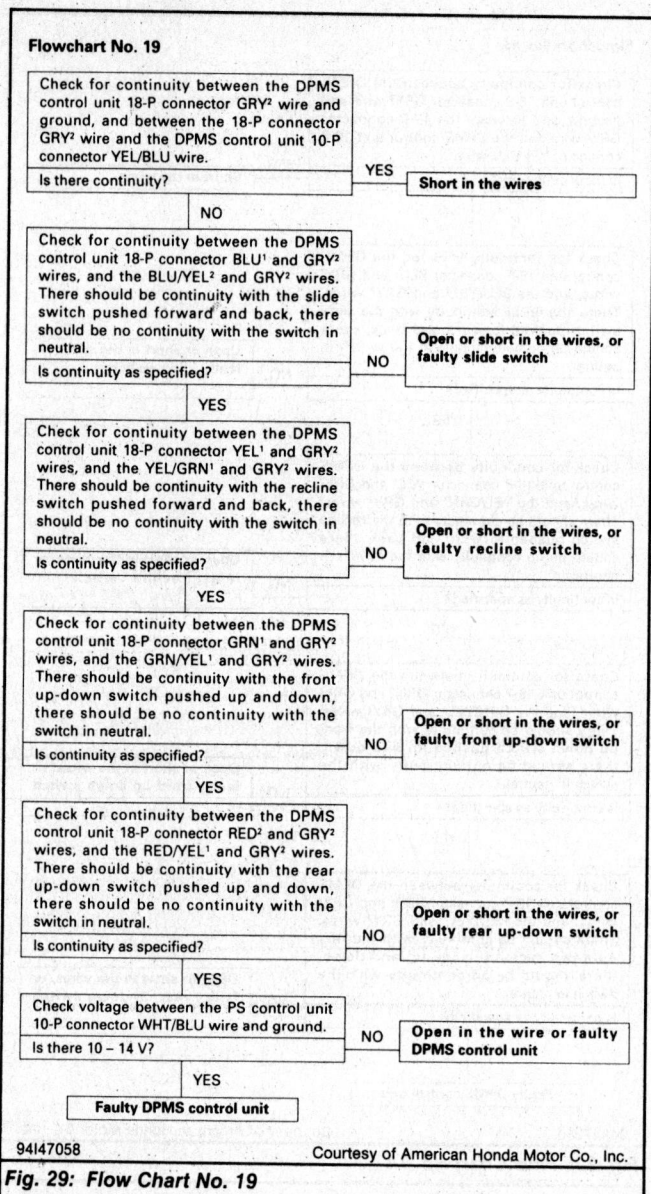

Flowchart No. 19

Check for continuity between the DPMS control unit 18-P connector GRY² wire and ground, and between the 18-P connector GRY² wire and the DPMS control unit 10-P connector YEL/BLU wire.

Is there continuity?

YES → **Short in the wires**

NO ↓

Check for continuity between the DPMS control unit 18-P connector BLU¹ and GRY² wires, and the BLU/YEL² and GRY² wires. There should be continuity with the slide switch pushed forward and back, there should be no continuity with the switch in neutral.

Is continuity as specified?

NO → **Open or short in the wires, or faulty slide switch**

YES ↓

Check for continuity between the DPMS control unit 18-P connector YEL¹ and GRY² wires, and the YEL/GRN¹ and GRY² wires. There should be continuity with the recline switch pushed forward and back, there should be no continuity with the switch in neutral.

Is continuity as specified?

NO → **Open or short in the wires, or faulty recline switch**

YES ↓

Check for continuity between the DPMS control unit 18-P connector GRN¹ and GRY² wires, and the GRN/YEL¹ and GRY² wires. There should be continuity with the front up-down switch pushed up and down, there should be no continuity with the switch in neutral.

Is continuity as specified?

NO → **Open or short in the wires, or faulty front up-down switch**

YES ↓

Check for continuity between the DPMS control unit 18-P connector RED² and GRY² wires, and the RED/YEL¹ and GRY² wires. There should be continuity with the rear up-down switch pushed up and down, there should be no continuity with the switch in neutral.

Is continuity as specified?

NO → **Open or short in the wires, or faulty rear up-down switch**

YES ↓

Check voltage between the PS control unit 10-P connector WHT/BLU wire and ground.

Is there 10 – 14 V?

NO → **Open in the wire or faulty DPMS control unit**

YES ↓

Faulty DPMS control unit

94I47058   Courtesy of American Honda Motor Co., Inc.

Fig. 29: Flow Chart No. 19

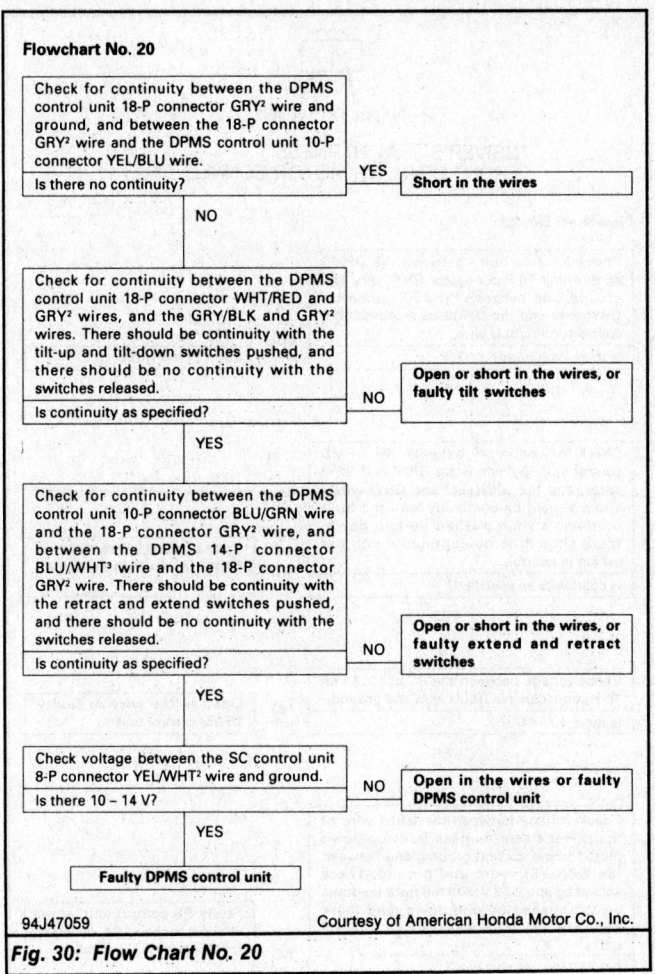

Fig. 30: Flow Chart No. 20

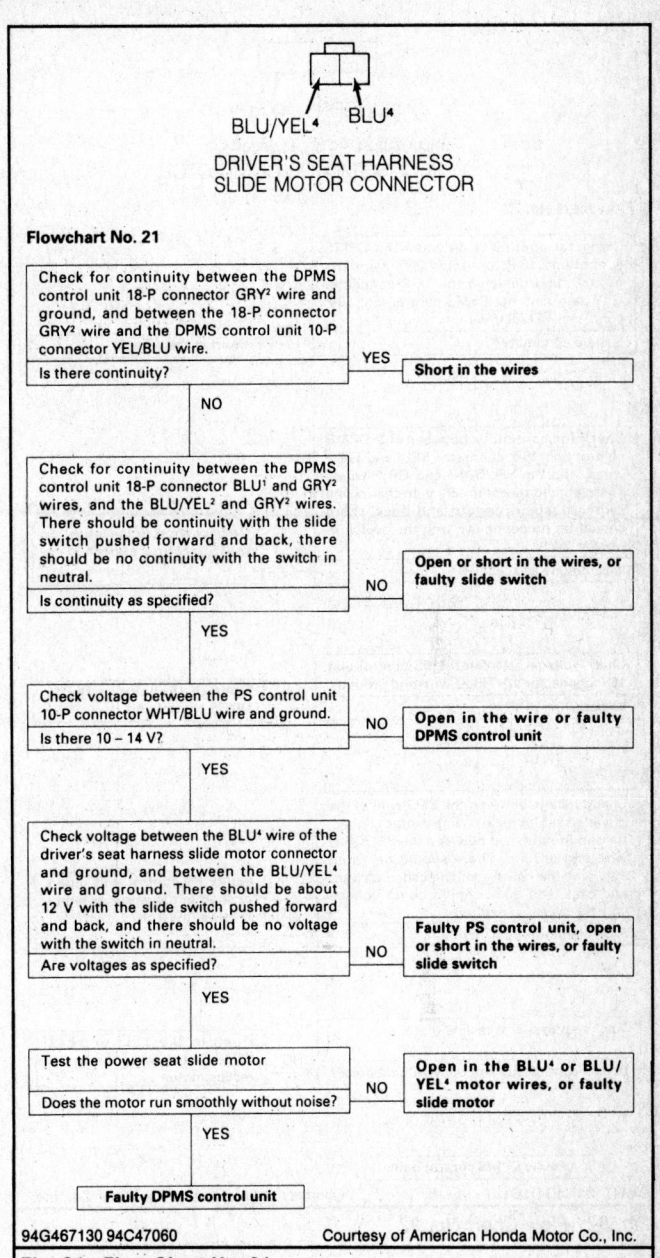

Fig. 31: Flow Chart No. 21

Flowchart No. 20

Check for continuity between the DPMS control unit 18-P connector GRY² wire and ground, and between the 18-P connector GRY² wire and the DPMS control unit 10-P connector YEL/BLU wire.

Is there no continuity? — YES → Short in the wires

NO

Check for continuity between the DPMS control unit 18-P connector WHT/RED and GRY² wires, and the GRY/BLK and GRY² wires. There should be continuity with the tilt-up and tilt-down switches pushed, and there should be no continuity with the switches released.

Is continuity as specified? — NO → Open or short in the wires, or faulty tilt switches

YES

Check for continuity between the DPMS control unit 10-P connector BLU/GRN wire and the 18-P connector GRY² wire, and between the DPMS 14-P connector BLU/WHT³ wire and the 18-P connector GRY² wire. There should be continuity with the retract and extend switches pushed, and there should be no continuity with the switches released.

Is continuity as specified? — NO → Open or short in the wires, or faulty extend and retract switches

YES

Check voltage between the SC control unit 8-P connector YEL/WHT² wire and ground.

Is there 10 – 14 V? — NO → Open in the wires or faulty DPMS control unit

YES

Faulty DPMS control unit

94J47059   Courtesy of American Honda Motor Co., Inc.

BLU/YEL⁴   BLU⁴

DRIVER'S SEAT HARNESS SLIDE MOTOR CONNECTOR

Flowchart No. 21

Check for continuity between the DPMS control unit 18-P connector GRY² wire and ground, and between the 18-P connector GRY² wire and the DPMS control unit 10-P connector YEL/BLU wire.

Is there continuity? — YES → Short in the wires

NO

Check for continuity between the DPMS control unit 18-P connector BLU¹ and GRY² wires, and the BLU/YEL² and GRY² wires. There should be continuity with the slide switch pushed forward and back, there should be no continuity with the switch in neutral.

Is continuity as specified? — NO → Open or short in the wires, or faulty slide switch

YES

Check voltage between the PS control unit 10-P connector WHT/BLU wire and ground.

Is there 10 – 14 V? — NO → Open in the wire or faulty DPMS control unit

YES

Check voltage between the BLU⁴ wire of the driver's seat harness slide motor connector and ground, and between the BLU/YEL⁴ wire and ground. There should be about 12 V with the slide switch pushed forward and back, and there should be no voltage with the switch in neutral.

Are voltages as specified? — NO → Faulty PS control unit, open or short in the wires, or faulty slide switch

YES

Test the power seat slide motor

Does the motor run smoothly without noise? — NO → Open in the BLU⁴ or BLU/YEL⁴ motor wires, or faulty slide motor

YES

Faulty DPMS control unit

94G467130 94C47060   Courtesy of American Honda Motor Co., Inc.

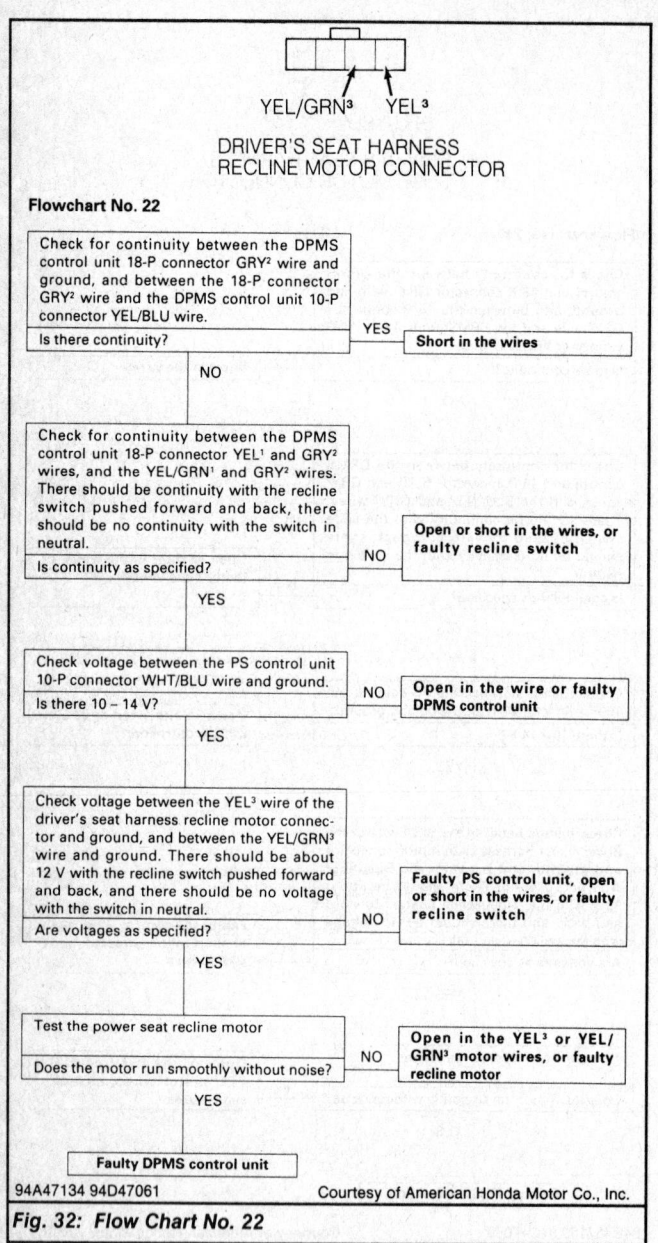

Fig. 32: Flow Chart No. 22

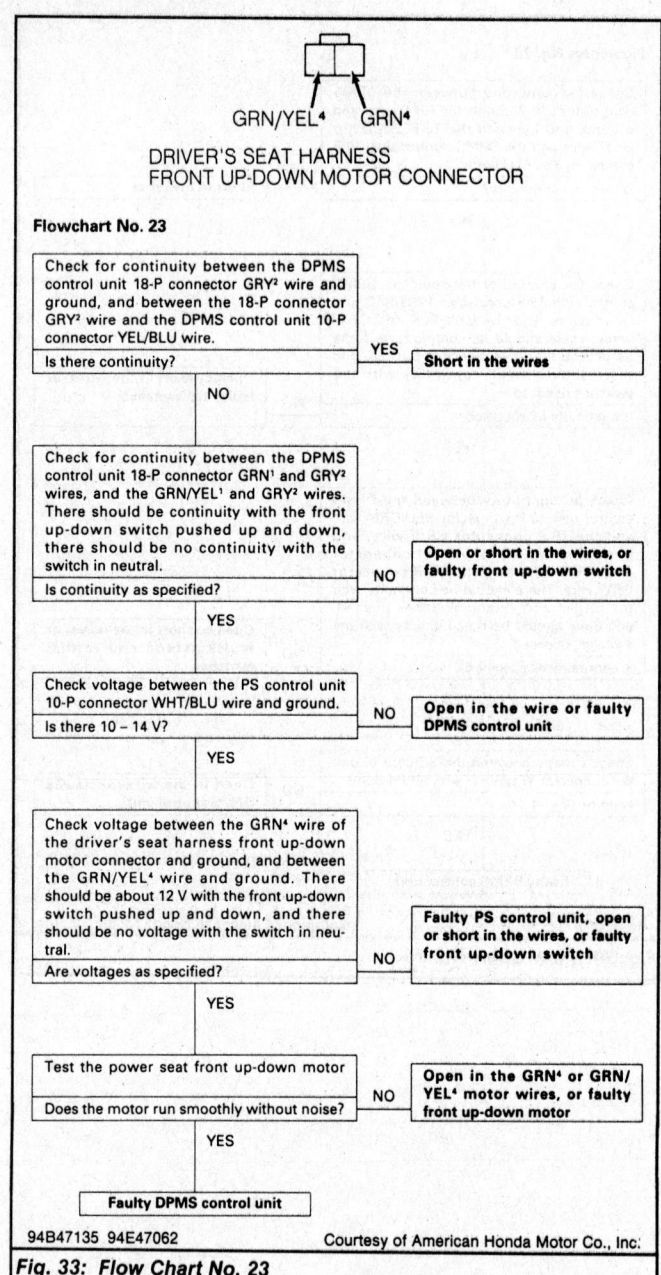

Fig. 33: Flow Chart No. 23

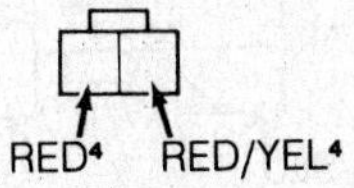

RED⁴   RED/YEL⁴

**DRIVER'S SEAT HARNESS
REAR UP-DOWN MOTOR CONNECTOR**

Flowchart No. 24

Check for continuity between the DPMS control unit 18-P connector GRY² wire and ground, and between the 18-P connector GRY² wire and the DPMS control unit 10-P connector YEL/BLU wire.
Is there continuity?

→ YES → **Short in the wires**

↓ NO

Check for continuity between the DPMS control unit 18-P connector RED² and GRY² wires, and the RED/YEL¹ and GRY² wires. There should be continuity with the rear up-down switch pushed up and down, there should be no continuity with the switch in neutral.
Is continuity as specified?

→ NO → **Open or short in the wires, or faulty rear up-down switch**

↓ YES

Check voltage between the PS control unit 10-P connector WHT/BLU wire and ground.
Is there 10 – 14 V?

→ NO → **Open in the wire or faulty DPMS control unit**

↓ YES

Check voltage between the RED⁴ wire of the driver's seat harness rear up-down motor connector and ground, and between the RED/YEL⁴ wire and ground. There should be about 12 V with the rear up-down switch pushed up and down, and there should be no voltage with the switch in neutral.
Are voltages as specified?

→ NO → **Faulty PS control unit, open or short in the wires, or faulty rear up-down switch**

↓ YES

Test the power seat rear up-down motor
Does the motor run smoothly without noise?

→ NO → **Open in the RED⁴ or RED/YEL⁴ motor wires, or faulty rear up-down motor**

↓ YES

Faulty DPMS control unit

94C47136 94F47063   Courtesy of American Honda Motor Co., Inc.

Fig. 34: Flow Chart No. 24

Flowchart No. 27

Check voltage between the DPMS control unit 12-P connector GRN/YEL⁴ and BLK¹ wires.
NOTE: All DPMS and PS control unit connectors must be connected.
Does voltage pulse between 1 V or less and 5 V or more with the slide motor running?

→ NO → **Open or short in the wires, or faulty slide memory sensor**

↓ YES

Faulty DPMS control unit

94H47065   Courtesy of American Honda Motor Co., Inc.

Fig. 35: Flow Chart No. 27

Flowchart No. 28

Check voltage between the DPMS control unit 12-P connector GRN/WHT and BLK¹ wires.
NOTE: All DPMS and PS control unit connectors must be connected.
Does voltage pulse between 1 V or less and 5 V or more with the recline motor running?

→ NO → **Open or short in the wires, or faulty recline memory sensor**

↓ YES

Faulty DPMS control unit

94I47066   Courtesy of American Honda Motor Co., Inc.

Fig. 36: Flow Chart No. 28

Flowchart No. 29

Check voltage between the DPMS control unit 12-P connector GRN/RED³ and BLK¹ wires.
NOTE: All DPMS and PS control unit connectors must be connected.
Does voltage pulse between 1 V or less and 5 V or more with the front up-down motor running?

→ NO → **Open or short in the wires, or faulty front up-down memory sensor**

↓ YES

Faulty DPMS control unit

94J47067   Courtesy of American Honda Motor Co., Inc.

Fig. 37: Flow Chart No. 29

Flowchart No. 30

Check voltage between the DPMS control unit 12-P connector GRN/BLU² and BLK¹ wires.
NOTE: All DPMS and PS control unit connectors must be connected.
Does voltage pulse between 1 V or less and 5 V or more with the rear up-down motor running?

→ NO → **Open or short in the wires, or faulty rear up-down memory sensor**

↓ YES

Faulty DPMS control unit

94I47082   Courtesy of American Honda Motor Co., Inc.

Fig. 38: Flow Chart No. 30

Flowchart No. 33

Check voltage between the DPMS control unit 12-P connector BLK/RED wire and ground. There should be 1 V or less with the ignition switch OFF, and there should be 10 V or more with the ignition switch ON.
Are voltages as specified?

→ NO → **Open or short in the wire, blown No. 20 (7.5 A) fuse in the under-dash fuse/relay box, or faulty ignition switch**

↓ YES

Check for continuity between the DPMS control unit 18-P connector GRY² wire and ground, and between the 18-P connector GRY² wire and the DPMS control unit 10-P connector YEL/BLU wire.
Is there continuity?

→ YES → **Short in the wires**

↓ NO

Check for continuity between the DPMS control unit 18-P connector YEL/WHT¹ wire and GRY² wire. There should be continuity with the MEMO button pushed, and there should be no continuity with the MEMO button released.
Is continuity as specified?

→ NO → **Open or short in the wires, or faulty MEMO button**

↓ YES

Faulty DPMS control unit

94J47083   Courtesy of American Honda Motor Co., Inc.

Fig. 39: Flow Chart No. 33

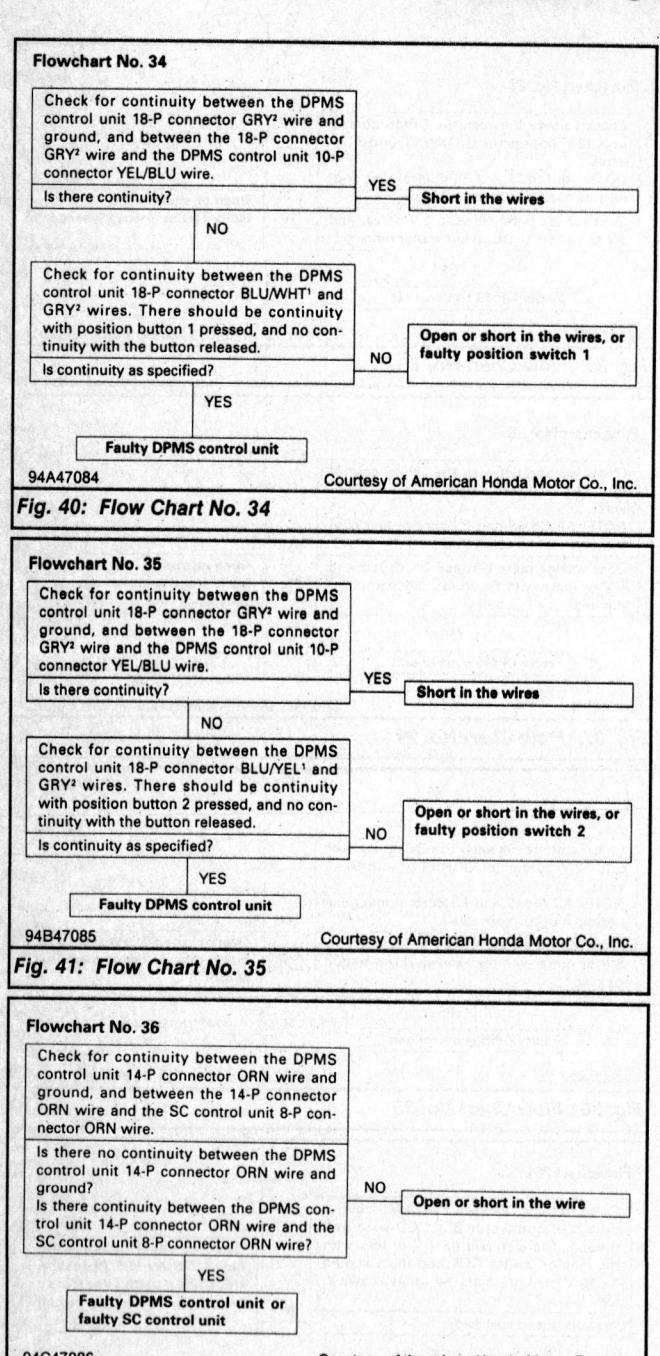

Flowchart No. 34

Check for continuity between the DPMS control unit 18-P connector GRY² wire and ground, and between the 18-P connector GRY² wire and the DPMS control unit 10-P connector YEL/BLU wire.

Is there continuity? — YES → **Short in the wires**

NO

Check for continuity between the DPMS control unit 18-P connector BLU/WHT¹ and GRY² wires. There should be continuity with position button 1 pressed, and no continuity with the button released.

Is continuity as specified? — NO → **Open or short in the wires, or faulty position switch 1**

YES

Faulty DPMS control unit

94A47084   Courtesy of American Honda Motor Co., Inc.

Fig. 40: Flow Chart No. 34

Flowchart No. 35

Check for continuity between the DPMS control unit 18-P connector GRY² wire and ground, and between the 18-P connector GRY² wire and the DPMS control unit 10-P connector YEL/BLU wire.

Is there continuity? — YES → **Short in the wires**

NO

Check for continuity between the DPMS control unit 18-P connector BLU/YEL¹ and GRY² wires. There should be continuity with position button 2 pressed, and no continuity with the button released.

Is continuity as specified? — NO → **Open or short in the wires, or faulty position switch 2**

YES

Faulty DPMS control unit

94B47085   Courtesy of American Honda Motor Co., Inc.

Fig. 41: Flow Chart No. 35

Flowchart No. 36

Check for continuity between the DPMS control unit 14-P connector ORN wire and ground, and between the 14-P connector ORN wire and the SC control unit 8-P connector ORN wire.

Is there no continuity between the DPMS control unit 14-P connector ORN wire and ground?
Is there continuity between the DPMS control unit 14-P connector ORN wire and the SC control unit 8-P connector ORN wire? — NO → **Open or short in the wire**

YES

Faulty DPMS control unit or faulty SC control unit

94C47086   Courtesy of American Honda Motor Co., Inc.

Fig. 42: Flow Chart No. 36

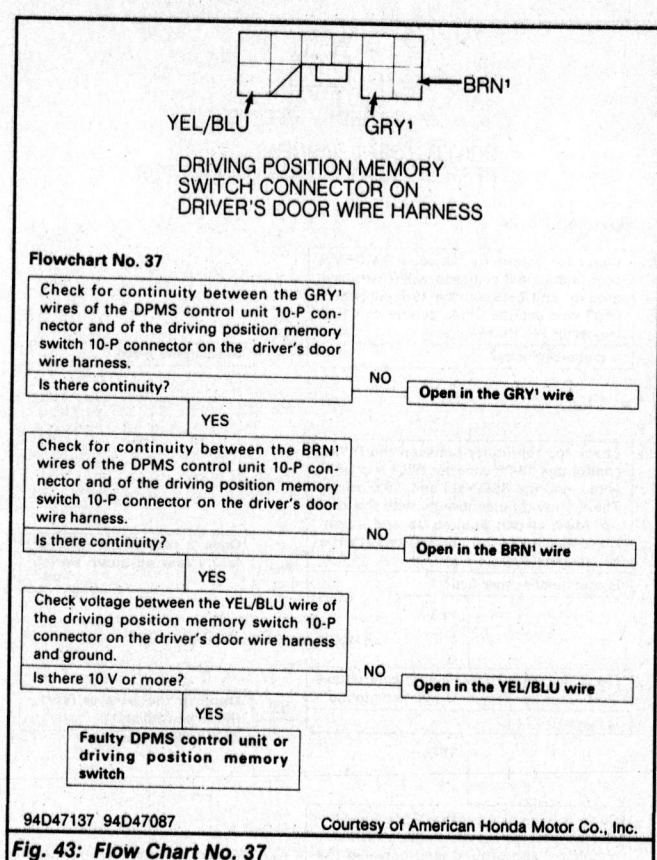

YEL/BLU   GRY¹   ← BRN¹

DRIVING POSITION MEMORY SWITCH CONNECTOR ON DRIVER'S DOOR WIRE HARNESS

Flowchart No. 37

Check for continuity between the GRY¹ wires of the DPMS control unit 10-P connector and of the driving position memory switch 10-P connector on the driver's door wire harness.

Is there continuity? — NO → **Open in the GRY¹ wire**

YES

Check for continuity between the BRN¹ wires of the DPMS control unit 10-P connector and of the driving position memory switch 10-P connector on the driver's door wire harness.

Is there continuity? — NO → **Open in the BRN¹ wire**

YES

Check voltage between the YEL/BLU wire of the driving position memory switch 10-P connector on the driver's door wire harness and ground.

Is there 10 V or more? — NO → **Open in the YEL/BLU wire**

YES

Faulty DPMS control unit or driving position memory switch

94D47137 94D47087   Courtesy of American Honda Motor Co., Inc.

Fig. 43: Flow Chart No. 37

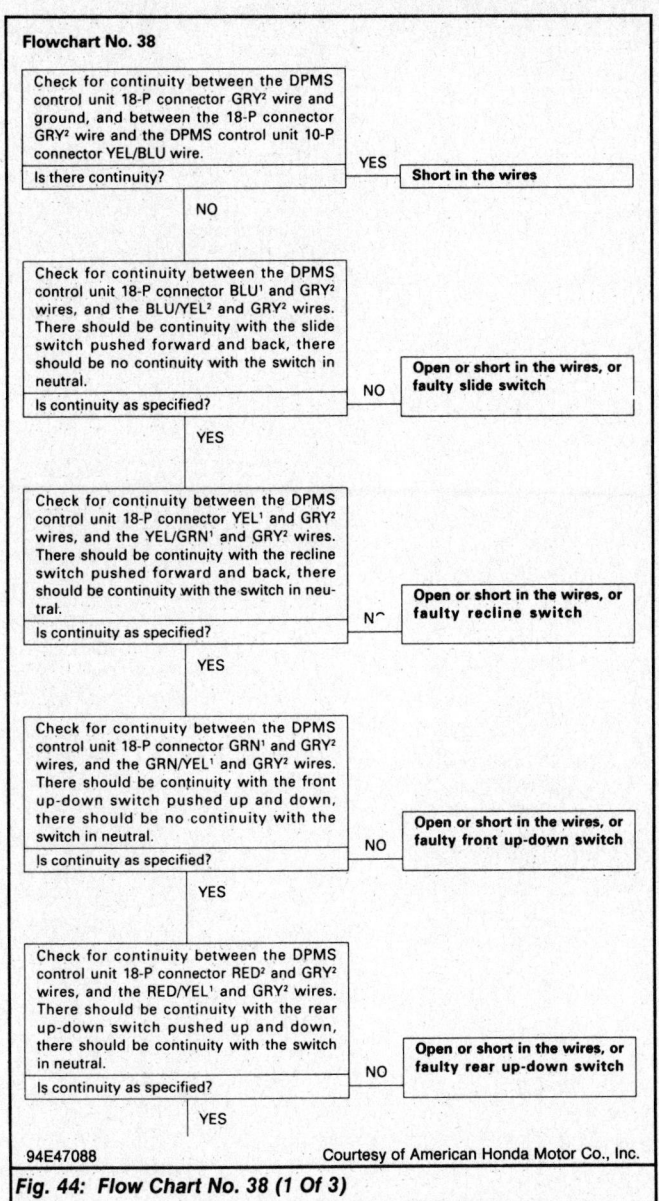

Flowchart No. 38

Check for continuity between the DPMS control unit 18-P connector GRY² wire and ground, and between the 18-P connector GRY² wire and the DPMS control unit 10-P connector YEL/BLU wire.
Is there continuity?

→ YES → **Short in the wires**

↓ NO

Check for continuity between the DPMS control unit 18-P connector BLU¹ and GRY² wires, and the BLU/YEL² and GRY² wires. There should be continuity with the slide switch pushed forward and back, there should be no continuity with the switch in neutral.
Is continuity as specified?

→ NO → **Open or short in the wires, or faulty slide switch**

↓ YES

Check for continuity between the DPMS control unit 18-P connector YEL¹ and GRY² wires, and the YEL/GRN¹ and GRY² wires. There should be continuity with the recline switch pushed forward and back, there should be continuity with the switch in neutral.
Is continuity as specified?

→ N~ → **Open or short in the wires, or faulty recline switch**

↓ YES

Check for continuity between the DPMS control unit 18-P connector GRN¹ and GRY² wires, and the GRN/YEL¹ and GRY² wires. There should be continuity with the front up-down switch pushed up and down, there should be no continuity with the switch in neutral.
Is continuity as specified?

→ NO → **Open or short in the wires, or faulty front up-down switch**

↓ YES

Check for continuity between the DPMS control unit 18-P connector RED² and GRY² wires, and the RED/YEL¹ and GRY² wires. There should be continuity with the rear up-down switch pushed up and down, there should be continuity with the switch in neutral.
Is continuity as specified?

→ NO → **Open or short in the wires, or faulty rear up-down switch**

↓ YES

94E47088
Courtesy of American Honda Motor Co., Inc.

Fig. 44: Flow Chart No. 38 (1 Of 3)

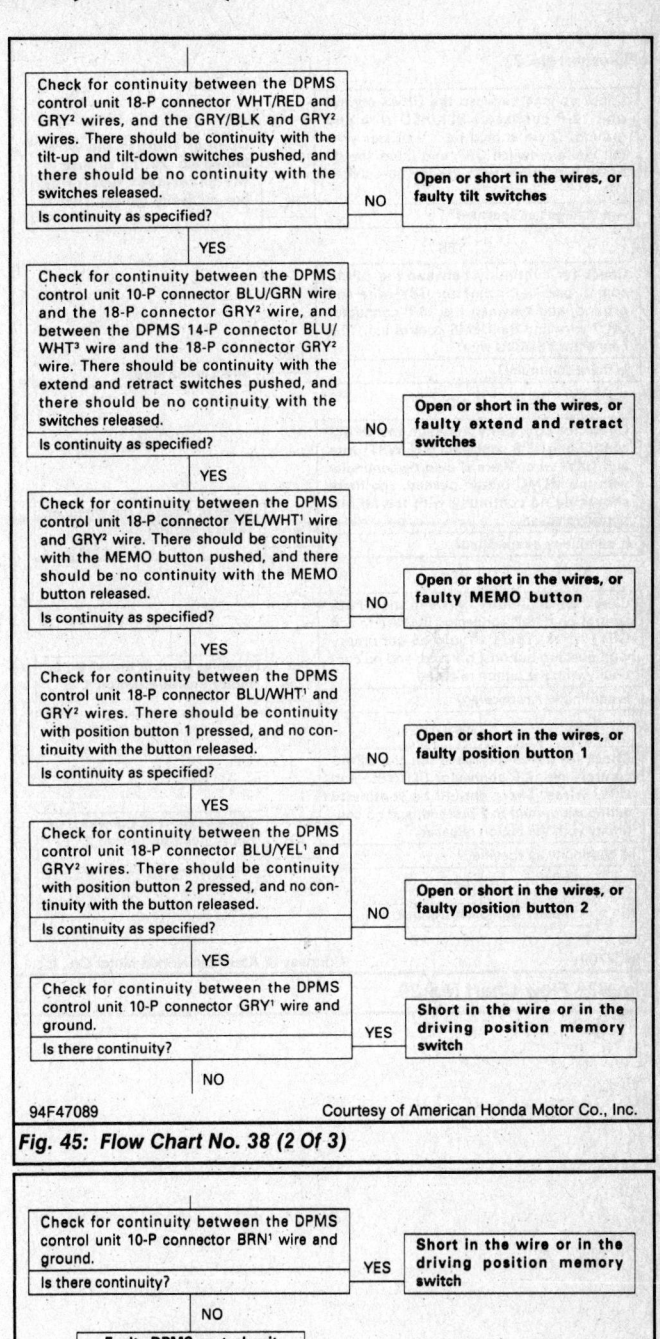

Check for continuity between the DPMS control unit 18-P connector WHT/RED and GRY² wires, and the GRY/BLK and GRY² wires. There should be continuity with the tilt-up and tilt-down switches pushed, and there should be no continuity with the switches released.
Is continuity as specified?

→ NO → **Open or short in the wires, or faulty tilt switches**

↓ YES

Check for continuity between the DPMS control unit 10-P connector BLU/GRN wire and the 18-P connector GRY² wire, and between the DPMS 14-P connector BLU/WHT³ wire and the 18-P connector GRY² wire. There should be continuity with the extend and retract switches pushed, and there should be no continuity with the switches released.
Is continuity as specified?

→ NO → **Open or short in the wires, or faulty extend and retract switches**

↓ YES

Check for continuity between the DPMS control unit 18-P connector YEL/WHT¹ wire and GRY² wire. There should be continuity with the MEMO button pushed, and there should be no continuity with the MEMO button released.
Is continuity as specified?

→ NO → **Open or short in the wires, or faulty MEMO button**

↓ YES

Check for continuity between the DPMS control unit 18-P connector BLU/WHT¹ and GRY² wires. There should be continuity with position button 1 pressed, and no continuity with the button released.
Is continuity as specified?

→ NO → **Open or short in the wires, or faulty position button 1**

↓ YES

Check for continuity between the DPMS control unit 18-P connector BLU/YEL¹ and GRY² wires. There should be continuity with position button 2 pressed, and no continuity with the button released.
Is continuity as specified?

→ NO → **Open or short in the wires, or faulty position button 2**

↓ YES

Check for continuity between the DPMS control unit 10-P connector GRY¹ wire and ground.
Is there continuity?

→ YES → **Short in the wire or in the driving position memory switch**

↓ NO

94F47089
Courtesy of American Honda Motor Co., Inc.

Fig. 45: Flow Chart No. 38 (2 Of 3)

Check for continuity between the DPMS control unit 10-P connector BRN¹ wire and ground.
Is there continuity?

→ YES → **Short in the wire or in the driving position memory switch**

↓ NO

Faulty DPMS control unit

94I47090
Courtesy of American Honda Motor Co., Inc.

Fig. 46: Flow Chart No. 38 (3 Of 3)

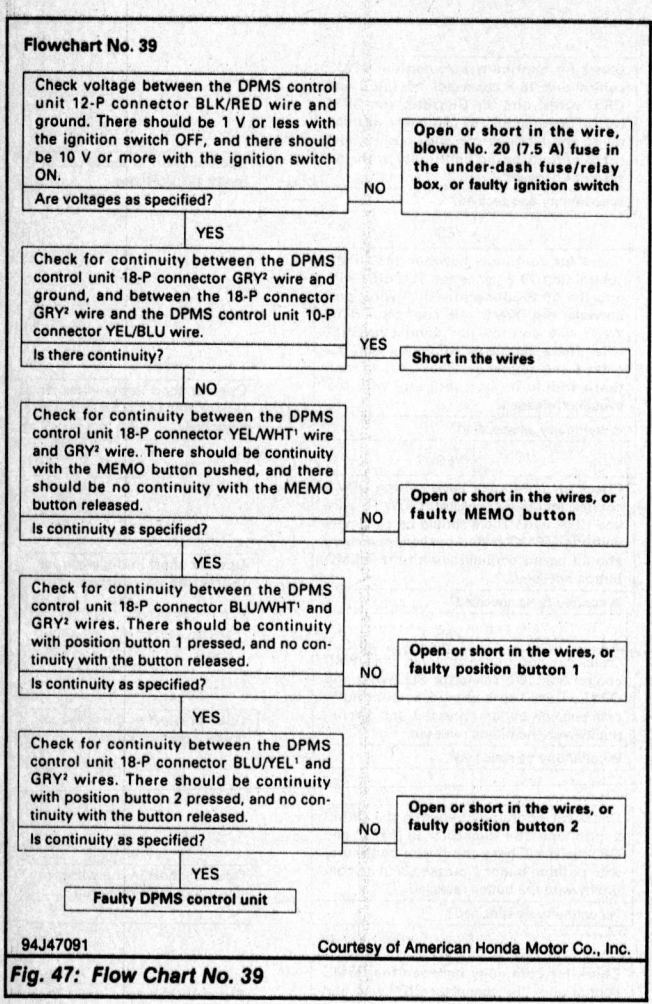

Flowchart No. 39

Check voltage between the DPMS control unit 12-P connector BLK/RED wire and ground. There should be 1 V or less with the ignition switch OFF, and there should be 10 V or more with the ignition switch ON.

Are voltages as specified?

NO → Open or short in the wire, blown No. 20 (7.5 A) fuse in the under-dash fuse/relay box, or faulty ignition switch

YES

Check for continuity between the DPMS control unit 18-P connector GRY² wire and ground, and between the 18-P connector GRY² wire and the DPMS control unit 10-P connector YEL/BLU wire.

Is there continuity?

YES → Short in the wires

NO

Check for continuity between the DPMS control unit 18-P connector YEL/WHT¹ wire and GRY² wire. There should be continuity with the MEMO button pushed, and there should be no continuity with the MEMO button released.

Is continuity as specified?

NO → Open or short in the wires, or faulty MEMO button

YES

Check for continuity between the DPMS control unit 18-P connector BLU/WHT¹ and GRY² wires. There should be continuity with position button 1 pressed, and no continuity with the button released.

Is continuity as specified?

NO → Open or short in the wires, or faulty position button 1

YES

Check for continuity between the DPMS control unit 18-P connector BLU/YEL¹ and GRY² wires. There should be continuity with position button 2 pressed, and no continuity with the button released.

Is continuity as specified?

NO → Open or short in the wires, or faulty position button 2

YES

Faulty DPMS control unit

94J47091   Courtesy of American Honda Motor Co., Inc.

Fig. 47: Flow Chart No. 39

TESTING

NOTE: *Different wires of the same color have been assigned a suffix number to distinguish them. See Fig 1. For example, the Green/Blue[1] wire is not the same as the Green/Blue[2] wire. Refer to Fig. 1 for all connector views.*

CONTROL UNIT INPUT TESTS

Legend – Seat control unit is located under front center of driver's seat. Driving Position Memory System (DPMS) Control Unit is located under left rear seat at left side. Unplug connectors. Check all connections and repair as necessary. *See Fig. 48-52.*

Use this chart for a quick check (with all connectors connected) of the input signals to and the output signals from the driving position memory system (DPMS) control unit.

Connector	Wire	Signal	Voltage should be	Symptom if voltage is not as specified
10-P	YEL/BLU	Battery power input	10 – 14 V	All functions don't work at all.
10-P	GRY[1]	Indicator 1 output	Indicator ON: 2 V or less Indicator OFF: 10 V or more	Indicator doesn't go on (open). Indicator doesn't go off (short).
10-P	BRN[1]	Indicator 2 output	Indicator ON: 2 V or less Indicator OFF: 10 V or more	Indicator doesn't go on (open). Indicator doesn't go off (short).
10-P	BLK[2]	DPMS control unit ground	No voltage	All functions don't work at all.
10-P	BLU/GRN	Input from steering column retract switch	Switch ON: 1 V or less Switch OFF: 4 V or more	Column doesn't retract (open). Column neither extends nor retracts (short).
10-P	YEL/WHT[2]	Power output to steering column control unit relays	10 – 14 V	Steering column doesn't move at all.
10-P	WHT/BLU	Power output to power seat control unit relays	10 – 14 V	Power seat doesn't move at all.
10-P	BLK[3]	DPMS control unit ground	No voltage	All functions don't work at all.
14-P	RED/YEL[2]	Output to steering column tilt-up relay	Relay ON: 1 V or less Relay OFF: 10 V or more	Column doesn't tilt up (open). Column neither tilts up nor down (short).
14-P	RED/BLU	Output to steering column tilt-down relay	Relay ON: 1 V or less Relay OFF: 10 V or more	Column doesn't tilt down (open). Column neither tilts up nor down (short).
14-P	GRN/BLU[1]	Output to steering column retract relay	Relay ON: 1 V or less Relay OFF: 10 V or more	Column doesn't retract (open). Column neither extends nor retracts (short).
14-P	GRN/YEL[2]	Output to steering column extend relay	Relay ON: 1 V or less Relay OFF: 10 V or more	Column doesn't extend (open). Column neither retracts nor extends (short).

94A47092

Courtesy of American Honda Motor Co., Inc.

Fig. 48: Testing DPMS Input & Output Signals (1 Of 5)

Connector	Wire	Signal	Voltage should be	Symptom if voltage is not as specified
14-P	BLU[3]	Output to power seat slide-forward relay	Relay ON: 1 V or less Relay OFF: 10 V or more	Seat doesn't slide forward (open). Seat slides neither forward nor back (short).
14-P	BLU/YEL[3]	Output to power seat slide-back relay	Relay ON: 1 V or less Relay OFF: 10 V or more	Seat doesn't slide back (open). Seat slides neither back nor forward (short).
14-P	YEL[2]	Output to power seat recline-forward relay	Relay ON: 1 V or less Relay OFF: 10 V or more	Seat doesn't recline forward (open). Seat reclines neither forward nor back (short).
14-P	YEL/GRN[2]	Output to power seat recline-back relay	Relay ON: 1 V or less Relay OFF: 10 V or more	Seat doesn't recline back (open). Seat reclines neither forward nor back (short).
14-P	GRN[2]	Output to power seat front-up relay	Relay ON: 1 V or less Relay OFF: 10 V or more	Seat front doesn't move up (open). Seat front moves neither up nor down (short).
14-P	GRN/YEL[3]	Output to power seat front-down relay	Relay ON: 1 V or less Relay OFF: 10 V or more	Seat front doesn't move down (open). Seat front moves neither down nor up (short).
14-P	RED[3]	Output to power seat rear-up relay	Relay ON: 1 V or less Relay OFF: 10 V or more	Seat rear doesn't move up (open). Seat rear moves neither up nor down (short).
14-P	RED/YEL[3]	Output to power seat rear-down relay	Relay ON: 1 V or less Relay OFF: 10 V or more	Seat rear doesn't move down (open). Seat rear moves neither down nor up (short).
14-P	ORN	Output to buzzer	Buzzer sounds: 10 V or more Buzzer is OFF: 1 V or less	Buzzer doesn't sound.
14-P	BLU/WHT[3]	Steering column extend switch input	Switch ON: 1 V or less Switch OFF: 4 V or more	Column doesn't extend (open). Column neither retracts nor extends (short).

94B47093

Courtesy of American Honda Motor Co., Inc.

Fig. 49: Testing DPMS Input & Output Signals (2 Of 5)

Connector	Wire	Signal	Voltage should be	Symptom if voltage is not as specified
12-P	GRN/RED[2]	AUTO switch input	Switch ON: 1 V or less Switch OFF: 4 V or more	Steering column doesn't tilt up and retract when the ignition key is pulled out (open). Steering column tilts up and retracts when the ignition switch is turned OFF (short).
12-P	WHT/GRN (M/T)	Parking brake switch input	Switch ON: 1 V or less (Parking brake lever up) Switch OFF: 4 V or more (Parking brake lever down)	Steering column doesn't tilt up and retract when the ignition key is pulled out (open). Steering column tilts up and retracts when the parking brake switch is OFF (short).
12-P	WHT/GRN (A/T)	A/T gear position switch input	1 V or less with shift lever in $\boxed{P}$ 4 V or more with shift lever in any other position than $\boxed{P}$	Steering column doesn't tilt up and retract when the ignition key is pulled out (open). Steering column tilts up and retracts when the shift lever is not in $\boxed{P}$ (short).
12-P	BLK/RED	Ignition switch input	Switch ON: 10 V or more Switch OFF: 1 V or less	Position can't be stored (open). Position can be stored (short).
12-P	BLU[2]	Tilt sensor input	As column tilts up, voltage changes from 0 to 5 V. As column tilts down, voltage changes from 5 V to 0.	Column can be manually tilted only for one second and doesn't tilt automatically.
12-P	PNK	Extend-retract sensor input	As column retracts, voltage changes from 0 to 5 V. As column extends, voltage changes from 5 V to 0.	Column can be manually extended or retracted for only one second and doesn't extend/retract automatically.
12-P	GRN/YEL[4]	Seat slide sensor input	As seat slides, voltages pulses from 1 V or less to 4 V or more.	Seat can be manually slided only for one second and doesn't slide automatically.
12-P	GRN/WHT	Seat recline sensor input	As seat reclines, voltage pulses from 1 V or less to 4 V or more.	Seat can be manually reclined only for one second and doesn't recline automatically.
12-P	GRN/RED[3]	Seat front up-down sensor input	As seat front moves up or down, voltage pulses from 1 V or less to 4 V or more.	Seat front can be manually moved up or down only for one second and doesn't move up/down automatically.

94E47138

Fig. 50: Testing DPMS Input & Output Signals (3 Of 5)

Connector	Wire	Signal	Voltage should be	Symptom if voltage is not as specified
12-P	GRN/BLU[2]	Seat rear up-down sensor input	As seat rear moves up or down, voltage pulses from 1 V or less to 4 V or more.	Seat rear can be manually moved up/down for only one second and doesn't move up/down automatically.
12-P	YEL/RED	Vehicle speed sensor (VSS) input	When the car runs, voltage pulses from 1 V or less to 5 V or more.	Adjustment mode 3 works when the car runs with the driver's door open.
12-P	BLK[1]	Seat sensor ground	1 V or less	Seat can be manually adjusted for only one second and doesn't adjust automatically (open).
12-P	BRN[2]	Steering column sensor ground	1 V or less	Steering column can be manually adjusted for only one second and doesn't adjust automatically (open).
18-P	BLU/WHT[2]	Ignition key switch input	Key inserted: 1 V or less Key removed: 10 V or more	Steering column doesn't tilt up and retract when the ignition key is pulled out.
18-P	YEL/WHT[1]	MEMO switch input	Switch ON: 1 V or less Switch OFF: 4 V or more	Position can't be stored; automatic adjustment can't be stopped by pushing the MEMO button.
18-P	BLU/WHT[1]	Position switch 1 input	Switch ON: 1 V or less Switch OFF: 4 V or more	Position 1 can't be retrieved; automatic adjustment can't be stopped by pushing position button 1
18-P	BLU/YEL[1]	Position switch 2 input	Switch ON: 1 V or less Switch OFF: 4 V or more	Position 2 can't be retrieved; automatic adjustment can't be stopped by pushing position button 2
18-P	GRY[3]	Constant voltage output to steering column sensors	About 5 V	Steering column can be manually adjusted only for one second and doesn't adjust automatically
18-P	WHT/RED	Tilt-up switch input	Switch ON: 1 V or less Switch OFF: 4 V or more	Column doesn't tilt up (open). Column tilts neither up nor down (short).

94F47139

Courtesy of American Honda Motor Co., Inc.

Fig. 51: Testing DPMS Input & Output Signals (4 Of 5)

Connector	Wire	Signal	Voltage should be	Symptom if voltage is not as specified
18-P	GRY/BLK	Tilt-down switch input	Switch ON: 1 V or less Switch OFF: 4 V or more	Column doesn't tilt down (open). Column tilts neither down nor up (short).
18-P	GRN/RED[1]	Driver's door switch input	Door open: 1 V or less Door closed: 10 V or more	Adjustment mode 4 works with the driver's door open (open). Adjustment mode 3 works with the car running (short).
18-P	BLU[1]	Seat slide-forward switch input	Switch ON: 1 V or less Switch OFF: 4 V or more	Seat doesn't slide forward (open). Seat slides neither forward nor back (short).
18-P	BLU/YEL[2]	Seat slide-back switch input	Switch ON: 1 V or less Switch OFF: 4 V or more	Seat doesn't slide back (open). Seat slides neither back nor forward (short).
18-P	YEL[1]	Seat recline-forward switch input	Switch ON: 1 V or less Switch OFF: 4 V or more	Seat doesn't recline forward (open). Seat reclines neither forward nor back (short).
18-P	YEL/GRN[1]	Seat recline-back switch input	Switch ON: 1 V or less Switch OFF: 4 V or more	Seat doesn't recline back (open). Seat reclines neither back nor forward (short).
18-P	GRN[1]	Seat front-up switch switch input	Switch ON: 1 V or less Switch OFF: 4 V or more	Seat front doesn't move up (open). Seat front moves neither up nor down (short).
18-P	GRN/YEL[1]	Seat front-down switch input	Switch ON: 1 V or less Switch OFF: 4 V or more	Seat front doesn't move down (open). Seat front moves neither down nor up (short).
18-P	RED[2]	Seat rear-up switch input	Switch ON: 1 V or less Switch OFF: 4 V or more	Seat rear doesn't move up (open). Seat rear moves neither up nor down (short).
18-P	RED/YEL[1]	Seat rear-down switch input	Switch ON: 1 V or less Switch OFF: 4 V or more	Seat rear doesn't move down (open). Seat rear moves neither down nor up (short).
18-P	GRY[2]	Common input from all seat, steering column, and position switches, and from the MEMO switch	Switch ON: 1 V or less Switch OFF: 4 V or more	Switches, adjustment modes 3 and 4 don't work, and positions can't be stored.
18-P	GRN[3]	Seat reclining limit switch input	Within 20° angle from most forward recline position: 1 V or less Beyond 25° angle from most forward recline position: 4 V or more	Seat doesn't stop at the reclining limit in adjustment modes 3 and 4

94I47140

Courtesy of American Honda Motor Co., Inc.

Fig. 52: Testing DPMS Input & Output Signals (5 Of 5)

MOTOR TEST

CAUTION: Disconnect power from motor immediately when motor stops.

Legend – Remove seat. Unplug connector from motor. Using jumper wires, connect motor terminals to battery voltage and ground. See WIRING DIAGRAMS for appropriate wire colors. Motor should run smoothly. Transpose jumper wires. Motor should run smoothly in opposite direction. Replace motor if operation is not as specified.

Vigor – 1) Remove seat. Unplug connector from slide motor. Remove seat switch from side of seat. Unplug 6-pin connector from switch. Connect battery voltage to terminal No. 7 and ground terminal No. 8. *See Fig. 53.* Seat should move backward. Reverse battery leads at motor and seat should slide forward.

2) Connect battery voltage to terminal No. 4 and ground terminal No. 3. *See Fig. 53.* Seat back should move forward. Reverse battery leads at motor and seat back should move backward (recline). If either motor does not work as described, replace motor(s).

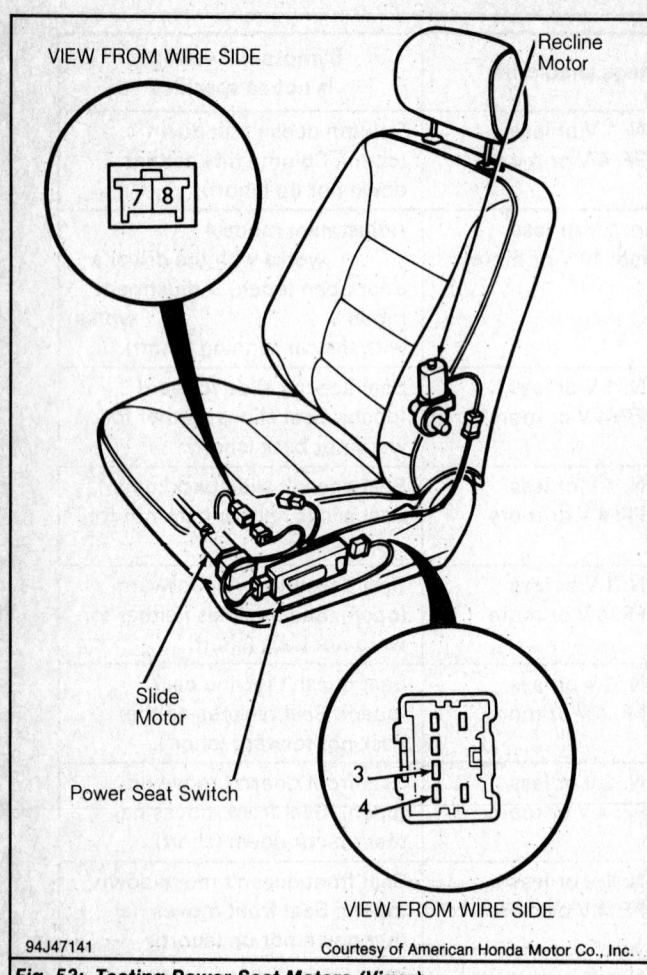

Fig. 53: Testing Power Seat Motors (Vigor)

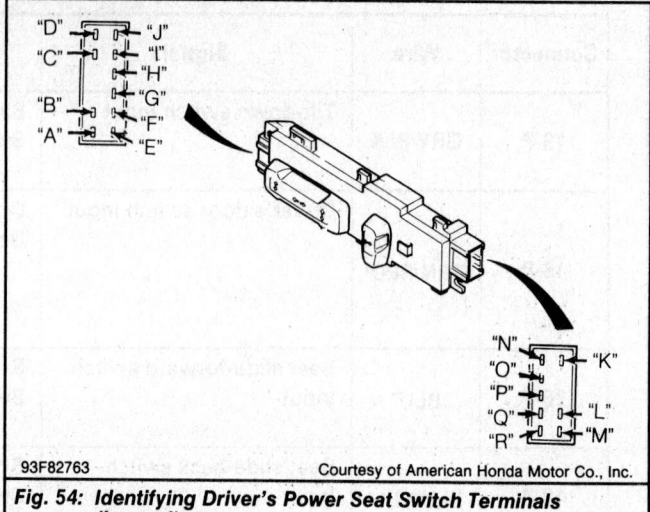

Fig. 54: Identifying Driver's Power Seat Switch Terminals (Legend)

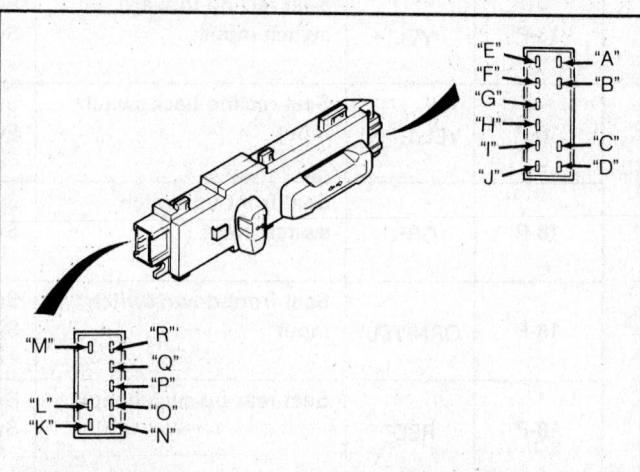

Fig. 55: Identifying Passenger Power Seat Switch Terminals (Legend)

SWITCH TEST

Seat Switch (Legend) – Remove seat. Remove switch. Check for continuity between specified terminals with switch held in each position. Replace switch if continuity is not as specified. See appropriate SEAT SWITCH TEST (LEGEND) table. See Fig. 54 or 55.

DRIVER'S SEAT SWITCH TEST (LEGEND)

Switch Position	Terminals
Forward/Back	
Forward	C-G
Back	C-F
Front Up/Down	
Up	C-H
Down	C-E
Rear Up/Down	
Up	I-J
Down	A-J
Recline	
Forward	C-F
Back	D-J

PASSENGER'S SEAT SWITCH TEST (LEGEND)

Switch Position	Terminals
Forward/Back	
Forward	B-I; C-F
Neutral	B-C-F
Back	C-I; B-F
Recline	
Forward	D-J; E-L
Neutral	D-E-L
Back	D-E; J-L

Memory Switch (Legend) – Remove driver's door panel. Unplug connector. Remove switch. Check for continuity between specified terminals with switch held in each position. Replace switch if continuity is not as specified. See MEMORY SWITCH TEST (LEGEND) table. See Fig. 56.

MEMORY SWITCH TEST (LEGEND)

Switch Position	Terminals
Memory Switch	
On	E-J
Off	No Continuity
Position Switch 1	
On	E-J
Off	No Continuity
Position Switch 2	
On	F-J
Off	No Continuity
Illumination	
No. 1	A-C
No. 2	A-D

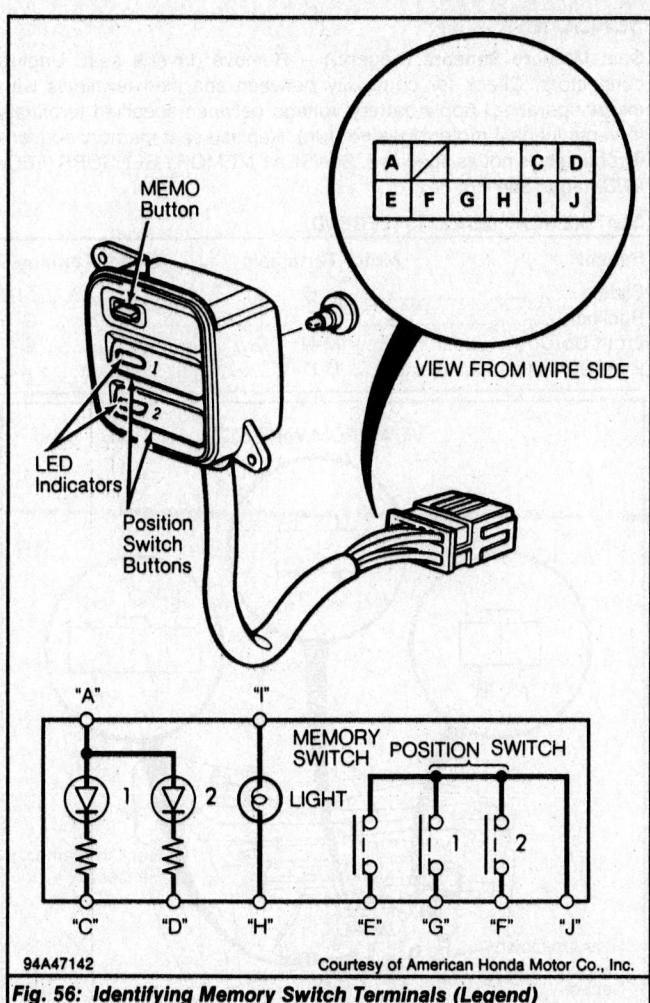

Fig. 56: Identifying Memory Switch Terminals (Legend)

94A47142   Courtesy of American Honda Motor Co., Inc.

Seat Switch (Vigor) – Remove retaining screws and switch. Unplug connectors. Check for continuity between specified terminals with switch in each position. Replace switch if continuity is not as specified. See POWER SEAT SWITCH TEST (VIGOR) table. *See Fig. 57.*

POWER SEAT SWITCH TEST (VIGOR)

Switch Position	Terminals
Forward/Back	
Forward	1-8
Neutral	2-7-8
Back	1-7
Recline	
Forward	4-5
Neutral	3-4-6
Back	3-5

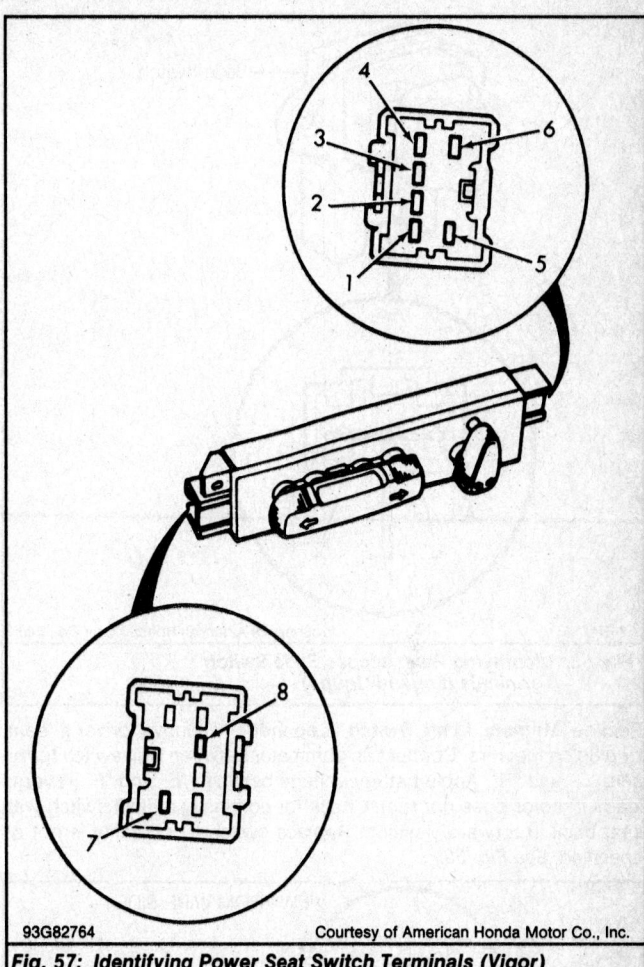

Fig. 57: Identifying Power Seat Switch Terminals (Vigor)

93G82764   Courtesy of American Honda Motor Co., Inc.

Rear Access Slide Switch (Legend Coupe) – Remove retaining screws and switch. Unplug connectors. Check for continuity between specified terminals with switch in each position. Replace switch if continuity is not as specified. See REAR ACCESS SLIDE SWITCH TEST (LEGEND COUPE) table. *See Fig. 58.*

REAR ACCESS SLIDE SWITCH TEST (LEGEND COUPE)

Switch Position	Terminals
Forward	A-D; B-E
Neutral	C-D; B-E
Back	A-B; C-D

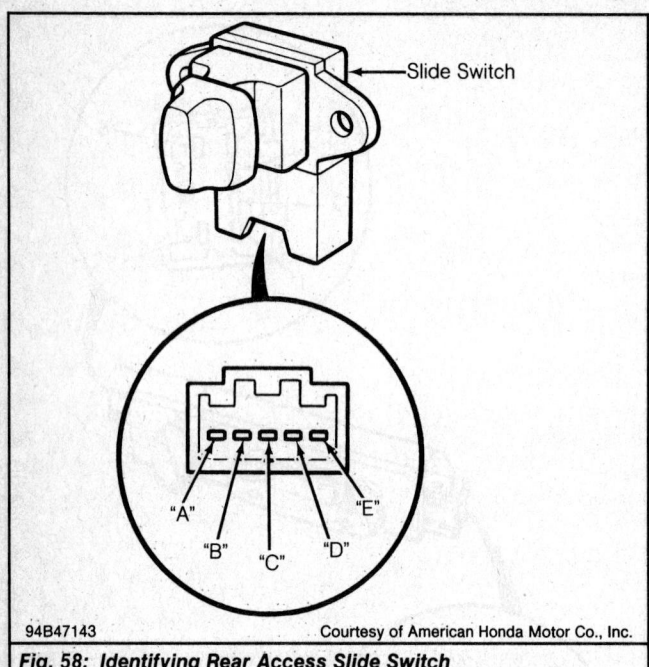

94B47143   Courtesy of American Honda Motor Co., Inc.

Fig. 58: Identifying Rear Access Slide Switch Terminals (Legend Coupe)

Recline Memory Limit Switch (Legend) – Remove driver's seat. Unplug connectors. Connect an ohmmeter between limit switch terminals "Q" and "R". Apply battery voltage between "E" and "F" (reverse leads if motor does not run). Check for continuity at limit switch with seat back in forward position. Replace switch if continuity is not as specified. *See Fig. 59.*

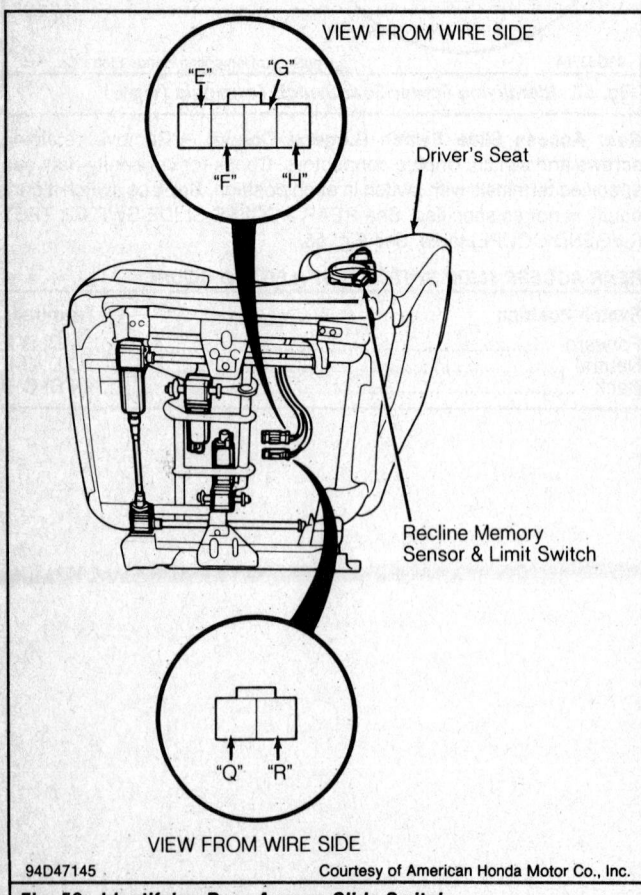

94D47145   Courtesy of American Honda Motor Co., Inc.

Fig. 59: Identifying Rear Access Slide Switch Terminals (Legend Coupe)

SENSORS

Seat Memory Sensors (Legend) – Remove driver's seat. Unplug connectors. Check for continuity between specified terminals with motor operating. Apply battery voltage between specified terminals (reverse leads if motor does not run). Replace seat memory sensors if continuity is not as specified. See SEAT MEMORY SENSORS (LEGEND) table. *See Fig. 60.*

SEAT MEMORY SENSORS (LEGEND)

Sensor	Motor Terminals	Sensor Terminals
Slide	A-B	I-J
Recline	E-F	G-H
Front Up/Down	M-N	O-P
Rear Up/Down	C-D	K-L

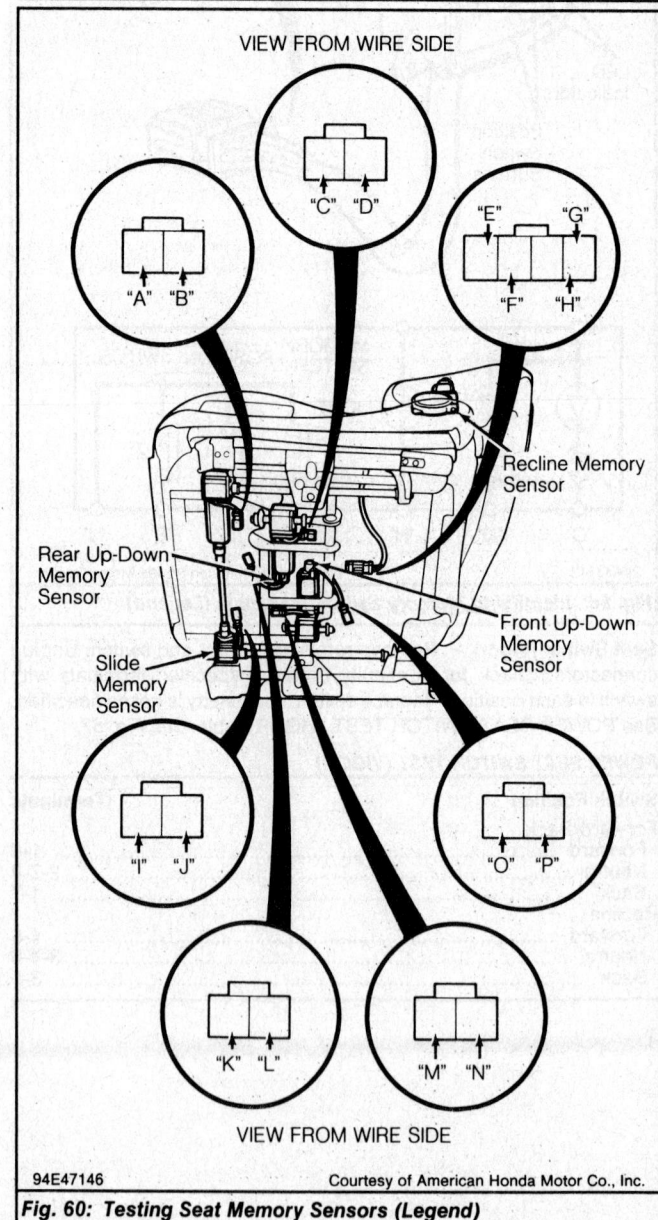

94E47146   Courtesy of American Honda Motor Co., Inc.

Fig. 60: Testing Seat Memory Sensors (Legend)

REMOVAL & INSTALLATION

CAUTION: When battery is disconnected, vehicle computer and memory systems may lose memory data. Driveability problems may exist until computer systems have completed a relearn cycle.

SEAT ASSEMBLY

Removal & Installation – Position seat fully rearward. Remove front seat track covers and front retaining bolts. Position seat fully forward. Remove rear seat track covers and retaining bolts. Unplug electrical connectors. Remove seat from vehicle.

MOTOR (LEGEND)

CAUTION: Wear protective gloves when removing and installing seat motors.

Removal & Installation (Forward/Back Motor) – Remove seat. Remove seat cushion. Remove slide joint cable. Remove retaining nuts and bolts. Remove motor and gearbox. To install, reverse removal procedure.

Removal & Installation (Recline Motor) – Remove seat. Remove seat cushion. Remove switch plate if necessary. Remove retaining nuts. Remove motor and gearbox. To install, reverse removal procedure. Apply molybdenum grease to gears. Apply thread lock cement to retaining nuts.

Removal & Installation (Up/Down Motor) – Raise rear of seat. Remove seat. Remove seat cushion. Remove harness protector from forward/rear adjuster. Remove springs. Remove plate from forward/rear and up/down adjuster. Unplug connectors. Remove retaining nuts and bolts. Slide pipe brackets inward. Remove motor. To install, reverse removal procedure. Apply molybdenum grease to lead screws. Replace bushings. Apply thread lock cement to retaining bolts.

SEAT ADJUSTER (LEGEND)

CAUTION: Wear protective gloves when removing and installing seat adjuster.

Removal & Installation – Raise front and rear of seat. Remove seat. Remove seat cushion and seat back. Remove switch. Separate recline adjuster from forward/back and up/down adjuster. Remove forward/back joint cable. Remove memory control unit. Remove harness protector. Unplug connectors. Remove lower seat rail caps. Remove any remaining clips and retaining bolts. Remove adjusters. To install, reverse removal procedure. Install new bushings.

MOTOR & SEAT ADJUSTER (VIGOR)

Removal & Installation – Use illustration as a guide. *See Fig. 61.*

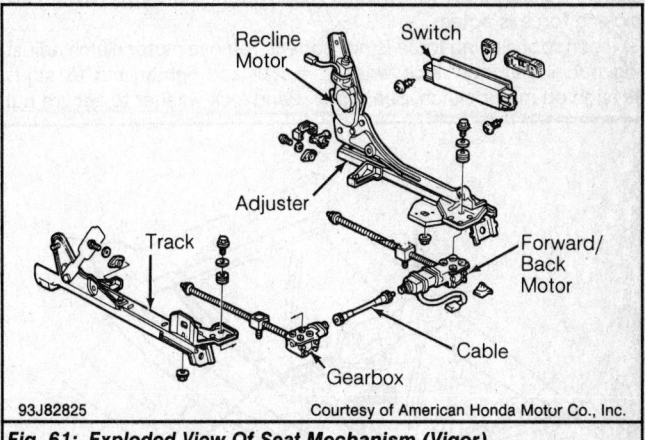

93J82825   Courtesy of American Honda Motor Co., Inc.

Fig. 61: Exploded View Of Seat Mechanism (Vigor)

WIRING DIAGRAMS

NOTE: See ACCESSORIES & EQUIPMENT, Volume 5.

1994 ACCESSORIES & EQUIPMENT
Power Sun Roof

Integra, Legend, Vigor

DESCRIPTION & OPERATION

All models use a permanent magnet motor to operate a cable drive which opens and closes the sun roof. If the drive mechanism fails, the sun roof can be operated manually.

ADJUSTMENTS

CLOSING FORCE

1) Open sun roof part way. Place a shop towel against front edge of glass. Attach a spring scale to glass. *See Fig. 1.* Have someone operate switch to close sun roof.
2) Sun roof should stop moving when closing force is 44-66 lbs. (200-300 N). Release sun roof switch as soon as sunroof stops moving and closing force is noted.
3) If sun roof closing force is not correct, remove motor clutch adjusting nut. Install new lock washer. Install and tighten nut to adjust tension on motor clutch. *See Fig. 2.* Bend lock washer to secure nut.

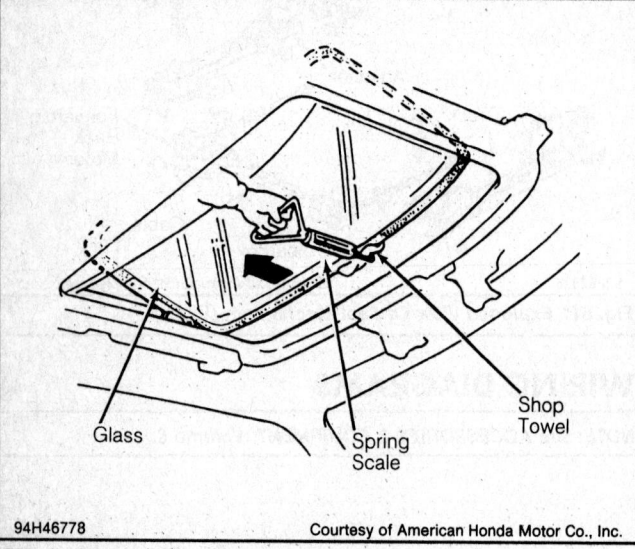

94H46778   Courtesy of American Honda Motor Co., Inc.
Fig. 1: Checking Sun Roof Closing Force

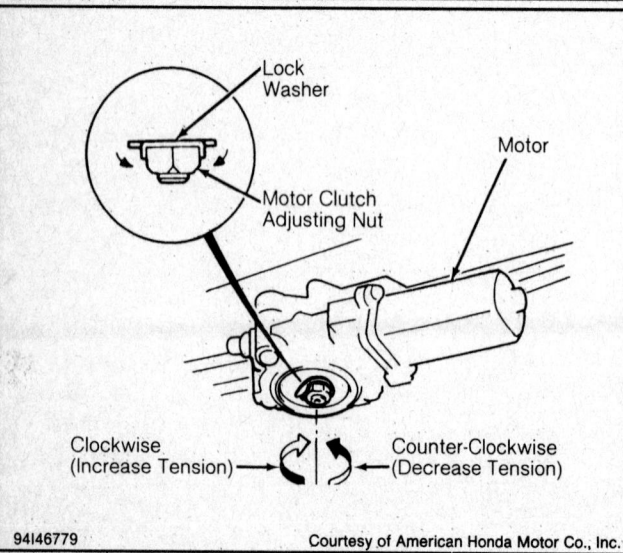

94I46779   Courtesy of American Honda Motor Co., Inc.
Fig. 2: Adjusting Sun Roof Motor Clutch Tension

SUN ROOF HEIGHT

Integra – Roof panel should be even with glass weatherstrip within 0.05-0.09" (1.3-2.3 mm). If adjustment is required, loosen nuts at side rails and move roof panel.

Legend – Roof panel should be even with glass weatherstrip within 0.06-0.10" (1.5-2.5 mm). If adjustment is required, pry out bracket cover and install or remove shims between glass and glass bracket.
Vigor – Roof panel should be even with glass weatherstrip within 0.02-0.06" (0.5-1.5 mm). If adjustment is required in front, install or remove shims between frame and sunshade rail. If adjustment is required in rear, install or remove shims between guide rail and sunshade rail.

TROUBLE SHOOTING

CAUTION: Legend and Vigor models are equipped with Supplemental Restraint System (SRS). SRS wiring harness is routed close to instrument cluster, steering wheel, and related components. All SRS wiring harnesses are covered by Yellow outer insulation. DO NOT use electrical test equipment on these circuits. Before working on steering column components, disable air bag system. See AIR BAG RESTRAINT SYSTEM article in ACCESSORIES & EQUIPMENT.

NOTE: Ensure all component terminals and ground connections are clean and tight. Check possible faults in order listed. Repair or replace components and circuits as necessary.

INTEGRA

Motor Runs, Sun Roof Does Not Move – Clutch out of adjustment. Foreign matter jammed in guide. Cable not properly attached.
Motor Does Not Run (With Either Switch) – Blown fuse No. 1 in underdash fuse/relay box. Blown fuse No. 14 in underdash fuse box. Faulty sun roof relay. Faulty sun roof motor. Faulty sun roof switch. Open in White, Green/Black, Green, or Black wire.
Motor Does Not Run With OPEN Switch – Faulty sun roof switch. Open in Green/Yellow wire.
Motor Does Not Run With CLOSE Switch – Faulty switch. Open in Green/Red wire.

LEGEND

Motor Runs, Sun Roof Does Not Move – Clutch out of adjustment. Foreign matter in guide. Outer cable not properly attached.
Motor Does Not Run With Either Switch – Blown fuse No. 51 in underhood fuse/relay box. Blown fuse No. 23 in underdash fuse box. Faulty sun roof switch. Faulty sun roof motor. Open in Green/White, Yellow/Green, Yellow, or Red wire.
Motor Does Not Run With OPEN Switch – Faulty OPEN relay. Faulty CLOSE relay. Faulty sun roof switch. Open in Yellow/Blue wire.
Motor Does Not Run With CLOSE Switch – Faulty CLOSE relay. Faulty OPEN relay. Faulty sun roof switch. Open in Yellow/Red wire.

VIGOR

Motor Runs, Sun Roof Does Not Move – Slipping clutch. Foreign matter in guide. Outer cable not properly attached.
Motor Does Not Run With Either Switch – Blown fuse No. 29 in underhood fuse/relay box. Blown fuse No. 5 in underdash fuse box. Faulty sun roof switch. Faulty sun roof motor. Poor ground. Open in Green, Yellow/Red, Green/Yellow, or Green/Red wire.
Motor Does Not Run With OPEN Switch – Faulty OPEN relay. Faulty CLOSE relay. Faulty sun roof switch. Open in Green/Yellow or Green/Red wire.
Motor Does Not Run With CLOSE Switch – Faulty CLOSE relay. Faulty OPEN relay. Faulty sun roof switch. Open in Green/Yellow or Green/Red wire.

TESTING

FUNCTION TEST

Integra – 1) Remove lower cover from instrument panel. Carefully pry sun roof control switch from instrument panel. Unplug connector. Check for continuity between Black connector terminal and ground. If continuity exists, go to next step. If continuity does not exist, repair Black wire or poor ground connection.

2) Turn ignition on. Check for voltage between Green and Black wires at connector. If battery voltage exists, go to step **3)**. If battery voltage does not exist, check for defective fuses No. 1 or No. 14, open in Green/Black, Green, or White wires, or faulty relay.

3) Turn ignition off. Connect jumper wire between Green and Green/Yellow wires. Connect Green/Red and Black wires. *See Fig. 3.* Turn ignition on. If sun roof opens, test switch. See SWITCH TEST. If sun roof does not open, test motor. See MOTOR TEST.

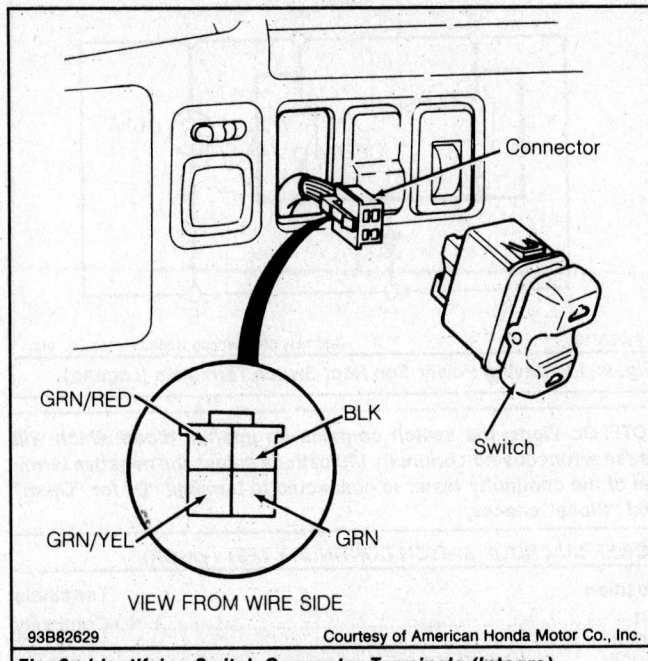

Connector

GRN/RED

BLK

GRN/YEL

GRN

Switch

VIEW FROM WIRE SIDE

93B82629   Courtesy of American Honda Motor Co., Inc.

Fig. 3: Identifying Switch Connector Terminals (Integra)

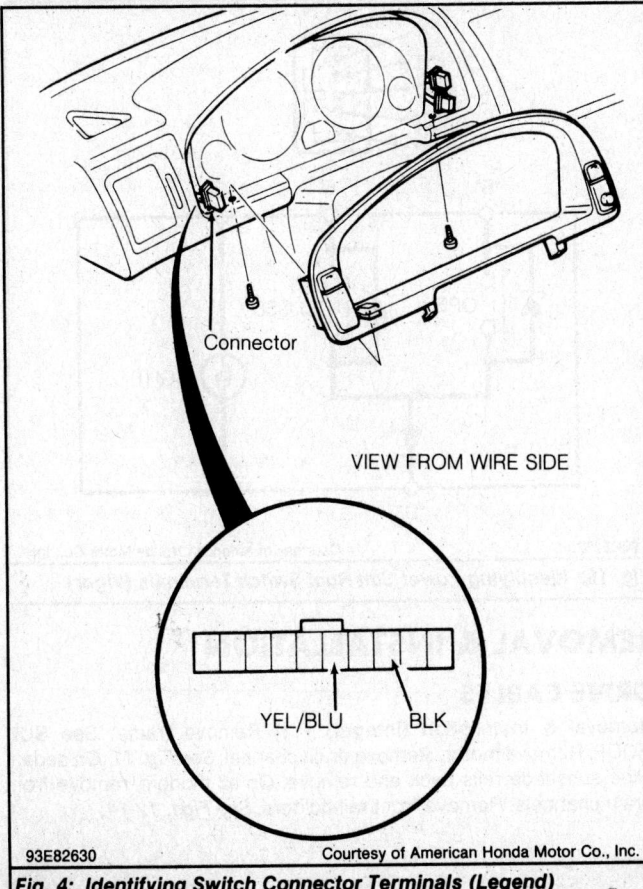

Connector

VIEW FROM WIRE SIDE

YEL/BLU   BLK

93E82630   Courtesy of American Honda Motor Co., Inc.

Fig. 4: Identifying Switch Connector Terminals (Legend)

Legend – 1) Remove 2 screws and instrument cluster trim panel. Unplug connector from switch. Check for continuity between Black wire and body ground. If continuity does not exist, check for open in Black wire. Repair as necessary.

2) Connect jumper wire between Yellow/Blue wire and body ground. *See Fig. 4.* Turn ignition on. If sun roof opens, test switch. See SWITCH TEST. If sun roof does not open, check for open in Yellow/Blue wire. If wire is okay, test motor. See MOTOR TEST.

Vigor – 1) Carefully pry sun roof control switch from instrument panel. Unplug connector. Check for continuity between Black connector terminal and ground. If continuity exists, go to next step. If continuity does not exist, repair Black wire or poor ground connection.

2) Using jumper wire, connect Green/Yellow wire to body ground. *See Fig. 5.* Turn ignition on. If sun roof opens, test switch. See SWITCH TEST. If sun roof does not open, check for open in Green/Yellow wire. If wiring is okay, test motor. See MOTOR TEST.

3) Using jumper wire, connect Green/Red wire to body ground. Turn ignition on. If sun roof closes, test switch. See SWITCH TEST. If sun roof does not close, check for open in Green/Red wire. If wiring is okay, test relays and motor. See RELAY TEST and MOTOR TEST.

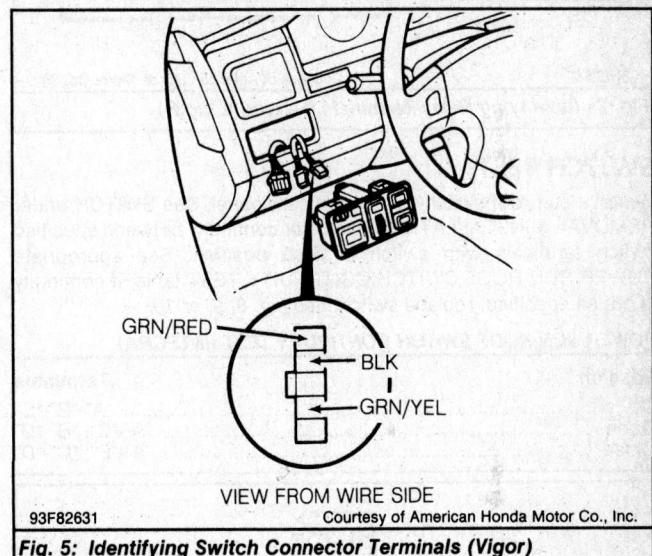

GRN/RED

BLK

GRN/YEL

VIEW FROM WIRE SIDE

93F82631   Courtesy of American Honda Motor Co., Inc.

Fig. 5: Identifying Switch Connector Terminals (Vigor)

MOTOR TEST

Remove headliner. Unplug connector from motor. Using jumper wires, connect battery voltage and ground to motor connector terminals. Check for motor operation. Transpose jumper wires and retest. Replace motor if it does not operate smoothly in both directions.

RELAY TEST

Integra – Remove power window relay from underdash fuse/relay box. Check for continuity between terminals "A" and "B". Continuity should not exist. Using jumper wires, connect terminals "C" and "D" to battery voltage and ground. *See Fig. 6.* Check for continuity between terminals "A" and "B". Continuity should exist. Replace relay if continuity is not as specified.

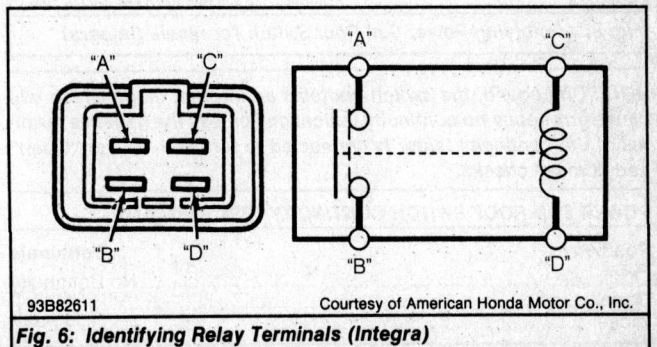

"A"   "C"

"B"   "D"

93B82611   Courtesy of American Honda Motor Co., Inc.

Fig. 6: Identifying Relay Terminals (Integra)

Legend & Vigor – **1)** Remove relay from socket. On Legend, relays are located near sun roof motor. On Vigor, relays are located in trunk, on right side. Check for continuity between terminals "A" and "C". Continuity should not exist. Check for continuity between terminals "B" and "C". *See Fig. 7.* Continuity should exist.

2) Using jumper wires, connect terminals "D" and "E" to battery voltage and ground. Check for continuity between terminals "A" and "C". Continuity should exist. Check for continuity between terminals "B" and "C". Continuity should not exist. Replace relay if operation is not as specified.

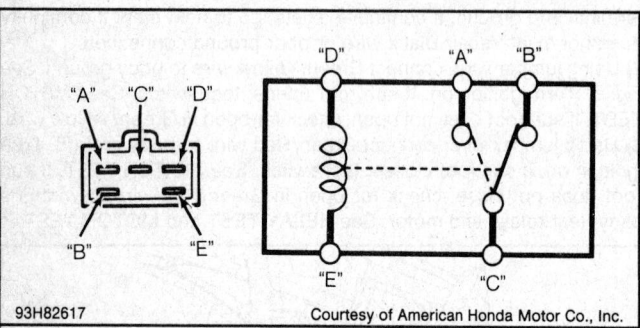

93H82617   Courtesy of American Honda Motor Co., Inc.

Fig. 7: Identifying Relay Terminals (Legend & Vigor)

SWITCH TEST

Remove sun roof switch from instrument panel. See SWITCH under REMOVAL & INSTALLATION. Check for continuity between specified switch terminals with switch in each position. See appropriate POWER SUN ROOF SWITCH CONTINUITY TEST table. If continuity is not as specified, replace switch. *See Fig. 8, 9, or 10.*

POWER SUN ROOF SWITCH CONTINUITY TEST (INTEGRA)

Position	Terminals
Off	"A"-"B"-"C"
Open	"A"-"C"; "B"-"D"
Close	"A"-"B"; "C"-"D"

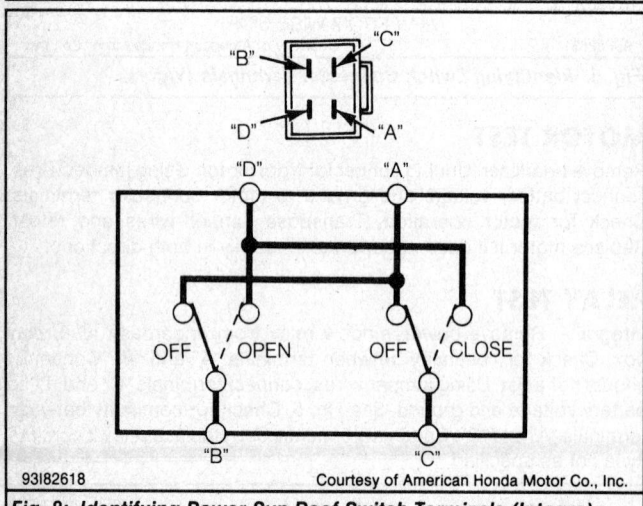

93I82618   Courtesy of American Honda Motor Co., Inc.

Fig. 8: Identifying Power Sun Roof Switch Terminals (Integra)

NOTE: *On Legend, the switch contains an internal diode which will cause erroneous no-continuity indications unless the negative terminal of the continuity tester is connected to terminal "H" for "Open" and "Close" checks.*

POWER SUN ROOF SWITCH CONTINUITY TEST (LEGEND)

Position	Terminals
Off	No Continuity
Open	"F"-"H"
Close	"G"-"H"

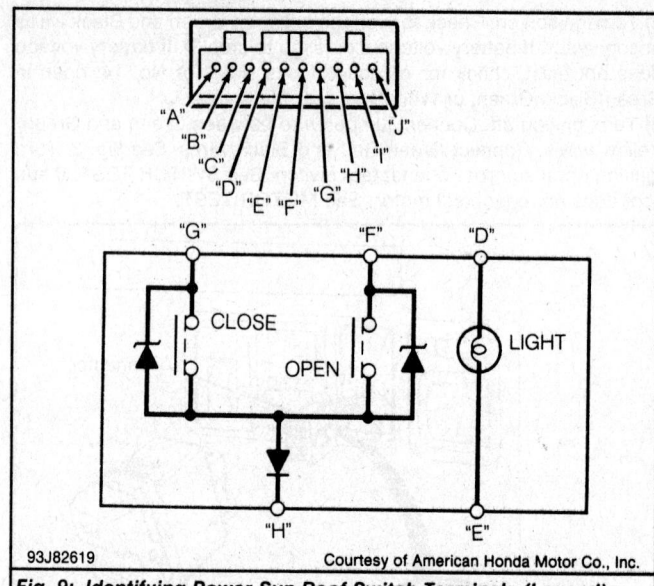

93J82619   Courtesy of American Honda Motor Co., Inc.

Fig. 9: Identifying Power Sun Roof Switch Terminals (Legend)

NOTE: *On Vigor, the switch contains an internal diode which will cause erroneous no-continuity indications unless the negative terminal of the continuity tester is connected to terminal "D" for "Open" and "Close" checks.*

POWER SUN ROOF SWITCH CONTINUITY TEST (VIGOR)

Position	Terminals
Off	No Continuity
Open	"B"-"D"
Close	"E"-"D"

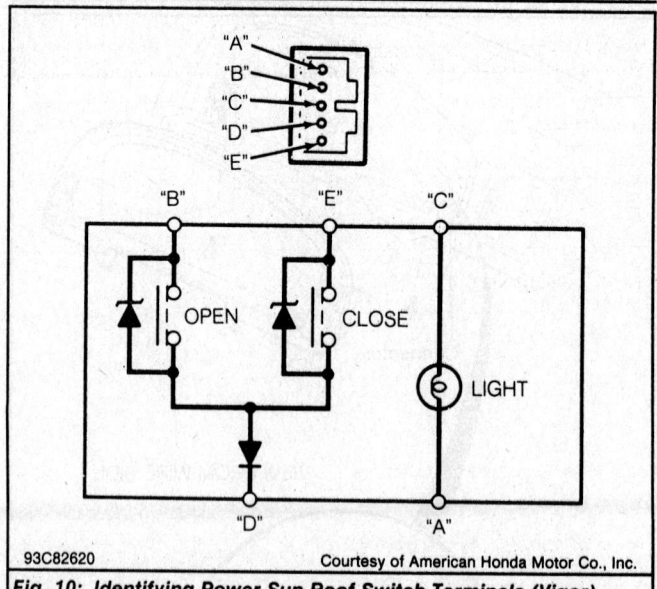

93C82620   Courtesy of American Honda Motor Co., Inc.

Fig. 10: Identifying Power Sun Roof Switch Terminals (Vigor)

REMOVAL & INSTALLATION
DRIVE CABLES

Removal & Installation (Integra) – **1)** Remove frame. See SUN ROOF. Remove motor. Remove drain channel. *See Fig. 11.* On sedan, slide sunshade rails back and remove. On all models, remove front drain channels. Remove front rail holders. *See Figs. 12-14.*

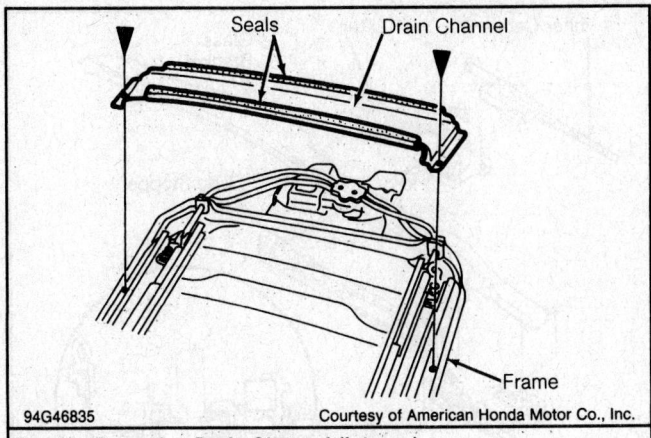

Fig. 11: Removing Drain Channel (Integra)

94G46835 — Courtesy of American Honda Motor Co., Inc.

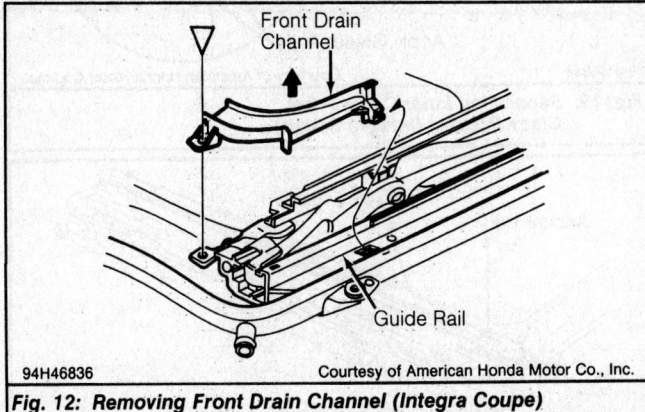

Fig. 12: Removing Front Drain Channel (Integra Coupe)

94H46836 — Courtesy of American Honda Motor Co., Inc.

guide rails. Remove cable assembly (with sliders attached) from frame. *See Fig. 23*. To install, reverse removal procedure.

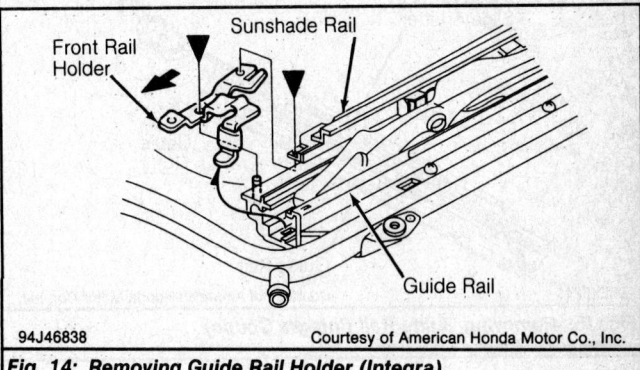

Fig. 14: Removing Guide Rail Holder (Integra)

94J46838 — Courtesy of American Honda Motor Co., Inc.

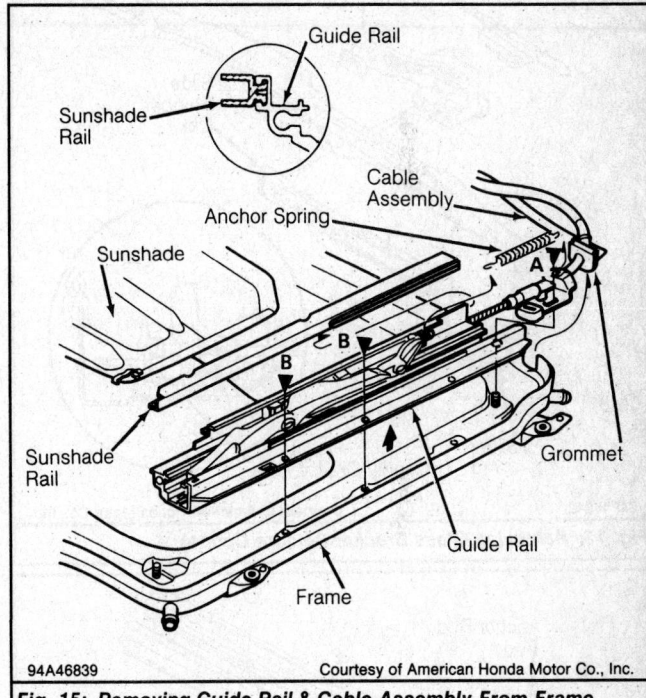

Fig. 15: Removing Guide Rail & Cable Assembly From Frame

94A46839 — Courtesy of American Honda Motor Co., Inc.

2) Remove anchor springs. Remove nuts and bolts from side guide rails and remove both guide rails with cable assembly. *See Fig. 13 or 15*. Remove sunshade and both sunshade rails.

3) On coupe, slide guide rail forward and remove from cable assembly. *See Fig. 16*. Remove glass bracket from cable assembly. *See Fig. 17*. Slide anchor rod forward to remove from guide rail. *See Fig. 18*.

4) On sedan, separate inner cable from glass bracket. *See Fig. 19*. Slide anchor rod forward to remove from guide rail. *See Fig. 20*. Slide guide rail back and remove from inner cable. *See Fig. 21*. Remove cable assembly from frame. *See Fig. 22*. On all models, to install, reverse removal procedure.

Removal & Installation (Legend & Vigor) – Remove frame. See SUN ROOF. Remove motor. Remove drain channel. *See Fig. 23*. Remove

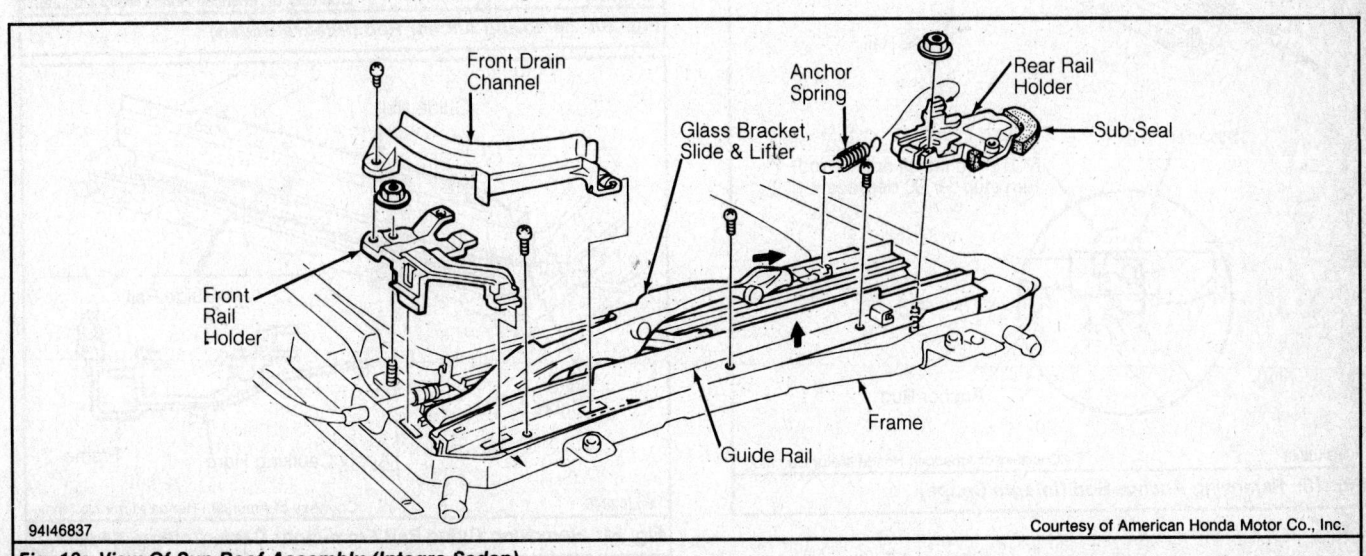

Fig. 13: View Of Sun Roof Assembly (Integra Sedan)

94I46837 — Courtesy of American Honda Motor Co., Inc.

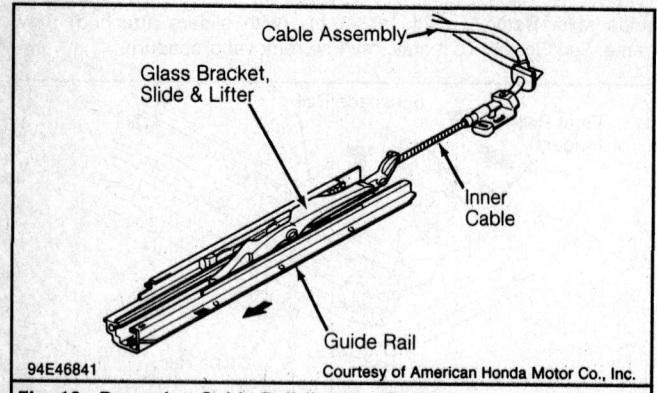

94E46841

Courtesy of American Honda Motor Co., Inc.

Fig. 16: Removing Guide Rail (Integra Coupe)

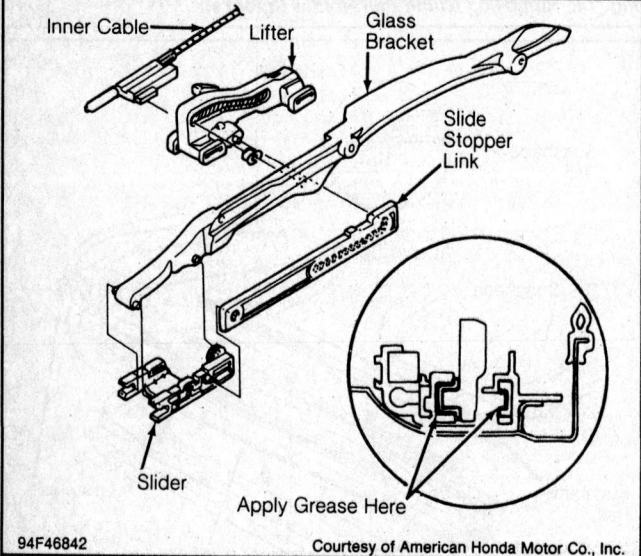

94F46842

Courtesy of American Honda Motor Co., Inc.

Fig. 17: Removing Glass Bracket (Integra Coupe)

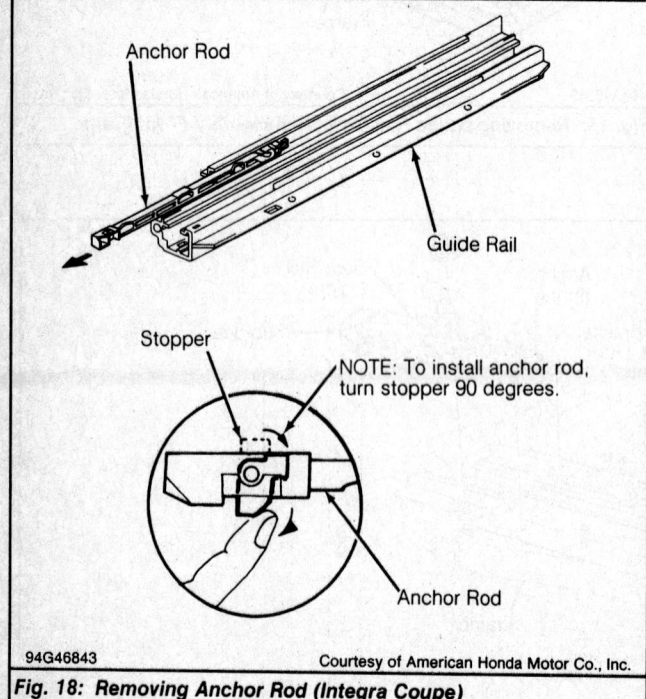

94G46843

Courtesy of American Honda Motor Co., Inc.

Fig. 18: Removing Anchor Rod (Integra Coupe)

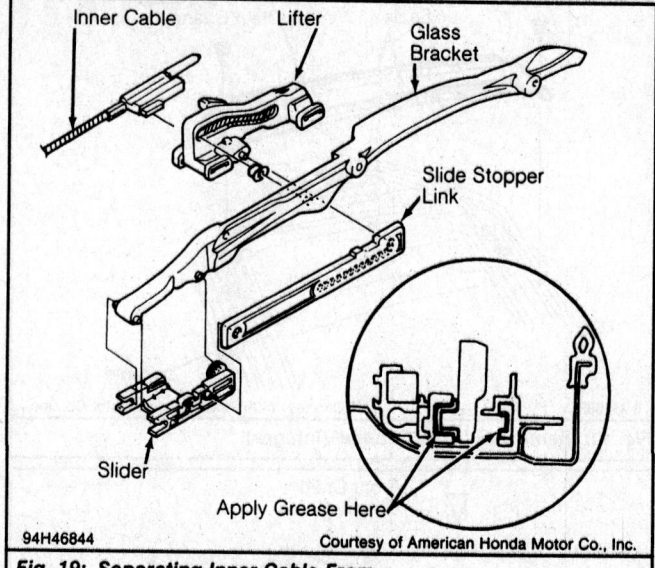

94H46844

Courtesy of American Honda Motor Co., Inc.

Fig. 19: Separating Inner Cable From Glass Bracket (Integra Sedan)

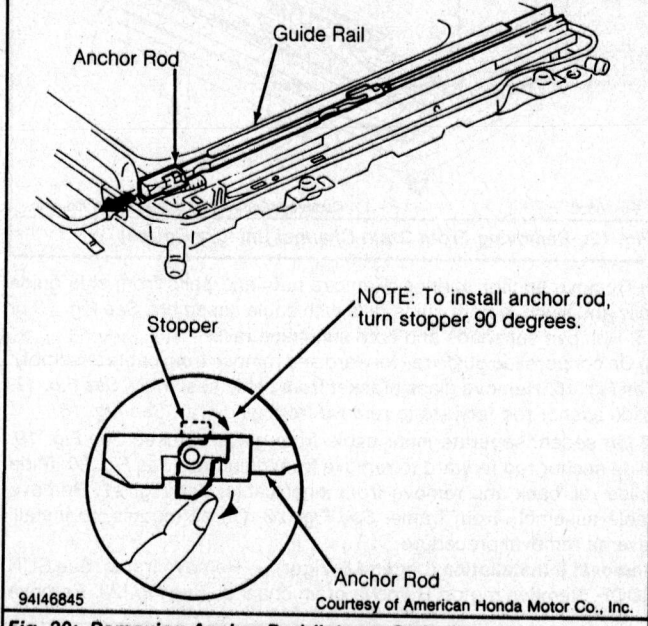

94I46845

Courtesy of American Honda Motor Co., Inc.

Fig. 20: Removing Anchor Rod (Integra Sedan)

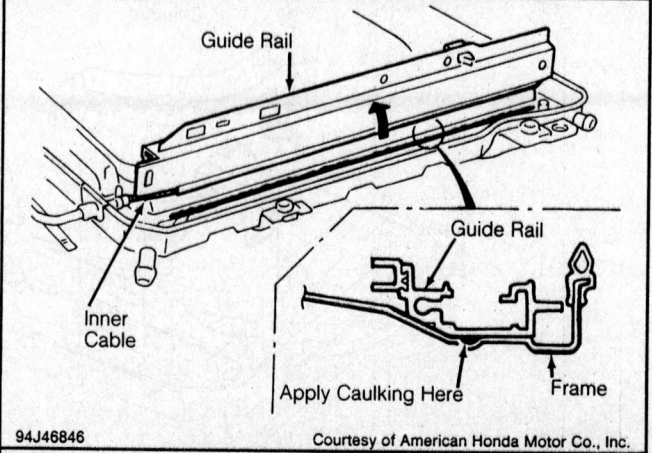

94J46846

Courtesy of American Honda Motor Co., Inc.

Fig. 21: Removing Guide Rail From Inner Cable (Integra Sedan)

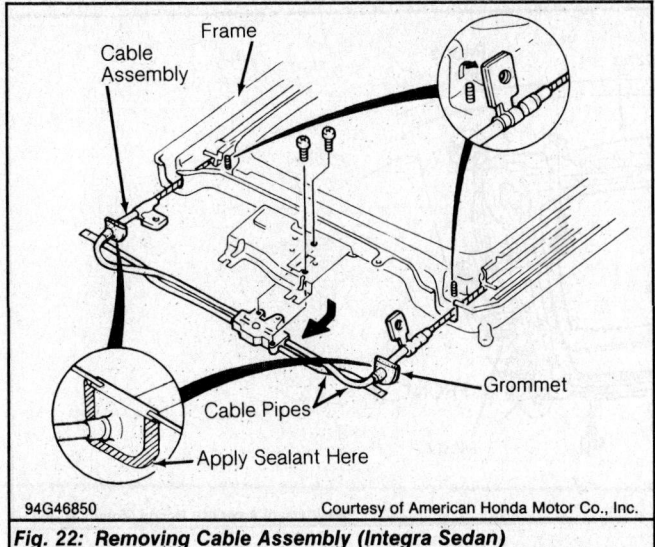

94G46850   Courtesy of American Honda Motor Co., Inc.

Fig. 22: Removing Cable Assembly (Integra Sedan)

DRIVE MOTOR

Removal & Installation – See SUN ROOF.

SUN ROOF

Removal & Installation (Integra) – **1)** Remove headliner. Open sun shade. Tilt glass up. Remove glass mounting bolts and remove glass. Remove sunshade rail screws and sunshade rails. Slide sunshade forward and out.

2) Unplug motor connector. Separate harness from clips. Remove motor. Disconnect drain tubes. Remove mounting bolts and hooks (if equipped). *See Fig. 24.* Remove frame.

3) To install, reverse removal procedure. Before installing sun roof motor, check glass opening drag. *See Fig. 25.* On Integra, if opening drag is more than 9 lbs. (40 N), adjust sun roof. See ADJUSTMENTS. On Legend and Vigor, if opening drag is more than 22 lbs. (100 N), adjust sun roof. See ADJUSTMENTS.

Removal & Installation (Legend & Vigor) – Remove headliner. On Legend, remove glass. On all models, unplug motor connector. Separate harness from clips. Remove motor. Disconnect drain tubes. Loosen rear mounting bolts. Remove mounting bolts and hooks (if equipped). Remove frame. To install, reverse removal procedure.

94H46851   Courtesy of American Honda Motor Co., Inc.

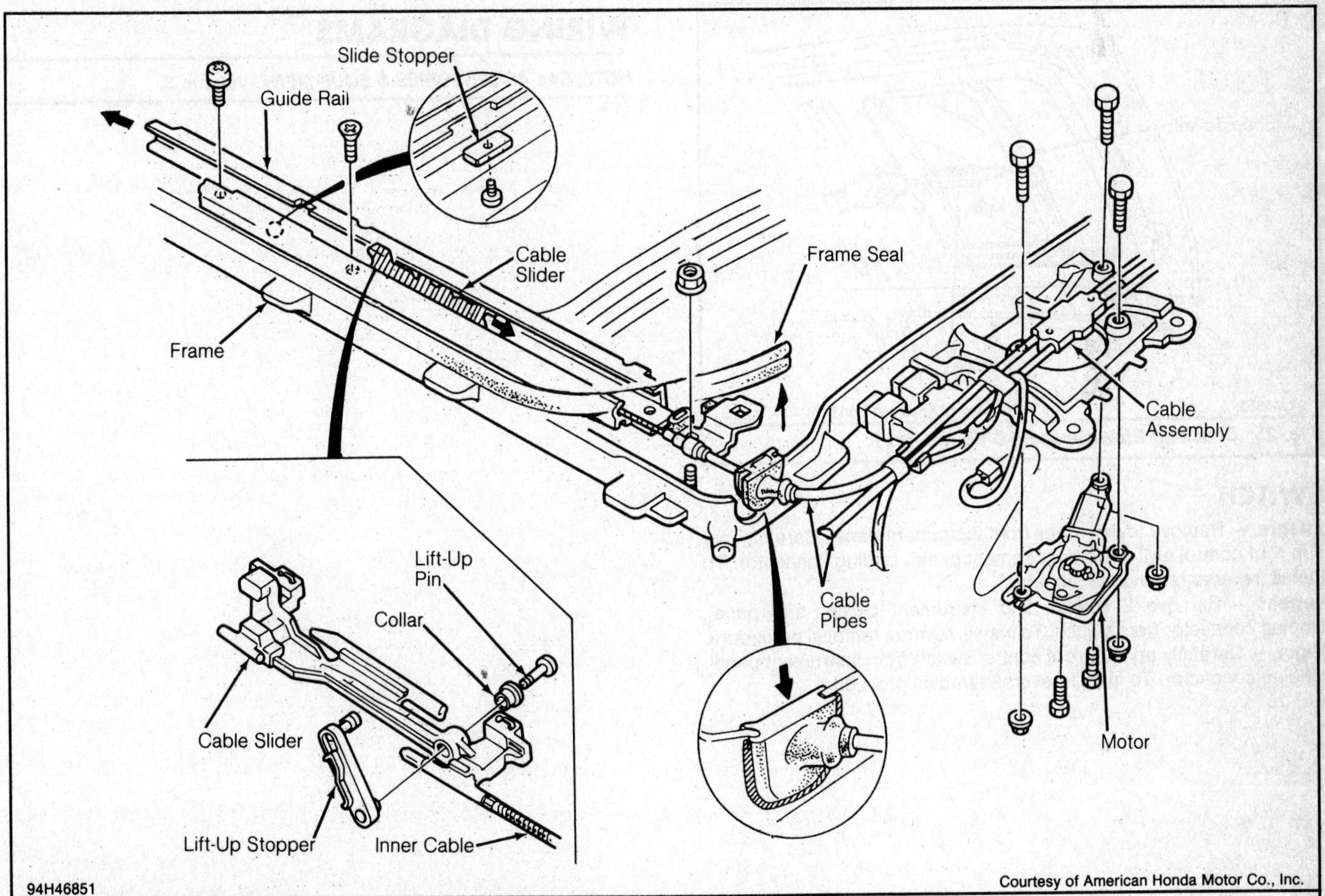

Fig. 23: View Of Sun Roof Assembly (Legend & Vigor)

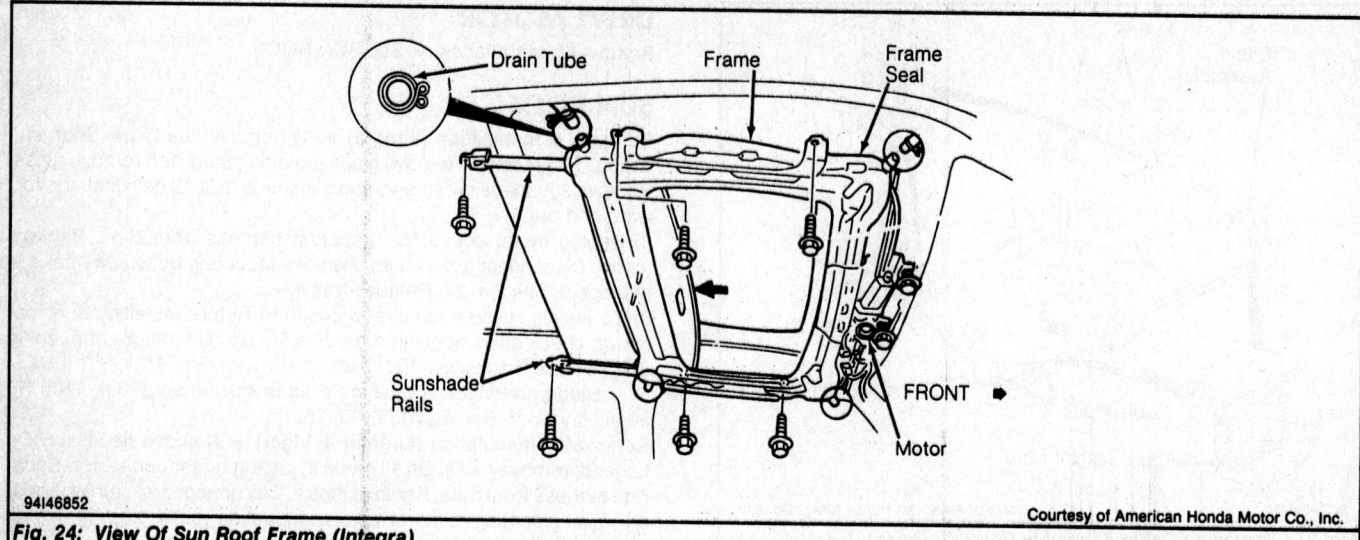

94I46852

Courtesy of American Honda Motor Co., Inc.

Fig. 24: View Of Sun Roof Frame (Integra)

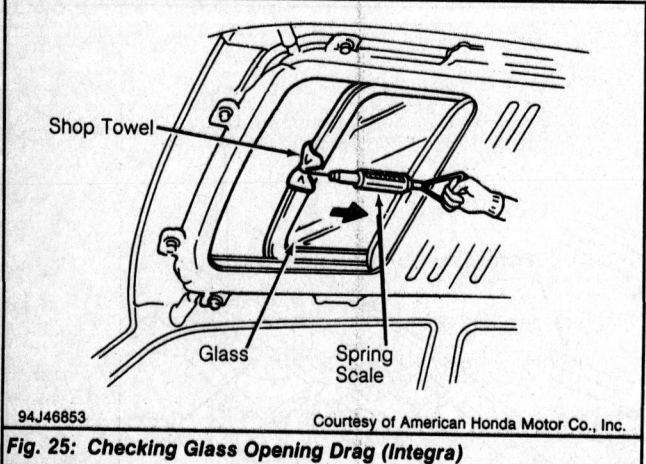

94J46853

Courtesy of American Honda Motor Co., Inc.

Fig. 25: Checking Glass Opening Drag (Integra)

WIRING DIAGRAMS

NOTE: See ACCESSORIES & EQUIPMENT, Volume 5.

SWITCH

Integra – Remove lower cover from instrument panel. Carefully pry sun roof control switch from instrument panel. Unplug connector. To install, reverse removal procedure.

Legend – Remove 2 screws and instrument cluster trim panel. Unplug connector from switch. To install, reverse removal procedure.

Vigor – Carefully pry sun roof control switch from instrument panel. Unplug connector. To install, reverse removal procedure.

Integra, Legend, Vigor

DESCRIPTION & OPERATION

A permanent magnet motor operates each power window. Driver's master switch controls all windows. Passenger switches control only the associated window. If the main switch is in OFF position, only the driver's window operates.

Legend and Vigor power windows may be operated until about 10 minutes after ignition switch is set from the "II" position to the "I" or "0" positions. Time delay function operates as long as neither front door has been opened.

AUTO mode permits driver's window to be fully lowered or raised without holding switch. Pressing switch past its first detent position will engage AUTO mode, fully lowering or raising window. AUTO function is controlled by an integral pulser within the driver's window motor assembly. The pulser cannot be serviced separately.

TROUBLE SHOOTING

CAUTION: All models are equipped with Supplemental Restraint System (SRS). SRS wiring harness is routed close to instrument cluster, steering wheel, and related components. All SRS wiring harnesses are covered by Yellow outer insulation. DO NOT use electrical test equipment on these circuits. Before working on steering column components, disable air bag system. See AIR BAG RESTRAINT SYSTEM article in ACCESSORIES & EQUIPMENT.

NOTE: Ensure all component terminals and ground connections are clean and tight. Check possible faults in order listed. Repair or replace components and circuits as necessary. Some wires have been assigned a superscript to distinguish them from other wires of the same color. For example, the Yellow/Green[1] wire is not the same as the Yellow/Green[2] wire.

INTEGRA

All Windows Inoperative – Blown fuse No. 14 in underdash fuse box. Faulty power window relay. Open in White/Red or Black/Yellow wire.

Driver's Window Inoperative – Blown fuse No. 5 in underdash fuse box. Faulty driver's window motor. Faulty window regulator. Driver's switch input. Open in White/Yellow wire.

Driver's Window Inoperative In AUTO – Driver's switch faulty. Faulty pulser (in driver's motor). Driver's switch input. Open in Blue or White/Yellow wire.

Passenger's Window Inoperative – Blown fuses No. 8 (right front), No. 4. (right rear) and/or No. 7 (left rear) in underdash fuse box. Faulty driver's master switch. Faulty passenger's switch. Faulty passenger's window motor. Faulty window regulator. Open in Blue/Black wire (right front), Green/Black wire (left rear), and/or Yellow/Black (right rear) wire.

LEGEND

All Windows Inoperative – Blown fuse No. 36 in underhood fuse box. Blown fuse No. 13 in underdash fuse box. Power window relay. Key-off timer circuit. Open in White/Yellow or White/Green wires.

Driver's Window inoperative – Blown fuse No. 17 in underdash fuse box. Faulty driver's window motor. Faulty window regulator. Faulty master switch. Faulty master switch input. Open in White/Yellow[2] wire.

Driver's Window Inoperative In AUTO – Faulty master switch. Master switch input. Open in Blue wire.

Passenger's Window Inoperative – Blown fuses No. 18 (right front), No. 24. (right rear), and/or No. 21 (left rear) in underdash fuse box. Faulty power window master switch. Faulty passenger's switch. Faulty passenger's window motor. Faulty window regulator. Open in Blue/Black (right front), Green/Black (left rear) or Yellow/Black (right rear) wire.

VIGOR

All Windows Inoperative – Blown fuse No. 15 in underhood fuse box. Blown fuse No. 37 in underhood relay box. Power window relay. Key-off timer circuit in integrated control unit. Open in Red wire.

Driver's Window Inoperative – Blown fuse No. 28 in underhood fuse box. Faulty driver's window motor. Faulty window regulator. Master switch input. Open in White/Yellow wire.

Driver's Window Inoperative In AUTO – Faulty master switch. Faulty pulser (in driver's motor). Master switch input. Open in Blue wire.

Passenger's Window Inoperative – Blown fuses No. 26 (right front), No. 24. (right rear), or No. 25 (left rear) in underhood fuse box. Faulty power window master switch. Faulty passenger's switch. Faulty passenger's window motor. Faulty window regulator. Open in Blue/Black (right front), Green/Black (left rear) or Yellow/Black (right rear) wire.

All Windows Inoperative Within 10 Minutes Of Ignition Switch Turned Off – Blown fuse No. 37 in underhood fuse box. Faulty door switches. Faulty key-off timer circuit in integrated control unit.

TESTING

MOTOR TEST

CAUTION: Disconnect one test immediately when motor stops running.

Driver's Window Motor Test (Integra) – Remove door panel. Unplug connector from motor. Using fused jumper wire, connect battery voltage to terminal No. 1. Connect terminal No. 2 to ground. See Fig. 1. Motor should run in "down" direction. Transpose jumper wires. Motor should run in "up" direction. Replace motor if it does not run smoothly in both directions.

Driver's Window Motor Test (Legend & Vigor) – Remove door panel. Unplug connector from motor. Using fused jumper wire, connect terminal No. 4 to battery voltage. Connect terminal No. 3 to ground. See Fig. 1. Motor should run in "up" direction. Transpose jumper wires. Motor should run in "down" direction. Replace motor if it does not run smoothly in both directions.

VIEW FROM WIRE SIDE

93H82526   Courtesy of American Honda Motor Co., Inc.

Fig. 1: Identifying Driver's Window Motor Terminals

Passenger Window Motor Test – Remove door panel. Unplug connector from motor. Using fused jumper wire, connect terminal No. 2 to battery voltage. Connect terminal No. 1 to ground. See Fig. 2. Motor should run in "up" direction. Transpose jumper wires. Motor should run in "down" direction. retest. Replace motor if it does not operate in both directions.

VIEW FROM WIRE SIDE

93I82527   Courtesy of American Honda Motor Co., Inc.

Fig. 2: Identifying Passenger's Window Motor Terminals

POWER WINDOW RELAY TEST

Remove power window relay from underhood fuse/relay box. Check for continuity between terminals "A" and "B". Continuity should not exist. Using jumper wires, connect terminals "C" and "D" to battery voltage and ground. See Fig. 3. If continuity does not exist between terminals "A" and "B", replace relay.

1994 ACCESSORIES & EQUIPMENT
Power Windows (Cont.)

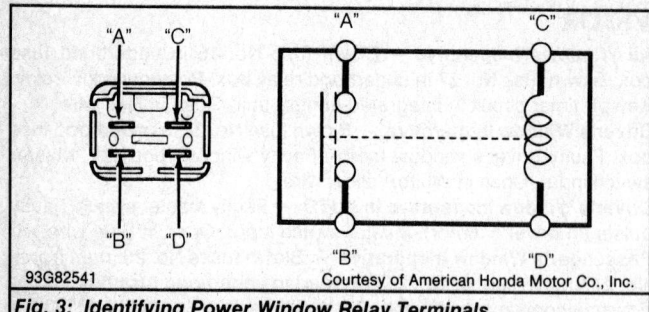

93G82541   Courtesy of American Honda Motor Co., Inc.

Fig. 3: Identifying Power Window Relay Terminals

PULSER TEST (DRIVER'S WINDOW MOTOR)

NOTE: Pulser is integral part of driver's window motor assembly. If pulser is defective, replace motor assembly.

Integra – Connect test leads of analog ohmmeter to motor connector terminals No. 3 and No. 4. Using jumper wires, connect terminals No. 1 and No. 2 to battery voltage and ground. *See Fig. 1.* If ohmmeter needle does not swing back and forth while motor operates, replace motor.

Legend & Vigor – Connect test leads of analog ohmmeter to motor connector terminals No. 1 and No. 2. Using jumper wires, connect terminals No. 3 and No. 4 to battery voltage and ground. *See Fig. 1.* If ohmmeter needle does not swing back and forth while motor operates, replace motor.

SWITCH INPUTS TEST

Turn ignition off. Remove driver's door panel. Unplug connectors from master switch. Using a DVOM, perform switch input tests in *Fig. 4, 5, 6 or 7.* If all input test results are okay, inspect connector and terminals for damage and proper fit. If connector is okay and power windows still malfunction, replace master switch.

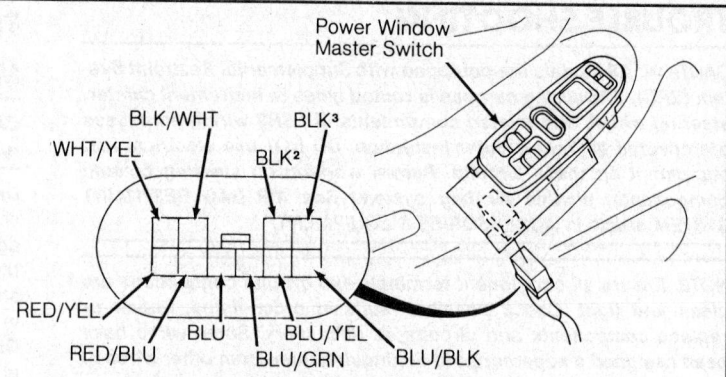

VIEW FROM WIRE SIDE

No.	Wire	Test condition	Test: Desired result	Possible cause if result is not obtained
1	BLK² BLK³	Under all conditions	Check for continuity to ground: There should be continuity.	• Poor ground • An open in the wire
2	WHT/YEL BLU/BLK	Ignition switch ON (II)	Check for voltage to ground: There should be battery voltage.	• Blown No. 14 (20 A) fuse in the under-dash fuse/relay box • Blown No. 5, or No. 8 (20 A) fuse in the under-dash fuse/relay box • Faulty power window relay • An open in the wire
3	RED/BLU¹ and RED/YEL¹	Connect the WHT/YEL and RED/YEL¹ terminals, and the RED/BLU¹ and BLK³ terminals with jumper wires, then turn the ignition switch ON (II).	Check the driver's window motor: It should run (the window moves down).	• Faulty driver's window motor • An open in the wire
4	BLU/YEL and BLU/GRN	Connect the BLU/BLK and BLU/GRN terminals, and the BLU/YEL and BLK² terminals with jumper wires, then turn the ignition switch ON (II).	Check the passenger's window motor: It should run (the window moves down).	• Faulty passenger's window motor • An open in the wire
5	BLU and BLK/WHT	Connect the WHT/YEL and RED/YEL¹ terminals, and the RED/BLU¹ and BLK³ terminals with jumper wires, then turn the ignition switch ON (II).	Connect an analog ohmmeter to the BLU and BLK/WHT terminals: The meter needle should move back and forth alternately as the driver's window motor runs.	• Faulty pulser • Faulty driver's window motor • An open in the wire

94J46911 94A46912   Courtesy of American Honda Motor Co., Inc.

Fig. 4: Switch Inputs Test (Integra Coupe)

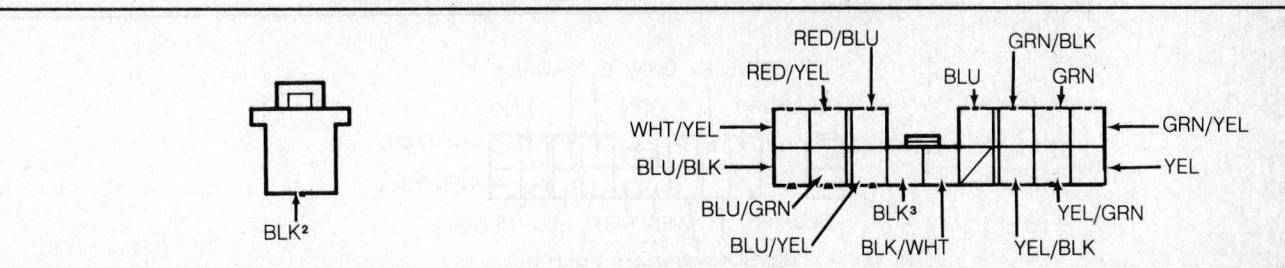

No.	Wire	Test condition	Test: Desired result	Possible cause if result is not obtained
1	BLK² and BLK³	Under all conditions	Check for continuity to ground: There should be continuity.	• Poor ground • An open in the wire
2	WHT/YEL BLU/BLK GRN/BLK YEL/BLK	Ignition switch ON (II)	Check for voltage to ground: There should be battery voltage.	• Blown No. 14 (20 A) fuse in the under-dash fuse/relay box • Blown No. 5, 8, 7 or 4 (20 A) fuse in the under-dash fuse/relay box • Faulty power window relay • An open in the wire
3	RED/BLU¹ and RED/YEL¹	Connect the WHT/YEL and RED/YEL¹ terminals, and the RED/BLU¹ and BLK³ terminals with jumper wires, then turn the ignition switch ON (II).	Check the driver's window motor: It should run (the window moves down).	• Faulty driver's window motor • An open in the wire
4	BLU/YEL and BLU/GRN	Connect the BLU/BLK and BLU/GRN terminals, and the BLU/YEL and BLK² terminals with jumper wires, then turn the ignition switch ON (II).	Check the front passenger's window motor: It should run (the window moves down).	• Faulty front passenger's window motor • An open in the wire
5	GRN/YEL and GRN	Connect the GRN/BLK and GRN terminals, and the GRN/YEL and BLK² terminals with jumper wires, then turn the ignition switch ON (II).	Check the left rear window motor: It should run (the window moves down).	• Faulty left rear window motor • Faulty left rear window switch • An open in the wire
6	YEL/GRN and YEL	Connect the YEL/BLK and YEL/GRN terminals, and the YEL and BLK² terminals with jumper wires, then turn the ignition switch ON (II).	Check the right rear window motor: It should run (the window moves down).	• Faulty right rear window motor • Faulty right rear window switch • An open in the wire
7	BLU and BLK/WHT	Connect the WHT/YEL and RED/YEL¹ terminals, and the RED/BLU¹ and BLK³ terminals with jumper wires, then turn the ignition switch ON (II).	Connect an analog ohmmeter to terminals BLU and BLK/WHT: The meter needle should move back and forth alternately as the driver's window motor runs.	• Faulty pulser • Faulty driver's window motor • An open in the wire

94B46913 94C46914

Courtesy of American Honda Motor Co., Inc.

Fig. 5: Switch Inputs Test (Integra Sedan)

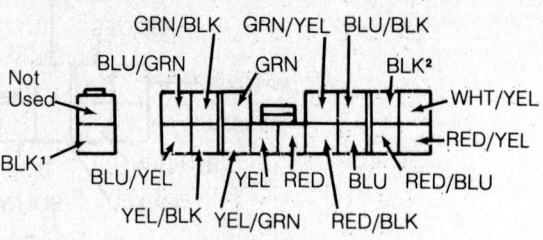

VIEW FROM WIRE SIDE

No.	Wire	Test condition	Test: Desired result	Possible cause if result is not obtained
1	BLK[1] and BLK[2]	Under all conditions	Check for continuity to gound: There should be continuity.	• Poor ground • An open in the wire
2	WHT/YEL BLU/BLK YEL/BLK GRN/BLK	Ignition switch ON	Check for voltage to ground: There should be battery voltage.	• Blown No. 17 (20 A), 18 (20 A), 21 (20 A), 24 (20 A) fuse • Faulty power window relay • Faulty key-off timer system • An open in the wire
3	RED/BLU and RED/YEL	Connect the WHT/YEL terminal to the RED/BLU terminal, and the RED/YEL terminal to the BLK[2] terminal, then turn the ignition switch ON.	Check the driver's motor operation: It should run.	• Faulty driver's window motor
4	BLU/YEL and BLU/GRN	Connect the BLU/BLK terminal to the BLU/YEL terminal, and the BLU/GRN terminal to the BLK[2] terminal, then turn the ignition switch ON.	Check the right front motor operation: It should run.	• Faulty right rear window motor • Faulty right rear switch • An open in the wire
5	YEL and YEL/GRN	Connect the YEL/BLK terminal to the YEL terminal, and the YEL/GRN terminal to the BLK[2] terminal, then turn the ignition switch ON.	Check the right rear motor operation: It should run.	• Faulty right rear window motor • Faulty right rear switch • An open in the wire
6	GRN/YEL and GRN	Connect the GRN/BLK terminal to the GRN/YEL terminal, and the GRN terminal to the BLK[2] terminal, then turn the ignition switch ON.	Check the left rear motor operation: It should run.	• Faulty left rear window motor • Faulty left rear switch • An open in the wire
7	BLU and BLK[2]	Connect the WHT/YEL terminal to the RED/YEL terminal, and the BLK[2] terminal to the RED/BLU terminal, then turn the ignition switch ON.	Check for voltage between the BLU (+) and BLK[2] (−) terminals with an analog voltmeter: It should indicate between 3—8 volts as the motor runs.	• Faulty pulser • Faulty driver's window motor • An open in the wire
8	RED/BLK and RED	Combination light switch ON and dash lights brightness controller dial rotated, dash lights should come on full bright.	Check for voltage between the RED/BLK (+) and RED (−) terminals: There should be battery voltage.	• Faulty dash lights brightness control system • An open in the wire

Fig. 6: Switch Inputs Test (Legend)

BLK

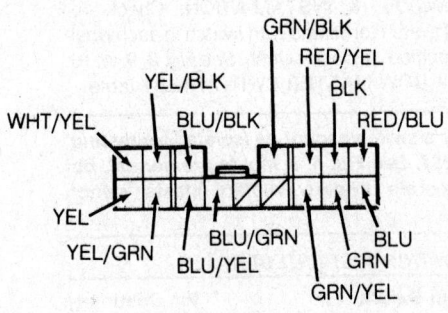

VIEW FROM WIRE SIDE

No.	Terminal	Test condition	Test: Desired result	Possible cause if result is not obtained
1	BLK[2]	Under all conditions.	Check for continuity to gound: There should be continuity.	• Poor ground • An open in the wire.
2	WHT/YEL BLU/BLK YEL/BLK GRN/BLK	Ignition switch ON.	Check for voltage to ground: There should be battery voltage.	• Blown No. 24, 25, 26 or 28 (20 A) fuse (in the under-hood fuse/relay box). • Faulty power window relay. • An open in the wire.
3	RED/BLU and RED/YEL	Connect the WHT/YEL terminal to the RED/BLU terminal, and the RED/YEL terminal to the BLK[2] terminal, then turn the ignition switch ON.	Check the driver's motor operation: It should run.	• Faulty driver's motor. • An open in the wire.
4	BLU/YEL and BLU/GRN	Connect the BLU/BLK terminal to the BLU/YEL terminal, and the BLU/GRN terminal to the BLK[2] terminal, then turn the ignition switch ON.	Check the front passenger's motor operation: It should run.	• Faulty front passenger's motor. • Faulty front passenger's switch. • An open in the wire.
5	YEL and YEL/GRN	Connect the YEL/BLK terminal to the YEL/GRN terminal, and the YEL terminal to the BLK[2] terminal, then turn the ignition switch ON.	Check the right rear motor operation: It should run (the window moves down).	• Faulty right rear motor. • Faulty right switch. • An open in the wire.
6	GRN/YEL and GRN	Connect the GRN/BLK terminal to the GRN terminal, and the GRN/YEL terminal to the BLK[2] terminal, then turn the ignition switch ON.	Check the left rear motor operation: It should run (the window moves down).	• Faulty left rear motor. • Faulty left rear switch. • An open in the wire.
7	BLU and BLK[2]	Connect the WHT/YEL terminal to the RED/YEL terminal, and the BLK[2] terminal to the RED/BLU terminal, then turn the ignition switch ON.	Check for resistance between the BLU and BLK[2] terminals: Between 20-50 ohms should be indicated as the driver's motor runs.	• Faulty pulser. • Faulty driver's motor. • An open in the wire.

Fig. 7: Switch Inputs Test (Vigor)

SWITCH TEST

Master Switch – Remove power window master switch. See WINDOW SWITCH under REMOVAL & INSTALLATION. Check for continuity between specified switch terminals with switch in each position. If continuity is not as specified, replace switch. *See Fig. 8, 9, or 10.* See appropriate POWER WINDOW MASTER SWITCH TEST table.

NOTE: On Legend, the driver's switch cannot be isolated for testing. Perform SWITCH INPUTS TEST. See Fig. 6. If inputs are normal, but driver's switch does not operate properly, replace master switch assembly.

POWER WINDOW MASTER SWITCH TEST (INTEGRA)

Position	Main Switch	Pin Continuity
Right Front Switch		
Coupe		
Off	On	"D"-"H"-"I"
Off	Off	"H"-"I"
Up	On	"D"-"H"; "I"-"J"
Up	Off	"I"-"J"
Down	On	"D"-"I"; "H"-"J"
Down	Off	"H"-"J"
Sedan		
Off	On	"I"-"J"-"Q"
	Off	"I"-"J"
Up	On	"J"-"H"; "I"-"Q"
	Off	"H"-"J"
Down	On	"H"-"I"; "J"-"Q"
	Off	"H"-"I"
Left Rear Switch		
Off	On	"F"-"G"-"Q"
	Off	"F"-"G"
Up	On	"E"-"G"; "F"-"Q"
	Off	"E"-"G"
Down	On	"E"-"F"; "G"-"Q"
	Off	"E"-"F"
Right Rear Switch		
Off	On	"O"-"P"-"Q"
	Off	"O"-"P"
Up	On	"N"-"P"; "O"-"Q"
	Off	"N"-"P"
Down	On	"F"-"J"; "P"-"Q"
	Off	"N"-"O"

[1] – Main switch position does not affect driver's switch operation.

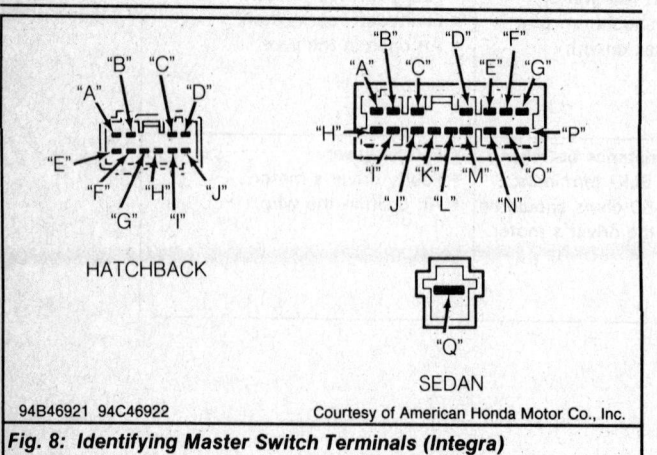

Fig. 8: Identifying Master Switch Terminals (Integra)

94B46921 94C46922   Courtesy of American Honda Motor Co., Inc.

POWER WINDOW MASTER SWITCH TEST (LEGEND)

Position	Main Switch	Pin Continuity
Right Front Switch		
Off	On	"G"-"P"-"Q"
	Off	"G"-"P"
Up	On	"C"-"P"; "G"-"Q"
	Off	"C"-"P"
Down	On	"C"-"G"; "P"-"Q"
	Off	"C"-"G"
Right Rear Switch		
Off	On	"M"-"N"-"Q"
	Off	"M"-"N"
Up	On	"O"-"M"; "N"-"Q"
	Off	"M"-"O"
Down	On	"N"-"O"; "M"-"Q"
	Off	"N"-"O"
Left Rear Switch		
Off	On	"D"-"E"-"Q"
	Off	"D"-"E"
Up	On	"D"-"F"; "E"-"Q"
	Off	"F"-"D"
Down	On	"E"-"F"; "D"-"Q"
	Off	"E"-"F"

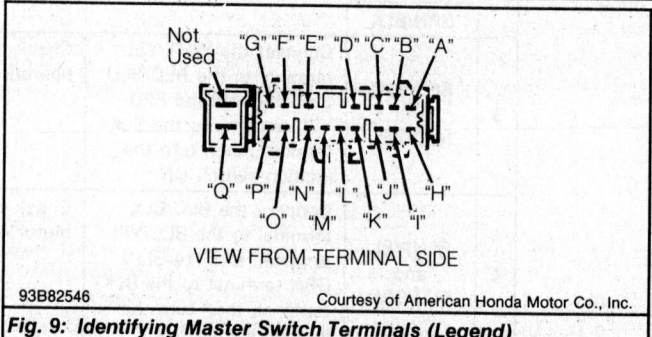

VIEW FROM TERMINAL SIDE

93B82546   Courtesy of American Honda Motor Co., Inc.

Fig. 9: Identifying Master Switch Terminals (Legend)

POWER WINDOW MASTER SWITCH TEST (VIGOR)

Position	Main Switch	Pin Continuity
Driver's Switch		
Off	1	"H"-"I"-"J"
Up	1	"H"-"N"
Down	1	"J"-"N"
Down (AUTO)	1	"J"-"N"
Right Front Switch		
Off	On	"D"-"E"-"O"
	Off	"D"-"E"
Up	On	"E"-"L"
	Off	"E"-"L"
Down	On	"D"-"L"
	Off	"D"-"L"
Left Rear Switch		
Off	On	"B"-"C"-"O"
	Off	"B"-"C"
Up	On	"C"-"K"
	Off	"C"-"K"
Down	On	"B"-"K"
	Off	"B"-"K"
Right Rear Switch		
Off	On	"F"-"G"-"O"
	Off	"F"-"G"
Up	On	"G"-"M"
	Off	"G"-"M"
Down	On	"F"-"M"
	Off	"F"-"M"

[1] – Main switch position does not affect driver's switch operation.

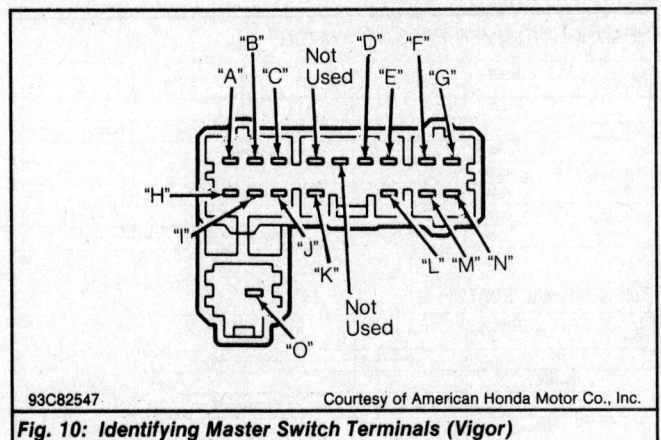

93C82547 — Courtesy of American Honda Motor Co., Inc.

Fig. 10: Identifying Master Switch Terminals (Vigor)

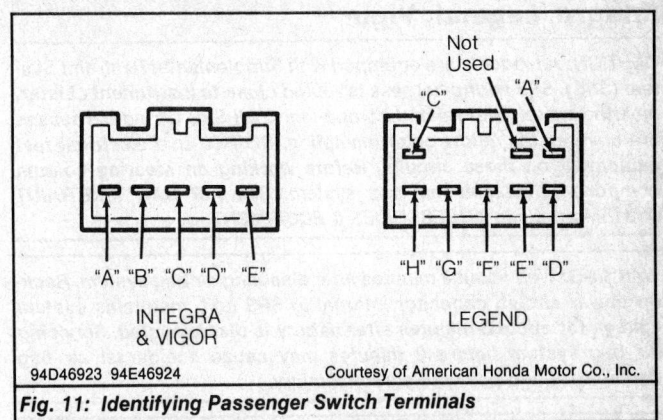

94D46923 94E46924 — Courtesy of American Honda Motor Co., Inc.

Fig. 11: Identifying Passenger Switch Terminals

PASSENGER WINDOW SWITCH TEST

Passenger Window Switch Test – Unplug connector from switch. See WINDOW SWITCH under REMOVAL & INSTALLATION. Check for continuity between specified switch terminals with switch in each position. If continuity is not as specified, replace switch. *See Fig. 11.* See PASSENGER POWER WINDOW SWITCH TEST table.

PASSENGER POWER WINDOW SWITCH TEST

Switch Position

	Continuity
Integra	
Front	
Off	"A"-"B"; "D"-"E"
Up	"B"-"C"; "D"-"E"
Down	"A"-"B"; "C"-"D"
Rear	
Off	"A"-"B"; "C"-"E"
Up	"A"-"B"; "D"-"E"
Down	"B"-"D"; "C"-"E"
Legend	
Off	"D"-"E"; "H"-"G"
Up	"D"-"E"; "C"-"G"
Down	"C"-"D"; "G"-"H"
Vigor	
Off	"A"-"C"; "D"-"E"
Up	"A"-"B"; "D"-"E"
Down	"A"-"C"; "B"-"D"

REMOVAL & INSTALLATION

WINDOW MOTOR

Removal & Installation – Information is not available from manufacturer.

WINDOW SWITCH

Removal & Installation – Remove door panel. Unplug connectors. Remove mounting screws. To install, reverse removal procedure.

WIRING DIAGRAMS

NOTE: See ACCESSORIES & EQUIPMENT, Volume 5.

1994 ACCESSORIES & EQUIPMENT
Steering Column Switches

Integra, Legend, Vigor

CAUTION: All models are equipped with Supplemental Restraint System (SRS). SRS wiring harness is routed close to instrument cluster, steering wheel, and related components. All SRS wiring harnesses are covered by Yellow outer insulation. DO NOT use electrical test equipment on these circuits. Before working on steering column components, disable air bag system. See AIR BAG RESTRAINT SYSTEM article in ACCESSORIES & EQUIPMENT.

WARNING: Wait about 3 minutes after disabling air bag system. Back-up power circuit, capacitor internal to SRS unit, maintains system voltage for about 3 minutes after battery is disconnected. Servicing air bag system before 3 minutes may cause accidental air bag deployment and possible personal injury.

NOTE: Radio/cassette or radio/CD player contains an anti-theft protection circuit. Whenever battery is disconnected, radio will go into anti-theft mode. When battery is reconnected, radio will display CODE and will be inoperative until proper code number is entered by vehicle owner.

TESTING

COMBINATION SWITCH (TURN SIGNAL/HEADLIGHT)

Integra – Remove steering column upper and lower covers. Unplug electrical connectors from switch. Check for continuity between specified terminals in each switch position. *See Fig. 1.* Replace switch if continuity is not as specified.

Legend – Remove instrument panel lower cover. Unplug 10-pin and 4-pin connectors. Check for continuity between specified terminals in each switch position. *See Fig. 2.* Replace switch if continuity is not as specified.

Vigor – Remove instrument panel lower cover. Remove knee bolster and instrument panel lower frame. Unplug 12-pin connector. Check for continuity between specified terminals in each switch position. *See Fig. 3.* Replace switch if continuity is not as specified.

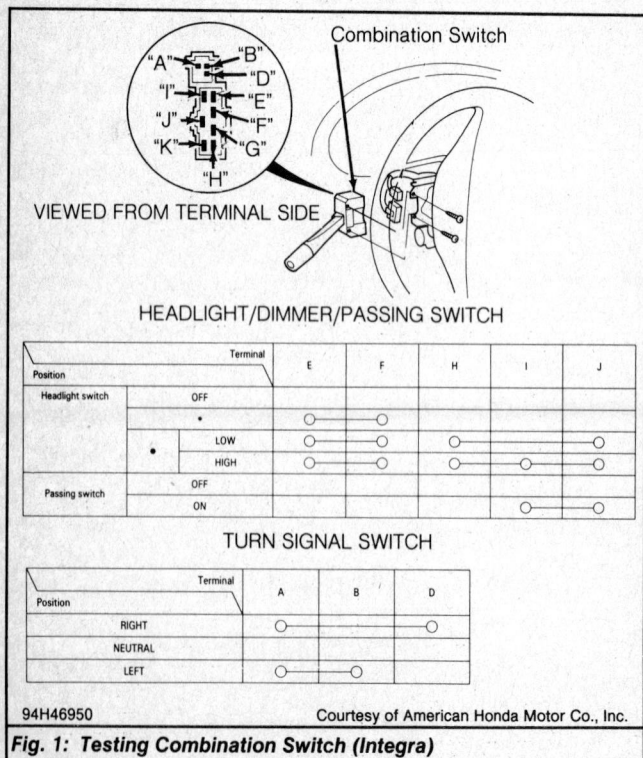

HEADLIGHT/DIMMER/PASSING SWITCH

Position	Terminal	E	F	H	I	J
Headlight switch	OFF					
	•	○——○				
	LOW	○——○		○——○		
	HIGH	○——○		○——○——○		
Passing switch	OFF					
	ON				○——○	

TURN SIGNAL SWITCH

Position	Terminal	A	B	D
RIGHT		○——○		
NEUTRAL				
LEFT		○—————○		

94H46950   Courtesy of American Honda Motor Co., Inc.

Fig. 1: Testing Combination Switch (Integra)

HEADLIGHT/DIMMER/PASSING SWITCH

Position	Terminal	2	3	11	12
Lighting Switch	OFF				
	•	○——○——○			
	•	○——○		○——————○	
Dimmer Switch	LOW				
	HIGH				
Passing Switch	OFF				
	ON	○——○		○——○	

TURN SIGNAL SWITCH

Position	Terminal	4	5	6
R				◄┤
NEUTRAL				
L			○——○	◄┤

VIEWED FROM TERMINAL SIDE

14-Pin Connector

92E00368   Courtesy of American Honda Motor Co., Inc.

Fig. 2: Testing Combination Switch (Legend)

DAYTIME RUNNING LIGHT CIRCUIT (CANADA)

Integra – **1)** Remove right kick panel. Unplug 8-pin and 4-pin connectors from daytime running light relay. *See Fig. 4.* Perform circuit test at daytime running light relay harness connectors.

2) Check for continuity between Black wire and ground. If continuity exists, go to next step. If continuity does not exist, check for poor ground connections at left front of engine compartment (next to washer reservoir) and behind left kick panel.

3) With ignition on, measure voltage between Yellow/Black wire and ground. If battery voltage exists, go to next step. If battery voltage does not exist, check for defective fuse No. 16 in under-dash fuse block. If fuse is okay, check for open in Yellow/Black wire. If Yellow/Black wire is okay, test ignition switch. See IGNITION SWITCH under TESTING.

4) Measure voltage between White/Yellow wire and ground. If battery voltage exists, go to next step. If battery voltage does not exist, check for defective fuse No. 17 in under-dash fuse block. If fuse is okay, repair open in White wire.

5) With headlight switch in ON position and dimmer switch in HI position, measure voltage between Red/White wire and ground. If battery voltage exists, go to next step. If battery voltage does not exist, repair open in Red/White wire. If okay, check combination switch. See COMBINATION SWITCH (TURN SIGNAL/HEADLIGHT) under TESTING.

6) Connect a jumper wire between Yellow/Black and White/Red wires. With ignition on, left and right headlight (high beam) and high beam indicator should be on. If operation is as specified, go to next step. If operation is not as specified, check for bad grounds or open in Yellow/Black and/or White/Red wires. If wires are okay, test daytime running resistor. See DAYTIME RUNNING RESISTOR (CANADA) under TESTING.

7) With ignition on, connect a jumper wire between Green/Red wire and ground. Brake warning light indicator should come on. If indicator light comes on, go to next step. If indicator light does not come on, check for bad indicator bulb. If bulb is okay, repair open in Green/Red wire.

8) With parking brake on, check for continuity between Red/Green wire and ground. If continuity exists, go to next step. If continuity does not exist, check parking brake switch. If switch is okay, repair open in Red/Green wire or fuse No. 15 in under-hood fuse panel.

9) If all test results are okay and system still does not work, replace daytime running light relay.

Legend – 1) Remove lower dash panel. Unplug 14-pin connector from daytime running light control unit. Perform circuit test at control unit relay connector.

NOTE: For testing purposes, wires of same color have been given superscript numbers for identification. See Fig. 5.

2) Check for continuity between Black wire and ground. If continuity exists, go to next step. If continuity does not exist, check for open in Black wire. If wire is okay, check for bad ground connection behind left kick panel, behind right kick panel and at right shock tower.

3) Measure voltage between Red/White [2] wire and ground. If battery voltage exists, go to next step. If battery voltage does not exist, check for defective fuse No. 16 in underdash fuse block. If fuse is okay, repair open in Red/White [2] wire.

4) Measure voltage between Blue/Red wire and ground. If battery voltage exists, go to next step. If battery voltage does not exist, check for open in Blue/Red wire. If wire is okay, test headlight relay. See HEADLIGHT RELAY.

5) With headlights off, check for continuity between Red/White [2] and ground. If continuity exists, go to next step. If continuity does not exist, check for bad ground connection at left front of engine compartment. If ground connection is okay, test dimmer relay. See DIMMER RELAY.

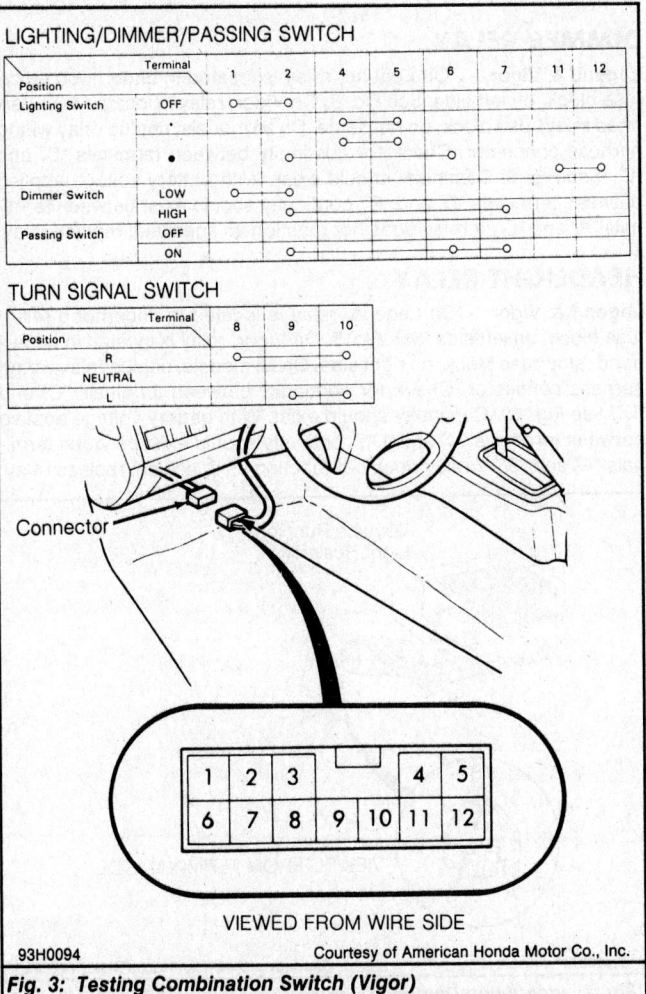

LIGHTING/DIMMER/PASSING SWITCH

Position	Terminal	1	2	4	5	6	7	11	12
Lighting Switch	OFF	○—○							
	•			○—○					
	●		○—		—○		○—○		
Dimmer Switch	LOW	○—○							
	HIGH		○—			—○			
Passing Switch	OFF								
	ON				○—	—○			

TURN SIGNAL SWITCH

Position	Terminal	8	9	10
R		○—	—○	
NEUTRAL				
L			○—	—○

VIEWED FROM WIRE SIDE

93H0094
Courtesy of American Honda Motor Co., Inc.

Fig. 3: Testing Combination Switch (Vigor)

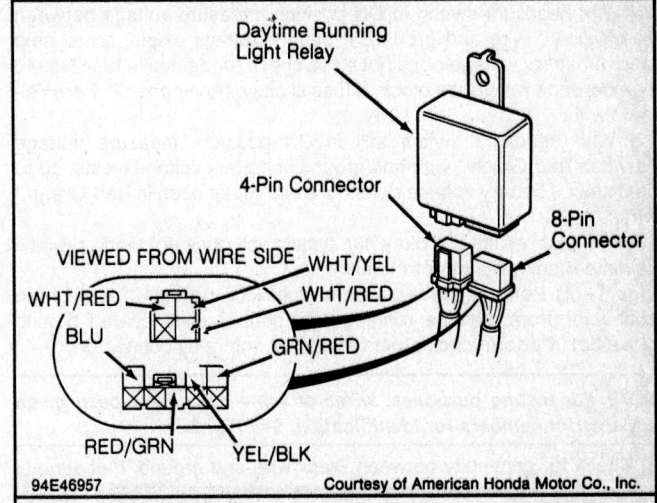

VIEWED FROM WIRE SIDE
- WHT/YEL
- WHT/RED
- WHT/RED
- BLU
- GRN/RED
- RED/GRN
- YEL/BLK

94E46957
Courtesy of American Honda Motor Co., Inc.

Fig. 4: Identifying Daytime Running Light Relay Connector Terminals (Integra – Canada)

6) With parking brake on, check for continuity between Green wire and ground. If continuity exists, go to next step. If continuity does not exist, check for open in Green wire. If wire is okay, check parking brake switch.

7) With ignition on, measure voltage between Black/Yellow wire and ground. If battery voltage exists, go to next step. If battery voltage does not exist, check for defective fuse No. 12 in underdash fuse block. If fuse is okay, repair open in Black/Yellow wire.

8) With ignition on, connect jumper wire between Green/Black wire and ground. Daytime running light indicator should come on. If indicator light comes on, go to next step. If indicator light does not come on, check for defective fuse No. 13 in underdash fuse block. If fuse is okay, check for bad indicator bulb. If bulb is okay, repair open in Green/Black wire.

9) With ignition on, use a jumper wire to ground Green/Red [1] wire. Brake warning indicator should come on. If indicator light comes on, go to next step. If brake warning indicator does not come on, check for defective fuse No. 13 in underdash fuse block. If fuse is okay, check for bad indicator bulb. If bulb is okay, repair open in Green/Red [1] wire.

10) Check for continuity between Red/Green [2], Red/Blue, and Red/Yellow [2] wires. If continuity exists between all 3 wires, go to next step. If continuity does not exist between any of these wires, repair open in suspect wire.

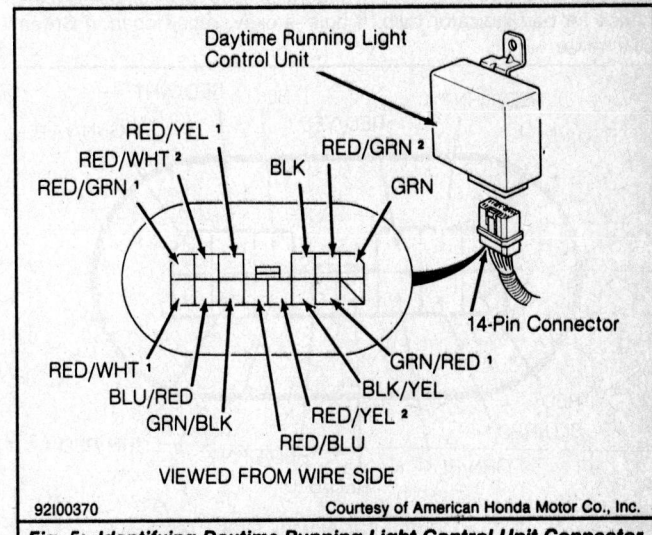

Daytime Running Light Control Unit
- RED/YEL [1]
- RED/WHT [2]
- RED/GRN [1]
- BLK
- RED/GRN [2]
- GRN
- RED/WHT [1]
- BLU/RED
- GRN/BLK
- RED/BLU
- RED/YEL [2]
- BLK/YEL
- GRN/RED [1]
- 14-Pin Connector

VIEWED FROM WIRE SIDE

92I00370
Courtesy of American Honda Motor Co., Inc.

Fig. 5: Identifying Daytime Running Light Control Unit Connector Terminals (Legend – Canada)

11) With headlight switch in ON position, measure voltage between Red/Yellow [1] wire and ground. If battery voltage exists, go to next step. If battery voltage does not exist, check for defective fuse No. 46 in underhood relay/fuse block. If fuse is okay, repair open in Red/Yellow [1] wire.

12) With headlight switch still in ON position, measure voltage between Red/Green [1] wire and ground. If battery voltage exists, go to next step. If battery voltage does not exist, repair open in Red/Green [1] wire.

13) If all test results are okay but system still does not work, replace daytime running light control unit.

Vigor – 1) Remove glove box and right kick panel. Unplug 14-pin connector from daytime running light control unit, located behind glove box. Perform circuit tests at control unit relay connector.

NOTE: *For testing purposes, wires of same color have been given superscript numbers for identification. See Fig. 6.*

---

2) Check for continuity between Black wire and ground. If continuity exists, go to next step. If continuity does not exist, repair open in Black wire.

3) Measure voltage between Red/Green [2] wire and ground. If battery voltage exists, go to next step. If battery voltage does not exist, check for defective fuse No. 21 in underdash fuse block. If fuse is okay, repair open in Red/Green [2] wire.

4) Measure voltage between Blue/Red wire and ground. If battery voltage exists, go to next step. If battery voltage does not exist, check for open in Blue/Red wire. If wire is okay, test dimmer relay. See DIMMER RELAY.

5) With headlights off, check for continuity between Red wire and ground. If continuity exists, go to next step. If continuity does not exist, check for open in Red wire. If wire is okay, check for bad ground connection, located at right side of engine compartment. If ground connection is okay, test dimmer relay. See DIMMER RELAY.

6) With parking brake on, measure voltage between Green/White wire and ground. If voltage is one volt or less, go to next step. If voltage is more than one volt, check for open in Green wire. If wire is okay, check parking brake switch.

7) With ignition on, measure voltage between Yellow/Black wire and ground. If battery voltage exists, go to next step. If battery voltage does not exist, check for defective fuse No. 10 in underdash fuse block. If fuse is okay, repair open in Yellow/Black wire.

8) With ignition on, connect jumper wire between Green/Black wire and ground. Daytime running light indicator should come on. If indicator light comes on, go to next step. If indicator light does not come on, check for defective fuse No. 1 in underdash fuse block. If fuse is okay, check for bad indicator bulb. If bulb is okay, repair open in Green/Black wire.

9) With ignition on, use a jumper wire to ground Green/Red wire. Brake warning indicator should come on. If indicator light comes on, go to next step. If brake warning indicator does not come on, check for defective fuse No. 1 in underdash fuse block. If fuse is okay, check for bad indicator bulb. If bulb is okay, repair open in Green/Red wire.

10) Check for continuity between Red/Yellow [2], Red/Green [3], and Red/Blue [1] wires. If continuity exists between all 3 wires, go to next step. If continuity does not exist for any of these wires, repair open in suspect wire.

11) With headlight switch in ON position, measure voltage between Red/Yellow [1] wire and ground. If battery voltage exists, go to next step. If battery voltage does not exist, check for defective fuse No. 19 in underdash fuse block. If fuse is okay, repair open in Red/Yellow wire [1].

12) With headlight switch still in ON position, measure voltage between Red/White wire and ground. If battery voltage exists, go to next step. If battery voltage does not exist, check for defective fuse No. 20 in underdash fuse block. If fuse is okay, repair open in Red/White wire.

13) If all test results are okay but system still does not work, replace daytime running light control unit.

DAYTIME RUNNING LIGHT RESISTOR (CANADA)

Integra – Unplug 3-pin connector from resistor. Resistor is located on left front of engine compartment. Measure resistance between terminals "A" and "B" and between terminals "C" and "B". *See Fig. 7.* Resistance should be 0.7-2.1 ohms. If resistance is not as specified, replace resistor.

DIMMER RELAY

Legend & Vigor – On Legend, relay is located in underhood relay/fuse block, on left side. *See Fig. 8.* On Vigor, relay is located in underhood relay/fuse block, on right side. On all models, unplug relay wiring harness connector. Check for continuity between terminals "B" and "C". *See Fig. 9.* Continuity should exist. With battery voltage applied between terminals "D" and "E", continuity should exist between terminals "A" and "C". If relay does not function as specified, replace relay.

HEADLIGHT RELAY

Legend & Vigor – On Legend, relay is located in underhood relay/fuse block, on left side. *See Fig. 8.* On Vigor, relay is located in underhood relay/fuse block, on right side. On all models, unplug relay wiring harness connector. Check for continuity between terminals "C" and "D". *See Fig. 10.* Continuity should exist. With battery voltage applied between terminals "C" and "D", continuity should exist between terminals "A" and "B". If relay does not function as specified, replace relay.

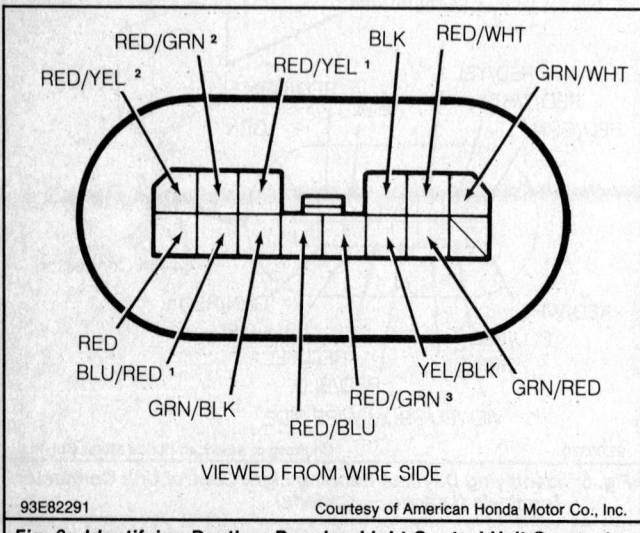

93E82291   Courtesy of American Honda Motor Co., Inc.

Fig. 6: Identifying Daytime Running Light Control Unit Connector Terminals (Vigor – Canada)

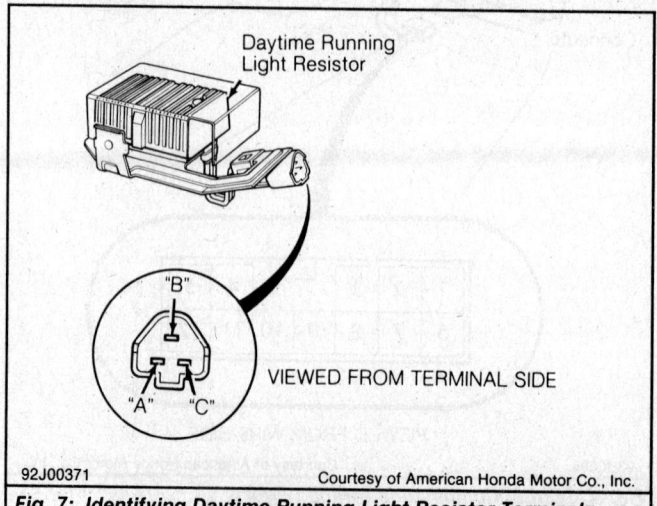

92J00371   Courtesy of American Honda Motor Co., Inc.

Fig. 7: Identifying Daytime Running Light Resistor Terminals (Integra – Canada)

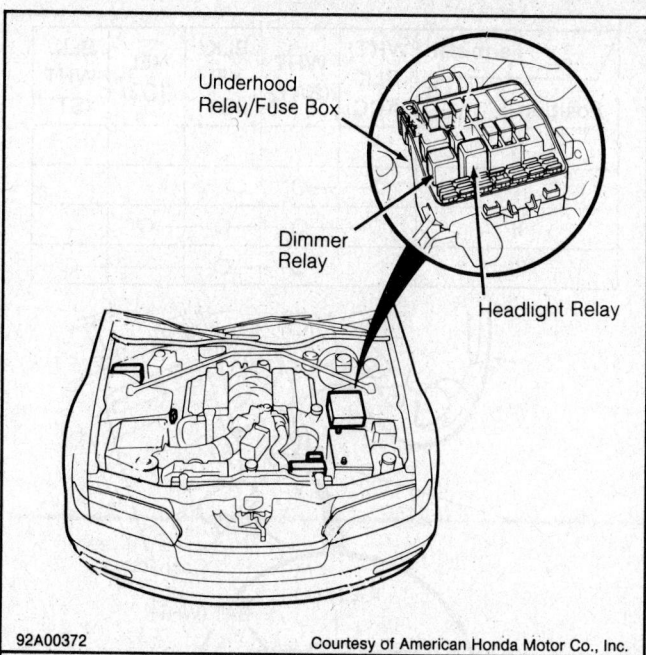

Underhood
Relay/Fuse Box

Dimmer
Relay

Headlight Relay

92A00372   Courtesy of American Honda Motor Co., Inc.

Fig. 8: Locating Headlight & Dimmer Relays (Legend)

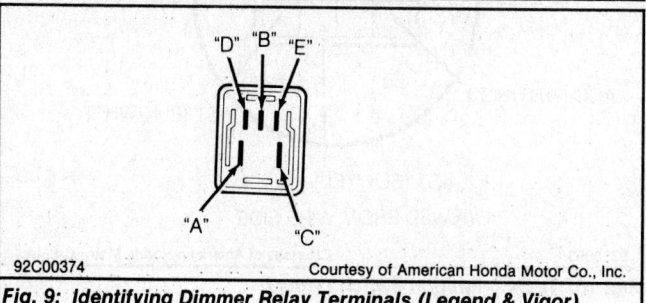

"D" "B" "E"

"A"   "C"

92C00374   Courtesy of American Honda Motor Co., Inc.

Fig. 9: Identifying Dimmer Relay Terminals (Legend & Vigor)

HORN

Integra & Vigor – 1) On Integra, remove fuse No. 32 from under-dash fuse panel. On all models, obtain radio anti-theft code. Position front wheels in straight-ahead position. Disconnect negative and positive battery cables. Remove lower instrument panel cover.
2) Disable air bag system. See AIR BAG RESTRAINT SYSTEM article in ACCESSORIES & EQUIPMENT. Unplug air bag connector from clockspring. Install shorting connector. Unplug 6-pin connector from vehicle harness. Install Test Harness (07LAZ-SL40300).
3) Check for continuity between terminal No. 3 on test harness and body ground. Continuity should exist with horn sounder pressed. Continuity should not exist with horn sounder released.

Legend – 1) Obtain radio anti-theft code. Position front wheels in straight-ahead position. Disconnect negative and positive battery cables. Remove lower instrument panel cover.

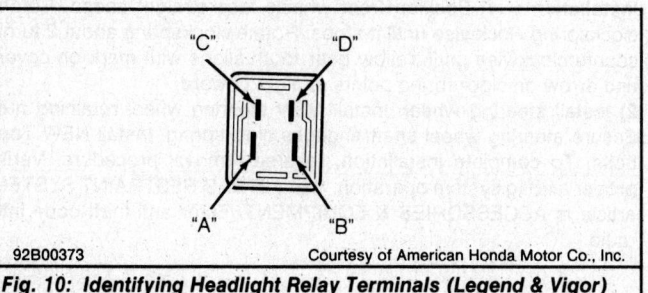

"C"   "D"

"A"   "B"

92B00373   Courtesy of American Honda Motor Co., Inc.

Fig. 10: Identifying Headlight Relay Terminals (Legend & Vigor)

2) Disable air bag system. See AIR BAG RESTRAINT SYSTEM article in ACCESSORIES & EQUIPMENT. Unplug air bag connector from clockspring. Install shorting connector. Unplug 7-pin connector from vehicle harness. Install Test Harness (07MAZ-SP00600).
3) Check for continuity between terminal No. 3 on test harness and body ground. Continuity should exist with horn sounder pressed. Continuity should not exist with horn sounder released.

IGNITION SWITCH

Integra – Disconect negative battery cable. Remove lower dashboard panel and left knee bolster. Unplug ignition switch 5-pin connector from dash fuse block. Unplug ignition switch 7-pin connector from main wiring harness. Check continuity at each switch position. See Fig. 11. Replace switch if continuity is not as specified.
Vigor – Remove lower instrument panel cover, left knee bolster and left kick panel. Unplug 7-pin connector from underdash fuse block. Check switch continuity at each switch position. See Fig. 13. Replace switch if continuity is not as specified.
Legend – Disconnect negative battery cable. Remove lower dashboard panel. Unplug ignition switch 7-pin connector from underdash fuse block. Test for continuity at each switch position. See Fig. 12. Replace switch if continuity is not as specified.

WINDSHIELD WIPER/WASHER SWITCH

For testing information, see WIPER/WASHER SYSTEMS article in ACCESSORIES & EQUIPMENT.

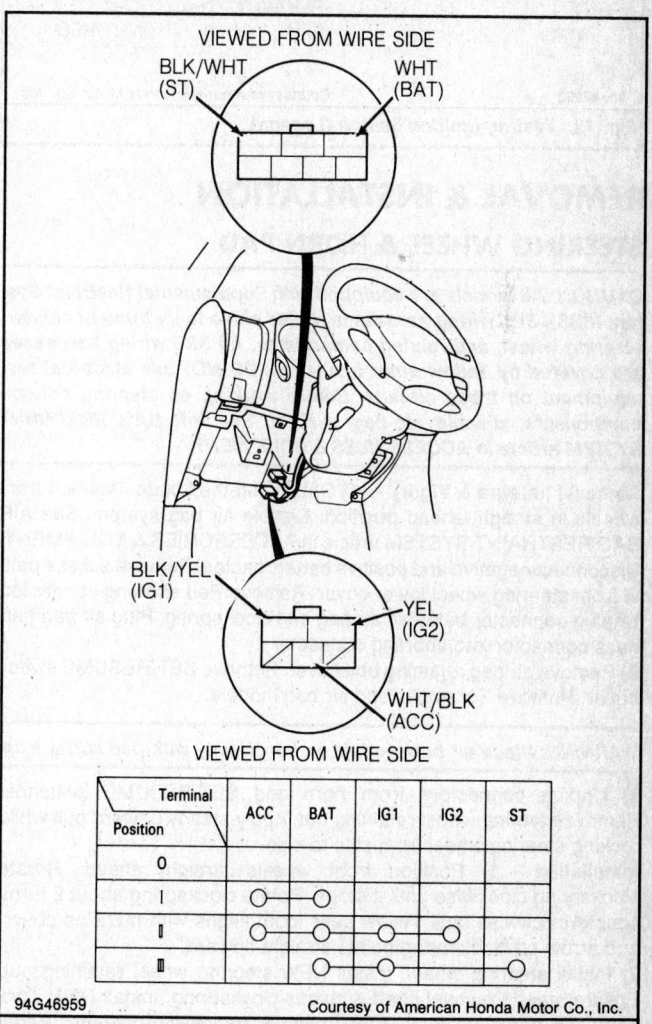

VIEWED FROM WIRE SIDE

BLK/WHT
(ST)   WHT
                        (BAT)

BLK/YEL
(IG1)

YEL
(IG2)

WHT/BLK
(ACC)

VIEWED FROM WIRE SIDE

Terminal Position	ACC	BAT	IG1	IG2	ST
0					
I	○—	—○			
II	○—	—○—	—○	○	
III		○—	—○		○

94G46959   Courtesy of American Honda Motor Co., Inc.

Fig. 11: Testing Ignition Switch (Integra)

Terminal / Position	WHT/RED (ACC)	WHT (BAT)	BLK/YEL (IG1)	YEL (IG2)	BLK/WHT (ST)
O					
I	○—————○			
II	○—————○	○—————○	
III			○—————○

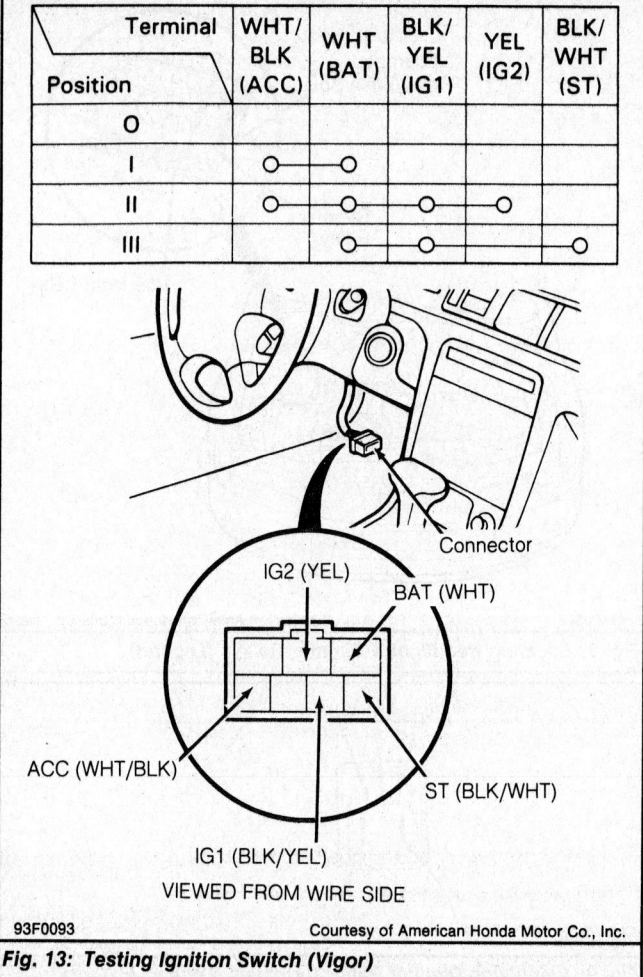

Terminal / Position	WHT/BLK (ACC)	WHT (BAT)	BLK/YEL (IG1)	YEL (IG2)	BLK/WHT (ST)
O					
I	○—————○			
II	○—————○—————○—————○	
III		○—————○————————————○

93F82292 — Courtesy of American Honda Motor Co., Inc.

Fig. 12: Testing Ignition Switch (Legend)

Labels in Fig. 12: Not Used; WHT (BAT); BLK/YEL (IG1); 7-Pin Connector; BLK/WHT (ST); WHT/RED (ACC); YEL (IG2)

93F0093 — Courtesy of American Honda Motor Co., Inc.

Fig. 13: Testing Ignition Switch (Vigor)

Labels in Fig. 13: Connector; IG2 (YEL); BAT (WHT); ACC (WHT/BLK); ST (BLK/WHT); IG1 (BLK/YEL); VIEWED FROM WIRE SIDE

REMOVAL & INSTALLATION

STEERING WHEEL & HORN PAD

CAUTION: All models are equipped with Supplemental Restraint System (SRS). SRS wiring harness is routed close to instrument cluster, steering wheel, and related components. All SRS wiring harnesses are covered by Yellow outer insulation. DO NOT use electrical test equipment on these circuits. Before working on steering column components, disable air bag system. See AIR BAG RESTRAINT SYSTEM article in ACCESSORIES & EQUIPMENT.

Removal (Integra & Vigor) – **1)** Obtain anti-theft code. Position front wheels in straight-ahead position. Disable air bag system. See AIR BAG RESTRAINT SYSTEM article in ACCESSORIES & EQUIPMENT. Disconnect negative and positive battery cables. Remove access panel from steering wheel lower cover. Remove Red shorting connector. Unplug connector between air bag and clockspring. Plug air bag harness connector into shorting connector.

2) Remove air bag retaining bolt cover. Remove SET/RESUME switch cover. Remove Torx bolts and air bag module.

WARNING: Place air bag module on bench only with pad surface up.

3) Unplug connectors from horn and SET/RESUME switches. Remove steering wheel retaining nut. Apply steady upward pull while rocking steering wheel from side to side.

Installation – **1)** Position front wheels straight ahead. Rotate clockspring clockwise until it stops. Rotate clockspring about 2 turns counterclockwise until Yellow gear tooth aligns with mark on cover, and arrow on clockspring points straight upward.

2) Install steering wheel. Install NEW steering wheel retaining nut. Ensure steering wheel shaft engages clockspring. Install NEW Torx bolts. To complete installation, reverse removal procedure. Verify proper air bag system operation. See AIR BAG RESTRAINT SYSTEM article in ACCESSORIES & EQUIPMENT. Enter anti-theft code into radio.

Removal (Legend) – **1)** Obtain anti-theft code. Disconnect negative and positive battery cables. Disable air bag system. See AIR BAG RESTRAINT SYSTEM article in ACCESSORIES & EQUIPMENT. Remove access panel from steering wheel lower cover. Remove Red shorting connector. Unplug connector between air bag and clockspring.

2) Plug air bag harness connector into shorting connector. On "L" and "LS" models, plug clockspring connector into Shorting Connector (07MAZ-SP00100). On all models, remove switch assembly covers. Remove Torx bolts and air bag module.

WARNING: Place air bag module on bench only with pad surface up.

3) Unplug connectors from horn, remote audio, and SET/RESUME switches. Remove steering wheel retaining nut. Remove steering wheel by applying steady upward pull while rocking steering wheel from side to side.

Installation – **1)** Position front wheels face straight ahead. Rotate clockspring clockwise until it stops. Rotate clockspring about 2 turns counterclockwise until Yellow gear tooth aligns with mark on cover, and arrow on clockspring points straight upward.

2) Install steering wheel. Install NEW steering wheel retaining nut. Ensure steering wheel shaft engages clockspring. Install NEW Torx bolts. To complete installation, reverse removal procedure. Verify proper air bag system operation. See AIR BAG RESTRAINT SYSTEM article in ACCESSORIES & EQUIPMENT. Enter anti-theft code into radio.

COMBINATION SWITCH (TURN SIGNAL/HEADLIGHT SWITCH)

Removal & Installation (Integra) – Disconnect negative battery cable. Remove steering column covers. Unplug 7-pin and 3-pin connectors. Remove combination switch mounting screws and switch. To install, reverse removal procedure.

Removal & Installation (Legend) – Remove switches from lower dashboard panel. Remove lower dashboard panel. Remove upper and lower steering column covers. Unplug 14-pin combination switch connector. Remove combination switch mounting screws and switch. To install, reverse removal procedure.

Removal & Installation (Vigor) – Remove lower dashboard panel and knee bolster. Remove upper and lower steering column covers. Unplug 12-pin combination switch connector. Remove combination switch mounting screws. Remove combination switch. To install, reverse removal procedure.

IGNITION SWITCH

Removal & Installation (Integra) – Disconnect negative battery cable. Remove steering wheel. Remove upper and lower steering column covers. Remove lower dashboard panel and left knee bolster. Unplug 5-pin connector from fuse/relay box under dash, and 7-pin connector from main harness. Rotate ignition switch to "O" position. Remove retaining screws and ignition switch. To install, reverse removal procedure.

Removal & Installation (Legend & Vigor) – Disconnect negative battery cable. Remove switches from lower instrument panel cover. Remove lower instrument panel cover. Unplug 7-pin ignition switch connector from underdash fuse block. Rotate ignition switch to "O" position. Remove retaining screws and ignition switch. To install, reverse removal procedure.

STEERING LOCK ASSEMBLY

Removal (Integra) – 1) Disconnect negative battery cable. Remove steering wheel. Remove upper and lower steering column covers. Remove lower dashboard panel and left knee bolster. Unplug 5-pin connector from fuse/relay box under dash, and 7-pin connector from main harness.

2) Remove steering column mounting bolts/nuts. Lower steering column assembly. Center-punch both shear bolts. Using a 3/16" bit, drill heads from bolts. Remove shear bolts and ignition lock assembly.

Installation – To install, reverse removal procedure. Tighten new shear bolts until heads twist off. Check for proper ignition switch steering lock operation.

Removal (Legend) – 1) Obtain radio anti-theft code. Disconnect negative battery cable. Remove switches from lower dashboard panel. Remove lower dashboard panel. Unplug wiring harness connectors as necessary. Remove steering column mounting bolts/nuts. Lower steering column assembly.

2) Grind slot into shear bolt. Using a screwdriver, remove shear bolt. Rotate ignition switch to "1" position. Push steering lock retaining pin inward. Remove steering lock assembly.

Installation – Rotate ignition switch to "1" position. Push steering lock retaining pin inward and insert steering lock assembly until it clicks into place. Install and loosely tighten new shear bolt. Insert ignition key, and check for proper steering lock operation. Tighten shear bolt until hex head twists off. To complete installation, reverse removal procedure. Enter anti-theft code into radio.

Removal & Installation (Vigor) – 1) Obtain radio anti-theft code. Disconnect negative battery cable. Remove left knee bolster, left kick panel, and lower panel. Remove steering column covers. Remove instrument cluster trim panel. Center-punch both shear bolts. Drill heads from bolts with a 3/16" bit. Remove shear bolts and ignition lock assembly.

2) To install, install new ignition switch without key inserted. Install new shear bolts loosely. Insert ignition key. Ensure key turns freely and steering wheel lock operates properly. Tighten shear bolts until heads break off. To complete installation, reverse removal procedure. Enter anti-theft code into radio.

WIPER/WASHER SWITCH

Removal & Installation (Integra) – Remove upper and lower steering column covers. Unplug wiper/washer wiring harness connectors. Remove 2 screws and wiper/washer switch. To install, reverse removal procedure.

Removal & Installation (Legend) – Remove switches from lower dashboard panel. Remove lower dashboard panel. Remove upper and lower steering column covers. Unplug wiper/washer connector. Remove wiper/washer switch. To install, reverse removal procedure.

Removal & Installation (Vigor) – Remove lower dashboard panel and knee bolster. Remove upper and lower steering column covers. Unplug 10-pin windshield wiper/washer switch connector. Remove wiper/washer switch. To install, reverse removal procedure.

TORQUE SPECIFICATIONS
TORQUE SPECIFICATIONS

Application	Ft. Lbs. (N.m)
Steering Wheel Nut [1]	37 (50)

	INCH Lbs. (N.m)
Air Bag Module Retaining Bolts	88 (10)

[1] – Always install NEW retaining nut.

WIRING DIAGRAMS

NOTE: See ACCESSORIES & EQUIPMENT, Volume 5.

Integra, Legend, Vigor

CAUTION: All models are equipped with Supplemental Restraint System (SRS). SRS wiring harness is routed close to instrument cluster, steering wheel, and related components. All SRS wiring harnesses are covered by Yellow outer insulation. DO NOT use electrical test equipment on these circuits. Before working on steering column components, disable air bag system. See AIR BAG RESTRAINT SYSTEM article in ACCESSORIES & EQUIPMENT.

WARNING: Wait about 3 minutes after disabling air bag system. An internal back-up power circuit maintains system voltage for about 3 minutes after battery is disconnected. Servicing air bag system before 3 minutes may cause accidental air bag deployment and possible personal injury.

NOTE: Radio/cassette or radio/CD player contains anti-theft protection circuit. Whenever battery is disconnected, radio enters anti-theft mode. When battery is reconnected, radio displays CODE and will be inoperative until proper code number is entered. Obtain radio code before disconnecting battery or radio fuse.

DESCRIPTION & OPERATION

All models are equipped with a 2-speed front wiper motor with intermittent feature. On some models, intermittent delay is adjustable. Integra hatchback is equipped with a rear wiper/washer system.

TESTING

FRONT WIPER MOTOR TEST

1) Remove wiper arms. To gain access to wiper motor connector, remove lower windshield molding, hood seal, and air scoop. Unplug wiper motor 5-pin connector.
2) To test low speed operation, connect battery voltage to Green/Black wire. Connect Blue wire to ground. Motor should run smoothly at low speed. If motor does not run smoothly, replace wiper motor.
3) To test high speed operation, connect battery voltage to Green/Black wire. Connect Blue/Yellow wire to ground. Motor should run smoothly at high speed. If motor does not run smoothly, replace wiper motor.

FRONT WIPER RELAY TEST

Intermittent Relay (Legend & Vigor) – **1)** On Legend, relay is located on underhood relay panel on left side, toward front. On Vigor, relay is located over radiator fan, on left side of vehicle. Unplug relay from socket.

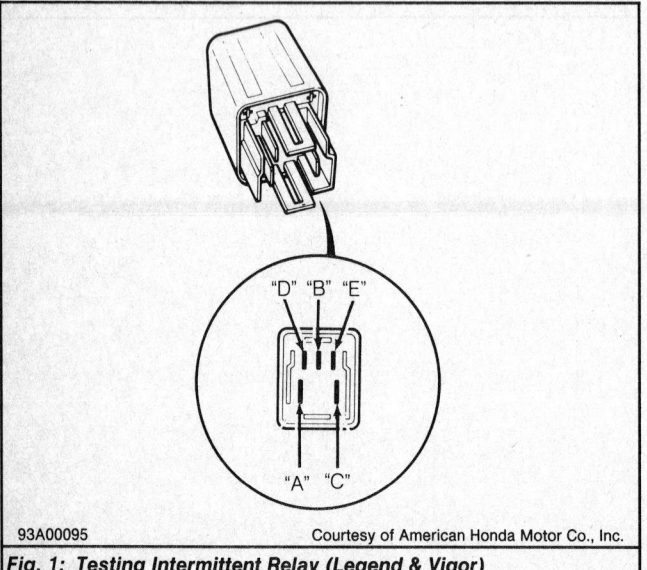

93A00095   Courtesy of American Honda Motor Co., Inc.

Fig. 1: Testing Intermittent Relay (Legend & Vigor)

2) Continuity should exist between terminals "B" and "C" with no power applied to relay coil. Continuity should not exist between terminals "A" and "C" with no power applied to relay coil. *See Fig. 1.*
3) Using fused jumper wires, apply battery voltage between coil terminals "D" and "E". Continuity should not exist between terminals "B" and "C". Continuity should exist between terminals "A" and "C". Replace relay if continuity is not as specified.

High-Speed Relay (Legend & Vigor) – **1)** On Legend, relay is located on underhood relay panel on left side, toward front. On Vigor, relay is located at relay panel under dash on right side. Unplug relay from socket.
2) Continuity should not exist between terminals "A" and "B" with no voltage applied to relay coil. *See Fig. 2.* Using fused jumper wires, apply battery voltage between coil terminals "C" and "D". Continuity should exist between terminals "A" and "B". Replace relay if continuity is not as specified.

Low-Speed Relay (Legend & Vigor) – **1)** On Legend, relay is located on underhood relay panel on left side, toward front. On Vigor, relay is located at relay panel under dash on right side. Unplug relay from socket.

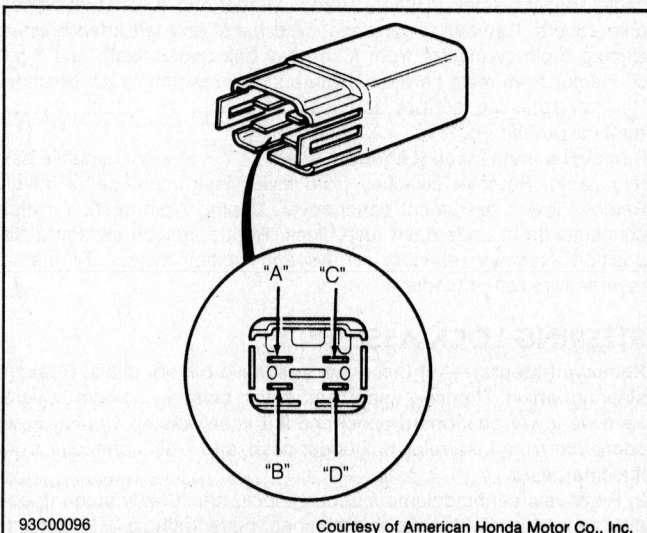

93C00096   Courtesy of American Honda Motor Co., Inc.

Fig. 2: Testing High-Speed Relay (Legend & Vigor)

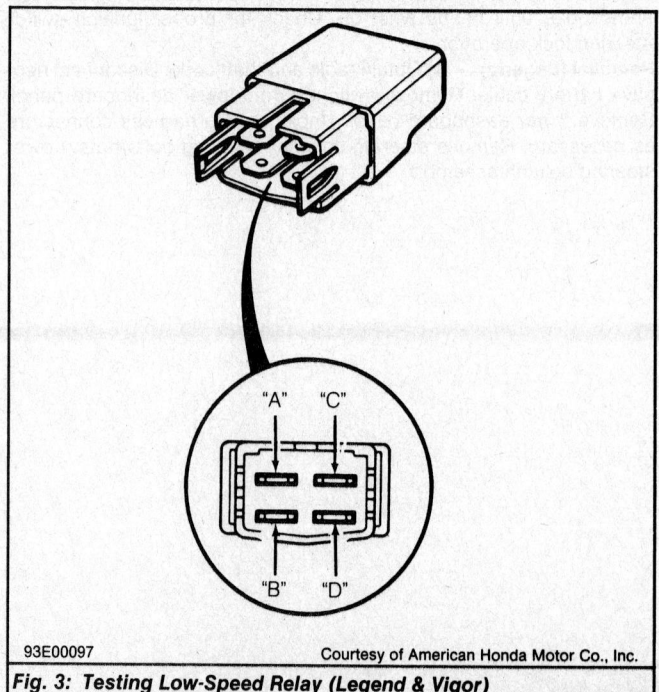

93E00097   Courtesy of American Honda Motor Co., Inc.

Fig. 3: Testing Low-Speed Relay (Legend & Vigor)

2) Continuity should exist between terminals "A" and "B" with no voltage applied to relay coil. *See Fig. 3.* Using fused jumper wires, apply battery voltage between coil terminals "C" and "D". No continuity should exist between terminals "A" and "B". Replace relay if continuity is not as specified.

WIPER/WASHER SWITCH TEST

Integra – Remove horn pad and steering wheel. Remove upper and lower steering column covers. Unplug 6-pin and 8-pin connectors from wiper/washer switch. Check for continuity between specified terminals in each switch position. *See Fig. 4.* If wiper/washer switch does not operate as specified, replace switch.

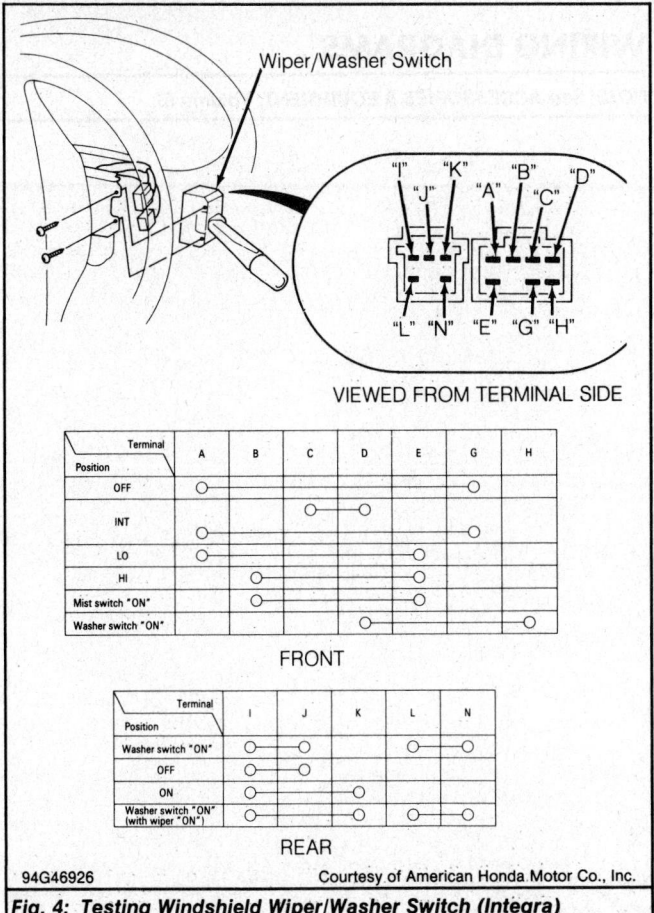

VIEWED FROM TERMINAL SIDE

Terminal / Position	A	B	C	D	E	G	H
OFF	O					O	
INT			O—O			O	
LO	O					O	
HI		O—O					
Mist switch "ON"		O—O		O			
Washer switch "ON"				O—O			O

FRONT

Terminal / Position	I	J	K	L	N
Washer switch "ON"	O—O				
OFF	O—O				
ON		O—O			
Washer switch "ON" (with wiper "ON")		O	O—O		

REAR

94G46926   Courtesy of American Honda Motor Co., Inc.

Fig. 4: Testing Windshield Wiper/Washer Switch (Integra)

Legend – Remove switches from lower dashboard panel. Remove lower dashboard panel. Unplug wiper/washer 10-pin connector. Check for continuity between specified terminals in each switch position. *See Fig. 5.* If wiper/washer switch does not operate as specified, replace switch.

Vigor – Remove lower dashboard panel. Unplug wiper/washer 10-pin connector. Check for continuity between specified terminals in each switch position. *See Fig. 6.* If wiper/washer switch does not operate as specified, replace switch.

WASHER MOTOR TEST

1) On Integra, remove front bumper. On Legend, remove left front inner fender. On Vigor, remove right front inner fender. On all models, unplug 2-pin connector at motor. Connect battery voltage across motor terminals. *See Fig. 7.*

2) Washer pump should run smoothly. Fluid should spray from outlet. If pump does not operate as specified, check for disconnected or blocked fluid lines. If fluid lines are okay, check for clogged washer pump outlet. If no faults are found, replace washer motor.

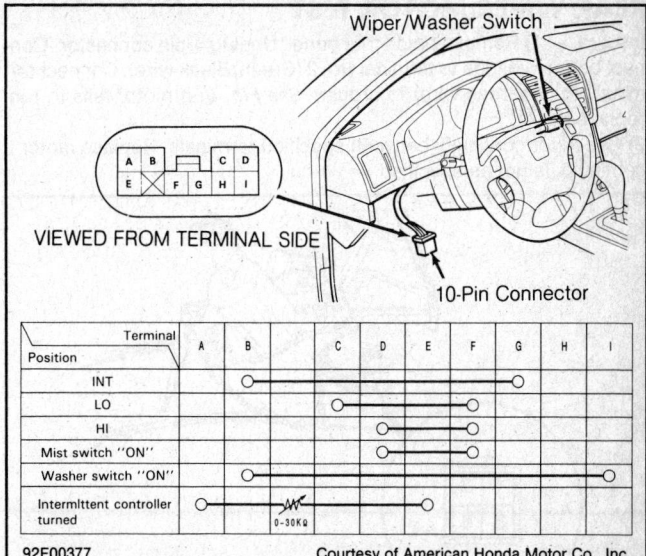

VIEWED FROM TERMINAL SIDE

10-Pin Connector

Terminal / Position	A	B	C	D	E	F	G	H	I
INT		O					O		
LO			O—O						
HI			O	O					
Mist switch "ON"			O	O					
Washer switch "ON"		O							O
Intermittent controller turned	O	—W— 0-30KΩ							

92F00377   Courtesy of American Honda Motor Co., Inc.

Fig. 5: Testing Windshield Wiper/Washer Switch (Legend)

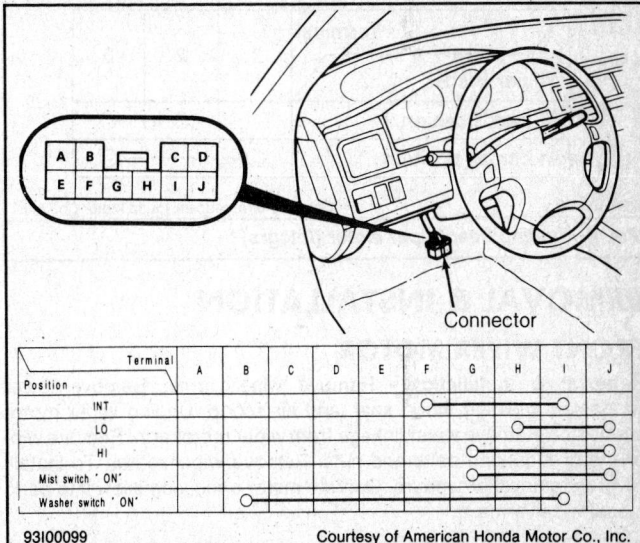

Connector

Terminal / Position	A	B	C	D	E	F	G	H	I	J
INT						O			O	
LO							O—O			
HI							O	O		
Mist switch "ON"						O	O			
Washer switch "ON"		O								O

93100099   Courtesy of American Honda Motor Co., Inc.

Fig. 6: Testing Windshield Wiper/Washer Switch (Vigor)

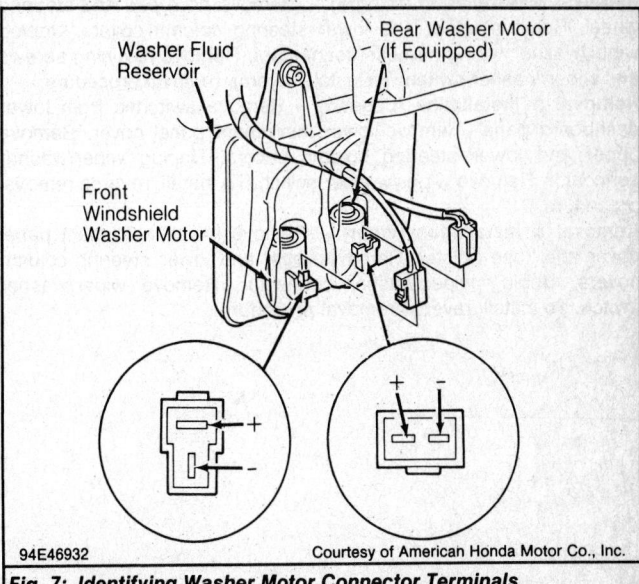

94E46932   Courtesy of American Honda Motor Co., Inc.

Fig. 7: Identifying Washer Motor Connector Terminals

REAR WIPER MOTOR TEST

Integra – 1) Remove hatch trim panel. Unplug 4-pin connector. Connect battery voltage to terminal No. 2 (Green/Black wire). Connect terminal No. 4 (Green wire) to ground. *See Fig. 8.* If motor fails to run, replace motor.
2) Check for continuity between specified terminals. Replace motor if continuity is not as specified.

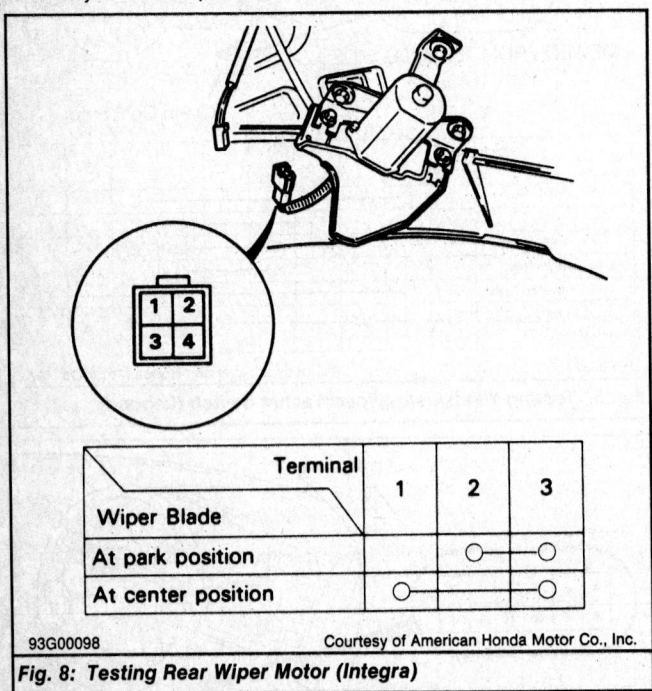

Terminal Wiper Blade	1	2	3
At park position		O———	———O
At center position	O———	———	———O

93G00098   Courtesy of American Honda Motor Co., Inc.

Fig. 8: Testing Rear Wiper Motor (Integra)

REMOVAL & INSTALLATION

FRONT WIPER MOTOR

Removal & Installation – Remove wiper arms. Remove lower windshield molding, hood seal, and air scoop. Unplug wiper motor connector. Remove wiper linkage from wiper motor arm. Remove wiper motor mounting bolts and nuts. Remove wiper motor. To install, reverse removal procedure. Operate motor once, and allow it to park. Install wiper arms.

WIPER/WASHER SWITCH

Removal & Installation (Integra) – Remove horn pad and steering wheel. Remove upper and lower steering column covers. Unplug wiper/washer wiring harness connectors. Remove retaining screws and wiper/washer switch. To install, reverse removal procedure.
Removal & Installation (Legend) – Remove switches from lower dashboard panel. Remove lower instrument panel cover. Remove upper and lower steering column covers. Unplug wiper/washer connector. Remove wiper/washer switch. To install, reverse removal procedure.
Removal & Installation (Vigor) – Remove lower instrument panel cover and knee bolster. Remove upper and lower steering column covers. Unplug wiper/washer connector. Remove wiper/washer switch. To install, reverse removal procedure.

WASHER MOTOR

Removal & Installation – On Integra, remove front bumper. On Legend, remove left front inner fender. On Vigor, remove right front inner fender. On all models, disconnect washer hoses and wiring harness connectors from washer motor. Remove mounting bolts and washer motor. To install, reverse removal procedure.

REAR WIPER MOTOR

Removal & Installation (Integra) – Remove rear hatch trim panel. Remove nut cover, retaining nut, wiper arm, cap, nut, washer, and rubber cushion. Unplug wiper motor connector. Remove mounting bolts and wiper motor. To install, reverse removal procedure.

WIRING DIAGRAMS

NOTE: See ACCESSORIES & EQUIPMENT, Volume 5.

Integra

NOTE: For repair procedures not covered in this article, see ENGINE OVERHAUL PROCEDURES article in GENERAL INFORMATION.

ENGINE IDENTIFICATION

Engine identification code is stamped on right rear of cylinder block as viewed from flywheel, below cylinder head mating surface. The first 5 characters of the code indicate engine type. The last 7 numbers of the code indicate engine serial number.

ENGINE IDENTIFICATION CODE

Application	Code
1.8L	B18A1

ADJUSTMENTS

VALVE CLEARANCE ADJUSTMENT

CAUTION: Always rotate engine in direction of normal rotation (counterclockwise as viewed from front of engine). Backward rotation may cause timing belt to jump time.

1) Adjust valves when engine temperature is 100°F (38°C) or less. Remove valve cover. Rotate crankshaft counterclockwise until No. 1 piston is at TDC of compression stroke.
2) Ensure UP marks on camshaft sprockets are at top, and TDC grooves on pulleys are aligned with TDC groove on back cover. *See Fig. 1.* Adjust clearance on both valves for No. 1 cylinder. Loosen lock nuts, and turn adjustment screw until clearance is as specified. Tighten lock nut to 18 ft. lbs. (25 N.m). Recheck adjustment. See VALVE CLEARANCE SPECIFICATIONS table.
3) Rotate crankshaft 180 degrees counterclockwise (camshaft sprockets turn 90 degrees) so No. 3 piston is at TDC of compression stroke. UP marks should point to exhaust side. Adjust clearance on both valves for No. 3 cylinder.

4) Rotate crankshaft 180 degrees counterclockwise so No. 4 piston is at TDC of compression stroke. Ensure UP marks are pointing down. Adjust clearance on both valves for No. 4 cylinder.
5) Rotate crankshaft 180 degrees counterclockwise so No. 2 piston is at TDC of compression stroke. Ensure UP marks are pointing to intake side. Adjust clearances on both valves for No. 2 cylinder. Install new valve cover gasket. Install valve cover. Retighten crankshaft pulley bolt to 133 ft. lbs. (180 N.m).

VALVE CLEARANCE SPECIFICATIONS

Application	In. (mm)
Exhaust	0.006-0.008 (0.16-0.20)
Intake	0.003-0.005 (0.08-0.12)

TIMING BELT TENSION ADJUSTMENT

CAUTION: Adjust timing belt with engine cold. DO NOT rotate crankshaft with timing belt tensioner adjusting bolt loose.

Remove valve cover. Rotate crankshaft counterclockwise until No. 1 piston is at TDC. Rotate crankshaft 5-6 revolutions counterclockwise on camshaft sprocket to create tension on timing belt. Loosen tension adjuster bolt to create tension on belt. *See Fig. 2.* Tighten tension adjuster bolt to specification. See TORQUE SPECIFICATIONS. Install valve cover using new gaskets.

REMOVAL & INSTALLATION

NOTE: For reassembly reference, label all electrical connectors, vacuum hoses, and fuel lines before removal. Place mating marks on engine hood and other major assemblies before removal.

FUEL PRESSURE RELEASE

CAUTION: Fuel system is under pressure. Release pressure before servicing fuel system components.

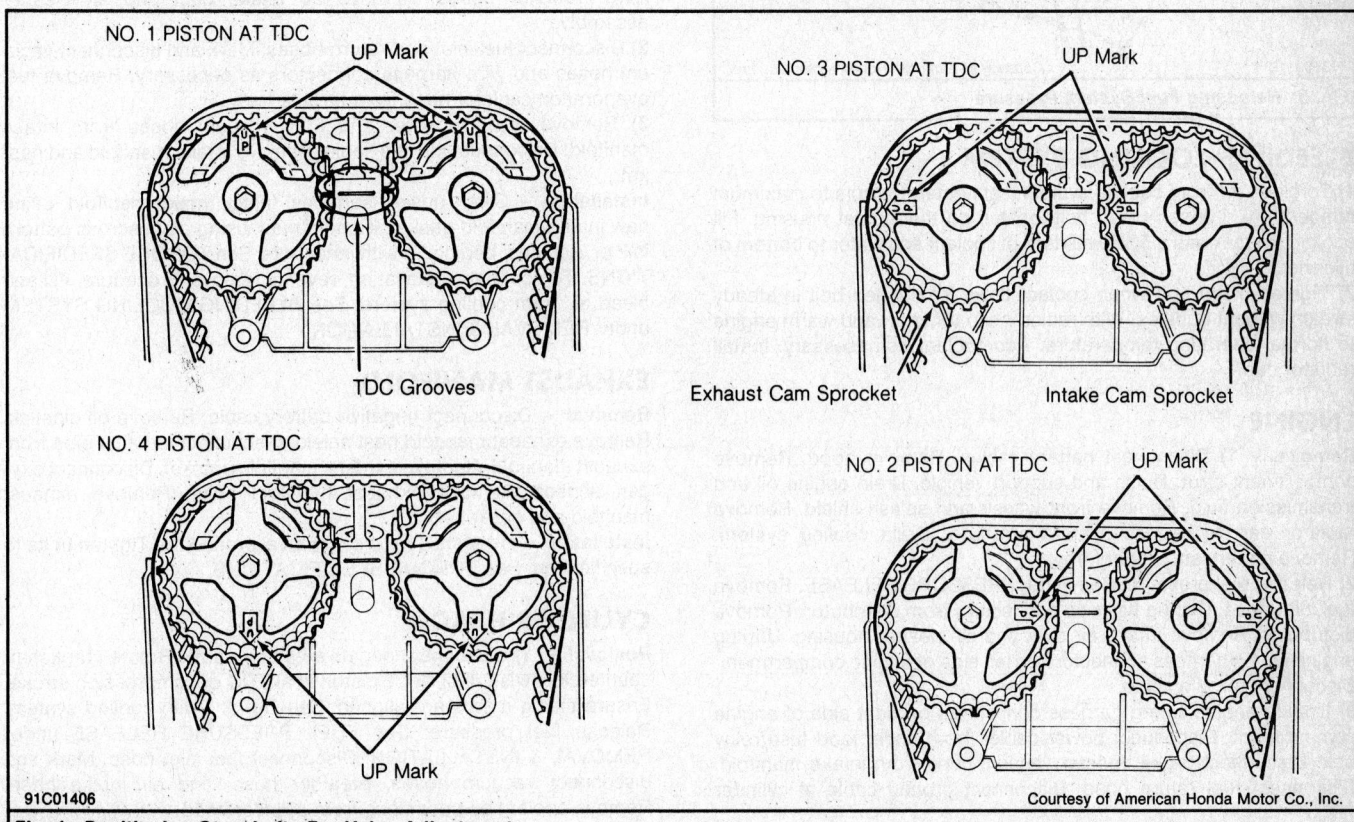

NO. 1 PISTON AT TDC — UP Mark — TDC Grooves

NO. 4 PISTON AT TDC — UP Mark

NO. 3 PISTON AT TDC — UP Mark — Exhaust Cam Sprocket — Intake Cam Sprocket

NO. 2 PISTON AT TDC — UP Mark

91C01406

Fig. 1: Positioning Camshafts For Valve Adjustment

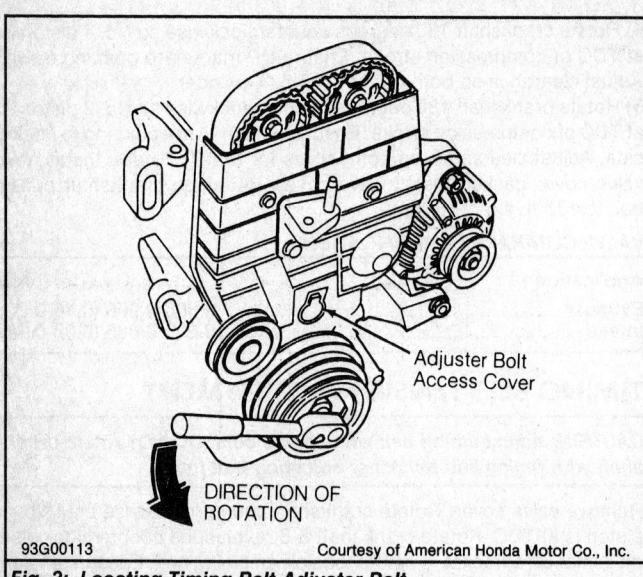

93G00113   Courtesy of American Honda Motor Co., Inc.

Fig. 2: Locating Timing Belt Adjuster Bolt

Disconnect negative battery cable. Remove fuel tank filler cap. Place a shop towel on top of fuel filter to absorb any fuel spray. Release fuel injection system pressure by slowly loosening fuel injection service bolt. See Fig. 3.

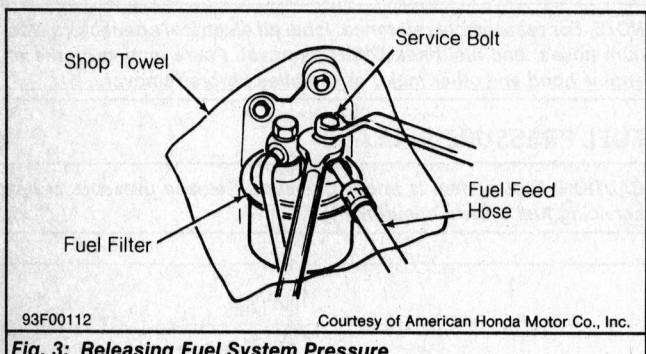

93F00112   Courtesy of American Honda Motor Co., Inc.

Fig. 3: Releasing Fuel System Pressure

BLEEDING COOLING SYSTEM

1) To bleed air from cooling system, set heater controls to maximum temperature. Loosen bleed bolt located on thermostat housing. Fill cooling system with a 50/50 mixture of coolant and water to bottom of filler neck.

2) Tighten bleed bolt when coolant flows from bleed bolt in steady stream without bubbles. With radiator cap off, start and warm engine to normal operating temperature. Add coolant as necessary. Install radiator cap.

ENGINE

Removal – 1) Disconnect battery cables. Remove hood. Remove compartment strut. Raise and support vehicle. Drain engine oil and transmission fluid. Remove front wheels and splash shield. Remove radiator cap to release system pressure. Drain cooling system. Remove battery and battery tray.

2) Release fuel pressure. See FUEL PRESSURE RELEASE. Remove fuel inlet hose. Unplug harness connectors from distributor. Remove distributor. Remove intake air duct and air cleaner housing. Unplug engine wiring harness connectors on left side of engine compartment. Disconnect throttle cable.

3) Unplug engine wiring harness connectors on right side of engine compartment. Disconnect power cables from underhood fuse/relay box. Disconnect brake booster vacuum hose from intake manifold. Disconnect fuel return hose. Disconnect ground cable at cylinder

head. Remove power steering pump with hoses attached. Set power steering pump aside.

4) Remove A/C compressor with hoses attached, and set it aside. Remove alternator. Disconnect transmission cooler lines. Remove radiator and heater hoses. Remove speed sensor, leaving hoses attached. Unplug cooling fan connectors. Remove radiator.

5) Remove exhaust pipe. Disconnect drive shafts. See FWD AXLE SHAFTS article in DRIVE AXLES. On M/T models, disconnect clutch cable, shift rod, and shift lever torque rod. On A/T models, remove torque converter cover and disconnect shift control cable.

6) On all models, attach chain hoist to engine. Raise hoist to take all slack from chain. Remove rear transmission mount and rear transmission mounting bracket. Remove front transmission mount. Remove side transmission mount and side transmission mounting bracket. Remove side engine mount.

7) Slowly raise engine/transaxle about 6 inches. Ensure all hoses and wiring have been disconnected. Carefully remove engine and transaxle from vehicle.

Installation – 1) To install, reverse removal procedure. To prevent excessive engine vibration and premature engine mount wear, tighten engine/transaxle mounts in specified sequence. See Fig. 4.

2) When installing drive axles, use new spring clips. Insert drive axles until spring clips click into groove of differential side gear. Ensure harness connectors and hoses are connected properly.

3) Ensure control cables are not bent or pinched and are adjusted properly. On M/T models, adjust clutch pedal free play. Verify transaxle shifts smoothly.

4) On all models, adjust drive belt tension. Fill or top off all fluids. Fill and bleed air from cooling system. See BLEEDING COOLING SYSTEM. Start engine and check for leaks.

INTAKE MANIFOLD

Removal – 1) Allow engine to cool. Disconnect negative battery cable. Release fuel pressure. See FUEL PRESSURE RELEASE under REMOVAL & INSTALLATION. Carefully remove radiator cap to release system pressure. Drain cooling system. Remove upper and lower radiator hoses. Remove air intake duct and air cleaner assembly.

2) Disconnect fuel inlet and return hoses. Mark and disconnect vacuum hoses and wire harness connectors as necessary. Remove fuel evaporation canister hose from throttle body.

3) Remove brake booster and PCV vacuum hoses from intake manifold. Disconnect throttle cable. Remove intake manifold and gasket.

Installation – Clean gasket surfaces. Install intake manifold, using new intake manifold gasket. Tighten nuts, using a crisscross pattern in 2 or 3 stages, beginning with inner nuts. See TORQUE SPECIFICATIONS. To complete installation, reverse removal procedure. Fill and bleed air from cooling system. See BLEEDING COOLING SYSTEM under REMOVAL & INSTALLATION.

EXHAUST MANIFOLD

Removal – Disconnect negative battery cable. Remove oil dipstick. Remove exhaust manifold heat shield. Disconnect exhaust pipe from exhaust manifold. Remove exhaust manifold bracket. Disconnect oxygen sensor. Remove exhaust manifold bolts. Remove exhaust manifold and gasket.

Installation – To install, reverse removal procedure. Tighten bolts to specification. See TORQUE SPECIFICATIONS.

CYLINDER HEAD

Removal – 1) Disconnect negative battery cable. Rotate crankshaft counterclockwise until No. 1 piston is at TDC of compression stroke. Ensure timing marks are aligned. See Fig. 5. Drain cooling system. Release fuel pressure. See FUEL PRESSURE RELEASE under REMOVAL & INSTALLATION. Disconnect fuel inlet hose. Mark and disconnect vacuum hoses, breather hose, and air intake hose. Remove coolant by-pass hose from cylinder head.

1994 ENGINES
1.8L 4-Cylinder (Cont.)

47 Ft. Lbs. (64 N.m)
54 Ft. Lbs. (74 N.m)
TRANSMISSION MOUNT
44 Ft. Lbs. (60 N.m)
44 Ft. Lbs. (60 N.m)
REAR MOUNT
38 Ft. Lbs. (54 N.m)
54 Ft. Lbs. (74 N.m)
SIDE ENGINE MOUNT
33 Ft. Lbs. (45 N.m)
60 Ft. Lbs. (83 N.m)
RIGHT FRONT MOUNT
60 Ft. Lbs. (83 N.m)
44 Ft. Lbs. (60 N.m)
33 Ft. Lbs. (44 N.m)
LEFT FRONT MOUNT

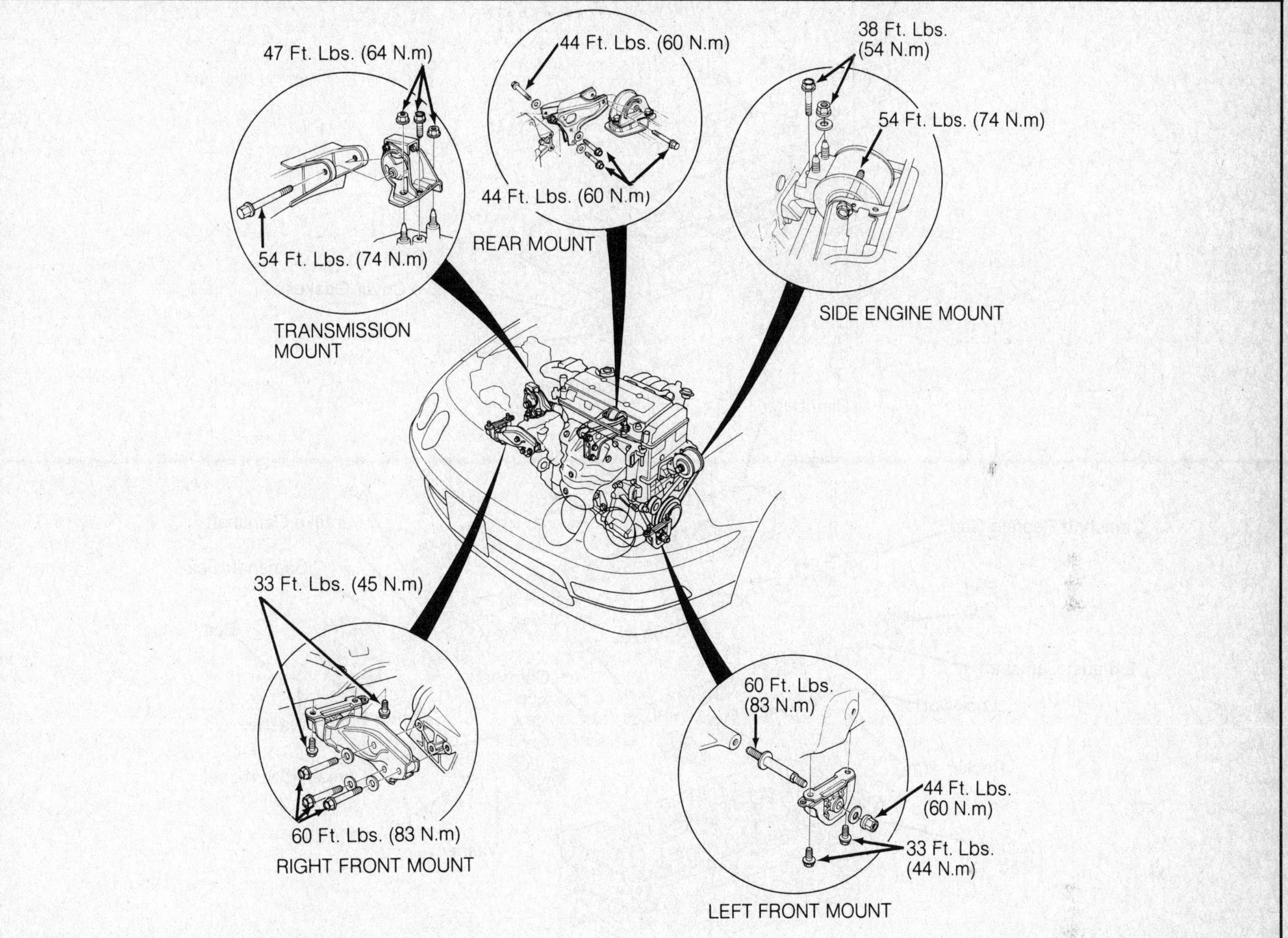

94C47193 Courtesy of American Honda Motor Co., Inc.

Fig. 4: Engine/Transaxle Mount Tightening Sequence

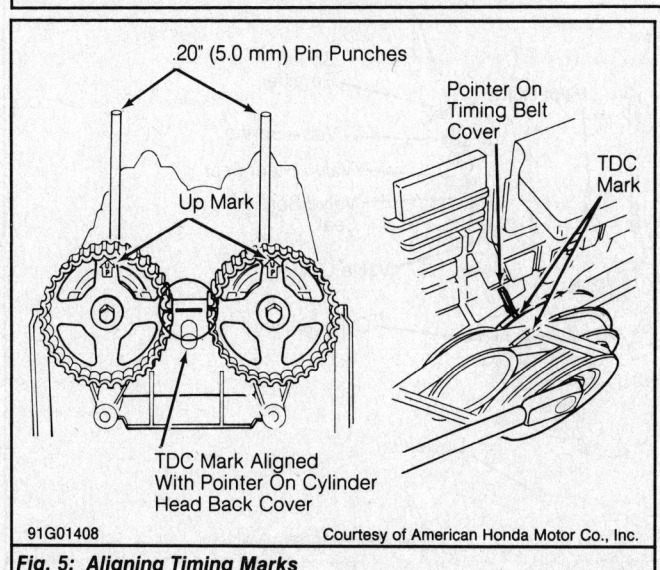

.20" (5.0 mm) Pin Punches
Pointer On Timing Belt Cover
TDC Mark
Up Mark
TDC Mark Aligned With Pointer On Cylinder Head Back Cover

91G01408 Courtesy of American Honda Motor Co., Inc.

Fig. 5: Aligning Timing Marks

2) Disconnect fuel evaporation canister hose from throttle body. Disconnect brake booster and PCV hoses from intake manifold. Disconnect fuel return hose. Disconnect throttle cable at throttle body.

3) Remove spark plug wires. Remove distributor. Disconnect any remaining hoses. Unplug engine harness connectors on left side of engine compartment. Disconnect engine wire harness clamps from cylinder head and intake manifold. Disconnect all remaining wiring from cylinder head.

4) Remove upper radiator hose, heater inlet hose, and by-pass hoses from intake manifold. Remove power steering pump, leaving hoses attached. Set power steering pump aside. Raise and support vehicle.

8
6
2
4
10
9
3
1
5
7
NOTE: Install Longest Cylinder Head Bolts At No. 1 & No. 2

91I01409 Courtesy of American Honda Motor Co., Inc.

Fig. 6: Cylinder Head Bolt Tightening Sequence

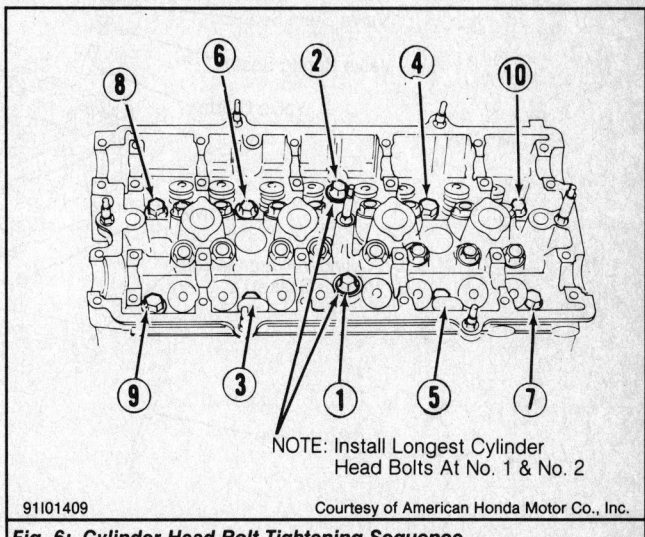

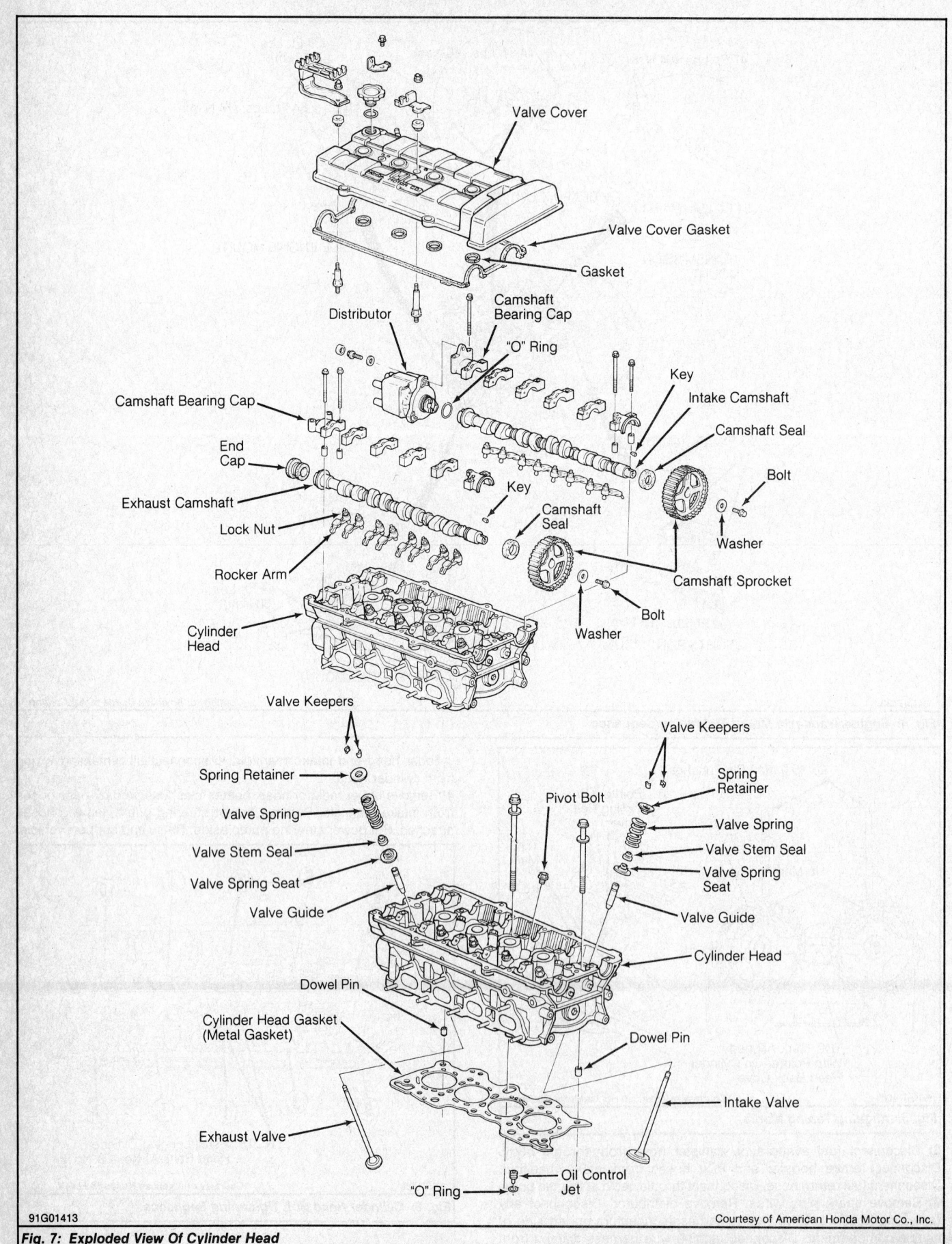

Valve Cover

Valve Cover Gasket

Gasket

Distributor

Camshaft
Bearing Cap

"O" Ring

Key

Intake Camshaft

Camshaft Bearing Cap

Camshaft Seal

End
Cap

Bolt

Exhaust Camshaft

Key

Washer

Lock Nut

Camshaft
Seal

Camshaft Sprocket

Rocker Arm

Bolt

Cylinder
Head

Washer

Valve Keepers

Valve Keepers

Spring Retainer

Pivot Bolt

Spring
Retainer

Valve Spring

Valve Spring

Valve Stem Seal

Valve Stem Seal

Valve Spring Seat

Valve Spring
Seat

Valve Guide

Valve Guide

Cylinder Head

Dowel Pin

Cylinder Head Gasket
(Metal Gasket)

Dowel Pin

Intake Valve

Exhaust Valve

Oil Control
Jet

"O" Ring

91G01413

Courtesy of American Honda Motor Co., Inc.

Fig. 7: Exploded View Of Cylinder Head

5) Remove left front wheel. Remove splash shield. Remove intake manifold bracket bolts. Remove exhaust manifold upper shroud and bracket. Remove exhaust pipe. Remove exhaust manifold. Remove cylinder head cover. Disconnect ground cable.

6) Remove upper timing belt cover. Loosen timing belt adjuster bolt, push timing belt to relieve tension, and retighten adjuster bolt. If timing belt is to be reused, mark an arrow on belt to indicate direction of rotation. Remove timing belt from camshaft sprockets.

7) Remove camshafts. Mark all parts for installation reference. Remove cylinder head bolts, 1/3 turn at a time, in reverse order of tightening sequence. *See Fig. 6.* Remove cylinder head. Separate intake manifold from cylinder head.

Inspection – Ensure all mating surfaces are clean. Check cylinder block surface for warpage. Measure cylinder head for warpage. Resurfacing is not required if warpage is less than 0.002" (0.05 mm). Resurface cylinder head if warpage is 0.002-0.008" (0.05-0.20 mm). Maximum resurface limit is 0.008" (0.20 mm). Ensure cylinder head dowel pins, oil control jet, and "O" ring are installed. *See Fig. 7.*

Installation – 1) Install new intake manifold gasket. Install intake manifold onto cylinder head. Tighten nuts in a crisscross pattern, beginning with inner nuts. See TORQUE SPECIFICATIONS.

2) Ensure No. 1 piston is at TDC. Apply a light coat of engine oil to cylinder head bolts and washers. Install longer cylinder head bolts into positions 1 and 2. Install remaining bolts. Tighten cylinder head bolts to specification, in sequence, in 2 stages. *See Fig. 6.*

3) Reverse removal procedure to complete installation. If reusing timing belt, install belt with arrow mark (made in removal procedure) in direction of original rotation. Adjust timing belt tension. See TIMING BELT TENSION ADJUSTMENT under ADJUSTMENTS. Fill and bleed cooling system. See BLEEDING COOLING SYSTEM under REMOVAL & INSTALLATION.

FRONT COVER OIL SEAL

Removal – Disconnect negative battery cable. Raise and support vehicle. Remove left front wheel. Remove left front wheelwell splash shield. Remove drive belts. Remove and set aside power steering pump with hoses attached. Remove crankshaft pulley. Remove front cover oil seal.

Installation – Apply a light coat of engine oil to crankshaft and lip of new seal. Install front seal using Seal Driver (07LAD-PR4010A). Ensure seal is fully seated. To complete installation, reverse removal procedure.

TIMING BELT

Removal – 1) Disconnect negative battery cable. Raise and support vehicle. Remove left front wheel. Remove left front wheelwell splash shield. Remove all drive belts. Remove power steering pump with hoses attached. Set power steering pump aside.

2) Remove valve cover and upper timing belt cover. *See Fig. 8.* Turn crankshaft counterclockwise to bring No. 1 piston to TDC of its compression stroke. Position UP mark on sprockets at top. *See Fig. 5.* Align grooves on sprockets. Remove crankshaft pulley.

3) Remove left engine mount bolts and nut. Remove engine mount. Remove lower timing belt cover. Loosen timing belt tension adjuster bolt. Push tensioner to relieve tension on timing belt. Retighten adjuster bolt. If reusing timing belt, mark direction of belt rotation before removing. Remove timing belt.

Installation – Ensure No. 1 piston is at TDC. Install timing belt onto sprockets. DO NOT bend or twist belt excessively. Ensure arrow (made during removal procedure) on used belt points in original rotation direction. Adjust timing belt tension. See TIMING BELT TENSION ADJUSTMENT under ADJUSTMENTS. To complete installation, reverse removal procedure. Tighten crankshaft pulley bolt to 147 ft. lbs. (200 N.m), loosen, then retighten to 133 ft. lbs. (180 N.m).

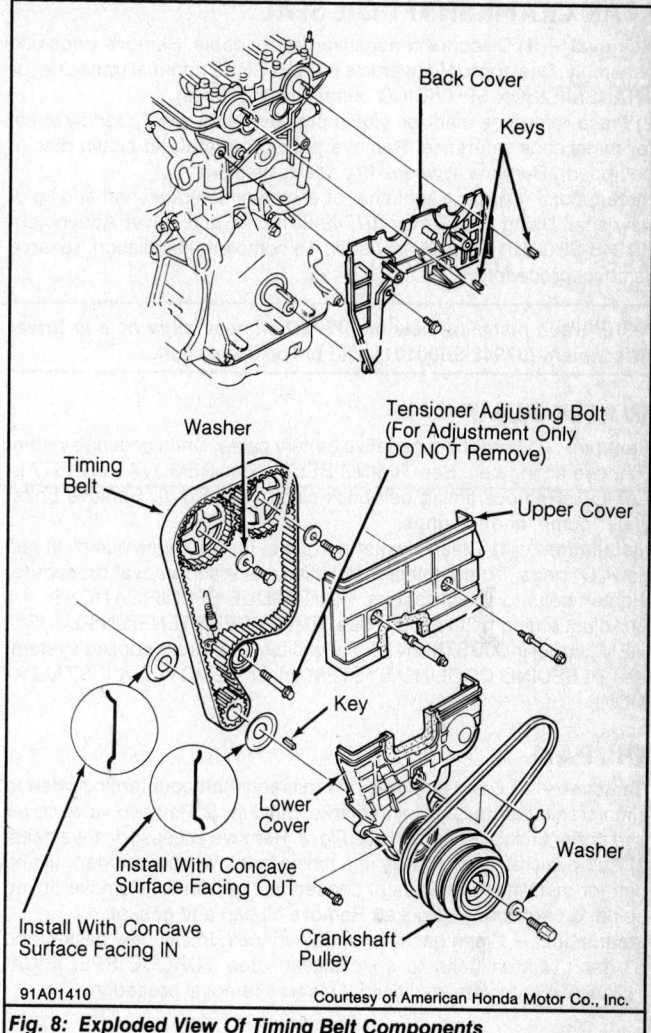

Fig. 8: Exploded View Of Timing Belt Components

91A01410 — Courtesy of American Honda Motor Co., Inc.

CAMSHAFTS

Removal – 1) Ensure No. 1 piston is at TDC. Position UP mark on sprockets at top. *See Fig. 5.* Align grooves on sprockets. Remove timing belt. See TIMING BELT under REMOVAL & INSTALLATION.

2) Remove camshaft sprockets. Camshafts may be held in place by installing 5-mm pin punches in No. 1 cam bearing caps. Mark position of distributor. Remove distributor. Loosen rocker arm adjuster screws.

3) Measure camshaft end play by prying camshaft toward front of cylinder head. Attach dial indicator, and zero it against sprocket end of camshaft. Pry camshaft away from dial indicator. Read dial indicator. Desired end play is 0.002-0.006" (0.05-0.15 mm). Maximum allowable end play is 0.020" (0.50 mm). If end play exceeds limit, replace camshaft.

4) Remove camshaft bearing cap bolts by turning bolts 2 turns at a time in a crisscross pattern. Tag all parts for installation reference. Remove camshafts. Remove rocker arms if necessary.

Installation – 1) Lubricate camshaft journals and bearing surfaces in caps and cylinder head. Install rocker arms (if removed) in their original positions. Install camshafts with keyways pointing upward (No. 1 piston at TDC). Install camshaft bearing caps in original positions.

2) Starting with center caps and working outward, tighten camshaft bearing cap bolts to 88 INCH lbs. (10 N.m) in 2 stages.

3) Install new camshaft seals (if removed). To complete installation, reverse removal procedure. Adjust timing belt tension. See TIMING BELT TENSION ADJUSTMENT under ADJUSTMENTS. Adjust valve clearance. See VALVE CLEARANCE ADJUSTMENT under ADJUSTMENTS.

REAR CRANKSHAFT OIL SEAL

Removal – **1)** Disconnect negative battery cable. Remove transaxle assembly. See appropriate article in CLUTCHES (manual transaxle) or TRANSMISSION SERVICING (automatic transaxle).
2) Place reference mark on clutch pressure plate (M/T) and flywheel for installation reference. Remove pressure plate and clutch disc (if equipped). Remove flywheel. Pry seal from cover.
Installation – Apply a light coat of engine oil to crankshaft and lip of new seal. Using Seal Driver (07749-0010000) and Driver Attachment (07948-SB00101), install new seal. To complete installation, reverse removal procedure.

NOTE: When installing new crankshaft oil seal, align hole in Driver Attachment (07948-SB00101) with pin on crankshaft.

WATER PUMP

Removal – Disconnect negative battery cable. Drain cooling system. Remove timing belt. See TIMING BELT under REMOVAL & INSTALLATION. Remove timing belt back cover. *See Fig. 8.* Remove bolts, water pump, and "O" rings.
Installation – **1)** Clean gasket surfaces. Install water pump. Install new "O" rings. To complete installation, reverse removal procedure. Tighten bolts to specifications. See TORQUE SPECIFICATIONS.
2) Adjust timing belt tension. See TIMING BELT TENSION ADJUSTMENT under ADJUSTMENTS. Fill and bleed air from cooling system. See BLEEDING COOLING SYSTEM under REMOVAL & INSTALLATION.

OIL PAN

Removal – **1)** Drain engine oil. Turn crankshaft counterclockwise to align crankshaft pulley timing marks. *See Fig. 5.* Remove valve cover and upper timing belt cover. *See Fig. 8.* Remove accessory drive belts.
2) Remove crankshaft pulley and timing belt lower cover. Mark timing belt for installation reference. Loosen belt tensioner. Remove timing belt and crankshaft sprocket. Remove oil pan and gasket.
Installation – Clean gasket mating surfaces. Install new gasket and oil pan. Tighten bolts to specification. See TORQUE SPECIFICATIONS. To complete installation, reverse removal procedure.

OVERHAUL

CYLINDER HEAD

Cylinder Head – Ensure all mating surfaces are clean. Measure cylinder head warpage. If warpage is less than 0.002" (0.05 mm), resurfacing is not required. If warpage is 0.002-0.008" (0.05-0.20 mm), resurface cylinder head. Maximum resurface limit is 0.008" (0.20 mm).
Valve Springs – Measure free length of valve springs. If measurements are not within specifications, replace valve springs. See VALVES & VALVE SPRINGS table under ENGINE SPECIFICATIONS.
Valve Stem Oil Seals – Intake and exhaust valve stem seals are not interchangeable. Intake valve stem seals have a White spring around neck of seal. Oil seals for exhaust valves have a Black spring around neck of seal. Use Valve Stem Seal Installer (07GAD-PH70100) to install valve stem seals.
Valve Guide Inspection – Measure valve guide clearance with a dial indicator placed on valve head. Zero dial indicator. Rock valve stem from side to side. Valve guides can be replaced if valve stem oil clearance is not within specification. See CYLINDER HEAD table under ENGINE SPECIFICATIONS at end of article.
Valve Guide Removal – **1)** Use a hot plate or oven to heat cylinder head to 300°F (150°C). Use Valve Guide Driver (07942-6570100), or fabricate valve guide remover from an air impact chisel. *See Fig. 9.* Using an air hammer and valve guide remover, drive valve guide 5/64" (2 mm) toward combustion chamber.

CAUTION: DO NOT heat cylinder head with a torch, or heat cylinder head hotter than 300°F (150°C). Excessive heat may loosen valve seats.

2) Turn head over. Working from combustion chamber side of head, drive valve guide out toward camshaft side of head. If valve guide does not move, drill valve guide using a 5/16" bit, then try to drive it out again.

CAUTION: Drill guides in extreme cases only. Cylinder head damage can occur if valve guide breaks.

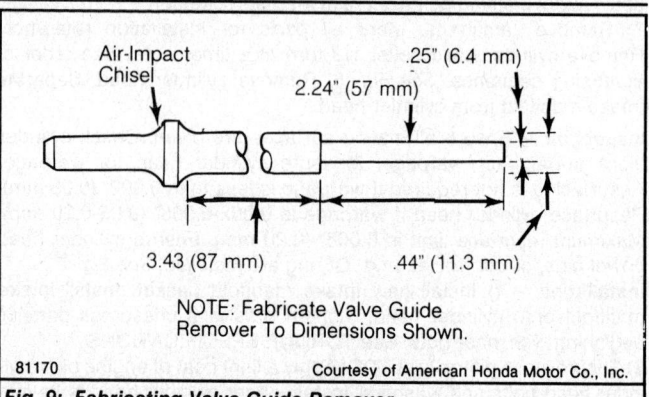

NOTE: Fabricate Valve Guide Remover To Dimensions Shown.

81170   Courtesy of American Honda Motor Co., Inc.
Fig. 9: Fabricating Valve Guide Remover

Valve Guide Installation – **1)** Cool new valve guides in freezer for about one hour. Remove new valve guides from freezer as needed. Install new valve guides from camshaft side of cylinder head.
2) Drive each guide into heated head until attachment bottoms against head. If replacing all valve guides, reheat cylinder head as necessary.
3) Intake valve guide installed height must be 0.55" (14 mm). Exhaust valve guide installed height must be 0.63" (16 mm). Using cutting oil, ream new valve guides by rotating Valve Guide Reamer (07984-657010C) clockwise the full length of valve guide bore. Measure valve stem oil clearance. See CYLINDER HEAD table under ENGINE SPECIFICATIONS.

NOTE: Always reface valve seat after replacing valve guide.

Valve Seat – Valve seat replacement procedure is not available from manufacturer.
Seat Correction Angles – If replacing valve guides, perform replacement before refacing valve seats. After refacing, if seat width is too wide, use 60-degree stone to raise seat, or 30-degree stone to lower seat. Ensure valve seat width is within specification. See CYLINDER HEAD table under ENGINE SPECIFICATIONS.
Valve Stem Installed Height – After servicing valves, measure valve stem installed height. *See Fig. 10.* If valve stem installed height exceeds 1.633" (41.485 mm) for intake valve, or 1.712" (43.485 mm) for exhaust valve, replace valve. If valve stem installed height still exceeds limit, replace cylinder head.

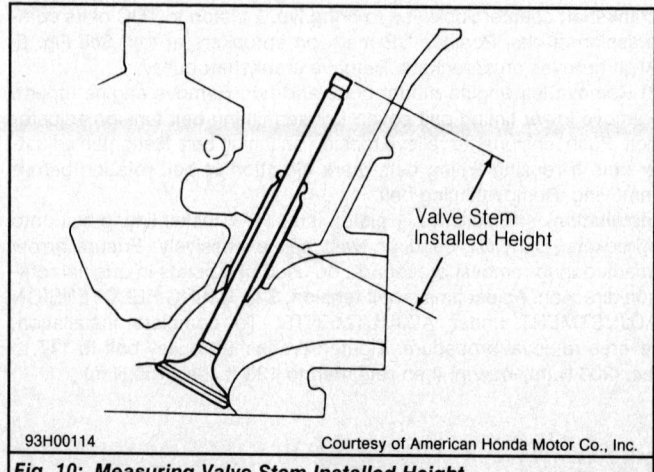

93H00114   Courtesy of American Honda Motor Co., Inc.
Fig. 10: Measuring Valve Stem Installed Height

CYLINDER BLOCK ASSEMBLY

Piston & Rod Assembly – 1) Each rod is sorted into one of 4 tolerance ranges. Size depends on crank journal bore. A number between 1 and 4 is stamped on split line of rod big end. Any combination of numbers between 1 and 4 may be found on any engine. See CONNECTING RODS under ENGINE SPECIFICATIONS.

NOTE: Reference numbers are for big end bore code, and do not indicate rod position in engine.

2) Connecting rod big end bore size range is 1.8898-1.8907" (48.000-48.024 mm). Install piston and connecting rod so arrow on top of piston is toward timing belt, and connecting rod oil hole is toward intake manifold side of engine. *See Fig. 11.*

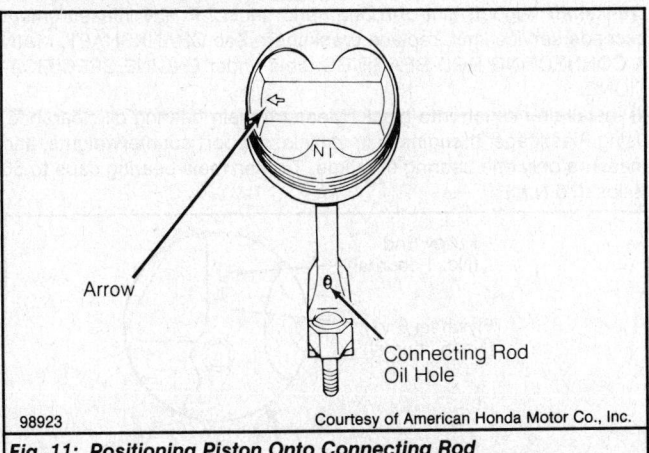

98923   Courtesy of American Honda Motor Co., Inc.

Fig. 11: Positioning Piston Onto Connecting Rod

Piston Pin Removal – 1) Install Piston Base Head (07HAF-PL20102) and Piston Pin Base Insert (07GAF-PH60300) into Base (07973-6570500). Turn handle on Piston Pin Driver Head (07973-PE00320) so piston driver length is 1.957" (49.70 mm). *See Fig. 12.*
2) Insert Piston Driver Shaft (07973-PE00310) into Pilot Collar (07LAF-PR30100). Place piston onto base. Press out piston pin. When removing or installing piston pin, place piston into press with embossed side facing up. Align recessed part of piston with lugs on base insert.

NOTE: Piston pins are available in oversize.

Piston Pin Inspection – 1) Measure diameter of piston pin. Measure diameter of piston pin bore in piston. Piston pin clearance is difference between the two measurements.
2) Piston pin clearance must be 0.0004-0.0009" (0.010-0.022 mm). If piston pin clearance is greater than 0.0009" (0.022 mm), install an oversize piston pin and recheck clearance. Oversize pin diameter is .8267-.8269" (20.997-21.003 mm).
3) Determine difference between piston pin diameter and connecting rod small end bore. Interference fit between piston pin and connecting rod must be 0.0005-0.0013" (0.013-0.032 mm).
Piston Pin Installation – 1) Ensure piston and connecting rod are positioned as shown. *See Fig. 12.* Turn handle on Piston Pin Driver (07973-PE00320) so piston driver length is 1.957" (49.70 mm).
2) Install Pilot Collar (07LAF-PR30100) into piston and connecting rod. Lubricate new piston pin lightly. Place piston onto base. Press in piston pin.
Fitting Pistons – 1) Using a feeler gauge, measure clearance between piston and cylinder bore. If clearance is near or exceeds 0.002" (0.05 mm), measure each piston and cylinder. Piston clearance is difference between cylinder bore and piston diameter. If piston clearance exceeds service limit, rebore cylinder and install oversize piston. New piston-to-bore clearance is .0004-.0014" (.010-.035 mm).
2) Remove all rings from piston. Clean piston thoroughly. Inspect piston for damage. Measure piston diameter at a point 0.6" (15 mm) from bottom of piston skirt. If diameter is not within specification, replace piston. See PISTON DIAMETERS table. See PISTONS, PINS & RINGS table under ENGINE SPECIFICATIONS.

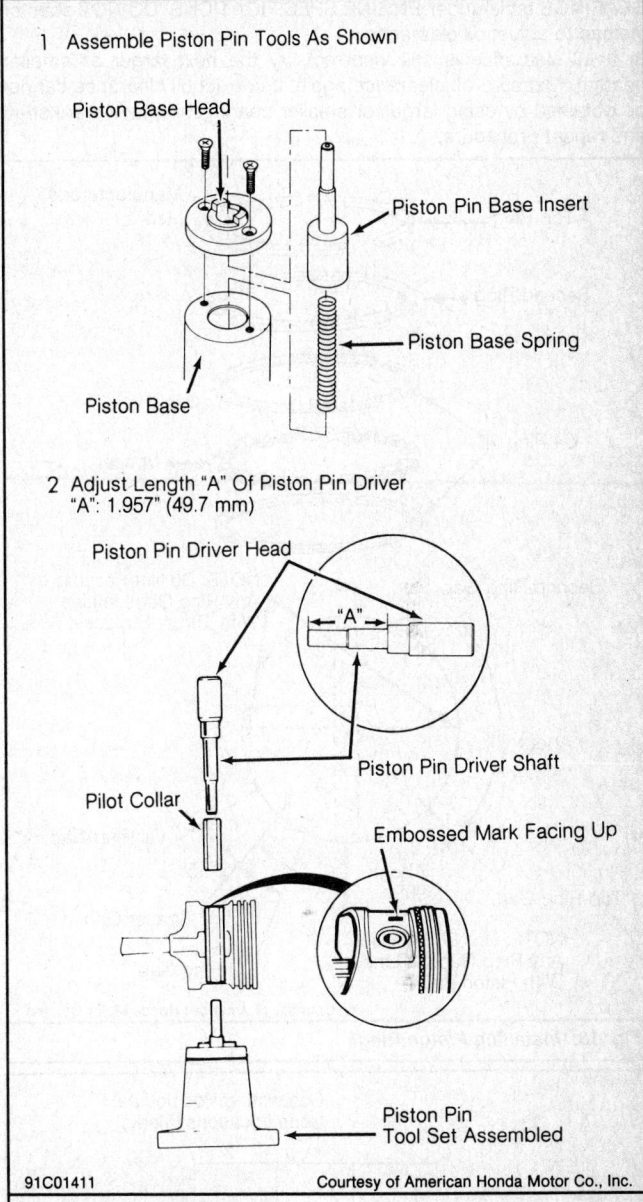

1 Assemble Piston Pin Tools As Shown

2 Adjust Length "A" Of Piston Pin Driver
   "A": 1.957" (49.7 mm)

91C01411   Courtesy of American Honda Motor Co., Inc.

Fig. 12: Removing Piston Pin

PISTON DIAMETERS [1]

Application	In. (mm)
Standard (New)	3.1882-3.1886 (80.98-80.99)
Service Limit	3.1878 (80.97)
Oversize 0.010 (0.25 mm)	3.1980-3.1984 (81.23-81.24)

[1] – Measured at 0.6" (15 mm) from bottom of piston skirt.

Piston Rings – 1) Using inverted piston, push new piston ring into cylinder bore 0.6-0.8" (15-20 mm) from bottom. Measure piston ring end gap using a feeler gauge. Repeat for each ring. See PISTONS, PINS & RINGS table under ENGINE SPECIFICATIONS.
2) Clean piston ring grooves thoroughly. Install piston rings with identification mark toward top of piston. Using a feeler gauge, measure piston ring side clearance between ring and ring land.
3) If ring lands are excessively worn, replace piston. See PISTONS, PINS & RINGS table. Align piston ring end gaps properly on piston. *See Fig. 13.*

Rod Bearings – 1) Using Plastigage, measure rod bearing oil clearance. Tighten bearing cap to 24 ft. lbs. (32 N.m). If oil clearance is incorrect, install a new bearing set (same color code) and recheck oil clearance. See CRANKSHAFT, MAIN & CONNECTING ROD

BEARINGS table under ENGINE SPECIFICATIONS. DO NOT shim or file cap to adjust oil clearance.

2) If oil clearance is still incorrect, try the next larger or smaller bearing. Measure oil clearance again. If correct oil clearance cannot be obtained by using larger or smaller bearings, replace crankshaft and repeat procedure.

NOTE: A number code indicating connecting rod big end bore is stamped on side of each connecting rod and cap. Connecting rod journal diameter codes (letters) are stamped on crankshaft counterweight pads. See Fig. 14. Use both codes when ordering replacement bearings.

Crankshaft & Main Bearings – 1) Remove rear crankshaft oil seal cover, oil screen, oil pump, and baffle plate. Rotate crankshaft so No. 2 and No. 3 crankpins are at bottom. Remove all connecting rod caps and bearings.

2) Mark all main bearing caps for assembly reference. Remove main bearing caps and bearing halves. Lift crankshaft from block, being careful not to damage journals.

3) Using a lathe or "V" blocks to support crankshaft, measure crankshaft runout, out-of-round, and taper. If any measurement exceeds service limit, replace crankshaft. See CRANKSHAFT, MAIN & CONNECTING ROD BEARINGS table under ENGINE SPECIFICATIONS.

4) Install crankshaft into block. Measure main bearing oil clearance, using Plastigage. If engine is in vehicle, support counterweights, and measure only one bearing at a time. Tighten main bearing caps to 56 ft. lbs. (76 N.m)

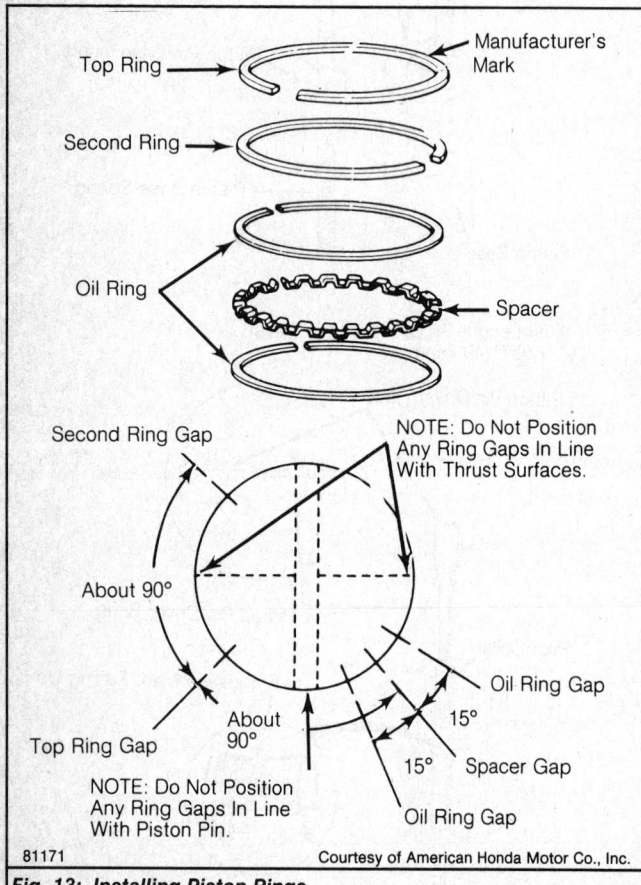

81171　　　　　　　　Courtesy of American Honda Motor Co., Inc.

Fig. 13: Installing Piston Rings

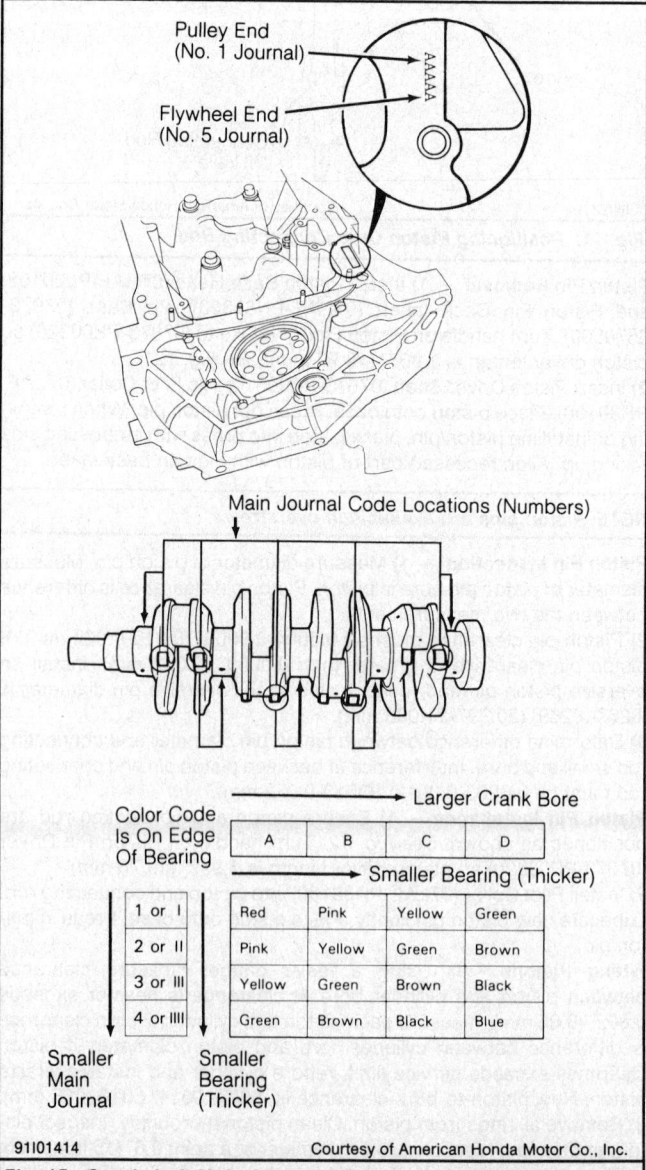

Fig. 15: Crankshaft Main Journal & Bearing Identification Codes

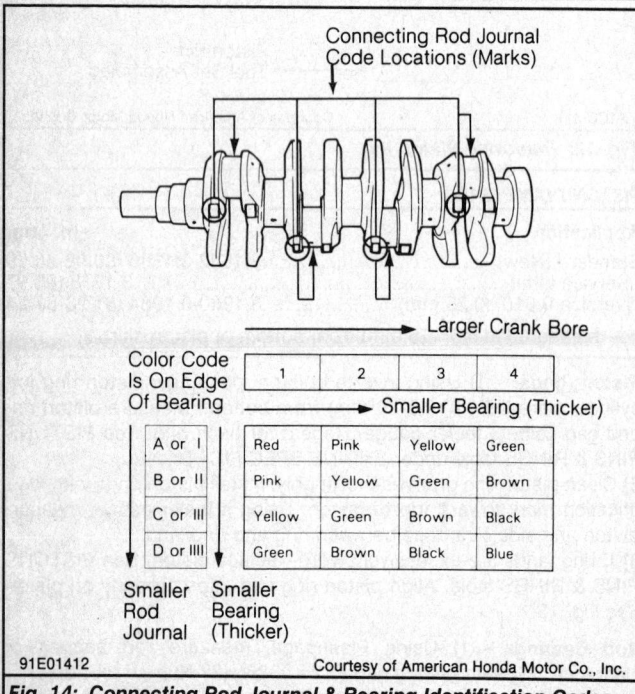

91E01412　　　　　　Courtesy of American Honda Motor Co., Inc.

Fig. 14: Connecting Rod Journal & Bearing Identification Codes

5) If oil clearance is incorrect, install a new bearing set (same color code) and recheck oil clearance. See CRANKSHAFT, MAIN & CONNECTING ROD BEARINGS table under ENGINE SPECIFICATIONS. If oil clearance is still incorrect, try next larger or smaller bearing and measure oil clearance once more.

6) If correct oil clearance cannot be obtained by using larger or smaller bearings, replace crankshaft and repeat procedure.

NOTE: A letter code indicating main journal bore diameters is stamped on cylinder block. See Fig. 15. Use these codes, together with crankshaft main journal diameter numbers, when ordering replacement bearings.

Thrust Bearing – **1)** Measure crankshaft end play, using a dial indicator. If end play exceeds specification, inspect thrust washers and thrust surface of crankshaft. See CRANKSHAFT, MAIN & CONNECTING ROD BEARINGS table under ENGINE SPECIFICATIONS.

2) Replace worn parts as necessary. Thrust washer thickness is fixed. DO NOT change thrust washer thickness by grinding or shimming. Install thrust washers with grooved side out.

Cylinder Block – **1)** Measure cylinder bore out-of-round and taper. If either out-of-round or taper exceeds 0.002" (0.05 mm), rebore cylinder for oversize pistons. If any cylinder exceeds oversize bore service limit, replace cylinder block. See CYLINDER BLOCK table under ENGINE SPECIFICATIONS at end of article.

2) Service limit is 0.004" (0.10 mm). If cylinder bore is okay, hone cylinder to obtain a 60-degree crosshatch pattern. After honing, wash cylinder bore with hot soapy water. Air-dry cylinder bore, and apply engine oil to prevent rusting. Using a feeler gauge and straightedge, measure cylinder block deck surface warpage.

ENGINE OILING

ENGINE LUBRICATION SYSTEM

A rotor-type oil pump draws oil from oil pan and delivers it under pressure to main and connecting rod bearings. An oil hole in each connecting rod lubricates thrust side of piston and cylinder wall. An oil passage carries oil to camshaft and rocker arms. Oil spray lubricates valve stems.

Crankcase Capacity – Crankcase capacity is 4.0 qts. (3.8L) including oil filter.

Oil Pressure – Oil pressure at idle should be 10 psi (0.7 kg/cm²) minimum. Oil pressure at 3000 RPM should be 50 psi (3.5 kg/cm²) minimum.

OIL PUMP

Removal & Disassembly – Remove oil pan. See OIL PAN under REMOVAL & INSTALLATION. Remove oil screen and oil pump assembly. Remove screws from oil pump housing. Separate housing and cover.

Inspection – Measure radial clearance between inner and outer rotors. Measure axial clearance between housing and outer rotor. Inspect both rotors and pump housing for scoring or other damage. Replace components if clearance measurements are not within specification. See OIL PUMP SPECIFICATIONS table.

OIL PUMP SPECIFICATIONS

Application	In. (mm)
Inner Rotor-To-Outer Rotor	
Radial Clearance	
Standard (New)	0.002-0.006 (0.05-0.15)
Service Limit	0.008 (0.20)
Housing-To-Outer Rotor	
Axial Clearance	
Standard (New)	0.001-0.003 (0.03-0.08)
Service Limit	0.006 (0.15)
Housing-To-Outer Rotor	
Radial Clearance	
Standard (New)	0.004-0.007 (0.10-0.18)
Service Limit	0.008 (0.20)

Reassembly & Installation – **1)** Reassemble oil pump, using Loctite on pump housing screws. Ensure oil pump turns freely. Install dowel pins and new "O" ring into cylinder block. Clean oil pump mating surfaces. Apply Liquid Sealant (08718-0001) to cylinder block mating surface of oil pump.

2) Apply sealant to threads of inner bolt holes. Install oil pump before sealant dries. Install oil screen and oil pump. Wait at least 30 minutes before filling crankcase with oil. To complete installation, reverse removal procedure.

TORQUE SPECIFICATIONS

TORQUE SPECIFICATIONS

Application	Ft. Lbs. (N.m)
A/C Compressor Bracket Bolts	17 (23)
Alternator Belt Adjustment Bolt	17 (23)
Alternator Mount Bolt	33 (45)
Camshaft Sprocket Bolts	27 (37)
Connecting Rod Nuts	[1] 24 (32)
Crankshaft Pulley Bolt	133 (180)
Cylinder Head Bolts	[2] 63 (85)
Distributor Mount Bolts	16 (22)
Engine Block-To-Transaxle Housing Bolts	47 (64)
Engine Mount Bolts	[3]
Exhaust Manifold Nuts	23 (31)
Exhaust Pipe Flange Nuts	40 (54)
Flexplate (A/T)	55 (75)
Flywheel Bolts (M/T)	[4] 77 (105)
Intake Manifold Nuts	17 (23)
Main Bearing Cap Bolts	[5] 58 (78)
Oil Pump Bolts	
6-mm Bolts	[6]
8-mm Bolts	17 (23)
Power Steering Mount Bolt	17 (23)
Rocker Arm Lock Nuts	18 (24)
Rocker Arm Pivot Bolt	46 (62)
Shift Lever Torque Rod Bolt	16 (22)
Timing Belt Tension Adjuster Bolt	40 (54)
	INCH Lbs. (N.m)
Camshaft Bearing Bolt	88 (10)
Crankshaft Baffle Plate	98 (11)
Crankshaft Rear Seal Cover Bolts	98 (11)
Fuel Service Bolt	132 (15)
Oil Pan Bolts	106 (12)
Oil Pump Screen Nuts	98 (11)
Timing Belt Cover Bolts	106 (12)
Valve Cover Nuts	88 (10)
Water Pump Bolt	106 (12)

[1] – Tighten connecting rod nuts in 2 stages. First tighten nuts to 15 ft. lbs. (20 N.m), then tighten them to 24 ft. lbs. (32 N.m).
[2] – Tighten cylinder head bolts in 2 stages. First tighten bolts to 22 ft. lbs. (30 N.m) and then to 63 ft. lbs. (85 N.m). *See Fig. 6.*
[3] – See Fig. 4.
[4] – Tighten in a crisscross pattern.
[5] – Tighten main bearing bolts in 2 stages. First tighten bolts to 22 ft. lbs. (30 N.m), then tighten them to 58 ft. lbs. (78 N.m).
[6] – Tighten to 96 INCH lbs. (11 N.m).

ENGINE SPECIFICATIONS

GENERAL SPECIFICATIONS

Application	Specification
Displacement	112 Cu. In. (1.8L)
Bore	3.19" (81 mm)
Stroke	3.50" (89 mm)
Compression Ratio	9.2:1
Fuel System	SFI
Horsepower @ RPM	140 @ 6000
Torque Ft. Lbs. @ RPM	126 @ 5000

1994 ENGINES
1.8L 4-Cylinder (Cont.)

CRANKSHAFT, MAIN & CONNECTING ROD BEARINGS

Application	In. (mm)
Crankshaft	
End Play	
Standard	0.004-0.014 (0.10-0.35)
Service Limit	0.018 (0.45)
Runout	
Standard	0.0012 (0.030)
Service Limit	0.0020 (0.040)
Main Bearings	
Journal Diameter	
Except No. 3	2.1644-2.1654 (54.976-55.000)
No. 3	2.1642-2.1651 (54.970-54.994)
Journal Out-Of-Round	
Standard	0.0002 (0.005)
Service Limit	0.0004 (0.010)
Journal Taper	
Standard	0.0002 (0.005)
Service Limit	0.0004 (0.010)
Oil Clearance	
Except No. 3 Journal	
Standard	0.0009-0.0017 (0.024-0.042)
Service Limit	0.0020 (0.050)
No. 3 Journal	
Standard	0.0012-0.0019 (0.030-0.048)
Service Limit	0.0024 (0.060)
Connecting Rod Bearings	
Journal Diameter	1.7707-1.7717 (44.976-45.000)
Journal Out-Of-Round	
Standard	0.0002 (0.005)
Service Limit	0.0004 (0.010)
Journal Taper	
Service Limit	0.0004 (0.010)
Oil Clearance	
Standard	0.0008-0.0015 (0.020-0.038)
Service Limit	0.0020 (0.050)

CONNECTING RODS

Application	In. (mm)
Bore Diameter	
Crankpin Bore [1]	
1	1.8898-1.8900 (48.000-48.006)
2	1.8900-1.8902 (48.006-48.012)
3	1.8902-1.8905 (48.012-48.018)
4	1.8905-1.8907 (48.018-48.024)
Pin Bore	0.8255-0.8260 (20.968-20.981)
Side Play	
Standard	0.006-0.012 (0.15-0.30)
Service Limit	0.016 (0.40)

[1] – Big end bore reference number is stamped on side of rod big end split line. Number is size reference and DOES NOT indicate position in engine or cylinder location.

PISTONS, PINS & RINGS

Application	In. (mm)
Pistons	
Clearance	
Standard	0.0004-0.0016 (0.010-0.040)
Service Limit	0.0020 (0.050)
Diameter [1]	
Standard	3.1882-3.1886 (80.980-80.990)
Service Limit	3.1878 (80.970)
Oversize 0.010" (0.25 mm)	3.1980-3.1984 (81.230-81.240)
Pins	
Diameter	0.8265-0.8268 (20.994-21.000)
Piston Fit	0.0004-0.0009 (0.010-0.022)
Rod Fit	0.0005-0.0013 (0.013-0.032)
Rings	
No. 1	
End Gap	0.008-0.014 (0.20-0.35)
Side Clearance	0.0018-0.0028 (0.045-0.070)
No. 2	
End Gap	0.016-0.022 (0.40-0.55)
Side Clearance	0.0018-0.0028 (0.045-0.070)
No. 3 (Oil)	
End Gap	0.008-0.020 (0.20-0.50)

[1] – Measure at 0.6" (15 mm) from bottom of skirt.

CYLINDER BLOCK

Application	In. (mm)
Cylinder Bore	
Standard Diameter	3.1890-3.1898 (81.000-81.020)
Service Limit	3.1917 (81.070)
Maximum Taper	0.002 (0.05)
Maximum Rebore Limit	0.010 (0.25)
Maximum Deck Warpage	0.004 (0.10)

VALVES & VALVE SPRINGS

Application	Specification
Intake Valves	
Face Angle	45°
Head Diameter	1.217-1.224" (30.90-31.10 mm)
Stem Diameter	
Standard	0.2591-0.2594" (6.58-6.59 mm)
Service Limit	0.258" (6.55 mm)
Minimum Margin	0.045" (1.15 mm)
Exhaust Valves	
Face Angle	45°
Head Diameter	1.098-1.106" (27.90-28.10 mm)
Stem Diameter	
Standard	0.2579-0.2583" (6.55-6.56 mm)
Service Limit	0.257" (6.52 mm)
Minimum Margin	0.057" (1.45 mm)
Valve Springs Free Length	
Intake	1.668" (42.36 mm)
Exhaust	1.578" (40.09 mm)

CYLINDER HEAD

Application	Specification
Cylinder Head	
Height	5.195-5.199" (131.95-132.05 mm)
Maximum Warpage	[1] 0.002-0.008" (0.05-0.20 mm)
Valve Seats	
Intake Valve	
Seat Angle	45°
Seat Width	
Standard	0.049-0.061" (1.25-1.55 mm)
Service Limit	0.079" (2.00 mm)
Exhaust Valve	
Seat Angle	45°
Seat Width	
Standard	0.049-0.061" (1.25-1.55 mm)
Service Limit	0.079" (2.00 mm)
Valve Guides	
Intake	
Valve Guide I.D.	
Standard	0.260-0.261" (6.61-6.63 mm)
Service Limit	0.262" (6.65 mm)
Valve Guide Installed Height	0.55" (14 mm)
Valve Stem-To-Guide Oil Clearance	
Standard	0.001-0.002" (0.02-0.05 mm)
Service Limit	0.003" (0.08 mm)
Exhaust Valve	
Valve Guide I.D.	
Standard	0.260-0.261" (6.61-6.63 mm)
Service Limit	0.262" (6.65 mm)
Valve Guide Installed Height	0.63" (16 mm)
Valve Stem-To-Guide Oil Clearance	
Standard	0.002-0.003" (0.05-0.08 mm)
Service Limit	0.004" (0.10 mm)

[1] – Maximum resurface limit is 0.008" (0.20 mm).

CAMSHAFT

Application	In. (mm)
End Play	
Standard	0.002-0.006 (0.05-0.15)
Service Limit	0.020 (0.50)
Journal Runout	
Standard	0.001 (0.03)
Service Limit	0.002 (0.06)
Oil Clearance	
Standard	0.002-0.004 (0.05-0.10)
Service Limit	0.006 (0.15)

VALVE STEM INSTALLED HEIGHT [1]

Application	In. (mm)
Intake	
Standard	1.605-1.623 (40.765-41.235)
Service Limit	1.633 (41.485)
Exhaust	
Standard	1.684-1.702 (42.765-43.235)
Service Limit	1.712 (43.485)

[1] – Measure from base of valve guide to tip of valve stem.

1994 ENGINES
1.8L VTEC 4-Cylinder

Integra GS-R

NOTE: For repair procedures not covered in this article, see ENGINE OVERHAUL PROCEDURES article in GENERAL INFORMATION.

ENGINE IDENTIFICATION

Engine identification code is stamped on right rear of cylinder block as viewed from flywheel, below cylinder head mating surface. First 5 numbers of code indicate engine type. Last 7 numbers of code indicate engine serial number.

ENGINE IDENTIFICATION CODE

Application	Code
1.8L	B18C1

ADJUSTMENTS

VALVE CLEARANCE

CAUTION: Always rotate engine only in direction of normal rotation (counterclockwise as viewed from front of engine). Backward rotation may cause timing belt to jump time.

1) Adjust valves when engine temperature is 100°F (38°C) or less. Remove valve cover. Rotate crankshaft counterclockwise until No. 1 piston is at TDC of compression stroke. Ensure UP marks on camshaft sprockets are at top and TDC grooves on pulleys are aligned with TDC groove on back cover. *See Fig. 1.*
2) Adjust valve clearance on both valves for No. 1 cylinder. Loosen lock nuts. Rotate adjuster screw until clearance is as specified. Tighten lock nut to 15 ft. lbs. (20 N.m). Recheck adjustment. See VALVE CLEARANCE SPECIFICATIONS table.

VALVE CLEARANCE SPECIFICATIONS

Application	In. (mm)
Exhaust	0.007-0.008 (0.17-0.21)
Intake	0.006-0.007 (0.15-0.19)

3) Rotate crankshaft 180 degrees counterclockwise (camshaft sprockets turn 90 degrees) until No. 3 piston is at TDC of compression stroke. UP marks should point to exhaust side. Adjust valve clearance on both valves for No. 3 cylinder.
4) Rotate crankshaft 180 degrees counterclockwise until No. 4 piston is at TDC of compression stroke. Ensure UP marks are pointing down. Adjust valve clearance on both valves for No. 4 cylinder.
5) Rotate crankshaft 180 degrees counterclockwise until No. 2 piston is at TDC of compression stroke. Ensure UP marks are pointing to intake side. Adjust valve clearances on both valves for No. 2 cylinder. Install new valve cover gasket. Retighten crankshaft pulley bolt to 133 ft. lbs. (180 N.m).

TIMING BELT TENSION

CAUTION: Adjust timing belt with engine cold. DO NOT rotate crankshaft with timing belt tensioner adjuster bolt loose.

Remove valve cover. Rotate crankshaft counterclockwise until No. 1 piston is at TDC. Rotate crankshaft 5-6 revolutions counterclockwise on camshaft sprocket to create tension on timing belt. Loosen tension adjuster bolt to create tension on belt. *See Fig. 2.* Tighten tension adjuster bolt to specification. See TORQUE SPECIFICATIONS. Install valve cover with new gaskets.

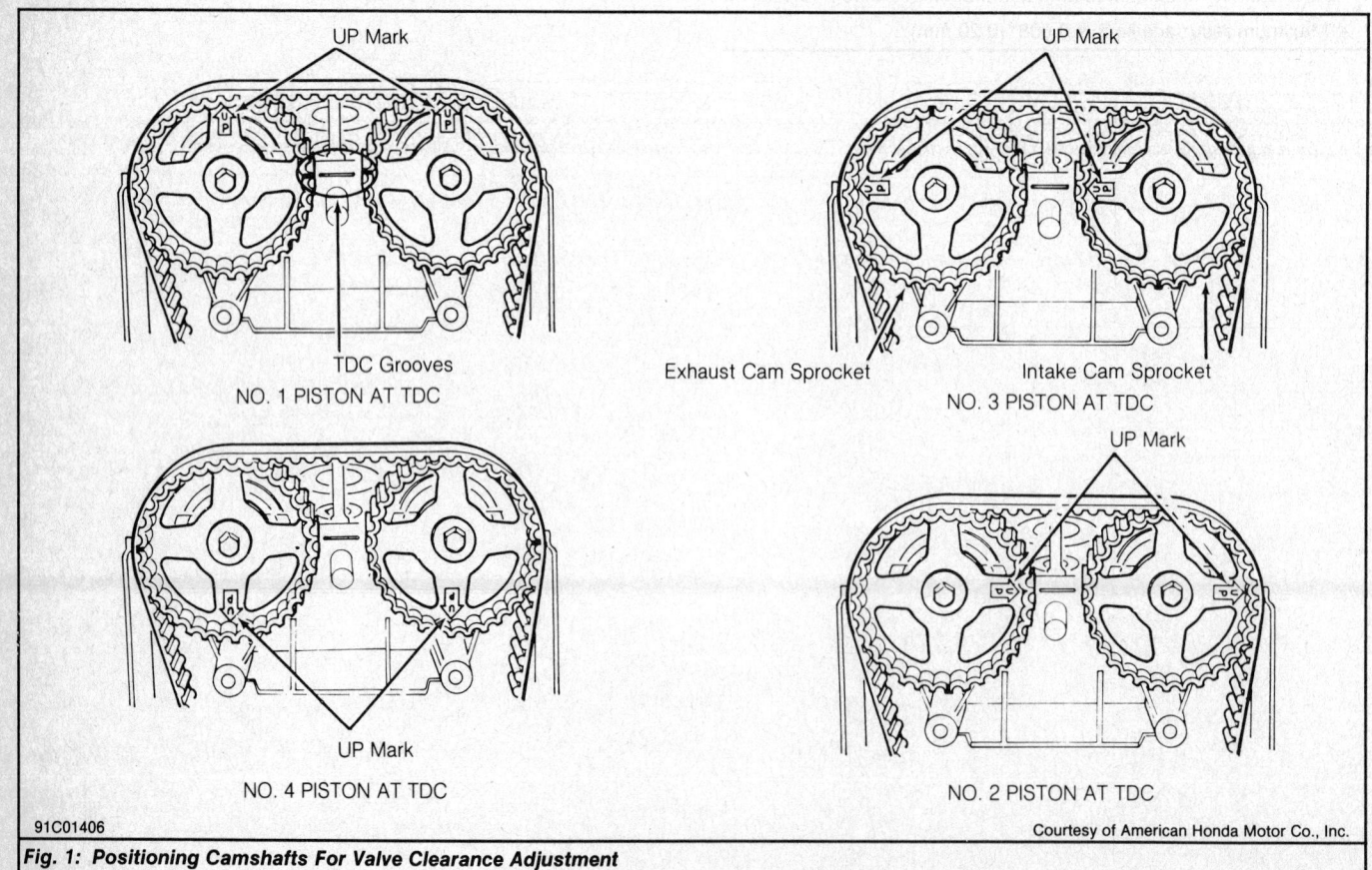

UP Mark

TDC Grooves
NO. 1 PISTON AT TDC

UP Mark

Exhaust Cam Sprocket   Intake Cam Sprocket
NO. 3 PISTON AT TDC

UP Mark
NO. 4 PISTON AT TDC

UP Mark
NO. 2 PISTON AT TDC

91C01406
Courtesy of American Honda Motor Co., Inc.

Fig. 1: Positioning Camshafts For Valve Clearance Adjustment

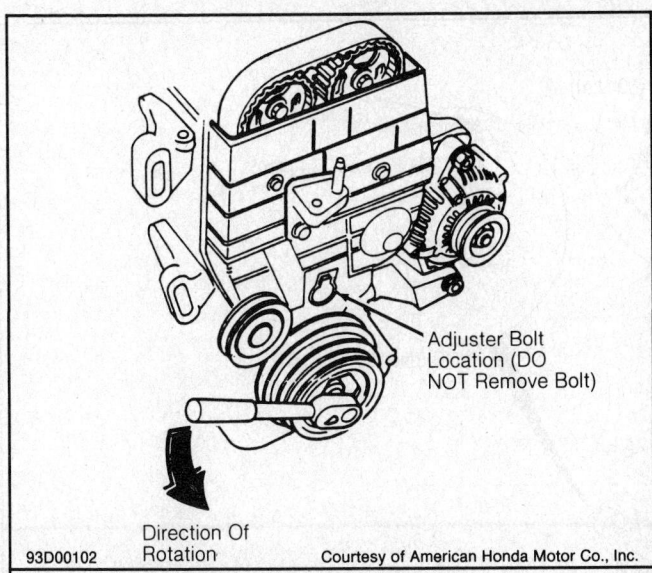

Fig. 2: Locating Timing Belt Adjuster Bolt

Adjuster Bolt Location (DO NOT Remove Bolt)

Direction Of Rotation

93D00102   Courtesy of American Honda Motor Co., Inc.

REMOVAL & INSTALLATION

NOTE: For reassembly reference, label all electrical connectors, vacuum hoses, and fuel lines before removal. Also place mating marks on engine hood and other major assemblies before removal.

NOTE: On some vehicles, radio/cassette or radio/CD player contains an anti-theft protection circuit. Whenever battery is disconnected, radio will go into anti-theft mode. When battery is reconnected, radio will display CODE and will be inoperative until proper code number is entered. Obtain code number before disconnecting battery.

CAUTION: Fuel system is under pressure. Release pressure before servicing fuel system components.

FUEL PRESSURE RELEASE

Disconnect negative battery cable. Remove fuel tank filler cap. Place a shop towel on top of fuel filter. Release fuel injection system pressure by slowly loosening fuel injection service bolt. *See Fig. 3.*

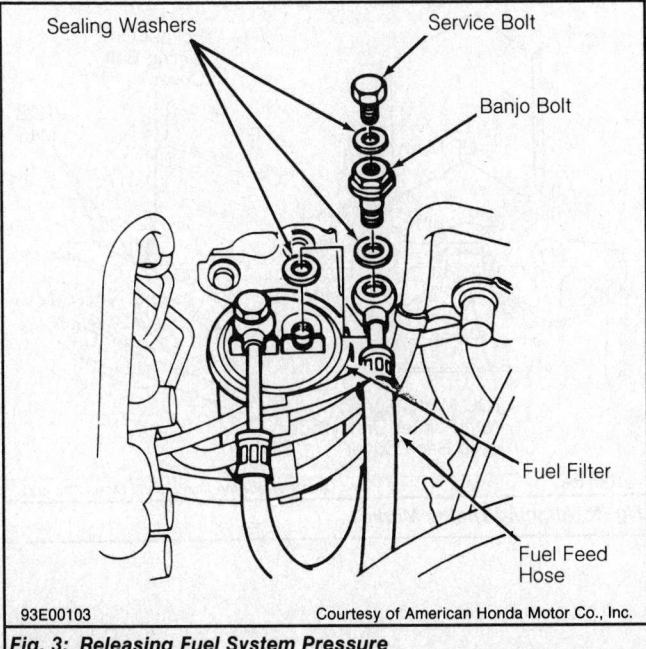

Sealing Washers   Service Bolt

Banjo Bolt

Fuel Filter

Fuel Feed Hose

93E00103   Courtesy of American Honda Motor Co., Inc.

Fig. 3: Releasing Fuel System Pressure

BLEEDING COOLING SYSTEM

1) To bleed air from cooling system, set heater controls to maximum temperature. Loosen bleed bolt located on thermostat housing. Fill cooling system with a 50/50 mixture of coolant and water to bottom of filler neck.

2) Tighten bleed bolt when coolant flows from bleed bolt in steady stream without bubbles. With radiator cap off, start and warm engine to normal operating temperature. Add coolant as necessary. Install radiator cap.

ENGINE

Removal – 1) Disconnect battery cables. Remove hood. Remove strut brace. Raise and support vehicle. Drain engine oil and transmission fluid. Remove front wheels and splash shield. Remove radiator cap to release system pressure. Drain cooling system. Remove battery and battery tray.

2) Release fuel pressure. See FUEL PRESSURE RELEASE. Remove fuel inlet hose. Unplug harness connectors from distributor. Remove distributor. Remove intake air duct and air cleaner housing. Unplug engine wiring harness connectors on left side of engine compartment. Disconnect throttle cable.

3) Unplug engine wiring harness connectors on right side of engine compartment. Disconnect power cables from underhood fuse/relay box. Disconnect brake booster vacuum hose from intake manifold. Disconnect fuel return hose. Disconnect ground cable at cylinder head. Remove power steering pump with hoses attached. Set power steering pump aside.

4) Remove A/C compressor with hoses attached, and set it aside. Remove alternator. Disconnect transmission cooler lines. Remove radiator and heater hoses. Remove speed sensor, leaving hoses attached. Unplug cooling fan connectors. Remove radiator.

5) Remove exhaust pipe. Disconnect drive shafts. See FWD AXLE SHAFTS article in DRIVE AXLES. On M/T models, disconnect clutch cable, shift rod, and shift lever torque rod. On A/T models, remove torque converter cover and disconnect shift control cable.

6) On all models, attach chain hoist to engine. Raise hoist to take all slack from chain. Remove rear transmission mount and rear transmission mounting bracket. Remove front transmission mount. Remove side transmission mount and side transmission mounting bracket. Remove side engine mount.

7) Slowly raise engine/transaxle about 6 inches. Ensure all hoses and wiring have been disconnected. Remove engine and transaxle from vehicle.

Installation – 1) To install, reverse removal procedure. To prevent excessive engine vibration and premature engine mount wear, tighten engine/transaxle mounts in specified sequence. *See Fig. 4.*

2) When installing drive axles, use new spring clips. Insert drive axles until spring clips click into groove of differential side gear. Ensure harness connectors and hoses are connected properly.

3) Ensure control cables are not bent or pinched and are adjusted properly. On M/T models, adjust clutch pedal free play. Verify transaxle shifts smoothly.

4) On all models, adjust drive belt tension. Fill or top off all fluids. Fill and bleed air from cooling system. See BLEEDING COOLING SYSTEM. Start engine and check for leaks.

INTAKE MANIFOLD

Removal – 1) Disconnect negative battery cable. Release fuel system pressure. See FUEL PRESSURE RELEASE. Carefully remove radiator cap to release cooling system pressure. Drain cooling system. Remove upper and lower radiator hoses. Remove air intake duct and air cleaner assembly.

2) Disconnect fuel inlet and return hoses. Mark and disconnect vacuum hoses and wiring harness connectors. Remove fuel evaporation canister hose from throttle body.

3) Remove brake booster and PCV hoses from intake manifold. Disconnect throttle cable. Remove coolant by-pass hoses. Remove intake manifold nuts, intake manifold, and gasket.

47 Ft. Lbs. (64 N.m)

44 Ft. Lbs. (60 N.m)

38 Ft. Lbs. (54 N.m)

54 Ft. Lbs. (74 N.m)

54 Ft. Lbs. (74 N.m)

44 Ft. Lbs. (60 N.m)

REAR MOUNT

SIDE ENGINE MOUNT

TRANSMISSION MOUNT

33 Ft. Lbs. (45 N.m)

60 Ft. Lbs. (83 N.m)

44 Ft. Lbs. (60 N.m)

60 Ft. Lbs. (83 N.m)

33 Ft. Lbs. (44 N.m)

RIGHT FRONT MOUNT

LEFT FRONT MOUNT

94C47193

Courtesy of American Honda Motor Co., Inc.

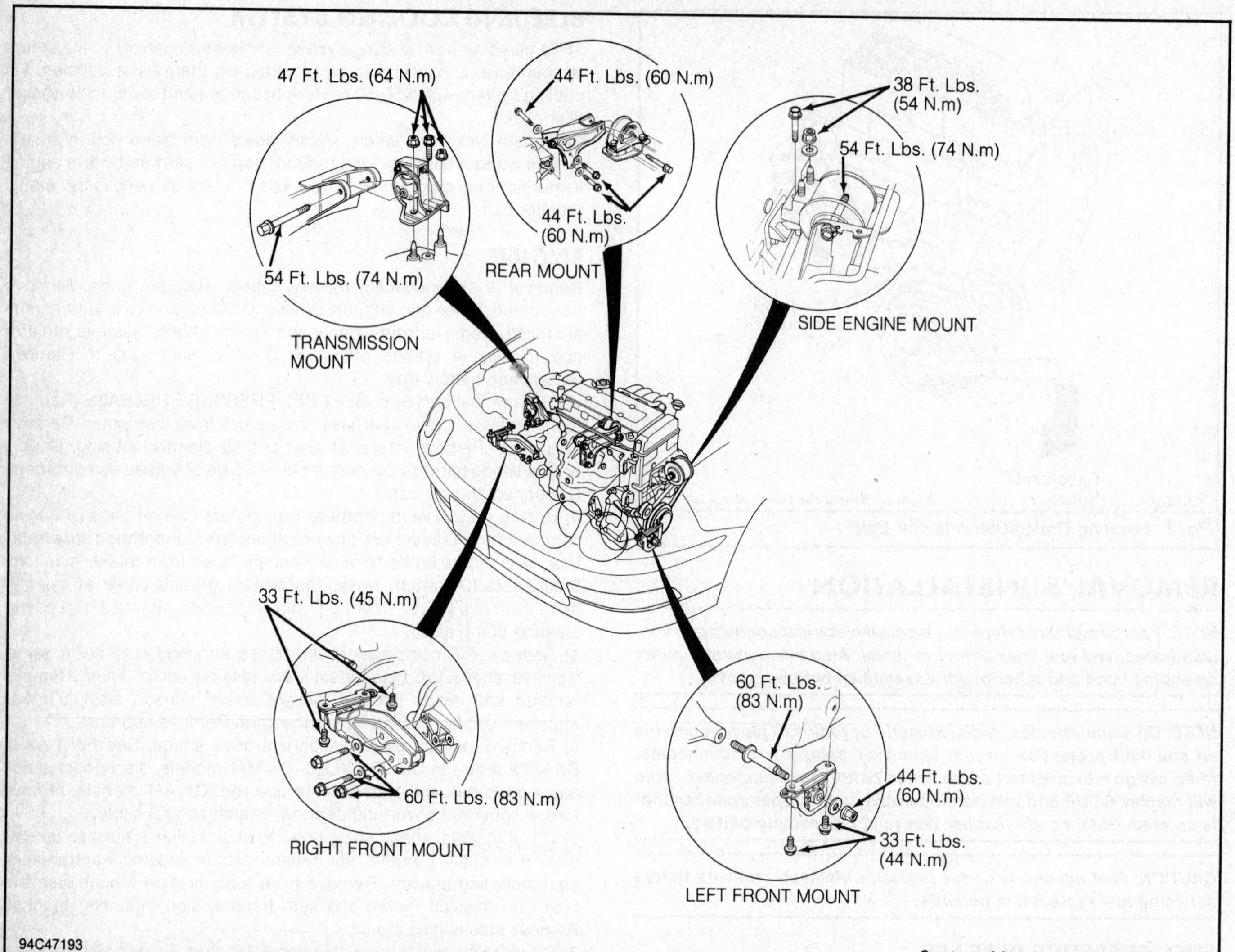

Fig. 4: Engine/Transaxle Mount Tightening Sequence

Installation – Clean gasket surfaces. Install intake manifold, using new intake manifold gasket. Tighten nuts to specification, using a crisscross pattern in 2-3 stages, beginning with inner nuts. See TORQUE SPECIFICATIONS. To complete installation, reverse removal procedure. Refill and bleed air from cooling system. See BLEEDING COOLING SYSTEM.

EXHAUST MANIFOLD

Removal – Disconnect negative battery cable. Remove oil dipstick. Remove exhaust manifold heat shield. Disconnect exhaust pipe from exhaust manifold. Remove exhaust manifold bracket. Disconnect oxygen sensor wiring. Remove exhaust manifold bolts. Remove exhaust manifold and gasket.

Installation – To install, reverse removal procedure. Tighten bolts to specification. See TORQUE SPECIFICATIONS.

CYLINDER HEAD

Removal – **1)** Allow engine to cool to less than 100°F (38°C). Disconnect negative battery cable. Drain cooling system. Release fuel system pressure. See FUEL PRESSURE RELEASE. Tag and disconnect all hoses. Remove engine strut. Rotate crankshaft pulley until No. 1 piston is at TDC of compression stroke and timing marks are aligned. *See Fig. 5.*

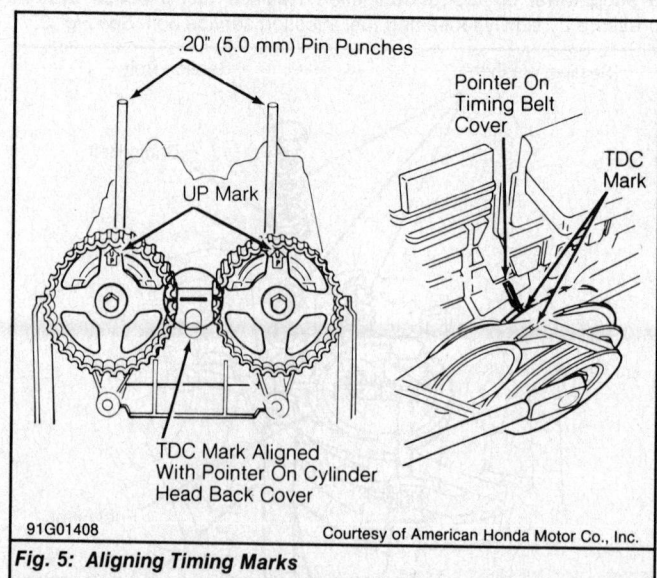

.20" (5.0 mm) Pin Punches

Pointer On Timing Belt Cover

UP Mark

TDC Mark

TDC Mark Aligned With Pointer On Cylinder Head Back Cover

91G01408

Courtesy of American Honda Motor Co., Inc.

Fig. 5: Aligning Timing Marks

2) Remove air inlet duct and air cleaner cover. Disconnect fuel feed line and charcoal canister hose from intake manifold. Disconnect throttle cable from throttle body. On A/T models, disconnect throttle control cable at throttle body.

3) On all models, disconnect fuel return line and brake booster vacuum line at intake manifold. Unplug all wiring connectors. Remove spark plug wire cover. Remove spark plug wires. Remove distributor. Remove by-pass hose, upper radiator hose, and heater hose. Disconnect engine ground cable at cylinder head cover.

4) Remove power steering pump with hoses attached, and set it aside. Remove heat shield. Remove intake manifold bracket. Remove exhaust manifold and exhaust pipe. Remove PCV hose and cylinder head cover. Remove middle timing belt cover. Remove right engine mount.

5) Loosen timing adjuster bolt 180 degrees. Push on timing belt tensioner to release tension from belt, then retighten adjuster bolt. Disengage timing belt from camshaft pulleys. Remove camshaft pulleys. Loosen valve adjuster screws and camshaft retainers. Remove rocker arms and camshafts. See CAMSHAFTS. Loosen cylinder head bolts 1/3 turn at a time until all are loose, in reverse order of tightening sequence. *See Fig. 6.* Remove cylinder head.

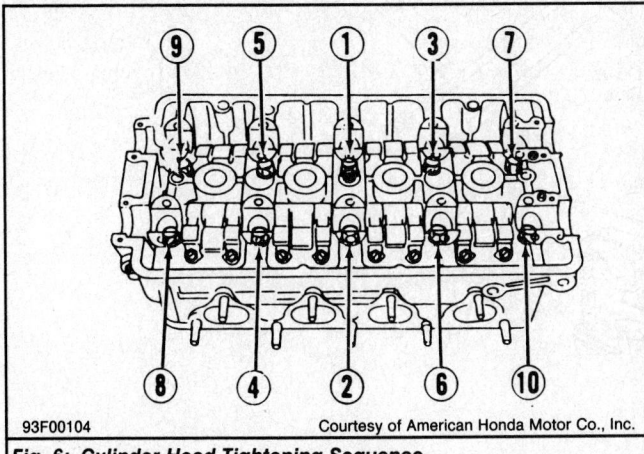

93F00104   Courtesy of American Honda Motor Co., Inc.

Fig. 6: Cylinder Head Tightening Sequence

Inspection – 1) Ensure all mating surfaces are clean. Measure cylinder block surface warpage. Cylinder block warpage must not exceed 0.003" (0.08 mm).

2) Measure cylinder head warpage. Resurfacing is not required if warpage is less than 0.002" (0.05 mm). Resurface cylinder head if warpage is 0.002-0.008" (0.05-0.20 mm). Maximum resurface limit is 0.008" (0.20 mm).

3) Ensure cylinder head dowel pins, oil control jet, and "O" ring are installed in block. *See Fig. 8.*

Installation – 1) Install new cylinder head gasket. Ensure No. 1 piston is at TDC of compression stroke. Apply a light coat of engine oil to cylinder head bolt threads and bottom of bolt head. Install and tighten cylinder head bolts to specification in 2 stages and in sequence. *See Fig. 6.*

2) Install intake manifold onto cylinder head. Tighten nuts to specification in a crisscross pattern, beginning with inner nuts. Install exhaust manifold with new nuts. Tighten nuts to specification in a crisscross pattern, beginning with inner nuts. See TORQUE SPECIFICATIONS.

3) Install camshafts. See CAMSHAFTS. Install camshaft pulleys. Install timing belt. See TIMING BELT. To complete installation, reverse removal procedure.

FRONT COVER OIL SEAL

Removal – Disconnect negative battery cable. Raise and support vehicle. Remove left front wheel. Remove left front wheelwell splash shield. Remove drive belts. Remove power steering pump with hoses attached, and set it aside. Remove crankshaft pulley. Remove front cover oil seal.

Installation – Apply a light coat of engine oil to crankshaft and lip of new seal. Install front seal using Seal Driver (07LAD-PR4010A). Ensure seal is fully seated. To complete installation, reverse removal procedure.

TIMING BELT

Removal – 1) Disconnect negative battery cable. Raise and support vehicle. Remove left front wheel. Remove left front wheelwell splash shield. Remove drive belts. Remove power steering pump with hoses attached, and set it aside. Remove right engine mount.

2) Remove valve cover and middle timing belt cover. *See Fig. 7.* Rotate crankshaft counterclockwise to bring No. 1 piston to TDC of its compression stroke. Position UP mark on sprockets at top. *See Fig. 5.* Align grooves on sprockets. Remove crankshaft pulley.

3) Remove left engine mount. Remove cylinder head cover. Remove crankshaft pulley. Loosen timing belt tension adjuster bolt 180 degrees. Push tensioner to relieve tension on timing belt. Retighten adjuster bolt. If reusing timing belt, mark direction of belt rotation before removing. Remove timing belt.

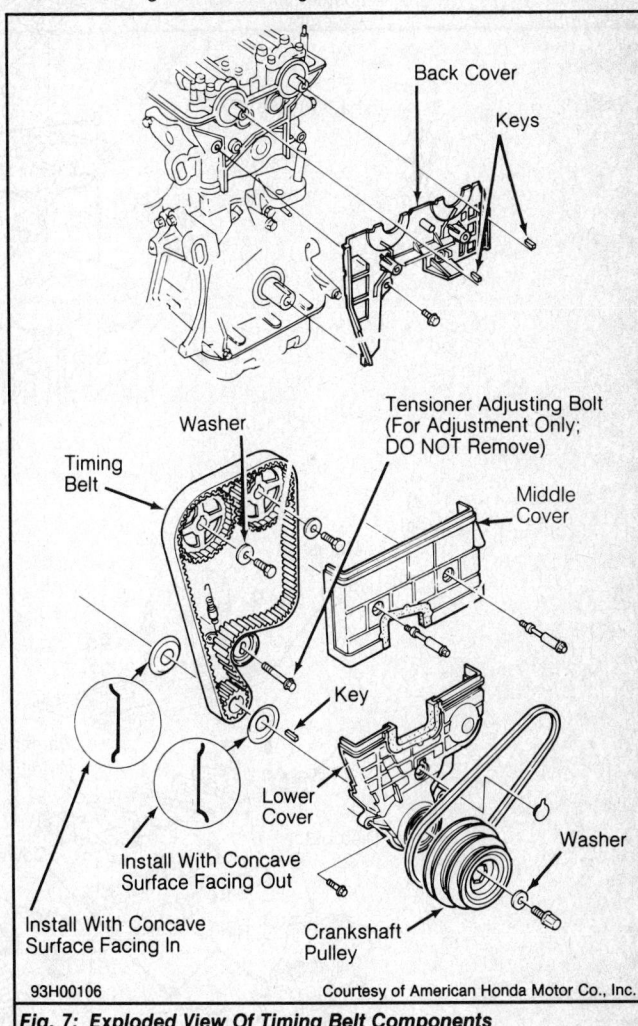

93H00106   Courtesy of American Honda Motor Co., Inc.

Fig. 7: Exploded View Of Timing Belt Components

Installation – 1) Ensure No. 1 piston is at TDC of compression stroke. Install timing belt onto sprockets. DO NOT bend or twist belt excessively. Ensure arrow on used belt points in original direction. Adjust timing belt tension. See TIMING BELT TENSION under ADJUSTMENTS.

2) To complete installation, reverse removal procedure. Lubricate threads only of crankshaft pulley bolt, leaving underside of bolt head dry. Tighten crankshaft pulley bolt to 147 ft. lbs. (200 N.m), loosen, then retighten to 133 ft. lbs. (180 N.m).

1994 ENGINES
1.8L VTEC 4-Cylinder (Cont.)

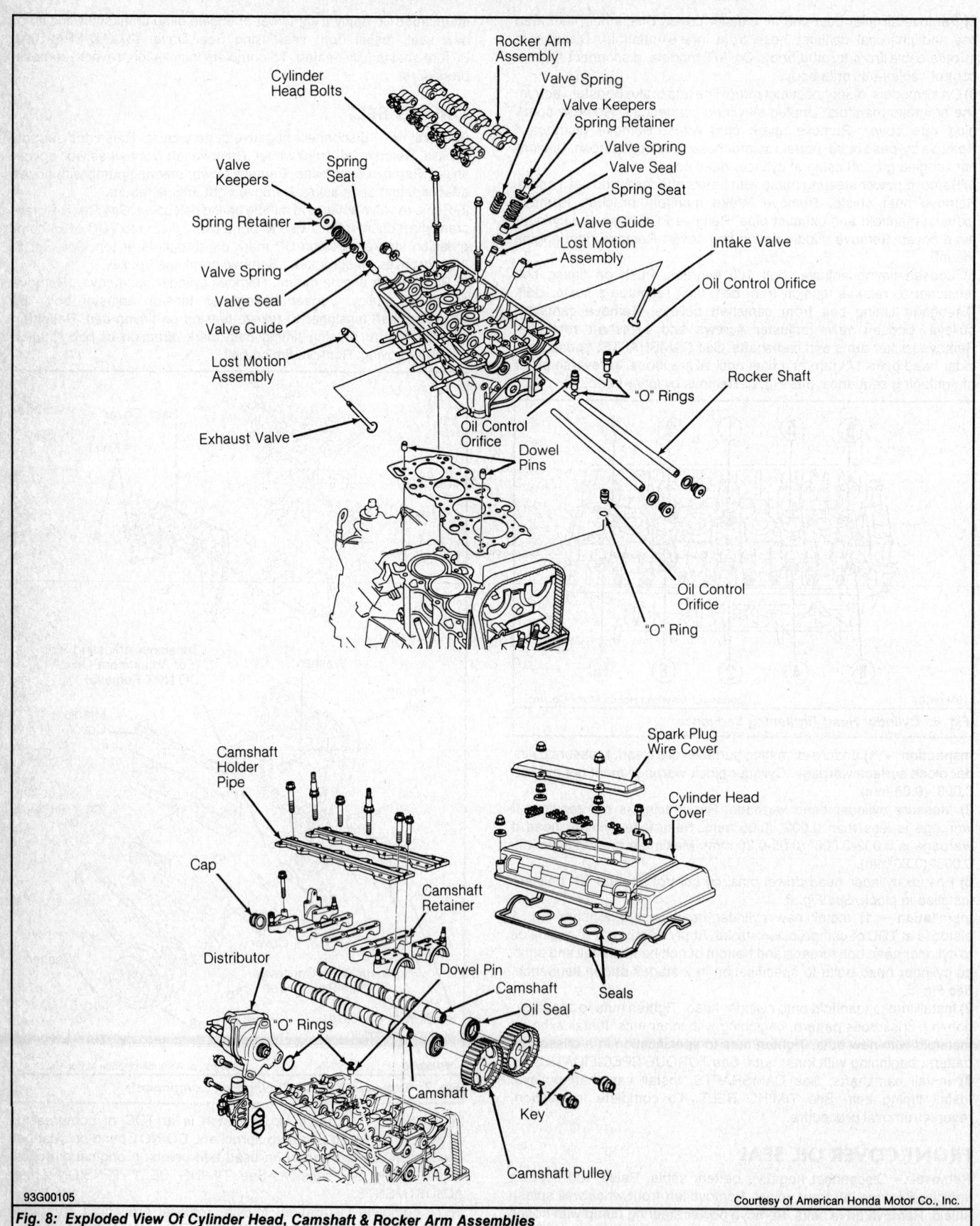

Rocker Arm Assembly
Valve Spring
Valve Keepers
Spring Retainer
Valve Spring
Valve Seal
Spring Seat
Valve Guide
Lost Motion Assembly
Intake Valve
Oil Control Orifice
Cylinder Head Bolts
Valve Keepers
Spring Seat
Spring Retainer
Valve Spring
Valve Seal
Valve Guide
Lost Motion Assembly
Exhaust Valve
Oil Control Orifice
Dowel Pins
"O" Rings
Rocker Shaft
Oil Control Orifice
"O" Ring

Camshaft Holder Pipe
Spark Plug Wire Cover
Cylinder Head Cover
Cap
Camshaft Retainer
Seals
Distributor
Dowel Pin
Camshaft
Oil Seal
"O" Rings
Camshaft
Key
Camshaft Pulley

93G00105

Fig. 8: Exploded View Of Cylinder Head, Camshaft & Rocker Arm Assemblies

CAMSHAFTS

Removal – **1)** Disconnect negative battery cable. Remove valve cover and middle timing belt cover. *See Fig. 7.* Rotate crankshaft counterclockwise to bring No. 1 piston to TDC of its compression stroke, with UP mark on sprockets at top. *See Fig. 5.* Remove distributor.

2) Loosen timing belt adjuster bolt 180 degrees. Push tensioner to release tension from belt. Retighten adjuster bolt. Disengage timing belt from camshaft pulleys. Remove camshaft pulleys. Loosen valve adjuster screws and camshaft retainer bolts. Remove camshaft and rocker arms.

Installation – **1)** Lubricate camshaft journals and bearings. Install rocker arms (if removed) into original positions. Install camshafts into cylinder head. Keyways must face upward. Apply sealant to mating surfaces of camshaft retainers at each end. Arrows on camshaft retainers must point toward timing belt. Temporarily tighten camshaft retainer bolts. Drive camshaft oil seals securely against bases of camshaft retainers.

2) Tighten camshaft bolts to specification in sequence. *See Fig. 9.* See TORQUE SPECIFICATIONS. To complete installation, reverse removal procedure. Adjust timing belt tension and valve clearance. See TIMING BELT TENSION and VALVE CLEARANCE under ADJUSTMENTS.

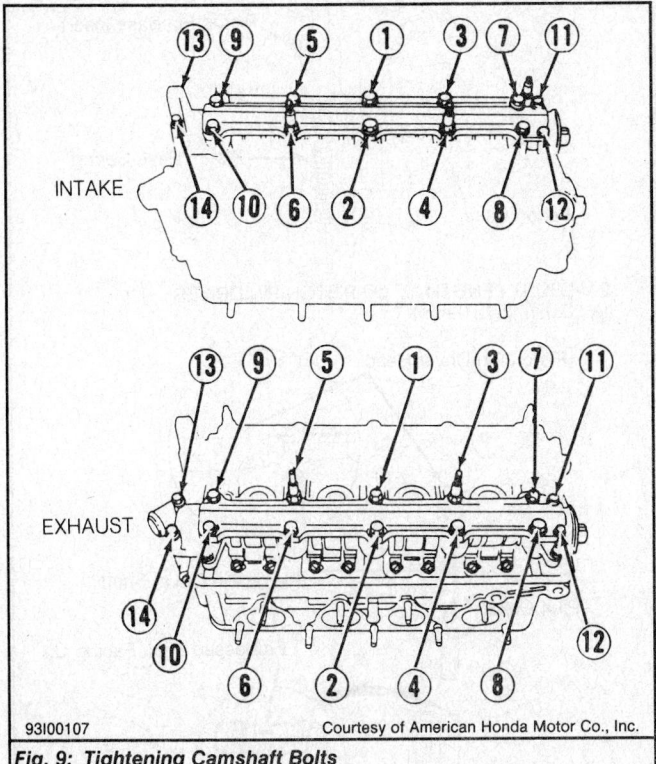

INTAKE

EXHAUST

93I00107   Courtesy of American Honda Motor Co., Inc.

Fig. 9: Tightening Camshaft Bolts

REAR CRANKSHAFT OIL SEAL

Removal – **1)** Disconnect negative battery cable. Remove transaxle assembly. See appropriate article in CLUTCHES (M/T models) or TRANSMISSION SERVICING (A/T models).

2) Place reference mark on clutch pressure plate (M/T models) and flywheel for reassembly reference. Remove pressure plate and clutch disc (if equipped). Remove flywheel. Pry seal from cover.

NOTE: When installing new crankshaft oil seal, align hole in Driver Attachment (07948-SB00101) with pin on crankshaft.

Installation – Apply a light coat of engine oil to crankshaft and lip of new seal. Using Seal Driver (07749-0010000) and Driver Attachment (07948-SB00101), install new seal. To complete installation, reverse removal procedure.

WATER PUMP

Removal – Disconnect negative battery cable. Drain cooling system. Remove timing belt. See TIMING BELT. Remove timing belt back cover. *See Fig. 7.* Remove retaining bolts, water pump, and "O" rings.
Installation – **1)** Clean gasket surfaces. Install water pump. Install new "O" rings. To complete installation, reverse removal procedure. Tighten bolts to specifications. See TORQUE SPECIFICATIONS.
2) Adjust timing belt tension. See TIMING BELT TENSION under ADJUSTMENTS. Fill and bleed air from cooling system. See BLEEDING COOLING SYSTEM.

OIL PAN

Removal – **1)** Drain engine oil. Rotate crankshaft counterclockwise to align crankshaft pulley timing marks. *See Fig. 5.* Remove valve cover and middle timing belt cover. *See Fig. 7.* Remove accessory drive belts.
2) Remove crankshaft pulley and timing belt lower cover. Mark timing belt for installation reference. Loosen belt tensioner. Remove timing belt and crankshaft sprocket. See TIMING BELT. Remove oil pan and gasket.
Installation – Clean gasket mating surfaces. Install new gasket and oil pan. Tighten bolts to specification. See TORQUE SPECIFICATIONS. To complete installation, reverse removal procedure.

OVERHAUL

CYLINDER HEAD

Cylinder Head – Ensure all mating surfaces are clean. Measure cylinder head warpage. If warpage is less than 0.002" (0.05 mm), resurfacing is not required. If warpage is 0.002-0.008" (0.05-0.20 mm), resurface cylinder head. Maximum resurface limit is 0.008" (0.20 mm).
Valve Springs – Measure free length of valve springs. If measurements are not within specifications, replace valve springs. See VALVES & VALVE SPRINGS table under ENGINE SPECIFICATIONS.
Valve Stem Oil Seals – Intake and exhaust valve stem seals are not interchangeable. Intake valve stem seals have a White spring around neck of seal. Oil seals for exhaust valves have a Black spring around neck of seal. Use Valve Stem Seal Installer (KD-2899) to install valve stem seals.
Valve Guide Inspection – Measure valve guide clearance using a dial indicator placed on valve head. Zero dial indicator. Rock valve stem from side to side. Valve guides can be replaced if valve stem oil clearance is not within specification. See CYLINDER HEAD table under ENGINE SPECIFICATIONS.
Valve Guide Removal – **1)** Use a hot plate or oven to heat cylinder head to 300°F (150°C). Use Valve Guide Driver (07742-0010100), or fabricate valve guide remover from an air-impact chisel. *See Fig. 10.* Using an air hammer and valve guide remover, drive valve guide 0.079" (2.0 mm) toward combustion chamber.

CAUTION: DO NOT heat cylinder head using a torch or heat cylinder head warmer than 300°F (150°C). Excessive heat may loosen valve seats.

2) Turn head over. Working from combustion chamber side of head, drive valve guide out toward camshaft side of head. If valve guide does not move, drill valve guide with a 5/16" bit and try again to drive out guide.

CAUTION: Drill guides in extreme cases only. Cylinder head damage can occur if valve guide breaks.

Valve Guide Installation – **1)** Cool new valve guides in freezer for about one hour. Remove new valve guides from freezer as needed. Slip a 15/64" (6 mm) steel washer and appropriate driver attachment over Valve Guide Driver (07742-0010100).
2) Install new valve guides from camshaft side of cylinder head. Drive each guide into heated head until driver attachment bottoms on head. If replacing all valve guides, reheat cylinder head as necessary.

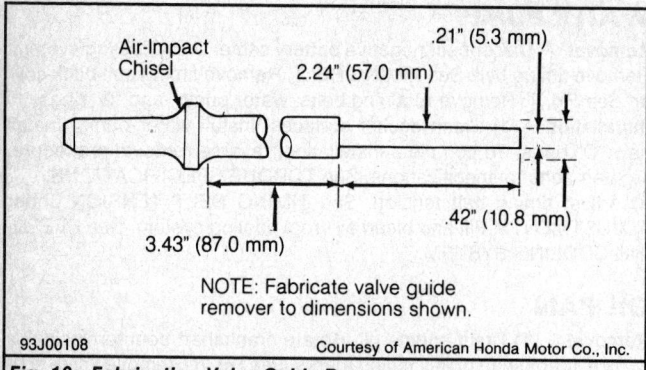

NOTE: Fabricate valve guide remover to dimensions shown.

93J00108

Courtesy of American Honda Motor Co., Inc.

Fig. 10: Fabricating Valve Guide Remover

3) Valve guide installed height must be 0.4941-0.5138" (12.55-13.05 mm). Using cutting oil, ream new valve guides by rotating Valve Guide Reamer (07HAH-PJ7010A) clockwise full length of valve guide bore. Measure valve stem oil clearance. See CYLINDER HEAD table under ENGINE SPECIFICATIONS.

NOTE: Always reface valve seat after replacing valve guide.

Valve Seat – Valve seat replacement procedure is not available.
Valve Seat Correction Angles – If valve guides are to be replaced, perform guide replacement before refacing valve seats. If seat width is too wide, use 60-degree stone to raise seat, or 30-degree stone to lower seat. Ensure valve seat width is within specification. See CYLINDER HEAD table under ENGINE SPECIFICATIONS.
Valve Stem Installed Height – After servicing valves, measure valve stem installed height. *See Fig. 11.* If valve stem installed height exceeds 1.5033" (38.185 mm) for intake valve or 1.4915" (37.885 mm) for exhaust valves, replace valve. If valve stem installed height still exceeds limit, replace cylinder head.

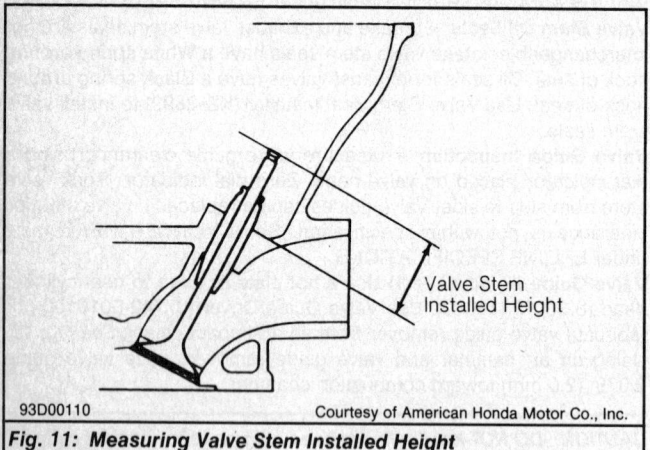

93D00110

Courtesy of American Honda Motor Co., Inc.

Fig. 11: Measuring Valve Stem Installed Height

VALVE TRAIN

Removal – Place a rubber band around each set of rocker arms to keep them together. Remove intake and exhaust rocker shaft oil control orifices. Thread a 12-mm bolt into end of rocker shaft. Pull bolt head to remove rocker shaft and rocker arms. Tag parts for installation reference as they are removed.
Installation – Lubricate all components before installation. Install all components into original locations. Back off valve adjuster screws before installation. If holes in cylinder head and rocker shafts are not in line, turn shaft with a 12-mm bolt threaded into end. To complete installation, reverse removal procedure.

CYLINDER BLOCK ASSEMBLY

Piston & Rod Assembly – 1) Each rod is sorted into one of 4 tolerance ranges. Size depends on crank journal bore. Number from 1 to 4 is stamped on side of rod big end. Any combination of numbers from 1 to 4 may be found on any engine.

NOTE: Reference numbers are for big end bore code and do not indicate rod position in engine.

2) Nominal connecting rod big bore size is 1.89" (48.0 mm). Install piston and connecting rod so arrow on top of piston is toward timing belt and numbers marked on connecting rod face timing belt.

NOTE: All replacement piston pins are oversize.

Piston Pin Removal – 1) Install Piston Base Head (07HAF-PL20102) and Piston Pin Base Insert (07GAF-PH60300) into Base (07973-6570500). Turn handle on Piston Pin Driver Head (07973-PE00320) so piston driver length is 2.035" (51.70 mm). *See Fig. 12.*
2) Insert Piston Driver Shaft (07973-PE00310) into Pilot Collar (07LAF-PR30100). Place piston onto base. Press out piston pin. When removing or installing piston pin, set piston in press with embossed side facing up. Align lugs on base insert with recessed part of piston.

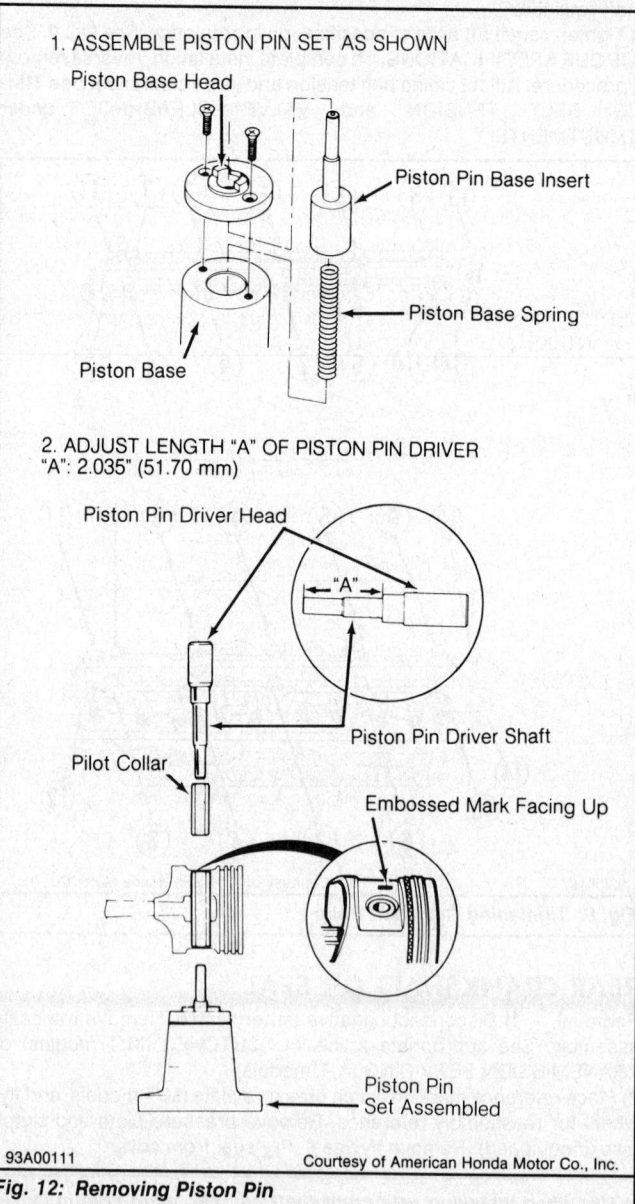

93A00111

Courtesy of American Honda Motor Co., Inc.

Fig. 12: Removing Piston Pin

Piston Pin Inspection – 1) Measure diameter of piston pin. Zero dial indicator to piston pin diameter. Insert gauge into piston boss to measure piston pin-to-piston clearance.
2) Piston pin clearance must be 0.0004-0.0009" (0.010-0.022 mm). If piston pin clearance is greater than 0.0009" (0.022 mm), install an oversize piston pin and recheck clearance.

3) Determine difference between piston pin diameter and connecting rod small end diameter. Interference fit between piston and connecting rod must be 0.0005-0.0013" (0.013-0.032 mm).

Piston Pin Installation – 1) Ensure piston and connecting rod are positioned so arrow on top of piston is toward timing belt and numbers marked on connecting rod face timing belt. Turn handle on Piston Pin Driver (07973-PE00320) so piston driver length is 2.035" (51.70 mm).
2) Install Pilot Collar (07LAF-PR30100) into piston and connecting rod. Lightly oil new piston pin. Place piston onto base. Press in piston pin.

Fitting Pistons – 1) Using a feeler gauge, measure piston-to-cylinder bore clearance. If clearance is near or exceeds 0.002" (0.05 mm), measure each piston and cylinder. If piston clearance exceeds service limit, rebore cylinder and install oversize piston.
2) Measure piston diameter at a point 0.6" (15 mm) from bottom of piston skirt. If diameter is not within specification, replace piston. See PISTON DIAMETER table. See PISTONS, PINS & RINGS table under ENGINE SPECIFICATIONS.

PISTON DIAMETER

Application [1]	In. (mm)
Standard (New)	3.1882-3.1886 (80.980-80.990)
Service Limit	3.1878 (80.970)
Oversize 0.010" (0.25 mm)	3.1980-3.1984 (81.230-81.240)

[1] – Measured at 0.6" (15 mm) from bottom of piston skirt.

Piston Rings – 1) Using inverted piston, push new piston ring into cylinder bore 0.6-0.8" (15-20 mm) from bottom. Measure piston ring end gap. Repeat for each ring. See PISTONS, PINS & RINGS table under ENGINE SPECIFICATIONS.
2) Clean piston ring grooves thoroughly. Install piston rings with identification mark toward top of piston. Using a feeler gauge, measure piston ring side clearance between ring and ring land.
3) If ring lands are excessively worn, replace piston. See PISTONS, PINS & RINGS table. Align piston ring end gaps properly on piston. *See Fig. 13.*

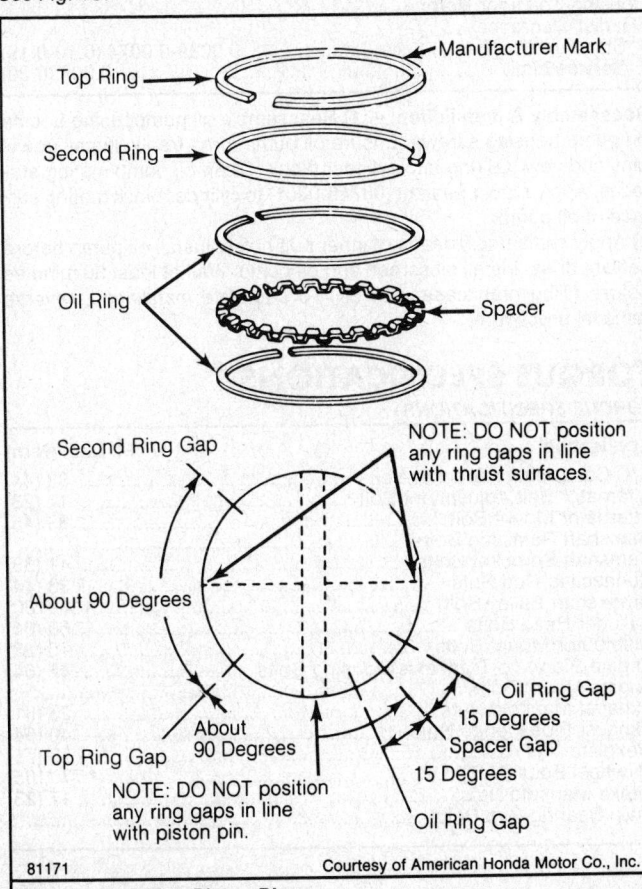

81171   Courtesy of American Honda Motor Co., Inc.

Fig. 13: Installing Piston Rings

Rod Bearings – 1) Using Plastigage, measure rod bearing oil clearance. Tighten bearing cap to 24 ft. lbs. (32 N.m).
2) If oil clearance is not within specification, install a new bearing set (same color code) and recheck oil clearance. DO NOT shim or file cap to adjust oil clearance.
3) If oil clearance is still incorrect, try next larger or smaller bearing. Measure oil clearance once more. If proper oil clearance cannot be obtained by using larger or smaller bearings, replace crankshaft and repeat procedure.

NOTE: A number indicating connecting rod bore is stamped on side of each connecting rod and cap. Connecting rod journal diameter codes (letters) are stamped on crankshaft counterweight pads. See Fig. 14. Use both codes when ordering replacement bearings.

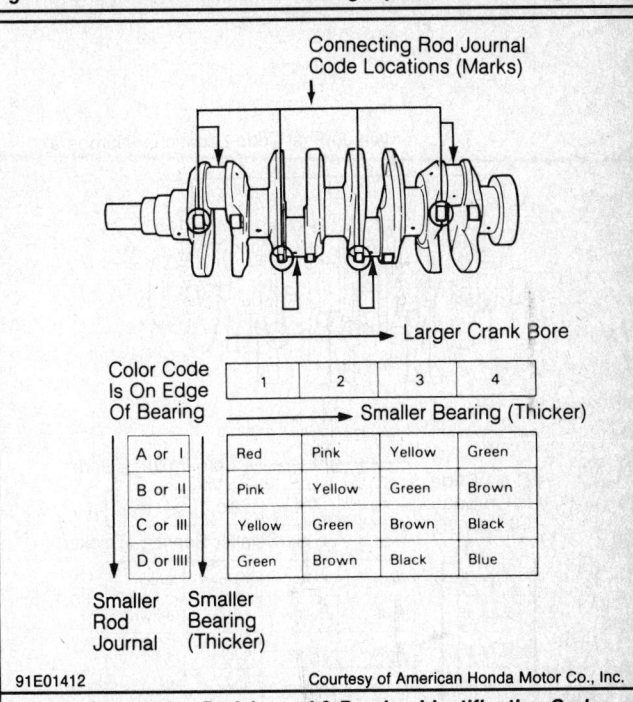

91E01412   Courtesy of American Honda Motor Co., Inc.

Fig. 14: Connecting Rod Journal & Bearing Identification Codes

Crankshaft & Main Bearings – 1) Remove rear crankshaft oil seal cover, oil screen, oil pump, and baffle plate. Rotate crankshaft so No. 2 and No. 3 crankpins are at bottom. Remove all connecting rod caps and bearings.
2) Mark all main bearing caps for assembly reference. Remove main bearing caps and bearing halves. Lift crankshaft from block, being careful not to damage journals.
3) Using a lathe or "V" blocks to support crankshaft, measure crankshaft runout, out-of-round, and taper. If any measurement exceeds service limit, replace crankshaft. See CRANKSHAFT, MAIN & CONNECTING ROD BEARINGS table under ENGINE SPECIFICATIONS.
4) Install crankshaft into block. Measure oil clearance with Plastigage. Tighten main bearing caps to 58 ft. lbs. (78 N.m). If oil clearance is not within specification, install a new bearing set (same color code) and recheck oil clearance.
5) If oil clearance is still incorrect, try next larger or smaller bearing and measure oil clearance once more. If proper oil clearance cannot be obtained by using larger or smaller bearings, replace crankshaft and repeat procedure.

NOTE: A letter indicating main journal bore diameters is stamped on cylinder block. See Fig. 15. Use these codes, together with crankshaft main journal diameter numbers, when ordering replacement bearings.

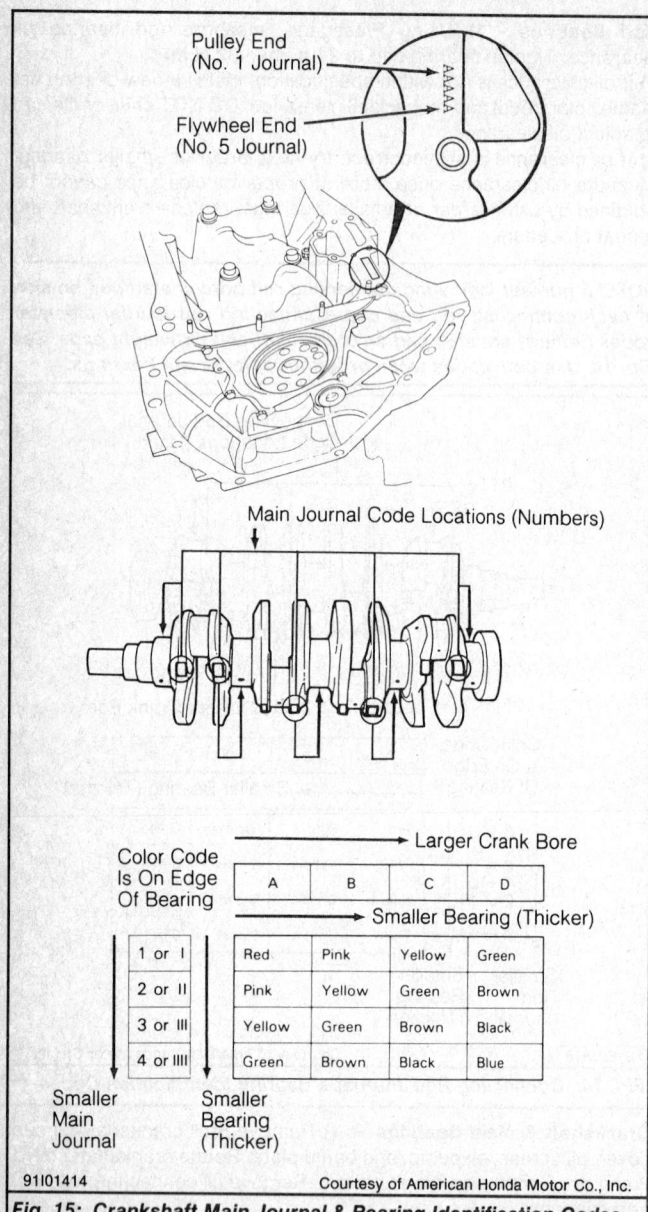

Fig. 15: Crankshaft Main Journal & Bearing Identification Codes

91I01414   Courtesy of American Honda Motor Co., Inc.

Thrust Bearing – **1)** Measure crankshaft end play with a dial indicator. If end play exceeds specification, inspect thrust washers and thrust surface of crankshaft. See CRANKSHAFT, MAIN & CONNECTING ROD BEARINGS table under ENGINE SPECIFICATIONS.

2) Replace worn parts as necessary. Thrust washer thickness is fixed. DO NOT change thrust washer thickness by grinding or shimming. Install thrust washers with grooved side out.

Cylinder Block – **1)** Measure cylinder bore out-of-round and taper. If either out-of-round or taper exceeds 0.002" (0.05 mm), rebore cylinder for oversize pistons. If any cylinder exceeds oversize bore service limit, replace cylinder block. See CYLINDER BLOCK table under ENGINE SPECIFICATIONS.

2) Using a feeler gauge and straightedge, measure cylinder block deck surface warpage. Service limit is 0.003" (0.08 mm). If cylinder bore is okay, hone cylinder to obtain a 60-degree crosshatch pattern. After honing, wash cylinder bore wish hot soapy water. Air-dry cylinder bore, and apply engine oil to prevent rusting.

ENGINE OILING

ENGINE LUBRICATION SYSTEM

A rotor-type oil pump draws oil from oil pan and delivers it under pressure to main and connecting rod bearings. Oil jets at bottom of block spray oil upward to lubricate piston and cylinder wall. An oil passage carries oil to camshaft and rocker arms. Oil spray lubricates valve stems.

Crankcase Capacity – Crankcase capacity is 4.0 qts. (3.8L) including oil filter. Oil capacity is 5.1 qts. (4.8L) after engine overhaul.

Oil Pressure – Oil pressure at idle should be 10 psi (0.7 kg/cm²) minimum. Oil pressure at 3000 RPM should be 50 psi (3.5 kg/cm²) minimum.

OIL PUMP

Removal & Disassembly – Remove oil pan. See OIL PAN under REMOVAL & INSTALLATION. Remove oil screen and oil pump assembly. Remove screws from oil pump housing. Separate housing and cover.

Inspection – Measure radial clearance between inner and outer rotors. Measure axial clearance between housing and outer rotor. Inspect both rotors and pump housing for scoring or other damage. Replace components if clearance measurements are not within specification. See OIL PUMP SPECIFICATIONS table.

OIL PUMP SPECIFICATIONS

Application	In. (mm)
Inner Rotor-To-Outer Rotor	
Radial Clearance	
Standard (New)	0.0016-0.0063 (0.04-0.16)
Service Limit	0.008 (0.20)
Housing-To-Outer Rotor	
Axial Clearance	
Standard (New)	0.0008-0.0027 (0.02-0.07)
Service Limit	0.006 (0.15)
Housing-To-Outer Rotor	
Radial Clearance	
Standard (New)	0.0039-0.0074 (0.10-0.19)
Service Limit	0.008 (0.20)

Reassembly & Installation – **1)** Reassemble oil pump, using Loctite on pump housing screws. Ensure oil pump turns freely. Install dowel pins and new "O" ring into cylinder block. Clean oil pump mating surfaces. Apply Liquid Sealant (08718-0001) to cylinder block mating surface of oil pump.

2) Apply sealant to threads of inner bolt holes. Install oil pump before sealant dries. Install oil screen and oil pump. Wait at least 30 minutes before filling crankcase with oil. To complete installation, reverse removal procedure.

TORQUE SPECIFICATIONS
TORQUE SPECIFICATIONS

Application	Ft. Lbs. (N.m)
A/C Compressor Bracket Bolts	33 (44)
Alternator Belt Adjustment Bolt	17 (23)
Alternator Mount Bolt	33 (45)
Camshaft Retaining Bolts	1
Camshaft Sprocket Bolts	41 (56)
Connecting Rod Nuts	2 33 (44)
Crankshaft Pulley Bolt	133 (180)
Cylinder Head Bolts	3 60 (81)
Distributor Mount Bolts	16 (22)
Engine Block-To-Transaxle Housing Bolts	47 (64)
Engine Mount Bolts	4
Exhaust Manifold Nuts	23 (31)
Exhaust Pipe Flange Nuts	40 (54)
Flexplate (A/T)	5 55 (75)
Flywheel Bolts (M/T)	5 77 (105)
Intake Manifold Nuts	17 (23)
Main Bearing Cap Bolts	6

TORQUE SPECIFICATIONS (Cont.)

Application	Ft. Lbs. (N.m)
Oil Pump Bolts	
6-mm Bolts	7
8-mm Bolts	17 (23)
Power Steering Mount Bolt	17 (23)
Rocker Arm Lock Nuts	14 (20)
Rocker Arm Shaft Sealing Bolt	47 (64)
Shift Lever Torque Rod Bolt	16 (22)
Timing Belt Tension Adjuster Bolt	40 (54)

Application	INCH Lbs. (N.m)
Crankshaft Baffle Plate	98 (11)
Crankshaft Rear Seal Cover Bolts	98 (11)
Fuel Service Bolt	106 (12)
Oil Pan Bolts	5 106 (12)
Oil Pump Screen Nuts	98 (11)
Timing Belt Cover Bolts	106 (12)
Valve Cover Nuts	88 (10)
Water Pump Bolt	106 (12)

1 – Tighten 6-mm bolts to 96 INCH lbs. (11 N.m). Tighten 8-mm bolts to 16 ft. lbs. (22 N.m). Bolts must be tightened in sequence shown. See Fig. 9.

2 – Tighten connecting rod nuts in 2 stages. First tighten nuts to 15 ft. lbs. (20 N.m), then tighten them to 33 ft. lbs. (44 N.m).

3 – Tighten cylinder head bolts in 2 stages. First tighten bolts to 22 ft. lbs. (30 N.m) and then to 60 ft. lbs. (81 N.m). See Fig. 6.

4 – See Fig. 4.

5 – Tighten in a crisscross pattern.

6 – Tighten main bearing bolts in 2 stages. First tighten bolts to 22 ft. lbs. (30 N.m), then tighten bearing caps 1 and 5 to 56 ft. lbs. (73 N.m) and bearing caps 2, 3 and 4 to 49 ft. lbs. (64 N.m).

7 – Tighten to 96 INCH lbs. (11 N.m).

ENGINE SPECIFICATIONS

GENERAL SPECIFICATIONS

Application	Specification
Displacement	110 Cu. In. (1.8L)
Bore	3.19" (81 mm)
Stroke	3.43" (87.2 mm)
Compression Ratio	10.0:1
Fuel System	SFI
Horsepower @ RPM	170 @ 7600
Torque Ft. Lbs. @ RPM	128 @ 6200

PISTONS, PINS & RINGS

Application	In. (mm)
Pistons	
Clearance	
Standard	0.0004-0.0016 (0.010-0.040)
Service Limit	0.0020 (0.050)
Diameter 1	
Standard	3.1882-3.1886 (80.980-80.990)
Service Limit	3.1878 (80.970)
Oversize 0.010" (0.25 mm)	3.1980-3.1984 (81.230-81.240)
Pins	
Diameter	0.8265-0.8268 (20.994-21.000)
Piston Fit	0.0004-0.0009 (0.010-0.022)
Rod Fit	0.0007-0.0013 (0.017-0.032)
Rings	
No. 1	
End Gap	0.008-0.014 (0.20-0.35)
Side Clearance	0.0018-0.0028 (0.045-0.070)
No. 2	
End Gap	0.016-0.022 (0.40-0.55)
Side Clearance	0.0018-0.0028 (0.045-0.070)
No. 3 (Oil)	
End Gap	0.008-0.020 (0.20-0.50)

1 – Measure at 0.6" (15 mm) from bottom of skirt.

CRANKSHAFT, MAIN & CONNECTING ROD BEARINGS

Application	In. (mm)
Crankshaft	
End Play	
Standard	0.004-0.014 (0.10-0.35)
Service Limit	0.018 (0.45)
Runout	
Standard	0.0008 (0.020)
Service Limit	0.0012 (0.030)
Main Bearings	
Journal Diameter	
Except No. 3	2.1644-2.1654 (54.976-55.000)
No. 3	2.1642-2.1651 (54.970-54.994)
Journal Out-Of-Round	
Standard	0.0002 (0.005)
Service Limit	0.0004 (0.010)
Journal Taper	
Standard	0.0002 (0.005)
Service Limit	0.0004 (0.010)
Oil Clearance	
Except No. 3 Journal	
Standard	0.0009-0.0017 (0.024-0.042)
Service Limit	0.0020 (0.050)
No. 3 Journal	
Standard	0.0012-0.0019 (0.030-0.048)
Service Limit	0.0024 (0.060)
Connecting Rod Bearings	
Journal Diameter	1.7707-1.7717 (44.976-45.000)
Journal Out-Of-Round	
Standard	0.0002 (0.005)
Service Limit	0.0004 (0.010)
Journal Taper	
Service Limit	0.0002 (0.005)
Oil Clearance	
Standard	0.0013-0.0020 (0.032-0.050)
Service Limit	0.0024 (0.060)

CONNECTING RODS

Application	In. (mm)
Bore Diameter	
Crankpin Bore	1.89 (48.0)
Pin Bore	0.8255-0.8260 (20.968-20.981)
Side Play	
Standard	0.006-0.012 (0.15-0.30)
Service Limit	0.016 (0.40)

CYLINDER BLOCK

Application	In. (mm)
Cylinder Bore	
Standard Diameter	3.1890-3.1898 (81.000-81.020)
Service Limit	3.1917 (81.070)
Maximum Taper	0.002 (0.05)
Maximum Rebore Limit	0.010 (0.25)
Maximum Deck Warpage	0.002 (0.05)

VALVES & VALVE SPRINGS

Application	Specification
Intake Valves	
Face Angle .... 45°	
Head Diameter .... 1.295-1.303" (32.90-33.10 mm)	
Margin	
Standard .... 0.041-0.053" (1.05-1.35 mm)	
Minimum Margin .... 0.033" (.85 mm)	
Stem Diameter	
Standard .... 0.2156-0.2159" (5.475-5.485 mm)	
Service Limit .... 0.2144" (5.445 mm)	
Exhaust Valves	
Face Angle .... 45°	
Head Diameter .... 1.098-1.106" (27.90-28.10 mm)	
Margin	
Standard .... 0.065-0.077" (1.65-1.95 mm)	
Minimum Margin .... 0.057" (1.45 mm)	
Stem Diameter	
Standard .... 0.2146-0.2150" (5.450-5.460 mm)	
Service Limit .... 0.2134" (5.420 mm)	
Valve Springs Free Length	
Intake	
Inner .... 1.39" (35.3 mm)	
Outer .... 1.611" (40.92 mm)	
Exhaust .... 1.651" (41.94 mm)	

CAMSHAFT

Application	In. (mm)
End Play	
Standard 0.002-0.006 (0.05-0.15)	
Service Limit 0.020 (0.50)	
Journal Runout	
Service Limit 0.00063 (0.015)	
Oil Clearance	
Standard 0.002-0.004 (0.05-0.10)	
Service Limit 0.006 (0.15)	

CYLINDER HEAD

Application	Specification
Cylinder Head	
Height .... 5.589-5.593" (141.95-142.05 mm)	
Maximum Warpage .... [1] 0.002-0.008" (0.05-0.20 mm)	
Valve Seats	
Intake & Exhaust	
Seat Angle .... 45°	
Seat Width	
Standard .... 0.049-0.061" (1.25-1.55 mm)	
Service Limit .... 0.079" (2.00 mm)	
Valve Guides	
Exhaust Valve	
Valve Guide I.D.	
Standard .... 0.217-0.218" (5.51-5.53 mm)	
Service Limit .... 0.219" (5.55 mm)	
Valve Guide Installed Height .... 0.494-0.514" (12.55-13.05 mm)	
Valve Stem-To-Guide Oil Clearance	
Standard .... 0.002-0.003" (0.05-0.08 mm)	
Service Limit .... 0.004" (0.10 mm)	
Intake	
Valve Guide I.D.	
Standard .... 0.217-0.218" (5.51-5.53 mm)	
Service Limit .... 0.219" (5.55 mm)	
Valve Guide Installed Height .... 0.494-0.514" (12.55-13.05 mm)	
Valve Stem-To-Guide Oil Clearance	
Standard .... 0.001-0.0022" (0.02-0.055 mm)	
Service Limit .... 0.003" (0.08 mm)	

[1] – Maximum resurface limit is 0.008" (0.20 mm).

VALVE STEM INSTALLED HEIGHT [1]

Application	In. (mm)
Intake	
Standard 1.4750-1.64935 (37.465-37.935)	
Service Limit 1.5033 (38.185)	
Exhaust	
Standard 1.4632-1.4817 (37.165-37.635)	
Service Limit 1.4915 (37.885)	

[1] – Measure from base of valve guide to tip of valve stem.

1994 ENGINES
2.5L 5-Cylinder

Vigor

NOTE: For repair procedures not covered in this article, see ENGINE OVERHAUL PROCEDURES article in GENERAL INFORMATION.

ENGINE IDENTIFICATION

Engine identification code is stamped on block, below cylinder head mating surface. First 5 characters of code indicate engine type. Sixth and seventh digits should be 20 (California) or 23 (Federal). Last 5 digits of code indicate engine serial number.

ENGINE IDENTIFICATION CODE

Application	Code
2.5L	G25A1

ADJUSTMENTS

VALVE CLEARANCE ADJUSTMENT

CAUTION: Always rotate engine in direction of normal rotation (counterclockwise as viewed from front of engine). Backward rotation may cause timing belt to jump time.

1) Adjust valves when engine temperature is less than 100°F (38°C). Remove cylinder head cover. Rotate crankshaft counterclockwise until No. 1 piston is at TDC of compression stroke.
2) Ensure No. 1 mark on camshaft pulley aligns with TDC groove on cam holder. *See Fig. 1.* Adjust clearance on valves for No. 1 cylinder. Slide feeler gauge between camshaft lobe and rocker arm. Loosen lock nuts, and turn adjustment screw until clearance is correct. Tighten lock nuts. See VALVE CLEARANCE SPECIFICATIONS table.
3) Rotate crankshaft 144 degrees counterclockwise (camshaft pulley turns 72 degrees) so No. 2 piston is at TDC of compression stroke. Ensure No. 2 mark on camshaft pulley aligns with TDC groove on cam holder. Adjust clearance on valves for No. 2 cylinder.
4) Rotate crankshaft 144 degrees counterclockwise (camshaft pulley turns 72 degrees) so No. 4 piston is at TDC of compression stroke. Ensure No. 4 mark on camshaft pulley aligns with TDC groove on cam holder. Adjust clearance on valves for No. 4 cylinder.
5) Rotate crankshaft 144 degrees counterclockwise (camshaft pulley turns 72 degrees) so No. 5 piston is at TDC of compression stroke. Ensure No. 5 mark on camshaft pulley aligns with TDC groove on cam holder. Adjust clearance on valves for No. 5 cylinder.
6) Rotate crankshaft 144 degrees counterclockwise (camshaft pulley turns 72 degrees) so No. 3 piston is at TDC of compression stroke. Ensure No. 3 mark on camshaft pulley aligns with TDC groove on cam holder. Adjust clearance on valves for No. 3 cylinder. Retighten crankshaft pulley bolt to 184 ft. lbs. (250 N.m).

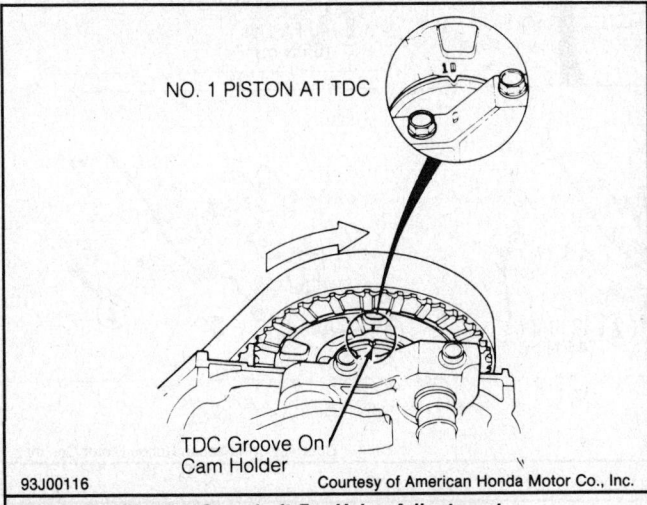

NO. 1 PISTON AT TDC

TDC Groove On Cam Holder

93J00116   Courtesy of American Honda Motor Co., Inc.

Fig. 1: Positioning Camshaft For Valve Adjustment (No. 1 Cylinder Shown; Others Similar)

VALVE CLEARANCE SPECIFICATIONS

Application	In. (mm)
Exhaust	0.011-0.013 (0.28-0.32)
Intake	0.009-0.011 (0.24-0.28)

TIMING BELT TENSION ADJUSTMENT

CAUTION: Adjust timing belt with engine cold. DO NOT rotate crankshaft with timing belt tension adjuster bolt loose.

1) Remove cylinder head cover. Rotate crankshaft counterclockwise until No. 1 piston is at TDC. Loosen adjuster bolt 180 degrees. *See Fig. 2.* Rotate crankshaft 3 teeth counterclockwise on camshaft pulley to create tension on timing belt.
2) Ensure timing belt and crankshaft pulley are securely engaged. Tighten tension adjuster bolt to specification. See TORQUE SPECIFICATIONS. Install cover and new gaskets. Retighten crankshaft pulley bolt to 181 ft. lbs. (250 N.m).

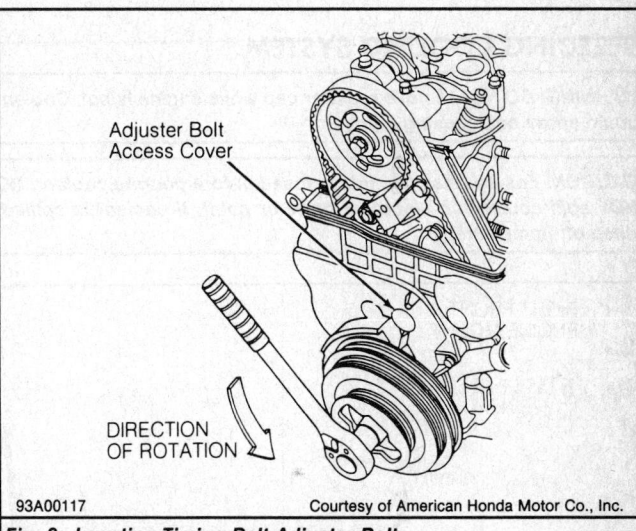

Adjuster Bolt Access Cover

DIRECTION OF ROTATION

93A00117   Courtesy of American Honda Motor Co., Inc.

Fig. 2: Locating Timing Belt Adjuster Bolt

REMOVAL & INSTALLATION

NOTE: For reassembly reference, label all electrical connectors, vacuum hoses, and fuel lines before removal. Also place mating marks on major assemblies before removal.

NOTE: Radio/cassette or radio/CD player is equipped with an anti-theft protection circuit. Whenever battery is disconnected, radio will go into anti-theft mode. When battery is reconnected, radio will display CODE, and will be inoperative until proper code number is entered. Obtain code number before disconnecting battery.

FUEL PRESSURE RELEASE

WARNING: Fuel system is under pressure. Release pressure before servicing fuel system components.

Disconnect negative battery cable. Remove fuel tank filler cap. Place shop towel on top of fuel filter to absorb any fuel spray. Release fuel injection system pressure by slowly loosening fuel injection service bolt. *See Fig. 3.*

NOTE: Replace washer between service bolt and banjo bolt whenever service bolt is loosened. Replace ALL washers if both bolts are removed.

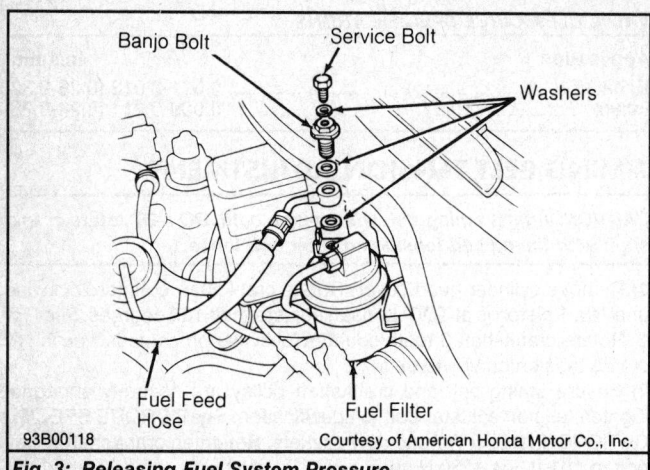

Fig. 3: Releasing Fuel System Pressure

BLEEDING COOLING SYSTEM

WARNING: DO NOT remove radiator cap while engine is hot. Coolant could spray out, causing injury.

CAUTION: Ensure relay box lid is closed before pouring coolant. DO NOT spill coolant on electrical parts or paint. If coolant is spilled, rinse off immediately.

1) Set heater controls for maximum heat. Ensure engine and radiator are cool to touch. Drain coolant from radiator, engine block and reservoir. Fill cooling system with a 50/50 mixture of coolant and water to bottom of filler neck. Loosen 2 bleed bolts on top of engine.

2) Tighten bleed bolts when coolant flows in steady stream without bubbles. Refill radiator to base of filler neck. Install cap on radiator and tighten to first stop only. Start and operate engine to normal operating temperature. Turn engine off. Check coolant level in radiator and top off if necessary. Fill coolant reservoir to MAX mark.

ENGINE

NOTE: Mark all wiring and hoses for installation reference. Ensure wiring and hoses do not interfere with other parts or with each other.

Removal – 1) Disconnect battery cables. Remove radiator cap. Raise and support vehicle. Remove splash shield. Drain engine coolant. Drain transmission and differential fluid. Drain engine oil. Lower vehicle. Secure hood as far open as possible. Disconnect ignition coil wire, condenser wire and engine ground wire.

2) Remove ABS relay box, battery heat shield and battery. Remove air inlet duct and air cleaner housing. Release fuel pressure. See FUEL PRESSURE RELEASE. Disconnect fuel inlet and return hoses. Disconnect throttle cable. Remove throttle cable clamp. Unplug fuel injector resistor connector.

3) Unplug engine wire harness connectors, and remove harness clamps. Disconnect hoses from intake manifold. Disconnect heater hoses. Unplug connectors at transmission. Disconnect ignition wires. Remove distributor. Disconnect power cables from underhood fuse/

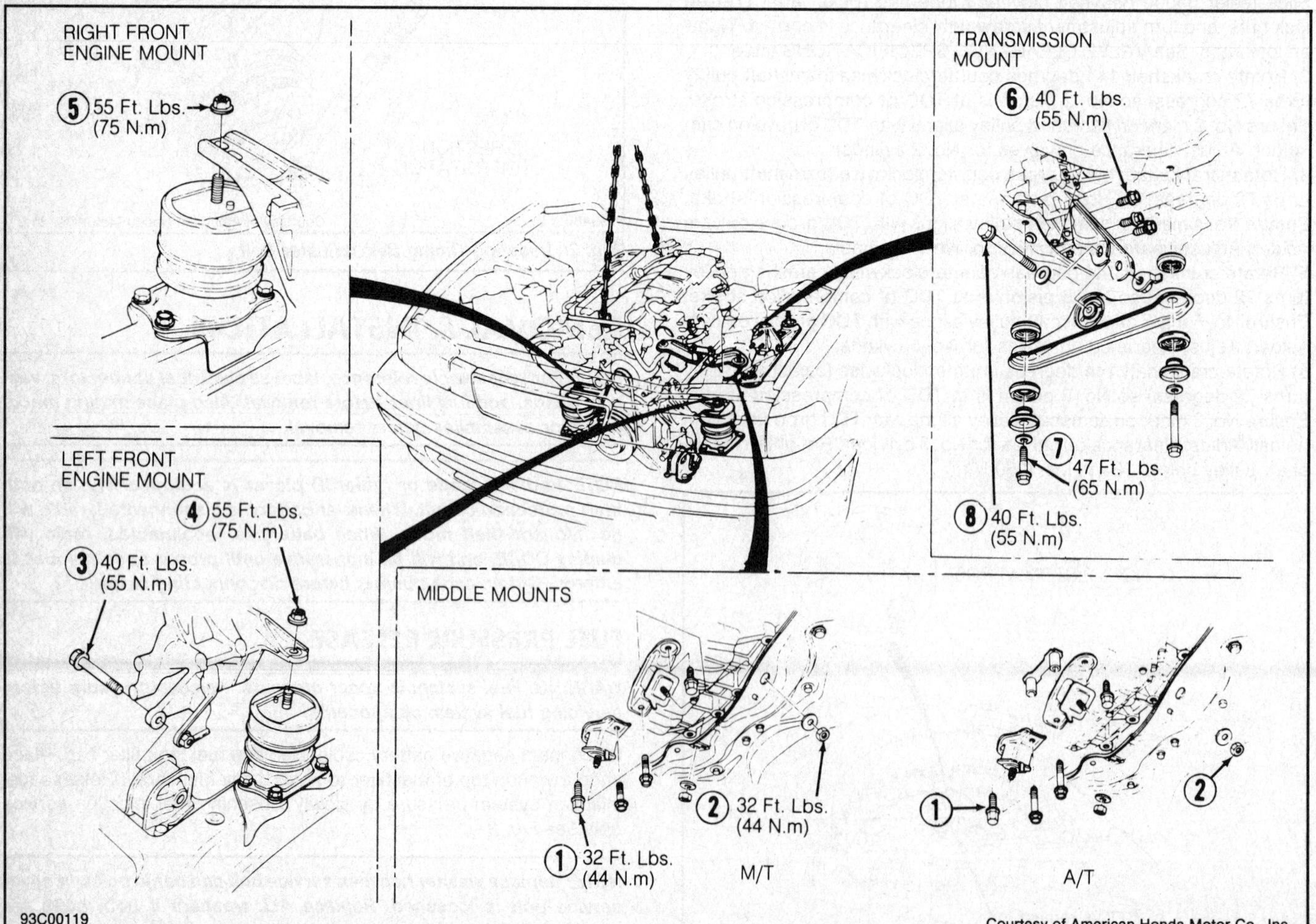

Fig. 4: Engine/Transmission Mount Tightening Sequence

relay box. Disconnect ground cables at cylinder head and transmission. Loosen adjusting bolt, and remove mounting bolt/nut and Power Steering (P/S) pump belt. Remove P/S pump with hoses attached. Set P/S pump aside.

4) Loosen idler pulley center nut and adjusting bolt. Remove A/C compressor belt. Remove A/C compressor with hoses attached. Disconnect connector, and set A/C compressor aside. Remove vehicle speed sensor and P/S speed sensor with hoses attached. Remove radiator. Disconnect connectors and ATF cooler hoses.

5) On A/T models, remove torque converter cover. Remove drive plate bolts, one at a time, while rotating crankshaft pulley. On all models, remove transmission housing bolts and 26-mm shim. Unplug wiring at transmission. Remove damper forks. Disconnect suspension lower arm ball joints using special tool. See appropriate article in SUSPENSION. Remove drive shafts. See FWD AXLE SHAFTS article in DRIVE AXLES.

6) Raise and support vehicle. Remove exhaust pipe. Remove transmission mount and mounting bracket. Shift transmission into Park (A/T) or 1st gear (M/T). Remove secondary cover and sealing bolt. Using Extension Shaft Puller (07LAC-PW50101), remove extension shaft from differential.

7) Attach chain hoist to engine. Remove left front engine mount nut and engine mount damper bolt. Remove right front engine mount nut. Remove middle engine mounts. Remove transmission housing mount bolts and side transmission mounting bracket. Remove side engine mount. Remove transmission housing mount bolts.

8) Remove clutch cover (M/T) or torque converter cover (A/T). Separate engine and transmission. Attach transmission jack and rubber pad or wooden block. Install middle engine mounts to transmission, and tighten mounting bolts to specification. *See Fig. 4.* Raise chain hoist to remove slack from chain.

9) Ensure all hoses and wires have been disconnected and set aside. Slowly raise engine about 6 inches. Carefully raise engine and remove from vehicle.

NOTE: If engine block and/or differential case are replaced, the 26-mm shim thickness must be adjusted. See DIFFERENTIAL article in DRIVE AXLES.

Installation – 1) To install, reverse removal procedure. To prevent excessive engine vibration and premature engine mount wear, tighten engine/transmission mounts in specified sequence. *See Fig. 4.*

2) When installing drive axles, use new spring clips. Insert drive axles until spring clips click into grooves of differential side gears. Before installing distributor, install collar on distributor and use new "O" rings. Ensure harness connectors and hoses are connected properly.

3) Ensure control cables are not bent or pinched, and are adjusted properly. On M/T vehicles, adjust clutch pedal free play. Verify transmission shifts smoothly.

4) On all models, adjust drive belt tension. Fill or top off all fluids. Turn ignition on, engine off, to operate fuel pump for about 2 seconds. Repeat procedure 2 or 3 times and check for fuel leaks. Fill and bleed air from cooling system. See BLEEDING COOLING SYSTEM. Start engine and check for leaks.

INTAKE MANIFOLD

NOTE: Reference mark all emission hoses before disconnecting.

Removal – 1) Allow engine to cool. Disconnect battery negative cable. Drain cooling system. Release fuel pressure. See FUEL PRESSURE RELEASE. Remove air intake duct and air cleaner assembly. Disconnect fuel inlet and return hoses. Disconnect throttle cable at throttle body. DO NOT bend cable.

2) Disconnect engine ground wire and evaporative emission control canister hoses from intake manifold. Remove heater hoses and brake booster vacuum hose. Remove ignition coil wire, condenser wire and engine ground cable. Remove ABS relay box and battery heat shield. Disconnect ignition wires, and remove distributor.

3) Remove engine wire harness connectors and clamps from cylinder head and intake manifold. Remove emission vacuum hoses and water by-pass hoses from intake manifold assembly. Remove upper radiator hose and water by-pass hose from thermostat case. Remove intake manifold nuts.

Installation – Clean gasket surfaces. Install intake manifold and new intake manifold gasket. Tighten nuts to specification in 2 or 3 steps using crisscross pattern, starting with inner nuts. See TORQUE SPECIFICATIONS. To complete installation, reverse removal procedure. Refill and bleed air from cooling system. See BLEEDING COOLING SYSTEM.

EXHAUST MANIFOLD

Removal – Disconnect negative battery cable. Remove heated O_2 sensor. Remove exhaust manifold bracket. Disconnect exhaust pipe from exhaust manifold. Remove exhaust manifold heat shields. Remove exhaust manifold bolts, exhaust manifold and gasket.

Installation – To install, reverse removal procedure. Tighten bolts to specification. See TORQUE SPECIFICATIONS.

CYLINDER HEAD

NOTE: Reference mark all emission hoses before disconnecting.

Removal – 1) Allow engine to cool. Disconnect battery negative cable. Drain cooling system. Rotate crankshaft counterclockwise until No. 1 piston is at TDC of compression stroke. Ensure No. 1 mark on camshaft pulley aligns with TDC groove on cam holder. *See Fig. 1.* Release fuel pressure. See FUEL PRESSURE RELEASE. Remove air intake duct and air cleaner assembly. Disconnect fuel inlet and return hoses. Disconnect throttle cable at throttle body. DO NOT bend cable.

2) Disconnect engine ground wire and evaporative emission control canister hoses from intake manifold. Remove heater hoses and brake booster vacuum hose. Remove ignition coil wire, condenser wire and engine ground cable. Remove ABS relay box and battery heat shield. Disconnect ignition wires, and remove distributor.

3) Remove engine wire harness connectors and clamps from cylinder head and intake manifold. Remove emission vacuum hoses and water by-pass hoses from intake manifold assembly. Remove upper radiator hose and water by-pass hose from thermostat case. Remove intake manifold bracket bolts.

4) Remove heated O_2 sensor. Remove exhaust manifold bracket. Disconnect exhaust pipe from exhaust manifold. Remove exhaust manifold heat shields. Remove exhaust manifold. Remove insulator plate. Remove PCV hose, and then remove cylinder head cover. Remove upper timing belt cover.

5) Loosen timing belt adjuster bolt 180 degrees. Push timing belt to relieve tension, and retighten adjuster bolt. If timing belt is to be reused, mark direction of belt rotation. Remove timing belt from camshaft pulley.

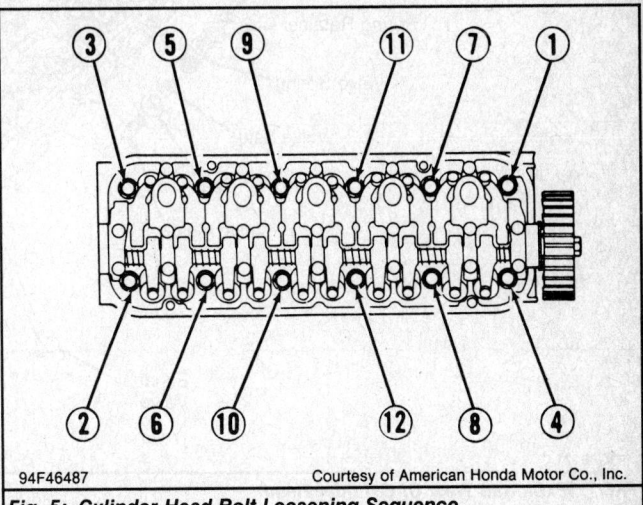

94F46487   Courtesy of American Honda Motor Co., Inc.

Fig. 5: Cylinder Head Bolt Loosening Sequence

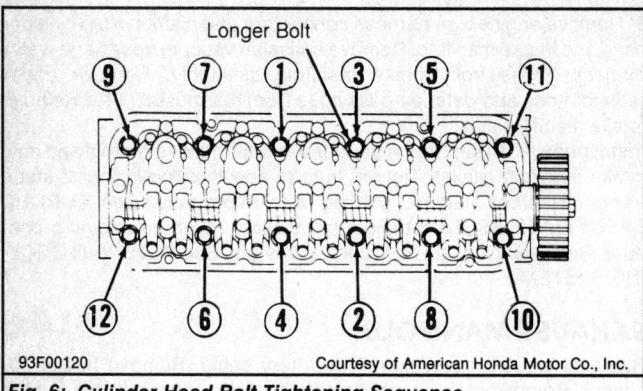

1994 ENGINES
2.5L 5-Cylinder (Cont.)

Longer Bolt
9
7
1
3
5
11
12
6
4
2
8
10
93F00120
Courtesy of American Honda Motor Co., Inc.

Fig. 6: Cylinder Head Bolt Tightening Sequence

6) Remove cylinder head bolts in sequence, 1/3 turn at a time. *See Fig. 5.* Remove cylinder head. Disconnect heater pipe from connecting pipe. Separate intake manifold from cylinder head.

Inspection – 1) Ensure all mating surfaces are clean. Check camshaft-to-holder oil clearance. Cylinder head cannot be resurfaced if oil clearance is not within specification. See CAMSHAFT table under ENGINE SPECIFICATIONS.

2) Measure cylinder head warpage. Resurface cylinder head if warpage is 0.002-0.008" (0.05-0.20 mm). Resurfacing is not required if warpage is less than 0.002" (0.05 mm). Maximum resurface limit is 0.008" (0.20 mm).

Installation – 1) Clean oil control orifice. Install oil control orifice, "O" ring, cylinder head dowel pins and new gasket in engine block. *See Fig. 7.* Install new intake manifold gasket. Install intake manifold onto cylinder head. Tighten nuts to specification in 2 or 3 steps using crisscross pattern, starting with inner nuts. See TORQUE SPECIFICATIONS.

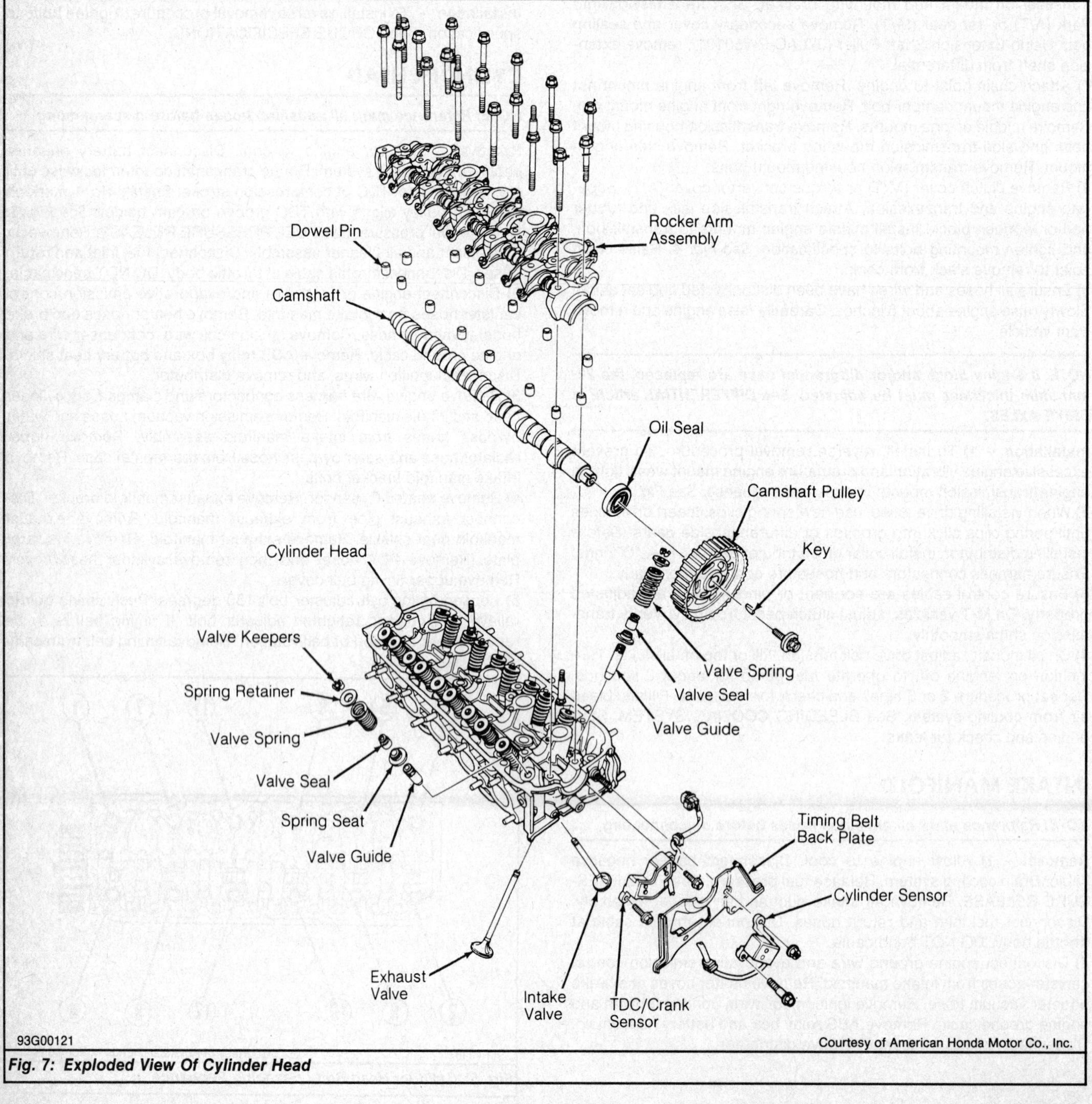

Dowel Pin
Rocker Arm
Assembly
Camshaft
Oil Seal
Camshaft Pulley
Cylinder Head
Key
Valve Keepers
Spring Retainer
Valve Spring
Valve Seal
Valve Guide
Valve Spring
Valve Seal
Spring Seat
Valve Guide
Timing Belt
Back Plate
Cylinder Sensor
Exhaust
Valve
Intake
Valve
TDC/Crank
Sensor
93G00121
Courtesy of American Honda Motor Co., Inc.

Fig. 7: Exploded View Of Cylinder Head

2) Ensure No. 1 piston and camshaft pulley are at TDC. Ensure cylinder head dowel pins and oil control orifice align. Apply light coat of engine oil to cylinder head bolts and washers. Install longer cylinder head bolt into position No. 3. *See Fig. 6.* Install remaining bolts. Tighten cylinder head bolts to specification in sequence, in 2 or 3 steps. See TORQUE SPECIFICATIONS.

3) Tighten intake manifold bracket bolts. Loosely install bracket to exhaust manifold. Install exhaust manifold and new gasket to cylinder head. Use new self-locking nuts. Apply oil to self-locking nut threads and tighten to specification in 2 or 3 steps in a crisscross pattern, starting with inner nuts.

4) To complete installation, reverse removal procedure. If reusing timing belt, ensure arrow mark on used belt points in direction of original rotation. Adjust timing belt tension. See TIMING BELT TENSION ADJUSTMENT under ADJUSTMENTS. Fill and bleed air from cooling system. See BLEEDING COOLING SYSTEM.

FRONT COVER OIL SEAL

Removal – Disconnect negative battery cable. Remove timing belt. See TIMING BELT. Remove crankshaft pulley. Remove front cover oil seal.

Installation – Apply a light coating of grease to crankshaft and lip of new seal. Install front seal using Seal Driver (07LAD-PT3010A). Ensure seal is fully seated. Clean excess grease value from crankshaft. Ensure oil seal lip is not distorted. To complete installation, reverse removal procedure. Tighten bolts to specification. See TORQUE SPECIFICATIONS.

TIMING BELT

Removal – **1)** Disconnect battery negative cable. Remove accessory drive belts. Remove valve cylinder head and upper timing belt cover. *See Fig. 8.* Rotate crankshaft counterclockwise to bring No. 1 piston to TDC of compression stroke. Remove crankshaft pulley. Remove lower timing belt cover.

2) Loosen timing belt tension adjuster bolt 180 degrees. Push tensioner to relieve tension on timing belt. Retighten adjuster bolt. If reusing timing belt, mark direction of belt rotation before removing. Remove timing belt.

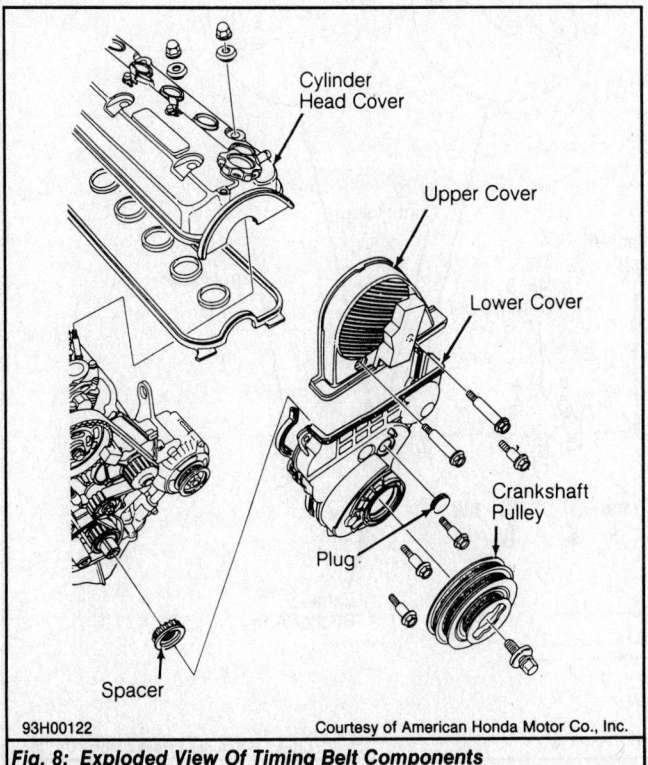

93H00122   Courtesy of American Honda Motor Co., Inc.

Fig. 8: Exploded View Of Timing Belt Components

Installation – Ensure No. 1 piston is at TDC. Position timing marks on camshaft pulley as shown. *See Fig. 9.* Install timing belt onto crankshaft pulley, tension adjuster pulley, water pump pulley and camshaft pulley. DO NOT bend or twist belt excessively. Ensure arrow on used belt points in original rotation direction. Adjust timing belt tension. See TIMING BELT TENSION ADJUSTMENT under ADJUSTMENTS. To complete installation, reverse removal procedure. Tighten bolts to specification. See TORQUE SPECIFICATIONS.

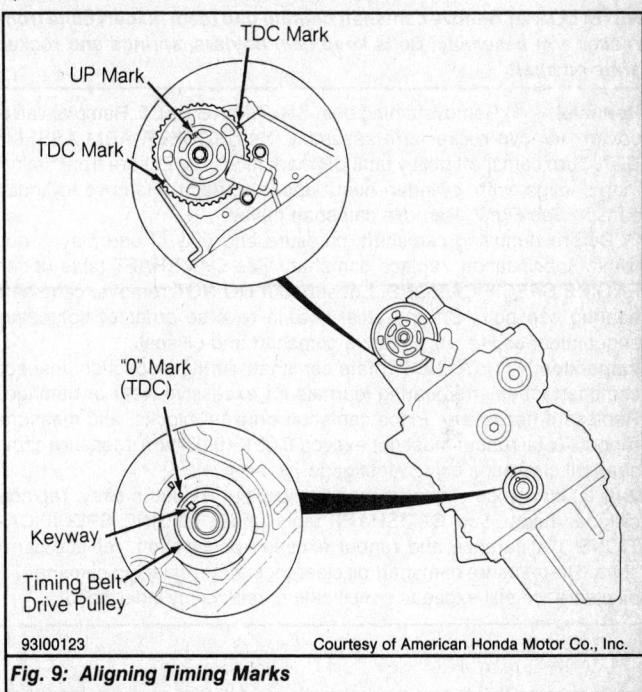

93I00123   Courtesy of American Honda Motor Co., Inc.

Fig. 9: Aligning Timing Marks

ROCKER ARM ASSEMBLY

NOTE: DO NOT remove camshaft bearing cap (cam holder) bolts from rocker arm assembly. Bolts keep cam holders, springs and rocker arms on shaft.

Removal – Loosen adjuster screws. Loosen, but DO NOT remove, camshaft bearing cap bolts 2 turns at a time, in reverse order of tightening sequence. Remove bolts, rocker arms, and rocker shaft as an assembly. If rocker shafts and arms are to be disassembled, tag all parts for reassembly reference, and carefully remove cam holder bolts one at a time.

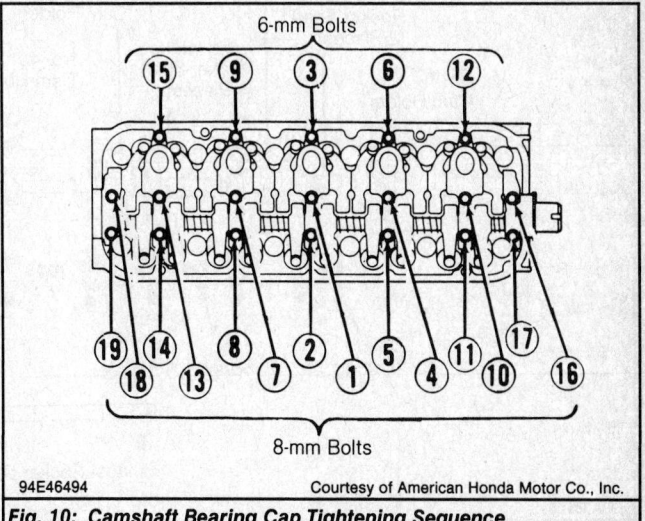

94E46494   Courtesy of American Honda Motor Co., Inc.

Fig. 10: Camshaft Bearing Cap Tightening Sequence

Installation – To install, reverse removal procedure. Clean all parts in solvent. Lubricate all moving parts. All parts must be installed into their original positions. Tighten bolts in sequence, 2 turns at a time. *See Fig. 10*. See TORQUE SPECIFICATIONS. Adjust valve clearance. See VALVE CLEARANCE ADJUSTMENT under ADJUSTMENTS.

CAMSHAFT

NOTE: DO NOT remove camshaft bearing cap (cam holder) bolts from rocker arm assembly. Bolts keep cam holders, springs and rocker arms on shaft.

Removal – 1) Remove timing belt. See TIMING BELT. Remove valve cover. Remove rocker arm assembly. See ROCKER ARM ASSEMBLY. Turn camshaft pulley until UP mark faces up. Ensure front timing marks align with cylinder head upper surface. Remove cylinder sensor. *See Fig. 7*. Remove camshaft pulley.

2) Before removing camshaft, measure end play. If end play is not within specification, replace camshaft. See CAMSHAFT table under ENGINE SPECIFICATIONS. Loosen, but DO NOT remove, camshaft bearing cap bolts 2 turns at a time, in reverse order of tightening sequence. *See Fig. 10*. Remove camshaft and oil seal.

Inspection – 1) DO NOT rotate camshaft during inspection. Inspect camshaft lobes and bearing journals for excessive wear or damage. Replace if necessary. Place camshaft onto "V" blocks, and measure runout. Total runout must not exceed 0.001" (0.03 mm). Measure camshaft oil clearance using Plastigage.

2) If oil clearance exceeds specification, but runout is okay, replace cylinder head. See CAMSHAFT table under ENGINE SPECIFICATIONS. If clearance and runout exceed specification, replace camshaft. Re-measure camshaft oil clearance after replacing camshaft. If oil clearance still exceeds specification, replace cylinder head.

4) If rocker arms must be removed from rocker shafts, note location of rocker arms for installation reference. Measure diameter of intake and exhaust rocker shafts at first rocker arm location. Measure inside diameter of rocker arm, and check for out-of-round condition.

5) Difference between the 2 measurements is rocker arm-to-shaft clearance. Repeat procedure for all rocker arms. If clearance exceeds specification, replace rocker shaft and any over-tolerance rocker arms. Inspect rocker arm faces for wear. Replace as necessary.

Installation – 1) Ensure rocker arms are assembled correctly onto rocker shaft. *See Fig. 11*. Lubricate camshaft journals and journal surfaces in caps and cylinder head. Position camshaft with keyway up. Install camshaft seal with spring facing in. Lubricate camshaft lobes. Apply gasket sealer to cylinder head mating surfaces of No. 1 and No. 7 cam holders.

2) Install rocker arm assembly, and tighten bolts finger tight. Ensure rocker arms are properly positioned onto valve stems. Tighten camshaft bearing cap bolts to specification in sequence, 2 turns at a time. *See Fig. 10*. See TORQUE SPECIFICATIONS. To complete installation, reverse removal procedure.

REAR CRANKSHAFT OIL SEAL

Removal & Installation – 1) Disconnect negative battery cable. Remove transmission. See FWD article in CLUTCHES (manual transmission) or AUTOMATIC TRANSMISSION article in TRANSMISSION SERVICING (automatic transmission).

2) On M/T models, place reference marks on clutch pressure plate and flywheel for installation reference. Remove pressure plate and clutch disc (if equipped).

3) On all models, remove flywheel or flexplate. Remove rear crankshaft oil seal. Apply light coating of grease to seal lip and crankshaft. Install new seal with part number facing out. Using Seal Driver

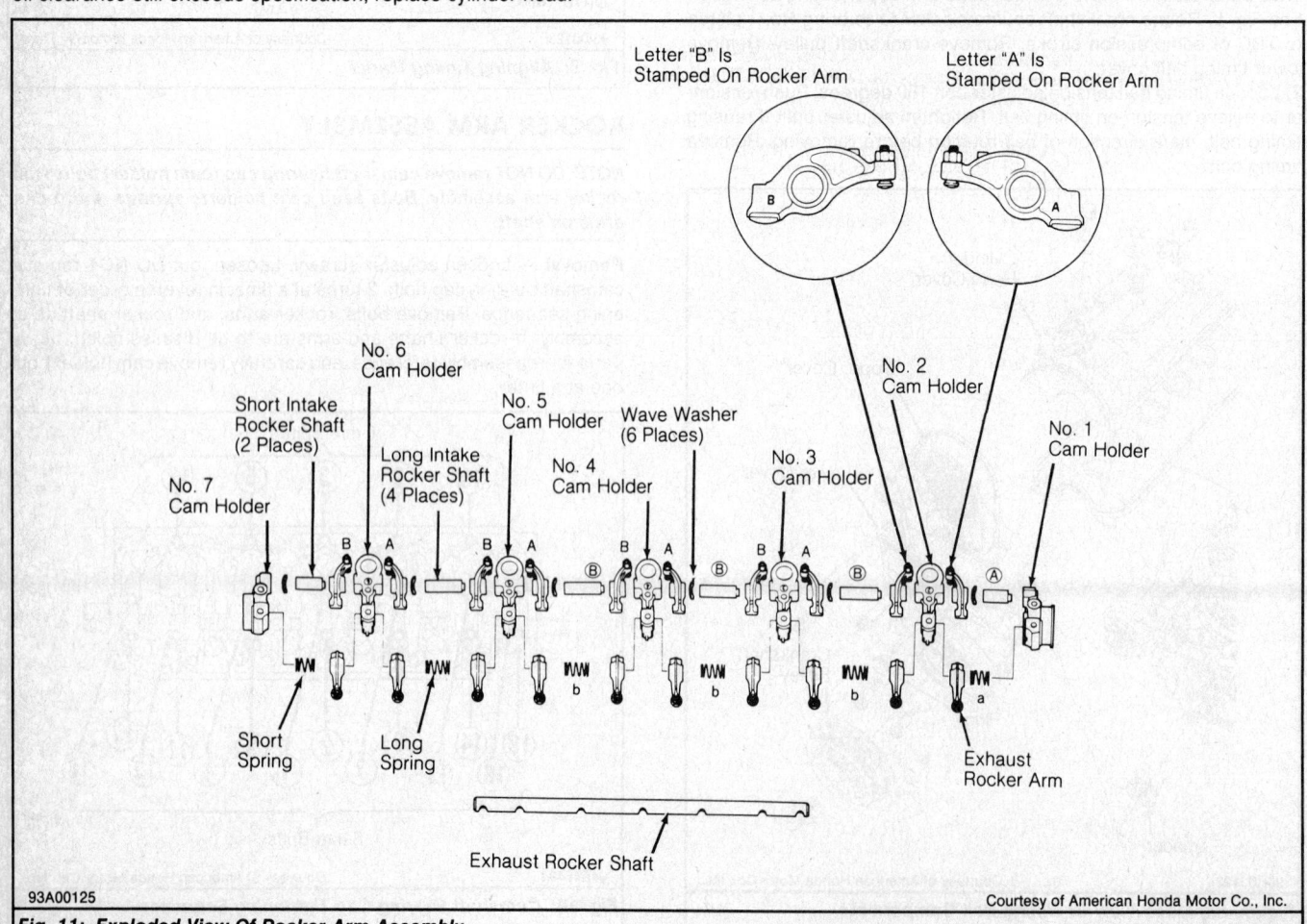

Letter "B" Is Stamped On Rocker Arm

Letter "A" Is Stamped On Rocker Arm

No. 7 Cam Holder

Short Intake Rocker Shaft (2 Places)

No. 6 Cam Holder

Long Intake Rocker Shaft (4 Places)

No. 5 Cam Holder

No. 4 Cam Holder

Wave Washer (6 Places)

No. 3 Cam Holder

No. 2 Cam Holder

No. 1 Cam Holder

Short Spring

Long Spring

Exhaust Rocker Arm

Exhaust Rocker Shaft

93A00125

Courtesy of American Honda Motor Co., Inc.

Fig. 11: *Exploded View Of Rocker Arm Assembly*

(07LAD-PT3010A), drive in new crankshaft oil seal until driver bottoms against oil pump. Clean excess grease from crankshaft. Ensure oil seal lip is not distorted.

4) Measure flywheel-end seal thickness and oil seal housing depth. Align hole in Driver Attachment (07948-SB00101) with pin on crankshaft. Using driver attachment and Driver (07749-0010000), drive crankshaft oil seal into rear cover until clearance between bottom of oil seal and rear cover is 0.02-0.03" (0.5-0.8 mm). Ensure clearance is the same all the way around. To complete installation, reverse removal procedure.

WATER PUMP

Removal & Installation – Drain cooling system. Remove timing belt. See TIMING BELT. Remove thermostat housing bolts. Remove water pump and "O" ring. To install, reverse removal procedure. Fill and bleed air from cooling system. See BLEEDING COOLING SYSTEM. Adjust timing belt tension. See TIMING BELT TENSION ADJUSTMENT under ADJUSTMENTS.

OIL PAN

Removal – **1)** Disconnect battery cables. Remove battery. Raise and support vehicle. Remove front wheels. Remove damper forks. Disconnect suspension lower arm ball joints. using special tool. See appropriate article in SUSPENSION.

2) Remove drive shafts. See FWD AXLE SHAFTS article in DRIVE AXLES. Remove air cleaner housing. Remove differential assembly. See DIFFERENTIAL article in DRIVE AXLES. Remove intermediate shaft. Remove A/C bracket. Remove set plate and oil pan inner pipe. Remove oil pan and "O" rings.

Installation – **1)** Clean oil pan and cylinder block mating surfaces. Install new oil pan "O" rings and seal. Apply a continuous bead of Liquid Gasket Sealer (08718-0001) to entire engine block, inside of bolt holes and bolt threads.

2) Install oil pan. Tighten bolts in sequence to specification. *See Fig. 12.* See TORQUE SPECIFICATIONS. Install oil pan inner pipe, then install retainer. Install differential. See DIFFERENTIALS article in DRIVE AXLES.

3) To complete installation, reverse removal procedure. Fill or top off all fluids. Wait a minimum of 30 minutes before filling crankcase with engine oil. Fill and bleed air from cooling system. See BLEEDING COOLING SYSTEM.

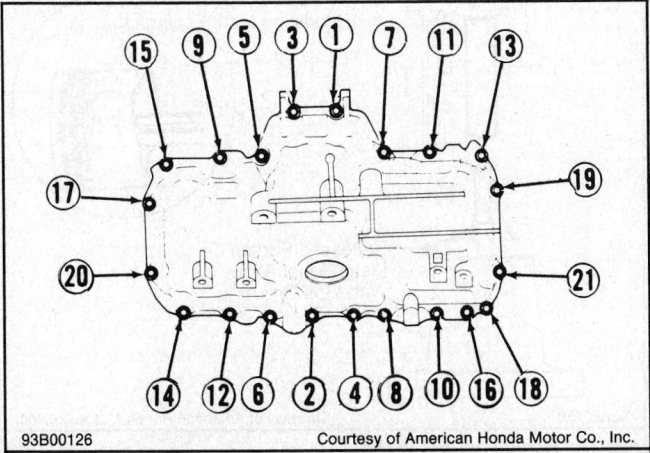

Fig. 12: Oil Pan Bolt Tightening Sequence

OVERHAUL

CYLINDER HEAD

Cylinder Head – **1)** Ensure all mating surfaces are clean. Check camshaft-to-holder oil clearance. Cylinder head cannot be resurfaced if oil clearance is not within specification. See CAMSHAFT table under ENGINE SPECIFICATIONS.

2) Measure cylinder head warpage. Resurface cylinder head if warpage exceeds 0.002" (0.05 mm). If warpage is less than 0.002" (0.05 mm), resurfacing is not required. Maximum resurface limit is 0.008" (0.20 mm). Minimum refinish thickness is 3.927" (99.75 mm). Standard (new) cylinder head thickness is 3.935-3.939" (99.95-100.05 mm).

Valve Springs – Measure free length of valve springs. If spring free lengths are not within specification, replace valve springs. See VALVES & VALVE SPRINGS table under ENGINE SPECIFICATIONS.

Valve Stem Oil Seals – Intake and exhaust valve stem seals are not interchangeable. Intake valve stem seals have a White spring around neck of seal. Oil seals for exhaust valves have a Black spring around neck of seal.

Valve Guide Inspection – Measure valve guide clearance with a dial indicator placed on valve head. Zero dial indicator. Lift valve 0.4" (10 mm) from seat. Rock valve stem from side to side. Valve guides can be replaced if valve stem oil clearance is not within specification. See CYLINDER HEAD table under ENGINE SPECIFICATIONS.

Valve Guide Removal – **1)** Use a hot plate or oven to heat cylinder head to 300°F (150°C). To remove valve guides, use Valve Guide Driver (07742-0010100), or fabricate valve guide remover from an air-impact chisel. *See Fig. 13.* Using an air hammer and valve guide remover, drive valve guide 5/64" (2 mm) toward combustion chamber.

CAUTION: DO NOT heat cylinder head with a torch, as head may warp. DO NOT heat cylinder head hotter than 300°F (150°C). Excessive heat may loosen valve seats.

2) Turn head over. Working from combustion chamber side of head, drive valve guide out toward camshaft side of head. If valve guide does not move, drill valve guide using a 5/16" bit, then try to drive it out again.

CAUTION: Drill guides in extreme cases only. Cylinder head damage can occur if valve guide breaks.

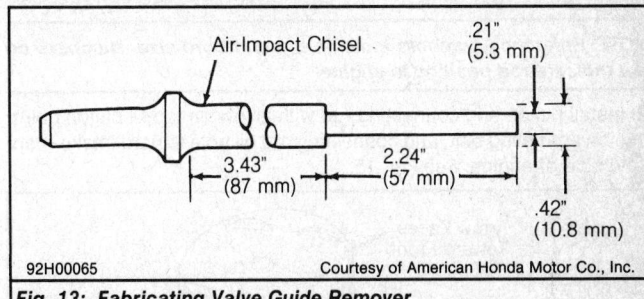

92H00065   Courtesy of American Honda Motor Co., Inc.

Fig. 13: Fabricating Valve Guide Remover

Valve Guide Installation – **1)** Chill new valve guides in freezer for about one hour. Remove new valve guides from freezer as needed. Slip a 15/64" (6 mm) steel washer over valve guide driver.

2) Intake valve guide installed height must be 0.974-0.994" (24.75-25.25 mm). Exhaust valve guide installed height must be 0.632-0.652" (16.05-16.55 mm). Install new valve guides from camshaft side of cylinder head. Drive each guide into heated head to specified installed height.

3) If replacing all valve guides, reheat cylinder head as necessary. Using cutting oil, ream new valve guides by rotating Valve Guide Reamer (07HAH-PJ7010A or 07HAH-PJ7010B) clockwise the full length of valve guide bore.

4) Continue rotating reamer clockwise while removing it from bore. Wash guide in detergent and water to remove any cutting oil residue. Measure valve stem-to-guide oil clearance. See CYLINDER HEAD table under ENGINE SPECIFICATIONS.

NOTE: Always reface valve seat after replacing valve guide.

Valve Seat – Valve seat replacement procedure is not available from manufacturer.

Seat Correction Angles – Replace valve guides, if necessary, before performing replacement before refacing valve seats. After refacing, if seat width is too wide, use 60-degree stone to raise seat, or 30-degree stone to lower seat. Ensure valve seat width is within specification. See CYLINDER HEAD table under ENGINE SPECIFICATIONS.

Valve Stem Installed Height – After servicing valves, measure valve stem installed height. *See Fig. 14.* If valve stem installed height exceeds 1.947" (49.465 mm) for any intake valve, or 2.048" (52.035 mm) for any exhaust valve, replace valve. If valve stem installed height still exceeds limit, replace cylinder head.

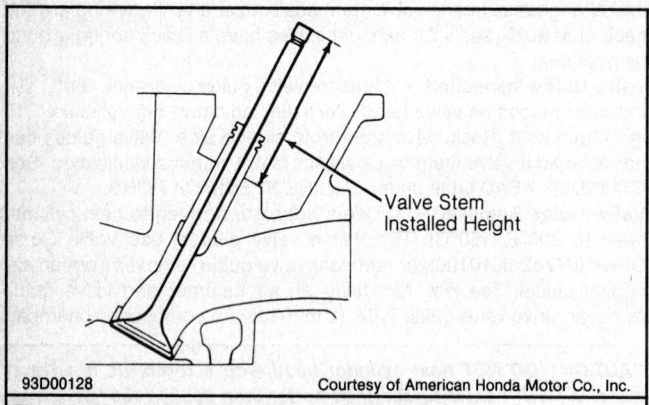

93D00128   Courtesy of American Honda Motor Co., Inc.

Fig. 14: Measuring Valve Stem Installed Height

CYLINDER BLOCK ASSEMBLY

Piston & Rod Assembly – 1) Each rod is sorted into one of 4 tolerance ranges. Size depends on crank journal bore. A number between 1 and 5 is stamped on side of rod's big end. Any combination of numbers between 1 and 5 may be found in engine. Ensure connecting rod crankpin bore and side play are within specification. See CONNECTING RODS table under ENGINE SPECIFICATIONS.

NOTE: Reference numbers indicate big end bore size. Numbers do not indicate rod position in engine.

2) Install piston and connecting rod with arrow on top of piston pointing toward timing belt, and connecting rod oil hole toward intake manifold side of engine. *See Fig. 15.*

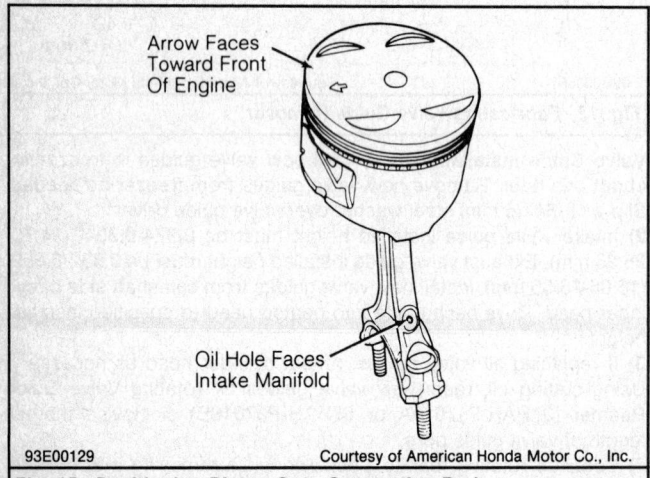

Arrow Faces Toward Front Of Engine

Oil Hole Faces Intake Manifold

93E00129   Courtesy of American Honda Motor Co., Inc.

Fig. 15: Positioning Piston Onto Connecting Rod

Piston Pin Removal – 1) Install Piston Base Head (07HAF-PL20102) and Piston Pin Base Insert (07GAF-PH60300) into Base (07973-6570500). Turn handle on Piston Pin Driver (07973-PE00320) so piston driver length is 2.03" (51.5 mm). *See Fig. 16.*

2) Insert Piston Driver Shaft (07973-PE00310) into Pilot Collar (07GAF-PH70100). Place piston onto base with embossed side facing up. Press out piston pin. Align recessed part of piston with lips on collar.

NOTE: All replacement piston pins are oversize.

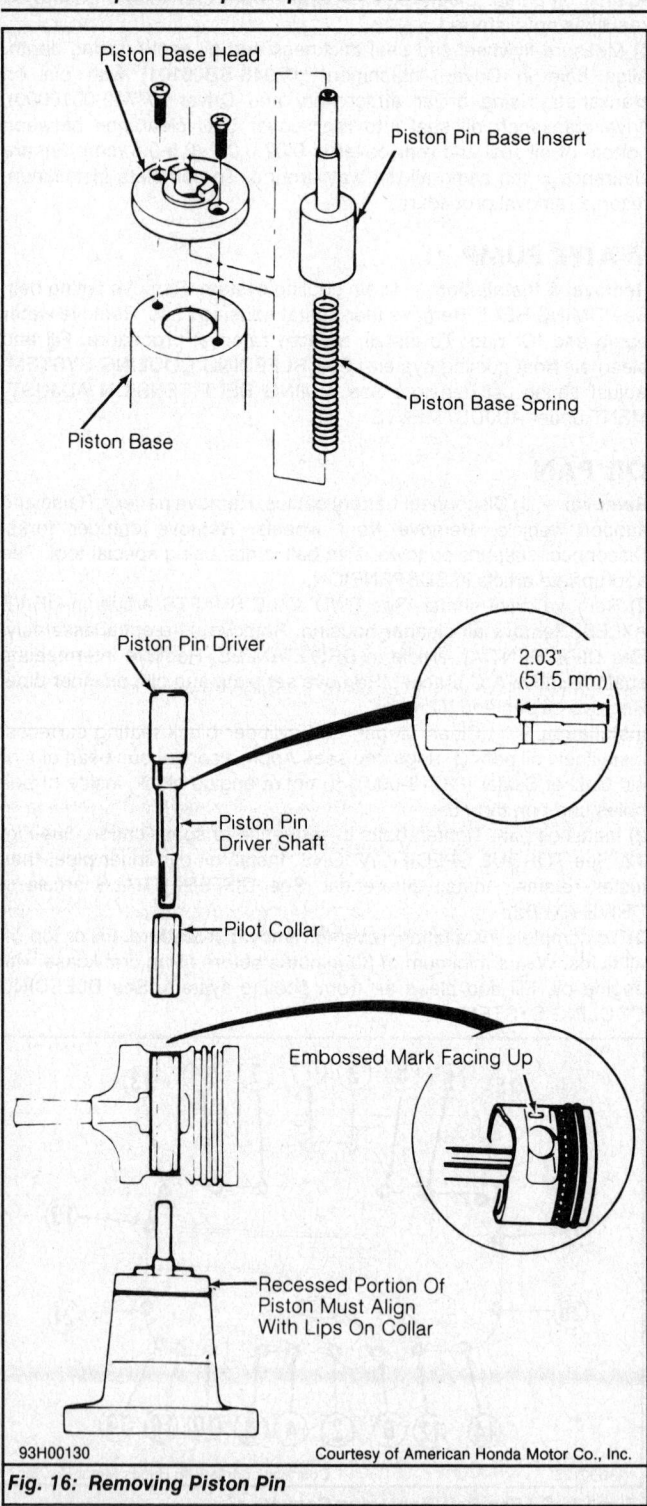

Piston Base Head

Piston Pin Base Insert

Piston Base Spring

Piston Base

Piston Pin Driver

2.03" (51.5 mm)

Piston Pin Driver Shaft

Pilot Collar

Embossed Mark Facing Up

Recessed Portion Of Piston Must Align With Lips On Collar

93H00130   Courtesy of American Honda Motor Co., Inc.

Fig. 16: Removing Piston Pin

Piston Pin Inspection – 1) Measure diameter of piston pin. Measure diameter of piston pin bore in piston. Piston pin clearance is difference between the 2 measurements.

2) Piston pin clearance must be 0.0005-0.0009" (0.013-0.024 mm). If piston pin clearance is greater than 0.0009" (0.024 mm), install an oversize piston pin and recheck clearance.

3) Determine difference between piston pin diameter and connecting rod small end bore. Interference fit between piston pin and connecting rod must be 0.0005-0.0013" (0.013-0.032 mm).

3) If oil clearance is still incorrect, try the next larger or smaller bearing. Measure oil clearance again. If changing bearing size still does not give proper oil clearance, replace crankshaft and repeat procedure.

NOTE: A number code, indicating connecting rod bore, is stamped on side of each connecting rod and cap. Code (letters) for connecting rod journal is stamped on crankshaft counterweight pad. See Fig. 18. Use both codes when ordering replacement bearings.

Crankshaft & Main Bearings – 1) Loosen main bearing cap bolts in sequence. *See Fig 19*. Remove all connecting rod and main bearing caps. Mark all bearing caps for reassembly reference. Lift crankshaft from block, being careful not to damage journals.

2) Using a lathe or "V" blocks to support crankshaft, measure crankshaft runout, out-of-round and taper. If any measurement exceeds service limit, replace crankshaft. See CRANKSHAFT, MAIN & CONNECTING ROD BEARINGS table under ENGINE SPECIFICATIONS.

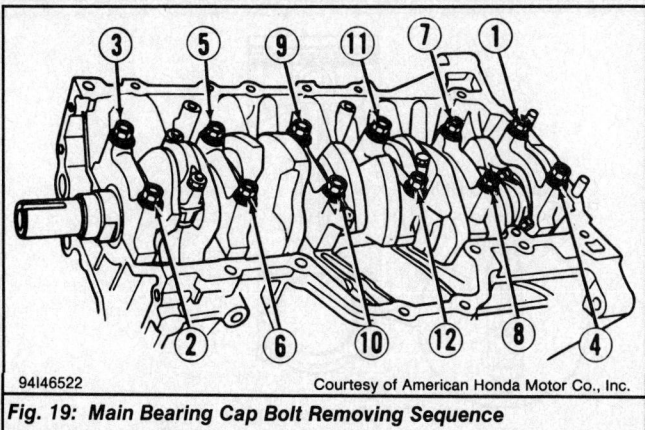

Fig. 19: *Main Bearing Cap Bolt Removing Sequence*

3) Install crankshaft into block. Measure main bearing oil clearance using Plastigage. If engine is in vehicle, support counterweights, and measure only one bearing at a time. Tighten main bearing caps to specification in 2 steps, in sequence. *See Fig. 20*. See TORQUE SPECIFICATION.

4) If oil clearance is not within specification, install a new bearing set (same color code) and recheck oil clearance. See CRANKSHAFT, MAIN & CONNECTING ROD BEARINGS table. DO NOT shim or file caps to adjust clearance.

5) If oil clearance is still incorrect, try next larger or smaller bearing and measure oil clearance once more. If changing bearing size still does not give proper oil clearance, replace crankshaft and repeat procedure.

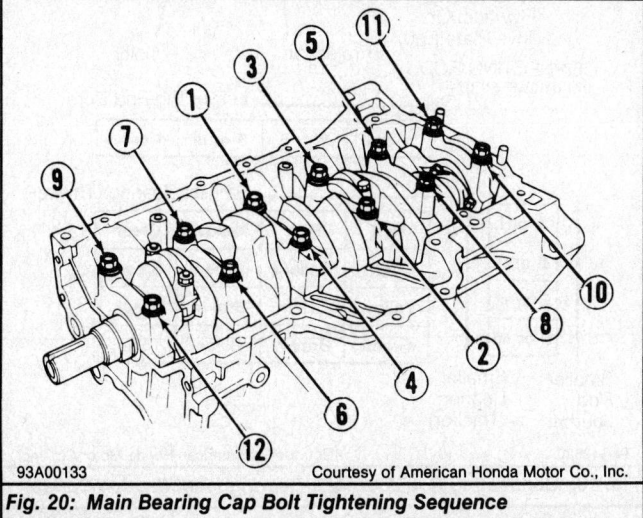

Fig. 20: *Main Bearing Cap Bolt Tightening Sequence*

NOTE: A letter code, indicating main journal bore, is stamped on cylinder block. Code for crankshaft main journal is stamped on crankshaft counterweight pad. Use both codes when ordering replacement bearings. See Fig. 21.

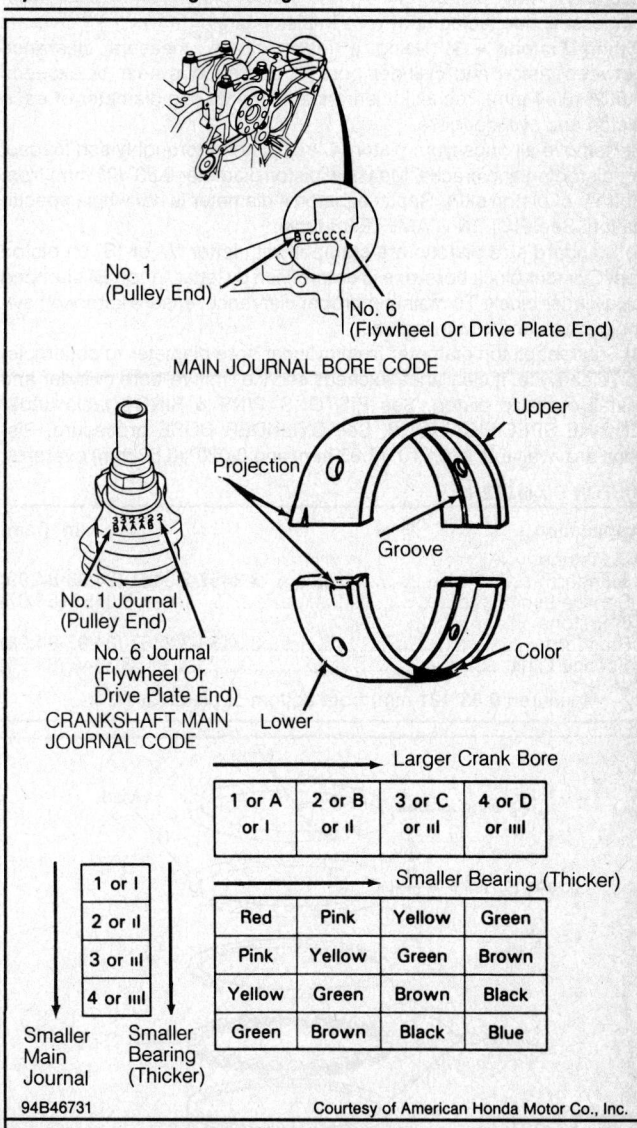

Fig. 21: *Crankshaft Main Journal & Bearing Identification Codes*

Thrust Bearing – 1) Measure crankshaft end play using dial indicator. If end play exceeds specification, inspect thrust washers and thrust surface of crankshaft. See CRANKSHAFT, MAIN & CONNECTING ROD BEARINGS table under ENGINE SPECIFICATIONS. Replace worn parts as necessary.

2) Thrust washer thickness is fixed. DO NOT change thrust washer thickness by grinding or shimming. Install thrust washers with grooved side out.

Cylinder Block – 1) Measure cylinder out-of-round and taper. If out-of-round or taper exceeds specification, re-bore cylinder for oversize pistons. See CYLINDER BLOCK table under ENGINE SPECIFICATIONS. If any cylinder bore exceeds oversize bore limit, replace cylinder block.

2) Cylinders can be bored 0.010" (0.25 mm) and 0.020" (0.50 mm) oversize. Maximum re-bore size is 0.020" (0.50 mm). Check piston-to-cylinder bore clearance after re-boring. See FITTING PISTONS procedure.

3) Using feeler gauge and straightedge, measure cylinder block deck surface warpage. Replace cylinder block if warped beyond service limit. See CYLINDER BLOCK table.

Piston Pin Installation – 1) Position piston and connecting rod as shown. *See Fig. 15.* Turn handle on Piston Pin Driver (07973-PE00320) so piston driver length is 2.03" (51.5 mm). *See Fig. 16.*

2) Install Pilot Collar (07GAF-PH70100) into piston and connecting rod. Lubricate new piston pin lightly. Place piston onto base with embossed side facing up. Press in piston pin.

Fitting Pistons – 1) Using a feeler gauge, measure clearance between piston and cylinder bore. If clearance is near or exceeds 0.002" (0.04 mm), recheck clearance by measuring diameter of each piston and cylinder bore.

2) Remove all rings from piston. Clean piston thoroughly and inspect for distortion and cracks. Measure piston diameter 0.83" (21 mm) from bottom of piston skirt. Replace piston if diameter is not within specification. See PISTON DIAMETERS table.

3) Standard size pistons are stamped with letter "A" or "B" on piston top. Cylinder block bore size is determined by letter "A" or "B" stamped on cylinder block. To maintain proper clearance, ensure letters on cylinder block and piston match.

4) Subtract piston diameter from cylinder bore diameter to obtain piston clearance. If clearance exceeds service limit, re-bore cylinder and install oversize piston. See PISTONS, PINS & RINGS table under ENGINE SPECIFICATIONS. See CYLINDER BORE procedure. Pistons are available in 0.010" (0.25 mm) and 0.020" (0.50 mm) oversize.

PISTON DIAMETERS [1]

Application	In. (mm)
"A" Pistons	
Standard	3.3457-3.3461 (84.98-84.99)
Service Limit	3.3453 (84.97)
"B" Pistons	
Standard	3.3453-3.3457 (84.97-84.98)
Service Limit	3.3449 (84.96)

[1] – Measured 0.83" (21 mm) from bottom of piston skirt.

Piston Rings – 1) Using inverted piston, push new piston ring into cylinder bore 0.6-0.8" (15-20 mm) from bottom. Measure piston ring end gap using a feeler gauge. Repeat procedure for each ring.

2) If gap is too small, ensure ring size is correct. If gap is too large, check cylinder bore diameter and re-bore if necessary. See CYLINDER BORE procedure. See PISTONS, PINS & RINGS table under ENGINE SPECIFICATIONS.

3) Clean piston ring grooves thoroughly. Install piston rings with identification mark toward top of piston. Using a feeler gauge, measure piston ring side clearance between ring and ring groove.

4) If ring grooves are excessively worn, replace piston. See PISTONS, PINS & RINGS table. Align piston ring end gaps properly on piston. *See Fig. 17.*

Rod Bearings – 1) Using Plastigage, measure rod bearing oil clearance. Tighten bearing cap to 24 ft. lbs. (33 N.m).

2) If oil clearance is incorrect, install a new bearing set (same color code) and recheck oil clearance. DO NOT shim or file cap to adjust oil clearance.

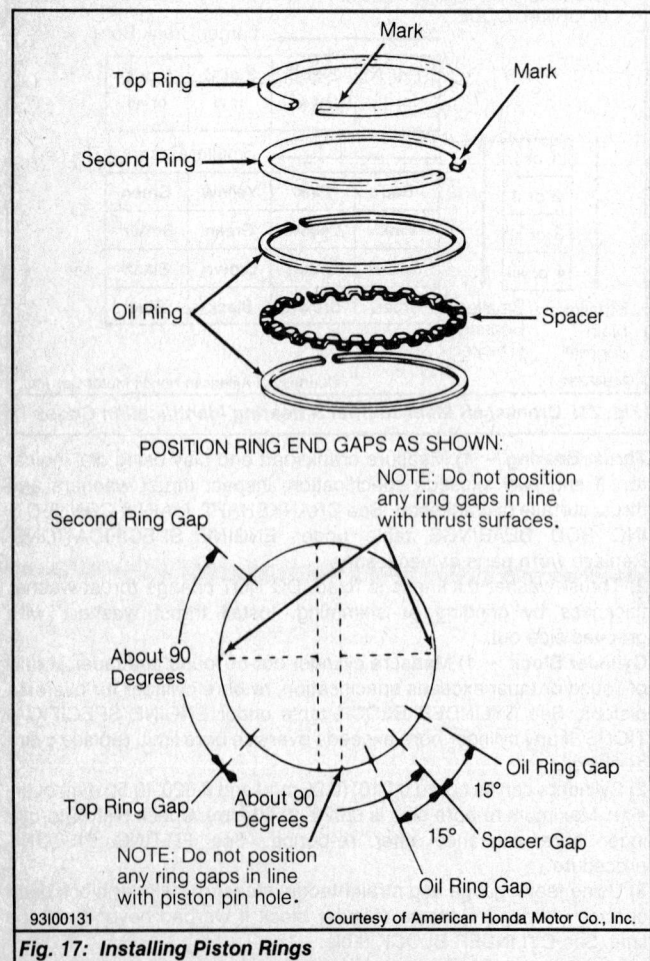

Fig. 17: *Installing Piston Rings*

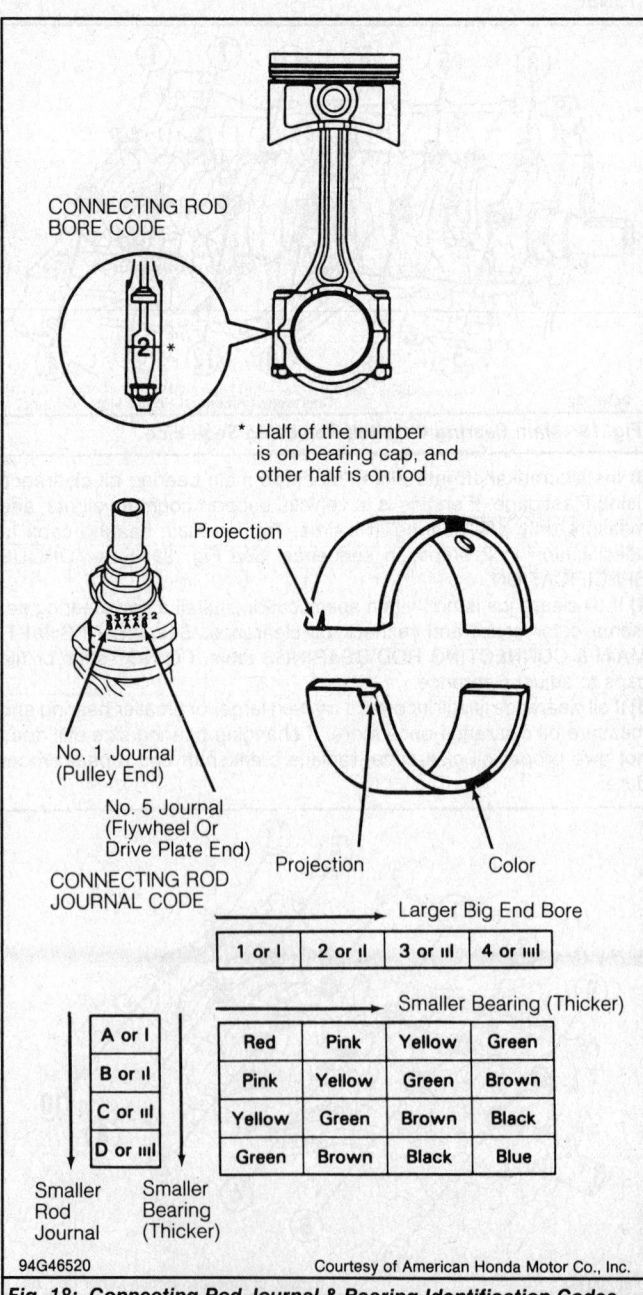

Fig. 18: *Connecting Rod Journal & Bearing Identification Codes*

4) If reusing cylinder block, hone cylinders to a 60-degree crosshatch pattern using 400-grit or finer stone. After honing, re-measure cylinder bores. Wash cylinder bore with hot soapy water. Air-dry cylinder bore, and apply engine oil to prevent rusting.

ENGINE OILING

ENGINE LUBRICATION SYSTEM

A rotor-type oil pump draws oil from oil pan and delivers it under pressure to main and connecting rod bearings. An oil hole in each connecting rod supplies oil to thrust side of piston and cylinder wall. An oil passage carries oil to camshaft and rocker arms. Oil spray lubricates valve stems.

Oil Pressure – Minimum oil pressure with engine at idle (hot) should be 10 psi (0.7 kg/cm²). Minimum oil pressure at 3000 RPM should be 50 psi (3.5 kg/cm²).

OIL PUMP

Removal & Disassembly – 1) Raise and support vehicle. Drain engine oil and differential oil. Remove spark plugs. Rotate crankshaft clockwise until No. 1 piston is at TDC of compression stroke. Remove timing belt. See TIMING BELT under REMOVAL & INSTALLATION. Remove oil pan. See OIL PAN under REMOVAL & INSTALLATION.
2) Remove oil pump screen. Remove oil pump assembly. Separate pump cover from pump housing. Using a screwdriver, pry oil seal from oil pump housing.
Inspection – Measure inner rotor-to-outer rotor radial clearance. Measure housing-to-rotor clearance. Measure housing-to-outer rotor radial clearance. Inspect rotors and pump housing for scoring or other defects. Replace components if not within specification or defective. See OIL PUMP SPECIFICATIONS table.

OIL PUMP SPECIFICATIONS

Application	In. (mm)
Inner Rotor-To-Outer Rotor	
Radial Clearance	
Standard	0.002-0.006 (0.04-0.16)
Service Limit	0.008 (0.20)
Housing-To-Outer Rotor	
Axial Clearance	
Standard	0.001-0.003 (0.02-0.07)
Service Limit	0.005 (0.12)
Housing-To-Outer Rotor	
Radial Clearance	
Standard	0.004-0.007 (0.10-0.18)
Service Limit	0.008 (0.20)

Reassembly & Installation – 1) Apply light coating of grease to crankshaft and lip of new seal. Using Seal Driver (07749-0010000) and Attachment (07746-0010400), install oil seal. Ensure seal is fully seated into oil pump housing.
2) Reassemble oil pump, applying Liquid Gasket Sealer (08718-0001) to pump housing cover. Ensure pump turns freely. Apply light coat of oil to lip of seal. Install dowel pins and new "O" ring into cylinder block. Clean oil pump and engine mating surfaces.
3) Apply liquid gasket sealer to cylinder block and oil pump mating surface. Apply liquid sealer to "O" ring grooves and inner threads of bolt holes. Install oil pump before liquid sealer dries. To complete installation, reverse removal procedure. Wait at least 30 minutes before filling crankcase with oil.

TORQUE SPECIFICATIONS

TORQUE SPECIFICATIONS

Application	Ft. Lbs. (N.m)
A/C Compressor Bolts	16 (22)
A/C Compressor Bracket Bolts	33 (45)
Alternator Bracket Bolts	33 (45)
Camshaft Bearing Cap Bolts [1]	
6-mm Bolts	[2]
8-mm Bolts	16 (22)

TORQUE SPECIFICATIONS (Cont.)

Application	Ft. Lbs. (N.m)
Camshaft Pulley Bolts	52 (70)
Clutch Slave Cylinder Bolts	16 (22)
Connecting Rod Cap Nuts	24 (33)
Crankshaft Pulley Bolt	184 (250)
Cylinder Head Bolts [3]	74 (100)
Engine Mounts	[4]
Engine Block-To-Transaxle Housing Bolts	
A/T	55 (75)
M/T	
With 26-mm Shim	55 (75)
Without 26-mm Shim	48 (65)
Exhaust Manifold	
Shroud Bolts	16 (22)
Nuts	23 (32)
Exhaust Pipe Flange Nuts	41 (55)
Flywheel Bolts [5]	77 (105)
Intake Manifold Bolts/Nuts	16 (22)
Main Bearing Cap Bolts [6]	
Stage 1	22 (30)
Stage 2	50 (68)
Oil Pan Bolts [7]	18 (24)
Oil Pump Housing Bolts	
6-mm Bolts	[2]
8-mm Bolts	16 (22)
Power Steering Pump Mount Bolt	33 (45)
Timing Belt Tension Adjuster Bolt	33 (45)
Torque Converter Drive Plate Bolts [5]	55 (75)

	INCH Lbs. (N.m)
Fuel Service Bolt	106 (12)
Oil Pump Screen Bolts	106 (12)
Speed Sensor Bolt	106 (12)
Timing Belt Cover Bolts	106 (12)
Valve Cover Bolts	106 (12)
Water Pump Bolts	106 (12)

[1] – Tighten bolts 2 turns at a time in sequence until camshaft is seated. Then tighten to specification in sequence. *See Fig. 10.*
[2] – Tighten to 106 INCH lbs. (12 N.m).
[3] – Tighten in sequence, in 2 or 3 steps. *See Fig. 6.*
[4] – Tighten in sequence to specification. *See Fig. 4.*
[5] – Tighten in a crisscross pattern.
[6] – Tighten in sequence. *See Fig. 20.*
[7] – Tighten in sequence. *See Fig. 12.*

ENGINE SPECIFICATIONS

GENERAL SPECIFICATIONS

Application	Specification
Displacement	150 Cu. In. (2.5L)
Bore	3.35" (85 mm)
Stroke	3.40" (86.4 mm)
Compression Ratio	9.0:1
Fuel System	SFI
Horsepower @ RPM	176 @ 6300
Torque Ft. Lbs. @ RPM	170 @ 3900

CONNECTING RODS

Application	In. (mm)
Bore Diameter	
Crankpin Bore	1.89 (48.00)
Side Play	
Standard	0.006-0.012 (0.15-0.30)
Service Limit	0.016 (0.40)

1994 ENGINES
2.5L 5-Cylinder (Cont.)

CRANKSHAFT, MAIN & CONNECTING ROD BEARINGS

Application	In. (mm)
Crankshaft	
End Play	
Standard	0.004-0.014 (0.10-0.35)
Service Limit	0.018 (0.45)
Maximum Journal Out-Of-Round	0.0004 (0.010)
Maximum Journal Taper	0.0004 (0.010)
Maximum Runout	0.002 (0.06)
Main Bearings	
Journal Diameter	2.1644-2.1654 (54.976-55.000)
Oil Clearance	
Standard	0.0007-0.0019 (0.018-0.048)
Service Limit	0.002 (0.053)
Connecting Rod Bearings	
Journal Diameter	1.7707-1.7717 (44.976-45.000)
Oil Clearance	
Standard	0.0006-0.0017 (0.015-0.043)
Service Limit	0.002 (0.05)

PISTONS, PINS & RINGS

Application	In. (mm)
Pistons	
Clearance	
Standard	0.0004-0.0016 (0.01-0.04)
Service Limit	0.002 (0.05)
Diameter	
Standard [1]	
"A" Piston	3.3457-3.3461 (84.98-84.99)
"B" Piston	3.3453-3.3457 (84.97-84.98)
Piston Pins	
Diameter	0.8659-0.8661 (21.994-22.000)
Piston Fit	0.0005-0.0009 (0.012-0.024)
Rod Interference Fit	0.0005-0.0013 (0.013-0.032)
Rings	
No. 1	
End Gap	
Standard	0.008-0.014 (0.20-0.35)
Service Limit	0.024 (0.60)
Side Clearance	0.0014-0.0024 (0.035-0.060)
No. 2	
End Gap	
Standard	0.016-0.022 (0.40-0.55)
Service Limit	0.028 (0.70)
Side Clearance	0.0012-0.0022 (0.030-0.055)
No. 3 (Oil)	
End Gap	
Standard	0.008-0.028 (0.20-0.70)
Service Limit	0.031 (0.80)

[1] – Piston identification letter is located on top of piston.

CYLINDER BLOCK

Application	In. (mm)
Cylinder Bore	
Diameter [1]	3.3465-3.3472 (85.000-85.020)
Maximum Taper	0.002 (0.05)
Deck Warpage	
Standard	0.003 (0.07)
Service Limit	0.004 (0.10)

[1] – Standard bore size is identified by "A" or "B" stamped on cylinder block deck surface.

VALVES & VALVE SPRINGS

Application	Specification
Intake Valves	
Face Angle	45°
Head Diameter	1.33-1.34" (33.9-34.1 mm)
Margin	
Standard	0.033-045" (0.85-1.15 mm)
Service Limit	0.026" (0.65 mm)
Stem Diameter	
Standard	0.2156-0.2159" (5.475-5.485 mm)
Service Limit	0.2144" (5.445 mm)
Valve Length	4.365-4.377" (110.88-111.18 mm)
Valve Stem Installed Height	
Standard	1.9191-1.9376" (48.745-49.215 mm)
Service Limit	1.9474" (49.465 mm)
Exhaust Valves	
Face Angle	45°
Head Diameter	1.14-1.15" (28.9-29.1 mm)
Margin	
Standard	0.061-073" (1.55-1.85 mm)
Service Limit	0.053" (1.36 mm)
Valve Length	4.848-4.860" (123.15-123.45 mm)
Stem Diameter	
Standard	0.2146-0.2150" (5.450-5.460 mm)
Service Limit	0.2134" (5.420 mm)
Valve Stem Installed Height	
Standard	2.0203-2.0238" (51.315-51.785 mm)
Service Limit	2.049" (52.035 mm)
Valve Springs	
Free Length	
Intake	2.052" (52.12 mm)
Exhaust	2.208" (56.08 mm)

CYLINDER HEAD

Application	Specification
Cylinder Head Height	3.935-3.939" (99.95-100.05 mm)
Maximum Warpage [1]	0.002" (0.05 mm)
Valve Seats	
Intake & Exhaust	
Seat Angle	45°
Seat Width	
Standard	0.049-0.061" (1.25-1.55 mm)
Service Limit	0.079" (2.00 mm)
Valve Guides	
Intake	
Valve Guide I.D.	0.2167-0.2173" (5.505-5.520 mm)
Valve Guide Installed Height	0.974-0.994" (24.75-25.25 mm)
Exhaust	
Valve Guide I.D.	0.217-0.218" (5.51-5.53 mm)
Valve Guide Installed Height	0.632-0.652" (16.05-16.55 mm)
Valve Stem-To-Guide Oil Clearance	
Intake	
Standard	0.0008-0.0018 (0.02-0.045 mm)
Service Limit	0.003 (0.075)
Exhaust	
Standard	0.002-0.003 (0.05-0.08 mm)
Service Limit	0.005 (0.12)

[1] – Maximum resurface limit is 0.008" (0.20 mm). Minimum cylinder head thickness is 3.927" (99.75 mm).

CAMSHAFT

Application	In. (mm)
End Play	0.002-0.006 (0.05-0.15)
Journal Runout	0.001 (0.03)
Lobe Height	
Intake	1.5434 (39.203)
Exhaust	1.5305 (38.875)
Oil Clearance	0.002-0.0035 (0.05-0.09)

Legend

NOTE: For repair procedures not covered in this article, see ENGINE OVERHAUL PROCEDURES article in GENERAL INFORMATION.

ENGINE IDENTIFICATION

Engine identification code is located on left front side of engine block, below cylinder head mating surface. First 5 characters of code indicate engine type. California models have number 40 or 41 as the sixth and seventh characters. Federal models have number 43 or 44 as the sixth and seventh characters. Last 5 digits of engine code indicate engine serial number.

ENGINE IDENTIFICATION CODES

Application	Code
3.2L	C32A1

ADJUSTMENTS

VALVE CLEARANCE ADJUSTMENT

NOTE: The 3.2L engine uses hydraulic valve lifters. Valve clearance adjustment is not necessary.

THROTTLE CABLE ADJUSTMENT

1) With engine at normal operating temperature, check throttle cable for binding and sticking. Repair as necessary. Check cable free play at throttle linkage.

2) Cable deflection should be 0.39-0.47" (10-12 mm). *See Fig. 1.* If deflection is not within specification, loosen lock nut and turn adjuster nut until deflection is within specification. With throttle cable properly adjusted, recheck throttle operation.

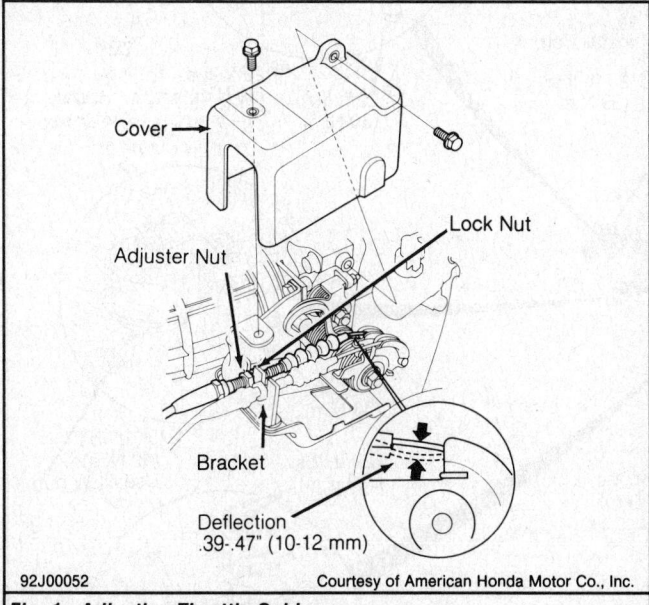

92J00052   Courtesy of American Honda Motor Co., Inc.

Fig. 1: Adjusting Throttle Cable

TIMING BELT TENSION ADJUSTMENT

CAUTION: Adjust timing belt with engine cold. DO NOT rotate crankshaft while belt tension adjuster bolt is loose.

Remove upper left camshaft cover. Remove damper from center bracket. Rotate crankshaft clockwise until No. 1 piston is at TDC of compression stroke. Rotate crankshaft 9 teeth clockwise on crankshaft pulley. Align Blue mark on crankshaft pulley with pointer on lower cover. *See Fig. 2.* Loosen tensioner adjusting bolt 1/2 turn (180°), and then tighten bolt to 32 ft. lbs. (43 N.m).

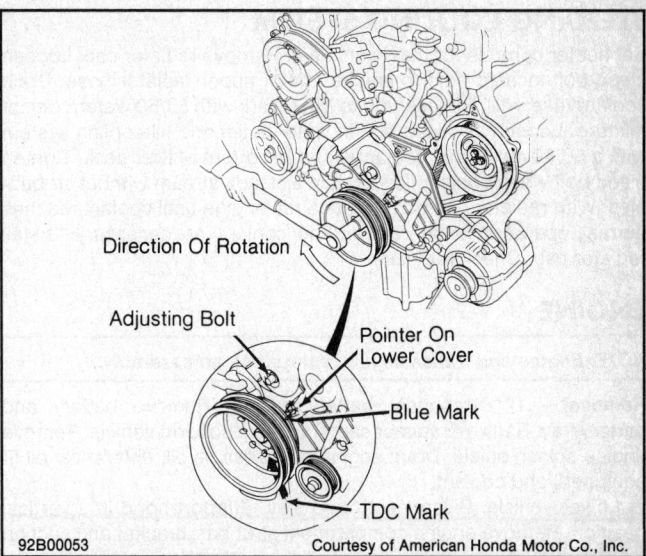

92B00053   Courtesy of American Honda Motor Co., Inc.

Fig. 2: Aligning Timing Marks For Timing Belt Tension Adjustment

REMOVAL & INSTALLATION

NOTE: For reassembly reference, label all electrical connectors, vacuum hoses and fuel lines before removal. Also place mating marks on other major assemblies before removal.

NOTE: Radio/cassette or radio/CD player is equipped with an anti-theft protection circuit. Whenever battery is disconnected, radio will go into anti-theft mode. When battery is reconnected, radio will display CODE, and will be inoperative until proper code number is entered. Obtain code number before disconnecting battery.

FUEL PRESSURE RELEASE

CAUTION: Fuel system is under pressure. Pressure must be released before servicing fuel system components.

Disconnect negative battery cable. Remove fuel tank filler cap. Place shop towel over fuel filter to absorb excess fuel. Slowly loosen fuel injection 6-mm service bolt one complete turn while holding banjo bolt. *See Fig. 3.* Fuel filter is located next to brake booster.

NOTE: Replace washer between service bolt and banjo bolt whenever service bolt is loosened. Replace all washers if both bolts are removed.

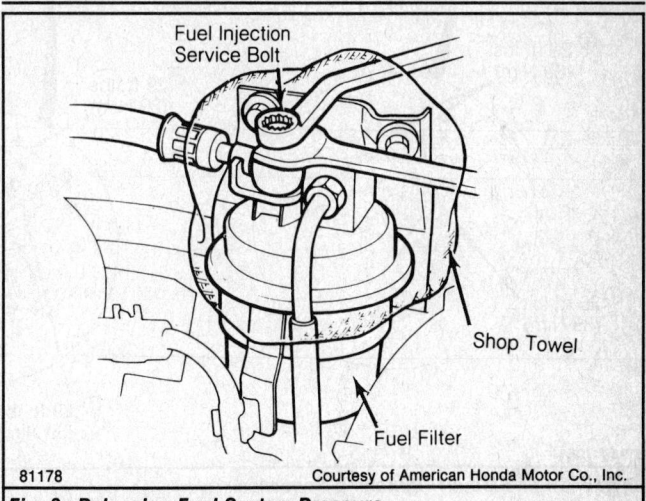

81178   Courtesy of American Honda Motor Co., Inc.

Fig. 3: Releasing Fuel System Pressure

1994 ENGINES
3.2L V6 (Cont.)

BLEEDING COOLING SYSTEM

Set heater controls for maximum heat. Remove radiator cap. Loosen bleed bolt located next to engine end of upper radiator hose. Drain coolant reservoir. Fill reservoir to MAX mark with 50/50 water/coolant mixture. Loosen air bleed bolt in water outlet, and fill cooling system with a 50/50 mixture of coolant/water to bottom of filler neck. Tighten bleed bolt when coolant flows out in a steady stream without air bubbles. With radiator cap off, start and run engine until coolant reaches normal operating temperature. Add coolant as necessary. Install radiator cap. Check for leaks

ENGINE

NOTE: Engine and transaxle are removed as an assembly.

Removal – 1) Disconnect battery cables. Remove battery and battery tray. Remove radiator cap. Raise and support vehicle. Remove engine splash shield. Drain engine oil, transaxle oil, differential oil (if equipped) and coolant.
2) Lower vehicle. Disconnect hood stay. Support hood in a vertical position. Remove engine compartment strut bar, bracket and suction pipe clamp. Unplug all necessary engine wiring harness connectors. Remove ground cable from cylinder block. Disconnect battery cable at

starter. Remove underhood relay box. Remove throttle cover. Remove throttle cable and cruise control cable. DO NOT bend cables. Replace cable if kinked.
3) Remove air cleaner and air duct. Unplug ignitor connector. Disconnect engine ground cable. Remove emission control box from firewall, leaving vacuum hoses connected. Release fuel pressure. See FUEL PRESSURE RELEASE. Disconnect fuel inlet and return hoses. Disconnect brake booster vacuum hose. Disconnect fuel vapor purge hose.
4) Unplug wiring harness connector at left rear of engine compartment. Remove necessary coolant hoses. Remove radiator, shroud, and fans as an assembly. Remove vacuum pipe, by-pass low and high control solenoid valves and vacuum tank. On Sedan GS and Coupe models, remove Traction Control System (TCS) lower bracket from Power Steering (P/S) bracket and TCS control valve assembly. On all models, remove P/S pump belt and pump, leaving hoses attached. Set power steering pump aside.
5) Raise and support vehicle. Remove front wheels. Remove damper forks. Disconnect lower arm ball joints using special tools. See appropriate article in SUSPENSION. Carefully pry drive shaft assembly straight out to avoid damaging differential oil seal or intermediate shaft dust seal. DO NOT pull on drive shaft, as CV joint may come apart. Suspend drive shafts aside with rope.

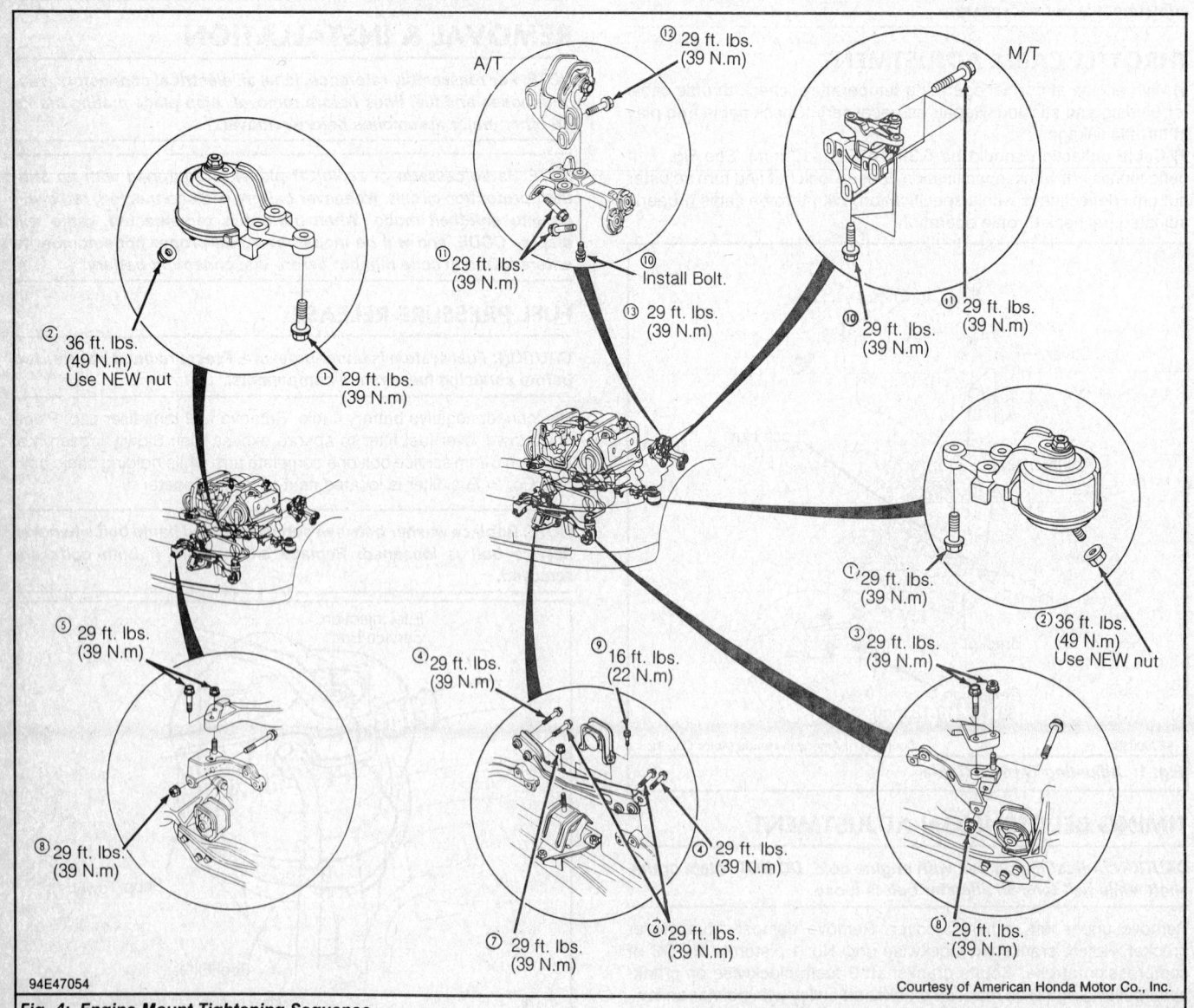

94E47054

Fig. 4: Engine Mount Tightening Sequence

NOTE: Coat all precision finished surfaces with clean engine oil or grease. Tie plastic bags over drive shaft ends.

6) Remove lower plate from rear crossmember, then retighten steering gear bolts. Remove vehicle speed sensor and P/S speed sensor, leaving hoses attached. Remove 3-way catalytic converter and heat shields. On Sedan GS and Coupe models, remove exhaust pipe and the warm-up 3-way catalytic converter. On all models, remove exhaust pipe covers, exhaust pipe and joint pipe assembly.

7) Remove A/C compressor belt and compressor, leaving hoses attached. On A/T models, disconnect shift control cable from transaxle. Remove rear transaxle mounting bracket. On M/T models, remove clutch slave cylinder, leaving hoses attached. Slide pin retainer back, and use a 5/16" pin punch to disconnect transaxle shift rod. Disconnect shift lever torque rod from rear of engine.

8) On all models, remove nuts and bolts from middle engine mounts. Lower hoist. Remove engine right and left brackets. Remove damper and engine center bracket. Remove EGR through-bolt and install a hook. Attach chain hoist to engine. Raise hoist to remove slack from chain.

9) Ensure all wiring harness connectors, vacuum, fuel, and coolant hoses affecting engine removal are disconnected. Slowly raise engine. Remove engine and transaxle assembly. DO NOT bend suction pipe.

Installation – 1) To install, reverse removal procedure. Tighten engine mounts in specified sequence. *See Fig. 4.* Improper engine mount tightening will result in excessive engine vibration and premature engine mount wear.

2) When installing drive shafts, use new spring clips. Insert each drive shaft until spring clip clicks into groove of differential side gear. Ensure all wire harness connectors and hoses are connected properly. Check throttle cable adjustment. See THROTTLE CABLE ADJUSTMENT under ADJUSTMENTS.

3) On manual transaxle, adjust clutch pedal free play. Verify transaxle shifts smoothly. On automatic transaxle, adjust transaxle range indicator to agree with actual drive range.

4) On all models, adjust accessory drive belt tension. Fill all fluids to proper level. Bleed air from cooling system. See COOLING SYSTEM BLEEDING.

INTAKE MANIFOLD

NOTE: Reference mark all emission hoses before disconnecting. Release fuel pressure before disconnecting fuel lines. See FUEL PRESSURE RELEASE.

Removal – 1) Allow engine to cool. Disconnect battery cables. Remove battery and battery tray. Remove throttle cover. Loosen throttle cable and cruise control cable lock nuts, and slip cable ends out of throttle bracket and throttle linkage. DO NOT bend cables. Replace cable if kinked. Remove air cleaner assembly and intake air duct.

2) Drain cooling system. Remove strut bar, bracket and suction pipe clamps. Disconnect engine ground wire and battery ground wire from cylinder head and cylinder block. Release fuel pressure. See FUEL PRESSURE RELEASE. Disconnect fuel feed hose from fuel filter. Disconnect fuel return hose from fuel pressure regulator. Disconnect brake booster vacuum hose.

3) Disconnect evaporative emission control canister hose from throttle body. Disconnect terminal and connectors, and remove underhood fuse/relay box. remove injector resistor and connector. Disconnect connectors, and remove ignition coils. Remove injector harness covers. *See Fig. 5.*

4) On right cylinder head, disconnect cylinders No. 1, 2 and 3 injector connectors. Disconnect Engine Coolant Temperature (ECT) sensor connector. Disconnect EGR valve lift sensor connector. On left cylinder head, disconnect cylinders No. 4, 5 and 6 injector connectors. Disconnect crank/cylinder sensor connector, ECT gauge sending unit connector and Intake Air Temperature (IAT) sensor connector. Disconnect left and right knock sensor connector.

5) Remove inlet air pipe. Remove vacuum pipes and hoses. On Sedan GS and Coupe models, remove Traction Control System (TCS) upper and lower brackets. Disconnect TCS throttle sensor and actuator connectors. Remove TCS control valve assembly.

6) On all models, remove Throttle Position (TP) sensor connectors. Remove left and right Heated Oxygen Sensors (HO2S). Remove clamps and engine wire harness. Remove breather pipe and EGR pipe. Remove intake manifold and coolant manifold as an assembly.

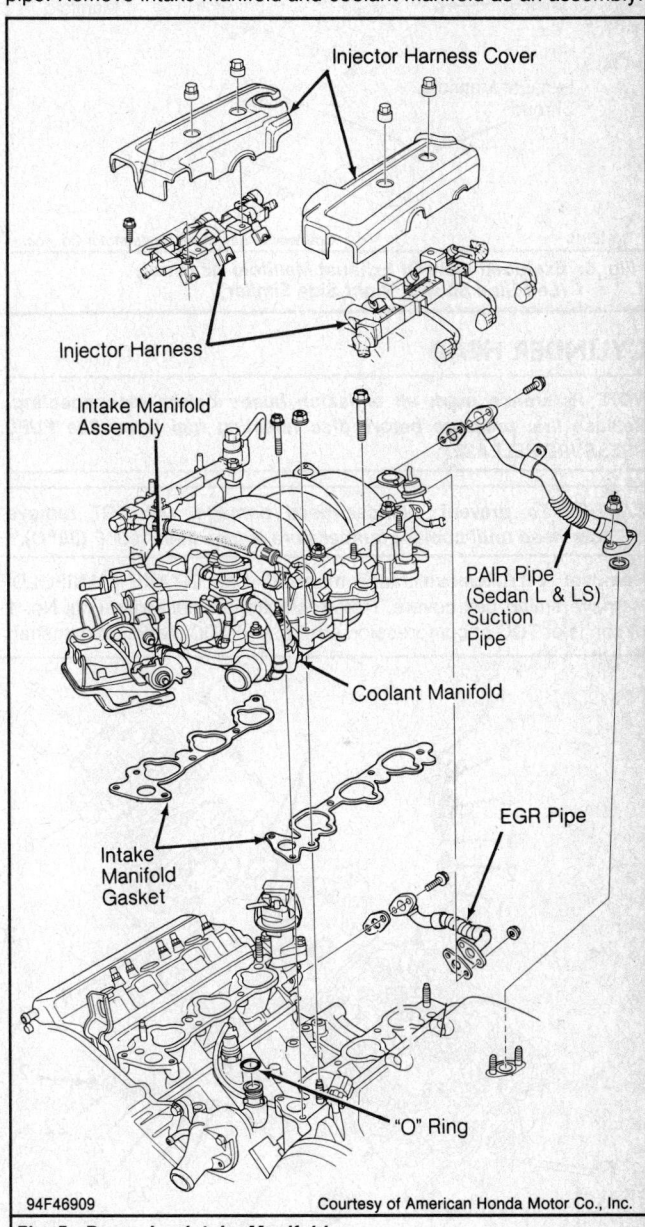

Injector Harness Cover

Injector Harness

Intake Manifold Assembly

PAIR Pipe (Sedan L & LS) Suction Pipe

Coolant Manifold

EGR Pipe

Intake Manifold Gasket

"O" Ring

94F46909   Courtesy of American Honda Motor Co., Inc.

Fig. 5: Removing Intake Manifold

Installation – 1) To install, reverse removal procedure. Clean intake manifold gasket mating surfaces. Install new gaskets and intake manifold. Install and tighten manifold bolts to specification. See TORQUE SPECIFICATIONS.

2) Check throttle cable adjustment. See THROTTLE CABLE ADJUSTMENT under ADJUSTMENTS. Fill and bleed air from cooling system. See COOLING SYSTEM BLEEDING.

EXHAUST MANIFOLD

Removal & Installation – Exhaust manifold removal and installation is part of cylinder head removal and installation. See CYLINDER HEAD. *See Fig. 6.*

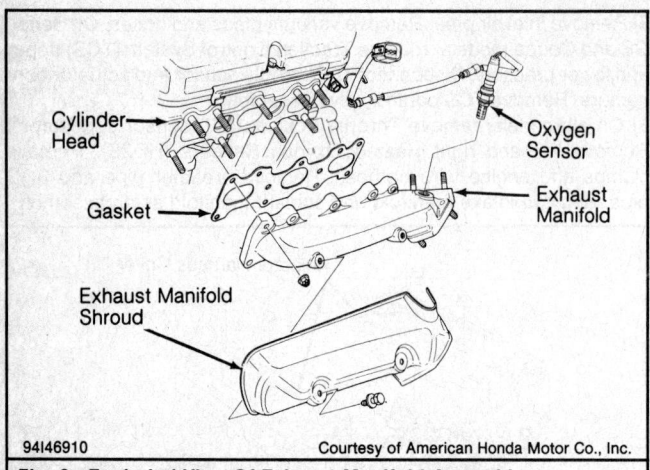

94I46910   Courtesy of American Honda Motor Co., Inc.

Fig. 6: Exploded View Of Exhaust Manifold Assembly (Left Side Shown; Right Side Similar)

CYLINDER HEAD

NOTE: Reference mark all emission hoses before disconnecting. Release fuel pressure before disconnecting fuel lines. See FUEL PRESSURE RELEASE.

CAUTION: To prevent cylinder head damage, DO NOT remove cylinder head until coolant temperature is less than 100°F (38°C).

Removal – 1) Remove intake manifold. See INTAKE MANIFOLD. Remove timing belt covers. Rotate crankshaft clockwise until No. 1 piston is at TDC of compression stroke, and TDC marks on camshaft

pulleys align with Yellow marks on cover plates. Loosen timing adjuster bolt 180 degrees. Push on right camshaft pulley to release belt tension, then retighten adjusting bolt. Disengage timing belt from camshaft pulleys. Remove camshaft pulleys. Remove timing belt cover plates.

2) If reusing timing belt, mark direction of belt rotation for installation reference. Remove crank/cylinder sensor from left cylinder head. Remove cylinder head covers. Remove 3 bolts from alternator bracket. Remove 2 bolts from power steering bracket.

CAUTION: DO NOT use air wrench or hammer to remove exhaust manifolds unless HO2S have been removed.

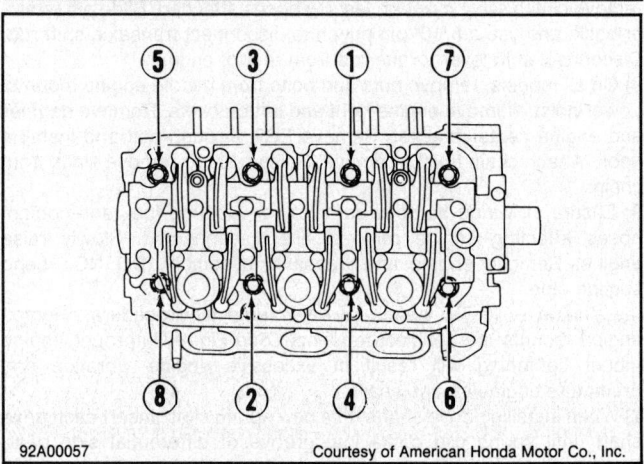

92A00057   Courtesy of American Honda Motor Co., Inc.

Fig. 7: Cylinder Head Bolt Tightening Sequence

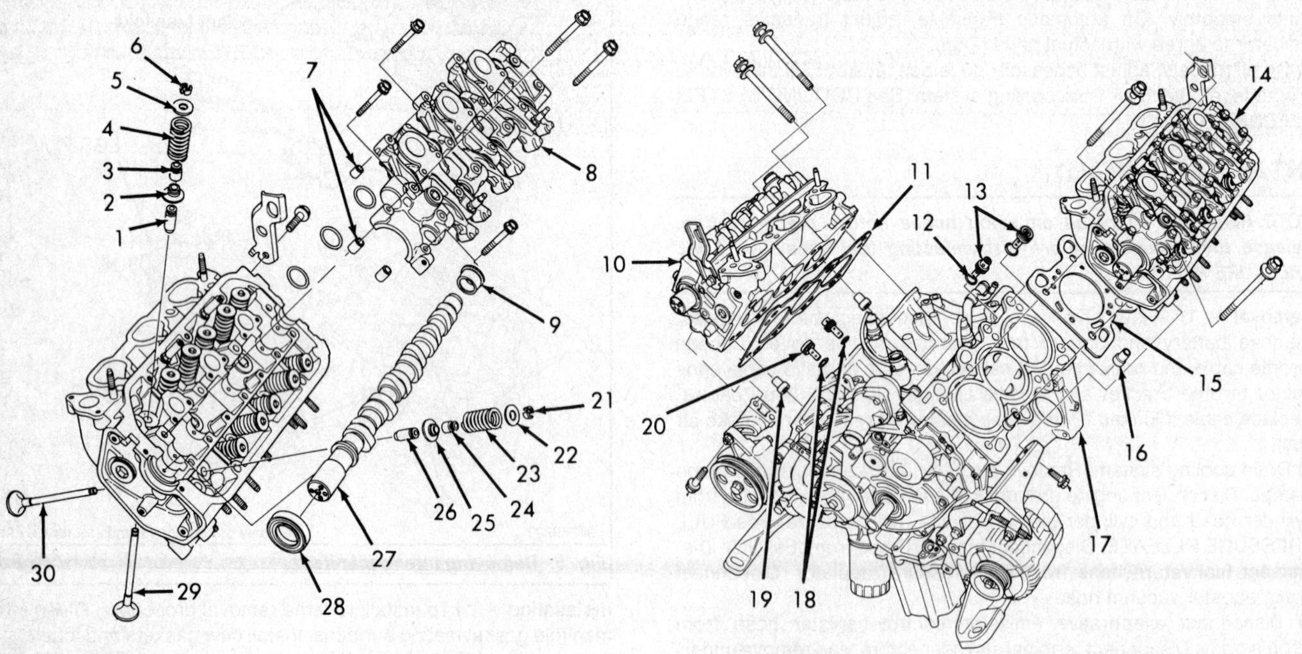

1. Valve Guide	9. Rubber Plug	17. Cylinder Block	24. Valve Stem Oil Seal
2. Spring Seat	10. Cylinder Head	18. "O" Ring	25. Spring Seat
3. Valve Stem Oil Seal	11. Head Gasket	19. Dowel Pin	26. Valve Guide
4. Intake Valve Spring	12. "O" Ring	20. Oil Control Orifice	27. Camshaft
5. Valve Spring Retainer	13. Oil Control Orifice	21. Valve Keepers	28. Camshaft Oil Seal
6. Valve Keepers	14. Cylinder Head	22. Valve Spring Retainer	29. Intake Valve
7. Dowel Pin	15. Head Gasket	23. Exhaust Valve Spring	30. Exhaust Valve
8. Rocker Arm Assembly	16. Dowel Pin		

94H46919   Courtesy of American Honda Motor Co., Inc.

Fig. 8: Exploded View Of Cylinder Head Components

3) Remove self-locking nuts on the warm-up 3-way catalytic converters. Disconnect catalytic converters from exhaust manifolds. Loosen cylinder head bolts 1/3 turn at a time, in reverse order of tightening sequence. *See Fig. 7.* Remove cylinder heads and gaskets. Remove exhaust manifold covers and exhaust manifolds.

Inspection – **1)** Clean gasket mating surfaces. Check camshaft-to-holder oil clearance. Cylinder head cannot be resurfaced if clearance is not within specification. See CAMSHAFT table under ENGINE SPECIFICATIONS.

2) Measure cylinder head warpage. If warpage is less than 0.002" (0.05 mm), resurfacing is not required. If warpage is 0.002-0.008" (0.05-0.20 mm), resurface cylinder head. Maximum resurface limit is 0.008" (0.20 mm). Remove and clean oil control orifices. *See Fig. 8.*

Installation – **1)** Ensure cylinder heads and cylinder block surface are clean. Install exhaust manifolds and new gaskets to cylinder heads. Apply oil to threads of exhaust manifold self-locking nuts. Using crisscross pattern, tighten self-locking nuts to specification in 2 or 3 steps, starting with inner nut. See TORQUE SPECIFICATIONS.

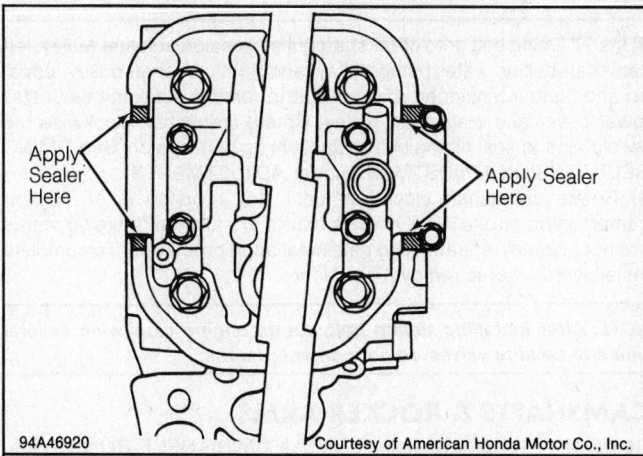

94A46920   Courtesy of American Honda Motor Co., Inc.

Fig. 9: Identifying Liquid Gasket Application Points

2) Install oil control orifices with new "O" rings. Install cylinder head dowel pins with new cylinder head gaskets. Ensure oil control orifices and dowel pins are aligned. Ensure No. 1 piston is at TDC.

3) Install cylinder heads on engine block. Apply clean engine oil to cylinder head bolt threads and washer contact surfaces. Tighten cylinder head bolts to specification in sequence, in 2 or 3 steps. *See Fig. 7.* See TORQUE SPECIFICATIONS.

4) Apply liquid gasket sealer to indicated areas (head mating surface of No. 1 and 7 camshaft holders). *See Fig. 9.* Install cylinder head cover. To complete installation, reverse removal procedure. Adjust timing belt tension. See TIMING BELT TENSION ADJUSTMENT under ADJUSTMENTS. To complete installation, reverse removal procedure. Fill and bleed cooling system. See BLEEDING COOLING SYSTEM.

FRONT COVER OIL SEAL

Removal & Installation – Remove crankshaft pulley and timing belt. See TIMING BELT. Pry oil seal from oil pump housing. Apply light coating of grease to crankshaft and lip on new seal. Using Seal Driver (07749-0010000) and Attachment (07746-0010500), install oil seal. Ensure seal is fully seated into housing. To complete installation, reverse removal procedure.

TIMING BELT

Removal – **1)** Remove negative battery cable. Remove damper, center bracket and center mount. On Sedan GS and Coupe models, remove Traction Control System (TCS) brackets. Disconnect TCS throttle sensor and actuator connectors. Remove TCS control valve assembly, leaving breather pipe by-pass hose connected.

2) Remove injector harness covers. *See Fig. 5.* Remove engine wiring harness. Remove oil pressure switch connector. Remove engine ground cable. Loosen mounting nuts/bolts, and remove accessory drive belts.

3) Remove timing belt upper covers. *See Fig. 10.* Rotate crankshaft clockwise until No. 1 piston is at TDC of compression stroke. Align timing marks. *See Fig. 11.* Remove crankshaft pulley. Remove A/C idler pulley. Remove engine oil dipstick tube.

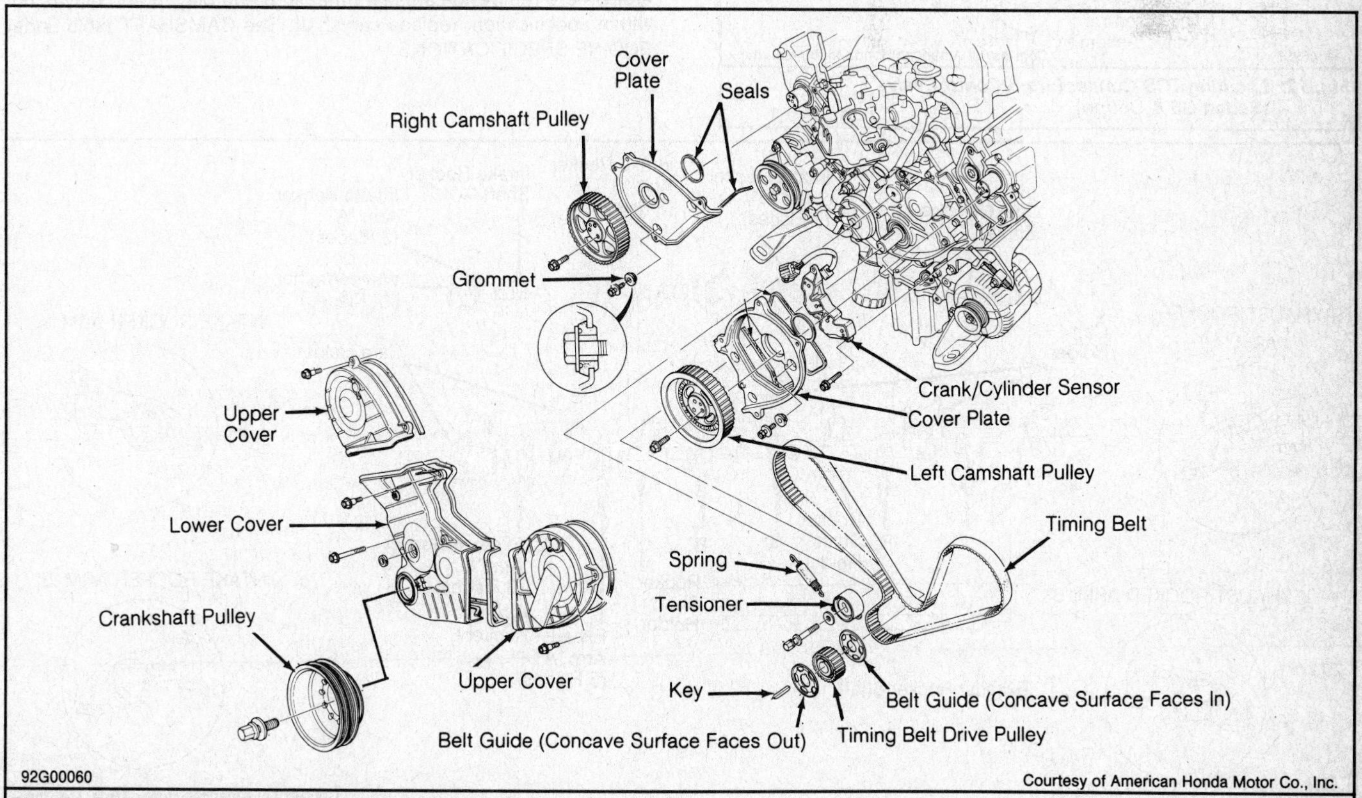

92G00060   Courtesy of American Honda Motor Co., Inc.

Fig. 10: Exploded View Of Timing Belt & Components

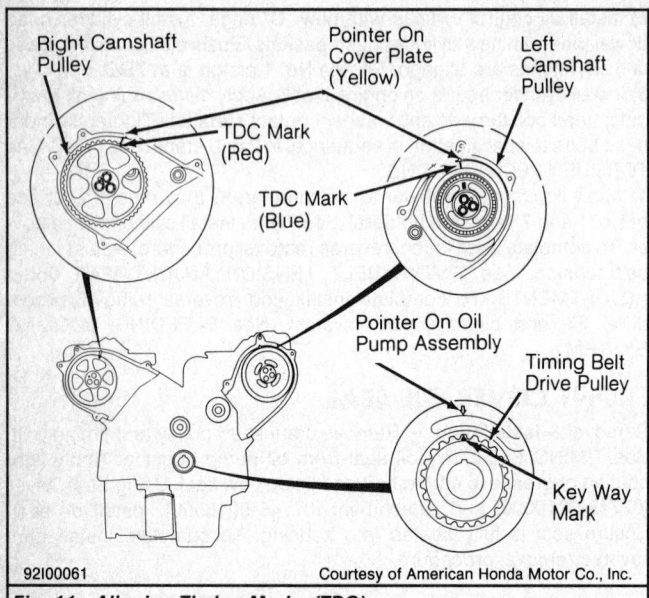

Fig. 11: Aligning Timing Marks (TDC)

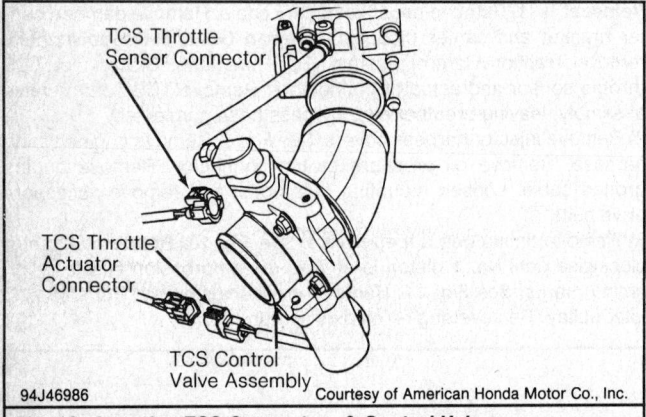

Fig. 12: Locating TCS Connectors & Control Valve (Sedan GS & Coupe)

4) Remove timing belt lower cover. If timing belt is to be reused, mark direction of belt rotation for installation reference. Loosen timing belt tensioner adjusting bolt 1/2 turn (180°). Push tensioner to release belt tension, then retighten bolt. Remove timing belt from pulleys.

CAUTION: DO NOT turn crankshaft or camshafts with timing belt removed, because pistons may hit valves, causing damage.

Installation – 1) Remove all spark plugs. Ensure No. 1 piston is at TDC of compression stroke. Position crankshaft and camshaft pulleys as shown. *See Fig. 11.*

2) Adjust camshaft pulley(s) until TDC mark on pulley and pointer on cover plate are aligned. If reusing timing belt, ensure arrow made in removal procedure points in direction of original rotation.

NOTE: When installing timing belt, turn crankshaft pulley 15 degree clockwise from TDC position. After adjusting left and right camshaft pulleys to TDC, turn crankshaft pulley counter clockwise to TDC position.

3) Install timing belt onto crankshaft pulley, tension adjuster pulley, left camshaft pulley, water pump pulley, and right camshaft pulley. Loosen and tighten tensioner adjuster bolt to remove slack in belt. Install lower cover and crankshaft pulley. Rotate crankshaft clockwise 5-6 revolutions to seat timing belt. Adjust timing belt tension. See TIMING BELT TENSION ADJUSTMENT under ADJUSTMENTS.

4) Rotate crankshaft clockwise until No. 1 piston is at TDC of compression stroke. Verify timing marks are aligned. If timing marks are not aligned, repeat timing belt installation procedure. To complete installation, reverse removal procedure.

NOTE: After installing timing belt, rotate engine clockwise several times to be sure valves do not contact pistons.

CAMSHAFTS & ROCKER ARMS

Removal – 1) Remove timing belt. See TIMING BELT. Remove camshaft pulleys. Remove upper cover plates. Remove cylinder head covers. Before removing camshaft, measure end play. If end play is not within specification, replace camshaft. See CAMSHAFT table under ENGINE SPECIFICATIONS.

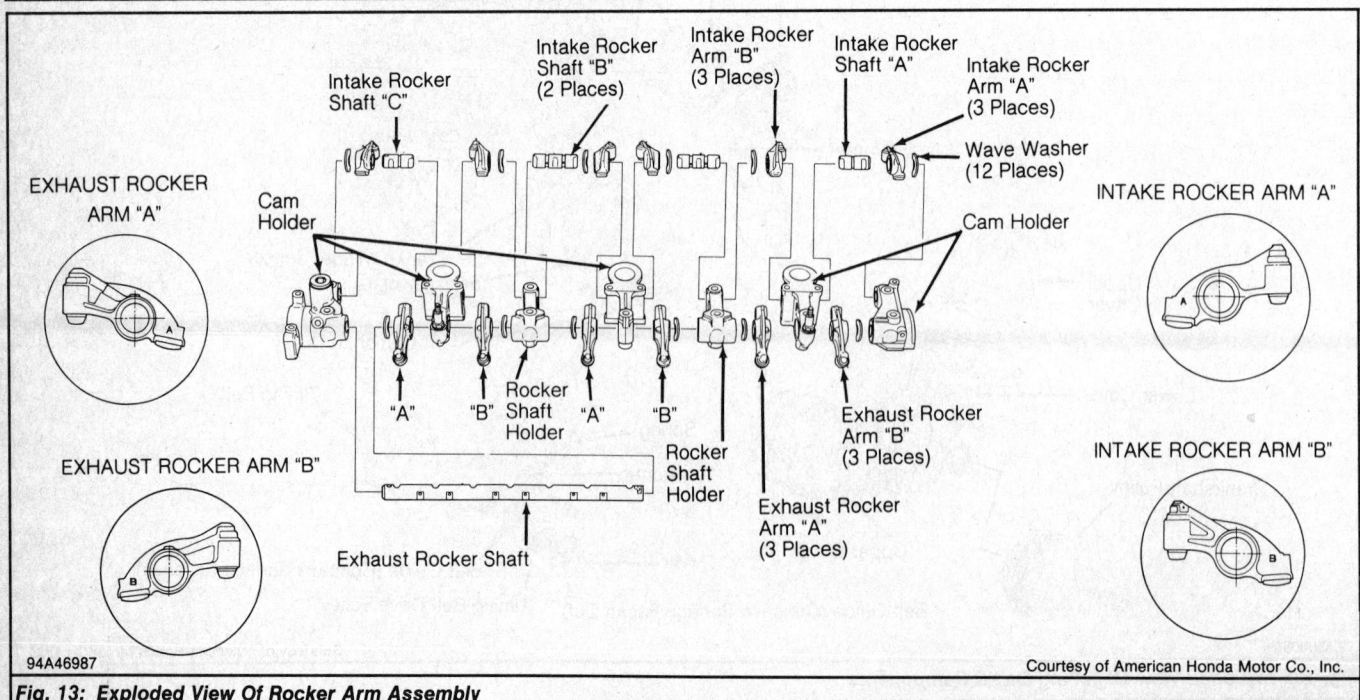

Fig. 13: Exploded View Of Rocker Arm Assembly

CAUTION: When removing rocker arm assembly, DO NOT remove camshaft holder bolts. Bolts keep camshaft holders, springs and rocker arms on shaft.

2) Remove camshaft bearing cap bolts 2 turns at a time, in reverse order of tightening sequence. *See Fig. 14.* Remove rocker shaft assembly. DO NOT remove lifters from rocker arms unless lifter replacement is necessary. Remove camshaft and oil seal.

Inspection – 1) DO NOT rotate camshaft during inspection. Inspect camshaft lobes and bearing journals for excessive wear or damage. Replace if necessary. Place camshaft onto "V" blocks, and measure runout. Total runout must not exceed 0.001" (0.03 mm). Measure camshaft oil clearance using Plastigage.

2) If oil clearance exceeds specification, but runout is okay, replace cylinder head. See CAMSHAFT table under ENGINE SPECIFICATIONS. If clearance and runout exceed specification, replace camshaft. Re-measure camshaft oil clearance after replacing camshaft. If oil clearance still exceeds specification, replace cylinder head.

3) If rocker arms must be removed from rocker shafts, note location of rocker arms for installation reference. Measure diameter of intake and exhaust rocker shafts at first rocker arm location. Measure inside diameter of rocker arm, and check for out-of-round condition.

4) Difference between the 2 measurements is rocker arm-to-shaft clearance. Repeat procedure for all rocker arms. If clearance exceeds specification, replace rocker shaft and any over-tolerance rocker arms. Inspect rocker arm faces for wear. Replace as necessary.

Installation – 1) Ensure rocker arms are assembled correctly onto rocker shaft. *See Fig. 13.* If lifters were replaced or removed from rocker arms, bleed air from lifters. Fill container with 10W-30 oil. Place lifter into container. Using a thin wire and a vertical motion, pump lifter plunger until no air bubbles emerge from lifter.

2) Install new "O" ring onto lifter. Install lifter into rocker arm. Lubricate camshaft journals and journal surfaces in caps and cylinder head. Position camshaft with pin hole at top. Install camshaft and camshaft seal. Apply gasket sealer to cylinder head mating surfaces of No. 1 and 7 camshaft holders.

3) Install rocker arm assembly, and tighten bolts finger tight. Ensure rocker arms are properly positioned onto valve stems. Tighten camshaft bearing cap bolts to specification 2 turns at a time and in sequence. *See Fig. 14.* See TORQUE SPECIFICATIONS. To complete installation, reverse removal procedure.

REAR CRANKSHAFT OIL SEAL

Removal & Installation – 1) Disconnect negative battery cable. Remove transaxle assembly. See FWD article in CLUTCHES (manual transaxle) or TRANSMISSION REMOVAL & INSTALLATION article in TRANSMISSION SERVICING (automatic transaxle).

2) On M/T models, mark clutch pressure plate and flywheel for installation reference. Remove pressure plate and clutch disc (if equipped).

3) On all models, remove flywheel or flexplate. Pry oil seal from rear oil seal cover. If oil seal cover is removed, use non-hardening liquid gasket to seal block mating surface. Apply light coat of oil to seal lip and crankshaft. Install new seal with part number facing out.

4) Using Seal Driver (07GAD-PH70201), drive in crankshaft oil seal until driver bottoms against oil pump. Clean excess grease from crankshaft. Ensure oil seal lip is not distorted.

5) Align hole in Driver Attachment (07948-SB00101) with pin on crankshaft. Using driver attachment and Driver (07749-0010000), drive crankshaft oil seal into rear cover until clearance between bottom of oil seal and rear cover is 0.02-0.03" (0.5-0.8 mm). Ensure clearance is the same all the way around. To complete installation, reverse removal procedure.

WATER PUMP

Removal & Installation – Drain cooling system. Remove timing belt. See TIMING BELT. Remove thermostat housing bolts. Remove water pump special bolts. Remove water pump and "O" ring. To install, reverse removal procedure. Fill and bleed air from cooling system. See BLEEDING COOLING SYSTEM.

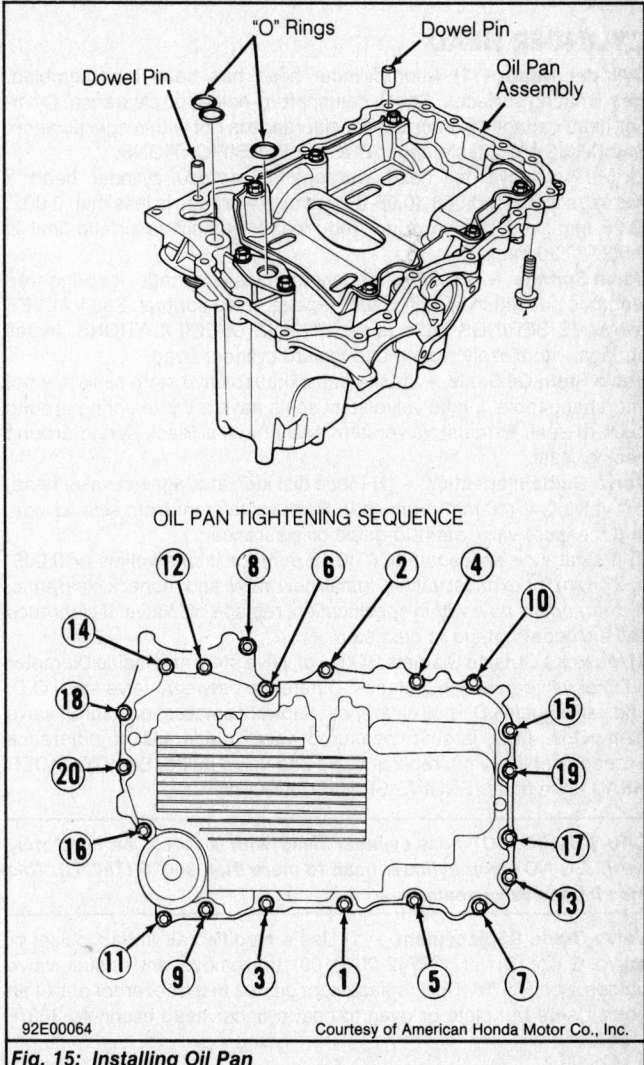

OIL PAN TIGHTENING SEQUENCE

92E00064   Courtesy of American Honda Motor Co., Inc.

Fig. 15: *Installing Oil Pan*

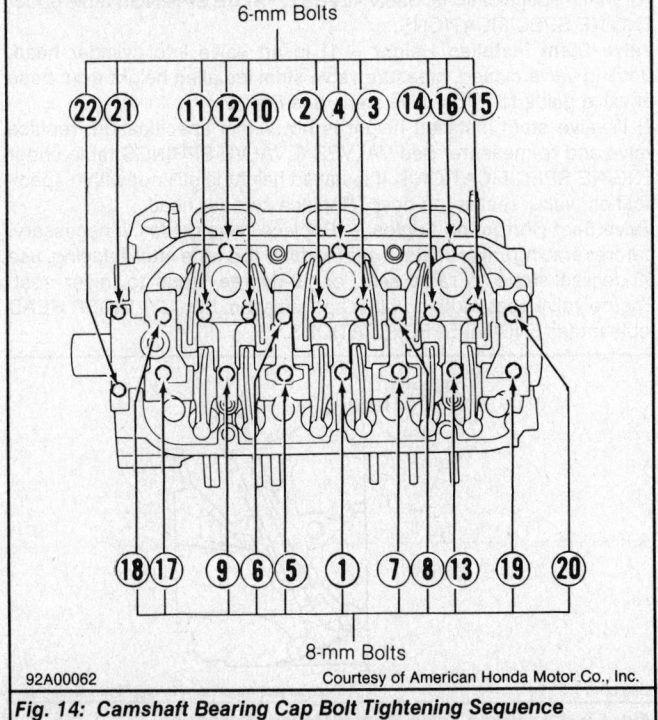

92A00062   Courtesy of American Honda Motor Co., Inc.

Fig. 14: *Camshaft Bearing Cap Bolt Tightening Sequence*

OIL PAN

Removal – 1) Disconnect battery cables. Remove battery. Remove radiator cap. Raise and support vehicle. Remove front wheels. Remove damper forks. Disconnect suspension lower arm ball joints using special tool. See appropriate article in SUSPENSION.

2) Remove driveshaft and suspend aside using rope. See FWD AXLE SHAFTS article in DRIVE AXLES. Remove engine splash shield and lower plate under rear beam. Drain engine and differential oil. Install drain bolt and plug using new washers. DO NOT over tighten drain bolt.

3) Drain engine coolant. Remove differential assembly. See DIFFERENTIAL article in DRIVE AXLES. Remove A/C compressor belt and compressor. Remove intermediate shaft. Remove engine stiffener (bracket). Remove flywheel (M/T) or drive plate (A/T) cover. Remove oil pan and "O" rings.

Installation – 1) Clean oil pan and cylinder block mating surface. Apply a continuous bead of Liquid Gasket Sealer (08718-0001) to cylinder block and inner threads of bolt holes. Apply liquid gasket sealer to bolt threads.

2) Coat new "O" rings with engine oil. Install oil pan and new "O" rings. Tighten bolts in sequence to specification. *See Fig. 15.* See TORQUE SPECIFICATIONS. To complete installation, reverse removal procedure.

3) Fill or top off all fluids. Wait a minimum of 30 minutes before filling crankcase with engine oil. Fill and bleed air from cooling system. See BLEEDING COOLING SYSTEM.

OVERHAUL

CYLINDER HEAD

Cylinder Head – 1) After cylinder head has been disassembled, clean mating surfaces. Check camshaft-to-holder oil clearance. Cylinder head cannot be resurfaced if clearance is not within specification. See CAMSHAFT table under ENGINE SPECIFICATIONS.

2) Measure cylinder head warpage. Resurface cylinder head if warpage is 0.002-0.008" (0.05-0.20 mm). If warpage is less than 0.002" (0.05 mm), resurfacing is not required. Maximum resurface limit is 0.008" (0.20 mm).

Valve Springs – Measure free length of valve springs. If spring free length is not within specification, replace valve springs. See VALVES & VALVE SPRINGS table under ENGINE SPECIFICATIONS. Install springs with closely wound end toward cylinder head.

Valve Stem Oil Seals – Intake and exhaust valve stem seals are not interchangeable. Intake valve stem seals have a White spring around neck of seal. Exhaust valve stem seals have a Black spring around neck of seal.

Valve Guide Inspection – 1) Place dial indicator against valve head. Lift valve 0.4" (10 mm) from seat. Rock valve stem from side to side, and measure valve stem-to-guide oil clearance.

2) If clearance exceeds 0.006" (0.16 mm) for intake valves or 0.009" (0.22 mm) for exhaust valves, install new valve and recheck clearance. If clearance is now within specification, replace old valve. If clearance still exceeds limit, go to next step.

3) Measure Outside Diameter (O.D.) of valve stem and Inside Diameter (I.D.) of valve guide, in 3 places. Difference between valve stem O.D. and valve guide I.D. is oil clearance. Subtract smallest measured valve stem O.D. from largest measured valve guide I.D. If difference exceeds service limit, replace valve and valve guide. See CYLINDER HEAD table under ENGINE SPECIFICATIONS.

CAUTION: DO NOT heat cylinder head with a torch, as head may warp. DO NOT heat cylinder head to more than 300°F (150°C). This may loosen valve seats.

Valve Guide Replacement – 1) Use a modified air impact chisel or Valve Guide Driver (07742-0010100) to remove and install valve guides. *See Fig. 16.* Chill replacement guides in a freezer for about an hour. Use a hot plate or oven to heat cylinder head evenly to 300°F (150°C).

2) Working from camshaft side, drive valve guide about 5/64" (2 mm) toward combustion chamber to dislodge carbon and make removal easier. Turn cylinder head over, and drive valve guide out toward camshaft side. If guide does not move, drill guide with 5/16" drill, and then try again.

CAUTION: Drill guides only in extreme cases. Cylinder head damage can occur if valve guide breaks.

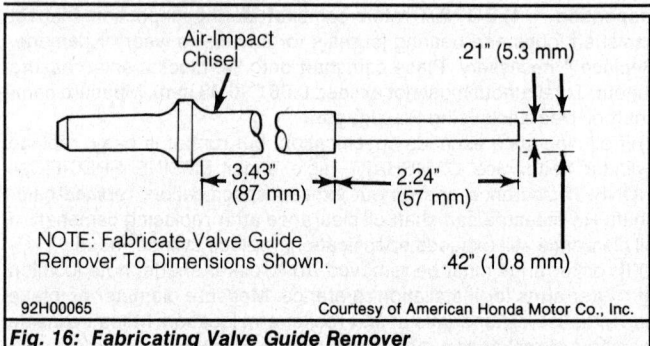

NOTE: Fabricate Valve Guide Remover To Dimensions Shown.

92H00065   Courtesy of American Honda Motor Co., Inc.

Fig. 16: Fabricating Valve Guide Remover

---

3) Individually remove new guides, as needed, from freezer. Slip a 15/64" (6 mm) steel washer over end of driver. Correct valve guide installed height is 0.62-0.64" (15.75-16.25 mm). Install new guides from camshaft side of head. Drive each guide into heated cylinder head to specified installed height.

4) If replacing all valve guides, reheat cylinder head as necessary. Using cutting oil, ream new valve guides by rotating Valve Guide Reamer (07HAH-PJ7010A or 07HAH-PJ7010B) clockwise the full length of valve guide bore.

5) Continue rotating reamer clockwise while removing it from bore. Thoroughly wash guide in detergent and water to remove any cutting residue. Check valve stem-to-guide oil clearance. See CYLINDER HEAD table under ENGINE SPECIFICATIONS.

NOTE: Always reface valve seat after replacing valve guide.

Valve Seat – Valve seat replacement procedure is not available from manufacturer.

Valves – Measure valve stem diameter and margin. Replace valve if not within specifications. See VALVES & VALVE SPRINGS table under ENGINE SPECIFICATIONS.

Valve Stem Installed Height – 1) Insert valve into cylinder head. Holding valve closed, measure valve stem installed height from base of valve guide to tip of valve stem. *See Fig. 17.*

2) If valve stem installed height is not within specification, replace valve and re-measure. See VALVES & VALVE SPRINGS table under ENGINE SPECIFICATIONS. If installed height is still not within specification, valve seat is too deep. Replace cylinder head.

Valve Seat Correction Angles – Replace valve guides, if necessary, before refacing valve seats. If seat width is too wide after refacing, use 60-degree stone to raise seat, or 30-degree stone to lower seat. Ensure valve seat width is within specification. See CYLINDER HEAD table under ENGINE SPECIFICATIONS.

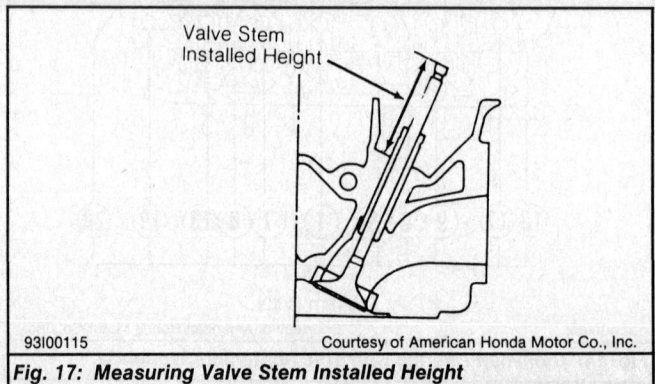

Valve Stem Installed Height

93I00115   Courtesy of American Honda Motor Co., Inc.

Fig. 17: Measuring Valve Stem Installed Height

CYLINDER BLOCK ASSEMBLY

Piston & Rod Assembly – **1)** Connecting rods are available in 4 tolerance ranges. Rod size depends on crank journal bore. A reference number between 1 and 4 is stamped on side of rod's big end. Any combination of numbers between 1 and 4 may be found in engine.

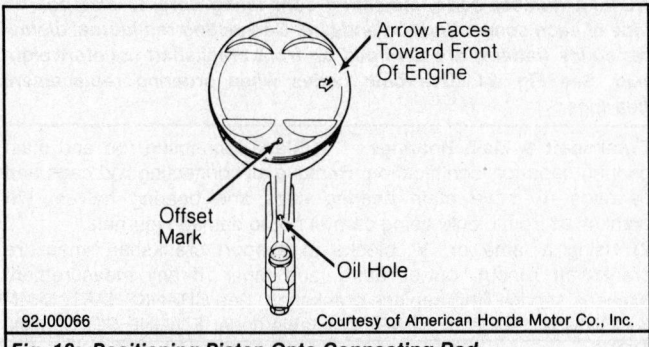

92J00066   Courtesy of American Honda Motor Co., Inc.

Fig. 18: Positioning Piston Onto Connecting Rod

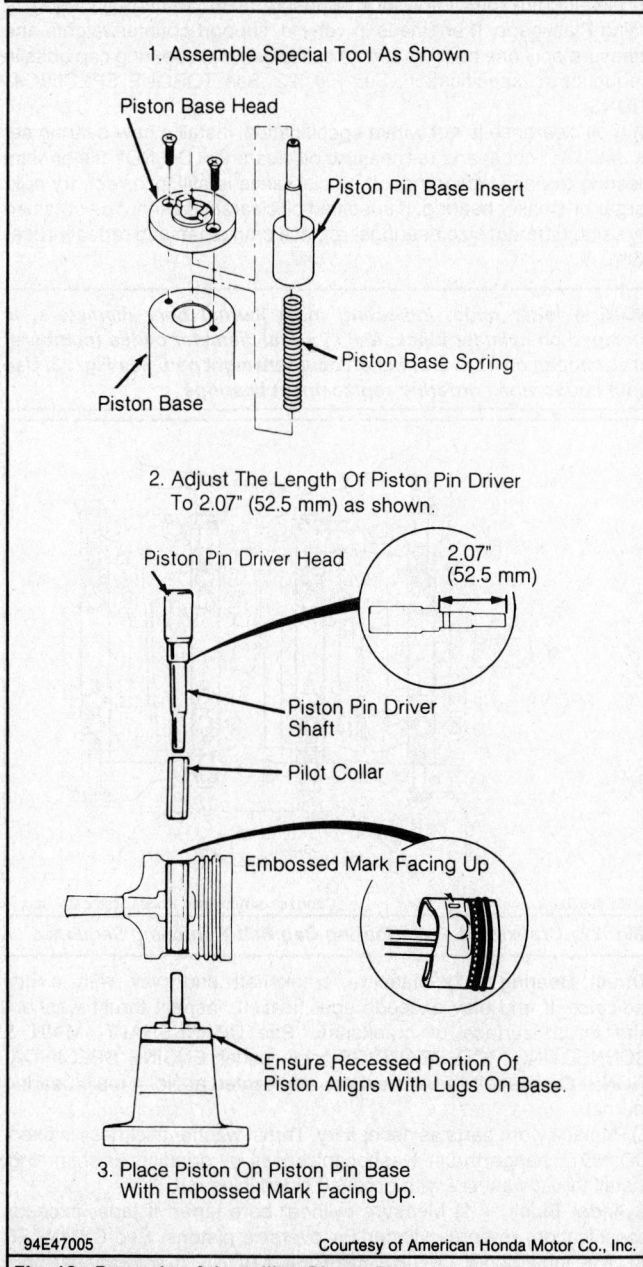

94E47005   Courtesy of American Honda Motor Co., Inc.

Fig. 19: Removing & Installing Piston Pin

NOTE: Reference numbers are for big end bore code. Numbers DO NOT indicate rod position in engine.

2) Nominal connecting rod's big end bore is 2.24" (57 mm). Install piston and connecting rod with arrow on top of piston toward front of engine, and connecting rod oil hole toward offset mark. *See Fig. 18.*

Piston Pin Removal – **1)** Install Piston Base Head (07HAF-PL20102 or 07HAF-PL20101), Piston Base Spring (07973-6570600), and Piston Pin Base Insert (07GAF-PH60300) into Piston Base (07973-6570500). *See Fig. 19.* Adjust Piston Pin Driver Head (07973-PE00320) so piston driver length is 2.07" (52.5 mm).
2) Insert Piston Pin Driver Shaft (07973-PE00310) into Pilot Collar (07GAF-PH70100). Position piston onto base with embossed mark facing up. Align recessed part of piston with lugs on base insert. Press out piston pin.

NOTE: All replacement piston pins are oversize.

Piston Pin Inspection – **1)** Measure diameter of piston pin. Zero dial indicator to piston pin diameter. Check piston for cracks or distortion. Measure piston pin bore in piston. Difference between the 2 measurements is pin-to-piston clearance.
2) Ensure clearance is 0.0005-0.0009" (0.012-0.024 mm). If clearance is greater than 0.0009" (0.024 mm), install an oversize piston pin and re-measure clearance.
3) Measure difference between piston pin diameter and connecting rod's small end bore. Interference fit between piston pin and connecting rod must be 0.0005-0.0013" (0.013-0.032 mm).
Piston Pin Installation – **1)** Position piston and connecting rod as shown. *See Fig. 18.* Adjust Piston Pin Driver Head (07973-PE00320) so piston driver length is 2.07" (52.5 mm). *See Fig. 19.*
2) Install Pilot Collar (07GAF-PH70100) into piston and connecting rod. Lubricate new piston pin lightly. Position piston onto base with embossed mark facing up. Press in piston pin.
Fitting Pistons – **1)** Using a feeler gauge, measure clearance between piston and cylinder bore. If clearance is near or exceeds 0.002" (0.04 mm), recheck piston clearance by measuring diameter of each piston and cylinder bore.
2) Remove all rings from piston. Clean piston thoroughly and inspect for distortion and cracks. Measure piston diameter 0.83" (21 mm) from bottom of piston skirt. Replace piston if diameter is not within specification. See PISTONS, PINS & RINGS table under ENGINE SPECIFICATIONS.
3) Standard size pistons are stamped with letter "A" or "B" on piston top. Cylinder block bore size is determined by letter "A" or "B" stamped on cylinder block. Identification letters on block read from front cylinder to rear cylinder. Letters for No. 1 through No. 3 cylinders are on first line, and letters for No. 4 through No. 6 cylinders are on second line. To maintain proper clearance, ensure letters on cylinder block and piston match.
4) Subtract piston diameter from cylinder bore diameter to obtain piston clearance. If clearance exceeds service limit, re-bore cylinder and install oversize piston. See PISTONS, PINS & RINGS table. See CYLINDER BORE procedure. Pistons are available in 0.010" (0.25 mm) and 0.020" (0.50 mm) oversize.
Piston Rings – **1)** Using inverted piston, push new piston ring into cylinder bore 0.6-0.8" (15-20 mm) from bottom. Using a feeler gauge, measure ring end gap. If gap is too large, check cylinder bore diameter and re-bore if necessary. See PISTONS, PINS & RINGS table under ENGINE SPECIFICATIONS. If gap is too small, check if ring size is correct.
2) Clean piston ring grooves thoroughly. Install rings onto piston with identification mark toward top of piston. Using a feeler gauge, measure side clearance between ring and ring groove.
3) If ring grooves are excessively worn, replace piston. See PISTONS, PINS & RINGS table. Ensure piston ring end gaps are properly spaced around piston. *See Fig. 20.*

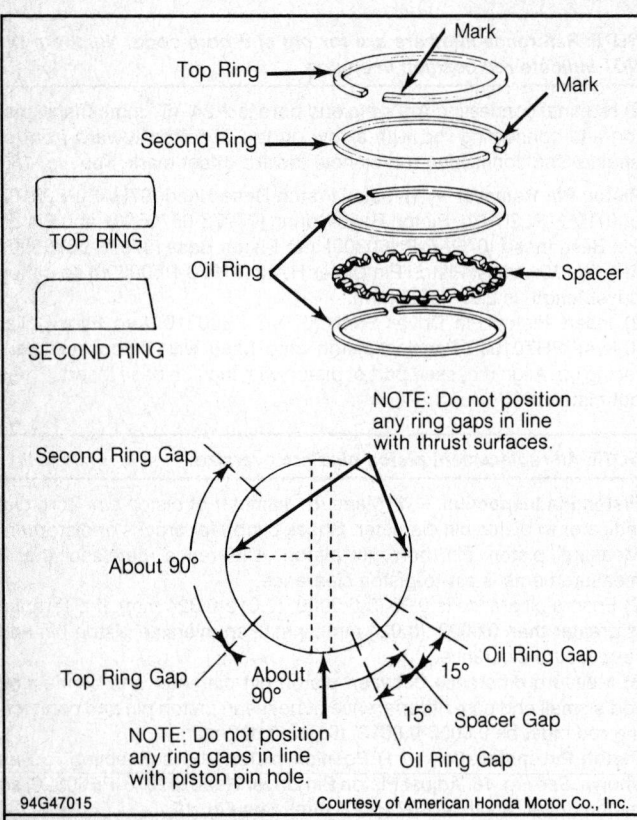

Fig. 20: Installing Piston Rings

94G47015   Courtesy of American Honda Motor Co., Inc.

Rod Bearings – 1) Measure oil clearance using Plastigage. Tighten bearing cap to 33 ft. lbs. (45 N.m). If oil clearance is not within specification, install a new bearing set (same color code) and recheck oil clearance. See CRANKSHAFT, MAIN & CONNECTING ROD BEARINGS table under ENGINE SPECIFICATIONS. DO NOT shim or file cap to adjust oil clearance.

2) If oil clearance is still incorrect, try next larger or smaller bearing and measure oil clearance again. If proper oil clearance cannot be obtained using different size bearings, replace crankshaft and repeat procedure.

NOTE: A number code, indicating connecting bore, is stamped on side of each connecting rod and cap. Connecting rod journal diameter codes (letters) are stamped on front crankshaft counterweight pad. See Fig. 21. Use both codes when ordering replacement bearings.

Crankshaft & Main Bearings – 1) Mark connecting rod and main bearing caps for identification. Remove all connecting rod caps and bearings. Remove main bearing caps and bearing halves. Lift crankshaft from block, being careful not to damage journals.

2) Using a lathe or "V" blocks to support crankshaft, measure crankshaft runout, out-of-round, and taper. If any measurement exceeds service limit, replace crankshaft. See CRANKSHAFT, MAIN & CONNECTING ROD BEARINGS table under ENGINE SPECIFICATIONS.

3) Install crankshaft into block. Measure main bearing oil clearance using Plastigage. If engine is in vehicle, support counterweights and measure only one bearing at a time. Tighten main bearing cap bolts in sequence to specification. *See Fig. 22.* See TORQUE SPECIFICATIONS.

4) If oil clearance is not within specification, install a new bearing set (same color code) and re-measure oil clearance. DO NOT file or shim bearing to adjust clearance. If oil clearance is still incorrect, try next larger or smaller bearing. If specified oil clearance cannot be obtained by using different size bearings, replace crankshaft and repeat procedure.

NOTE: A letter code, indicating main journal bore diameters, is stamped on cylinder block. Main journal diameter codes (numbers) are stamped on front crankshaft counterweight pad. See Fig. 23. Use both codes when ordering replacement bearings.

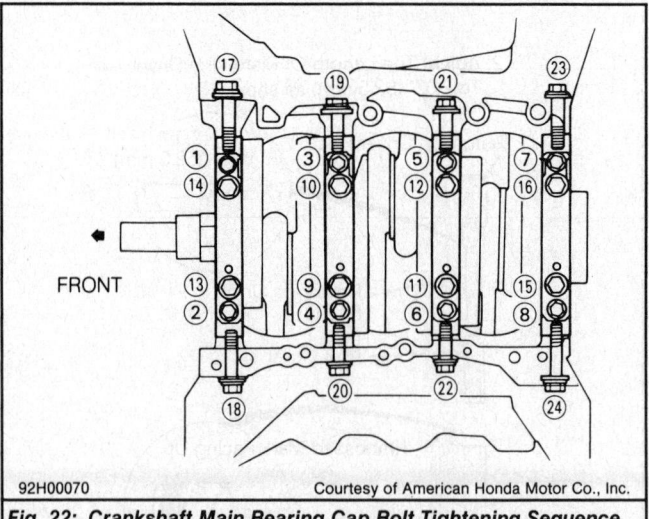

Fig. 22: Crankshaft Main Bearing Cap Bolt Tightening Sequence

92H00070   Courtesy of American Honda Motor Co., Inc.

Thrust Bearing – 1) Measure crankshaft end play with a dial indicator. If end play exceeds specification, inspect thrust washers and thrust surface of crankshaft. See CRANKSHAFT, MAIN & CONNECTING ROD BEARINGS table under ENGINE SPECIFICATIONS. Crankshaft thrust washers are located at No. 4 main bearing journal.

2) Replace worn parts as necessary. Thrust washer thickness is fixed. DO NOT change thrust washer thickness by grinding or shimming. Install thrust washers with grooved side facing out.

Cylinder Block – 1) Measure cylinder bore taper. If taper exceeds specification, re-bore cylinder for oversize pistons. See CYLINDER BLOCK table under ENGINE SPECIFICATIONS. If any cylinder bore exceeds oversize bore limit, replace cylinder block.

Note: On bearing sets with 2 colors, such as Green/Brown, it does not matter which color is in top or bottom as long as set has one of each bearing.

92D00068   Courtesy of American Honda Motor Co., Inc.

Fig. 21: Connecting Rod Journal & Bearing Identification Codes

	1 or I	2 or II	3 or III	4 or IIII
A or I	Pink	Pink Yellow	Yellow	Yellow Green
B or II	Pink Yellow	Yellow	Yellow Green	Green
C or III	Yellow	Yellow Green	Green	Green Brown
D or IIII	Yellow Green	Green	Green Brown	Brown
E or IIIII	Green	Green Brown	Brown	Brown Black
F or IIIIII	Green Brown	Brown	Brown Black	Black

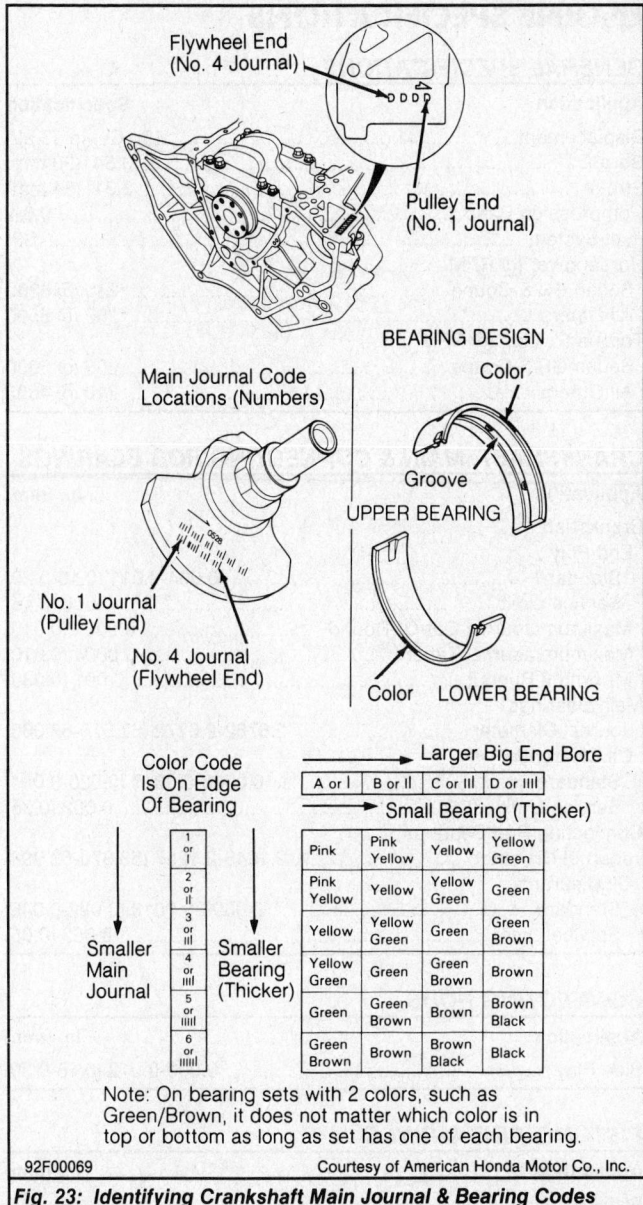

Fig. 23: Identifying Crankshaft Main Journal & Bearing Codes

2) Cylinders can be bored for 0.010" (0.25 mm) and 0.020" (0.50 mm) oversize. Maximum re-boring is 0.020" (0.50 mm). Check piston-to-cylinder bore clearance after re-boring. See FITTING PISTONS procedure.

3) Using feeler gauge and straightedge, measure cylinder block deck warpage. Replace cylinder block if warped beyond service limit. See CYLINDER BLOCK table.

4) If reusing cylinder block, hone cylinders to 60-degree crosshatch pattern. After honing, re-measure cylinder bores. Wash cylinder bore with hot soapy water. Air-dry cylinder bore, and apply engine oil to prevent rusting.

ENGINE OILING

ENGINE LUBRICATION SYSTEM

Oil pump draws oil from oil pan and delivers it under pressure to main and connecting rod bearings. An oil hole in each connecting rod supplies oil to thrust side of piston and cylinder wall. An oil passage carries oil to camshaft and rocker arms. Oil spray lubricates valve stems.

Oil Pressure – Minimum oil pressure with engine at idle should be 10 psi (0.7 kg/cm²). Minimum oil pressure at 3000 RPM should be 50 psi (3.5 kg/cm²).

OIL PUMP

Removal & Disassembly – 1) Raise and support vehicle. Drain engine oil and differential oil. Rotate crankshaft clockwise until No. 1 piston is at TDC of compression stroke. Remove timing belt. See TIMING BELT under REMOVAL & INSTALLATION. Remove oil pan. See OIL PAN under REMOVAL & INSTALLATION.

2) Remove oil cooler (Sedan GS and Coupe) or oil pump cap (all others). Remove special bolts and oil pump assembly. *See Fig. 24.* Remove screen screws from oil pump housing. Separate pump cover from pump housing. Using a screwdriver, pry oil seal from oil pump housing.

Inspection – Measure inner-to-outer rotor clearance. Measure housing-to-rotor axial clearance. Measure housing-to-outer rotor clearance. Replace components if not within specification. See OIL PUMP SPECIFICATIONS table. Inspect both rotors and pump housing for scoring or other damage and replace if necessary.

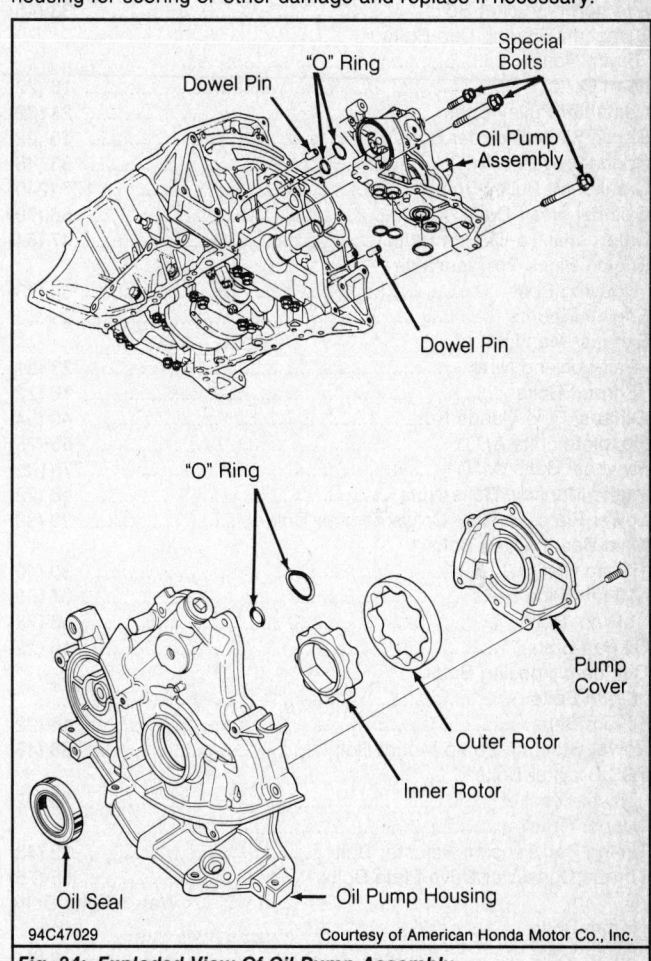

Fig. 24: Exploded View Of Oil Pump Assembly

OIL PUMP SPECIFICATIONS

Application	In. (mm)
Inner Rotor-To-Outer Rotor Clearance	
Standard (New)	0.002-0.006 (0.04-0.16)
Service Limit	0.008 (0.20)
Housing-To-Rotor Axial Clearance	
Standard (New)	0.001-0.003 (0.02-0.07)
Service Limit	0.005 (0.13)
Housing-To-Outer Rotor Clearance	
Standard (New)	0.004-0.007 (0.10-0.18)
Service Limit	0.008 (0.20)

Reassembly & Installation – 1) Apply light coating of grease to crankshaft and lip of new seal. Using Seal Driver (07749-0010000) and Attachment (07746-0010500), install oil seal. Ensure seal is fully seated into oil pump housing.

2) Reassemble oil pump. Apply Liquid Gasket Sealer (08718-0001) to pump housing screws. Ensure oil pump turns freely. Install dowel pins and "O" ring into cylinder block. Clean oil pump and engine mating surfaces.

3) Apply liquid gasket sealer oil pump and cylinder block mating surface. Apply sealer to threads of inner bolt holes. Install oil pump before sealant dries. Wait at least 30 minutes before filling crankcase with oil. To complete installation, reverse removal procedure.

TORQUE SPECIFICATIONS

TORQUE SPECIFICATIONS

Application	Ft. Lbs. (N.m)
A/C Compressor Bolts	16 (22)
A/C Compressor Bracket Bolts	33 (45)
Alternator Bracket Bolts	33 (45)
Camshaft Bearing Cap Bolts [1]	
6-mm Bolts	[2]
8-m Bolts	16 (22)
Camshaft Pulley Bolts	24 (32)
Clutch Slave Cylinder Bolts	16 (22)
Connecting Rod Nuts	33 (45)
Crankshaft Pulley Bolt	177 (240)
Cylinder Head Bolts [3]	58 (78)
Differential-To-Oil Pan Bolts	47 (64)
Engine Block-To-Transaxle	
Housing Bolts	54 (73)
Engine Mounts	[4]
Exhaust Manifold	
Self-Locking Nuts	23 (31)
Shroud Bolts	16 (22)
Exhaust Pipe Flange Nuts	40 (54)
Flexplate bolts A/T) [5]	55 (75)
Flywheel Bolts (M/T) [5]	77 (105)
Intake Manifold Bolts/Nuts	16 (22)
Lower Plate-To-Rear Crossmember Bolts	29 (39)
Main Bearing Cap Bolts [6]	
9-mm Bolts	30 (40)
10-mm Side Bolts	37 (50)
11-mm Bolts	58 (78)
Oil Pan Bolts [7]	16 (22)
Oil Pump Housing Bolts	
6 mm Bolts	[2]
8 mm Bolts	16 (22)
Power Steering Pump Mount Bolt	33 (45)
TCS Bracket Bolts	
Lower Bracket	16 (22)
Upper Bracket	[2]
Timing Belt Tension Adjuster Bolt	32 (43)
Torque Converter Drive Plate Bolts [5]	55 (75)
Water Pump Bolts	
6-mm Bolts	[2]
8-mm Bolts	16 (22)

Application	INCH Lbs. (N.m)
Coolant Passage Manifold Bolts	106 (12)
Crankshaft Rear Seal Cover Bolts	106 (12)
Fuel Service Bolt	106 (12)
Oil Pump Screen Bolts	106 (12)
Timing Belt Cover Bolts	106 (12)
Valve Cover Bolts	89 (10)

[1] – Tighten bolts 2 turns at a time in sequence. *See Fig. 14.*
[2] – Tighten to 106 INCH lbs. (12 N.m).
[3] – Tighten in sequence, in 2-3 steps. *See Fig. 7.*
[4] – Tighten in sequence to specification. *See Fig. 4.*
[5] – Tighten in a crisscross pattern.
[6] – Tighten in sequence. *See Fig. 22.*
[7] – Tighten in sequence. *See Fig. 15.*

ENGINE SPECIFICATIONS

GENERAL SPECIFICATIONS

Application	Specification
Displacement	196 Cu. In. (3.2L)
Bore	3.54" (90 mm)
Stroke	3.31" (84 mm)
Compression Ratio	9.6:1
Fuel System	SFI
Horsepower @ RPM	
Sedan GS & Coupe	230 @ 6200
All Others	200 @ 5500
Torque Ft. Lbs. @ RPM	
Sedan GS & Coupe	206 @ 5000
All Others	210 @ 4500

CRANKSHAFT, MAIN & CONNECTING ROD BEARINGS

Application	In. (mm)
Crankshaft	
End Play	
Standard	0.004-0.011 (0.10-0.29)
Service Limit	0.018 (0.45)
Maximum Journal Out-Of-Round	0.0004 (0.010)
Maximum Journal Taper	0.0004 (0.010)
Maximum Runout	0.001 (0.030)
Main Bearings	
Journal Diameter	2.6762-2.6772 (67.976-68.000)
Oil Clearance	
Standard	0.0008-0.0017 (0.020-0.044)
Service Limit	0.002 (0.05)
Connecting Rod Bearings	
Journal Diameter	2.1248-2.1257 (53.970-53.994)
Oil Clearance	
Standard	0.0009-0.0018 (0.022-0.046)
Service Limit	0.002 (0.05)

CONNECTING RODS

Application	In. (mm)
Side Play	0.006-0.012 (0.15-0.30)

PISTONS, PINS & RINGS

Application	In. (mm)
Pistons	
Clearance	
Standard	0.001-0.002 (0.02-0.04)
Service Limit	0.003 (0.08)
Diameter	
Standard [1]	
"A" Piston	3.5425-3.5429 (89.980-89.990)
"B" Piston	3.5421-3.5425 (89.970-89.980)
Oversize	
.010" (0.25 mm)	3.5520-3.5524 (90.220-90.230)
.020" (0.50 mm)	3.5618-3.5622 (90.470-90.480)
Piston Pins	
Diameter	
Standard	0.8659-0.8661 (21.994-22.000)
Oversize	0.8660-0.8663 (21.997-22.003)
Pin-To-Piston Clearance	0.0005-0.0009 (0.012-0.024)
Rod Interference Fit	0.0005-0.0013 (0.013-0.032)
Rings	
No. 1	
End Gap	
Standard	0.010-0.016 (0.25-0.40)
Service Limit	0.028 (0.70)
Side Clearance	0.0014-0.0024 (0.035-0.060)

[1] – Piston identification letter is located on top of piston.

PISTONS, PINS & RINGS (Cont.)

Application	In. (mm)
No. 2	
End Gap	
Standard	0.016-0.022 (0.40-0.55)
Service Limit	0.033 (0.85)
Side Clearance	0.0012-0.0022 (0.030-0.055)
No. 3 (Oil)	
End Gap	
Standard	0.008-0.028 (0.20-0.70)
Service Limit	0.031 (0.80)

[1] – Piston identification letter is located on top of piston.

CYLINDER BLOCK

Application	In. (mm)
Cylinder Bore	
Standard Diameter	
"A" Piston [1]	3.5437-3.5441 (90.010-90.020)
"B" Piston [1]	3.5433-3.5437 (90.000-90.010)
Service Limit	3.546 (90.07)
Oversize	
.25 O/S	3.553-3.554 (90.25-90.27)
.50 O/S	3.563-3.564 (90.50-90.52)
Maximum Taper	0.002 (0.05)
Maximum Deck Warpage	0.004 (0.10)

[1] – Standard bore size is identified by "A" or "B" stamped on cylinder block deck surface (right front). Letters on block read from front cylinder to rear cylinder. Identification letters for No. 1 through No. 3 cylinders are on first line, and letters for No. 4 through No. 6 cylinders are on second line.

VALVES & VALVE SPRINGS

Application	Specification
Intake Valves	
Face Angle	45°
Head Diameter	
Sedan GS & Coupe	1.335-1.343" (33.90-34.10 mm)
All Others	1.295-1.303" (32.90-33.10 mm)
Margin	
Standard	0.033-0.045" (0.85-1.15 mm)
Service Limit	0.026" (0.65 mm)
Stem Diameter	
Standard	0.2157-0.2161" (5.480-5.490 mm)
Service Limit	0.2146" (5.450 mm)
Valve Length	4.472-4.483" (113.58-113.88 mm)
Valve Stem Installed Height	
Standard	1.8478-1.8652" (46.935-47.375 mm)
Service Limit	1.8750" (47.625 mm)
Exhaust Valves	
Face Angle	45°
Head Diameter	1.098-1.106" (27.90-28.10 mm)
Margin	
Standard	0.053-0.065" (1.35-1.65 mm)
Service Limit	0.045" (1.15 mm)
Stem Diameter	
Standard	0.2146-0.2150" (5.450-5.460 mm)
Service Limit	0.213" (5.42 mm)
Valve Length	4.568-4.580" (116.03-116.33 mm)
Valve Stem Installed Height	
Standard	1.8852-1.9045" (47.885-48.375 mm)
Service Limit	1.9124" (48.575 mm)
Valve Springs Free Length	
Intake	
Sedan GS & Coupe	1.935" (49.15 mm)
All Others	1.975" (50.17 mm)
Exhaust	
Sedan GS & Coupe	1.975" (50.17 mm)
All Others	1.983" (50.36 mm)

CYLINDER HEAD

Application	Specification
Cylinder Head Height	3.935-3.939" (99.95-100.05 mm)
Maximum Warpage [1]	0.002" (0.05 mm)
Valve Seats	
Intake & Exhaust	
Seat Angle	45°
Seat Width	
Standard	0.049-0.061" (1.25-1.55 mm)
Service Limit	0.080" (2.00 mm)
Valve Guides	
Intake & Exhaust	
Valve Guide I.D.	
Standard	0.217-0.218" (5.51-5.53 mm)
Service Limit	0.219" (5.55 mm)
Valve Guide Installed Height	0.620-0.640" (15.75-16.25 mm)
Valve Stem-To-Guide Oil Clearance	
Intake	
Standard	0.001-0.002" (0.02-0.05 mm)
Service Limit	0.003" (0.08 mm)
Exhaust	
Standard	0.002-0.003" (0.05-0.08 mm)
Service Limit	0.004" (0.11 mm)

[1] – Maximum resurface limit is 0.008" (0.20 mm).

CAMSHAFT

Application	In. (mm)
End Play	
Standard	0.002-0.006 (0.05-0.15)
Service Limit	0.006 (0.15)
Maximum Journal Runout	0.001 (0.03)
Lobe Height	
Intake	
Sedan GS & Coupe	1.588 (40.3450)
All Others	1.575 (40.0050)
Exhaust	
All Others	1.487 (37.7660)
Sedan GS & Coupe	1.493 (37.9340)
Oil Clearance	
Standard	0.0020-0.0035 (0.050-0.090)
Service Limit	0.004 (0.10)

1994 ENGINE COOLING
Specifications & Electric Cooling Fans

Integra, Legend, Vigor

SPECIFICATIONS

BELT ADJUSTMENT

BELT ADJUSTMENT

Application	¹ Deflection – In. (mm)
A/C Compressor	
Integra	
RS & LS Models	19/64-3/8 (7.5-9.5)
GS-R Models	21/64-13/32 (8.5-10.5)
Legend	5/16-3/8 (8.0-10.0)
Vigor	15/64-23/64 (6.0-9.0)
Alternator	
Integra	23/64-7/16 (9.0-11)
Legend	11/32-13/32 (9.0-10.5)
Vigor	19/64-3/8 (7.5-9.5)
Power Steering	
Integra	29/64-17/32 (11.5-13.5)
Legend	29/64-17/32 (11.5-13.5)
Vigor	1/4-23/64 (6.5-9.0)

¹ – Deflection is with 22 lbs. (10 kg) pressure applied midway on longest belt run, after belt has run at least 5 minutes.

COOLING SYSTEM SPECIFICATIONS

COOLING SYSTEM SPECIFICATIONS

Model	Specification
Coolant Replacement Interval	¹ 45,000 Miles
Coolant Capacity	
Integra	
RS & LS Models	
A/T	7.1 qts. (6.7L)
M/T	6.8 qts. (6.4L)
GS-R Models	7.1 qts. (6.7L)
Legend	
A/T	9.2 qts. (8.7L)
M/T	9.3 qts. (8.8L)
Vigor	
A/T	7.9 qts. (7.5L)
M/T	8.0 qts. (7.6L)
Pressure Cap	
Integra	13.5-18 psi
Legend	14-18 psi
Vigor	13.5-18 psi
Thermostat Opens	
Integra & Legend	
Starts	169-176°F (76-80°C)
Fully Open	194°F (90°C)
Vigor	
Primary	
Starts	176-183°F (80-84°C)
Fully Open	203°F (95°C)
Secondary	
Starts	181-189°F (83-87°C)
Fully Open	203°F (95°C)

¹ – Replace every 2 years or 30,000 miles thereafter.

BLEEDING COOLING SYSTEM

Always bleed air from cooling system after replacing coolant. Set heater for maximum heat. Remove radiator cap. Loosen drain plug and remove drain bolt (if equipped) from engine block. Drain coolant reservoir. Fill coolant reservoir to MAX mark with 50/50 water-coolant mixture. Loosen bleed bolt and fill radiator up to base of filler neck. Close bleed bolt when coolant flows out without bubbles. Tighten bleed bolt to 89 INCH lbs. (10 N.m). With radiator cap removed, start and run engine until normal operating temperature is reached. Top off coolant if necessary.

ELECTRIC COOLING FANS

DESCRIPTION

All models have electric cooling fans. Integra without A/C uses one cooling fan. All others have 2 cooling fans (radiator and condenser).

OPERATION

Integra – On models without A/C fan is controlled by an Engine Coolant Temperature (ECT) switch and relay. On models with A/C, fans (radiator and condenser) are controlled by ETC switch, radiator fan relay and condenser fan relay.
Legend – A Fan Control Unit (FCU) controls the radiator and condenser fans. Both fans run whenever engine is running. Fans run at either low or high speed, depending on engine temperature. If A/C system pressure is higher than normal, both fans run at high speed regardless of engine temperature. The FCU is located underneath a cover at passenger's front floor area. The FCU receives input from radiator fan control sensor, ECM, radiator fan control module, and A/C pressure switches.

An engine oil temperature sensor sends signal to radiator fan control module, which then operates condenser fan for up to 15 minutes after engine is shut off, depending on engine temperature. Module is located on right kick panel.
Vigor – Fans are controlled by Engine Coolant Temperature (ECT) switch and relays. If engine coolant temperature is higher than 226°F (108°C) when engine is shut off, a radiator fan control module continues to power fan for up to 15 minutes. Module is located under right side of dash.

TROUBLE SHOOTING & TESTING

To trouble shoot cooling fans, use appropriate cooling fan wiring diagrams. See WIRING DIAGRAMS.

COMPONENT TESTING

Fan Motor – Unplug appropriate fan motor connector. Apply battery voltage between fan motor terminals. If fan motor operates, check related components and wiring. If fan motor does not operate, reverse battery leads. If fan still does not operate, replace it.
Engine Coolant Temperature (ECT) Switch (Integra & Vigor) – 1) Remove ECT switch. On Integra, switch is located on rear of engine cylinder block. On Vigor, one sensor is located on the thermostat housing, the other is threaded into radiator tank, on driver's side.
2) Suspend switch and thermometer in container partially filled with coolant. Heat coolant while monitoring temperature. Check continuity of switch at specified temperatures. See ECT SWITCH CONTINUITY TEST (INTEGRA & VIGOR) table. If continuity is not as specified, replace ECT switch. If continuity is as specified, check relay and related wiring.
Radiator Fan Control Sensor (Legend) – 1) Remove sensor from thermostat housing. Suspend switch and thermometer in container partially filled with coolant. Heat coolant while monitoring temperature.
2) Measure sensor resistance at specified temperatures. See RADIATOR CONTROL FAN SENSOR RESISTANCE (LEGEND) table. If continuity is not as specified, replace sensor. If continuity is as specified, check relay and related wiring.

ECT SWITCH CONTINUITY TEST (INTEGRA & VIGOR)

Application	Specification
Integra	
Less Than 181-189°F (83-87°C)	No Continuity
Greater Than 196-203°F (91-95°C)	Continuity
Vigor	
ECT Switch "A"	
Less Than 187-196°F (86-91°C)	No Continuity
Greater Than 217-228°F (103-109°C)	Continuity
ECT Switch "B"	
Less Than 207-216°F (97-102°C)	No Continuity
Greater Than 217-228°F (103-109°C)	Continuity

RADIATOR CONTROL FAN SENSOR RESISTANCE (LEGEND)

Application	Ohms
183°F (84°C)	1047-1255
194°F (90°C)	872-1024
230°F (110°C)	489-541

Oil Temperature Sensor (Legend) – 1) Remove oil temperature sensor from cylinder head cover. Suspend sensor and thermometer in a container of water. Heat water while monitoring temperature.

2) Check continuity between sensor terminals at specified temperatures. See OIL TEMPERATURE SENSOR CONTINUITY TEST table. If continuity is not as specified, replace sensor. If continuity is as specified, check relay, other components, and all related wiring.

OIL TEMPERATURE SENSOR CONTINUITY TEST (LEGEND)

Application	Specification
Less Than 156-185°F (69-85°C)	No Continuity
Greater Than 192-203°F (89-95°C)	Continuity

Fan Relays – 1) Basic relay operation is the same, although physical appearance of relays may be different. Remove relay to be tested. *See Fig. 1, 2 or 3.* Check continuity between relay terminals "A" and "B". *See Fig. 4.* Continuity should not exist.

2) Apply battery voltage between terminals "C" and "D". Ensure continuity exists between terminals "A" and "B". If continuity is not as specified, replace relay. If continuity is as specified.

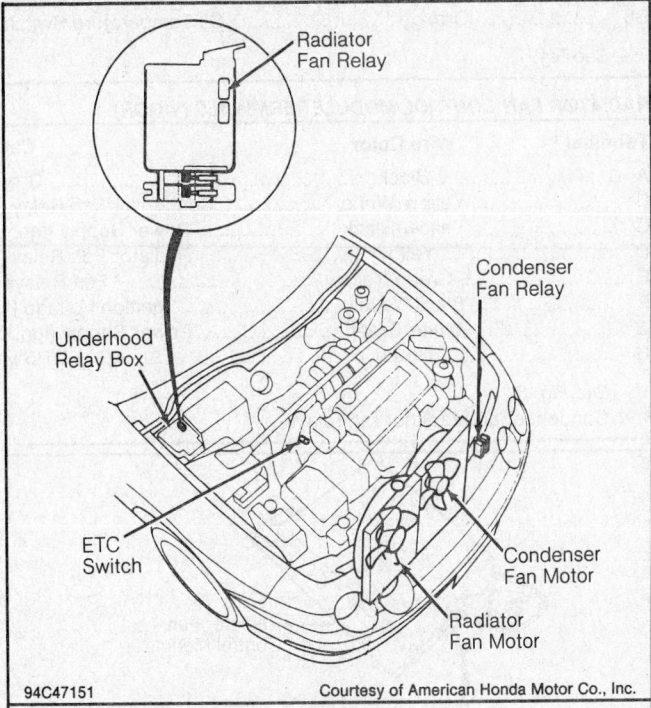

94C47151   Courtesy of American Honda Motor Co., Inc.

Fig. 1: Locating Fan Relays (Integra)

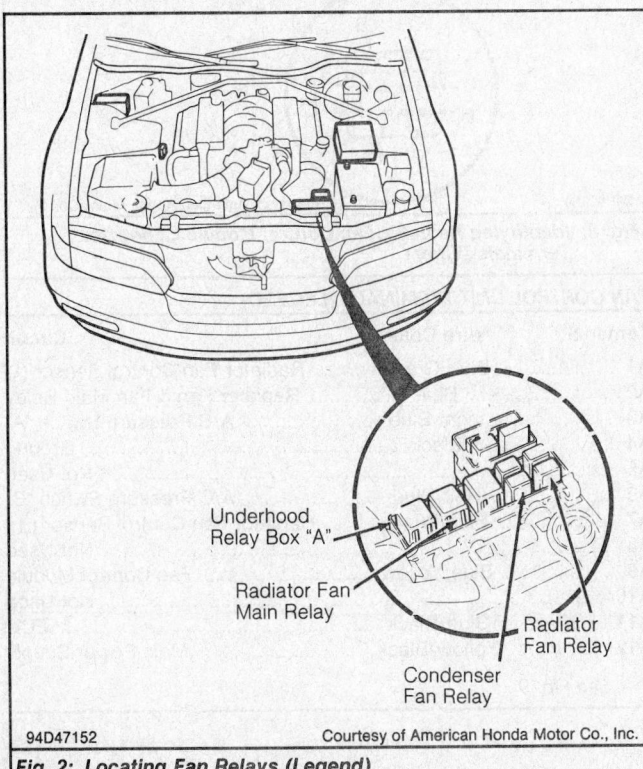

94D47152   Courtesy of American Honda Motor Co., Inc.

Fig. 2: Locating Fan Relays (Legend)

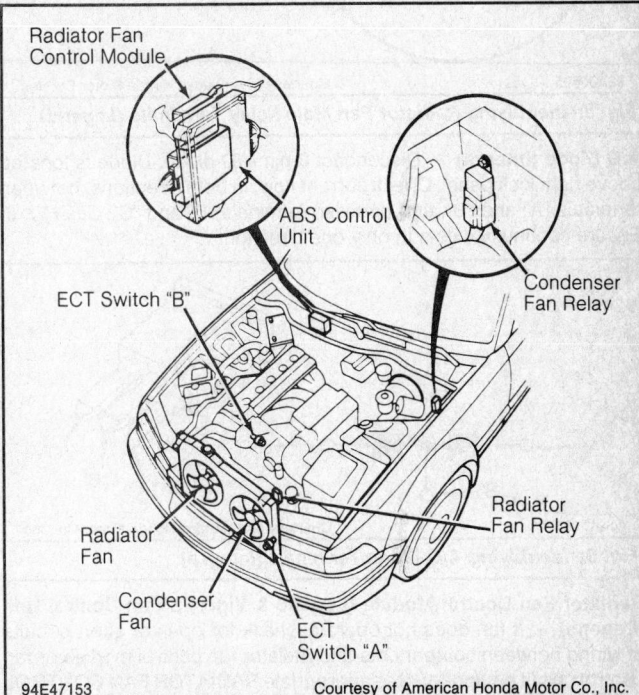

94E47153   Courtesy of American Honda Motor Co., Inc.

Fig. 3: Locating Fan Relays & Related Components (Vigor)

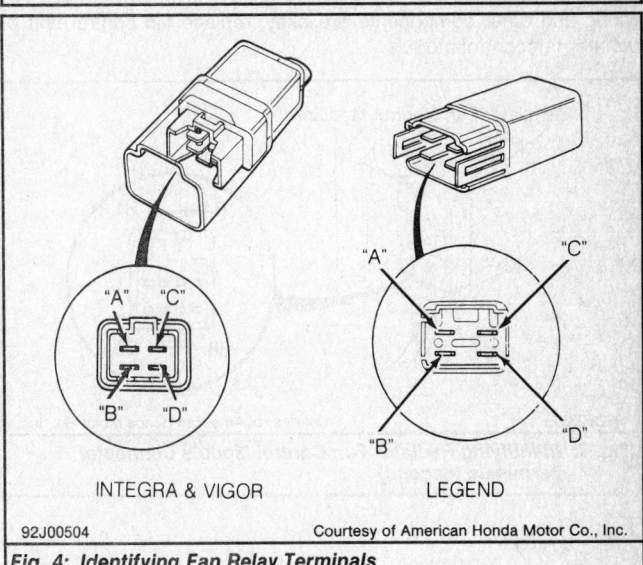

92J00504   Courtesy of American Honda Motor Co., Inc.

Fig. 4: Identifying Fan Relay Terminals

Radiator Fan Main Relay (Legend) – Remove radiator fan main relay. Relay is located in underhood relay box "A". *See Fig. 2.* Continuity should exist between terminals "A" and "C" with battery voltage applied between terminals "D" and "E". *See Fig. 5.* With battery voltage disconnected, continuity should exist between terminals "B" and "C". If relay does not operate as specified, replace relay.

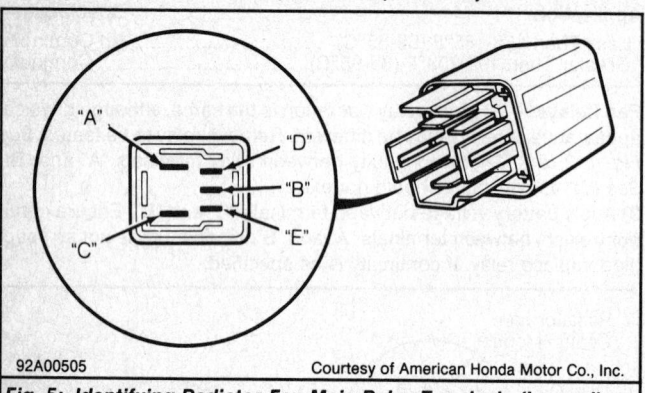

92A00505 — Courtesy of American Honda Motor Co., Inc.

Fig. 5: Identifying Radiator Fan Main Relay Terminals (Legend)

A/C Diode (Integra) – Disconnect 3-pin A/C diode. Diode is located above right kick panel. Check current flow, in both directions, between terminals "A" and "B", and between terminals "B" and "C". *See Fig. 6.* Ensure continuity exists in only one direction.

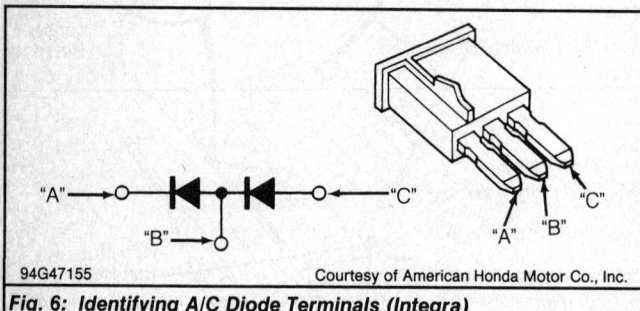

94G47155 — Courtesy of American Honda Motor Co., Inc.

Fig. 6: Identifying A/C Diode Terminals (Integra)

Radiator Fan Control Module (Legend & Vigor) & Fan Control Unit (Legend) – If fan does not operate, check for open or short circuits in wiring between components and radiator fan control module or fan control unit (if equipped). See appropriate RADIATOR FAN CONTROL MODULE TERMINALS table or FAN CONTROL UNIT TERMINALS (LEGEND) table. *See Fig. 7, 8 or 9.* Also see WIRING DIAGRAMS. If all wiring and other components are okay, replace fan control unit or radiator fan control module.

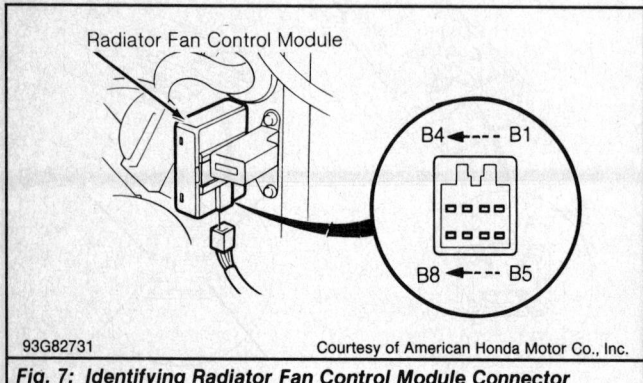

93G82731 — Courtesy of American Honda Motor Co., Inc.

Fig. 7: Identifying Radiator Fan Control Module Connector Terminals (Legend)

RADIATOR FAN CONTROL MODULE TERMINALS (LEGEND)

Terminal [1]	Wire Color	Circuit
B1	Black	Ground
B2	Blue/Yellow	Fan Control Unit
B3	Blue/Red	Condenser Fan Relay (+)
B4	Yellow/Blue	Power Supply (Ign. On)
B5	Green	Condenser Fan Relay (–)
B6	Black/Red	Power Supply (Ign. Off)
B7		Not Used
B8	Orange	Oil Temperature Switch

[1] – See Fig. 7.

RADIATOR FAN CONTROL MODULE TERMINALS (VIGOR)

Terminal [1]	Wire Color	Circuit
A	Black	Ground
B	Yellow/White	Condenser Fan Relay (+)
C	Yellow/Black	Power Supply (Ign. On)
D	Yellow	Radiator Fan Relay (+)
E	Lt. Green/Yellow	[2] Fan Relays (–)
F	Black/Yellow	Ignition Voltage (IG1)
G	White/Green	Power Supply (Ign. Off)
H	Green	ECT Switch

[1] – See Fig. 8.
[2] – Condenser and radiator fan relays.

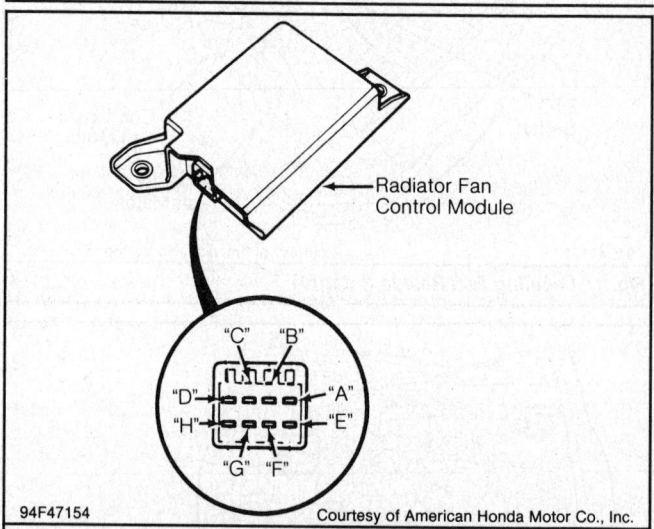

94F47154 — Courtesy of American Honda Motor Co., Inc.

Fig. 8: Identifying Radiator Fan Control Module Connector Terminals (Vigor)

FAN CONTROL UNIT TERMINALS (LEGEND)

Terminal [1]	Wire Color	Circuit
A1	Blue/Green	Radiator Fan Control Sensor (–)
A2	Blue	Radiator Fan & Fan Main Relay
A3	Light Blue	A/C Pressure Switch "A"
A4	Black	Ground
A5		Not Used
A6	Red/Blue	A/C Pressure Switch "B"
A7	Blue/White	Radiator Fan Control Sensor (+)
A8		Not Used
A9	Blue/Yellow	Fan Control Module
A10		Not Used
A11	Blue/Black	ECU
A12	Yellow/Black	Main Power Supply

[1] – See Fig. 9.

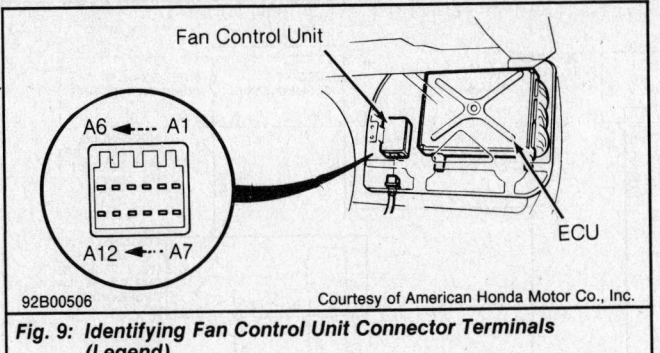

92B00506

Courtesy of American Honda Motor Co., Inc.

Fig. 9: Identifying Fan Control Unit Connector Terminals (Legend)

WIRING DIAGRAMS

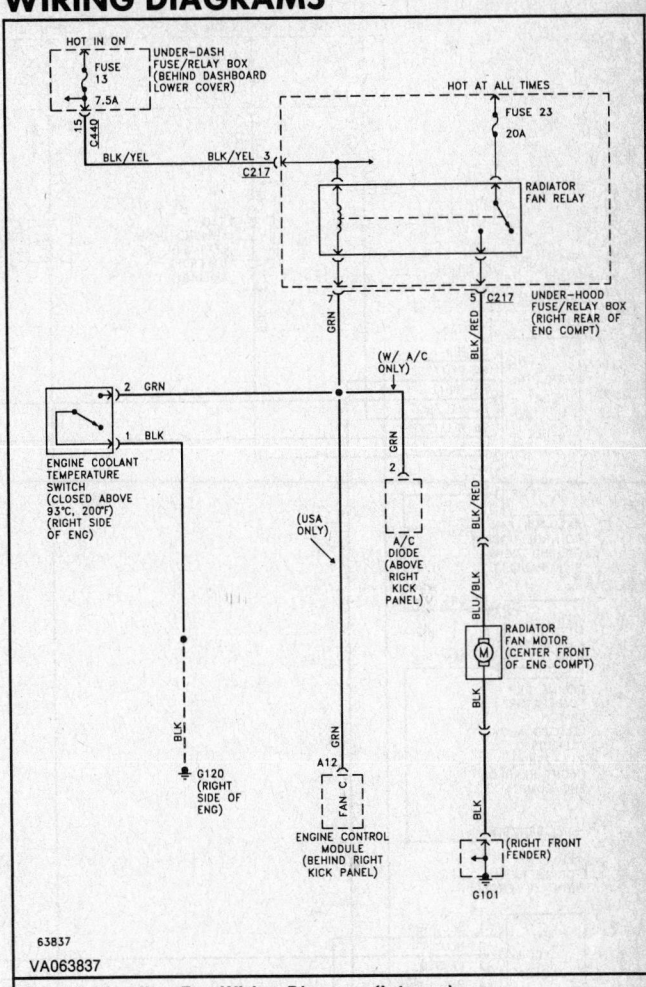

63837

VA063837

Fig. 10: Cooling Fan Wiring Diagram (Integra)

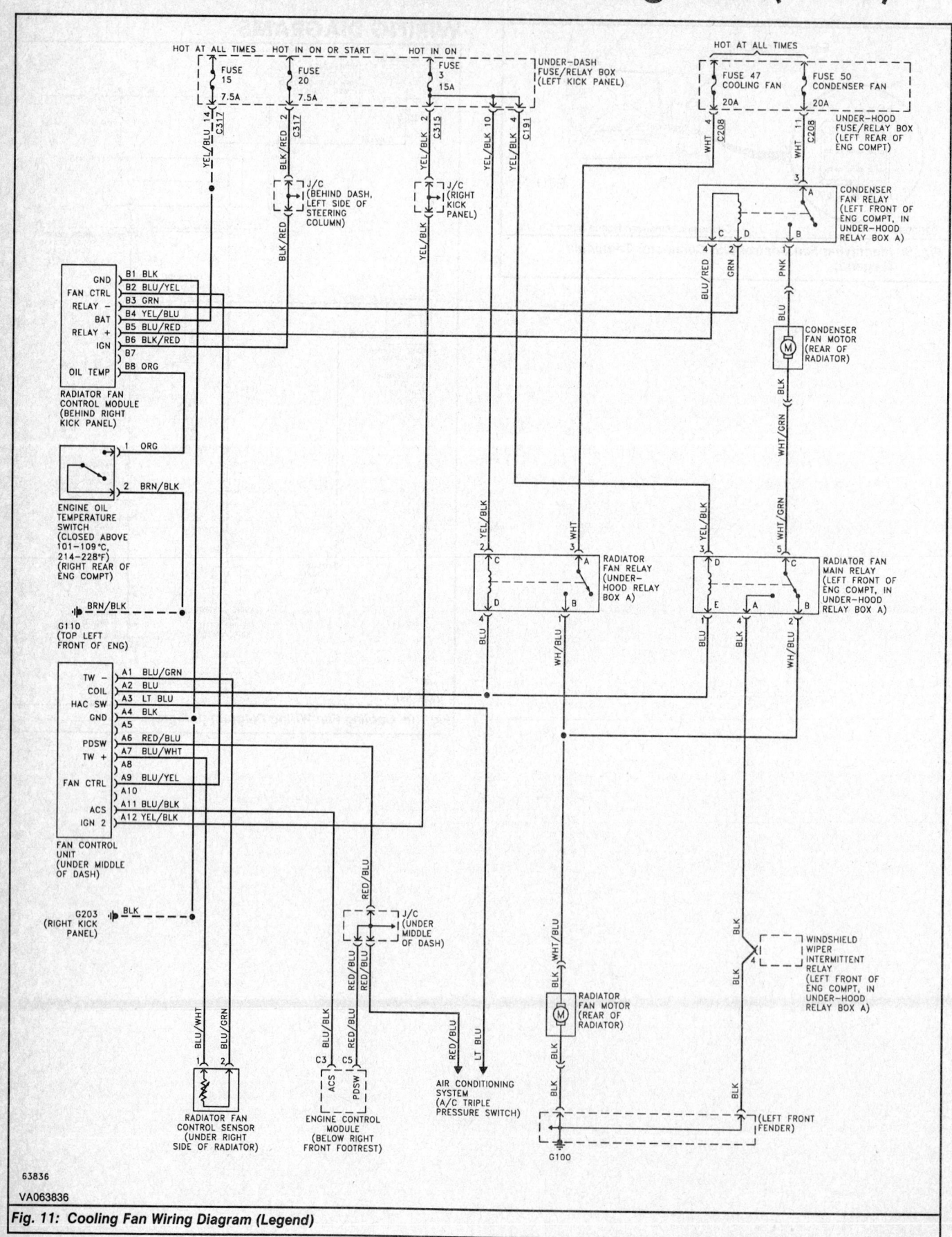

63836
VA063836

Fig. 11: Cooling Fan Wiring Diagram (Legend)

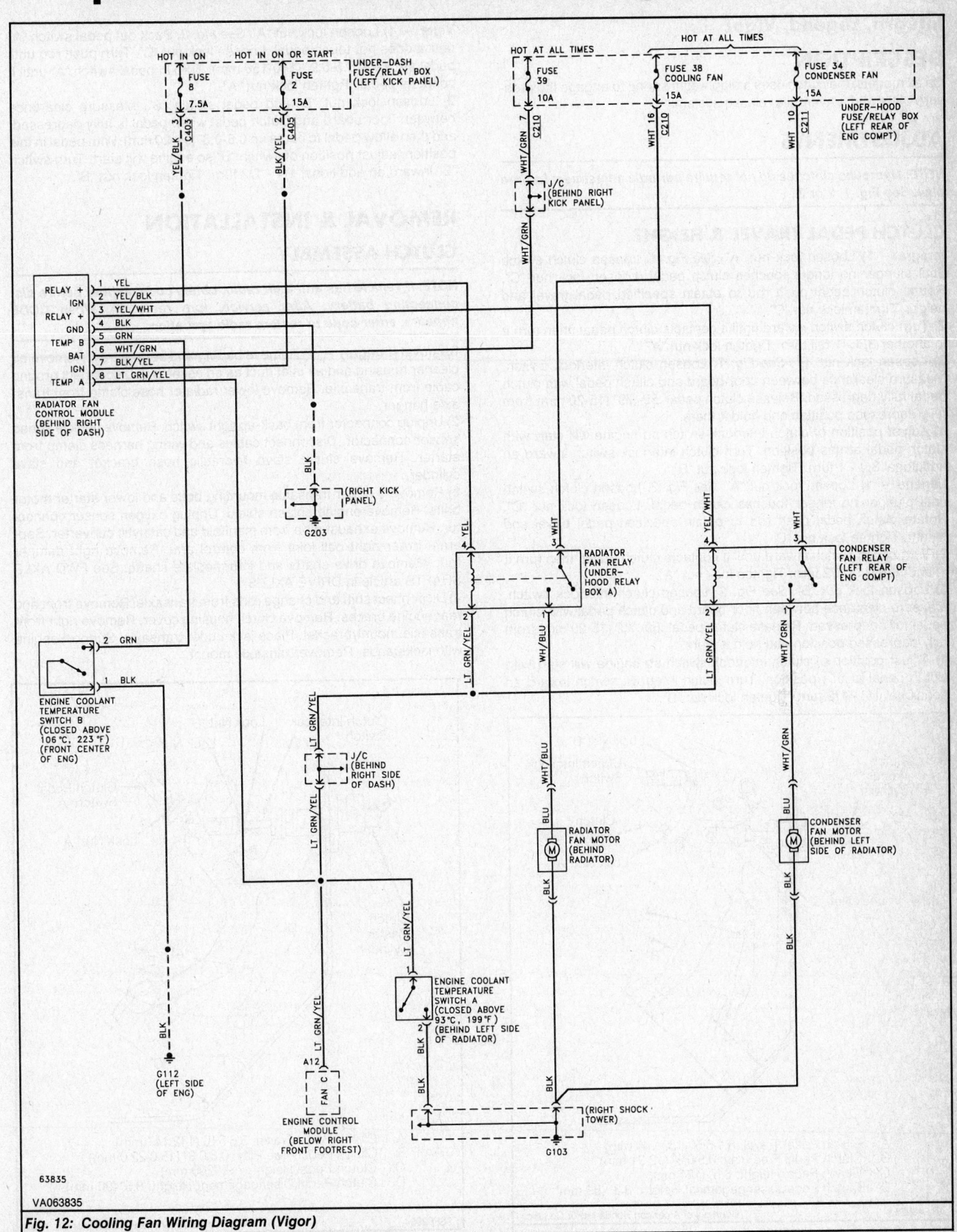

63835

VA063835

Fig. 12: Cooling Fan Wiring Diagram (Vigor)

Integra, Legend, Vigor

DESCRIPTION

On all models, the clutch uses a diaphragm spring to engage the pressure plate and a hydraulic release system.

ADJUSTMENTS

NOTE: Hydraulic clutches do not require periodic adjustment for free play. See Fig. 1, 2 or 3.

CLUTCH PEDAL TRAVEL & HEIGHT

Integra – 1) Loosen lock nut "A". *See Fig. 1.* Loosen clutch switch until plunger no longer touches clutch pedal. Loosen lock nut "C". Rotate clutch pedal push rod to obtain specified pedal travel and height. Tighten lock nut "C".

2) Turn clutch switch inward until it contacts clutch pedal, then turn it in another 3/4 - 1 full turn. Tighten lock nut "A".

3) Loosen lock nut "B". *See Fig. 1.* Loosen clutch interlock switch. Measure clearance between floor board and clutch pedal with clutch pedal fully depressed. Release clutch pedal .59-.79" (15-20 mm) from fully depressed position and hold it there.

4) Adjust position of clutch interlock switch so engine will start with clutch pedal at this position. Turn clutch interlock switch inward an additional 3/4 - 1 turn. Tighten lock nut "B".

Legend – 1) Loosen lock nut "A". *See Fig. 2.* Loosen clutch switch until plunger no longer touches clutch pedal. Loosen lock nut "C". Rotate clutch pedal push rod to obtain specified pedal travel and height. Tighten lock nut "C".

2) Turn clutch switch inward until it contacts clutch pedal, then turn it in another 1/4 - 1/2 turn. Tighten lock nut "A".

3) Loosen lock nut "B". *See Fig. 2.* Loosen clutch interlock switch. Measure clearance between floor board and clutch pedal with clutch pedal fully depressed. Release clutch pedal .59-.79" (15-20 mm) from fully depressed position and hold it there.

4) Adjust position of clutch interlock switch so engine will start with clutch pedal at this position. Turn clutch interlock switch inward an additional 1/4 - 1/2 turn. Tighten lock nut "B".

Vigor – 1) Loosen lock nut "A". *See Fig. 3.* Back out pedal switch "A" until it does not touch pedal. Loosen lock nut "C". Turn push rod until pedal stroke is 5.5-5.9" (140-150 mm). Turn in pedal switch "A" until it contacts pedal. Tighten lock nut "A".

2) Loosen lock nut "B" and pedal switch "B". Measure clearance between floor board and clutch pedal when pedal is fully depressed, and then allow pedal to come up 0.6-0.8" (15-20 mm). With pedal in this position, adjust position of switch "B" so engine will start. Turn switch "B" inward an additional 1/4 - 1/2 turn. Tighten lock nut "B".

REMOVAL & INSTALLATION

CLUTCH ASSEMBLY

NOTE: If vehicle has anti-theft radio, obtain code number before disconnecting battery. After service, turn radio on. When CODE appears, enter code to restore radio operation.

Removal (Integra) – 1) Remove battery and battery tray. Remove air cleaner housing and air inlet duct as an assembly. Disconnect ground cable from transaxle. Remove lower radiator hose clamp from transaxle hanger.

2) Unplug connector from back-up light switch. Remove vehicle speed sensor connector. Disconnect cables and wiring harness clamp from starter. Remove clutch slave hydraulic hose bracket and slave cylinder.

3) Remove 3 upper transaxle mounting bolts and lower starter motor bolts. Remove engine splash shield. Unplug oxygen sensor connector. Remove exhaust pipe from manifold and catalytic converter. Separate lower right ball joint from control arm. Remove right damper fork. Remove drive shafts and intermediate shafts. See FWD AXLE SHAFTS article in DRIVE AXLES.

4) Disconnect shift and change rods from transaxle. Remove front and rear engine braces. Remove clutch housing cover. Remove right front transaxle mount/bracket. Place jack under transaxle. Support engine with jackstands. Remove transaxle mount.

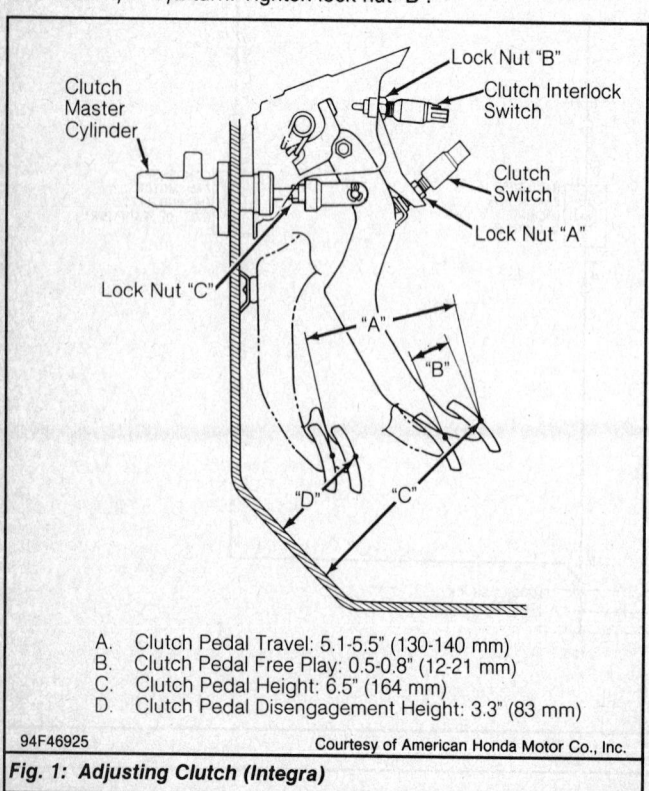

A. Clutch Pedal Travel: 5.1-5.5" (130-140 mm)
B. Clutch Pedal Free Play: 0.5-0.8" (12-21 mm)
C. Clutch Pedal Height: 6.5" (164 mm)
D. Clutch Pedal Disengagement Height: 3.3" (83 mm)

94F46925   Courtesy of American Honda Motor Co., Inc.

Fig. 1: Adjusting Clutch (Integra)

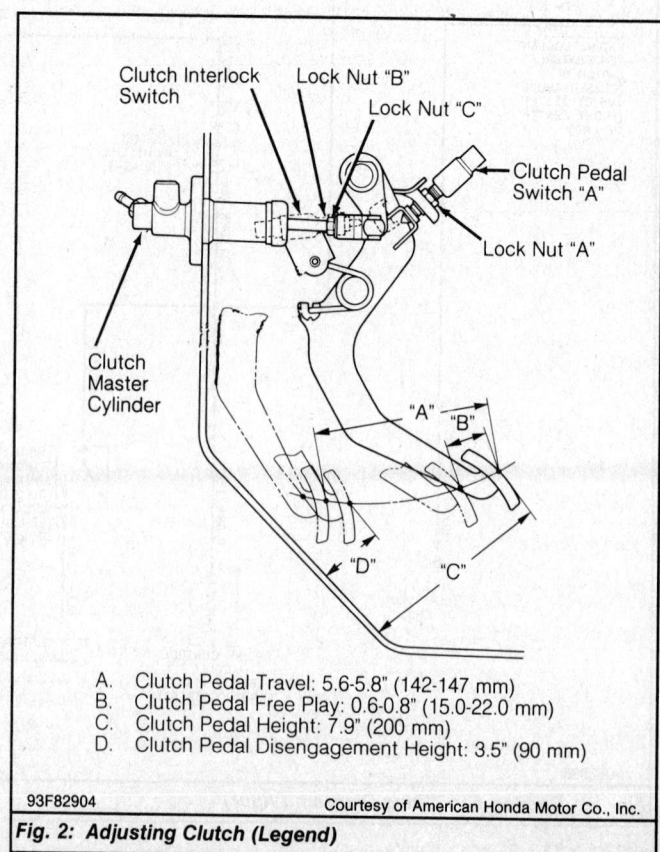

A. Clutch Pedal Travel: 5.6-5.8" (142-147 mm)
B. Clutch Pedal Free Play: 0.6-0.8" (15.0-22.0 mm)
C. Clutch Pedal Height: 7.9" (200 mm)
D. Clutch Pedal Disengagement Height: 3.5" (90 mm)

93F82904   Courtesy of American Honda Motor Co., Inc.

Fig. 2: Adjusting Clutch (Legend)

5) Remove rear transaxle mount bracket and mount bolts from side of transaxle. Move transaxle away from engine until shaft clears clutch. Lower transaxle to remove from vehicle.

6) Before removing clutch from flywheel, measure diaphragm spring fingers wear with feeler gauge, Handle (07936-3710100), Clutch Alignment Shaft (07NAF-PR30100), and Clutch Alignment Disc (07JAF-PM7011A). Wear limit is 0.03" (.8 mm). Install flywheel holder. Unscrew pressure plate bolts 2 turns at a time in a crisscross pattern, to prevent warpage.

Inspection – 1) Inspect pressure plate surface for wear, cracks, burning, or warpage in excess of 0.006" (0.15 mm). Measure warpage with straightedge and feeler gauge at several different points. Inspect clutch pilot bearing for smooth operation. Clutch release bearing must turn smoothly. Replace bearings if necessary.

2) Inspect clutch disc lining for excessive wear and burned or oil-soaked condition. Measure disc thickness and rivet depth. Inspect clutch disc for loose torsion dampers. Measure clutch disc runout and flywheel runout. See CLUTCH SPECIFICATIONS table.

NOTE: Use new spring clips on both axle shafts. Slide axles in until spring clips engage differential.

Installation – 1) Align dowel holes in pressure plate with flywheel dowels. Using clutch alignment tool and ring gear holder, install disc and pressure plate. Tighten pressure plate bolts to specification in a crisscross pattern. See TORQUE SPECIFICATIONS.

2) Ensure both dowel pins are installed in clutch housing. Clean release bearing sliding surface. Apply molybdenum disulfide grease to surface. Apply a light coating of grease to input shaft splines. Keep clutch disc and pressure plate surfaces free of grease and dirt.

3) To complete installation, reverse removal procedure. Refill all fluids to proper level. Adjust clutch pedal height and free play. See CLUTCH PEDAL TRAVEL & HEIGHT under ADJUSTMENTS.

CLUTCH SPECIFICATIONS

Application	In. (mm)
Disc Thickness	
Standard (New)	0.33-0.36 (8.4-9.1)
Service Limit	0.24 (6.0)
Disc Runout	0.04 (1.0)
Maximum Flywheel Runout	
Standard (New)	0.002 (0.05)
Service Limit	0.006 (0.15)
Rivet Depth	
Standard (New)	0.05 (1.30)
Service Limit	0.008 (0.20)

NOTE: Obtain radio anti-theft code number before disconnecting battery. After service, turn radio on. When CODE appears, enter code to restore radio operation.

Removal (Legend) – 1) Disconnect battery cables. Remove strut bar. Drain transaxle fluid. Without removing vacuum lines, remove emission control box and set it aside. Unplug harness connectors (if necessary). Remove transaxle housing bolts.

2) Remove release cylinder hose bracket from rear engine hanger. Remove exhaust pipe and catalytic converter. Remove secondary cover and 36-mm sealing bolt. *See Fig. 4.* Remove heat shield and bracket. Shift transaxle into first gear to lock secondary gear. Using Puller (07LAC-PW50100), separate extension shaft from differential. *See Fig. 5.* Disconnect shift rod and torque rod from transaxle. Remove clutch release fork cover. Remove clutch release cylinder. Disconnect oil cooler hoses from oil pump pipes.

3) Remove lower engine shield. Temporarily reinstall steering gear bolts. Remove exhaust pipe bracket, transaxle mount, and transaxle bracket. Pull out release fork to disengage it from pivot and release bearing. Let fork hang from housing.

4) Place jack under transaxle. Remove transaxle mounts. Remove engine-to-transaxle bracket. Remove flywheel inspection cover. Remove transaxle housing mounting bolts and 26-mm shim. *See Fig.*

6. Check for wires, hoses, or any other components that may still be attached. Pull transaxle away from engine until clear. Lower transaxle to remove from vehicle.

5) If reusing clutch, mark pressure plate and flywheel for installation reference. Unscrew pressure plate bolts 2 turns at a time in a crisscross pattern. If necessary, remove flywheel and clutch pilot bearing.

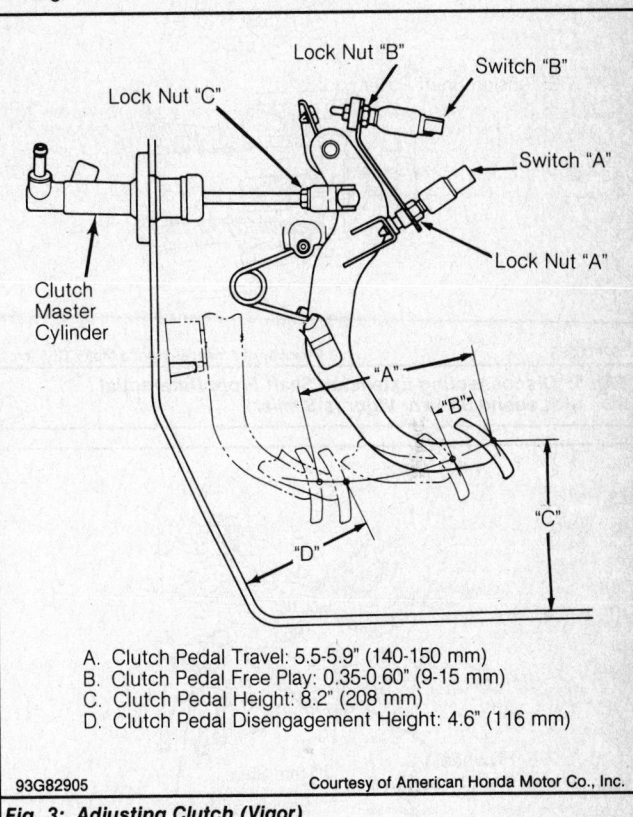

A. Clutch Pedal Travel: 5.5-5.9" (140-150 mm)
B. Clutch Pedal Free Play: 0.35-0.60" (9-15 mm)
C. Clutch Pedal Height: 8.2" (208 mm)
D. Clutch Pedal Disengagement Height: 4.6" (116 mm)

93G82905 Courtesy of American Honda Motor Co., Inc.

Fig. 3: Adjusting Clutch (Vigor)

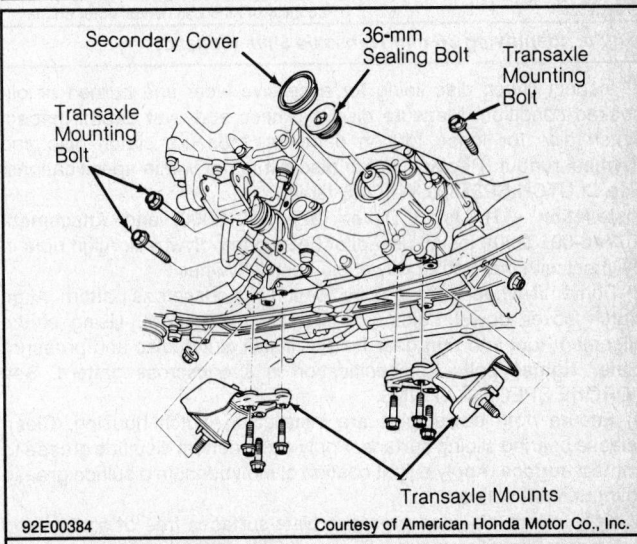

92E00384 Courtesy of American Honda Motor Co., Inc.

Fig. 4: Identifying Differential Secondary Cover & Sealing Bolt (Legend)

Inspection – 1) Inspect pressure plate surface for wear, cracks, burning, or warpage in excess of 0.006" (0.15 mm). Measure warpage with straightedge and feeler gauge at several different points. Inspect clutch pilot bearing for smooth operation. Clutch release bearing must turn smoothly. Replace bearings if necessary.

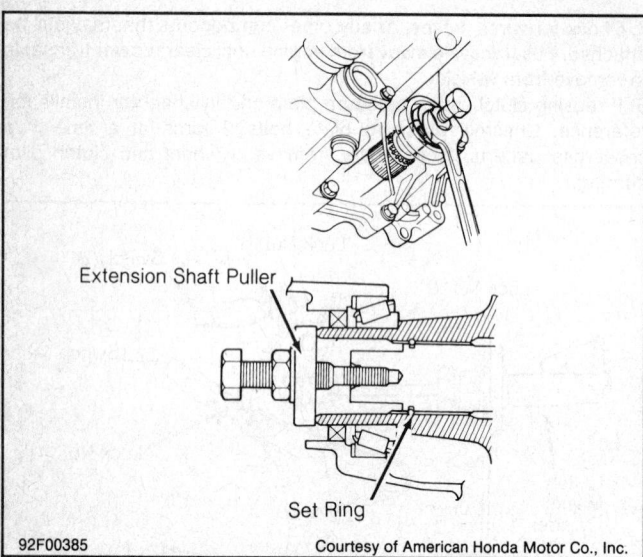

Extension Shaft Puller

Set Ring

92F00385   Courtesy of American Honda Motor Co., Inc.

Fig. 5: Disconnecting Extension Shaft From Differential (Legend Shown; Vigor Is Similar)

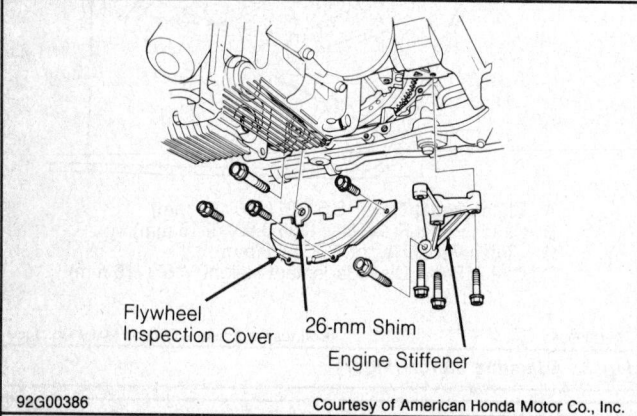

Flywheel Inspection Cover

26-mm Shim

Engine Stiffener

92G00386   Courtesy of American Honda Motor Co., Inc.

Fig. 6: Identifying 26-mm Transaxle Shim (Legend)

2) Inspect clutch disc lining for excessive wear and burned or oil-soaked condition. Measure disc thickness and rivet depth. Inspect clutch disc for loose torsion dampers. Measure clutch disc and flywheel runout. Replace clutch disc if it is not within specifications. See CLUTCH SPECIFICATIONS table.

Installation – 1) Using Driver (07749-0010000) and Attachment (07746-0010200), install new pilot bearing into flywheel. Align hole in flywheel with crankshaft dowel pin. Install flywheel.

2) Tighten flywheel bolts to specification in a crisscross pattern. Align clutch cover dowel holes with dowels in flywheel. Using clutch alignment tool and ring gear holder, install clutch disc and pressure plate. Tighten bolts to specification in a crisscross pattern. See TORQUE SPECIFICATIONS.

3) Ensure both dowel pins are installed in clutch housing. Clean release bearing sliding surface. Apply molybdenum disulfide grease to contact surface. Apply a light coating of molybdenum disulfide grease to input shaft splines.

4) Keep clutch disc and pressure plate surfaces free of grease and dirt. Apply High Temp Urea Grease (08798-9002) to extension shaft splines. Install new extension shaft set ring. Ensure open slot in set ring is facing upward.

5) Using Extension Shaft Installer (07MAF-PY40100), install extension shaft. Ensure set ring locks into extension shaft groove. Install 36-mm sealing bolt and tighten it to specification. See TORQUE SPECIFICATIONS.

6) To complete installation, reverse removal procedure. Refill all fluids to proper level. Adjust clutch pedal travel and height. See CLUTCH PEDAL TRAVEL & HEIGHT under ADJUSTMENTS.

NOTE: *Obtain radio anti-theft code number before disconnecting battery. After service, turn radio on. When CODE appears, enter code to restore radio operation.*

Removal (Vigor) – 1) Remove battery and battery tray. Remove ABS relay box, located near corner of battery. Leave wiring harness connected to relay box. Remove heat shield. Remove distributor, leaving wiring connected. Remove control box, leaving vacuum hoses connected.

2) Unplug back-up switch connector. Disconnect transaxle ground wire. Remove clutch release cylinder. Remove transaxle housing bolts and 26-mm shim. Remove transaxle mount beam and transaxle mount bracket. Remove secondary cover and 33-mm sealing bolt.

3) Shift transaxle into low gear. Using Extension Shaft Puller (07LAC-PW50100), disengage extension shaft from differential. *See Fig. 5.* Remove exhaust pipe and exhaust pipe brace. Remove shift rod and extension rod. *See Fig. 7.* Remove transaxle mount nuts. Place jack under transaxle. Remove transaxle mounts. *See Fig. 8.*

4) Remove clutch housing cover. Remove transaxle housing bolt. Pull transaxle away from engine until clear. Lower transaxle from vehicle to remove.

5) If reusing clutch, mark pressure plate and flywheel for installation reference. Install flywheel holder. Unscrew pressure plate bolts 2 turns at a time in a crisscross pattern.

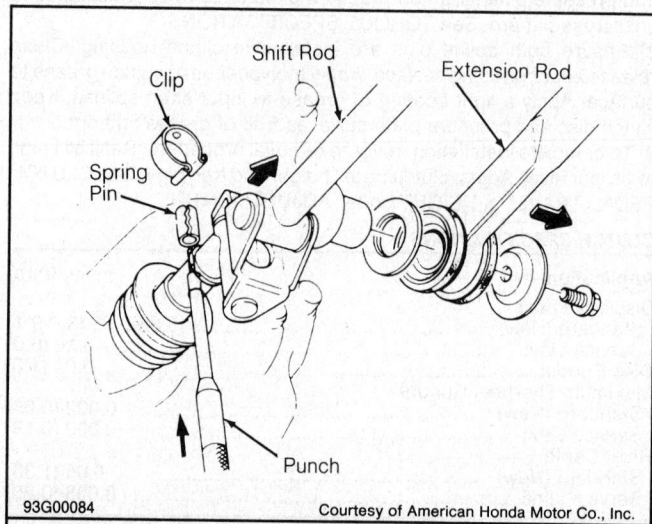

Clip   Shift Rod   Extension Rod

Spring Pin

Punch

93G00084   Courtesy of American Honda Motor Co., Inc.

Fig. 7: Removing Shift Rod (Vigor)

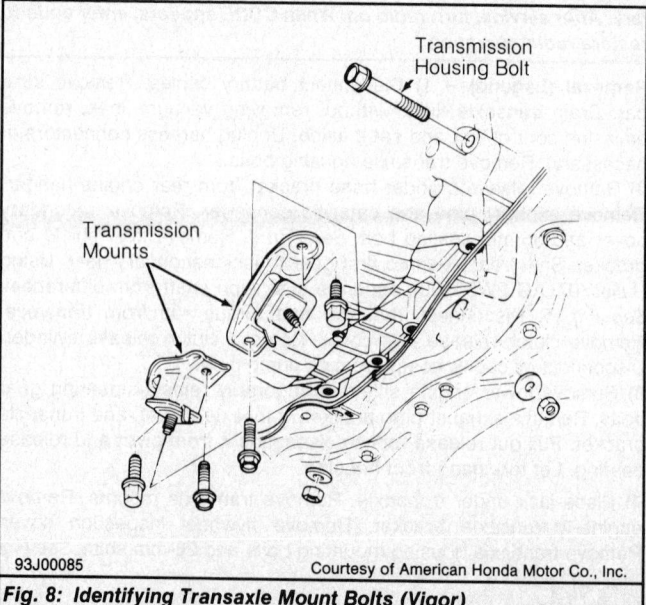

Transmission Housing Bolt

Transmission Mounts

93J00085   Courtesy of American Honda Motor Co., Inc.

Fig. 8: Identifying Transaxle Mount Bolts (Vigor)

Inspection – 1) Inspect pressure plate surface for wear, cracks, burning and warpage in excess of 0.006" (0.15 mm). Measure warpage with straightedge and feeler gauge at several different points. Check clutch pilot bearing for smooth operation. Clutch release bearing must turn smoothly. Replace bearings if necessary.

2) Inspect clutch disc lining for excessive wear and burned or oil-soaked condition. Measure disc thickness and rivet depth. Inspect clutch disc for loose torsion dampers. Measure disc runout and flywheel runout. Replace clutch disc if it does not meet specifications. See CLUTCH SPECIFICATIONS table.

Installation – 1) Ensure both locating dowels are in place. Pack clutch release bearing, release fork, and release guide with molybdenum disulfide grease. Apply high temperature molybdenum disulfide grease to extension shaft splines. Pack secondary gear and extension shaft cavity with high temperature molybdenum disulfide grease.

2) Install new shift rod retainer pin and extension shaft retaining ring. Turn release fork upward, then guide it into groove on release bearing. To complete installation, reverse removal procedure. Tighten bolts to specification. See TORQUE SPECIFICATIONS.

CLUTCH MASTER CYLINDER

Removal & Installation (Integra) – Remove brake fluid from master cylinder. Disconnect fluid lines and reservoir hose from master cylinder. Plug end of line from fluid reservoir. Remove master cylinder. Reverse removal procedure to install. Bleed hydraulic system. See BLEEDING CLUTCH HYDRAULIC SYSTEM.

Removal & Installation (Legend) – Remove clevis pin from master cylinder push rod, located at clutch pedal. Disconnect fluid lines at master cylinder. Plug end of line from fluid reservoir. Remove master cylinder. Reverse removal procedure to install. Bleed hydraulic system. See BLEEDING CLUTCH HYDRAULIC SYSTEM.

Removal & Installation (Vigor) – Leaving hoses connected, remove charcoal canister and set it aside. Disconnect fluid lines at master cylinder. Plug end of line from fluid reservoir. Remove lower dashboard panel. Remove clevis pin from master cylinder push rod, located at clutch pedal. Remove master cylinder. Reverse removal procedure to install. Bleed hydraulic system. See BLEEDING CLUTCH HYDRAULIC SYSTEM.

BLEEDING CLUTCH HYDRAULIC SYSTEM

Attach hose to bleeder fitting, located on clutch release cylinder, next to hydraulic line. Submerge other end of hose in container half full of clean brake fluid. Fill reservoir with DOT 3 or DOT 4 brake fluid. Open bleeder fitting. Have assistant press clutch pedal to full release position. Close bleeder fitting. Repeat until air bubbles no longer emerge from hose. Refill reservoir.

OVERHAUL

NOTE: Manufacturer recommends replacement of faulty clutch master and release cylinders, and does not provide overhaul procedures.

TORQUE SPECIFICATIONS
TORQUE SPECIFICATIONS (INTEGRA)

Application	Ft. Lbs. (N.m)
Ball Joint Castle Nut	40 (54)
Damper Fork Pinch Bolt	47 (64)
Engine Stiffener Bracket-To-Engine Bolt	17 (23)
Engine Stiffener Bracket-To-Transaxle Bolt	42 (57)
Flywheel-To-Crankshaft Bolt [1]	76 (103)
Intermediate Shaft Support Bolt	29 (39)
Pressure Plate-To-Flywheel Bolt [1]	19 (26)
Radius Arm Nut	32 (43)
Rear Mount-To-Transaxle Bolt	43 (58)
Release Fork Bolt	22 (29)
Starter Motor Bolt	32 (43)
Transaxle Mounting Bolt/Nut (Firewall Side)	54 (73)
Transaxle Mounting Bolt/Nut (Front)	47 (64)
Transaxle-To-Engine Mounting Bolt	42 (57)
Transaxle Torque Rod Bolt	16 (22)

[1] – Tighten bolts in a crisscross pattern.

TORQUE SPECIFICATIONS (LEGEND)

Application	Ft. Lbs. (N.m)
Engine Stiffener Mounting Bolt	16 (22)
Exhaust Pipe Bracket-To-Transaxle Bolt	26 (35)
Exhaust Pipe-To-Manifold Nut	40 (54)
Extension Shaft 36-mm Sealing Bolt	58 (79)
Flywheel-To-Crankshaft Bolt [1]	76 (103)
Master Cylinder Mounting Bolt	10 (14)
Pressure Plate-To-Flywheel Bolt [1]	16 (22)
Release Cylinder-To-Housing Bolt	16 (22)
Transaxle Mount Bolt	29 (39)
Transaxle Mount Nut	36 (49)
Transaxle Shift Rod Bolt	16 (22)
Transaxle-To-Engine Bolt	55 (75)
Transaxle Torque Rod Bolt	16 (22)

[1] – Tighten bolts in a crisscross pattern.

TORQUE SPECIFICATIONS (VIGOR)

Application	Ft. Lbs. (N.m)
Exhaust Pipe Bracket Bolt	16 (22)
Exhaust Manifold Nut	40 (54)
Extension Shaft Sealing Bolt	58 (79)
Flywheel-To-Crankshaft Bolt [1]	76 (103)
Pressure Plate-To-Flywheel Bolt [1]	19 (26)
Release Cylinder Bolt	16 (22)
Torque Rod Bolt	16 (22)
Transaxle Mount Nut	36 (49)
Transaxle Shift Rod Bolt	16 (22)
Transaxle-To-Engine Bolt	55 (75)

[1] – Tighten bolts in a crisscross pattern.

1994 DRIVE AXLES
FWD Axle Shafts

Integra, Legend, Vigor

DESCRIPTION & OPERATION

Each axle shaft consists of a shaft and a Constant Velocity (CV) joint at each end. Inner CV joint is splined to transaxle. Outer CV joint is splined to hub assembly and secured by a spindle nut. Inner and outer CV joints are enclosed by boots. Inner CV joints can be repaired; outer CV joints can be serviced only as an assembly.

TROUBLE SHOOTING

NOTE: See TROUBLE SHOOTING article in GENERAL INFORMATION.

REMOVAL, DISASSEMBLY, REASSEMBLY & INSTALLATION

FWD AXLE SHAFTS

Removal – **1)** Pry lock tab away from spindle nut. Loosen spindle nut and wheel lug nuts. Raise and support vehicle. Drain transaxle fluid. On Integra and Legend, draining transaxle fluid is not necessary if removing only left axle shaft. On Vigor, draining transaxle fluid is not necessary if removing only right axle shaft. On all models, remove front wheels and spindle nut. Remove damper pinch bolt and damper fork bolt. Remove damper fork. *See Fig. 1.*

2) Remove lower ball joint cotter pin. Back off castle nut until outer surface is flush with end of stud. Using ball joint puller, separate ball joint from lower control arm. Remove ball joint castle nut and ball joint from lower control arm. Pull steering knuckle outward. Remove axle shaft from hub assembly. If necessary, use plastic mallet to drive axle from hub.

NOTE: DO NOT pull on inner CV joint; it may come apart. Be careful not to damage seals.

3) Using a large screwdriver, carefully pry inner CV joint and shaft assembly outward to disengage retaining ring from groove at end of inner drive axle. Grip both sides of inner CV joint, and remove axle shaft and CV joint from vehicle.

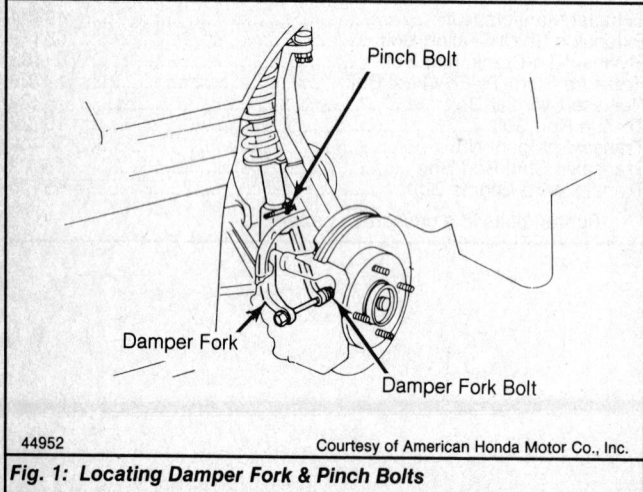

Fig. 1: Locating Damper Fork & Pinch Bolts

NOTE: DO NOT disassemble outer CV joint. If service is necessary, replace it as an assembly. On inner CV joint, mark rollers and roller grooves for reassembly reference.

Disassembly – **1)** Remove axle shaft from vehicle, and place on work bench. Remove and discard inner CV joint boot clamps. Slide boot toward outer CV joint for access to inner CV joint. *See Fig. 2.*
2) Mark axle shaft, inner CV joint housing, and spider roller for reassembly reference. Remove housing from spider assembly. Mark rollers and spider for reassembly reference. Remove rollers from spider.

3) Remove snap ring retaining spider to axle shaft. Remove spider. Remove stopper ring. Slide boot from axle shaft. Remove outer CV joint boot clamps. Slide boot from axle shaft inner CV joint end.

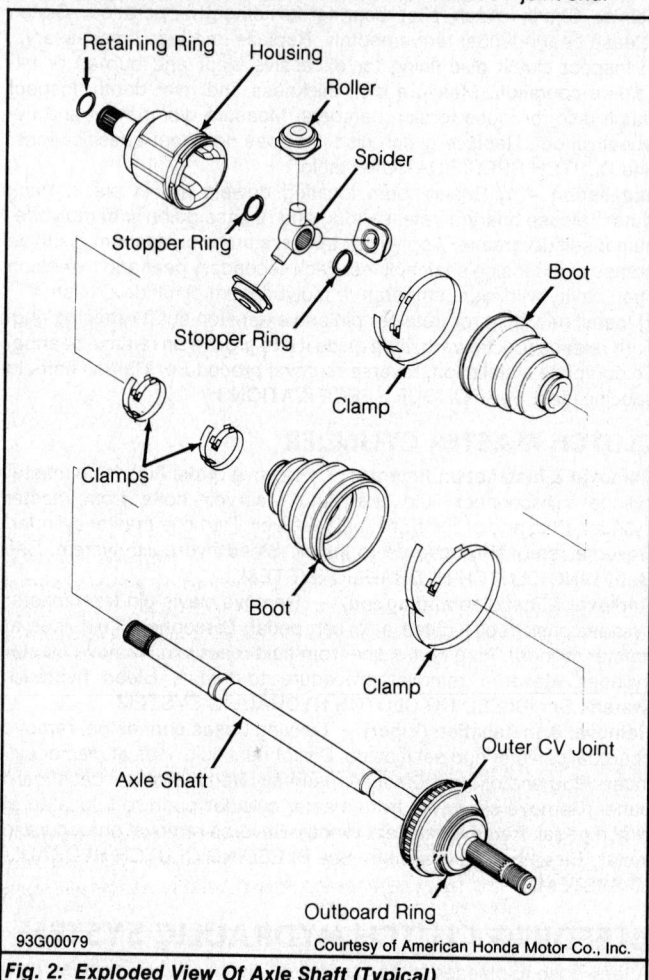

Fig. 2: Exploded View Of Axle Shaft (Typical)

Reassembly – **1)** Thoroughly clean axle shaft, and inspect for wear. Replace all defective parts. Wrap axle shaft splines with vinyl tape to prevent damage to CV joint boots.
2) Install inner and outer CV joint boots. Remove vinyl tape from axle shaft. DO NOT install CV joint boot clamps yet.

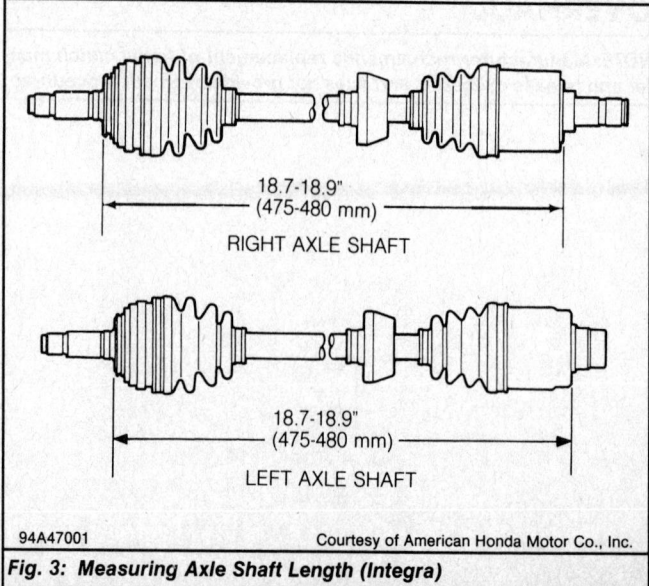

Fig. 3: Measuring Axle Shaft Length (Integra)

3) Install stopper ring into groove on axle shaft. Install spider onto axle shaft with reference marks aligned. Install snap ring into groove. Pack outer CV joint boot with grease supplied with joint kit. Lubricate spider and inner bore of rollers.

4) Align rollers with marks made at disassembly. Ensure high sides of rollers face outward. Install rollers. Pack inner CV joint and boot with grease. Install housing onto spider assembly. Align reference marks made at disassembly while installing housing onto spider assembly. Adjust length of axle shaft. See Fig. 3, 4 or 5.

5) Position boots halfway between full compression and full extension. Install new boot clamps. Lightly tap boot clamp to reduce clamp height. Install new retaining ring onto end of inner CV joint. Install axle shaft.

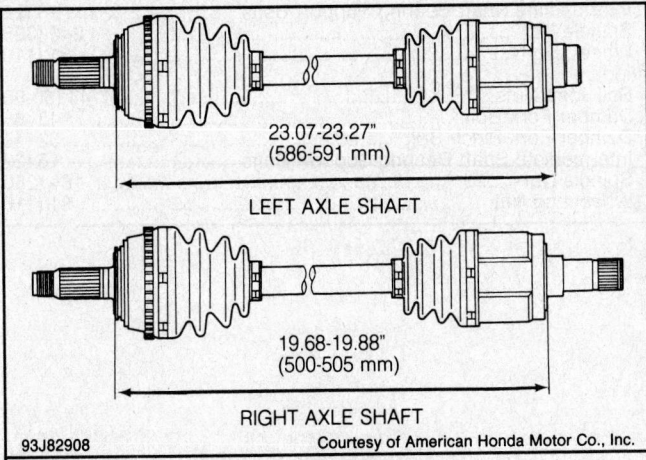

23.07-23.27"
(586-591 mm)

LEFT AXLE SHAFT

19.68-19.88"
(500-505 mm)

RIGHT AXLE SHAFT

93J82908   Courtesy of American Honda Motor Co., Inc.

Fig. 4: Measuring Axle Shaft Length (Legend)

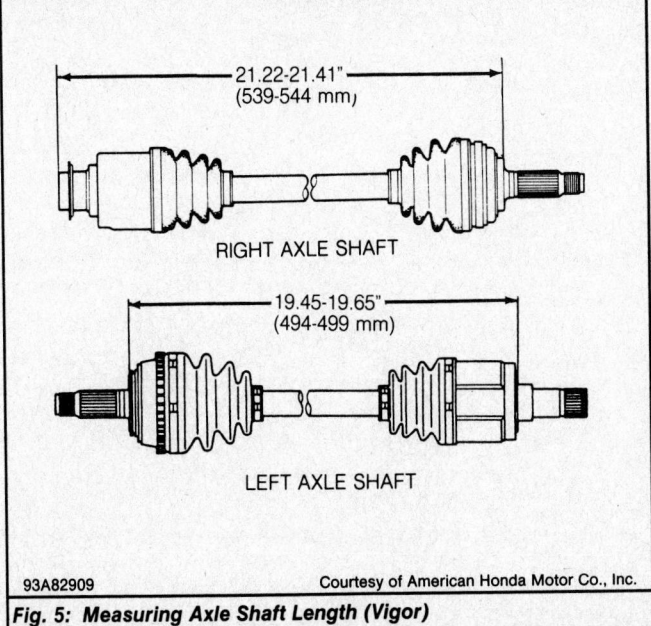

21.22-21.41"
(539-544 mm)

RIGHT AXLE SHAFT

19.45-19.65"
(494-499 mm)

LEFT AXLE SHAFT

93A82909   Courtesy of American Honda Motor Co., Inc.

Fig. 5: Measuring Axle Shaft Length (Vigor)

CAUTION: Always use a NEW retaining ring when installing axle shaft.

Installation – 1) Ensure length of assembled axle shaft is within specification. See Fig. 3, 4 or 5. Install new retaining ring into groove at end of axle shaft. Install new clamps onto boots.

2) Slide axle into transaxle or intermediate shaft. Seat retaining ring fully into groove. Check by attempting to pull axle out of installed position.

3) Pull hub assembly away from axle shaft. Slide axle into hub assembly. Install and lightly tighten spindle nut. Position ball joint into hub.

Raise lower control arm with floor jack. Install ball joint nut. Tighten ball joint nut to specification. See TORQUE SPECIFICATIONS.

4) Install and secure cotter pin. Remove floor jack. Tighten spindle nut to specification. To complete installation, reverse removal procedure.

INTERMEDIATE SHAFT

Removal (Integra) – 1) Drain fluid from transaxle. Remove left axle shaft. See FWD AXLE SHAFTS. Remove bearing support bolts. See Fig. 6.

CAUTION: To prevent damaging oil seal when removing intermediate shaft, hold shaft in horizontal position until shaft is clear of seal.

2) Lower bearing support. Remove intermediate shaft from differential. To prevent damage to seal, hold intermediate shaft in horizontal position when removing.

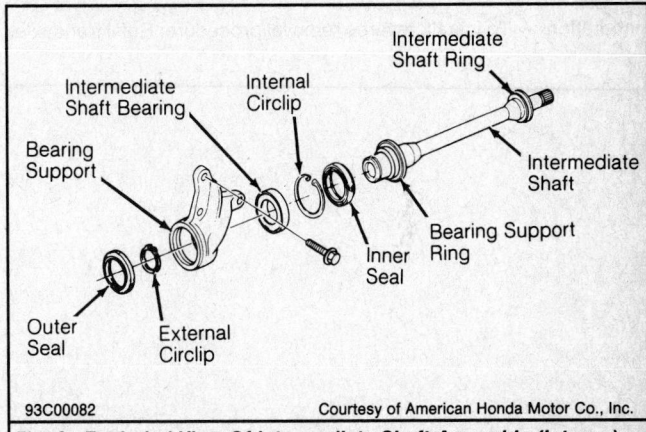

Intermediate Shaft Bearing

Bearing Support

Internal Circlip

Intermediate Shaft Ring

Intermediate Shaft

Bearing Support Ring

Inner Seal

Outer Seal

External Circlip

93C00082   Courtesy of American Honda Motor Co., Inc.

Fig. 6: Exploded View Of Intermediate Shaft Assembly (Integra)

Disassembly – Remove intermediate shaft outer seal. Remove external circlip. Press intermediate shaft from shaft bearing. Remove intermediate shaft inner seal. Remove internal circlip. Press intermediate shaft bearing from bearing support. Inspect all components for wear or damage. Replace as necessary.

Reassembly – 1) Press intermediate shaft bearing into bearing support. Seat internal circlip into groove of bearing support. Install circlip so tapered end faces outward.

2) Press intermediate shaft inner seal into bearing support. Press intermediate shaft into shaft bearing. Install external circlip into intermediate shaft groove so tapered end faces outward. Press outer seal into bearing support.

Installation – To install, reverse removal procedure. Refill transaxle.

Removal (Legend & Vigor) – Drain fluid from transaxle. Remove left axle shaft. See FWD AXLE SHAFTS. Remove bearing support bolts. See Fig. 7. Remove intermediate shaft assembly from oil pan.

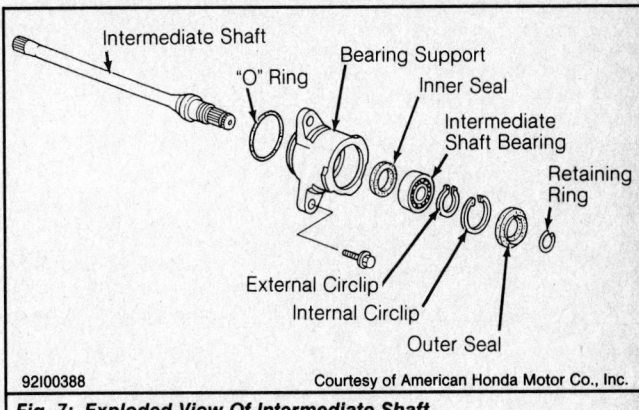

Intermediate Shaft

"O" Ring

Bearing Support

Inner Seal

Intermediate Shaft Bearing

Retaining Ring

External Circlip

Internal Circlip

Outer Seal

92I00388   Courtesy of American Honda Motor Co., Inc.

Fig. 7: Exploded View Of Intermediate Shaft (Legend Shown; Vigor Is Similar)

CAUTION: Bearing support is made of aluminum. DO NOT overstess when servicing intermediate shaft.

Disassembly – Remove intermediate shaft outer seal from bearing support. Remove external and internal circlips. Press intermediate shaft from shaft bearing. Press intermediate shaft bearing from bearing support. Remove intermediate shaft inner seal from bearing support. Remove "O" ring. Inspect all components for wear or damage. Replace as necessary.

Reassembly – 1) Press intermediate shaft inner seal into bearing support. Seat internal circlip into bearing support groove so tapered end faces outward.

2) Press intermediate shaft into shaft bearing. Install external circlip into intermediate shaft groove so tapered end faces outward. On Legend, press in seal until it is flush with bearing support. On Vigor, press seal into bearing support until seal is 0.28" (7 mm) from end of bearing support.

Installation – To install, reverse removal procedure. Refill transaxle.

TORQUE SPECIFICATIONS
TORQUE SPECIFICATIONS

Application	Ft. Lbs. (N.m)
Integra	
Ball Joint Nut	41 (55)
Damper Fork Bolt	48 (65)
Damper Pinch Bolt	32 (44)
Intermediate Shaft Bearing Support Bolts	29 (40)
Spindle Nut	136 (185)
Wheel Lug Nut	81 (110)
Legend	
Ball Joint Nut	52-59 (70-80)
Damper Fork Bolt	52 (70)
Damper Pinch Bolt	37 (50)
Intermediate Shaft Bearing Support Bolts	16 (22)
Spindle Nut	240 (325)
Wheel Lug Nut	81 (110)
Vigor	
Ball Joint Nuts	37-44 (50-60)
Damper Fork Bolt	48 (65)
Damper Fork Pinch Bolt	32 (44)
Intermediate Shaft Bearing Support Bolts	16 (22)
Spindle Nut	184 (250)
Wheel Lug Nut	81 (110)

Legend

DESCRIPTION

Although Legend has FWD, it is equipped with a separate differential assembly that is bolted to right side of engine oil pan and to transaxle. Differential assembly is linked internally to transaxle by an extension shaft.

AXLE RATIO

Axle ratio is determined by dividing number of ring gear teeth by number of drive pinion teeth.

AXLE RATIO SPECIFICATIONS

Application	Ratio
Automatic Transaxle (A/T)	4.35:1
Manual Transaxle (M/T)	4.48:1

LUBRICATION

CAPACITY

DIFFERENTIAL OIL CAPACITY & TYPE

Qt. (L)	Type
1.11 (1.05) After Drain	[1] API GL-4 Or GL-5 SAE 90
1.16 (1.10) After Overhaul	[1] API GL-4 Or GL-5 SAE 90

[1] – Below 0°F (–18°C), use API GL-4 or GL-5 SAE 80 or SAE 80W 90.

TROUBLE SHOOTING

NOTE: See TROUBLE SHOOTING article in GENERAL INFORMATION.

REMOVAL & INSTALLATION

DIFFERENTIAL CARRIER

Removal – 1) Disconnect negative battery cable. Raise and support vehicle. Drain cooling system. Drain differential fluid. Remove drive axles and intermediate shaft. See FWD AXLE SHAFTS article in DRIVE AXLES. Remove lower engine splash shield.

NOTE: Reinstall steering gearbox mounting bolts after removing engine splash shield.

2) Disconnect differential cooler lines. Remove speed sensor. Remove secondary cover 36-mm sealing bolt from transaxle. See Fig. 1. Shift transaxle into 1st gear or Park to lock secondary gear.

3) Using Extension Shaft Puller (07LAC-PW50100), disconnect extension shaft from differential. Remove and discard set ring. Note location of 26-mm diameter shim. See Fig. 2. Remove differential carrier mounting bolts, shim, and carrier.

Installation – 1) To install, reverse removal procedure. Install new oil pan-to-differential "O" ring. Install differential carrier. Using a feeler gauge, measure clearance between differential and transaxle. See Fig. 3. Use clearance measurement to determine appropriate shim to be installed.

2) Shims are available in 0.004" (0.10 mm) increments, ranging from 0.0748" (1.900 mm) to 0.1181" (3.000 mm). Tighten bolt retaining shim first, then tighten remaining carrier bolts. Apply High Temp Urea Grease (08798-9002) to extension shaft splines. Install new extension shaft set ring.

3) Ensure open slot of set ring faces up. Using Installer (07MAF-PY40100), install extension shaft. Ensure set ring locks into extension shaft groove. Apply high temperature Urea grease around end of extension shaft.

4) Coat threads with Loctite and install 36-mm sealing bolt. Tighten bolt to specification. See TORQUE SPECIFICATIONS. Replenish all fluids.

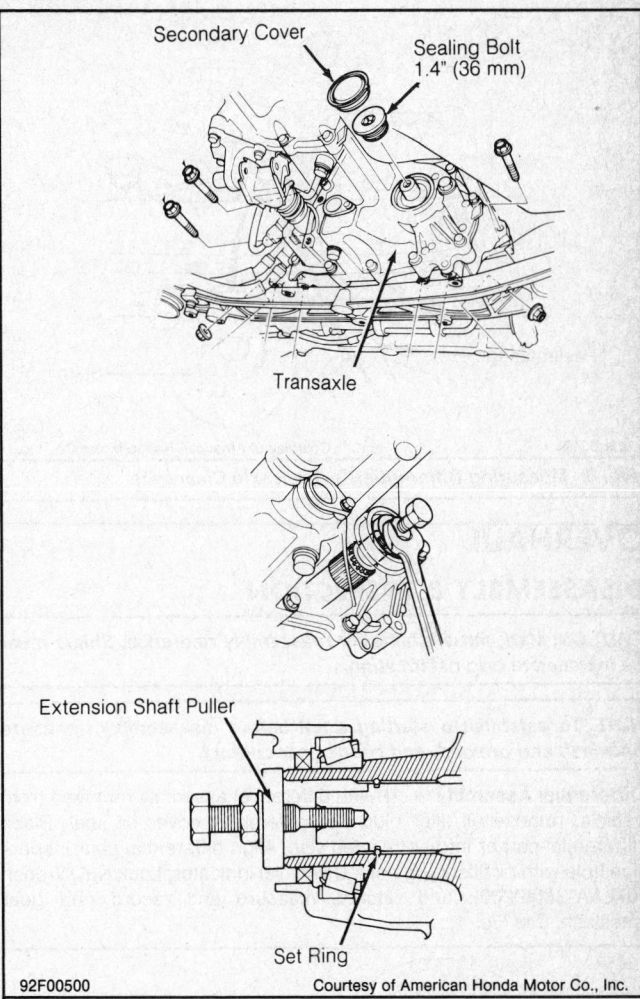

92F00500   Courtesy of American Honda Motor Co., Inc.

Fig. 1: Disconnecting Extension Shaft From Differential

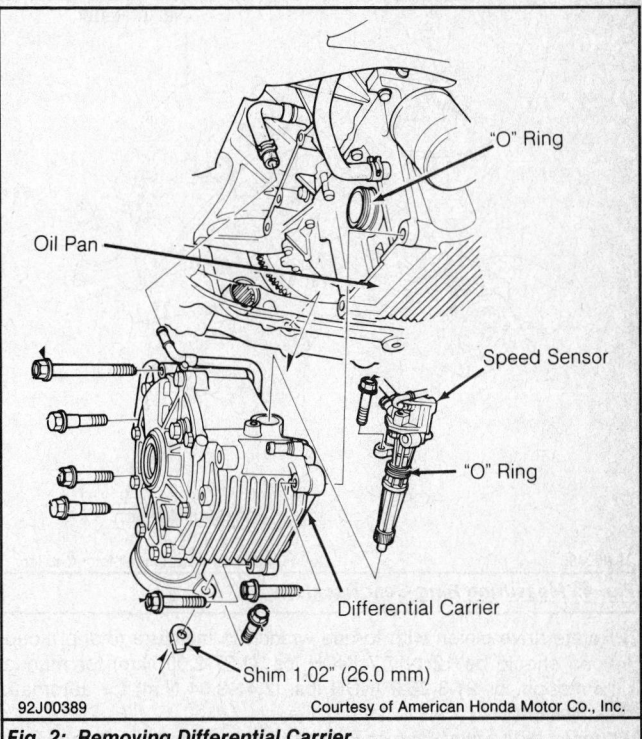

92J00389   Courtesy of American Honda Motor Co., Inc.

Fig. 2: Removing Differential Carrier

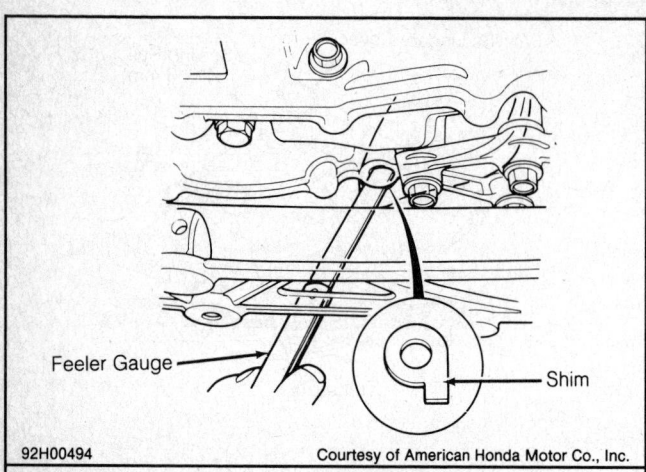

Fig. 3: Measuring Differential-To-Transaxle Clearance

Feeler Gauge — Shim

92H00494   Courtesy of American Honda Motor Co., Inc.

OVERHAUL

DISASSEMBLY & INSPECTION

CAUTION: Mark thrust shims for reassembly reference. Shims must be installed in original location.

NOTE: To establish a starting point before disassembly, measure backlash and preload, and check gear contact.

Differential Assembly – 1) With differential assembly removed from vehicle, remove oil filler plug and differential cover oil seal. Place differential carrier into soft-jawed vise. Align differential gear inspection hole with oil filler plug hole. Using dial indicator, Lock Nut Wrench (07LAA-SM40200), and ratchet, measure and record ring gear backlash. *See Fig. 4.*

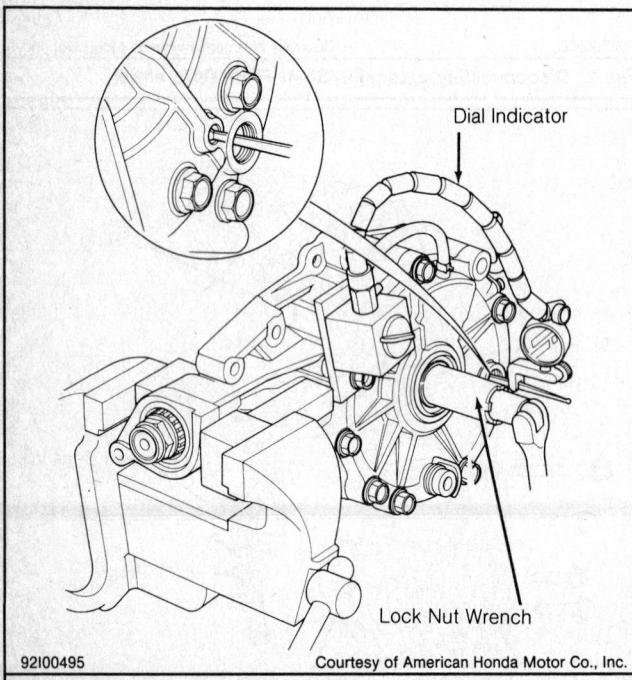

Dial Indicator

Lock Nut Wrench

92I00495   Courtesy of American Honda Motor Co., Inc.

Fig. 4: Measuring Ring Gear Backlash

2) Rotate drive pinion with torque wrench to measure total preload. Preload should be 12.1-17.7 INCH lbs. (1.37-2.00 N.m) for manual transmission, or 21.3-26.9 INCH lbs. (2.41-3.04 N.m) for automatic transmission.
3) Loosen differential case cover in a crisscross pattern. Remove differential case cover. Clean gear teeth, then coat lightly with Prussian

Blue dye on both sides of each gear tooth. Reinstall cover. Tighten bolts in a crisscross pattern to 33 ft. lbs. (45 N.m). Using Locknut Wrench (07HAA-SF10100), rotate ring gear one full turn while applying resistance to drive pinion. Remove differential case cover and check tooth contact pattern. See GEAR TOOTH CONTACT PATTERNS article in GENERAL INFORMATION.
4) On M/T vehicles, use Attachment (07GAD-PG40100) and Driver (07749-0010000) to remove outer bearing race and 79.5-mm diameter shims from differential cover. On A/T vehicles, pry up on bearing race, or heat differential housing to maximum of 212°F (100°C) to remove race.

CAUTION: On A/T vehicles, DO NOT reuse thrust shim(s) if prying method was used to remove bearing race.

5) On all vehicles, remove breather plate from differential cover. *See Fig. 5.* Remove differential case assembly from carrier. Invert carrier and remove oil cooler lines from carrier. Remove nuts securing oil cooler. Remove oil cooler, "O" rings, and oil guide pipe.
6) Hold drive pinion with 17-mm hex wrench and vise. *See Fig. 6.* Raise pinion shaft lock nut tab from groove on pinion drive gear. Remove lock nut, thrust washer, and pinion hub. Remove drive pinion oil seal, thrust washer, and bearing.
7) Remove drive pinion, pinion spacer, and thrust washer. On M/T vehicles, use a punch to remove inner and outer bearing races from carrier. On A/T vehicles, pry out bearing race, or heat differential housing to maximum of 212°F (100°C) to remove outer and inner bearing races.

CAUTION: On A/T vehicles, DO NOT reuse thrust shim(s) if bearing race was removed by prying.

8) On all vehicles, use bearing separator and hydraulic press to remove differential case bearings. Install left axle shaft and intermediate shaft into differential case. Set differential case onto "V" blocks. Measure backlash at both pinion gears. If pinion backlash exceeds 0.012" (0.30 mm), replace differential assembly.
9) Remove ring gear from differential case. Remove roll pin from pinion shaft. Keeping in order of removal, remove pinion shaft, pinion gears, side gears, thrust washers, and thrust shims. Clean all parts thoroughly in solvent. Blow dry with compressed air. Inspect parts for wear or damage. Replace if necessary.

NOTE: If replacement of ring gear or pinion is necessary, replace drive pinion and ring gear as a set.

REASSEMBLY

Differential Case – 1) Coat differential side gears on both sides with molybdenum disulfide grease. Install gears and thrust shims into differential case. Coat pinion gears with grease. Install gears and thrust washers into differential case. Pinion thrust washers must be of equal thickness.
2) Rotate gears until shaft holes in pinion gears align with shaft holes in differential case. Install pinion shaft, and align roll pin holes in shaft with hole in case. Install new roll pin into pinion shaft.
3) Measure pinion gear backlash. See step **1)** under DISASSEMBLY & INSPECTION. Install ring gear. Tighten bolts to specification. See TORQUE SPECIFICATIONS. Using hydraulic press and Attachment (07MAD-PR90100), install side bearings into differential case.

NOTE: Manufacturer recommends measuring drive pinion depth only when installing new drive pinion and ring gear.

Drive Pinion Inner Bearing – If installing new drive pinion and ring gear, measure drive pinion depth before installing inner bearing. See DRIVE PINION DEPTH under ADJUSTMENTS. Install 43-mm diameter thrust shim and roller bearing onto drive pinion. Using used pinion spacer, Attachment (07746-0030400), Driver (07746-0030100), and hydraulic press, install bearing. *See Fig. 7.* Discard used spacer after installing bearing.

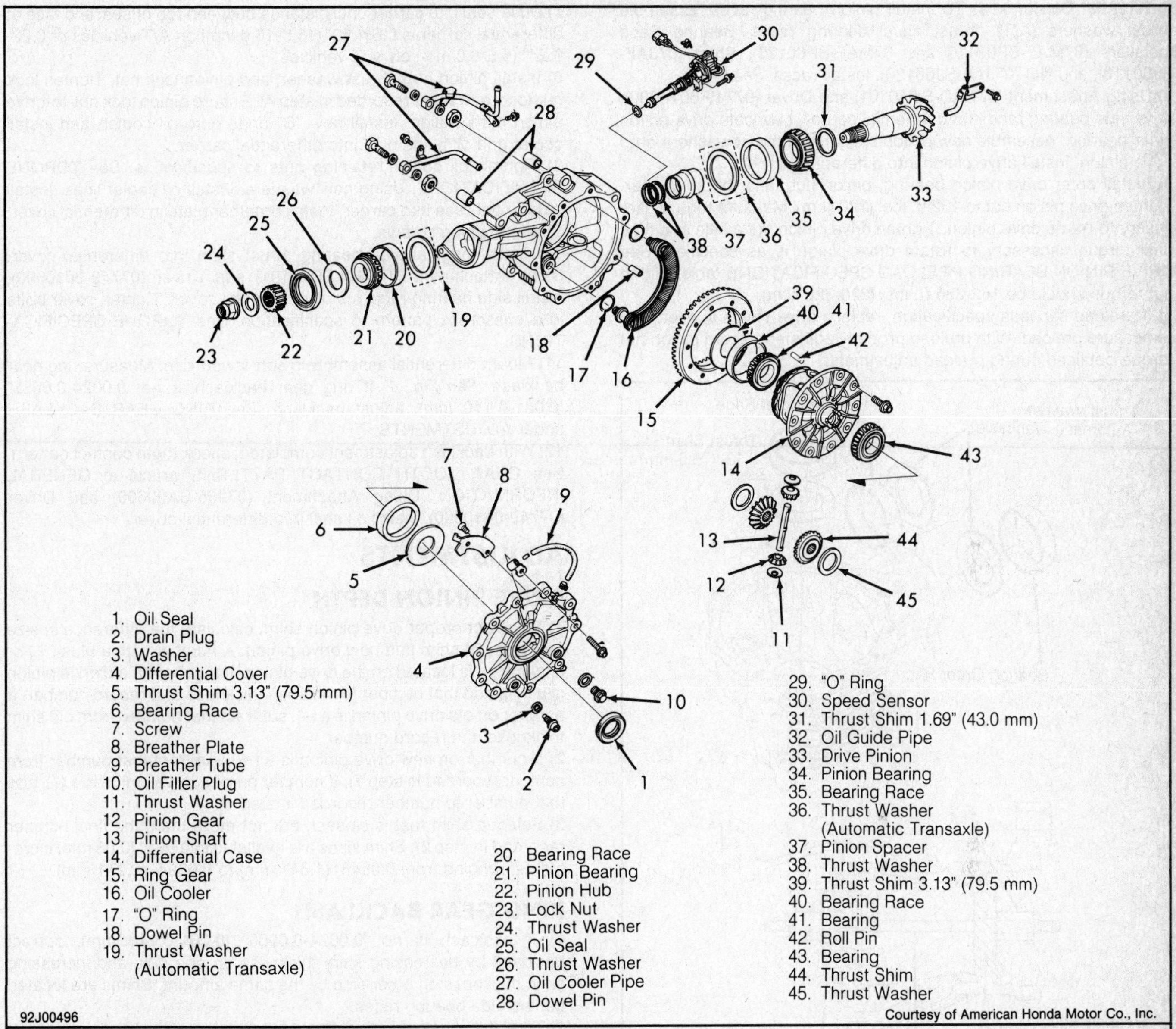

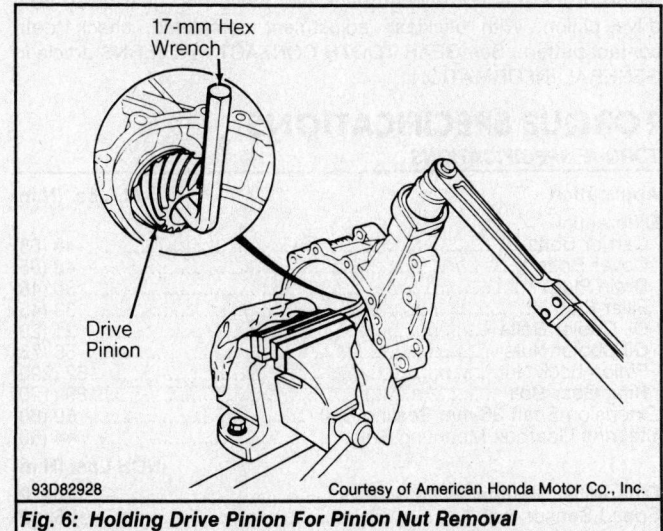

1. Oil Seal
2. Drain Plug
3. Washer
4. Differential Cover
5. Thrust Shim 3.13" (79.5 mm)
6. Bearing Race
7. Screw
8. Breather Plate
9. Breather Tube
10. Oil Filler Plug
11. Thrust Washer
12. Pinion Gear
13. Pinion Shaft
14. Differential Case
15. Ring Gear
16. Oil Cooler
17. "O" Ring
18. Dowel Pin
19. Thrust Washer
   (Automatic Transaxle)

20. Bearing Race
21. Pinion Bearing
22. Pinion Hub
23. Lock Nut
24. Thrust Washer
25. Oil Seal
26. Thrust Washer
27. Oil Cooler Pipe
28. Dowel Pin

29. "O" Ring
30. Speed Sensor
31. Thrust Shim 1.69" (43.0 mm)
32. Oil Guide Pipe
33. Drive Pinion
34. Pinion Bearing
35. Bearing Race
36. Thrust Washer
   (Automatic Transaxle)
37. Pinion Spacer
38. Thrust Washer
39. Thrust Shim 3.13" (79.5 mm)
40. Bearing Race
41. Bearing
42. Roll Pin
43. Bearing
44. Thrust Shim
45. Thrust Washer

92J00496

Courtesy of American Honda Motor Co., Inc.

Fig. 5: Exploded View Of Differential Assembly

17-mm Hex Wrench

Drive Pinion

93D82928

Courtesy of American Honda Motor Co., Inc.

Fig. 6: Holding Drive Pinion For Pinion Nut Removal

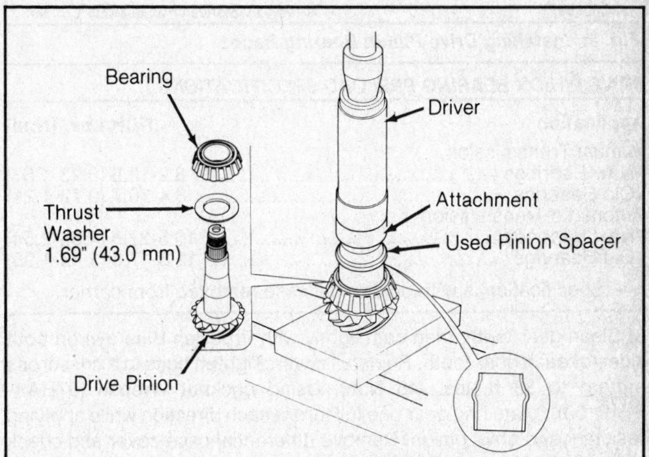

Bearing

Driver

Thrust Washer 1.69" (43.0 mm)

Attachment

Used Pinion Spacer

Drive Pinion

92B00498

Courtesy of American Honda Motor Co., Inc.

Fig. 7: Installing Drive Pinion Inner Bearing

Differential Carrier – 1) To install pinion bearing races, assemble thrust washers (A/T), thrust shim, bearing races, Bearing Race Installers (07MAF-SP00110 and 07MAF-SP00120), Shaft (07JAF-SJ80110), and Nut (07JAF-SJ80120). Install races. See Fig. 8.

2) Using Attachment (07GAD-SD40101) and Driver (07749-0010000), drive side bearing race into differential carrier. Lubricate drive pinion inner bearing. Assemble new pinion spacer and thrust washers onto drive pinion. Install drive pinion into differential carrier.

3) Install outer drive pinion bearing, pinion hub, and thrust washer. Tighten drive pinion nut to 162 ft. lbs. (220 N.m). Measure torque necessary to rotate drive pinion. Tighten drive pinion nut a little at a time until torque necessary to rotate drive pinion is as specified. See DRIVE PINION BEARING PRELOAD SPECIFICATIONS table. Pinion nut torque should be 162-236 ft. lbs. (220-320 N.m).

4) If preload exceeds specification, replace drive pinion spacer, and remeasure preload. With preload properly adjusted, record pinion nut torque obtained during preload adjustment.

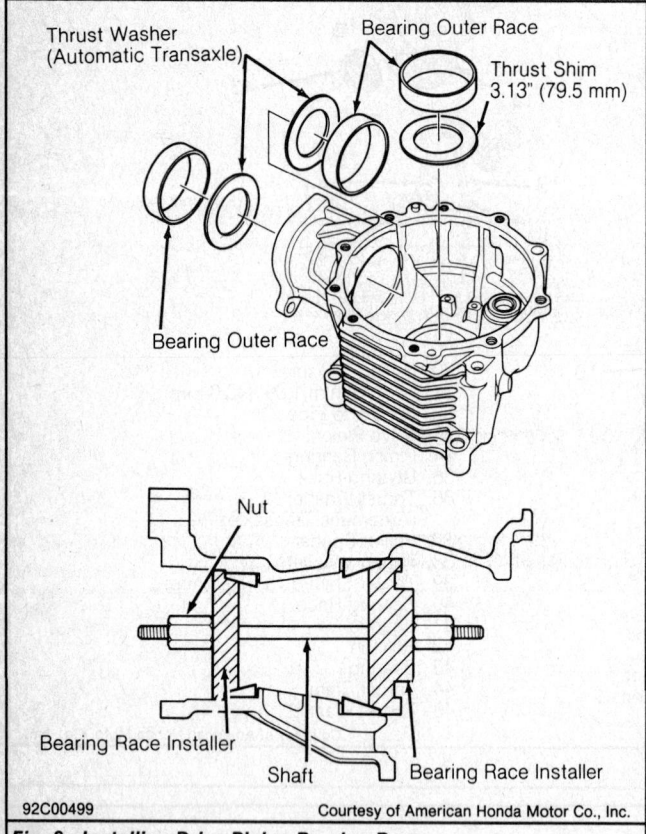

Thrust Washer (Automatic Transaxle)

Bearing Outer Race

Thrust Shim 3.13" (79.5 mm)

Bearing Outer Race

Nut

Bearing Race Installer

Shaft

Bearing Race Installer

92C00499   Courtesy of American Honda Motor Co., Inc.

Fig. 8: Installing Drive Pinion Bearing Races

DRIVE PINION BEARING PRELOAD SPECIFICATIONS [1]

Application	INCH Lbs. (N.m)
Manual Transmission	
New Bearings	8.2-13.9 (0.93-1.57)
Old Bearings	6.4-10.7 (0.72-1.21)
Automatic Transmission	
New Bearings	16.5-22.5 (1.86-2.54)
Old Bearings	12.8-17.3 (1.45-1.95)

[1] – Specification is with differential case removed from carrier.

5) Clean gear teeth, then coat lightly with Prussian Blue dye on both sides of each gear tooth. Reinstall cover. Tighten bolts in a crisscross pattern to 33 ft. lbs. (45 N.m). Using Locknut Wrench (07HAA-SF10100), rotate ring gear one full turn in each direction while applying resistance to drive pinion. Remove differential case cover and check tooth contact pattern. See GEAR TOOTH CONTACT PATTERNS article in GENERAL INFORMATION.

6) Mark pinion lock nut-to-drive pinion location. Remove pinion lock nut, thrust washer, and pinion hub. Using Attachment (07MAD-SP00200) and Driver (07749-0010000), install pinion oil seal.

7) Drive seal into carrier until distance between top of seal and face of differential carrier is 0.61-.63" (15.5-16.0 mm) on A/T vehicles or 0.22-0.24" (5.5-6.0 mm) on M/T vehicles.

8) Install pinion hub, thrust washer, and pinion lock nut. Tighten lock nut to torque value recorded in step **4)**. Ensure pinion lock nut-to-drive pinion marks align. Install new "O" rings onto oil cooler, and install cooler and oil guide pipe into differential carrier.

9) Tighten oil cooler retaining nuts to specification. See TORQUE SPECIFICATIONS. Using new washers, install oil cooler lines. Install differential case into carrier. Install breather plate in differential cover. Stake retaining screws.

10) Install original side bearing thrust shim into differential cover. Using Attachment (07GAD-SD40101) and Driver (07749-0010000), install side bearing race. Install differential cover. Tighten cover bolts in a crisscross pattern to specification. See TORQUE SPECIFICATIONS.

11) Mount differential assembly in soft-jawed vise. Measure ring gear backlash. See Fig. 4. If ring gear backlash is not 0.0024-0.0055" (0.061-0.140 mm), adjust backlash. See RING GEAR BACKLASH under ADJUSTMENTS.

12) With backlash adjustment completed, check tooth contact pattern. See GEAR TOOTH CONTACT PATTERNS article in GENERAL INFORMATION. Using Attachment (07965-SA00600) and Driver (07749-0010000), install oil seal into differential cover.

ADJUSTMENTS

DRIVE PINION DEPTH

1) To select proper drive pinion shim, calculate the difference in size between old shim and new drive pinion. A number with a plus (+) or a minus (–) is located on the drive pinion. If number on old drive pinion is a (+), add that number to old shim thickness and record number. If number on old drive pinion is a (–), subtract that number from old shim thickness and record number.

2) If number on new drive pinion is a (+), subtract that number from number recorded in step **1)**. If number on new drive pinion is a (–), add that number to number recorded in step **1)**.

3) Select a shim that is closest, but not more than, the final number recorded in step **2)**. Shim sizes are available in 0.001" (0.03 mm) increments, ranging from 0.0646" (1.641 mm) to 0.0894" (2.271 mm).

RING GEAR BACKLASH

1) If backlash is not 0.0024-0.0055" (0.061-0.140 mm), correct backlash by decreasing shim thickness on one side and increasing shim thickness on other side by the same amount. Shims are located behind side bearing races.

2) Total thickness of both shims must equal total thickness of original shims. If there is too much backlash, move ring gear toward drive pinion. If there is not enough backlash, move ring gear away from drive pinion. With backlash adjustment completed, check tooth contact pattern. See GEAR TOOTH CONTACT PATTERNS article in GENERAL INFORMATION.

TORQUE SPECIFICATIONS
TORQUE SPECIFICATIONS

Application	Ft. Lbs. (N.m)
Differential	
Carrier Bolts	48 (65)
Cover Bolts [1]	48 (65)
Drain Plug	30 (40)
Filler Plug	33 (45)
Oil Cooler Bolts	21 (29)
Oil Cooler Nuts	55 (75)
Pinion Lock Nut	162 (220)
Ring Gear Bolt	89 (120)
Extension Shaft 36-mm Sealing Bolt	59 (80)
Steering Gearbox Mounting Bolts	44 (60)

	INCH Lbs. (N.m)
Differential Breather Plate Screws	106 (12)
Speed Sensor Bolt	106 (12)

[1] – Tighten in a crisscross pattern.

Integra, Legend, Vigor

DESCRIPTION

Integra, Legend, and Vigor are equipped with front and rear disc brakes. A cable operates parking brake at rear wheels.

WARNING: DO NOT use air pressure or a dry brush to clean brake assemblies. Avoid breathing brake dust. Use OSHA-approved vacuum cleaner for cleaning and collecting dust. Avoid contaminating brake pads and discs with brake fluid or grease.

BLEEDING BRAKE SYSTEM

BLEEDING PROCEDURES

CAUTION: Use only clean DOT 3 or 4 brake fluid. Ensure no dirt or other foreign matter contaminates brake fluid. DO NOT mix different brands of brake fluid as they may not be compatible. Avoid spilling brake fluid on car, as it will damage paint. If brake fluid contacts paint, immediately flush with water.

1) Reservoir on master cylinder must be full at start of bleeding procedure. Refill reservoir after bleeding each wheel. Have an assistant slowly pump brake pedal several times then apply steady pressure. Loosen brake bleed screw to allow air to escape from system.
2) Tighten bleed screw securely. Repeat procedure until air bubbles no longer appear in fluid. Bleed brakes in following sequence.
* Right Rear
* Left Front
* Left Rear
* Right Front
3) Road test vehicle and check brake performance.

ADJUSTMENTS

PEDAL PLAY & HEIGHT

1) Measure pedal height from center of pedal pad to floorboard, with carpet removed. To adjust pedal height, loosen stoplight switch lock nut, and back off switch until it no longer touches brake pedal.
2) Loosen power brake unit push rod lock nut, and rotate push rod to adjust pedal height. See BRAKE PEDAL HEIGHT table.
3) Tighten lock nut. Adjust stoplight switch. See STOPLIGHT SWITCH. After adjustment, brake pedal free play should be 0.04-0.20" (1.0-5.0 mm).

BRAKE PEDAL HEIGHT

Application	In. (mm)
Integra	
Automatic Transaxle	6.5 (165)
Manual Transaxle	6.3 (160)
Legend	8.4 (213)
Vigor	
Automatic Transaxle	7.6 (194)
Manual Transaxle	7.8 (199)

STOPLIGHT SWITCH

Stoplight switch is located under dash, above brake pedal. To adjust switch, loosen lock nuts, then turn switch until plunger is fully inward, with threaded end touching pedal arm pad. Back off switch 1/2 turn, then tighten lock nuts. Ensure brakelights go off when pedal is released.

PARKING BRAKE

Integra & Vigor – 1) Raise and support rear of vehicle. Ensure rear brake caliper lever contacts brake caliper pin. *See Fig. 1.* Pull parking brake lever up one notch.
2) Remove end panel from rear of parking brake lever cover. Tighten equalizer nut until rear wheels drag slightly when turned. Release brake lever. Rear wheels should rotate freely. Rear wheels should lock when lever is pulled up 6-10 (Integra) or 7-11 (Vigor) clicks.

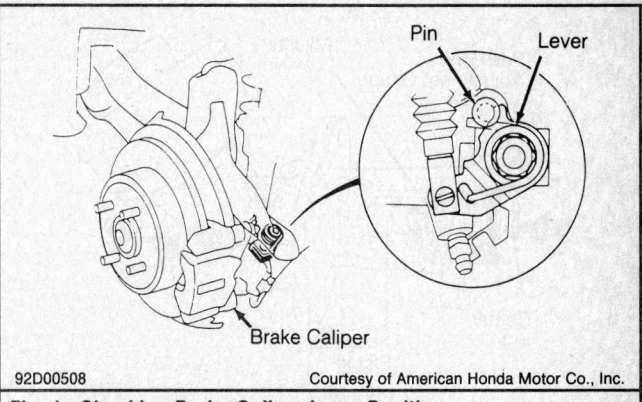

92D00508 — Courtesy of American Honda Motor Co., Inc.

Fig. 1: Checking Brake Caliper Lever Position (Integra Shown; Vigor Similar)

Legend – 1) Parking brake shoes are located inside of rear brake disc. Parking brake should hold when parking brake lever is pulled up 8-12 clicks. If number of clicks to fully set brake is excessive, minor adjustments (1-2 clicks) can be made by adjusting equalizer. For minor adjustment, go to next step. For major adjustment, see step 3).
2) Remove end cover from parking brake console. Pull parking brake lever up one click. Raise and support rear of vehicle. Tighten equalizer adjusting nut until slight drag is felt when wheels are turned. Release parking brake lever. Wheels should not drag. Readjust if necessary. With equalizer properly adjusted, parking brake should be fully applied when parking brake lever is pulled 6-8 clicks.

NOTE: Ensure parking brakes are not worn beyond service limit of 0.004" (1.0 mm). Replace both brake shoes if either lining is worn beyond limit.

3) Release parking brake lever. Remove end cover from parking brake console. Back off equalizer adjusting nut. Raise and support rear of vehicle. Remove rear wheels. Using flat-blade screwdriver, turn adjuster up until brake shoes lock, and then back off 8 stops.
4) Tighten equalizer adjusting nut so parking brake is fully applied when parking brake lever is pulled up 8 to 12 clicks. Install rear wheels. Rear wheels should not drag when parking brake lever is released. Readjust if necessary. Install console rear cover.

BRAKE WARNING LIGHT

Brake warning light indicates parking brake is engaged and/or low brake fluid level. To adjust parking brake light operation, remove center console. Turn ignition on. Bend switch plate downward until light comes on when parking brake lever is pulled one notch and goes out when lever is released.

MASTER CYLINDER PUSH ROD CLEARANCE

NOTE: Master cylinder push rod-to-piston clearance must be checked and adjusted before installing master cylinder.

1) Mount Push Rod Adjustment Gauge (07JAG-SD40100) on master cylinder. Rotate adjuster nut until top of center shaft contacts end of secondary piston. *See Fig. 2.*
2) Remove push rod adjustment gauge from master cylinder, and mount it upside down on master booster. Tighten master cylinder nuts to 11 ft. lbs. (15 N.m). Using engine or outside vacuum source, apply a minimum of 20 in. Hg vacuum to brake booster.
3) Using a feeler gauge, verify clearance between gauge body and adjusting nut is 0-0.016" (0-0.40 mm) on Integra, or 0-0.008" (0-0.20 mm) on Legend and Vigor. *See Fig. 3.* If clearance is not as specified, go to next step.
4) On Integra and Vigor, loosen star lock nut and rotate adjuster in or out to adjust clearance. On Legend, remove adjustment gauge. Hold push rod, and rotate adjuster on booster in or out to adjust clearance. DO NOT pull push rod out of brake booster.

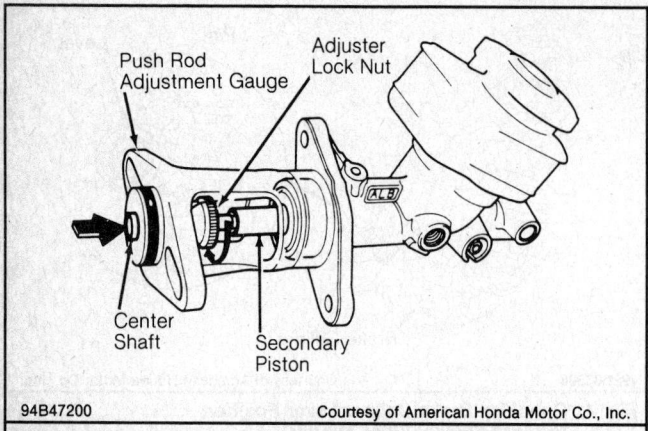

Fig. 2: Setting Push Rod Adjustment Gauge (Typical)

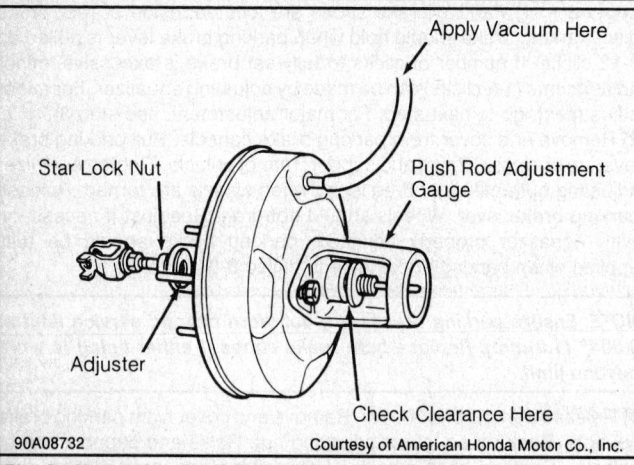

Fig. 3: Measuring Push Rod Clearance (Typical)

BRAKE BOOSTER PUSH ROD

If brake booster is removed, on Integra and Legend, adjust push rod length to 4.58-4.62" (115.5-116.5 mm). On Vigor, adjust length to 4.78-4.82" (121.5-122.5 mm). *See Fig. 4.* Check pedal height and free play after installing master cylinder. See PEDAL PLAY & HEIGHT.

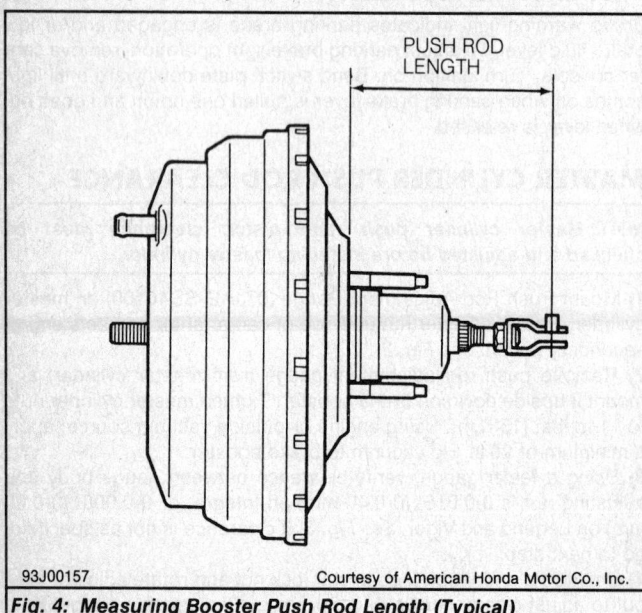

Fig. 4: Measuring Booster Push Rod Length (Typical)

PARKING BRAKE LINING BREAK-IN

Legend – 1) Perform this procedure only when new parking brake shoes or new rear brake discs have been installed. Pull up on parking brake lever while counting number of clicks. If number of clicks to fully set parking brake is not 8-12, adjust parking brake. See PARKING BRAKE.

2) With parking brake adjusted correctly, park car on firm, level surface. Tape end of parking brake release lever so release button is held in. Attach spring scale to center of parking brake lever.

3) Drive vehicle about 30 MPH for 1/4 mile, and have assistant pulls up on parking brake lever with a force of 20 lbs. (9 kg). Release parking brake lever. Park vehicle for 5-10 minutes to allow brake discs to cool.

4) Repeat step **3)**. Remove tape from parking brake lever. Check and adjust parking brake as necessary. See PARKING BRAKE.

TESTING

POWER BRAKE UNIT

CAUTION: DO NOT disassemble brake booster. Replace booster assembly if faulty.

Functional Test – 1) Start engine. Turn ignition off. Press brake pedal several times. Press and hold pedal firmly for 15 seconds. If pedal sinks, master cylinder, brakeline, or caliper piston is faulty.

2) Start engine with pedal pressed. If pedal sinks slightly, vacuum unit is working properly. If pedal height does not change, booster or check valve is faulty.

Leak Test – 1) Press brake pedal with engine running. Turn ignition off. If pedal height does not change with pedal pressed for 30 seconds, vacuum booster is okay. If pedal rises, vacuum booster is leaking.

2) With engine stopped, press brake pedal several times with normal pressure. Pedal should be low when first pressed. On consecutive applications, pedal height should gradually increase. If pedal height does not change, check power brake booster check valve.

Check Valve Test – Disconnect power brake unit vacuum hose at booster. Start and idle engine. Check for vacuum at booster end of hose. If vacuum is not available, vacuum source or check valve is faulty. Repair vacuum source or replace check valve, and retest.

REMOVAL & INSTALLATION

FRONT DISC BRAKE PADS

Removal – 1) Raise and support front of vehicle. Remove front wheels. Remove caliper bolts, and move caliper aside.

2) Remove pads, pad shims, and pad retainers. Measure thickness of brake lining. Minimum brake pad thickness is 0.06" (1.60 mm). Remove caliper bracket and bracket bolts. Thoroughly clean caliper and bracket. Check for cracks or grooves.

NOTE: Replace brake pads in axle sets. Do not allow grease, brake fluid, or other contaminants to contact lining surface. Inspect, clean, and resurface rotor as necessary.

Installation – 1) Install bracket and bracket bolts. Tighten bolts to 81 ft. lbs. (110 N.m). Lubricate shim and sliding surfaces with high-temperature silicone grease. Install pad retainers. Apply Molykote® M77 compound to both sides of pad shims and back of pads.

2) Install inner and outer pad shims. Install brake pads in brackets. Install inner brake pad with pad wear indicator on the inside. Push piston into caliper bore with finger pressure so caliper will fit over pads.

3) Position caliper and install caliper bolts. Tighten bolts to specification. See TORQUE SPECIFICATIONS. Press brake pedal several times to seat pads. Bleed brakes as necessary. See BLEEDING BRAKE SYSTEM.

REAR DISC BRAKE PADS

Removal (Integra & Vigor) – **1)** Raise and support rear of vehicle. Remove wheels. Remove caliper shield. Remove lock pin and clevis pin. Disconnect parking brake cable by removing cable-to-caliper clip (if necessary).

2) Remove caliper mounting bolts and caliper from bracket. Remove shims, brake pads, and retainers. Measure friction pad thickness. Service limit is 0.06" (1.6 mm).

Installation – **1)** Clean caliper thoroughly. Remove rust and check for grooves or cracks. Install pad retainers in appropriate positions. Apply Molykote® M77 compound to both sides of inner and outer pad shims. Install brake pads and shims. Rotate caliper piston clockwise in caliper to position piston (if necessary). Align cut-out in piston with tab on inner pad.

2) Avoid twisting piston boot. Install brake caliper and caliper bracket. Install parking brake cable. Pump brake pedal several times to seat pads. Bleed brakes as necessary. See BLEEDING BRAKE SYSTEM. Adjust parking brake if necessary. See PARKING BRAKE.

Removal (Legend) – **1)** Raise and support rear of vehicle. Remove rear wheels. Remove lower caliper mounting bolt, and pivot caliper aside. Remove shims, pads, and retainers. Measure thickness of pad lining. Service limit is 0.06" (1.6 mm).

2) If removing caliper, remove upper caliper mounting bolt, and support caliper aside using wire. Remove caliper bracket bolts and caliper bracket. Thoroughly clean caliper and bracket. Remove any rust, and check for grooves or cracks.

Installation – **1)** Install caliper bracket and mounting bolts. Tighten bolts to 28 ft. lbs. (39 N.m). Install pad retainers. Apply Molykote® M77 compound to both sides of inner and outer pad shims. Install brake pads and shims on caliper bracket. Install inner pad with wear indicator mark on the inside. Ensure pad spring is installed onto caliper body.

2) Push in piston so caliper will fit over brake pads. Install brake caliper and mounting bolts. Tighten caliper mounting bolts to specification. See TORQUE SPECIFICATIONS. Pump brake pedal several times to seat pads. Bleed brakes if necessary. See BLEEDING BRAKE SYSTEM.

FRONT DISC BRAKE CALIPER

Removal – Raise and support front of vehicle. Remove wheels. Remove banjo bolts. Disconnect brake hose from caliper. Plug hydraulic line and caliper. Remove caliper mounting bolts and caliper. Remove pads, pad shims, and pad retainers.

Installation – To install, reverse removal procedure. Replace copper banjo bolt washers when connecting brake hose. Install brake pads. See FRONT DISC BRAKE PADS. Bleed brake system. See BLEEDING BRAKE SYSTEM.

REAR DISC BRAKE CALIPER

Removal – Raise and support rear of vehicle. Remove wheels. Remove caliper shield (if equipped). Remove banjo bolts. On Integra and Vigor, disconnect parking brake cable. On all models, disconnect brake hose from caliper. Plug hydraulic line and caliper. Remove caliper mounting bolts and caliper. Remove pads, pad shims and pad retainers.

Installation – To install, reverse removal procedure. Replace copper banjo bolt washers when connecting brake hose. Install brake pads. See REAR DISC BRAKE PADS. Bleed brake system. See BLEEDING BRAKE SYSTEM.

DISC BRAKE ROTOR

Removal (Front & Rear) – **1)** Raise and support vehicle. Remove wheels. Remove caliper assembly and wire aside. See FRONT DISC BRAKE CALIPER or REAR DISC BRAKE CALIPER. Measure rotor runout before removal. Remove rotor retaining screws.

2) Install two 8 x 12 mm bolts into existing holes. To prevent warpage, turn bolts alternately 2 turns at a time until rotor can be removed from hub. Clean rust from rotor. Inspect rotor surfaces for cracks or grooves. Resurface or replace rotor as necessary.

Installation – To install, reverse removal procedure. Tighten retaining screws. Bleed hydraulic system (if necessary). See BLEEDING BRAKE SYSTEM.

MASTER CYLINDER & BOOSTER

CAUTION: DO NOT disassemble master cylinder or booster. Service these components as complete assembly.

Removal & Installation (Integra) – **1)** Empty brake fluid from master cylinder. Unplug brake fluid level switch connectors. Disconnect brakelines from master cylinder. Remove master cylinder mounting nuts and master cylinder. See Fig. 5. Disconnect vacuum hose from brake booster. Remove vacuum hose bracket.

2) Remove clevis pin from booster push rod. Remove booster mounting nuts and booster. To install, reverse removal procedure after checking push rod clearance and length. After installation, check and adjust pedal height. Fill and bleed brake system.

Removal & Installation (Legend) – Removal and installation procedure is not available. Refer to illustration for exploded view of master cylinder and booster assembly. See Fig. 6.

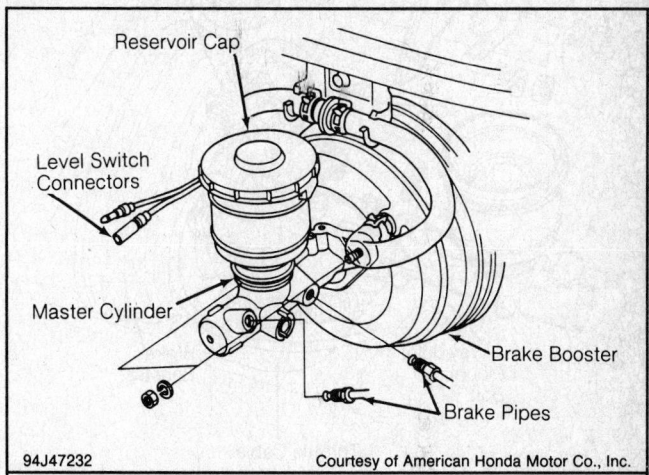

Fig. 5: Exploded View Of Master Cylinder & Booster (Integra)

94J47232   Courtesy of American Honda Motor Co., Inc.

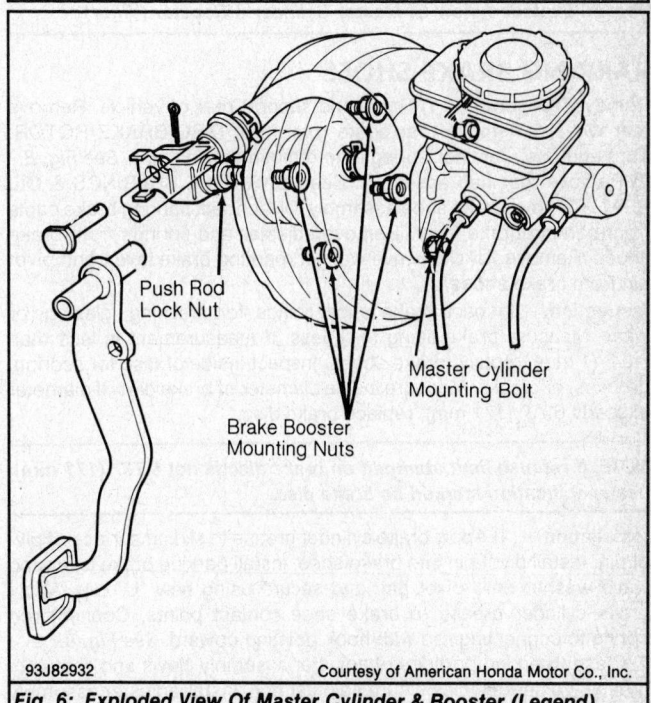

93J82932   Courtesy of American Honda Motor Co., Inc.

Fig. 6: Exploded View Of Master Cylinder & Booster (Legend)

Removal & Installation (Vigor) – **1)** Empty master cylinder reservoir. Remove 4-way joint mounting bolt. See Fig. 7. Disconnect check valve and throttle cable from 4-way joint bracket. Remove master cylinder mounting nuts, washers, and 4-way joint bracket. Remove master cylinder from brake booster.

2) Remove throttle cable clamp bolt. Disconnect vacuum tube from brake booster. Remove cotter pin and joint pin. Remove brake booster mounting nuts and brake booster. To install, reverse removal procedure after measuring push rod clearance and length. See MASTER CYLINDER PUSH ROD CLEARANCE. After installation, check and adjust pedal height. See PEDAL PLAY & HEIGHT under ADJUSTMENTS. Fill and bleed brake system.

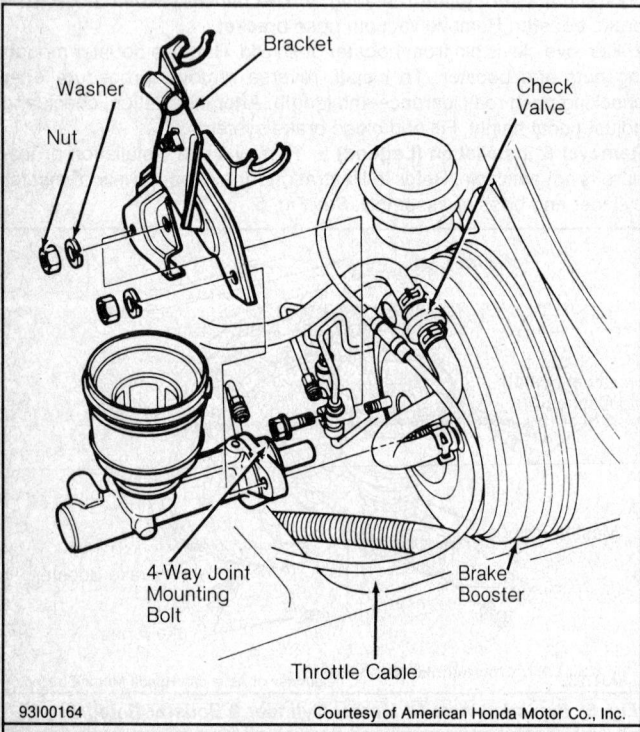

93I00164   Courtesy of American Honda Motor Co., Inc.

Fig. 7: Exploded View Of Master Cylinder & Booster (Vigor)

PARKING BRAKE SHOES

Removal (Legend) – **1)** Raise and support rear of vehicle. Remove rear wheels. Remove rear brake rotor. See DISC BRAKE ROTOR. Turn and push retainer spring in to remove tension pins. See Fig. 8.

2) Remove rear hub assembly. See REAR AXLE BEARINGS & OIL SEAL. Remove brake shoe assembly. Disconnect parking brake cable from parking brake lever. Remove adjuster and springs from brake shoes. Remove "U" clip, wave washer, parking brake lever, and pivot pin from brake shoes.

Inspection – Inspect brake shoe linings for cracking, glazing, or wear. Measure brake lining thickness. If measurement is less than 0.04" (1 mm), replace brake shoes. Inspect inside of disc for scoring, grooves, or cracks. Measure inside diameter of brake disc. If diameter exceeds 6.73" (171 mm), replace brake disc.

NOTE: If refinish limit stamped on brake disc is not 6.73" (171 mm), use specification marked on brake disc.

Installation – **1)** Apply brake cylinder grease to sliding surface of pivot pin. Install pivot pin into brake shoe. Install parking brake lever and wave washer onto pivot pin, and secure using new "U" clip. Apply brake cylinder grease to brake shoe contact points. Connect rod spring to connecting rod with hook pointing upward. See Fig. 8.

2) Clean threaded portions of adjuster assembly clevis and coat with grease. To shorten clevis, turn adjuster bolt. Install adjuster assembly and return spring "B". Connect parking brake cable to parking brake

lever. Install tension pins and retainer spring. Install return springs. Install hub assembly, if removed, and tighten spindle nut to specification. See TORQUE SPECIFICATION.

3) Install disc and 6-mm screws. Adjust parking brake. See PARKING BRAKE under ADJUSTMENTS. Install rear brake caliper. Bleed hydraulic system if necessary. See BLEEDING BRAKE SYSTEM. If new parking brake shoes or new brake discs have been installed, perform brake shoe lining break-in procedure. See PARKING BRAKE LINING BREAK-IN under ADJUSTMENTS.

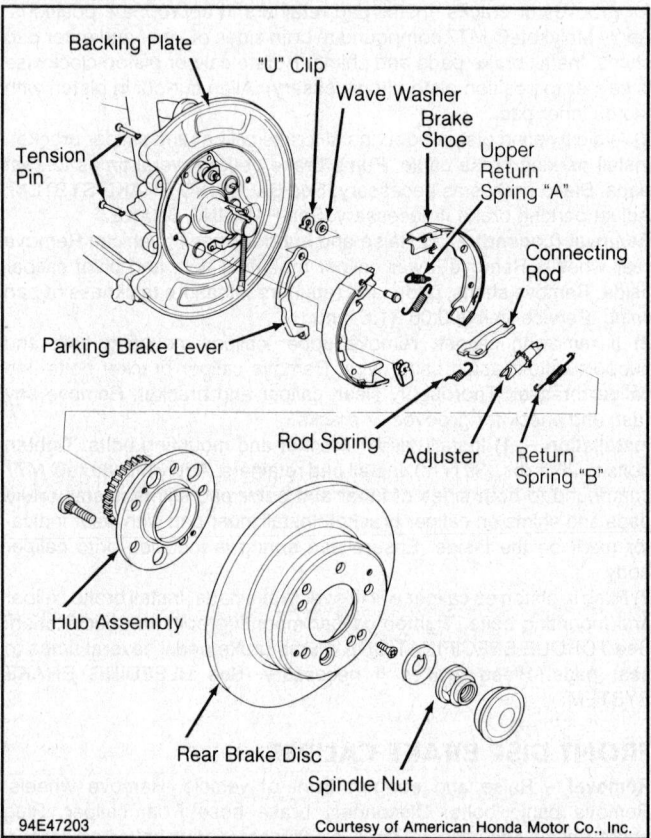

94E47203   Courtesy of American Honda Motor Co., Inc.

Fig. 8: Exploded View Of Parking Brake Assembly (Legend)

REAR AXLE BEARINGS & OIL SEAL

NOTE: Rear axle bearing and hub are replaced as an assembly.

Removal & Installation – Raise rear of vehicle and support with safety stands. Remove wheel assembly. Remove caliper and wire aside. See REAR DISC BRAKE CALIPER. Remove brake disc. Remove hub cap. Pry spindle nut lock tab away from spindle and loosen nut. Remove hub/bearing assembly. To install, reverse removal procedure. Tighten spindle nut to specification. See TORQUE SPECIFICATIONS.

OVERHAUL
FRONT DISC BRAKE CALIPER

NOTE: Legend Coupe and Legend Sedan GS have dual-piston caliper.

Disassembly – **1)** Disconnect brake hose from caliper. Remove caliper. See FRONT DISC BRAKE CALIPER under REMOVAL & INSTALLATION. Remove pad spring from caliper. See Fig. 9. Place wooden block or shop towel in caliper, opposite piston.

2) Slowly apply 30-psi (2.1 kg/cm²) air pressure to brake fluid inlet port to force piston from caliper bore. Remove piston boot and piston seal. Ensure caliper bore is not scored or damaged during removal of seal. Discard rubber components.

CAUTION: DO NOT put hand in front of piston when using air pressure to remove piston.

NOTE: Ensure brake fluid does not spill on painted surfaces, as damage to finish will result.

Reassembly – 1) Clean piston and caliper bore with clean brake fluid. Inspect for wear or damage. Apply silicone grease to new piston seal and piston boot. Install piston seal and piston boot into cylinder groove.

2) Lubricate caliper cylinder and piston with clean brake fluid. Install piston into cylinder with dished end facing inward. To complete reassembly, reverse removal procedure. Replace washers when installing brakeline. Bleed system after installation. See BLEEDING BRAKE SYSTEM.

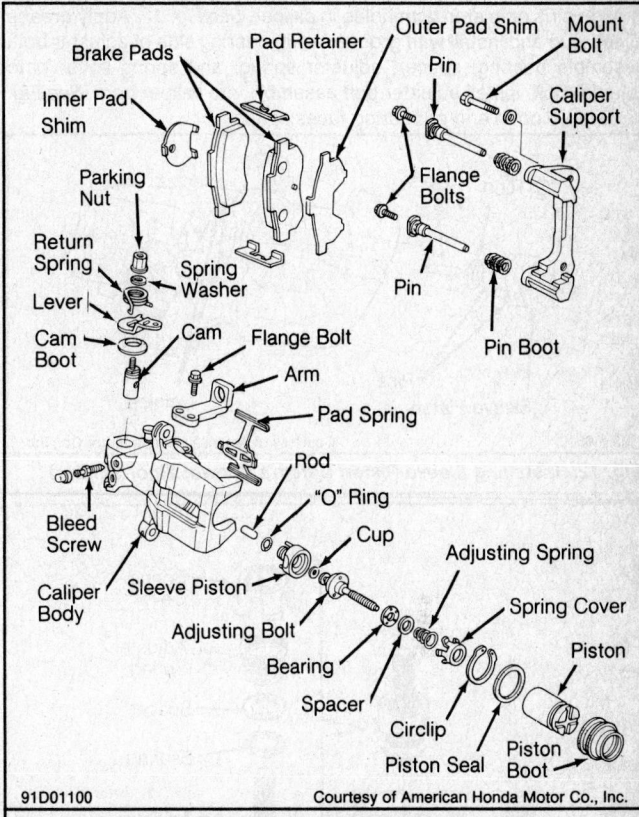

Fig. 10: Exploded View Of Rear Brake Caliper Assembly
(Integra Shown; Vigor Similar)

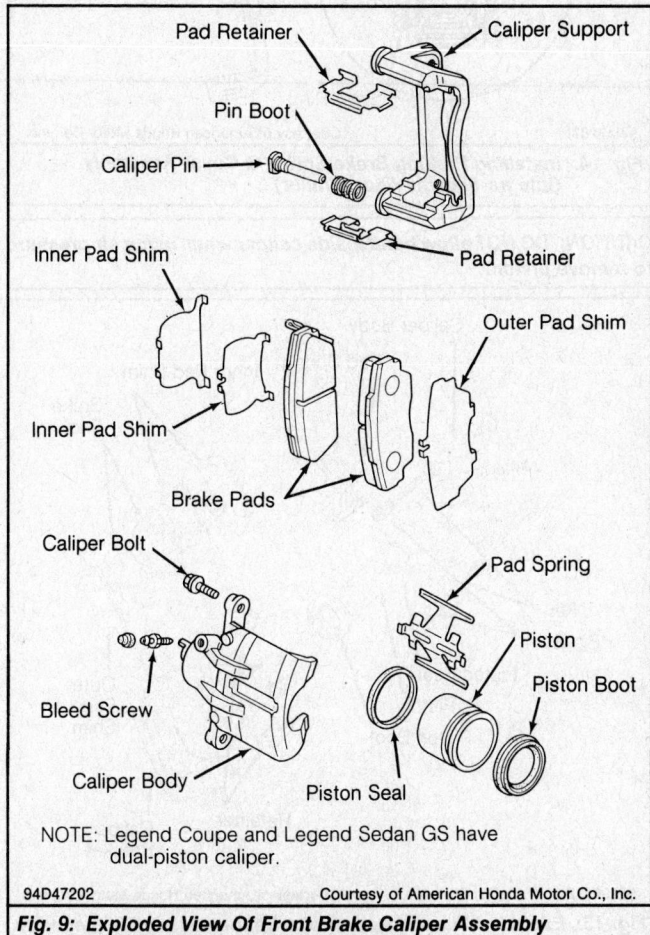

NOTE: Legend Coupe and Legend Sedan GS have dual-piston caliper.

Fig. 9: Exploded View Of Front Brake Caliper Assembly
(Integra Shown; Legend & Vigor Similar)

REAR DISC BRAKE CALIPER

Disassembly (Integra & Vigor) – 1) Remove brake caliper. See REAR DISC BRAKE CALIPER under REMOVAL & INSTALLATION. Remove pad spring from caliper. Using Wrench (07916-6390001), rotate piston counterclockwise to remove. See Fig. 10. Ensure caliper bore or piston components are not damaged. Replace if necessary.

2) Install Brake Spring Compressor (07HAE-SG00100) between caliper body and spring cover. Position lock nuts as shown, then rotate shaft until plate just contacts caliper body. See Fig. 11. Rotate shaft clockwise 1/4 – 1/2 turn to compress spring. DO NOT turn shaft more than 1/2 turn, as inner components may be damaged.

3) Lower lock nuts to plate, then tighten securely. Remove retaining ring. Relax spring compressor before removing it. Remove adjuster bolt. Remove spring cover, adjuster spring, spacer, bearing and cup. Remove sleeve piston and "O" ring. Remove pin from cam. Remove return spring, parking nut, spring washer, lever, cam, and cam boot.

4) Remove cam boot. Clean all parts in clean brake fluid. Inspect components for excessive wear or damage. Replace as required. Replace all rubber components.

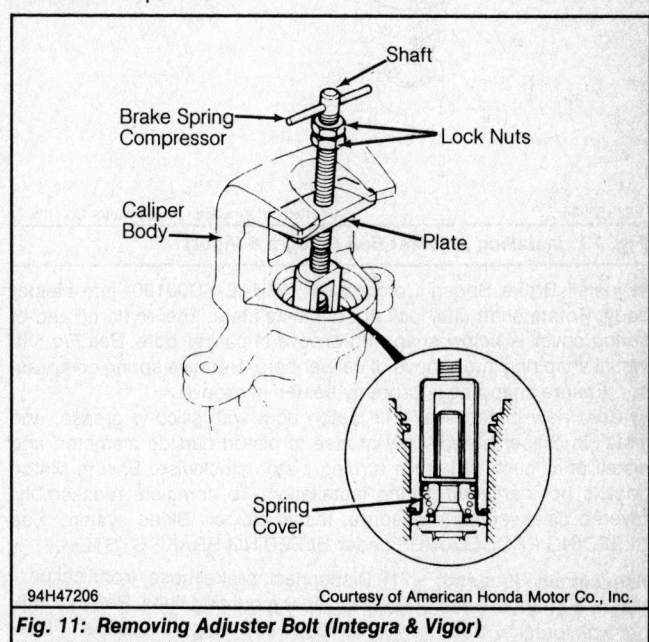

Fig. 11: Removing Adjuster Bolt (Integra & Vigor)

Reassembly – 1) Pack needle bearing with Brake Cylinder Grease (08733-B020E). Pack new cam boot with brake cylinder grease and install into cylinder body. Lubricate pin contact area of cam with brake cylinder grease. Install cam and lever assembly in caliper body.

2) Install return spring. Install lever and spring washer. Apply Loctite to parking nut and install. Tighten nut to 21 ft. lbs. (28 N.m). Install rod into cam. Install new "O" ring onto sleeve piston. Align hole in bottom of sleeve piston with rod in cam.

3) Align pins on piston with holes in caliper. *See Fig. 12*. Apply grease to new cup and install with groove facing bearing side of adjuster bolt. Assemble bearing, spacer, adjuster spring, and spring cover onto adjuster bolt. Install adjuster bolt assembly into caliper bore. *See Fig. 13*. Ensure open end of bearing faces spacer.

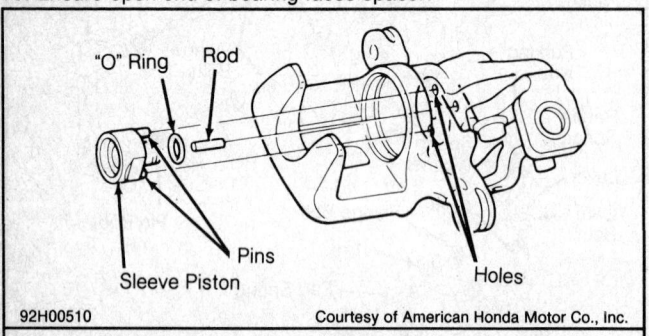

92H00510   Courtesy of American Honda Motor Co., Inc.

Fig. 12: Installing Sleeve Piston (Integra Shown; Vigor Similar)

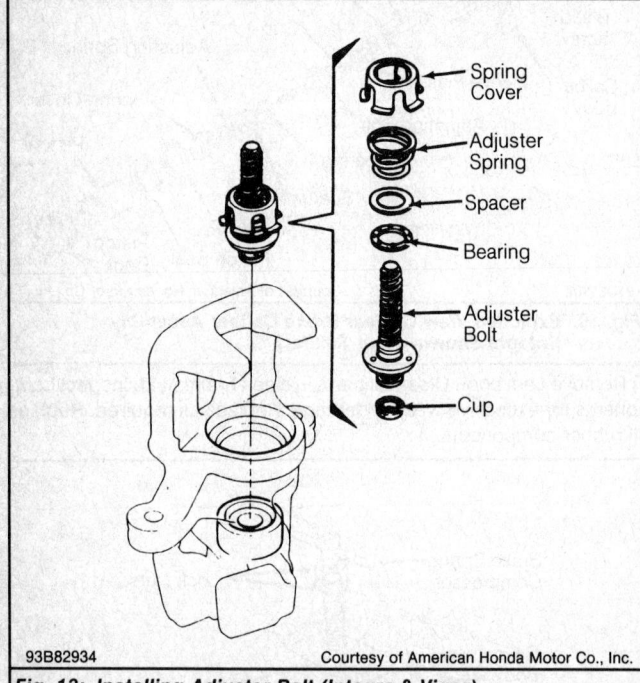

93B82934   Courtesy of American Honda Motor Co., Inc.

Fig. 13: Installing Adjuster Bolt (Integra & Vigor)

4) Install Brake Spring Compressor (07HAE-SG00100) into caliper body. Rotate shaft until lock nut contacts plate. Ensure flared end of spring cover is below snap ring groove in caliper bore. *See Fig. 14*. Install snap ring into groove of caliper bore. Remove spring compressor. Ensure snap ring is properly seated in groove.

5) Coat new piston seal and piston boot with silicone grease, and install in caliper bore. Apply grease to piston outside diameter, and install onto push rod while turning piston clockwise. Ensure piston boot is not damaged during installation. To complete reassembly, reverse disassembly procedure. Install caliper. Bleed system. See BLEEDING PROCEDURES under BLEEDING BRAKE SYSTEM.

Disassembly (Legend) – 1) Disconnect brake hose from caliper. Plug end of brake hose. Remove caliper mounting bolts. Remove caliper from bracket. *See Fig. 15*. Remove pad spring from caliper. Place wooden block or shop towel into caliper, opposite piston.

2) Slowly apply 30-psi (2.1 kg/cm²) air pressure to brake fluid inlet port to force piston from caliper bore. Remove piston boot and piston seal. Ensure caliper bore is not scored or damaged during removal of seal. Discard rubber components.

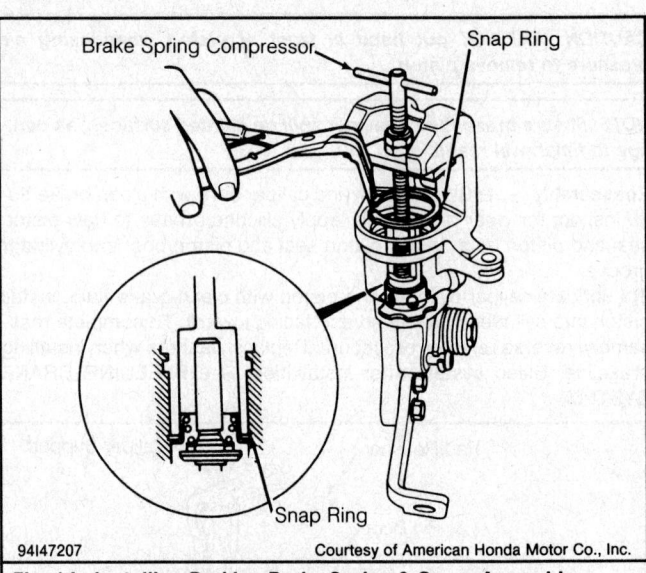

94I47207   Courtesy of American Honda Motor Co., Inc.

Fig. 14: Installing Parking Brake Spring & Cover Assembly (Integra Shown; Vigor Similar)

CAUTION: *DO NOT allow hand inside caliper when using air pressure to remove piston.*

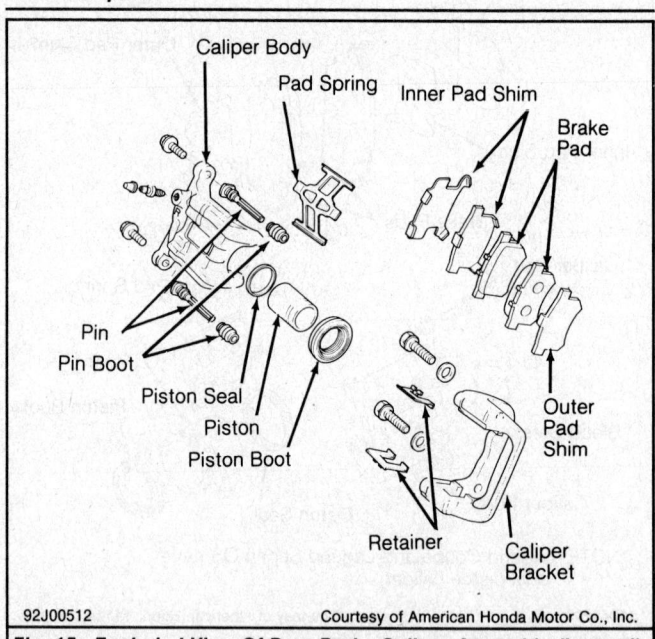

92J00512   Courtesy of American Honda Motor Co., Inc.

Fig. 15: Exploded View Of Rear Brake Caliper Assembly (Legend)

Reassembly – Coat new piston seal and boot with silicone grease, and install into caliper. Lubricate caliper bore and piston with brake fluid. Install piston into cylinder with dished end facing inward. To complete reassembly, reverse disassembly procedure. Replace washers when installing brakeline. Bleed system after installation. See BLEEDING BRAKE SYSTEM.

MASTER CYLINDER

Disassembly & Reassembly – DO NOT disassemble master cylinder. Replace master cylinder if defective.

POWER BRAKE BOOSTER

Disassembly & Reassembly – DO NOT disassemble power brake unit. Replace power brake booster if defective.

TORQUE SPECIFICATIONS

TORQUE SPECIFICATIONS

Application	Ft. Lbs. (N.m)
Caliper Body Mounting Bolt	
Front	
Integra	23 (31)
Legend & Vigor	36 (50)
Rear	17 (23)
Caliper Mount Bracket Bolt	
Integra & Vigor	28 (39)
Legend	
Front	81 (110)
Rear	28 (39)
Flex Hose-To-Caliper Banjo Bolt	26 (35)
Master Cylinder Mounting Nut	11 (15)
Push Rod Lock Nut	11 (15)
Rear Caliper Parking Nut	
Integra & Vigor	21 (28)
Rear Spindle Nut	
Integra & Vigor	134 (181)
Legend	210 (285)
Wheel Lug Nut	81 (110)
	INCH Lbs. (N.m)
Brake Bleed Screw	80 (9)
Brake Booster Mounting Nut	115 (13)

DISC BRAKE SPECIFICATIONS

DISC BRAKE SPECIFICATIONS

Application	In. (mm)
Integra	
Disc Diameter	
Front	10.3 (262)
Rear	9.4 (239)
Parallelism	0.0006 (0.015)
Maximum Runout	0.004 (0.10)
Original Thickness	
Front	0.83 (21)
Rear	0.36 (9.1)
Minimum Refinish Thickness	
Front	0.75 (19.0)
Rear	0.31 (8)
Discard Thickness	[1]
Legend	
Disc Diameter	11 (280)
Parallelism	0.0006 (0.015)
Maximum Runout	0.004 (0.10)
Original Thickness	
Front	0.91 (23)
Rear	0.35 (9.0)
Minimum Refinish Thickness	
Front	0.83 (21)
Rear	0.30 (7.5)
Discard Thickness	[1]
Parking Brake Drum (Rear)	
Diameter	
Standard	6.69 (170.0)
Service Limit	6.73 (171.0)
Lining Thickness	
Standard	0.10 (2.5)
Service Limit	0.40 (1.0)
Vigor	
Disc Diameter	
Front	11.1 (282)
Rear	10.2 (258)
Parallelism	0.0006 (0.015)
Maximum Runout	0.004 (0.10)
Original Thickness	
Front	0.91 (23.0)
Rear	0.4 (10.0)
Minimum Refinish Thickness	
Front	0.83 (21.0)
Rear	0.31 (8.0)
Discard Thickness	[1]

[1] – Use discard thickness stamped on rotor if different from minimum refinish thickness shown in table.

1994 BRAKES
Anti-Lock

Integra, Legend, Vigor

DESCRIPTION

The Anti-Lock Brake System (ABS) is designed to prevent wheel lock-up during hard braking. This effect allows driver to maintain control of vehicle under severe braking conditions. System consists of ABS control unit, accumulator, pressure switch, pump assembly, wheel sensors, gear pulsers, modulator, warning light, master cylinder, power booster assembly, motor and fail-safe relays and connecting wiring. *See Fig. 1, 2 or 3.*

NOTE: For more information on brake system, see DISC article.

OPERATION

The control unit receives an AC signal (wheel speed) from each wheel sensor. With this information, control unit electronically opens or closes the solenoids, located inside modulator, to prevent wheel lock-up.

CAUTION: See ANTI-LOCK BRAKE SAFETY PRECAUTIONS article in GENERAL INFORMATION.

SERVICING

Replace brake fluid every 30,000 miles. Replace ABS high-pressure hose every 60,000 miles.

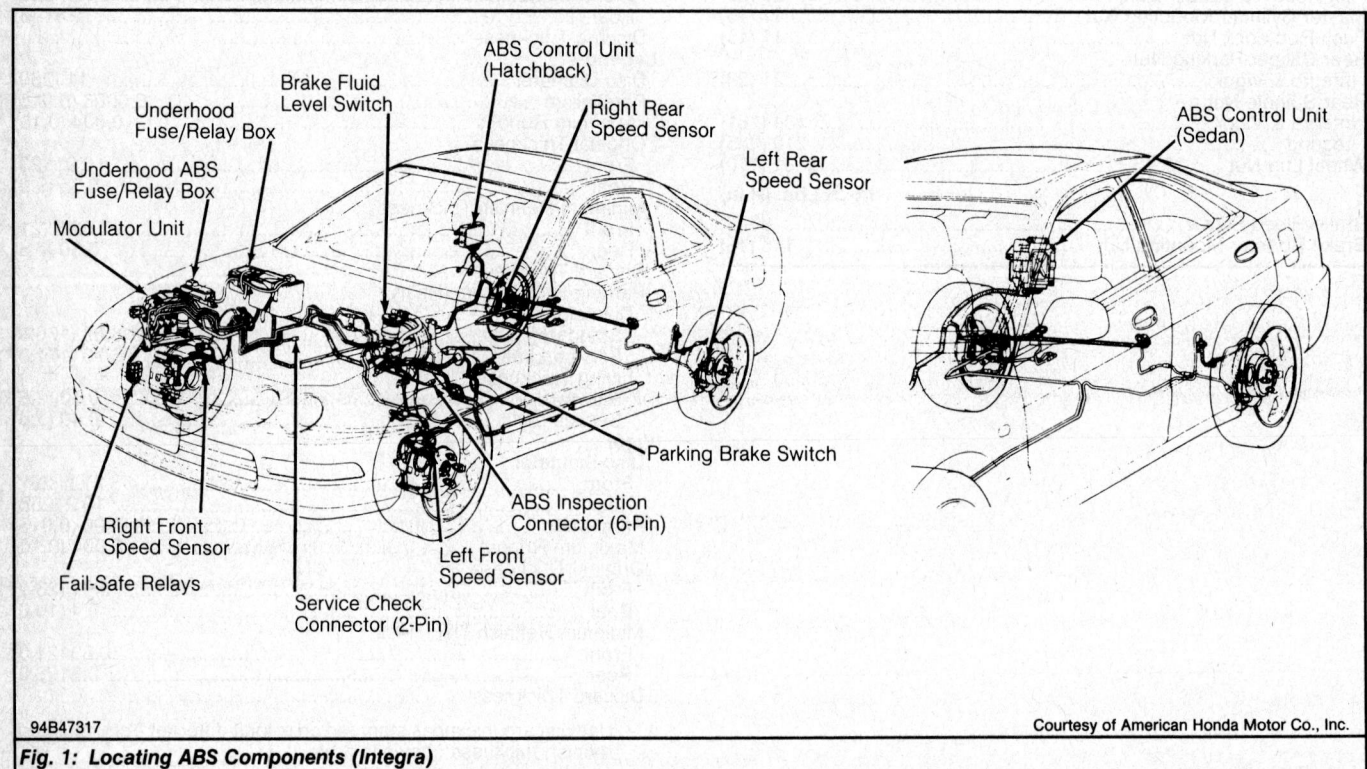

94B47317

Courtesy of American Honda Motor Co., Inc.

Fig. 1: Locating ABS Components (Integra)

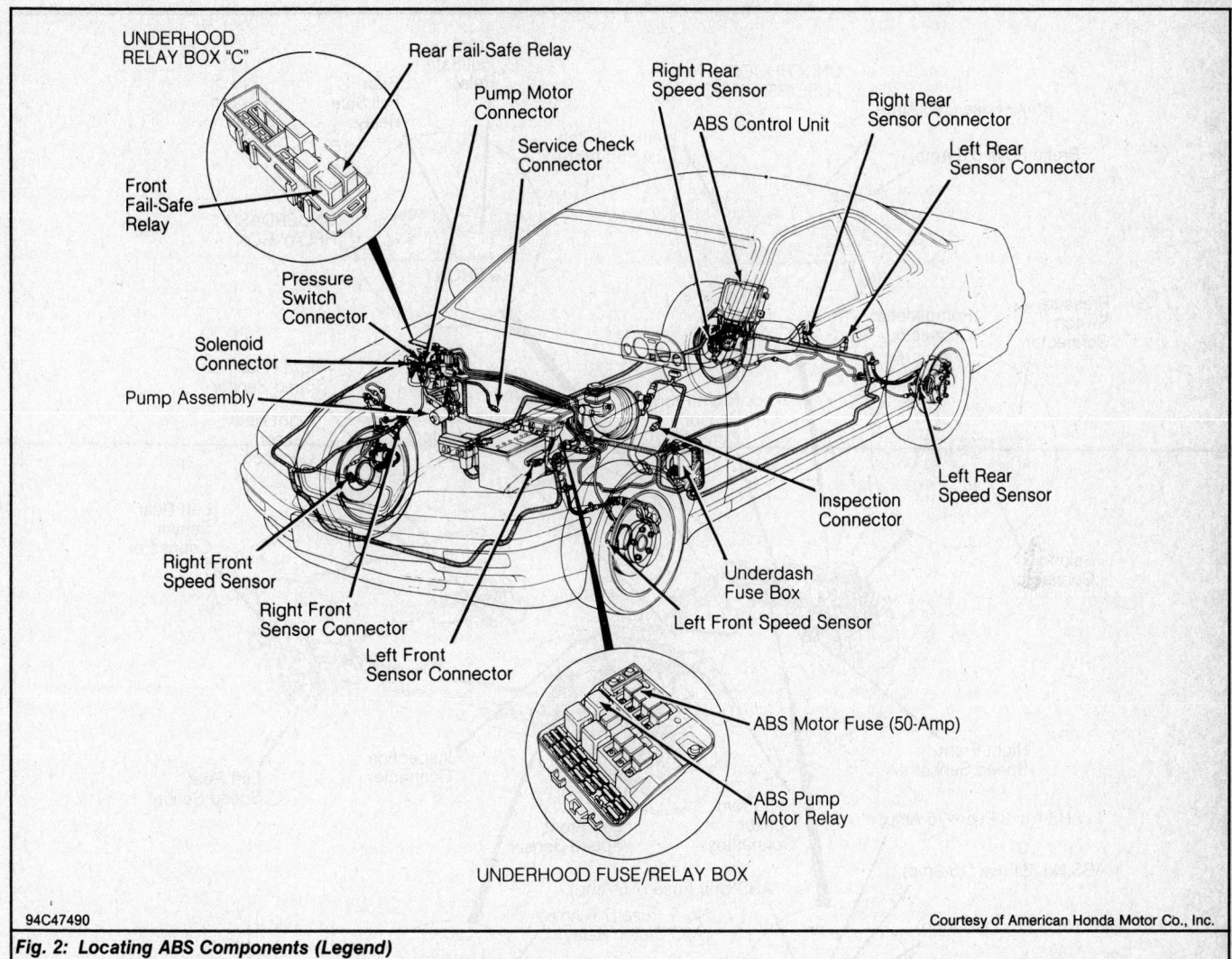

UNDERHOOD RELAY BOX "C"

Rear Fail-Safe Relay

Pump Motor Connector

Service Check Connector

Right Rear Speed Sensor

ABS Control Unit

Right Rear Sensor Connector

Left Rear Sensor Connector

Front Fail-Safe Relay

Pressure Switch Connector

Solenoid Connector

Pump Assembly

Right Front Speed Sensor

Right Front Sensor Connector

Left Front Sensor Connector

Inspection Connector

Underdash Fuse Box

Left Front Speed Sensor

Left Rear Speed Sensor

ABS Motor Fuse (50-Amp)

ABS Pump Motor Relay

UNDERHOOD FUSE/RELAY BOX

94C47490

Courtesy of American Honda Motor Co., Inc.

Fig. 2: *Locating ABS Components (Legend)*

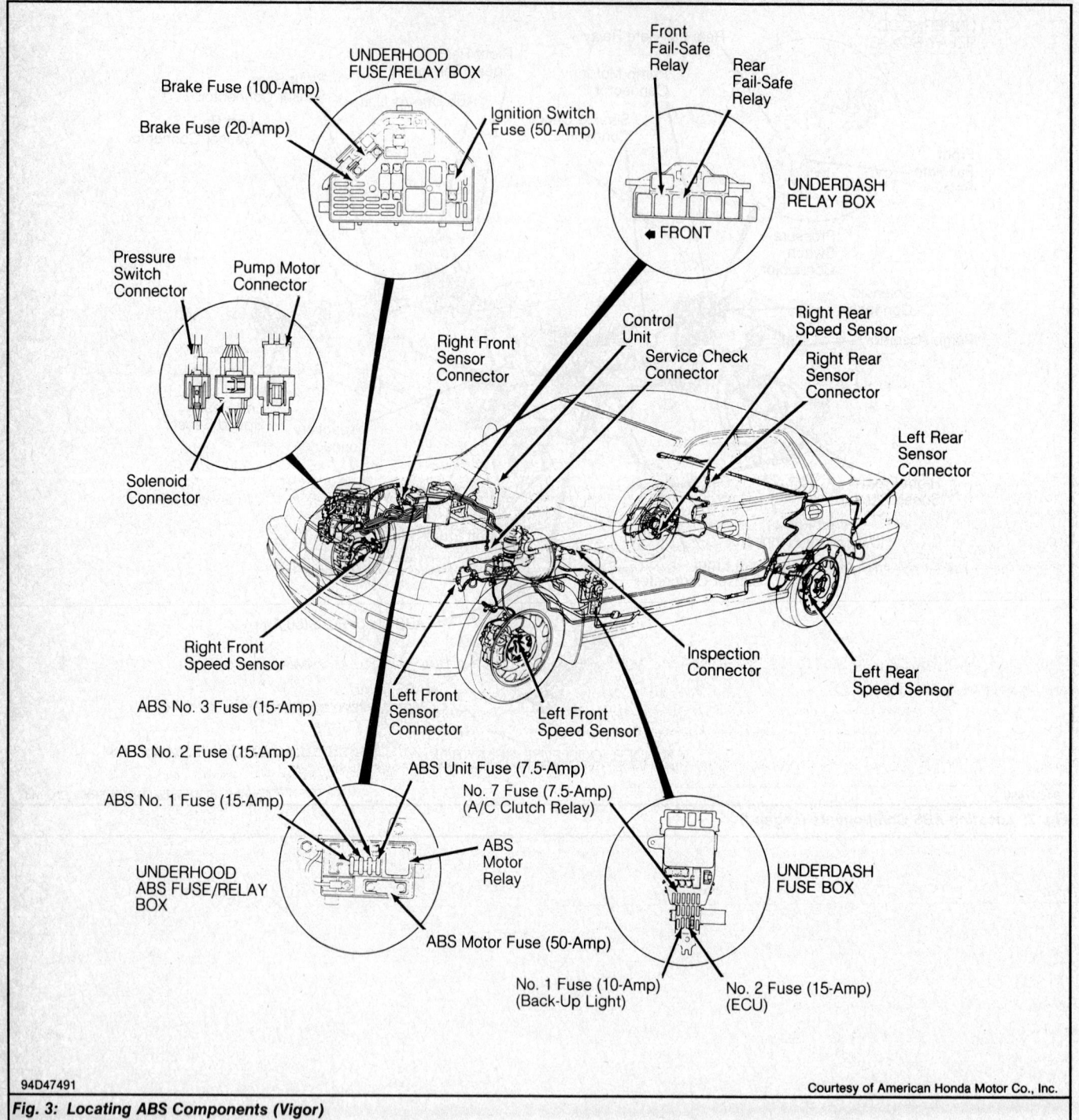

Fig. 3: Locating ABS Components (Vigor)

94D47491

Courtesy of American Honda Motor Co., Inc.

BLEEDING BRAKE SYSTEM

NOTE: Relieve system pressure before servicing modulator, accumulator or ABS pump motor.

RELIEVING SYSTEM PRESSURE

Integra – Remove bleeder cap from maintenance bleeder on modulator. *See Fig. 4.* Attach wrench to maintenance bleeder. Connect a rubber tube of appropriate diameter to maintenance bleeder, and place other end in a suitable container. Hold rubber tube, and slowly loosen maintenance bleeder 1/8 - 1/4 turn to drain brake fluid from modulator. After fluid stops flowing, loosen bleeder further to relieve pressure completely.

Legend & Vigor – **1)** Drain brake fluid from master cylinder and modulator reservoir. Remove Red cap from maintenance bleeder screw. *See Fig. 5.*

2) Using ABS "T" Wrench (07HAA-SG00100 or 07HAA-SG00101), loosen maintenance bleeder screw 1/4 turn to release high pressure fluid into reservoir. Turn "T" wrench one complete turn to relieve remaining accumulator line pressure. Tighten bleeder screw, and install Red cap.

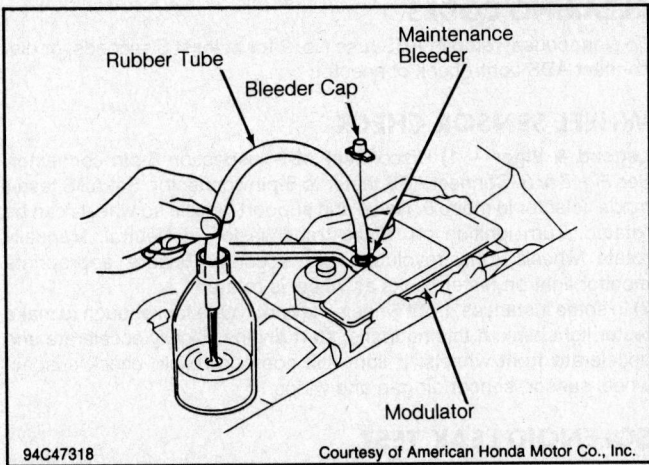

Rubber Tube

Maintenance
Bleeder

Bleeder Cap

Modulator

94C47318   Courtesy of American Honda Motor Co., Inc.

Fig. 4: Locating Maintenance Bleeder Screw (Integra)

Maintenance
Bleeder With
Red Cap

Reservoir Tank

Modulator

To Left Rear Brake
To Right Rear Brake
To Left Front Brake

Pump Assembly

Accumulator

Master
Cylinder

Brake
Booster

Pressure
Switch

To Right
Front Brake

94E47492   Courtesy of American Honda Motor Co., Inc.

**Fig. 5: Locating Maintenance Bleeder Screw
(Legend Shown; Vigor Similar)**

AIR BLEEDING

Using ABS Tester (Legend & Vigor) – 1) Park vehicle on level ground, and block wheels. Set transmission in Park (A/T) or Neutral (M/T). Release parking brake. Connect ABS Tester (07HAJ-SG0010B) to 6-pin inspection connector. *See Fig. 2 or 3.*
2) Fill modulator reservoir to MAX level. Start engine and allow to idle for a few minutes. Stop engine, and check fluid level in modulator reservoir. Refill to MAX level, if necessary.
3) Bleed high-pressure fluid from maintenance bleeder using ABS "T" wrench. *See Fig. 5.* Start engine and allow to idle for a few minutes. Stop engine, and check fluid level in modulator reservoir. Refill to MAX level, if necessary. Turn ABS tester mode selector to mode 2.
4) Depress brake pedal firmly, and press START TEST button. Kickback should be felt. If kickback is not felt, repeat step **3)**. If kickback is felt, repeat step **4)** for ABS tester modes 3, 4 and 5.
5) Fill modulator reservoir to MAX level. Perform system function test. See ABS FUNCTION TEST under DIAGNOSIS & TESTING.

TROUBLE SHOOTING

ANTI-LOCK WARNING LIGHT

ANTI-LOCK warning light will come on for any of following reasons:
- Brake fluid pump runs longer than preset value.
- Vehicle driven longer than 30 seconds with parking brake applied.
- Rear wheels locked longer than specified time.
- Wheel speed sensor not transmitting a signal.
- Operation time of solenoid valves exceeds a specified value or solenoid circuit is open.
- Output signals from control unit are not transmitted to solenoid valves.
- Strong radio frequency interference (Integra).
- Temporary loss of traction due to excessive cornering speed or starting from stuck condition (mud, snow or sand).
- Vehicle driven on extremely rough road.
- Low battery voltage.

If low battery voltage caused problem, recharge battery. Remove ABS fuse No. 2 for 3 seconds. Reinstall fuse, and check light. To reset light for any other condition, turn ignition off. ABS is okay if light goes our after engine is started. If light remains on, check system for trouble codes. See RETRIEVING CODES.

ANTI-LOCK WARNING LIGHT DOES NOT COME ON

1) If light does not come on when ignition is on, check bulb. On Integra, check back-up light fuse (10 amps) in underdash fuse relay box. Check Yellow wire between back-up light fuse and instrument panel.
2) On Legend, check Yellow wire between instrument panel and back-up light/turn signal fuse in underdash fuse relay box. On Vigor, check Yellow wire between instrument panel and back-up light fuse in underdash fuse relay box.
3) On all models, check Blue/Red wire between instrument panel to control unit. Check control unit ground circuit. If circuits are okay, check control unit connectors. If connectors are okay, install known-good control unit and recheck.

ANTI-LOCK WARNING LIGHT REMAINS ON, BUT DOES NOT FLASH TROUBLE CODES

1) If warning light stays on after 3 seconds, but does not flash trouble codes, check for loose or poor connection at connector. If connector is okay, check ABS fuse No. 2. Check for open White wire between ABS fuse No. 2 and control unit.
2) On Integra, check Black/Yellow wire between control unit and rear defroster/cooling fan relay fuse in underdash fuse relay box. Check wire between battery and underhood fuse/relay box. Check for open circuit inside underhood ABS fuse/relay box.
3) On Legend, check Yellow/Black wire between control unit and rear defroster/cooling fan relay fuse in underdash fuse/relay box. On Vigor, check Black/Yellow wire between control unit and heater control relay fuse in underdash fuse/relay box.
4) On all models, check for short in Blue/Red wire between instrument panel and control unit. Check for open in White/Blue wire between alternator and control unit. If problem cannot be found, install a known-good control unit and retest.

DIAGNOSIS & TESTING

NOTE: On Legend, after performing ABS function check, disconnect ABS fuse No. 2 for at least 3 seconds to erase TCS control unit memory.

ABS FUNCTION TEST

Perform ABS function test after any ABS component repair or replacement, system bleeding or repair affecting sensors or wiring.

WARNING: DO NOT drive vehicle with ABS tester connected to vehicle. Loss of braking can occur.

Preliminary Procedure – ANTI-LOCK warning light should come on when ignition is on and go off after engine is started. If light remains on, see ANTI-LOCK WARNING LIGHT under TROUBLESHOOTING. If light goes off, park vehicle on level surface. Block wheels, and place transmission in Park (A/T) or Neutral (M/T).

Testing – **1)** Turn ignition switch to OFF position. Connect ABS Tester (07HAJ-SG0010B) to 6-pin inspection connector. *See Fig. 1, 2 or 3.* Start engine, and release parking brake. Place mode selector in mode 1. Push START TEST button. TEST-IN-PROGRESS light should come on. DO NOT turn mode selector switch while TEST-IN-PROGRESS light is on.

2) Ensure all 4 monitor lights on ABS tester come on within 1-2 seconds. ANTI-LOCK light should not come on. If light is on, check system for codes. See RETRIEVING CODES.

3) Turn mode selector to mode 2. Depress brake pedal firmly, and push START TEST button. ANTI-LOCK warning light should not come on and kickback should be felt at brake pedal. If light comes on or kickback is not felt, see ANTI-LOCK WARNING LIGHT under TROUBLE SHOOTING.

4) Repeat step **3)** for remaining ABS tester modes (3, 4 and 5). Results should be as described in mode 2. If results differ, see ANTI-LOCK WARNING LIGHT. Breakdown of modes is as follows:

Mode 1 – Sends simulated driving signal of each wheel to control unit to check self-diagnostic circuit. No kickback should be felt in brake pedal.

Mode 2 – Sends driving signal of each wheel and then sends lock signal of left rear wheel to control unit. Kickback should be felt in brake pedal.

Mode 3 – Sends driving signal of each wheel and then sends lock signal of right rear wheel to control unit. Kickback should be felt in brake pedal.

Mode 4 – Sends driving signal of each wheel and then sends lock signal of left front wheel to control unit. Kickback should be felt in brake pedal.

Mode 5 – Sends driving signal of each wheel and then sends lock signal of right front wheel to control unit. Kickback should be felt in brake pedal.

Mode 6 – Not used.

If kickback is not felt as described in modes No. 2-5, repeat test several times before trouble shooting other parts of system.

RETRIEVING CODES

1) Turn engine off. Turn ignition on. Ensure ANTI-LOCK warning light comes on. Start engine and check ANTI-LOCK warning light. If warning light goes out, no fault codes exist.

2) If light remains on, turn engine off. Disconnect service check connector. *See Fig. 1, 2 or 3.* On Legend and Vigor, connect jumper wire between service check connector terminals. On Integra, connect SSC Short Connector (07PAZ-0010100) to service check connector.

3) Turn ignition on, but DO NOT start engine. ANTI-LOCK warning light should start flashing Diagnostic Trouble Codes (DTC). If light does not flash DTC, go to ANTI-LOCK WARNING LIGHT REMAINS ON, BUT DOES NOT FLASH TROUBLE CODES under TROUBLE SHOOTING.

4) First flashing sequence indicates main code of DTC, and second number indicates sub code of DTC. *See Fig. 6.* A one-second pause separates main and sub codes. Total of 3 DTC's can be set at one time. There is a 5-second pause between DTC's.

5) To recheck DTC sequence, turn ignition off for a few seconds and then turn it back on. After codes are retrieved, go to appropriate test under TROUBLE CODES to diagnose system.

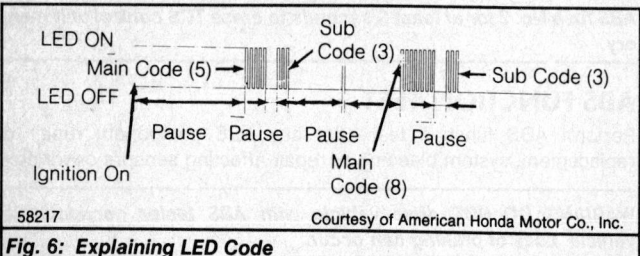

58217   Courtesy of American Honda Motor Co., Inc.

Fig. 6: Explaining LED Code

CLEARING CODES

To clear codes, remove ABS fuse No. 2 for at least 3 seconds, or disconnect ABS control unit connector.

WHEEL SENSOR CHECK

Legend & Vigor – **1)** Disconnect ABS inspection 6-pin connector. *See Fig. 2 or 3.* Connect ABS tester to 6-pin connector. Set ABS tester mode selector in mode 0. Raise and support vehicle so wheels can be rotated. Turn ignition on. Place transmission in Neutral. Manually rotate wheels (one revolution per second). Ensure appropriate monitor light on tester blinks as wheel is rotated.

2) In some instances, front wheels may not rotate fast enough to make tester light blink. If this happens, start engine. Slowly accelerate and decelerate front wheels. If light still does not blink, check suspect wheel sensor, sensor air gap and wiring.

SOLENOID LEAK TEST

NOTE: If solenoid leaks excessively, brake fluid in modulator reservoir will rise when ABS power unit is operated.

Legend & Vigor – **1)** Disconnect pressure switch connector and pump motor connector. Connect ohmmeter between Yellow wires of accumulator pressure switch connector. *See Fig. 7.*

2) Apply battery voltage to Red/White wire on pump motor connector. Ground Green terminal. Install an on-off switch in negative lead. Turn switch to ON position. Allow pressure to build inside accumulator. Check for continuity at pressure switch.

3) If continuity exists, allow pump to operate for 10 more seconds. Turn switch to OFF position. If solenoid hisses or squeaks, replace modulator. Check for continuity at pressure switch within 30 minutes. Continuity should exist. If continuity does not exist, solenoid is faulty. Replace modulator.

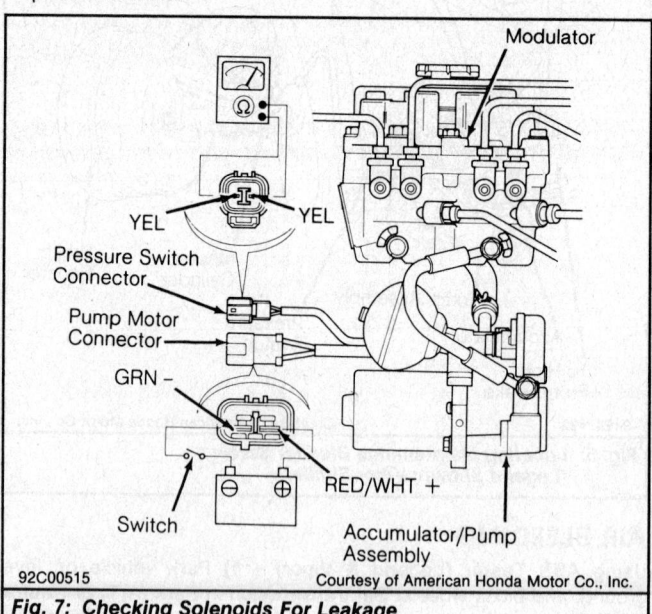

92C00515   Courtesy of American Honda Motor Co., Inc.

**Fig. 7: Checking Solenoids For Leakage
(Legend Shown; Vigor Similar)**

MODULATOR FUNCTION CHECK

NOTE: Bleed high-pressure fluid from modulator unit before performing modulator function check. See RELIEVING SYSTEM PRESSURE under BLEEDING BRAKE SYSTEM.

Integra – **1)** Bleed high-pressure fluid from modulator unit. See RELIEVING SYSTEM PRESSURE under BLEEDING BRAKE SYSTEM. Raise and support vehicle with safety stands. Have an assistant depress brake pedal firmly. Ensure wheels cannot be rotated. Remove cap and slowly fill reservoir to MAX level with clean brake fluid.

2) Wait a few minutes, then start engine and allow to idle for a few minutes. Turn engine off. Check brake fluid in reservoir. Fluid should be below MAX level. Fill reservoir to MAX level with clean fluid. Start engine and ensure ANTI-LOCK light goes off.

RELAY TEST

Remove relay to be tested. *See Fig. 1, 2 or 3.* Using ohmmeter, check continuity between terminals "A" and "B". *See Fig. 8.* Continuity should not exist. Apply battery voltage between terminals "C" and "D". Continuity should now exist between terminals "A" and "B". If continuity is not as specified, replace relay.

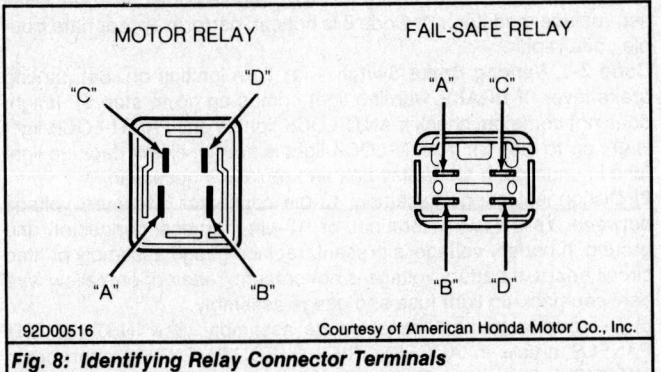

Fig. 8: *Identifying Relay Connector Terminals*

TROUBLE CODES

CONTROL UNIT TROUBLE CODES (INTEGRA)

Code	System Affected
1	Pump Motor
1-2	Pump Motor Circuit
1-3	High Pressure Leakage
1-4	Pressure Switch
1-8	Accumulator Gas Leakage
2-1	Parking Brake Switch
3-1 To 3-8	Pulser(s)
3-12	Different Diameter Tire Used
4-1 To 4-8	Wheel Speed Sensor(s)
5-4 & 5-8	Rear Wheel Lock(s)
6	Front & Rear Fail-Safe Relays
6-1	Front Fail-Safe Relay
6-4	Rear Fail-Safe Relay
7-1 & 7-2	Front Solenoid(s) Circuit
7-4	Rear Solenoid Circuit
8-1	ABS Function
8-2	CPU Comparison
8-1	Integrated Circuit

CONTROL UNIT TROUBLE CODES (LEGEND & VIGOR)

Code	System Affected
1	Pump Motor
1-2	Pump Motor Circuit
1-3	High Pressure Leakage
1-4	Pressure Switch
1-8	Accumulator Gas Leakage
2-1	Parking Brake Switch
3-1 To 3-4	Pulser(s)
4-1 To 4-8	Wheel Speed Sensor(s)
5-4 & 5-8	Rear Speed Sensor(s)
6-1	Front Fail-Safe Relay
6-4	Rear Fail-Safe Relay
7-1 & 7-2	Front Solenoid(s) Circuit
7-4	Rear Solenoid Circuit

NOTE: Use only high impedance Digital Volt-Ohmmeter (DVOM) for testing.

INTEGRA

Code 1, Pump Motor Overrun – 1) Start engine and allow to idle for one minute. Check pump motor and ANTI-LOCK light operation. If pump motor runs for 40 seconds then light comes on, go to next step. If pump motor and light do not operate as described, vehicle is okay at this time.

2) Check fluid level in modulator reservoir. *See Fig. 9.* If fluid level is not okay, replace modulator. If fluid level is okay, stop engine and go to next step.

3) Disconnect modulator 14-pin connector. Check continuity between Yellow wire and Black wire terminals of 14-pin connector. If continuity exists, go to next step. If continuity is not present, replace modulator unit.

4) Measure voltage between Yellow wire terminal of 14-pin connector and ground. If battery voltage is not present, go to next step. If battery voltage exists, check pressure switch ground connection. If ground connection is okay, repair open Black wire between pressure switch and ground.

5) Measure voltage between Yellow wire terminal of control unit 26-pin connector and ground. If battery voltage exists, repair open Yellow wire between pressure switch and control unit. If battery voltage is not present, check control unit connectors. If connectors are okay, install known-good control unit and retest.

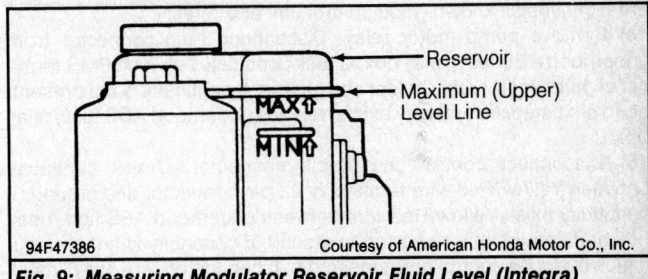

Reservoir
Maximum (Upper) Level Line

Fig. 9: *Measuring Modulator Reservoir Fluid Level (Integra)*

Code 1-2, Pump motor circuit – 1) Check ABS fuses and replace if necessary. Remove pump motor relay. Test relay and replace if necessary. See RELAY TEST under DIAGNOSIS & TESTING. If relay is okay, bleed high pressure fluid from modulator bleed screw. See RELIEVING SYSTEM PRESSURE under BLEEDING BRAKE SYSTEM.

2) Connect jumper wire between "B+" terminal and motor terminal of pump motor relay holder. *See Fig. 10.* If pump motor runs, go to next step. If pump motor does not run, go to step **8)**.

3) Remove jumper wire. Disconnect 3-pin connector from underhood ABS fuse/relay box. Turn ignition on. Measure voltage between motor terminal of pump motor relay holder and ground. If battery voltage does not exist, go to step **11)**. If battery voltage exists, go to next step.

4) Measure voltage between Black/Yellow wire of 3-pin connector and ground. If battery voltage is present, go to next step. If battery voltage is not present, repair open Black/Yellow wire between underdash fuse/relay box and underhood ABS fuse/relay box.

5) Reconnect 3-pin connector to underhood ABS fuse/relay box. Install pump motor relay. If relay clicks, go to step **14)**. If relay does not click, measure voltage between Yellow/Red wire terminal of underhood ABS fuse/relay box 3-pin connector and ground. If battery voltage exists, go to next step. If battery voltage does not exist, replace underhood ABS fuse/relay box.

6) Measure voltage between Yellow/Red wire terminal of control unit 22-pin connector and ground. If battery voltage is not present, repair open Yellow/Red wire between underhood ABS fuse/relay box and control unit. If battery voltage exists, go to next step.

7) Reconnect connectors. Bleed high pressure fluid. See RELIEVING SYSTEM PRESSURE under BLEEDING BRAKE SYSTEM. Add clean brake fluid if necessary. Start engine and check for DTC 2-1. If DTC 2-1 is still present, replace control unit.

8) Measure voltage between battery terminal of underhood ABS fuse/relay box and ground. If battery voltage is not present, repair open White wire between battery and underhood ABS fuse/relay box. If battery voltage is present, go to next step.

9) Disconnect ABS pump motor 2-pin connector. Measure voltage between White wire terminal of pump motor connector and ground. If battery voltage exists, go to next step. If battery voltage is not present, repair open White wire between underhood ABS fuse/relay box and pump motor.

10) Measure voltage between pump motor connector terminals. If battery voltage exists, replace pump motor. If battery voltage is not present, check pump motor ground connection. If ground connection is okay, repair open Black wire between pump motor and ground.

11) Disconnect 4-pin connector from underhood ABS fuse/relay box. Measure voltage between Brown/Yellow wire terminal of 4-pin connector and ground. If battery voltage is not present, go to next step. If battery voltage exists, replace underhood ABS fuse/relay box.

12) Measure voltage between Brown/Yellow wire terminal of control unit 26-pin connector and ground. If battery voltage is not present, go to next step. If battery voltage exists, repair open Brown/Yellow wire between underhood ABS fuse/relay box and control unit.

13) Turn ignition off. Disconnect control unit 26-pin connector. Check continuity between Brown/Yellow wire terminal of 2-6 pin connector and ground. If continuity exists, Brown/Yellow wire between underhood fuse/relay box and control unit is shorted to ground. If continuity does not exist, check for loose control unit connectors. If connectors are okay, install known-good control unit and retest.

14) Remove pump motor relay. Disconnect 3-pin connector from underhood ABS fuse/relay box. Check continuity between PMR terminal of pump motor relay holder and ground. If continuity is not present, go to next step. If continuity exists, replace underhood ABS fuse/relay box.

15) Disconnect control unit 22-pin connector. Check continuity between Yellow/Red wire terminal of 22-pin connector and ground. If continuity exist, Yellow/Red wire between underhood ABS fuse/relay box and control unit is shorted to ground. If continuity is not present, check for loose control unit connectors. If connectors are okay, install and known-good control unit and recheck.

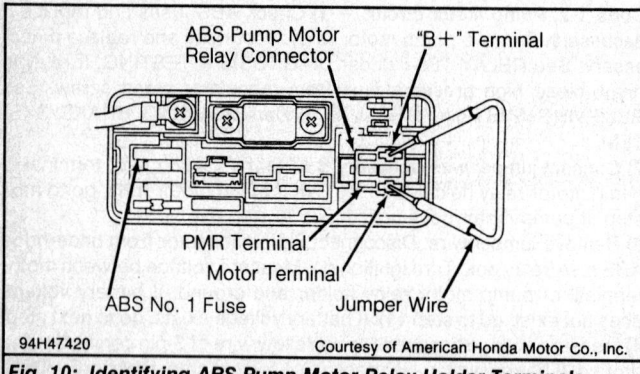

94H47420   Courtesy of American Honda Motor Co., Inc.

Fig. 10: Identifying ABS Pump Motor Relay Holder Terminals

Code 1-3, High Pressure Leakage – 1) Check modulator for brake fluid leak. If there is no fluid leak, go to next step. If there is fluid leak, tighten modulator fitting or replace modulator if necessary.

2) Start engine. If ABS pump motor does not operate, go to next step. If pump motor operates, turn engine off after pump motor stops. Wait 30 minutes, and then restart engine. If pump motor does not operate, go to next step. If pump motor operates, wait until motor stops and then go to next step.

3) Turn engine off. Disconnect modulator 14-pin connector. Wait 30 minutes, then check continuity between modulator connector Yellow wire and Black wire terminals. If continuity does not exist, replace modulator. If continuity exists, problem is intermittent. Check for loose connectors and terminals in pressure switch circuit.

Code 1-4, Pressure Switch – 1) Bleed high pressure fluid from modulator. See RELIEVING SYSTEM PRESSURE. Disconnect modulator 14-pin connector. Check continuity between modulator connector Yellow wire and Black wire terminals. If continuity does not exist, go to next step. If continuity exists, visually inspect modulator wire harness. If wire harness is okay, replace modulator.

2) Disconnect control unit 26-pin connector. Check continuity between Yellow wire terminal of control unit connector and ground. If continuity does not exist, go to next step. If continuity exists, Yellow wire between control unit and modulator is shorted to ground.

3) Reconnect control unit 26-pin connector. Turn ignition on. Measure voltage between control unit Yellow wire terminal and ground. If battery voltage is present, pressure switch signal is okay. If battery voltage is not present, check for loose control unit connectors. If connectors are okay, install known-good control unit and retest.

Code 1-8, Accumulator Gas Leakage – 1) Check accumulator relief plug. If plug is damaged, replace accumulator. If plug is okay, start and run engine until ANTI-LOCK light goes off. Turn engine off. Repeat procedure 10 times.

2) If light goes off each time engine is started, system is okay at this time. If symptom reappears, replace modulator. If light does not go off after each engine start, check for ABS trouble codes. If Code 1-8 is set, replace modulator. If Code 8 is not set, perform appropriate trouble code repair.

Code 2-1, Parking Brake Switch – 1) Turn ignition on. Set parking brake lever. If BRAKE warning light comes on go to step **5)**. If light does not come on, check if ANTI-LOCK light is on. If ANTI-LOCK light is on, go to step **3)**. If ANTI-LOCK light is not on, check back-up light fuse in underdash fuse/relay box and replace if necessary.

2) Disconnect gauge assembly 13-pin connector. Measure voltage between Yellow wire terminal of 13-pin harness connector and ground. If battery voltage is present, replace gauge assembly printed circuit board. If battery voltage is not present, repair open Yellow wire between back-up light fuse and gauge assembly.

3) Remove instrument panel gauge assembly. See INSTRUMENT PANELS article in ACCESSORIES & EQUIPMENT of appropriate MITCHELL ® manual. Check BRAKE warning light bulb. Replace as necessary. Reconnect gauge assembly 13-pin and 16-pin connectors if disconnected. Connect jumper wire between Green/Red wire terminal of 16-pin connector and ground.

4) If BRAKE warning light does not come on, replace gauge assembly printed circuit board. If light comes on, connect jumper wire between parking brake switch connector and ground. If BRAKE warning light comes on, replace parking brake switch. If light does not come on, repair open Green/Red wire between gauge assembly and parking brake switch.

5) Release parking brake lever. If BRAKE warning light does not go off, go to step **7)**. If light goes off, measure voltage between Green/Red wire terminal of control unit 26-pin harness connector and ground. If battery voltage is present, go to next step. If battery voltage is not present, repair open Green/Red wire between gauge assembly and control unit.

6) Test drive vehicle at minimum speed of 6 MPH for at least 30 seconds. If ANTI-LOCK light comes on, replace control unit. If light does not come on, code was probably set because vehicle was driven with parking brake applied for more than 30 seconds.

7) Check brake fluid level in master cylinder reservoir. If brake fluid level is correct, go to next step. If fluid level is not correct, check front brake pad and brake system for leaks. If no problem is found, fill master cylinder reservoir to the correct level.

8) Disconnect brake fluid level switch connectors. If BRAKE warning light goes off, replace brake fluid level switch. If light does not go off, check parking brake switch and replace if necessary. If switch is okay, disconnect control unit 26-pin connector.

9) If BRAKE warning light goes off, replace control unit. If light does not go off, Green/Red wire between BRAKE warning light, parking brake switch and brake fluid level switch is shorted to ground.

Codes 3-1 To 3-8, Pulser – Probable cause is chipped pulser gear or improperly installed speed sensor. No other information is available from manufacturer.

Code 3-12, Different Tire Size Used On Vehicle – Code may set if different diameter tires are used on vehicle. No other information is available from manufacturer.

Code 4-1, Right Front Wheel Speed Sensor – 1) Disconnect right front wheel speed sensor 2-pin connector. Measure resistance between speed sensor harness connector terminals. If resistance is not 600-900 ohms, replace speed sensor. If resistance is 600-900 ohms, go to next step.

2) Check continuity between Green/Black wire terminal of sensor harness connector and ground. If continuity exists, replace sensor. If continuity

tinuity does not exist, disconnect control unit 22-pin connector. Check continuity between Green/Black wire terminal of control unit 22-pin connector and ground.

3) If continuity exists, Green/Black wire between control unit and speed sensor is shorted to ground. If continuity does not exist, check continuity between Green wire terminal of control unit 22-pin connector and ground.

4) If continuity exists, Green wire between control unit and speed sensor is shorted to ground. If continuity does not exist, reconnect speed sensor 2-pin connector. Measure resistance between Green wire and Green/Black wire terminals of control unit 22-pin connector.

5) If resistance is 600-900 ohms, go to step **7)**. If resistance is not 600-900 ohms, connect jumper wire between Green/Black wire terminal of control unit 22-pin connector and ground. Disconnect right front speed sensor 2-pin connector.

6) Check continuity between speed sensor Green/Black wire terminal and ground. If continuity exists, repair open Green wire between control unit and speed sensor. If continuity does not exist, repair open Green/Black wire between control unit and speed sensor.

7) Check right front speed sensor air gap and correct if necessary. See WHEEL SENSOR AIR GAP SPECIFICATIONS table under REMOVAL & INSTALLATION. If gap is okay, go to next step if ABS tester is available, or step **10)** if ABS tester is not available.

8) Connect ABS tester to inspection 6-pin connector. *See Fig. 1*. Start engine. Turn mode selector on ABS tester to mode 5. Firmly depress and hold brake pedal down. Push START TEST switch.

9) Have assistant manually rotate right front wheel. If wheel cannot be rotated, replace modulator. If wheels can be rotated, problem is intermittent. Test drive vehicle. If symptom reappears, replace control unit.

10) Disconnect modulator 14-pin connector. Connect battery positive terminal to Red/Black wire and Yellow/Black wire terminals of modulator 14-pin connector. Connect battery negative terminal and an on-off switch to White/Black wire and Green/Black wire terminals of 14-pin connector.

11) Firmly depress brake pedal, and momentarily turn on switch to apply ABS function to right front wheel. Have assistant manually rotate right front wheel. If wheel cannot be rotated, replace modulator. If wheel can be rotated, problem is intermittent. Test drive vehicle. If symptom reappears, replace control unit.

Code 4-2, Left Front Wheel Speed Sensor – **1)** Disconnect left front wheel speed sensor 2-pin connector. Measure resistance between speed sensor harness connector terminals. If resistance is not 600-900 ohms, replace speed sensor. If resistance is 600-900 ohms, go to next step.

2) Check continuity between Green/Blue wire terminal of sensor harness connector and ground. If continuity exists, replace sensor. If continuity does not exist, disconnect control unit 22-pin connector. Check continuity between Green/Blue (Green/Orange or Green/Blue on hatchback) wire terminal of control unit 22-pin connector and ground.

3) If continuity exists, Green/Blue wire or Green/Orange wire between control unit and speed sensor is shorted to ground. If continuity does not exist, check continuity between Brown (Light Green/Black or Brown on hatchback) wire terminal of control unit 22-pin connector and ground.

4) If continuity exists, Brown wire or Light Green/Black wire between control unit and speed sensor is shorted to ground. If continuity does not exist, reconnect speed sensor 2-pin connector. Measure resistance between Brown (Light Green/Black on hatchback) wire and Green/Blue (Green/Orange on hatchback) wire terminals of control unit 22-pin connector.

5) If resistance is 600-900 ohms, go to step **7)**. If resistance is not 600-900 ohms, connect jumper wire between Green/Blue wire or Green/Orange wire terminal of control unit 22-pin connector and ground. Disconnect left front speed sensor 2-pin connector.

6) Check continuity between speed sensor Green/Blue wire or Green/Orange wire terminal and ground. If continuity exists, repair open Brown wire or Light Green/Black wire between control unit and speed sensor. If continuity does not exist, repair open Green/Blue wire or Green/Orange wire between control unit and speed sensor.

7) Check left front speed sensor air gap and correct if necessary. See WHEEL SENSOR AIR GAP SPECIFICATIONS table under REMOVAL & INSTALLATION. If gap is okay, go to next step if ABS tester is available, or step **10)** if ABS tester is not available.

8) Connect ABS tester to inspection 6-pin connector. *See Fig. 1*. Start engine. Turn mode selector on ABS tester to mode 4. Firmly depress and hold brake pedal down. Push START TEST switch.

9) Have assistant manually rotate left front wheel. If wheel cannot be rotated, replace modulator. If wheels can be rotated, problem is intermittent. Test drive vehicle. If symptom reappears, replace control unit.

10) Disconnect modulator 14-pin connector. Connect battery positive terminal to Red/Blue wire and Yellow/Blue wire terminals of modulator 14-pin connector. Connect battery negative terminal and an on-off switch to White/Blue wire and Gray/Blue wire terminals of 14-pin connector.

11) Firmly depress brake pedal, and momentarily turn on switch to apply ABS function to left front wheel. Have assistant manually rotate left front wheel. If wheel cannot be rotated, replace modulator. If wheel can be rotated, problem is intermittent. Test drive vehicle. If symptom reappears, replace control unit.

Code 4-4, Right Rear Wheel Speed Sensor – **1)** Disconnect right rear wheel speed sensor 2-pin connector. Measure resistance between speed sensor harness connector terminals. If resistance is not 700-1100 ohms, replace speed sensor. If resistance is 700-1100 ohms, go to next step.

2) Check continuity between Green/Yellow wire terminal of sensor harness connector and ground. If continuity exists, replace sensor. If continuity does not exist, disconnect control unit 22-pin connector. Check continuity between Green/Yellow wire terminal of control unit 22-pin connector and ground.

3) If continuity exists, Green/Yellow wire between control unit and speed sensor is shorted to ground. If continuity does not exist, check continuity between Blue/Yellow wire terminal of control unit 22-pin connector and ground.

4) If continuity exists, Blue/Yellow wire between control unit and speed sensor is shorted to ground. If continuity does not exist, reconnect speed sensor 2-pin connector. Measure resistance between Green/Yellow wire and Blue/Yellow wire terminals of control unit 22-pin connector.

5) If resistance is 700-1100 ohms, go to step **7)**. If resistance is not 700-1100 ohms, connect jumper wire between Green/Yellow wire terminal of control unit 22-pin connector and ground. Disconnect right rear speed sensor 2-pin connector.

6) Check continuity between speed sensor Green/Yellow wire terminal and ground. If continuity exists, repair open Blue/Yellow wire between control unit and speed sensor. If continuity does not exist, repair open Green/Yellow wire between control unit and speed sensor.

7) Check right rear speed sensor air gap and correct if necessary. See WHEEL SENSOR AIR GAP SPECIFICATIONS table under REMOVAL & INSTALLATION. If gap is okay, go to next step if ABS tester is available, or step **10)** if ABS tester is not available.

8) Connect ABS tester to inspection 6-pin connector. *See Fig. 1*. Start engine. Turn mode selector on ABS tester to mode 3. Firmly depress and hold brake pedal down. Push START TEST switch.

9) Have assistant manually rotate right front wheel. If wheel cannot be rotated, replace modulator. If wheels can be rotated, problem is intermittent. Test drive vehicle. If symptom reappears, replace control unit.

10) Disconnect modulator 14-pin connector. Connect battery positive terminal to Red/White wire and Yellow/White wire terminals of modulator 14-pin connector. Connect battery negative terminal and an on-off switch to White wire and Gray/White wire terminals of 14-pin connector.

11) Firmly depress brake pedal, and momentarily turn on switch to apply ABS function to right rear wheel. Have assistant manually rotate right rear wheel. If wheel cannot be rotated, replace modulator. If wheel can be rotated, problem is intermittent. Test drive vehicle. If symptom reappears, replace control unit.

Code 4-8, Left Rear Wheel Speed Sensor – **1)** Disconnect left rear wheel speed sensor 2-pin connector. Measure resistance between speed sensor harness connector terminals. If resistance is not 700-1100 ohms, replace speed sensor. If resistance is 700-1100 ohms, go to next step.

2) Check continuity between Light Blue wire terminal of sensor harness connector and ground. If continuity exists, replace sensor. If continuity does not exist, disconnect control unit 22-pin connector. Check continuity between Light Blue wire terminal of control unit 22-pin connector and ground.

3) If continuity exists, Light Blue wire between control unit and speed sensor is shorted to ground. If continuity does not exist, check continuity between Gray wire terminal of control unit 22-pin connector and ground.

4) If continuity exists, Gray wire between control unit and speed sensor is shorted to ground. If continuity does not exist, reconnect speed sensor 2-pin connector. Measure resistance between Light Blue wire and Brown wire terminals of control unit 22-pin connector.

5) If resistance is 700-1100 ohms, go to step 7). If resistance is not 700-1100 ohms, connect jumper wire between Light Blue wire terminal of control unit 22-pin connector and ground. Disconnect left rear speed sensor 2-pin connector.

6) Check continuity between speed sensor Light Blue wire terminal and ground. If continuity exists, repair open Gray wire between control unit and speed sensor. If continuity does not exist, repair open Light Blue wire between control unit and speed sensor.

7) Check left rear speed sensor air gap and correct if necessary. See WHEEL SENSOR AIR GAP SPECIFICATIONS table under REMOVAL & INSTALLATION. If gap is okay, go to next step if ABS tester is available, or step 10) if ABS tester is not available.

8) Connect ABS tester to inspection 6-pin connector. See Fig. 1. Start engine. Turn mode selector on ABS tester to mode 2. Firmly depress and hold brake pedal down. Push START TEST switch.

9) Have assistant manually rotate left rear wheel. If wheel cannot be rotated, replace modulator. If wheels can be rotated, problem is intermittent. Test drive vehicle. If symptom reappears, replace control unit.

10) Disconnect modulator 14-pin connector. Connect battery positive terminal to Red/White wire and Yellow/White wire terminals of modulator 14-pin connector. Connect battery negative terminal and an on-off switch to White wire and Gray/White wire terminals of 14-pin connector.

11) Firmly depress brake pedal, and momentarily turn on switch to apply ABS function to left rear wheel. Have assistant manually rotate left rear wheel. If wheel cannot be rotated, replace modulator. If wheel can be rotated, problem is intermittent. Test drive vehicle. If symptom reappears, replace control unit.

Codes 5-4 To 5-8, Rear Wheel Lock – 1) Turn ignition on. Set parking brake lever. If BRAKE warning light comes on, go to next step. If light does not come on, repair open wire between parking brake switch and underdash fuse/relay box, or replace parking brake switch.

2) Test drive vehicle at speed of 6 MPH. If ANTI-LOCK light does not come on, go to next step. If light comes on, check for ABS trouble codes. If Code 4-4 or 4-8 is set, perform rear wheel speed sensor trouble code test. If Codes 4-4 and 4-8 are not set, perform appropriate trouble code test.

3) Raise and support vehicle. Spin left and/or right rear wheels and check for brake drag and repair if necessary. If ABS tester is available, go to next step. If ABS tester is not available, go to step 5).

4) Connect ABS tester to inspection 6-pin connector. See Fig. 1. Start engine. Turn mode selector on ABS tester to mode 2. Firmly depress and hold brake pedal down. Have assistant manually rotate rear wheels. If wheels cannot be rotated, replace modulator. If wheels cannot be rotated, problem is intermittent. Replace modulator if symptom reappears.

5) Disconnect modulator 14-pin connector. Connect battery positive terminal to Red/White wire and Yellow/White wire terminals of modulator 14-pin connector. Connect battery negative terminal and an on-off switch to White wire and Gray/White wire terminals of 14-pin connector.

6) Firmly depress brake pedal, and momentarily turn on switch to apply ABS function to rear wheels. Have assistant manually rotate

rear wheels. If wheel cannot be rotated, replace modulator. If wheel can be rotated, problem is intermittent. If symptom reappears, replace control unit.

Code 6, Front & Rear Fail-Safe Relays – 1) Start engine. If ANTI-LOCK light does not go off, go to next step. If light goes off, system is okay at this time. Check for damaged wire harness between control unit, solenoids and fail-safe relays.

2) Check for ABS trouble codes. If Code 6 is not set, perform appropriate trouble code test. If Code 6 is set, disconnect control unit 22-pin connector. Start engine. Measure voltage between Yellow/Green wire terminal of 22-pin connector and ground.

3) If battery voltage is present, Yellow/Green wire between control unit and fail-safe relays is shorted to ground. If battery voltage is not present, turn ignition off. Reconnect control unit 22-pin connector. Turn ignition on.

4) Measure voltage between Yellow/Green wire terminal of 22-pin connector and ground. If battery voltage is present, replace control unit. If battery voltage is not present, perform CODE 6-1 and CODE 6-4 tests.

Code 6-1, Front Fail-Safe Relay – 1) Start engine. If ANTI-LOCK light does not go off, go to next step. If light goes off, system is okay at this time. Check for damaged wire harness between control unit, solenoids and front fail-safe relay.

2) Check for ABS trouble codes. If Code 6-1 is not set, perform appropriate trouble code test. If Code 6-1 is set, test front fail-safe relay and replace if necessary. See RELAY TEST under DIAGNOSIS & TESTING. Disconnect modulator 14-pin connector.

3) Visually check modulator wire harness for short to power and repair or replace as necessary. If wire harness is okay, start engine. Measure voltage between Brown/Black wire terminal of front fail-safe relay connector and ground.

4) If battery voltage is not present, go to next step. If battery voltage is present, Brown/Black wire between front fail-safe relay and modulator is shorted to power.

5) Stop engine. Disconnect control unit 26-pin connector. Start engine. Measure voltage between Red/Black wire terminal of 26-pin connector and ground. If battery voltage is not present, go to next step. If battery voltage is present, Red/Black wire between control unit and modulator is shorted to power.

6) Measure voltage between Red/Blue wire terminal of 26-pin connector and ground. If battery voltage is not present, go to next step. If battery voltage is present, Red/Blue wire between control unit and modulator is shorted to power.

7) Measure voltage between Yellow/Black wire terminal of 26-pin connector and ground. If battery voltage is not present, go to next step. If battery voltage is present, Yellow/Black wire between control unit and modulator is shorted to power.

8) Measure voltage between Yellow/Blue wire terminal of 26-pin connector and ground. If battery voltage is present, Yellow/Blue wire between control unit and modulator is shorted to power. If battery voltage is not present, check for loose control unit connectors. If connectors are okay, install known-good control unit and retest.

Code 6-4, Rear Fail-Safe Relay – 1) Start engine. If ANTI-LOCK light does not go off, go to next step. If light goes off, system is okay at this time. Check for damaged wire harness between control unit, solenoids and rear fail-safe relay.

2) Check for ABS trouble codes. If Code 6-4 is not set, perform appropriate trouble code test. If Code 6-4 is set, test rear fail-safe relay and replace if necessary. See RELAY TEST under DIAGNOSIS & TESTING. Disconnect modulator 14-pin connector.

3) Visually check modulator wire harness for short to power and repair or replace as necessary. If wire harness is okay, start engine. Measure voltage between Blue/Black wire terminal of rear fail-safe relay connector and ground.

4) If battery voltage is not present, go to next step. If battery voltage is present, Blue/Black wire between rear fail-safe relay and modulator is shorted to power.

5) Stop engine. Disconnect control unit 26-pin connector. Start engine. Measure voltage between Red/White wire terminal of 26-pin connector and ground. If battery voltage is not present, go to next step. If bat-

tery voltage is present, Red/White wire between control unit and modulator is shorted to power.

6) Measure voltage between Yellow/White wire terminal of 26-pin connector and ground. If battery voltage is present, Yellow/White wire between control unit and modulator is shorted to power. If battery voltage is not present, check for loose control unit connectors. If connectors are okay, install known-good control unit and retest.

Code 7-1, Right Front Solenoid – **1)** Start engine. If ANTI-LOCK light does not go off, go to next step. If light goes off, system is okay at this time. Check connectors and wire harness between control unit, fail-safe relay and modulator.

2) Check for ABS trouble codes. If Code 7-1 is not set, perform appropriate trouble code test. If Code 7-1 is set, disconnect modulator 14-pin connector. Remove front fail-safe relay. Connect jumper wire between White/Green wire and Brown/Black wire terminals of fail-safe relay harness connector.

NOTE: Modulator 14-pin connector has more than one Brown/Black wires. Ensure appropriate wire is tested.

3) Measure voltage between modulator terminal No. 5 and ground. *See Fig. 11.* If battery voltage is present, go to next step. If battery voltage is not present, repair open Brown/Black wire between front fail-safe relay and modulator.

4) Measure voltage between modulator terminal No. 8 and ground. If battery voltage is present, go to next step. If battery voltage is not present, repair open Brown/Black wire between front fail-safe relay and modulator.

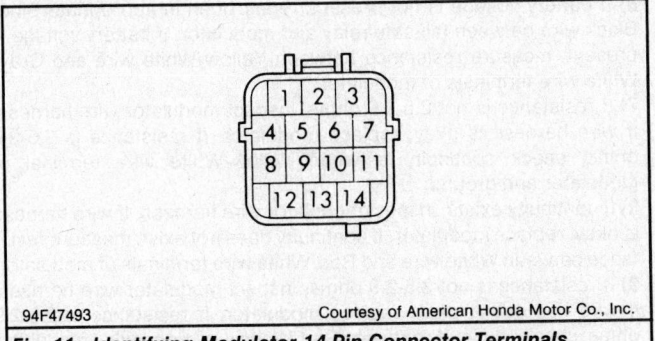

94F47493   Courtesy of American Honda Motor Co., Inc.
Fig. 11: Identifying Modulator 14-Pin Connector Terminals

5) Measure resistance between modulator connector terminals No. 1 and 3. *See Fig. 11.* If resistance is 2.5-2.9 ohms, go to next step. If resistance is not 2.5-2.9 ohms, inspect modulator wire harness. If wire harness is okay, replace modulator

6) Check continuity between modulator connector terminal No. 1 and ground. If continuity does not exist, go to next step. If continuity exists, inspect modulator wire harness. If wire harness is okay, replace modulator.

7) Measure resistance between modulator connector terminals No. 8 and 13. If resistance is 2.5-2.9 ohms, go to next step. If resistance is not 2.5-2.9 ohms, inspect modulator wire harness. If wire harness is okay, replace modulator

8) Check continuity between modulator connector terminal No. 12 and ground. If continuity does not exist, go to next step. If continuity exists, inspect modulator wire harness. If wire harness is okay, replace modulator.

9) Check continuity between modulator connector terminals No. 1 and 12. If continuity does not exist, go to next step. If continuity exists, replace modulator wire harness.

10) Disconnect control unit 26-pin connector. Check continuity between Yellow/Black wire terminal of 26-pin connector and ground. If continuity is not present, go to next step. If continuity is present, Yellow/Black wire between control unit and modulator is shorted to ground.

11) Check continuity between Red/Black wire terminal of 26-pin connector and ground. If continuity is not present, go to next step. If continuity is present, Red/Black wire between control unit and modulator is shorted to ground.

12) Check continuity between Red/Black wire and Yellow/Black wire terminals of 26-pin connector. If continuity is not present, go to next step. If continuity is present, repair shorted Red/Black wire Yellow/Black wire between control unit.

13) Reconnect modulator 14-pin connector. Measure voltage between Yellow/Black wire terminal of control unit 26-pin connector and ground. If battery voltage exists, go to next step. If battery voltage is not present, repair open Yellow/Black wire between control unit and modulator.

14) Measure voltage between Red/Black wire terminal of control unit 26-pin connector and ground. If battery voltage exists, go to next step. If battery voltage is not present, repair open Red/Black wire between control unit and modulator.

15) Check continuity between Black wire terminal of 26-pin connector and ground. If continuity is not present, check ground connection. If ground connection is okay, repair open Black wire between control unit and ground.

16) If continuity is present, check for loose control unit connectors. If connectors are okay, install a known-good control unit and retest.

Code 7-2, Left Front Solenoid – **1)** Start engine. If ANTI-LOCK light does not go off, go to next step. If light goes off, system is okay at this time. Check connectors and wire harness between control unit, fail-safe relay and modulator.

2) Check for ABS trouble codes. If Code 7-2 is not set, perform appropriate trouble code test. If Code 7-2 is set, check ABS No. 1 fuse in underhood ABS fuse/relay box. If fuse is okay, go to step **8)**. If fuse is not okay, measure voltage between ABS No. 1 fuse holder terminals. *See Fig. 10.*

3) If battery voltage is not present, go to step **5)**. If battery voltage is present, disconnect 4-pin connector from underhood ABS fuse/relay box. Measure voltage between ABS No. 1 fuse holder terminals. *See Fig. 10.*

4) If battery voltage exists, replace underhood ABS fuse/relay box. If battery voltage is not present, White/Green wire between underhood ABS fuse/relay box and front fail-safe relay is shorted to ground.

5) Disconnect modulator 14-pin connector. Install new ABS No.1 fuse (20-amp) in underhood ABS fuse/relay box. Disconnect front fail-safe relay connector. Measure voltage between White/Green wire and Brown/Black wire terminals of front fail-safe relay connector.

6) If battery voltage is present, Brown/Black wire between front fail-safe relay and modulator is shorted to ground. If battery voltage is not present check continuity between ground and following modulator terminals: No. 5 (Gray/Black wire), No. 7 (Gray/Blue wire), No. 8 (White/Black wire) and No. 10 (White/Blue wire). *See Fig. 11.*

7) If continuity exists, inspect modulator wire harness. If wire harness is okay, replace modulator. If continuity does not exist, reconnect front fail-safe relay connector and modulator 14-pin connector and retest.

8) Reinstall ABS No. 1 fuse in fuse/relay box. Measure voltage between White/Green wire terminal of underhood ABS fuse/relay box 4-pin connector and ground. If battery voltage is present, go to next step. If battery voltage is not present, replace underhood ABS fuse/relay box.

9) Disconnect front fail-safe relay connector. Measure voltage between White/Green wire terminal of fail-safe relay connector and ground. If battery voltage is present, go to next step. If battery voltage is not present, repair open White/Green wire between underhood ABS fuse/relay box and fail-safe relay.

10) Test front fail-safe relay and replace as necessary. See RELAY TEST under DIAGNOSIS & TESTING. Disconnect modulator 14-pin connector. Connect jumper wire between White/Green wire and Brown/Black wire terminals of front fail-safe relay connector.

NOTE: Modulator 14-pin connector has more than one Brown/Black wires. Ensure appropriate wire is tested.

11) Measure voltage between 14-pin harness connector terminal No. 7 and ground. *See Fig. 11.* If battery voltage is present, go to next step. If battery voltage is not present, repair open in appropriate Brown/Black wire between front fail-safe relay and modulator.

12) Measure voltage between 14-pin harness connector terminal No. 10 and ground. If battery voltage is present, go to next step. If battery voltage is not present, repair open in appropriate Brown/Black wire between front fail-safe relay and modulator.

13) Measure resistance between Yellow/Blue wire and Gray/Blue wire terminals of modulator. If resistance is 2.5-2.9 ohms, go to next step. If resistance is not 2.5-2.9 ohms, inspect modulator wire harness. If wire harness is okay, replace modulator.

14) Check continuity between Yellow/Blue wire terminal of modulator and ground. If continuity does not, go to next step. If continuity exists, inspect modulator wire harness. If wire harness is okay, replace modulator.

15) Measure resistance between White/Blue wire and Red/Blue wire terminals of modulator. If resistance is 2.5-2.9 ohms, go to next step. If resistance is not 2.5-2.9 ohms, inspect modulator wire harness. If wire harness is okay, replace modulator.

16) Check continuity between Red/Blue wire terminal of modulator and ground. If continuity does not exist, go to next step. If continuity exists, inspect modulator wire harness. If wire harness is okay, replace modulator.

17) Check continuity between following terminals of modulator: Red/Blue wire and Yellow/Blue wire; Red/Blue wire and Red/Black wire; Red/Blue wire and Yellow/Black wire. If continuity does not exist, go to next step. If continuity exists, replace modulator wire harness.

18) Check continuity between following terminals of modulator: Yellow/Blue wire and Red/Black wire; Yellow/Blue wire and Yellow/Black wire. If continuity does not exist, go to next step. If continuity exists, replace modulator wire harness.

19) Disconnect control unit 26-pin connector. Check continuity between Yellow/Blue wire terminal of 26-pin connector and ground. If continuity does not exist, go to next step. If continuity exists, Yellow/Blue wire between control unit and modulator is shorted to ground.

20) Check continuity between Red/Blue wire terminal of 26-pin connector and ground. If continuity does not exist, go to next step. If continuity exists, Red/Blue wire between control unit and modulator is shorted to ground.

21) Check continuity between following terminals of 26-pin connector terminals: Red/Blue wire and Yellow/Blue wire; Red/Blue wire and Red/Black wire; Red/Blue wire and Yellow/Black wire. If continuity does not exist, go to next step. If continuity exits, repair shorted wire(s) between control unit and modulator.

22) Check continuity between following terminals of 26-pin connector terminals: Yellow/Blue wire and Red/Black wire; Yellow/Blue wire and Yellow/Black wire. If continuity does not exist, go to next step. If continuity exists, repair shorted wire(s) between control unit and modulator.

23) Connect modulator 14-pin connector. Measure voltage between Yellow/Blue wire terminal of 26-pin connector and ground. If battery voltage exists, go to next step. If battery voltage is not present, repair open Yellow/Blue wire between control unit and modulator.

24) Measure voltage between Red/Blue wire terminal of 26-pin connector and ground. If battery voltage exists, go to next step. If battery voltage is not present, repair open Red/Blue wire between control unit and modulator.

25) Check continuity between Black wire terminal of control unit 26-pin connector and ground. If continuity exists, go to next step. If continuity does not exist, check ground connection. If ground connection is okay, repair open Black wire between control unit and ground.

26) Disconnect control unit 22-pin connector. Connect jumper wire between Yellow/Green wire terminal of 22-pin connector and ground. Remove jumper wire from front fail-safe relay.

27) Disconnect rear fail-safe relay connector. Check continuity between Yellow/Green wire terminal of front fail-safe relay connector and ground. If continuity exists, go to next step. If continuity does not exist, repair open Yellow/Green wire between control unit and front fail-safe relay.

28) Remove jumper wire from Yellow/Green wire terminal of 22-pin connector. Check continuity between Yellow/Green wire terminal of front fail-safe relay connector and ground. If continuity does not exist, go to next step. If continuity exists, Yellow/Green wire between control unit and front fail-safe relay is shorted to ground.

29) Check continuity between Black wire terminal of front fail-safe relay connector and ground. If continuity does not exist, check ground

connection. If ground connection is okay, repair open Black wire between front fail-safe relay and ground.

30) If continuity exists, check for loose control unit connectors. If connectors are okay, install known-good control unit and retest.

Code 7-4, Rear Solenoid – **1)** Start engine. If ANTI-LOCK light does not go off, go to next step. If light goes off, system is okay at this time. Check connectors and wire harness between control unit, fail-safe relay and modulator.

2) Check for ABS trouble codes. If Code 7-4 is not set, perform appropriate trouble code test. If Code 7-4 is set, disconnect rear fail-safe relay connector. Measure voltage between White wire terminal of fail-safe relay connector and ground.

3) If battery voltage is not present, repair open White wire between underhood ABS fuse/relay box and rear fail-safe relay. If continuity exists, test rear fail-safe relay and replace if necessary. See RELAY TEST under DIAGNOSIS & TESTING.

NOTE: Modulator 14-pin connector has more than one Blue/Black wires. Ensure appropriate Blue/Black wire is tested.

---

4) Disconnect modulator 14-pin connector. Connect jumper wire between White wire and Blue/Black wire terminals of rear fail-safe relay. Measure voltage between modulator 14-pin harness connector terminal No. 6 and ground. *See Fig. 11.*

5) If battery voltage is not present, repair open in appropriate Blue/Black wire between fail-safe relay and modulator. If battery voltage is present, measure voltage between 14-pin harness connector terminal No. 9 and ground.

6) If battery voltage is not present, repair open in appropriate Blue/Black wire between fail-safe relay and modulator. If battery voltage is present, measure resistance between Yellow/White wire and Gray/White wire terminals of modulator.

7) If resistance is not 2.5-2.9 ohms, inspect modulator wire harness. If wire harness is okay, replace modulator. If resistance is 2.5-2.9 ohms, check continuity between Yellow/White wire terminal of modulator and ground.

8) If continuity exists, inspect modulator wire harness. If wire harness is okay, replace modulator. If continuity does not exist, measure resistance between White wire and Red/White wire terminals of modulator.

9) If resistance is not 2.5-2.9 ohms, inspect modulator wire harness. If wire harness is okay, replace modulator. If resistance is 2.5-2.9 ohms, check continuity between Red/White wire terminal of modulator and ground.

10) If continuity exists, inspect modulator wire harness. If wire harness is okay, replace modulator. If continuity does not exist, check continuity between Yellow/White wire and Red/White wire terminals of modulator. If continuity does not exist, go to next step. If continuity exists, replace modulator wire harness.

11) Check continuity between following modulator terminals: Red/White wire and Red/Black wire; Red/White wire and Yellow/Black wire; Red/White wire and Red/Blue wire; Red/White wire and Yellow/Blue wire.

12) If continuity exists, replace modulator wire harness. If continuity does not exist, check continuity between following modulator terminals: Yellow/White wire and Red/Black wire; Yellow/White wire and Yellow/Black wire; Yellow/White wire and Red/Blue wire; Yellow/White wire and Yellow/Blue wire.

13) If continuity exists, replace modulator wire harness. If continuity does not exist, disconnect control unit 26-pin connector. Check continuity between Yellow/White wire terminal of 26-pin connector and ground.

14) If continuity exists, Yellow/White wire between control unit and modulator is shorted to ground. If continuity does not exist, check continuity between Red/White wire terminal of 26-pin connector and ground.

15) If continuity exists, Red/White wire between control unit and modulator is shorted to ground. If continuity does not exist, check continuity between Red/White wire and Yellow/White wire terminals of 26-pin connector.

16) If continuity exists, repair shorted Yellow/White wire and Red/White wire between control unit and modulator. If continuity does not exist, check continuity between following terminals of 26-pin connector: Red/White wire and Red/Black wire; Red/White wire and Yellow/Black wire; Red/White wire and Red/Blue wire; Red/White wire and Yellow/Blue wire.

17) If continuity exists, repair shorted wire(s) between control unit and modulator. If continuity does not exist, check continuity between following terminals of 26-pin connector: Yellow/White wire and Red/Black wire; Yellow/White wire and Yellow/Black wire; Yellow/White wire and Red/Blue wire; Yellow/White wire and Yellow/Blue wire.

18) If continuity exists, repair shorted wire(s) between control unit and modulator. If continuity does not exist, Reconnect modulator 14-pin connector. Measure voltage between Yellow/White wire terminal of 26-pin connector and ground.

19) If battery voltage is not present, repair open Yellow/White wire between control unit and modulator. If battery voltage is present, measure voltage between Red/White wire terminal of 26-pin connector and ground.

20) If battery voltage is not present, repair open Red/White wire between control unit and modulator. If battery voltage is present, check continuity between Black wire terminal of 22-pin connector and ground.

21) If continuity does not exist, check ground connection. If ground connection is okay, repair open Black wire between control unit and ground. If continuity exists, disconnect control unit 22-pin connector. Connect jumper wire between Yellow/Green wire terminal of 22-pin connector and ground.

22) Remove jumper wire from rear fail-safe relay. Disconnect front fail-safe relay connector. Check continuity between Yellow/Green wire terminal of rear fail safe relay connector and ground.

23) If continuity does not exist, repair open Yellow/Green wire control unit and rear fail-safe relay. If continuity exists, remove jumper wire from Yellow/Green wire terminal of control unit 22-pin connector.

24) Check continuity between Black wire terminal of rear fail-safe relay connector and ground. If continuity does not exist, check ground connection. If ground connection is okay, repair open Black wire between rear fail-safe relay and ground.

25) If continuity exists, check for loose control connectors. If connectors are okay, install known-good control unit and retest.

Code 8-1, ABS Function – 1) Test drive vehicle at minimum speed of 12 MPH for at least 2 minutes. If ANTI-LOCK light comes on, go to next step. If light does not come on, system is okay at this time. Check wheel speed sensor connections. If connections are okay, code was probably caused by rough road condition.

2) Check for ABS trouble codes. If Code 8-1 is set, replace control unit. If Code 8-1 is not set, perform appropriate trouble code test.

Code 8-2, CPU Comparison – Start engine. If ANTI-LOCK light does not come on, system is okay at this time. If light comes on, check for ABS trouble codes. If Code 8-2 is set, replace control unit. If Code 8-2 is not set, perform appropriate trouble code test.

Code 8-4, Integrated Circuit (IC) – Replace control unit if Code 8-4 is set. No other information is available from manufacturer.

LEGEND

NOTE: DO NOT disassemble ABS pump assembly. If any part is defective (accumulator, pump motor or pressure switch), replace entire assembly.

Code 1, Pump Motor Overrun – 1) Bleed high-pressure fluid from maintenance bleeder using ABS "T" wrench. See RELIEVING SYSTEM PRESSURE under BLEEDING BRAKE SYSTEM. Remove pump motor relay from underhood fuse/relay box. *See Fig. 2.* Connect jumper wire between terminals No. 1 and 2 about 8 seconds. *See Fig. 12.*

2) If pump motor runs with a constant soft sound, bleed air from ABS using ABS tester. See AIR BLEEDING under BLEEDING BRAKE SYSTEM. Recheck pump sound. If pump motor runs with an increasingly loud, raspy sound, check fluid level in accumulator by bleeding high pressure line using ABS "T" wrench. *See Fig. 13.*

3) If fluid level is 40-70 cc, go to next step. If fluid level is not 40-70 cc, connect jumper wire between terminals No. 1 and 2 of pump motor relay connector for about 10 seconds. Check for changes in fluid level.

If fluid level does not change, relief valve in pump motor is defective. Replace ABS pump assembly. If fluid level changes, solenoid is defective (leaking). Replace modulator unit.

4) Connect jumper wire between terminals No. 1 and 2 of pump motor relay connector for about 10 seconds. Disconnect pressure switch 2-pin connector. Check continuity between pressure switch terminals. If continuity does not exist, pressure switch is defective. Replace pump motor assembly. If continuity exists, system is okay at this time.

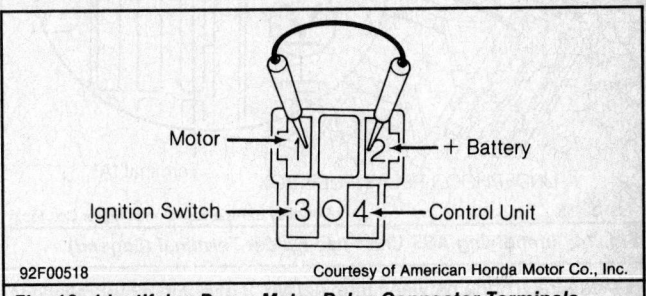

Motor — 1 — + Battery
Ignition Switch — 3 O 4 — Control Unit

92F00518   Courtesy of American Honda Motor Co., Inc.

Fig. 12: Identifying Pump Motor Relay Connector Terminals (Legend)

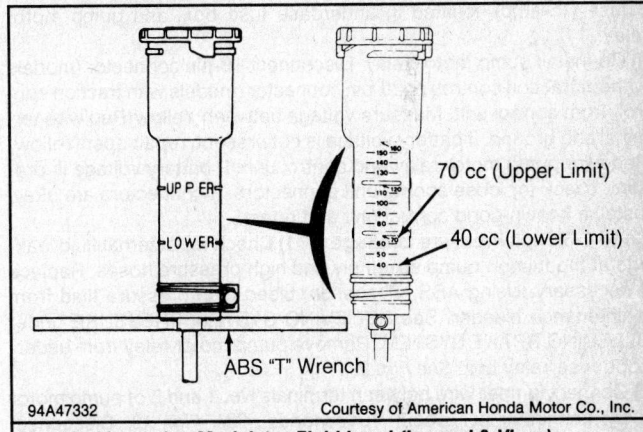

UPPER
LOWER

70 cc (Upper Limit)
40 cc (Lower Limit)

ABS "T" Wrench

94A47332   Courtesy of American Honda Motor Co., Inc.

Fig. 13: Measuring Modulator Fluid Level (Legend & Vigor)

Code 1-2, Pump Motor Circuit – 1) Check ABS and rear defroster/cooling fan relay fuses and replace if necessary. Remove pump motor relay. Test relay and replace if necessary. See RELAY TEST under DIAGNOSIS & TESTING. If relay is okay, connect jumper wire between terminals No. 1 and 2 of pump motor relay connector. If pump motor does not run, go to next step. If pump motor runs, go to step **5)**.

2) Using DVOM, measure voltage between pump motor relay connector terminal No. 2 and ground. If battery voltage is present, go to next step. If battery voltage is not present, replace underhood fuse/relay box.

3) Disconnect pump motor 2-pin connector. Measure voltage between White/Blue wire terminal and ground. If battery voltage is present, go to next step. If battery voltage is not present, repair open White/Blue wire between pump motor relay and pump motor.

4) Measure voltage between White/Blue wire and Black wire terminals of pump motor connector. If battery voltage is present, pump motor is defective. Replace pump assembly. If battery voltage is not present, check ground connection at right rear corner of engine compartment. If ground connection is okay, repair open Black wire.

5) Disconnect jumper wire. Remove ABS unit fuse from underhood fuse/relay box. Turn ignition on. Measure voltage between indicated fuse holder terminal and ground. *See Fig. 14.* If battery voltage is present, go to next step. If battery voltage is not present, repair open White/Blue wire between ABS unit fuse holder and control unit.

6) Re-install ABS unit fuse. Disconnect ABS pump motor connector. Measure voltage between pump relay connector terminal No. 1 and ground. *See Fig. 12.* If battery voltage is present, go to next step. If battery voltage is not present, replace underhood fuse/relay box.

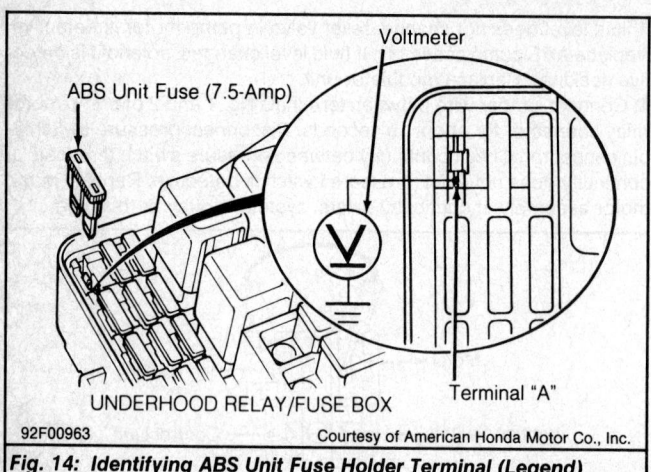

ABS Unit Fuse (7.5-Amp)

Voltmeter

UNDERHOOD RELAY/FUSE BOX

Terminal "A"

92F00963   Courtesy of American Honda Motor Co., Inc.

Fig. 14: Identifying ABS Unit Fuse Holder Terminal (Legend)

7) Measure voltage between terminal No. 3 of pump motor relay connector and ground. If battery voltage is present, go to next step. If battery voltage is not present, repair open Yellow/Black wire between No. 3 fuse (15-amp), located in underdash fuse box, and pump motor relay.

8) Re-install pump motor relay. Disconnect 18-pin connector (models without traction control) or 20-pin connector (models with traction control) from control unit. Measure voltage between Yellow/Red wire terminal and ground. If battery voltage is not present, repair open Yellow/Red wire pump motor relay and control unit. If battery voltage is present, check for loose control unit connectors. If connectors are okay, install a known-good control unit and retest.

Code 1-3, High Pressure Leakage – **1)** Check for external fluid leakage at modulator, pump assembly and high pressure hoses. Replace if necessary. Using ABS "T" wrench, bleed high pressure fluid from maintenance bleeder. See RELIEVING SYSTEM PRESSURE under BLEEDING BRAKE SYSTEM. Remove pump motor relay from underhood fuse/relay box. *See Fig. 2.*

2) Connect jumper wire between terminals No. 1 and 2 of pump motor relay connector for about 10 seconds. *See Fig. 12.* Disconnect pressure switch 2-pin connector. Wait 30 minutes, then check continuity between pressure switch terminals. If continuity exists, system is okay. If continuity does not exist, solenoid is defective (leaking). Replace modulator unit.

Code 1-4, Pressure Switch Circuit – **1)** Using ABS "T" wrench, bleed high pressure fluid from maintenance bleeder. See RELIEVING SYSTEM PRESSURE under BLEEDING BRAKE SYSTEM. Disconnect pressure switch 2-pin connector. Check continuity between pressure switch terminals. If continuity does not exist, go to next step. If continuity exists, pressure switch is defective. Replace pump assembly.

2) Check continuity between Yellow wire terminal of pressure switch connector and ground. If continuity exists, repair short in Yellow wire between pressure switch and control unit. If continuity does not exist, check for loose control unit connectors. If connectors are okay, install a known-good control unit and retest.

Code 1-8, Accumulator Gas Leakage – Ensure relief plug on accumulator is tight. Ensure relief plug "O" ring is not out of place or defective. Using ABS "T" wrench, bleed high pressure fluid from maintenance bleeder. See RELIEVING SYSTEM PRESSURE under BLEEDING BRAKE SYSTEM. If no fluid or more than 70 cc of fluid comes out, replace pump assembly.

Code 2-1, Parking Brake Switch – **1)** Remove ABS fuse No. 2 (15-amp) for at least 3 seconds to clear control unit memory. Test drive vehicle. If ANTI-LOCK warning light and control unit LED are off (no code), vehicle was probably driven with parking brake applied.

2) If parking brake was not applied, check for low brake fluid level in master cylinder reservoir. Refill if necessary. Check for shorted Green/Red wire between BRAKE warning light and parking brake switch. Check for shorted Green/Red wire between BRAKE warning light and brake fluid level switch.

3) Also check for blown bulb in BRAKE warning light. Check for open Green/Red wire between BRAKE warning light and control unit. If all items are okay, check for loose or damaged control unit connectors. If connectors are okay, install a known-good control unit and retest.

Codes 3-1 To 3-4 – No testing is available from manufacturer.

Codes 4-1 To 4-8, Front & Rear Speed Sensor(s) – **1)** Disconnect 18-pin connector (models without traction control) or 20-pin connector (models with traction control) from control unit. Using DVOM, measure resistance between indicated connector terminals. See SPEED SENSOR RESISTANCE table.

SPEED SENSOR RESISTANCE

Terminals [1]	Speed Sensor	Ohms
GRN/BLK & GRN	Right Front	500-1000
GRN/BLU & BRN	Left Front	500-1000
GRN/YEL & BLU/YEL	Right Rear	1000-1500
LT BLU & GRY	Left Rear	1000-1500

[1] – Measure resistance between indicated 18-pin or 20-pin connector terminals.

2) If resistance is not as specified, go to next step. If resistance is as specified, check continuity between sensor wires and ground. If continuity does not exist, check sensor and control unit connection. If connectors are okay, install a known-good control unit and retest. If continuity exists, repair shorted sensor wire or replace faulty speed sensor.

3) Disconnect speed sensor connector. Measure resistance between speed sensor terminals. Ensure resistance is 500-1000 ohms (front sensors) or 1000-1500 ohms (rear sensors). If resistance is as specified, go to next step. If resistance is not as specified, replace defective speed sensor.

4) Reconnect 18-pin or 20-pin connector. Check continuity between speed sensor harness connector wires and ground. If continuity does not exist, repair open circuit. If continuity exists, check for loose control unit connectors. If connectors are okay, install a known-good control unit and retest.

Codes 5-4 To 5-8, Rear Speed Sensor(s) – **1)** Disconnect 18-pin (models without traction control) or 20-pin (models with traction control) connector from control unit. Using DVOM, measure resistance between indicated terminals. See REAR SENSOR RESISTANCE table.

REAR SENSOR RESISTANCE

Terminals [1]	Speed Sensor	Ohms
GRN/YEL & BLU/YEL	Right Rear	1000-1500
LT BLU & GRY	Left Rear	1000-1500

[1] – Measure resistance between indicated 18-pin or 20-pin connector terminals.

2) If resistance is not as specified, go to step **4)**. If resistance is as specified, check continuity between sensor wires and ground. If continuity exists, repair shorted wire or replace sensor. If continuity does not exist, go to next step.

3) Reconnect 18-pin or 20-pin connector. Connect ABS Tester (07HAJ-SG0010B) to inspection connector. *See Fig. 2.* Check ABS function in modes 2 and 3. If ABS does not function properly, replace defective modulator. If ABS functions properly, check for rear brake drag. If brake drag is okay, install a known-good control unit and retest.

4) Disconnect speed sensor wiring harness connector. Measure resistance between sensor terminals. If resistance is not 1000-1500 ohms, replace defective speed sensor. If resistance is 1000-1500 ohms, go to next step.

5) Reconnect 18-pin or 20-pin connector. Check continuity between speed sensor harness connector wires and ground. If continuity does not exist, repair open circuit. If continuity exists, check for loose control unit connectors. If connectors are okay, install a known-good control unit, and retest.

Code 6-1, Front Fail-Safe Relay Circuit – **1)** Remove front fail-safe relay. Test relay and replace if necessary. See RELAY TEST under DIAGNOSIS & TESTING. If relay is okay, turn ignition on. Measure voltage between Yellow/Black wire terminal of fail-safe relay and ground.

2) If battery voltage does not exist, repair open Yellow/Black wire between fuse No. 3 (in underdash fuse/relay box) and front fail-safe relay. If battery voltage is present, turn ignition off. Disconnect solenoid connector, located on right side of engine compartment, near shock tower.

3) Using DVOM, check continuity between Brown/Black wire terminal of fail-safe relay and ground. If continuity does not exist, go to next step. If continuity exists, repair shorted Brown/Black wire between solenoid and front fail-safe relay.

4) Check continuity between ground and following solenoid connector terminals: Brown/Black wire and Brown/Blue wire. If continuity does not exist, go to next step. If continuity exists, solenoid is defective. Replace modulator unit.

5) Disconnect 12-pin (models without traction control) or 14-pin (models with traction control) connector from control unit. Check continuity between ground and following connector (12-pin or 14-pin) terminals: Red/Black, Yellow/Black, Red/Blue and Yellow/Blue wires. If continuity does not exist, go to next step. If continuity exits, repair shorted wire(s) between solenoid and control unit connector.

6) Remove rear fail-safe relay from underhood fuse/relay box. Disconnect 18-pin (without traction control) or 20-pin (with traction control) connector. Check continuity between Yellow/Green wire terminal of connector (18- or 20-pin) and ground. If continuity exists, repair shorted Yellow/Green wire control unit and front fail-safe relay. If continuity does not exist, go to next step.

7) Reinstall front fail-safe relay. Turn ignition on. Measure voltage between Yellow/Green wire terminal of control unit and ground. If battery voltage does not exist, repair open Yellow/Green wire between control unit and front fail-safe relay. If battery voltage exists, check for loose control unit connectors. If connectors are okay, install a known-good control unit and retest.

Code 6-4, Rear Fail-Safe Relay Circuit – **1)** Remove rear fail-safe relay. Test relay and replace if necessary. See RELAY TEST under DIAGNOSIS & TESTING. If relay is okay, turn ignition on. Measure voltage between Yellow/Black wire terminal of fail-safe relay and ground.

2) If battery voltage does not exist, repair open Yellow/Black wire between fuse No. 1 (in underdash fuse/relay box) and rear fail-safe relay. If battery voltage exists, turn ignition off. Disconnect solenoid connector, located on right side of engine compartment, near shock tower.

3) Using DVOM, check for continuity between Blue/Black wire terminal of fail-safe relay and ground. If continuity does not exist, go to next step. If continuity exists, repair shorted Blue/Black wire between solenoid and rear fail-safe relay.

4) Check continuity between Brown/White wire terminal of solenoid connector and ground. If continuity does not exist, go to next step. If continuity exists, solenoid is defective. Replace modulator.

5) Disconnect 12-pin (models without traction control) or 14-pin (models with traction control) connector. Check continuity of Red/White wire and Yellow/White wire between control unit and ground. If continuity does not exist, go to next step. If continuity exists, repair shorted wire(s).

6) Remove front fail-safe relay. Disconnect 18-pin (without traction control) or 20-pin (with traction control) connector. Check continuity between Yellow/Green wire terminal and ground. If continuity exists, repair shorted Yellow/Green wire between control unit connector and rear fail-safe relay. If continuity does not exist, go to next step.

7) Reinstall rear fail-safe relay. Turn ignition on. Measure voltage between Yellow/Green wire terminal and ground. If battery voltage does not exist, repair open Yellow/Green wire between control unit and rear fail-safe relay. If battery voltage exists, check for loose control unit connectors. If connectors are okay, install a known-good control unit and retest.

Codes 7-1 & 7-2, Front Solenoid Circuit (Open) – **1)** Disconnect solenoid connector, located on right side of engine compartment, near shock tower. Using DVOM, measure resistance between following solenoid connector terminals: Red/Black wire and Brown/Black wire (right inlet); Red/Blue wire and Brown/Blue wire (left inlet).

2) If resistance is not 1-3 ohms, solenoid is faulty. Replace modulator. If resistance is 1-3 ohms, measure resistance between following solenoid connector terminals: Yellow/Black wire and Brown/Black wire (right outlet); Yellow/Blue wire and Brown/Blue wire (left outlet). If resistance is 1-3 ohms, go to next step. If resistance is not 1-3 ohms, solenoid is defective. Replace modulator.

3) Disconnect 12-pin (models without traction control) or 14-pin (models with traction control) connector from control unit. Check continuity of following wires between control unit and front solenoid: Red/Black wire, Yellow/Black wire, Red/Blue wire and Yellow/Blue wire. If continuity exists, go to next step. If continuity does not exist, repair open wire(s).

4) Check continuity of following wires between control unit and ground: Red/Black wire, Yellow/Black wire, Red/Blue wire and Yellow/Blue wire. If continuity does not exist, go to next step. If continuity exists, repair shorted wire(s).

5) Remove front fail-safe relay. Test relay and replace if necessary. See RELAY TEST under DIAGNOSIS & TESTING. If relay is okay, check continuity between Black wire terminal of fail-safe relay connector and ground. If continuity exists, go to next step. If continuity does not exist, check poor ground connection located behind right kick panel. If ground is okay, repair open Black wire.

6) Check continuity of Brown/Black wire between solenoids and front fail-safe relay. If continuity does not exist, repair open Brown/Black wire between solenoids and relay. If continuity exists, check for loose control unit connectors. If connectors are okay, install a known-good control unit and retest.

Code 7-4, Rear Solenoid Circuit (Open) – **1)** Disconnect 10-pin connector from solenoids. Connector is located on right side of engine compartment, near shock tower.

2) Using DVOM, measure resistance between following solenoid terminals: Red/White wire and Brown/White wire (rear inlet); Yellow/White wire and Brown/White wire (rear outlet). If resistance is 1-3 ohms, go to next step. If resistance is not 1-3 ohms, solenoid is defective. Replace modulator.

3) Disconnect 12-pin (models without traction control) or 14-pin (models with traction control) connector from control unit. Check continuity of following wires between control unit and rear solenoid: Red/White wire and Yellow/White wire. If continuity exists, go to next step. If continuity does not exist, repair open wire(s).

4) Check continuity of following wires between control unit and ground: Red/White wire and Yellow/White wire. If continuity does not exist, go to next step. If continuity exists, repair shorted wire(s).

5) Remove rear fail-safe relay. Test relay and replace if necessary. See RELAY TEST under DIAGNOSIS & TESTING. If relay is okay, check continuity between Black wire terminal of fail-safe relay connector and ground. If continuity exists, go to next step. If continuity does not exist, check fail-safe relay ground connection, located behind right kick panel. If ground connection is okay, repair open Black wire.

6) Check continuity of Blue/Black wire between solenoid and rear fail-safe relay. If continuity does not exist, repair open Blue/Black wire. If continuity exists, check for loose control unit connectors. If connectors are okay, install a known-good control unit and retest.

VIGOR

NOTE: DO NOT disassemble ABS pump assembly. If any part is defective (accumulator, pump motor or pressure switch), replace entire assembly.

Code 1, Pump Motor Overrun – **1)** Bleed high-pressure fluid from maintenance bleeder using ABS "T" wrench. See RELIEVING SYSTEM PRESSURE under BLEEDING BRAKE SYSTEM. Remove pump motor relay. *See Fig. 3.* Connect jumper wires between terminals No. 3 and 8. *See Fig. 15.*

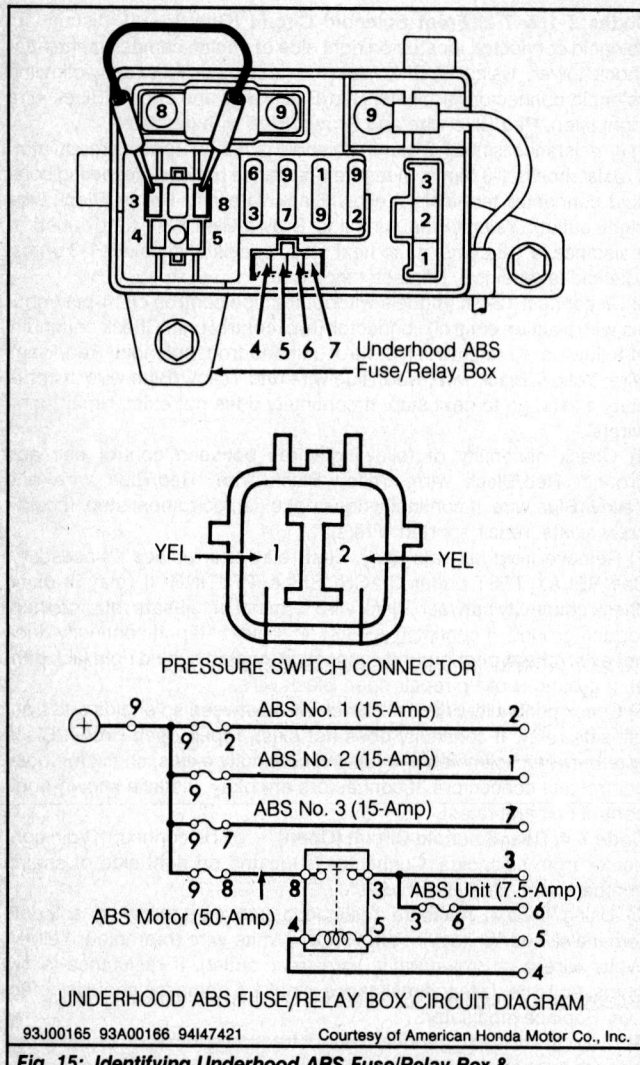

YEL → 1 2 ← YEL

PRESSURE SWITCH CONNECTOR

ABS No. 1 (15-Amp) — 2
ABS No. 2 (15-Amp) — 1
ABS No. 3 (15-Amp) — 7
3
ABS Unit (7.5-Amp) — 6
ABS Motor (50-Amp) — 5
4

UNDERHOOD ABS FUSE/RELAY BOX CIRCUIT DIAGRAM

93J00165 93A00166 94I47421   Courtesy of American Honda Motor Co., Inc.

Fig. 15: Identifying Underhood ABS Fuse/Relay Box & Pressure Switch Connector Terminals (Vigor)

2) If pump motor runs with a constant soft sound, bleed air from ABS using ABS tester. See AIR BLEEDING under BLEEDING BRAKE SYSTEM. Recheck pump sound. If pump motor runs with an increasingly loud, raspy sound, check fluid level in accumulator by bleeding high pressure line using ABS "T" wrench. See Fig. 13.

3) If 40-70 cc is measured, go to next step. If fluid measured is not 40-70 cc, connect jumper wire between terminals No. 3 and 8 for about 10 seconds. See Fig. 15. Check for changes in fluid level. If fluid level does not change, relief valve in pump motor is defective. Replace pump assembly. If fluid level changes, solenoid is defective (leaking). Replace modulator.

4) Connect jumper wire between terminals No. 3 and 8 for about 10 seconds. See Fig. 15. Disconnect pressure switch 2-pin connector. Check continuity between pressure switch terminals. If continuity does not exist, replace pressure switch is defective. Replace pump assembly. If continuity exists, vehicle is okay at this time.

Code 1-2, Pump Motor Circuit – 1) Check ABS and rear defroster/cooling fan relay fuses. Remove pump motor relay. Test relay and replace if defective. See RELAY TEST under DIAGNOSIS & TESTING. If relay is okay, connect jumper wire between terminals No. 3 and 8. See Fig. 15. If pump motor does not run, go to next step. If pump motor runs, go to step **5)**.

2) Using DVOM, measure voltage between pump motor relay terminal No. 8 and ground. If battery voltage exists, go to next step. If battery voltage does not exist, replace underhood ABS fuse/relay.

3) Disconnect 2-pin connector from pump motor. Measure voltage between White/Blue wire terminal and ground. If battery voltage

exists, go to next step. If battery voltage does not exist, repair open White/Blue wire.

4) Measure voltage between White/Blue wire and Black wire terminals of pump motor connector. If battery voltage exists, pump motor is defective. Replace pump assembly. If battery voltage does not exist, check ground connection. If ground connection is okay, repair open Black wire.

5) Remove jumper wire. Remove ABS unit fuse from underhood relay/fuse box. Turn ignition on. Measure voltage between fuse holder No. 6 terminal and ground. See Fig. 15. If battery voltage exists, go to next step. If battery voltage does not exist, repair open White/Red wire between ABS unit fuse holder and control unit.

6) Reinstall ABS unit fuse. Disconnect pump motor 2-pin connector. Measure voltage between pump motor relay connector terminal No. 3 and ground. See Fig. 15. If battery voltage exists, go to next step. If battery voltage does not exist, replace fuse/relay box.

7) Measure voltage between terminal No. 4 of pump motor relay connector and ground. If battery voltage exists, go to next step. If battery voltage does not exist, repair open Black/Yellow wire between fuse No. 7 (15-amp), located in underdash fuse box, and pump motor relay.

8) Reinstall pump motor relay. Disconnect 18-pin connector from control unit. Measure voltage between Yellow/Red wire terminal and ground. If battery voltage does not exist, repair open Yellow/Red wire. If battery voltage exists, check for loose control unit connectors. If connectors are okay, install a known-good control unit and retest.

Code 1-3, High Pressure Leakage – 1) Check for external fluid leakage at modulator, pump motor and high pressure hoses. Replace if necessary. Using ABS "T" wrench, bleed high-pressure fluid from maintenance bleeder. See RELIEVING SYSTEM under BLEEDING BRAKE SYSTEM. Remove pump motor relay. See Fig. 3.

2) Connector jumper wire between terminals No. 3 and 8 of pump motor relay connector for about 10 seconds. See Fig. 15. Disconnect 2-pin connector from pressure switch. Wait 30 minutes, then check continuity between pressure switch terminals. If continuity exists, system is okay at this time. If continuity does not exist, solenoid is defective (leaking). Replace modulator.

Code 1-4, Pressure Switch Circuit – 1) Using ABS "T" wrench, bleed high pressure fluid from maintenance bleeder. See RELIEVING SYSTEM PRESSURE under BLEEDING BRAKE SYSTEM. Disconnect 2-pin connector from pressure switch. Check continuity between pressure switch terminals. If continuity does not exist, go to next step. If continuity exists, pressure switch is defective. Replace pump assembly.

2) Check continuity between Yellow wire terminal of pressure switch harness connector and ground. If continuity exists, repair shorted Yellow wire between pressure switch and control unit. If continuity does not exist, check for loose control unit connectors. If connectors are okay, install a known-good control unit and retest.

Code 1-8, Accumulator Gas Leakage – Ensure relief plug on accumulator is tight. Ensure relief plug "O" ring is not out of place or defective. Using ABS "T" wrench, bleed high pressure fluid from maintenance bleeder. See RELIEVING SYSTEM PRESSURE under BLEEDING BRAKE SYSTEM. If no fluid or more than 70 cc of fluid is bled, replace pump assembly.

Code 2-1, Parking Brake Switch – 1) Remove ABS fuse No. 2 (15-amp) for at least 3 seconds to clear trouble codes. Test drive vehicle. If ANTI-LOCK warning light and control unit LED are off (no code), vehicle was probably driven with parking brake applied.

2) If parking brake was not applied, check for low brake fluid level in master cylinder reservoir. Refill if necessary. Check for shorted Green/Red wire between BRAKE warning light and parking brake switch. Check for shorted Green/Red wire between BRAKE warning light and brake fluid level switch.

3) Also check for blown bulb in BRAKE warning light. Check for open Green/Red wire between BRAKE warning light and control unit. If all items are okay, check for loose or damaged control unit connectors. If connectors are okay, install a known-good control unit and retest.

Codes 3-1 To 3-8 – No testing is available from manufacturer.

Codes 4-1 To 4-8, Front & Rear Speed Sensor(s) – 1) Disconnect 18-pin connector from control unit. Using DVOM, measure resistance between indicated terminals. See SPEED SENSOR RESISTANCE table.

SPEED SENSOR RESISTANCE

Terminals [1]	Speed Sensor	Ohms
GRN/BLK & GRN	Right Front	750-1200
GRN/BLU & BRN	Left Front	750-1200
GRN/YEL & BLU/YEL	Right Rear	1100-1600
LT BLU & GRY	Left Rear	1100-1600

[1] – Measure resistance between indicated 18-pin connector terminals.

2) If resistance is not as specified, go to next step. If resistance is as specified, check continuity between sensor wires and ground. If continuity does not exist, check sensor and control unit connection. If connectors are okay, install a known-good control unit and retest. If continuity exists, repair shorted sensor wire or replace faulty speed sensor.

3) Disconnect speed sensor 2-pin connector. Measure resistance between speed sensor terminals. Ensure resistance is 750-1200 ohms (front sensors) or 1100-1600 ohms (rear sensors). If resistance is as specified, go to next step. If resistance is not as specified, replace defective speed sensor.

4) Reconnect 18-pin connector. Check continuity between speed sensor harness connector wires and ground. If continuity does not exist, repair open circuit. If continuity exists, check for loose control unit connectors. If connectors are okay, install a known-good control unit and retest.

Codes 5-4 To 5-8, Rear Speed Sensor(s) – 1) Disconnect 18-pin connector from control unit. Using DVOM, measure resistance between indicated terminals. See REAR SENSOR RESISTANCE table.

REAR SENSOR RESISTANCE

Terminals [1]	Speed Sensor	Ohms
GRN/YEL & BLU/YEL	Right Rear	1100-1600
LT BLU & GRY	Left Rear	1100-1600

[1] – Measure resistance between indicated 18-pin connector terminals.

2) If resistance is not as specified, go to step **4)**. If resistance is as specified, check continuity between sensor wires and ground. If continuity exists, repair shorted wire or replace sensor. If continuity does not exist, go to next step.

3) Reconnect 18-pin connector. Connect ABS tester to inspection connector. See Fig. 3. Check ABS function in modes 2 and 3. If ABS does not function properly, replace modulator unit. If ABS functions okay, check for rear brake drag. If brake drag, is okay, install a known-good control unit and retest.

4) Disconnect speed sensor wiring harness connector. Measure resistance between sensor terminals. If resistance is not 1100-1600 ohms, replace defective speed sensor. If resistance is 1100-1600 ohms, go to next step.

5) Reconnect 18-pin connector. Check continuity between speed sensor harness connector wires and ground. If continuity does not exist, repair open circuit. If continuity exists, check for loose control unit connectors. If connectors are okay, install a known-good control unit and retest.

Code 6-1, Front Fail-Safe Relay Circuit – 1) Check ABS fuses. Remove front fail-safe relay. Test relay and replace if necessary. See RELAY TEST under DIAGNOSIS & TESTING. If relay is okay, turn ignition on.

2) Using DVOM, measure voltage between Black/Yellow wire terminal of fail-safe relay and ground. If battery voltage does not exists, repair open Black/Yellow wire. If battery voltage is present, go to next step.

3) Turn ignition switch to OFF position. Disconnect 10-pin connector from solenoid. Check continuity between Brown/Black wire terminal of fail-safe relay and ground. If continuity exists, repair shorted Brown/Black wire. If continuity does not exist, go to next step.

4) Remove rear fail-safe relay. Check continuity of following wires between solenoid and ground: Brown/Black wire and Brown/Blue wire. If continuity is not present, go to next step. If continuity exists, solenoid is shorted. Replace modulator.

5) Disconnect 18-pin and 12-pin connectors from control unit. Check continuity of following wires between control unit and ground: Red/Black wire, Yellow/Black wire, Red/Blue wire and Yellow/Blue wire. If continuity exists, replace shorted wire(s) between solenoid and control unit.

6) If continuity does not exist, check continuity between Yellow/Green wire terminal of 18-pin connector and ground. If continuity exists, repair shorted Yellow/Green wire between control unit and front fail-safe relay.

7) If continuity does not exist, reinstall front fail-safe relay. Turn ignition switch to ON position. Check voltage between Yellow/Green wire terminal of control unit and ground. If battery voltage is not present, repair open Yellow/Green wire between front fail-safe relay and control unit.

8) If battery voltage exists, check for loose control unit connectors. If connections are okay, install a known-good control unit and retest.

Code 6-4, Rear Fail-Safe Relay Circuit – 1) Remove fail-safe relay. Test relay and replace if necessary. See RELAY TEST under DIAGNOSIS & TESTING. If relay is okay, turn ignition switch to ON position.

2) Measure voltage between Black/Yellow wire terminal of fail-safe relay and ground. If battery voltage is not present, repair open Black/Yellow wire between fuse and fail-safe relay.

3) If battery voltage is present, turn ignition switch to OFF position. Disconnect 10-pin connector from solenoid. Using DVOM, check continuity between Blue/Black wire terminal of fail-safe relay and ground. If continuity does not exist, go to next step. If continuity exists, repair shorted Blue/Black wire between solenoid and rear fail-safe relay.

4) Remove front fail-safe relay. Check continuity between Brown/White wire terminal of solenoid and ground. If continuity does not exist, go to next step. If continuity exists, solenoid is defective. Replace modulator.

5) Disconnect 18-pin and 12-pin connectors from control unit. Check continuity of following wires between control unit and ground: Red/White wire and Yellow/White wire. If continuity does not exist, go to next step. If continuity exists, repair shorted wire(s) between solenoid and control unit connector.

6) Check continuity between 18-pin connector Yellow/Green wire terminal and ground. If continuity does not exist, go to next step. If continuity exists, repair shorted Yellow/Green wire between control unit and rear fail-safe relay.

7) Reinstall rear fail-safe relay. Turn ignition switch to ON position. Measure voltage between Yellow/Green wire terminal of control unit connector and ground. If battery voltage is not present, repair open Yellow/Green wire between rear fail-safe relay and control unit. If battery voltage exists, check for loose control unit connectors. If connectors are okay, install a known-good control unit and retest.

Codes 7-1 & 7-2, Front Solenoid Circuit (Open) – 1) Disconnect 10-pin connector from solenoids. Connector is located on right side of engine compartment, near shock tower.

2) Using DVOM, measure resistance of solenoid inlet wires. Measure voltage between following solenoid terminals: Red/Black wire and Brown/Black wire (right inlet); Red/Blue wire and Brown/Blue wire (left inlet). If resistance is 1-3 ohms, go to next step. If resistance is not 1-3 ohms, solenoid is defective. Replace modulator.

3) Measure resistance of solenoid outlet wires. Measure between following solenoid terminals: Yellow/Black wire and Brown/Black wire (right outlet); Yellow/Blue wire and Brown/Blue wire (left outlet). If resistance is 1-3 ohms, go to next step. If resistance is not 1-3 ohms, solenoid is defective. Replace modulator.

4) Disconnect 12-pin connector from control unit. Check continuity of following wires between control unit and front solenoid: Red/Black wire, Yellow/Black wire, Red/Blue wire and Yellow/Blue wire. If continuity exists, go to next step. If continuity does not exist, repair open wire(s) between solenoid and control unit.

5) Check continuity of following wires between control unit and ground: Red/Black wire, Yellow/Black wire, Red/Blue wire and Yellow/Blue wire. If continuity does not exist, go to next step. If continuity exists, repair shorted wire(s).

6) Remove front fail-safe relay. Test relay and replace if necessary. See RELAY TEST under DIAGNOSIS & TESTING. If relay is okay, check continuity between Black wire terminal of fail-safe relay connector and ground. If continuity exists, go to next step. If continuity does not exist, check fail-safe relay ground connection, located behind right kick panel. If ground connection is okay, repair open Black wire.

7) Check continuity of Brown/Black wire between solenoid connector and front fail-safe relay connector. If continuity does not exist, repair open Brown/Black wire. If continuity exists, check for loose control unit connectors. If connectors are okay, install a known-good control unit and retest.

Code 7-4, Rear Solenoid Circuit (Open) – 1) Disconnect 10-pin connector from solenoids. Connector is located on right side of engine compartment, near shock tower.

2) Using DVOM, measure resistance of following solenoid terminals: Red/White wire and Brown/White wire (rear inlet); Yellow/White wire and Brown/White wire (rear outlet). If resistance is 1-3 ohms, go to next step. If resistance is not 1-3 ohms, solenoid is defective. Replace modulator.

3) Disconnect 12-pin connector from control unit. Check continuity of following wires between control unit and solenoid: Red/White wire and Yellow/White wire. If continuity exists, go to next step. If continuity does not exist, repair open wire(s).

4) Check continuity of following wires between control unit and ground: Red/White wire and Yellow/White wire. If continuity does not exist, go to next step. If continuity exists, repair shorted wire(s).

5) Remove rear fail-safe relay. Test relay and replace if necessary. See RELAY TEST under DIAGNOSIS & TESTING. If relay is okay, check continuity between Black wire terminal of fail-safe relay connector and ground. If continuity exists, go to next step. If continuity does not exist, check fail-safe relay ground connection, located behind right kick panel. If ground connection is okay, repair open Black wire.

6) Check continuity of Blue/Black wire between solenoid and rear fail-safe relay. If continuity does not exist, repair open Blue/Black wire. If continuity exists, check for loose control unit connectors. If connectors are okay, install a known-good control unit and retest.

REMOVAL & INSTALLATION

MODULATOR/ABS PUMP ASSEMBLY

WARNING: Accumulator contains high-pressure nitrogen gas. DO NOT puncture, expose to flame or attempt to disassemble accumulator. It could explode and cause severe injury.

Removal & Installation (Integra) – 1) Bleed high-pressure fluid from maintenance bleeder. See RELIEVING SYSTEM PRESSURE under BLEEDING BRAKE SYSTEM. Remove flange bolts. Disconnect 14-pin connector from modulator. *See Fig. 1.* Disconnect pump motor 2-pin connector.

2) Remove wire harness clips from modulator bracket. Remove nuts (8-mm) and remove modulator from bracket. Remove 8-mm flange bolts, and remove pump motor from modulator.

3) Relieve pressure from accumulator before disposing. Secure modulator in vise with relief plug pointing straight up. *See Fig. 16.* Slowly turn relief plug 3 1/2 turns, and wait at least 3 minutes for all pressure to escape. Remove accumulator from modulator. Remove relief plug, and dispose accumulator.

4) To install new modulator/pump assembly, reverse removal procedure. Check letters stamped on modulator to ensure brake pipes are properly connected. Start engine and allow it to idle from one minute. Ensure ANTI-LOCK light is off and brake fluid is not leaking from brake pipe joints.

5) Stop engine. Fill modulator reservoir to MAX line with clean brake fluid. Bleed brake system. See BRAKE SYSTEM BLEEDING in DISC article.

NOTE: On Legend and Vigor, DO NOT disassemble ABS pump assembly. Replace accumulator, pump motor and pressure switch as an assembly.

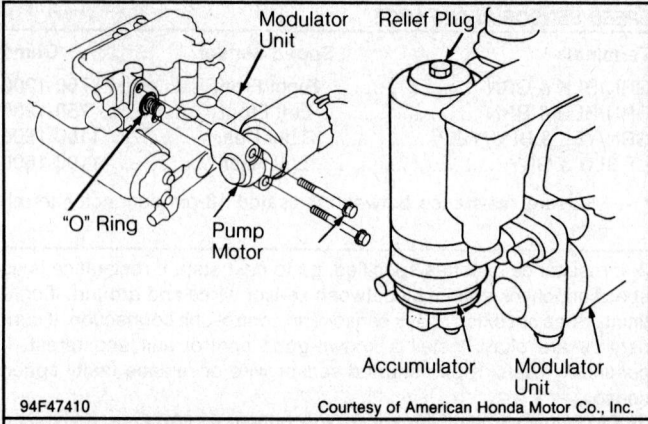

94F47410   Courtesy of American Honda Motor Co., Inc.

Fig. 16: Identifying Modulator/ABS Pump Assembly Components (Integra)

Removal & Installation (Legend) – 1) Disconnect connectors, and remove emission control box from bulkhead. Remove brakeline bracket bolt to remove brakeline fitting. Disconnect engine wire harness connector, and remove harness clamp. Disconnect solenoid/pump connectors.

2) Remove upper heat shield mounting bolts. Raise and support vehicle. Loosen but DO NOT remove lower heat shield mounting bolt. Lower vehicle. Remove heat shield. Bleed high pressure fluid from maintenance bleeder. See RELIEVING SYSTEM PRESSURE under BLEEDING BRAKE SYSTEM.

3) Disconnect 6 steel brakelines from modulator. Cap 2 lines from master cylinder to prevent fluid loss. *See Fig. 5.* Loosen but DO NOT remove lower modulator bracket bolt. Remove 2 upper modulator bracket bolts. Remove modulator, pump assembly and bracket as an assembly. Remove pump assembly from modulator.

4) Relieve pressure from accumulator before disposing. Remove accumulator. Secure accumulator in vise with relief plug pointing straight up. *See Fig. 17.* Slowly turn relief plug 3 1/2 turns, and wait at least 3 minutes for all pressure to escape. Remove relief plug, and dispose of accumulator.

5) To install modulator/pump assembly, reverse removal procedure. When installing steel brakelines, have assistant depress brake pedal lightly to bleed lines. Bleed all 4 calipers. See BLEEDING BRAKE SYSTEM in DISC article. Remove ABS No. 2 fuse from underhood fuse relay box for at least 3 seconds to clear control unit's memory. Test ABS function. See ABS FUNCTION TEST under BLEEDING BRAKE SYSTEM.

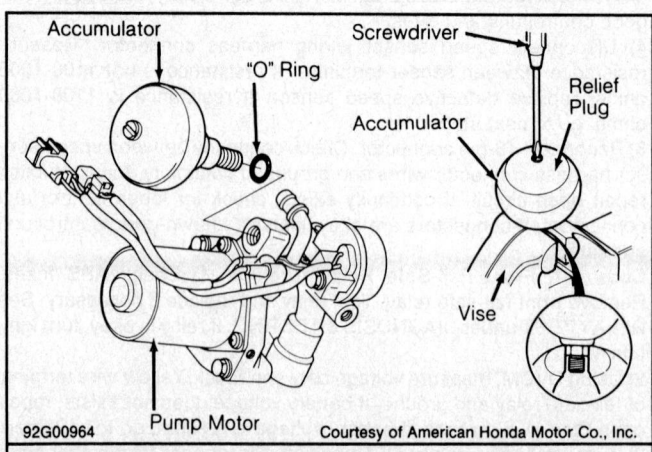

92G00964   Courtesy of American Honda Motor Co., Inc.

Fig. 17: Disposing Accumulator (Legend Shown; Vigor Similar)

Removal & Installation (Vigor) – 1) DO NOT bend or damage brakelines when removing modulator. Bleed modulator and accumulator/line high-pressure from maintenance bleeder. See RELIEVING SYSTEM PRESSURE under BLEEDING BRAKE SYSTEM. Remove heat shield. Remove underhood fuse/relay box mounting bolts. *See Fig. 3.*

2) Disconnect connectors from modulator. Remove modulator bracket bolts, and remove modulator/pump assembly and bracket. See Fig. 5. Remove pump assembly from modulator.

3) Relieve pressure from accumulator before disposing. Mount pump assembly in vise. Using an open-end wrench, turn accumulator counterclockwise to remove. Secure accumulator in vise with relief plug pointing straight up. See Fig. 17. Slowly turn relief plug 3 1/2 turns, and wait at least 3 minutes for all pressure to escape. Remove relief plug, and dispose accumulator.

4) To install modulator/ABS pump assembly, reverse removal procedure. Use new "O" ring. Fill modulator reservoir and bleed air from system. See AIR BLEEDING under BLEEDING BRAKE SYSTEM. Refill modulator reservoir to MAX level.

WHEEL SENSOR

Removal & Installation – Unplug wheel sensor connector. Remove wheel sensor from vehicle. See Fig. 1, 2 or 3. To install, reverse removal procedure. Ensure wheel sensor-to-pulser air gap is within specification. See WHEEL SENSOR AIR GAP SPECIFICATIONS table.

WHEEL SENSOR AIR GAP SPECIFICATIONS

Application	In. (mm)
Integra	.016-.039 (.40-1.00)
Legend	
Front	.024-.047 (.60-1.20)
Rear	.012-.051 (.30-1.30)
Vigor	
Front	.024-.035 (.60-.90)
Rear	.020-.035 (.50-.90)

TORQUE SPECIFICATIONS

TORQUE SPECIFICATIONS

Application	Ft. Lbs. (N.m)
Caliper Body Mounting Bolt	
Front	
Integra	23 (31)
Legend & Vigor	36 (50)
Rear	28 (39)
Caliper Mount Bracket Bolt	
Integra & Vigor	28 (39)
Legend	
Front	81 (110)
Rear	28 (39)
Flex Hose-To-Caliper Banjo Bolt	28 (39)
Master Cylinder Mounting Bolt	11 (15)
Modulator Set Plate Bolts	11 (15)
Push Rod Lock Nut	11 (15)
Rear Caliper Parking Nut	
Integra & Vigor	21 (28)
Rear Spindle Nut	
Integra & Vigor	134 (181)
Legend	210 (285)
Speed Sensor Mounting Bolts	
Integra	[1]
Legend	
Front	16 (22)
Rear	[1]
Vigor	16 (22)
Wheel Lug Nut	81 (110)
	INCH Lbs. (N.m)
Brake Bleed Screw	80 (9.0)
Control Unit Mounting Bolt	106 (12)
Maintenance Bleeder Screw	
Integra	97 (11)
Legend & Vigor	80 (9)
Brake Booster Mounting Nut	115 (13)

[1] – Tighten bolts to 89 INCH lbs. (10 N.m).

WIRING DIAGRAMS

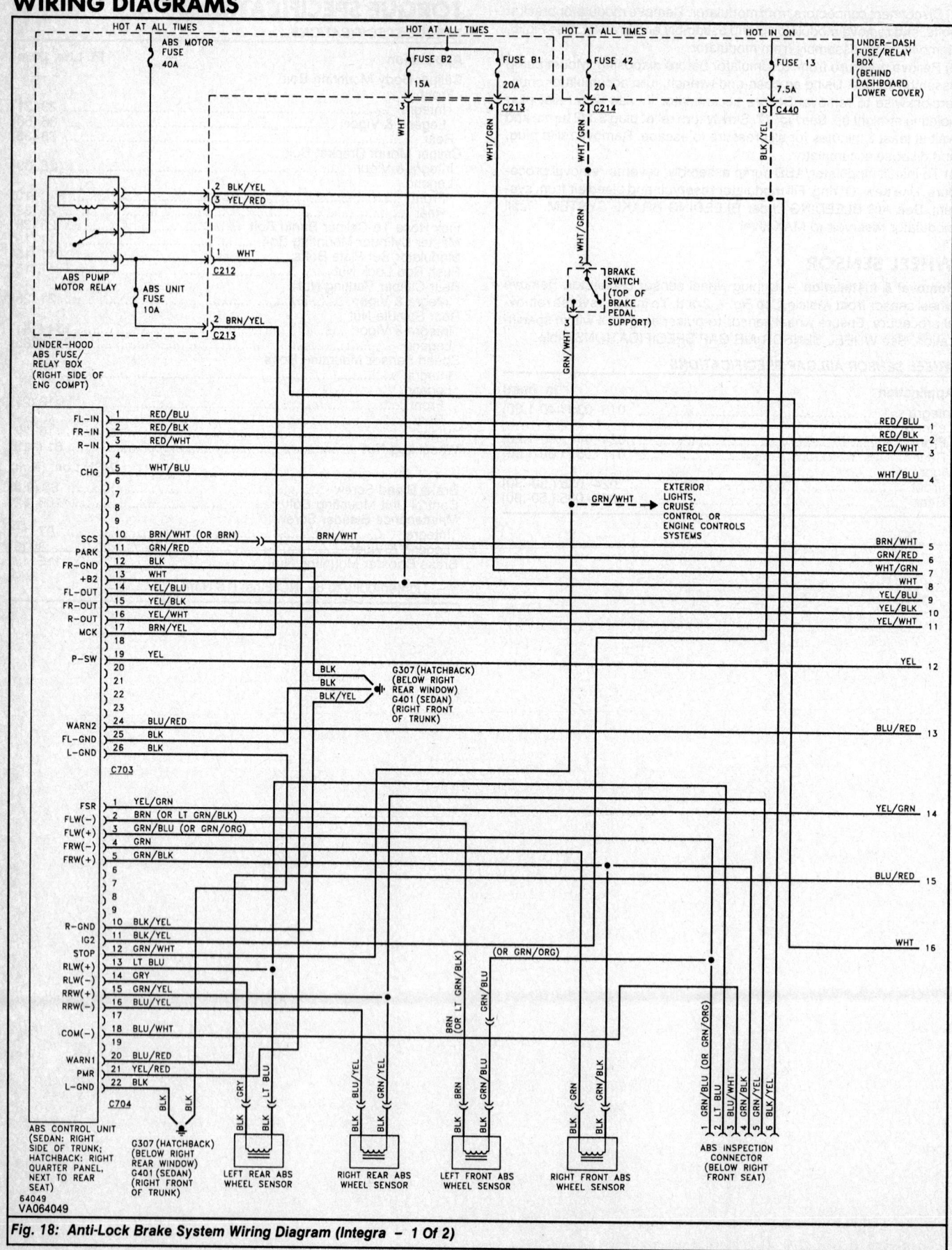

Fig. 18: Anti-Lock Brake System Wiring Diagram (Integra – 1 Of 2)

64049
VA064049

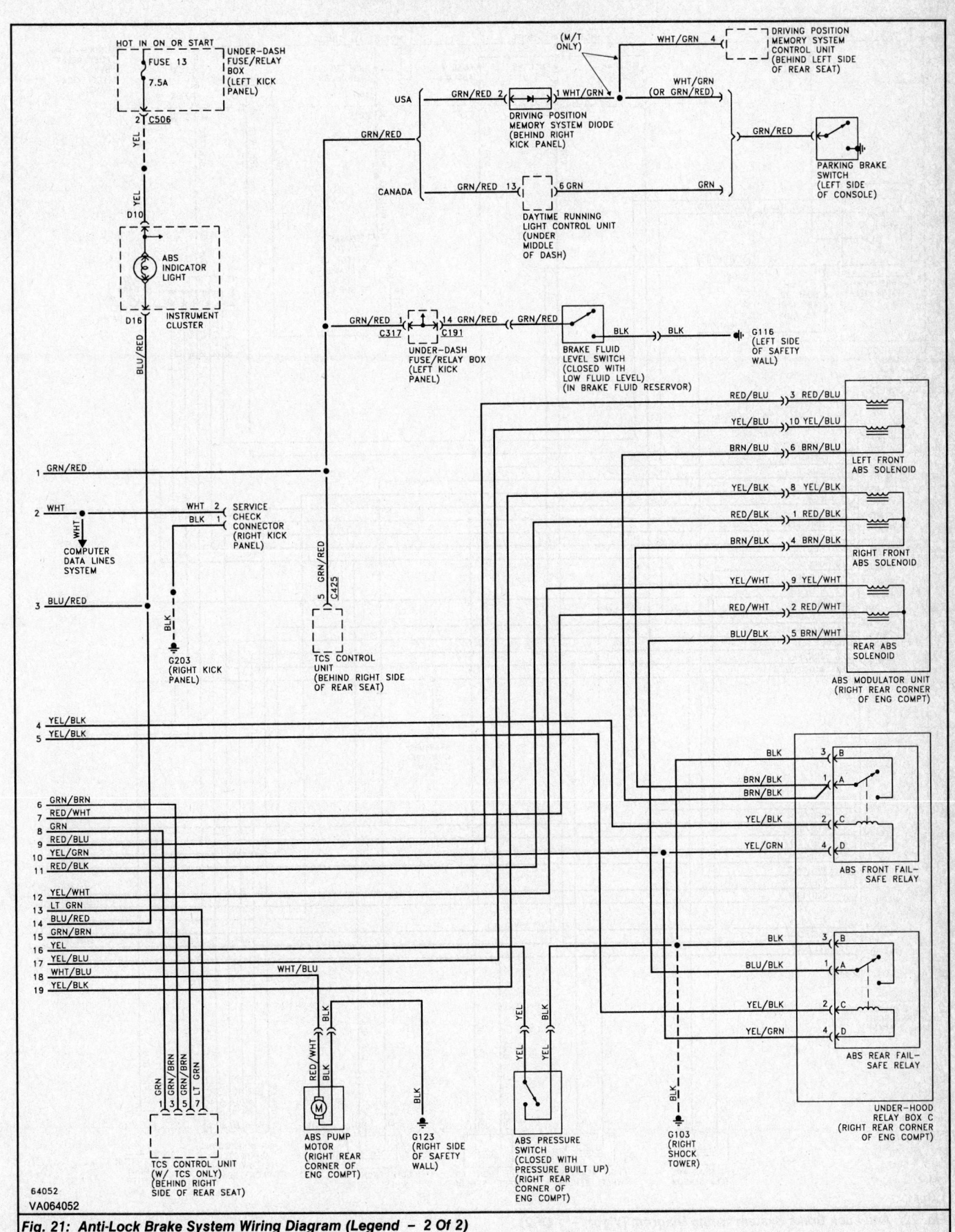

Fig. 21: Anti-Lock Brake System Wiring Diagram (Legend – 2 Of 2)

64052

VA064052

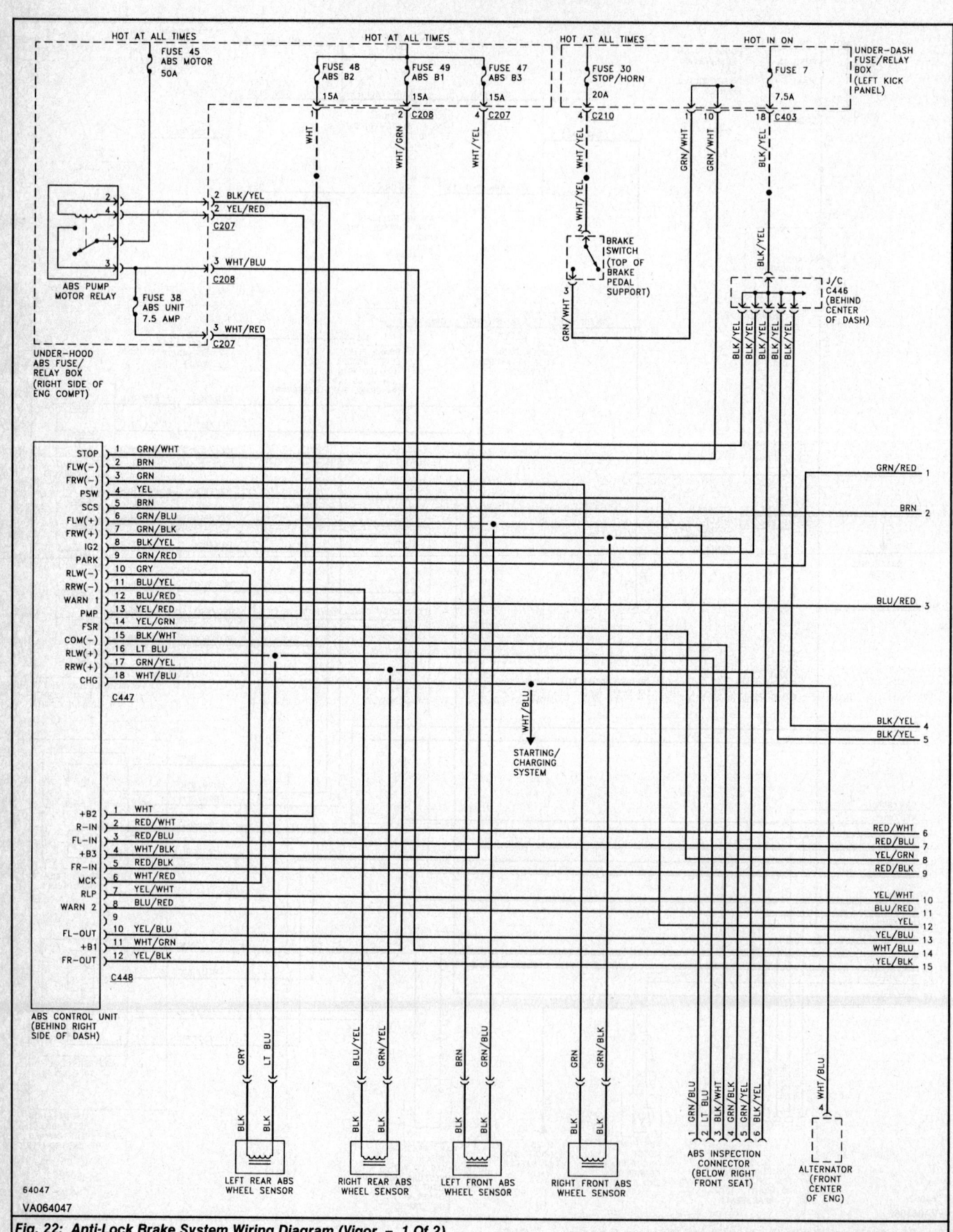

64047

VA064047

Fig. 22: Anti-Lock Brake System Wiring Diagram (Vigor – 1 Of 2)

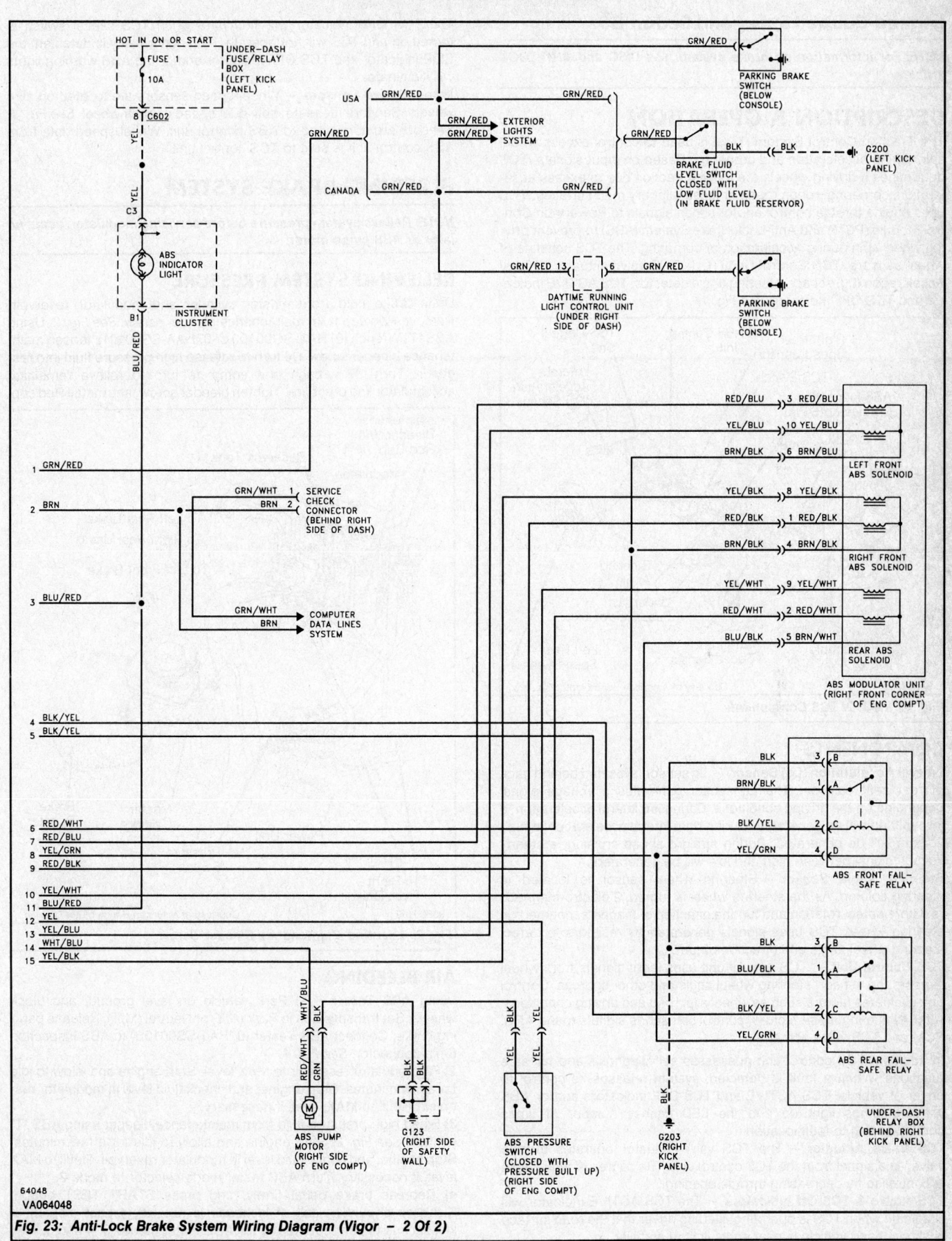

Fig. 23: Anti-Lock Brake System Wiring Diagram (Vigor – 2 Of 2)

Legend Coupe LS, Legend Sedan GS

NOTE: For information on brake system, see DISC and ANTI-LOCK articles.

DESCRIPTION & OPERATION

The Traction Control System (TCS) is used to control excess wheel spin during acceleration and cornering. Based on input signals, TCS determines if driving wheels are loosing traction due to excess acceleration, cornering, rough roads or loose/slippery road surfaces. TCS uses engine throttle control and/or sends signals to Powertrain Control Module (PCM) and Anti-Lock Brake System (ABS) to prevent driving wheel spin during acceleration or cornering. The TCS consists of wheel sensors, TCS Control Unit (TCU), TCS valve actuator, Lateral Acceleration (Lg) sensor, steering angle detector, TCS ACTIVE indicator and TCS OFF indicator. *See Fig. 1.*

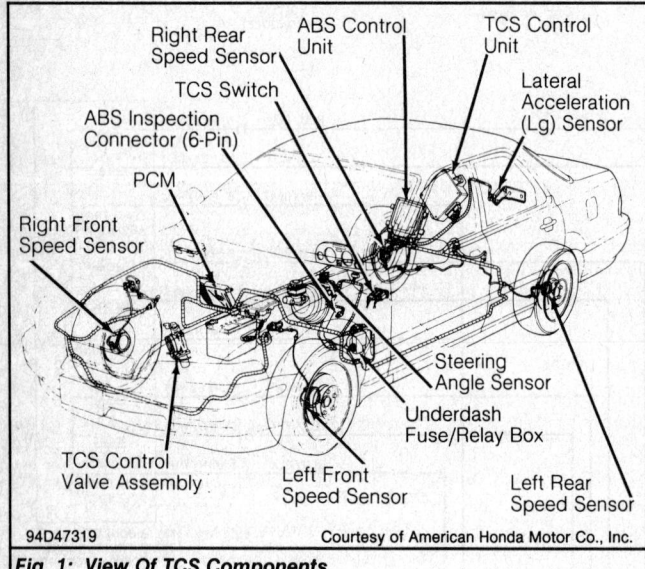

94D47319   Courtesy of American Honda Motor Co., Inc.

Fig. 1: View Of TCS Components

COMPONENTS

Lateral Acceleration (Lg) Sensor – Lg sensor is located behind back of rear seat cushion. The Lg sensor generates a voltage signal depending on the driving conditions. During left lateral acceleration, a low voltage will be generated. During right lateral acceleration, a high voltage will be generated. During straight ahead cruising, a steady voltage signal between high and low will be generated.

Steering Angle Sensor – Steering wheel sensor is located in steering column. As the steering wheel is turned, 2 electro-magnetic resistors detect rotation and turning direction of magnets mounted on steering wheel. TCS uses signals generated by resistors to detect steering wheel angle and direction of turn.

TCS Control Unit – TCS control unit uses input signals from wheel sensors, Lg sensor, steering wheel angle and other sources. Control unit evaluates factors such as wheel slip, road and driving conditions. After evaluating these factors, control unit sends signals to the ABS, PCM and TCS valve actuator.

In addition, TCS control unit possesses self-diagnosis and fail-safe functions. When a fault is detected, system releases its control to driver of vehicle. TCS ACTIVE and TCS OFF indicators and/or ABS warning lamps light up and the LED flashes number of times corresponding to fault location.

TCS Valve Actuator – The TCS valve actuator operates throttle valve via a signal from the TCS control unit. The degree of wheel spin is controlled by decreasing throttle opening.

TCS Active & TCS Off Indicators – The TCS ACTIVE indicator will illuminate when TCS is operating, alerting driver that the road surface is slippery and vehicle is nearing its limit of stability.

The TCS OFF indicator will illuminate when TCS cancel switch is turned on and TCS will not operate. If an abnormality is detected, the SLIP indicator and TCS OFF indicator and/or the ABS warning lights will illuminate.

Wheel Speed Sensors – Wheel speed sensors are located on all 4 wheels. Sensors measure individual speed of each wheel. *See Fig. 1.* Sensors are connected to ABS control unit. Wheel speed data from ABS control unit is sent to TCS control unit.

BLEEDING BRAKE SYSTEM

NOTE: Relieve system pressure before servicing modulator, accumulator or ABS pump motor.

RELIEVING SYSTEM PRESSURE

Drain brake fluid from master cylinder and modulator reservoir. Remove Red cap from maintenance bleeder screw. *See Fig. 2.* Using ABS "T" Wrench (07HAA-SG00100 or 07HAA-SG00101), loosen maintenance bleeder screw 1/4 turn to release high pressure fluid into reservoir. Turn "T" wrench one complete turn to relieve remaining accumulator line pressure. Tighten bleeder screw, and install Red cap.

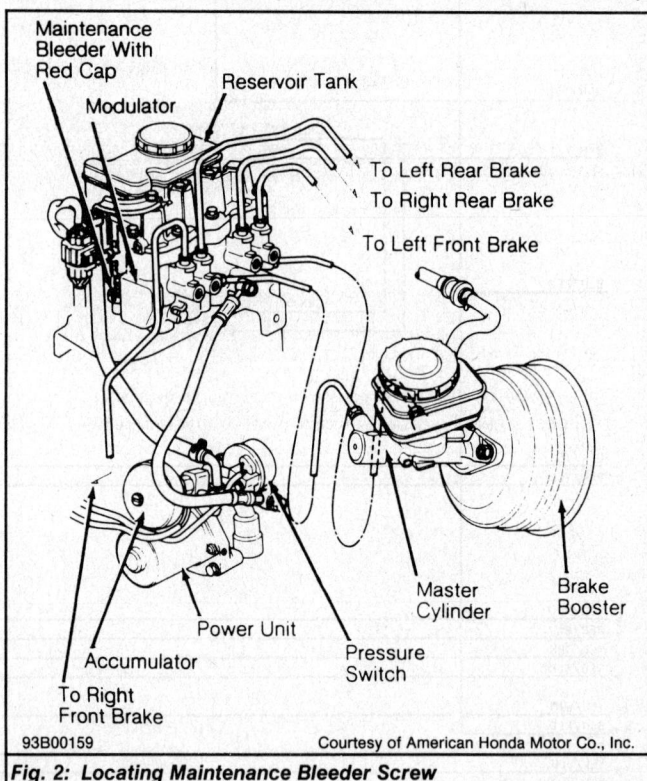

93B00159   Courtesy of American Honda Motor Co., Inc.

Fig. 2: Locating Maintenance Bleeder Screw

AIR BLEEDING

Using ABS Tester – 1) Park vehicle on level ground, and block wheels. Set transmission in Park (A/T) or Neutral (M/T). Release parking brake. Connect ABS Tester (07HAJ-SG0010B) to ABS inspection 6-pin connector. *See Fig. 1.*

2) Fill modulator reservoir to MAX level. Start engine and allow to idle for a few minutes. Stop engine, and check fluid level in modulator reservoir. Refill to MAX level, if necessary.

3) Bleed high-pressure fluid from maintenance bleeder using ABS "T" wrench. *See Fig. 2.* Start engine and allow to idle for a few minutes. Stop engine, and check fluid level in modulator reservoir. Refill to MAX level, if necessary. Turn ABS tester mode selector to mode 2.

4) Depress brake pedal firmly, and press START TEST button. Kickback should be felt. If kickback is not felt, repeat step **3)**. If kickback is felt, repeat step **4)** for ABS tester modes 3, 4 and 5.

5) Fill modulator reservoir to MAX level. Perform system function test. See ABS FUNCTION TEST under DIAGNOSIS & TESTING.

COMPONENT TESTS

FAIL-SAFE RELAY

1) Relay is located on underhood relay panel on left side, toward front. Unplug relay from socket. Using fused jumper wires, apply battery voltage between coil terminals No. 1 and 3.

2) Continuity should exist between terminals No. 2 and 4 with voltage applied to relay coil. *See Fig. 3.* No continuity should exist between terminals No. 1 and 4 with no battery voltage. Replace relay if continuity is not as specified.

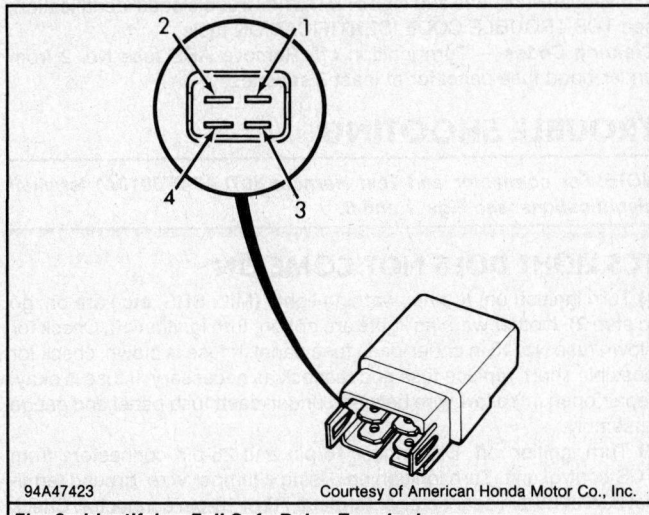

94A47423   Courtesy of American Honda Motor Co., Inc.

Fig. 3: Identifying Fail-Safe Relay Terminals

LATERAL ACCELERATOR (Lg) SENSOR

1) Remove Lg sensor with bracket and harness connector attached. Turn ignition on. Measure voltage between terminals No. 2 and 3. *See Fig. 4.*

2) Voltage should be about 2.5 volts with sensor held vertical. Voltage should be about 1.5 volts with sensor bracket down. Voltage should be about 3.5 volts with sensor harness connector held down.

3) If voltage is as described, Lg sensor is okay. If voltage is not as described, repair related circuits or replace Lg sensor.

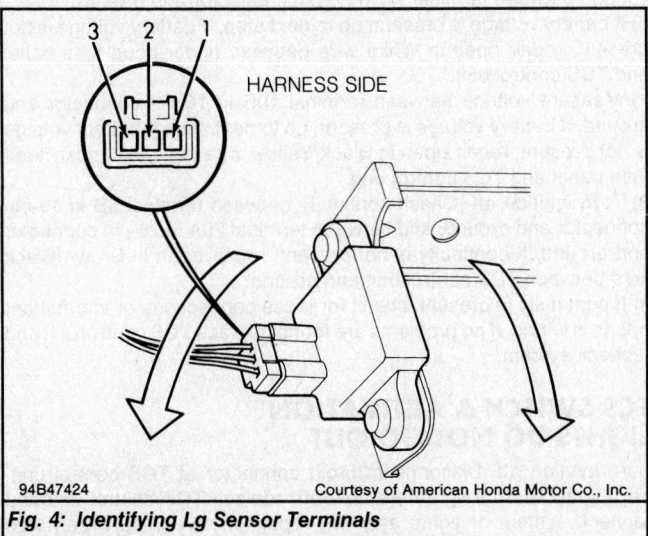

HARNESS SIDE

94B47424   Courtesy of American Honda Motor Co., Inc.

Fig. 4: Identifying Lg Sensor Terminals

TCS SWITCH

Remove connector from TCS switch. Check for continuity between terminals "A" and "B" with button pressed and no continuity with button released. *See Fig. 5.* Continuity should be present between terminals "C" and "D", and "E" and "F". If switch does not work as described, replace switch.

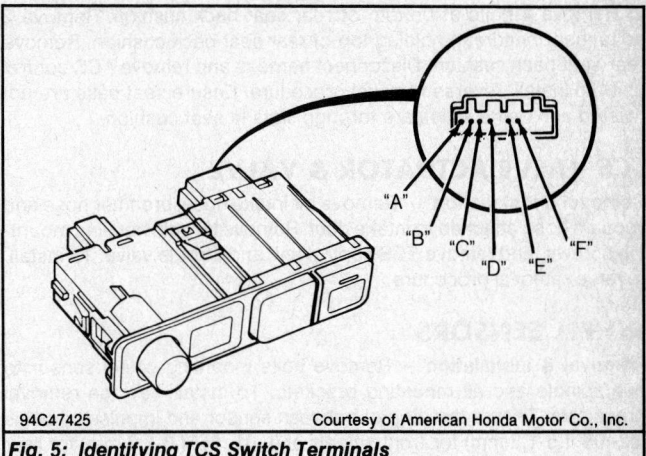

94C47425   Courtesy of American Honda Motor Co., Inc.

Fig. 5: Identifying TCS Switch Terminals

REMOVAL & INSTALLATION

Lg SENSOR

Removal & Installation – 1) Pull both tabs forward at front edge of rear lower seat cushion. Lift and remove rear lower seat cushion. Remove headrests.

2) Remove 4 bolts at bottom of rear seat back cushion. Remove 2 bolts (near headrest) holding top of rear seat back cushion. Remove rear seat back cushion. Disconnect harness and remove Lg sensor with bracket attached. To install, reverse removal procedure.

STEERING ANGLE SENSOR

Removal & Installation – 1) Remove steering column covers. Disconnect steering angle sensor connector and remove sensor from steering column. *See Fig. 6* DO NOT lose any adjustment shims. Shims are reused during installation.

NOTE: DO NOT apply grease or glue to hold adjustment shims in place during installation. Use existing adjustment shims for original or new steering angle sensor installation.

---

2) Install all removed adjustment shims and mounting bolts to steering angle sensor. Tighten steering angle sensor mounting screws. Reconnect harness connector. Install steering column covers. Perform system check to ensure steering angle sensor is operating.

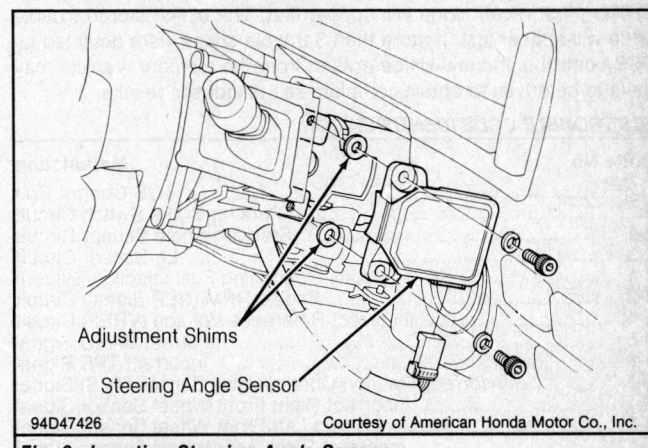

Adjustment Shims

Steering Angle Sensor

94D47426   Courtesy of American Honda Motor Co., Inc.

Fig. 6: Locating Steering Angle Sensor

TCS CONTROL UNIT

Removal & Installation – 1) Pull both tabs forward at front edge of rear lower seat cushion. Lift and remove rear lower seat cushion. Remove headrests.

2) Remove 4 bolts at bottom of rear seat back cushion. Remove 2 bolts (near headrest) holding top of rear seat back cushion. Remove rear seat back cushion. Disconnect harness and remove TCS control unit. To install, reverse removal procedure. Ensure seat belts are not twisted and belt buckles are through slots in seat cushion.

TCS VALVE ACTUATOR & VALVE

Removal & Installation – Remove air intake hose, breather hose and vacuum hose attached to intake duct. Remove throttle housing mounting screws, and remove TCS control unit and throttle valve. To install, reverse removal procedure.

WHEEL SENSORS

Removal & Installation – Remove bolts mounting wheel sensor to hub/spindle and all mounting brackets. To install, reverse removal procedure. Ensure the air gap between sensor and impulse wheel is .02-.05" (.6-1.2 mm) for front wheels and .01-.05" (.3-1.2 mm) for rear wheels.

TORQUE SPECIFICATIONS

TORQUE SPECIFICATIONS

Application	INCH Lbs. (N.m)
Front Wheel Sensor Harness Bracket Bolts	84 (10)
Front Wheel Sensor Retaining Bolts	1
Front Wheel Sensor Harness Bracket Bolts	84 (10)
Rear Wheel Sensor Retaining Bolts	84 (10)
Steering Angle Sensor	84 (10)
Throttle Housing Nuts	1

1 – Tighten bolts/nuts to 16 ft. lbs. (22 N.m).

DIAGNOSIS

NOTE: Before starting TCS diagnostic checks, road test vehicle and confirm customer's complaint. If tire pressure is low or incorrect tire size is installed, clear trouble code(s) and road test vehicle.

DIAGNOSTIC SYSTEM

TCS Control Unit – 1) TCS control unit includes self-diagnostics. It will store up to 3 codes. Self-diagnostic system is functioning as long as engine is running. When a problem occurs, the TCS indicator light will come on and trouble code(s) will be stored. If the ignition is turned off and engine restarted, the TCS light will not come on (unless another problem is present). Any trouble codes will remain in memory.

2) The most recent code will appear first. The oldest stored trouble code will appear last. If more than 3 trouble codes were detected by TCS control unit, they will be erased from the memory. Vehicle may have to be driven to obtain complete self-diagnostic results.

TCS TROUBLE CODE IDENTIFICATION 1

Code No.	Malfunction
1-2	TCS Control Unit
2	Parking Brake Switch Circuit
2-1	Steering Angle Sensor Circuit
2-3	Lg Sensor Circuit
3-1	PCM Circuits Controlling Fuel Injection System
3-2	Engine RPM (NEP Signal) Circuit
3-4	Incorrect Reference Voltage (VREF) Circuit
3-5	Incorrect BARO Signal
3-6	Incorrect TPS Signal
3-7	Incorrect Traction Control Valve Sensor (TCS) Signal
4-1	Incorrect Right Front Wheel Sensor Signal
4-2	Incorrect Left Front Wheel Sensor Signal
4-4	Incorrect Right Rear Wheel Sensor Signal
4-8	Incorrect Left Rear Wheel Sensor Signal
4-9	Incorrect Signals All Wheels
5-1	Incorrect TCS Valve Assembly Or Fail-Safe Relay
5-2	Incorrect TCS Valve Operation
5-3	Incorrect Back-Up Voltage (VB)
6-1	Incorrect PCM Circuit Signals

1 – See DIAGNOSTIC CHARTS for DTC repair information.

Retrieving Codes – 1) Turn ignition on, with engine off. Ensure TCS light comes on. If TCS light does not come on, go to TCS LIGHT DOES NOT COME ON under TROUBLE SHOOTING. Turn ignition off.

2) Locate 2-pin self-diagnostic connector at passenger-side toe board. Install a jumper wire between White and Black wires of self-diagnostic connector. Turn ignition on, but do not start engine. TCS light should start flashing any stored code(s). If TCS light stays on and trouble code(s) are not flashes, go to TCS LIGHT DOES NOT GO OFF under DIAGNOSIS.

3) A long (1.2 second) flash indicates main digit of DTC, and short flash (0.3 second) indicates sub digit of DTC. For trouble code identification, see TCS TROUBLE CODE IDENTIFICATION table.

Clearing Codes – Turn ignition off. Remove ABS fuse No. 2 from under-hood fuse panel for at least 3 seconds.

TROUBLE SHOOTING

NOTE: For connector and Test Harness (07LA3-PT3010A) terminal identifications, see Figs. 7 and 8.

TCS LIGHT DOES NOT COME ON

1) Turn ignition on. If other warning lights (MIL, SRS, etc.) are on, go to step 2). If other warning lights are not on, turn ignition off. Check for blown fuse No. 13 in under-dash fuse panel. If fuse is blown, check for possible short, replace fuse and recheck as necessary. If fuse is okay, repair open in Yellow wire between under-dash fuse panel and gauge assembly.

2) Turn ignition off. Disconnect 16-pin and 26-pin connectors from TCS control unit. Turn ignition on. Using a jumper wire, ground terminal 23A of 26-pin connector or terminal 7B of 16-pin connector. Check for TCS indicator light being on.

3) Ground terminal 10A of 26-pin connector. Check for TCS activation light being on. Ground terminal 6A of 26-pin connector. Check for TCS switch indicator light being on.

4) If all lights came on when terminals were grounded, go to next step. If one or more lights stayed off, check gauge assembly for bad bulb. Replace bulbs as necessary. If bulbs are okay, check appropriate circuit between TCS control unit and gauge assembly.

5) Check for blown ABS fuse No. 2 in under-hood fuse panel and fuse No. 22 in under-dash fuse panel. If fuse(s) is blown, check for possible short, replace fuse and recheck as necessary. If fuse is okay, measure voltage between terminal 1A in 26-pin connector and ground.

6) If battery voltage is present, go to next step. If battery voltage is not present, repair open in White wire between under-hood fuse panel and TCS control unit.

7) Measure voltage between terminal 10B in 16-pin connector and ground. If battery voltage is present, go to next step. If battery voltage is not present, repair open in Black/Yellow wire between under-hood fuse panel and TCS control unit.

8) Turn ignition off. Check continuity between terminal 5B in 16-pin connector and ground, and between terminal 20A in 26-pin connector and ground. If continuity is not present, repair open in Brown/Black wire between TCS control unit and ground.

9) If continuity is present, check for loose connections or intermittent opens in wiring. If no problems are found, replace TCS control unit and recheck system.

TCS SWITCH & ACTIVATION LIGHTS DO NOT GO OUT

Turn ignition off. Disconnect 26-pin connector at TCS control unit. Turn ignition on. If lights are now off, replace TCS control unit and recheck system. If lights stay on, repair short in Red/Green wire between TCS control unit and gauge assembly or Gray/Red wire between TCS control unit and TCS switch.

TCS LIGHT DOES NOT GO OFF

1) Turn ignition on. If TCS switch indicator and TCS activation lights stay off, see TCS LIGHT DOES NOT COME ON under TROUBLE SHOOTING. If lights stay on longer than 2 seconds, start engine.

2) If engine Malfunction Indication Light (MIL) comes on, perform self-diagnostic procedure in appropriate ENGINE PERFORMANCE article. Ensure engine Diagnostic Trouble Codes (DTC) 35 and 36 are not present.

NOTE: DTC 35 indicates a circuit problem in Gray/Yellow wire between terminal 14B of 16-pin connector at TCS control unit and PCM. DTC 36 indicates a circuit problem in Gray/Blue wire between terminal 19A of 26-pin connector at TCS control unit and PCM.

---

3) If DTC 35 and/or 36 are present, perform tests to correct circuit problems. See appropriate ENGINE PERFORMANCE article. If there is no DTC, start engine.

4) Measure voltage between terminal 9B of 16-pin TCS control unit connector and ground. If less than 2 volts is present, go to step **6)**. If more than 2 volts is present, turn ignition off. Disconnect 16-pin and 26-pin connectors from TCS control unit.

5) Turn ignition on. If TCS indicator light is on, repair short in Blue/Red wire between TCS control unit and gauge assembly. If TCS indicator light is off, replace TCS control unit and recheck system.

6) Turn ignition off. Connect Test Harness (07LAJ-PT3010A) to PCM. Start engine. Measure voltage between terminal C6 of test harness and ground. If more than 2 volts is present, repair open in Gray/Black wire between TCS control unit and PCM.

7) If less than 2 volts is present, turn ignition off. Disconnect 12-pin PCM connector and 16-pin TCS control unit connector. Check for continuity between terminal 9B of 16-pin TCS control unit connector and ground.

8) If continuity is present, repair open in Gray/Black wire between TCS control unit and PCM. If continuity is not present, reconnect 16-pin TCS control unit connector.

9) Measure resistance between terminals 9B and 5B of 16-pin TCS control unit connector. Also measure resistance between terminal 9B of 16-pin and terminal 20A of 26-pin TCS control unit connectors.

10) If resistance is zero (or almost zero), replace TCS control unit. If resistance is not zero (or almost zero), check for poor electrical connections. If no problems are found, replace PCM and recheck system.

DIAGNOSTIC CHARTS

NOTE: For connector and Test Harness (07LAJ-PT3010A) terminal identifications, see Figs. 7 and 8.

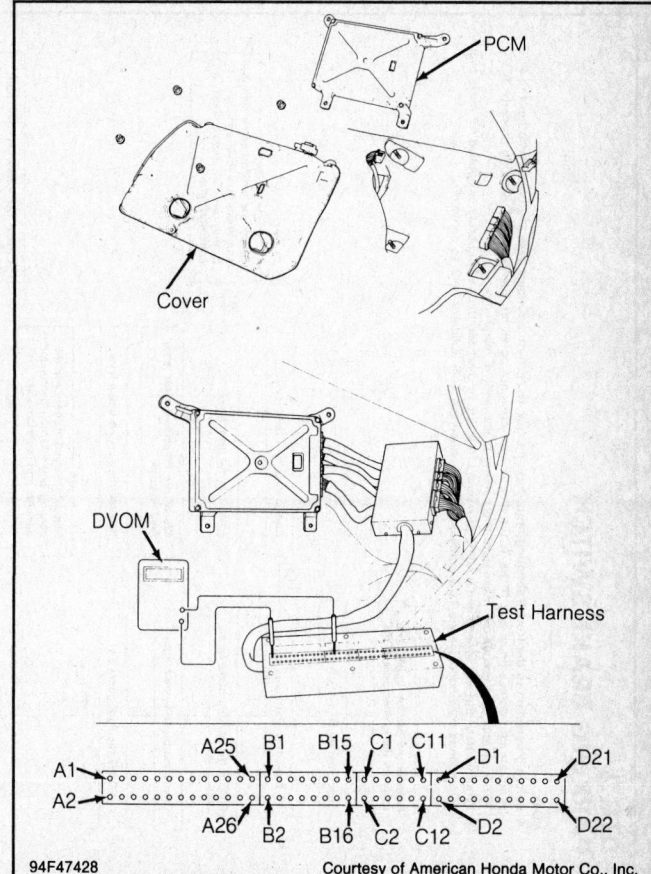

94F47428   Courtesy of American Honda Motor Co., Inc.

Fig. 8: Identifying Test Harness Connector Terminals

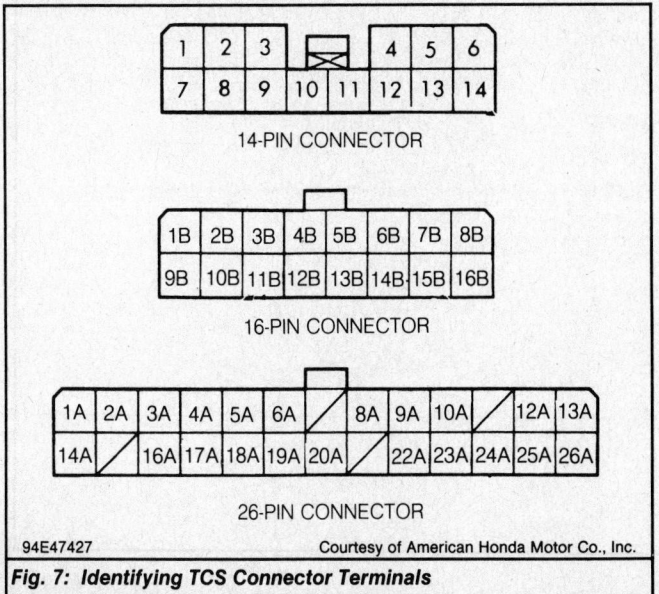

94E47427   Courtesy of American Honda Motor Co., Inc.

Fig. 7: Identifying TCS Connector Terminals

DTC 1-2 OR TCS INDICATOR LIGHT STAYS ON TCS CONTROL UNIT

NOTE:
- If DTC 1-2 is indicated, replace TCS control unit.
- If TCS indicator light remains on, check Blue/Red wire between TCS control unit and TCS indicator light for short to ground. If wire is okay, replace TCS control unit.

DTC 2 PARKING BRAKE SWITCH

NOTE:
- Before proceeding to the troubleshooting procedure, be sure to perform a running test and check whether the TCS indicator light comes on or not. If the TCS indicator light does not come on, the system is working properly. If the TCS indicator light comes on, make sure the parking brake lever is released.
- When both of the rear wheels are running at 6 mph (10 km/h) or over and the parking brake is applied for more than 30 seconds continuously, the TCS control unit will cause the TCS indicator light to come on.

Release the parking brake lever and turn the ignition switch ON.

Check the brake system light.

Does the light come on?

NO → Pull up the parking brake lever.
Check the brake system light.
Does the light come on?
YES → Release the parking brake lever.
Measure the voltage between the TCS control unit terminal 9A (+) and body ground.
Is there battery voltage?
YES → Substitute a known-good TCS control unit and recheck.
• Check for poor connections or loose wires.
NO → Repair open in the GRN/RED wire between the TCS control unit and gauge assembly.

YES → Check the brake fluid level.
Is the level low?
YES → Check the brake pad wear and fluid leakage.
NO → Check the parking brake switch and brake fluid level switch. If they are OK, repair short in GRN/RED wire.

Release the parking brake lever.
Measure the voltage between the parking brake switch connector terminal and body ground.
Is there battery voltage?
YES → Check the parking brake switch.
NO → Check the brake system light bulb. If it is OK, repair open in the GRN/RED wire between the parking brake switch and gauge assembly.

94G47429

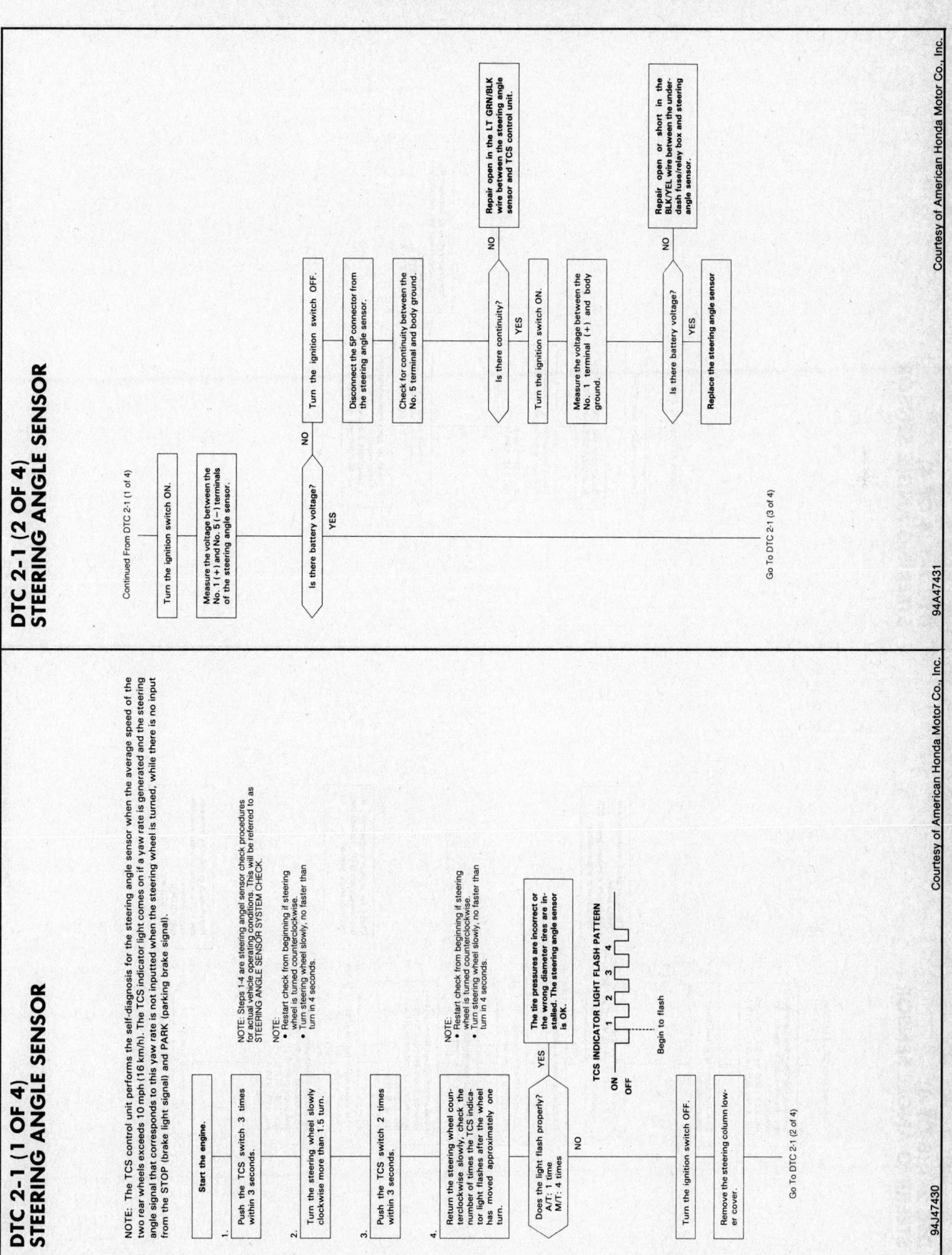

DTC 2-1 (1 OF 4)
STEERING ANGLE SENSOR

NOTE: The TCS control unit performs the self-diagnosis for the steering angle sensor when the average speed of the two rear wheels exceeds 10 mph (16 km/h). The TCS indicator light comes on if a yaw rate is generated and the steering angle signal that corresponds to this yaw rate is not inputted when the steering wheel is turned, while there is no input from the STOP (brake light signal) and PARK (parking brake signal).

Start the engine.

1. Push the TCS switch 3 times within 3 seconds.

2. Turn the steering wheel slowly clockwise more than 1.5 turn.

NOTE: Steps 1-4 are steering angle sensor check procedures for actual vehicle operating conditions. This will be referred to as STEERING ANGLE SENSOR SYSTEM CHECK.

NOTE:
• Restart check from beginning if steering wheel is turned counterclockwise.
• Turn steering wheel slowly, no faster than turn in 4 seconds.

3. Push the TCS switch 2 times within 3 seconds.

4. Return the steering wheel counterclockwise slowly, check the number of times the TCS indicator light flashes after the wheel has moved approximately one turn.

NOTE:
• Restart check from beginning if steering wheel is turned counterclockwise.
• Turn steering wheel slowly, no faster than turn in 4 seconds.

The tire pressures are incorrect or the wrong diameter tires are installed. The steering angle sensor is OK.

Does the light flash properly?
A/T: 1 time
M/T: 4 times

YES →

NO

TCS INDICATOR LIGHT FLASH PATTERN

```
           1  2  3  4
ON  ┌─┐ ┌─┐ ┌─┐ ┌─┐
OFF─┘ └─┘ └─┘ └─┘ └─
```

Begin to flash

Turn the ignition switch OFF.

Remove the steering column lower cover.

Go To DTC 2-1 (2 of 4)

DTC 2-1 (2 OF 4)
STEERING ANGLE SENSOR

Continued From DTC 2-1 (1 of 4)

Turn the ignition switch ON.

Measure the voltage between the No. 1 (+) and No. 5 (−) terminals of the steering angle sensor.

Is there battery voltage?

YES ↓   NO →

NO → Turn the ignition switch OFF.

Disconnect the 5P connector from the steering angle sensor.

Check for continuity between the No. 5 terminal and body ground.

Is there continuity?

YES ↓   NO → Repair open in the LT GRN/BLK wire between the steering angle sensor and TCS control unit.

Turn the ignition switch ON.

Measure the voltage between the No. 1 terminal (+) and body ground.

Is there battery voltage?

YES ↓   NO → Repair open or short in the BLK/YEL wire between the under-dash fuse/relay box and steering angle sensor.

Replace the steering angle sensor

Go To DTC 2-1 (3 of 4)

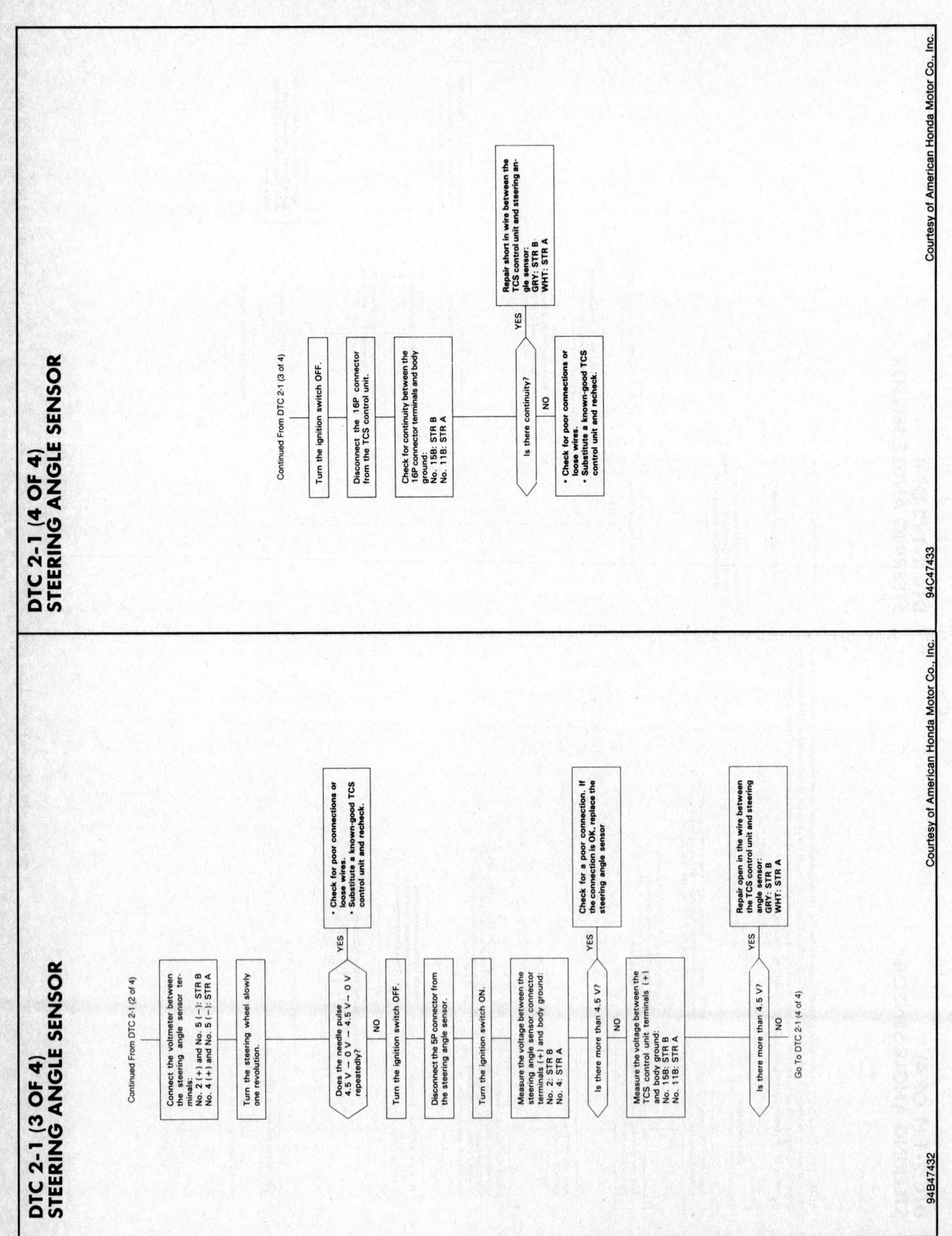

DTC 2-1 (3 OF 4)
STEERING ANGLE SENSOR

Continued From DTC 2-1 (2 of 4)

Connect the voltmeter between the steering angle sensor terminals:
No. 2 (+) and No. 5 (−): STR B
No. 4 (+) and No. 5 (−): STR A

Turn the steering wheel slowly one revolution.

Does the needle pulse 4.5 V − 0 V − 4.5 V − 0 V repeatedly?

YES —
- Check for poor connections or loose wires.
- Substitute a known-good TCS control unit and recheck.

NO

Turn the ignition switch OFF.

Disconnect the 5P connector from the steering angle sensor.

Turn the ignition switch ON.

Measure the voltage between the steering angle sensor connector terminals (+) and body ground:
No. 2: STR B
No. 4: STR A

Is there more than 4.5 V?

YES — Check for a poor connection. If the connection is OK, replace the steering angle sensor

NO

Measure the voltage between the TCS control unit terminals (+) and body ground:
No. 15B: STR B
No. 11B: STR A

Is there more than 4.5 V?

YES — Repair open in the wire between the TCS control unit and steering angle sensor:
GRY: STR B
WHT: STR A

NO

Go To DTC 2-1 (4 of 4)

DTC 2-1 (4 OF 4)
STEERING ANGLE SENSOR

Continued From DTC 2-1 (3 of 4)

Turn the ignition switch OFF.

Disconnect the 16P connector from the TCS control unit.

Check for continuity between the 16P connector terminals and body ground:
No. 15B: STR B
No. 11B: STR A

Is there continuity?

YES — Repair short in wire between the TCS control unit and steering angle sensor:
GRY: STR B
WHT: STR A

NO

- Check for poor connections or loose wires.
- Substitute a known-good TCS control unit and recheck.

94B47432

94C47433

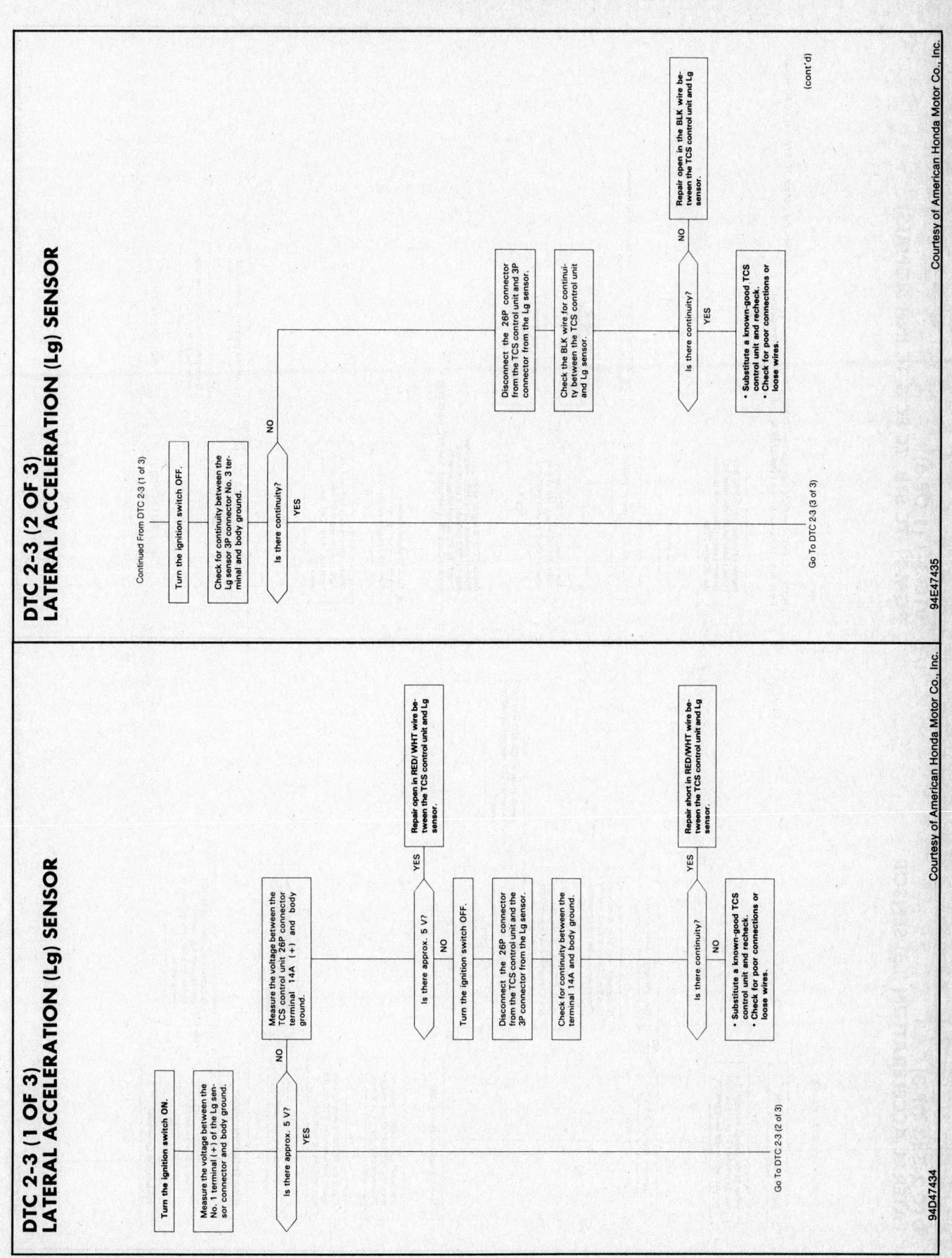

DTC 2-3 (1 OF 3)
LATERAL ACCELERATION (Lg) SENSOR

Turn the ignition switch ON.

Measure the voltage between the No. 1 terminal (+) of the Lg sensor connector and body ground.

Is there approx. 5 V?

YES — Go To DTC 2-3 (2 of 3)

NO — Measure the voltage between the TCS control unit 26P connector terminal 14A (+) and body ground.

Is there approx. 5 V?

YES — Repair open in RED/WHT wire between the TCS control unit and Lg sensor.

NO — Turn the ignition switch OFF.

Disconnect the 26P connector from the TCS control unit and the 3P connector from the Lg sensor.

Check for continuity between the terminal 14A and body ground.

Is there continuity?

YES — Repair short in RED/WHT wire between the TCS control unit and Lg sensor.

NO — • Substitute a known-good TCS control unit and recheck.
• Check for poor connections or loose wires.

DTC 2-3 (2 OF 3)
LATERAL ACCELERATION (Lg) SENSOR

Continued From DTC 2-3 (1 of 3)

Turn the ignition switch OFF.

Check for continuity between the Lg sensor 3P connector No. 3 terminal and body ground.

Is there continuity?

YES — Go To DTC 2-3 (3 of 3)

NO — Disconnect the 26P connector from the TCS control unit and 3P connector from the Lg sensor.

Check the BLK wire for continuity between the TCS control unit and Lg sensor.

Is there continuity?

YES — • Substitute a known-good TCS control unit and recheck.
• Check for poor connections or loose wires.

NO — Repair open in the BLK wire between the TCS control unit and Lg sensor.

(cont'd)

94D47434

94E47435

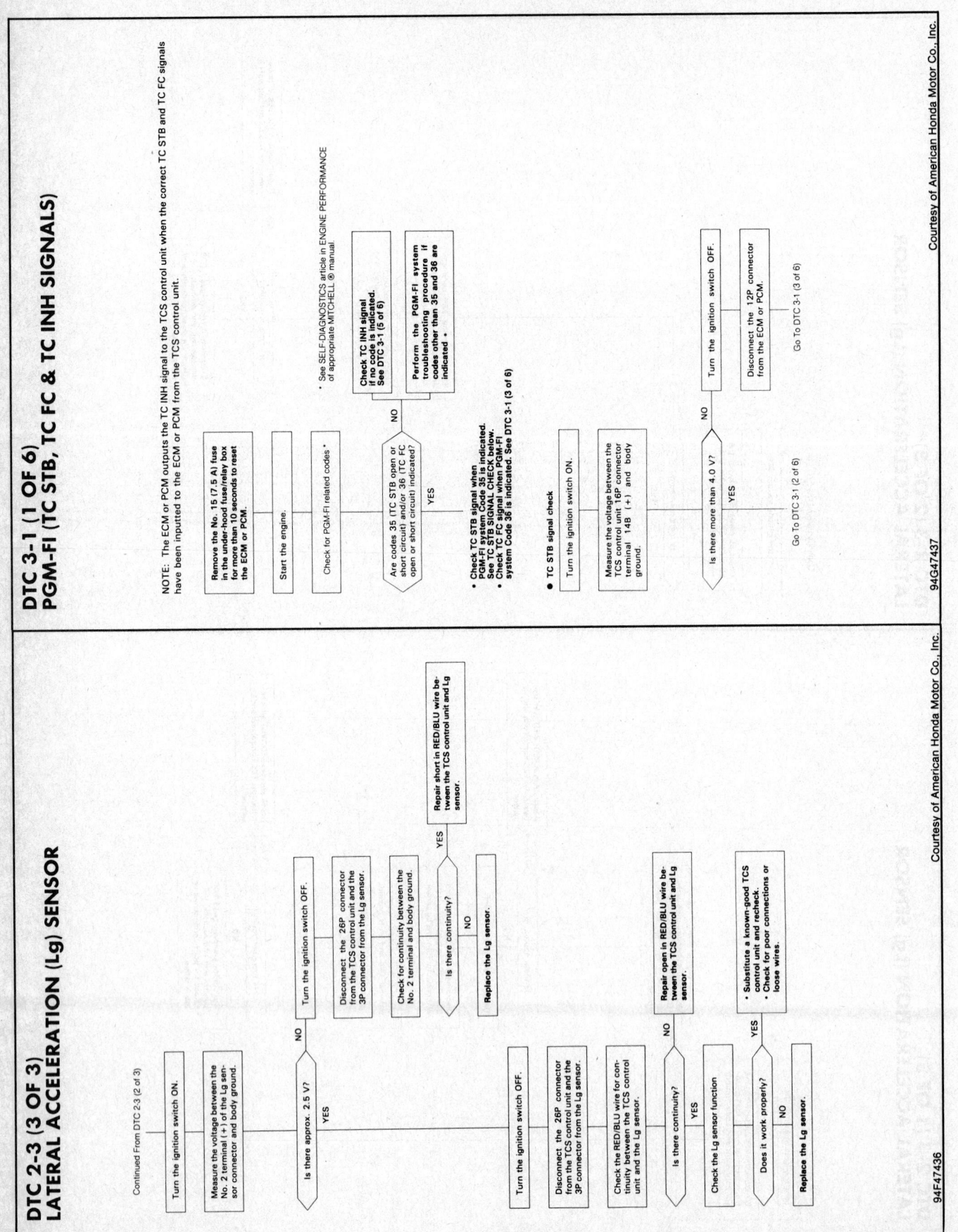

DTC 3-1 (1 OF 6)
PGM-FI (TC STB, TC FC & TC INH SIGNALS)

NOTE: The ECM or PCM outputs the TC INH signal to the TCS control unit when the correct TC STB and TC FC signals have been inputted to the ECM or PCM from the TCS control unit.

Remove the No. 15 (7.5 A) fuse in the under-hood fuse/relay box for more than 10 seconds to reset the ECM or PCM.

Start the engine.

Check for PGM-FI related codes *

Are codes 35 (TC STB open or short circuit) and/or 36 (TC FC open or short circuit) indicated?

* See SELF-DIAGNOSTICS article in ENGINE PERFORMANCE of appropriate MITCHELL ® manual.

YES / NO

Check TC INH signal if no code is indicated. See DTC 3-1 (5 of 6)

Perform the PGM-FI system troubleshooting procedure if codes other than 35 and 36 are indicated *

- Check TC STB signal when PGM-FI system Code 35 is indicated. See TC STB SIGNAL CHECK below.
- Check TC FC signal when PGM-FI system Code 36 is indicated. See DTC 3-1 (3 of 6)

● TC STB signal check

Turn the ignition switch ON.

Measure the voltage between the TCS control unit 16P connector terminal 14B (+) and body ground.

Is there more than 4.0 V?

YES / NO

YES → Go To DTC 3-1 (2 of 6)

NO →
Turn the ignition switch OFF.

Disconnect the 12P connector from the ECM or PCM.

Go To DTC 3-1 (3 of 6)

94G47437

DTC 2-3 (3 OF 3)
LATERAL ACCELERATION (Lg) SENSOR

Continued From DTC 2-3 (2 of 3)

Turn the ignition switch ON.

Measure the voltage between the No. 2 terminal (+) of the Lg sensor connector and body ground.

Is there approx. 2.5 V?

YES / NO

NO →
Turn the ignition switch OFF.

Disconnect the 26P connector from the TCS control unit and the 3P connector from the Lg sensor.

Check for continuity between the No. 2 terminal and body ground.

Is there continuity?

YES / NO

YES →
Repair short in RED/BLU wire between the TCS control unit and Lg sensor.

NO →
Replace the Lg sensor.

YES →
Turn the ignition switch OFF.

Disconnect the 26P connector from the TCS control unit and the 3P connector from the Lg sensor.

Check the RED/BLU wire for continuity between the TCS control unit and the Lg sensor.

Is there continuity?

YES / NO

NO →
Repair open in RED/BLU wire between the TCS control unit and Lg sensor.

YES →
Check the Lg sensor function

Does it work properly?

YES / NO

YES →
- Substitute a known-good TCS control unit and recheck.
- Check for poor connections or loose wires.

NO →
Replace the Lg sensor.

94F47436

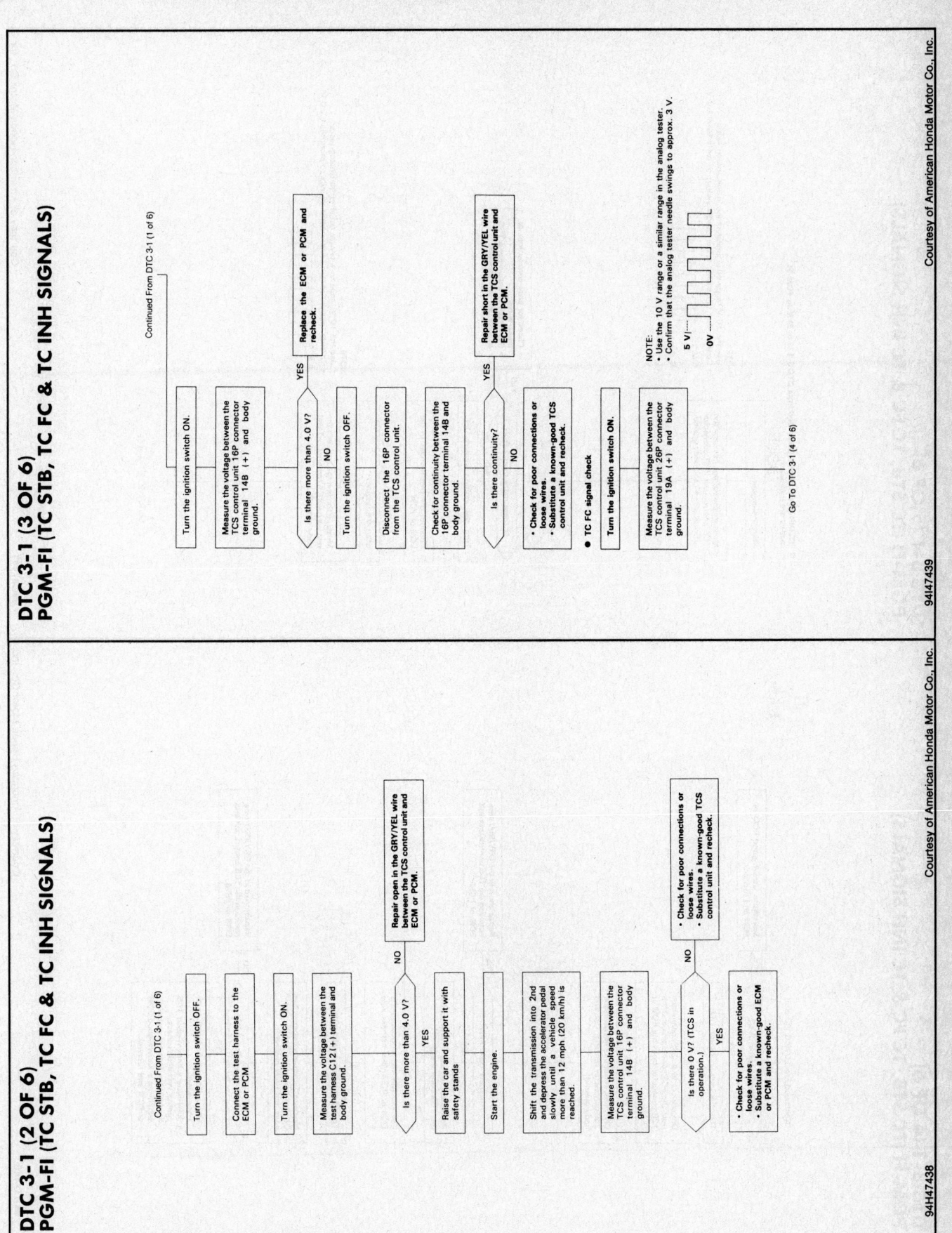

DTC 3-1 (3 OF 6)
PGM-FI (TC STB, TC FC & TC INH SIGNALS)

Continued From DTC 3-1 (1 of 6)

Turn the ignition switch ON.

Measure the voltage between the TCS control unit 16P connector terminal 14B (+) and body ground.

Is there more than 4.0 V? — YES → Replace the ECM or PCM and recheck.

NO

Turn the ignition switch OFF.

Disconnect the 16P connector from the TCS control unit.

Check for continuity between the 16P connector terminal 14B and body ground.

Is there continuity? — YES → Repair short in the GRY/YEL wire between the TCS control unit and ECM or PCM.

NO

- Check for poor connections or loose wires.
- Substitute a known-good TCS control unit and recheck.

● TC FC signal check

Turn the ignition switch ON.

Measure the voltage between the TCS control unit 26P connector terminal 19A (+) and body ground.

Go To DTC 3-1 (4 of 6)

NOTE:
- Use the 10 V range or a similar range in the analog tester.
- Confirm that the analog tester needle swings to approx. 3 V.

5 V
0V

94147439

Courtesy of American Honda Motor Co., Inc.

DTC 3-1 (2 OF 6)
PGM-FI (TC STB, TC FC & TC INH SIGNALS)

Continued From DTC 3-1 (1 of 6)

Turn the ignition switch OFF.

Connect the test harness to the ECM or PCM.

Turn the ignition switch ON.

Measure the voltage between the test harness C12 (+) terminal and body ground.

Is there more than 4.0 V? — NO → Repair open in the GRY/YEL wire between the TCS control unit and ECM or PCM.

YES

Raise the car and support it with safety stands.

Start the engine.

Shift the transmission into 2nd and depress the accelerator pedal slowly until a vehicle speed more than 12 mph (20 km/h) is reached.

Measure the voltage between the TCS control unit 16P connector terminal 14B (+) and body ground.

Is there 0 V? (TCS in operation.) — NO → - Check for poor connections or loose wires.
- Substitute a known-good TCS control unit and recheck.

YES

- Check for poor connections or loose wires.
- Substitute a known-good ECM or PCM and recheck.

94H47438

Courtesy of American Honda Motor Co., Inc.

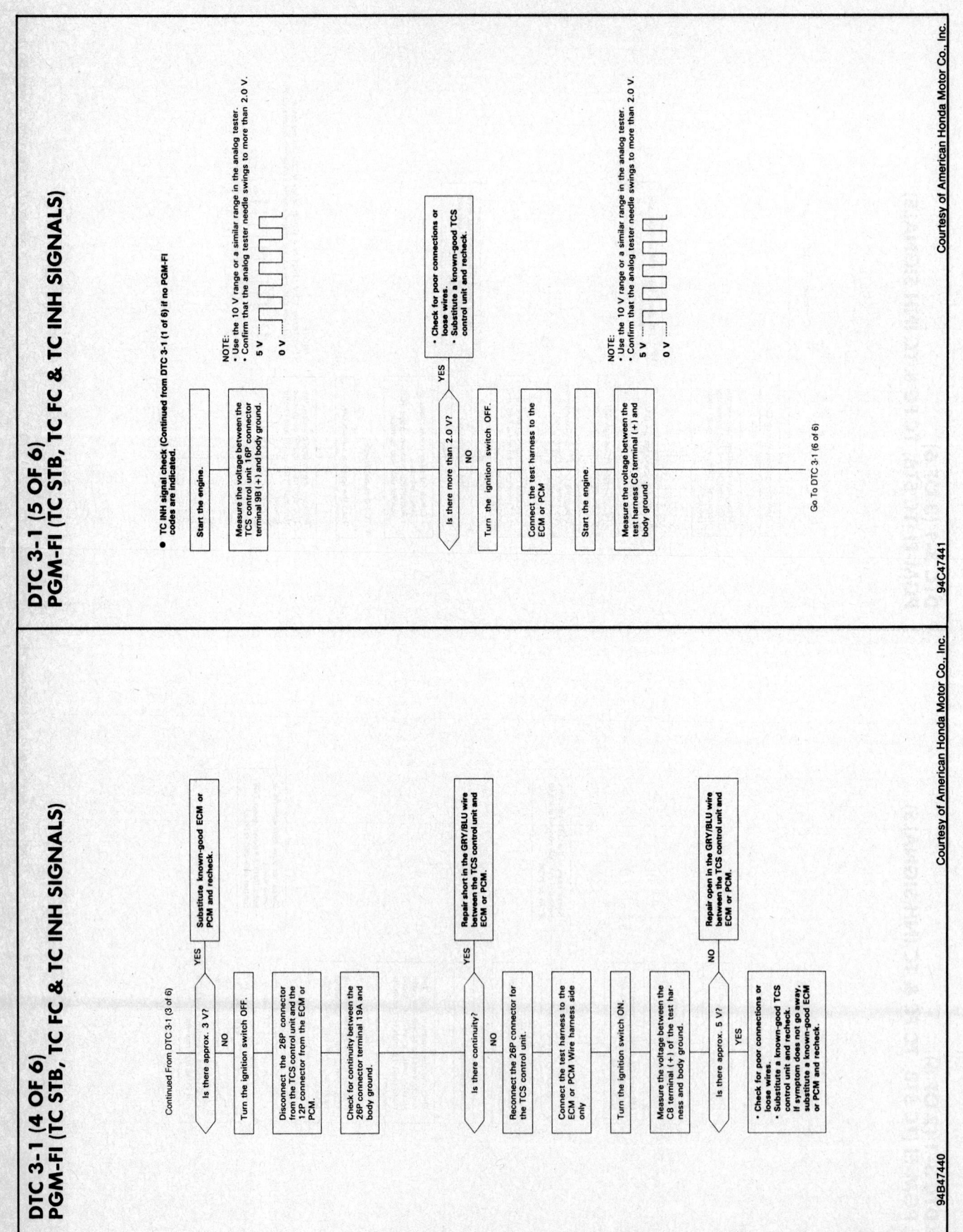

DTC 3-1 (5 OF 6)
PGM-FI (TC STB, TC FC & TC INH SIGNALS)

- TC INH signal check (Continued from DTC 3-1 (1 of 6) if no PGM-FI codes are indicated.)

Start the engine.

Measure the voltage between the TCS control unit 16P connector terminal 9B (+) and body ground.

NOTE:
• Use the 10 V range or a similar range in the analog tester.
• Confirm that the analog tester needle swings to more than 2.0 V.

5 V
0 V

Is there more than 2.0 V?

YES → • Check for poor connections or loose wires.
• Substitute a known-good TCS control unit and recheck.

NO

Turn the ignition switch OFF.

Connect the test harness to the ECM or PCM.

Start the engine.

Measure the voltage between the test harness C6 terminal (+) and body ground.

NOTE:
• Use the 10 V range or a similar range in the analog tester.
• Confirm that the analog tester needle swings to more than 2.0 V.

5 V
0 V

Go To DTC-3-1 (6 of 6)

DTC 3-1 (4 OF 6)
PGM-FI (TC STB, TC FC & TC INH SIGNALS)

Continued From DTC 3-1 (3 of 6)

Is there approx. 3 V?

YES → Substitute known-good ECM or PCM and recheck.

NO

Turn the ignition switch OFF.

Disconnect the 26P connector from the TCS control unit and the 12P connector from the ECM or PCM.

Check for continuity between the 26P connector terminal 19A and body ground.

Is there continuity?

YES → Repair short in the GRY/BLU wire between the TCS control unit and ECM or PCM.

NO

Reconnect the 26P connector for the TCS control unit.

Connect the test harness to the ECM or PCM Wire harness side only

Turn the ignition switch ON.

Measure the voltage between the C8 terminal (+) of the test harness and body ground.

Is there approx. 5 V?

YES → • Check for poor connections or loose wires.
• Substitute a known-good TCS control unit and recheck. If symptom does not go away, substitute a known-good ECM or PCM and recheck.

NO → Repair open in the GRY/BLU wire between the TCS control unit and ECM or PCM.

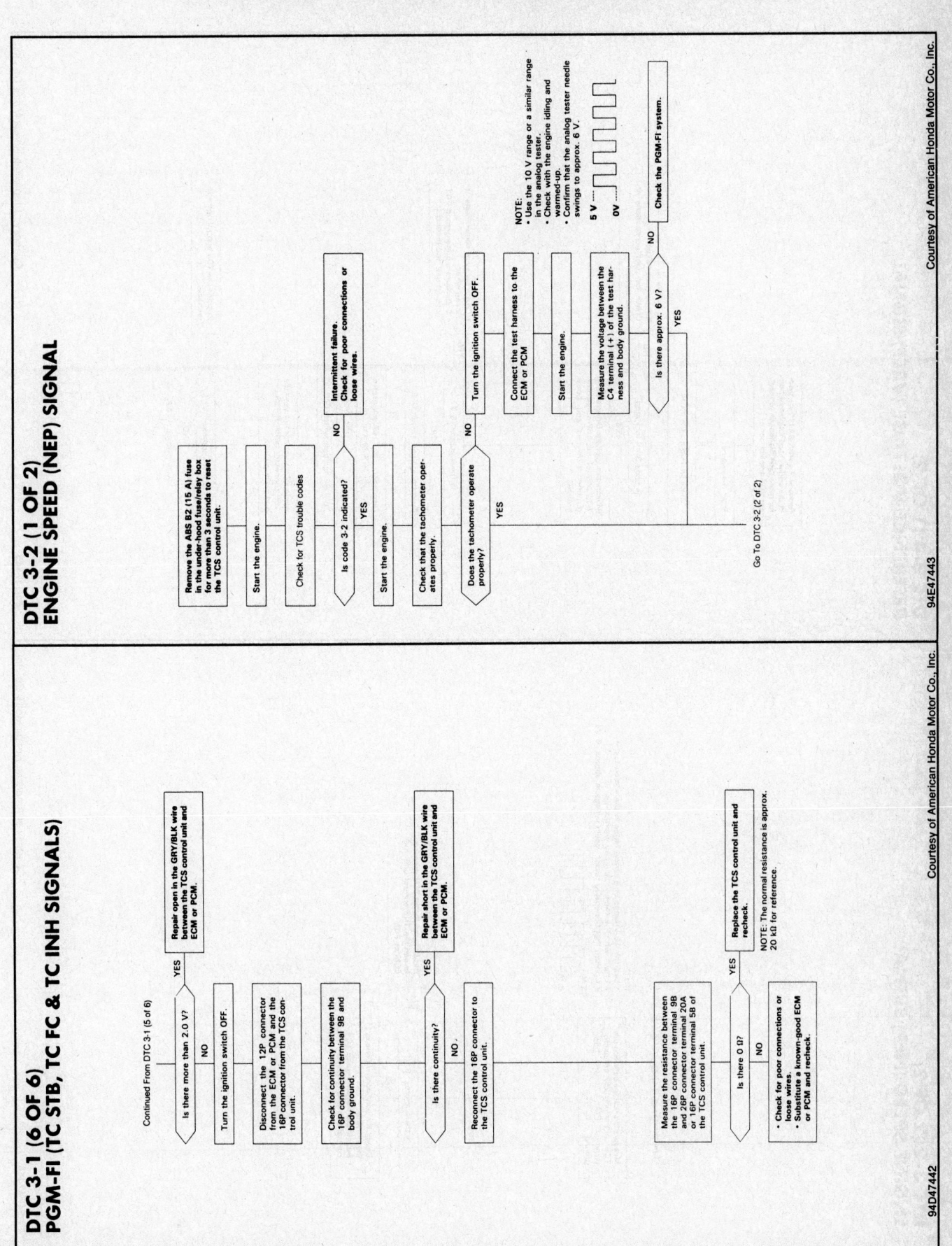

DTC 3-1 (6 OF 6)
PGM-FI (TC STB, TC FC & TC INH SIGNALS)

Continued From DTC 3-1 (5 of 6)

Is there more than 2.0 V?

YES → Repair open in the GRY/BLK wire between the TCS control unit and ECM or PCM.

NO

Turn the ignition switch OFF.

Disconnect the 12P connector from the ECM or PCM and the 16P connector from the TCS control unit.

Check for continuity between the 16P connector terminal 9B and body ground.

Is there continuity?

YES → Repair short in the GRY/BLK wire between the TCS control unit and ECM or PCM.

NO

Reconnect the 16P connector to the TCS control unit.

Measure the resistance between the 16P connector terminal 9B and 26P connector terminal 20A or 16P connector terminal 5B of the TCS control unit.

Is there 0 Ω?

YES → Replace the TCS control unit and recheck.

NOTE: The normal resistance is approx. 20 kΩ for reference.

NO

- Check for poor connections or loose wires.
- Substitute a known-good ECM or PCM and recheck.

DTC 3-2 (1 OF 2)
ENGINE SPEED (NEP) SIGNAL

Remove the ABS B2 (15 A) fuse in the under-hood fuse/relay box for more than 3 seconds to reset the TCS control unit.

Start the engine.

Check for TCS trouble codes

Is code 3-2 indicated?

NO → Intermittent failure. Check for poor connections or loose wires.

YES

Start the engine.

Check that the tachometer operates properly.

Does the tachometer operate properly?

NO → Turn the ignition switch OFF.

Connect the test harness to the ECM or PCM

Start the engine.

Measure the voltage between the C4 terminal (+) of the test harness and body ground.

Is there approx. 6 V?

NO → Check the PGM-FI system.

YES

NOTE:
- Use the 10 V range or a similar range in the analog tester.
- Check with the engine idling and warmed-up.
- Confirm that the analog tester needle swings to approx. 6 V.

5 V ----
0V ----

YES

Go To DTC 3-2 (2 of 2)

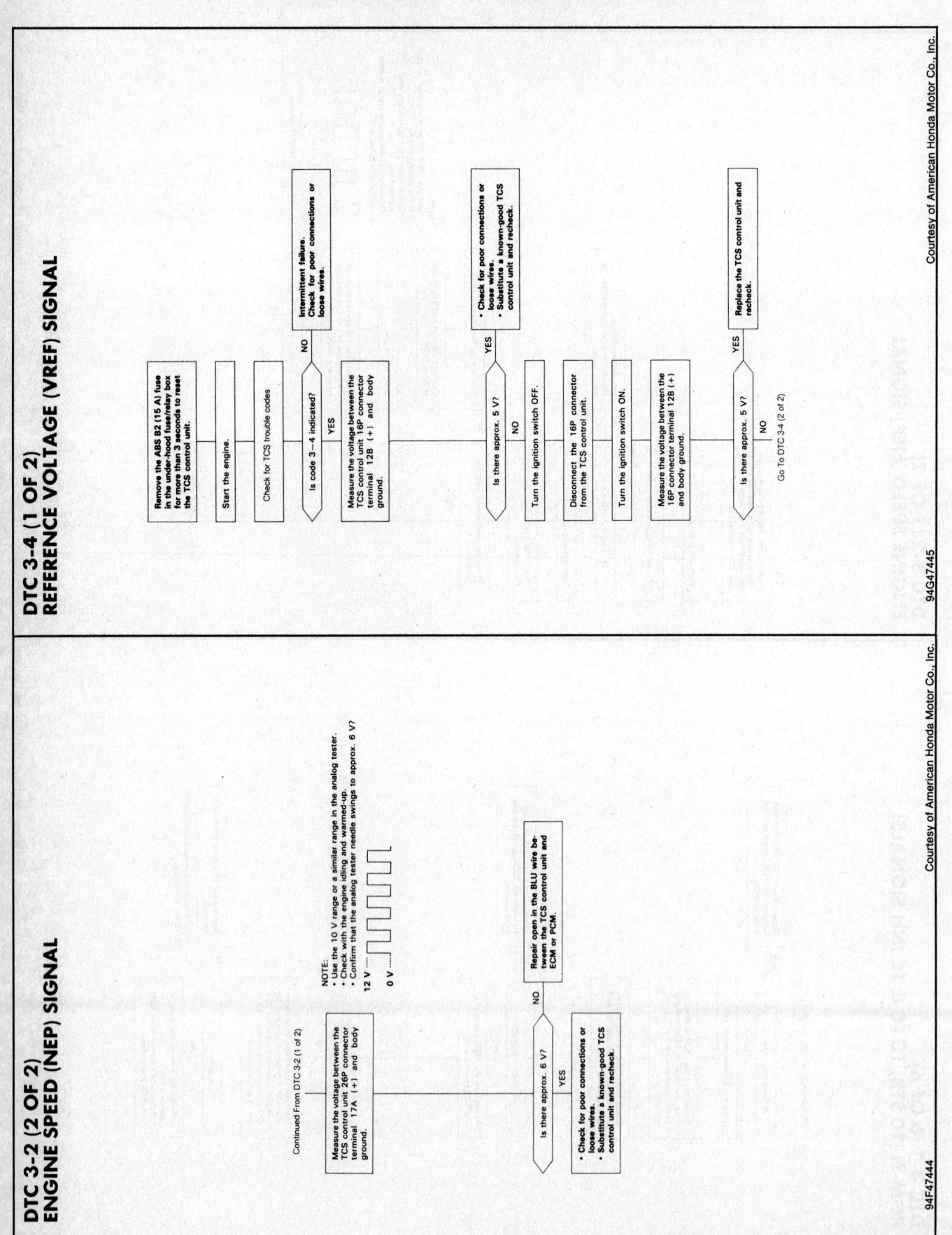

DTC 3-4 (1 OF 2)
REFERENCE VOLTAGE (VREF) SIGNAL

Remove the ABS B2 (15 A) fuse in the under-hood fuse/relay box for more than 3 seconds to reset the TCS control unit.

Start the engine.

Check for TCS trouble codes

Is code 3—4 indicated?

NO → Intermittent failure. Check for poor connections or loose wires.

YES

Measure the voltage between the TCS control unit 16P connector terminal 12B (+) and body ground.

Is there approx. 5 V?

YES → • Check for poor connections or loose wires.
• Substitute a known-good TCS control unit and recheck.

NO

Turn the ignition switch OFF.

Disconnect the 16P connector from the TCS control unit.

Turn the ignition switch ON.

Measure the voltage between the 16P connector terminal 12B (+) and body ground.

Is there approx. 5 V?

YES → Replace the TCS control unit and recheck.

NO

Go To DTC 3-4 (2 of 2)

94G47445

DTC 3-2 (2 OF 2)
ENGINE SPEED (NEP) SIGNAL

Continued From DTC 3-2 (1 of 2)

Measure the voltage between the TCS control unit 26P connector terminal 17A (+) and body ground.

NOTE:
• Use the 10 V range or a similar range in the analog tester.
• Check with the engine idling and warmed-up.
• Confirm that the analog tester needle swings to approx. 6 V?

12 V —
0 V —

Is there approx. 6 V?

NO → Repair open in the BLU wire between the TCS control unit and ECM or PCM.

YES

• Check for poor connections or loose wires.
• Substitute a known-good TCS control unit and recheck.

94F47444

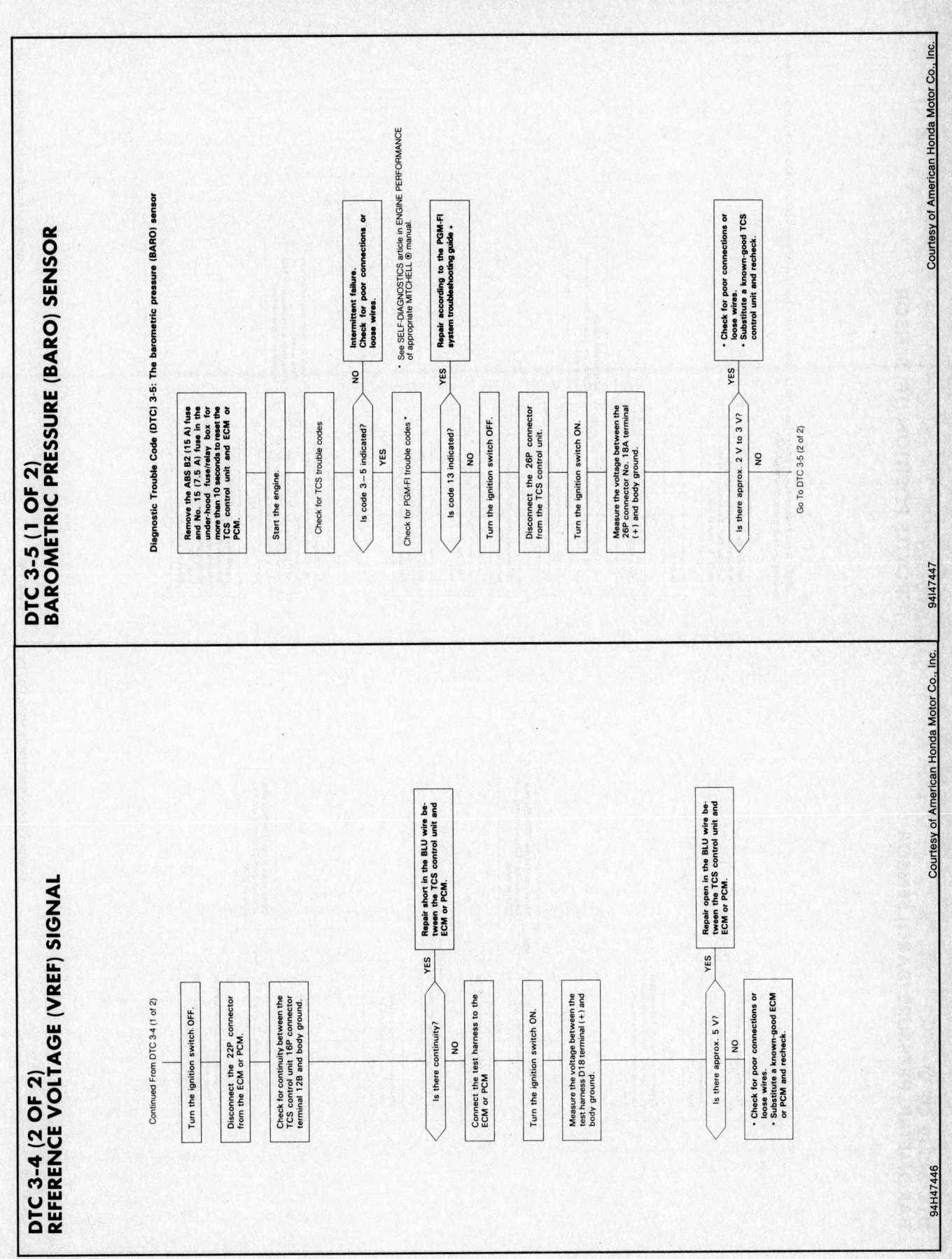

DTC 3-5 (1 OF 2) BAROMETRIC PRESSURE (BARO) SENSOR

Diagnostic Trouble Code (DTC) 3-5: The barometric pressure (BARO) sensor

- Remove the ABS B2 (15 A) fuse and No. 15 (7.5 A) fuse in the under-hood fuse/relay box for more than 10 seconds to reset the TCS control unit and ECM or PCM.
- Start the engine.
- Check for TCS trouble codes
- Is code 3—5 indicated?
  - NO → Intermittent failure. Check for poor connections or loose wires.
  - YES →
- Check for PGM-FI trouble codes *
  - * See SELF-DIAGNOSTICS article in ENGINE PERFORMANCE of appropriate MITCHELL ® manual.
- Is code 13 indicated?
  - YES → Repair according to the PGM-FI system troubleshooting guide *
  - NO →
- Turn the ignition switch OFF.
- Disconnect the 26P connector from the TCS control unit.
- Turn the ignition switch ON.
- Measure the voltage between the 26P connector No. 13A terminal (+) and body ground.
- Is there approx. 2 V to 3 V?
  - YES → Check for poor connections or loose wires. Substitute a known-good TCS control unit and recheck.
  - NO → Go To DTC 3-5 (2 of 2)

DTC 3-4 (2 OF 2) REFERENCE VOLTAGE (VREF) SIGNAL

Continued From DTC 3-4 (1 of 2)

- Turn the ignition switch OFF.
- Disconnect the 22P connector from the ECM or PCM.
- Check for continuity between the TCS control unit 16P connector terminal 12B and body ground.
- Is there continuity?
  - YES → Repair short in the BLU wire between the TCS control unit and ECM or PCM.
  - NO →
- Connect the test harness to the ECM or PCM
- Turn the ignition switch ON.
- Measure the voltage between the test harness D18 terminal (+) and body ground.
- Is there approx. 5 V?
  - YES → Repair open in the BLU wire between the TCS control unit and ECM or PCM.
  - NO → Check for poor connections or loose wires. Substitute a known-good ECM or PCM and recheck.

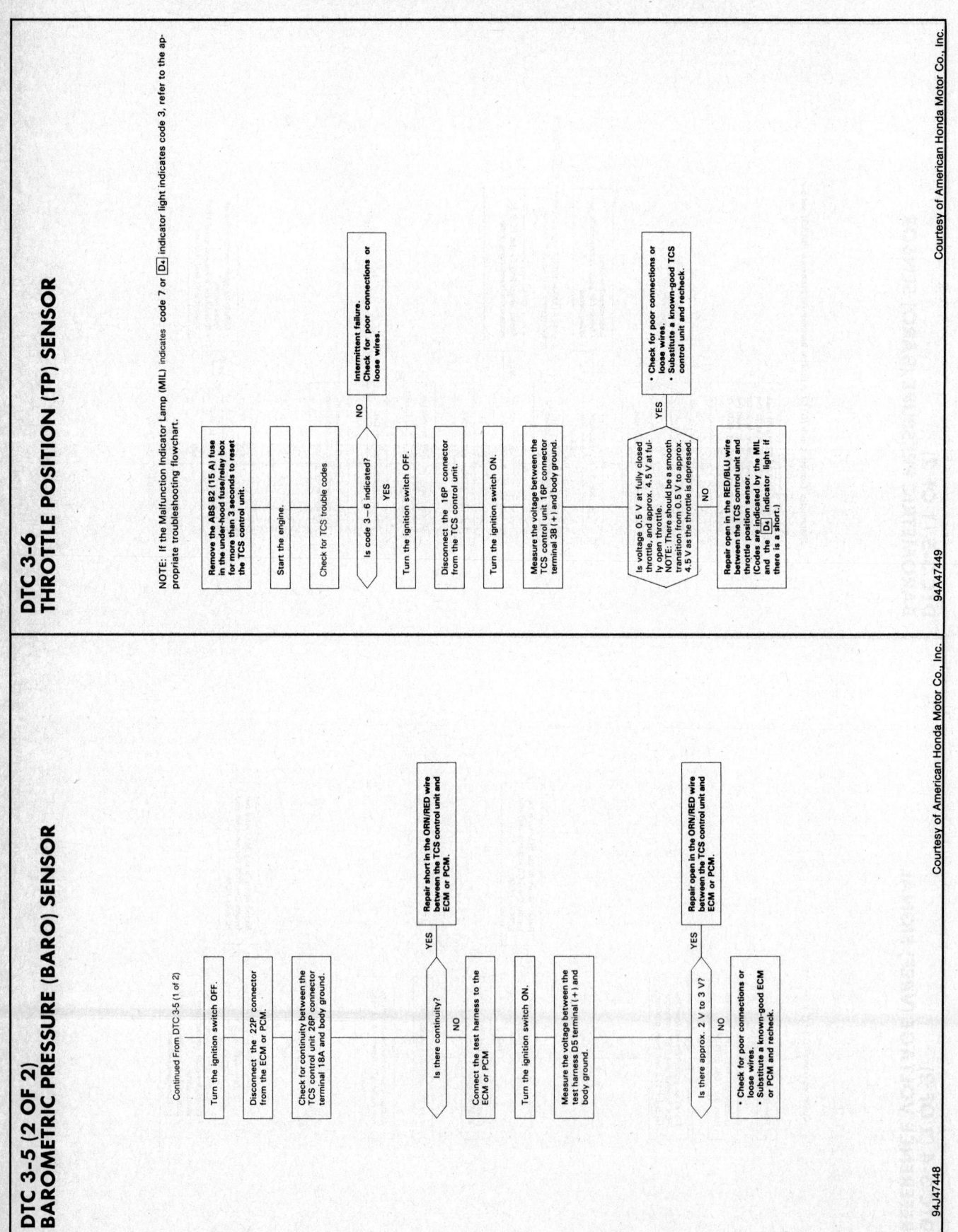

DTC 3-6
THROTTLE POSITION (TP) SENSOR

NOTE: If the Malfunction Indicator Lamp (MIL) indicates code 7 or [D4] indicator light indicates code 3, refer to the appropriate troubleshooting flowchart.

Remove the ABS B2 (15 A) fuse in the under-hood fuse/relay box for more than 3 seconds to reset the TCS control unit.

Start the engine.

Check for TCS trouble codes

Is code 3—6 indicated?

NO → Intermittent failure.
Check for poor connections or loose wires.

YES

Turn the ignition switch OFF.

Disconnect the 16P connector from the TCS control unit.

Turn the ignition switch ON.

Measure the voltage between the TCS control unit 16P connector terminal 3B (+) and body ground.

Is voltage 0.5 V at fully closed throttle, and approx. 4.5 V at fully open throttle.
NOTE: There should be a smooth transition from 0.5 V to approx. 4.5 V as the throttle is depressed.

YES → • Check for poor connections or loose wires.
• Substitute a known-good TCS control unit and recheck.

NO

Repair open in the RED/BLU wire between the TCS control unit and throttle position sensor.
(Codes are indicated by the MIL and the [D4] indicator light if there is a short.)

94J47449

DTC 3-5 (2 OF 2)
BAROMETRIC PRESSURE (BARO) SENSOR

Continued From DTC 3-5 (1 of 2)

Turn the ignition switch OFF.

Disconnect the 22P connector from the ECM or PCM.

Check for continuity between the TCS control unit 26P connector terminal 18A and body ground.

Is there continuity?

YES → Repair short in the ORN/RED wire between the TCS control unit and ECM or PCM.

NO

Connect the test harness to the ECM or PCM

Turn the ignition switch ON.

Measure the voltage between the test harness D5 terminal (+) and body ground.

Is there approx. 2 V to 3 V?

YES → Repair open in the ORN/RED wire between the TCS control unit and ECM or PCM.

NO

• Check for poor connections or loose wires.
• Substitute a known-good ECM or PCM and recheck.

94J47448

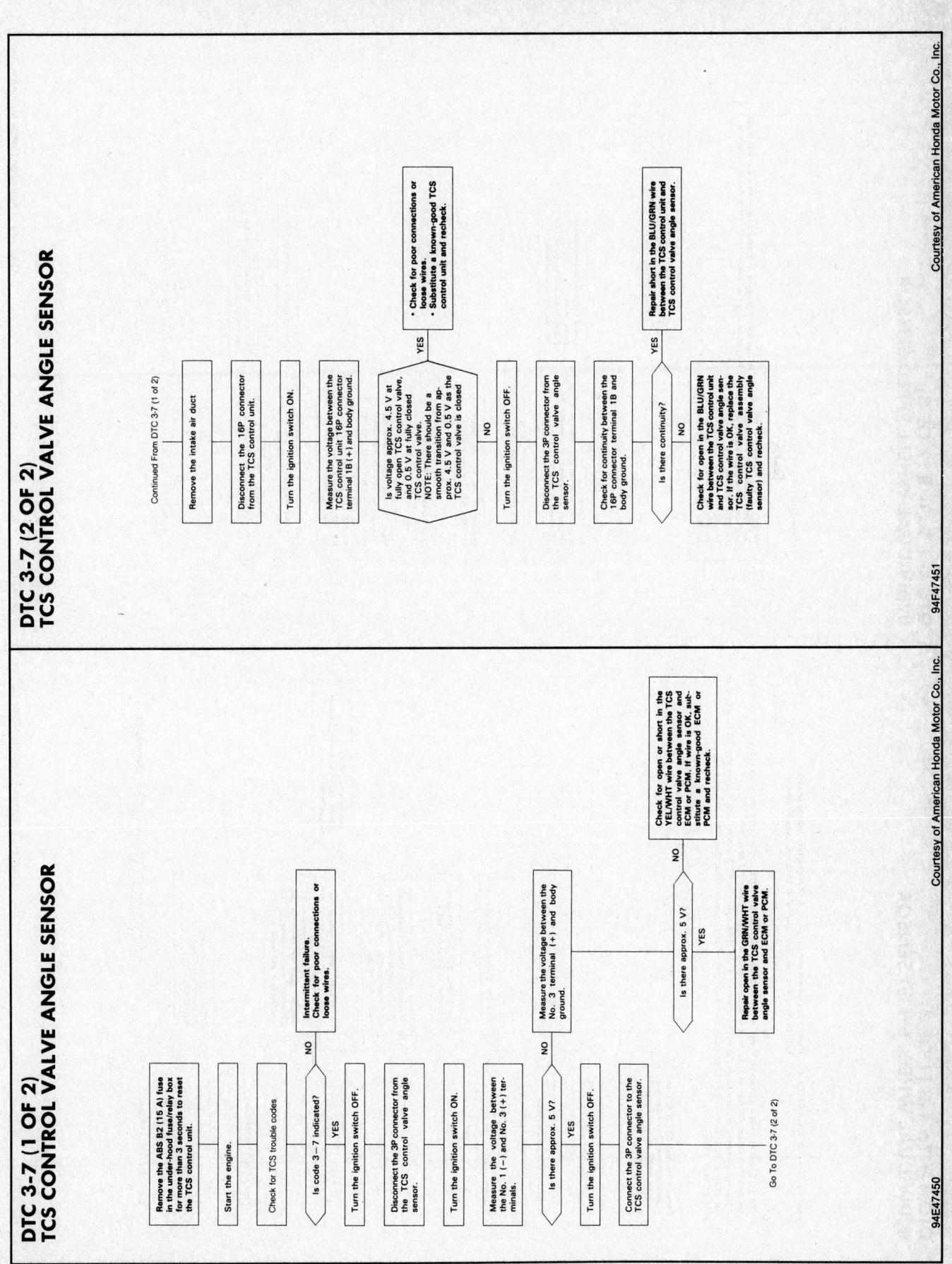

DTC 3-7 (2 OF 2)
TCS CONTROL VALVE ANGLE SENSOR

Continued From DTC 3-7 (1 of 2)

Remove the intake air duct

Disconnect the 16P connector from the TCS control unit.

Turn the ignition switch ON.

Measure the voltage between the TCS control unit 16P connector terminal 1B (+) and body ground.

Is voltage approx. 4.5 V at fully open TCS control valve, and 0.5 V at fully closed TCS control valve. NOTE: There should be a smooth transition from approx. 4.5 V and 0.5 V as the TCS control valve is closed

YES → • Check for poor connections or loose wires.
• Substitute a known-good TCS control unit and recheck.

NO

Turn the ignition switch OFF.

Disconnect the 3P connector from the TCS control valve angle sensor.

Check for continuity between the 16P connector terminal 1B and body ground.

Is there continuity? YES → Repair short in the BLU/GRN wire between the TCS control unit and TCS control valve angle sensor.

NO

Check for open in the BLU/GRN wire between the TCS control unit and TCS control valve angle sensor. If the wire is OK, replace the TCS control valve assembly (faulty TCS control valve angle sensor) and recheck.

94F47451

Courtesy of American Honda Motor Co., Inc.

DTC 3-7 (1 OF 2)
TCS CONTROL VALVE ANGLE SENSOR

Remove the ABS B2 (15 A) fuse in the under-hood fuse/relay box for more than 3 seconds to reset the TCS control unit.

Start the engine.

Check for TCS trouble codes

Is code 3—7 indicated? NO → Intermittent failure. Check for poor connections or loose wires.

YES

Turn the ignition switch OFF.

Disconnect the 3P connector from the TCS control valve angle sensor.

Turn the ignition switch ON.

Measure the voltage between the No. 1 (—) and No. 3 (+) terminals.

Is there approx. 5 V? NO → Measure the voltage between the No. 3 terminal (+) and body ground.

YES

Turn the ignition switch OFF.

Connect the 3P connector to the TCS control valve angle sensor.

Go To DTC 3-7 (2 of 2)

Is there approx. 5 V? NO → Check for open or short in the YEL/WHT wire between the TCS control valve angle sensor and ECM or PCM. If wire is OK, substitute a known-good ECM or PCM and recheck.

YES

Repair open in the GRN/WHT wire between the TCS control valve angle sensor and ECM or PCM.

94E47450

Courtesy of American Honda Motor Co., Inc.

Courtesy of American Honda Motor Co., Inc.

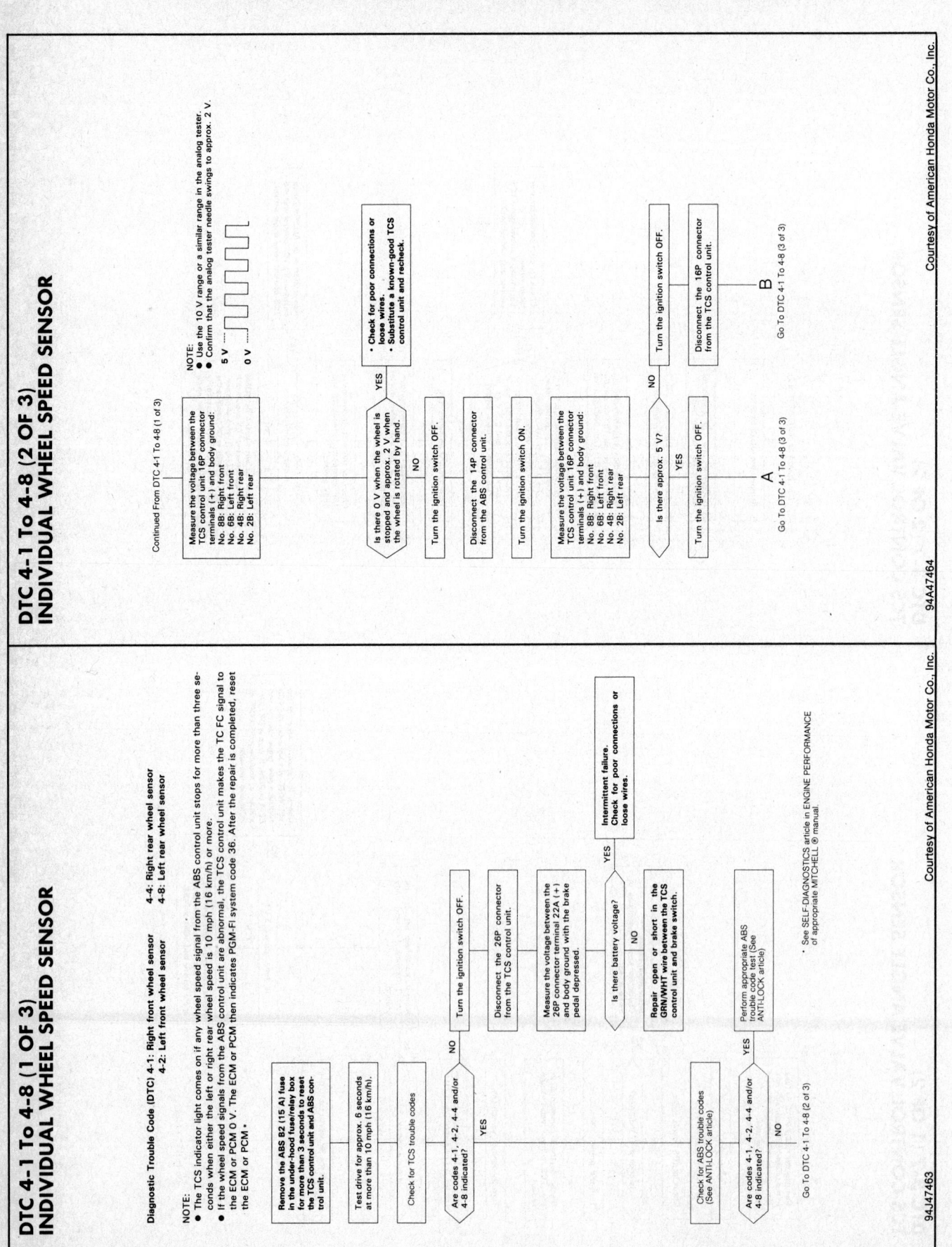

DTC 4-1 To 4-8 (1 OF 3) INDIVIDUAL WHEEL SPEED SENSOR

Diagnostic Trouble Code (DTC) 4-1: Right front wheel sensor   4-4: Right rear wheel sensor
4-2: Left front wheel sensor   4-8: Left rear wheel sensor

NOTE:
• The TCS indicator light comes on if any wheel speed signal from the ABS control unit stops for more than three seconds when either the left or right rear wheel speed is 10 mph (16 km/h) or more.
• If the wheel speed signals from the ABS control unit are abnormal, the TCS control unit makes the TC FC signal to the ECM or PCM 0 V. The ECM or PCM then indicates PGM-FI system code 36. After the repair is completed, reset the ECM or PCM.*

Remove the ABS B2 (15 A) fuse in the under-hood fuse/relay box for more than 3 seconds to reset the TCS control unit and ABS control unit.

Test drive for approx. 6 seconds at more than 10 mph (16 km/h).

Check for TCS trouble codes

Are codes 4-1, 4-2, 4-4 and/or 4-8 indicated?

YES — Turn the ignition switch OFF.

Disconnect the 26P connector from the TCS control unit.

Measure the voltage between the 26P connector terminal 22A (+) and body ground with the brake pedal depressed.

Is there battery voltage?

YES — Intermittent failure. Check for poor connections or loose wires.

NO — Repair open or short in the GRN/WHT wire between the TCS control unit and brake switch.

NO — Check for ABS trouble codes (See ANTI-LOCK article)

Are codes 4-1, 4-2, 4-4 and/or 4-8 indicated?

YES — Perform appropriate ABS trouble code test (See ANTI-LOCK article)

NO — Go To DTC 4-1 To 4-8 (2 of 3)

* See SELF-DIAGNOSTICS article in ENGINE PERFORMANCE of appropriate MITCHELL ® manual.

DTC 4-1 To 4-8 (2 OF 3) INDIVIDUAL WHEEL SPEED SENSOR

Continued From DTC 4-1 To 4-8 (1 of 3)

Measure the voltage between the TCS control unit 16P connector terminals (+) and body ground:
No. 8B: Right front
No. 6B: Left front
No. 4B: Right rear
No. 2B: Left rear

Is there 0 V when the wheel is stopped and approx. 2 V when the wheel is rotated by hand.

YES — • Check for poor connections or loose wires.
• Substitute a known-good TCS control unit and recheck.

NO — Turn the ignition switch OFF.

Disconnect the 14P connector from the ABS control unit.

Turn the ignition switch ON.

Measure the voltage between the TCS control unit 16P connector terminals (+) and body ground:
No. 8B: Right front
No. 6B: Left front
No. 4B: Right rear
No. 2B: Left rear

Is there approx. 5 V?

YES — Turn the ignition switch OFF.

A — Go To DTC 4-1 To 4-8 (3 of 3)

NO — Turn the ignition switch OFF.

Disconnect the 16P connector from the TCS control unit.

B — Go To DTC 4-1 To 4-8 (3 of 3)

NOTE:
• Use the 10 V range or a similar range in the analog tester.
• Confirm that the analog tester needle swings to approx. 2 V.
5 V ----
0 V ----

DTC 4-9 (1 OF 2)
ALL WHEEL SPEED SENSORS

Diagnostic Trouble Code (DTC) 4-9: All wheel sensors

NOTE: The TCS indicator light comes on if all wheel speed signals from the ABS control unit stop for more than five seconds while the engine is running.

Remove the ABS B2 (15 A) fuse in the under-hood fuse/relay box for more than 3 seconds to reset the TCS control unit and ABS control unit.

Start the engine.

Check for TCS trouble codes

Is code 4-9 indicated?

NO → Intermittent failure. Check for poor connections or loose wires.

YES

Check the ABS indicator light.

Is the ABS indicator light ON?

YES → Perform appropriate ABS trouble code test (See ANTI-LOCK article).

NO

Measure the voltage between the TCS control unit 16P connector terminals (+) and body ground with the wheels stopped.
No. 8B: Right front
No. 6B: Left front
No. 4B: Right rear
No. 2B: Left rear

Is there approx. 5 V?

NO → Check for poor connections or loose wires. Substitute a known-good TCS control unit and recheck.

YES

Go to DTC 4-9 (2 of 2)

94C47466

DTC 4-1 To 4-8 (3 OF 3)
INDIVIDUAL WHEEL SPEED SENSOR

Continued From DTC 4-1 To 4-8 (2 of 3)

Continued From DTC 4-1 To 4-8 (2 of 3)

B

Check for continuity between the 16P connector terminals and body ground:
No. 8B: Right front
No. 6B: Left front
No. 4B: Right rear
No. 2B: Left rear

Is there continuity?

NO → Check for poor connections or loose wires. Substitute a known-good TCS control unit and recheck.

YES

Repair short in wire between the TCS control unit and ABS control unit:
GRN: Right front
GRN/BRN: Left front
GRN/ORN: Right rear
LT GRN: Left rear

A

Measure the voltage between the ABS control unit 14P connector terminals (+) and body ground:
No. 5: Left front
No. 6: Right front
No. 13: Right rear
No. 14: Left rear

Is there approx. 5 V?

YES → Check for poor connections or loose wires. Substitute a known-good ABS control unit and recheck.

NO

Repair open in wire between the TCS control unit and ABS control unit:
GRN: Right front
GRN/BRN: Left front
GRN/ORN: Right rear
LT GRN: Left rear

94B47465

Courtesy of American Honda Motor Co., Inc.

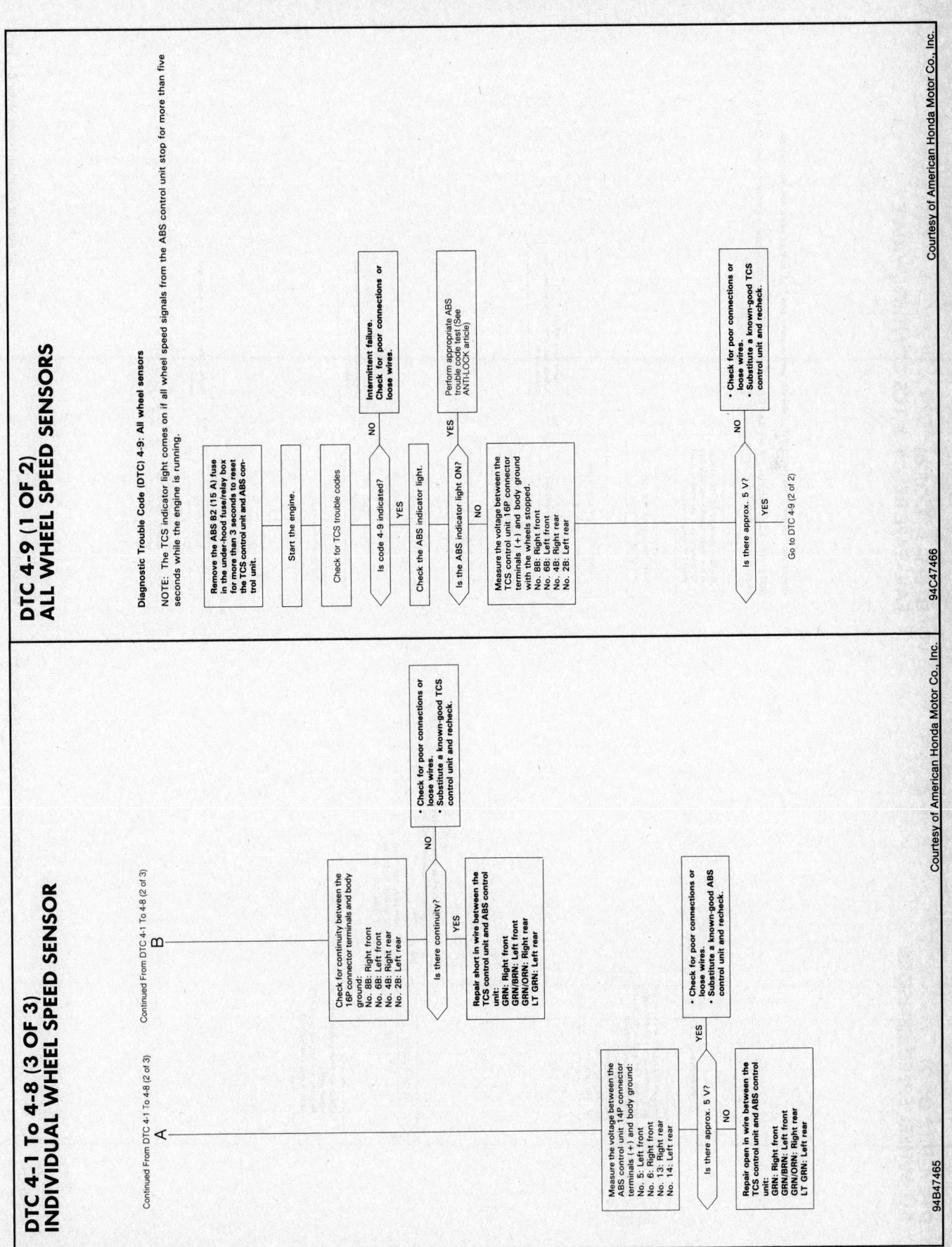

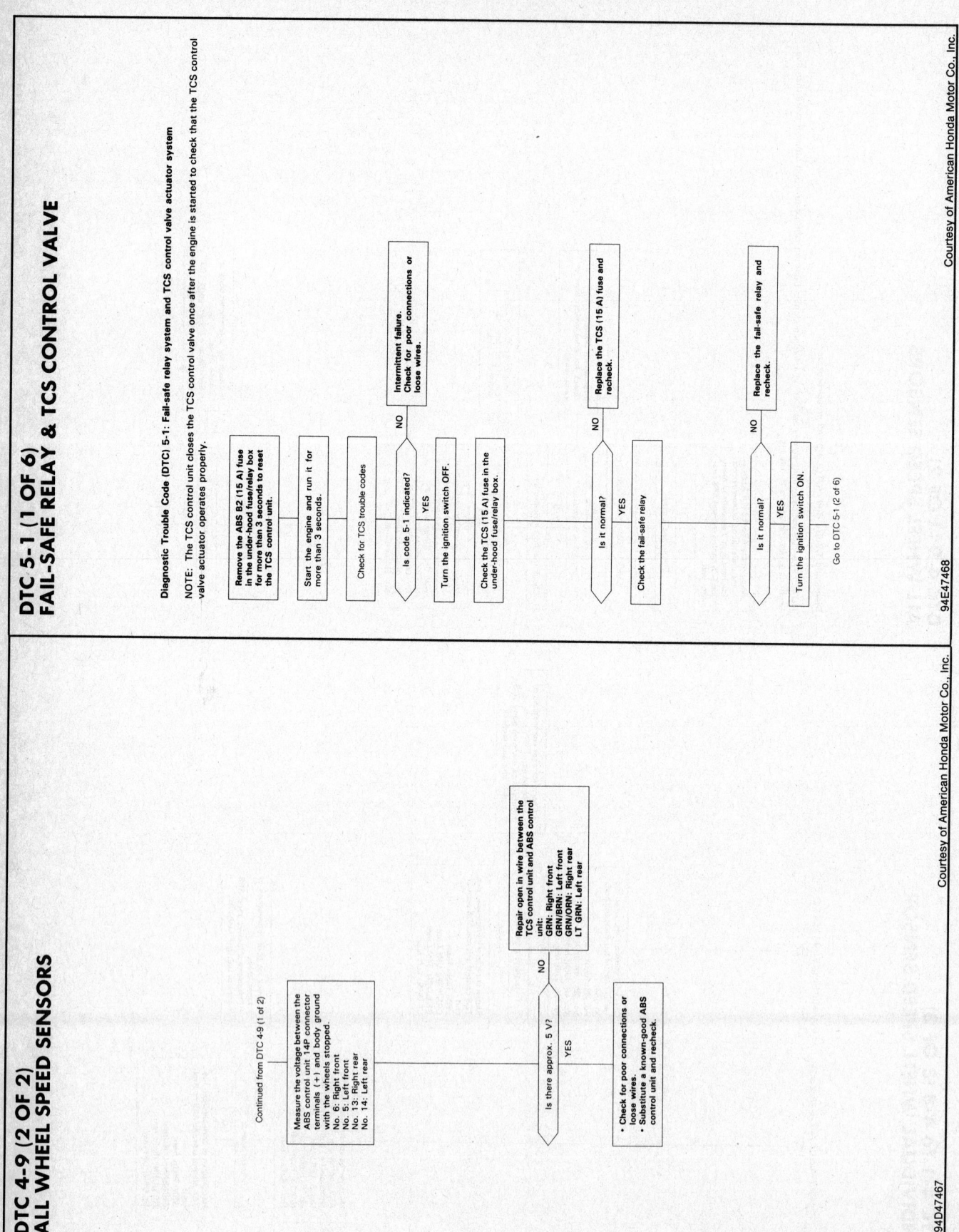

DTC 5-1 (1 OF 6) FAIL-SAFE RELAY & TCS CONTROL VALVE

Diagnostic Trouble Code (DTC) 5-1: Fail-safe relay system and TCS control valve actuator system

NOTE: The TCS control unit closes the TCS control valve once after the engine is started to check that the TCS control valve actuator operates properly.

- Remove the ABS B2 (15 A) fuse in the under-hood fuse/relay box for more than 3 seconds to reset the TCS control unit.
- Start the engine and run it for more than 3 seconds.
- Check for TCS trouble codes

Is code 5-1 indicated? → NO → Intermittent failure. Check for poor connections or loose wires.

YES

- Turn the ignition switch OFF.
- Check the TCS (15 A) fuse in the under-hood fuse/relay box.

Is it normal? → NO → Replace the TCS (15 A) fuse and recheck.

YES

- Check the fail-safe relay

Is it normal? → NO → Replace the fail-safe relay and recheck.

YES

- Turn the ignition switch ON.

Go to DTC 5-1 (2 of 6)

94E47468

DTC 4-9 (2 OF 2) ALL WHEEL SPEED SENSORS

Continued from DTC 4-9 (1 of 2)

- Measure the voltage between the ABS control unit 14P connector terminals (+) and body ground with the wheels stopped.
  No. 6: Right front
  No. 5: Left front
  No. 13: Right rear
  No. 14: Left rear

Is there approx. 5 V? → NO → Repair open in wire between the TCS control unit and ABS control unit:
GRN: Right front
GRN/BRN: Left front
GRN/ORN: Right rear
LT GRN: Left rear

YES

- Check for poor connections or loose wires.
- Substitute a known-good ABS control unit and recheck.

94D47467

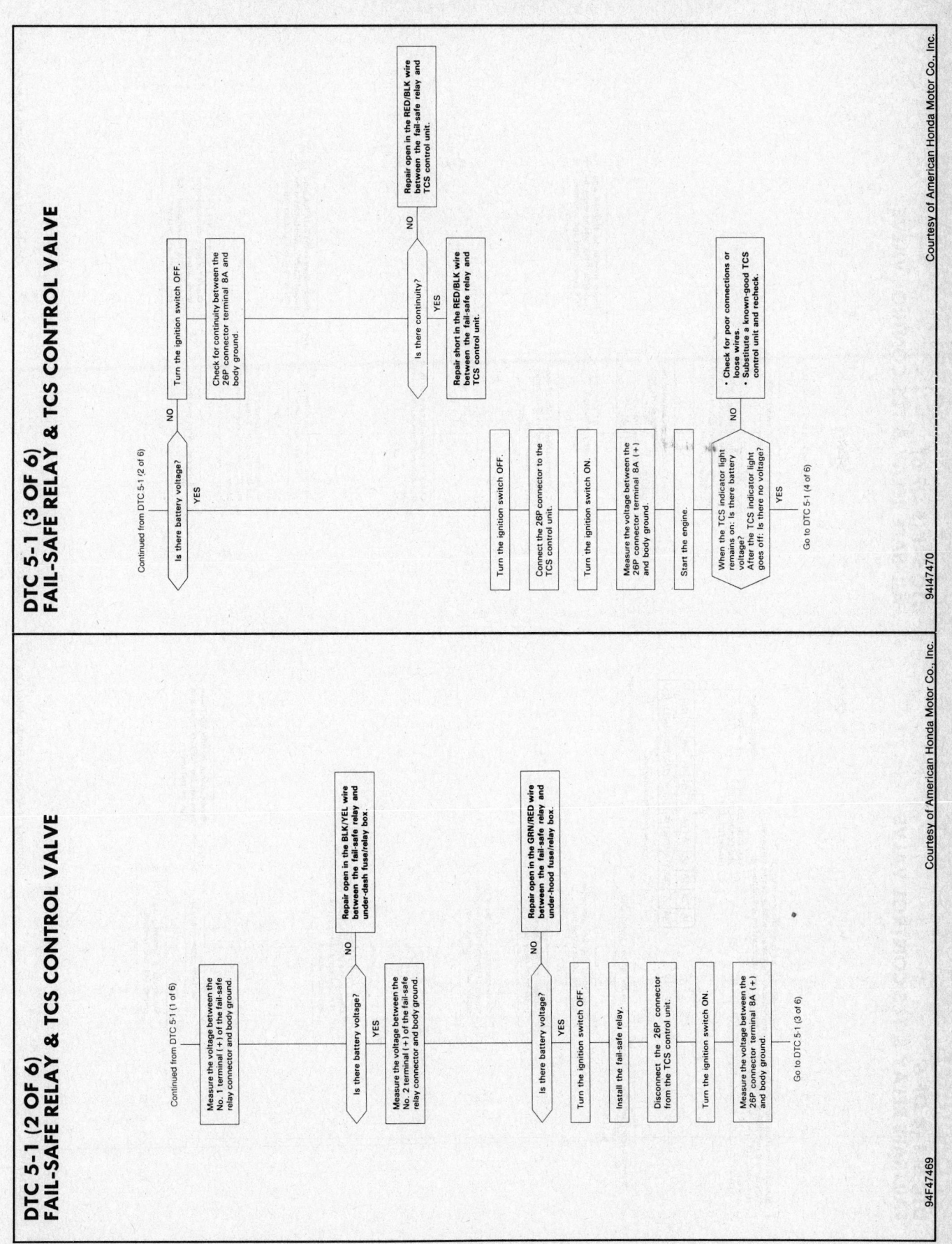

DTC 5-1 (2 OF 6)
FAIL-SAFE RELAY & TCS CONTROL VALVE

Continued from DTC 5-1 (1 of 6)

Measure the voltage between the No. 1 terminal (+) of the fail-safe relay connector and body ground.

Is there battery voltage?

NO → Repair open in the BLK/YEL wire between the fail-safe relay and under-dash fuse/relay box.

YES

Measure the voltage between the No. 2 terminal (+) of the fail-safe relay connector and body ground.

Is there battery voltage?

NO → Repair open in the GRN/RED wire between the fail-safe relay and under-hood fuse/relay box.

YES

Turn the ignition switch OFF.

Install the fail-safe relay.

Disconnect the 26P connector from the TCS control unit.

Turn the ignition switch ON.

Measure the voltage between the 26P connector terminal 8A (+) and body ground.

Go to DTC 5-1 (3 of 6)

94F47469

Courtesy of American Honda Motor Co., Inc.

DTC 5-1 (3 OF 6)
FAIL-SAFE RELAY & TCS CONTROL VALVE

Continued from DTC 5-1 (2 of 6)

Is there battery voltage?

NO → Turn the ignition switch OFF.

Check for continuity between the 26P connector terminal 8A and body ground.

Is there continuity?

NO → Repair open in the RED/BLK wire between the fail-safe relay and TCS control unit.

YES

Repair short in the RED/BLK wire between the fail-safe relay and TCS control unit.

YES

Turn the ignition switch OFF.

Connect the 26P connector to the TCS control unit.

Turn the ignition switch ON.

Measure the voltage between the 26P connector terminal 8A (+) and body ground.

Start the engine.

When the TCS indicator light remains on: Is there battery voltage?
After the TCS indicator light goes off: Is there no voltage?

NO → • Check for poor connections or loose wires.
• Substitute a known-good TCS control unit and recheck.

YES

Go to DTC 5-1 (4 of 6)

94F47470

Courtesy of American Honda Motor Co., Inc.

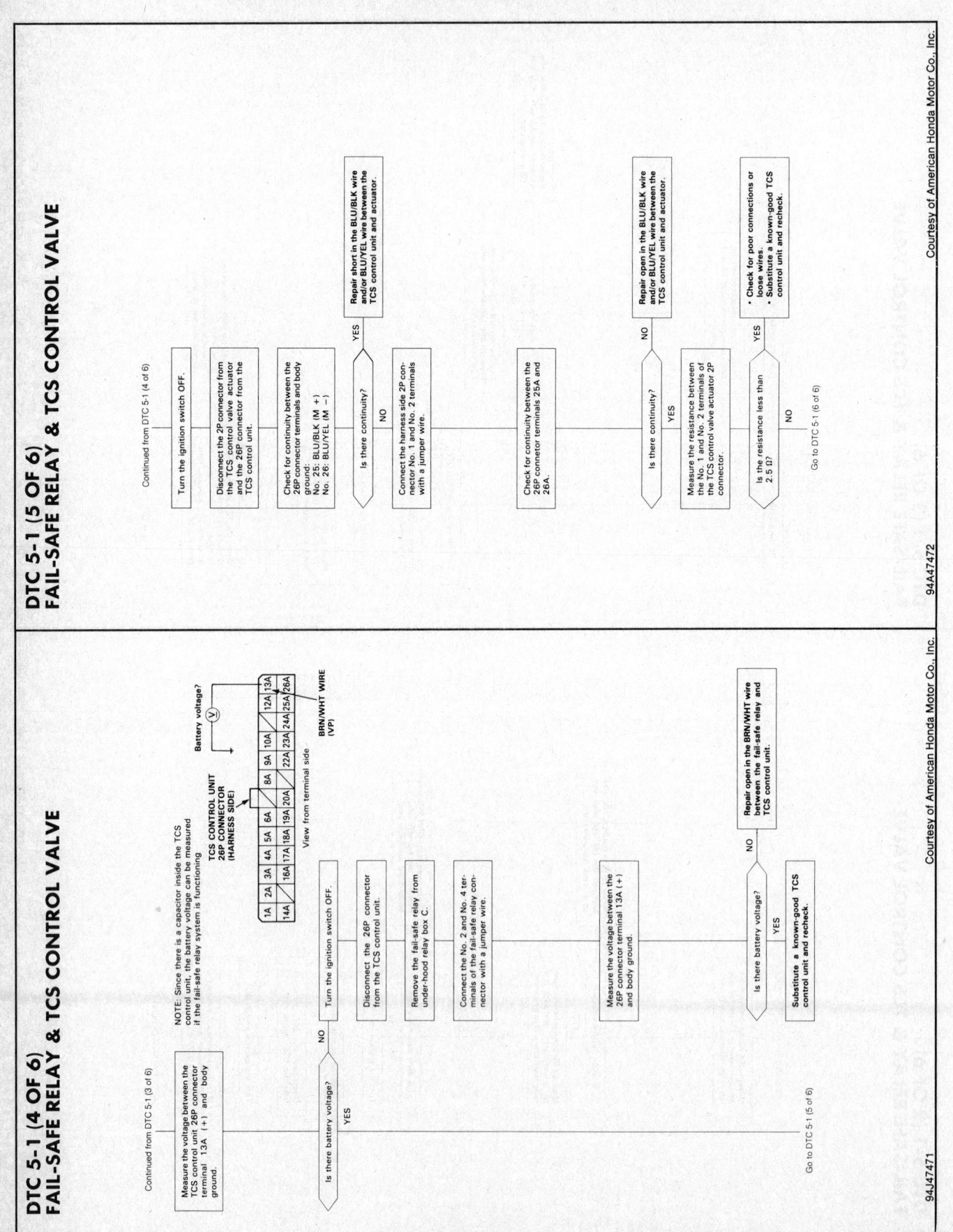

DTC 5-1 (4 OF 6)
FAIL-SAFE RELAY & TCS CONTROL VALVE

Continued from DTC 5-1 (3 of 6)

Measure the voltage between the TCS control unit 26P connector terminal 13A (+) and body ground.

NOTE: Since there is a capacitor inside the TCS control unit, the battery voltage can be measured if the fail-safe relay system is functioning.

Battery voltage?

TCS CONTROL UNIT
26P CONNECTOR
(HARNESS SIDE)

| 1A | 2A | 3A | 4A | 5A | 6A | | 8A | 9A | 10A | | 12A | 13A |
| 14A | | 16A | 17A | 18A | 19A | 20A | | 22A | 23A | 24A | 25A | 26A |

BRN/WHT WIRE
(VP)

View from terminal side

Is there battery voltage?

NO → Turn the ignition switch OFF.

Disconnect the 26P connector from the TCS control unit.

Remove the fail-safe relay from under-hood relay box C.

Connect the No. 2 and No. 4 terminals of the fail-safe relay connector with a jumper wire.

Measure the voltage between the 26P connector terminal 13A (+) and body ground.

Is there battery voltage?

NO → Repair open in the BRN/WHT wire between the fail-safe relay and TCS control unit.

YES → Substitute a known-good TCS control unit and recheck.

YES →

Go to DTC 5-1 (5 of 6)

94J47471

Courtesy of American Honda Motor Co., Inc.

DTC 5-1 (5 OF 6)
FAIL-SAFE RELAY & TCS CONTROL VALVE

Continued from DTC 5-1 (4 of 6)

Turn the ignition switch OFF.

Disconnect the 2P connector from the TCS control valve actuator and the 26P connector from the TCS control unit.

Check for continuity between the 26P connector terminals and body ground:
No. 25: BLU/BLK (M +)
No. 26: BLU/YEL (M −)

Is there continuity?

YES → Repair short in the BLU/BLK wire and/or BLU/YEL wire between the TCS control unit and actuator.

NO →

Connect the harness side 2P connector No. 1 and No. 2 terminals with a jumper wire.

Check for continuity between the 26P connector terminals 25A and 26A.

Is there continuity?

NO → Repair open in the BLU/BLK wire and/or BLU/YEL wire between the TCS control unit and actuator.

YES →

Measure the resistance between the No. 1 and No. 2 terminals of the TCS control valve actuator 2P connector.

Is the resistance less than 2.5 Ω?

YES → • Check for poor connections or loose wires.
• Substitute a known-good TCS control unit and recheck.

NO →

Go to DTC 5-1 (6 of 6)

94A47472

Courtesy of American Honda Motor Co., Inc.

DTC 5-1 (6 OF 6)
FAIL-SAFE RELAY & TCS CONTROL VALVE

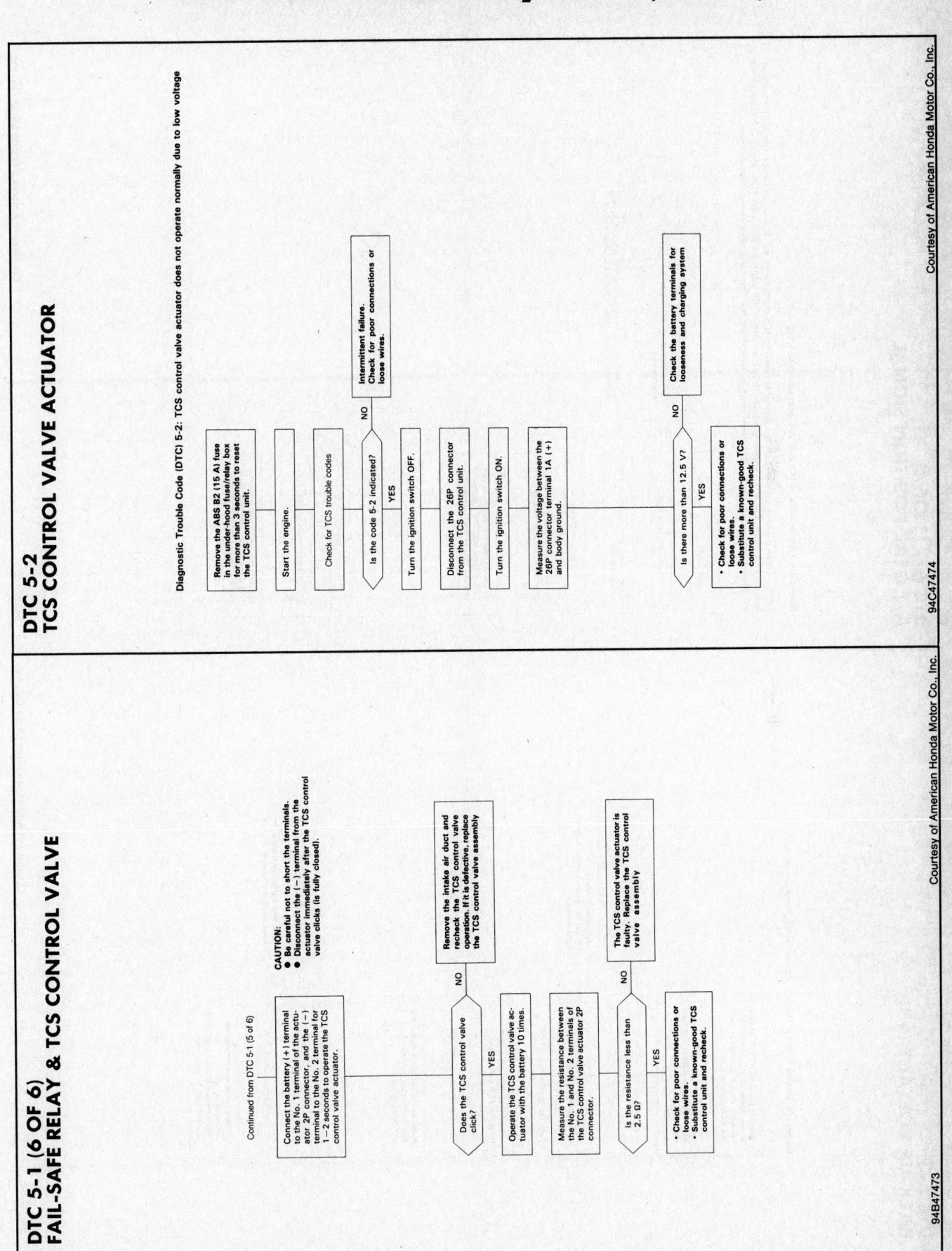

Continued from DTC 5-1 (5 of 6)

Connect the battery (+) terminal to the No. 1 terminal of the actuator 2P connector, and the (−) terminal to the No. 2 terminal for 1—2 seconds to operate the TCS control valve actuator.

CAUTION:
- Be careful not to short the terminals.
- Disconnect the (−) terminal from the actuator immediately after the TCS control valve clicks (is fully closed).

Does the TCS control valve click?

NO → Remove the intake air duct and recheck the TCS control valve operation. If it is defective, replace the TCS control valve assembly

YES

Operate the TCS control valve actuator with the battery 10 times.

Measure the resistance between the No. 1 and No. 2 terminals of the TCS control valve actuator 2P connector.

Is the resistance less than 2.5 Ω?

NO → The TCS control valve actuator is faulty. Replace the TCS control valve assembly

YES

- Check for poor connections or loose wires.
- Substitute a known-good TCS control unit and recheck.

94B47473

DTC 5-2
TCS CONTROL VALVE ACTUATOR

Diagnostic Trouble Code (DTC) 5-2: TCS control valve actuator does not operate normally due to low voltage

Remove the ABS B2 (15 A) fuse in the under-hood fuse/relay box for more than 3 seconds to reset the TCS control unit.

Start the engine.

Check for TCS trouble codes

Is the code 5-2 indicated?

NO → Intermittent failure. Check for poor connections or loose wires.

YES

Turn the ignition switch OFF.

Disconnect the 26P connector from the TCS control unit.

Turn the ignition switch ON.

Measure the voltage between the 26P connector terminal 1A (+) and body ground.

Is there more than 12.5 V?

NO → Check the battery terminals for looseness and charging system

YES

- Check for poor connections or loose wires.
- Substitute a known-good TCS control unit and recheck.

94C47474

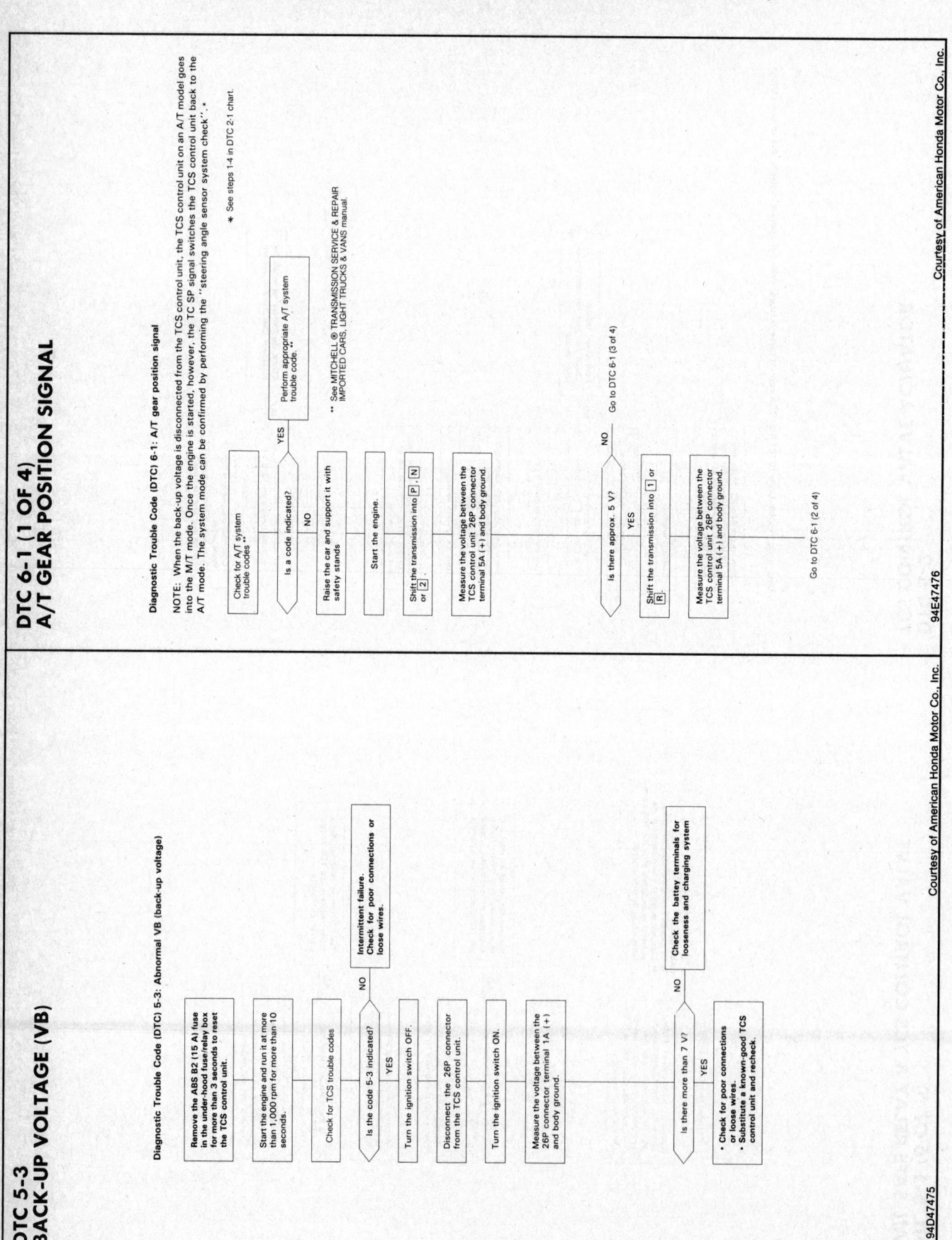

DTC 6-1 (1 OF 4)
A/T GEAR POSITION SIGNAL

Diagnostic Trouble Code (DTC) 6-1: A/T gear position signal

NOTE: When the back-up voltage is disconnected from the TCS control unit, the TCS control unit on an A/T model goes into the M/T mode. Once the engine is started, however, the TC SP signal switches the TCS control unit back to the A/T mode. The system mode can be confirmed by performing the "steering angle sensor system check". *

```
Check for A/T system
trouble codes **

        │

Is a code indicated?  ──YES──►  Perform appropriate A/T system
                                trouble code. **
        │
        NO

Raise the car and support it with
safety stands

        │

Start the engine.

        │

Shift the transmission into [P], [N]
or [2]

        │

Measure the voltage between the
TCS control unit 26P connector
terminal 5A (+) and body ground.

        │

Is there approx. 5 V?  ──NO──►  Go to DTC 6-1 (3 of 4)
        │
        YES

Shift the transmission into [1] or
[R].

        │

Measure the voltage between the
TCS control unit 26P connector
terminal 5A (+) and body ground.

        │

Go to DTC 6-1 (2 of 4)
```

* See steps 1-4 in DTC 2-1 chart.

** See MITCHELL® TRANSMISSION SERVICE & REPAIR IMPORTED CARS, LIGHT TRUCKS & VANS manual.

94E47476

DTC 5-3
BACK-UP VOLTAGE (VB)

Diagnostic Trouble Code (DTC) 5-3: Abnormal VB (back-up voltage)

```
Remove the ABS B2 (15 A) fuse
in the under-hood fuse/relay box
for more than 3 seconds to reset
the TCS control unit.

        │

Start the engine and run it at more
than 1,000 rpm for more than 10
seconds.

        │

Check for TCS trouble codes

        │

Is the code 5-3 indicated?  ──NO──►  Intermittent failure.
        │                            Check for poor connections or
        YES                          loose wires.

Turn the ignition switch OFF.

        │

Disconnect the 26P connector
from the TCS control unit.

        │

Turn the ignition switch ON.

        │

Measure the voltage between the
26P connector terminal 1A (+)
and body ground.

        │

Is there more than 7 V?  ──NO──►  Check the battery terminals for
        │                         looseness and charging system
        YES

• Check for poor connections
  or loose wires.
• Substitute a known-good TCS
  control unit and recheck.
```

94D47475

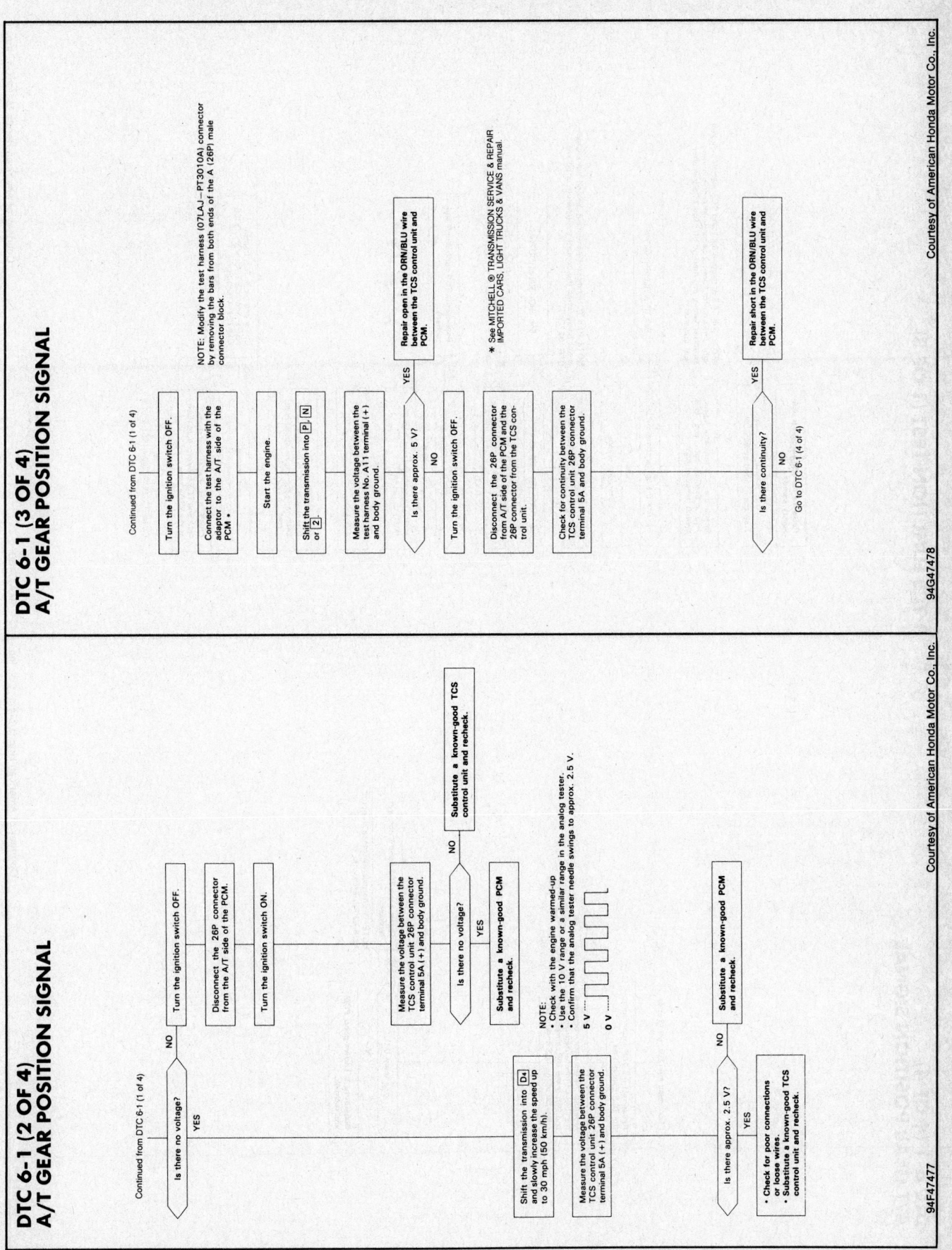

DTC 6-1 (2 OF 4)
A/T GEAR POSITION SIGNAL

Continued from DTC 6-1 (1 of 4)

Is there no voltage?

NO → Turn the ignition switch OFF.

Disconnect the 26P connector from the A/T side of the PCM.

Turn the ignition switch ON.

Measure the voltage between the TCS control unit 26P connector terminal 5A (+) and body ground.

Is there no voltage?

NO → Substitute a known-good TCS control unit and recheck.

YES → Substitute a known-good PCM and recheck.

NOTE:
• Check with the engine warmed-up
• Use the 10 V range or a similar range in the analog tester.
• Confirm that the analog tester needle swings to approx. 2.5 V.

5 V
0 V

YES

Shift the transmission into D4 and slowly increase the speed up to 30 mph (50 km/h).

Measure the voltage between the TCS control unit 26P connector terminal 5A (+) and body ground.

Is there approx. 2.5 V?

NO → Substitute a known-good PCM and recheck.

YES → • Check for poor connections or loose wires.
• Substitute a known-good TCS control unit and recheck.

94F47477   Courtesy of American Honda Motor Co., Inc.

DTC 6-1 (3 OF 4)
A/T GEAR POSITION SIGNAL

Continued from DTC 6-1 (1 of 4)

Turn the ignition switch OFF.

Connect the test harness with the adaptor to the A/T side of the PCM. *

Start the engine.

Shift the transmission into P, N or 2.

Measure the voltage between the test harness No. A11 terminal (+) and body ground.

Is there approx. 5 V?

YES → Repair open in the ORN/BLU wire between the TCS control unit and PCM.

NO

Turn the ignition switch OFF.

Disconnect the 26P connector from A/T side of the PCM and the 26P connector from the TCS control unit.

Check for continuity between the TCS control unit 26P connector terminal 5A and body ground.

Is there continuity?

YES → Repair short in the ORN/BLU wire between the TCS control unit and PCM.

NO

Go to DTC 6-1 (4 of 4)

NOTE: Modify the test harness (07LAJ—PT3010A) connector by removing the bars from both ends of the A (26P) male connector block.

* See MITCHELL ® TRANSMISSION SERVICE & REPAIR IMPORTED CARS, LIGHT TRUCKS & VANS manual.

94G47478   Courtesy of American Honda Motor Co., Inc.

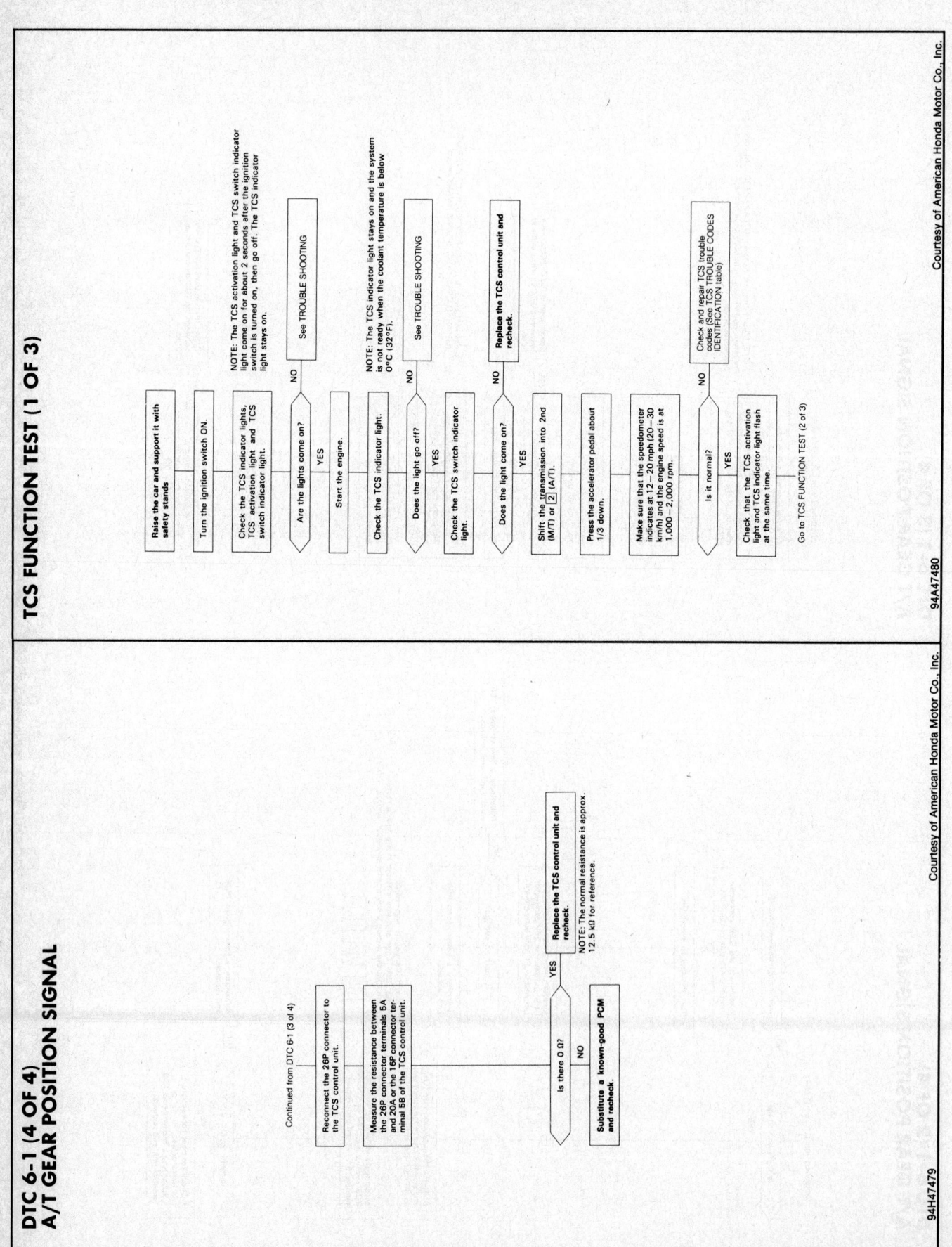

TCS FUNCTION TEST (1 OF 3)

Raise the car and support it with safety stands

Turn the ignition switch ON.

Check the TCS indicator lights, TCS activation light and TCS switch indicator light.

Are the lights come on? — NO → See TROUBLE SHOOTING

NOTE: The TCS activation light and TCS switch indicator light come on for about 2 seconds after the ignition switch is turned on, then go off. The TCS indicator light stays on.

YES

Start the engine.

Check the TCS indicator light.

Does the light go off? — NO → See TROUBLE SHOOTING

NOTE: The TCS indicator light stays on and the system is not ready when the coolant temperature is below 0°C (32°F).

YES

Check the TCS switch indicator light.

Does the light come on? — NO → Replace the TCS control unit and recheck.

YES

Shift the transmission into 2nd (M/T) or ② (A/T).

Press the accelerator pedal about 1/3 down.

Make sure that the speedometer indicates at 12—20 mph (20—30 km/h) and the engine speed is at 1,000—2,000 rpm.

Is it normal? — NO → Check and repair TCS trouble codes (See TCS TROUBLE CODES IDENTIFICATION table)

YES

Check that the TCS activation light and TCS indicator light flash at the same time.

Go to TCS FUNCTION TEST (2 of 3)

94A47480

DTC 6-1 (4 OF 4)
A/T GEAR POSITION SIGNAL

Continued from DTC 6-1 (3 of 4)

Reconnect the 26P connector to the TCS control unit.

Measure the resistance between the 26P connector terminals 5A and 20A or the 16P connector terminal 5B of the TCS control unit.

Is there 0 Ω? — NO → Substitute a known-good PCM and recheck.

YES

Replace the TCS control unit and recheck.

NOTE: The normal resistance is approx. 12.5 kΩ for reference.

94H47479

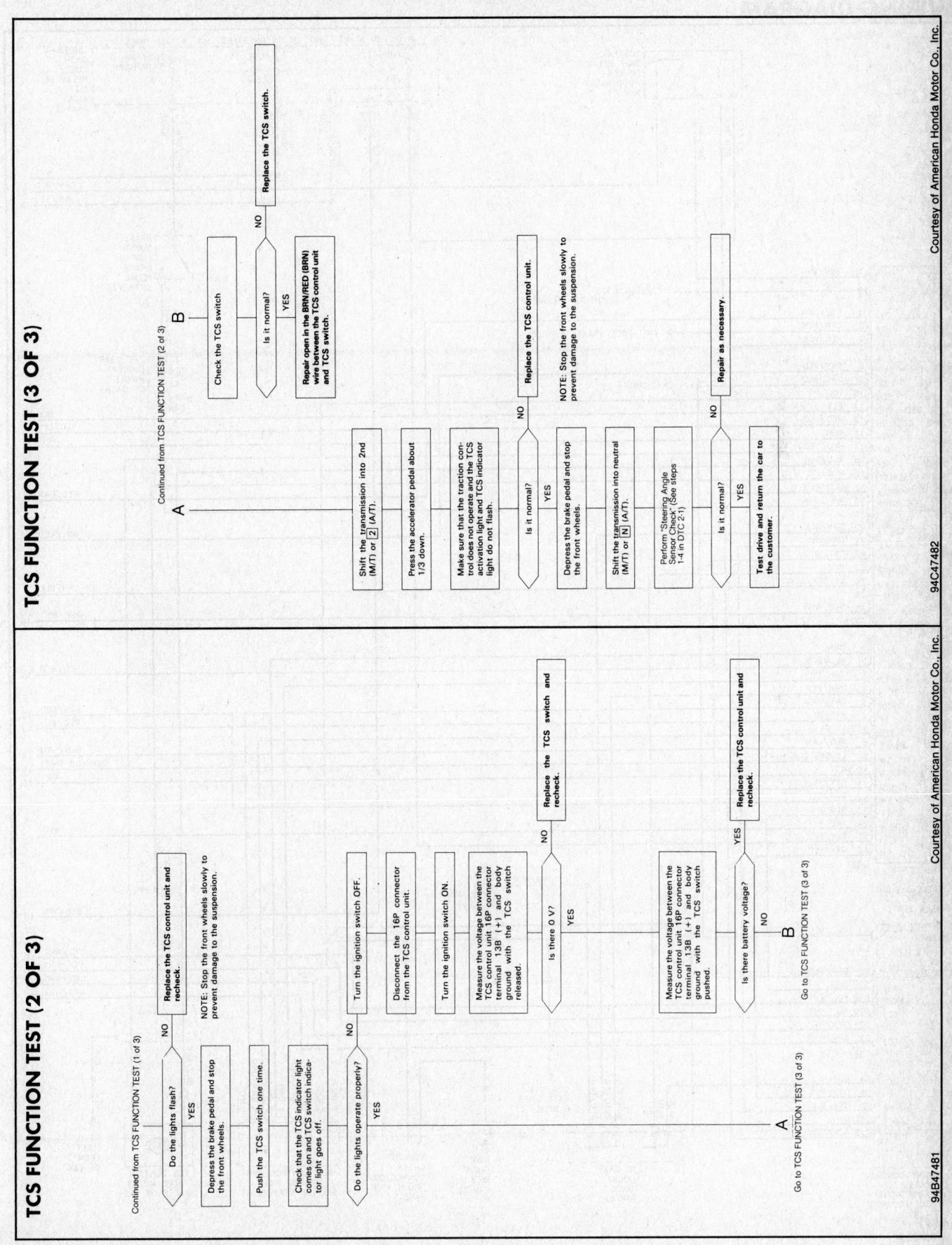

TCS FUNCTION TEST (3 OF 3)

Continued from TCS FUNCTION TEST (2 of 3)

B

Check the TCS switch

Is it normal?

NO → Replace the TCS switch.

YES

Repair open in the BRN/RED (BRN) wire between the TCS control unit and TCS switch.

A

Shift the transmission into 2nd (M/T) or ② (A/T).

Press the accelerator pedal about 1/3 down.

Make sure that the traction control does not operate and the TCS activation light and TCS indicator light do not flash.

Is it normal?

NO → Replace the TCS control unit.

YES

Depress the brake pedal and stop the front wheels.

NOTE: Stop the front wheels slowly to prevent damage to the suspension.

Shift the transmission into neutral (M/T) or Ⓝ (A/T).

Perform "Steering Angle Sensor Check" (See steps 1-4 in DTC 2-1)

Is it normal?

NO → Repair as necessary.

YES

Test drive and return the car to the customer.

TCS FUNCTION TEST (2 OF 3)

Continued from TCS FUNCTION TEST (1 of 3)

Do the lights flash?

NO → Replace the TCS control unit and recheck.

YES

NOTE: Stop the front wheels slowly to prevent damage to the suspension.

Depress the brake pedal and stop the front wheels.

Push the TCS switch one time.

Check that the TCS indicator light comes on and TCS switch indicator light goes off.

Do the lights operate properly?

NO → Turn the ignition switch OFF.

Disconnect the 16P connector from the TCS control unit.

Turn the ignition switch ON.

Measure the voltage between the TCS control unit 16P connector terminal 13B (+) and body ground with the TCS switch released.

Is there 0 V?

NO → Replace the TCS switch and recheck.

YES

Measure the voltage between the TCS control unit 16P connector terminal 13B (+) and body ground with the TCS switch pushed.

Is there battery voltage?

YES → Replace the TCS control unit and recheck.

NO

B

Go to TCS FUNCTION TEST (3 of 3)

YES

A

Go to TCS FUNCTION TEST (3 of 3)

94C47482

94B47481

WIRING DIAGRAM

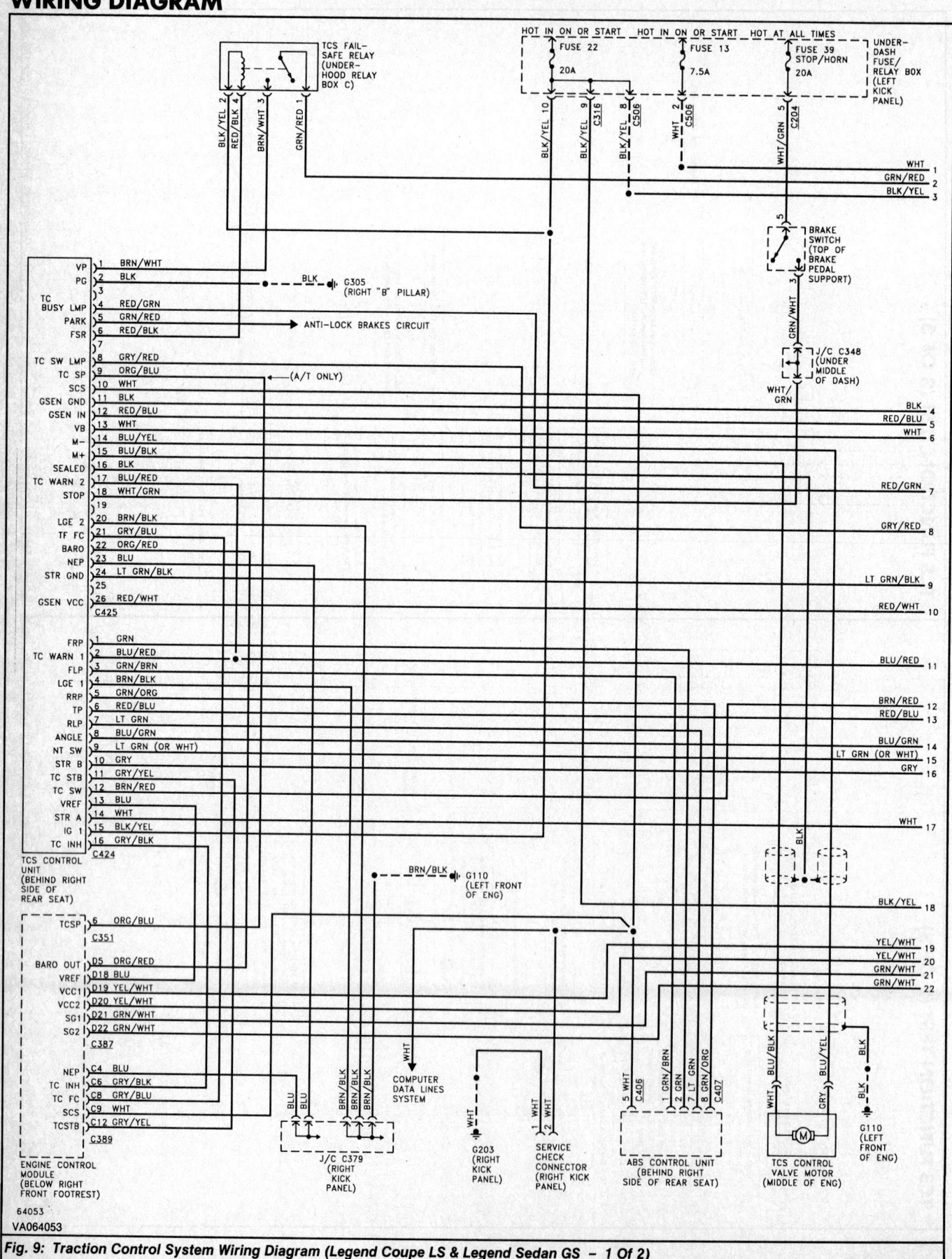

64053
VA064053

Fig. 9: Traction Control System Wiring Diagram (Legend Coupe LS & Legend Sedan GS - 1 Of 2)

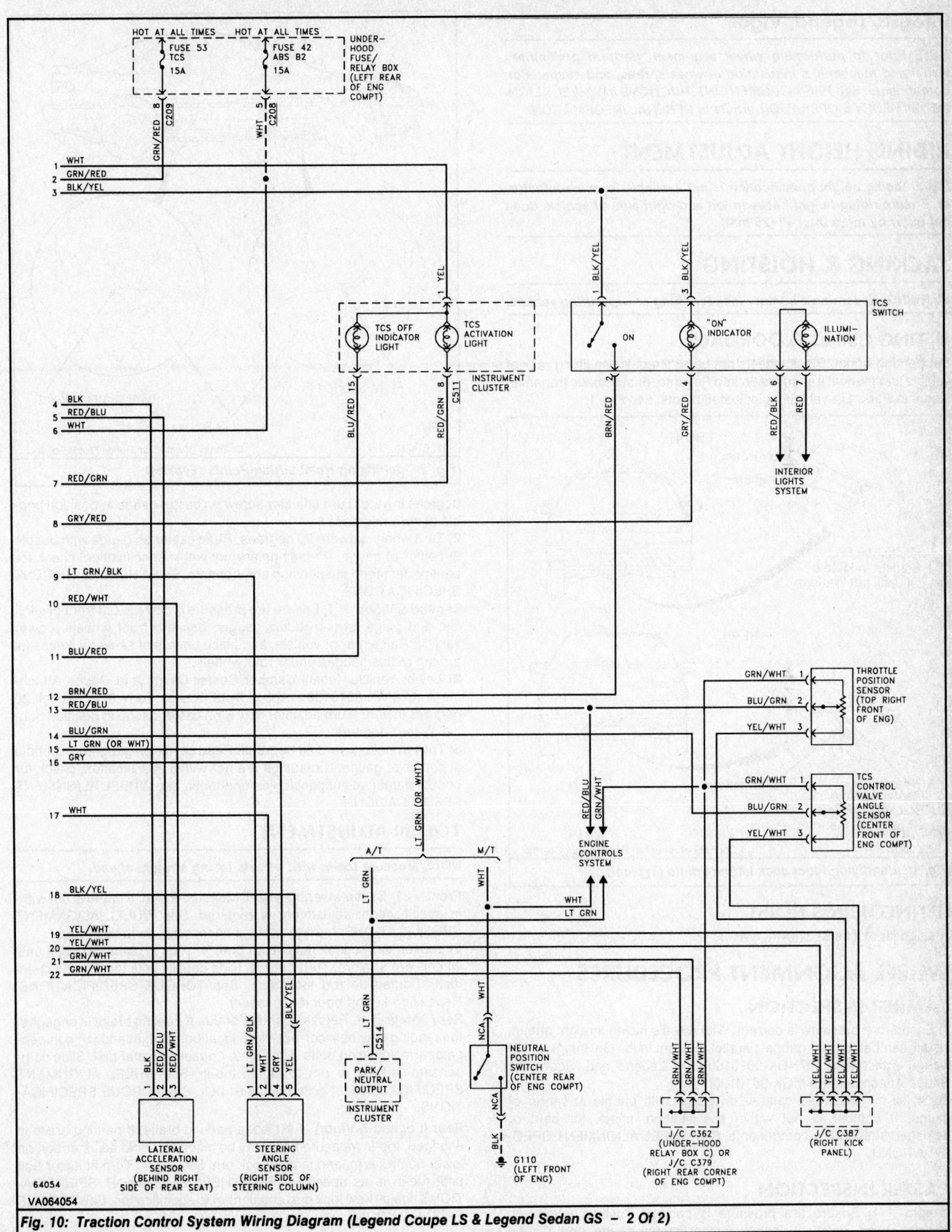

Fig. 10: Traction Control System Wiring Diagram (Legend Coupe LS & Legend Sedan GS — 2 Of 2)

64054
VA064054

1994 WHEEL ALIGNMENT
Specifications & Procedures

Integra, Legend, Vigor

NOTE: Prior to performing wheel alignment, perform preliminary visual and mechanical inspection of wheels, tires, and suspension components. See PRE-ALIGNMENT INSTRUCTIONS in WHEEL ALIGNMENT THEORY & OPERATION article in GENERAL INFORMATION.

RIDING HEIGHT ADJUSTMENT

NOTE: Riding height specification is not available from manufacturer. Ensure riding height between left and right side of vehicle does not differ by more than 1" (25 mm).

JACKING & HOISTING

WARNING: Never use a bumper jack for lifting or supporting vehicle.

LIFTING USING FLOOR JACK

Set parking brake. Block wheels not being lifted. When lifting rear of vehicle, set manual transmission into Reverse, or automatic transmission into Park. Lift vehicle at indicated points. *See Fig. 1.*

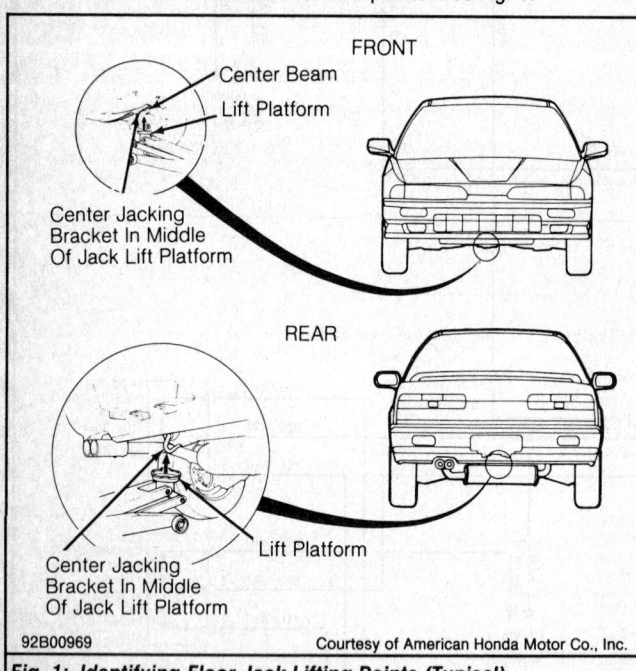

Fig. 1: Identifying Floor Jack Lifting Points (Typical)

LIFTING USING HOIST

Position lift blocks as shown. *See Fig. 2.*

WHEEL ALIGNMENT PROCEDURES

CAMBER INSPECTION

1) Ensure tire pressure is correct. With wheels facing straight ahead, install camber/caster gauge parallel to front hub. On Integra, use Gauge Attachment (07HGK-0010100). On Legend and Vigor, use Gauge Attachment (07MGK-0010100).

2) On all models, read camber on gauge with bubble at center of gauge. If camber is not within specification, check for bent or damaged suspension components. See WHEEL ALIGNMENT SPECIFICATIONS.

CASTER INSPECTION

Integra – 1) Ensure tire pressure is correct. Position wheels in straight-ahead position. Install camber/caster gauge and Gauge Attachment (07HGK-0010100). Apply front brake. Turn front wheel 20

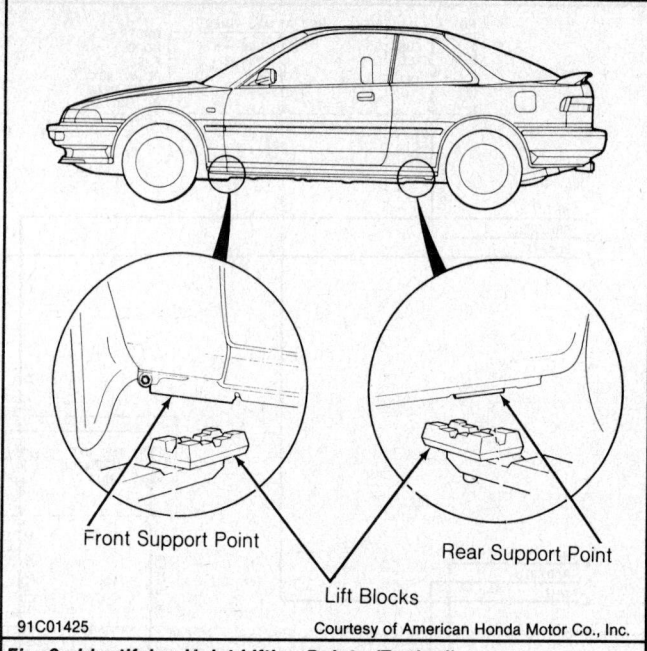

Fig. 2: Identifying Hoist Lifting Points (Typical)

degrees inward. Turn adjuster screw on caster gauge to position bubble at zero degrees.

2) Turn wheel outward 20 degrees. Read caster on gauge with bubble at center of gauge. If readings are not within specification, check for bent or damaged suspension components. See WHEEL ALIGNMENT SPECIFICATIONS.

Legend & Vigor – 1) Ensure tire pressure is correct. Lift front of vehicle, and place turning radius gauges beneath front wheels. Lower vehicle. Raise rear of vehicle, and place boards of same thickness as turning radius gauges under rear wheels.

2) Lower vehicle. Install Camber/Caster Gauge and Gauge Attachment (07MGK-0010100). Apply front brake. Turn front wheel 20 degrees inward. Turn adjuster screw on caster gauge to position bubble at zero degrees.

3) Turn wheel outward 20 degrees. Read caster on gauge with bubble at center of gauge. If readings are not within specification, check for bent or damaged suspension components. See WHEEL ALIGNMENT SPECIFICATIONS.

TOE-IN ADJUSTMENT

NOTE: Measure toe-in with wheels facing straight ahead.

Front – 1) Center steering wheel. Measure toe-in. If toe-in is not within specification, adjustment is required. See WHEEL ALIGNMENT SPECIFICATIONS. If adjustment is necessary, go to next step.

2) Loosen tie rod lock nuts. Turn both tie rods in same direction until wheels are straight. Turn both tie rods equally until toe-in is as specified. Tighten tie rod lock nuts. See TORQUE SPECIFICATIONS. Reposition tie rod boot if necessary.

Rear (Integra) – Release parking brake. If parking brake is engaged, toe reading may be incorrect. Note locations of right and left compensator arm adjusting bolts. *See Fig. 3.* Loosen adjuster bolt. Slide compensator arm in or out to adjust toe-in. See WHEEL ALIGNMENT SPECIFICATIONS. Tighten adjuster bolt. See TORQUE SPECIFICATIONS.

Rear (Legend & Vigor) – Release parking brake. If parking brake is engaged, toe-in measurement may be incorrect. Hold adjuster bolt on lower control arm, and loosen lock nut. *See Fig. 4.* Turn adjuster bolt until toe-in is as specified. See WHEEL ALIGNMENT SPECIFICATIONS. Install new lock nut, and tighten to specification. See TORQUE SPECIFICATIONS.

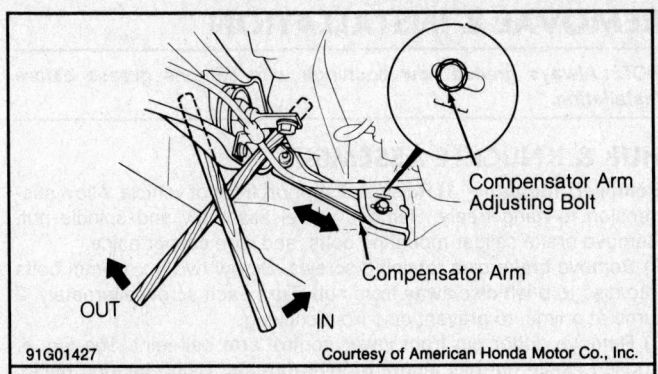

91G01427   Courtesy of American Honda Motor Co., Inc.

Fig. 3: Adjusting Rear Toe-In (Integra)

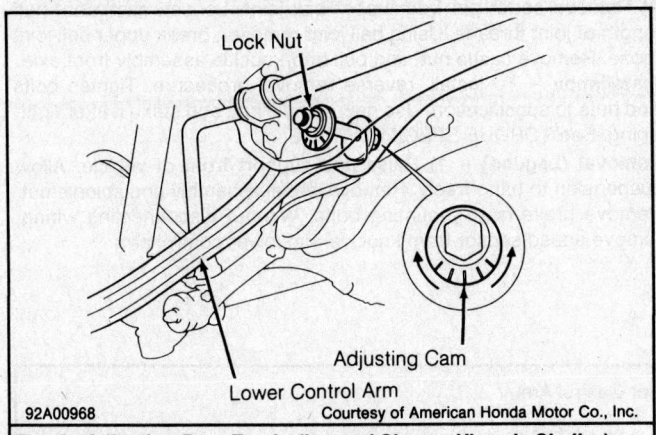

92A00968   Courtesy of American Honda Motor Co., Inc.

Fig. 4: Adjusting Rear Toe-In (Legend Shown; Vigor Is Similar)

TORQUE SPECIFICATIONS
TORQUE SPECIFICATIONS

Application	Ft. Lbs. (N.m)
Integra	
Compensator Arm Adjusting Bolt	48 (65)
Spindle Nut	
Front	136 (185)
Rear	136 (185)
Tie Rod Lock Nut	41 (55)
Wheel Lug Nut	81 (110)
Legend	
Radius Rod	63 (85)
Rear Control Arm Lock Nut	41 (55)
Spindle Nut	
Front	247 (335)
Rear	210 (285)
Tie Rod Lock Nut	33 (45)
Wheel Lug Nut	81 (110)
Vigor	
Radius Rod Lock Nut	32 (44)
Rear Control Arm	41 (55)
Spindle Nut	
Front	184 (250)
Rear	100 (134)
Tie Rod Lock Nut	33 (45)
Wheel Lug Nut	81 (110)

WHEEL ALIGNMENT SPECIFICATIONS
WHEEL ALIGNMENT SPECIFICATIONS

Application	Preferred	Range
Integra		
Camber [1]		
Front	0	– 1 To 1
Rear	– 0.67	– 1.67 To 0.33
Caster [1]		
Front	1.5	0.5 To 2.5
Toe-In [1]		
Front	0	– 0.16 To 0.16
Rear	0.16	0 To 0.24
Toe-In [2]		
Front	0 (0)	– 0.08 To 0.08 (– 2 To 2)
Rear	0.08 (2)	0 To 0.12 (0 To 3)
Toe-Out On Turns [1]		
Inner	40.5	N/A
Outer	32	N/A
Legend		
Camber [1]		
Front	0	– 1 To 1
Rear	– 0.33	1.33 To 0.67
Caster [1]		
Front	3.75	2.75 To 4.75
Toe-In [1]		
Front	– 0.08	– 0.24 To 0.08
Rear	0.16	0 To 0.32
Toe-In [2]		
Front	– 0.04 (– 1)	– 0.12 To 0.04 (– 3 To 1)
Rear	0.08 (2)	0 To 0.16 (0 To 4)
Toe-Out On Turns [1]		
Inner	44	N/A
Outer	35	N/A
Vigor		
Camber [1]		
Front	0	– 1 To 1
Rear	– 0.5	– 1.5 To 0.5
Caster [1]		
Front	1.63	0.63 To 2.63
Toe-In [1]		
Front	0	– 0.16 To 0.16
Rear	0.24	0.06 To 0.4
Toe-In [2]		
Front	0 (0)	– 0.08 To 0.08 (– 2 To 2)
Rear	0.12 (3)	0.04 To 0.2 (1 To 5)
Toe-Out On Turns [1]		
Inner	39.4	N/A
Outer	33.6	N/A

[1] – Measurements are in degrees.
[2] – Measurements are in inches (mm).

Integra, Legend, Vigor

CAUTION: Use extreme care when working around Supplemental Restraint System (SRS) wiring and components at front fenderwells. All SRS wiring harnesses and connectors are color-coded Yellow. DO NOT damage this wiring.

DESCRIPTION

All models use independent wishbone MacPherson strut front suspension. Vertically mounted strut assembly is attached to lower control arm by a fork assembly. *See Fig. 1, 2, or 3.* Steering knuckle is attached to upper and lower control arms by ball joints. A stabilizer bar and radius rod are attached to the lower control arm.

ADJUSTMENTS & INSPECTION

WHEEL ALIGNMENT SPECIFICATIONS & PROCEDURES

NOTE: See SPECIFICATIONS & PROCEDURES article in WHEEL ALIGNMENT.

WHEEL BEARINGS

Wheel bearings are not adjustable.

BALL JOINT CHECKING

Information is not available from manufacturer.

REMOVAL & INSTALLATION

NOTE: Always grease new bushings with silicone grease before installation.

HUB & KNUCKLE ASSEMBLY

Removal (Integra) – 1) Raise and support front of vehicle. Allow suspension to hang freely. Remove wheel assembly and spindle nut. Remove brake caliper mounting bolts, and wire caliper aside.
2) Remove brake disc retaining screws. Screw two 8 x 10-mm bolts into disc to push disc away from hub. Turn each screw alternately, 2 turns at a time, to prevent disc from cocking.
3) Remove cotter pin from lower control arm ball joint. *See Fig. 4.* Loosen castle nut half length of joint threads. Using bearing puller, break lower control arm ball joint loose.
4) Remove cotter pin from upper ball joint. Loosen castle nut half length of joint threads. Using ball joint remover, break upper ball joint loose. Remove castle nut, and pull hub/knuckle assembly from axle.
Installation – To install, reverse removal procedure. Tighten bolts and nuts to specification. Use new spindle nut, and stake it after tightening. See TORQUE SPECIFICATIONS.

Removal (Legend) – 1) Raise and support front of vehicle. Allow suspension to hang freely. Remove wheel assembly and spindle nut. Remove brake hose mounting bolts. Without disconnecting wiring, remove speed sensor from knuckle and lower control arm.

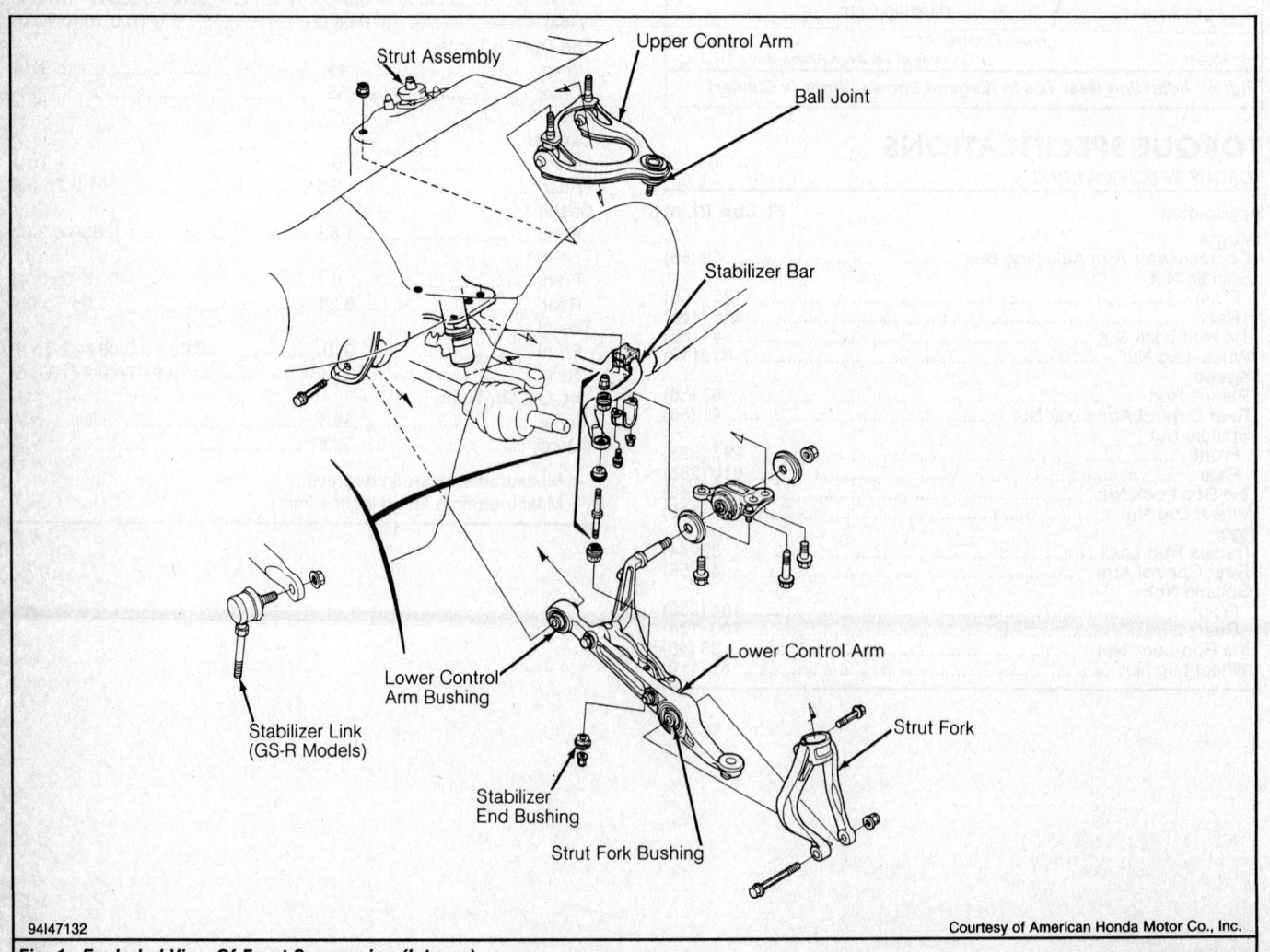

94I47132

Fig. 1: Exploded View Of Front Suspension (Integra)

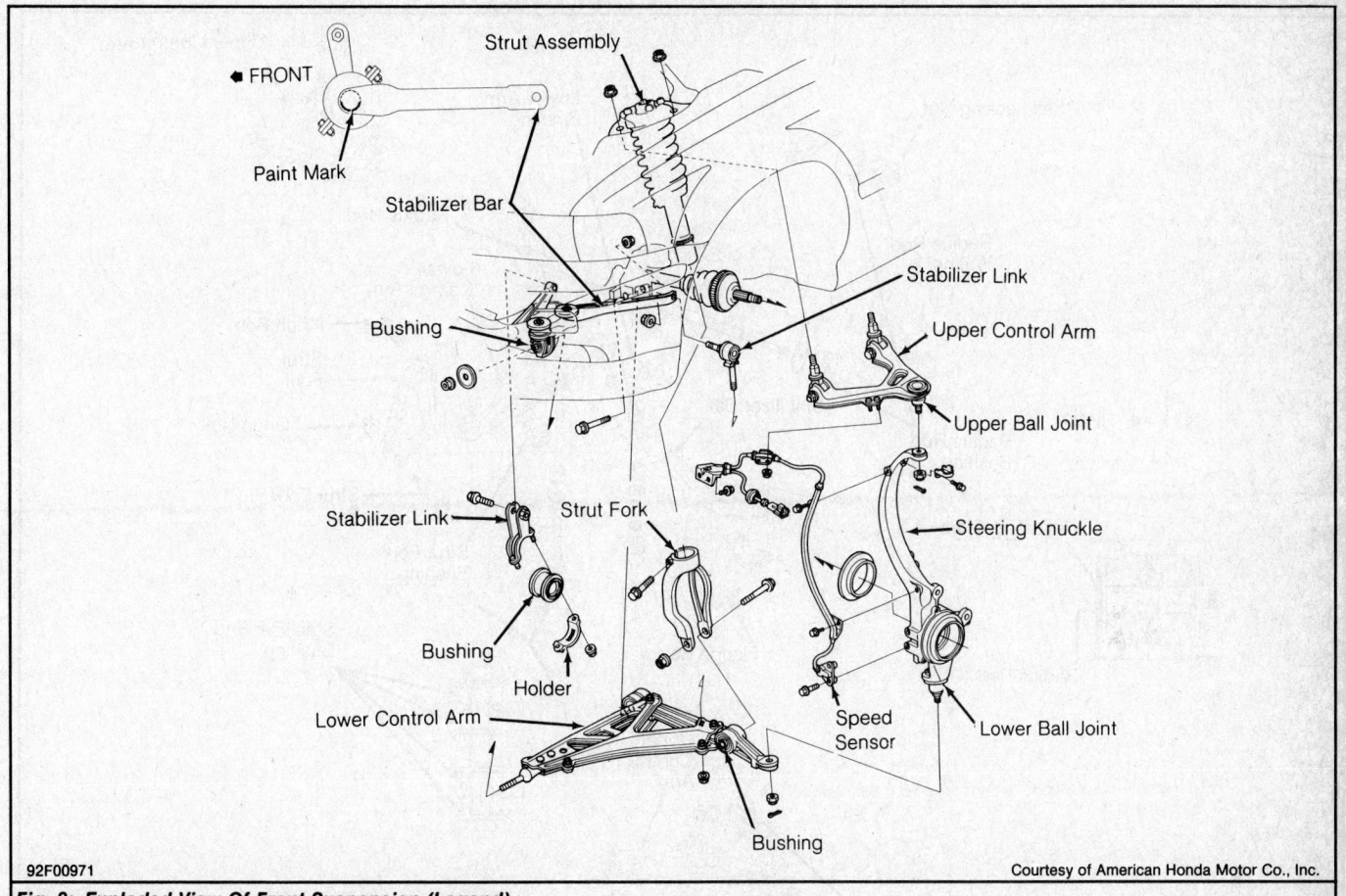

FRONT

Strut Assembly

Paint Mark

Stabilizer Bar

Bushing

Stabilizer Link

Upper Control Arm

Upper Ball Joint

Stabilizer Link

Strut Fork

Steering Knuckle

Bushing

Holder

Lower Control Arm

Speed Sensor

Lower Ball Joint

Bushing

92F00971

Courtesy of American Honda Motor Co., Inc.

Fig. 2: Exploded View Of Front Suspension (Legend)

2) Without disconnecting hydraulic hose, remove brake caliper and wire it aside. Remove brake disc retaining screws. Screw two 8 x 12-mm bolts into disc to push disc away from hub. Turn each screw alternately, 2 turns at a time, to prevent disc from cocking.

3) Remove cotter pin from tie rod ball joint, and remove castle nut. Using Ball Joint Remover (07MAC-SL00200), break tie rod ball joint loose. Separate tie rod from knuckle. Remove cotter pin from lower control arm ball joint, and loosen castle nut half length of joint threads.

4) Using bearing puller, break lower control arm ball joint loose. Remove castle nut, and pull arm down until ball joint is clear of knuckle. Remove cotter pin from upper ball joint, and loosen castle nut half length of joint threads. Using ball joint remover, break upper ball joint loose. Remove castle nut, and pull hub/knuckle assembly from axle.

Installation – To install, reverse removal procedure. Tighten bolts and nuts to specification. Use NEW spindle nut, and stake it after tightening. See TORQUE SPECIFICATIONS.

Removal (Vigor) – **1)** Lift spindle nut locking tab. Remove nut. Loosen wheel nuts slightly. Raise and support front of vehicle. Remove wheel nuts and wheel.

2) Remove mounting bolt for brake hose bracket. Remove caliper mounting bolts, and wire caliper aside. Without disconnecting speed sensor wire, remove speed sensor wire bracket and speed sensor from knuckle.

3) Remove cotter pin from tie rod ball joint, and remove castle nut. Install a 12-mm hex nut flush with ball joint pin as a thread protector. Using Ball Joint Remover (07MAC-SL00200), break tie rod ball joint loose. Separate tie rod from knuckle.

4) Remove cotter pin from lower arm ball joint, and remove castle nut. Install a 14-mm hex nut flush with ball joint pin as a thread protector. Using Ball Joint Remover (07MAC-SL00100), break lower arm ball joint loose and separate ball joint and lower arm.

5) Remove knuckle protector. Remove cotter pin and upper ball joint castle nut. Install a 10-mm hex nut flush with ball joint pin as a thread protector. Using Ball Joint Remover (07MAC-SL00200), break ball joint loose and separate it from knuckle.

6) Pull knuckle outward, and separate drive shaft outboard joint from knuckle with a plastic mallet. Remove hub/knuckle assembly from vehicle.

Installation – To install hub/knuckle assembly, reverse removal procedure. Tighten bolts and nuts to specification. Use NEW spindle nut, and stake it after tightening. See TORQUE SPECIFICATIONS.

LOWER BALL JOINT

Removal (Integra) – **1)** Remove steering knuckle. See HUB & KNUCKLE ASSEMBLY. Remove dust boot snap ring, dust boot, and ball joint snap ring.

2) Position Ball Joint Installer/Remover (07965-SB00100) so narrow end of tool fits over tapered end of ball joint shaft. Install and tighten ball joint nut. Position Ball Joint Removal Base (07965-SB00300) between ball joint housing and steering knuckle, and place assembly in vise. Press ball joint from knuckle. *See Fig. 5.*

Installation – **1)** Position ball joint into steering knuckle. Position ball joint installer wide end on ball joint shaft. Position Ball Joint Installation Base (07965-SB00300) over end of ball joint. Press ball joint into knuckle. *See Fig. 5.*

2) Install ball joint snap ring and dust boot. Install dust boot clip with Boot Clip Guide (07974-SA50700). To complete installation, reverse removal procedure.

Removal & Installation (Legend) – Remove steering knuckle. See HUB & KNUCKLE ASSEMBLY. Remove cotter pin and lower ball joint nut. Using Balll Joint Remover (07MAC-SL00200), separate ball joint from lower arm.

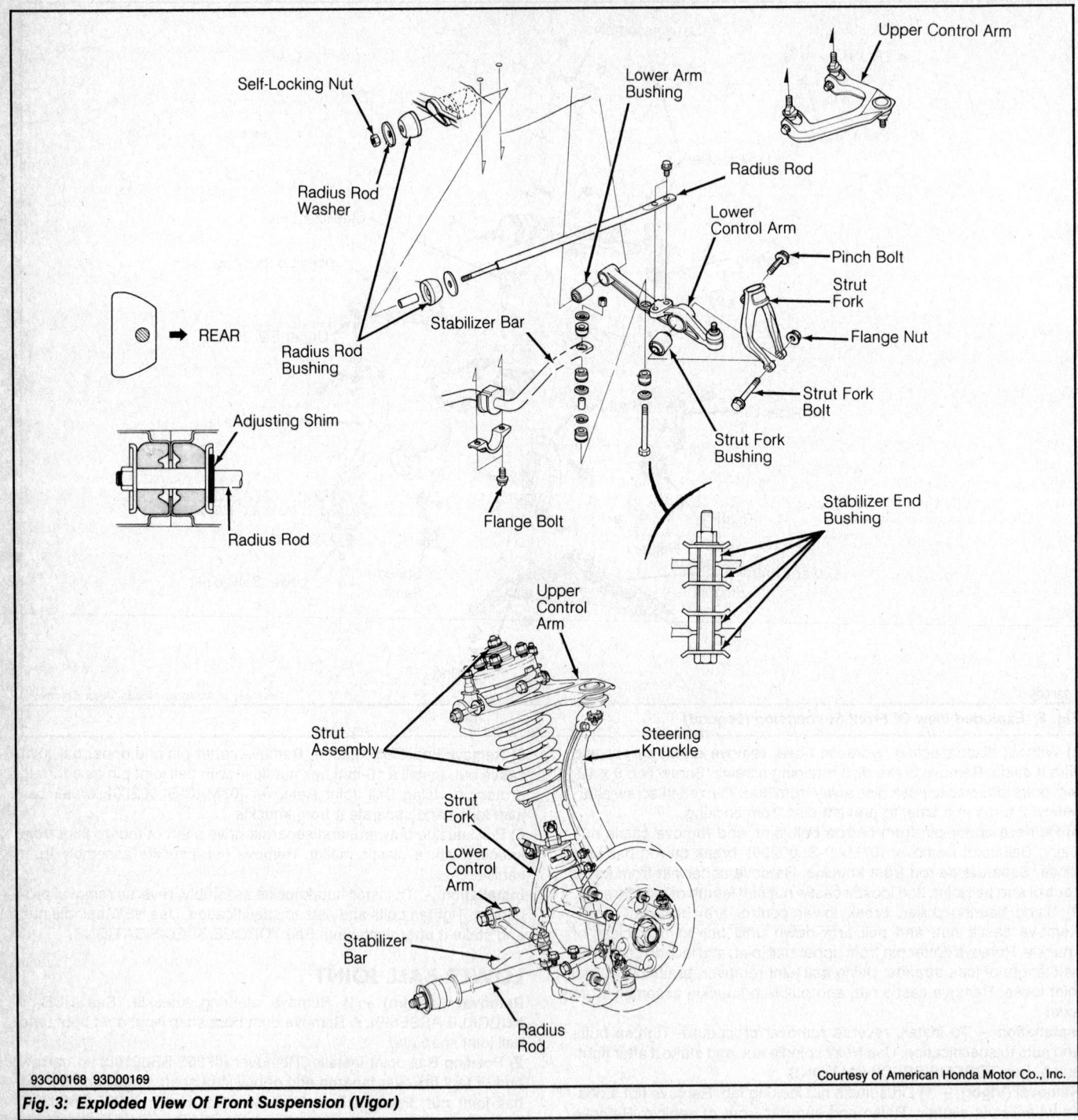

93C00168 93D00169

Courtesy of American Honda Motor Co., Inc.

Fig. 3: Exploded View Of Front Suspension (Vigor)

Removal (Vigor) – 1) Remove steering knuckle. See HUB & KNUCKLE ASSEMBLY. Remove dust boot snap ring, dust boot, and ball joint snap ring.

2) Position Ball Joint Installer/Remover (07GAF-SD40330) so narrow end of tool fits over tapered end of ball joint shaft. Install and tighten ball joint nut. Position Ball Joint Removal Base (07GAF-SD40310) between ball joint housing and steering knuckle, and place assembly in vise. Press ball joint from knuckle. *See Fig. 5.*

Installation – 1) Position ball joint into steering knuckle. Position ball joint installer wide end on ball joint shaft. Position Ball Joint Installation Base (07GAF-SD40320) over end of ball joint. Press ball joint into knuckle. *See Fig. 5.*

2) Install ball joint snap ring and dust boot. Install dust boot clip with Boot Clip Guide (07GOG-SD40700). To complete installation, reverse removal procedure.

LOWER CONTROL ARM

Removal (Integra) – 1) Raise and support front of vehicle. Remove wheel assembly. Remove strut fork and strut rod (radius arm) bolts. Remove nut, bolt, and bushings from stabilizer bar.

2) Remove cotter pin from lower control arm ball joint, and remove castle nut. Break lower control arm ball joint loose, and pull arm down until ball joint is clear of knuckle. Remove lower control arm pivot bolt. Remove control arm.

Installation – Inspect parts for deterioration and damage. Replace worn or damaged parts. Reverse removal procedure to install control arm.

Removal & Installation (Legend & Vigor) – *See Fig. 2 or 3.*

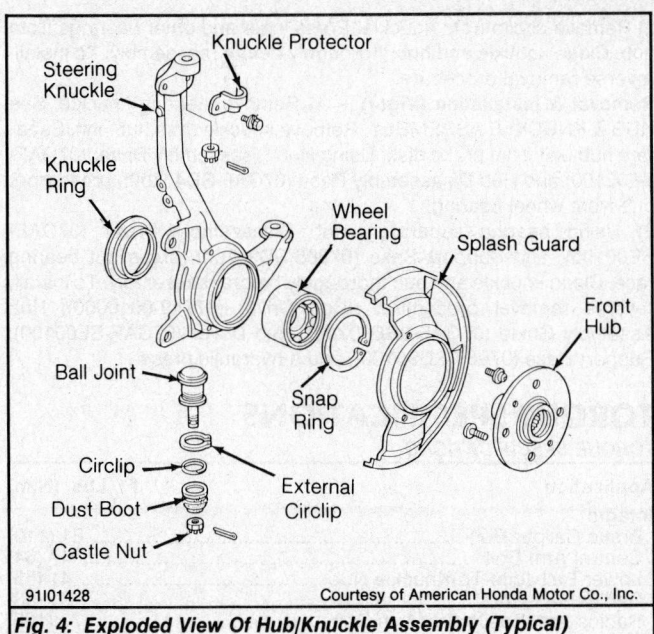

Fig. 4: Exploded View Of Hub/Knuckle Assembly (Typical)

STABILIZER BAR

Removal & Installation – See Fig. 1, 2, or 3.

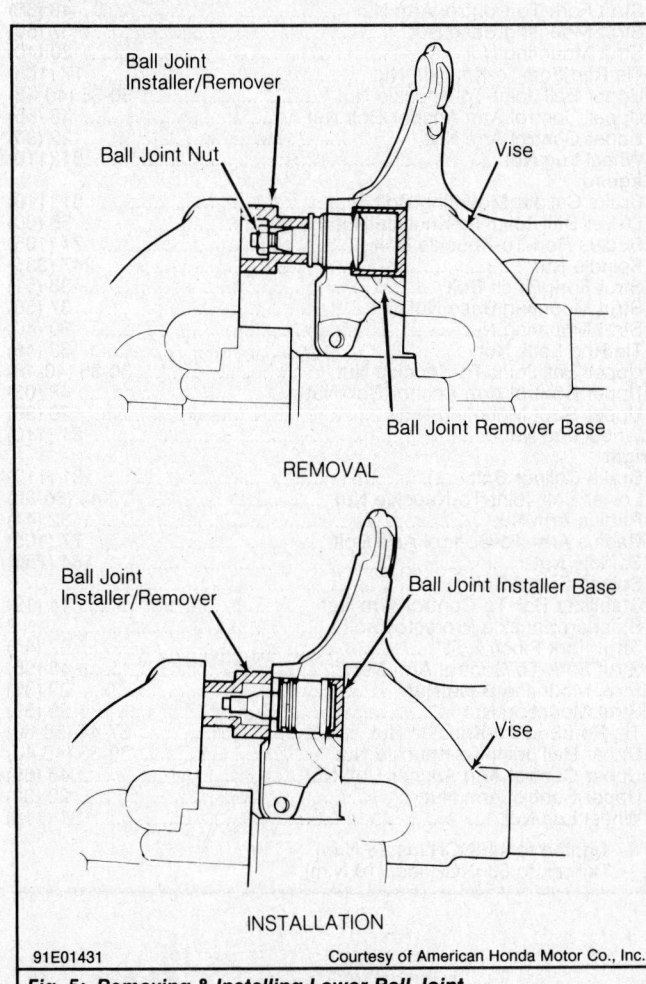

Fig. 5: Removing & Installing Lower Ball Joint
(Integra Shown; Vigor Is Similar)

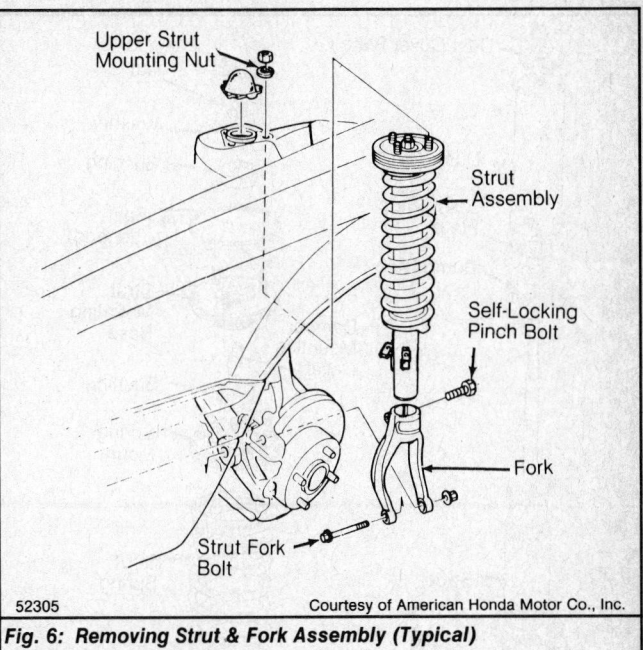

Fig. 6: Removing Strut & Fork Assembly (Typical)

STRUT ASSEMBLY

Removal – Raise and support front of vehicle. Remove wheel assembly and brake hose clamp from strut. Remove strut-to-fork pinch bolt and strut fork bolt. See Fig. 6. Remove strut fork assembly. Remove cap and nuts from top of strut. Remove strut assembly.

NOTE: Struts and strut forks are not interchangeable from side to side.

Disassembly – Using a spring compressor, compress spring slightly to remove spring tension. Hold strut rod with Allen wrench and remove spring seat nut. Slowly release spring compressor. Remove spring. Disassemble strut, noting relative position of parts. See Fig. 7.

Reassembly – Inspect parts for cracks, deterioration, or damage. Check shock absorber for leaks and improper operation. Replace strut if resistance is weak, uneven, or jerky when strut is compressed. Replace worn or damaged parts. Position mounting base with one stud aligned with tab on strut housing. To complete reassembly, reverse disassembly procedure.

Installation – **1)** Install strut fork onto lower control arm. Position strut assembly so tab on strut housing aligns with slot in fork. Align upper strut studs with strut tower holes. Place jack under knuckle, and raise it until vehicle just lifts from safety stand.

NOTE: Strut mount base nuts must be tightened with strut under vehicle weight.

2) Install upper strut mount nuts. Tighten strut assembly while strut is under load. Reverse removal procedure to complete installation. Tighten nuts and bolts to specification. See TORQUE SPECIFICATIONS.

UPPER CONTROL ARM

Inspection – Raise and support front of vehicle. Remove wheel assembly. Rock upper ball joint front to back. Replace upper arm bushings if any play exists.

Removal (Integra) – **1)** Raise and support front of vehicle. Remove wheel assembly. Remove cotter pin from upper ball joint, and remove castle nut.

2) Break upper control arm ball joint loose, and push arm up until ball joint is clear of knuckle. Remove anchor bolt nuts. Remove bolts and upper control arm. Clamp each upper arm anchor bolt in a vise. Remove upper arm bushings.

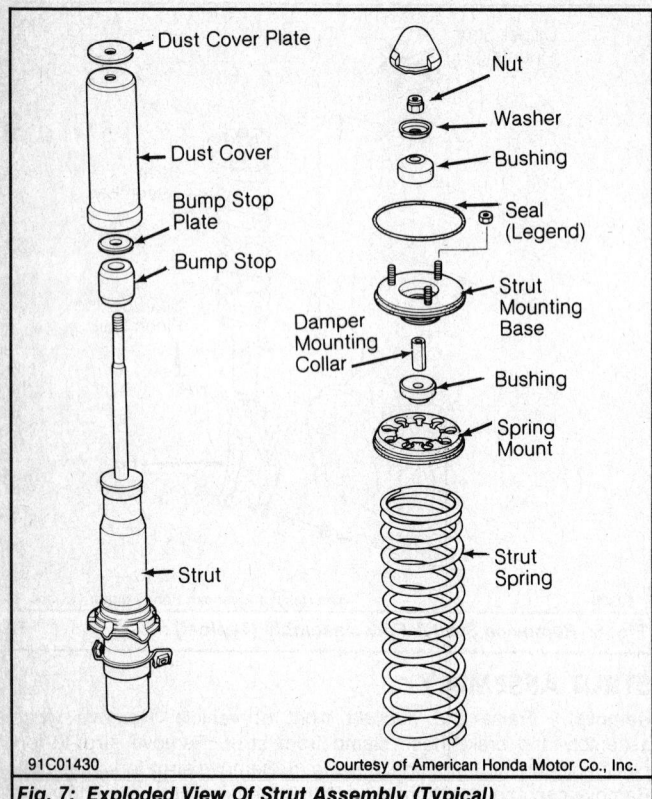

Dust Cover Plate	Nut
Dust Cover	Washer
Bump Stop Plate	Bushing
Bump Stop	Seal (Legend)
Damper Mounting Collar	Strut Mounting Base
	Bushing
	Spring Mount
Strut	Strut Spring

91C01430   Courtesy of American Honda Motor Co., Inc.

Fig. 7: Exploded View Of Strut Assembly (Typical)

Installation – Coat new upper arm bushings with grease. Install upper arm bushings into upper arm anchor bolts. Center bushing so that 0.4" (10 mm) protrudes from each side of anchor bolt. Install and tighten upper arm bolts/nuts. See TORQUE SPECIFICATIONS. To complete installation, reverse removal procedure. Check camber, and adjust if necessary.

Removal & Installation (Legend & Vigor) – See Fig. 2 or 3.

UPPER BALL JOINT

Removal & Installation (Legend) – Upper ball joint is not replaceable as a separate component. If ball joint is worn excessively, replace upper control arm.

WHEEL BEARING

Removal (Integra) – 1) Remove steering knuckle. See HUB & KNUCKLE ASSEMBLY. Remove splash guard screws and splash guard. Using Front Hub Remover/Installer (07GAF-SE00100) and hydraulic press, press hub from steering knuckle. Remove bearing retaining snap ring and knuckle ring from knuckle.

2) Press bearing from knuckle. Using bearing puller, remove outboard bearing from hub. Clean knuckle and hub thoroughly before reassembly.

Installation – Press new bearing into knuckle. Install snap ring into knuckle groove. Install splash guard. Invert knuckle. Press new bearing into hub. Press hub into knuckle. To complete installation, reverse removal procedure.

Removal & Installation (Legend) – 1) Remove steering knuckle. See HUB & KNUCKLE ASSEMBLY. Clamp steering knuckle into soft-jawed vise. Using universal hub puller, separate hub from knuckle. Remove splash guard screws and splash guard.

2) Remove circlip from knuckle. Press inner and outer bearings from hub. Clean knuckle and hub thoroughly before reassembly. To install, reverse removal procedure.

Removal & Installation (Vigor) – 1) Remove steering knuckle. See HUB & KNUCKLE ASSEMBLY. Remove knuckle from hub unit. Separate hub unit from brake disk. Using Hub Disassembly Driver (07GAF-SE00100) and Hub Disassembly Base (07GAF-SD40700), press front hub from wheel bearing.

2) Using bearing separator, Hub Disassembly Driver (07GAF-SE00100), and Support Base (07965-SD90100), press out bearing race. Clean knuckle and hub thoroughly before reassembly. To install, reverse removal procedure, using Driver (07749-0010000), Hub Assembly Guide (07GAF-0SE00200), Hub Driver (07GAF-SE00100), Support Base (07965-SD90100), and a hydraulic press.

TORQUE SPECIFICATIONS
TORQUE SPECIFICATIONS

Application	Ft. Lbs. (N.m)
Integra	
Brake Caliper Bolt	81 (110)
Control Arm Bolt	47 (64)
Lower Ball Joint-To-Knuckle Nut	41 (55)
Radius Arm Nut	61 (83)
Radius Arm-To-Control Arm Bolt	77 (105)
Spindle Nut	134 (181)
Splash Guard Bolt	[1]
Stabilizer Bar-To-Control Arm Nut	16 (22)
Steering Knuckle Protector Bolt	[2]
Strut Fork Pinch Bolt	32 (44)
Strut Fork-To-Control Arm Nut	48 (65)
Strut Mounting Base Nut	37 (50)
Strut Mounting Nut	30 (40)
Tie Rod End-To-Knuckle Nut	77 (105)
Upper Ball Joint-To-Knuckle Nut	30-35 (40-48)
Upper Control Arm Anchor Bolt Nut	48 (65)
Upper Control Arm Nut	22 (30)
Wheel Lug Nut	81 (110)
Legend	
Brake Caliper Mounting Bolt	81 (110)
Lower Ball Joint-To-Knuckle Nut	59 (80)
Radius Rod-To-Knuckle Bolt	77 (105)
Spindle Nut	247 (335)
Strut Fork Pinch Bolt	38 (51)
Strut Mounting Base Nut	37 (50)
Strut Mounting Nut	30 (40)
Tie Rod Lock Nut	33 (45)
Upper Ball Joint-To-Knuckle Nut	30-35 (40-48)
Upper Control Arm Anchor Bolt Nut	48 (65)
Upper Strut Mounting Nut	29 (39)
Wheel Lug Nut	81 (110)
Vigor	
Brake Caliper Bolt	81 (110)
Lower Ball Joint-To-Knuckle Nut	37-44 (50-60)
Radius Arm Nut	32 (44)
Radius Arm-To-Control Arm Bolt	77 (105)
Spindle Nut	184 (250)
Splash Guard Bolt	[2]
Stabilizer Bar-To-Control Arm Nut	14 (19)
Steering Knuckle Protector Bolt	[2]
Strut Fork Pinch Bolt	32 (44)
Strut Fork-To-Control Arm Nut	48 (65)
Strut Mounting Base Nut	29 (39)
Strut Mounting Nut	29 (39)
Tie Rod End-To-Knuckle Nut	37-44 (50-60)
Upper Ball Joint-To-Knuckle Nut	30-35 (40-48)
Upper Control Arm Anchor Bolt Nut	48 (65)
Upper Control Arm Nut	22 (30)
Wheel Lug Nut	81 (110)

[1] – Tighten to 44 INCH lbs. (5 N.m).
[2] – Tighten to 88 INCH lbs. (10 N.m).

Integra, Legend, Vigor

DESCRIPTION

All models use an independent control arm suspension system. Suspension consists of a vertically mounted strut with coil spring connected to a knuckle/spindle assembly, upper control arm, one or 2 lower control arms, trailing arm (Integra and Vigor), and a stabilizer bar. *See Figs. 1, 2, and 3.*

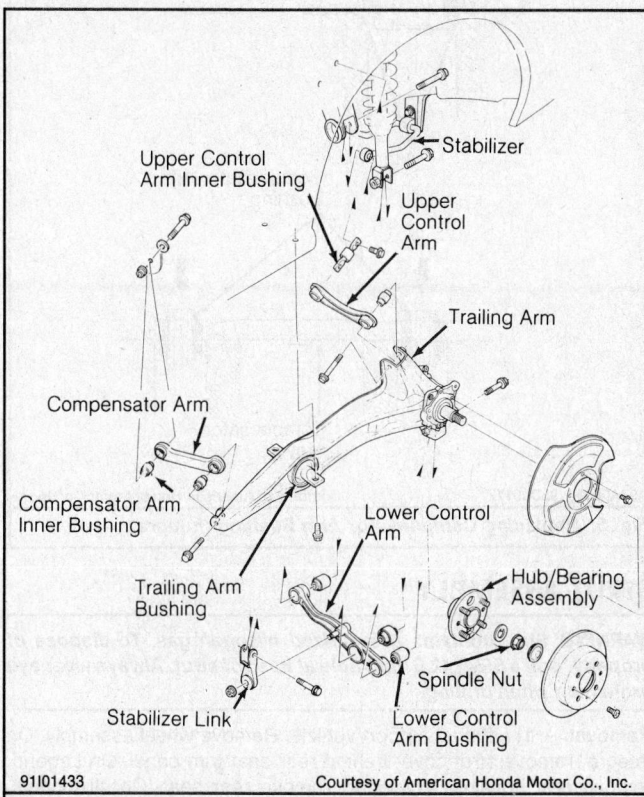

Fig. 1: Exploded View Of Rear Suspension (Integra)

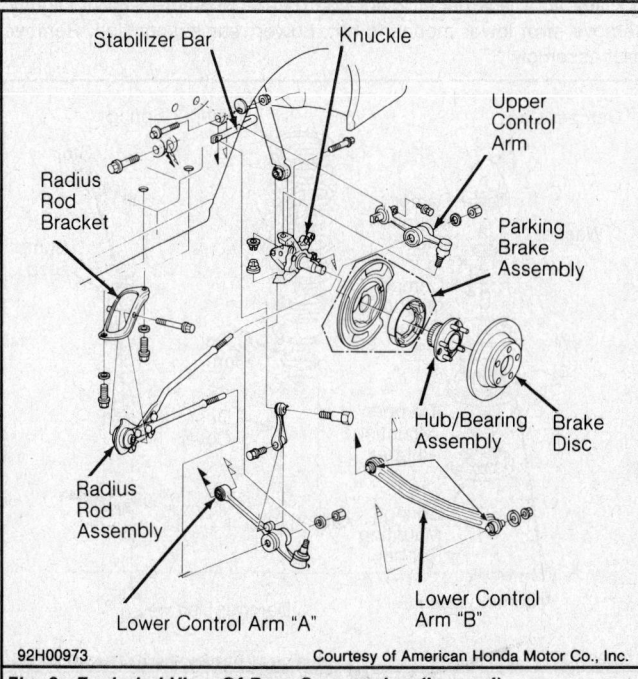

Fig. 2: Exploded View Of Rear Suspension (Legend)

Fig. 3: Exploded View Of Rear Suspension (Vigor)

ADJUSTMENTS & INSPECTION

WHEEL ALIGNMENT
SPECIFICATIONS & PROCEDURES

NOTE: See SPECIFICATIONS & PROCEDURES article in WHEEL ALIGNMENT.

WHEEL BEARING

Wheel bearings are not adjustable.

REMOVAL & INSTALLATION

HUB/BEARING ASSEMBLY

Removal & Installation – Raise and support rear of vehicle. Remove wheel assembly. Remove caliper, and wire it aside. Remove brake disc. Remove hub cap. Pry spindle nut lock tab away from spindle, and remove nut. Remove hub/bearing assembly. *See Fig. 1, 2, or 3.* To install, reverse removal procedure.

UPPER & LOWER CONTROL ARMS

Removal & Installation (Integra) – *See Fig. 1.*
Removal & Installation (Legend) – 1) Remove hub/bearing assembly. See HUB/BEARING ASSEMBLY. Without disconnecting wiring, remove speed sensor from knuckle and lower control arm. Remove parking brake cable retaining brackets.
2) Remove parking brake assembly. Separate strut from knuckle by removing strut mounting bolt. Remove cotter pin from lower control arm ball joint, and loosen castle nut half length of joint threads.
3) Using Ball Joint Remover (07MAC-SL00200), break lower ball joint loose from knuckle. Remove castle nut. Remove cotter pin from upper control arm ball joint, and loosen castle nut half length of joint threads. Using ball joint remover, break upper control arm ball joint loose. Remove castle nut.
4) Remove lower control arm "B". *See Fig. 2.* Remove knuckle. Remove upper radius rod nut. Remove upper control arm. Remove stabilizer link from lower control arm "A". Remove lower radius rod nut. Remove lower control arm "A". Remove radius rod assembly. To install, reverse removal procedure.

NOTE: Control arms are not interchangeable. Painted identification mark is SPO-L-UP for left lower control arm or SPO-R-UP for right control arm. Install control arm so painted identification mark faces toward front. Upper control arms are marked POL for left upper control arm, or POR for right upper control arm.

Removal & Installation (Vigor) – *See Fig. 3.*

UPPER ARM BUSHING

Removal & Installation (Integra) – Drive out upper arm inner bushing and upper arm bushing. *See Fig. 4.* Scribe a line on upper arm inner bushing in line with bolt mounting surface. Mark upper arm at 2 points so they are in line and make a right angle with arm. *See Fig. 4.* Drive in upper arm inner bushing with marks aligned. Drive upper arm bushing into upper arm until their leading edges are flush with upper arm. *See Fig. 4.*

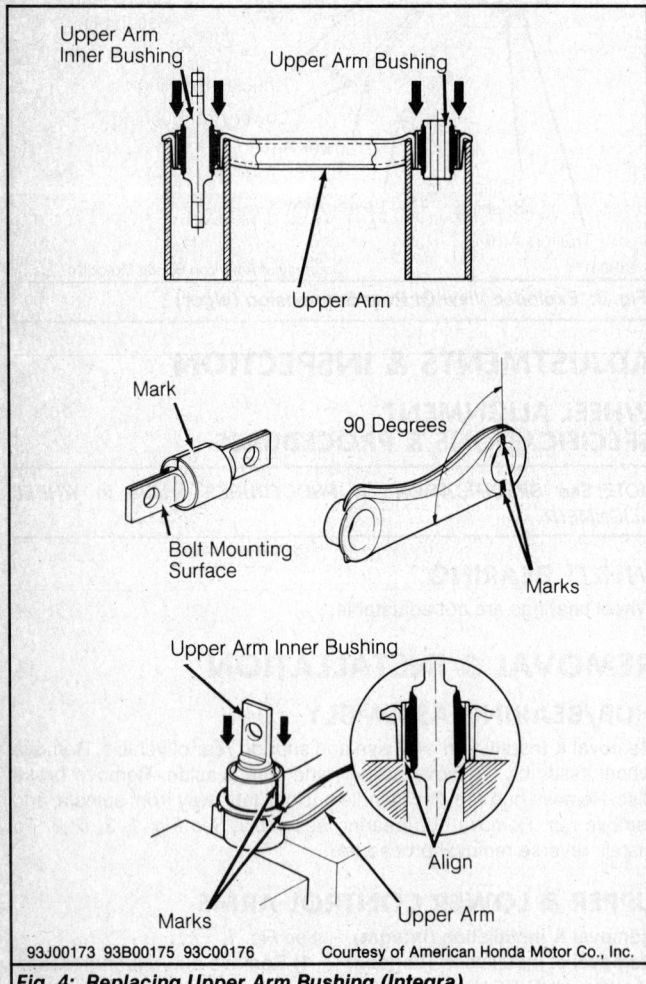

Fig. 4: Replacing Upper Arm Bushing (Integra)

COMPENSATOR ARM BUSHING

Removal & Installation (Integra) – Drive compensator arm bushing out of compensator arm in appropriate direction. *See Fig. 5.* Drive bushings in from indicated direction, with leading edges flush with compensator arm. *See Fig. 5.*

TRAILING ARM

Removal & Installation (Integra & Vigor) – *See Fig. 1 or 3.*

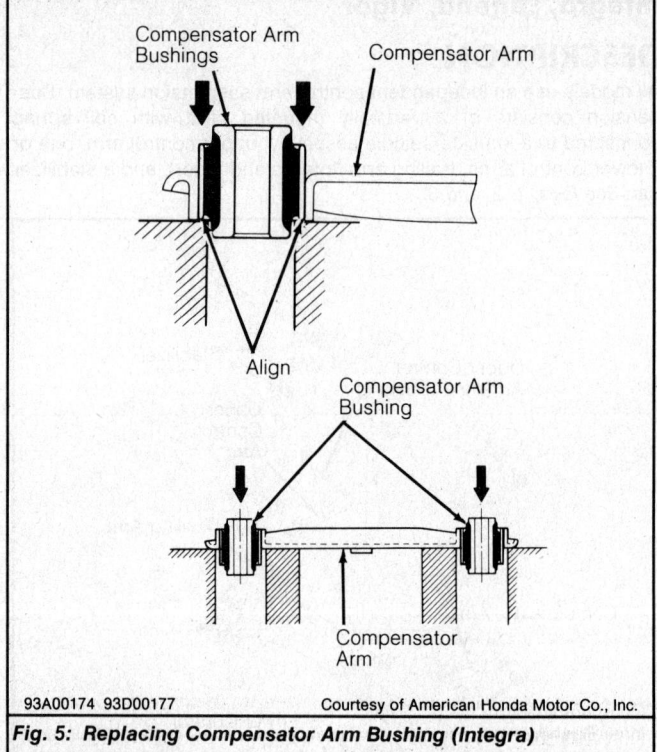

Fig. 5: Replacing Compensator Arm Bushing (Integra)

STRUT ASSEMBLY

WARNING: Strut contains pressurized nitrogen gas. To dispose of properly, drill a 5/64" (2.0 mm) hole at base of strut. Always wear eye protection when drilling.

Removal – **1)** Lift and support vehicle. Remove wheel assembly. On Integra, remove strut cover behind rear seat trim panel. On Legend, remove rear speaker. On Vigor, remove rear seat. On all models, remove strut mounting base nuts. *See Fig. 6 or 7.*
2) Place floor jack under lower control arm. Compress strut slightly. Remove strut lower mounting nut. Lower rear suspension. Remove strut assembly.

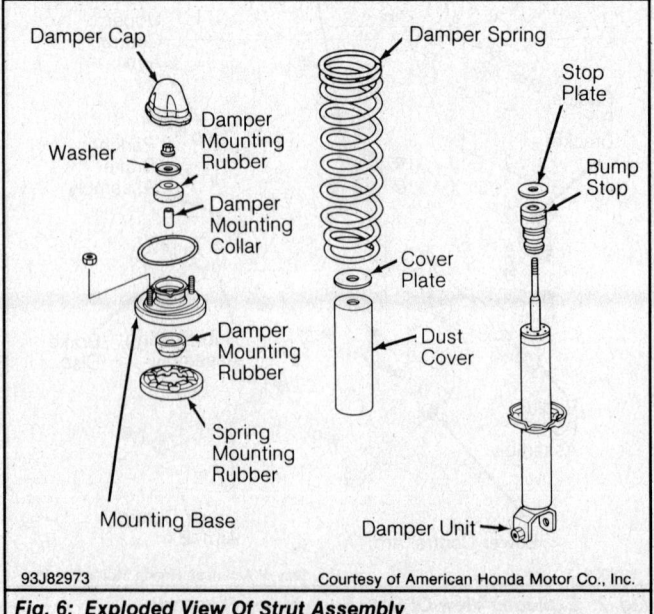

Fig. 6: Exploded View Of Strut Assembly (Integra Shown; Legend Is Similar)

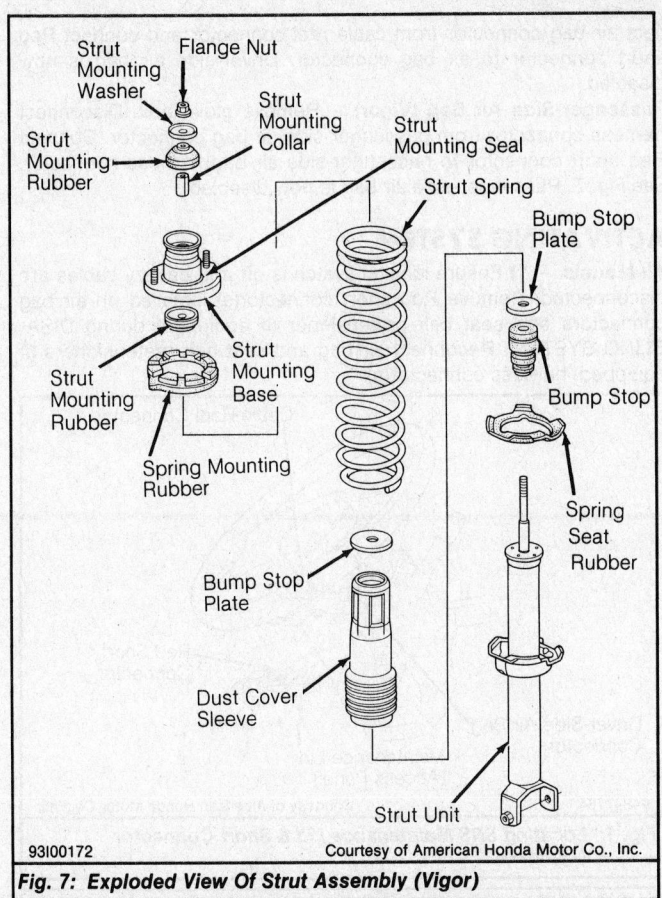

93I00172   Courtesy of American Honda Motor Co., Inc.

Fig. 7: Exploded View Of Strut Assembly (Vigor)

Disassembly – 1) Compress strut spring with spring compressor. DO NOT compress spring more than necessary to remove 10-mm self-locking nut. Remove 10-mm self-locking nut from strut assembly. **2)** Remove spring compressor. Note component locations, and complete disassembly by removing components.

Inspection – Check for smooth operation in both compression and extension strokes. Check for oil leaks, abnormal noises, or and binding. Replace strut as necessary.

Reassembly & Installation – To reassemble, reverse disassembly procedure. To install, reverse removal procedure.

TORQUE SPECIFICATIONS
TORQUE SPECIFICATIONS

Application	Ft. Lbs. (N.m)
Integra	
Brake Caliper Bolt	17 (23)
Brake Caliper Bracket Bolt	29 (40)
Compensator Arm Adjusting Bolt	29 (40)
Compensator-To-Frame Bolt	29 (40)
Lower Strut Mounting Bolt	41 (55)
Spindle Nut	136 (185)
Stabilizer Assembly Bolts	16 (22)
Stabilizer Link Nut	30 (40)
Strut Mounting Base Nuts	30 (40)
Trailing Arm-To-Compensator Arm Bolt	30 (40)
Trailing Arm-To-Upper Arm	41 (55)
Upper Strut Mounting Nut	22 (30)
Wheel Lug Nut	81 (110)
Legend	
Ball Joint Nut	41 (55)
Brake Caliper Bracket Bolt	29 (39)
Brake Caliper Mounting Bolt	29 (39)
Lower Control Arm "B"-To-Knuckle Bolt	41 (55)
Lower Strut Mounting Bolt	77 (105)
Radius Rod Bracket Bolt	77 (105)
Spindle Nut	210 (285)
Stabilizer Link Bolt	16 (22)
Strut Mounting Base Nuts	29 (39)
Upper Control Arm-To-Upper Radius Rod Nut	62 (85)
Upper Strut Mounting Nut	22 (30)
Wheel Lug Nut	81 (110)
Vigor	
Brake Caliper Bracket Bolt	29 (39)
Brake Caliper Mounting Bolt	17 (23)
Lower Strut Mounting Bolt	41 (55)
Spindle Nut	136 (185)
Stabilizer Assembly Bolts	16 (22)
Stabilizer Link Nut	[1]
Strut Mounting Base Nuts	29 (39)
Trailing Arm-To-Frame Bolt	48 (65)
Trailing Arm-To-Knuckle Nut	27 (36)
Upper Strut Mounting Nut	22 (30)
Wheel Lug Nut	81 (110)

[1] – Tighten nut to 115 INCH lbs. (13 N.m).

Integra, Legend, Vigor

DESCRIPTION

All models use a 2-piece safety steering column with a slip joint flange connection. The steering column is supported by a column tube.

WARNING: All models are equipped with Supplemental Restraint System (SRS). All SRS wiring is color coded Yellow. Before performing any repairs on steering column, disable air bag system. See DISABLING SYSTEM under DISABLING & ACTIVATING AIR BAG SYSTEM.

DISABLING & ACTIVATING AIR BAG SYSTEM

DISABLING SYSTEM

WARNING: Wait at least 3 minutes after deactivating air bag system. System maintains voltage for about 3 minutes after battery is disconnected. Servicing air bag system before 3 minutes may cause accidental air bag deployment and possible personal injury.

CAUTION: Radio has a coded theft protection circuit. Before disconnecting battery cables, obtain radio anti-theft code number from customer. After reconnecting power, turn radio on. Word CODE will be displayed. Enter customer 5-digit code to restore radio operation.

WARNING: If SRS Red short connectors are not properly installed, static electricity can deploy air bags and seat belt pretensioners (if equipped).

Driver-Side Air Bag (Integra) – 1) Turn ignition off. Disconnect both battery cables. Remove access panel from steering wheel. *See Fig. 1.* Remove Red short connector from holder on access panel.
2) Disconnect air bag connector from cable reel connector. Connect Red short connector to air bag connector. Driver-side air bag is now disabled. Disable passenger-side air bag (if equipped).
Passenger-Side Air Bag (Integra) – Remove glove box. Disconnect harness connector from passenger-side air bag connector. Connect Red short connector to passenger-side air bag connector. *See Fig. 2.* Passenger-side air bag is now disabled.
Driver-Side Air Bag (Legend) – 1) To disable SRS, turn ignition off. Wait at least 3 minutes to allow capacitor in back-up circuit to discharge, preventing a malfunction of seat belt pretensioner or accidental deployment of air bag.
2) Disconnect both battery cables. Remove maintenance lid below driver-side air bag. *See Fig. 1.* Remove Red short connector. Unplug 3-pin connector between air bag and cable reel. Connect Red short connector to air bag side of connector. On models equipped with anti-theft circuit, connect SRS Short Connector "A" (07MAZ-SP00200) to cable reel side of connector. *See Fig. 3.* Driver-side air bag is now disabled.
Passenger-Side Air Bag (Legend) – 1) Remove glove box. Disconnect passenger-side air bag connector from SRS main harness. Connect passenger-side air bag connector to Red short connector. *See Fig. 4.* Connect another SRS short connector "A" to SRS main harness 3-pin connector. *See Fig. 5.*
2) Access both seat belt pretensioner connectors. Locate and remove Red short connector from connector holder on seat belt pretensioner. *See Fig. 6.* Disconnect SRS seat belt pretensioner harness connector. Install SRS Red short connector to SRS seat belt pretensioner connector.
3) Cover seat belt pretensioner harness connector to keep terminals clean. Repeat procedure for remaining seat belt pretensioner. SRS is disabled when all Red short connectors are installed to both air bags and both seat belt pretensioners.
Driver-Side Air Bag (Vigor) – Turn ignition off. Disconnect both battery cables. Remove access panel from steering wheel. *See Fig. 1.* Remove Red short connector from holder on access panel. Discon-

nect air bag connector from cable reel connector and connect Red short connector to air bag connector. Driver-side air bag is now disabled.
Passenger-Side Air Bag (Vigor) – Remove glove box. Disconnect harness connector from passenger-side air bag connector. Connect Red short connector to passenger-side air bag harness connector. *See Fig. 7.* Passenger-side air bag is now disabled.

ACTIVATING SYSTEM

All Models – 1) Ensure ignition switch is off and battery cables are disconnected. Remove Red short connector(s) installed on air bag connectors and seat belt pretensioner (if equipped) during DISABLING SYSTEM. Reconnect air bag and seat belt pretensioners (if equipped) harness connector(s).

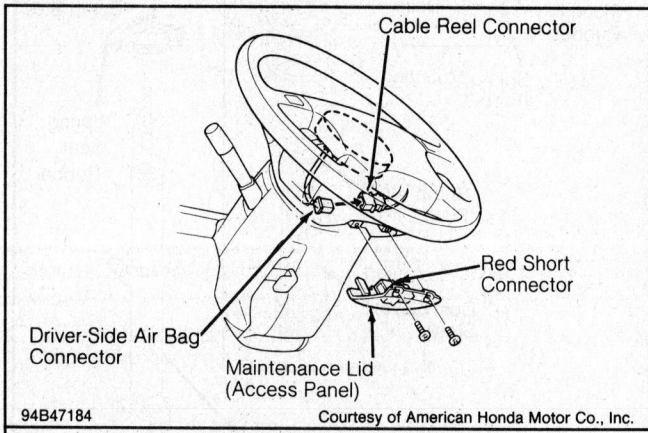

94B47184   Courtesy of American Honda Motor Co., Inc.
Fig. 1: Locating SRS Maintenance Lid & Short Connector (Typical)

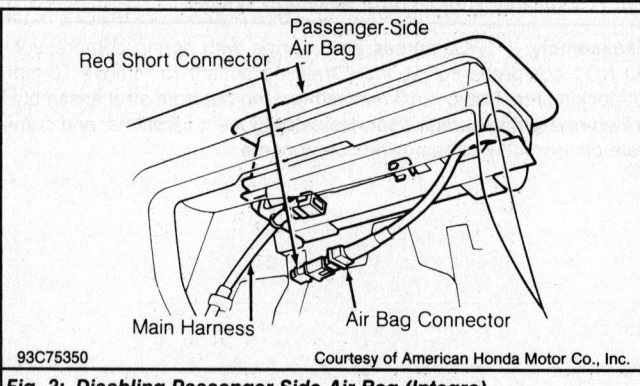

93C75350   Courtesy of American Honda Motor Co., Inc.
Fig. 2: Disabling Passenger-Side Air Bag (Integra)

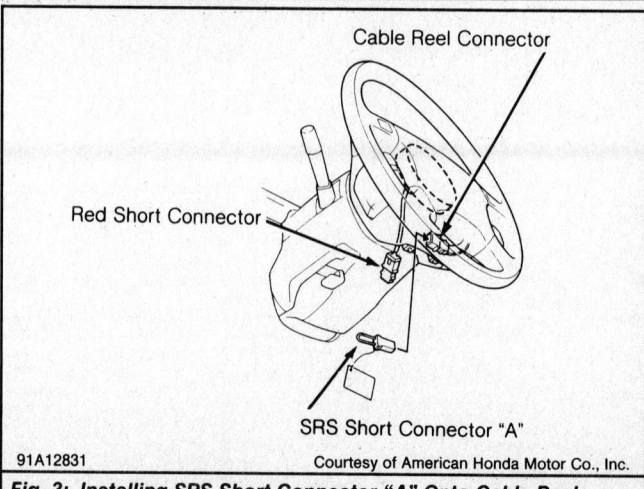

91A12831   Courtesy of American Honda Motor Co., Inc.
Fig. 3: Installing SRS Short Connector "A" Onto Cable Reel Connector (Typical)

2) Install Red short connectors in respective holders. Install access panel to steering wheel and trim panels to seat belt pretensioners. Install glove box. Reconnect battery cables.

3) Turn ignition on. Observe SRS indicator light to verify system is functioning properly. SRS indicator light should come on for about 6 seconds and then go off. While vehicle is driven, SRS light should not come on or flash. If SRS indicator light does not operate as indicated, system must be inspected/repaired as soon as possible. Refer to 1994 MITCHELL ® AIR BAG SERVICE & REPAIR MANUAL.

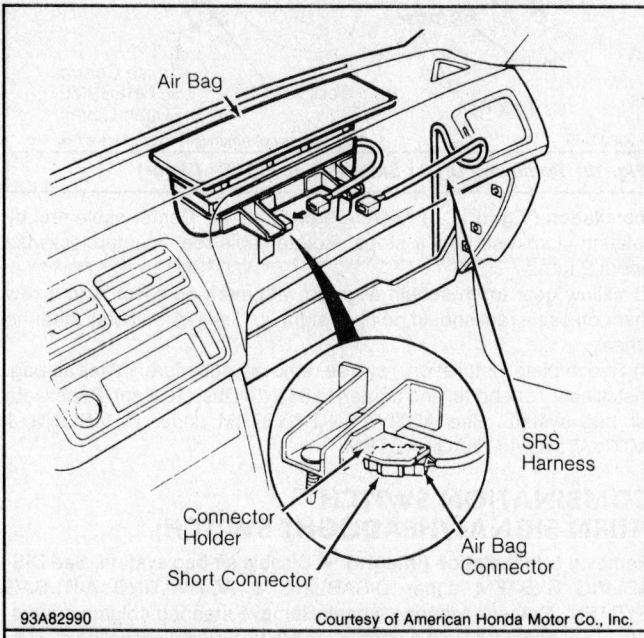

Fig. 4: *Installing Passenger-Side Air Bag Short Connector (Legend)*

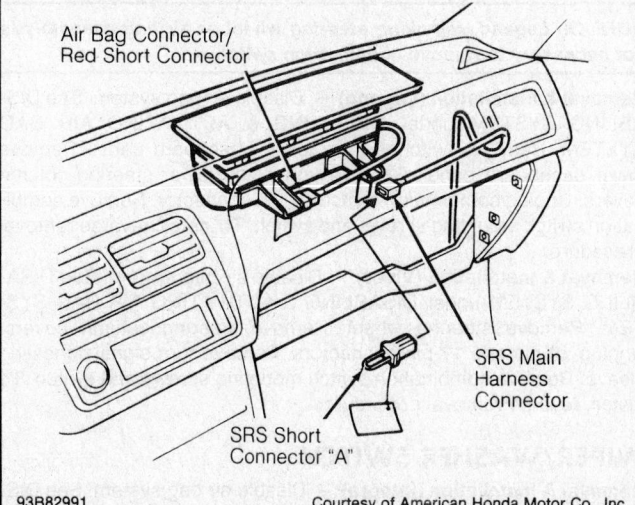

Fig. 5: *Installing Passenger-Side SRS Harness Short Connector (Legend)*

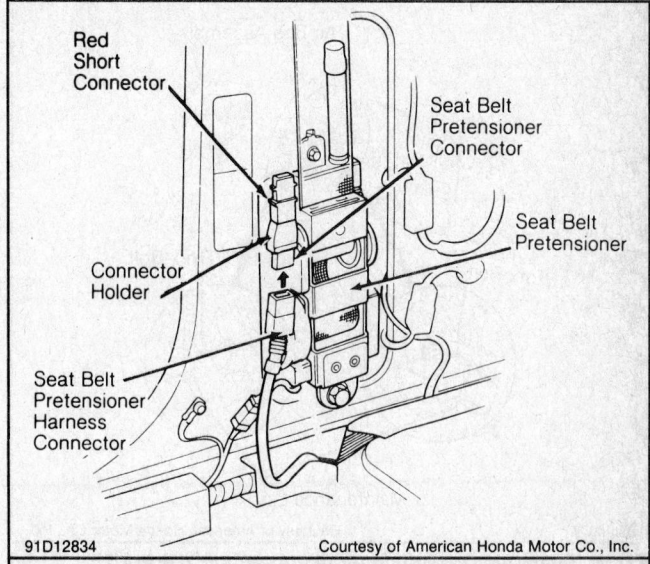

Fig. 6: *Locating Seat Belt Pretensioner Short Connector (Legend)*

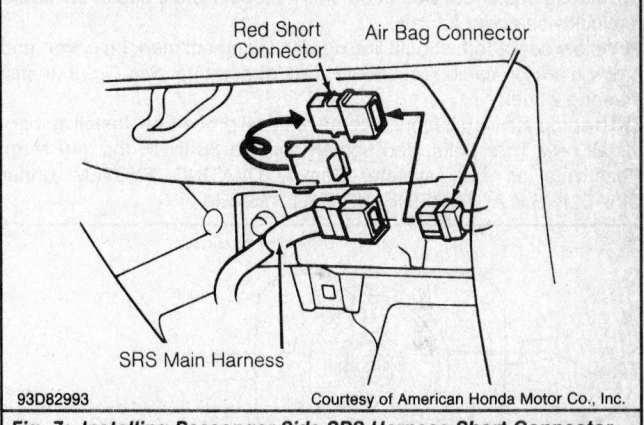

Fig. 7: *Installing Passenger-Side SRS Harness Short Connector (Vigor)*

REMOVAL & INSTALLATION

STEERING WHEEL & HORN PAD

WARNING: Never store air bag upside down. Accidental deployment could cause serious injury. Store air bag with pad surface up and away from work area. DO NOT disassemble or tamper with air bag assembly.

Removal & Installation (Integra) – **1)** Deactivate air bag system. See DISABLING SYSTEM under DISABLING & ACTIVATING AIR BAG SYSTEM. Position front wheels straight ahead. Disconnect all electrical harness connectors. Mark steering wheel and shaft for installation reference. Remove steering wheel shaft nut.

2) Remove steering wheel by rocking slightly while pulling steadily with both hands. To install, reverse removal procedure. Align marks properly upon assembly.

Removal (Legend) – **1)** Deactivate air bag system. See DISABLING SYSTEM under DISABLING & ACTIVATING AIR BAG SYSTEM. Position front wheels straight ahead. Remove maintenance lids from headlight/turn signal switch and wiper/washer switch. *See Fig. 8.* Remove and discard Torx bolts. Remove air bag assembly.

2) Mark steering wheel and shaft for installation reference. Note position of all connectors, and unplug as necessary. Remove steering wheel nut. Remove steering wheel by rocking slightly while pulling steadily with both hands.

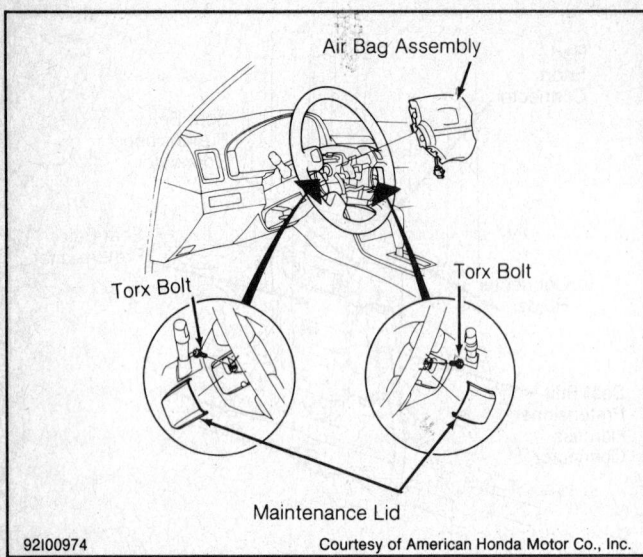

Fig. 8: Removing Driver-Side Air Bag Assembly (Legend)

92I00974   Courtesy of American Honda Motor Co., Inc.

Installation (Legend) – 1) Align reference marks. Center cable reel by rotating cable reel clockwise until it stops. Rotate cable reel counterclockwise about 2 turns.
2) Yellow gear tooth should line up with alignment mark on cover, and arrow mark on cable reel should point straight up. *See Fig. 9.* Install steering wheel.
3) To complete installation, reverse removal procedure. Install air bag. Install new Torx bolts, and tighten bolts to 88 INCH lbs. (10 N.m). Reactivate air bag system. See ACTIVATING SYSTEM under DISABLING & ACTIVATING AIR BAG SYSTEM.

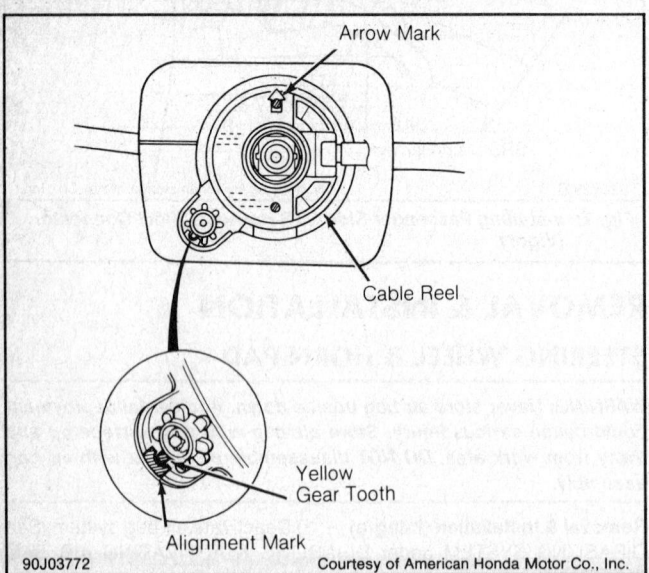

Fig. 9: Centering Cable Reel (Legend Shown; Vigor Is Similar)

90J03772   Courtesy of American Honda Motor Co., Inc.

Removal (Vigor) – 1) Deactivate air bag system. See DISABLING SYSTEM under DISABLING & ACTIVATING AIR BAG SYSTEM. Position front wheels straight ahead.
2) Remove access panel from steering wheel lower cover. Remove short connector. Unplug connector between air bag and cable reel. Connect short connector to air bag side of connector. *See Fig. 1.*
3) Remove lid "B" and cruise control SET/RESUME switch cover. *See Fig. 10.* Remove and discard Torx bolts. Remove air bag assembly.
4) Unplug connectors from horn and cruise control SET/RESUME switches. Remove steering wheel nut. Mark steering wheel and shaft for reassembly. Remove steering wheel by rocking slightly while pulling steadily with both hands.

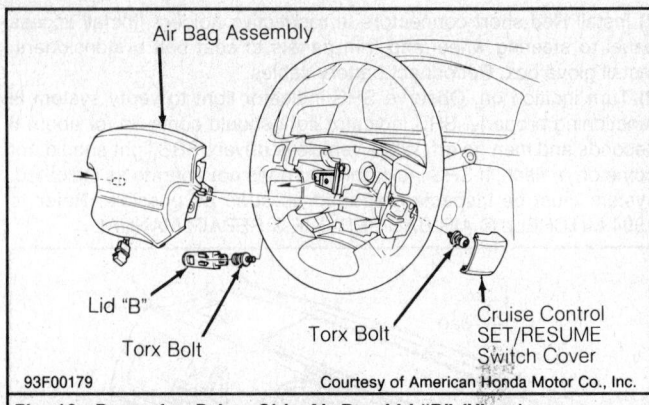

Fig. 10: Removing Driver-Side Air Bag Lid "B" (Vigor)

93F00179   Courtesy of American Honda Motor Co., Inc.

Installation (Vigor) – 1) Align reference marks. Center cable reel by rotating clockwise until it stops. Rotate cable reel counterclockwise about 2 turns.
2) Yellow gear tooth should align up with mark on cover, and arrow mark on cable reel should point straight up. *See Fig. 9.* Install steering wheel.
3) To complete installation, reverse removal procedure. Install air bag. Install new Torx bolts, and tighten to 88 INCH lbs. (10 N.m). Reactivate air bag system. See ACTIVATING SYSTEM under DISABLING & ACTIVATING AIR BAG SYSTEM.

COMBINATION SWITCH
(TURN SIGNAL/HEADLIGHT SWITCH)

Removal & Installation (Integra) – Disable air bag system. See DISABLING SYSTEM under DISABLING & ACTIVATING AIR BAG SYSTEM. Remove steering wheel. Remove steering column covers. Unplug connectors from switch. Remove turn signal canceling sleeve. Remove combination switch mounting screws and switch. To install, reverse removal procedure.

NOTE: On Legend, removing steering wheel or air bag assembly is not necessary to remove combination switch.

Removal & Installation (Legend) – Disable air bag system. See DISABLING SYSTEM under DISABLING & ACTIVATING AIR BAG SYSTEM. Remove switches from lower dashboard panel. Remove lower dashboard panel. Remove upper and lower steering column covers. Unplug combination switch 14-pin connector. Remove combination switch mounting screws and switch. To install, reverse removal procedure.
Removal & Installation (Vigor) – Disable air bag system. See DISABLING SYSTEM under DISABLING & ACTIVATING AIR BAG SYSTEM. Remove steering wheel. Remove steering column covers. Unplug 10-pin and 12-pin connectors. Remove turn signal canceling sleeve. Remove combination switch mounting screws and switch. To install, reverse removal procedure.

WIPER/WASHER SWITCH

Removal & Installation (Integra) – Disable air bag system. See DISABLING SYSTEM under DISABLING & ACTIVATING AIR BAG SYSTEM. Remove horn pad and steering wheel. Remove upper and lower steering column covers. Unplug wiper/washer wiring harness connectors. Remove cruise control slip ring (if equipped). Remove 2 screws and wiper/washer switch. To install, reverse removal procedure.
Removal & Installation (Legend) – Disable air bag system. See DISABLING SYSTEM under DISABLING & ACTIVATING AIR BAG SYSTEM. Remove switches from lower dashboard panel. Remove lower dashboard panel. Remove upper and lower steering column covers. Unplug wiper/washer connector. Remove wiper/washer switch. To install, reverse removal procedure.

Removal & Installation (Vigor) – Disable air bag system. See DISABLING SYSTEM under DISABLING & ACTIVATING AIR BAG SYSTEM. Remove dashboard lower panel and knee bolster. Remove steering column covers. Unplug 10-pin connector. Remove mounting screws and washer/wiper switch. To install, reverse removal procedure.

IGNITION SWITCH

Removal & Installation (Integra) – Disable air bag system. See DISABLING SYSTEM under DISABLING & ACTIVATING AIR BAG SYSTEM. Remove steering wheel. Remove upper and lower steering column covers. Remove lower dashboard panel and left knee bolster. Unplug 4-pin connector from underdash fuse block. Unplug 5-pin connector from main wire harness. Set ignition switch to "O" position. Remove 2 screws and ignition switch. To install, reverse removal procedure.

Removal & Installation (Legend) – Disable air bag system. See DISABLING SYSTEM under DISABLING & ACTIVATING AIR BAG SYSTEM. Remove switches from lower dashboard panel. Remove lower dashboard panel. Unplug ignition switch 7-pin connector from underdash fuse box. Set ignition switch to "O" position. Remove 2 screws and ignition switch. To install, reverse removal procedure.

Removal & Installation (Vigor) – Disable air bag system. See DISABLING SYSTEM under DISABLING & ACTIVATING AIR BAG SYSTEM. Remove dashboard lower cover and knee bolster. Unplug 7-pin connector from underdash fuse block. Remove steering column covers. Set ignition switch to "O" position. Remove 2 screws and ignition switch. To install, reverse removal procedure.

STEERING LOCK ASSEMBLY

Removal & Installation (Integra) – 1) Disable air bag system. See DISABLING SYSTEM under DISABLING & ACTIVATING AIR BAG SYSTEM. Remove steering wheel. Remove upper and lower steering column covers. Remove lower dashboard panel and left knee bolster. Unplug ignition switch 7-pin connector from main wiring harness.

2) Remove steering column mounting bolts/nuts. Lower steering column. Center-punch both shear bolts. Using a 3/16" bit, drill heads from bolts. Remove shear bolts and ignition lock assembly.

3) To install, reverse removal procedure. Tighten new shear bolts until heads twist off. Check for proper ignition switch steering lock operation.

Removal & Installation (Legend) – 1) Disconnect negative battery terminal. Remove switches from lower dashboard panel. Remove lower dashboard panel. Unplug wiring harness connectors as necessary. Remove steering column mounting bolts/nuts. Lower steering column assembly.

2) Grind slot into shear bolt. Using a screwdriver, remove shear bolt. Set ignition switch to "I" position. Push in on steering lock retaining pin. Remove steering lock assembly.

3) To install, set ignition switch to "I" position. Push in on steering lock retaining pin and insert steering lock assembly until assembly clicks into place. Loosely install new shear bolt. Insert ignition key and check for proper steering lock operation. Tighten shear bolt until hex head twists off. To complete installation, reverse removal procedure.

Removal & Installation (Vigor) – 1) Disable air bag system. See DISABLING SYSTEM under DISABLING & ACTIVATING AIR BAG SYSTEM. Remove lower dashboard panel and left knee bolster. Unplug ignition switch 7-pin connector from main wiring harness. On models with A/T, unplug 8-pin connector from main wiring harness.

2) On all models, remove upper and lower steering column covers. Remove instrument panel trim panel. Center-punch both shear bolts. Using a 3/16" bit, drill heads from bolts. Remove shear bolts and lock assembly.

3) Install new switch without key inserted. Finger-tighten new shear bolts. Insert key. Check for proper operation. Tighten shear bolts until heads break off. To complete installation, reverse removal procedure.

STEERING COLUMN ASSEMBLY

Removal (Integra) – 1) Deactivate air bag system. See DISABLING SYSTEM under DISABLING & ACTIVATING AIR BAG SYSTEM. Remove steering wheel. See STEERING WHEEL & HORN PAD. Remove left and right lower covers from instrument panel. Remove front console. Remove left knee bolster from steering hanger.

2) Remove steering joint cover. Remove steering shaft joint pinch bolts. Mark steering joint and pinion shaft for installation reference. Remove steering joint.

3) Remove upper and lower steering column covers. Remove turn signal canceling sleeve and combination switch. Unplug all wiring harness connectors. Remove steering column assembly.

Installation (Integra) – Position steering column assembly into hole in floorboard. Align reference marks, and install steering joint onto pinion shaft. Install and tighten steering joint pinch bolts. See TORQUE SPECIFICATIONS. Install steering joint cover. Install steering column to underside of dashboard. To complete installation, reverse removal procedure.

Removal (Legend) – 1) Deactivate air bag system. See DISABLING SYSTEM under DISABLING & ACTIVATING AIR BAG SYSTEM. Remove steering wheel. See STEERING WHEEL & HORN PAD.

2) Remove pinch bolt from lower steering joint in engine compartment. Remove courtesy light control switch from lower dashboard panel. Remove lower dashboard panel. Remove upper and lower steering column covers.

CAUTION: DO NOT disconnect cable reel connector and SRS wiring harness.

---

3) Remove steering joint cover. Without unplugging connector, remove cable reel box from underneath steering column, and place it aside on floor. *See Fig. 11.* Remove clip. Remove cable reel, turn signal canceling sleeve, and combination switch from column assembly, and place them aside on floor.

4) Unplug ignition switch connector from underdash fuse box. Remove steering column mounting bolts/nuts. Carefully remove steering column assembly.

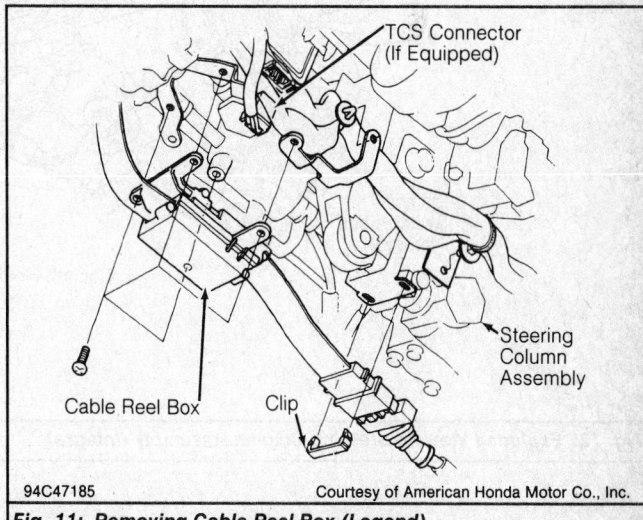

94C47185   Courtesy of American Honda Motor Co., Inc.

Fig. 11: Removing Cable Reel Box (Legend)

Installation (Legend) – 1) Position steering column assembly into hole on floorboard. Align bolt hole in steering joint with slot in steering shaft. Insert shaft into steering joint.

2) Install steering column mounting bolts/nuts, and tighten them to specification. See TORQUE SPECIFICATIONS. Install and tighten lower steering joint pinch bolt. To complete installation, reverse removal procedure.

Removal (Vigor) – 1) Deactivate air bag system. See DISABLING SYSTEM under DISABLING & ACTIVATING AIR BAG SYSTEM. Remove steering wheel. See STEERING WHEEL & HORN PAD.

2) Remove pinch bolt from lower steering joint in engine compartment. Remove lower cover and driver-side knee bolster. Remove upper and lower steering column covers.

3) Remove steering joint cover. Remove SRS wiring harness from underside of column bracket by removing clip. Remove cable reel assembly and turn signal canceling sleeve from combination switch assembly. Remove combination switch assembly.

NOTE: Place combination switch assembly aside on floor gently. DO NOT disconnect cables from combination switch assembly.

4) Disconnect wire coupler of ignition switch. Remove steering column assembly attaching nuts and bolts. Remove steering column.

Installation (Vigor) – 1) Guide steering shaft through engine bulkhead. Align bolt hole in steering joint with slot in steering shaft, insert shaft into steering joint, and install bolt.

2) Install steering column assembly and nuts and steering column holder. Connect ignition switch wiring. Install combination switch.

NOTE: Ensure wires are not caught or pinched by any parts when connecting combination switch and cable reel.

3) Install turn signal switch canceling sleeve and cable reel onto steering column. Align slot in canceling sleeve with projection on cable reel.

4) Install SRS wiring harness onto underside of column bracket with clip. Install steering joint cover. Install upper and lower column covers. Install knee bolster and lower cover. Install steering wheel and air bag assembly.

OVERHAUL

NOTE: For exploded view of steering column, see Fig. 12, 13 or 14.

TORQUE SPECIFICATIONS
TORQUE SPECIFICATIONS

Application	Ft. Lbs. (N.m)
Column Holder Bolts/Nuts	
Integra & Legend	16 (22)
Vigor	29 (39)
Dash Sensor Mounting Bolt	16 (22)
Seat Belt Pretensioner Lower Mounting	
Bolt (Legend)	23 (32)
Shoulder Harness Upper & Lower Anchor	
Bolts (Legend)	23 (32)
Steering Joint Pinch Bolt	16 (22)
Steering Wheel Nut	37 (50)
Upper Column Mounting Bolts/Nuts	
Integra	1
Legend & Vigor	12 (16)
	INCH Lbs. (N.m)
Air Bag Torx Bolts (Driver & Passenger Side)	88 (10)
Seat Belt Pretensioner Upper Mounting	
Bolt (Legend)	88 (10)
SRS Unit Torx Bolts	88 (10)

¹ – Tighten to 88 INCH lbs. (10 N.m)

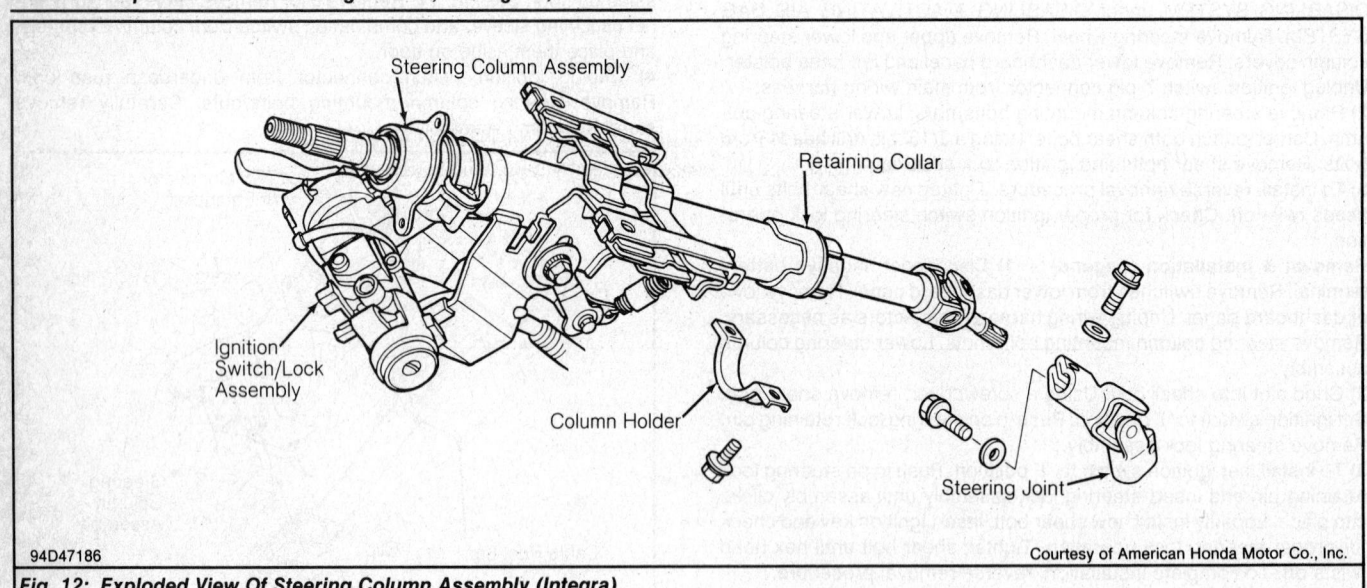

94D47186   Courtesy of American Honda Motor Co., Inc.

Fig. 12: Exploded View Of Steering Column Assembly (Integra)

Labels in figure: Steering Column Assembly; Retaining Collar; Ignition Switch/Lock Assembly; Column Holder; Steering Joint

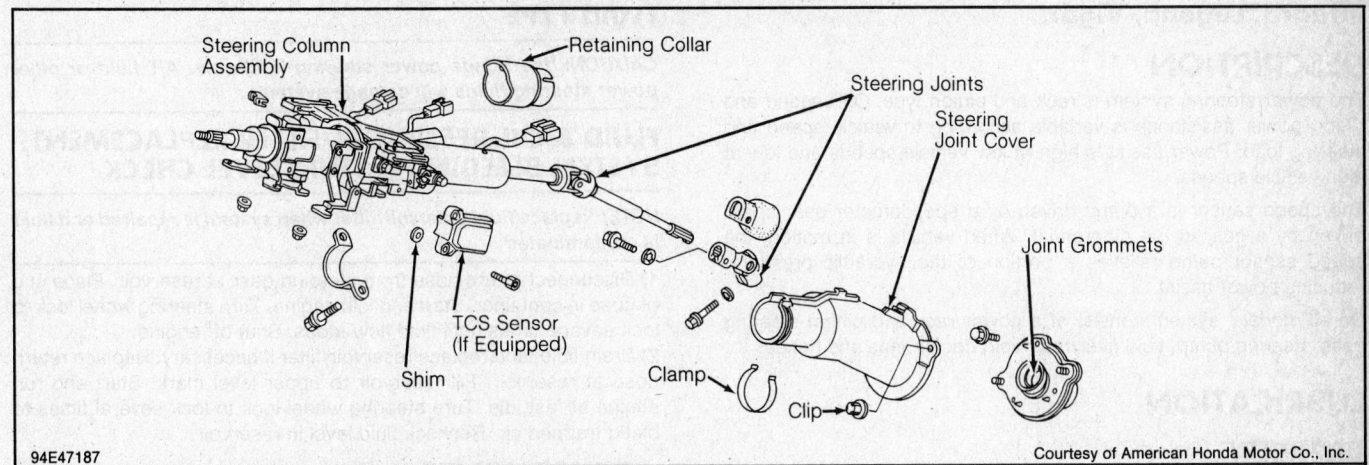

Fig. 13: Exploded View Of Steering Column Assembly (Legend)

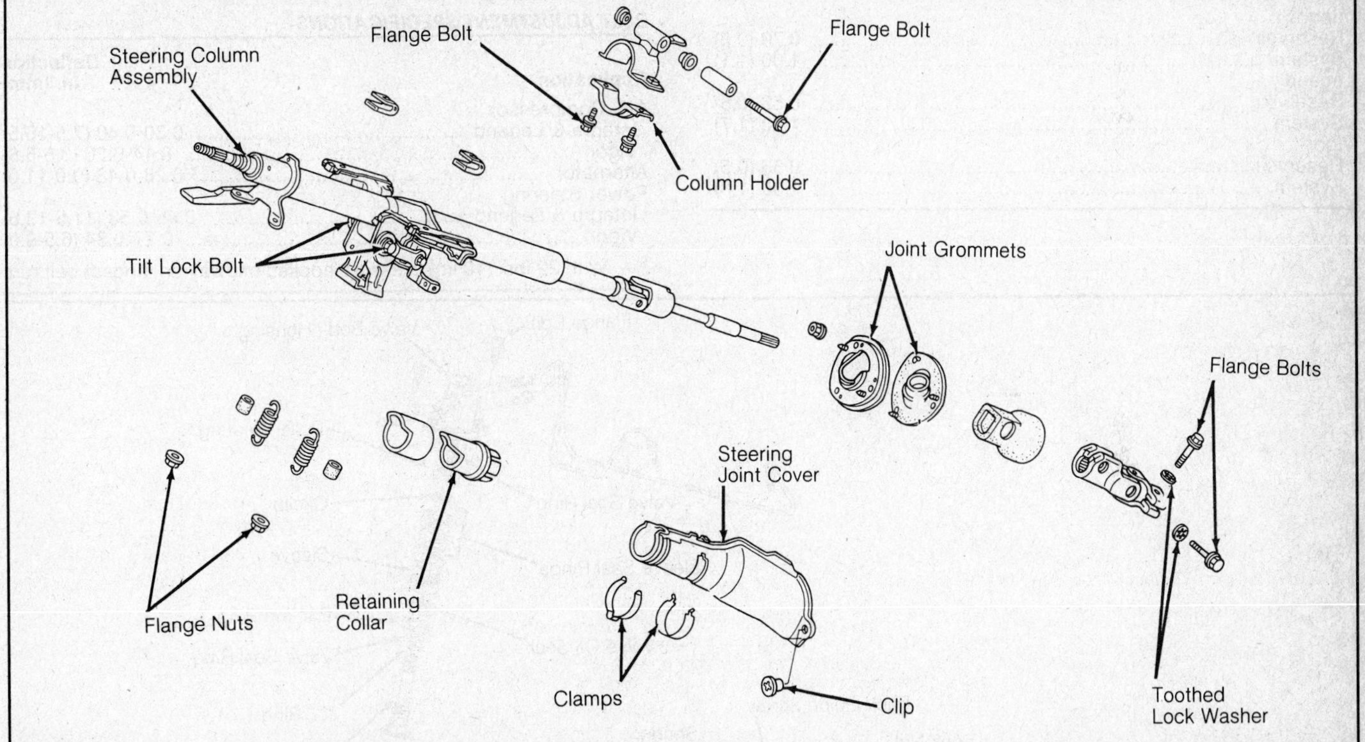

Fig. 14: Exploded View Of Steering Column Assembly (Vigor)

1994 STEERING
Power Rack & Pinion

Integra, Legend, Vigor

DESCRIPTION

The power steering system is rack and pinion type. On Legend and Vigor, power assistance is variable according to vehicle speed and steering load. Power assist is high at low vehicle speeds and low at high vehicle speeds.

The speed sensor is a pump driven by a speedometer gear shaft, driven by a gear in the differential. When vehicle is in motion, the speed sensor pump relieves a portion of the hydraulic pressure, reducing power assist.

On all models, system consist of a power rack and pinion steering gear, steering pump, fluid filter/reservoir, cooler lines and hoses.

LUBRICATION

CAPACITY

SYSTEM CAPACITY

Application	Qts. (L)
Integra	
Reservoir	0.79 (0.8)
System	1.00 (1.1)
Legend	
Reservoir	0.53 (0.5)
System	1.80 (1.7)
Vigor	
Reservoir	0.53 (0.5)
System	1.90 (1.8)

FLUID TYPE

CAUTION: Use Honda power steering fluid only. A/T fluid or other power steering fluids will damage system.

FLUID & OIL RESERVOIR/FILTER REPLACEMENT, SYSTEM BLEEDING & FLUID LEVEL CHECK

NOTE: Replace fluid reservoir/filter when system is repaired or if fluid is contaminated.

1) Disconnect return hose from steering gear at reservoir. Place end of hose in container. Start and idle engine. Turn steering wheel lock to lock several times until fluid flow stops. Shut off engine.
2) Drain fluid, and replace reservoir/filter if necessary. Replace return hose at reservoir. Fill reservoir to upper level mark. Start and run engine at fast idle. Turn steering wheel lock to lock several times to bleed trapped air. Recheck fluid level in reservoir.

ADJUSTMENTS

BELT TENSION

BELT ADJUSTMENT SPECIFICATIONS

Application	[1] Deflection In. (mm)
A/C Compressor	
Integra & Legend	0.30-0.40 (7.5-10.5)
Vigor	0.14-0.20 (3.5-5.5)
Alternator	0.28-0.43 (9.0-11.0)
Power Steering	
Integra & Legend	0.45-0.53 (11.5-13.5)
Vigor	0.27-0.34 (6.5-9.0)

[1] – With 22 lbs. (10 kg) pressure applied midway on longest belt run.

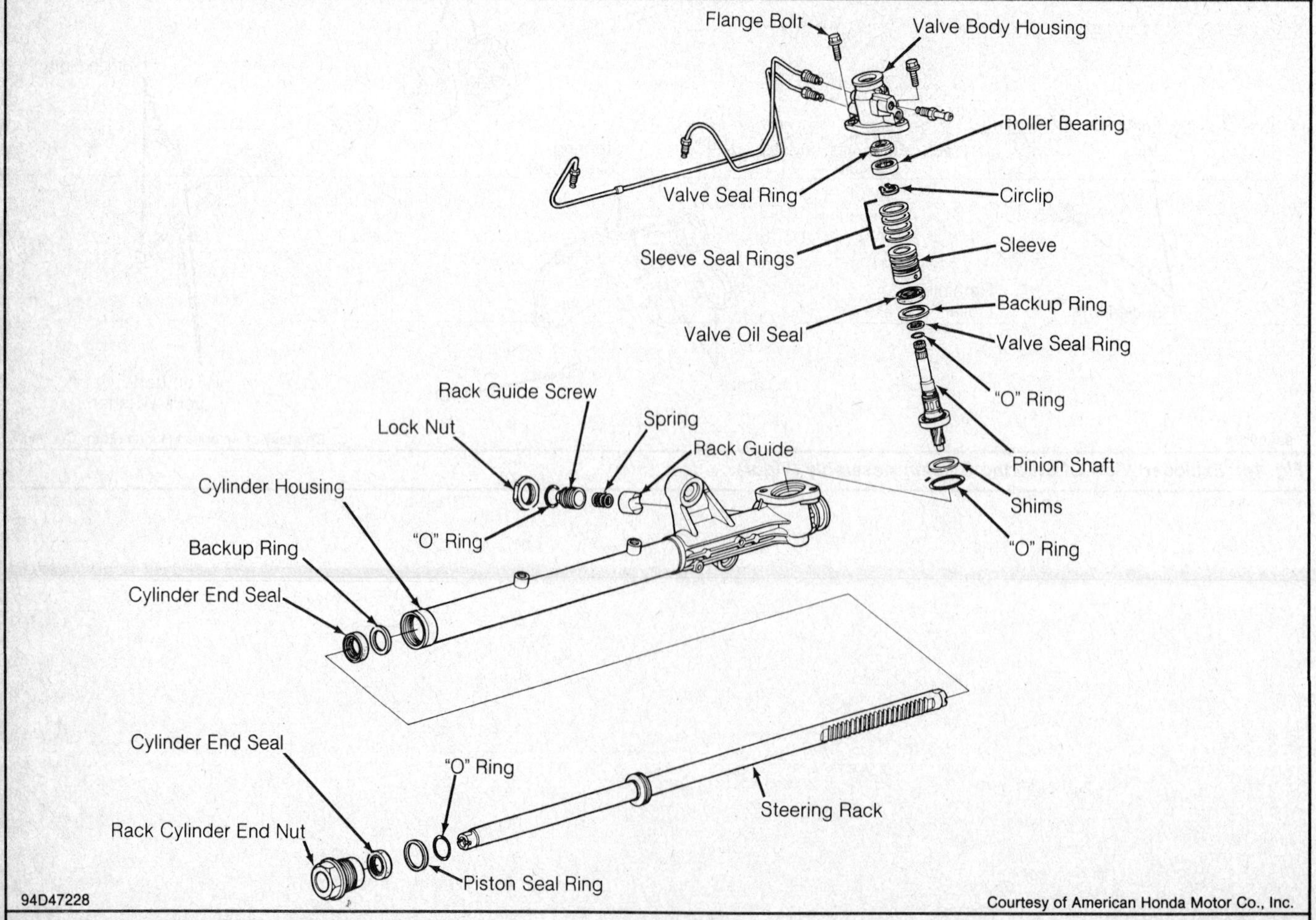

94D47228

Fig. 1: Exploded View Of Power Steering Gear (Integra)

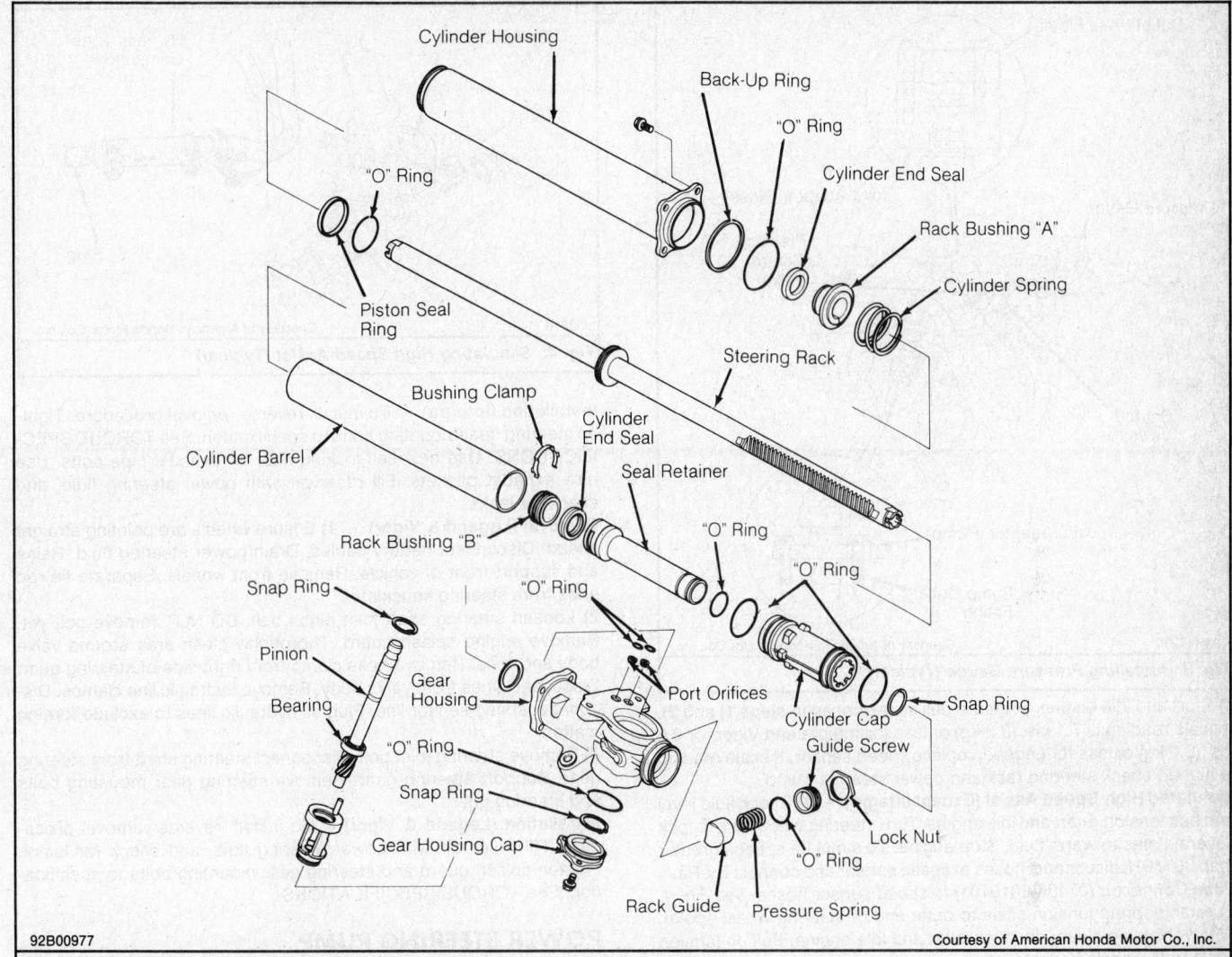

92B00977

Courtesy of American Honda Motor Co., Inc.

Fig. 2: Exploded View Of Power Steering Gear (Legend Shown; Vigor Is Similar)

PUMP PRELOAD

Integra & Vigor – Measure power steering pump preload with torque wrench after overhauling pump or installing replacement pump. Check preload with pump mounted in a vise. Maximum preload should be 36 INCH lbs. (4 N.m) for Integra and 71 INCH lbs. (8 N.m) for Vigor. If preload is higher than specification, disassemble and inspect pump.
Legend – Information is not available from manufacturer.

RACK GUIDE

1) Using Lock Nut Wrench (07916-SA50001), loosen rack guide screw lock nut. See Fig. 1 or 2. Tighten rack guide screw until spring is compressed against guide.
2) Loosen rack guide screw, and retighten it to 36 INCH lbs. (4 N.m). Back off rack guide screw about 25 degrees. Holding rack guide screw in place, tighten lock nut to 18 ft. lbs. (24 N.m). Measure steering effort. See STEERING WHEEL TURNING FORCE under TESTING.

TESTING

PUMP PRESSURE CHECK

1) Check fluid level and belt tension. Adjust as necessary. Disconnect outlet hose from pump. Install Pump Joint Adapter (07NAK-SR3011A on Integra, 07GAK-SE00112 on Legend or 07LAK-SM40110 on Vigor) onto pump outlet fitting. See Fig. 3.

2) Install Hose Joint Adapter (07NAK-SSR3012A on Integra, 07GAK-SE00120 on Legend or 07LAK-SM40120 on Vigor) onto outlet hose. Install Pressure Gauge Set (07406-0010000) between pump and hose joint adapters. Fully open shutoff and pressure control valves.
3) Start and idle engine. Turn steering wheel lock to lock several times to warm fluid. Completely close shutoff valve.
4) Gradually close pressure control valve until pressure gauge needle stabilizes. Read pressure. Immediately open shutoff valve. Pump pressure should be at least 1140 psi (80 kg/cm²). Repair or replace pump if pressure is not within specification.

CAUTION: To prevent damage to pump, DO NOT keep shutoff valve closed for longer than 5 seconds.

STEERING WHEEL TURNING FORCE

Low-Speed Assist (Integra, Legend & Vigor) – 1) Check fluid level and belt tension. Start and idle engine. Turn steering wheel lock to lock several times to warm fluid. Attach a spring tension scale to steering wheel at outer end of spoke.
2) Ensure vehicle is on a clean, dry surface. With engine at idle, pull tension scale. Read scale as soon as wheels begin to move. Reading should be a maximum of 7.1 lbs. (3.2 kg) for Integra and Vigor, or 6.6 lbs. (3.0 kg) for Legend.
3) If reading does not meet specification, stop engine and disconnect hose between control unit and speed sensor at sensor. Plug hose and sensor fitting.

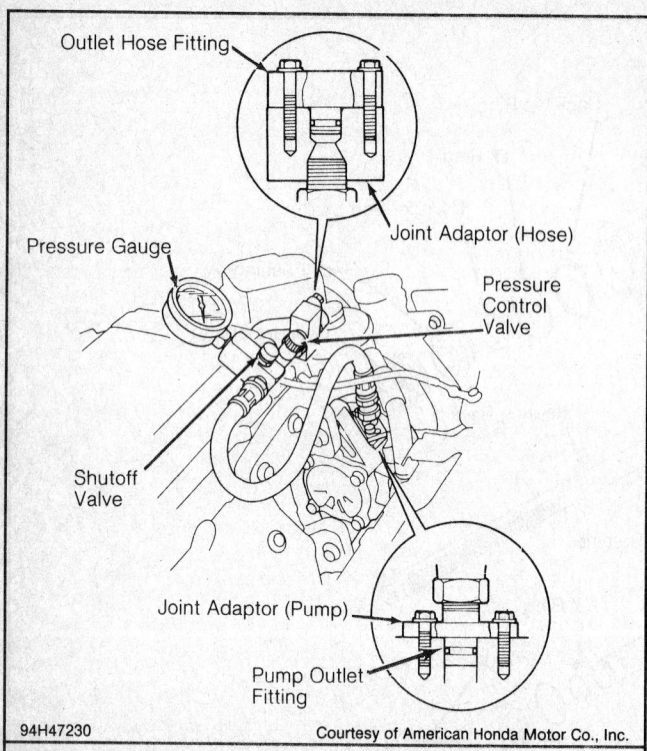

94H47230   Courtesy of American Honda Motor Co., Inc.

Fig. 3: Installing Pressure Gauge (Typical)

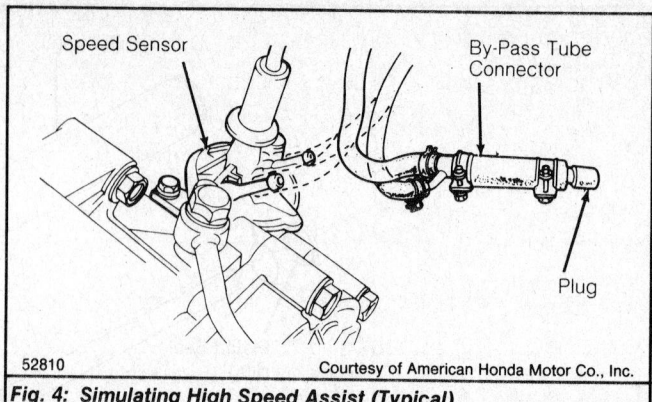

52810   Courtesy of American Honda Motor Co., Inc.

Fig. 4: Simulating High Speed Assist (Typical)

4) Start and idle engine. Measure pull as described in steps **1)** and **2)**. If scale reading is 7.1 lbs. (3.2 kg) or less for Integra and Vigor, or 6.6 lbs. (3.0 kg) or less for Legend, replace speed sensor. If scale reading is higher, check steering rack and power steering pump.

Simulated High-Speed Assist (Except Integra) – 1) Check fluid level and belt tension. Start and idle engine. Turn steering wheel lock to lock several times to warm fluid. Stop engine. To simulate speeds greater than 30 MPH, disconnect hoses at speed sensor and connect By-Pass Tube Connector (07406-0010101) to speed sensor hoses. See Fig. 4.

2) Attach spring tension scale to outer end of steering wheel spoke. With vehicle on clean, dry floor, start and idle engine. Pull on tension scale until wheels begin to move.

3) If turning force is less than 11 lbs. (5.0 kg) on Vigor, or less than 9 lbs. (4.0 kg) on Legend, speed sensor is okay. Check for pinched or bent sensor feed. If feed line is okay, problem is in pump or control unit. If turning force is 11 lbs. (5.0 kg) or more on Vigor, or 9 lbs. (4.0 kg) or more on Legend, replace faulty speed sensor.

REMOVAL & INSTALLATION

POWER RACK & PINION

Removal (Integra) – 1) Remove steering joint cover. Remove steering shaft joint pinch bolt. Disconnect steering shaft from steering gear. Drain power steering fluid. Remove steering gear shield.

2) Thoroughly clean area around valve body. Raise and support front of vehicle. Remove front wheels. Separate tie rod ends from steering knuckles. On M/T models, remove shift rod from transaxle case. Slide shift retaining pin cover back away from transaxle. Using a drift, drive shift rod retaining pin from shift rod. Disconnect shift rod from transaxle.

3) On A/T models, remove shift cable holder and cable clamp. Remove shift cable from transaxle.

4) On all models, remove exhaust pipe between exhaust header pipe and converter. Remove steering fluid tubes from valve body. Remove crossmember from below steering gear. Remove steering gear mounting bolts. Slide assembly to right until left tie rod clears frame. Lower steering gear, and remove it through left side.

Installation (Integra) – To install, reverse removal procedure. Tighten steering gear mounting bolts to specification. See TORQUE SPECIFICATIONS. Use new self-locking nuts on exhaust pipe bolts. Use new exhaust gaskets. Fill reservoir with power steering fluid, and check for leaks.

Removal (Legend & Vigor) – 1) Ensure wheels are pointing straight ahead. Disconnect battery cables. Drain power steering fluid. Raise and support front of vehicle. Remove front wheels. Separate tie rod ends from steering knuckles.

2) Loosen steering shaft joint pinch bolt. DO NOT remove bolt yet. Remove engine splash guard. Thoroughly clean area around valve body and lines. Remove hose clamp from right side of steering gear. Disconnect lines from valve body. Remove hydraulic line clamps. Disconnect speed sensor line. Plug all hydraulic lines to exclude foreign matter.

3) Remove steering joint bolt. Disconnect steering shaft from steering gear. Support steering gear. Remove steering gear mounting bolts and steering gear.

Installation (Legend & Vigor) – To install, reverse removal procedure. Fill reservoir with power steering fluid, and check for leaks. Tighten splash guard and steering gear mounting bolts to specification. See TORQUE SPECIFICATIONS.

POWER STEERING PUMP

Removal & Installation – Drain fluid. Disconnect inlet and outlet hoses at pump. On Legend, remove air cleaner cover and duct. On all models, remove power steering belt. Remove pump retaining bolts. Remove pump. To install, reverse removal procedure. Adjust belt tension. Fill reservoir with new fluid. Check for leaks.

SPEED SENSOR

Removal (Legend & Vigor) – Remove rear mount bracket stay. Unplug speed sensor connector. Disconnect and plug speed sensor hoses. Remove speed sensor mounting bolt and speed sensor.

Installation (Legend & Vigor) – Install NEW speed sensor "O" ring. After replacing sensor, turn steering wheel lock to lock several times with engine idling to bleed air from system. Check power steering fluid, and top off if necessary. Check for leaks.

VALVE BODY

Removal & Installation (Integra) – Drain power steering fluid. Remove gear box shield. Thoroughly clean area around valve body. Disconnect fluid lines from valve body, and remove flange bolts. See Fig. 5. Remove valve body from gear box. To install, reverse removal procedure. Check for leaks.

Removal & Installation (Legend & Vigor) – Remove steering gear. See POWER RACK & PINION under REMOVAL & INSTALLATION. Remove pinion dust cover. See Fig. 6. Thoroughly clean area around valve body. Remove flange bolts and valve body from gear box. To install, reverse removal procedure. Check for leaks.

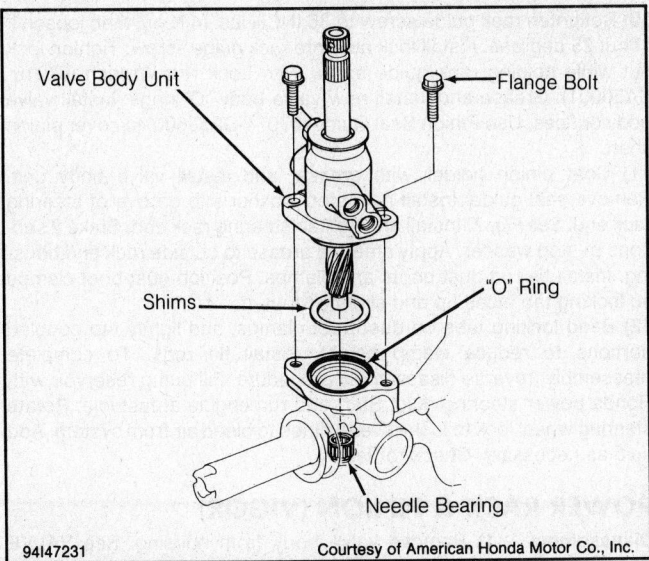

Fig. 5: Removing Valve Body (Integra)

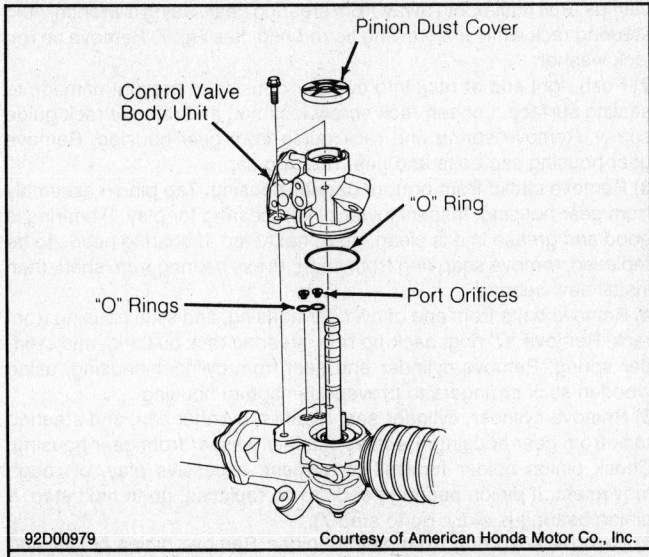

Fig. 6: Removing Valve Body (Legend Shown; Vigor Is Similar)

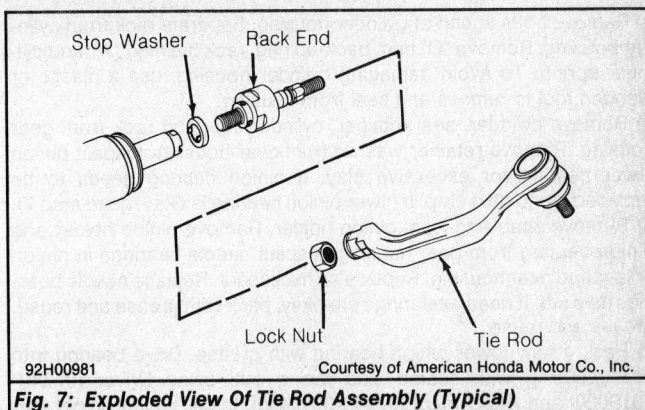

Fig. 7: Exploded View Of Tie Rod Assembly (Typical)

OVERHAUL

POWER RACK & PINION (INTEGRA)

Disassembly – 1) Remove valve body from housing. See VALVE BODY under REMOVAL & INSTALLATION. Carefully clamp steering gear in soft-jawed vise. Loosen dust boot clamps. Pull dust boots away from steering gear. Remove tie rods from rack. See Fig. 7.

2) Push right end of rack into cylinder to prevent rack from being scratched. Loosen rack guide screw lock nut. See Fig. 1. Remove rack guide screw, "O" ring, spring, and rack guide from gear housing. Remove hydraulic lines from cylinder housing. Move steering rack back and forth to drain fluid from cylinder fittings.

3) Remove valve body from gearbox. See Fig. 5. Using a 1/8" (3 mm) drill, drill out staked point on cylinder end. Do not allow metal shavings from entering cylinder housing.

4) Install a puller yoke to steering gearbox. Clamp puller in a soft-jawed vise. Loosen and remove cyliner end nut. Set gearbox facing upwards on press. Using a 12 x170 mm flange bolt with a nut installed on bolt, install flange bolt into the end of steering rack until it threads into rack hole. Back out flange bolt about 1/4" turn and tighten flange nut againt rack by hand.

5) Press cylinder end seal and steering rack out of gearbox. Remove flange bolt and nut from steering rack. Install a 24" long 3/8" drive extension and Cylinder Seal Remover Attachment (07NAD-SR30200) into cylinder from gear box side. Press out cylinder and end seal from cylinder. Remove piston seal ring and "O" ring from rack piston.

Reassembly – 1) Install NEW "O" ring and piston seal onto rack with narrow edge facing out. Coat Pinion Seal Ring Guide (07GAG-SD40100) with power steering fluid, and slide it onto rack, big end first. Position new piston seal ring on seal ring guide big end. Push new seal into piston seal ring guide groove so it sits on top of "O" ring.

2) Coat piston seal ring and Piston Seal Ring Sizer (07GAG-SD40200) with power steering fluid. Slide ring sizer onto rack and over piston seal ring. Rotate ring sizer while moving it up and down to seat piston seal ring. Coat sliding surface of Cylinder End Seal Slider (07974-6890801) and cylinder end seal with power steering fluid. Position seal on slider with grooved side facing out.

3) Grease sliding surface of steering rack. Install cylinder end seal on steering rack with grooved side facing piston. Remove tool from steering rack. Install backup ring on steering rack, behind cylinder end seal. Grease steering rack teeth, then insert steering rack into gear housing. See Fig. 1.

4) Position gear box in press facing upwards. Install flange bolt on end of steering rack. Install cylinder end seal into bottom of cylinder by using press on flange. Do not push on bolt with excessive force, as it may damage cylinder end seal.

5) Remove flange bolt and center steering rack. Install vinyl tape or Cylinder End Seal Guide (07GAG-SD40400) onto end of steering rack. Coat guide or vinyl tape and new cylinder end seal with power steering fluid. Install cylinder end seal onto steering rack with grooved end facing inside of cylinder.

6) Install puller yoke to steering gearbox, then clamp puller yoke to a soft-jawed vise. Grease inside surface of cylinder end, then install cylinder end by screwing it into cylinder housing. Stake the end of cylinder housing after tightening cylinder end nut. Reinstall valve body assembly to steering gear.

7) Fill pump reservoir with Honda power steering fluid. Start and run engine at fast idle. Rotate steering wheel lock to lock several times to bleed air from system. Add fluid as necessary. Check for leaks.

POWER RACK & PINION (LEGEND)

Disassembly – 1) Remove valve body from housing. See VALVE BODY under REMOVAL & INSTALLATION. Carefully clamp steering gear in soft-jawed vise. Remove tie rod assembly. Loosen dust boot clamps. Pull dust boots away from steering gear. Using a wrench, hold steering rack. Unscrew and remove tie rod end. Remove stop washer. See Fig. 7.

2) Push right end of rack into cylinder to prevent rack from being scratched. Loosen rack guide screw lock nut. See Fig. 2. Remove rack guide screw, "O" ring, spring, and rack guide. Remove gear housing cap. Remove snap ring from bottom of gear housing. Tap pinion from gear housing with soft hammer. Inspect upper pinion bearing for excessive play. If bearing is defective, replace pinion assembly.

3) Remove bolts at end of cylinder housing. Separate rack from cylinder housing. Remove "O" ring, back-up ring, rack bushing "A", and cylinder spring. To avoid damaging cylinder housing, use a plastic or wooden tool to remove end seal from housing.

4) Remove cylinder, seal retainer, cylinder cap, and rack from gear housing. Remove retainer washer from gear housing. Inspect pinion lower bearing for excessive play. If pinion bearing needs to be replaced, go to next step. If lower pinion bearing is okay, go to step 7).

5) Remove snap ring from pinion holder. Remove pinion holder and pinion bearing from gear housing. Inspect needle bearings in pinion holder and gear housing. Replace as necessary. Replace needle bearings as a set. If needle bearings are okay, pack with grease and reuse. grease and reuse.

6) Pack a new lower pinion bearing with grease. Drive bearing into gear housing with sealed side facing out, using Driver (07749-0010000) and Attachment (07746-0010400). Install pinion holder into gear housing. Install snap ring with tapered side facing away from housing. Align snap ring ends with flat part of pinion holder.

7) Remove cylinder and seal retainer from rack. Remove "O" rings and snap ring from seal retainer. Remove cylinder cap from seal retainer. Remove "O" rings from cylinder cap. Remove bushing clamp from seal retainer. Remove rack bushing "B" and cylinder end seal with back-up ring.

8) Carefully pry piston seal ring and "O" ring from rack. Clean all parts, and inspect for wear or damage. In addition to standard overhaul kit replacement parts, replace any other parts showing excessive wear or damage.

Reassembly – 1) Install new "O" ring onto rack, with narrow edge facing out. Coat Pinion Seal Ring Guide (07MAG-SP00100) with power steering fluid, and slide it onto rack, big end first. Position new piston seal ring onto seal ring guide big end. Push new seal into piston seal ring guide groove so that it sits on top of "O" ring.

2) Coat piston seal ring and Piston Seal Ring Sizer (07LAG-SM40200) with power steering fluid. Slide ring sizer onto rack and over piston seal ring. Rotate ring sizer while moving it up and down to seat piston seal ring. Coat new "O" rings with grease, and install rings onto cylinder cap.

3) Slide cylinder cap onto seal retainer. Install snap ring and "O" ring onto seal retainer. Grease sliding surface of steering rack bushing "B". Install bushing onto steering rack with groove in bushing facing steering rack piston. Grease sliding surfaces of new cylinder end seal and Cylinder End Seal Slider (07GAG-SD40300).

4) Position seal and back-up ring onto seal slider, with groove facing opposite slider. Grease rack, and slide seal slider onto rack past gear tooth section. Remove seal slider from cylinder end seal, then separate seal slider and remove it from rack. Fit seal retainer onto rack.

5) Push rack bushing "B" toward seal retainer by hand until cylinder end seal is seated in retainer. Fit bushing clamp in groove of seal retainer. Grease steering rack. Install retainer washer into gear housing. Insert seal retainer and rack into gear housing. Coat inside of cylinder with power steering fluid.

6) Slide cylinder over rack and into gear housing. Press cylinder into gear housing until it seats. Install cylinder spring over rack. Coat rack bushing "A" with power steering fluid, and install it onto spring. Wrap end of steering rack with vinyl tape. Coat tape with grease.

7) Coat inside of cylinder housing with power steering fluid. Install cylinder end seal with lip of seal facing toward inside of cylinder. Install "O" ring and back-up ring onto gear housing. Carefully position cylinder onto gear housing, and loosely install bolts. Remove vinyl tape from steering rack.

8) Tighten cylinder housing bolts to specification. See TORQUE SPECIFICATIONS. Carefully insert rack into cylinder housing without damaging rack sliding surface. Install pinion shaft into pinion holder. Install snap ring into pinion holder groove, with tapered side facing out. Grease new "O" ring, and place it into groove in gear housing cap. Install gear housing cap.

9) Install new "O" ring onto rack guide screw. Coat rack guide with grease. Install rack guide, spring, and rack guide screw onto gear housing. Tighten rack guide screw until it compresses spring and seats against rack guide, then loosen screw.

10) Retighten rack guide screw to 36 INCH lbs. (4 N.m), then loosen it about 25 degrees. Install lock nut onto rack guide screw. Tighten lock nut while holding rack guide screw with Lock Nut Wrench (07916-SA50001). Grease and install new valve body "O" rings. Install valve body orifices. Use Pinion Seal Guide (07974-SA50600) to cover pinion shaft.

11) Coat pinion holder with grease, and install valve body unit. Remove seal guide. Install new stop washer into groove of steering rack end. See Fig. 7. Install and tighten steering rack end. Stake 2 sections of stop washer. Apply steering grease to outside rack end housing. Install tie rod dust boots and clamps. Position dust boot clamps so locking tab faces up and slightly forward.

12) Bend locking tabs on dust boot clamps, and lightly tap doubled portions to reduce clamp height. Install tie rods. To complete reassembly, reverse disassembly procedure. Fill pump reservoir with Honda power steering fluid. Start and run engine at fast idle. Rotate steering wheel lock to lock several times to bleed air from system. Add fluid as necessary. Check for leaks.

POWER RACK & PINION (VIGOR)

Disassembly – 1) Remove valve body from housing. See VALVE BODY under REMOVAL & INSTALLATION. Carefully clamp steering gear in soft-jawed vise. Remove tie rod assembly. Loosen dust boot clamps. Pull dust boots away from steering gear. Using a wrench, hold steering rack while unscrewing tie rod end. See Fig. 7. Remove tie rod lock washer.

2) Push right end of rack into cylinder housing to prevent damage to sealing surface. Loosen rack screw lock nut, and remove rack guide screw. Remove spring and rack guide from gear housing. Remove gear housing cap bolts and gear housing cap.

3) Remove circlip from bottom of gear housing. Tap pinion assembly from gear housing. Inspect lower pinion bearing for play. If bearing is good and grease in it is clean, go to next step. If bearing needs to be replaced, remove snap ring from shaft. Press bearing from shaft, then install new bearing.

4) Remove bolts from end of cylinder housing, and slide housing from rack. Remove "O" ring, back-up ring, steering rack bushing, and cylinder spring. Remove cylinder end seal from cylinder housing, using wooden stick or fingers to prevent damage to housing.

5) Remove cylinder, cylinder seal retainer, cylinder cap, and steering rack from gear housing. Remove retainer washer from gear housing. Check pinion holder for free movement, excessive play, or rough movement. If pinion bearing needs to be replaced, go to next step. If pinion bearing is okay, go to step 7).

6) Remove snap ring from pinion holder. Remove pinion holder and pinion upper bearing from gear housing. Inspect needle bearings in pinion holder and gear housing. If replacing needle bearings, replace them as a set. If needle bearings are okay, pack them with grease and reuse them. Replace damaged pinion bearings as necessary.

7) Remove cylinder and seal retainer from steering rack. Remove "O" ring and snap ring from seal retainer. Remove cylinder cap from seal retainer. Remove "O" rings from cylinder cap. Remove bushing stopper ring from seal retainer. Remove cylinder end seal and rack bushing. Carefully pry piston seal ring and "O" ring from rack.

Reassembly – 1) Install new "O" ring onto rack, with narrow edge facing out. Coat Pinion Seal Ring Guide (07HAG-SF10100) with power steering fluid, and slide it onto rack, big end first. Position new piston seal ring onto seal ring guide big end. Push new seal into piston seal ring guide groove so it sits on top of "O" ring.

2) Coat piston seal ring and Piston Seal Ring Sizer (07HAG-SF10200) with power steering fluid. Slide ring sizer onto rack and over piston seal ring. Rotate ring sizer while moving it up and down to seat piston seal ring. Coat new "O" rings with grease, and install onto cylinder cap.

3) Slide cylinder cap onto seal retainer. Install snap ring and "O" ring onto seal retainer. Grease sliding surface of steering rack bushing "B", and install bushing onto steering rack with groove in bushing facing steering rack piston. Grease sliding surfaces of new cylinder end seal and Cylinder End Seal Slider (07GAG-SD40300).

4) Position seal and back-up ring onto seal slider, with groove facing opposite slider. Grease rack, and position seal slider onto rack past gear tooth section. Remove seal slider from cylinder end seal. Separate seal slider and remove it from rack. Fit seal retainer onto rack.

5) Push rack bushing "B" toward seal retainer by hand until cylinder end seal is seated in retainer. Fit bushing clamp in groove of seal retainer. Grease steering rack. Install retainer washer into gear housing. Insert seal retainer and rack into gear housing. Coat inside of cylinder with power steering fluid.

6) Slide cylinder over rack and into gear housing. Press cylinder into gear housing until it seats. Install cylinder spring over rack. Coat rack bushing "A" with power steering fluid, and install it onto spring. Wrap end of steering rack with vinyl tape. Coat tape with grease.

7) Coat inside of cylinder housing with power steering fluid. Install cylinder end seal with lip of seal facing toward inside of cylinder. Install "O" ring and back-up ring onto gear housing. Carefully position cylinder onto gear housing, and loosely install bolts. Remove vinyl tape from steering rack.

8) Tighten cylinder housing bolts to specification. See TORQUE SPECIFICATIONS. Carefully insert rack into cylinder housing without damaging rack sliding surface. Install pinion shaft into pinion holder. Install snap ring into pinion holder groove, with tapered side facing out. Grease new "O" ring, and place into groove in gear housing cap. Install gear housing cap.

9) Install new "O" ring onto rack guide screw. Coat rack guide with grease. Install rack guide, spring, and rack guide screw onto gear housing. Tighten rack guide screw until it compresses spring and seats against rack guide, then loosen screw.

10) Retighten rack guide screw to 36 INCH lbs. (4 N.m), then loosen it about 25 degrees. Install lock nut onto rack guide screw. Tighten lock nut while holding rack guide screw with Lock Nut Wrench (07916-SA50001). Grease and install new valve body "O" rings. Install valve body orifices. Use Pinion Seal Guide (07974-SA50600) to cover pinion shaft.

11) Coat pinion holder with grease. Install valve body unit. Remove seal guide. Install new stop washer into groove of steering rack end. See Fig. 7. Install and tighten steering rack end. Stake 2 sections of stop washer. Apply steering grease to outside rack end housing. Install tie rod dust boots and clamps. Position dust boot clamps so locking tab faces up and slightly forward.

12) Bend locking tabs on dust boot clamps, and lightly tap on doubled portions to reduce clamp height. Install tie rods. To complete reassembly, reverse disassembly procedure. Fill pump reservoir with Honda power steering fluid. Start and run engine at fast idle. Rotate steering wheel lock to lock several times to bleed air from system. Add fluid as necessary. Check for leaks.

POWER STEERING PUMP

Disassembly & Reassembly (Integra) – 1) Remove power steering pump from vehicle. See POWER STEERING PUMP under REMOVAL & INSTALLATION. Using Universal Holder (07725-0030000) to hold pump pulley, remove pulley bolt. Pulley bolt has left-hand threads. Remove pump pulley and pump front cover. Remove port fitting and control valve. Control valves are available in 2 sizes. "A" is stamped on control valve "A" for identification. Control valve "B" has no identification mark. Ensure same size control valve is returned to pump on reassembly. Remove "O" ring from control valve. See Fig. 8.

2) Remove dowel pins and housing seal from pump housing. Remove dowel pins, plunger seal, and "O" ring. Separate port housing from pump housing. Remove housing seal and dowel pins.

3) Remove dowel pins from pump housing. Remove housing seal and "O" ring from port housing. Remove pump drive and driven gears from housing. Remove plunger seal and plungers.

4) Pry out oil seal from front pump cover. Clean and inspect all parts, and replace as necessary. To reassemble, reverse disassembly procedure. Coat new oil seal with Power Steering Grease (08733-B070E) before assembly. Coat all other parts with power steering fluid. Use a 30-mm socket to install front pump cover seal.

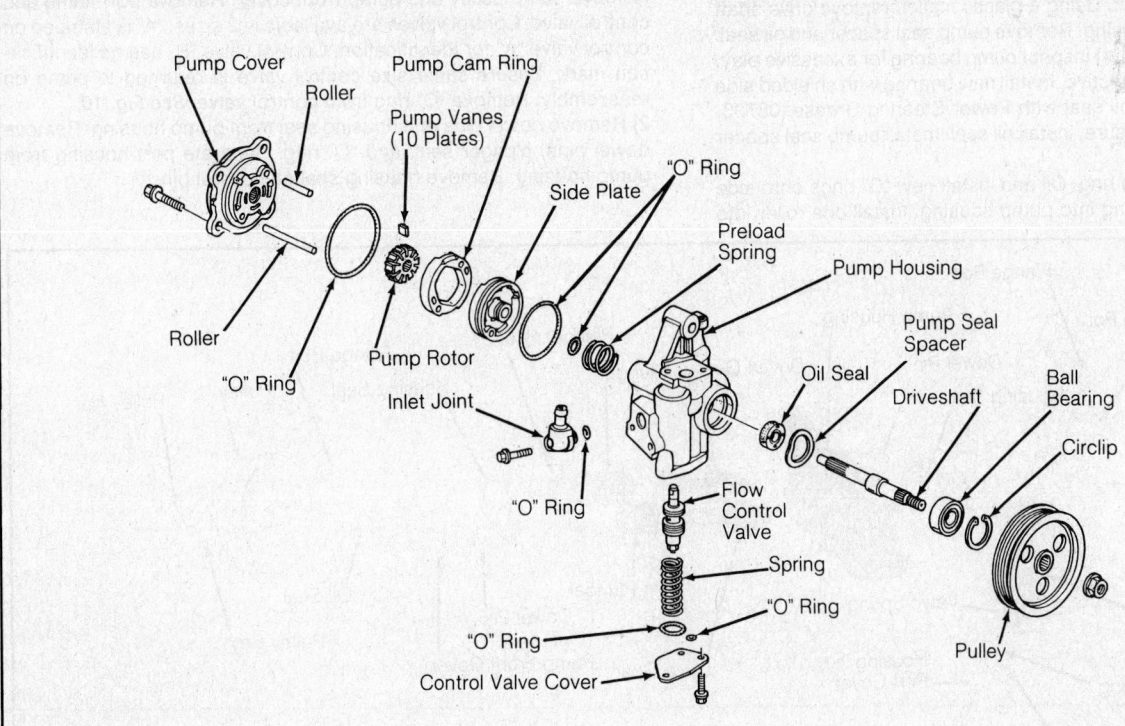

94A47233 — Courtesy of American Honda Motor Co., Inc.

Fig. 8: Exploded View Of Power Steering Pump (Integra)

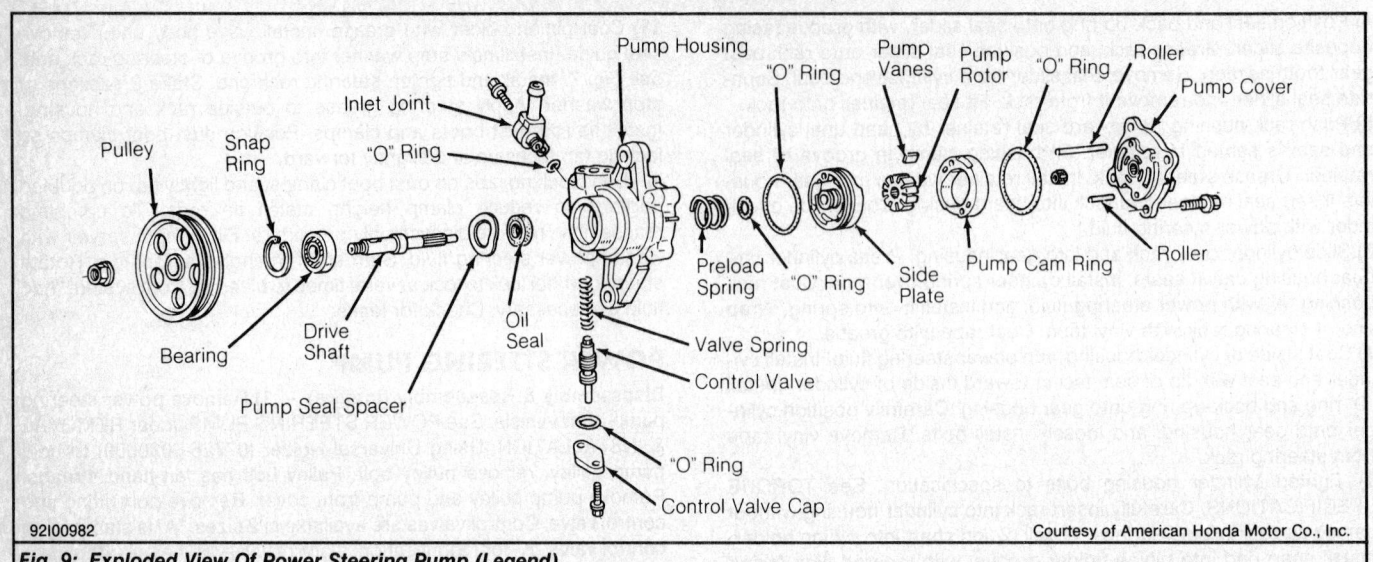

Fig. 9: Exploded View Of Power Steering Pump (Legend)

92I00982   Courtesy of American Honda Motor Co., Inc.

Disassembly (Legend) – 1) Remove power steering pump from vehicle. See POWER STEERING PUMP under REMOVAL & INSTALLATION. Using Universal Holder (07725-0030000) to hold pump pulley, remove pulley bolt and pulley. Pulley bolt has right-hand threads.

2) Remove control valve cap. *See Fig. 9.* Remove control valve, spring, and "O" ring. Inspect control valve for wear and damage. Check that valve moves in and out of pump smoothly. Control valves are available in 2 sizes. "A" is stamped on control valve "A" for identification. Control valve "B" has no identification mark. Remove inlet joint and "O" ring. Remove pump front cover.

3) Remove pump cam ring from pump housing. Remove pump rotor and vanes. Remove rollers, side plate, and preload spring. Remove snap ring from drive shaft. Using a plastic mallet, remove drive shaft assembly from pump housing. Remove pump seal spacer and oil seal.

Reassembly (Legend) – 1) Inspect pump bearing for excessive play. Replace bearing if it is defective. Install new bearing with shielded side facing down. Coat new oil seal with Power Steering Grease (08733-B070E). Using hand pressure, install oil seal. Install pump seal spacer and pump drive shaft.

2) Install drive shaft snap ring. Oil and install new "O" rings onto side plate. Install preload spring into pump housing. Install one roller into hole in pump housing. Align hole in side plate with roller, and install side plate. *See Fig. 9.* Install remaining roller into side plate.

3) Install pump cam ring with "0" (zero) mark on cam ring facing upward. Install pump rotor onto drive shaft with "0" (zero) mark on rotor facing upward. Install vanes into rotor grooves. Rounded ends of vanes face toward cam ring. To complete reassembly, reverse disassembly procedure. Ensure pump turns smoothly when rotating pump pulley.

Disassembly & Reassembly (Vigor) – 1) Remove power steering pump from vehicle. See POWER STEERING PUMP under REMOVAL & INSTALLATION. Using Universal Holder (07725-0030000) to hold pump pulley, remove pulley bolt. Pulley bolt has left-hand threads. Remove pump pulley and pump front cover. Remove port fitting and control valve. Control valves are available in 2 sizes. "A" is stamped on control valve "A" for identification. Control valve "B" has no identification mark. Ensure same size control valve is returned to pump on reassembly. Remove "O" ring from control valve. *See Fig. 10.*

2) Remove dowel pins and housing seal from pump housing. Remove dowel pins, plunger seal, and "O" ring. Separate port housing from pump housing. Remove housing seal and dowel pins.

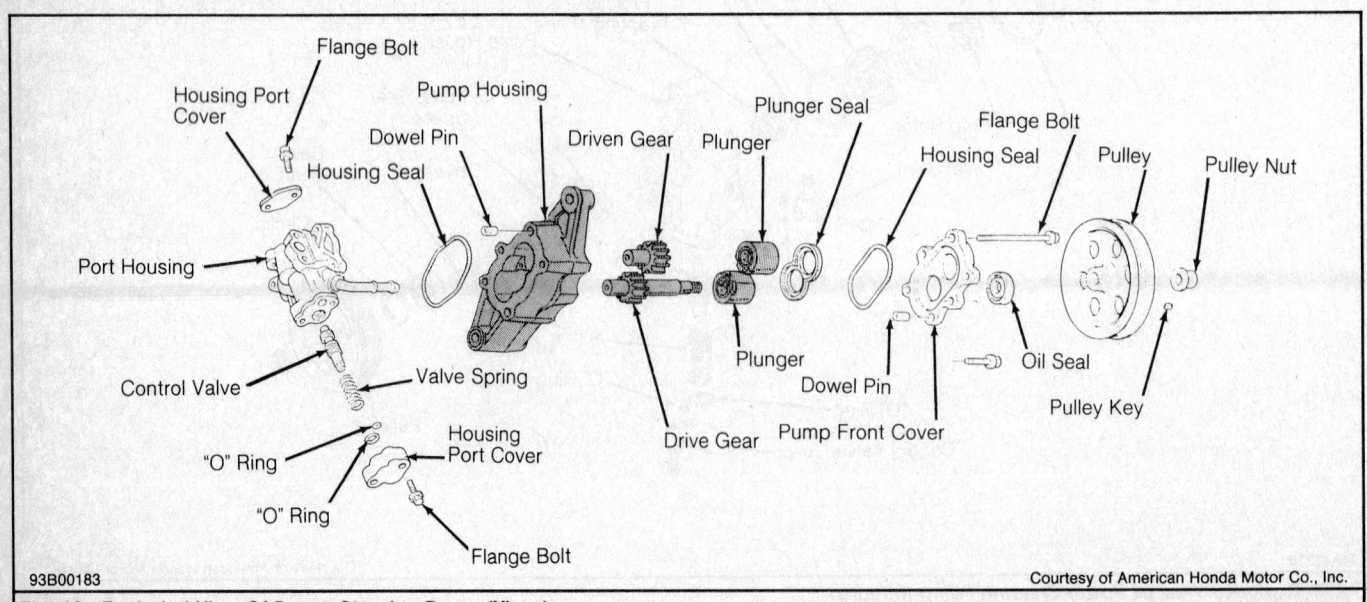

93B00183   Courtesy of American Honda Motor Co., Inc.

Fig. 10: Exploded View Of Power Steering Pump (Vigor)

3) Remove dowel pins from pump housing. Remove housing seal and "O" ring from port housing. Remove pump drive and driven gears from housing. Remove plunger seal and plungers.

4) Pry oil seal from front pump cover. Clean and inspect all parts, and replace as necessary. To reassemble, reverse disassembly procedure. Coat new oil seal with Power Steering Grease (08733-B070E) before assembly. Coat all other parts with power steering fluid. Use a 30-mm socket to install front pump cover seal.

VALVE BODY

Disassembly & Reassembly (Integra) – 1) Remove valve body flange bolts. *See Fig. 1 or 5.* Remove valve body from gear box. Wrap pinion shaft with vinyl tape. Press out pinion shaft from valve housing. Check valve housing inner wall for ridges. Replace valve housing if ridges are present.

2) If valve housing is replaced, install NEW 32 mm shim(s) on bearing surface of housing to adjust thickness. Check for signs of wear, burr or other damage to edges of sleeve groove. If necessary, replace both pinion shaft and sleeve as a set.

3) Remove pinion shaft sleeve from pinion shaft. Remove seal rings and "O" rings from sleeve. Press out oil seal and bearing from valve body. Inspect all parts for wear or damage. Always replace "O" rings and seals before assembly. To reassemble, reverse removal procedure. Coat all parts with Power Steering Grease (08733-B070E) before reassembly.

Disassembly & Reassembly (Legend & Vigor) – 1) On Legend, remove pinion dust seal. On Vigor models, remove valve body flange bolts. Remove cap from valve body. *See Fig. 11 or 12.* Remove cap seal from cap. Remove pressure control valve and spring from valve body. Inspect pressure control valve for wear or damage. Replace valve as necessary.

2) Remove gain control valve and spring from valve body. Inspect gain control valve for wear or damage. Replace as necessary. Separate valve body and port housing. Remove port seal and dowel from port housing. Remove rollers from control valve by pushing valve out one side and then the other.

3) Remove plungers, return springs, and control valve from valve body. Inspect plungers and control valve for wear or damage. Using a 1/16" (1.5 mm) drill bit, remove sensor orifice and "O" ring. If valve body is damaged, replace it as an assembly. Inspect all parts for wear or damage, and replace as necessary.

4) To reassemble, reverse disassembly procedure. Coat all parts with Power Steering Grease (08733-B070E) before assembly.

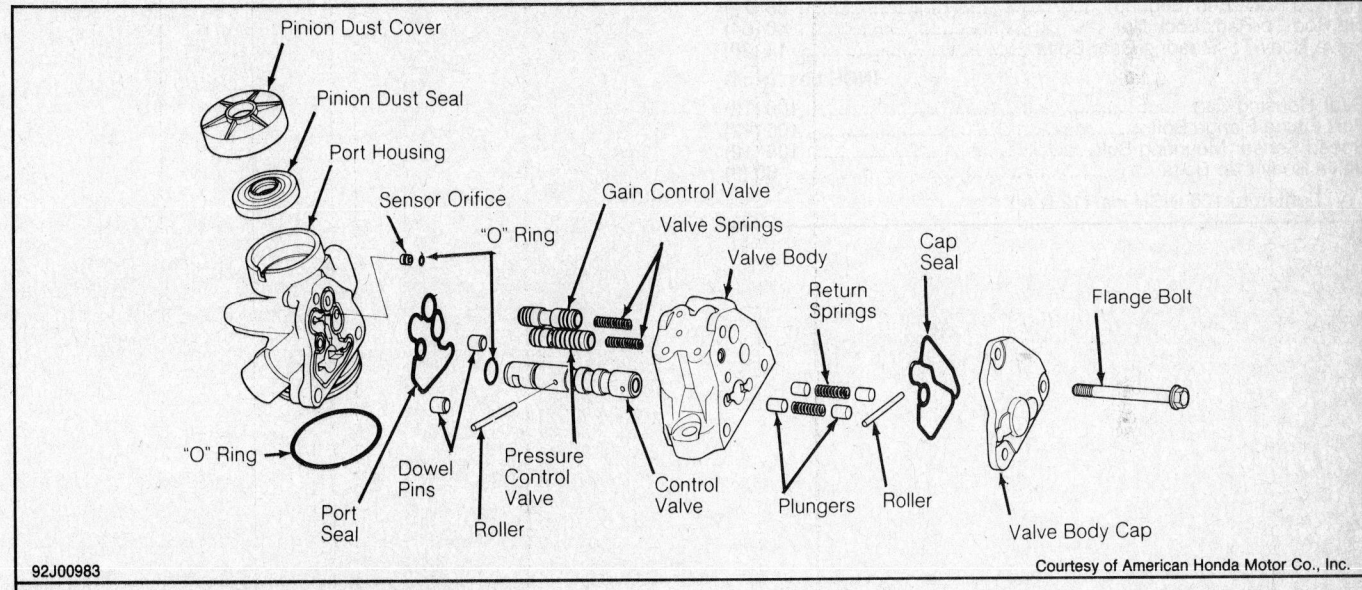

92J00983

Courtesy of American Honda Motor Co., Inc.

Fig. 11: Exploded View Of Valve Body (Legend)

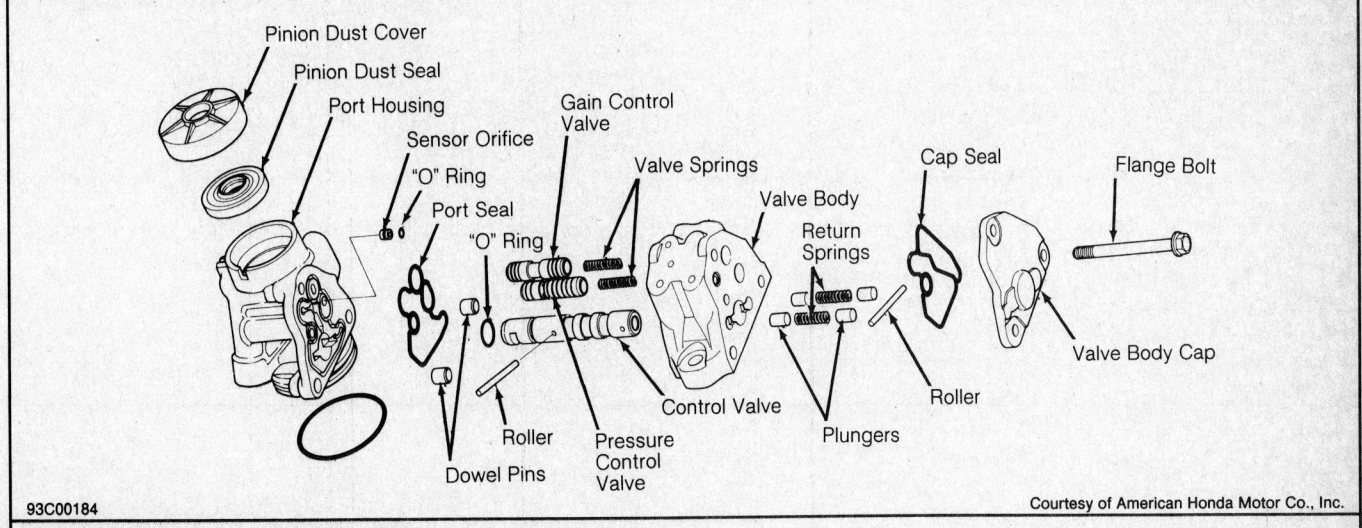

93C00184

Courtesy of American Honda Motor Co., Inc.

Fig. 12: Exploded View Of Valve Body (Vigor)

TORQUE SPECIFICATIONS
TORQUE SPECIFICATIONS

Application	Ft. Lbs. (N.m)
Hydraulic Lines	
Integra	
Pump (Outlet Hose)	1
Steering Rack Cylinder	12 (17)
Valve Body	20 (26)
Legend & Vigor	
Return Line	
6 mm	1
10 mm	21 (28)
Pump Front Cover Bolts	
Integra & Legend	14 (19)
Vigor	1
Pump Pulley Nut	47 (64)
Pump-To-Bracket Bolt	
Integra	18 (24)
Legend & Vigor	33 (45)
Rack Cylinder-To-Gear Housing Bolt	16 (22)
Rack Guide Lock Nut	18 (24)
Rack Cylinder End Nut (Integra)	51 (69)
Shift Cable Holder (Legend)	20 (27)
Steering Gear Mounting Bolts	28 (38)
Tie Rod End Nuts	32 (43)
Tie Rod Rack End (Legend)	58 (79)
Tie Rod-To-Rack Lock Nut	40 (54)
Valve Body-To-Steering Gear Bolts	14 (20)
	INCH Lbs. (N.m)
Gear Housing Cap	106 (12)
Port Fitting Flange Bolt	106 (12)
Speed Sensor Mounting Bolt	106 (12)
Valve Body Cap Bolts	80 (9)

1 – Tighten to 106 INCH lbs. (12 N.m).

Integra, Legend, Vigor

IDENTIFICATION

AUTOMATIC TRANSAXLE APPLICATIONS

Model	Transaxle
Integra	Model MP7A
Legend	Model MPYA
Vigor	Model MPWA

LUBRICATION

SERVICE INTERVALS

Change fluid every 30,000 miles. No filter service or band adjustment is required.

CHECKING FLUID LEVEL

Start and run engine until it reaches normal operating temperature. Turn ignition off. Check fluid level with vehicle on level floor. Fluid level should be between FULL and LOW marks. Add fluid if necessary. On Integra, DO NOT use a wrench to secure dipstick.

RECOMMENDED FLUID

Use Honda premium formula Automatic Transmission Fluid (ATF) or Dexron-II transmission fluid.

FLUID CAPACITIES

TRANSAXLE REFILL CAPACITIES

Application	Refill Qts. (L)	Dry Fill Qts. (L)
Integra	3.0 (2.8)	6.2 (5.9)
Legend	3.5 (3.3)	9.2 (8.7)
Vigor	2.6 (2.5)	7.6 (7.2)

DIFFERENTIAL REFILL CAPACITIES

Application	Refill Qts. (L)	Dry Fill Qts. (L)
Legend [1]	1.1 (1.00)	1.2 (1.10)
Vigor [1]	1.0 (0.95)	1.1 (1.00)

[1] – Use Hypoid SAE 90 fluid above 0°F (-18°C). Use SAE 80W-90 below 0°F (-18°C).

DRAINING & REFILLING

Warm transaxle to normal operating temperature. Remove transaxle drain plug. Using new gasket, replace drain plug when fluid is drained. Tighten drain plug to specification. See TORQUE SPECIFICATIONS. Refill transaxle to FULL mark on dipstick. See TRANSAXLE REFILL CAPACITIES table under FLUID CAPACITIES.

ADJUSTMENTS

WARNING: Legend and Vigor are equipped with Supplemental Restraint System (SRS). All SRS wiring is color-coded Yellow. DO NOT use electrical test equipment on these circuits. Disconnect negative and positive battery cables before removing console. Wait at least 3 minutes after deactivating air bag system. System maintains voltage for about 3 minutes after battery is disconnected. Servicing air bag system before 3 minutes may cause accidental air bag deployment and possible personal injury.

CAUTION: Radio has a coded theft protection circuit. Before disconnecting battery cables, obtain radio anti-theft code number from customer. After reconnecting power, turn radio on. Word CODE will be displayed. Enter customer 5-digit code to restore radio operation.

SHIFT CONTROL CABLE

Integra & Legend – 1) Start engine. Shift to Reverse. Verify transaxle engages in Reverse. With engine off, remove console. Shift gear selector into Neutral (Integra) or Reverse (Legend) position. Remove lock pin from cable adjuster. Align hole in adjuster with hole in shift cable. *See Fig. 1.*

2) Two holes in end of shift cable are positioned at 90 degrees to allow cable adjustments in 1/4-turn increments. Loosen lock nut on shift cable, and adjust if necessary. *See Fig. 1.* Tighten lock nut. Install lock pin.

3) Lock pin should not bind as it is installed. If it binds, cable is still out of adjustment. Repeat adjustment procedure. Start engine, and check shift lever selection of all gears.

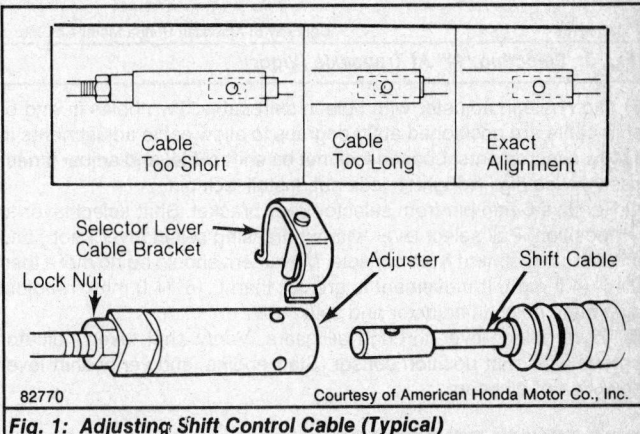

82770   Courtesy of American Honda Motor Co., Inc.

Fig. 1: Adjusting Shift Control Cable (Typical)

Vigor – 1) Start engine. Shift to Reverse. Verify transaxle engages in Reverse. With engine off, remove console. Shift gear selector into Neutral position. Remove lock pin from cable adjuster. Insert a 6-mm pin into selector lever bracket through lock pin sliding hole. *See Fig. 2.*

2) Verify shift position is in "N" position on transaxle. *See Fig. 3.* Mark on indicator should align with "N" mark at shift indicator panel. If marks are not aligned, loosen indicator panel mounting screws and adjust by moving panel. Set ignition switch to ON position, and verify "N" indicator light comes on.

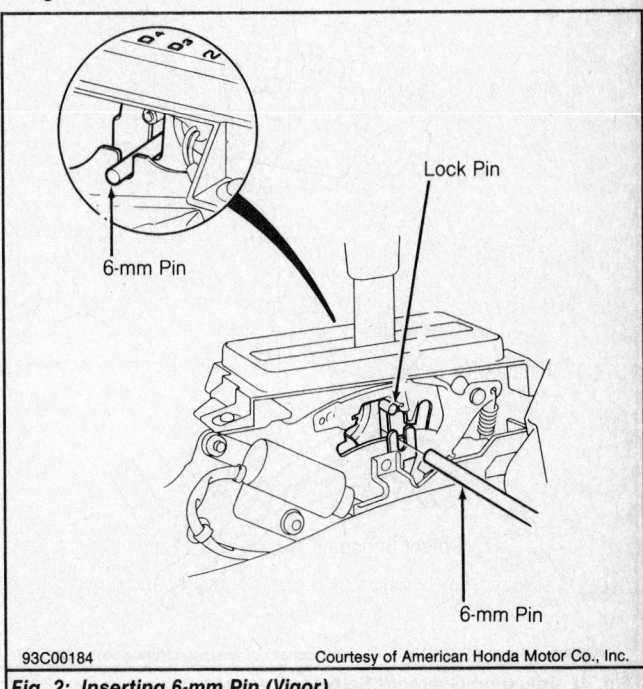

93C00184   Courtesy of American Honda Motor Co., Inc.

Fig. 2: Inserting 6-mm Pin (Vigor)

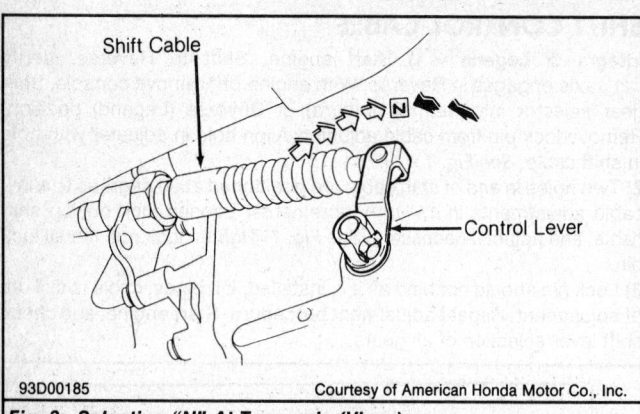

93D00185   Courtesy of American Honda Motor Co., Inc.

Fig. 3: Selecting "N" At Transaxle (Vigor)

3) Align hole in adjuster with hole in shift cable. Two holes in end of shift cable are positioned at 90 degrees to allow cable adjustments in 1/4-turn increments. Loosen lock nut on shift cable, and adjust if necessary. *See Fig. 1.* Tighten lock nut. Install lock pin.

4) Remove 6-mm pin from selector lever bracket. Shift select lever to "P" position. Pull select lever without pressing select lever knob, and measure movement from console. Movement should be no more than 0.16" (4.0 mm). If movement is greater than 0.16" (4.0 mm), readjust alignment holes in adjuster and shift cable.

5) Move select lever through all gears. Verify shift lever indicator agrees with shift position sensor. Start engine, and verify shift lever selection of all gears.

GEARSHIFT SELECTOR

Legend – Remove center console. Shift gear selector into Neutral position. Measure clearance between lock pin and lock pin gate. Clearance should be 0.008-0.020" (0.20-0.51 mm). *See Fig. 4.* If clearance is not within specification, loosen bolt "B" and adjust. After adjustment, verify gearshift selector movement.

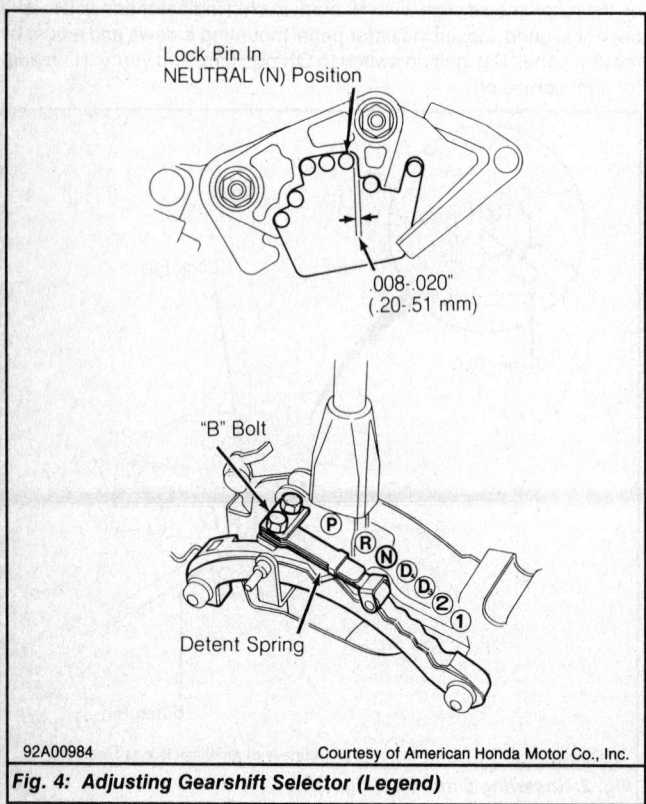

92A00984   Courtesy of American Honda Motor Co., Inc.

Fig. 4: Adjusting Gearshift Selector (Legend)

SHIFT INDICATOR PANEL

Legend & Vigor – Shift gear selector into Neutral position. Index mark on shift indicator should align with "N" mark on shift indicator panel. *See Fig. 5.* If index mark is not aligned, remove center console. Remove shift indicator panel mounting screws, and adjust by moving panel.

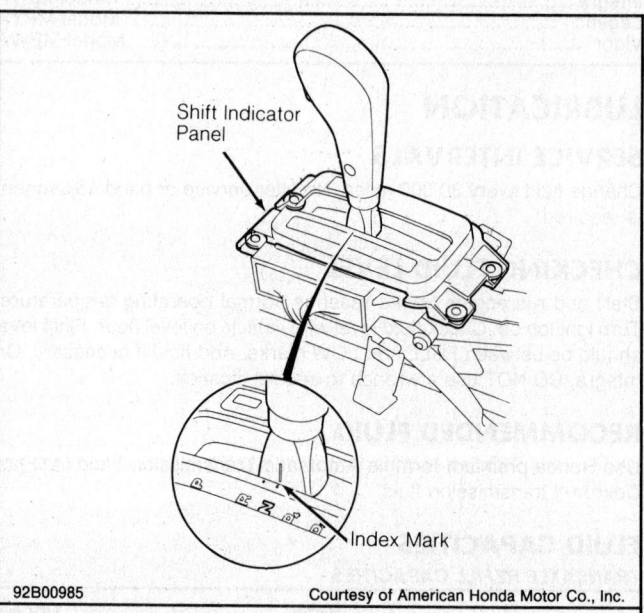

92B00985   Courtesy of American Honda Motor Co., Inc.

Fig. 5: Adjusting Shift Indicator Panel (Legend Shown; Vigor Is Similar)

NEUTRAL SAFETY SWITCH

Neutral safety switch is located at bottom of shift lever, under console. Engine should start in Park and Neutral only. If vehicle does not operate as described, loosen 2 switch mounting screws and readjust.

TORQUE SPECIFICATIONS
TORQUE SPECIFICATIONS

Application	Ft. Lbs. (N.m)
Differential Drain Plug	
Legend	33 (45)
Vigor	35 (48)
Transaxle Drain Plug	
Integra	29 (39)
Legend & Vigor	37 (50)
	INCH Lbs. (N.m)
Shift Cable Lock Nut	62 (7)

Integra, Legend, Vigor

IDENTIFICATION
MANUAL TRANSAXLE APPLICATIONS

Model	Transaxle
Integra	5-Speed – Model Y80
Legend	5-Speed – Model K4A6
Vigor	5-Speed – Model L3A3

LUBRICATION

SERVICE INTERVALS
Change fluid every 30,000 miles.

CHECKING FLUID LEVEL
Ensure fluid level is at bottom of fill hole. Drain plug is located on bottom of case. Replace drain plug gasket whenever fluid is changed.

RECOMMENDED FLUID
Use SAE 10W-30 or 10W-40 engine oil API grade SF or SG.

FLUID CAPACITIES
TRANSAXLE REFILL CAPACITIES

Application	Refill Qts. (L)	Dry Fill Qts. (L)
Integra	2.3 (2.2)	2.4 (2.3)
Legend	2.4 (2.3)	2.7 (2.6)
Vigor	1.9 (1.8)	2.1 (2.0)

DIFFERENTIAL REFILL CAPACITIES

Application	Refill Qts. (L)	Dry Fill Qts. (L)
Legend [1]	1.10 (1.0)	1.20 (1.1)
Vigor [1]	0.95 (0.9)	1.06 (1.0)

[1] – Use Hypoid SAE 90 fluid.

ADJUSTMENTS

LINKAGE
No external adjustments are required.

1994 TRANSMISSION SERVICING
Transaxle Removal & Installation

Integra, Legend, Vigor

MANUAL

NOTE: For manual transaxle replacement procedures, see FWD article in CLUTCHES.

AUTOMATIC

WARNING: All models are equipped with Supplemental Restraint System (SRS). All SRS wiring is color-coded Yellow. Before performing any repairs, disable air bag system. See AIR BAG RESTRAINT SYSTEM article in ACCESSORIES & EQUIPMENT. Wait at least 3 minutes after deactivating air bag system. System maintains voltage for about 3 minutes after battery is disconnected. Servicing air bag system before 3 minutes may cause accidental air bag deployment and possible personal injury.

CAUTION: Radio has a coded theft protection circuit. Before disconnecting battery cables, obtain radio anti-theft code number from customer. After reconnecting power, turn radio on. Word CODE will be displayed. Enter customer 5-digit code to restore radio operation.

INTEGRA

Removal – 1) Disconnect negative and then positive battery cable. Remove battery. Remove air intake hose and battery base. Disconnect starter wiring. Remove starter retaining bolts and starter. Disconnect transaxle ground strap. Unplug speed sensor connector. Leaving hydraulic hose attached, remove speed sensor.

2) Unplug lock-up control solenoid valve connectors. Disconnect hose from vacuum modulator. Drain transaxle fluid. Disconnect and plug transaxle cooler lines. On all models except GS-R, remove center crossmember. On all models, remove exhaust pipe. Turn ignition switch to release steering lock. Shift transaxle to Neutral.

3) Remove left and right axle shafts. See FWD AXLE SHAFTS article in DRIVE AXLES. Remove intermediate shaft. Remove engine and right wheelwell splash shields. Remove right damper bolt, and separate damper from damper fork.

4) Remove right radius rod. Remove front and rear engine stiffeners. Remove flywheel inspection cover and shift cable holder. Disconnect shift cable by removing cotter pin, control pin, and control lever roller. Remove shift cable guide. Remove drive plate bolts.

5) Remove bolt from front engine mount. Remove mounting bolts from rear engine mount bracket. Remove front and rear transaxle housing mounting bolts. Loosen differential housing mounting bolts. Attach a hoist to transaxle housing hoist bracket and differential housing-to-engine mounting bolt. Lift engine slightly to unload mounts.

6) Place a jack under transaxle, and raise transaxle just enough to take weight from mounts. Remove front engine mount. Remove transaxle mount and mount bracket bolts. Pull transaxle away from engine until it clears dowel pins. Lower transaxle and remove from vehicle.

Installation – To install transaxle, reverse removal procedure. Replace all exhaust system gaskets and self-locking bolts and nuts. Use new spring clips on ends of both axle shafts. Tighten bolts to specification. See TORQUE SPECIFICATIONS. Refill with A/T fluid.

LEGEND

Removal – 1) Disconnect negative and then positive battery cable. Remove strut bar. Drain transaxle fluid. Without removing vacuum lines, remove ignition timing control box and set it aside. Unplug wiring harness connectors as necessary. Remove fluid fill tube. Remove transaxle housing bolts.

2) Remove exhaust pipe from exhaust manifolds. Remove catalytic converter. Remove heat shield and bracket. Disconnect oil cooler hoses from joint pipes. See Fig. 1. Remove shift cable cover. Remove shift cable holder from shift cable holder base.

3) Remove control lever from control shaft. See Fig. 1. Remove lower plate, and reinstall steering gear assembly mounting bolts. See Fig. 2. Rotate control shaft and shift transaxle into "P" position (Park).

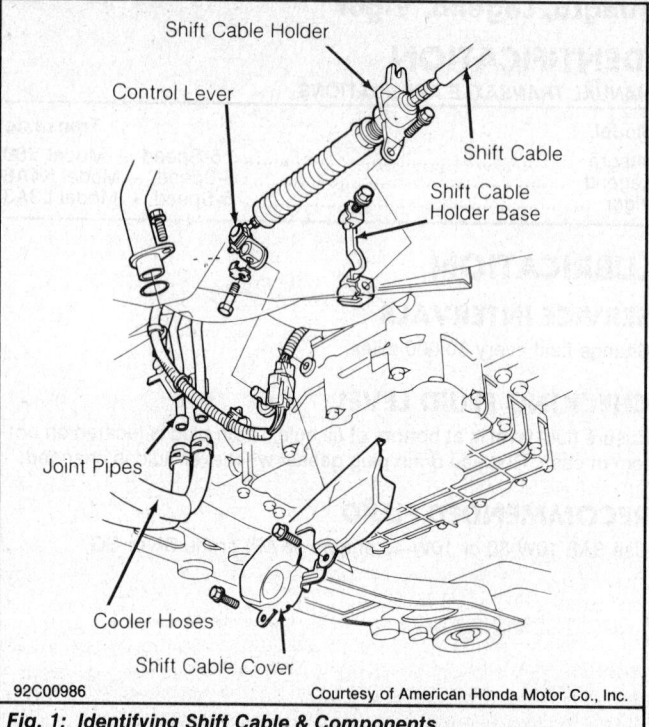

Fig. 1: Identifying Shift Cable & Components
(Legend Shown; Vigor Is Similar)

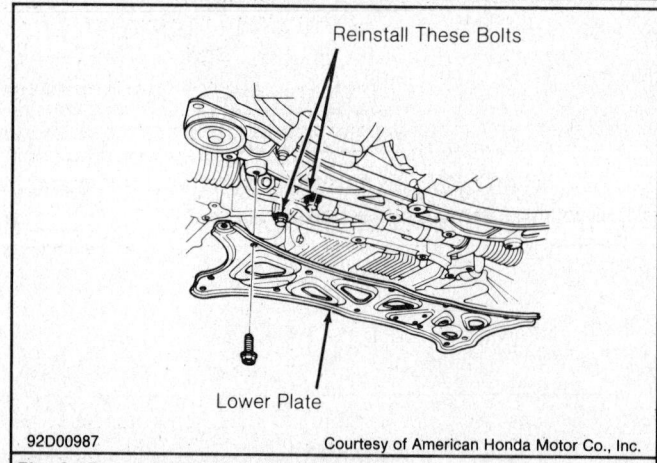

Fig. 2: Removing Lower Plate (Legend)

4) Remove secondary cover and 36-mm sealing bolt from transaxle. See Fig. 3. Using Extension Shaft Puller (07LAC-PW50100), disconnect extension shaft from differential. Remove and discard set ring. Place jack under transaxle.

5) Raise transaxle high enough to take weight from middle transaxle mounts. Remove middle transaxle mounts. Remove shift cable guide from transaxle. Remove rear transaxle mount/mount bracket and exhaust pipe bracket. Remove engine stiffener. Remove flywheel inspection cover.

6) Remove drive plate bolts. Remove transaxle housing mounting bolts and 26-mm shim. See Fig. 4. Check for wires, hoses, or other components that may still be attached. Pull transaxle away from engine until it clears dowel pins. Remove transaxle.

Installation – 1) Ensure both dowel pins are installed into torque converter housing. Apply Honda Grease (UM264) to extension shaft splines. Position secondary spring into differential side of extension housing. See Fig. 5.

2) Place transaxle on transmission jack, and raise it to engine level. Install 26-mm shim and transaxle housing mounting bolt. Install remaining transaxle housing bolts. Install drive plate bolts, and tighten to specification. See TORQUE SPECIFICATIONS.

Contents

Contents

WIRING DIAGRAMS (Cont.)

ACCESSORIES & EQUIPMENT

AIR BAG RESTRAINT SYSTEM

PASSIVE RESTRAINTS

ANTI-THEFT SYSTEM

ACCESSORIES & EQUIPMENT (Cont.)

1994 CHRYSLER CORP./MITSUBISHI
Contents (Cont.)

BRAKES

BRAKES (Cont.)

WHEEL ALIGNMENT

STEERING (Cont.)

TRANSMISSION SERVICING

1994 MODEL COVERAGE

MODEL	BODY CODE [1]	ENGINE [2]	ENGINE ID [3]	FUEL SYSTEM	IGNITION SYSTEM [4]
Colt	1, 6	1.5L 4-Cyl. (4G15) SOHC	A	MFI	Optical
		1.8L 4-Cyl. (4G93) SOHC	C	MFI	Hall Effect
Colt Vista	0	1.8L 4-Cyl. (4G93) SOHC	C	MFI	Hall Effect
		2.4L 4-Cyl. (4G64) SOHC	G	MFI	Hall Effect
Diamante	7	3.0L V6 (6G72) SOHC	H	MFI	Optical
		3.0L V6 (6G72) DOHC	J	MFI	DIS
Diamante Wagon	7	3.0L V6 (6G72) SOHC	S	MFI	Optical
Eclipse	4	1.8L 4-Cyl. (4G37) SOHC	B	MFI	Optical
		2.0L 4-Cyl. (4G63) DOHC	E	MFI	DIS
		2.0L 4-Cyl. (4G63) DOHC Turbo	F	MFI	DIS
Expo	0, 9	1.8L 4-Cyl. (4G93) SOHC	C	MFI	Hall Effect
		2.4L 4-Cyl. (4G64) SOHC	G	MFI	Hall Effect
Galant	6	2.4L 4-Cyl. (4G64) SOHC	G	MFI	Optical
		2.4L 4-Cyl. (4G64) DOHC	L	MFI	DIS
Mirage	1, 6	1.5L 4-Cyl. (4G15) SOHC	A	MFI	Optical
		1.8L 4-Cyl. (4G93) SOHC	C	MFI	Hall Effect
Montero	1	3.0L V6 (6G72) SOHC	H	MFI	Optical
		3.5L V6 (6G74) DOHC	M	MFI	DIS
Pickup	1, 2, 3	2.4L 4-Cyl. (4G64) SOHC	G	MFI	Optical
		3.0L V6 (6G72) SOHC	H	MFI	Optical
Precis	D	1.5L 4-Cyl. (G4AJK) SOHC	J	MFI	Optical
Stealth	4	3.0L V6 (6G72) SOHC	H	MFI	Optical
		3.0L V6 (6G72) DOHC	J	MFI	DIS
		3.0L V6 (6G72) DOHC Turbo	K	MFI	DIS
Summit	1, 6	1.5L 4-Cyl. (4G15) SOHC	A	MFI	Optical
		1.8L 4-Cyl. (4G93) SOHC	C	MFI	Hall Effect
Summit Wagon	0	1.8L 4-Cyl. (4G93) SOHC	C	MFI	Hall Effect
		2.4L 4-Cyl. (4G64) SOHC	G	MFI	Hall Effect
3000GT	4	3.0L V6 (6G72) DOHC	J	MFI	DIS
		3.0L V6 (6G72) DOHC Turbo	K	MFI	DIS

[1] – Body code is seventh character (fifth character on Precis) of Vehicle Identification Number (VIN). VIN is located on upper left corner of instrument panel.

[2] – See ENGINE CODE LOCATION.

[3] – Engine ID is eighth character of VIN.

[4] – Ignition timing is computer-controlled. On all models with Distributorless Ignition System (DIS), crankshaft position sensor is mounted in place of distributor.

VIN DEFINITION (EXCEPT PRECIS)

JB3CU14L1RU123456
①②③④⑤⑥⑦⑧⑨⑩⑪⑫⑬⑭⑮⑯⑰

① Indicates Nation of Origin.
② Indicates Manufacturer.
③ Indicates Vehicle Type.
④ Indicates Restraint System. [1]
⑤ Indicates Model.
⑥ Indicates Vehicle Series.
⑦ Indicates Body Type.
⑧ **Indicates Engine Type and Make.**
⑨ Indicates Check Digit.
⑩ **Indicates Model Year.**
⑪ Indicates Assembly Plant.
⑫⑬⑭⑮⑯⑰ Indicates Plant Sequential Number.

[1] – On Pickup and Montero, fourth character of VIN indicates GVWR.

VIN DEFINITION (PRECIS ONLY)

KMHVF32J9RU000047
①②③④⑤⑥⑦⑧⑨⑩⑪⑫⑬⑭⑮⑯⑰

①②③ Indicates Manufacturer.
④ Indicates Drive Line Type.
⑤ Indicates Body Type.
⑥ Indicates Vehicle Series.
⑦ Indicates Restraint Type.
⑧ **Indicates Engine Type and Make.**
⑨ Indicates Check Digit.
⑩ **Indicates Model Year.**
⑪ Indicates Assembly Plant.
⑫⑬⑭⑮⑯⑰ Indicates Plant Sequential Number.

MODEL YEAR VIN CODE APPLICATION

VIN Code	Model Year
N	1992
P	1993
R	1994

1994 ENGINE PERFORMANCE
Chrysler Corp./Eagle/Mitsubishi Introduction (Cont.)

ENGINE CODE LOCATION

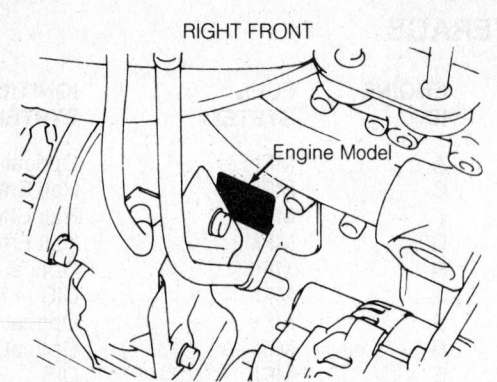

RIGHT FRONT

Engine Model

**COLT, MIRAGE & SUMMIT – 1.5L
& ECLIPSE – 1.8L & 2.0L**

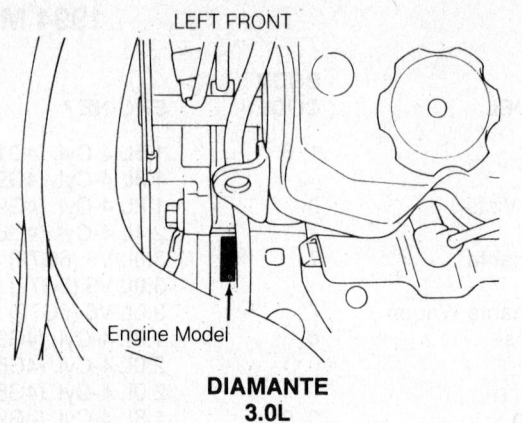

LEFT FRONT

Engine Model

**DIAMANTE
3.0L**

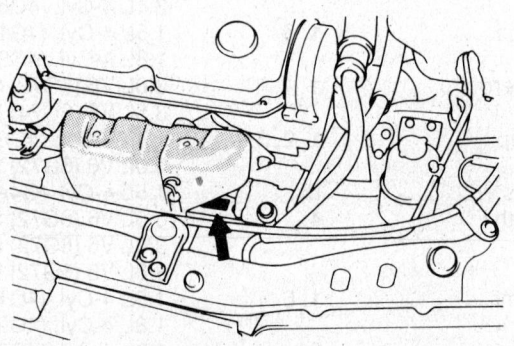

**COLT VISTA, EXPO & SUMMIT WAGON
2.4L**

RIGHT FRONT

Engine Model

**COLT, COLT VISTA, EXPO, MIRAGE
SUMMIT & SUMMIT WAGON
1.8L**

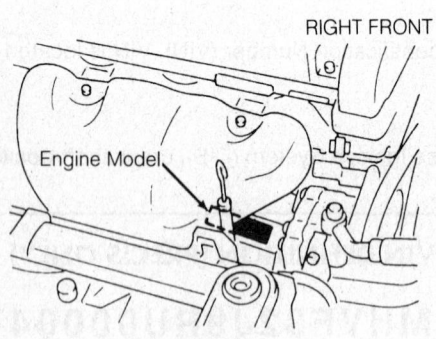

RIGHT FRONT

Engine Model

**GALANT
2.4L**

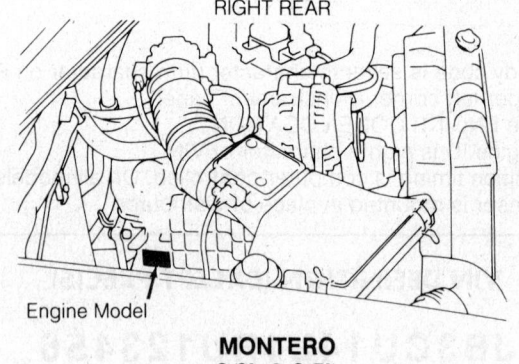

RIGHT REAR

Engine Model

**MONTERO
3.0L & 3.5L**

94B44124 92A25569 94C44125 93B78064 94D44126 94E44127

Courtesy of Chrysler Corp.

ENGINE CODE LOCATION (Cont.)

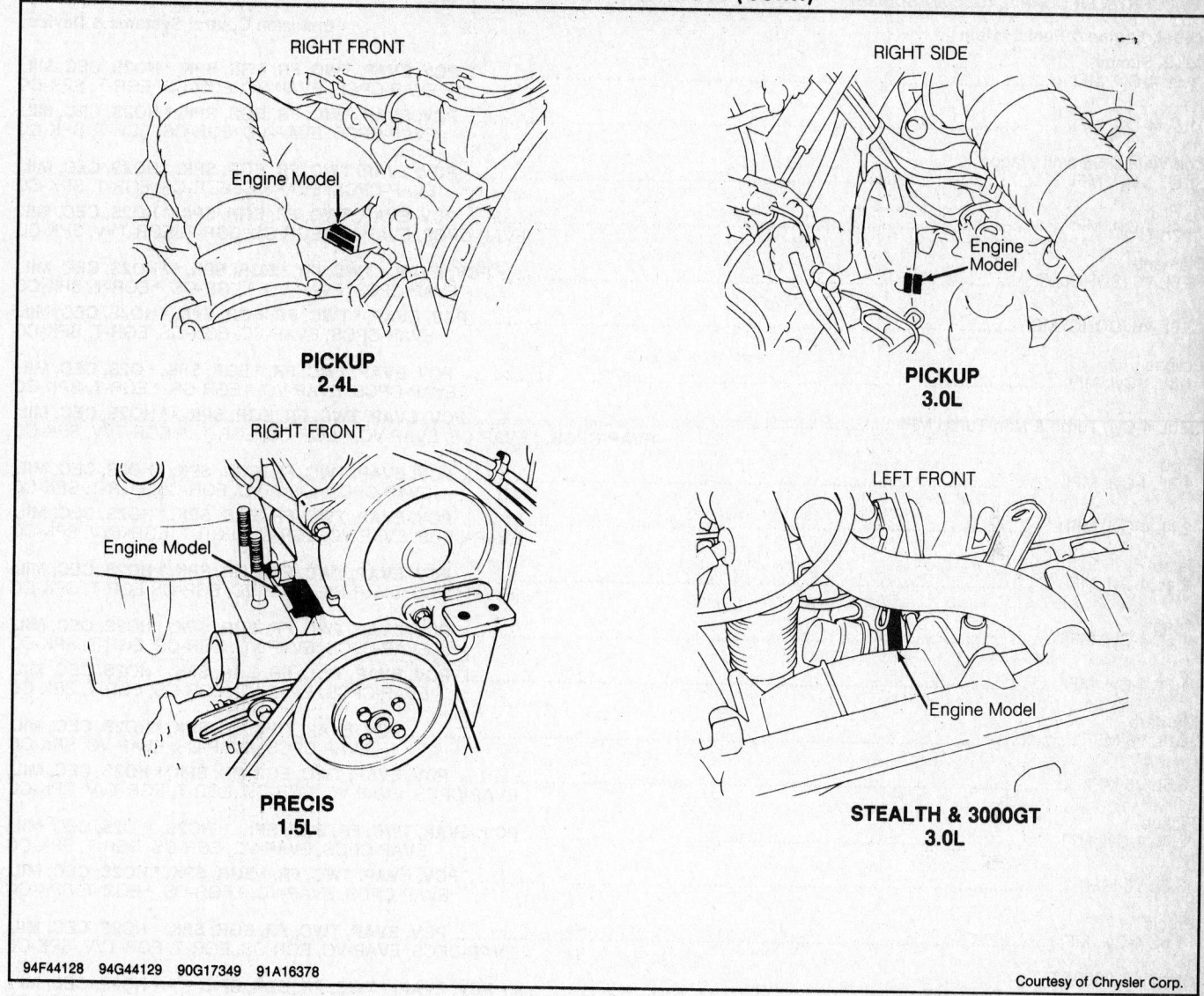

RIGHT FRONT

Engine Model

PICKUP
2.4L

RIGHT SIDE

Engine Model

PICKUP
3.0L

RIGHT FRONT

Engine Model

PRECIS
1.5L

LEFT FRONT

Engine Model

STEALTH & 3000GT
3.0L

94F44128   94G44129   90G17349   91A16378

Courtesy of Chrysler Corp.

1994 ENGINE PERFORMANCE
Emission Applications

1994 CHRYSLER CORP./EAGLE/MITSUBISHI

Model, Engine & Fuel System	Emission Control Systems & Devices
Colt & Summit	
1.5L 4-Cyl. MFI	**PCV, EVAP, TWC, FR, EGR, SPK,** [1] **HO2S, CEC, MIL,** EVAP-CPCS, EVAP-VC, EGR-CS, EGR-T, SPK-CC
1.8L 4-Cyl. MFI	**PCV, EVAP, TWC, FR, EGR, SPK,** [1] **HO2S, CEC, MIL,** EVAP-CPCS, EVAP-VC, EGR-CS, EGR-T, SPK-CC
Colt Vista & Summit Wagon	
1.8L 4-Cyl. MFI	**PCV, EVAP, TWC, FR, EGR, SPK,** [1] **HO2S, CEC, MIL,** EVAP-CPCS, EVAP-VC, EGR-CS, EGR-T, SPK-CC
2.4L 4-Cyl. MFI	**PCV, EVAP, TWC, FR, EGR, SPK,** [1] **HO2S, CEC, MIL,** EVAP-CPCS, EVAP-VC, EGR-CS, EGR-T, EGR-TVV, SPK-CC
Diamante	
3.0L V6 (SOHC) MFI	**PCV, EVAP,** [2] **TWC, FR,** [3] **EGR, SPK,** [4] [5] **HO2S, CEC, MIL,** EVAP-CPCS, EVAP-VC, [3] EGR-CS, [3] EGR-T, SPK-CC
3.0L V6 (DOHC) MFI	**PCV, EVAP,** [2] **TWC, FR, EGR, SPK,** [6] **HO2S, CEC, MIL,** EVAP-CPCS, EVAP-VC, EGR-CS, EGR-T, SPK-CC
Eclipse	
1.8L 4-Cyl. MFI	**PCV, EVAP, TWC, FR,** [3] **EGR, SPK,** [7] **O2S, CEC, MIL,** EVAP-CPCS, EVAP-VC, [3] EGR-CS, [3] EGR-T, SPK-CC
2.0L 4-Cyl. Turbo & Non-Turbo MFI	**PCV, EVAP, TWC, FR, EGR, SPK,** [3] [8] **HO2S, CEC, MIL,** EVAP-CPCS, [9] EVAP-CS, EVAP-VC, [3] EGR-CS, EGR-T, [10] EGR-TVV, SPK-CC
Expo	
1.8L 4-Cyl. MFI	**PCV, EVAP, TWC, FR, EGR, SPK,** [1] **HO2S, CEC, MIL,** EVAP-CPCS, EVAP-VC, EGR-CS, EGR-T, SPK-CC
2.4L 4-Cyl. MFI	**PCV, EVAP, TWC, FR, EGR, SPK,** [1] **HO2S, CEC, MIL,** EVAP-CPCS, EVAP-VC, EGR-CS, EGR-T, EGR-TVV, SPK-CC
Galant	
2.4L 4-Cyl. MFI	**PCV, EVAP, TWC, FR, EGR, SPK,** [1] **HO2S, CEC, MIL,** EVAP-CPCS, EVAP-CS, EVAP-VC, EGR-CS EGR-T, SPK-CC
Mirage	
1.5L 4-Cyl. MFI	**PCV, EVAP, TWC, FR, EGR, SPK,** [1] **HO2S, CEC, MIL,** EVAP-CPCS, EVAP-VC, EGR-CS, EGR-T, SPK-CC
1.8L 4-Cyl. MFI	**PCV, EVAP, TWC, FR, EGR, SPK,** [1] **HO2S, CEC, MIL,** EVAP-CPCS, EVAP-VC, EGR-CS, EGR-T, SPK-CC
Montero	
3.0L V6 MFI	**PCV, EVAP, TWC, FR, SPK,** [8] **HO2S, CEC, MIL,** EVAP-CPCS, EVAP-CS, EVAP-VC, SPK-CC
3.5L V6 MFI	**PCV, EVAP, TWC, EGR, FR, SPK,** [8] **HO2S, CEC, MIL,** EVAP-CPCS, EVAP-VC, EGR-CS, EGR-T, EGR-TVV, SPK-CC
Pickup	
2.4L 4-Cyl. MFI	**PCV, EVAP, TWC, FR, EGR, SPK,** [11] **HO2S,** [12] **O2S, CEC, MIL,** EVAP-CPCS, EVAP-VC, EGR-CS, EGR-T, SPK-CC
3.0L V6 MFI	**PCV, EVAP, TWC, FR,** [3] **EGR, SPK,** [8] **HO2S, CEC, MIL,** EVAP-CPCS, EVAP-VC, [3] EGR-CS, [3] EGR-T, SPK-CC
Precis	
1.5L 4-Cyl. MFI	**PCV, EVAP, TWC, FR, EGR, SPK,** [1] **HO2S, CEC, MIL,** EVAP-CPCS, EVAP-VC, EGR-CS, EGR-T, EGR-TVV, SPK-CC
Stealth & 3000GT	
3.0L V6 Turbo & Non-Turbo MFI	**PCV, EVAP,** [2] **TWC, FR, EGR, SPK,** [5] [13] [14] **HO2S, CEC, MIL,** EVAP-CPCS, [9] EVAP-CS, EVAP-VC, [3] EGR-CS, [3] EGR-T, SPK-CC

[1] – Equipped with 2 HO2S.
[2] – Vehicles equipped with 4 HO2S, are equipped with 3 catalytic converters.
[3] – Calif.
[4] – Federal, equipped with one HO2S.
[5] – Calif., equipped with 4 HO2S.
[6] – Equipped with 4 HO2S.
[7] – Equipped with one O2S.
[8] – Equipped with one HO2S.
[9] – Turbo.
[10] – Federal.
[11] – Calif. (RWD).
[12] – Federal and Calif. (4WD).
[13] – Federal (SOHC), equipped with one HO2S.
[14] – Federal (DOHC), equipped with 2 HO2S.

NOTE: For quick reference, major emission control systems and devices are listed in bold type; components and other related devices are listed in light type.

CEC – Computerized Engine Control
EGR – Exhaust Gas Recirculation
EGR-CS – EGR Control Solenoid
EGR-T – EGR Temperature Sensor
EGR-TVV – EGR Thermal Vacuum Valve
EVAP – Fuel Evaporative System
EVAP-CS – EVAP Control Solenoid
EVAP-CPCS – EVAP Canister Purge Control Solenoid
EVAP-VC – EVAP Vapor Canister

FR – Fill Pipe Restrictor
HO2S – Heated Oxygen Sensor
MFI – Multiport Fuel Injection
MIL – Malfunction Indicator Light
O2S – Oxygen Sensor
PCV – Positive Crankcase Ventilation
SPK – Spark Controls
SPK-CC – SPK Computer Controlled
TWC – Three-Way Catalyst

1994 ENGINE PERFORMANCE
Service & Adjustment Specifications

Chrysler Corp.: Colt, Colt Vista, Stealth
Eagle: Summit, Summit Wagon
Mitsubishi: Diamante, Eclipse, Expo, Galant,
Mirage, Montero, Pickup, Precis, 3000GT

INTRODUCTION

Use this article to quickly find specifications related to servicing and on-vehicle adjustments. This is a quick reference article to use when you are familiar with an adjustment procedure and only need a specification.

CAPACITIES

BATTERY SPECIFICATIONS

Application	Group Size	CCA Rating
Colt, Mirage & Summit	24R	430
Diamante	26R	490
Eclipse	86	430
Colt Vista, Expo & Summit Wagon		
1.8L	26R	350
2.4L	26R	490
Galant	26	490
Montero	26R	490
Pickup		
2.4L	24F	430
3.0L	26R	490
Precis	24	420
Stealth & 3000GT	26R	520

NOTE: Refill capacities are approximate. Correct fluid level should be determined by mark on dipstick, if applicable.

FLUID CAPACITIES

Application	Quantity
Automatic Transaxle (Mitsubishi Plus/Mopar Plus/Dexron-II)	
Colt, Mirage, Precis & Summit	6.3 Qts. (6.0L)
Colt Vista & Summit Wagon	
AWD	6.9 Qts. (6.5L)
FWD	6.4 Qts. (6.1L)
Diamante, Stealth & 3000GT	7.9 Qts. (7.5L)
Galant	
SOHC	6.3 Qts. (6.0L)
DOHC	7.9 Qts. (7.5L)
Eclipse	
Except Turbo	6.4 Qts. (6.1L)
Turbo	7.4 Qts. (7.0L)
Expo	
AWD	6.9 Qts. (6.5L)
FWD	6.3 Qts. (6.0L)
Automatic Transmission (Mitsubishi Plus/Mopar Plus/Dexron II)	
Montero	7.6 Qts. (7.2L)
Pickup	7.7 Qts. (7.3L)
Cooling System (Includes Heater & Reserve Tank)	
Colt, Mirage & Summit	
1.5L	5.3 Qts. (5.0L)
1.8L	6.3 Qts. (6.0L)
Colt Vista, Expo & Summit Wagon	
1.8L	6.3 Qts. (6.0L)
2.4L	6.8 Qts. (6.4L)
Diamante	8.5 Qts. (8.0L)
Montero	10.0 Qts. (9.5L)
Eclipse	
1.8L	6.6 Qts. (6.2L)
2.0L	7.6 Qts. (7.2L)
Galant	7.4 Qts. (7.0L)
Pickup	
2WD	
Auto. Trans.	6.4 Qts. (6.1L)
Man. Trans.	6.3 Qts. (6.0L)
4WD	8.9 Qts. (8.4L)
Precis	5.6 Qts. (5.3L)
Stealth & 3000GT	8.5 Qts. (8.0L)

FLUID CAPACITIES (Cont.)

Application	Quantity
Crankcase (Includes Filter)	
Colt, Mirage & Summit	
1.5L	3.5 Qts. (3.3L)
1.8L	4.0 Qts. (3.8L)
Colt Vista, Expo & Summit Wagon	
1.8L & 2.4L (8-Valve)	4.0 Qts. (3.8L)
2.4L (16-Valve)	4.5 Qts. (4.3L)
Diamante	4.5 Qts. (4.3L)
Eclipse	
1.8L	4.1 Qts. (3.9L)
2.0L Non-Turbo	4.6 Qts. (4.4L)
2.0L Turbo	4.8 Qts. (4.5L)
Galant	4.7 Qts. (4.4L)
Montero	5.5 Qts. (4.9L)
Pickup	
2.4L	4.0 Qts. (3.8L)
3.0L	5.0 Qts. (4.6L)
Precis	3.6 Qts. (3.4L)
Stealth & 3000GT	
Non-Turbo	4.5 Qts. (4.3L)
Turbo	5.0 Qts. (4.6L)
Differential (SAE 80W-90/API GL-5)	
Eclipse	.75 Qts. (.7L)
Colt Vista, Expo, Stealth	
Summit Wagon & 3000GT	1.2 Qts. (1.1L)
Montero	
Front	1.3 Qts. (1.2L)
Rear	2.7 Qts. (2.6L)
Pickup	
2WD	1.6 Qts. (1.5L)
4WD	
Front	1.2 Qts. (1.1L)
Rear	2.7 Qts. (2.6L)
Manual Transaxle (SAE 75W-85/API GL-4)	
Colt, Mirage & Summit	1.9 Qts. (1.8L)
Colt Vista, Expo & Summit Wagon	
FWD	
1.8L	1.9 Qts. (1.8L)
2.4L	2.4 Qts. (2.3L)
AWD	2.4 Qts. (2.3L)
Eclipse	
Non-Turbo	1.9 Qts. (1.8L)
Turbo	2.4 Qts. (2.3L)
Galant	2.2 Qts. (2.1L)
Precis	
KM 201	1.9 Qts. (1.8L)
KM 200	1.8 Qts. (1.7L)
Stealth & 3000GT	
FWD	2.4 Qts. (2.3L)
AWD	2.5 Qts. (2.4L)
Manual Transmission (SAE 75W-85/API GL-4)	
Montero	2.6 Qts. (2.5L)
Pickup	
2WD	2.4 Qts. (2.3L)
4WD	2.6 Qts. (2.5L)
Power Steering (Dexron-II)	
Diamante	1.9 Pts. (.9L)
Montero	2.1 Pts. (1.0L)
Stealth & 3000GT	
2-Wheel Steering	1.9 Pts. (.9L)
4-Wheel Steering	1.6 Pts. (1.5L)
All Others	1.9 Pts. (.9L)
Transfer Case (SAE 75W-85/API GL-4)	
Colt Vista, Eclipse,	
Expo & Summit Wagon	1.2 Pts. (.6L)
Montero	
V5MT1 & V4AW2	4.8 Pts. (2.3L)
V4AW3	5.0 Pts. (2.6L)
Pickup	4.7 Pts. (2.2L)
Stealth & 3000GT	.7 Pt. (.3L)

1994 ENGINE PERFORMANCE
Service & Adjustment Specifications (Cont.)

QUICK-SERVICE

SERVICE INTERVALS & SPECIFICATIONS
REPLACEMENT INTERVALS

Component	Miles
Colt, Mirage & Summit	
Air Filter	30,000
Automatic Transaxle Fluid	30,000
Coolant	30,000
Oil	7500
Oil Filter	15,000
Spark Plugs	30,000
Timing Belt	60,000
Colt Vista, Expo & Summit Wagon	
Air Filter	30,000
Automatic Transaxle Fluid	30,000
Coolant	30,000
Oil	7500
Oil Filter	15,000
Rear Axle Fluid	30,000
Spark Plugs	30,000
Timing Belt	60,000
Diamante	
Air Filter	30,000
Automatic Transaxle Fluid	30,000
Coolant	30,000
Oil	7500
Oil Filter	15,000
Spark Plugs	
SOHC	30,000
DOHC	60,000
Timing Belt	60,000
Eclipse	
Air Filter	30,000
Automatic Transaxle Fluid	30,000
Coolant	30,000
Oil	
Non-Turbo	7500
Turbo	5000
Oil Filter	
Non-Turbo	15,000
Turbo	10,000
Spark Plugs	30,000
Timing Belt	60,000
Galant	
Air Filter	30,000
Automatic Transaxle Fluid	30,000
Coolant	30,000
Oil	7500
Oil Filter	15,000
Rear Axle Fluid	30,000
Spark Plugs	30,000
Timing & Balance Shaft Belts	60,000
Montero	
Air Filter	30,000
Automatic Transmission Fluid	30,000
Coolant	30,000
Front & Rear Axle Fluid	30,000
Oil	7500
Oil Filter	15,000
O[2] Sensor [1]	80,000
Spark Plugs	30,000
Spark Plug Wires [1]	60,000
Timing Belt	60,000
Transfer Case Fluid	30,000
Vapor Canister [1]	100,000
Pickup	
Air Filter	30,000
Automatic Transmission Fluid	30,000
Coolant	30,000
EGR Valve (2.4L) [1]	50,000
Front & Rear Axle Fluid	30,000
Oil	7500
Oil Filter	15,000
O[2] Sensor [1]	80,000
Spark Plugs	30,000
Spark Plug Wires [1]	60,000
Timing Belt	60,000
Transfer Case Fluid	30,000
Vapor Canister [1]	100,000

[1] – Federal models only.

REPLACEMENT INTERVALS (Cont.)

Component	Miles
Precis	
Air Filter	30,000
Automatic Transaxle Fluid	30,000
Brake Fluid	30,000
Coolant	30,000
Fuel Filter	60,000
Oil & Filter	7500
Spark Plugs	30,000
Timing Belt	60,000
Stealth & 3000GT	
Air Filter	30,000
Automatic Transaxle Fluid	30,000
Coolant	30,000
Rear Axle Fluid (AWD)	30,000
Fuel Filter	30,000
Oil	
Non-Turbo	7500
Turbo	5000
Oil Filter	
Non-Turbo	15,000
Turbo	10,000
Spark Plugs	
SOHC	30,000
DOHC	60,000
Timing Belt	60,000

[1] – Federal models only.

BELT ADJUSTMENT

Application	[1] Deflection New Belt – In. (mm)	[1] Deflection Used Belt – In. (mm)
Colt, Mirage & Summit		
1.5L		
Alternator	.22-.28 (5.5-7.0)	.31 (7.8)
A/C	.20-.24 (5.0-6.0)	.24-.28 (6.0-7.0)
P/S	.16-.22 (4.0-5.5)	.22-.30 (5.5-7.6)
1.8L		
Alternator	.28-.34 (7.0-8.5)	.37 (9.5)
P/S (w/o A/C)	.22-.24 (5.5-6.0)	.27-.30 (6.8-7.6)
P/S (w/ A/C)	.30-.35 (7.6-9.0)	.37-.45 (9.5-11.4)
Colt Vista, Expo & Summit Wagon		
1.8L		
Alternator	.28-.34 (7.0-8.5)	.37 (9.5)
P/S	.30-.35 (7.6-9.0)	.37-.45 (9.5-11.4)
A/C	.22-.24 (5.5-6.0)	.27-.30 (6.8-7.6)
2.4L		
Alternator	.30-.35 (7.6-9.0)	.40 (10.0)
P/S	.18-.26 (4.5-6.6)	.24-.35 (6.0-9.0)
A/C	.17-.19 (4.3-4.8)	.21-.24 (5.3-6.0)
Diamante		
SOHC		
Alternator & P/S	.15-.19 (3.8-4.8)	.23-.31 (5.8-7.8)
A/C	.25-.27 (6.3-6.8)	.29-.33 (7.3-8.3)
DOHC		
Alternator & A/C	.13-.15 (3.3-3.8)	.15-.19 (3.8-4.8)
P/S	.30-.35 (7.6-9.0)	.41-.49 (10.5-12.5)
Eclipse		
1.8L		
Alternator	.31-.43 (7.8-10.9)	[2]
A/C	.16-.20 (4.0-5.0)	.22-.24 (5.5-6.0)
P/S	.23-.35 (5.8-9.0)	[2]
2.0L		
Alternator	.35-.45 (9.0-11.4)	[2]
A/C	.16-.20 (4.0-5.0)	.22-.24 (5.6-6.1)
P/S	.23-.35 (5.8-9.0)	[2]

[1] – With 22 lbs. (10 kg) pressure applied midway on belt run.
[2] – Information is not available from manufacturer.

BELT ADJUSTMENT (Cont.)

Application	[1] Deflection New Belt – In. (mm)	[1] Deflection Used Belt – In. (mm)
Galant		
Alternator Belt	.29-.35 (7.3-8.8)	.39 (10.0)
A/C Belt	.22-.24 (5.5-6.0)	.26-.30 (6.5-7.6)
Montero		
3.0L		
Alternator	.25-.31 (6.3-7.8)	.35 (9.0)
P/S	.31 (7.8)	.39 (10.0)
A/C	.19-.23 (4.8-5.8)	.25-.29 (6.3-7.3)
3.5L		
Alternator	.16-.20 (4.0-5.0)	.22-.26 (5.5-6.5)
P/S	.43-.51 (11.0-13.0)	.55-.63 (14.0-16.0)
A/C	.26-.30 (6.5-7.5)	.20-.24 (5.0-6.0)
Pickup		
2.4L		
Alternator	.27-.39 (6.8-10.0)	[2]
P/S	.23-.35 (5.8-8.8)	[2]
A/C	.33-.39 (8.3-10.0)	[2]
3.0L		
Alternator	.31-.39 (7.8-10.0)	[2]
P/S	.35-.47 (8.8-12.0)	[2]
A/C	.33-.39 (8.3-10.0)	[2]
Precis		
A/C	.34-.42 (8.6-10.6)	[2]
Alternator	.28-.32 (7.0-8.2)	[2]
P/S	.28-.39 (7.0-10.0)	[2]
Stealth		
SOHC		
Alternator & P/S	.15-.19 (3.8-4.8)	.23-.31 (5.8-7.8)
A/C	.25-.27 (6.3-6.8)	.29-.33 (7.3-8.3)
DOHC		
Alternator	.13-.15 (3.3-3.8)	.15-.19 (3.8-4.8)
P/S	.29-.35 (7.3-8.8)	.41-.49 (10.4-12.4)
3000GT		
Alternator	.13-.15 (3.3-3.8)	.15-.19 (3.8-4.8)
P/S	.29-.35 (7.3-8.8)	.41-.49 (10.4-12.4)

[1] – With 22 lbs. (10 kg) pressure applied midway on belt run.
[2] – Information is not available from manufacturer.

MECHANICAL CHECKS

ENGINE COMPRESSION

Check engine compression with engine at normal operating temperature, all spark plugs removed and throttle wide open.

COMPRESSION SPECIFICATIONS

Application [1]	Specification
Compression Ratio	
1.5L (VIN A)	9.2:1
1.5L (VIN J)	9.4:1
1.8L (VIN B)	9.0:1
1.8L (VIN C)	
Colt, Expo & Summit	9.5:1
Colt Vista, Expo & Summit Wagon	8.5:1
2.0L (VIN E)	9.0:1
2.0L (VIN F)	7.8:1
2.4L (VIN G)	
8-Valve	8.5:1
16-Valve	9.5:1
2.4L (VIN L)	10.0:1
3.0L (VIN J)	10.0:1
3.0L (VIN K)	8.0:1
3.0L (VIN H)	
Diamante	10.0:1
Montero, Pickup & Stealth	8.9:1
3.5L (VIN M)	9.5:1

COMPRESSION SPECIFICATIONS (Cont.)

Application [1]	Specification
Compression Pressure	
1.5L (VIN A)	192 psi (13.4 kg/cm²)
1.5L (VIN J)	192 psi (13.4 kg/cm²)
1.8L (VIN C)	199 psi (13.9 kg/cm²)
1.8L (VIN B)	185 psi (13.0 kg/cm²)
2.0L (VIN E)	192 psi (13.4 kg/cm²)
2.0L (VIN F)	164 psi (11.5 kg/cm²)
2.4L (VIN G)	
8-Valve	171 psi (12.0 kg/cm²)
16-Valve	185 psi (13.0 kg/cm²)
Galant (SOHC)	192 psi (13.4 kg/cm²)
2.4L (VIN L)	206 psi (14.6 kg/cm²)
3.0L (VIN J)	185 psi (13.0 kg/cm²)
3.0L (VIN K)	156 psi (10.9 kg/cm²)
3.0L (VIN H)	
Diamante	196 psi (13.8 kg/cm²)
Except Diamante	171 psi (12.0 kg/cm²)
3.5L (VIN M)	185 psi (13.0 kg/cm²)
Maximum Variation Between Cylinders	14 psi (1.0 kg/cm²)

[1] – See CHRYSLER CORP./EAGLE/MITSUBISHI INTRODUCTION article for VIN information.

VALVE CLEARANCE

NOTE: Valve adjustment is required on 1.5L and 1.8L engines only. Check adjustment at 15,000 mile intervals.

VALVE CLEARANCE SPECIFICATIONS

Application	[1] In. (mm)
1.5L (VIN A & J)	
Hot Engine	
Intake	.008 (.20)
Exhaust	.010 (.25)
1.8L (VIN C)	
Hot Engine	
Intake	.008 (.20)
Exhaust	.012 (.30)

[1] – Adjust valves with engine hot.

IGNITION SYSTEM

IGNITION COIL

IGNITION COIL RESISTANCE – Ohms @ 68°F (20°C)

Application	Primary	Secondary
1.5L (VIN A)	.9-1.2	20,000-29,000
1.5L (VIN J)	.72-.88	10,300-13,900
1.8L (VIN B)	.9-1.2	19,000-27,000
1.8L (VIN C)	.9-1.2	20,000-29,000
2.0L (VIN E & F)	.70-.86	11,300-15,300
2.4L (VIN G)		
Except Pickup	.9-1.2	20,000-29,000
Pickup	.72-.88	10,300-13,900
2.4L (VIN L)	.67-.81	11,310-15,300
3.0L (VIN H)	.72-.88	10,300-13,900
3.0L (VIN J & K)	.67-.81	11,310-15,300
3.5L (VIN M)	.69-.85	15,300-20,700

HIGH TENSION WIRE RESISTANCE

NOTE: Following resistance specifications are preferred. Wire resistance should not exceed 22 k/ohms for all models except Montero 3.5L. On Montero 3.5L, resistance should not exceed 26 k/ohms. Individual wire specificatios are not available for 2.4L (VIN L) and Montero 3.5L.

1994 ENGINE PERFORMANCE
Service & Adjustment Specifications (Cont.)

HIGH TENSION WIRE RESISTANCE

Application [1]	Ohms
1.5L (VIN A)	
Coil Wire	[2]
No. 1 Wire	11,500
No. 2 Wire	9100
No. 3 Wire	9000
No. 4 Wire	6600
1.5L (VIN J)	
Coil Wire	[2]
No. 1 Wire	10,100
No. 2 Wire	11,800
No. 3 Wire	11,800
No. 4 Wire	14,200
1.8L (VIN C)	
Coil Wire	[2]
No. 1 Wire	12,500
No. 2 Wire	11,700
No. 3 Wire	9300
No. 4 Wire	8500
1.8L (VIN B)	
Coil Wire	[2]
No. 1 Wire	10,100
No. 2 Wire	11,500
No. 3 Wire	12,000
No. 4 Wire	13,000
2.0L (VIN E & F)	
Coil Wire	Not Used
No. 1 Wire	5800
No. 2 Wire	8400
No. 3 Wire	10,600
No. 4 Wire	9700
2.4L (VIN G)	
Pickup	
Coil Wire	3000
No. 1 Wire	10,000
No. 2 Wire	12,000
No. 3 Wire	12,000
No. 4 Wire	14,000
Except Pickup	
Coil Wire	[2]
No. 1 Wire	12,500
No. 2 Wire	11,700
No. 3 Wire	9300
No. 4 Wire	8500
3.0L (VIN J & K)	
Coil Wire	Not Used
No. 1 Wire	8600
No. 2 Wire	13,900
No. 3 Wire	6400
No. 4 Wire	11,500
No. 5 Wire	4500
No. 6 Wire	11,780
3.0L (VIN H)	
Stealth	
Coil Wire	[2]
No. 1 Wire	7800
No. 2 Wire	6400
No. 3 Wire	9600
No. 4 Wire	7500
No. 5 Wire	10,400
No. 6 Wire	8600
Diamante	
Coil Wire	[2]
No. 1 Wire	7800
No. 2 Wire	6400
No. 3 Wire	9600
No. 4 Wire	7500
No. 5 Wire	10,400
No. 6 Wire	8600
Montero & Pickup	
Coil Wire	3000
No. 1 Wire	9000
No. 2 Wire	8500
No. 3 Wire	10,000
No. 4 Wire	9000
No. 5 Wire	12,000
No. 6 Wire	10,000

[1] – See CHRYSLER CORP./EAGLE/MITSUBISHI INTRODUCTION article for VIN information.
[2] – Information is not available from manufacturer.

SPARK PLUGS
SPARK PLUG TYPE

Application	Nippondenso No.
1.5L (VIN A)	W16EPR-11
1.5L (VIN J)	[1] RN9YC4
1.8L (VIN B)	W20EPR-11
1.8L (VIN C)	
Colt, Mirage & Summit	K20PR-U11
Colt Vista, Expo & Summit Wagon	K16PR-U11
2.0L (VIN E)	W20EPR-11
2.0L (VIN F)	
Eclipse	W20EPR
2.4L (VIN G, 8-Valve)	W20EPR-11
2.4L (VIN G, 16-Valve)	K16PR-U11
2.4L (VIN L)	W20EPR-11
3.0L (VIN J & K)	PK20PR-P11
3.0L (VIN H)	
Diamante	W20EPR-11
Montero, Pickup & Stealth	W16EPR-11
3.5L (VIN M)	PK16PR-P11

[1] – Champion spark plug.

SPARK PLUG SPECIFICATIONS

Application	Gap In. (mm)	Torque Ft. Lbs. (N.m)
Eclipse (2.0L Turbo)	.028-.031 (.7-.8)	15-21 (20-30)
All Others	.039-.043 (1.0-1.1)	15-21 (20-30)

FIRING ORDER & TIMING MARKS

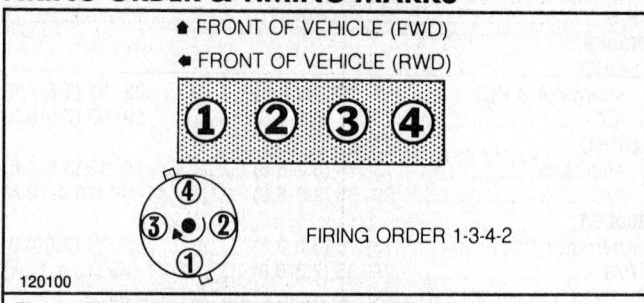

Fig. 1: Firing Order & Distributor Rotation (1.5L, 1.8L, 2.0L SOHC & 2.4L SOHC)

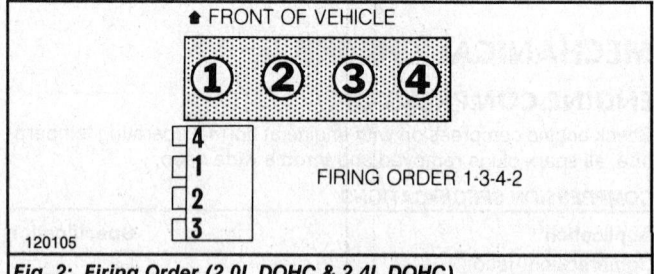

Fig. 2: Firing Order (2.0L DOHC & 2.4L DOHC)

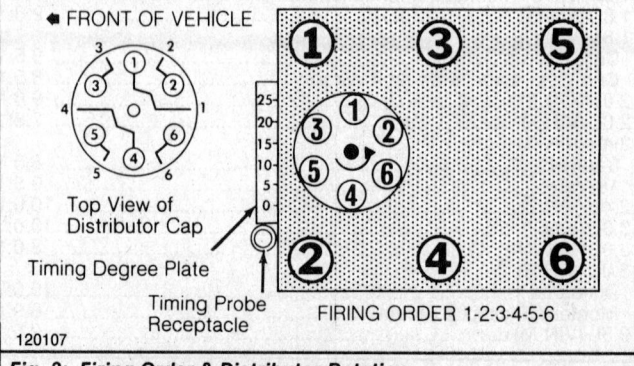

Fig. 3: Firing Order & Distributor Rotation (3.0L Montero & Pickup)

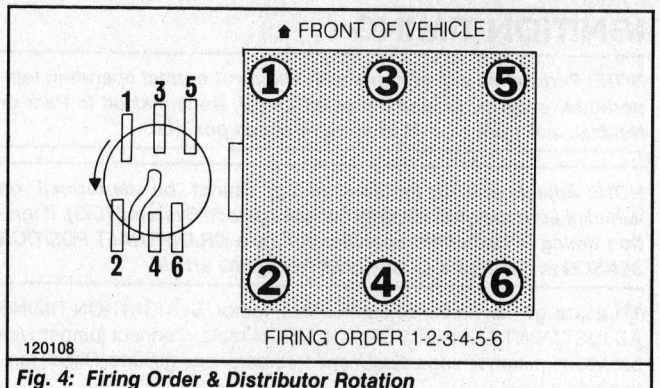

Fig. 4: Firing Order & Distributor Rotation (3.0L SOHC Diamante & Stealth)

FRONT OF VEHICLE

FIRING ORDER 1-2-3-4-5-6

120108

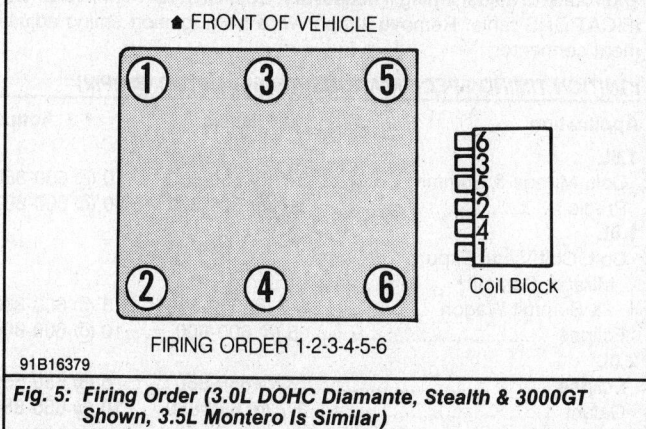

Fig. 5: Firing Order (3.0L DOHC Diamante, Stealth & 3000GT Shown, 3.5L Montero Is Similar)

FRONT OF VEHICLE

Coil Block

FIRING ORDER 1-2-3-4-5-6

91B16379

IGNITION TIMING

IGNITION TIMING (Degrees BTDC @ RPM)

Application	[1] Basic	[2][3] Actual
1.5L		
Colt, Mirage & Summit	3-7 @ 650-850	10 @ 650-850
Precis	3-7 @ 600-800	10 @ 600-800
1.8L		
Colt, Colt Vista, Expo, Mirage, Summit, & Summit Wagon	3-7 @ 600-800	5 @ 600-800
Eclipse	5 @ 600-800	10 @ 600-800
2.0L		
Eclipse	5 @ 650-850	8 @ 650-850
2.4L		
Colt Vista, Expo & Summit Wagon	3-7 @ 650-850	8 @ 650-850
Galant		
SOHC	3-7 @ 650-850	10 @ 650-850
DOHC	2-8 @ 700-900	8 @ 700-900
Pickup	3-7 @ 600-800	8 @ 600-800
3.0L		
Diamante & Montero	3-7 @ 600-800	15 @ 600-800
Pickup	3-7 @ 650-850	15 @ 650-850
Stealth & 3000GT	2-8 @ 600-800	15 @ 600-800
3.5L		
Montero	3-7 @ 600-800	15 @ 600-800

[1] – With ignition timing adjustment connector grounded or vacuum hose (farthest from distributor) disconnected.

[2] – With ignition timing adjustment connector ungrounded or vacuum hose (farthest from distributor) connected. Ignition timing may fluctuate.

[3] – If vehicle altitude is more than 2300 ft. above sea level, actual timing may be advanced (5 degrees).

FUEL SYSTEM

FUEL PUMP
REGULATED FUEL PRESSURE

Application	At Idle w/Vacuum psi (kg/cm²)	At Idle w/o Vacuum psi (kg/cm²)
Eclipse (Turbo)		
Man. Trans.	27 (1.8)	36-38 (2.5-2.6)
Auto. Trans.	33 (2.3)	41-46 (2.8-3.2)
Stealth (Turbo) & 3000GT	34 (2.4)	43-45 (3.0-3.1)
All Others	38 (2.6)	47-50 (3.3-3.5)

IDLE SPEED

IDLE SPEED SPECIFICATIONS

Application	Curb Idle	Basic Idle
1.5L		
Colt, Mirage & Summit	650-850	650-850
Precis	600-800	600-800
1.8L		
Colt Vista, Expo & Summit Wagon	600-800	600-800
Eclipse	600-800	600-800
2.0L		
Eclipse, Galant	650-850	650-850
2.4L		
Colt Vista, Expo & Summit Wagon	650-850	650-850
Galant		
SOHC	650-850	10650-850
DOHC	700-900	700-900
Pickup	600-800	600-800
3.0L		
Diamante, Montero, Stealth & 3000GT	600-800	600-800
Pickup	650-850	650-850
3.5L		
Montero	600-800	600-800

INJECTOR RESISTANCE

INJECTOR RESISTANCE

Application	Ohms
Non-Turbo [1]	13-16
Turbo	2-3

[1] – Includes all Eclipse models.

THROTTLE POSITION SENSOR (TPS)

TPS SPECIFICATIONS

Application	[1] Volts
Colt, Mirage & Summit	.3-1.0
Diamante (w/Traction Control)	.58-.69
Eclipse & Pickup (2.4L)	.48-.52
All Others	.4-1.0

[1] – At idle.

1994 ENGINE PERFORMANCE
On-Vehicle Adjustments

Chrysler Corp.: Colt, Colt Vista, Stealth
Eagle: Summit, Summit Wagon
Mitsubishi: Diamante, Eclipse, Expo, Galant,
  Mirage, Montero, Pickup, Precis, 3000GT

ENGINE MECHANICAL

Before performing any on-vehicle adjustments to fuel or ignition system, ensure engine mechanical condition is okay (i.e. engine compression).

VALVE CLEARANCE

NOTE: Valve clearance is adjustable on 1.5L and 1.8L (VIN C) engines only. All other models use hydraulic lash adjusters.

VALVE ADJUSTMENT

CAUTION: DO NOT rotate crankshaft in opposite direction of normal engine rotation.

1.5L & 1.8L (VIN C) – 1) Ensure engine is at normal operating temperature. Remove all spark plugs and valve cover. Rotate crankshaft clockwise to position cylinder No. 1 at TDC of compression stroke. Adjust intake valves on cylinders No. 1 and 2, and exhaust valves on cylinders No. 1 and 3. See VALVE CLEARANCE SPECIFICATIONS table.
2) Rotate crankshaft 360 degrees to position cylinder No. 4 at TDC of compression stroke. Adjust intake valves on cylinders No. 3 and 4, and exhaust valves on cylinders No. 2 and 4. Install spark plugs and valve cover.

VALVE CLEARANCE SPECIFICATIONS

Application	[1] In. (mm)
1.5L (VIN A & J)	
Hot Engine	
Intake	.008 (.20)
Exhaust	.010 (.25)
1.8L (VIN C)	
Hot Engine	
Intake	.008 (.20)
Exhaust	.012 (.30)

[1] – Adjust valves with engine hot.

CHECKING HYDRAULIC VALVE LIFTERS

Except 1.5L & 1.8L – 1) Warm engine to normal operating temperature. Remove valve cover. Position cylinder No. 1 at TDC on compression stroke. On 4-cylinder engines, check intake rockers on cylinders No. 1 and 2. Check exhaust rockers on cylinders No. 1 and 3. On 6-cylinder engines, check intake rockers on cylinders No. 1, 5 and 6. Check exhaust rockers on cylinders No. 1, 2 and 3.
2) Push downward on end of rocker arm above lash adjuster. Rotate crankshaft 360 degrees. On 4-cylinder engines, check intake rockers on cylinders No. 3 and 4. Check exhaust rockers on cylinders No. 2 and 4. On 6-cylinder engines, check intake rockers on cylinders No. 2, 3 and 4. Check exhaust rockers on cylinders No. 4, 5 and 6. If lash adjuster is normal, it will feel solid.
3) If lash adjuster moves downward easily when pushed, replace adjuster. If lash adjuster feels soft or spongy, air has probably entered lash adjuster. If this occurs, check engine oil level. If engine oil level is okay, check oil screen and oil screen gasket for damage.
4) After repairing cause of air leak, warm engine to operating temperature. Drive vehicle at low speed for approximately 5 minutes. Turn engine off for a few minutes.
5) Restart engine and drive at low speed for approximately 5 minutes. Repeat this step several times for about one hour. This helps remove air from engine oil.

IGNITION TIMING

NOTE: Perform all adjustments with engine at normal operating temperature, cooling fan and accessories off, transmission in Park or Neutral, and front wheels in straight-ahead position.

NOTE: Adjustment of ignition timing cannot be performed on vehicles equipped with Distributorless Ignition Systems (DIS). If ignition timing is not within specification, see CRANKSHAFT POSITION SENSOR in SYSTEM & COMPONENT TESTING article.

1) Locate ignition timing adjustment connector. See IGNITION TIMING ADJUSTMENT CONNECTOR LOCATION table. Connect jumper wire between ignition timing adjustment connector and ground. Check ignition basic timing.
2) If ignition basic timing is not within specification, loosen distributor and rotate to adjust timing if necessary. See IGNITION TIMING SPECIFICATIONS table. Remove jumper wire from ignition timing adjustment connector.

IGNITION TIMING SPECIFICATIONS (Degrees BTDC @ RPM)

Application	[1] Basic	[2] [3] Actual
1.5L		
Colt, Mirage & Summit	3-7 @ 650-850	10 @ 650-850
Precis	3-7 @ 600-800	10 @ 600-800
1.8L		
Colt, Colt Vista, Expo, Mirage, Summit, & Summit Wagon	3-7 @ 600-800	5 @ 600-800
Eclipse	5 @ 600-800	10 @ 600-800
2.0L		
Eclipse	5 @ 650-850	8 @ 650-850
Galant	3-7 @ 650-850	10 @ 650-850
2.4L		
Colt Vista, Expo & Summit Wagon	3-7 @ 650-850	8 @ 650-850
Galant		
SOHC	3-7 @ 650-850	10 @ 650-850
DOHC	2-8 @ 700-900	8 @ 700-900
Pickup	3-7 @ 600-800	8 @ 600-800
3.0L		
Diamante & Montero	3-7 @ 600-800	15 @ 600-800
Pickup	3-7 @ 650-850	15 @ 650-850
Stealth & 3000GT	2-8 @ 600-800	15 @ 600-800
3.5L		
Montero	3-7 @ 600-800	15 @ 600-800

[1] – With ignition timing adjustment connector grounded or vacuum hose (farthest from distributor) disconnected.
[2] – With ignition timing adjustment connector ungrounded or vacuum hose (farthest from distributor) connected. Ignition timing may fluctuate.
[3] – If vehicle altitude is more than 2300 ft. above sea level, actual timing may be advanced (5 degrees).

NOTE: Ignition timing adjustment connector is either round or oval with protective cover. Connector is either Black or Brown and is secured to harness with colored transparent tape.

IGNITION TIMING ADJUSTMENT CONNECTOR LOCATION

Application	[1][2] Wire Color	Location
Colt, Mirage & Summit	Black/Blue	3
Colt Vista, Expo & Summit Wagon	Blue	4
Diamante	White/Yellow	3
Eclipse	Yellow/Red	5
Galant	Black/Blue	3
Montero	White/Yellow	8
Pickup		
2.4L	Black/Blue	6
3.0L	White/Yellow	6
Precis	Light Green/Red	7
Stealth (SOHC & DOHC)	Black/Green	4
3000GT	Black/Green	4

[1] – Remove waterproof female connector (if equipped) for access to wire.
[2] – Ground connector at wire end for basic timing adjustment.
[3] – On main wiring harness, near center of firewall.
[4] – On main wiring harness, near master cylinder reservoir on firewall, near strut tower.
[5] – On main wiring harness, near wiper motor on firewall, behind battery.
[6] – Near left rear corner of engine compartment, below cruise control actuator (if equipped).
[7] – Between air filter housing and upper radiator hose.
[8] – On main wiring harness, near wiper motor on firewall.

IDLE SPEED & MIXTURE

NOTE: *Perform adjustments with engine at normal operating temperature, cooling fan and accessories off, transmission in Park or Neutral, and front wheels in straight-ahead position.*

CURB (SLOW) IDLE SPEED

NOTE: *Curb idle speed is controlled by Idle Air Control (IAC) motor. Adjustment is usually not necessary. For curb idle speed specifications, see IDLE SPEED SPECIFICATIONS table under BASIC IDLE SPEED.*

1) Check ignition timing and adjust if necessary. See IGNITION TIMING. Run engine at 2000-3000 RPM for more than 5 seconds. Allow engine to idle for 2 minutes. Check curb idle speed.
2) If curb idle speed is not within specification, check IAC system. See SYSTEM & COMPONENT TESTING article. If IAC system is okay, adjust basic idle speed. See BASIC IDLE SPEED.

BASIC IDLE SPEED

NOTE: *ALWAYS check TPS adjustment after adjusting basic idle speed. See THROTTLE POSITION SENSOR (TPS).*

NOTE: *For Data Link Connector (DLC) location, see SELF-DIAGNOSTICS article.*

NOTE: *Ensure vehicle is at normal operating temperature with all lights, cooling fan and accessories off. Shift transmission into Neutral or Park position.*

Colt, Colt Vista, Diamante, Eclipse (2.0L), Expo, Galant, Mirage, Montero, Pickup, Stealth, Summit, Summit Wagon & 3000GT – 1) Insert paper clip or appropriate probe into tachometer connector. See TACHOMETER CONNECTOR LOCATION table. Connect a primary voltage detecting type tachometer to paper clip.
2) On all models with 16-pin DLC connector, connect a jumper wire between data link terminal No. 1 and vehicle ground. See Fig. 1. On all models with 12-pin DLC connector, connect a jumper wire between data link terminal No. 10 and vehicle ground. See Fig. 1.

3) Connect a jumper wire between ignition timing adjustment connector and vehicle ground. See IGNITION TIMING ADJUSTMENT CONNECTOR LOCATION table under IGNITION TIMING.
4) Start and run engine at idle. Check basic idle speed. See IDLE SPEED SPECIFICATIONS table. If idle speed is not within specification, turn engine speed adjusting screw until correct engine speed is obtained. See Fig. 2. Access to speed adjusting screw is obtained by removing rubber plug on throttle body.
5) If idle speed cannot be lowered by turning engine speed adjusting screw, determine if fixed speed adjusting screw (stop screw contacting throttle lever) has been adjusted. See FIXED SPEED ADJUSTING SCREW for procedure.
6) After all adjustments are verified correct, possible cause of incorrect idle speed is deterioration of fast idle air control motor. Throttle valve must be replaced to correct symptom. Disconnect jumper wires and recheck idle speed.
Eclipse (1.8L) & Precis – 1) Insert paper clip or appropriate probe into tachometer connector. See TACHOMETER CONNECTOR LOCATION table. Connect a primary voltage detecting type tachometer to paper clip. Run engine and read idle speed. See IDLE SPEED SPECIFICATIONS table.
2) If idle speed is not within specification, loosen accelerator cable adjusting bracket. Turn ignition switch to ON position with engine off, (KOEO). Leave ignition on for 15 seconds to allow Idle Air Control (IAC) motor plunger to fully retract.
3) Turn ignition off and disconnect IAC motor connector. Loosen the Fixed Speed Adjusting Screw (FSAS). Start engine and adjust IAC adjusting screw to appropriate idle speed. See Fig. 3. Adjust FSAS until screw contacts throttle lever and then loosen 1/2 turn. Tighten lock nut. Connect IAC motor connector. Tighten accelerator cable adjusting bracket.

TACHOMETER CONNECTOR LOCATION

Application	Type	Location
Colt, Mirage & Summit	1-Pin	1
Colt Vista, Expo & Summit Wagon	1-Pin	2
Diamante	1- Or 3-Pin	3
Eclipse (1.8L)	3-Pin	4
Eclipse (2.0L)	1-Pin	5
Montero (3.0L) & Pickup (3.0L)	1-Pin	6
Montero (3.5L)	1-Pin	7
Precis	1-Pin	8
Pickup (2.4L)	1-Pin	9
Stealth & 3000GT	3-Pin	10, 11

[1] – Next to EGR solenoid, near center of firewall.
[2] – On main harness, on firewall below Vehicle Identification Plate.
[3] – On DOHC engine, 1-pin Blue connector is attached to main harness on center of firewall. On SOHC engine, 3-pin connector (White/Blue wire) is mounted to ignition coil bracket and must be backprobed.
[4] – Backprobe double wire side (White wire) of noise filter connector, located on right side of intake plenum above distributor.
[5] – On firewall, behind throttle body.
[6] – Backprobe connector to noise filter (White/Black wire) mounted on ignition coil bracket.
[7] – Next to ignition timing adjustment connector.
[8] – Backprobe 1-pin connector to noise filter mounted on right front side of intake plenum.
[9] – On main harness, on firewall to left of Vehicle Identification Plate.
[10] – On SOHC, backprobe double wire portion of connector to noise filter (White/Black wire) behind intake plenum, near ignition coil.
[11] – On DOHC, blue connector (Black/White wire) below wiper motor.

IDLE SPEED SPECIFICATIONS

Application	Curb Idle	Basic Idle
1.5L		
Colt, Mirage & Summit	650-850	650-850
Precis	600-800	600-800
1.8L		
Colt Vista, Expo &		
Summit Wagon	600-800	600-800
Eclipse	600-800	600-800
2.0L		
Eclipse, Galant	650-850	650-850
2.4L		
Colt Vista, Expo &		
Summit Wagon	650-850	650-850
Galant		
SOHC	650-850	10650-850
DOHC	700-900	700-900
Pickup	600-800	600-800
3.0L		
Diamante, Montero,		
Stealth & 3000GT	600-800	600-800
Pickup	650-850	650-850
3.5L		
Montero	600-800	600-800

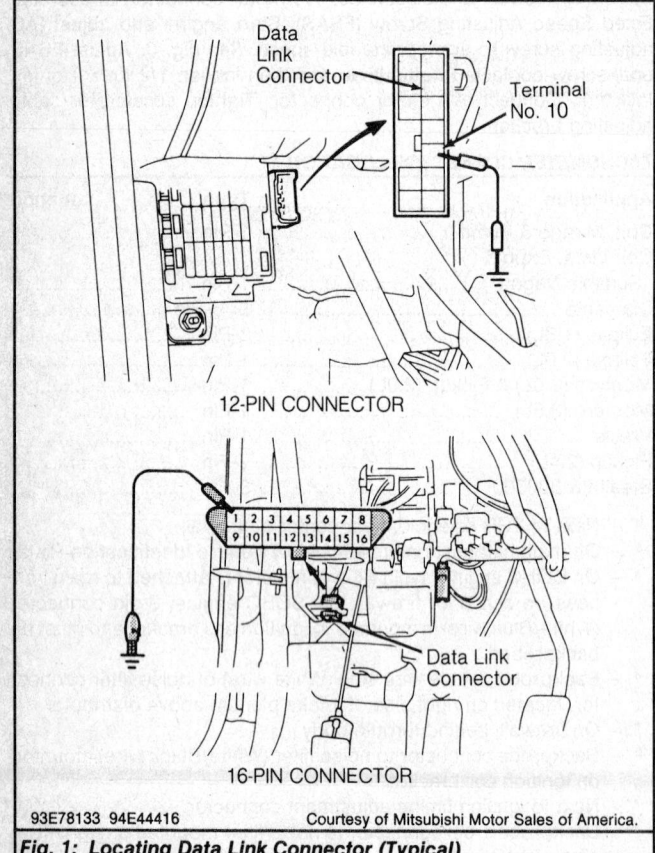

12-PIN CONNECTOR

16-PIN CONNECTOR

93E78133 94E44416   Courtesy of Mitsubishi Motor Sales of America.

Fig. 1: Locating Data Link Connector (Typical)

FIXED SPEED ADJUSTING SCREW

NOTE: Fixed Speed Adjusting Screw (FSAS) is preset by manufacturer and usually does not require adjustment. Only adjust FSAS if other adjustment procedures require it, or if manufacturer's original setting has been changed.

Colt, Colt Vista, Expo, Diamante, Galant, Mirage, Montero, Pickup, Stealth, Summit, Summit Wagon & 3000GT – 1) Loosen throttle cable. Loosen FSAS lock nut. *See Fig. 4.* Turn FSAS counterclockwise

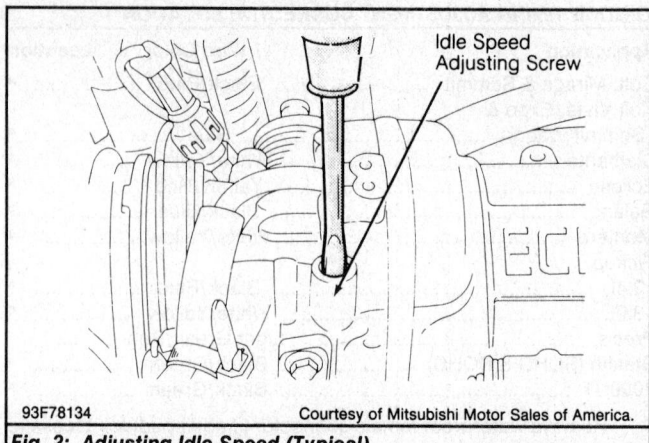

93F78134   Courtesy of Mitsubishi Motor Sales of America.

Fig. 2: Adjusting Idle Speed (Typical)

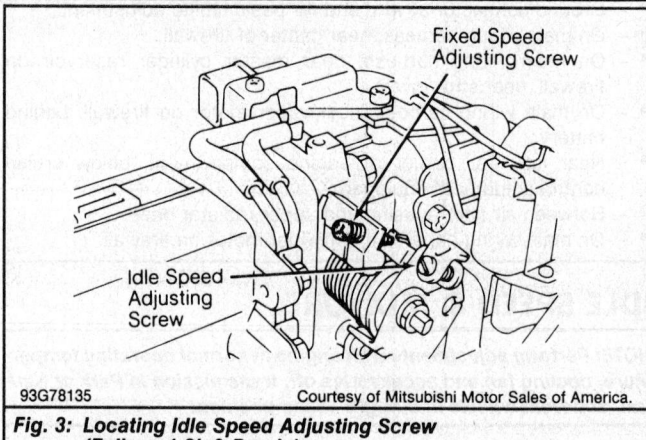

93G78135   Courtesy of Mitsubishi Motor Sales of America.

Fig. 3: Locating Idle Speed Adjusting Screw (Eclipse 1.8L & Precis)

until throttle valve is fully closed. Turn FSAS clockwise until throttle valve begins to open. Turn FSAS clockwise 1 1/4 turns after throttle valve begins to open.

2) Tighten lock nut while holding FSAS in position. Adjust throttle cable. Adjust basic idle speed. See BASIC IDLE SPEED under IDLE SPEED & MIXTURE. Adjust throttle position sensor. See THROTTLE POSITION SENSOR (TPS).

NOTE: Eclipse 2.0L DOHC uses an idle position switch as the Fixed Speed Adjusting Screw (FSAS). For adjustment, see IDLE POSITION SWITCH under THROTTLE POSITION SENSOR (TPS).

Eclipse (1.8L) & Precis – To adjust Fixed Speed Adjusting Screw (FSAS), adjust basic idle speed. See BASIC IDLE SPEED under IDLE SPEED & MIXTURE.

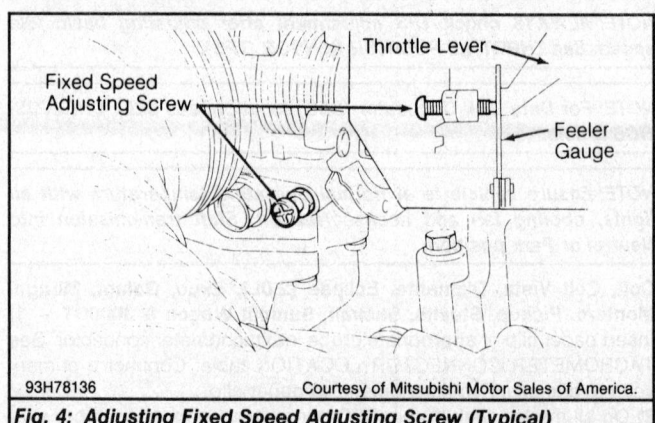

93H78136   Courtesy of Mitsubishi Motor Sales of America.

Fig. 4: Adjusting Fixed Speed Adjusting Screw (Typical)

IDLE MIXTURE

NOTE: Idle mixture is computer controlled on fuel injected engines and is nonadjustable. CO level should not exceed .5%. HC level should not exceed 100 ppm. If mixture levels exceed limits, see SELF-DIAGNOSTICS article.

THROTTLE POSITION SENSOR (TPS)

TPS ADJUSTMENT

NOTE: Ensure basic idle speed is set to specification before adjusting TPS. See BASIC IDLE SPEED under IDLE SPEED & MIXTURE. Perform all adjustments with engine at normal operating temperature, front wheels in straight-ahead position, cooling fan and all accessories off, and transmission in Park or Neutral.

TPS SPECIFICATIONS

Application	¹ Volts
Colt, Mirage & Summit	.3-1.0
Diamante (w/Traction Control)	.58-.69
Eclipse & Pickup (3.0L)	.48-.52
All Others	.4-1.0

¹ – At idle.

Colt Vista, Expo, Montero & Summit Wagon – 1) Disconnect TPS connector. Using external ohmmeter, measure resistance between TPS terminals No. 1 and 2. *See Fig. 5.* Insert .025" (.65 mm) feeler gauge between fixed speed adjusting screw and throttle lever.
2) Loosen TPS mounting screws and rotate TPS fully clockwise. Ensure there is continuity between terminals No. 1 and 2. Rotate TPS counterclockwise until there is no continuity and tighten screws. Install Test Harness (MB991348) between TPS and harness connector.
3) Turn ignition on. Using external voltmeter, measure TPS output voltage between terminals No. 1 and 3. See TPS SPECIFICATION table. If voltage is not within specifications, check harness and sensor. See SYSTEM & COMPONENT TESTING article.
Colt, Diamante, Galant, Mirage, Pickup, Stealth, Summit & 3000GT –
1) Disconnect TPS connector. Using external ohmmeter, measure resistance between TPS terminals No. 3 and 4. *See Fig. 5.* Insert .025" (.65 mm) feeler gauge between fixed speed adjusting screw and throttle lever.
2) Loosen TPS mounting screws and rotate TPS fully clockwise. Ensure there is continuity between terminals No. 3 and 4. Rotate TPS counterclockwise until there is no continuity and tighten screws. Install Test Harness (MB991348) between TPS and harness connector.
3) Turn ignition on. Using external voltmeter, measure TPS output voltage between terminals No. 2 and 4. See TPS SPECIFICATIONS table. If voltage is not within specification, check harness and sensor. See SYSTEM & COMPONENT TESTING article.
Precis – Disconnect TPS connector. Install Test Harness (MB991348) between TPS and harness connector. Turn ignition on. Using external voltmeter, measure TPS output voltage between terminals No. 3 and 4. See TPS SPECIFICATIONS table. If voltage is not within specification, check harness and sensor. See SYSTEM & COM-
PONENT TESTING article.
Eclipse – Disconnect TPS connector. Install Test Harness (MB991348) between TPS and harness connector. Turn ignition on. Using external voltmeter, measure TPS output voltage between terminals No. 2 and 4. See TPS SPECIFICATIONS table. If voltage is not within specifications, check harness and sensor. See SYSTEM & COMPONENT TESTING article.

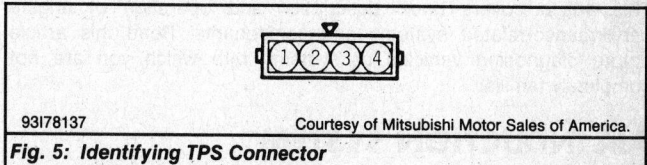

93I78137 — Courtesy of Mitsubishi Motor Sales of America.

Fig. 5: Identifying TPS Connector

IDLE POSITION SWITCH

NOTE: Idle position switch is preset by manufacturer. Adjustment is usually not necessary. If other procedures require adjustment of idle position switch or if switch setting has been changed, adjust switch as follows.

2.0L Eclipse DOHC – 1) Loosen throttle cable. Disconnect electrical connector from idle position switch. *See Fig. 6.* Loosen lock nut at base of switch. Turn switch counterclockwise until throttle valve is fully closed.
2) Connect ohmmeter between switch terminal and switch body (ground). Turn idle position switch clockwise until ohmmeter registers continuity. At this point, throttle valve should begin to open.
3) Turn switch 15/16 of a turn beyond contact point. Tighten lock nut at base of idle position switch, holding switch to prevent it from turning while tightening.
4) Adjust throttle cable. Adjust basic idle speed. See BASIC IDLE SPEED under IDLE SPEED & MIXTURE. Adjust TPS. See TPS ADJUSTMENT.
All Other Models – Idle position switch is incorporated into IAC motor and is automatically adjusted when TPS is adjusted. See TPS ADJUSTMENT.

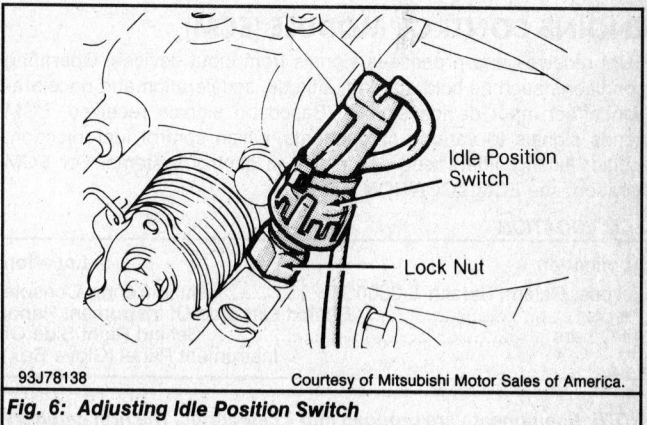

Idle Position Switch

Lock Nut

93J78138 — Courtesy of Mitsubishi Motor Sales of America.

Fig. 6: Adjusting Idle Position Switch

1994 ENGINE PERFORMANCE
Theory & Operation

Chrysler Corp.: Colt, Colt Vista, Stealth
Eagle: Summit, Summit Wagon
Mitsubishi: Diamante, Eclipse, Expo, Galant,
  Mirage, Montero, Pickup, Precis, 3000GT

INTRODUCTION

This article covers basic description and operation of engine performance-related systems and components. Read this article before diagnosing vehicles or systems with which you are not completely familiar.

AIR INDUCTION SYSTEM

NON-TURBOCHARGED ENGINES

Colt, Mirage & Summit (1.5L) – Colt, Mirage and Summit models equipped with 1.5L engines use a Manifold Absolute Pressure (MAP) sensor instead of an airflow sensor. A air filter is ducted to a plenum-mounted throttle body.

All Other Models – All remaining models use same basic air induction system. Remote air filter (with airflow sensor) is ducted to a plenum-mounted throttle body.

TURBOCHARGED ENGINES

In addition to basic air induction system, turbocharging system components include turbocharger(s), air-to-air intercooler(s), air by-pass valve(s), wastegate actuator(s), wastegate control solenoid valve(s) and intake duct.

Wastegate Control Solenoid Valve – Engine Control Module (ECM) energizes solenoid valve, controlling leakage rate of turbocharger pressure to wastegate actuator.

COMPUTERIZED ENGINE CONTROLS

Multi-Point Fuel Injection (MFI) is a computerized engine control system, which controls fuel injection, ignition timing, idle speed and emission control systems.

ENGINE CONTROL MODULE (ECM)

ECM receives and processes signals from input devices. Operating conditions such as cold starting, altitude, acceleration and deceleration affect input device signals. Based on signals received, ECM sends signals to various components, which control fuel injection, ignition timing, idle speed and emission control systems. For ECM location, see ECM LOCATION table.

ECM LOCATION

Application	Location
Eclipse, Galant, Stealth & 3000GT	Behind Center Console
Precis	Behind Left Side Of Instrument Panel
All Others	Behind Right Side Of Instrument Panel (Glove Box)

NOTE: *Components are grouped into 2 categories. The first category covers INPUT DEVICES, which control or produce voltage signals monitored by Engine Control Module (ECM). The second category covers OUTPUT SIGNALS, which are components controlled by ECM.*

INPUT DEVICES

Vehicles are equipped with different combinations of input devices. Not all input devices are used on all models. To determine input device usage on specific models, see appropriate wiring diagram in WIRING DIAGRAMS article. The following are available input devices.

Air Conditioner Switch – When A/C is turned on, signal is sent to ECM. With engine at idle, ECM increases idle speed through Idle Air Control (IAC) motor.

Airflow Sensor – Incorporated in airflow sensor assembly, airflow sensor is a Karmen vortex-type sensor which measures intake airflow rate. Intake air flows through tunnel in airflow sensor assembly. Airflow sensor transmits radio frequency signals across direction of incoming airflow, downstream of vortex. Intake air encounters vortex, causing turbulence in tunnel.

Turbulence disrupts radio frequency, causing variations in transmission. Airflow sensor converts frequency transmitted into a proportionate electrical signal, which is sent to ECM.

Airflow Sensor Assembly – Assembly is mounted inside air cleaner, and incorporates airflow sensor, atmospheric pressure sensor and intake air temperature sensor.

Atmospheric (Barometric) Pressure Sensor – Sensor is incorporated in airflow sensor assembly. Sensor converts atmospheric pressure to electrical signal, which is sent to ECM. ECM adjusts air/fuel ratio and ignition timing according to altitude.

Camshaft Position Sensor – Assembly is located in distributor on SOHC engines. On DOHC 4-cylinder engines, assembly is a separate unit mounted in place of distributor. On DOHC 6-cylinder engines, sensor is located beside camshaft in front of engine. ECM determines TDC based on pulse signals received from sensor and then controls MFI timing.

Closed Throttle Position Switch – Closed throttle position switch is located in the Throttle Position Sensor (TPS) on all models except Eclipse. On Eclipse models, switch is separately located on throttle body. ECM senses whether accelerator pedal is depressed or not. High voltage (open) or low voltage (closed) signal is input to ECM, which then controls IAC motor based on input signal.

Coolant Temperature Sensor – Sensor converts coolant temperature to electrical signal for use by ECM. ECM uses coolant temperature information to control fuel enrichment when engine is cold.

Crankshaft Position Sensor Assembly – Assembly is located in distributor on SOHC engines. On DOHC 4-cylinder engines, assembly is a separate unit mounted in place of distributor. On DOHC 6-cylinder engines, sensor is located beside crankshaft in front of engine. ECM determines crankshaft position on pulse signals received from sensor and then controls MFI timing and ignition timing.

Electrical Load Switch – Electrical load switch inputs on/off state of taillight relay, defogger relay and stoplight relay to ECM. ECM signals IAC to increase or decrease RPM depending on on/off state of relays.

Engine Speed (Tach Signal) – ECM uses ignition coil tach signal to determine engine speed.

Heated Oxygen Sensor (HO2S) – HO2S detects oxygen content in exhaust gas and sends this information to ECM. ECM uses input signals from sensor to vary duration of fuel injection. Oxygen sensor heater stabilizes sensor temperature regardless of exhaust gas temperature to allow for more accurate exhaust oxygen content readings.

Ignition Timing Adjustment Terminal – Used for adjusting base ignition timing. When terminal is grounded, ECM timing control function is by-passed, allowing base timing to be adjusted.

Inhibitor Switch (Automatic Transmission) – Inhibitor switch senses position of transmission select lever, indicating engine load due to automatic transmission engagement. Based on this signal, ECM commands IAC motor to increase throttle angle, maintaining optimum idle speed.

Intake Air Temperature Sensor – Sensor is incorporated in airflow sensor assembly. This resistor-based sensor measures temperature of incoming air and supplies air density information to ECM.

Knock Sensor (Turbo) – Sensor is located in cylinder block and senses engine vibration during detonation (knock). Sensor converts vibration into electrical signal. ECM retards ignition timing based on this signal.

Motor Position Sensor (MPS) – Sensor is incorporated in IAC motor (or separate unit on some models). MPS senses IAC motor plunger position and sends electrical signal to ECM.

Oxygen (O₂) Sensor – O_2 sensor is located in exhaust system and generates an output voltage. Output voltage varies with oxygen content of exhaust gas stream. ECM adjusts air/fuel mixture based on signals from O_2 sensor.

Power Steering Oil Pressure Switch – Switch detects increase in power steering oil pressure. When power steering oil pressure increases, switch contacts close, signaling ECM. ECM commands IAC motor, raising idle speed to compensate for drop in engine RPM due to power steering load.

TDC Sensor – See CRANKSHAFT POSITION & TDC SENSOR ASSEMBLY under INPUT DEVICES.

Throttle Position Sensor (TPS) – TPS is a variable resistor mounted on throttle body. ECM uses voltage signal from TPS to determine throttle plate angle.

Vehicle Speed Sensor – Sensor is located in speedometer in instrument cluster, and uses a reed switch to sense speedometer gear revolutions. ECM uses gear revolutions to determine vehicle speed.

OUTPUT SIGNALS

NOTE: *Vehicles are equipped with various combinations of computer-controlled components. Not all components listed below are used on every vehicle. For theory and operation on each output component, refer to system indicated after component.*

Accelerator Pedal Position Sensor (APPS) – See MISCELLANEOUS CONTROLS.

Data Link Connector – See SELF-DIAGNOSTIC SYSTEM.

EGR Control Solenoid Valve – See EXHAUST GAS RECIRCULATION (EGR) CONTROL under EMISSION SYSTEMS.

Fuel Injectors – See FUEL CONTROL under FUEL SYSTEM.

Fuel Pressure Control Solenoid Valve (Turbo) – See FUEL DELIVERY under FUEL SYSTEM.

Fuel Pressure Regulator – See FUEL DELIVERY under FUEL SYSTEM.

Idle Speed Control Servo – See IDLE SPEED under FUEL SYSTEM.

Malfunction Indicator Light – See SELF-DIAGNOSTIC SYSTEM.

Power Transistor(s) & Ignition Coils – See IGNITION SYSTEMS.

Purge Control Solenoid Valve – See EVAPORATIVE CONTROL under EMISSION SYSTEMS.

Variable Induction Control (VIC) Motor Sensor – See MISCELLANEOUS CONTROLS.

Wastegate Control Solenoid Valve – See TURBOCHARGED ENGINES under AIR INDUCTION SYSTEM.

FUEL SYSTEM

FUEL DELIVERY

Electric fuel pump, located in gas tank, feeds fuel through in-tank fuel filter, external fuel filter (located in engine compartment) and fuel injector rail.

Fuel Pump – Fuel pump consists of a motor-driven impeller. Pump has an internal check valve to maintain system pressure, and a relief valve to protect fuel pressure circuit. Pump receives voltage supply from MFI control relay.

Fuel Pressure Control Solenoid Valve (Turbo) – Valve prevents rough idle due to fuel percolation. On engine restart, if engine coolant or intake air temperature reaches a preset value, ECM applies voltage to fuel pressure control solenoid valve for 2 minutes after engine restart. Valve will open, allowing atmospheric pressure to be applied to fuel pressure regulator diaphragm. This allows maximum available fuel pressure at injectors, enriching fuel mixture and maintaining stable idle at high engine temperatures.

Fuel Pressure Regulator – Located on fuel injector rail, this diaphragm-operated relief valve adjusts fuel pressure according to engine manifold vacuum.

As engine manifold vacuum increases (closed throttle), fuel pressure regulator diaphragm opens relief valve, allowing pressure to bleed off through fuel return line, reducing fuel pressure.

As engine manifold vacuum decreases (open throttle), fuel pressure regulator diaphragm closes valve, preventing pressure from bleeding off through fuel return line, increasing fuel pressure.

FUEL CONTROL

Fuel Injectors – Fuel is supplied to engine through electronically pulsed (timed) injector valves located on fuel rail(s). ECM controls amount of fuel metered through injectors based on information received from sensors.

IDLE SPEED

Air Conditioner (A/C) Relay – When A/C is turned on with engine at idle, ECM signals IAC motor to increase idle speed. To prevent A/C compressor from switching on before idle speed has increased, ECM momentarily opens A/C relay circuit.

Idle Air Control (IAC) Motor – Motor controls pintle-type air valve (DOHC engines) or throttle plate angle (SOHC engines) to regulate volume of intake air at idle.

During start mode, ECM controls idle intake air volume according to coolant temperature input. After starting, with idle position switch activated (throttle closed), fast idle speed is controlled by IAC motor and fast idle air control valve (if equipped).

When idle switch is deactivated (throttle open), IAC motor moves to a preset position in accordance with coolant temperature input.

ECM signals IAC motor to increase engine RPM in the following situations: A/T (if applicable) is shifted from Neutral to Drive, A/C is turned on, or power steering pressure reaches a preset value.

Fast Idle Air Control Valve – Some models use a coolant temperature-sensitive fast idle air control valve, located on throttle body, to admit additional intake air volume during engine warm-up. Control valve closes as temperature increases, restricting by-pass airflow rate. At engine warm-up, valve closes completely.

IGNITION SYSTEMS

DIRECT IGNITION SYSTEM (DOHC ENGINES)

Depending on number of cylinders, ignition system is a 2 or 3-coil distributorless ignition system. Crankshaft position and TDC sensor assembly, mounted in place of distributor, are optically controlled.

Power Transistors & Ignition Coils – Based on crankshaft position and TDC sensor inputs, ECM controls timing and directly activates each power transistor to fire coils. On 4-cylinder engines, power transistor "A" controls primary current of ignition coil "A" to fire spark plugs on cylinders No. 1 and No. 4 at the same time. Power transistor "B" controls primary current of ignition coil "B" to fire spark plugs on cylinders No. 2 and No. 3 at the same time. On V6 engines, companion cylinders No. 1 and 4, 2 and 5, and 3 and 6 are fired together.

On all models, although each coil fires 2 plugs at the same time, ignition takes place in only one cylinder, since the other cylinder is on its exhaust stroke when plug fires.

ELECTRONIC IGNITION SYSTEM (SOHC ENGINES)

Breakerless electronic ignition system uses a disc and optical sensing unit to trigger power transistor.

Power Transistor & Ignition Coil – Power transistor is mounted inside distributor with disc and optical sensing unit. When ignition is on, ignition coil primary circuit is energized. As distributor shaft rotates, disc rotates, triggering optical sensing unit. ECM receives signals from optical sensing unit. Signals are converted and sent to power transistor, interrupting primary current flow and inducing secondary voltage.

IGNITION TIMING CONTROL SYSTEM

Ignition timing is controlled by ECM. ECM adjusts timing based on various conditions such as engine temperature, altitude and detonation (turbo).

EMISSION SYSTEMS

EXHAUST GAS RECIRCULATION (EGR) CONTROL

Federal (Non-Turbo) – To lower oxides of nitrogen (NOx) exhaust emissions, a non-computer controlled exhaust gas recirculation system is used. EGR operation is controlled by throttle body ported vacuum. Vacuum is routed through thermovalve to prevent EGR operation at low engine temperatures.

Spring pressure holds EGR valve closed during low vacuum conditions (engine idling or wide open throttle). When vacuum pressure increases and overcomes EGR spring pressure, EGR valve is lifted to allow exhaust gases to flow into intake manifold for combustion.

California & Turbo – ECM controls EGR operation by activating EGR control solenoid valve according to engine load. When engine is cold, ECM signals EGR control solenoid valve to deactivate EGR.

California models are equipped with an EGR temperature sensor. When EGR malfunction occurs, EGR temperature decreases and ECM illuminates MIL (CHECK ENGINE light).

EGR Control Solenoid Valve – Valve denies or allows vacuum supply to EGR valve based on ECM commands.

Thermovalve – Thermovalve denies or allows vacuum supply to EGR valve based on coolant temperature.

EVAPORATIVE CONTROL

Fuel evaporation system prevents fuel vapor from entering atmosphere. System consists of the following: special fuel tank with vapor separator tanks (if equipped), vacuum relief filler cap, overfill limiter (2-way valve), fuel check valve, thermovalve (if equipped), charcoal canister, purge control valve, purge control solenoid valve, and connecting lines and hoses.

Purge Control Solenoid Valve – When engine is off, fuel vapors are vented into charcoal canister. When engine is warmed to normal operating temperature and running at speeds greater than idle, ECM energizes purge control solenoid valve, allowing vacuum to purge valve.

Canister vapors are then drawn through purge valve into intake manifold for burning. Purge control solenoid valve remains closed during idle and engine warm-up to reduce HC (hydrocarbons) and CO (carbon monoxide) emissions.

HIGH ALTITUDE CONTROL (HAC)

HAC system compensates for variations in altitude. When atmospheric (barometric) pressure sensor determines vehicle is at altitude greater than preset value, ECM compensates by adjusting air/fuel mixture and ignition timing. If HAC system is inoperative, there will be an increase in emissions.

POSITIVE CRANKCASE
VENTILATION (PCV) VALVE

PCV valve operates in closed crankcase ventilation system. Closed crankcase ventilation system consists of PCV valve, oil separator, breather and ventilation hoses.

PCV valve is a one-way check valve located in valve cover. When engine is running, manifold vacuum pulls PCV valve open, allowing crankcase fumes to enter intake manifold. If engine backfires through intake manifold, PCV valve closes to prevent crankcase combustion.

MISCELLANEOUS CONTROLS

NOTE: Although not considered true engine performance-related systems, some controlled devices may affect driveability if they malfunction.

Accelerator Pedal Position Sensor (APPS) – ECM supplies one end of APPS resistor with a 5-volt signal. The other end of resistor is grounded at ECM. Accelerator pedal position sensor converts amount accelerator pedal is depressed into variable voltage input to traction control module for traction control.

Variable Induction Control (VIC) Motor Sensor – ECM controls VIC valve opening or closing. VIC valve controls length of intake air path to intake manifold. VIC valve closes at higher RPM to shorten intake air path and opens at lower RPM to lengthen intake air path. The result is more engine torque in a wider RPM range.

SELF-DIAGNOSTIC SYSTEM

NOTE: ECM diagnostic memory is retained by direct power supply from battery. Memory is not erased by turning off ignition, but it will be erased if battery or ECM is disconnected.

Self-diagnostic system monitors input and output signals through the data link connector. On all models, codes can be read using analog voltmeter. Scan tester can be used to read codes on some models. For additional information, see SELF-DIAGNOSTICS article.

Malfunction Indicator Light (MIL) – MIL (CHECK ENGINE light) comes on when ignition is turned on. MIL remains on for several seconds after engine has started. If an abnormal input signal occurs, MIL comes on and code is stored in memory. If an abnormal input signal returns to normal, ECM turns MIL off, but code remains stored in memory until it is cleared. If ignition is turned on again, MIL will not come on until ECM detects malfunction during system operation.

Chrysler Corp.: Colt, Colt Vista, Stealth
Eagle: Summit, Summit Wagon
Mitsubishi: Diamante, Eclipse, Expo, Galant,
 Mirage, Montero, Pickup, Precis, 3000GT

INTRODUCTION

The following diagnostic steps will help prevent overlooking a simple problem. This is also where to begin diagnosis for a no-start condition. The first step in diagnosing any driveability problem is verifying the customer's complaint with a test drive under the conditions the problem reportedly occurred.

Before entering self-diagnostics, perform a careful and complete visual inspection. Most engine control problems result from mechanical breakdowns, poor electrical connections or damaged/misrouted vacuum hoses. Before condemning the computerized system, perform each test listed in this article.

NOTE: *Perform all voltage tests with a Digital Volt-Ohmmeter (DVOM) with a minimum 10-megohm input impedance, unless stated otherwise in test procedure.*

PRELIMINARY INSPECTION & ADJUSTMENTS

VISUAL INSPECTION

Visually inspect all electrical wiring, looking for chafed, stretched, cut or pinched wiring. Ensure electrical connectors fit tightly and are not corroded. Ensure vacuum hoses are properly routed and are not pinched or cut. See VACUUM DIAGRAMS article to verify routing and connections (if necessary). Inspect air induction system for possible vacuum leaks.

MECHANICAL INSPECTION

Compression – Check engine mechanical condition with a compression gauge, vacuum gauge, or an engine analyzer. See engine analyzer manual for specific instructions.

WARNING: *DO NOT use ignition switch during compression tests on fuel injected vehicles. Use a remote starter to crank engine. Fuel injectors on many models are triggered by ignition switch during cranking mode, which can create a fire hazard or contaminate the engine's oiling system.*

COMPRESSION SPECIFICATIONS

Application [1]	psi (kg/cm²)
Compression Pressure	
1.5L (VIN A)	192 psi (13.4 kg/cm²)
1.5L (VIN J)	192 psi (13.4 kg/cm²)
1.8L (VIN B)	185 psi (13.0 kg/cm²)
1.8L (VIN C)	199 psi (13.9 kg/cm²)
2.0L (VIN E)	192 psi (13.4 kg/cm²)
2.0L (VIN F)	164 psi (11.5 kg/cm²)
2.4L (VIN G)	
8-Valve	171 psi (12.0 kg/cm²)
16-Valve	185 psi (13.0 kg/cm²)
Galant (SOHC)	192 psi (13.4 kg/cm²)
2.4L (VIN L)	206 psi (14.6 kg/cm²)
3.0L (VIN H)	
Diamante	196 psi (13.8 kg/cm²)
Except Diamante	171 psi (12.0 kg/cm²)
3.0L (VIN J)	185 psi (13.0 kg/cm²)
3.0L (VIN K)	156 psi (10.9 kg/cm²)
3.5L (VIN M)	185 psi (13.0 kg/cm²)
Maximum Variation Between Cylinders	14 psi (1.0 kg/cm²)

[1] – See CHRYSLER CORP./EAGLE/MITSUBISHI INTRODUCTION article for VIN information.

Exhaust System Backpressure – Exhaust system can be checked with a vacuum or pressure gauge. Remove O_2 sensor or air injection check valve (if equipped). Connect a 0-5 psi pressure gauge and run engine at 2500 RPM. If exhaust system backpressure is greater than 1 3/4 - 2 psi, exhaust system or catalytic converter is plugged.

If using a vacuum gauge, connect vacuum gauge hose to intake manifold vacuum port and start engine. Observe vacuum gauge. Open throttle part way and hold steady. If vacuum gauge reading slowly drops after stabilizing, exhaust system should be checked for a restriction.

FUEL SYSTEM

WARNING: *ALWAYS relieve fuel pressure before disconnecting any fuel injection-related component. DO NOT allow fuel to contact engine or electrical components.*

FUEL PRESSURE

Relieving Fuel Pressure – **1)** On Diamante, Eclipse (FWD), Pickup and Precis, disconnect fuel pump harness connector at fuel tank from underneath vehicle. On Colt, Colt Vista, Eclipse (AWD), Expo, Galant, Mirage, Montero, Stealth, Summit, Summit Wagon and 3000GT, remove rear seat cushion and remove access plate if required to disconnect fuel pump harness connector.

2) On all models, start engine. Let engine run until it stops. Turn ignition off. Disconnect negative battery terminal. Connect fuel pump harness connector. Reinstall rear seat (if necessary.)

WARNING: *Before disconnecting high pressure fuel hose at fuel delivery pipe, cover fuel hose connection with a rag. Some residual fuel pressure may still be in system.*

Pressure Testing – **1)** Disconnect high pressure fuel hose at fuel delivery pipe. Remove throttle body bracket (if necessary). Connect fuel pressure gauge with adapter between fuel delivery pipe and high pressure hose. See Fig. 1.

2) Connect negative battery terminal. Operate fuel pump by connecting battery voltage to fuel pump test terminal. See FUEL PUMP TEST TERMINAL LOCATION table. Ensure no fuel leaks are present. Disconnect battery voltage from fuel pump test terminal.

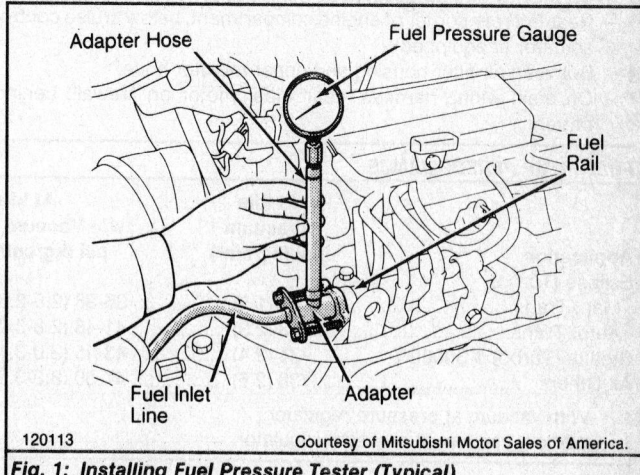

120113   Courtesy of Mitsubishi Motor Sales of America.

Fig. 1: Installing Fuel Pressure Tester (Typical)

3) Start engine and let idle. Measure fuel pressure with vacuum hose connected to fuel pressure regulator. Record fuel pressure reading. See FUEL PUMP PERFORMANCE table. Disconnect and plug vacuum hose from fuel pressure regulator. Record fuel pressure reading.

4) Check for fuel pressure in fuel return hose by gently pinching hose while increasing engine speed. If fuel volume is low, fuel pressure in return hose will not be felt. Increase engine speed to 2500-3000 RPM, 2-3 times. Return engine to idle. Fuel pressure should not drop when engine is returned to idle.

5) Turn ignition off. On all models except Precis, ensure fuel pressure reading does not decrease within 2 minutes. On Precis, fuel pressure reading should not decrease within 5 minutes. On all models, if a decrease is noted, monitor speed of decrease.

6) If fuel pressure is lower than specification, fuel pressure drops at idle after increasing engine speed to 2500-3000 RPM, or no fuel pressure in fuel return hose can be felt, check for clogged fuel filter, or faulty fuel pressure regulator or fuel pump.

7) If fuel pressure is greater than specification, check for a faulty fuel pressure regulator or plugged fuel return line. If fuel pressure does not change when vacuum hose to regulator is connected or disconnected, check for a leaking or clogged vacuum hose to fuel pressure regulator or faulty fuel pressure regulator.

8) If fuel pressure decreases suddenly after engine is stopped, check valve in fuel pump is not seated. Replace fuel pump. If fuel pressure drops slowly, fuel injector is leaking or fuel pressure regulator valve seat is leaking. Check for faulty fuel injector or fuel pressure regulator. Repair as necessary.

9) When fuel pressure test is complete, repeat fuel pressure release procedure before disconnecting fuel pressure gauge. Install new "O" ring at end of high pressure hose. Check for fuel leaks.

FUEL PUMP TEST TERMINAL LOCATION

Application	Wire Color	Location
Colt, Mirage & Summit	Black/Blue	1
Diamante	Black/Blue	1
Eclipse	Black/White	2
Colt Vista, Expo & Summit Wagon	Black/Blue	3
Galant	Black/Blue	3
Montero	Black/White	4
Pickup	Black/Blue	5
Precis	Yellow	6
Stealth & 3000GT	Black/Blue	7

1 – On main wiring harness, near center of firewall.
2 – On main wiring harness, near wiper motor on firewall, behind battery.
3 – On main wiring harness, near left center of firewall.
4 – On main wiring harness, near wiper motor on firewall.
5 – Near left rear corner of engine compartment, below cruise control actuator (if equipped).
6 – Between air filter housing and upper radiator hose.
7 – On main wiring harness, near wiper motor on firewall, behind battery.

FUEL PUMP PERFORMANCE

Application	At Idle w/Vacuum [1] psi (kg/cm²)	At Idle w/o Vacuum [2] psi (kg/cm²)
Eclipse (Turbo)		
Man. Trans.	27 (1.8)	36-38 (2.5-2.6)
Auto. Trans.	33 (2.3)	41-46 (2.8-3.2)
Stealth (Turbo) & 3000GT	34 (2.4)	43-45 (3.0-3.1)
All Others	38 (2.6)	47-50 (3.3-3.5)

1 – With vacuum at pressure regulator.
2 – Without vacuum at pressure regulator.

MFI Control Relay – Multipurpose relay switches power to vehicle sensors and actuators including airflow sensor, crank angle sensor, idle speed control, injectors and fuel pump. When ignition switch is turned to ON position, ECM energizes coils controlling injectors, airflow sensor and idle speed control. When ignition switch is turned to START position, ECM energizes coils (through inhibitor switch on A/T models) to supply power to fuel pump. Relay failure will cause a no-start condition. For testing procedure, see SYSTEM & COMPONENT TESTING article.

IGNITION CHECKS
SPARK

Check for spark at coil wire (if applicable) and at each spark plug wire using a high output spark tester. Check spark plug wire resistance on suspect wires. For wire resistance specification, see SERVICE & ADJUSTMENT SPECIFICATIONS article.

CAMSHAFT POSITION SENSOR

For camshaft position sensor testing procedure, see SYSTEM & COMPONENT TESTING article.

CRANKSHAFT POSITION SENSOR

For crankshaft position sensor testing procedure, see SYSTEM & COMPONENT TESTING article.

DISTRIBUTORLESS IGNITION SYSTEM (DIS) 4-CYLINDER

Ignition Coil Resistance – 1) Disconnect ignition coil connector. Using a Digital Volt-Ohmmeter (DVOM), measure primary coil resistance between ignition coil connector terminals No. 2 and 3 (coils for cylinders No. 1 and 4) and terminals No. 1 and 3 (coils for cylinders No. 2 and 3). See Fig. 2.

2) Remove ignition wires from coil. Measure secondary coil resistance between coil towers for cylinders No. 1 and 4 and between coil towers for cylinders No. 2 and 3. Primary and secondary coil resistance should be within specification. See IGNITION COIL RESISTANCE (4-CYLINDER) table. Connect coil harness connector. Connect ignition wires to coil.

IGNITION COIL RESISTANCE (4-CYLINDER) – Ohms @ 68°F (20°C)

Application	Primary	Secondary
Eclipse	.70-.86	11,300-15,300
Galant (DOHC)	.67-.81	11,310-15,300

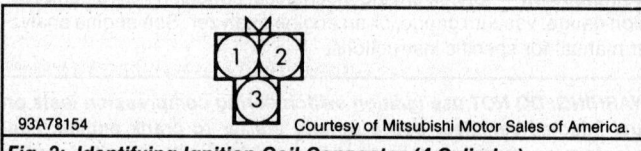

93A78154   Courtesy of Mitsubishi Motor Sales of America.

Fig. 2: Identifying Ignition Coil Connector (4-Cylinder)

Power Transistor – 1) To test the section of the power transistor that controls cylinders No. 1 and 4 of the ignition coil, disconnect power transistor connector. Using a 1.5-volt dry cell battery, connect negative end of battery to terminal No. 3 of power transistor and positive end to terminal No. 7. See Fig. 3.

2) Using an analog ohmmeter, check for continuity between terminals No. 3 and 8 of power transistor. Continuity should exist. With positive end of 1.5-volt battery disconnected, there should be no continuity. Replace power transistor if it fails test.

3) To test the section of the power transistor that controls cylinders No. 2 and 4 , connect negative end of 1.5-volt dry cell battery to terminal No. 3 of power transistor and positive end to terminal No. 2.

4) Using an analog ohmmeter, check for continuity between terminals No. 1 and 3 of power transistor. Continuity should exist. With positive end of 1.5-volt battery disconnected, there should be no continuity. Replace power transistor if it fails test.

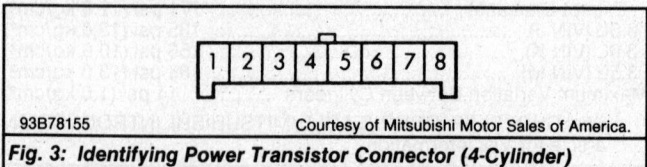

93B78155   Courtesy of Mitsubishi Motor Sales of America.

Fig. 3: Identifying Power Transistor Connector (4-Cylinder)

DISTRIBUTORLESS IGNITION SYSTEM (DIS) V6

Ignition Coil Resistance – 1) On Stealth and 3000GT, measure primary coil resistance between terminal No. 3 (power terminal) and each individual coil terminal using a DVOM. See Fig. 4. To check secondary coil resistance, measure resistance between towers of each individual coil.

2) On Montero 3.5L, measure between each individual coil primary terminals to determine primary resistance. To measure secondary resistance, remove coil and measure between spark plug connector and high tension wire connector.

3) Replace coil if primary and secondary coil resistances are not within specification. See IGNITION COIL RESISTANCE (V6) table.

IGNITION COIL RESISTANCE (V6) – Ohms @ 68°F (20°C)

Application	Primary	Secondary
3.0L	.67-.81	11,300-15,300
3.5L	.69-.85	15,300-20,700

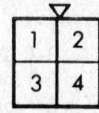

93C78156   Courtesy of Mitsubishi Motor Sales of America.

Fig. 4: Identifying Ignition Coil Connector (V6)

Power Transistor – 1) To test section of power transistor that controls cylinders No. 1 and 4 of ignition coil, disconnect power transistor connector. Using a 1.5-volt dry cell battery, connect negative end of 1.5-volt battery to terminal No. 4 of power transistor and positive end to terminal No. 3. See Fig. 5.

2) Using an analog ohmmeter, check for continuity between terminals No. 4 and 13 of power transistor. Continuity should exist. With positive end of 1.5-volt battery disconnected, there should be no continuity. Replace power transistor if it fails test.

3) To test section of power transistor that controls cylinders No. 2 and 5 of ignition coil, connect negative end of 1.5-volt battery to terminal No. 4 of power transistor and positive end to terminal No. 2. See Fig. 5.

4) Using an analog ohmmeter, check for continuity between terminals No. 4 and 12 of power transistor. Continuity should exist. With positive end of 1.5-volt battery disconnected, there should be no continuity. Replace power transistor if it fails test.

5) To test section of power transistor that controls cylinders No. 3 and 6 of ignition coil, connect negative end of 1.5-volt battery to terminal No. 4 of power transistor and positive end to terminal No. 1. See Fig. 5.

6) Using an analog ohmmeter, check for continuity between terminals No. 4 and 11 of power transistor. Continuity should exist. With positive end of 1.5-volt battery disconnected, there should be no continuity. Replace power transistor if it fails test.

93D78157   Courtesy of Mitsubishi Motor Sales of America.

Fig. 5: Identifying Power Transistor Connector (V6)

HALL EFFECT & OPTICAL IGNITION

Ignition Coil Resistance – Using a DVOM, measure primary coil resistance between positive and negative terminals of coil. See Fig. 6. Measure secondary coil resistance between coil positive terminal and ignition coil tower. Primary and secondary coil resistance should be within specification. See IGNITION COIL RESISTANCE table.

IGNITION COIL RESISTANCE – Ohms @ 68°F (20°C)

Application	Primary	Secondary
1.5L (VIN A)	.9-1.2	20,000-29,000
1.5L (VIN J)	.72-.88	10,300-13,900
1.8L (VIN B)	.9-1.2	19,000-27,000
1.8L (VIN C)	.9-1.2	20,000-29,000
2.0L (VIN E & F)	.70-.86	11,300-15,300
2.4L (VIN G)		
Except Pickup	.9-1.2	20,000-29,000
Pickup	.72-.88	10,300-13,900
2.4L (VIN L)	.67-.81	11,310-15,300
3.0L (VIN J & K)	.67-.81	11,310-15,300
3.0L (VIN H)	.72-.88	10,300-13,900
3.5L (VIN M)	.69-.85	15,300-20,700

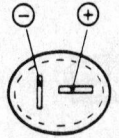

DIAMANTE, MONTERO (3.0L)
STEALTH (SOHC)

ECLIPSE
1 = POSITIVE
2 = NEGATIVE

COLT, COLT VISTA (1.8L, 2.4L 16-VALVE)
EXPO (1.8L, 2.4L 16-VALVE),
GALANT, MIRAGE, SUMMIT,
SUMMIT WAGON (1.8L, 2.4L 16-VALVE)
11 = POSITIVE
12 = NEGATIVE

COLT VISTA (2.4L 8-VALVE),
EXPO (2.4L 8-VALVE), PICKUP (3.0L),
SUMMIT WAGON (2.4L 8-VALVE)

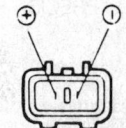

PICKUP (2.4L), PRECIS

93H78177 93I78178 93J78179
93C78180 93D78181   Courtesy of Mitsubishi Motor Sales of America.

Fig. 6: Identifying Ignition Coil Connectors

Power Transistor (Colt, Colt Vista – 1.8L & 2.4L 16-Valve, Expo – 1.8L & 2.4L 16-Valve, Galant, Mirage, Summit & Summit Wagon – 1.8L & 2.4L 16-Valve – 1) Disconnect power transistor connector. Using a 1.5-volt dry cell battery, connect negative end of 1.5-volt battery to terminal No. 5 of power transistor and positive end to terminal No. 6. See Fig. 7.

2) Using an analog ohmmeter, check for continuity between terminals No. 5 and 12 of power transistor. Continuity should exist. With positive end of 1.5-volt battery disconnected, there should be no continuity. Replace power transistor if it fails test.

Power Transistor (Eclipse) – 1) Disconnect power transistor connector. Using a 1.5-volt dry cell battery, connect negative end of 1.5-volt battery to terminal No. 5 of power transistor and positive end to terminal No. 6. See Fig. 7.

2) Using an analog ohmmeter, check for continuity between terminals No. 5 and 8 of power transistor. Continuity should exist. With positive end of 1.5-volt battery disconnected, there should be no continuity. Replace power transistor if it fails test.

1994 ENGINE PERFORMANCE
Basic Diagnostic Procedures (Cont.)

Power Transistor (Precis) – **1)** Disconnect power transistor connector. Using a 3.0-volt power source, connect negative end of power source to terminal No. 2 of power transistor and positive end to terminal No. 1. *See Fig. 7.*

2) Using an analog ohmmeter, check for continuity between terminals No. 1 and 2 of power transistor. Continuity should exist. With positive end of 3.0-volt power source disconnected, there should be no continuity. Replace power transistor if it fails test.

Power Transistor (All Others) – **1)** Disconnect power transistor connector. Using a 1.5-volt dry cell battery, connect negative end of 1.5-volt battery to terminal No. 2 of power transistor and positive end to terminal No. 1. *See Fig. 7.*

2) Using an analog ohmmeter, check for continuity between terminals No. 2 and 3 of power transistor. Continuity should exist. With positive end of 1.5-volt battery disconnected, there should be no continuity. Replace power transistor if it fails test.

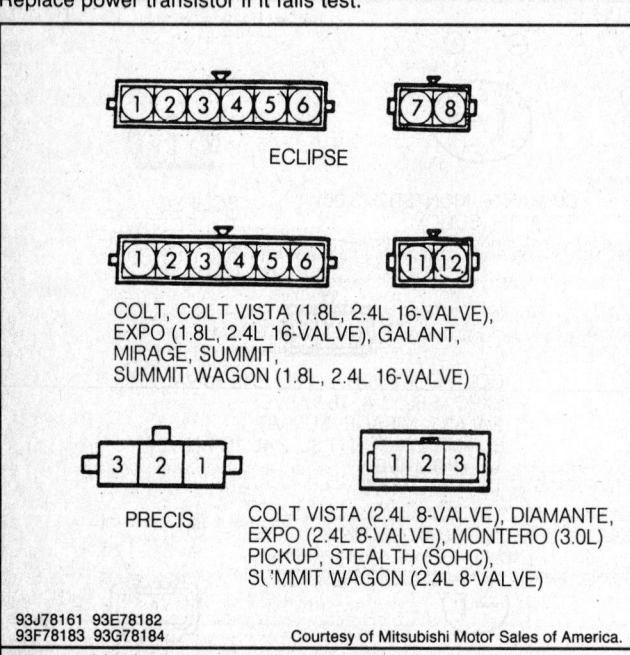

ECLIPSE

COLT, COLT VISTA (1.8L, 2.4L 16-VALVE),
EXPO (1.8L, 2.4L 16-VALVE), GALANT,
MIRAGE, SUMMIT,
SUMMIT WAGON (1.8L, 2.4L 16-VALVE)

PRECIS

COLT VISTA (2.4L 8-VALVE), DIAMANTE,
EXPO (2.4L 8-VALVE), MONTERO (3.0L)
PICKUP, STEALTH (SOHC),
SUMMIT WAGON (2.4L 8-VALVE)

93J78161 93E78182
93F78183 93G78184

Courtesy of Mitsubishi Motor Sales of America.

Fig. 7: Identifying Power Transistor Connectors

IDLE SPEED & IGNITION TIMING

Ensure idle speed and ignition timing are set to specification. See IGNITION TIMING SPECIFICATIONS table. For adjustment procedures, see ON-VEHICLE ADJUSTMENTS article.

IGNITION TIMING (Degrees BTDC @ RPM)

Application	[1] Basic	[2] [3] Actual
1.5L		
Colt, Mirage & Summit	3-7 @ 650-850	10 @ 650-850
Precis	3-7 @ 600-800	10 @ 600-800
1.8L		
Colt, Colt Vista, Expo, Mirage, Summit & Summit Wagon	3-7 @ 600-800	5 @ 600-800
Eclipse	5 @ 600-800	10 @ 600-800
2.0L		
Eclipse	5 @ 650-850	8 @ 650-850
2.4L		
Colt Vista, Expo & Summit Wagon	3-7 @ 650-850	8 @ 650-850
Galant		
SOHC	3-7 @ 650-850	10 @ 650-850
DOHC	2-8 @ 700-900	8 @ 700-900
Pickup	3-7 @ 600-800	8 @ 600-800
3.0L		
Diamante & Montero	3-7 @ 600-800	15 @ 600-800
Pickup	3-7 @ 650-850	15 @ 650-850
Stealth & 3000GT	2-8 @ 600-800	15 @ 600-800
3.5L		
Montero	3-7 @ 600-800	15 @ 600-800

[1] – With ignition timing adjustment connector grounded or vacuum hose (farthest from distributor) disconnected.

[2] – With ignition timing adjustment connector ungrounded or vacuum hose (farthest from distributor) connected. Ignition timing may fluctuate.

[3] – If vehicle altitude is more than 2300 ft. above sea level, actual timing may be advanced.

SUMMARY

If no faults were found while performing BASIC DIAGNOSTIC PROCEDURES, proceed to SELF-DIAGNOSTICS article. If no hard codes are found in self-diagnostics, proceed to TROUBLE SHOOTING – NO CODES article for diagnosis by symptom (i.e., ROUGH IDLE, NO START, etc.) or intermittent diagnostic procedures.

Chrysler Corp.: Colt, Colt Vista, Stealth
Eagle: Summit, Summit Wagon
Mitsubishi: Diamante, Eclipse, Expo, Galant,
Mirage, Montero, Pickup, Precis, 3000GT

NOTE: For Precis self-diagnostics information, see Hyundai SELF-DIAGNOSTICS – ELANTRA, EXCEL & SONATA article.

INTRODUCTION

If no faults were found while performing BASIC DIAGNOSTIC PROCEDURES, proceed with self-diagnostics. If no trouble codes or only pass codes are present after entering self-diagnostics, proceed to TROUBLE SHOOTING – NO CODES article for diagnosis by symptom (i.e., ROUGH IDLE, NO START, etc.).

SELF-DIAGNOSTIC SYSTEM

SYSTEM DIAGNOSIS

System diagnosis can be accomplished using an appropriate scan tester, a voltmeter or the Malfunction Indicator Light (MIL). See RETRIEVING CODES. Engine Control Module (ECM) monitors several different engine control system circuits. If an abnormal input signal occurs, a trouble code is stored in ECM memory and assigned a trouble code number. Each circuit has its own trouble code number and message. A specific trouble code indicates a particular system failure, but does not indicate that cause of failure is necessarily within system.

A trouble code does not condemn any specific component; it simply points out a probable malfunctioning area. If a trouble code is set, ECM will turn on MIL. System malfunctions encountered are identified as either hard failures or intermittent failures as determined by ECM.

Hard Failures – Hard failures cause MIL to glow and remain on until malfunction is repaired. If MIL comes on and remains on (MIL may flash) during vehicle operation, cause of malfunction may be determined by using trouble codes. See TROUBLE CODES. If a sensor fails, ECM will use a substitute value in its calculations to continue engine operation. In this condition, (limp-in mode) vehicle is functional, but loss of good driveability may result.

Intermittent Failures – Intermittent failures may cause MIL to flicker or glow and go out after intermittent trouble code goes away. However, corresponding trouble code will be retained in ECM memory. If related trouble code does not reoccur within a certain time frame, related trouble code will be erased from ECM memory. Intermittent failures may be caused by a sensor, connector or wiring problems. See INTERMITTENTS in TROUBLE SHOOTING – NO CODES article.

SERVICE PRECAUTIONS

Before proceeding with diagnosis, following precautions must be observed:

- Ensure vehicle has a fully charged battery and functional charging system.
- Visually inspect connectors and circuit wiring being worked on.
- DO NOT disconnect battery or ECM. This will erase any trouble codes stored in ECM.
- DO NOT cause short circuits when performing electrical tests. This will set additional trouble codes, making diagnosis of original problem more difficult.
- DO NOT use a test light in place of a voltmeter.
- When checking for spark, ensure coil wire is NOT more than 1/4" from chassis ground. If coil wire is more than 1/4" from chassis ground, damage to vehicle electronics and/or engine may result.
- DO NOT prolong testing of fuel injectors. Engine may hydrostatically (liquid) lock.
- When a vehicle has multiple trouble codes, always repair lowest number trouble code first.

RETRIEVING CODES

Manufacturers recommend using a scan tester to retrieve codes. If scan tester is not available, trouble codes may be retrieved using a voltmeter or Malfunction Indicator Light (MIL). See RETRIEVING CODES table for code retrieval method available by model and proceed to appropriate method.

RETRIEVING CODES

Application	Use Voltmeter	Use MIL
Colt, Mirage & Summit	Yes	No
Colt Vista, Expo & Summit Wagon	No	Yes
Diamante	No	Yes
Eclipse	Yes	No
Galant	No	Yes
Montero	[1] Yes	[2] Yes
Pickup	Yes	No
Stealth & 3000GT	No	Yes

[1] – On vehicles equipped with 3.0L engine.
[2] – On vehicles equipped with 3.5L engine.

Using Scan Tester – 1) Refer to manufacturer's operation manual for instructions in use of scan tester. Before entering on-board diagnostics, see SERVICE PRECAUTIONS. Turn ignition switch to OFF position. Locate Data Link Connector (DLC), next to fuse block. Connect power source terminal of scan tester to cigarette lighter socket.

2) Connect scan tester to DLC. Turn ignition switch to ON position. Read and record scan tester self-diagnostic output. Perform necessary repair(s). See TROUBLE CODES.

Using Voltmeter – 1) Before entering on-board diagnostics, see SERVICE PRECAUTIONS. Turn ignition switch to OFF position. Locate Data Link Connector (DLC), next to fuse block. Connect voltmeter positive lead to DLC self-diagnostic test mode terminal and negative lead to either DLC ground terminal. See Fig. 1.

2) Turn ignition switch to ON position. Disclosure of ECM memory will begin. If 2 or more systems are non-functional, they are indicated by order of increasing code number. Indication is made by 12-volt pulses of voltmeter pointer. A constant repetition of short 12-volt pulses indicates system is normal. If system is abnormal, voltmeter will pulse between zero and 12 volts.

3) Signals will appear on voltmeter as long and short 12-volt pulses. Long pulses represent tens; short pulses represent ones. For example, 4 long pulses and 3 short pulses indicate Code 43. After recording trouble code(s), perform necessary repair(s) to indicated circuit(s). See TROUBLE CODES.

Using Malfunction Indicator Light (MIL) – 1) Before entering on-board diagnostics, see SERVICE PRECAUTIONS. Turn ignition switch to OFF position. Locate Data Link Connector (DLC), next to fuse block. Connect Diagnostic Harness (MB99159) between DLC self-diagnostic output terminal and chassis ground. See Fig. 1.

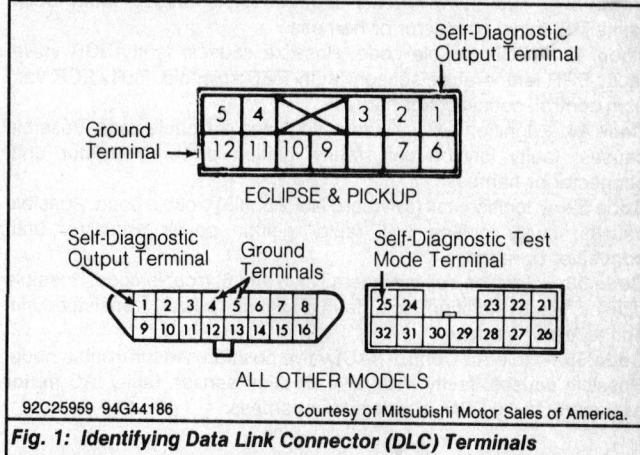

ECLIPSE & PICKUP

ALL OTHER MODELS

92C25959 94G44186   Courtesy of Mitsubishi Motor Sales of America.

Fig. 1: Identifying Data Link Connector (DLC) Terminals

2) Turn ignition switch to ON position. Disclosure of ECM memory will begin. If 2 or more systems are non-functional, they are indicated by order of increasing code number. Indication is made by MIL flashes. A constant repetition of short flashes indicates system is normal.

3) If system is abnormal, signals will appear on MIL as long and short flashes. Long flashes represent tens; short flashes represent ones. For example, 4 long flashes and 3 short flashes indicate Code 43. After recording trouble code(s), perform necessary repair(s) to indicated circuit(s). See TROUBLE CODES.

TROUBLE CODES

NOTE: Codes listed in TROUBLE CODES are not used on all vehicles.

MIL Stays On – ECM trouble code. Possible cause: faulty ECM.
Code 11 – Oxygen Sensor (O2S) trouble code. Possible causes: faulty O2S sensor, connector or harness, low or high fuel pressure, defective injector(s), intake air leaks.
Code 12 – Airflow sensor trouble code. Possible causes: faulty airflow sensor, connector or harness.
Code 13 – Intake air temperature sensor trouble code. Possible causes: faulty intake air temperature sensor, connector or harness.
Code 14 – Throttle Position Sensor (TPS) trouble code. Possible causes: faulty TPS, connector or harness, closed throttle position switch.
Code 15 – Idle Speed Control (ISC) motor position sensor trouble code. Possible causes: faulty ISC motor position sensor, faulty throttle position sensor, connector or harness.
Code 21 – Engine Coolant Temperature (ECT) sensor trouble code. Possible causes: faulty coolant temperature sensor, connector or harness.
Code 22 – Crankshaft Position (CKP) sensor trouble code. Possible causes: faulty distributor assembly (if equipped), faulty CKP sensor, connector or harness.
Code 23 – Camshaft Position (CMP) sensor trouble code. Possible causes: faulty distributor assembly (if equipped), faulty CMP sensor, connector or harness.
Code 24 – Vehicle Speed Sensor (VSS) trouble code. Possible causes: faulty VSS, connector or harness.
Code 25 – Barometric (BARO) pressure sensor trouble code. Possible causes: faulty BARO pressure sensor, connector or harness.
Code 31 – Knock sensor trouble code. Possible causes: faulty knock sensor, connector or harness.
Code 32 – MAP sensor faulty. Possible causes: faulty MAP sensor, connector or harness.
Code 36 – Ignition timing adjustment signal trouble code. Possible causes: connector or harness.
Code 39 – Oxygen Sensor (O2S) trouble code. Possible causes: faulty O2S sensor, faulty O2S sensor heater, connector or harness, low or high fuel pressure, defective injector(s), intake air leaks.
Code 41 – Fuel Injector(s) trouble code. Possible causes: low or high injector coil resistance, connector or harness.
Code 42 – Fuel pump trouble code. Possible causes: faulty ECM, faulty MFI relay, connector or harness.
Code 43 – EGR trouble code. Possible causes: faulty EGR valve, faulty EGR temperature sensor, faulty EGR solenoid, faulty EGR vacuum control, connector or harness.
Code 44 – Ignition coil (cylinders No. 1 and 4) trouble code. Possible causes: faulty ignition coil, faulty ignition power transistor unit, connector or harness.
Code 52 – Ignition coil (cylinders No. 2 and 5) trouble code. Possible causes: faulty ignition coil, faulty ignition power transistor unit, connector or harness.
Code 53 – Ignition coil (cylinders No. 3 and 6) trouble code. Possible causes: faulty ignition coil, faulty ignition power transistor unit, connector or harness.
Code 55 – Idle Air Control (IAC) valve position sensor trouble code. Possible causes: faulty IAC valve position sensor, faulty IAC motor assembly, faulty ECM, connector or harness.

Code 59 – Rear Oxygen Sensor (O2S), or left rear O2S sensor on vehicles equipped with 4 O2S sensors, trouble code. Possible causes: faulty O2S sensor, faulty O2S sensor heater, faulty ECM, connector or harness.
Code 61 – Transaxle control module torque reduction signal trouble code. Possible causes: faulty transaxle control module, connector or harness.
Code 62 – Variable Induction Control (VIC) Valve position sensor trouble code. Possible causes: faulty VIC valve position sensor, connector or harness.
Code 69 – Right rear Oxygen Sensor (O2S) trouble code. Possible causes: faulty O2S sensor, faulty O2S sensor heater, faulty ECM, connector or harness.
Code 71 – Traction Control (TC) vacuum valve solenoid trouble code. Possible causes: faulty TC vacuum valve solenoid, connector or harness.
Code 72 – Traction Control (TC) vent valve solenoid trouble code. Possible causes: faulty TC vent valve solenoid, connector or harness.

CLEARING CODES

CAUTION: When battery is disconnected, vehicle computer and memory systems may lose memory data. Driveability problems may exist until computer systems have completed a relearn cycle. See COMPUTER RELEARN PROCEDURES article in GENERAL INFORMATION before disconnecting battery.

To clear codes using a scan tester, refer to owners manual supplied with scan tester. If scan tester is not available, codes may also be cleared by disconnecting negative battery cable for at least 15 seconds, allowing ECM to clear trouble codes. Reconnect negative battery cable and check for codes to confirm repair.

ECM LOCATION
ECM LOCATION

Application	Location
Eclipse, Galant, Stealth & 3000GT	Behind Radio Console
All Other Models	Behind Right Side Of Instrument Panel

SUMMARY

If no hard trouble codes (or only pass codes) are present, driveability symptoms exist, or intermittent codes exist, proceed to TROUBLE SHOOTING – NO CODES article for diagnosis by symptom (i.e., ROUGH IDLE, NO START, etc.) or intermittent diagnostic procedures.

TERMINAL IDENTIFICATION

NOTE: The following terminals are shown as viewed from component side of connector.

TERMINAL IDENTIFICATION DIRECTORY

Connector	See Fig.
Airflow Sensor	2
CKP/CMP Sensor	3
Coolant Temperature Sensor	4
ECM	5
EGR Temperature Sensor	6
Fuel Injector	7
Fuel Pump	8
Idle Air Control Valve Position Sensor	9
Idle Speed Control Motor & Position Sensor	10
Ignition Coil	11
Induction Control Valve Position Sensor	12
Knock Sensor	13
MAP Sensor	14
MFI Relay	15
Oxygen Sensor (O2S)	16
Throttle Position Sensor	17
Traction Control Vacuum Solenoid	18
Traction Control Vent Solenoid	19
Transaxle Control Module	20

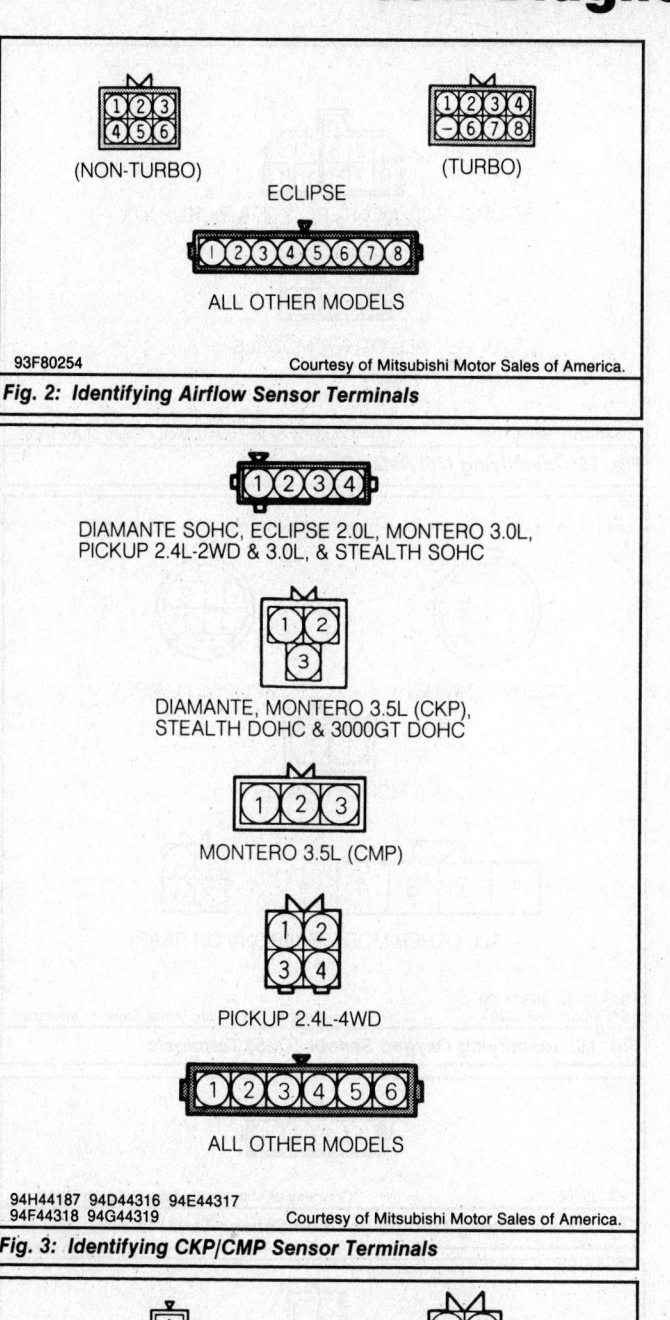

Fig. 2: Identifying Airflow Sensor Terminals

Fig. 3: Identifying CKP/CMP Sensor Terminals

Fig. 4: Identifying Engine Coolant Temperature (ECT) Sensor Terminals

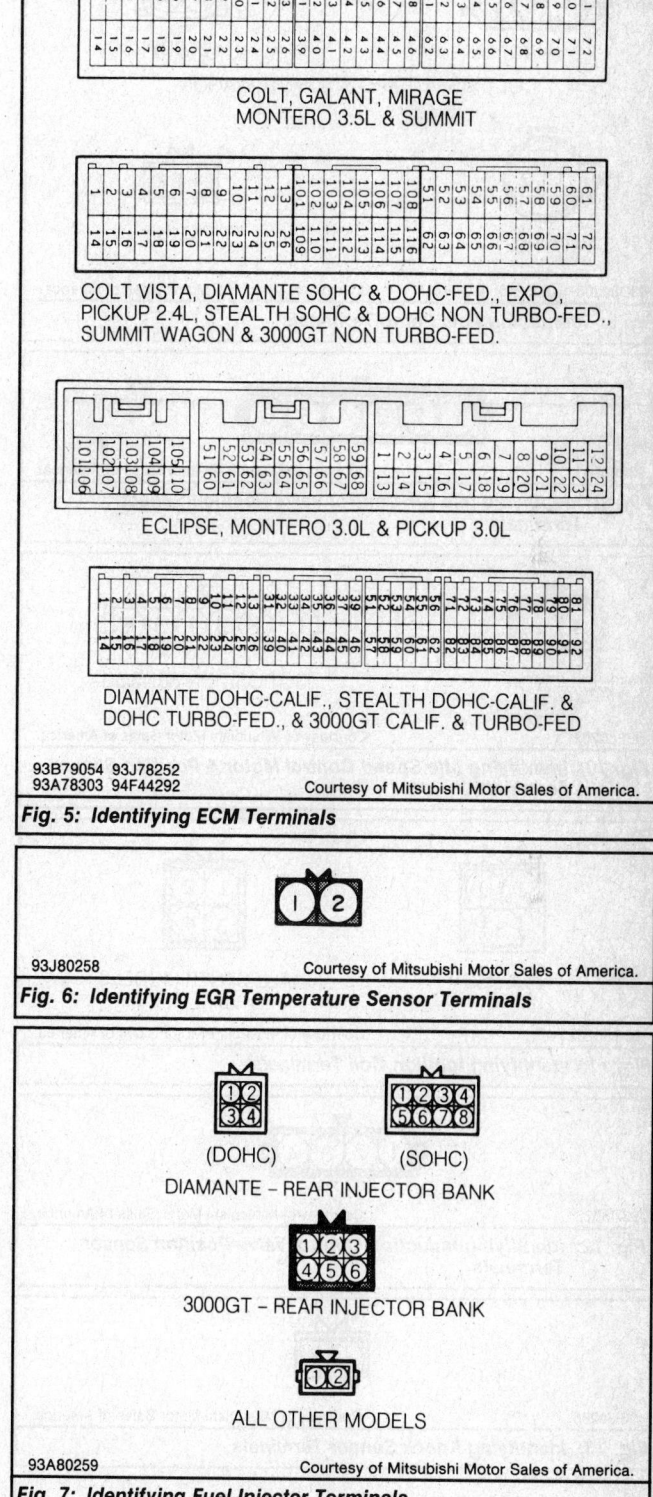

Fig. 5: Identifying ECM Terminals

Fig. 6: Identifying EGR Temperature Sensor Terminals

Fig. 7: Identifying Fuel Injector Terminals

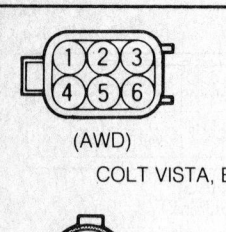

(AWD) (FWD)

COLT VISTA, EXPO & SUMMIT WAGON

ECLIPSE PICKUP

93D80260 94F45216 94G45217   Courtesy of Mitsubishi Motor Sales of America.

Fig. 8: Identifying Fuel Pump Terminals

93E80261   Courtesy of Mitsubishi Motor Sales of America.

Fig. 9: Identifying Idle Air Control Valve Position Sensor Terminals

ISC MOTOR ISC POSITION SENSOR

93F80262   Courtesy of Mitsubishi Motor Sales of America.

Fig. 10: Identifying Idle Speed Control Motor & Position Sensor Terminals

ECLIPSE ALL OTHER MODELS

93G80263   Courtesy of Mitsubishi Motor Sales of America.

Fig. 11: Identifying Ignition Coil Terminals

93H80264   Courtesy of Mitsubishi Motor Sales of America.

Fig. 12: Identifying Induction Control Valve Position Sensor Terminals

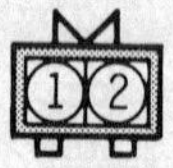

93I80265   Courtesy of Mitsubishi Motor Sales of America.

Fig. 13: Identifying Knock Sensor Terminals

93J80266   Courtesy of Mitsubishi Motor Sales of America.

Fig. 14: Identifying Map Sensor Terminals

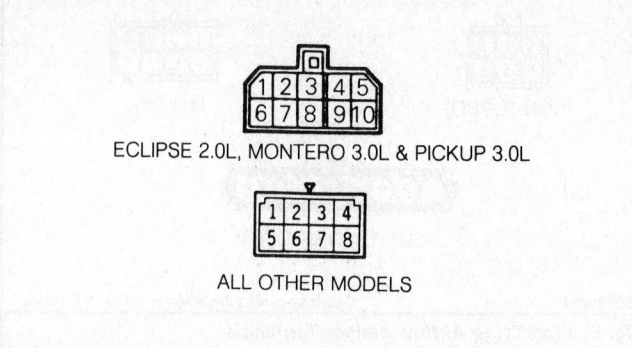

ECLIPSE 2.0L, MONTERO 3.0L & PICKUP 3.0L

ALL OTHER MODELS

93A80267 94H44559   Courtesy of Mitsubishi Motor Sales of America.

Fig. 15: Identifying MFI Relay Terminals

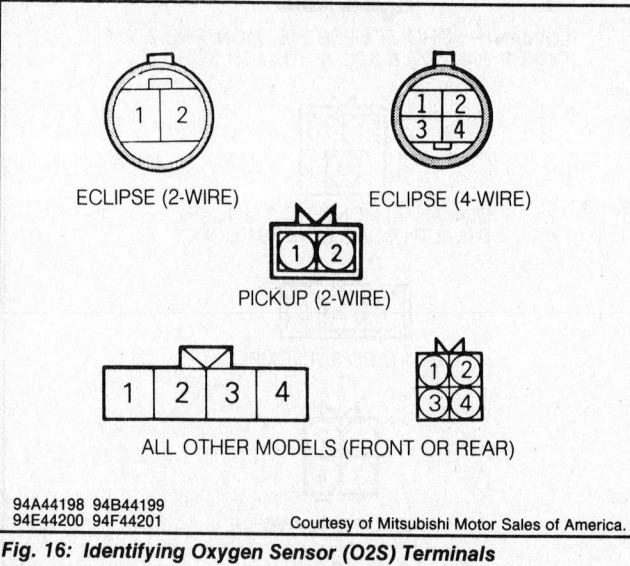

ECLIPSE (2-WIRE) ECLIPSE (4-WIRE)

PICKUP (2-WIRE)

ALL OTHER MODELS (FRONT OR REAR)

94A44198 94B44199
94E44200 94F44201   Courtesy of Mitsubishi Motor Sales of America.

Fig. 16: Identifying Oxygen Sensor (O2S) Terminals

93C80269   Courtesy of Mitsubishi Motor Sales of America.

Fig. 17: Identifying Throttle Position Sensor Terminals

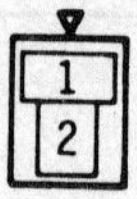

93F80270   Courtesy of Mitsubishi Motor Sales of America.

Fig. 18: Identifying Traction Control Vacuum Solenoid Terminals

93G80271   Courtesy of Mitsubishi Motor Sales of America.

Fig. 19: Identifying Traction Control Vent Solenoid Terminals

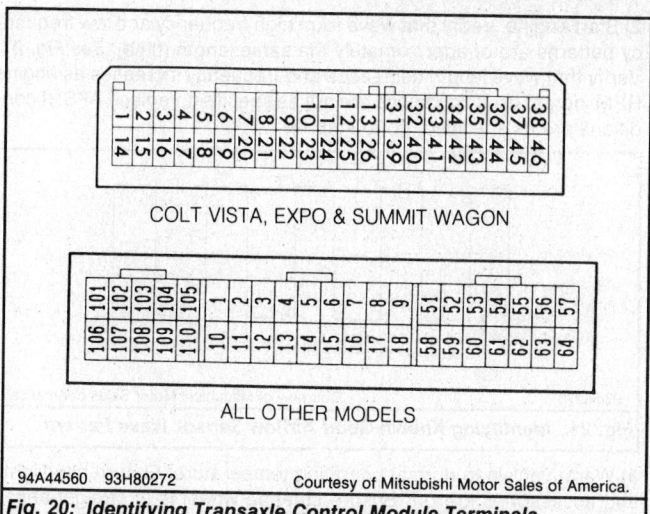

COLT VISTA, EXPO & SUMMIT WAGON

ALL OTHER MODELS

94A44560   93H80272   Courtesy of Mitsubishi Motor Sales of America.

Fig. 20: Identifying Transaxle Control Module Terminals

DIAGNOSTIC TESTS

CAUTION: *Ensure ignition switch is in OFF position when performing resistance tests.*

NOTE: *Perform all resistance and voltage tests using a Digital Volt-Ohmmeter (DVOM) with a minimum 10-megohm impedance, unless stated otherwise in test procedures.*

NOTE: *For wire color identification at ECM terminals, see appropriate pin voltage chart in PIN VOLTAGE CHARTS article.*

Clear trouble codes after each repair. See CLEARING CODES under SELF-DIAGNOSTIC SYSTEM. Recheck for codes to confirm repair. See RETRIEVING CODES under SELF-DIAGNOSTIC SYSTEM.

CODE 11: OXYGEN SENSOR (O2S) (2-WIRE OXYGEN SENSOR)

NOTE: *For component terminal identification, see TERMINAL IDENTI-FICATION. For wiring diagrams, see WIRING DIAGRAMS article.*

1) If using scan tester, go to step **2)**. Start and warm engine to operating temperature. Disconnect O2S connector. Connect DVOM between chassis ground and O2S terminal No. 1. While repeatedly racing engine, measure O2S output voltage. If voltage is not .6-1.0 volt, replace O2S. If voltage is within specification, go to step **4)**.
2) Using scan tester, read O2S voltage. While monitoring scan tester, accelerate to 4000 RPM. Suddenly decelerate. Scan tester should read .3 volt or less. Suddenly accelerate. Scan tester should read .5-1.0 volt. If voltage is not as specified, replace O2S. If voltage is as specified, go to next step.
3) While monitoring scan tester, accelerate to 2000 RPM and decelerate to 700 RPM (idle). Scan tester should switch between .6-1.0 volt and .4 volt or less. If voltage is not as specified, replace O2S. If voltage is as specified, go to next step.
4) Disconnect O2S connector and ECM connector. Using DVOM, check for continuity between O2S terminal No. 1 and ECM connector terminal No. 4. If continuity does not exist, repair wiring harness as necessary. If continuity exists, go to next step.
5) Using DVOM, check continuity between chassis ground and O2S connector terminal No. 2. If continuity does not exist, replace O2S. If continuity exists, condition required to set trouble code is not present at this time. Test is complete. Intermittent problem may exist. See TROUBLE SHOOTING – NO CODES article.

CODE 11: HEATED OXYGEN SENSOR (HO2S) (4-WIRE OXYGEN SENSOR)

NOTE: *For component terminal identification, see TERMINAL IDENTI-FICATION. For wiring diagrams, see WIRING DIAGRAMS article.*

1) If using scan tester, go to step **3)**. Disconnect HO2S connector. On all models except Diamante, Pickup, Stealth non-turbo and 3000GT non-turbo, install Test Harness (MB998464) between HO2S and HO2S connector. On all models, use DVOM to check resistance between specified HO2S connector heater terminals. See 4-WIRE HO2S CONNECTOR TERMINAL IDENTIFICATION table. HO2S resistance should be 20 ohms at 68°F (20°C). If resistance is not as specified, replace HO2S. If resistance is as specified, go to next step.
2) Using jumper wires, apply 12 volts to specified HO2S connector heater terminals. See HO2S CONNECTOR TERMINAL IDENTIFICA-TION table. Using DVOM, check voltage between specified HO2S connector output terminals, while repeatedly racing engine. If voltage is not .6-1.0 volt, replace HO2S. If voltage is .6-1.0 volt, go to step **5)**.

HO2S CONNECTOR TERMINAL IDENTIFICATION

Application	¹ Heater Terminals No.	Output Terminals No.
Colt, Mirage & Summit (1.5L), Montero, & Stealth & 3000GT (Turbo)	1 & 3	2 & 4
Colt, Mirage & Summit (1.8L), Colt Vista, Expo, Galant, Pickup & Summit Wagon	2 & 4	1 & 3
Diamante, Eclipse (2.0L), & Stealth & 3000GT (Non-Turbo)	3 & 4	1 & 2

¹ – First terminal listed is positive. Second terminal listed is negative.

3) Start and warm engine to operating temperature. Using scan tester, read HO2S voltage. While monitoring scan tester, accelerate to 4000 RPM. Suddenly decelerate. Scan tester should read .3 volt or less. Suddenly accelerate. Scan tester should read .5-1.0 volt. If voltage is not as specified, replace HO2S. If voltage is as specified, go to next step.
4) While monitoring scan tester, accelerate to 2000 RPM and decelerate to 700 RPM (idle). Scan tester should switch between .6-1.0 volt and .4 volt or less. If voltage is not as specified, replace HO2S. If voltage is as specified, go to next step.
5) Disconnect HO2S connector. On Eclipse, Galant, Pickup 3.0L, Stealth and 3000GT, go to next step. On all other models, disconnect MFI relay connector. Using DVOM, check for continuity between specified HO2S connector terminals and MFI connector terminals. See HO2S-TO-MFI WIRING HARNESS TERMINAL IDENTIFICATION table. If continuity does not exist, repair wiring harness as necessary. If continuity exists, go to step **7)**.

HO2S-TO-MFI WIRING HARNESS TERMINAL IDENTIFICATION

Application	HO2S Terminal No.	MFI Terminal No.
All 1.5L Models	1	2
Diamante	3	5
Montero		
3.0L	1	5
3.5L	1	3
All Other Models	2	2

6) Turn ignition switch to ON position. Using DVOM, check voltage between specified HO2S connector terminal and chassis ground. See HO2S CONNECTOR VOLTAGE CIRCUIT IDENTIFICATION table. If system voltage does not exist, repair wiring harness as necessary. If system voltage exists, go to next step.

HO2S CONNECTOR VOLTAGE CIRCUIT IDENTIFICATION

Application	Terminal No.
Eclipse, Stealth & 3000GT (Non-Turbo)	3
Galant & Pickup 3.0L	2
Stealth & 3000GT (Turbo)	1

7) On Galant, go to next step. Using DVOM, check for continuity between specified HO2S connector terminals and ECM connector terminals. See HO2S-TO-ECM WIRING HARNESS TERMINAL IDENTIFICATION table. If continuity does not exist on either circuit, repair appropriate circuit for open or short to ground as necessary. If continuity exists, go to next step.

HO2S-TO-ECM WIRING HARNESS TERMINAL IDENTIFICATION

Application	HO2S Terminal No.	ECM Terminal No.
Colt, Colt Vista, Expo, Mirage, Pickup, & Summit Wagon		
1.5L	3	56
	4	35
1.8L Except Summit Wagon	3	5
	4	35
2.4L & Summit Wagon	3	56
	4	105
3.0L	3	4
Diamante	1	56
Eclipse 2.0L	1	4
Montero		
3.0L	4	4
3.5L	3	56
Stealth & 3000GT		
Non-Turbo	1	56
Turbo	4	56

8) Disconnect HO2S connector. Using DVOM, check for continuity between specified HO2S connector terminal and chassis ground. See HO2S CONNECTOR GROUND CIRCUIT IDENTIFICATION table. If continuity does not exist, repair wiring harness as necessary. On Galant, if no system or component malfunctions occur in preceding tests, go to next step. On all other models, if no system or component malfunctions occur in preceding tests, condition required to set trouble code is not present at this time. Test is complete. Intermittent problem may exist. See TROUBLE SHOOTING – NO CODES article.

HO2S CONNECTOR GROUND CIRCUIT IDENTIFICATION

Application	Terminal No.
Colt 1.8L, Colt Vista, Expo, Galant, Mirage 1.8L, Pickup, Summit 1.8L & Summit Wagon	1
Eclipse	4
All Other Models	2

9) Disconnect ECM connector. Turn ignition switch to ON position. Using DVOM, check voltage between ECM connector terminal No. 35 and chassis ground. If system voltage does not exist, repair wiring harness as necessary. If system voltage exists and no system or component malfunctions occur in preceding tests, condition required to set trouble code is not present at this time. Test is complete. Intermittent problem may exist. See TROUBLE SHOOTING – NO CODES article.

CODE 12: AIRFLOW SENSOR

NOTE: For component terminal identification, see TERMINAL IDENTIFICATION. For wiring diagrams, see WIRING DIAGRAMS article.

NOTE: Procedures are provided by manufacturer for component testing using an engine analyzer with oscilloscope capability. Refer to manufacturer's operation manual for instructions in use of oscilloscope. If using a scan tester, go to step 3).

1) If using scan tester, go to step 3). Disconnect Airflow Sensor (AFS) connector. Install Test Harness (MB991348) between AFS and AFS connector. Using engine analyzer with oscilloscope capability, connect special patterns probe to AFS connector terminal No. 3.

2) Start engine. Verify that wave form high frequency and low frequency patterns are of approximately the same length (time). *See Fig. 21.* Verify that wave length decreases and frequency increases as engine RPM increases. If conditions are not as specified, replace AFS. If conditions are as specified, go to step 4).

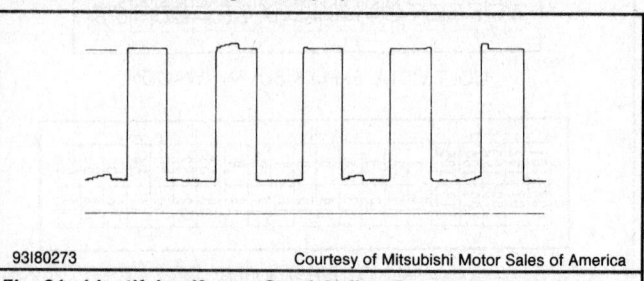

93I80273   Courtesy of Mitsubishi Motor Sales of America

Fig. 21: Identifying Known-Good Airflow Sensor Wave Pattern

3) Warm vehicle to normal operating temperature. Ensure headlights and accessories are off. Ensure steering wheel is in straight-ahead position. Using scan tester, read Airflow Sensor (AFS) volume (frequency) value. See AIRFLOW SENSOR VALUES table. Frequency should increase when engine is raced. If values are not as specified, replace AFS. If values are as specified, go to next step.

AIRFLOW SENSOR VALUES

Application	Hz @ 700 RPM	Hz @ 2000 RPM
1.8L		
Colt, Colt Vista, Expo, Mirage, Summit & Summit Wagon	23-49	51-91
Eclipse	25-40	67-88
2.0L		
Eclipse		
Non-Turbo	25-50	70-90
Turbo	25-50	60-85
2.4L		
Colt Vista, Expo & Summit Wagon	18-44	43-83
Galant	18-44	64-104
SOHC	21-47	28-54
DOHC	42-82	45-85
Pickup	40-60	85-105
3.0L		
Diamante & Stealth SOHC	21-47	57-97
Montero	22-48	60-100
Pickup	25-45	70-90
Stealth & 3000GT		
DOHC Non-Turbo	22-48	50-90
DOHC Turbo	22-48	68-108
3.5L		
Montero	27-53	60-100

4) On Eclipse, Galant, Pickup 2.4L – 4WD and 3.0L, Stealth and 3000GT, go to step 8). On all other models, disconnect AFS connector and MFI relay connector. Using DVOM, check for continuity between specified AFS connector terminal and MFI relay connector terminal. See AFS-TO-MFI RELAY TERMINAL WIRING HARNESS IDENTIFICATION table. If continuity does not exist, repair wiring harness as necessary. If continuity exists, go to next step.

AFS-TO-MFI RELAY TERMINAL WIRING HARNESS IDENTIFICATION

Application	AFS Terminal No.	MFI RELAY Terminal No.
Diamante & Montero 3.0L	4	4
Montero 3.5L	2	4
All Other Models	4	3

5) Using DVOM, check for continuity between chassis ground and AFS connector terminal No. 5 (terminal No. 4 on Galant). If continuity does not exist, repair wiring harness as necessary. If continuity exists, go to next step.

6) Disconnect AFS connector and ECM connector. Using DVOM, check for continuity between specified AFS connector terminal and ECM connector terminal. See AFS-TO-ECM WIRING HARNESS TERMINAL IDENTIFICATION table. If continuity does not exist on specified circuit(s), repair appropriate circuit for open or short to ground as necessary. If continuity exists, go to next step.

AFS-TO-ECM WIRING HARNESS TERMINAL IDENTIFICATION

Application	AFS Terminal No.	ECM Terminal No.
Montero 3.0L	3	10
	7	57
All Other Models	3	70
	7	19

7) Turn ignition switch to ON position. Using DVOM, check voltage between chassis ground and AFS harness connector terminal No. 3. If voltage is not 4.8-5.2 volts, replace ECM. If voltage is as specified, condition required to set trouble code is not present at this time. Test is complete. Intermittent problem may exist. See TROUBLE SHOOTING – NO CODES article.

8) Disconnect AFS connector. Turn ignition switch to ON position. Using DVOM, check voltage between specified terminal and chassis ground. See AFS CONNECTOR POWER SUPPLY CIRCUIT IDENTIFICATION table. If system voltage does not exist, repair wiring harness as necessary. If system voltage exists, go to next step.

AFS CONNECTOR POWER SUPPLY CIRCUIT IDENTIFICATION

Application	Terminal No.
Eclipse	
1.8L & 2.0L Turbo	2
2.0L Non-Turbo	1
Galant, Pickup 2.4L – 4WD,	
Stealth & 3000GT	4
Pickup 3.0L	5

9) With ignition switch in ON position, use DVOM to check voltage between specified terminal and chassis ground. See AFS CONNECTOR VOLTAGE CIRCUIT IDENTIFICATION table. If voltage is not 4.8-5.2 volts, repair wiring harness as necessary. If voltage is as specified, go to next step.

AFS CONNECTOR VOLTAGE CIRCUIT IDENTIFICATION

Application	Terminal No.
Eclipse	
1.8L	1
2.0L Non-Turbo	2
All Other Models	3

10) Using DVOM, check for continuity between specified AFS connector terminal and chassis ground. See AFS CONNECTOR GROUND CIRCUIT IDENTIFICATION table. If continuity does not exist, repair wiring harness as necessary. If continuity exists on Eclipse 1.8L or 2.0L non-turbo, condition required to set trouble code is not present at this time. Test is complete. Intermittent problem may exist. See TROUBLE SHOOTING – NO CODES article. On all other models, go to next step.

AFS CONNECTOR GROUND CIRCUIT IDENTIFICATION

Application	Terminal No.
Eclipse	
1.8L & 2.0L Non-Turbo	4
2.0L Turbo	6
All Other Models	5

11) Disconnect AFS connector and ECM connector. Using DVOM, check for continuity between specified AFS connector terminal and ECM connector terminal. See ECM-TO-AFS WIRING HARNESS TERMINAL IDENTIFICATION table. If continuity does not exist on specified circuit(s), repair appropriate circuit for open or short to ground as necessary. If continuity exists, condition required to set trouble code is not present at this time. Test is complete. Intermittent problem may exist. See TROUBLE SHOOTING – NO CODES article.

ECM-TO-AFS WIRING HARNESS TERMINAL IDENTIFICATION

Application	ECM Terminal No.	AFS Terminal No.
Eclipse 2.0L Turbo	6	1
Galant, Stealth & 3000GT	19	7
All Other Models	57	7

CODE 13: INTAKE AIR TEMPERATURE SENSOR

NOTE: On all models except 1.5L engines, intake air temperature sensor is built into airflow sensor. For CODE 13 test purposes, airflow sensor will be referred to as intake air temperature sensor. For component terminal identification, see AIRFLOW SENSOR under TERMINAL IDENTIFICATION. For component terminal identification on 1.5L engines, see Fig. 22. For wiring diagrams, see WIRING DIAGRAMS article.

1) If using scan tester, go to step 3). Disconnect Intake Air Temperature (IAT) sensor connector. Using a thermometer, check engine compartment ambient temperature. Using DVOM, check resistance between specified IAT sensor terminals. See IAT SENSOR TERMINAL IDENTIFICATION table. Resistance should be 6000 ohms at 32°F (0°C), 2700 ohms at 68°F (20°C) or 400 ohms at 176°F (80°C). If resistance is not as specified, replace IAT sensor. If resistance is as specified, go to next step.

IAT SENSOR TERMINAL IDENTIFICATION

Application	Terminals No.
All 1.5L Models	1 & 2
Eclipse	
1.8L & 2.0L Non-Turbo	4 & 5
2.0L Turbo	6 & 8
All Other Models	5 & 6

93J80274   Courtesy of Mitsubishi Motor Sales of America

Fig. 22: Identifying IAT Component Terminals (1.5L)

2) Using a hair dryer, warm IAT sensor while monitoring DVOM. Resistance should decrease evenly as temperature rises. If resistance remains unchanged, replace IAT sensor. If resistance changes, go to step 4).

3) Turn ignition switch to ON or RUN position. Using a thermometer, check engine compartment ambient temperature. Using scan tester, read Intake Air Temperature (IAT) sensor temperature. See IAT SENSOR TEMPERATURE table. If temperatures are not as specified, replace IAT sensor. If temperatures are as specified, go to next step.

IAT SENSOR TEMPERATURE

Ambient Temperature	Standard Value
–4°F (–20°C)	–20°C
32°F (0°C)	0°C
68°F (20°C)	20°C
104°F (40°C)	40°C
176°F (80°C)	80°C

4) Disconnect IAT sensor connector. Using DVOM, check for continuity between chassis ground and specified IAT sensor connector terminal. See IAT SENSOR GROUND CIRCUIT TERMINAL IDENTIFICATION table. If continuity does not exist, repair wiring harness as necessary. If continuity exists, go to next step.

1994 ENGINE PERFORMANCE
Self-Diagnostics (Cont.)

IAT SENSOR GROUND CIRCUIT TERMINAL IDENTIFICATION

Application	Terminal No.
All 1.5L Models	1
Eclipse	
1.8L	4
2.0L Non-Turbo	6
2.0L Turbo	8
All Other Models	5

5) On Eclipse 1.8L and 2.0L turbo, Pickup 2.4L – 4WD and 3.0L, Stealth and 3000GT, go to next step. On all other models, with IAT sensor connector and ECM connector disconnected, check for continuity between specified IAT sensor connector terminal and ECM connector terminal. See IAT-TO-ECM WIRING HARNESS TERMINAL IDENTIFICATION table. If continuity does not exist, repair wiring harness as necessary. If continuity exists, go to next step.

IAT-TO-ECM WIRING HARNESS TERMINAL IDENTIFICATION

Application	IAT Connector Terminal No.	ECM Connector Terminal No.
All 1.5L Models	2	52
Eclipse 2.0L Non-Turbo	5	16
Montero 3.0L	6	8
All Other Models	6	52

6) Turn ignition switch to ON position. Check voltage between chassis ground and specified IAT sensor connector. See IAT SENSOR CONNECTOR VOLTAGE SUPPLY CIRCUIT TERMINAL IDENTIFICATION table. If voltage is not 4.5-4.9 volts, replace ECM. If voltage is as specified, replace IAT sensor.

IAT SENSOR CONNECTOR VOLTAGE SUPPLY CIRCUIT TERMINAL IDENTIFICATION

Application	Terminal No.
All 1.5L Models	2
Eclipse 2.0L	
Non-Turbo	3
Turbo	4
All Other Models	6

CODE 14: THROTTLE POSITION SENSOR

NOTE: For component terminal identification, see TERMINAL IDENTIFICATION. For wiring diagrams, see WIRING DIAGRAMS article.

1) If using scan tester, go to step **3)**. Disconnect Throttle Position Sensor (TPS) connector. Using DVOM, check resistance between TPS terminals No. 1 and No. 4. If resistance is not 3500-6500 ohms, replace TPS. If resistance is as specified, go to next step.

2) Check resistance between specified TPS terminals. See TPS TERMINAL IDENTIFICATION table. While monitoring DVOM, slowly open throttle from idle to fully open position. If resistance does not change smoothly, replace TPS. If resistance changes smoothly, go to step **4)**.

TPS TERMINAL IDENTIFICATION

Application	Terminals No.
Colt Vista, Expo, Montero, Pickup 3.0L & Summit Wagon	1 & 3
All Other Models	2 & 4

3) Turn ignition switch to ON position. Using scan tester, read Throttle Position Sensor (TPS) voltage. With throttle at idle, voltage should read .3-1.0 volt. Voltage should increase while slowly opening throttle. At wide open throttle, voltage should read 4.5-5.5 volts. If voltage is not as specified, replace TPS. If voltage is as specified, go to next step.

4) On Eclipse, Galant, Pickup 2.4L – 4WD and 3.0L, Stealth and 3000GT, go to step **7)**. On all other models, disconnect TPS connector. Using DVOM, check continuity between chassis ground and specified TPS connector terminal. See TPS CONNECTOR GROUND CIRCUIT IDENTIFICATION table. If continuity does not exist, repair wiring harness as necessary. If continuity exists, go to next step.

TPS CONNECTOR GROUND CIRCUIT IDENTIFICATION

Application	Terminal No.
Colt Vista, Expo, Montero & Summit Wagon	1
All Other Models	4

5) Disconnect TPS connector and ECM connector. Check for continuity between specified TPS connector terminal and ECM connector terminal. See TPS-TO-ECM WIRING HARNESS TERMINAL IDENTIFICATION table. If continuity does not exist, repair wiring harness as necessary. If continuity exists, go to next step.

TPS-TO-ECM WIRING HARNESS TERMINAL IDENTIFICATION

Application	TPS Terminal No.	ECM Terminal No.
Colt, Diamante, Mirage & Summit	1	61
	2	64
Colt Vista, Expo & Summit Wagon	3	64
	4	61
Pickup 2.4L – RWD	1	64
	2	61
Montero		
3.0L	3	19
	4	23
3.5L	3	61
	4	64

6) Check voltage between chassis ground and specified TPS connector terminal. See TPS VOLTAGE CIRCUIT IDENTIFICATION table. If voltage is not 4.8-5.2 volts, replace ECM. If voltage is as specified, condition required to set trouble code is not present at this time. Test is complete. Intermittent problem may exist. See TROUBLE SHOOTING – NO CODES article.

TPS VOLTAGE CIRCUIT IDENTIFICATION

Application	TPS Terminal No.
Colt, Diamante, Mirage, Pickup 2.4L – RWD & Summit	1
Colt Vista, Expo, Montero & Summit Wagon	4

7) Disconnect TPS connector. Turn ignition switch to ON position. Using DVOM, check voltage between chassis ground and specified TPS connector terminal. See TPS VOLTAGE SUPPLY IDENTIFICATION table. If voltage is not 4.8-5.2 volts, repair wiring harness as necessary. If voltage is as specified, go to next step.

TPS VOLTAGE SUPPLY IDENTIFICATION

Application	TPS Terminal No.
Eclipse, Galant, Stealth & 3000GT	4
Pickup	
2.4L – 4WD	4
3.0L	1

8) Check continuity between chassis ground and specified TPS connector terminal. See TPS CONNECTOR GROUND CIRCUIT IDENTIFICATION table. If continuity does not exist, repair wiring harness as necessary. If continuity exists, go to next step.

TPS CONNECTOR GROUND CIRCUIT IDENTIFICATION

Application	TPS Terminal No.
Galant	5
Pickup 3.0L	1
All Other Models	4

9) With TPS connector and ECM connector disconnected, check for continuity between specified TPS connector terminal and ECM connector terminal. See ECM-TO-TPS HARNESS IDENTIFICATION table. If continuity does not exist, repair wiring harness as necessary. If continuity exists, condition required to set trouble code is not present at this time. Test is complete. Intermittent problem may exist. See TROUBLE SHOOTING – NO CODES article.

ECM-TO-TPS HARNESS IDENTIFICATION

Application	ECM Terminal No.	TPS Terminal No.
Galant	61	2
Pickup 3.0L	19	3
Stealth & 3000GT	84	2
All Other Models	9	2

CODE 15: IDLE SPEED CONTROL POSITION SENSOR

NOTE: For component terminal identification, see TERMINAL IDENTIFICATION. For wiring diagrams, see WIRING DIAGRAMS article.

1) If using scan tester, go to step 3). Disconnect Idle Speed Control (ISC) motor position sensor connector. Using DVOM, check resistance between ISC motor position sensor terminals No. 2 and No. 3. If resistance is not 4000-6000 ohms, replace ISC motor position sensor. If resistance is as specified, go to next step.

CAUTION: Apply only 6 volts DC or less to ISC motor connector. Higher voltage could cause servo gears to lock up.

2) Disconnect ISC motor connector. Connect a 6-volt DC power supply between ISC motor connector terminals No. 1 and No. 2 to operate ISC motor. Check resistance between ISC motor position sensor terminals No. 3 and No. 5. Ensure ISC motor position sensor resistance changes smoothly as motor extends and retracts. If resistance does not change smoothly, replace ISC motor assembly. If resistance changes smoothly, go to step 4).

3) Ensure engine coolant temperature is 185-205°F (85-95°C). Place transmission in Park or Neutral. Turn off all accessories except A/C. Ensure A/C clutch is operating when A/C system is on. With engine at idle, use scan tester to read Idle Speed Control (ISC) motor position sensor voltage. See ISC VOLTAGE SPECIFICATIONS table. If voltage is not as specified, replace IAC motor position sensor. If voltage is as specified, go to next step.

ISC VOLTAGE SPECIFICATIONS

Application	A/C Switch Position	Standard Voltage
Eclipse	Off	.5-1.3
	On	.8-1.8
	[1]	.9-1.9
All Other Models	Off	.5-1.3
	On	.9-2.3
	[1]	.9-2.3

[1] – On A/T models only, apply brakes, place transmission selector in "D" position and A/C switch in ON position.

4) Disconnect ISC motor position sensor connector. Turn ignition switch to ON position. Using DVOM, check voltage between chassis ground and sensor connector terminal No. 2. Check voltage between chassis ground and sensor connector terminal No. 6. Voltage should be 4.8-5.2 volts on both circuits. If voltage is not as specified, repair appropriate wiring harness circuit(s) as necessary. If voltage is as specified, go to next step.

5) Check for continuity between chassis ground and sensor connector terminal No. 3. If continuity does not exist, repair wiring harness as necessary. If continuity exists, condition required to set trouble code is not present at this time. Test is complete. Intermittent problem may exist. See TROUBLE SHOOTING – NO CODES article.

CODE 21: ENGINE COOLANT TEMPERATURE (ECT) SENSOR

NOTE: For component terminal identification, see TERMINAL IDENTIFICATION. For wiring diagrams, see WIRING DIAGRAMS article.

1) If using scan tester, go to step 2). Remove Engine Coolant Temperature (ECT) sensor from intake manifold. Submerge temperature sensing portion of ECT sensor in hot water. Using DVOM, check resistance across ECT sensor terminals. See ECT SENSOR RESISTANCE SPECIFICATIONS table. If resistance is not as specified, replace ECT sensor. If resistance is as specified, go to step 3).

ECT SENSOR RESISTANCE SPECIFICATIONS

Water Temperature	Approximate Ohms
32°F (0°C)	5800
68°F (20°C)	2400
104°F (40°C)	1100
176°F (80°C)	300

2) Turn ignition switch to ON or RUN position. Using a thermometer, check engine compartment ambient temperature. Using scan tester, read Engine Coolant Temperature (ECT) sensor voltage. See ECT SENSOR VOLTAGE SPECIFICATIONS table. If voltage is not within specifications, replace ECT sensor. If voltage is within specification, go to next step.

ECT SENSOR VOLTAGE SPECIFICATIONS

Ambient Temperature	Standard Value °F (°C)
–4°F (–20°C)	–20°C
32°F (0°C)	0°C
68°F (20°C)	20°C
104°F (40°C)	40°C
176°F (80°C)	80°C

3) Disconnect ECT sensor connector. Using DVOM, check continuity between chassis ground and specified connector terminal. See ECT SENSOR GROUND CIRCUIT TERMINAL IDENTIFICATION table. If continuity does not exist, repair wiring harness as necessary. If continuity exists, go to next step.

ECT SENSOR GROUND CIRCUIT TERMINAL IDENTIFICATION

Application	Terminal No.
All 1.5L Models, Eclipse 1.8L & Pickup 2.4L – 4WD	1
All Other Models	2

4) On Eclipse 2.0L, Pickup 2.4L – 4WD and 3.0L, Stealth, and 3000GT, go to next step. On all other models, Disconnect ECT sensor connector and ECM connector. Check continuity between specified ECT sensor connector terminals and ECM connector terminals. See ECT SENSOR-TO-ECM WIRING HARNESS TERMINAL IDENTIFICATION table. If continuity does not exist, repair wiring harness as necessary. If continuity exists, go to next step.

ECT SENSOR-TO-ECM WIRING HARNESS TERMINAL IDENTIFICATION

Application	ECT SENSOR Terminal No.	ECM Terminal No.
All 1.5L Models	2	63
Montero 3.0L	1	20
All Other Models	1	63

5) Turn ignition switch to ON position. Check voltage between chassis ground and specified ECT sensor connector terminal. See ECT SENSOR VOLTAGE CIRCUIT IDENTIFICATION table. If voltage is not 4.5-4.9 volts, replace ECM. If voltage is as specified, condition required to set trouble code is not present at this time. Test is complete. Intermittent problem may exist. See TROUBLE SHOOTING – NO CODES article.

ECT SENSOR VOLTAGE CIRCUIT IDENTIFICATION

Application	Terminal No.
All 1.5L Models, Eclipse 1.8L & Pickup 2.4L – 4WD	1
All Other Models	2

CODE 22: CRANKSHAFT POSITION (CKP) SENSOR

NOTE: *For component terminal identification, see TERMINAL IDENTIFICATION. For wiring diagrams, see WIRING DIAGRAMS article.*

NOTE: *Procedures are provided by manufacturer for component testing using an engine analyzer with oscilloscope capability. Refer to manufacturer's operation manual for instructions in use of oscilloscope. If using a scan tester, go to step 3).*

1) If using a scan tester, go to step **3)**. On all models except Eclipse, Galant SOHC, Pickup, Stealth and 3000GT, disconnect Crankshaft/Camshaft Position (CKP/CMP) sensor connector. Install Test Harness (MB991348) between sensor and connector. On all models, using engine analyzer with oscilloscope capability, connect special patterns probe to specified connector terminal. See CKP PATTERN PICK-UP TERMINAL IDENTIFICATION table.

CKP PATTERN PICK-UP TERMINAL IDENTIFICATION

Application	Terminal No.
Diamante, Eclipse 2.0L, Galant DOHC, Montero, Pickup 3.0L, Stealth & 3000GT	2
Pickup 2.4L	1
All Other Models	3

2) Start engine. Compare oscilloscope wave pattern with known-good wave pattern. *See Fig. 23*. Verify that wave length (time) decreases as engine RPM increases. If a wave pattern is output and it fluctuates to left or right, check for loose timing belt or an abnormality in sensor pick-up disc. If a rectangular wave pattern is output even when engine is not started, substitute known-good CKP sensor. Repeat test. If wave pattern is still abnormal, go to step **5)**.

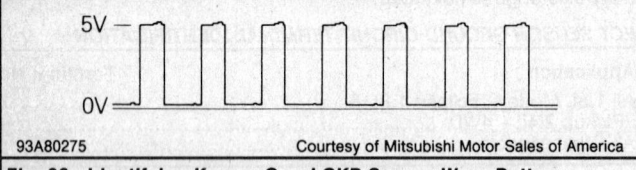

93A80275   Courtesy of Mitsubishi Motor Sales of America

Fig. 23: Identifying Known-Good CKP Sensor Wave Pattern

3) Connect an engine tachometer. Crank engine. Ensure ignition coil primary current toggles on and off. Using tachometer and scan tester, compare cranking speed and scan tester read out. If engine fails to start and tachometer reads zero RPM when engine is cranked, check for broken timing belt or faulty CKP sensor. If CKP sensor is suspected, substitute known-good CKP sensor. Repeat test procedure. If engine fails to start, tachometer reads zero RPM, and ignition coil primary current fails to toggle on and off, check for faulty ignition coil, ignition circuit or power transistor. If engine starts and readouts agree, go to next step.

4) Ensure A/C switch is in ON position to activate closed throttle position switch. Allow engine to idle. Check coolant temperature. Using scan tester, read idle speed. See IDLE RPM SPECIFICATIONS table. If RPM is not to specification, check for faulty coolant temperature sensor, basic idle speed adjustment, or idle air control motor. If RPM is within specifications, go to next step.

IDLE RPM SPECIFICATIONS

Coolant Temperature	Engine RPM
–4°F (–20°C)	
Colt, Colt Vista, Expo, Mirage, Pickup, Summit & Summit Wagon	
1.5L	1460-1660
1.8L	1380-1580
2.4L	1300-1500
3.0L	1500-1700
Diamante, Stealth & 3000GT	1300-1500
Eclipse & Montero	1500-1700
Galant	1280-1480
32°F (0°C)	
Colt, Colt Vista, Expo, Mirage, Pickup, Summit & Summit Wagon	
1.5L	1350-1550
1.8L	1330-1530
2.4L	1300-1500
3.0L	1250-1450
Diamante, Montero, Stealth & 3000GT	1250-1450
Eclipse	1350-1550
Galant	1220-1420
68°F (20°C)	
Colt, Colt Vista, Expo, Mirage, Pickup 2.4L, Summit & Summit Wagon	
1.5L	1180-1380
1.8L	1250-1450
2.4L	1150-1350
Diamante DOHC, Galant, Stealth DOHC & 3000GT	1100-1300
Diamante SOHC, Montero, Pickup 3.0L, & Stealth SOHC	1050-1250
Eclipse	
1.8L	1150-1350
2.0L	1180-1380
104°F (40°C)	
Colt, Colt Vista, Expo, Mirage, Pickup, Summit & Summit Wagon	
1.5L	940-1140
1.8L	1000-1200
2.4L	950-1150
3.0L	850-1050
Diamante DOHC, Eclipse, Galant, Stealth DOHC & 3000GT	950-1150
Eclipse	
1.8L	950-1150
2.0L	1000-1200
Diamante SOHC, Montero & Stealth SOHC	850-1050
176°F (80°C)	
Colt, Colt Vista, Expo, Mirage, Pickup, Summit & Summit Wagon	
1.5L	650-850
1.8L	600-800
2.4L	650-850
3.0L	600-800
Diamante, Eclipse 1.8L, Montero, Stealth & 3000GT	600-800
Eclipse 2.0L	650-850
Galant	
SOHC	650-850
DOHC	700-900

5) On all models except Colt, Mirage and Summit, go to next step. Disconnect CKP/CMP sensor connector and Ignition (IG) switch connector. Using DVOM, check for continuity between CKP/CMP sensor connector terminal No. 2 and IG switch connector terminal No. 3. See Fig. 24. If continuity does not exist, repair wiring harness as necessary. If continuity exists, go to step **8)**.

93B80276   Courtesy of Mitsubishi Motor Sales of America

Fig. 24: Identifying Ignition Switch Terminals

6) On all other models except Diamante and Montero, go to next step. Disconnect CKP/CMP connector and MFI relay connector. Using DVOM, check for continuity between CKP/CMP connector terminal No. 3 and MFI relay connector terminal No. 5 (terminal No. 3 on Montero 3.5L). If continuity does not exist, repair wiring harness as necessary. If continuity exists, go to step **8)**.

7) On all other models, disconnect CKP/CMP sensor connector. Turn IG switch to ON position. Using DVOM, check voltage between chassis ground and specified CKP/CMP sensor connector terminal. See CKP SENSOR VOLTAGE TERMINAL IDENTIFICATION table. If battery voltage does not exist, repair ignition circuit between CKP/CMP sensor connector and IG switch. If battery voltage exists, go to next step.

CKP SENSOR VOLTAGE TERMINAL IDENTIFICATION

Application	Terminal No.
Colt Vista, Eclipse 1.8L, Expo, Galant SOHC & Summit Wagon	2
All Other Models	3

8) With CKP/CMP sensor connector disconnected, check for continuity between chassis ground and specified CKP/CMP sensor connector terminal. See CKP SENSOR GROUND CIRCUIT TERMINAL IDENTIFICATION table. If continuity does not exist, repair wiring harness as necessary. If continuity exists, go to next step.

CKP SENSOR GROUND CIRCUIT TERMINAL IDENTIFICATION

Application	Terminal No.
Diamante SOHC, Eclipse 2.0L, Montero 3.0L, Pickup 3.0L & Stealth SOHC	4
Pickup 2.4L	2
All Other Models	1

9) On Eclipse, Pickup 2.4L – 4WD and 3.0L, Stealth and 3000GT, go to next step. On all other models, with CKP/CMP sensor connector and ECM connector disconnected, check for continuity between specified CKP/CMP sensor connector terminal and ECM connector terminal. See CKP-TO-ECM CONNECTOR TERMINAL IDENTIFICATION table. If continuity does not exist, repair wiring harness as necessary. If continuity exists, go to next step.

CKP-TO-ECM CONNECTOR TERMINAL IDENTIFICATION

Application	CKP Terminal No.	ECM Terminal No.
Diamante & Galant DOHC	1	69
Montero		
3.0L	1	22
	2	21
3.5L	2	69
Pickup 2.4L – RWD	1	69
All Other Models	3	69

10) With ignition switch in ON position, check for voltage between chassis ground and specified CKP/CMP sensor connector terminal. See CKP SENSOR SUPPLY CIRCUIT IDENTIFICATION table. If 4.8-5.2 volts do not exist, replace ECM. If voltage is to specification and CKP sensor is suspected, replace CKP sensor.

CKP SENSOR SUPPLY CIRCUIT IDENTIFICATION

Application	Terminal No.
Diamante, Eclipse 2.0L, Galant DOHC, Montero, Pickup 3.0L, Stealth & 3000GT	2
Galant & Pickup 2.4L	1
All Other Models	3

CODE 23: CAMSHAFT POSITION SENSOR

NOTE: For component terminal identification, see TERMINAL IDENTIFICATION. For wiring diagrams, see WIRING DIAGRAMS article.

NOTE: Procedures are provided by manufacturer for component testing using an engine analyzer with oscilloscope capability. Refer to manufacturer's operation manual for instructions in use of oscilloscope. Manufacturer does not provide procedures for testing component using a scan tester.

1) On all models except Eclipse, Galant, Pickup, Stealth and 3000GT, disconnect Crankshaft/Camshaft Position (CKP/CMP) sensor connector. Install Test Harness (MB991348) between sensor and connector. On all models, using engine analyzer with oscilloscope capability, connect special patterns probe to specified connector terminal. See CMP PATTERN PICK-UP TERMINAL IDENTIFICATION table.

CMP PATTERN PICK-UP TERMINAL IDENTIFICATION

Application	Terminal No.
Diamante SOHC, Eclipse 2.0L, Montero 3.0L, Pickup 3.0L, Stealth & 3000GT	1
Diamante DOHC, Galant DOHC & Montero 3.5L	2
All Other Models	4

2) Start engine. Compare oscilloscope wave pattern with known-good wave pattern. *See Fig. 25.* Verify that wave length (time) decreases as engine RPM increases. If a wave pattern is output and it fluctuates to left or right, check for loose timing belt or an abnormality in sensor pick-up disc. If a rectangular wave pattern is output even when engine is not started, substitute known-good CMP sensor. Repeat test. If wave pattern is still abnormal, go to next step.

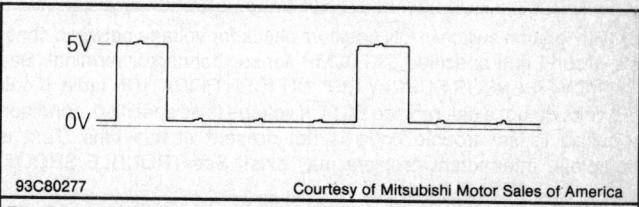

93C80277   Courtesy of Mitsubishi Motor Sales of America

Fig. 25: Identifying Known-Good CMP Sensor Wave Pattern

3) On all models except Colt, Mirage and Summit, go to step **4)**. Disconnect CKP/CMP sensor connector and Ignition (IG) switch connector. Using DVOM, check for continuity between CKP/CMP sensor connector terminal No. 2 and ignition switch connector terminal No. 3. *See Fig. 24.* If continuity does not exist, repair wiring harness as necessary. If continuity exists, go to step **6)**.

4) On all other models except Diamante and Montero, go to next step. Disconnect CKP/CMP connector and MFI relay connector. Using DVOM, check for continuity between CKP/CMP connector terminal No. 3 and MFI relay connector terminal No. 5 (terminal No. 3 on Montero 3.5L). If continuity does not exist, repair wiring harness as necessary. If continuity exists, go to step **6)**.

5) On all other models, disconnect CKP/CMP sensor connector. Turn ignition switch to ON position. Using DVOM, check voltage between chassis ground and specified CKP/CMP sensor connector terminal. See CMP SENSOR VOLTAGE TERMINAL IDENTIFICATION table. If battery voltage does not exist, repair ignition circuit between CKP/CMP sensor connector and IG switch. If battery voltage exists, go to next step.

CMP SENSOR VOLTAGE TERMINAL IDENTIFICATION

Application	Terminal No.
Colt Vista, Eclipse 1.8L, Expo, Galant SOHC, & Summit Wagon	2
All Other Models	3

6) With CKP/CMP sensor connector disconnected, check for continuity between chassis ground and specified CKP/CMP sensor connector terminal. See CMP SENSOR GROUND CIRCUIT TERMINAL IDENTIFICATION table. If continuity does not exist, repair wiring harness as necessary. If continuity exists, go to next step.

CMP SENSOR GROUND CIRCUIT TERMINAL IDENTIFICATION

Application	Terminal No.
Diamante SOHC, Eclipse 2.0L, Montero 3.0L, Pickup 3.0L & Stealth SOHC	4
Pickup 2.4L	2
All Other Models	1

7) On Eclipse, Pickup 2.4L – 4WD and 3.0L, Stealth and 3000GT, go to next step. On all other models, with CKP/CMP sensor connector and ECM connector disconnected, check for continuity between specified CKP/CMP sensor connector terminal and ECM connector terminal. See ECM-TO-CKP/CMP CONNECTOR TERMINAL IDENTIFICATION table. If continuity does not exist, repair wiring harness as necessary. If continuity exists, go to next step.

ECM-TO-CKP/CMP CONNECTOR TERMINAL IDENTIFICATION

Application	CKP/CMP Terminal No.	ECM Terminal No.
Diamante		
SOHC	1	68
DOHC	2	68
Galant DOHC	2	68
Montero		
3.0L	1	22
	2	21
3.5L	2	68
All Other Models	4	68

8) With ignition switch in ON position, check for voltage between chassis ground and specified CKP/CMP sensor connector terminal. See CKP/CMP SENSOR SUPPLY CIRCUIT IDENTIFICATION table. If 4.8-5.2 volts do not exist, replace ECM. If voltage is as specified, condition required to set trouble code is not present at this time. Test is complete. Intermittent problem may exist. See TROUBLE SHOOTING – NO CODES article.

CKP/CMP SENSOR SUPPLY CIRCUIT IDENTIFICATION

Application	Terminal No.
Diamante SOHC, Montero 3.0L, Pickup 3.0L & Stealth SOHC	1
Diamante DOHC, Galant DOHC, Montero 3.5L, Stealth DOHC & 3000GT	2
All Other Models	4

CODE 24: VEHICLE SPEED SENSOR

NOTE: For component terminal identification, see TERMINAL IDENTIFICATION. For wiring diagrams, see WIRING DIAGRAMS article.

1) Manufacturer does not provide Vehicle Speed Sensor (VSS) testing procedures using scan tester. On Galant, Montero, Stealth turbo and 3000GT turbo, go to step **3)**. On all other models, VSS is located in speedometer. VSS component testing procedures using DVOM require removal of instrument panel. Removal and installation of instrument panel is basically an unbolt and bolt-on procedure.

2) Use DVOM to check continuity between indicated VSS terminals. *See Fig. 26.* Ensure continuity pulses on and off 4 times per speedometer shaft revolution. If continuity is not as specified, replace VSS. If continuity is as specified, go to step **4)**.

3) VSS is located at end of speedometer cable in transmission. Remove VSS. Connect battery, resistor (3-10 ohms) and voltmeter to indicated terminals. *See Fig. 26.* Ensure voltage pulses 4 times per speedometer shaft revolution. If voltage is not as specified, replace VSS. If voltage is as specified, go to next step.

4) Disconnect ECM connector. Using DVOM, check continuity between chassis ground and specified ECM connector terminal. See VSS OUTPUT CIRCUIT IDENTIFICATION table. Move vehicle. Ensure continuity pulses on and off 4 times per tire revolution. If continuity is as specified: on Colt, Mirage and Summit, go to next step; on Eclipse, Galant, Stealth and 3000GT, conditions required to set code are not present at this time, test is complete; on all other models, go to step **7)**. If continuity is not as specified: on Colt, Mirage and Summit, go to step **7)**; on Eclipse, Galant, Pickup 2.4L – 4WD and 3.0L, Stealth and 3000GT, go to step **6)**; on all other models, go to next step.

VSS OUTPUT CIRCUIT IDENTIFICATION

Application	Terminal No.
Eclipse, Montero SOHC & Pickup	18
All Other Models	66

5) With ECM connector disconnected, disconnect VSS connector. Ground ECM connector VSS output terminal. See VSS OUTPUT CIRCUIT IDENTIFICATION table. Using DVOM, check for continuity between chassis ground and specified VSS connector terminal. See ECM-TO-VSS CIRCUIT IDENTIFICATION table. If continuity does not exist, repair wiring harness as necessary. If continuity exists, go to next step.

ECM-TO-VSS CIRCUIT IDENTIFICATION

Application	Terminal No.
Colt, Mirage & Summit	43
Montero & Pickup 2.4L – RWD	1
All Other Models	9

6) With VSS connector disconnected, check for continuity between chassis ground and specified VSS connector terminal. See VSS GROUND CIRCUIT IDENTIFICATION table. If continuity does not exist, repair wiring harness as necessary. If continuity exists, go to next step.

VSS GROUND CIRCUIT IDENTIFICATION

Application	Terminal No.
Colt, Mirage & Summit	12
Colt Vista, Expo & Summit Wagon	5
Diamante & Montero 3.0L	13
Eclipse	2
Galant	16
Montero 3.5L	43
Pickup	10
Stealth & 3000GT	102

7) With VSS connector and ECM connector disconnected, turn ignition switch to ON position. Using DVOM, check for voltage between chassis ground and specified VSS connector terminal. See VSS VOLTAGE FEED CIRCUIT IDENTIFICATION table. If voltage is not 4.5-4.9 volts, replace ECM. If voltage is as specified, condition required to set trouble code is not present at this time. Test is complete. Intermittent problem may exist. See TROUBLE SHOOTING – NO CODES article.

VSS VOLTAGE FEED CIRCUIT IDENTIFICATION

Application	Terminal No.
Colt, Mirage & Summit	43
Eclipse	59
Montero & Pickup	1
Stealth & 3000GT	109
All Other Models	9

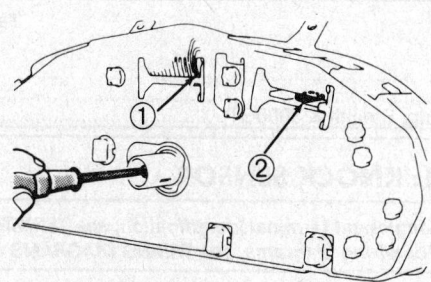

COLT, MIRAGE & SUMMIT

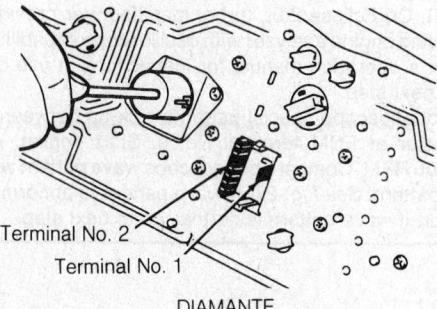

Terminal No. 2
Terminal No. 1

DIAMANTE

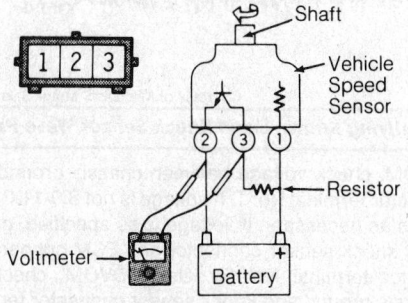

GALANT, MONTERO, STEALTH & 3000GT TURBO

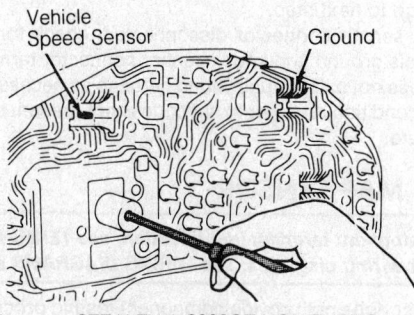

STEALTH & 3000GT NON-TURBO

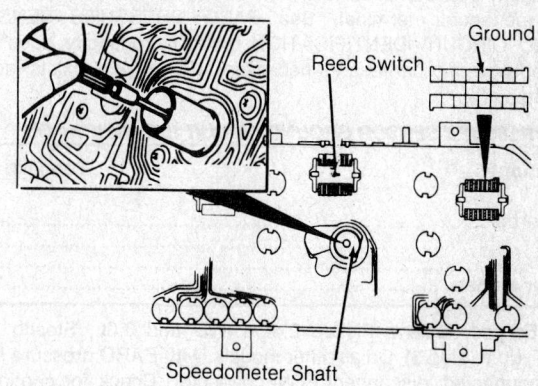

COLT VISTA, EXPO & SUMMIT WAGON

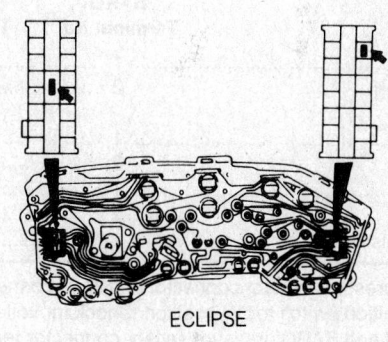

ECLIPSE

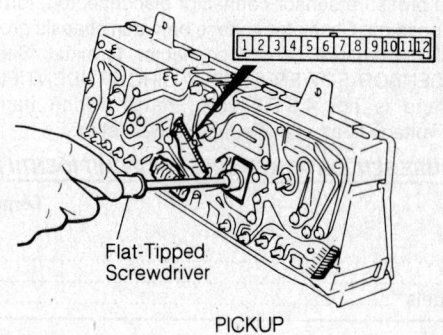

Flat-Tipped
Screwdriver

PICKUP

Courtesy of Mitsubishi Motor Sales of America.

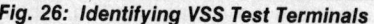

93D80278 93B02405 93H02371 93A01839 93C01840 93F81096 93E01841

Fig. 26: Identifying VSS Test Terminals

CODE 25: BAROMETRIC PRESSURE SENSOR

NOTE: Barometric (BARO) pressure sensor is built into airflow sensor. For code 25 test purposes, the airflow sensor will be referred to as the BARO pressure sensor. For component terminal identification, see AIRFLOW SENSOR under TERMINAL IDENTIFICATION. For wiring diagrams, see WIRING DIAGRAMS article.

1) Manufacturer does not provide component testing procedure without scan tester. Turn ignition switch to ON position. Using scan tester, read sensor pressure. See BARO PRESSURE SENSOR SPECIFICA-

TIONS table. If pressure is not as specified, replace BARO pressure sensor. If pressure is as specified, go to next step.

BARO PRESSURE SENSOR SPECIFICATIONS

Altitude Ft. (M)	Pressure In. Hg
0 (0)	29.92
1969 (600)	27.95
3937 (1200)	25.98
5906 (1800)	24.02

1994 ENGINE PERFORMANCE
Self-Diagnostics (Cont.)

2) Disconnect BARO pressure sensor connector. Using DVOM, check for continuity between chassis ground and specified BARO pressure sensor connector terminal. See BARO PRESSURE SENSOR GROUND CIRCUIT IDENTIFICATION table. If continuity does not exist, repair wiring harness as necessary. If continuity exists, go to next step.

BARO PRESSURE SENSOR GROUND CIRCUIT IDENTIFICATION

Application	Terminal No.
Eclipse	
Non-Turbo	4
Turbo	6
Galant	1
All Other Models	5

3) On Eclipse, Galant, Pickup 2.4L – 4WD and 3.0L, Stealth and 3000GT, go to step 5). On all other models, with BARO pressure sensor disconnected, disconnect ECM connector. Check for continuity between specified ECM connector terminal and BARO pressure sensor connector terminal. See BARO PRESSURE SENSOR TO ECM CIRCUIT IDENTIFICATION table. If continuity does not exist, repair wiring harness as necessary. If continuity exists, go to next step.

BARO PRESSURE SENSOR TO ECM CIRCUIT IDENTIFICATION

Application	BARO Terminal No.	ECM Terminal No.
Diamante	1	61
	2	65
Montero		
3.0L	1	23
	2	16
3.5L	1	65
	2	61
All Other Models	2	65

4) With BARO pressure sensor connector and ECM connector disconnected, turn ignition switch to ON position. Check for voltage between chassis ground and BARO pressure sensor connector terminal No. 1. If voltage is not 4.8-5.2 volts, replace ECM. If voltage is as specified, condition required to set code is not present at this time. Test is complete. Intermittent problem may exist. See TROUBLE SHOOTING – NO CODES article.

5) With BARO pressure sensor connector disconnected, turn ignition switch to ON position. Check for voltage between chassis ground and specified BARO pressure sensor connector terminal. See BARO PRESSURE SENSOR POWER SUPPLY CIRCUIT IDENTIFICATION table. If voltage is not 4.8-5.2 volts, repair wiring harness as necessary. If voltage is as specified, go to next step.

BARO PRESSURE SENSOR POWER SUPPLY CIRCUIT IDENTIFICATION

Application	Terminal No.
Eclipse	
Non-Turbo	3
Turbo	4
All Other Models	1

6) With BARO pressure sensor connector and ECM connector disconnected, ground ECM connector terminal No. 16 (terminal No. 65 on Galant, Stealth and 3000GT). Using DVOM, check for continuity between chassis ground and specified BARO pressure sensor connector terminal. See ECM-TO-BARO PRESSURE SENSOR GROUND CIRCUIT IDENTIFICATION table. If continuity does not exist, repair wiring harness as necessary. If continuity exists, condition required to set code is not present at this time. Test is complete. Intermittent problem may exist. See TROUBLE SHOOTING – NO CODES article.

ECM-TO-BARO PRESSURE SENSOR GROUND CIRCUIT IDENTIFICATION

Application	Terminal No.
Eclipse	
Non-Turbo	3
Turbo	4
Galant, Pickup, Stealth & 3000GT	1

CODE 31: KNOCK SENSOR

NOTE: For component terminal identification, see TERMINAL IDENTIFICATION. For wiring diagrams, see WIRING DIAGRAMS article.

1) Manufacturer does not provide component testing procedure using scan tester. On Diamante, Galant, Montero 3.5L, Stealth and 3000GT, go to step 4). On Eclipse 2.0L turbo, manufacturer provides testing procedure using engine analyzer with oscilloscope capability. Refer to manufacturer's operation manual for instructions in use of oscilloscope. Go to next step.

2) Connect oscilloscope special patterns pick-up between ECM and ECM connector at ECM terminal No. 9. Start engine. Accelerate engine to 5000 RPM. Compare oscilloscope wave pattern with known-good wave pattern. *See Fig. 27.* If wave pattern is abnormal, replace knock sensor. If wave pattern is normal, go to next step.

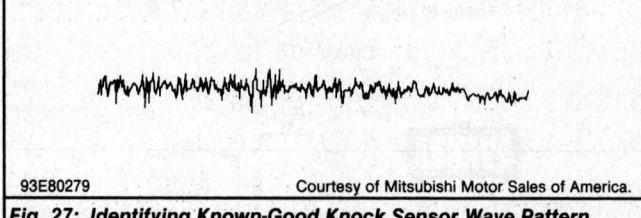

93E80279   Courtesy of Mitsubishi Motor Sales of America.

Fig. 27: Identifying Known-Good Knock Sensor Wave Pattern

3) Using DVOM, check voltage between chassis ground and knock sensor connector terminal No. 1. If voltage is not 8.0-11.0 volts, repair wiring harness as necessary. If voltage is as specified, go to step 5).

4) Disconnect knock sensor connector and ECM connector. Ground ECM connector terminal No. 58. Using DVOM, check continuity between chassis ground and knock sensor connector terminal No. 1. If continuity does not exist, repair wiring harness as necessary. If continuity exists, go to next step.

5) With knock sensor connector disconnected, check for continuity between chassis ground and knock sensor connector terminal No. 2. If continuity does not exist, repair wiring harness as necessary. If continuity exists, condition required to set code is not present at this time. Test is complete.

CODE 32: MAP SENSOR

NOTE: For component terminal identification, see TERMINAL IDENTIFICATION. For wiring diagrams, see WIRING DIAGRAMS article.

1) Manufacturer does not provide component testing procedure without scan tester. Ensure coolant temperature is 176-203°F (80-95°C). Ensure all accessories are off, transmission is in Neutral, and ignition switch is in ON position. Using scan tester, read intake manifold plenum pressure. See INTAKE MANIFOLD PLENUM PRESSURE SPECIFICATIONS table. If conditions are not as specified, replace Manifold Absolute Pressure (MAP) sensor. If conditions are as specified, go to next step.

2) Disconnect MAP sensor connector. Using DVOM, check continuity between chassis ground and MAP sensor connector terminal No. 3. If continuity does not exist, repair wiring harness as necessary. If continuity exists, go to next step.

3) With MAP sensor connector disconnected, disconnect ECM connector. Ground ECM connector terminal No. 70. Using DVOM, check continuity between chassis ground and MAP sensor connector terminal No. 2. If continuity does not exist, repair wiring harness as necessary. If continuity exists, go to next step.

INTAKE MANIFOLD PLENUM PRESSURE SPECIFICATIONS

Engine State	Altitude Ft. (M)	Pressure In. Hg
Off	0 (0)	29.92
	1969 (600)	27.95
	3937 (1200)	25.98
	5906 (1800)	24.02
Idle (750 RPM)		6.70-10.62
Suddenly Raced		[1]

[1] – Pressure should increase.

4) With MAP sensor connector and ECM connector disconnected, turn ignition switch to ON position. Check voltage between chassis ground and MAP sensor connector terminal No. 1. If 4.8-5.2 volts do not exist, replace ECM. If voltage is as specified, condition required to set code is not present at this time. Test is complete. Intermittent problem may exist. See TROUBLE SHOOTING – NO CODES article.

CODE 36: IGNITION TIMING ADJUSTMENT SIGNAL

NOTE: *For component terminal identification, see TERMINAL IDENTIFICATION. For wiring diagrams, see WIRING DIAGRAMS article.*

Turn ignition switch to ON position. Using DVOM, check voltage at ignition timing adjustment terminal (located at firewall) with terminal grounded and ungrounded. With terminal grounded, voltage should be 0-1.0 volt. With terminal ungrounded, voltage should be 4.0-5.5 volts. If voltage is not as specified, repair ignition timing adjustment terminal wiring harness or connector as necessary. If voltage is as specified, replace ECM.

CODE 39: OXYGEN SENSOR (O2S)

NOTE: *For component terminal identification, see TERMINAL IDENTIFICATION. For wiring diagrams, see WIRING DIAGRAMS article.*

1) If using scan tester, go to step **3)**. Disconnect O2S connector. Install Test Harness (MB998464) between O2S and O2S connector. Using DVOM, check resistance between O2S connector terminals No. 1 and No. 3. O2S resistance should be 20 ohms at 68°F (20°C). If resistance is not as specified, replace O2S. If resistance is as specified, go to next step.
2) Start and warm engine to operating temperature. Using jumper wires, ground O2S connector terminal No. 3 and apply 12 volts to O2S connector terminal No. 1. Using DVOM, check voltage between O2S connector terminals No. 2 and No. 4 while repeatedly racing engine. If voltage is not .6-1.0 volt, replace O2S. If voltage is as specified, go to step **5)**.
3) Start and warm engine to operating temperature. Using scan tester, read O2S voltage. While monitoring scan tester, accelerate engine to 4000 RPM. Suddenly decelerate engine. Scan tester should read .2 volt or less. Suddenly accelerate engine. Scan tester should read .6-1.0 volt. If voltage is not as specified, replace O2S. If voltage is as specified, go to next step.
4) While monitoring scan tester, accelerate to 2000 RPM and decelerate to 700 RPM (idle). Scan tester should switch between .6-1.0 volt and .4 volt or less. If voltage is not as specified, replace O2S. If voltage is as specified, go to next step.
5) With O2S connector disconnected, turn ignition switch to ON position. Using DVOM, check voltage between chassis ground and O2S connector terminal No. 1. If system voltage does not exist, repair wiring harness as necessary. If system voltage exists, go to next step.
6) Using DVOM, check for continuity between O2S connector terminal No. 4 and ECM connector terminal No. 56. If continuity does not exist, repair wiring harness as necessary. If continuity exists, go to next step.

7) With O2S connector disconnected, check for continuity between chassis ground O2S connector terminal No. 2. If continuity does not exist, repair wiring harness as necessary. If continuity exists, condition required to set fault is not present at this time. Test is complete. Intermittent problem may exist. See TROUBLE SHOOTING – NO CODES article.

CODE 41: FUEL INJECTOR

NOTE: *For component terminal identification, see TERMINAL IDENTIFICATION. For wiring diagrams, see WIRING DIAGRAMS article.*

1) Using a stethoscope or long-bladed screwdriver, listen for clicking sound from each injector while engine is running or being cranked. If no sound is heard from injector(s), check injector connections. If connections are not okay, repair connections as necessary. If connections are okay, go to next step.
2) Disconnect injector connector. Using DVOM, check resistance across injector terminals. If resistance is not 13-16 ohms, replace injector. If resistance is as specified, go to next step.
3) Using scan tester, read injector drive time while cranking engine. See INJECTOR CRANKING DRIVE TIME SPECIFICATIONS table. Go to next step.

INJECTOR CRANKING DRIVE TIME SPECIFICATIONS

Coolant Temperature	Drive Time
32°F (0°C)	
Colt, Colt Vista, Diamante DOHC, Eclipse Non-Turbo, Expo, Galant, Mirage, Pickup 2.4L, Summit & Summit Wagon	17-20 ms
Diamante SOHC, Montero 3.0L, Pickup 3.0L, Stealth Non-Turbo & 3000GT Non-Turbo	14-16 ms
Eclipse Turbo	24 ms
Montero 3.5L	90-110 ms
Stealth Turbo & 3000GT Turbo	9 ms
68°F (20°C)	
Except 1.5L Models, Diamante DOHC, Eclipse Turbo, Stealth DOHC & 3000GT	38-41 ms
All 1.5L Models	35 ms
Diamante DOHC, Stealth DOHC Non-Turbo & 3000GT Non-Turbo	45-46 ms
Eclipse Turbo	12 ms
Montero	
3.0L	36-44 ms
3.5L	42-51 ms
Stealth Turbo & 3000GT Turbo	28 ms
176°F (80°C)	
Except Diamante DOHC, Eclipse Turbo, Stealth SOHC & Turbo & 3000GT Turbo	9-10 ms
Diamante DOHC	11 ms
Eclipse Turbo	4-5 ms
Montero	
3.0L	8-10ms
3.5L	9-11
Stealth SOHC	8 ms
Stealth Turbo & 3000GT Turbo	6 ms

4) Ensure coolant temperature is at 176-205°F (80-95°C), all accessories are off and transaxle is in Neutral position. Using scan tester, read injector drive time under specified engine conditions. See INJECTOR OPERATING DRIVE TIME SPECIFICATIONS table. Go to next step.
5) Allow engine to idle after warm up. Using scan tester, shut off injectors in sequence. Idle should change when good injectors are shut off. If idle state does not change, check injector connection, spark plug and cable, and cylinder compression. If conditions are not as specified in preceding steps, go to next step.
6) On Eclipse, Pickup 2.4L – 4WD and 3.0L, Stealth and 3000GT, go to step **8)**. On all other models, disconnect MFI relay connector and injector connector at faulty injector. Using DVOM, check for continuity between specified MFI relay connector terminal and injector connector terminal. See MFI-TO-FUEL INJECTOR HARNESS TERMINAL IDENTIFICATION table. If continuity does not exist, repair wiring harness as necessary. If continuity exists, go to next step.

1994 ENGINE PERFORMANCE
Self-Diagnostics (Cont.)

INJECTOR OPERATING DRIVE TIME SPECIFICATIONS

Engine State	Drive Time
750 RPM	
All 1.5L Models	1.7-2.9 ms
All 1.8L Models	2.5-3.7 ms
Colt Vista 2.4L, Expo 2.4L &	
Summit Wagon 2.4L	2.0-3.2 ms
Diamante, Stealth Non-Turbo & 3000GT Non-Turbo	2.3-3.5 ms
Eclipse 2.0L	[1]
Galant	2.2-3.4 ms
Montero	2.4-3.6 [2]
Pickup 2.4L	[2]
Stealth Turbo & 3000GT Turbo	1.6-3.8 ms
2000 RPM	
All 1.5L Models	1.5-2.7 ms
Colt Vista 2.4L, Expo 2.4L	
& Summit Wagon 2.4L	1.8-3.0 ms
Eclipse	[3]
Galant	1.7-2.9 ms
Montero 3.0L	2.3-3.5
Pickup 3.0L	2.6-3.1 ms
Stealth Turbo & 3000GT Turbo	1.4-2.6 ms
All Other Models	2.0-3.3 ms
Suddenly Accelerated	
All Models	[4]

[1] – On non-turbo model, drive time is 2.4-3.2 ms. On turbo model, drive time is 1.6-2.2 ms.
[2] – On 2.4L, drive time is 3.0-4.0 ms. On 3.0L, drive time is 2.7-3.2 ms.
[3] – On 1.8L, drive time is 2.3-3.9 ms. On 2.0L non-turbo, drive time is 1.9-2.7 ms. On 2.0L turbo, drive time is 1.4-2.2 ms.
[4] – Drive time should increase.

MFI-TO-FUEL INJECTOR HARNESS TERMINAL IDENTIFICATION

Application	MFI Terminal No.	Fuel Injector Terminal No.
Colt, Mirage & Summit	2	2
Diamante & Montero	5	1
Montero		
3.0L	5	1
3.5L	3	1
All Other Models	2	1

7) Using a DVOM, check for continuity between injector connector terminal No. 2 (terminal No. 5 for No. 4 injector or terminal No. 6 for No. 6 injector on Diamante DOHC, or terminal No. 3 for No. 5 injector or terminal No. 4 for No. 6 injector on Diamante SOHC), and specified ECM connector terminal. See INJECTOR-TO-ECM CIRCUIT IDENTIFICATION table. If continuity does not exist, repair wiring harness as necessary. If continuity exists, condition required to set code is not present at this time. Intermittent problem may exist. See TROUBLE SHOOTING – NO CODES article.

8) On Eclipse 2.0L, Stealth and 3000GT, go to step **10)**. Disconnect injector connector at faulty injector. Turn ignition switch to ON position. Using DVOM, check for voltage between chassis ground and injector connector terminal No. 1 (terminal No. 2 on Pickup 3.0L). If battery voltage does not exist, repair wiring harness as necessary. If battery voltage exists, go to next step.

9) With injector connector disconnected, disconnect ECM connector. Check for continuity between injector connector terminal No. 2 and ECM connector terminal No. 51 (No. 1 on Galant) for injector No. 1, No. 52 (No. 14 on Galant) for injector No. 2, No. 60 (No. 2 on Galant) for injector No. 3, or No. 61 (No. 15 on Galant) for injector No. 4 (ECM connector terminal No. 105 for injector No. 5 or terminal No. 109 for injector No. 6 on Pickup 3.0L). If continuity does not exist, repair wiring harness as necessary. If continuity exists, condition required to set code is not present at this time. Test is complete. Intermittent problem may exist. See TROUBLE SHOOTING – NO CODES article.

10) On Stealth and 3000GT, go to step **15)**. Turn ignition switch to ON position. With MFI relay connector connected, check for voltage between chassis ground and MFI relay connector terminals No. 4 and No. 5. If battery voltage does not exist, check MFI relay. If battery voltage exists: on turbo models, go to next step; on non-turbo models, go to step **13)**.

INJECTOR-TO-ECM CIRCUIT IDENTIFICATION

Application	Injector No.	ECM Terminal No.
Diamante	1	1
	2	14
	3	2
	4	15
	5	3
	6	16
Montero		
3.0L	1	51
	2	52
	3	60
	4	61
	5	105
	6	109
3.5L	1	1
	2	14
	3	2
	4	15
	5	3
	6	16
All Other Models	1	1
	2	14
	3	2
	4	15

11) Disconnect MFI relay resistor connector. Turn ignition switch to ON position. Check for voltage between chassis ground and relay resistor connector terminal No. 3. If battery voltage does not exist, repair wiring harness between MFI relay and relay resistor. If battery voltage exists, go to next step.

12) With relay resistor connector disconnected and injector connector connected, check resistance between relay resistor terminals No. 3 and No. 1 for injector No. 1, No. 3 and No. 4 for injector No. 2, No. 3 and No. 5 for injector No. 3, or No. 3 and No. 6 for injector No. 4. If resistance is not 5.5-6.5 ohms at 68°F (20°C), replace relay resistor. If resistance is as specified, go to next step.

13) Disconnect injector connector at faulty injector. Using DVOM, check voltage between chassis ground and injector connector terminal No. 1 (non-turbo) or injector connector terminal No. 2 (turbo). If battery voltage does not exist, repair wiring harness as necessary. If battery voltage exists, go to next step.

14) With injector connector disconnected, disconnect ECM connector. Ground ECM connector terminal No. 51 for injector No.1, No. 52 for injector No. 2, No. 60 for injector No. 3, or No. 61 for injector No. 4. Check for continuity between chassis ground and injector connector terminal No. 1 (non-turbo) or No. 2 (turbo). If continuity does not exist, repair wiring harness as necessary. If continuity exists, condition required to set code is not present at this time. Test is complete. Intermittent problem may exist. See TROUBLE SHOOTING – NO CODES article.

15) Disconnect MFI relay resistor connector. Turn ignition switch to ON position. Using DVOM, check for voltage between chassis ground and resistor connector terminal No. 2. *See Fig. 28.* If battery voltage does not exist, repair wiring harness as necessary between MFI relay resistor connector and MFI relay. If battery voltage exists, reconnect MFI relay resistor connector. Go to next step.

VIEWED FROM HARNESS SIDE

93H80280   Courtesy of Mitsubishi Motor Sales of America

Fig. 28: Identifying MFI Relay Resistor Terminals

16) If faulty injector is on rear injector bank, go to next step. Disconnect injector connector at faulty front injector. Turn ignition switch to ON position. Using DVOM, check voltage between chassis ground and injector connector terminal No. 1. If battery voltage does not exist, repair wiring harness as necessary between injector connector and MFI relay. If voltage exists, go to step **18**).

17) Disconnect rear bank injector connector. Using DVOM, check voltage between chassis ground and injector connector terminal No. 1. If battery voltage does not exist, repair wiring harness as necessary between injector connector and MFI relay. If voltage exists, go to step **19**).

18) With injector connector disconnected, disconnect ECM connector. Ground ECM connector terminal No. 1 for injector No. 1, No. 2 for injector No. 3, or No. 3 for injector No. 3. Using DVOM, check for continuity between chassis ground and injector connector terminal No. 2. If continuity does not exist, repair wiring harness as necessary between appropriate injector connector and ECM connector terminal. If continuity exists, condition required to set code is not present at this time. Test is complete. Intermittent problem may exist. See TROUBLE SHOOTING – NO CODES article.

19) With rear bank injector connector disconnected, disconnect ECM connector. Ground ECM connector terminal No. 14 for injector No. 2, No. 15 for injector No. 4, or No. 16 for injector No. 6. Using DVOM, check for continuity between chassis ground and rear bank injector connector terminal No. 2 for injector No. 2, No. 3 for injector No. 4, or No. 4 for injector No. 6. If continuity does not exist, repair wiring harness between rear bank injector connector and ECM connector. If continuity exists, condition required to set code is not present at this time. Test is complete. Intermittent problem may exist. See TROUBLE SHOOTING – NO CODES article.

CODE 42: FUEL PUMP

NOTE: For component terminal identification, see TERMINAL IDENTIFICATION. For wiring diagrams, see WIRING DIAGRAMS article.

1) Turn ignition switch to ON position. Using a scan tester, actuate fuel pump. Crank engine with fuel pump actuated. Operating noise should be heard. Pinch fuel pump return hose and feel for fuel flow pulsations. If operating noise is not heard or fuel flow is not felt, replace fuel pump. If conditions are as specified, go to next step.

2) Apply 12 volts to fuel pump check terminal. *See Fig. 29.* If fuel pump operates, go to step **5**). If fuel pump does not operate, go to next step.

3) Disconnect fuel pump connector, located at front of fuel tank. Using DVOM, check for continuity between chassis ground and specified fuel pump connector terminal. See FUEL PUMP GROUND CIRCUIT IDENTIFICATION table. If continuity does not exist, repair wiring harness as necessary. If continuity exists, go to next step.

FUEL PUMP GROUND CIRCUIT IDENTIFICATION

Application	Terminal No.
Colt Vista, Expo & Summit Wagon	
FWD	2
AWD	3
All Other Models	1

4) Ground fuel pump check terminal. With fuel pump connector disconnected, disconnect MFI relay connector. Check for continuity between chassis ground and specified fuel pump connector terminal. See FUEL PUMP DRIVE CIRCUIT IDENTIFICATION table. If continuity does not exist, repair wiring harness as necessary. If continuity exists, go to next step.

FUEL PUMP DRIVE CIRCUIT IDENTIFICATION

Application	Terminal No.
Colt Vista, Expo & Summit Wagon	
FWD	1
AWD	6
All Other Models	2

5) Disconnect MFI relay connector. Check voltage between chassis ground and specified MFI relay connector terminal. See MFI RELAY VOLTAGE SUPPLY TERMINAL IDENTIFICATION table. With ignition switch in OFF position, voltage should be zero. With engine cranking,

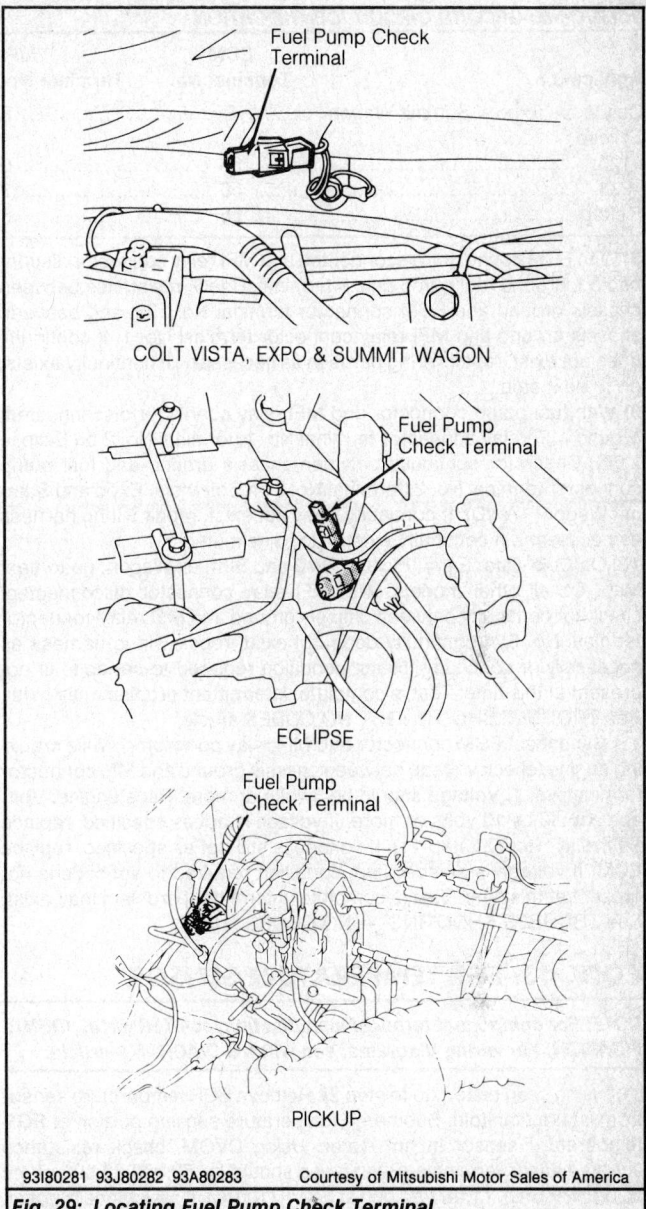

93I80281 93J80282 93A80283   Courtesy of Mitsubishi Motor Sales of America

Fig. 29: Locating Fuel Pump Check Terminal

voltage should be 8.0 volts or more. If voltage is not as specified, repair ignition switch or wiring harness as necessary. If voltage is as specified, go to next step.

MFI RELAY VOLTAGE SUPPLY TERMINAL IDENTIFICATION

Application	Terminal No.
Eclipse	
1.8L	4
2.0L	3
All Other Models	7

6) Turn ignition to OFF position. With MFI connector disconnected, disconnect ECM connector. Ground specified ECM connector terminal and check continuity between chassis ground and specified MFI relay connector terminal. See ECM-TO-MFI GROUND CIRCUIT IDENTIFICATION table. If continuity does not exist, repair wiring harness as necessary. If continuity exists, go to next step.

7) On Eclipse and Pickup 4WD, go to next step. On all other models, with fuel pump connector and MFI relay connector disconnected, ground fuel pump check terminal. Check for continuity between chassis ground and MFI relay connector terminal No. 1. If continuity does not exist, repair wiring harness as necessary. If continuity exists, go to step **9**).

1994 ENGINE PERFORMANCE
Self-Diagnostics (Cont.)

ECM-TO-MFI GROUND CIRCUIT IDENTIFICATION

Application	ECM Terminal No.	MFI Terminal No.
Colt Vista, Expo & Summit Wagon	8	5
Eclipse		
1.8L	56	5
2.0L	56	7
Pickup	56	5

8) With ECM connector disconnected and MFI relay connector disconnected, ground fuel pump check terminal. Check resistance between chassis ground and ECM connector terminal No. 109, and between chassis ground and MFI relay connector terminal No. 1. If continuity does not exist, repair wiring harness as necessary. If continuity exists, go to next step.

9) With fuel pump connector and MFI relay connector disconnected, ground MFI relay connector terminal No. 1 (terminal No. 2 on Eclipse 2.0L). Check for continuity between chassis ground and fuel pump connector terminal No. 2 (terminal No. 3 on Colt Vista, Expo and Summit Wagon – AWD). If continuity does not exist, repair wiring harness as necessary. If continuity exists, go to next step.

10) On Colt Vista, Expo, Pickup RWD and Summit Wagon, go to next step. On all other models, with MFI relay connector disconnected, check for continuity between chassis ground and MFI relay connector terminal No. 6. If continuity does not exist, repair wiring harness as necessary. If continuity exists, condition required to set code is not present at this time. Test is complete. Intermittent problem may exist. See TROUBLE SHOOTING – NO CODES article.

11) Reconnect ECM connector and MFI relay connector. While cranking engine, check voltage between chassis ground and MFI connector terminal No. 1. Voltage should be 8 volts or more. Race engine. Voltage should be 12 volts or more. If voltage is not as specified, replace MFI relay. Repeat step **11)**. If voltage is still not as specified, replace ECM. If voltage is as specified, condition required to set code is not present at this time. Test is complete. Intermittent problem may exist. See TROUBLE SHOOTING – NO CODES article.

CODE 43: EGR TEMPERATURE SENSOR

NOTE: *For component terminal identification, see TERMINAL IDENTIFICATION. For wiring diagrams, see WIRING DIAGRAMS article.*

1) If using scan tester, go to step **2)**. Remove EGR temperature sensor from intake manifold. Submerge temperature sensing portion of EGR temperature sensor in hot water. Using DVOM, check resistance across sensor terminals. Resistance should be 60,000-83,000 ohms at 122°F (50°C), 11,000-14,000 at 212°F (100°C). If resistance is not as specified, replace EGR temperature sensor. If resistance is as specified, go to step **3)**.

2) Warm engine to operating temperature. Allow engine to idle for 2 minutes. Squeeze green-striped hose between EGR valve and EGR solenoid. Using scan tester, read EGR temperature sensor temperature. At 700-750 RPM, scan tester should read 70°F (158°C) or less on Colt, Colt Vista, Eclipse, Expo, Galant, Mirage, Summit and Summit Wagon. On all other models, scan tester should read 212°F (100°C) or less. At 3500-4000 RPM, scan tester should read 158°F (70°C) or more on Colt, Colt Vista, Eclipse, Expo, Mirage, Summit and Summit Wagon. On all other models, scan tester should read 248°F (120°C) or more. If reading is not as specified, replace EGR temperature sensor. If reading is as specified, go to next step.

3) On Montero, go to next step. Disconnect EGR temperature sensor connector. Using DVOM, check continuity between chassis ground and EGR temperature sensor terminal No. 2 on Eclipse 2.0L and Pickup 3.0L (terminal No. 1 on all other models). If continuity does not exist, repair wiring harness as necessary. If continuity exists, go to next step.

4) On Eclipse, Galant, Pickup 2.4L – 4WD and 3.0L, Stealth and 3000GT, go to next step. On all other models, with EGR temperature sensor disconnected, disconnect ECM connector. Check for continuity between EGR temperature sensor connector terminal No. 2 and

ECM connector terminal No. 53. (No. 6 on Montero). If continuity does not exist, repair wiring harness as necessary. If continuity exists, go to next step.

5) On all models, with EGR temperature sensor connector and ECM connector disconnected, turn ignition switch to ON position. Check voltage between chassis ground and EGR connector terminal No. 2 on Eclipse 2.0L, Galant and Pickup 3.0L (terminal No. 1 on all other models). Voltage should be 3.3-4.7 volts. If voltage is not as specified on Eclipse, Pickup 2.4L – 4WD and 3.0L, Stealth and 3000GT, repair wiring harness as necessary. If voltage is not as specified on all other models, replace ECM. If voltage is as specified, condition required to set code is not present at this time. Test is complete. Intermittent problem may exist. See TROUBLE SHOOTING – NO CODES article.

CODES 44, 52 & 53: IGNITION COILS

NOTE: *For component terminal identification, see TERMINAL IDENTIFICATION. For wiring diagrams, see WIRING DIAGRAMS article.*

NOTE: *Procedures are provided by manufacturer for component testing using an engine analyzer with oscilloscope capability. Refer to manufacturer's operation manual for instructions in use of oscilloscope.*

1) If using a scan tester, go to step **4)**. On Diamante and Montero, disconnect power transistor connector. Install Test Harness (MB991348) between transistor and connector. Start engine and accelerate to 1200 RPM. Using engine analyzer with oscilloscope capability, sequentially connect special pattern probe to ignition power transistor connector terminals No. 4 on Diamante or No. 1 on Montero (coils No. 3 and No. 6), No. 5 on Diamante or No. 2 on Montero (coils No. 2 and No. 5) and No. 6 on Diamante or No. 3 on Montero (coils No. 1 and No. 4). *See Fig. 30.* Observe oscilloscope wave pattern at each terminal. Go to step **3)**.

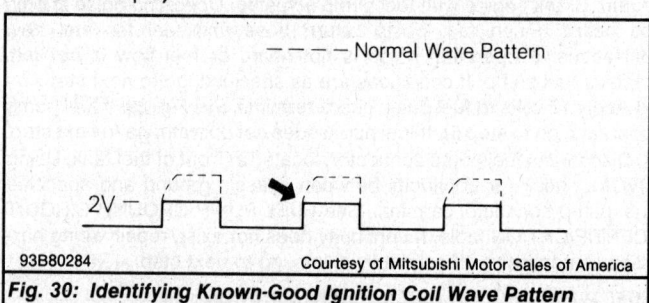

Courtesy of Mitsubishi Motor Sales of America

Fig. 30: Identifying Known-Good Ignition Coil Wave Pattern

2) On Eclipse, Stealth and 3000GT, start engine and let idle. Idle speed is 750 RPM for Eclipse, and 700 RPM for Stealth and 3000GT. Using engine analyzer with oscilloscope capability, connect special pattern probe at ignition power transistor terminal No. 1 for Eclipse, or terminal No. 13 for Stealth and 3000GT. Observe oscilloscope wave pattern. *See Fig. 30.* Connect special pattern probe at ignition power transistor terminal No. 2 for Eclipse and Montero, or terminal No. 3 for Stealth and 3000GT.

3) On all models, if oscilloscope wave pattern rise fluctuates to right and is between 2-4.5 volts for each transistor terminal, system is okay. If wave pattern is rectangular and is 2 volts or less, check for broken wire in primary ignition circuit. If wave pattern is rectangular and is 12 volts or more, replace defective ignition power transistor.

4) On all models, using scan tester, check for continuity between chassis ground and ignition timing adjustment terminal. With engine at idle, ground ignition timing adjustment terminal (located at firewall). Scan tester should display ON. With ignition timing adjustment terminal not grounded, scan tester should display OFF. If conditions are not as specified, repair circuit between ignition timing adjustment connector and ECM terminal No. 104 on Diamante, Stealth and 3000GT, ECM terminal No. 12 on Eclipse or ECM terminal No. 34 on Galant and Montero. If conditions are as specified, go to next step.

5) Connect timing light and tachometer. Ensure engine is at normal operating temperature. With engine at idle (750 RPM for Diamante, Eclipse and Montero, or 700 RPM for Stealth and 3000GT), check ignition timing. Timing should be 7-23 degrees BTDC for Diamante, Stealth and 3000GT, 5-15 degrees BTDC for Eclipse, or 2-18 degrees for Montero.

6) With engine at 2000 RPM, timing should be 20-40 degrees BTDC for Diamante, 33-41 degrees BTDC on Eclipse non-turbo models, 30-40 degrees BTDC on Eclipse turbo models, 18-38 degrees on Montero, 30-50 degrees BTDC on Stealth and 3000GT non-turbo models, or 23-43 degrees BTDC on Stealth and 3000GT turbo models. Ground ignition timing adjustment terminal. On all models, with engine idling, ignition timing should be 3-7 degrees BTDC.

7) On Diamante and Montero, disconnect ignition switch and ignition coil connectors. Using a DVOM, check for continuity between ignition switch connector terminal No. 4 and ignition coil connector terminal No. 3 on Diamante or No. 2 on Montero. If continuity does not exist, repair wiring between ignition switch and ignition coil. If continuity exists, go to next step.

8) Disconnect ignition power transistor connector. Check for continuity between power transistor connector terminal No. 9 on Diamante or No. 6 on Montero, and ignition coil connector terminal No. 3 on Diamante or No. 2 on Montero. If continuity does not exist, repair wiring between ignition power transistor and ignition coil. If continuity exists, go to next step.

9) Check for continuity between ignition power resistor connector terminal No. 1 on Diamante or No. 11 and ignition coil connector terminal No. 4 on Diamante or No. 1 on Montero. Check for continuity between ignition power resistor connector terminal No. 2 on Diamante or No. 12 on Montero, and ignition coil connector terminal No. 1. Check for continuity between ignition power resistor connector terminal No. 3 on Diamante or No. 13 on Montero, and ignition coil terminal No. 2. on Diamante or No. 1 on Montero. If continuity does not exist, repair appropriate circuit between ignition power resistor connector and ignition coil connector. If continuity exists, go to next step.

10) Check for continuity between chassis ground and ignition coil connector terminals No. 1, 2 and 4 on Diamante or No. 1 on Montero. If continuity does not exist, check for short to ground between ignition power transistor and ignition coil. If continuity exists, go to step **13)**.

11) On Eclipse, Stealth and 3000GT, disconnect ignition coil connector. Turn ignition switch to ON position. Using a DVOM, check voltage at ignition coil connector terminal No. 3. If battery voltage is not present, repair wiring between ignition coil and ignition switch. If battery voltage is present, go to next step.

12) Disconnect ignition power resistor connector. Check voltage at ignition power resistor connector terminal No. 6. If battery voltage is not present, repair wiring between ignition power resistor connector and ignition switch. If battery voltage is present, go to next step.

13) On all models, disconnect ECM connector. Ground ECM connector terminal No. 11 on Diamante and Montero, No. 109 on Eclipse, or No. 101 on Stealth and 3000GT. Check for continuity between chassis ground and ignition power transistor connector terminal No. 4 on Diamante and Eclipse, terminal No. 1 on Montero, or terminal No. 5 on Stealth and 3000GT. On Diamante and Montero, ground ECM connector terminal No. 10. Check for continuity between chassis ground and ignition power transistor connector terminal No. 6 on Diamante or No. 3 on Montero. Ground ECM connector terminal No. 23. Check for continuity between chassis ground and ignition power transistor connector terminal No. 5 on Diamante or No. 2 on Montero.

14) Ground ECM connector terminal No. 58 on Diamante or No. 101 on Montero. Check for continuity between chassis ground and ignition power transistor connector terminal No. 8 on Diamante or No. 5 on Montero. On all models, if continuity does not exist, check appropriate circuit for open or short to ground between ignition power transistor and ECM. If continuity exists, on Diamante and Montero, go to step **17)**. On all other models, go to next step.

15) Check for continuity between ignition power transistor connector terminal No. 1 and ignition coil connector terminal No. 1 on Eclipse, or terminals No. 11 and No. 4 on Stealth and 3000GT. Check for continu-

ity between ignition power resistor connector terminal No. 8 and ignition coil terminal No. 2 on Eclipse or terminals No. 12 and No. 1 on Stealth and 3000GT.

16) Check for continuity between ignition power transistor connector terminal No. 13 and ignition coil connector terminal No. 2 on Stealth and 3000GT. If continuity does not exist, repair appropriate between ignition power transistor and ignition coil. If continuity exists, go to next step.

17) Check for continuity between chassis ground and ignition power transistor connector terminal No. 7 on Diamante, No. 3 on Eclipse, or No. 4 on Montero, Stealth and 3000GT. If continuity does not exist, repair wiring between ignition power transistor connector and ground. If continuity exists, go to next step.

18) With ignition switch in START position, check voltage at ignition power transistor connector terminals No. 4, 5 and 6 on Diamante, terminals No. 2 and No. 7 on Eclipse, or terminals No. 1, 2 and 3 on Montero, Stealth and 3000GT. Voltage should be 0.5-4.0 volts. If voltage is not as specified, repair appropriate circuit between ignition power transistor connector and ECM connector. If voltage is as specified, go to next step.

19) With ignition switch in ON position, check voltage at ignition timing adjustment connector. On all models, voltage should be 4.0-5.2 volts. If voltage is as specified, circuit is okay. If voltage is not as specified, repair wiring between ignition timing adjustment connector and ECM connector.

CODE 55: IDLE AIR CONTROL POSITION SENSOR

NOTE: For component terminal identification, see TERMINAL IDENTIFICATION. For wiring diagrams, see WIRING DIAGRAMS article.

1) Manufacturer does not provide component testing procedure without using scan tester. Ensure engine coolant temperature is 185-205°F (85-95°C). Place transmission in Park or Neutral. Turn off all accessories except A/C. Ensure A/C clutch is operating when A/C system is on. Allow engine to idle.

2) Using scan tester, read Idle Air Control (IAC) position sensor step. See IAC POSITION SENSOR STEP SPECIFICATIONS table. If scan tester does not read as specified, replace IAC position sensor. If readings are as specified, go to next step.

IAC POSITION SENSOR STEP SPECIFICATIONS

A/C Switch Position	Standard Step Value
Off	2-20
On	Increase From 8-50
1	Increase From 3-40

1 – For A/T models. Brakes applied, transmission selector in "D" and A/C on.

3) Disconnect ECM connector and IAC position sensor connector. Ground specified ECM connector terminal and using DVOM, check continuity between chassis ground and specified IAC connector terminal. See ECM-TO-IAC HARNESS CIRCUIT IDENTIFICATION table. If continuity does not exist, repair wiring harness as necessary. If continuity exists, go to next step.

ECM-TO-IAC HARNESS CIRCUIT IDENTIFICATION

Application	ECM Terminal No.	IAC Terminal No.
Colt Vista, Expo & Summit Wagon	13 & 23	1
	67	2
	68	4
All Other Models	5	4
	18	2
	61	1

4) With IAC position sensor connector disconnected, check continuity between chassis ground and IAC position sensor connector terminal No. 3. If continuity does not exist, repair wiring harness as necessary. If continuity exists, go to next step.

5) With IAC position sensor connector disconnected and ECM connector connected, turn ignition switch to ON position. Check for voltage between chassis ground and IAC connector terminals No. 2 and No. 4. If voltage is not 4.8-5.2 volts on either circuit, replace ECM. If voltage is as specified, go to next step.

6) Check voltage between chassis ground and IAC position sensor connector terminal No. 1. If voltage is not 4.8-5.2 volts, replace ECM. If voltage is as specified, condition required to set code is not present at this time. Test is complete. Intermittent problem may exist. See TROUBLE SHOOTING – NO CODES article.

CODES 59 & 69: REAR OXYGEN SENSOR (O2S)

NOTE: For component terminal identification, see TERMINAL IDENTIFICATION. For wiring diagrams, see WIRING DIAGRAMS article.

1) If using scan tester, go to next step. Disconnect O2S connector. Using DVOM, check continuity between O2S terminals No. 3 and No. 4. If continuity does not exist, replace O2S. If continuity exists, go to step **3)**.

2) With an assistant, road test vehicle. Drive vehicle with wide open throttle in 2nd gear (M/T) or "L" position (A/T). Using scan tester, read O2S voltage. If O2S voltage is not .6-1.0 volt at 3500 RPM, replace O2S. If voltage is as specified, go to next step.

3) Disconnect O2S connector and MFI relay connector. Using DVOM, check for continuity between O2S connector terminal No. 3 and MFI relay connector No. 2. If continuity does not exist, repair wiring harness as necessary. If continuity exists, go to next step.

4) With O2S connector disconnected, disconnect ECM connector. Check for continuity between O2S connector terminal No. 1 and ECM connector terminal No. 55. If continuity does not exist, repair wiring harness as necessary. If continuity exists, go to next step.

5) With O2S connector disconnected, check for continuity between chassis ground and O2S connector terminals No. 2 and No. 4. If continuity does not exist on either circuit, repair wiring harness as necessary. If continuity exists and preceding test procedure did not discover any trouble codes, replace O2S.

CODE 61: TRANSAXLE CONTROL MODULE SIGNAL

NOTE: For component terminal identification, see TERMINAL IDENTIFICATION. For wiring diagrams, see WIRING DIAGRAMS article.

1) Disconnect Transaxle Control Module (TCM) and ECM connectors. Ground TCM connector terminal No. 7 (No. 18 on Colt Vista, Expo and Summit Wagon). Using DVOM, check continuity between chassis ground and ECM connector terminal No. 116. If continuity does not exist, repair wiring harness as necessary. If continuity exists, go to next step.

2) Ground TCM connector terminal No. 9 (No. 4 on Colt Vista, Expo and Summit Wagon). Check continuity between chassis ground and ECM connector terminal No. 59. If continuity does not exist, repair wiring harness as necessary. If continuity exists, go to next step.

3) Ground TCM connector terminal No. 108 (No. 17 on Colt Vista, Expo and Summit Wagon). Check continuity between chassis ground and ECM connector terminal No. 7. If continuity does not exist, repair wiring harness as necessary. If continuity exists, test is complete. Intermittent problem may exist. See TROUBLE SHOOTING – NO CODES article.

CODE 62: INDUCTION CONTROL VALVE POSITION SENSOR

NOTE: For component terminal identification, see TERMINAL IDENTIFICATION. For wiring diagrams, see WIRING DIAGRAMS article. Induction control valve position sensor is built into induction control motor.

1) Disconnect induction control motor connector and ECM connector. Ground ECM connector terminal No. 61. Using DVOM, check continu-ity between chassis ground and induction control motor connector terminal No. 1.

2) Ground ECM connector terminal No. 111. Check continuity between chassis ground and induction control motor connector terminal No. 2.

3) Ground ECM connector terminal No. 103. Check continuity between chassis ground and induction control motor connector terminal No. 4.

4) If continuity exists in previous steps, go to next step. If continuity does not exist in previous steps, check for open or short to ground in appropriate circuit between ECM connector and induction control motor.

5) With induction control motor connector disconnected, check continuity between chassis ground and induction control motor connector terminal No. 3. If continuity does not exist, repair wiring harness as necessary. If continuity exists, go to next step.

6) Turn ignition switch to ON position. Ensure control motor connector is disconnected and ECM connector is connected. Using DVOM, check voltage at induction control motor connector terminals No. 2 and No. 4. If voltage is not 4.8-5.2 volts, repair wiring harness as necessary. If wiring harness is okay, replace ECM. If voltage is as specified, go to next step.

7) Ensure ignition switch is in ON position. Ensure control motor connector is disconnected and ECM connector is connected. Using DVOM, check voltage at induction control motor connector terminal No. 1. If voltage is not 4.8-5.2 volts, repair wiring harness as necessary. If wiring harness is okay, replace ECM. If voltage is as specified, test is complete. Intermittent problem may exist. See appropriate TROUBLE SHOOTING – NO CODES article. If wiring harness, connectors and induction control motor are okay, replace air intake plenum assembly. See appropriate article in ENGINES in appropriate MITCHELL® manual.

CODE 71: TRACTION CONTROL VACUUM SOLENOID

NOTE: For component terminal identification, see TERMINAL IDENTIFICATION. For wiring diagrams, see WIRING DIAGRAMS article.

1) Turn ignition switch to ON position. Using a scan tester, actuate vacuum solenoid. With solenoid actuated, operating noise should be heard. If operating noise is not heard, go to next step. If operating noise is heard, go to step **4)**.

2) Disconnect vacuum solenoid and MFI relay connectors. Using DVOM, check for continuity between vacuum solenoid connector terminal No. 1 and MFI relay connector terminal No. 5. If continuity does not exist, repair wiring harness between MFI relay and vacuum solenoid as necessary. If continuity exists, go to next step.

3) Disconnect ECM connector. Ground ECM connector terminal No. 102. Check continuity between chassis ground and vacuum solenoid connector terminal No. 2. If continuity does not exist, repair wiring harness as necessary. If continuity exists, check solenoid vacuum. Go to next step.

4) Remove vacuum hoses from solenoid. Ensure solenoid harness connector is disconnected. Connect a vacuum pump to solenoid

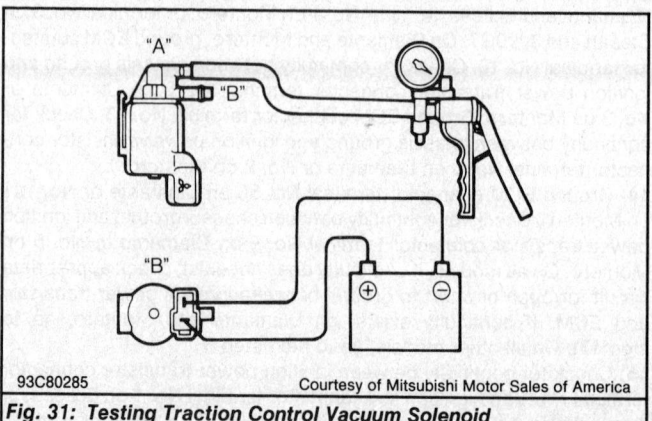

93C80285   Courtesy of Mitsubishi Motor Sales of America

Fig. 31: Testing Traction Control Vacuum Solenoid

nipple "A". Use jumper wires to connect battery voltage to solenoid terminals. *See Fig. 31*. With vacuum applied, nipple "B" unplugged, and negative jumper wire disconnected, solenoid should hold vacuum.

5) With vacuum applied, nipple "B" unplugged, and negative jumper wire connected, solenoid should not hold vacuum. With vacuum applied, nipple "B" plugged, and negative jumper wire connected, solenoid should hold vacuum.

6) If solenoid tests as described, check resistance between solenoid terminals. Resistance should be 36-44 ohms at 68°F (20°C). If resistance is not as specified, replace solenoid. If resistance is as specified, inspect throttle valve operation. Clean or repair as necessary.

7) Connect a vacuum pump to 90 degree vacuum nipple on vacuum tank. Apply 19.8" Hg of vacuum to tank and ensure vacuum holds. Connect vacuum pump to straight nipple on vacuum tank. Plug 90 degree nipple. Apply 19.8" Hg of vacuum. Unplug 90 degree nipple and ensure vacuum releases. Replace tank as necessary.

8) Remove Green stripe vacuum hose from vacuum actuator, located near throttle valve. Connect vacuum pump to actuator. With accelerator pedal depressed, apply 7.9" Hg of vacuum to actuator. Ensure actuator rod is pulled upward and vacuum is held. Repair actuator as necessary.

CODE 72: TRACTION CONTROL VENT SOLENOID

NOTE: For component terminal identification, see TERMINAL IDENTIFICATION. For wiring diagrams, see WIRING DIAGRAMS article.

1) Turn ignition switch to ON position. Using a scan tester, actuate ventilation solenoid. With solenoid actuated, operating noise should be heard. If operating noise is not heard, go to next step. If operating noise is heard, go to step **4)**.

2) Disconnect ventilation solenoid and MFI relay connectors. Using DVOM, check for continuity between ventilation solenoid connector terminal No. 1 and MFI relay connector terminal No. 5. If continuity does not exist, repair wiring harness as necessary. If continuity exists, go to next step.

3) Disconnect ECM connector. Ground ECM connector terminal No. 105. Check continuity between chassis ground and ventilation solenoid connector terminal No. 2. If continuity does not exist, repair wiring harness as necessary. If continuity exists, check solenoid vacuum. Go to next step.

4) Remove vacuum hoses from solenoid. Ensure solenoid harness connector is disconnected. Connect a vacuum pump to solenoid nipple "A". Use jumper wires to connect battery voltage to solenoid terminals. *See Fig. 32*. With vacuum applied, nipple "B" unplugged, and negative jumper wire connected, solenoid should hold vacuum.

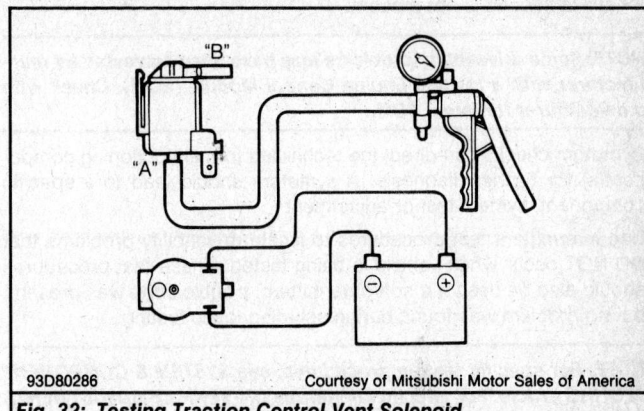

93D80286   Courtesy of Mitsubishi Motor Sales of America

Fig. 32: Testing Traction Control Vent Solenoid

5) With vacuum applied, nipple "B" unplugged, and negative jumper wire disconnected, solenoid should not hold vacuum. With vacuum applied, nipple "B" plugged, and negative jumper wire disconnected, solenoid should hold vacuum.

6) If solenoid tests as described, check resistance between solenoid terminals. If resistance is not 36-44 ohms at 68°F (20°C), replace solenoid. If resistance is as specified, go to Code 71: TRACTION CONTROL VACUUM SOLENOID.

1994 ENGINE PERFORMANCE
Trouble Shooting – No Codes

**Chrysler Corp.: Colt, Colt Vista, Stealth
Eagle: Summit, Summit Wagon
Mitsubishi: Diamante, Eclipse, Expo, Galant,
 Mirage, Montero, Pickup, Precis, 3000GT**

INTRODUCTION

Before diagnosing symptoms or intermittent faults, perform steps in BASIC DIAGNOSTIC PROCEDURES and SELF-DIAGNOSTICS articles. Use this article to diagnose driveability problems existing when a hard fault code is not present.

NOTE: Some driveability problems may have been corrected by manufacturer with a revised Engine Control Module (ECM). Check with manufacturer for latest ECM.

Symptom checks can direct the technician to malfunctioning component(s) for further diagnosis. A symptom should lead to a specific component, system test or adjustment.

Use intermittent test procedures to locate driveability problems that DO NOT occur when vehicle is being tested. These test procedures should also be used if a soft (intermittent) trouble code was present, but no problem was found during self-diagnostic testing.

NOTE: For specific testing procedures, see SYSTEM & COMPONENT TESTING article. For specifications, see ON-VEHICLE ADJUSTMENTS or SERVICE & ADJUSTMENT SPECIFICATIONS article.

SYMPTOMS

SYMPTOM DIAGNOSIS

Symptom checks cannot be used unless problem occurs while vehicle is being tested. To reduce diagnostic time, ensure steps in BASIC DIAGNOSTIC PROCEDURES and SELF-DIAGNOSTICS articles were performed before diagnosing a symptom. Following symptoms are available for diagnosis.

- Difficult To Start/No Start (Cranks Okay)
- Rough Or Unstable Idle
- Engine Hesitates Or Poor Acceleration
- Engine Surges
- Detonation Or Knocking
- Poor Fuel Mileage

DIFFICULT TO START/NO START (CRANKS OKAY)

- Check idle speed control servo (if applicable).
- Check stepper motor (if applicable).
- Check ignition switch.
- Check camshaft position sensor.
- Check crankshaft position sensor.
- Check park/neutral position switch (A/T).
- Check airflow sensor.
- Check coolant temperature sensor.
- Check power supply to ECM ground.
- Check fuel pressure.
- Check for disconnected or damaged vacuum hoses.
- Check for control relay malfunction.
- Check for MFI system malfunction.
- Check for fuel pump drive control system malfunction.
- Check for ignition coil malfunction.
- Check for ignition timing malfunction.
- Check for power transistor malfunction.
- Check for fuel injector malfunction.
- Check for ECM malfunction.
- Ensure electrical harness, connectors and wires are not broken or loose.

ROUGH OR UNSTABLE IDLE

- Check intake air temperature sensor.
- Check purge control solenoid valve (if applicable).
- Check vehicle speed sensor.
- Check engine coolant temperature sensor.
- Check barometric pressure sensor.
- Check ignition switch.
- Check throttle position sensor.
- Check camshaft position sensor.
- Check crankshaft position sensor.
- Check power steering oil pressure switch.
- Check A/C switch and power relay (if applicable).
- Check park/neutral position switch.
- Check oxygen sensor.
- Check airflow sensor.
- Check motor position sensor (if equipped).
- Check fuel pressure.
- Check for disconnected or damaged vacuum hoses.
- Check MFI system malfunction.
- Check for stepper motor malfunction (if applicable).
- Check for fuel injector malfunction.
- Check for power transistor malfunction.
- Check for vehicle speed switch malfunction.
- Check for ECM malfunction.
- Ensure electrical harness, connectors and wires are not broken or loose.

ENGINE HESITATES OR POOR ACCELERATION

- Check intake air temperature sensor.
- Check engine coolant temperature sensor.
- Check barometric pressure sensor.
- Check ignition switch.
- Check ignition coil.
- Check EGR control solenoid valve (if applicable).
- Check throttle position sensor.
- Check camshaft position sensor.
- Check crankshaft position sensor.
- Check power steering oil pressure switch.
- Check A/C switch (if applicable).
- Check park/neutral position switch (A/T).
- Check oxygen sensor.
- Check airflow sensor.
- Check motor position sensor (if applicable).
- Check fuel pressure.
- Check for disconnected or damaged vacuum hoses.
- Check for MFI system malfunction.
- Check for stepper motor malfunction (if applicable).
- Check for fuel injector malfunction.
- Check for power transistor malfunction.
- Check for A/C power relay control system malfunction.
- Check for ECM malfunction.
- Ensure electrical harness, connectors and wires are not broken or loose.

ENGINE SURGES

- Check coolant temperature sensor.
- Check EGR control solenoid valve (if applicable).
- Check fuel pressure.
- Check for fuel injector malfunction.

DETONATION OR KNOCKING

- Check airflow sensor.
- Check for cooling system problems.
- Check fuel quality.
- Check intake air temperature sensor.
- Check barometric pressure sensor.
- Check ignition coil.
- Check power transistor.
- Check for EGR system malfunction.

POOR FUEL MILEAGE

- Check intake air temperature sensor.
- Check engine coolant temperature sensor.
- Check barometric pressure sensor.
- Check ignition switch.
- Check throttle position sensor.
- Check camshaft position sensor.
- Check crankshaft position sensor.
- Check power steering oil pressure switch.
- Check A/C switch (if applicable).
- Check park/neutral position switch (A/T).
- Check oxygen sensor.
- Check airflow sensor.
- Check motor position sensor (if applicable).
- Check fuel pressure.
- Check for MFI system malfunction.
- Check for stepper motor malfunction.
- Check for fuel injector malfunction.
- Check for power transistor malfunction.

INTERMITTENTS

INTERMITTENT PROBLEM DIAGNOSIS

Intermittent fault testing requires duplicating circuit or component failure to identify problem. These procedures may lead to computer setting a fault code (on some systems) which may help in diagnosis.

If problem vehicle does not produce fault codes, monitor voltage or resistance values using a DVOM while attempting to reproduce conditions causing intermittent fault. A status change on DVOM indicates a fault has been located.

Use a DVOM to pinpoint faults. When monitoring voltage, ensure ignition switch is in ON position or engine is running. Ensure ignition switch is in OFF position or negative battery cable is disconnected when monitoring circuit resistance. Status changes on DVOM during test procedures indicate area of fault.

TEST PROCEDURES

Intermittent Simulation – To reproduce conditions creating an intermittent fault, use following methods:

- Lightly vibrate component.
- Heat component.
- Wiggle or bend wiring harness.
- Spray component with water mist.
- Remove/apply vacuum source.

Monitor circuit/component voltage or resistance while simulating intermittent. If engine is running, monitor for self-diagnostic codes. Use test results to identify a faulty component or circuit.

1994 ENGINE PERFORMANCE
System & Component Testing

**Chrysler Corp.: Colt, Colt Vista, Stealth
Eagle: Summit, Summit Wagon
Mitsubishi: Diamante, Eclipse, Expo, Galant, Mirage, Montero, Pickup, Precis, 3000GT**

INTRODUCTION

NOTE: Testing individual components does not isolate shorts or opens. Perform all voltage tests using a Digital Volt-Ohmmeter (DVOM) with minimum 10-megohm input impedance, unless stated otherwise in test procedure. Use ohmmeter to isolate wiring harness shorts or opens.

Before testing separate components or systems, perform procedures in BASIC DIAGNOSTIC PROCEDURES article. Since many computer-controlled and monitored components set a trouble code if they malfunction, also perform procedures in SELF-DIAGNOSTICS article.

AIR INDUCTION SYSTEMS

TURBOCHARGED

Turbocharger Pressure Check – 1) Disconnect turbocharger pressure control Black hose at wastegate solenoid valve, and plug valve nipple. Attach pressure gauge to hose. Drive vehicle and accelerate engine, in 2nd gear, to 3500 RPM or greater. Measure turbocharger pressure when pressure gauge stabilizes. See TURBOCHARGER PRESSURE SPECIFICATIONS table.
2) If pressure gauge reading is more than specified, check wastegate actuator. See WASTEGATE ACTUATOR TEST. Replace wastegate actuator as required. If pressure gauge reading is less than specified, check for malfunctioning wastegate valve, turbocharger pressure leaks and faulty turbocharger.

TURBOCHARGER PRESSURE SPECIFICATIONS

Application	Pressure psi (kg/cm²)
Eclipse	
A/T	5.4-10.0 (37-68)
M/T	6.0-10.8 (41-75)
Stealth & 3000GT	2.9-8.7 (20-60)

Air By-Pass Valve – Remove air by-pass valve. Valve is mounted to intake air duct between air-to-air intercooler and intake plenum. Apply vacuum to diaphragm of vacuum valve. Valve should begin opening at approximately 7.7 in. Hg (Eclipse) or 16 in. Hg (Stealth and 3000GT). Observe operation of valve through by-pass opening.
Wastegate Actuator Test – Actuator is mounted on turbocharger. Apply vacuum to wastegate actuator to ensure actuator rod moves. Ensure diaphragm holds vacuum. DO NOT apply excessive vacuum to wastegate actuator or attempt to adjust wastegate valve.
Wastegate Control Solenoid Valve Test – 1) On Eclipse, valve is mounted to top back section of air cleaner. On Stealth and 3000GT, valve is mounted to firewall beside EGR solenoid. Disconnect White vacuum hose at valve, and connect vacuum pump. Apply vacuum to valve to check leakage. Disconnect harness connector at valve. Connect 12 volts across valve terminals. Valve should open and release vacuum.
2) Disconnect harness connector at valve. Using external ohmmeter, check resistance between valve terminals. Solenoid valve resistance should be 36-44 ohms.
3) Connect DVOM between Red wire terminal of valve harness connector and ground. Turn ignition on. Battery voltage should be present. If battery voltage is not present, check for open in circuit between MFI relay and solenoid harness connector. Repair as necessary. If circuit is okay, inspect MFI relay. See RELAYS under MOTORS, RELAYS & SOLENOIDS. MFI relay is located near ECM, behind radio, under console.
4) If battery voltage is present, disconnect ECM connector. See ENGINE CONTROL MODULE (ECM) LOCATION table under COMPUTERIZED ENGINE CONTROLS. Connect DVOM between Orange

wire terminal (Eclipse) or Red/Yellow wire terminal (Stealth & 3000GT) of wastegate control solenoid valve harness connector and ground.
5) Ground ECM harness connector terminal No. 105 (Eclipse) or No. 32 (Stealth & 3000GT). *See Fig. 1.* Check for continuity in circuit between ECM harness connector and wastegate control solenoid valve harness connector. If continuity does not exist, check and repair circuit as necessary. If continuity exists and all preceding tests do not show any system or component malfunction and ECM is suspected, substitute ECM with known good component and retest.

NON-TURBOCHARGED

NOTE: For diagnosis and testing information concerning Variable Induction Control (VIC) motor position sensor, see SELF-DIAGNOSTICS article.

Variable Induction Control Solenoid Valve Test (Montero 3.5L) – 1) Valve is mounted on front of intake plenum. Disconnect White vacuum hose at valve, and connect vacuum pump. Apply vacuum to valve to check leakage. Disconnect harness connector at valve. Connect 12 volts across valve terminals. Valve should open and release vacuum.
2) Disconnect harness connector at valve. Using external ohmmeter, check resistance between valve terminals. Solenoid valve resistance should be 36-44 ohms.
3) Connect DVOM between Red wire terminal of valve harness connector and ground. Turn ignition on. Battery voltage should be present. If battery voltage is not present, check for open in circuit between MFI relay and solenoid harness connector. Repair as necessary. If circuit is okay, inspect MFI relay. See RELAYS under MOTORS, RELAYS & SOLENOIDS. MFI relay is located above ECM, behind glove box.
4) If battery voltage is present, disconnect ECM connector. See ENGINE CONTROL MODULE (ECM) LOCATION table under COMPUTERIZED ENGINE CONTROLS. Connect DVOM between Blue/Red wire terminal of variable induction control solenoid valve harness connector and ground.
5) Ground ECM harness connector terminal No. 20. *See Fig. 1.* Check for continuity in circuit between ECM harness connector and solenoid valve harness connector. If continuity does not exist, check and repair circuit as necessary. If continuity exists and all preceding tests do not show any system or component malfunction and ECM is suspected, substitute ECM with known good component and retest.
Variable Induction Control Motor (Diamante, Stealth & 3000GT) – 1) Disconnect VIC motor harness connector. Using DVOM, measure resistance between motor connector terminals. Resistance should be 5-35 ohms. Replace VIC motor if resistance is not as specified.
2) Apply 6 volts between both servo connector terminals. Ensure variable induction control motor shaft turns smoothly. Reverse voltage to motor connector terminals. Motor shaft should turn smoothly in opposite direction. If shaft does not function properly, replace air intake plenum assembly.
3) Check for continuity in circuit between control motor harness connector and ECM. Disconnect VIC motor connector and ECM connector. Connect DVOM to Green/Black wire of VIC connector and vehicle ground. Ground terminal No. 109 (Fed. models) or terminal No. 39 (Calif. models) of ECM. If continuity exists, go to next step. If continuity does not exist, repair as needed.
4) Connect DVOM to Green/White wire of VIC connector and vehicle ground. Ground terminal No. 110 (Fed. models) or terminal No. 40 (Calif. models) of ECM. If continuity does not exist, repair as needed. If continuity exists and all preceding tests do not show any system or component malfunction and ECM is suspected, substitute ECM with known good component and retest.

COMPUTERIZED ENGINE CONTROLS

CONTROL UNIT

NOTE: For Engine Control Module (ECM) location, see ENGINE CONTROL MODULE (ECM) LOCATION table. To identify ECM power and ground circuits, see appropriate wiring diagram in WIRING DIAGRAMS article.

Ground Circuits – 1) Turn ignition off. Using an ohmmeter, check continuity between chassis ground and ECM ground terminals. See GROUND TERMINAL IDENTIFICATION table. Ohmmeter should indicate zero ohms. If reading is not zero ohms, check and repair open circuit between ECM connector and ground.

2) Connect voltmeter negative lead to chassis ground. Connect positive lead to ECM ground terminals. See GROUND TERMINAL IDENTIFICATION table. *See Fig. 1.* With engine running, voltmeter should indicate less than one volt. If voltmeter reading is greater than one volt, check for open, corrosion or loose connection in ground circuit.

Power Circuits – Turn ignition on. Check for battery voltage on ECM power terminals. See POWER TERMINAL IDENTIFICATION table. If battery voltage is not present, check operation of MFI relay. See RELAYS under MOTORS, RELAYS & SOLENOIDS.

POWER TERMINAL IDENTIFICATION

Application	ECM Terminals No.
Eclipse, Montero (3.0L) & Pickup (3.0L)	102 & 107
Precis	
California (Connector C50-4)	2 & 15
Federal (Connector C50-3)	4 & 9
Except Eclipse, Montero (3.0L),	
Pickup (3.0L) & Precis	12 & 25

ENGINE CONTROL MODULE (ECM) LOCATION

Application	Location
Eclipse, Galant, Stealth & 3000GT	Behind Center Console
Precis	Behind Left Side Of Instrument Panel
All Others	Behind Right Side Of Instrument Panel (Glove Box)

ENGINE SENSORS & SWITCHES

Barometric Pressure Sensor – Sensor is a part of airflow sensor assembly. See SELF-DIAGNOSTICS article.

Camshaft Position Sensor – See SELF-DIAGNOSTICS article.

Closed Throttle Position Switch – See THROTTLE POSITION SENSOR in SELF-DIAGNOSTICS article.

Coolant Temperature Sensor – See SELF-DIAGNOSTICS article.

Crankshaft Position Sensor – See SELF-DIAGNOSTICS article.

EGR Temperature Sensor – See SELF-DIAGNOSTICS article.

Idle Position Switch – See THROTTLE POSITION SENSOR in SELF-DIAGNOSTICS article.

NOTE: Park/neutral position switch on Precis model is not connected to ECM. For circuit identification, see appropriate wiring diagram in WIRING DIAGRAMS article.

Park/Neutral Position (PNP) Switch (A/T Models) – 1) Switch is mounted to automatic transmission, near shift lever mechanism. Ensure switch is adjusted properly. Switch output can be affected by improper adjustment. Using DVOM, check continuity between selected terminals. Continuity should exist between ignition switch and ECM when shift selector lever is in Park or Neutral position. See PARK/NEUTRAL POSITION (PNP) SWITCH TERMINAL IDENTIFICATION table.

2) Using DVOM, measure supply voltage from ignition switch in start position. Disconnect ECM harness connector. See ENGINE CONTROL MODULE (ECM) LOCATION table under COMPUTERIZED ENGINE CONTROLS. Disconnect park/neutral position switch connector. Turn ignition switch to START position. Measure voltage

COLT, GALANT, MIRAGE
MONTERO (3.5L) & SUMMIT

COLT VISTA, DIAMANTE (SOHC & DOHC-FED.), EXPO, PICKUP (2.4L), STEALTH (SOHC & DOHC NON TURBO-FED.), SUMMIT WAGON & 3000GT (NON TURBO-FED.)

ECLIPSE, MONTERO (3.0L) & PICKUP (3.0L)

DIAMANTE (DOHC-CALIF.), STEALTH (DOHC-CALIF. & DOHC TURBO-FED.), 3000GT (CALIF. & TURBO-FED.)

PRECIS (CALIFORNIA)

PRECIS (FEDERAL)

93B79054 93A78303 93J78252
94F44292 93J78278 93J78302
Courtesy of Mitsubishi Motor Sales of America.

Fig. 1: Identifying ECM Connectors

GROUND TERMINAL IDENTIFICATION

Application	ECM Terminals No.
Eclipse, Montero (3.0L) & Pickup (3.0L)	101 & 106
Precis	
California (Connector C50-4)	1 & 14
Federal (Connector C50-3)	5 & 10
Except Eclipse, Montero (3.0L),	
Pickup (3.0L) & Precis	13 & 26

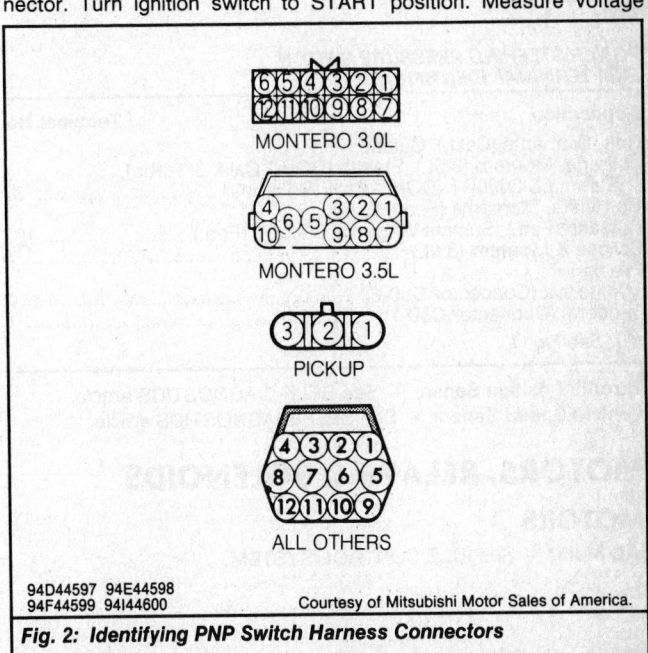

MONTERO 3.0L

MONTERO 3.5L

PICKUP

ALL OTHERS

94D44597 94E44598
94F44599 94I44600
Courtesy of Mitsubishi Motor Sales of America.

Fig. 2: Identifying PNP Switch Harness Connectors

1994 ENGINE PERFORMANCE
System & Component Testing (Cont.)

PARK/NEUTRAL POSITION (PNP) SWITCH TERMINAL IDENTIFICATION [1]

Application	PNP Terminal No. To ECM Terminal No. (Start)	PNP Terminal No. To ECM Terminal No. (Run)
Colt Vista (AWD), Diamante (Fed.), Expo (AWD), Stealth (Fed.), Summit Wagon (AWD) & 3000GT (Fed.)	8 & 71	7 & 51
Colt, Colt Vista (FWD), Expo (FWD), Galant, Mirage, Summit & Summit Wagon (FWD)	5 & 71	8 & 51
Diamante (Calif.), Stealth (Calif.) & 3000GT (Calif.)	8 & 91	7 & 71
Eclipse Non-Turbo	5 & 104	8 & 108
Eclipse Turbo	8 & 104	7 & 108
Pickup	Grounded [2]	2 & 71

[1] – For PNP harness connector terminal identification, *see Fig. 2.*
[2] – PNP switch case is grounded. Starting system utilizes a starter relay. See appropriate wiring diagram in WIRING DIAGRAMS article.

between switch (start circuit) and vehicle ground. See PARK/NEUTRAL POSITION (PNP) SWITCH TERMINAL IDENTIFICATION table. If battery voltage is present, go to next step. If voltage is less than battery voltage, inspect and repair circuit.

3) Using DVOM, check continuity between PNP switch and ECM. See PARK/NEUTRAL POSITION SWITCH TERMINAL IDENTIFICATION table. If continuity does not exist in either circuit, inspect and repair faulty circuit as needed. If continuity exists and all preceding tests do not show any system or component malfunction and ECM is suspected, substitute ECM with known good component and retest.

Intake Air Temperature Sensor – See SELF-DIAGNOSTICS article.
Oxygen (O₂) Sensor – See SELF-DIAGNOSTICS article.
Power Steering Oil Pressure Switch – 1) Disconnect switch connector at pump. Using DVOM, check continuity between switch and vehicle ground. Continuity should not exist with wheels straight ahead and engine idling. Continuity should be present when wheels are turned to lock position or when pump pressure is increased.
2) Check continuity of circuit between switch and ECM. Disconnect power steering oil pressure switch harness connector and ECM harness connector. See ENGINE CONTROL MODULE (ECM) LOCATION table under COMPUTERIZED ENGINE CONTROLS. Connect jumper wire between ECM terminal and vehicle ground. See POWER STEERING PRESSURE SWITCH ECM TERMINAL IDENTIFICATION table. Using DVOM, check for continuity between switch harness connector and vehicle ground. Check and repair circuit if no continuity exists. Go to step 3) if continuity exists.
3) Connect ECM harness connector. Turn ignition on. Using DVOM, measure voltage at switch harness connector. System is okay if battery voltage exists. Substitute ECM with known good unit if voltage does not exist.

POWER STEERING PRESSURE SWITCH ECM TERMINAL IDENTIFICATION

Application	[1] Terminal No.
Colt, Diamante (Calif.), Galant, Mirage, Montero (3.5L), Stealth (DOHC-Calif. & Turbo), Summit & 3000GT (DOHC-Calif. & Turbo)	37
Colt Vista, Diamante (Fed.), Expo, Stealth (Fed.), Summit Wagon & 3000GT (Fed.)	107
Eclipse & Montero (3.0L)	5
Precis California (Connector C50-6)	2
Federal (Connector C50-1)	8

[1] – See Fig. 1.

Throttle Position Sensor – See SELF-DIAGNOSTICS article.
Vehicle Speed Sensor – See SELF-DIAGNOSTICS article.

MOTORS, RELAYS & SOLENOIDS
MOTORS

IAC Motor – See IDLE CONTROL SYSTEM.

RELAYS

NOTE: *Cooling fan control relay for Eclipse, Montero and Pickup is not controlled by ECM. For circuit identification, see appropriate wiring diagram in WIRING DIAGRAMS article.*

Cooling Fan Control Relay (Hi & Lo) – 1) Remove suspected relay from underhood relay block. Connect 12-volt power supply to relay terminals No. 2 and 4. See Fig. 3. Continuity should exist between terminals No. 1 and 3. Replace relay if continuity is not present. If continuity is present, go to next step.
2) With ignition on, check voltage between each relay receptacle terminal No. 4 and vehicle ground. If battery voltage is not present, inspect and repair circuit between ignition switch and relay. If battery voltage is present, go to next step.
3) Using ohmmeter, check continuity between each relay receptacle terminal No. 3 and vehicle ground. If continuity does not exist, inspect and repair ground circuit as needed. If continuity exists, go to next step.
4) Disconnect ECM harness connector. See ENGINE CONTROL MODULE (ECM) LOCATION table under COMPUTERIZED ENGINE CONTROLS. Using ohmmeter check continuity between relay receptacle terminal No. 2 and appropriate ECM terminal. See FAN CONTROL RELAY ECM CIRCUIT IDENTIFICATION table.
5) If continuity does not exist, inspect and repair faulty circuit(s) as needed. If continuity exists and all preceding tests do not show any system or component malfunction and ECM is suspected, substitute ECM with known good component and retest.

FAN CONTROL RELAY ECM CIRCUIT IDENTIFICATION

Application	Lo Fan Circuit No.	Hi Fan Circuit No.
Colt, Mirage & Summit	16	3
Colt Vista, Expo & Summit Wagon	11	3
Diamante, Stealth & 3000GT (Federal Models)	6	53
Diamante, Stealth & 3000GT (Calif. Models)	20	21
Galant	16	3

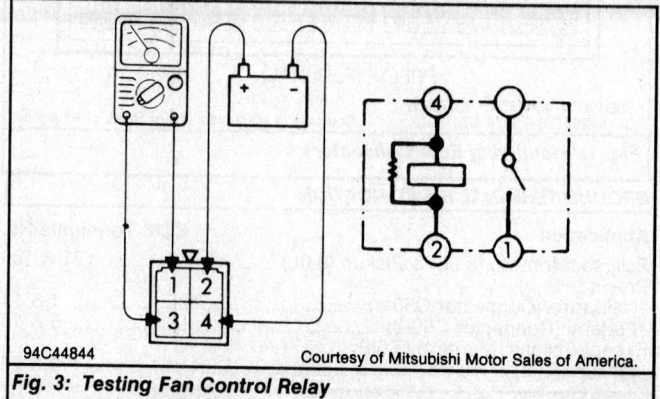

94C44844   Courtesy of Mitsubishi Motor Sales of America.

Fig. 3: Testing Fan Control Relay

NOTE: For MFI relay location, see MFI RELAY LOCATION table.

MFI RELAY LOCATION

Application	Location
Colt Vista, Diamante, Expo, Galant & Summit Wagon	Behind glove box, next to ECM.
Montero	Under right corner of dash.
Pickup	Behind kick panel.
Precis	Behind glove box.
All Others	Behind center console.

MFI Relay (Colt, Colt Vista, Expo, Mirage, Pickup 2.4L, Summit & Summit Wagon) – **1)** This step checks ignition switch supply voltage of MFI relay. Disconnect MFI relay harness connector. Turn ignition on. Using DVOM, measure voltage between terminal No. 8 of relay harness connector and vehicle ground. See Fig. 4. If battery voltage is present, go to step **2)**. If battery voltage is not present, check and repair circuit between ignition switch and MFI relay.

2) This step checks continuity of MFI relay ground circuit. Turn ignition off. Using DVOM, check continuity between MFI relay harness connector terminal No. 6 and vehicle ground. If continuity exists, go to step **3)**. If continuity does not exist, check and repair circuit between MFI relay and vehicle ground.

3) This step checks battery supply voltage of MFI relay. Using DVOM, measure voltage between terminal No. 4 of relay harness connector and vehicle ground. If voltage is battery voltage, go to step **4)**. If voltage is not battery voltage, check and repair circuit between battery and MFI relay.

4) This step checks continuity of circuit between MFI relay and ECM. Disconnect ECM harness connector. See ENGINE CONTROL MODULE (ECM) LOCATION table under COMPUTERIZED ENGINE CONTROLS. Using DVOM, check continuity between MFI relay harness connector terminal No. 3 and ECM harness connector terminals No. 12 and 25. See Figs. 1 and 4. If continuity exists, go to step **5)**. If continuity does not exist, check and repair circuits between MFI relay harness connector and ECM.

5) This step checks supply voltage to MFI relay actuator. Connect ECM and MFI relay harness connectors. Using DVOM, backprobe MFI relay terminal No. 2. With engine cranking, voltage should be 8 volts or greater. Start engine and run at 2500 RPM or greater. If battery voltage is present, harness is okay. If voltage is not battery voltage, go to step **6)**.

6) If MFI relay tests okay in steps **6)** through **8)**, substitute ECM with known good unit and retest. Removal of relay may assist in testing. Measure resistance between MFI relay terminals No. 5 and 7. Resistance should be approximately 90 ohms. Check continuity between terminals No. 6 and 8. Continuity should exist in only one direction. Replace MFI relay if continuity is not as specified.

7) Connect 12-volt power source between relay terminals No. 5 and 7. Connect positive lead to terminal No. 7. With relay energized, battery voltage should exist between terminals No. 1 and 5. With power source removed, voltage should not exist.

8) Move 12-volt power source to relay terminals No. 6 and 8. Connect positive lead to terminal No. 8. With relay energized, continuity should exist between terminals No. 2 and 4 and between terminals No. 3 and 4. With power source removed, continuity should not exist. Replace MFI relay if measurements are not as specified.

MFI Relay (Diamante SOHC & DOHC-Fed., Galant, Montero 3.5L, Stealth SOHC & DOHC Non Turbo-Fed. & 3000GT Non Turbo-Fed.) – **1)** This step checks ignition supply voltage to ECM. Disconnect ECM harness connector. Turn ignition on. Using DVOM, measure voltage between ECM harness connector terminal No. 62 and vehicle ground. See Fig. 1. If battery voltage is present, go to step **2)**. If battery voltage is not present, check and repair circuit between ignition switch and ECM harness connector.

2) This step checks continuity of circuit between MFI relay and ECM. Disconnect ECM harness connector. Using DVOM, check continuity between MFI relay harness connector terminal No. 6 and ECM harness connector terminal No. 108. If continuity exists, go to step **4)**. If continuity does not exist, check and repair circuits between MFI relay harness connector and ECM.

3) This step checks continuity of circuit between MFI relay and ECM. Check continuity between MFI relay harness connector terminal No. 2 (except Galant) or terminal No. 3 (Galant) and ECM harness connector terminals No. 12 and 25. If continuity exists, go to step **5)**. If continuity does not exist, check and repair circuits between MFI relay harness connector and ECM.

4) If MFI relay tests okay in following steps, substitute ECM with known good unit and retest. Measure resistance between MFI relay terminals No. 5 and 7. Resistance should be approximately 90 ohms. Check continuity between terminals No. 6 and 8. Continuity should exist in only one direction. Replace MFI relay if continuity is not as specified.

5) Connect 12-volt power source between relay terminals No. 5 and 7. Connect positive lead to terminal No. 7. With relay energized, battery voltage should exist between terminals No. 1 and 5. With power source removed, voltage should not exist.

6) Move 12-volt power source to relay terminals No. 6 and 8. Connect positive lead to terminal No. 8. With relay energized, continuity should exist between terminals No. 2 and 4 and between terminals No. 3 and 4. With power source removed, continuity should not exist. Replace MFI relay if measurements are not as specified.

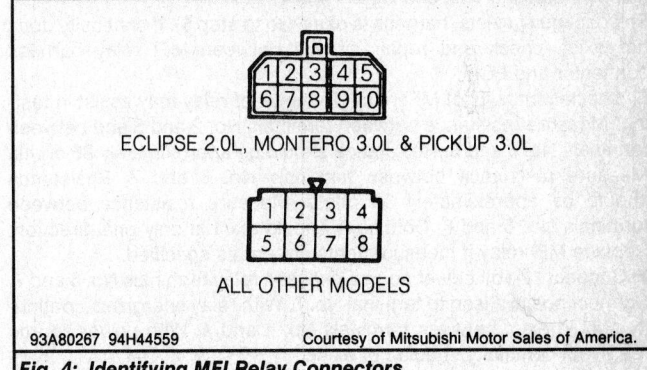

ECLIPSE 2.0L, MONTERO 3.0L & PICKUP 3.0L

ALL OTHER MODELS

93A80267 94H44559   Courtesy of Mitsubishi Motor Sales of America.

Fig. 4: Identifying MFI Relay Connectors

MFI Relay (Diamante DOHC-Calif., Stealth DOHC Calif. & Turbo & 3000GT Calif. & Turbo) – **1)** This step checks ignition supply voltage to ECM. Disconnect ECM harness connector. Turn ignition on. Using DVOM, measure voltage between ECM harness connector terminal No. 82 and vehicle ground. See Fig. 1. If battery voltage is present, go to step **2)**. If battery voltage is not present, check and repair circuit between ignition switch and ECM harness connector.

2) This step checks continuity of circuit between MFI relay and ECM. Disconnect ECM harness connector. See ENGINE CONTROL MODULE (ECM) LOCATION table under COMPUTERIZED ENGINE CONTROLS. Using DVOM, check continuity between MFI relay harness connector terminal No. 6 and ECM harness connector terminal No. 38. If continuity exists, go to step **4)**. If continuity does not exist, check and repair circuits between MFI relay harness connector and ECM.

3) This step checks continuity of circuit between MFI relay and ECM. Check continuity between MFI relay harness connector terminal No. 2 and ECM harness connector terminals No. 12 and 25. If continuity exists, go to step **5)**. If continuity does not exist, check and repair circuits between MFI relay harness connector and ECM.

4) If MFI relay tests okay in following steps, substitute ECM with known good unit and retest. Measure resistance between relay terminals No. 5 and 7. Resistance should be approximately 90 ohms. Check continuity between terminals No. 6 and 8. Continuity should exist in only one direction. Replace MFI relay if continuity is not as specified.

5) Connect 12-volt power source between relay terminals No. 5 and 7. Connect positive lead to terminal No. 7. With relay energized, battery voltage should exist between terminals No. 1 and 5. With power source removed, voltage should not exist.

6) Move 12-volt power source to relay terminals No. 6 and 8. Connect positive lead to terminal No. 8. With relay energized, continuity should exist between terminals No. 2 and 4 and between terminals No. 3 and 4. With power source removed, continuity should not exist. Replace MFI relay if measurements are not as specified.

MFI Relay (Eclipse 1.8L) – **1)** This step checks ignition switch supply voltage of MFI relay. Disconnect MFI relay connector. Turn ignition on. Measure voltage between terminal No. 8 of relay harness connector and vehicle ground. *See Fig. 4.* If battery voltage is present, go to step **2)**. If battery voltage is not present, check and repair circuit between ignition switch and MFI relay.

2) This step checks continuity of MFI relay ground circuit. Turn ignition off. Using DVOM, check continuity between MFI relay harness connector terminal No. 6 and vehicle ground. If continuity exists, go to step **3)**. If continuity does not exist, check and repair circuit between MFI relay and vehicle ground.

3) This step checks battery supply voltage of MFI relay. Using DVOM, measure voltage between terminal No. 4 of relay harness connector and vehicle ground. If battery voltage is present, go to step **4)**. If battery voltage is not present, check and repair circuit between battery and MFI relay.

4) This step checks continuity of circuit between MFI relay and ECM. Disconnect ECM harness connector. See ENGINE CONTROL MODULE (ECM) LOCATION table under COMPUTERIZED ENGINE CONTROLS. Using DVOM, check continuity between MFI relay harness connector terminal No. 3 and ECM harness connector terminals No. 102 and 107. *See Figs. 1 and 4.*

5) If continuity exists, harness is okay. Go to step **6)**. If continuity does not exist, check and repair circuits between MFI relay harness connector and ECM.

6) Check continuity of MFI relay. Removal of relay may assist in testing. Measure resistance between terminals No. 2 and 5 and between terminals No. 3 and 5. Resistance should be approximately 95 ohms. Measure resistance between terminals No. 6 and 7. Resistance should be approximately 35 ohms. Measure resistance between terminals No. 6 and 8. Continuity should exist in only one direction. Replace MFI relay if measurements are not as specified.

7) Connect 12-volt power source between relay terminals No. 6 and 7. Connect positive lead to terminal No. 7. With relay energized, continuity should exist between terminals No. 1 and 4. With power source removed, continuity should not exist.

8) Move 12-volt power source to relay terminals No. 2 and 5. Connect positive lead to terminal No. 2. With relay energized, continuity should exist between terminals No. 1 and 4. With power source removed, continuity should not exist.

9) Move 12-volt power source to relay terminals No. 6 and 8. Connect positive lead to terminal No. 8. With relay energized, continuity should exist between terminals No. 2 and 4. With power source removed, continuity should not exist. Replace MFI relay if any measurements are not as specified.

MFI Relay (Eclipse 2.0L) – **1)** This step checks ignition supply voltage to ECM. Disconnect ECM harness connector. See ENGINE CONTROL MODULE (ECM) LOCATION table under COMPUTERIZED ENGINE CONTROLS. Turn ignition on. Using DVOM, measure voltage between ECM harness connector terminal No. 110 and vehicle ground. *See Fig. 1.* If battery voltage is present, go to step **2)**. If battery voltage is not present, check and repair circuit between ignition switch and ECM harness connector.

2) This step checks battery supply voltage of MFI relay. Using DVOM, measure voltage between terminal No. 10 of relay harness connector and vehicle ground. *See Fig. 4.* If voltage is battery voltage, go to step **3)**. If voltage is not battery voltage, check and repair circuit between battery and MFI relay.

3) This step checks continuity of circuit between MFI relay and ECM. Disconnect ECM harness connector. Using DVOM, check continuity between MFI relay harness connector terminal No. 8 and ECM connectors No. 63 and 66. If continuity exists, go to step **4)**. If continuity does not exist, check and repair circuits between MFI relay harness connector and ECM.

4) Check continuity between MFI relay harness connector terminal No. 4 and ECM harness connector terminals No. 102 and 107. If continuity exists, go to step **5)**. If continuity does not exist, check and repair circuits between MFI relay harness connector and ECM.

5) Disconnect ECM harness connector. Using DVOM, check continuity between MFI relay harness connector terminal No. 5 and ECM har-

ness connector terminals No. 102 and 107. If continuity exists, harness is okay. Go to step **6)**. If continuity does not exist, check and repair circuits between MFI relay harness connector and ECM.

6) Connect 12-volt power source between relay terminals No. 8 and 10. Connect positive lead to terminal No. 10. With relay energized, battery voltage should exist between terminals No. 4 and 8 and between terminals No. 5 and 8. With power source removed, voltage should not exist.

7) Move 12-volt power source to relay terminals No. 6 and 9. Connect positive lead to terminal No. 9. With relay energized, continuity should exist between terminals No. 2 and 3. With power source removed, continuity should not exist.

8) Move 12-volt power source to relay terminals No. 3 and 7. Connect positive lead to terminal No. 3. With relay energized, battery voltage should exist between terminals No. 2 and 7. With power source removed, voltage should not exist. Replace MFI relay if any measurements are not as specified.

MFI Relay (Montero 3.0L & Pickup 3.0L) – **1)** This step checks ignition supply voltage to ECM. Disconnect ECM harness connector. See ENGINE CONTROL MODULE (ECM) LOCATION table under COMPUTERIZED ENGINE CONTROLS. Turn ignition on. Measure voltage between ECM harness connector terminal No. 110 and vehicle ground. *See Fig. 1.* If battery voltage is present, go to step **2)**. If battery voltage is not present, repair circuit between ignition switch and ECM harness connector.

2) This step checks battery supply voltage of MFI relay. Measure voltage between terminal No. 10 of relay harness connector and vehicle ground. *See Fig. 4.* If battery voltage is present, go to step **3)**. If battery voltage is not present, check and repair circuit between battery and MFI relay.

3) This step checks continuity of circuit between MFI relay and ECM. Disconnect ECM harness connector. Check continuity between MFI relay harness connector terminal No. 8 and ECM harness connectors No. 63 and 66. If continuity exists, go to step **4)**. If continuity does not exist, check and repair circuits between MFI relay harness connector and ECM.

4) This step checks continuity of circuit between MFI relay and ECM. Check continuity between MFI relay harness connector terminal No. 4 and ECM harness connector terminals No. 102 and 107. If continuity exists, go to step **5)**. If continuity does not exist, check and repair circuits between MFI relay harness connector and ECM.

5) Connect 12-volt power source between relay terminals No. 8 and 10. Connect positive lead to terminal No. 10. With relay energized, battery voltage should exist between terminals No. 4 and 8 and between terminals No. 5 and 8. With power source removed, voltage should not exist.

6) Move 12-volt power source to relay terminals No. 6 and 9. Connect positive lead to terminal No. 6. With relay energized, continuity should exist between terminals No. 2 and 3. With power source removed, continuity should not exist.

7) Move 12-volt power source to relay terminals No. 3 and 7. Connect positive lead to terminal No. 3. With relay energized, voltage should exist between terminals No. 2 and 7. With power source removed, voltage should not exist. Replace MFI relay if any measurements are not as specified.

MFI Relay (Precis) – **1)** This step checks ignition switch supply voltage of MFI relay. Disconnect MFI relay harness connector. Turn ignition on. Using DVOM, measure voltage between terminal No. 5 of relay harness connector and vehicle ground. *See Fig. 5.* If voltage is battery voltage, go to step **2)**. If voltage is not battery voltage, check and repair circuit between ignition switch and MFI relay.

2) This step checks continuity of MFI relay ground circuit. Turn ignition off. Using DVOM, check continuity between MFI relay harness connector terminal No. 7 and vehicle ground. If continuity exists, go to step **3)**. If continuity does not exist, check and repair circuit between MFI relay and vehicle ground.

3) This step checks battery supply voltage of MFI relay. Using DVOM, measure voltage between terminal No. 1 of relay harness connector and vehicle ground. If voltage is battery voltage, go to step **4)**. If voltage is not battery voltage, check and repair circuit between battery and MFI relay.

4) This step checks continuity of circuit between MFI relay and ECM. Disconnect ECM harness connector. Check continuity between MFI relay harness connector terminal No. 2 and ECM terminals No. 2 and 15 of connector C50-4 on California models or terminals No. 9 and 4 of connector C50-3 on Federal models. *See Figs. 1 and 5.*

5) If continuity exists, harness is okay. Go to step **6)**. If continuity does not exist, check and repair circuits between MFI relay harness connector and ECM.

6) This step checks continuity of MFI relay. Removal of relay may assist in testing. Measure resistance between terminals No. 2 and 8 and between terminals No. 3 and 8. Resistance should be about 95 ohms. Measure resistance between terminals No. 6 and 7. Resistance should be about 35 ohms. Measure resistance between terminals No. 5 and 7. Continuity should exist in only one direction. Replace MFI relay if any measurements are not as specified.

7) Connect 12-volt power source between relay terminals No. 6 and 7. Connect positive lead to terminal No. 6. With relay energized, continuity should exist between terminals No. 1 and 4. With power source removed, continuity should not exist.

8) Move 12-volt power source to relay terminals No. 5 and 7. Connect positive lead to terminal No. 5. With relay energized, continuity should exist between terminals No. 1 and 3. With power source removed, continuity should not exist. Replace MFI relay if any measurements are not as specified.

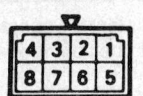 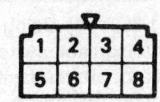

COMPONENT CONNECTOR   HARNESS CONNECTOR

93E78455   Courtesy of Mitsubishi Motor Sales of America.

Fig. 5: Identifying MFI Relay Connectors (Precis)

SOLENOIDS

EGR Control Solenoid Valve – See EXHAUST GAS RECIRCULATION (EGR) under EMISSION SYSTEMS & SUB-SYSTEMS.
Fuel Pressure Regulator Control Solenoid Valve (Turbo Models) – See FUEL DELIVERY under FUEL SYSTEM.
Purge Control Solenoid Valve – See FUEL EVAPORATION under EMISSION SYSTEMS & SUB-SYSTEMS.
Variable Induction Control Solenoid Valve (Montero 3.5L) – See NON-TURBOCHARGED under AIR INDUCTION SYSTEMS.
Wastegate Control Solenoid Valve – See TURBOCHARGED under AIR INDUCTION SYSTEMS.

FUEL SYSTEM

FUEL DELIVERY

NOTE: For fuel system pressure testing, see BASIC DIAGNOSTIC PROCEDURES article.

Fuel Pressure Regulator Control Solenoid Valve (Turbo Models) –
1) Label and remove vacuum hoses from solenoid valve. Disconnect wiring harness. Connect vacuum pump to nipple where Black vacuum hose was connected. Leave pump connected throughout procedure.
2) Apply vacuum and ensure valve leaks. Plug nipple where Blue-striped hose was connected. Apply vacuum and ensure vacuum holds. Remove plug from Blue-striped hose nipple. Apply battery voltage across valve terminals. Apply vacuum and ensure vacuum holds.
3) Using an ohmmeter, check resistance across terminals of solenoid. Resistance should be 36-46 ohms at 68°F (20°C). If resistance is not within specification, replace solenoid valve.
4) If resistance is within specification, disconnect solenoid harness connector. Turn ignition on. Using DVOM, measure voltage between harness connector terminal (Red wire) and vehicle ground.
5) If battery voltage is present, go to step **6)**. If battery voltage is not present, inspect and repair circuit between MFI relay and solenoid. If

circuit is okay, inspect MFI relay. See RELAYS under MOTORS, RELAYS & SOLENOIDS. MFI relay is located near ECM, behind radio, under console.
6) Disconnect ECM connector. See ENGINE CONTROL MODULE (ECM) LOCATION table under COMPUTERIZED ENGINE CONTROLS. Connect jumper wire between ECM terminal No. 6 (No. 57 on Eclipse) and vehicle ground. *See Fig. 1.* Using DVOM, measure continuity between solenoid harness connector terminal Blue/Red wire (White wire on Eclipse) and vehicle ground.
7) If continuity does not exist, check and repair circuit between solenoid and ECM. If continuity exists and all preceding tests do not show any system or component malfunction and ECM is suspected, substitute ECM with known good component and retest.

FUEL CONTROL

Fuel Injectors – See SELF-DIAGNOSTICS article.

IDLE CONTROL SYSTEM

ELECTRICAL LOAD SWITCH

Diamante DOHC, Stealth DOHC & 3000GT DOHC – **1)** Disconnect ECM connector. See ENGINE CONTROL MODULE (ECM) LOCATION table under COMPUTERIZED ENGINE CONTROLS. Using DVOM, measure input voltage between terminal No. 24 and vehicle ground. Turn headlights on. Measure voltage. Turn headlights off.
2) Turn defogger on. Measure voltage. Turn defogger off. Depress brake pedal. Measure voltage. Release brake pedal. If any measurement is less than battery voltage, check and repair malfunctioning circuit. See appropriate wiring diagram under WIRING DIAGRAMS article.

IDLE AIR CONTROL (IAC) MOTOR

CAUTION: DO NOT apply more than 6 volts to IAC motor.

NOTE: For diagnosis and testing information concerning IAC motor position sensor, see SELF-DIAGNOSTICS article.

Colt, Colt Vista, Expo, Mirage, Pickup 2.4L, Summit & Summit Wagon – **1)** Using a stethoscope, listen for operating sound of IAC motor when ignition switch is placed in ON position. If no operating sound can be heard, proceed with following tests.
2) This step checks for continuity between IAC motor and ECM. Disconnect IAC motor harness connector and ECM harness connector. See ENGINE CONTROL MODULE (ECM) LOCATION table under COMPUTERIZED ENGINE CONTROLS. Connect a jumper wire between ECM harness connector terminal No. 4 and vehicle ground. *See Fig. 1.* Using DVOM, check continuity between IAC harness connector No. 5 and vehicle ground. *See Fig. 6.*
3) Move jumper wire to ECM harness connector terminal No. 17 and vehicle ground. Using DVOM, check continuity between IAC harness connector No. 6 and vehicle ground. If continuity does not exist, check and repair appropriate circuit. If continuity exists, go to step **4)**.
4) If preceding tests do not show any system or component malfunction and ECM is suspected, replace ECM and retest system.

COMPONENT CONNECTOR   HARNESS CONNECTOR

93I78475   Courtesy of Mitsubishi Motor Sales of America.

Fig. 6: Identifying IAC Motor Connectors (All 4-Cylinder Models Except Eclipse 2.0L & Galant)

1994 ENGINE PERFORMANCE
System & Component Testing (Cont.)

NOTE: Procedures are provided by manufacturer for component testing using an engine analyzer with oscilloscope capability. Refer to manufacturer's operation manual for instructions in use of oscilloscope. Go to step 10) for test procedures using oscilloscope.

Diamante, Eclipse 2.0L, Galant, Montero, Pickup 3.0L, Stealth & 3000GT – 1) Using a stethoscope, listen for operating sound of IAC motor when ignition switch is placed in ON position. If no operating sound can be heard, proceed with following tests.

2) Disconnect IAC harness connector. Install Test Harness (MD998463-01) if necessary to aid testing. Using DVOM, measure resistance between IAC terminals No. 1 and 2 and between terminals No. 1 and 3. *See Fig. 7.* Resistance should be 28-33 ohms.

3) Measure resistance between terminals No. 4 and 5 and between terminals No. 5 and 6. Resistance should be 28-33 ohms. If resistance measurements are not within specification, replace IAC motor. Go to step **4)** if IAC motor is within specification.

4) Remove throttle body. See REMOVAL, OVERHAUL & INSTALLATION article. Remove stepper motor from throttle body. Connect Test Harness (MD998463-01) to IAC motor.

5) Hold IAC motor in hand. Place thumb on top of plunger. Connect positive lead of 6-volt power source to White and Green clips of test harness. Individually connect, then disconnect, negative lead of power source to Red and Black clips, Blue and Black clips, Blue and Yellow clips, and Red and Yellow clips. Finish by connecting negative lead to Red and Black clips again.

6) Connect negative lead to test leads in reverse sequence of step **5)**. Stepper motor should vibrate with each connection. Replace IAC motor if vibration is not felt with each connection.

7) Ensure MFI relay is functioning properly. See RELAYS under MOTORS, RELAYS & SOLENOIDS. Disconnect IAC motor harness connector. Turn ignition on. Using DVOM, check for battery voltage between terminal No. 2 and vehicle ground and terminal No. 5 and vehicle ground. If voltage is not battery voltage, check and repair circuits between MFI relay and IAC motor. If battery voltage exists, go to step **8)**.

8) This step checks for continuity between MFI relay and IAC motor. Check for continuity between MFI relay terminals No. 4 and 5 and IAC motor terminals No. 2 and 5. *See Figs. 4 and 7.* If continuity exists, go to step **9)**. If continuity does not exist, check and repair circuits.

9) This step checks for continuity between ECM and IAC motor. Disconnect ECM harness connector. Check continuity of specified circuits. *See Figs. 1 and 7.* See IAC TO ECM CIRCUIT CONTINUITY CHECK table. Check and repair any circuits without continuity.

IAC TO ECM CIRCUIT CONTINUITY CHECK

IAC Terminal No.	ECM Terminal No.
Eclipse 2.0L, Montero 3.0L & Pickup 3.0L	
1	58
3	59
4	67
6	68
Diamante, Galant, Montero 3.5L, Stealth & 3000GT	
1	4
3	17
4	5
6	18

10) Connect ECM harness connector. Install harness connector and Test Harness (MB998463-01). Using engine analyzer with oscilloscope capability, connect special patterns probe to selected leads of test harness. Leads used are Red, Green, Black and Yellow clips.

11) Start engine, and allow it to idle. Connect special patterns probe to one test lead. Turn A/C on. When IAC motor operates to increase engine speed to compensate for A/C system, a waveform should be displayed. Conduct test with each remaining test lead and compare pattern to illustration. *See Fig. 8.*

12) If waveform is different, replace IAC motor. If all preceding tests do not show any system or component malfunction and ECM is suspected, replace ECM and retest system.

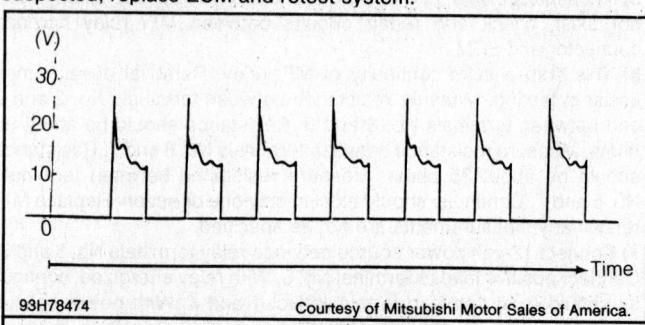

93H78474   Courtesy of Mitsubishi Motor Sales of America.

Fig. 8: Identifying Good IAC Motor Waveform

IDLE SPEED CONTROL MOTOR

NOTE: For diagnosis and testing information concerning ISC motor position sensor, see SELF-DIAGNOSTICS article.

Eclipse 1.8L – 1) Using a stethoscope, listen for operation of ISC motor when ignition switch is placed in ON position. If operation cannot be heard, proceed with following tests.

2) Disconnect ISC harness connector. Connect a 6-volt power source across ISC motor connectors. Check if motor operates. Reverse power source leads. Check if motor operates in opposite direction. Replace motor if it does not function properly.

3) Using DVOM, measure resistance between ISC motor connectors. Resistance should be 5-35 ohms. Replace motor if resistance is not within specification.

4) This step checks for continuity between ISC motor and ECM. Disconnect ISC motor harness connector and ECM harness connector. See ENGINE CONTROL MODULE (ECM) LOCATION table under COMPUTERIZED ENGINE CONTROLS. Connect a jumper wire between ECM harness connector terminal No. 58 and vehicle ground. *See Fig. 1.* Using DVOM, check continuity between ISC harness connector No. 1 (Blue/White wire) and vehicle ground.

5) Move jumper wire to ECM harness connector terminal No. 59 and vehicle ground. Using DVOM, check continuity between ISC harness connector No. 2 and vehicle ground. If continuity does not exist, check and repair appropriate circuit. If continuity exists, go to step **6)**.

6) If preceding tests do not show any system or component malfunction and ECM is suspected, replace ECM and retest system.

Precis – 1) Using a stethoscope, listen for operation of ISC motor when ignition switch is placed in ON position. If operation cannot be heard, proceed with following tests.

2) Disconnect ISC harness connector. Connect a 6-volt power source across ISC motor connectors. Check if motor operates. Reverse power source leads and check if motor operates in opposite direction. Replace motor if does not function properly.

3) Using DVOM, measure resistance between ISC motor connectors. Resistance should be 5-70 ohms. Replace motor if resistance is not within specification.

4) This step checks for continuity between ISC motor and ECM. Disconnect ISC motor harness connector and ECM harness connector. Connect a jumper wire between selected ECM harness connector terminal and vehicle ground. See ECM TERMINAL SELECTION table. Using DVOM, check continuity between ISC harness connector No. 1 (Red wire) and vehicle ground.

5) Move jumper wire to selected ECM harness connector terminal and vehicle ground. See ECM TERMINAL SELECTION table. Using DVOM, check continuity between ISC harness connector No. 2 (Orange wire) and vehicle ground. If continuity does not exist, check and repair appropriate circuit. If continuity exists, go to step **6)**.

6) If preceding tests do not show any system or component malfunction and ECM is suspected, replace ECM and retest system.

 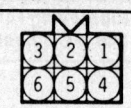

COMPONENT CONNECTOR   HARNESS CONNECTOR

93G78473   Courtesy of Mitsubishi Motor Sales of America.

Fig. 7: Identifying IAC Motor Connectors (All V6 Models, Eclipse 2.0L & Galant)

ECM TERMINAL SELECTION

Terminal No. [1]	ISC Motor Terminal No.
California (Connector No. C50-4)	
23	1
10	2
Federal (Connector No. C50-2)	
1	1
2	2

[1] – See Fig. 1.

IGNITION SYSTEM

NOTE: *For basic ignition checks, see BASIC DIAGNOSTIC PROCE-DURES article.*

TIMING CONTROL SYSTEMS

Camshaft Position Sensor – See SELF-DIAGNOSTICS article.
Crankshaft Position Sensor – See SELF-DIAGNOSTICS article.
Knock Sensor – See SELF-DIAGNOSTICS article.

EMISSION SYSTEMS & SUB-SYSTEMS

EXHAUST GAS RECIRCULATION (EGR)

EGR Temperature Sensor – See SELF-DIAGNOSTICS article.
EGR Control Solenoid Valve – **1)** Label and disconnect both vacuum hoses from solenoid valve. See VACUUM DIAGRAMS article. Disconnect electrical connector. Connect hand vacuum pump to solenoid valve nipple where Green-striped hose was connected. Apply vacuum to solenoid valve. Vacuum should hold.

2) Apply battery voltage to terminals of solenoid valve. Vacuum should bleed down when voltage is applied to terminals. Using an ohmmeter, check resistance across solenoid valve terminals. Reading should be 36-44 ohms at 68°F (20°C). If reading is not within specification, replace valve.

3) Disconnect EGR solenoid harness connector. Turn ignition on. Using DVOM, measure voltage at harness connector MFI relay power supply terminal. See EGR CONTROL SOLENOID HARNESS CONNECTOR TERMINAL IDENTIFICATION table.

4) If battery voltage is present, go to step **5)**. If battery voltage is not present, check and repair circuit between purge solenoid and MFI relay. If circuit is okay, inspect MFI relay. See RELAYS under MOTORS, RELAYS & SOLENOIDS.

5) Disconnect ECM harness connector. See ENGINE CONTROL MODULE (ECM) LOCATION table under COMPUTERIZED ENGINE CONTROLS. Connect jumper wire between ECM terminal No. 6 (No. 53 on Eclipse and Pickup 3.0L) and vehicle ground. See Fig. 1.

6) Using DVOM, check for continuity between harness connector ECM control circuit terminal and vehicle ground. See PURGE CONTROL SOLENOID HARNESS CONNECTOR TERMINAL IDENTIFICATION table. If continuity does not exist, check and repair circuit as needed. If continuity exists and preceding tests do not show any system or component malfunction and ECM is suspected, substitute ECM with known good unit and retest system.

EGR CONTROL SOLENOID HARNESS CONNECTOR TERMINAL IDENTIFICATION

Application	Terminal No.	Wire Color
MFI Relay Circuit		
Colt, Mirage & Summit	1	Black/Red
Colt Vista, Expo & Summit Wagon	1	Black/Red
Diamante	1	Red
Eclipse		
1.8L	1	Yellow/White
2.0L	1	Red
Galant	1	Black/Red
Montero	1	Black/Red
Pickup		
2.4L	1	Black/Red
3.0L	1	Red
Stealth & 3000GT	2	Red
ECM Control Circuit		
Colt, Mirage & Summit		
1.5L	2	Black/Red
1.8L	2	Brown
Colt Vista, Expo & Summit Wagon	2	Brown/Green
Diamante	2	White
Eclipse		
1.8L	2	Brown/White
2.0L Non-Turbo	2	Brown/White
2.0L Turbo	1	Black/Yellow
Galant	2	Brown
Montero	2	Black/Red
Pickup		
2.4L	2	Brown
3.0L	2	Lt. Green/Yellow
Stealth & 3000GT	1	Lt. Green/Red

FUEL EVAPORATION

Purge Control Valve – Remove purge control valve. Valve is mounted between canister and purge control solenoid valve. See VACUUM DIAGRAMS article. Apply vacuum to diaphragm of vacuum valve. Valve should begin opening at approximately 15.7 in. Hg. Observe operation of valve through by-pass opening.

Purge Control Solenoid Valve – **1)** Label and disconnect both vacuum hoses from solenoid valve. Disconnect electrical connector. Connect hand vacuum pump to solenoid valve nipple where Red-striped hose was connected. Apply vacuum to solenoid valve. Vacuum should hold.

2) Apply battery voltage to terminals of solenoid valve. Vacuum should bleed down when voltage is applied to terminals. Using an ohmmeter, check resistance across solenoid valve terminals. Reading should be 36-44 ohms at 68°F (20°C). If reading is not within specification, replace valve.

3) Disconnect purge solenoid harness connector. Turn ignition on. Using DVOM, measure voltage at harness connector MFI relay power supply terminal. See PURGE CONTROL SOLENOID HARNESS CONNECTOR TERMINAL IDENTIFICATION table.

4) If battery voltage is present, go to step **5)**. If battery voltage is not present, check and repair circuit between purge solenoid and MFI relay. If circuit is okay, inspect MFI relay. See RELAYS under MOTORS, RELAYS & SOLENOIDS.

5) Disconnect ECM harness connector. See ENGINE CONTROL MODULE (ECM) LOCATION table under COMPUTERIZED ENGINE CONTROLS. Connect jumper wire between ECM terminal No. 9 (No. 62 on Eclipse, Montero 3.0L and Pickup 3.0L) and vehicle ground. See Fig. 1.

6) Using DVOM, check for continuity between harness connector ECM control circuit terminal and vehicle ground. See PURGE CONTROL SOLENOID HARNESS CONNECTOR TERMINAL IDENTIFICATION table. If continuity does not exist, check and repair circuit as needed. If continuity exists and preceding tests do not show any system or component malfunction and ECM is suspected, substitute ECM with known good unit and retest system.

PURGE CONTROL SOLENOID HARNESS CONNECTOR TERMINAL IDENTIFICATION

Application	Terminal No.	Wire Color
MFI Relay Circuit		
Colt, Mirage &		
Summit	2	Black/Red
Colt Vista, Expo &		
Summit Wagon	2	Black/Red
Diamante	1	Red
Eclipse		
1.8L	1	Yellow/White
2.0L	1	Red
Galant		
SOHC	2	Black/Red
DOHC	2	Red
Montero	1	Black/Red
Pickup	1	Red
Stealth & 3000GT	2	Red
ECM Control Circuit		
Colt, Mirage &		
Summit	1	Green/Red
Colt Vista, Expo &		
Summit Wagon	1	Green/Red
Diamante	2	Brown/Green
Eclipse	1	Black/White
Galant		
SOHC	1	Green/Red
DOHC	1	Brown/Yellow
Montero	2	Black/Red
Pickup		
2.4L	2	Green/Red
3.0L	2	Brown/Yellow
Stealth & 3000GT	1	Lt. Green/Blue

POSITIVE CRANKCASE VENTILATION (PCV)

PCV Valve – Remove PCV valve. Shake valve by hand. Valve should rattle if moving freely. Apply air pressure to valve. Air should flow in one direction only. Connect PCV valve to vacuum hose and start engine. Ensure vacuum is flowing through valve.

MISCELLANEOUS CONTROLS

NOTE: Although some of the controlled devices listed here are not technically engine performance components, they can affect driveability if they malfunction.

Accelerator Pedal Position Sensor (Diamante With Traction Control) – **1)** Sensor is connected to throttle valve. Disconnect sensor connector. Measure resistance between terminals No. 1 and No. 4. Resistance should be 3.5-6.5 ohms.

2) Using analog ohmmeter, measure resistance between terminals No. 1 and 3. Monitor ohmmeter while slowly opening throttle from idle position to WOT. Resistance should change smoothly in proportion with throttle opening. Replace sensor if ohmmeter displays erratic changes in resistance when opening throttle.

3) Check for open or short in circuit between accelerator pedal position sensor and ECM. Disconnect sensor and ECM connectors. Connect ohmmeter between sensor connector terminal No. 4 and vehicle ground. Ground ECM connector terminal No. 61 (Fed. models) or terminal No. 81 (Calif. models). Repair circuit as needed if continuity does not exist.

4) Check for continuity between sensor connector terminal No. 1 and vehicle ground. Repair circuit between sensor connector terminal No. 1 and ECM terminal No. 72 (Fed. models) or terminal No. 92 (Calif. models) as needed if continuity does not exist. Connect ECM connector. Turn ignition on. Using DVOM, measure voltage between sensor connector terminal No. 4 and vehicle ground. Voltage should be 4.8-5.2 volts. Replace ECM is voltage is not within specification.

A/C Switch & Compressor Clutch Relay – Using DVOM, measure power supply voltage of ECM. Disconnect ECM connector. Turn A/C switch and ignition switch to ON positions. Measure voltage between specified ECM terminals and vehicle ground. See A/C POWER ECM TERMINAL LOCATION table. Voltage should be 6 volts or greater. If voltage is not battery voltage, check and repair circuit.

A/C POWER ECM TERMINAL LOCATION

Application	[1] Terminal No.
Colt, Mirage & Summit	22 & 45
Colt Vista, Expo & Summit Wagon	22 & 115
Diamante (Calif.)	22 & 45
Diamante (Fed.)	22 & 115
Eclipse	7 & 65
Galant	22 & 45
Montero (3.0L)	7 & 65
Montero (3.5L)	22 & 45
Pickup	7 & 65
Precis (California)	[2] 6 & 13 [3]
Precis (Federal)	[4] 10 & 18 [5]
Stealth & 3000GT (Calif. & Turbo)	22 & 45
Stealth & 3000GT (Fed. & Non Turbo)	22 & 115

[1] – See Fig. 1.
[2] – ECM connector C50-1. See Fig. 1.
[3] – ECM connector C50-2. See Fig. 1.
[4] – ECM connector C50-6. See Fig. 1.
[5] – ECM connector C50-4. See Fig. 1.

Chrysler Corp.: Colt, Colt Vista, Stealth
Eagle: Summit, Summit Wagon
Mitsubishi: Diamante, Eclipse, Expo, Galant,
 Mirage, Montero, Pickup, 3000GT

NOTE: Manufacturer does not provide ECM pin voltage information for Precis.

INTRODUCTION

NOTE: Unless stated otherwise in testing procedures, perform all voltage tests using a Digital Volt-Ohmmeter (DVOM) with a minimum 10-megohm input impedance. Voltage readings may vary slightly due to battery condition or charging rate.

Pin voltage charts are supplied to reduce diagnostic time. Checking pin voltages at the ECM connector determines whether it is receiving and transmitting proper voltage signals. Diagnostic charts may also help determine if ECM harness is shorted or open.

TEST PROCEDURE

CAUTION: Shorting positive DVOM lead between connector terminal and ground could damage vehicle wiring, sensor and ECM.

1) If necessary, remove module to access harness connector. Using DVOM, backprobe terminals with positive lead. Connect negative lead to ECM ground terminal. See appropriate chart for identification of ground terminal. *See Figs. 1-25.*
2) All measurements are applicable to vehicle at normal operating temperature at sea level. Unless otherwise noted, engine is idling when specification requires engine running. Ensure transmission shift selector is in Neutral or Park (as applicable). If DVOM displays measurement that is not within specification, see SELF-DIAGNOSTICS or SYSTEM & COMPONENT TESTING article.

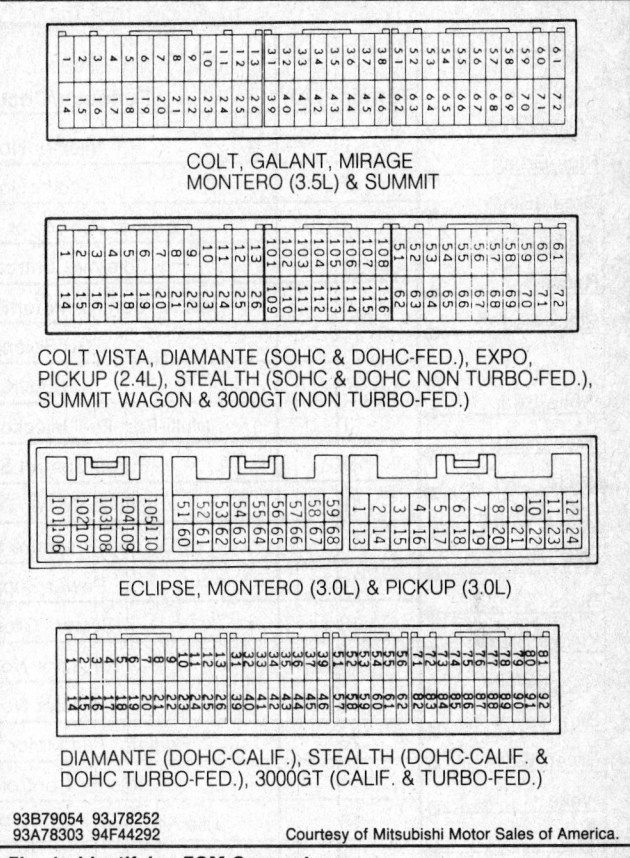

COLT, GALANT, MIRAGE
MONTERO (3.5L) & SUMMIT

COLT VISTA, DIAMANTE (SOHC & DOHC-FED.), EXPO,
PICKUP (2.4L), STEALTH (SOHC & DOHC NON TURBO-FED.),
SUMMIT WAGON & 3000GT (NON TURBO-FED.)

ECLIPSE, MONTERO (3.0L) & PICKUP (3.0L)

DIAMANTE (DOHC-CALIF.), STEALTH (DOHC-CALIF. &
DOHC TURBO-FED.), 3000GT (CALIF. & TURBO-FED.)

93B79054 93J78252
93A78303 94F44292

Courtesy of Mitsubishi Motor Sales of America.

Fig. 1: Identifying ECM Connectors

1994 ENGINE PERFORMANCE
Pin Voltage Charts (Cont.)

	Terminal ID.	Function/Description	Voltage Value (DC Volts Unless Otherwise Specified)
Yellow/Blue	1	Injector No. 1	Battery Voltage With KOER [1]
Blue/Green	2	Injector No. 3	Battery Voltage With KOER [1]
Green/Black	3	Radiator Fan Motor Relay (High)	Battery Voltage With Fan Off
Blue/Yellow	4	Idle Air Control Motor	0-1 Volt With KOEO [2]
Red	5	Idle Air Control Motor Position Sensor	0-1 or 4.5-5.5 Volts With KOEO [2]
Black/Red [3]	6	EGR Solenoid	Battery Voltage With KOEO [2]
	7	BLANK	N/A
White/Red	8	Multi-Port Fuel Injection Pump Relay	Battery Voltage With KOEO [2]
Green/Red	9	Purge Control Solenoid	Battery Voltage With KOEO [2]
White	10	Ignition Power Transistor	0.3-3.0 Volts With Engine @ 3000 RPM
Green/White	11	A/C Triple Pressure Switch (1.8L)	Battery Voltage, A/C System-199 PSI (1373 kPa) [4]
Red	12	Power Supply	Battery Voltage With KOEO [2]
Black	13	System Ground	Not Applicable
Yellow/Black	14	Injector No. 2	Battery Voltage With KOER [1]
Green/White	15	Injector No. 4	Battery Voltage With KOER [1]
Blue/Yellow	16	Radiator Fan Motor Relay (Low)	Battery Voltage With Fan Off
Green/Black	17	Idle Air Control Motor	0-1 Volt With KOEO [2]
White	18	Idle Air Control Motor Position Sensor	0-1 Or 4.5-5.5 Volts With KOEO [2]
Blue	19	Airflow Sensor (1.8L)	0-1 Volt With KOER [1]
	20	BLANK	N/A
	21	BLANK	N/A
Black/White	22	Air Conditioning Clutch Relay	Battery Voltage With KOER [1]
	23	BLANK	N/A
Black/Blue	24	Electric Load Switch (1.8L)	0-3 Volts With KOEO [2] (Accessories Off)
Red	25	Power Supply	Battery Voltage With KOEO [2]
Black	26	System Ground	Not Applicable
	31	BLANK	N/A
Black/Yellow	32	Heated Oxygen Sensor (Rear)	0-3 Volts With KOER [1]
	33	BLANK	N/A
Black/Blue	34	Ignition Timing Adjustment Terminal	4.0-5.5 Volts With KOEO [2]
Black/Yellow	35	Heated Oxygen Sensor (Front)	0-3 Volts With KOER [1]
Lt. Green/Red	36	Malfunction Indicator Light	Battery Voltage With KOEO [2]
Yellow	37	Power Steering Pressure Switch	Battery Voltage With KOER [1]

[1] – KOER – Key On, Engine Running.
[2] – KOEO – Key On, Engine Off.
[3] – On 1.8L, wire color is Brown.
[4] – High side pressure measurement.

94H44138

Fig. 2: Pin Voltage Chart (Colt, Mirage & Summit – 1 Of 2)

	Terminal ID.	Function/Description	Voltage Value (DC Volts Unless Otherwise Specified)
	38	BLANK	N/A
	39	BLANK	N/A
	40	BLANK	N/A
	41	BLANK	N/A
Yellow	42	Data Link Connector	Not Available
Green/White	43	Data Link Connector	Not Available
	44	BLANK	N/A
Green/Yellow	45	Air Conditioning Switch	Battery Voltage With KOER [1] (A/C On)
	46	BLANK	N/A
Black/Red [2]	51	Ignition Switch (Start Circuit)	8 Volts Or More (Engine Cranking)
Red/Black	52	Intake Air Temperature Sensor	0.4-1.0 Volt With KOEO [3] (Sensor @ 176°F)
Blue	53	EGR Temperature Sensor	2.2-3.0 Volts With KOEO [3] (Sensor @ 212°F)
	54	BLANK	N/A
White	55	Heated Oxygen Sensor (Rear)	.6-1.0 Volt With KOER [1] (WOT) [4]
White	56	Heated Oxygen Sensor (Front)	0-.9 Volt With KOER [1] (2000 RPM)
	57	BLANK	N/A
	58	BLANK	N/A
	59	BLANK	N/A
Black/Yellow	60	Back-Up Power Supply	Battery Voltage With Ignition Off
Green/Blue	61	Manifold Absolute Pressure Sensor [5]	4.5-5.5 Volts With KOEO [3]
	62	BLANK	N/A
Yellow/Green	63	Coolant Temperature Sensor	.3-.9 Volt With KOEO [3] (Sensor @ 176°F)
Green/White	64	Throttle Position Sensor	0.3-1.0 Volt With KOEO [3]
Pink	65	Barometric Pressure Sensor (1.8L)	3.7-4.3 Volts With KOEO [3] (Sea Level)
Yellow/White	66	Vehicle Speed Sensor	0-5 Volts (Pulse) With KOEO [3] (Sensor Rotating)
Yellow/Red	67	Closed Throttle Position Switch	0-1 Volt With KOEO [3]
Brown/Red	68	Camshaft Position Sensor	0.5-2.0 Volts With KOER [1]
Brown/Green	69	Crankshaft Position Sensor	1.5-2.5 Volts With KOER [1]
White/Black	70	Manifold Absolute Pressure Sensor (1.5L)	0.9-1.5 Volts With KOER [1]
White/Black	70	Intake Airflow Sensor (1.8L)	2.2-3.2 Volts With KOER [1]
Black/Yellow [6]	71	Ignition Switch (A/T)	Battery Voltage With KOEO [3]
Black	72	Coolant Temperature Switch	Not Available

[1] – KOER – Key On, Engine Running.
[2] – On M/T models, wire color is Black/Yellow.
[3] – KOEO – Key On, Engine Off.
[4] – Drive vehicle in 2nd gear (M/T) or "L" (A/T) @ WOT.
[5] – Barometric sensor on 1.8L.
[6] – On M/T models, wire color is Black.

94I44139

Fig. 3: Pin Voltage Chart (Colt, Mirage & Summit – 2 Of 2)

1994 ENGINE PERFORMANCE
Pin Voltage Charts (Cont.)

	Terminal ID.	Function/Description	Voltage Value (DC Volts Unless Otherwise Specified)
Yellow/Blue →	1	Injector No. 1	Battery Voltage With KOER [1]
Blue/Green →	2	Injector No. 3	Battery Voltage With KOER [1]
Blue/Red →	3	Radiator Fan Motor Relay-Hi	Battery Voltage With KOER [1] (Fan Off)
Blue/Yellow →	4	Idle Air Control Motor	Battery Voltage/0-3 Volts (Load Controlled)
Green →	5	Idle Air Control Motor	Battery Voltage/0-3 Volts (Load Controlled)
Brown/Green →	6	EGR Solenoid	Battery Voltage With KOEO [2]
Brown/Red →	7	Transmission Control Module	1-4 Volts With KOER [1]
White/Red →	8	Multi-Port Fuel Injection Pump Relay	Battery Voltage With KOEO [2]
Green/Red →	9	Purge Control Solenoid	Battery Voltage With KOEO [2]
White →	10	Ignition Power Transistor	0.3-3.0 Volts With Engine @ 3000 RPM
Green →	11	Radiator Fan Motor Relay-Lo	Battery Voltage With KOER [1] (Fan Off)
Red →	12	Power Supply	Battery Voltage With KOEO [2]
Black →	13	Ground Circuit	Not Applicable
Yellow/Black →	14	Injector No. 2	Battery Voltage With KOER [1]
Lt. Green/White →	15	Injector No. 4	Battery Voltage With KOER [1]
Green/Yellow →	16	Triple Pressure Switch (A/C)	Battery Voltage With KOER [1], [3]
Green/Black →	17	Idle Air Control Motor	Battery Voltage/0-3 Volts (Load Controlled)
White →	18	Idle Air Control Motor	Battery Voltage/0-3 Volts (Load Controlled)
Yellow/White →	19	Airflow Sensor Reset Signal	0-1 Volt With KOER [1]
	20	BLANK	N/A
	21	BLANK	N/A
Black/White →	22	Air Conditioning Clutch Relay	Battery Voltage With KOER [1] (A/C Off)
	23	BLANK	N/A
	24	BLANK	N/A
Red →	25	Power Supply	Battery Voltage With KOEO [2]
Black →	26	Ground Circuit	Not Applicable
Black/Yellow [4] →	51	Ignition Switch	8 Volts Or More With Engine Cranking
Red/Black →	52	Intake Air Temperature Sensor	0.4-1.0 Volt With KOEO [2] (Sensor @ 176°F)
Brown/White →	53	EGR Temperature Sensor	2.2-3.0 Volts With KOEO [2] (Sensor @ 212°F)
	54	BLANK	N/A
White →	55	Heated Oxygen Sensor	0-.8 Volt (Pulse) With KOER [1]
White →	56	Heated Oxygen Sensor	0.6-1.0 Volt With Engine @ 3000 RPM

[1] – KOER – Key On, Engine Running.
[2] – KOEO – Key On, Engine Off.
[3] – A/C high side pressure is 199 PSI (1373 kPa) or less.
[4] – On A/T models, wire color is Black/Red.

94F44169

Fig. 4: Pin Voltage Chart (Colt Vista, Expo & Summit Wagon – 1 Of 2)

	Terminal ID.	Function/Description	Voltage Value (DC Volts Unless Otherwise Specified)
	57	BLANK	N/A
	58	BLANK	N/A
White/Red	59	Transmission Control Module	0-1 Volt With KOER [1]
Black/Yellow	60	Back-Up Power Supply	Battery Voltage With Ignition Off
Green/Red	61	Throttle Position Sensor	4.5-5.5 Volts With KOEO [2]
	62	BLANK	N/A
Yellow/Green	63	Coolant Temperature Sensor	.3-.9 Volt With KOEO [2] (Sensor @ 176°F)
Green/White	64	Throttle Position Sensor	0.3-0.6 Volt With KOEO [2]
Pink	65	Barometric Pressure Sensor	3.7-4.3 Volts With KOER [1] (Sea Level)
Yellow/White	66	Vehicle Speed Sensor	0-5 Volts (Pulse) With KOEO [2] (Sensor Rotating)
Yellow/Red	67	Closed Throttle Position Switch	0-1 Volt With KOEO [2]
Brown/Red	68	Camshaft Position Sensor	0.2-3.0 Volts With KOER [1]
Brown/Green	69	Crankshaft Position Sensor	0.2-3.0 Volts With KOER [1]
White/Black	70	Airflow Sensor	2.2-3.2 Volts With KOER [1]
Black [3]	71	Park/Neutral Position Switch	0-3 Volts With KOEO [2] In Park
Black	72	Throttle Position Sensor	Not Available
	101	BLANK	N/A
	102	BLANK	N/A
	103	BLANK	N/A
Black/Blue	104	Ignition Timing Adjustment Terminal	4.0-5.5 Volts With KOEO [2] (GND Disconnected)
Black	105	Oxygen Sensor Heater	0-3 Volts With KOER [1]
Lt. Green/Red	106	Malfunction Indicator Light	0-3 Volts With KOEO [2] (Initially)
Yellow	107	Power Steering Pressure Switch	Battery Voltage With KOER [1]
	108	BLANK	N/A
	109	BLANK	N/A
	110	BLANK	N/A
	111	BLANK	N/A
Yellow	112	Data Link Connector	Not Available
Green/White	113	Data Link Connector	Not Available
	114	BLANK	N/A
Green/Red	115	Air Conditioning Switch	0-3 Volts With KOER [1] (A/C Off)
	116	BLANK	N/A

[1] – KOER – Key On, Engine Running.
[2] – KOEO – Key On, Engine Off.
[3] – On A/T models, wire color is Black/Yellow.

94I44170

Fig. 5: Pin Voltage Chart (Colt Vista, Expo & Summit Wagon – 2 Of 2)

	Terminal ID.	Function/Description	Voltage Value (DC Volts Unless Otherwise Specified)
Blue/Yellow	1	Injector No. 1	Battery Voltage With KOER [1]
Yellow/Red	2	Injector No. 3	Battery Voltage With KOER [1]
Yellow	3	Injector No. 5	Battery Voltage With KOER [1]
Green/Black	4	Idle Air Control Motor	Battery Voltage/0-3 Volts (Load Controlled)
Gray/Blue	5	Idle Air Control Motor	Battery Voltage/0-3 Volts (Load Controlled)
White	6	EGR Solenoid (Calif.)	Battery Voltage With KOEO [2]
Green/White	6	Radiator Fan Motor Relay-Lo (SOHC-Fed.)	Battery Voltage With KOEO [2] (Fan Off)
Brown/Red	7	Transmission Control Module	1-4 Volts With KOER [1]
White/Red	8	Multi-Port Fuel Injection Pump Relay	Battery Voltage With KOEO [2]
Brown/Green	9	Purge Control Solenoid	Battery Voltage With KOEO [2]
White/Green [3]	10	Ignition Power Transistor	0.3-3.0 Volts With Engine @ 3000 RPM
Brown	11	Ignition Power Transistor (DOHC)	0.3-3.0 Volts With Engine @ 3000 RPM
Brown/Red [4]	12	Power Supply	Battery Voltage With KOEO [2]
Black	13	Ground Circuit	Not Applicable
Yellow/Black	14	Injector No. 2	Battery Voltage With KOER [1]
Lt. Green/White	15	Injector No. 4	Battery Voltage With KOER [1]
Yellow/Green	16	Injector No. 6	Battery Voltage With KOER [1]
Green/Red	17	Idle Air Control Motor	Battery Voltage/0-3 Volts (Load Controlled)
Green/Blue	18	Idle Air Control Motor	Battery Voltage/0-3 Volts (Load Controlled)
Green/White	19	Airflow Sensor Reset Signal	0-1 Volt With KOER [1]
Green/White	20	Radiator Fan Motor Relay-Lo (SOHC-Calif.)	Battery Voltage With KOEO [2] (Fan Off)
Black	20	Traction Control Module (DOHC)	Not Available
Brown/Red	21	Traction Control Module (DOHC)	Not Available
Green/Black	21	Radiator Fan Motor Relay-Hi (SOHC-Calif.)	Battery Voltage With KOEO [2] (Fan Off)
Brown/Yellow	22	Air Conditioning Clutch Relay (A/C On)	Battery Voltage With KOER [1]
Black	23	Ignition Power Transistor (DOHC)	0.3-3.0 Volts With Engine @ 3000 RPM
Red/Green	24	Electrical Load Switch (DOHC)	0-3 Volts With KOER [1] (Accessories Off)
Black/Red	25	Power Supply	Battery Voltage With KOEO [2]
Black	26	Ground Circuit	Not Applicable
Black/Blue	51	Ignition Switch	8 Volts Or More With Engine Cranking
Red/Blue	52	Intake Air Temperature Sensor	0.4-1.0 Volt With KOEO [2] (Sensor @ 176°F)
Blue/Black	53	EGR Temperature Sensor (Calif.)	2.2-3.0 Volts With KOEO [2] (Sensor @ 212°F)
Green/Black	53	Radiator Fan Motor Relay-Hi (SOHC-Fed.)	Battery Voltage With KOEO [2] (Fan Off)
Black	54	Heated Oxygen Sensor R.F. (SOHC-Calif.)	0-3 Volts With KOER [1]
White	55	Heated Oxygen Sensor R.F. (SOHC-Calif.)	0-.8 Volt (Pulse) With KOER [1]
White	56	Heated Oxygen Sensor [5]	0-.8 Volt (Pulse) With KOER [1]
Black	57	Heated Oxygen Sensor L.F. (SOHC-Calif.)	0-3 Volts With KOER [1]

[1] – KOER – Key On, Engine Running.
[2] – KOEO – Key On, Engine Off.
[3] – On DOHC models, wire color is Black/Blue.
[4] – On DOHC models, wire color is Black/Red.
[5] – Left front sensor on Calif. models, only sensor on Fed. models.

94J44171

Fig. 6: Pin Voltage Chart (Diamante SOHC & DOHC (Federal) – 1 Of 2)

	Terminal ID.	Function/Description	Voltage Value (DC Volts Unless Otherwise Specified)
Black [1]	58	Knock Sensor	Not Available
White	59	Transmission Control Module (DOHC)	0-1 Volt With KOER [2]
Red/Yellow [3]	60	Back-Up Power Supply	Battery Voltage With Ignition Off
Green/Yellow	61	Throttle Position Sensor	4.5-5.5 Volts With KOEO [4]
Black/White	62	Ignition Supply Voltage	Battery Voltage With KOEO [4]
Yellow/Green	63	Coolant Temperature Sensor	.3-.9 Volt With KOEO [4] (Sensor @ 176°F)
Brown/Red	64	Throttle Position Sensor	0.3-1.0 Volt With KOEO [4]
Pink	65	Barometric Pressure Sensor	Battery Voltage With KOER [2] (Sea Level)
Yellow/White	66	Vehicle Speed Sensor	0-5 Volts (Pulse) With KOEO [4], Sensor Rotating
Yellow/Red	67	Closed Throttle Position Switch	0-1 Volt With KOEO [4]
Red/Black [5]	68	Camshaft Position Sensor	0.2-3.0 Volts With KOER [2]
Black/White [6]	69	Crankshaft Position Sensor	0.2-3.0 Volts With KOER [2]
White/Black	70	Airflow Sensor	2.2-3.2 Volts With KOER [2]
Black/Yellow	71	Park/Neutral Position Switch	0-3 Volts With KOEO [4] In Park
Black	72	Coolant Temperature Sensor	Not Available
White	101	Ignition Signal (DOHC)	0.3-3.0 Volts With Engine @ 3000 RPM
White	102	Heated Oxygen Sensor L.R. (Calif.)	.6-1.0 Volt In 1st Gear Or "L" @ WOT
Green/Black	102	Traction Control Vacuum Solenoid (DOHC-Fed.)	Battery Voltage With KOEO [4]
Black/Blue	103	Variable Induction Control Position Sensor	0-1 Volt Or 4.5-5.5 Volts With KOEO [4]
White/Yellow	104	Ignition Timing Adjustment Terminal	4.0-5.5 Volts With KOEO [4]
Green	105	Heated Oxygen Sensor R.R. (Calif.)	.6-1.0 Volt In 1st Gear Or "L" @ WOT
Green/Black	105	Traction Control Ventilation Solenoid (DOHC-Fed.)	Battery Voltage With KOEO [4]
Green/Yellow	106	Engine Alarm Light	0-3 Volts With KOEO [4] (Initially)
Blue/White	107	Power Steering Pressure Switch	Battery Voltage With KOER [2]
Blue/Green	108	MFI Relay Supply Voltage	Battery Voltage With Ignition Off
Green/Black	109	Variable Induction Control Motor	0-1 Volt With KOER [2]
Green/Red	110	Variable Induction Control Motor	0-1 Volt With KOER [2]
Green/White	111	Variable Induction Control Position Sensor	0-1 Volt Or 4.5-5.5 Volts With KOEO [4]
Yellow	112	Data Link Connector	Not Available
Gray/Red	113	Data Link Connector	Not Available
	114	BLANK	N/A
Green/White	115	Air Conditioning Switch	0-3 Volts With KOER [2] (A/C Off)
Yellow/Green	116	Traction Control Module	4.5-5.5 Volts With KOER [2] (DOHC)

[1] – On DOHC models, wire color is White.
[2] – KOER – Key On, Engine Running.
[3] – On DOHC models, wire color is Red/Black.
[4] – KOEO – Key On, Engine Off.
[5] – On DOHC models, wire color is Blue/Red.
[6] – On DOHC models, wire color is Blue/Yellow.

94A44172

Fig. 7: Pin Voltage Chart (Diamante SOHC & DOHC (Federal) – 2 Of 2)

1994 ENGINE PERFORMANCE
Pin Voltage Charts (Cont.)

Blue/Yellow →
Yellow/Red →
Yellow →
Green/Black →
Gray/Blue →
White →
Brown/Red →
White/Red →
Brown/Green →
Black/Blue →
Brown →
Black/Red →
Black →
Yellow/Black →
Lt. Green/White →
Yellow/Green →
Green/Red →
Green/Blue →
Green/White →
Green/White →
Green/Black →
Brown/Yellow →
Black →
Red/Green →
Black/Red →
Black →
Green/White →
Green/Black →
Black/Blue →
Green/Yellow →
Blue/White →
Blue/Green →
Green/Black →
Green/Red →
Green/White →
White →

Terminal ID.	Function/Description	Voltage Value (DC Volts Unless Otherwise Specified)
1	Injector No. 1	Battery Voltage With KOER [1]
2	Injector No. 3	Battery Voltage With KOER [1]
3	Injector No. 5	Battery Voltage With KOER [1]
4	Idle Air Control Motor	Battery Voltage/0-3 Volts (Load Controlled)
5	Idle Air Control Motor	Battery Voltage/0-3 Volts (Load Controlled)
6	EGR Solenoid	Battery Voltage With KOEO [2]
7	Transmission Control Module	1-4 Volts With KOER [1]
8	Multi-Port Fuel Injection Pump Relay	0-3 Volts With KOER [1]
9	Purge Control Solenoid	Battery Voltage With KOEO [2]
10	Ignition Power Transistor	0.3-3.0 Volts With Engine @ 3000 RPM
11	Ignition Power Transistor (DOHC)	0.3-3.0 Volts With Engine @ 3000 RPM
12	Power Supply	Battery Voltage With KOEO [2]
13	Ground Circuit	Not Applicable
14	Injector No. 2	Battery Voltage With KOER [1]
15	Injector No. 4	Battery Voltage With KOER [1]
16	Injector No. 6	Battery Voltage With KOER [1]
17	Idle Air Control Motor	Battery Voltage/0-3 Volts (Load Controlled)
18	Idle Air Control Motor	Battery Voltage/0-3 Volts (Load Controlled)
19	Airflow Sensor Reset Signal	0-1 Volt With KOER [1]
20	Radiator Fan Motor Relay-Lo	Battery Voltage With KOEO [2] (Fan Off)
21	Radiator Fan Motor Relay-Hi	Battery Voltage With KOEO [2] (Fan Off)
22	Air Conditioning Clutch Relay (A/C On)	Battery Voltage With KOER [1]
23	Ignition Power Transistor	0.3-3.0 Volts With Engine @ 3000 RPM
24	Electrical Load Switch	0-3 Volts With KOER [1] (Accessories Off)
25	Power Supply	Battery Voltage With KOEO [2]
26	Ground Circuit	Not Applicable
31	Traction Control Ventilation Solenoid	Battery Voltage With KOEO [2]
32	Traction Control Vacuum Solenoid	Battery Voltage With KOEO [2]
33	Variable Induction Control Position Sensor	0-1 Volt Or 4.5-5.5 Volts With KOEO [2]
34	BLANK	N/A
35	BLANK	N/A
36	Engine Alarm Light	0-3 Volts With KOEO [2] (Initially)
37	Power Steering Pressure Switch	Battery Voltage With KOER [1]
38	MFI Relay Supply Voltage	Battery Voltage With Ignition Off
39	Variable Induction Control Motor	0-1 Volt With KOER [1] (Decelerating)
40	Variable Induction Control Motor	0-1 Volt With KOER [1] (Accelerating)
41	Variable Induction Control Position Sensor	0-1 Volt Or 4.5-5.5 Volts With KOEO [2]
42	BLANK	N/A
43	Transmission Control Module (DOHC)	0-1 Volt With KOER [1]
44	BLANK	N/A

[1] – KOER – Key On, Engine Running.
[2] – KOEO – Key On, Engine Off.

94F44136

Fig. 8: Pin Voltage Chart (Diamante DOHC (California) – 1 Of 2)

	Terminal ID.	Function/Description	Voltage Value (DC Volts Unless Otherwise Specified)
Green/White	45	Air Conditioning Switch	0-3 Volts With KOER [1] (A/C Off)
Yellow/Green	46	Traction Control Module	4.5-5.5 Volts With KOER [1]
	51	BLANK	N/A
White/Yellow	52	Ignition Timing Adjustment Terminal	4.0-5.5 Volts With KOEO [2] (Ground Disconnected)
White	53	Transmission Control Module	Not Available
	54	BLANK	N/A
	55	BLANK	N/A
Gray/Red	56	Data Link Connector	Not Available
	57	BLANK	N/A
White	58	Engine Ignition Signal	.3-3.0 Volt With KOER [1] (3000 RPM)
Black	59	Transmission Control Module	Not Available
White	60	Heated Oxygen Sensor R.R.	.6-1.0 Volt In 1st Gear Or "L" @ WOT
Yellow	61	BLANK	N/A
Black/Blue	62	Data Link Connector	Not Available
Red/Blue	71	Ignition Switch	8 Volts Or More With Engine Cranking
Yellow	72	Intake Air Temperature Sensor	0.4-1.0 Volt With KOEO [2] (Sensor @ 176°F)
Black	73	EGR Temperature Sensor	2.2-3.0 Volts With KOEO [2] (Sensor @ 212°F)
White	74	Heated Oxygen Sensor R.F.	0-3 Volts With KOER [1]
White	75	Heated Oxygen Sensor R.F.	0-.8 Volt (Pulse) With KOER [1] (2000 RPM)
Black	76	Heated Oxygen Sensor L.F.	0-.8 Volt (Pulse) With KOER [1] (2000 RPM)
Black	77	Heated Oxygen Sensor L.F.	0-3 Volts With KOER [1]
White	78	Knock Sensor	Not Available
Red/Yellow	79	Heated Oxygen Sensor L.R.	.6-1.0 Volt In 1st Gear Or "L" @ WOT
Green/Yellow	80	Back-Up Power Supply	Battery Voltage With Ignition Off
Black/White	81	Throttle Position Sensor	4.5-5.5 Volts With KOEO [2]
Yellow/Green	82	Ignition Supply Voltage	Battery Voltage With KOEO [2]
Brown/Red	83	Coolant Temperature Sensor	.3-.9 Volt With KOEO [2] (Sensor @ 176°F)
Pink	84	Throttle Position Sensor	0.3-1.0 Volt With KOEO [2]
Yellow/White	85	Barometric Pressure Sensor	3.7-4.3 Volts With KOER [1] (Sea Level)
Yellow/Red	86	Vehicle Speed Sensor	0-5 Volts (Pulse) With KOEO [2] (Sensor Rotating)
Blue/Red	87	Closed Throttle Position Switch	0-1 Volt With KOEO [2]
Blue/Yellow	88	Camshaft Position Sensor	0.2-3.0 Volts With KOER [1]
White/Black	89	Crankshaft Position Sensor	0.2-3.0 Volts With KOER [1]
Black/Yellow	90	Airflow Sensor	2.2-3.2 Volts With KOER [1]
Black	91	Park/Neutral Position Switch	0-3 Volts With KOEO [2] In Park
	92	Coolant Temperature Sensor	Not Applicable

[1] – KOER – Key On, Engine Running.
[2] – KOEO – Key On, Engine Off.

94G44137

Fig. 9: Pin Voltage Chart (Diamante DOHC (California) – 2 Of 2)

1994 ENGINE PERFORMANCE
Pin Voltage Charts (Cont.)

	Terminal ID.	Function/Description	Voltage Value (DC Volts Unless Otherwise Specified)
Yellow	1	Data Link Connector	Not Available
White	2	Data Link Connector	Not Available
Black/Red	3	Boost Meter (Turbo)	4-13 Volts With KOEO [1]
White	4	Heated Oxygen Sensor	0-.8 Volt With KOER [2] (2000 RPM)
Yellow/Black	5	Power Steering Pressure Switch	Battery Voltage With KOER [2]
Green	6	Closed Throttle Position Switch (1.8L)	0-1 Volt With KOEO [1]
Green/White	6	Intake Airflow Sensor Reset Signal (2.0L)	0-1 Volt With KOER [2]
Black/Green	7	Air Conditioning Switch	Battery Voltage With KOER [2] (A/C On)
Green/Orange	8	Intake Air Temperature Sensor	0.4-1.0 Volt With KOEO [1] (Sensor @ 176°F)
White	9	Knock Sensor	Not Available
Green/Blue	10	Intake Airflow Sensor	2.2-3.2 Volts With KOER [2]
Red/Blue	11	Anti-Lock Braking Signal	Battery Voltage With KOER [2]
Yellow/Red	12	Ignition Timing Adjustment Terminal	4.0-5.5 Volts With KOEO [1] (GND Disconnected)
Green/Red	13	Idle Speed Control Motor Position Sensor	Not Available
Black/White	13	Fuel Pump Drive Signal (2.0L)	Battery Voltage With KOER [2]
Green/Black	14	Closed Throttle Position Switch (2.0L)	0-1 Volt With KOEO [1]
Blue/Yellow	15	EGR Temperature Sensor	2.2-3.0 Volts With KOEO [1] (Sensor @ 212°F)
Green/Yellow	16	Barometric Pressure Sensor	3.7-4.3 Volts With KOEO [1] (Sea Level)
Brown	17	Idle Speed Control Motor Position Sensor (1.8L)	0.7-1.1 Volts With KOEO [1]
Green/Black	17	Coolant Temperature Sensor (2.0L)	Not Available
Yellow/White	18	Vehicle Speed Sensor	0-5 Volts (Pulse) With KOEO [1] (Sensor Rotating)
Green/White	19	Throttle Position Sensor	0.3-1.0 Volt With KOEO [1]
Yellow/Green	20	Coolant Temperature Sensor	.3-.9 Volt With KOEO [1] (Sensor @ 176°F)
Brown/Yellow [3]	21	Crankshaft Position Sensor	0.2-3.0 Volts With KOER [2]
Black/Blue [4]	22	Camshaft Position Sensor	0.1-3.0 Volts With KOER [2]
Green/Red	23	Throttle Position Sensor	4.5-5.5 Volts With KOEO [1]
Green/Black	24	Sensor Ground	Not Applicable
Yellow/Blue	51	Injector No. 1	Battery Voltage With KOER [2]
Yellow/Black	52	Injector No. 2	Battery Voltage With KOER [2]
Brown/White [5]	53	EGR Solenoid	Battery Voltage With KOEO [1]
Green/Yellow [6]	54	Ignition Power Transistor	0.3-3.0 Volts With Engine @ 3000 RPM

[1] – KOEO – Key On, Engine Off.
[2] – KOER – Key On, Engine Running.
[3] – On A/T models, wire color is Black.
[4] – On A/T models, wire color is White.
[5] – On 2.0L, wire color is Black/Yellow.
[6] – On 2.0L, wire color is Yellow.

94B44173

Fig. 10: Pin Voltage Chart (Eclipse – 1 Of 2)

	Terminal ID.	Function/Description	Voltage Value (DC Volts Unless Otherwise Specified)
Yellow/Red	55	Ignition Power Transistor Unit "B"	0.3-3.0 Volts With Engine @ 3000 RPM
White/Red	56	Multi-Port Fuel Injection Pump Relay	Battery Voltage With KOEO [1]
White	57	Fuel Pressure Solenoid	Battery Voltage With KOEO [1]
Blue/White	58	Idle Air Control Motor (1.8L)	0-1 Volt With KOEO [1]
Green/Black	59	Idle Air Control Motor (1.8L)	0-1 Volt With KOEO [1]
Blue	58	Idle Air Control Motor (2.0L)	Battery Voltage/0-3 Volts (Fluctuating)
Yellow	59	Idle Air Control Motor (2.0L)	Battery Voltage/0-3 Volts (Fluctuating)
Lt. Green	60	Injector No. 3	Battery Voltage With KOER [2]
Lt. Green/White	61	Injector No. 4	Battery Voltage With KOER [2]
Black/White	62	Purge Control Solenoid	Battery Voltage With KOEO [1]
Black/Blue	63	Multi-Port Fuel Injection Relay	Battery Voltage With Ignition Off
Red/Green	64	Malfunction Indicator Light	0-3 Volts With KOEO [1] (Initially)
Red/Black	65	Air Conditioning Clutch Relay	Battery Voltage With KOER [2] (A/C On)
Black/Blue	66	Multi-Port Fuel Injection Relay	Battery Voltage With Ignition Off
White	67	Idle Air Control Motor	Battery Voltage/0-3 Volts (Fluctuating)
Black	68	Idle Air Control Motor	Battery Voltage/0-3 Volts (Fluctuating)
Black	101	System Ground	Not Applicable
Red	102	Power Supply	Battery Voltage With KOEO [1]
Red/Black	103	Back-Up Power Supply	Battery Voltage With Ignition Off
Black [3]	104	Park/Neutral Position Switch	0-3 Volts With KOEO [1] (Park Or Neutral)
Orange	105	Turbocharger Wastegate Solenoid	Battery Voltage With KOEO [1]
Black	106	System Ground	Not Applicable
Red	107	Power Supply	Battery Voltage With KOEO [1]
Black/Yellow	108	Ignition Switch	8 Volts Or More (Engine Cranking)
Black/White	109	Fuel Pump Drive Signal (1.8L)	Battery Voltage With KOER [2]
White	109	Engine Ignition Signal	0.3-3.0 Volts With KOER [2] (3000 RPM)
Black/White	110	Ignition Switch	Battery Voltage With KOEO [1]

[1] – KOEO – Key On, Engine Off.
[2] – KOER – Key On, Engine Running.
[3] – On A/T models, wire color is Black/Yellow.

94C44174

Fig. 11: Pin Voltage Chart (Eclipse – 2 Of 2)

1994 ENGINE PERFORMANCE
Pin Voltage Charts (Cont.)

	Terminal ID.	Function/Description	Voltage Value (DC Volts Unless Otherwise Specified)
Yellow/Blue	1	Injector No. 1	Battery Voltage With KOER [1]
Blue/Green	2	Injector No. 3	Battery Voltage With KOER [1]
Blue/Red	3	Radiator Fan Motor Relay-Hi	Battery Voltage With Fan Off
Blue/Yellow	4	Idle Air Control Motor (SOHC)	0-1 Volt With KOEO [2]
Blue	4	Stepper Motor (DOHC)	Battery Voltage/0-3 Volts (Load Controlled)
White	5	Idle Air Control Motor (SOHC)	0-1 or 4.5-5.5 Volts (Load Controlled)
White	5	Stepper Motor (DOHC)	Not Available
Black/Red	6	EGR Solenoid	Battery Voltage With KOEO [2]
Green	7	Transmission Control Module	Not Available
Black/Blue [3]	8	Multi-Port Fuel Injection Pump Relay	Battery Voltage With KOEO [2]
Green/Red [4]	9	Purge Control Solenoid	Battery Voltage With KOEO [2]
White [5]	10	Ignition Power Transistor	0.3-3.0 Volts With Engine @ 3000 RPM
Green	11	A/C Pressure Switch	Battery Voltage With KOER [1, 6]
Red	12	Power Supply	Battery Voltage With KOEO [2]
Black	13	System Ground	Not Applicable
Yellow/Black	14	Injector No. 2	Battery Voltage With KOER [1]
Lt. Green/White	15	Injector No. 4	Battery Voltage With KOER [1]
Green/Yellow	16	Radiator Fan Motor Relay-Lo	Battery Voltage With KOER [1] (Fan Off)
Green/Black	17	Idle Air Control Motor (SOHC)	0-1 Volt With KOEO [2]
Yellow	17	Stepper Motor (DOHC)	Not Available
Green	18	Idle Air Control Motor (SOHC)	0-1 or 4.5-5.5 Volts (Load Controlled)
Green	18	Stepper Motor (DOHC)	Not Available
Blue	19	Airflow Sensor Reset Signal	0-1 Volt With KOER [1]
	20	BLANK	N/A
	21	BLANK	N/A
Green	22	Air Conditioning Clutch Relay	Battery Voltage With KOER [1] (A/C Off)
Yellow/Red	23	Ignition Power Transistor	0.3-3.0 Volts With Engine @ 3000 RPM
Red/Green	24	Electric Load Switch	Battery Voltage With KOER [1] (Headlights On)
Red	25	Power Supply	Battery Voltage With KOEO [2]
Black	26	System Ground	Not Applicable
White	31	Engine Ignition Signal (DOHC)	Battery Voltage With KOER [1]
	32	BLANK	N/A
	33	BLANK	N/A
Black/Blue	34	Ignition Timing Adjustment Terminal	4.0-5.5 Volts With KOEO [2] (GND Disconnected)
Black	35	Heated Oxygen Sensor	0-3 Volts With KOER [1]

[1] – KOER – Key On, Engine Running.
[2] – KOEO – Key On, Engine Off.
[3] – Wire color is White/Red on DOHC.
[4] – Wire color is Brown/Yellow on DOHC.
[5] – Wire color is Yellow/White on DOHC.
[6] – A/C System high side pressure of 199 PSI (1373 kPa) or less.

94E44176

Fig. 12: Pin Voltage Chart (Galant – 1 Of 2)

	Terminal ID.	Function/Description	Voltage Value (DC Volts Unless Otherwise Specified)
Lt. Green/Red →	36	Malfunction Indicator Light	Battery Voltage With KOEO [1] (Initially)
Yellow →	37	Power Steering Pressure Switch	Battery Voltage With KOER [2]
Blue/Black →	38	Multi-Port Fuel Injection Relay Power Supply	Battery Voltage With Ignition Off
	39	BLANK	N/A
	40	BLANK	N/A
	41	BLANK	N/A
Yellow →	42	Data Link Connector	Not Available
Green/Red →	43	Data Link Connector	Not Available
	44	BLANK	N/A
Green/White →	45	Air Conditioning Switch	0-3 Volts With KOER [2] (A/C Off)
Green/Red →	46	Transmission Control Module	Not Available
Black/Yellow →	51	Ignition Switch (Start Circuit)	8 Volts Or More (Engine Cranking)
Red/Black →	52	Intake Air Temperature Sensor	0.4-1.0 Volt With KOEO [1] (Sensor @ 176°F)
Yellow/Green [3] →	53	EGR Temperature Sensor	2.2-3.0 Volts With KOEO [1] (Sensor @ 212°F)
	54	BLANK	N/A
White →	55	Heated Oxygen Sensor	0-.8 Volt With KOER [2] (2000 RPM)
White →	56	Heated Oxygen Sensor (Front)	0-.8 Volt With KOER [2] (2000 RPM)
	57	BLANK	N/A
White →	58	Knock Sensor	Not Available
	59	BLANK	N/A
Red/Black [4] →	60	Back-Up Power Supply	Battery Voltage With Ignition Off
Green/Blue [5] →	61	Throttle Position Sensor	4.5-5.5 Volts With KOEO [1]
Lt. Green/Red →	62	Ignition Switch (DOHC)	Battery Voltage With KOEO [2]
Yellow/Green →	63	Coolant Temperature Sensor	.3-.9 Volt With KOEO [1] (Sensor @ 176°F)
Green/White →	64	Throttle Position Sensor	0.3-1.0 Volt With KOEO [1]
Pink →	65	Barometric Pressure Sensor	3.7-4.3 Volts With KOEO [1] (Sea Level)
Yellow/White →	66	Vehicle Speed Sensor	0-5 Volts (Pulse) With KOEO [1] (Sensor Rotating)
Yellow/Red →	67	Closed Throttle Position Switch	0-1 Volt With KOEO [1]
Brown/Red [6] →	68	Camshaft Position Sensor	0.5-2.0 Volts With KOER [2]
Brown/Green [7] →	69	Crankshaft Position Sensor	1.5-2.5 Volts With KOER [2]
White/Black →	70	Airflow Sensor	2.2-3.2 Volts With KOER [2]
Black/Yellow →	71	Park/Neutral Switch	0-3 Volts With KOEO [1] In Park
Black →	72	Coolant Temperature Switch	Not Available

[1] – KOEO – Key On, Engine Off.
[2] – KOER – Key On, Engine Running.
[3] – Wire color is Black/Blue on DOHC.
[4] – Wire color is Black/Yellow on DOHC.
[5] – Wire color is Green/Red on DOHC.
[6] – Wire color is White on DOHC.
[7] – Wire color is Black on DOHC.

94F44177

Fig. 13: Pin Voltage Chart (Galant – 2 Of 2)

1994 ENGINE PERFORMANCE
Pin Voltage Charts (Cont.)

	Terminal ID.	Function/Description	Voltage Value (DC Volts Unless Otherwise Specified)
Yellow	1	Data Link Connector	Not Available
Green/Red	2	Data Link Connector	Not Available
	3	BLANK	N/A
White	4	Heated Oxygen Sensor	0-.8 Volt (Fluctuating) With KOER [1] (2000 RPM)
Blue/White	5	Power Steering Pressure Switch	Battery Voltage With KOER [1]
	6	BLANK	N/A
Green/Blue	7	Air Conditioning Switch	Battery Voltage With KOER [1] (A/C On)
Red/Black	8	Intake Air Temperature Sensor	0.4-1.0 Volt With KOEO [2] (Sensor @ 176°F)
Green/Black	9	Anti-Lock Braking Signal	Battery Voltage With KOER [1]
White/Black	10	Intake Airflow Sensor	2.2-3.2 Volts With KOER [1]
	11	BLANK	N/A
White/Yellow	12	Ignition Timing Adjustment Terminal	4.0-5.5 Volts With KOEO [2] (GND Disconnected)
	13	BLANK	N/A
Yellow/Red	14	Closed Throttle Position Switch	0-1 Volt With KOEO [2]
	15	BLANK	N/A
Pink	16	Barometric Pressure Sensor	3.7-4.3 Volts With KOEO [2] (Sea Level)
Black	17	Sensor Ground	Not Applicable
Yellow/White	18	Vehicle Speed Sensor	0-5 Volts (Pulse) With KOEO [2] (Sensor Rotating)
Red/Green	19	Throttle Position Sensor	0.3-1.0 Volt With KOEO [2]
Yellow/Green	20	Coolant Temperature Sensor	.3-.9 Volt With KOEO [2] (Sensor @ 176°F)
Green	21	Crankshaft Position Sensor	0.2-3.0 Volts With KOER [1]
White	22	Camshaft Position Sensor	0.2-3.0 Volts With KOER [1]
Green/Yellow	23	Throttle Position Sensor	4.5-5.5 Volts With KOEO [2]
Black	24	Throttle Position Sensor	Not Applicable
Yellow/Blue	51	Injector No. 1	Battery Voltage With KOER [1]
Yellow/Black	52	Injector No. 2	Battery Voltage With KOER [1]
	53	BLANK	N/A

[1] – KOER – Key On, Engine Running.
[2] – KOEO – Key On, Engine Off.

94G44178

Fig. 14: Pin Voltage Chart (Montero 3.0L – 1 Of 2)

	Terminal ID.	Function/Description	Voltage Value (DC Volts Unless Otherwise Specified)
White	54	Ignition Power Transistor	0.3-3.0 Volts With Engine @ 3000 RPM
White/Red	55	BLANK	N/A
Blue/Black	56	Multi-Port Fuel Injection Pump Relay	Battery Voltage With KOEO [1]
Green/Red	57	Intake Airflow Sensor Reset Signal	0-1 Volt With KOEO [1]
Green/Black	58	Idle Air Control Motor	Battery Voltage/0-3 Volts (Fluctuating)
Blue/Yellow	59	Idle Air Control Motor	Battery Voltage/0-3 Volts (Fluctuating)
Lt. Green/Red	60	Injector No. 3	Battery Voltage With KOEO [1]
Black/Red	61	Injector No. 4	Battery Voltage With KOEO [1]
Blue/Green	62	Purge Control Solenoid	Not Available
Black/White	63	Multi-Port Fuel Injection Relay	0-3 Volts With KOEO [1]
Green/White	64	Malfunction Indicator Light	Battery Voltage With KOEO [1]
Blue/Green	65	Air Conditioning Clutch Relay	Battery Voltage With KOER [2] (A/C Off)
Gray/Blue	66	Multi-Port Fuel Injection Relay	0-3 Volts With KOEO [1]
Green/Blue	67	Idle Air Control Motor	Battery Voltage/0-3 Volts (Fluctuating)
Black	68	Idle Air Control Motor	Battery Voltage/0-3 Volts (Fluctuating)
Black/Red	101	System Ground	Not Applicable
Black/Green	102	Power Supply	Battery Voltage With KOEO [1]
Black/Yellow	103	Back-Up Power Supply	Battery Voltage With Ignition Off
Yellow/White	104	Park/Neutral Position Switch	0-3 Volts With KOEO [1] (Park Or Neutral)
Black	105	Injector No. 5	Battery Voltage With KOER [2]
Black/Red	106	System Ground	Not Applicable
Black/Blue	107	Power Supply	Battery Voltage With KOEO [1]
Yellow/Green	108	Ignition Switch	Battery Voltage With KOEO [1] (Engine Cranking)
Black/White	109	Injector No. 6	Battery Voltage With KOER [2]
	110	Ignition Switch	Battery Voltage With KOEO [1]

[1] – KOEO – Key On, Engine Off.
[2] – KOER – Key On, Engine Running.

94H44179

Fig. 15: Pin Voltage Chart (Montero 3.0L – 2 Of 2)

	Terminal ID.	Function/Description	Voltage Value (DC Volts Unless Otherwise Specified)
Yellow/Blue	1	Injector No. 1	Battery Voltage With KOER [1]
Blue/Yellow	2	Injector No. 3	Battery Voltage With KOER [1]
Yellow/White	3	Injector No. 5	Battery Voltage With KOER [1]
Green/Red	4	Idle Air Control Motor	Battery Voltage/0-3 Volts (Load Controlled)
Gray/Blue	5	Idle Air Control Motor	Battery Voltage/0-3 Volts (Load Controlled)
Black/Red	6	EGR Solenoid	Battery Voltage With KOEO [2]
	7	BLANK	N/A
White/Red	8	Multi-Port Fuel Injection Pump Relay	Battery Voltage With KOEO [2]
Black/Red	9	Purge Control Solenoid	Battery Voltage With KOEO [2]
White	10	Ignition Power Transistor	0.3-3.0 Volts With Engine @ 3000 RPM
Red/Blue	11	Ignition Power Transistor	0.3-3.0 Volts With Engine @ 3000 RPM
Black/Red	12	Power Supply	Battery Voltage With KOEO [2]
Black	13	Ground Circuit	Not Applicable
Yellow/Black	14	Injector No. 2	Battery Voltage With KOER [1]
Lt. Green/Red	15	Injector No. 4	Battery Voltage With KOER [1]
Yellow/Green	16	Injector No. 6	Battery Voltage With KOER [1]
Green/Black	17	Idle Air Control Motor	Battery Voltage/0-3 Volts (Load Controlled)
Green/Blue	18	Idle Air Control Motor	Battery Voltage/0-3 Volts (Load Controlled)
Blue/Black	19	Airflow Sensor Reset Signal	0-1 Volt With KOER [1]
Blue/Red	20	Variable Induction Control Motor	0-3 Volts With KOER [1]
	21	BLANK	N/A
Green/White	22	Air Conditioning Clutch Relay (A/C On)	Battery Voltage With KOER [1]
Black/Green	23	Ignition Power Transistor	0.3-3.0 Volts With Engine @ 3000 RPM
Red/Green	24	Electrical Load Switch	0-3 Volts With KOER [1] (Accessories Off)
Black/Red	25	Power Supply	Battery Voltage With KOEO [2]
Black	26	Ground Circuit	Not Applicable
White	31	Ignition Signal	0.3-3.0 Volts With Engine @ 3000 RPM
White	32	Heated Oxygen Sensor	.6-1.0 Volt In 1st Gear Or "L" @ WOT
	33	BLANK	N/A
White/Yellow	34	Ignition Timing Adjustment Terminal	4.0-5.5 Volts With KOEO [2] (GND Disconnected)
	35	BLANK	N/A
Black/White	36	Check Engine Light	0-3 Volts With KOEO [2] (Initially)
Blue/White	37	Power Steering Pressure Switch	Battery Voltage With KOER [1]

[1] – KOER – Key On, Engine Running.
[2] – KOEO – Key On, Engine Off.

94A44180

Fig. 16: Pin Voltage Chart (Montero 3.5L – 1 Of 2)

	Terminal ID.	Function/Description	Voltage Value (DC Volts Unless Otherwise Specified)
Blue/Green	38	MFI Relay Supply Voltage	Battery Voltage With Ignition Off
	39	BLANK	N/A
	40	BLANK	N/A
	41	BLANK	N/A
Yellow	42	Data Link Connector	Not Available
Green/Red	43	Data Link Connector	Not Available
Green/Black	44	ABS Signal	Battery Voltage With KOER [1]
Green/Blue	45	Air Conditioning Switch	0-3 Volts With KOER [1] (A/C Off)
	46	BLANK	N/A
Black/Blue	51	Ignition Switch	8 Volts Or More With Engine Cranking
Red/Black	52	Intake Air Temperature Sensor	0.4-1.0 Volt With KOEO [2] (Sensor @ 176°F)
Red/Yellow	53	EGR Temperature Sensor (Calif.)	2.2-3.0 Volts With KOEO [2] (Sensor @ 212°F)
	54	BLANK	N/A
	55	BLANK	N/A
White	56	Heated Oxygen Sensor	0-.8 Volt (Pulse) With KOER [1] (2000 RPM)
	57	BLANK	N/A
Black	58	Knock Sensor	Not Available
White	59	Transmission Control Module (DOHC)	0-1 Volt With KOER [1]
Black/Green	60	Back-Up Power Supply	Battery Voltage With Ignition Off
Green/Yellow	61	Throttle Position Sensor	4.5-5.5 Volts With KOEO [2]
Black/White	62	Ignition Supply Voltage	Battery Voltage With KOEO [2]
Yellow/Green	63	Coolant Temperature Sensor	.3-.9 Volt With KOEO [2] (Sensor @ 176°F)
Red/Green	64	Throttle Position Sensor	0.3-1.0 Volt With KOEO [2]
Pink	65	Barometric Pressure Sensor	Battery Voltage With KOER [1] (Sea Level)
Yellow/White	66	Vehicle Speed Sensor	0-5 Volts (Pulse) With KOEO [2], Sensor Rotating
Yellow/Red	67	Closed Throttle Position Switch	0-1 Volt With KOEO [2]
White	68	Camshaft Position Sensor	0.2-3.0 Volts With KOER [1]
Blue/Yellow	69	Crankshaft Position Sensor	0.2-3.0 Volts With KOER [1]
White/Black	70	Airflow Sensor	2.2-3.2 Volts With KOER [1]
Black/Yellow	71	Park/Neutral Position Switch	0-3 Volts With KOEO [2] In Park
Black	72	Coolant Temperature Sensor	Not Available

[1] – KOER – Key On, Engine Running.
[2] – KOEO – Key On, Engine Off.

94B44181

Fig. 17: Pin Voltage Chart (Montero 3.5L – 2 Of 2)

1994 ENGINE PERFORMANCE
Pin Voltage Charts (Cont.)

Color	Terminal ID.	Function/Description	Voltage Value (DC Volts Unless Otherwise Specified)
Yellow/Blue →	1	Injector No. 1	Battery Voltage With KOER [1]
Blue/Green →	2	Injector No. 3	Battery Voltage With KOER [1]
	3	BLANK	N/A
Blue/Yellow →	4	Idle Air Control Motor	2 Volts Or More/0-1 Volts (Load Controlled)
White →	5	Idle Air Control Motor	1.5-4.0/0-1 Volts (Load Controlled)
Brown →	6	EGR Solenoid	Battery Voltage With KOEO [2]
	7	BLANK	N/A
Black/Blue →	8	Multi-Port Fuel Injection Pump Relay	Battery Voltage With KOEO [2]
Brown/Yellow →	9	Purge Control Solenoid	Battery Voltage With KOEO [2]
White →	10	Ignition Power Transistor	0.3-3.0 Volts With Engine @ 3000 RPM
	11	BLANK	N/A
Red →	12	Power Supply	Battery Voltage With KOEO [2]
Black →	13	Ground Circuit	Not Applicable
Yellow/Blue →	14	Injector No. 2	Battery Voltage With KOER [1]
Lt. Green/White →	15	Injector No. 4	Battery Voltage With KOER [1]
	16	BLANK	N/A
Green/Black →	17	Idle Air Control Motor	4 Volts Or More/0-1 Volts (Load Controlled)
Green →	18	Idle Air Control Motor	1.5-4.0 Volts/0-1 Volts (Load Controlled)
Blue →	19	Airflow Sensor Reset Signal	0-1 Volt With KOER [1]
	20	BLANK	N/A
	21	BLANK	N/A
Blue →	22	Air Conditioning Clutch Relay	Battery Voltage With KOER [1] (A/C Off)
	23	BLANK	N/A
	24	BLANK	N/A
Red →	25	Power Supply	Battery Voltage With KOEO [2]
Black →	26	Ground Circuit	Not Applicable
Black/Yellow →	51	Ignition Switch	8 Volts Or More With Engine Cranking
Red/Black →	52	Intake Air Temperature Sensor	0.4-1.0 Volt With KOEO [2] (Sensor @ 176°F)
Black/Blue →	53	EGR Temperature Sensor	2.2-3.0 Volts With KOEO [2] (Sensor @ 212°F)
	54	BLANK	N/A

[1] – KOER – Key On, Engine Running.
[2] – KOEO – Key On, Engine Off.

94C44182

Fig. 18: Pin Voltage Chart (Pickup 2.4L – 1 Of 2)

	Terminal ID.	Function/Description	Voltage Value (DC Volts Unless Otherwise Specified)
White →	55	Heated Oxygen Sensor (Rear)	0.6-1.0 Volt With Engine @ WOT
White →	56	Heated Oxygen Sensor (Front)	0-.8 Volt (Pulse) With KOER [1]
	57	BLANK	N/A
	58	BLANK	N/A
	59	BLANK	N/A
Black/Yellow →	60	Back-Up Power Supply	Battery Voltage With Ignition Off
Green/Blue →	61	Throttle Position Sensor	4.5-5.5 Volts With KOEO [2]
	62	BLANK	N/A
Yellow/Green →	63	Coolant Temperature Sensor	.3-.9 Volt With KOEO [2] (Sensor @ 176°F)
Green/White →	64	Throttle Position Sensor	0.3-.6 Volt With KOEO [2]
Pink →	65	Barometric Pressure Sensor	3.7-4.3 Volts With KOER [1] (Sea Level)
Yellow/White →	66	Vehicle Speed Sensor	0-5 Volts (Pulse) With KOEO [2] (Sensor Rotating)
Yellow/Red →	67	Closed Throttle Position Switch	0-1 Volt With KOEO [2]
Brown/Red →	68	Camshaft Position Sensor	0.2-3.0 Volts With KOER [1]
Brown/Green →	69	Crankshaft Position Sensor	0.2-3.0 Volts With KOER [1]
White/Black →	70	Airflow Sensor	2.2-3.2 Volts With KOER [1]
Black/Yellow →	71	Park/Neutral Position Switch	0-3 Volts With KOEO [2] (In Park)
Black →	72	Throttle Position Sensor	Not Available
	101	BLANK	N/A
	102	BLANK	N/A
	103	BLANK	N/A
Black/Blue →	104	Ignition Timing Adjustment Terminal	4.0-5.5 Volts With KOEO [2] (GND Disconnected)
Black →	105	Oxygen Sensor Heater	0-3 Volts With KOER [1]
Lt. Green/Red →	106	Malfunction Indicator Light	0-3 Volts With KOEO [2] (Initially)
	107	BLANK	N/A
	108	BLANK	N/A
	109	BLANK	N/A
	110	BLANK	N/A
	111	BLANK	N/A
Yellow →	112	Data Link Connector	Not Available
Green/White →	113	Data Link Connector	Not Available
	114	BLANK	N/A
Green/Red →	115	Air Conditioning Switch	0-3 Volts With KOER [1] (A/C Off)
	116	BLANK	N/A

[1] – KOER – Key On, Engine Running.
[2] – KOEO – Key On, Engine Off.

94D44183

Fig. 19: Pin Voltage Chart (Pickup 2.4L – 2 Of 2)

1994 ENGINE PERFORMANCE
Pin Voltage Charts (Cont.)

	Terminal ID.	Function/Description	Voltage Value (DC Volts Unless Otherwise Specified)
Yellow →	1	Data Link Connector	Not Available
Green/White →	2	Data Link Connector	Not Available
	3	BLANK	N/A
White →	4	Heated Oxygen Sensor	0-.8 Volt With KOER [1] (Fluctuating)
	5	BLANK	N/A
	6	BLANK	N/A
Green/Red →	7	Air Conditioning Switch	Battery Voltage With KOER [1] (A/C On)
Red/Blue →	8	Intake Air Temperature Sensor	0.4-1.0 Volt With KOEO [2]
	9	BLANK	N/A
White/Black →	10	Intake Airflow Sensor	2.2-3.2 Volts With KOER [1]
	11	BLANK	N/A
White/Yellow →	12	Ignition Timing Adjustment Terminal	4.0-5.5 Volts With KOEO [2]
	13	BLANK	N/A
Yellow/Red →	14	Closed Throttle Position Switch	0-1 Volt With KOEO [2]
Lt. Green/Blue →	15	EGR Temperature Sensor	2.2-3.0 Volts With KOER [1] (Sensor @ 212°F)
Pink →	16	Barometric Pressure Sensor	3.7-4.3 Volts With KOEO [2]
Black →	17	Sensor Ground	Not Applicable
Yellow/White →	18	Vehicle Speed Sensor	0-5 Volts (Pulse) With KOEO [2] (Sensor Rotating)
Green/White →	19	Throttle Position Sensor	0.3-1.0 Volt With KOEO [2]
Yellow/Green →	20	Coolant Temperature Sensor	.3-.9 Volt With KOEO [2] (Sensor @ 176°F)
Blue/White →	21	Crankshaft Position Sensor	0.2-3.0 Volts With KOER [1]
Blue/Red →	22	Camshaft Position Sensor	0.2-3.0 Volts With KOER [1]
Green/Yellow →	23	Throttle Position Sensor	4.5-5.5 Volts With KOEO [2]
Black →	24	Throttle Position Sensor	Not Applicable
Yellow →	51	Injector No. 1	Battery Voltage With KOER [1]
Yellow/Blue →	52	Injector No. 2	Battery Voltage With KOER [1]
Lt. Green/Yellow →	53	EGR Solenoid	Battery Voltage With KOEO [2]
White →	54	Ignition Power Transistor	0.3-3.0 Volts With Engine @ 3000 RPM
	55	BLANK	N/A

[1] – KOER – Key On, Engine Running.
[2] – KOEO – Key On, Engine Off.

94E44184

Fig. 20: Pin Voltage Chart (Pickup 3.0L – 1 Of 2)

	Terminal ID.	Function/Description	Voltage Value (DC Volts Unless Otherwise Specified)
White/Red →	56	Multi-Port Fuel Injection Relay	Battery Voltage With KOEO [1]
Red/Green →	57	Intake Airflow Sensor Reset Signal	0-1 Volt With KOEO [1]
Green/Yellow →	58	Idle Air Control Motor	Battery Voltage/0-3 Volts (Fluctuating)
Green/Black →	59	Idle Air Control Motor	Battery Voltage/0-3 Volts (Fluctuating)
Blue/Green →	60	Injector No. 3	Battery Voltage With KOEO [1]
Lt. Green/White →	61	Injector No. 4	Battery Voltage With KOEO [1]
Brown/Blue →	62	Purge Control Solenoid	Not Available
Blue/Green →	63	Multi-Port Fuel Injection Relay	Battery Voltage With KOEO [1]
Lt. Green/Red →	64	Malfunction Indicator Light	Battery Voltage With KOEO [1]
Blue →	65	Air Conditioning Clutch Relay	Battery Voltage With KOER [2] (A/C Off)
Blue/Green →	66	Multi-Port Fuel Injection Relay	Battery Voltage With KOEO [1]
Green/Red →	67	Idle Air Control Motor	Battery Voltage/0-3 Volts (Fluctuating)
Green/Blue →	68	Idle Air Control Motor	Battery Voltage/0-3 Volts (Fluctuating)
Black →	101	System Ground	Not Applicable
Red →	102	Power Supply	Battery Voltage With KOEO [1]
Black/Yellow →	103	Back-Up Power Supply	Battery Voltage With Ignition Off
Black/Yellow →	104	Ignition Switch	Battery Voltage (Engine Cranking)
Yellow/White →	105	Injector No. 5	Battery Voltage With KOER [2]
Black →	106	System Ground	Not Applicable
Red →	107	Power Supply	Battery Voltage With KOEO [1]
Black/Red →	108	Ignition Switch	8 Volts Or More With KOEO [1]
Yellow/Green →	109	Injector No. 6	Battery Voltage With KOER [2]
Black/White →	110	Ignition Switch	Battery Voltage With KOEO [1]

[1] – KOEO – Key On, Engine Off.
[2] – KOER – Key On, Engine Running.

94F44185

Fig. 21: Pin Voltage Chart (Pickup 3.0L – 2 Of 2)

1994 ENGINE PERFORMANCE
Pin Voltage Charts (Cont.)

Wire Color	Terminal ID.	Function/Description	Voltage Value (DC Volts Unless Otherwise Specified)
Green	1	Injector No. 1	Battery Voltage With KOER [1]
Green/Yellow	2	Injector No. 3	Battery Voltage With KOER [1]
Green/Black	3	Injector No. 5	Battery Voltage With KOER [1]
Green/Black	4	Idle Air Control Motor	Battery Voltage/0-3 Volts (Load Controlled)
Gray/Blue	5	Idle Air Control Motor	Battery Voltage/0-3 Volts (Load Controlled)
Lt. Green/Red	6	EGR Solenoid (Calif.)	Battery Voltage With KOEO [2]
Green/Yellow	6	Radiator Fan Motor Relay-Lo (DOHC)	Battery Voltage With KOER [1] (Fan Off)
Blue/White	7	Transaxle Control Module	1-4 Volts With KOER [1]
White/Red	8	Multi-Port Fuel Injection Relay	Battery Voltage With KOEO [2]
Black/Red	9	Purge Control Solenoid	Battery Voltage With KOEO [2]
Black/Blue	10	Ignition Power Transistor	0.3-3.0 Volts With Engine @ 3000 RPM
Brown/Red	11	Ignition Power Transistor (DOHC)	0.3-3.0 Volts With Engine @ 3000 RPM
Black/Red	12	Power Supply	Battery Voltage With KOEO [2]
Black	13	Ground Circuit	Not Applicable
Yellow/Black	14	Injector No. 2	Battery Voltage With KOER [1]
Green/Red	15	Injector No. 4	Battery Voltage With KOER [1]
Green/White	16	Injector No. 6	Battery Voltage With KOER [1]
Green/Black	17	Idle Air Control Motor	Battery Voltage/0-3 Volts (Load Controlled)
Green/Yellow	18	Idle Air Control Motor	Battery Voltage/0-3 Volts (Load Controlled)
Red/White	19	Airflow Sensor Reset Signal	0-1 Volt With KOER [1]
Green/Yellow	20	Radiator Fan Motor Relay-Lo (SOHC)	Battery Voltage With KOER [1] (Fan Off)
Blue/Orange	20	Air Conditioning Switch No. 2 (DOHC)	0-3 Volts (A/C Off)
Blue/Red [3]	21	Radiator Fan Motor Relay-Hi	Battery Voltage With KOER [1] (Fan Off)
Green	22	Air Conditioning Clutch Relay	Battery Voltage With KOER [1] (A/C Off)
Black/White	23	Ignition Power Transistor (DOHC)	0.3-3.0 Volts With Engine @ 3000 RPM
Red/Green	24	Electrical Load Switch	0-3 Volts With KOER [1] (Accessories Off)
Black/Red	25	Power Supply	Battery Voltage With KOEO [2]
Black	26	Ground Circuit	Not Applicable
Black/White [4]	51	Ignition Switch	8 Volts Or More With Engine Cranking
Red/Blue	52	Intake Air Temperature Sensor	0.4-1.0 Volt With KOEO [2] (Sensor @ 176°F)
Blue/Red	53	Radiator Fan Motor Relay-Hi	Battery Voltage With KOER [1] (Fan Off)
	54	BLANK	N/A

[1] – KOER – Key On, Engine Running.
[2] – KOEO – Key On, Engine Off.
[3] – Wire color is Green/Yellow on DOHC.
[4] – On M/T models, wire color is Black/Yellow.

94E44309

Fig. 22: Pin Voltage Chart Stealth (SOHC & DOHC Non – Turbo – Federal) & 3000GT (Non – Turbo – Federal) – 1 Of 2

	Terminal ID.	Function/Description	Voltage Value (DC Volts Unless Otherwise Specified)
White	55	Heated Oxygen Sensor	0-.8 Volt (Pulse) With KOER [1]
White	56	Heated Oxygen Sensor	0-.8 Volt (Pulse) With KOER [1]
White	57	BLANK	N/A
White/Red	58	Knock Sensor (DOHC)	Not Available
Red/Black	59	Transaxle Control Module	0-1 Volt With KOER [1]
Green/Yellow	60	Back-Up Power Supply	Battery Voltage With Ignition Off
Black/White	61	Throttle Position Sensor	4.5-5.5 Volts With KOEO [2]
Black/White	62	Ignition Supply Voltage	Battery Voltage With KOEO [2]
Brown/Red	63	Coolant Temperature Sensor	.3-.9 Volt With KOEO [2] (Sensor @ 176°F)
Orange	64	Throttle Position Sensor	0.3-1.0 Volt With KOEO [2]
Yellow/White	65	Barometric Pressure Sensor	3.7-4.3 Volts With KOER [1] (Sea Level)
Yellow/Red	66	Vehicle Speed Sensor	0-5 Volts (Pulse) With KOEO [1] (Sensor Rotating)
Blue/Red	67	Closed Throttle Position Switch	0-1 Volt With KOEO [2]
Blue/Red	68	Camshaft Position Sensor	0.2-3.0 Volts With KOER [1]
Blue/Yellow	69	Crankshaft Position Sensor	0.2-3.0 Volts With KOER [1]
Black/Yellow	70	Airflow Sensor	2.2-3.2 Volts With KOER [1]
Black	71	Park/Neutral Position Switch	0-3 Volts With KOEO [2] In Park
Blue/Orange	72	Throttle Position Sensor	Not Available
White	101	Air Conditioning Switch (SOHC)	0-3 Volts (A/C Off)
White	101	Ignition Signal (DOHC)	0.3-3.0 Volts With Engine @ 3000 RPM
Black/Blue	102	Heated Oxygen Sensor (Calif.)	0.6-1.0 Volts With KOER [1] (WOT-Low Gear)
Black/Green	103	Induction Control Valve Position Sensor (DOHC)	0-1 Or 4.5-5.5 With KOEO [2]
White	104	Ignition Timing Adjustment Terminal	4.0-5.5 Volts With KOEO [2] (GND Disconnected)
Green/Red	105	Heated Oxygen Sensor (Calif.)	0.6-1.0 Volts With KOER [1] (WOT-Low Gear)
Blue/White	106	Malfunction Indicator Light	0-3 Volts With KOEO [2] (Initially)
Blue/Green	107	Power Steering Pressure Switch	Battery Voltage With KOER [1]
Green/Black	108	MFI Relay Supply Voltage	Battery Voltage With Ignition Off
Green/White	109	Variable Induction Control Motor (Closed)	0-1 Volt With KOER [1] (Decelerating)
Red/White	110	Variable Induction Control Motor (Open)	0-1 Volt With KOER [1] (Accelerating)
Yellow	111	Variable Induction Control Position Sensor [3]	0-1 Volt Or 4.5-5.5 Volts With KOEO [2]
Pink	112	Data Link Connector	Not Available
	113	Data Link Connector	Not Available
Blue/Red	114	BLANK	N/A
White/Blue	115	Air Conditioning Switch	0-3 Volts With KOER [1] (A/C Off)
	116	Transaxle Control Module	4.5-5.5 Volts With KOER [1] (DOHC)

[1] – KOER – Key On, Engine Running.
[2] – KOEO – Key On, Engine Off.

94H44310

Fig. 23: Pin Voltage Chart (Stealth (SOHC & DOHC Non – Turbo – Federal) & 3000GT (Non – Turbo – Federal) – 2 Of 2)

1994 ENGINE PERFORMANCE
Pin Voltage Charts (Cont.)

Green
Green/Yellow
Green/Black
Gray
Gray/Blue
Lt. Green/Red
Blue/Red
White/Red
Lt. Green/Red
Black/Blue
Brown/Red
Black/Red
Black
Yellow/Black
Green/Red
Green/White
Green/Black
Green/Yellow
Red/White
Blue/Red
Green/Yellow
Green
Black/White
Red/Green
Black/Red
Black
Black/White
Red/Yellow
Red
Red/White
Green
Blue/White
Blue/Green
Green/Black
Green/White
Red/White
White/Red
Red/Blue

Terminal ID.	Function/Description	Voltage Value (DC Volts Unless Otherwise Specified)
1	Injector No. 1	Battery Voltage With KOER [1]
2	Injector No. 3	Battery Voltage With KOER [1]
3	Injector No. 5	Battery Voltage With KOER [1]
4	Idle Air Control Motor	Battery Voltage/0-3 Volts (Load Controlled)
5	Idle Air Control Motor	Battery Voltage/0-3 Volts (Load Controlled)
6	EGR Solenoid	Battery Voltage With KOEO [2]
7	Transmission Control Module	1-4 Volts With KOER [1]
8	Multi-Port Fuel Injection Pump Relay	0-3 Volts With KOER [1]
9	Purge Control Solenoid	Battery Voltage With KOEO [2]
10	Ignition Power Transistor	0.3-3.0 Volts With Engine @ 3000 RPM
11	Ignition Power Transistor	0.3-3.0 Volts With Engine @ 3000 RPM
12	Power Supply	Battery Voltage With KOEO [2]
13	Ground Circuit	Not Applicable
14	Injector No. 2	Battery Voltage With KOER [1]
15	Injector No. 4	Battery Voltage With KOER [1]
16	Injector No. 6	Battery Voltage With KOER [1]
17	Idle Air Control Motor	Battery Voltage/0-3 Volts (Load Controlled)
18	Idle Air Control Motor	Battery Voltage/0-3 Volts (Load Controlled)
19	Airflow Sensor Reset Signal	0-1 Volt With KOER [1]
20	Radiator Fan Motor Relay-Hi	Battery Voltage With KOEO [2] (Fan Off)
21	Radiator Fan Motor Relay-Lo	Battery Voltage With KOEO [2] (Fan Off)
22	Air Conditioning Clutch Relay (A/C On)	Battery Voltage With KOER [1]
23	Ignition Power Transistor	0.3-3.0 Volts With Engine @ 3000 RPM
24	Electrical Load Switch	0-3 Volts With KOER [1] (Accessories Off)
25	Power Supply	Battery Voltage With KOEO [2]
26	Ground Circuit	Not Applicable
31	Fuel Pump Relay No. 2	0-3 Volts With KOER [1] (Snap Throttle)
32	Turbo Wastegate Solenoid	Battery Voltage With KOEO [2]
33	BLANK	N/A
34	Exhaust Mode Switch	0-3 Volts With KOEO [2] (Switch On)
35	Exhaust Mode Indicator Signal	0-3 Volts With KOER [1] (Switch On)
36	Check Engine Light	0-3 Volts With KOEO [2] (Initially)
37	Power Steering Pressure Switch	Battery Voltage With KOER [1]
38	MFI Relay Supply Voltage	Battery Voltage With Ignition Off
39	Variable Induction Control Motor	0-1 Volt With KOER [1] (Decelerating)
40	Variable Induction Control Motor	0-1 Volt With KOER [1] (Accelerating)
41	Variable Induction Control Position Sensor	0-1 Volt Or 4.5-5.5 Volts With KOEO [2]
42	BLANK	N/A
43	Transmission Control Module	0-1 Volt With KOER [1]
44	ABS Signal	Battery Voltage With KOER [1]

[1] – KOER – Key On, Engine Running.
[2] – KOEO – Key On, Engine Off.

94I44311

Fig. 24: Pin Voltage Chart Stealth (DOHC – Calif. & DOHC Turbo – Federal) & 3000GT (Calif. & Turbo – Federal) – 1 Of 2)

	Terminal ID.	Function/Description	Voltage Value (DC Volts Unless Otherwise Specified)
Green/Red →	45	Air Conditioning Switch	0-3 Volts With KOER [1] (A/C Off)
White/Blue →	46	Traction Control Module	4.5-5.5 Volts With KOER [1]
	51	BLANK	N/A
Blue/Green →	52	Ignition Timing Adjustment Terminal	4.0-5.5 Volts With KOEO [2] (GND Disconnected)
	53	BLANK	N/A
	54	BLANK	N/A
	55	BLANK	N/A
Pink →	56	Data Link Connector	Not Available
	57	BLANK	N/A
White →	58	Engine Ignition Signal	.3-3.0 Volt With KOER [1] (3000 RPM)
Blue/Orange →	59	Air Conditioning Switch	0-3 Volts With KOER [1] (A/C Off)
White →	60	Heated Oxygen Sensor R.R.	.6-1.0 Volt In 2nd Gear Or "L" @ WOT
	61	BLANK	N/A
Yellow →	62	Data Link Connector	Not Available
Black/Yellow →	71	Ignition Switch	8 Volts Or More With Engine Cranking
Red/Blue →	72	Intake Air Temperature Sensor	0.4-1.0 Volt With KOEO [2] (Sensor @ 176°F)
Yellow →	73	EGR Temperature Sensor	2.2-3.0 Volts With KOEO [2] (Sensor @ 212°F)
Black →	74	Oxygen Sensor Heater	0-3 Volts With KOER [1]
White →	75	Heated Oxygen Sensor R.F.	0-.8 Volt (Pulse) With KOER [1] (2000 RPM)
White →	76	Heated Oxygen Sensor L.F.	0-.8 Volt (Pulse) With KOER [1] (2000 RPM)
Black →	77	Oxygen Sensor Heater	0-3 Volts With KOER [1]
Black →	78	Knock Sensor	Not Available
White →	79	Heated Oxygen Sensor L.R.	.6-1.0 Volt In 2nd Gear Or "L" @ WOT
Red/Black →	80	Back-Up Power Supply	Battery Voltage With Ignition Off
Green/Yellow →	81	Throttle Position Sensor	4.5-5.5 Volts With KOEO [2]
Black/White →	82	Ignition Supply Voltage	Battery Voltage With KOEO [2]
Black/White →	83	Coolant Temperature Sensor	.3-.9 Volt With KOEO [2] (Sensor @ 176°F)
Brown/Red →	84	Throttle Position Sensor	0.3-1.0 Volt With KOEO [2]
Orange →	85	Barometric Pressure Sensor	3.7-4.3 Volts With KOER [1] (Sea Level)
Yellow/White →	86	Vehicle Speed Sensor	0-5 Volts (Pulse) With KOEO [2], Sensor Rotating
Yellow/Red →	87	Closed Throttle Position Switch	0-1 Volt With KOEO [2]
Blue/Red →	88	Camshaft Position Sensor	0.2-3.0 Volts With KOER [1]
Blue/White →	89	Crankshaft Position Sensor	0.2-3.0 Volts With KOER [1]
Blue/Yellow →	90	Airflow Sensor	2.2-3.2 Volts With KOER [1]
Black/Yellow →	91	Park/Neutral Position Switch	0-3 Volts With KOEO [2] In Park
Black →	92	Coolant Temperature Sensor	Not Applicable

[1] – KOER – Key On, Engine Running.
[2] – KOEO – Key On, Engine Off.

94J44312

Fig. 25: Pin Voltage Chart Stealth (DOHC-Calif. & DOHC Turbo – Federal) & 3000GT (Calif. & Turbo – Federal) – 2 Of 2)

1994 ENGINE PERFORMANCE
Sensor Operating Range Charts

Chrysler Corp.: Colt, Colt Vista, Stealth
Eagle: Summit, Summit Wagon
Mitsubishi: Diamante, Eclipse, Expo, Galant,
Mirage, Montero, Pickup, Precis, 3000GT

INTRODUCTION

Sensor operating range information can help determine if a sensor is out of calibration. An out-of-calibration sensor may not set a trouble code, but it may cause driveability problems.

NOTE: Unless stated otherwise in test procedure, perform all voltage tests using a Digital Volt-Ohmmeter (DVOM) with a minimum 10-megohm input impedance. For connector and terminal identification, see WIRING DIAGRAMS article.

AIRFLOW METER HERTZ TEST [1]

Condition	Hz
Colt, Mirage & Summit	
1.8L	
700 RPM	23-49
2000 RPM	51-91
Colt Vista, Expo & Summit Wagon	
1.8L	
750 RPM	23-49
2000 RPM	51-91
2.4L	
750 RPM	18-44
2000 RPM	43-83
Diamante	
700 RPM	21-47
2000 RPM	57-97
Eclipse	
1.8L	
700 RPM	25-40
2000 RPM	67-88
2.0L	
750 RPM	25-50
2000 RPM	
Non-Turbo	70-90
Turbo	60-85
Galant	
SOHC	
750 RPM	18-44
2000 RPM	64-104
DOHC	
800 RPM	28-54
2000 RPM	45-85
Montero	
3.0L	
700 RPM	22-48
2000 RPM	60-100
3.5L	
700 RPM	27-53
2000 RPM	60-100
Pickup	
2.4L	
750 RPM	40-60
2000 RPM	85-105
3.0L	
700 RPM	25-45
2000 RPM	70-90
Precis	
750 RPM	27-33
2000 RPM	60-80
Stealth & 3000GT	
SOHC	
700 RPM	21-47
2000 RPM	57-97
DOHC (Non-Turbo)	
700 RPM	22-48
2000 RPM	50-90
DOHC (Turbo)	
700 RPM	21-47
2000 RPM	68-108

[1] – Measure hertz frequency with Multi-Use Tester (MUT-II).

COOLANT TEMPERATURE SENSOR RESISTANCE

Temperature °F (°C)	Ohms
Eclipse	
68 (20)	2200-2600
176 (80)	264-328
Galant	
32 (0)	5100-6500
68 (20)	2100-2700
104 (40)	900-1300
176 (80)	260-360
Pickup 2.4L	
32 (0)	5900
68 (20)	2500
104 (40)	1100
176 (80)	300
All Others	
32 (0)	5800
68 (20)	2400
104 (40)	1100
176 (80)	300

EGR TEMPERATURE SENSOR RESISTANCE TEST [1] [2]

Temperature °F (°C)	Ohms
122 (50)	60-83
212 (100)	11-14

[1] – Measure resistance across disconnected sensor terminals.
[2] – Specifications apply to all models except Montero.

INTAKE AIR TEMPERATURE SENSOR RESISTANCE

Temperature °F (°C)	Ohms
Galant & Precis	
32 (0)	5300-6700
68 (20)	2300-3000
176 (80)	300-420
All Others	
32 (0)	6000
68 (20)	2700
176 (80)	400

OXYGEN SENSOR VOLTAGE TEST [1]

Application	Volts
All Models	
Lean	0.1
Rich	1.0

[1] – Test at normal operating temperature.

Throttle Position Sensor (TPS) – Measure total and variable resistance between specified TPS connector terminals. See TPS TEST TERMINALS table. Total resistance should be 3500-6500 ohms. Variable resistance should change smoothly between 3500 and 6500 ohms as throttle valve is moved from closed to wide open throttle.

TPS TEST TERMINALS

Application	Terminals No.
Total Resistance	1 & 4
Variable Resistance	
Colt Vista, Expo, Montero, Pickup 3.0L, Precis & Summit Wagon	1 & 3
All Others	2 & 4

VEHICLE SPEED SENSOR CONTINUITY TEST [1]

Application   [2] **Continuity**

All Models .... 4 Changes Per Revolution

[1] – Measure continuity at back of speedometer. See appropriate wiring diagram in WIRING DIAGRAMS article.

[2] – With ECM connector disconnected, turn speedometer cable to cycle reed switch on and off.

VEHICLE SPEED SENSOR VOLTAGE TEST [1]

Application   [2] **Volts**

All Models
  Ignition Switch Off .... 1 Or Less
  Ignition Switch On 4.5-4.9

[1] – Measure voltage at back of speedometer. See appropriate wiring diagram in WIRING DIAGRAMS article.

[2] – With ECM connector disconnected, turn speedometer cable to cycle reed switch on and off.

1994 ENGINE PERFORMANCE
Vacuum Diagrams

**Chrysler Corp.: Colt, Colt Vista, Stealth
Eagle: Summit, Summit Wagon
Mitsubishi: Diamante, Eclipse, Expo, Galant,
Mirage, Montero, Pickup, Precis, 3000GT**

INTRODUCTION

This article contains underhood views or schematics of vacuum hose routing. Use these vacuum diagrams during the visual inspection in BASIC DIAGNOSTIC PROCEDURES article. This will assist in identifying improperly routed vacuum hoses, which cause driveability and/or computer-indicated malfunctions.

NOTE: Always refer to Emission Control label in engine compartment before attempting service. If manual and label differ, always use emission label specifications.

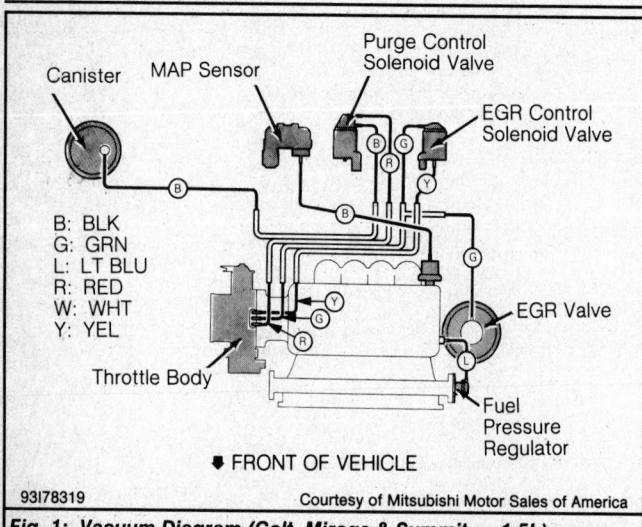

93I78319   Courtesy of Mitsubishi Motor Sales of America

Fig. 1: Vacuum Diagram (Colt, Mirage & Summit – 1.5L)

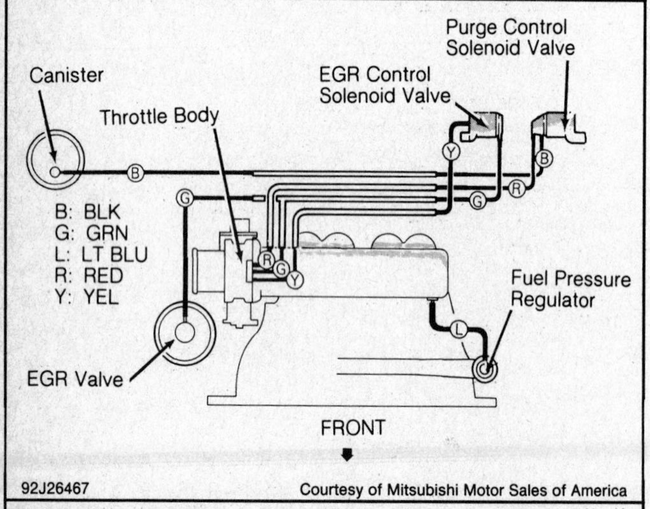

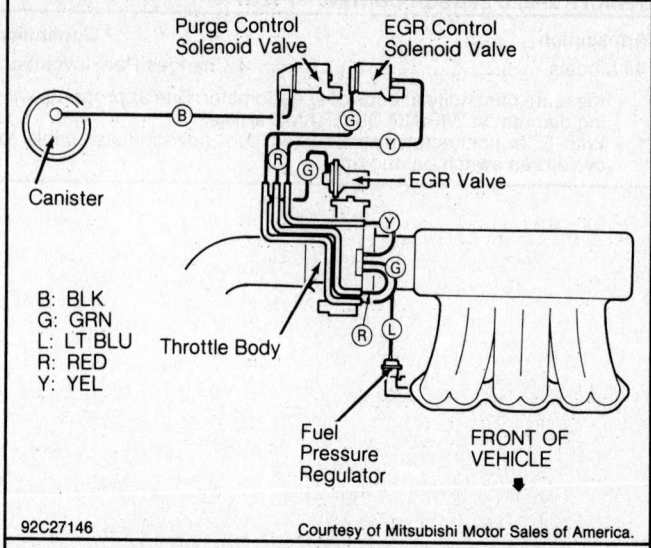

92C27146   Courtesy of Mitsubishi Motor Sales of America.

Fig. 3: Vacuum Diagram (Diamante SOHC & DOHC Without Traction Control – California)

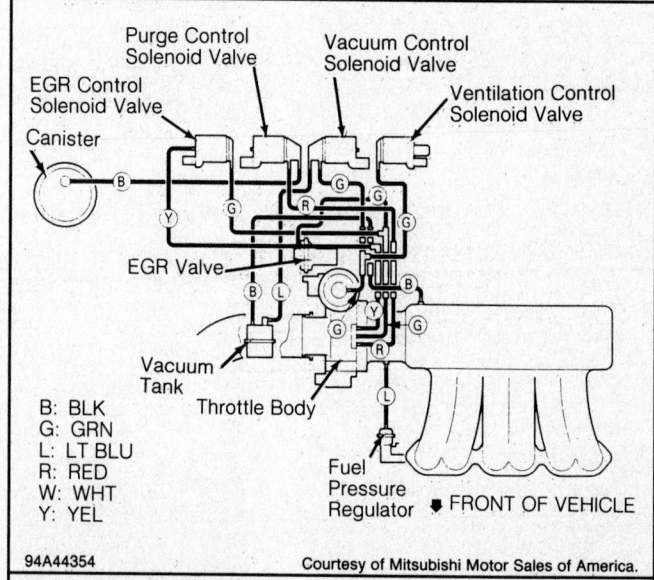

94A44354   Courtesy of Mitsubishi Motor Sales of America.

Fig. 4: Vacuum Diagram (Diamante DOHC With Traction Control – California)

92J26467   Courtesy of Mitsubishi Motor Sales of America

Fig. 2: Vacuum Diagram (Colt, Mirage, Summit – 1.8L, & Colt Vista, Expo & Summit Wagon – 1.8L & 2.4L)

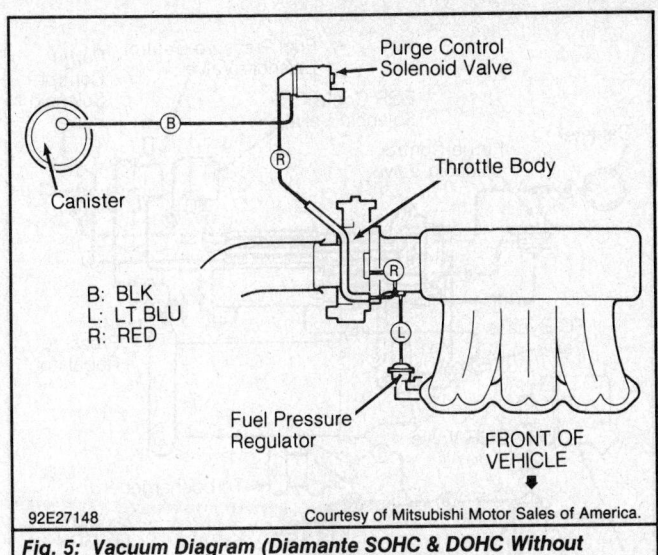

Purge Control
Solenoid Valve

Throttle Body

Canister

B: BLK
L: LT BLU
R: RED

Fuel Pressure
Regulator

FRONT OF
VEHICLE

92E27148

Courtesy of Mitsubishi Motor Sales of America.

Fig. 5: Vacuum Diagram (Diamante SOHC & DOHC Without Traction Control – Federal)

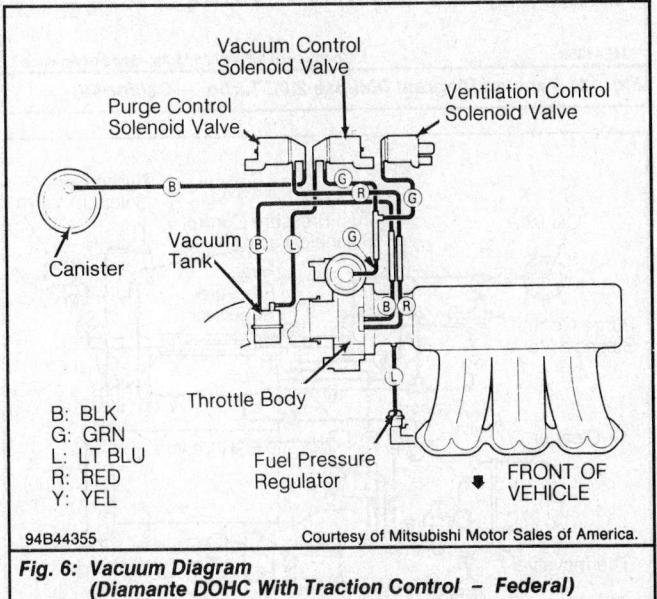

Vacuum Control
Solenoid Valve

Ventilation Control
Solenoid Valve

Purge Control
Solenoid Valve

Vacuum
Tank

Canister

Throttle Body

B: BLK
G: GRN
L: LT BLU
R: RED
Y: YEL

Fuel Pressure
Regulator

FRONT OF
VEHICLE

94B44355

Courtesy of Mitsubishi Motor Sales of America.

Fig. 6: Vacuum Diagram (Diamante DOHC With Traction Control – Federal)

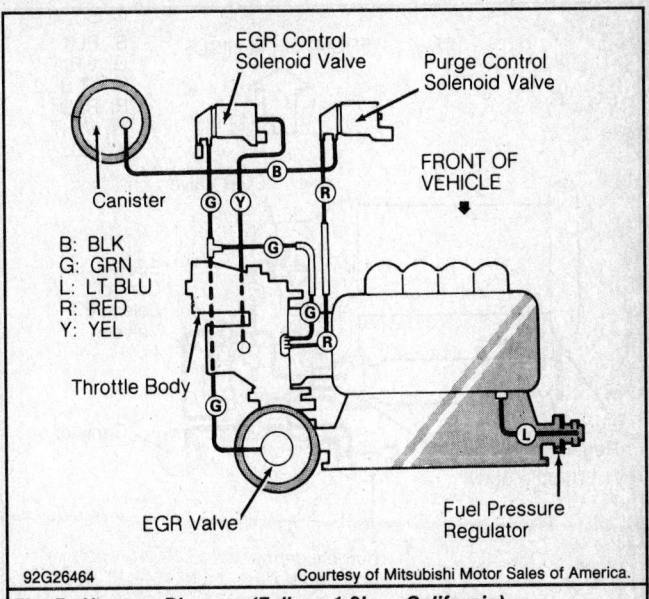

EGR Control
Solenoid Valve

Purge Control
Solenoid Valve

FRONT OF
VEHICLE

Canister

B: BLK
G: GRN
L: LT BLU
R: RED
Y: YEL

Throttle Body

EGR Valve

Fuel Pressure
Regulator

92G26464

Courtesy of Mitsubishi Motor Sales of America.

Fig. 7: Vacuum Diagram (Eclipse 1.8L – California)

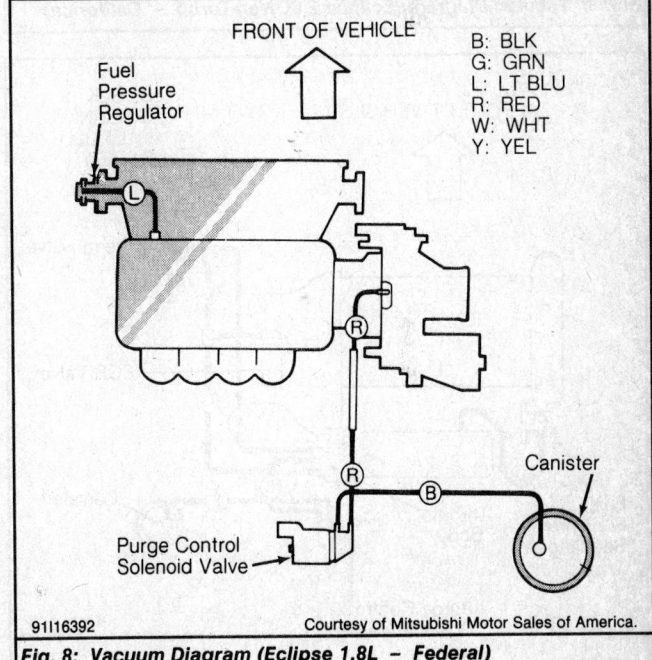

FRONT OF VEHICLE

Fuel
Pressure
Regulator

B: BLK
G: GRN
L: LT BLU
R: RED
W: WHT
Y: YEL

Canister

Purge Control
Solenoid Valve

91I16392

Courtesy of Mitsubishi Motor Sales of America.

Fig. 8: Vacuum Diagram (Eclipse 1.8L – Federal)

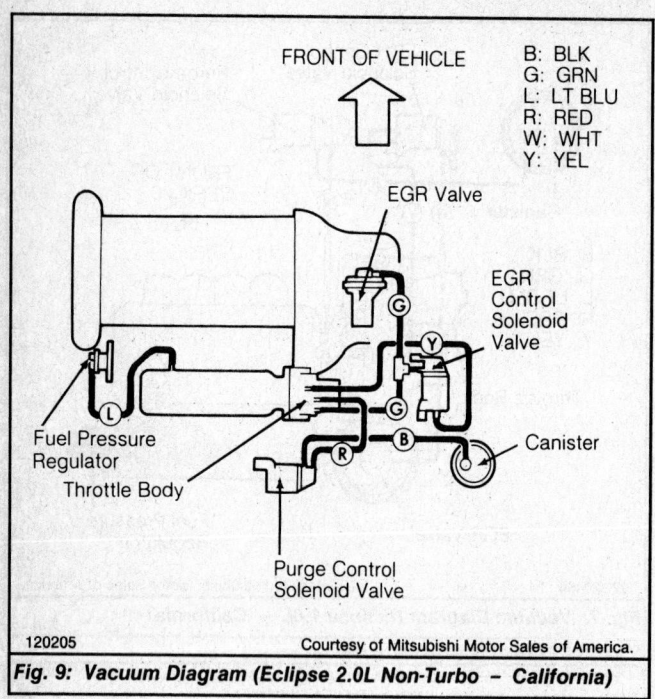

Fig. 9: Vacuum Diagram (Eclipse 2.0L Non-Turbo – California)

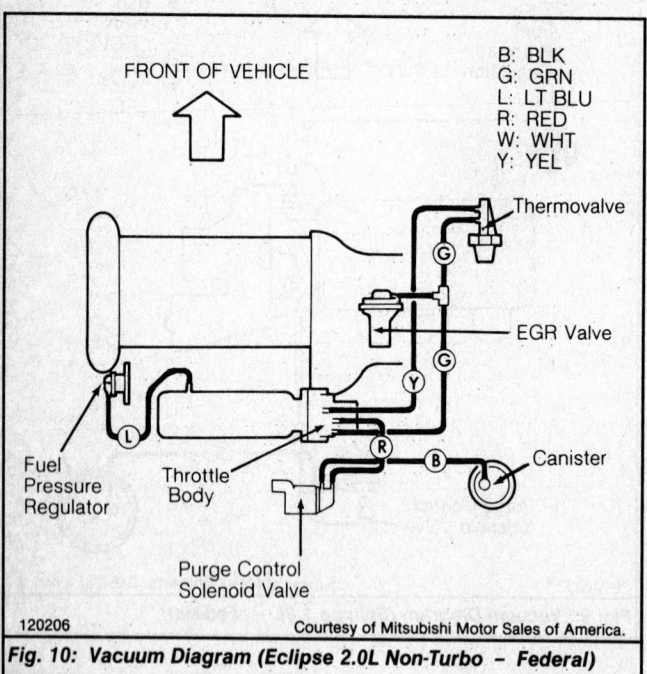

Fig. 10: Vacuum Diagram (Eclipse 2.0L Non-Turbo – Federal)

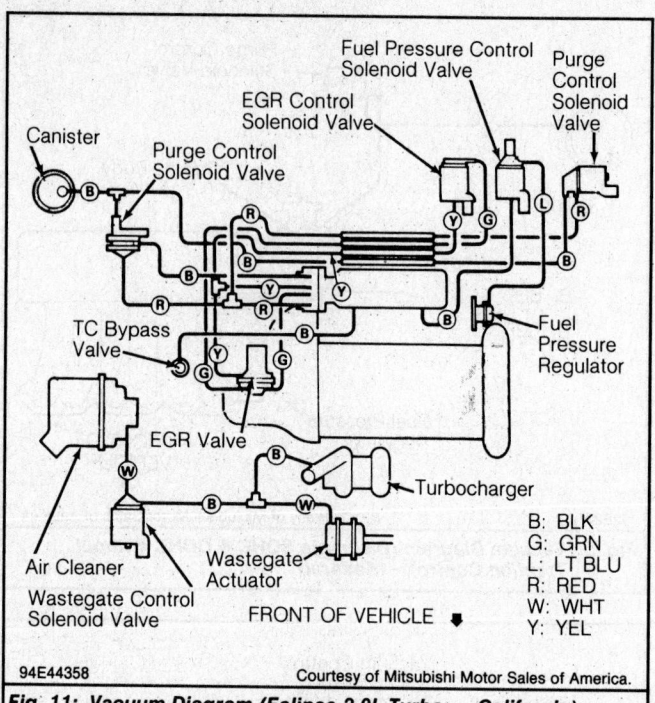

Fig. 11: Vacuum Diagram (Eclipse 2.0L Turbo – California)

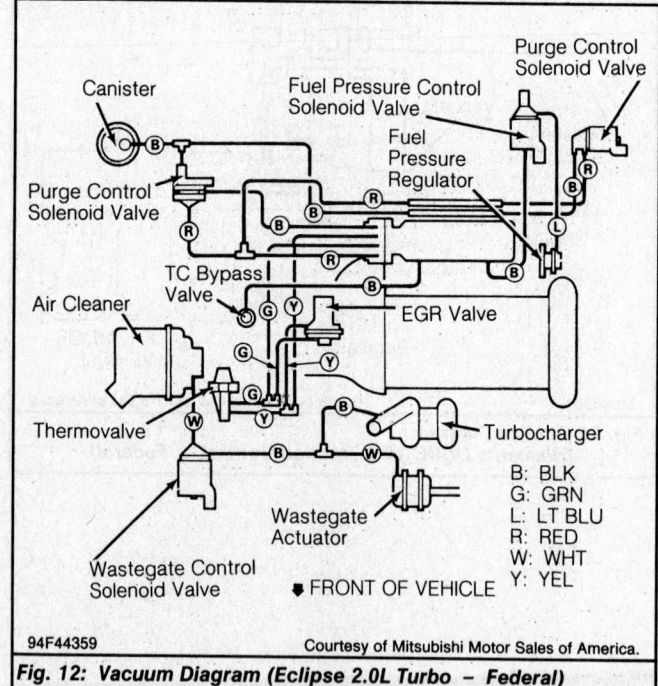

Fig. 12: Vacuum Diagram (Eclipse 2.0L Turbo – Federal)

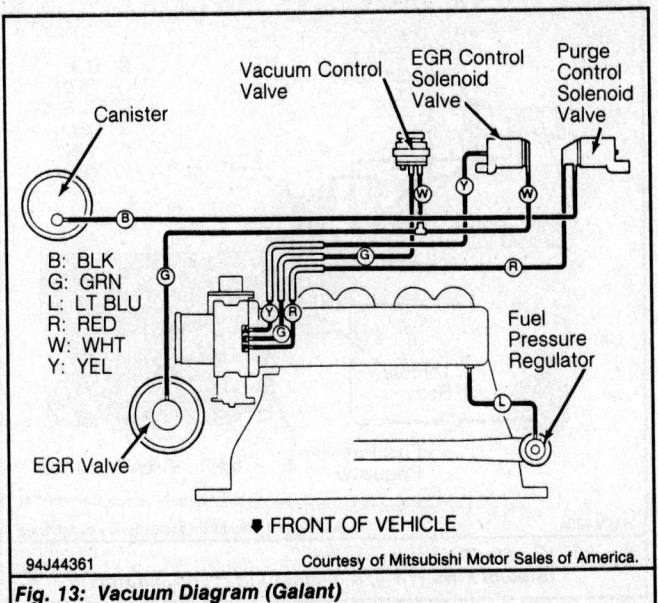

Fig. 13: Vacuum Diagram (Galant)

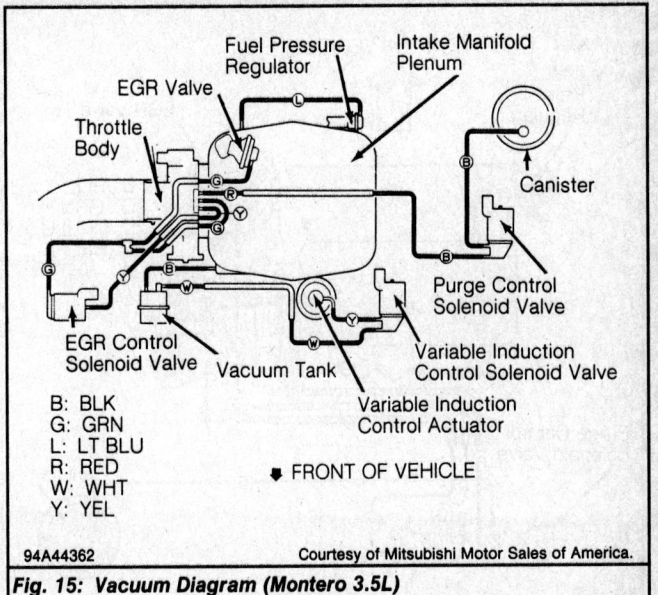

Fig. 15: Vacuum Diagram (Montero 3.5L)

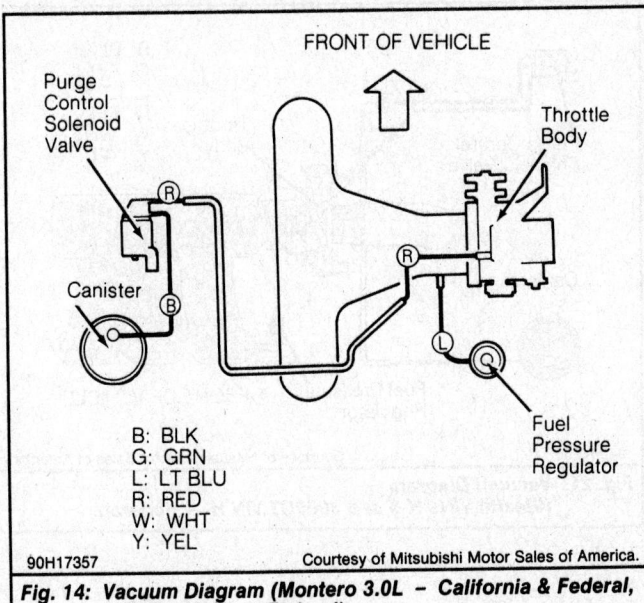

Fig. 14: Vacuum Diagram (Montero 3.0L – California & Federal, & Pickup 3.0L – Federal)

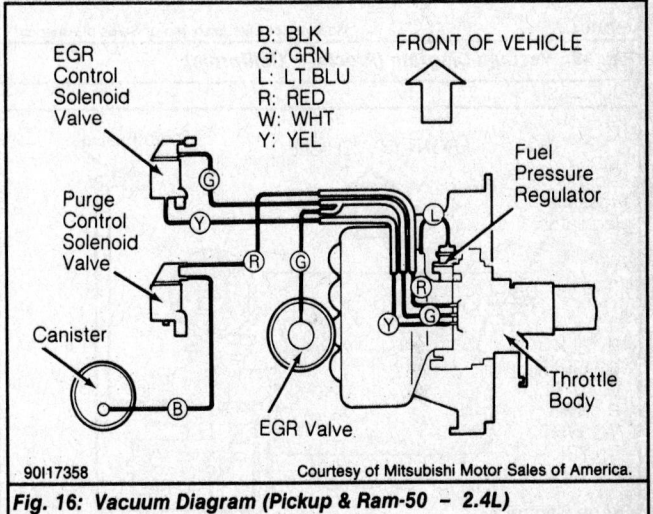

Fig. 16: Vacuum Diagram (Pickup & Ram-50 – 2.4L)

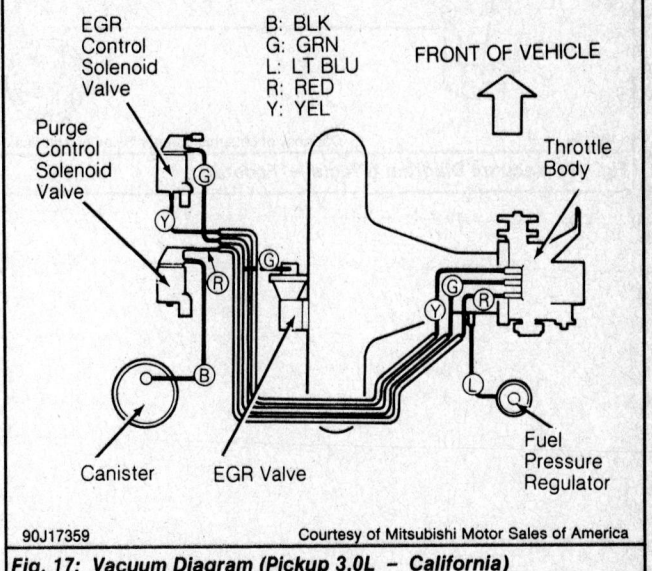

Fig. 17: Vacuum Diagram (Pickup 3.0L – California)

1994 ENGINE PERFORMANCE
Vacuum Diagrams (Cont.)

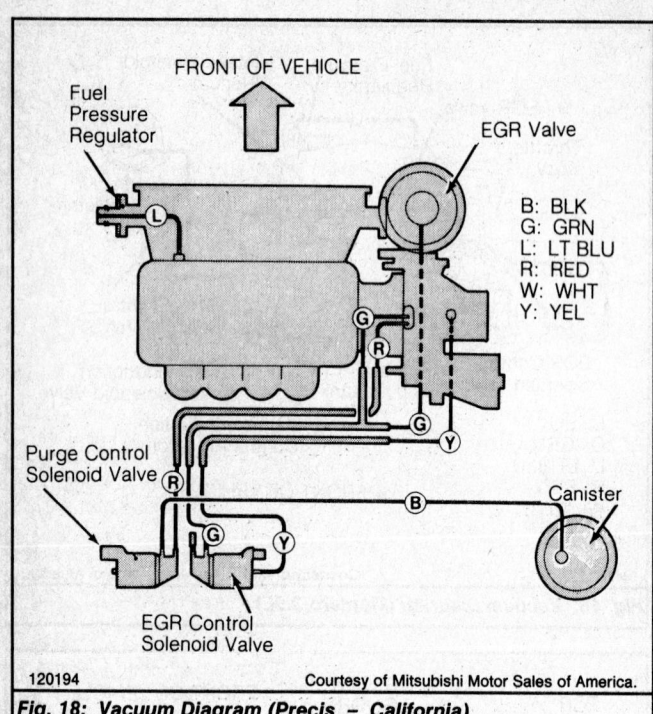

Fig. 18: Vacuum Diagram (Precis – California)

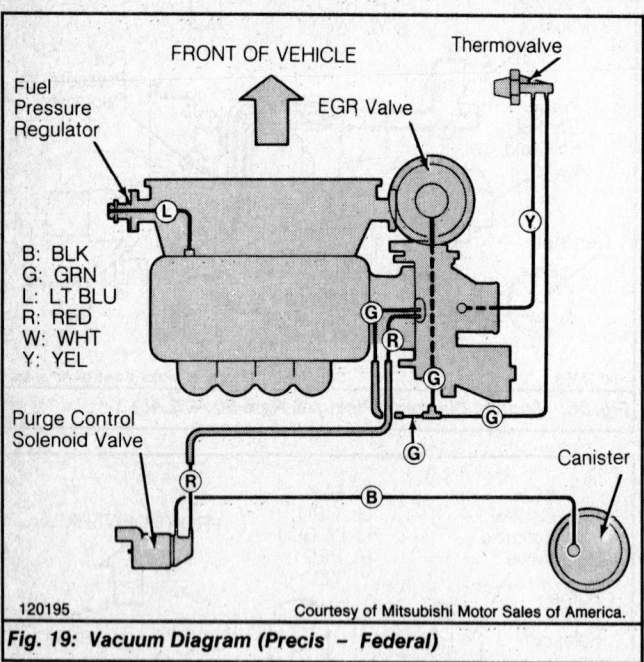

Fig. 19: Vacuum Diagram (Precis – Federal)

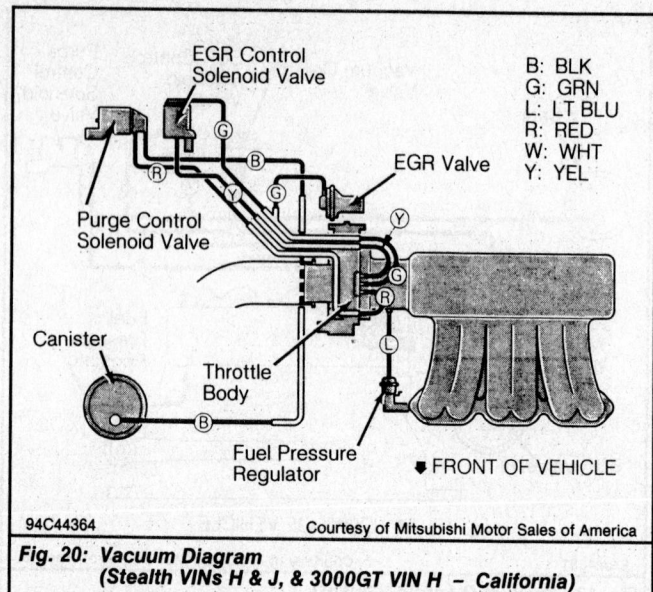

Fig. 20: Vacuum Diagram (Stealth VINs H & J, & 3000GT VIN H – California)

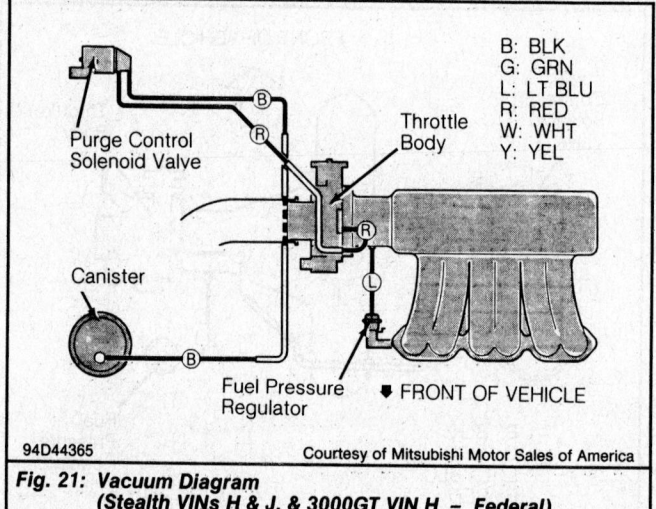

Fig. 21: Vacuum Diagram (Stealth VINs H & J, & 3000GT VIN H – Federal)

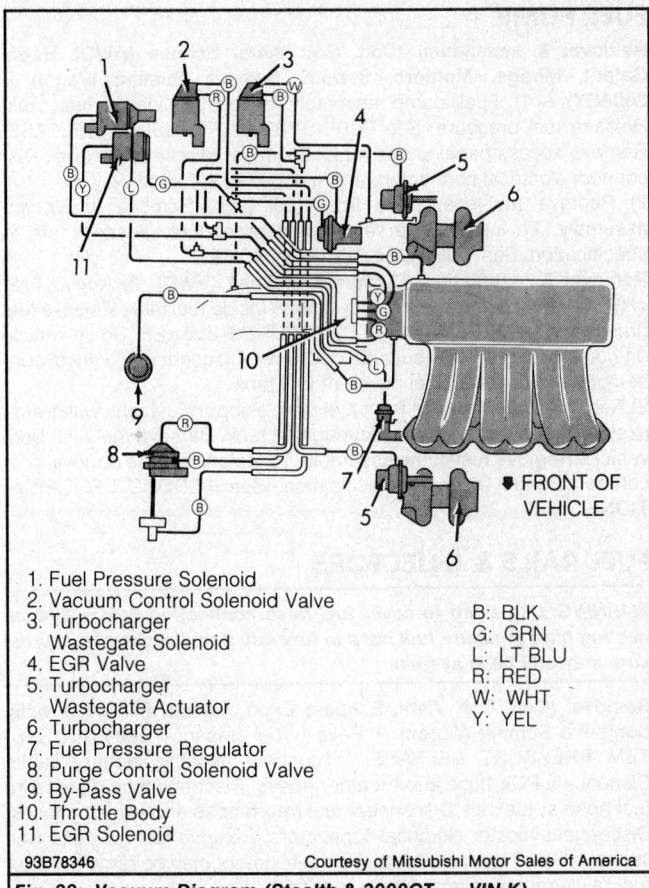

1. Fuel Pressure Solenoid
2. Vacuum Control Solenoid Valve
3. Turbocharger
   Wastegate Solenoid
4. EGR Valve
5. Turbocharger
   Wastegate Actuator
6. Turbocharger
7. Fuel Pressure Regulator
8. Purge Control Solenoid Valve
9. By-Pass Valve
10. Throttle Body
11. EGR Solenoid

B: BLK
G: GRN
L: LT BLU
R: RED
W: WHT
Y: YEL

↓ FRONT OF
VEHICLE

93B78346   Courtesy of Mitsubishi Motor Sales of America

Fig. 22: Vacuum Diagram (Stealth & 3000GT – VIN K)

1994 ENGINE PERFORMANCE
Removal, Overhaul & Installation

Chrysler Corp.: Colt, Colt Vista, Stealth
Eagle: Summit, Summit Wagon
Mitsubishi: Diamante, Eclipse, Expo, Galant,
Mirage, Montero, Pickup, Precis, 3000GT

INTRODUCTION

Removal, overhaul and installation procedures are covered in this article. If component removal and installation is primarily an unbolt and bolt-on procedure, only a torque specification may be furnished.

IGNITION SYSTEM

DISTRIBUTOR

NOTE: *Diamante 3.0L DOHC, Eclipse 2.0L, Galant 2.4L DOHC, Montero 3.5L, Stealth 3.0L DOHC & 3000GT use Distributorless Ignition System (DIS). All models (except Precis) with distributor type ignition systems have non-serviceable distributors. See Fig. 1 for exploded view of Precis distributor.*

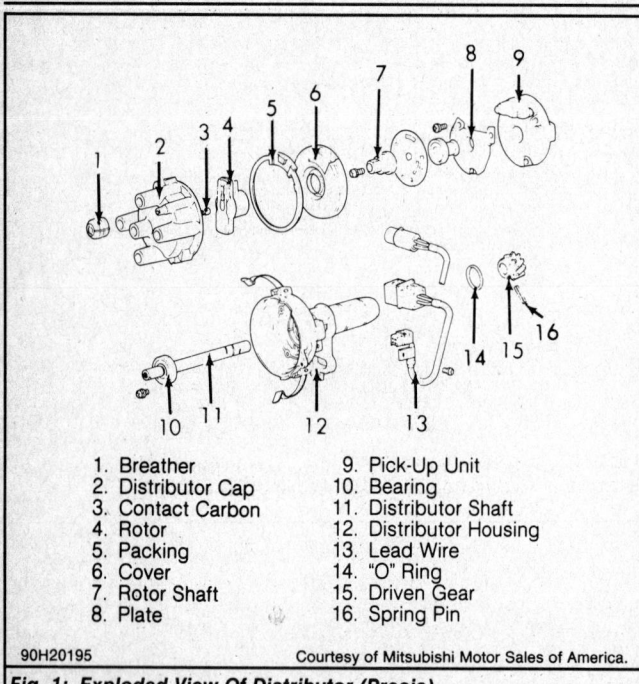

1. Breather
2. Distributor Cap
3. Contact Carbon
4. Rotor
5. Packing
6. Cover
7. Rotor Shaft
8. Plate
9. Pick-Up Unit
10. Bearing
11. Distributor Shaft
12. Distributor Housing
13. Lead Wire
14. "O" Ring
15. Driven Gear
16. Spring Pin

90H20195   Courtesy of Mitsubishi Motor Sales of America.

Fig. 1: Exploded View Of Distributor (Precis)

FUEL SYSTEM

WARNING: *Always relieve fuel pressure before disconnecting any fuel injection-related component. DO NOT allow fuel to contact engine or electrical components.*

FUEL SYSTEM PRESSURE RELEASE

Relieving Fuel Pressure – 1) On Diamante, Eclipse (FWD), Pickup and Precis, disconnect fuel pump harness connector at fuel tank from underneath vehicle. On Colt, Colt Vista, Eclipse (AWD), Expo, Galant, Mirage, Montero, Stealth, Summit, Summit Wagon and 3000GT, remove rear seat cushion and remove access plate if required to disconnect fuel pump harness connector.
2) On all models, start engine. Let engine run until it stops. Turn ignition off. Disconnect negative battery terminal. Connect fuel pump harness connector. Reinstall rear seat (if necessary.)

WARNING: *Before disconnecting high pressure fuel hose at fuel delivery pipe, cover fuel hose connection with a rag. Some residual fuel pressure may still be in system.*

FUEL PUMP

Removal & Installation (Colt, Colt Vista, Eclipse (AWD), Expo, Galant, Mirage, Montero, Stealth, Summit, Summit Wagon & 3000GT) – 1) Fuel pump assembly is located inside fuel tank. Release fuel pressure. See FUEL SYSTEM PRESSURE RELEASE. Remove access panel under seat, in trunk or in rear cargo area. Disconnect electrical connectors and fuel hoses at fuel tank.
2) Remove fuel filler hose from fuel tank. Remove fuel pump assembly. To install, reverse removal procedure. Tighten nuts to specification. See TORQUE SPECIFICATIONS.
Removal & Installation (Diamante, Eclipse (FWD), Pickup & Precis) – 1) Fuel pump assembly is located inside fuel tank. Release fuel pressure. See FUEL SYSTEM PRESSURE RELEASE. Raise vehicle on hoist. Drain fuel into suitable container. Disconnect electrical connectors and breather/fuel hoses at fuel tank.
2) Remove fuel filler hose from fuel tank. Support fuel tank with transmission jack. Remove nuts securing fuel tank. Remove fuel tank from vehicle. Remove fuel pump assembly. To install, reverse removal procedure. Tighten nuts to specification. See TORQUE SPECIFICATIONS.

FUEL RAILS & INJECTORS

WARNING: *Use a rag to cover fuel hose connection before disconnecting high pressure fuel hose at fuel rail. Some residual fuel pressure may still be in system.*

Removal (Colt, Colt Vista, Eclipse, Expo, Galant, Mirage, Precis, Summit & Summit Wagon) – Relieve fuel pressure. See FUEL SYSTEM PRESSURE RELEASE. Disconnect negative battery cable. Disconnect PCV hose and breather hoses. Disconnect high pressure fuel hose at fuel rail. Disconnect fuel return hose and vacuum hoses. Disconnect injector electrical connectors. Remove fuel rail bolts, and lift fuel rail and injectors from engine. Injectors may be removed after fuel rail is removed from intake manifold.
Installation – 1) To install, reverse removal procedure. Use new insulators and "O" rings when installing injectors.
2) Use lubricant on "O" rings. Install injectors into fuel rail with a twisting motion. Ensure injectors rotate smoothly when installing. DO NOT drop injectors while removing or installing fuel rail.
Removal (Pickup 2.4L) – 1) Relieve fuel pressure. See FUEL SYSTEM PRESSURE RELEASE. Drain enough coolant to ensure coolant level is below throttle body. Disconnect negative battery cable. Remove air intake and breather hoses. Disconnect throttle body wiring harness connectors. Disconnect accelerator cable.
2) On A/T models, disconnect kickdown cable. On all models, disconnect coolant hoses from throttle body. Label and disconnect vacuum hoses as necessary. Remove throttle body and gasket. Disconnect fuel injector wiring harness connectors.
3) Disconnect high pressure fuel hose at fuel rail. Disconnect fuel return hose. Disconnect vacuum hoses. Disconnect injector electrical connectors. Remove fuel rail bolts and lift fuel rail and injectors from engine. Injectors may be removed after fuel rail is removed from intake manifold.
Installation – 1) To install, reverse removal procedure. Use new insulators and "O" rings when installing injectors.
2) Use lubricant on "O" rings. Install injectors into fuel rail using a twisting motion. Ensure injectors rotate smoothly when installing. Adjust throttle and kickdown cable (if necessary). DO NOT drop injectors while removing or installing fuel rail.
Removal (Pickup 3.0L & Montero) – 1) Relieve fuel pressure. See FUEL SYSTEM PRESSURE RELEASE. Disconnect negative battery cable. Remove air intake hose. Remove accelerator cable adjusting bolts. On A/T models, remove throttle control cable. On all models, remove accelerator cable. Label and disconnect all vacuum hoses from throttle body and upper intake manifold (air intake plenum).
2) Remove EGR pipe and gasket. Remove ignition coil (if necessary). Remove engine oil filler neck bracket. Disconnect PCV hose. Remove throttle body leaving coolant hoses connected. Remove throttle body gasket. Remove front and rear intake plenum brackets. Remove intake plenum mounting bolts. Remove intake plenum and gasket.

3) Disconnect high pressure fuel hose at fuel rail. Disconnect fuel return hose. Disconnect vacuum hoses. Disconnect injector electrical connectors. Remove fuel rail bolts and lift fuel rail and injectors from engine. Injectors may be removed after fuel rail is removed from intake manifold.

Installation – 1) To install, reverse removal procedure. Use new insulators and "O" rings when installing injectors.

2) Use lubricant on "O" rings. Install injectors into fuel rail using a twisting motion. Ensure injectors rotate smoothly when installing. DO NOT drop injectors while removing or installing fuel rail. Adjust throttle control and accelerator cables (if necessary). Refill cooling system.

Removal (Diamante, Stealth & 3000GT) – 1) Relieve fuel pressure. See FUEL SYSTEM PRESSURE RELEASE. Disconnect negative battery cable. Drain coolant. Remove air intake hose. Remove throttle body and gasket with control cables and vacuum hoses attached.

2) Remove EGR pipe (if equipped). Disconnect power brake hose. Label and disconnect vacuum hoses and wiring harness connectors as necessary. Remove intake plenum brackets and mounting bolts. Remove intake plenum and gasket.

3) Disconnect high pressure fuel hose at fuel rail. Disconnect fuel return hose. Disconnect vacuum hoses. Disconnect injector electrical connectors. Remove fuel rail bolts, and lift fuel rail and injectors from engine. Injectors may be removed after fuel rail is removed from intake manifold.

Installation – To install, reverse removal procedure. Use new insulators and "O" rings when installing injectors. Install injectors into fuel rail with a twisting motion. Ensure injectors rotate smoothly when installing. DO NOT drop injectors while removing or installing fuel rail. Refill cooling system.

OXYGEN (O₂) SENSOR

Removal & Installation – 1) O₂ sensor is mounted in exhaust pipe below exhaust header. It is equipped with a permanent pigtail which must be protected from damage when sensor is removed. Ensure sensor is free of contaminants. Avoid using cleaning solvents of any type.

2) Sensor may be difficult to remove when engine temperature is less than 120°F (48°C). Always use anti-seize compound on threads before installation. Tighten O₂ sensor to specification. See TORQUE SPECIFICATIONS.

THROTTLE BODY

Removal – Disconnect air intake hose. Remove accelerator, cruise control and A/T throttle valve cables (if equipped). Disconnect fuel vapor hose, electrical harness connector, vacuum hose and coolant hoses. Remove throttle body retaining bolts.

Disassembly – Remove throttle position sensor. Remove idle speed control motor. Remove throttle bracket and connector bracket (if equipped). Remove idle position switch and adjusting nut (if equipped).

NOTE: DO NOT remove throttle valve. DO NOT use cleaning solvents on throttle position sensor, idle speed control motor or idle position switch.

Cleaning – Clean all parts except throttle position sensor, idle speed control motor and idle position switch in solvent. Check vacuum port and passage for clogging. Clean vacuum, vapor and fuel passages using compressed air.

Reassembly – To reassemble, reverse disassembly procedure.

Installation – To install, reverse removal procedure.

THROTTLE POSITION SENSOR

Removal & Installation – Throttle Position Sensor (TPS) is located on throttle body. Disconnect TPS electrical connector. Remove TPS screws and TPS. To install, reverse removal procedure. Tighten TPS screws to specification. See TORQUE SPECIFICATIONS. For TPS adjustment procedure, see ON-VEHICLE ADJUSTMENTS article.

TURBOCHARGERS

Removal (Eclipse) – 1) Disconnect negative battery cable. Drain engine coolant and oil. On models equipped with A/C, remove condenser fan motor assembly. Remove O₂ sensor. Remove oil dipstick guide and "O" ring.

2) Disconnect air intake hose and vacuum hoses. Remove air hose and air outlet housing. Remove heat protectors. Disconnect exhaust pipe. Remove power steering oil pump and bracket. Remove engine hanger bracket. Disconnect oil inlet pipe.

3) Disconnect coolant hose and tubes. Remove nuts and bolts securing exhaust manifold. Remove exhaust manifold and gaskets. Disconnect oil return pipe. Remove turbocharger assembly.

Removal (Stealth & 3000GT – Front) – 1) Disconnect negative battery cable. Drain engine oil and coolant. Remove radiator. Disconnect exhaust pipe. Remove air intake hose, air hoses and air pipe. Remove alternator and belt. Remove oil dipstick guide.

2) Remove heat protector. Disconnect oxygen sensor electrical connector. Remove oil return pipe. Remove turbocharger support bracket, and remove turbocharger from exhaust manifold.

Removal (Stealth & 3000GT – Rear) – 1) Disconnect battery cables, and remove battery. Drain engine oil and cooling system. Remove accelerator cable. Remove air hose, air pipe and heat protectors. Disconnect clutch booster vacuum hose. Remove air intake hoses and EGR pipe. Disconnect O₂ sensor electrical connector.

2) Remove oil pipe and EGR valve. Disconnect exhaust fitting, and remove rear heat protector. Remove oil return pipe. Remove turbocharger assembly.

Inspection (All Models) – Check turbine and compressor wheels for cracking and other damage. Ensure turbine and compressor wheels turn smoothly. Check for oil leakage from turbocharger assembly. Check for proper wastegate valve operation. See SYSTEM & COMPONENT TESTING article.

Installation (All Models) – 1) To install, reverse removal procedure. Before oil pipe flare nut (above turbocharger) is installed, pour clean engine oil into oil pipe installation hole of turbocharger. Ensure oil and air hoses are properly installed and securely clamped.

2) Use new gaskets. Adjust accelerator cable (if necessary). Refill engine oil and coolant. Check for oil and coolant leaks. Tighten all bolts to specification. See TORQUE SPECIFICATIONS table.

TORQUE SPECIFICATIONS

TORQUE SPECIFICATIONS

Applications	Ft. Lbs. (N.m)
Coolant Temperature Sensor	22 (29)
Exhaust Manifold-To-Engine Nuts	18-22 (24-29)
Exhaust Manifold-To-Turbocharger Bolts	40-47 (54-64)
Exhaust Pipe Bolts	22-29 (29-39)
Fuel Tank Drain Plug	11-18 (15-24)
Fuel Tank Nuts	15-22 (20-29)
Knock Sensor	15-18 (20-24)
Oil Pipe-To-Engine	10-14 (14-19)
Oxygen (O₂) Sensor	29-36 (39-49)
Plenum-To-Intake Manifold Bolts	11-15 (15-20)
Water Pipe-To-Turbocharger	
Except Stealth & 3000GT	25-36 (34-49)
Stealth & 3000GT	22 (30)

	INCH Lbs. (N.m)
Camshaft Position Sensor	84 (9)
Crankshaft Position Sensor	84 (9)
Distributor Hold-Down Bolt	108 (12)
EGR Temperature Sensor	89 (10)
Fuel Rail Bolts	84-108 (9.0-12.0)
Heat Protector Bolts	108-132 (12.0-15.0)
ISC Switch Screws	20-54 (2.5-4.5)
TPS Switch Screws	13-20 (1.5-2.5)
Wastegate Actuator Bolts	84-108 (9.0-12.0)

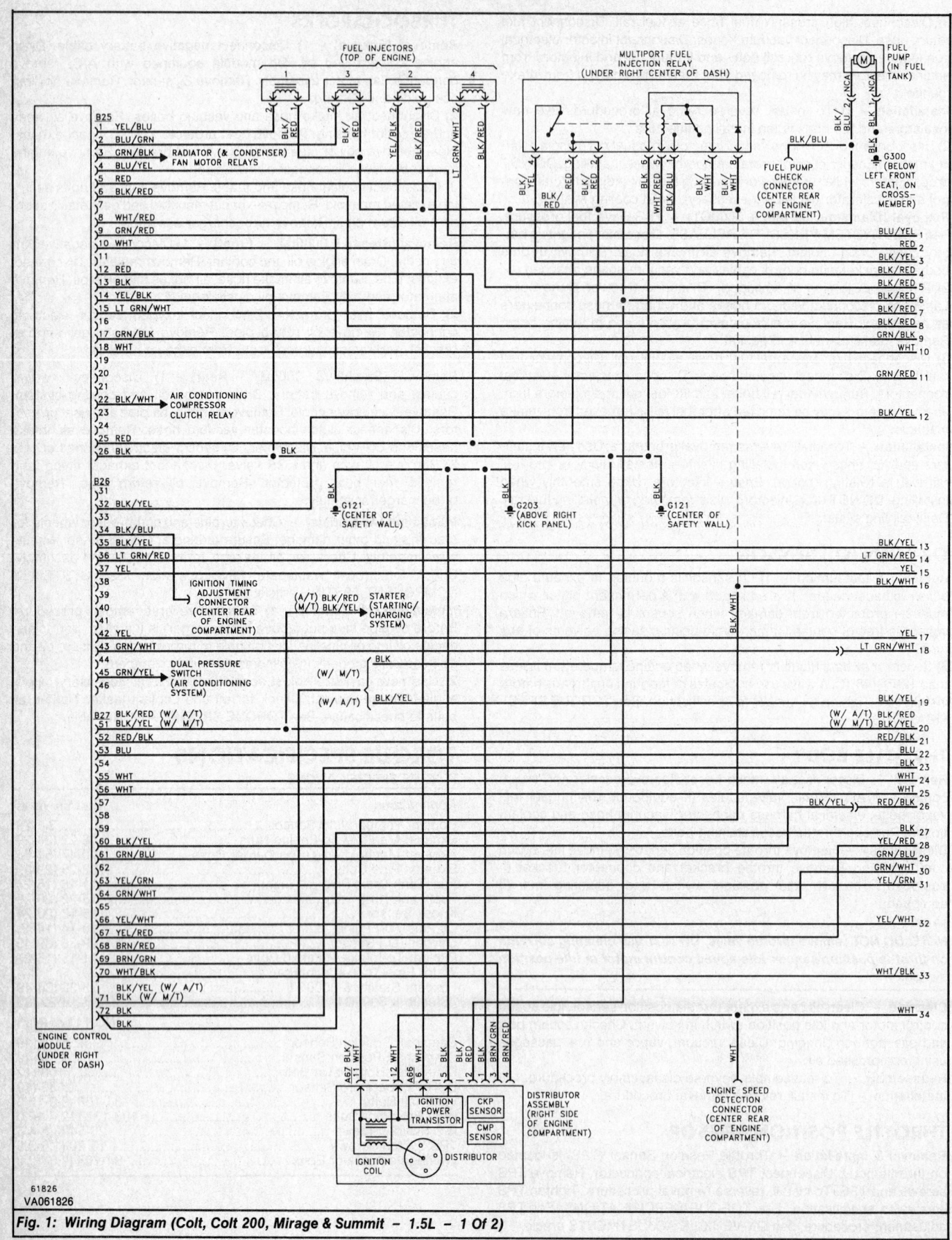

Fig. 1: Wiring Diagram (Colt, Colt 200, Mirage & Summit – 1.5L – 1 Of 2)

61826
VA061826

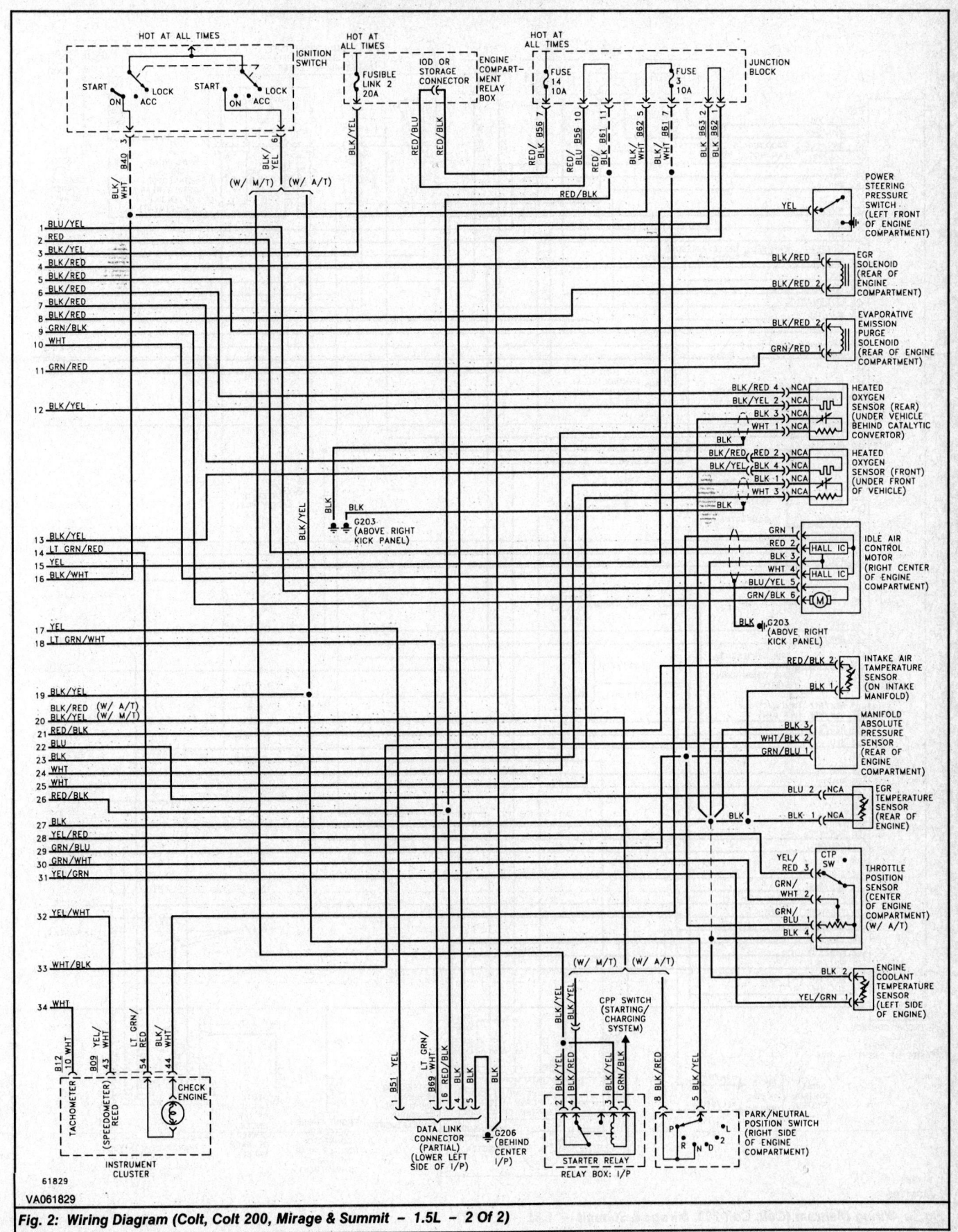

Fig. 2: Wiring Diagram (Colt, Colt 200, Mirage & Summit – 1.5L – 2 Of 2)

VA061829

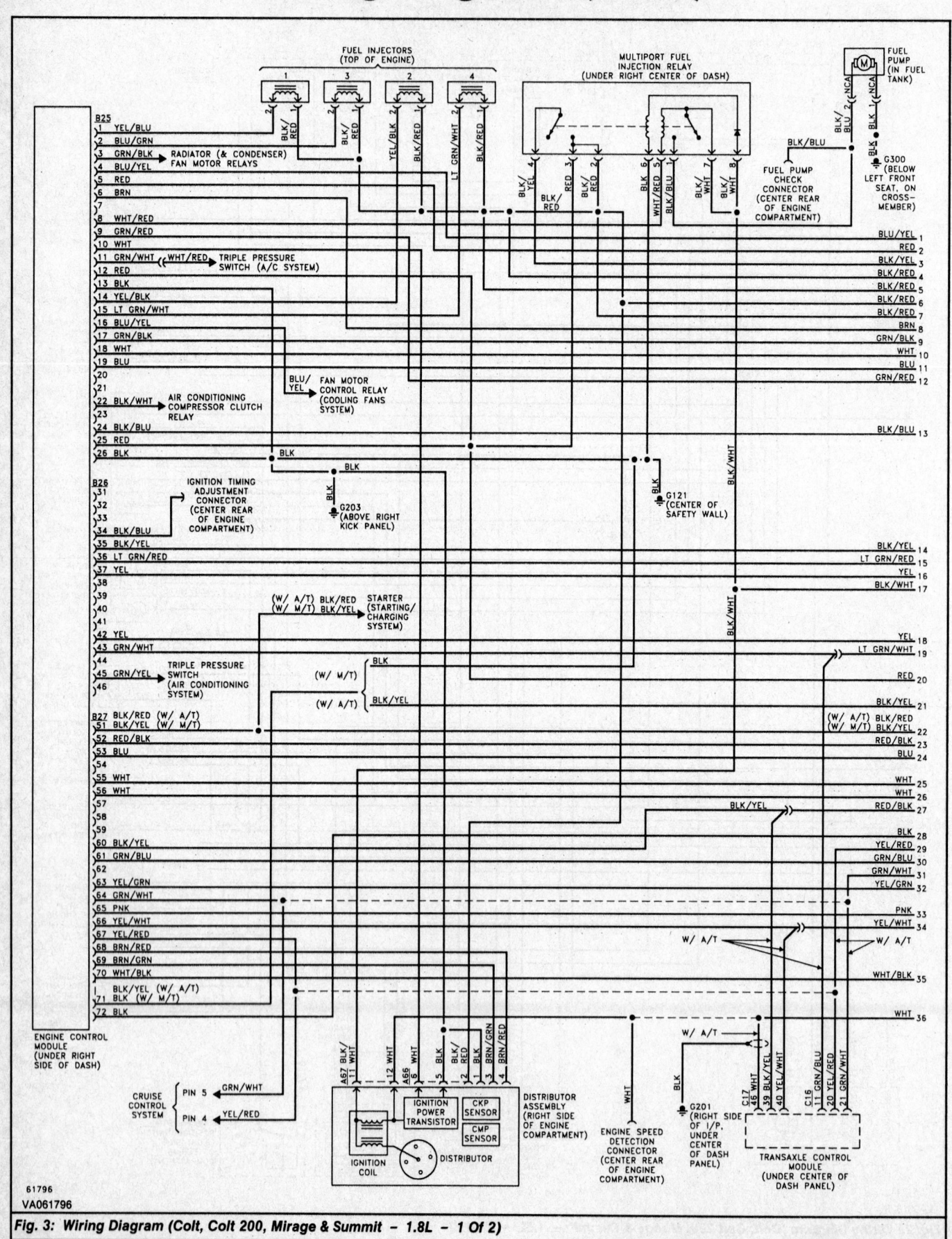

Fig. 3: Wiring Diagram (Colt, Colt 200, Mirage & Summit - 1.8L - 1 Of 2)

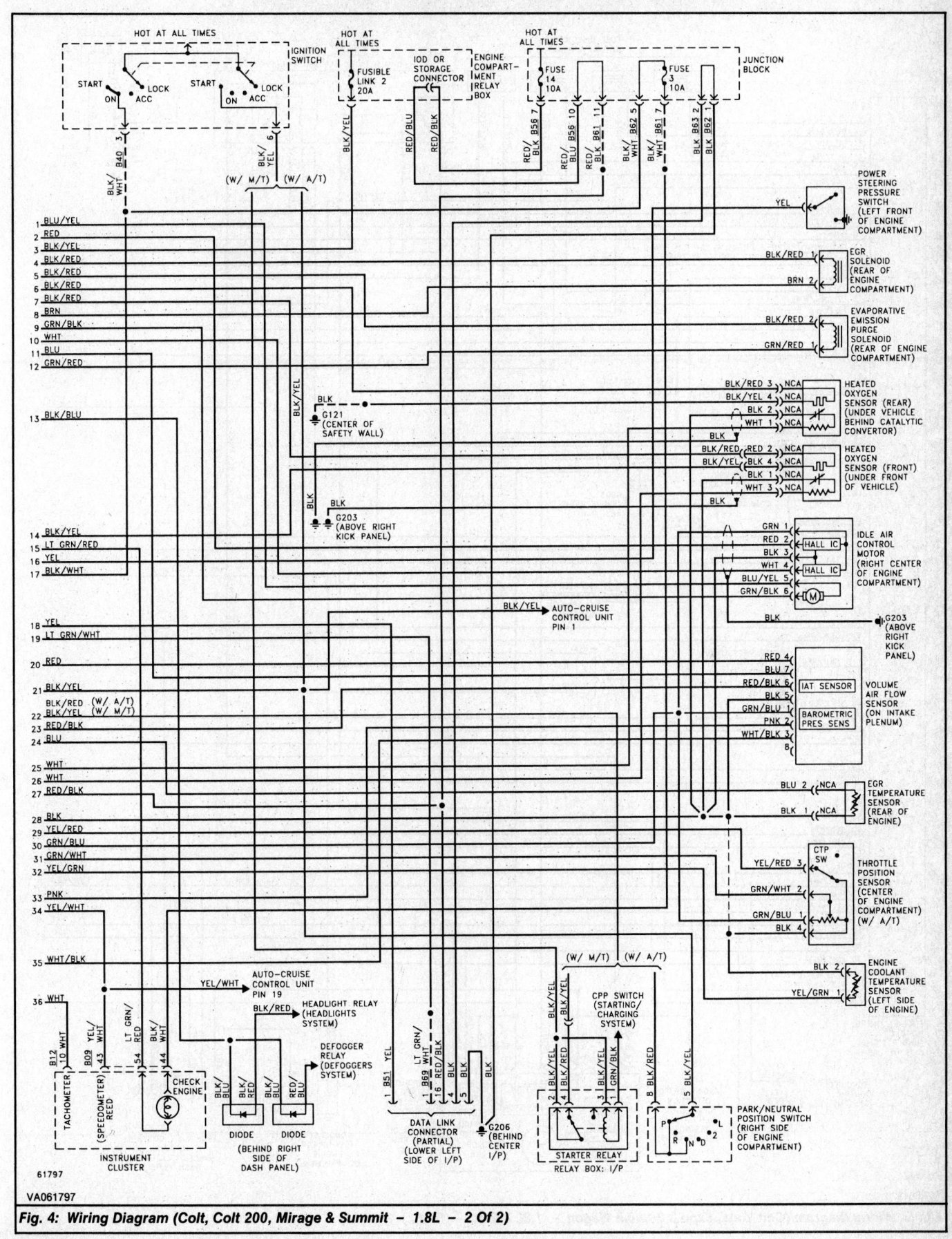

Fig. 4: Wiring Diagram (Colt, Colt 200, Mirage & Summit - 1.8L - 2 Of 2)

61797

VA061797

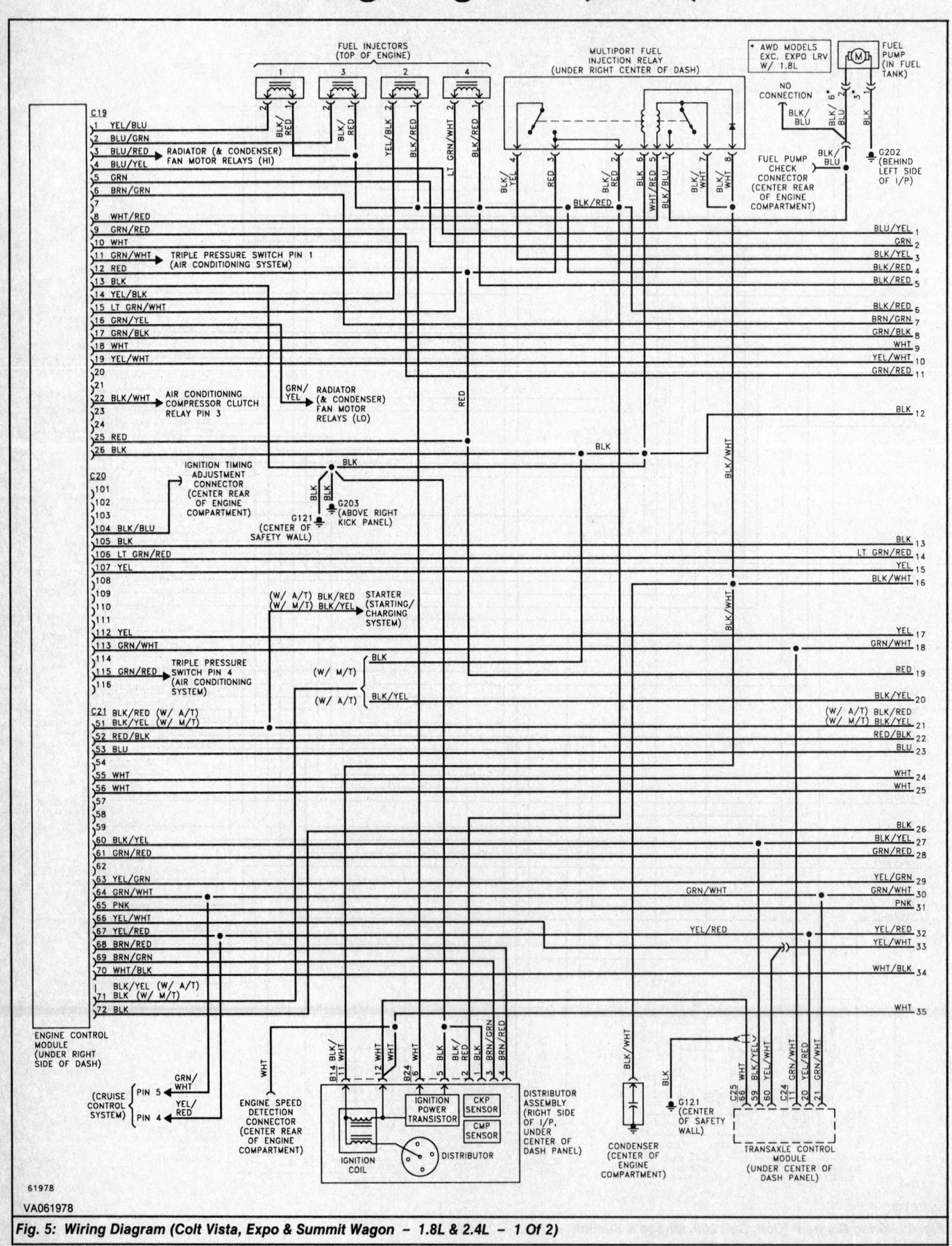

Fig. 5: Wiring Diagram (Colt Vista, Expo & Summit Wagon - 1.8L & 2.4L - 1 Of 2)

1994 ENGINE PERFORMANCE
Wiring Diagrams (Cont.)

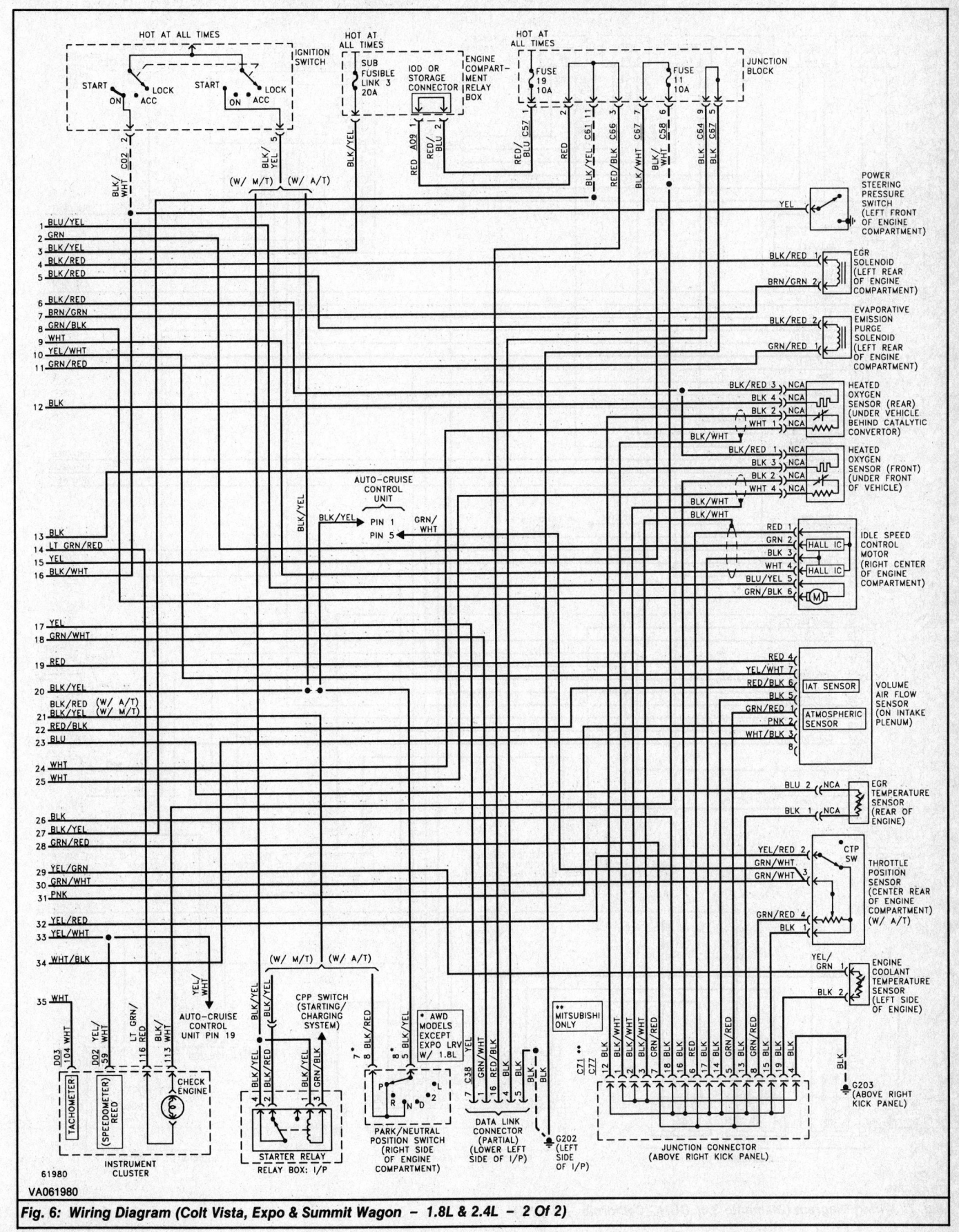

Fig. 6: Wiring Diagram (Colt Vista, Expo & Summit Wagon – 1.8L & 2.4L – 2 Of 2)

1994 ENGINE PERFORMANCE
Wiring Diagrams (Cont.)

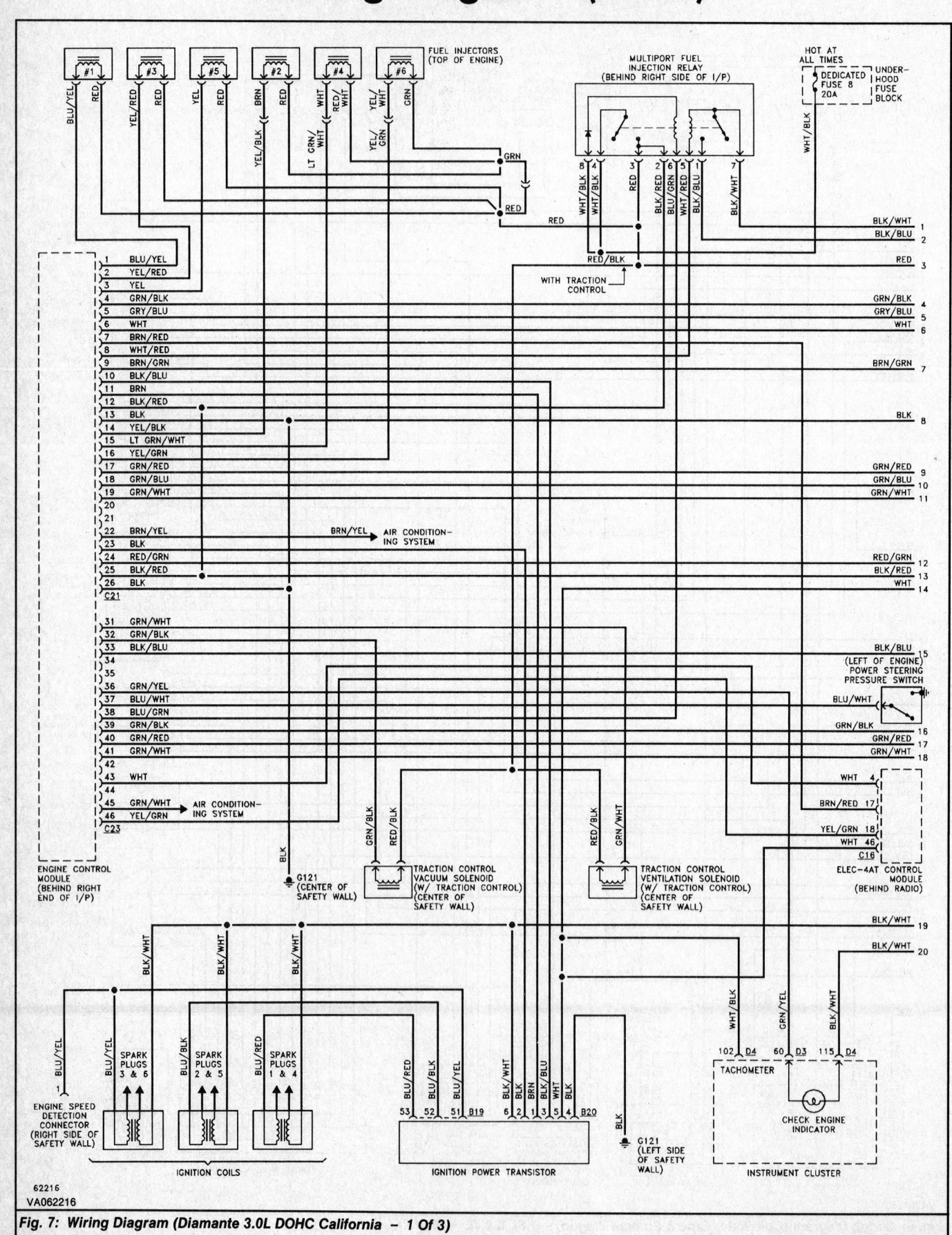

Fig. 7: Wiring Diagram (Diamante 3.0L DOHC California – 1 Of 3)

62216

VA062216

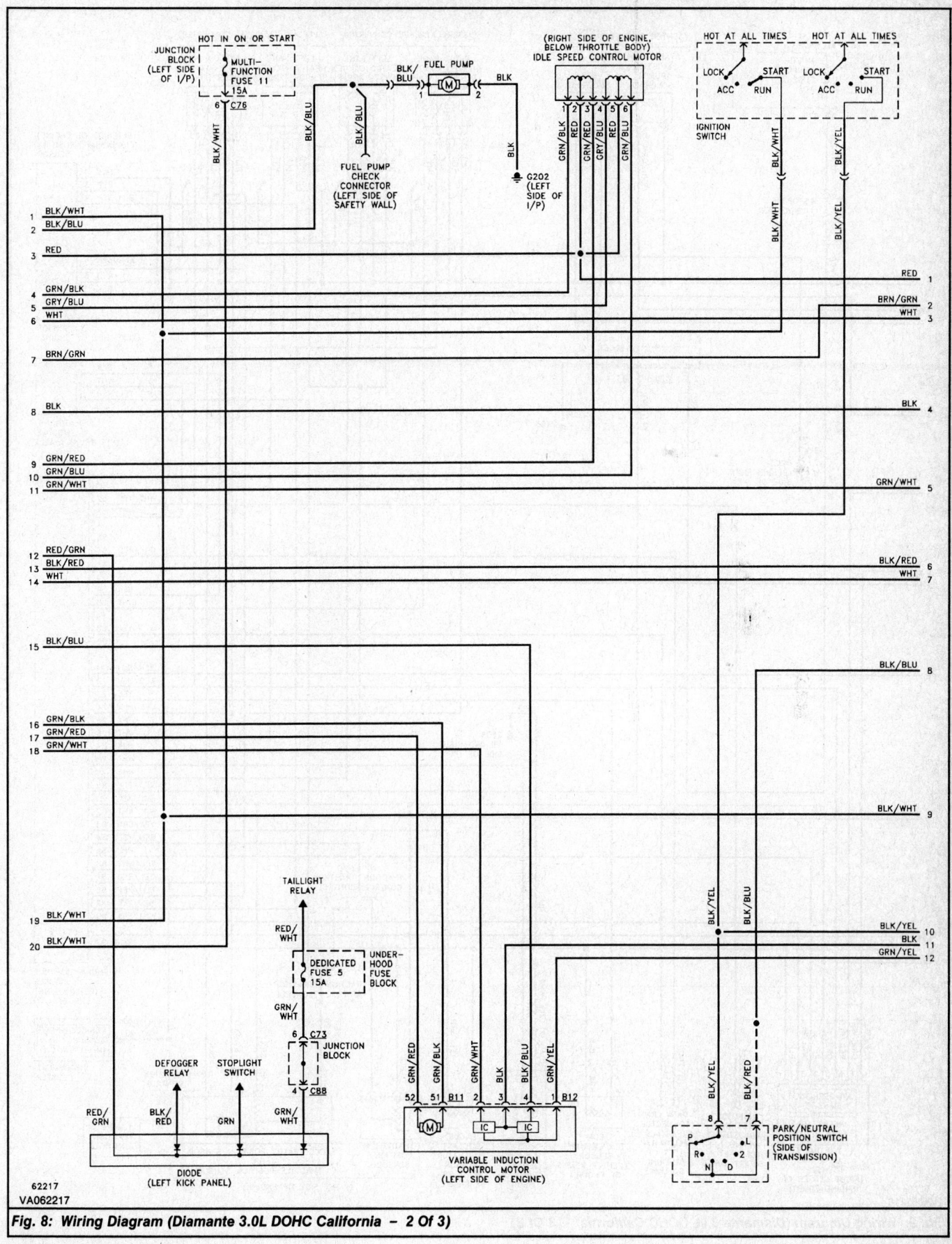

Fig. 8: Wiring Diagram (Diamante 3.0L DOHC California – 2 Of 3)

1994 ENGINE PERFORMANCE
Wiring Diagrams (Cont.)

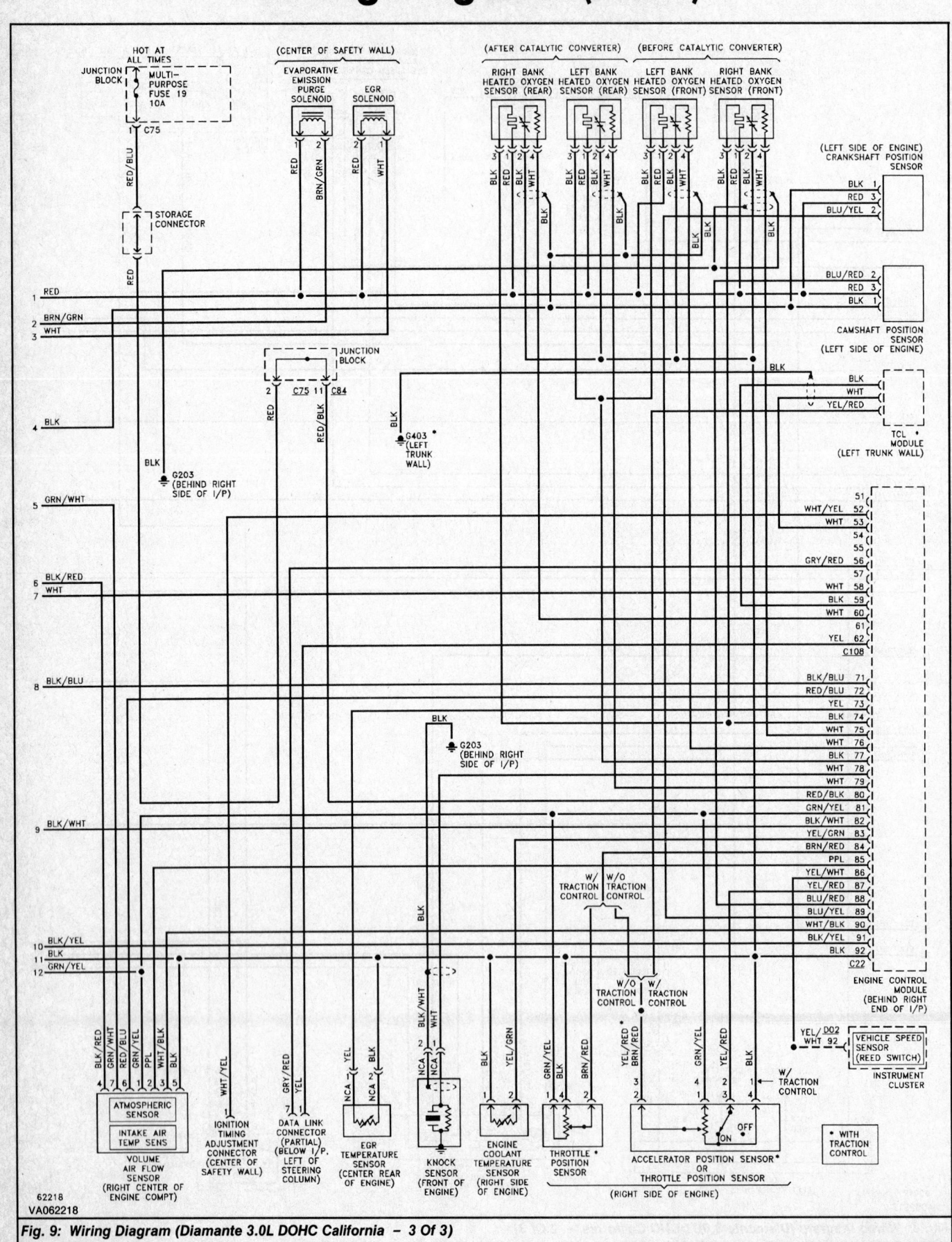

Fig. 9: Wiring Diagram (Diamante 3.0L DOHC California – 3 Of 3)

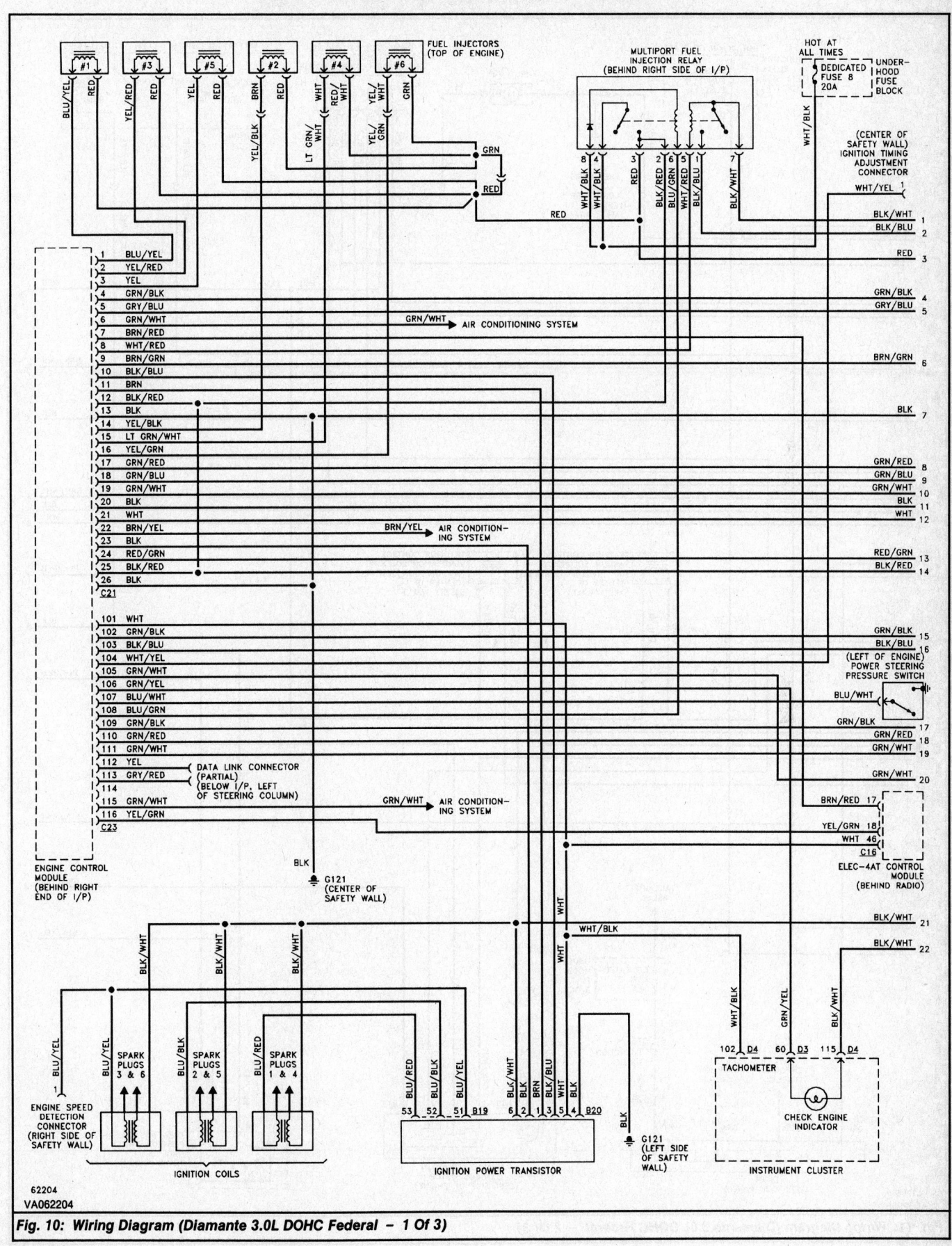

Fig. 10: Wiring Diagram (Diamante 3.0L DOHC Federal – 1 Of 3)

62204
VA062204

1994 ENGINE PERFORMANCE
Wiring Diagrams (Cont.)

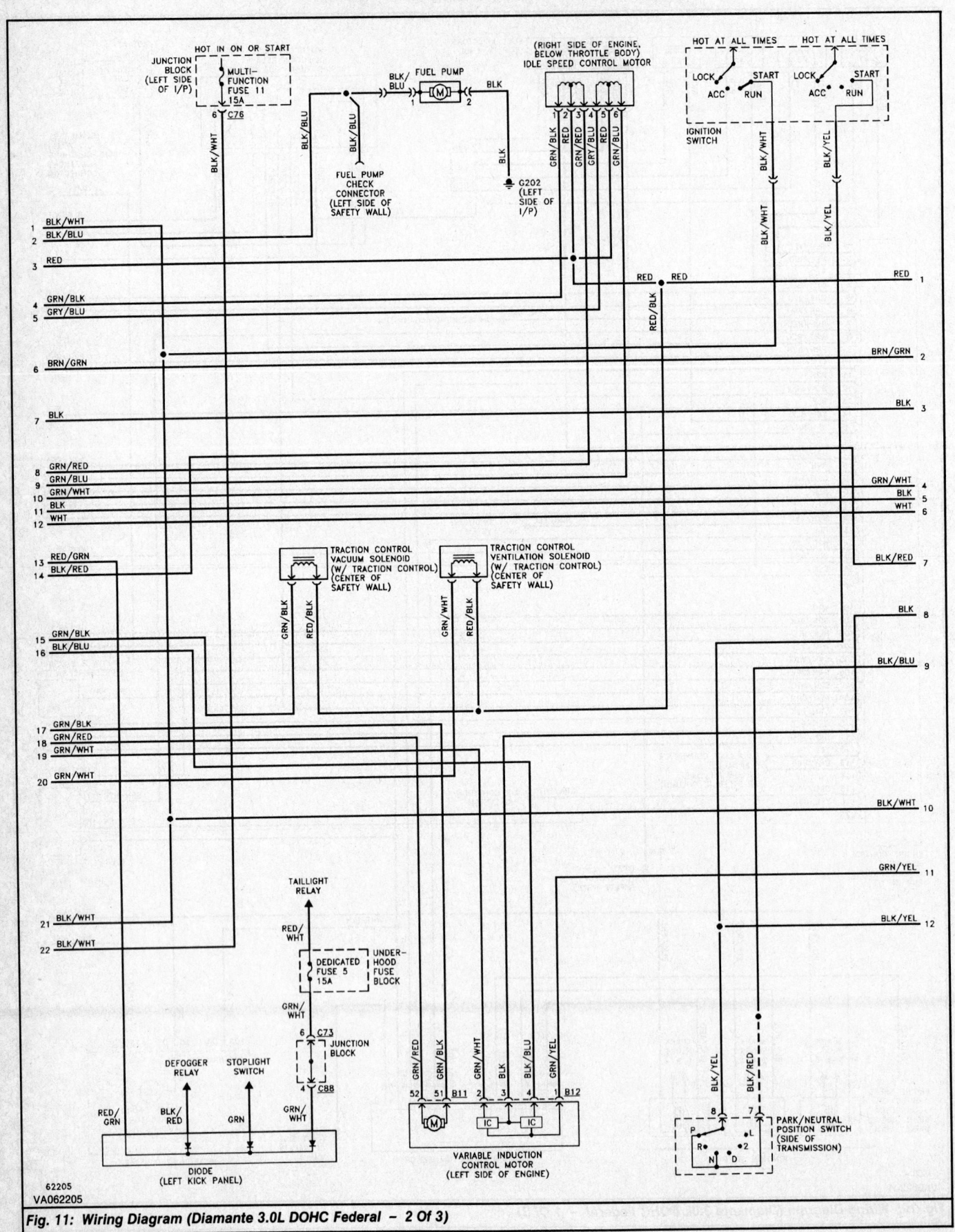

Fig. 11: Wiring Diagram (Diamante 3.0L DOHC Federal – 2 Of 3)

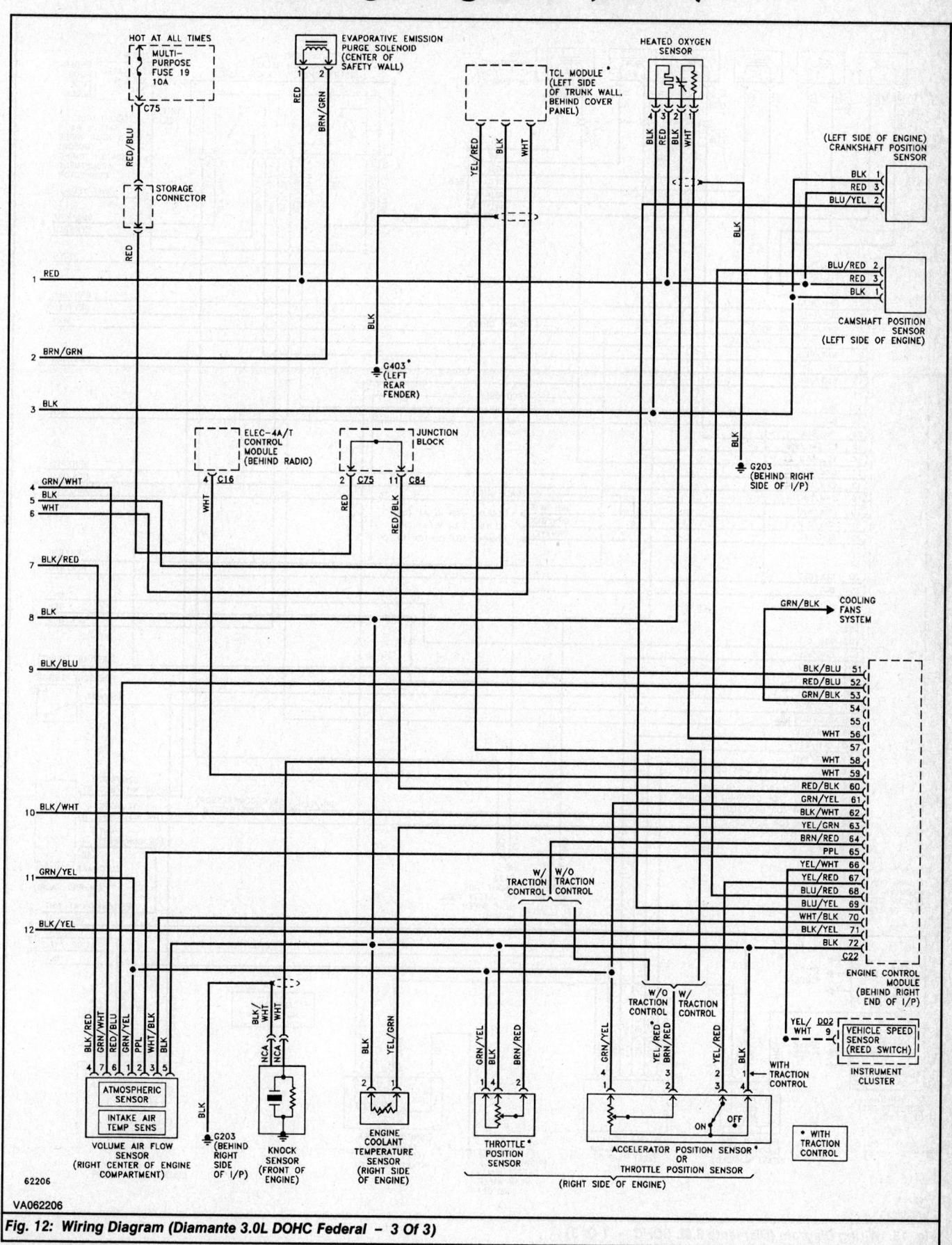

Fig. 12: Wiring Diagram (Diamante 3.0L DOHC Federal – 3 Of 3)

1994 ENGINE PERFORMANCE
Wiring Diagrams (Cont.)

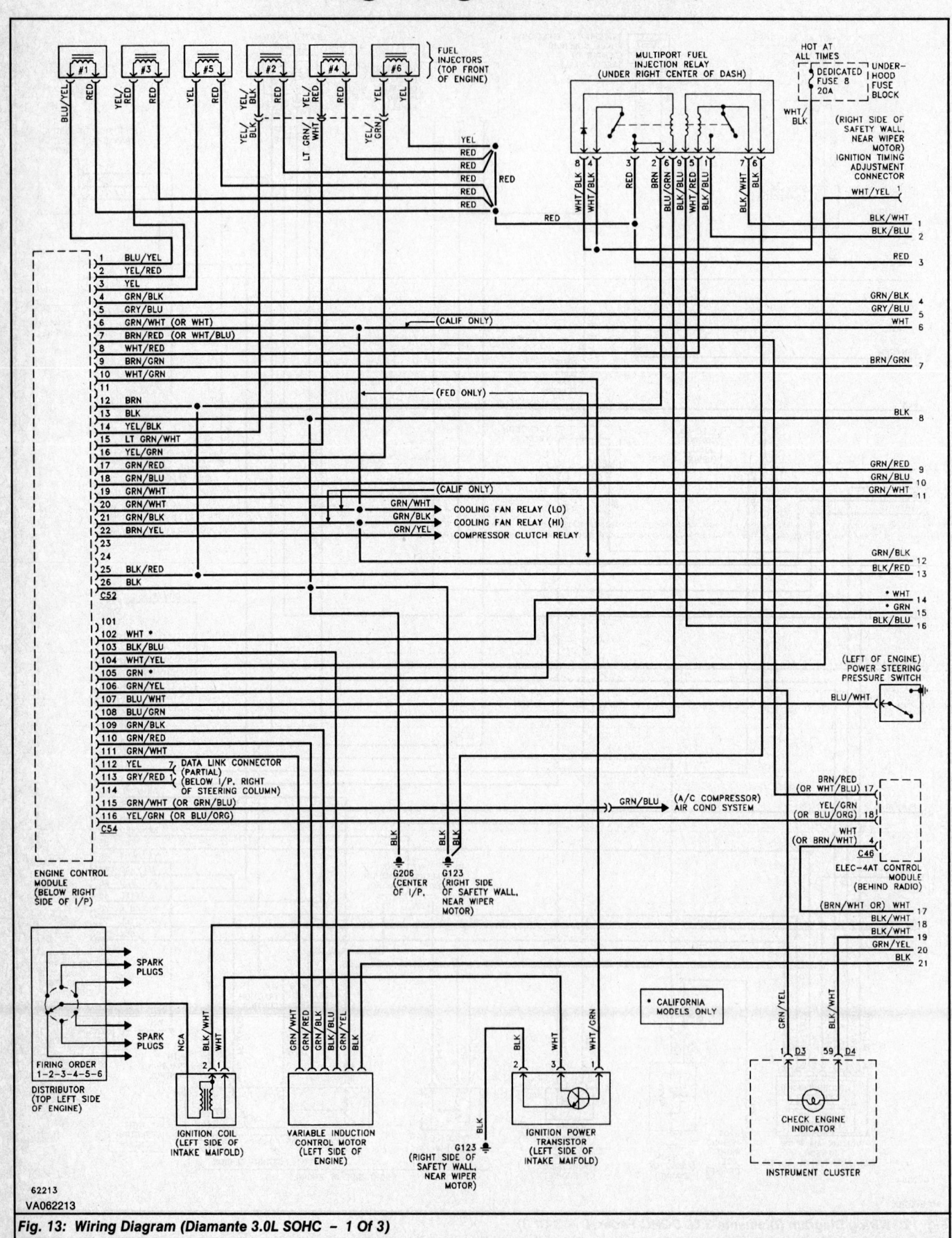

62213

VA062213

Fig. 13: Wiring Diagram (Diamante 3.0L SOHC – 1 Of 3)

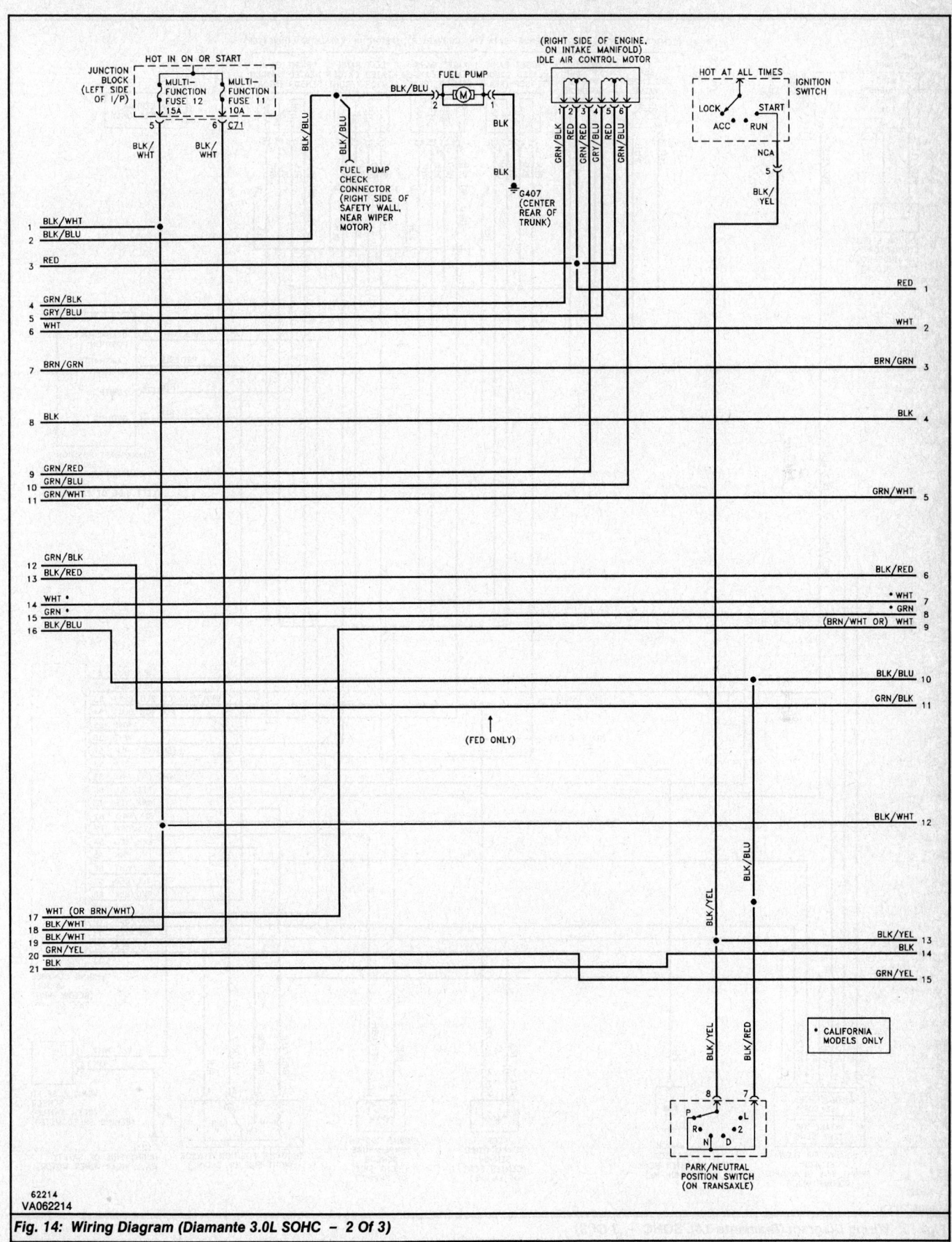

62214
VA062214

Fig. 14: *Wiring Diagram (Diamante 3.0L SOHC – 2 Of 3)*

1994 ENGINE PERFORMANCE
Wiring Diagrams (Cont.)

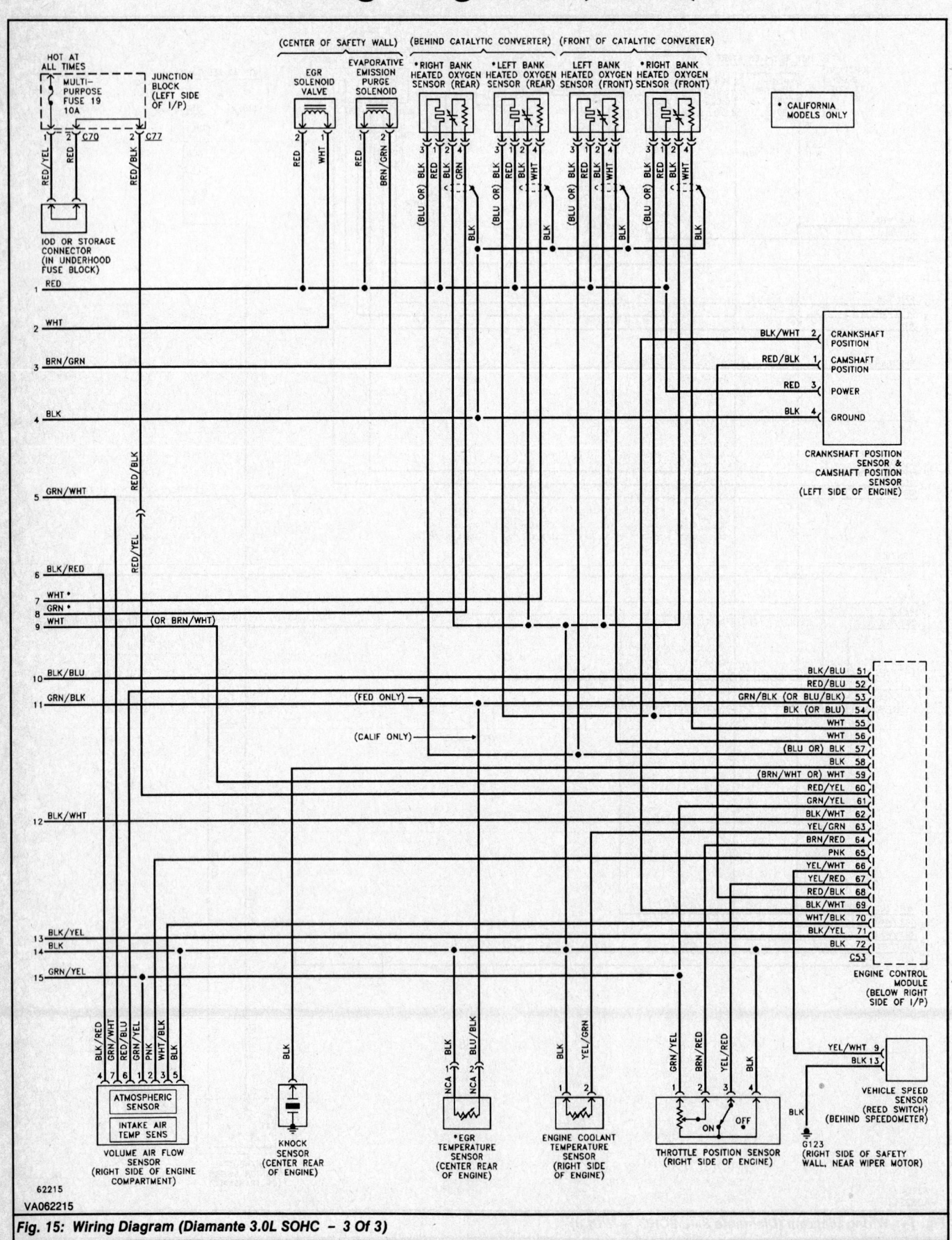

Fig. 15: Wiring Diagram (Diamante 3.0L SOHC – 3 Of 3)

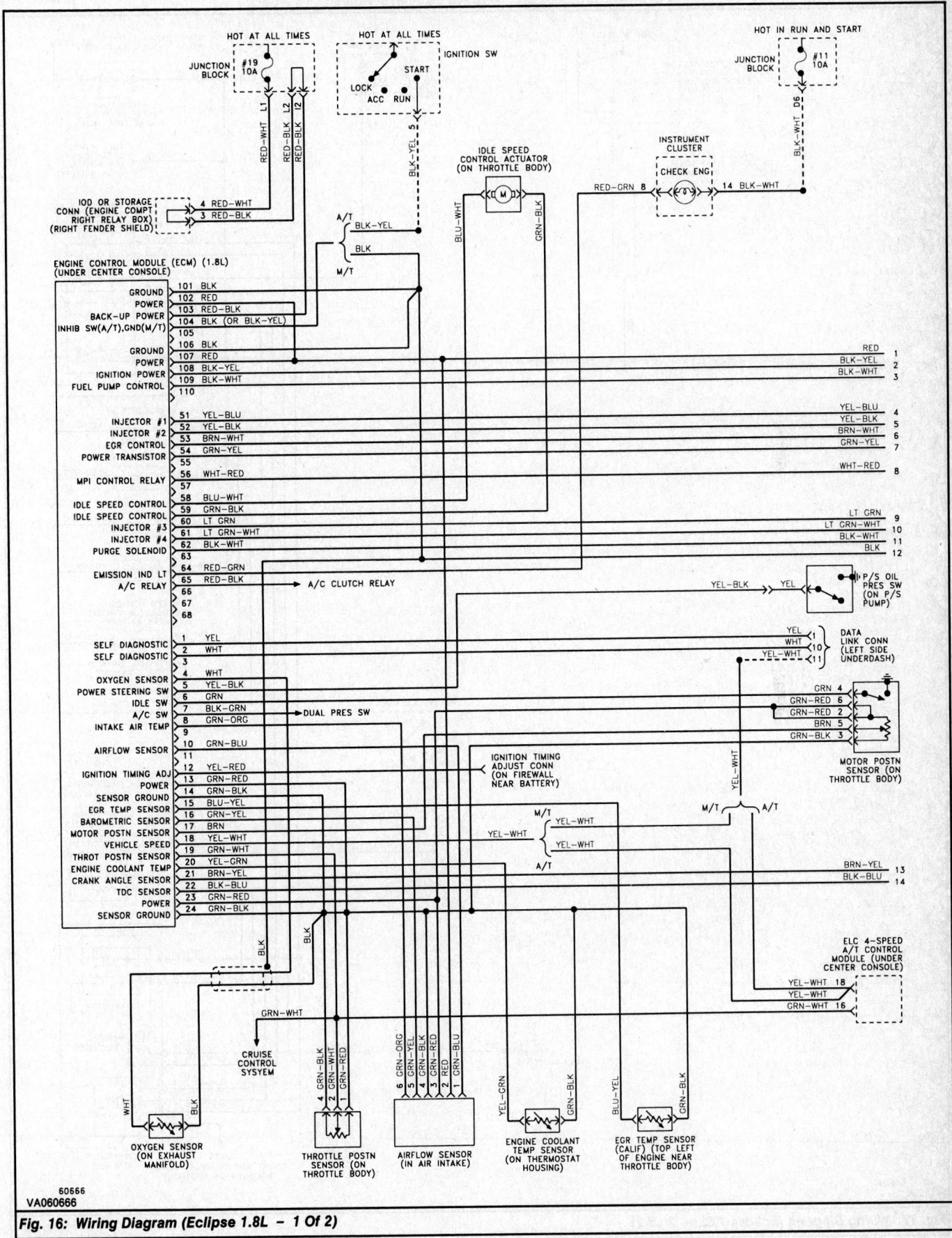

Fig. 16: Wiring Diagram (Eclipse 1.8L - 1 Of 2)

VA060666
60666

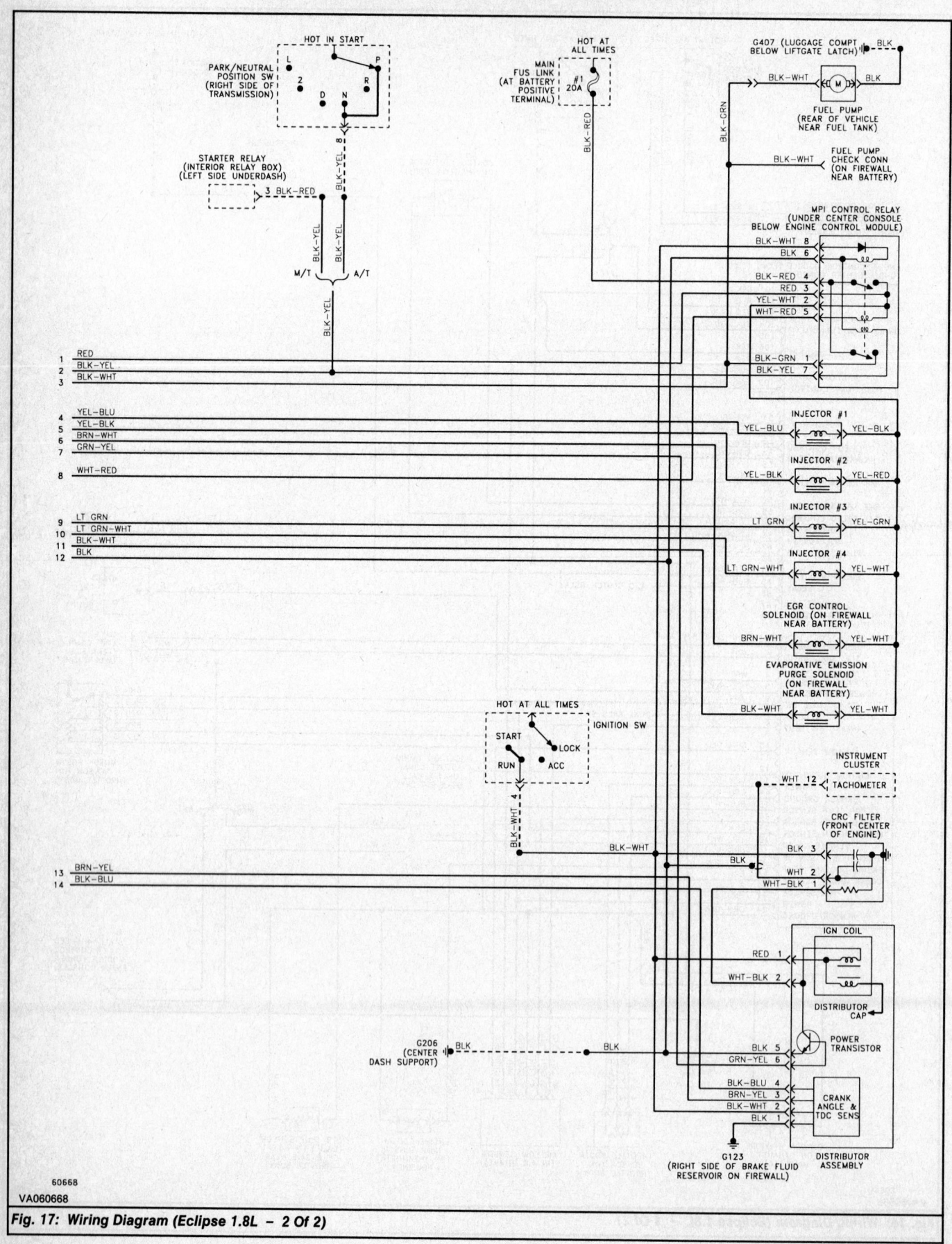

Fig. 17: Wiring Diagram (Eclipse 1.8L – 2 Of 2)

VA060668

60668

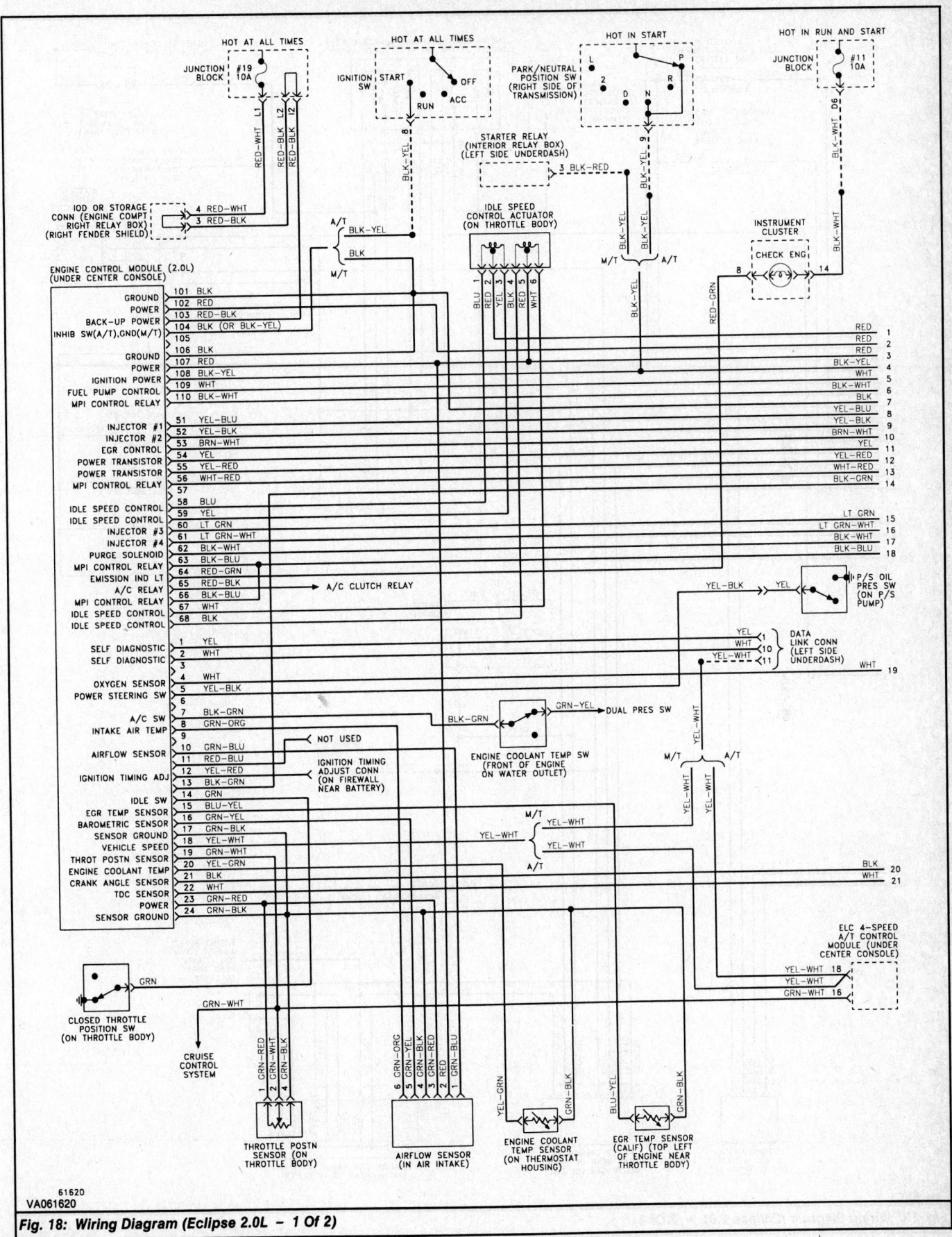

1994 ENGINE PERFORMANCE
Wiring Diagrams (Cont.)

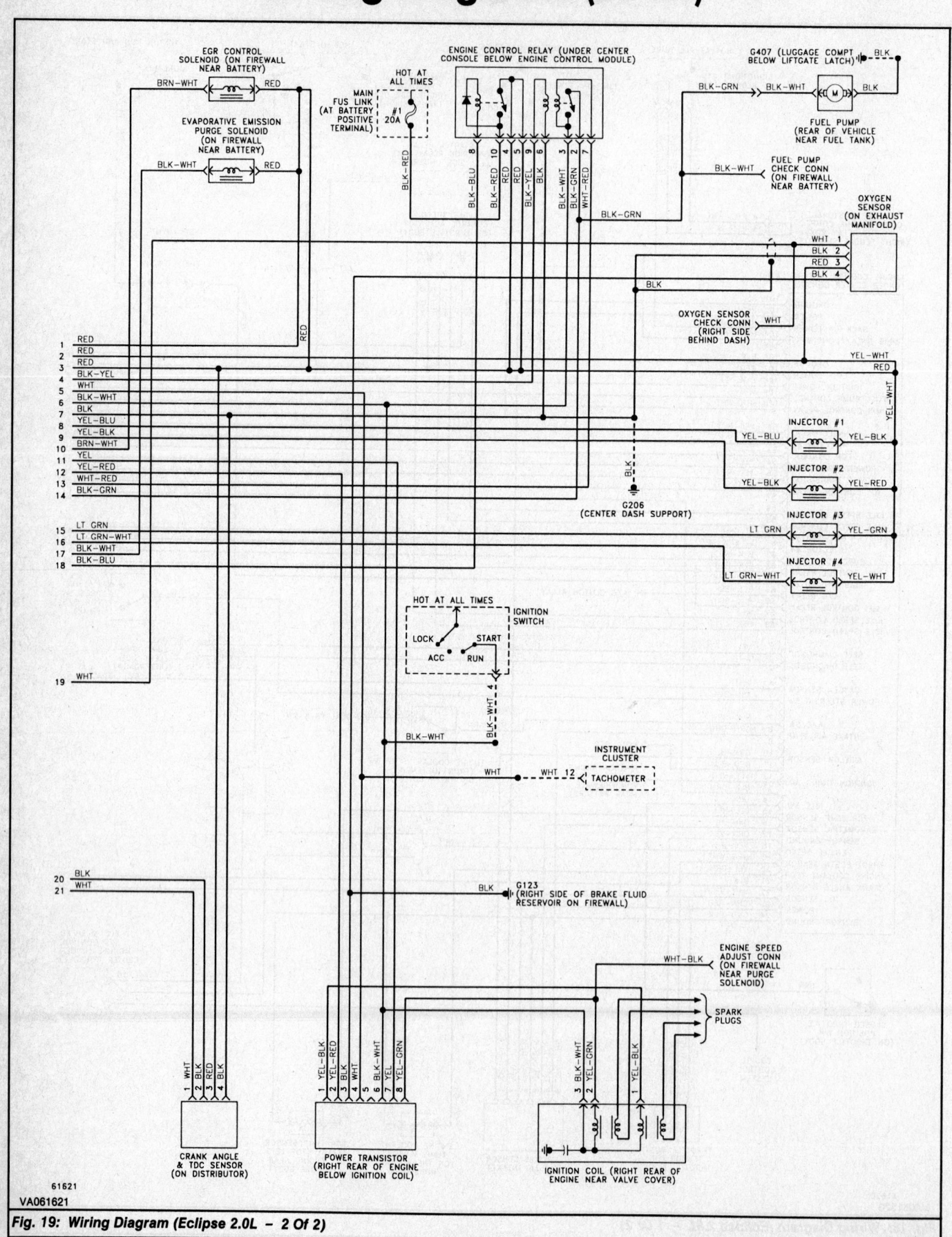

Fig. 19: Wiring Diagram (Eclipse 2.0L - 2 Of 2)

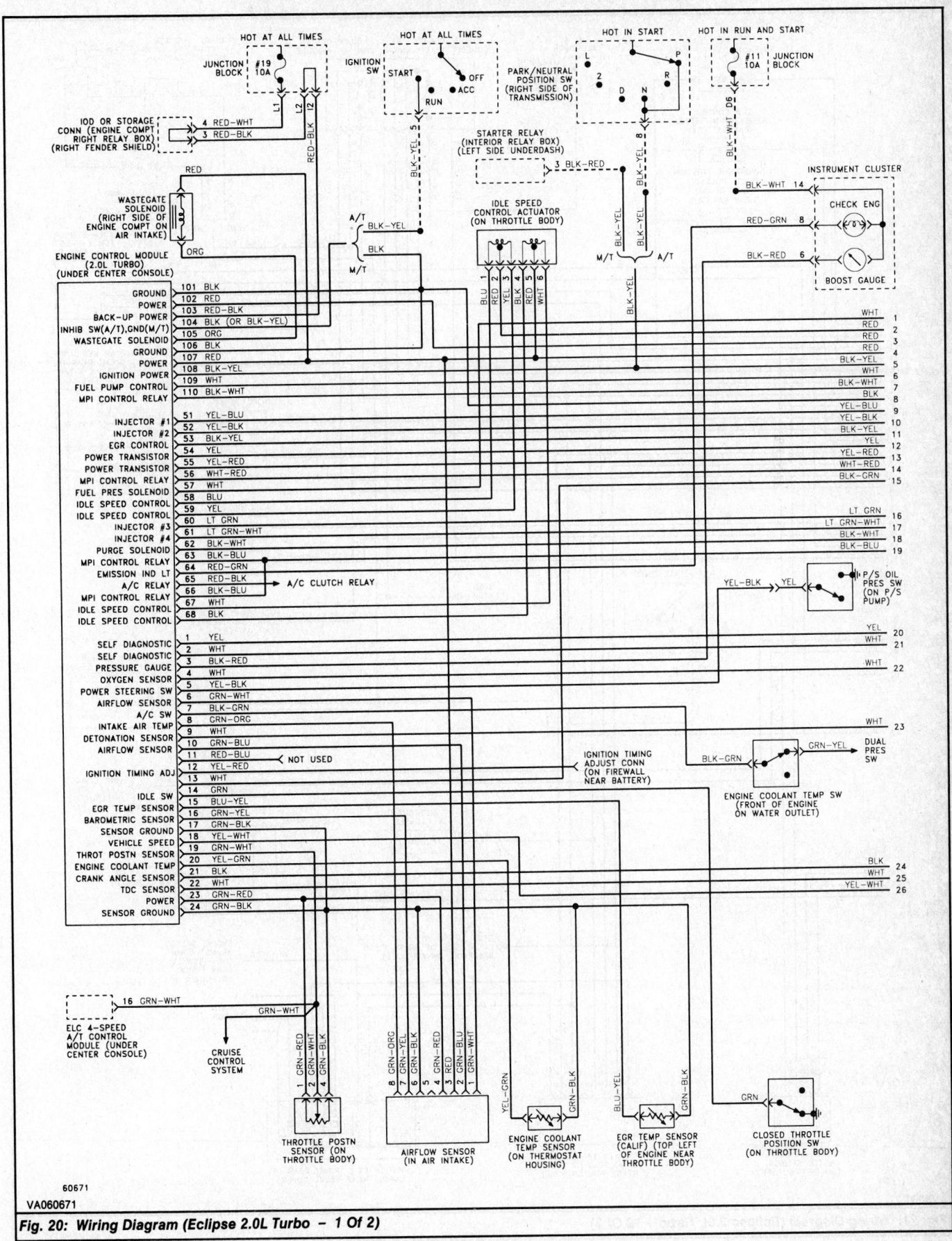

Fig. 20: Wiring Diagram (Eclipse 2.0L Turbo – 1 Of 2)

VA060671

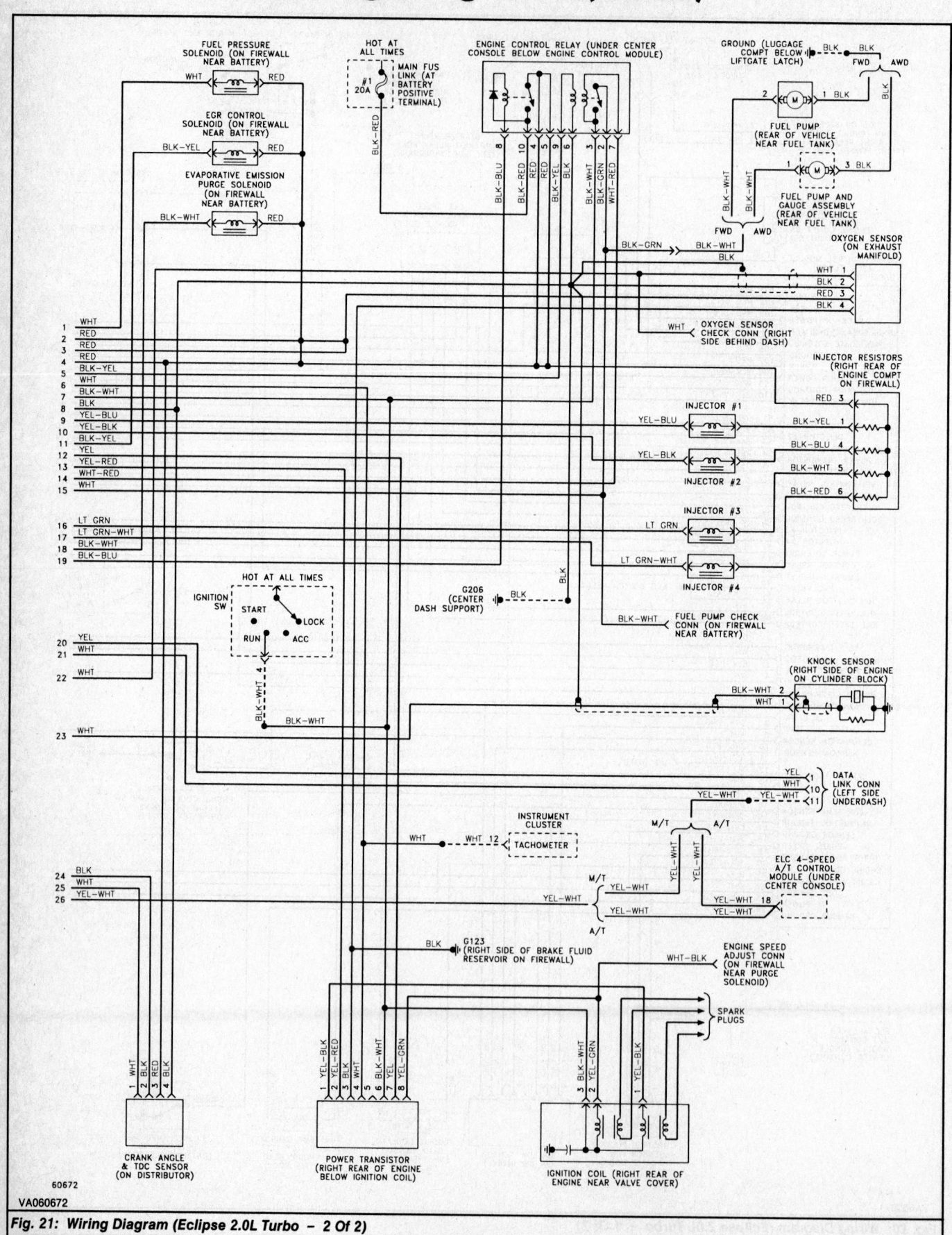

Fig. 21: *Wiring Diagram (Eclipse 2.0L Turbo – 2 Of 2)*

60672

VA060672

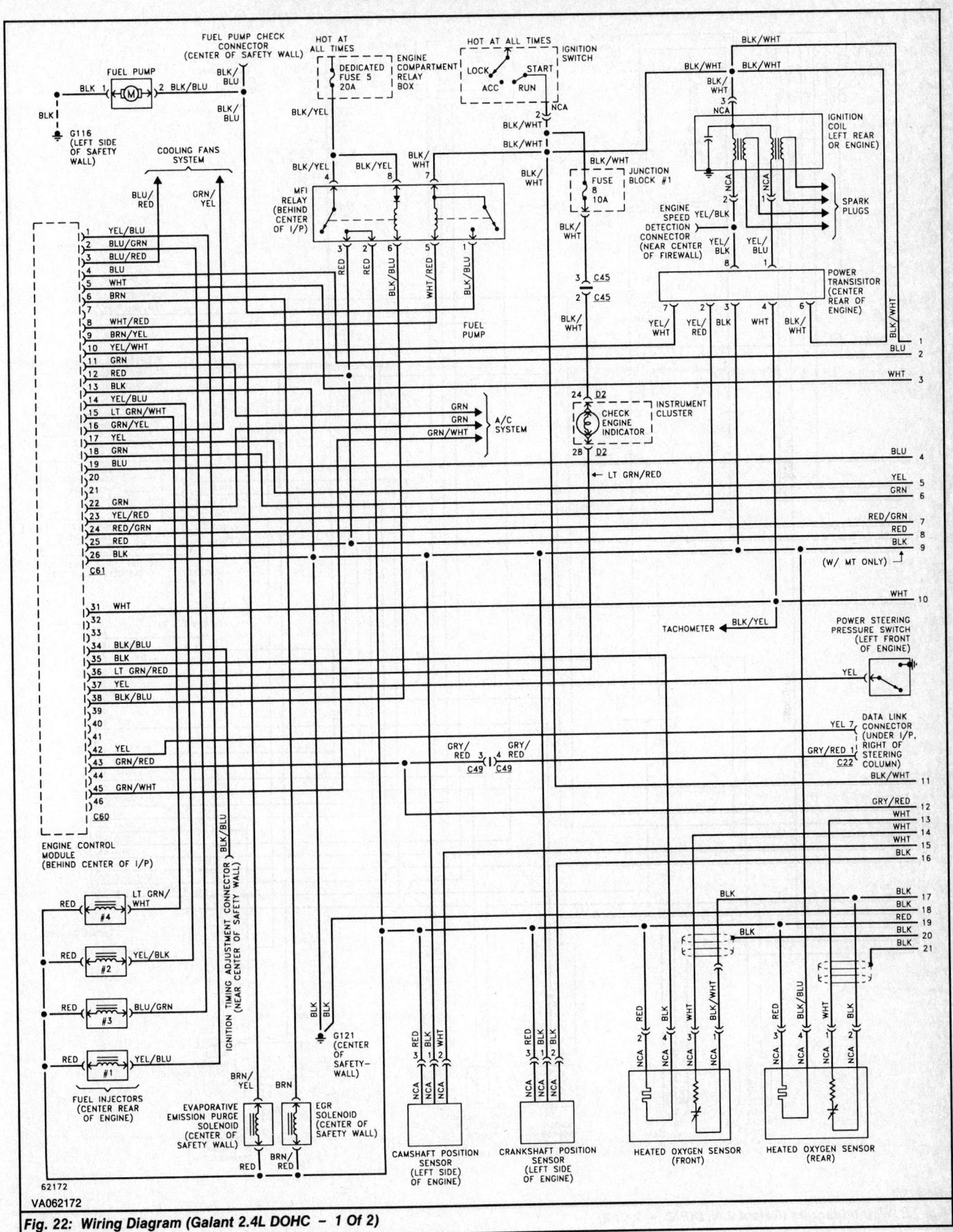

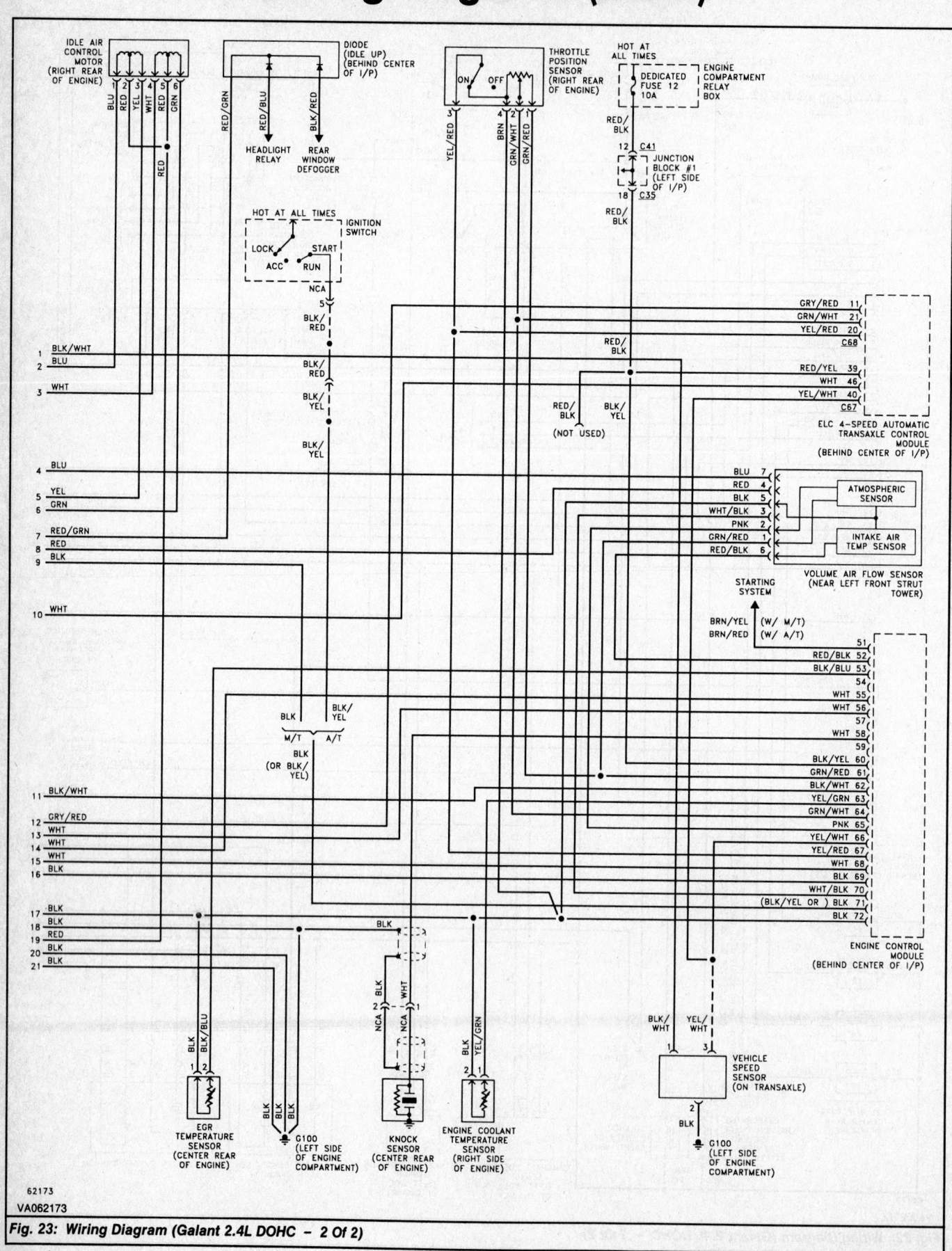

62173

VA062173

Fig. 23: Wiring Diagram (Galant 2.4L DOHC - 2 Of 2)

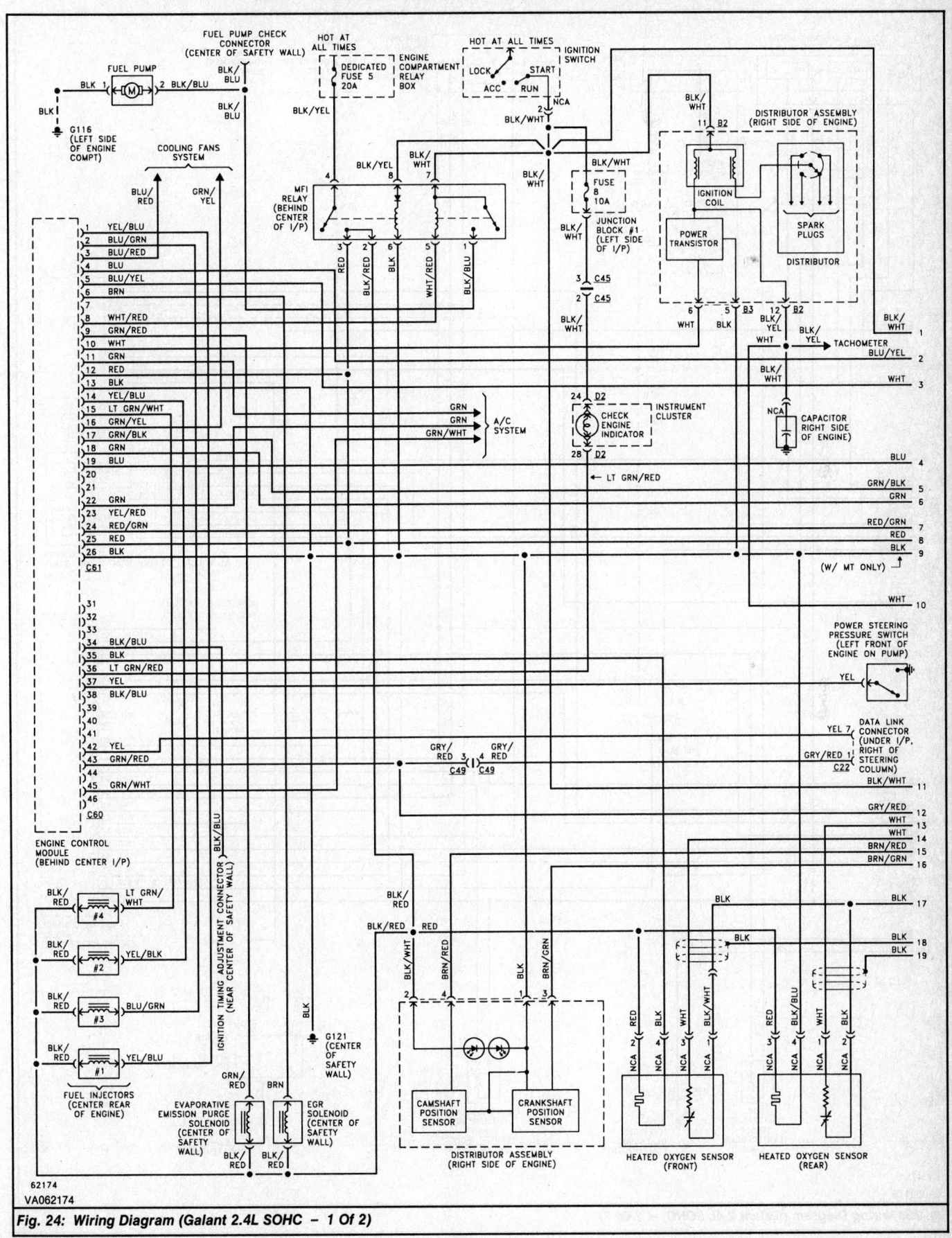

Fig. 24: Wiring Diagram (Galant 2.4L SOHC – 1 Of 2)

62174

VA062174

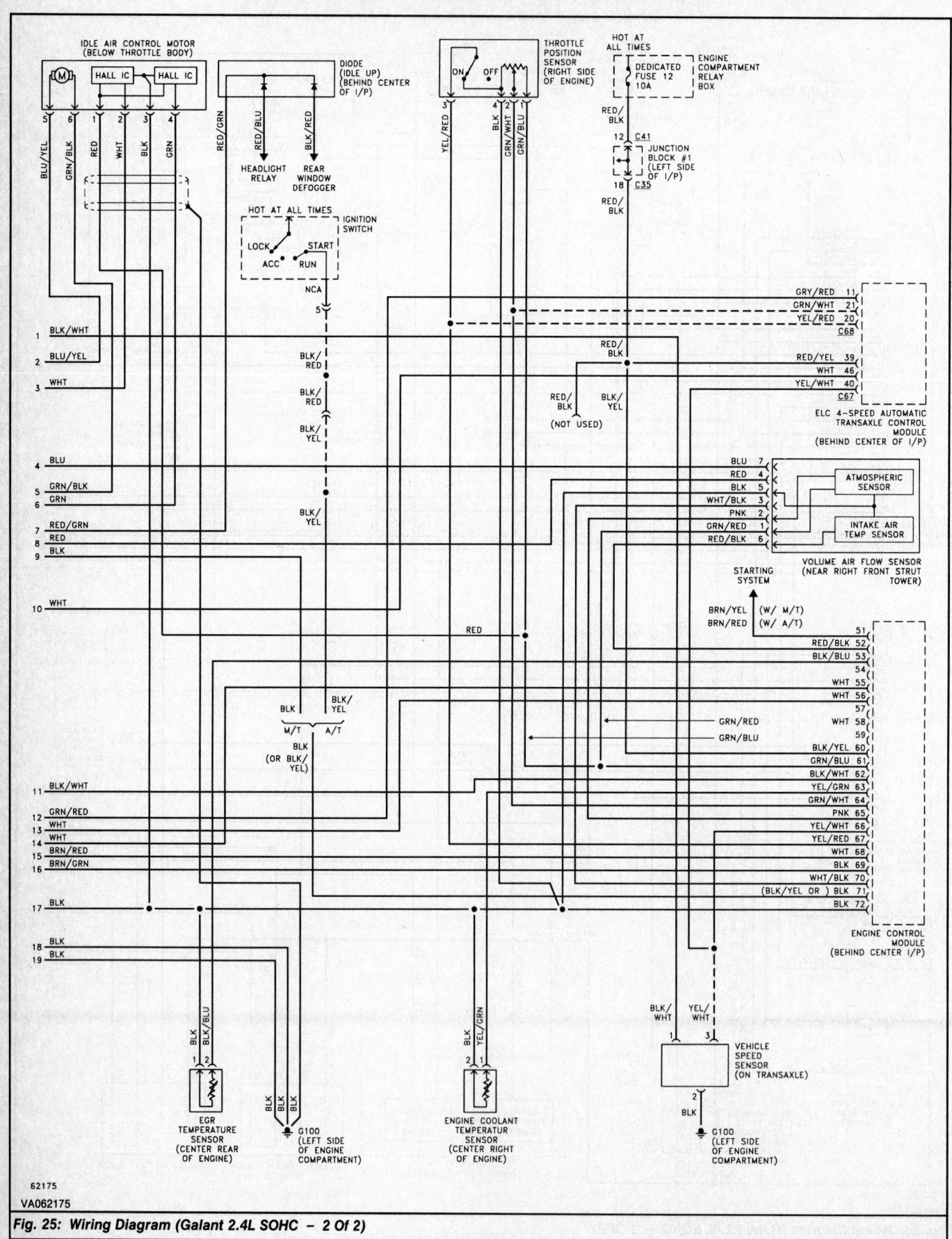

Fig. 25: Wiring Diagram (Galant 2.4L SOHC - 2 Of 2)

62175

VA062175

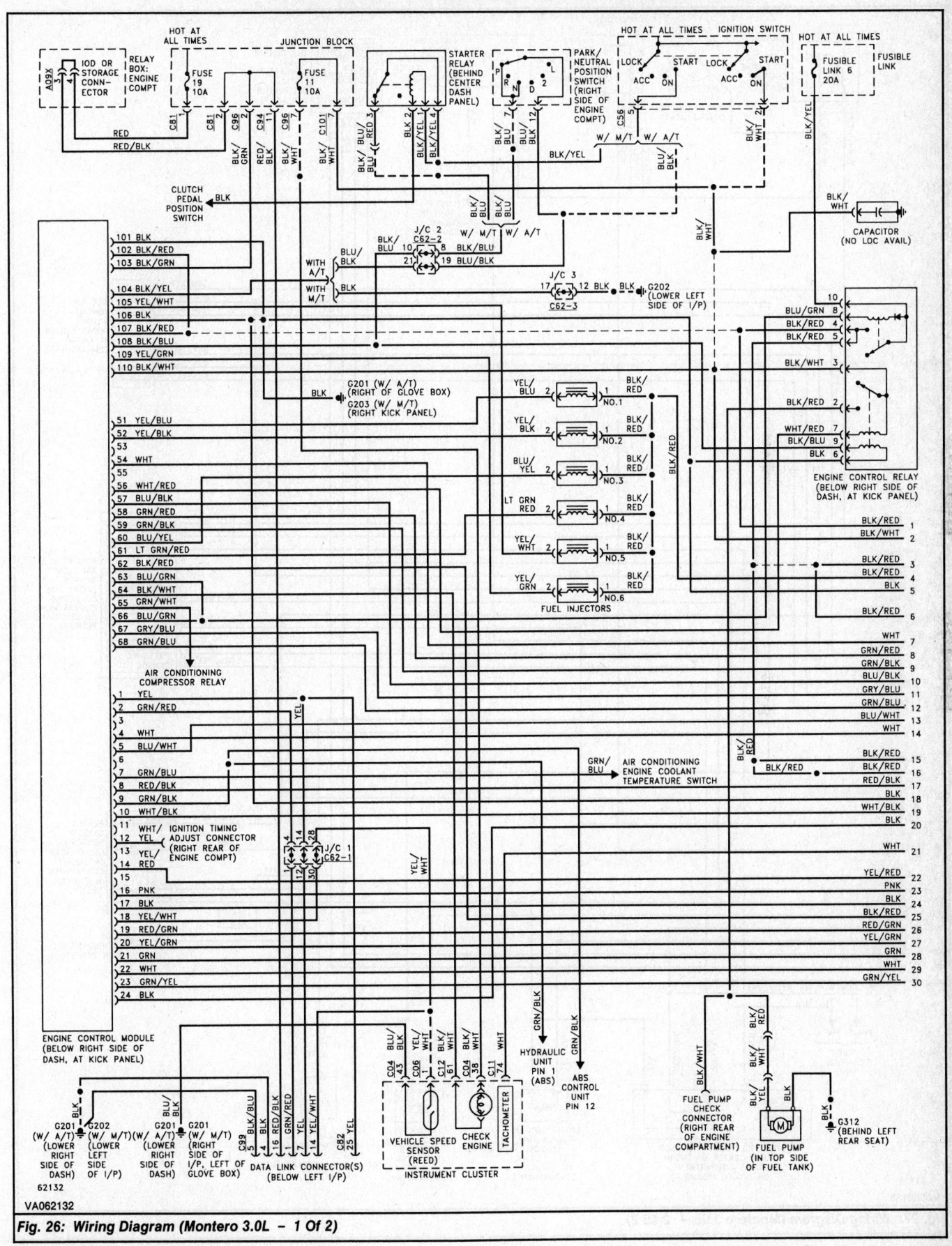

Fig. 26: Wiring Diagram (Montero 3.0L - 1 Of 2)

62132

VA062132

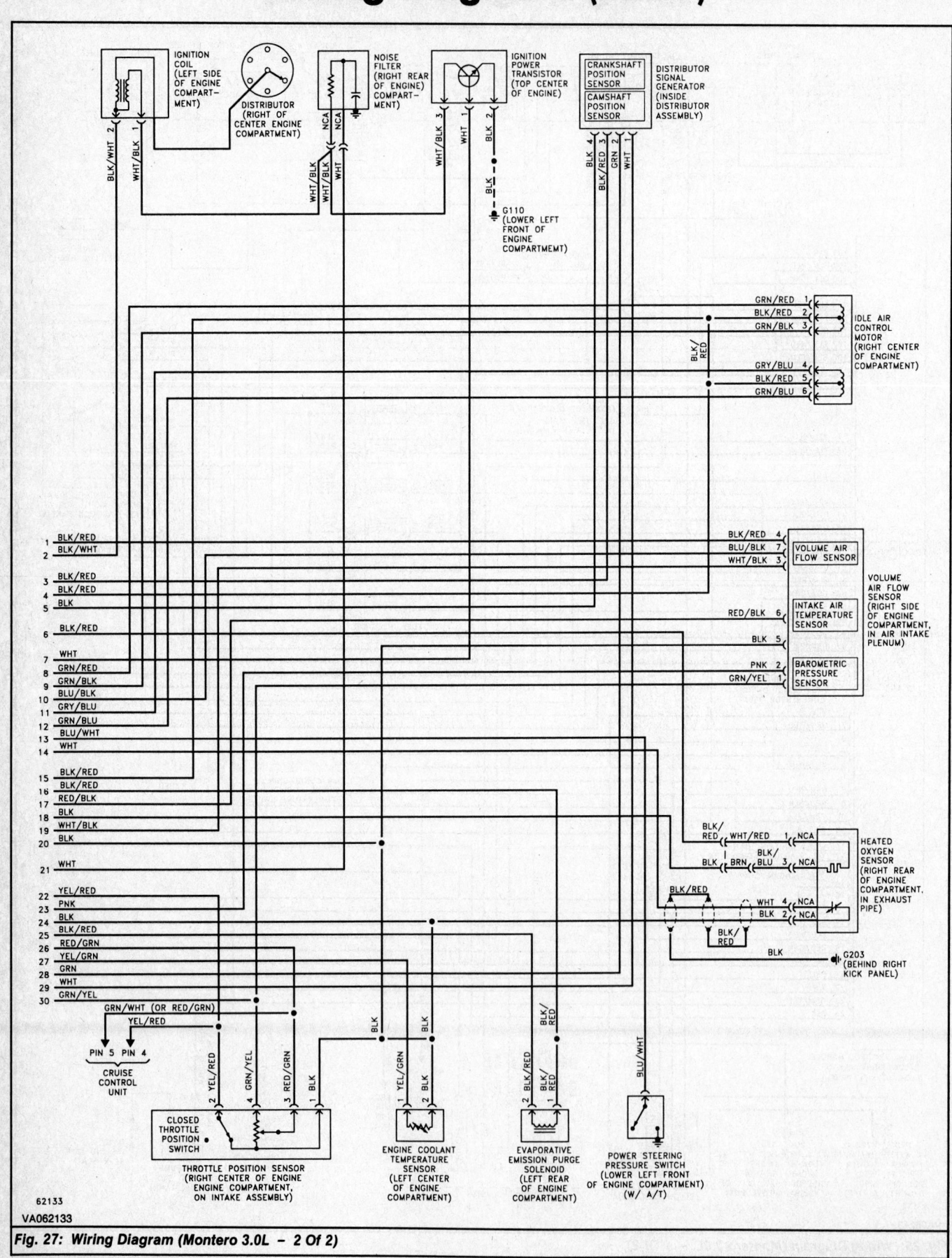

Fig. 27: Wiring Diagram (Montero 3.0L - 2 Of 2)

62133

VA062133

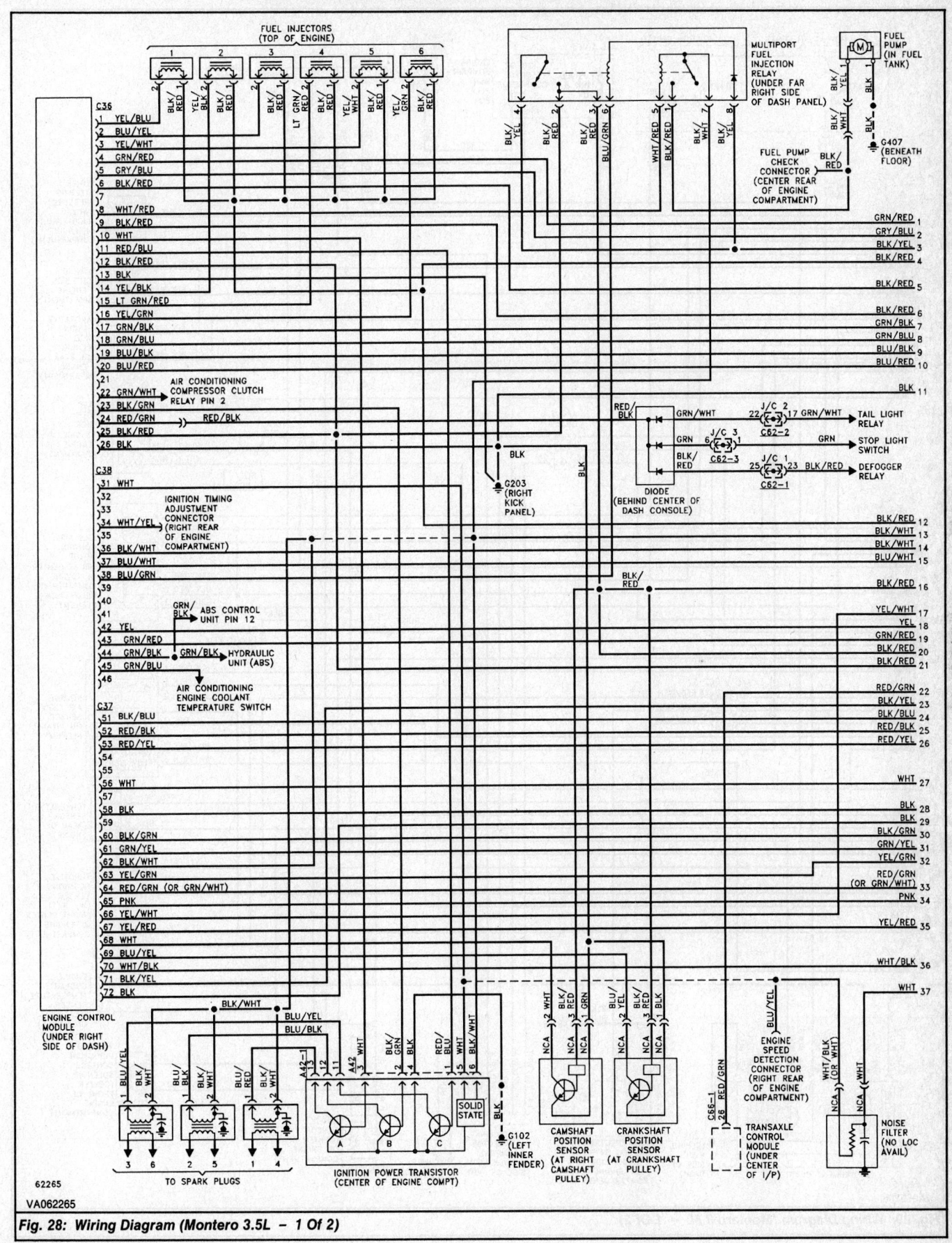

Fig. 28: Wiring Diagram (Montero 3.5L – 1 Of 2)

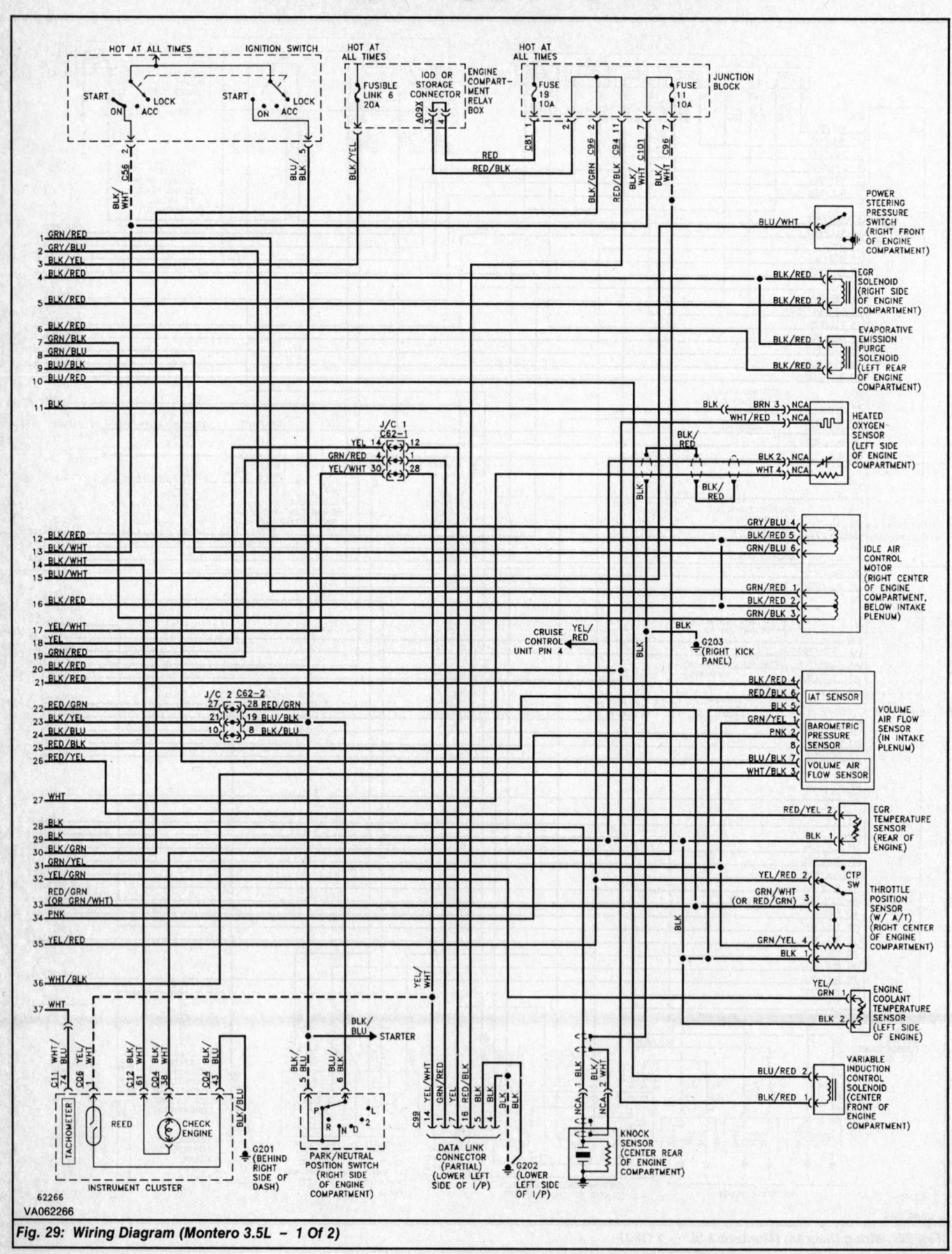

Fig. 29: Wiring Diagram (Montero 3.5L – 1 Of 2)

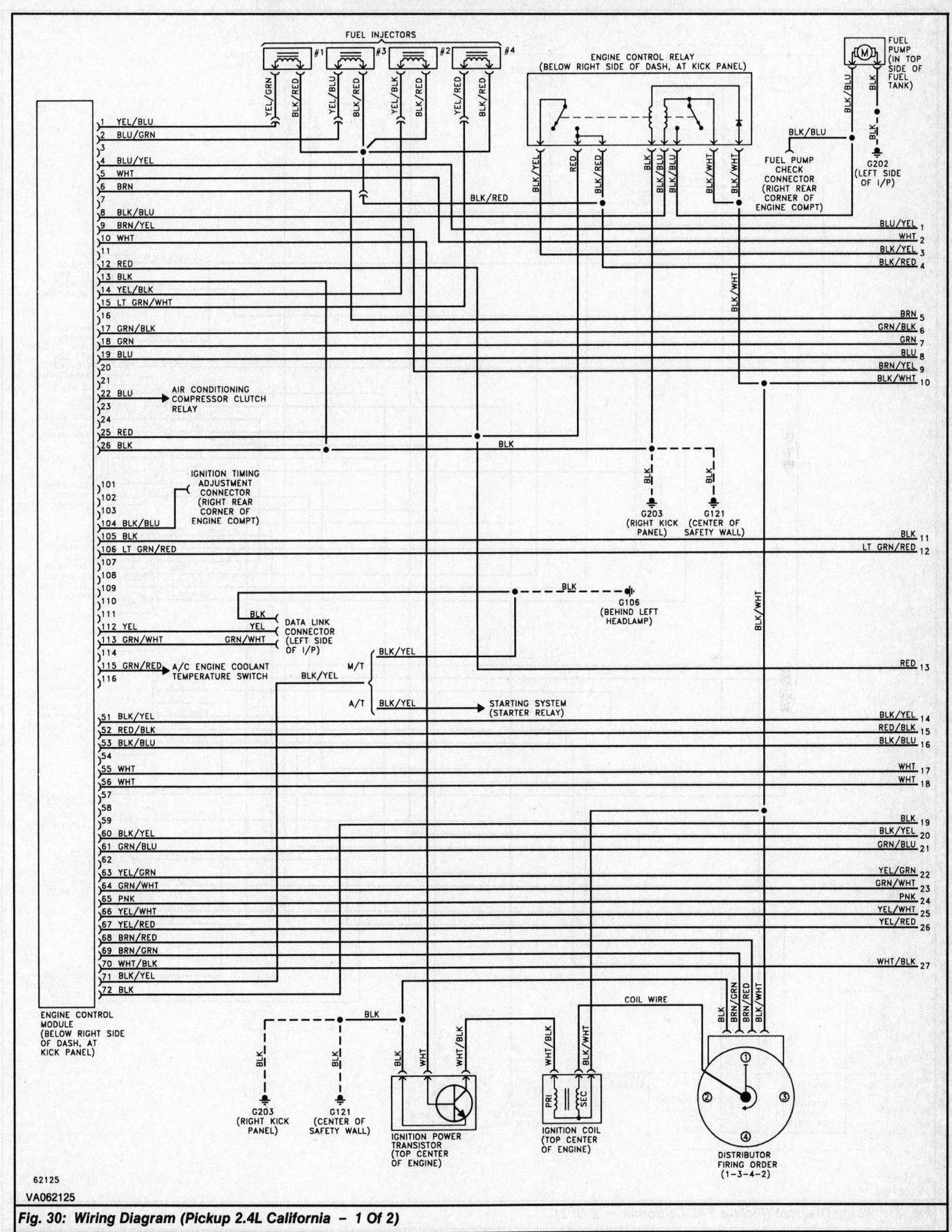

Fig. 30: Wiring Diagram (Pickup 2.4L California – 1 Of 2)

1994 ENGINE PERFORMANCE
Wiring Diagrams (Cont.)

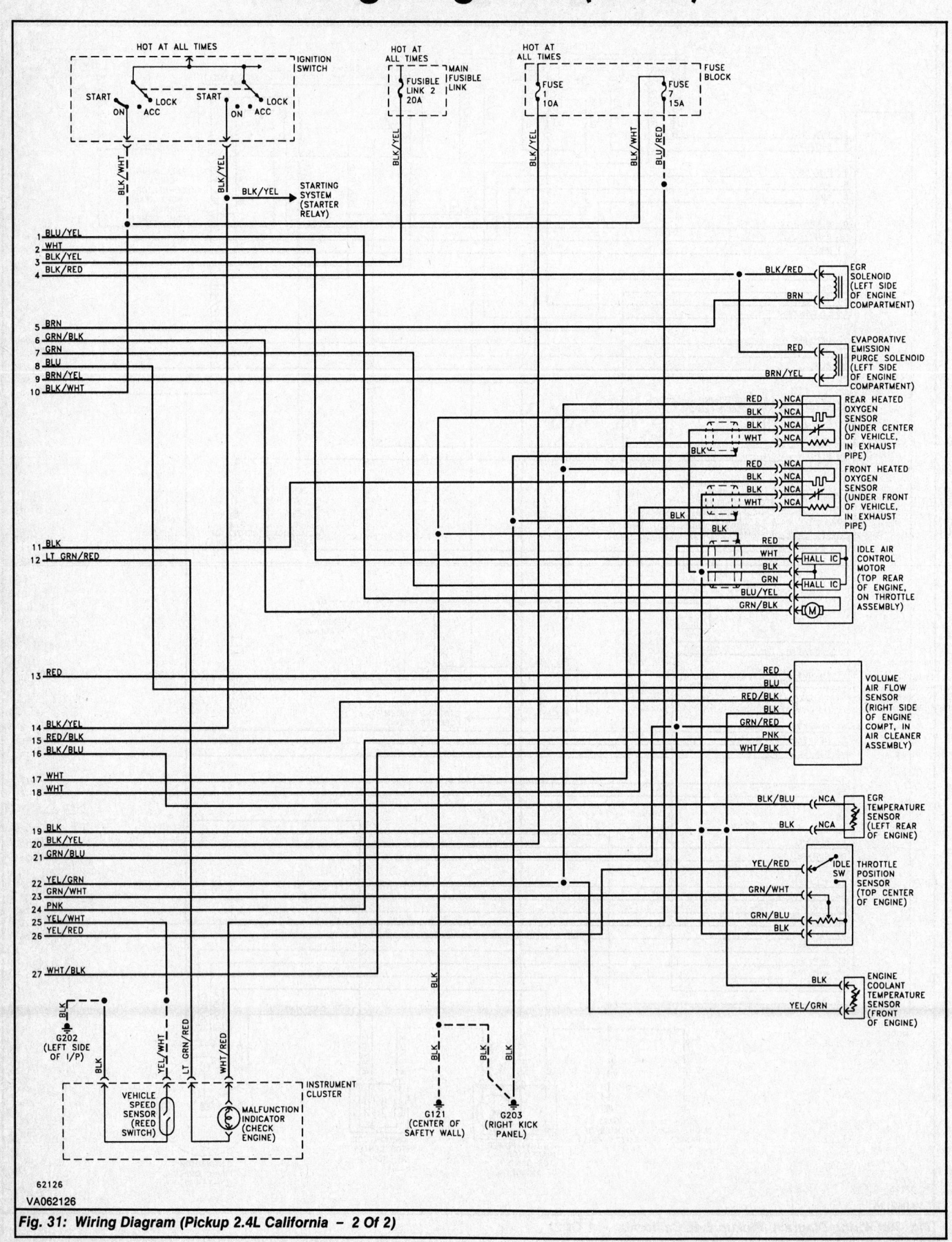

Fig. 31: Wiring Diagram (Pickup 2.4L California – 2 Of 2)

62126

VA062126

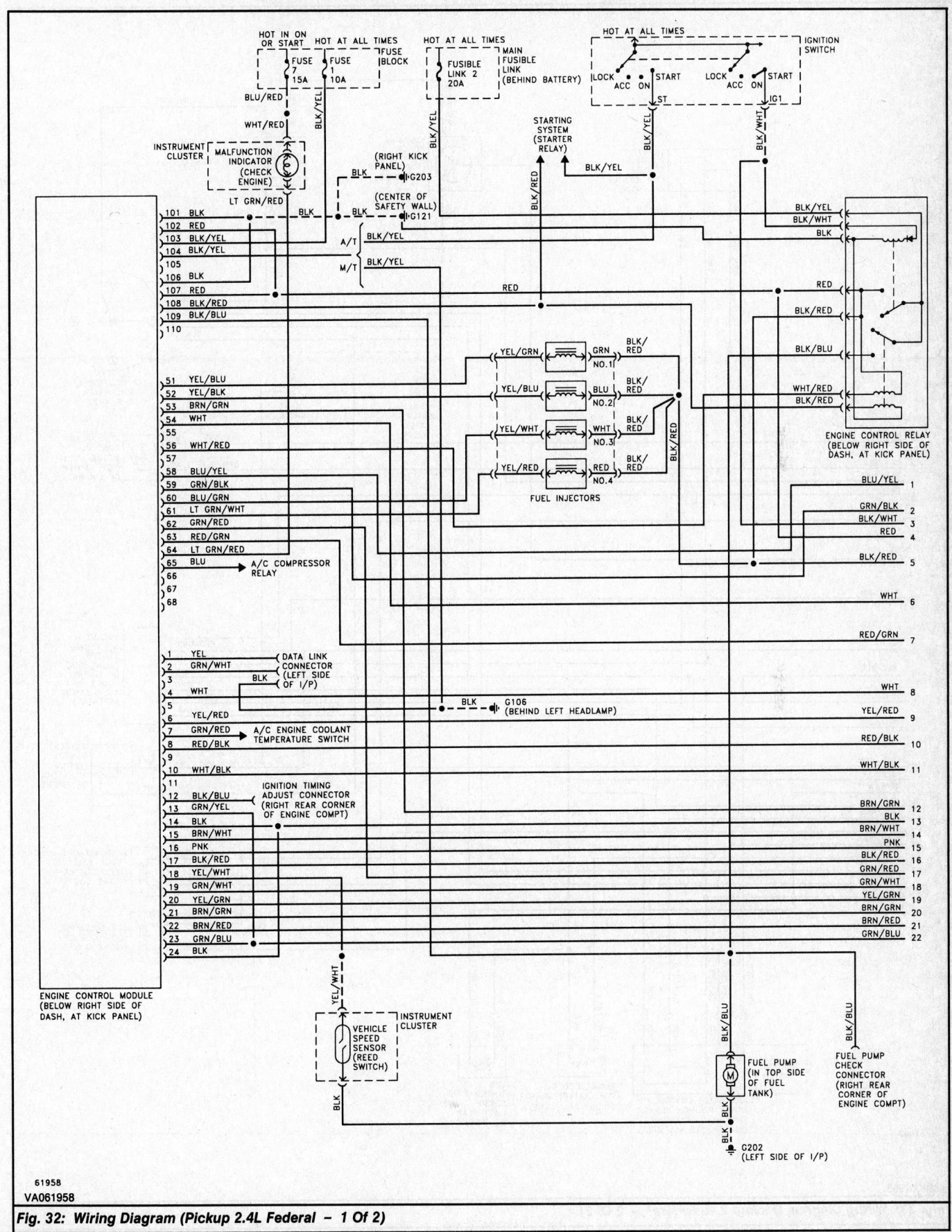

Fig. 32: Wiring Diagram (Pickup 2.4L Federal — 1 Of 2)

61958

VA061958

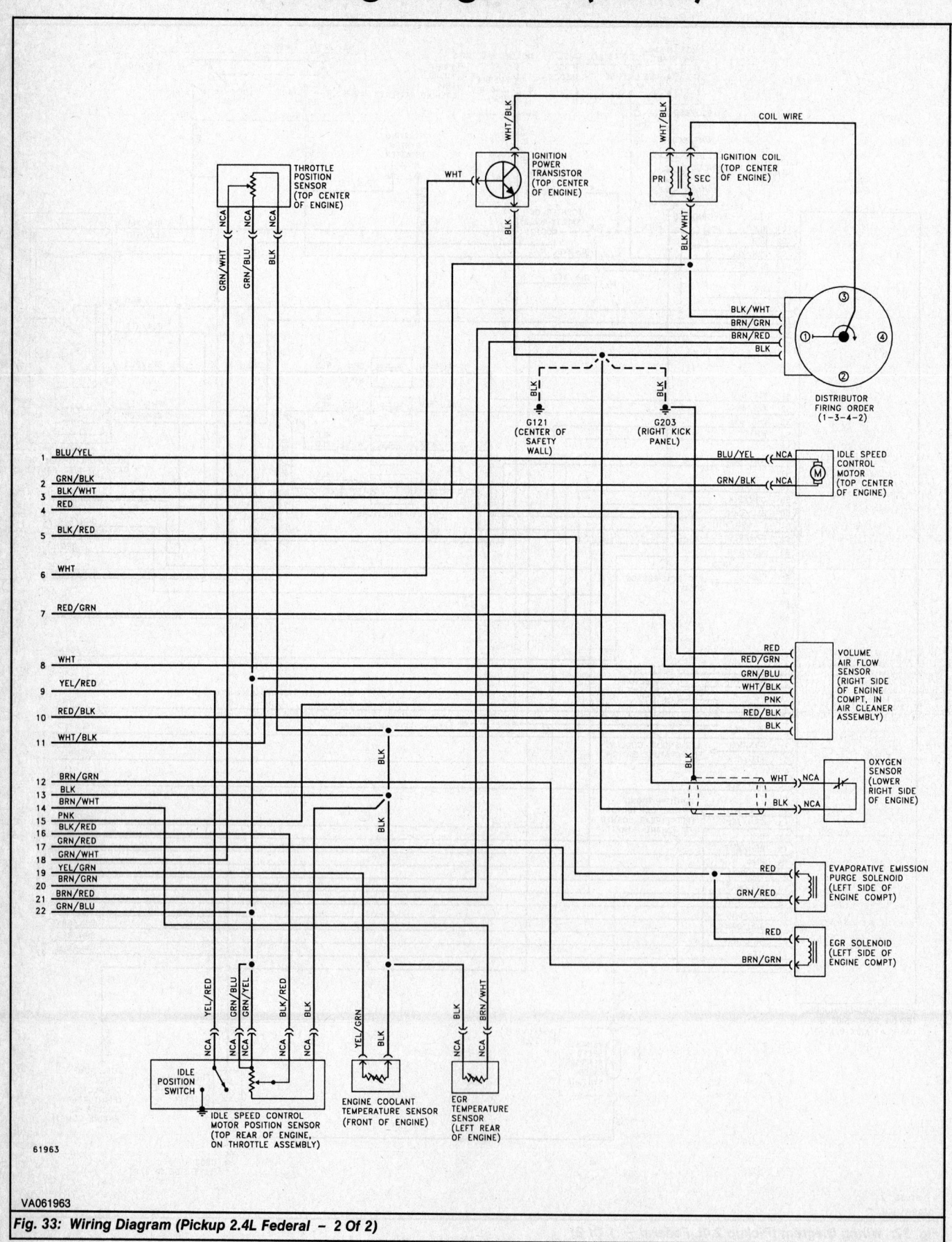

Fig. 33: Wiring Diagram (Pickup 2.4L Federal – 2 Of 2)

61963

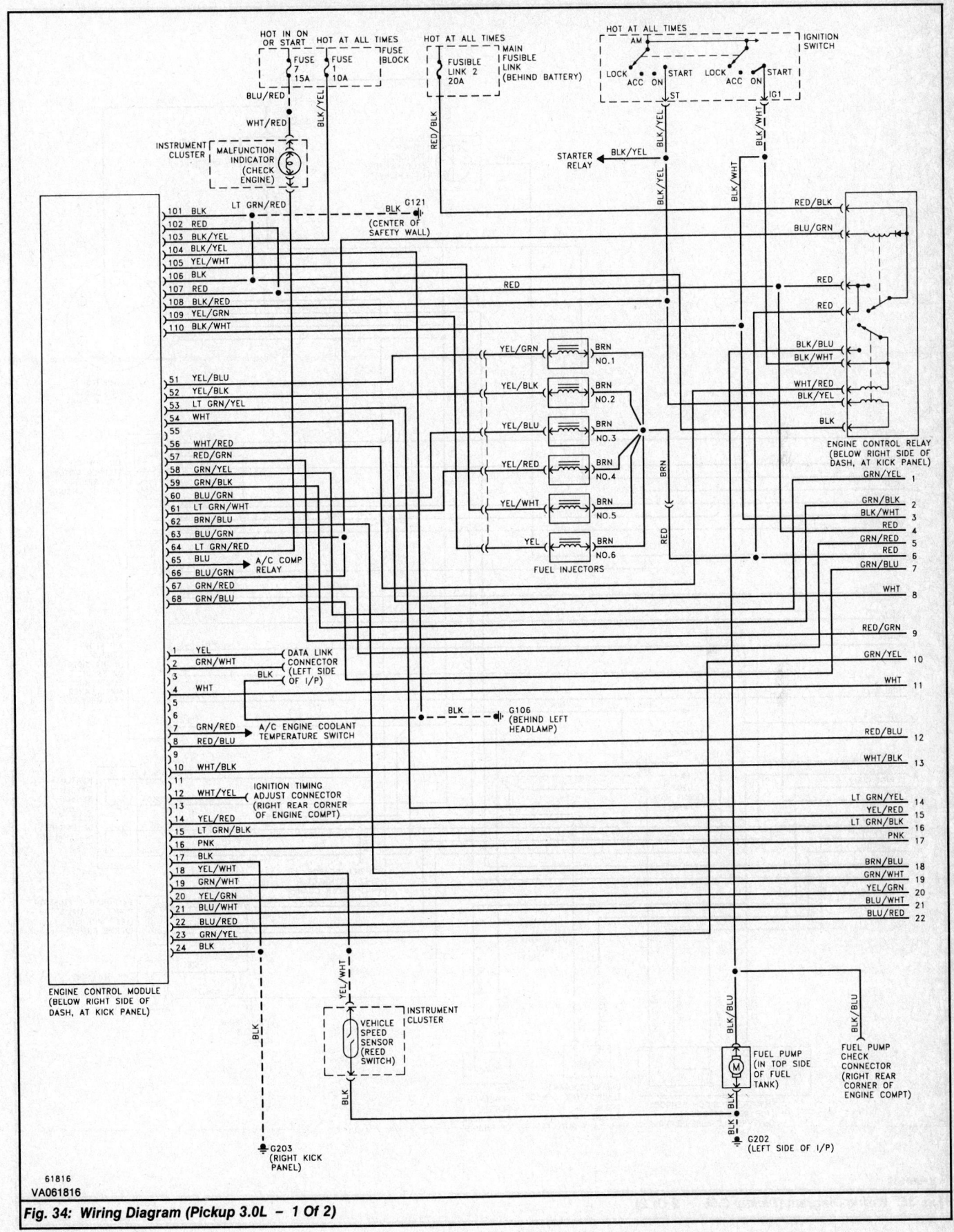

Fig. 34: Wiring Diagram (Pickup 3.0L – 1 Of 2)

61816

VA061816

1994 ENGINE PERFORMANCE
Wiring Diagrams (Cont.)

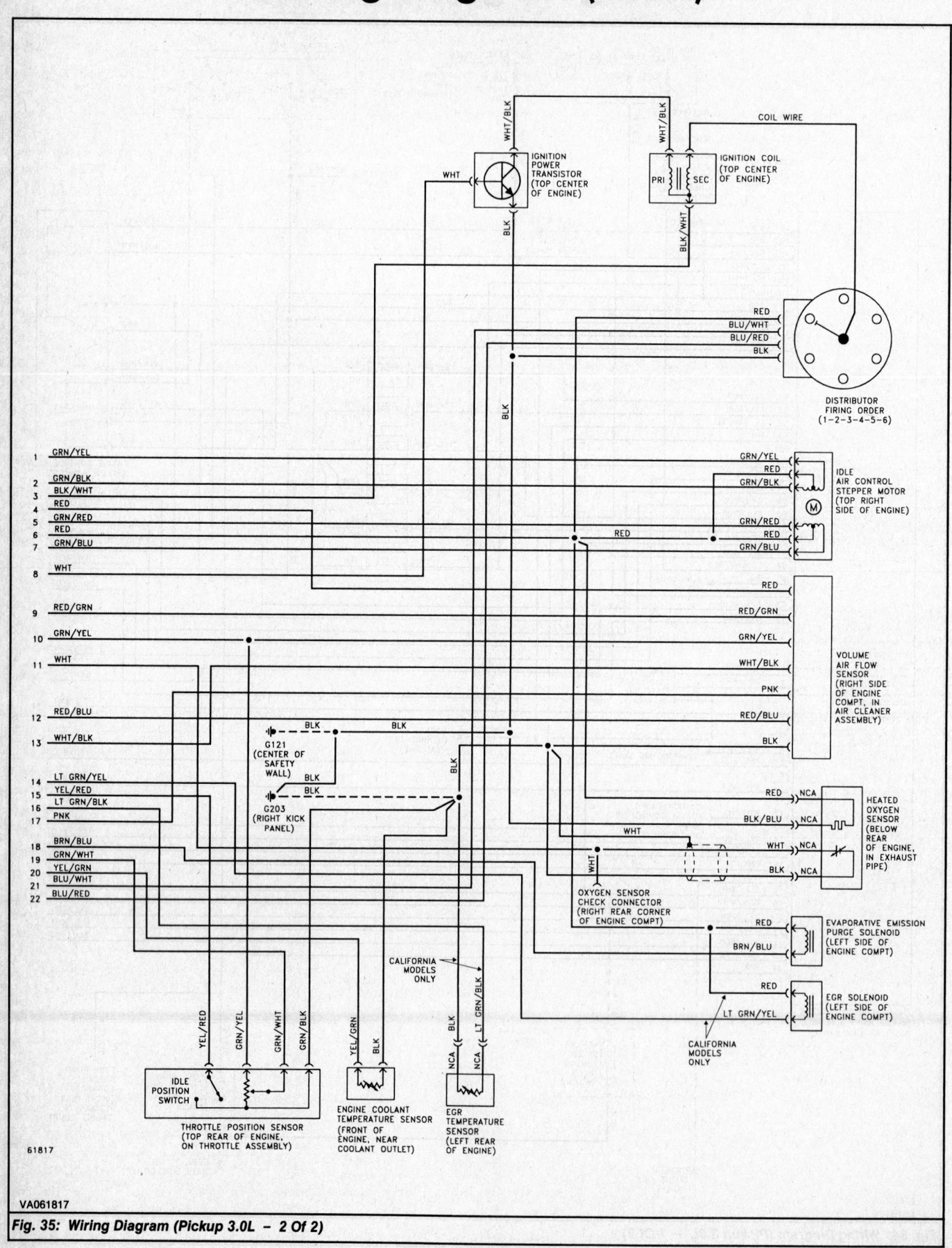

Fig. 35: Wiring Diagram (Pickup 3.0L - 2 Of 2)

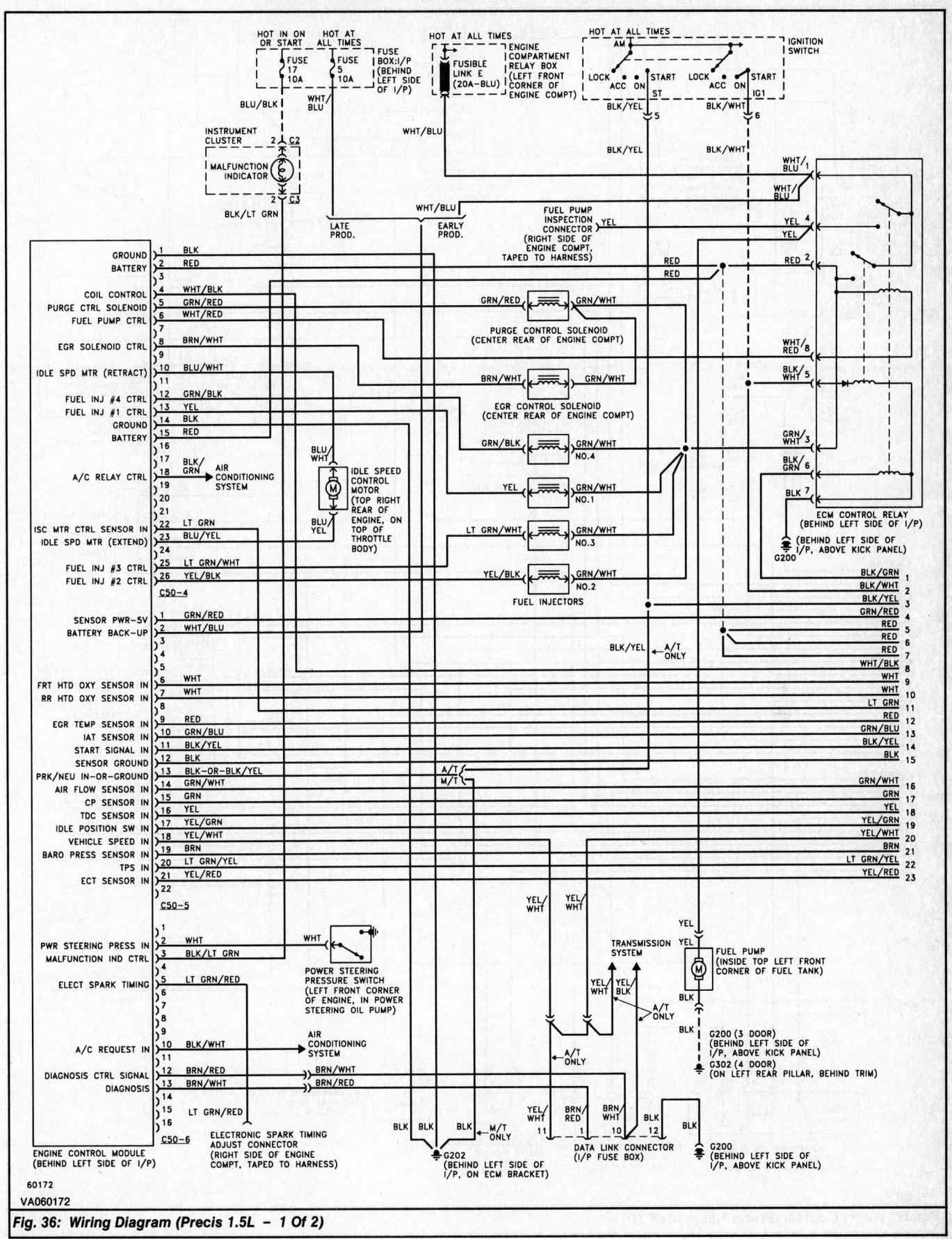

Fig. 36: Wiring Diagram (Precis 1.5L - 1 Of 2)

60172

VA060172

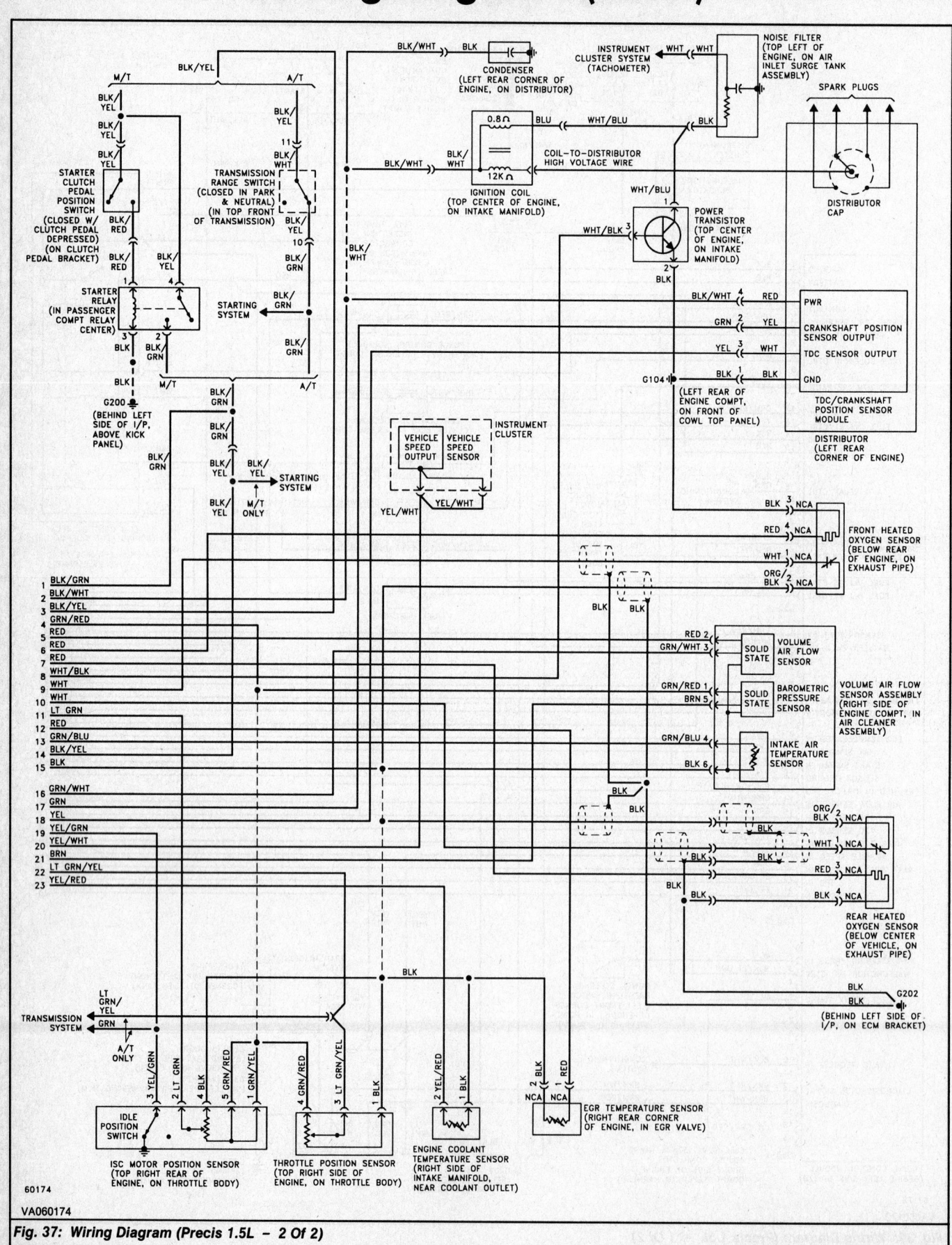

Fig. 37: Wiring Diagram (Precis 1.5L - 2 Of 2)

60174

VA060174

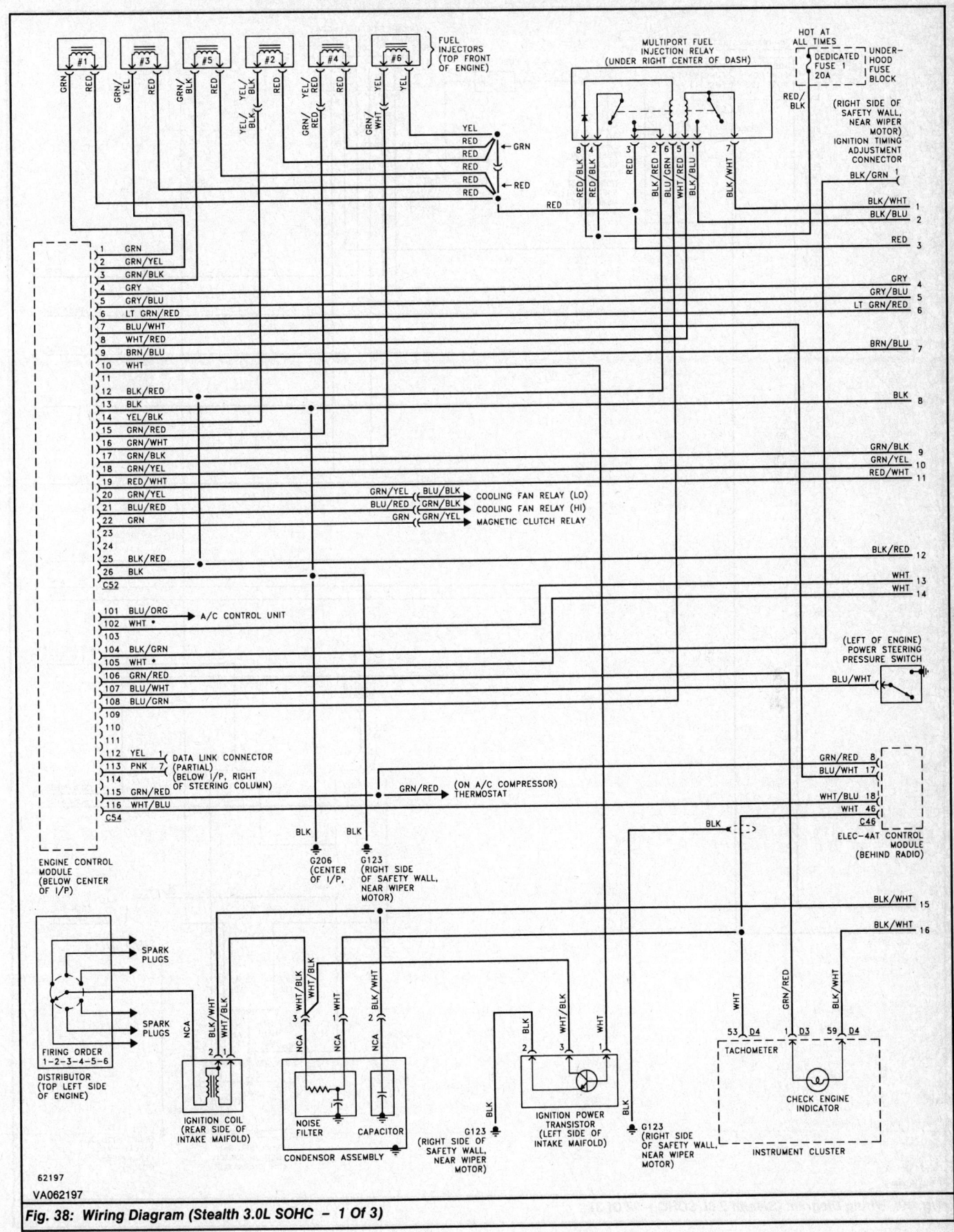

Fig. 38: Wiring Diagram (Stealth 3.0L SOHC – 1 Of 3)

62197
VA062197

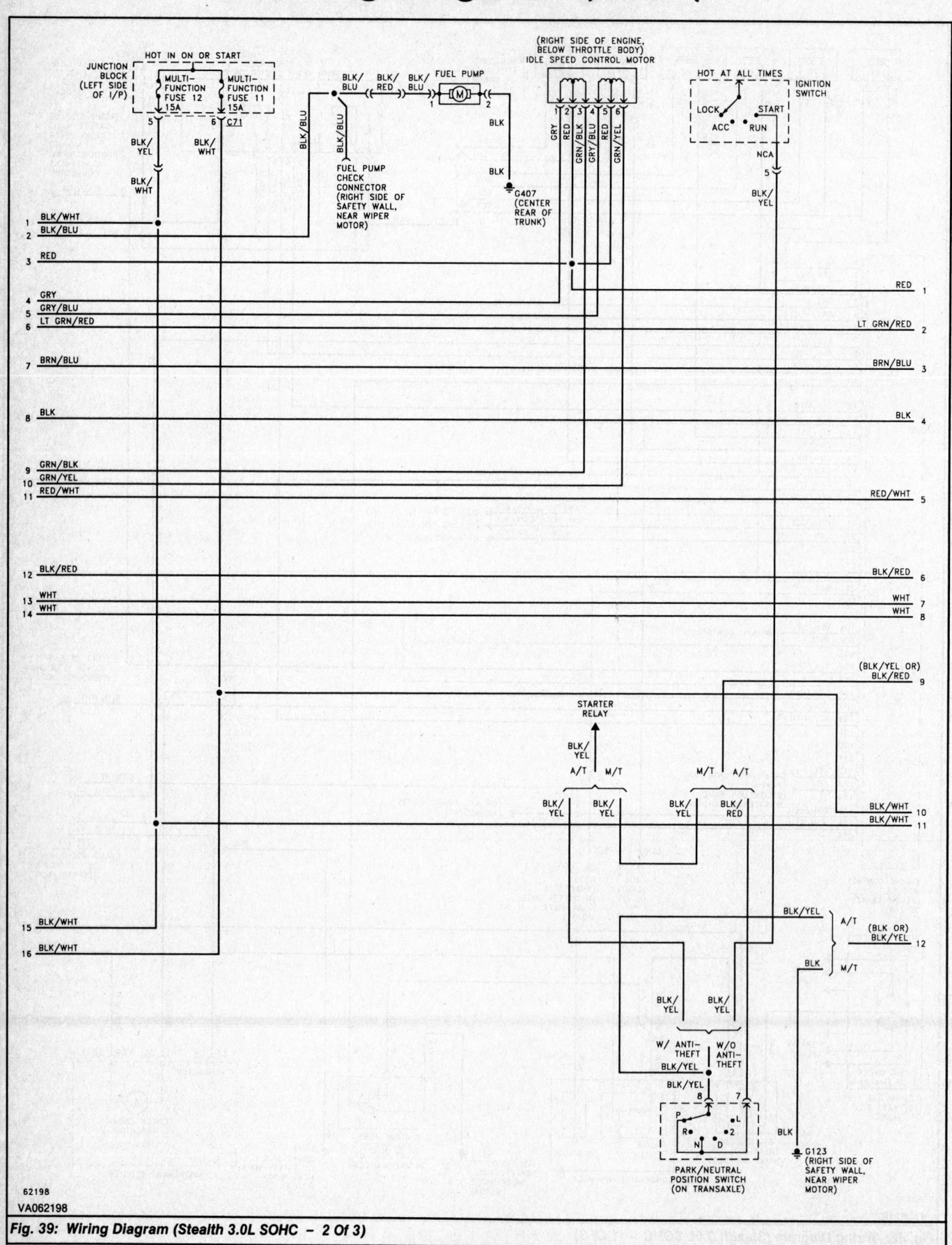

Fig. 39: Wiring Diagram (Stealth 3.0L SOHC – 2 Of 3)

62198
VA062198

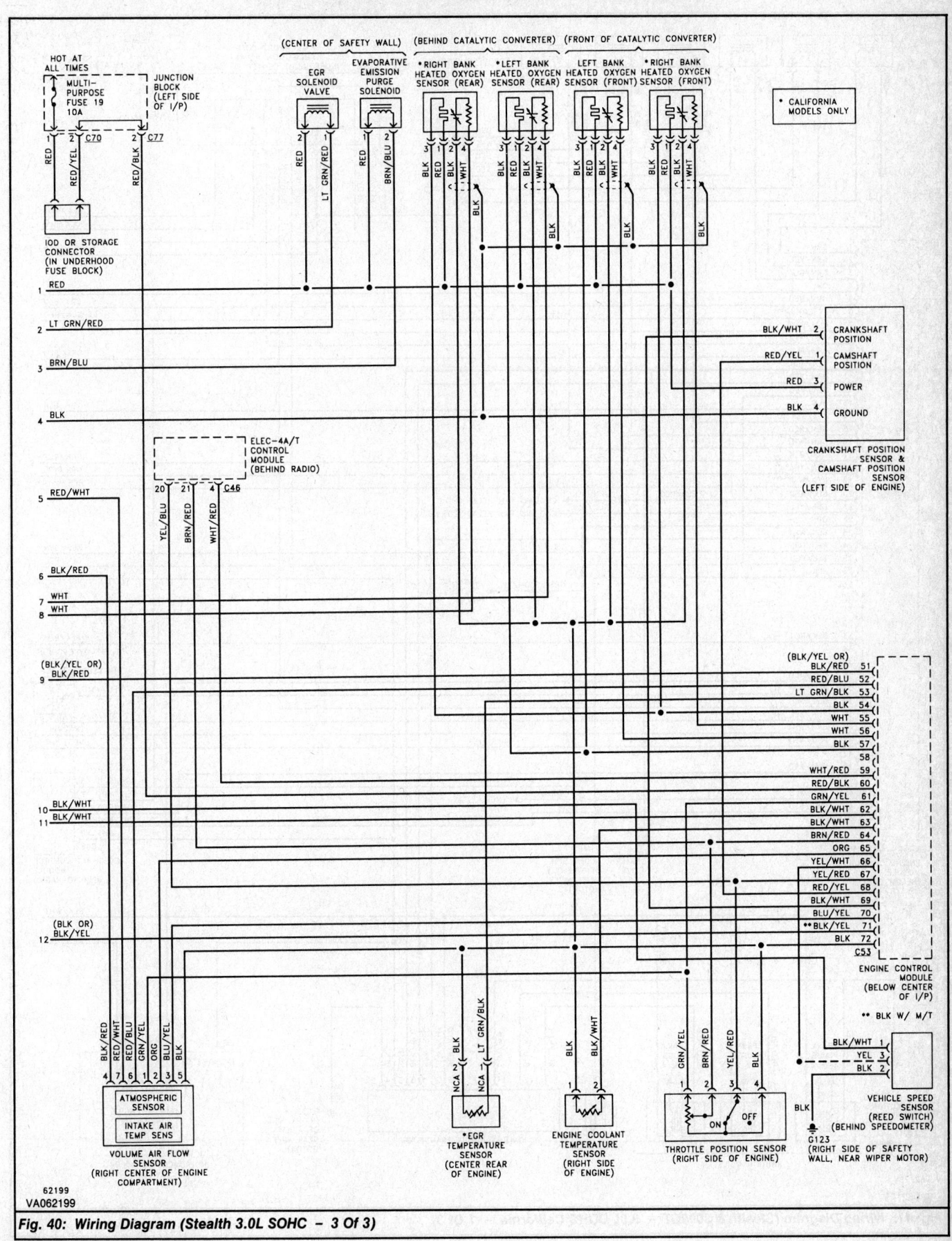

Fig. 40: Wiring Diagram (Stealth 3.0L SOHC – 3 Of 3)

62199
VA062199

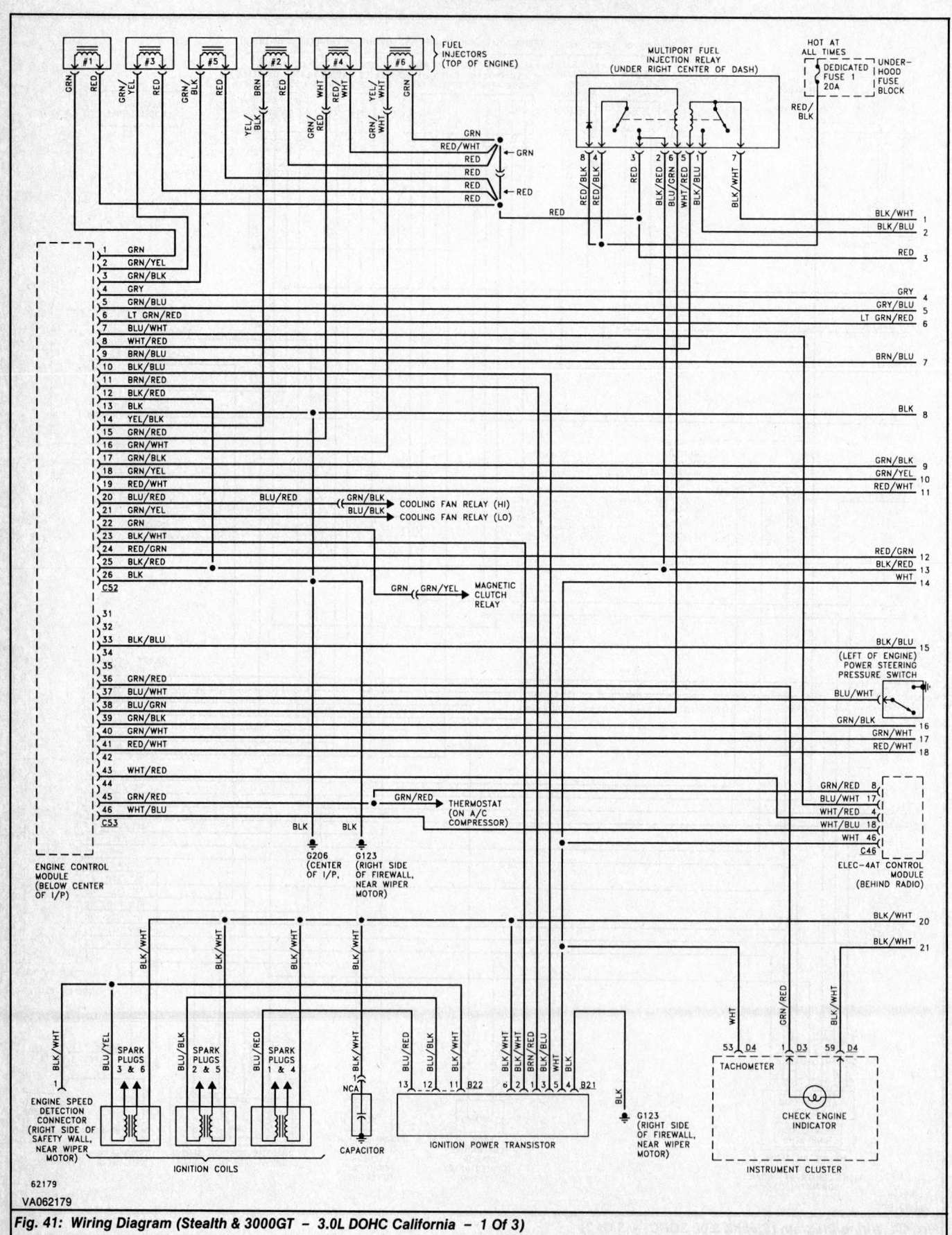

Fig. 41: Wiring Diagram (Stealth & 3000GT – 3.0L DOHC California – 1 Of 3)

62179

VA062179

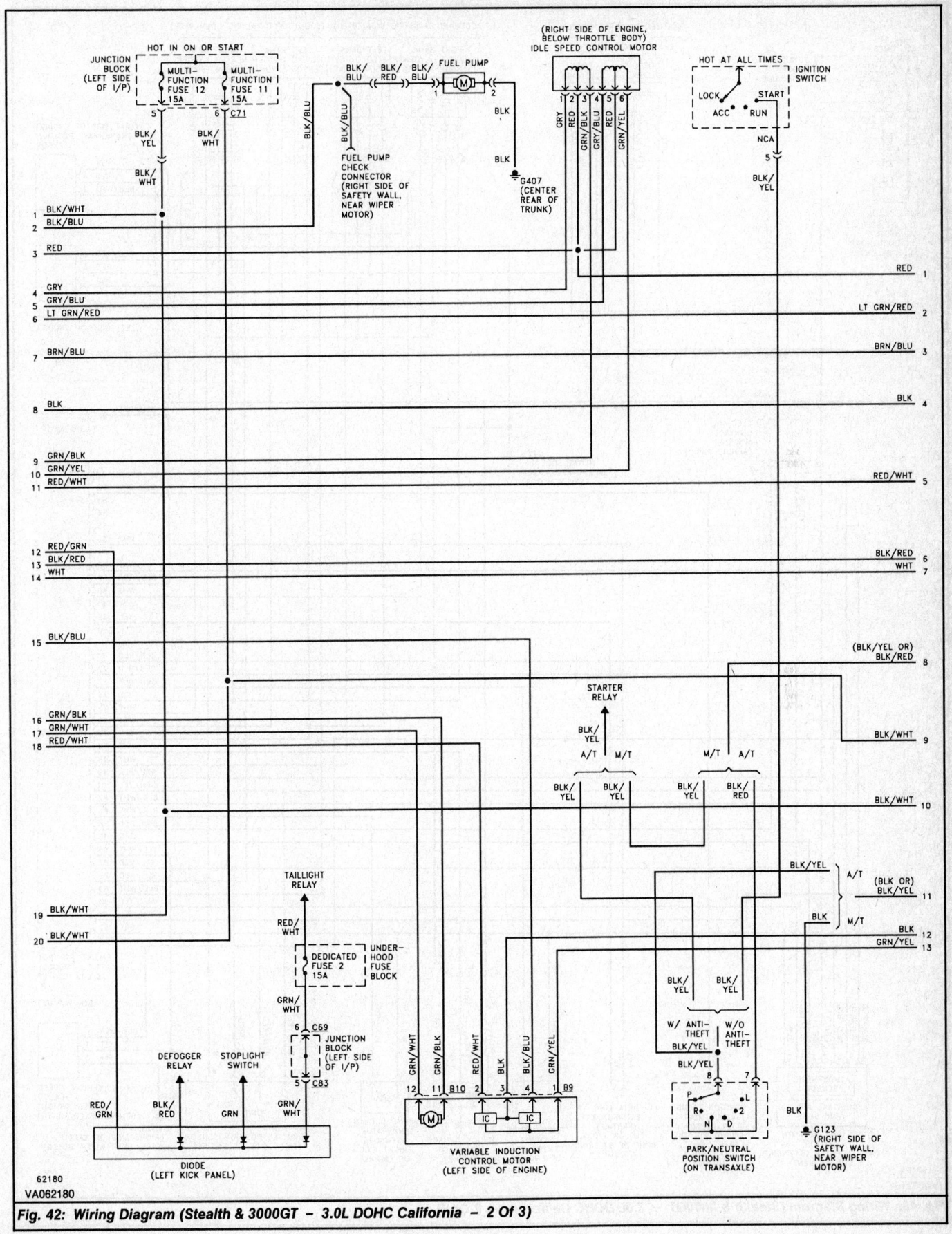

Fig. 42: Wiring Diagram (Stealth & 3000GT – 3.0L DOHC California – 2 Of 3)

1994 ENGINE PERFORMANCE
Wiring Diagrams (Cont.)

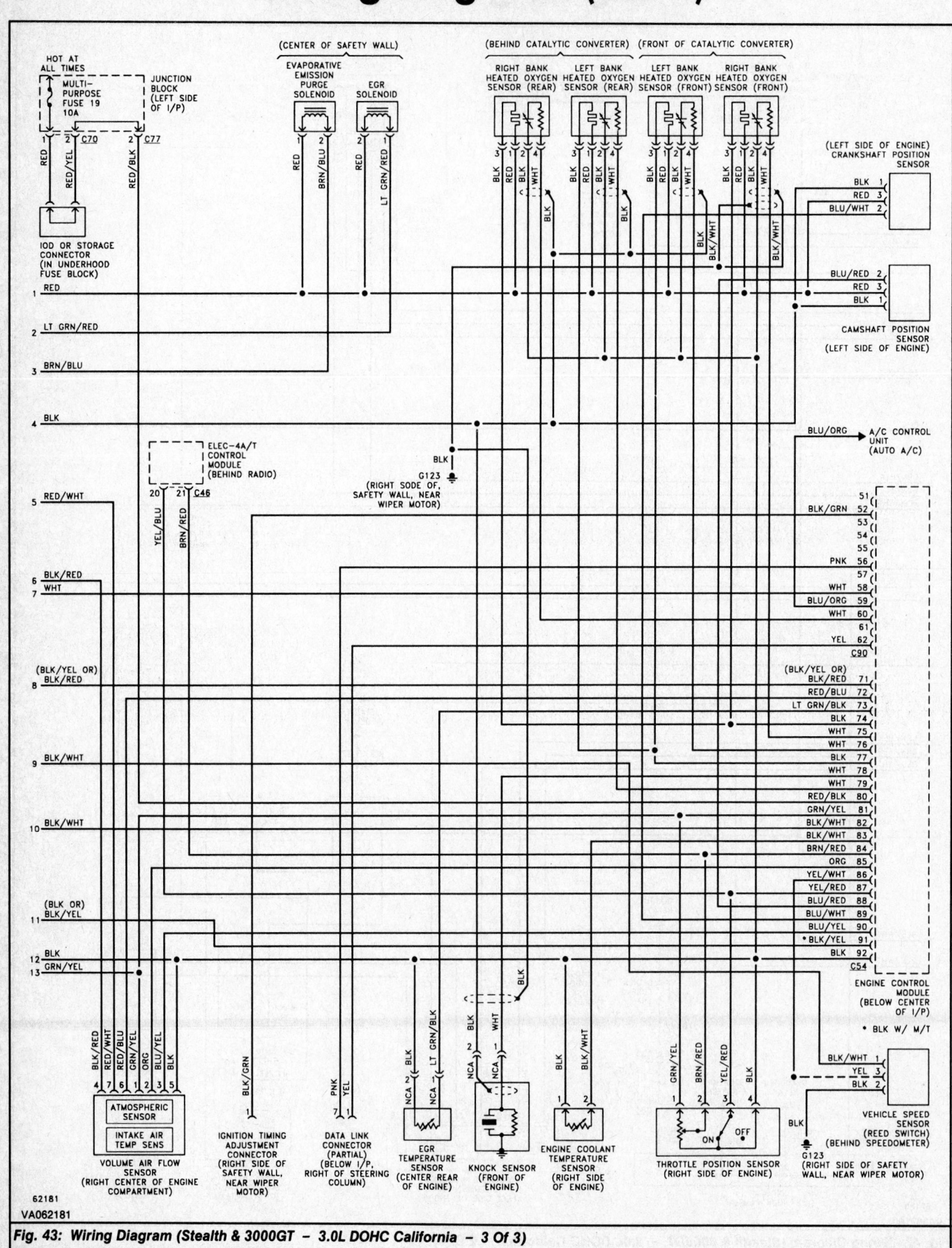

Fig. 43: Wiring Diagram (Stealth & 3000GT - 3.0L DOHC California - 3 Of 3)

62181

VA062181

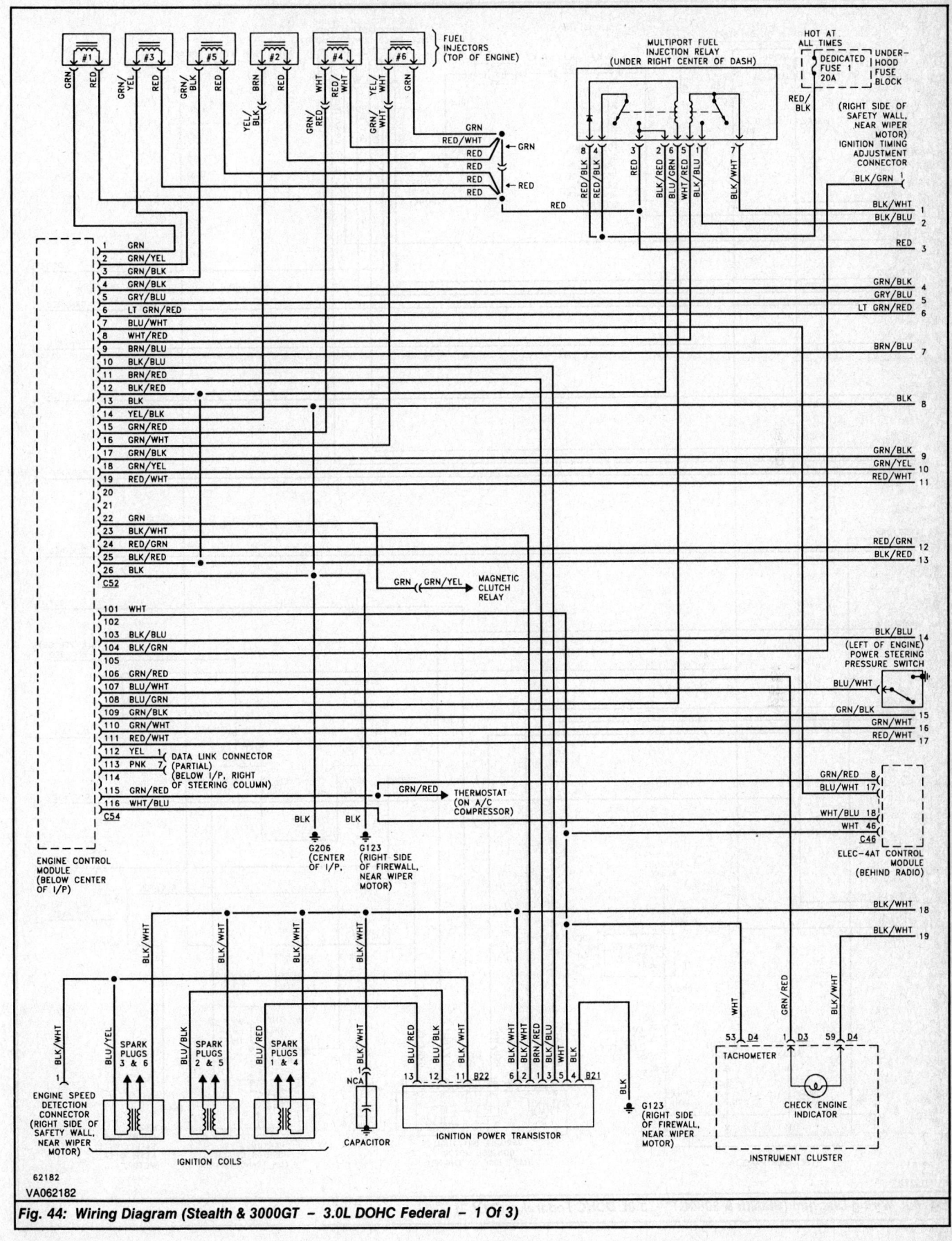

Fig. 44: Wiring Diagram (Stealth & 3000GT – 3.0L DOHC Federal – 1 Of 3)

62182

VA062182

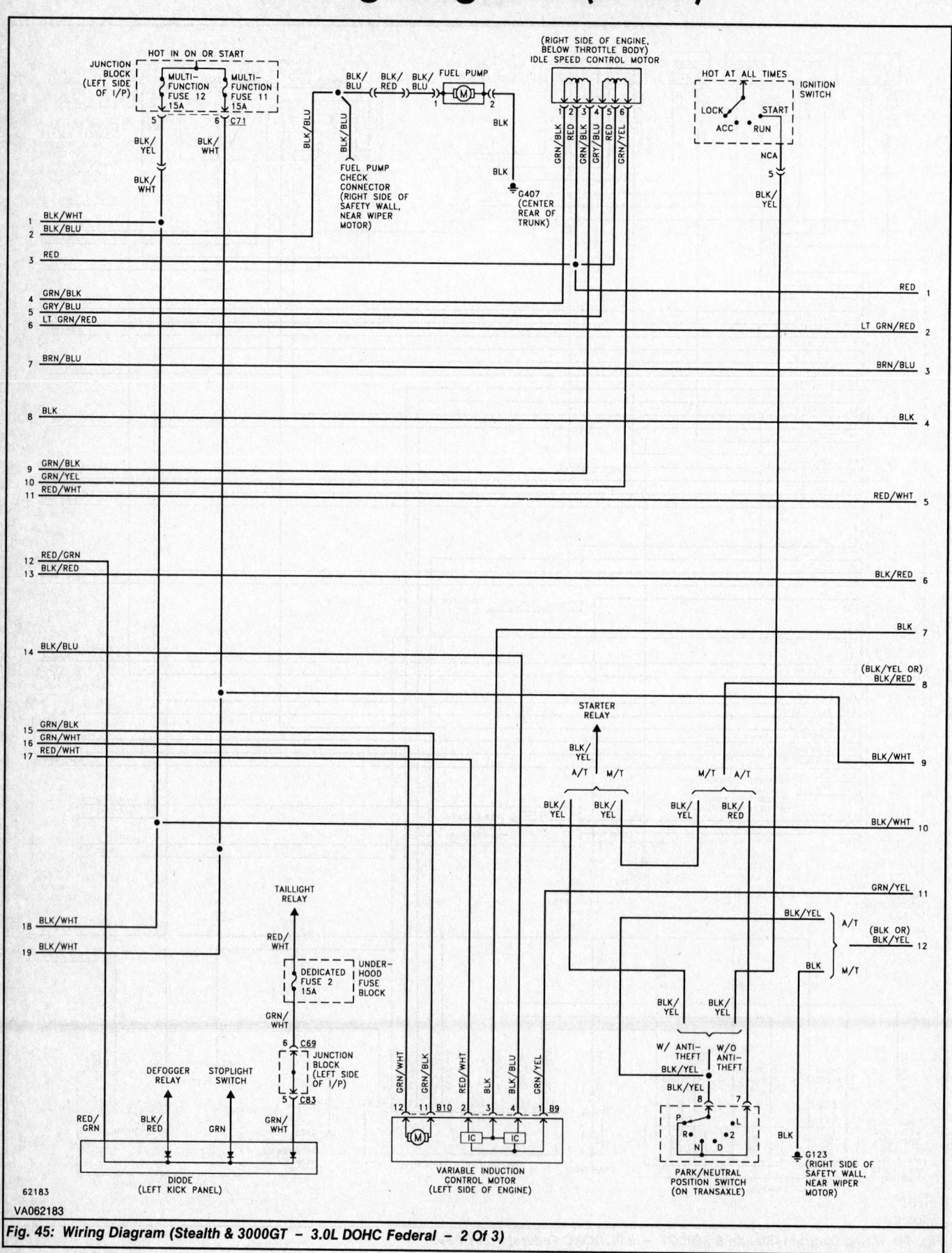

Fig. 45: Wiring Diagram (Stealth & 3000GT - 3.0L DOHC Federal - 2 Of 3)

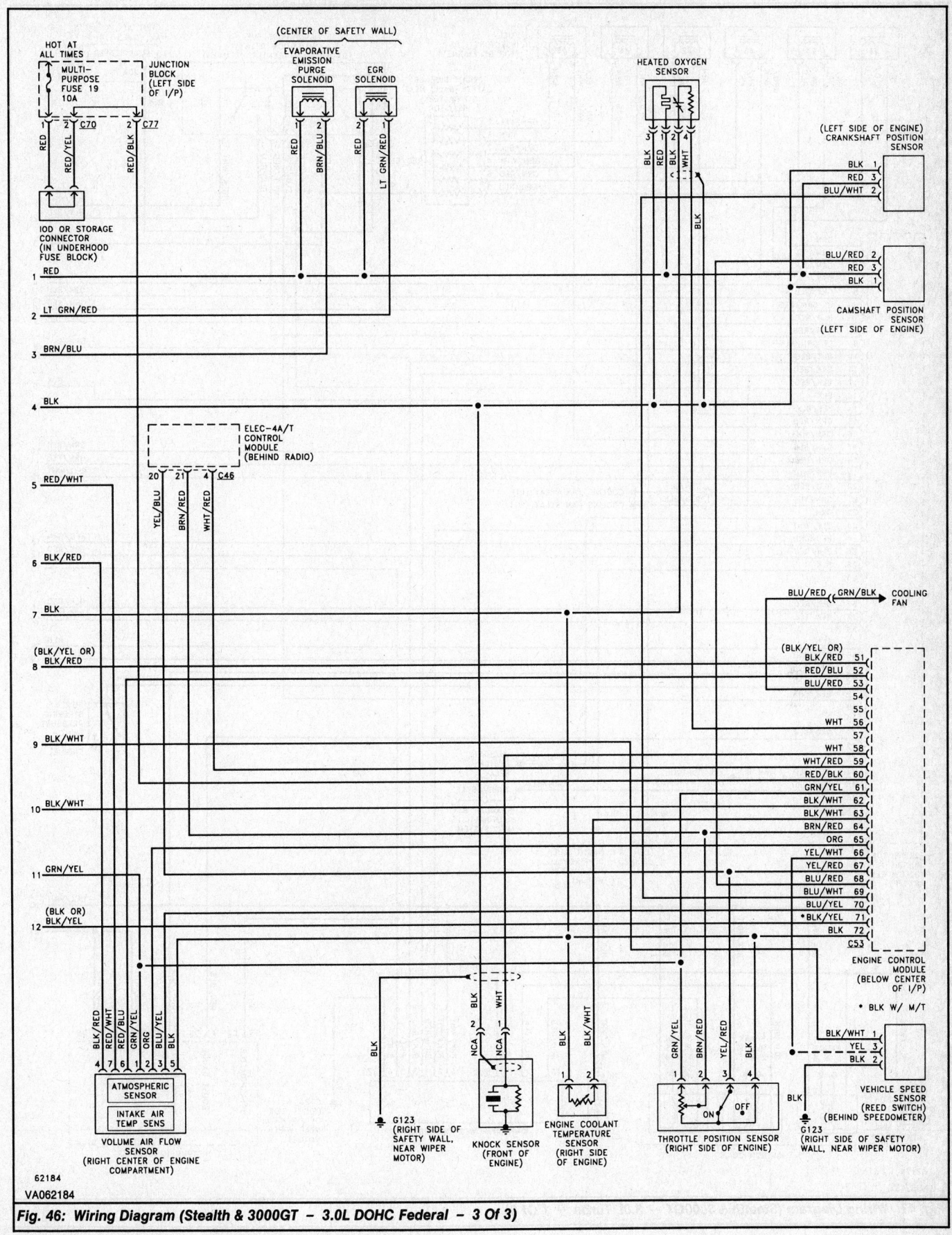

Fig. 46: Wiring Diagram (Stealth & 3000GT - 3.0L DOHC Federal - 3 Of 3)

1994 ENGINE PERFORMANCE
Wiring Diagrams (Cont.)

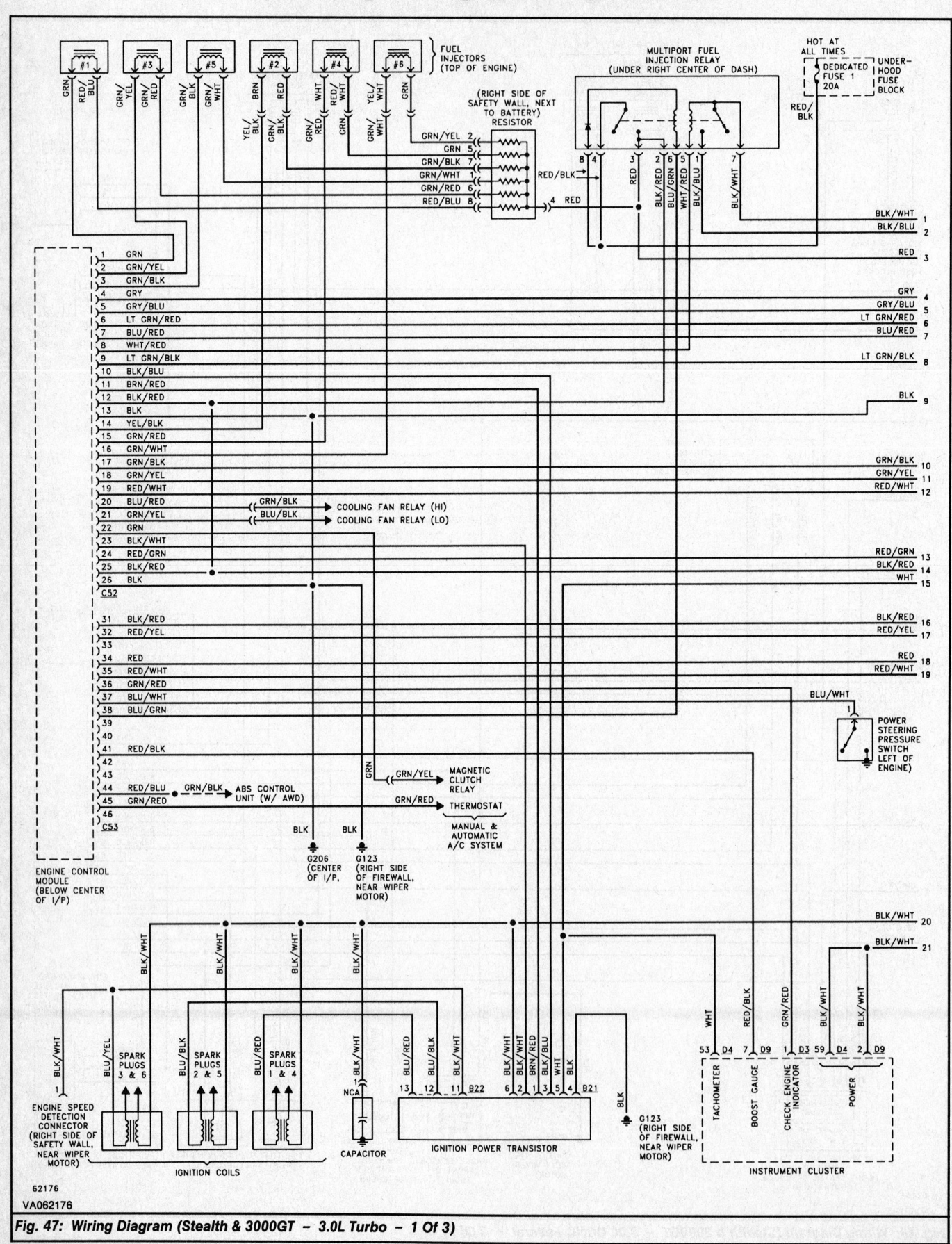

Fig. 47: *Wiring Diagram (Stealth & 3000GT - 3.0L Turbo - 1 Of 3)*

62176

VA062176

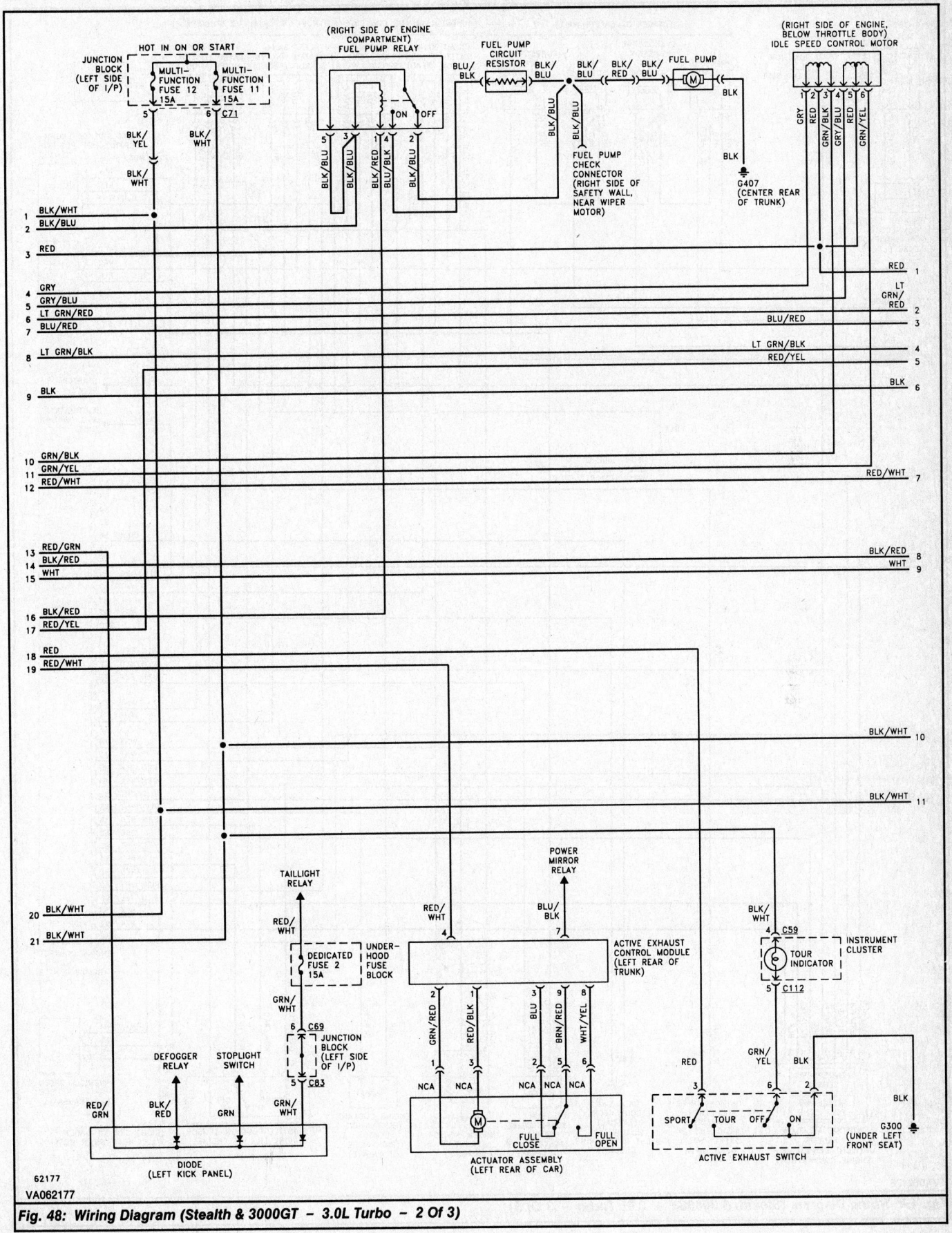

Fig. 48: Wiring Diagram (Stealth & 3000GT – 3.0L Turbo – 2 Of 3)

62177

VA062177

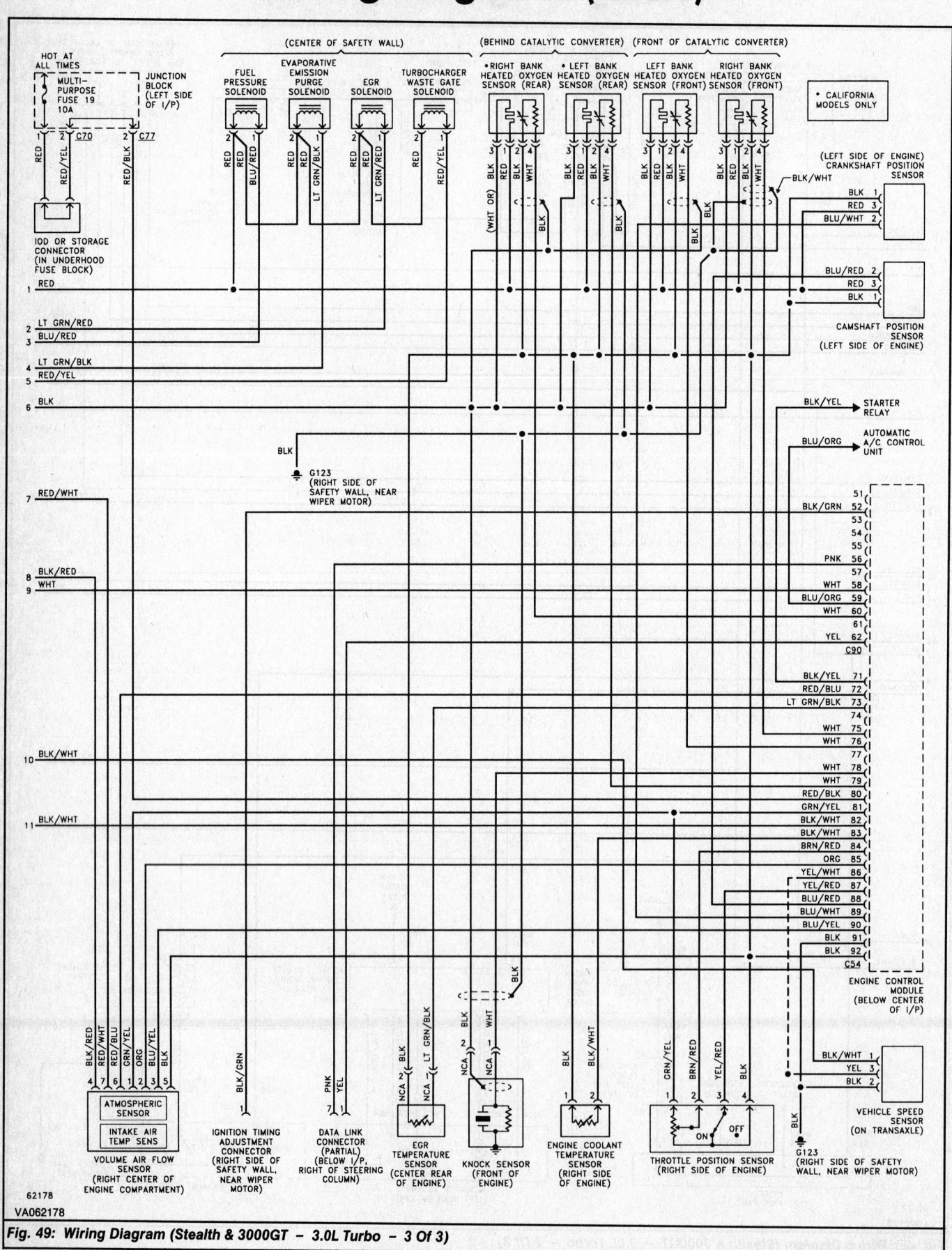

62178

VA062178

Fig. 49: Wiring Diagram (Stealth & 3000GT – 3.0L Turbo – 3 Of 3)

1994 ELECTRICAL
Alternators & Regulators

Chrysler Corp.: Colt, Colt Vista, Stealth
Eagle: Summit, Summit Wagon
Mitsubishi: Diamante, Eclipse, Expo, Galant,
Mirage, Montero, Pickup, Precis, 3000GT

DESCRIPTION

Mitsubishi alternators are conventional 3-phase, self-rectifying type units containing 6 diodes (3 positive and 3 negative) which are used to rectify current. All models use a case-mounted Integrated Circuit (IC) voltage regulator.

Alternator relay or resistor with diode is used to ensure charging of battery even if charging indicator light is defective.

ADJUSTMENTS
DRIVE BELT ADJUSTMENT

Application	Deflection [1] New Belt In. (mm)	Deflection [1] Used Belt In. (mm)
Colt, Mirage & Summit		
1.5L	.22-.28 (5.6-7.1)	.31 (7.9)
1.8L	.28-.34 (7.1-8.6)	.37 (9.5)
Colt Vista, Expo & Summit Wagon		
1.8L	.28-.34 (7.1-8.6)	.37 (9.5)
2.4L	.30-.35 (7.6-8.9)	.39 (10.0)
Diamante		
SOHC	.16-.20 (4.0-5.0)	.24-.31 (6.0-7.9)
DOHC	.14-.16 (3.5-4.0)	.16-.20 (4.0-5.0)
Eclipse		
1.8L	.26-.31 (6.5-7.9)	.37 (9.5)
2.0L	.30-.35 (7.6-9.0)	.39 (10.0)
Galant	.30-.35 (7.6-9.0)	.39 (10.0)
Montero		
3.0L	.26-.31 (6.5-7.9)	.35 (9.0)
3.5L [2]	.16-.20 (4.0-5.0)	.22-.26 (5.6-6.5)
Pickup		
2.4L	.28-.39 (7.1-10.0)	[3]
3.0L	.32-.39 (8.0-10.0)	[3]
Precis	.22-.28 (5.6-7.1)	.31 (7.9)
Stealth		
SOHC	.24-.35 (6.0-9.0)	[3]
DOHC	.16-.22 (4.0-5.6)	[3]
3000GT	.16-.22 (4.0-5.6)	[3]

[1] – With 22 lbs. (10 kg) pressure applied midway on belt run.
[2] – Measure between water pump pulley and crankshaft pulley.
[3] – Information is not available from manufacturer.

TROUBLE SHOOTING

NOTE: See TROUBLE SHOOTING article in GENERAL INFORMATION.

ON-VEHICLE TESTING
ALTERNATOR TO BATTERY CONTINUITY TEST

NOTE: Check alternator wiring harness connections and drive belt tension and ensure battery is fully charged before performing test.

1) Turn ignition switch to OFF position. Disconnect negative battery cable. Remove output lead from alternator terminal "B". See Fig. 1. Install a 100-amp ammeter in series with terminal "B" and disconnected output lead. Install positive lead of ammeter to terminal "B" and negative lead to disconnected output wire.

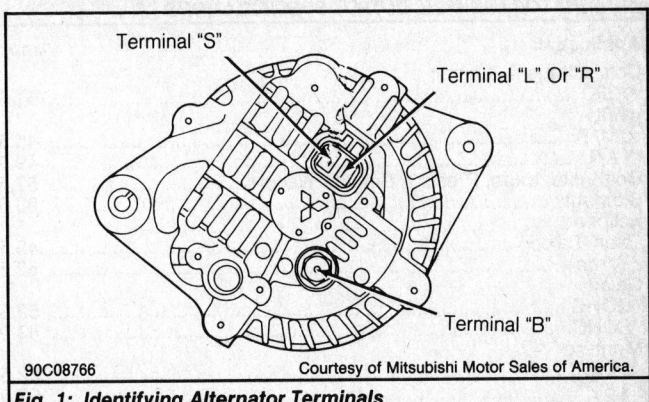

Fig. 1: Identifying Alternator Terminals

2) Install a digital voltmeter between alternator terminal "B" and positive battery terminal. Install positive voltmeter lead to terminal "B" and negative lead to positive battery terminal. Reconnect negative battery cable.

3) Start engine. Turn accessories on and adjust engine speed until ammeter indicates 20 amps, and note voltmeter reading. If voltmeter indicates .2 volt or less, system is okay.

4) If voltage is greater than .2 volt, wiring is defective between alternator terminal "B", fusible link and positive battery terminal. Disconnect negative battery cable, and remove test equipment.

ALTERNATOR OUTPUT TEST

NOTE: During alternator output test, a slightly discharged battery should be used as a fully charged battery may not allow full alternator output.

1) Turn ignition switch to OFF position. Disconnect negative battery cable. Disconnect alternator output wire from terminal "B". Install positive lead of 100-amp ammeter to terminal "B" and negative lead to disconnected output lead.

CAUTION: Tighten each connection securely as heavy current flow will exist. DO NOT use clips on ammeter.

2) Connect positive voltmeter lead (0-20 volts) to alternator terminal "B" and negative lead to ground. Install tachometer, and reconnect negative battery cable.

3) Ensure voltmeter indicates battery voltage. If no voltage exists, an open circuit is present in wire between alternator terminal "B" and negative battery terminal. Check grounds and fusible link.

4) Turn headlights on, and start engine. Set headlights at high beam and heater switch on HIGH. Quickly accelerate engine speed to 2500 RPM and note alternator output current on ammeter. Minimum output should be within specification. See ALTERNATOR MINIMUM OUTPUT SPECIFICATIONS table.

NOTE: Output voltage changes with electrical load and temperature. Ensure proper electrical load is applied while checking output. Nominal output may not be obtained if alternator or ambient temperature is excessive. Allow alternator or temperature to cool, and recheck output. Alternator output is stamped on metal plate attached to alternator case.

5) If minimum output is not obtained and alternator wiring is okay, repair alternator. Disconnect negative battery cable, and remove test equipment.

1994 ELECTRICAL
Alternators & Regulators (Cont.)

ALTERNATOR MINIMUM OUTPUT SPECIFICATIONS

Application	Amps
Colt, Mirage & Summit	
1.5L	52.5
1.8L	
M/T	45.5
A/T	49.0
Colt Vista, Expo, Precis & Summit Wagon	52.5
Diamante	63.0
Eclipse	
Non-Turbo	45.5
Turbo	52.5
Galant	
DOHC	52.5
SOHC	63.0
Montero	
3.0L	52.5
3.5L	63.0
Pickup	
2.4L	28.0
3.0L	45.5
Stealth	
DOHC	77.0
SOHC	63.0
3000GT	77.0

REGULATED VOLTAGE TEST

NOTE: Ensure battery is fully charged and proper drive belt tension exists.

1) Turn ignition switch to OFF position. Disconnect negative battery cable. Connect positive voltmeter lead to terminal "S" of alternator. See Fig. 1. Connect negative voltmeter lead to ground.
2) Disconnect alternator output wire from terminal "B". Install a 100-amp ammeter in series with terminal "B" and disconnected output lead. Install positive lead of ammeter to terminal "B" and negative lead to disconnected output wire. Install a tachometer, and reconnect negative battery cable.

3) Turn ignition switch to ON position and ensure voltmeter indicates battery voltage. If no voltage exists, there is an open in wire between alternator terminal "S" and positive battery terminal or fusible link is blown.
4) Start engine. Ensure all lights and accessories are off. Operate engine at 2500 RPM and read voltmeter when alternator output current drops to 10 amps or less. Voltage regulator is okay if voltage output is within specification. See REGULATOR VOLTAGE SPECIFICATIONS table.

REGULATOR VOLTAGE SPECIFICATIONS

Ambient Temperature	Voltage
-4°F (-20°C)	14.2-15.4
68°F (20°C)	13.9-14.9
140°F (60°C)	13.4-14.6
176°F (80°C)	13.1-14.5

BENCH TESTING
RECTIFIER ASSEMBLY

1) Using ohmmeter, check for continuity between diodes and stator coil lead connection. See Fig. 2. Reverse leads. If continuity exists in both directions, diode is shorted. Replace rectifier assembly.
2) To check entire diode assembly, use an ohmmeter to check for continuity between both ends of each diode. See Fig. 2. Switch ohmmeter leads. Continuity should exist in one direction only. If no continuity exists in both directions, diode is defective. Replace rectifier assembly.

ROTOR

1) Check continuity across rotor slip rings. Resistance should be 3-5 ohms (3.1 ohms on Precis). Replace rotor if no continuity exists or resistance is not within specification.
2) Check continuity between individual slip rings and rotor shaft. If continuity exists, rotor coil or slip ring is grounded. Replace rotor.

STATOR

Ensure no continuity exists between stator coil leads and stator core. Check continuity between leads of stator coil. If no continuity exists between coil leads, replace stator.

OVERHAUL

Replace brushes if worn to limit line. Limit line is line closest to rotor contact end of brush. Brushes can be retained in brush holder while installing rotor by inserting wire into back of rear housing. See Fig. 3.

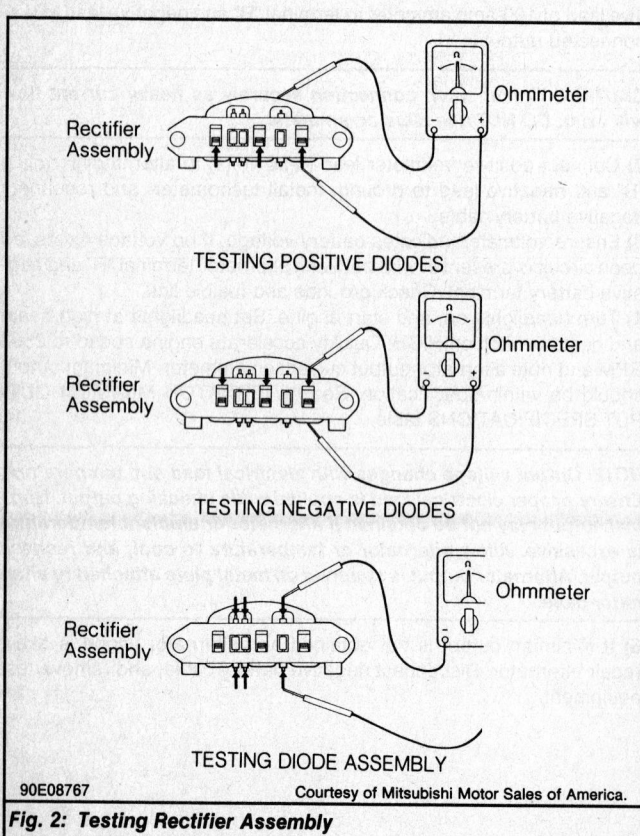

TESTING POSITIVE DIODES

TESTING NEGATIVE DIODES

TESTING DIODE ASSEMBLY

90E08767   Courtesy of Mitsubishi Motor Sales of America.

Fig. 2: Testing Rectifier Assembly

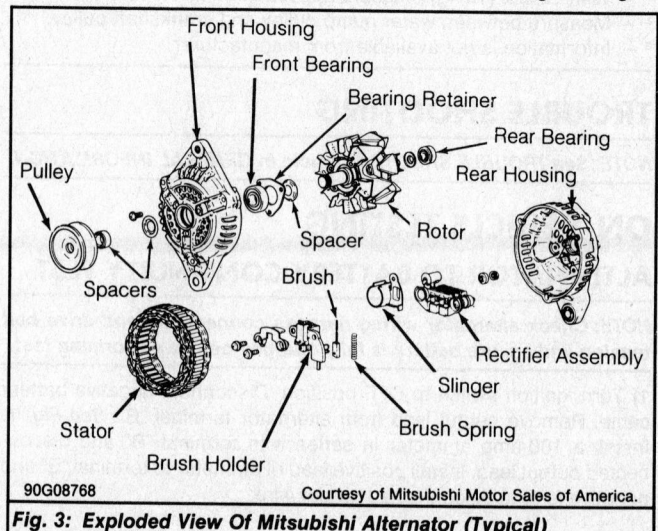

90G08768   Courtesy of Mitsubishi Motor Sales of America.

Fig. 3: Exploded View Of Mitsubishi Alternator (Typical)

WIRING DIAGRAMS

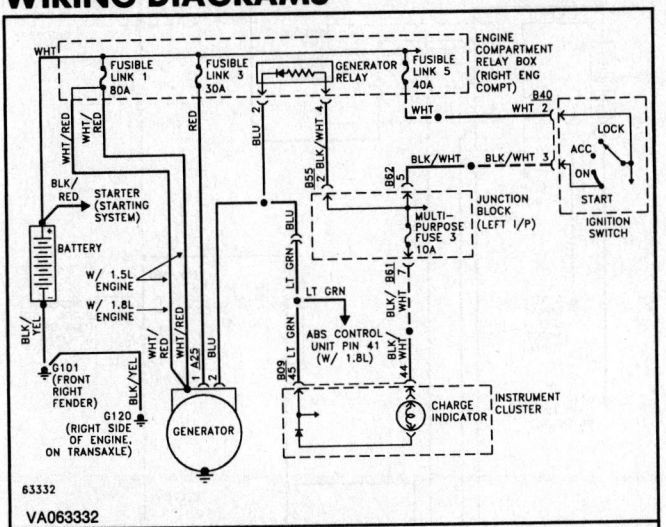

Fig. 4: Charging System Wiring Diagram (Colt, Mirage & Summit)

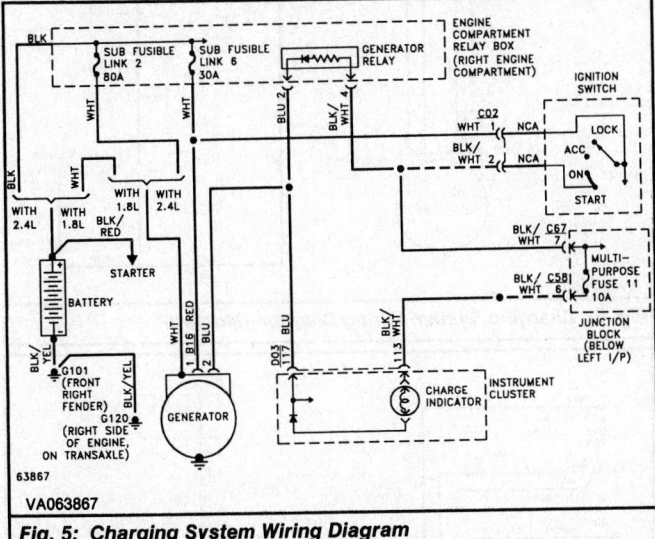

Fig. 5: Charging System Wiring Diagram (Colt Vista, Expo & Summit Wagon)

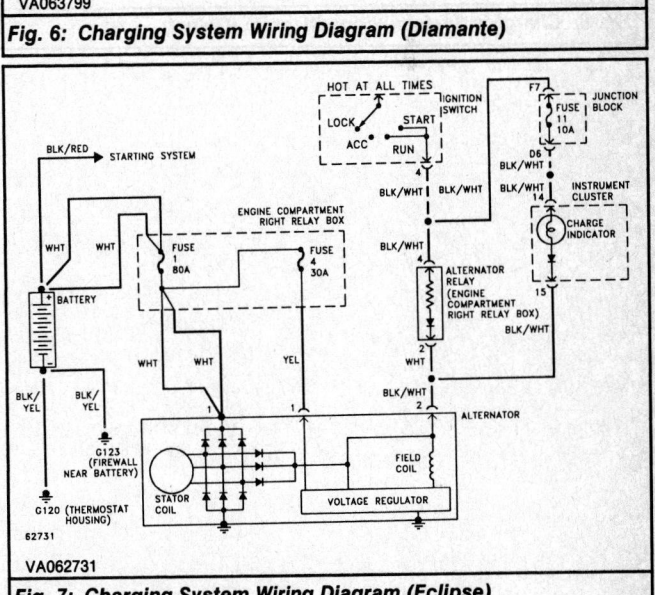

Fig. 6: Charging System Wiring Diagram (Diamante)

Fig. 7: Charging System Wiring Diagram (Eclipse)

1994 ELECTRICAL
Alternators & Regulators (Cont.)

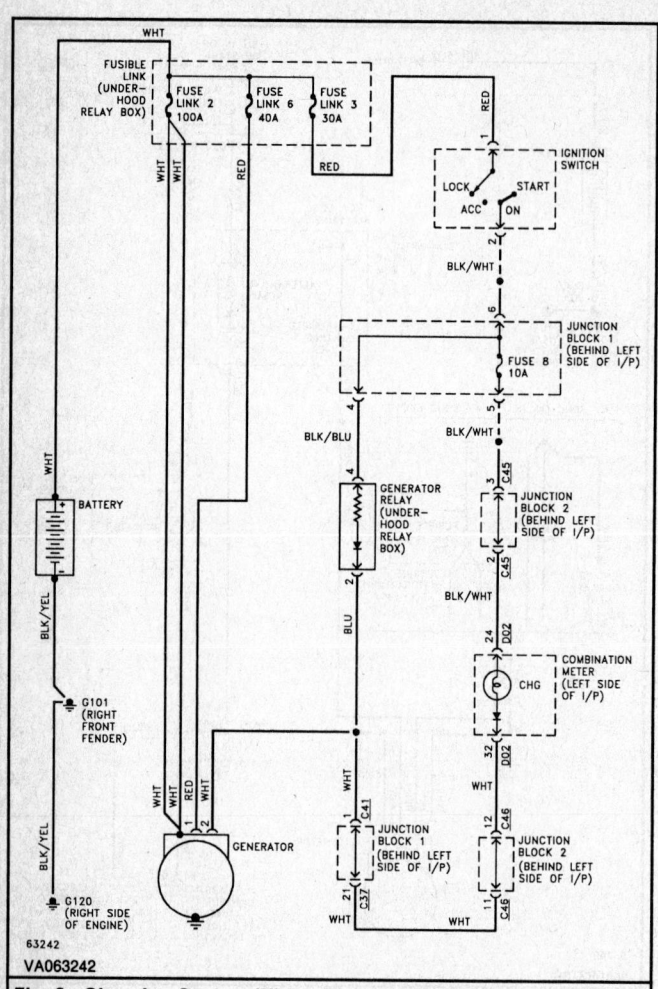

Fig. 8: Charging System Wiring Diagram (Galant)

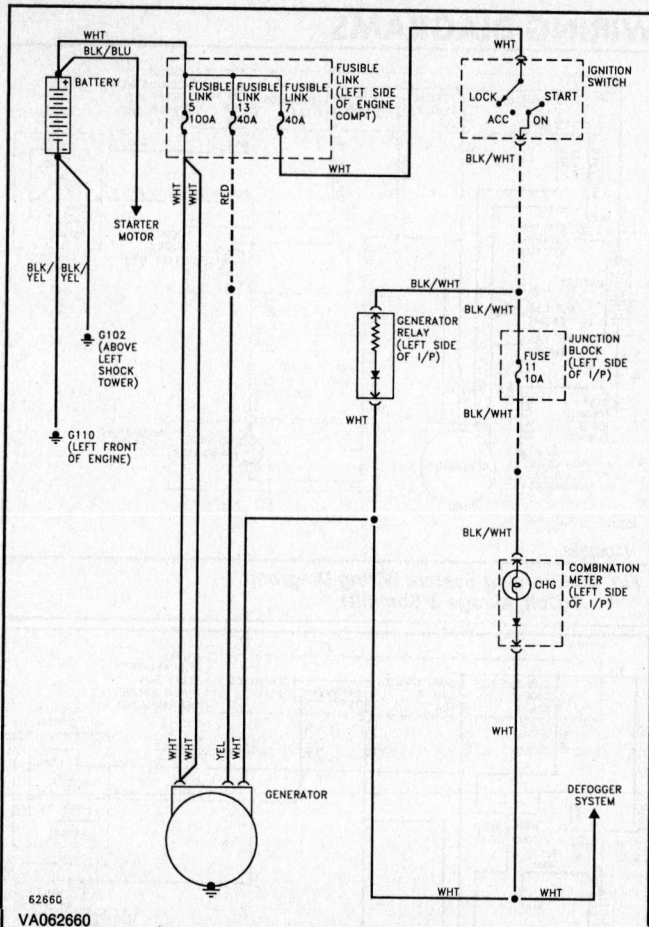

Fig. 9: Charging System Wiring Diagram (Montero)

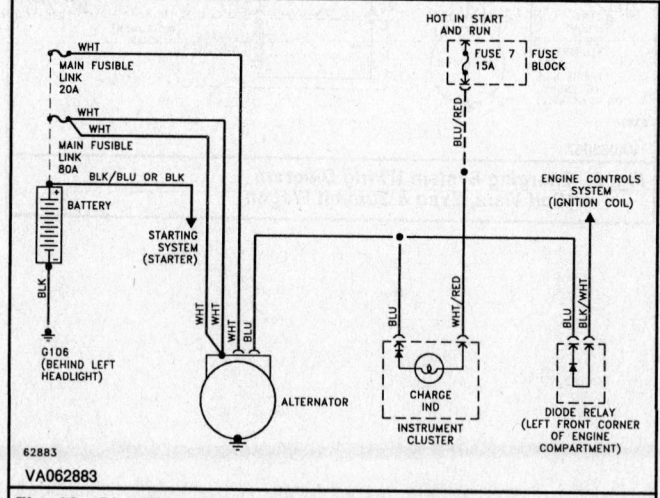

Fig. 10: Charging System Wiring Diagram (Pickup)

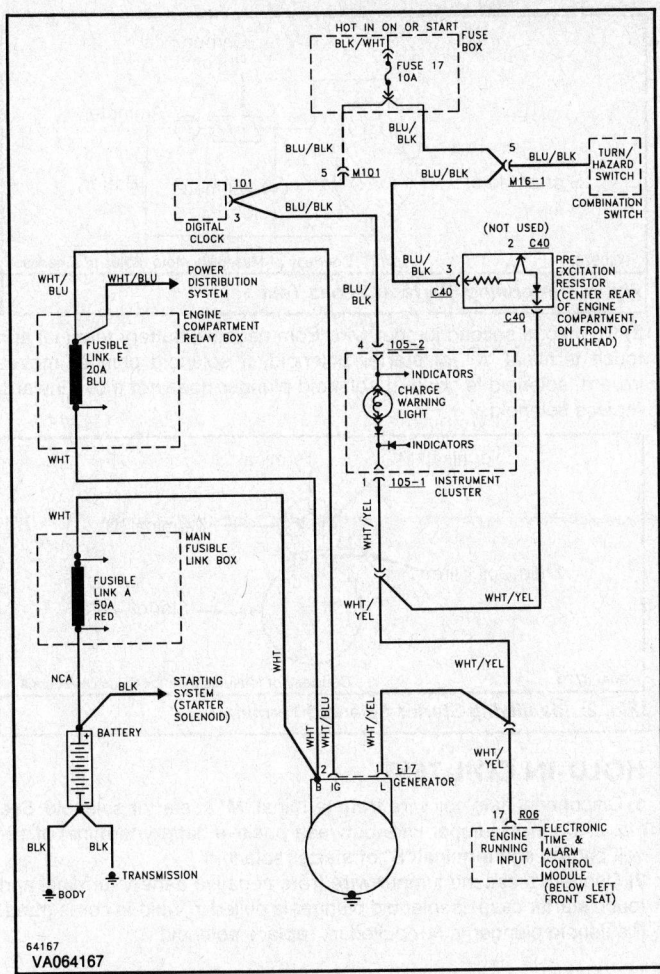

Fig. 11: Charging System Wiring Diagram (Precis)

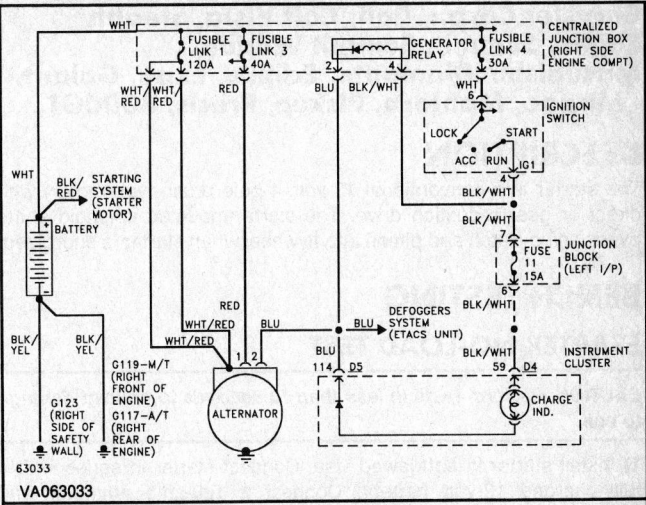

Fig. 12: Charging System Wiring Diagram (Stealth & 3000GT – DOHC)

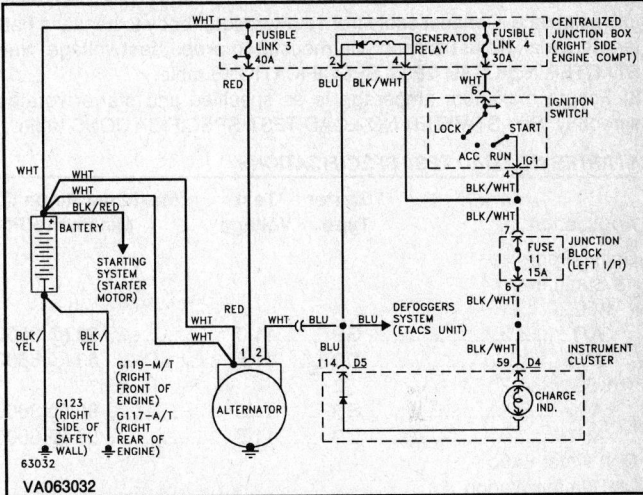

Fig. 13: Charging System Wiring Diagram (Stealth & 3000GT – SOHC)

Chrysler Corp.: Colt, Colt Vista, Stealth
Eagle: Summit, Summit Wagon
Mitsubishi: Diamante, Eclipse, Expo, Galant,
Mirage, Montero, Pickup, Precis, 3000GT

DESCRIPTION

The starter is a conventional 12-volt, 4-pole brush-type motor, with direct or gear reduction drive. The starter-mounted solenoid shifts overrunning clutch and pinion into flywheel when starter is energized.

BENCH TESTING

STARTER NO-LOAD TEST

CAUTION: Perform tests in less than 10 seconds to prevent damage to coil.

1) Install starter in soft-jawed vise. Connect starter in series with a fully-charged 12-volt battery. Connect a 100-amp ammeter and carbon pile rheostat in series with positive battery post and starter motor terminal. *See Fig. 1.*
2) Install voltmeter across starter motor. Adjust carbon pile rheostat to full resistance. Connect cable from starter motor body to negative battery terminal. Adjust carbon pile rheostat to proper test voltage. See STARTER NO-LOAD TEST SPECIFICATIONS table.
3) Ensure maximum amperage is as specified and starter rotates smoothly. See STARTER NO-LOAD TEST SPECIFICATIONS table.

STARTER NO-LOAD TEST SPECIFICATIONS

Application	[1] Starter Type	Test Voltage	Maximum Amps @ Minimum RPM
Colt, Mirage & Summit			
1.5L			
A/T	GR	11.0	90 @ 3000
M/T	DD	11.5	60 @ 6600
1.8L			
A/T	GR	11.0	90 @ 3000
M/T	DD	11.5	53 @ 6000
Colt Vista, Expo & Summit Wagon			
1.8L			
A/T	GR	11.0	90 @ 3000
M/T	DD	11.5	53 @ 6000
2.4L			
A/T	GR	11.0	90 @ 3000
M/T	DD	11.5	60 @ 6600
Diamante, Galant, Montero, Stealth & 3000GT	GR	11.0	90 @ 3000
Eclipse			
1.8L	DD	11.5	60 @ 6600
2.0L	GR	11.0	90 @ 3000
Pickup			
2.4L			
A/T	GR	11.0	90 @ 3000
M/T	DD	11.5	60 @ 6600
3.0L	GR	11.0	90 @ 3000
Precis			
A/T	DD	11.5	60 @ 6600
M/T	DD	11.5	60 @ 6500

[1] – DD indicates direct drive. GR indicates gear reduction.

PULL-IN COIL TEST

1) Disconnect field coil wire from terminal "M" at starter solenoid. *See Fig. 2.* Connect jumper wire between positive battery terminal of 12-volt battery and terminal "S" of solenoid.

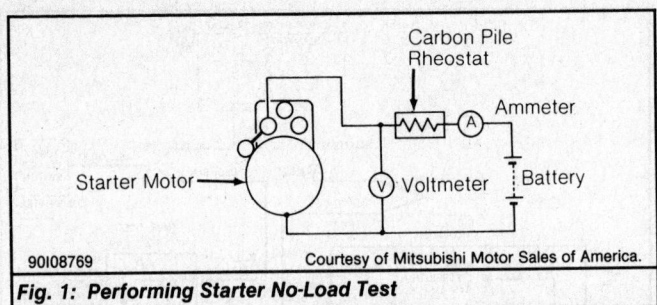

Fig. 1: *Performing Starter No-Load Test*

2) Connect a second jumper wire from negative battery terminal and touch terminal "M" of starter solenoid. If solenoid plunger moves inward, solenoid is good. If solenoid plunger does not move inward, replace solenoid.

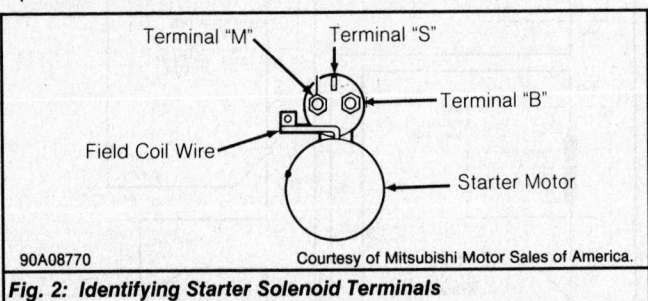

Fig. 2: *Identifying Starter Solenoid Terminals*

HOLD-IN COIL TEST

1) Disconnect field coil wire from terminal "M" at starter solenoid. *See Fig. 2.* Connect jumper wire between positive battery terminal of 12-volt battery and terminal "S" of starter solenoid.
2) Connect a second jumper wire from negative battery terminal and touch starter case. If solenoid plunger is pulled in, hold-in coil is good. If solenoid plunger is not pulled in, replace solenoid.

RETURN TEST

1) Disconnect field coil wire from terminal "M" at starter solenoid. *See Fig. 2.* Connect jumper wire between positive battery terminal of 12-volt battery and terminal "M" of starter solenoid.
2) Connect a second jumper wire from negative battery terminal and touch starter case. Pull pinion outward and release it. Replace solenoid if pinion remains out.

PINION GAP MEASUREMENT

1) Disconnect field coil wire from terminal "M" at starter solenoid. *See Fig. 2.* Connect jumper wire between positive battery terminal of 12-volt battery and terminal "S" of starter solenoid.
2) Connect a second jumper wire from negative battery terminal and touch terminal "M" of starter solenoid. Measure clearance between pinion and stopper. *See Fig. 3.*
3) Clearance should be within specification. See STARTER SPECIFICATIONS table. Adjust clearance by adding or removing gaskets between solenoid and front housing.

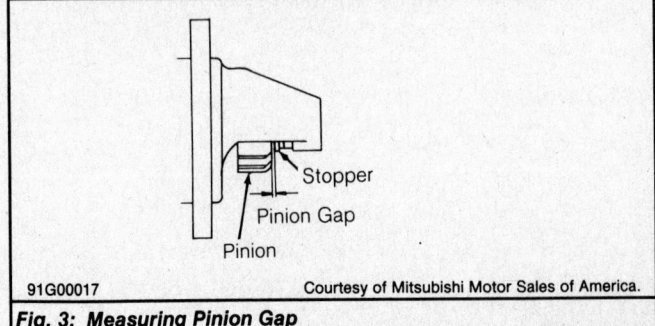

Fig. 3: *Measuring Pinion Gap*

REMOVAL & INSTALLATION

Removal & Installation – Disconnect negative battery cable. If necessary, raise vehicle on hoist. Remove starter mounting bolts and starter. To install, reverse removal procedure.

NOTE: On Montero with A/T, it may be necessary to disconnect transmission oil cooler line for starter removal.

OVERHAUL

Check commutator for out-of-round and proper amount of undercut. Replace or repair armature if not within specification. See STARTER SPECIFICATIONS table. Ensure brushes are not worn beyond wear line (outer line closest to commutator contact surface). Check pinion gap. See PINION GAP MEASUREMENT under BENCH TESTING. *See Figs. 4 and 5.*

STARTER SPECIFICATIONS

Application	In. (mm)
Commutator Maximum Runout [1]	
Except Pickup, Stealth & 3000GT	.002 (.05)
Pickup, Stealth & 3000GT	.004 (1.0)
Commutator Minimum Diameter [1]	
Colt, Colt Vista, Expo, Mirage	
Summit & Summit Wagon	
Direct Drive Type Starter	1.26 (32.0)
Gear Reduction Type Starter	1.16 (29.4)
Pickup	
2.4L	
A/T	1.16 (29.4)
M/T	1.26 (32.0)
Stealth & 3000GT	1.12 (28.4)
All Other Models	1.16 (29.4)
Commutator Undercut Depth [1]	.020 (.51)
Pinion Gap	.020-.079 (.51-2.01)

[1] – Information is not available for Precis.

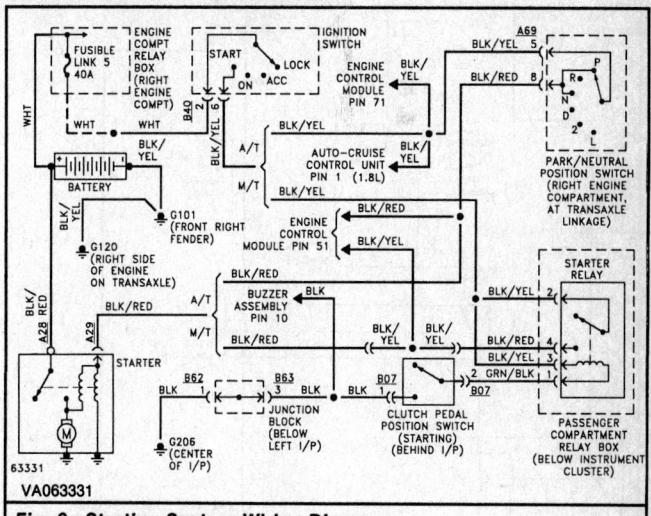

1. Packing	11. Pinion
2. Ball	12. Internal Gear
3. Starter Solenoid	13. Planetary Gear Holder
4. Gasket	14. Planetary Gear
5. Packing	15. Rear Housing
6. Plate	16. Brush Holder
7. Lever	17. Brush
8. Front Housing	18. Rear Bearing
9. Snap Ring	19. Armature
10. Stopper	20. Yoke Assembly

90I08774   Courtesy of Mitsubishi Motor Sales of America.

Fig. 5: Exploded View Of Gear Reduction Starter (Typical)

WIRING DIAGRAMS

VA063331

Fig. 6: Starting System Wiring Diagram (Colt, Mirage & Summit)

1. Front Housing	9. Washers
2. Washer	10. Armature
3. Stopper	11. Pinion
4. Lever	12. Snap Ring
5. Plate	13. Rear Housing
6. Packing	14. Rear Bearing
7. Gasket	15. Brush Holder Assembly
8. Starter Solenoid	16. Yoke Assembly

90E08772   Courtesy of Mitsubishi Motor Sales of America.

Fig. 4: Exploded View Of Direct Drive Starter (Typical)

1994 ELECTRICAL
Starters (Cont.)

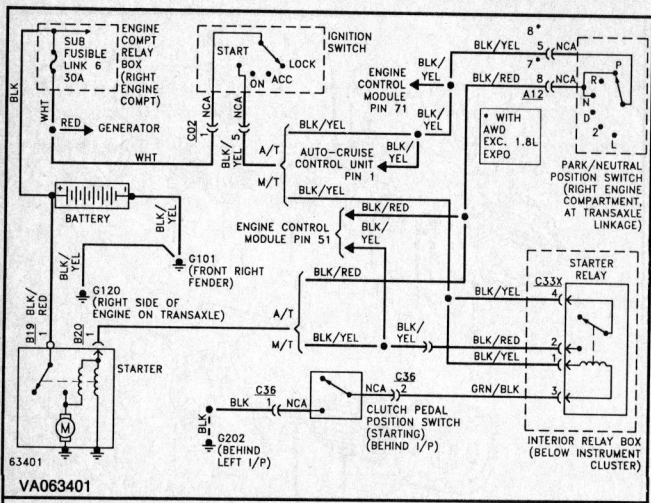

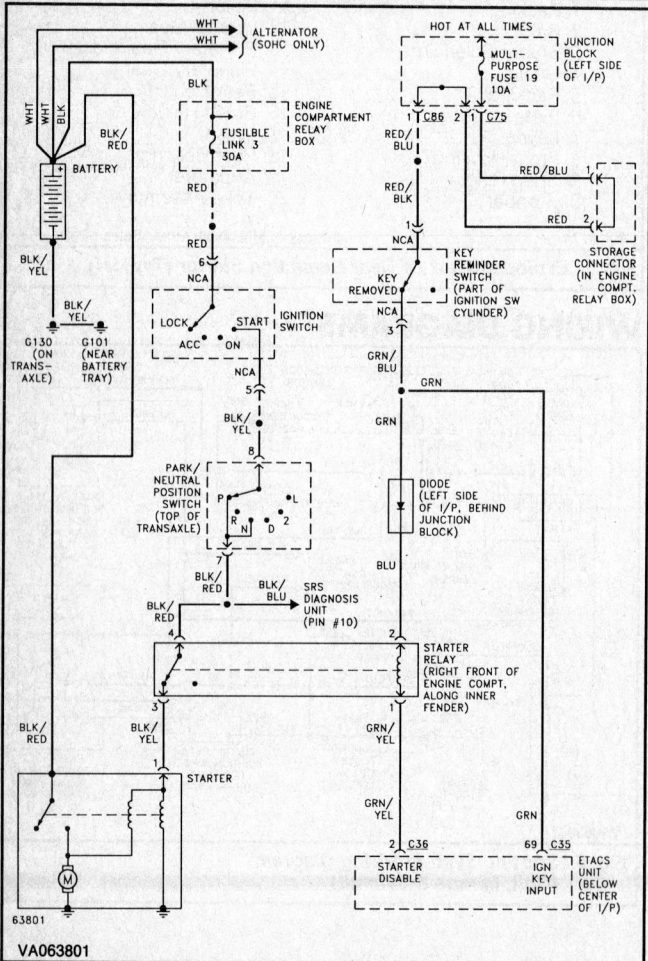

Fig. 7: Starting System Wiring Diagram (Colt Vista, Expo & Summit Wagon)

VA063401

Fig. 8: Starting System Wiring Diagram (Diamante)

VA063801

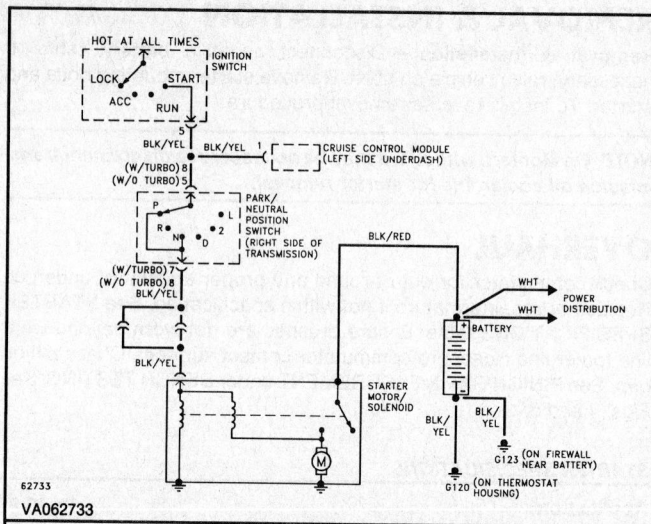

Fig. 9: Starting System Wiring Diagram (Eclipse A/T)

VA062733

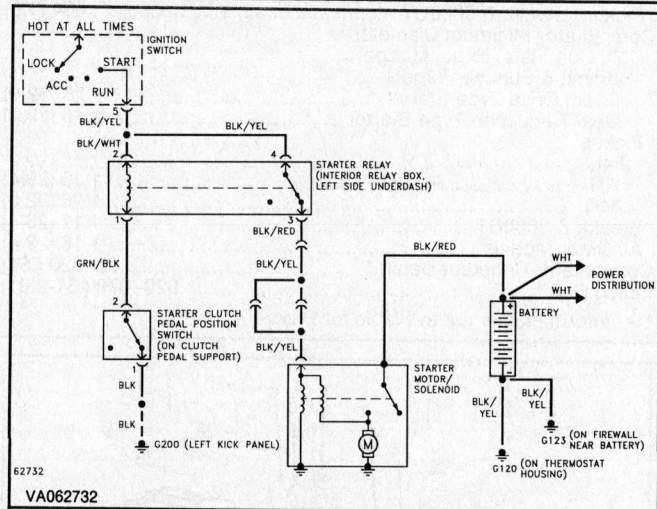

Fig. 10: Starting System Wiring Diagram (Eclipse M/T)

VA062732

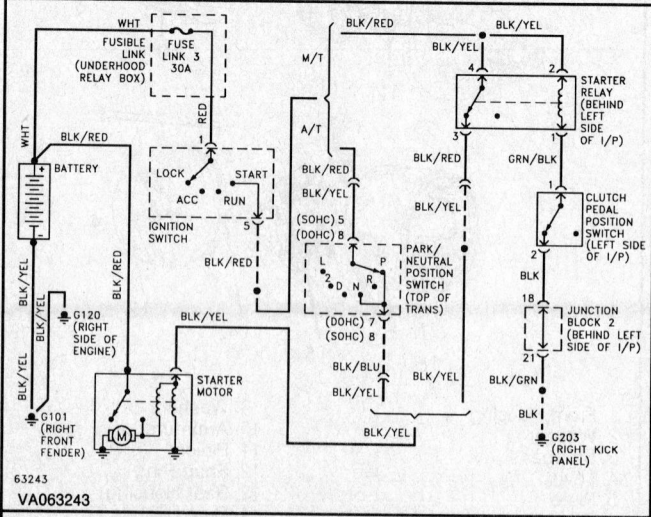

Fig. 11: Starting System Wiring Diagram (Galant)

VA063243

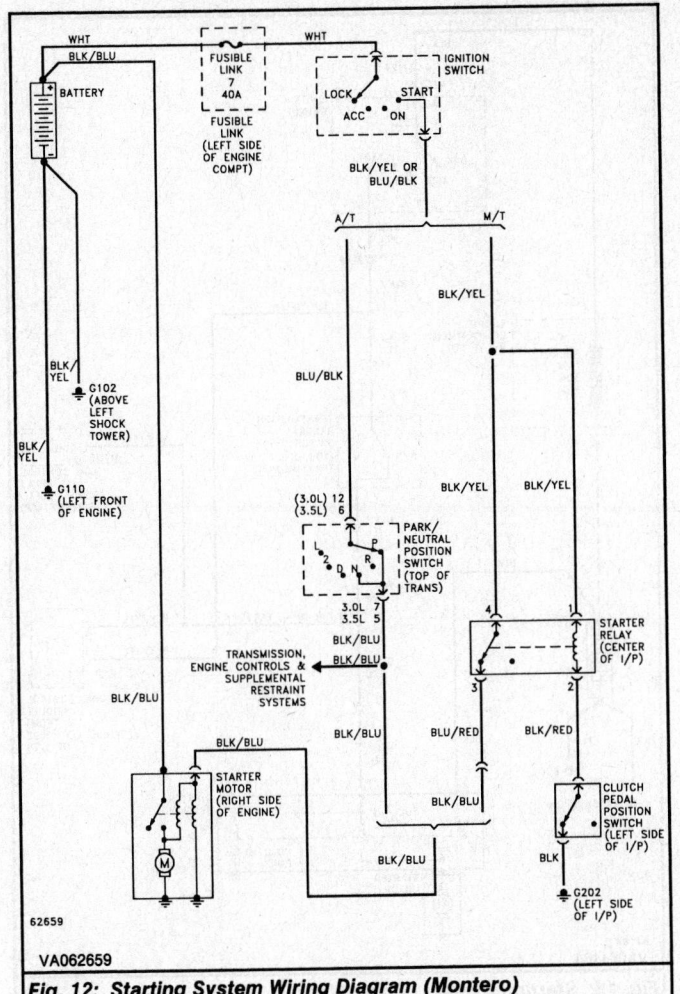

Fig. 12: Starting System Wiring Diagram (Montero)

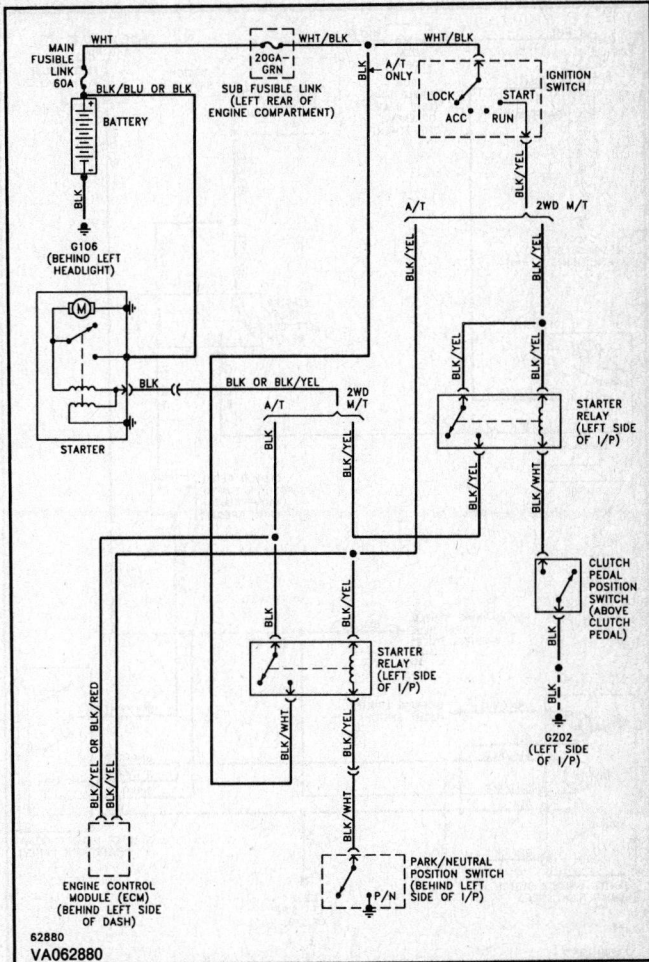

Fig. 13: Starting System Wiring Diagram (Pickup A/T & 2WD M/T)

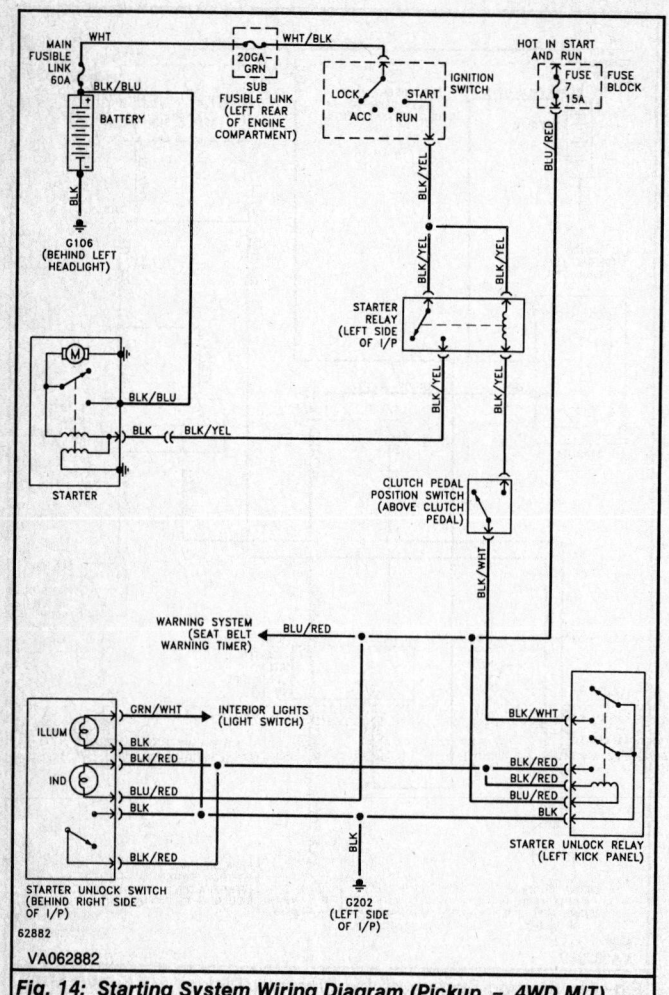

Fig. 14: Starting System Wiring Diagram (Pickup – 4WD M/T)

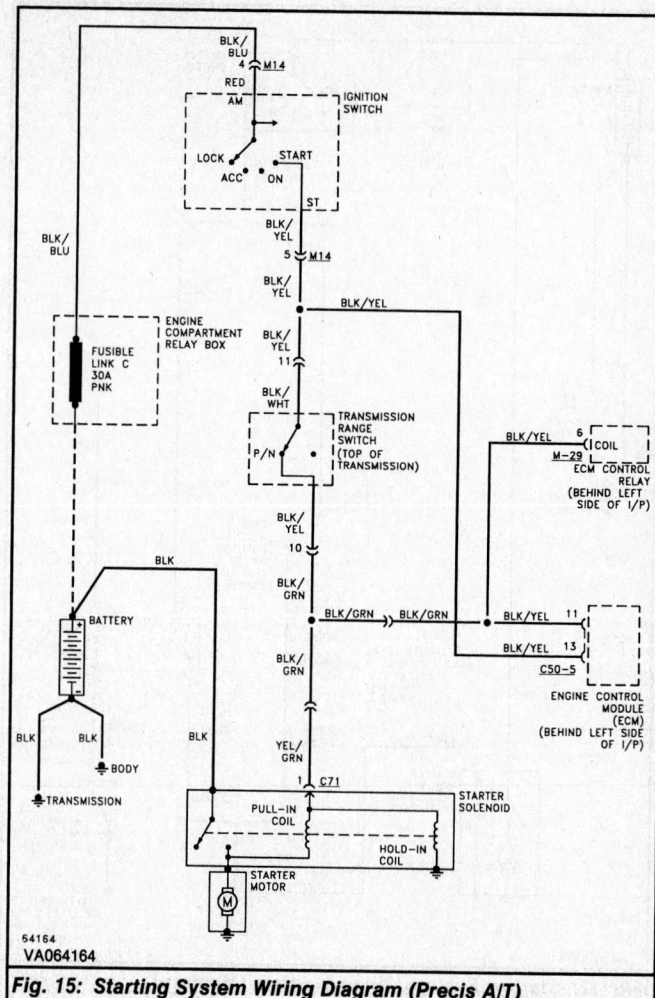

Fig. 15: Starting System Wiring Diagram (Precis A/T)

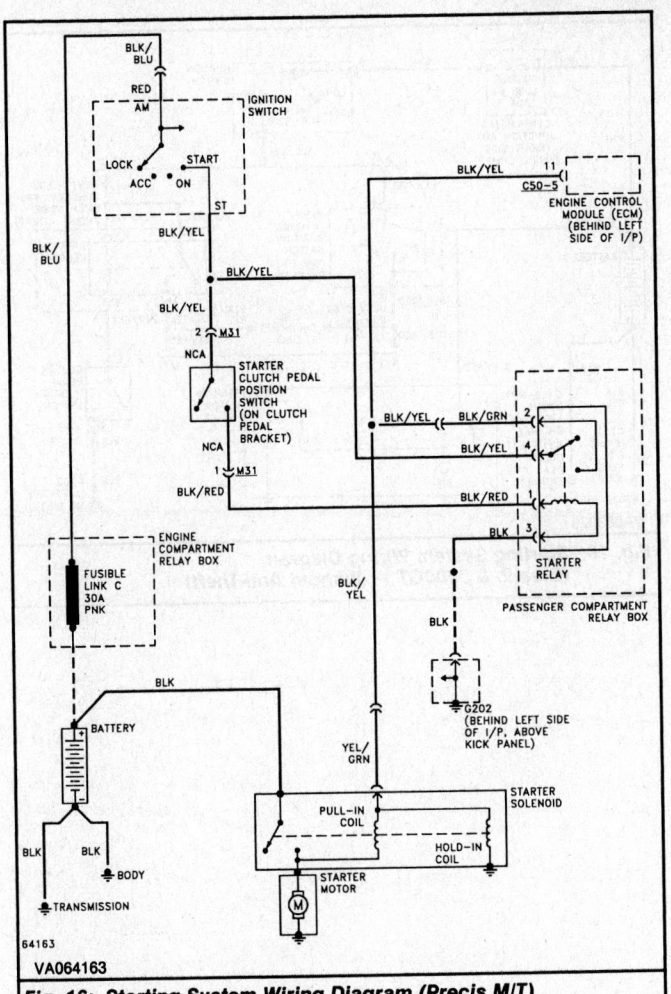

Fig. 16: Starting System Wiring Diagram (Precis M/T)

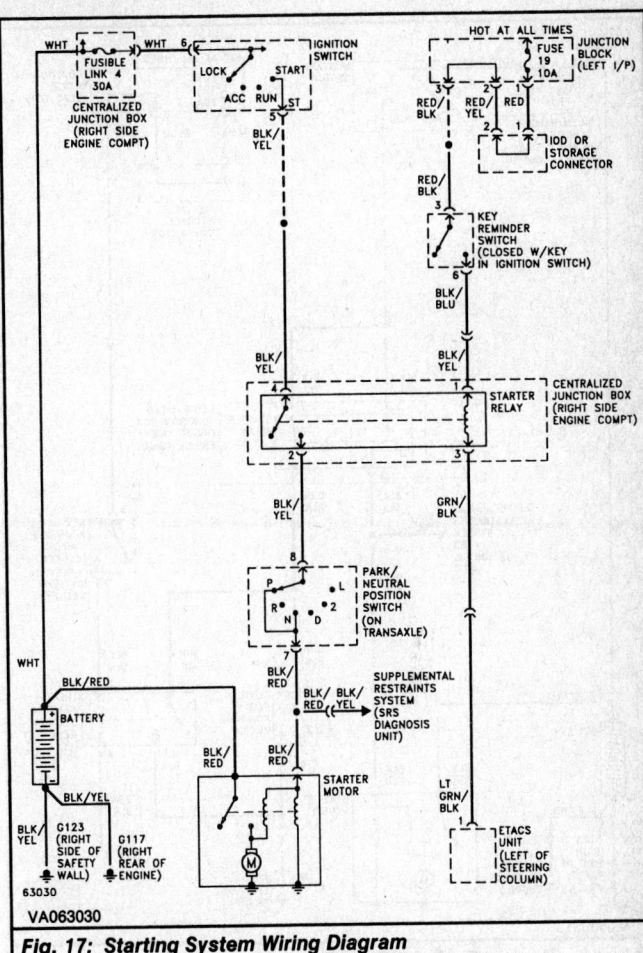

Fig. 17: Starting System Wiring Diagram (Stealth & 3000GT – A/T With Anti-Theft)

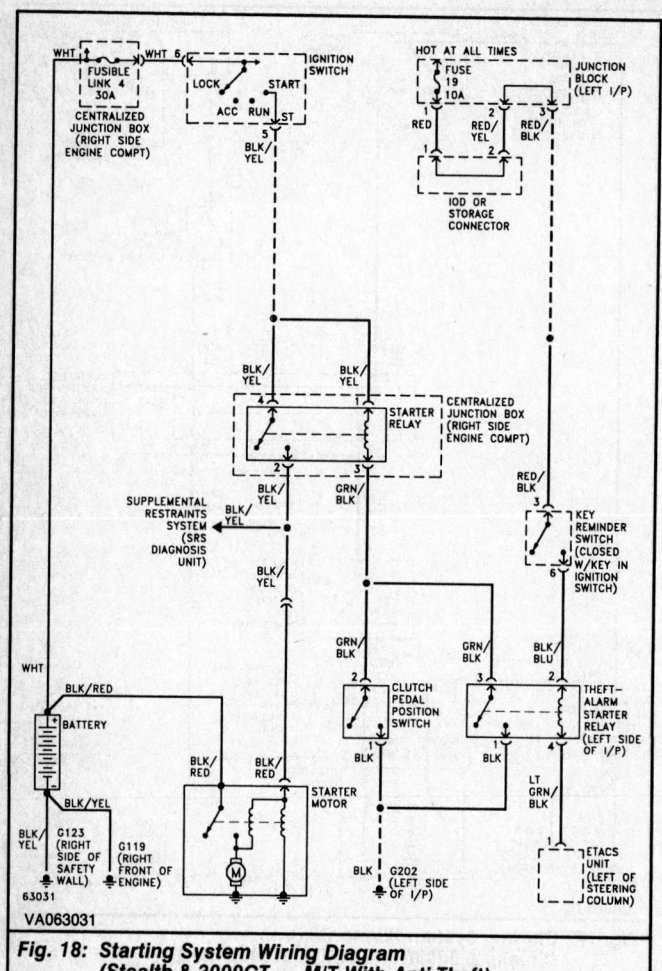

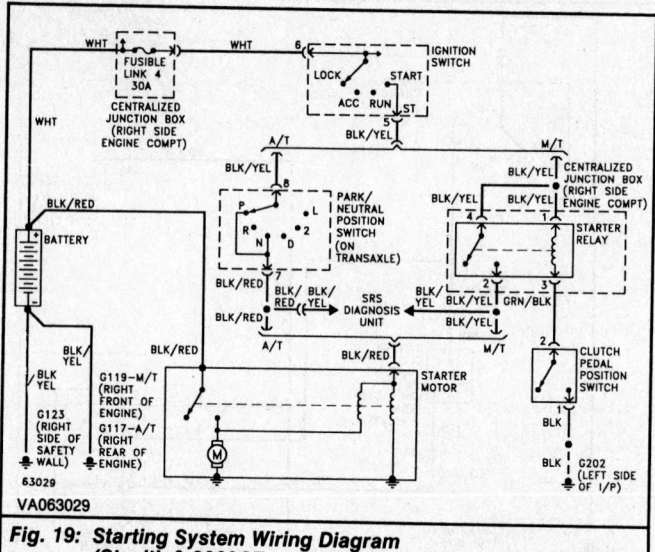

Fig. 19: Starting System Wiring Diagram
(Stealth & 3000GT – Without Anti-Theft)

Fig. 18: Starting System Wiring Diagram
(Stealth & 3000GT – M/T With Anti-Theft)

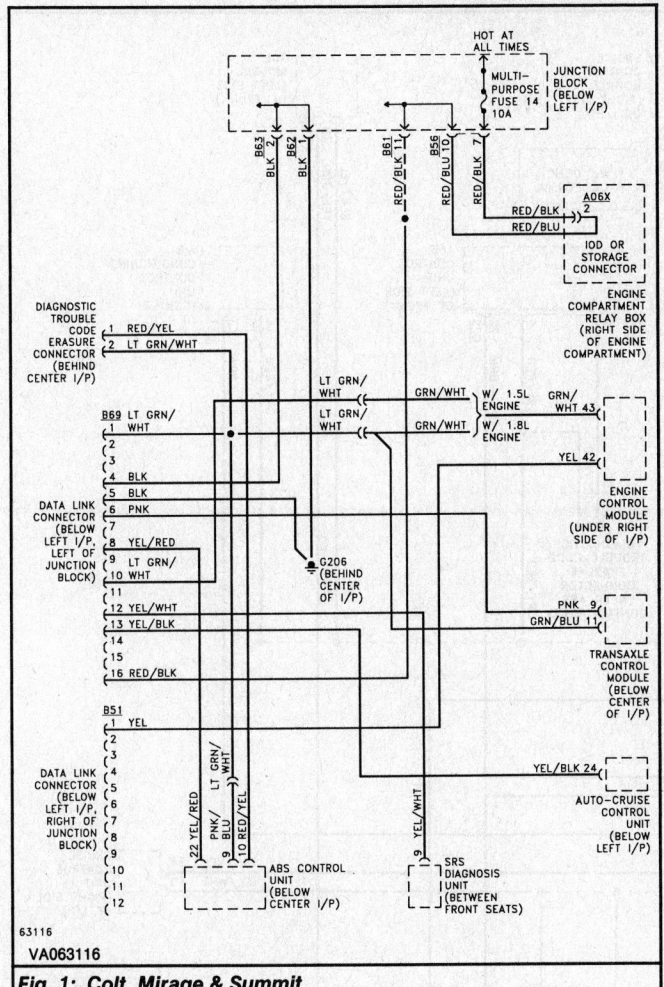

Fig. 1: *Colt, Mirage & Summit*

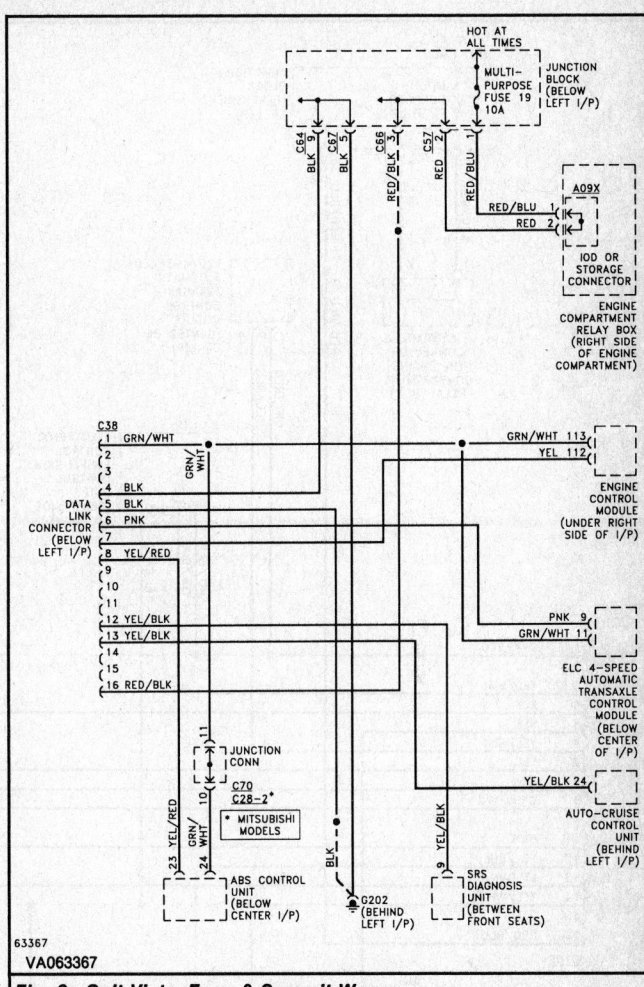

Fig. 3: *Colt Vista, Expo & Summit Wagon*

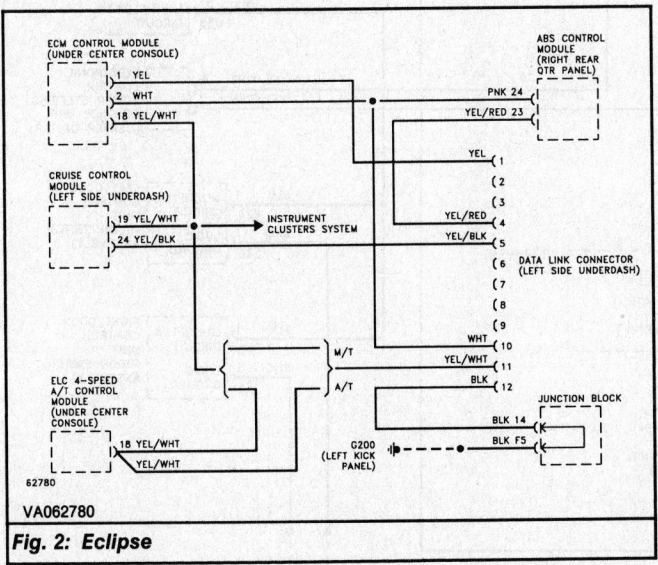

Fig. 2: *Eclipse*

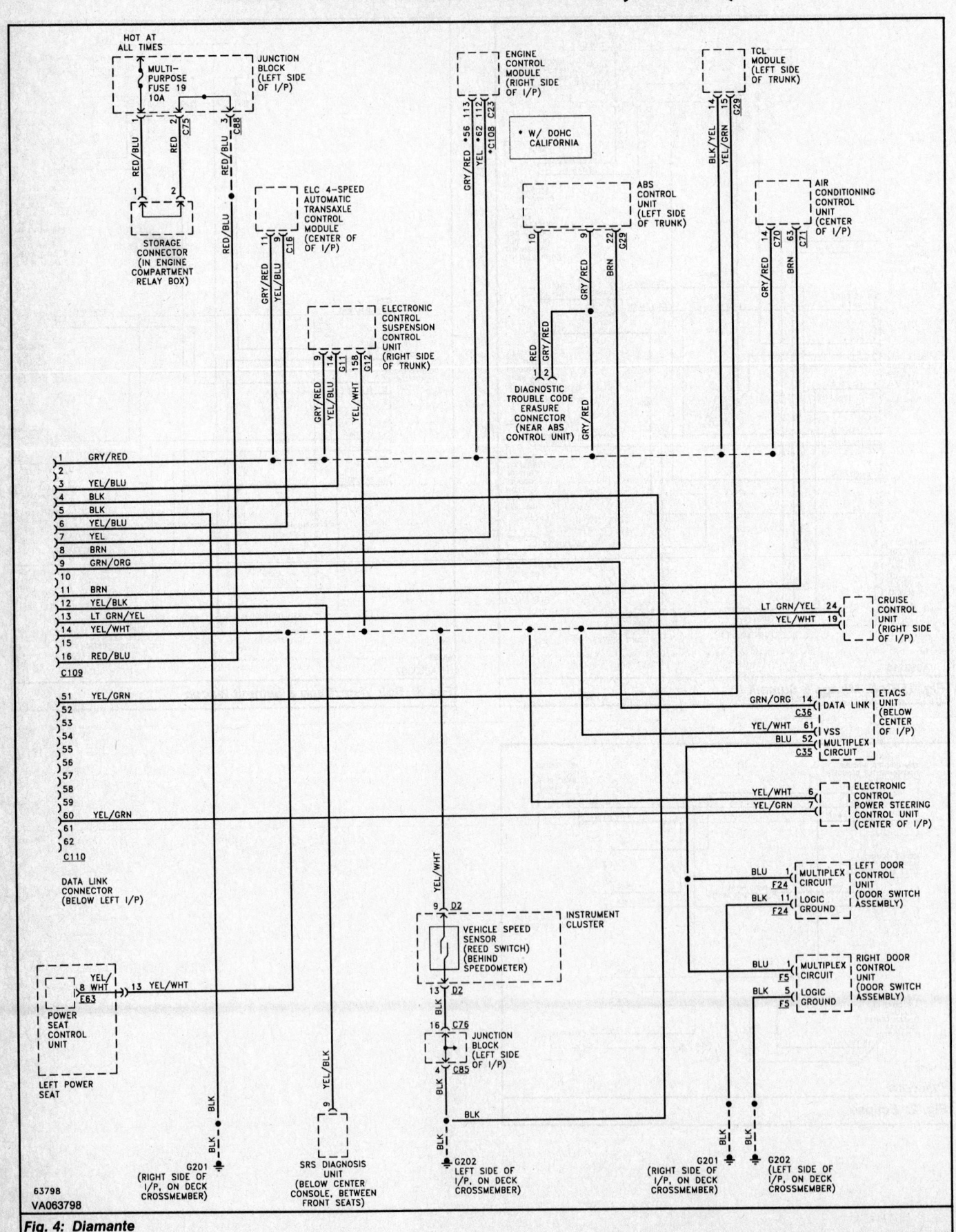

Fig. 4: Diamante

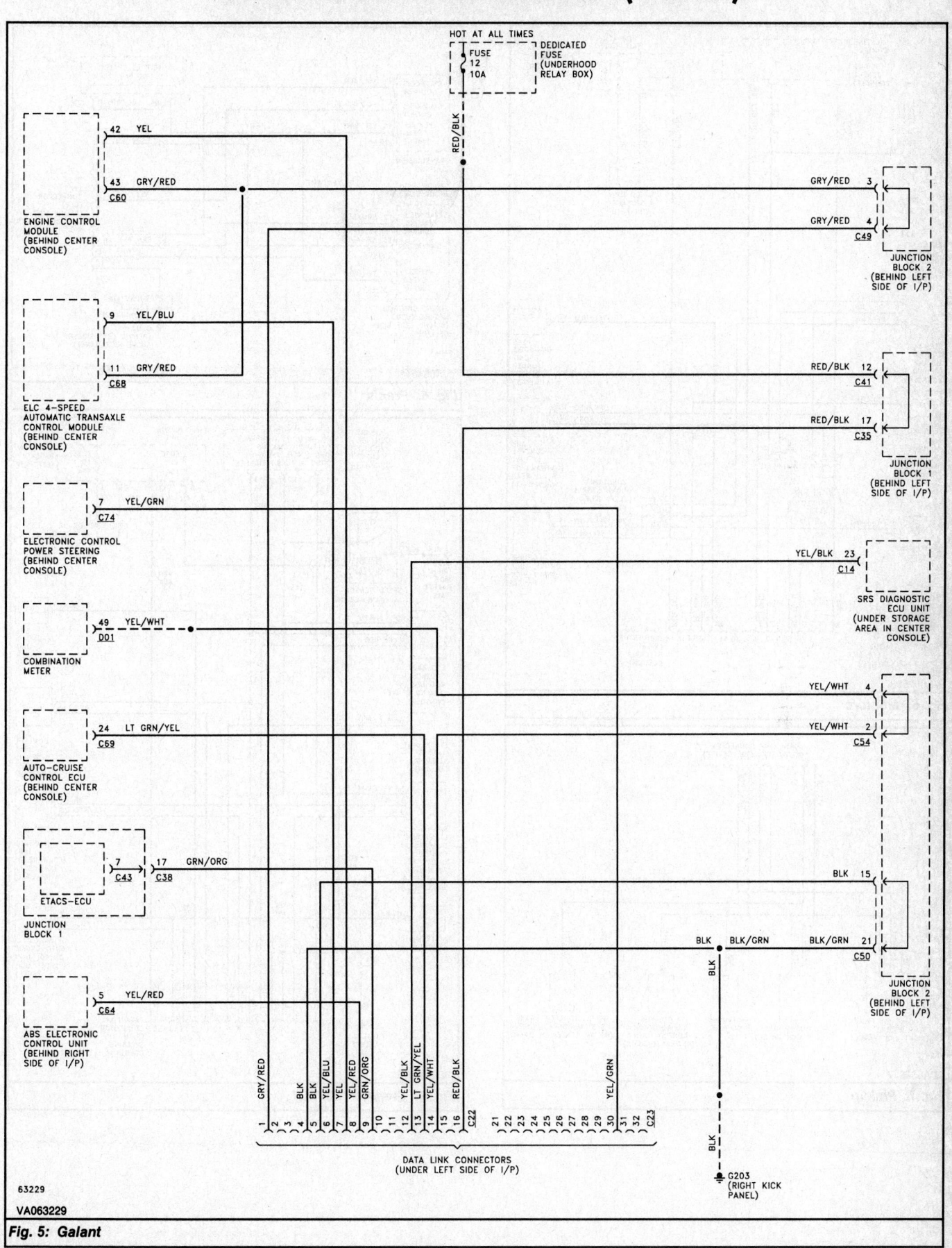

Fig. 5: Galant

63229

VA063229

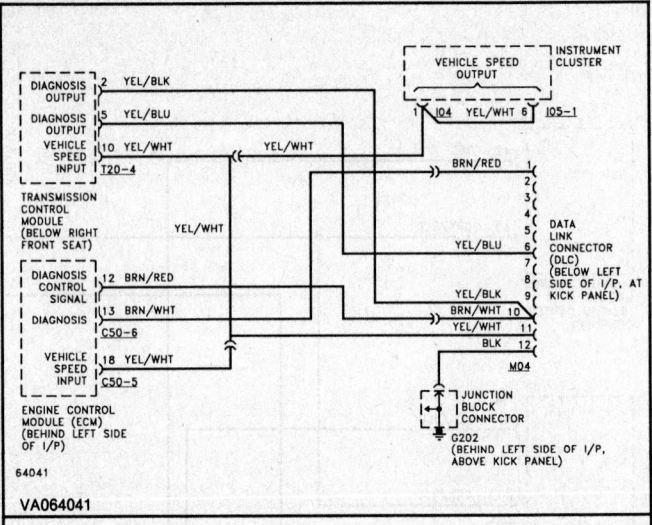

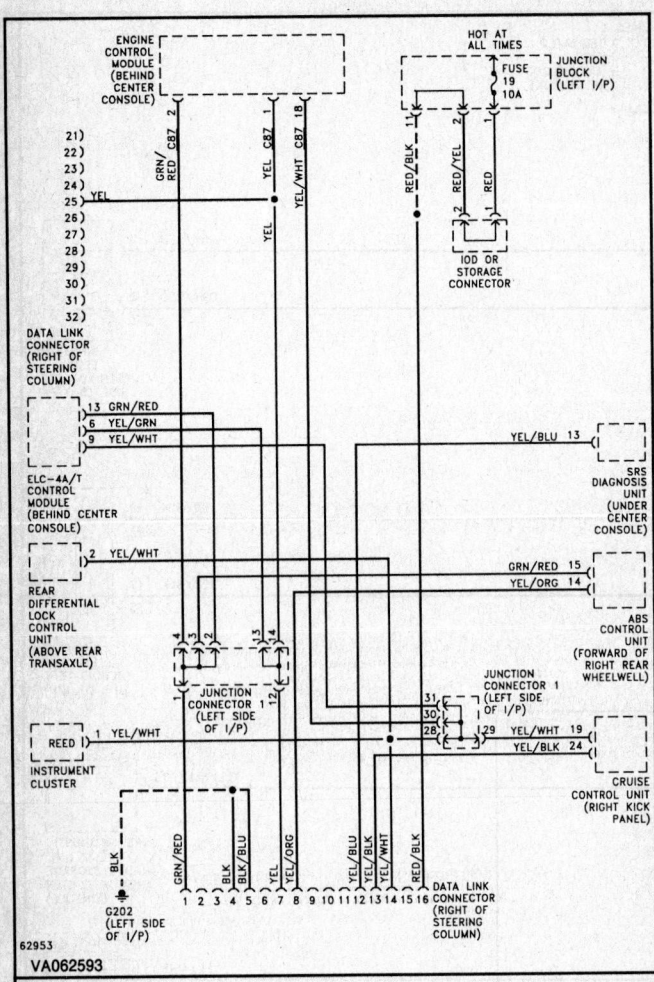

Fig. 6: Montero

Fig. 8: Precis

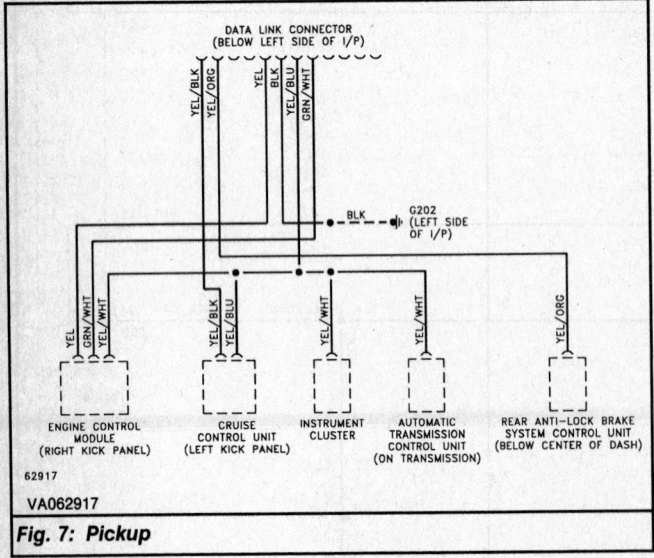

Fig. 7: Pickup

Fig. 9: Stealth & 3000GT

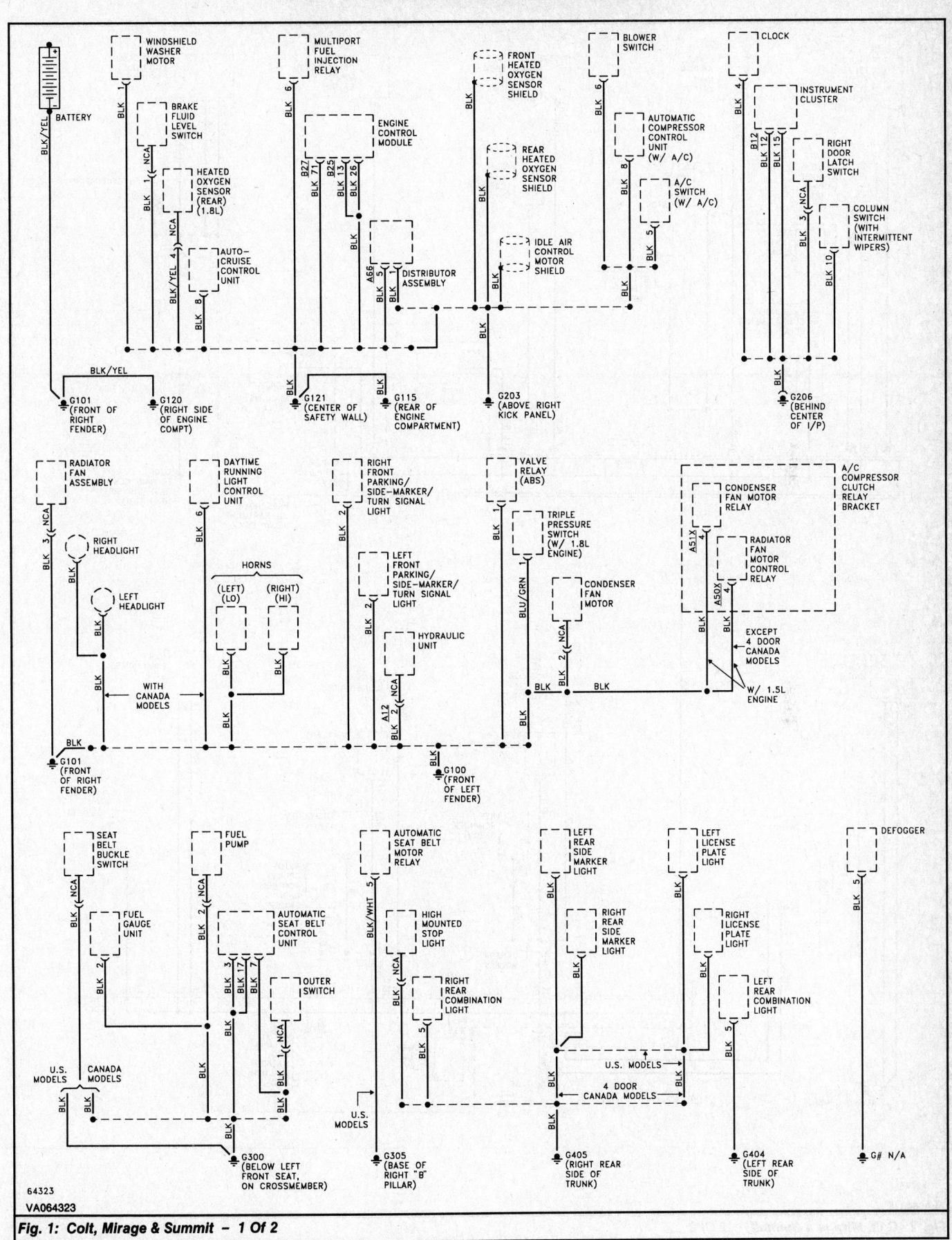

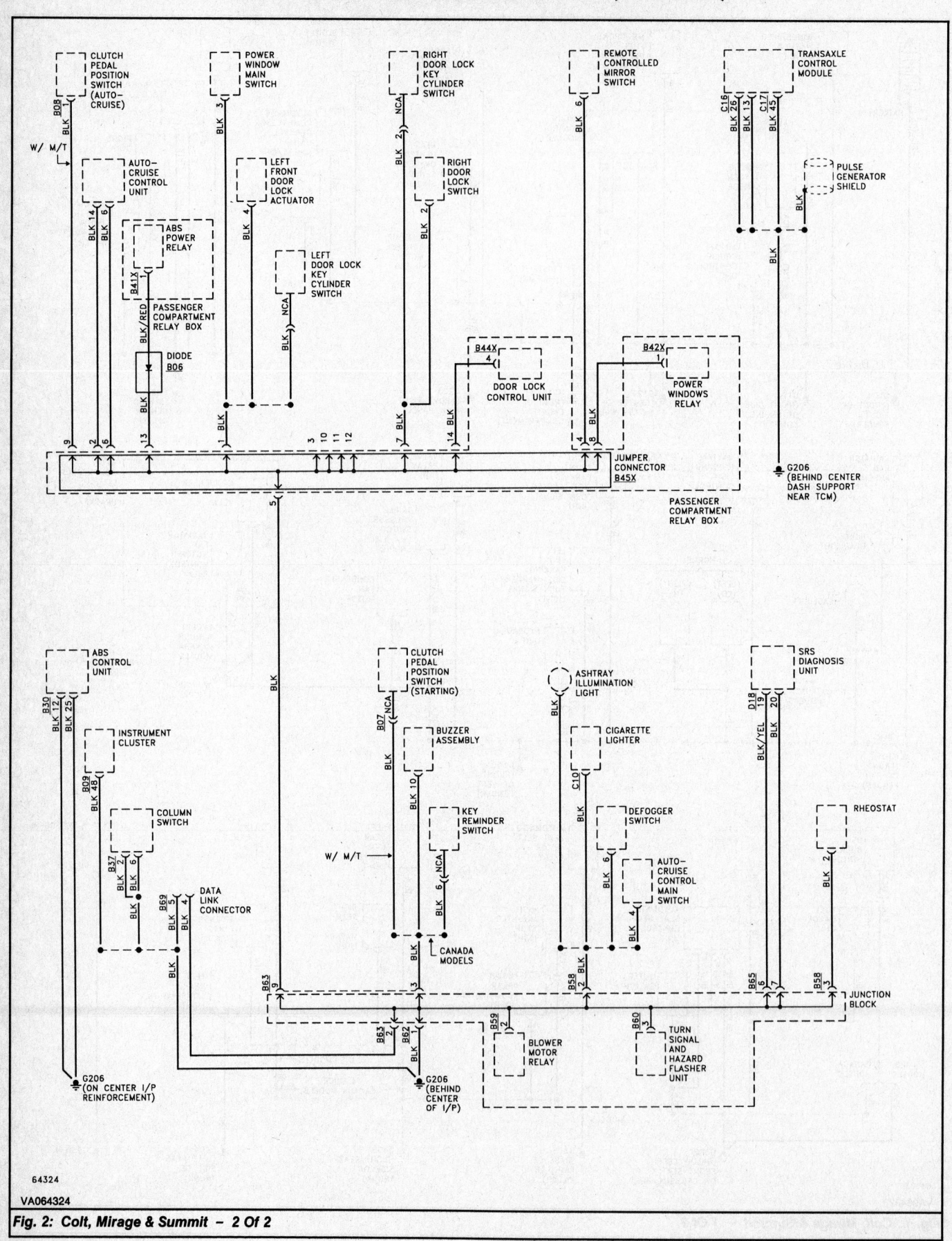

Fig. 2: Colt, Mirage & Summit – 2 Of 2

64324

VA064324

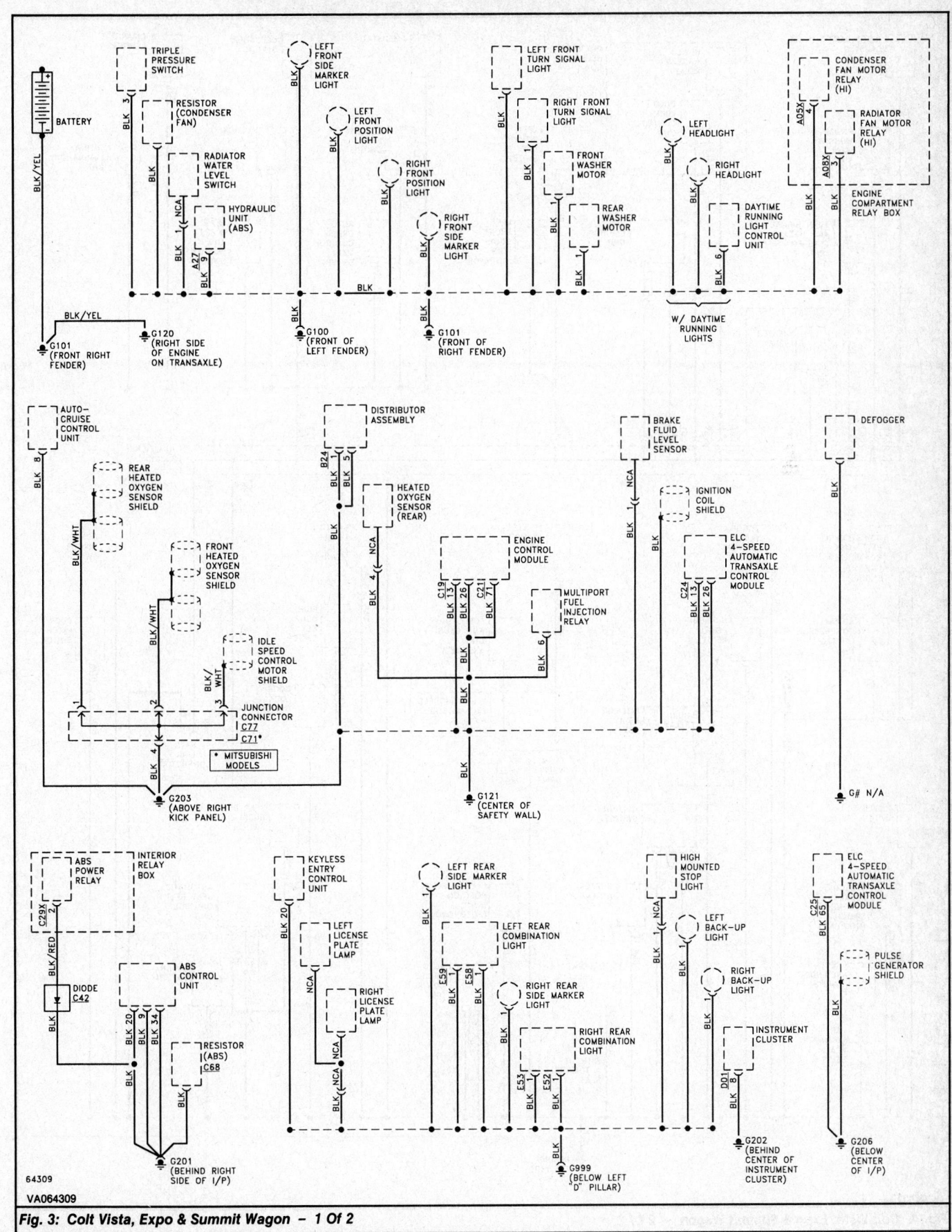

1994 WIRING DIAGRAMS
Ground Distribution (Cont.)

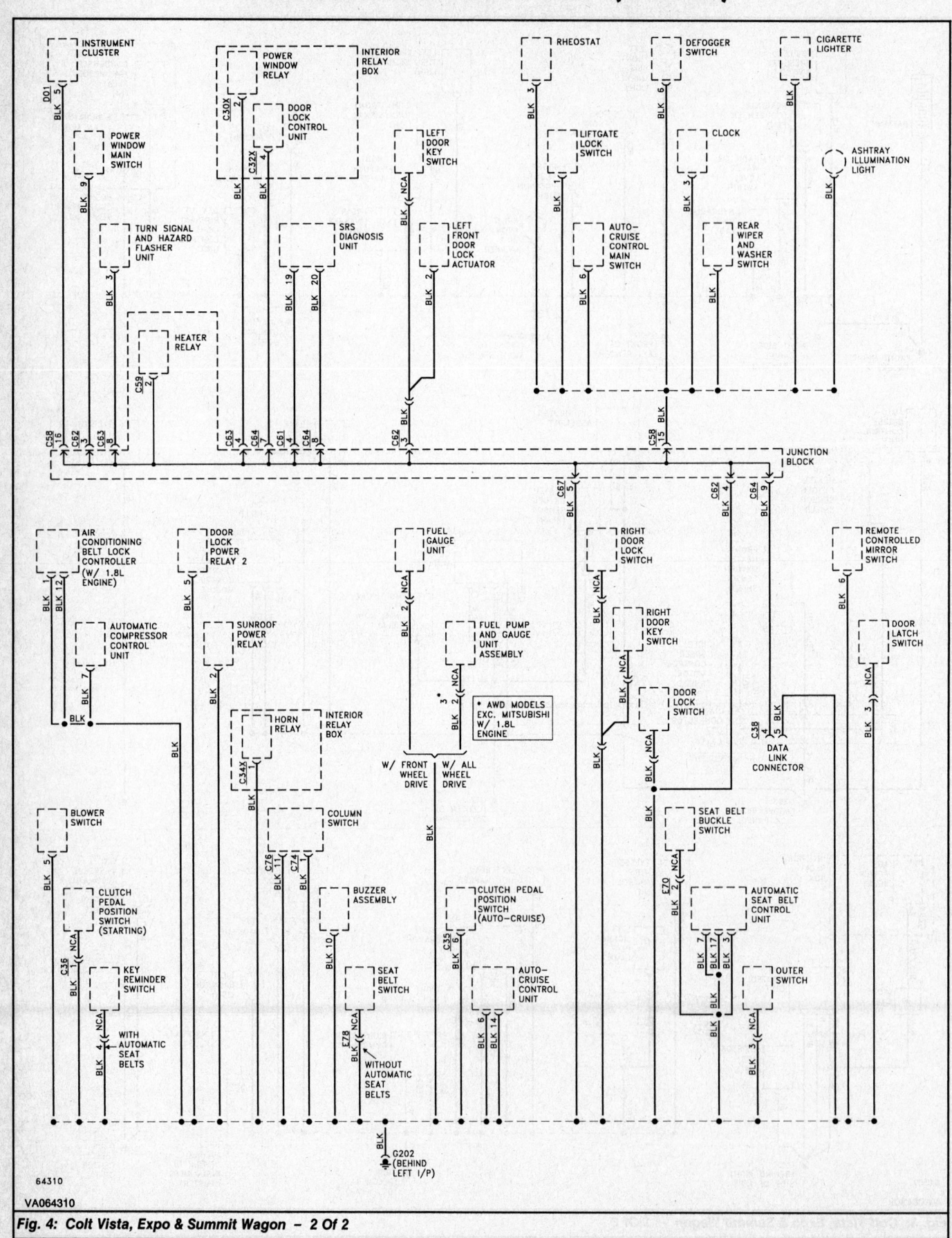

64310

VA064310

Fig. 4: Colt Vista, Expo & Summit Wagon – 2 Of 2

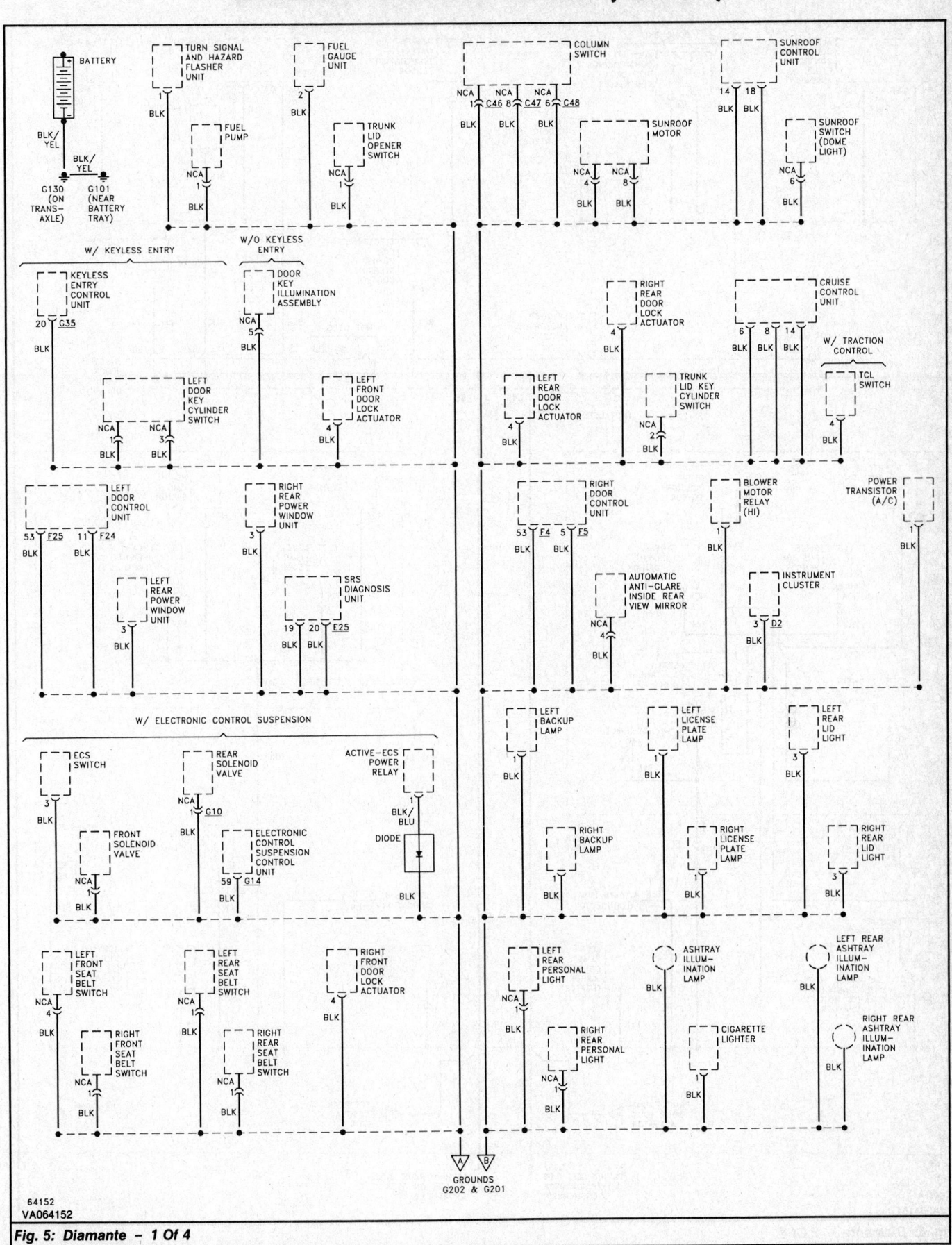

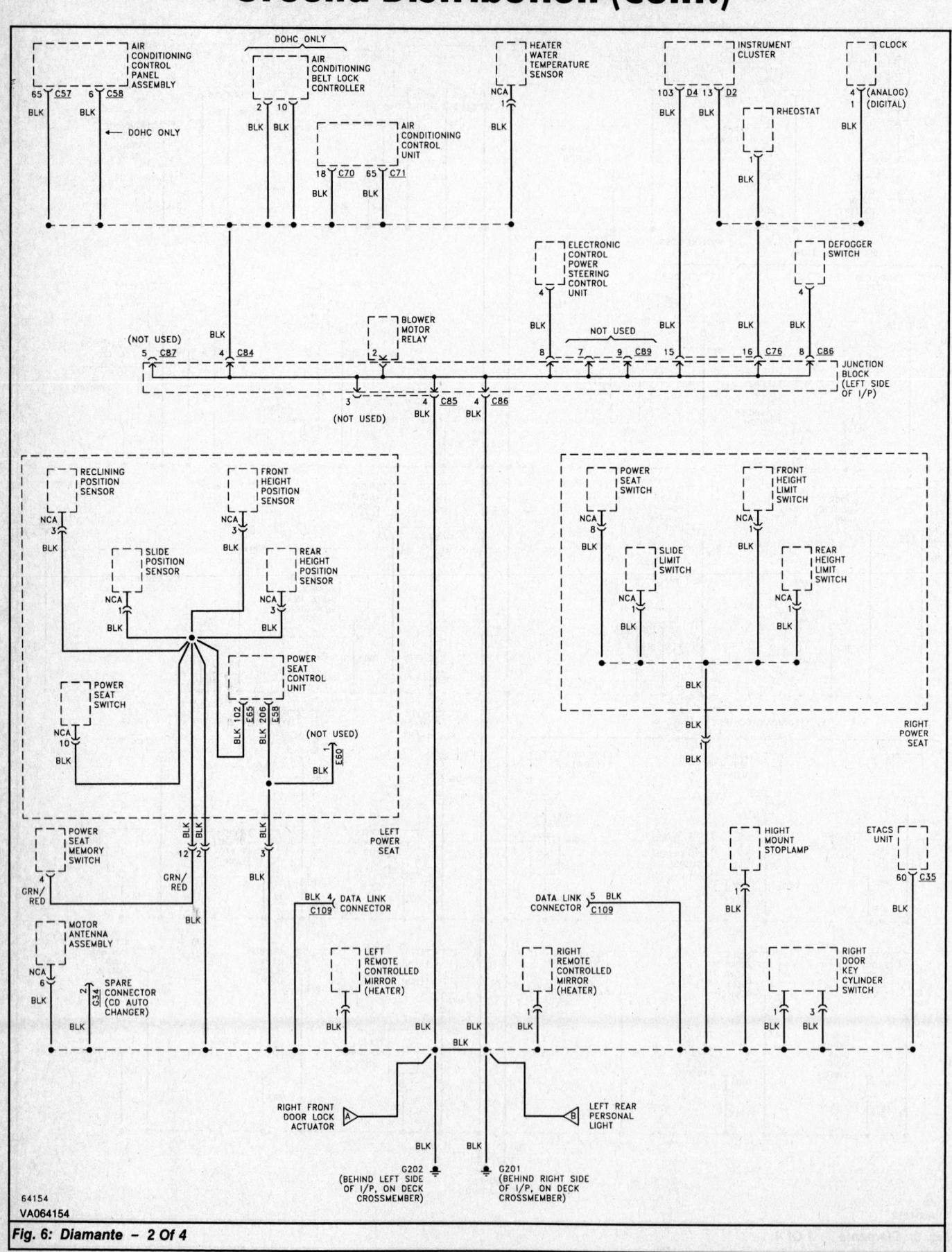

64154
VA064154

Fig. 6: Diamante – 2 Of 4

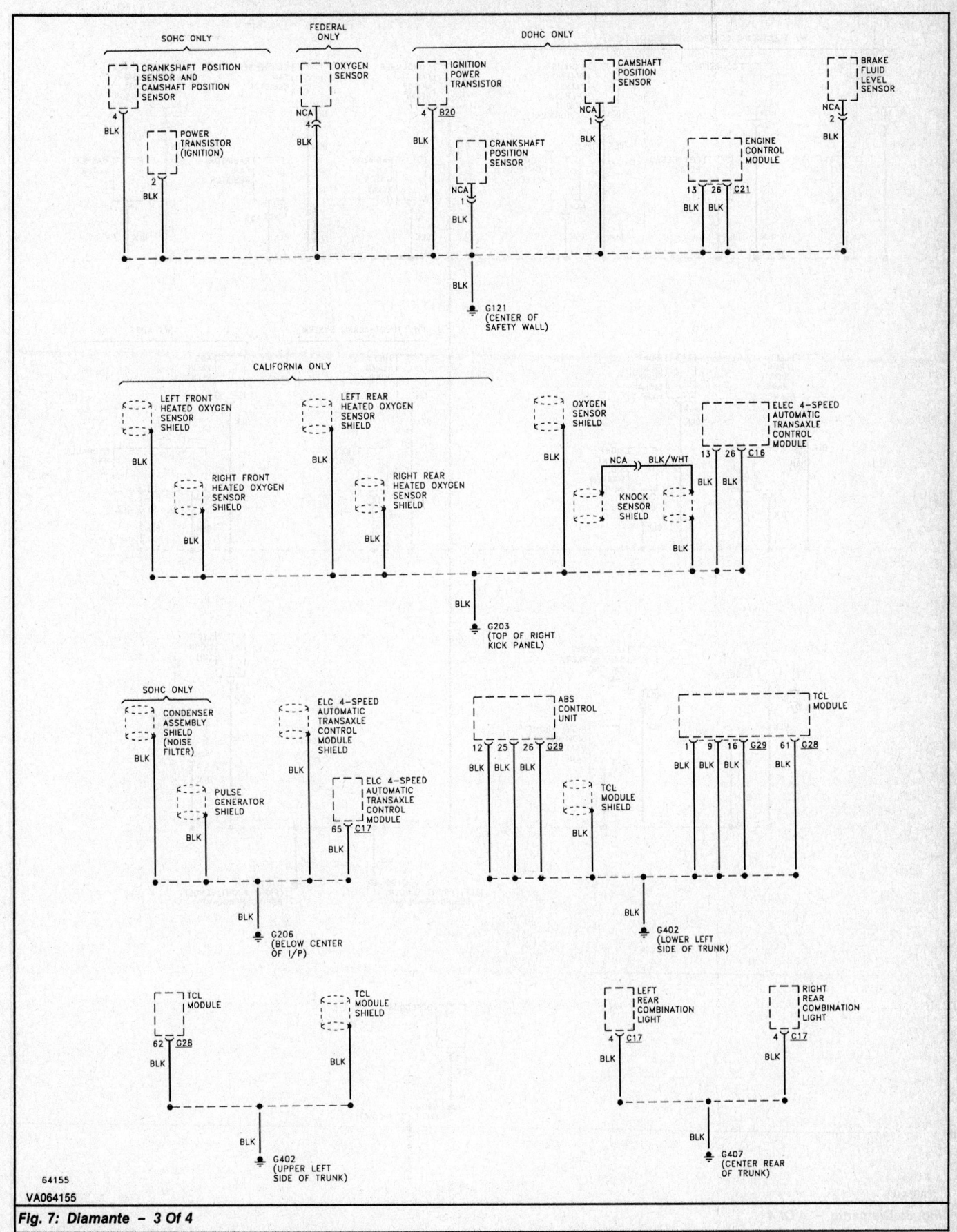

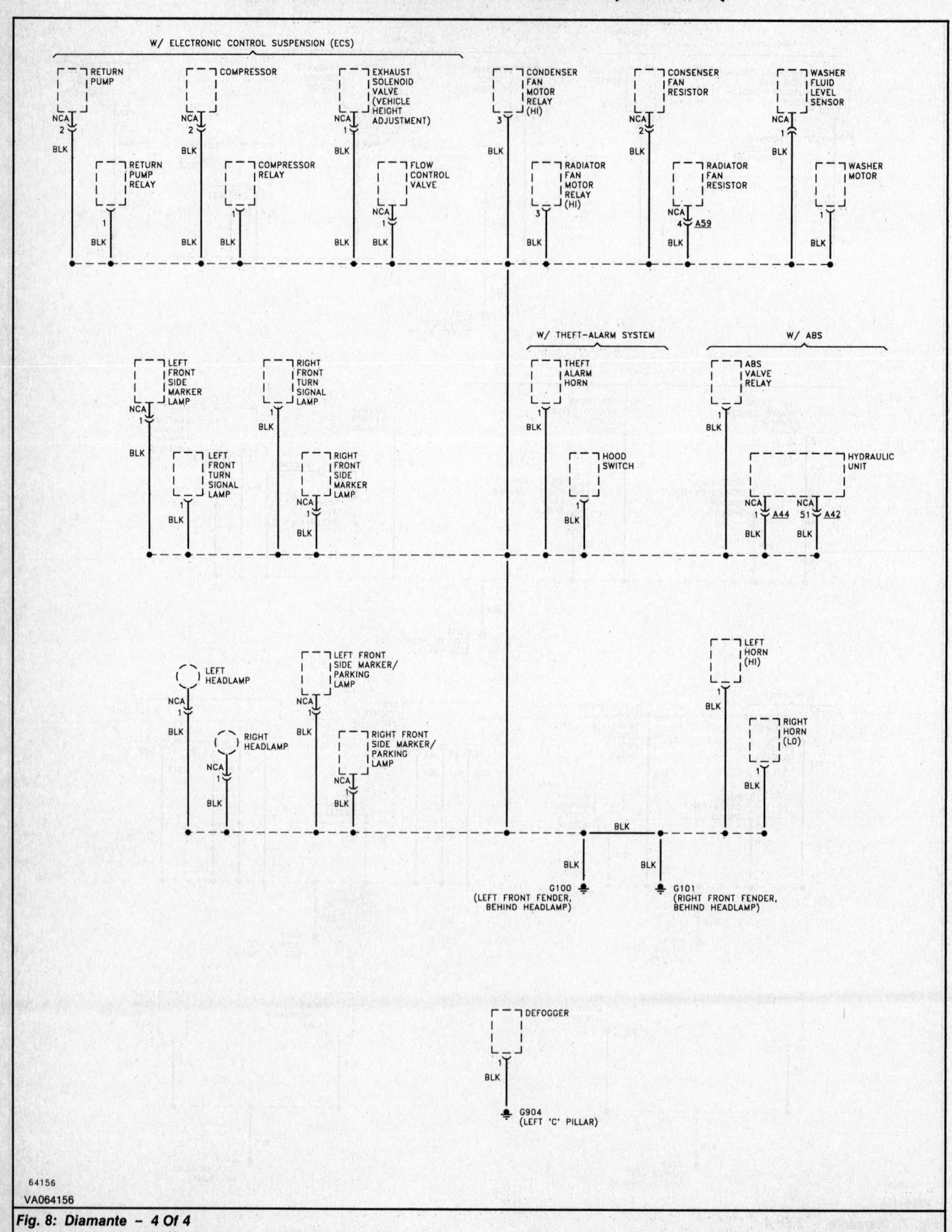

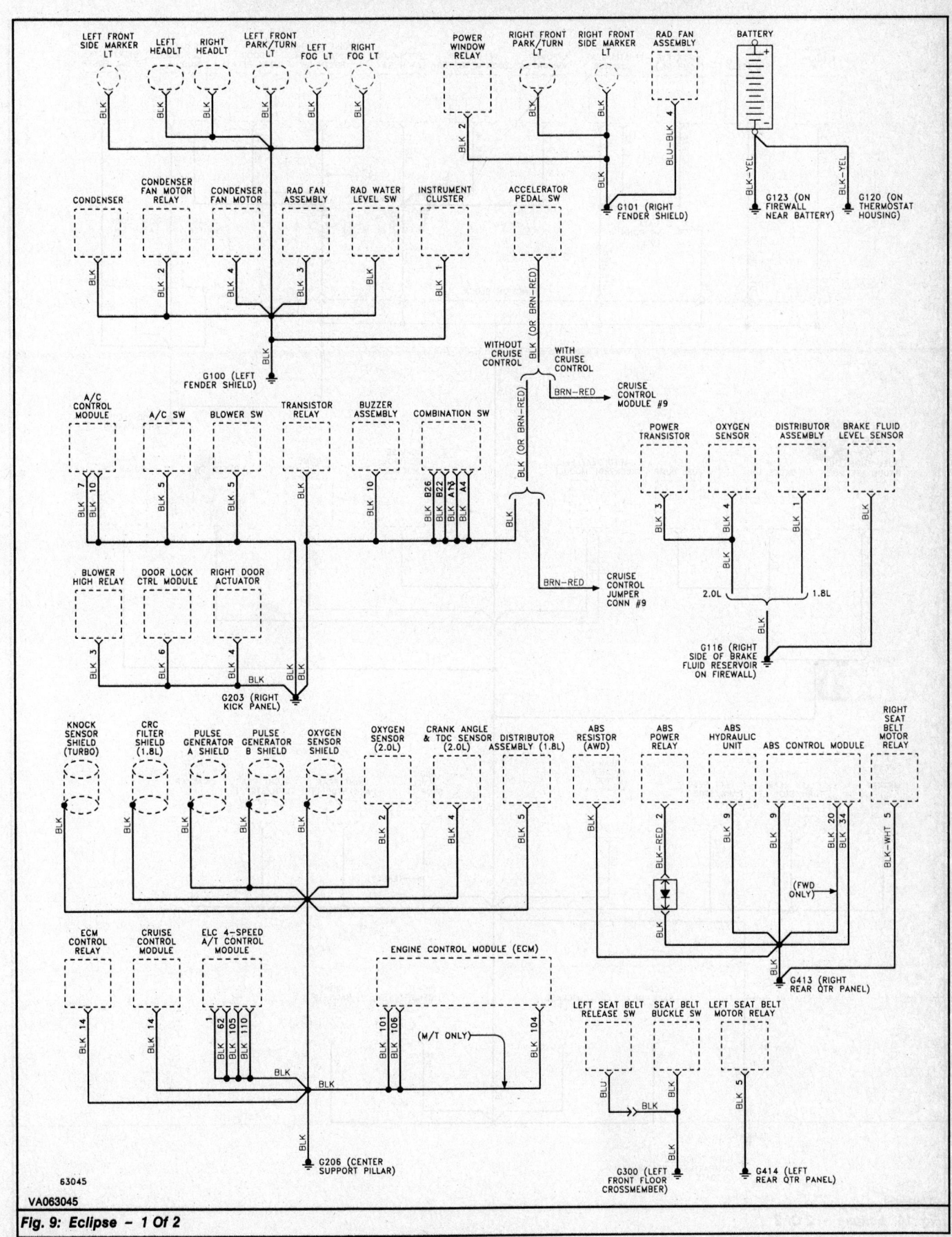

Fig. 9: Eclipse – 1 Of 2

63045

VA063045

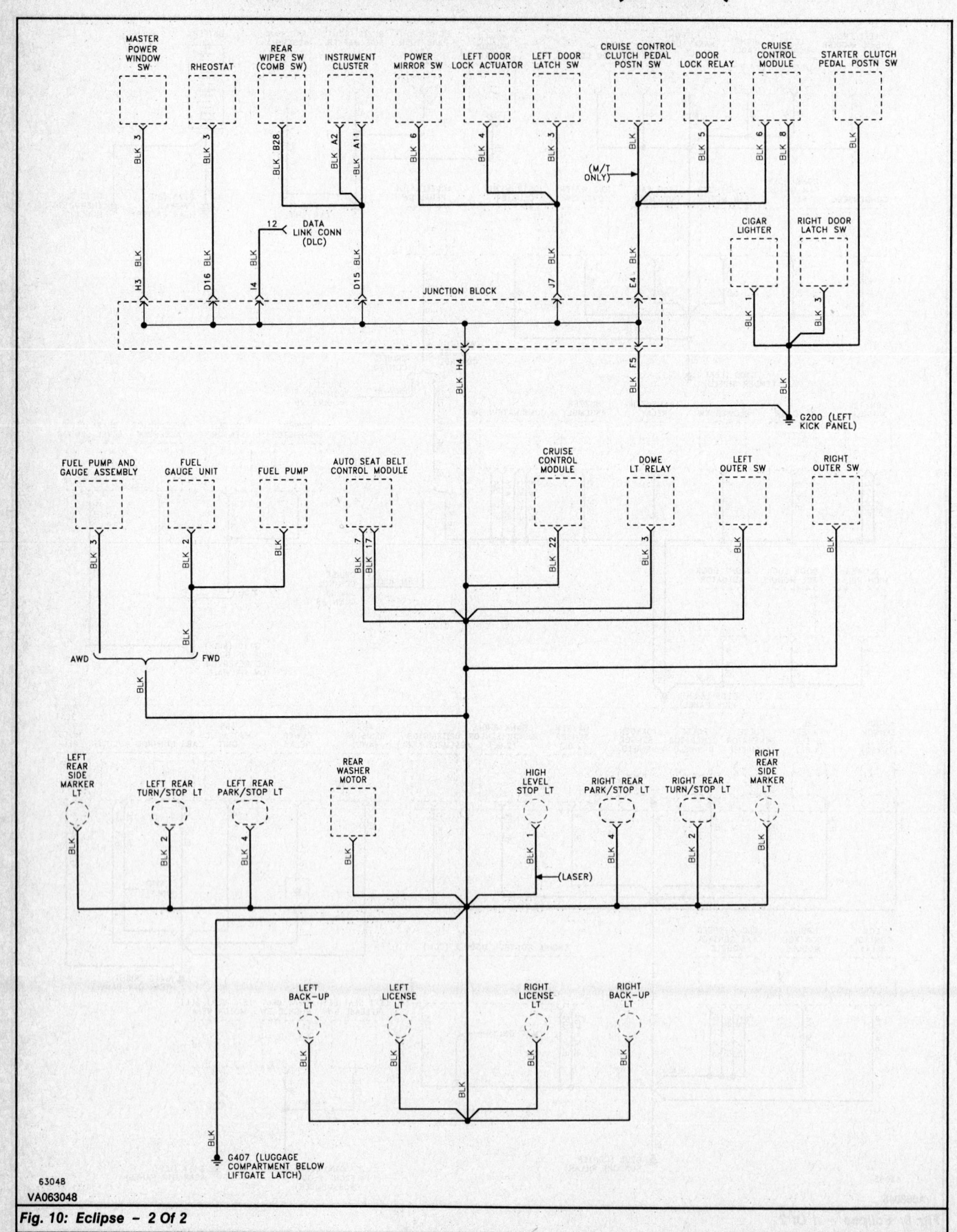

63048
VA063048

Fig. 10: Eclipse – 2 Of 2

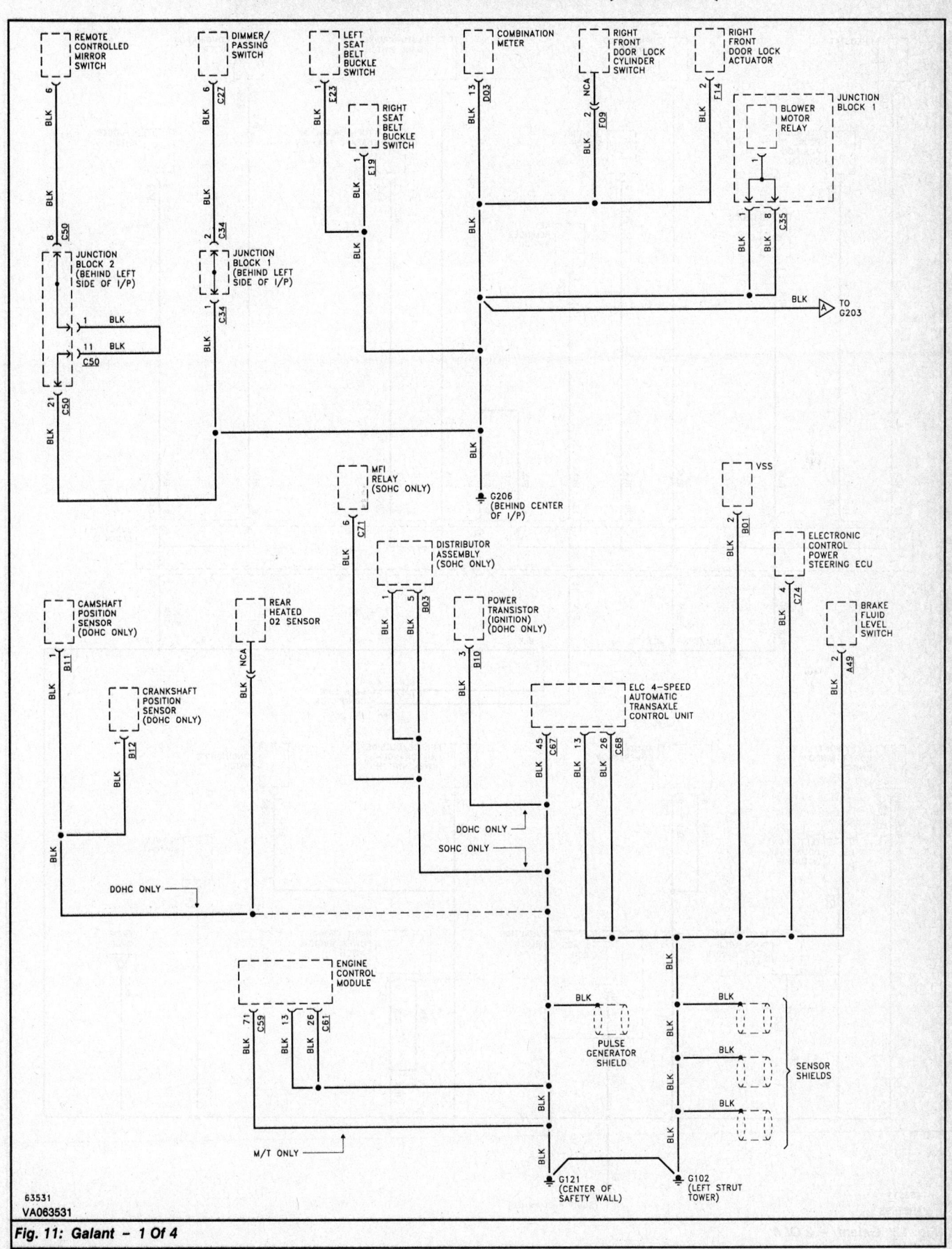

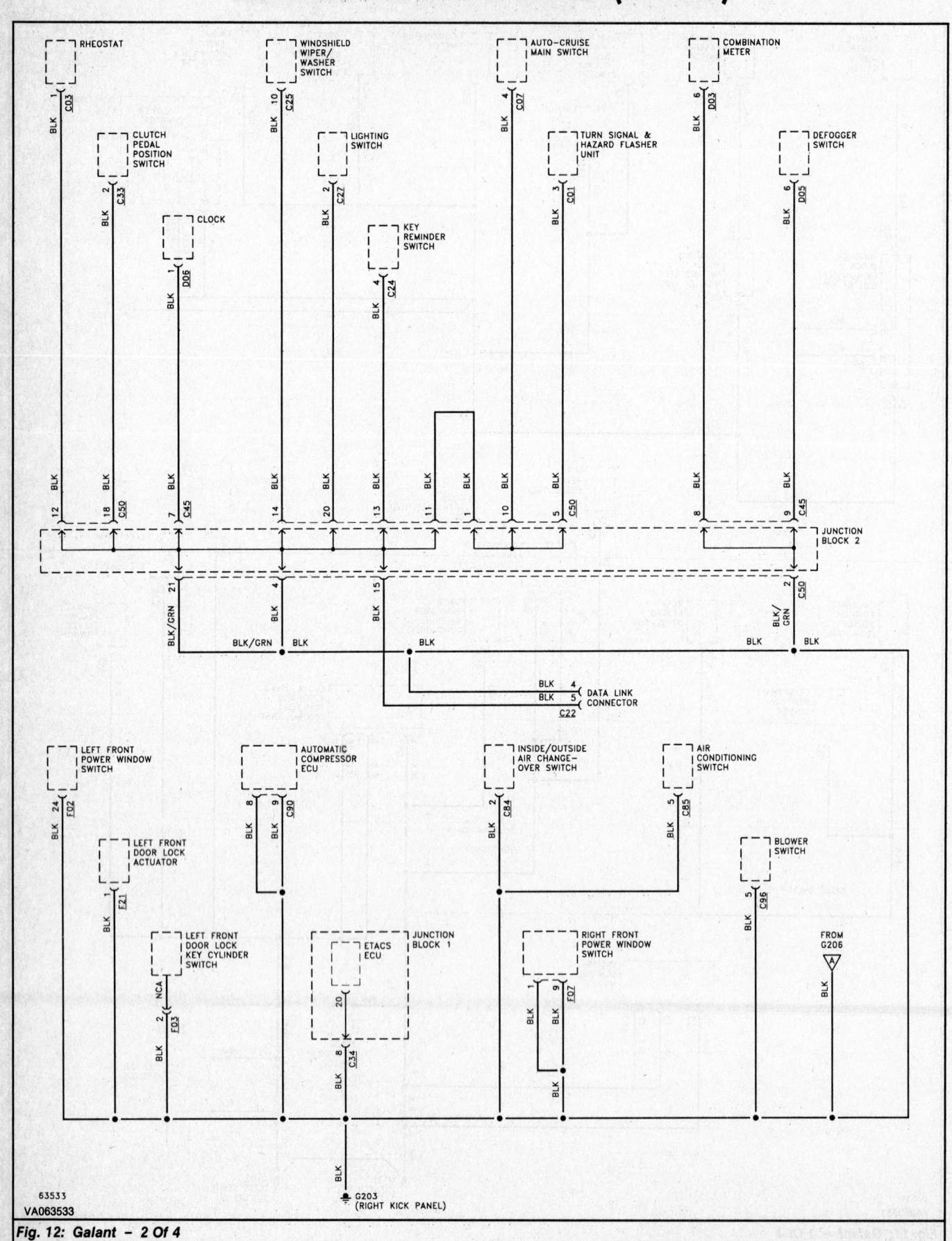

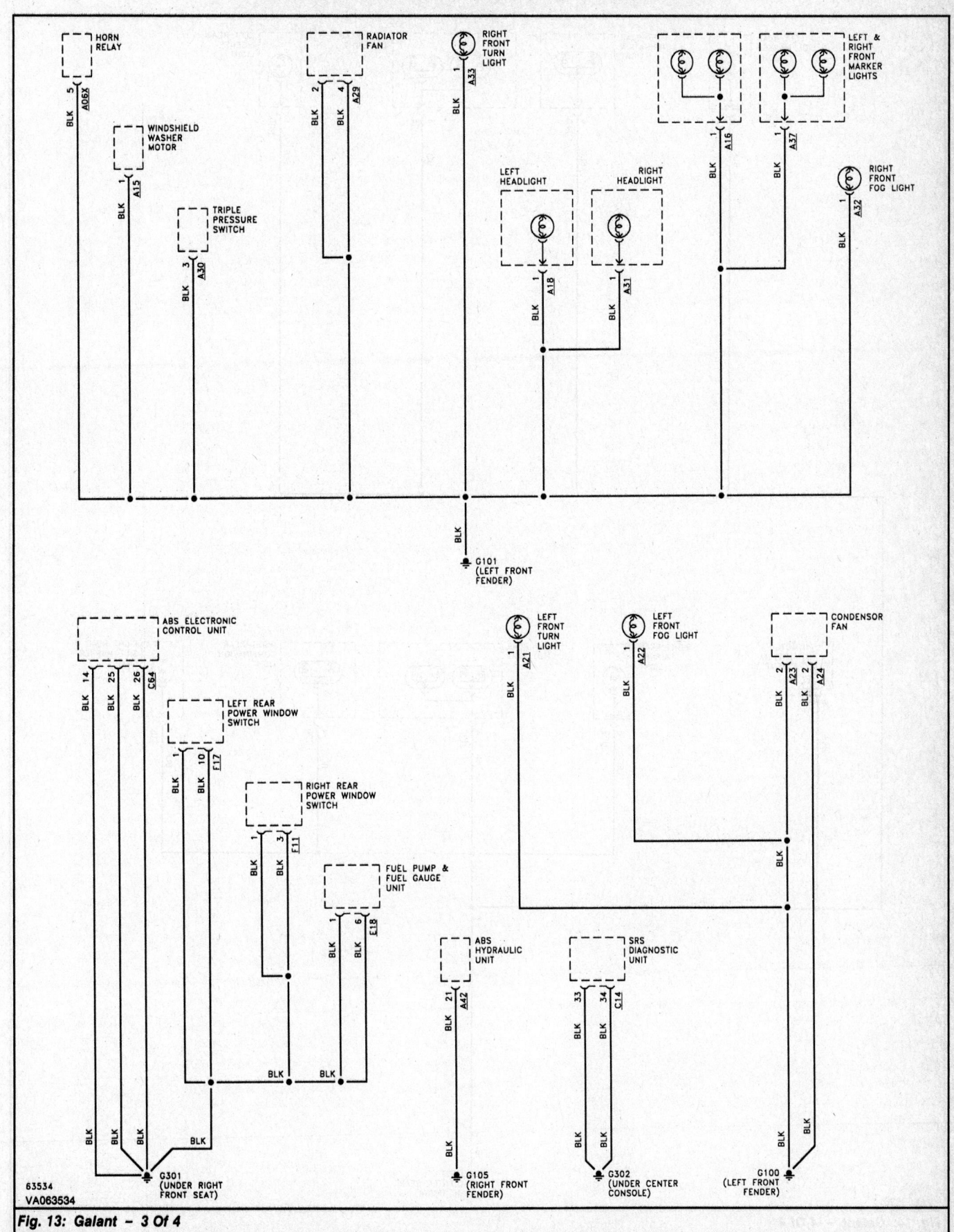

63534
VA063534

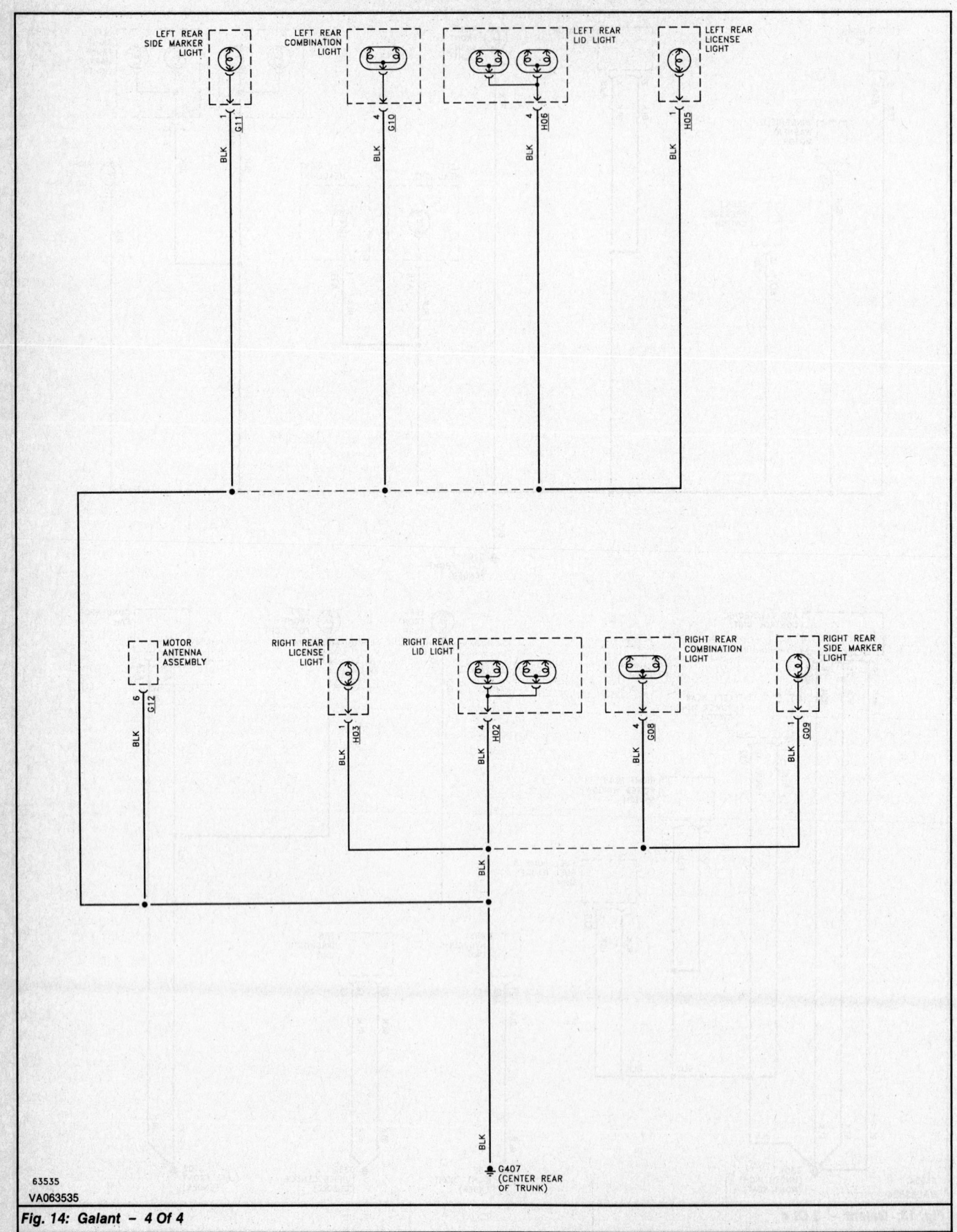

63535
VA063535

Fig. 14: Galant – 4 Of 4

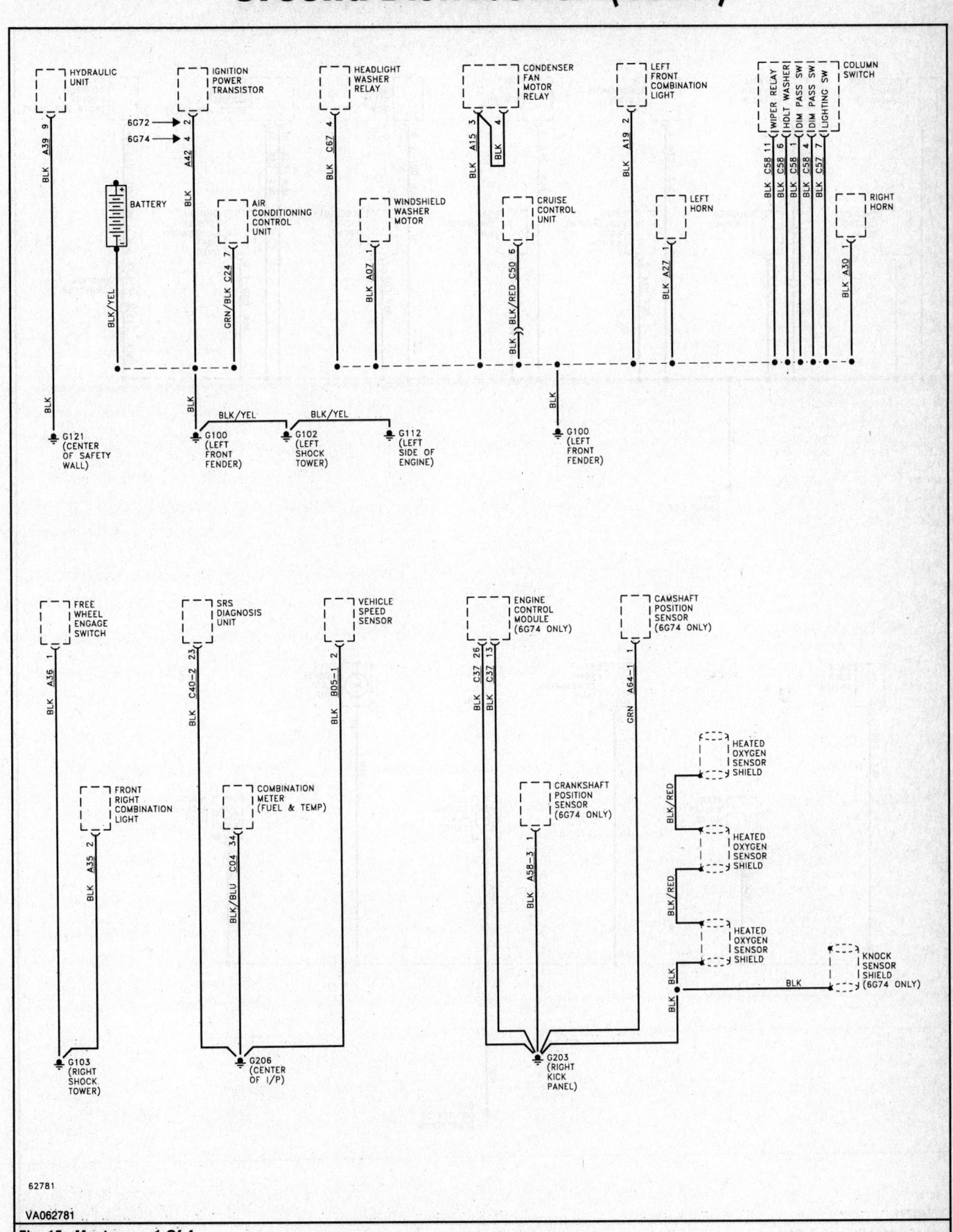

Fig. 15: Montero – 1 Of 4

62781

VA062781

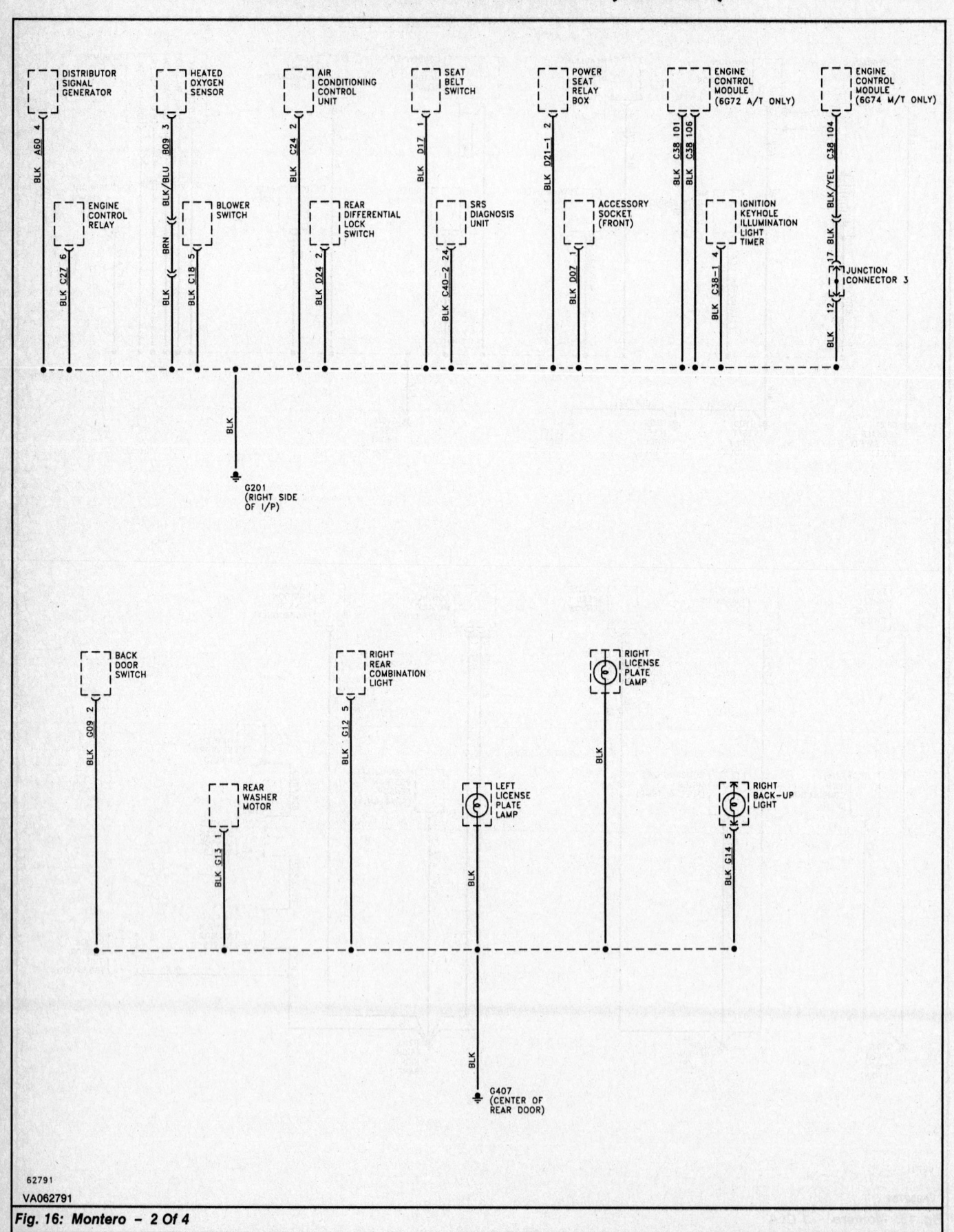

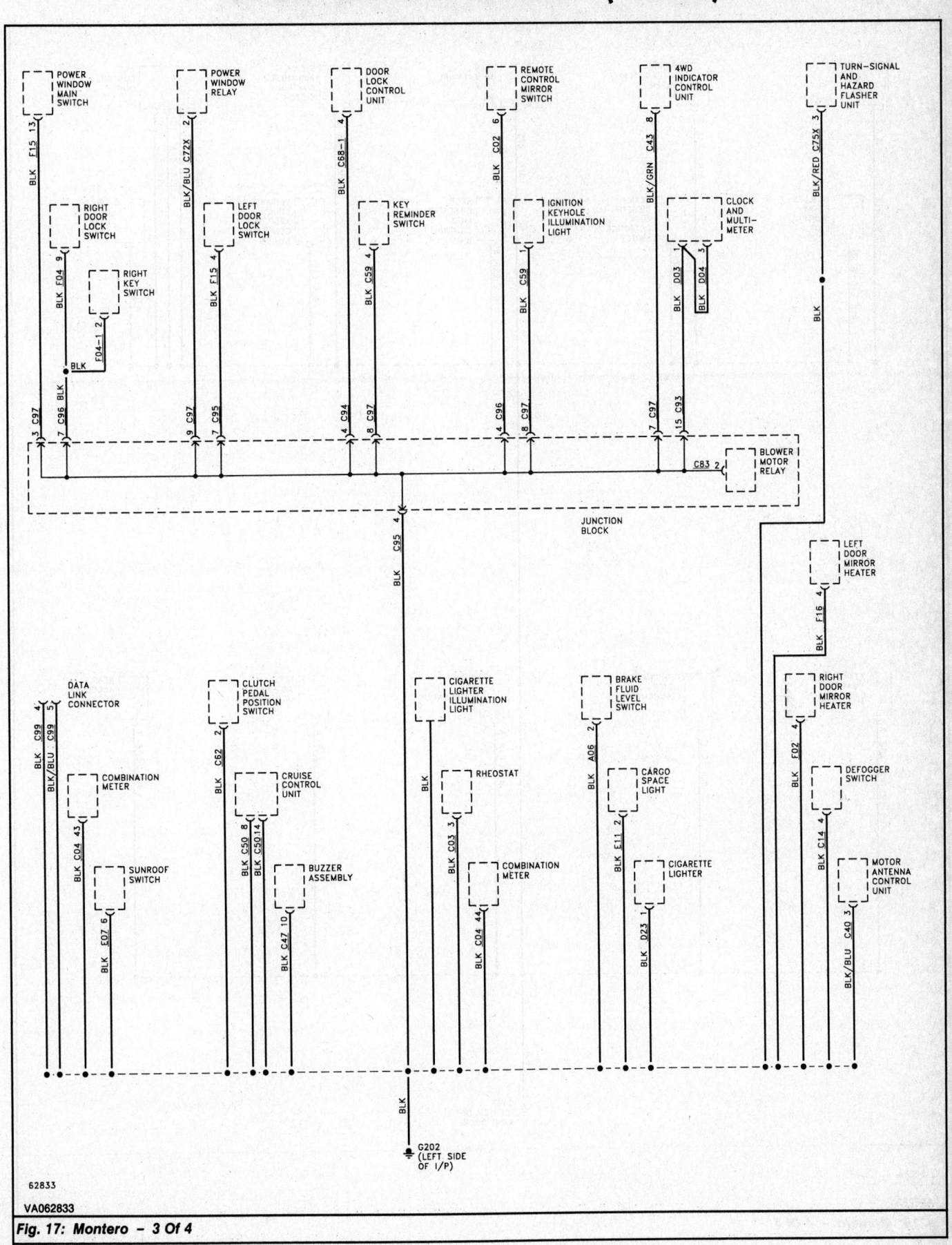

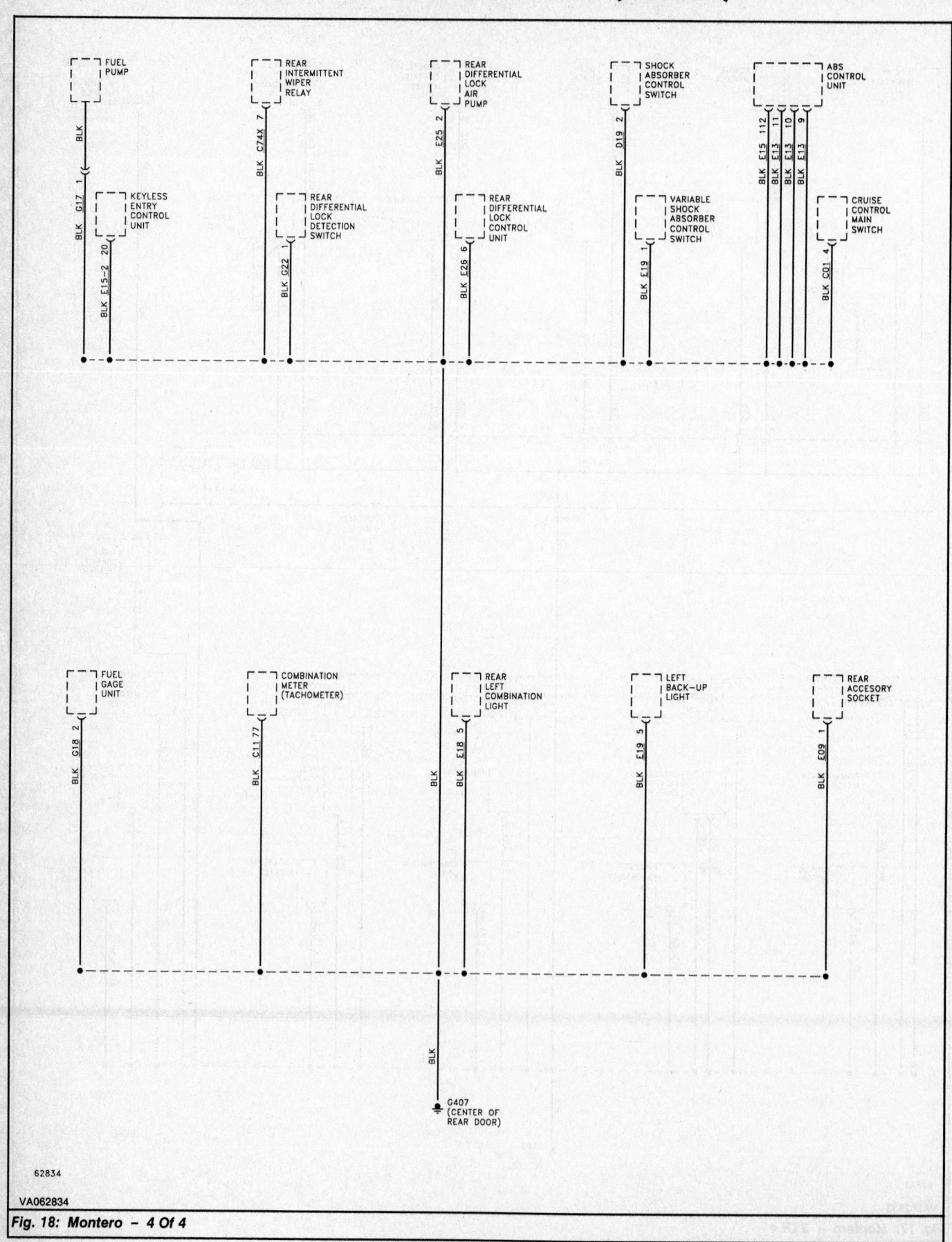

62834

VA062834

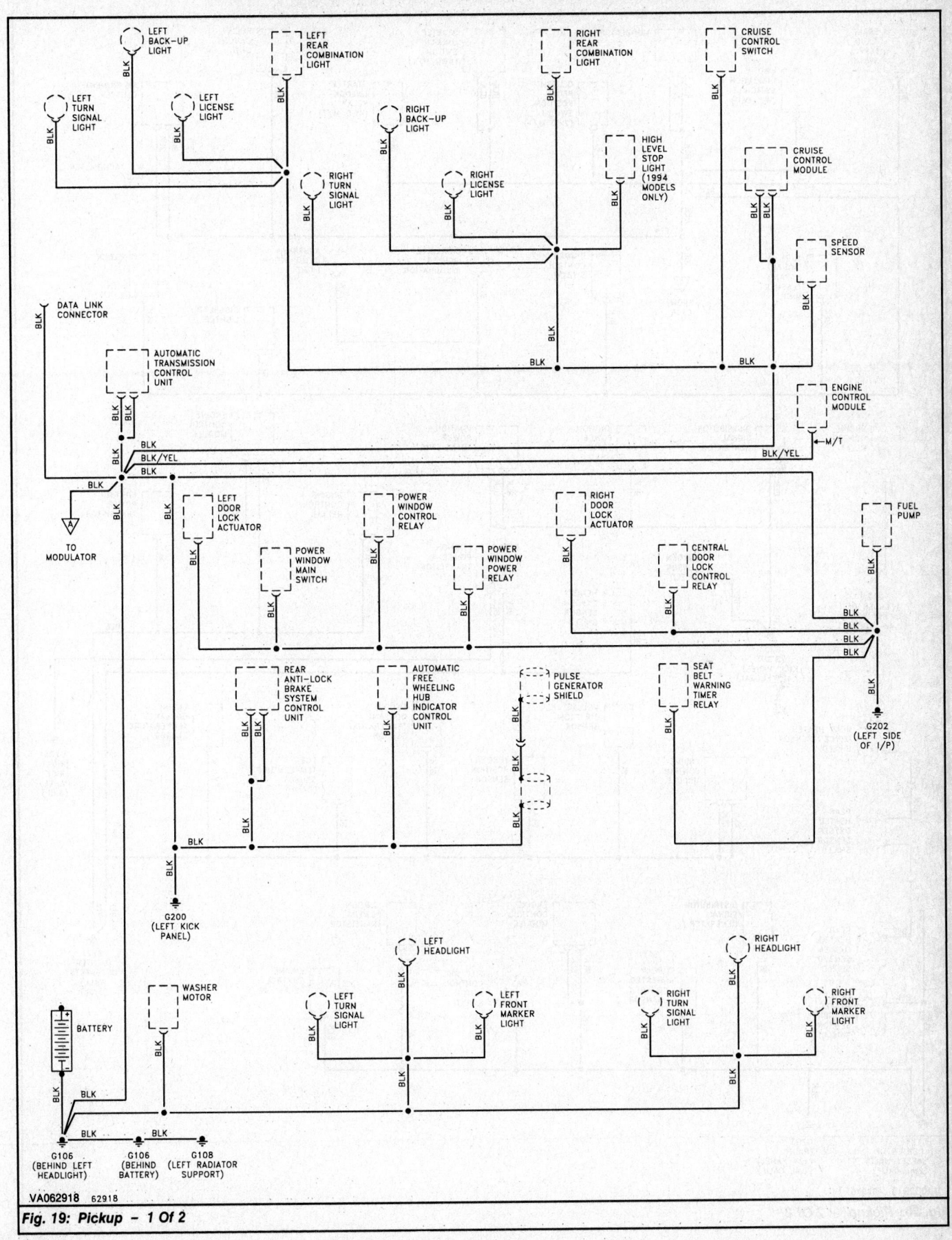

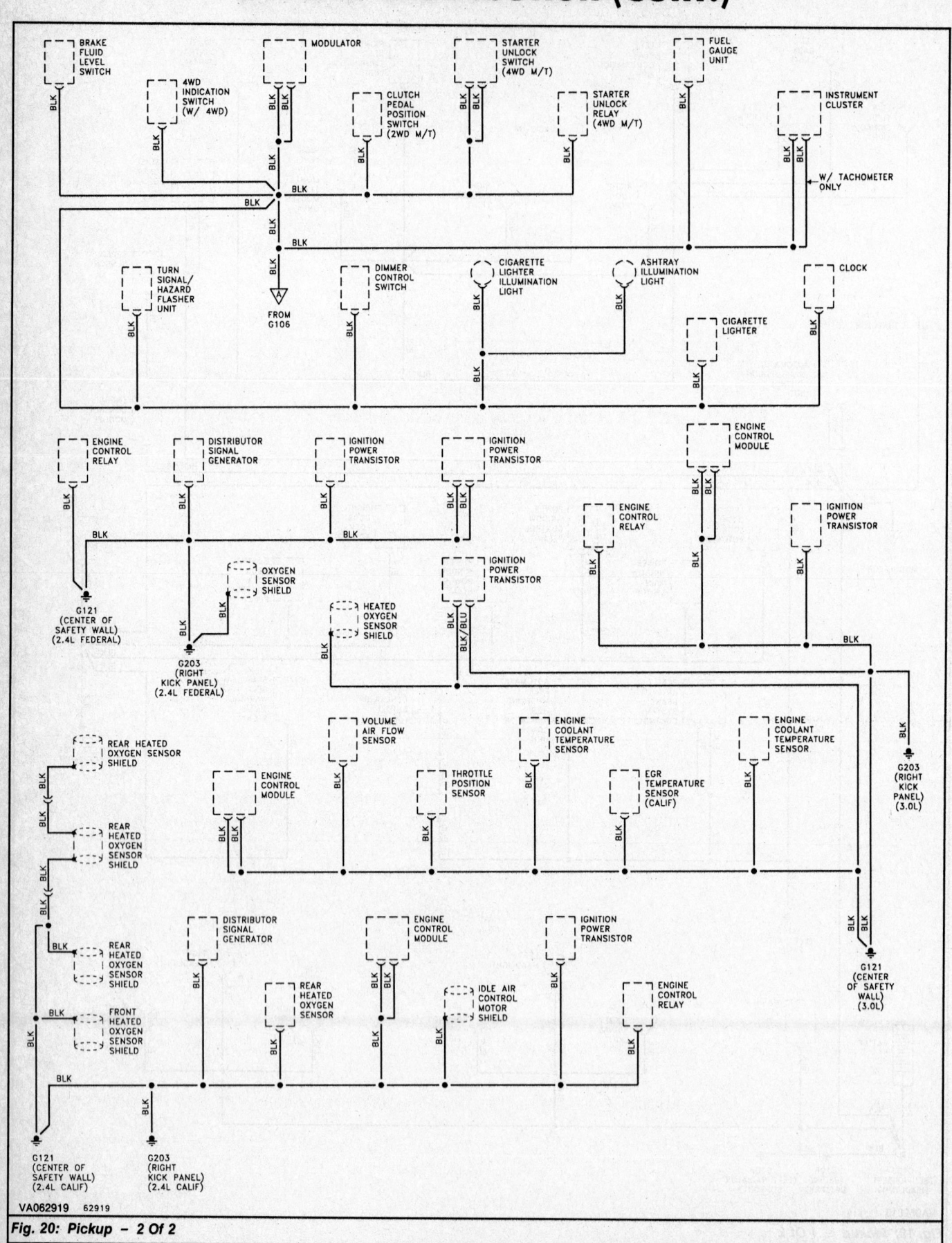

Fig. 20: Pickup – 2 Of 2

VA062919   62919

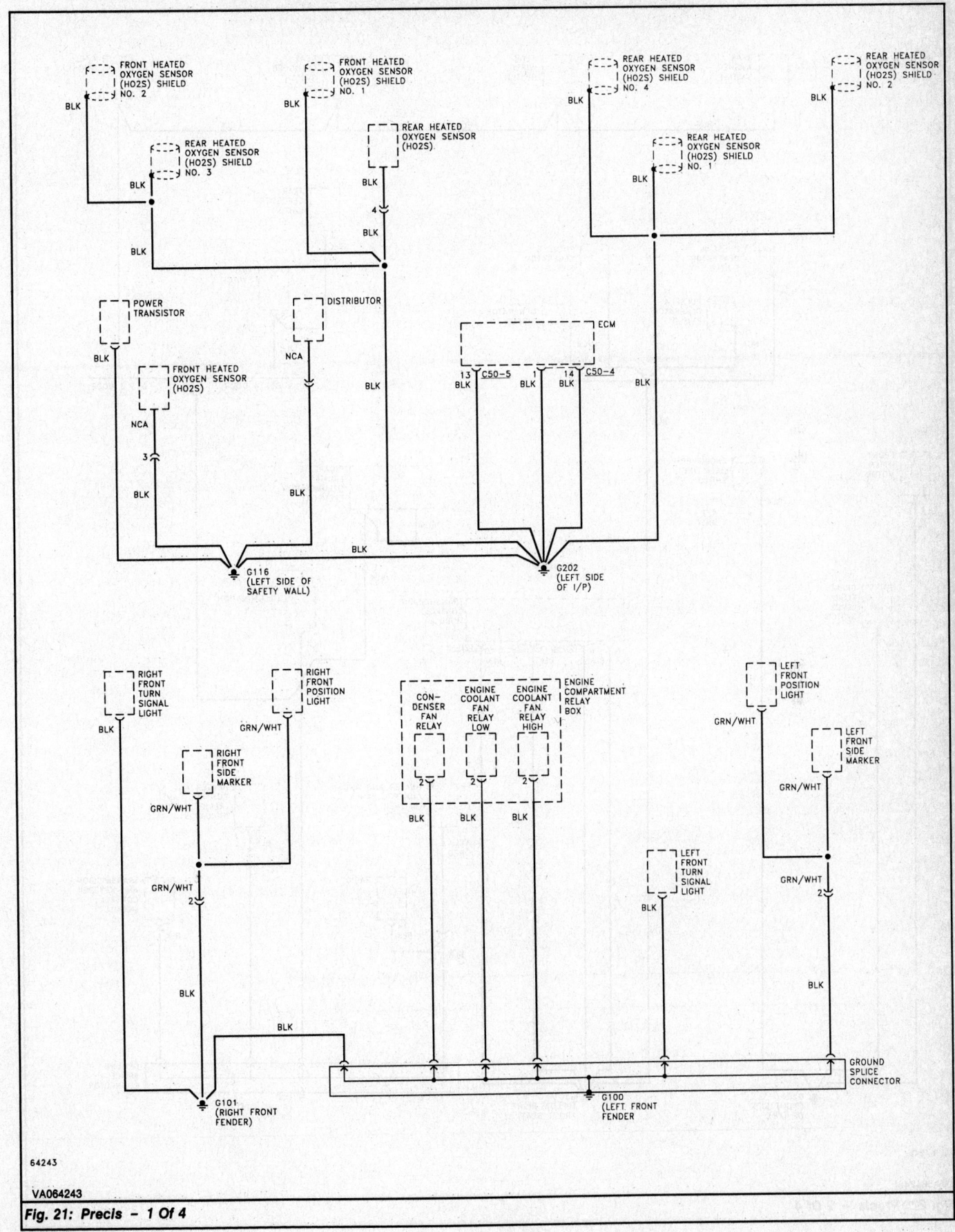

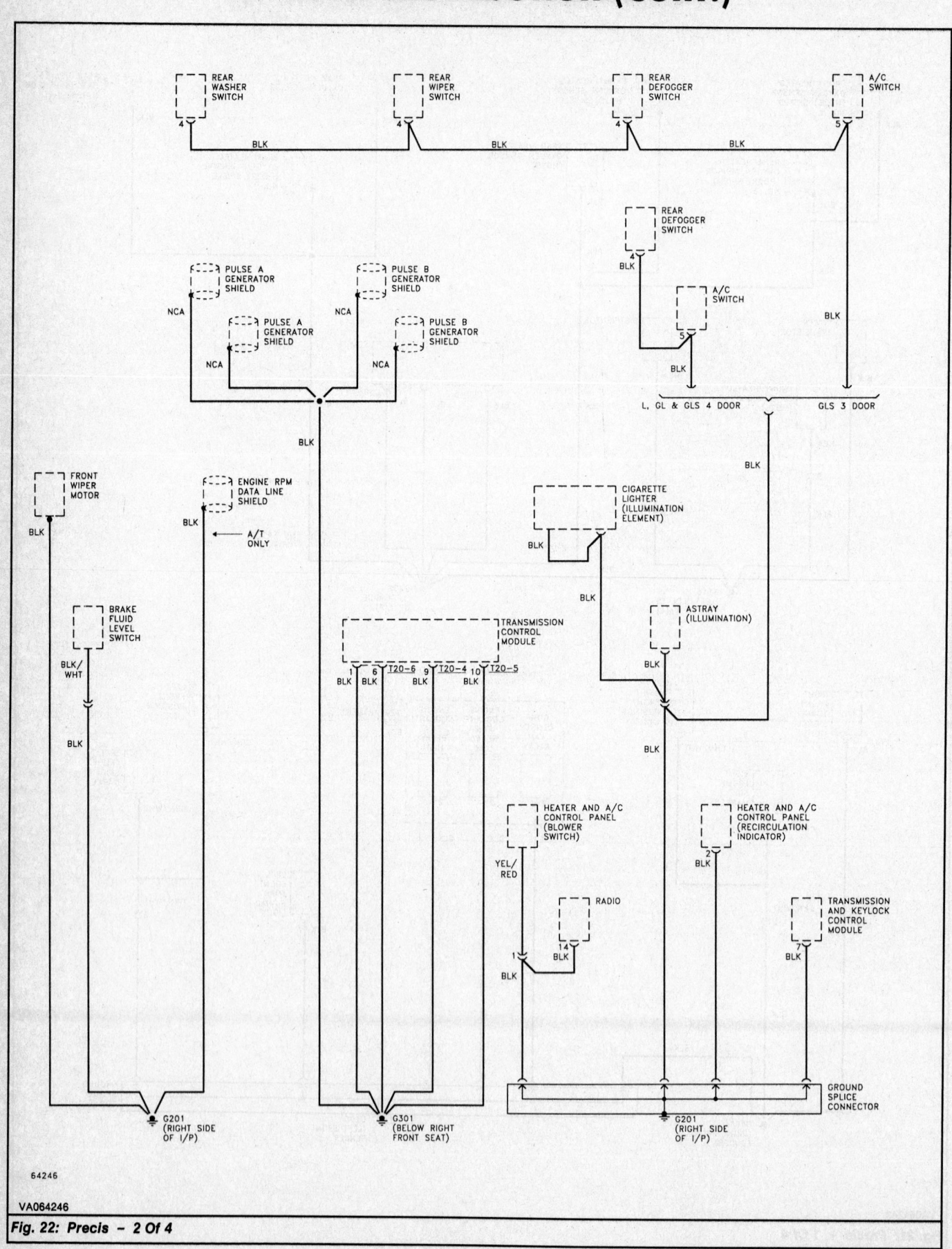

64246

VA064246

Fig. 22: Precis – 2 Of 4

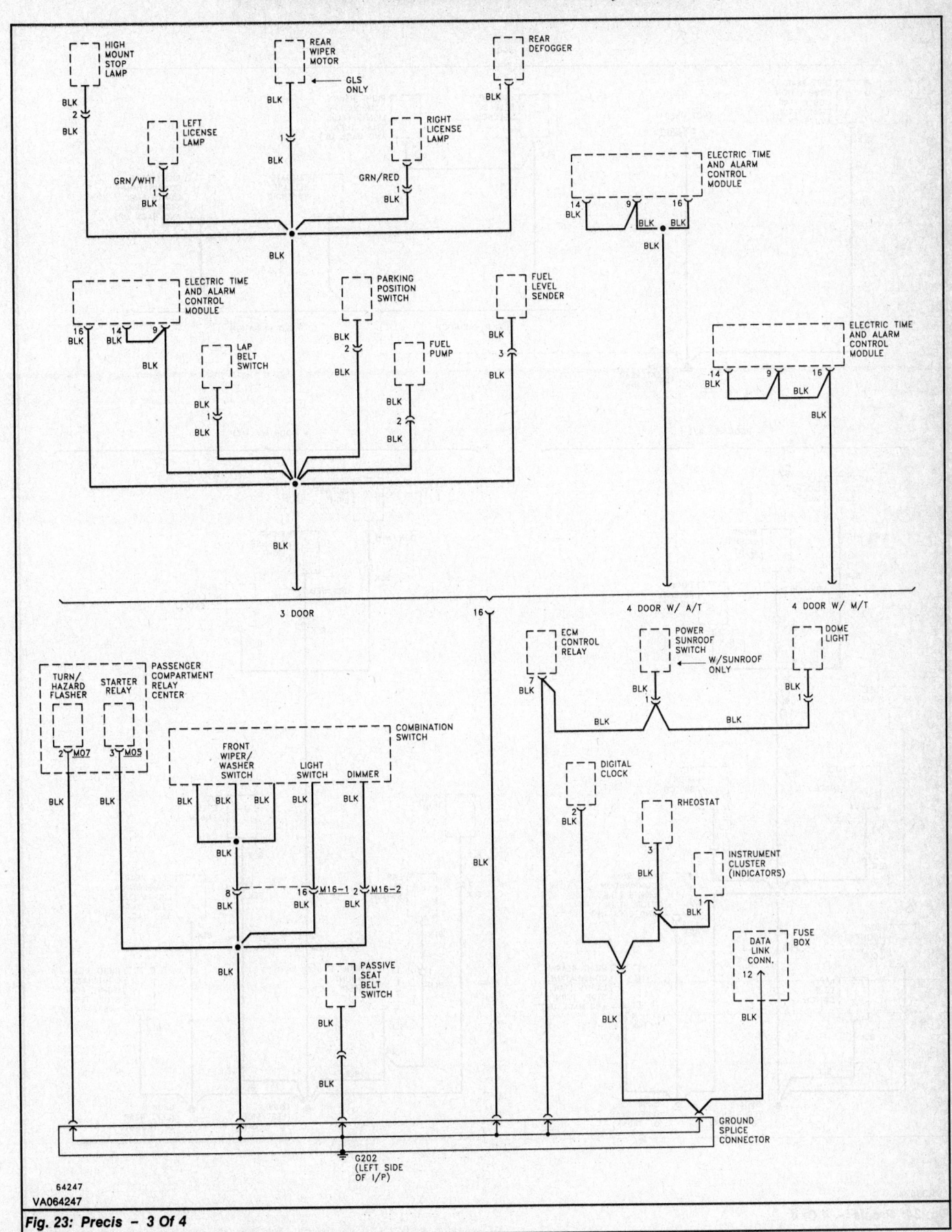

64247
VA064247

Fig. 23: Precis - 3 Of 4

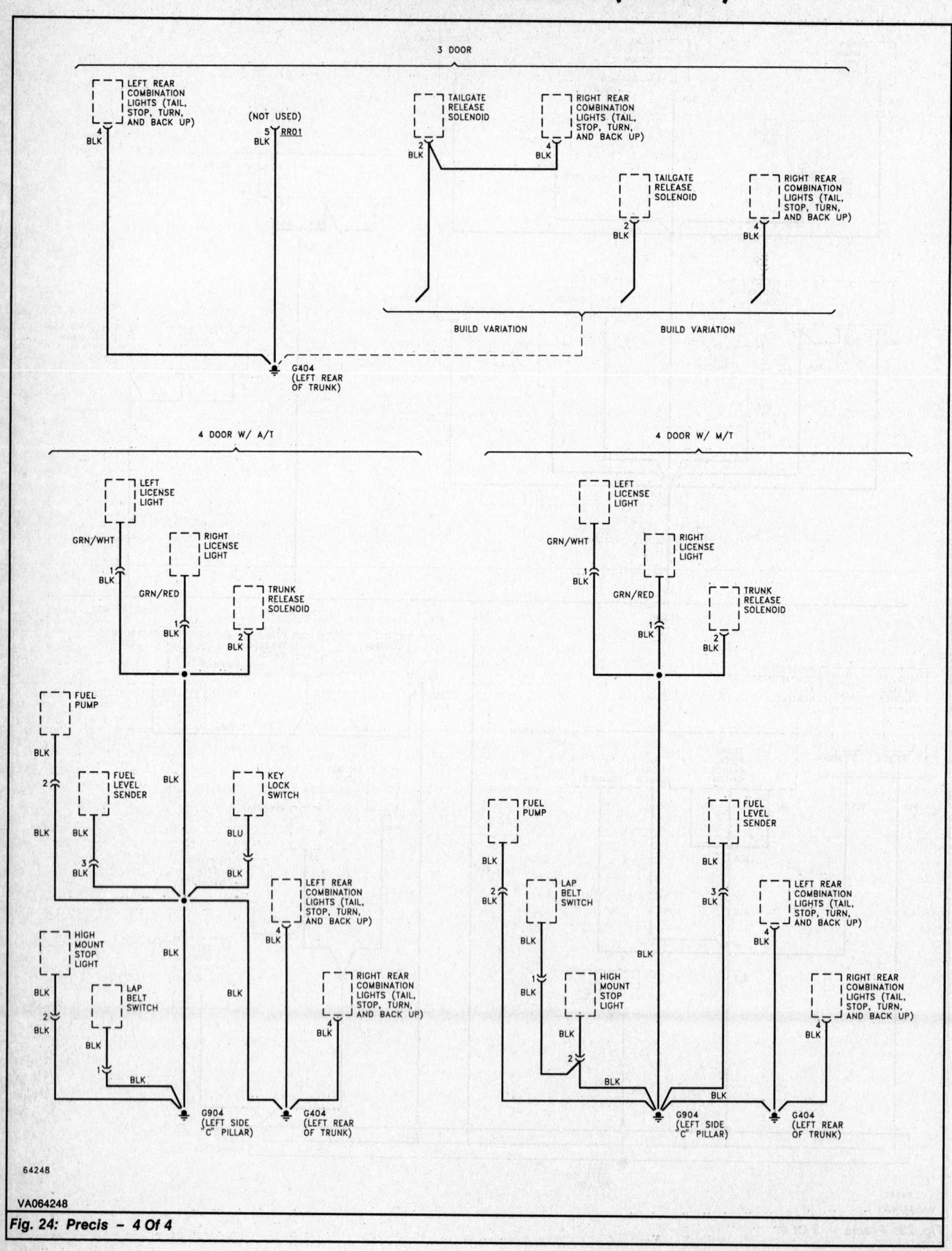

64248

VA064248

Fig. 24: Precis – 4 Of 4

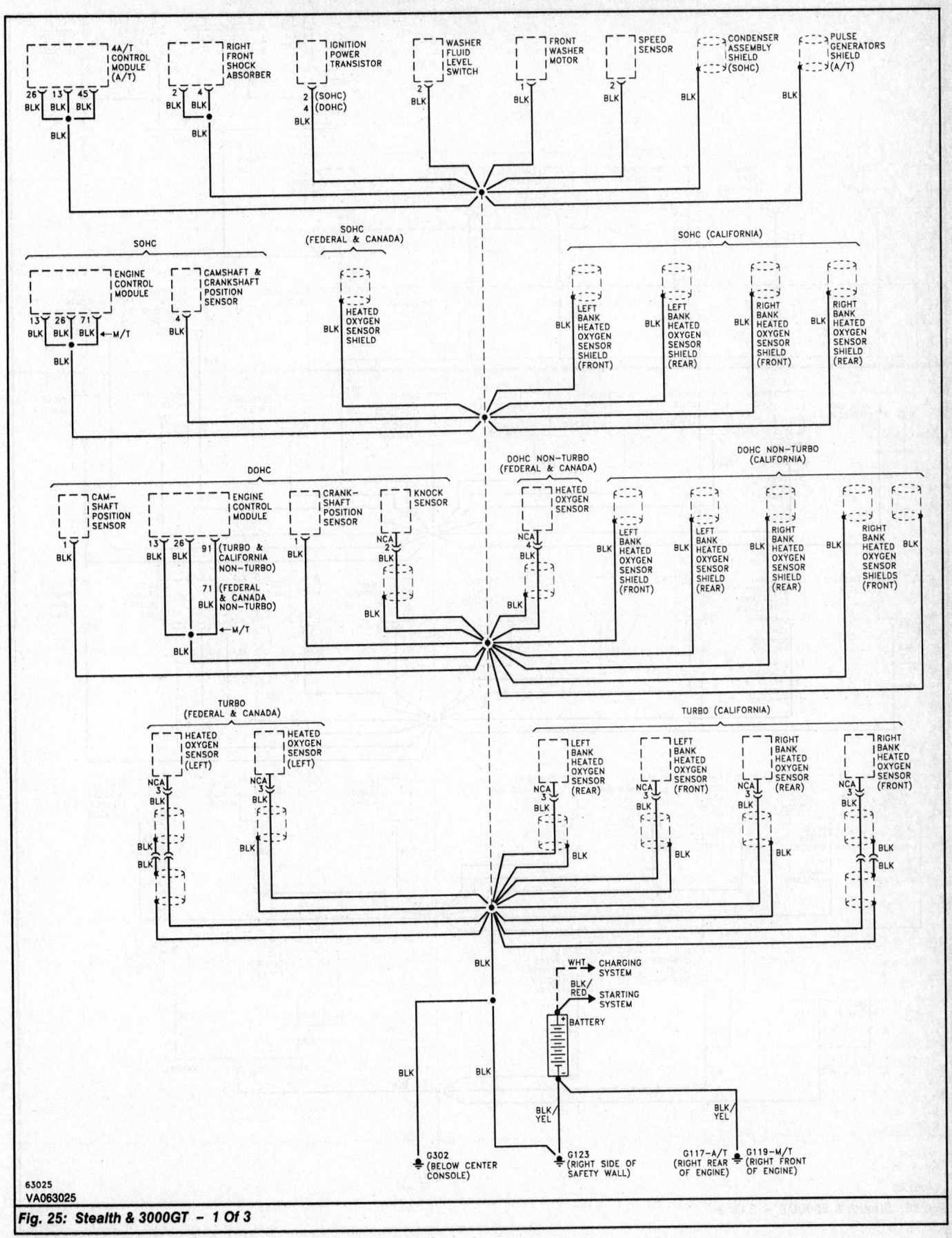

63025
VA063025

Fig. 25: Stealth & 3000GT – 1 Of 3

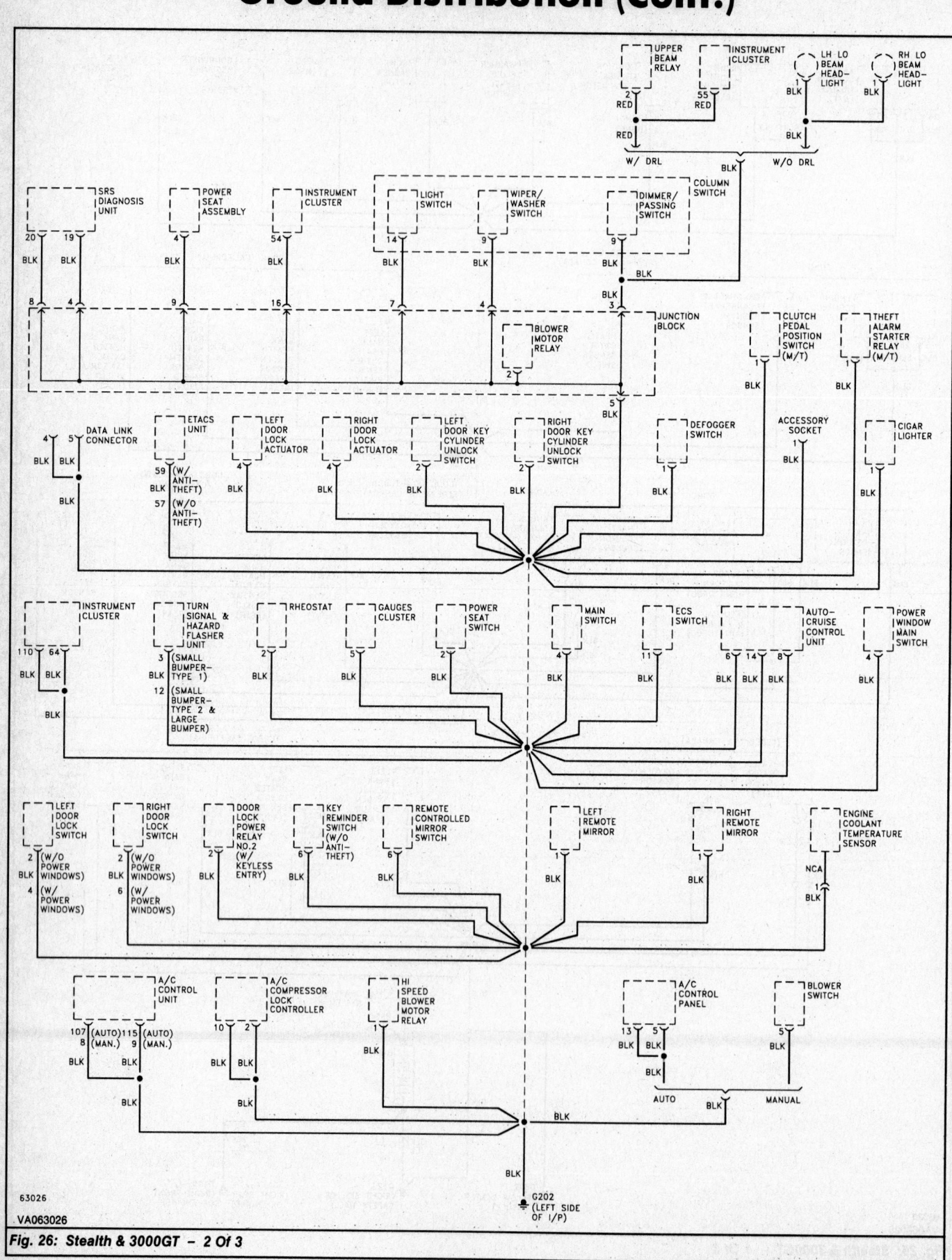

63026

VA063026

Fig. 26: Stealth & 3000GT - 2 Of 3

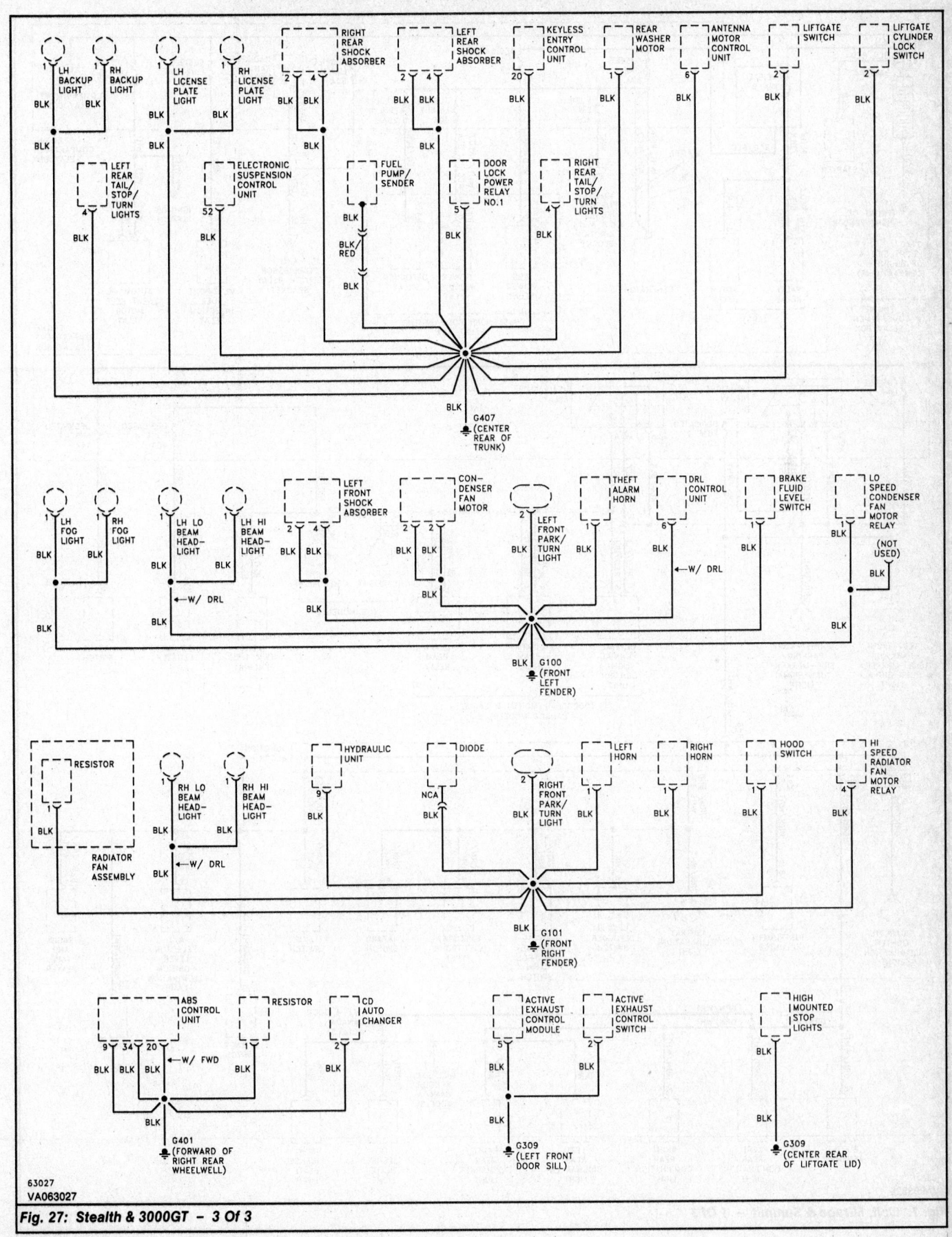

63027
VA063027

Fig. 27: Stealth & 3000GT – 3 Of 3

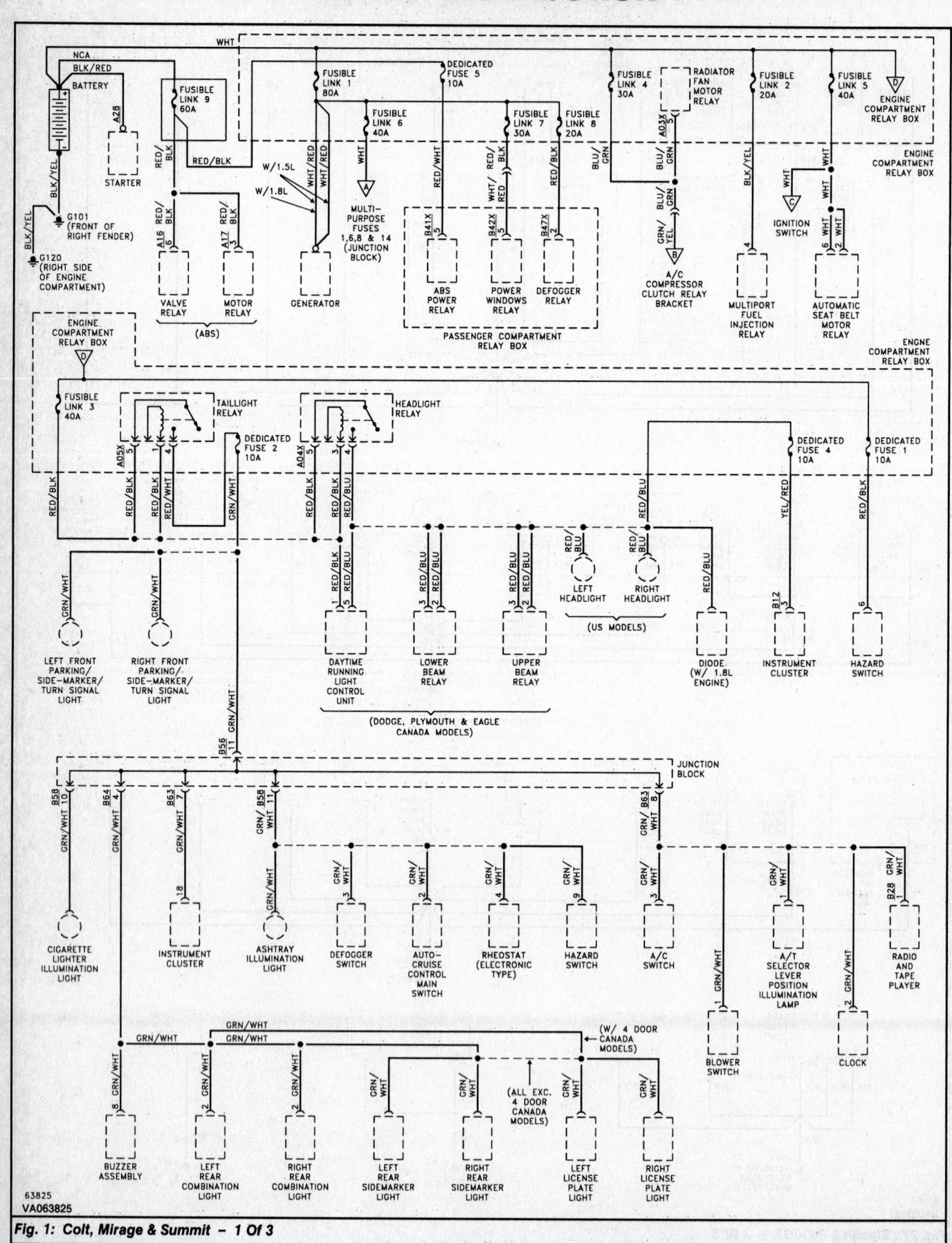

Fig. 1: Colt, Mirage & Summit — 1 Of 3

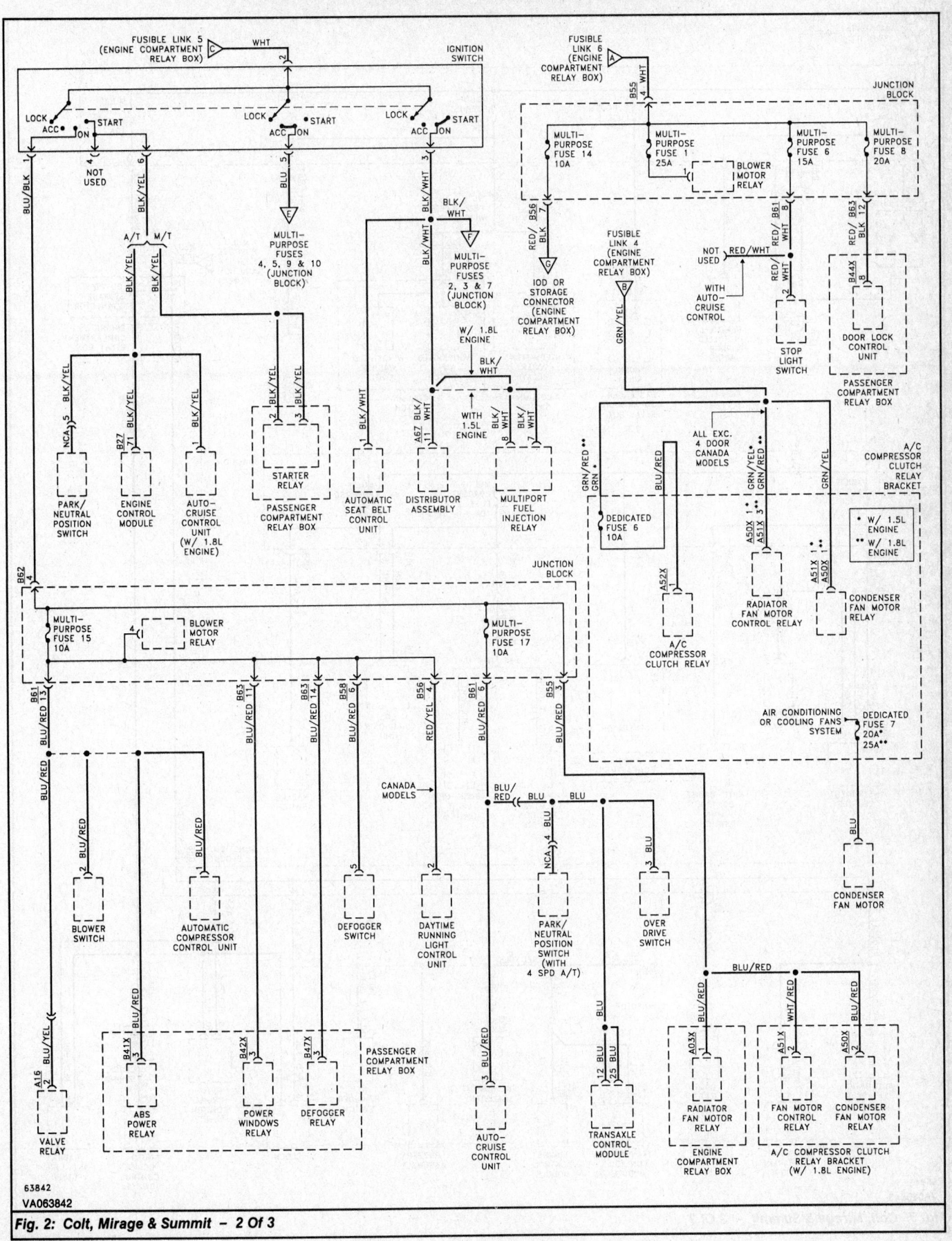

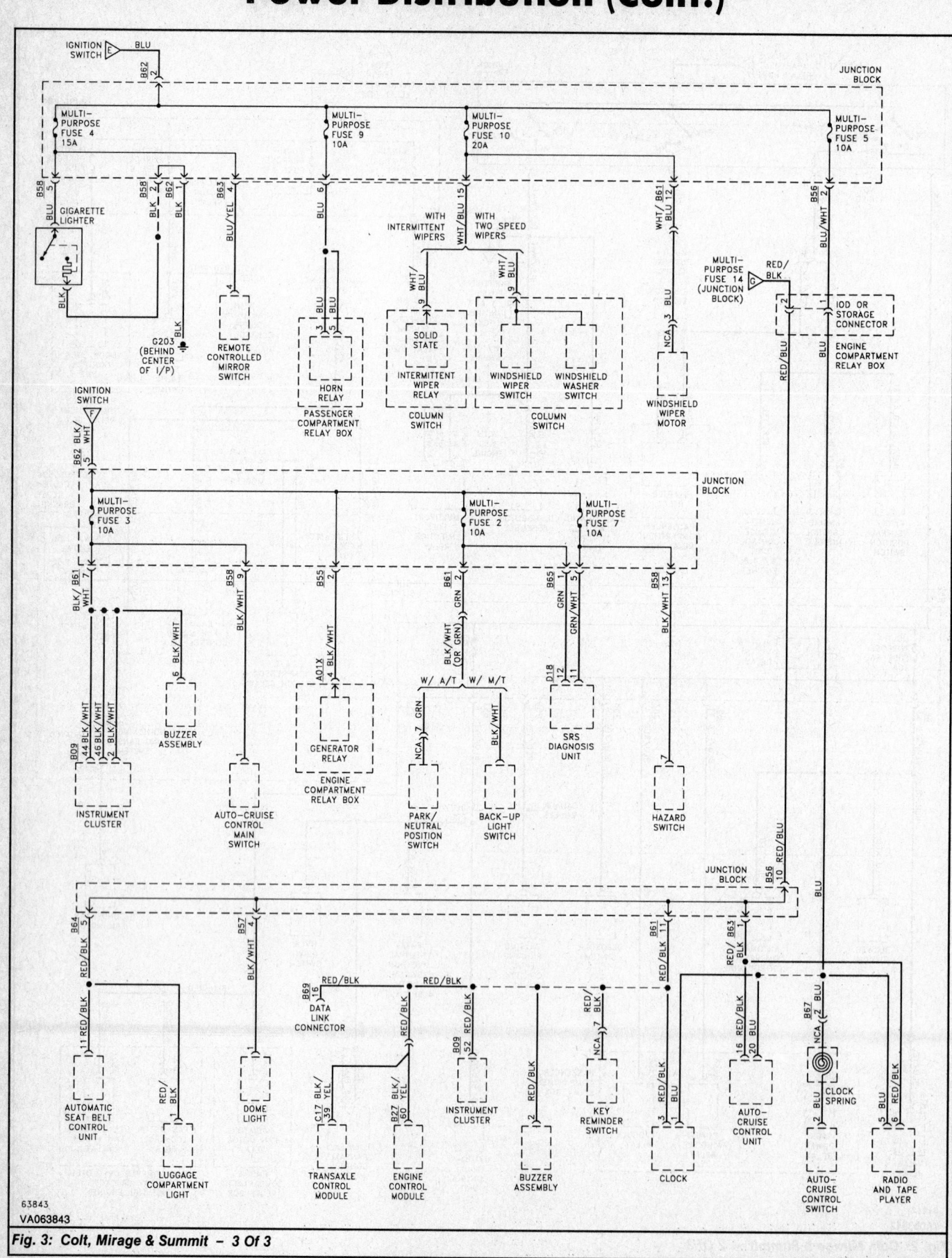

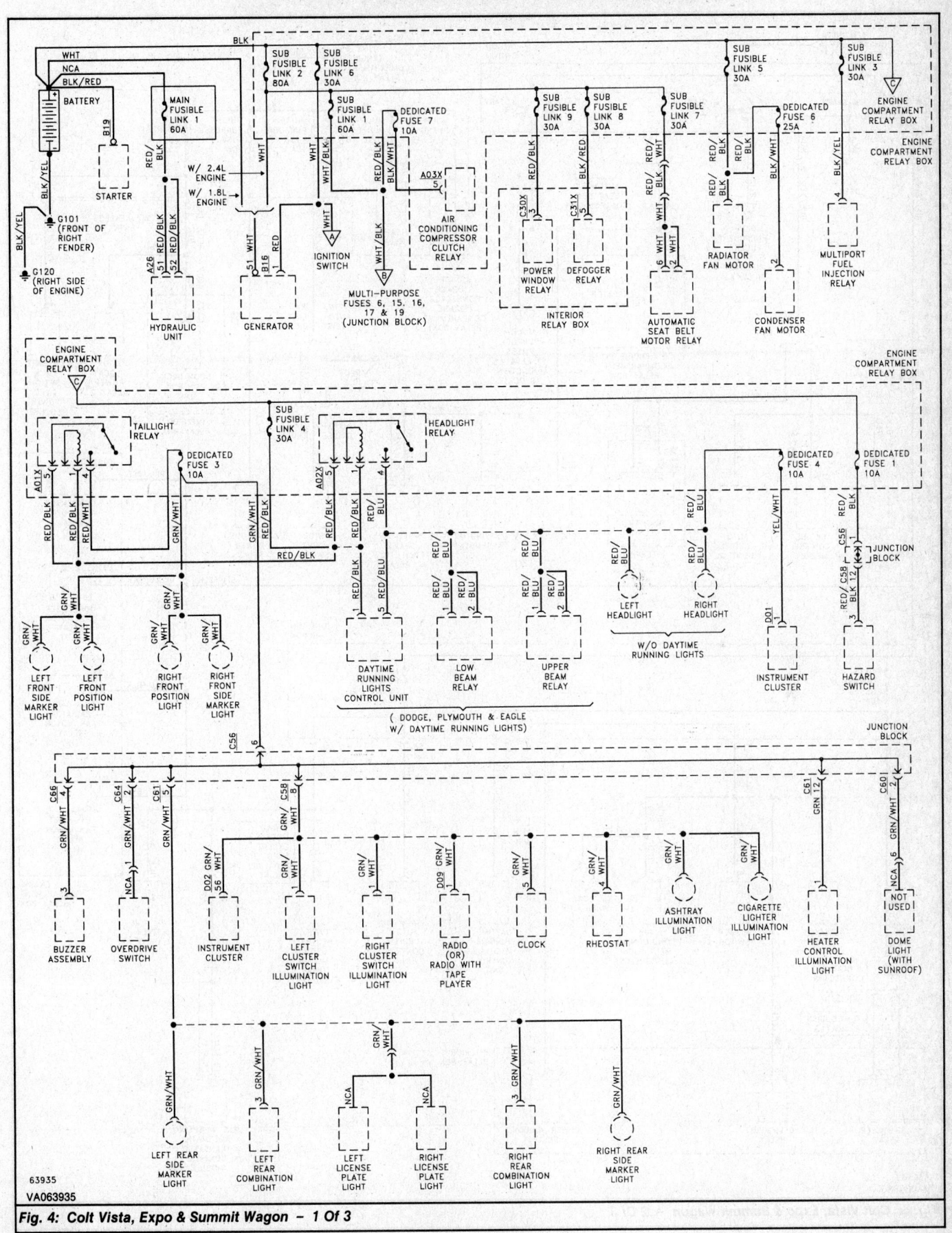

63935

VA063935

Fig. 4: Colt Vista, Expo & Summit Wagon – 1 Of 3

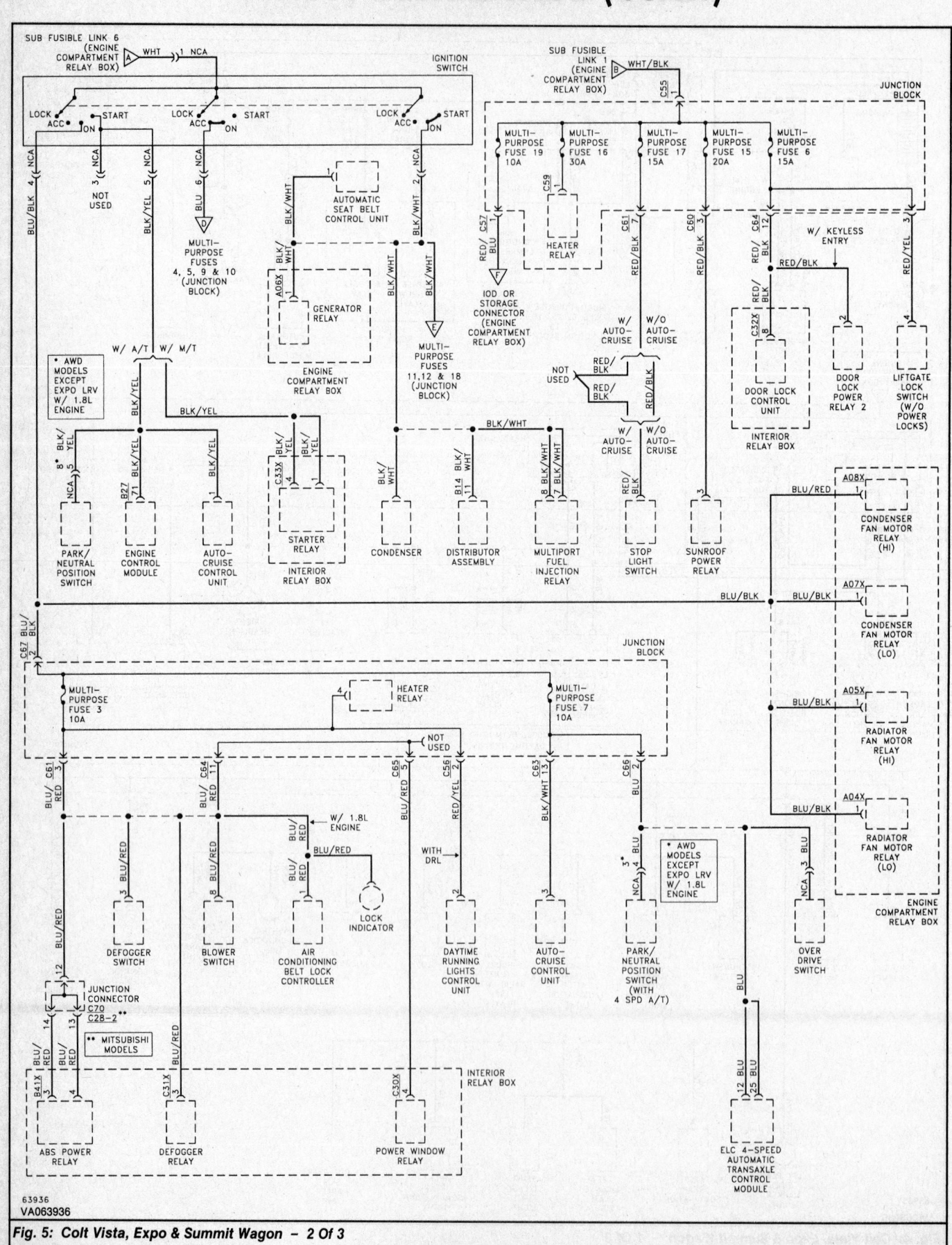

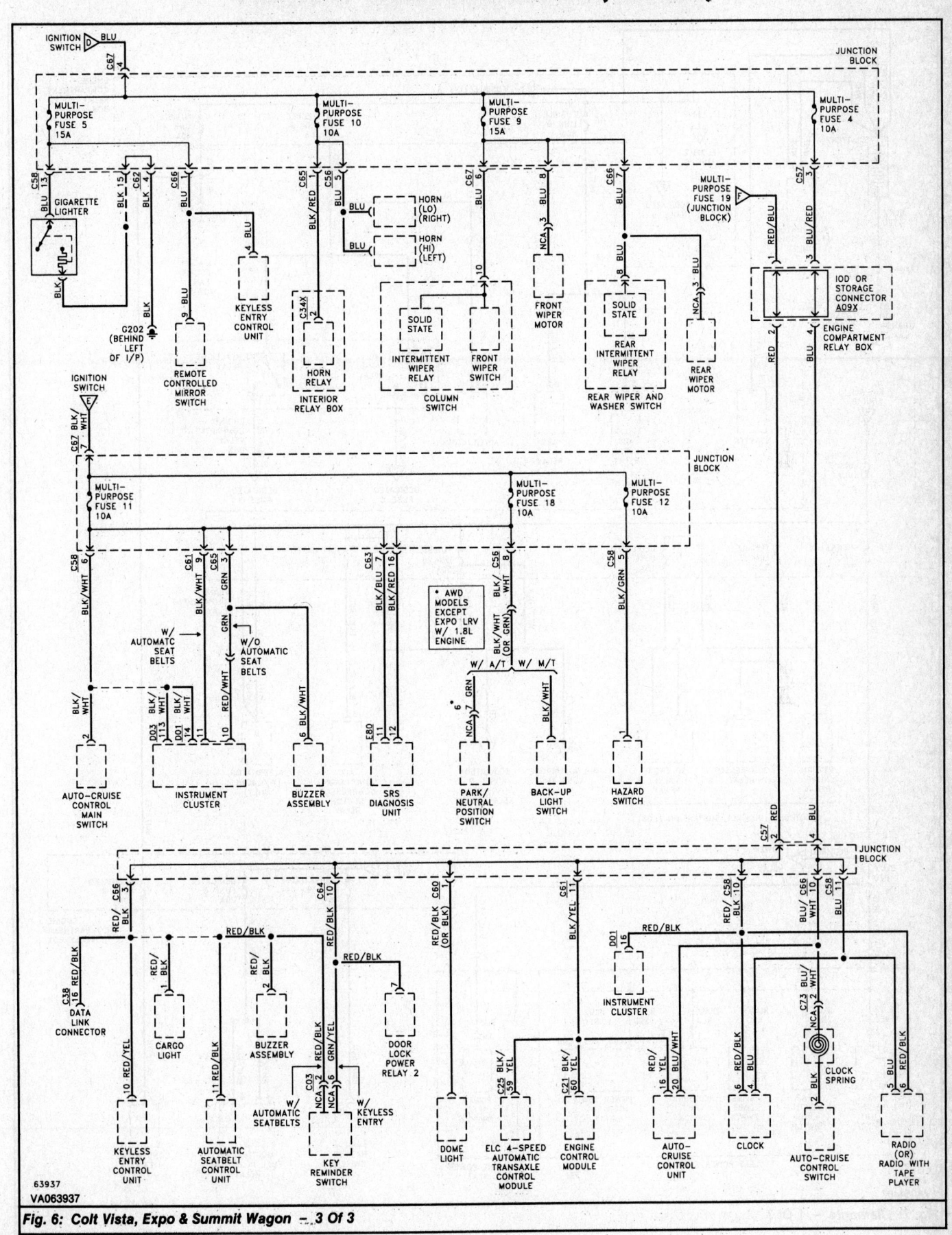

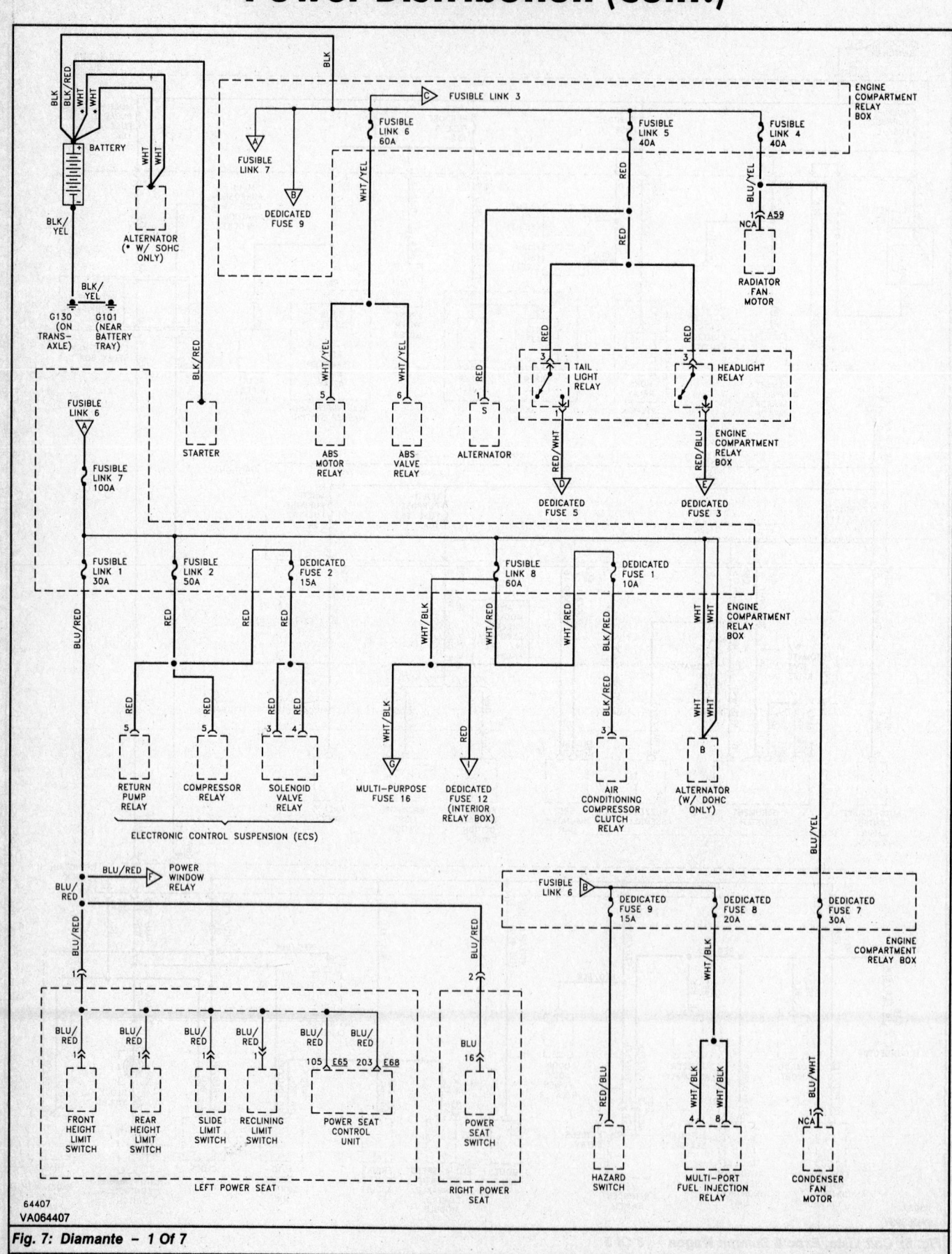

64407
VA064407

Fig. 7: Diamante - 1 Of 7

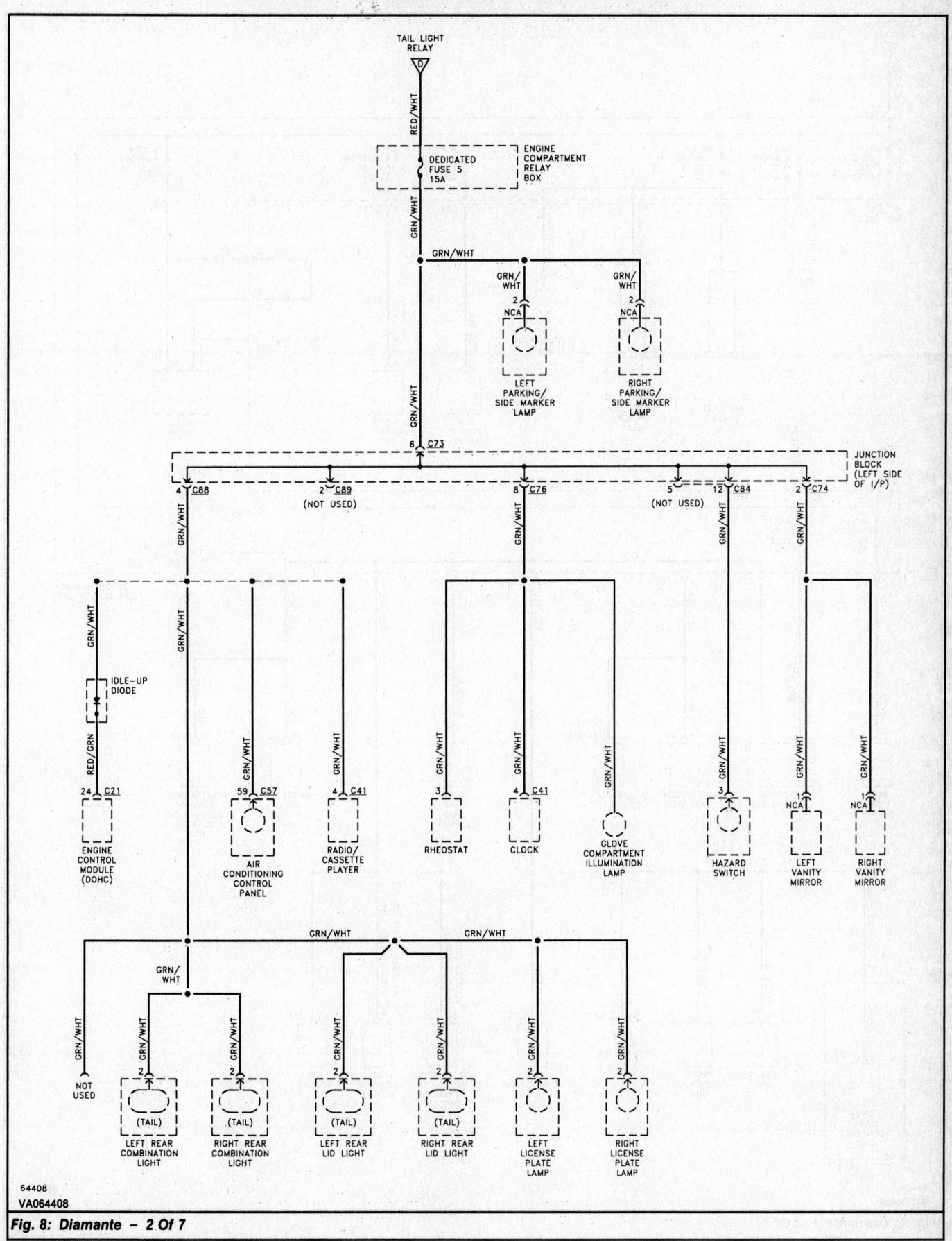

64408

VA064408

Fig. 8: Diamante - 2 Of 7

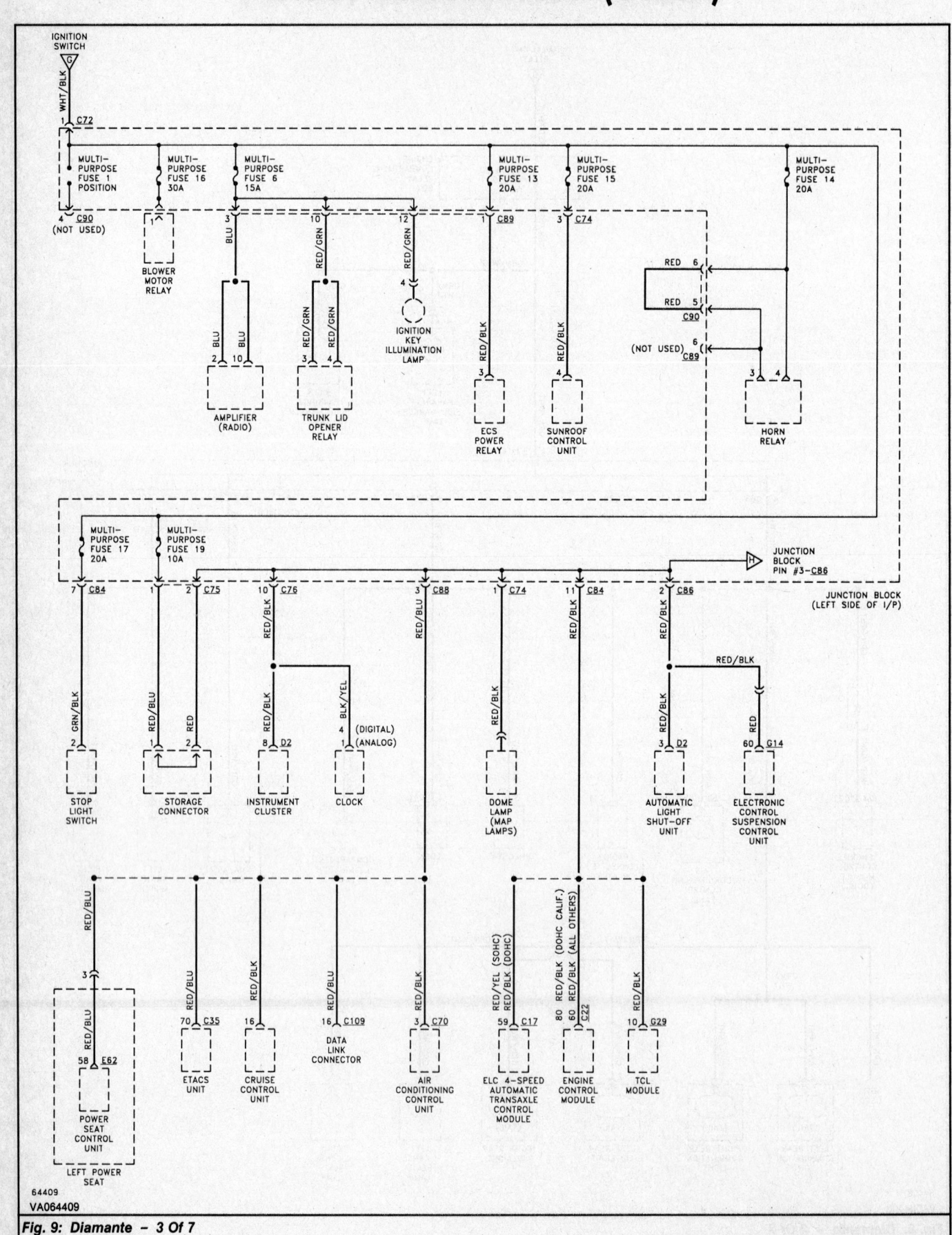

64409

VA064409

Fig. 9: Diamante – 3 Of 7

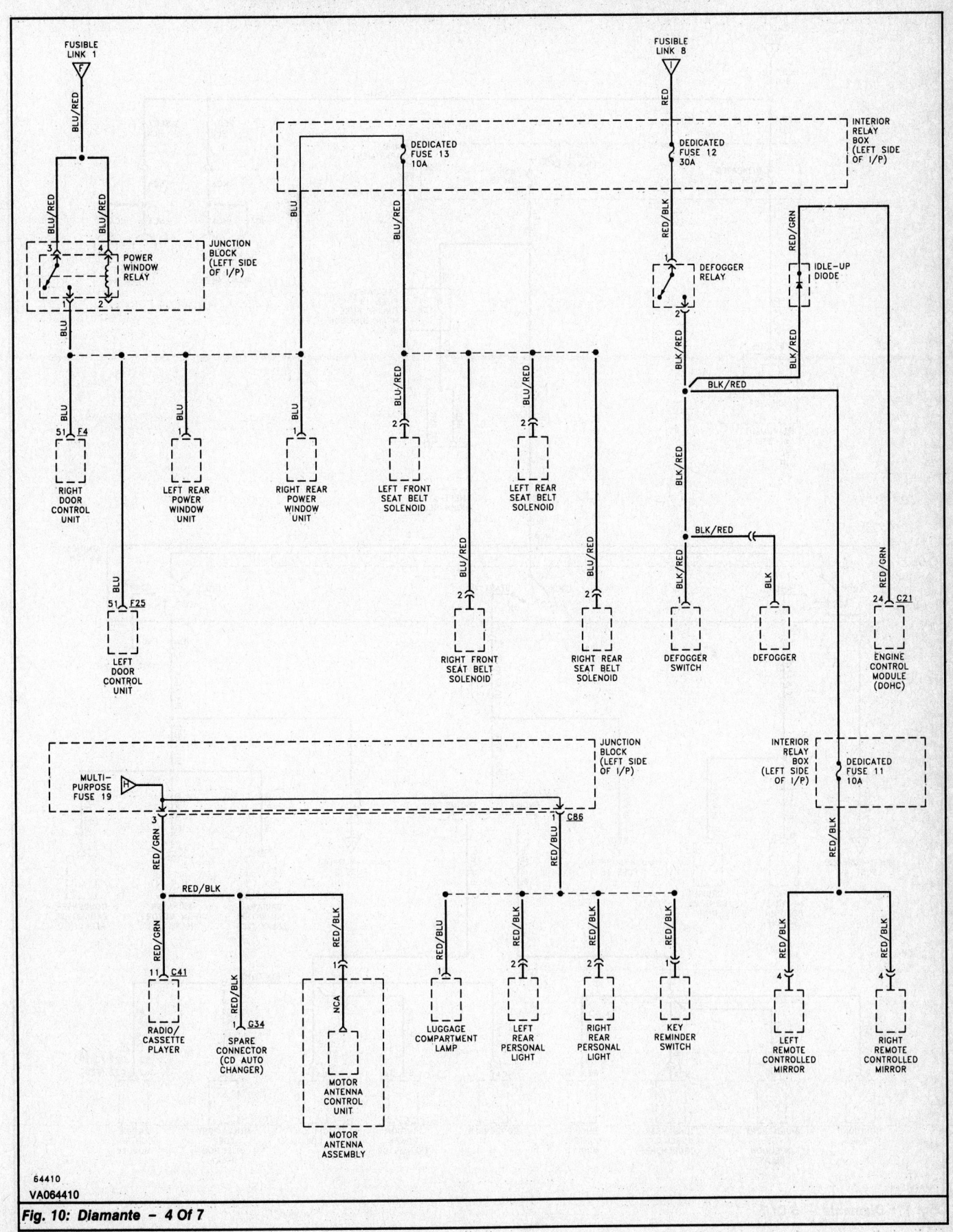

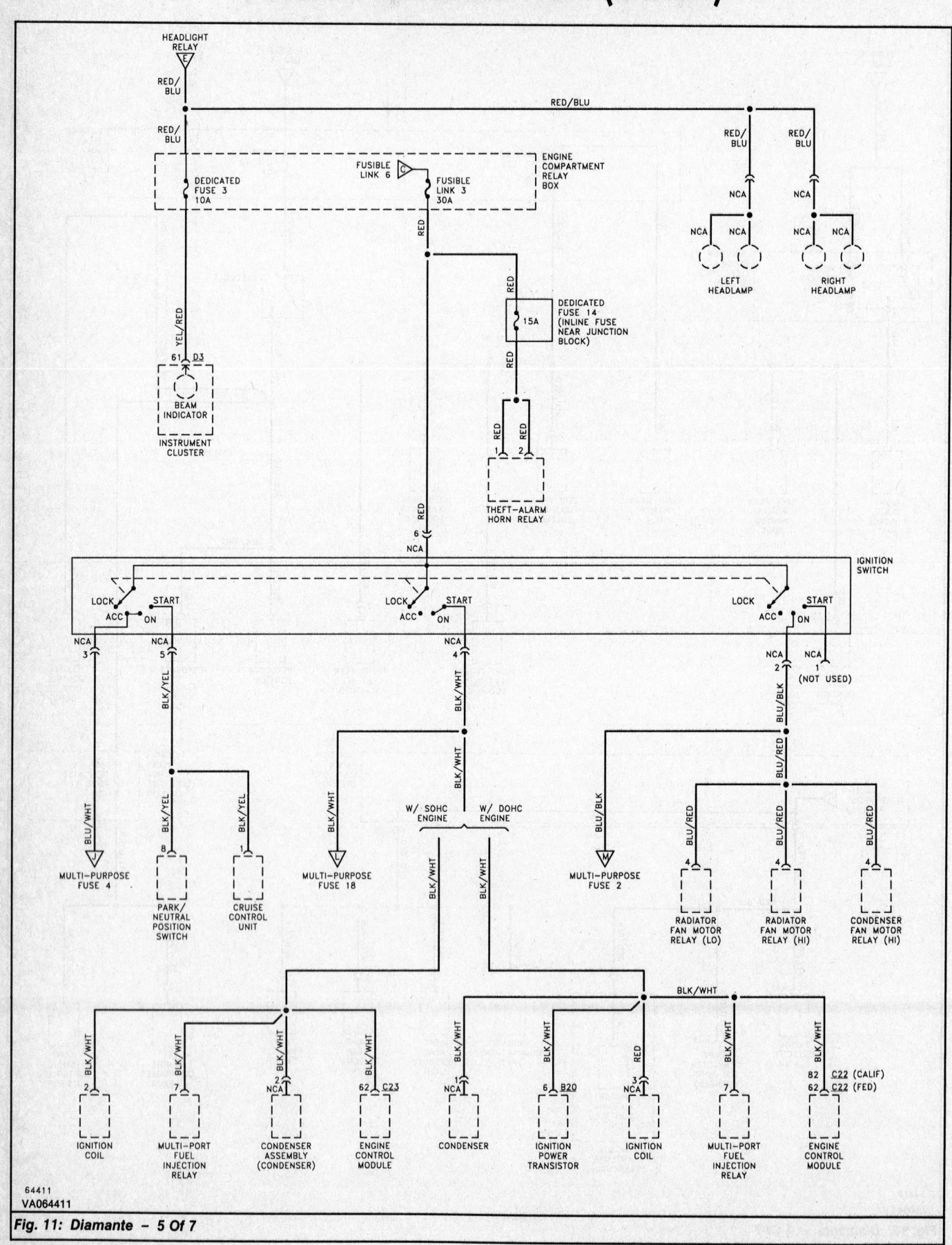

64411
VA064411

Fig. 11: Diamante – 5 Of 7

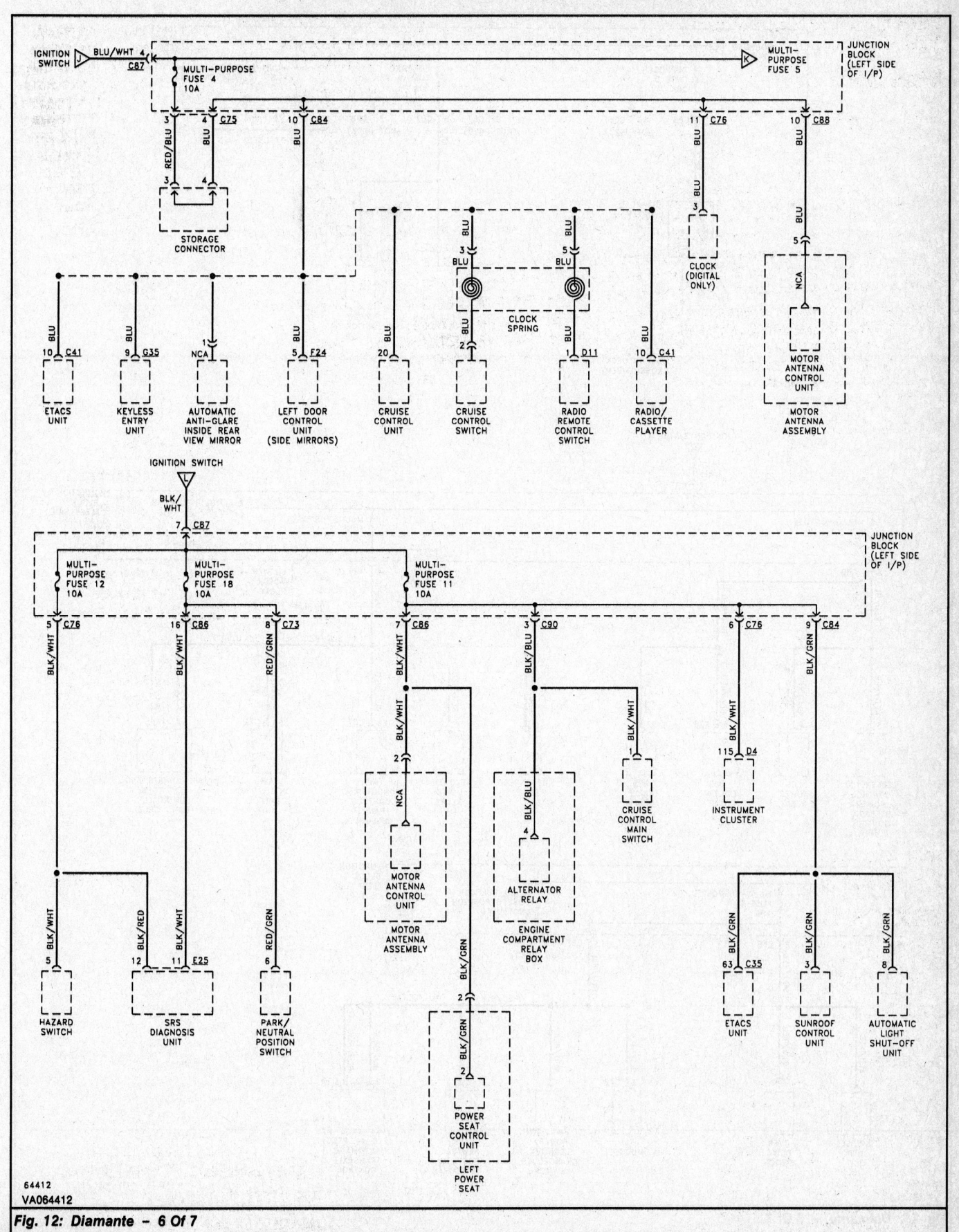

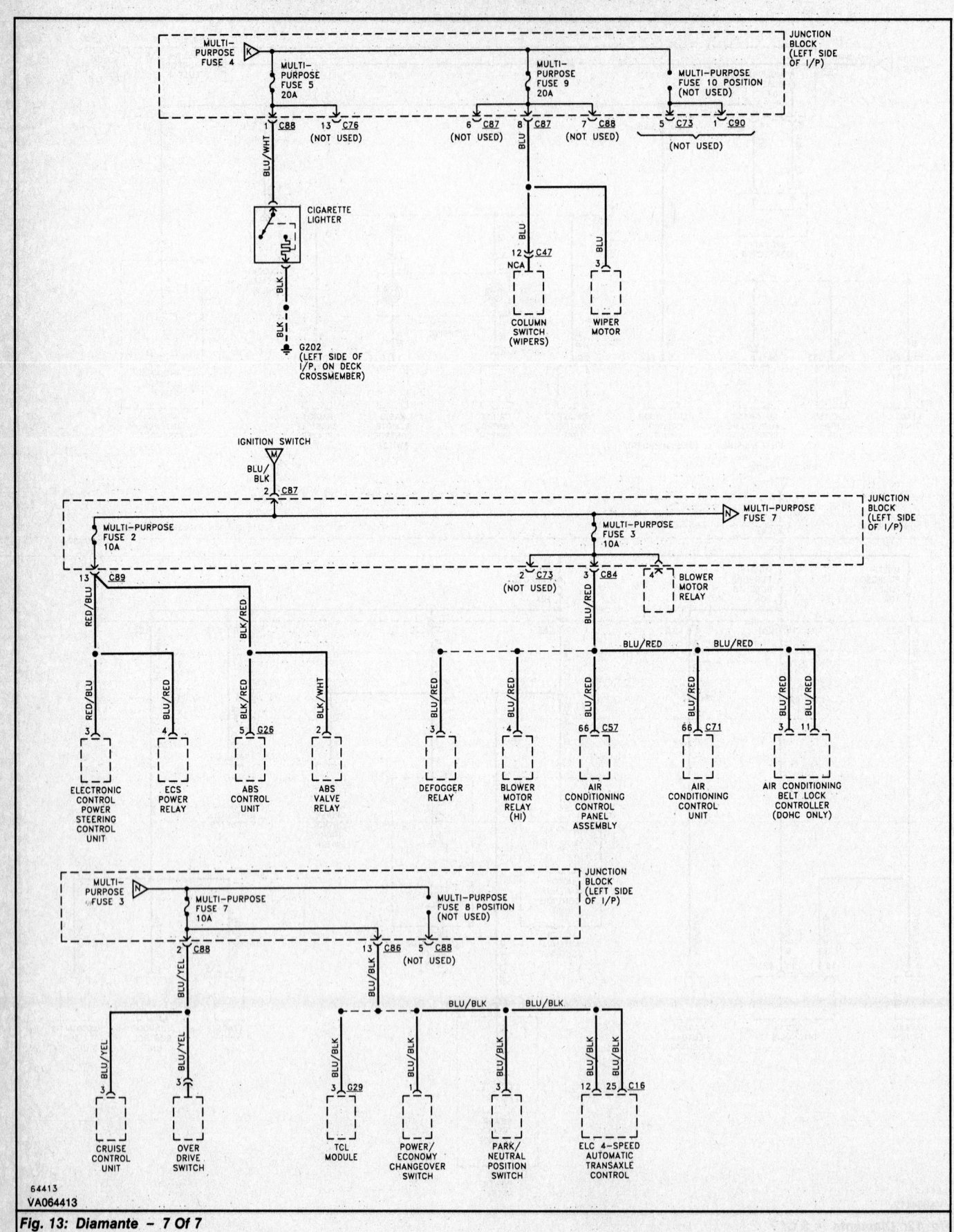

64413
VA064413

Fig. 13: Diamante – 7 Of 7

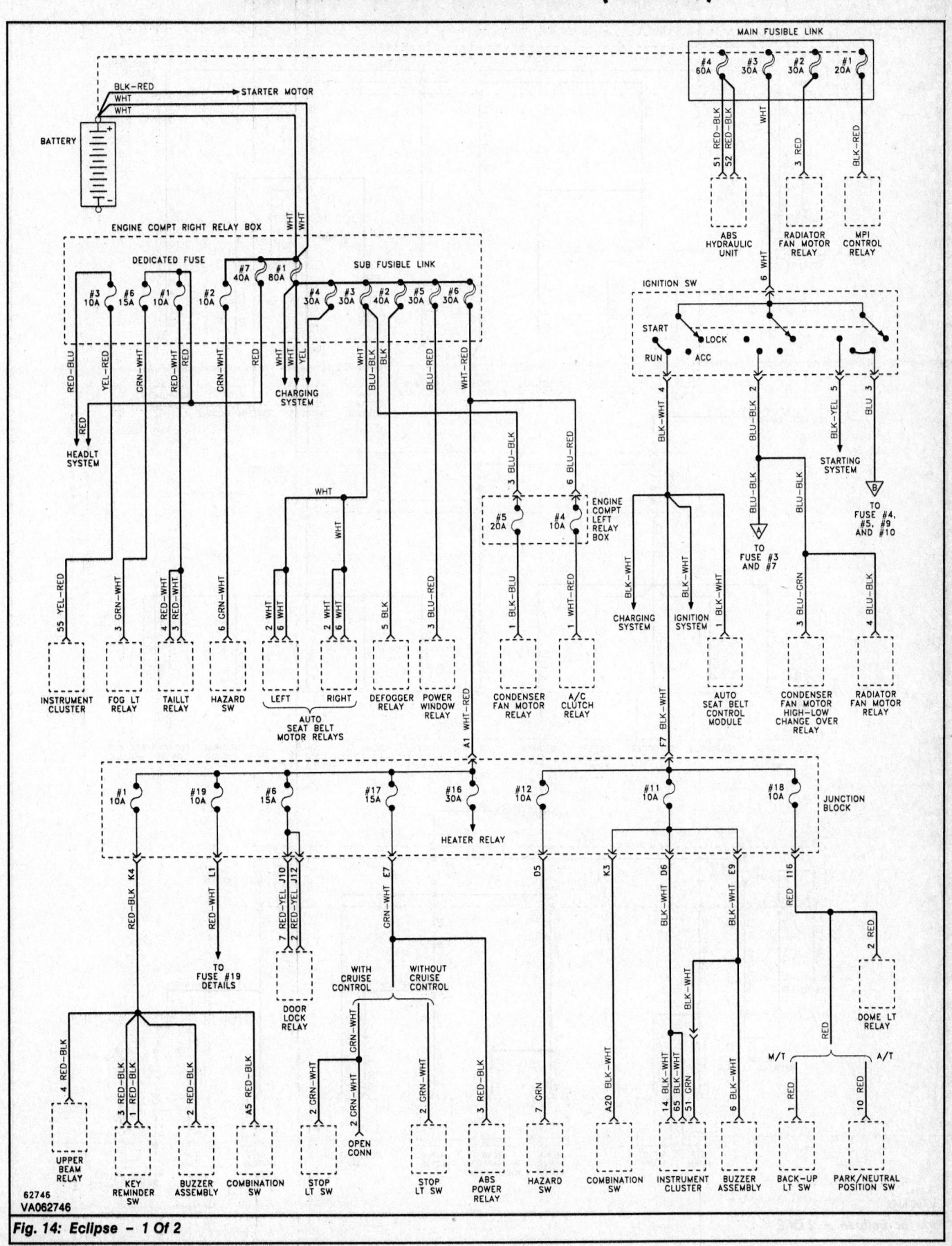

Fig. 14: Eclipse – 1 Of 2

62746
VA062746

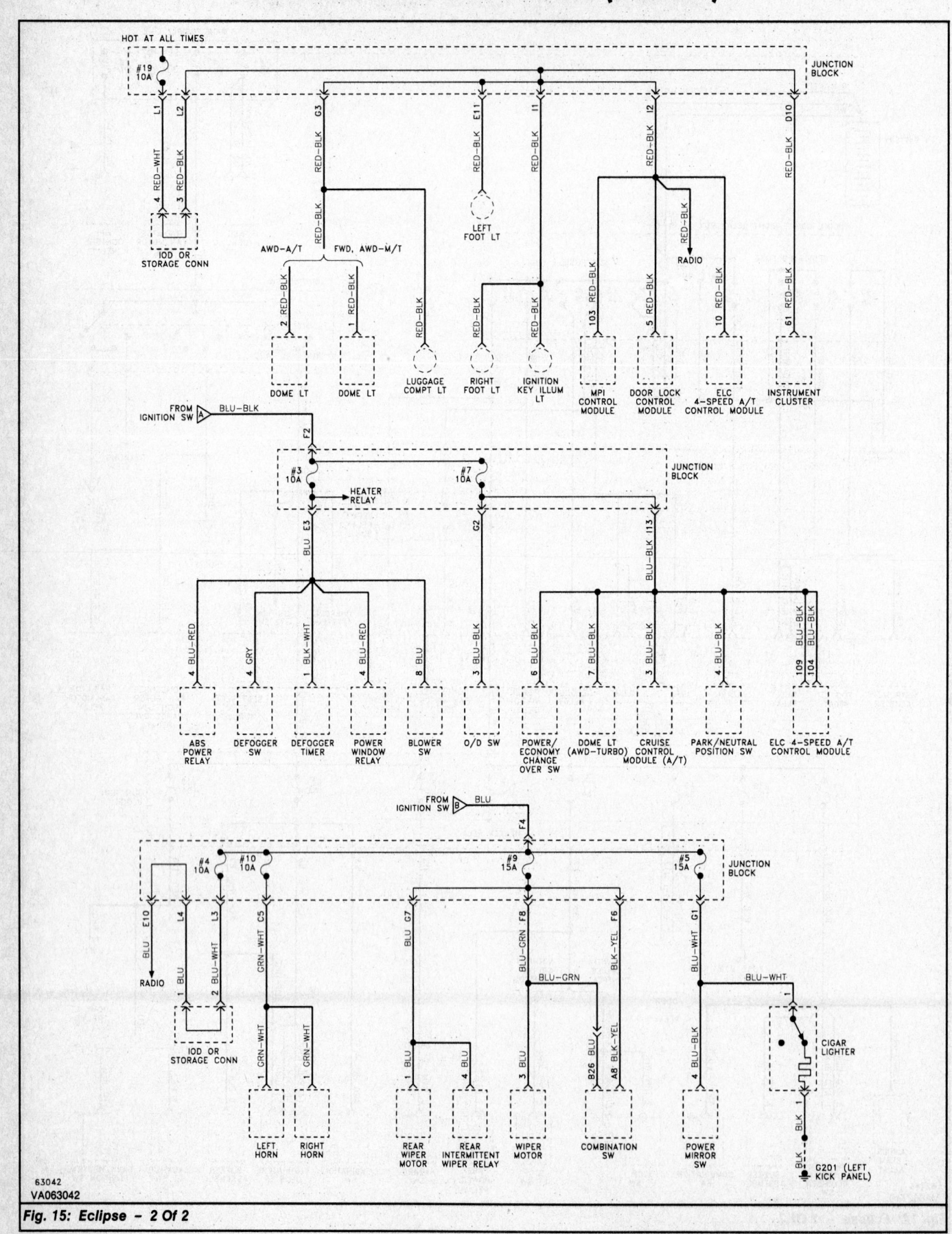

63042
VA063042

Fig. 15: Eclipse - 2 Of 2

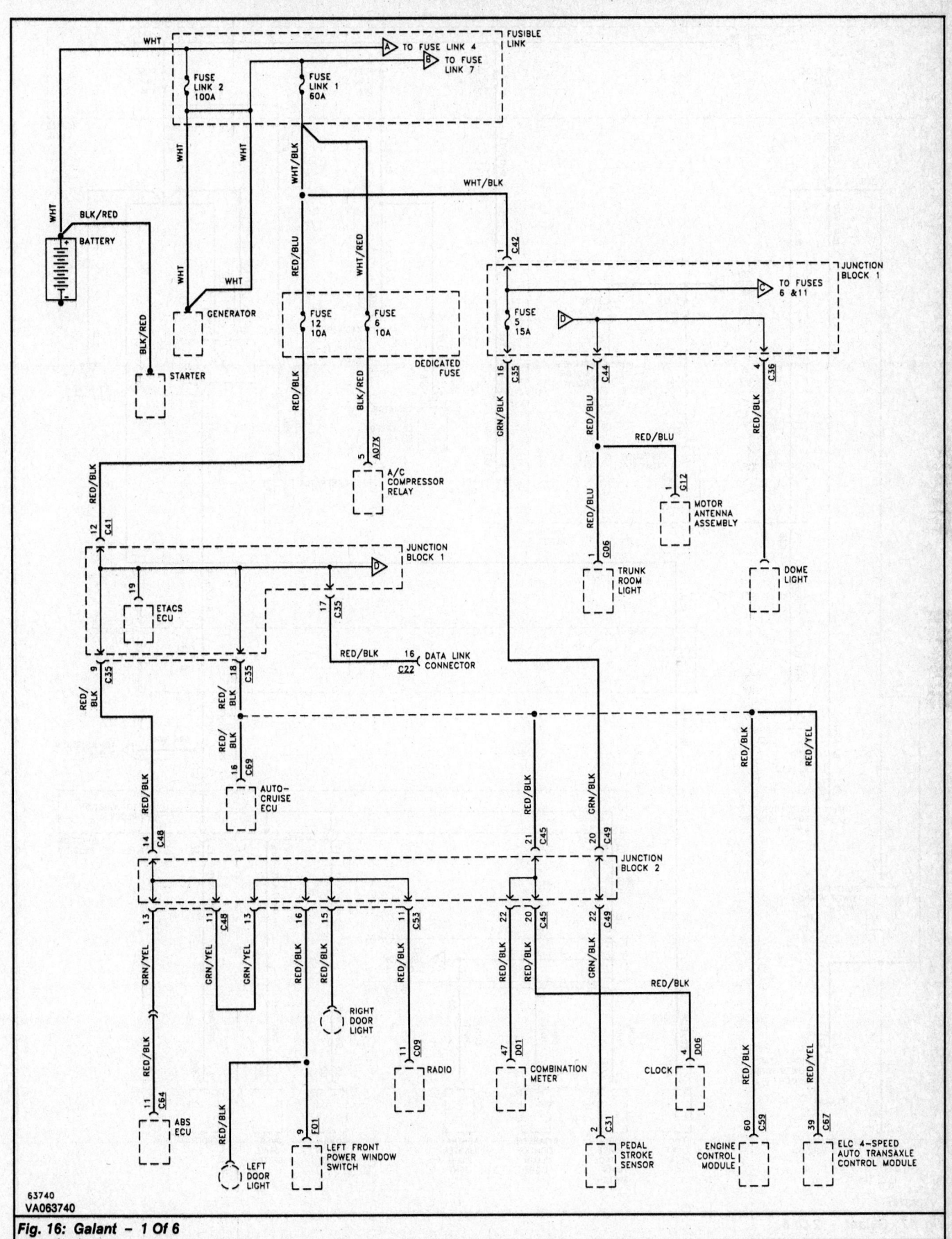

63740
VA063740

Fig. 16: Galant – 1 Of 6

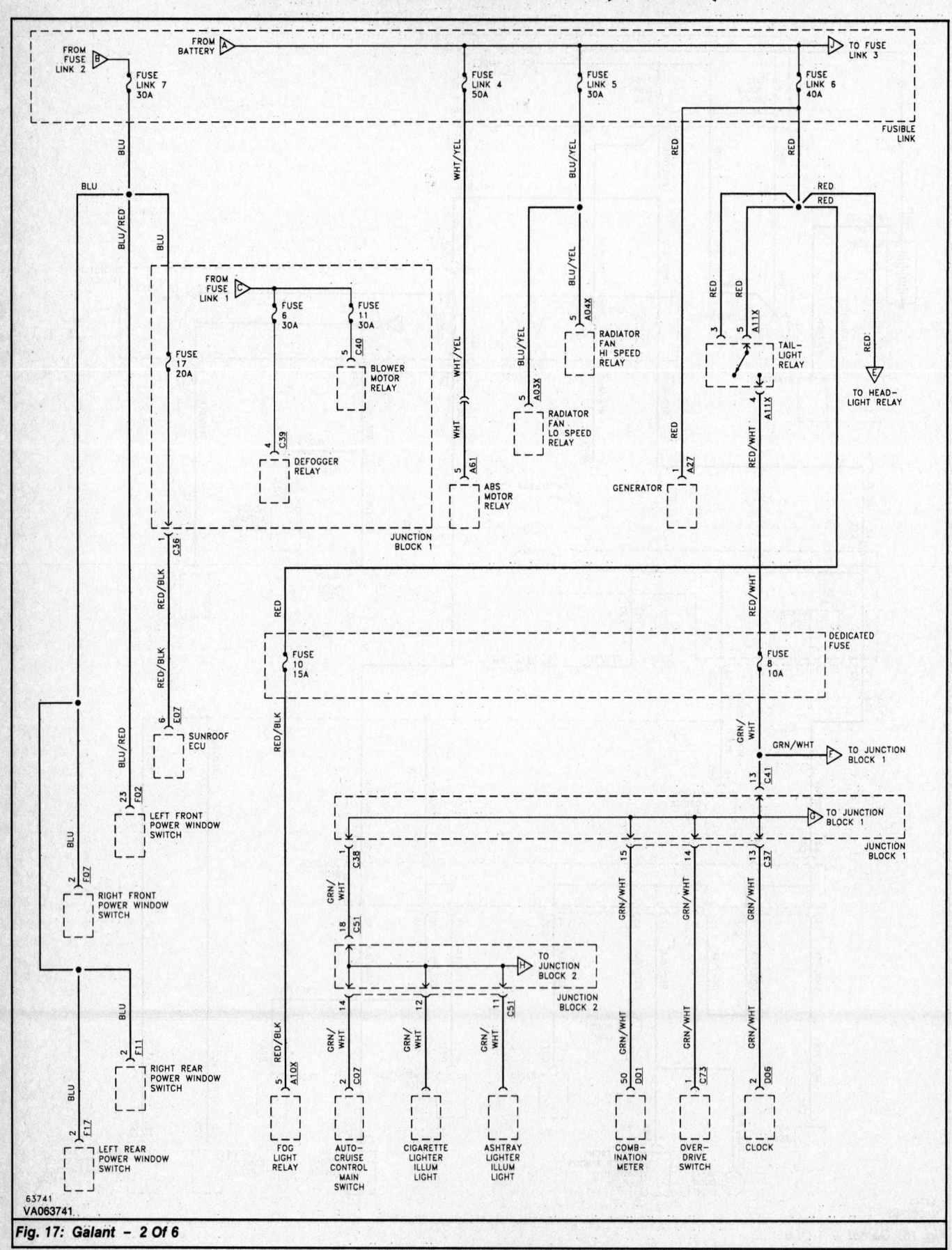

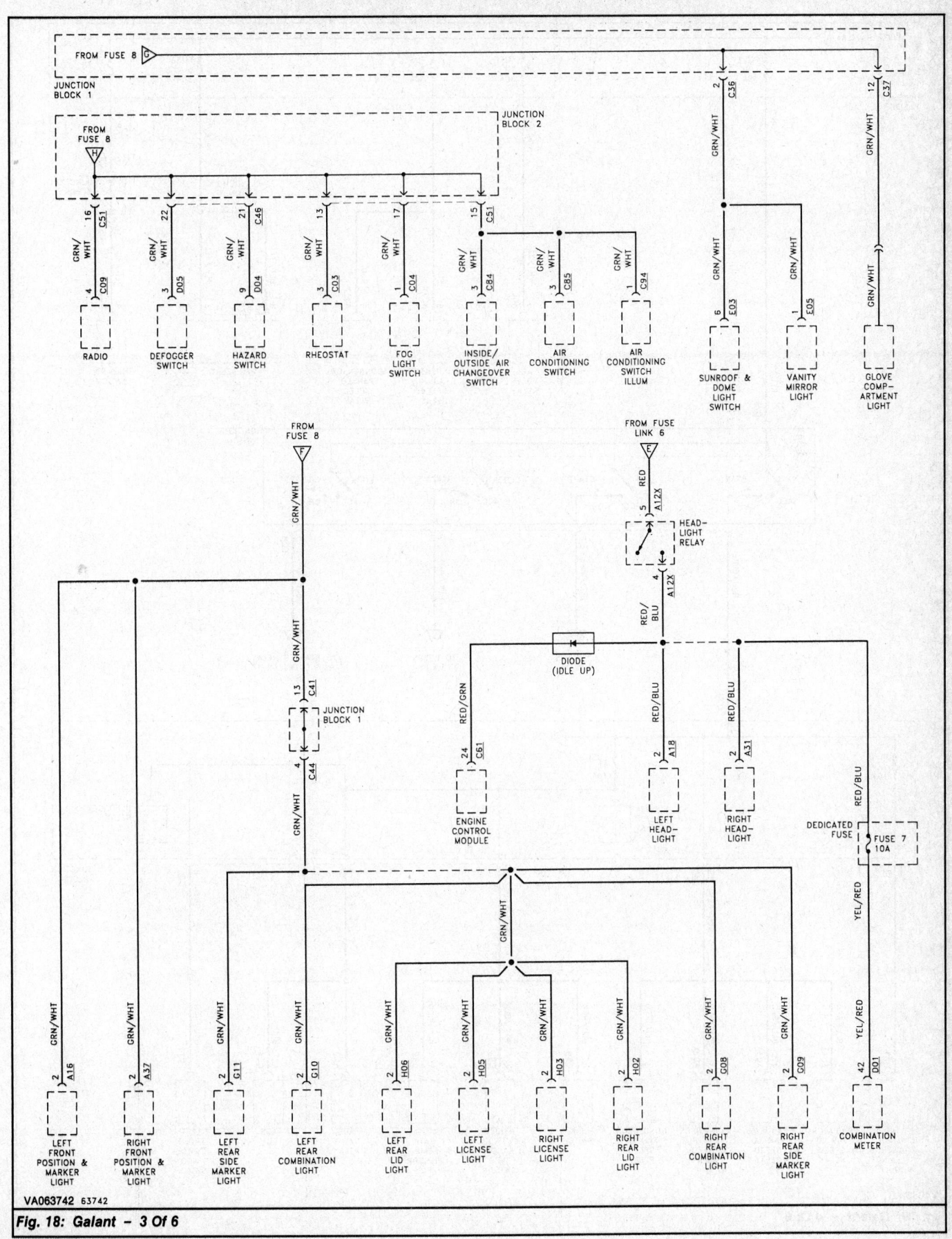

Fig. 18: Galant – 3 Of 6

VA063742 63742

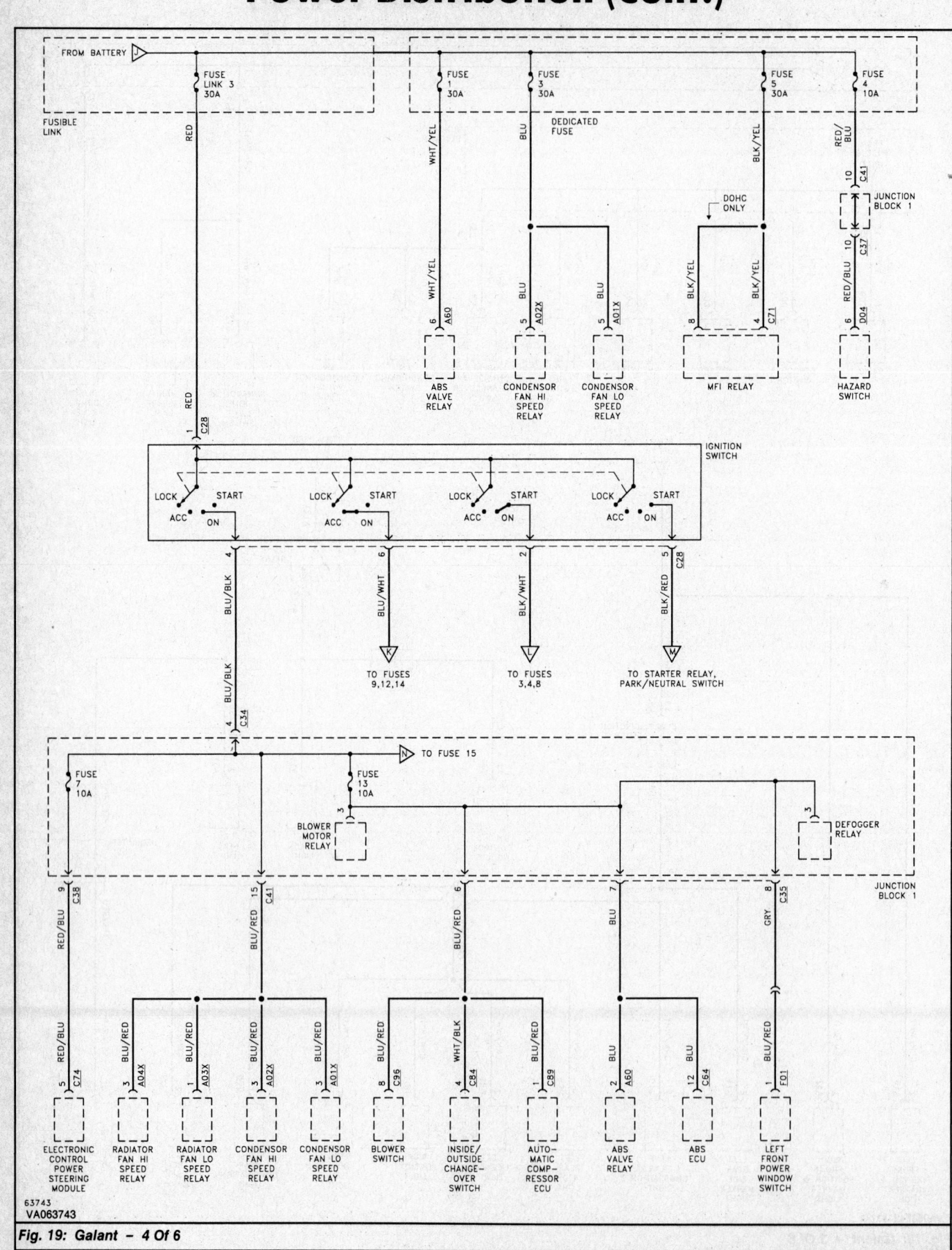

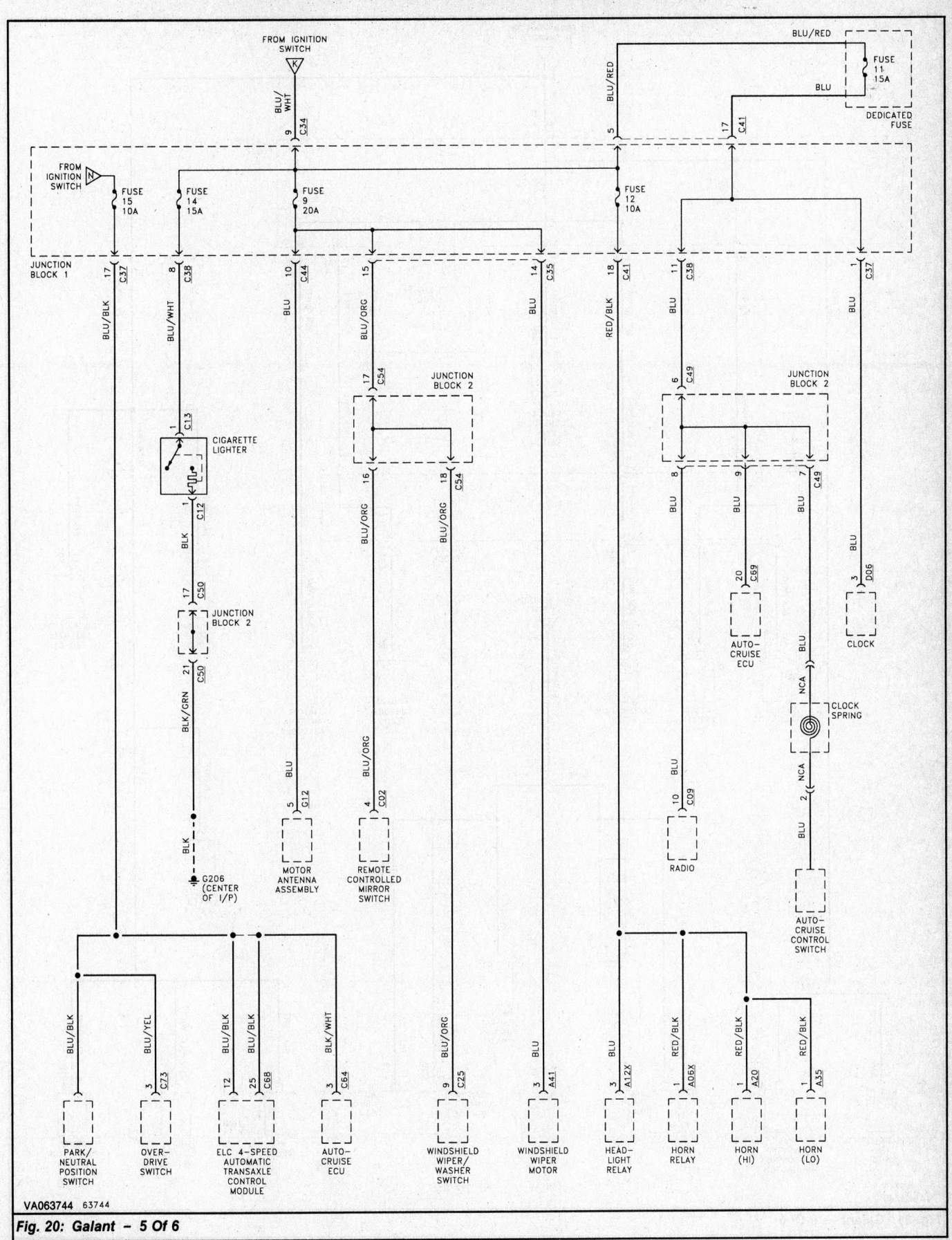

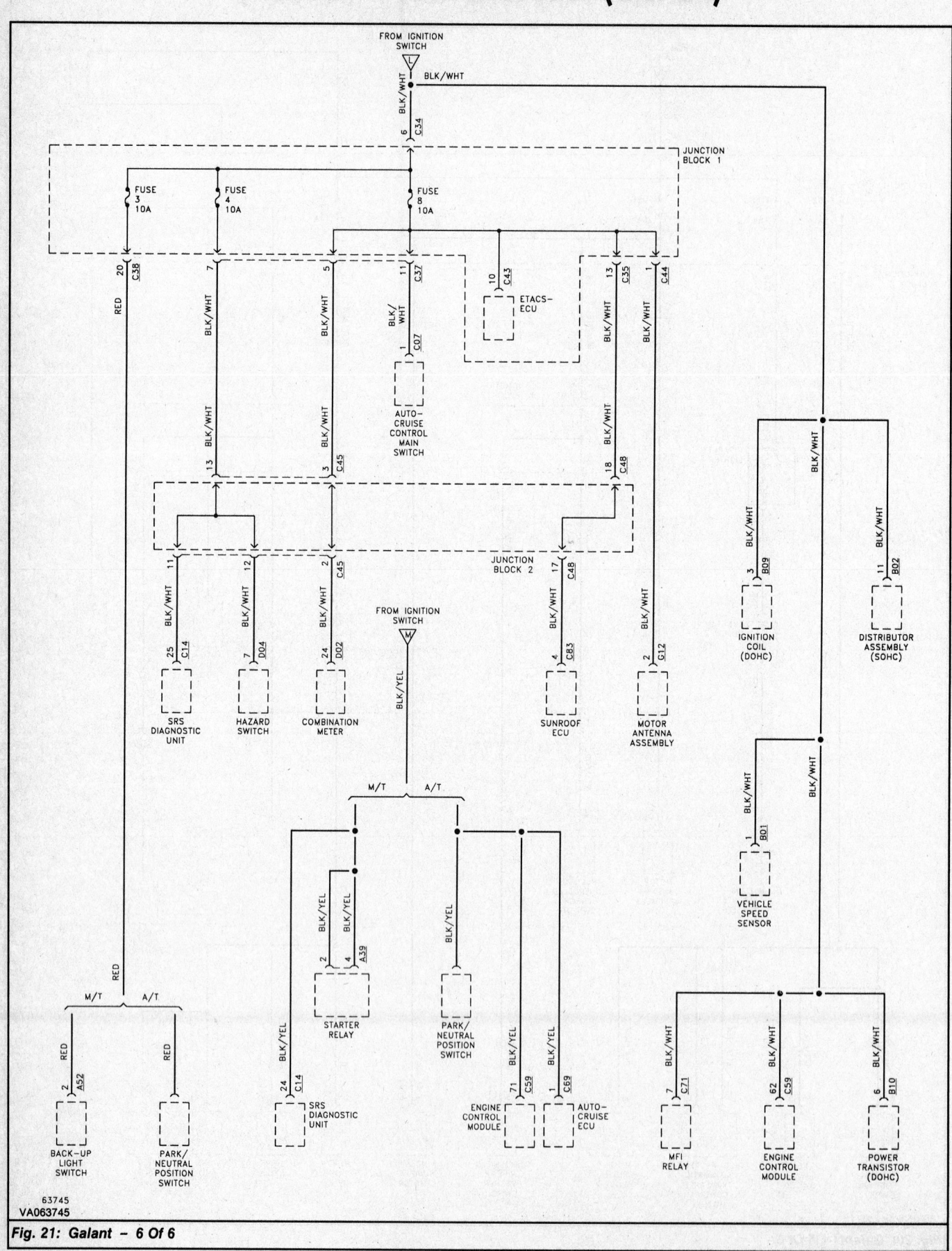

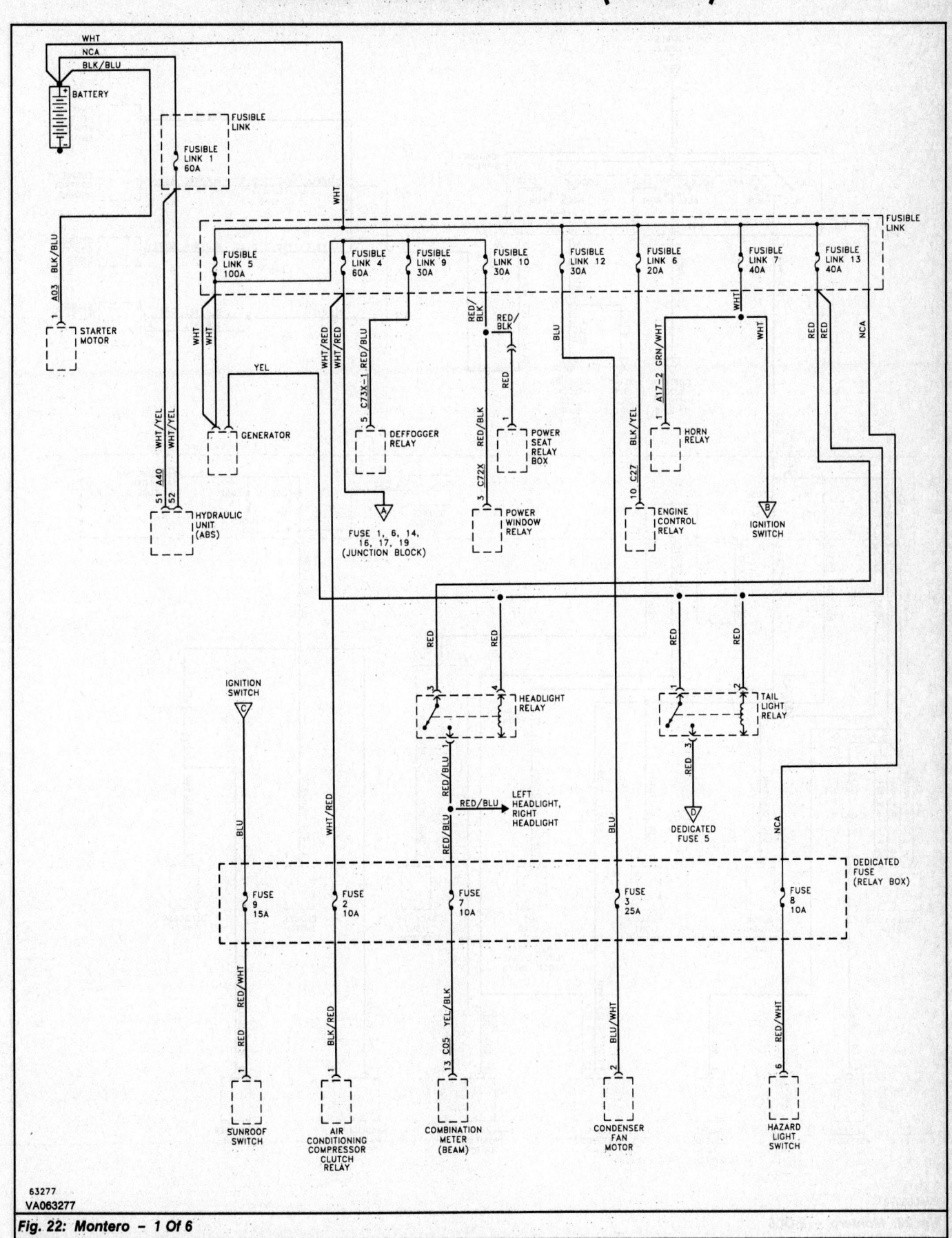

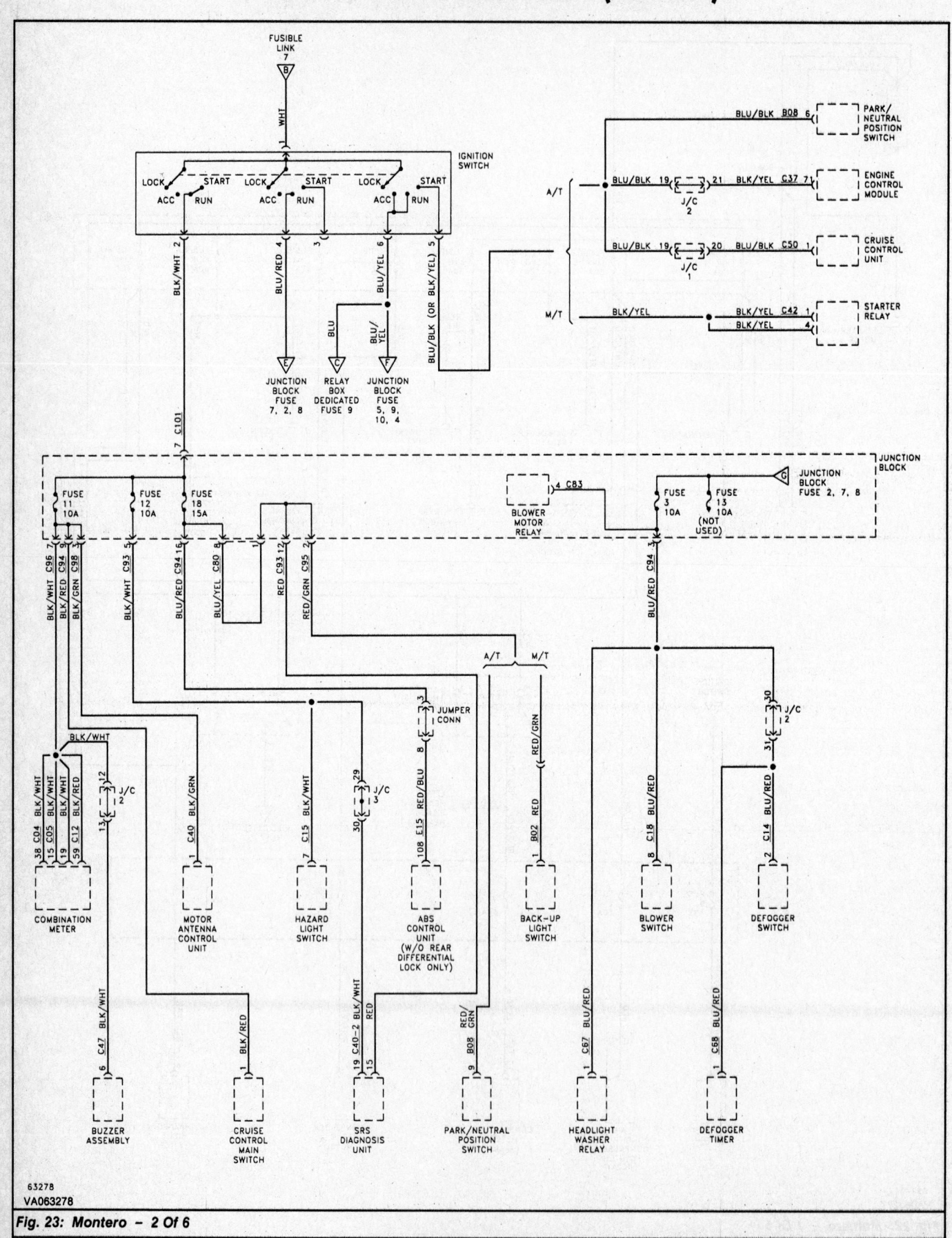

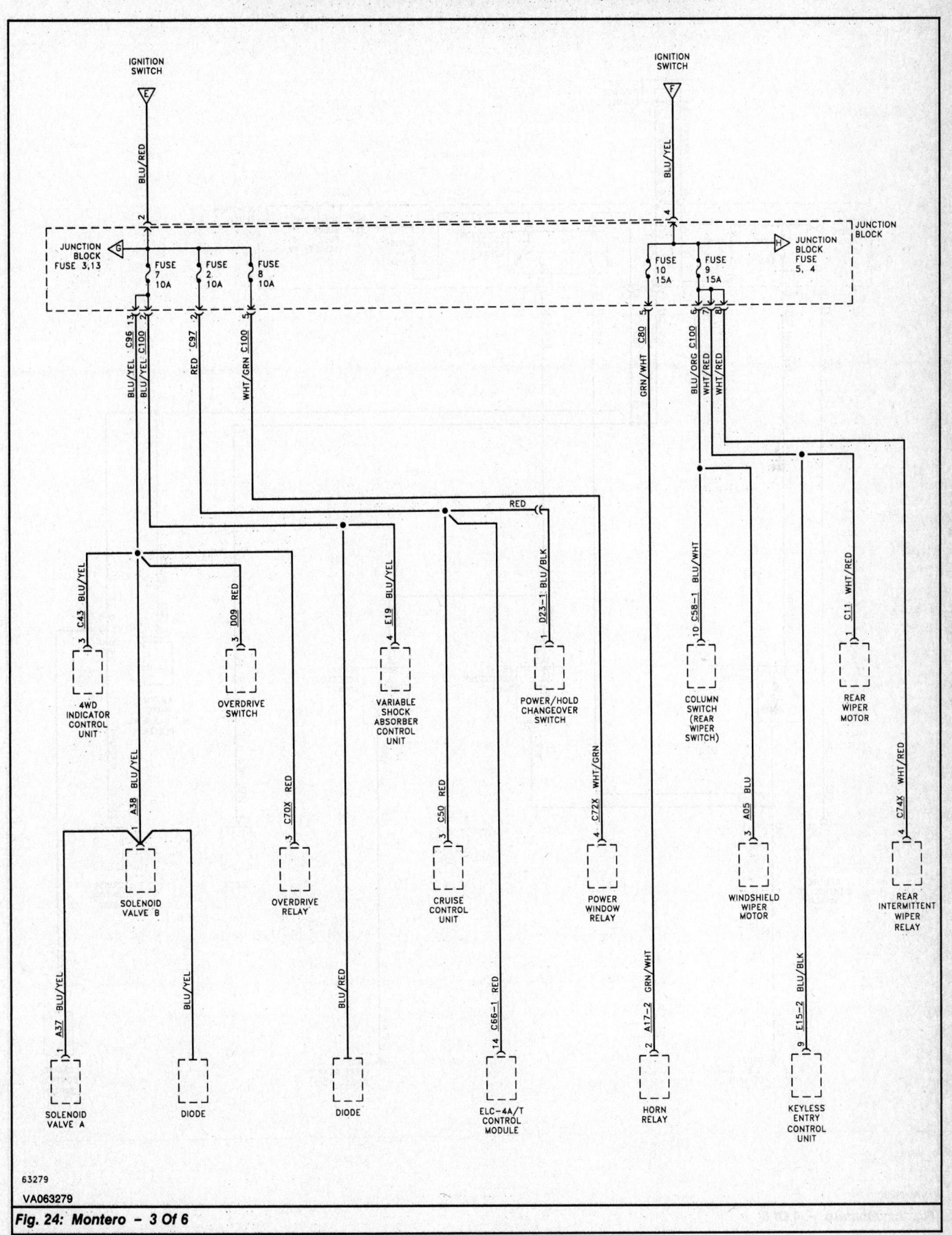

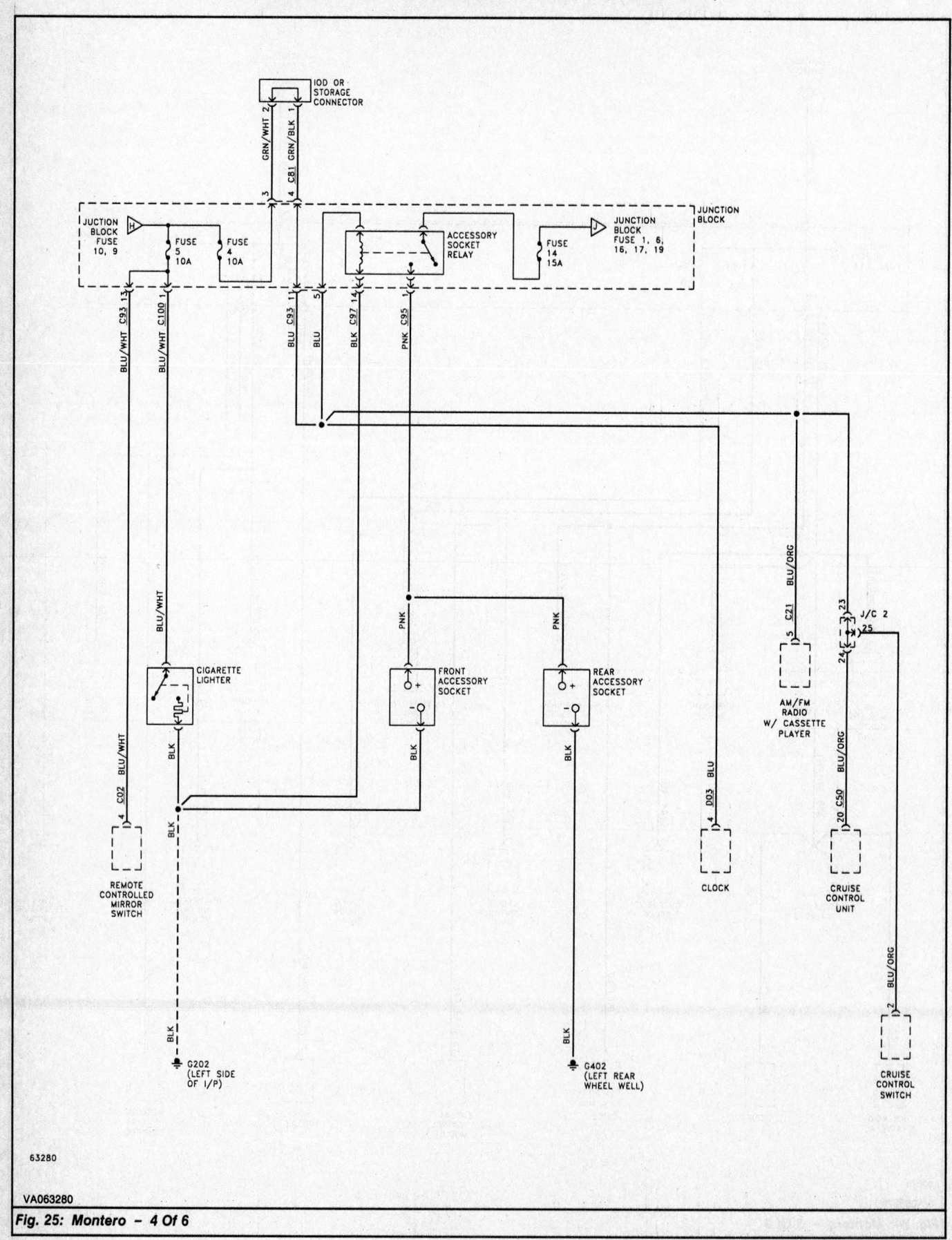

63280

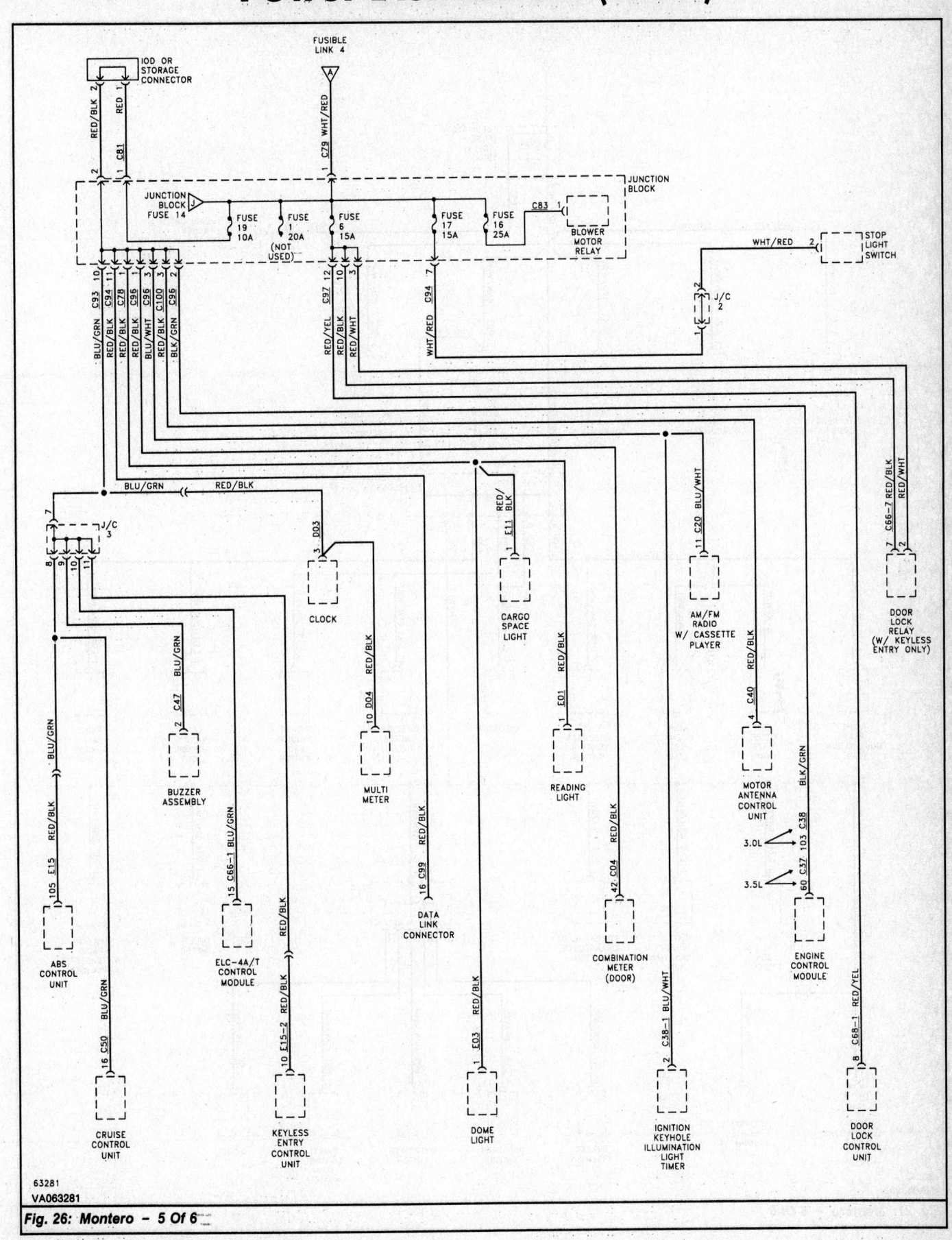

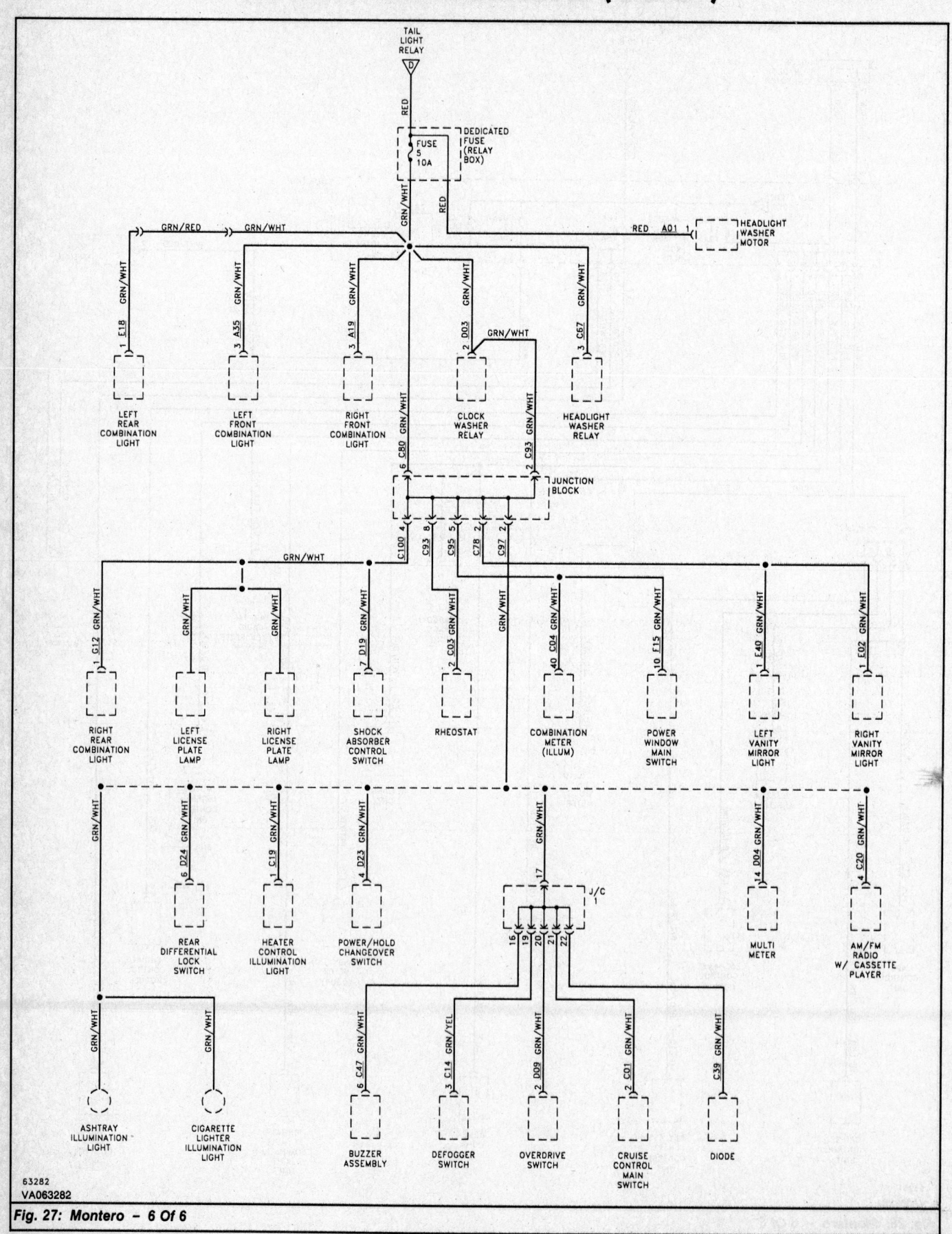

Fig. 27: Montero – 6 Of 6

63282
VA063282

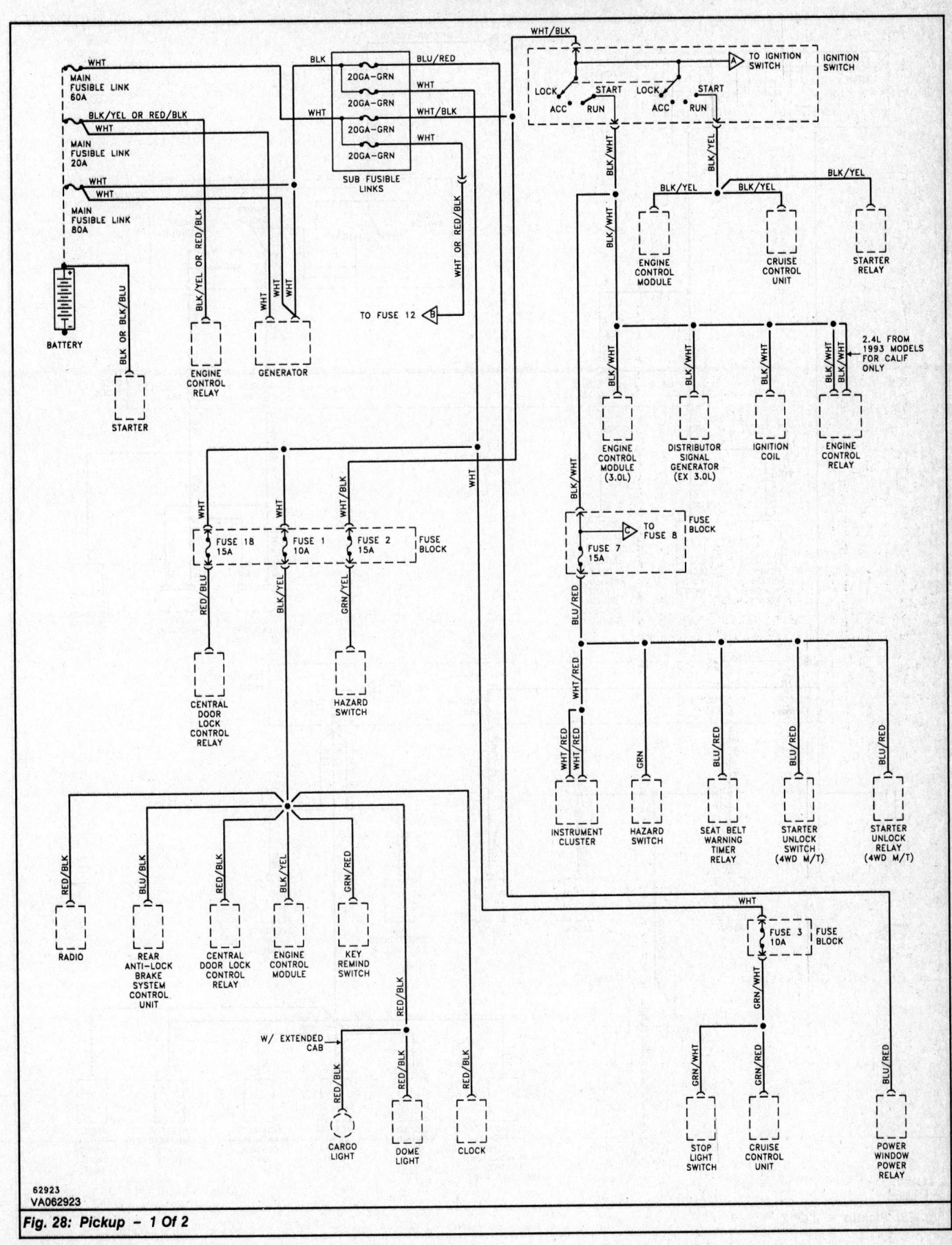

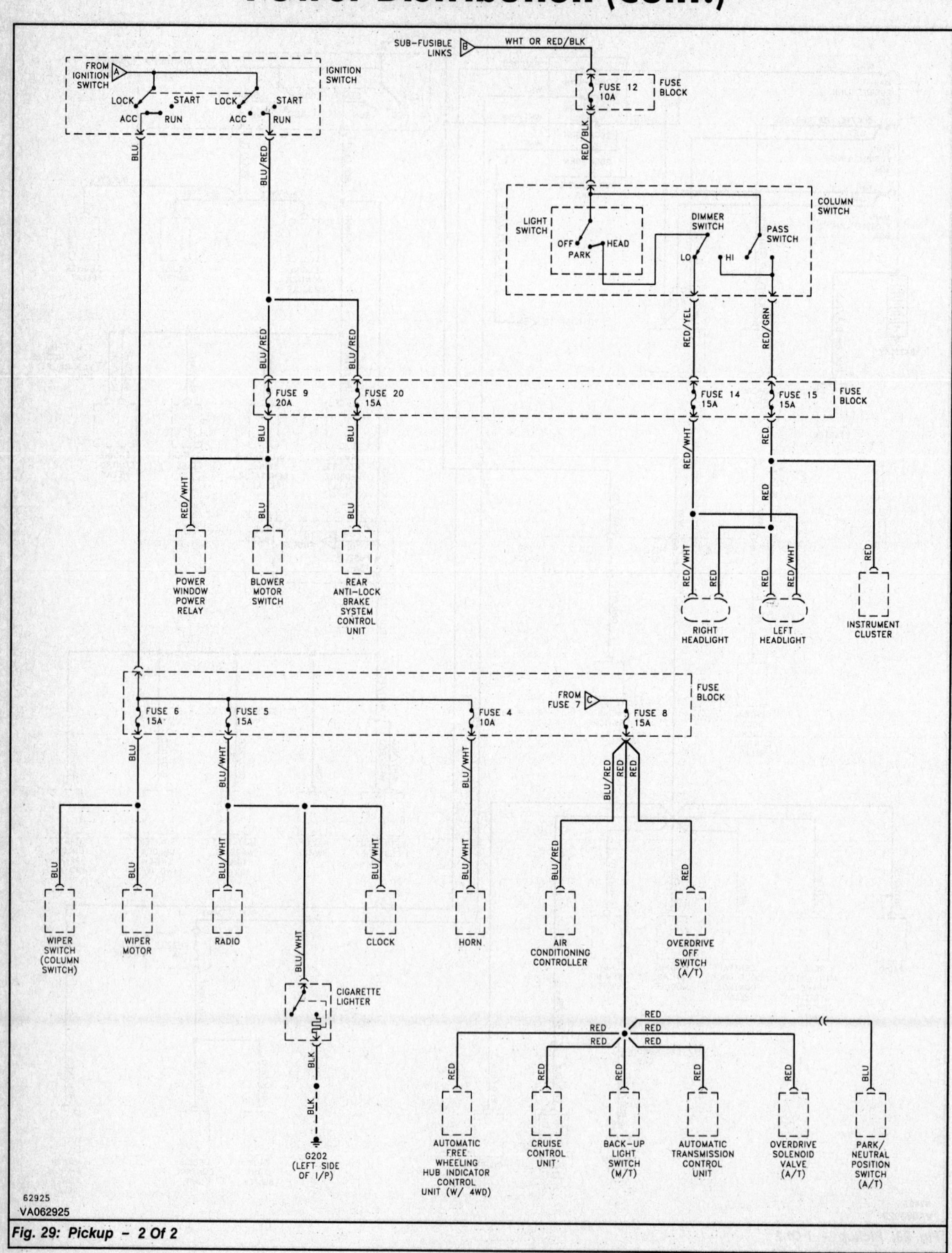

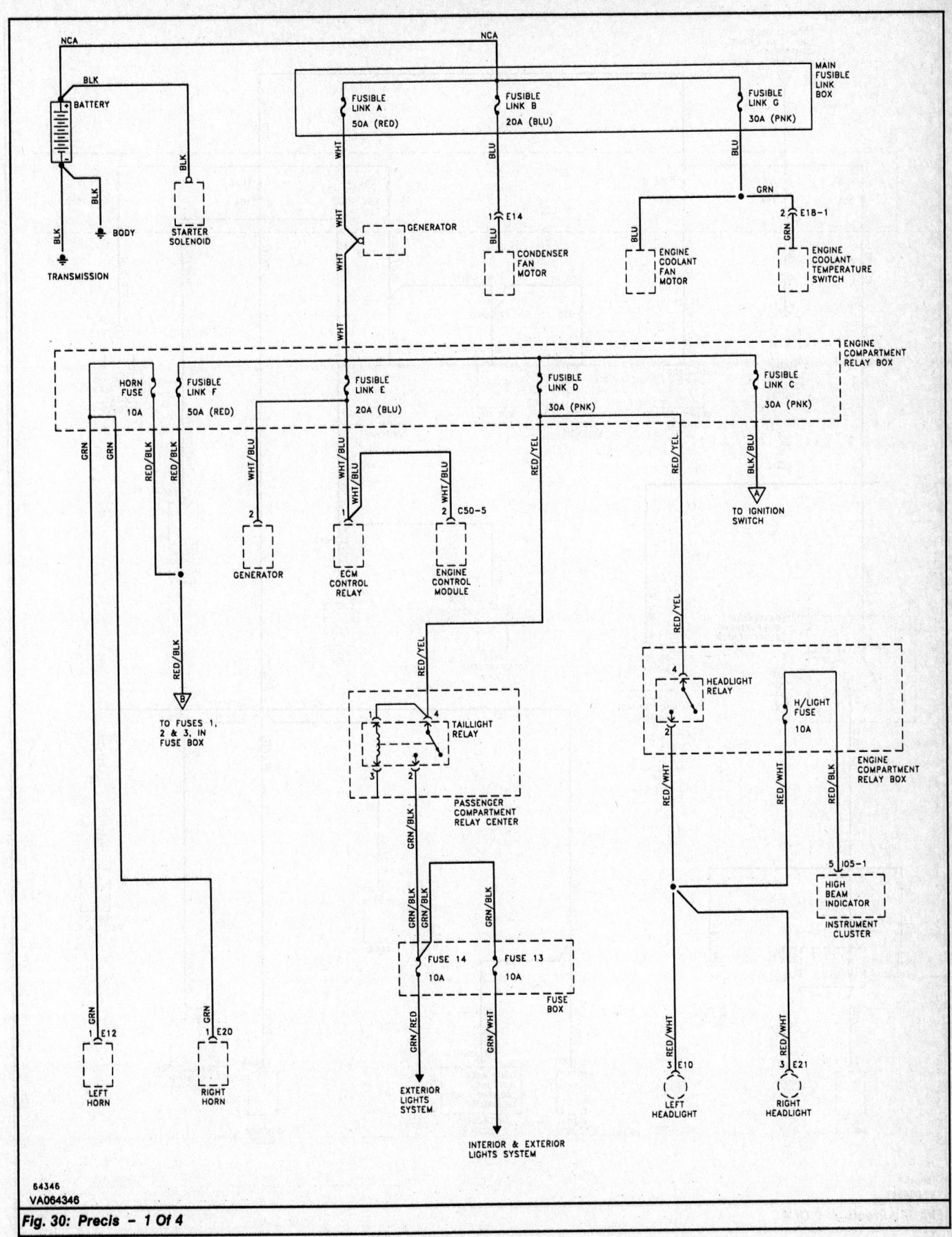

64346
VA064346

Fig. 30: Precis - 1 Of 4

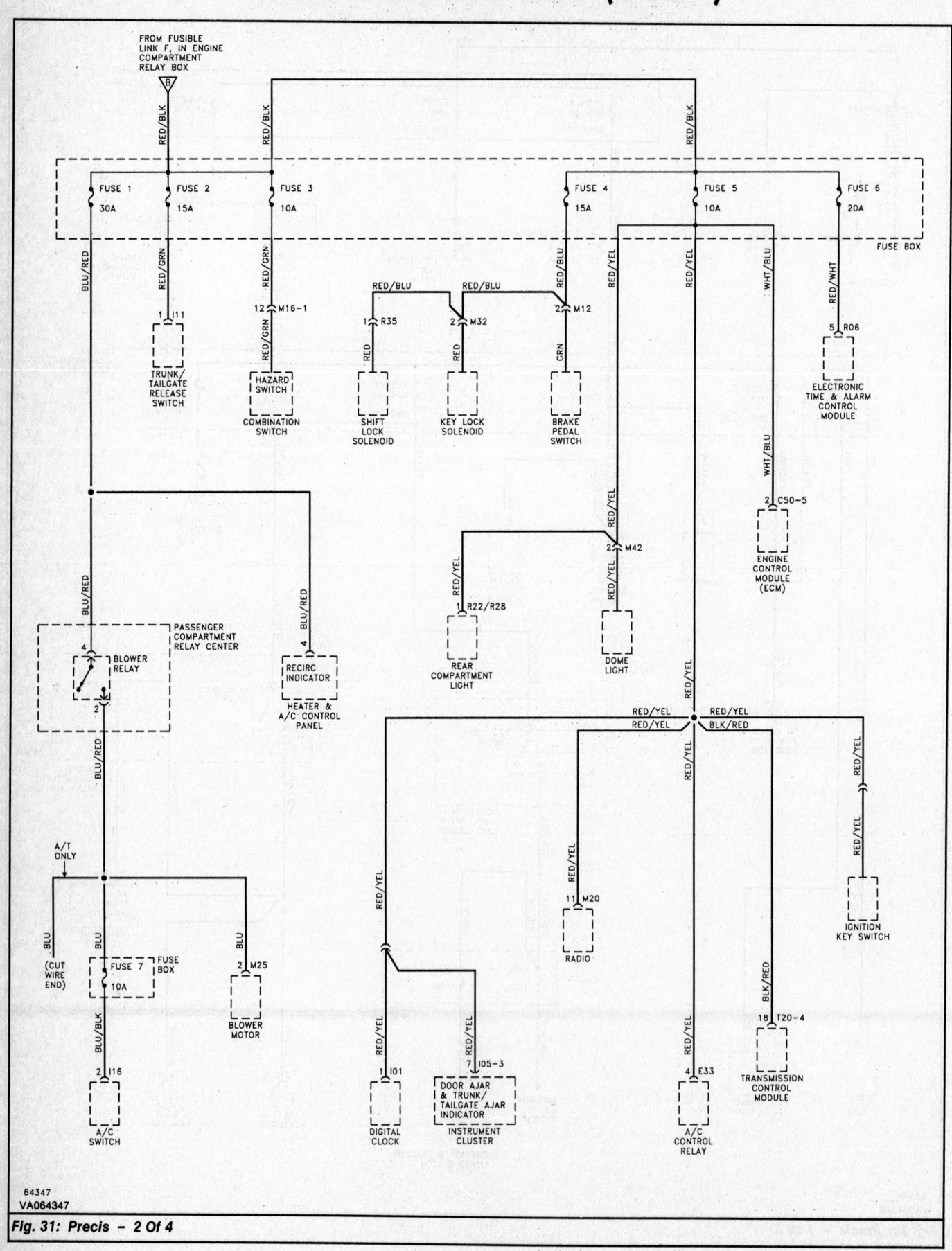

Fig. 31: Precis - 2 Of 4

64347
VA064347

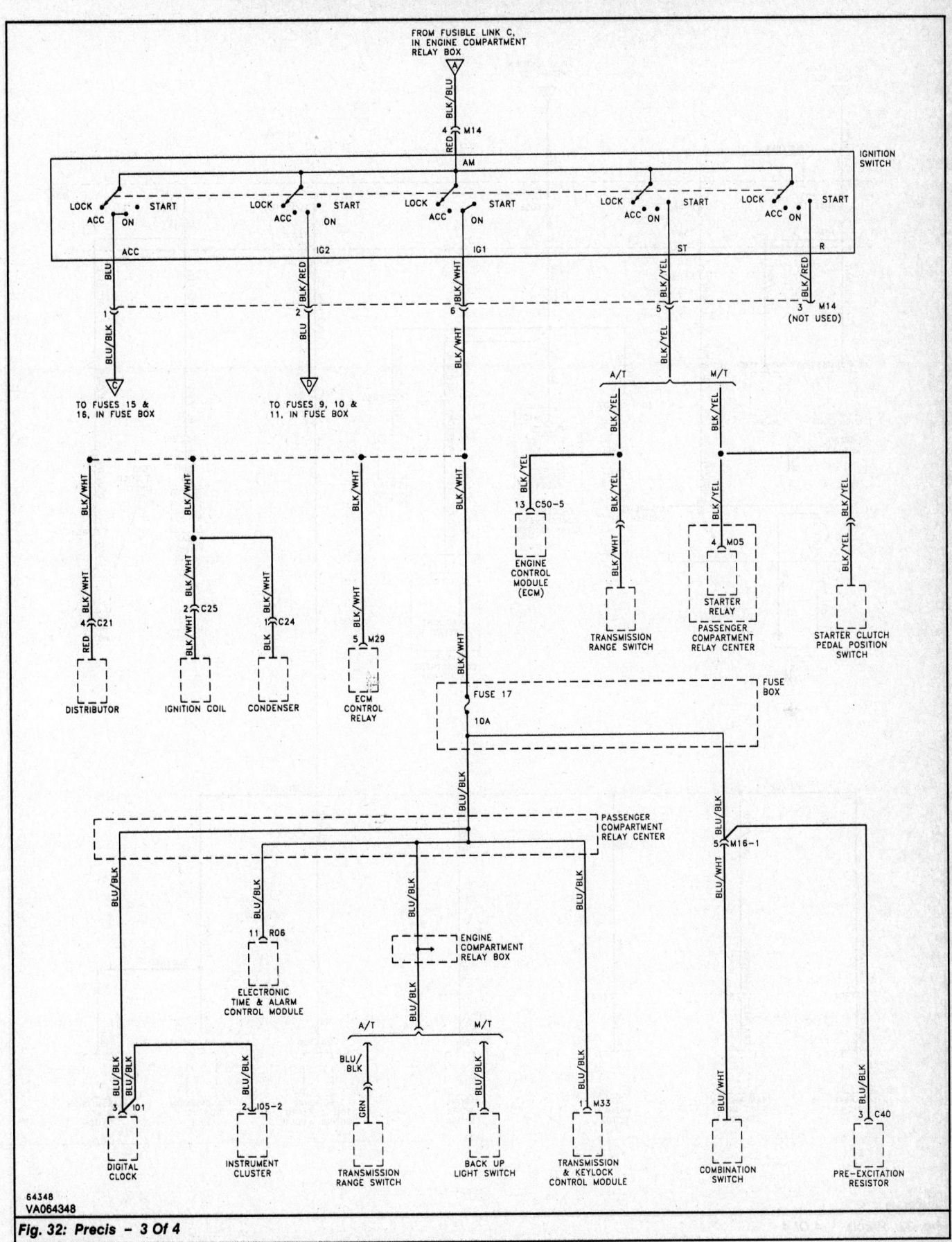

Fig. 32: Precis - 3 Of 4

64348
VA064348

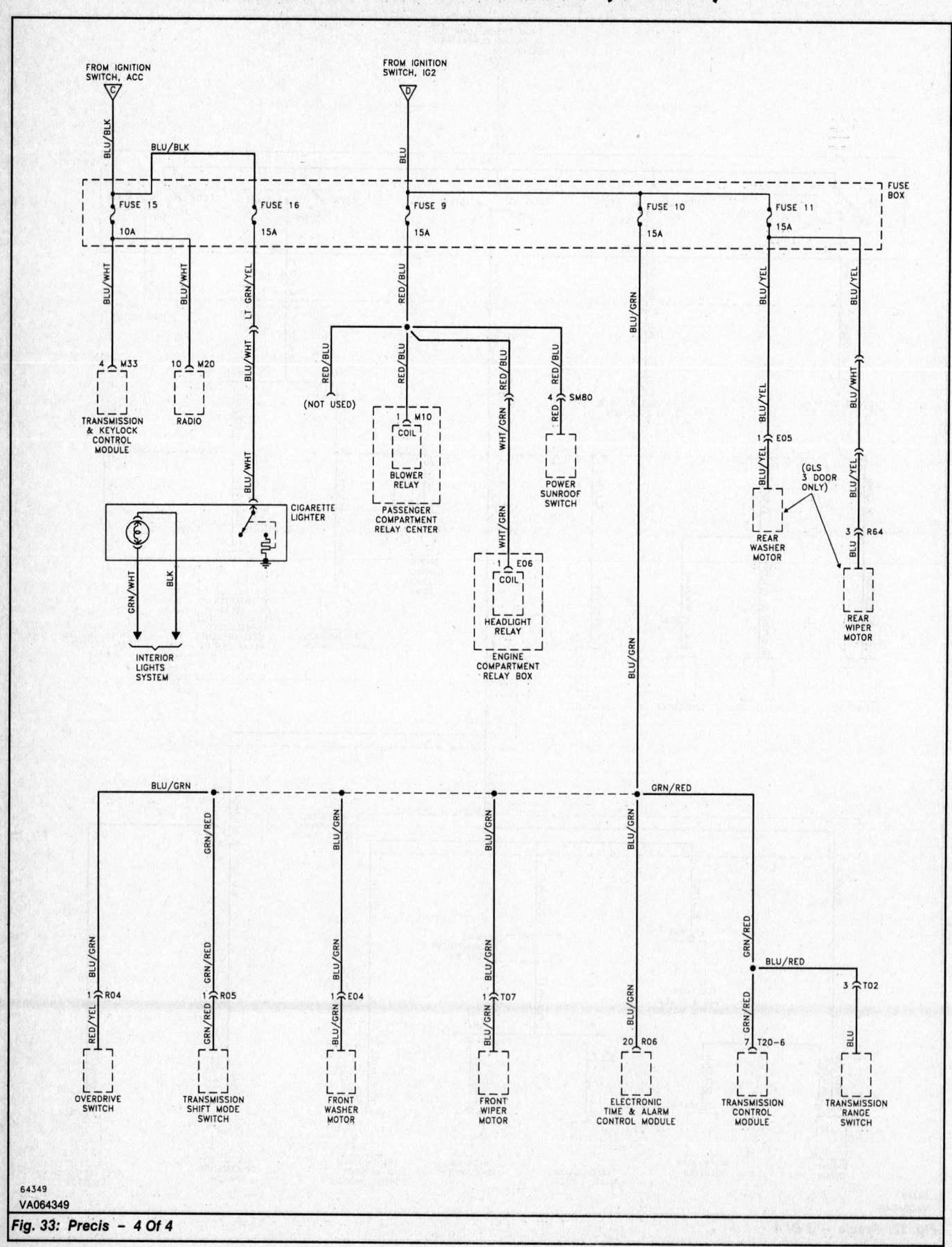

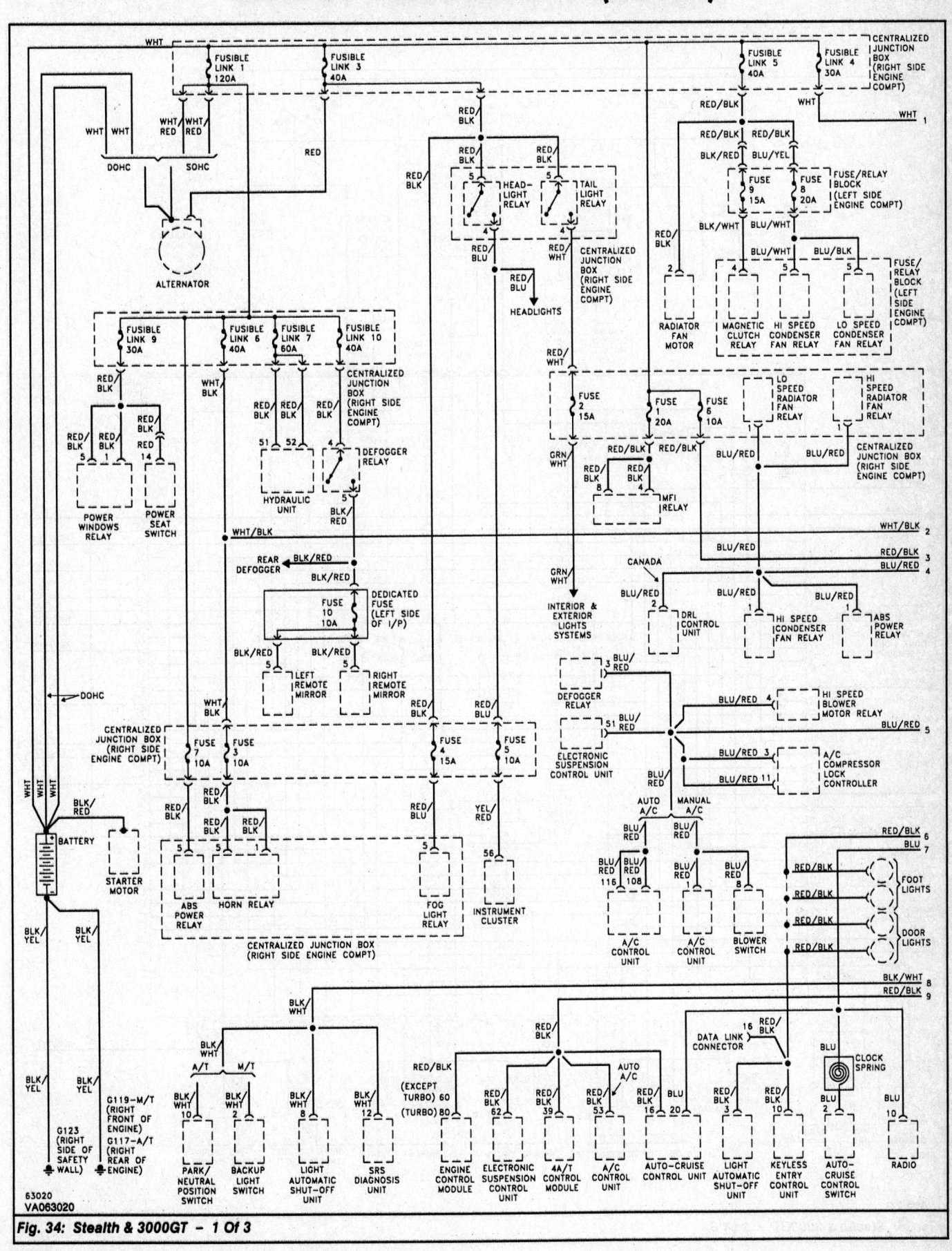

Fig. 34: Stealth & 3000GT - 1 Of 3

63020
VA063020

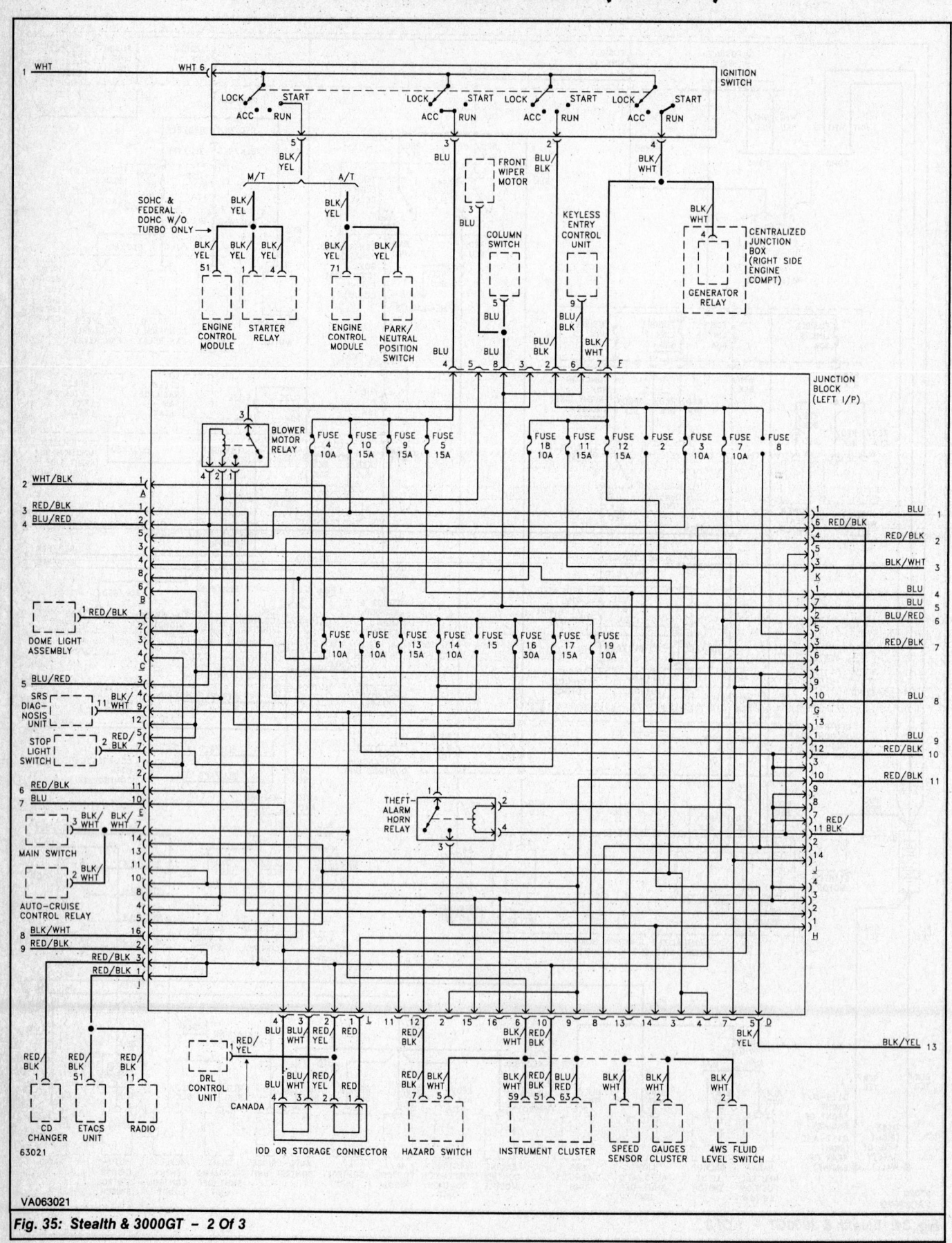

Fig. 35: Stealth & 3000GT - 2 Of 3

VA063021

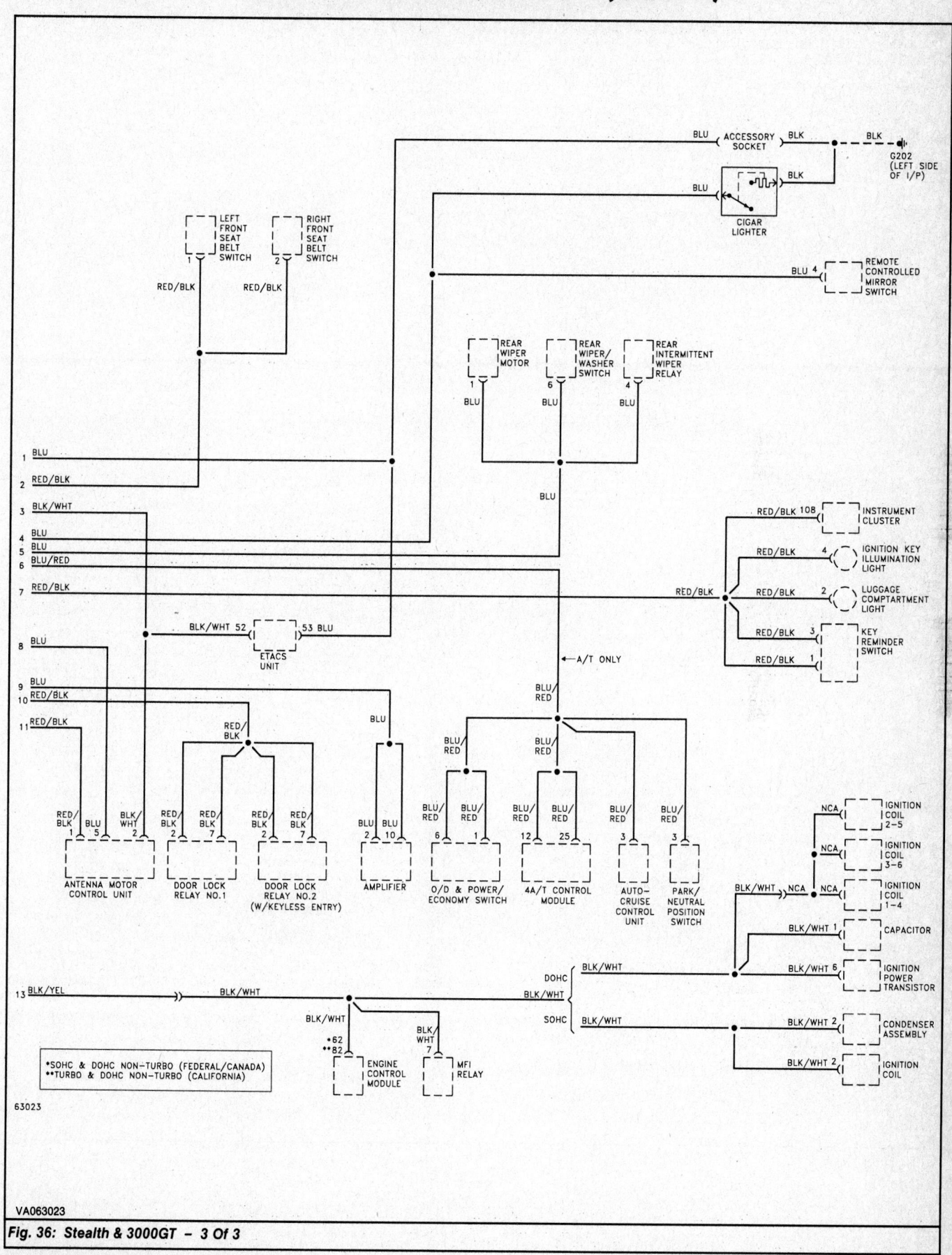

63023

VA063023

Fig. 36: Stealth & 3000GT – 3 Of 3

Chrysler Corp.: Colt, Colt Vista, Stealth
Eagle: Summit, Summit Wagon
Mitsubishi: Diamante, Expo, Galant, Mirage, Montero, 3000GT

WARNING: To avoid injury from accidental air bag deployment, read and carefully follow all WARNINGS and SERVICE PRECAUTIONS.

CAUTION: When battery is disconnected, radio will go into anti-theft protection mode. Obtain radio anti-theft protection code from owner prior to servicing vehicle.

NOTE: For information on air bag DIAGNOSIS & TESTING or DISPOSAL PROCEDURES, see MITCHELL® AIR BAG SERVICE & REPAIR MANUAL, DOMESTIC & IMPORTED MODELS.

DESCRIPTION & OPERATION

Supplemental Restraint System (SRS) consists of a driver-side air bag module, passenger-side air bag module (if equipped), SRS warning light, clockspring, impact sensor(s), and SRS Diagnostic Unit (SDU). *See Fig. 1 or 2.*

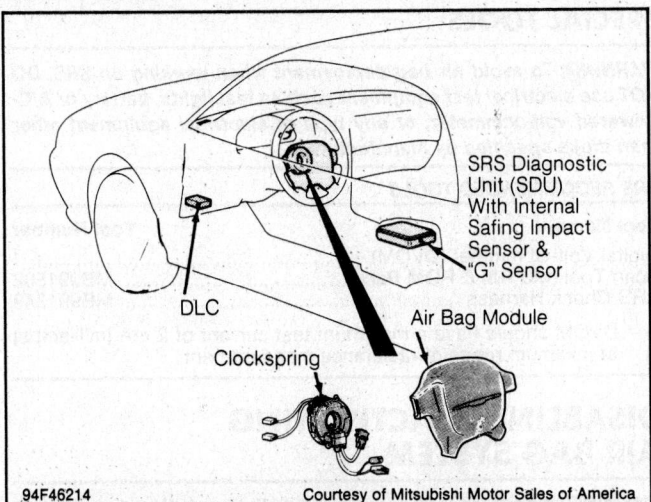

94F46214   Courtesy of Mitsubishi Motor Sales of America

Fig. 1: Identifying Supplemental Restraint System Components (Colt, Colt Vista, Expo, Mirage, Summit & Summit Wagon)

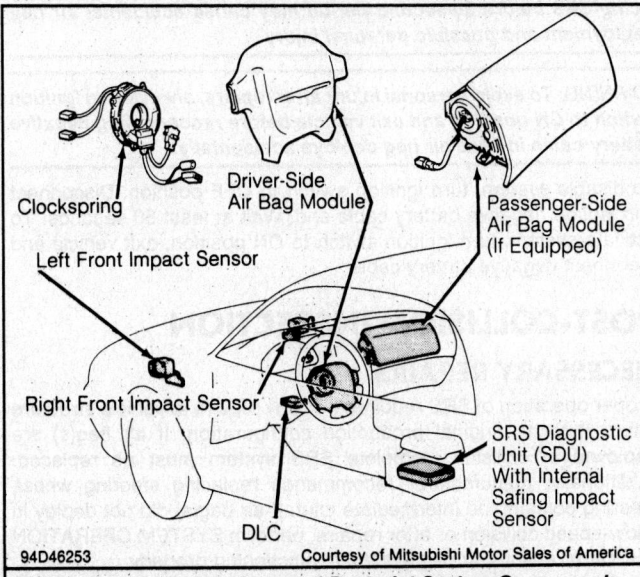

94D46253   Courtesy of Mitsubishi Motor Sales of America

Fig. 2: Identifying Supplemental Restraint System Components (Diamante, Galant, Montero, Stealth & 3000GT)

SDU contains a safing impact sensor. On Colt, Colt Vista, Expo, Mirage, Summit and Summit Wagon, SDU also contains an analog "G" sensor. All other models are equipped with left front and right front impact sensors.

During a front-end collision, SRS is designed to deploy air bag(s) only when safing impact sensor plus either or both front impact sensors or "G " sensor activate simultaneously.

SRS WARNING LIGHT

When ignition switch is in the ON or START position, SRS warning light on instrument panel will illuminate for about 7 seconds and then turn off. This indicates SDU has checked SRS system and found it free of faults. If SRS warning light blinks, stays on all the time or does not come on, a malfunction in SRS exists.

IMPACT SENSORS

The impact sensors verify the direction and severity of impact. Impact sensors are inertia switches, which complete an electrical circuit when impact provides sufficient "G" force. Front impact sensors are located under front fenders.

AIR BAG MODULE(S)

Driver-side air bag module is mounted on steering wheel, and passenger-side air bag module (if equipped) is mounted on dash above glove box. *See Fig. 1 or 2.* Air bag module inflator assembly produces nitrogen gas to fill air bag. When a small amount of current from SDU is applied, ignitor starts a thermal reaction, which spreads an ignitor charge.

Surrounding ignitor charge is a pellet-filled area that produces nitrogen gas. Gas pressure builds and discharges from inflator through a diffuser and screen assembly, forcing trim cover to burst along its seams until air bag is fully inflated. When air bag is fully inflated, gas escapes through vents on sides of air bag.

SRS DIAGNOSTIC UNIT (SDU)

The SDU stores trouble codes and provides system information to SRS warning light and data link connector. Safing impact sensor is an integral part of SDU. On Colt, Colt Vista, Expo, Mirage, Summit and Summit Wagon, SDU also contains an analog "G" sensor.

CLOCKSPRING

Clockspring connects air bag module to steering column wiring, forming SRS circuit. The clockspring is a flat, ribbon-like tape of conductive material, which winds and unwinds with steering wheel movement. Because of clockspring's constant movement, it is the most fragile part in system.

SERVICING

NOTE: To ensure long-term operation of SRS, manufacturer recommends inspecting SRS system 10 years from vehicle manufacture date. See certification label on driver-side center pillar. The following items should be checked.

AIR BAG MODULE(S), STEERING WHEEL & CLOCKSPRING

1) Remove air bag module(s) from steering wheel and from above glove box (if equipped). See AIR BAG MODULE(S) and CLOCKSPRING under REMOVAL & INSTALLATION. DO NOT apply excessive force when disconnecting air bag module clockspring connector.
2) Check air bag module trim cover for dents, cracks or deformities. Check hooks and connectors for damage, terminals for deformities, and wiring harness for binds. Check air bag inflator case for dents, cracks or deformities.
3) Check wiring harness (built into steering wheel) and connectors for damage, and terminals for deformities. Remove clockspring. See AIR BAG MODULE(S) and CLOCKSPRING under REMOVAL & INSTALLATION.

4) Check clockspring connectors and protective tube for damage, and check terminals for deformities. Visually inspect case and gears for damage. Turn front wheels to straight-ahead position. Install and adjust clockspring. See CLOCKSPRING CENTERING under ADJUSTMENTS.

5) Install steering wheel, column covers and air bag module(s). Check steering wheel for noise, binds, difficult operation, or excessive free play.

6) Check all connectors for poor connections. Check wiring harness for binds, connectors for damage, and terminals for deformities. Replace connectors or wiring harness as required.

IMPACT SENSORS

Remove right and left splash shields. Check sensors to ensure arrow marks face front of vehicle. Check upper frame and sensor brackets for deformities or rust. Check sensors for dents, cracks and rust. Check sensor harness for binds, connectors for damage, and terminals for deformities. Replace sensor and/or sensor harness as required.

SRS DIAGNOSTIC UNIT (SDU)

Check SDU case and brackets for dents, cracks or deformities. Check connectors and lock lever for damage, and terminals for deformities. Replace SDU as required.

SYSTEM OPERATION CHECK

Turn ignition switch to ON or START position. SRS warning light on instrument panel should illuminate for approximately 7 seconds then turn off. This indicates SRS is functioning properly. If SRS warning light does not illuminate as described, SRS system is malfunctioning. If any of the following conditions exist, SRS is malfunctioning and needs repair.

- SRS warning light does not illuminate as described.
- SRS warning light stays on for more than 7 seconds.
- SRS warning light illuminates while driving.

SERVICE PRECAUTIONS

The following precautions should be observed when working with SRS:

- Disable SRS before servicing any SRS or steering column component. Failure to do this may result in accidental air bag deployment and possible personal injury. See DISABLING & ACTIVATING AIR BAG SYSTEM.
- Wait at least 60 SECONDS after disabling air bag system. SRS system retains enough voltage, for a short time after system is disabled, to deploy air bag(s).
- After repairs, always turn ignition switch to ON position and exit vehicle before reconnecting negative battery cable in case of accidental air bag deployment. Ensure SRS warning light is working properly and no system faults are indicated. See SYSTEM OPERATION CHECK.
- Always wear safety glasses when servicing or handling an air bag.
- The SDU must be stored in its original special container until used for service. It must be stored in a clean, dry place, away from sources of extreme heat, sparks and high electrical energy.
- DO NOT expose air bag module and clockspring to temperatures greater than 200°F (93°C).
- When placing a live air bag on a bench or other surface, always face air bag and trim cover up, away from surface. This will reduce motion of module if air bag accidentally deploys.
- After air bag deploys, air bag surface may contain deposits of sodium hydroxide, which irritate skin. Always wear safety glasses, rubber gloves and long-sleeved shirt during clean-up. Wash hands using mild soap and water. Follow correct clean-up and disposal procedures.
- Because of critical system operating requirements, DO NOT service any SRS components. Repairs are only made by replacing defective part(s).

- DO NOT allow any electrical source near inflator on the back of air bag module.
- When carrying live air bag module, trim cover should be pointed away from body to minimize injury in case of accidental air bag deployment.
- When testing voltage or continuity at SDU, use terminal side (not the wire end) of connector.
- DO NOT probe a wire through insulator, as this will damage it and eventually cause failure due to corrosion.
- When performing electrical tests, prevent accidental shorting of terminals. Such shorts can damage fuses or components, and may cause a second trouble code to set, making diagnosis of original problem more difficult.
- Never use an analog volt-ohmmeter or test light in place of a Digital Volt-Ohmmeter (DVOM). When performing tests, use a DVOM with a maximum test current of 2 mA (milliamps) at minimum range of resistance measurement. Also see SPECIAL TOOLS.
- If SRS is not fully functional for any reason, DO NOT drive vehicle until system is repaired and is fully functional. DO NOT remove bulbs, modules, sensors or other components, or in any way disable system from operating normally. If SRS is not functional, park vehicle until repairs are made.

SPECIAL TOOLS

WARNING: To avoid air bag deployment when working on SRS, DO NOT use electrical test equipment such as test lights, battery or A/C-powered volt-ohmmeter, or any type of electrical equipment other than those specified by manufacturer.

SRS RECOMMENDED TOOLS

Tool Name	Tool Number
Digital Volt-Ohmmeter (DVOM)	1
Scan Tool (MUT-II) & ROM Pack	MB991502
SRS Check Harness	MB991349

1 – DVOM should have a maximum test current of 2 mA (milliamps) at minimum range of resistance measurement.

DISABLING & ACTIVATING AIR BAG SYSTEM

WARNING: Wait at least 60 seconds after disconnecting negative battery cable before servicing SRS. System reserve capacitor maintains SRS voltage for about 60 seconds after battery is disconnected. Servicing SRS before 60-second period may cause accidental air bag deployment and possible personal injury.

WARNING: To avoid personal injury after repairs, always turn ignition switch to ON position and exit vehicle before reconnecting negative battery cable in case air bag deploys accidentally.

To disable system, turn ignition switch to OFF position. Disconnect and isolate negative battery cable end. Wait at least 60 seconds. To activate system, turn ignition switch to ON position, exit vehicle and reconnect negative battery cable.

POST-COLLISION INSPECTION

NECESSARY REPAIRS

Proper operation of SRS requires that any repairs to vehicle structure return it to its original production configuration. If air bag(s) are deployed in collision, complete SRS system must be replaced. Additionally, manufacturer recommends replacing steering wheel, steering column and intermediate joint. If air bag(s) did not deploy in a low-speed collision or after repairs, perform SYSTEM OPERATION CHECK to ensure air bag system is functioning properly.

IMPACT SENSORS

Remove right and left splash shields. Check sensors to ensure arrow marks face front of vehicle. Check upper frame and sensor brackets for deformities or rust. Check sensors for dents, cracks and rust. Check sensor harness for binds, connectors for damage, and terminals for deformities. Replace sensor and/or sensor harness as required.

SRS DIAGNOSTIC UNIT (SDU)

Check SDU case and brackets for dents, cracks or deformities. Check connectors and lock lever for damage, and terminals for deformities. Replace SDU as required.

AIR BAG MODULE(S), STEERING WHEEL & CLOCKSPRING

1) Remove air bag modules from steering wheel and from above glove box (if equipped). See AIR BAG MODULE(S) and CLOCKSPRING under REMOVAL & INSTALLATION. DO NOT apply excessive force when disconnecting air bag module clockspring connector.
2) Check air bag module(s) trim cover for dents, cracks or deformities. Check hooks and connectors for damage, terminals for deformities, and wiring harness for binds. Check air bag inflator case for dents, cracks or deformities.
3) Check wiring harness (built into steering wheel) and connectors for damage, and terminals for deformities. Remove clockspring. See AIR BAG MODULE(S) and CLOCKSPRING under REMOVAL & INSTALLATION.
4) Check clockspring connectors and protective tube for damage, and terminals for deformities. Visually inspect case and gears for damage. Turn front wheels to straight-ahead position. Install and adjust clockspring. See CLOCKSPRING CENTERING under ADJUSTMENTS.
5) Install steering wheel, column covers and air bag module(s). Check steering wheel for noise, binds, difficult operation, or excessive free play.
6) Check all connectors for poor connections. Check wiring harness for binds, connectors for damage, and terminals for deformities. Replace connectors or wiring harness as required.

REMOVAL & INSTALLATION

WARNING: Failure to follow air bag service precautions may result in air bag deployment and personal injury. See SERVICE PRECAUTIONS. After component replacement, perform a system operational check to ensure proper system operation. See SYSTEM OPERATION CHECK.

CAUTION: Replace faulty SRS components; NEVER repair or disassemble. Handle all SRS components carefully. Replace any component that is dented, cracked, deformed or rusted. Replace components after air bag has deployed.

SRS DIAGNOSTIC UNIT (SDU)

WARNING: SDU contains safing impact sensor, which enables SRS to activate air bag(s). To avoid accidental deployment, NEVER connect SDU electrically to system unless it is bolted to vehicle.

Removal – 1) If replacing a deployed air bag, SDU must be replaced. Before proceeding, follow air bag service precautions. See SERVICE PRECAUTIONS. Ensure front wheels are in straight-ahead position. Turn ignition off. Disable SRS. See DISABLING & ACTIVATING AIR BAG SYSTEM.

CAUTION: A double-lock connector locking mechanism is used on SDU. DO NOT use excessive force when disconnecting connector, or damage to connector may occur.

2) Gain access to SDU located under center console. Using a screwdriver, push in SDU lock spring to unlock wiring connector lock lever. See Fig. 3. Disconnect wiring connectors. Remove SDU-to-bracket bolts. See Fig. 4. Remove SDU.

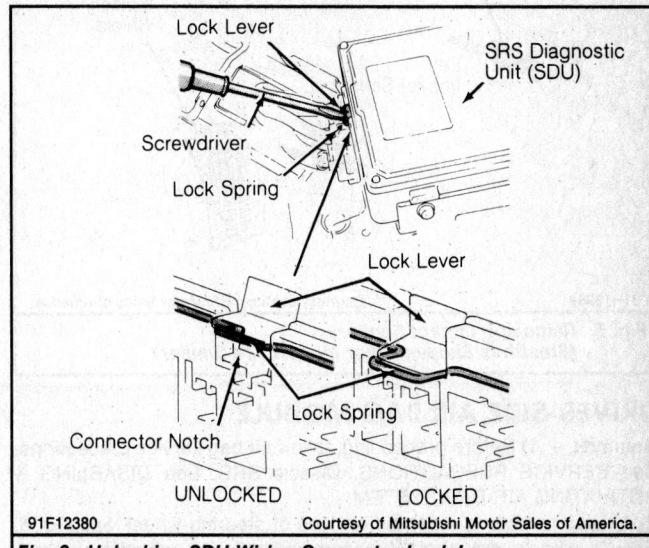

Fig. 3: Unlocking SDU Wiring Connector Lock Lever

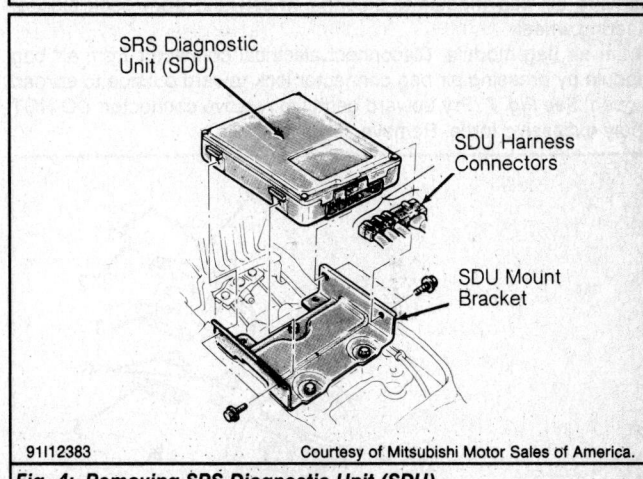

Fig. 4: Removing SRS Diagnostic Unit (SDU)

Installation – 1) To install SDU, reverse removal procedure. Install SDU with NEW screws and tighten to 15-20 INCH lbs. (1.7-2.2 N.m). Use only screws supplied with new SDU. When connecting SDU wiring connectors, press down SDU lock lever to lock connectors in place. See Fig. 3.
2) After SDU is installed, check SRS warning light to ensure system is functioning properly. See SYSTEM OPERATION CHECK.

IMPACT SENSORS

Removal – 1) If replacing a deployed air bag, right and left impact sensors must be replaced. Before proceeding, follow air bag service precautions. See SERVICE PRECAUTIONS. Disable SRS. See DISABLING & ACTIVATING AIR BAG SYSTEM.
2) Ensure front wheels are in straight-ahead position. Turn ignition switch to OFF position. Remove splash shield or extensions. See Fig. 5. Disconnect electrical connector. Remove bolts attaching sensor. Remove sensor.
Installation – To install impact sensor, reverse removal procedure. Tighten impact sensor screws to 90-120 INCH lbs. (10.1-13.6 N.m). After sensors are installed, check SRS warning light to ensure system is functioning properly. See SYSTEM OPERATION CHECK.

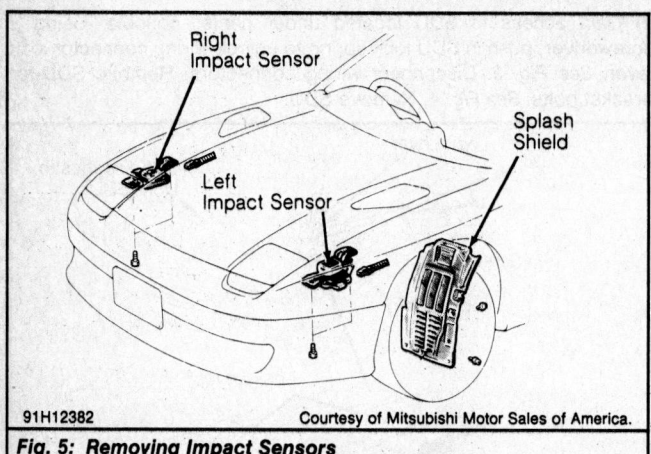

91H12382   Courtesy of Mitsubishi Motor Sales of America.

*Fig. 5: Removing Impact Sensors
(Stealth Is Shown; Other Models Are Similar)*

DRIVER-SIDE AIR BAG MODULE

Removal – **1)** Before proceeding, follow air bag service precautions. See SERVICE PRECAUTIONS. Disable SRS. See DISABLING & ACTIVATING AIR BAG SYSTEM.

2) Air bag module is mounted on face of steering wheel. *See Fig. 6.* Ensure wheels are straight ahead and steering wheel is locked. Remove air bag module-to-steering wheel nuts from back side of steering wheel.

3) Lift air bag module. Disconnect electrical connector from air bag module by pressing air bag connector lock toward outside to spread it open. *See Fig. 7.* Pry upward gently to remove connector. DO NOT apply excessive force. Remove air bag module.

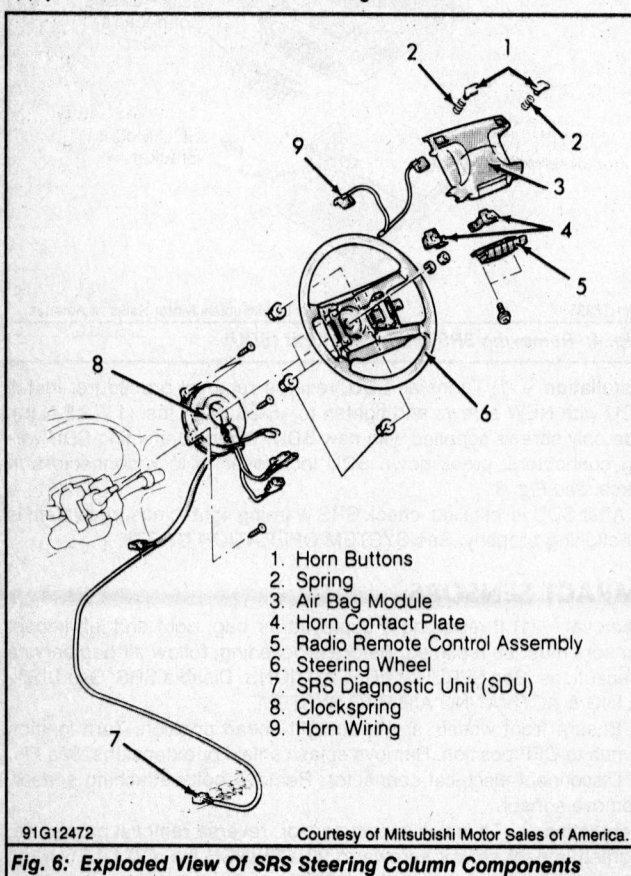

1. Horn Buttons
2. Spring
3. Air Bag Module
4. Horn Contact Plate
5. Radio Remote Control Assembly
6. Steering Wheel
7. SRS Diagnostic Unit (SDU)
8. Clockspring
9. Horn Wiring

91G12472   Courtesy of Mitsubishi Motor Sales of America.

Fig. 6: Exploded View Of SRS Steering Column Components

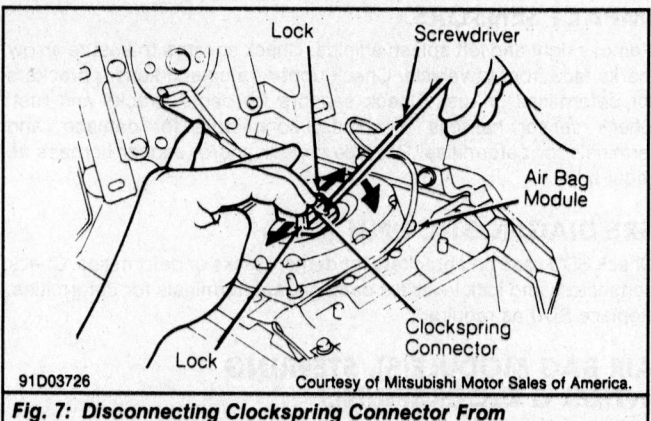

91D03726   Courtesy of Mitsubishi Motor Sales of America.

*Fig. 7: Disconnecting Clockspring Connector From
Air Bag Module*

Installation – **1)** To install, reverse removal procedure. Ensure horn switch wires are properly positioned. *See Fig. 8.* Tighten air bag module-to-steering wheel nuts to 48 INCH lbs. (5 N.m).

2) Check SRS warning light to ensure system is functioning properly. See SYSTEM OPERATION CHECK.

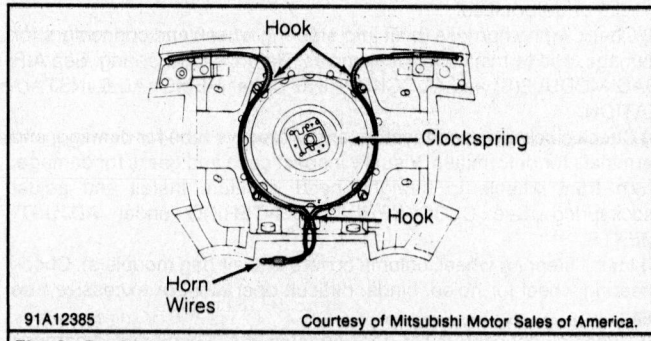

91A12385   Courtesy of Mitsubishi Motor Sales of America.

Fig. 8: Positioning Horn Switch Wiring

PASSENGER-SIDE AIR BAG MODULE

Removal – **1)** Before proceeding, follow air bag service precautions. See SERVICE PRECAUTIONS. Disable SRS. See DISABLING & ACTIVATING AIR BAG SYSTEM.

2) Remove glove box and glove box cover. *See Fig. 9.* Disconnect electrical connector from air bag module. Remove air bag module bolts. Remove air bag module. To install, reverse removal procedure. Tighten air bag module bolts to 48 INCH lbs. (5 N.m).

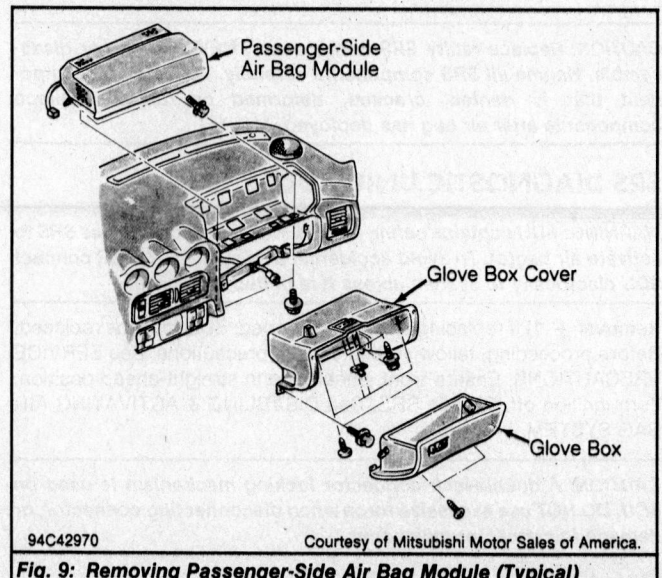

94C42970   Courtesy of Mitsubishi Motor Sales of America.

Fig. 9: Removing Passenger-Side Air Bag Module (Typical)

CLOCKSPRING

CAUTION: When installing steering wheel, if rotating part of clockspring is not properly centered with steering column and front wheels, clockspring failure will result. See CLOCKSPRING CENTERING under ADJUSTMENTS.

Removal – 1) If replacing a deployed air bag, clockspring must be replaced. Before proceeding, follow air bag service precautions. See SERVICE PRECAUTIONS. Disable SRS. See DISABLING & ACTIVATING AIR BAG SYSTEM.

2) Clockspring is located behind steering wheel. *See Fig. 6.* Ensure wheels are straight ahead and steering wheel is locked. Remove air bag module. See AIR BAG MODULE under REMOVAL & INSTALLATION. Remove steering wheel. Remove rear console assembly.

3) Using a screwdriver, push in SDU lock spring to unlock wiring connector lock lever. *See Fig. 3.* Disconnect 2-pin Red clockspring connector at SDU. *See Fig. 10.* Remove knee protector. Remove steering column covers. Remove screws attaching clockspring. Remove clockspring.

Installation – 1) To install, reverse removal procedure. Adjust clockspring. See CLOCKSPRING CENTERING under ADJUSTMENTS. When connecting SDU wiring connectors, press down SDU lock lever to lock connectors in place. *See Fig. 3.* Tighten steering wheel nut to specification. See TORQUE SPECIFICATIONS. Ensure horn switch wires are properly positioned. *See Fig. 8.*

2) Turn steering wheel all the way in both directions to ensure steering is normal. Check SRS warning light to ensure system is functioning properly. See SYSTEM OPERATION CHECK.

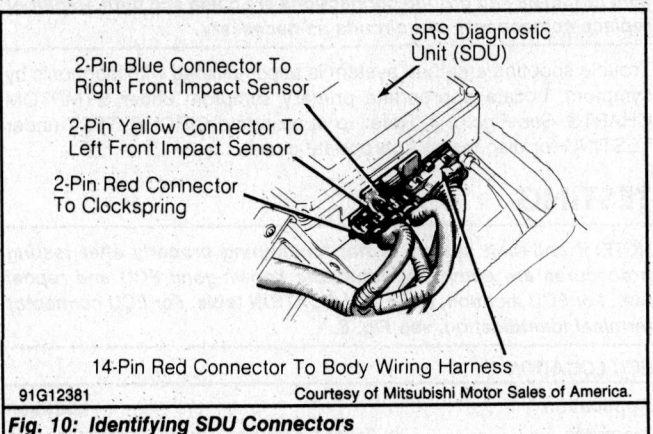

2-Pin Blue Connector To Right Front Impact Sensor

2-Pin Yellow Connector To Left Front Impact Sensor

2-Pin Red Connector To Clockspring

SRS Diagnostic Unit (SDU)

14-Pin Red Connector To Body Wiring Harness

91G12381   Courtesy of Mitsubishi Motor Sales of America.

Fig. 10: Identifying SDU Connectors

ADJUSTMENTS
CLOCKSPRING CENTERING

CAUTION: If rotating part of clockspring is not properly centered with steering column and front wheels, clockspring failure will result. The following procedure must be used to center clockspring.

1) Ensure wheels are straight ahead and steering wheel is locked. With air bag module and steering wheel removed, align clockspring mating mark and neutral position indicator. *See Fig. 11.*

2) Ensure horn switch wires are properly positioned. *See Fig. 8.* Install steering wheel and air bag module. Turn steering wheel all the way in both directions to ensure steering is normal.

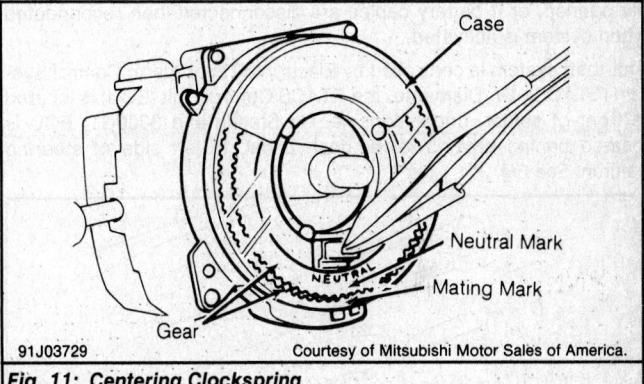

Case

Neutral Mark

Mating Mark

Gear

91J03729   Courtesy of Mitsubishi Motor Sales of America.

Fig. 11: Centering Clockspring

TORQUE SPECIFICATIONS
TORQUE SPECIFICATIONS

Application	Ft. Lbs. (N.m)
Steering Wheel Nut	29 (39)

	INCH Lbs. (N.m)
Air Bag Module Bolts/Nuts	48 (5)
Front Impact Sensor Screws	90-120 (10.1-13.6)
SRS Diagnostic Unit Bolts	15-20 (1.7-2.2)

WIRING DIAGRAMS

See ACCESSORIES & EQUIPMENT, Volume 5.

1994 ACCESSORIES & EQUIPMENT
Anti-Theft System

Chrysler Corp.: Stealth
Mitsubishi: Diamante, 3000GT

DESCRIPTION

CAUTION: All models are equipped with Supplemental Restraint System (SRS). SRS wiring harness is routed close to instrument cluster, steering wheel, and related components. DO NOT use electrical test equipment on these circuits. Before working on steering column components, disable air bag system. See AIR BAG RESTRAINT SYSTEM article in ACCESSORIES & EQUIPMENT.

The anti-theft system electrically disables starter, flashes lights and sounds an alarm if any doors, luggage compartment or hood is forcibly opened, or if battery cables are disconnected then reconnected when system is activated.

Anti-theft system is controlled by Electronic Timer Alarm Control System (ETACS). On Diamante, the ETACS Control Unit (ECU) is located in front of shifter, under console. On Stealth and 3000GT, ECU is located behind driver's lower dash panel, to left side of steering column. See Fig. 1.

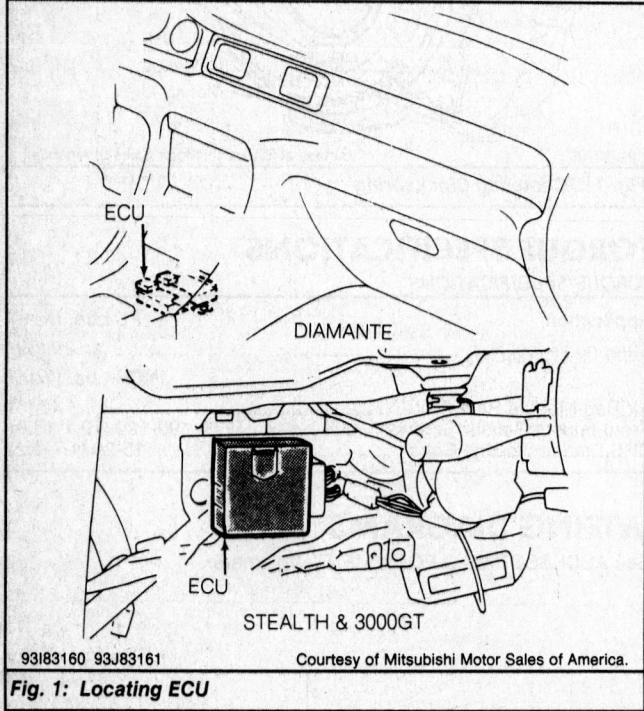

93J83160 93J83161   Courtesy of Mitsubishi Motor Sales of America.

Fig. 1: Locating ECU

OPERATION

Setting Anti-Theft System – Close all doors, hood and luggage compartment. Remove ignition key from ignition switch. Lock vehicle using one of 3 methods listed:
- Using key, lock left or right front door (all doors are locked through key-interlinked lock operation).
- Lock all doors using wireless door lock control system.
- With rear doors locked and one of the front doors locked, lock other front door using keyless door lock (without key).

After performing one method listed above, indicator light on instrument panel will light continuously for approximately 30 seconds. After 30 seconds, indicator light will blink once per second. When anti-theft system is set, doors cannot be locked or unlocked using door lock control switch and luggage compartment cannot be opened with luggage compartment door opener switch.

Canceling Anti-Theft System (System Set, No Alarm) – Anti-theft system operation can be canceled performing one of 4 methods listed:
- Unlock left or right front door using key.
- Unlock all doors using wireless door lock control system.

- Insert key in ignition switch and turn to ACC or ON position (this is operative only when anti-theft system has never operated).
- Using key, unlock luggage compartment. Anti-theft system is temporarily canceled only while luggage compartment door is open. Approximately 2 seconds after luggage compartment is closed, anti-theft system is reset.

Checking Anti-Theft System Operation – Ensure anti-theft system is activated and indicator light is blinking. When hood is opened or any door is unlocked without using key, vehicle horns and anti-theft horn will sound, and headlights and taillights will flash for approximately one minute. If doors are not locked when alarm is sounding, anti-theft system will repeat door locking operation every 2 seconds during the one minute alert time.

Canceling Anti-Theft System (System Set, Alarm Sounding) – Anti-theft system can be canceled by performing one of 4 methods listed:
- Unlock left or right front door with key.
- Unlock doors with wireless door lock control system.
- Insert key into ignition cylinder and turn to ACC or ON position.
- Wait for approximately one minute to elapse after alarm has started. After one minute has elapsed, anti-theft system will automatically reset in about 2 seconds if all doors are closed.

TROUBLE SHOOTING

NOTE: Verify power door lock system is operating properly before trouble shooting anti-theft system. See KEYLESS ENTRY & POWER DOOR LOCKS under ACCESSORIES & EQUIPMENT. Ensure all component terminals and ground connections are clean and tight. Repair or replace components and circuits as necessary.

Trouble shooting anti-theft system is accomplished with diagnosis by symptom. Locate appropriate primary symptom under SYMPTOM CHARTS. See Figs. 2-7. Refer to appropriate CIRCUIT TEST under TESTING for diagnosing appropriate circuit.

TESTING

NOTE: If anti-theft system is not functioning properly after testing procedures are complete, substitute known-good ECU and repeat test. For ECU location, see ECU LOCATION table. For ECU connector terminal identification, see Fig. 8.

ECU LOCATION

Application	¹ Location
Diamante	In Front Of Shifter, Under Center Console
Stealth & 3000GT	Behind Driver's Side Lower Dash, To Left Side Of Steering Column

¹ – See Fig. 1.

SYSTEM INPUT TEST

1) Access Data Link Connector (DLC). DLC is located behind lower dash panel to left of steering column on Diamante or behind lower dash panel to right of steering column on Stealth and 3000GT. Using Special Tool (MB991529), connect positive lead of voltmeter to terminal No. 9 and negative lead to terminal No. 4 or No. 5. See Fig. 9. Check if input signals from system components are being received by ECU.

2) Voltmeter needle should sweep when each of the following switches is operated:
- Driver and front passenger door switches.
- Headlight switch.
- Front passenger door lock switch.
- Hood switch.
- Luggage compartment light switch.
- Front passenger door key cylinder switch.
- Trunk lid key cylinder switch.

3) If switch or related components are not functioning, voltmeter will not operate when switch is activated. Replace appropriate component or repair circuit as necessary. Check following for possible cause:

SYMPTOM CHARTS

Trouble symptom	Cause	Circuit Test	Remedy
The system is not armed (The SECURITY light doesn't illuminate, and the alarm doesn't function.) (The central door locking system functions normally.)	Damaged or disconnected wiring of ECU power supply circuit	No. 1	Replace the fusible link No. ⑧ or the fuse No. ⑲. Repair the harness.
	Damaged or disconnected wiring of door switch input circuit	No. 4	Repair the harness or replace the door switch.
The arming procedures are followed, but the SECURITY light does not illuminate. (There is an alarm, however, when an alarm test is conducted after about 20 seconds have passed.)	Damaged or disconnected wiring of SECURITY light activation circuit.	No. 8	Replace the fusible link No. ⑧ or the fuse No. ⑲. Repair the harness.
	Blown SECURITY light bulb		Replace the bulb.
	Malfunction of the ECU.	—	Replace the ECU.
The alarm sounds in error when, while the system is armed, a door or the trunk lid is unlocked by using the key.	Damaged or disconnected wiring of a door key cylinder and the trunk lid key cylinder switch input circuit.	No. 6	Repair the harness or replace a door key cylinder and the trunk lid key cylinder switch.
	Malfunction of a door key cylinder and the trunk lid key cylinder switch.		
	Malfunction of the ECU.	—	Replace the ECU.

93F83035

Courtesy of Mitsubishi Motor Sales of America.

Fig. 2: Symptom Chart (Diamante – 1 Of 3)

Trouble symptom	Cause	Circuit Test	Remedy
There is no alarm when, as an alarm test, a door is opened without using the key. (The arming and disarming are normal, and the alarm is activated when the trunk lid or hood is opened.)	Damaged or disconnected wiring of door switch (all doors) input circuit	No. 4	Repair the harness or replace the door switch.
	Malfunction of the door switch		
	Malfunction of the ECU	—	Replace the ECU.
There is no alarm when, as an alarm test, the trunk lid is opened without using the key. (The alarm is activated, however, by opening a door or the hood.)	Damaged or disconnected wiring of luggage compartment light switch input circuit	No. 7	Repair the harness or replace the luggage compartment light switch.
	Malfunction of the luggage compartment light switch		
	Malfunction of the ECU.	—	Replace the ECU.
There is no alarm when, as an alarm test the hood is opened from within the vehicle. (The alarm is activated, however, by opening a door or the trunk lid.)	Damaged or disconnected wiring of hood switch input circuit.	No. 3	Repair the harness or replace the hood switch.
	Malfunction of the hood switch.		
	Malfunction of the ECU.	—	Replace the ECU.

93G83036

Courtesy of Mitsubishi Motor Sales of America.

Fig. 3: Symptom Chart (Diamante – 2 Of 3)

- Open fuse, circuit breaker or fusible link caused by short to body ground.
- Wire connector or pin inside connector disengaged at any connector or component system.
- Defective ETACS Control Unit (ECU).
- Defective switch, relay or actuator.
- Subfreezing weather conditions, mechanical failure or corroded or misaligned assemblies.

CIRCUIT TESTS (DIAMANTE)

CAUTION: Ensure ignition switch is in OFF position when connecting or disconnecting component connectors.

NOTE: For ECU connector terminal identification, see Fig. 8. For appropriate wiring diagram, see WIRING DIAGRAMS.

Test No. 1 (Power & Ground Circuit) – 1) With ECU connector connected, connect voltmeter positive lead to ECU connector terminal No. 70 (Red/Blue wire). Connect negative lead to ground. If battery voltage is present, go to next step. If voltage is not as specified, repair open circuit between ECU and fusible link No. 8 as necessary.

2) Turn ignition switch to OFF position. Disconnect ECU connector. Using an ohmmeter, check continuity between ECU wiring harness connector terminal No. 60 (Black wire) and ground. If continuity does not exist, repair open circuit.

Test No. 2 (Key Reminder Switch Input Circuit) – 1) With ECU connector connected, connect voltmeter positive lead to ECU connector terminal No. 69 (Green wire). Connect negative lead to ground. Battery voltage should be present with ignition key removed. No voltage should exist with ignition key inserted. If voltage is as specified, go to next step. If voltage is not as specified, repair open circuit between ECU and fusible link No. 8.

Trouble symptom	Cause	Circuit Test	Remedy
Engine would not start	• Malfunction of the starter relay • Damage or disconnected wiring of starter relay activation circuit.	No. 15	Repair the harness. Replace the starter relay. Replace the magnet switch.
	Malfunction of the ECU.		Replace the ECU.
When, as a test of the alarm, a door or the trunk lid is opened without using the key, or the hood is opened from within the vehicle, the horn and the theft-alarm horn sound but the headlights don't flash. (The headlights can, however, be switched ON by using the passing switch.)	Damaged or disconnected wiring of headlight power supply circuit or headlight activation circuit	Nos. 13 & 14	Repair the harness. Replace the headlight relay or the headlight.
	Malfunction of the ECU.		Replace the ECU.
The headlights flash during an alarm test but the horn or the theft-alarm horn does not sound.	Damaged or disconnected wiring of horn relay power supply circuit or horn activation circuit Damaged or disconnected wiring of the theft-alarm horn relay power supply circuit or the theft-alarm horn activation circuit.	Nos. 9, 10, 11 & 12	Repair the harness. Replace the t-alarm horn or the horn. Replace dedicated fuse or fusible link ⑧. Replace the horn relay or the theft-alarm horn relay.
	Malfunction of the ECU.		Replace the ECU.
The system is not deactivated when, during an alarm test in which the alarm is intentionally activated, the door or liftgate is unlocked by using the key. (The system also cannot be disarmed.)	Damaged or disconnected wiring of door key cylinder and trunk lid key cylinder switch input circuit	No. 6	Repair the harness. Replace the key cylinder switch or the trunk lid key cylinder switch.
	Malfunction of door key cylinder or trunk lid key cylinder switch.		
	Malfunction of the ECU.		Replace the ECU.

93H83037

Courtesy of Mitsubishi Motor Sales of America.

Fig. 4: Symptom Chart (Diamante – 3 Of 3)

Trouble symptom	Cause	Circuit Test	Remedy
The system is not armed (The SECURITY light doesn't illuminate, and the alarm doesn't function.)	Damaged or disconnected wiring of ECU power supply circuit	No. 1	Replace the fusible link No. ⑥ or the fuse No. ⑲. Repair the harness.
	Damaged or disconnected wiring of door switch input circuit	No. 4	Repair the harness or replace the door switch.
The arming procedures are followed, but the SECURITY light does not illuminate. (There is an alarm, however, when an alarm test is conducted after about 20 seconds have passed.)	Damaged or disconnected wiring of SECURITY light activation circuit	No. 8	Replace the fusible link No. ⑥ or the fuse No. ⑲. Repair the harness.
	Blown SECURITY light bulb		Replace the bulb.
	Malfunction of the ECU.	—	Replace the ECU.
The alarm sounds in error when, while the system is armed, a door or the liftgate is unlocked by using the key.	Damaged or disconnected wiring of a door key cylinder and the liftgate unlock switch input circuit.	No. 6	Repair the harness or replace a door key cylinder and the liftgate unlock switch.
	Malfunction of a door key cylinder and the liftgate unlock switch.		
	Malfunction of the ECU.	—	Replace the ECU.

93I83038

Courtesy of Mitsubishi Motor Sales of America.

Fig. 5: Symptom Chart (Stealth & 3000GT – 1 Of 3)

2) Turn ignition switch to OFF position. Disconnect ECU connector. Using an ohmmeter, check continuity between ECU wiring harness connector terminal No. 69 (Green wire) and ground. If continuity does not exist, repair open circuit.

NOTE: Voltage measurement requires use of an oscilloscope in the following test. Follow oscilloscope manufacturer's operating instructions.

Test No. 3 (Hood Switch Input Circuit) – **1)** With ECU connector connected, check voltage on ECU connector terminal No. 54 (Brown wire) using an oscilloscope. When hood is closed, 5 volts should exist. No voltage should exist when hood is open. If voltage is as specified, go to next step. If voltage is not as specified, repair open circuit between ECU and hood switch.
2) Turn ignition switch to OFF position. Disconnect ECU connector. Using an ohmmeter, check continuity between ECU wiring harness connector terminal No. 54 (Brown wire) and ground. Continuity should

Trouble symptom	Cause	Circuit Test	Remedy
There is no alarm when, as an alarm test, a door is opened without using the key. (The arming and disarming are normal, and the alarm is activated when the liftgate or hood is opened.)	Damaged or disconnected wiring of door switch (all doors) input circuit	No. 4	Repair the harness or replace the door switch.
	Malfunction of the door switch		
	Malfunction of the ECU	–	Replace the ECU.
There is no alarm when, as an alarm test, the liftgate is opened without using the key. (The alarm is activated, however, by opening a door or the hood.)	Damaged or disconnected wiring of liftgate switch input circuit	No. 7	Repair the harness or replace the liftgate switch.
	Malfunction of the liftgate switch.		
	Malfunction of the ECU.	–	Replace the ECU.

93J83039

Courtesy of Mitsubishi Motor Sales of America.

Fig. 6: Symptom Chart (Stealth & 3000GT – 2 Of 3)

Trouble symptom	Cause	Circuit Test	Remedy
There is no alarm when, as an alarm test, the hood is opened from within the vehicle. (The alarm is activated, however, by opening a door or the liftgate.)	Damaged or disconnected wiring of hood switch input circuit.	No. 3	Repair the harness or replace the hood switch.
	Malfunction of the hood switch.		
	Malfunction of the ECU.	–	Replace the ECU.
Engine would not start [Engine starting is possible when the starter relay is in the switched-off (normally closed) condition, with the clutch switch in the switch-off and the ECU harness connector disconnected.]	There is a short-circuit of the starter relay activation circuit	No. 15	Repair the harness.
When, as a test of the alarm, a door or the liftgate is opened without using the key, or the hood is opened from within the vehicle, the horn and the theft-alarm horn sound but the headlights don't flash. (The headlights can, however, be switched ON by using the passing switch.)	Damaged or disconnected wiring of headlight power supply circuit or headlight activation circuit	Nos. 13 & 14	Repair the harness or replace the diode D₂. Replace the headlight relay or the headlight.
	Malfunction of the ECU.		Replace the ECU.
The headlights flash during an alarm test but the horn or the theft alarm horn does not sound.	Damaged or disconnected wiring of horn relay power supply circuit or horn activation circuit Damaged or disconnected wiring of the theft-alarm horn relay power supply circuit or the theft-alarm horn activation circuit.	Nos. 9, 10 & 11	Repair the harness. Replace the horn. Replace dedicated fuse No. ⑥ or the fusible link No. ⑥.
	Malfunction of the ECU.		Replace the ECU.
The system is not deactivated when, during an alarm test in which the alarm is intentionally activated, the door or liftgate is unlocked by using the key. (The system also cannot be disarmed.)	Damaged or disconnected wiring of door key cylinder and liftgate unlock switch input circuit	Nos. 6 & 7 26)	Repair the harness. Replace the key cylinder switch or the liftgate switch.
	Malfunction of door key cylinder and liftgate unlock switch.		
	Malfunction of the ECU		Replace the ECU.

93C83040

Courtesy of Mitsubishi Motor Sales of America.

Fig. 7: Symptom Chart (Stealth & 3000GT – 3 Of 3)

exist when hood is open. No continuity should exist when hood is closed. If continuity is not as specified, repair circuit between ECU and hood switch as necessary.

NOTE: Voltage measurement requires use of an oscilloscope in the following test. Follow oscilloscope manufacturer's operating instructions.

Test No. 4 (Door Switch Input Circuit) – 1) With ECU connector connected, check voltage on ECU connector terminal No. 56 (Green/Red wire) using an oscilloscope. Open and close each door in turn. Voltage

should be 5 volts with all doors closed. Voltage should be zero volts with any door open. If voltage is as specified, go to next step. If voltage is not as specified, repair circuit between ECU and appropriate door switch as necessary.

2) Turn ignition switch to OFF position. Disconnect ECU connector. Using an ohmmeter, check continuity between ECU wiring harness connector terminal No. 56 (Green/Red wire) and ground. Continuity should exist when any door is open. No continuity should exist when all doors are closed. If continuity is not as specified, repair open circuit between ECU and appropriate door switch.

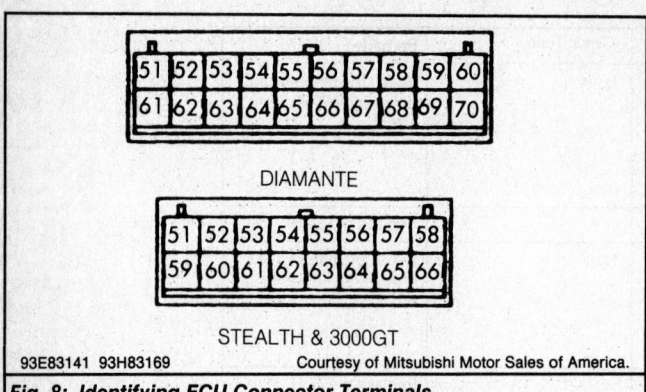

DIAMANTE

STEALTH & 3000GT

93E83141 93H83169   Courtesy of Mitsubishi Motor Sales of America.

Fig. 8: Identifying ECU Connector Terminals

NOTE: *Voltage measurement requires use of an oscilloscope in the following test. Follow oscilloscope manufacturer's operating instructions.*

Test No. 5 (Door Lock Actuator Switch Input Circuit) – 1) With ECU connector connected, check voltage on ECU connector terminals No. 58 (Red/Yellow wire) for right front door, and No. 68 (Red/White wire) for both rear doors using an oscilloscope. Lock and unlock each door in turn. With door(s) locked, voltage should be 5 volts. With door(s) unlocked, voltage should be zero volts. If voltage is as specified, go to next step. If voltage is not as specified, repair circuit between ECU and appropriate door lock actuator switch.

2) Access left front door control unit, located in left front door armrest. Using an oscilloscope, with connectors connected, check voltage on left front door control unit connector terminal No. 4 (Red/White wire). *See Fig. 10*. Lock and unlock left front door. With door locked, voltage should be 5 volts. With door unlocked, voltage should be zero volts. If voltage is as specified, go to next step. If voltage is not at specified, repair circuit between left front door control unit and left front door lock actuator switch as necessary.

3) Turn ignition switch to OFF position. Disconnect ECU connector. Using an ohmmeter, check continuity between ground and ECU wiring harness connector terminals No. 58 (Red/Yellow wire) for right front door, and No. 68 (Red/White wire) for rear doors. Lock and unlock each door in turn. With door(s) locked, continuity should not exist. With door(s) unlocked, continuity should exist. If continuity is as specified, go to next step. If continuity is not as specified, repair open circuit between ECU and appropriate door lock actuator switch.

4) Disconnect left front door control unit connector. Using an ohmmeter, check continuity between left front control unit wiring connector terminal No. 4 (Red/White wire) and ground. With door locked, no continuity should exist. With door unlocked, continuity should exist. If continuity is not as specified, repair open circuit between left front door control unit and left front door lock actuator switch.

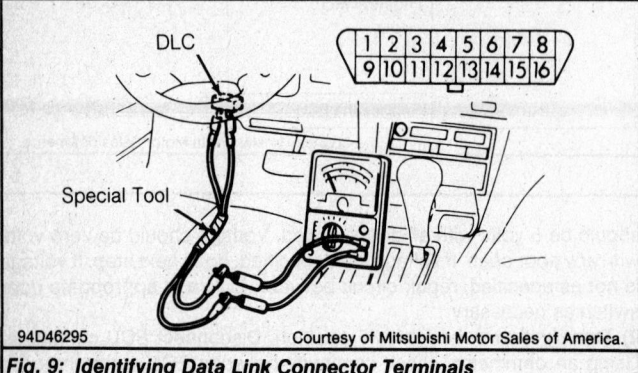

94D46295   Courtesy of Mitsubishi Motor Sales of America.

Fig. 9: Identifying Data Link Connector Terminals

93H83136   Courtesy of Mitsubishi Motor Sales of America.

Fig. 10: Identifying Left Front Door Control Unit Connector Terminals

---

NOTE: *Voltage measurement requires use of an oscilloscope in the following test. Follow oscilloscope manufacturer's operating instructions.*

Test No. 6 (Door & Trunk Lid Key Cylinder Switch Input Circuit) – 1) With ECU connector connected, check voltage on ECU connector terminals No. 11 (Red/Yellow wire) for right front door, and No. 51 (Brown/Green wire) for trunk lid using an oscilloscope. Lock and unlock right front door and trunk lid in turn. With door and trunk lid locked, voltage should be 5 volts. With door and trunk lid unlocked, voltage should be zero volts. If voltage is as specified, go to next step. If voltage is not as specified, repair appropriate circuit between ECU and door key cylinder switch or trunk lid key cylinder switch.

2) Check voltage on ECU connector terminal No. 62 (Brown/Red wire) for right front door using an oscilloscope. Lock and unlock right front door. With door locked, voltage should be zero volts. With door unlocked, voltage should be 5 volts. If voltage is as specified, go to next step. If voltage is not as specified, repair circuit between ECU and door key cylinder switch.

3) Access left front door control unit, located in left front door armrest. Using an oscilloscope, with connectors connected, check voltage on left front door control unit connector terminal No. 2 (Brown/Red wire). *See Fig. 10*. Lock and unlock left front door. With door locked, voltage should be zero volts. With door unlocked, voltage should be 5 volts. If voltage is as specified, go to next step. If voltage is not as specified, repair circuit between left front door control unit and left front door key cylinder switch as necessary.

4) Check voltage on left front door control unit connector terminal No. 12 (Red/Yellow wire). Lock and unlock left front door. With door locked, voltage should be 5 volts. With door unlocked, voltage should be zero volts. If voltage is as specified, go to next step. If voltage is not as specified, repair circuit between left front door control unit and left front door key cylinder switch as necessary.

5) Turn ignition switch to OFF position. Disconnect ECU connector. Using an ohmmeter, check continuity between ground and ECU wiring harness connector terminals No. 11 (Red/Yellow wire) for right front door, and No. 51 (Brown/Green wire) for trunk lid. Lock and unlock right front door and trunk lid in turn. With door and trunk lid locked, continuity should not exist. With door or trunk lid unlocked, continuity should exist. If continuity is as specified, go to next step. If continuity is not as specified, repair appropriate open circuit between ECU and right front door key cylinder switch or trunk lid switch.

6) Check continuity between ground and ECU wiring harness connector terminal No. 62 (Brown/Red wire) for right front door lock and unlock right front door. With door locked, continuity should exist. With door unlocked, continuity should not exist. If continuity is as specified, go to next step. If continuity is not as specified, repair open circuit between ECU and right front door key cylinder switch.

7) Disconnect left front door control unit connector. Using an ohmmeter, check continuity between left front control unit wiring connector terminal No. 2 (Brown/Red wire) and ground. With door locked, continuity should exist. With door unlocked, continuity should not exist. If continuity is not as specified, repair open circuit between left front door control unit and left front door key cylinder switch.

NOTE: *Voltage measurement requires use of an oscilloscope in the following test. Follow oscilloscope manufacturer's operating instructions.*

Test No. 7 (Luggage Compartment Light Switch Input Circuit) – 1) With ECU connector connected, check voltage on ECU connector terminal No. 64 (Brown/Blue wire) using an oscilloscope. When trunk lid is closed, 5 volts should exist. No voltage should exist when trunk lid is open. If voltage is as specified, go to next step. If voltage is not as specified, repair circuit between ECU and luggage compartment light switch terminal.

2) Turn ignition switch to OFF position. Disconnect ECU connector. Using an ohmmeter, check continuity between ECU wiring harness connector terminal No. 64 (Brown/Blue wire) and ground. No continuity should exist when trunk lid is closed. Continuity should exist when trunk lid is open. If continuity is not as specified, repair open circuit between ECU and luggage compartment light switch.

Test No. 8 (Security Light Activation Circuit) – 1) Turn ignition switch to OFF position. Disconnect ECU connector. Gain access to instrument panel combination meter connector. Using a voltmeter, check voltage on combination meter connector terminal No. 8 (Red/Black wire). See Fig. 11. Battery voltage should exist. If voltage is as specified, go to next step. If voltage is not as specified, check circuit between combination meter connector and fuse No. 19. Repair circuit as necessary.

2) Check voltage on combination meter terminal No. 1 (Brown/White wire). Battery voltage should exist. If voltage is not as specified, check circuit between combination meter connector and ECU wiring connector terminal No. 16 (Brown/White wire). Repair circuit as necessary.

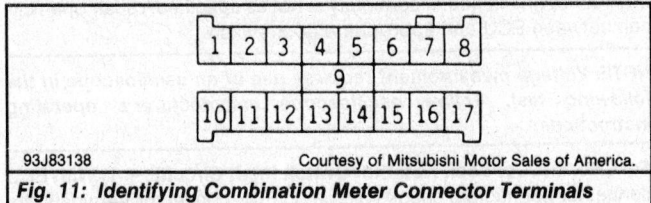

Fig. 11: Identifying Combination Meter Connector Terminals (Diamante)

93J83138 — Courtesy of Mitsubishi Motor Sales of America.

CAUTION: When battery is disconnected, radio will go into anti-theft protection mode. Obtain radio anti-theft protection code from owner prior to servicing vehicle.

Test No. 9 (Theft Alarm Horn Relay Power Circuit) – 1) Disconnect and remove battery. Remove intake air cleaner duct from right side inner fender panel. Disconnect theft alarm horn relay. See Fig. 12. Reconnect battery.

2) Using a voltmeter, check voltage on theft alarm horn relay wiring connector terminal No. 1 (Red wire). Battery voltage should exist. If voltage is not as specified, repair circuit between theft alarm horn relay connector and fusible link No. 3.

CAUTION: When battery is disconnected, radio will go into anti-theft protection mode. Obtain radio anti-theft protection code from owner prior to servicing vehicle.

Test No. 10 (Theft Alarm Horn Activation Circuit) – 1) Turn ignition switch to OFF position. Disconnect battery. Disconnect ECU connector. Gain access to theft alarm horn relay, located behind battery and intake air duct on right side inner fender panel. See Fig. 12. Reconnect battery.

2) Ground ECU wiring harness connector terminal No. 10 (Green/Black wire). Using a voltmeter, check voltage on theft alarm horn relay terminal No. 3 (Green/White wire). Battery voltage should exist. If voltage is as specified, go to next step. If voltage is not as specified, replace horn relay.

3) Check voltage at theft alarm horn Black wire. Battery voltage should exist. If voltage is as specified and horn does not sound, replace horn. If voltage is not as specified, repair circuit between horn ground and horn relay as necessary.

Test No. 11 (Horn Relay Power Supply Circuit) – Disconnect horn relay, located above fuse box. See Fig. 13. Using a voltmeter, check voltage on horn relay wiring connector terminal No. 1 (White/Black wire). Battery voltage should exist. If voltage is not as specified, repair circuit between horn relay connector and fuse No. 14 as necessary.

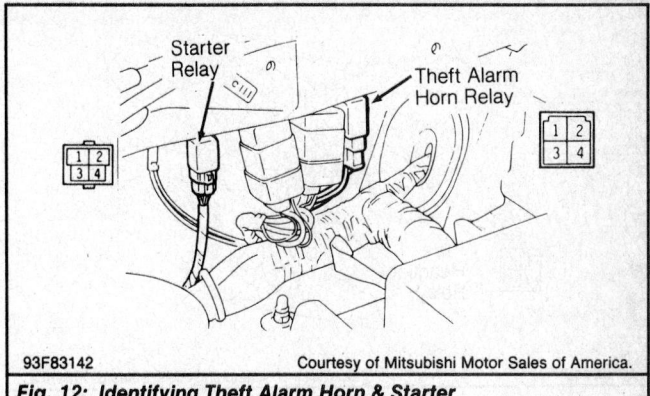

Fig. 12: Identifying Theft Alarm Horn & Starter Relays & Relay Terminals

93F83142 — Courtesy of Mitsubishi Motor Sales of America.

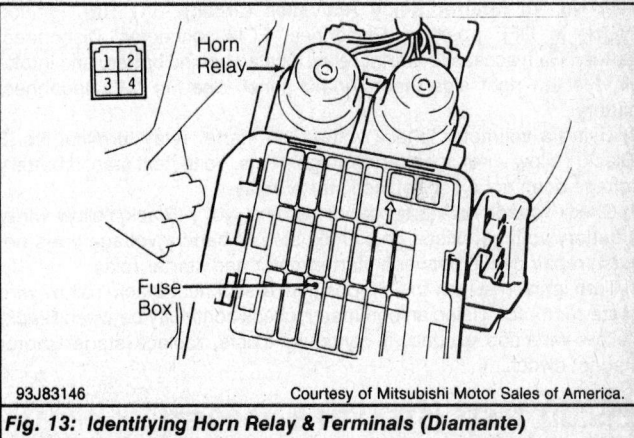

Fig. 13: Identifying Horn Relay & Terminals (Diamante)

93J83146 — Courtesy of Mitsubishi Motor Sales of America.

Test No. 12 (Horn Activation Circuit) – 1) Turn ignition switch to OFF position. Disconnect ECU connector. Ground ECU wiring connector terminal No. 10 (Green/Black wire). Using a voltmeter, check voltage on horn relay terminal No. 1 (White/Black wire). See Fig. 13. Battery voltage should exist. If voltage is as specified, go to next step. If voltage is not as specified, replace horn relay.

2) Check voltage at horn Black wire. Battery voltage should exist. If voltage is as specified and horn does not sound, replace horn. If voltage is not as specified, repair circuit between horn ground and horn relay as necessary.

Test No. 13 (Headlight Power Supply Circuit) – Disconnect headlight relay. See Fig. 14. Using a voltmeter, check voltage on headlight relay wiring connector terminal No. 3 (Red wire). If battery voltage does not exist, repair circuit between headlight relay wiring connector and fusible link No. 5.

Test No. 14 (Headlight Activation Relay) – 1) Turn ignition switch to OFF position. Disconnect ECU connector. Ground ECU wiring connector terminal No. 10 (Green/Black wire). Using a voltmeter, check voltage on headlight relay connector terminal No. 1 (Red/Blue wire). Battery voltage should exist. If voltage is as specified, go to next step. If voltage is not as specified, replace headlight relay.

2) Check voltage on appropriate headlight connector terminal No. 2 (Red/Blue wire). Battery voltage should exist. If voltage is as specified, go to next step. If voltage is not as specified, repair circuit between headlight and headlight relay as necessary.

3) Check voltage on headlight connector terminal No. 1 (Black wire). No battery voltage should exist. If battery voltage does not exist and headlight does not glow, replace headlight. If battery voltage exists, repair circuit between headlight and headlight relay as necessary.

CAUTION: When battery is disconnected, radio will go into anti-theft protection mode. Obtain radio anti-theft protection code from owner prior to servicing vehicle.

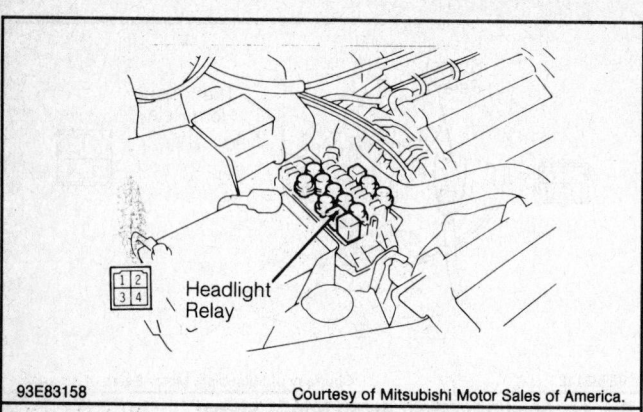

93E83158   Courtesy of Mitsubishi Motor Sales of America.

Fig. 14: Identifying Headlight Relay & Terminals (Diamante)

Test No. 15 (Starter Relay Activation Circuit) – 1) Turn ignition switch to OFF position. Disconnect ECU connector. Disconnect battery. Gain access to starter relay, located behind battery and intake air duct on right side inner fender panel. *See Fig. 12.* Reconnect battery.

2) Using a voltmeter, check voltage on starter relay terminal No. 3 (Black/Yellow wire). If battery voltage exists, go to next step. If battery voltage does not exist, replace starter relay.

3) Check voltage on starter motor terminal No. 1 (Black/Yellow wire). If battery voltage exists, go to next step. If battery voltage does not exist, repair circuit between starter motor and starter relay.

4) Turn ignition switch to OFF position. Disconnect Black/Yellow wire at starter motor. Using an ohmmeter, check continuity between Black/Yellow wire and ground. If continuity exists, replace starter motor magnet switch.

CIRCUIT TESTS (STEALTH & 3000GT)

CAUTION: Ensure ignition switch is in OFF position whenever disconnecting component connectors.

NOTE: For ECU connector terminal identification, see Fig. 8. For appropriate wiring diagram, see WIRING DIAGRAMS.

Test No. 1 (Power & Ground Circuit) – 1) With ECU connector connected, connect voltmeter positive lead to ECU connector terminal No. 51 (Red/Blue wire). Connect negative lead to ground. If battery voltage is present, go to next step. If voltage is not as specified, repair open circuit between ECU and fusible link No. 6 as necessary.

2) Turn ignition switch to OFF position. Disconnect ECU connector. Using an ohmmeter, check continuity between ECU wiring harness connector terminal No. 59 (Black wire) and ground. If continuity does not exist, repair open circuit.

Test No. 2 (Key Reminder Switch Input Circuit) – 1) With ECU connector connected, connect voltmeter positive lead to ECU connector terminal No. 64 (Black/Blue wire). Connect negative lead to ground. Battery voltage should be present with ignition key removed. No voltage should exist with ignition key inserted. If voltage is as specified, go to next step. If voltage is not as specified, repair open circuit between ECU and fusible link No. 6.

2) Turn ignition switch to OFF position. Disconnect ECU connector. Using an ohmmeter, check continuity between ECU wiring harness connector terminal No. 64 (Black/Blue wire) and ground. If continuity does not exist, repair open circuit.

NOTE: Voltage measurement requires use of an oscilloscope in the following test. Follow oscilloscope manufacturer's operating instructions.

Test No. 3 (Hood Switch Input Circuit) – 1) With ECU connector connected, check voltage on ECU connector terminal No. 18 (Blue/Black wire) using an oscilloscope. When hood is closed, 5 volts should exist.

No voltage should exist when hood is open. If voltage is as specified, go to next step. If voltage is not as specified, repair open circuit between ECU and hood switch.

2) Turn ignition switch to OFF position. Disconnect ECU connector. Using an ohmmeter, check continuity between ECU wiring harness connector terminal No. 18 (Blue/Black wire) and ground. Continuity should exist when hood is open. No continuity should exist when hood is closed. If continuity is not as specified, repair circuit between ECU and hood switch as necessary.

NOTE: Voltage measurement requires use of an oscilloscope in the following test. Follow oscilloscope manufacturer's operating instructions.

Test No. 4 (Door Switch Input Circuit) – 1) With ECU connector connected, check voltage on ECU connector terminal No. 10 (Red/Green wire) using an oscilloscope. Open and close each door in turn. Voltage should be 5 volts with both doors closed. Voltage should be zero volts with either door open. If voltage is as specified, go to next step. If voltage is not as specified, repair circuit between ECU and appropriate door switch as necessary.

2) Turn ignition switch to OFF position. Disconnect ECU connector. Using an ohmmeter, check continuity between ECU wiring harness connector terminal No. 10 (Red/Green wire) and ground. Continuity should exist when either door is open. No continuity should exist when both doors are closed. If continuity is not as specified, repair open circuit between ECU and appropriate door switch.

NOTE: Voltage measurement requires use of an oscilloscope in the following test. Follow oscilloscope manufacturer's operating instructions.

Test No. 5 (Door Lock Actuator Switch Input Circuit) – 1) With ECU connector connected, check voltage on ECU connector terminals No. 13 (Brown/Yellow wire) for left door, and No. 14 (Brown wire) for right door using an oscilloscope. Lock and unlock both doors in turn. With door(s) locked, voltage should be 5 volts. With door(s) unlocked, voltage should be zero volts. If voltage is as specified, go to next step. If voltage is not as specified, repair circuit between ECU and appropriate door lock actuator switch.

2) Turn ignition switch to OFF position. Disconnect ECU connector. Using an ohmmeter, check continuity between ground and ECU wiring harness connector terminals No. 13 (Brown/Yellow wire) for left door, and No. 14 (Brown wire) for right door. Lock and unlock each door in turn. With door(s) locked, continuity should not exist. With door(s) unlocked, continuity should exist. If continuity is not as specified, repair open circuit between ECU and appropriate door lock actuator switch.

NOTE: Voltage measurement requires use of an oscilloscope in the following test. Follow oscilloscope manufacturer's operating instructions.

Test No. 6 (Door & Liftgate Key Cylinder Switch Input Circuit) – 1) With ECU connector connected, check voltage on ECU connector terminals No. 19 (Black wire) for both doors, and No. 20 (Blue/Red wire) for liftgate using an oscilloscope. Lock and unlock doors and liftgate in turn. With doors and liftgate locked, voltage should be 5 volts. With either door or liftgate unlocked, voltage should be zero volts. If voltage is as specified, go to next step. If voltage is not as specified, repair appropriate circuit between ECU and door cylinder switch or liftgate key cylinder switch.

2) Turn ignition switch to OFF position. Disconnect ECU connector. Using an ohmmeter, check continuity between ground and ECU wiring harness connector terminals No. 19 (Black wire) for both doors, and No. 20 (Blue/Red wire) for liftgate. Lock and unlock doors and liftgate in turn. With doors and liftgate locked, continuity should not exist. With either door or liftgate unlocked, continuity should exist. If continuity is not as specified, repair appropriate open circuit between ECU and door cylinder switch or liftgate switch.

NOTE: Voltage measurement requires use of an oscilloscope in the following test. Follow oscilloscope manufacturer's operating instructions.

Test No. 7 (Liftgate Light Switch Input Circuit) – **1)** With ECU connector connected, check voltage on ECU connector terminal No. 17 (Blue/White wire) using an oscilloscope. When liftgate is closed, 5 volts should exist. No voltage should exist when liftgate is open. If voltage is as specified, go to next step. If voltage is not as specified, repair circuit between ECU and liftgate switch.

2) Turn ignition switch to OFF position. Disconnect ECU connector. Using an ohmmeter, check continuity between ECU wiring harness connector terminal No. 17 (Blue/White wire) and ground. No continuity should exist when liftgate lid is closed. Continuity should exist when liftgate is open. If continuity is not as specified, repair open circuit between ECU and liftgate switch.

Test No. 8 (Security Light Activation Circuit) – **1)** Turn ignition switch to OFF position. Disconnect ECU connector. Gain access to instrument panel combination meter connector. Using a voltmeter, check voltage on combination meter connector terminal No. 51 (Red/Black wire). *See Fig. 15.* Battery voltage should exist. If voltage is as specified, go to next step. If voltage is not as specified, check circuit between combination meter connector and fuse No. 19. Repair circuit as necessary.

2) Check voltage on combination meter terminal No. 52 (Green wire). Battery voltage should exist. If voltage is not as specified, check circuit between combination meter connector and ECU wiring connector terminal No. 57 (Green wire). Repair circuit as necessary.

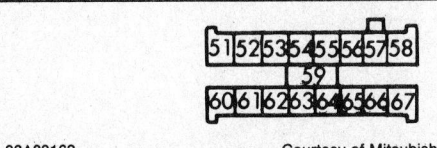

93A83162   Courtesy of Mitsubishi Motor Sales of America.

Fig. 15: Identifying Combination Meter Connector Terminals (Stealth & 3000GT)

Test No. 9 (Horn Relay Power Supply Circuit) – Disconnect horn relay, located in right side of engine compartment. *See Fig. 16.* Using a voltmeter, check voltage on horn relay wiring connector terminal No. 5 (Red/Black wire). Battery voltage should exist. If voltage is not as specified, repair circuit between horn relay connector and fuse No. 6 as necessary.

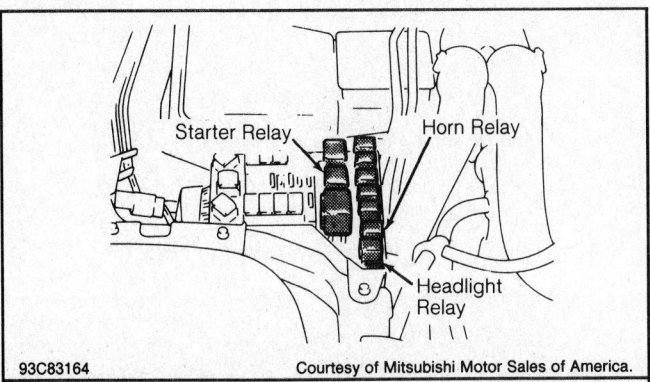

93C83164   Courtesy of Mitsubishi Motor Sales of America.

Fig. 16: Identifying Relays & Terminals (Stealth & 3000GT)

Test No. 10 (Horn Activation Circuit) – **1)** Turn ignition switch to OFF position. Disconnect ECU connector. Ground ECU wiring connector terminal No. 58 (Blue/Green wire). Using a voltmeter, check voltage on horn relay terminal No. 4 (Green/Red wire). *See Fig. 16.* Battery voltage should exist. If voltage is as specified, go to next step. If voltage is not as specified, replace horn relay.

2) Check voltage at horn Black wire. Battery voltage should exist. If voltage is as specified and horn does not sound, replace horn. If voltage is not as specified, repair circuit between horn and horn relay as necessary.

Test No. 11 (Theft Alarm Horn Relay Power Circuit) – Disconnect theft alarm horn relay, located above fuse box. *See Fig. 17.* Using a voltmeter, check voltage on theft alarm horn relay wiring connector terminal No. 1 (White/Black wire). Battery voltage should exist. If voltage is not as specified, repair circuit between theft alarm horn relay connector and fusible link No. 6.

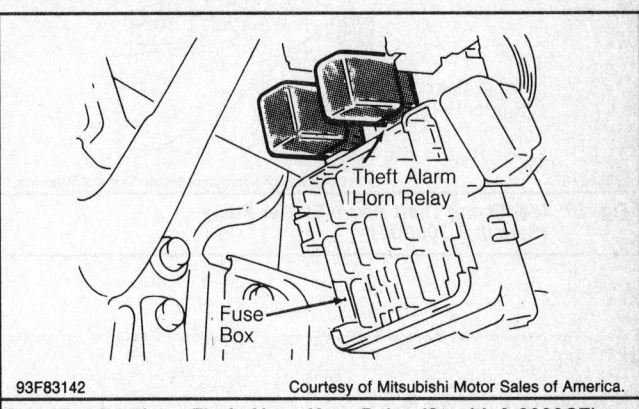

93F83142   Courtesy of Mitsubishi Motor Sales of America.

Fig. 17: Identifying Theft Alarm Horn Relay (Stealth & 3000GT)

Test No. 12 (Theft Alarm Horn Activation Circuit) – **1)** Turn ignition switch to OFF position. Disconnect ECU connector. Ground ECU wiring harness connector terminal No. 58 (Blue/Green wire). Using a voltmeter, check voltage on theft alarm horn relay terminal No. 1 (White/Black wire). *See Fig. 17.* Battery voltage should exist. If voltage is as specified, go to next step. If voltage is not as specified, replace horn relay.

2) Check voltage at theft alarm horn Red/Black wire. Battery voltage should exist. If voltage is as specified and horn does not sound, replace horn. If voltage is not as specified, repair circuit between horn and horn relay as necessary.

Test No. 13 (Headlight Power Supply Circuit) – Disconnect headlight relay. *See Fig. 16.* Using a voltmeter, check voltage on headlight relay wiring connector terminal No. 5 (Red/Black wire). If battery voltage does not exist, repair circuit between headlight relay wiring connector and fusible link No. 3.

Test No. 14 (Headlight Activation Relay) – **1)** Turn ignition switch to OFF position. Disconnect ECU connector. Ground ECU wiring connector terminal No. 2 (Red/Yellow wire). Using a voltmeter, check voltage on headlight relay connector terminal No. 4 (Red/Blue wire). *See Fig. 16.* Battery voltage should exist. If voltage is as specified, go to next step. If voltage is not as specified, replace headlight relay.

2) Check voltage on appropriate (left or right) headlight connector Red/Blue wire. Battery voltage should exist. If voltage is as specified, go to next step. If voltage is not as specified, repair circuit between headlight and headlight relay as necessary.

3) Check voltage on appropriate (left or right) headlight connector Red wire with light switch in LOW position and Red/White wire with light switch in HI position. No battery voltage should exist. If battery voltage does not exist and headlight does not glow, replace headlight or repair headlight switch as necessary. See appropriate STEERING COLUMN SWITCHES article in ACCESSORIES & EQUIPMENT. If battery voltage exists, repair circuit between headlight and headlight relay as necessary.

Test No. 15 (Starter Relay Activation Circuit) – **1)** Turn ignition switch to OFF position. Disconnect ECU connector. Using a voltmeter, check voltage on starter relay terminal No. 3 (Black/Yellow wire). *See Fig. 18.* If battery voltage exists, go to next step. If battery voltage does not exist, replace starter relay.

2) Check voltage on starter motor terminal No. 1 (Black/Yellow wire). If battery voltage exists, go to next step. If battery voltage does not exist, repair circuit between starter motor and starter relay.

3) Turn ignition switch to OFF position. Disconnect Brown/Red wire at starter motor. Using an ohmmeter, check continuity between Brown/Red wire and ground. If continuity exists, replace starter motor magnet switch.

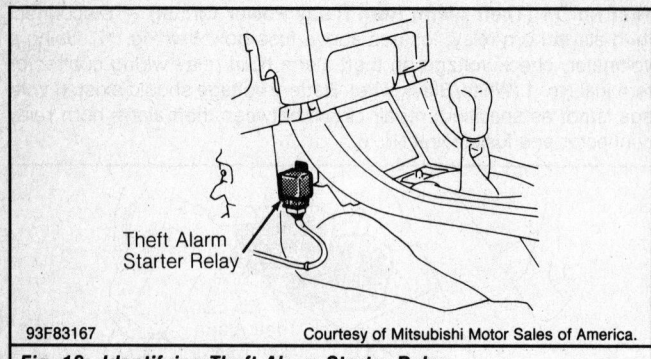

Theft Alarm
Starter Relay

93F83167   Courtesy of Mitsubishi Motor Sales of America.

**Fig. 18: Identifying Theft Alarm Starter Relay
(Stealth & 3000GT)**

REMOVAL & INSTALLATION

CAUTION: When battery is disconnected, vehicle computer and memory systems may lose memory data. Driveability problems may exist until computer systems have completed a relearn cycle. Obtain radio anti-theft protection code from owner prior to servicing vehicle.

Manufacturers do not provide a step by step procedure for removing and installing anti-theft system components.

WIRING DIAGRAMS
See ACCESSORIES & EQUIPMENT, Volume 5.

Cruise Control Systems – Colt, Eclipse, Galant Mirage, Stealth, Summit & 3000GT

DESCRIPTION & OPERATION

The cruise control system is electronically controlled and vacuum actuated. System components include an Electronic Control Unit (ECU), vacuum pump, actuator, cruise control switch, clutch pedal switch, accelerator pedal switch, cruise indicator light, diode (if equipped), Park/Neutral (P/N) switch (A/T), closed throttle position switch, overdrive switch, stoplight switch, throttle position sensor, vehicle speed sensor and A/T control unit.

The system also has self-diagnostic capability. When self-diagnostic mode is activated, each switch and sensor is checked for defects. If cruise control system has been canceled without using a normal cancel method, a code will be set and stored in ECU. Codes can be retrieved to help determine which circuit is malfunctioning.

PRELIMINARY INSPECTION

Before performing TROUBLE SHOOTING steps, inspect vacuum pump, linkage assembly, actuator, cables and vacuum hoses. Ensure linkage and cables move smoothly. Ensure cables do not have excessive slack or tension.

TROUBLE SHOOTING

NOTE: *For further trouble shooting information, see appropriate* **CHECK RESULTS & SYMPTOM CHARTS. See Figs. 4-11.**

SYSTEM CANCELS OR WILL NOT RESET AFTER CANCELLATION

1) Check trouble codes. See SELF-DIAGNOSTICS under DIAGNOSIS & TESTING. If no trouble codes are stored, check to see if cruise control can be set.
2) If cruise control can be set, system may have been canceled because of driving on steep hills or loose wiring connection. If cruise control still cannot be set, perform SYSTEM INPUT TESTS under DIAGNOSIS & TESTING.

NOTE: *If vacuum pump circuit and parts of actuator check okay, replace ECU.*

3) If SYSTEM INPUT TESTS check okay, check vacuum pump. See TEST NO. 5 under appropriate CIRCUIT TESTS. If SYSTEM INPUT TESTS do not check okay, see INPUT CODE CHART. *See Fig. 3.*

ADJUSTMENTS

CRUISE CONTROL CABLE

Colt, Eclipse, Mirage & Summit – 1) Warm engine to normal operating temperature. On all models except Eclipse, remove air cleaner. On all models, remove cable protector. Ensure cable is free of bends and folds. Turn ignition on for 15 seconds. Loosen lock nut "C". *See Fig. 1.*
2) With the end of linkage "C" held in contact with stopper on linkage "B", adjust play in cruise control cable (inner cable) to .04-.08" (1-2 mm). Tighten lock nut.
Galant, Stealth & 3000GT – 1) Warm engine to normal operating temperature. Ensure cable is free of bends and folds. Remove cable protector. Loosen adjusting and lock nuts of link "A". Turn ignition on. *See Fig. 1.*
2) Turn adjusting nut "A" to reduce free play of inner cable of cruise control cable. When lever of link "A" contacts intermediate link "B", back off adjusting nut one turn.
3) Free play of inner cable should be .04-.08" (1-2 mm). Tighten lock nut. Ensure end of fixed Speed Adjusting Screw (SAS) is in contact with stopper of throttle lever.

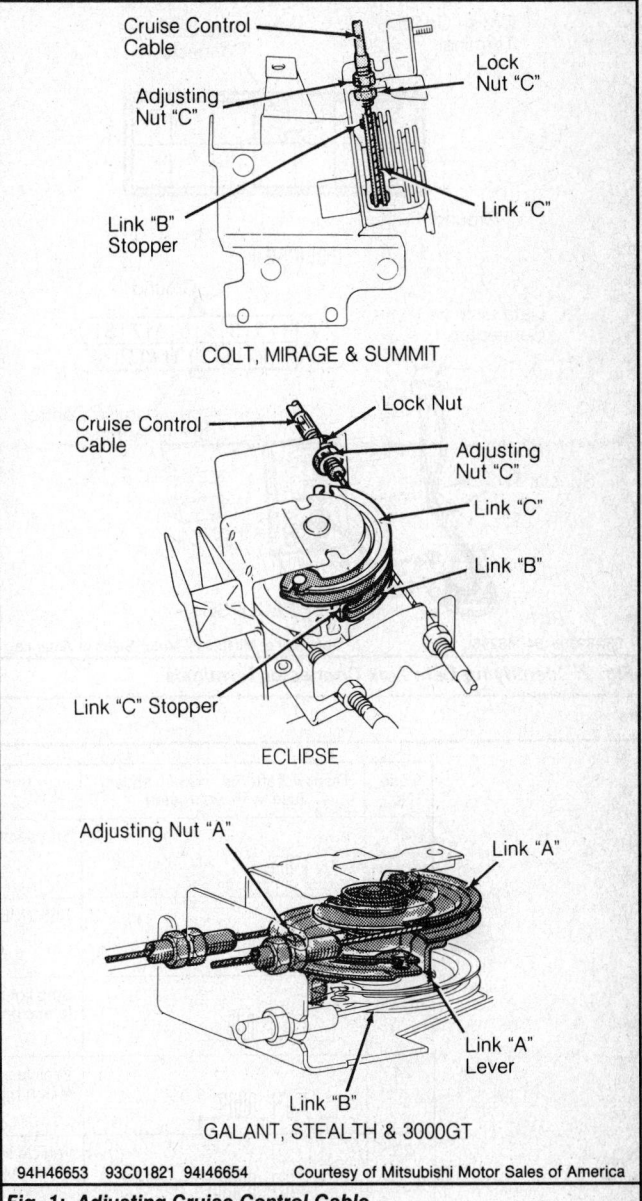

94H46653 93C01821 94I46654 Courtesy of Mitsubishi Motor Sales of America

Fig. 1: Adjusting Cruise Control Cable

DIAGNOSIS & TESTING

CRUISE CONTROL SWITCH FUNCTION TEST

NOTE: *If vehicle speed decreases approximately 9 MPH below set speed, set speed will be canceled.*

Colt, Eclipse, Galant, Mirage & Summit – 1) Cruise control switch is part of multifunction switch mounted on steering column. To operate cruise control system, turn cruise control switch to ON position. Ensure indicator light inside switch comes on.

NOTE: *Speed will not set beyond system limit of 90 MPH.*

2) With cruise control switch in ON position, drive vehicle 25-90 MPH. Press and release SET button. Vehicle speed should stay at set speed. Instrument cluster cruise indicator light should come on. To increase set speed, turn control switch to RESUME position and hold until new set speed is reached.

CHRYSLER/MITSU.
4-16

1994 ACCESSORIES & EQUIPMENT
Cruise Control Systems – Colt, Eclipse, Galant, Mirage, Stealth, Summit & 3000GT (Cont.)

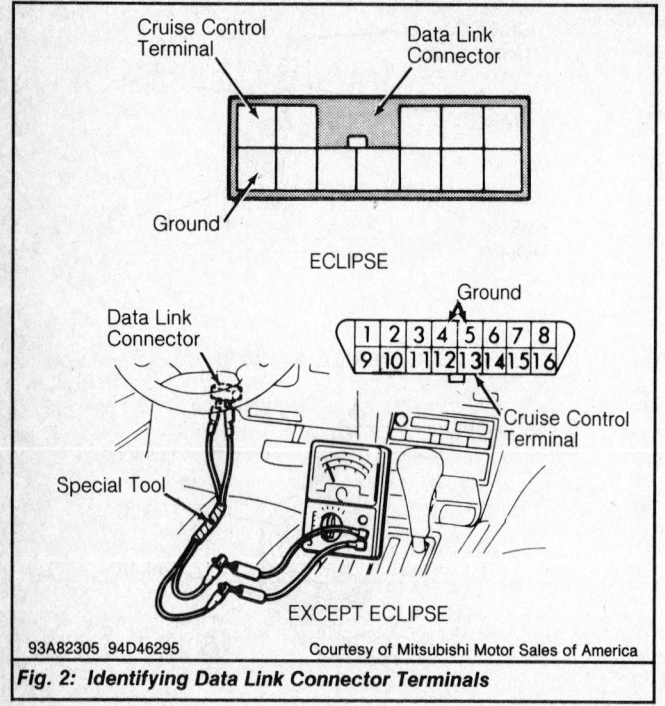

93A82305 94D46295

Courtesy of Mitsubishi Motor Sales of America

Fig. 2: Identifying Data Link Connector Terminals

3) To lower set speed, press SET button and hold until new set speed is reached. To return to set speed after cancellation, move RESUME switch from ON to OFF position. Vehicle speed should return to previous setting before cancellation. Set speed should cancel when any of the following occurs:
- Brake pedal is pressed.
- Clutch pedal is pressed.
- Transmission is shifted to Neutral or Park.
- Cruise control main switch is turned to OFF position.
- Ignition switch is turned to OFF position.

Stealth & 3000GT – 1) Cruise control switch is mounted separately to steering wheel. Turn main cruise control switch to ON position. Cruise control indicator on instrument cluster should come on.

2) To operate cruise control system, drive vehicle at desired speed between 25 and 90 MPH. Move cruise control switch downward to set desired speed. Set indicator light should come on.

3) Vehicle speed should stay at set speed. To increase set speed, move control switch upward to RESUME position and hold until new set speed is reached. To lower set speed, move control switch down to COAST position. Hold until new set speed is reached.

4) To return to set speed after cancellation, move control switch upward to RESUME position. Vehicle speed should return to previous setting before cancellation. Set speed should cancel when any of the following occurs:
- Cruise control switch is pulled toward driver.
- Brake pedal is pressed.
- Clutch pedal is pressed.
- Transmission is shifted to Neutral.

Code No.	Display patterns (output codes) (use with voltmeter)	Input operation		Check results
21		SET switch ON		SET switch circuit normal
22		RESUME switch ON		RESUME switch normal
23		Stop light switch ON (brake pedal depressed)		Stop light switch circuit normal
24		Vehicle speed more than approx. 40 km/h (25 mph)		Vehicle speed sensor circuit normal if code Nos. 24 and 25 are displayed
25		Vehicle speed less than approx. 40 km/h (25 mph)		
26		M/T	Clutch pedal position switch ON (clutch pedal depressed)	Clutch pedal position switch circuit normal
		A/T	Park/neutral position switch ON (SELECT lever placed in "N" position)	Park/neutral position switch circuit normal
27		CANCEL switch ON		CANCEL switch circuit normal
28		TPS output voltage 1.5 V or more (Accelerator pedal depressed more than half the way)		Throttle position sensor circuit normal
29		Closed throttle position switch OFF (Accelerator pedal depressed)		Closed throttle position switch circuit normal

94D46477

Courtesy of Mitsubishi Motor Sales of America

Fig. 3: Input Code Chart

SELF-DIAGNOSTICS

1) Self-diagnostics should be performed when cruise control cancels without driver using normal cancel modes. Data Link Connector (DLC) is located on right side of fuse box.

2) Use Scan Tester (MB991341) or an analog voltmeter for code retrieval. Plug scan tester connectors into cigarette lighter and DLC. Read trouble codes. If using voltmeter, connect leads of analog voltmeter between cruise control terminal and ground terminal of DLC. *See Fig. 2.* Read voltmeter needle sweeps to determine trouble code.

NOTE: On all models, Codes No. 15 and 16 will be displayed whether malfunction is present or not. On Stealth & 3000GT, a Code 17 will not cause system to cancel.

---

3) Once trouble codes have been displayed, see SELF-DIAGNOSTIC TROUBLE CODES to find appropriate CIRCUIT TEST. See appropriate CIRCUIT TESTS. To clear trouble codes, disconnect positive battery cable or go to next step.

4) Turn ignition on. Turn cruise control set switch on. Turn cruise switch on and, in less than one second after cruise switch is turned on, turn resume switch on.

5) Press set switch and brake pedal simultaneously, holding them for more than 5 seconds. Ensure codes are cleared.

SELF-DIAGNOSTIC TROUBLE CODES

Code 11 – Possible cause: faulty vacuum pump circuit. Perform CIRCUIT TEST NO. 5.

Code 12 – Possible cause: faulty vehicle speed sensor circuit. Perform CIRCUIT TEST NO. 4.

Code 15 – Possible cause: faulty control switch. Perform CIRCUIT TEST NO. 2. On Eclipse, also perform CIRCUIT TEST NO. 3.

Code 16 – Possible cause: faulty control unit. Substitute known-good control unit.

Code 17 – Possible cause: faulty closed throttle position switch or throttle position sensor. On Eclipse, perform CIRCUIT TEST NO. 11. On all other models, perform CIRCUIT TEST NO. 9.

SYSTEM INPUT TESTS

1) System input tests should be performed if no trouble codes are stored when performing SELF-DIAGNOSTICS.

2) System input tests cycle each cruise control switch and sensor. Use Scan Tester (MB991341) or an analog voltmeter for system input check.

3) The scan tester setting is the same as setting for self-diagnostics. Plug scan tester connectors into cigarette lighter and data link connector.

4) If using voltmeter, connect leads of analog voltmeter between cruise control terminal and ground terminal of diagnostic connector. *See Fig. 2.* Turn ignition on. Turn cruise control switch to OFF position. Turn cruise control set switch to ON position.

5) Turn cruise control switch to ON position and within one second, turn resume switch to ON position. Perform each switch input test as specified in INPUT CODE CHART. *See Fig. 3.*

6) Cycle each switch until code is displayed. If code is not displayed, that switch or sensor is defective. When each switch or sensor is cycled and signals are reaching control unit, codes will continue to display.

7) When switch or sensor cycling stops, code display stops. If system input tests check okay, check vacuum pump. See TEST NO. 5 under appropriate CIRCUIT TESTS.

	Check results	Probable cause	Remedy	Circuit Test
	Even if an attempt is made to enter data, no code appears.	Open circuit in auto-cruise control unit power supply circuit	Replace control switch or repair harness.	No. 1
		Open circuit in control switch circuit		
		Defective auto-cruise control unit	Replace auto-cruise control unit.	–
	Code No. 21 remains even though SET switch is set to OFF.	SET switch ON malfunction	Replace the control switch.	No. 2
	Code No. 22 remains even though RESUME switch is set to OFF.	RESUME switch ON malfunction	Replace the control switch.	No. 3
	Code No. 23 does not appear when brake pedal is depressed.	Defective stop light switch circuit	Replace stop light switch or repair harness.	No. 7
	Code No. 23 does not disappear when brake pedal is released.			
	Code No. 26 does not disappear when clutch pedal is released. <M/T>	Defective clutch switch circuit	Replace clutch switch or repair harness.	No. 8
	Code No. 26 does not disappear when SELECT lever is placed in a position other than "N" and "P". <A/T>	Defective Park/Neutral position switch circuit	Replace Park/Neutral position switch or repair harness.	No. 9
	Code No. 25 does not appear when vehicle is traveling at less than 40 km/h (25 mph).	Defective vehicle speed sensor circuit	Check or repair vehicle speed sensor circuit.	No. 5
	Code No. 25 does not disappear or code No. 24 does not appear when vehicle speed is increased to more than approximately 40 km/h (25 mph).			

94E46478

Fig. 4: *Check Results Chart (Colt, Galant, Mirage & Summit)*

CHRYSLER/MITSU.
4-18

1994 ACCESSORIES & EQUIPMENT
Cruise Control Systems – Colt, Eclipse, Galant, Mirage, Stealth, Summit & 3000GT (Cont.)

Trouble symptom	Probable cause	Circuit Test	Remedy
• The set vehicle speed varies greatly upward or downward. • "Hunting" (repeated alternating acceleration and deceleration) occurs after setting is made.	Malfunction of the vehicle speed sensor circuit	No. 5	Repair the vehicle speed sensor system, or replace the part.
	Malfunction of the speedometer cable or speedometer drive gear		
	Auto-cruise vacuum pump circuit poor contact	No. 6	Repair the auto-cruise vacuum pump system, or replace the part.
	Malfunction of the auto-cruise vacuum pump		
	Malfunction of the auto-cruise control unit	–	Replace the auto-cruise control unit.
The auto-cruise control system is not canceled when the brake pedal is depressed.	Brake switch (for auto-cruise control) malfunction (short-circuit)	No. 7	Repair the harness or replace the stop light switch.
	Auto-cruise vacuum pump drive circuit short-circuit	No. 6	Repair the harness or replace the auto-cruise vacuum pump.
	Malfunction of the auto-cruise control unit	–	Replace the auto-cruise control unit.
The auto-cruise control system is not canceled when the clutch pedal is depressed. <M/T> (It is canceled, however, when the brake pedal is depressed.)	Damaged or disconnected wiring of clutch switch input circuit	If the input check code No. 26 indicates a malfunction. No. 8	Repair the harness, or repair or replace the clutch switch.
	Clutch switch improper installation (won't switch ON)		
	Malfunction of the auto-cruise control unit	–	Replace the auto-cruise control unit.
The auto-cruise control system is not canceled when the shift lever is moved to the "N" position. <A/T> (It is canceled, however, when the brake pedal is depressed.)	Damaged or disconnected wiring of Park/Neutral position switch input circuit	If the input check code No. 26 indicates a malfunction. No. 9	Repair the harness, or repair or replace the Park/Neutral position switch.
	Improper adjustment of Park/Neutral position switch		
	Malfunction of the auto-cruise control unit	–	Replace the auto-cruise control unit.

94H46513

Fig. 5: Symptom Chart (Colt, Galant, Mirage & Summit – 1 Of 2)

Trouble symptom	Probable cause	Circuit Test	Remedy
Cannot decelerate by using the SET switch.	Temporary damaged or disconnected wiring of SET switch input circuit	No. 2	Repair the harness or replace the SET switch.
	Auto-cruise vacuum pump circuit poor contact	No. 6	Repair the harness or replace the auto-cruise vacuum pump and actuator.
	Malfunction of the auto-cruise vacuum pump and actuator (including blocking of negative pressure passage)		
	Malfunction of the auto-cruise control unit	–	Replace the auto-cruise control unit.
Cannot accelerate or resume speed by using the RESUME switch.	Open or short circuit in RESUME switch circuit in control switch	No. 3	Replace the control switch.
	Auto-cruise vacuum pump circuit poor contact	No. 6	Repair the harness or replace the auto-cruise vacuum pump and actuator.
	Malfunction of the auto-cruise vacuum pump and actuator (including air leaks from negative pressure passage)		
	Malfunction of the auto-cruise control unit	–	Replace the auto-cruise control unit.
Auto-cruise control system can be set while traveling at a vehicle speed of less than 40 km/h (25 mph), or there is no automatic cancellation at that speed.	Malfunction of the vehicle speed sensor circuit	No. 5	Repair the vehicle speed sensor system, or replace the part.
	Malfunction of the speedometer cable or the speedometer drive gear		
	Malfunction of the auto-cruise control unit	–	Replace the auto-cruise control unit.
The auto-cruise control switch indicator light does not illuminate. (But auto-cruise control system is normal.)	Damaged or disconnected bulb of auto-cruise control switch indicator	No. 4	Repair the harness or replace the control switch.
	Harness damaged or disconnected		
Overdrive is not canceled during fixed speed driving. <A/T>	Malfunction of circuit related to overdrive cancellation, or malfunction of auto-cruise control unit	**No. 10**	Repair the harness or replace the part.
No shift to overdrive during manual driving. <A/T>			
The auto-cruise control indicator light does not illuminate. (But auto-cruise control system is normal.)	Damaged or disconnected bulb of indicator light	No. 4	Repair the harness or replace the bulb.
	Harness damaged or disconnected		

93D82308

Fig. 6: Symptom Chart (Colt, Galant, Mirage & Summit – 2 Of 2)

CHRYSLER/MITSU.
4-20

1994 ACCESSORIES & EQUIPMENT
Cruise Control Systems – Colt, Eclipse, Galant, Mirage, Stealth, Summit & 3000GT (Cont.)

Check results	Probable cause	Remedy	Circuit Test
Code 21 remains even though SET switch is set to OFF.	SET switch ON malfunction	Replace the control switch.	No. 2
	SET switch input line short-circuit	Repair the harness.	
Code 22 remains even though RESUME switch is set to OFF.	RESUME switch ON malfunction	Replace the control switch.	No. 3
	RESUME switch input line short-circuit	Repair the harness.	
Code 23 is not canceled even if the stop light switch is turned OFF by releasing the brake pedal.	Malfunction of stop light switch circuit.	Replace stop light switch or repair harness.	No. 6
Code 25 does not disappear, and code 24 does not appear, even though vehicle speed reaches approximately 40 km/h (25 mph) or higher.	Malfunction of the vehicle-speed sensor circuit (damaged or disconnected wiring, or short-circuit)	Check or repair the vehicle speed sensor circuit.	No. 4
Code 26 is not canceled even if the clutch pedal position switch is turned OFF by releasing the clutch pedal.	Malfunction of clutch pedal position switch circuit.	Replace clutch pedal position switch or repair harness.	No. 8
Code 26 is not canceled even if the select lever is moved to anything but N, P <A/T>.	Malfunction of park/neutral position switch circuit.	Replace park/neutral position switch or repair harness.	No. 7

CHECK RESULTS CHART

Trouble symptom	Probable cause	Circuit Test	Remedy
Cannot accelerate or resume speed by using the RESUME switch.	Damaged or disconnected wiring, or short-circuit, of RESUME switch input circuit	No. 3	Repair the harness or replace the RESUME switch.
	Auto-cruise vacuum pump circuit poor contact	No. 5	Repair the harness or replace the auto-cruise vacuum pump and actuator.
	Malfunction of the auto-cruise vacuum pump and actuator (including air leak from negative pressure passage)		
	Malfunction of the ECU	–	Replace the ECU.
Auto-cruise control system can be set while traveling at a vehicle speed of less than 40 km/h (25 mph), or there is no automatic cancellation at that speed.	Malfunction of the vehicle-speed sensor circuit	No. 4	Repair the vehicle-speed sensor system, or replace the part.
	Malfunction of the speedometer cable or the speedometer drive gear		
	Malfunction of the ECU	–	Replace the ECU.
The indicator light of combination meter does not illuminate. (But auto-cruise control system is normal.)	Damaged or disconnected bulb of indicator light	–	Repair the harness or replace the bulb.
	Harness damaged or disconnected		
Malfunction of control function by ON/OFF switching of ELC 4 A/T accelerator switch (Non-operation of damper clutch, 2nd gear hold, etc.)	Malfunction of circuit related to accelerator switch OFF function	No. 9	Repair the harness or replace the part.
	Malfunction of the ECU		
Overdrive is not canceled during fixed speed driving. <A/T>	Malfunction of circuit related to overdrive cancellation, or malfunction of ECU	No. 10	Repair the harness or replace the part.
No shift to overdrive during manual driving. <A/T>			

SYMPTOM CHART (1 OF 2)

94F46479 93B01825

Courtesy of Mitsubishi Motor Sales of America

Fig. 7: Check Results Chart & Symptom Chart (Eclipse – 1 Of 2)

1994 ACCESSORIES & EQUIPMENT
Cruise Control Systems – Colt, Eclipse, Galant, Mirage, Stealth, Summit & 3000GT (Cont.)

CHRYSLER/MITSU.
4-21

Trouble symptom	Probable cause	Circuit Test	Remedy
• The set vehicle speed varies greatly upward or downward. • "Hunching" (repeated alternating acceleration and deceleration) occurs after setting is made.	Malfunction of the vehicle speed sensor circuit	No.4	Repair the vehicle speed sensor system, or replace the part.
	Malfunction of the speedometer cable or speedometer drive gear		
	Auto-cruise vacuum pump circuit poor contact	No.5	Repair the auto-cruise vacuum pump or replace the part.
	Malfunction of the auto-cruise vacuum pump		
	Malfunction of the ECU	–	Replace the ECU.
The auto-cruise control system is not canceled when the brake pedals is depressed.	Damaged or disconnected wiring of the stop light switch input circuit; brake switch (for auto-cruise control) malfunction (short-circuit)	If the input check code No.23 indicates a malfunction. No.6	Repair the harness or replace the stop light switch.
	Auto-cruise vacuum pump drive circuit short-circuit.	No.5	Repair the harness or replace the auto-cruise vacuum pump.
	Malfunction of the ECU	–	Replace the ECU.
The auto-cruise control system is not canceled when the clutch pedal is depressed. (vehicles with a manual transaxle) (It is canceled, however, when the brake pedal is depressed.)	Damaged or disconnected wiring of clutch pedal position switch input circuit	If the input check code No.26 indicates a malfunction. No.8	Repair the harness, or repair or replace the clutch pedal position switch.
	Clutch pedal position switch improper installation (won't switch ON)		
	Malfunction of the ECU	–	Replace the ECU.
The auto-cruise control system is not canceled when the shift lever is moved to the "N" position. (vehicles with an automatic transaxle) (It is canceled, however, when the brake pedal is depressed.)	Damaged or disconnected wiring of park/neutral position switch input circuit	If the input check code No.26 indicates a malfunction. No.7	Repair the harness, or repair or replace the park/neutral position switch.
	Improper adjustment of park/neutral position switch		
	Malfunction of the ECU	–	Replace the ECU.
Cannot decelerate by using the SET switch	Temporary damaged or disconnected wiring of SET switch input circuit	No.2	Repair the harness or replace the SET switch.
	Auto-cruise vacuum pump circuit poor contact	No.5	Repair the harness or replace the auto-cruise vacuum pump and actuator.
	Malfunction of the auto-cruise vacuum pump and actuator (including clogging of negative pressure passage)		
	Malfunction of the ECU	–	Replace the ECU.

SYMPTOM CHART (2 OF 2)

94146480

Courtesy of Mitsubishi Motor Sales of America

Fig. 8: Symptom Chart (Eclipse – 2 Of 2)

CHRYSLER/MITSU.
4-22

1994 ACCESSORIES & EQUIPMENT
Cruise Control Systems – Colt, Eclipse, Galant, Mirage, Stealth, Summit & 3000GT (Cont.)

Result of check	Probable cause	Remedy	Circuit Test
None of the codes appear even if input operations are performed.	Open circuit in control unit power supply circuit.	Replace main switch or repair harness.	No. 1
	Open circuit in control switch circuit	Replace control switch or repair harness.	No. 2
	Defective control unit	Replace control unit.	
Even when SET switch is set to OFF, code No. 21 does not go away.	SET switch ON malfunction	Replace the control switch.	No. 2
Even when RESUME switch is set to OFF, code No. 22 does not go away.	RESUME switch ON malfunction	Replace control switch.	No. 2
Even when CANCEL switch is set to OFF, code No. 27 does not go away.	CANCEL switch ON malfunction	Replace control switch.	No. 2
Even when brake pedal is depressed, code No. 23 is not displayed.	Defective stop light switch circuit	Replace stop light switch or repair harness.	No. 7
Even when brake pedal is released, code No. 23 does not go away.			
Even when clutch pedal is released, code No. 26 does not go away. <M/T>	Defective clutch pedal position switch circuit	Replace clutch pedal position switch or repair harness.	No. 7
Even when select lever is placed in any position other than "N" and "P", code No. 26 does not go away. <A/T>	Defective park/neutral position switch circuit	Replace park/neutral position switch or repair harness.	No. 8
Code No. 25 is not displayed even when vehicle speed is less than about 40 km/h (25 mph).	Defective vehicle speed sensor circuit	Check and repair vehicle speed sensor circuit.	No. 4
Even when vehicle speed is increased to more than about 40 km/h (25 mph), code No. 25 does not go away. Code No. 24 is not displayed, either.			

94J46481

Courtesy of Mitsubishi Motor Sales of America

Fig. 9: Check Results Chart (Stealth & 3000GT)

Trouble symptom	Probable cause	Circuit Test	Remedy
• The set vehicle speed varies greatly upward or downward. • "Hunting" (repeated alternating acceleration and deceleration) occurs after setting is made.	Malfunction of the vehicle speed sensor circuit	No. 4	Repair the vehicle speed sensor system, or replace the part.
	Malfunction of the speedometer cable or speedometer drive gear <Up to 1993 models (Non turbo)>		
	Vacuum pump assembly circuit poor contact	No. 5	Repair the actuator system, or replace the part.
	Malfunction of the vacuum pump assembly (including air leaks from negative pressure passage)		
	Malfunction of the ECU	–	Replace the ECU.
The cruise control system is not canceled when the brake pedal is depressed.	Brake switch (for cruise control) malfunction (short-circuit)	No. 6	Repair the harness or replace the stop light switch.
	Vacuum pump assembly drive circuit short-circuit	No. 5	Repair the harness or replace the vacuum pump assembly.
	Malfunction of the ECU	–	Replace the ECU.
The cruise control system is not canceled when the clutch pedal is depressed. <M/T> (It is canceled, however, when the brake pedal is depressed.)	Damaged or disconnected wiring of clutch switch input circuit	If the input check code No. 26 indicates a malfunction. No. 7	Repair the harness, or repair or replace the clutch switch.
	Clutch switch improper installation (won't switch ON)		
	Malfunction of the ECU	–	Replace the ECU.
The cruise control system is not canceled when the shift lever is moved to the "N" position. <A/T> (It is canceled, however, when the brake pedal is depressed.)	Damaged or disconnected wiring of park/neutral position switch input circuit	If the input check code No. 26 indicates a malfunction. No. 8	Repair the harness, or repair or replace the park/neutral position switch.
	Improper adjustment of park/neutral position switch		
	Malfunction of the ECU	–	Replace the ECU.
Cannot decelerate by using the SET switch.	Temporary damaged or disconnected wiring of control switch input circuit	No. 2	Repair the harness or replace the control switch.
	Vacuum pump assembly circuit poor contact	No. 5	Repair the harness or replace the vacuum pump assembly.
	Malfunction of the vacuum pump assembly		
	Malfunction of the ECU	–	Replace the ECU.

94A46482

Fig. 10: Symptom Chart (Stealth & 3000GT – 1 Of 2)

CHRYSLER/MITSU. 4-24

1994 ACCESSORIES & EQUIPMENT
Cruise Control Systems – Colt, Eclipse, Galant, Mirage, Stealth, Summit & 3000GT (Cont.)

Trouble symptom	Probable cause	Circuit Test	Remedy
Cannot accelerate or resume speed by using the RESUME switch.	Open or short circuit in RESUME switch circuit in control switch	No. 2	Replace the control switch.
	Vacuum pump assembly circuit poor contact	No. 5	Repair the harness or replace the vacuum pump assembly.
	Malfunction of the vacuum pump assembly (including air leaks from negative pressure passage)		
	Malfunction of the ECU	–	Replace the ECU.
Even when CANCEL switch is set to ON, cruise control is not canceled (Cruise control, however, is canceled when brake pedal is depressed.)	Open or short circuit in CANCEL switch circuit in control switch	If the input check code No. 27 indicates a malfunction. No. 2	Replace the control switch.
	Malfunction of the ECU	–	Replace the ECU
The cruise control system can be set while traveling at a vehicle speed of less than 40 km/h (25 mph), or there is no automatic cancellation at that speed.	Malfunction of the vehicle-speed sensor circuit	No. 4	Repair the vehicle speed sensor system, or replace the part.
	Malfunction of the speedometer cable or the speedometer drive gear <Non turbo>		
	Malfunction of the ECU	–	Replace the ECU.
The cruise control indicator light of the combination meter does not illuminate. (But cruise control system is normal)	Damaged or disconnected bulb of indicator light	No. 3	Repair the harness or replace the light bulb.
	Harness damaged or disconnected		
	Malfunction of the ECU	–	Replace the ECU.
Cruise control ON indicator light does not come on. (However, cruise control is functional.)	Burned-out indicator light bulb	No. 3	Repair the harness or replace the main switch.
	Open or short circuit in harness		
Malfunction of control function by ON/OFF switching of ELC 4 A/T accelerator switch. (Non-operation of damper clutch, 2nd gear hold, etc.)	Malfunction of circuit related to accelerator switch OFF function	No. 10	Repair the harness or replace the part.
	Malfunction of the ECU		
Overdrive is not canceled during fixed speed driving <A/T>	Malfunction of circuit related to overdrive cancellation, or malfunction of ECU	No. 11	Repair the harness or replace the part.
No shift to overdrive during manual driving. <A/T>			

93182311

Courtesy of Mitsubishi Motor Sales of America

Fig. 11: Symptom Chart (Stealth & 3000GT – 2 Of 2)

CIRCUIT TESTS (EXCEPT ECLIPSE)

NOTE: To identify circuit connector terminals, see Fig. 13. See appropriate wiring diagram.

Test No. 1 (Power Supply Circuit) – 1) When cruise control switch is turned to ON position, battery voltage should be present on terminal No. 2 of control unit. If voltage is not present, check fuse No. 2 and replace as necessary. If fuse is okay, replace switch or repair harness.
2) Control unit should be grounded at all times through terminals No. 8 and 14. If circuit is not grounded, repair harness. On Colt, Galant, Mirage and Summit, control unit back-up power supply should have battery voltage at all times through terminal No. 16. If voltage is not present, check fuse No. 8 and replace as necessary. If fuse is okay, replace switch or repair harness.
Test No. 2 (Set, Resume & Cancel Switch Circuits) – 1) When all switches are turned to OFF position, voltage should not be present on terminal No. 18 of cruise control unit. When set switch is turned to ON position, 3 volts should be present on terminal No. 18 of control unit.
2) When resume switch is turned to ON position, 6 volts should be present on terminal No. 18 of control unit. When resume switch is turned to OFF position, voltage should not be present on terminal No. 18 of control unit.
3) When cancel switch is turned to ON position, battery voltage should be present on terminal No. 18 of control unit. When cancel switch is turned to OFF position, voltage should not be present on terminal No. 18 of control unit. If circuit does not test correctly, replace switch or repair harness.
Test No. 3 (Indicator Light Circuit) – When cruise control is active, battery voltage should be present on terminal No. 23 of control unit. When cruise control is turned to OFF position, voltage should not be present on terminal No. 23 of control unit. If circuit does not test correctly, replace switch or repair harness.

Test No. 4 (Vehicle Speed Sensor Circuit) – When vehicle moves slowly, voltage should alternate from zero volts to 2 or more volts at terminal No. 19 of control unit. If circuit does not test correctly, replace sensor or repair harness.

Test No. 5 (Vacuum Pump Circuit) – **1)** When release valve is on, battery voltage should not be present on terminal No. 9 (No. 12 on Stealth and 3000GT) of control unit. When release valve is off, battery voltage should be present on terminal No. 9 (No. 12 on Stealth and 3000GT) of control unit.

2) When control valve is on, battery voltage should not be present on terminal No. 13 of control unit. When control valve is off, battery voltage should be present on terminal No. 13 of control unit.

3) When DC motor is driven, battery voltage should not be present on terminal No. 26 of control unit. When DC motor is stopped, battery voltage should be present on terminal No. 26 of control unit.

4) When cruise control switch is turned to ON position, battery voltage should be present on terminal No. 25 of control unit. When DC motor is stopped, battery voltage should be present on terminal No. 26 of control unit. See Fig. 12. If circuit does not test correctly, replace vacuum pump or repair harness.

Auto-cruise control operations	DC motor (ON: Current supplied OFF: No current supplied)	Solenoid valve (ON: Closed OFF: Opened)	
		Control valve	Release valve
Acceleration	ON	ON	ON
Hold	OFF	ON	ON
Deceleration	OFF	OFF	ON
Cancellation	OFF	OFF	OFF

93J01141   Courtesy of Mitsubishi Motor Sales of America

Fig. 12: Testing Vacuum Pump Circuit (Except Eclipse)

Test No. 6 (Stoplight Switch Circuit) – When brake pedal is pressed, battery voltage should be present on terminal No. 15 of control unit. When brake pedal is released, voltage should not be present on terminal No. 15 of control unit. If circuit does not test correctly, replace switch or repair harness.

Test No. 7 (Clutch Switch Circuit) – When clutch pedal is pressed, battery voltage should not be present on terminal No. 1 of control unit. When clutch pedal is released, voltage should be present on terminal No. 1 of control unit. If circuit does not test correctly, replace switch or repair harness.

Test No. 8 (Park/Neutral Switch Circuit) – **1)** When park/neutral switch is placed in Neutral or Park, battery voltage should not be present on terminal No. 1 of control unit.

2) When park/neutral switch is placed in Drive, Second, Low or Reverse positions, battery voltage should be present on terminal No. 1 of control unit. If circuit does not test correctly, replace switch or repair harness.

Test No. 9 (Throttle Position Sensor & Closed Throttle Position Switch Circuit) – **1)** When checking closed throttle position switch, if accelerator pedal is pressed, battery voltage should be present on terminal No. 4 of control unit. When accelerator pedal is released, battery voltage should not be present on terminal No. 4 of control unit.

2) When checking throttle position sensor, if throttle valve is in idle position, .45-.55 volt (.48-.72 volt on Stealth and 3000GT) should be present on terminal No. 5 of control unit.

3) When throttle valve is in wide open throttle position, 4.5-5.5 volts should be present on terminal No. 5 of control unit. If circuit does not test correctly, replace switch or repair harness.

Test No. 10 (Overdrive Cancellation Circuit) – **1)** When ignition switch is in ON position, battery voltage should be present on terminal No. 3 of control unit. When overdrive is activated, battery voltage should be present on terminal No. 10 of control unit.

2) When overdrive is off, battery voltage should not be present on terminal No. 10 of control unit. When overdrive switch is in ON position, battery voltage should be present on terminal No. 11 of control unit.

3) When overdrive switch is in OFF position, battery voltage should not be present on terminal No. 11 of control unit. If circuit does not test correctly, replace switch or repair harness.

CLUTCH & ACCELERATOR SWITCH CONNECTOR (ALL MODELS)

CRUISE CONTROL RELAY CONNECTOR (STEALTH & 3000GT)

CRUISE CONTROL SWITCH CONNECTOR (EXCEPT ECLIPSE, STEALTH & 3000GT)

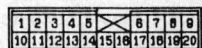
CRUISE CONTROL SWITCH CONNECTOR (ECLIPSE)

ELECTRONIC CRUISE CONTROL UNIT (ECU) CONNECTOR (ALL MODELS)

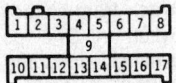
INSTRUMENT CLUSTER CONNECTOR (ALL MODELS)

MAIN CRUISE CONTROL SWITCH CONNECTOR (STEALTH & 3000GT)

MAIN CRUISE CONTROL SWITCH CONNECTOR (EXCEPT ECLIPSE, STEALTH & 3000GT)

MOTOR POSITION SENSOR CONNECTOR (EXCEPT ECLIPSE, STEALTH & 3000GT)

OVERDRIVE SWITCH CONNECTOR (ECLIPSE)

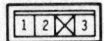
OVERDRIVE SWITCH CONNECTOR (EXCEPT ECLIPSE)

PARK/NEUTRAL SWITCH CONNECTOR (EXCEPT ECLIPSE)

PARK/NEUTRAL SWITCH CONNECTOR (EXCEPT ECLIPSE)

STOPLIGHT SWITCH CONNECTOR (ALL MODELS)

THROTTLE POSITION SENSOR CONNECTOR (ALL MODELS)

VACUUM PUMP CONNECTOR (ALL MODELS)

93B01830 93I01838 93D01826 93C01835 93J02211 93J01872 93G01837 93B02212
93F01832 93G01836 93J01834 93C02217 93E82226 93D02213 93D02374 93F02214

Courtesy of Mitsubishi Motor Sales of America

Fig. 13: Identifying Cruise Control Circuit Connector Terminals

CHRYSLER/MITSU.
4-26

1994 ACCESSORIES & EQUIPMENT
Cruise Control Systems – Colt, Eclipse, Galant, Mirage, Stealth, Summit & 3000GT (Cont.)

CIRCUIT TESTS (ECLIPSE)

NOTE: To identify circuit connector terminals, see Fig. 13. See appropriate wiring diagram.

Test No. 1 (Power Supply Circuit) – 1) When cruise control switch is turned to ON position, battery voltage should be present on terminal No. 2 of control unit connector. If battery voltage is not present, check fuse No. 11.

2) If fuse is okay, repair harness. Control unit should be grounded at all times through terminals No. 8 and 14. If circuit is not grounded, repair harness.

Test No. 2 (Set & Coast Switch Circuits) – When set switch is turned to ON position, voltage should not be present on terminal No. 17 of control unit. When set switch is turned to OFF position, voltage should be present on terminal No. 17 of control unit. If circuit does not test correctly, replace switch or repair harness.

Test No. 3 (Resume Switch Circuit) – When resume switch is turned to ON position, voltage should not be present on terminal No. 18 of control unit. When resume switch is turned to off position, voltage should be present on terminal No. 18 of control unit. If circuit does not test correctly, replace switch or repair harness.

Test No. 4 (Vehicle Speed Sensor Circuit) – When vehicle moves slowly, voltage should alternate from zero volts to 2 or more volts at terminal No. 19 of control unit. If circuit does not test correctly, replace sensor or repair harness.

Test No. 5 (Vacuum Pump Circuit) – 1) When release valve is in release mode, battery voltage should be present on terminal No. 12 of control unit. When release valve is in acceleration or deceleration mode, voltage should not be present on terminal No. 12 of control unit.

2) When control valve is in release or deceleration modes, battery voltage should be present on terminal No. 13 of control unit. When control valve is in acceleration mode, battery voltage should not be present on terminal No. 13 of control unit.

3) When vacuum pump is in release or deceleration mode, battery voltage should be present on terminal No. 26 of control unit. When vacuum pump is in acceleration mode, battery voltage should not be present on terminal No. 26 of control unit. If circuit does not test correctly, replace vacuum pump or repair harness.

Test No. 6 (Stoplight Switch Circuit) – When brake pedal is pressed, battery voltage should be present on terminal No. 15 of control unit. When brake pedal is released, voltage should not be present on terminal No. 15 of control unit. If circuit does not test correctly, replace switch or repair harness.

Test No. 7 (Park/Neutral Switch Circuit) – 1) When P/N switch is placed in "N" or "P", battery voltage should not be present on terminal No. 1 of control unit.

2) When P/N switch is placed in "D", "2", "L" or "R" position, battery voltage should be present on terminal No. 1 of control unit. If circuit does not test correctly, replace switch or repair harness.

Test No. 8 (Clutch Switch Circuit) – When clutch pedal is pressed, battery voltage should not be present on terminal No. 1 of control unit. When clutch pedal is released, voltage should be present on terminal No. 1 of control unit. If circuit does not test correctly, replace switch or repair harness.

Test No. 9 (Accelerator Switch Circuit) – 1) When ignition switch is in ON position, battery voltage should be present on terminal No. 3 of control unit. When accelerator pedal is pressed, battery voltage should not be present on terminal No. 9 of control unit.

2) When accelerator pedal is released, battery voltage should be present on terminal No. 9 of control unit. If circuit does not test correctly, replace switch or repair harness.

Test No. 10 (Overdrive Cancellation Circuit) – 1) When ignition switch is in ON position, battery voltage should be present on terminal No. 3 of control unit. When overdrive is activated, battery voltage should be present on terminal No. 10 of control unit.

2) When overdrive is off, battery voltage should not be present on terminal No. 10 of control unit. When overdrive switch is in ON position, battery voltage should be present on terminal No. 11 of control unit.

3) When overdrive switch is in OFF position, battery voltage should not be present on terminal No. 11 of control unit. If circuit does not test correctly, replace switch or repair harness.

Test No. 11 (Throttle Position Sensor & Closed Throttle Position Switch Circuit) – 1) When checking closed throttle position switch, if accelerator pedal is pressed, battery voltage should be present on terminal No. 4 of control unit. When accelerator pedal is released, battery voltage should not be present on terminal No. 4 of control unit.

2) When checking throttle position sensor, if throttle valve is in idle position, .45-.55 volt should be present on terminal No. 5 of control unit. When throttle valve is in wide open throttle position, 4.5-5.5 volt should be present on terminal No. 5 of control unit. If circuit does not test correctly, replace switch or repair harness.

CRUISE CONTROL SWITCHES, RELAYS & SENSORS TESTS

Resume & Set Switch (Colt, Galant, Mirage & Summit) – 1) Remove knee protector or lower panel assembly and column cover. Disconnect 4-pin cruise control switch connector. For resume circuit, check continuity between terminal No. 1 and ground wire.

2) For set circuit, check continuity between terminal No. 2 and ground wire. If continuity is not present, replace cruise control switch.

Resume & Set Switch (Eclipse) – 1) Remove knee protector and lower column cover. Disconnect cruise control switch connector. With switch in resume position, continuity should exist between terminals No. 13 and 19.

2) With switch in set position, continuity should exist between terminals No. 13 and 8. If continuity is not present, replace cruise control switch.

CAUTION: The capacitor in the SRS diagnostic unit holds enough voltage to deploy air bag even after battery cable has been disconnected. Remove negative battery cable and wait for more than 60 seconds before removing air bag module.

Resume & Set Switch (Stealth & 3000GT) – 1) Remove air bag module. See AIR BAG MODULE under REMOVAL & INSTALLATION. Disconnect cruise control switch 2-pin connector.

2) With switch in OFF position, continuity should not be present between terminals. When switch is pulled toward you for cancel mode, zero ohms should be present.

3) When switch is in RESUME position, resistance should be 820 ohms. When switch is in SET position, resistance should be 2700 ohms. Replace cruise control switch if resistance is not correct.

Main Switch (Stealth & 3000GT) – 1) Pry main switch bezel with switch from console. Check continuity in each switch position. With switch in OFF position, continuity should be present between terminals No. 2 and 6 for illumination light circuit. *See Fig. 13.*

2) With switch in Neutral position, continuity should be present between terminals No. 2 and 6, and between terminals No. 1 and 4. With switch in ON position, continuity should be present between terminals No. 2 and 6, and between terminals No. 1, 3 and 4. If continuity is not present, replace main switch.

Cruise Control Relay (Stealth & 3000GT) – 1) Remove relay. Relay is located behind center of dash, below radio. Continuity should be present between terminals No. 2 and 4. *See Fig. 13.*

2) Apply battery voltage to terminal No. 2 and ground terminal No. 4. Continuity should be present between terminals No. 1 and 3. If continuity is not correct, replace cruise control relay.

Brakelight/Stoplight Switch – Disconnect switch connector. When brake pedal is pressed, continuity should exist between terminals No. 2 and 3. *See Fig. 13.* When brake pedal is released, continuity should exist between terminals No. 1 and 4. If continuity is not correct, replace switch.

Clutch Switch – Disconnect switch connector. Continuity should be present between clutch switch terminals when clutch pedal is pressed. If continuity is not correct, replace switch.

Park/Neutral Switch – Disconnect switch connector. On Eclipse, continuity should exist between connector terminals No. 8 and 9 when

1994 ACCESSORIES & EQUIPMENT
Cruise Control Systems – Colt, Eclipse, Galant, Mirage, Stealth, Summit & 3000GT (Cont.)

CHRYSLER/MITSU.
4-27

shift lever is in "P" or "N". On Stealth & 3000GT, continuity should exist between connector terminals No. 7 and 8 when shift lever is in "P" or "N". On all other models, continuity should exist between connector terminals No. 5 and 8 when shift lever is in "P" or "N". *See Fig. 13*. If continuity is not correct, replace switch.

Throttle Position Switch – 1) Disconnect throttle position sensor connector. Measure resistance between terminals No. 1 and 4. *See Fig. 13*. Resistance should be 3.5-6.5 ohms.

2) Connect an analog ohmmeter between terminals No. 2 and 4. *See Fig. 13*. Operate throttle valve slowly from idle to wide open throttle. Resistance should change smoothly as throttle valve is opened and closed. Replace throttle position sensor as necessary.

Closed Throttle Position Switch – 1) Disconnect switch connector. Closed throttle position switch is incorporated in throttle position sensor. Continuity should exist between terminals No. 3 and 4 with accelerator pedal released. *See Fig. 13*.

2) With accelerator pedal pressed, continuity should not be present between terminals No. 3 and 4. Replace closed throttle position switch if continuity is not correct.

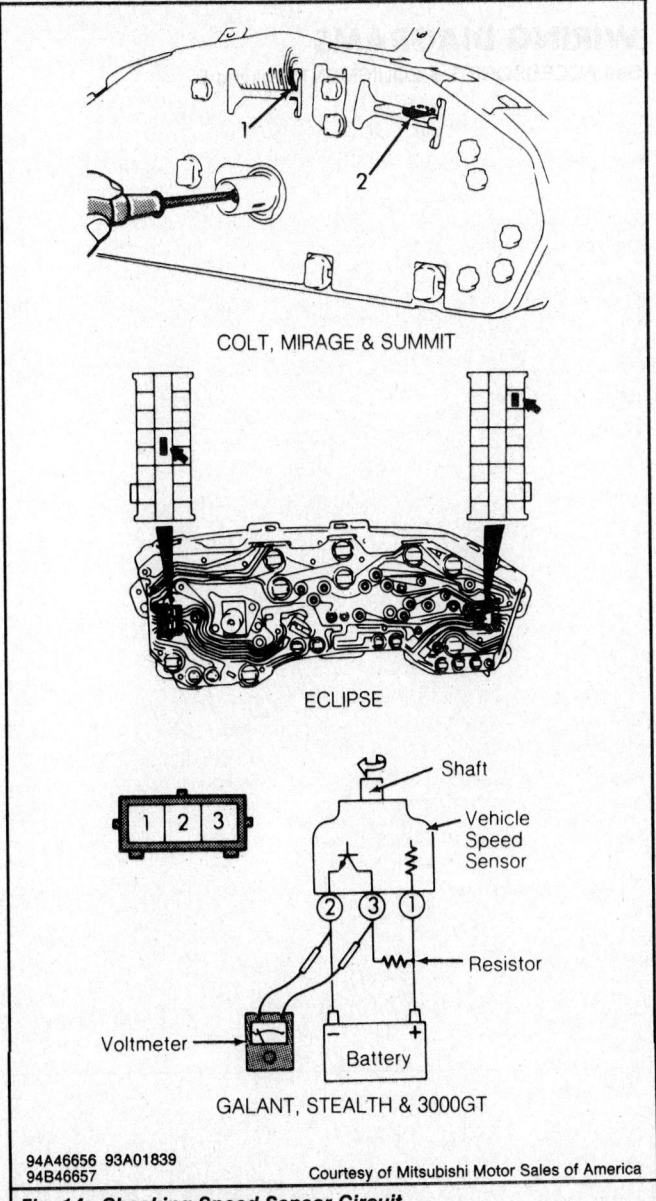

COLT, MIRAGE & SUMMIT

ECLIPSE

GALANT, STEALTH & 3000GT

94A46656 93A01839
94B46657
Courtesy of Mitsubishi Motor Sales of America

Fig. 14: Checking Speed Sensor Circuit

ACCELERATOR SWITCH TEST

NOTE: Accelerator pedal switch testing information is not available from manufacturer.

VACUUM PUMP ASSEMBLY TEST

Solenoid Valves – Remove vacuum pump connector. Resistance should be 50-60 ohms between terminals No. 1 and 2, and between terminals No. 1 and 3. *See Fig. 13*. Ensure solenoid valve makes operating noise when battery voltage is applied between terminals No. 1 and 2, and between terminals No. 1 and 3. If solenoid valve does not make noise, replace vacuum pump assembly.

Pump Motor – Remove vacuum pump connector. Apply battery voltage between terminals No. 1 and 4. *See Fig. 13*. Motor should operate. Replace motor if it does not operate.

ACTUATOR TEST

Remove actuator. Apply vacuum to actuator. Actuator linkage holder should move more than 1.38" (35 mm). Actuator diaphragm should hold vacuum.

VEHICLE SPEED SENSOR

Colt, Eclipse, Mirage & Summit – 1) Remove instrument cluster. See INSTRUMENT CLUSTER under REMOVAL & INSTALLATION. On Colt, Mirage and Summit, check continuity between vehicle speed sensor terminals No. 1 and 2. *See Fig. 14*. On Eclipse, check continuity between vehicle speed sensor terminals.

2) Ensure continuity pulses on and off 4 times per revolution of speedometer shaft connection. If continuity is not as specified, replace sensor.

Galant, Stealth & 3000GT – Remove speed sensor from transmission. Connect battery, resistor (3-10 ohms) and voltmeter to speed sensor terminals. *See Fig. 14*. When speedometer shaft is turned several times, voltage should pulse 4 times each revolution. Replace speed sensor if operation is not correct.

REMOVAL & INSTALLATION

AIR BAG MODULE

CAUTION: The capacitor in the SRS diagnostic unit holds enough voltage to deploy air bag even after battery cable has been disconnected. Remove negative battery cable and wait for more than 60 seconds before removing air bag module.

Removal & Installation – 1) Remove air bag module mounting nuts from back of steering wheel. When disconnecting clockspring connector, press connector toward the outer side to spread it open.

2) Disconnect clockspring connector from air bag module. DO NOT apply excessive force to connector. Lay air bag with pad cover face up. To install, reverse removal procedure.

ACTUATOR

Removal & Installation – Remove linkage protector. Remove cruise control cable. Remove accelerator and throttle cables. Disconnect vacuum hoses and electrical connectors. Remove linkage assembly. Remove vacuum pump and bracket. Remove actuator and bracket. To install, reverse removal procedure.

CRUISE CONTROL STEERING COLUMN SWITCH

WARNING: DO NOT hammer steering wheel. Collapsible steering column mechanism may be damaged.

Removal & Installation – Remove knee protector and lower panel. Remove column covers. Remove air bag module and bracket. See AIR BAG MODULE. Remove clip and column switch. To install, reverse removal procedure.

CHRYSLER/MITSU.
4-28

1994 ACCESSORIES & EQUIPMENT
Cruise Control Systems – Colt, Eclipse, Galant, Mirage, Stealth, Summit & 3000GT (Cont.)

VEHICLE SPEED SENSOR

Removal & Installation (Except Galant, Stealth & 3000GT) – Remove instrument cluster. See INSTRUMENT CLUSTER. Speed sensor is located in speedometer. To install, reverse removal procedure.

INDICATOR LIGHT

Removal & Installation – Indicator light is located in instrument cluster. Remove instrument cluster. See INSTRUMENT CLUSTER. To install, reverse removal procedure.

INSTRUMENT CLUSTER

Removal & Installation (Colt, Galant, Mirage, Stealth, Summit & 3000GT) – 1) Disconnect negative battery cable. Remove center panel, knee protector, gauge bezel, combination meter and adapter. Remove bulb socket, bulb, gauge glass and speedometer.
2) Remove gauge cluster (or tachometer and gauge), left indicator lens and turn and high beam indicator lens. Remove A/T position indicator light, lens, printed circuit board and meter case. To install, reverse removal procedure.

Eclipse – 1) Disconnect negative battery cable. Remove cluster cover. Remove cluster mounting screws. Remove cluster by turning upper part toward front. Disconnect all necessary electrical connectors. Remove instrument cluster.
2) Disconnect speedometer cable at transaxle end. Pull speedometer cable slightly toward vehicle interior. Release adapter by turning left or right, and remove adapter. To install, reverse removal procedure.

CONTROL UNIT

Removal & Installation (Colt, Galant, Mirage & Summit) – Cruise control unit is located behind left side of lower dash, behind fuse block. Remove mounting screws and remove control unit. To install, reverse removal procedure.
Removal & Installation (Eclipse) – Cruise control unit is located behind left kick panel. Remove kick panel and cruise control unit. To install, reverse removal procedure.
Removal & Installation (Stealth & 3000GT) – Cruise control unit is located behind right kick panel. Remove kick panel and cruise control unit. To install, reverse removal procedure.

WIRING DIAGRAMS

See ACCESSORIES & EQUIPMENT, Volume 5.

DESCRIPTION & OPERATION

The cruise control system is electronically controlled and vacuum actuated. System components include a control unit, actuator, vacuum pump, cruise control switch, clutch pedal switch, cruise indicator light, diode, Park/Neutral (P/N) or inhibitor switch (A/T), stoplight switch, Vehicle Speed Sensor (VSS) and A/T control unit (if equipped).

The system also has self-diagnostic capability. When self-diagnostic mode is activated, each switch and sensor is checked for defects. If cruise control system has been canceled without using a normal cancel method, a code will be set and stored in control unit. Codes can be retrieved to help determine which circuit is malfunctioning.

PRELIMINARY INSPECTION

Before performing TROUBLE SHOOTING steps, inspect linkage assembly, actuator, cables and vacuum hoses. Ensure linkage and cables move smoothly. Ensure cables do not have excessive slack or tension.

TROUBLE SHOOTING

NOTE: *For further trouble shooting information, see CHECK RESULTS & SYMPTOM CHARTS. See Figs. 3-5.*

SYSTEM CANCELS OR WILL NOT RESET AFTER CANCELLATION

1) Check trouble codes. See SELF-DIAGNOSTICS under DIAGNOSIS & TESTING. If no trouble codes are stored, check to see if cruise control can be set.
2) If cruise control can be set, system may have canceled because of driving on steep hills or loose wiring connection. If cruise control still cannot be set, perform SYSTEM INPUT TESTS under DIAGNOSIS & TESTING.
3) If SYSTEM INPUT TESTS check okay, check vacuum pump circuit. See TEST NO. 5 under CIRCUIT TESTS. If SYSTEM INPUT TESTS do not check okay, see INPUT CODE CHART & CHECK RESULTS CHART. *See Fig. 3.*

ADJUSTMENTS

CRUISE CONTROL CABLE

1) Ensure cruise control cable is free of bends and folds. Ensure idle speed is correct. Turn ignition off. Remove actuator cover. Turn link "C" until contact point touches contact point of link "B". *See Fig. 1.*
2) With links "B" and "C" in that position, turn adjusting nut "C" until free play in cruise control cable is .04-.08" (1-2 mm). Tighten adjusting nut "C" until link "C" can touch link "B". Then back off adjusting nut "C" one turn.

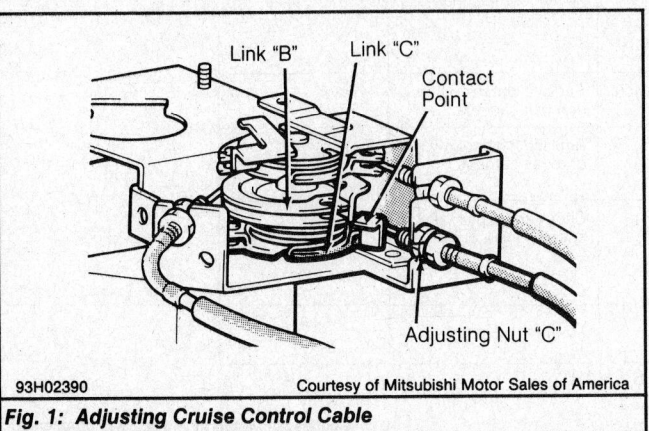

93H02390   Courtesy of Mitsubishi Motor Sales of America

Fig. 1: Adjusting Cruise Control Cable

DIAGNOSIS & TESTING

CRUISE CONTROL SWITCH FUNCTION TEST

NOTE: *If vehicle speed decreases approximately 9 MPH below set speed, set speed will be canceled.*

1) Cruise control switch is mounted on steering column. To operate cruise control system, turn ignition on. Turn main cruise control switch to ON position. Ensure switch indicator light comes on.

NOTE: *Speed will not set beyond system limit of 90 MPH.*

2) Drive vehicle between 25 and 90 MPH. Move cruise control switch lever to set position. Vehicle speed should stay at set speed. To increase set speed, turn control switch to RESUME position and hold until new set speed is reached.
3) To lower set speed, press set button and hold until new set speed is reached. To return to set speed after cancellation, move resume switch from ON to OFF position. Vehicle speed should return to previous setting before cancellation. Set speed should cancel when any of the following occurs:
- Brake pedal is pressed.
- Cancel switch is activated.
- Transmission is shifted to Neutral or Park.
- Cruise control main switch is turned to OFF position.
- Ignition switch is turned to OFF position.

SELF-DIAGNOSTICS

NOTE: *Problem represented by Code No. 17 will not cancel cruise control system.*

1) Self-diagnostics should be performed when cruise control cancels without the driver using normal cancel modes. Data Link Connector (DLC) is located on right side of fuse box.
2) Use analog voltmeter or Scan Tester (MB991341) for code retrieval. Connect leads of scan tester or analog voltmeter to diagnostic connector. *See Fig. 2.*
3) When using a scan tester, turn ignition switch to OFF position before connecting or disconnecting tester. Turn ignition on. Select self-diagnostic mode according to scan tester instructions. Read trouble codes. See SELF-DIAGNOSTIC CODES to find appropriate circuit test.
4) When using voltmeter, turn ignition and main cruise control switches to ON position. Using Special Tool (MB992529), connect voltmeter positive lead to DLC terminal No. 6 and negative lead to terminal No. 4 or 5. Read voltmeter needle sweeps to determine trouble code. Once trouble codes have been displayed, see SELF-DIAGNOSTIC CODES to find appropriate circuit test.
5) To clear trouble codes, either disconnect battery cable or turn ignition on. Turn main cruise control switch and set switch to ON position. Within one second, turn resume switch to ON position.
6) Depress brake pedal and hold cruise control switch in ON position for more than 5 seconds. Verify codes are cleared.

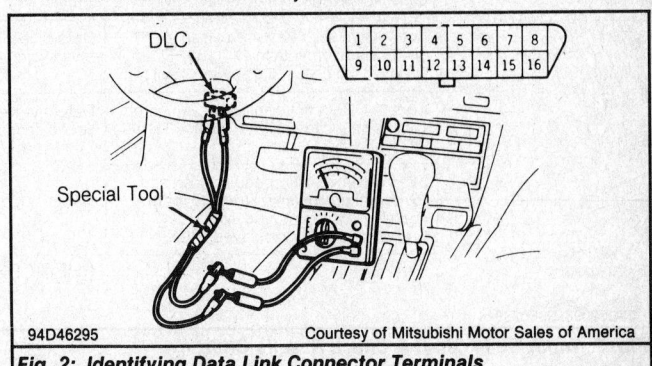

94D46295   Courtesy of Mitsubishi Motor Sales of America

Fig. 2: Identifying Data Link Connector Terminals

CHRYSLER/MITSU. 4-30

1994 ACCESSORIES & EQUIPMENT
Cruise Control Systems
Colt Vista, Expo & Summit Wagon (Cont.)

Code No.	Display patterns (output codes) (use with voltmeter)	Input operation		Check results
21	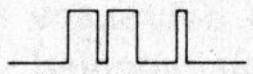	SET switch ON		SET switch circuit normal
22	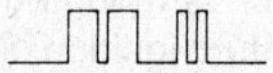	RESUME switch ON		RESUME switch normal
23	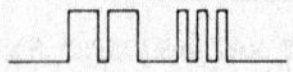	Stop light switch ON (brake pedal depressed)		Stop light switch circuit normal
24		Vehicle speed more than approx. 40 km/h (25 mph)		Vehicle speed sensor circuit normal if code Nos. 24 and 25 are displayed
25	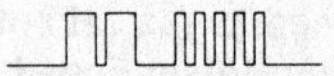	Vehicle speed less than approx. 40 km/h (25 mph)		
26	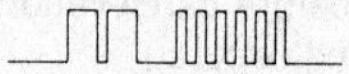	M/T	Clutch switch ON (clutch pedal depressed)	Clutch switch circuit normal
		A/T	Inhibitor switch ON (SELECT lever placed in "N" position)	Inhibitor switch circuit normal
27		CANCEL switch ON		CANCEL switch circuit normal
28	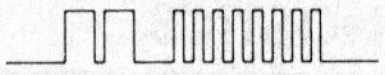	TPS output voltage 1.5 V or more (Accelerator pedal depressed more than half the way)		Throttle position sensor circuit normal
29		Idle switch OFF (Accelerator pedal depressed)		Idle switch circuit normal

INPUT CODE CHART

Result of check	Probable cause	Remedy	Circuit Test
None of the codes appear even if input operations are performed.	Open circuit in control unit power supply circuit.	Replace main switch or repair harness.	No. 1
	Open circuit in control switch circuit	Replace control switch or repair harness.	No. 2
	Defective control unit	Replace control unit.	—
Even when SET switch is set to OFF, code No. 21 does not go away.	SET switch ON malfunction	Replace the control switch.	No. 2
Even when RESUME switch is set to OFF, code No. 22 does not go away.	RESUME switch ON malfunction	Replace control switch.	No. 2
Even when CANCEL switch is set to OFF, code No. 27 does not go away.	CANCEL switch ON malfunction	Replace control switch.	No. 2
Even when brake pedal is depressed, code No. 23 is not displayed.	Defective stop light switch circuit	Replace stop light switch or repair harness.	No. 6
Even when brake pedal is released, code No. 23 does not go away.			
Even when clutch pedal is released, code No. 26 does not go away. <M/T>	Defective clutch switch circuit	Replace clutch switch or repair harness.	No. 7
Even when select lever is placed in any position other than "N" and "P", code No. 26 does not go away. <A/T>	Defective inhibitor switch circuit	Replace inhibitor switch or repair harness.	No. 8
Code No. 25 is not displayed even when vehicle speed is less than about 40 km/h (25 mph).	Defective vehicle speed sensor circuit	Check and repair vehicle speed sensor circuit.	No. 4
Even when vehicle speed is increased to more than about 40 km/h (25 mph), code No. 25 does not go away. Code No. 24 is not displayed, either.			

CHECK RESULTS CHART

Fig. 3: Input Code Chart & Check Results Chart

1994 ACCESSORIES & EQUIPMENT
Cruise Control Systems
Colt Vista, Expo & Summit Wagon (Cont.)

CHRYSLER/MITSU.
4-31

Trouble symptom	Probable cause	Circuit Test	Remedy
• The set vehicle speed varies greatly upward or downward. • "Hunching" (repeated alternating acceleration and deceleration) occurs after setting is made.	Malfunction of the vehicle speed sensor circuit	No. 4	Repair the vehicle speed sensor system, or replace the part.
	Malfunction of the speedometer cable or speedometer drive gear		
	Vacuum pump assembly circuit poor contact	No. 5	Repair the actuator system, or replace the part.
	Malfunction of the vacuum pump assembly (including air leaks from negative pressure passage)		
	Malfunction of the ECU	–	Replace the ECU.
The cruise control system is not canceled when the brake pedal is depressed.	Brake switch (for cruise control) malfunction (short-circuit)	No. 6	Repair the harness or replace the stop light switch.
	Vacuum pump assembly drive circuit short-circuit	No. 5	Repair the harness or replace the vacuum pump assembly.
	Malfunction of the ECU	–	Replace the ECU.
The cruise control system is not canceled when the clutch pedal is depressed. <M/T> (It is canceled, however, when the brake pedal is depressed.)	Damaged or disconnected wiring of clutch switch input circuit	If the input check code No. 26 indicates a malfunction. No. 7	Repair the harness, or repair or replace the clutch switch.
	Clutch switch improper installation (won't switch ON)		
	Malfunction of the ECU	–	Replace the ECU.
The cruise control system is not canceled when the shift lever is moved to the "N" position. <A/T> (It is canceled, however, when the brake pedal is depressed.)	Damaged or disconnected wiring of inhibitor switch input circuit	If the input check code No. 26 indicates a malfunction. No. 8	Repair the harness, or repair or replace the inhibitor switch.
	Improper adjustment of inhibitor switch		
	Malfunction of the ECU	–	Replace the ECU.
Cannot decelerate by using the SET switch.	Temporary damaged or disconnected wiring of control switch input circuit	No. 2	Repair the harness or replace the control switch.
	Vacuum pump assembly circuit poor contact	No. 5	Repair the harness or replace the vacuum pump assembly.
	Malfunction of the vacuum pump assembly		
	Malfunction of the ECU	–	Replace the ECU.

93I02395

Courtesy of Mitsubishi Motor Sales of America

Fig. 4: Symptom Chart (1 Of 2)

SELF-DIAGNOSTIC CODES

Code 11 – Possible cause: faulty vacuum pump circuit. Perform CIRCUIT TEST NO. 5.
Code 12 – Possible cause: faulty vehicle speed sensor circuit. Perform CIRCUIT TEST NO. 4.
Code 15 – Possible cause: faulty control switch. Perform CIRCUIT TEST NO. 2.
Code 16 – Possible cause: faulty control unit. Substitute known-good control unit.
Code 17 – Possible cause: faulty closed throttle position switch or throttle position sensor. Perform CIRCUIT TEST NO. 9

SYSTEM INPUT TESTS

1) System input tests should be performed if no trouble codes are stored when performing SELF-DIAGNOSTICS.
2) System input tests cycle each cruise control switch and sensor. Use analog voltmeter or Scan Tester (MB991341) for system input check. Connect leads of analog voltmeter or scan tester to DLC. See Fig. 2.

3) Turn ignition on. Move set switch to ON position. Turn main cruise control switch to ON position. Within one second, turn resume switch to ON position.

NOTE: Cruise control system cannot be set during input test.

4) Perform each input operation according to INPUT CODE CHART and read codes. See Fig. 3. Each code will be displayed in order of priority starting with No. 1. If no display is present, a malfunction may exist in the cruise control unit power supply circuit or the set and/or resume switch. Check for malfunction according to TEST NO. 1 or TEST NO. 2 under CIRCUIT TESTS.

CIRCUIT TESTS

NOTE: To identify circuit connector terminals, see Fig. 6.

Test No. 1 (Power Supply Circuit) – **1)** When main cruise control switch is turned to ON position, battery voltage should be present on terminal No. 2 of cruise control unit. If voltage is not present, check fuse No. 11 and replace as necessary. If fuse is okay, replace switch or repair wiring harness as necessary.

CHRYSLER/MITSU.
4-32

1994 ACCESSORIES & EQUIPMENT
Cruise Control Systems
Colt Vista, Expo & Summit Wagon (Cont.)

Trouble symptom	Probable cause	Circuit Test	Remedy
Cannot accelerate or resume speed by using the RESUME switch.	Open or short circuit in RESUME switch circuit in control switch	No. 2	Replace the control switch.
	Vacuum pump assembly circuit poor contact	No. 5	Repair the harness or replace the vacuum pump assembly.
	Malfunction of the vacuum pump assembly (including air leaks from negative pressure passage)		
	Malfunction of the ECU	–	Replace the ECU.
Even when CANCEL switch is set to ON, cruise control is not canceled (Cruise control, however, is canceled when brake pedal is depressed.)	Open or short circuit in CANCEL switch circuit in control switch	If the input check code No. 27 indicates a malfunction. No. 2	Replace the control switch.
	Malfunction of the ECU	–	Replace the ECU
The cruise control system can be set while traveling at a vehicle speed of less than 40 km/h (25 mph), or there is no automatic cancellation at that speed.	Malfunction of the vehicle-speed sensor circuit	No. 4	Repair the vehicle speed sensor system, or replace the part.
	Malfunction of the speedometer cable or the speedometer drive gear		
	Malfunction of the ECU	–	Replace the ECU.
The cruise control indicator light of the combination meter does not illuminate. (But cruise control system is normal)	Damaged or disconnected bulb of indicator light	No. 3	Repair the harness or replace the light bulb.
	Harness damaged or disconnected		
	Malfunction of the ECU	–	Replace the ECU.
Main switch indicator light does not come on. (However, cruise control is functional.)	Burned-out indicator light bulb	No. 3	Replace the main switch.
Overdrive is not canceled during fixed speed driving <A/T>	Malfunction of circuit related to overdrive cancellation, or malfunction of ECU	No. 10	Repair the harness or replace the part.
No shift to overdrive during manual driving. <A/T>			

93B82256

Fig. 5: Symptom Chart (2 Of 2)

2) Cruise control unit should be grounded at all times through terminals No. 6, 8 and 14. If circuit is not grounded, repair wiring harness as necessary. Cruise control unit back-up power supply should have battery voltage to it at all times through terminal No. 16. If voltage is not present, check fuse No. 19 and replace as necessary. If fuse is okay, replace switch or repair wiring harness as necessary.

Test No. 2 (Set, Resume & Cancel Switch Circuits) – 1) When all switches are turned to OFF position, voltage should not be present on terminal No. 18 of cruise control unit. When set switch is turned to ON position, 3 volts should be present on terminal No. 18 of cruise control unit.

2) When resume switch is turned to ON position, 6 volts should be present on terminal No. 18 of cruise control unit. When resume switch is turned to OFF position, voltage should be present on terminal No. 18 of cruise control unit.

3) When cancel switch is turned to ON position, battery voltage should be present on terminal No. 18 of cruise control unit. When cancel switch is turned to OFF position, voltage should not be present on terminal No. 18 of cruise control unit. If circuit does not test correctly, replace switch or repair wiring harness as necessary.

Test No. 3 (Indicator Light Circuit) – When cruise control is active, battery voltage should be present on terminal No. 23 of cruise control unit. When cruise control is turned to OFF position, voltage should not be present on terminal No. 23 of cruise control unit. If circuit does not test correctly, replace switch or repair wiring harness as necessary.

Test No. 4 (Vehicle Speed Sensor Circuit) – When vehicle moves slowly, voltage should alternate between zero volts and 2 or more volts at terminal No. 19 of cruise control unit. If circuit does not test correctly, replace sensor or repair wiring harness as necessary.

Test No. 5 (Vacuum Pump Circuit) – 1) When release valve is on, voltage should not be present on terminal No. 12 of cruise control unit. When release valve is off, battery voltage should be present on terminal No. 12 of cruise control unit.

2) When control valve is on, voltage should not be present on terminal No. 13 of cruise control unit. When control valve is off, battery voltage should be present on terminal No. 13 of cruise control unit.

3) When DC motor is driven, voltage should not be present on terminal No. 26 of cruise control unit. When DC motor is stopped, battery voltage should be present on terminal No. 26 of cruise control unit.

4) When main cruise control switch is turned to ON position, battery voltage should be present on terminal No. 25 of cruise control unit. If circuit does not test correctly, replace vacuum pump or repair wiring harness as necessary.

Test No. 6 (Stoplight Switch Circuit) – When brake pedal is pressed, battery voltage should be present on terminal No. 15 of cruise control unit. When brake pedal is released, voltage should not be present on terminal No. 15 of cruise control unit. If circuit does not test correctly, replace switch or repair wiring harness as necessary.

1994 ACCESSORIES & EQUIPMENT
Cruise Control Systems
Colt Vista, Expo & Summit Wagon (Cont.)

CHRYSLER/MITSU.
4-33

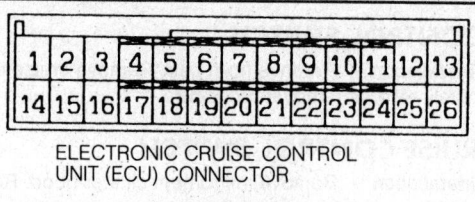

ELECTRONIC CRUISE CONTROL
UNIT (ECU) CONNECTOR

CRUISE CONTROL
SWITCH CONNECTOR

CRUISE CONTROL MAIN
SWITCH CONNECTOR

P/N SWITCH
CONNECTOR

THROTTLE POSITION SENSOR
CONNECTOR

VACUUM PUMP
CONNECTOR

INSTRUMENT CLUSTER
CONNECTORS

93J02211 94I46423 93E02398 93I02404 93E82226 93D82225 93I82261

Courtesy of Mitsubishi Motor Sales of America

Fig. 6: Cruise Control Circuit Connectors

Test No. 7 (Clutch Switch Circuit) – When clutch pedal is pressed, battery voltage should not be present on terminal No. 1 of cruise control unit. When clutch pedal is released, voltage should be present on terminal No. 1 of cruise control unit. If circuit does not test correctly, replace switch or repair wiring harness as necessary.

Test No. 8 (Park/Neutral (P/N) Switch Circuit) – 1) When P/N or inhibitor switch is placed in Neutral or Park, battery voltage should not be present on terminal No. 1 of cruise control unit.

2) When P/N switch is placed in Drive, 2nd, Low or Reverse positions, battery voltage should be present on terminal No. 1 of cruise control unit. If circuit does not test correctly, replace switch or repair wiring harness as necessary.

Test No. 9 (Closed Throttle Position Switch & Throttle Position Sensor Circuit) – 1) When checking closed throttle position (idle) switch, if accelerator pedal is pressed, voltage should not be present on terminal No. 4 of cruise control unit. When accelerator pedal is released, 4.5-5.5 volts should be present on terminal No. 4 of cruise control unit.

2) When checking throttle position sensor, if throttle valve is in idle position, .48-.72 volt should be present on terminal No. 5 of cruise control unit. When throttle valve is in wide open throttle position, 4.0-5.5 volts should be present on terminal No. 5 of cruise control unit. If circuit does not test correctly, replace switch or repair wiring harness as necessary.

Test No. 10 (Overdrive Cancellation Circuit) – 1) When ignition switch is in ON position, battery voltage should be present on terminal No. 3 of cruise control unit. When overdrive is activated, battery voltage should be present on terminal No. 10 of cruise control unit.

2) When overdrive is off, voltage should not be present on terminal No. 10 of cruise control unit. When overdrive switch is in ON position, battery voltage should be present on terminal No. 11 of cruise control unit.

3) When overdrive switch is in OFF position, voltage should not be present on terminal No. 11 of cruise control unit. If circuit does not test correctly, replace switch or repair wiring harness as necessary.

CRUISE CONTROL SWITCH TESTS

Cancel, Resume & Set Switch – 1) Remove screw from bottom of horn pad. Remove horn pad. Disconnect cruise control switch 5-pin connector. With switch in OFF position, continuity should not be present between any terminals.

2) Measure resistance between terminals No. 1 and 2. When switch is pulled toward you for cancel mode, continuity should be present. When switch is in RESUME position, resistance should be 820 ohms. When switch is in SET position, resistance should be 2700 ohms. Replace cruise control switch if resistance is not correct.

Main Switch – 1) When switch is moved to Neutral position, continuity should be present between terminals No. 4 and 6. See Fig. 6. When switch is moved to ON position, continuity should be present between terminals No. 2, 4 and 6.

2) Connect battery voltage to terminal No. 2 and ground terminal No. 6. Battery voltage should be present on terminal No. 4 when main switch is moved to ON position. Replace switch if it does not test correctly.

VACUUM PUMP TEST

1) Remove vacuum pump connector. Resistance should be 50-60 ohms between terminals No. 1 and 2, and between terminals No. 1 and 3. See Fig. 6. Ensure solenoid valve makes operating noise when battery voltage is applied between terminals No. 1 and 2, and between terminals No. 1 and 3.

2) If solenoid valve does not make noise, replace vacuum pump assembly. Remove vacuum pump connector. Apply battery voltage between terminals No. 1 and 4. Motor should operate. Replace motor if it does not operate.

ACTUATOR TEST

Remove actuator. Apply vacuum to actuator. Actuator linkage holder should move more than 1.38" (35 mm). Actuator diaphragm should hold vacuum. Replace actuator if actuator does not test correctly.

VEHICLE SPEED SENSOR TEST

1) Remove instrument cluster. See INSTRUMENT CLUSTER under REMOVAL & INSTALLATION. Check continuity between reed switch terminal and ground terminal shown in illustration. See Fig. 7.

2) Ensure continuity pulses on and off 4 times per revolution of speedometer shaft connection. If continuity is not as specified, replace sensor.

STOPLIGHT SWITCH TEST

Disconnect switch connector. When brake pedal is pressed, continuity should be present between terminals No. 2 and 3. When brake pedal is released, continuity should be present between terminals No. 1 and 4. Replace switch if it does not test correctly.

PARK/NEUTRAL (P/N) SWITCH TEST

Disconnect P/N switch connector. Continuity should be present between terminals No. 5 and 8 (FWD) or terminals No. 7 and 8 (AWD). Replace switch if it does not test correctly.

CHRYSLER/MITSU.
4-34

1994 ACCESSORIES & EQUIPMENT
Cruise Control Systems
Colt Vista, Expo & Summit Wagon (Cont.)

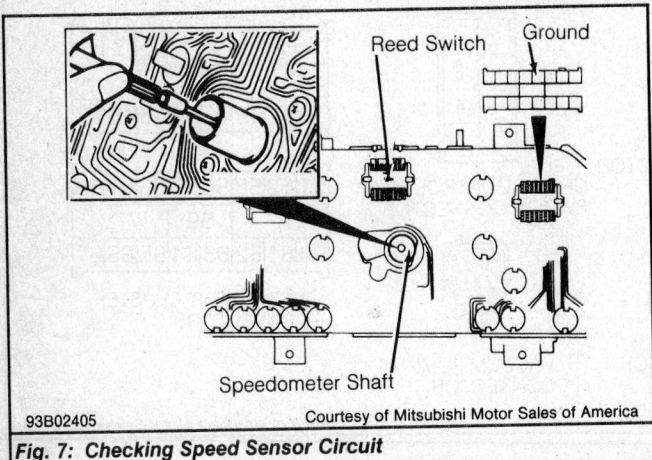

Reed Switch Ground

Speedometer Shaft

93B02405 Courtesy of Mitsubishi Motor Sales of America

Fig. 7: Checking Speed Sensor Circuit

THROTTLE POSITION SENSOR TEST

1) Disconnect sensor connector. Resistance between terminals No. 1 and 4 should be 3500-6500 ohms. Use an analog ohmmeter to measure resistance between terminals No. 1 and 3. *See Fig. 6.*
2) Slowly open throttle valve to wide open throttle. Resistance should change smoothly as throttle is opened. Replace throttle position sensor if it does not test correctly.

REMOVAL & INSTALLATION

ACTUATOR

Removal & Installation – 1) Remove linkage protector. Disconnect throttle cable, accelerator cable and cruise control cable link connections. Disconnect vacuum pump connector. Remove linkage assembly.
2) Remove throttle cable, accelerator cable and cruise control cables. Remove vacuum pump bracket. Remove vacuum pump assembly. Remove actuator bracket, and remove actuator. To install, reverse removal procedure.

CRUISE CONTROL SWITCH

Removal & Installation – Remove horn pad. Remove cruise control switch. To install, reverse removal procedure.

MAIN CRUISE CONTROL SWITCH

Removal & Installation – Remove instrument cluster hood. Remove main cruise control switch from hood. To install, reverse removal procedure.

VEHICLE SPEED SENSOR

Removal & Installation – Remove instrument cluster. See INSTRUMENT CLUSTER. Speed sensor is a part of speedometer. To install, reverse removal procedure.

INSTRUMENT CLUSTER

Removal & Installation – Disconnect negative battery cable. Remove cluster hood. Remove instrument cluster. To install, reverse removal procedure.

CONTROL UNIT

Removal & Installation – Cruise control system control unit is located under left side of dash. Remove control unit. To install, reverse removal procedure.

WIRING DIAGRAM

See ACCESSORIES & EQUIPMENT, Volume 5.

DESCRIPTION & OPERATION

The cruise control system is electronically controlled and vacuum actuated. System components include an Electronic Control Unit (ECU), actuator, vacuum pump, cruise control switch, clutch pedal switch, cruise indicator light, diode, Park/Neutral (P/N) switch (A/T), stoplight switch, Vehicle Speed Sensor (VSS) and A/T control unit.

The system also has self-diagnostic capability. When self-diagnostic mode is activated, each switch and sensor is checked for defects. Also when cruise control system has been canceled without using a normal cancel method, a code will be set and stored in ECU. Codes can be retrieved to help determine which circuit is malfunctioning.

PRELIMINARY INSPECTION

Before performing TROUBLE SHOOTING steps, inspect linkage assembly, actuator, cables and vacuum hoses. Ensure linkage and cables move smoothly. Ensure cables do not have excessive slack or tension.

TROUBLE SHOOTING

NOTE: For further trouble shooting information, see CHECK RESULTS CODES and SYMPTOM CHARTS. See Figs. 3-5.

SYSTEM CANCELS OR WILL NOT RESET AFTER CANCELLATION

1) Check trouble codes, see SELF-DIAGNOSTICS under DIAGNOSIS & TESTING. If no trouble codes are stored, check to see if cruise control can be set.
2) If cruise control can be set, system may have canceled because of driving on steep hills or loose wiring connection. If cruise control still cannot be set, perform SYSTEM INPUT TESTS under DIAGNOSIS & TESTING.
3) If SYSTEM INPUT TESTS check okay, check actuator circuit. See TEST NO. 6 under CIRCUIT TESTS. If SYSTEM INPUT TESTS do not check okay, see INPUT CODES

ADJUSTMENTS

CRUISE CONTROL CABLE

1) Ensure cruise control and accelerator cables are free of bends and folds. Remove actuator cover. Loosen lock nut and adjusting nut "A" to free cables. See Fig. 1. Tighten adjusting nut "A" in direction that will reduce inner cable free play.
2) Just when intermediate link "A" touches intermediate link "B", back off adjustment nut "A" one turn. Inner cable free play should be 0-.04" (0-1.0 mm). Tighten lock nut. Press accelerator pedal to ensure links "A" and "B" operate smoothly. Install actuator cover.

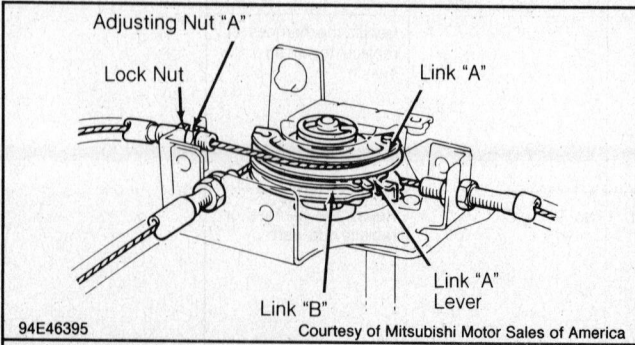

94E46395　　　Courtesy of Mitsubishi Motor Sales of America

Fig. 1: Adjusting Cruise Control Cable

DIAGNOSIS & TESTING

CRUISE CONTROL SWITCH FUNCTION TEST

NOTE: If vehicle speed decreases approximately 9 MPH below set speed, set speed will be canceled.

1) Cruise control switch is mounted on steering column. To operate cruise control system, turn ignition on. Turn main cruise control switch to ON position. Ensure switch indicator light comes on.

NOTE: Speed will not set beyond system limit of 90 MPH.

2) Drive vehicle at more than 25 MPH. Move cruise control switch lever to SET position. Vehicle speed should stay at set speed. To increase set speed, turn control switch to Resume (RES) position and hold until new set speed is reached.
3) To lower set speed, press SET button and hold until new set speed is reached. To return to set speed after cancellation, move RES switch from ON to OFF position. Vehicle speed should return to previous setting before cancellation. Set speed should cancel when any of the following occur:
- Brake pedal is pressed.
- Cancel switch is activated.
- Transmission is shifted to Neutral or Park.
- Cruise control main switch is turned to OFF position.
- Ignition switch is turned to OFF position.

SELF-DIAGNOSTICS

1) Self-diagnostics should be performed when cruise control cancels without the driver using normal cancel modes. Data Link Connector (DLC) is located behind lower dash panel to left of steering column. See Fig. 2.
2) Use analog voltmeter or Scan Tester (MUT-II) for code retrieval. Use scan tester according to operating instructions provided with tester. Using Special Tool (MB991529), connect leads of analog voltmeter between DLC terminal No. 13 (cruise control) and terminal No. 4 or 5 (ground terminals).

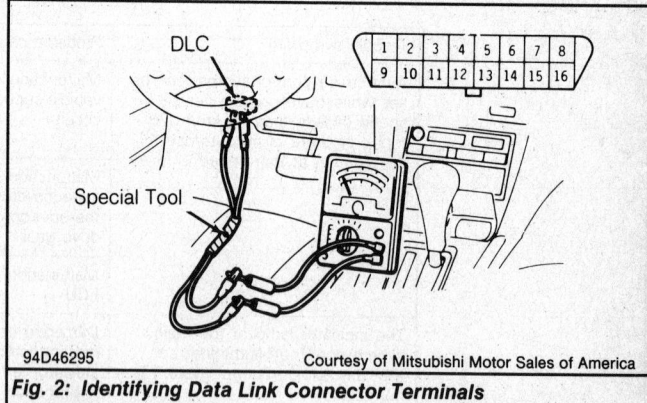

94D46295　　　Courtesy of Mitsubishi Motor Sales of America

Fig. 2: Identifying Data Link Connector Terminals

3) Read voltmeter needle sweeps to determine trouble code. Once trouble codes have been displayed, see SELF-DIAGNOSTIC CODES to find appropriate circuit test.
4) To clear trouble codes, either disconnect battery cable or turn ignition on. Turn main cruise control switch and set switch to ON position, and, within one second, turn RES switch to ON position.
5) Depress brake pedal and hold cruise control switch in ON position for more than 5 seconds. Verify codes are cleared.

SELF-DIAGNOSTIC CODES

Code 11 – Possible cause: faulty vacuum pump drive system. Perform CIRCUIT TEST NO. 6.
Code 12 – Possible cause: faulty vehicle speed signal system. Perform CIRCUIT TEST NO. 5.
Code 15 – Possible cause: faulty control switch. Perform CIRCUIT TESTS NO. 2 and 3.

Code 16 – Possible cause: faulty ECU. Substitute known-good ECU.

Code 17 – Possible cause: faulty throttle position sensor, accelerator sensor or closed throttle position switch. Perform CIRCUIT TEST NO. 10.

CHECK RESULTS CODES

Code 21 Remains After SET Switch Is Moved To OFF Position – Possible causes: faulty set switch; replace control switch. Set switch input line short circuit; repair wiring harness as necessary and perform CIRCUIT TEST NO. 2.

Code 22 Remains After RES Switch Is Moved To OFF Position – Possible causes: faulty RES switch; replace control switch. RES switch input line short circuit; repair wiring harness as necessary and perform CIRCUIT TEST NO. 3.

Code 23 Does Not Cancel After Releasing Brake Pedal – Possible cause: faulty stoplight switch circuit. Replace stoplight switch or repair wiring harness as necessary. Perform CIRCUIT TEST NO. 7.

Code 25 Remains Set And Code 24 Does Not Set Even Though Vehicle Speed Reaches 25 MPH Or More – Possible cause; faulty Vehicle Speed Sensor (VSS) circuit. Repair VSS circuit. Perform CIRCUIT TEST NO. 5.

Code 26 Remains Set After Selector Lever Is Moved To Anything But "N" Or "P" Position – Possible cause: faulty Park/Neutral (P/N) position switch. Replace P/N switch or repair wiring harness as necessary. Perform CIRCUIT TEST NO. 8.

Code 27 Remains After CANCEL Switch Is Moved To OFF Position – Possible cause: faulty CANCEL switch circuit. Replace control switch or repair wiring harness as necessary. Perform CIRCUIT TEST NO. 4.

Code 28 Remains Set After Accelerator Pedal Is Released – Possible causes: faulty throttle position sensor circuit or accelerator sensor circuit. Replace appropriate sensor or repair wiring harness as necessary. Perform CIRCUIT TEST NO. 10.

Code 29 Remains Set After Closed Throttle Position Switch (TPS) Is Moved To ON Position – Possible cause: faulty TPS circuit. Replace TPS or repair wiring harness as necessary. Perform CIRCUIT TEST NO. 10.

SYSTEM INPUT TESTS

1) System input tests should be performed if no trouble codes are stored when performing SELF-DIAGNOSTICS. System input tests cycle each cruise control switch and sensor.

2) Use analog voltmeter or Scan Tester (MUT-II) for system input check. Use scan tester according to operating instructions provided with tester. Using Special Tool (MB991529), connect leads of analog voltmeter between DLC terminal No. 13 (cruise control) and terminal No. 4 or 5 (ground terminals). See Fig. 2.

3) When using scan tester or voltmeter, turn ignition on and main cruise control switch to OFF position. Select a cruise control circuit on scan tester menu. Turn SET switch to ON position. Turn main cruise control switch to ON position.

4) Within one second, turn RES switch to ON position. Select input test code from scan tester menu. Perform each input test according to INPUT CODES. Read codes.

5) Each code is displayed in order of priority. If no codes are displayed, control unit, SET switch or RES switch may be at fault. Perform CIRCUIT TESTS NO. 1 and 2. See CIRCUIT TESTS. Turn main cruise control switch to OFF position.

INPUT CODES

NOTE: When both Code 24 and Code 25 can be confirmed, vehicle speed sensor circuit is operating normally.

Code 21 – SET switch in ON position.
Code 22 – RES switch in ON position.
Code 23 – Brake pedal depressed.
Code 24 – Driving at 25 MPH or more.
Code 25 – Driving at less than 25 MPH or stopped.
Code 26 – Selector lever in PARK or NEUTRAL position.
Code 27 – CANCEL switch in ON position.
Code 28 – Accelerator pedal depressed more than halfway.
Code 29 – Accelerator pedal depressed.

Trouble symptom	Probable cause	Circuit Test	Remedy
Auto-cruise control system can be set while traveling at a vehicle speed of less than 40 km/h (25 mph), or there is no automatic cancellation at that speed.	Malfunction of the vehicle-speed sensor circuit	No. 5	Repair the vehicle-speed sensor system, or replace the part.
	Malfunction of the speedometer cable or the speedometer drive gear		
	Malfunction of the ECU	—	Replace the ECU.
The indicator lamp of the main switch does not illuminate. (But auto-cruise control system is normal.)	Damaged or disconnected bulb of indicator lamp Malfunction of the main switch	—	Repair the harness or replace the main switch.
	Harness damaged or disconnected		
Overdrive is not canceled during fixed speed driving.	Malfunction of circuit related to overdrive cancelation, or malfunction of ECU	No. 9	Repair the harness or replace the part.
No shift to overdrive during manual driving.			

Fig. 3: Symptom Chart (1 Of 3)

Trouble symptom	Probable cause	Circuit Test	Remedy
The auto-cruise control system is not canceled when the selector lever is moved to the "N" position. (Vehicles with an automatic transaxle) (It is canceled, however, when the brake pedal is depressed.)	Damaged or disconnected wiring of park/neutral position switch input circuit	No. 8	Repair the harness, or repair or replace the park/neutral position switch
	Improper adjustment of park/neutral position switch		
	Malfunction of the ECU	—	Replace the ECU.
Cannot decelerate by using the SET switch	Temporary damaged or disconnected wiring of SET switch input circuit	No. 2	Repair the harness or replace the auto-cruise control switch.
	Auto-cruise vacuum pump circuit poor contact	No. 6	Repair the harness or replace the auto-cruise vacuum pump.
	Malfunction of the vacuum pump assembly (including air leaks from negative pressure passage)		
	Malfunction of the ECU	—	Replace the ECU.
Cannot accelerate or resume speed by using the RESUME switch.	Damaged or disconnected wiring, or short-circuit, of RESUME switch input circuit	No. 2	Repair the harness or replace the auto-cruise control switch.
	Auto-cruise vacuum pump circuit poor contact	No. 6	Repair the harness or replace the auto-cruise vacuum pump.
	Malfunction of the vacuum pump assembly (including air leaks from negative pressure passage)		
	Malfunction of the ECU	—	Replace the ECU.
Cruise control does not cancel even when the CANCEL switch is set to ON. (However, it is cancelled when the brake pedal is depressed.)	Broken wire in the CANCEL switch circuit inside the control switch	No. 4	Repair the harness or replace the auto-cruise control switch.
	Malfunction of the ECU	—	Replace the ECU.

93B2223

Courtesy of Mitsubishi Motor Sales of America

Fig. 4: Symptom Chart (2 Of 3)

Trouble symptom	Probable cause	Circuit Test	Remedy
• The set vehicle speed varies gratly upward or downward. • "Hunching" (repeated alternating acceleration and deceleration) occurs after setting is made.	Malfunction of the vehicle speed sensor circuit	No. 5	Repair the vehicle speed sensor system, or replace the part.
	Malfunction of the speedometer cable or speedometer drive gear		
	Auto-cruise vacuum pump circuit poor contact	No. 6	Repair auto-cruise vacuum pump assembly or replace the part.
	Malfunction of the ECU	—	Replace the ECU.
The auto-cruise control system is not canceled when the brake pedal is depressed.	Damaged or disconnected wiring of the stop light switch input circuit: brake switch (for auto-cruise control) malfunction (short-circuit)	No. 7	Repair the harness or replace the stop light switch.
	Auto-cruise vacuum pump drive circuit short-circuit	No. 6	Repair the harness or replace the auto-cruise vacuum pump.
	Malfunction of the ECU	—	Replace the ECU.

93C2224

Fig. 5: Symptom Chart (3 Of 3)

CIRCUIT TESTS

NOTE: To identify circuit connector terminals, see Fig. 6. See wiring diagram.

Test No. 1 (Power Supply Circuit) – **1)** Turn ignition on. When cruise control switch is turned to ON position, battery voltage should be present on terminal No. 2 of cruise control unit connector. If voltage is not present, check fuse No. 11 and replace as necessary.

2) If fuse is okay, check and repair harness as necessary. Battery voltage should never be present on terminal No. 8 of cruise control unit connector. If voltage is present on terminal No. 8 of cruise control unit connector, repair harness or replace cruise control unit.

Test No. 2 (SET Switch Circuit) – When SET switch is turned to ON position, 3 volts should be present on terminal No. 18 of cruise control unit. When SET switch is turned to OFF position, voltage should not be present on terminal No. 18 of cruise control unit. If circuit does not test correctly, replace switch or repair harness.

Test No. 3 (RES Switch Circuit) – When RES switch is turned to ON position, 6 volts should be present on terminal No. 18 of cruise control unit. When RES switch is turned to OFF position, voltage should not be present on terminal No. 18 of cruise control unit. If circuit does not test correctly, replace switch or repair harness.

Test No. 4 (Cancel Switch Circuit) – When cancel switch is turned to ON position, battery voltage should be present on terminal No. 18 of cruise control unit. When cancel switch is turned to OFF position, voltage should not be present on terminal No. 18 of cruise control unit. If circuit does not test correctly, replace switch or repair harness.

Test No. 5 (Vehicle Speed Sensor Circuit) – When vehicle moves slowly, voltage should alternate from zero volts to 2 volts and should not exceed 5 volts at terminal No. 19 of cruise control unit. If circuit does not test correctly, replace sensor or printed circuit board.

Test No. 6 (Vacuum Pump Circuit) – **1)** When cruise system is in deceleration or release modes, battery voltage should be present on terminals No. 13 and 26 of cruise control unit.

ACCELERATOR POSITION SENSOR, CLOSED THROTTLE POSITION SENSOR & THROTTLE POSITION SENSOR

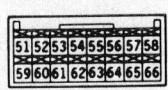

A/T CONTROL UNIT CONNECTOR

ELECTRONIC CRUISE CONTROL UNIT (ECU) CONNECTOR

VACUUM PUMP CONNECTOR

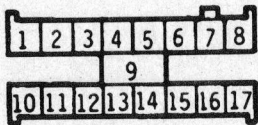

INSTRUMENT CLUSTER CONNECTOR

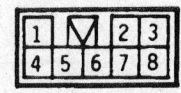

MAIN CRUISE CONTROL SWITCH CONNECTOR

OVERDRIVE SWITCH CONNECTOR

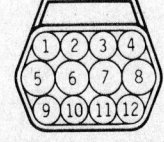

PARK/NEUTRAL SWITCH CONNECTOR

93D02374 93D82225 93J02211 93F02214 93J01872 93B02212 93E02218 93E82226

Fig. 6: Cruise Control Circuit Connectors

2) When cruise system is in release mode, battery voltage should be present on terminal No. 12 of cruise control unit. If circuit does not test correctly, replace vacuum pump or repair harness.

Test No. 7 (Stoplight Switch Circuit) – When brake pedal is pressed, battery voltage should be present on terminal No. 15 of cruise control unit. If voltage is not present, adjust or replace brake switch. If switch is okay, repair harness.

Test No. 8 (Park/Neutral Switch Circuit) – Voltage should not be present on terminal No. 1 of P/N switch when shift lever is in Neutral position. If circuit does not test correctly, replace switch or repair harness.

Test No. 9 (Overdrive Switch Circuit) – When overdrive switch is pushed to ON position, battery voltage should be present on terminal No. 10 of A/T control unit and terminal No. 11 of cruise control unit. If circuit does not test correctly, replace switch or repair harness.

Test No. 10 (Closed Throttle Position Switch & Throttle Position Sensor Circuit) – 1) When accelerator pedal is pressed, 4.5-5.5 volts should be present on terminal No. 4 (closed throttle position switch) of cruise control unit. When accelerator pedal is released, voltage should not be present on terminal No. 4 of cruise control unit.

2) When accelerator pedal is pressed to wide open throttle, 4.0-5.5 volts should be present on terminal No. 5 (throttle position sensor) of cruise control unit. When accelerator pedal is released, .5-.7 volt should be present on terminal No. 5 of cruise control unit. If circuit does not test correctly, replace switch or repair harness.

CRUISE CONTROL SWITCH TESTS

CANCEL, SET & RES Switches – 1) Remove air bag module. See AIR BAG MODULE under REMOVAL & INSTALLATION. Disconnect cruise control switch 2-pin connector. With cruise control switch in CANCEL position, continuity should be present between terminals.

2) With switch in RES position, 820 ohms should be present between terminals. With switch in SET position, 2700 ohms should be present between terminals. If switch does not test correctly, replace cruise control switch.

PARK/NEUTRAL SWITCH TEST

Disconnect switch connector. Shift transaxle into Neutral and Park positions. Continuity should be present between terminals No. 7 and 8. *See Fig. 6.* If continuity is not present, adjust P/N switch. If switch is adjusted properly, replace switch.

VACUUM PUMP TEST

Remove vacuum pump connector. Resistance should be 50-60 ohms between terminal No. 1 and terminals No. 2 and 3. *See Fig. 6.* Ensure solenoid valve makes operating noise when battery voltage is applied between terminal No. 1 and terminals No. 2 and 3. If solenoid valve does not make noise, replace vacuum pump assembly.

ACTUATOR TEST

Remove actuator. Apply vacuum to actuator. Actuator linkage holder should move more than 1.38" (35 mm). Actuator diaphragm should hold vacuum. Replace actuator if actuator does not test correctly.

VEHICLE SPEED SENSOR TEST

1) Remove instrument cluster. See INSTRUMENT CLUSTER under REMOVAL & INSTALLATION. Check continuity between vehicle speed sensor terminals. *See Fig. 7.*

2) Ensure continuity pulses on and off 4 times per revolution of speedometer shaft connection. If continuity is not as specified, replace sensor.

BRAKELIGHT/STOPLIGHT SWITCH TEST

Disconnect switch connector. When brake pedal is pressed, continuity should be present between terminals No. 1 (Blue/Red wire) and No. 3 (Green wire). When brake pedal is released, continuity should be present between terminals No. 2 (Green/Black wire) and No. 4 (Blue/White wire). Replace switch if it does not test correctly.

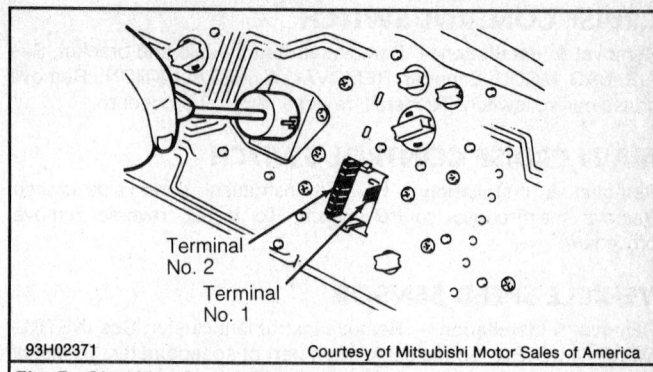

93H02371   Courtesy of Mitsubishi Motor Sales of America

Fig. 7: Checking Speed Sensor Circuit

CLOSED THROTTLE POSITION SWITCH & THROTTLE POSITION SENSOR TESTS

Throttle Position Sensor – 1) Disconnect sensor connector. Resistance between terminals No. 1 and 4 should be 3500-6500 ohms. Use an analog ohmmeter to measure resistance between terminals No. 2 and 4.

2) Slowly open throttle valve to wide open throttle. Resistance should change smoothly as throttle is opened. Replace throttle position sensor if it does not test correctly.

Closed Throttle Position Switch (SOHC) – 1) Disconnect throttle position sensor connector. Continuity should be present between terminals No. 3 and 4 with accelerator pedal released. Continuity should not be present with accelerator pedal pressed.

2) If continuity is not present with accelerator released, loosen throttle position sensor mounting screw. Turn throttle position sensor completely clockwise. Recheck continuity. Replace throttle position sensor if closed throttle position switch does not test correctly.

Closed Throttle Position Switch (DOHC) – 1) Disconnect throttle position sensor connector. Continuity should be present between terminals No. 1 and 2 with accelerator pedal released. Continuity should not be present with accelerator pedal pressed.

2) If continuity is not present with accelerator released, loosen throttle position sensor mounting screw. Turn throttle position sensor completely clockwise. Recheck continuity. Replace throttle position sensor if closed throttle position switch does not test correctly.

REMOVAL & INSTALLATION

AIR BAG MODULE

CAUTION: The capacitor in diagnostic unit holds enough voltage to deploy air bag for approximately 60 seconds after disconnection of battery. If an operation is performed during that time, air bag could deploy and cause serious injury. See AIR BAG RESTRAINT SYSTEM article in ACCESSORIES & EQUIPMENT.

Removal & Installation – 1) Disconnect negative battery cable and wait for more than 60 seconds. Remove air bag module mounting nuts from back of steering wheel. When disconnecting clockspring connector, press connector toward outside to spread it open.

2) Disconnect clockspring connector from air bag module. DO NOT apply excessive force to connector. Lay air bag with pad cover face up. To install, reverse removal procedure.

ACTUATOR

Removal & Installation – 1) Remove linkage protector. Disconnect throttle cable, accelerator cable and cruise control cable link connections. Disconnect vacuum pump connector. Remove linkage assembly. Remove vacuum pump bracket. Remove vacuum pump assembly.

2) Remove linkage assembly. Remove accelerator and throttle cables. Remove actuator bracket. Remove cruise control cable. Remove actuator. To install, reverse removal procedure.

CRUISE CONTROL SWITCH

Removal & Installation – Remove air bag module and bracket. See AIR BAG MODULE under REMOVAL & INSTALLATION. Remove cruise control switch. To install, reverse removal procedure.

MAIN CRUISE CONTROL SWITCH

Removal & Installation – Pry out instrument panel side switch. Remove main cruise control switch. To install, reverse removal procedure.

VEHICLE SPEED SENSOR

Removal & Installation – Remove instrument cluster. See INSTRUMENT CLUSTER. Speed sensor is a part of speedometer. To install, reverse removal procedure.

INSTRUMENT CLUSTER

Removal & Installation – Disconnect negative battery cable. Remove cluster bezel. Remove instrument cluster. To install, reverse removal procedure.

CONTROL UNIT

Removal & Installation – Cruise control system control unit is located behind center console. Remove ash tray and radio. Remove control unit. To install, reverse removal procedure.

WIRING DIAGRAM

See ACCESSORIES & EQUIPMENT, Volume 5.

DESCRIPTION & OPERATION

The cruise control system is electronically and vacuum controlled. System components include a control unit, actuator, vacuum pump, cruise control switch, clutch pedal switch, cruise indicator light, diode, Park/Neutral (P/N) switch (A/T), stoplight switch, vehicle speed sensor and A/T control unit.

The system has self-diagnostic capability. When self-diagnostic mode is activated, each switch and sensor is checked for defects. When cruise control system has been canceled without using a normal cancel method, a code will be set and stored in control unit. Codes can be retrieved to help determine which circuit is malfunctioning.

PRELIMINARY INSPECTION

Before performing TROUBLE SHOOTING steps, inspect linkage assembly, actuator, cables and vacuum hoses. Ensure linkage and cables move smoothly. Ensure cables do not have excessive slack or tension.

TROUBLE SHOOTING

NOTE: For further trouble shooting information, see CHECK RESULTS & SYMPTOM CHARTS. See Figs. 5-7.

SYSTEM CANCELS OR WILL NOT RESET AFTER CANCELLATION

1) Check trouble codes, see SELF-DIAGNOSTICS under DIAGNOSIS & TESTING. If no trouble codes are stored, ensure cruise control can be set.
2) If cruise control can be set, system may have canceled because of driving on steep hills or loose wiring connection. If cruise control still cannot be set, perform SYSTEM INPUT TESTS under DIAGNOSIS & TESTING.
3) If SYSTEM INPUT TESTS check okay, check vacuum pump circuit. See TEST NO. 6 under CIRCUIT TESTS. If SYSTEM INPUT TESTS do not check okay, see INPUT CODE CHART. See Fig. 4.

ADJUSTMENTS

CRUISE CONTROL CABLE

Remove link protector. Loosen lock nut. Hold link "A" so that it touches link "B". Adjust free play by turning adjusting nut until free play is .04-.08" (1-2 mm). Tighten lock nut. *See Fig. 1.*

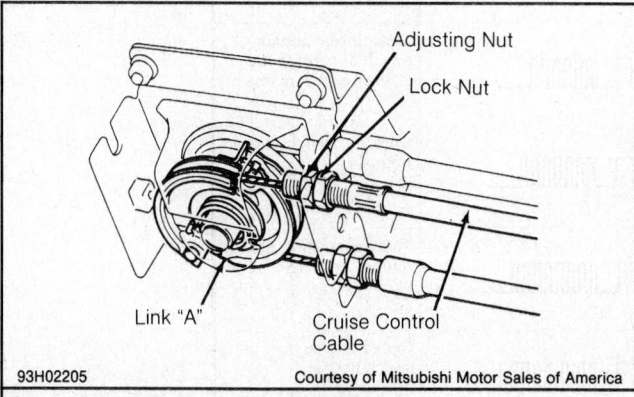

93H02205   Courtesy of Mitsubishi Motor Sales of America

Fig. 1: Adjusting Cruise Control Cable

DIAGNOSIS & TESTING

CRUISE CONTROL SWITCH FUNCTION TEST

NOTE: If vehicle speed decreases approximately 9 MPH below set speed, set speed will be canceled.

1) Cruise control switch is part of multifunction switch mounted on steering column. To operate cruise control system, turn ignition on. Turn cruise control switch to ON position. Ensure switch indicator light comes on.

NOTE: Speed will not set beyond system limit of 90 MPH.

2) With cruise control switch in ON position, drive vehicle between 25 and 90 MPH. Press and release SET button. Vehicle speed should stay at set speed. Instrument cluster cruise indicator light should come on. To increase set speed, turn control switch to RESUME position and hold until new set speed is reached.
3) To lower set speed, press SET button and hold until new set speed is reached. To return to set speed after cancellation, move resume switch from ON to OFF position. Vehicle speed should return to previous setting before cancellation. Set speed should cancel when any of the following occurs:
 • Brake pedal is pressed.
 • Clutch pedal is pressed.
 • Transmission is shifted to Neutral or Park.
 • Cruise control main switch is turned to OFF position.
 • Ignition switch is turned to OFF position.

SELF-DIAGNOSTICS

1) Self-diagnostics should be performed when cruise control cancels without the driver using normal cancel modes. Data Link Connector (DLC) is located on right side of fuse box. Use analog voltmeter or Scan Tester (MB991341) for code retrieval.
2) Use scan tester according to operating instructions provided with tester. Connect leads of analog voltmeter between cruise control terminal and ground terminal of DLC. *See Fig. 2.* Read voltmeter needle sweeps to determine trouble code.
3) Once trouble codes have been displayed, see SELF-DIAGNOSTIC CODE CHART to determine appropriate CIRCUIT TEST. *See Fig. 3.*
4) To clear trouble codes, either disconnect battery cable or turn ignition on. Turn main cruise control switch and set switch to ON position. Within one second turn resume switch to ON position.
5) Hold stoplight switch and cruise control switch in ON position for more than 5 seconds. Verify codes are cleared.

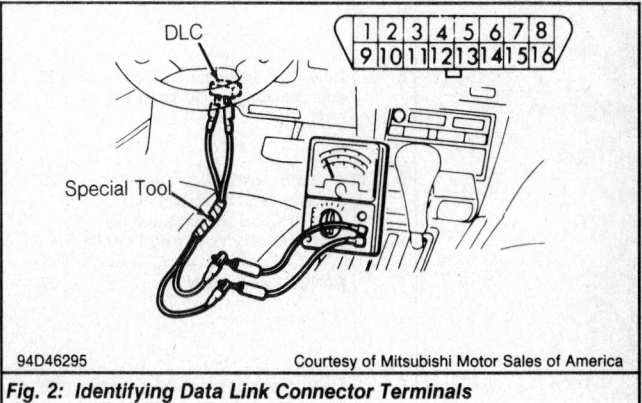

94D46295   Courtesy of Mitsubishi Motor Sales of America

Fig. 2: Identifying Data Link Connector Terminals

SYSTEM INPUT TESTS

1) System input tests should be performed if no trouble codes are stored when performing SELF-DIAGNOSTICS. System input tests cycle each cruise control switch and sensor.
2) Use Scan Tester (MB991341) for system input check. Use scan tester according to operating instructions provided with tester. Connect leads of analog voltmeter between cruise control terminal and ground terminal of data link connector. *See Fig. 2.* Turn ignition switch to ON position. Follow INPUT CODE CHART sequence. *See Fig. 4.*
3) To display results of input check, move SET switch to ON position. Then turn MAIN switch to ON position. Within one second, activate RESUME switch. Codes will display if circuit tested is okay.

Code No.	Display patterns (output codes) (Use with voltmeter)	Probable cause	Circuit Test
11	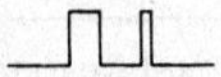	Abnormal condition of motor-driven vacuum pump system	No. 6
12	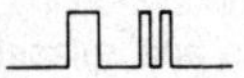	Abnormal condition of vehicle-speed signal system	No. 5
15	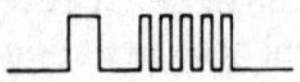	Control switch malfunction (when SET and RESUME switches switched ON simultaneously.)	No. 2, 3
16	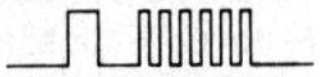	Abnormal condition of ECU	No. 7, 8, 9
17	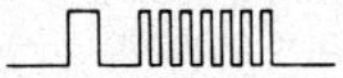	Abnormal condition of throttle position sensor Abnormal condition of idle switch	No. 11

93E02195

Fig. 3: Self-Diagnostic Code Chart

Check No.	Input operation	Code No.	Diagnostic code pattern (with voltmeter)	Check results
1	SET switch ON	21	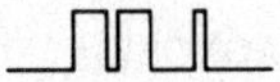	SET switch circuit normal
2	RESUME switch ON	22	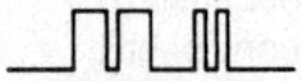	RESUME switch circuit normal
3	Stop light switch (brake pedal depressed)	23	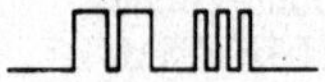	Stop light switch normal
4	Driving at approximately to 40 km/h (25 mph) or higher	24	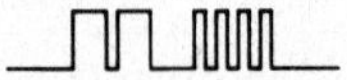	When both No. 4 and No. 5 can be confirmed, vehicle-speed sensor circuit normal.
5	Driving at less than approximately to 40 km/h (25 mph)	25	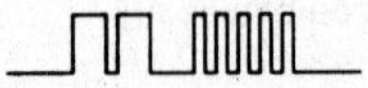	
6	1. Clutch pedal position switch ON (clutch pedal depressed) <M/T> 2. Park/Neutral position switch ON (selector lever to "N" range) <A/T>	26	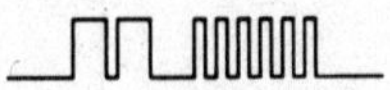	Clutch pedal position switch or park/neutral position switch normal
7	CANCEL switch ON	27	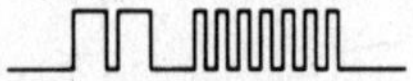	CANCEL switch circuit normal
8	Throttle position sensor output (when the accelerator pedal is pressed more than half way)	28	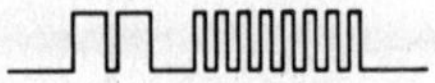	Throttle position sensor normal
9	Closed throttle position switch OFF (accelerator pedal depressed)	29	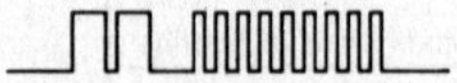	Closed throttle position switch normal

94D46451

Fig. 4: Input Code Chart

Check results	Probable cause	Remedy	Check chart No.
Code 21 remains even though SET switch is set to OFF.	SET switch ON malfunction	Replace the control switch.	No. 2
	SET switch input line short-circuit	Repair the harness.	
Code 22 remains even though RESUME switch is set to OFF.	RESUME switch ON malfunction	Replace the control switch.	No. 3
	RESUME switch input line short-circuit	Repair the harness.	
Code 23 remains even if the stop light switch is turned OFF by releasing the brake pedal.	Malfunction of stop light switch circuit.	Replace stop light switch or repair harness.	No. 7
Code 25 remains, and code 24 does not appear, even though vehicle speed reaches approximately 40 km/h (25 mph) or higher.	Malfunction of the vehicle-speed sensor circuit (damaged or disconnected wiring, or short-circuit)	Check or repair the vehicle speed sensor circuit.	No. 5
Code 26 remains even if the clutch pedal position switch is turned OFF by releasing the clutch pedal. <M/T>	Malfunction of clutch pedal position switch circuit.	Replace clutch pedal position switch or repair harness.	No. 8
Code 26 remains even if the selector lever is moved to anything but N, P. <A/T>	Malfunction of park/neutral position switch circuit.	Replace park/neutral position switch or repair harness.	No. 9
Code 27 remains even though CANCEL switch is set to OFF.	Malfunction of CANCEL switch circuit.	Replace the control switch or repair harness.	No. 4
Code 28 remains even if the accelerator is released.	Malfunction of throttle position sensor circuit.	Replace the sensor or repair harness.	No. 11
Code 29 remains even though the closed throttle position switch is set to ON.	Malfunction of closed throttle position switch circuit	Replace the switch or repair harness.	No. 11

94E46452

Courtesy of Mitsubishi Motor Sales of America

Fig. 5: Check Results Chart

CIRCUIT TESTS

NOTE: To identify circuit connector terminals, see Fig. 8.

Test No. 1 (Power & Ground Circuit) – 1) Turn ignition on. When cruise control main switch is turned to ON position, battery voltage should be present on terminal No. 2 of cruise control unit connector. **2)** If voltage is not present, check fuse No. 11 and replace as necessary. If fuse is okay, check and repair harness as necessary. Terminal No. 8 should be grounded at all times. If terminal No. 8 is not grounded, repair harness.

Test No. 2 (Set Switch Circuits) – When set switch is turned to ON position, 3 volts should be present on terminal No. 18 of cruise control unit. When set switch is turned to OFF position, voltage should not be present on terminal No. 18 of cruise control unit. If circuit does not test correctly, replace switch as necessary or repair harness.

Test No. 3 (Resume Switch Circuit) – When resume switch is turned to ON position, 6 volts should be present on terminal No. 18 of cruise control unit. When resume switch is turned to OFF position, voltage should not be present on terminal No. 18 of cruise control unit. If circuit does not test correctly, replace switch as necessary or repair harness.

Test No. 4 (Cancel Switch Circuit) – When cancel switch is turned to ON position, battery voltage should be present on terminal No. 18 of cruise control unit. When cancel switch is in OFF position, voltage should not be present on terminal No. 18 of cruise control unit. If circuit does not test correctly, replace switch as necessary or repair harness.

Test No. 5 (Vehicle Speed Sensor Circuit) – When vehicle moves slowly, voltage should alternate between zero and 2 or more volts at terminal No. 19 of cruise control unit. If circuit does not test correctly, replace sensor as necessary or repair harness.

Test No. 6 (Vacuum Pump Circuit) – 1) When cruise system is in deceleration or release mode, battery voltage should be present on terminals No. 26 and 13 of cruise control unit. If circuit does not test correctly, replace vacuum pump as necessary or repair harness.

2) When cruise system is in release mode, battery voltage should be present on terminal No. 12 of cruise control unit. When cruise system is in hold mode, voltage on terminals No. 12, 13 and 26 will go from battery voltage to zero volts depending on driving conditions. If circuit does not test correctly, replace vacuum pump as necessary or repair harness.

Test No. 7 (Stoplight Switch Circuit) – When brake pedal is pressed, battery voltage should be present on terminal No. 15 of cruise control unit. If voltage is not present, adjust or replace brake switch. If circuit does not test correctly, replace switch as necessary or repair harness.

Test No. 8 (Clutch Switch Circuit) – When clutch pedal is pressed, battery voltage should be present at terminal No. 1 of cruise control unit. If circuit does not test correctly, replace switch as necessary or repair harness.

Test No. 9 (Park/Neutral Switch Circuit) – When transmission is in Park/Neutral position, battery voltage should be present on terminal No. 1 of cruise control unit. If circuit does not test correctly, replace switch as necessary or repair harness.

Test No. 10 (Overdrive Switch Circuit) – When overdrive switch is pushed to ON position, battery voltage should be present on terminal No. 11 of cruise control unit. If circuit does not test correctly, replace switch as necessary or repair harness.

Test No. 11 (Closed Throttle Position Switch & Throttle Position Sensor Circuit) – 1) When accelerator pedal is pressed, 4.5-5.5 volts should be present on terminal No. 4 (closed throttle position switch) of cruise control unit. When accelerator pedal is released, voltage should not be present on terminal No. 4 of cruise control unit.

2) When accelerator pedal is pressed to wide open throttle, 4.0-5.5 volts should be present on terminal No. 5 (throttle position sensor) of cruise control unit. When accelerator pedal is released, .5-.7 volt should be present on terminal No. 5 of cruise control unit. If circuit does not test correctly, replace sensor as necessary or repair harness.

1994 ACCESSORIES & EQUIPMENT
Cruise Control Systems – Montero (Cont.)

Trouble symptom	Probable cause	Check chart No.	Remedy
• The set vehicle speed varies greatly upward or downward. • "Hunching" (repeated alternating acceleration and deceleration) occurs after setting is made.	Malfunction of the vehicle speed sensor circuit	No. 5	Repair the vehicle speed sensor system, or replace the part.
	Malfunction of the speedometer cable or speedometer drive gear		
	Motor-driven vacuum pump circuit poor contact	No. 6	Repair the motor-driven vacuum pump or replace the part.
	Malfunction of the motor-driven vacuum pump		
	Malfunction of the ECU	—	Replace the ECU.
The cruise control system is not canceled when the brake pedal is depressed.	Damaged or disconnected wiring of the stop light switch input circuit or stop light switch (for cruise control) poor contact (short-circuit)	If the input check code No. 23 indicates a malfunction, see the check chart No. 7	Repair the harness or replace the stop light switch.
	Motor-driven vacuum pump drive circuit short-circuit	No. 6	Repair the harness or replace the motor-driven vacuum pump.
	Malfunction of the ECU	—	Replace the ECU.
The cruise control system is not canceled when the clutch pedal is depressed. <M/T> (It is canceled, however, when the brake pedal is depressed.)	Damaged or disconnected wiring of clutch pedal position switch input circuit	If the input check code No. 23 indicates a malfunction, see the check chart No. 8	Repair the harness, or repair or replace the clutch pedal position switch
	Clutch pedal position switch improper installation (won't switch ON)		
	Malfunction of the ECU	—	Replace the ECU.
The cruise control system is not canceled when the selector lever is moved to the "N" position. <A/T> (It is canceled, however, when the brake pedal is depressed.)	Damaged or disconnected wiring of park/neutral position switch input circuit	If the input check code No. 23 indicates a malfunction, see the check chart No. 9	Repair the harness, or repair or replace the park/neutral position switch.
	Improper adjustment of park/neutral position switch		
	Malfunction of the ECU	—	Replace the ECU.

94F46453

Courtesy of Mitsubishi Motor Sales of America

Fig. 6: Symptom Chart (1 Of 2)

Trouble symptom	Probable cause	Circuit Test	Remedy
Cannot decelerate by using the SET switch	Temporary damaged or disconnected wiring of SET switch input circuit	No. 2	Repair the harness or replace the control switch.
	Motor-driven vacuum pump circuit poor contact	No. 6	Repair the harness or replace the motor-driven vacuum pump.
	Malfunction of the auto-cruise actuator		
	Malfunction of the ECU	—	Replace the ECU.
Cannot accelerate or resume speed by using the RESUME switch.	Damaged or disconnected wiring, or short-circuit, of RESUME switch input circuit	No. 3	Repair the harness or replace the control switch.
	Motor-driven vacuum pump circuit poor contact	No. 6	Repair the harness or replace the motor-driven vacuum pump.
	Malfunction of the motor-driven vacuum pump		
	Malfunction of the ECU	—	Replace the ECU.
Auto-cruise control system can be set while traveling at a vehicle speed of less than 40 km/h (25 mph), or there is no automatic cancellation at that speed.	Malfunction of the vehicle-speed sensor circuit	No. 5	Repair the vehicle-speed sensor system, or replace the part.
	Malfunction of the speedometer cable or the speedometer drive gear		
	Malfunction of the ECU	—	Replace the ECU.
The indicator light of the main switch does not illuminate. (But auto-cruise control system is normal.)	Damaged or disconnected bulb of indicator light or malfunction of the main switch	—	Repair the harness or replace the main switch.
	Harness damaged or disconnected		
Overdrive is not canceled during fixed speed driving. <A/T>	Malfunction of circuit related to overdrive cancelation, or malfunction of ECU	No. 10	Repair the harness or replace the part.
No shift to overdrive during manual driving. <A/T>			

93C02203

Courtesy of Mitsubishi Motor Sales of America

Fig. 7: Symptom Chart (2 Of 2)

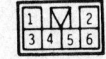

CRUISE CONTROL UNIT CONNECTOR

MAIN CRUISE CONTROL SWITCH CONNECTOR

STOPLIGHT SWITCH CONNECTOR

VACUUM PUMP CONNECTOR

INSTRUMENT CLUSTER CONNECTOR

OVERDRIVE SWITCH CONNECTOR

PARK/NEUTRAL SWITCH CONNECTOR

CLOSED THROTTLE POSITION SWITCH & THROTTLE POSITION SENSOR CONNECTOR

93J02211 93B02212 93D02213 93F02214 93I02215 93A02218 93C02217 93D02374

Courtesy of Mitsubishi Motor Sales of America

Fig. 8: Identifying Cruise Control Circuit Connectors

CRUISE CONTROL SWITCH TESTS

Set & Resume Switches – 1) Remove lower steering column cover. Disconnect 2-pin switch connector. Operate and test switch. When cancel switch is operated, continuity should be present between terminals No. 1 and 2. Zero ohms resistance should be indicated.

2) When resume switch is operated, 820 ohms resistance should be present between terminals No. 1 and 2. When set switch is operated, 2700 ohms resistance should be present between terminals No. 1 and 2. Replace cruise control switch if it does not test correctly.

Main Switch – 1) In each switch position, continuity should be present between terminals No. 2 and 7 for switch illumination. *See Fig. 8.* When switch is moved to Neutral position, continuity should be present between terminals No. 1 and 4.

2) When switch is moved to ON position, continuity should be present between terminals No. 1, 4 and 5. Connect battery voltage to terminal No. 5 and ground terminal No. 4.

3) Battery voltage should be present on terminal No. 1 when main switch is moved to ON position. Replace switch if it does not test correctly.

BRAKELIGHT/STOPLIGHT SWITCH TEST

Disconnect switch connector. When brake pedal is pressed, continuity should be present between terminals No. 2 and 3. *See Fig. 8.* When brake pedal is released, continuity should be present between terminals No. 1 and 4. Replace switch if it does not test correctly.

CLOSED THROTTLE POSITION SWITCH & THROTTLE POSITION SENSOR TESTS

Closed Throttle Position Switch – 1) Disconnect throttle position sensor connector. Continuity should be present between terminals No. 1 and 2 with accelerator pedal released. *See Fig. 8.* Continuity should not be present with accelerator pedal pressed.
2) If continuity is not present with accelerator released, loosen throttle position sensor mounting screw. Turn throttle position sensor completely clockwise. Recheck continuity. Replace throttle position sensor if closed throttle position switch does not test correctly.
Throttle Position Sensor – 1) Disconnect sensor connector. Resistance between terminals No. 1 and 4 should be 3500-6500 ohms. Use an analog ohmmeter to measure resistance between terminals No. 1 and 3. *See Fig. 8.*
2) Slowly open throttle valve to wide open throttle. Resistance should change smoothly as throttle is opened. Replace throttle position sensor if it does not test correctly.

PARK/NEUTRAL SWITCH TEST

Disconnect switch connector. Shift transaxle into Neutral and Park positions. Continuity should be present between terminals No. 7 and 12. *See Fig. 8.* If continuity is not present, adjust park/neutral switch. If switch is adjusted properly, replace switch.

VACUUM PUMP TEST

1) Remove vacuum pump connector. Resistance should be 50-60 ohms between terminal No. 1 and terminals No. 2 and 3. *See Fig. 8.* Ensure solenoid valve makes operating noise when battery voltage is applied between terminal No. 1 and terminals No. 2 and 3.
2) If solenoid valve does not make noise, replace vacuum pump assembly. Apply battery voltage to terminals No. 1 and 4, motor should operate. Replace vacuum pump if motor does not operate.

ACTUATOR TESTS

Remove actuator. Apply vacuum to actuator. Actuator linkage holder should move more than 1.38" (35 mm). Actuator diaphragm should hold vacuum. Replace actuator if actuator does not test correctly.

VEHICLE SPEED SENSOR TEST

Remove speed sensor from transmission. Connect speed sensor, resistor (3000-10,000 ohms) and battery. *See Fig. 9.* Using a voltmeter, ensure voltage pulses on and off 4 times per revolution of speedometer shaft. Replace sensor if voltage is not as specified.

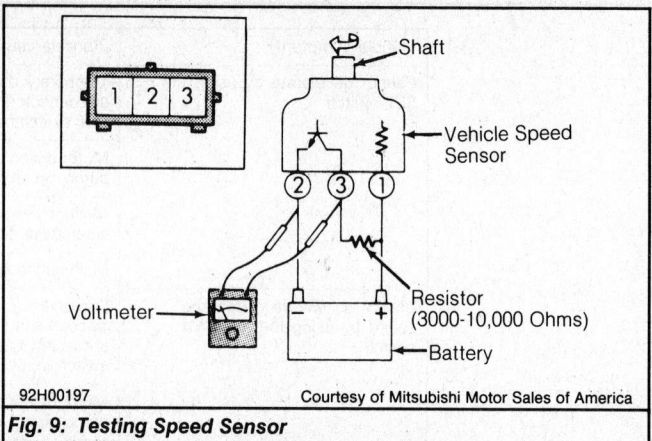

92H00197   Courtesy of Mitsubishi Motor Sales of America
Fig. 9: Testing Speed Sensor

REMOVAL & INSTALLATION

ACTUATOR

Removal & Installation – Disconnect cruise control cable from link. Disconnect actuator wiring connector. Remove vacuum pump and vacuum pump bracket. Remove actuator and actuator bracket. To install, reverse removal procedure.

CONTROL UNIT

Removal & Installation – Cruise control unit is located behind center of dash panel. Remove center trim panel and radio or radio plug bezel. Remove control unit. To install, reverse removal procedure.

CRUISE CONTROL SWITCH

Removal & Installation – Remove lower steering column cover. Disconnect electrical connectors. Remove screws attaching cruise control switch to steering column. Remove switch. To install, reverse removal procedure.

INSTRUMENT CLUSTER

Removal & Installation – Disconnect negative battery cable. Remove cluster cover. Disconnect speedometer cable. Remove instrument cluster. To install, reverse removal procedure.

WIRING DIAGRAM

See ACCESSORIES & EQUIPMENT, Volume 5.

DESCRIPTION & OPERATION

The cruise control system is electronically controlled and vacuum actuated. System components include a control unit, actuator, vacuum pump, cruise control switch, clutch pedal switch, cruise indicator light, diode, Park/Neutral switch (A/T), stoplight switch, vehicle speed sensor and A/T control unit.

The system also has self-diagnostic capability. When self-diagnostic mode is activated, each switch and sensor is checked for defects. Also, when cruise control system has been canceled without using a normal cancel method, a code will be set and stored in control unit. Codes can be retrieved to help determine which circuit is malfunctioning.

PRELIMINARY INSPECTION

Before performing TROUBLE SHOOTING steps, inspect linkage assembly, actuator, cables and vacuum hoses. Ensure linkage and cables move smoothly. Ensure cables do not have excessive slack or tension.

TROUBLE SHOOTING

NOTE: *For further trouble shooting information, see SYMPTOM CHARTS. See Fig. 4.*

SYSTEM CANCELS OR WILL NOT RESET AFTER CANCELLATION

1) Check trouble codes, see SELF-DIAGNOSTICS under DIAGNOSIS & TESTING. If no trouble codes are stored, check to see if cruise control can be set.
2) If cruise control can be set, system may have canceled because of driving on steep hills or loose wiring connection. If cruise control still cannot be set, perform SYSTEM INPUT TESTS under DIAGNOSIS & TESTING.
3) If SYSTEM INPUT TESTS check okay, check actuator circuit. See TEST NO. 5 under CIRCUIT TESTS. If SYSTEM INPUT TESTS do not check okay, see INPUT CODE CHART. *See Fig. 5.*

ADJUSTMENTS

ACCELERATOR CABLE

1) To adjust accelerator cable "A", ensure accelerator cables are free of bends and folds. Remove actuator cover. Loosen lock nuts of accelerator cables "A" and "B". *See Fig. 1.* While keeping lever "P" and stopper in contact with each other, turn adjusting nut until lever "P" begins to move.
2) Back off adjusting nut 1/2 turn and tighten lock nut. To adjust accelerator cable "B", adjust nuts on carburetor. Ensure clearance between levers "C" and "P" is 0-.08" (0-2 mm), after adjustment. *See Fig. 1.*

DIAGNOSIS & TESTING

CRUISE CONTROL SWITCH FUNCTION TEST

NOTE: *If vehicle speed decreases approximately 9 MPH below set speed, set speed will be canceled.*

1) Cruise control switch is part of multifunction switch, mounted on steering column. To operate cruise control system, turn ignition on. Turn main cruise control switch to ON position. Ensure switch indicator light comes on.

NOTE: *Speed will not set beyond system limit of 90 MPH.*

2) With main cruise control switch in ON position, drive vehicle between 25 and 90 MPH. Press and release SET button. Vehicle speed should stay at set speed. Instrument cluster cruise indicator light should come on. To increase set speed, turn control switch to RESUME position and hold until new set speed is reached.

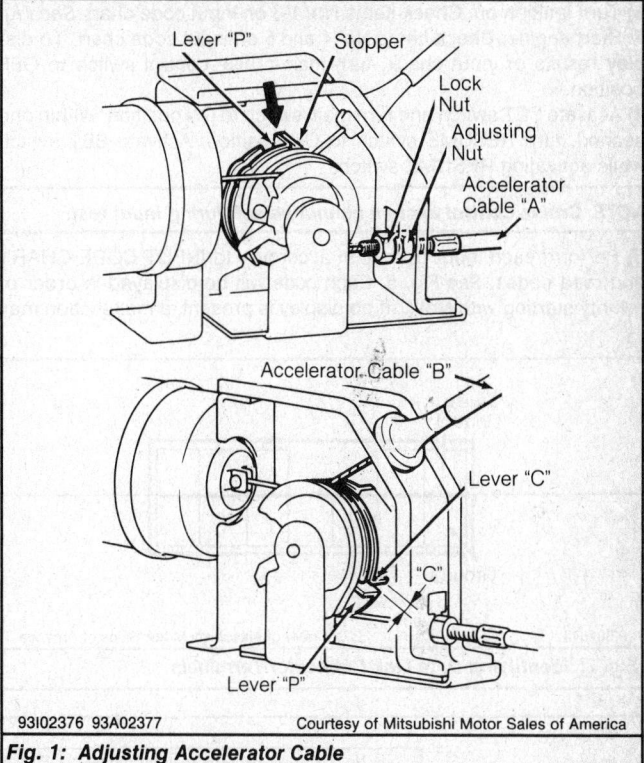

93I02376 93A02377   Courtesy of Mitsubishi Motor Sales of America

Fig. 1: Adjusting Accelerator Cable

3) To lower set speed, press SET button and hold until new set speed is reached. To return to set speed after cancellation, move RESUME switch from ON to OFF position. Vehicle speed should return to previous setting before cancellation. Set speed should cancel when any of the following occurs:
- Brake pedal is pressed.
- Clutch pedal is pressed.
- Cruise control main switch is turned to OFF position.

SELF-DIAGNOSTICS

NOTE: *Codes No. 13, 14, 15 & 16 will be displayed even if system is okay.*

1) Self-diagnostics should be performed when cruise control cancels without the driver using normal cancel modes. Data link connector is located below fuse box.
2) Use analog voltmeter or Scan Tester (MB991341) for code retrieval. Use scan tester according to operating instructions provided with tester. Connect leads of analog voltmeter between cruise control terminal and ground terminal of data link connector. *See Fig. 2.*
3) Read voltmeter needle sweeps to determine trouble code. Once trouble codes have been displayed, read SELF-DIAGNOSTIC CODE CHART & CHECK RESULTS CHART to find appropriate CIRCUIT TEST. *See Fig. 3.*
4) To clear trouble codes, either disconnect battery cable or turn ignition on. Turn main cruise control switch and SET switch to ON position, and, within one second, turn RESUME switch to ON position.
5) Depress brake pedal and hold cruise control switch in ON position for more than 5 seconds. Verify codes are cleared.

SYSTEM INPUT TESTS

1) System input tests should be performed if no trouble codes are stored when performing SELF-DIAGNOSTICS.
2) System input tests cycle each cruise control switch and sensor. Use analog voltmeter or Scan Tester (MB991341) for system input check. Use scan tester according to operating instructions provided with tester. Connect leads of analog voltmeter between cruise control terminal and ground terminal of data link connector. *See Fig. 2.*

3) Turn ignition on. Check items No. 1-3 on input code chart. *See Fig. 5.* Start engine. Check items No. 4 and 5 on input code chart. To display results of input check, turn main cruise control switch to OFF position.

4) Activate SET switch and turn main switch to ON position. Within one second, turn RESUME switch to ON position. Activate SET switch while activating RESUME switch.

NOTE: Cruise control system cannot be set during input test.

5) Perform each input operation according to INPUT CODE CHART and read codes. *See Fig. 5.* Each code will be displayed in order of priority starting with No. 1. If no display is present, a malfunction may

exist in the cruise control unit power supply circuit or the SET and/or RESUME switch. Check for malfunction according to circuit tests No. 1, 2 and 3.

CIRCUIT TESTS

NOTE: To identify circuit connector terminals, see Fig. 6. See wiring diagram.

Test No. 1 (Power Supply Circuit) – **1)** Turn ignition on. When main cruise control switch is turned to ON position, battery voltage should be present on terminal No. 5 of cruise control unit connector. If voltage is not present, check fuse No. 7 and replace as necessary.

2) If fuse is okay, check and repair harness as necessary. Battery voltage should never be present on terminal No. 20 of cruise control unit connector. If voltage is present on terminal No. 20 of cruise control unit connector, repair harness or replace cruise control unit.

Test No. 2 (SET Switch Circuit) – When SET switch is turned to ON position, voltage should not be present on terminal No. 11 of cruise control unit. When SET switch is turned to OFF position, battery voltage should be present on terminal No. 11 of cruise control unit. If circuit does not test correctly, replace switch or repair harness.

Test No. 3 (RESUME Switch Circuit) – When RESUME switch is turned to ON position, voltage should not be present on terminal No. 13 of cruise control unit. When RESUME switch is turned to OFF position, battery voltage should be present on terminal No. 13 of cruise control unit. If circuit does not test correctly, replace switch or repair harness.

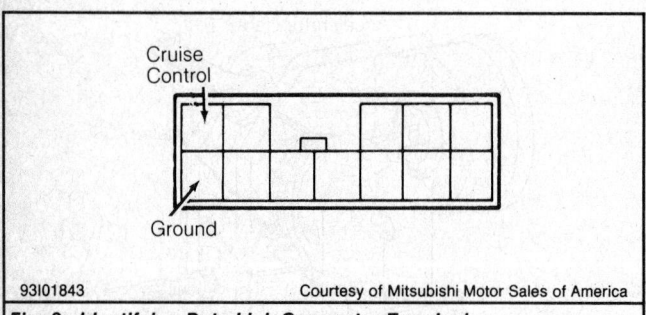

93I01843   Courtesy of Mitsubishi Motor Sales of America

Fig. 2: Identifying Data Link Connector Terminals

Code No.	Display patterns (output codes)	Probable cause	Circuit Test
11	12V / 0V 1 1	Abnormal condition of actuator drive system	No. 5
12	12V / 0V 1 2	Abnormal condition of vehicle-speed signal system	No. 4
13	12V / 0V 1 3	Low-speed limitter activation (The system is normal if it can be reset.)	–
14	12V / 0V 1 4	Automatic cancelation activated by vehicle speed reduction. (The system is normal if it can be reset.)	–
15	12V / 0V 1 5	Control switch malfunction (when SET and RESUME switches switched on simultaneously)	No. 2, 3
16	12V / 0V 1 6	Cancel switch ON signal input (including input wiring damage, disconnection or when trouble has occurred in the circuitry inside the control unit)	No. 6, 7

SELF-DIAGNOSTIC CODE CHART

Check results	Probable cause	Remedy	Circuit Test
Code No. 21 remains even though SET switch is set to OFF.	SET switch ON malfunction	Replace the control switch.	No. 2
	SET switch input line short-circuit	Repair the harness.	
Code No. 22 remains even though RESUME switch is set to OFF.	RESUME switch ON malfunction	Replace the control switch.	No. 3
	RESUME switch input line short-circuit	Repair the harness.	
Code No. 23 remains even though CANCEL switch is set to OFF.	Malfunction of the CANCEL circuit (ON malfunction)	Check or repair each CANCEL circuit.	No. 6, 7
Code No. 25 does not disappear, and code No. 24 does not appear, even though vehicle speed reaches approximately 40 km/h (25 mph) or higher.	Malfunction of the vehicle-speed sensor circuit (damaged or disconnected wiring, or short-circuit)	Check or repair the vehicle speed sensor circuit.	No. 4

CHECK RESULTS CHART

93C02378 93E02379   Courtesy of Mitsubishi Motor Sales of America

Fig. 3: Self-Diagnostic Code Chart & Check Results Chart

Cruise Control Systems – Pickup (Cont.)

Symptom	Probable cause	Circuit Test	Remedy
The auto-cruise control system is not canceled when the clutch pedal is depressed. (It is canceled, however, when the brake pedal is depressed.)	Damaged or disconnected wiring of clutch switch input circuit	If the input check code No. 23 indicates a malfunction. No. 7	Repair the harness, or repair or replace the clutch switch.
	Clutch switch improper installation (won't switch ON)		
	Malfunction of the auto-cruise control unit	–	Replace the auto-cruise control unit.
Cannot decelerate by using the SET switch	Temporary damaged or disconnected wiring of SET switch input circuit	No. 2	Repair the harness or replace the SET switch.
	Actuator circuit poor contact	No. 5	Repair the harness or replace the actuator.
	Malfunction of the actuator		
	Malfunction of the auto-cruise control unit	–	Replace the auto-cruise control unit.
Cannot accelerate or resume speed by using the RESUME switch.	Damaged or disconnected wiring, or short-circuit, of RESUME switch input circuit	No. 3	Repair the harness or replace the RESUME switch.
	Actuator circuit poor contact	No. 5	Repair the harness or replace the actuator.
	Malfunction of the actuator		
	Malfunction of the auto-cruise control unit	–	Replace the auto-cruise control unit.
Auto-cruise control system can be set while traveling at a vehicle speed of less than 40 km/h (25 mph), or there is no automatic cancelation at that speed.	Malfunction of the vehicle-speed sensor circuit	No. 4	Repair the vehicle speed sensor system, or replace the part.
	Malfunction of the speedometer cable or the speedometer drive gear		
	Malfunction of the auto-cruise control unit	–	Replace the auto-cruise control unit.

Symptom	Probable cause	Circuit Test	Remedy
• The set vehicle speed varies greatly upward or downward. • "Hunching" (repeated alternating acceleration and deceleration) occurs after setting is made.	Malfunction of the vehicle speed sensor circuit	No.4	Repair the vehicle-speed sensor system, or replace the part.
	Malfunction of the speedometer cable or speedometer drive gear		
	Malfunction of the vacuum circuit	No. 8	Repair vacuum system, or replace the part.
	Actuator circuit poor contact	No. 5	Repair the actuator system, or replace the part.
	Malfunction of the actuator		
	Malfunction of the Auto-cruise control unit	–	Replace the auto-cruise control unit.
The auto-cruise control system is not canceled when the brake pedal is depressed.	Damaged or disconnected wiring of the stop light switch input circuit; brake switch (for auto-cruise control) malfunction (short-circuit)	If the input check code No. 23 indicates a malfunction. No. 6	Repair the harness or replace the stop light switch.
	Actuator drive circuit short-circuit	No. 5	Repair the harness or replace the actuator.
	Malfunction of the auto-cruise control unit	–	Replace the auto-cruise control unit.

93I02381 93A02382

Courtesy of Mitsubishi Motor Sales of America

Fig. 4: Symptom Charts

Check No.	Input operation	Code No.	Display patterns (output codes)	Check results
1	SET switch ON	21	12V / 0V	SET switch circuit normal
2	RESUME switch ON	22	12V / 0V	RESUME switch circuit normal
3	Each CANCEL switch ON 1 Stop light switch (brake pedal depressed) 2 Clutch switch (clutch pedal depressed)	23	12V / 0V	Each CANCEL circuit normal
4	Driving at approximately to 40 km/h (25 mph) or higher	24	12V / 0V	When both No. 4 and No. 5 can be confirmed, vehicle-speed sensor circuit normal.
5	Driving at less than approximately 40 km/h (25 mph) or stopped	25	12V / 0V	

93G02380

Courtesy of Mitsubishi Motor Sales of America

Fig. 5: Input Code Chart

Test No. 4 (Vehicle Speed Sensor Circuit) – When vehicle moves slowly, voltage should alternate from zero volt to 3 volts and should not exceed 5 volts at terminal No. 10 of cruise control unit. If circuit does not test correctly, replace sensor or printed circuit board.

Test No. 5 (Actuator Circuit) – 1) When vehicle is accelerated using RESUME switch, battery voltage should be present on terminals No. 1, 2 and 3 of cruise control unit.
2) When vehicle is coasting by using SET switch, battery voltage should not be present on terminals No. 1, 2 and 3 of cruise control unit. If circuit does not test correctly, replace actuator as necessary or repair harness.

Test No. 6 (Stoplight Switch Circuit) – 1) Battery voltage should be present at all times on terminal No. 18 of cruise control unit. If battery voltage is not present at all times, check fuse No. 3 and replace as necessary. If fuse is okay, repair harness.
2) When brake pedal is pressed, battery voltage should be present on terminal No. 15 of cruise control unit. If voltage is not present, adjust or replace brake switch. If switch is okay, repair harness.

Test No. 7 (Clutch Switch Circuit) – When clutch pedal is pressed, battery voltage should be present on terminal No. 19 of control unit. When clutch pedal is released, voltage should not be present on terminal No. 19 of control unit. If circuit does not test correctly, replace switch or repair harness.

CRUISE CONTROL SWITCH TEST

Main, RESUME & SET Switches – 1) Disconnect 20-pin column switch connector. With main switch in ON position, continuity should be present between terminals No. 5 and 6. See Fig. 6. With SET switch in ON position, continuity should be present between terminals No. 4 and 17.

2) With RESUME switch in ON position, continuity should be present between terminals No. 16 and 17 and between terminals No. 5 and 6. If continuity is not present in any position, replace switch.

VACUUM PUMP TEST

1) Remove vacuum pump connector. Disconnect check valve vacuum hose from actuator. Connect a vacuum gauge to vacuum pump. Connect battery voltage to terminal "L" and ground terminal "B". See Fig. 7.
2) Vacuum pump should operate and create at least 6 in. Hg vacuum. Release vacuum and reconnect power source to vacuum pump. Disconnect power source. Vacuum pump should hold vacuum temporarily. Replace vacuum pump if it does not operate properly.

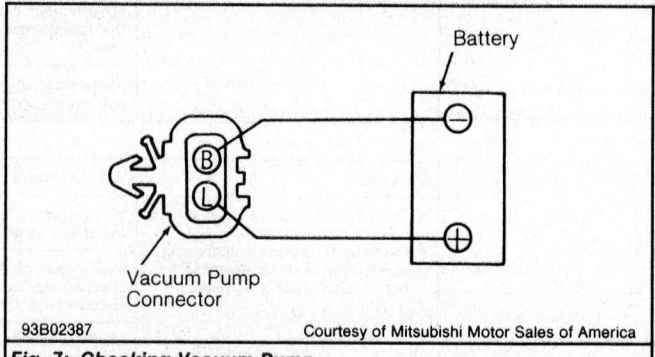

93B02387

Courtesy of Mitsubishi Motor Sales of America

Fig. 7: Checking Vacuum Pump

VACUUM SWITCH TEST

Disconnect wiring connector. Using a hand-held vacuum pump, apply vacuum to vacuum switch. With vacuum applied to vacuum switch continuity should be present between vacuum switch terminals. Vacuum should not drop suddenly. Replace vacuum switch if vacuum drops suddenly or if continuity is not present.

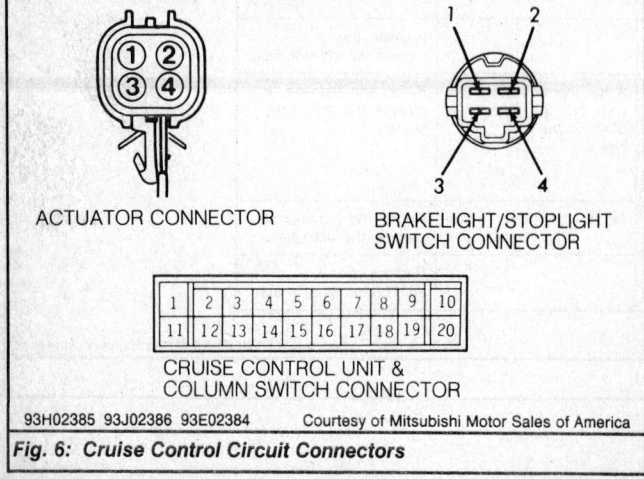

ACTUATOR CONNECTOR

BRAKELIGHT/STOPLIGHT SWITCH CONNECTOR

CRUISE CONTROL UNIT & COLUMN SWITCH CONNECTOR

93H02385 93J02386 93E02384   Courtesy of Mitsubishi Motor Sales of America

Fig. 6: Cruise Control Circuit Connectors

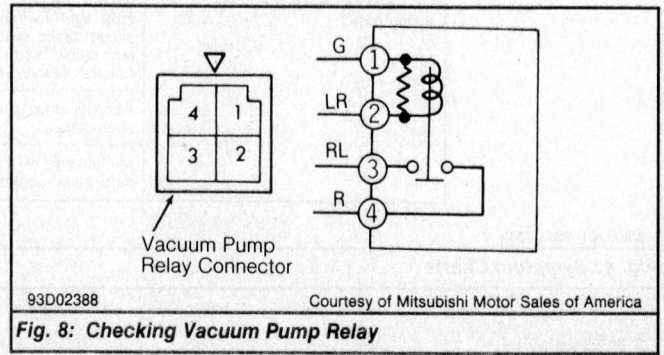

93D02388

Courtesy of Mitsubishi Motor Sales of America

Fig. 8: Checking Vacuum Pump Relay

VACUUM PUMP RELAY TEST

1) Check relay when voltage and ground are applied and not applied. When relay is not energized, 70 ohms should be present between terminals No. 1 and 2. *See Fig. 8.*

2) Continuity should not be present between terminals No. 3 and 4. Connect battery voltage and ground between terminals No. 1 and 2. Continuity should be present between terminals No. 3 and 4.

ACTUATOR TESTS

Resistance Test – 1) Turn ignition off. With actuator connector disconnected, measure resistance between actuator terminals. *See Fig. 6.* Terminals No. 1 and 4 should have 18-28 ohms present.

2) Terminals No. 1 and 3 should have 25-35 ohms present. Terminals No. 1 and 2 should have 45-65 ohms present. Replace actuator if resistance is not as specified.

Operational Test – 1) With connector disconnected, connect battery voltage to terminal No. 1. *See Fig. 6.* Ground terminals No. 2 and 3. Connect ammeter between positive side of battery and terminal No. 1 of actuator connector.

2) Apply 16 in. Hg vacuum to actuator. Vacuum should hold steady and ammeter should read .5-.6 amp. Disconnect ground from terminal No. 2 or 3. Vacuum should hold and ammeter should read .2-.4 amp. If actuator does not test correctly, replace actuator.

VEHICLE SPEED SENSOR TEST

Remove instrument cluster. See INSTRUMENT CLUSTER under REMOVAL & INSTALLATION. Connect ohmmeter between terminals No. 1 and 10. *See Fig. 9.* Ensure continuity pulses on and off 4 times per revolution of speedometer shaft connection. If continuity is not as specified, replace sensor.

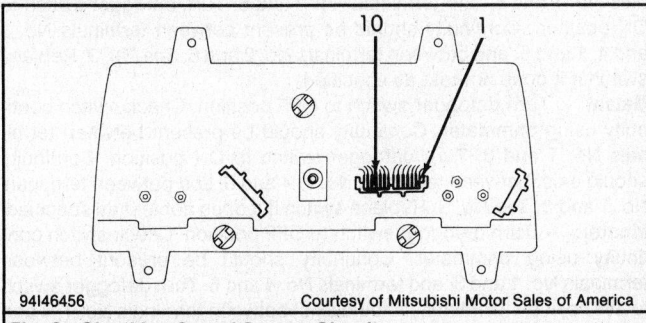

94146456   Courtesy of Mitsubishi Motor Sales of America

Fig. 9: Checking Speed Sensor Circuit

BRAKELIGHT/STOPLIGHT SWITCH TEST

Disconnect switch connector. When brake pedal is pressed, continuity should be present between terminals No. 1 and 3. *See Fig. 6.* When brake pedal is released, continuity should be present between terminals No. 2 and 4. Replace switch if it does not test correctly.

CLOSED THROTTLE POSITION SWITCH & THROTTLE POSITION SENSOR TESTS

Throttle Position Sensor – 1) Disconnect sensor connector. Resistance between terminals No. 1 (Green/Yellow wire) and No. 4 (Green/Black wire) should be 3500-6500 ohms. Use an analog ohmmeter to measure resistance between terminals No. 2 (Green/White wire) and No. 4 (Green/Black wire).

2) Slowly open throttle valve to wide open throttle. Resistance should change smoothly as throttle is opened. Replace throttle position sensor if it does not test correctly.

Closed Throttle Position Switch – 1) Disconnect throttle position sensor connector. Continuity should be present between terminals No. 3 (Yellow/Red wire) and No. 4 (Green/Black wire) with accelerator pedal released. Continuity should not be present with accelerator pedal pressed.

2) If continuity is not present with accelerator released, loosen throttle position sensor mounting screw. Turn throttle position sensor completely clockwise. Recheck continuity. Replace throttle position sensor if closed throttle position switch does not test correctly.

REMOVAL & INSTALLATION

ACTUATOR

Removal & Installation – 1) Remove linkage protector. Disconnect throttle cable, accelerator cable and cruise control cable link connections. Disconnect vacuum pump connector. Remove linkage assembly. Remove vacuum pump bracket. Remove vacuum pump assembly.

2) Remove linkage assembly. Remove accelerator and throttle cables. Remove actuator bracket. Remove cruise control cable. Remove actuator. To install, reverse removal procedure.

CRUISE CONTROL SWITCH

Removal & Installation – Remove horn pad. Remove steering wheel. Remove upper and lower steering column covers. Remove column switch. To install, reverse removal procedure.

MAIN CRUISE CONTROL SWITCH

Removal & Installation – Pry out instrument panel side switch. Remove main cruise control switch. To install, reverse removal procedure.

VEHICLE SPEED SENSOR

Removal & Installation – Remove instrument cluster. See INSTRUMENT CLUSTER. Speed sensor is a part of speedometer. To install, reverse removal procedure.

INSTRUMENT CLUSTER

Removal & Installation – Disconnect negative battery cable. Remove cluster bezel. Remove instrument cluster. To install, reverse removal procedure.

CONTROL UNIT

Removal & Installation – Cruise control unit is located behind center console. Remove ashtray and radio. Remove control unit. To install, reverse removal procedure.

WIRING DIAGRAM

See ACCESSORIES & EQUIPMENT, Volume 5.

1994 ACCESSORIES & EQUIPMENT
Rear Window Defoggers – Except Precis

Chrysler Corp.: Colt, Colt Vista, Stealth
Eagle: Summit, Summit Wagon
Mitsubishi: Diamante, Eclipse, Expo, Galant, Mirage, Montero, 3000GT

DESCRIPTION & OPERATION

The rear window defogger is a heating filament grid bonded to the inside of the window. Heat is regulated by a control switch located on the instrument panel.

TROUBLE SHOOTING

DEFOGGER DOES NOT WORK

Check for blown fuse, poor contact, defective defogger switch, poor connection or open wire.

DEFOGGER TIMER INOPERATIVE

Check defogger switch. Timer is integrated into defogger switch.

INDICATOR LIGHT DOES NOT WORK

Check for burned out bulb, open wire or poor connection.

INDICATOR LIGHT IS DIM

Check rheostat or indicator bulb.

TESTING

NOTE: Testing information for all components on all vehicles is not available from manufacturer.

DEFOGGER RELAY TEST

Colt, Colt Vista, Expo, Mirage, Summit & Summit Wagon – 1) Remove defogger relay, located in right front corner of engine compartment. Ground relay terminal No. 1, and apply battery voltage to terminal No. 3. Check relay continuity using ohmmeter.
2) Continuity should exist between terminals No. 2 and 5. With voltage disconnected, continuity should not exist between terminals No. 2 and 5. Ensure continuity exists between terminals No. 1 and 3. *See Fig. 1.* Replace relay if it does not test as specified.
Diamante, Montero, Stealth & 3000GT – 1) Remove defogger relay, located in right front corner of engine compartment. Ground relay terminal No. 3, and apply battery voltage to terminal No. 5. Check relay continuity using ohmmeter.
2) Continuity should exist between terminals No. 1 and 2. With voltage disconnected, continuity should not exist between terminals No. 1 and 2. Ensure continuity exists between terminals No. 3 and 5. *See Fig. 2.* Replace relay if it does not test as specified.
Eclipse – 1) Remove defogger relay, located to the right of fuse block. Ground relay terminal No. 4, and apply battery voltage to terminal No. 2. Check relay continuity using ohmmeter.

2) Continuity should exist between terminals No. 1 and 2. With voltage disconnected, continuity should not be present between terminals No. 1 and 2. Ensure continuity is present between terminals No. 3 and 4. *See Fig. 2.* Replace relay if it does not test as specified.
Galant – 1) Remove defogger relay, located in right front corner of engine compartment. Ground relay terminal No. 3, and apply battery voltage to terminal No. 1. Check relay continuity using ohmmeter.
2) Continuity should exist between terminals No. 4 and 5. With voltage disconnected, continuity should not exist between terminals No. 4 and 5. Ensure continuity exists between terminals No. 1 and 3. *See Fig. 1.* Replace relay if it does not test as specified.

DEFOGGER SWITCH TEST

NOTE: Remove window defogger switch and disconnect switch connector for the following test.

Colt, Colt Vista, Expo, Mirage, Summit & Summit Wagon – Turn defogger switch to OFF position. Check switch continuity using ohmmeter. Continuity should be present between terminals No. 1 and 2. Turn defogger switch to ON position. Continuity should exist between terminals No. 1, 2 and 4. *See Fig. 3 or 4.* Replace switch if it does not test as specified.
Diamante – Turn defogger switch to OFF position. Check switch continuity using ohmmeter. Continuity should be present between terminals No. 1 and 4, and terminals No. 2 and 5. Turn defogger switch to ON position. Continuity should exist between terminals No. 1, 4 and 6, and between terminals No. 2 and 5. *See Fig. 3.* Replace switch if it does not test as specified.
Eclipse – Turn defogger switch to OFF position. Check switch continuity using ohmmeter. Continuity should be present between terminals No. 1 and 5, and terminals No. 2 and 6. Turn defogger switch to ON position. Continuity should be present between terminals No. 3 and 4, 1 and 5, and between terminals No. 2 and 6. *See Fig. 3.* Replace switch if it does not test as specified.
Galant – Turn defogger switch to OFF position. Check switch continuity using ohmmeter. Continuity should be present between terminals No. 1 and 3. Turn defogger switch to ON position. Continuity should exist between terminals No. 2, 4 and 6, and between terminals No. 1 and 3. *See Fig. 3.* Replace switch if it does not test as specified.
Montero – Turn defogger switch to OFF position. Check switch continuity using ohmmeter. Continuity should be present between terminals No. 1 and 3, and terminals No. 4 and 6. Turn defogger switch to ON position. Continuity should exist between terminals No. 1, 4 and 6, and between terminals No. 1 and 3. *See Fig. 3.* Replace switch if it does not test as specified.

94I46605 — Courtesy of Mitsubishi Motor Sales of America.

Fig. 1: Identifying Defogger Relay Terminals (Colt, Colt Vista, Expo, Galant, Mirage, Summit & Summit Wagon)

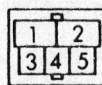

94J46606 — Courtesy of Mitsubishi Motor Sales of America.

Fig. 2: Identifying Defogger Relay Terminals (Diamante, Eclipse, Montero, Stealth & 3000GT)

94A46607 — Courtesy of Mitsubishi Motor Sales of America.

Fig. 3: Identifying Defogger Switch Terminals (Colt, Diamante, Eclipse, Galant, Mirage, Montero & Summit)

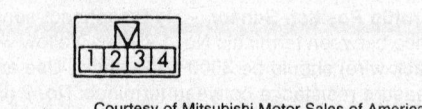

94B46608 — Courtesy of Mitsubishi Motor Sales of America.

Fig. 4: Identifying Defogger Switch Terminals (Colt Vista, Expo & Summit Wagon)

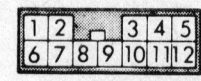

94C46609 — Courtesy of Mitsubishi Motor Sales of America.

Fig. 5: Identifying Defogger Switch Terminals (Stealth & 3000GT)

Stealth & 3000GT – 1) Remove defogger switch assembly from instrument cluster bezel. With defogger switch in OFF position, check switch continuity using ohmmeter.

2) Continuity should exist between terminals No. 3 and 4. With defogger switch in ON position, continuity should exist between terminals No. 1 and 2, 1 and 6, and between terminals No. 3 and 4. See Fig. 5. Replace switch if it does not test as specified.

DEFOGGER TIMER TEST

NOTE: *Information for defogger timer test is available from manufacturer for Eclipse and Montero only.*

1) Remove defogger timer from interior relay block. Connect battery voltage and test light to timer. See Fig. 6. Ensure test light illuminates for approximately 11 seconds when battery voltage is applied to terminal No. 3.

2) Reapply battery voltage to terminal No. 3 and observe test light. Test light should go off. Replace timer if it does not test as specified.

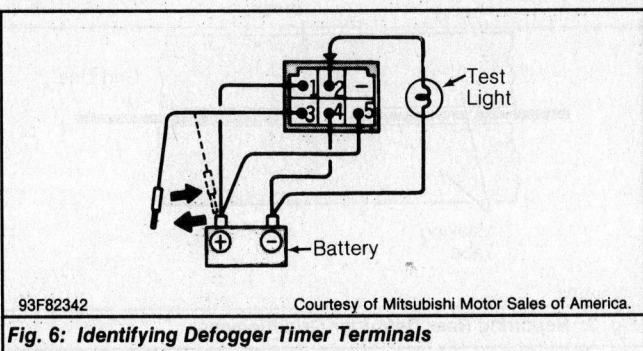

93F82342   Courtesy of Mitsubishi Motor Sales of America.

Fig. 6: Identifying Defogger Timer Terminals

GRID TEST

1) Start and run engine at 2000 RPM. Ensure battery is fully charged. Turn defogger switch to ON position. Using a voltmeter, check voltage at center section of each grid filament.

2) If voltage is approximately 6 volts, grid filament is okay. If voltage is approximately 12 volts, an open is present in the negative circuit. Move probe slowly toward the negative terminal to determine location of open circuit.

3) If voltage is zero volts, an open is present in the positive circuit. Move probe slowly toward the positive terminal to determine location of open circuit. Repair grid as necessary. See Fig. 7.

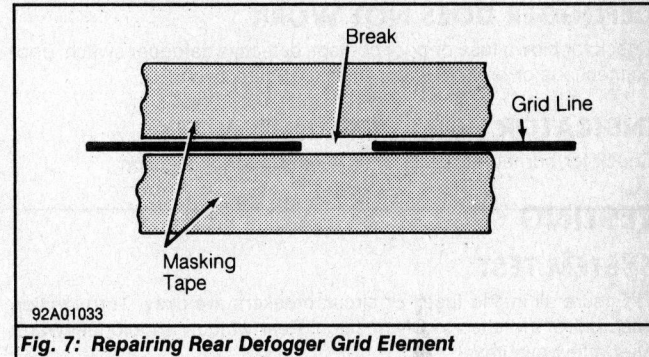

92A01033

Fig. 7: Repairing Rear Defogger Grid Element

WIRING DIAGRAMS

See ACCESSORIES & EQUIPMENT, Volume 5.

DESCRIPTION & OPERATION

Rear window defogger system uses a heating filament grid bonded to the inside of rear window. Heat is regulated by a control switch and the Electronic Timer Alarm Control System (ETACS). The ETACS Control Unit (ECU) is located under left front seat. System has an indicator light to show when system is operating. Power is supplied to the control switch through the ECU. ECU will supply power to the grid for 10 minutes or until the ignition is turned off.

TROUBLE SHOOTING

DEFOGGER DOES NOT WORK

Check for blown fuse or poor contact, defective defogger switch, poor connections or broken wires. Check for defective ECU.

INDICATOR LIGHT DOES NOT WORK

Check for burned out bulb, open wire or poor connection.

TESTING

SYSTEM TEST

1) Ensure all in-line fuses or circuit breakers are okay. Turn ignition and control switches to ON position. Rear window should feel warm after a few minutes.
2) If glass is not warm, use a test light or voltmeter to check for battery voltage at grid feed wire. If battery voltage is not present, check wiring harness, control switch and ECU.

DEFOGGER SWITCH TEST

Disconnect defogger switch from wiring harness. Defogger switch is located on upper center console. Depress defogger switch to ON position. Check switch continuity. Continuity should be present between terminals No. 2 and 4. *See Fig. 1.* If continuity does not exist, replace switch.

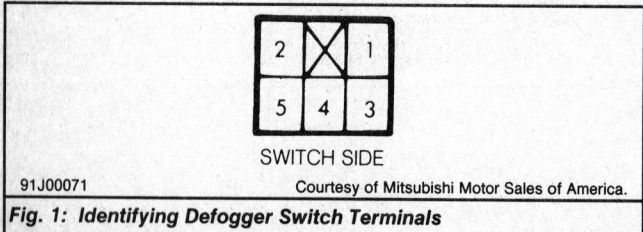

91J00071
Courtesy of Mitsubishi Motor Sales of America.

Fig. 1: Identifying Defogger Switch Terminals

GRID FILAMENT TEST

1) Turn defogger switch to ON position. Use voltmeter to measure voltage at center point of each filament line. *See Fig. 2.* A reading of approximately 6 volts indicates a good filament. A reading of 12 volts indicates a break in the filament between center and positive side.
2) A reading of zero volts indicates a break in the filament between center and negative side. To locate break, move probe along filament until meter needle moves abruptly. A broken filament may be repaired using conductive paint. *See Fig. 3.*

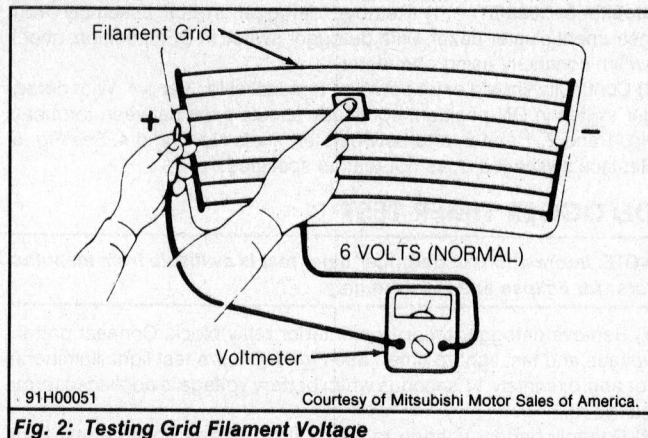

91H00051
Courtesy of Mitsubishi Motor Sales of America.

Fig. 2: Testing Grid Filament Voltage

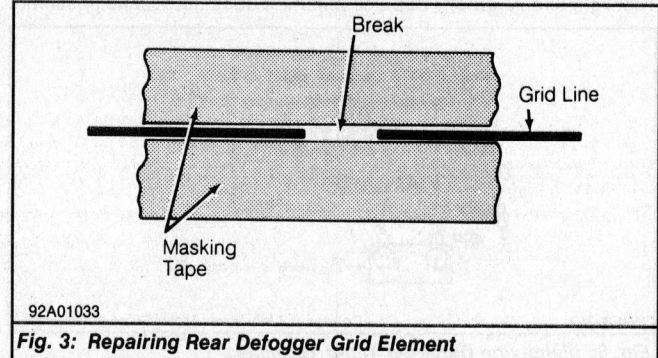

92A01033

Fig. 3: Repairing Rear Defogger Grid Element

ETACS CONTROL UNIT (ECU) TEST

After tracing problem to ECU (located under left front seat), manufacturer suggests testing with a known good unit. If system then operates properly, replace ECU.

WIRING DIAGRAM

See ACCESSORIES & EQUIPMENT, Volume 5.

Chrysler Corp.: Stealth
Mitsubishi: Diamante, 3000GT

DESCRIPTION & OPERATION

Headlight system features an automatic shutoff system. With headlights on, system will turn all lights off when driver's door is opened with ignition in OFF position. Also lights will turn off when ignition is turned off when driver's door is already open.

Headlight system is controlled by Electronic Timer Alarm Control System (ETACS). On Diamante, the ETACS Control Unit (ECU) is located in front of shifter, under console. On Stealth and 3000GT, ECU is located behind driver's lower dash panel, to left side of steering column. See Fig. 1. Current flows from fuse No. 6 to headlight switch, headlight relay, ECU and automatic light shutoff unit.

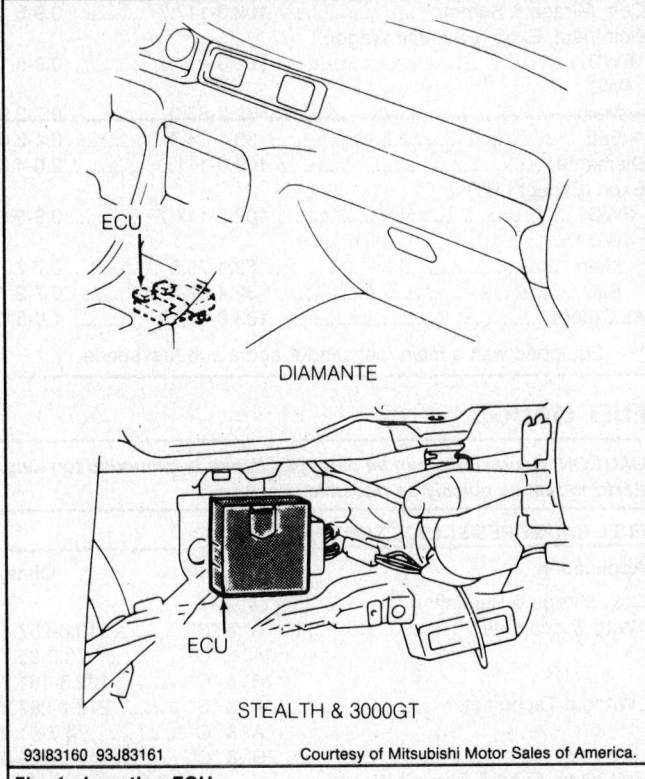

Fig. 1: Locating ECU

TROUBLE SHOOTING

HEADLIGHTS DO NOT TURN OFF AUTOMATICALLY

Close driver's door. Turn ignition switch to ON position. Turn on headlights. Turn ignition switch to OFF position. Open driver's door. If headlights do not turn off, check for following possible causes:

- Wire connector or pin inside connector disengaged at any connector or component in system.
- Open or short circuit in wiring harness.
- Defective automatic light shutoff unit.
- Defective ECU.

TESTING

NOTE: If system is not functioning properly after testing procedures are completed, substitute known-good ECU and retest.

HEADLIGHT AUTOMATIC SHUTOFF UNIT

1) To access headlight automatic shutoff unit, remove passenger rear quarter trim. Using 12-volt test light, backprobe connector terminal No. 7. See Fig. 2.

2) Test light should illuminate during following circumstances:
- Headlight and ignition switch are both in OFF position.
- Headlight switch in TAIL or HEAD position and ignition switch is in ACC or ON position.
- Headlight switch in TAIL or HEAD position. Ignition switch is turned to OFF position and driver's door is opened.
- Headlight switch in TAIL or HEAD position. Driver's door is open. Ignition switch is turned to OFF position.
- Headlight switch in TAIL or HEAD position. Driver's door is open. Ignition switch is turned to ON position.

3) Ensure headlight switch is in TAIL or HEAD position. Turn ignition switch to OFF position and open driver's door. Turn headlight switch from TAIL or HEAD position to OFF position and then back to TAIL or HEAD position. After following this procedure, test light should not be illuminated.

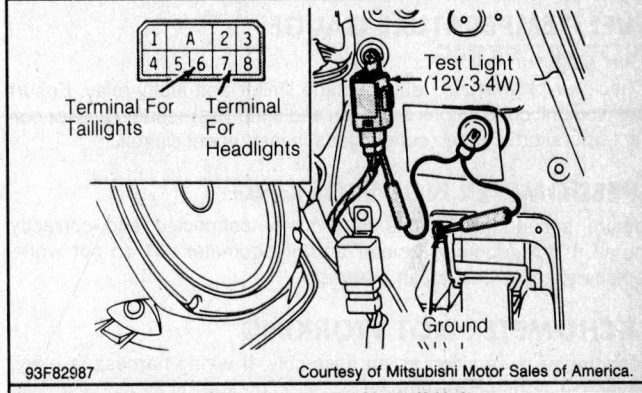

Fig. 2: Testing Headlight Automatic Shutoff Unit

INPUT SIGNAL

1) Access Data Link Connector (DLC). DLC is located behind lower dash panel to left of steering column on Diamante or behind lower dash panel to right of steering column on Stealth and 3000GT. Using Special Tool (MB991529), connect positive lead of voltmeter to terminal No. 9 and negative lead to terminal No. 4 or No. 5. See Fig. 3. Check if input signals from system components are being received by ECU.

2) Voltmeter needle should sweep when each switch is operated (i.e. headlight switch, ignition switch or door switch). If switch or related component is not functioning, voltmeter will not operate when switch is activated. Check related circuit and/or component. Replace appropriate component or repair circuit as necessary.

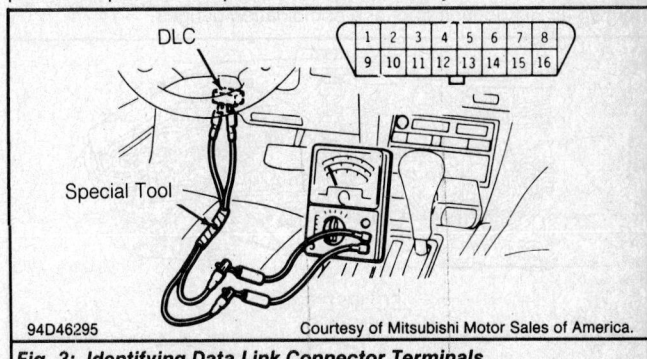

Fig. 3: Identifying Data Link Connector Terminals

REMOVAL & INSTALLATION

CAUTION: When battery is disconnected, vehicle computer and memory systems may lose memory data. Driveability problems may exist until computer systems have completed a relearn cycle. Obtain radio anti-theft protection code from owner prior to servicing vehicle.

Manufacturers do not provide a step by step procedure for removing and installing headlight automatic shutoff system components.

1994 ACCESSORIES & EQUIPMENT
Instrument Panels – Except Precis

Chrysler Corp.: Colt, Colt Vista, Stealth
Eagle: Summit, Summit Wagon
Mitsubishi: Diamante, Eclipse, Expo, Galant,
Mirage, Montero, Pickup, 3000GT

DESCRIPTION & OPERATION

Instrument cluster includes speedometer, fuel gauge and temperature gauge. Fuel gauge has a built-in voltage limiter to keep voltage supply to gauges at 7 volts. Some models may also have a shunt-type ammeter, oil pressure gauge, tachometer, voltmeter and/or turbo boost pressure gauge. Oil pressure gauge uses full battery voltage. The tachometer operates by pulse feed.

TROUBLE SHOOTING

FUEL/TEMPERATURE GAUGE NOT WORKING

Check for blown fuse, faulty voltage limiter and faulty relay. Ensure sending unit connections are clean and tight. Test sending unit for correct operation. Tighten connections in instrument cluster.

SPEEDOMETER NOT WORKING

Ensure speedometer cable is properly connected and correctly routed. If speedometer pointer and/or odometer still do not work, replace speedometer as an assembly.

TACHOMETER NOT WORKING

Tachometer is serviced as an assembly. If wiring harness is okay, replace tachometer assembly.

WARNING LIGHTS NOT WORKING

Test for defective sending unit, burned-out bulb and broken printed circuit. Ensure all connections are clean and tight.

TESTING

BOOST PRESSURE GAUGE

NOTE: Boost pressure gauge testing procedures for Galant are not available from manufacturer.

Resistance Test (Eclipse, Stealth & 3000GT – Turbo) – 1) Remove instrument cluster from instrument panel. See INSTRUMENT CLUSTER under REMOVAL & INSTALLATION. On Stealth and 3000GT, remove air distribution duct and combination gauges.

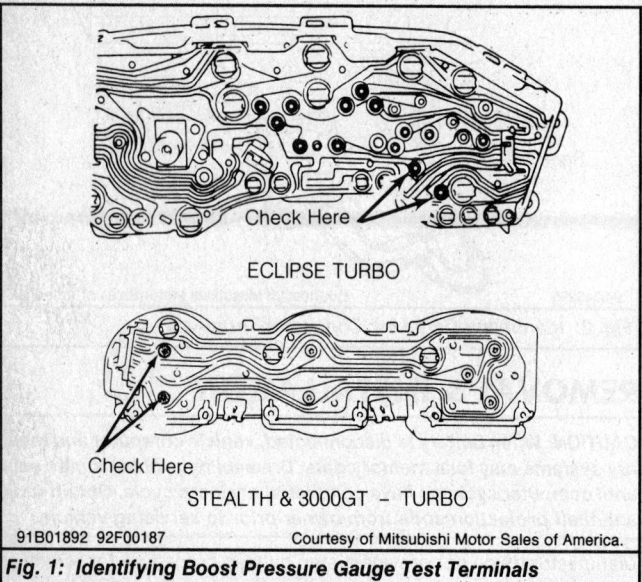

Check Here
ECLIPSE TURBO

Check Here
STEALTH & 3000GT – TURBO

91B01892 92F00187   Courtesy of Mitsubishi Motor Sales of America.

Fig. 1: Identifying Boost Pressure Gauge Test Terminals

2) On all models, measure resistance between boost pressure gauge terminals on back of instrument cluster or combination gauges using ohmmeter. *See Fig. 1.* Resistance should be 72 ohms. If resistance is not as specified, replace gauge.

FUEL TANK SENDING UNIT

Resistance Test – Remove fuel tank sending unit from fuel tank. Measure resistance between appropriate terminals with fuel float in FULL and EMPTY positions. *See Fig. 2.* Compare resistance reading to FUEL TANK SENDING UNIT RESISTANCE SPECIFICATIONS table. If resistance is not to specification, replace fuel tank sending unit.

FUEL TANK SENDING UNIT RESISTANCE SPECIFICATIONS

Application	Empty	Full
Colt, Mirage & Summit	102.3-117.7	0.9-5.1
Colt Vista, Expo & Summit Wagon		
FWD	102.3-117.7	0.9-5.1
4WD [1]		
Main	72.2-83.0	0.7-2.9
Sub	30.1-34.7	0.4-2.0
Diamante	109.0-111.0	2.0-4.0
Expo (Except LRV)		
FWD	102.3-117.7	0.9-5.1
4WD [1]		
Main	69.4-79.5	0.7-2.7
Sub	32.4-37.7	0.7-2.7
All Others	103.0-117.0	1.0-5.0

[1] – Equipped with a main fuel sender and a sub fuel sender.

FUEL GAUGE

CAUTION: Gauge coils can be damaged if wire is grounded too long. Perform test as quickly as possible.

FUEL GAUGE RESISTANCE SPECIFICATIONS

Application	Terminals	Ohms
Colt, Mirage & Summit		
With Tachometer	"A" & "B"	210.6-257.4
	"A" & "C"	78.3-95.7
	"B" & "C"	132.3-161.7
Without Tachometer	"A" & "B"	218.7-267.3
	"A" & "C"	74.7-91.3
	"B" & "C"	144.0-176.0
Colt Vista, Expo & Summit Wagon		
With Tachometer	"A" & "B"	82.8-101.2
	"A" & "C"	58.5-71.5
	"B" & "C"	85.5-104.5
Without Tachometer	"A" & "B"	218.7-267.3
	"A" & "C"	24.7-91.3
	"B" & "C"	144.0-176.0
Diamante	"A" & "B"	247.0-301.0
	"A" & "C"	78.0-94.0
	"B" & "C"	170.0-206.0
Eclipse	"A" & "B"	230.0
	"A" & "C"	102.0
	"B" & "C"	102.0
Galant	"A" & "B"	99.0
	"A" & "C"	262.0
	"B" & "C"	163.0
Montero	No. 2 & 3	209.7-256.3
	No. 1 & 2	77.4-94.6
	No. 1 & 3	132.3-161.7
Pickup	IGN & "E"	62.0-78.0
	7V & FU	49.0-61.0
Stealth & 3000GT	"A" & "B"	254.0
	"A" & "C"	101.0
	"B" & "C"	153.0

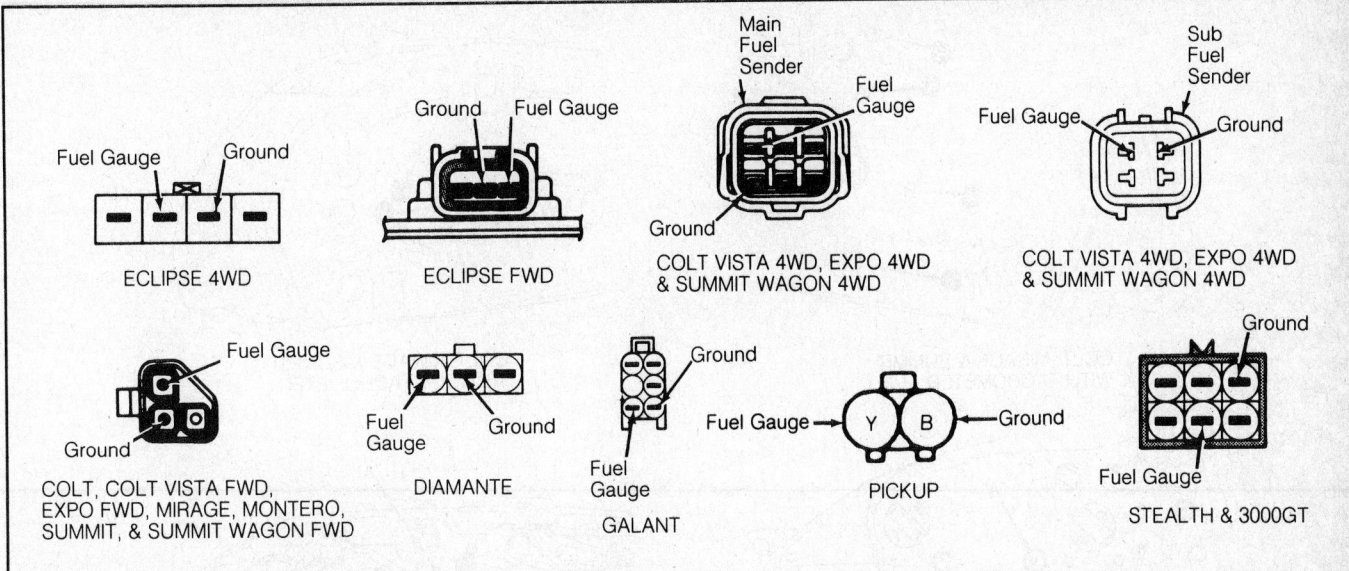

93J01075 93B01076 93E82390 93F82391 93H01079 93J01080 94E46650 93B01081 93D01082

Courtesy of Mitsubishi Motor Sales of America.

Fig. 2: Identifying Fuel Gauge Test Connections

Simple Test – 1) Disconnect fuel gauge sending unit connector wire in luggage compartment, in cargo space or at tank unit. Connect a 12-volt, 3.4-watt bulb to harness side of connector, between appropriate terminals. See Fig. 2.

2) Turn ignition switch to ON position. Ensure test bulb flashes, or stays on, and fuel gauge needle moves. If bulb or gauge needle does not function as described, check and repair fuel gauge circuit.

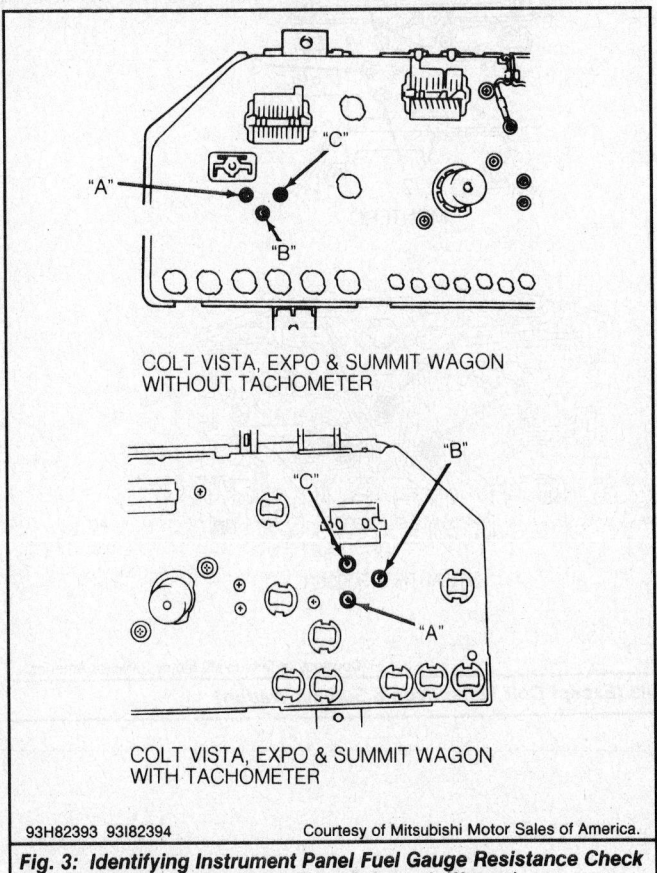

93H82393 93I82394

Courtesy of Mitsubishi Motor Sales of America.

Fig. 3: Identifying Instrument Panel Fuel Gauge Resistance Check Terminals (Colt Vista, Expo & Summit Wagon)

NOTE: Fuel gauge resistance test must be completed with instrument panel cluster removed. Use ohmmeter for all measurements. If resistance is extremely low, a short may exist in coil. If resistance is extremely high, a broken wire or similar problem may exist in gauge.

Resistance Test – 1) Remove instrument cluster. See INSTRUMENT CLUSTER under REMOVAL & INSTALLATION. On Stealth and 3000GT, remove air distribution duct and combination gauges.

2) On all models, measure resistance between appropriate terminals of instrument cluster or combination gauges. See Figs. 3 and 4. See FUEL GAUGE RESISTANCE SPECIFICATIONS table. If resistance readings are not to specification, replace fuel gauge.

OIL PRESSURE GAUGE

Circuit Test (Eclipse, Montero, Pickup, Stealth & 3000GT) – 1) Disconnect oil pressure gauge wiring connector from sending unit inside engine compartment. Connect a 12-volt test light between harness connector terminal and ground. Turn ignition on, but DO NOT start engine.

2) If test light comes on and gauge needle moves, go to GAUGE RESISTANCE TEST. If test light does not come on and gauge needle does not move, repair wiring to sending unit.

Gauge Resistance Test (Eclipse, Montero, Pickup, Stealth & 3000GT) – 1) Remove instrument cluster from instrument panel. See INSTRUMENT CLUSTER under REMOVAL & INSTALLATION. On Stealth and 3000GT, remove air distribution duct and combination gauges.

2) On all models, check continuity between oil pressure gauge terminals. See Fig. 5. See OIL PRESSURE GAUGE RESISTANCE SPECIFICATIONS table. If resistance is not within specification, replace oil pressure gauge.

OIL PRESSURE GAUGE RESISTANCE SPECIFICATIONS

Application	Ohms
Eclipse, Stealth & 3000GT	42
Montero	50
Pickup	37-47

REED SWITCH

Continuity Check (Except Pickup) – 1) Remove instrument cluster. See INSTRUMENT CLUSTER under REMOVAL & INSTALLATION. Check continuity between reed switch terminals No. 1 and 2. See Fig. 7.

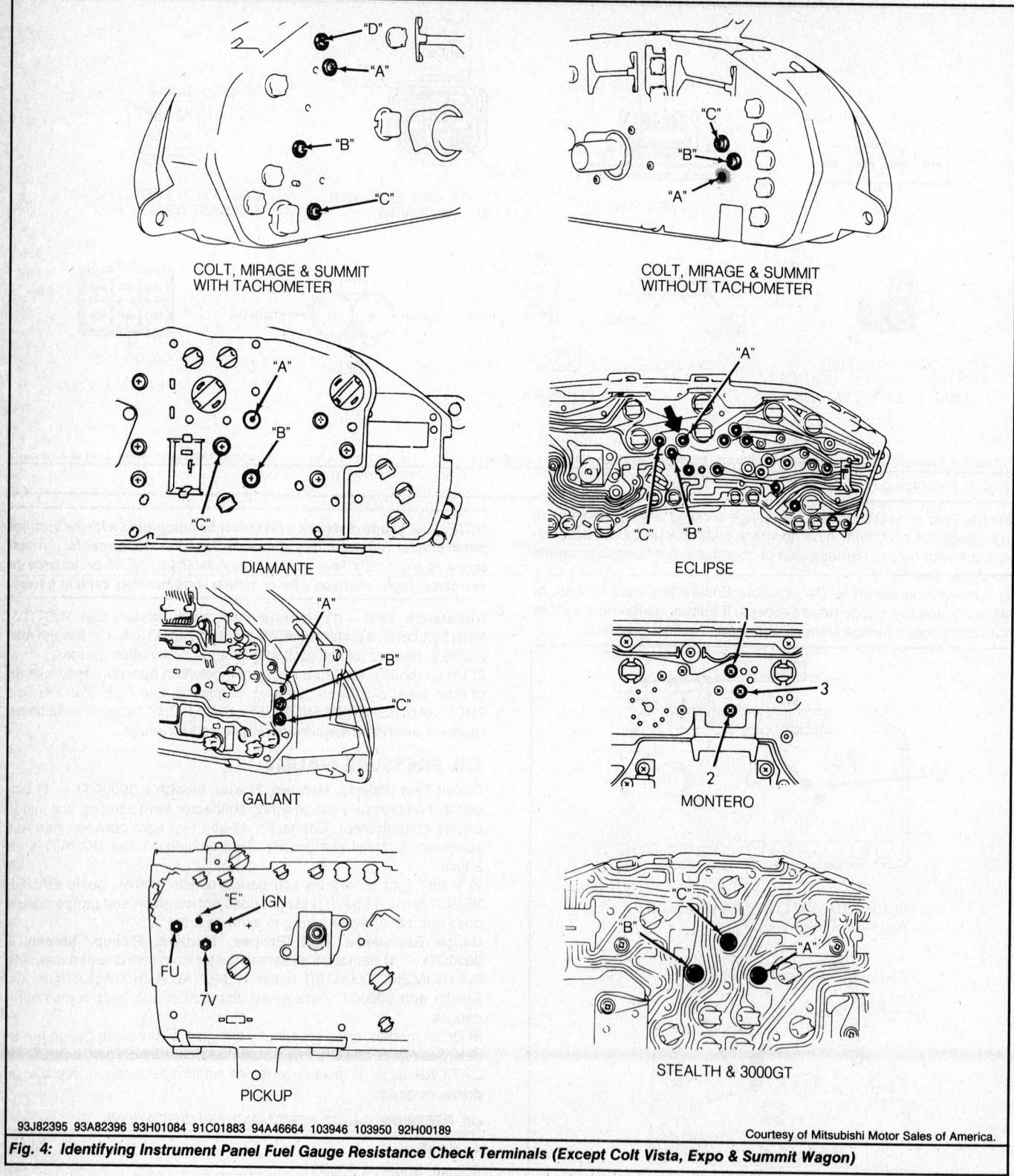

COLT, MIRAGE & SUMMIT
WITH TACHOMETER

COLT, MIRAGE & SUMMIT
WITHOUT TACHOMETER

DIAMANTE

ECLIPSE

GALANT

MONTERO

PICKUP

STEALTH & 3000GT

93J82395 93A82396 93H01084 91C01883 94A46664 103946 103950 92H00189

Courtesy of Mitsubishi Motor Sales of America.

Fig. 4: Identifying Instrument Panel Fuel Gauge Resistance Check Terminals (Except Colt Vista, Expo & Summit Wagon)

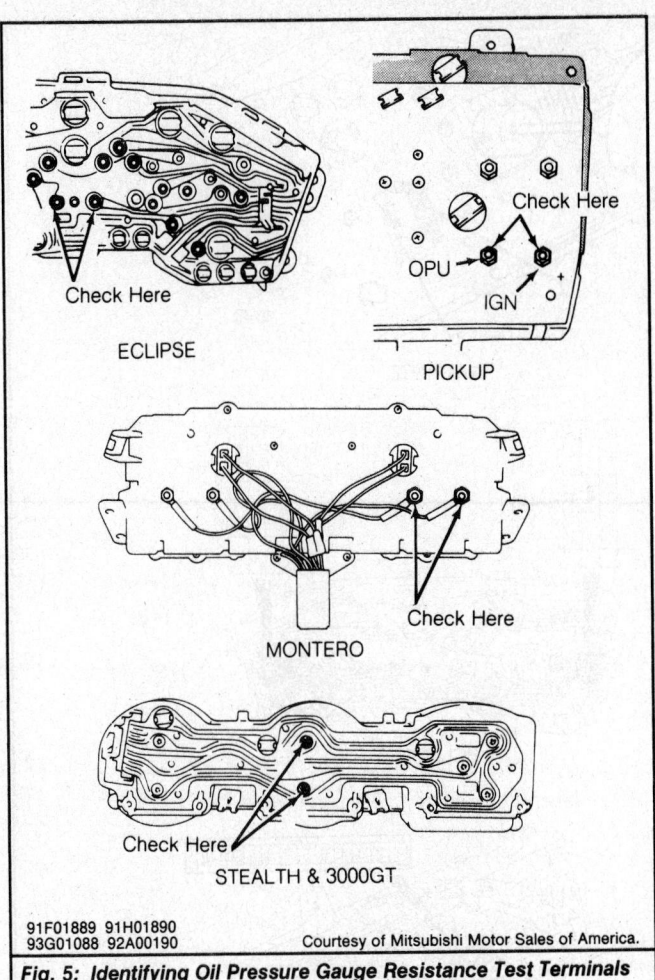

91F01889 91H01890
93G01088 92A00190

Courtesy of Mitsubishi Motor Sales of America.

Fig. 5: Identifying Oil Pressure Gauge Resistance Test Terminals (Eclipse, Montero, Pickup, Stealth & 3000GT)

2) Ensure continuity pulses on and off 4 times per revolution of speedometer shaft connection. If continuity is not as specified, replace reed switch.

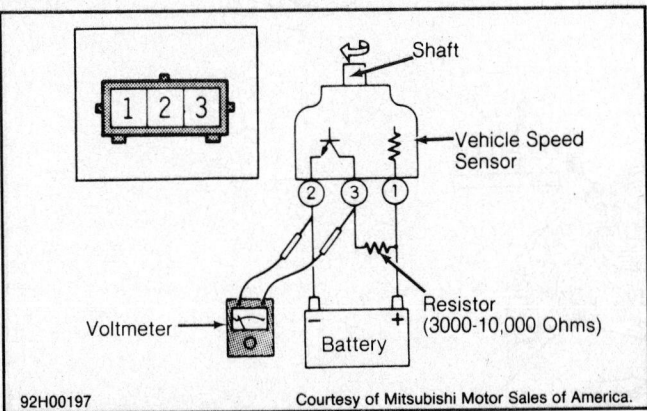

92H00197

Courtesy of Mitsubishi Motor Sales of America.

Fig. 6: Testing Speed Sensor (Galant, Stealth & 3000GT – With Electronic Speedometer)

SPEED SENSOR

Voltage Test (Stealth & 3000GT – With Electronic Speedometer) – Remove speed sensor from transmission. Connect speed sensor, resistor (3000-10,000 ohms) and battery. See Fig. 6. Using a voltmeter, ensure voltage pulses on and off 4 times per revolution of speedometer shaft. Replace sensor if voltage is not as specified.

SPEEDOMETER

Calibration Test – Adjust tire pressure to standard value. Using a calibrated, reliable speedometer tester, compare reading of vehicle speedometer to speedometer tester. See SPEEDOMETER ALLOWABLE VARIATION table. Replace speedometer if necessary.

SPEEDOMETER ALLOWABLE VARIATION

MPH (km/h)	Allowable Variation MPH (km/h)
20 (32)	19-22 (31-35)
40 (64)	38-44 (61-71)
60 (97)	57-66 (92-106)
80 (129)	76-88 (122-142)
100 (161)	94-110 (151-177)

TACHOMETER

NOTE: DO NOT reverse polarity when installing tachometer; diode and transistor may be damaged.

Calibration Test – Connect a calibrated, reliable tach-dwell meter to vehicle ignition system. Operate engine at various speeds (RPM). See TACHOMETER ALLOWABLE VARIATION table. If comparison between tach-dwell meter and vehicle tachometer readings are not within permissible variation, replace vehicle tachometer.

TACHOMETER ALLOWABLE VARIATION

Engine Speed (RPM)	Allowable Variation (RPM)
Colt, Mirage & Summit	
1000	900-1100
3000	2800-3100
5000	4625-5100
6000	5550-6100
Colt Vista, Diamante, Expo, Montero, Stealth, Summit Wagon & 3000GT	
1000	900-1100
3000	2850-3150
5000	4750-5250
6000	5700-6300
Eclipse	
8000-RPM Tachometer	
700	600-800
3000	2850-3150
5000	4750-5250
9000-RPM Tachometer	
700	600-800
3000	2900-3225
5000	4900-5325
Galant	
1000	900-1100
3000	2850-3150
5000	4750-5250
6000	5700-6300
Pickup	
1000	900-1100
3000	2850-3150
6000	5700-6300

TEMPERATURE GAUGE

CAUTION: DO NOT connect sender wire directly to ground during test.

Circuit Test – 1) Disconnect temperature sender wire from sending unit. Connect a 12-volt, 3.4-watt test light between connector terminal and ground. Turn ignition switch to ON position.
2) If test light flashes and temperature gauge needle moves, go to SENSOR RESISTANCE TEST. If test light does not flash or gauge needle does not move, repair wiring to sending unit.
Sensor Resistance Test – 1) Remove Coolant Temperature Sensor (CTS) from engine. See COOLANT TEMPERATURE SENSOR LOCATION table. Place sending unit in 158°F (70°C) water. Check sensor resistance using ohmmeter.
2) CTS resistance should be 90-117 ohms. If CTS resistance is okay, go to GAUGE RESISTANCE TEST. Replace CTS if resistance is not as specified.

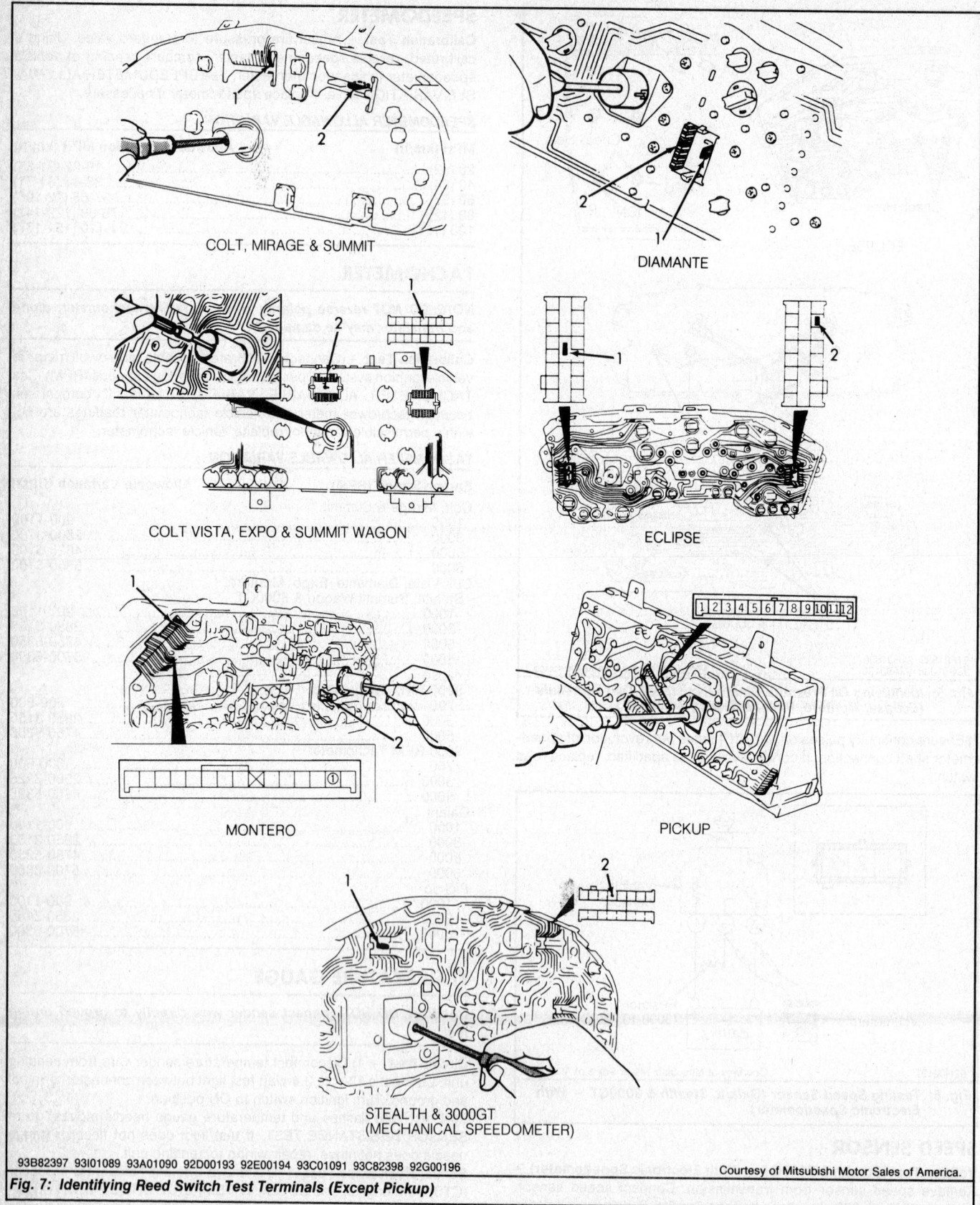

COLT, MIRAGE & SUMMIT

DIAMANTE

COLT VISTA, EXPO & SUMMIT WAGON

ECLIPSE

MONTERO

PICKUP

STEALTH & 3000GT
(MECHANICAL SPEEDOMETER)

93B82397 93I01089 93A01090 92D00193 92E00194 93C01091 93C82398 92G00196

Courtesy of Mitsubishi Motor Sales of America.

Fig. 7: Identifying Reed Switch Test Terminals (Except Pickup)

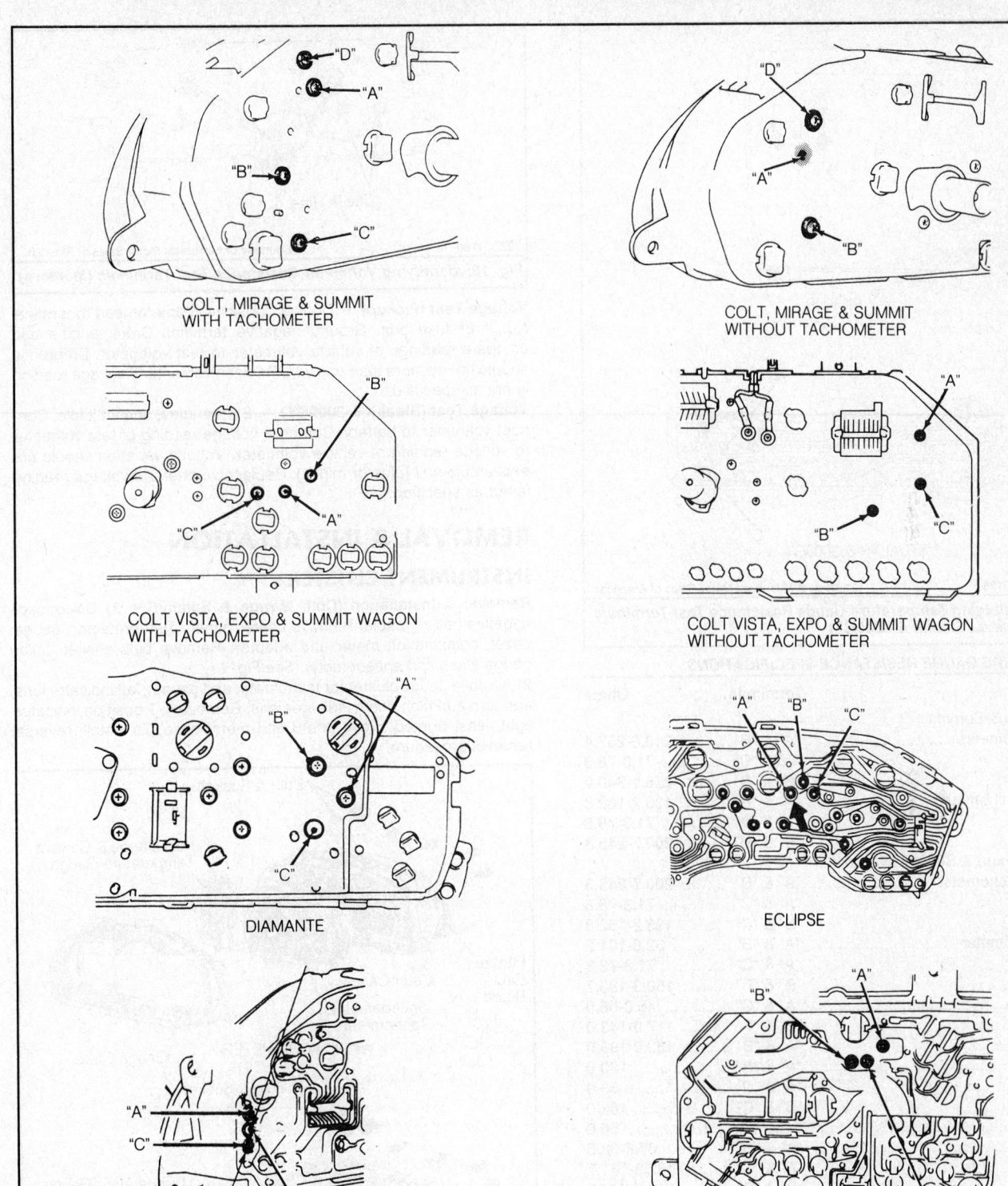

93J82395 93D82399 93I01094 93B01095 93G01093 91D01888 94G46660 93D01096

Courtesy of Mitsubishi Motor Sales of America.

Fig. 8: Identifying Temperature Gauge Resistance Test Terminals (Except Pickup, Stealth & 3000GT)

COOLANT TEMPERATURE SENSOR LOCATION

Model	Location
Colt Vista, Diamante, Expo, Stealth DOHC, Summit Wagon & 3000GT	Thermostat Housing
All Others	Intake Manifold

Gauge Resistance Test – **1)** Remove instrument cluster from instrument panel. See INSTRUMENT CLUSTER under REMOVAL & INSTALLATION. On Stealth and 3000GT, remove air distribution duct and combination gauges.

2) On all models, measure resistance between temperature gauge terminals at rear of cluster or combination gauges. See TEMPERATURE GAUGE RESISTANCE SPECIFICATIONS table. *See Figs. 8 and 9.*

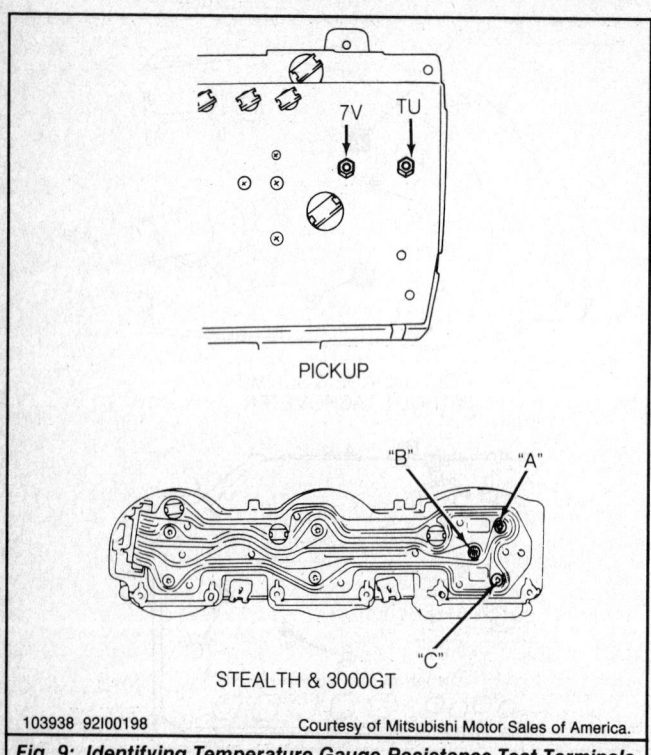

Fig. 9: Identifying Temperature Gauge Resistance Test Terminals (Pickup, Stealth & 3000GT)

103938 92I00198   Courtesy of Mitsubishi Motor Sales of America.

TEMPERATURE GAUGE RESISTANCE SPECIFICATIONS

Application	Terminals	Ohms
Colt, Mirage & Summit		
With Tachometer	"A" & "B"	210.6-257.4
	"A" & "C"	71.3-78.8
	"B" & "D"	278.1-340.0
Without Tachometer	"A" & "B"	133.2-162.8
	"A" & "D"	71.3-78.8
	"B" & "D"	200.7-245.3
Colt Vista, Expo & Summit Wagon		
Without Tachometer	"A" & "B"	200.7-245.3
	"A" & "C"	71.3-78.8
	"B" & "C"	133.2-162.8
With Tachometer	"A" & "B"	82.8-101.2
	"A" & "C"	71.3-78.8
	"B" & "C"	150.3-183.7
Diamante	"A" & "C"	46.0-56.0
	"B" & "C"	117.0-143.0
	"A" & "B"	163.0-199.0
Eclipse	"A" & "B"	130.0
	"A" & "C"	53.0
	"B" & "C"	162.0
Galant	"B" & "C" [1]	50.0
Montero	"A" & "B"	67.5-82.5
	"A" & "C"	132.3-161.7
	"B" & "C"	199.8-244.2
Pickup	7V & TU	49.0-61.0
Stealth & 3000GT	"A" & "B"	51.0
	"A" & "C"	139.0
	"B" & "C"	190.0

[1] – With 12-volt battery voltage applied to terminal "A" and battery ground applied to terminal "C".

VOLTMETER

Resistance Test (Montero) – Using an ohmmeter, measure resistance between voltmeter terminals. See Fig. 10. Resistance should be 380-460 ohms.

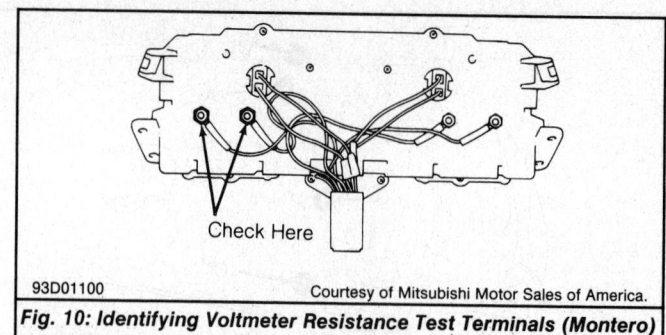

93D01100   Courtesy of Mitsubishi Motor Sales of America.

Fig. 10: Identifying Voltmeter Resistance Test Terminals (Montero)

Voltage Test (Pickup) – Connect positive voltmeter lead to terminal No. 7 of fuse box. Ground negative terminal. Crank engine and compare readings of vehicle voltmeter to test voltmeter. Difference should not be more than one volt. Replace voltmeter if voltage reading is not as specified.

Voltage Test (Stealth & 3000GT) – Start engine, and let it idle. Connect voltmeter to battery. Compare voltage reading of test voltmeter to voltage reading of vehicle voltmeter. Voltage variation should not exceed 0.5 volt (plus or minus). Replace voltmeter if voltage reading is not as specified.

REMOVAL & INSTALLATION

INSTRUMENT CLUSTER

Removal & Installation (Colt, Mirage & Summit) – 1) Disconnect negative battery cable. Remove center panel, knee protector, gauge bezel, combination meter and adapter. Remove bulb socket, bulb, gauge glass and speedometer. See Fig. 11.

2) Remove gauge cluster (or tachometer and gauge), left indicator lens and turn and high beam indicator lens. Remove A/T position indicator light, lens, printed circuit board and meter case. To install, reverse removal procedure.

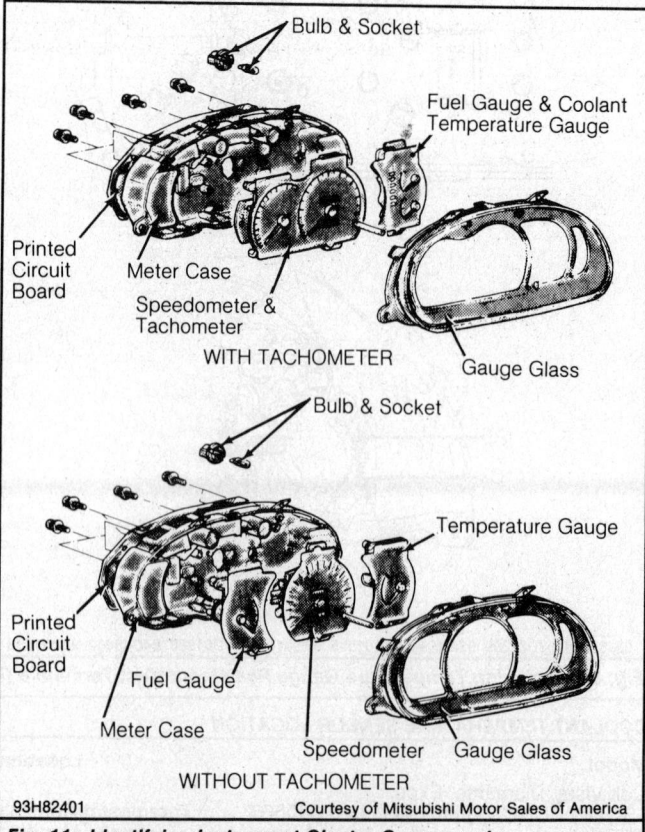

93H82401   Courtesy of Mitsubishi Motor Sales of America

Fig. 11: Identifying Instrument Cluster Components (Colt, Mirage & Summit)

Removal & Installation (Diamante) – Disconnect negative battery cable. Remove gauge bezel. Remove screws holding gauge assembly in place. Remove instrument cluster. Remove trip meter reset button. *See Fig. 12.* Remove gauge glass and plate. Remove gauges as necessary. To install, reverse removal procedure.

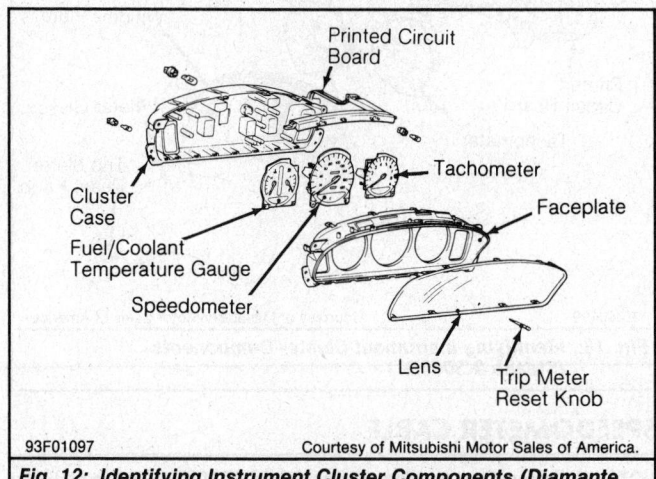

Fig. 12: Identifying Instrument Cluster Components (Diamante W/Tachometer Is Shown; W/O Tachometer Is Similar)

Removal & Installation (Colt Vista, Expo & Summit Wagon) – **1)** Disconnect negative battery cable. Remove cluster hood. Remove cluster mounting screws. Disconnect necessary electrical connectors.
2) Remove cluster. On models without tachometer, remove printed circuit board. On all models, remove cluster glass. Remove gauges as necessary. *See Fig. 13.* To install, reverse removal procedure.

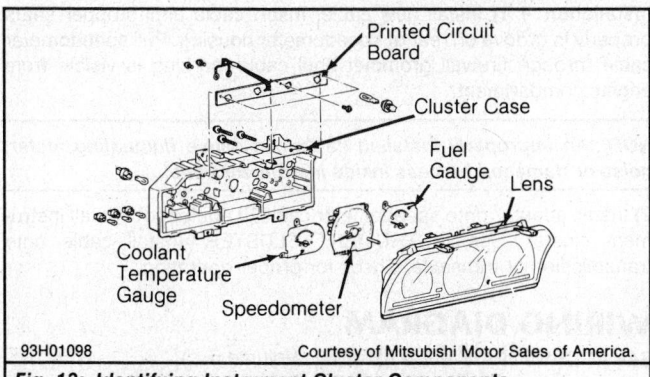

Fig. 13: Identifying Instrument Cluster Components (Colt Vista, Expo & Summit Wagon)

Removal & Installation (Eclipse) – **1)** Disconnect negative battery cable. Remove cluster cover. Remove cluster mounting screws. Remove cluster by turning upper part toward front. Disconnect all necessary electrical connectors. Remove instrument cluster.
2) Disconnect speedometer cable at transaxle end. Pull speedometer cable slightly toward vehicle interior. Release adapter by turning left or right, and remove adapter. To install, reverse removal procedure. *See Fig. 14.*

Removal & Installation (Galant) – Disconnect negative battery cable. Remove trip meter reset knob and gauge cluster bezel. *See Fig. 15.* Remove 4 cluster mounting screws. Remove cluster by turning upper part toward front. Disconnect electrical connectors and speedometer cable adapter. To install, reverse removal procedure.

Removal & Installation (Montero) – **1)** Disconnect negative battery cable. Remove instrument cluster cover plug. Remove cluster cover. Remove screws from instrument cluster.
2) Disconnect speedometer cable from back of instrument cluster. Disconnect all connectors attaching cluster. Remove cluster. To install, reverse removal procedure. *See Fig. 16.*

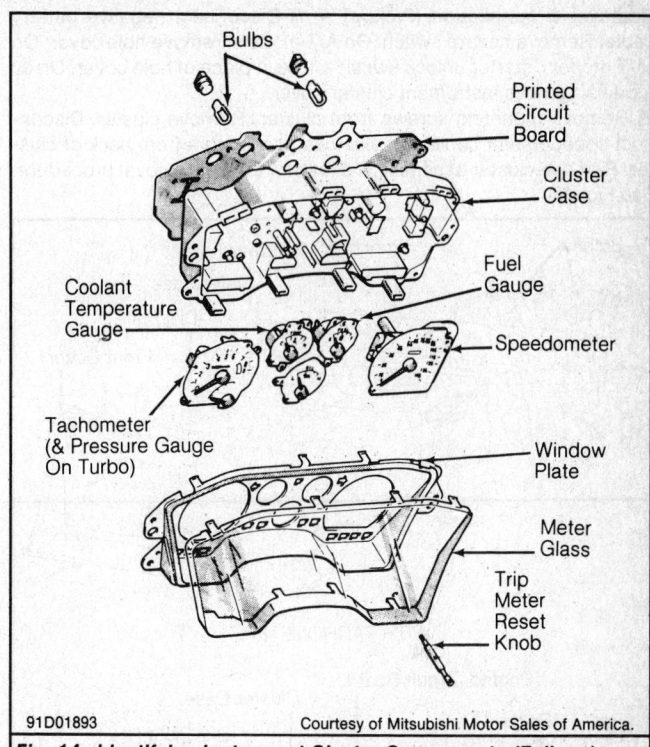

Fig. 14: Identifying Instrument Cluster Components (Eclipse)

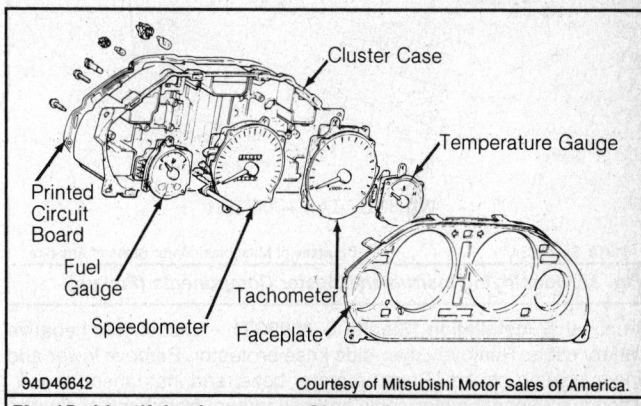

Fig. 15: Identifying Instrument Cluster Components (Galant)

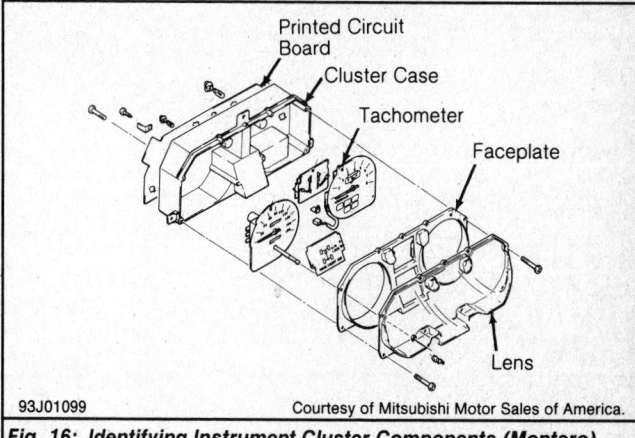

Fig. 16: Identifying Instrument Cluster Components (Montero)

Removal & Installation (Pickup) – 1) Disconnect negative battery cable. Remove hazard switch. On A/T models, remove hole cover. On M/T models, starter unlock switch will be in place of hole cover. On all models, remove instrument cluster cover.

2) Remove mounting screws from cluster. Remove cluster. Disconnect speedometer cable and electrical connectors from back of cluster. Remove cluster assembly. To install, reverse removal procedure. *See Fig. 17.*

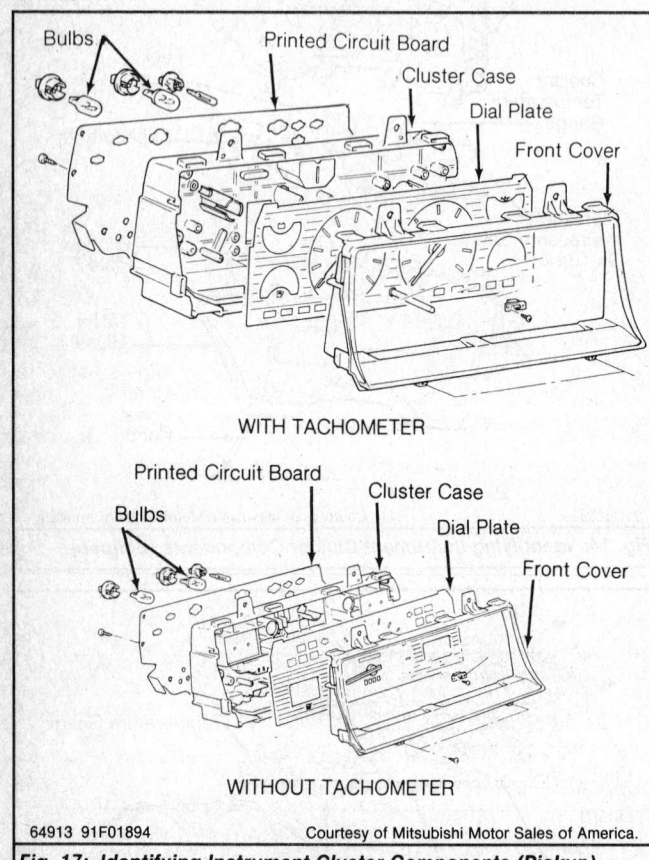

WITH TACHOMETER

WITHOUT TACHOMETER

64913 91F01894   Courtesy of Mitsubishi Motor Sales of America.

Fig. 17: Identifying Instrument Cluster Components (Pickup)

Removal & Installation (Stealth & 3000GT) – Disconnect negative battery cable. Remove driver-side knee protector. Remove lower and upper column covers. Remove meter bezel and instrument cluster. Disconnect speedometer cable and connectors from back of cluster. Remove cluster. To install, reverse removal procedure. *See Fig. 18.*

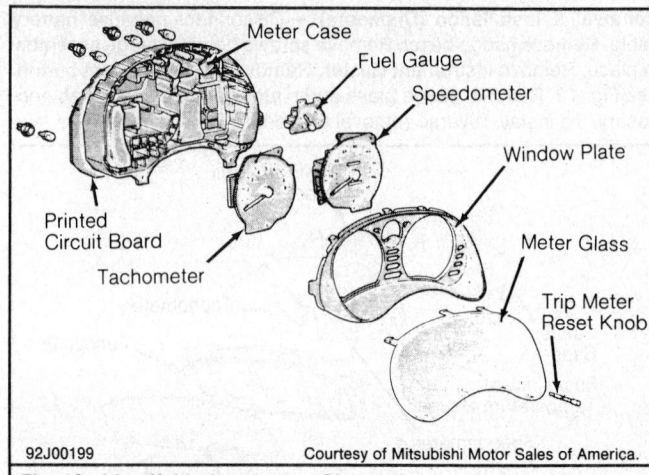

92J00199   Courtesy of Mitsubishi Motor Sales of America.

Fig. 18: Identifying Instrument Cluster Components (Stealth & 3000GT)

SPEEDOMETER CABLE

NOTE: When routing speedometer cable, DO NOT bend cable sharply. Minimum bending radius is 6" (150 mm). Speedometer cable length varies with transmission type.

Removal – Disconnect speedometer cable from transmission or transaxle. Remove instrument cluster from instrument panel. See INSTRUMENT CLUSTER. Disconnect speedometer cable from instrument cluster and/or adapter (if equipped). Remove speedometer cable from firewall grommet.

Installation – 1) Install new cable. Insert cable until stopper seats properly in groove on rear of speedometer housing. Pull speedometer cable through firewall grommet until cable marking is visible from engine compartment.

NOTE: An improperly installed cable can cause fluctuating meter, noise or damaged harness inside instrument panel.

2) Install adapter onto speedometer cable (if equipped). Install instrument cluster. See INSTRUMENT CLUSTER. Install cable onto transmission or transaxle. Check for proper operation.

WIRING DIAGRAM

See ACCESSORIES & EQUIPMENT, Volume 5.

DESCRIPTION

Standard instrument cluster includes speedometer, tachometer, Engine Coolant Temperature (ECT) and fuel gauges. Oil pressure, brake fluid level and seat belt reminder are indicated by warning/reminder lights.

TESTING

BRAKE WARNING LIGHT

Continuity Test (Brake Fluid Level Switch) – Disconnect brake fluid level switch connector at reservoir. Using an ohmmeter, ensure continuity exists between switch terminals while pressing down on switch float. Repair or replace switch if continuity does not exist.

Inspection (Brake Fluid Level Warning Light) – Start engine. Release parking brake. Disconnect brake fluid level warning switch at reservoir. Jumper harness connector terminals together. Warning light should come on. If light does not come on, check wiring. Repair or replace as necessary.

Continuity Test (Parking Brake Switch) – Remove rear console assembly. Disconnect parking brake switch. Check continuity of switch terminal to ground while moving parking brake lever. Ensure continuity is not present when lever is released. Continuity should be present when parking brake is applied (lever pulled up). If switch does not function as described, check wiring harness. Repair or replace switch and/or harness as necessary.

FUEL GAUGE

Simple Test (Fuel Gauge Sending Unit) – Raise and support vehicle. Disconnect harness connector at fuel gauge sending unit. Connect a 12-volt, 3.4-watt test light to fuel gauge sending unit harness connector terminal No. 2 and ground. See Fig. 1. Turn ignition on. Ensure test light flashes and fuel gauge indicator moves toward "F" position. If test light does not flash and fuel gauge indicator does not move, check wiring harness and repair as necessary.

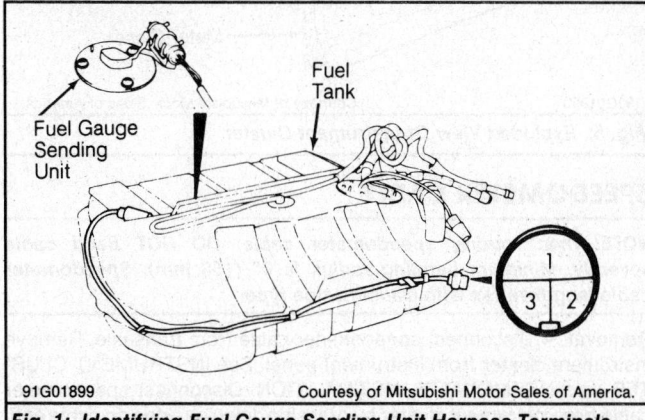

91G01899   Courtesy of Mitsubishi Motor Sales of America.

Fig. 1: Identifying Fuel Gauge Sending Unit Harness Terminals

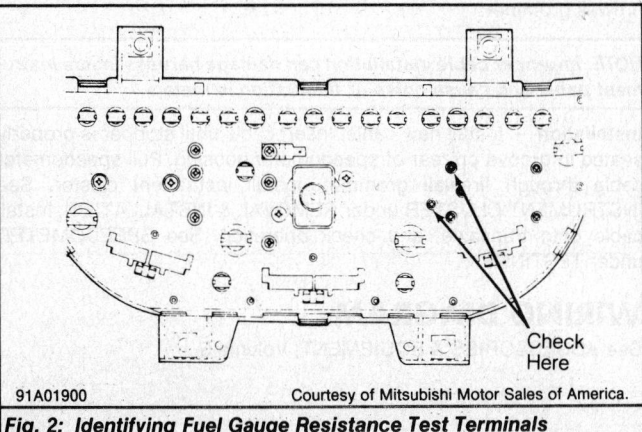

91A01900   Courtesy of Mitsubishi Motor Sales of America.

Fig. 2: Identifying Fuel Gauge Resistance Test Terminals

Resistance Test (Fuel Gauge) – Remove instrument cluster. See INSTRUMENT CLUSTER under REMOVAL & INSTALLATION. Attach ohmmeter leads between fuel gauge connector terminals. See Fig. 2. Resistance should be 55 ohms. If resistance is less than 55 ohms, check for shorted fuel gauge coil. If resistance is greater than 55 ohms, check for open wire to gauge coil.

Resistance Test (Fuel Gauge Sending Unit) – Access fuel gauge sending unit through luggage compartment. Remove sending unit assembly. Using an ohmmeter, check sending unit resistance between terminals No. 2 and 3 with float in each position. See FUEL GAUGE SENDING UNIT RESISTANCE SPECIFICATIONS table. See Fig. 3.

FUEL GAUGE SENDING UNIT RESISTANCE SPECIFICATIONS

Sending Unit Positions	Ohms
F (Full)	1-5
1/2	28.5-36.5
E (Empty)	103-117

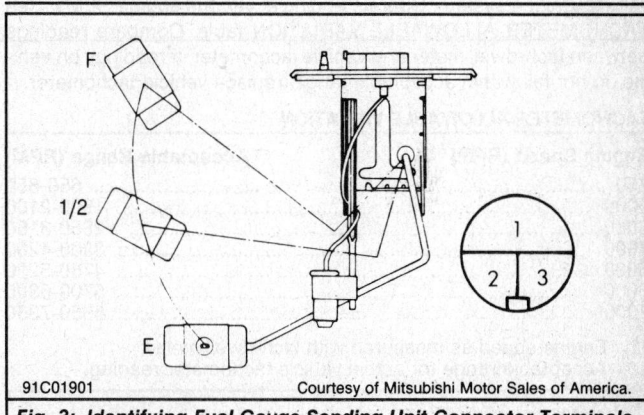

91C01901   Courtesy of Mitsubishi Motor Sales of America.

Fig. 3: Identifying Fuel Gauge Sending Unit Connector Terminals & Float Positions

OIL PRESSURE WARNING LIGHT

Continuity Test (Oil Pressure Switch) – Disconnect wire to oil pressure switch. Using an ohmmeter, check continuity between switch terminal and body ground. With engine off, continuity should not exist. Ensure continuity exists when engine is running and oil pressure is at least 4.3 psi (.30 kg/cm²). Replace switch if it does not function as described.

SEAT BELT WARNING LIGHT

Continuity Test (Lap Belt Switch) – Disconnect wiring connector from seat belt switch. Check continuity between switch terminals. Ensure continuity is only present when seat belt is not fastened. Continuity should not be present when seat belt is fastened. Replace switch if it does not function as specified.

Continuity Test (Passive Seat Belt Switch) – Disconnect wiring connector from passive seat belt switch. Check continuity between outer switch connector terminals. Ensure continuity is only present when seat belt is not fastened. Continuity should not be present when seat belt is fastened. Replace switch if it does not function as specified.

Inspection (Warning Light) – Turn ignition on. With seat belt fastened, warning light should not come on. Unfasten seat belt. Warning light should come on for about 6 seconds. If light does not function as described, check bulb, switch and circuit. Repair or replace defective component(s) as necessary.

SPEEDOMETER

Cable Inspection – Check cable for kinks, bends and improper routing. Disconnect cable at each end, and check cable core for kinks, burrs and bent tips. Repair or replace cable as necessary.

Calibration Test – Ensure tire pressure is at proper level. Using a reliable speedometer tester, compare reading on vehicle speedometer to reading on speedometer tester. See SPEEDOMETER ALLOWA-

BLE VARIATION table. If reading on vehicle speedometer does not fall within acceptable range, replace speedometer.

SPEEDOMETER ALLOWABLE VARIATION

Vehicle Speed [1] MPH (KM/H)	[2] Acceptable Range MPH (KM/H)
10 (16)	8.5-11.5 (13.7-18.5)
20 (32)	18.5-21.5 (29.8-34.6)
40 (64)	38.5-41.5 (62.0-66.8)
60 (96.5)	58.5-61.5 (94.1-98.9)
80 (128.7)	78.5-81.5 (126.3-131.2)
100 (161)	98.5-101.5 (158.5-163.3)
120 (193.1)	118.5-121.5 (190.7-195.5)

[1] – Vehicle speed as measured with speedometer tester.
[2] – Acceptable range for actual vehicle speedometer reading.

TACHOMETER

Calibration Test – Connect a reliable calibrated tach-dwell meter to vehicle ignition system. Operate engine at various engine RPMs. See TACHOMETER ALLOWABLE VARIATION table. Compare readings between tach-dwell meter and vehicle tachometer. If readings on vehicle do not fall within acceptable range, replace vehicle tachometer.

TACHOMETER ALLOWABLE VARIATION

Engine Speed (RPM) [1]	[2] Acceptable Range (RPM)
750	650-850
2000	1900-2100
3000	2850-3150
4000	3900-4200
5000	4750-5250
6000	5700-6300
7000	6650-7350

[1] – Engine speed as measured with tach-dwell meter.
[2] – Acceptable range for actual vehicle tachometer reading.

ENINGE COOLANT TEMPERATURE (ECT) GAUGE

Simple Test – Disconnect harness connector from ECT sending unit, located in engine compartment. Connect a 12-volt, 3.4-watt test light between harness connector and ground. Turn ignition on. Ensure test light flashes and temperature gauge indicator moves toward "H" position. If test light does not flash and gauge indicator does not move, check wiring harness, and repair as necessary. If test light flashes but gauge indicator does not move, replace gauge.

Resistance Test (ECT Sending Unit) – Using an ohmmeter, measure resistance between ECT sending unit terminal and ground. *See Fig. 4*. If resistance is not within specification, replace sending unit. See ECT SENDING UNIT RESISTANCE SPECIFICATIONS table.

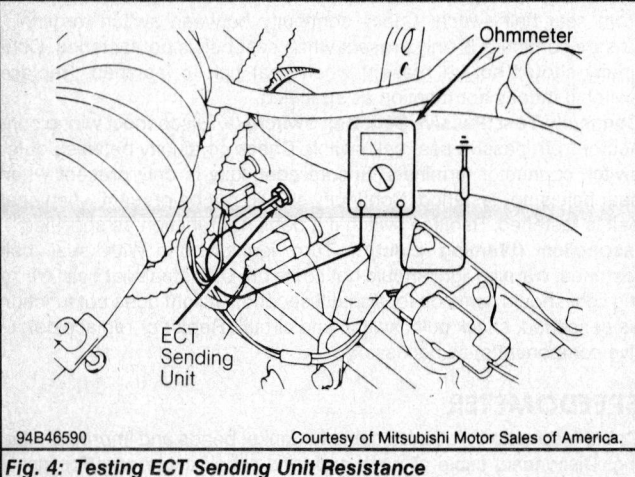

94B46590   Courtesy of Mitsubishi Motor Sales of America.

Fig. 4: Testing ECT Sending Unit Resistance

ECT SENDING UNIT RESISTANCE SPECIFICATIONS

Coolant Temperature °F (°C)	Ohms
112 (50)	230
140 (60)	155
158 (70)	90.5-117.5
239 (115)	21.3-26.3
248 (120)	21
252 (122)	19.5

REMOVAL & INSTALLATION

INSTRUMENT CLUSTER

Removal & Installation – Disconnect negative battery cable. Remove instrument cluster bezel screws, and remove bezel. Remove instrument cluster retaining screws. Pull cluster rearward enough to disengage speedometer cable. Disconnect harness connectors and remove cluster. *See Fig. 5*. To install, reverse removal procedure.

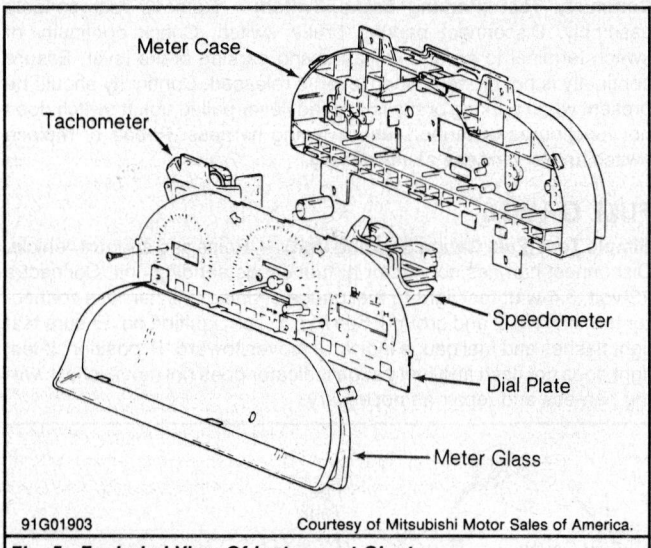

91G01903   Courtesy of Mitsubishi Motor Sales of America.

Fig. 5: Exploded View Of Instrument Cluster

SPEEDOMETER CABLE

NOTE: When routing speedometer cable, DO NOT bend cable severely. Minimum bending radius is 6" (150 mm). Speedometer cable length varies with transmission type.

Removal – Disconnect speedometer cable from transaxle. Remove instrument cluster from instrument panel. See INSTRUMENT CLUSTER under REMOVAL & INSTALLATION. Disconnect speedometer cable from instrument cluster by pressing down on ridge on cable end, and separate cable from cluster. Remove speedometer cable from firewall grommet.

NOTE: Improper cable installation can damage harness inside instrument panel and cause noise or fluctuation in meter.

Installation – Install new cable. Insert cable until stopper is properly seated in groove on rear of speedometer housing. Pull speedometer cable through firewall grommet. Install instrument cluster. See INSTRUMENT CLUSTER under REMOVAL & INSTALLATION. Install cable onto transaxle, and check operation. See SPEEDOMETER under TESTING.

WIRING DIAGRAM

See ACCESSORIES & EQUIPMENT, Volume 5.

Chrysler Corp.: Colt, Colt Vista, Stealth
Eagle: Summit, Summit Wagon
Mitsubishi: Diamante, Eclipse, Expo, Galant,
 Mirage, Montero, Pickup, 3000GT

DESCRIPTION & OPERATION

On Diamante, Eclipse, Galant, Stealth and 3000GT, power door locks are controlled by driver or front passenger switches which send signals to a Electronic Timer Alarm Control System (ETACS) module. The ETACS module sends appropriate signals to individual door lock actuators through individual relays.

On Colt, Colt Vista, Expo, Mirage, Montero, Pickup, Summit and Summit Wagon, power door lock actuator receives signal from individual control relay that is operated by a switch incorporated in actuator. On all models except Colt Vista, Expo and Summit Wagon, all door locks are actuated with the operation of one lock. Colt Vista, Expo and Summit Wagon use a separate tailgate lock switch mounted on dash.

The following features are incorporated in power door lock systems that have an ETACS module:

* Once locked door is closed, system will unlock door if key remains in ignition switch.
* Continuous switching between lock and unlock of door will disable system for approximately one minute.
* On Diamante, doors automatically lock once vehicle exceeds 12 MPH.

Colt Vista, Diamante, Expo, Stealth, Summit Wagon and 3000GT offer optional keyless entry system. Use of a 2 button portable remote control operates door locks within a range of 33 ft. (10 m). Dome light flashes twice once doors are locked and illuminates for 3 seconds when doors are unlocked. If after 30 seconds, door(s) have not been opened when unlocked with keyless entry system, doors will relock.

Diamante uses a switch, located on driver's dash, that activates a solenoid which releases the trunk lid. Trunk release can be disabled with ON/OFF switch located in glove compartment (valet security).

TROUBLE SHOOTING

POWER DOOR LOCK INOPERATIVE

Operate door lock(s) with ignition switch in OFF position. If door lock(s) do not operate, check for following possible causes:

* Burned fuse, circuit breaker or fusible link caused by short to body ground.
* Wire connector or pin inside connector disengaged at any connector or component in system.
* Defective ETACS module (if equipped).
* Defective door lock switch, relay or actuator.
* Subfreezing weather conditions, mechanical failure, or corroded or misaligned assemblies.

KEY REMINDER SYSTEM INOPERATIVE
(ETACS CONTROLLED SYSTEM)

With key inserted in ignition switch, lock driver's or passenger's door and close door. If door locks do not unlock, check for following possible causes:

* Defective key reminder switch or no input signal to ETACS module.
* Defective front door switch or no input signal to ETACS module.
* Defective vehicle speed sensor or no input signal to ETACS module.

TESTING

NOTE: If after all testing procedures are completed, system is not functioning properly, substitute ETACS module with known good unit and retest. See ETACS MODULE LOCATION table.

ETACS MODULE LOCATION

Application	Location
Diamante	In Front Of Shifter, Under Console
Eclipse [1]	Behind Right Kick Panel
Galant	Behind Dash, Above Steering Column
Stealth & 3000GT	Behind Lower Dash, Left Side Of Steering Column

[1] – Eclipse uses door lock control unit.

INPUT SIGNAL

1) Access data link connector at lower left corner of dash. Connect positive lead of voltmeter to terminal No. 9 and negative lead to terminal No. 12. *See Fig. 1.* Check if input signals from system components are being received by ETACS module.

2) Voltmeter needle should sweep when each switch is operated (i.e., headlight switch or pop-up switch). If switch or related component is not functioning, voltmeter will not operate when switch is activated. Check related circuit and/or component.

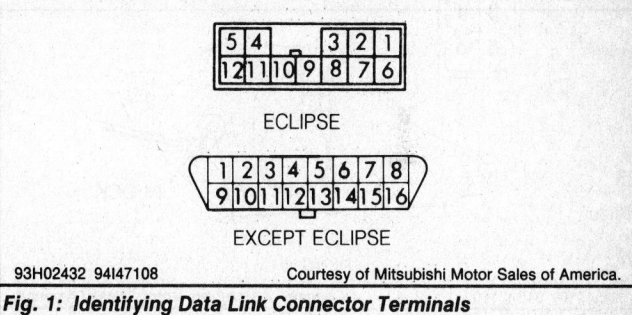

93H02432 94I47108   Courtesy of Mitsubishi Motor Sales of America.

Fig. 1: Identifying Data Link Connector Terminals

DOOR LOCK ACTUATOR

Except Pickup – **1)** Access left front or right rear door lock actuator. See DOOR LOCK ACTUATOR under REMOVAL & INSTALLATION. Disconnect harness connector. Set actuator to LOCK position. Connect positive lead of 12-volt power source to terminal No. 1 of actuator. *See Fig. 2.* Actuator should operate to UNLOCK position when terminal No. 3 is connected to negative lead.

2) With actuator set to UNLOCK position, connect positive lead of 12-volt power source to terminal No. 3 of actuator. *See Fig. 2.* Actuator should operate to LOCK position when terminal No. 1 is connected to negative lead.

3) Access right front or left rear door lock actuator. See DOOR LOCK ACTUATOR under REMOVAL & INSTALLATION. Disconnect harness connector. Set actuator to LOCK position. Connect positive lead of 12-volt power source to terminal No. 3 of actuator. *See Fig. 2.* Actuator should operate to UNLOCK position when terminal No. 1 is connected to negative lead.

4) With actuator set to UNLOCK position, connect positive lead of 12-volt power source to terminal No. 1 of actuator. *See Fig. 2.* Actuator should operate to LOCK position when terminal No. 3 is connected to negative lead.

5) On left or right door lock actuator, there should be continuity between terminals No. 2 and 4 when actuator is in UNLOCK position. There should be no continuity in LOCK position. Replace actuator if it fails any preceding tests.

Pickup – **1)** Access door lock actuator. See DOOR LOCK ACTUATOR under REMOVAL & INSTALLATION. Disconnect harness connector. Set actuator to LOCK position. Connect positive lead of 12-volt power source to terminal No. 4 of actuator. *See Fig. 2.* Actuator should operate to UNLOCK position when terminal No. 1 is connected to negative lead.

2) With actuator set to UNLOCK position, connect positive lead of 12-volt power source to terminal No. 1 of actuator. *See Fig. 2.* Actuator should operate to LOCK position when terminal No. 4 is connected to negative lead.

1994 ACCESSORIES & EQUIPMENT
Keyless Entry & Power Door Locks (Cont.)

3) Using ohmmeter, check for continuity between terminals No. 2 and 5 when actuator is in UNLOCK position and continuity between terminals No. 3 and 5 in LOCK position. Replace actuator if it fails any preceding tests.

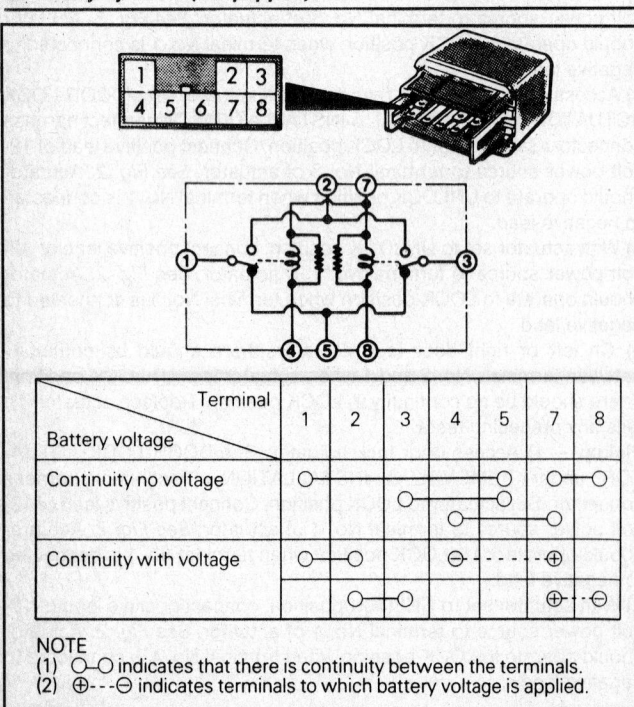

94J47109 94C47110   Courtesy of Mitsubishi Motor Sales of America.

Fig. 2: Identifying Actuator Connectors

DOOR LOCK POWER RELAY

NOTE: Manufacturer does not provide testing information for Pickup door lock power relay/control unit.

NOTE: Following testing applies to door lock power relay "2" for keyless entry systems (if equipped).

Terminal	1	2	3	4	5	7	8
Battery voltage							
Continuity no voltage	○—				—○	○—	—○
			○—	—○—	—○		
Continuity with voltage	○—	—○			⊖—	- - -	—⊕
		○—	—○			⊕—	—⊖

NOTE
(1) ○—○ indicates that there is continuity between the terminals.
(2) ⊕- - -⊖ indicates terminals to which battery voltage is applied.

93D82977   Courtesy of Mitsubishi Motor Sales of America.

Fig. 3: Testing Door Lock Power Relay

Check continuity of relay using following chart. *See Fig. 3.* Replace relay as needed. For relay location, *see Fig. 5.*

KEYLESS CONTROL UNIT

NOTE: Manufacturer does not provide testing information for keyless control unit on Stealth and 3000GT.

NOTE: If after all testing procedures are completed, system is not functioning properly, substitute keyless control unit with known good unit and retest.

Colt Vista, Expo & Summit Wagon – Disconnect keyless control unit harness connector. On Colt Vista, Expo LRV and Summit Wagon, keyless control unit is located behind left quarter panel, above wheelwell. On Expo, keyless control unit is located behind right quarter panel, above wheelwell. Using DVOM, measure voltage between selected terminal and vehicle ground. *See Figs. 4 and 6.* If voltage is not within specification, inspect and repair circuit as needed. See appropriate wiring diagram under WIRING DIAGRAMS.

Diamante – Disconnect keyless control unit harness connector. Control unit is located under rear shelf, accessed through trunk. Using DVOM, measure voltage between selected terminal and vehicle ground. *See Figs. 4 and 7.* If voltage is not within specification, inspect and repair circuit as needed. See appropriate wiring diagram under WIRING DIAGRAMS.

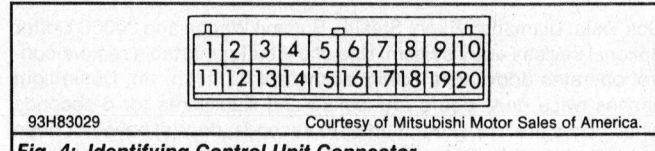

93H83029   Courtesy of Mitsubishi Motor Sales of America.

Fig. 4: Identifying Control Unit Connector

POWER DOOR LOCK CONTROL UNIT (DIAMANTE)

1) Turn ignition on. Using DVOM, backprobe terminal No. 1 (Blue wire) of left control unit. *See Fig. 4.* If voltage measured between terminal No. 1 and ground is battery voltage, go to next step. If voltage is not within specification, go to step **3)**.

2) Disconnect left control unit harness connector and measure voltage between harness connector terminal No. 1 and ground. If voltage is less than battery voltage, inspect and repair circuit between ETACS harness connector terminal No. 52 (Blue wire) and left control unit harness connector terminal No. 1. If battery voltage exists, replace left control unit.

3) Disconnect ETACS harness connector. See ETACS MODULE LOCATION table. Disconnect both left and right front door control unit harness connectors. Using ohmmeter, check for continuity between terminal No. 1 of left control unit and vehicle ground. If continuity exists, inspect and repair short to ground. If continuity does not exist, go to next step.

4) Connect ETACS harness connector. Using DVOM, measure voltage between left control unit harness connector terminal No. 1 and ground. If battery voltage does not exist, replace ETACS module and retest. If battery voltage exists, go to next step.

5) Connect right door control unit harness connector. Using DVOM, measure voltage between left control unit harness connector terminal No. 1 and ground. If battery voltage does not exist, replace right control unit and retest. If battery voltage exists, replace left control unit and retest.

POWER DOOR LOCK CONTROL UNIT (ECLIPSE)

Using DVOM, backprobe power door lock control unit connector. Measure voltage between selected terminal and vehicle ground. *See Figs. 8 and 9.* If voltage is not within specification, inspect and repair circuit as needed. See appropriate wiring diagram under WIRING DIAGRAMS.

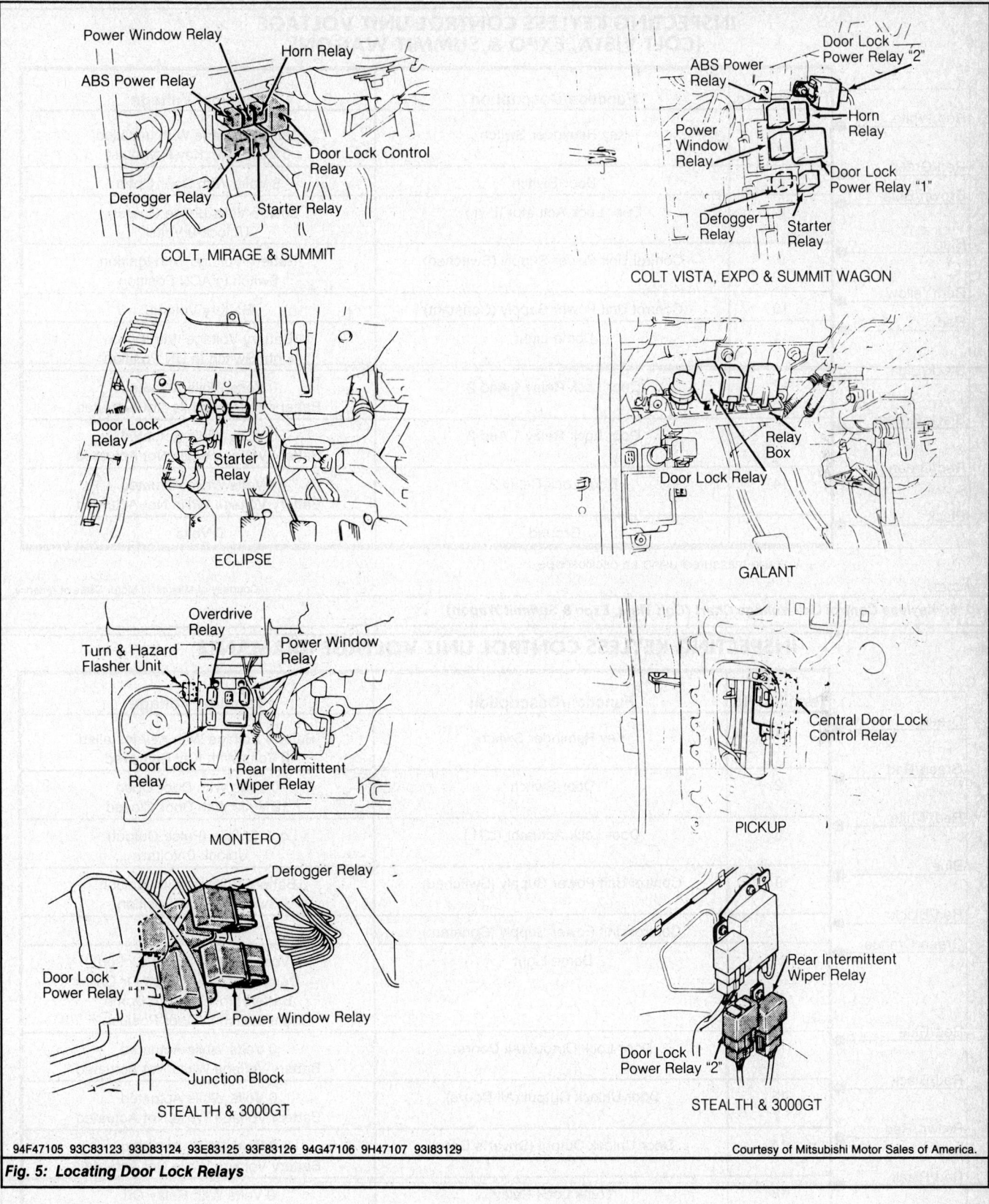

Fig. 5: Locating Door Lock Relays

94F47105 93C83123 93D83124 93E83125 93F83126 94G47106 9H47107 93I83129

Courtesy of Mitsubishi Motor Sales of America.

INSPECTING KEYLESS CONTROL UNIT VOLTAGE
(COLT VISTA, EXPO & SUMMIT WAGON)

	Terminal No.	Function/Description	Terminal Voltage
Red/White	1	Key Reminder Switch	Battery Voltage With Installed 0 Volts With Key Removed
Red/Green	2	Door Switch	5 Volts With Door Open
Brown/Blue	6	Door Lock Actuator (L.H.)	Lock-5 Volts (Pulse Output) [1] Unlock-0 Volts
Blue	9	Control Unit Power Supply (Switched)	Battery Voltage With Ignition Switch In ACC Position
Red/Yellow	10	Control Unit Power Supply (Constant)	Battery Voltage
Red	11	Dome Light	Battery Voltage With Dome Light Switch In ON Position
Black/Blue	12	Door Lock Relay 1 And 2	0 Volts While Actuated Battery Voltage While Not Actuated
Black/Green	13	Door Lock Relay 1 And 2	0 Volts While Actuated Battery Voltage While Not Actuated
Red/Green	14	Door Lock Relay 2	0 Volts While Actuated Battery Voltage While Not Actuated
Black	20	Ground	0 Volts

[1] – Voltage measured using an oscilloscope.

93A83030

Courtesy of Mitsubishi Motor Sales of America.

Fig. 6: Keyless Control Unit Voltage Chart (Colt Vista, Expo & Summit Wagon)

INSPECTING KEYLESS CONTROL UNIT VOLTAGE (DIAMANTE)

	Terminal No.	Function/Description	Terminal Voltage
Green	1	Key Reminder Switch	Battery Voltage With Key Installed 0 Volts With Key Removed
Green/Red	2	Door Switch	0 Volts With Door Open 12 Volts With Door Closed
Red/White	6	Door Lock Actuator (L.H.)	Lock-5 Volts (Pulse Output) [1] Unlock-0 Volts
Blue	9	Control Unit Power Supply (Switched)	Battery Voltage With Ignition Switch In ACC Position
Red/Black	10	Control Unit Power Supply (Constant)	Battery Voltage
Green/Orange	11	Dome Light	0 Volts With All Doors Closed, Dome Light Switch Off Or On Battery Voltage With Dome Light Switch In Door Position [2]
Red/Blue	12	Door Lock Output (All Doors)	0 Volts While Actuated Battery Voltage While Not Actuated
Red/Black	13	Door Unlock Output (All Doors)	0 Volts While Actuated Battery Voltage While Not Actuated
Brown/Red	14	Door Unlock Output (Driver's Door)	0 Volts While Actuated Battery Voltage While Not Actuated
Red/Black	18	Trunk Lock Relay	0 Volts With Relay Off Battery Voltage With Relay On
Black	20	Ground	0 Volts

[1] – Voltage measured using an oscilloscope.
[2] – Door position indicated on switch by black dot (•).

93B83031

Courtesy of Mitsubishi Motor Sales of America.

Fig. 7: Keyless Control Unit Voltage Chart (Diamante)

93C83032   Courtesy of Mitsubishi Motor Sales of America.

Fig. 8: Identifying Door Lock Control Unit Connector

REAR DOOR LOCK ACTUATOR (COLT VISTA, EXPO, MONTERO & SUMMIT WAGON)

Access door lock actuator. See DOOR LOCK ACTUATOR under REMOVAL & INSTALLATION. Disconnect rear door release solenoid harness connector. Remove solenoid if needed. Connect positive lead of 12-volt power source to solenoid connector. Solenoid should operate when negative lead contacts solenoid housing. Replace solenoid as needed. On Colt Vista, Expo and Summit Wagon, check continuity of release switch. See Fig. 10. Replace switch as needed.

TRUNK RELEASE SOLENOID & SWITCH (DIAMANTE)

1) Remove trunk release main switch from glove compartment. Disconnect harness connector. Using ohmmeter, check for continuity across switch terminals when switch is in ON position. Replace as needed.

2) Remove trunk release opener switch from lower driver's dash. Disconnect harness connector. Using ohmmeter, check for continuity across switch terminals when switch is depressed. Replace switch as needed.

3) Open trunk lid. Disconnect trunk release solenoid harness connector. Remove solenoid if needed. Connect positive lead of 12-volt power source to solenoid connector. Solenoid should operate when negative lead contacts solenoid housing. Replace switch as needed.

REMOVAL & INSTALLATION

CAUTION: When battery is disconnected, vehicle computer and memory systems may lose memory data. Driveability problems may exist until computer systems have completed a relearn cycle.

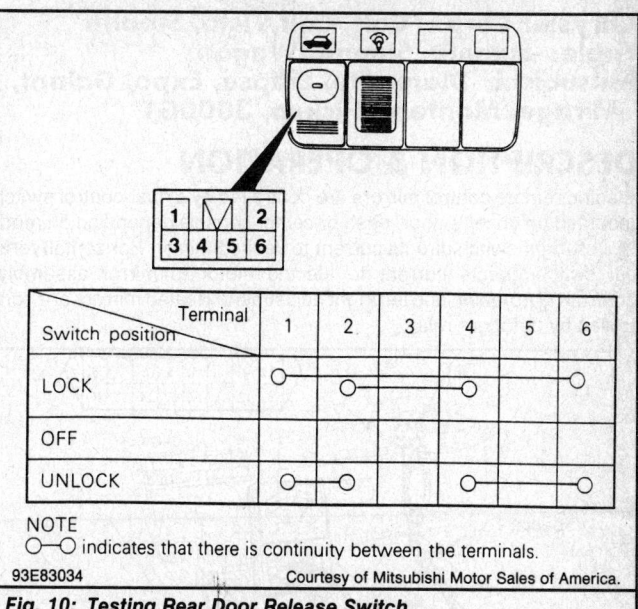

Switch position \ Terminal	1	2	3	4	5	6
LOCK	○—	—○	○—	—○		
OFF						
UNLOCK	○—	—○			○—	—○

NOTE
○—○ indicates that there is continuity between the terminals.

93E83034   Courtesy of Mitsubishi Motor Sales of America.

Fig. 10: Testing Rear Door Release Switch (Colt Vista, Expo & Summit Wagon)

DOOR LOCK ACTUATOR

Except Rear Door Or Hatch – Remove inner door panel. Remove delta cover (access to mirror mounting). Remove door light, switch panel and armrest. Remove mounting screws, and slide panel up to remove. Remove waterproof film. Remove actuator. To install, reverse removal procedure.

Rear Door Or Hatch – Remove door pull handle. Remove window trim. Remove door release handle trim. Remove tool kit (if equipped). Remove door panel and waterproof film. Remove actuator solenoid. To install, reverse removal procedure.

WIRING DIAGRAMS

See ACCESSORIES & EQUIPMENT, Volume 5.

INSPECTING POWER DOOR LOCK CONTROL UNIT VOLTAGE (ECLIPSE)

	Terminal No.	Function/Description	Terminal Voltage
Brown/White	1	Door Lock Relay Signal	Battery Voltage With Lock Not Operated .5 Volt When Lock Is Operated
Brown	2	Door Lock Signal (Driver's Door)	Battery Voltage In Lock Position 0 Volts In Unlock Position
Brown/Blue	3	Door Lock Relay Signal	Battery Voltage With Lock Not Operated .5 Volt When Lock Is Operated
Brown/Yellow	4	Door Lock Signal (Passenger's Door)	Battery Voltage In Lock Position 0 Volts In Unlock Position
Red/Black	5	Control Unit Power Supply (Constant)	Battery Voltage
Black	6	Ground	0 Volts

93D83033   Courtesy of Mitsubishi Motor Sales of America.

Fig. 9: Power Door Lock Control Unit Voltage Chart (Eclipse)

1994 ACCESSORIES & EQUIPMENT
Power Mirrors

Chrysler Corp.: Colt, Colt Vista, Stealth
Eagle: Summit, Summit Wagon
Mitsubishi: Diamante, Eclipse, Expo, Galant,
Mirage, Montero, Pickup, 3000GT

DESCRIPTION & OPERATION

Electric remote control mirrors are controlled by a dual-control switch mounted on driver's door, dash or center console depending on model. Left/right switch directs current to desired mirror. Horizontal/vertical switch directs current to electric motor in mirror assembly, controlling up/down and left/right adjustment. Heated mirrors are controlled by defogger relay.

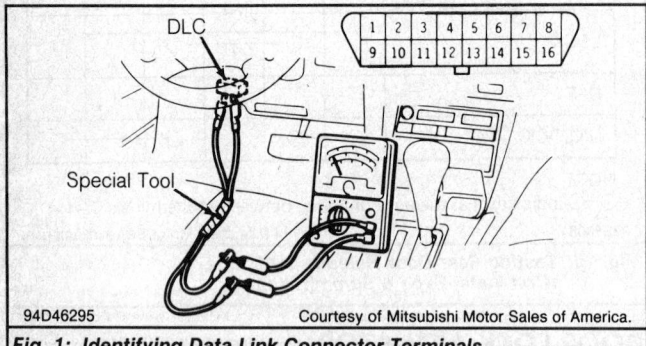

94D46295   Courtesy of Mitsubishi Motor Sales of America.

Fig. 1: Identifying Data Link Connector Terminals

TROUBLE SHOOTING

POWER MIRRORS INOPERATIVE

Check for faulty fuse, faulty power mirror switch or faulty power mirror motor. See POWER MIRROR FUSE IDENTIFICATION table.

POWER MIRROR FUSE IDENTIFICATION

Application	Fuse No.
Colt, Mirage & Summit	4
Diamante	4 & 19
Galant	9
All Others	5

TESTING

INPUT SIGNAL (DIAMANTE)

NOTE: If after all testing has been completed, power mirror is still not functioning, substitute ETACS unit with known good unit and retest.

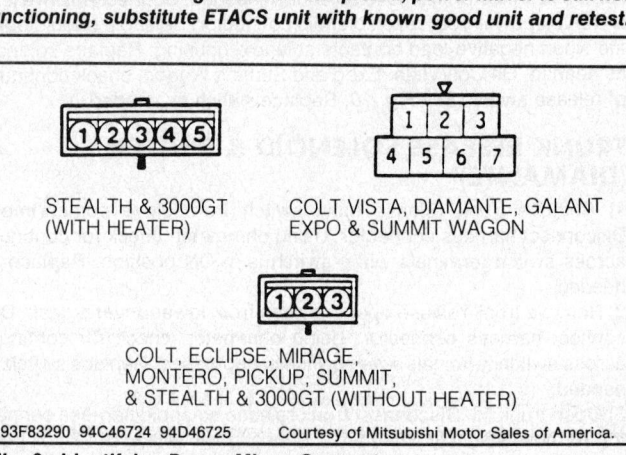

STEALTH & 3000GT (WITH HEATER)   COLT VISTA, DIAMANTE, GALANT EXPO & SUMMIT WAGON

COLT, ECLIPSE, MIRAGE, MONTERO, PICKUP, SUMMIT, & STEALTH & 3000GT (WITHOUT HEATER)

93F83290 94C46724 94D46725   Courtesy of Mitsubishi Motor Sales of America.

Fig. 2: Identifying Power Mirror Connector

Connection Direction of operation	Battery ⊕	Battery ⊖	Terminal 1	Terminal 2	Terminal 3
Up	O—————————————————O				O
		O——————O			O
Down	O—————————O				O
		O———————————O			O
Left	O—————————O			O	
		O———————————O		O	
Right	O—————————O			O	
		O———————————O		O	

COLT, COLT VISTA, EXPO, MIRAGE, MONTERO, SUMMIT & SUMMIT WAGON

Connection Direction of operation	Battery ⊕	Battery ⊖	Terminal 5	Terminal 6	Terminal 7	Terminal 1*	Terminal 4*
Up	O	O	O		O		
Down	O	O	O		O		
Left	O	O	O	O			
Right	O	O	O	O			

NOTE
O——O indicates each terminal is connected to the battery.
*: Vehicles with heated mirror

DIAMANTE & GALANT

Connection Direction	Battery (+)	Battery (−)	Terminal 1	Terminal 2	Terminal 3
UP	O		O		
		O			O
DOWN	O				O
		O	O		
RIGHT	O			O	
		O		O	
LEFT	O				O
		O			O

ECLIPSE & PICKUP

Connection Direction	Battery (+)	Battery (−)	Terminal 2 (1)*	Terminal 3 (2)*	Terminal 4 (3)*	Terminal 1	Terminal 5
UP	O				O		
		O	O				
DOWN	O				O		
		O	O				
RIGHT	O			O			
		O		O			
LEFT	O			O			
		O		O			

NOTE
(1) O—O indicates that each terminal is connected to the battery.
(2) * indicates door mirror terminal on vehicles without heater.

STEALTH & 3000GT

Courtesy of Mitsubishi Motor Sales of America.

94F46727 94G46728 94H46729 93B83296

Fig. 3: Power Mirror Operational Test Charts

1) Access Data Link Connector (DLC) at lower left corner of dash. Using Special Tool (MB991529), connect positive lead of voltmeter to terminal No. 9 and negative lead to terminal No. 4 or 5. *See Fig. 1.* Check if input signals from power mirror switch are being received by ETACS module.

2) Voltmeter needle should sweep when each switch is operated. If switch or related component is not functioning, voltmeter will not operate when switch is activated. Check related circuit and/or component.

POWER MIRROR MOTOR TEST

Connect 12-volt power source to mirror connector terminals. *See Figs. 2 and 3.* Replace mirror as necessary.

POWER MIRROR SWITCH TEST

Remove mirror switch. Using ohmmeter, check continuity of switch. See appropriate POWER MIRROR SWITCH CONTINUITY CHART. *See Fig. 4 or 5.* Replace switch if switch continuity is not as specified.

POWER MIRROR SWITCH CONTINUITY CHART (ECLIPSE)

Switch Position	[1] Check Continuity Between
Left Side	
UP	Pins No. 3 & 6; Pins No. 4 & 5
DOWN	Pins No. 3 & 5; Pins No. 4 & 6
LEFT	Pins No. 2 & 4; Pins No. 3 & 5
RIGHT	Pins No. 2 & 3; Pins No. 4 & 5
Right Side	
UP	Pins No. 1 & 3; Pins No. 4 & 5
DOWN	Pins No. 1 & 4; Pins No. 3 & 5
LEFT	Pins No. 3 & 5; Pins No. 4 & 7
RIGHT	Pins No. 3 & 7; Pins No. 4 & 5

[1] – See Fig. 4.

POWER MIRROR SWITCH CONTINUITY CHART (ALL OTHERS)

Switch Position	[1] Check Continuity Between
Left Side	
UP	Pins No. 4 & 8; Pins No. 6 & 7
DOWN	Pins No. 4 & 7; Pins No. 6 & 8
LEFT	Pins No. 3 & 6; Pins No. 4 & 7
RIGHT	Pins No. 3 & 4; Pins No. 6 & 7
Right Side	
UP	Pins No. 2 & 4; Pins No. 6 & 7
DOWN	Pins No. 2 & 6; Pins No. 4 & 7
LEFT	Pins No. 4 & 7; Pins No. 6 & 9
RIGHT	Pins No. 4 & 9; Pins No. 6 & 7

[1] – See Fig. 5.

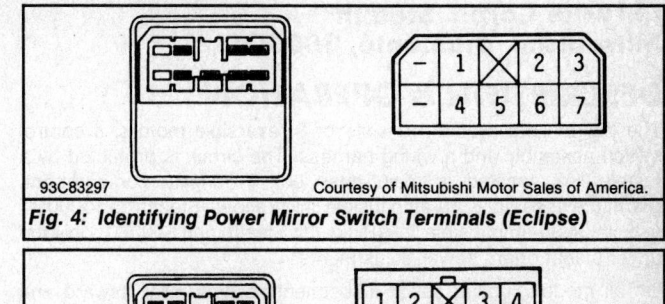

93C83297   Courtesy of Mitsubishi Motor Sales of America.

Fig. 4: Identifying Power Mirror Switch Terminals (Eclipse)

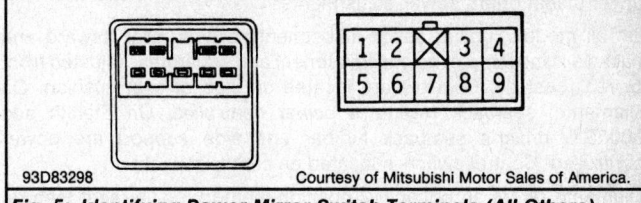

93D83298   Courtesy of Mitsubishi Motor Sales of America.

Fig. 5: Identifying Power Mirror Switch Terminals (All Others)

REMOVAL & INSTALLATION

POWER MIRROR ASSEMBLY

Remove delta cover (trim cover), screws and electrical connector. Remove mirror assembly. To install, reverse removal procedure.

WIRING DIAGRAMS

See ACCESSORIES & EQUIPMENT, Volume 5.

1994 ACCESSORIES & EQUIPMENT
Power Seats

Chrysler Corp.: Stealth
Mitsubishi: Diamante, 3000GT

DESCRIPTION & OPERATION

The power seat system consists of 3 reversible motors, a control switch assembly and a wiring harness. The circuit is protected by a fusible link, located in main relay box in engine compartment. Diamante uses No. 8, 60-amp fusible link (Yellow). Stealth and 3000GT use No. 9, 30-amp fusible link (Pink). On Stealth and 3000GT, only the driver's seat offers power adjustments.

On all models, power assist adjustments offered are: forward and backward movement, height adjustment and separately adjusted front or rear seat tilt. Controls are located on side of seat cushion. On Diamante, seatback recline is power controlled. On Stealth and 3000GT, driver's seatback lumbar and side support are power controlled. Control switch is located on center console.

Diamante offers an optional 2 position memory power seat feature. Power memory seat control panel is located above rear view mirror. Once seat is adjusted to desired position, memory of seat position is retained by pressing "M" button and then pressing button "1" or "2" within 5 seconds. To adjust seat, press either "1" or "2" to achieve desired seat position. If incorrect memory button is pressed, operation can be canceled by pressing "STOP" button.

TESTING

LIMIT SWITCH/SENSOR

(Diamante – Driver's Seat) – 1) Disconnect each motor harness connector. Limit sensor in incorporated into each motor except slide motor. Slide motor limit sensor connector is separate. Operate each motor. See POWER SEAT MOTORS under TESTING.

2) Connect ohmmeter to left side of motor connector on all connectors except slide sensor connector. Connect ohmmeter directly to slide sensor connector. Check sensor resistance as motor operates until stopped. Reverse direction of motor and check resistance until motor stops. Resistance readings should not change erratically. Replace power seat adjuster assembly if any switch fails testing.

(Diamante – Front Passenger's Seat) – Disconnect each limit switch harness connector. Operate each switch to check continuity between terminals using ohmmeter. See LIMIT SWITCH CONTINUITY (DIAMANTE) table and *Fig. 1*. Replace power seat adjuster assembly if any switch fails testing.

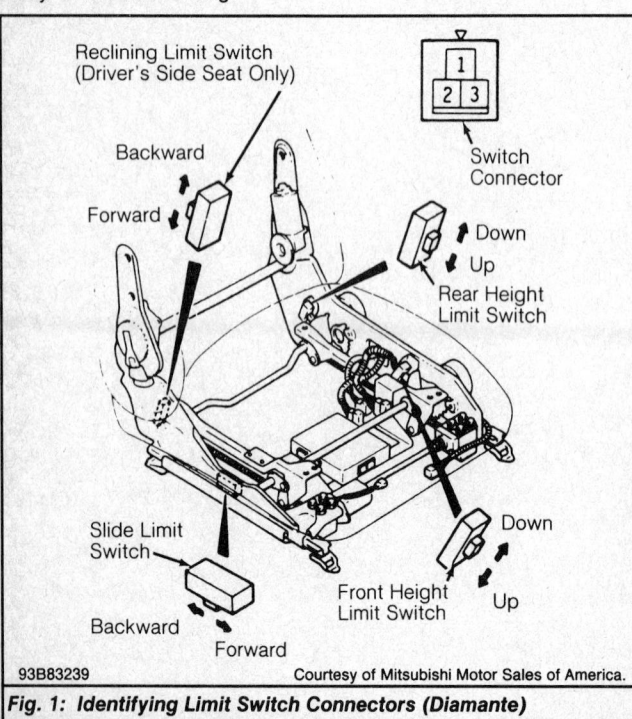

Reclining Limit Switch
(Driver's Side Seat Only)

Backward

Forward

Switch Connector

Down
Up
Rear Height Limit Switch

Slide Limit Switch

Backward
Forward

Down
Up
Front Height Limit Switch

93B83239   Courtesy of Mitsubishi Motor Sales of America.

Fig. 1: Identifying Limit Switch Connectors (Diamante)

LIMIT SWITCH CONTINUITY (DIAMANTE)

Switch Position	Check Continuity Between
Slide Limit Switch	
Forward	Pins No. 1 & 2
Backward	Pins No. 1 & 3
Front & Rear Height Limit Switch	
Up	Pins No. 1 & 3
Down	Pins No. 1 & 2
Reclining Limit Switch	
Forward	Pins No. 1 & 3
Backward	Pins No. 1 & 2
All Limit Switches	
Middle (ON)	Pins No. 1, 2 & 3

(Stealth & 3000GT – Driver's Seat) – Disconnect each limit switch harness connector. Operate each switch to check continuity between terminals using ohmmeter. See LIMIT SWITCH CONTINUITY table and *Fig. 2*. Replace power seat adjuster assembly if any switch fails testing.

LIMIT SWITCH CONTINUITY (STEALTH & 3000GT)

Switch Position	Check Continuity Between
Slide Limit Switch	
Forward	Pins No. 1 & 3
Backward	Pins No. 1 & 2
Middle (ON)	Pins No. 1, 2 & 3
Front & Rear Height Limit Switch	
Front Up	Pins No. 1 & 3
Front Down	Pins No. 1 & 2
Front Middle (ON)	Pins No. 1, 2 & 3
Rear Up	Pins No. 4, 5 & 6
Rear Down	Pins No. 4 & 5
Rear Middle (ON)	Pins No. 4, 5 & 6

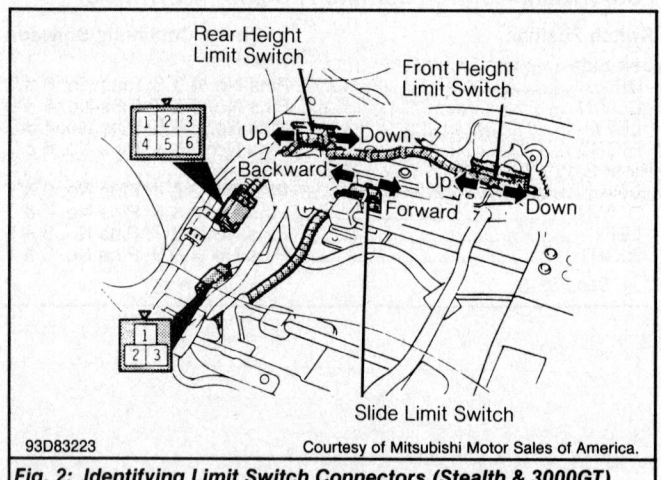

Rear Height Limit Switch

Front Height Limit Switch

Up   Down
Backward
Up
Forward   Down

Slide Limit Switch

93D83223   Courtesy of Mitsubishi Motor Sales of America.

Fig. 2: Identifying Limit Switch Connectors (Stealth & 3000GT)

LUMBAR/SIDE ADJUSTMENT SWITCH (STEALTH & 3000GT)

Remove switch from center console. Using ohmmeter, check continuity of switch. See LUMBAR/SIDE ADJUSTMENT SWITCH CONTINUITY (STEALTH & 3000GT) table and *Fig. 3*. Replace switch as necessary if switch continuity is not as specified.

LUMBAR/SIDE ADJUSTMENT SWITCH CONTINUITY (STEALTH & 3000GT)

Switch Position	Check Continuity Between
Lumbar Support	
Push	Pins No. 2 & 3; Pins No. 5 & 7
Off	Pins No. 2, 3 & 5
Release	Pins No. 2 & 5; Pins No. 3 & 7
Side Support	
Spread	Pins No. 1 & 2; Pins No. 7 & 8
Off	Pins No. 1, 2 & 8
Close	Pins No. 1 & 7; Pins No. 2 & 8

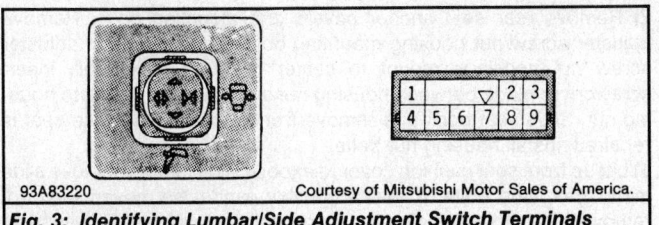

93A83220   Courtesy of Mitsubishi Motor Sales of America.

Fig. 3: Identifying Lumbar/Side Adjustment Switch Terminals

MEMORY POWER SEAT CONTROL UNIT (DIAMANTE)

Control unit is located below driver's seat. Manufacturer does not provide information for diagnosis or repair of memory power seat control unit or system.

MEMORY POWER SEAT SWITCH (DIAMANTE)

Remove switch from overhead console. Using ohmmeter, check continuity of switch. See MEMORY POWER SEAT SWITCH CONTINUITY (DIAMANTE) table and *Fig. 4*. Replace switch as necessary if switch continuity is not as specified.

MEMORY POWER SEAT SWITCH CONTINUITY (DIAMANTE)

Switch Position	Check Continuity Between
Memory Button ON	Pins No. 3 & 7
Position Button "1" ON	Pins No. 3 & 9
Position Button "2" ON	Pins No. 3 & 8
Stop Button ON	Pins No. 3 & 6
All Buttons Off	No Continuity, All Terminals

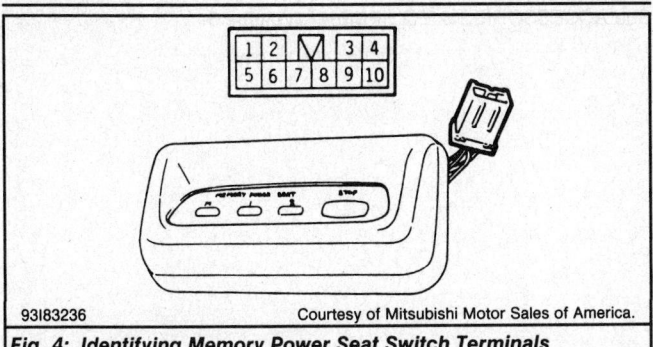

93I83236   Courtesy of Mitsubishi Motor Sales of America.

Fig. 4: Identifying Memory Power Seat Switch Terminals

POWER SEAT MOTORS

(Diamante) – **1)** Disconnect each motor harness connector. On all connectors except slide motor connector, connect 12-volt power supply to motor both right side connector terminals. Reverse power supply leads to reverse direction of motor operation. Motor should operate freely and smoothly. If any motor does not operate correctly, replace power seat adjuster assembly. Motors are not able to be replaced individually.

2) On slide motor connector, connect 12-volt power supply to motor connector terminals. Reverse power supply leads to reverse direction of motor operation. Motor should operate freely and smoothly. If any motor does not operate correctly, replace power seat adjuster assembly. Motor is not able to be replaced individually.

(Stealth & 3000GT) – Disconnect each motor harness connector. To access lumbar and side support motor harness connectors, remove seatback panel. Connect 12-volt power supply to motor connector terminals. Reverse power supply leads to reverse direction of motor operation. Motor should operate freely and smoothly. If any motor does not operate correctly, replace power seat adjuster assembly or seatback assembly. Motors are not able to be replaced individually.

POWER SEAT SWITCH

(Diamante) – Disconnect power seat switch harness connector. Using ohmmeter, check continuity of switch. See POWER SEAT SWITCH CONTINUITY (DIAMANTE) table and *Fig. 5*. Replace switch as necessary if continuity is not as specified.

POWER SEAT SWITCH CONTINUITY (DIAMANTE)

Switch Position	Check Continuity Between
Driver's Seat	
Front Height Switch	
UP	Pins No. 2 & 10
DOWN	Pins No. 7 & 10
Rear Height Switch	
UP	Pins No. 3 & 10
DOWN	Pins No. 8 & 10
Slide Switch	
Forward	Pins No. 1 & 10
Backward	Pins No. 6 & 10
Reclining Switch	
Forward	Pins No. 9 & 10
Backward	Pins No. 5 & 10
All Switches	
Off	No Continuity, All Terminals
Passenger's Seat	
Front Height Switch	
UP	Pins No. 9 & 12; Pins No. 11 & 16
DOWN	Pins No. 10 & 11; Pins No. 12 & 16
Rear Height Switch	
UP	Pins No. 5 & 16; Pins No. 6 & 7
DOWN	Pins No. 5 & 15; Pins No. 6 & 16
Slide Switch	
Forward	Pins No. 1 & 4; Pins No. 3 & 16
Backward	Pins No. 2 & 3; Pins No. 4 & 16
Reclining Switch	
Forward	Pins No. 8 & 14; Pins No. 13 & 16
Backward	Pins No. 8 & 13; Pins No. 14 & 16
All Switches	
Off	No Continuity, All Terminals

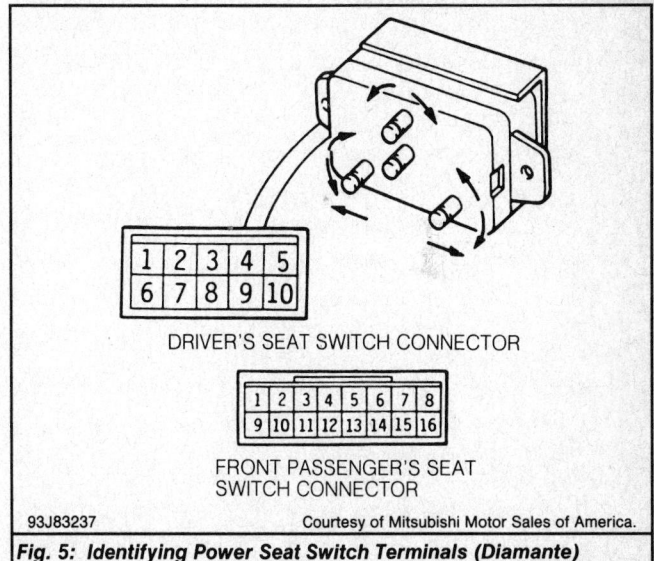

DRIVER'S SEAT SWITCH CONNECTOR

FRONT PASSENGER'S SEAT SWITCH CONNECTOR

93J83237   Courtesy of Mitsubishi Motor Sales of America.

Fig. 5: Identifying Power Seat Switch Terminals (Diamante)

(Stealth & 3000GT) – Disconnect power seat switch harness connector. Using ohmmeter, check continuity of switch. See POWER SEAT SWITCH CONTINUITY (STEALTH & 3000GT) table and *Fig. 6*. Replace switch as necessary if continuity is not as specified.

POWER SEAT SWITCH CONTINUITY (STEALTH & 3000GT)

Switch Position	Check Continuity Between
Slide Switch	
Forward	Pins No. 2 & 3; Pins No. 4 & 14
Backward	Pins No. 1 & 4; Pins No. 3 & 14
Front Height Switch	
Up	Pins No. 9 & 10; Pins No. 11 & 14
Down	Pins No. 8 & 11; Pins No. 10 & 14
Rear Height Switch	
Up	Pins No. 6 & 12; Pins No. 7 & 14
Down	Pins No. 5 & 7; Pins No. 12 & 14
All Switches	
All Off	No Continuity, All Terminals

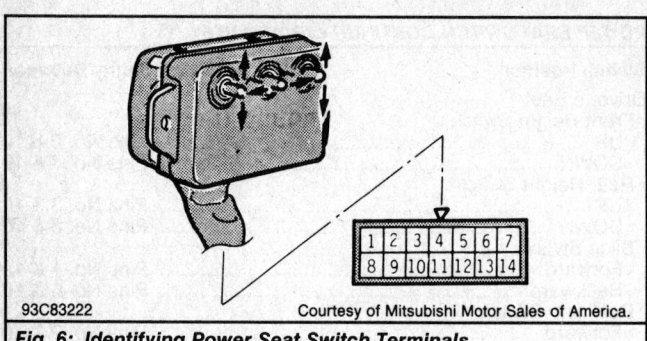

93C83222   Courtesy of Mitsubishi Motor Sales of America.

Fig. 6: Identifying Power Seat Switch Terminals (Stealth & 3000GT)

REMOVAL & INSTALLATION

SEAT ASSEMBLY

Removal & Installation (Normal Removal) – With ignition on, move seat fully rearward. Remove front seat anchor covers and remove nuts. Move seat fully forward. Remove rear seat anchor covers and remove bolts. Turn ignition off. Disconnect electrical harness connectors. Remove seat assembly. To install, reverse removal procedure.

Removal & Installation (Malfunctioning Power Seat Mechanism) –
1) Removal of seat assembly front or rear mounting bolt is not possible due to malfunction of slide motor, slide switch or frozen slide rails. If seat is stuck in forward position, go to next step. If seat is stuck in rearward position, go to step **3)**.

2) Remove rear seat anchor covers and mounting bolts. Remove adjuster screw nut housing mounting bolt. *See Fig. 7.* Both adjuster screw nut housings mount to center of slider frame rail. Insert screwdriver blade between housing nut and rail. Lift and rotate housing nut. Slide seat back and remove front anchor nuts. Once seat is repaired, install housing nut bolts.
3) Lift up front seat cushion cover to expose slide motor. Remove slide motor mounting bolts. If seat assembly cannot be moved forward, remove slide motor bracket mounting bolts. Move seat forward and remove rear anchor bolts. Once seat is repaired, install slide motor mounting bolts.

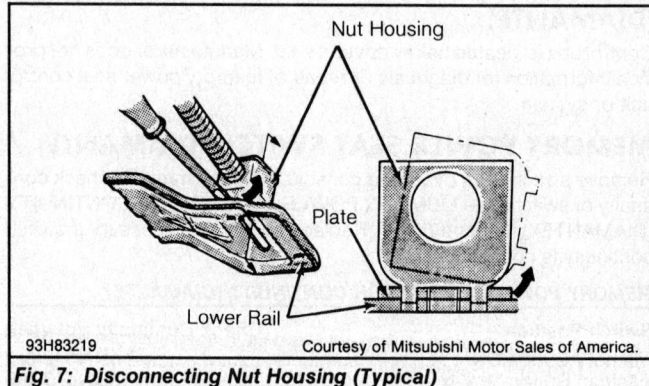

93H83219   Courtesy of Mitsubishi Motor Sales of America.

Fig. 7: Disconnecting Nut Housing (Typical)

WIRING DIAGRAMS

See ACCESSORIES & EQUIPMENT, Volume 5.

Chrysler Corp.: Colt Vista
Eagle: Summit Wagon
Mitsubishi: Diamante, Expo, Galant, Montero

DESCRIPTION & OPERATION

The sun roof is actuated by a overhead console mounted switch. The motor, located near the switch, moves the sun roof panel by means of drive cables. If necessary, sun roof can be closed manually, using crank handle stored in tool pouch.

On vehicles equipped with Electronic Timer Alarm Control System (ETACS), sun roof can be operated up to 30 seconds after ignition switch is turned to OFF position.

Sun roof motor incorporates feature to initially limit opening or closing of roof glass panel (safety feature). For example, sun roof will not fully close from fully open position without releasing, then depressing slide switch during operation. Sun roof initially stops approximately 8" short of fully closed position.

ADJUSTMENTS

ROOF GLASS PANEL

Colt Vista, Diamante, Expo, Galant & Summit Wagon – 1) Fully close sun roof. Ensure roof glass panel is parallel with roof opening. If roof glass panel parallelism is within .04" (1 mm), go to next step. If parallelism is greater than specification, go to step **4)**.
2) Open sun shade and remove side trim strips. See Fig. 1. Lightly pull down on strip to remove. Loosen mounting nuts on each side. Move glass panel as needed. Once panel is correctly adjusted, tighten nuts and install trim strip.
3) Once forward/backward adjustment has been completed, ensure sliding roof assembly's guide and link reference holes are correctly aligned. See Fig. 2. If reference hole adjustment cannot be corrected, fully closed position of roof glass panel to fully closed position of motor is not correctly indexed. To correct, go to next step.
4) To correct roof glass panel parallelism, remove motor. See DRIVE MOTOR under REMOVAL & INSTALLATION. Manually move roof glass panel into fully closed position, parallel with roof opening. Using manual closure wrench (located in tool pouch), rotate drive motor drive gear until mating marks are aligned. See Fig. 3. Install drive motor. If minor adjustment is needed, repeat step **2)**. Install side trim strips.

MAINTENANCE

LUBRICATION

NOTE: Manufacturer only provides lubrication procedures during reassembly of sliding roof assembly components.

TROUBLE SHOOTING

Check following items listed below symptom to aid in diagnosis and repair of sun roof assembly.

SUN ROOF INOPERATIVE

- Fusible link or multipurpose fuse.
- Sun roof switch.
- Drive motor.
- Control relay.
- Power relay.

ROOF GLASS PANEL DOES NOT OPERATE CORRECTLY

- Foreign matter lodged in guide rail.
- Drive motor drive gear not correctly indexed with drive cables.
- Decrease in clutch slipping force of drive motor.
- Misaligned roof glass panel causing binding.

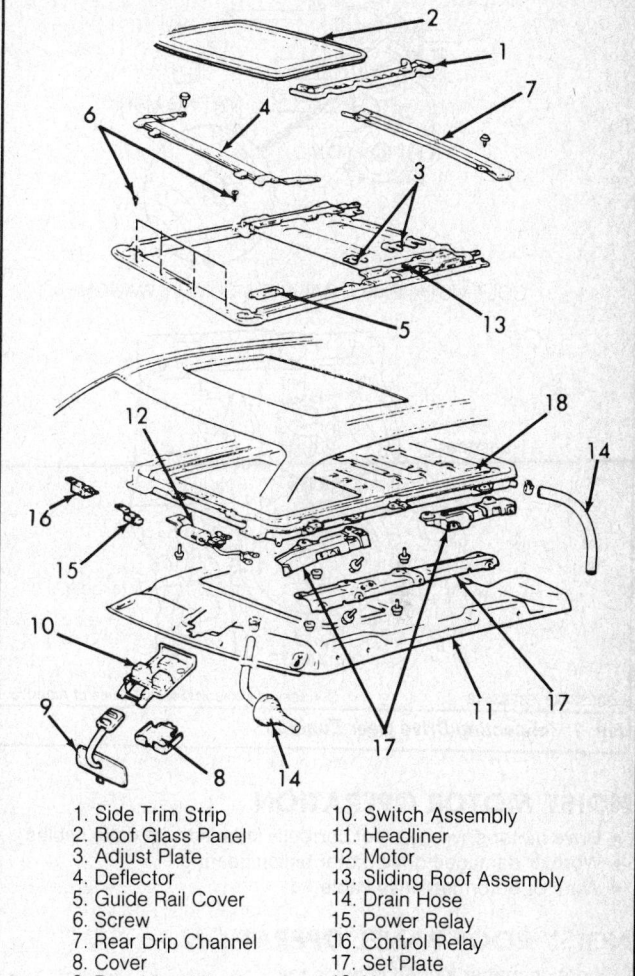

1. Side Trim Strip	10. Switch Assembly
2. Roof Glass Panel	11. Headliner
3. Adjust Plate	12. Motor
4. Deflector	13. Sliding Roof Assembly
5. Guide Rail Cover	14. Drain Hose
6. Screw	15. Power Relay
7. Rear Drip Channel	16. Control Relay
8. Cover	17. Set Plate
9. Rear View Mirror	18. Housing Assembly

93B83445   Courtesy of Mitsubishi Motor Sales of America.

Fig. 1: Exploded View Of Sun Roof Assembly (Typical)

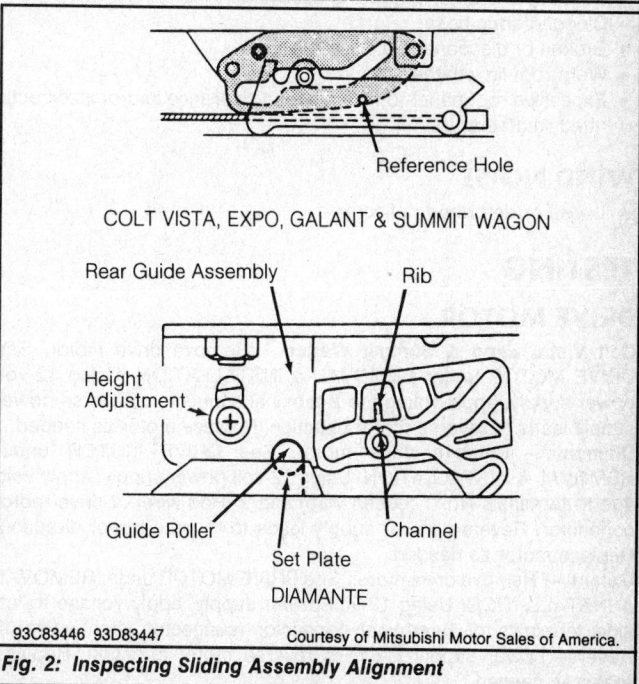

Reference Hole

COLT VISTA, EXPO, GALANT & SUMMIT WAGON

Rear Guide Assembly   Rib

Height Adjustment

Guide Roller   Channel

Set Plate

DIAMANTE

93C83446 93D83447   Courtesy of Mitsubishi Motor Sales of America.

Fig. 2: Inspecting Sliding Assembly Alignment

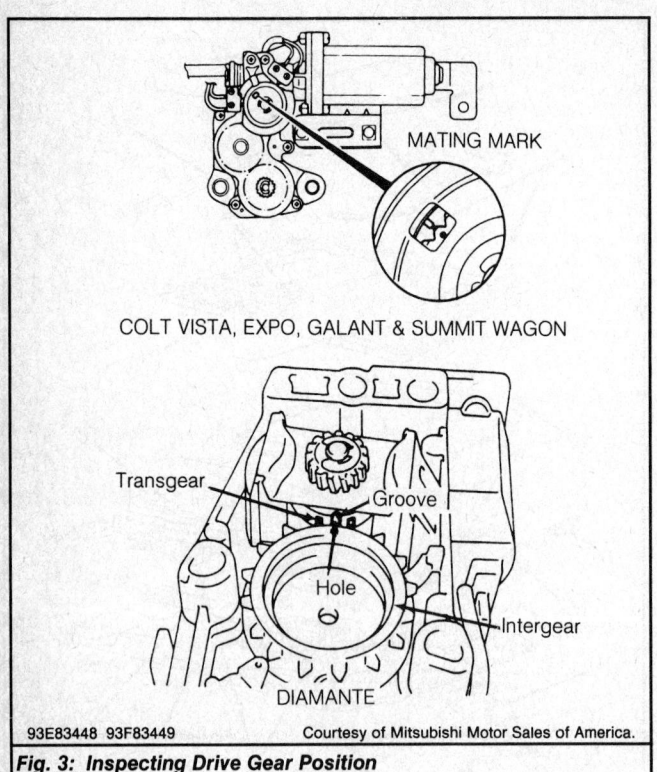

COLT VISTA, EXPO, GALANT & SUMMIT WAGON

MATING MARK

Transgear
Groove
Hole
Intergear

DIAMANTE

93E83448 93F83449   Courtesy of Mitsubishi Motor Sales of America.

Fig. 3: Inspecting Drive Gear Position

NOISY MOTOR OPERATION

- Drive motor drive gear not correctly indexed with drive cables.
- Worn or damaged drive motor pinion bearing.
- Worn or deformed drive cable.

NOISY ROOF PANEL OPERATION

- Foreign matter lodged in guide rail.
- Loose guide rail and lid.

WATER LEAKS

- Dust accumulation in housing assembly.
- Clogged drain hose.
- Broken or disconnected drain hose.
- Worn roof lid weatherstrip.
- Excessive roof panel-to-roof opening clearance and/or incorrectly fitted weatherstrip.

WIND NOISE

- Loose or deformed deflector.

TESTING

DRIVE MOTOR

Colt Vista, Expo & Summit Wagon – Remove drive motor. See DRIVE MOTOR under REMOVAL & INSTALLATION. Using 12-volt power supply, apply voltage to 2-terminal connector. Reverse power supply leads to reverse motor direction. Replace motor as needed.

Diamante – Remove drive motor. See DRIVE MOTOR under REMOVAL & INSTALLATION. Using 12-volt power supply, apply voltage to terminals No. 1 (Green wire) and 2 (Red wire) of drive motor connector. Reverse power supply leads to reverse motor direction. Replace motor as needed.

Galant – Remove drive motor. See DRIVE MOTOR under REMOVAL & INSTALLATION. Using 12-volt power supply, apply voltage to left side terminals of 6-terminal connector (connector latch upward). Reverse power supply leads to reverse motor direction. Replace motor as needed.

Montero – Remove drive motor. See DRIVE MOTOR under REMOVAL & INSTALLATION. Using 12-volt power supply, apply voltage to left side terminals of 4-terminal connector (connector latch upward). Reverse power supply leads to reverse motor direction. Replace motor as needed.

DRIVE MOTOR LIMIT SWITCH

Colt Vista, Expo, & Summit Wagon – Remove limit switches from drive motor. Using ohmmeter, check continuity of each switch. See Fig. 4. Continuity should exist between terminals No. 1 and 2 for switch No. 1, and terminals No. 1 and 3 for switch No. 2. Replace switches as needed. Install switches. See Fig. 4.

Diamante – Remove limit switches from drive motor. Using ohmmeter, check continuity of each switch. Continuity should exist between terminals No. 4 (Black wire) and No. 5 (Blue wire) for switch No. 1, and terminals No. 4 (Black wire) and No. 6 (Blue/Black wire) for switch No. 2. Replace switches as needed.

Galant – Remove limit switches from drive motor. Using ohmmeter, check continuity of each switch. Continuity should exist between terminals No. 3 (White/Black wire) and No. 5 (Red wire) for switch No. 1, and terminals No. 3 (White/Black wire) and No. 6 (Red/Yellow wire) for switch No. 2. Replace switches as needed.

Montero – Using ohmmeter, check continuity of limit switch. When intermittent gear cam of drive motor depresses switch lever, continuity should exist between right side terminals of drive motor 4-terminal connector (connector latch upward). Replace drive motor if switch fails test.

INPUT SIGNAL (DIAMANTE)

NOTE: If after all testing has been completed, sun roof is still not functioning, substitute ETACS unit with known good unit and retest.

1) Access data link connector at lower left corner of dash. Using Special Tool (MB991529), connect positive lead of voltmeter to terminal No. 9 and negative lead to terminal No. 4 or 5. See Fig. 5. Check if input signals from sun roof switch are being received by ETACS module.

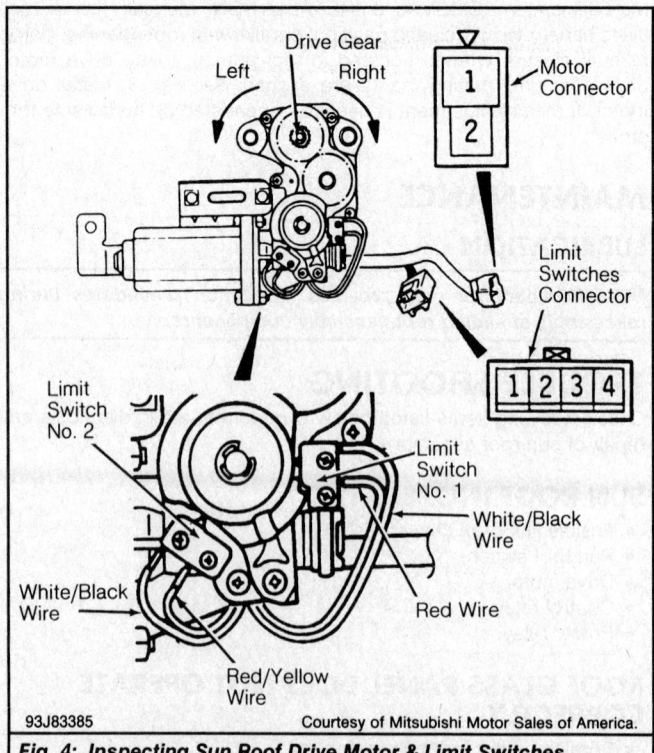

Drive Gear
Left   Right
Motor Connector
1
2
Limit Switches Connector
1 2 3 4
Limit Switch No. 2
Limit Switch No. 1
White/Black Wire
White/Black Wire
Red Wire
Red/Yellow Wire

93J83385   Courtesy of Mitsubishi Motor Sales of America.

Fig. 4: Inspecting Sun Roof Drive Motor & Limit Switches (Colt Vista, Expo & Summit Wagon)

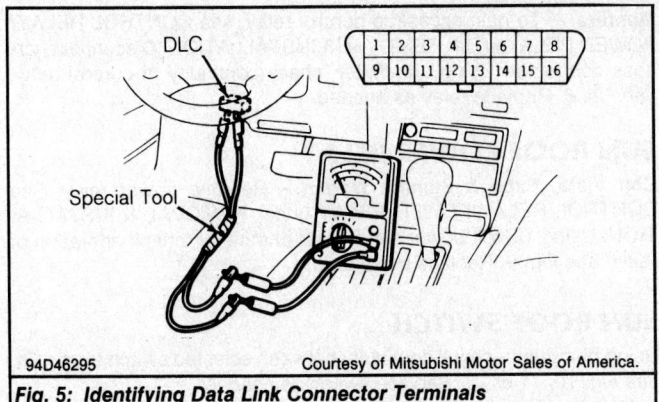

94D46295   Courtesy of Mitsubishi Motor Sales of America.

Fig. 5: Identifying Data Link Connector Terminals

2) Voltmeter needle should sweep when each switch is operated. If switch or related component is not functioning, voltmeter will not operate when switch is activated. Check related circuit and/or component.

SUN ROOF CONTROL RELAY

NOTE: Manufacturer does not supply sun roof control unit testing information for Diamante and Galant.

Colt Vista, Expo & Summit Wagon – To gain access to control relay, see CONTROL RELAY/POWER RELAY under REMOVAL & INSTALLATION. Remove limit switches from drive motor. Ensure limit switch harness connectors are connected. Turn ignition on. Using DVOM, backprobe control unit between connector terminal and vehicle ground. *See Figs. 6 and 7.* Once testing is completed, remount limit switches. *See Fig. 4.*

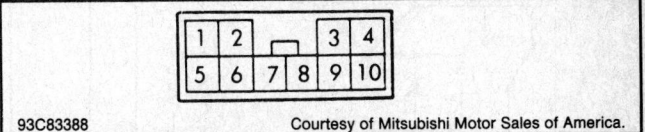

93C83388   Courtesy of Mitsubishi Motor Sales of America.

Fig. 7: Identifying Sun Roof Control Unit Terminals (Colt Vista, Expo & Summit Wagon)

Check sequence	Tester connection terminal	Checking conditions			Standard	Countermeasure if deviation from standard
		Always/ Usually	Limit switch	Sunroof switch		
1	5	Always			Continuity	Check the harness (between the control relay and ground).
2	10	Always			Battery Positive Voltage	Check the harness (between the control relay and the battery).
3	6		No. 1 OFF		Battery Positive Voltage	Replace the control relay or the motor.
			No. 1 ON		0 V	Check the harness (between the control relay and ground).
4	2		No. 2 OFF		Battery Positive Voltage	Replace the control relay or the motor.
			No.2 ON		0 V	Check the harness (between the control relay and ground).
5	3	Usually			Battery Positive Voltage	Replace the control relay or the motor.
				Tilt up	0 V	Check the harness (between the control relay and ground). Check the tilt switch.
6	7	Usually			Battery Positive Voltage	Replace the control relay or the motor.
				Tilt down	0 V	Check the harness (between the control relay and ground). Check the tilt switch.
7	9	Usually			Battery Positive Voltage	Replace the control relay or the motor.
				Slide open	0 V	Check the harness (between the control relay and ground). Check the slide switch.
8	8	Usually			Battery Positive Voltage	Replace the control relay or the motor.
				Slide close	0 V	Check the harness (between the control relay and ground). Check the slide switch.
9	4		No. 2 OFF	Tilt up	Battery Positive Voltage	Replace the control relay.
10	1		① No. 2 OFF	② Tilt down	–	–
			③ No. 1 OFF → ON		Battery Positive Voltage → 0V	Replace the control relay.
11	1		① No. 1 ON	② Slide open	–	–
			③ No. 2 ON		Battery Positive Voltage	Replace the control relay.
12	4		① No. 1 ON	② Slide close	–	–
			③ No. 2 ON → OFF		Battery Positive Voltage → 0V	Replace the control relay.
13	4		① No. 1 OFF		–	–
			② No. 2 ON	③ Slide close	Battery Positive Voltage (for 0.5 sec.)	Replace the control relay.

93D83389   Courtesy of Mitsubishi Motor Sales of America.

Fig. 6: Sun Roof Control Unit Testing Chart (Colt Vista, Expo & Summit Wagon)

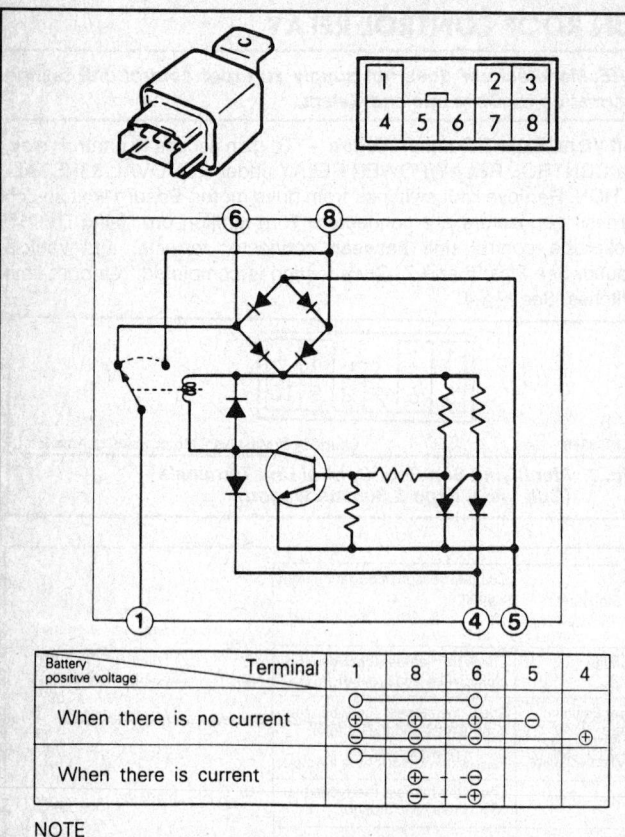

Battery positive voltage	Terminal	1	8	6	5	4
When there is no current		⊖ ⊕ ⊕	⊕ ⊕	⊕ ⊖	⊖	⊕
When there is current		⊖ ⊕ ⊖	⊕ ⊖	⊖ ⊕		

NOTE
(1) O—O indicates that there is continuity between the terminals.
(2) ⊕—⊖ indicates that there is continuity when the (+) is connected to the tester plus terminal, and the (−) is connected to the tester minus terminal.
(3) ⊕· ⊖ indicates terminals to which battery positive voltage is applied.

93G83416 93H83417   Courtesy of Mitsubishi Motor Sales of America.

Fig. 8: Testing Control Relay (Montero)

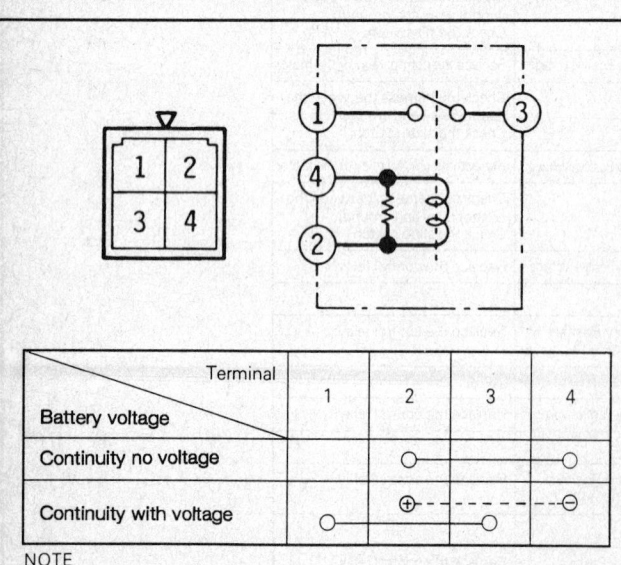

	Terminal	1	2	3	4
Battery voltage					
Continuity no voltage			O	O	
Continuity with voltage		O	⊕		⊖

NOTE
(1) O—O indicates that there is continuity between the terminals.
(2) +—— indicates terminals to which battery voltage is applied.

93I83384   Courtesy of Mitsubishi Motor Sales of America.

Fig. 9: Inspecting Sun Roof Power Relay Continuity (Colt Vista, Expo & Summit Wagon)

Montero – To gain access to control relay, see CONTROL RELAY/POWER RELAY under REMOVAL & INSTALLATION. Disconnect harness connector. Using ohmmeter, check continuity of control relay. *See Fig. 8.* Replace relay as needed.

SUN ROOF POWER RELAY

Colt Vista, Expo & Summit Wagon – Remove power relay. See CONTROL RELAY/POWER RELAY under REMOVAL & INSTALLATION. Using 12-volt power supply and ohmmeter, check operation of relay. *See Fig. 9.* Replace as needed.

SUN ROOF SWITCH

Using ohmmeter, check continuity between selected switch terminals. *See Fig. 10, 11 or 12.* Replace switch as needed.

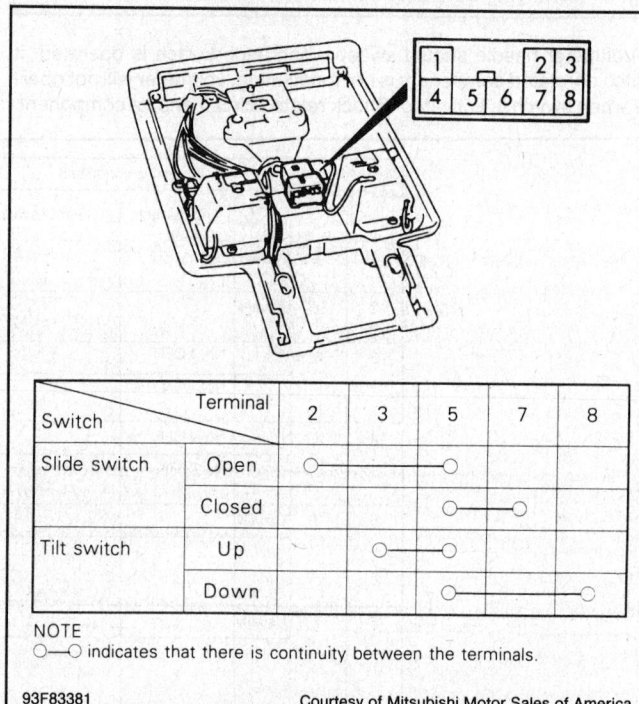

Switch	Terminal	2	3	5	7	8
Slide switch	Open	O		O		
	Closed			O	O	
Tilt switch	Up		O	O		
	Down				O	O

NOTE
O—O indicates that there is continuity between the terminals.

93F83381   Courtesy of Mitsubishi Motor Sales of America.

Fig. 10: Inspecting Sun Roof Switch Continuity (Colt Vista, Expo, Galant & Summit Wagon)

Switch	Terminal	4	5	8	9	10
Slide switch	Open	O		O		
	Close			O		O
Tilt switch	Up			O	O	
	Down				O	O

NOTE
O—O indicates that there is continuity between the terminals.

93J83450 93A83451   Courtesy of Mitsubishi Motor Sales of America.

Fig. 11: Inspecting Sun Roof Switch Continuity (Diamante)

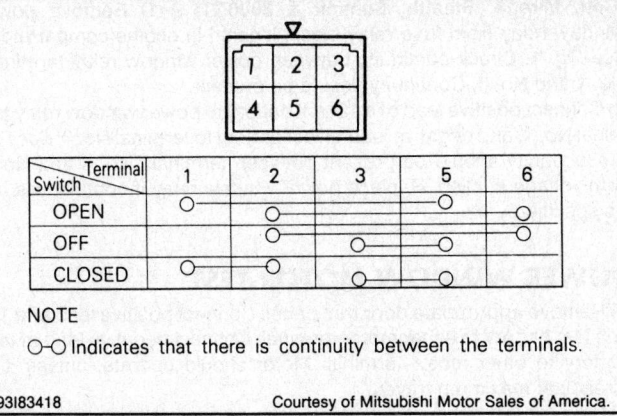

Switch \ Terminal	1	2	3	5	6
OPEN	○──	──○	────	○──	──○
OFF		○──	──○	──○	
CLOSED	○──	──○	──○	──○	

NOTE
○─○ Indicates that there is continuity between the terminals.

93183418   Courtesy of Mitsubishi Motor Sales of America.

Fig. 12: Inspecting Sun Roof Switch Continuity (Montero)

REMOVAL & INSTALLATION

CONTROL RELAY/POWER RELAY

Removal & Installation – Remove overhead switch assembly. Lower headliner to gain access to relays. See DRIVE MOTOR under REMOVAL & INSTALLATION. Remove relays. To install, reverse removal procedure.

DRIVE CABLES

NOTE: Manufacturer does not supply drive cable removal & installation information for Diamante.

Removal & Installation (Colt Vista, Expo, Galant & Summit Wagon) –
1) Remove sliding roof assembly. See SUN ROOF under REMOVAL & INSTALLATION. Remove sun shade and stopper at rear end of drive rail. Remove sliding roof drive cable assembly from rear part of guide rail. Depress assembly into guide rail to slide past notches if necessary.
2) Once sliding assembly is removed, ensure plastic sliding shoes attached to assembly are retained for reassembly. Ensure guide rail, sliding assembly and drive cables are clean before reassembly.
3) To reassemble, reverse disassembly procedure. Apply multipurpose grease to all moving components. To install sliding roof assembly, reverse removal procedure.
Removal & Installation (Montero) – 1) With sun roof assembly removed from vehicle, remove plastic mounting cover and roof glass panel. Remove front guide bracket and deflector assembly. Remove front guide rail end cover. Remove set plate and guide rail assembly. Remove sun shade and drive cable tube. Remove lifter assembly and slider assembly from housing assembly.
2) Ensure guide rail, sliding assembly and drive cables are clean before reassembly. To reassemble, reverse disassembly procedure. Apply multipurpose grease to all moving components. To install sliding roof assembly, reverse removal procedure.

DRIVE MOTOR

Removal (Colt Vista, Expo, Galant & Summit Wagon) – 1) To remove sun roof drive motor, headliner must be lowered enough to gain access to motor. Remove overhead switch assembly. Remove front and rear door scuff plate.
2) Remove center pillar lower and upper trim. Remove roof rail and sun roof trim strips. Remove front pillar trim. Remove assist handle (if needed). Lower headliner to gain access to motor assembly. Disconnect motor harness connector. Remove motor mounting bolts and remove motor.

Inspection – Check each drive gear tooth for abrasion or wear. Check both drive cables for wear. Replace as needed.
Installation – Ensure sun roof glass panel is fully closed. Sun roof drive cables must be properly indexed to drive motor drive gear. Remove drive motor cam gear cover. Using manual closure wrench (included in vehicle tool pouch), rotate motor to correct position. See Fig. 3. Install motor. To complete installation, reverse removal procedure.
Removal & Installation (Diamante) – Remove sun roof switch assembly. Remove drive motor. To install, ensure sun roof glass panel is fully closed. Sun roof drive cables must be properly indexed to drive motor drive gear. Using manual closure wrench (located in tool pouch), rotate drive motor until alignment hole of intermittent gear is aligned with center of drive gear. See Fig. 3. To complete installation, reverse removal procedure.
Removal & Installation (Montero) – Remove sun roof switch assembly. Remove drive motor. To install, open roof glass panel approximately 7.9" (200 mm). Using manual closure wrench, rotate drive motor until alignment hole of intermittent gear is aligned with center of drive gear. See Fig. 3. To complete installation, reverse removal procedure.

SUN ROOF

Removal & Installation (Colt Vista, Diamante, Expo, Galant & Summit Wagon) – **1)** Remove side trim panels. Trim panels are removed by lightly pulling straight down. Unbolt and remove roof glass panel with adjust plates. See Fig. 1. Operate sun roof drive cable assembly to fully open position. Remove deflector. Remove guide rail cover. Operate sun roof drive cable assembly to fully closed position and remove rear drip channel.
2) Remove overhead switch assembly. Remove rear seat. Push down on rear seat cushion and pull seat release lever. Unbolt and remove seat back. Remove front and rear door scuff plate.
3) Remove center pillar lower and upper trim. Remove roof rail and sun roof trim strips. Remove front and rear pillar trim. Remove assist handle. Remove headliner. Disconnect motor harness connector. Remove motor mounting bolts and remove motor.
4) Attach protective tape around roof opening. Pull sliding roof assembly forward through roof opening. Disconnect drain hoses. If drain hoses need replacement, attach cord to exterior end of drain hose. Pull drain hose from interior end. To install hose, reverse removal procedure. Remove housing assembly and set brackets.
5) To install remaining components, reverse removal procedure. Sun roof drive cables must be properly indexed to drive motor drive gear. Remove drive motor cam gear cover. Using manual closure wrench (included in vehicle tool pouch), rotate motor to correct position. See Fig. 3. Install motor. Install remaining components. To adjust roof glass panel, see ROOF GLASS PANEL under ADJUSTMENTS.
Removal & Installation (Montero) – **1)** Remove decoration covers. Unbolt roof glass panel from sliding assembly and remove. Remove sun roof switch assembly and drive motor. Remove front and rear door scuff plate.
2) Remove center pillar lower and upper trim. Remove roof rail and sun roof trim strips. Remove front and rear pillar trim. Remove assist handle. Remove headliner. Remove rear set bracket. Remove sun roof assembly. Disconnect drain hoses.
3) If drain hoses need replacement, attach cord to exterior end of drain hose. Pull drain hose from interior end. To install hose, reverse removal procedure. To install, reverse removal procedure. See DRIVE MOTOR for installation procedures.

WIRING DIAGRAMS

See ACCESSORIES & EQUIPMENT, Volume 5.

Chrysler Corp.: Colt, Colt Vista, Stealth
Eagle: Summit, Summit Wagon
Mitsubishi: Diamante, Eclipse, Expo, Galant,
  Mirage, Montero, Pickup, 3000GT

DESCRIPTION & OPERATION

With the ignition switch in RUN position, battery voltage is applied to the master power window switch, located on the driver's door. The master power window switch provides power and ground for all power window switches and motors. The master power window switch offers one-touch operation of driver's window. A solid state control unit, incorporated in the master switch, fully lowers driver's window when switch is completely depressed. Master switch also includes lock-out feature to prevent passengers from operating any of the other power window door switches. On Diamante, Stealth and 3000GT, power windows are able to be operated for up to 30 seconds after ignition is turned off.

TROUBLE SHOOTING

POWER WINDOWS INOPERATIVE

Check for faulty sub fusible link, faulty power window relay or faulty power window switches. See POWER WINDOW FUSIBLE LINK IDENTIFICATION table.

POWER WINDOW FUSIBLE LINK IDENTIFICATION

Application	Fusible Link No.
Colt, Mirage & Summit	7
Colt Vista, Expo & Summit Wagon	9
Diamante	1
Eclipse	5
Galant	2
Montero	10
Pickup	9
Stealth & 3000GT	9

ONE WINDOW FAILS TO OPERATE

If one window does not operate, even if both master and passenger side power window switches are pressed, check for faulty master power window switch or power window motor that is inoperative. If one window does not operate, only when either master or passenger side power window switch is pressed, but does operate when both switches are pressed, check power window switch that is inoperative.

ONE-TOUCH SWITCH FUNCTION INOPERATIVE

Replace master power window switch.

TESTING

CIRCUIT BREAKER TEST

Press UP switch to fully close window. Continue to press switch for 10 seconds. Release UP switch and immediately press DOWN switch. If window begins to open within 60 seconds, circuit breaker is okay. Circuit breaker is part of window motor.

POWER WINDOW RELAY TEST

(All Models Except Colt, Mirage, Stealth, Summit & 3000GT) – 1) Remove power window relay from fuse/relay block, located in engine compartment. *See Fig. 1.* Check continuity between power window relay terminals No. 2 and No. 4. Continuity should be present.
2) Connect positive lead of a 12-volt battery to power window relay terminal No. 2, and negative lead of test battery to terminal No. 4. *See Fig. 3.* Continuity should be present between terminals No. 1 and No. 3 with voltage applied. Replace power window relay if continuity is not as specified.

(Colt, Mirage, Stealth, Summit & 3000GT) – 1) Remove power window relay from fuse/relay block, located in engine compartment. *See Fig. 1.* Check continuity between power window relay terminals No. 1 and No. 3. Continuity should be present.
2) Connect positive lead of a 12-volt battery to power window relay terminal No. 1, and negative lead of test battery to terminal No. 3. *See Fig. 4.* Continuity should be present between terminals No. 4 and No. 5 with voltage applied. Replace power window relay if continuity is not as specified.

POWER WINDOW MOTOR TEST

1) Remove appropriate door trim panel. Connect positive lead of a 12-volt test battery to either motor terminal. Connect negative lead of test battery to other motor terminal. Motor should operate, unless it is already at maximum travel.
2) Reverse test battery leads. Motor should operate in opposite direction. If motor does not operate, inspect wiring. If wiring is okay, replace motor. Reverse test battery leads again to complete full function test of motor.

POWER WINDOW SWITCH TEST

NOTE: Manufacturer does not supply information for Diamante and Pickup.

Remove control switch from trim panel. Using ohmmeter, check continuity of switch. See appropriate WINDOW SWITCH CONTINUITY CHART. *See Fig. 2.* Replace appropriate switch as necessary if switch continuity is not as specified.

MASTER WINDOW SWITCH CONTINUITY CHART (COLT, MIRAGE & SUMMIT)

Switch Position [1]	Check Continuity Between
Normal Position	
Left Front OFF	Pins 2, 3 & 10
Left Rear OFF	Pins 1, 3 & 7
Left Front UP	Pins 2 & 4; Pins 3 & 10
Left Rear UP	Pins 1 & 3; Pins 4 & 7
Left Front DOWN	Pins 2 & 3; Pins 4 & 10
Left Rear DOWN	Pins 1 & 4; Pins 3 & 7
Right Front OFF	Pins 3, 5 & 11
Right Rear OFF	Pins 3, 6 & 14
Right Front UP	Pins 3 & 5; Pins 4 & 11
Right Rear UP	Pins 3 & 14; Pins 4 & 6
Right Front DOWN	Pins 3 & 11; Pins 4 & 5
Right Rear DOWN	Pins 3 & 6; Pins 4 & 14
Lock Position	
Left Front OFF	Pins 2, 3 & 10
Left Rear OFF	Pins 1 & 7
Left Front UP	Pins 2 & 4; Pins 3 & 10
Left Rear UP	Pins 4 & 7
Left Front DOWN	Pins 2 & 3; Pins 4 & 10
Left Rear DOWN	Pins 1 & 4
Right Front OFF	Pins 5 & 11
Right Rear OFF	Pins 6 & 14
Right Front UP	Pins 4 & 11
Right Rear UP	Pins 4 & 6
Right Front DOWN	Pins 4 & 5
Right Rear DOWN	Pins 4 & 14

[1] – Left side of vehicle refers to driver's side.

PASSENGER SIDE WINDOW SWITCH CONTINUITY CHART (COLT, MIRAGE & SUMMIT)

Switch Position	Check Continuity Between
OFF	Pins 1 & 2; Pins 3 & 6
UP	Pins 2 & 4; Pins 3 & 6
DOWN	Pins 1 & 2; Pins 3 & 4

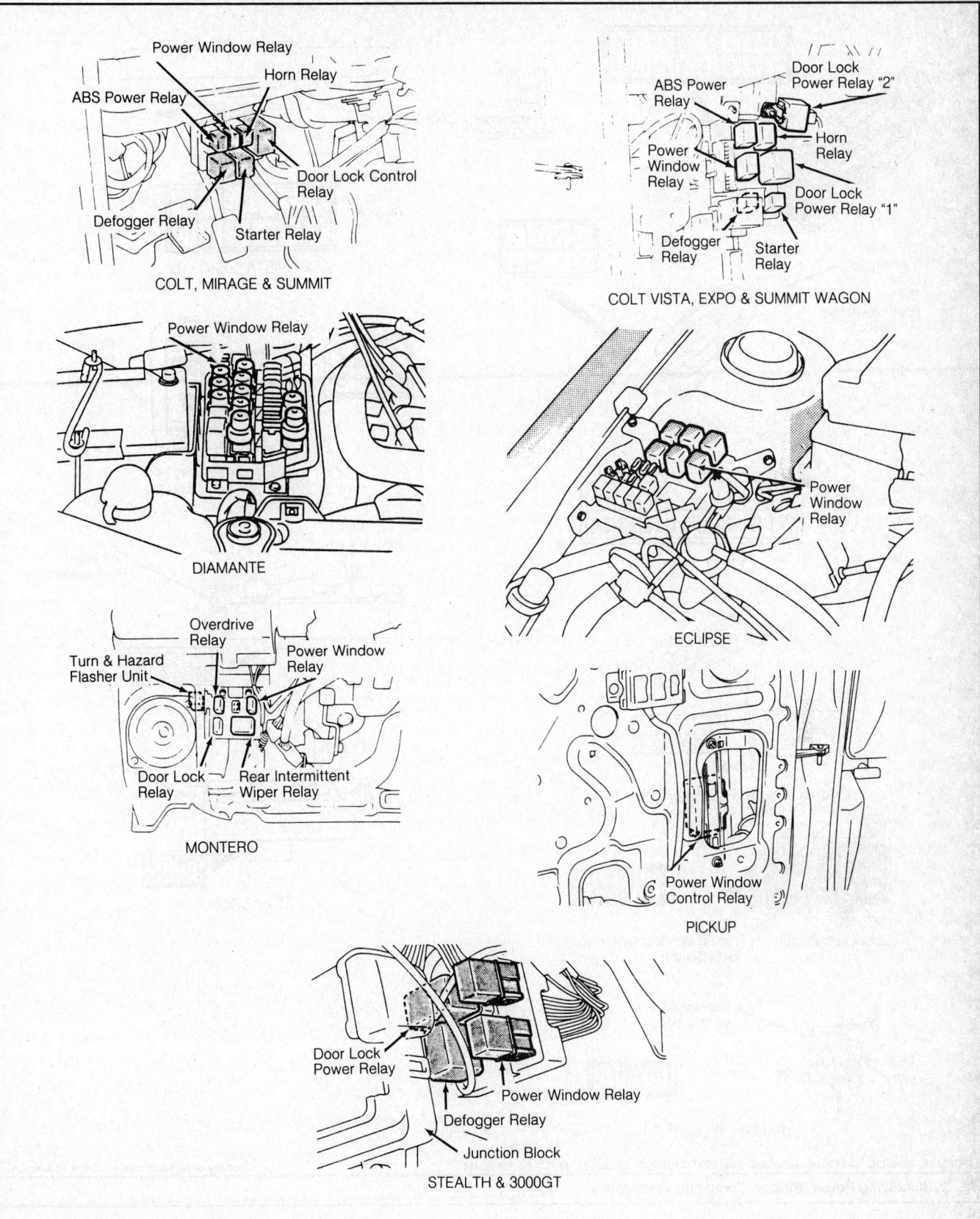

Power Window Relay

Horn Relay

ABS Power Relay

Door Lock Control Relay

Defogger Relay

Starter Relay

COLT, MIRAGE & SUMMIT

ABS Power Relay

Door Lock Power Relay "2"

Horn Relay

Power Window Relay

Door Lock Power Relay "1"

Defogger Relay

Starter Relay

COLT VISTA, EXPO & SUMMIT WAGON

Power Window Relay

DIAMANTE

Power Window Relay

ECLIPSE

Overdrive Relay

Turn & Hazard Flasher Unit

Power Window Relay

Door Lock Relay

Rear Intermittent Wiper Relay

MONTERO

Power Window Control Relay

PICKUP

Door Lock Power Relay

Power Window Relay

Defogger Relay

Junction Block

STEALTH & 3000GT

94H46885 93C83123 93E83174 93H40987 93F83126 94I46886 93H83128

Courtesy of Mitsubishi Motor Sales of America.

Fig. 1: Locating Power Window Relay

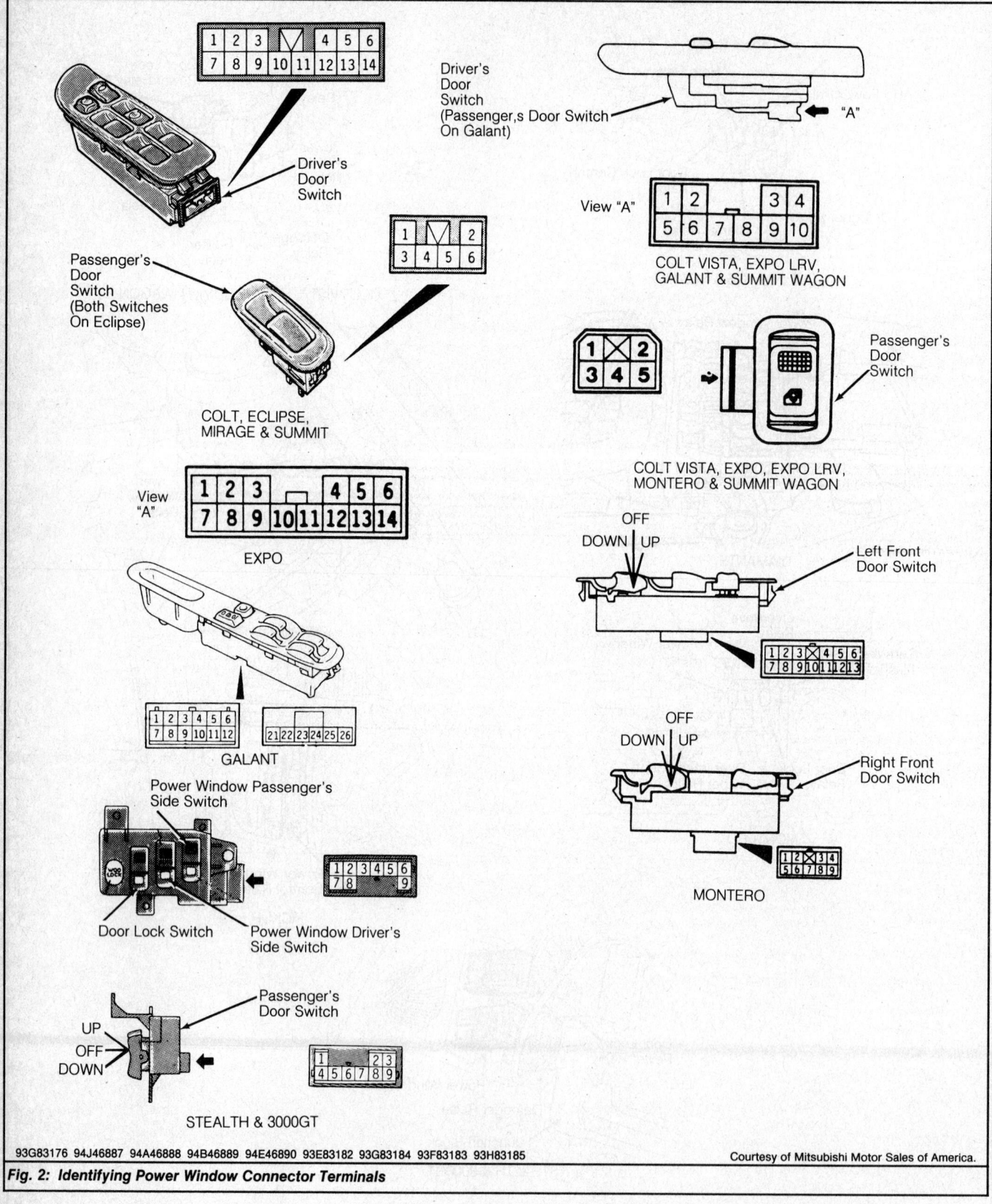

Fig. 2: Identifying Power Window Connector Terminals

93G83176 94J46887 94A46888 94B46889 94E46890 93E83182 93G83184 93F83183 93H83185

Courtesy of Mitsubishi Motor Sales of America.

MASTER WINDOW SWITCH CONTINUITY CHART (COLT VISTA, EXPO LRV & SUMMIT WAGON)

Switch Position [1]	Check Continuity Between
Normal Position	
Left Front OFF	Pins 1, 2 & 9
Left Front UP	Pins 1 & 9; Pins 2 & 6
Left Front DOWN	Pins 1 & 6; Pins 2 & 9
Right Front OFF	Pins 5, 8 & 9
Right Front UP	Pins 5 & 6; Pins 8 & 9
Right Front DOWN	Pins 5 & 9; Pins 6 & 8
Lock Position	
Left Front OFF	Pins 1, 2 & 9
Left Front UP	Pins 1 & 9; Pins 2 & 6
Left Front DOWN	Pins 1 & 6; Pins 2 & 9
Right Front OFF	Pins 5 & 8
Right Front UP	Pins 5 & 6
Right Front DOWN	Pins 6 & 8

[1] – Left side of vehicle refers to driver's side.

MASTER WINDOW SWITCH CONTINUITY CHART (ECLIPSE)

Switch Position [1]	Check Continuity Between
Normal Position	
Left Front OFF	Pins 2, 3 & 6
Left Front UP	Pins 2 & 3; Pins 5 & 6
Left Front DOWN	Pins 2 & 5; Pins 3 & 6
Right Front OFF	Pins 1, 3 & 4
Right Front UP	Pins 1 & 3; Pins 4 & 5
Right DOWN	Pins 1 & 5; Pins 3 & 4
Lock Position	
Left OFF	Pins 2, 3 & 6
Left UP	Pins 2 & 3; Pins 5 & 6
Left DOWN	Pins 2 & 5; Pins 3 & 6
Right OFF	Pins 1 & 4
Right UP	Pins 4 & 5
Right DOWN	Pins 1 & 5

[1] – Left side of vehicle refers to driver's side.

PASSENGER SIDE WINDOW SWITCH CONTINUITY CHART (ECLIPSE)

Switch Position	Check Continuity Between
OFF	Pins 2 & 4; Pins 3 & 5
UP	Pins 2 & 4; Pins 5 & 6
DOWN	Pins 3 & 5; Pins 4 & 6

MASTER WINDOW SWITCH CONTINUITY CHART (EXPO)

Switch Position [1]	Check Continuity Between
Normal Position	
Left Front OFF	Pins 1, 5 & 8
Left Rear OFF	Pins 5, 11 & 12
Left Front UP	Pins 1 & 13; Pins 5 & 8
Left Rear UP	Pins 5 & 12; 11 & 13
Left Front DOWN	Pins 1 & 5; Pins 8 & 13
Left Rear DOWN	Pins 5 & 11; Pins 12 & 13
Right Front OFF	Pins 2, 5 & 9
Right Rear OFF	Pins 5, 7 & 10
Right Front UP	Pins 2 & 5; Pins 9 & 13
Right Rear UP	Pins 5 & 7; Pins 10 & 13
Right Front DOWN	Pins 2 & 13; Pins 5 & 9
Right Rear DOWN	Pins 5 & 10; Pins 7 & 13
Lock Position	
Left Front OFF	Pins 1, 5 & 8
Left Rear OFF	Pins 5, 11 & 12
Left Front UP	Pins 1 & 13; Pins 5 & 8
Left Rear UP	Pins 5 & 12
Left Front DOWN	Pins 1 & 5; Pins 8 & 13
Left Rear DOWN	Pins 5 & 11
Right Front OFF	Pins 2, 5 & 9
Right Rear OFF	Pins 5, 7 & 10
Right Front UP	Pins 2 & 5; Pins 9 & 13
Right Rear UP	Pins 10 & 13
Right Front DOWN	Pins 2 & 13; Pins 5 & 9
Right Rear DOWN	Pins 5 & 10

[1] – Left side of vehicle refers to driver's side.

RIGHT FRONT SIDE WINDOW SWITCH CONTINUITY CHART (EXPO)

Switch Position	Check Continuity Between
OFF	Pins 1 & 2; Pins 4 & 5
UP	Pins 2 & 3; Pins 4 & 5
DOWN	Pins 1 & 2; Pins 3 & 4

REAR DOOR SIDE WINDOW SWITCH CONTINUITY CHART (EXPO)

Switch Position [1]	Check Continuity Between
Left Rear OFF	Pins 1 & 2; Pins 3 & 4
Left Rear UP	Pins 1 & 2; Pins 4 & 5
Left Rear DOWN	Pins 1 & 5; Pins 3 & 4
Right Rear OFF	Pins 1 & 2; Pins 3 & 4
Right Rear UP	Pins 1 & 5; Pins 3 & 4
Right Rear DOWN	Pins 1 & 2; Pins 4 & 5

[1] – Left side of vehicle refers to driver's side.

MASTER WINDOW SWITCH CONTINUITY CHART (GALANT)

Switch Position [1]	Check Continuity Between
Normal Position	
Left Front OFF	Pins 21, 22 & 24
Left Rear OFF	Pins 10 & 24
Left Front UP	Pins 21 & 24; Pins 22 & 23
Left Rear UP	Pins 10 & 24; Pins 11 & 24
Left Front DOWN	Pins 21 & 23; Pins 22 & 24
Left Rear DOWN	Pins 10 & 24; Pins 11 & 24
Right Front OFF	Pins 10 & 24
Right Rear OFF	Pins 10 & 24
Right Front UP	Pins 10 & 24; Pins 11 & 24
Right Rear UP	Pins 10 & 24; Pins 11 & 24
Right Front DOWN	Pins 10 & 24; Pins 11 & 24
Right Rear DOWN	Pins 10 & 24; Pins 11 & 24
Lock Position	
Left Rear UP	Pins 11 & 24
Left Rear DOWN	Pins 11 & 24
Right Front UP	Pins 11 & 24
Right Rear UP	Pins 11 & 24
Right Front DOWN	Pins 11 & 24
Right Rear DOWN	Pins 11 & 24

[1] – Left side of vehicle refers to driver's side.

PASSENGER SIDE WINDOW SWITCH CONTINUITY CHART (GALANT)

Switch Position	Check Continuity Between
OFF	Pins 1, 7 & 8
UP	Pins 1 & 2; Pins 1 & 7; Pins 2 & 8
DOWN	Pins 1 & 2; Pins 1 & 8; Pins 2 & 7

MASTER WINDOW SWITCH CONTINUITY CHART (MONTERO)

Switch Position [1]	Check Continuity Between
Normal Position	
Left Front OFF	Pins 2, 8 & 13
Left Rear OFF	Pins 4, 11 & 13
Left Front UP	Pins 2 & 9; Pins 8 & 13
Left Rear UP	Pins 4 & 9; 11 & 13
Left Front DOWN	Pins 2 & 13; Pins 8 & 9
Left Rear DOWN	Pins 4 & 13; Pins 9 & 11
Right Front OFF	Pins 1, 7 & 13
Right Rear OFF	Pins 5, 12 & 13
Right Front UP	Pins 1 & 9; Pins 7 & 13
Right Rear UP	Pins 5 & 9; Pins 12 & 13
Right Front DOWN	Pins 1 & 13; Pins 7 & 9
Right Rear DOWN	Pins 5 & 13; Pins 9 & 12
Lock Position	
Left Front OFF	Pins 2, 8 & 13
Left Rear OFF	Pins 4 & 11
Left Front UP	Pins 2 & 9; Pins 8 & 13
Left Rear UP	Pins 4 & 9
Left Front DOWN	Pins 2 & 13; Pins 8 & 9
Left Rear DOWN	Pins 9 & 11
Right Front OFF	Pins 1 & 7
Right Rear OFF	Pins 5 & 12
Right Front UP	Pins 1 & 9
Right Rear UP	Pins 5 & 9
Right Front DOWN	Pins 7 & 9
Right Rear DOWN	Pins 9 & 12

[1] – Left side of vehicle refers to driver's side.

RIGHT FRONT SIDE WINDOW SWITCH CONTINUITY CHART (MONTERO)

Switch Position	Check Continuity Between
OFF	Pins 1 & 7; Pins 2 & 5
UP	Pins 2 & 5; Pins 6 & 7
DOWN	Pins 1 & 7; Pins 5 & 6

REAR DOOR SIDE WINDOW SWITCH CONTINUITY CHART (MONTERO)

Switch Position	Check Continuity Between
OFF	Pins 1 & 2; Pins 3 & 5
UP	Pins 1 & 2; Pins 3 & 4
DOWN	Pins 2 & 4; Pins 3 & 5

MASTER WINDOW SWITCH CONTINUITY CHART (STEALTH & 3000GT)

Switch Position [1]	Check Continuity Between
Normal Position	
Left Front OFF	Pins 2, 6 & 9
Left Front UP	Pins 1 & 2; Pins 6 & 9
Left Front DOWN	Pins 1 & 9; Pins 2 & 6
Right Front OFF	Pins 3, 4 & 6
Right Front UP	Pins 1 & 4; Pins 3 & 6
Right Front DOWN	Pins 1 & 3; Pins 4 & 6
Lock Position	
Left Front OFF	Pins 2, 6 & 9
Left Front UP	Pins 1 & 2; Pins 6 & 9
Left Front DOWN	Pins 1 & 9; Pins 2 & 6
Right Front OFF	Pins 3 & 4
Right Front UP	Pins 1 & 4
Right Front DOWN	Pins 1 & 3

[1] – Left side of vehicle refers to driver's side.

PASSENGER SIDE WINDOW SWITCH CONTINUITY CHART (STEALTH & 3000GT)

Switch Position	Check Continuity Between
OFF	Pins 3 & 8; Pins 5 & 7
UP	Pins 3 & 8; Pins 5 & 9
DOWN	Pins 3 & 9; Pins 5 & 7

REMOVAL & INSTALLATION

POWER WINDOW MOTOR

Removal & Installation – Remove door trim panel and waterproof shield. Remove glass retaining screws and glass. See Fig. 5. Remove motor and slider assembly retaining bolts and remove motor and slider assembly from door. To install, reverse removal procedure.

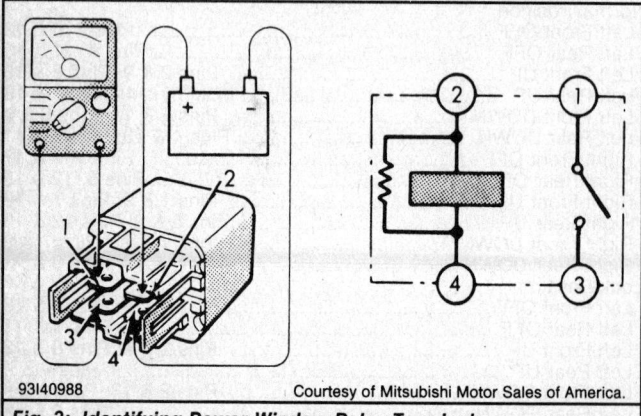

93I40988   Courtesy of Mitsubishi Motor Sales of America.

**Fig. 3: Identifying Power Window Relay Terminals
(Except Colt, Galant, Mirage, Stealth, Summit & 3000GT)**

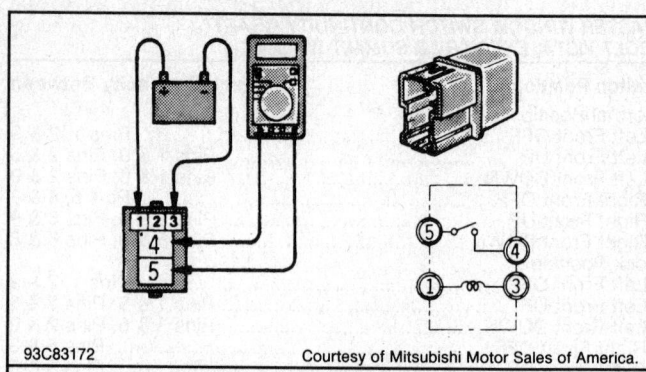

93C83172   Courtesy of Mitsubishi Motor Sales of America.

**Fig. 4: Identifying Power Window Relay Terminals
(Colt, Mirage, Stealth, Summit & 3000GT)**

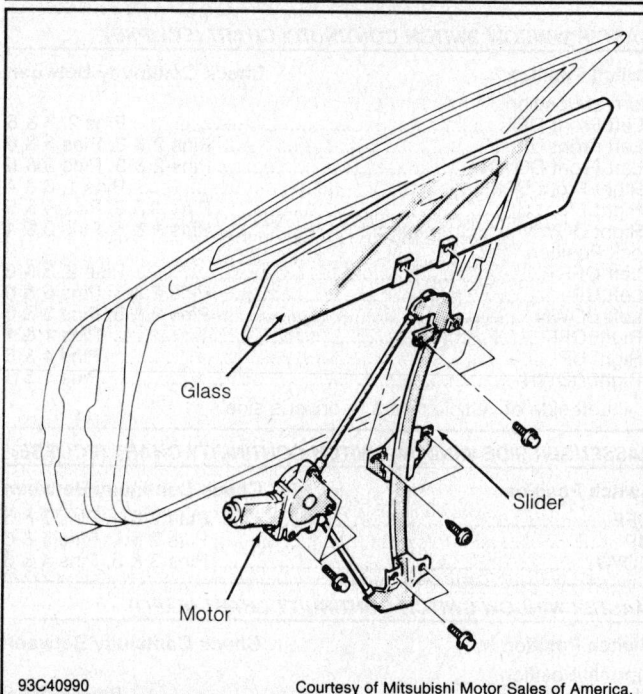

Glass

Slider

Motor

93C40990   Courtesy of Mitsubishi Motor Sales of America.

Fig. 5: Removing Power Window Motor & Slider Assembly

WIRING DIAGRAMS

See ACCESSORIES & EQUIPMENT, Volume 5.

Chrysler Corp.: Colt, Colt Vista, Stealth,
Eagle: Summit, Summit Wagon
Mitsubishi: Diamante, Eclipse, Expo, Galant,
 Mirage, Montero, Pickup, 3000GT

TESTING

For steering column switch testing, see STEERING COLUMN SWITCH TESTING/REMOVAL & INSTALLATION table for figure reference.

STEERING COLUMN SWITCH TESTING/REMOVAL & INSTALLATION

Model	See Fig.
Colt, Mirage & Summit	1
Colt Vista, Expo & Summit Wagon	2
Diamante	3
Eclipse	4
Galant	5
Montero	6
Pickup	7
Stealth & 3000GT	8

REMOVAL & INSTALLATION

WARNING: Wait at least 60 seconds after disconnecting negative battery cable before servicing air bag system. System voltage is maintained for about 60 seconds after battery is disconnected. Failure to wait 60 seconds before servicing system may cause accidental air bag deployment and possible personal injury.

NOTE: For service procedures relating to air bag module removal and installation, and disabling and activation of air bag system, see AIR BAG RESTRAINT SYSTEM article.

IGNITION SWITCH

Removal & Installation (Colt, Mirage & Summit) – Remove knee protector. Remove steering column cover. See Fig. 1. Remove clip and cover. On A/T models, remove key interlock cable, spring and slide lever. On all models, remove ignition switch. To install, reverse removal procedure.

Removal & Installation (Colt Vista, Expo & Summit Wagon) – 1) Remove hood lock release handle. Remove instrument panel undercover. Remove lower steering column cover. Remove instrument cluster hood.
2) Remove upper steering column cover. See Fig. 2. Remove steering lock cylinder. Remove key reminder switch. Remove ignition switch. To install, reverse removal procedure.

Removal & Installation (Diamante) – Remove knee protector. Remove upper and lower steering column covers. See Fig. 3. Remove ignition switch. To install, reverse removal procedure.

Removal & Installation (Eclipse) – **1)** Remove knee protector mount screw plugs. Remove knee protector. Remove hood lock release handle. Remove upper and lower steering column covers. See Fig. 4. Remove ignition key illumination light.
2) Remove steering lock cylinder. Remove lap cooler and shower ducts. On A/T models, remove key interlock cable and slide lever. On all models, remove ignition switch. To install, reverse removal procedure.

Removal & Installation (Galant) – Remove knee protector. Remove upper and lower column covers. See Fig. 5. Remove ignition switch. To install, reverse removal procedure.

Removal & Installation (Montero) – Remove instrument panel undercover. Remove upper and lower column covers. See Fig. 6. Remove ignition switch. To install, reverse removal procedure.

Removal & Installation (Pickup) – Remove steering column cover. See Fig. 7. Remove ignition switch. To install, reverse removal procedure.

Removal & Installation (Stealth & 3000GT) – Remove knee protector. Remove upper and lower steering column covers. Remove lap cooler duct and foot shower duct. Remove key reminder switch. See Fig. 8. Remove ignition switch. To install, reverse removal procedure.

STEERING COLUMN SWITCH

WARNING: DO NOT hammer on steering wheel. Collapsible steering column mechanism may be damaged.

Removal & Installation (Colt, Mirage & Summit) – Remove knee protector and lower panel. Remove column covers. Remove horn pad and steering wheel. See Fig. 1. Remove clip and column switch. To install, reverse removal procedure.

Removal & Installation (Colt Vista, Expo & Summit Wagon) – Remove hood lock release handle. Remove instrument panel undercover. Remove steering wheel. Remove lower steering column cover. Remove instrument cluster hood. Remove upper steering column cover. See Fig. 2. Remove column switch. To install, reverse removal procedure.

Removal & Installation (Diamante) – Remove air bag module. See AIR BAG RESTRAINT SYSTEM article. Remove steering wheel. Remove knee protector. Remove upper and lower steering column covers. See Fig. 3. Remove left or right column switch. To install, reverse removal procedure.

Removal & Installation (Eclipse) – Remove horn pad and steering wheel. Remove hood lock release handle. Remove knee protector and upper and lower column covers. Remove lap cooler duct and foot shower duct. See Fig. 4. Remove column switch. To install, reverse removal procedure.

Removal & Installation (Galant) – Remove horn pad. Remove steering wheel. Remove knee protector. Remove upper and lower steering column covers. See Fig. 5. Remove column switch. To install, reverse removal procedure.

Removal & Installation (Montero) – Remove instrument panel under cover. Remove horn pad. Remove steering wheel. Remove upper and lower steering column covers. See Fig. 6. Remove column switch. To install, reverse removal procedure.

Removal & Installation (Pickup) – Remove horn pad. Remove steering wheel. Remove upper and lower steering column covers. See Fig. 7. Remove column switch. To install, reverse removal procedure.

Removal & Installation (Stealth & 3000GT) – **1)** Remove air bag module. See AIR BAG RESTRAINT SYSTEM article. Remove steering wheel. Remove knee protector.
2) Remove upper and lower steering column covers. See Fig. 8. Remove lap cooler duct and foot shower duct. Remove left or right column switch. To install, reverse removal procedure.

WIRING DIAGRAMS

See ACCESSORIES & EQUIPMENT, Volume 5.

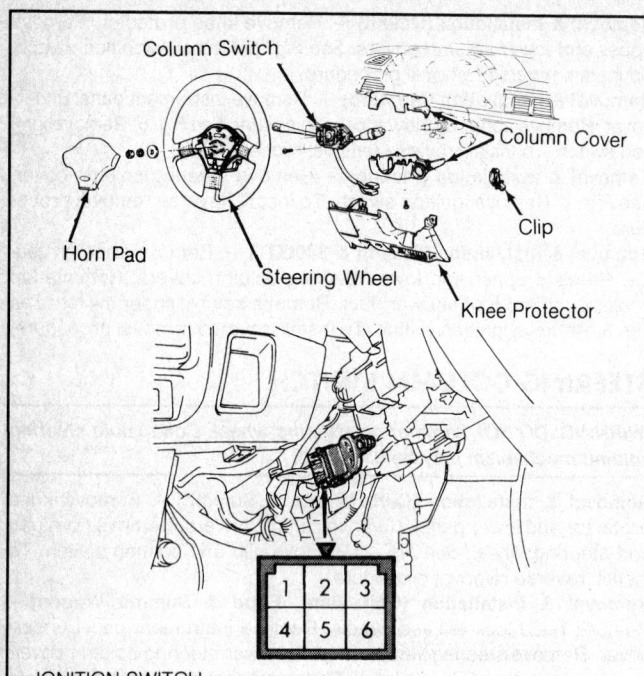

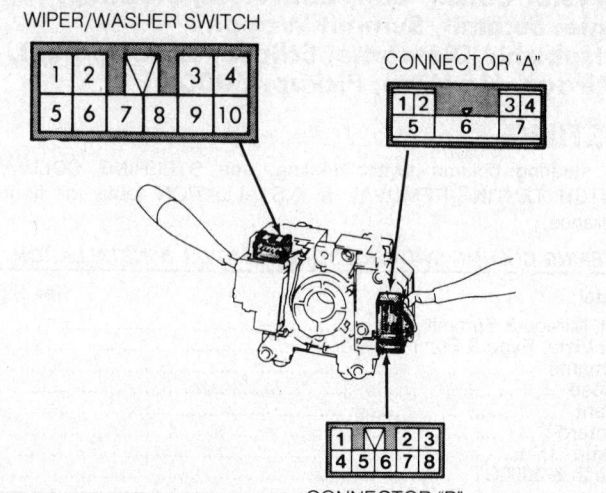

IGNITION SWITCH

Ignition key position	Terminal	1	2	3	4	5	6
LOCK							
ACC			○			○	
ON		○	○	○	○		
START			○	○	○		○

NOTE
○—○ indicates that there is continuity between the terminals.

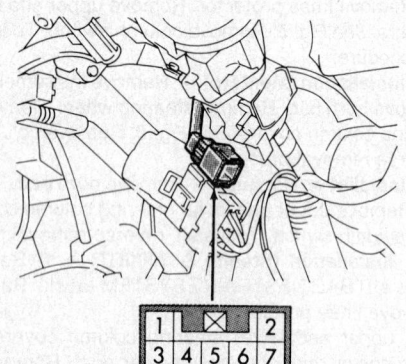

KEY REMINDER SWITCH

Ignition key position	Terminal	1	2	3	4	5	6	7
Pull out				○			○	
Insert <Vehicles with automatic seat belts>				○				○

LIGHTING, DIMMER/PASSING & TURN SIGNAL SWITCHES

Switch position		Connector A							Connector B		
Terminal No.		1	2	3	4	5	6	7	5	7	8
LIGHTING	OFF										
	TAIL		○	○							
	HEAD		○	○	○						
DIMMER/ PASSING	LOWER						○	○			
	UPPER					○	○				
	PASSING	○	○				○				
TURN SIGNAL	RH								○	○	
	OFF										
	LH									○	○

NOTE
○—○ indicates that there is continuity between the terminals.

WASHER/WIPER SWITCH

Switch position		Terminal	5	6	7	8	9
Wiper switch	OFF			○	○		
	1 (LO)				○		○
	2 (HI)					○	○
Washer switch	ON		○				○

93A82438

Courtesy of Mitsubishi Motor Sales of America.

Fig. 1: Testing, Removing & Installing Steering Column Switches (Colt, Mirage & Summit)

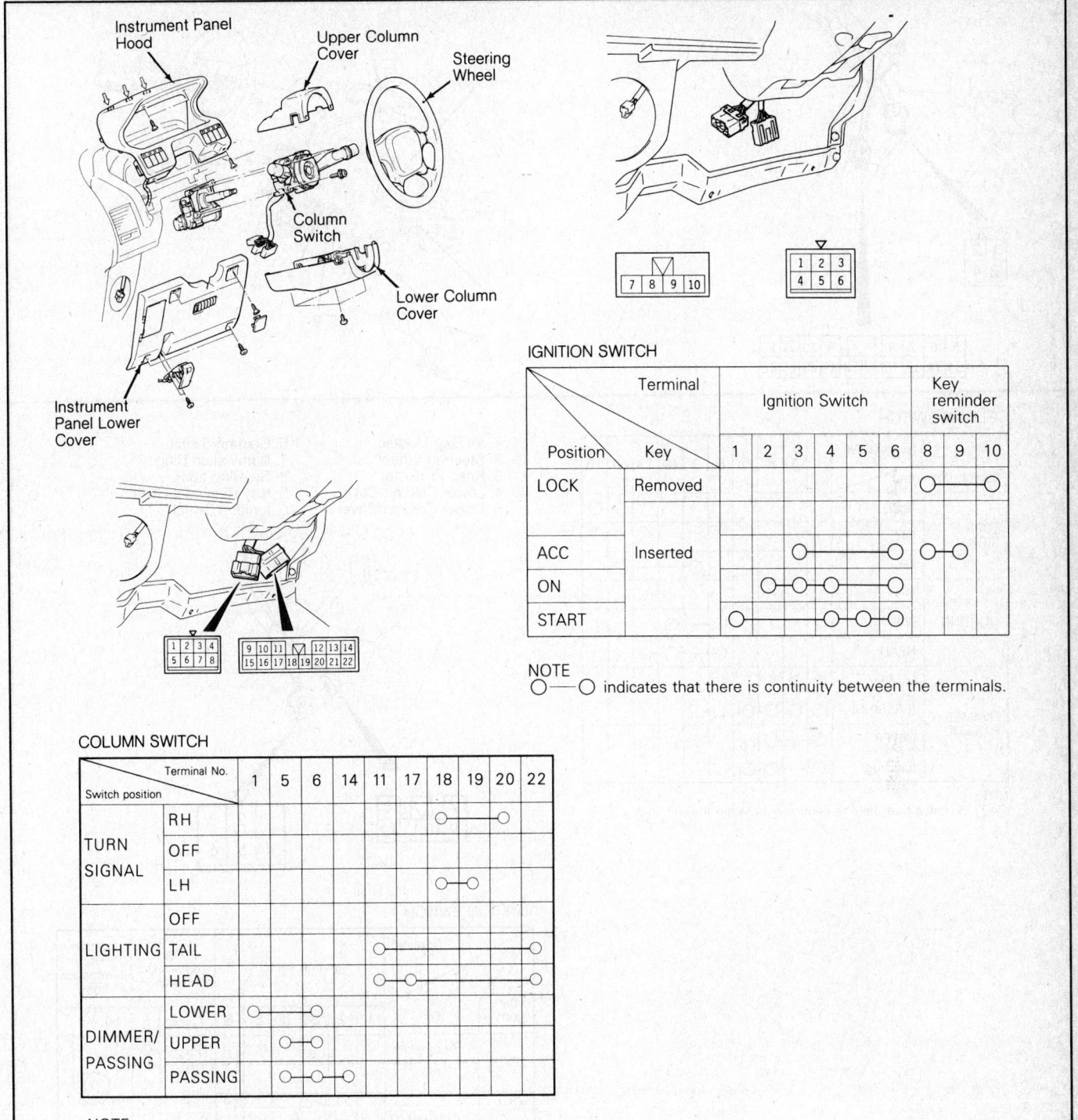

IGNITION SWITCH

Position	Terminal / Key	Ignition Switch						Key reminder switch		
		1	2	3	4	5	6	8	9	10
LOCK	Removed							O—	—	—O
ACC	Inserted			O—	—	—O		O—	—O	
ON			O—	—O			O			
START		O			O—|—O—|—O				

NOTE
O——O indicates that there is continuity between the terminals.

COLUMN SWITCH

Switch position	Terminal No.	1	5	6	14	11	17	18	19	20	22
TURN SIGNAL	RH							O—	—O		
	OFF										
	LH							O—O			
LIGHTING	OFF										
	TAIL					O—|—|—|—O				
	HEAD					O—O—|—|—O				
DIMMER/ PASSING	LOWER	O—	—O								
	UPPER		O—O								
	PASSING		O—O—O							

NOTE
O—O indicates that there is continuity between the terminals.

93H01102

Courtesy of Mitsubishi Motor Sales of America.

Fig. 2: Testing, Removing & Installing Steering Column Switches (Colt Vista, Expo & Summit Wagon)

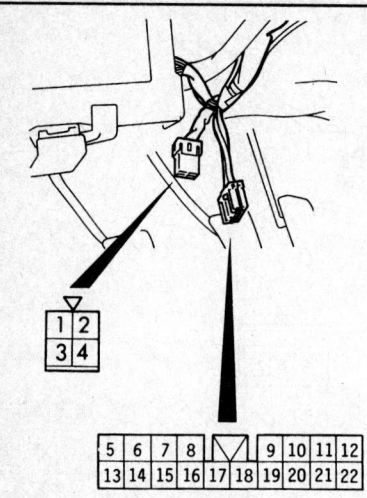

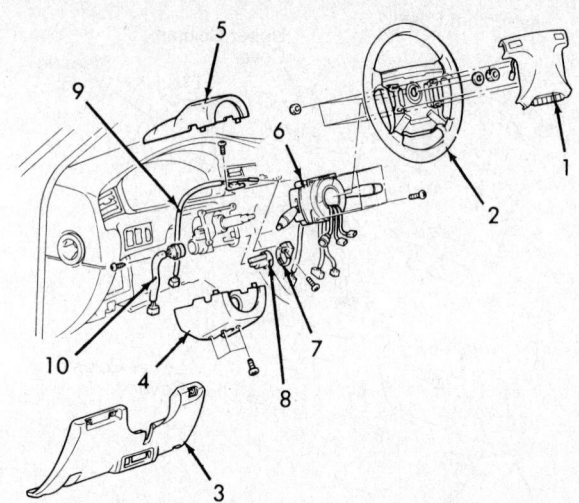

1. Air Bag Module
2. Steering Wheel
3. Knee Protector
4. Lower Column Cover
5. Upper Column Cover
6. Column Switch
7. Illumination Ring
8. Steering Lock
9. Key Reminder Switch
10. Ignition Switch

COLUMN SWITCH

Switch position		Terminal No. 1	3	4	5	8	9	10	17	18	19
TURN SIGNAL	RH									O—O	
	OFF										
	LH						O—		—O		
LIGHTING	OFF										
	TAIL					O—	—O				
	HEAD					O—	—O—	—O			
DIMMER/ PASSING	LOWER	O—O									
	(PASSING)	(O—	—O—	—O—	—O)						
	UPPER	O—	—O—	—O							
	(passing)	(O—	—O—	—O)							

NOTE
O—O indicates that there is continuity between the terminals.

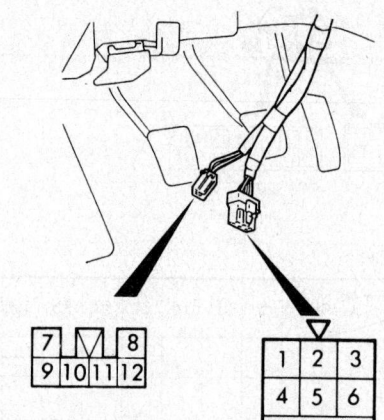

IGNITION SWITCH

Position	Terminal Key	Ignition switch						Key reminder switch			Ignition key illumination light	
		1	2	3	4	5	6	7	8	9	10	11
LOCK	Removed							O—		—O		
ACC	Inserted			O—		—O—	—O					
ON			O—	—O—	—O—	—O—	—O	O—	—O			
START		O—			—O—	—O—	—O					

NOTE
O—O indicates that there is continuity between the terminals.

93F01101

Fig. 3: Testing, Removing & Installing Steering Column Switches (Diamante)

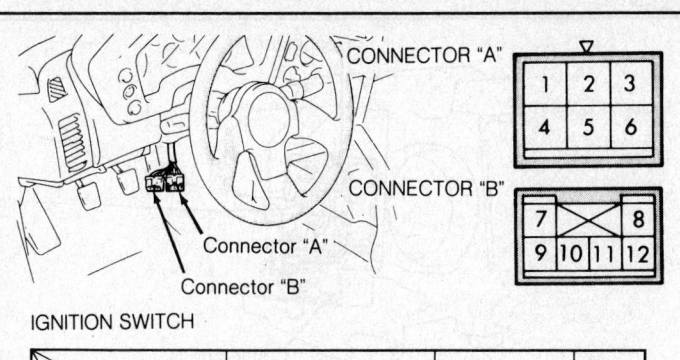

CONNECTOR "A"

1	2	3
4	5	6

CONNECTOR "B"

7		8
9	10	11	12

Connector "A"

Connector "B"

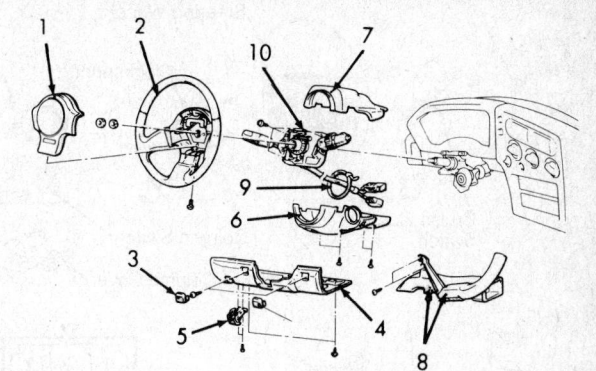

1. Horn Pad
2. Steering Wheel
3. Plug
4. Knee Protector
5. Hood Lock Release Handle
6. Lower Column Cover
7. Upper Column Cover
8. Lap Cooler Duct
9. Cable Band
10. Column Switch

IGNITION SWITCH

Position	Key	Ignition switch						Key reminder switch				Ignition key illumination light	
Terminal		6	3	4	2	5	1	7	8	9	12	10	11
LOCK	Removed									O—O		O—O	
ACC	Inserted	O—O						O—O					
ON		O—O—O—O						O—O					
START		O—O			O—O—O								

NOTE
O—O indicates that there is continuity between the terminals.

TURN SIGNAL SWITCH

Switch position	Terminal 15	16	17
Left	O—O		
Neutral			
Right		O——O	

CONNECTOR "A"

1	2	3	4	5		6	7	8	9
10	11	12	13	14	15	16	17	18	19	20

Connector "A"

Connector "B"

CONNECTOR "B"

21	22	23	24
25	26	27	28

DIMMER/PASSING SWITCH

Switch position		Terminal 11	21	22	25	26
Dimmer switch	Low		O—O			
	High			O—O		
Passing switch	P1	O——O			O——O	
	P2	O——O			O—O——O	

NOTE
(1) O—O indicates that there is continuity between the terminals.
(2) P1 represents the passing operation when the dimmer switch is in the "Low" position, and P2 represents the operation when it is in the "High" position.

LIGHTING SWITCH

Switch position	Terminal 3	4	12	5	6	14
OFF				O—O		
≡O O≡	O——O			O—O		
≡O	O—O——O			O——O		

NOTE
O—O indicates that there is continuity between the terminals.

91J02937

Fig. 4: Testing, Removing & Installing Steering Column Switches (Eclipse)

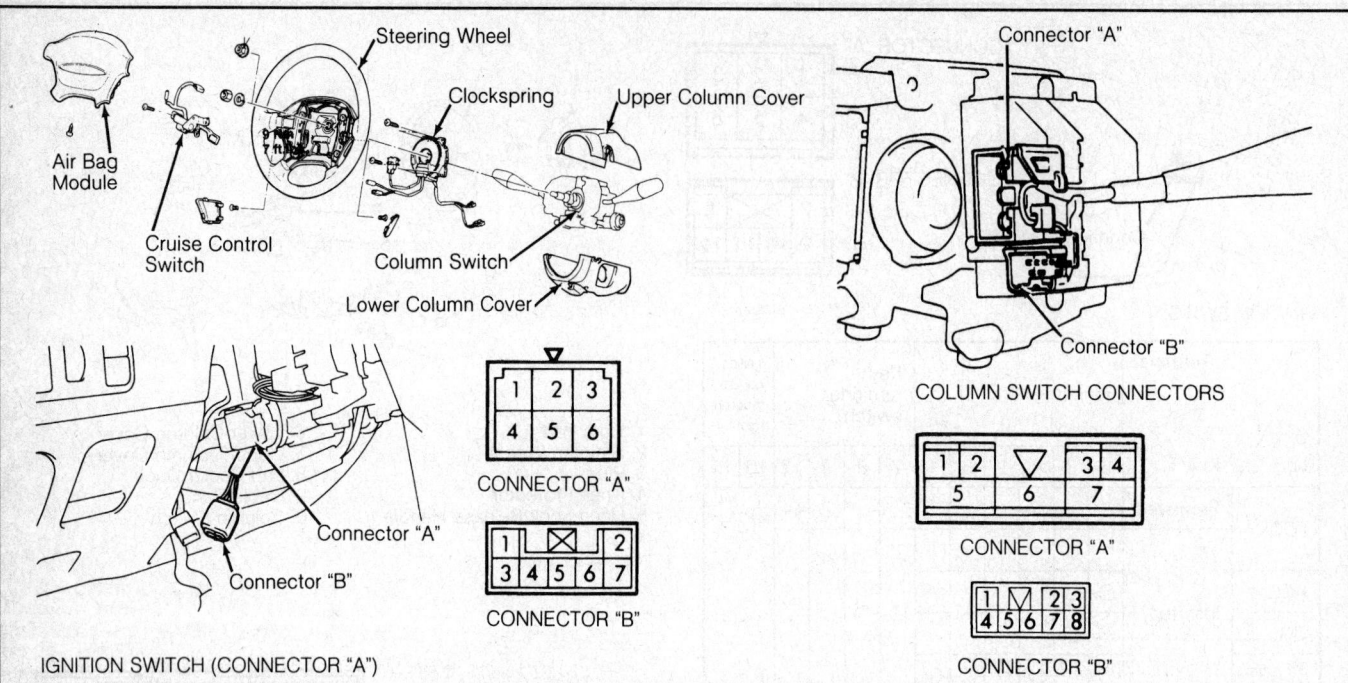

COLUMN SWITCH CONNECTORS

CONNECTOR "A"

CONNECTOR "B"

IGNITION SWITCH (CONNECTOR "A")

Ignition key position	Terminal No. 1	2	3	4	5	6
LOCK						
ACC	O					O
ON	O	O		O		O
START	O	O	O		O	

NOTE
O——O indicates that there is continuity between the terminals.

KEY REMINDER SWITCH (CONNECTOR "B")

Ignition key	Terminal No. Key reminder switch 4	6	Key hole illumination light 1	2
Removed	O	O		
Inserted			O——O	

NOTE
O——O indicates that there is continuity between the terminals.

LIGHTING & DIMMER/PASSING SWITCH (CONNECTOR "A")

Switch position		Terminal No. 1	2	3	4	5	6	7
LIGHTING SWITCH	OFF							
	TAIL		O		O			
	HEAD		O	O	O			
DIMMER/ PASSING SWITCH	Low-beam						O	O
	High-beam							
	PASSING	O	O			O	O	*1
						O	O	*2

NOTE
1. O——O indicates that there is low-beam continuity between the terminals.
2. *1 indicates that the dimmer switch has continuity at the low-beam position.
3. *2 indicates that the dimmer switch has continuity at the high-beam position.

TURN SIGNAL SWITCH (CONNECTOR "B")

Switch position		Terminal No. 5	7	8
TURN-SIGNAL LIGHT SWITCH	RH	O		O
	OFF			
	LH		O	O

NOTE
O——O indicates that there is continuity between the terminals.

94G47080

Courtesy of Mitsubishi Motor Sales of America.

Fig. 5: *Testing, Removing & Installing Steering Column Switches (Galant)*

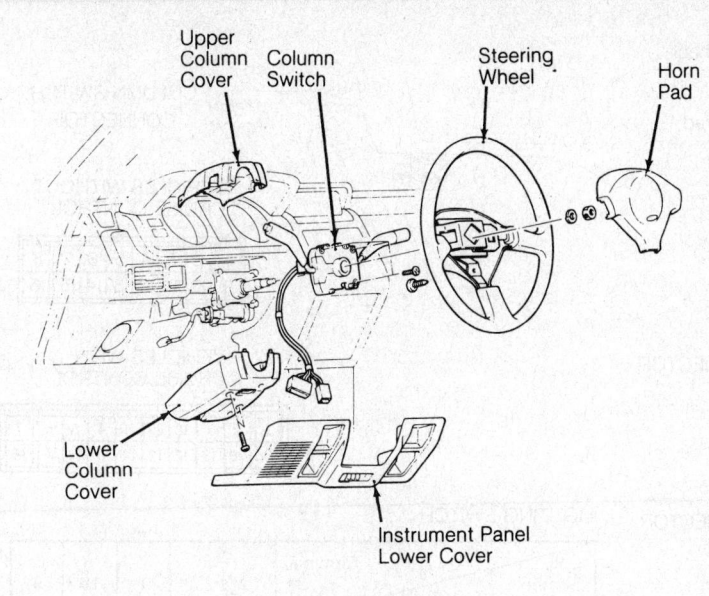

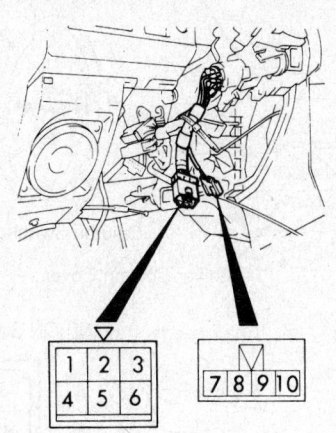

1	2	3
4	5	6

7	8	9	10

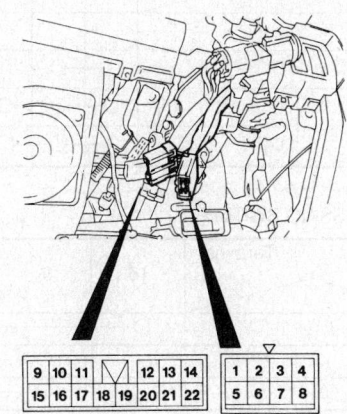

9	10	11		12	13	14
15	16	17	18	19	20	21	22

1	2	3	4
5	6	7	8

IGNITION SWITCH

	Terminal	Ignition switch						Key reminder switch	
Position	Key	1	2	3	4	5	6	7	10
LOCK	Removed								
ACC	Inserted			O	O		O	O	O
ON			O	O	O		O		
START		O		O	O	O	O		

NOTE
O—O indicates that there is continuity between the terminals.

COLUMN SWITCH

	Terminal	1	5	6	11	14	17	18	19	20	22
Switch position											
Lighting switch	OFF										
	TAIL				O						O
	HEAD				O		O				O
Dimmer switch	LOW BEAM	O		O							
	HIGH BEAM		O	O							
Passing switch	P₁	O	O	O	O		O				
	P₂		O	O			O				
Turn-signal switch	RH							O		O	
	OFF										
	LH							O	O		

NOTE
(1) O—O indicates that there is continuity between the terminals.

93J01103

Courtesy of Mitsubishi Motor Sales of America.

Fig. 6: Testing, Removing & Installing Steering Column Switches (Montero)

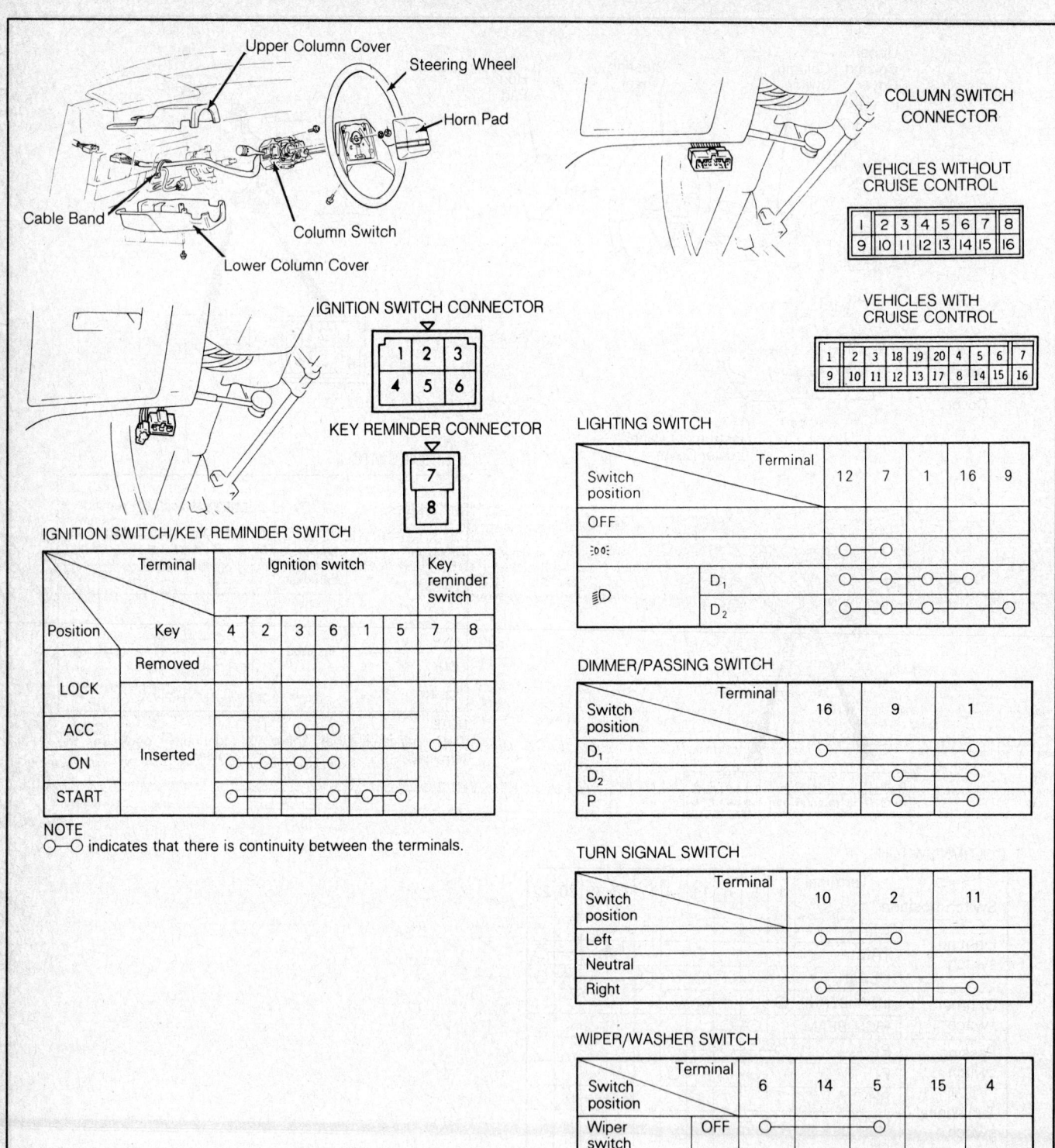

93B82439

Fig. 7: Testing, Removing & Installing Steering Column Switches (Pickup)

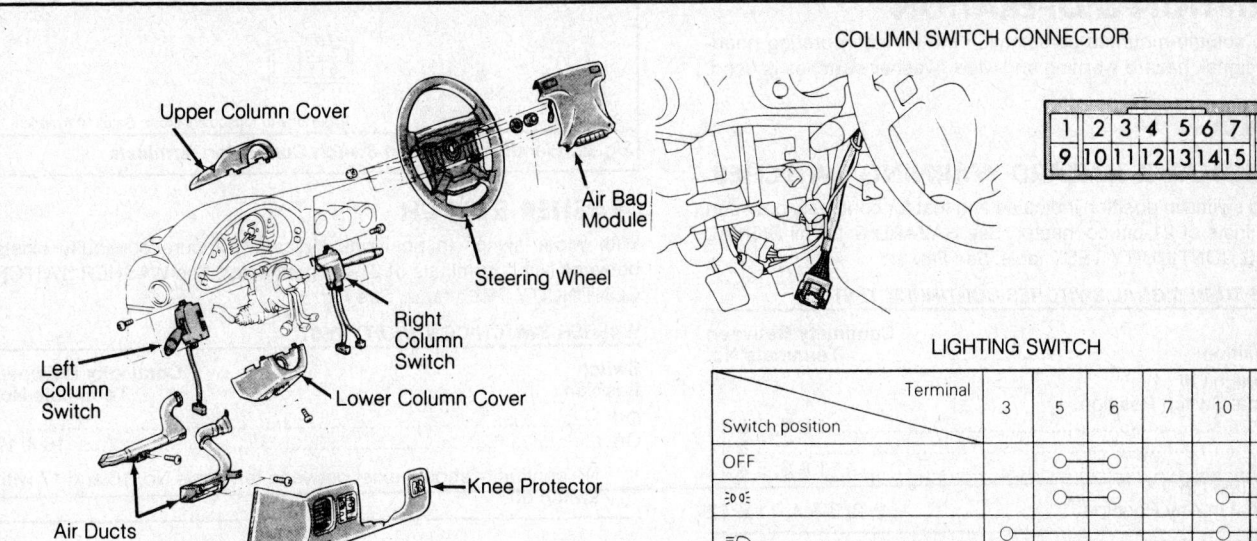

COLUMN SWITCH CONNECTOR

| 1 | 2 | 3 | 4 | 5 | 6 | 7 | 8 |
| 9 | 10 | 11 | 12 | 13 | 14 | 15 | 16 |

LIGHTING SWITCH

Switch position \ Terminal	3	5	6	7	10	14
OFF		O—	—O			
⊃O⊂		O—	—O		O—	—O
⊒D	O—	—O			O—	—O

TURN SIGNAL SWITCH

Switch position \ Terminal	1	12	13
Left	O—	—O	
Neutral			
Right	O—	—O

DIMMER/PASSING SWITCH

Switch position \ Terminal		2	8	9	16
Dimmer switch	LOW			O—	—O
	HIGH		O—	—O	
Passing switch		O—	—O—	—O	

WIPER/WASHER SWITCH

Switch position \ Terminal No.		3	4	5	6	7	8	9	10
Wiper switch	OFF				O—|—O				O
	INT	O			O—|—O			O	
	LO		O—	—O					
	HI		O—	—O	O			
Variable intermittent wiper control switch		O					O	
Washer switch			O—	—O			O	

NOTE
O—O denotes that there is continuity between the terminals.

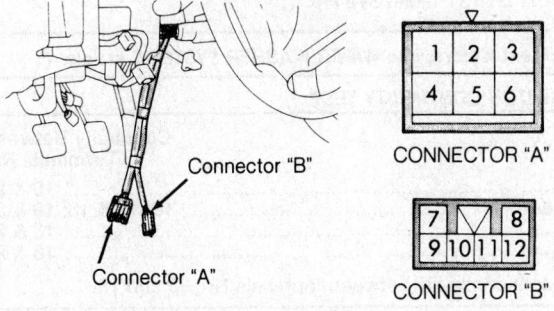

IGNITION SWITCH/KEY REMINDER
SWITCH CONNECTORS

| 1 | 2 | 3 |
| 4 | 5 | 6 |

CONNECTOR "A"

| 7 | | 8 |
| 9 | 10 | 11 | 12 |

CONNECTOR "B"

IGNITION SWITCH/KEY REMINDER SWITCH

Position \ Terminal	Key	Ignition switch						Key reminder switch			Ignition key illumination light	
		1	2	3	4	5	6	7	8	9	12	10	11
LOCK	Removed								O—	—O		⦵
ACC	Inserted		O—	—O—	—O		O		
ON		O—	—O—	—O—	—O		O—	—O		
START		O—	—O—	—O—	—O				

NOTE
O—O indicates that there is continuity between the terminals.

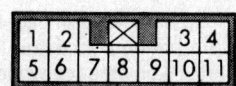

| 1 | 2 | ✕ | | 3 | 4 |
| 5 | 6 | 7 | 8 | 9 | 10 | 11 |

WIPER/WASHER SWITCH CONNECTOR

93B01104

Fig. 8: Testing, Removing & Installing Steering Column Switches (Stealth & 3000GT)

DESCRIPTION & OPERATION

A steering column-mounted combination switch incorporating headlight, turn signal, hazard warning and wiper/washer switches is used.

TESTING

TURN SIGNAL & HAZARD WARNING SWITCHES

Set hazard switch in position indicated and test for continuity between listed terminals of 21-pin connector. See HAZARD & TURN SIGNAL SWITCHES CONTINUITY TEST table. *See Fig. 1.*

HAZARD & TURN SIGNAL SWITCHES CONTINUITY TEST

Switch Position	Continuity Between Terminals No.
Hazard Switch Off	
Turn Signal Switch Position	
Left	1 & 2; 5 & 11
Neutral	5 & 11
Right	1 & 3; 5 & 11
Hazard Switch On	
Turn Signal In Any Position	1, 2, 3 & 4; 11 & 12

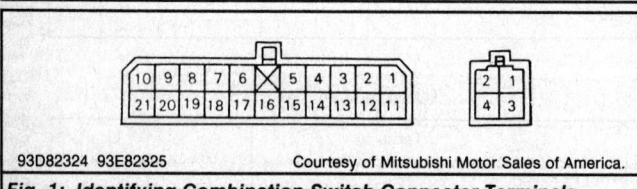

93D82324 93E82325   Courtesy of Mitsubishi Motor Sales of America.

Fig. 1: Identifying Combination Switch Connector Terminals

HEADLIGHT SWITCH

With headlight switch in positions indicated, ensure continuity exists between listed terminals of 21-pin connector. See LIGHTING SWITCH CONTINUITY TEST table. *See Fig. 1.*

LIGHTING SWITCH CONTINUITY TEST

Switch Position	Continuity Between Terminals No.
Off	[1]
I	8 & 10
II	8, 9 & 10

[1] – No continuity should exist between terminals No. 8, 9 and 10 with switch off.

DIMMER/PASSING SWITCH

With dimmer/passing switch in positions indicated, ensure continuity exists between listed terminals of 4-pin connector. See DIMMER/PASSING SWITCH CONTINUITY TEST table. *See Fig. 1.*

DIMMER/PASSING SWITCH CONTINUITY TEST

Switch Position	Continuity Between Terminals No.
High Beam	2 & 3
Low Beam	1 & 2
Passing	2, 3 & 4

IGNITION SWITCH

With ignition switch in positions indicated, ensure continuity exists between terminals listed. See IGNITION SWITCH CONTINUITY TEST table. *See Fig. 2.*

IGNITION SWITCH CONTINUITY TEST

Switch Position	Continuity Between Terminals No.
Lock	[1]
Accessory	1 & 4
On	1, 2, 4 & 6
Start	4, 5 & 6

[1] – No continuity should exist between terminals No. 1, 2, 3, 4, 5 or 6 with switch in lock position.

91J02089   Courtesy of Mitsubishi Motor Sales of America.

Fig. 2: Identifying Ignition Switch Connector Terminals

WASHER SWITCH

With wiper switch in positions indicated, ensure continuity exists between listed terminals of 21-pin connector. See WASHER SWITCH CONTINUITY TEST table. *See Fig. 1.*

WASHER SWITCH CONTINUITY TEST

Switch Position	Continuity Between Terminals No.
Off	[1]
On	16 & 17

[1] – No continuity should exist between terminals No. 16 and 17 with switch off.

WIPER SWITCH

With wiper switch in positions indicated, ensure continuity exists between listed terminals of 21-pin connector. See WIPER SWITCH CONTINUITY TEST table. *See Fig. 1.*

NOTE: To test wipers, see WIPER/WASHER SYSTEMS article.

WIPER SWITCH CONTINUITY TEST

Switch Position	Continuity Between Terminals No.
Off	19 & 21
Intermittent	[1] 13, 16 & 18; 19 & 21
Low	16 & 21
High	18 & 20

[1] – Variable continuity between terminals No. 13 and 16.

REAR WIPER SWITCH

For testing information, see WIPER/WASHER SYSTEMS article.

REMOVAL & INSTALLATION

WARNING: Wait at least 60 seconds after disconnecting negative battery cable before servicing air bag system. System voltage is maintained for about 60 seconds after battery is disconnected. Failure to wait 60 seconds before servicing system may cause accidental air bag deployment and possible personal injury.

NOTE: For service procedures relating to air bag module removal and installation, and disabling and activation of air bag system, see AIR BAG RESTRAINT SYSTEM article.

STEERING WHEEL & HORN PAD

Removal – Remove air bag module/horn pad. Remove horn contact plates and disconnect horn button connector. Remove lock nut and washer. Make alignment mark on steering wheel and shaft for installation reference. Install steering wheel puller, and pull steering wheel from shaft.

Installation – To install, align reference mark on steering shaft and steering wheel. To complete installation, reverse removal procedure.

COMBINATION SWITCH

Removal & Installation – Disconnect negative battery cable. Remove steering wheel. Remove steering column cover. Disconnect combination switch and rheostat connectors. Remove combination switch from steering shaft. To install, reverse removal procedure.

IGNITION SWITCH & LOCK CYLINDER

Removal – 1) Remove steering wheel, upper and lower steering column covers, and combination switch (if necessary). Disconnect ignition switch harness connectors.

2) If shear bolt studs are accessible, use a hacksaw to cut a slot into exposed studs. Using a screwdriver, remove studs.

3) If shear bolt studs are recessed or hard to reach with a hacksaw, center punch studs. Using a drill bit and a screw extractor, remove studs. Remove steering lock and ignition switch.

Installation – To install, reverse removal procedure. Install new shear bolts and tighten finger tight. Ensure proper operation of steering lock and ignition switch. Tighten shear bolts until heads break off. Install combination switch, steering column covers and steering wheel.

WIRING DIAGRAM

See ACCESSORIES & EQUIPMENT, Volume 5.

1994 ACCESSORIES & EQUIPMENT
Wiper/Washer Systems

Chrysler Corp.: Colt, Colt Vista, Stealth
Eagle: Summit, Summit Wagon
Mitsubishi: Diamante, Eclipse, Expo, Galant,
Mirage, Montero, Pickup, Precis, 3000GT

DESCRIPTION & OPERATION

All models are equipped with a 2-speed wiper motor with an optional intermittent wiper feature. Some models are equipped with a rear wiper/washer.

Galant is equipped with a wiper system that varies the intermittent setting speed with vehicle speed. The system uses the ignition switch, wiper switch, intermittent switch, washer switch, vehicle speed sensor, and the Electronic Time and Alarm Control System (ETACS) control unit. The ETACS control unit is located behind left side of dash.

ADJUSTMENTS

FRONT WIPER ARM ADJUSTMENT

Ensure wiper motor is in park position. Position wiper arm and blade assembly so tip of blade is specified distance above front window trim. See FRONT WIPER ADJUSTMENT SPECIFICATIONS table.

FRONT WIPER ADJUSTMENT SPECIFICATIONS

Model	Driver's Side In. (mm)	Passenger's Side In. (mm)
Colt, Mirage & Summit	.79-1.18 (20-30)	.59-.98 (15-25)
Colt Vista, Expo & Summit Wagon	.98-1.38 (25-35)	1.38-1.77 (35-45)
Diamante		
2-Speed	.79-1.18 (20-30)	.79-1.18 (20-30)
Intermittent	.91-1.30 (23-33)	.91-1.30 (23-33)
Eclipse	1.0 (25)	1.0 (25)
Galant	.39-.79 (10-20)	.39-.79 (10-20)
Montero	.98-1.38 (25-35)	1.38-1.77 (35-45)
Pickup	.56-.98 (14-25)	.56-.98 (14-25)
Precis	1.18 (30)	1.18 (30)
Stealth & 3000GT	.59-.79 (15-20)	.59-.79 (15-20)

REAR WIPER ARM ADJUSTMENT

NOTE: Colt, Diamante, Galant, Mirage, Pickup and Summit are not equipped with rear wipers.

Ensure wiper motor is in park position. Position wiper arm and blade assembly so tip of blade is specified distance from edge of window. See REAR WIPER ADJUSTMENT SPECIFICATIONS table.

REAR WIPER ADJUSTMENT SPECIFICATIONS

Model	In. (mm)
Colt Vista, Expo & Summit Wagon	.79-1.18 (20-30)
Eclipse	1.18 (30)
Montero	2.56-2.95 (65-75)
Precis	[1]
Stealth & 3000GT	[2]

[1] – Information is not available from manufacturer.
[2] – Position blade tip along ceramic edge of window.

TESTING

FRONT WIPER MOTOR TEST

Checking Wiper Motor Operation (Except Pickup & Precis) – Disconnect wiring connector from wiper motor. Connect battery voltage to wiper motor connector as shown, and ensure wiper motor operates at low and high speeds. See Fig. 1.

Checking Automatic Stop (Except Pickup & Precis) – 1) Operate wiper motor at low speed. See Fig. 1. Disconnect battery voltage during operation to stop motor.

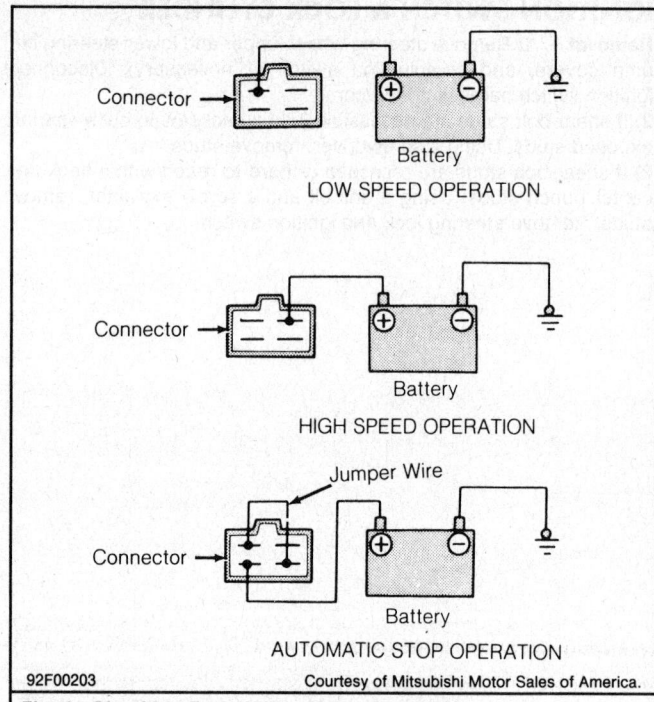

Fig. 1: Checking Front Wiper Motor Operation (Except Pickup & Precis)

2) Using a jumper wire, connect terminals as shown. See Fig. 1. Connect 12 volts to indicated terminal, and ground wiper motor bracket. Ensure wiper arm is correctly parked.

Checking Wiper Motor Operation (Pickup & Precis) – Disconnect wiring connector from wiper motor. Connect battery voltage to appropriate wiper motor terminal, and ground other terminal. See WIPER MOTOR OPERATION CHECK table. See Fig. 2. Ensure wiper motor operates in both low and high speeds.

WIPER MOTOR OPERATION CHECK

Model & Application	Ground Terminal No.	Apply Voltage To Terminal No.
Low Speed Operation		
Pickup	1	3
Precis	5	1
High Speed Operation		
Pickup	2	3
Precis	2	1

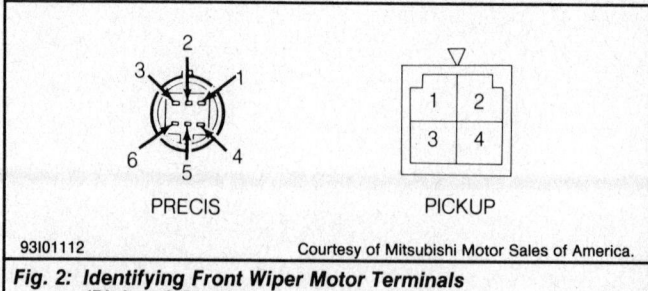

Fig. 2: Identifying Front Wiper Motor Terminals (Pickup & Precis)

Checking Automatic Stop (Pickup & Precis) – 1) Operate wiper motor at low speed. See CHECKING WIPER MOTOR OPERATION (PICKUP & PRECIS). Disconnect battery voltage to stop motor in any position except park.

2) Using a jumper wire, connect terminals indicated. See AUTOMATIC STOP CHECK table. See Fig. 2. Connect 12 volts to terminal indicated in table, and ground wiper motor bracket. Ensure motor parks wiper arm.

AUTOMATIC STOP CHECK

Model	Jumper Wire Terminals No.	Apply Voltage To Terminal No.
Pickup	1 & 4	3
Precis	5 & 6	[1] 1

[1] – Attach negative battery lead to terminal No. 3.

INTERMITTENT WIPER RELAY (FRONT) TEST

NOTE: *On Colt, Eclipse, Mirage, Montero and Summit, intermittent wiper relay is incorporated into wiper switch. Information on testing is not available from manufacturer. Information on Precis is not available from manufacturer.*

Voltage Check (Colt Vista, Expo & Summit Wagon) – Disconnect column switch connector. Place wiper switch in intermittent position. Turn ignition switch to accessory position. Ensure alternating voltage (0-12 volts) is present at terminal No. 3 of column switch connector. *See Fig. 3.*

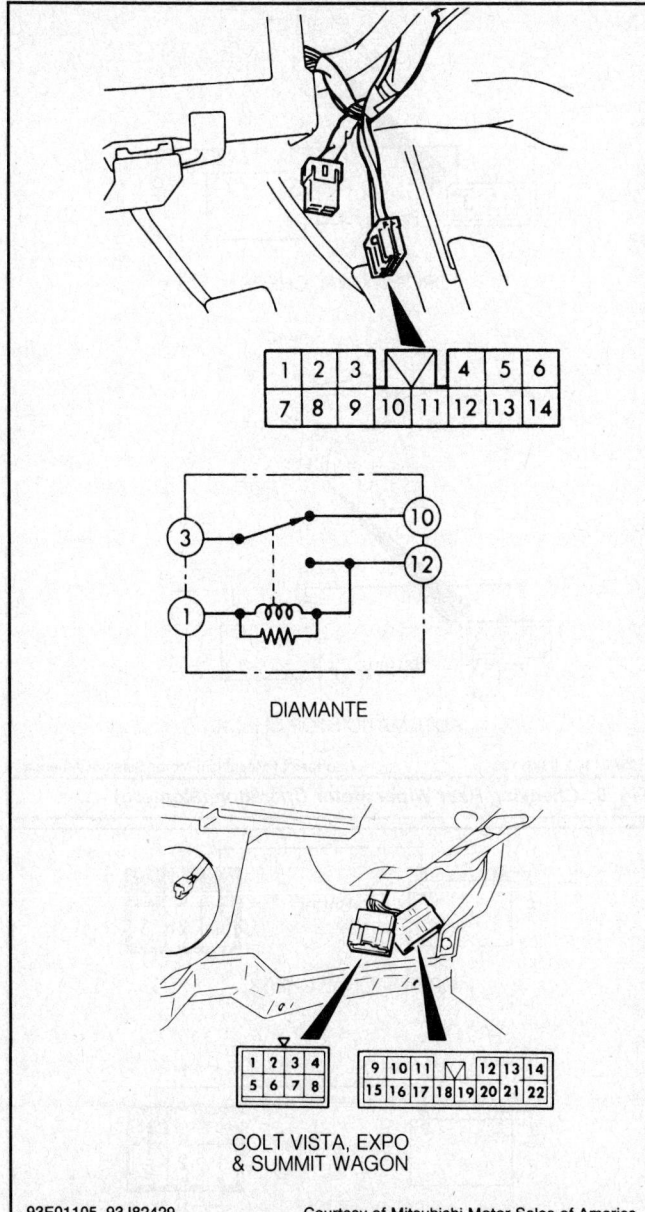

DIAMANTE

COLT VISTA, EXPO
& SUMMIT WAGON

93E01105 93J82429   Courtesy of Mitsubishi Motor Sales of America.

Fig. 3: Identifying Front Wiper Relay Terminals (Colt Vista, Diamante, Expo & Summit Wagon)

Continuity & Voltage Check (Diamante) – **1)** Disconnect column switch connector. Turn wiper switch to OFF or AUTO position. Ensure continuity is present between terminals No. 3 and 10, and 1 and 12. Ensure there is no continuity between terminals No. 3 and 12.
2) Connect battery voltage to relay terminal No. 12 and ground terminal No. 1. Battery voltage should be present on terminal No. 3. Replace relay if continuity and voltage are not present. *See Fig. 3.*

Continuity Check (Galant) – Relay is built into column switch assembly. *See Fig. 4.* With relay installed, check for continuity as specified in WIPER/WASHER CONTINUITY CHECK table. Replace column switch assembly if continuity is not as specified.

WIPER/WASHER CONTINUITY CHECK

Switch Position	[1] Check Continuity Between
Wiper Switch	
Off	Pins No. 6 & 7
1	Pins No. 7 & 9
2	Pins No. 8 & 9
Washer Switch	
On	Pins No. 5 & 9

[1] – *See Fig. 4.*

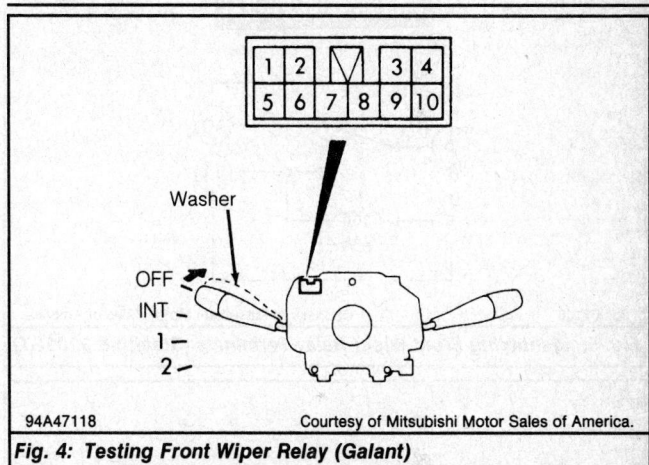

94A47118   Courtesy of Mitsubishi Motor Sales of America.

Fig. 4: Testing Front Wiper Relay (Galant)

Voltage Check (Pickup) – Intermittent relay is located next to wiper motor. With relay installed, place wiper switch in intermittent position. Turn ignition switch to accessory position. Ensure alternating voltage (0-12 volts) is present at Blue wire terminal of intermittent relay connector.

Continuity & Voltage Check (Stealth & 3000GT) – **1)** Disconnect column switch connector. Ensure continuity is present between terminals No. 5 and 11, and between terminals No. 6 and 10. Ensure there is no continuity between terminals No. 6 and 11.
2) Connect battery voltage to terminal No. 5 and ground terminal No. 11. Battery voltage should be present on terminal No. 6. Replace relay if continuity and voltage are not present. *See Fig. 5.*

FRONT WIPER SWITCH TEST

NOTE: *Front wiper switch is part of combination switch on steering column. See appropriate STEERING COLUMN SWITCHES article.*

REAR WIPER MOTOR TEST

NOTE: *Information on Precis not available from manufacturer.*

Operational Check (Except Diamante) – Disconnect wiring connector from wiper motor. Connect battery voltage to wiper motor connector as shown, and ensure motor housing is well grounded. Motor should run at low speed. *See Figs. 6-9.*

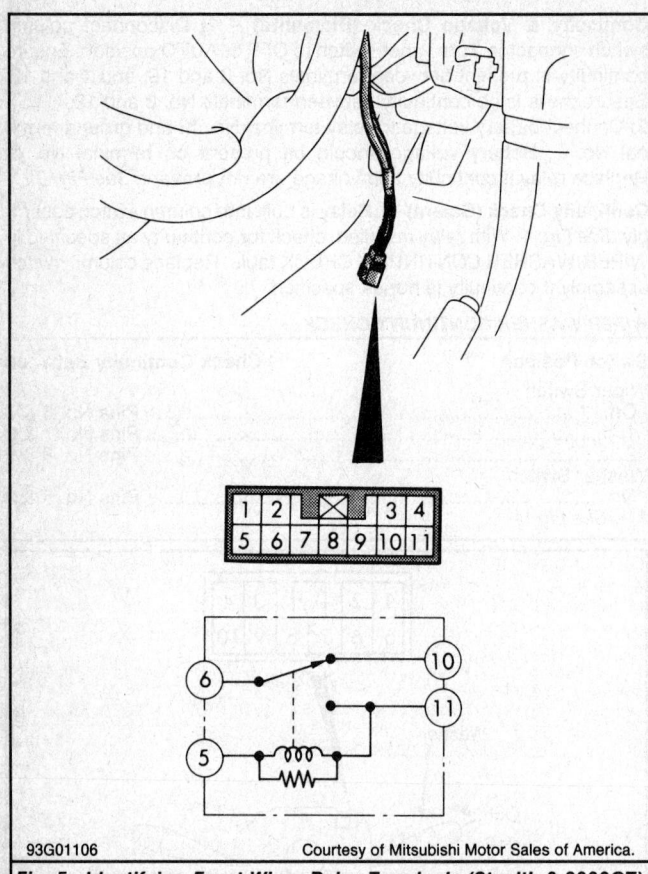

93G01106   Courtesy of Mitsubishi Motor Sales of America.

Fig. 5: Identifying Front Wiper Relay Terminals (Stealth & 3000GT)

93I01107 93G01125   Courtesy of Mitsubishi Motor Sales of America

Fig. 6: Checking Rear Wiper Motor Operation (Colt Vista, Expo & Summit Wagon)

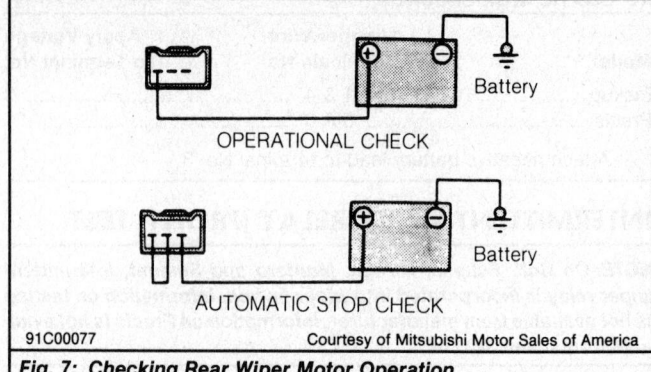

91C00077   Courtesy of Mitsubishi Motor Sales of America

Fig. 7: Checking Rear Wiper Motor Operation (Eclipse)

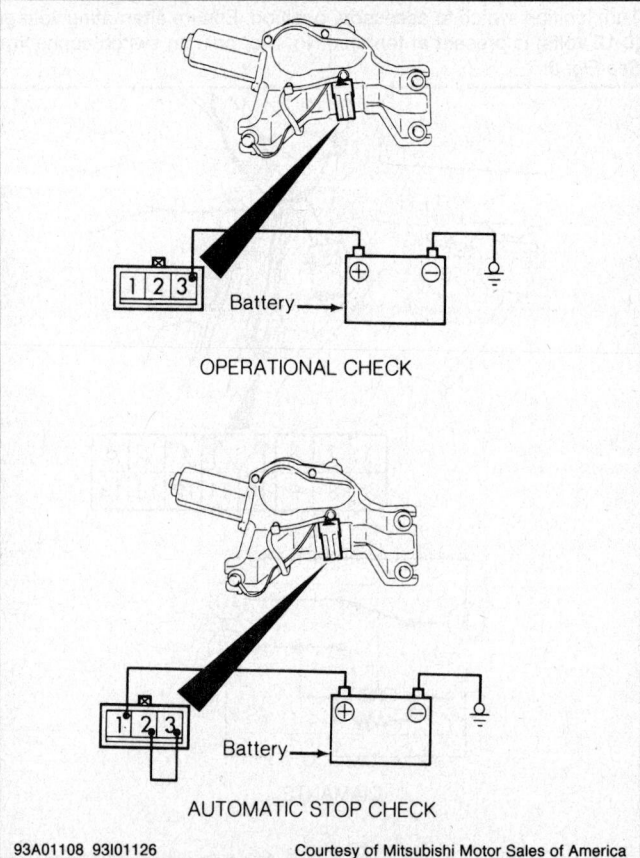

93A01108 93I01126   Courtesy of Mitsubishi Motor Sales of America

Fig. 8: Checking Rear Wiper Motor Operation (Montero)

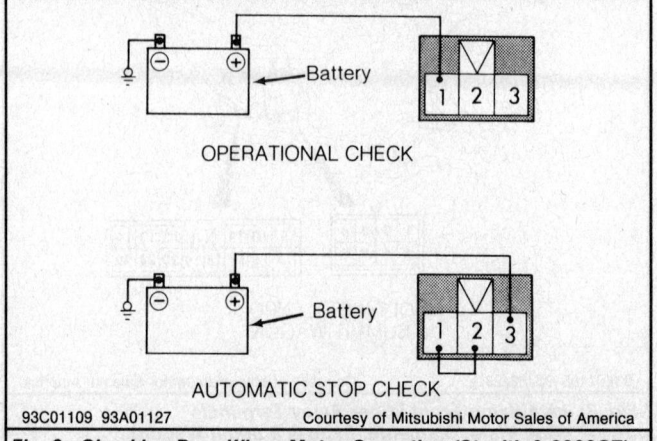

93C01109 93A01127   Courtesy of Mitsubishi Motor Sales of America

Fig. 9: Checking Rear Wiper Motor Operation (Stealth & 3000GT)

Automatic Stop Check (Except Diamante) – Operate wiper motor, and then disconnect wiring connector from wiper motor to stop motor operation at a point other than park position. Connect battery voltage and jumper wire to wiper motor connector as shown, and ensure motor housing is well grounded. *See Figs. 6-9.* Motor should return to park position.

REAR WIPER RELAY TEST

NOTE: Information on Precis not available from manufacturer.

Operational Check (Colt Vista, Expo & Summit Wagon) – **1)** Rear wiper relay is a part of wiper switch. With wiper switch connector installed on relay, turn ignition switch to accessory position. Turn wiper switch to intermittent position.

2) Check voltage between terminal No. 5 and ground. *See Fig. 10.* Voltage should alternate between zero and 5 volts. Replace wiper switch if voltage does not alternate.

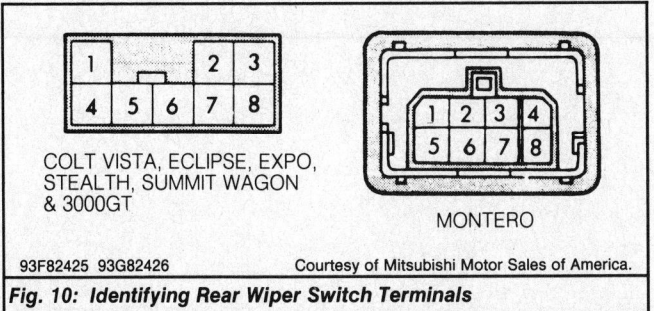

COLT VISTA, ECLIPSE, EXPO,
STEALTH, SUMMIT WAGON
& 3000GT

MONTERO

93F82425 93G82426   Courtesy of Mitsubishi Motor Sales of America.

Fig. 10: Identifying Rear Wiper Switch Terminals

Operational Check (Eclipse, Stealth & 3000GT) – Remove quarter trim. Leave intermittent relay connected to wiring harness. Operate rear wiper and check voltage at terminal No. 2. *See Fig. 11.* Zero volts should be present when rear wiper stops. There should be 12 volts when rear wiper operates.

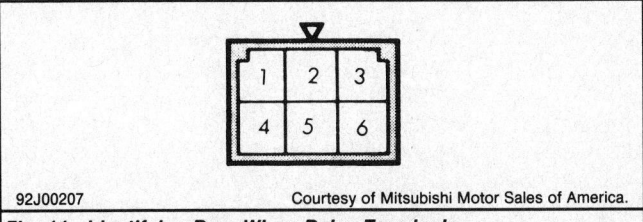

92J00207   Courtesy of Mitsubishi Motor Sales of America.

Fig. 11: Identifying Rear Wiper Relay Terminals

Operational Check (Montero) – **1)** Relay is on left side of steering column, behind dash. Disconnect relay from wiring harness. Connect positive voltmeter lead to terminal No. 2. Connect negative voltmeter lead to terminal No. 5. Connect battery voltage to terminal No. 4 and ground terminal No. 5. *See Fig. 12.*

2) Jumper terminals No. 1 and 4 for 2 seconds. Remove jumper. Jumper terminals No. 1 and 5 for about 8 seconds. Voltmeter should show zero volts. After terminals No. 1 and 5 have been connected for at least 8 seconds, battery voltage should be present on terminal No. 2. Replace relay if voltage is not as specified.

REAR WIPER SWITCH TEST

NOTE: Testing information for Precis rear wiper switch not available from manufacturer.

Colt Vista, Expo & Summit Wagon – **1)** Remove wiper switch from instrument panel and disconnect wiper switch. Place wiper switch in OFF position. Continuity should exist between terminals No. 4 and 5. *See Fig. 10.* Place wiper switch in ON position. Continuity should exist between terminals No. 5 and 8.

2) Place wiper switch in INT position. Continuity should exist between terminals No. 4 and 5, and between terminals No. 1 and 8. Depress washer switch. Continuity should exist between terminals No. 7 and 8.

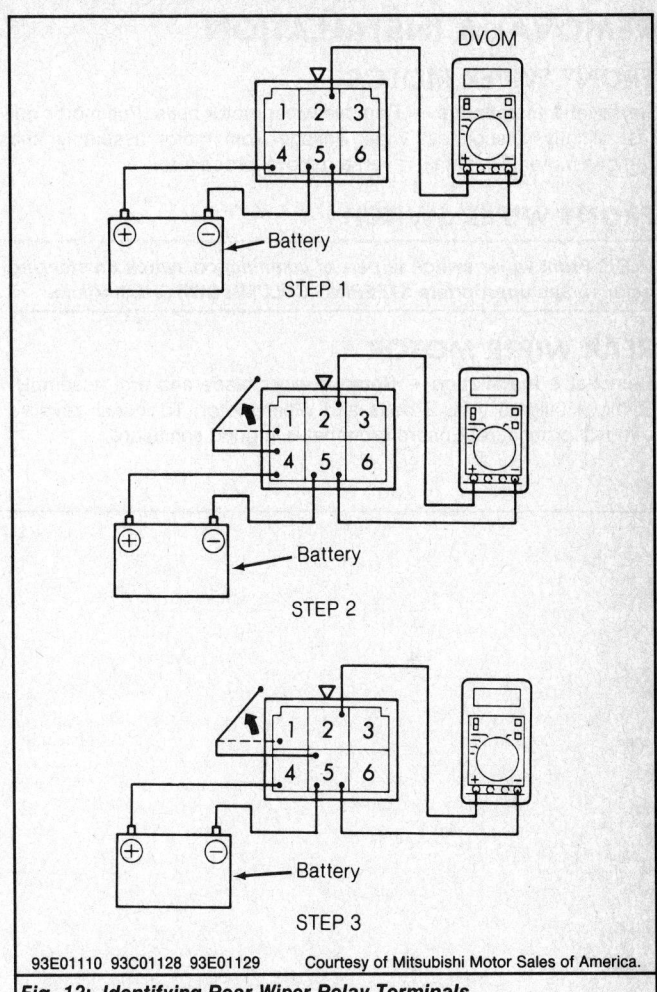

DVOM

STEP 1

Battery

STEP 2

Battery

STEP 3

Battery

93E01110 93C01128 93E01129   Courtesy of Mitsubishi Motor Sales of America.

Fig. 12: Identifying Rear Wiper Relay Terminals

Eclipse – **1)** Remove wiper switch from instrument panel and disconnect wiper switch. Place wiper switch in OFF position. Continuity should exist between terminals No. 4 and 5. *See Fig. 10.* Place wiper switch in ON position. Continuity should exist between terminals No. 5 and 6.

2) Place wiper switch in INT position. Continuity should exist between terminals No. 2 and 8, and between terminals No. 4 and 5. Depress washer switch. Continuity should exist between terminals No. 6 and 7. Continuity between terminals No. 1 and 3 should exist in all positions (light circuit).

Montero – Remove wiper switch from instrument panel and disconnect wiper switch. Place wiper switch in OFF position. Continuity should exist between terminals No. 4 and 7. *See Fig. 10.* Place wiper switch in ON position. Continuity should exist between terminals No. 2 and 7. Place wiper switch in INT position. Continuity should exist between terminals No. 4 and 7, and between terminals No. 1 and 6. Depress washer switch. Continuity should exist between terminals No. 2 and 3.

Stealth & 3000GT – **1)** Remove wiper switch from instrument panel and disconnect wiper switch. Place wiper switch in OFF position. Continuity should exist between terminals No. 4 and 5. *See Fig. 10.* Place wiper switch in ON position. Continuity should exist between terminals No. 5 and 6.

2) Place wiper switch in INT position. Continuity should exist between terminals No. 4 and 5, and between terminals No. 7 and 8. Depress washer switch. Continuity should exist between terminals No. 2 and 6. Continuity between terminals No. 1 and 3 should exist in all positions (light circuit).

REMOVAL & INSTALLATION

FRONT WIPER MOTOR

Removal & Installation – Remove wiper motor bolts. Pull motor out just slightly. Disconnect wiper linkage from motor assembly and remove motor. To install, reverse removal procedure.

FRONT WIPER SWITCH

NOTE: Front wiper switch is part of combination switch on steering column. See appropriate STEERING COLUMN SWITCHES article.

REAR WIPER MOTOR

Removal & Installation – Remove wiper blade and arm assembly. Remove tailgate trim, 2 bolts and wiper motor. To install, reverse removal procedure. Ensure grommet is in good condition.

REAR WIPER RELAY

Removal & Installation – On all models equipped with rear wiper relay except Montero, relay is located behind right rear quarter trim. On Montero, relay is located on left side of steering column, behind dash.

REAR WIPER SWITCH

Removal & Installation – Pry rear wiper switch from instrument panel and disconnect wiper switch. To install switch, reverse removal procedure.

WIRING DIAGRAMS

See ACCESSORIES & EQUIPMENT, Volume 5.

EXHAUST MANIFOLD

Removal – Disconnect exhaust pipe from manifold. Remove exhaust manifold outer heat shield, oxygen sensor, and engine hanger (if equipped) from manifold. Remove manifold bolts, manifold, gasket, and manifold inner heat shield.

Installation – To install, reverse removal procedure. Use new gaskets and exhaust manifold retaining nuts.

CYLINDER HEAD

NOTE: On all models except Precis, cylinder head can be removed with intake and exhaust manifolds installed.

Removal (1.5L – Except Precis) – 1) Release fuel pressure. See FUEL PRESSURE RELEASE under REMOVAL & INSTALLATION. Drain cooling system. Disconnect upper radiator hose, by-pass hose, and heater hoses. Remove spark plugs.

2) Disconnect air intake and breather hoses, accelerator cable, and throttle control cable (A/T models). Disconnect fuel and vacuum lines. Disconnect necessary electrical connections.

CAUTION: DO NOT rotate engine counterclockwise (as viewed from timing belt end of engine).

3) Remove rocker cover and upper timing belt cover. Rotate engine clockwise, as viewed from timing belt end of engine, to align timing marks. Secure timing belt to camshaft sprocket with wire. Remove camshaft sprocket with timing belt installed. Wire sprocket and belt aside, being careful to maintain sprocket and belt relationship.

CAUTION: Ensure timing belt does not come off of crankshaft sprocket. DO NOT rotate engine with timing belt disengaged from camshaft. See TIMING BELT.

4) Remove support brace (if equipped) from intake manifold. Disconnect exhaust pipe from exhaust manifold. Loosen cylinder head bolts in sequence, in 2 stages. *See Fig. 5.* Remove cylinder head and gasket.

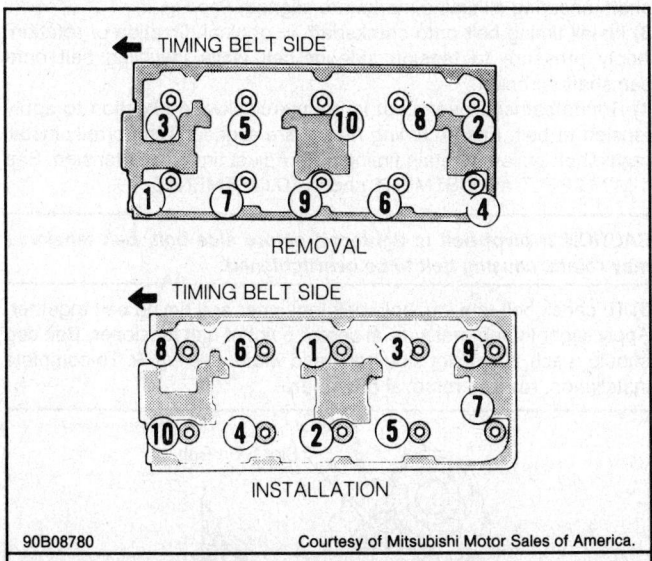

Fig. 5: Cylinder Head Bolt Removal & Installation Sequence (1.5L)

Inspection – Inspect cylinder head for warpage. Resurface cylinder head if warpage exceeds specification. See CYLINDER HEAD table under ENGINE SPECIFICATIONS.

Installation – 1) Install cylinder head gasket with identification mark toward timing belt, facing up. *See Fig. 6.* Install cylinder head. DO NOT apply sealant to head gasket. Tighten bolts to specification in sequence, in 2 stages. *See Fig. 5.* See TORQUE SPECIFICATIONS.

2) Install timing belt and camshaft sprocket in original location. Ensure timing marks are aligned. See TIMING BELT. To complete installation, reverse removal procedure. Refill cooling system. Adjust all control cables.

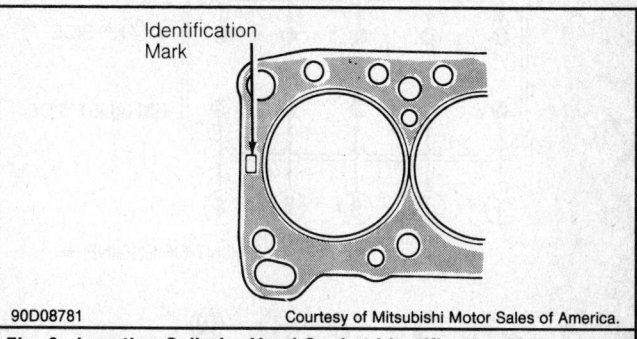

Fig. 6: Locating Cylinder Head Gasket Identification Mark (1.5L – Except Precis)

Removal (1.5L – Precis) – 1) Release fuel pressure. See FUEL PRESSURE RELEASE under REMOVAL & INSTALLATION. Remove air cleaner. Drain coolant. Remove upper radiator hose. Remove distributor and spark plug wires. Remove intake and exhaust manifolds. See INTAKE MANIFOLD and EXHAUST MANIFOLD under REMOVAL & INSTALLATION.

2) Remove fan, spacer, water pump pulley, and upper timing belt cover. Align timing marks. Loosen timing belt tensioner. Move belt tensioner toward water pump. Temporarily tighten tensioner bolt.

CAUTION: Ensure timing belt does not come off of crankshaft sprocket. DO NOT rotate engine with timing belt disengaged from camshaft. See TIMING BELT under REMOVAL & INSTALLATION.

3) Mark location of timing belt on camshaft sprocket for installation reference. Remove timing belt from camshaft sprocket.

4) Remove rocker cover. Using Wrench (09221-11000), loosen head bolts in proper sequence. *See Fig. 5.* Remove cylinder head.

Inspection – Inspect cylinder head for warpage. Resurface cylinder head if warpage exceeds specification. See CYLINDER HEAD table under ENGINE SPECIFICATIONS.

Installation – 1) Install cylinder head. Use new gasket. DO NOT apply sealant to head gasket. Tighten bolts to specification in proper sequence. See TORQUE SPECIFICATIONS. *See Fig. 5.*

2) Install timing belt onto camshaft sprocket in original location. Ensure timing marks are aligned. Adjust timing belt. See TIMING BELT under REMOVAL & INSTALLATION. To complete installation, reverse removal procedure.

Removal (1.8L) – 1) Release residual fuel pressure from fuel system. See FUEL PRESSURE RELEASE under REMOVAL & INSTALLATION. Drain cooling system.

2) Disconnect all necessary electrical connectors, vacuum hoses, coolant hoses, fuel hoses and cables. Support timing belt end of engine from below. Remove engine mount at timing belt end of engine.

CAUTION: DO NOT rotate engine counterclockwise (as viewed from timing belt end of engine).

3) Remove rocker cover. Remove timing belt upper front cover. Rotate crankshaft clockwise (as viewed from timing belt end of engine) until timing mark on camshaft sprocket aligns with timing mark on upper rear cover. *See Fig. 10.*

4) Wire timing belt and sprocket together to maintain correct position. Remove camshaft sprocket with timing belt attached, and allow it to rest on lower front cover. Remove timing belt upper rear cover. Disconnect exhaust pipe from exhaust manifold.

5) Remove intake manifold support bracket. Using Cylinder Head Bolt Wrench (MD998051), loosen cylinder head bolts (in 2-3 steps) in proper sequence. *See Fig. 7.* Remove cylinder head and gasket.

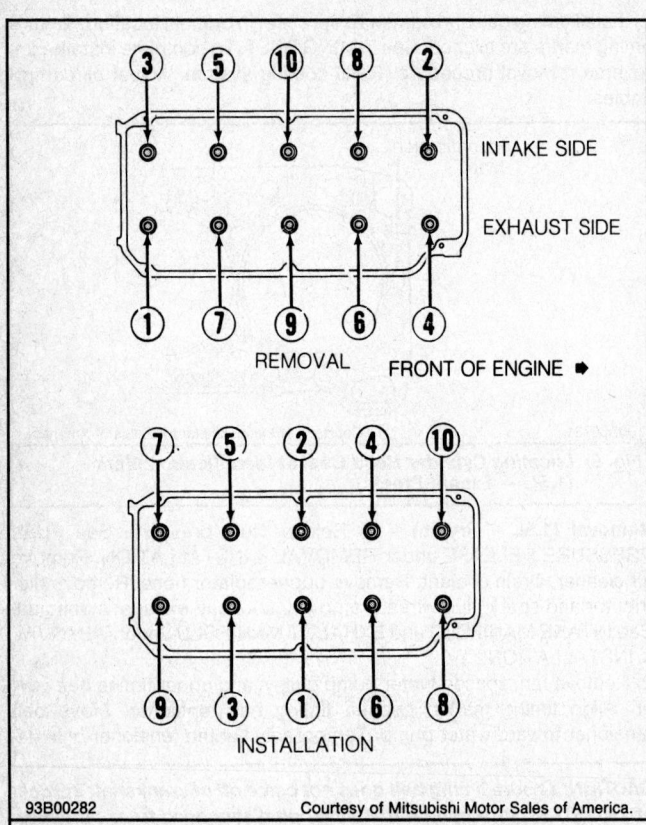

93B00282   Courtesy of Mitsubishi Motor Sales of America.

Fig. 7: Cylinder Head Bolt Removal & Installation Sequence (1.8L)

Inspection – Inspect cylinder head for warpage at deck surface. Resurface cylinder head if warpage exceeds specification. See CYLINDER HEAD table under ENGINE SPECIFICATIONS.

Installation – **1)** Install cylinder head using new gasket. Ensure identification mark at timing belt end of gasket faces upward. DO NOT apply sealant to head gasket. Install and tighten cylinder head bolts (in 2-3 steps) to specification in proper sequence. See Fig. 7.

2) To complete installation, reverse removal procedure. Apply sealant to contact surfaces of semi-circular packing. Apply gasoline to "O" ring on fuel line before installing fuel line in fuel delivery pipe. Adjust all control cables. Fill cooling system.

FRONT COVER OIL SEAL

NOTE: FRONT COVER refers to cover at front of cylinder block. Cover contains oil pump, front cover oil seal (crankshaft front seal), and oil filter mount. Manufacturer specifies oil seal removal procedure with front cover removed from engine. See OIL PUMP & FRONT COVER under ENGINE OILING.

TIMING BELT

Removal (1.5L) – **1)** Remove protective cover under engine. Support engine. Remove engine mount located near timing belt cover. Remove all drive belts and drive pulleys from crankshaft and water pump.

CAUTION: DO NOT rotate engine counterclockwise (as viewed from timing belt end of engine). If reusing timing belt, place reference mark on timing belt to indicate direction of rotation before removing.

2) Remove timing belt covers and gaskets, noting bolt lengths and locations as they are removed. Rotate engine clockwise to align timing mark on camshaft sprocket with mark on cylinder head. Ensure all timing marks are aligned. See Fig. 8.

3) Place mark on timing belt to indicate direction of belt rotation. Loosen timing belt tensioner bolts. Move tensioner inward toward water pump. Temporarily tighten bolt in slot side of tensioner. Remove timing belt.

4) If removing crankshaft belt sprocket, remove sprocket bolt, sprocket, and flange (located behind sprocket). Note orientation of installed flange.

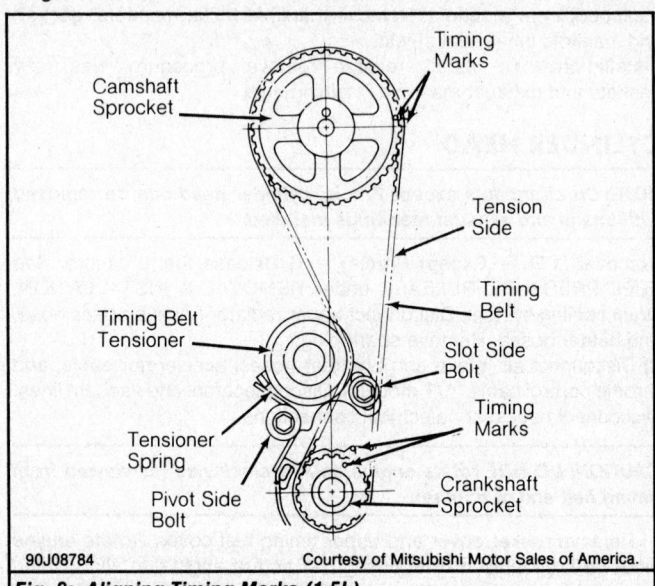

90J08784   Courtesy of Mitsubishi Motor Sales of America.

Fig. 8: Aligning Timing Marks (1.5L)

Inspection – Inspect belt teeth for cracks, damage, or oil contamination. Inspect all sprockets for damage. Examine belt tensioner for grease leakage and roughness when pulley is rotated. Replace components if defective.

Installation – **1)** Install flange onto crankshaft, with chamfered edge facing away from cylinder block. Install camshaft sprocket. Tighten sprocket bolt to specification. See TORQUE SPECIFICATIONS.

2) Install belt tensioner, tension spring, and spacer. Ensure spring is properly engaged against front case. Rotate tensioner toward water pump. Temporarily tighten retaining bolts. Rotate camshaft and crankshaft, ensuring all timing marks are aligned. See Fig. 8.

3) Install timing belt onto crankshaft, in original direction of rotation. Apply pressure to tension side of belt while installing belt onto camshaft sprocket.

4) Rotate camshaft sprocket in counterclockwise direction to apply tension to belt. Ensure timing marks are aligned. Temporarily install crankshaft pulley to retain timing belt. Adjust timing belt tension. See TIMING BELT ADJUSTMENT under ADJUSTMENTS.

CAUTION: If pivot bolt is tightened before side bolt, belt tensioner may rotate, causing belt to be overtightened.

5) To check belt tension, hold belt tensioner and timing belt together. Apply slight thumb pressure at center point of belt tensioner. Belt cog should reach 1/2 of slot side bolt head width. See Fig. 9. To complete installation, reverse removal procedure.

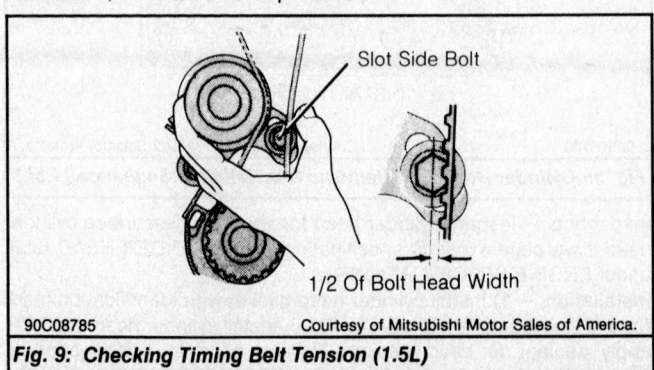

90C08785   Courtesy of Mitsubishi Motor Sales of America.

Fig. 9: Checking Timing Belt Tension (1.5L)

Removal (1.8L) – **1)** Remove condenser tank. Remove A/C and power steering hose mounting bracket from upper engine mount at timing

OVERHAUL

CYLINDER HEAD

Cylinder Head – Measure cylinder head warpage. Resurface cylinder head if warpage exceeds specification. See CYLINDER HEAD table under ENGINE SPECIFICATIONS.

Valve Springs – Measure valve spring free length and out-of-square. Replace valve springs if not within specification. See VALVES & VALVE SPRINGS table under ENGINE SPECIFICATIONS. Install all valve springs with painted area toward rocker arm.

Valve Stem Oil Seals – Install seals, using valve seal installer to properly position oil seal. On 1.5L engines (except Precis), use Valve Seal Installer (MD998760). On Precis, use Valve Seal Installer (MD998302). On 1.8L engines, use Valve Seal Installer (MD998774).

CAUTION: DO NOT install valve guide with same diameter as that removed.

Valve Guides – 1) Measure valve stem diameter. Replace valve if stem diameter is not within specification. Measure valve stem oil clearance. See CYLINDER HEAD and VALVES & VALVE SPRINGS tables under ENGINE SPECIFICATIONS.

2) If clearance exceeds service limit, valve guide can be replaced with an oversized valve guide. See OVERSIZED VALVE GUIDE SPECIFICATIONS table.

3) On Precis, remove valve guide from cylinder head, using Valve Guide Remover/Installer (09222-21200). On all other models, use commercial valve guide remover to remove valve guide. On all models, drive valve guide out toward combustion chamber side of cylinder head.

4) Note intake valve guides are shorter than exhaust valve guides. Using valve guide installer, press new valve guide into cylinder head from top. Install valve guide to proper height. Measure guide clearance of new valve guides. Ream valve guide as necessary. Reface valves and seats. See OVERSIZED VALVE GUIDE SPECIFICATIONS table. See CYLINDER HEAD table under ENGINE SPECIFICATIONS.

OVERSIZED VALVE GUIDE SPECIFICATIONS [1]

Size Mark	Guide Size In. (mm)	Cylinder Head Bore In. (mm)
Precis		
5	.002 (.05)	.4766-.4770 (12.105-12.115)
25	.010 (.25)	.4844-.4848 (12.305-12.315)
50	.020 (.50)	.4943-.4947 (12.555-12.565)
All Others		
5	.002 (.05)	.4744-.4751 (12.050-12.070)
25	.010 (.25)	.4823-.4830 (12.250-12.270)
50	.020 (.50)	.4921-.4928 (12.500-12.520)

[1] – For installed valve guide height, see CYLINDER HEAD table under ENGINE SPECIFICATIONS.

Valve Seats – 1) To replace valve seats, cut valve seat to designated dimension. *See Fig. 15.* Machine cylinder head to proper dimension. See OVERSIZED VALVE SEAT SPECIFICATIONS table.

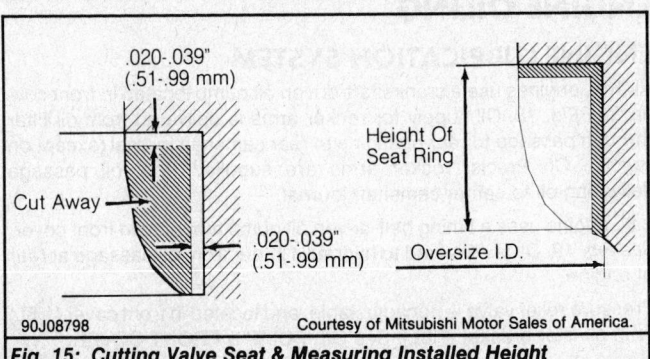

90J08798   Courtesy of Mitsubishi Motor Sales of America.

Fig. 15: Cutting Valve Seat & Measuring Installed Height

2) Heat cylinder head to 480°F (250°C). Press replacement seat into cylinder head. Ensure valve seat height is within specification. Cut valve seat to proper angle to obtain correct seat width.

Valves – Measure valve stem diameter and margin. Replace valve if measurements are not within specification. See VALVES & VALVE SPRINGS table under ENGINE SPECIFICATIONS.

OVERSIZED VALVE SEAT SPECIFICATIONS

Size Mark	Seat Size In. (mm)	Cyl. Head Bore In. (mm)	Seat Height In. (mm)
1.5L (Except Precis)			
Intake			
Primary			
30	.012 (.30)	1.079-1.080 (27.42-27.44)	.276-.283 (7.01-7.19)
60	.024 (.60)	1.091-1.092 (27.72-27.74)	.287-.295 (7.29-7.49)
Secondary			
30	.012 (.30)	1.276-1.277 (32.420-32.440)	.276-.283 (7.01-7.19)
60	.024 (.60)	1.288-1.289 (32.720-32.740)	.287-.295 (7.29-7.49)
Exhaust			
30	.012 (.30)	1.394-1.395 (35.42-35.44)	.291-.299 (7.39-7.59)
60	.024 (.60)	1.406-1.407 (35.72-35.74)	.303-.311 (7.70-7.90)
1.5L (Precis)			
Intake			
30	.012 (.30)	1.429-1.430 (36.30-36.32)	.280 (7.10)
60	.024 (.60)	1.441-1.442 (36.60-36.63)	.291 (7.39)
Exhaust			
30	.012 (.30)	1.272-1.273 (32.31-32.33)	.295 (7.49)
60	.024 (.60)	1.283-1.285 (32.59-32.64)	.307 (7.79)
1.8L			
Intake			
30	.012 (.30)	1.390-1.391 (35.31-35.33)	.311-.319 (7.90-8.10)
60	.024 (.60)	1.402-1.403 (35.60-35.64)	.323-.331 (8.20-8.40)
Exhaust			
30	.012 (.30)	1.311-1.312 (32.30-33.32)	.311-.319 (7.90-8.10)
60	.024 (.60)	1.323-1.324 (33.60-33.63)	.323-.331 (8.20-8.40)

VALVE TRAIN

Rocker Arm Shaft Assembly (1.5L) – 1) Note location of all components for reassembly reference. Remove bolts from shafts, and separate components. On Precis, note lengths of springs. Intake rocker arm springs are longer than exhaust rocker arm springs. On all others, springs are only on intake rocker arm shaft. On all models, inspect components for damage and wear.

2) To install components, reverse removal procedure. Install components into original locations. On Precis, rocker arms are marked "1" or "3" for odd cylinders and "2" or "4" for even cylinders. On all others, rocker arms are marked "A" to "D" for location. *See Figs. 13 and 16.* Ensure large chamfer on rocker arm bore is facing timing belt side of engine.

3) Tighten rocker arm assembly bolts to specification. See TORQUE SPECIFICATIONS. Adjust valve clearance. See VALVE CLEARANCE ADJUSTMENT under ADJUSTMENTS.

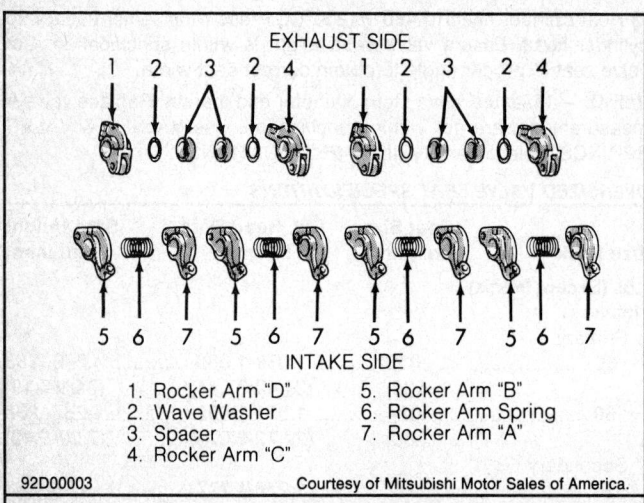

EXHAUST SIDE

1 2 3 2 4   1 2 3 2 4

5 6 7 5 6 7   5 6 7 5 6 7

INTAKE SIDE

1. Rocker Arm "D"   5. Rocker Arm "B"
2. Wave Washer   6. Rocker Arm Spring
3. Spacer   7. Rocker Arm "A"
4. Rocker Arm "C"

92D00003   Courtesy of Mitsubishi Motor Sales of America.

Fig. 16: Identifying Rocker Arm Components (1.5L Except Precis)

Rocker Arm Shaft Assembly (1.8L) – **1)** For reassembly reference, note location and order of assembly for all components. Remove bolts from shafts, and separate components. Note length of springs. Intake rocker arm shaft springs are longer than exhaust rocker arm shaft springs.

2) Inspect components for wear and damage. Install components in original location when reassembling shaft assembly. Tighten rocker arm assembly bolts to specification. See TORQUE SPECIFICATIONS.

3) Before installing lash adjuster, submerge lash adjuster in oil. Use a small wire to hold down internal check valve. Pump plunger up and down 4 or 5 times to bleed air from lash adjuster.

CYLINDER BLOCK ASSEMBLY

Piston & Rod Assembly – Mark piston and rod assembly with corresponding cylinder number before removal. Install piston and rod assembly into cylinder block, with front mark on piston top toward timing belt side of engine.

Fitting Pistons – **1)** Measure piston skirt diameter .08" (2 mm) above bottom of highest point on piston skirt, at 90-degree angle to piston pin. If piston diameter is not within specification, replace piston. See PISTONS, PINS & RINGS table under ENGINE SPECIFICATIONS.

2) Measure cylinder diameter in 3 places: .47" (12 mm) from top of bore, .47" (12 mm) from bottom of bore, and near center of bore. If cylinder diameter or taper is not within specification, rebore cylinder. See CYLINDER BLOCK table under ENGINE SPECIFICATIONS.

3) If clearance between piston and cylinder bore clearance is not within specification, replace piston and/or machine cylinder bore. See PISTONS, PINS & RINGS table.

Piston Rings – **1)** Using inverted piston, push new piston ring to bottom of cylinder bore. Measure piston ring end gap, using a feeler gauge. Repeat for each ring. See PISTONS, PINS & RINGS table under ENGINE SPECIFICATIONS.

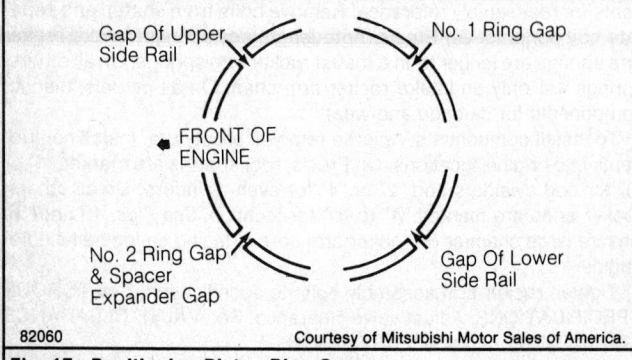

Gap Of Upper Side Rail

No. 1 Ring Gap

FRONT OF ENGINE

No. 2 Ring Gap & Spacer Expander Gap

Gap Of Lower Side Rail

82060   Courtesy of Mitsubishi Motor Sales of America.

Fig. 17: Positioning Piston Ring Gaps

2) Clean piston ring grooves thoroughly. Install piston rings with identification mark toward top of piston. DO NOT use ring expander to install oil ring side rails. Measure piston ring side clearance between ring and ring land.

3) If ring lands are excessively worn, replace piston. See PISTONS, PINS & RINGS table. Align piston ring end gaps properly on piston. See Fig. 17.

Rod Bearings – **1)** Using Plastigage, measure rod bearing oil clearance. Tighten bearing cap nuts to 15 ft. lbs. (20 N.m), then an additional 1/4 turn. See CRANKSHAFT, MAIN & CONNECTING ROD BEARINGS and CONNECTING RODS tables under ENGINE SPECIFICATIONS.

NOTE: Before installing connecting bearing caps, attempt to run nuts down bolts by hand. Replace bolt if nut does not run down smoothly for the entire length.

---

2) If oil clearance is incorrect, install a new bearing set and again measure oil clearance. If proper oil clearance cannot be obtained by using new bearings, replace crankshaft.

Crankshaft & Main Bearings – **1)** Measure main and connecting rod bearing journals diameters. Measure journal taper and out-of-round. Measure crankshaft end play. See CRANKSHAFT, MAIN & CONNECTING ROD BEARINGS table under ENGINE SPECIFICATIONS. Replace crankshaft if measurements are not within specification.

2) Using Plastigage, measure main bearing oil clearance. Tighten bearing cap bolts to 37-41 ft. lbs. (50-55 N.m). See CRANKSHAFT, MAIN & CONNECTING ROD BEARINGS and CONNECTING RODS tables under ENGINE SPECIFICATIONS.

3) If oil clearance is incorrect, install a new bearing set and again measure oil clearance. Undersize bearings are available. If proper oil clearance cannot be obtained by using new bearings, replace crankshaft.

4) On 1.5L, install main bearing caps in numerical order, according to number stamped on cap. Install bearing caps so arrow on top of cap points toward timing belt end of engine. Tighten main bearing caps in 2 stages to specification, starting at center and working outward. See TORQUE SPECIFICATIONS.

5) On 1.8L, install main bearing caps with arrow on top of cap pointing toward timing belt end of engine. "F" stamped on top of cap (next to arrow) indicates front main bearing cap; "R" indicates rear main bearing cap.

Thrust Bearing – Replace thrust bearing if crankshaft end play is not within specification. See CRANKSHAFT, MAIN & CONNECTING ROD BEARINGS table under ENGINE SPECIFICATIONS.

Cylinder Block – **1)** Measure cylinder block deck warpage. See CYLINDER BLOCK table under ENGINE SPECIFICATIONS. If warpage exceeds specification, machine surface. DO NOT remove more than a combined total of .008" (0.20 mm) material from cylinder head and cylinder block gasket surfaces.

2) Measure cylinder bore diameter in 3 places: .47" (12 mm) from top of bore, .47" (12 mm) from bottom of bore, and near center of bore. If cylinder bore diameter or taper is not within specification, rebore cylinders and install oversize pistons. See CYLINDER BLOCK table.

ENGINE OILING

ENGINE LUBRICATION SYSTEM

All 1.5L engines use a crankshaft-driven oil pump located in front cover. See Fig. 18. Oil supply for rocker arms is delivered from oil filter through passage to rear of engine to rear camshaft journal (except on Precis). On Precis, rocker arms are supplied from oil passage delivering oil to center camshaft journal.

1.8L engine uses a timing belt-driven oil pump mounted in front cover. See Fig. 19. Oil is delivered to hydraulic lifters from oil passage at rear of engine.

Pressure relief valve is nonadjustable, and located in front cover (1.5L) or in oil filter bracket (1.8L). See OIL PUMP & FRONT COVER.

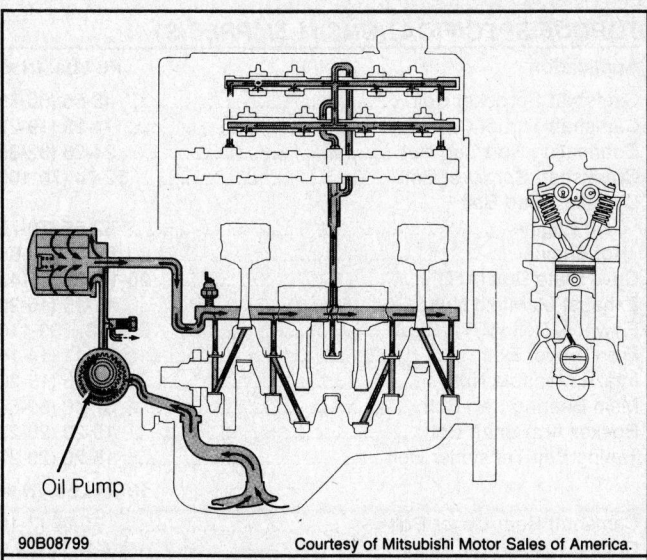

Oil Pump

90B08799

Courtesy of Mitsubishi Motor Sales of America.

**Fig. 18: Engine Oiling System
(Precis Shown; Other 1.5L Engines Are Similar)**

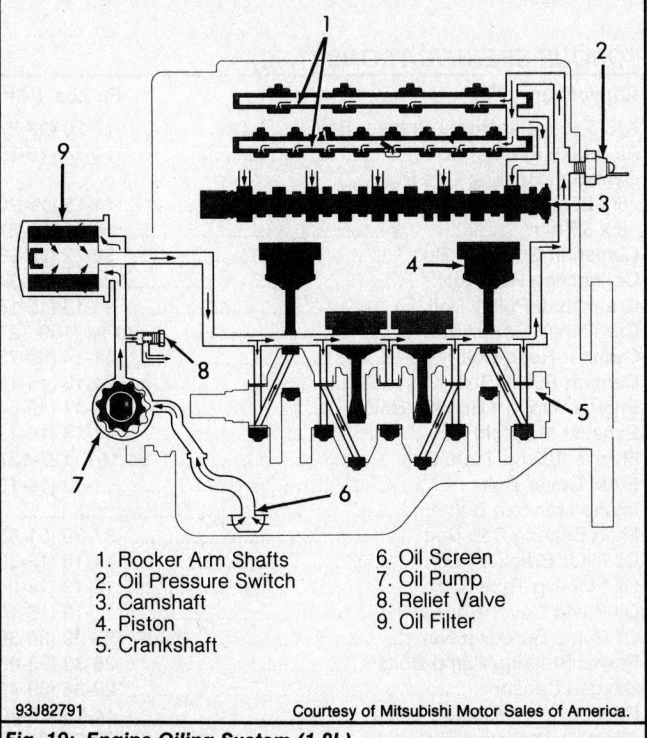

1. Rocker Arm Shafts
2. Oil Pressure Switch
3. Camshaft
4. Piston
5. Crankshaft
6. Oil Screen
7. Oil Pump
8. Relief Valve
9. Oil Filter

93J82791

Courtesy of Mitsubishi Motor Sales of America.

Fig. 19: Engine Oiling System (1.8L)

Crankcase Capacity – See CRANKCASE CAPACITY table.

CRANKCASE CAPACITY

Application	[1] Qts. (L)
1.5L	3.6 (3.4)
1.8L	4.6 (4.4)

[1] – Capacities listed include oil filter change.

Oil Pressure – At curb idle and with oil temperature 167-194°F (75-90°C), normal oil pressure should be at least 11 psi (.77 kg/cm²).

OIL PUMP & FRONT COVER

Removal (1.5L) – Remove timing belt and crankshaft sprocket. See TIMING BELT under REMOVAL & INSTALLATION. Remove oil filter and oil pressure switch. Remove oil pan, oil screen, and oil filter bracket. Remove front cover and oil pump assembly.

Disassembly & Inspection – **1)** Remove gear cover. Note and mark direction of installed gear for reassembly reference, using felt pen. **2)** Measure clearance between outer gear and cover. Measure clearance between inner gear tip and outer gear (except Precis). On Precis, measure clearance between crescent and gears.
3) On all models, place straightedge across front cover housing. Measure gear end play clearance between each gear and straightedge.
4) Inspect pressure relief valve for freedom of movement in bore. Measure spring tension and free length of relief valve spring. Replace components if not within specifications. See OIL PUMP SPECIFICATIONS table. Inspect oil pan for cracks or damage. Inspect oil screen for clogging.

OIL PUMP SPECIFICATIONS

Application	Specification
1.5L (Except Precis)	
Gear End Play	[1] .0016-.0039" (.040-.100 mm)
Inner Gear-To-Outer Gear Tip	[2] .0024-.0071" (.060-.180 mm)
Outer Gear-To-Case	[2] .0039-.0071" (.100-.180 mm)
Relief Valve Spring	
Free Length	1.835" (46.60 mm)
Spring Pressure	13 Lbs. @ 1.579" (6 kg @ 40.10 mm)
1.5L (Precis)	
Gear End Play	.0016-.0039" (.040-.100 mm)
Inner Gear-To-Crescent	.0083-.0126" (.210-.320 mm)
Outer Gear-To-Case	.0039-.0079" (.100-.200 mm)
Outer Gear-To-Crescent	.0087-.0134" (.220-.340 mm)
Relief Valve Spring	
Free Length	1.850" (47.00 mm)
Spring Pressure	13.4 Lbs. @ 1.579" (6.1 kg @ 40.10 mm)
1.8L	
Gear End Play	
Drive Gear	[3] .0031-.0055" (.080-.140 mm)
Driven Gear	[3] .0024-.0047" (.060-.120 mm)
Gear Tip-To-Body Clearance	
Drive Gear	[3] .0063-.0083" (.160-.210 mm)
Driven Gear	[3] .0051-.0071" (.130-.180 mm)
Relief Valve Spring	
Free Length	1.835" (46.60 mm)
Spring Pressure	13.4 Lbs. @ 1.579" (6.1 kg @ 40.10 mm)

[1] – Wear limit is .0079" (.200 mm).
[2] – Wear limit is .0138" (.350 mm).
[3] – Wear limit is .0098" (.250 mm).

Reassembly & Installation – **1)** Lubricate all components with engine oil. Assemble all components into housing in original locations.
2) Install front cover with new gasket. Install front cover bolts in appropriate locations. See Fig. 20. Tighten to specifications. See TORQUE SPECIFICATIONS. Coat outer surface of Seal Guide (MD998285 for Precis and MD998305 for all other models). Install seal guide over end of crankshaft.
3) Slide seal into front cover. Using Seal Installer (MD998375 for Precis and MD998304 for all others), install front seal in front cover. To complete installation, reverse removal procedure.

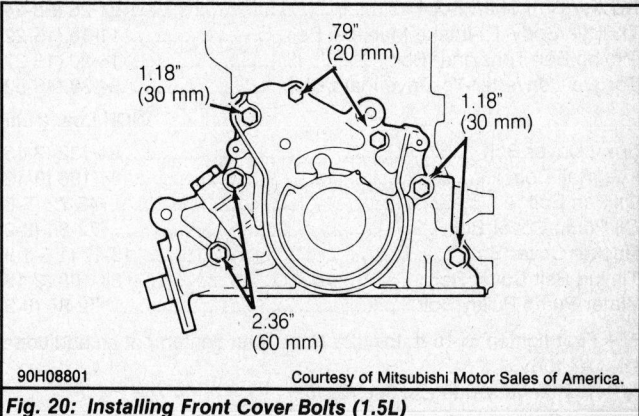

.79"
(20 mm)

1.18"
(30 mm)

1.18"
(30 mm)

2.36"
(60 mm)

90H08801

Courtesy of Mitsubishi Motor Sales of America.

Fig. 20: Installing Front Cover Bolts (1.5L)

Removal (1.8L) – **1)** Remove oil pan. See OIL PAN under REMOVAL & INSTALLATION. If necessary, remove oil filter bracket assembly. Remove oil pick-up assembly.

1994 ENGINES
1.5L & 1.8L 4-Cylinder (Cont.)

2) Remove timing belt and sprockets. See TIMING BELT under REMOVAL & INSTALLATION. Remove oil pump drive gear. Remove oil pump cover and gasket. Remove front cover from cylinder block.
3) If front cover sticks to cylinder block, pry cover from cylinder block at screwdriver slot. Remove plug, spring and relief plunger. Remove crankshaft oil seal from front cover.

Inspection – 1) Inspect components for damage. Install oil pump gears in front cover. Using feeler gauge, measure gear-to-front cover clearance between tip of teeth on each gear and front cover.
2) Place straightedge across front cover above gears. Using feeler gauge, check clearance between gear (rotor) tips.
3) Check for ridge on oil pump cover in gear operating area. Ensure relief plunger slides freely in bore. Ensure spring free length is 1.85" (47.0 mm). Replace components if not within specification. See OIL PUMP SPECIFICATIONS (1.8L) table.

OIL PUMP SPECIFICATIONS (1.8L)

Application	Specification
Gear Side Clearance	.0015-.0039" (.04-.10 mm)
Gear Tip Clearance	.0024-.0071" (.06-.18 mm)
Gear-To-Front Cover Clearance	
Standard	.0039-.0071" (.10-.18 mm)
Limit	.0138" (.351 mm)

Installation – 1) If crankshaft oil seal was removed, use Seal Installer (MD998717) to install seal in front cover. Install gears in oil pump case. Attach oil pump case cover.
2) To complete installation, reverse removal procedure. Tighten bolts to specification. See TORQUE SPECIFICATIONS.

TORQUE SPECIFICATIONS

TORQUE SPECIFICATIONS (1.5L EXCEPT PRECIS)

Application	Ft. Lbs. (N.m)
Camshaft Sprocket Bolt	52-74 (70-100)
Connecting Rod Cap Bolt	[1]
Crankshaft Pulley Bolt	10-11 (14-15)
Crankshaft Sprocket Bolt	52-74 (70-100)
Cylinder Head Bolt [2]	52-55 (70-75)
Drive Plate-To-Crankshaft Bolt	96-103 (130-140)
Exhaust Manifold-To-Engine Bolt	11-14 (15-19)
Exhaust Pipe-To-Manifold Bolt	29-37 (40-50)
Flywheel-To-Crankshaft Bolt	96-103 (130-140)
Intake Manifold Bolt	11-15 (15-20)
Intake Manifold Brace Bolt	13-18 (18-25)
Main Bearing Cap Bolt	37-41 (50-55)
Oil Pressure Switch	11-16 (15-22)
Oil Pump Relief Valve Plug	29-37 (40-50)
Oil Screen Bolt	11-16 (15-22)
Rocker Arm Adjuster Lock Nut	10-13 (14-18)
Rocker Arm Shaft Bolt	21-25 (28-34)
Throttle Body-To-Intake Manifold Bolt	11-16 (15-22)
Timing Belt Tensioner Bolt	14-20 (19-27)
Torque Converter-To-Drive Plate Bolt	34-38 (46-52)
	INCH Lbs. (N.m)
Front Cover Bolt	84-132 (9-15)
Fuel Rail Bolt	84-108 (9-12)
Oil Pan Bolt	48-72 (5-8)
Oil Pump Cover Bolt	72-84 (8-9)
Rocker Cover Bolt	13-17 (1.5-1.9)
Timing Belt Cover Bolt	84-108 (9-12)
Water Pump Pulley Bolt	72-84 (8-9)

[1] – First tighten to 15 ft. lbs. (20 N.m), then tighten nut an additional 1/4 turn.
[2] – Tighten in sequence. See Fig. 5.

TORQUE SPECIFICATIONS (1.5L PRECIS)

Application	Ft. Lbs. (N.m)
Camshaft Sprocket Bolt	48-55 (65-75)
Camshaft Thrust Case Bolt	14-20 (19-27)
Connecting Rod Cap Nut	24-26 (32-35)
Crankshaft Sprocket Bolt	52-74 (70-100)
Cylinder Head Bolt [1]	
Cold Engine	52-55 (70-75)
Hot Engine	59-63 (80-85)
Drive Plate Bolt (A/T)	96-103 (130-140)
Exhaust Manifold Nut	11-15 (15-20)
Flywheel Bolt (M/T)	96-103 (130-140)
Front Cover Bolt	10-11 (14-15)
Intake Manifold Nut	11-15 (15-20)
Main Bearing Cap Bolt	37-40 (50-54)
Rocker Arm Shaft Bolt	15-20 (20-27)
Timing Belt Tensioner Bolt	15-20 (20-27)
	INCH Lbs. (N.m)
Camshaft Rear Cover Bolt	70-86 (7-10)
Rocker Cover Bolt	13-18 (1.5-2.0)
Timing Belt Cover Bolt	86-104 (10-12)

[1] – Tighten in sequence. See Fig. 5.

TORQUE SPECIFICATIONS (1.8L)

Application	Ft. Lbs. (N.m)
A/C Tensioner Pulley Bracket Bolt	17-20 (23-27)
Air Intake Plenum Bolt	11-14 (15-19)
Camshaft Bearing Cap Bolt	
6 x 20-mm	14-15 (19-20)
8 x 65-mm	15-20 (20-27)
Camshaft Sprocket Bolt	58-72 (79-98)
Connecting Rod Nut	24-25 (33-34)
Crankshaft Pulley Bolt	11-13 (15-18)
Crankshaft Sprocket Bolt	80-94 (109-127)
Cylinder Head Bolt [1]	51-54 (69-73)
Damper Pulley Bolt	11-13 (15-18)
Engine Support Bracket Bolt	36-47 (49-64)
Exhaust Manifold Nut	11-14 (15-19)
Flywheel/Drive Plate Bolt	94-101 (127-137)
Front Cover Bolt	11-13 (15-18)
Intake Manifold Bolt	[2]
Main Bearing Cap Bolt	37-39 (51-53)
Oil Filter Bracket Bolt	11-16 (15-22)
Oil Pick-Up Tube Nut	13-18 (18-24)
Oil Pump Cover Bolt	11-13 (15-18)
Oil Pump Sprocket Nut	26-29 (35-39)
Power Steering Pump Bolts	26-33 (35-45)
Oxygen Sensor	29-36 (39-49)
Rocker Arm Assembly Bolts	14-15 (19-20)
Silent Shaft Sprocket Bolt	25-29 (34-39)
Throttle Body Bolt	11-16 (15-22)
Timing Belt "A" Tensioner Bolt	16-22 (22-30)
Timing Belt "B" Tensioner Bolt	11-16 (15-22)
Water Pump Bolt	
Except 8 x 65-mm	10 (14)
8 x 65-mm	15-19 (20-26)
	INCH Lbs. (N.m)
Fuel Rail Bolt	84-108 (9-12)
Oil Pan Bolt/Nut	48-60 (5-7)
Timing Belt Cover Bolt	84-108 (9-12)
Valve Cover Bolt	48-60 (5-7)
Water Pump Pulley Bolt	72-84 (8-9)

[1] – Tighten bolts to specification in sequence. See Fig. 7.
[2] – Information is not available from manufacturer.

ENGINE SPECIFICATIONS

GENERAL SPECIFICATIONS

Application	Specification
1.5L	
Displacement	89.6 Cu. In. (1.5L)
Bore	2.97" (75.5 mm)
Stroke	3.23" (82.0 mm)
Compression Ratio	9.4:1
Fuel System	MFI
Horsepower @ RPM	
Except Precis	92 @ 6000
Precis	81 @ 5500
Torque Ft. Lbs. @ RPM	
Except Precis	93 @ 3000
Precis	91 @ 3000
1.8L	
Displacement	111 Cu. In. (1.8L)
Bore	3.19" (81.0 mm)
Stroke	3.50" (89.0 mm)
Compression Ratio	8.5:1
Fuel System	MFI
Horsepower @ RPM	[1]
Torque Ft. Lbs. @ RPM	[1]

[1] – Information is not available from manufacturer.

CRANKSHAFT, MAIN & CONNECTING ROD BEARINGS

Application	In. (mm)
1.5L (Except Precis)	
Crankshaft	
End Play	
Standard	.002-.007 (.05-.18)
Service Limit	.010 (.25)
Main Bearings	
Journal Diameter	1.8898 (48.00)
Journal Out-Of-Round	.0006 (.015) Maximum
Journal Taper	.0006 (.015) Maximum
Oil Clearance	
Standard	.0008-.0028 (.020-.070)
Service Limit	.0059 (.150)
Connecting Rod Bearings	
Journal Diameter	1.6535 (42.000)
Journal Out-Of-Round	.0006 (.015) Maximum
Journal Taper	.0006 (.015) Maximum
Oil Clearance	
Standard	.0008-.0024 (.020-.060)
Service Limit	.0059 (.150)
1.5L (Precis)	
Crankshaft	
End Play	
Standard	.002-.007 (.05-.18)
Service Limit	.010 (.25)
Main Bearings	
Journal Diameter	1.8898 (48.00)
Journal Out-Of-Round	.0004 (.010) Maximum
Journal Taper	.0004 (.010) Maximum
Oil Clearance	.0008-.0028 (.020-.070)
Connecting Rod Bearings	
Journal Diameter	1.6535 (42.000)
Journal Out-Of-Round	.0004 (.010) Maximum
Journal Taper	.0004 (.010) Maximum
Oil Clearance	.0006-.0017 (.015-.045)

CRANKSHAFT, MAIN & CONNECTING ROD BEARINGS (Cont.)

Application	In. (mm)
1.8L	
Crankshaft End Play	
Standard	.002-.007 (.05-.18)
Service Limit	.016 (.41)
Main Bearings	
Journal Diameter	2.244 (57.00)
Journal Out-Of-Round	.0006 (.015)
Journal Taper	.0002 (.005)
Oil Clearance	
Standard	.0008-.0016 (.02-.04)
Service Limit	.004 (.10)
Connecting Rod Bearings	
Journal Diameter	1.771 (45.00)
Journal Out-Of-Round	.0006 (.015)
Journal Taper	.0002 (.005)
Oil Clearance	
Standard	.0008-.0020 (.02-.05)
Service Limit	.004 (.10)

CONNECTING RODS

Application	In. (mm)
1.5L	
Maximum Bend	.002 (.05)
Maximum Twist	.004 (.10)
Side Play	
Standard	.004-.010 (.10-.25)
Service Limit	.016 (.41)
1.8L	
Maximum Bend	.002 Per 3.937 (.05 Per 100.00)
Maximum Twist	.0039 Per 3.937 (.099 Per 100.00)
Side Play	
Standard	.0039-.0098 (.099-.249)
Service Limit	.016 (.41)

PISTONS, PINS [1] & RINGS

Application	In. (mm)
1.5L	
Pistons	
Clearance	.0008-.0016 (.020-.040)
Diameter [2]	2.9713-2.9724 (75.470-75.500)
Rings	
No. 1	
End Gap	
Standard	.008-.014 (.20-.35)
Service Limit	.031 (.80)
Side Clearance	
Standard	.0012-.0028 (.030-.070)
Service Limit	
Except Precis	.004 (.10)
Precis	.006 (.15)
No. 2	
End Gap	
Standard	.008-.014 (.20-.35)
Service Limit	.031 (.80)
Side Clearance	
Standard	.0008-.0024 (.020-.060)
Service Limit	
Except Precis	.004 (.10)
Precis	.005 (.13)
No. 3 (Oil)	
End Gap	
Standard	.008-.028 (.20-.70)
Service Limit	.040 (1.0)

1994 ENGINES
1.5L & 1.8L 4-Cylinder (Cont.)

PISTONS, PINS [1] & RINGS (Cont.)

Application	In. (mm)
1.8L	
Pistons	
Clearance	.0008-.0016 (.020-.040)
Diameter	3.1882-3.1886 (80.980-80.990)
Pins	
Rod Fit	[1]
Rings	
No. 1	
End Gap	
Standard	.0098-.0157 (.250-.400)
Service Limit	.031 (.79)
Side Clearance	
Standard	.0012-.0028 (.030-.070)
Service Limit	.004 (.100)
No. 2	
End Gap	
Standard	.0157-.0217 (.400-.550)
Service Limit	.031 (.79)
Side Clearance	
Standard	.0008-.0024 (.020-.060)
Service Limit	.004 (.10)
Oil Ring Side Rail	.0079-.0236 (.200-.600)

[1] – Pin specifications are not available from manufacturer.

[2] – Diameter is measured at specified location and at 90 degree angle to piston pin. See CYLINDER BLOCK ASSEMBLY under OVERHAUL.

CYLINDER BLOCK

Application	In. (mm)
1.5L	
Cylinder Bore	
Standard Diameter	2.9724-2.9736 (75.500-75.530)
Maximum Taper	.0008 (.020)
Maximum Out-Of-Round	.0008 (.020)
Minimum Deck Height	[1] 10.067 (255.70)
Maximum Deck Warpage	[1] .002 (.05)
1.8L	
Cylinder Bore	
Standard Diameter	3.1734 (80.600)
Maximum Taper	.0004 (.010)
Maximum Out-Of-Round	.0004 (.010)
Deck Height	11.228 (285.20)
Maximum Deck Warpage	[1] .0039 (.099)

[1] – If deck warpage exceeds specification, machine deck surface. DO NOT remove more than a combined total of .008" (.20 mm) material from original surfaces of cylinder head and cylinder block.

VALVES & VALVE SPRINGS

Application	Specification
1.5L	
Intake Valves	
Face Angle	45°
Minimum Margin	
Standard	.040" (1.00 mm)
Service Limit	
Except Precis	.020" (.50 mm)
Precis	.028" (.70 mm)
Stem Diameter	
Except Precis	.259" (6.58 mm)
Precis	.260" (6.60 mm)
Exhaust Valves	
Face Angle	45°
Minimum Margin	
Standard	.059" (1.50 mm)
Service Limit	.040" (1.00 mm)
Stem Diameter	
Except Precis	.258" (6.55 mm)
Precis	.260" (6.60 mm)
Valve Springs	
Free Length	
Except Precis	
Intake	
Standard	1.815" (46.10 mm)
Service Limit	1.776" (45.10 mm)
Exhaust	
Standard	1.843" (46.80 mm)
Service Limit	1.803" (45.80 mm)
Precis	
Standard	1.756" (44.60 mm)
Service Limit	1.717" (43.60 mm)
Installed Height	
Except Precis	[1]
Precis	
Standard	1.42" (36.0 mm)
Service Limit	1.46" (37.0 mm)
Out-Of-Square	
Except Precis	
Standard	2°
Service Limit	4°
Precis	
Standard	1.5°
Service Limit	3°
1.8L	
Intake Valves	
Face Angle	45-45.5°
Minimum Margin	.019" (.48 mm)
Stem Diameter	.235" (5.97 mm)
Exhaust Valves	
Face Angle	45-45.5°
Minimum Margin	.039" (1.0 mm)
Stem Diameter	.234" (5.95 mm)
Valve Springs	
Free Length	1.965-2.004" (48.21-49.20 mm)
Installed Height	[1]
Out-Of-Square	
Standard	Less Than 2°
Service Limit	4°

[1] – Information is not available from manufacturer.

CYLINDER HEAD

Application	Specification
1.5L (Except Precis)	
Cylinder Head Height	4.209-4.217" (106.90-107.10 mm)
Maximum Warpage	[1] .002" (.05 mm)
Valve Seats	
Intake Valve	
Seat Angle	44°
Seat Width	.035-.051" (.90-1.30 mm)
Exhaust Valve	
Seat Angle	44°
Seat Width	.035-.051" (.90-1.30 mm)
Valve Guides	
Valve Guide Installed Height	.670" (17.00 mm)
Intake Valve	
Valve Stem-To-Guide Oil Clearance	
Standard	.0008-.0020" (.020-.050 mm)
Service Limit	.004" (.10 mm)
Exhaust Valve	
Valve Stem-To-Guide Oil Clearance	
Standard	.0020-.0035" (.050-.090 mm)
Service Limit	.0059" (.150 mm)
1.5L (Precis)	
Maximum Warpage	[1] .002" (.05 mm)
Valve Seats	
Intake Valve	
Seat Angle	45°
Seat Width	.035-.051" (.90-1.30 mm)
Exhaust Valve	
Seat Angle	45°
Seat Width	.035-.051" (.90-1.30 mm)
Valve Guides	
Valve Guide Installed Height	.539-.563" (13.7-14.3 mm)
Intake Valve	
Valve Stem-To-Guide Oil Clearance	
Standard	.0012-.0024" (.030-.060 mm)
Service Limit	.004" (.10 mm)
Exhaust Valve	
Valve Stem-To-Guide Oil Clearance	
Standard	.0020-.0035" (.050-.090 mm)
Service Limit	.0059" (.150 mm)
1.8L	
Cylinder Head Height	4.720" (119.9 mm)
Maximum Warpage	[1] .0012" (.03 mm)
Valve Seats	
Intake Valve	
Seat Angle	43.5-44.0°
Seat Width	.0354-.0512" (.899-1.300 mm)
Exhaust Valve	
Seat Angle	43.5-44.0°
Seat Width	.0354-.0512" (.899-1.300 mm)
Valve Guides	
Intake Valve	
Valve Stem-To-Guide Oil Clearance	
Standard	.0008-.0020" (.02-.05 mm)
Service Limit	.004" (.10 mm)
Exhaust Valve	
Valve Stem-To-Guide Oil Clearance	
Standard	.0020-.0035" (.05-.09 mm)
Service Limit	.006" (.15 mm)

[1] – If deck warpage exceeds specification, machine surface. DO NOT remove more than a combined total of .008" (.20 mm) material from original surfaces of cylinder head and cylinder block.

CAMSHAFT

Application	In. (mm)
1.5L	
End Play	
Except Precis	[1]
Precis	
Standard	.002-.008 (.05-.20)
Service Limit	.016 (.40)
Journal Diameter	
Except Precis	1.020 (25.90)
Precis	[1]
Lobe Height	
Except Precis	
Intake	
Standard	1.3858 (35.200)
Service Limit	1.3661 (34.700)
Exhaust	
Standard	1.3743 (34.907)
Service Limit	1.3546 (34.407)
Precis	
Intake	
Standard	1.5318 (38.908)
Service Limit	1.5118 (38.400)
Exhaust	
Standard	1.5344 (38.975)
Service Limit	1.5144 (38.465)
Oil Clearance	
Except Precis	
Standard	.0024-.0039 (.060-.0990)
Service Limit	.0055 (.140)
Precis	[1]
1.8L	
End Play	.004-.008 (.10-.20)
Journal Diameter	1.7689-1.7693 (44.93-44.94)
Lobe Height	
Intake	1.4677-1.4876 (37.28-37.78)
Exhaust	1.4799-1.4996 (37.59-38.09)
Oil Clearance	.0020-.0035 (.051-.089)

[1] – Information is not available from manufacturer.

1994 ENGINES
1.8L, 2.0L & 2.4L 4-Cylinder

Chrysler Corp.: Colt Vista
Eagle: Summit Wagon
Mitsubishi: Eclipse, Expo, Pickup

NOTE: For repair procedures not covered in this article, see ENGINE OVERHAUL PROCEDURES article in GENERAL INFORMATION.

ENGINE IDENTIFICATION

Vehicle Identification Number (VIN) is stamped on a metal plate located at upper left corner of instrument panel, near windshield. The eighth character of VIN identifies engine, and tenth character (R) identifies model year (1994).

Engine model code and serial number are stamped on right side of cylinder block, near front. For specific location, see CHRYSLER CORP./MITSUBISHI INTRODUCTION article in ENGINE PERFORMANCE.

ENGINE IDENTIFICATION CODES

Application	Engine Model	Engine Code
Colt Vista, Expo & Summit Wagon		
1.8L	4G93	C
2.4L	4G64	G
Eclipse		
1.8L	4G37	B
2.0L	4G63	E
2.0L Turbo	4G63	F
Pickup	4G64	G

ADJUSTMENTS

VALVE CLEARANCE ADJUSTMENT

1.8L (Colt Vista, Expo & Summit Wagon) – 1) Adjust valves when engine temperature is 176-203°F (80-95°C). Remove spark plugs and valve cover. Rotate crankshaft counterclockwise until "T" mark is lined up with notch on crankshaft pulley.

CAUTION: Always rotate engine in direction of normal rotation (counterclockwise as viewed from front of engine).

2) Ensure valve stem-to-rocker arm clearance is present at cylinder No. 1. If clearance is not present, rotate crankshaft another 360 degrees. Ensure "T" mark on timing indicator is lined up with notch on crankshaft pulley. Adjust clearance on both valves for cylinder No. 1 and exhaust valve for cylinder No. 3. Adjust cylinder No. 2 intake valve. *See Fig. 1.* See VALVE CLEARANCE SPECIFICATIONS (1.8L) table.
3) Rotate crankshaft 360 degrees counterclockwise so piston No. 4 is at TDC of compression stroke. Ensure "T" mark on timing indicator is

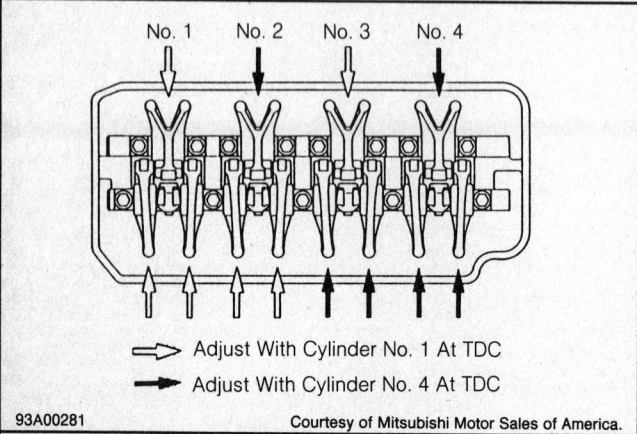

93A00281   Courtesy of Mitsubishi Motor Sales of America.

Fig. 1: Valve Clearance Adjusting Sequence (Colt Vista, Expo & Summit Wagon – 1.8L)

lined up with notch on crankshaft pulley. Adjust clearance on both valves for cylinder No. 4. Adjust cylinder No. 3 intake valve and cylinder No. 2 exhaust valve. *See Fig. 1.* Install new valve cover gasket. Install valve cover.

VALVE CLEARANCE SPECIFICATIONS (1.8L)

Application	In. (mm)
Exhaust	.012 (.30)
Intake	.008 (.20)

1.8L (Eclipse), 2.0L & 2.4L – Hydraulic lash adjusters are used. Valve adjustment is not required.

REMOVAL & INSTALLATION

CAUTION: When battery is disconnected, vehicle computer and memory systems may lose memory data. Driveability problems may exist until computer systems have completed a relearn cycle.

NOTE: For reassembly reference, label all electrical connectors, vacuum hoses and fuel lines before removal. Also place mating marks on engine hood and other major assemblies before removal.

FUEL PRESSURE RELEASE

Disconnect fuel pump connector near fuel tank. Start engine, and allow it to idle until it stalls. Turn ignition off. Reconnect fuel pump connector. Disconnect negative battery cable before disconnecting fuel lines.

ENGINE

CAUTION: To prevent fire hazard, release residual pressure in fuel system before disconnecting fuel lines.

Removal (Eclipse) – 1) Remove hood. Drain cooling system. Release residual fuel pressure from fuel system. See FUEL PRESSURE RELEASE under REMOVAL & INSTALLATION.
2) Drain engine oil and transaxle oil. Remove transaxle. On M/T models, see appropriate article in CLUTCHES. On A/T models, see TRANSMISSION REMOVAL & INSTALLATION article in TRANSMISSION SERVICING.
3) Remove radiator and cooling fan assembly. Disconnect all necessary electrical connectors, vacuum hoses, fuel hoses and cables. Leaving hoses connected, remove power steering pump and A/C compressor, and support aside using wire.
4) Disconnect exhaust pipe from exhaust manifold. Using lifting device, support weight of engine. Remove upper engine mount bracket assembly. Raise engine slightly. Ensure all cables, hoses and electrical harnesses are disconnected from engine. Lift engine upward from engine compartment.
Installation – To install, reverse removal procedure. Ensure all hoses and wires are cleared when lowering engine assembly into compartment. Perform final tightening of mounting bolts and nuts with weight of engine on insulators. See TORQUE SPECIFICATIONS. Replace all fluids, and adjust all cables and linkages.
Removal (Colt Vista, Expo & Summit Wagon – 1.8L) – 1) Release residual fuel pressure from fuel system. See FUEL PRESSURE RELEASE under REMOVAL & INSTALLATION. Remove hood and air cleaner assembly.
2) Remove all necessary electrical connectors, vacuum hoses, fuel hoses, coolant hoses and cables. Remove accelerator cable. Drain cooling system. Drain engine oil and transaxle oil. Remove transaxle. For M/T models, see appropriate article in CLUTCHES. For A/T models, see TRANSMISSION REMOVAL & INSTALLATION article in TRANSMISSION SERVICING.
3) Remove radiator. Leaving hoses connected, remove power steering pump and A/C compressor, and support aside using wire. Remove all drive belts. Remove exhaust manifold heat shield. Disconnect exhaust pipe from exhaust manifold. Disconnect front and rear lower engine mounts.

4) Support engine using hoist. Remove engine mount brackets. Raise engine slightly. Ensure all cables, hoses and electrical harnesses are disconnected from engine. Lift engine assembly upward from vehicle to remove from engine compartment.

Installation – To install, reverse removal procedure. Ensure all wiring and hoses are cleared when lowering engine into engine compartment. With weight of engine on insulators, tighten mounting bolts and nuts to specification. See TORQUE SPECIFICATIONS. Replace all fluids. Adjust all cables and linkages.

Removal (Colt Vista, Expo & Summit Wagon – 2.4L) – 1) Release residual fuel pressure from fuel system. See FUEL PRESSURE RELEASE under REMOVAL & INSTALLATION. Remove hood and engine undercover assembly. Drain cooling system. Remove radiator.

2) Remove all necessary electrical connectors, vacuum hoses, fuel hoses, coolant hoses and cables. Remove A/C and power steering hoses. Remove alternator. Drain engine oil and transaxle oil. Remove transaxle. For M/T models, see appropriate article in CLUTCHES. For A/T models, see TRANSMISSION REMOVAL & INSTALLATION article in TRANSMISSION SERVICING.

3) Remove air cleaner and intake hose assembly. Remove condenser tank. Remove all drive belts. Remove exhaust manifold heat shield. Disconnect exhaust pipe from exhaust manifold. Disconnect front and rear lower engine mounts.

4) Support engine using hoist. Remove engine mount brackets. Raise engine slightly. Ensure all cables, hoses and electrical harnesses are disconnected from engine. Lift engine assembly upward from vehicle to remove from engine compartment.

Installation – To install, reverse removal procedure. Ensure all wiring and hoses are cleared when lowering engine assembly into engine compartment. With weight of engine on insulators, tighten mounting bolts and nuts to specification. See TORQUE SPECIFICATIONS. Replace all fluids, and adjust all cables and linkages.

Removal (Pickup) – 1) Remove hood. Drain cooling system. Release residual fuel pressure from fuel system. See FUEL PRESSURE RELEASE under REMOVAL & INSTALLATION.

2) Drain engine oil and transmission oil. On 4WD models, remove transfer case. On all models, remove transmission. For M/T models, see appropriate article in CLUTCHES. For A/T models, see TRANSMISSION REMOVAL & INSTALLATION article in TRANSMISSION SERVICING.

3) Remove radiator and cooling fan assembly. Disconnect all necessary electrical connectors, vacuum hoses, fuel hoses, coolant hoses and cables. Leaving hoses connected, remove power steering pump and A/C compressor, and support aside.

4) Disconnect exhaust pipe from exhaust manifold. Using lift device, support weight of engine. Remove bolts from engine mounting brackets. Remove engine.

Installation – To install, reverse removal procedure. Clear all wiring and hoses when lowering engine into engine compartment. Tighten mounting bolts and nuts to specification with weight of engine on insulators. See TORQUE SPECIFICATIONS (2.4L) table. Replace all fluids. Adjust all cables and linkages.

INTAKE MANIFOLD

CAUTION: To prevent fire hazard, release residual pressure in fuel system before disconnecting fuel lines.

Removal (1.8L & 2.0L) – 1) Release residual fuel pressure from fuel system. See FUEL PRESSURE RELEASE under REMOVAL & INSTALLATION.

2) Disconnect negative battery cable. Drain cooling system. Disconnect air intake hose or turbo supply hose from throttle body inlet. Remove air cleaner assembly (if necessary).

CAUTION: DO NOT allow fuel injectors to fall out when removing fuel delivery pipe.

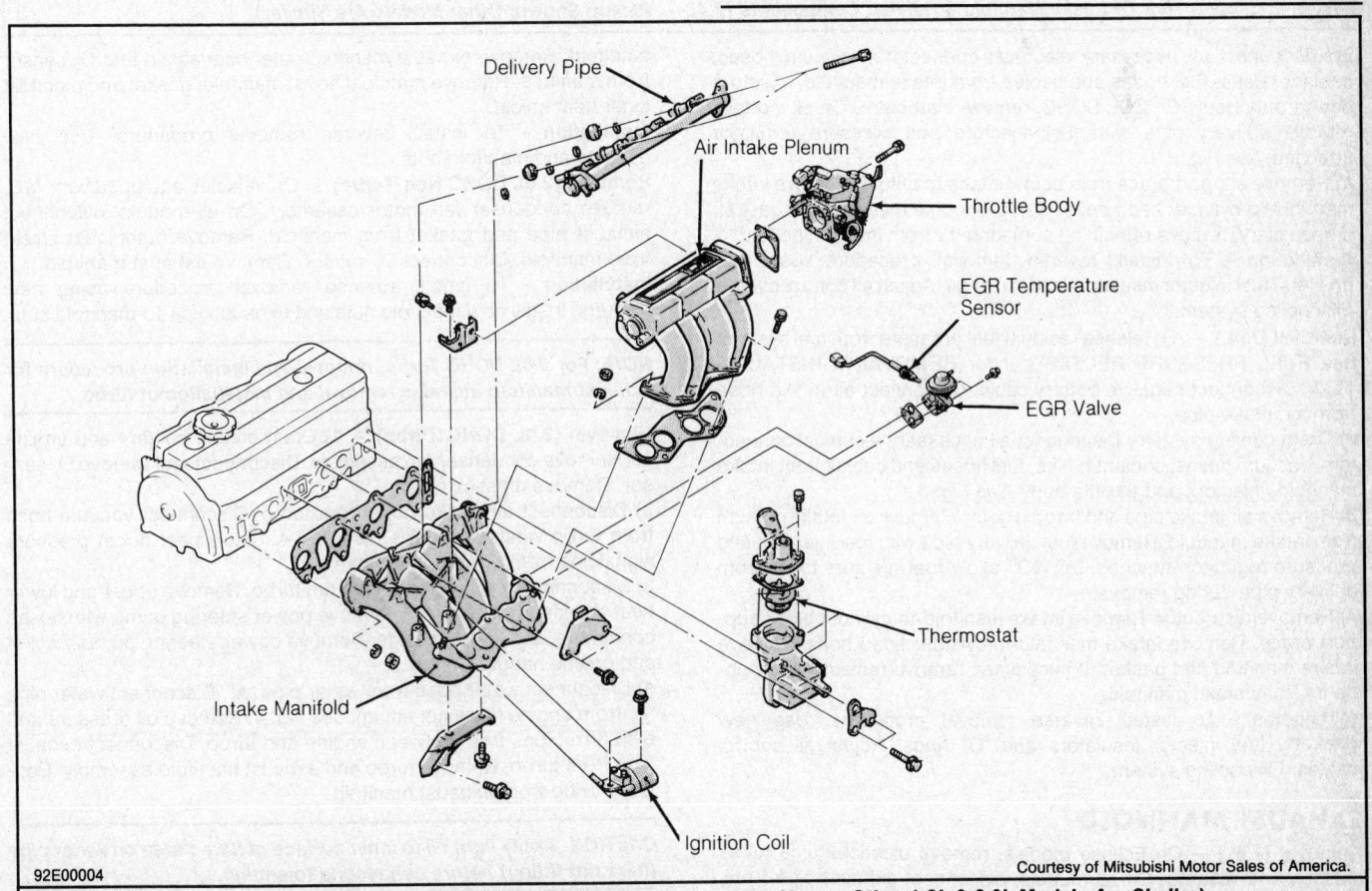

92E00004

Courtesy of Mitsubishi Motor Sales of America.

Fig. 2: Exploded View Of Intake Manifold & Related Components (Eclipse 1.8L Shown; Other 1.8L & 2.0L Models Are Similar)

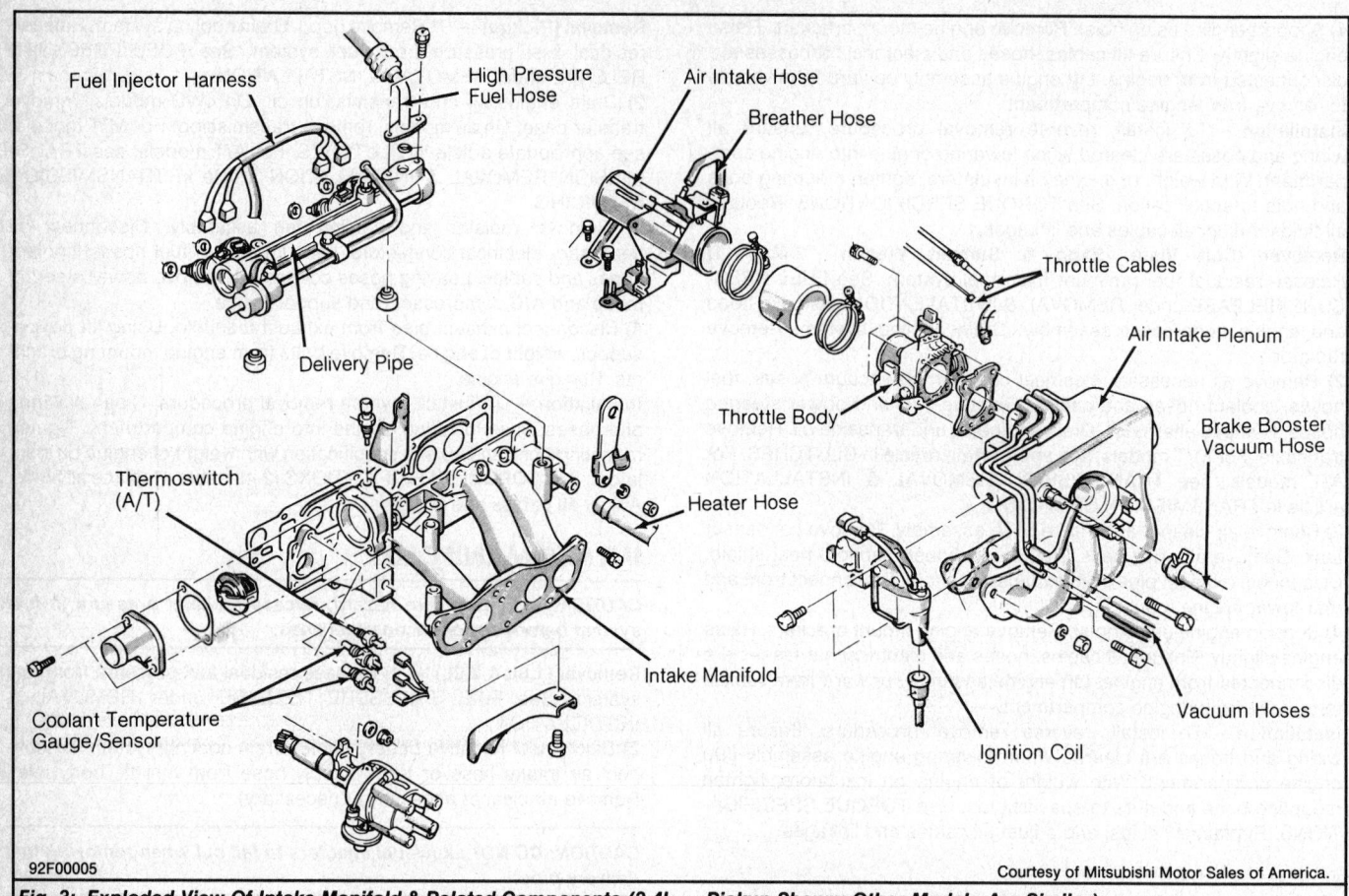

Fuel Injector Harness

High Pressure
Fuel Hose

Air Intake Hose

Breather Hose

Throttle Cables

Air Intake Plenum

Throttle Body

Brake Booster
Vacuum Hose

Delivery Pipe

Heater Hose

Thermoswitch
(A/T)

Intake Manifold

Coolant Temperature
Gauge/Sensor

Vacuum Hoses

Ignition Coil

92F00005

Courtesy of Mitsubishi Motor Sales of America.

Fig. 3: Exploded View Of Intake Manifold & Related Components (2.4L – Pickup Shown; Other Models Are Similar)

3) Disconnect all necessary electrical connectors, vacuum hoses, coolant hoses, fuel hoses and cables from intake manifold, injectors and throttle body. On 2.0L SOHC, remove distributor. On all models, remove delivery pipe with fuel injectors and pressure regulator attached. *See Fig. 2.*

4) Remove support brace from below intake manifold. Remove intake manifold-to-cylinder head bolts. Remove intake manifold and gasket. If necessary, remove remaining components from intake manifold.
Installation – To install, reverse removal procedure. Use new gaskets, fuel injector insulators and "O" rings. Adjust all control cables. Fill cooling system.

Removal (2.4L) – **1)** Release residual fuel pressure from fuel system. See FUEL PRESSURE RELEASE under REMOVAL & INSTALLATION. Disconnect negative battery cable. Disconnect air intake hose from air intake pipe.

2) Drain cooling system. Disconnect all necessary electrical connectors, vacuum hoses, coolant hoses, fuel hoses and cables from intake manifold, injectors and throttle body. *See Fig. 3.*

3) Remove air intake pipe and throttle body. Remove air intake plenum from intake manifold. Remove fuel delivery pipe with fuel injectors and pressure regulator attached. DO NOT allow fuel injectors to fall from delivery pipe during removal.

4) Remove distributor. Remove intake manifold-to-cylinder block support brace. Remove intake manifold-to-cylinder head bolts. Remove intake manifold and gasket. If necessary, remove remaining components from intake manifold.
Installation – To install, reverse removal procedure. Use new gaskets, fuel injector insulators and "O" rings. Adjust all control cables. Fill cooling system.

EXHAUST MANIFOLD
Removal (1.8L) – On Eclipse models, remove dipstick guide tube, dipstick and "O" ring. On all models, disconnect exhaust pipe from

manifold. Remove exhaust manifold outer heat shield and O₂ sensor from manifold. Remove manifold bolts, manifold, gasket and manifold inner heat shield.
Installation – To install, reverse removal procedure. Use new gaskets and manifold nuts.
Removal (2.0L DOHC Non-Turbo) – On vehicles equipped with A/C, remove condenser fan motor assembly. On all models, disconnect exhaust pipe and gasket from manifold. Remove outer heat shield from manifold. Disconnect O₂ sensor. Remove exhaust manifold.
Installation – To install, reverse removal procedure using new gaskets. Install new manifold nuts and exhaust pipe-to-manifold nuts.

NOTE: For 2.0L DOHC Turbo, removal and installation procedure for exhaust manifold includes removal and installation of turbo.

Removal (2.0L DOHC Turbo) – **1)** Drain engine coolant and engine oil. Remove condenser fan assembly. Disconnect and remove O₂ sensor. Remove dipstick tube.

2) Disconnect air intake hose from turbo. Disconnect vacuum hose from turbo wastegate valve. *See Fig. 4.* Disconnect boost pressure signal line from turbo output hose.

3) Disconnect turbo output hose from turbo. Remove upper and lower heat shields from manifold. Remove power steering pump with hoses connected, and support aside. Remove power steering pump bracket and engine hanger.

4) Disconnect water hose from water pipe "A". Disconnect water pipe "B" from engine (flare nut fitting). *See Fig. 4.* Remove oil pressure and oil return pipes from between engine and turbo. Disconnect exhaust pipe from turbo. Remove turbo and exhaust manifold assembly. Separate turbo from exhaust manifold.

CAUTION: Apply light oil to inner surface of flared area on water pipe (flare nut fitting) before connecting to engine.

Installation – To install, reverse removal procedure. Use new gaskets, manifold nuts and exhaust pipe-to-turbo nuts. Refill all necessary fluids.

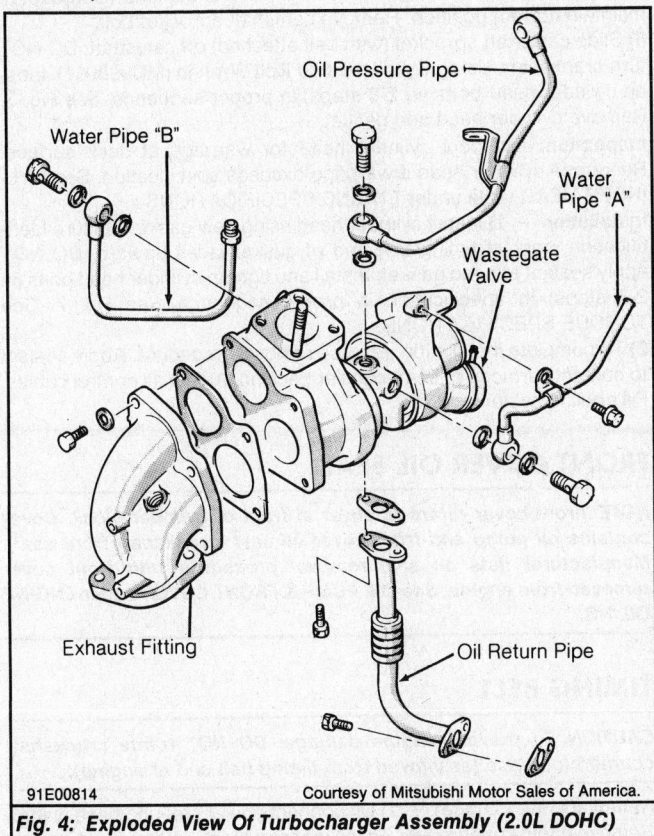

Fig. 4: Exploded View Of Turbocharger Assembly (2.0L DOHC)

Removal (2.0L SOHC & 2.4L) – Remove exhaust manifold heat shield. Disconnect exhaust pipe and gasket from manifold. Remove O_2 sensor. Remove exhaust manifold.

Installation – To install, reverse removal procedure. Use new gaskets and exhaust pipe-to-manifold nuts.

TURBOCHARGER

NOTE: For turbocharger removal and installation procedures, see EXHAUST MANIFOLD under REMOVAL & INSTALLATION.

CYLINDER HEAD

CAUTION: Release residual pressure in fuel system before disconnecting fuel lines.

Removal (1.8L & 2.0L SOHC) – 1) Release residual fuel pressure from fuel system. See FUEL PRESSURE RELEASE under REMOVAL & INSTALLATION. Drain cooling system.
2) Disconnect all necessary electrical connectors, vacuum hoses, coolant hoses, fuel hoses and cables. Support timing belt end of engine from below. Remove engine mount at timing belt end of engine.

CAUTION: DO NOT rotate engine counterclockwise (as viewed from timing belt end of engine).

3) Remove rocker cover. Remove timing belt upper front cover. Rotate crankshaft clockwise (as viewed from timing belt end of engine) until timing mark on camshaft sprocket aligns with timing mark on upper rear cover (1.8L) or cylinder head (2.0L). *See Fig. 9 or 26.*
4) Wire timing belt and sprocket together to maintain correct position. Remove camshaft sprocket with timing belt attached, and allow it to rest on lower front cover. On 1.8L, remove timing belt upper rear cover. On all models, disconnect exhaust pipe from exhaust manifold.

5) Remove intake manifold support bracket. Using Cylinder Head Bolt Wrench (MD998051 for 1.8L or MD998360 for 2.0L), loosen cylinder head bolts (in 2-3 steps) in proper sequence. *See Fig. 5 or 6.* Remove cylinder head and gasket.

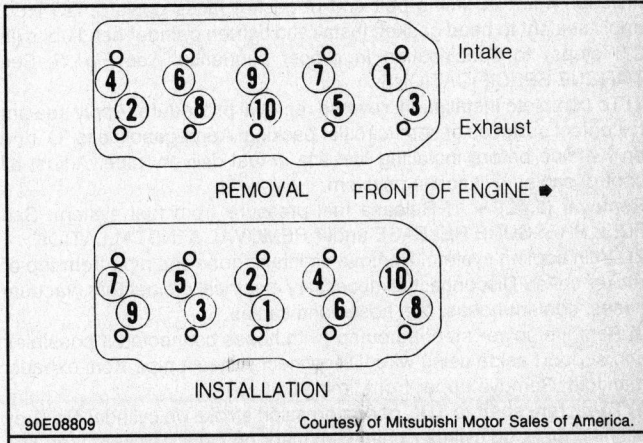

Fig. 5: Cylinder Head Bolt Removal & Installation Sequence (1.8L Eclipse & 2.0L)

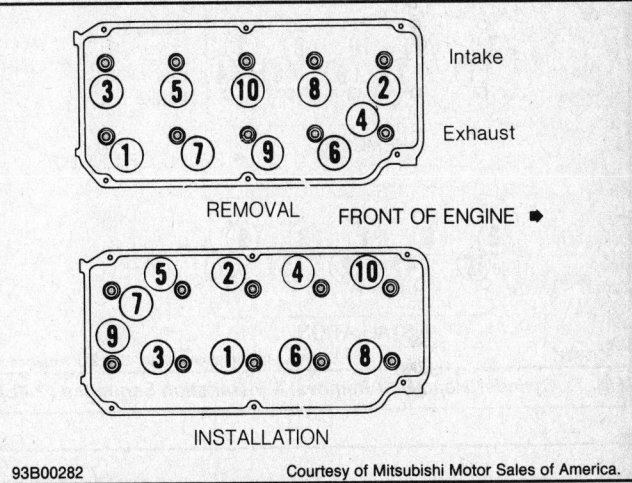

Fig. 6: Cylinder Head Bolt Removal & Installation Sequence (1.8L Except Eclipse)

Inspection – Inspect cylinder head for warpage at deck surface. Resurface cylinder head if warpage exceeds specification. See CYLINDER HEAD table under ENGINE SPECIFICATIONS.
Installation – 1) Install cylinder head using new gasket. Ensure identification mark at timing belt end of gasket faces upward. DO NOT apply sealant to head gasket. Install and tighten cylinder head bolts (in 2-3 steps) to specification in proper sequence. *See Fig. 5 or 6.* See TORQUE SPECIFICATIONS.
2) To complete installation, reverse removal procedure. Apply sealant to contact surfaces of semi-circular packing. Apply gasoline to "O" ring on fuel line before installing fuel line in fuel delivery pipe. Adjust all control cables. Fill cooling system.
Removal (2.0L DOHC) – 1) Release residual fuel pressure from fuel system. See FUEL PRESSURE RELEASE under REMOVAL & INSTALLATION. Drain cooling system. Remove air cleaner assembly.
2) Disconnect all necessary electrical connectors, vacuum hoses, coolant hoses, fuel hoses and cables. Remove timing belt. See TIMING BELT under REMOVAL & INSTALLATION.
3) Remove rocker cover. On non-turbo engines, disconnect exhaust pipe from exhaust manifold. On turbo engines, disconnect exhaust manifold from turbo.
4) On all models, loosen cylinder head bolts (in 2-3 steps) in proper sequence using Cylinder Head Bolt Wrench (MD998051-01). *See Fig. 5.* Remove cylinder head and gasket.

Inspection – Inspect cylinder head for warpage at deck surface. Resurface cylinder head if warpage exceeds specification. See CYLINDER HEAD table under ENGINE SPECIFICATIONS.

Installation – **1)** Install cylinder head using new gasket. Ensure identification mark at timing belt end of gasket faces upward. DO NOT apply sealant to head gasket. Install and tighten cylinder head bolts (in 2-3 steps) to specification in proper sequence. *See Fig. 5.* See TORQUE SPECIFICATIONS.

2) To complete installation, reverse removal procedure. Apply sealant to contact surfaces of semi-circular packing. Apply gasoline to "O" ring on fuel line before installing fuel line in fuel delivery pipe. Adjust all control cables. Fill cooling system.

Removal (2.4L) – **1)** Release fuel pressure from fuel system. See FUEL PRESSURE RELEASE under REMOVAL & INSTALLATION.

2) Drain cooling system. Remove air intake hose and pipe from top of rocker cover. Disconnect all necessary electrical connectors, vacuum hoses, coolant hoses, fuel hoses and cables.

3) Remove power steering pump (with hoses connected if possible), and support aside using wire. Disconnect exhaust pipe from exhaust manifold. Remove upper front timing belt cover.

4) Turn crankshaft to TDC of compression stroke on cylinder No. 1 by aligning mark on cylinder head with mark on camshaft sprocket. *See Fig. 26.* Remove rocker cover. Remove distributor cap.

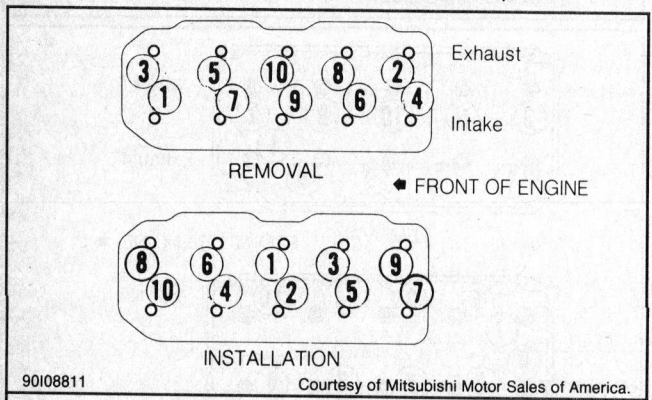

Exhaust

Intake

REMOVAL

← FRONT OF ENGINE

INSTALLATION

90I08811

Courtesy of Mitsubishi Motor Sales of America.

Fig. 7: Cylinder Head Bolt Removal & Installation Sequence (2.4L)

5) Mark rotor-to-distributor position. Mark distributor-to-cylinder head position. Remove distributor. Mark timing belt in alignment with timing mark on camshaft sprocket. Wire timing belt to camshaft sprocket to maintain correct position. Remove camshaft sprocket bolt.

6) Slide camshaft sprocket (with belt attached) off camshaft. DO NOT turn crankshaft. Using Cylinder Head Bolt Wrench (MD998051), loosen cylinder head bolts (in 2-3 steps) in proper sequence. *See Fig. 7.* Remove cylinder head and gasket.

Inspection – Inspect cylinder head for warpage at deck surface. Resurface cylinder head if warpage exceeds specification. See CYLINDER HEAD table under ENGINE SPECIFICATIONS.

Installation – **1)** Install cylinder head using new gasket. Ensure identification mark at timing belt end of gasket faces upward. DO NOT apply sealant to head gasket. Install and tighten cylinder head bolts (in 2-3 steps) to specification in proper sequence. *See Fig. 7.* See TORQUE SPECIFICATIONS.

2) To complete installation, reverse removal procedure. Apply sealant to contact surfaces of semi-circular packing. Adjust all control cables. Fill cooling system.

FRONT COVER OIL SEAL

NOTE: Front cover refers to cover at front of cylinder block. Cover contains oil pump and front cover oil seal (crankshaft front seal). Manufacturer lists oil seal removal procedure with front cover removed from engine. See OIL PUMP & FRONT COVER under ENGINE OILING.

TIMING BELT

CAUTION: To prevent engine damage, DO NOT rotate crankshaft counterclockwise (as viewed from timing belt end of engine).

Removal (1.8L Eclipse) – **1)** Disconnect power steering hose clamp. Remove engine undercover. Place wooden block between jack and oil pan. Raise engine slightly.

2) Remove engine mount assembly near timing belt cover. Remove all drive belts and tensioner pulley bracket. *See Fig. 8.* Remove power steering, water pump and damper pulleys. Remove adapter and crankshaft pulley.

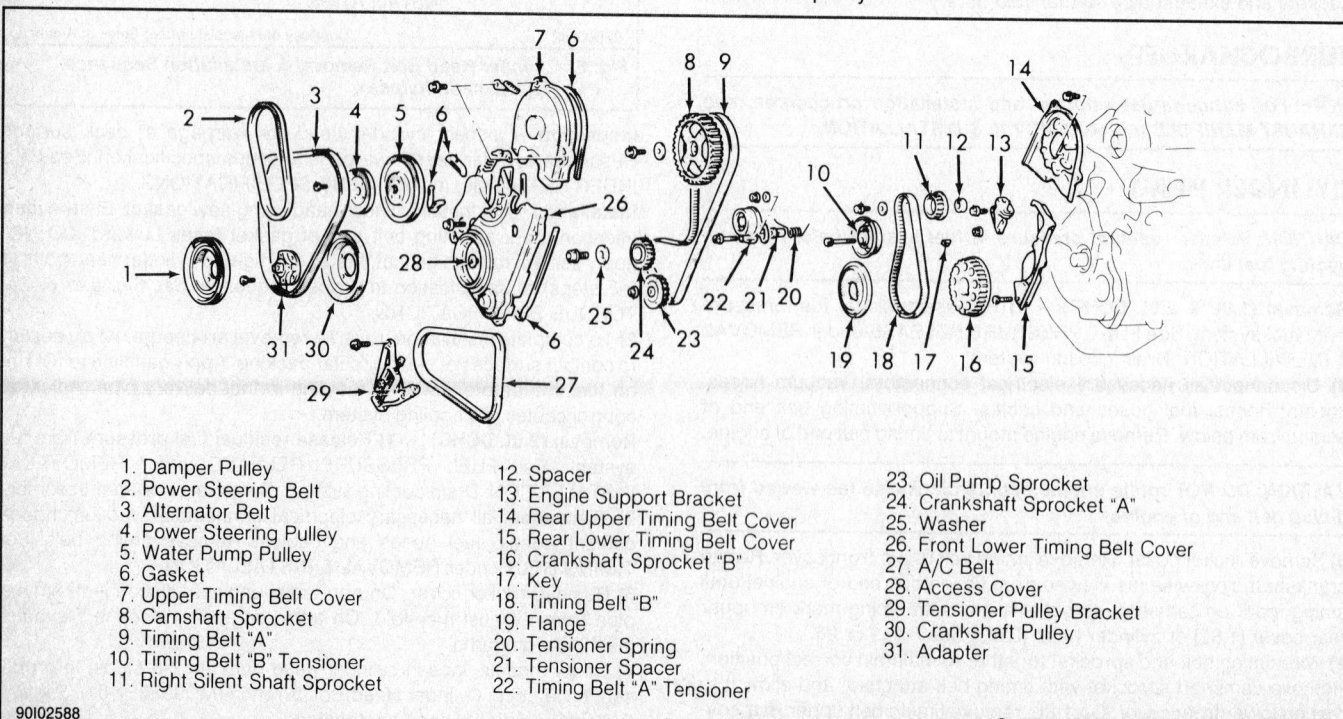

1. Damper Pulley
2. Power Steering Belt
3. Alternator Belt
4. Power Steering Pulley
5. Water Pump Pulley
6. Gasket
7. Upper Timing Belt Cover
8. Camshaft Sprocket
9. Timing Belt "A"
10. Timing Belt "B" Tensioner
11. Right Silent Shaft Sprocket
12. Spacer
13. Engine Support Bracket
14. Rear Upper Timing Belt Cover
15. Rear Lower Timing Belt Cover
16. Crankshaft Sprocket "B"
17. Key
18. Timing Belt "B"
19. Flange
20. Tensioner Spring
21. Tensioner Spacer
22. Timing Belt "A" Tensioner
23. Oil Pump Sprocket
24. Crankshaft Sprocket "A"
25. Washer
26. Front Lower Timing Belt Cover
27. A/C Belt
28. Access Cover
29. Tensioner Pulley Bracket
30. Crankshaft Pulley
31. Adapter

90I02588

Courtesy of Mitsubishi Motor Sales of America.

Fig. 8: Exploded View Of Timing Belts & Related Components (1.8L Eclipse Shown; 2.0L SOHC & 2.4L Engines Are Similar)

NOTE: Ensure timing marks are aligned. Mark direction of rotation of all timing belts.

3) Remove upper and lower timing belt covers and gaskets. Remove access cover. Remove crankshaft sprocket "A" bolt and washer. Rotate crankshaft clockwise (as viewed from timing belt side of engine), and align timing mark on camshaft sprocket with timing mark on rear upper timing belt cover. See Fig. 9.

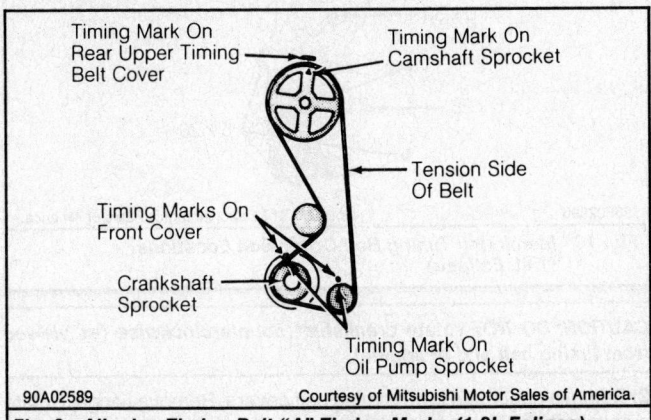

Fig. 9: Aligning Timing Belt "A" Timing Marks (1.8L Eclipse)

90A02589   Courtesy of Mitsubishi Motor Sales of America.

4) If timing belts are to be reused, mark timing belts to indicate direction of belt rotation for reassembly reference. Loosen timing belt tensioner bolt for timing belt "A". Move tensioner toward water pump, and tighten tensioner bolt. Remove timing belt.

5) Remove timing belt tensioner, tensioner spacer and tensioner spring. See Fig. 8. Remove camshaft sprocket. Remove plug from side of cylinder block, and install a .31" (8.0 mm) diameter Phillips screwdriver to hold left silent shaft. See Fig. 10.

6) Remove oil pump sprocket nut, and remove sprocket. Remove crankshaft sprocket "A" and flange. Remove timing belt tensioner "B". If timing belt "B" is to be reused, mark direction of timing belt rotation for reassembly reference. Remove timing belt "B".

7) Remove right silent shaft sprocket and spacer. Before removing crankshaft sprocket "B", note direction of sprocket installation. Remove key from crankshaft. Remove left engine support bracket. Remove rear timing belt covers.

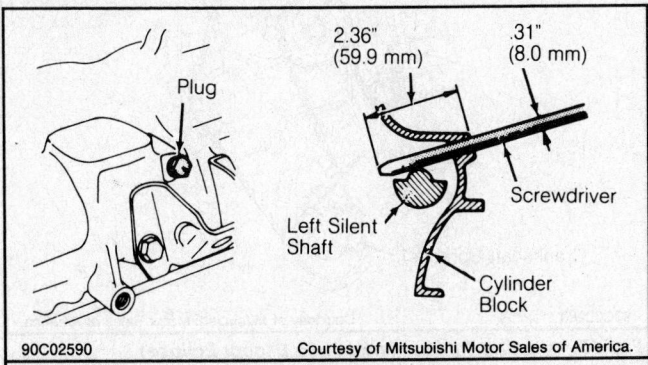

Fig. 10: Holding Silent Shaft In Stationary Position (1.8L Shown; Others Are Similar)

90C02590   Courtesy of Mitsubishi Motor Sales of America.

Inspection – Inspect timing belts for damaged teeth or cracks. Ensure belts are not contaminated by oil. Check tensioners for freedom of rotation. Replace components if damaged.

Installation – **1)** Install rear timing belt covers, engine support bracket and crankshaft key. Install crankshaft sprocket "B" so undercut side is toward crankshaft. See Fig. 11.

CAUTION: Ensure right silent shaft spacer is installed with chamfered side toward oil seal, or damage to oil seal will result.

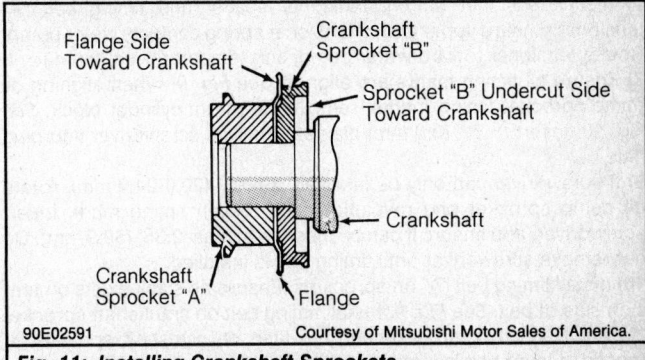

Fig. 11: Installing Crankshaft Sprockets (1.8L Eclipse Shown; 2.0L Is Similar)

90E02591   Courtesy of Mitsubishi Motor Sales of America.

2) Coat outer diameter of right silent shaft spacer with engine oil. Install spacer with chamfered side toward oil seal. Install right silent shaft sprocket.

3) Align crankshaft sprocket "B" and right silent shaft timing marks. See Fig. 12. Install timing belt "B" on sprockets. Ensure belt is installed in original direction of rotation and no slack exists in belt.

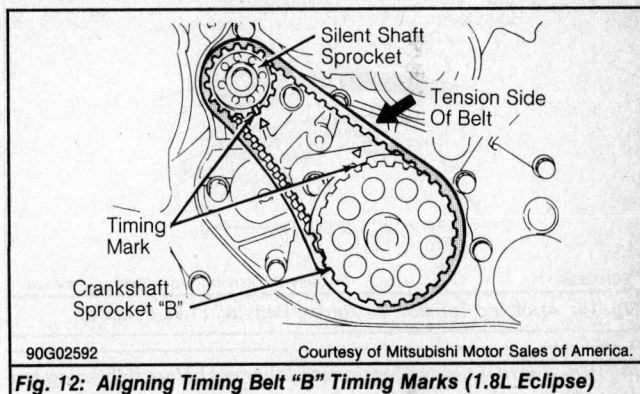

Fig. 12: Aligning Timing Belt "B" Timing Marks (1.8L Eclipse)

90G02592   Courtesy of Mitsubishi Motor Sales of America.

CAUTION: When tightening bolt, ensure tensioner does not rotate, or excessive pressure will be applied to timing belt.

4) Install timing belt tensioner "B" so center of pulley is located left of tensioner bolt. See Fig. 13. Ensure flange on tensioner pulley is toward front of engine. Rotate tensioner inward toward timing belt until belt is tight. Tighten tensioner bolt.

5) Check belt deflection at designated area. See Fig. 13. Belt deflection should be .20-.28" (5.0-7.1 mm). Readjust timing belt if belt deflection is not within specification.

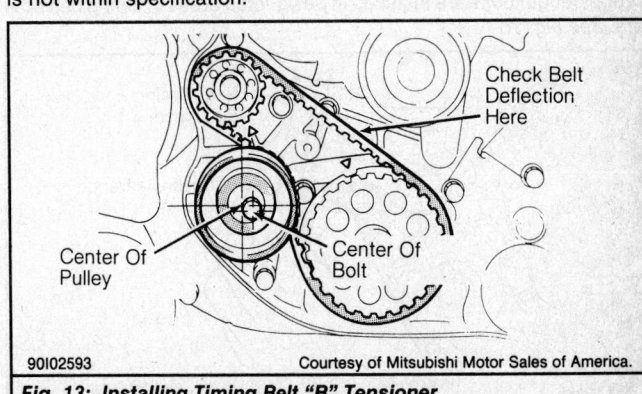

Fig. 13: Installing Timing Belt "B" Tensioner (1.8L Eclipse Shown; Others Are Similar)

90I02593   Courtesy of Mitsubishi Motor Sales of America.

6) Install flange in front of crankshaft sprocket "B", with offset toward crankshaft. See Fig. 11. Install crankshaft sprocket "A". Install camshaft and oil pump sprockets. Tighten bolts to specification. See TORQUE SPECIFICATIONS.

7) Install tensioner spring, tensioner spacer and timing belt "A" tensioner. Ensure upper end of tensioner spring contacts water pump. Rotate tensioner toward water pump, and temporarily tighten nut.

8) Ensure all timing marks are aligned. *See Fig. 9.* When aligning oil pump sprocket timing marks, remove plug from cylinder block. *See Fig. 10.* Insert a .31" (8.0 mm) diameter Phillips screwdriver into plug hole.

9) If screwdriver can only be inserted .79-.98" (20.0-24.9 mm), rotate oil pump sprocket one revolution, and realign timing mark. Insert screwdriver, and ensure it can be inserted at least 2.36" (59.9 mm). Do not remove screwdriver until timing belt is installed.

10) Install timing belt "A" on sprockets. Ensure no slack exists on tension side of belt. *See Fig. 9.* Install timing belt on crankshaft sprocket "A", then on oil pump sprocket and then on camshaft sprocket. If reused, ensure belt is installed in original direction of rotation.

11) Loosen tensioner nut to allow spring tension to be applied to timing belt. Ensure all timing marks are aligned. Remove screwdriver and install plug.

12) To apply tension on timing belt, rotate crankshaft clockwise so camshaft sprocket moves 2 teeth past timing mark on rear timing belt cover. *See Fig. 14.* DO NOT rotate crankshaft counterclockwise.

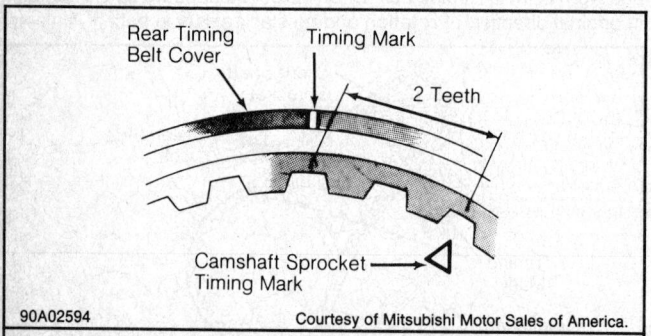

Fig. 14: Applying Tension To Timing Belt "A" (1.8L Eclipse)

CAUTION: DO NOT tighten tensioner spacer nut before tightening tensioner bolt, or timing belt tensioner will rotate and apply excessive pressure on timing belt.

13) Rotate tensioner inward toward timing belt. Ensure timing belt fully engages camshaft sprocket. Tighten timing belt tensioner bolt. Tighten tensioner spacer nut.

14) At midway location between camshaft sprocket and oil pump sprocket, push timing belt "A" outward toward lower timing belt cover. Note clearance between timing belt and cover. *See Fig. 15.* Clearance should be .47" (12.0 mm). Timing belt may need to be readjusted.

15) To complete installation, reverse removal procedure. Ensure proper length bolts are installed in designated areas in timing belt covers. *See Fig. 16.*

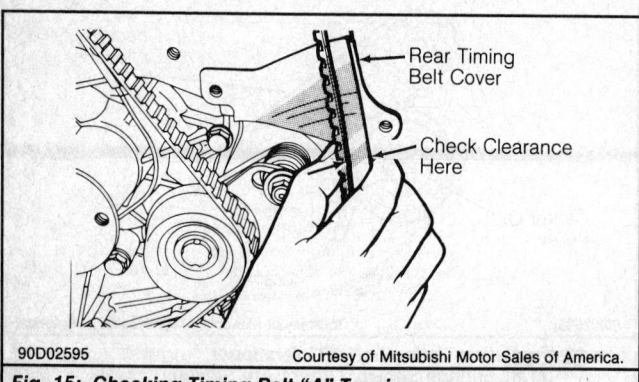

Fig. 15: Checking Timing Belt "A" Tension (1.8L Eclipse Shown; Others Are Similar)

Removal (1.8L Except Eclipse) – **1)** Remove condenser tank. Remove A/C and power steering hose mounting bracket from upper engine mount at timing belt cover. Remove all drive belts. Using End

Yoke Holder (MB990767) and Crankshaft Pulley Holder (MD998718), remove crankshaft pulley bolt and pulley.

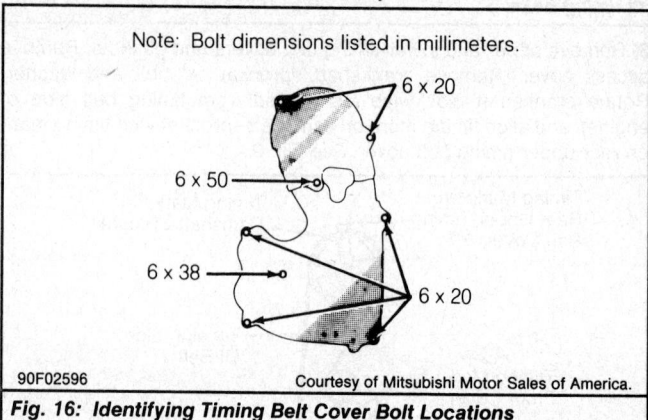

Fig. 16: Identifying Timing Belt Cover Bolt Locations (1.8L Eclipse)

CAUTION: DO NOT rotate crankshaft counterclockwise (as viewed from timing belt end of engine).

2) Remove upper and lower timing belt covers. Remove flange. Rotate crankshaft clockwise (as viewed from timing belt end of engine) until cylinder No. 1 is at TDC of compression stroke, and timing mark on camshaft sprocket and crankshaft sprocket align with timing mark on engine. *See Fig. 17.*

3) If timing belt is to be reused, mark direction of rotation before removing. Loosen timing belt tensioner bolt. Using a screwdriver, move tensioner away from timing belt. Tighten bolt to secure tensioner. Remove timing belt.

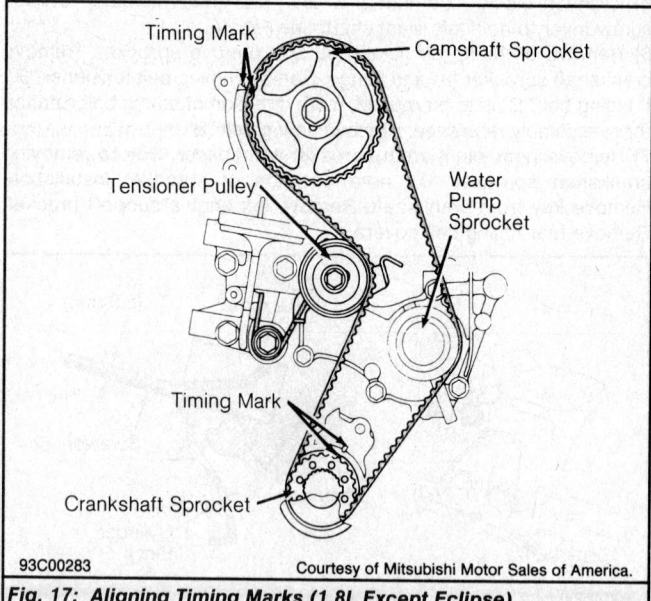

Fig. 17: Aligning Timing Marks (1.8L Except Eclipse)

Inspection – Check belt teeth for cracks, damage and oil contamination. Inspect all sprockets for damage. Check belt tensioner for grease leakage or roughness in tensioner rotation. Replace components if damaged.

Installation – **1)** Install timing belt tensioner, leaving bolt loose. Using a screwdriver, push tensioner toward engine mount. Tighten timing belt tensioner bolt.

2) Align camshaft sprocket and crankshaft sprocket timing marks with timing marks on engine. Install timing belt. Loosen timing belt tensioner to apply spring pressure to timing belt. Ensure timing marks are still aligned.

3) Tighten timing belt tensioner bolt. Rotate camshaft in reverse direction and ensure that there is no slack in timing belt. Rotate crankshaft

2 complete revolutions clockwise (as viewed from timing belt end of engine) and ensure timing marks are still aligned.

4) Ensure timing belt teeth are properly seated in sprockets. Install flange. *See Fig. 18.* To complete installation, reverse removal procedure. Ensure proper length bolts are installed in designated areas in timing belt covers. *See Fig. 19.*

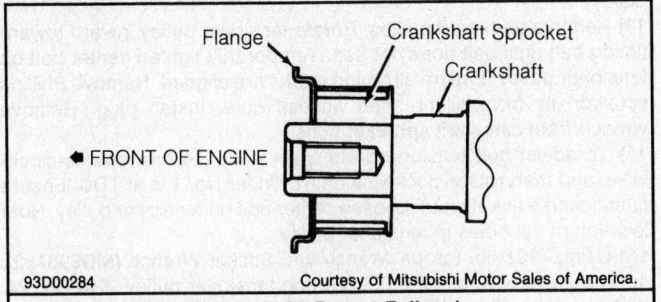

Flange   Crankshaft Sprocket   Crankshaft

◄ FRONT OF ENGINE

93D00284   Courtesy of Mitsubishi Motor Sales of America.

Fig. 18: Installing Flange (1.8L Except Eclipse)

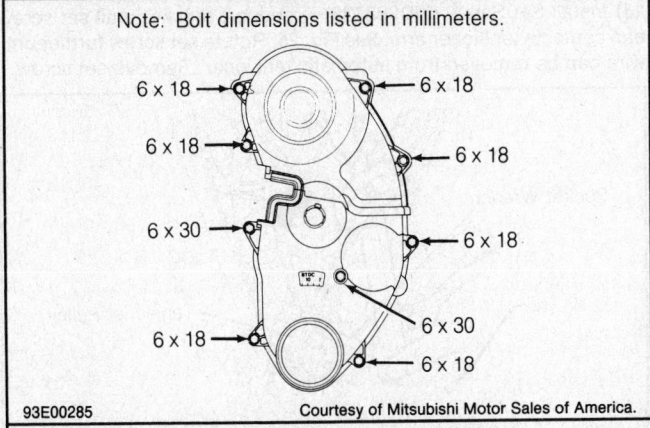

Note: Bolt dimensions listed in millimeters.

6 x 18   6 x 18
6 x 18   6 x 18
6 x 30   6 x 18
6 x 30
6 x 18   6 x 18

93E00285   Courtesy of Mitsubishi Motor Sales of America.

Fig. 19: Identifying Timing Belt Cover Bolt Locations (1.8L Except Eclipse)

Removal (2.0L DOHC) – **1)** Remove protective cover from below engine. Remove A/C and power steering hose mounting bracket. Support engine. Remove upper engine mount located near timing belt cover. Remove all drive belts and drive pulleys from crankshaft and water pump.
2) Remove drive belt tensioner. Remove upper and lower timing belt cover with gasket. Note bolt lengths and locations. Remove breather hose, PCV hose and center shield from valve cover. Disconnect spark plug wires from spark plugs.

CAUTION: DO NOT rotate crankshaft counterclockwise (as viewed from timing belt end of engine).

3) Remove rocker cover and semi-circular packing (located at rear of rocker cover). Remove rubber plug. Rotate crankshaft clockwise (as viewed from timing belt end of engine) until all timing marks align and cylinder No. 1 is at TDC of compression stroke. *See Fig. 20.*
4) Remove automatic tensioner. *See Fig. 21.* If timing belt is to be reused, mark timing belt to indicate original direction of rotation. Remove timing belt. Remove tensioner pulley, tensioner arm and idler pulley (if necessary). Inspect sprockets for damage.
5) To remove camshaft sprockets, hold camshaft hexagon (between camshaft journals No. 2 and 3) while removing camshaft sprocket bolt. Remove camshaft sprockets. Remove silent shaft access plug from cylinder block. Insert .31" (8.0 mm) diameter Phillips screwdriver to block left silent shaft. *See Fig. 10.* Remove oil pump sprocket nut and sprocket.
6) Remove bolt, washer, crankshaft sprocket and flange. Note direction of flange installation. Remove rear timing belt tensioner assembly. Remove rear timing belt. Remove right silent shaft sprocket with spacer. Remove rear crankshaft sprocket, key and inner cover.

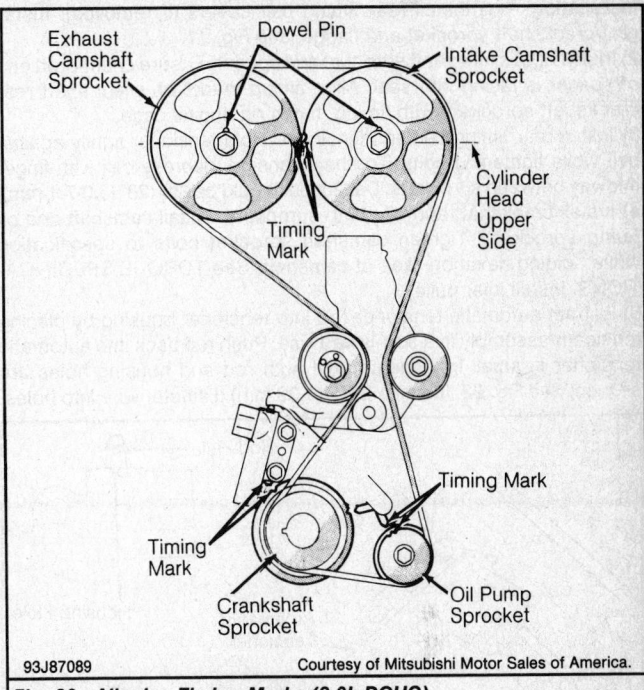

Exhaust Camshaft Sprocket   Dowel Pin   Intake Camshaft Sprocket

Cylinder Head Upper Side

Timing Mark

Timing Mark

Timing Mark

Crankshaft Sprocket   Oil Pump Sprocket

93J87089   Courtesy of Mitsubishi Motor Sales of America.

Fig. 20: Aligning Timing Marks (2.0L DOHC)

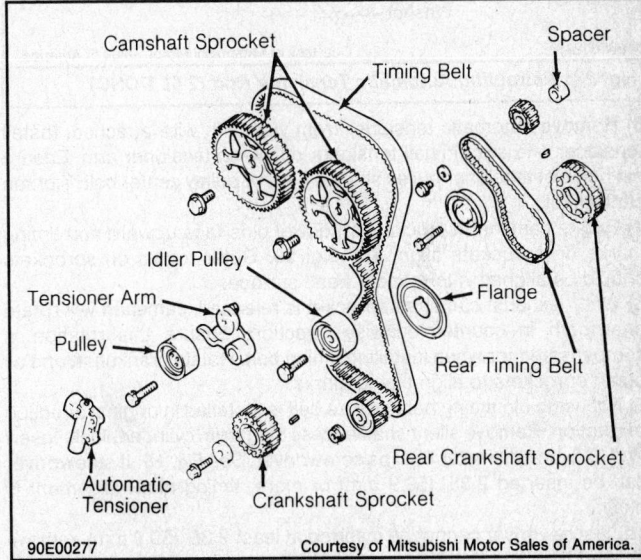

Camshaft Sprocket   Timing Belt   Spacer

Idler Pulley   Flange

Tensioner Arm   Rear Timing Belt

Pulley

Rear Crankshaft Sprocket

Automatic Tensioner   Crankshaft Sprocket

90E00277   Courtesy of Mitsubishi Motor Sales of America.

Fig. 21: Exploded View Of Timing Belt & Related Components (2.0L DOHC)

Inspection – **1)** Check belt teeth for damage and oil contamination. Inspect belt for glossy, hardened or non-elastic surface. Ensure belt is not cracked, separated or showing canvas fiber.
2) Inspect all sprockets for damage. Check tensioner pulley and idler pulley for grease leakage and roughness in rotation. Replace components if damaged.
3) Inspect automatic tensioner for leaks. Check rod end of automatic tensioner for wear. Measure distance from tensioner rod end to tensioner housing. Distance should be .47" (11.9 mm).

NOTE: If plug at bottom of tensioner protrudes past tensioner housing, place a washer over plug to prevent it from contacting vise when pushing rod into tensioner housing.

4) Retract rod into tensioner housing by placing automatic tensioner assembly in a soft-jawed vise. Close vise to push rod back into tensioner. Replace automatic tensioner assembly if rod can be easily pushed into automatic tensioner.

Installation – **1)** Install rear timing belt covers (if removed). Install rear crankshaft sprocket and flange. *See Fig. 11.*

2) Install right silent shaft sprocket and spacer. Ensure chamfered end of spacer is facing into seal. Align timing marks on silent shaft rear crankshaft sprockets with timing marks on engine case.

3) Install rear timing belt and tensioner. Hold tensioner tightly against belt while tightening bolts. To check tension, depress belt with finger midway between sprockets. Deflection should be .20-.28" (5.0-7.1 mm).

4) Install crankshaft and oil pump sprockets. Install camshaft and oil pump sprockets. Tighten camshaft sprocket bolts to specification while holding hexagon area of camshaft. See TORQUE SPECIFICATIONS. Install idler pulley.

5) Retract automatic tensioner rod into tensioner housing by placing tensioner assembly in a soft-jawed vise. Push rod back into automatic tensioner in small increments until both rod and housing holes are aligned. *See Fig. 22.* Install a .055" (1.39 mm) diameter wire into holes.

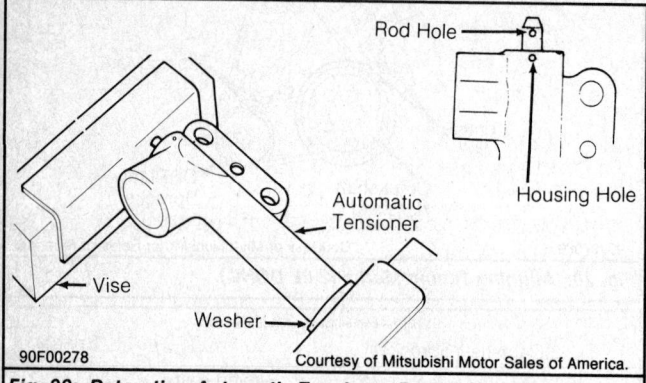

Fig. 22: *Retracting Automatic Tensioner Rod (2.0L DOHC)*

6) Remove automatic tensioner from vise with wire attached. Install tensioner and arm. Install tensioner pulley on tensioner arm. Ensure pin holes of tensioner pulley shaft are left of pulley center bolt. Tighten center bolt.

7) Rotate camshaft sprockets so dowel pins face upward and timing marks on sprockets align. *See Fig. 20.* Outer marks on sprockets should be aligned with cylinder head surface.

8) When exhaust camshaft sprocket is released, camshaft will rotate one tooth in counterclockwise direction. Ensure this rotation is compensated for when installing timing belt. Rotate crankshaft and oil pump sprockets to align timing marks.

9) If reusing old timing belt, ensure belt is installed in original direction of rotation. Remove silent shaft access plug from cylinder block. Insert .31" (8.0 mm) diameter Phillips screwdriver. *See Fig. 10.* If screwdriver can be inserted 2.36" (59.9 mm) or more, timing mark alignment is okay.

10) If screwdriver cannot be inserted at least 2.36" (59.9 mm), remove screwdriver and rotate oil pump sprocket one full turn. Reinsert screwdriver. Leave screwdriver in place until timing belt is installed. Install timing belt on intake camshaft sprocket. Use spring clip to hold belt on sprocket. *See Fig. 23.*

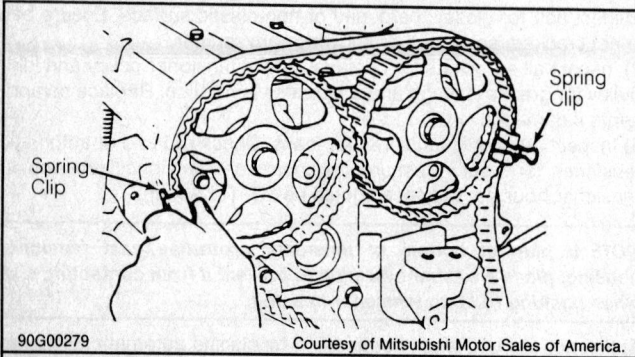

Fig. 23: *Installing Timing Belt On Camshaft Sprockets (2.0L DOHC)*

11) Install wrench on both camshaft sprocket bolts. Install timing belt around exhaust camshaft sprocket while holding camshaft sprocket bolt so timing mark on camshaft sprocket is aligned with timing mark.

12) Install another spring clip on timing belt and camshaft sprocket to hold belt on sprocket. Install timing belt in following sequence: around idler pulley, oil pump sprocket, crankshaft sprocket and tensioner pulley.

13) Remove both spring clips. Rotate tensioner pulley inward toward timing belt until belt does not sag. Temporarily tighten center bolt on tensioner pulley. Ensure all timing marks are aligned. Remove Phillips screwdriver from silent shaft access hole. Install plug. Remove wrench from camshaft sprocket bolts.

14) To adjust belt tension, rotate crankshaft 1/4 turn counterclockwise, and then rotate clockwise until cylinder No. 1 is at TDC. Ensure timing marks are aligned. Loosen center bolt on tensioner pulley. Note location of pin holes in tensioner pulley.

15) Using INCH-lb. torque wrench and Socket Wrench (MD998752), apply 22-24 INCH lbs. (2.6-2.8 N.m) on tensioner pulley. *See Fig. 24.* With torque applied to tensioner pulley, tighten tensioner pulley center bolt to 31-40 ft. lbs. (42-54 N.m).

16) Install Set Screw (MD998738) in support bracket until set screw end contacts tensioner arm. *See Fig. 25.* Rotate set screw further until wire can be removed from automatic tensioner. Remove set screw.

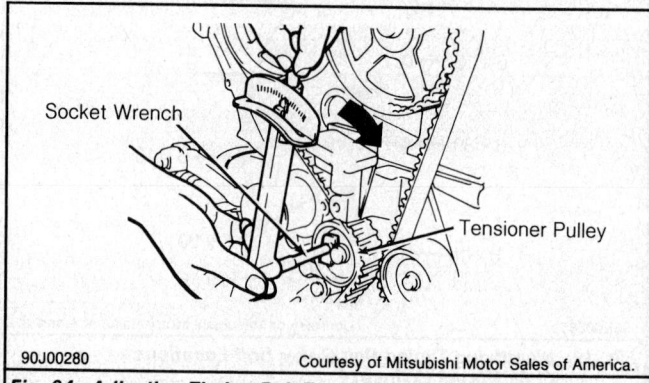

Fig. 24: *Adjusting Timing Belt Tensioner Pulley (2.0L DOHC)*

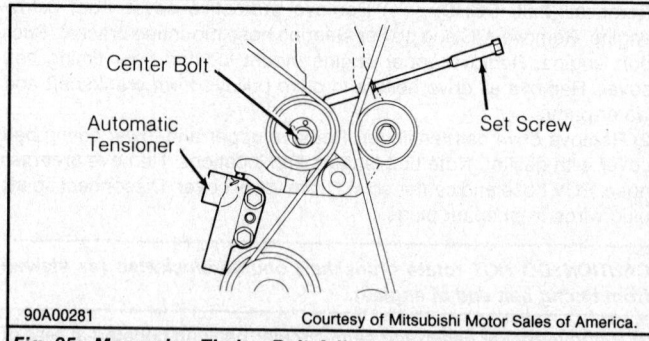

Fig. 25: *Measuring Timing Belt Adjustment (2.0L DOHC)*

17) Rotate crankshaft clockwise 2 complete revolutions, and allow to remain in this position for about 15 minutes. Measure distance between tensioner arm and automatic tensioner body. Distance should be .15-.18" (3.8-4.5 mm).

18) If distance cannot be measured due to lack of clearance, use alternate method. Install set screw until it contacts tensioner arm.

19) Rotate set screw inward while counting number of turns until tensioner arm contacts automatic tensioner housing. Number of turns should be 2 1/2-3 if belt tension is correct. Remove set screw. Install rubber plug in rear timing belt cover.

20) To complete installation, reverse removal procedure. Apply sealant to contact areas on semi-circular packing and rocker cover before installing. Ensure correct bolts are installed in proper location in timing belt covers.

Removal (2.0L SOHC) – 1) Remove A/C and power steering hose mounting bracket or O$_2$ sensor connector bracket from upper engine mount at timing belt cover. Support engine, and remove upper engine mount. Remove all drive belts and drive pulleys from crankshaft and water pump.

2) Remove drive belt tensioner. Remove upper and lower timing belt covers. Note bolt lengths and locations. Longer (2) bolts are located above crankshaft seal. Remove crankshaft sprocket bolt access cover, crankshaft sprocket bolt and washer. If necessary, remove rocker arm cover for clearance.

CAUTION: DO NOT rotate crankshaft counterclockwise (as viewed from timing belt end of engine). If timing belt is to be reused, mark direction of rotation before removing.

---

3) Rotate crankshaft clockwise (as viewed from timing belt end of engine) until cylinder No. 1 is at TDC of compression stroke. Align timing mark on camshaft sprocket with timing mark on cylinder head. *See Fig. 26.* Loosen timing belt tensioner adjustment bolt, and move tensioner toward water pump. Tighten bolt to secure tensioner. Remove front timing belt and camshaft sprocket.

4) If oil pump sprocket removal is necessary, remove left silent shaft access plug from cylinder block. Insert .31" (8.0 mm) diameter Phillips screwdriver to block left silent shaft. *See Fig. 10.* Remove oil pump sprocket nut and sprocket.

5) Remove front crankshaft sprocket and flange. Note direction and order of installation. Remove rear timing belt tensioner assembly. Remove rear timing belt. Remove right silent shaft sprocket with spacer. Remove rear crankshaft sprocket with key and inner cover.

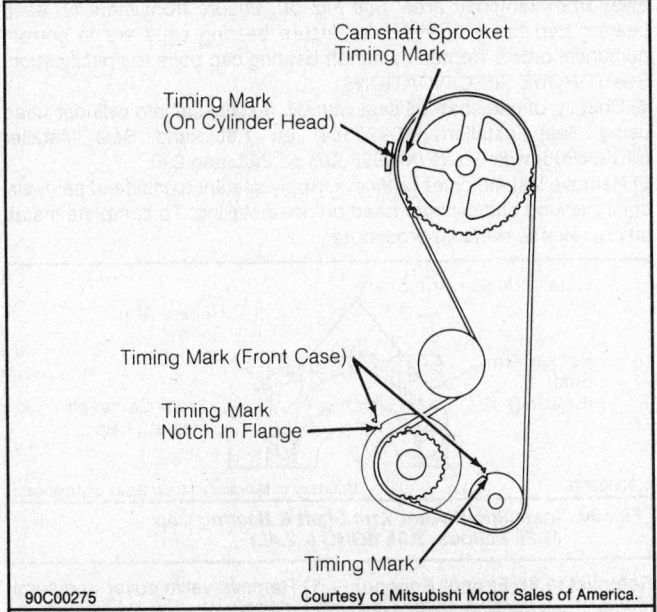

Courtesy of Mitsubishi Motor Sales of America.
90C00275

Fig. 26: Aligning Front Timing Belt (2.0L SOHC & 2.4L)

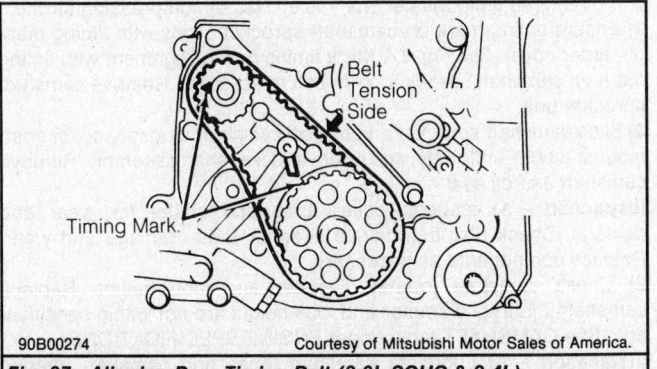

Courtesy of Mitsubishi Motor Sales of America.
90B00274

Fig. 27: Aligning Rear Timing Belt (2.0L SOHC & 2.4L)

Inspection – Check belt teeth for cracks, damage and contamination. Inspect sprockets for damage. Check belt tensioner for leakage or roughness in rotation. Replace components as necessary.

Installation – 1) Install rear crankshaft sprocket and flange onto crankshaft. *See Fig. 11.* Lubricate and install right silent shaft spacer and sprocket. Ensure chamfered side of spacer is installed into silent shaft seal. If reused, install rear timing belt in original direction of rotation. Ensure timing marks are aligned. *See Fig. 27.*

2) Install rear timing belt tensioner. Hold tensioner tightly against belt while tightening bolts. Depress belt between sprockets to ensure deflection is .20-28" (5.0-7.1 mm). Adjust as necessary.

3) Install crankshaft front sprocket. Install oil pump sprocket. Hold left silent shaft using a .31" (8.0 mm) diameter Phillips screwdriver through access hole. *See Fig. 10.* Ensure screwdriver can be inserted at least 2.36" (59.9 mm).

4) Remove screwdriver if it cannot be inserted at least 2.36" (59.9 mm), and rotate oil pump sprocket one revolution. Align timing mark. Insert screwdriver, and ensure it can be inserted at least 2.36" (59.9 mm).

5) DO NOT remove screwdriver until timing belt is installed. Install camshaft sprocket. Tighten bolts to specification. See TORQUE SPECIFICATIONS (2.0L).

6) Install front timing belt tensioner, tension spring and spacer(s). Ensure spring is properly engaged against water pump case. Rotate tensioner toward water pump, and temporarily tighten bolts. Ensure timing marks are aligned. *See Fig. 26.*

7) If reused, install timing belt in original direction of rotation. Apply pressure on tension side of belt while installing belt on camshaft sprocket. Loosen timing belt tensioner to apply spring pressure to timing belt. Ensure timing marks are still aligned.

8) To apply tension on belt, rotate crankshaft clockwise until camshaft sprocket timing mark is offset by 2 teeth. Tighten tensioner bolt. Tighten tensioner nut.

9) To check belt tension, apply slight thumb pressure and measure deflection between camshaft and oil pump sprocket. *See Fig. 15.* Belt deflection should be .55" (14.0 mm). To complete installation, reverse removal procedure.

Removal (2.4L) – 1) Remove radiator shroud, cooling fan and pulley. Remove all drive belts and crankshaft pulleys. Remove upper timing belt covers and gaskets. Note bolt length and location.

CAUTION: DO NOT rotate crankshaft counterclockwise (as viewed from timing belt end of engine). If timing belt is to be reused, mark direction of rotation before removing.

---

2) Remove crankshaft sprocket bolt and washer. Rotate crankshaft clockwise (as viewed from timing belt end of engine) until cylinder No. 1 is at TDC of compression stroke. Align timing mark on camshaft sprocket with mark on cylinder head. *See Fig. 26.*

3) Loosen timing belt tensioner adjustment bolt, and move tensioner toward water pump. Tighten bolt to secure tensioner. Remove front timing belt and tensioner. DO NOT rotate crankshaft after timing belt has been removed.

4) Remove camshaft sprocket (if necessary). Remove oil pump sprocket access plug from cylinder block. *See Fig. 10.* Insert a .31" (8.0 mm) diameter Phillips screwdriver to block left silent shaft.

5) Remove oil pump sprocket nut, and remove sprocket. Remove front crankshaft sprocket and flange. Note direction and order of installation for reassembly reference.

6) Remove rear timing belt tensioner assembly. Remove rear timing belt. Remove right silent shaft sprocket with spacer (if necessary). Remove rear crankshaft sprocket with key.

Inspection – Check belt teeth for cracks, damage and contamination. Inspect sprockets for damage. Check belt tensioner for leakage and roughness in rotation. Replace components if damaged.

Installation – 1) Install rear crankshaft sprocket and flange. Install right silent shaft sprocket and spacer. Spacer should be installed with chamfered end into oil seal. Align timing marks. *See Fig. 27.*

2) Install rear tensioner. Hold tensioner tightly against belt while tightening bolts. Ensure deflection is .20-.28" (5.0-7.1 mm). *See Fig. 13.* Install camshaft sprocket. Tighten camshaft sprocket bolt to specification. See TORQUE SPECIFICATIONS.

3) Install front timing belt tensioner, tension spring and spacer. Ensure spring is properly engaged against water pump case. Rotate tensioner toward water pump, and temporarily tighten bolts. Ensure timing marks are aligned. *See Fig. 26.* Install timing belt on crankshaft.

4) Apply pressure on tension side of timing belt while installing belt (in order) on crankshaft, oil pump and camshaft sprockets. Loosen tensioner to apply spring pressure to timing belt.

5) To apply tension to belt, rotate crankshaft clockwise until camshaft sprocket timing mark is offset by 2 teeth. Tighten tensioner bolt. Tighten tensioner spacer nut.

6) To check belt tension, apply slight thumb pressure and measure deflection between camshaft and oil pump sprocket. Belt deflection should be .55" (14.0 mm). *See Fig. 15.* To complete installation, reverse removal procedure.

ROCKER ARM & VALVE LASH ADJUSTER

CAUTION: DO NOT rotate crankshaft if timing belt has been removed. DO NOT rotate crankshaft counterclockwise (as viewed from timing belt end of engine).

Removal (1.8L Eclipse, 2.0L SOHC & 2.4L) – **1)** Remove valve cover and semi-circular packing from rear of cylinder head. Remove upper front timing belt cover.

2) Rotate crankshaft clockwise (as viewed from timing belt end of engine) until cylinder No. 1 is at TDC of compression stroke and timing mark on camshaft sprocket aligns with timing mark on upper cover (1.8L) or cylinder head (2.0L SOHC and 2.4L). *See Fig. 9 or 26.*

3) Mark timing belt in alignment with timing mark on camshaft sprocket. Wire belt to sprocket. Remove camshaft sprocket bolt. Slide camshaft sprocket and belt off camshaft.

NOTE: Check lash adjuster free play before rocker arm removal. See INSPECTION procedure.

4) Install Lash Adjuster Retainer (MD998443) on rocker arm to prevent adjuster from falling out of rocker arm. *See Fig. 28.* Loosen rocker shaft mounting bolts uniformly, and remove rocker shaft assembly. Remove camshaft and oil seal. If removing lash adjusters from rocker arms, mark for installation reference.

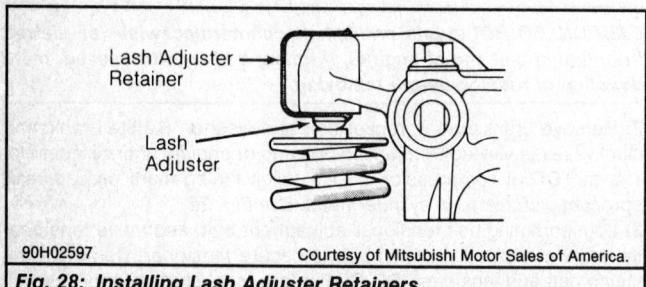

90H02597   Courtesy of Mitsubishi Motor Sales of America.
Fig. 28: Installing Lash Adjuster Retainers
(1.8L Eclipse, 2.0L SOHC & 2.4L)

Inspection – **1)** Before removing rocker arms from engine, insert a small wire through rocker arm bleed hole and into lash adjuster. With wire lightly holding lash adjuster internal check ball down, move rocker arm up and down to check for free play. If no free play is present, replace adjuster.

2) Inspect rocker arms and shafts for wear and damage. Check distributor drive gear for tooth damage and wear. Replace components as necessary.

3) Check camshaft journal diameter and lobe height. Replace camshaft if journal diameter and lobe height are not within specification. See CAMSHAFT table under ENGINE SPECIFICATIONS.

Installation – **1)** Lubricate camshaft lobes and camshaft bearing journals, and install camshaft into cylinder head. Install lash adjuster in rocker arm (if removed). Install lash adjuster retainer.

2) Ensure rocker arm components are installed in original location and wave washers are properly positioned. *See Fig. 29.* Rocker arms for cylinders No. 1 and 3 are marked 1-3. Rocker arms for cylinders No. 2 and 4 are marked 2-4.

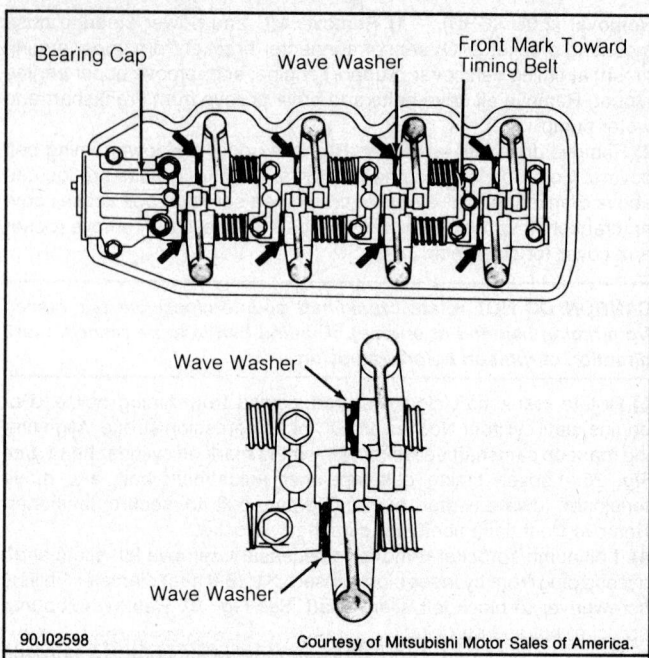

90J02598   Courtesy of Mitsubishi Motor Sales of America.
Fig. 29: Installing Rocker Arm Shaft Components
(1.8L Eclipse, 2.0L SOHC & 2.4L)

3) Install bearing cap No. 1 on rocker arm shafts so cut areas face away from camshaft area. *See Fig. 30.* Ensure front mark on each bearing cap faces timing belt. Ensure bearing caps are in correct numerical order. Tighten camshaft bearing cap bolts to specification. See TORQUE SPECIFICATIONS.

4) Coat lip of camshaft oil seal with oil. Install seal into cylinder head using Seal Installer (MD998364) on 1.8L, and Seal Installer (MD998306) with Guide (MD998307) on 2.0L and 2.4L.

5) Remove lash adjuster retainers. Apply sealant to inside of semi-circular packing and cylinder head before installing. To complete installation, reverse removal procedure.

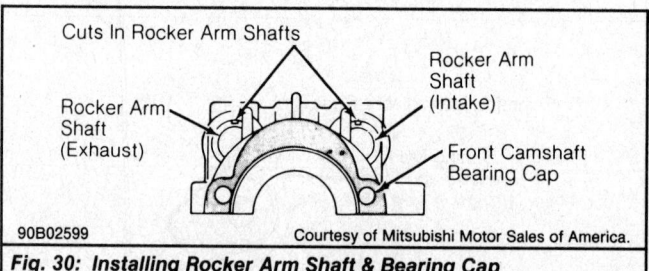

90B02599   Courtesy of Mitsubishi Motor Sales of America.
Fig. 30: Installing Rocker Arm Shaft & Bearing Cap
(1.8L Eclipse, 2.0L SOHC & 2.4L)

Removal (1.8L Except Eclipse) – **1)** Remove valve cover and semi-circular packing from rear of cylinder head. Remove upper front timing belt cover. Rotate crankshaft clockwise (as viewed from timing belt end of engine) until cylinder No. 1 is at TDC of compression stroke.

2) Ensure timing mark on camshaft sprocket aligns with timing mark on upper cover. *See Fig. 17.* Mark timing belt in alignment with timing mark on camshaft sprocket. Wire belt to sprocket. Remove camshaft sprocket bolt.

3) Slide camshaft sprocket and belt off camshaft. Loosen rocker shaft mounting bolts uniformly, and remove rocker shaft assembly. Remove camshaft and oil seal.

Inspection – **1)** Inspect rocker arms and shafts for wear and damage. Check distributor drive gear for tooth damage and wear. Replace components as necessary.

2) Check camshaft journal diameter and lobe height. Replace camshaft if journal diameter and lobe height are not within specification. See CAMSHAFT table under ENGINE SPECIFICATIONS.

Installation – **1)** Lubricate camshaft lobes and camshaft bearing journals. Install camshaft into cylinder head.

2) Ensure rocker arms are installed in original location. Tighten camshaft bearing cap bolts to specification. See TORQUE SPECIFI-CATIONS.

3) Coat lip of camshaft oil seal with oil. Install seal into cylinder head using Seal Installer (MD998713-01). To complete installation, reverse removal procedure.

Removal (2.0L DOHC) – 1) Disconnect throttle cable bracket from intake plenum. Remove timing belt. See TIMING BELT under REMOVAL & INSTALLATION.

2) Remove crankshaft position sensor. *See Fig. 31.* Using wrench, secure exhaust camshaft at hexagon. Remove sprocket bolt and sprocket. Repeat procedure for intake cam. Loosen front camshaft bearing cap bolts uniformly in 3 steps. Remove caps and seals.

3) Repeat procedure for remaining camshaft bearing cap bolts. Remove rear bearing caps last. Remove remaining camshaft bearing caps. If necessary, tap bearing cap using plastic hammer to break loose. Remove intake and exhaust camshafts. Remove rocker arms and lash adjusters from cylinder head.

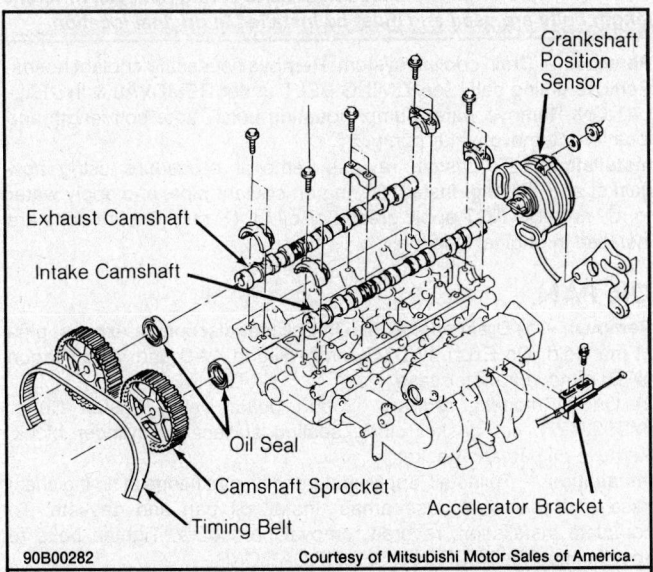

Exhaust Camshaft
Intake Camshaft
Crankshaft Position Sensor
Oil Seal
Camshaft Sprocket
Accelerator Bracket
Timing Belt

90B00282   Courtesy of Mitsubishi Motor Sales of America.

Fig. 31: Exploded View Of Camshaft & Related Components (2.0L DOHC)

Inspection – Check rocker arm friction surfaces for wear and damage. Check rocker arm rollers for smooth rotation. Check camshaft journal diameter and lobe height. Replace camshaft if journal diameter and lobe height are not within specification. See CAMSHAFT table under ENGINE SPECIFICATIONS.

Installation – 1) If new camshafts are installed, position camshaft in cylinder head without bearing caps. Ensure rotation is smooth. Lubricate journals, and install bearing caps.

2) Camshafts should turn easily by hand. If camshafts are okay, remove bearing caps and camshafts. Install lash adjusters and rocker arms on cylinder head.

3) Lubricate camshaft lobes and bearing journals. Install camshafts in cylinder head with dowel pins at 12 o'clock position. Note intake camshaft is slotted at rear. *See Fig. 32.*

4) Install camshaft bearing caps in original location, and tighten in sequence in 2-3 steps. *See Fig. 33.* See TORQUE SPECIFICATIONS.

NOTE: *To ensure correct fuel and ignition timing, install crankshaft position sensor so mark on housing aligns with notch on plate. See Fig. 32.*

5) Lubricate inside diameter of camshaft oil seal. Using Seal Installer (MD998306 and MD998307), install camshaft oil seal. To complete installation, reverse removal procedure.

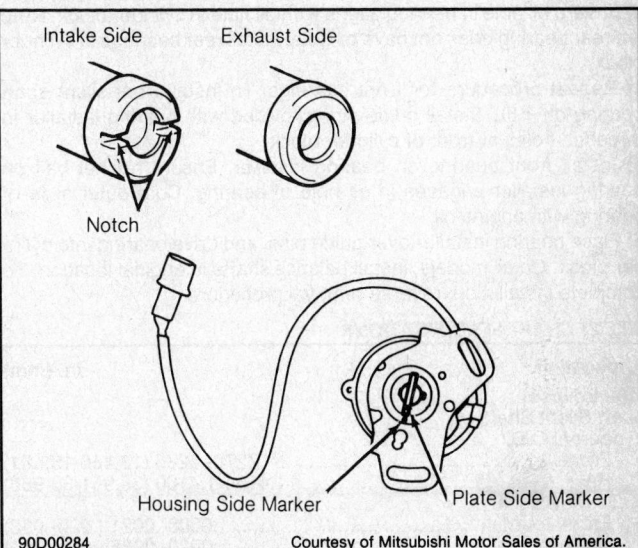

Intake Side   Exhaust Side

Notch

Housing Side Marker   Plate Side Marker

90D00284   Courtesy of Mitsubishi Motor Sales of America.

Fig. 32: Aligning Crankshaft Position Sensor To Intake Camshaft (2.0L DOHC)

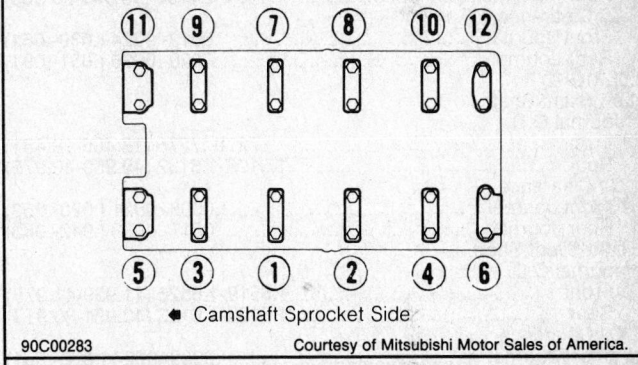

⑪ ⑨ ⑦ ⑧ ⑩ ⑫

⑤ ③ ① ② ④ ⑥

◄ Camshaft Sprocket Side

90C00283   Courtesy of Mitsubishi Motor Sales of America.

Fig. 33: Camshaft Bearing Cap Bolt Tightening Sequence (2.0L DOHC)

CAMSHAFT

NOTE: *For removal and installation of camshaft, see ROCKER ARM & VALVE LASH ADJUSTER under REMOVAL & INSTALLATION.*

SILENT SHAFTS & BEARINGS

NOTE: *1.8L models, except Eclipse, are not equipped with silent shaft.*

Removal – Remove front cover and oil pump. See OIL PUMP & FRONT COVER under ENGINE OILING. Remove silent shafts from cylinder block.

NOTE: *Rear bearing(s) cannot be removed unless front bearings have been removed from block.*

Inspection – 1) Inspect silent shaft and bearings for damage. Ensure silent shaft journal O.D. and oil clearance is within specification. See SILENT SHAFT SPECIFICATIONS table. Replace components if not within specification.

2) If bearings need replacing, use indicated puller. See SILENT SHAFT BEARING REMOVAL & INSTALLATION table.

NOTE: *Install rear bearings before installing front bearings.*

Installation – 1) Coat bearing outer area with engine oil before installing. Mount rear silent shaft bearing on indicated installer. See SILENT SHAFT BEARING REMOVAL & INSTALLATION table.

2) Ensure oil hole in bearing aligns with oil hole in cylinder block. Note left rear bearing does not have oil hole. Install rear bearings in cylinder block.

3) Repeat procedure for front bearings. To install front silent shaft bearing on 1.8L, install guide pins provided with bearing installer in threaded holes at front of cylinder block.

4) Install front bearing on bearing installer. Ensure ratchet ball on bearing installer engages in oil hole of bearing. Coat outer area of bearing with engine oil.

5) Place bearing installer over guide pins, and drive bearing into cylinder block. On all models, install balance shafts in original location. To complete installation, reverse removal procedure.

SILENT SHAFT SPECIFICATIONS

Application	In. (mm)
1.8L Eclipse	
Left Silent Shaft	
Journal O.D.	
Front	.7270-.7276 (18.466-18.481)
Rear	1.4154-1.4160 (35.951-35.966)
Oil Clearance	
Front Journal	.0008-.0021 (.020-.053)
Rear Journal	.0020-.0036 (.051-.091)
Right Silent Shaft	
Journal O.D.	
Front	1.5338-1.5344 (38.959-38.974)
Rear	1.4154-1.4160 (35.951-35.966)
Oil Clearance	
Front Journal	.0012-.0024 (.030-.061)
Rear Journal	.0020-.0036 (.051-.091)
2.0L DOHC	
Left Silent Shaft	
Journal O.D.	
Front	.7270-.7276 (18.466-18.481)
Rear	1.6126-1.6132 (40.959-40.975)
Oil Clearance	
Front Journal	.0008-.0021 (.020-.053)
Rear Journal	.0017-.0033 (.042-.083)
Right Silent Shaft	
Journal O.D.	
Front	1.6519-1.6526 (41.959-41.975)
Rear	1.6122-1.6129 (40.951-35.967)
Oil Clearance	
Front Journal	.0008-.0024 (.020-.061)
Rear Journal	.0020-.0036 (.051-.091)
2.0L SOHC & 2.4L	
Left Silent Shaft	
Journal O.D.	
Front	.728 (18.49)
Rear	1.61 (40.9)
Oil Clearance	
Front Journal	.0011-.0020 (.028-.051)
Rear Journal	.0020-.0036 (.051-.091)
Right Silent Shaft	
Journal O.D.	
Front	1.65 (42.0)
Rear	1.61 (40.9)
Oil Clearance	
Front Journal	.0011-.0024 (.028-.061)
Rear Journal	.0020-.0036 (.051-.091)

SILENT SHAFT BEARING REMOVAL & INSTALLATION

Application	Tool No.
1.8L Eclipse	
Installer	
Front Bearing	MD998280
Rear Bearing	MD998286
Puller	
Front Bearing	MD998282
Rear Bearing	MD998283
2.0L & 2.4L	
Installer	MD990938
Front & Rear Bearing Adapter	MD998373
Left Rear Bearing Guide Plate	MD998374
Puller	MIT304204
Front Bearing Adapter	MD998371
Rear Bearing Adapter	MD998372
Left Rear Bearing Guide Plate	MD998374

REAR CRANKSHAFT OIL SEAL

Removal – **1)** Remove transaxle/transmission. For A/T vehicles, see TRANSMISSION REMOVAL & INSTALLATION article in TRANSMISSION SERVICING. For M/T vehicles, see appropriate article in CLUTCHES.

2) Remove flywheel or drive plate. Remove rear main oil seal case and gasket from rear of cylinder block. Remove oil separator and oil seal from seal case.

Installation – **1)** Coat seal lip with oil. Using Seal Installer (MD998011 for 1.8L Eclipse, MD998776 for 1.8L except Eclipse, or MD998376 for 2.0L and 2.4L), install seal in seal case until it bottoms.

2) Install oil separator in seal case with hole of separator at bottom of seal case (toward oil pan). Install seal case and gasket. Install flywheel or drive plate. To complete installation, reverse removal procedure.

WATER PUMP

CAUTION: Note length and location of bolts during removal. Different length bolts are used and must be installed in original location.

Removal – Drain cooling system. Remove necessary coolant hoses. Remove timing belt. See TIMING BELT under REMOVAL & INSTALLATION. Remove water pump mounting bolts. Note bolt length and location. Remove water pump.

Installation – To install, reverse removal procedure using new gasket and "O" ring. Install "O" ring on coolant pipe, and apply water to "O" ring. DO NOT apply grease or oil to "O" ring. Ensure bolts are installed in original location.

OIL PAN

Removal – **1)** Drain engine oil. On Eclipse, disconnect exhaust pipe at manifold. On Expo 4WD, Summit Wagon 4WD and Vista Wagon 4WD, remove transfer case.

2) On all models, remove oil pan bolts. Using Gasket Cutter (MD998727), cut gasket along sealing surface of cylinder block. Remove oil pan and gasket.

Installation – To install, apply sealant to oil pan flange at timing chain case and rear seal case areas. Install oil pan and gaskets. To complete installation, reverse removal procedure. Tighten bolts to specification. See TORQUE SPECIFICATIONS.

OVERHAUL

CYLINDER HEAD

Cylinder Head – Inspect cylinder head for warpage at deck surface. Resurface cylinder head if warpage exceeds specification. See CYLINDER HEAD table under ENGINE SPECIFICATIONS.

Valve Springs – Inspect valve spring free length, out-of-square and installed height. Replace valve spring if not within specification. See VALVES & VALVE SPRINGS table under ENGINE SPECIFICATIONS. Install all valve springs with painted area toward rocker arm.

Valve Stem Oil Seals – DO NOT reuse oil seals. Install valve spring seat before installing oil seals. To provide proper positioning of oil seal, install new oil seals using Valve Seal Installer (MD998728 for 1.8L Eclipse, MD998774 for 1.8L except Eclipse, MD998737 for 2.0L DOHC, MD998737 for 2.0L SOHC or MD998729 for 2.4L).

Valve Guides – Ensure valve stem diameter is within specification. Check valve stem clearance. Clearance should be within specification. See VALVES & VALVE SPRINGS and CYLINDER HEAD tables under ENGINE SPECIFICATIONS. If clearance exceeds service limits, replace valve guide with an oversized valve guide.

Valves – Ensure valve stem diameter and margin are within specification. See VALVES & VALVE SPRINGS table under ENGINE SPECIFICATIONS.

Valve Seat – See ENGINE OVERHAUL PROCEDURES article in GENERAL INFORMATION.

Valve Seat Correction Angles – See ENGINE OVERHAUL PROCEDURES article in GENERAL INFORMATION.

VALVE TRAIN

Rocker Arm Shaft Assembly – 1) For reassembly reference, note location and order of assembly for all components. Remove bolts from shafts, and separate components. Note length of springs. Intake rocker arm shaft springs are longer than exhaust rocker arm shaft springs. **2)** Inspect components for wear and damage. Install components in original location when reassembling shaft assembly. Tighten rocker arm assembly bolts to specification. See TORQUE SPECIFICATIONS.

Lash Adjusters – Before installing lash adjuster, submerge lash adjuster in oil. Use a small wire to hold down internal check valve. Pump plunger up and down 4 or 5 times to bleed air from lash adjuster.

CYLINDER BLOCK ASSEMBLY

Piston & Rod Assembly – 1) Mark piston and rod assembly with corresponding cylinder number before removing. Center piston pin in piston. Measure and record piston pin installation depth. Use Piston Pin Removal & Installation Set (MD998780) with hydraulic press to remove piston pin.

2) Piston pin should be easily pushed into piston. If looseness or resistance is encountered, replace piston and pin as a set. Check connecting rod for damage and excessive bend and twist. See CONNECTING RODS table under ENGINE SPECIFICATIONS.

3) Position piston, piston pin and rod on press. Ensure front mark on piston will face timing belt side of engine when installed. Using piston pin removal and installation set, install piston pin into piston and rod to depth recorded in step 1). Ensure piston pin is centered in piston.

Fitting Pistons – 1) Measure piston skirt diameter at 90-degree angle to piston pin. If piston diameter is not within specification, replace piston. See PISTONS, PINS & RINGS table under ENGINE SPECIFICATIONS.

2) Measure cylinder bore diameter at 3 places: near top of bore, bottom of bore and center of bore. If cylinder bore diameter or taper is not within specification, machine cylinder bore. See CYLINDER BLOCK table under ENGINE SPECIFICATIONS.

3) If piston-to-cylinder bore clearance is not within specification, replace piston and/or machine cylinder bore. See PISTONS, PINS & RINGS table under ENGINE SPECIFICATIONS.

Piston Rings – Ensure ring end gap and side clearance are within specification. See PISTONS, PINS & RINGS table under ENGINE SPECIFICATIONS. DO NOT use a ring expander to install oil ring side rails. Properly position ring end gaps around circumference of piston before installing. See Fig. 34.

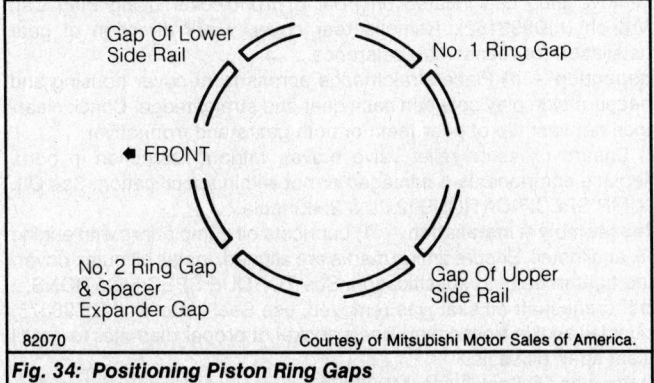

Fig. 34: Positioning Piston Ring Gaps

(Labels: Gap Of Lower Side Rail; No. 1 Ring Gap; FRONT; No. 2 Ring Gap & Spacer Expander Gap; Gap Of Upper Side Rail; 82070; Courtesy of Mitsubishi Motor Sales of America.)

Rod Bearings – Note position of connecting rod in relation to bearing cap before removing. Ensure bearing oil clearance and side play are within specification. See CRANKSHAFT, MAIN & CONNECTING ROD BEARINGS and CONNECTING RODS tables under ENGINE SPECIFICATIONS.

Crankshaft & Main Bearings – Check diameter of crankshaft main bearing journals and connecting rod bearing journals. Check journals for taper and out-of-round. Check crankshaft end play. See CRANKSHAFT, MAIN & CONNECTING ROD BEARINGS table under ENGINE SPECIFICATIONS.

Thrust Bearing – Replace thrust bearing if crankshaft end play is not within specification. See CRANKSHAFT, MAIN & CONNECTING ROD BEARINGS table under ENGINE SPECIFICATIONS.

Cylinder Block – 1) Check cylinder block head surface warpage. If warpage exceeds specification, machine surface. See CYLINDER BLOCK table under ENGINE SPECIFICATIONS. DO NOT remove more than a combined total .008" (0.20 mm) material from original surfaces of cylinder head or cylinder block.

2) Check cylinder bore wear and taper. Measure cylinder bore diameter at 3 places: near top of bore, bottom of bore and center of bore. If cylinder bore diameter or taper is not within specification, machine cylinder bore. See CYLINDER BLOCK table.

ENGINE OILING

ENGINE LUBRICATION SYSTEM

Oil pressure is provided by a belt-driven oil pump mounted in front cover. Pressure relief valve is not adjustable, and is located either in front cover or oil filter bracket. See Fig. 35.

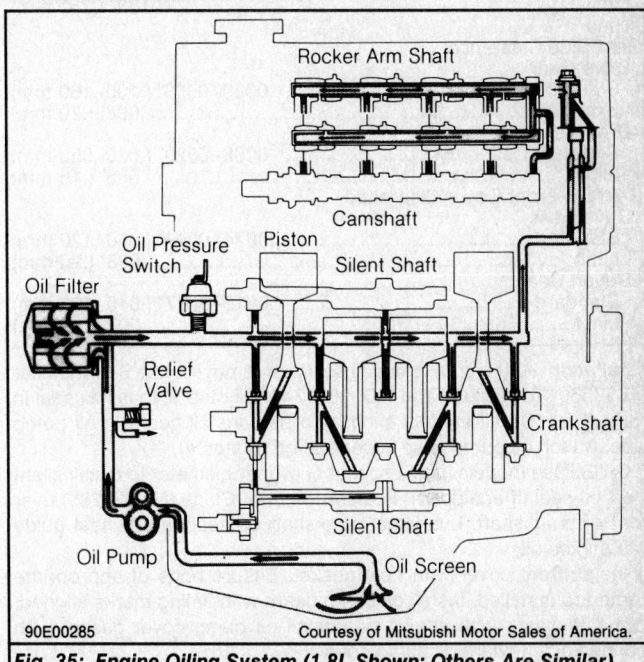

Fig. 35: Engine Oiling System (1.8L Shown; Others Are Similar)

(Labels: Rocker Arm Shaft; Camshaft; Oil Pressure Switch; Piston; Silent Shaft; Oil Filter; Relief Valve; Crankshaft; Silent Shaft; Oil Pump; Oil Screen; 90E00285; Courtesy of Mitsubishi Motor Sales of America.)

CRANKCASE CAPACITY SPECIFICATIONS

Application	¹ Qts. (L)
Colt Vista, Expo & Summit Wagon	
1.8L	4.0 (3.8)
2.4L	4.1 (3.9)
Eclipse	
1.8L	4.1 (3.9)
2.0L	4.6 (4.4)
Pickup	4.1 (3.9)

¹ – Includes oil filter.

Oil Pressure – Oil pressure should be at least 11.4 psi (.80 kg/cm²) at curb idle, and oil temperature should be 167-194°F (75-90°C).

OIL PUMP & FRONT COVER

Removal (1.8L) – 1) Remove oil pan. See OIL PAN under REMOVAL & INSTALLATION. If necessary, remove oil filter bracket assembly. Remove oil pick-up assembly.

2) Remove timing belt and sprockets. See TIMING BELT under REMOVAL & INSTALLATION. Remove oil pump drive gear. Remove oil pump cover and gasket. Remove front cover from cylinder block.

3) If front cover sticks to cylinder block, pry cover from cylinder block at screwdriver slot. Remove plug, spring and relief plunger. Remove silent shaft and crankshaft oil seal from front cover.

Inspection – 1) Inspect components for damage. Install oil pump gears in front cover. Using feeler gauge, measure gear-to-front cover clearance between tip of teeth on each gear and front cover.

2) Place straightedge across front cover above gears. Using feeler gauge, check gear side clearance between straightedge and both oil pump gears. On Colt Vista, Expo and Summit Wagon, check clearance between gear (rotor) tips.

3) Check for ridge on oil pump cover in gear operating area. Ensure relief plunger slides freely in bore. Ensure spring free length is 1.73" (44.0 mm) for Eclipse and 1.85" (47.0 mm) for all others. Replace components if not within specification. See OIL PUMP SPECIFICATIONS (1.8L) table.

OIL PUMP SPECIFICATIONS (1.8L)

Application	Specification
Colt Vista, Expo & Summit Wagon	
Gear Side Clearance	.0015-.0039" (.040-.100 mm)
Gear Tip Clearance	.0024-.0071" (.060-.180 mm)
Gear-To-Front Cover Clearance	
Standard	.0039-.0071" (.100-.180 mm)
Limit	.0138" (.351 mm)
Eclipse	
Gear Side Clearance	
Drive Gear	
Standard	.0039-.0063" (.100-.160 mm)
Limit	.008" (.20 mm)
Driven Gear	
Standard	.0008-.0020" (.020-.050 mm)
Limit	.006" (.15 mm)
Gear-To-Front Cover Clearance	
Drive Gear	
Standard	.0024-.0047" (.060-.120 mm)
Limit	.008" (.20 mm)
Driven Gear	
Standard	.0015-.0047" (.040-.120 mm)
Limit	.007" (.18 mm)

Installation – 1) If crankshaft oil seal was removed, use Seal Installer (MD998304 for Eclipse and MD998717 for all others) to install seal in front cover. On all models except Eclipse, install gears in oil pump case. Attach oil pump case cover and go to step **4)**.

2) On Eclipse models, use a socket of proper diameter to install silent shaft oil seal (if equipped). Position Oil Seal Guide (MD998285) over front of crankshaft. Lubricate crankshaft oil seal and oil seal guide with engine oil.

3) Install front cover with new gasket. Ensure bolts of appropriate length are installed. Install oil pump gears with timing marks aligned. Lubricate gears with engine oil. Install oil pump cover gasket with rounded side toward oil pump cover.

4) On all models, to complete installation, reverse removal procedure. Tighten bolts to specification. See TORQUE SPECIFICATIONS.

Removal (2.0L DOHC) – 1) Remove timing belt and sprockets. See TIMING BELT under REMOVAL & INSTALLATION. Remove oil pan. See OIL PAN under REMOVAL & INSTALLATION. Remove oil filter. Using Socket (MD998054), remove oil pressure switch.

2) Remove oil pressure gauge sending unit. On turbo models, remove oil cooler and oil cooler by-pass valve. Remove oil jets and check valves from cylinder block.

3) On all models, remove oil pick-up tube, oil filter bracket and gasket. Remove plug, gasket, spring and relief plunger. Using Plug Cap Wrench (MD998162), remove plug cap and "O" ring from front cover.

4) Remove front cover and gasket from cylinder block. Remove silent shaft and crankshaft oil seals from front cover. Remove oil pump cover. Note timing marks on oil pump gears, and remove gears from front cover.

Inspection – 1) Inspect components for damage. Install oil pump gears in front cover. Using feeler gauge, measure gear-to-front cover clearance between tip of teeth on each gear and front cover.

2) Place straightedge across front cover above oil pump gears. Using feeler gauge, check gear side clearance between straightedge and gears. Check for ridge on oil pump cover in gear operating area.

3) Ensure pressure relief valve moves without restriction in bore. Replace components if damaged or not within specification. See OIL PUMP SPECIFICATIONS (2.0L & 2.4L) table.

4) On turbo models, ensure oil jets and check valves are not clogged or damaged. Ensure oil cooler by-pass valve slides freely. Remove valve, and measure distance from valve body to tip of valve at room temperature. Distance should be 1.358" (34.49 mm).

5) Heat oil to 212°F (100°C), and submerge valve in heated oil for 2 minutes. Distance from valve body to tip of valve should be at least 1.57" (39.88 mm). Replace valve assembly if measurements are not as specified.

Installation – 1) Lubricate oil pump gears with engine oil, and install. Ensure timing marks are aligned. Install oil pump cover, and tighten bolts to specification. See TORQUE SPECIFICATIONS.

2) If crankshaft oil seal was removed, use Seal Installer (MD998375-01) to install seal in front cover. Use a socket of proper diameter to install silent shaft oil seals.

3) Position Oil Seal Guide (MD998285) over front of crankshaft. Lubricate crankshaft oil seal and oil seal guide with engine oil. Install front cover with new gasket, and temporarily tighten bolts. Install oil filter bracket. Ensure correct length bolts are installed.

4) To complete installation, reverse removal procedure. Install plug cap using new "O" ring, and tighten to specification. Apply thread sealant to oil pressure switch threads before installing. Tighten all bolts to specification. See TORQUE SPECIFICATIONS.

OIL PUMP SPECIFICATIONS (2.0L & 2.4L)

Application	Specification
Gear Side Clearance	
Drive Gear	
Standard	.0031-.0055" (.080-.140 mm)
Limit	.0098" (.250 mm)
Driven Gear	
Standard	.0024-.0047" (.060-.120 mm)
Limit	.0098" (.250 mm)
Gear-To-Front Cover Clearance	
Drive Gear	
Standard	.0063-.0083" (.160-.210 mm)
Limit	.0098" (.250 mm)
Driven Gear	
Standard	.0051-.0071" (.130-.180 mm)
Limit	.0098" (.250 mm)

Removal & Disassembly (2.0L SOHC & 2.4L) – 1) Remove timing belt and crankshaft sprocket. See TIMING BELT under REMOVAL & INSTALLATION. Remove oil filter, oil pressure switch, oil pan and oil screen.

2) Remove oil filter bracket, front cover and oil pump assembly. Remove plug cap located on front of front cover using Plug Cap Wrench (MD998162). Remove rear cover. Mark direction of gear installation for reassembly reference.

Inspection – 1) Place straightedge across front cover housing and measure side play between each gear and straightedge. Check clearance between tip of gear teeth of both gears and front cover.

2) Ensure pressure relief valve moves without restriction in bore. Replace components if damaged or not within specification. See OIL PUMP SPECIFICATIONS (2.0L & 2.4L) table.

Reassembly & Installation – 1) Lubricate oil pump gears with engine oil, and install. Ensure timing marks are aligned. Install oil pump cover, and tighten bolts to specification. See TORQUE SPECIFICATIONS.

2) If crankshaft oil seal was removed, use Seal Installer (MD998375) to install seal in front cover. Use a socket of proper diameter to install silent shaft oil seals.

3) Position Oil Seal Guide (MD998285) over front of crankshaft. Lubricate crankshaft oil seal and oil seal guide with engine oil. Install front cover with new gasket, and temporarily tighten bolts. Install oil filter bracket. Ensure correct length bolts are installed.

4) To complete installation, reverse removal procedure. Install plug cap using new "O" ring, and tighten to specification. Apply thread sealant to oil pressure switch threads before installing. Tighten all bolts to specification. See TORQUE SPECIFICATIONS.

TORQUE SPECIFICATIONS

TORQUE SPECIFICATIONS (1.8L)

Application	Ft. Lbs. (N.m)
A/C Tensioner Pulley Bracket Bolt	17-20 (23-27)
Air Intake Plenum Bolt	11-14 (15-19)
Camshaft Bearing Cap Bolt	
6 x 20-mm	14-15 (19-20)
8 x 65-mm	15-20 (20-27)
Camshaft Sprocket Bolt	58-72 (79-98)
Connecting Rod Nut	24-25 (33-34)
Crankshaft Pulley Bolt	11-13 (15-18)
Crankshaft Sprocket Bolt	80-94 (109-127)
Cylinder Head Bolt [1]	51-54 (69-73)
Damper Pulley Bolt	11-13 (15-18)
Engine Support Bracket Bolt	36-47 (49-64)
Exhaust Manifold Nut	11-14 (15-19)
Flywheel/Drive Plate Bolt	94-101 (127-137)
Front Cover Bolt	11-13 (15-18)
Intake Manifold Bolt	[2]
Main Bearing Cap Bolt	37-39 (51-53)
Oil Filter Bracket Bolt	11-16 (15-22)
Oil Pick-Up Tube Nut	13-18 (18-24)
Oil Pump Cover Bolt	11-13 (15-18)
Oil Pump Sprocket Nut	26-29 (35-39)
Power Steering Pump Bolts	26-33 (35-45)
Oxygen Sensor	29-36 (39-49)
Rocker Arm Assembly Bolts	14-15 (19-20)
Silent Shaft Sprocket Bolt	25-29 (34-39)
Throttle Body Bolt	11-16 (15-22)
Timing Belt "A" Tensioner Bolt	16-22 (22-30)
Timing Belt "B" Tensioner Bolt	11-16 (15-22)
Water Pump Bolt	
Except 8 x 65-mm	10 (14)
8 x 65-mm	15-19 (20-26)

	INCH Lbs. (N.m)
Fuel Rail Bolt	84-108 (9-12)
Oil Pan Bolt/Nut	48-60 (5-7)
Timing Belt Cover Bolt	84-108 (9-12)
Valve Cover Bolt	48-60 (5-7)
Water Pump Pulley Bolt	72-84 (8-9)

[1] – Tighten bolts to specification in sequence. *See Fig. 5 or 6.*
[2] – Information is not available from manufacturer.

TORQUE SPECIFICATIONS (2.0L)

Application	Ft. Lbs. (N.m)
A/C Tensioner Pulley Bracket Bolt	17-20 (23-27)
Auto Tensioner Bolt (DOHC)	14-20 (19-27)
Camshaft Bearing Cap Bolt	
DOHC [1]	14-15 (19-20)
SOHC	
Large	14-15 (19-20)
Small	14-20 (19-27)
Camshaft Sprocket Bolt	58-72 (79-98)
Connecting Rod Nut	36-38 (49-52)
Crankshaft Pulley Bolt	14-22 (19-30)
Crankshaft Sprocket Bolt	80-94 (109-127)
Cylinder Head Bolt [2]	65-72 (88-98)
Engine Support Bracket Bolt	
Front	36-51 (49-69)
Left	22-30 (30-41)
Exhaust Manifold Nut	
DOHC	18-22 (24-30)
SOHC	11-15 (15-20)
Exhaust Pipe-To-Manifold Nut	22-29 (30-39)

[1] – Tighten bolts in sequence. *See Fig. 33.*
[2] – Tighten bolts in sequence. *See Fig. 5.*

TORQUE SPECIFICATIONS (2.0L) (Cont.)

Application	Ft. Lbs. (N.m)
Exhaust Pipe-To-Turbo Nut	29-43 (39-58)
Flywheel/Drive Plate Bolt	94-101 (127-137)
Front Cover Bolt	
DOHC	14-16 (19-22)
SOHC	14-20 (19-27)
Front Tensioner Pulley Bolt (DOHC)	31-40 (42-54)
Idler Pulley Bolt (DOHC)	25-30 (34-41)
Intake Manifold Bolt/Nut	
DOHC	
8-mm	11-14 (15-19)
10-mm	22-30 (30-41)
SOHC	11-14 (15-19)
Intake Manifold Stay Bolt	
DOHC	18-22 (24-30)
SOHC	13-18 (18-24)
Main Bearing Cap Bolt	
DOHC	47-51 (64-69)
SOHC	37-39 (50-53)
Oil Cooler By-Pass Valve	37-43 (50-58)
Oil Filter Bracket Bolt	11-16 (15-22)
Oil Jet Bolt	22-25 (30-34)
Oil Pump Cover Bolt	11-13 (15-18)
Oil Pump Driven Gear Bolt	25-29 (34-39)
Oil Pump Pick-Up Tube Bolt	11-16 (15-22)
Oil Pump Sprocket Nut	36-43 (49-58)
Oxygen Sensor	29-36 (39-49)
Plug Cap	14-20 (19-27)
Power Steering Pump Bolts	26-33 (35-45)
Rear Tensioner Retaining Bolt	11-16 (15-22)
Rocker Arm Assembly Bolts	14-15 (19-20)
Silent Shaft Sprocket Bolt	
DOHC	31-35 (42-47)
SOHC	
.08" (2.0 mm) Washer	25-29 (34-39)
.10" (2.5 mm) Washer	31-35 (42-47)
Throttle Body Bolt (DOHC)	11-16 (15-22)
Turbo Coolant Line At Turbo Banjo Bolt	25-36 (34-49)
Turbo Coolant Line-To-Engine Flare Nut	29-36 (39-49)
Turbo Oil Pipe-To-Cylinder Block Banjo Bolt	10-14 (14-19)
Turbo Oil Pipe-To-Turbo Banjo Bolt	20-25 (27-34)
Turbo-To-Manifold Bolt/Nut	40-47 (54-64)
Water Pump Bolt	
Except 8 x 65-mm	10 (14)
8 x 65-mm	15-19 (20-26)

	INCH Lbs. (N.m)
Crankshaft Position Sensor Nut	84-108 (9-12)
Distributor Nut	84-108 (9-12)
Fuel Rail Bolt	84-108 (9-12)
Oil Pan Bolt	48-72 (5-8)
Oil Pressure Switch	72-108 (8-12)
Rear Crankshaft Oil Seal Case Bolt	84-108 (9-12)
Throttle Body Bolt (SOHC)	84-108 (9-12)
Timing Belt Cover Bolt	84-108 (9-12)
Turbo Oil Drain Line Bolt	72-84 (8-9)
Valve Body Bolt (DOHC)	84-108 (9-12)
Valve Cover Bolt	
DOHC	24-36 (3-4)
SOHC	48-60 (5-7)
Water Pump Pulley Bolt	72-84 (8-9)

[1] – Tighten bolts in sequence. *See Fig. 33.*
[2] – Tighten bolts in sequence. *See Fig. 5.*

TORQUE SPECIFICATIONS (2.4L)

Application	Ft. Lbs. (N.m)
Camshaft Bearing Cap Bolts	
8 x 25-mm	15-19 (20-26)
8 x 65-mm	14-15 (19-20)
Camshaft Sprocket Bolt	58-72 (79-98)
Connecting Rod Cap Nuts	37-38 (50-52)
Crankshaft Pulley Bolt	15-21 (20-28)
Crankshaft Sprocket Bolt	80-94 (109-127)
Cylinder Head Bolt (Cold Engine) [1]	65-72 (88-98)
Engine Support Bracket Bolts	29-36 (39-49)
Exhaust Manifold-To-Engine Bolt	11-14 (15-19)
Exhaust Pipe-To-Manifold Bolt	29-40 (39-54)
Flywheel/Drive Plate Bolt	94-101 (127-137)
Front Cover Bolt	15-19 (20-26)
Front Tensioner Bolt	30-40 (41-54)
Intake Manifold Bolt	11-14 (15-19)
Intake Manifold Stay Bolt	13-18 (18-24)
Main Bearing Cap Bolt	37-39 (50-53)
Oil Filter Bracket Bolt	11-15 (15-20)
Oil Pan Drain Plug	26-32 (35-43)
Oil Pump Cover Bolt	11-13 (15-18)
Oil Pump Driven Gear Bolt	25-28 (34-38)
Oil Pump Relief Valve Plug	29-36 (39-49)
Oil Pump Sprocket Nut	36-43 (49-58)
Oil Screen Bolt	11-15 (15-20)
Oil Screen Stay Nut	11-15 (15-20)
Power Steering Pump Bolt	18-24 (24-33)
Rear Tensioner Bolt	11-15 (15-20)
Rocker Arm Assembly Bolts	14-15 (19-20)
Silent Shaft Sprocket Bolt	25-28 (34-38)
Throttle Body Bolt	11-16 (15-22)

	INCH Lbs. (N.m)
Cooling Fan Nut	84-108 (9-12)
Delivery Pipe Bolt	84-108 (9-12)
High Pressure Fuel Hose Bolt	12-24 (1.4-2.7)
Oil Pan Bolt	48-72 (5-8)
Oil Pressure Switch	72-108 (8-12)
Radiator Upper Shroud	24-48 (3-5)
Rear Oil Seal Case Bolt	84-108 (9-12)
Rocker Cover Bolt	48-60 (5-7)
Timing Belt Upper Cover Bolts	84-108 (9-12)

[1] – Tighten bolts in sequence. *See Fig. 7.*

ENGINE SPECIFICATIONS

GENERAL SPECIFICATIONS

Application	Specification
1.8L	
Displacement	
Eclipse	107 Cu. In. (1.8L)
Except Eclipse	111 Cu. In. (1.8L)
Bore	
Eclipse	3.17" (80.6 mm)
Except Eclipse	3.19" (81.0 mm)
Stroke	
Eclipse	3.39" (86.1 mm)
Except Eclipse	3.50" (89.0 mm)
Compression Ratio	
Eclipse	9.0:1
Except Eclipse	8.5:1
Fuel System	MFI
Horsepower @ RPM	[1]
Torque Ft. Lbs. @ RPM	[1]

[1] – Information is not available from manufacturer.

GENERAL SPECIFICATIONS (Cont.)

Application	Specification
2.0L	
Displacement	122 Cu. In. (2.0L)
Bore	3.35" (85.1 mm)
Stroke	3.46" (87.9 mm)
Compression Ratio	
DOHC	
Non-Turbo	9.0:1
Turbo	7.8:1
SOHC	8.5:1
Fuel System	MFI
Horsepower @ RPM	
DOHC	
Non-Turbo	135 @ 6000
Turbo	190 @ 6000
SOHC	96 @ 5000
Torque Ft. Lbs. @ RPM	
DOHC	
Non-Turbo	125 @ 3000
Turbo	203 @ 3000
SOHC	113 @ 3500
2.4L	
Displacement	143.4 Cu. In. (2.4L)
Bore	3.41" (86.5 mm)
Stroke	3.94" (100.0 mm)
Compression Ratio	8.5:1
Fuel System	MFI
Horsepower @ RPM	116 @ 5000
Torque Ft. Lbs. @ RPM	136 @ 3500

[1] – Information is not available from manufacturer.

CRANKSHAFT, MAIN & CONNECTING ROD BEARINGS

Application	In. (mm)
Crankshaft End Play	
Standard	.0020-.0070 (.051-.178)
Wear Limit	.016 (.41)
Main Bearings	
Journal Diameter	2.244 (57.00)
Journal Out-Of-Round	.0006 (.015)
Journal Taper	.0002 (.005)
Oil Clearance	
Standard	.0008-.0016 (.020-.040)
Wear Limit	.004 (.10)
Connecting Rod Bearings	
Journal Diameter	1.771 (45.00)
Journal Out-Of-Round	.0006 (.015)
Journal Taper	.0002 (.005)
Oil Clearance	
Standard	.0008-.0020 (.020-.050)
Wear Limit	.004 (.10)

CONNECTING RODS

Application	In. (mm)
Maximum Bend	.0020 Per 3.937 (.051 Per 100.00)
Maximum Twist	.0039 Per 3.937 (.01 Per 100.00)
Side Play	
Standard	.0039-.0098 (.010-.250)
Wear Limit	.016 (.41)

PISTONS, PINS & RINGS (1.8L)

Application	In. (mm)
Eclipse	
Pistons	
Clearance	.0004-.0012 (.010-.030)
Diameter	3.1732 (80.599)
Pins	
Rod Fit	[1]
Rings	
No. 1	
End Gap	
Standard	.0118-.0177 (.300-.450)
Wear Limit	.031 (.79)
Side Clearance	
Standard	.0018-.0033 (.045-.085)
Wear Limit	.004 (.10)
No. 2	
End Gap	
Standard	.0079-.0138 (.200-.350)
Wear Limit	.031 (.79)
Side Clearance	
Standard	.0008-.0024 (.020-.060)
Wear Limit	.004 (.10)
Oil Ring Side Rail	.0079-.0276 (.200-.700)
Except Eclipse	
Pistons	
Clearance	.0008-.0016 (.020-.040)
Diameter	3.1882-3.1886 (80.980-80.990)
Pins	
Rod Fit	[1]
Rings	
No. 1	
End Gap	
Standard	.0098-.0157 (.250-.400)
Wear Limit	.031 (.79)
Side Clearance	
Standard	.0012-.0028 (.030-.070)
Wear Limit	.004 (.10)
No. 2	
End Gap	
Standard	.0157-.0217 (.400-.550)
Wear Limit	.031 (.79)
Side Clearance	
Standard	.0008-.0024 (.020-.060)
Wear Limit	.004 (.10)
Oil Ring Side Rail	.0079-.0236 (.200-.600)

[1] – Press fit with load of 1100-3300 lbs. (499-1497 kg).

PISTONS, PINS & RINGS (2.0L)

Application	In. (mm)
Pistons	
Clearance	
DOHC Non-Turbo	.0008-.0016 (.020-.041)
DOHC Turbo	.0012-.0020 (.030-.051)
SOHC	.0004-.0012 (.010-.030)
Diameter	3.3464 (85.000)
Pins	
Rod Fit	[1]
Rings	
No. 1	
End Gap	
Standard	
DOHC	.0098-.0177 (.250-.450)
SOHC	.0098-.0157 (.250-.400)
Wear Limit	.031 (.79)
Side Clearance	
Standard	.0012-.0028 (.030-.071)
Wear Limit	.004 (.10)
No. 2	
End Gap	
Standard	
DOHC	.0138-.0197 (.350-.500)
SOHC	.0079-.0138 (.200-.350)
Wear Limit	.031 (.79)
Side Clearance	
Standard	
DOHC	.0012-.0028 (.030-.071)
SOHC	.0008-.0024 (.020-.061)
Wear Limit	.004 (.10)

[1] – Press fit with load of 1653-3858 lbs. (750-1750 kg).

PISTONS, PINS & RINGS (2.0L) (Cont.)

Application	In. (mm)
No. 3 (Oil)	
End Gap	
Standard	.0079-.0276 (.200-.700)
Wear Limit	.039 (.99)

[1] – Press fit with load of 1653-3858 lbs. (750-1750 kg).

PISTONS, PINS & RINGS (2.4L)

Application	In. (mm)
Pistons	
Clearance	.0008-.0016 (.020-.041)
Diameter	3.406 (86.51)
Pins	
Rod Fit	[1]
Rings	
No. 1	
End Gap	
Standard	.0098-.0157 (.250-.400)
Wear Limit	.031 (.79)
Side Clearance	
Standard	.0012-.0028 (.030-.071)
Wear Limit	.004 (.10)
No. 2	
End Gap	
Standard	.0079-.0157 (.200-.400)
Wear Limit	.031 (.79)
Side Clearance	
Standard	.0008-.0024 (.020-.061)
Wear Limit	.004 (.10)
No. 3 (Oil)	
End Gap	
Standard	.0079-.0276 (.200-.700)
Wear Limit	.039 (.99)

[1] – Press fit with load of 1653-3858 lbs. (750-1750 kg).

CYLINDER BLOCK

Application	In. (mm)
1.8L (Eclipse)	
Cylinder Bore	
Standard Diameter	3.1734 (80.600)
Maximum Taper	.0004 (.010)
Maximum Out-Of-Round	.0004 (.010)
Deck Height	11.228 (285.20)
Maximum Deck Warpage	[1] .0039 (.099)
1.8L (Except Eclipse)	
Cylinder Bore	
Standard Diameter	3.1894-3.1898 (81.010-81.020)
Maximum Taper	.0004 (.010)
Maximum Out-Of-Round	.0004 (.010)
Deck Height	[2]
Maximum Deck Warpage	[1] .0039 (.099)
2.0L	
Cylinder Bore	
Standard Diameter	3.347 (85.001)
Maximum Taper	.0004 (.010)
Maximum Out-Of-Round	.0004 (.010)
Deck Height	11.18 (283.9)
Maximum Deck Warpage	[1] .002 (.05)
2.4L	
Cylinder Bore	
Standard Diameter	3.406 (86.51)
Maximum Taper	.0008 (.020)
Maximum Out-Of-Round	.0008 (.020)
Deck Height	11.42 (290.1)
Maximum Deck Warpage	[1] .002 (.05)

[1] – Combined maximum total grind limit of cylinder head and cylinder block is .008" (.20 mm).

[2] – Information is not available from manufacturer.

1994 ENGINES
1.8L, 2.0L & 2.4L 4-Cylinder (Cont.)

VALVES & VALVE SPRINGS

Application	Specification
1.8L (Eclipse)	
Intake Valves	
Face Angle	45-45.5°
Minimum Margin	.028" (.71 mm)
Stem Diameter	.31" (8.0 mm)
Exhaust Valves	
Face Angle	45-45.5°
Minimum Margin	.020" (.51 mm)
Stem Diameter	.31" (8.0 mm)
Valve Springs	
Free Length	1.898-1.937" (48.21-49.20 mm)
Installed Height	1.469-1.516" (37.31-38.51 mm)
Out-Of-Square	
Standard	Less Than 2°
Wear Limit	4°
1.8L (Except Eclipse)	
Intake Valves	
Face Angle	45-45.5°
Minimum Margin	.019" (.48 mm)
Stem Diameter	.235" (5.97 mm)
Exhaust Valves	
Face Angle	45-45.5ᶜ
Minimum Margin	.039" (1.00 mm)
Stem Diameter	.234" (5.95 mm)
Valve Springs	
Free Length	1.965-2.004" (48.21-49.20 mm)
Installed Height	[1]
Out-Of-Square	
Standard	Less Than 2°
Wear Limit	4°
2.0L	
Intake Valves	
Face Angle	45-45.5°
Minimum Margin	
Standard	
DOHC	.040" (1.02 mm)
SOHC	.047" (1.19 mm)
Wear Limit	.028" (.71 mm)
Stem Diameter	
DOHC	.2585-.2591" (6.565-6.581 mm)
SOHC	.31" (8.0 mm)
Valve Length	
DOHC	4.311" (109.50 mm)
SOHC	4.323" (109.80 mm)
Exhaust Valves	
Face Angle	45-45.5°
Minimum Margin	
DOHC	
Standard	.059" (1.50 mm)
Wear Limit	.039" (1.00 mm)
SOHC	
Standard	.079" (2.01 mm)
Wear Limit	.059" (1.50 mm)
Stem Diameter	
DOHC	.2571-.2579" (6.530-6.551 mm)
SOHC	.31" (8.0 mm)
Valve Length	
DOHC	4.319" (109.70 mm)
SOHC	4.280" (108.71 mm)

[1] - Information is not available from manufacturer.

VALVES & VALVE SPRINGS (Cont.)

Application	Specification
2.0L (Cont.)	
Valve Springs	
Free Length	
DOHC	1.862-1.902" (47.29-48.31 mm)
SOHC	1.921-1.961" (48.79-49.81 mm)
Installed Height	
DOHC	1.575-1.614" (40.01-41.00 mm)
SOHC	1.591-1.630" (40.41-41.40 mm)
Out-Of-Square	
Standard	Less Than 2°
Wear Limit	4°
2.4L	
Intake Valves	
Face Angle	45-45.5°
Minimum Margin	
Standard	.047" (1.19 mm)
Wear Limit	.028" (.71 mm)
Stem Diameter	.31" (8.0 mm)
Valve Length	4.1953" (106.560 mm)
Exhaust Valves	
Face Angle	45-45.5°
Minimum Margin	
Standard	.079" (2.01 mm)
Wear Limit	.059" (1.50 mm)
Stem Diameter	.31" (8.0 mm)
Valve Length	4.1401" (105.159 mm)
Valve Springs	
Free Length	1.961" (49.81 mm)
Installed Height	1.591-1.630" (40.41-41.40 mm)
Out-Of-Square	
Standard	Less Than 2°
Wear Limit	4°

[1] - Information is not available from manufacturer.

CYLINDER HEAD (1.8L)

Application	Specification
Eclipse	
Cylinder Head Height	3.484" (88.49 mm)
Maximum Warpage	[1] .0019" (.048 mm)
Valve Seats	
Intake Valve	
Seat Angle	44-44.5°
Seat Width	.0354-.0512" (.899-1.300 mm)
Exhaust Valve	
Seat Angle	44-44.5°
Seat Width	.0354-.0512" (.899-1.300 mm)
Valve Guides	
Intake Valve	
Valve Stem-To-Guide Oil Clearance	
Standard	.0012-.0024" (.030-.061 mm)
Wear Limit	.004" (.10 mm)
Exhaust Valve	
Valve Stem-To-Guide Oil Clearance	
Standard	.0020-.0035" (.051-.089 mm)
Wear Limit	.006" (.15 mm)
Except Eclipse	
Cylinder Head Height	4.720" (119.90 mm)
Maximum Warpage	[1] .0012" (.030 mm)
Valve Seats	
Intake Valve	
Seat Angle	43.5-44.0°
Seat Width	.0354-.0512" (.899-1.300 mm)
Exhaust Valve	
Seat Angle	43.5-44.0°
Seat Width	.0354-.0512" (.899-1.300 mm)

[1] – Combined maximum total grind limit of cylinder head and cylinder block is .008" (.20 mm).

CYLINDER HEAD (1.8L) (Cont.)

Application	Specification
Except Eclipse (Cont.)	
Valve Guides	
Intake Valve	
Valve Stem-To-Guide Oil Clearance	
Standard	.0008-.0020" (.020-.050 mm)
Wear Limit	.004" (.10 mm)
Exhaust Valve	
Valve Stem-To-Guide Oil Clearance	
Standard	.0020-.0035" (.050-.090 mm)
Wear Limit	.006" (.15 mm)

[1] – Combined maximum total grind limit of cylinder head and cylinder block is .008" (.20 mm).

CYLINDER HEAD (2.0L)

Application	Specification
Cylinder Head Height	
DOHC	5.197" (132.00 mm)
SOHC	3.544" (90.00 mm)
Maximum Warpage	[1] .0020" (.051 mm)
Valve Seats	
Intake Valve	
Seat Angle	
DOHC	44-44.5°
SOHC	45°
Seat Width	.035-.051" (.89-1.30 mm)
Exhaust Valve	
Seat Angle	
DOHC	44-44.5°
SOHC	45°
Seat Width	.035-.051" (.89-1.30 mm)
Valve Guides	
Intake Valve	
Guide Length	
DOHC	1.791" (45.49 mm)
SOHC	1.85" (47.0 mm)
Valve Stem-To-Guide Oil Clearance	
Standard	
DOHC	.0008-.0019" (.020-.048 mm)
SOHC	.0012-.0024" (.030-.061 mm)
Wear Limit	.004" (.10 mm)
Exhaust Valve	
Guide Length	
DOHC	1.988" (50.50 mm)
SOHC	2.05" (52.1 mm)
Valve Stem-To-Guide Oil Clearance	
Standard	
DOHC	.0020-.0033" (.051-.084 mm)
SOHC	.0020-.0035" (.051-.089 mm)
Wear Limit	.006" (.15 mm)

[1] – Combined maximum total grind limit of cylinder head and cylinder block is .008" (.20 mm).

CYLINDER HEAD (2.4L)

Application	Specification
Cylinder Head Height	3.544" (90.00 mm)
Maximum Warpage	[1] .0020" (.051 mm)
Valve Seats	
Intake Valve	
Seat Angle	44-44.5°
Seat Width	.035-.051" (.89-1.30 mm)
Exhaust Valve	
Seat Angle	44-44.5°
Seat Width	.035-.051" (.89-1.30 mm)
Valve Guides	
Intake Valve	
Guide Length	1.85" (47.0 mm)
Valve Stem-To-Guide	
Oil Clearance	.0012-.0024" (.030-.061 mm)
Exhaust Valve	
Guide Length	2.05" (52.1 mm)
Valve Stem-To-Guide	
Oil Clearance	.0020-.0035" (.051-.089 mm)

[1] – Combined maximum total grind limit of cylinder head and cylinder block is .008" (.20 mm).

CAMSHAFT

Application	In. (mm)
1.8L (Eclipse)	
End Play	.004-.008 (.10-.20)
Journal Diameter	1.3360-1.3366 (33.934-33.950)
Lobe Height	1.3941-1.4138 (35.410-35.911)
Oil Clearance	.0020-.0035 (.051-.089)
1.8L (Except Eclipse)	
End Play	.004-.008 (.10-.20)
Journal Diameter	1.7689-1.7693 (44.930-44.940)
Lobe Height	
Intake	1.4677-1.4876 (37.280-37.780)
Exhaust	1.4799-1.4996 (37.590-38.090)
Oil Clearance	.0020-.0035 (.051-.089)
2.0L	
End Play	.004-.008 (.10-.20)
Journal Diameter	
DOHC	1.0217-1.0224 (25.951-25.969)
SOHC	1.339 (34.01)
Lobe Height	
DOHC	
Intake	
Non-Turbo & Turbo M/T	1.3777-1.3974 (34.994-35.494)
Turbo A/T	1.3661-1.3858 (34.699-35.199)
Exhaust	
Non-Turbo & Turbo A/T	1.3661-1.3858 (34.699-35.199)
Turbo M/T	1.3777-1.3974 (34.994-35.494)
SOHC	1.6370-1.6567 (41.580-42.080)
Oil Clearance	.0020-.0035 (.051-.089)
2.4L	
End Play	.004-.008 (.10-.20)
Journal Diameter	1.339 (34.01)
Lobe Height	1.6496-1.6693 (41.900-42.400)
Oil Clearance	.0020-.0035 (.051-.089)

1994 ENGINES
2.4L 4-Cylinder

Mitsubishi: Galant

NOTE: For repair procedures not covered in this article, see ENGINE OVERHAUL PROCEDURES article in GENERAL INFORMATION.

ENGINE IDENTIFICATION

Vehicle Identification Number (VIN) is stamped on a metal plate located at upper left corner of instrument panel, near windshield. The eighth character of VIN identifies engine, and tenth character (R) identifies model year (1994).

Engine model code and serial number are stamped on right side of cylinder block, near front. For specific location, see CHRYSLER CORP./MITSUBISHI INTRODUCTION article in ENGINE PERFORMANCE.

ENGINE IDENTIFICATION CODES

Application	Engine Model	Engine Code
DOHC	4G64	L
SOHC	4G64	G

ADJUSTMENTS

VALVE CLEARANCE ADJUSTMENT

Hydraulic lash adjusters are used. Valve adjustment is not required.

REMOVAL & INSTALLATION

CAUTION: When battery is disconnected, vehicle computer and memory systems may lose memory data. Driveability problems may exist until computer systems have completed a relearn cycle.

NOTE: For reassembly reference, label all electrical connectors, vacuum hoses and fuel lines before removal. Also place mating marks on engine hood and other major assemblies before removal.

FUEL PRESSURE RELEASE

Disconnect fuel pump connector near fuel tank. Start engine, and allow it to idle until it stalls. Turn ignition off. Reconnect fuel pump connector. Disconnect negative battery cable before disconnecting fuel lines.

ENGINE

CAUTION: To prevent fire hazard, release residual pressure in fuel system before disconnecting fuel lines.

Removal – **1)** Remove hood. Drain cooling system. Release residual fuel pressure from fuel system. See FUEL PRESSURE RELEASE under REMOVAL & INSTALLATION.
2) Drain engine oil and transaxle oil. Remove transaxle. On M/T models, see appropriate article in CLUTCHES. On A/T models, see TRANSMISSION REMOVAL & INSTALLATION article in TRANSMISSION SERVICING.
3) Remove radiator and cooling fan assembly. Disconnect all necessary electrical connectors, vacuum hoses, fuel hoses and cables. Leaving hoses connected, remove power steering pump and A/C compressor, and support aside using wire.
4) Disconnect exhaust pipe from exhaust manifold. Using lifting device, support weight of engine. Remove upper engine mount bracket assembly. Raise engine slightly. Ensure all cables, hoses and electrical harnesses are disconnected from engine. Lift engine upward from engine compartment.
Installation – To install, reverse removal procedure. Ensure all hoses and wires are cleared when lowering engine assembly into compartment. Perform final tightening of mounting bolts and nuts with weight of engine on insulators. See TORQUE SPECIFICATIONS. Replace all fluids, and adjust all cables and linkages.

INTAKE MANIFOLD

CAUTION: To prevent fire hazard, release residual pressure in fuel system before disconnecting fuel lines.

Removal – **1)** Release residual fuel pressure from fuel system. See FUEL PRESSURE RELEASE under REMOVAL & INSTALLATION. Disconnect negative battery cable. Disconnect air intake hose from air intake pipe.
2) Drain cooling system. Disconnect all necessary electrical connectors, vacuum hoses, coolant hoses, fuel hoses and cables from intake manifold, injectors and throttle body. *See Fig. 1 or 2.*
3) Remove air intake pipe and throttle body. Remove air intake plenum from intake manifold. Remove fuel delivery pipe with fuel injectors and pressure regulator attached. DO NOT allow fuel injectors to fall from delivery pipe during removal.
4) On SOHC, remove distributor. On all models, remove intake manifold-to-cylinder block support brace. Remove intake manifold-to-cylinder head bolts. Remove intake manifold and gasket. If necessary, remove remaining components from intake manifold.
Installation – To install, reverse removal procedure. Use new gaskets, fuel injector insulators and "O" rings. Adjust all control cables. Fill cooling system.

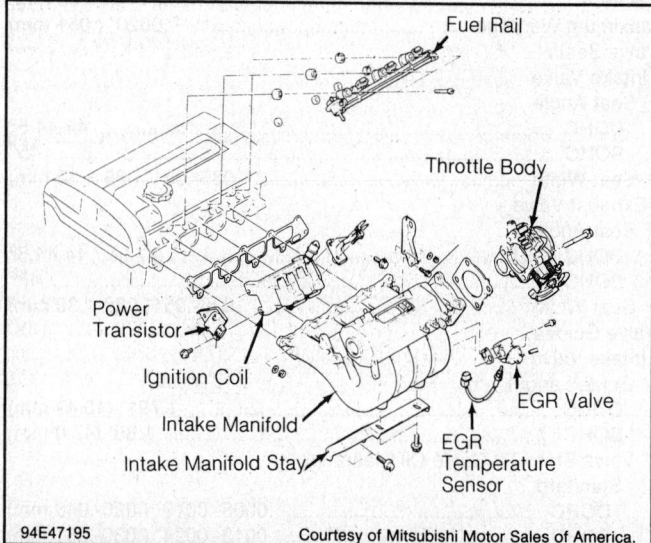

94E47195   Courtesy of Mitsubishi Motor Sales of America.

Fig. 1: Exploded View Of Intake Manifold & Related Components (DOHC)

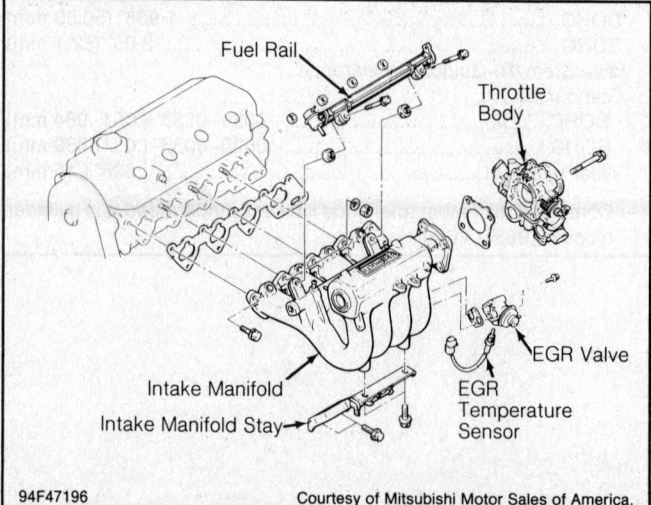

94F47196   Courtesy of Mitsubishi Motor Sales of America.

Fig. 2: Exploded View Of Intake Manifold & Related Components (SOHC)

EXHAUST MANIFOLD

Removal – Remove exhaust manifold heat shield. Disconnect exhaust pipe and gasket from manifold. Remove oxygen sensor. Remove exhaust manifold.

Installation – To install, reverse removal procedure. Use new gaskets and exhaust pipe-to-manifold nuts.

CYLINDER HEAD

CAUTION: Release residual pressure in fuel system before disconnecting fuel lines.

Removal – 1) Release fuel pressure from fuel system. See FUEL PRESSURE RELEASE under REMOVAL & INSTALLATION.

2) Drain cooling system. Remove air intake hose and pipe from top of rocker cover. Disconnect all necessary electrical connectors, vacuum hoses, coolant hoses, fuel hoses and cables.

3) Remove power steering pump (with hoses connected if possible), and support aside using wire. Disconnect exhaust pipe from exhaust manifold. Remove upper front timing belt cover.

4) Turn crankshaft to TDC of compression stroke on cylinder No. 1 by aligning mark on cylinder head with mark on camshaft sprocket. *See Fig. 14.* Remove rocker cover.

5) On SOHC, remove distributor cap. Mark rotor-to-distributor position. Mark distributor-to-cylinder head position. Remove distributor. On all models, mark timing belt in alignment with timing mark on camshaft sprocket. Wire timing belt to camshaft sprocket to maintain correct position. Remove camshaft sprocket bolt.

6) Slide camshaft sprocket (with belt attached) off camshaft. DO NOT turn crankshaft. Loosen cylinder head bolts (in 2-3 steps) in proper sequence. *See Fig. 3 or 4.* Remove cylinder head and gasket.

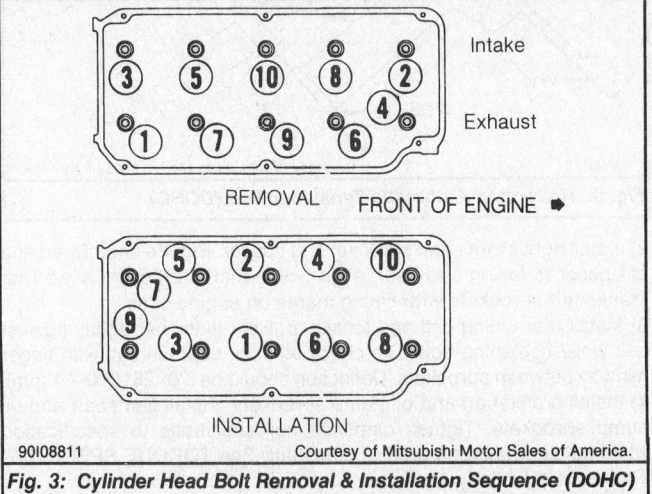

REMOVAL   FRONT OF ENGINE ➡

INSTALLATION

90I08811   Courtesy of Mitsubishi Motor Sales of America.

Fig. 3: Cylinder Head Bolt Removal & Installation Sequence (DOHC)

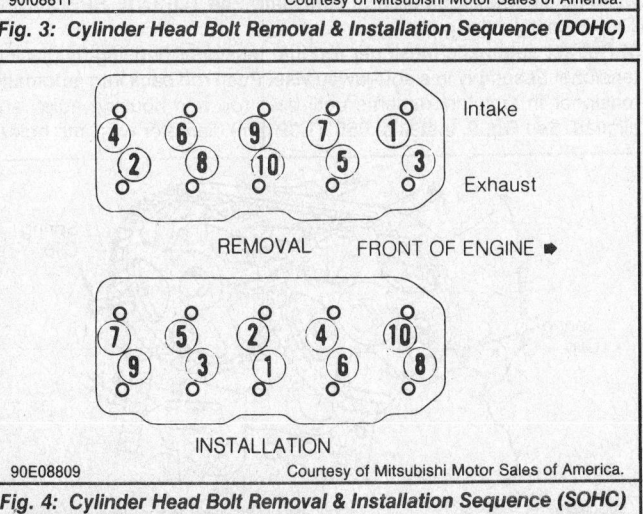

REMOVAL   FRONT OF ENGINE ➡

INSTALLATION

90E08809   Courtesy of Mitsubishi Motor Sales of America.

Fig. 4: Cylinder Head Bolt Removal & Installation Sequence (SOHC)

Inspection – Inspect cylinder head for warpage at deck surface. Resurface cylinder head if warpage exceeds specification. See CYLINDER HEAD table under ENGINE SPECIFICATIONS.

Installation – 1) Install cylinder head using new gasket. Ensure identification mark at timing belt end of gasket faces upward. DO NOT apply sealant to head gasket. Install and tighten cylinder head bolts (in 2-3 steps) to specification in proper sequence. *See Fig. 3 or 4.* See TORQUE SPECIFICATIONS.

2) To complete installation, reverse removal procedure. Apply sealant to contact surfaces of semi-circular packing. Adjust all control cables. Fill cooling system.

FRONT COVER OIL SEAL

NOTE: Front cover refers to cover at front of cylinder block. Cover contains oil pump and front cover oil seal (crankshaft front seal). Manufacturer lists oil seal removal procedure with front cover removed from engine. See OIL PUMP & FRONT COVER under ENGINE OILING.

TIMING BELT

CAUTION: To prevent engine damage, DO NOT rotate crankshaft counterclockwise (as viewed from timing belt end of engine).

NOTE: Ensure timing marks are aligned. Mark direction of rotation of all timing belts.

Removal (DOHC) – 1) Remove protective cover from below engine. Remove A/C and power steering hose mounting bracket. Support engine. Remove upper engine mount located near timing belt cover. Remove all drive belts and drive pulleys from crankshaft and water pump.

2) Remove drive belt tensioner. Remove upper and lower timing belt cover with gasket. Note bolt lengths and locations. Remove breather hose, PCV hose and center shield from valve cover. Disconnect spark plug wires from spark plugs.

CAUTION: DO NOT rotate crankshaft counterclockwise (as viewed from timing belt end of engine).

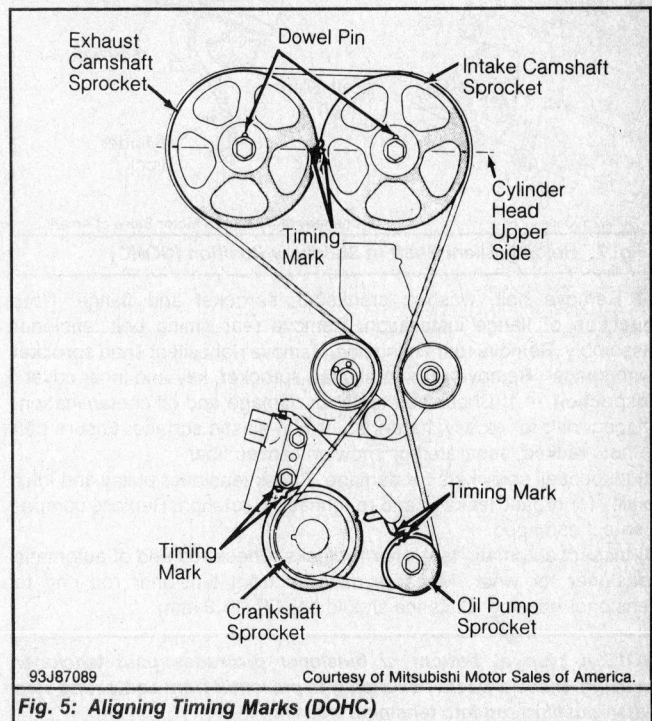

93J87089   Courtesy of Mitsubishi Motor Sales of America.

Fig. 5: Aligning Timing Marks (DOHC)

3) Remove rocker cover and semi-circular packing (located at rear of rocker cover). Remove rubber plug. Rotate crankshaft clockwise (as viewed from timing belt end of engine) until all timing marks align and cylinder No. 1 is at TDC of compression stroke. *See Fig. 5.*

4) Remove automatic tensioner. *See Fig. 6.* If timing belt is to be reused, mark timing belt to indicate original direction of rotation. Remove timing belt. Remove tensioner pulley, tensioner arm and idler pulley (if necessary). Inspect sprockets for damage.

5) To remove camshaft sprockets, hold camshaft hexagon (between camshaft journals No. 2 and 3) while removing camshaft sprocket bolt. Remove camshaft sprockets. Remove silent shaft access plug from cylinder block. Insert .31" (8.0 mm) diameter Phillips screwdriver to block left silent shaft. *See Fig. 7.* Remove oil pump sprocket nut and sprocket.

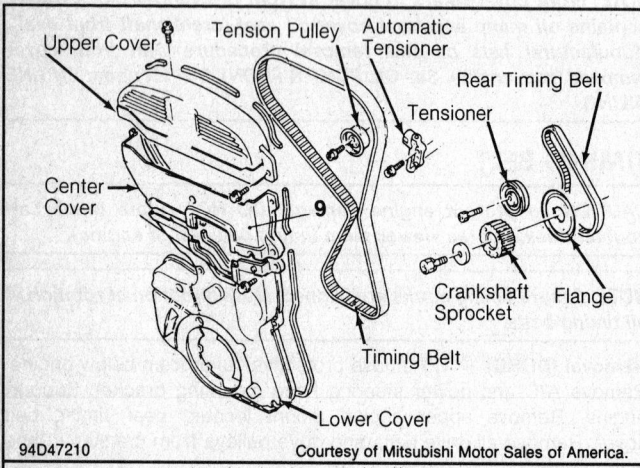

Fig. 6: **Exploded View Of Timing Belt & Related Components (DOHC)**

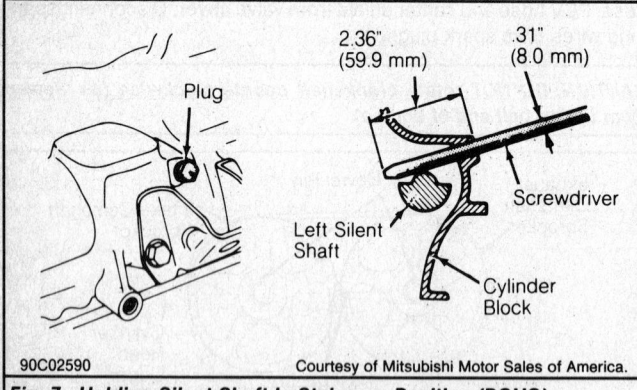

Fig. 7: **Holding Silent Shaft In Staionary Position (DOHC)**

6) Remove bolt, washer, crankshaft sprocket and flange. Note direction of flange installation. Remove rear timing belt tensioner assembly. Remove rear timing belt. Remove right silent shaft sprocket with spacer. Remove rear crankshaft sprocket, key and inner cover.

Inspection – 1) Check belt teeth for damage and oil contamination. Inspect belt for glossy, hardened or non-elastic surface. Ensure belt is not cracked, separated or showing canvas fiber.

2) Inspect all sprockets for damage. Check tensioner pulley and idler pulley for grease leakage and roughness in rotation. Replace components if damaged.

3) Inspect automatic tensioner for leaks. Check rod end of automatic tensioner for wear. Measure distance from tensioner rod end to tensioner housing. Distance should be .47" (11.9 mm).

NOTE: *If plug at bottom of tensioner protrudes past tensioner housing, place a washer over plug to prevent it from contacting vise when pushing rod into tensioner housing.*

4) Retract rod into tensioner housing by placing automatic tensioner assembly in a soft-jawed vise. Close vise to push rod back into tensioner. Replace automatic tensioner assembly if rod can be easily pushed into automatic tensioner.

Installation – 1) Install rear timing belt covers (if removed). Install rear crankshaft sprocket and flange. *See Fig. 8.*

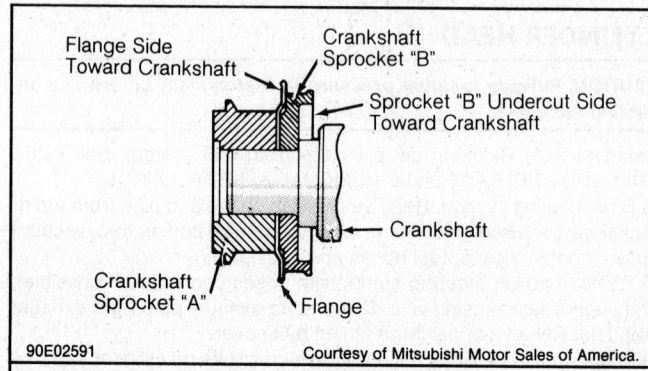

Fig. 8: **Installing Crankshaft Sprockets (DOHC)**

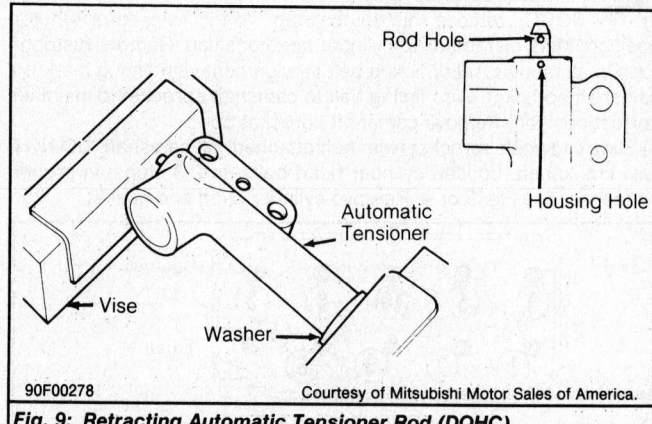

Fig. 9: **Retracting Automatic Tensioner Rod (DOHC)**

2) Install right silent shaft sprocket and spacer. Ensure chamfered end of spacer is facing into seal. Align timing marks on silent shaft rear crankshaft sprockets with timing marks on engine case.

3) Install rear timing belt and tensioner. Hold tensioner tightly against belt while tightening bolts. To check tension, depress belt with finger midway between sprockets. Deflection should be .20-.28" (5.0-7.1 mm).

4) Install crankshaft and oil pump sprockets. Install camshaft and oil pump sprockets. Tighten camshaft sprocket bolts to specification while holding hexagon area of camshaft. See TORQUE SPECIFICATIONS. Install idler pulley.

5) Retract automatic tensioner rod into tensioner housing by placing tensioner assembly in a soft-jawed vise. Push rod back into automatic tensioner in small increments until both rod and housing holes are aligned. *See Fig. 9.* Install a .055" (1.39 mm) diameter wire into holes.

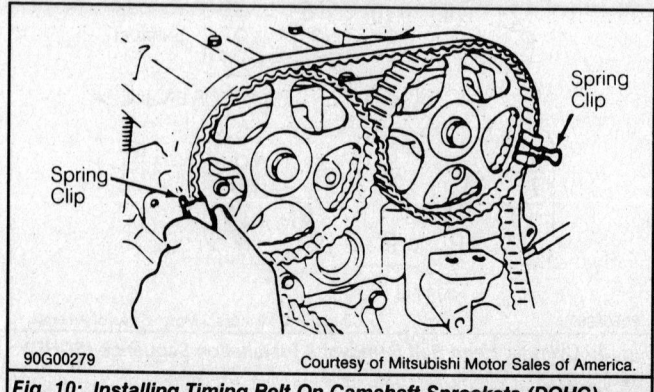

Fig. 10: **Installing Timing Belt On Camshaft Sprockets (DOHC)**

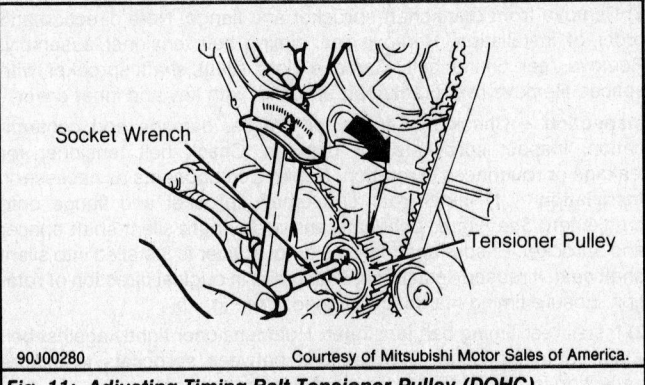

Fig. 11: Adjusting Timing Belt Tensioner Pulley (DOHC)

90J00280 Courtesy of Mitsubishi Motor Sales of America.

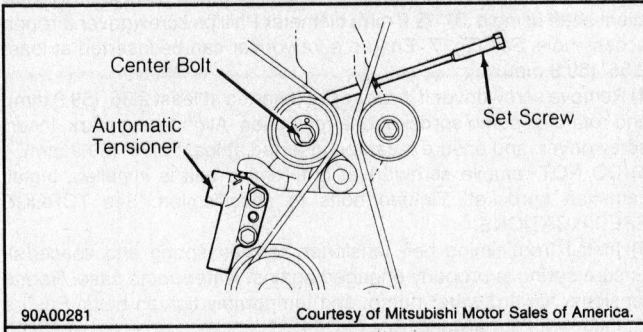

Fig. 12: Measuring Timing Belt Adjustment (DOHC)

90A00281 Courtesy of Mitsubishi Motor Sales of America.

compensated for when installing timing belt. Rotate crankshaft and oil pump sprockets to align timing marks.

9) If reusing old timing belt, ensure belt is installed in original direction of rotation. Remove silent shaft access plug from cylinder block. Insert .31" (8.0 mm) diameter Phillips screwdriver. *See Fig. 7.* If screwdriver can be inserted 2.36" (59.9 mm) or more, timing mark alignment is okay.

10) If screwdriver cannot be inserted at least 2.36" (59.9 mm), remove screwdriver and rotate oil pump sprocket one full turn. Reinsert screwdriver. Leave screwdriver in place until timing belt is installed. Install timing belt on intake camshaft sprocket. Use spring clip to hold belt on sprocket. *See Fig. 10.*

11) Install wrench on both camshaft sprocket bolts. Install timing belt around exhaust camshaft sprocket while holding camshaft sprocket bolt so timing mark on camshaft sprocket is aligned with timing mark.

12) Install another spring clip on timing belt and camshaft sprocket to hold belt on sprocket. Install timing belt in following sequence: around idler pulley, oil pump sprocket, crankshaft sprocket and tensioner pulley.

13) Remove both spring clips. Rotate tensioner pulley inward toward timing belt until belt does not sag. Temporarily tighten center bolt on tensioner pulley. Ensure all timing marks are aligned. Remove Phillips screwdriver from silent shaft access hole. Install plug. Remove wrench from camshaft sprocket bolts.

14) To adjust belt tension, rotate crankshaft 1/4 turn counterclockwise, and then rotate clockwise until cylinder No. 1 is at TDC. Ensure timing marks are aligned. Loosen center bolt on tensioner pulley. Note location of pin holes in tensioner pulley.

15) Using INCH-lb. torque wrench and Socket Wrench (MD998767), apply 22 INCH lbs. (2.6 N.m) on tensioner pulley. *See Fig. 11.* With torque applied to tensioner pulley, tighten tensioner pulley center bolt to 35 ft. lbs. (48 N.m).

16) Install set screw in support bracket until set screw end contacts tensioner arm. *See Fig. 12.* Rotate set screw further until wire can be removed from automatic tensioner. Remove set screw.

17) Rotate crankshaft clockwise 2 complete revolutions, and allow to remain in this position for about 15 minutes. Measure distance between tensioner arm and automatic tensioner body. Distance should be .15-.18" (3.8-4.5 mm).

6) Remove automatic tensioner from vise with wire attached. Install tensioner and arm. Install tensioner pulley on tensioner arm. Ensure pin holes of tensioner pulley shaft are left of pulley center bolt. Tighten center bolt.

7) Rotate camshaft sprockets so dowel pins face upward and timing marks on sprockets align. *See Fig. 5.* Outer marks on sprockets should be aligned with cylinder head surface.

8) When exhaust camshaft sprocket is released, camshaft will rotate one tooth in counterclockwise direction. Ensure this rotation is

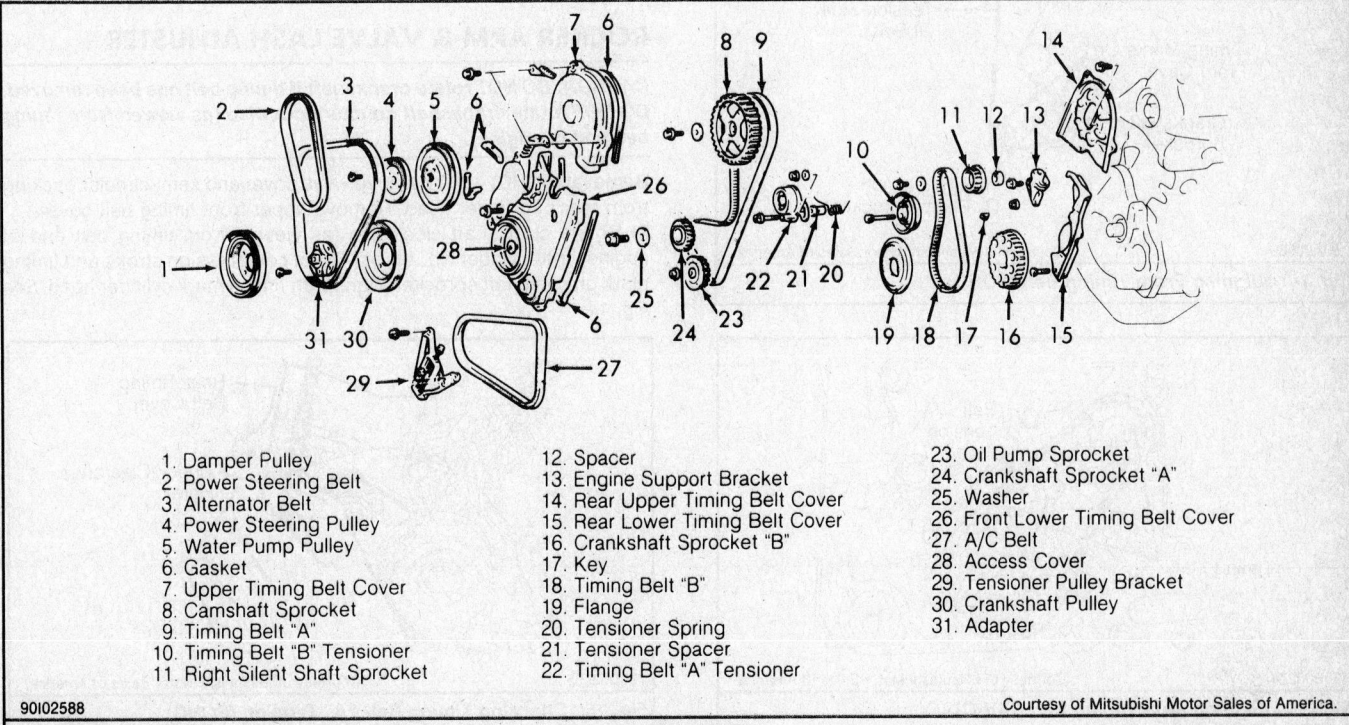

1. Damper Pulley	12. Spacer
2. Power Steering Belt	13. Engine Support Bracket
3. Alternator Belt	14. Rear Upper Timing Belt Cover
4. Power Steering Pulley	15. Rear Lower Timing Belt Cover
5. Water Pump Pulley	16. Crankshaft Sprocket "B"
6. Gasket	17. Key
7. Upper Timing Belt Cover	18. Timing Belt "B"
8. Camshaft Sprocket	19. Flange
9. Timing Belt "A"	20. Tensioner Spring
10. Timing Belt "B" Tensioner	21. Tensioner Spacer
11. Right Silent Shaft Sprocket	22. Timing Belt "A" Tensioner

23. Oil Pump Sprocket
24. Crankshaft Sprocket "A"
25. Washer
26. Front Lower Timing Belt Cover
27. A/C Belt
28. Access Cover
29. Tensioner Pulley Bracket
30. Crankshaft Pulley
31. Adapter

90I02588 Courtesy of Mitsubishi Motor Sales of America.

Fig. 13: Exploded View Of Typical Timing Belts & Related Components (SOHC)

18) If distance cannot be measured due to lack of clearance, use alternate method. Install set screw until it contacts tensioner arm.

19) Rotate set screw inward while counting number of turns until tensioner arm contacts automatic tensioner housing. Number of turns should be 2 1/2-3 if belt tension is correct. Remove set screw. Install rubber plug in rear timing belt cover.

20) To complete installation, reverse removal procedure. Apply sealant to contact areas on semi-circular packing and rocker cover before installing. Ensure correct bolts are installed in proper location in timing belt covers.

Removal (SOHC) – 1) Remove A/C and power steering hose mounting bracket or oxygen sensor connector bracket from upper engine mount. Remove all drive belts and drive pulleys from crankshaft and water pump. See Fig. 13.

2] Remove drive belt tensioner. Remove upper and lower timing belt covers. Note bolt lengths and locations. Longer (2) bolts are located above crankshaft seal. Remove crankshaft sprocket bolt access cover, crankshaft sprocket bolt and washer. If necessary, remove rocker arm cover for clearance.

CAUTION: DO NOT rotate crankshaft counterclockwise (as viewed from timing belt end of engine). If timing belt is to be reused, mark direction of rotation before removing.

---

3) Rotate crankshaft clockwise (as viewed from timing belt end of engine) until cylinder No. 1 is at TDC of compression stroke. Align timing mark on camshaft sprocket with timing mark on cylinder head. See Fig. 14. Loosen timing belt tensioner bolt, and remove tensioner toward water pump. Tighten bolt to secure tensioner. Remove front timing belt and camshaft sprocket.

4) If oil pump sprocket removal is necessary, remove left silent shaft access plug from cylinder block. Insert .31" (8.0 mm) diameter Phillips screwdriver to block left silent shaft. See Fig. 7. Remove oil pump sprocket nut and sprocket.

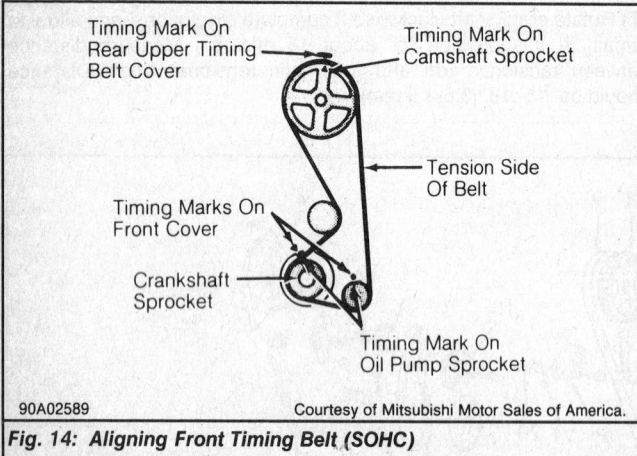

Fig. 14: Aligning Front Timing Belt (SOHC)

5) Remove front crankshaft sprocket and flange. Note direction and order of installation. Remove rear timing belt tensioner assembly. Remove rear timing belt. Remove right silent shaft sprocket with spacer. Remove rear crankshaft sprocket with key and inner cover.

Inspection – Check belt teeth for cracks, damage and contamination. Inspect sprockets for damage. Check belt tensioner for leakage or roughness in rotation. Replace components as necessary.

Installation – 1) Install rear crankshaft sprocket and flange onto crankshaft. See Fig. 8. Lubricate and install right silent shaft spacer and sprocket. Ensure chamfered side of spacer is installed into silent shaft seal. If reused, install rear timing belt in original direction of rotation. Ensure timing marks are aligned. See Fig. 15.

2) Install rear timing belt tensioner. Hold tensioner tightly against belt while tightening bolts. Depress belt between sprockets to ensure deflection is .20-28" (5.0-7.1 mm). Adjust as necessary.

3) Install crankshaft front sprocket. Install oil pump sprocket. Hold left silent shaft using a .31" (8.0 mm) diameter Phillips screwdriver through access hole. See Fig. 7. Ensure screwdriver can be inserted at least 2.36" (59.9 mm).

4) Remove screwdriver if it cannot be inserted at least 2.36" (59.9 mm), and rotate oil pump sprocket one revolution. Align timing mark. Insert screwdriver, and ensure it can be inserted at least 2.36" (59.9 mm).

5) DO NOT remove screwdriver until timing belt is installed. Install camshaft sprocket. Tighten bolts to specification. See TORQUE SPECIFICATIONS.

6) Install front timing belt tensioner, tension spring and spacer(s). Ensure spring is properly engaged against water pump case. Rotate tensioner toward water pump, and temporarily tighten bolts. Ensure timing marks are aligned. See Fig. 14.

7) If reused, install timing belt in original direction of rotation. Apply pressure on tension side of belt while installing belt on camshaft sprocket. Loosen timing belt tensioner to apply spring pressure to timing belt. Ensure timing marks are still aligned.

8) To apply tension on belt, rotate crankshaft clockwise until camshaft sprocket timing mark is offset by 2 teeth. Tighten tensioner bolt. Tighten tensioner nut.

9) To check belt tension, apply slight thumb pressure and measure deflection between camshaft and oil pump sprocket. See Fig. 16. Belt deflection should be .55" (14.0 mm). To complete installation, reverse removal procedure.

ROCKER ARM & VALVE LASH ADJUSTER

CAUTION: DO NOT rotate crankshaft if timing belt has been removed. DO NOT rotate crankshaft counterclockwise (as viewed from timing belt end of engine).

Removal (SOHC) – 1) Remove valve cover and semi-circular packing from rear of cylinder head. Remove upper front timing belt cover.

2) Rotate crankshaft clockwise (as viewed from timing belt end of engine) until cylinder No. 1 is at TDC of compression stroke and timing mark on camshaft sprocket aligns with timing mark cylinder head. See Fig. 14.

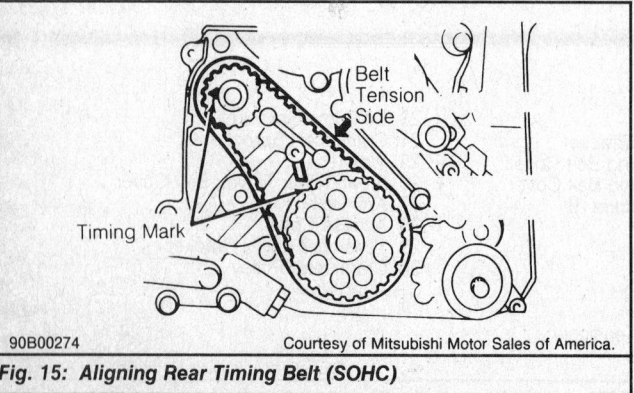

Fig. 15: Aligning Rear Timing Belt (SOHC)

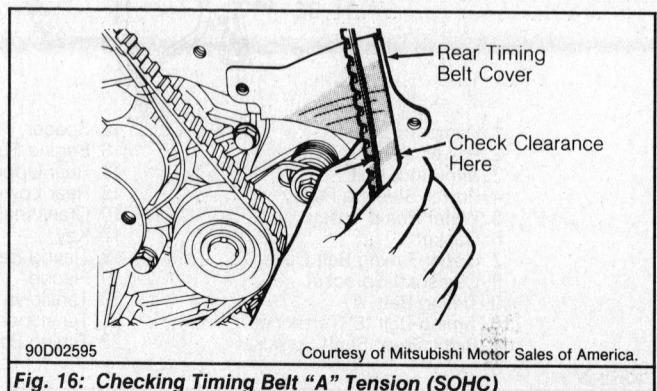

Fig. 16: Checking Timing Belt "A" Tension (SOHC)

3) Mark timing belt in alignment with timing mark on camshaft sprocket. Wire belt to sprocket. Remove camshaft sprocket bolt. Slide camshaft sprocket and belt off camshaft.

NOTE: Check lash adjuster free play before rocker arm removal. See INSPECTION procedure.

4) Install Lash Adjuster Retainer (MD998443) on rocker arm to prevent adjuster from falling out of rocker arm. *See Fig. 17.* Loosen rocker shaft mounting bolts uniformly, and remove rocker shaft assembly. Remove camshaft and oil seal. If removing lash adjusters from rocker arms, mark for installation reference.

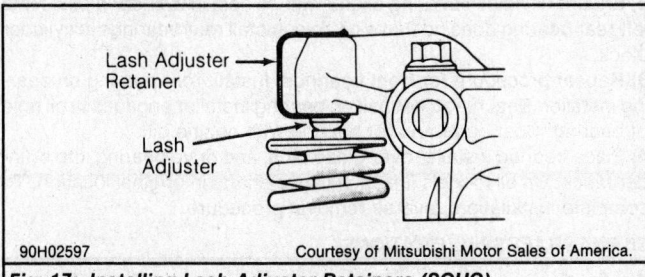

90H02597   Courtesy of Mitsubishi Motor Sales of America.

Fig. 17: Installing Lash Adjuster Retainers (SOHC)

Inspection – 1) Before removing rocker arms from engine, insert a small wire through rocker arm bleed hole and into lash adjuster. With wire lightly holding lash adjuster internal check ball down, move rocker arm up and down to check for free play. If no free play is present, replace adjuster.

2) Inspect rocker arms and shafts for wear and damage. Check distributor drive gear for tooth damage and wear. Replace components as necessary.

3) Check camshaft journal diameter and lobe height. Replace camshaft if journal diameter and lobe height are not within specification. See CAMSHAFT table under ENGINE SPECIFICATIONS.

Installation – 1) Lubricate camshaft lobes and camshaft bearing journals, and install camshaft into cylinder head. Install lash adjuster in rocker arm (if removed). Install lash adjuster retainer.

2) Ensure rocker arm components are installed in original location and wave washers are properly positioned. *See Fig. 18.* Rocker arms for cylinders No. 1 and 3 are marked 1-3. Rocker arms for cylinders No. 2 and 4 are marked 2-4.

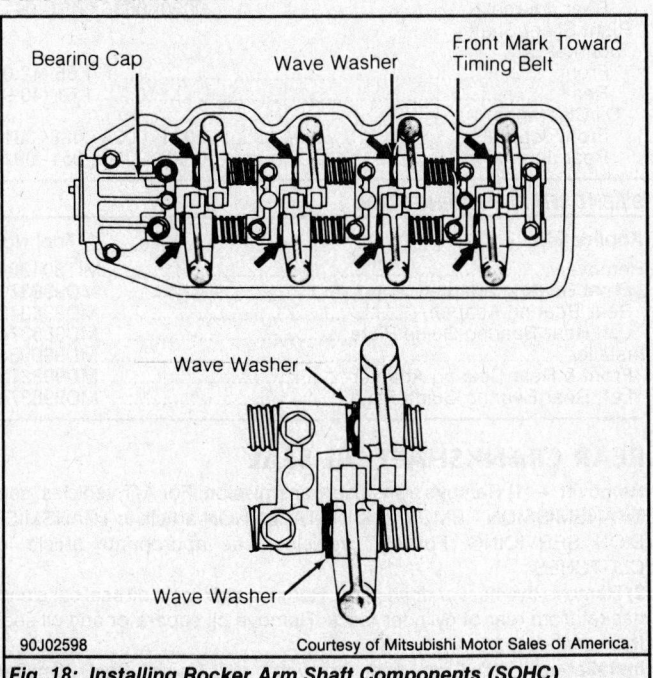

90J02598   Courtesy of Mitsubishi Motor Sales of America.

Fig. 18: Installing Rocker Arm Shaft Components (SOHC)

3) Install bearing cap No. 1 on rocker arm shafts so cut areas face away from camshaft area. *See Fig. 19.* Ensure front mark on each bearing cap faces timing belt. Ensure bearing caps are in correct numerical order. Tighten camshaft bearing cap bolts to specification. See TORQUE SPECIFICATIONS.

4) Coat lip of camshaft oil seal with oil. Install seal into cylinder head using Seal Installer (MD998306) with Guide (MD998307).

5) Remove lash adjuster retainers. Apply sealant to inside of semi-circular packing and cylinder head before installing. To complete installation, reverse removal procedure.

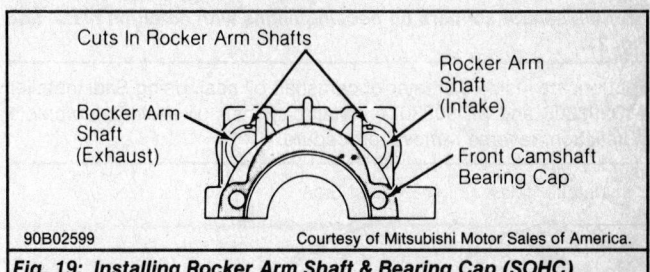

90B02599   Courtesy of Mitsubishi Motor Sales of America.

Fig. 19: Installing Rocker Arm Shaft & Bearing Cap (SOHC)

Removal (DOHC) – 1) Disconnect throttle cable bracket from intake plenum. Remove timing belt. See TIMING BELT under REMOVAL & INSTALLATION.

2) Remove crankshaft position sensor. *See Fig. 20.* Using wrench, secure exhaust camshaft at hexagon. Remove sprocket bolt and sprocket. Repeat procedure for intake camshaft. Loosen front camshaft bearing cap bolts uniformly in 3 steps. Remove caps and seals.

3) Repeat procedure for remaining camshaft bearing cap bolts. Remove rear bearing caps last. Remove remaining camshaft bearing caps. If necessary, tap bearing cap using plastic hammer to break loose. Remove intake and exhaust camshafts. Remove rocker arms and lash adjusters from cylinder head.

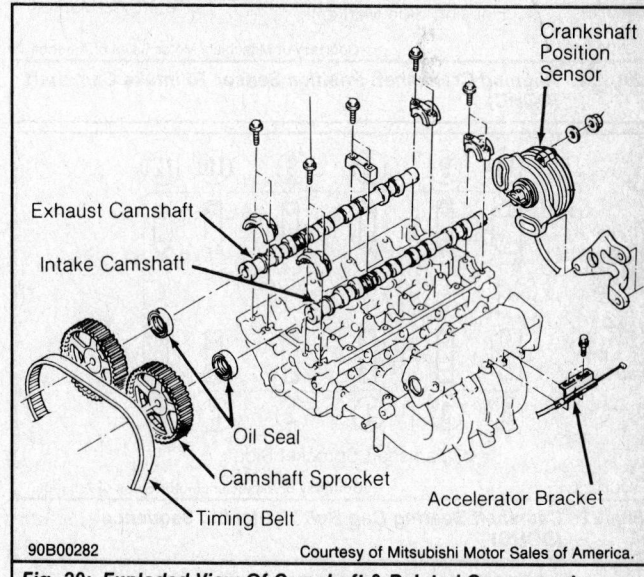

90B00282   Courtesy of Mitsubishi Motor Sales of America.

Fig. 20: Exploded View Of Camshaft & Related Components (DOHC)

Inspection – Check rocker arm friction surfaces for wear and damage. Check rocker arm rollers for smooth rotation. Check camshaft journal diameter and lobe height. Replace camshaft if journal diameter and lobe height are not within specification. See CAMSHAFT table under ENGINE SPECIFICATIONS.

Installation – 1) If new camshafts are installed, position camshafts in cylinder head without bearing caps. Ensure rotation is smooth. Lubricate journals, and install bearing caps.

2) Camshafts should turn easily by hand. If camshafts are okay, remove bearing caps and camshafts. Install lash adjusters and rocker arms on cylinder head.

3) Lubricate camshaft lobes and bearing journals. Install camshafts in cylinder head with dowel pins at 12 o'clock position. Note intake camshaft is slotted at rear. *See Fig. 21.*

4) Install camshaft bearing caps in original location, and tighten in sequence in 2-3 steps. *See Fig. 22. See TORQUE SPECIFICATIONS.*

NOTE: To ensure correct fuel and ignition timing, install crankshaft position sensor so mark on housing aligns with notch on plate. See Fig. 21.

5) Lubricate inside diameter of camshaft oil seal. Using Seal Installer (MD998306 and MD998307), install camshaft oil seal. To complete installation, reverse removal procedure.

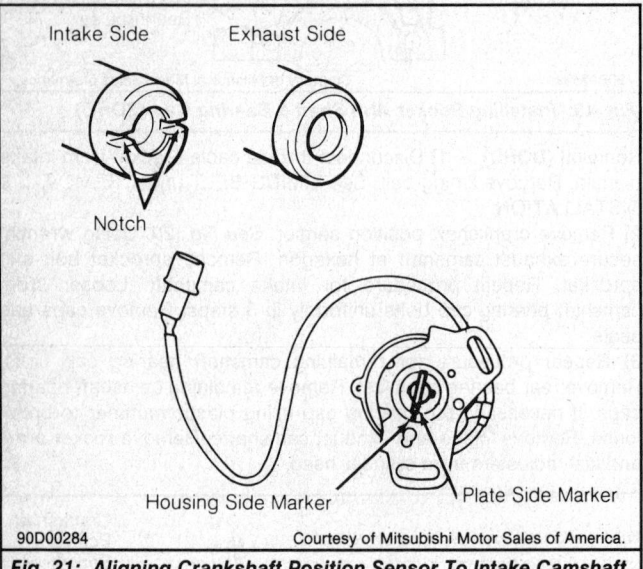

Fig. 21: Aligning Crankshaft Position Sensor To Intake Camshaft (DOHC)

90D00284 — Courtesy of Mitsubishi Motor Sales of America.

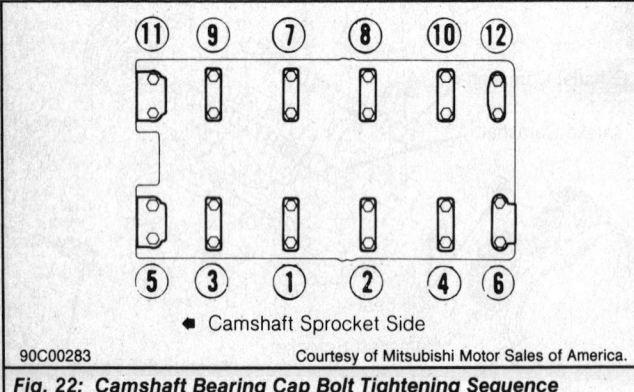

Fig. 22: Camshaft Bearing Cap Bolt Tightening Sequence (DOHC)

90C00283 — Courtesy of Mitsubishi Motor Sales of America.

CAMSHAFT

NOTE: For removal and installation of camshaft, see ROCKER ARM & VALVE LASH ADJUSTER under REMOVAL & INSTALLATION.

SILENT SHAFTS & BEARINGS

Removal – Remove front cover and oil pump. See OIL PUMP & FRONT COVER under ENGINE OILING. Remove silent shafts from cylinder block.

NOTE: Rear bearing(s) cannot be removed unless front bearings have been removed from block.

Inspection – **1)** Inspect silent shaft and bearings for damage. Ensure silent shaft journal O.D. and oil clearance is within specification. See SILENT SHAFT SPECIFICATIONS table. Replace components if not within specification.

2) If bearings need replacing, use indicated puller. See SILENT SHAFT BEARING TOOL table.

NOTE: Install rear bearings before installing front bearings.

Installation – **1)** Coat bearing outer area with engine oil before installing. Mount rear silent shaft bearing on indicated installer. See SILENT SHAFT BEARING TOOL table.

2) Ensure oil hole in bearing aligns with oil hole in cylinder block. Note left rear bearing does not have oil hole. Install rear bearings in cylinder block.

3) Repeat procedure for front bearings. Install front bearing on bearing installer. Ensure ratchet ball on bearing installer engages in oil hole of bearing. Coat outer area of bearing with engine oil.

4) Place bearing installer over guide pins, and drive bearing into cylinder block. On all models, install balance shafts in original location. To complete installation, reverse removal procedure.

SILENT SHAFT SPECIFICATIONS

Application	In. (mm)
DOHC	
Left Silent Shaft	
Journal O.D.	
Front	.7270-.7276 (18.466-18.481)
Rear	1.6126-1.6132 (40.959-40.975)
Oil Clearance	
Front Journal	.0008-.0021 (.020-.053)
Rear Journal	.0017-.0033 (.042-.083)
Right Silent Shaft	
Journal O.D.	
Front	1.6519-1.6526 (41.959-41.975)
Rear	1.6122-1.6129 (40.951-35.967)
Oil Clearance	
Front Journal	.0008-.0024 (.020-.061)
Rear Journal	.0020-.0036 (.051-.091)
SOHC	
Left Silent Shaft	
Journal O.D.	
Front	.728 (18.49)
Rear	1.61 (40.9)
Oil Clearance	
Front Journal	.0011-.0020 (.028-.051)
Rear Journal	.0020-.0036 (.051-.091)
Right Silent Shaft	
Journal O.D.	
Front	1.65 (42.0)
Rear	1.61 (40.9)
Oil Clearance	
Front Journal	.0011-.0024 (.028-.061)
Rear Journal	.0020-.0036 (.051-.091)

SILENT SHAFT BEARING TOOL

Application	Tool No.
Remover	MIT304204
Front Bearing Adapter	MD998371
Rear Bearing Adapter	MD998372
Left Rear Bearing Guide Plate	MD998374
Installer	MD990938
Front & Rear Bearing Adapter	MD998373
Left Rear Bearing Guide Plate	MD998374

REAR CRANKSHAFT OIL SEAL

Removal – **1)** Remove transaxle/transmission. For A/T vehicles, see TRANSMISSION REMOVAL & INSTALLATION article in TRANSMISSION SERVICING. For M/T vehicles, see appropriate article in CLUTCHES.

2) Remove flywheel or drive plate. Remove rear main oil seal case and gasket from rear of cylinder block. Remove oil separator and oil seal from seal case.

Installation – **1)** Coat seal lip with oil. Using Seal Installer (MD998376), install seal in seal case until it bottoms.

2) Install oil separator in seal case with hole of separator at bottom of seal case (toward oil pan). Install seal case and gasket. Install flywheel or drive plate. To complete installation, reverse removal procedure.

WATER PUMP

CAUTION: Note length and location of bolts during removal. Different length bolts are used and must be installed in original location.

Removal – Drain cooling system. Remove necessary coolant hoses. Remove timing belt. See TIMING BELT under REMOVAL & INSTALLATION. Remove water pump mounting bolts. Note bolt length and location. Remove water pump.
Installation – To install, reverse removal procedure using new gasket and "O" ring. Install "O" ring on coolant pipe, and apply water to "O" ring. DO NOT apply grease or oil to "O" ring. Ensure bolts are installed in original location.

OIL PAN

Removal – **1)** Drain engine oil. Disconnect exhaust pipe at manifold. Disconnect and remove axle shaft at cylinder block. See FWD AXLE SHAFTS article in DRIVE AXLES.
2) Remove oil pan bolts. Using Gasket Cutter (MD998727), cut gasket along sealing surface of cylinder block. Remove oil pan and gasket. Clean oil pan and block gasket surfaces.
Installation – To install, apply sealant to oil pan flange at timing chain case and rear seal case areas. Install oil pan and gaskets. To complete installation, reverse removal procedure. Tighten bolts to specification. See TORQUE SPECIFICATIONS.

OVERHAUL

CYLINDER HEAD

Cylinder Head – Inspect cylinder head for warpage at deck surface. Resurface cylinder head if warpage exceeds specification. See CYLINDER HEAD table under ENGINE SPECIFICATIONS.
Valve Springs – Inspect valve spring free length, out-of-square and installed height. Replace valve spring if not within specification. See VALVES & VALVE SPRINGS table under ENGINE SPECIFICATIONS. Install all valve springs with painted area toward rocker arm.
Valve Stem Oil Seals – DO NOT reuse oil seals. Install valve spring seat before installing oil seals. To provide proper positioning of oil seal, install new oil seals using Valve Seal Installer (MD998737 for DOHC or MD998729 for SOHC).
Valve Guides – Ensure valve stem diameter is within specification. Check valve stem clearance. Clearance should be within specification. See VALVES & VALVE SPRINGS and CYLINDER HEAD tables under ENGINE SPECIFICATIONS. If clearance exceeds service limits, replace valve guide with an oversized valve guide.
Valves – Ensure valve stem diameter and margin are within specification. See VALVES & VALVE SPRINGS table under ENGINE SPECIFICATIONS.
Valve Seat – See ENGINE OVERHAUL PROCEDURES article in GENERAL INFORMATION.
Valve Seat Correction Angles – See ENGINE OVERHAUL PROCEDURES article in GENERAL INFORMATION.

VALVE TRAIN

Rocker Arm Shaft Assembly – **1)** For reassembly reference, note location and order of assembly for all components. Remove bolts from shafts, and separate components. Note length of springs. Intake rocker arm shaft springs are longer than exhaust rocker arm shaft springs.
2) Inspect components for wear and damage. Install components in original location when reassembling shaft assembly. Tighten rocker arm assembly bolts to specification. See TORQUE SPECIFICATIONS.
Lash Adjusters – Before installing lash adjuster, submerge lash adjuster in oil. Use a small wire to hold down internal check valve. Pump plunger up and down 4 or 5 times to bleed air from lash adjuster.

CYLINDER BLOCK ASSEMBLY

Piston & Rod Assembly – **1)** Mark piston and rod assembly with corresponding cylinder number before removing. Center piston pin in piston. Measure and record piston pin installation depth. Use Piston Pin Removal & Installation Set (MD998780) with hydraulic press to remove piston pin.
2) Piston pin should be easily pushed into piston. If looseness or resistance is encountered, replace piston and pin as a set. Check connecting rod for damage and excessive bend and twist. See CONNECTING RODS table under ENGINE SPECIFICATIONS.
3) Position piston, piston pin and rod on press. Ensure front mark on piston will face timing belt side of engine when installed. Using piston pin removal and installation set, install piston pin into piston and rod to depth recorded in step **1)**. Ensure piston pin is centered in piston.
Fitting Pistons – **1)** Measure piston skirt diameter at 90-degree angle to piston pin. If piston diameter is not within specification, replace piston. See PISTONS, PINS & RINGS table under ENGINE SPECIFICATIONS.
2) Measure cylinder bore diameter at 3 places: near top of bore, bottom of bore and center of bore. If cylinder bore diameter or taper is not within specification, machine cylinder bore. See CYLINDER BLOCK table under ENGINE SPECIFICATIONS.
3) If piston-to-cylinder bore clearance is not within specification, replace piston and/or machine cylinder bore. See PISTONS, PINS & RINGS table under ENGINE SPECIFICATIONS.
Piston Rings – Ensure ring end gap and side clearance are within specification. See PISTONS, PINS & RINGS table under ENGINE SPECIFICATIONS. DO NOT use a ring expander to install oil ring side rails. Properly position ring end gaps around circumference of piston before installing. *See Fig. 23.*

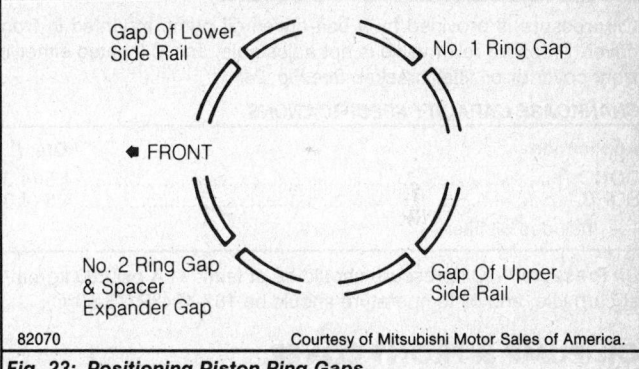

Fig. 23: Positioning Piston Ring Gaps

Rod Bearings – Note position of connecting rod in relation to bearing cap before removing. Ensure bearing oil clearance and side play are within specification. See CRANKSHAFT, MAIN & CONNECTING ROD BEARINGS and CONNECTING RODS tables under ENGINE SPECIFICATIONS.
Crankshaft & Main Bearings – Check diameter of crankshaft main bearing journals and connecting rod bearing journals. Check journals for taper and out-of-round. Check crankshaft end play. See CRANKSHAFT, MAIN & CONNECTING ROD BEARINGS table under ENGINE SPECIFICATIONS.
Thrust Bearing – Replace thrust bearing if crankshaft end play is not within specification. See CRANKSHAFT, MAIN & CONNECTING ROD BEARINGS table under ENGINE SPECIFICATIONS.
Cylinder Block – **1)** Check cylinder block head surface warpage. If warpage exceeds specification, machine surface. See CYLINDER BLOCK table under ENGINE SPECIFICATIONS. DO NOT remove more than a combined total .008" (0.20 mm) material from original surfaces of cylinder head or cylinder block.
2) Check cylinder bore wear and taper. Measure cylinder bore diameter at 3 places: near top of bore, bottom of bore and center of bore. If cylinder bore diameter or taper is not within specification, machine cylinder bore. See CYLINDER BLOCK table.

1994 ENGINES
2.4L 4-Cylinder (Cont.)

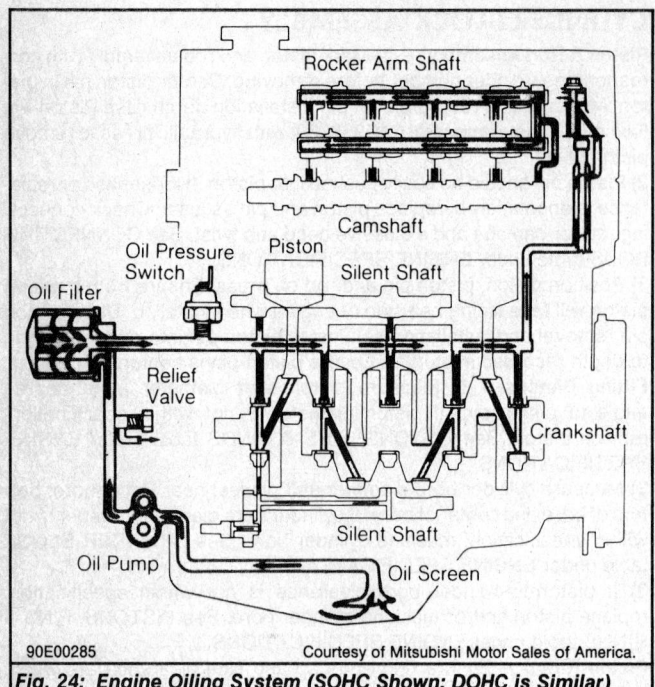

90E00285   Courtesy of Mitsubishi Motor Sales of America.

Fig. 24: Engine Oiling System (SOHC Shown; DOHC is Similar)

ENGINE OILING

ENGINE LUBRICATION SYSTEM

Oil pressure is provided by a belt-driven oil pump mounted in front cover. Pressure relief valve is not adjustable, and is located either in front cover or oil filter bracket. *See Fig. 24.*

CRANKCASE CAPACITY SPECIFICATIONS

Application	[1] Qts. (L)
DOHC	4.5 (4.3)
SOHC	4.5 (4.3)

[1] – Includes oil filter.

Oil Pressure – Oil pressure should be at least 11.4 psi (.80 kg/cm²) at curb idle, and oil temperature should be 167-194°F (75-90°C).

OIL PUMP & FRONT COVER

Removal & Disassembly – 1) Remove timing belt and crankshaft sprocket. See TIMING BELT under REMOVAL & INSTALLATION. Remove oil filter, oil pressure switch, oil pan and oil screen.
2) Remove oil filter bracket, front cover and oil pump assembly. Remove plug cap located on front of front cover using Plug Cap Wrench (MD998162). Remove rear cover. Mark direction of gear installation for reassembly reference.
Inspection – 1) Place straightedge across front cover housing and measure side play between each gear and straightedge. Check clearance between tip of gear teeth of both gears and front cover.
2) Ensure pressure relief valve moves without restriction in bore. Replace components if damaged or not within specification. See OIL PUMP SPECIFICATIONS table.

Reassembly & Installation – 1) Lubricate oil pump gears with engine oil, and install. Ensure timing marks are aligned. Install oil pump cover, and tighten bolts to specification. See TORQUE SPECIFICATIONS.
2) If crankshaft oil seal was removed, use Seal Installer (MD998375) to install seal in front cover. Use a socket of proper diameter to install silent shaft oil seals.

OIL PUMP SPECIFICATIONS

Application	Specification
Gear Side Clearance	
Drive Gear	
Standard	.0031-.0055" (.080-.140 mm)
Limit	.0098" (.250 mm)
Driven Gear	
Standard	.0024-.0047" (.060-.120 mm)
Limit	.0098" (.250 mm)
Gear-To-Front Cover Clearance	
Drive Gear	
Standard	.0063-.0083" (.160-.210 mm)
Limit	.0098" (.250 mm)
Driven Gear	
Standard	.0051-.0071" (.130-.180 mm)
Limit	.0098" (.250 mm)

3) Position Oil Seal Guide (MD998285) over front of crankshaft. Lubricate crankshaft oil seal and oil seal guide with engine oil. Install front cover with new gasket, and temporarily tighten bolts. Install oil filter bracket. Ensure correct length bolts are installed.
4) To complete installation, reverse removal procedure. Install plug cap using new "O" ring, and tighten to specification. Apply thread sealant to oil pressure switch threads before installing. Tighten all bolts to specification. See TORQUE SPECIFICATIONS.

TORQUE SPECIFICATIONS

TORQUE SPECIFICATIONS

Application	Ft. Lbs. (N.m)
A/C Tensioner Pulley Bracket Bolt	17-20 (23-27)
Auto Tensioner Bolt (DOHC)	14-20 (19-27)
Camshaft Bearing Cap Bolt	
DOHC [1]	14-15 (19-20)
SOHC	
Large	14-15 (19-20)
Small	14-20 (19-27)
Camshaft Sprocket Bolt	58-72 (79-98)
Connecting Rod Nut	36-38 (49-52)
Crankshaft Pulley Bolt	14-22 (19-30)
Crankshaft Sprocket Bolt	80-94 (109-127)
Cylinder Head Bolt [2]	65-72 (88-98)
Engine Support Bracket Bolt	
Front	36-51 (49-69)
Left	22-30 (30-41)
Exhaust Manifold Nut	
DOHC	18-22 (24-30)
SOHC	11-15 (15-20)
Exhaust Pipe-To-Manifold Nut	22-29 (30-39)
Flywheel/Drive Plate Bolt	94-101 (127-137)
Front Cover Bolt	
DOHC	14-16 (19-22)
SOHC	14-20 (19-27)
Front Tensioner Pulley Bolt (DOHC)	31-40 (42-54)
Idler Pulley Bolt (DOHC)	25-30 (34-41)
Intake Manifold Bolt/Nut	
DOHC	
8-mm	11-14 (15-19)
10-mm	22-30 (30-41)
SOHC	11-14 (15-19)
Intake Manifold Stay Bolt	
DOHC	18-22 (24-30)
SOHC	13-18 (18-24)
Main Bearing Cap Bolt	
DOHC	47-51 (64-69)
SOHC	37-39 (50-53)

[1] – Tighten bolts in sequence. See Fig. 22.
[2] – Tighten bolts in sequence. See Fig. 3 or 4.

TORQUE SPECIFICATIONS (Cont.)

Application	Ft. Lbs. (N.m)
Oil Cooler By-Pass Valve	37-43 (50-58)
Oil Filter Bracket Bolt	11-16 (15-22)
Oil Jet Bolt	22-25 (30-34)
Oil Pump Cover Bolt	11-13 (15-18)
Oil Pump Driven Gear Bolt	25-29 (34-39)
Oil Pump Pick-Up Tube Bolt	11-16 (15-22)
Oil Pump Sprocket Nut	36-43 (49-58)
Oxygen Sensor	29-36 (39-49)
Plug Cap	14-20 (19-27)
Power Steering Pump Bolts	26-33 (35-45)
Rear Tensioner Retaining Bolt	11-16 (15-22)
Rocker Arm Assembly Bolts	14-15 (19-20)
Silent Shaft Sprocket Bolt	
DOHC	31-35 (42-47)
SOHC	
.08" (2.0 mm) Washer	25-29 (34-39)
.10" (2.5 mm) Washer	31-35 (42-47)
Throttle Body Bolt (DOHC)	11-16 (15-22)
Water Pump Bolt	
Except 8 x 65-mm	10 (14)
8 x 65-mm	15-19 (20-26)

Application	INCH Lbs. (N.m)
Crankshaft Position Sensor Nut	84-108 (9-12)
Distributor Nut	84-108 (9-12)
Fuel Rail Bolt	84-108 (9-12)
Oil Pan Bolt	48-72 (5-8)
Oil Pressure Switch	72-108 (8-12)
Rear Crankshaft Oil Seal Case Bolt	84-108 (9-12)
Throttle Body Bolt (SOHC)	84-108 (9-12)
Timing Belt Cover Bolt	84-108 (9-12)
Valve Body Bolt (DOHC)	84-108 (9-12)
Valve Cover Bolt	
DOHC	24-36 (3-4)
SOHC	48-60 (5-7)
Water Pump Pulley Bolt	72-84 (8-9)

ENGINE SPECIFICATIONS

GENERAL SPECIFICATIONS

Application	Specification
Displacement	143.4 Cu. In. (2.4L)
Bore	3.41" (86.5 mm)
Stroke	3.94" (100.0 mm)
Compression Ratio	
DOHC	10.0:1
SOHC	9.5:1
Fuel System	MFI
Horsepower @ RPM	141 @ 5500
Torque Ft. Lbs. @ RPM	148 @ 3000

CYLINDER BLOCK

Application	In. (mm)
Cylinder Bore	
Standard Diameter	3.406-3.407 (86.50-86.53)
Maximum Taper	.0004 (.010)
Maximum Out-Of-Round	.0004 (.010)
Deck Height	11.41-11.42 (289.9-290.1)
Maximum Deck Warpage	[1] .002 (.05)

[1] – Combined maximum total grind limit of cylinder head and cylinder block is .008" (.20 mm).

CYLINDER HEAD

Application	Specification
Cylinder Head Height	
DOHC	5.193-5.201" (131.90-132.10 mm)
SOHC	4.720-4.728'' (119.90-120.10 mm)
Maximum Warpage	[1] .0020" (.051 mm)
Valve Seats	
Intake Valve	
Seat Angle	45-45.5°
Seat Width	.035-.051" (.89-1.30 mm)
Exhaust Valve	
Seat Angle	45-45.5°
Seat Width	.035-.051" (.89-1.30 mm)
Valve Guides	
Intake Valve	
Guide Length	
DOHC	1.791" (45.49 mm)
SOHC	1.85" (47.0 mm)
Valve Stem-To-Guide Oil Clearance	
Intake Valve	
Standard	.0008-.0020" (.020-.050 mm)
Wear Limit	.0040" (.10 mm)
Exhaust Valve	
Standard	
DOHC	.0020-.0035" (.050-.090 mm)
SOHC	.0012-.0028" (.030-.070 mm)
Wear Limit	.006" (.15 mm)

[1] – Combined maximum total grind limit of cylinder head and cylinder block is .008" (.20 mm).

PISTONS, PINS & RINGS

Application	In. (mm)
Pistons	
Clearance	.0008-.0016 (.020-.041)
Diameter	3.4051 (86.490)
Pins	
Rod Fit	[1]
Rings	
No. 1	
End Gap	
Standard	
DOHC	.0098-.0138 (.250-.350)
SOHC	.0098-.0157 (.250-.400)
Wear Limit	.031 (.79)
Side Clearance	
Standard	.0012-.0028 (.030-.071)
Wear Limit	.004 (.10)
No. 2	
End Gap	
Standard	.0157-.0217 (.400-.550)
Wear Limit	.031 (.79)
Side Clearance	
Standard	
DOHC	.0012-.0028 (.030-.071)
SOHC	.0008-.0024 (.020-.061)
Wear Limit	.004 (.10)
No. 3 (Oil)	
End Gap	
Standard	.0039-.0150 (.100-.400)
Wear Limit	.039 (.99)

[1] – Press fit with load of 1653-3858 lbs. (750-1750 kg).

CONNECTING RODS

Application	In. (mm)
Side Play	
Standard	.0039-.0098 (.010-.250)

1994 ENGINES
2.4L 4-Cylinder (Cont.)

CAMSHAFT [1]

Application	In. (mm)
End Play	.004-.008 (.10-.20)
Journal Diameter	
DOHC	1.022 (25.96)
SOHC	1.768 (44.93)
Lobe Height	
DOHC	
Intake Valve	
"A" & "D"	1.378-1.397 (34.99-35.49)
"B" & "E"	1.366-1.386 (34.70-35.20)
"K"	1.373-1.393 (34.88-35.38)
Exhaust Valve	
"A"	1.366-1.386 (34.70-35.20)
"C"	1.378-1.397 (34.99-35.49)
"H"	1.355-1.374 (34.41-34.91)
SOHC	
Intake Valve	
"D"	1.650-1.669 (41.90-42.40)
1 & 2	1.452-1.472 (36.89-37.39)
Exhaust Valve	
"D"	1.650-1.669 (41.90-42.40)
1 & 2	1.456-1.475 (36.97-37.47)

[1] – Camshaft identification mark is stamped on end opposite camshaft sprocket.

CRANKSHAFT, MAIN & CONNECTING ROD BEARINGS

Application	In. (mm)
Crankshaft End Play	
Standard	.0020-.0071 (.051-.180)
Wear Limit	.0098 (.25)
Main Bearings	
Journal Diameter [1]	
"1"	2.2439-2.2441 (56.994-57.000)
"2"	2.2436-2.2439 (56.988-56.994)
"3"	2.2434-2.2436 (56.982-56.988)
Oil Clearance	
Standard	.0008-.0016 (.020-.041)
Wear Limit	.004 (.10)
Connecting Rod Bearings	
Journal Diameter	1.8898-1.8904 (48.000-48105)
Oil Clearance	
Standard	.0008-.0016 (.020-.041)
Wear Limit .004 (.10) Wear Limit	.016 (.41)

[1] – Identification mark is stamped on crankshaft.

VALVES & VALVE SPRINGS

Application	Specification
Intake Valves	
Face Angle	45-45.5°
Minimum Margin	
Standard	.039" (1.00 mm)
Wear Limit	.020" (.50 mm)
Stem Diameter	
DOHC	.260" (6.6 mm)
SOHC	.236" (6.0 mm)
Exhaust Valves	
Face Angle	45-45.5°
Minimum Margin	
DOHC	
Standard	.059" (1.50 mm)
Wear Limit	.039" (1.00 mm)
SOHC	
Standard	.047" (1.20 mm)
Wear Limit	.028" (0.70 mm)
Stem Diameter	
DOHC	.256" (6.50 mm)
SOHC	.232" (5.90 mm)
Valve Springs	
Free Length	
DOHC	1.85" (47.0 mm)
SOHC	2.01" (51.0 mm)
Installed Height	
DOHC	1.57" (40.0 mm)
SOHC	1.74" (44.2 mm)
Out-Of-Square	
Standard	
DOHC	Less Than 1.5°
SOHC	Less Than 2°
Wear Limit	4°

Chrysler Corp.: Stealth
Mitsubishi: Diamante, Montero, Pickup, 3000GT

NOTE: For repair procedures not covered in this article, see ENGINE OVERHAUL PROCEDURES article in GENERAL INFORMATION.

ENGINE IDENTIFICATION

Engine may be identified by Vehicle Identification Number (VIN) stamped on a metal pad located near lower left corner of windshield. The eighth character of VIN identifies engine, and tenth character (R) identifies model year (1994). Engine model number is stamped on front upper edge of cylinder block, below cylinder head, or on vehicle information plate on firewall. Engine serial number is stamped near the engine model number.

ENGINE IDENTIFICATION CODES

Application	Engine Model	Engine Code
Diamante		
SOHC	6G72	H
DOHC	6G72	J
Montero	6G72	H
Pickup	6G72	H
Stealth		
SOHC	6G72	H
DOHC Non-Turbo	6G72	J
DOHC Turbo	6G72	K
3000GT		
DOHC Non-Turbo	6G72	J
DOHC Turbo	6G72	K

ADJUSTMENTS

VALVE CLEARANCE ADJUSTMENT

NOTE: All engines are equipped with hydraulic lash adjusters. Adjustment is not required.

REMOVAL & INSTALLATION

CAUTION: When battery is disconnected, vehicle computer and memory systems may lose memory data. Driveability problems may exist until computer systems have completed a relearn cycle.

NOTE: For reassembly reference, label all electrical connectors, vacuum hoses, and fuel lines before removal. Also place mating marks on engine hood and other major assemblies before removal.

FUEL PRESSURE RELEASE

Perform these steps to release fuel system pressure:
- Disconnect fuel pump harness connector at fuel tank.
- Start engine. After it stalls, turn ignition switch to OFF position.
- Disconnect battery (-) terminal. Reconnect fuel pump harness.
- Wrap shop towels around fuel return and high pressure hoses to prevent fuel splashing on engine. Disconnect fuel return hose and high pressure fuel hose to drain any residual fuel.

ENGINE

Removal (Diamante) – 1) Remove hood. Drain cooling system. Remove radiator. Release fuel system pressure. See FUEL PRESSURE RELEASE. Disconnect negative battery cable. Drain engine oil and transaxle oil. Remove front exhaust pipe. Remove transaxle assembly. See appropriate CLUTCHES or TRANSMISSION SERVICING article.

2) Disconnect accelerator cable, brake booster vacuum hose, fuel supply and return lines, and heater hoses. Disconnect EGR tempera-ture sensor (if equipped). Unplug vacuum hose connector. Remove drive belts. Remove power steering pump and A/C compressor, leaving hoses attached.

3) Unplug all harness connectors. Remove bolt from body ground connection. Disconnect alternator wiring inside relay box. Remove relay box and engine wiring harness connection. On models with ABS, remove radiator overflow tank and bracket.

4) Attach engine hoist. Raise engine enough to take weight from mounts. Remove engine mount bracket. Remove damper. Remove rear roll stopper bracket mount bolt. Remove front roll stopper bracket mount bolt. Carefully lift engine from car.

Installation – To install, reverse removal procedure. Install engine mount bracket so that arrow points away from engine, toward body. Install new "O" rings on fuel lines. Install new exhaust gaskets and nuts. Adjust throttle cable. See TORQUE SPECIFICATIONS. Replenish fluids.

Removal (Montero & Pickup) – 1) Remove hood. Drain cooling system. Remove radiator. Remove skid plate and splash shields. Release fuel system pressure. See FUEL PRESSURE RELEASE. Disconnect negative battery cable.

2) Remove air cleaner ducts. Remove accessory drive belts. Remove and support A/C compressor and power steering pump, leaving hoses connected. Disconnect oil cooler hoses. Cover fuel hose with shop towel, and disconnect high pressure fuel hose and "O" ring. Disconnect fuel return hose.

3) Label and disconnect all vacuum hoses. Disconnect cooling system hoses. Label and unplug all electrical connections from engine. Remove heat shield from motor mounts. Remove motor mount bolts. Ensure all hoses and wires are disconnected and set aside.

4) Disconnect exhaust pipe from exhaust manifolds. Remove starter. Attach engine hoist to engine. Support transmission. Disconnect engine from transmission. See appropriate article in CLUTCHES or TRANSMISSION SERVICING. Remove engine.

Installation – To install, reverse removal procedure. Install new "O" rings onto fuel lines. Install new exhaust gaskets and nuts. See TORQUE SPECIFICATIONS. Replenish fluids.

CAUTION: DO NOT allow foreign material into turbocharger air intake hoses or pipes.

Removal (Stealth & 3000GT) – 1) Release fuel pressure. See FUEL PRESSURE RELEASE. Remove hood. Remove cruise control vacuum pump and linkage. On turbo models, remove necessary turbo air intake hoses and pipes. On all other models, remove air cleaner hoses.

2) On all models, drain cooling system. Drain engine oil and transaxle oil. Remove heater hoses and radiator hoses. Remove transaxle assembly. See appropriate article in CLUTCHES or TRANSMISSION SERVICING.

3) Remove radiator. Label and disconnect all vacuum hoses. Label and unplug all electrical connections and harnesses from engine. Remove accessory drive belts.

4) Remove and support A/C compressor and power steering pump. DO NOT disconnect hoses from compressor or pump. Cover fuel hose with shop towel, and disconnect high pressure fuel hose and "O" ring. Disconnect fuel return hose.

5) On turbo models, disconnect oil cooler and vacuum hoses. On all models, remove motor mount bolts and brackets. Ensure all hoses and wires are disconnected and set aside. Attach engine hoist to engine. Remove engine.

Installation – To install, reverse removal procedure. Install new "O" ring on fuel line. Install new exhaust gaskets and nuts. See TORQUE SPECIFICATIONS. Replenish fluids.

INTAKE MANIFOLD

CAUTION: Fuel system is under pressure. Fuel pressure must be released before disconnecting fuel lines. See FUEL PRESSURE RELEASE.

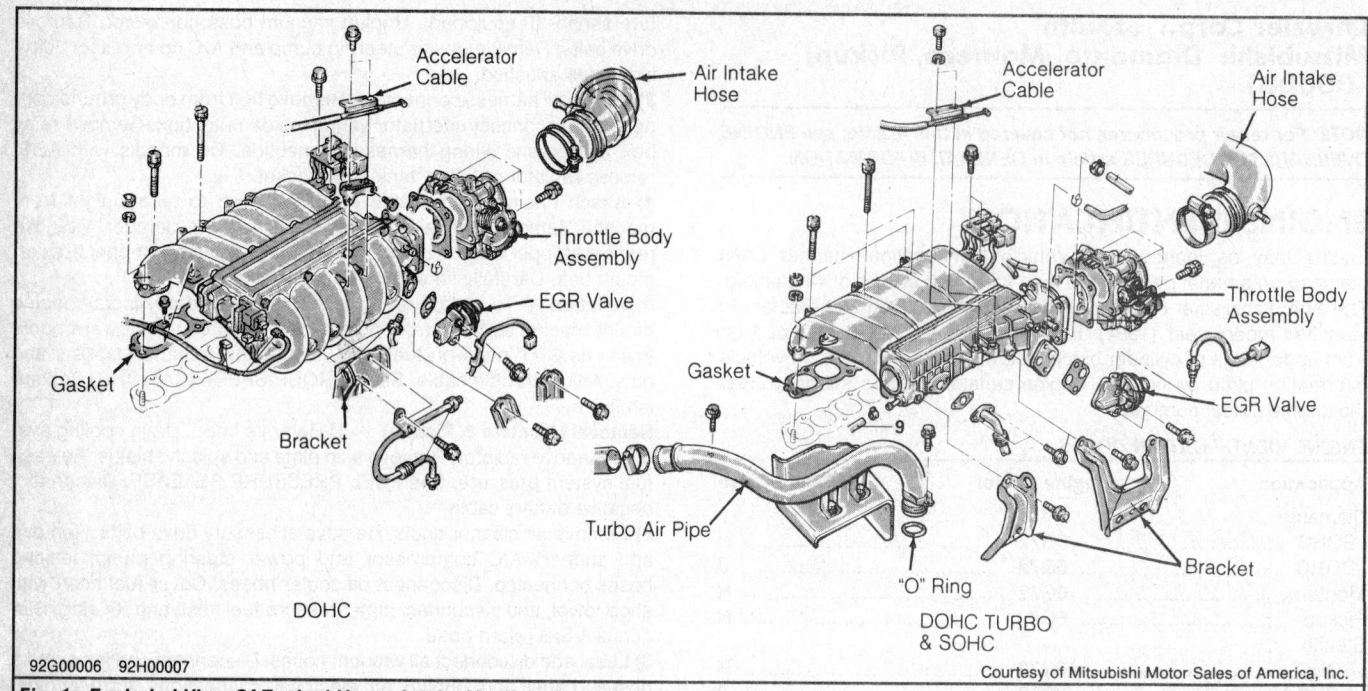

92G00006 92H00007 Courtesy of Mitsubishi Motor Sales of America, Inc.

Fig. 1: Exploded View Of Typical Upper Intake Manifold Components

Removal (Diamante SOHC) – 1) Release fuel pressure. Drain cooling system. Remove air intake hose. Remove EGR tube (if equipped). Remove ignition coil and cable. Remove front and rear intake plenum braces. Remove EGR valve and gasket (if equipped). Remove throttle body. Remove power transistor.

2) Remove plenum. Remove distributor and spark plugs. Remove fuel injector wiring harness. Remove fuel pressure regulator, fuel rails, fuel injectors, and grommets. Remove coolant outlet fitting and thermostat. Remove retaining nuts and intake manifold.

Removal (SOHC Except Diamante) – 1) Release fuel pressure. Drain cooling system. Remove air intake hose. Remove throttle body. Remove EGR valve and tube (if equipped). Remove front and rear manifold brackets. Remove upper intake manifold. See Fig. 1.

2) Remove spark plug cables, spark plugs, distributor, and coil. Remove fuel pressure regulator, fuel injectors, fuel rails, and grommets. Remove coolant and heater hoses. Remove temperature sensors and thermoswitch. Remove coolant outlet fitting and thermostat. Remove retaining nuts and intake manifold.

Removal (DOHC Non-Turbo) – 1) Release fuel pressure. Remove air intake hose. Remove EGR tube (if equipped). Remove front and rear intake plenum braces. Remove EGR valve. Remove throttle body. Remove intake plenum.

2) Remove center cover. Remove spark plug cables, spark plugs, and ignition coil. Remove power transistor. Remove crank angle sensor. Remove fuel injector harness. Remove fuel pressure regulator, fuel injectors, fuel rails, and grommets. Remove retaining nuts and intake manifold. See Fig. 2.

Removal (DOHC Turbo) – 1) Release fuel pressure. Drain cooling system. Remove air intake hose. Remove EGR tube (if equipped). Remove front and rear intake plenum braces. Remove EGR valve. Remove throttle body. Remove intake plenum.

2) Remove center cover. Remove spark plug cables and spark plugs. Remove clamp, located in coil area. Remove ignition coil. Remove decking hook. Remove power transistor. Remove crank angle sensor. Remove fuel injector harness. Remove fuel pressure regulator, fuel rails, and grommets. Remove retaining nuts and intake manifold.

Installation (All Models) – Clean all gasket mating surfaces. Inspect for damage and cracks on all mounting surfaces. To install, reverse removal procedure using new gaskets and "O" rings. Tighten bolts and nuts to specification. See TORQUE SPECIFICATIONS.

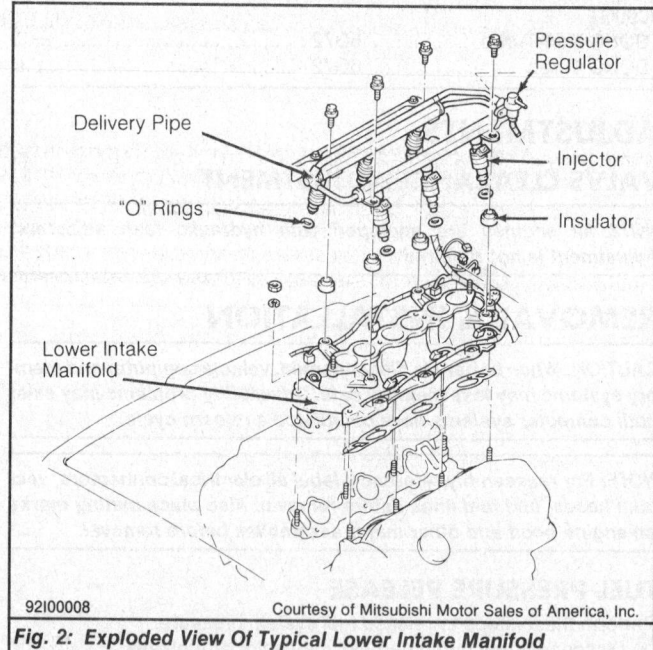

92I00008 Courtesy of Mitsubishi Motor Sales of America, Inc.

Fig. 2: Exploded View Of Typical Lower Intake Manifold

TURBOCHARGER

CAUTION: DO NOT allow foreign material into turbocharger air intakes or coolant and oil passages.

Removal (Front) – 1) Drain coolant. Remove radiator. Remove right transaxle brace. Disconnect exhaust pipe from turbocharger. Remove all air intake ducts. Note match marks and installation depth on air pipes and hoses for reinstallation reference. Remove accessory drive belt. Remove alternator. Remove A/C compressor and bracket, leaving hoses connected, and support aside.

2) Remove O_2 sensor. Remove dipstick assembly. Remove turbocharger heat shield. Disconnect turbo coolant feed and return lines. Disconnect turbocharger oil feed and return lines. Remove turbocharger assembly.

Removal (Rear) – 1) Drain coolant. Remove battery. Disconnect accelerator cable at bracket and throttle body. Disconnect exhaust pipe from turbo. Remove all air intake pipes and heat shields. Disconnect accelerator cable at pedal.

2) Remove clutch booster vacuum hose. Remove O_2 sensor. Remove EGR tube. Remove turbocharger heat shield. Disconnect turbocharger coolant feed and return lines. Disconnect turbocharger oil feed and return lines. Remove turbocharger assembly.

Installation (Front & Rear) – Inject clean engine oil into turbocharger through oil pipe installation hole. To complete installation, reverse removal procedure. Align match marks, and install air ducts and hoses to proper depth.

EXHAUST MANIFOLDS

Removal (Diamante SOHC) – 1) Disconnect exhaust pipe from both exhaust manifolds. To remove front manifold, remove heat shield. Remove dipstick assembly. Remove retaining nuts and exhaust manifold.

2) To remove rear manifold, remove roll stopper brace. Remove heat shield. Remove intake plenum brace and bracket. Remove EGR tube (if equipped). Remove retaining nuts and exhaust manifold.

Removal (Diamante DOHC) – 1) Disconnect exhaust pipe from both exhaust manifolds. To remove front manifold remove condenser fan assembly. Remove alternator drive belt, alternator bracket, and alternator. Remove A/C compressor, leaving hoses connected. Remove dipstick assembly. Remove heat shield. Remove retaining nuts and exhaust manifold.

2) To remove rear manifold, remove studs from bottom of exhaust manifold. Remove roll stopper brace. Remove heat shield. Remove EGR tube (if equipped). Remove retaining nuts and exhaust manifold.

Removal (Montero & Pickup) – 1) Remove O_2 sensor. Disconnect exhaust pipes from manifolds. Lower exhaust pipes. Remove heat shields. Before removing right manifold, remove decking hook and alternator brace.

2) Before removing left exhaust manifold, remove EGR tube (if equipped) and gasket. Remove front intake manifold plenum bracket. Remove exhaust manifolds and gaskets.

Removal (Stealth & 3000GT) – 1) Remove turbocharger(s) (if equipped). See TURBOCHARGER. On front manifold, remove drive belt and alternator. Remove oil dipstick. On rear manifold, remove EGR tube (if equipped).

NOTE: Note locations and orientation of exhaust manifold washers for installation reference. DO NOT mix these fasteners.

---

2) On all manifolds, remove exhaust pipe-to-manifold nuts. Lower exhaust pipe. Remove heat shield. Remove exhaust manifold nuts and washers. Note locations and orientation of all washers for reinstallation reference. DO NOT mix these fasteners. Remove exhaust manifold and gasket.

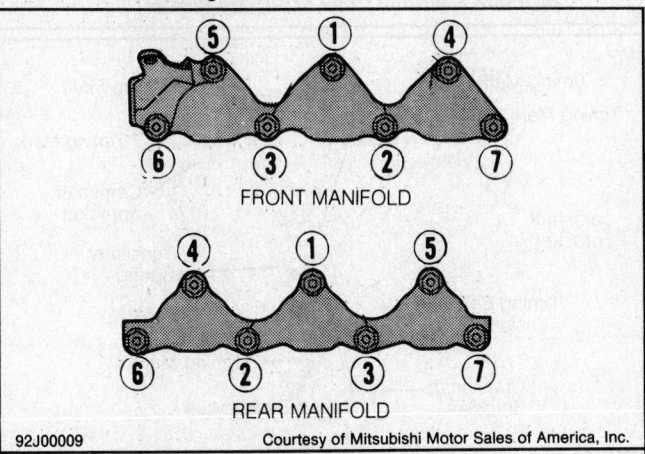

92J00009   Courtesy of Mitsubishi Motor Sales of America, Inc.

Fig. 3: Exhaust Manifold Tightening Sequence (Diamante, Stealth & 3000GT)

Installation (All Models) – To install, reverse removal procedure. Install new gaskets. Lubricate new dipstick tube "O" ring with engine oil before installation. Install manifold nuts and washers in original locations. On Diamante, Stealth and 3000GT, tighten nuts in sequence. *See Fig. 3.* On all models, tighten nuts to specification. See TORQUE SPECIFICATIONS.

CYLINDER HEADS

Removal (SOHC) – 1) Drain cooling system. Remove intake manifolds and brackets. See INTAKE MANIFOLD. Remove spark plug wires. Remove splash shields. Disconnect O_2 sensor. Remove heat shields and exhaust manifolds. See EXHAUST MANIFOLDS.

2) Remove distributor. Remove timing belt outer covers, camshaft sprockets, timing belt, and timing belt inner covers. See TIMING BELT. Remove accessory bracket bolts from front of cylinder head. Remove rocker cover and gasket.

NOTE: To prevent cylinder head warpage and cracking, loosen cylinder head bolts in 2 or 3 stages in proper sequence.

---

3) Using Socket (MD998051), unscrew cylinder head bolts in 2 or 3 stages in proper sequence. *See Fig. 4.* Remove cylinder head and camshaft assemblies. Note orientation of washers under cylinder head bolts.

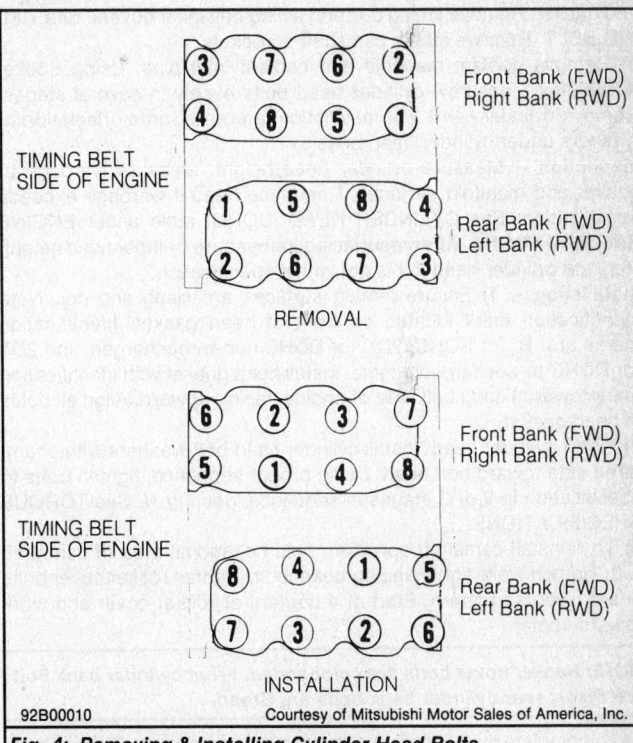

92B00010   Courtesy of Mitsubishi Motor Sales of America, Inc.

Fig. 4: Removing & Installing Cylinder Head Bolts

Inspection – Measure cylinder head height. Measure warpage at gasket and manifold surfaces. Resurface head if warpage exceeds specification. See CYLINDER HEAD (SOHC) table under ENGINE SPECIFICATIONS. Replace cylinder head if it is not within specification after resurfacing.

Installation – 1) Ensure mating surfaces are clean and dry. Note identification mark located on front of head gasket. Identification marks are "R" for SOHC, 2DN for DOHC non-turbocharged, and 2DT for DOHC turbocharged engine. Install head gasket with identification mark toward timing belt side of engine, facing upward.

2) Install cylinder head. Install cylinder head bolt washers with chamfered side toward bolt head. Using proper sequence, tighten bolts to specification in 2 or 3 stages in proper sequence. *See Fig. 4.* See TORQUE SPECIFICATIONS.

3) Apply sealant to rocker cover sealing surfaces before installation. *See Fig. 5.* Align rocker cover gasket projections with notches in rocker cover. Lubricate all "O" rings with engine oil before installation. Install new "O" rings onto distributor adapter and oil dipstick tube.

4) Lubricate camshaft area with oil prior to installing distributor adapter. To complete installation, reverse removal procedure. Tighten bolts and nuts to specification. See TORQUE SPECIFICATIONS. After engine reaches normal operating temperature, allow engine to cool. Retighten cylinder head bolts to specification.

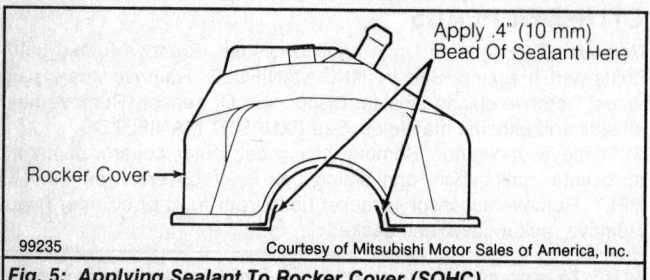

Fig. 5: Applying Sealant To Rocker Cover (SOHC)

Removal (DOHC) – **1)** Drain cooling system. Remove manifolds and brackets. See INTAKE MANIFOLD. Remove turbocharger(s) (if equipped). See TURBOCHARGER. Remove exhaust manifolds. See EXHAUST MANIFOLDS.

2) Remove spark plug wires and ignition coils. Remove rocker cover and gasket. Remove timing belt and timing belt inner covers. See TIMING BELT. Remove intake camshaft sprockets.

3) Remove coolant manifold and coolant inlet pipe. Using Socket (MD998051), unscrew cylinder head bolts evenly in several stages. Remove cylinder head. For installation reference, note orientation of washers under cylinder head bolts.

Inspection – Measure cylinder head height. Measure warpage at gasket and manifold surfaces. Resurface head if warpage exceeds specification. See CYLINDER HEAD (DOHC) table under ENGINE SPECIFICATIONS. After resurfacing, remeasure cylinder head height. Replace cylinder head if it is not within specification.

Installation – **1)** Ensure mating surfaces are clean and dry. Note identification mark located on front of head gasket. Identification marks are "R" for SOHC, 2DN for DOHC non-turbocharged, and 2DT for DOHC turbocharged engine. Install head gasket with identification mark toward timing belt side of engine, facing upward. Align all holes in head gasket.

2) Install cylinder head. Install cylinder head bolt washers with chamfered side toward bolt head. Using proper sequence, tighten bolts to specification in 2 or 3 stages in sequence. See Fig. 4. See TORQUE SPECIFICATIONS.

3) To reinstall camshaft sprocket, hold hexagonal area of camshaft with wrench while tightening sprocket bolt. Tighten rocker cover bolts in a crisscross pattern. Start at 4 corners of rocker cover and work toward center.

NOTE: *Rocker cover bolts are color-coded. Front cylinder bank bolts are Black; rear cylinder bank bolts are Green.*

4) To complete installation, reverse removal procedure. Tighten bolts and nuts to specification. See TORQUE SPECIFICATIONS.

FRONT CRANKSHAFT OIL SEAL

Removal & Installation – Remove timing belt and crankshaft sprocket. See TIMING BELT. Pry oil seal from oil pump. Before installation, coat seal lip with grease. Using Seal Driver (MD998717), install seal in oil pump. Install remaining components. See TORQUE SPECIFICATIONS.

TIMING BELT

Removal (Diamante SOHC) – **1)** Remove left front and left side splash shields. Using engine hoist, lift engine just enough to remove weight from engine mounts. Remove drive belts. Remove A/C tensioner pulley and bracket. Remove engine mount bracket bolts in sequence. Lubricate reamer bolt with penetrating oil before and during removal. See Fig. 6. Remove power steering pump, leaving hoses attached.

2) Remove engine support bracket. Remove crankshaft pulley. Remove timing belt covers. Remove flange from crankshaft. See Fig. 7. Rotate crankshaft to align all timing marks. See Fig. 8. Loosen belt tensioner bolt, and rotate belt tensioner counterclockwise to release belt tension.

3) If reusing timing belt, mark belt to indicate direction of belt rotation. Loosen tensioner bolt. Pry tensioner counterclockwise to relieve belt tension. While holding tensioner, tighten tensioner bolt. Remove timing belt.

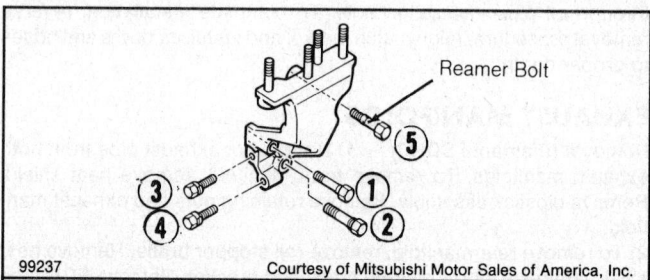

Fig. 6: Removing Engine Support Bracket

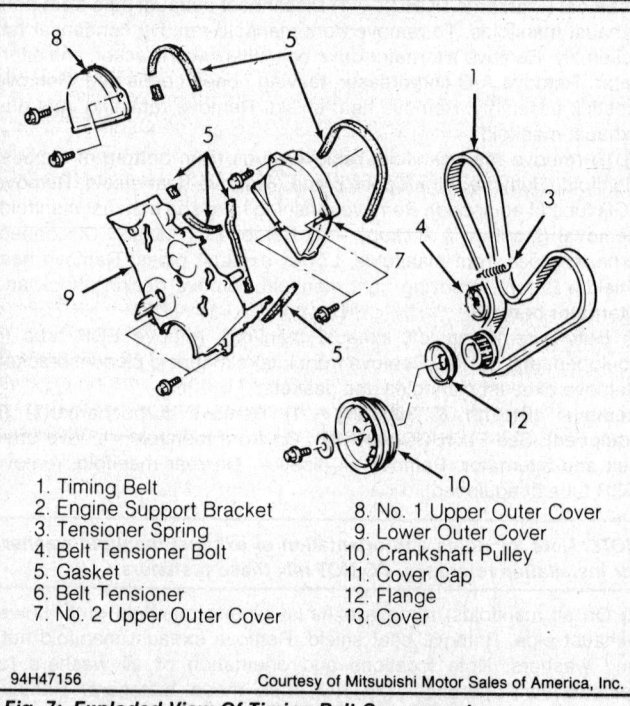

1. Timing Belt
2. Engine Support Bracket
3. Tensioner Spring
4. Belt Tensioner Bolt
5. Gasket
6. Belt Tensioner
7. No. 2 Upper Outer Cover
8. No. 1 Upper Outer Cover
9. Lower Outer Cover
10. Crankshaft Pulley
11. Cover Cap
12. Flange
13. Cover

Fig. 7: Exploded View Of Timing Belt Components (Montero & Pickup; Other SOHC Are Similar)

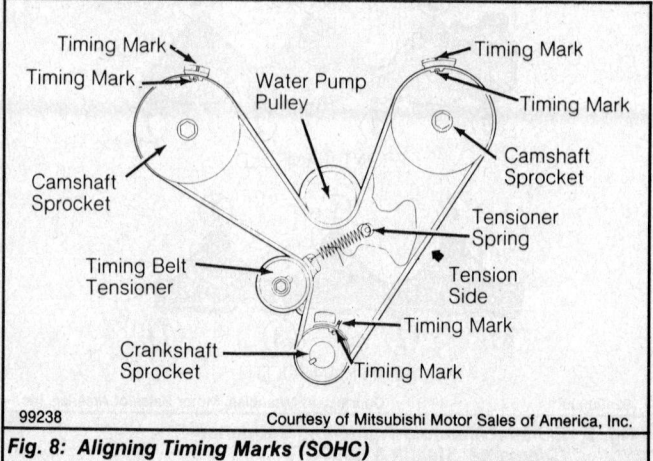

Fig. 8: Aligning Timing Marks (SOHC)

Installation – 1) If original belt is to be reinstalled, install in original running direction. Install timing belt onto crankshaft sprocket, then around left camshaft sprocket, with all slack removed from tension side of belt. Route timing belt onto water pump pulley, right camshaft sprocket, and tensioner. Apply torque to rear camshaft pulley to tighten belt. Ensure all timing marks are aligned.

2) Install flange onto crankshaft. Loosen belt tensioner bolts slightly, and allow tensioner to apply belt tension. Using Crankshaft Socket (MD998716-01), rotate crankshaft 2 revolutions clockwise. DO NOT rotate counterclockwise. Realign all timing marks. Tighten belt tensioner bolts to specification. Using belt tension gauge, measure belt tension halfway between crankshaft sprocket and camshaft sprocket on side opposite belt tensioner.

3) Belt tension should be 44-66 lbs. (20-30 kg). To install remaining components, reverse removal procedure. Install proper length bolts in timing belt covers. *See Fig. 9.* Tighten bolts to specification. See TORQUE SPECIFICATIONS.

Note: Bolt measurements indicated in millimeters.

Thread Diameter & Length
"A" – 6 x 60 mm
"B" – 6 x 20 mm
"C" – 6 x 55 mm

94I47157   Courtesy of Mitsubishi Motor Sales of America, Inc.

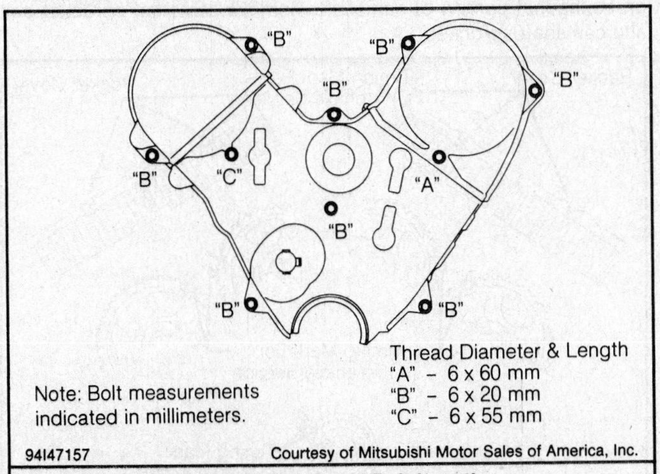

Fig. 9: Identifying Timing Belt Cover Bolt Lengths (Montero & Pickup)

Removal (Montero & Pickup) – 1) Drain cooling system. Disconnect upper radiator hose. Remove upper radiator shroud. Remove cooling fan and fan clutch assembly. Remove cooling fan pulley. Remove drive belts. Remove power steering pump, leaving hoses connected. Set power steering pump aside.

2) Remove power steering pump brackets. Remove A/C tensioner pulley and mounting bracket. Remove A/C compressor with hoses connected, and remove mounting bracket. Remove cooling fan bracket assembly. Note location and length of bolts for reassembly reference.

NOTE: "V" belt will be damaged by tool. DO NOT use engine "V" belt to hold crankshaft pulley unless belt is to be replaced.

3) Remove upper timing belt covers and gaskets. *See Fig. 7.* Remove lower timing belt cover and gaskets. Using Holder (MB998747) and a used "V" belt, remove crankshaft pulley bolt. Remove crankshaft pulley.

4) Remove flange. *See Fig. 7.* Rotate crankshaft to align all timing marks. *See Fig. 8.* Loosen belt tensioner bolt, and rotate belt tensioner counterclockwise to relieve belt tension.

5) If reusing timing belt, place arrow on belt to indicate belt running direction. Remove timing belt and belt tensioner. If camshaft sprocket requires removal, install Holder (MB990775) onto camshaft sprocket. Remove retaining bolt and camshaft sprocket. Remove rear timing belt cover if necessary.

Installation – 1) Install rear timing belt cover. Tighten bolts to specification. See TORQUE SPECIFICATIONS. Install camshaft sprockets (if removed). Using holder, hold camshaft and tighten retaining bolt to specification.

2) Install belt tensioner and spring. Ensure spring is secured on pin of water pump and engaged in hole of belt tensioner, with hook of spring pointing away from cylinder block.

3) Rotate belt tensioner counterclockwise as far as possible, and temporarily tighten bolt. Align all timing marks with No. 1 cylinder at TDC of compression stroke. *See Fig. 8.*

4) Install timing belt onto crankshaft sprocket first, then onto left camshaft sprocket, with all slack removed from tension side of belt. Route timing belt onto water pump pulley, right camshaft sprocket, and tensioner. Remove any slack from belt by rotating left and then right camshaft sprockets counterclockwise.

5) Ensure belt is installed in original direction of rotation, and all timing marks are aligned. Install flange on crankshaft. Loosen belt tensioner bolts slightly, and allow tensioner to apply belt tension.

6) Using Crankshaft Socket (MD998716), rotate crankshaft 2 revolutions clockwise. DO NOT rotate counterclockwise. Realign all timing marks. Tighten belt tensioner bolts to specification. Using belt tension gauge, measure belt tension halfway between crankshaft sprocket and camshaft sprocket on side opposite belt tensioner.

7) Belt tension should be 57-84 lbs. (26-38 kg). To install remaining components, reverse removal procedure. Install bolts in proper holes. *See Fig. 9.* Tighten bolts to specification. See TORQUE SPECIFICATIONS.

Removal (Stealth SOHC) – 1) Remove lower splash shields. Remove cruise control actuator (if equipped). Remove all drive belts. Unplug electrical connector at power steering pump. Remove A/C tensioner pulley and mounting bracket.

2) Remove power steering pump, leaving hoses connected, and wire aside. Support engine. Remove front engine mount through-bolt and front engine mount. Remove timing belt No. 1 upper cover and gaskets. *See Fig. 7.*

NOTE: Engine support bracket reamer bolt may be seized. Apply penetrating lubricant to bolt during removal.

3) Remove engine support bracket bolts in proper sequence. *See Fig. 6.* Remove engine support bracket. Remove timing cover cap, timing belt cover, and gaskets. Using Holder (MB990767) and Adapter Bolts (MD998719), remove crankshaft pulley.

4) Remove lower timing belt cover, gaskets, and flange. *See Fig. 7.* Rotate crankshaft to align all timing marks. *See Fig. 8.* Loosen belt tensioner bolt. Rotate belt tensioner counterclockwise to relieve belt tension.

5) If reusing timing belt, place arrow on belt to indicate belt running direction. Remove timing belt and belt tensioner.

6) If camshaft sprocket requires removal, install Holder (MB990767) with Adapter Bolts (MD998719) onto camshaft sprocket. Remove camshaft sprocket bolt and camshaft sprocket. Remove rear timing belt cover if necessary.

Installation – 1) Install rear timing belt cover. Tighten bolts to specification. See TORQUE SPECIFICATIONS. Install camshaft sprockets (if removed). Using holder, hold camshaft and tighten camshaft sprocket bolt to specification.

2) Install belt tensioner and spring. Ensure spring is secured on pin of water pump and engaged in hole of belt tensioner, with hook of spring pointing away from cylinder block.

3) Rotate belt tensioner counterclockwise as far as possible. Temporarily tighten bolt. Align all timing marks with No. 1 cylinder at TDC of compression stroke. *See Fig. 8.*

4) Install timing belt onto crankshaft sprocket, rear cylinder bank camshaft sprocket, water pump pulley, front cylinder bank camshaft sprocket, and timing belt tensioner. Ensure belt is installed in original direction of rotation, and all timing marks are aligned. Install flange onto crankshaft. Loosen belt tensioner bolts slightly, and allow tensioner to apply belt tension.

5) Using Crankshaft Socket (MD998716), rotate crankshaft 2 revolutions clockwise. DO NOT rotate counterclockwise. Realign all timing marks. Tighten belt tensioner bolts to specification. See TORQUE SPECIFICATIONS. Using belt tension gauge, measure belt tension halfway between crankshaft sprocket and camshaft sprocket on side opposite belt tensioner.

NOTE: Engine support bracket reamer bolt must be tightened slowly. Apply lubricant onto bolt during installation.

6) Belt tension should be 44-66 lbs. (20-30 kg). To install remaining components, reverse removal procedure. Install bolts into proper holes. Install covers and engine support bracket. *See Figs. 6 and 10.* Tighten bolts to specification. See TORQUE SPECIFICATIONS.

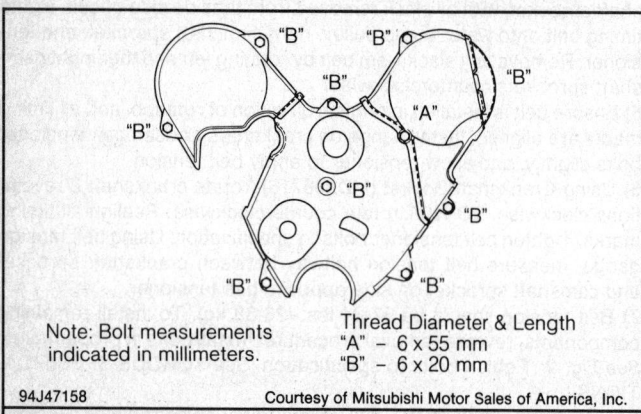

Note: Bolt measurements indicated in millimeters.

Thread Diameter & Length
"A" – 6 x 55 mm
"B" – 6 x 20 mm

94J47158   Courtesy of Mitsubishi Motor Sales of America, Inc.

Fig. 10: Identifying Timing Belt Cover Bolts (Stealth SOHC)

Removal (Diamante DOHC) – 1) Disconnect negative battery cable. Remove left front and left side splash shields. Using engine hoist, lift engine to remove weight from engine mounts. Remove alternator and drive belt tensioner assembly. Remove crankshaft pulley. On vehicles with ABS, remove overflow tank and bracket.

2) Remove engine mount brakcet bolts in sequence. Lubricate reamer bolt with penetrating oil before and during removal. *See Fig. 6.* Remove timing belt covers. Turn crankshaft clockwise to align all timing marks. Loosen center bolt on tensioner pulley to relieve belt tension. Remove belt. Mark running direction if belt is to be reused.

Removal (Stealth & 3000GT – DOHC) – 1) Remove lower splash shields. Remove cruise control actuator (if equipped). Remove drive belts. Remove alternator. Remove drive belt tensioner assembly.

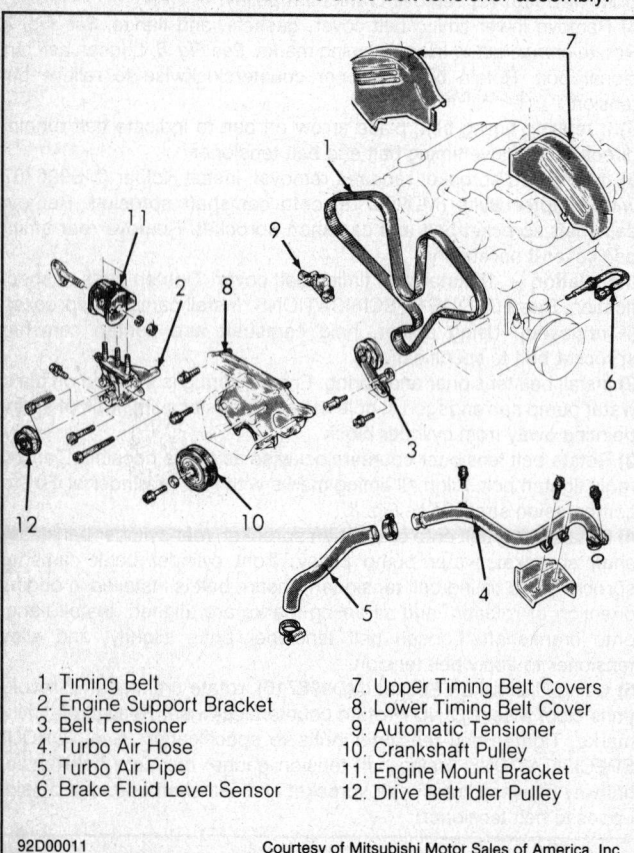

1. Timing Belt
2. Engine Support Bracket
3. Belt Tensioner
4. Turbo Air Hose
5. Turbo Air Pipe
6. Brake Fluid Level Sensor
7. Upper Timing Belt Covers
8. Lower Timing Belt Cover
9. Automatic Tensioner
10. Crankshaft Pulley
11. Engine Mount Bracket
12. Drive Belt Idler Pulley

92D00011   Courtesy of Mitsubishi Motor Sales of America, Inc.

Fig. 11: Exploded View Of Timing Belt Components (DOHC)

2) Using Holder (MB990767) and Adapter Bolts (MD998754), remove crankshaft pulley. *See Fig. 11.* Disconnect brake fluid level sensor. Remove upper timing belt covers. Support engine. Remove front engine mount through-bolt and front engine mount.

NOTE: Engine support bracket reamer bolt may be seized. Apply penetrating lubricant to bolt during removal.

3) Remove drive belt idler pulley. Remove engine support bracket bolts in sequence. *See Fig. 6.* Remove engine support bracket. Remove timing belt upper and lower covers, noting length and location of cover bolts.

4) If reusing timing belt, place arrow on belt to indicate running direction. Remove timing belt and belt tensioner. Rotate crankshaft to align all timing marks. *See Fig. 12.* Loosen tensioner center bolt. Remove timing belt.

5) If camshaft sprocket requires removal, hold camshaft with wrench on hexagonal portion of camshaft. Remove camshaft sprocket bolt and camshaft sprocket.

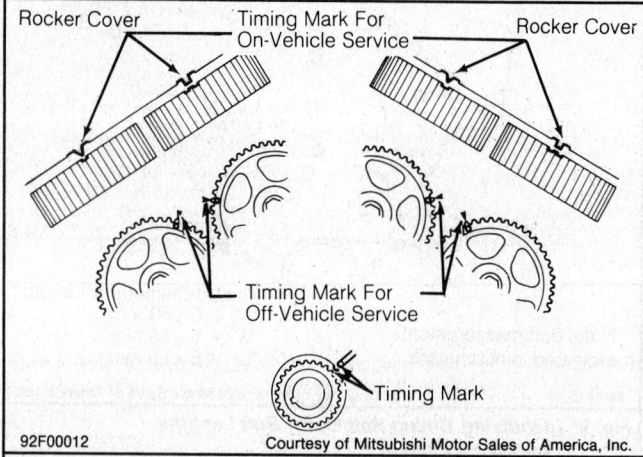

92F00012   Courtesy of Mitsubishi Motor Sales of America, Inc.

Fig. 12: Aligning Timing Marks – Initial Alignment (DOHC)

Installation (Diamante, Stealth & 3000GT – DOHC) – 1) Install camshaft sprockets (if removed). See TORQUE SPECIFICATIONS.

2) Place automatic tensioner assembly in a soft-jawed vise. Slowly close vise to press rod back into tensioner until both rod and housing holes are aligned. Install a .055" (1.40 mm) diameter wire through both holes.

3) Remove tensioner from vise, and install assembly with wire in place. Install crankshaft sprocket (if removed). Align timing marks on crankshaft and camshaft sprockets. *See Fig. 12.*

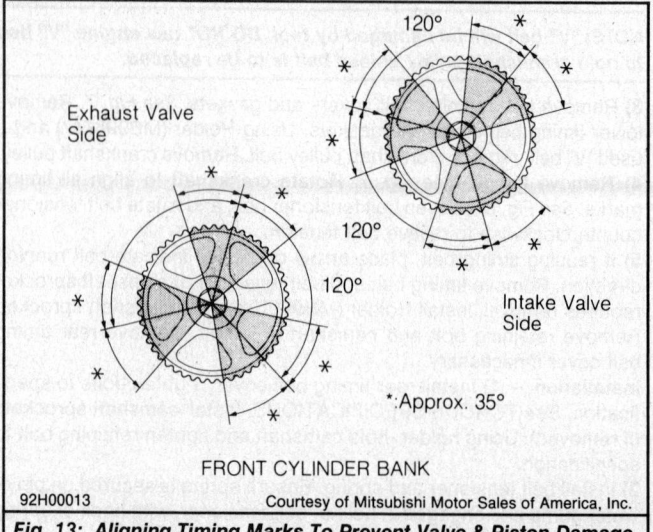

92H00013   Courtesy of Mitsubishi Motor Sales of America, Inc.

Fig. 13: Aligning Timing Marks To Prevent Valve & Piston Damage (DOHC)

CAUTION: Turning camshaft sprockets while No. 1 cylinder is at TDC may damage valve and piston. Use care when aligning timing marks.

4) To lower No. 1 piston from TDC and prevent valve and piston contact, turn crankshaft back 3 sprocket teeth (measured at timing mark). Starting with front bank of cylinders, verify intake and exhaust camshaft timing marks are not within shaded area of figure. *See Fig. 13.*

WARNING: Use care when aligning timing marks. When camshaft sprocket timing marks are in indicated area, camshaft is under valve spring pressure and may rotate suddenly, pinching hand between sprockets.

5) If camshaft sprocket timing mark is within indicated area, carefully rotate camshaft sprocket until timing mark is located in nearest safe area. *See Fig. 13.*

6) Rotate either camshaft sprocket clockwise to align timing marks as shown in illustration. *See Fig. 14.* If camshaft sprocket is rotated past timing mark, rotate it counterclockwise to realign it. Repeat procedure for other front bank camshaft sprocket.

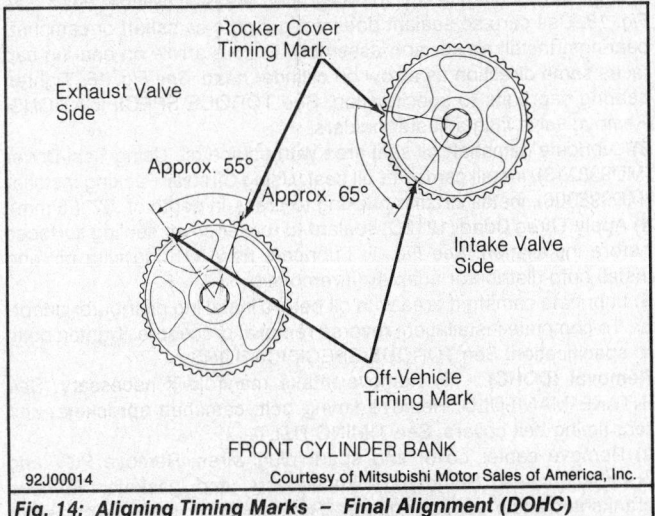

Fig. 14: Aligning Timing Marks – Final Alignment (DOHC)

NOTE: If necessary, crankshaft sprocket may be turned one tooth counterclockwise to aid belt installation.

7) Repeat steps **4)** through **6)** for rear cylinder bank camshafts. Align crankshaft timing mark. Install timing belt onto sprockets in sequence. *See Fig. 15.* Use spring-type paper clips to secure belt on sprockets. Use wrenches on camshaft sprocket bolts to prevent camshafts from turning during belt installation.

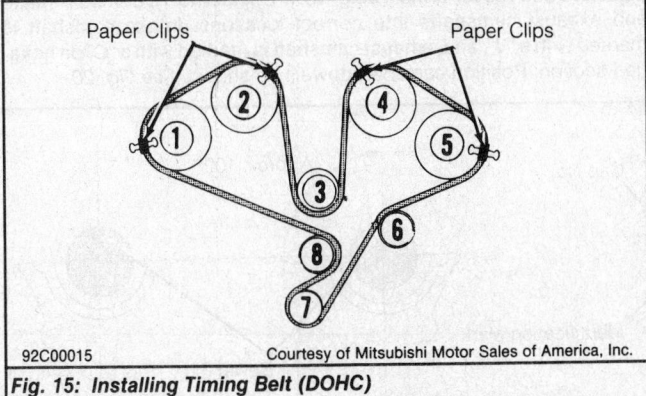

Fig. 15: Installing Timing Belt (DOHC)

8) Rotate timing belt tensioner pulley until pin holes are located above center bolt. *See Fig. 16.* Push tensioner pulley against belt, and temporarily tighten center bolt. Ensure all timing marks are aligned, and remove clips.

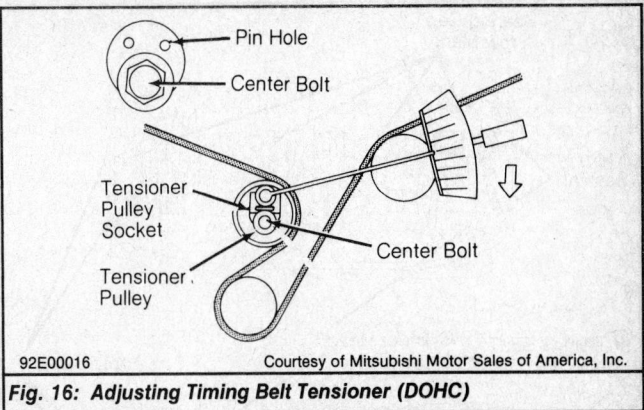

Fig. 16: Adjusting Timing Belt Tensioner (DOHC)

9) Rotate crankshaft 1/4 revolution counterclockwise. Rotate crankshaft clockwise until timing marks are realigned. Loosen tensioner center bolt. Using Tensioner Pulley Socket (MD998767), apply approximately 90 INCH lbs. (10 N.m) torque to tensioner pulley to prevent it from turning. *See Fig. 16.* Retighten center bolt to specification. See TORQUE SPECIFICATIONS. Ensure tensioner pulley does not rotate while tightening center bolt.

10) Rotate crankshaft 2 revolutions clockwise. Wait 5 minutes. Verify wire can still be moved easily, or automatic tensioner rod projects from tensioner body .15-.18" (3.8-4.5 mm). If wire does not move easily, or rod projection is not to specification, repeat steps **6)** and **10)**. Remove wire.

NOTE: Lubricate engine support bracket reamer bolt while it is tightened slowly.

11) To complete installation, reverse removal procedure. Install bolts into correct timing belt cover holes. Install bolts into engine support bracket in reverse order of removal sequence. *See Fig. 6.* Tighten bolts to specification. See TORQUE SPECIFICATIONS.

CAMSHAFT & ROCKER ARMS

Removal (SOHC) – 1) Remove PCV valve and breather hoses. Remove timing belt, camshaft sprocket, and rear timing belt cover. See TIMING BELT. Remove rocker covers and gaskets. Remove circular packing from rear of camshafts.

2) Remove camshaft oil seal from front of cylinder head or distributor adapter. Remove distributor adapter and "O" ring. Install Valve Lash Adjuster Holder (MD998443) onto rocker arm. *See Fig. 17.* Note arrow marks on bearing caps and cylinder head. *See Fig. 18.*

3) Bearing cap location number is stamped on front side of bearing cap. Remove bearing cap bolts. Keep components in order for reassembly reference. Remove rocker arm assembly. Remove camshaft from cylinder head.

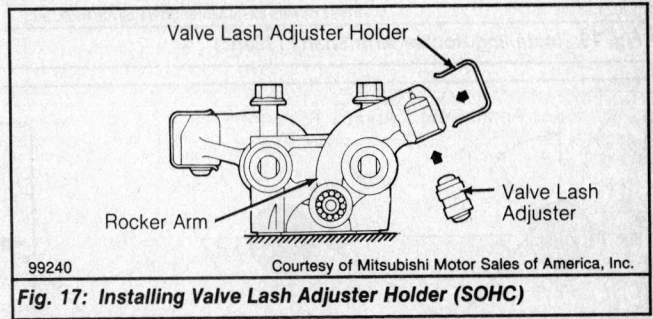

Fig. 17: Installing Valve Lash Adjuster Holder (SOHC)

Inspection – 1) Remove bearing caps, rocker arms, and springs from shafts. Mark component location for reassembly reference. Inspect rocker arm and shaft for damaged roller and flaking. Measure rocker arm I.D. and rocker arm shaft O.D. Determine oil clearance. Measure spring free length. Replace components if not within specification. See ROCKER ARM & SHAFT SPECIFICATIONS (SOHC) table.

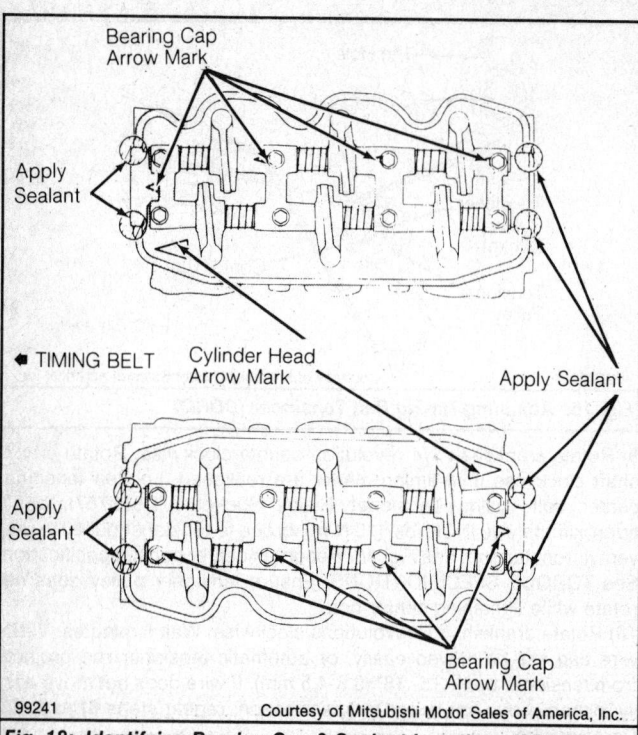

Fig. 18: Identifying Bearing Cap & Sealant Locations (SOHC)

99241   Courtesy of Mitsubishi Motor Sales of America, Inc.

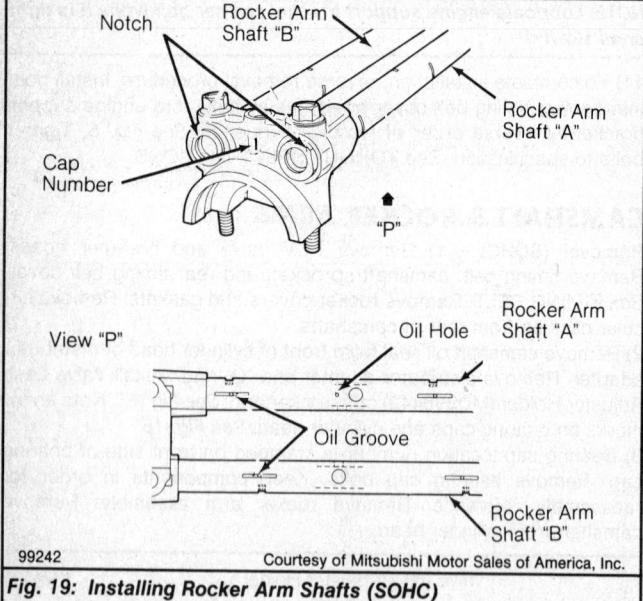

Fig. 19: Installing Rocker Arm Shafts (SOHC)

99242   Courtesy of Mitsubishi Motor Sales of America, Inc.

2) Inspect camshaft and distributor gear for damage. Measure camshaft end play, journal diameter, and lobe height. Replace camshaft if it is not within specification. See CAMSHAFT (SOHC) table under ENGINE SPECIFICATIONS.

3) Lubricate components with engine oil. Reassemble rocker arms, springs, and bearing caps. Install bearing caps with identification number toward camshaft sprocket. Ensure oil holes and notch of shafts are properly positioned. See Fig. 19.

ROCKER ARM & SHAFT SPECIFICATIONS (SOHC)

Application	In. (mm)
Oil Clearance	[1] .0004-.0016 (.010-.041)
Rocker Arm I.D.	.7444 (18.91)
Rocker Arm Shaft O.D.	.7440 (18.90)
Spring Free Length	2.173 (55.19)

[1] – Maximum clearance is .004" (.10 mm).

Installation – 1) Lubricate camshaft with engine oil, and install into cylinder head. Install valve lash adjusters and valve lash adjuster holders (if removed). See Fig. 17.

2) Apply 3M Sealant (4171) to designated areas of cylinder head. See Fig. 18. Use care so sealant does not get onto camshaft or camshaft bearings. Install rocker arm assembly. Ensure arrow on bearing cap faces same direction as arrow on cylinder head. See Fig. 18. Tighten bearing cap bolts to specification. See TORQUE SPECIFICATIONS. Remove valve lash adjuster holders.

3) Lubricate camshaft oil seal area with engine oil. Using Seal Driver (MD998713), install camshaft oil seal. Using Circular Packing Installer (MD998306), install circular packing to press-in depth of .02" (.5 mm).

4) Apply Three Bond (1212D) sealant to rocker cover sealing surfaces before installation. See Fig. 5. Lubricate new "O" ring with oil, and install onto distributor adapter (if removed).

5) Lubricate camshaft area with oil before installing distributor adapter. To complete installation, reverse removal procedure. Tighten bolts to specification. See TORQUE SPECIFICATIONS.

Removal (DOHC) – 1) Remove intake manifold if necessary. See INTAKE MANIFOLD. Remove timing belt, camshaft sprockets, and rear timing belt covers. See TIMING BELT.

2) Remove center cover and spark plug wires. Remove PCV and breather hoses. Remove rocker covers and gaskets. Remove crankshaft angle sensor adapter. Remove front and rear camshaft bearing caps together with seals and packings.

3) Remove remaining camshaft bearing caps in sequence: No. 2, No. 4, and No. 3. Remove camshaft, rocker arms, and lash adjusters. Mark component location for reassembly reference.

Inspection – Inspect rocker arms for damage. Inspect camshaft for damage. Measure camshaft end play, journal diameter, and lobe height. Replace camshaft if it is not within specification. See CAMSHAFT (DOHC) table under ENGINE SPECIFICATIONS.

Installation – 1) Lubricate components with engine oil. Install lash adjusters and rocker arms. Bring No. 1 cylinder to TDC. Install intake and exhaust camshafts into correct locations. Intake camshaft is marked with a "V", and exhaust camshaft is marked with a "C" on hexagon section. Position camshaft dowels as shown. See Fig. 20.

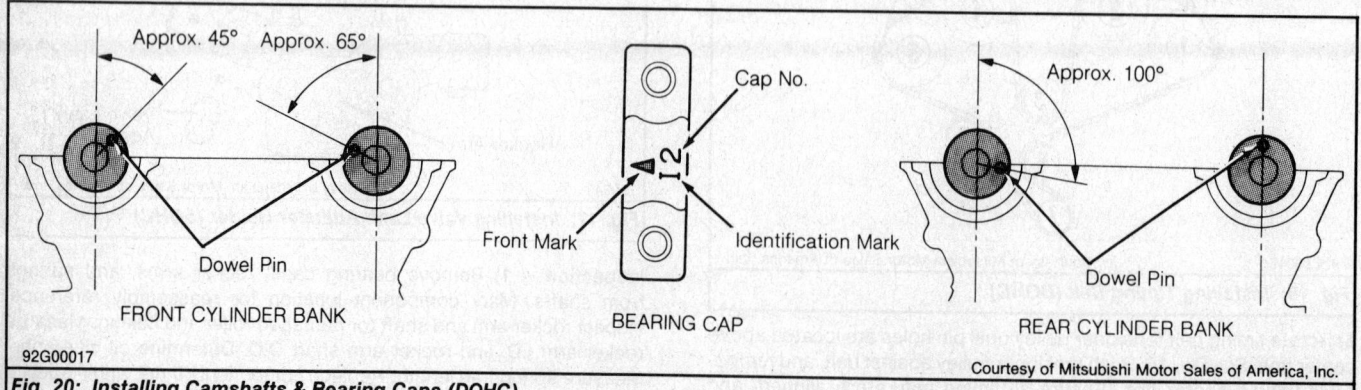

Fig. 20: Installing Camshafts & Bearing Caps (DOHC)

92G00017   Courtesy of Mitsubishi Motor Sales of America, Inc.

NOTE: If cylinder head is off vehicle, support cylinder head at least .4" (10 mm) above work surface to prevent valve damage while installing camshaft bearing caps.

2) Install camshaft bearing caps in sequence: No. 3, No. 4, and No. 2. Install bearing caps with front mark arrow facing the same direction as similar mark on cylinder head beside bearing journal. Note bearing cap number and identification mark ("I" for intake camshaft and "E" for exhaust). See Fig. 20.

3) Install front and rear bearing caps. Tighten bearing cap bolts to specification. See TORQUE SPECIFICATIONS. Lubricate camshaft oil seal area with engine oil. Using Seal Driver (MD998761), install camshaft oil seal. Using Circular Packing Installer (MD998761), install packing.

4) Install crankshaft angle sensor adapter. To complete installation, reverse removal procedure. Tighten bolts to specification. See TORQUE SPECIFICATIONS.

REAR CRANKSHAFT OIL SEAL

Removal – Remove transaxle/transmission. See appropriate article in TRANSMISSION SERVICING or CLUTCHES. Remove flywheel or drive plate. Remove rear oil seal housing. Pry seal from seal housing.

Installation – Lubricate seal lip with engine oil. Using Seal Driver (MD998718), install seal into seal housing. Apply sealant to sealing surface of seal case. Install seal case. Install flywheel or drive plate. Tighten bolts to specification. See TORQUE SPECIFICATIONS. To complete installation, reverse removal procedure.

WATER PUMP

Removal – Drain cooling system. Remove timing belt and crankshaft sprocket. See TIMING BELT. Remove coolant ducts to water pump if necessary. Remove water pump bolts, noting length and location for reassembly reference. Remove water pump.

Installation – To install, reverse removal procedure, using new gasket and "O" rings. Coat all "O" rings with water before installation. Install water pump and gasket. Tighten bolts to specification. See TORQUE SPECIFICATIONS.

OIL PAN

Removal (Diamante) – Raise and support vehicle. Drain engine oil. Remove splash shield. Remove exhaust pipe. If equipped with 4-wheel steering, remove right crossmember. On all models, remove left crossmember. Remove starter. Remove roll stopper brace. Remove front and rear transaxle braces. Remove bellhousing cover. Remove retaining bolts and oil pan.

Removal (Montero) – 1) Remove hood. Remove skid plate and lower covers. Raise and support vehicle. Disconnect and remove exhaust pipe from exhaust manifolds. Drain engine oil. Remove starter cover and starter. Unplug oil pressure sending unit connector. Remove front suspension crossmember.

2) Remove transmission braces. Remove ground cable. Remove engine mount heat shields. Attach engine hoist. Remove motor mount bolts. Raise engine and insert a 1" wood spacer between front insulator and mounts. Lower engine onto wood blocks.

3) Raise and support vehicle. Remove oil pan bolts. Using Seal Cutter (MD998727), separate oil pan from cylinder block. Remove oil pan.

Removal (Pickup) – 1) Remove skid plate and lower covers. Raise and support vehicle. Drain engine oil. Using Steering Linkage Puller (C-3894-A or MB990635), disconnect relay rod from idler arm and steering box.

2) Remove oil pan bolts. Using Seal Cutter (MD998727), separate oil pan from cylinder block. Remove pan from vehicle.

Removal (Stealth & 3000GT) – 1) Raise and support vehicle. Remove engine undercovers. Drain engine oil. Unplug O_2 sensor connector. Disconnect front exhaust pipe from manifolds. On All-Wheel Drive (AWD) models, drain transfer case. Remove front air dam. Remove AWD drive shaft and transfer case.

2) On turbocharged models, remove oil return lines from oil pan. On all models, remove starter. Remove crossmember and transaxle braces.

Remove bellhousing cover. Remove oil pan bolts. Using Seal Cutter (MD998727), separate oil pan from cylinder block. Remove oil pan.

Inspection (All Models) – Clean sealant from mating surfaces on engine block and oil pan. Inspect oil pan for cracks and damage. Inspect sealing surface for damage and deformation. Inspect oil pick-up screen for damage.

Installation (All Models) – 1) To install, reverse removal procedure. Apply sealant to oil pan flange in a continuous .16" (4 mm) diameter bead. See Fig. 21. Install oil pan within 15 minutes of applying sealant.

2) Tighten bolts to specification in proper sequence. See TORQUE SPECIFICATIONS. Wait at least 30 minutes before adding oil and starting engine. On AWD models, refill transfer assembly with GL-4 hypoid gear oil. On all models, complete installation by reversing removal procedure.

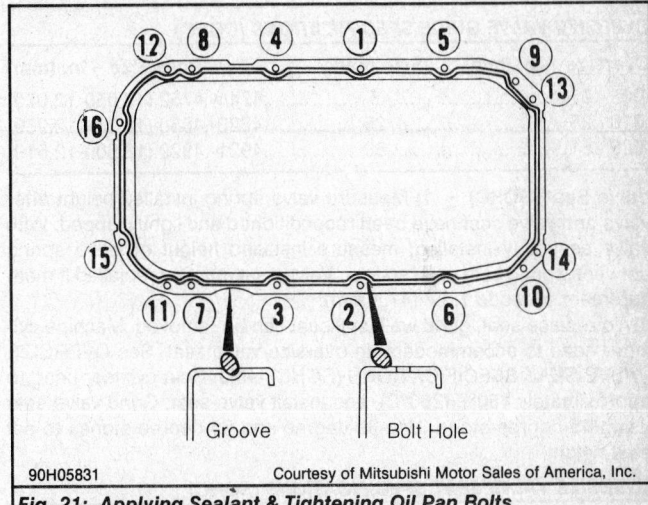

Groove   Bolt Hole

90H05831   Courtesy of Mitsubishi Motor Sales of America, Inc.

Fig. 21: Applying Sealant & Tightening Oil Pan Bolts

OVERHAUL

CYLINDER HEAD

Cylinder Head – Measure cylinder head height. Measure warpage at gasket and manifold surfaces. Resurface head if warpage exceeds specification. See appropriate CYLINDER HEAD table under ENGINE SPECIFICATIONS. Replace cylinder head if it is not within specification after resurfacing.

NOTE: Install valve springs with enamel-coated side toward valve spring retainer.

Valve Springs – Measure free length of valve springs. Measure spring pressure at specified height. Replace springs if not within specification. See appropriate VALVES & VALVE SPRINGS table under ENGINE SPECIFICATIONS. Inspect valve spring for squareness. Replace spring if out-of-square exceeds 4 degrees.

Valve Stem Oil Seals – With valves removed, remove oil seals from cylinder head. Lubricate new seals with engine oil. Using Valve Stem Oil Seal Installer (MD998377 for Montero, MD998729 for Pickup and Stealth SOHC, or MD998763 for DOHC), install valve stem oil seal.

Valve Guides – 1) Measure valve stem oil clearance. Replace valve guide if not within specification. See appropriate VALVES & VALVE SPRINGS table under ENGINE SPECIFICATIONS.

2) Using rod of Valve Guide Remover/Installer (MD998115) for SOHC, drive out valve guide toward combustion chamber side of cylinder head. Note length of valve guides. On DOHC, use press and appropriate driver to press valve guide out toward combustion chamber side of head.

3) On all models, cylinder head must be bored to install oversized valve guide once guide is removed. DO NOT install valve guide of same O.D. as old guide. Bore cylinder head to specification for oversize valve guide. See appropriate OVERSIZE VALVE GUIDE SPECIFICATIONS table.

4) On SOHC, install proper length valve guide. Intake guide is 1.73" (43.9 mm) long; exhaust guide is 1.89" (48.0 mm) long. On all models, position cylinder head with combustion chamber downward.

5) Using valve guide remover/installer, install valve guide. Remover/installer sets valve guide height on SOHC. On DOHC, install valve guide to .689" (17.5 mm), measured from cylinder head spring seating area to top of valve guide. On all models, ensure valve slides smoothly in valve guide. Recondition valve seat.

OVERSIZE VALVE GUIDE SPECIFICATIONS (SOHC)

Oversize – In. (mm)	Size Mark	Bore Size – In. (mm)
.002 (.05)	5	.5138-.5147 (13.050-13.073)
.010 (.25)	25	.5217-.5224 (13.251-13.269)
.020 (.51)	50	.5315-.5323 (13.500-13.520)

OVERSIZE VALVE GUIDE SPECIFICATIONS (DOHC)

Oversize – In. (mm)	Size Mark	Bore Size – In. (mm)
.002 (.05)	5	.4744-.4752 (12.050-12.070)
.010 (.25)	25	.4823-.4830 (12.251-12.269)
.020 (.51)	50	.4921-.4929 (12.500-12.519)

Valve Seat (SOHC) – **1)** Measure valve spring installed height after valve and valve seat have been reconditioned and lightly lapped. With valve assembly installed, measure installed height of valve spring between spring seat and retainer. Valve seat must be replaced if measurement exceeds 1.63" (41.4 mm).

2) To replace seat, grind wall until seat can be removed. Machine cylinder head to accommodate an oversize valve seat. See OVERSIZE VALVE SEAT SPECIFICATIONS (SOHC) table. Heat cylinder head to approximately 480°F (250°C), and install valve seat. Grind valve seat using 45-degree stone. Use 30-degree and 60-degree stones to set seat height.

OVERSIZE VALVE SEAT SPECIFICATIONS (SOHC)

Application	In. (mm)
Intake	
Bore Depth	
.012" (.3 mm) Oversize	.311-.319 (7.9-8.1)
.024" (.6 mm) Oversize	.323-.331 (8.2-8.4)
Bore Diameter	
.012" (.3 mm) Oversize	1.7441-1.7453 (44.300-44.330)
.024" (.6 mm) Oversize	1.7559-1.7571 (44.600-44.630)
Exhaust	
Bore Depth	
.012" (.3 mm) Oversize	.311-.319 (7.9-8.1)
.024" (.6 mm) Oversize	.323-.331 (8.2-8.4)
Bore Diameter	
.012" (.3 mm) Oversize	1.5079-1.5091 (38.300-38.331)
.024" (.6 mm) Oversize	1.5197-1.5209 (38.600-38.630)

Valve Seat (DOHC) – Grind seat wall thickness until seat can be removed. Machine cylinder head to accommodate an oversize valve seat. See OVERSIZE VALVE SEAT SPECIFICATIONS (DOHC) table. Heat cylinder head to approximately 480°F (250°C), or chill valve seat with liquid nitrogen, and install valve seat. Grind valve seat using 45-degree stone. Use 30-degree and 60-degree stones to adjust seat height.

OVERSIZE VALVE SEAT SPECIFICATIONS (DOHC)

Application	In. (mm)
Intake	
Bore Depth	
.012" (.3 mm) Oversize	.295-.303 (7.5-7.7)
.024" (.6 mm) Oversize	.307-.315 (7.8-8.0)
Bore Diameter	
.012" (.3 mm) Oversize	1.4291-1.4303 (36.300-36.329)
.024" (.6 mm) Oversize	1.4409-1.4421 (36.600-36.629)
Exhaust	
Bore Depth	
.012" (.3 mm) Oversize	.311-.319 (7.9-8.1)
.024" (.6 mm) Oversize	.323-.331 (8.2-8.4)
Bore Diameter	
.012" (.3 mm) Oversize	1.3110-1.3122 (33.300-33.330)
.024" (.6 mm) Oversize	1.3228-1.3240 (33.600-33.630)

Valves – Disassemble cylinder head. Measure valve stem diameter, valve margin, and overall length. See appropriate VALVES & VALVE SPRINGS table under ENGINE SPECIFICATIONS. Inspect valve for worn stem tip. Measure valve margin after grinding valves. Replace valves if not within specification.

Lash Adjusters – Before installation, submerge lash adjuster in diesel fuel. Using a small wire, hold down internal check valve. Pump plunger up and down 4 or 5 times to bleed air from lash adjuster.

CYLINDER BLOCK ASSEMBLY

Cylinder Block – **1)** Inspect cylinder block for cracks, warpage, cylinder bore taper, and out-of-round. Replace or repair cylinder block if it is not within specification. See CYLINDER BLOCK table under ENGINE SPECIFICATIONS.

2) Measure cylinder bore and piston skirt diameter. Piston skirt diameter should be measured at 90-degree angle to piston pin. Clearance between piston and cylinder bore must be within specification. See appropriate PISTONS, PINS & RINGS table under ENGINE SPECIFICATIONS.

Piston & Rod Assembly – **1)** Remove cylinder heads and oil pan. See CYLINDER HEADS and OIL PAN under REMOVAL & INSTALLATION. Remove cylinder ridge. Mark connecting rod and cap for cylinder identification.

2) Note front mark on piston and connecting rod. *See Fig. 22.* Mark is positioned toward timing belt side of engine. Remove rod cap and piston assembly.

3) Piston ring end gap and side clearance must be within specification. See appropriate PISTONS, PINS & RINGS table under ENGINE SPECIFICATIONS. Install rings onto piston with ring code identification marks toward top of piston. On DOHC, top ring is marked "T", and No. 2 ring is marked T2. On SOHC, top ring is marked T1, and No. 2 ring is marked 2R. Lubricate piston, rings, and cylinder bore with engine oil.

NOTE: Front mark "R" on piston indicates installation in cylinders No. 1, 3, or 5; front mark "L" indicates installation in cylinders No. 2, 4, or 6. Ensure front mark on piston and connecting rod are toward timing belt side of engine. See Fig. 22.

4) Distribute ring end gaps properly around piston. *See Fig. 22.* Install piston and rod into cylinder bore, with front mark toward timing belt side of engine.

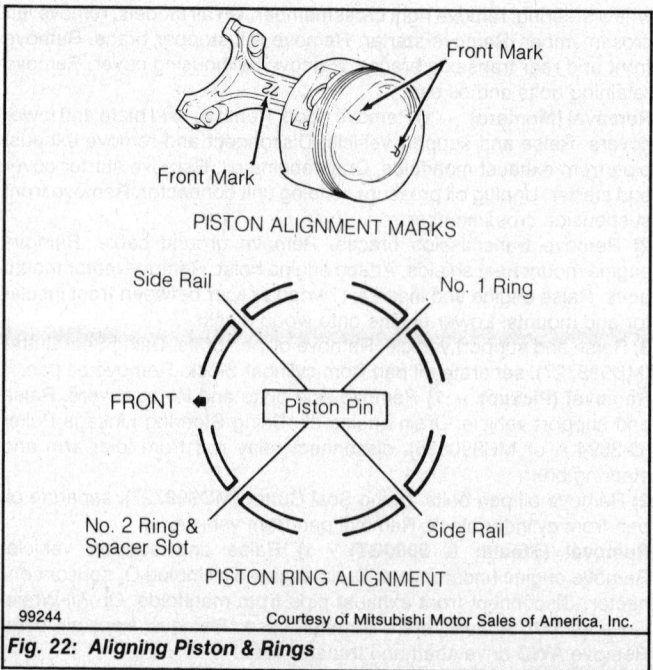

PISTON ALIGNMENT MARKS

PISTON RING ALIGNMENT

99244   Courtesy of Mitsubishi Motor Sales of America, Inc.

Fig. 22: Aligning Piston & Rings

5) Measure bearing clearance using Plastigage. Tighten rod cap nuts to specification. See TORQUE SPECIFICATIONS. Connecting rod must move freely on crankshaft. Measure connecting rod side play. Repair or replace connecting rod if not within specification. See CONNECTING RODS table under ENGINE SPECIFICATIONS.

Fitting Pistons – Measure cylinder bore and piston skirt diameter. Piston skirt diameter should be measured at 90-degree angle to piston pin. Clearance between piston and cylinder bore must be within specification. See appropriate PISTONS, PINS & RINGS table under ENGINE SPECIFICATIONS.

Piston Pin Replacement – **1)** Note reference mark on top of piston and connecting rod. *See Fig. 22.* Using press and Piston Pin Remover/Installer (MD998184 for SOHC, or MD998765 for DOHC), remove pin.

2) Inspect piston for cracks and damage. Measure ring side clearance. Replace piston if not within specification. See appropriate PISTONS, PINS & RINGS table under ENGINE SPECIFICATIONS.

3) Measure connecting rod for bend and twist. Replace connecting rod if twist exceeds .004" (.10 mm) or bend exceeds .002" (.05 mm).

NOTE: Install piston with reference mark aligned with connecting rod reference mark. See Fig. 22.

---

4) Position piston onto connecting rod. Align reference marks on top of piston and connecting rod. *See Fig. 22.* Lubricate all components with oil. Press piston pin into piston and connecting rod. To install, reverse removal procedure. Ensure piston pin is centered in piston.

Crankshaft & Main Bearings – **1)** Remove flywheel or drive plate. Remove transaxle/transmission mounting plate and rear seal case. Remove oil pump, oil pan, and oil pick-up tube. Mark connecting rod and main bearing caps for location.

2) Remove connecting rod caps and bearings. Note direction of arrow on main bearing cap. Remove main bearing cap. *See Fig. 23.* Remove crankshaft. Remove main bearings from cylinder block. Mark bearings for location.

3) Inspect crankshaft for cracks and damaged gear or threads. Measure crankshaft for taper and out-of-round. Replace or repair crankshaft if it is not within specification. See CRANKSHAFT, MAIN & CONNECTING ROD BEARINGS table under ENGINE SPECIFICATIONS.

4) Install upper main bearings into cylinder block. Ensure oil holes are aligned, and bearings are properly seated. Lubricate bearings with engine oil. Install thrust bearing with oil grooves toward crankshaft thrust surface.

5) Install crankshaft into block. Install thrust bearing with oil grooves toward crankshaft thrust surface. Install main bearing caps with arrow toward front of engine.

6) Measure oil clearance using Plastigage. Tighten bolts to specification in proper sequence. *See Fig. 23.* See TORQUE SPECIFICATIONS. Clearance must be within specification. See CRANKSHAFT, MAIN & CONNECTING ROD BEARINGS table. If oil clearance is not within specification, replace bearings or crankshaft.

7) Ensure crankshaft rotates freely with main bearing cap installed. Measure crankshaft end play. See CRANKSHAFT, MAIN & CONNECTING ROD BEARINGS table.

8) Install connecting rod caps and bearings. Install components in original locations. Tighten rod nuts to specification. See TORQUE SPECIFICATIONS. To complete installation, reverse removal procedure. Tighten bolts to specification.

Connecting Rod Bearings – **1)** Mark bearing cap and connecting rod for location. Remove connecting rod cap and bearing. Install replacement bearing.

2) Align reference marks on rod cap and connecting rod. Measure bearing clearance with Plastigage. Connecting rods must move freely on crankshaft. Measure connecting rod side play. See CONNECTING RODS table under ENGINE SPECIFICATIONS.

Crankshaft End Play – If end play is not within specification, inspect thrust bearings and crankshaft. Replace thrust bearing or crankshaft to obtain correct end play. See CRANKSHAFT, MAIN & CONNECTING ROD BEARINGS table under ENGINE SPECIFICATIONS.

ENGINE OILING

ENGINE LUBRICATION SYSTEM

Oil pressure is provided by a rotor-type pump driven by crankshaft. Pressure relief valve is located in oil pump body.

Crankcase Capacity – On Diamante, crankcase capacity is 4.9 qts (4.3L) including filter. Montero and Pickup oil capacity is 5.0 qts. (4.7L). Add .5 qt. (.4L) when filter is replaced. Add .5 qt. (.4L) with oil cooler. Stealth and 3000GT oil capacity is 4.2 qts. (4.0L). Add .5 qt. (.4L) with filter replacement. Add .5 qt. (.4L) with oil cooler.

Oil Pressure – Oil pressure should be at least 11 psi (.8 kg/cm²) at idle and engine oil temperature of 167-194°F (75-90°C).

OIL PUMP

Removal – Remove timing belt and crankshaft sprocket. See TIMING BELT under REMOVAL & INSTALLATION. Remove oil pan. See OIL PAN under REMOVAL & INSTALLATION. Remove oil filter and mounting bracket. Remove oil pump and gasket from cylinder block. Note bolt length and location for installation reference.

Disassembly & Inspection – **1)** Disassemble pump. Inspect for scoring and cracks. Install rotors into pump body. Measure clearance between driven rotor and pump body. See OIL PUMP SPECIFICATIONS table.

2) Measure rotor side clearance. Replace rotor set or pump assembly if not within specification. Ensure relief valve slides freely in pump body bore. Inspect relief valve spring for damage.

OIL PUMP SPECIFICATIONS

Application	In. (mm)
Driven Rotor-To-Pump Body	.0039-.0071 (.099-.180)
Rotor Side Clearance	.0016-.0037 (.041-.094)

Reassembly & Installation – **1)** Reassemble pump. Tighten pump rear cover bolts to specification. See TORQUE SPECIFICATIONS. Install oil pump and gasket. Align splined teeth of oil pump with crankshaft. Install bolts, and tighten to specification.

2) If oil seal was removed, coat new seal with grease. Using Seal Driver (MD998717), install seal in oil pump until flush with case. Install remaining components.

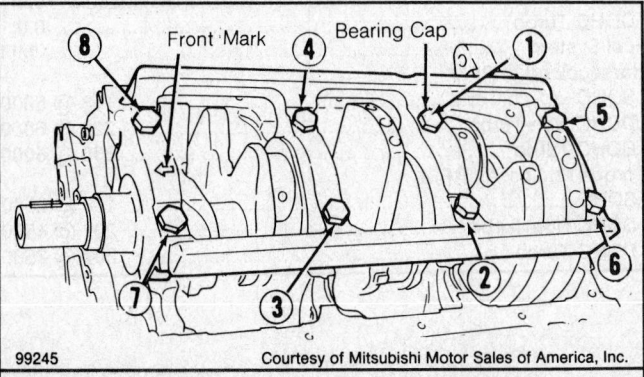

99245   Courtesy of Mitsubishi Motor Sales of America, Inc.

Fig. 23: Tightening Sequence For Main Bearing Cap Bolts

TORQUE SPECIFICATIONS

TORQUE SPECIFICATIONS (DIAMANTE, STEALTH & 3000GT)

Application	Ft. Lbs. (N.m)
Air Intake Plenum Brace Bolts	13 (18)
Automatic Tensioner Bolt	17 (23)
Camshaft Bearing Cap Bolt	
Front & Rear	15 (20)
No. 2, 3 & 4	[1]
Camshaft Sprocket Bolt	66 (90)
Connecting Rod Nut	38 (52)
Crankshaft Pulley Bolt	136 (185)
Cylinder Head Bolt [2]	
DOHC Turbo	92 (125)
Except DOHC Turbo	59 (80)
Distributor Adapter Bolt	11 (15)
Drive Plate Bolt	55 (75)
Engine Support Bracket Bolt	
Except 10 x 40-mm	76-83 (103-113)
10 x 40-mm	47-54 (64-73)
Exhaust Manifold Nut	13 (18)
Flywheel Bolt	55 (75)
Intake Manifold Bolt	13 (18)
Main Bearing Cap Bolt	
Head Mark "9"	59 (80)
Head Mark "10"	70 (95)
Oil Filter Bracket Bolt	11 (15)
Oil Pick-Up Tube Bolt	14 (19)
Oil Pump Mounting Bolt	11 (15)
Rear Engine Support Bracket-To-Engine Bolt	13-18 (18-25)
Relief Valve Plug	33 (45)
Rocker Shaft	15 (20)
Roll Stopper Bracket Through-Bolts	36-43 (49-58)
Turbocharger-To-Exhaust Fitting	40-47 (54-64)
Timing Belt Tensioner Arm Bolt	31 (42)
Timing Belt Tensioner Pulley Nut	36 (49)
Water Pump Bolt	17 (23)

	INCH Lbs. (N.m)
Delivery Pipe Bolt	108 (12)
Oil Pan Bolt	48-60 (5-7)
Oil Pump Cover Bolt	96 (11)
Rear Seal Case Bolt	96 (11)
Rocker Cover Bolt	
DOHC	26 (3)
SOHC	72-84 (8-9)
Throttle Body Bolt	84-108 (9-12)
Timing Belt Cover Bolt	84-108 (9-12)
Transmission Mounting Plate Bolt	84-108 (9-12)

[1] - Tighten to 97 INCH lbs. (8 N.m)
[2] - Tighten in 2 stages in sequence. See Fig. 4.

TORQUE SPECIFICATIONS (MONTERO & PICKUP)

Application	Ft. Lbs. (N.m)
Air Intake Plenum Stay Bolts	11-14 (15-19)
Camshaft Bearing Cap Bolt	14-15 (19-20)
Camshaft Sprocket Bolt	58-72 (79-98)
Connecting Rod Nut	37-38 (50-52)
Crankshaft Pulley Bolt	
Montero	108-116 (146-157)
Pickup	130-137 (176-186)
Cylinder Head Bolt [1]	
Cold Engine	65-72 (88-98)
Drive Plate Bolt	53-55 (72-75)
Exhaust Manifold Nut	11-16 (15-22)
Flywheel Bolt	53-55 (72-75)
Intake Manifold Bolts	11-15 (15-20)
Left Engine Support Bracket Bolt	15-21 (20-30)
Main Bearing Cap Bolt	55-61 (75-83)
Oil Pick-Up Tube Bolt	11-15 (15-20)
Rear Engine Support Bracket-To-Engine Bolt	13-18 (18-25)
Relief Valve Plug	29-36 (39-49)
Right Engine Support Bracket Bolt	
10 x 22-mm	25-36 (34-49)
12 x 22-mm & 12 x 32 mm	47-61 (64-83)
Rocker Shaft	14-15 (19-20)
Timing Belt Tensioner Bolt	16-21 (22-29)
Water Pump Bolt	14-20 (19-27)

	INCH Lbs. (N.m)
Delivery Pipe Bolt	84-108 (9-12)
Distributor Adapter Bolt	108-132 (12-15)
Oil Filter Bracket Bolt	108-120 (12-14)
Oil Pan Bolt	48-60 (5-7)
Oil Pump Cover Bolt	72-108 (8-12)
Oil Pump Mounting Bolt	108-120 (12-14)
Rear Seal Case Bolt	84-108 (9-12)
Rocker Cover Bolt	72-84 (8-9)
Throttle Body Bolt	84-108 (9-12)
Timing Belt Cover Bolt	84-108 (9-12)
Transmission Mounting Plate Bolt	84-108 (9-12)

[1] - Tighten in 2 stages in proper sequence. See Fig. 4.

ENGINE SPECIFICATIONS

GENERAL SPECIFICATIONS

Application	Specification
Displacement	181.4 Cu. In.
Bore	3.587" (91.1 mm)
Stroke	2.992" (76.0 mm)
Compression Ratio	
SOHC	8.9:1
DOHC Non-Turbo	10.0:1
DOHC Turbo	8.0:1
Fuel System	MFI
Horsepower @ RPM	
SOHC	143 @ 5000
DOHC Non-Turbo	222 @ 6000
DOHC Turbo	300 @ 6000
Torque Ft. Lbs. @ RPM	
SOHC	168 @ 2500
DOHC Non-Turbo	201 @ 4500
DOHC Turbo	307 @ 2500

CRANKSHAFT, MAIN & CONNECTING ROD BEARINGS

Application	In. (mm)
Crankshaft	
End Play	
Standard	.0020-.0098 (.050-.250)
Limit	.012 (.30)
Main Bearings	
Journal Diameter	2.36 (59.9)
Journal Out-Of-Round	
SOHC	.0002 (.005)
DOHC	.00012 (.003)
Journal Taper	
SOHC	.0002 (.005)
DOHC	.00012 (.003)
Oil Clearance	
Standard	
SOHC	.0008-.0020 (.020-.051)
DOHC	.0007-.0017 (.018-.043)
Limit	.004 (.10)
Connecting Rod Bearings	
Journal Diameter	1.965 (49.91)
Journal Out-Of-Round	
SOHC	.0002 (.005)
DOHC	.00012 (.003)
Journal Taper	.0002 (.005)
Oil Clearance	
Standard	.0008-.0020 (.020-.051)
Limit	.004 (.10)

CONNECTING RODS

Application	In. (mm)
Maximum Bend	.002 (.05)
Maximum Twist (Total Rod Length)	.004 (.10)
Side Play	
Standard	.0039-.0099 (.099-.251)
Limit	.016 (.41)

PISTONS, PINS & RINGS (SOHC)

Application	In. (mm)
Pistons	
Clearance	.0008-.0016 (.020-.040)
Diameter	3.587 (91.11)
Pins	
Piston Fit	[1]
Rod Fit	[2]
Rings	
No. 1	
End Gap	
Standard	.0118-.0177 (.300-.450)
Limit	.031 (.79)
Side Clearance	
Standard	.0020-.0035 (.051-.089)
Limit	.004 (.10)
No. 2	
End Gap	
Standard	.0098-.0157 (.249-.399)
Limit	.031 (.79)
Side Clearance	
Standard	.0008-.0024 (.020-.060)
Limit	.004 (.10)
No. 3 (Oil)	
End Gap	
Standard	
Except Stealth	.008-.024 (.20-.60)
Stealth	.012-.035 (.30-.89)
Limit	.039 (.99)

[1] – Slip.
[2] – At press load of 1653-3858 lbs. (750-1750 kg).

PISTONS, PINS & RINGS (DOHC)

Application	In. (mm)
Pistons	
Clearance	.0012-.0020 (.030-.051)
Diameter	3.587 (91.11)
Pins	
Piston Fit	[1]
Rod Fit	[2]
Rings	
No. 1	
End Gap	.0118-.0177 (.300-.450)
Side Clearance	
Standard	.0012-.0028 (.030-.071)
Limit	.004 (.10)
No. 2	
End Gap	.0177-.0236 (.450-.599)
Side Clearance	
Standard	.0008-.0024 (.020-.060)
Limit	.004 (.10)
No. 3 (Oil)	
End Gap	
Standard	.008-.024 (.20-.60)
Limit	.039 (.99)

[1] – Slip.
[2] – At press load of 1686-3934 lbs. (759-1770 kg).

CYLINDER BLOCK

Application	In. (mm)
Cylinder Bore	
Standard Diameter	3.590 (91.19)
Maximum Taper & Out-Of-Round	.0008 (.020)
Maximum Deck Warpage	
Standard	.002 (.05)
Limit	.0040 (.102)

VALVES & VALVE SPRINGS (SOHC)

Application	Specification
Intake Valves	
Face Angle	45-45.5°
Minimum Margin	.028" (.71 mm)
Standard Length	4.055" (103.00 mm)
Stem Diameter	.3134-.3140" (7.960-7.976 mm)
Exhaust Valves	
Face Angle	45-45.5°
Minimum Margin	.059" (1.50 mm)
Standard Length	4.043" (102.70 mm)
Stem Diameter	.3122-.3130" (7.930-7.950 mm)
Valve Springs	
Free Length	
Standard	1.960" (49.78 mm)
Limit	1.920" (48.77 mm)
Installed Height	1.591" (40.41 mm)
Out-Of-Square	
Standard	2°
Limit	4°

	Lbs. @ In. (kg @ mm)
Pressure (Valves Closed)	74 @ 1.591 (33.6 @ 40.41)

1994 ENGINES
3.0L V6 (Cont.)

VALVES & VALVE SPRINGS (DOHC)

Application	Specification
Intake Valves	
Face Angle	45-45.5°
Minimum Margin	.019" (.48 mm)
Standard Length	4.185" (106.30 mm)
Stem Diameter	.260" (6.60 mm)
Exhaust Valves	
Face Angle	45-45.5°
Minimum Margin	.039" (.99 mm)
Standard Length	4.150" (105.41 mm)
Stem Diameter	.260" (6.60 mm)
Valve Springs	
Free Length	
Standard	1.830" (46.48 mm)
Limit	1.790" (45.47 mm)
Installed Height	1.492" (37.90 mm)
Out-Of-Square	
Standard	2°
Limit	4°

	Lbs. @ In. (kg @ mm)
Pressure (Valves Closed)	62 @ 1.492 (28.1 @ 37.90)

CYLINDER HEAD (SOHC)

Application	Specification
Cylinder Head Height	3.310" (84.07 mm)
Maximum Warpage	.008" (.20 mm)
Valve Seats (Intake & Exhaust)	
Seat Angle	45-45.5°
Seat Width	.035-.051" (.90-1.30 mm)
Seat Bore Diameter	1.732-1.742" (44.00-44.25 mm)
Valve Guides	
Intake Valve	
Valve Guide Cyl. Head Bore I.D.	.5118-.5189" (13.00-13.18 mm)
Valve Guide Length	1.732" (44 mm)
Stem-To-Guide Clearance	
Standard	.0012-.0024" (.030-.060 mm)
Limit	.004" (.10 mm)
Exhaust Valve	
Valve Guide Cyl. Head Bore I.D.	.5118-.5189" (13.00-13.18 mm)
Valve Guide Length	1.890" (48 mm)
Stem-To-Guide Clearance	
Standard	.0020-.0035" (.051-.089 mm)
Limit	.006" (.15 mm)

CYLINDER HEAD (DOHC)

Application	Specification
Cylinder Head Height	5.20" (132.1 mm)
Maximum Warpage	.008" (.20 mm)
Valve Seats (Intake & Exhaust)	
Seat Angle	45-45.5°
Seat Width	.035-.051" (.90-1.30 mm)
Seat Bore Diameter	1.417-1.427" (35.99-36.25 mm)
Valve Guides	
Intake Valve	
Valve Guide Cyl. Head Bore I.D.	.5118-.5189" (13.00-13.18 mm)
Valve Guide Installed Height	.689" (17.50 mm)
Stem-To-Guide Clearance	
Standard	.0008-.0020" (.020-.051 mm)
Limit	.0040" (.102 mm)
Exhaust Valve	
Valve Guide Cyl. Head Bore I.D.	.5118-.5189" (13.00-13.18 mm)
Valve Guide Installed Height	.689" (17.50 mm)
Valve Stem-To-Guide Clearance	
Standard	.0020-.0035" (.051-.089 mm)
Limit	.0060" (.152 mm)

CAMSHAFT (SOHC)

Application	In. (mm)
End Play	
Standard	.004-.008 (0.1-0.2)
Limit	.015 (0.4)
Journal Diameter	1.34 (34.0)
Lobe Height	
Standard	1.620 (41.15)
Limit	1.600 (40.64)
Oil Clearance	.0020-.0035 (.050-.090)

CAMSHAFT (DOHC)

Application	In. (mm)
End Play	
Standard	.004-.008 (0.1-0.2)
Limit	.015 (0.4)
Journal Diameter	1.020 (25.91)
Lobe Height	
Intake	
Standard	1.370 (34.80)
Limit	1.350 (34.29)
Exhaust	
Standard	1.370 (34.80)
Limit	1.350 (34.29)
Oil Clearance	.0020-.0040 (.050-.102)

Mitsubishi: Montero

NOTE: For repair procedures not covered in this article, see ENGINE OVERHAUL PROCEDURES article in GENERAL INFORMATION.

ENGINE IDENTIFICATION

Engine may be identified by Vehicle Identification Number (VIN) stamped on a metal pad located near lower left corner of windshield. The eighth character of VIN identifies engine, and tenth character (R) identifies model year (1994). Engine model number is stamped on front upper edge of cylinder block, below cylinder head, or on vehicle information plate on firewall. Engine serial number is stamped near the engine model number.

ENGINE IDENTIFICATION CODES

Application	Engine Model	Engine Code
Montero	6G74	M

ADJUSTMENTS

VALVE CLEARANCE ADJUSTMENT

NOTE: 3.5L engines are equipped with hydraulic lash adjusters. Adjustment is not required.

REMOVAL & INSTALLATION

CAUTION: When battery is disconnected, vehicle computer and memory systems may lose memory data. Driveability problems may exist until computer systems have completed a relearn cycle.

NOTE: For reassembly reference, label all electrical connectors, vacuum hoses, and fuel lines before removal. Also place mating marks on engine hood and other major assemblies before removal.

FUEL PRESSURE RELEASE

Perform these steps to release fuel system pressure:
- Disconnect fuel pump harness connector at fuel tank.
- Start engine. After it stalls, turn ignition switch to OFF position.
- Disconnect battery (-) terminal. Reconnect fuel pump harness.
- Wrap shop towels around fuel return and high pressure hoses to prevent fuel splashing on engine. Disconnect fuel return hose and high pressure fuel hose to drain any residual fuel.

ENGINE

Removal – **1)** Remove hood. Drain cooling system. Remove radiator. Remove skid plate and splash shields. Release fuel system pressure. See FUEL PRESSURE RELEASE. Disconnect negative battery cable.
2) Remove air cleaner ducts. Remove accessory drive belts. Remove and support A/C compressor and power steering pump, leaving hoses connected. Disconnect oil cooler hoses. Cover fuel hose with shop towel, and disconnect high pressure fuel hose and "O" ring. Disconnect fuel return hose.
3) Label and disconnect all vacuum hoses. Disconnect cooling system hoses. Label and unplug all electrical connections from engine. Remove heat shield from motor mounts. Remove motor mount bolts. Ensure all hoses and wires are disconnected and set aside.
4) Disconnect exhaust pipe from exhaust manifolds. Remove starter. Attach engine hoist to engine. Support transmission. Disconnect engine from transmission. See appropriate article in CLUTCHES or TRANSMISSION SERVICING. Remove engine.
Installation – To install, reverse removal procedure. Install new "O" rings onto fuel lines. Install new exhaust gaskets and nuts. See TORQUE SPECIFICATIONS. Replenish fluids.

INTAKE MANIFOLD

CAUTION: Fuel system is under pressure. Fuel pressure must be released before disconnecting fuel lines. See FUEL PRESSURE RELEASE.

Removal – **1)** Release fuel pressure. Remove EGR pipe. Remove intake plenum stays. Remove EGR valve. Remove throttle body. Remove intake plenum cover and intake plenum. Remove variable induction control assembly. *See Fig. 1.*
2) Remove center cover. Remove spark plug cables and spark plugs. Remove ignition power transistor. Remove crankshaft position sensor. Remove fuel injector harness. Remove fuel pressure regulator, fuel injectors, fuel rails, and grommets. Remove retaining nuts and intake manifold. *See Fig. 2.*
Installation – Clean all gasket mating surfaces. Inspect for damage and cracks on all mounting surfaces. To install, reverse removal procedure using, new gaskets and "O" rings. Tighten bolts and nuts to specification. See TORQUE SPECIFICATIONS.

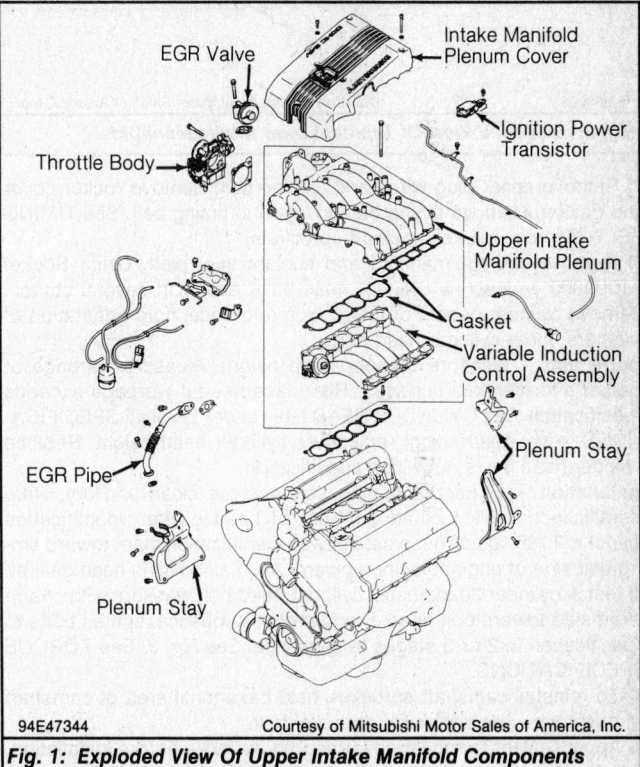

94E47344 Courtesy of Mitsubishi Motor Sales of America, Inc.

Fig. 1: Exploded View Of Upper Intake Manifold Components

EXHAUST MANIFOLDS

NOTE: Note locations and orientation of exhaust manifold washers for installation reference. DO NOT mix these fasteners.

Removal – **1)** Remove oxygen sensor. Disconnect exhaust pipes from manifolds. Lower exhaust pipes. Remove heat shields. Before removing right manifold, remove decking hook and alternator brace.
2) Before removing left exhaust manifold, remove EGR tube and gasket. Remove front intake manifold plenum bracket. Remove exhaust manifolds and gaskets.
Installation – To install, reverse removal procedure. Install new gaskets. Lubricate new dipstick tube "O" ring with engine oil before installation. Install manifold nuts and washers in original locations. Tighten nuts to specification. See TORQUE SPECIFICATIONS.

CYLINDER HEADS

Removal – **1)** Drain cooling system. Remove manifolds and brackets. See INTAKE MANIFOLD. Remove exhaust manifolds. See EXHAUST MANIFOLDS.

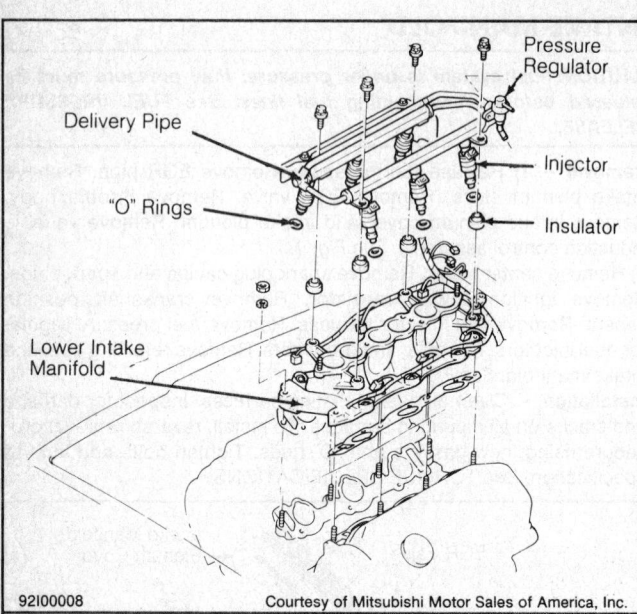

Fig. 2: Exploded View Of Typical Lower Intake Manifold

2) Remove spark plug wires and ignition coil. Remove rocker cover and gasket. Remove timing belt covers and timing belt. See TIMING BELT. Remove intake camshaft sprockets.

3) Remove coolant manifold and coolant inlet pipe. Using Socket (MD998051), unscrew cylinder head bolts evenly in several stages. Remove cylinder head. For installation reference, note orientation of washers under cylinder head bolts.

Inspection – Measure cylinder head height. Measure warpage at gasket and manifold surfaces. Resurface head if warpage exceeds specification. See CYLINDER HEAD table under ENGINE SPECIFICATIONS. After resurfacing, remeasure cylinder head height. Replace cylinder head if it is not within specification.

Installation – 1) Ensure mating surfaces are clean and dry. Note identification mark located on front of head gasket. Identification marks is T136. Install head gasket with identification mark toward timing belt side of engine, facing upward. Align all holes in head gasket.

2) Install cylinder head. Install cylinder head bolt washers with chamfered side toward bolt head. Using proper sequence, tighten bolts to specification in 2 or 3 stages in sequence. See Fig. 3. See TORQUE SPECIFICATIONS.

3) To reinstall camshaft sprocket, hold hexagonal area of camshaft with wrench while tightening sprocket bolt.

4) Apply sealant to rocker cover sealing surfaces before installation. See Fig. 4. Align rocker cover gasket projections with notches in rocker cover. Tighten rocker cover bolts in a crisscross pattern. Start at 4 corners of rocker cover and work toward center.

5) Lubricate all "O" rings with engine oil before installation. Install new "O" ring on oil dipstick tube. To complete installation, reverse removal procedure. Tighten bolts and nuts to specification. See TORQUE SPECIFICATIONS.

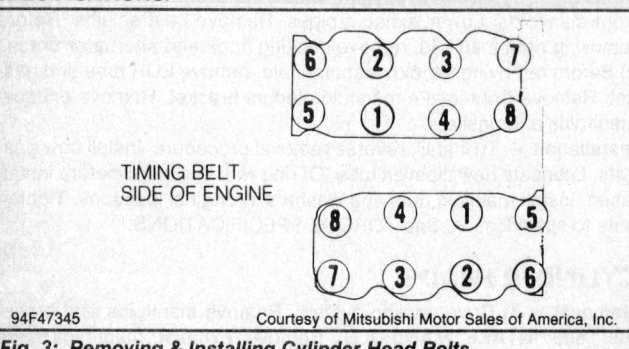

Fig. 3: Removing & Installing Cylinder Head Bolts

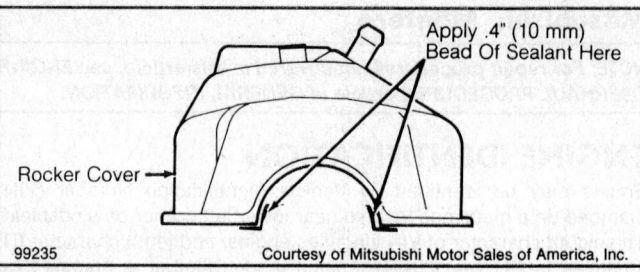

Fig. 4: Applying Sealant To Rocker Cover

FRONT CRANKSHAFT OIL SEAL

Removal & Installation – Remove timing belt and crankshaft sprocket. See TIMING BELT. Pry oil seal from oil pump. Before installation, coat seal lip with grease. Using Seal Driver (MD998717), install seal in oil pump. Install remaining components. See TORQUE SPECIFICATIONS.

TIMING BELT

CAUTION: To prevent engine damage, DO NOT rotate crankshaft counterclockwise (as viewed from timing belt end of engine).

NOTE: Ensure timing marks are aligned. Mark direction of rotation of timing belt.

Removal – 1) Disconnect negative battery cable. Remove radiator. Remove alternator. Remove battery and battery tray. Remove lower splash shields.

2) Remove drive belts. Remove cooling fan clutch assembly. Remove water pump pulley. Remove A/C compressor and compressor bracket. Remove accessory mount cover. Remove power steering pump. Remove accessory mount.

CAUTION: Note length and location of timing belt cover bolts during removal. Different length bolts are used and must be installed in original location.

3) Remove timing belt upper cover. Remove crankshaft position sensor connector. Using Holder (MB990767) and Bolts (MB998754), remove crankshaft pulley. See Fig. 5.

4) If reusing timing belt, place arrow on belt to indicate running direction. Rotate crankshaft to align all timing marks. See Fig. 6. Loosen tensioner center bolt. Remove timing belt and belt tensioner.

5) If camshaft sprocket requires removal, hold camshaft with wrench on hexagonal portion of camshaft. Remove camshaft sprocket bolt and camshaft sprocket.

Installation – 1) Install camshaft sprockets (if removed). See TORQUE SPECIFICATIONS.

2) Place automatic tensioner assembly in a soft-jawed vise. Slowly close vise to press rod back into tensioner until both rod and housing holes are aligned. Install a .055" (1.40 mm) diameter wire through both holes.

3) Remove tensioner from vise, and install assembly with wire in place. Install crankshaft sprocket (if removed). Align timing marks on crankshaft and camshaft sprockets. See Fig. 6.

CAUTION: Turning camshaft sprockets while No. 1 cylinder is at TDC may damage valve and piston. Use care when aligning timing marks.

4) To lower No. 1 piston from TDC and prevent valve and piston contact, turn crankshaft back 3 sprocket teeth (measured at timing mark). Starting with front bank of cylinders, verify intake and exhaust camshaft timing marks are not within shaded area of figure. See Fig. 7.

WARNING: Use care when aligning timing marks. When camshaft sprocket timing marks are in indicated area, camshaft is under valve spring pressure and may rotate suddenly, pinching hand between sprockets.

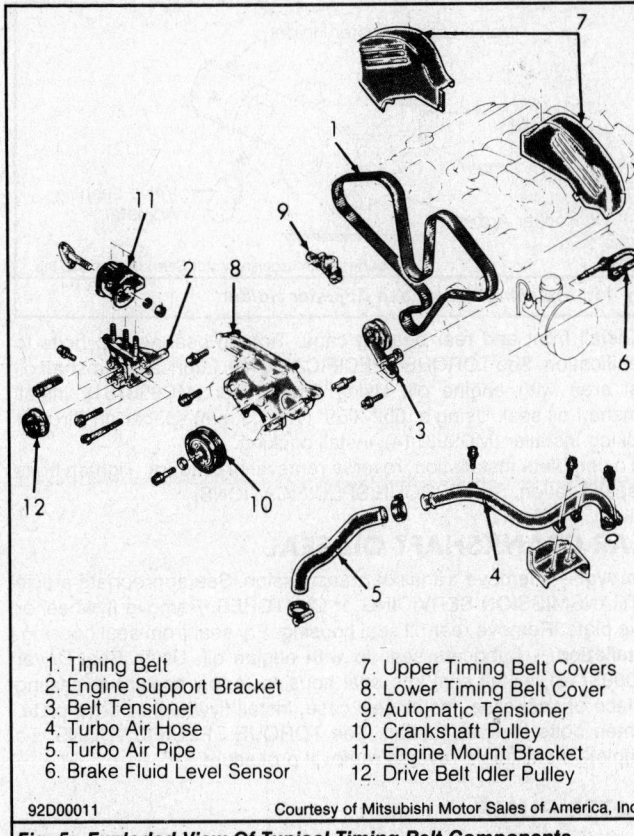

1. Timing Belt
2. Engine Support Bracket
3. Belt Tensioner
4. Turbo Air Hose
5. Turbo Air Pipe
6. Brake Fluid Level Sensor
7. Upper Timing Belt Covers
8. Lower Timing Belt Cover
9. Automatic Tensioner
10. Crankshaft Pulley
11. Engine Mount Bracket
12. Drive Belt Idler Pulley

92D00011   Courtesy of Mitsubishi Motor Sales of America, Inc.

Fig. 5: Exploded View Of Typical Timing Belt Components

5) If camshaft sprocket timing mark is within indicated area, carefully rotate camshaft sprocket until timing mark is located in nearest safe area. See Fig. 7.

6) Rotate either camshaft sprocket clockwise to align timing marks as shown in illustration. See Fig. 8. If camshaft sprocket is rotated past timing mark, rotate it counterclockwise to realign it. Repeat procedure for other front bank camshaft sprocket.

NOTE: If necessary, crankshaft sprocket may be turned one tooth counterclockwise to aid belt installation.

7) Repeat steps 4) through 6) for rear cylinder bank camshafts. Align crankshaft timing mark. Install timing belt onto sprockets in sequence. See Fig. 9. Use spring-type paper clips to secure belt on sprockets. Use wrenches on camshaft sprocket bolts to prevent camshafts from turning during belt installation.

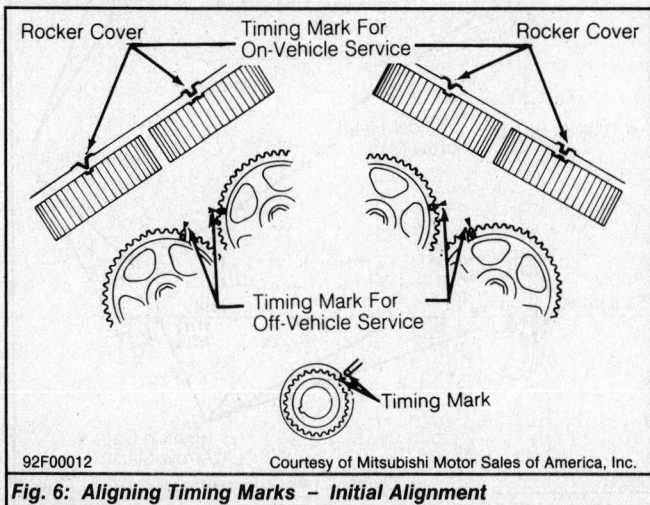

92F00012   Courtesy of Mitsubishi Motor Sales of America, Inc.

Fig. 6: Aligning Timing Marks – Initial Alignment

FRONT CYLINDER BANK

92H00013   Courtesy of Mitsubishi Motor Sales of America, Inc.

Fig. 7: Aligning Timing Marks To Prevent Valve & Piston Damage

8) Rotate timing belt tensioner pulley until pin holes are located above center bolt. See Fig. 10. Push tensioner pulley against belt, and temporarily tighten center bolt. Ensure all timing marks are aligned, and remove clips.

9) Rotate crankshaft 1/4 revolution counterclockwise. Rotate crankshaft clockwise until timing marks are realigned. Loosen tensioner center bolt. Using Tensioner Pulley Socket (MD998767), apply approximately 83 INCH lbs. (9.4 N.m) torque to tensioner pulley to prevent it from turning. See Fig. 10. Retighten center bolt to specification. See TORQUE SPECIFICATIONS. Ensure tensioner pulley does not rotate while tightening center bolt.

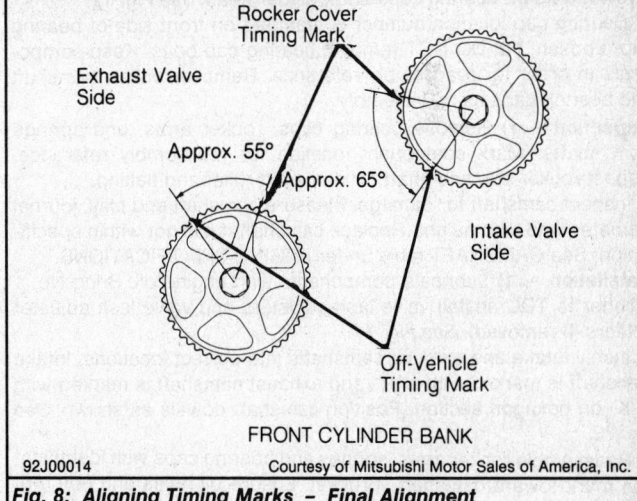

FRONT CYLINDER BANK

92J00014   Courtesy of Mitsubishi Motor Sales of America, Inc.

Fig. 8: Aligning Timing Marks – Final Alignment

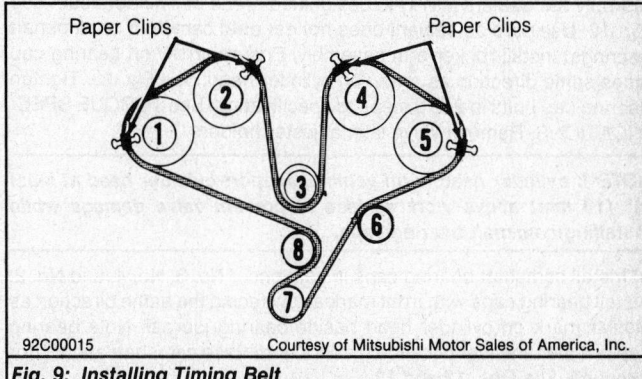

92C00015   Courtesy of Mitsubishi Motor Sales of America, Inc.

Fig. 9: Installing Timing Belt

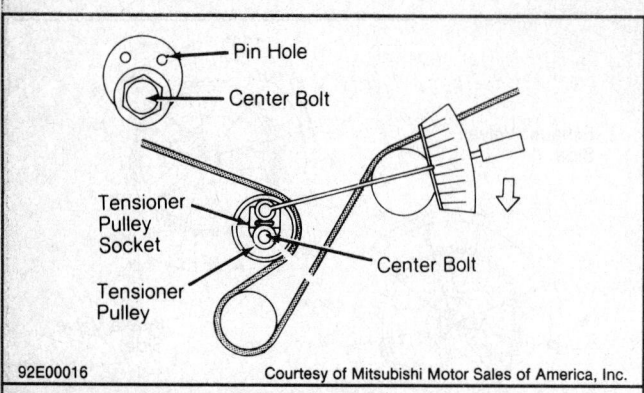

92E00016   Courtesy of Mitsubishi Motor Sales of America, Inc.

Fig. 10: Adjusting Timing Belt Tensioner

10) Rotate crankshaft 2 revolutions clockwise. Wait 5 minutes. Verify wire can still be moved easily, or automatic tensioner rod projects from tensioner body .15-.18" (3.8-4.5 mm). If wire does not move easily, or rod projection is not to specification, repeat steps **6)** and **10)**. Remove wire.

11) To complete installation, reverse removal procedure. Install bolts into correct timing belt cover holes. Tighten bolts to specification. See TORQUE SPECIFICATIONS.

CAMSHAFT & ROCKER ARMS

Removal – 1) Remove PCV valve and breather hoses. Remove timing belt and camshaft sprockets. See TIMING BELT. Remove rocker covers and gaskets. Remove circular packing from rear of camshafts.

2) Remove camshaft oil seals from front of cylinder head. Install Valve Lash Adjuster Holder (MD998443) onto rocker arm. *See Fig. 11.* Note arrow marks on bearing caps and cylinder head. *See Fig. 12.*

3) Bearing cap location number is stamped on front side of bearing cap. Loosen, but DO NOT remove, bearing cap bolts. Keep components in order for reassembly reference. Remove rocker, camshaft and bearing caps as an assembly.

Inspection – 1) Remove bearing caps, rocker arms, and springs from shafts. Mark component location for reassembly reference. Inspect rocker arm and shaft for damaged roller and flaking.

2) Inspect camshaft for damage. Measure camshaft end play, journal diameter, and lobe height. Replace camshaft if it is not within specification. See CAMSHAFT table under ENGINE SPECIFICATIONS.

Installation – 1) Lubricate components with engine oil. Bring No. 1 cylinder to TDC. Install valve lash adjusters and valve lash adjuster holders (if removed). *See Fig. 11.*

2) Install intake and exhaust camshafts into correct locations. Intake camshaft is marked with a "P", and exhaust camshaft is marked with a "K" on hexagon section. Position camshaft dowels as shown. *See Fig. 13.*

3) Reassemble rocker arms, springs and bearing caps with identification mark toward camshaft sprocket. Ensure oil holes and notch of shafts are properly positioned. *See Fig. 14.*

4) Apply 3M Sealant (4171) to designated areas of cylinder head. *See Fig. 12.* Use care so sealant does not get onto camshaft or camshaft bearings. Install rocker arm assembly. Ensure arrow on bearing cap faces same direction as arrow on cylinder head. *See Fig. 12.* Tighten bearing cap bolts in 2 to 3 steps to specification. See TORQUE SPECIFICATIONS. Remove valve lash adjuster holders.

NOTE: If cylinder head is off vehicle, support cylinder head at least .4" (10 mm) above work surface to prevent valve damage while installing camshaft bearing caps.

5) Install camshaft bearing caps in sequence: No. 3, No. 4, and No. 2. Install bearing caps with front mark arrow facing the same direction as similar mark on cylinder head beside bearing journal. Note bearing cap number and identification mark ("I" for intake camshaft and "E" for exhaust). *See Figs. 12 and 13.*

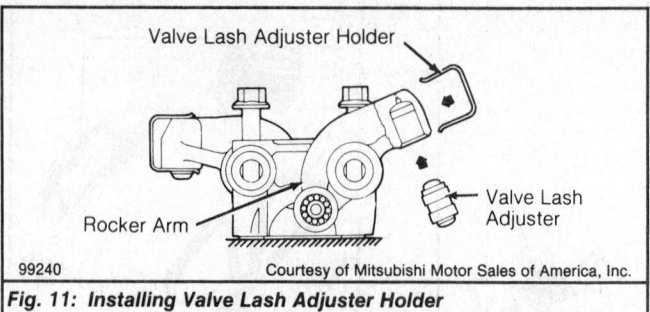

Valve Lash Adjuster Holder

Rocker Arm

Valve Lash Adjuster

99240   Courtesy of Mitsubishi Motor Sales of America, Inc.

Fig. 11: Installing Valve Lash Adjuster Holder

6) Install front and rear bearing caps. Tighten bearing cap bolts to specification. See TORQUE SPECIFICATIONS. Lubricate camshaft oil seal area with engine oil. Using Seal Driver (MD998761), install camshaft oil seal. Using a .052-.059" (1.3-1.5 mm) spacer on Circular Packing Installer (MD998714), install packing.

7) To complete installation, reverse removal procedure. Tighten bolts to specification. See TORQUE SPECIFICATIONS.

REAR CRANKSHAFT OIL SEAL

Removal – Remove transaxle/transmission. See appropriate article in TRANSMISSION SERVICING or CLUTCHES. Remove flywheel or drive plate. Remove rear oil seal housing. Pry seal from seal housing.

Installation – Lubricate seal lip with engine oil. Using Seal Driver (MD998718), install seal into seal housing. Apply sealant to sealing surface of seal case. Install seal case. Install flywheel or drive plate. Tighten bolts to specification. See TORQUE SPECIFICATIONS. To complete installation, reverse removal procedure.

WATER PUMP

Removal – Drain cooling system. Remove timing belt and crankshaft sprocket. See TIMING BELT. Remove coolant ducts to water pump if necessary. Remove water pump bolts, noting length and location for reassembly reference. Remove water pump.

Installation – To install, reverse removal procedure, using new gasket and "O" rings. Coat all "O" rings with water before installation. Install water pump and gasket. Tighten bolts to specification. See TORQUE SPECIFICATIONS.

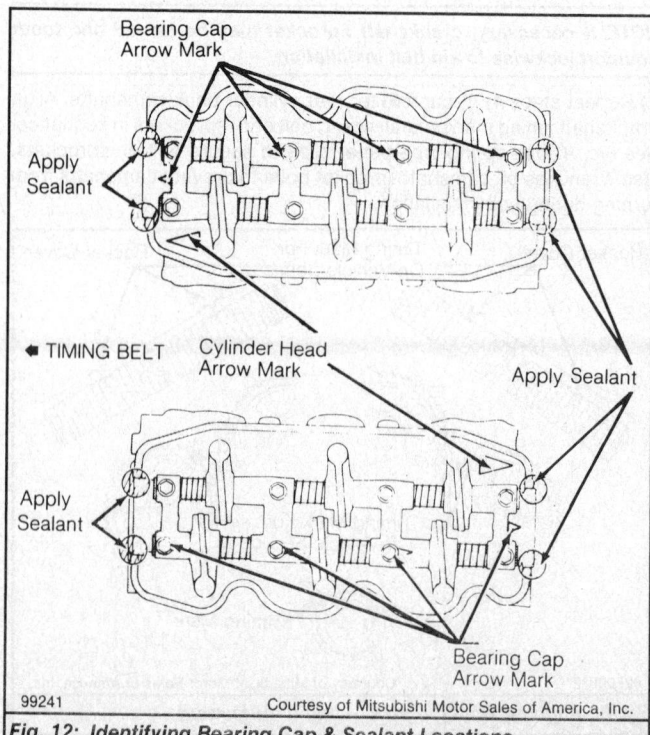

Bearing Cap Arrow Mark

Apply Sealant

TIMING BELT   Cylinder Head Arrow Mark

Apply Sealant

Apply Sealant

Bearing Cap Arrow Mark

99241   Courtesy of Mitsubishi Motor Sales of America, Inc.

Fig. 12: Identifying Bearing Cap & Sealant Locations

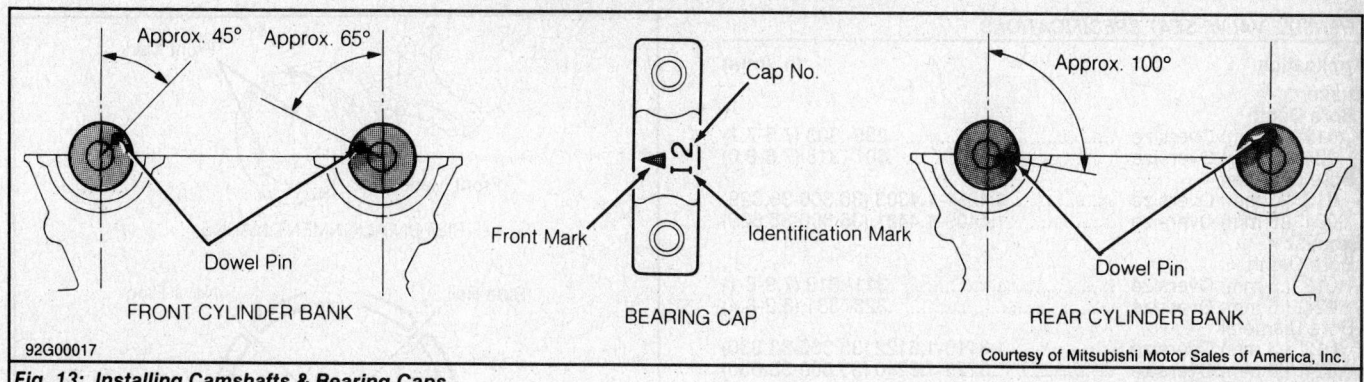

Fig. 13: Installing Camshafts & Bearing Caps

OIL PAN

Removal – 1) Remove hood. Remove skid plate and lower covers. Raise and support vehicle. Disconnect and remove exhaust pipe from exhaust manifolds. Drain engine oil. Remove starter cover and starter. Unplug oil pressure sending unit connector. Remove front suspension crossmember.

2) Remove transmission braces. Remove ground cable. Remove engine mount heat shields. Attach engine hoist. Remove motor mount bolts. Raise engine and insert a 1" wood spacer between front insulator and mounts. Lower engine onto wood blocks.

3) Raise and support vehicle. Remove oil pan bolts. Using Seal Cutter (MD998727), separate oil pan from cylinder block. Remove oil pan.

Inspection – Clean sealant from mating surfaces on engine block and oil pan. Inspect oil pan for cracks and damage. Inspect sealing surface for damage and deformation. Inspect oil pick-up screen for damage.

Installation – 1) To install, reverse removal procedure. Apply sealant to oil pan flange in a continuous .16" (4 mm) diameter bead. See Fig. 15. Install oil pan within 15 minutes of applying sealant.

2) Tighten bolts to specification in proper sequence. See TORQUE SPECIFICATIONS. Wait at least 30 minutes before adding oil and starting engine. To complete installation, reverse removal procedure.

OVERHAUL

CYLINDER HEAD

Cylinder Head – Measure cylinder head height. Measure warpage at gasket and manifold surfaces. Resurface head if warpage exceeds specification. See CYLINDER HEAD table under ENGINE SPECIFICATIONS. Replace cylinder head if it is not within specification after resurfacing.

NOTE: Install valve springs with enamel-coated side toward valve spring retainer.

Valve Springs – Measure free length of valve springs. Measure spring pressure at specified height. Replace springs if not within specification. See VALVES & VALVE SPRINGS table under ENGINE SPECIFICATIONS. Inspect valve spring for squareness. Replace spring if out-of-square exceeds 4 degrees.

Valve Stem Oil Seals – With valves removed, remove oil seals from cylinder head. Lubricate new seals with engine oil. Using Valve Stem Oil Seal Installer (MD998377), install valve stem oil seal.

Valve Guides – 1) Measure valve stem oil clearance. Replace valve guide if not within specification. See VALVES & VALVE SPRINGS table under ENGINE SPECIFICATIONS.

2) Using press and appropriate driver, press valve guide out toward combustion chamber side of head. Cylinder head must be bored to install oversized valve guide once guide is removed. DO NOT install valve guide of same O.D. as old guide. Bore cylinder head to specification for oversize valve guide. See OVERSIZE VALVE GUIDE SPECIFICATIONS table.

3) Position cylinder head with combustion chamber downward. Using valve guide remover/installer, install valve guide. Install valve guide to .689" (17.5 mm), measured from cylinder head spring seating area to top of valve guide. Ensure valve slides smoothly in valve guide. Recondition valve seat.

OVERSIZE VALVE GUIDE SPECIFICATIONS

Oversize – In. (mm)	Size Mark	Bore Size – In. (mm)
.002 (.05)	5	.4744-.4752 (12.050-12.070)
.010 (.25)	25	.4823-.4830 (12.251-12.269)
.020 (.51)	50	.4921-.4929 (12.500-12.519)

Valve Seat – Grind seat wall thickness until seat can be removed. Machine cylinder head to accommodate an oversize valve seat. See OVERSIZE VALVE SEAT SPECIFICATIONS table. Heat cylinder head to approximately 480°F (250°C), or chill valve seat with liquid nitrogen, and install valve seat. Grind valve seat using 45-degree stone. Use 30-degree and 60-degree stones to adjust seat height.

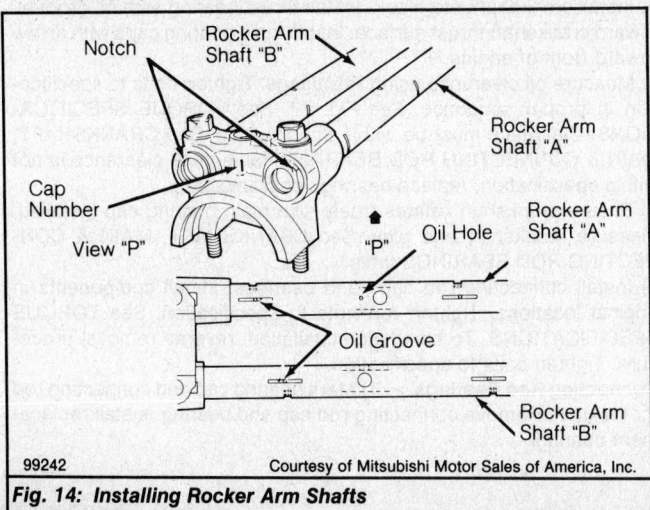

Fig. 14: Installing Rocker Arm Shafts

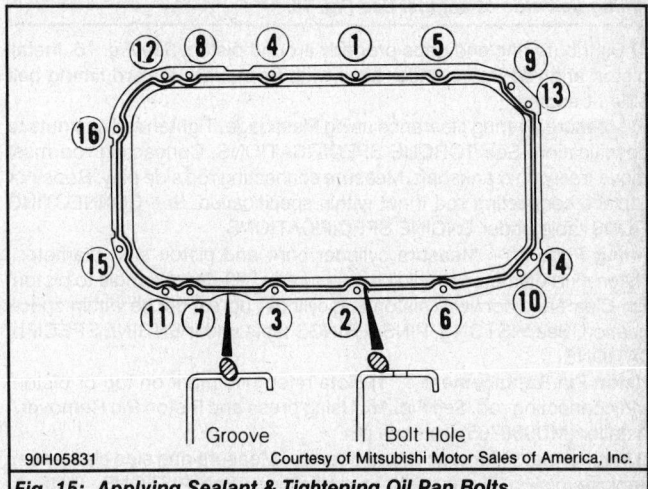

Fig. 15: Applying Sealant & Tightening Oil Pan Bolts

OVERSIZE VALVE SEAT SPECIFICATIONS

Application	In. (mm)
Intake	
Bore Depth	
.012" (.3 mm) Oversize	.295-.303 (7.5-7.7)
.024" (.6 mm) Oversize	.307-.315 (7.8-8.0)
Bore Diameter	
.012" (.3 mm) Oversize	1.4291-1.4303 (36.300-36.329)
.024" (.6 mm) Oversize	1.4409-1.4421 (36.600-36.629)
Exhaust	
Bore Depth	
.012" (.3 mm) Oversize	.311-.319 (7.9-8.1)
.024" (.6 mm) Oversize	.323-.331 (8.2-8.4)
Bore Diameter	
.012" (.3 mm) Oversize	1.3110-1.3122 (33.300-33.330)
.024" (.6 mm) Oversize	1.3228-1.3240 (33.600-33.630)

Valves – Disassemble cylinder head. Measure valve stem diameter, valve margin, and overall length. See appropriate VALVES & VALVE SPRINGS table under ENGINE SPECIFICATIONS. Inspect valve for worn stem tip. Measure valve margin after grinding valves. Replace valves if not within specification.

Lash Adjusters – Before installation, submerge lash adjuster in diesel fuel. Using a small wire, hold down internal check valve. Pump plunger up and down 4 or 5 times to bleed air from lash adjuster.

CYLINDER BLOCK ASSEMBLY

Cylinder Block – 1) Inspect cylinder block for cracks, warpage, cylinder bore taper, and out-of-round. Replace or repair cylinder block if it is not within specification. See CYLINDER BLOCK table under ENGINE SPECIFICATIONS.

2) Measure cylinder bore and piston skirt diameter. Piston skirt diameter should be measured at 90-degree angle to piston pin. Clearance between piston and cylinder bore must be within specification. See appropriate PISTONS, PINS & RINGS table under ENGINE SPECIFICATIONS.

Piston & Rod Assembly – 1) Remove cylinder heads and oil pan. See CYLINDER HEADS and OIL PAN under REMOVAL & INSTALLATION. Remove cylinder ridge. Mark connecting rod and cap for cylinder identification.

2) Note front mark on piston and connecting rod. *See Fig. 16.* Mark is positioned toward timing belt side of engine. Remove rod cap and piston assembly.

3) Piston ring end gap and side clearance must be within specification. See PISTONS, PINS & RINGS table under ENGINE SPECIFICATIONS. Install rings onto piston with ring code identification marks toward top of piston. Top ring is marked "1T", and No. 2 ring is marked "2T". Lubricate piston, rings, and cylinder bore with engine oil.

NOTE: Front mark "R" on piston indicates installation in cylinders No. 1, 3, or 5; front mark "L" indicates installation in cylinders No. 2, 4, or 6. Ensure front mark on piston and connecting rod are toward timing belt side of engine. See Fig. 16.

4) Distribute ring end gaps properly around piston. *See Fig. 16.* Install piston and rod into cylinder bore, with front mark toward timing belt side of engine.

5) Measure bearing clearance using Plastigage. Tighten rod cap nuts to specification. See TORQUE SPECIFICATIONS. Connecting rod must move freely on crankshaft. Measure connecting rod side play. Repair or replace connecting rod if not within specification. See CONNECTING RODS table under ENGINE SPECIFICATIONS.

Fitting Pistons – Measure cylinder bore and piston skirt diameter. Piston skirt diameter should be measured at 90-degree angle to piston pin. Clearance between piston and cylinder bore must be within specification. See PISTONS, PINS & RINGS table under ENGINE SPECIFICATIONS.

Piston Pin Replacement – 1) Note reference mark on top of piston and connecting rod. *See Fig. 16.* Using press and Piston Pin Remover/Installer (MD998765), remove pin.

2) Inspect piston for cracks and damage. Measure ring side clearance. Replace piston if not within specification. See PISTONS, PINS & RINGS table under ENGINE SPECIFICATIONS.

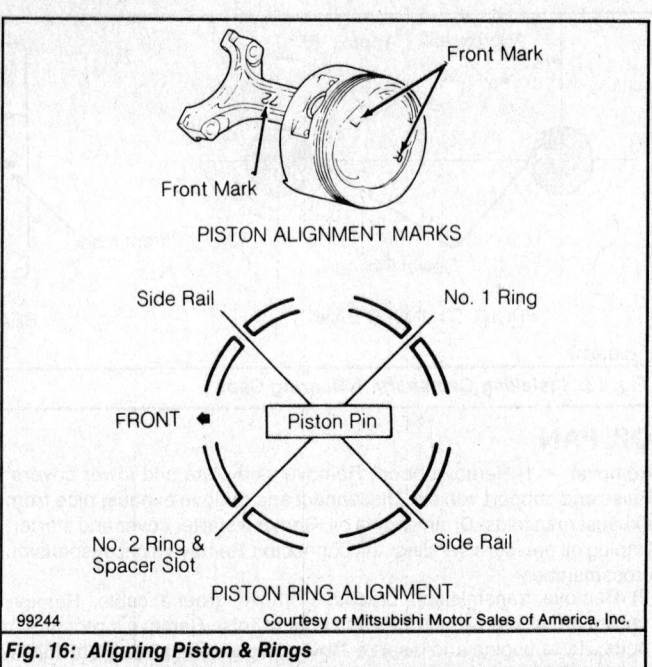

PISTON ALIGNMENT MARKS

PISTON RING ALIGNMENT

99244   Courtesy of Mitsubishi Motor Sales of America, Inc.

Fig. 16: Aligning Piston & Rings

NOTE: Install piston with reference mark aligned with connecting rod reference mark. See Fig. 16.

3) Position piston onto connecting rod. Align reference marks on top of piston and connecting rod. *See Fig. 16.* Lubricate all components with oil. Press piston pin into piston and connecting rod. To install, reverse removal procedure. Ensure piston pin is centered in piston.

Crankshaft & Main Bearings – 1) Remove flywheel or drive plate. Remove transaxle/transmission mounting plate and rear seal case. Remove oil pump, oil pan, and oil pick-up tube. Mark connecting rod and main bearing caps for location.

2) Remove connecting rod caps and bearings. Note direction of arrow on main bearing cap. Remove main bearing cap. *See Fig. 17.* Remove crankshaft. Remove main bearings from cylinder block. Mark bearings for location.

3) Inspect crankshaft for cracks and damaged gear or threads. Measure crankshaft for taper and out-of-round. Replace or repair crankshaft if it is not within specification. See CRANKSHAFT, MAIN & CONNECTING ROD BEARINGS table under ENGINE SPECIFICATIONS.

4) Install upper main bearings into cylinder block. Ensure oil holes are aligned, and bearings are properly seated. Lubricate bearings with engine oil. Install thrust bearing with oil grooves toward crankshaft thrust surface.

5) Install crankshaft into block. Install thrust bearing with oil grooves toward crankshaft thrust surface. Install main bearing caps with arrow toward front of engine.

6) Measure oil clearance using Plastigage. Tighten bolts to specification in proper sequence. *See Fig. 17.* See TORQUE SPECIFICATIONS. Clearance must be within specification. See CRANKSHAFT, MAIN & CONNECTING ROD BEARINGS table. If oil clearance is not within specification, replace bearings or crankshaft.

7) Ensure crankshaft rotates freely with main bearing cap installed. Measure crankshaft end play. See CRANKSHAFT, MAIN & CONNECTING ROD BEARINGS table.

8) Install connecting rod caps and bearings. Install components in original locations. Tighten rod nuts to specification. See TORQUE SPECIFICATIONS. To complete installation, reverse removal procedure. Tighten bolts to specification.

Connecting Rod Bearings – 1) Mark bearing cap and connecting rod for location. Remove connecting rod cap and bearing. Install replacement bearing.

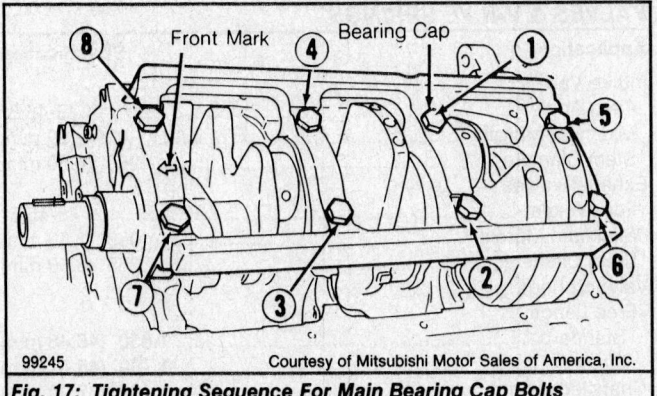

99245   Courtesy of Mitsubishi Motor Sales of America, Inc.

Fig. 17: Tightening Sequence For Main Bearing Cap Bolts

2) Align reference marks on rod cap and connecting rod. Measure bearing clearance with Plastigage. Connecting rods must move freely on crankshaft. Measure connecting rod side play. See CONNECTING RODS table under ENGINE SPECIFICATIONS.

Crankshaft End Play – If end play is not within specification, inspect thrust bearings and crankshaft. Replace thrust bearing or crankshaft to obtain correct end play. See CRANKSHAFT, MAIN & CONNECTING ROD BEARINGS table under ENGINE SPECIFICATIONS.

ENGINE OILING

ENGINE LUBRICATION SYSTEM

Oil pressure is provided by a rotor-type pump driven by crankshaft. Pressure relief valve is located in oil pump body.

Crankcase Capacity – Capacity is 5.2 qts (4.9L) including filter and oil cooler.

Oil Pressure – Oil pressure should be at least 11 psi (.8 kg/cm²) at idle and engine oil temperature of 167-194°F (75-90°C).

OIL PUMP

Removal – Remove timing belt and crankshaft sprocket. See TIMING BELT under REMOVAL & INSTALLATION. Remove oil pan. See OIL PAN under REMOVAL & INSTALLATION. Remove oil filter and mounting bracket. Remove oil pump and gasket from cylinder block. Note bolt length and location for installation reference.

Disassembly & Inspection – 1) Disassemble pump. Inspect for scoring and cracks. Install rotors into pump body. Measure clearance between driven rotor and pump body. See OIL PUMP SPECIFICATIONS table.

2) Measure rotor side clearance. Replace rotor set or pump assembly if not within specification. Ensure relief valve slides freely in pump body bore. Inspect relief valve spring for damage.

OIL PUMP SPECIFICATIONS

Application	In. (mm)
Driven Rotor-To-Pump Body	.0039-.0071 (.099-.180)
Rotor Side Clearance	.0016-.0037 (.041-.094)

Reassembly & Installation – 1) Reassemble pump. Tighten pump rear cover bolts to specification. See TORQUE SPECIFICATIONS. Install oil pump and gasket. Align splined teeth of oil pump with crankshaft. Install bolts, and tighten to specification.

2) If oil seal was removed, coat new seal with grease. Using Seal Driver (MD998717), install seal in oil pump until flush with case. Install remaining components.

TORQUE SPECIFICATIONS

TORQUE SPECIFICATIONS

Application	Ft. Lbs. (N.m)
Accessory Mount Bolts	
10 x 80 mm	28-30 (38-41)
10 x 100 mm	32-34 (43-46)
12 x 100 mm	53-55 (72-75)
Camshaft Bearing Cap Bolt	14-15 (19-20)
Camshaft Sprocket Bolt	66-67 (89-91)
Connecting Rod Nut	37-38 (50-52)
Coolant Fan Bracket Bolt	29-31 (39-42)
Crankshaft Pulley Bolt	108-116 (146-157)
Cylinder Head Bolt (Cold Engine) [1]	76-83 (103-113)
Drive Plate Bolt	53-55 (72-75)
Engine Support Bracket Bolt	15-21 (20-28)
Front	34-36 (46-49)
Rear	14-19 (19-26)
Exhaust Manifold Nut	11-16 (15-22)
Flywheel Bolt	53-55 (72-75)
Intake Manifold Bolts	11-15 (15-20)
Intake Manifold Plenum Stay Bolts	11-14 (15-19)
Main Bearing Cap Bolt	55-61 (75-83)
Oil Pick-Up Tube Bolt	11-15 (15-20)
Power Steering Pump Bolt	28-30 (38-41)
Relief Valve Plug	29-36 (39-49)
Rocker Shaft	14-15 (19-20)
Timing Belt Tensioner Bolt	34-36 (46-49)
Water Pump Bolt	14-20 (19-27)

	INCH Lbs. (N.m)
Cooling Fan Bolt	89-106 (10-12)
Crankshaft Position Sensor	71-89 (8-10)
Delivery Pipe Bolt	80-106 (9-12)
Intake Manifold Plenum Cover Bolts	80-106 (9-12)
Oil Filter Bracket Bolt	106-124 (12-14)
Oil Pan Bolt	44-62 (5-7)
Oil Pump Cover Bolt	71-106 (8-12)
Oil Pump Mounting Bolt	106-124 (12-14)
Rear Seal Case Bolt	80-106 (9-12)
Rocker Cover Bolt	27-35 (3-4)
Throttle Body Bolt	80-106 (9-12)
Timing Belt Cover Bolt	80-106 (9-12)
Transmission Mounting Plate Bolt	80-106 (9-12)

[1] – Tighten in 2 stages in proper sequence. *See Fig. 3.*

ENGINE SPECIFICATIONS

GENERAL SPECIFICATIONS

Application	Specification
Displacement	213.4 Cu. In.
Bore	3.66" (93.0 mm)
Stroke	3.38" (85.8 mm)
Compression Ratio	9.5:1
Fuel System	MFI
Horsepower @ RPM	215 @ 5000
Torque Ft. Lbs. @ RPM	228 @ 3000

1994 ENGINES
3.5L V6 (Cont.)

CRANKSHAFT, MAIN & CONNECTING ROD BEARINGS

Application	In. (mm)
Crankshaft	
End Play	
Standard	.0020-.0098 (.051-.250)
Limit	.012 (.30)
Main Bearings	
Journal Diameter	2.36 (59.9)
Journal Out-Of-Round	.00012 (.003)
Journal Taper	.00012 (.003)
Oil Clearance	
Standard	.0007-.0017 (.018-.043)
Limit	.004 (.10)
Connecting Rod Bearings	
Journal Diameter	1.965 (49.91)
Journal Out-Of-Round	.00012 (.003)
Journal Taper	.0002 (.005)
Oil Clearance	
Standard	.0008-.0020 (.020-.051)
Limit	.004 (.10)

CONNECTING RODS

Application	In. (mm)
Maximum Bend	.002 (.05)
Maximum Twist (Total Rod Length)	.004 (.10)
Side Play	
Standard	.0039-.0099 (.099-.251)
Limit	.016 (.41)

PISTONS, PINS & RINGS

Application	In. (mm)
Pistons	
Clearance	.0012-.0020 (.030-.051)
Diameter	3.66 (93.0)
Pins	
Piston Fit	[1]
Rod Fit	[2]
Rings	
No. 1	
End Gap	.0118-.0177 (.300-.450)
Side Clearance	
Standard	.0012-.0028 (.030-.071)
Limit	.004 (.10)
No. 2	
End Gap	.0177-.0236 (.450-.599)
Side Clearance	
Standard	.0008-.0024 (.020-.060)
Limit	.004 (.10)
No. 3 (Oil)	
End Gap	
Standard	.0039-.0138 (.099-.351)
Limit	.039 (.99)

[1] – Slip.
[2] – At press load of 1653-3858 lbs. (750-1750 kg).

CYLINDER BLOCK

Application	In. (mm)
Cylinder Bore	
Standard Diameter	3.66 (93.0)
Maximum Taper & Out-Of-Round	.0008 (.020)
Maximum Deck Warpage	
Standard	.002 (.05)
Limit	.0040 (.102)

VALVES & VALVE SPRINGS

Application	Specification
Intake Valves	
Face Angle	45-45.5°
Minimum Margin	.039" (.99 mm)
Stem Diameter	.260" (6.60 mm)
Exhaust Valves	
Face Angle	45-45.5°
Minimum Margin	.059" (1.50 mm)
Stem Diameter	.256" (6.50 mm)
Valve Springs	
Free Length	
Standard	1.830" (46.48 mm)
Limit	1.790" (45.47 mm)
Installed Height	1.492" (37.90 mm)
Out-Of-Square	
Standard	Less Than 2°
Limit	Less Than 4°
	Lbs. @ In. (kg @ mm)
Pressure (Valves Closed)	62 @ 1.492 (28.1 @ 37.90)

CYLINDER HEAD

Application	Specification
Cylinder Head Height	5.20" (132.1 mm)
Maximum Warpage	.008" (.20 mm)
Valve Seats (Intake & Exhaust)	
Seat Angle	45°-45.5
Seat Width	.035-.051" (.90-1.30 mm)
Seat Bore Diameter	1.417-1.427" (35.99-36.25 mm)
Valve Guides	
Intake Valve	
Valve Guide Cyl. Head Bore I.D.	.476" (12.1 mm)
Valve Guide Installed Height	.689" (17.50 mm)
Stem-To-Guide Clearance	
Standard	.0008-.0020" (.020-.051 mm)
Limit	.0040" (.102 mm)
Exhaust Valve	
Valve Guide Cyl. Head Bore I.D.	.476" (12.1 mm)
Valve Guide Installed Height	.689" (17.50 mm)
Valve Stem-To-Guide Clearance	
Standard	.0020-.0035" (.051-.089 mm)
Limit	.0060" (.152 mm)

CAMSHAFT

Application	In. (mm)
End Play	
Standard	.004-.008 (.1-.2)
Limit	.015 (.4)
Journal Diameter	1.020 (25.91)
Lobe Height	
Intake	
Standard	1.386 (35.20)
Limit	1.366 (34.70)
Exhaust	
Standard	1.374 (34.91)
Limit	1.355 (34.41)
Oil Clearance	.0020-.0040 (.050-.102)

**Chrysler Corp.: Colt, Colt Vista, Stealth
Eagle: Summit, Summit Wagon
Mitsubishi: Diamante, Eclipse, Expo, Galant,
 Mirage, Montero, Pickup, Precis, 3000GT**

SPECIFICATIONS

BELT ADJUSTMENT

NOTE: For belt routing, see Figs. 1-6.

BELT ADJUSTMENT

Application	Deflection [1] In. (mm)
Colt, Mirage & Summit	
1.5L	.22-.30 (5.5-7.5)
1.8L	[2]
Colt Vista, Expo & Summit Wagon	
1.8L	[2]
2.4L	.30-.35 (7.5-9.0)
Diamante	[3]
Eclipse	
1.8L	.26-.31 (6.5-8.0)
2.0L	.30-.35 (7.5-9.0)
Galant	.30-.35 (7.5-9.0)
Montero	
3.0L	.26-31 (6.5-8.0)
3.5L	
Alternator Belt	[4] .16-20 (4.0-5.0)
Power Steering Belt	.43-.51 (11.0-13.0)
Pickup	
2.4L	.28-.39 (7.1-10.0)
3.0L	.31-.39 (8.0-10.0)
Precis	.22-.28 (5.5-7.0)
Stealth & 3000GT	[5]

[1] – With 22 lbs. (10 kg) pressure applied midway on belt run.
[2] – Water pump is driven by timing belt. Tension is correct when
 space between cover and belt ("A"), under thumb pressure, is
 approximately 1.18" (30 mm). *See Fig. 2.*
[3] – Water pump is driven by timing belt. On SOHC, belt tension is
 44.1-66.1 lbs. (20-30 kg) using tension gauge. *See Fig. 4.* On
 DOHC, timing belt deflection is controlled by an automatic
 tensioner.
[4] – Measure between water pump pulley and crankshaft pulley.
[5] – Water pump is driven by timing belt. On SOHC, belt tension is
 46.3-68.3 lbs. (21-31 kg) using tension gauge. *See Fig. 4.* On
 DOHC, timing belt deflection is controlled by an automatic
 tensioner.

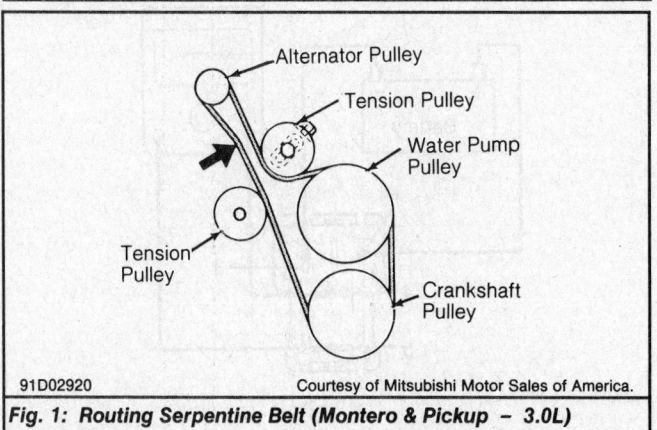

91D02920   Courtesy of Mitsubishi Motor Sales of America.

Fig. 1: Routing Serpentine Belt (Montero & Pickup – 3.0L)

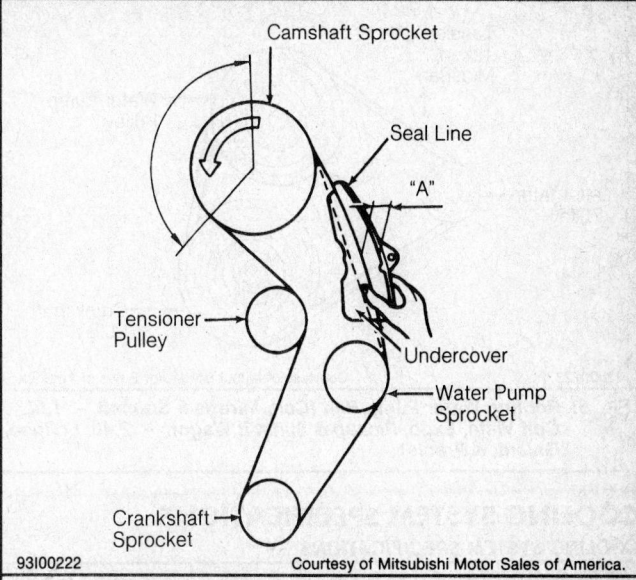

93I00222   Courtesy of Mitsubishi Motor Sales of America.

Fig. 2: Routing Timing/Water Pump Belt (Colt, Colt Vista, Expo, Mirage, Summit & Summit Wagon – 1.8L)

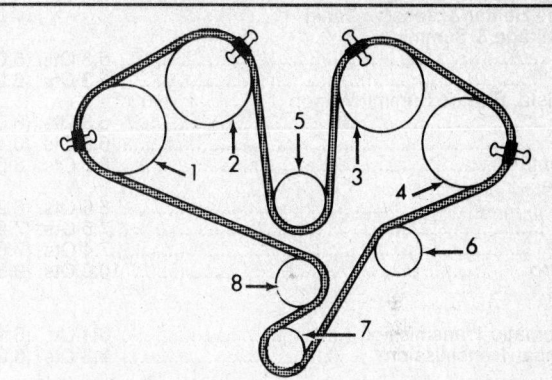

1. Exhaust Camshaft Sprocket (Front Bank)
2. Intake Camshaft Sprocket (Front Bank)
3. Intake Camshaft Sprocket (Rear Bank)
4. Exhaust Camshaft Sprocket (Rear Bank)
5. Water Pump Pulley
6. Idler Pulley
7. Crankshaft Sprocket
8. Tensioner Pulley

94F46156   Courtesy of Mitsubishi Motor Sales of America.

Fig. 3: Routing Timing/Water Pump Belt (Diamante, Stealth & 3000GT – DOHC)

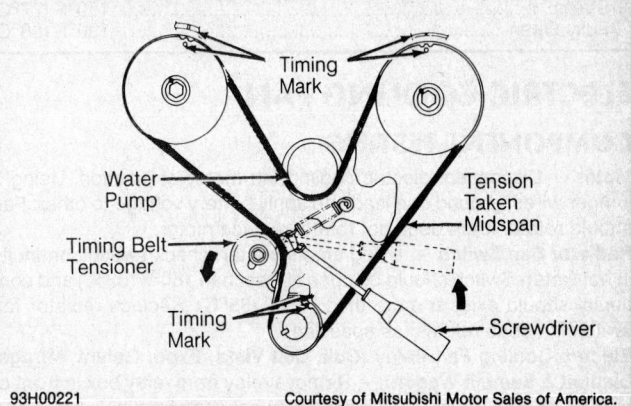

93H00221   Courtesy of Mitsubishi Motor Sales of America.

Fig. 4: Routing Timing/Water Pump Belt (Diamante, Stealth & 3000GT – SOHC)

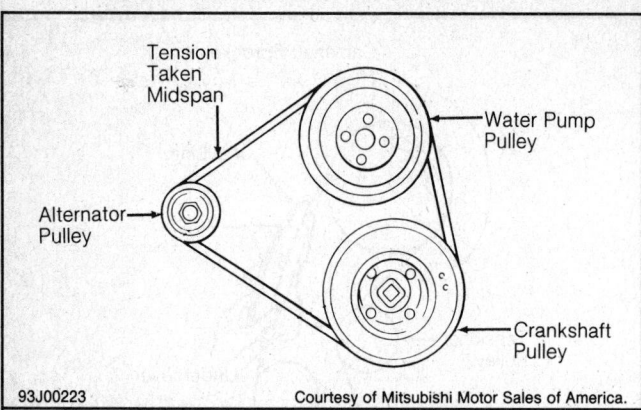

93J00223 — Courtesy of Mitsubishi Motor Sales of America.

Fig. 5: Routing Water Pump Belt (Colt, Mirage & Summit – 1.5L; Colt Vista, Expo, Pickup & Summit Wagon – 2.4L; Eclipse, Galant, & Precis)

COOLING SYSTEM SPECIFICATIONS

COOLING SYSTEM SPECIFICATIONS

Application	Specification
Coolant Replacement Interval	30,000 Miles Or 24 Months
Coolant Capacity	
(Includes Heater & Reserve Tank)	
Colt, Mirage & Summit	
1.5L	5.3 Qts. (5.0L)
1.8L	6.3 Qts. (6.0L)
Colt Vista, Expo & Summit Wagon	
1.8L	6.3 Qts. (6.0L)
2.4L	6.8 Qts. (6.4L)
Diamante	8.5 Qts. (8.0L)
Eclipse	
1.8L	6.6 Qts. (6.2L)
2.0L	7.6 Qts. (7.2L)
Galant	7.4 Qts. (7.0L)
Montero	10.0 Qts. (9.5L)
Pickup	
2.4L	
Automatic Transmission	6.4 Qts. (6.1L)
Manual Transmission	6.3 Qts. (6.0L)
4WD	
2.4L	
Automatic Transmission	6.4 Qts. (6.1L)
Manual Transmission	6.6 Qts. (6.2L)
3.0L	8.9 Qts (8.4L)
Precis	5.6 Qts. (5.3L)
Stealth & 3000GT	8.8 Qts. (8.3L)
Pressure Cap	11-15 psi
Thermostat Opens	
Except Stealth & 3000GT (DOHC)	
Starts	180°F (82°C)
Fully Open	212°F (100°C)
Stealth & 3000GT (DOHC)	
Starts	170°F (77°C)
Fully Open	190°F (88°C)

ELECTRIC COOLING FAN

COMPONENT TESTING

Motor – Disconnect electric cooling fan motor at junction. Using 2 jumper wires, ground one lead and apply battery voltage to other. Fan should rotate. If fan does not rotate, replace motor.

Radiator Fan Switch – Using an ohmmeter, check switch continuity in hot water. Switch should be open at less than 180°F (82°C) and continuity should exist at more than 185°F (85°C). Replace radiator fan switch if it does not test as specified.

Electric Cooling Fan Relay (Colt, Colt Vista, Expo, Galant, Mirage, Summit & Summit Wagon) – Remove relay from relay box in front of right front strut tower. Check continuity between terminals No. 4 and 5 with battery connected between terminals No. 1 and 3. See Fig. 7. With battery connected, there should be continuity between terminals No. 4 and 5. With battery disconnected, there should be continuity

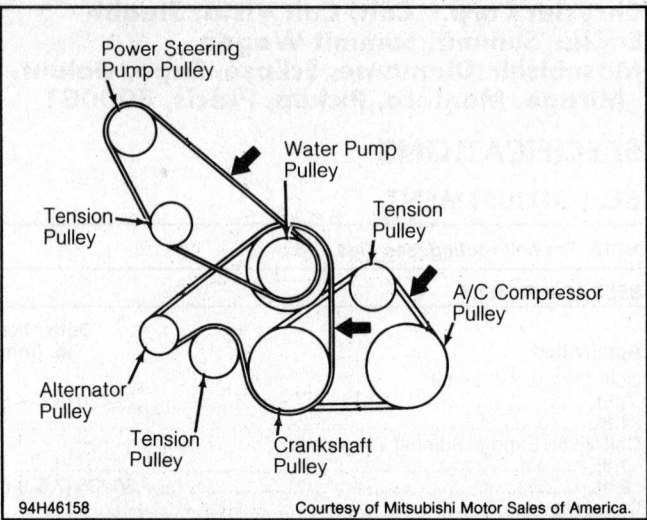

94H46158 — Courtesy of Mitsubishi Motor Sales of America.

Fig. 6: Routing Water Pump/Alternator Belt & Water Pump/Power Steering Belt (Montero – 3.5L)

between terminals No. 1 and 3 and no continuity between terminals No. 4 and 5. Replace relay if it does not test as specified.

Electric Cooling Fan Relay (Diamante, Eclipse, Stealth & 3000GT) –
1) Remove radiator fan motor relay from relay box located at right side of engine compartment. Check for continuity between terminals with battery power applied to terminal No. 2 and terminal No. 4 grounded. See Fig. 8.
2) With power on, there should be continuity between terminals No. 1 and 3. With power disconnected, there should be no continuity between terminals No. 1 and 3, and there should be continuity between terminals No. 2 and 4. Replace relay if it does not test as specified.

Electric Cooling Fan Relay (Precis) – Remove relay from relay box in front of right front strut tower. Connect battery between terminals No. 1 and 2. See Fig. 9. Continuity should exist between terminals No. 3 and 4. With battery disconnected, continuity should exist between terminals No. 1 and 2 and should not exist between terminals No. 3 and 4. Replace relay if it does not test as specified.

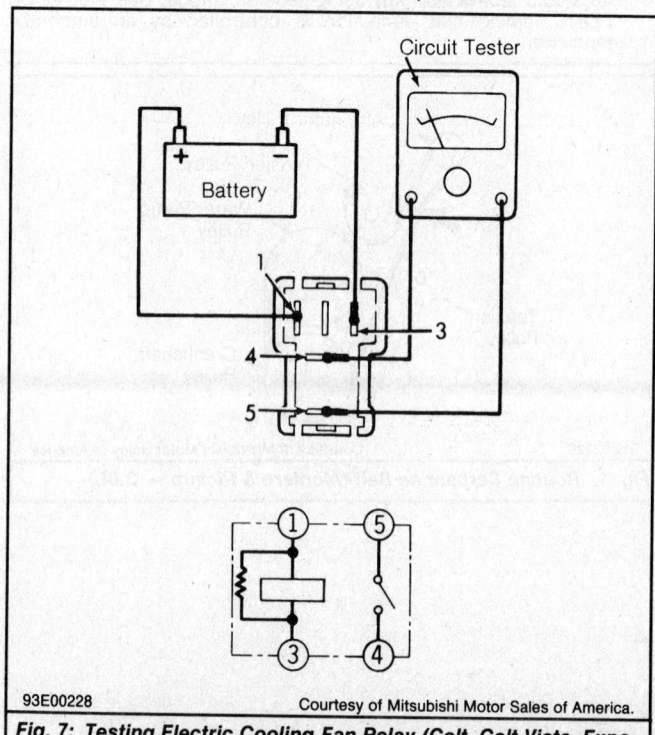

93E00228 — Courtesy of Mitsubishi Motor Sales of America.

Fig. 7: Testing Electric Cooling Fan Relay (Colt, Colt Vista, Expo, Galant, Mirage, Summit & Summit Wagon)

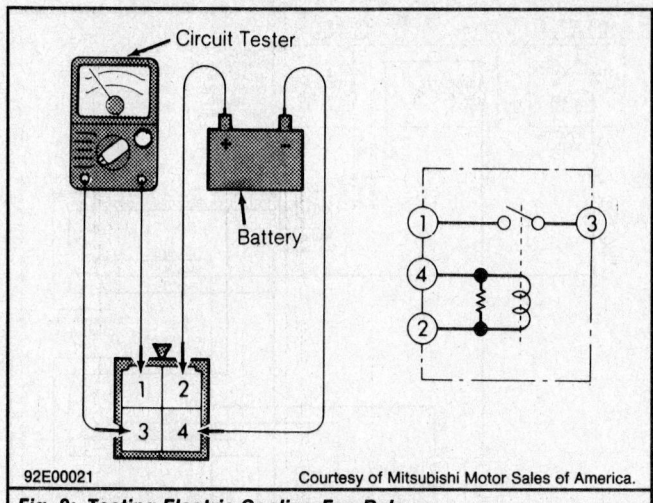

Fig. 8: Testing Electric Cooling Fan Relay (Diamante, Eclipse, Stealth & 3000GT)

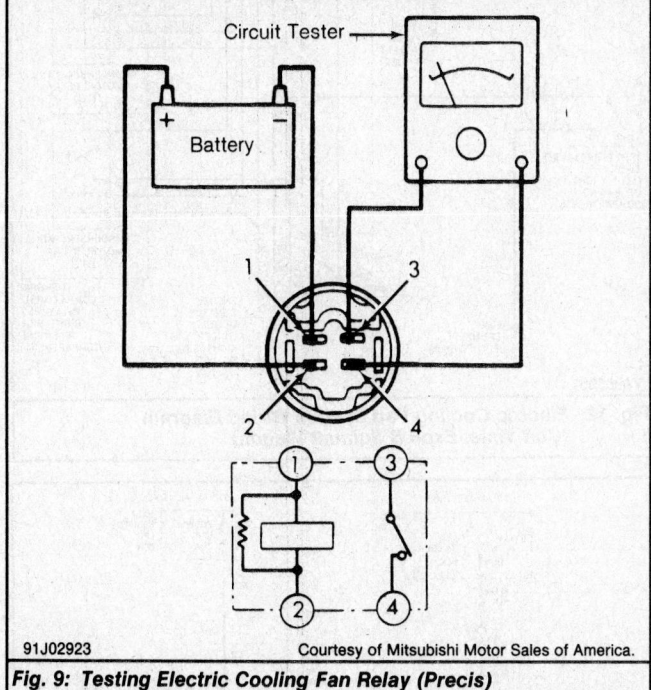

Fig. 9: Testing Electric Cooling Fan Relay (Precis)

SYSTEM TESTING

NOTE: For appropriate wiring diagram, see WIRING DIAGRAMS.

Colt, Mirage & Summit – 1) With A/C switch in LOW position, ignition on and engine coolant temperature greater than 185°F (85°C), thermosensor completes path to ground, closing radiator fan motor relay contacts and providing current to radiator fan motor.
2) With A/C switch in HIGH position and ignition on, power supply from automatic compressor control unit causes condenser fan motor relay and condenser fan motor control relay to turn on, causing condenser fan and radiator cooling fan to operate.

Diamante – 1) With ignition on, A/C switch off and engine coolant temperature greater than 185°F (85°C), thermosensor completes path to ground, closing radiator fan motor relay contacts and providing current to radiator fan motor (low) but not condenser fan motor. With coolant temperature 208°F (98°C), current path will turn both radiator and condenser fans on high.
2) With ignition on, A/C switch on and coolant temperature less than 185°F (85°C), radiator and condenser fans are on low. With coolant temperature over 185°F (85°C), radiator and condenser fans run on high.

Eclipse, Galant, Precis, Stealth & 3000GT – With ignition on and engine coolant temperature greater than 185°F (85°C), thermosensor completes path to ground, closing radiator fan motor relay contacts and providing current to radiator fan.

Colt Vista, Expo & Summit Wagon – 1) With A/C switch in LOW position, ignition on and engine coolant temperature greater than 185°F (85°C), thermosensor completes path to ground, closing radiator fan motor relay contacts and providing current to radiator fan motor.
2) With A/C switch in HIGH position and ignition on, power supply from auto compressor control unit causes condenser fan motor relay to turn on, using a resistor to cause condenser fan and radiator cooling fan to operate at a low speed.
3) If pressure switch is activated by excessive pressure or if thermosensor is on when engine coolant temperature exceeds 185°F (85°C), condenser fan motor control relay is activated, causing condenser fan and radiator cooling fan to operate at a high speed.

WIRING DIAGRAMS

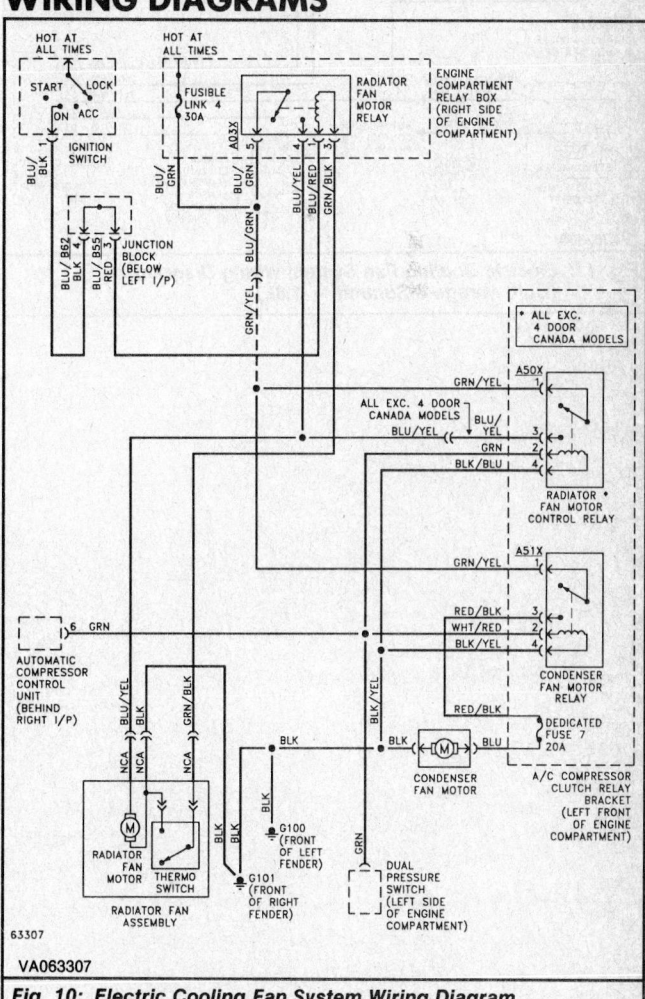

Fig. 10: Electric Cooling Fan System Wiring Diagram (Colt, Mirage & Summit – 1.5L)

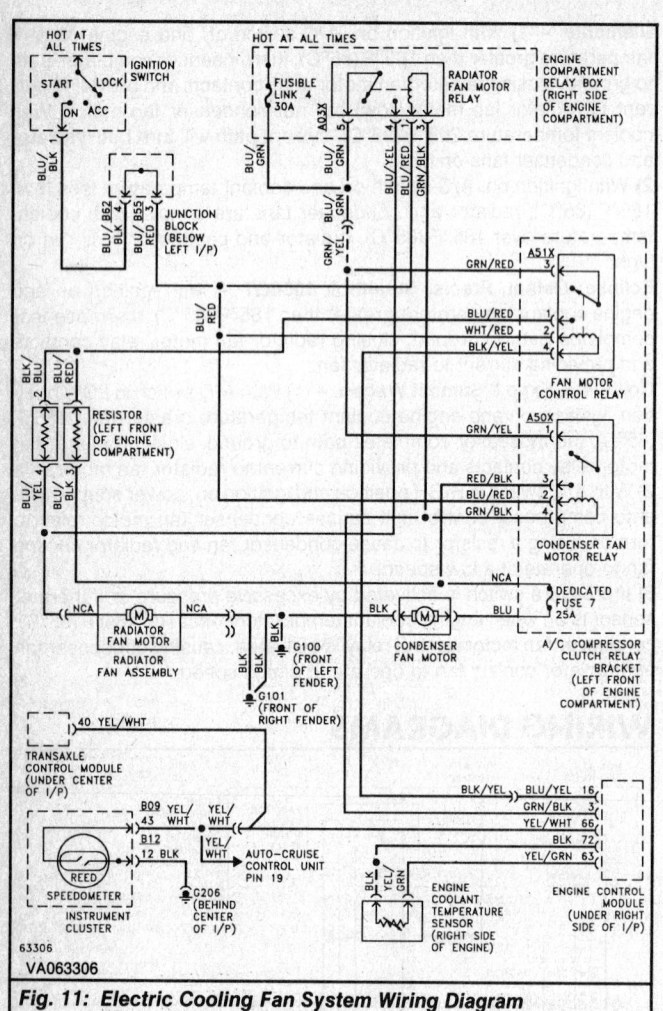

Fig. 11: Electric Cooling Fan System Wiring Diagram (Colt, Mirage & Summit – 1.8L)

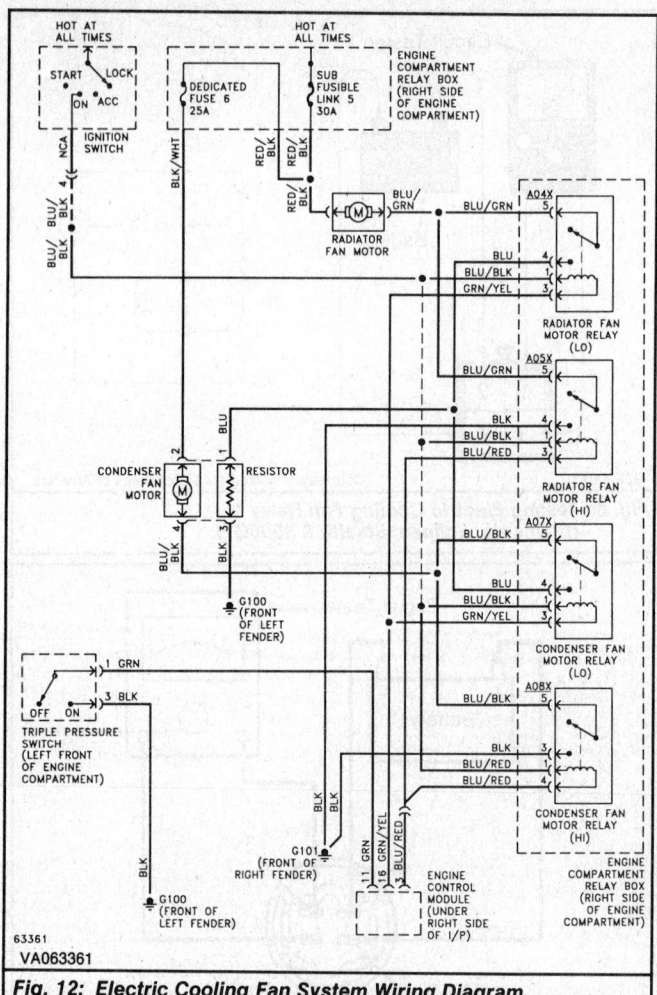

Fig. 12: Electric Cooling Fan System Wiring Diagram (Colt Vista, Expo & Summit Wagon)

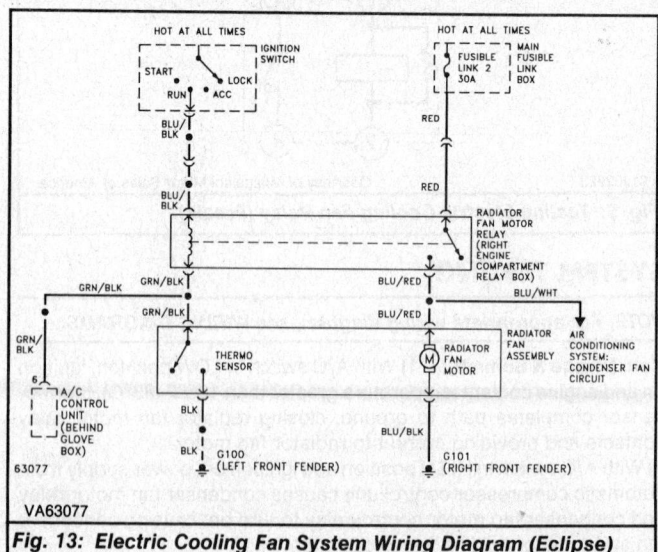

Fig. 13: Electric Cooling Fan System Wiring Diagram (Eclipse)

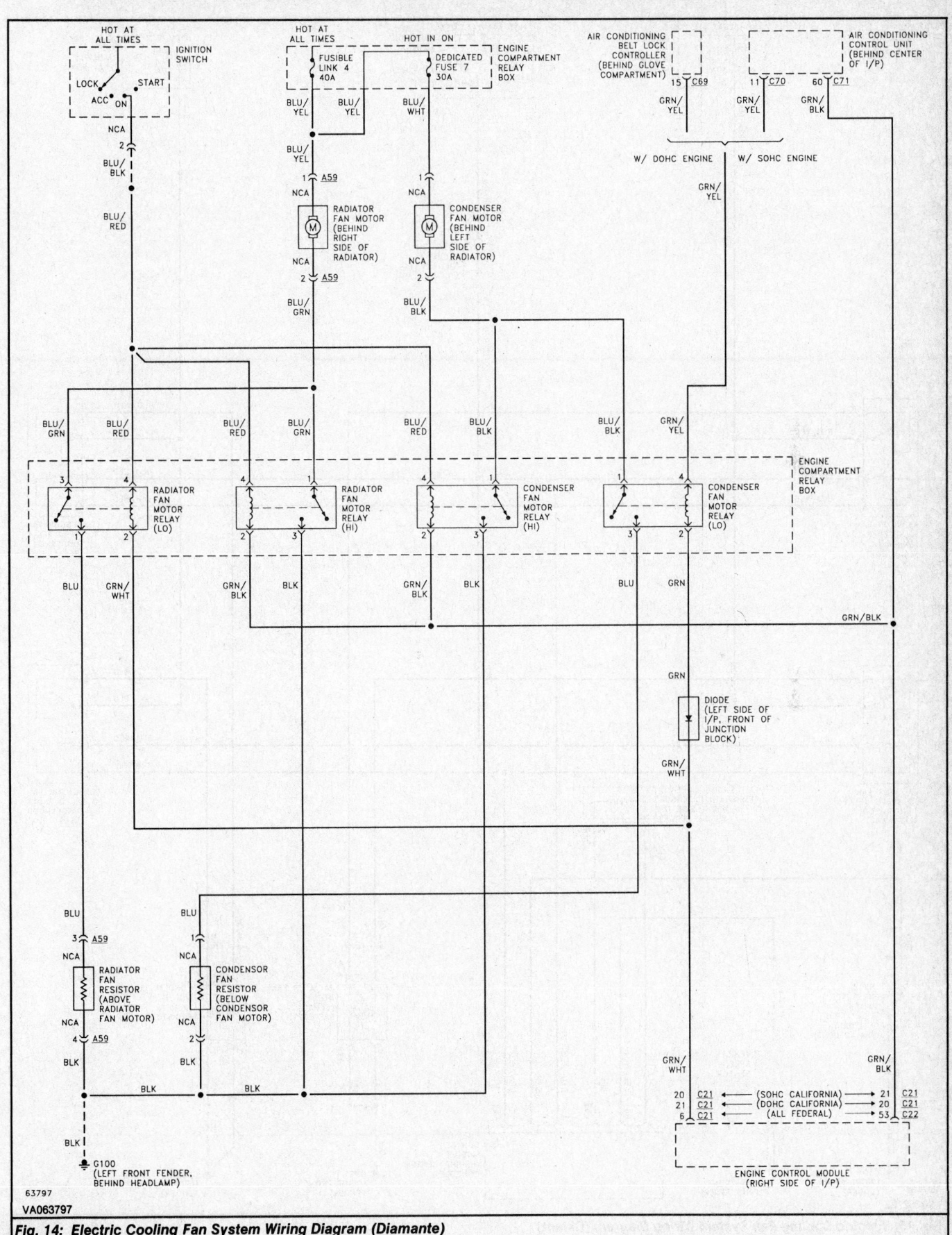

Fig. 14: Electric Cooling Fan System Wiring Diagram (Diamante)

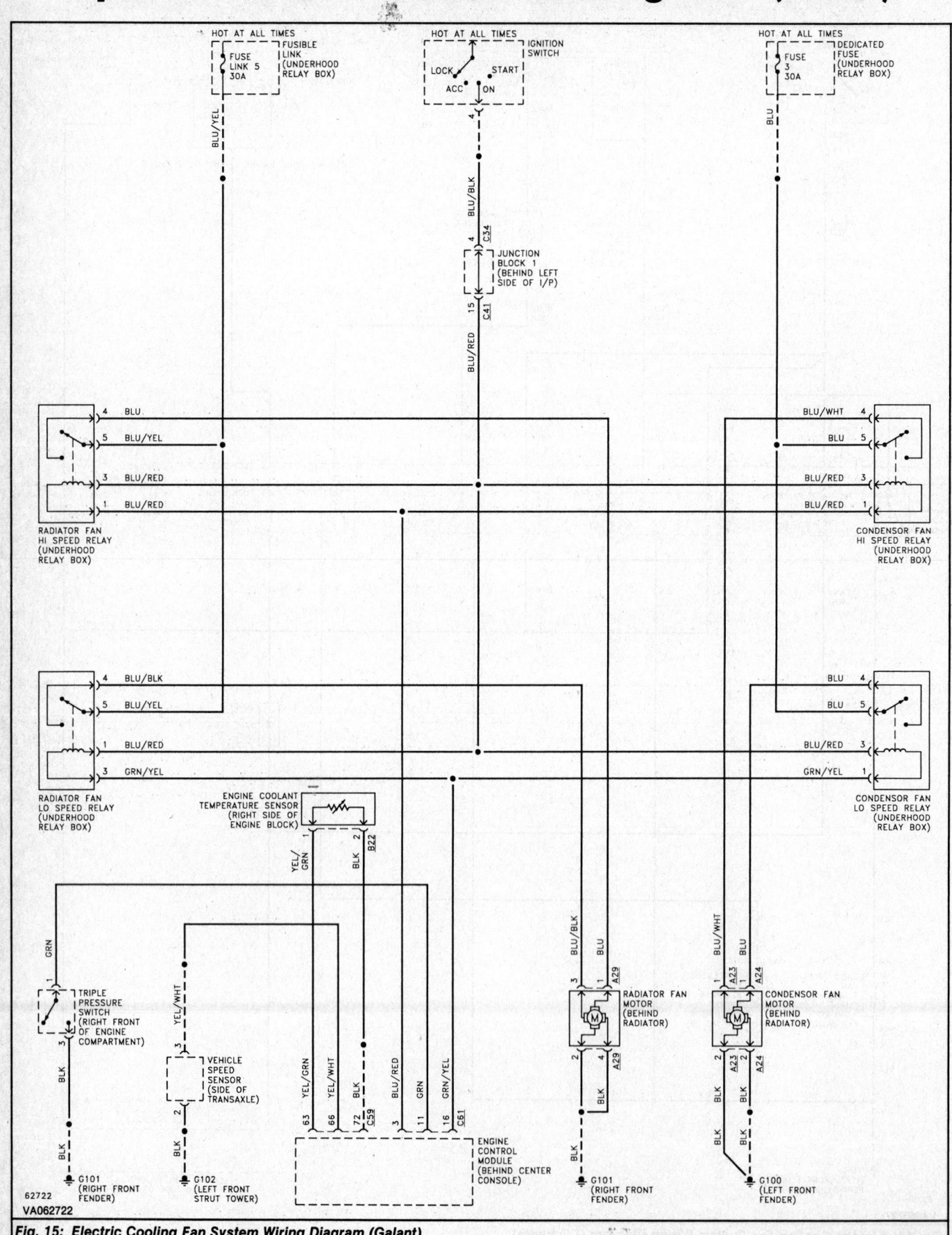

Fig. 15: Electric Cooling Fan System Wiring Diagram (Galant)

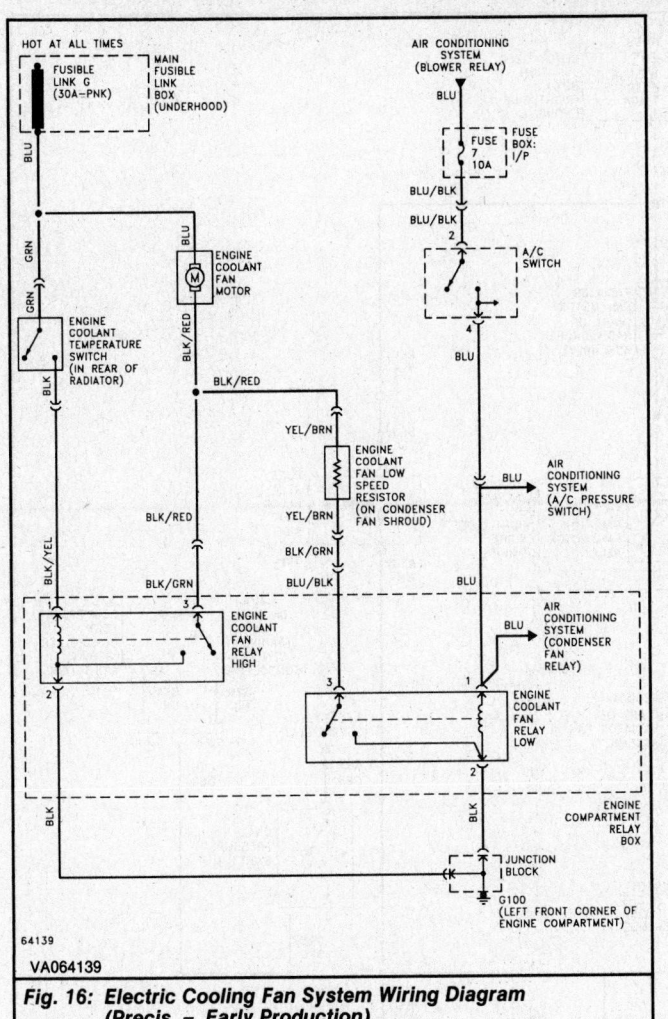

Fig. 16: Electric Cooling Fan System Wiring Diagram (Precis – Early Production)

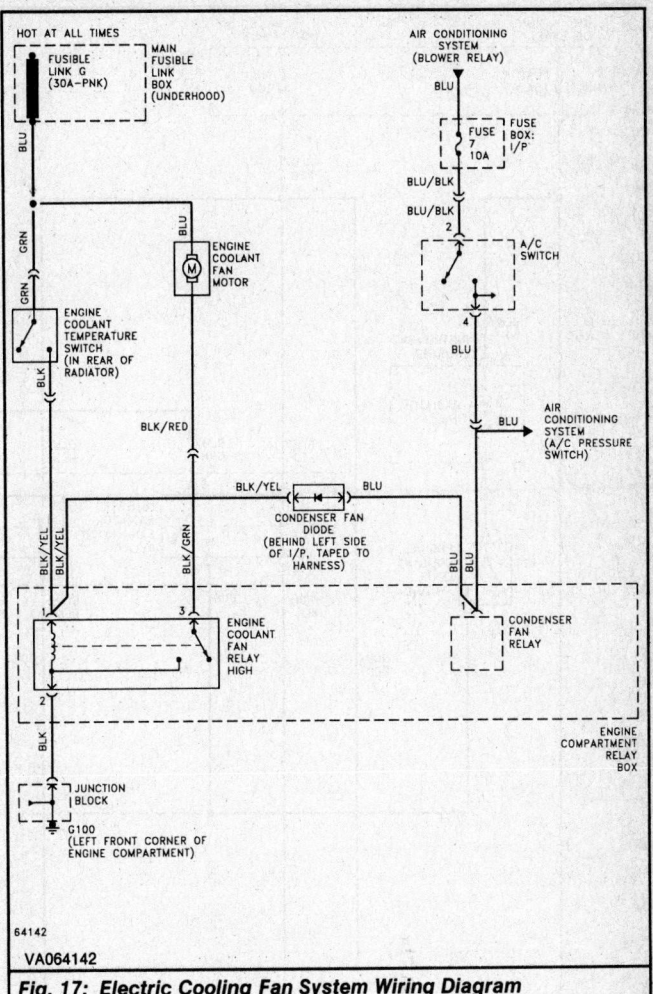

Fig. 17: Electric Cooling Fan System Wiring Diagram (Precis – Late Production)

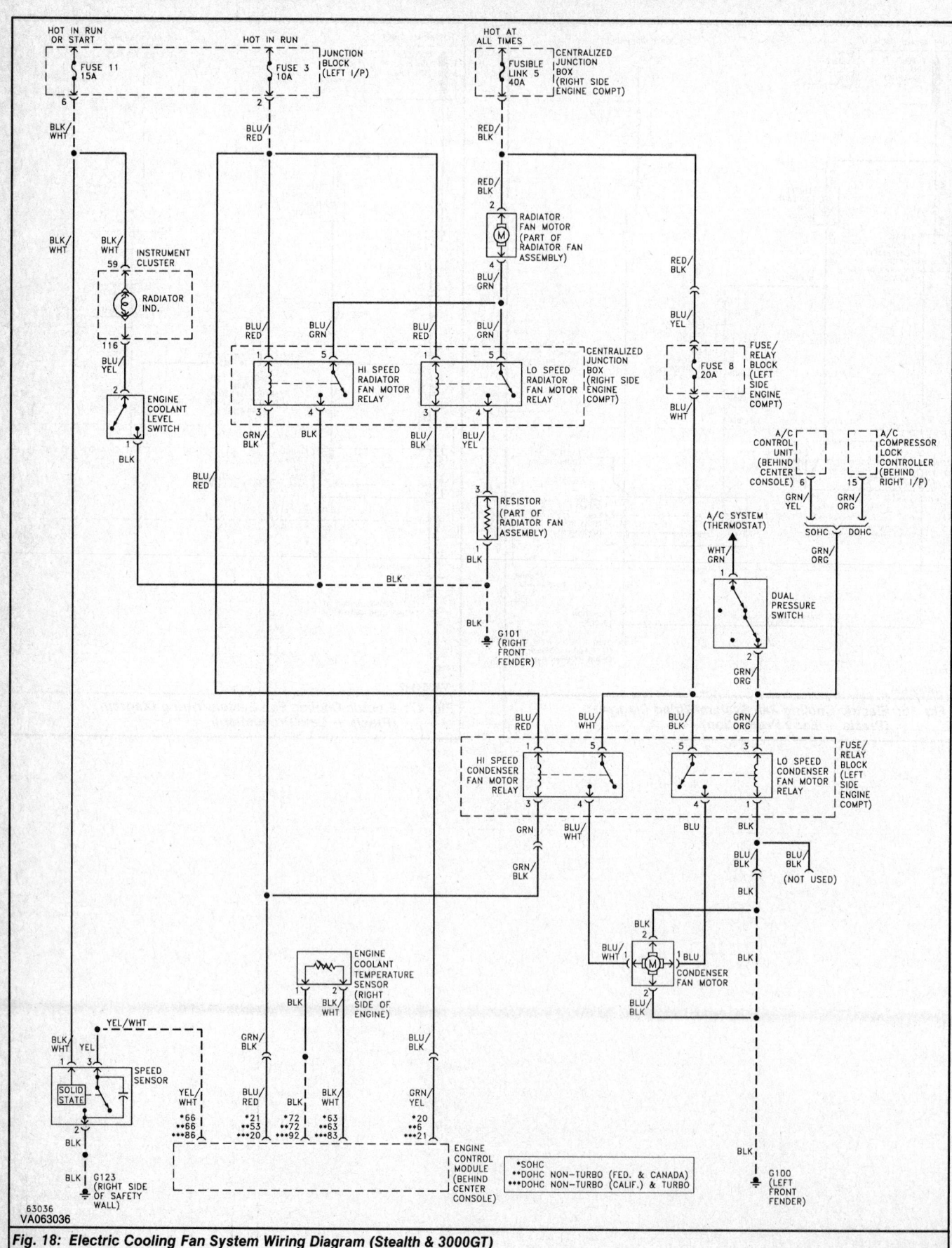

Fig. 18: Electric Cooling Fan System Wiring Diagram (Stealth & 3000GT)

Chrysler Corp.: Colt, Colt Vista,
 Stealth, Summit, Summit Wagon
Mitsubishi: Eclipse, Expo, Galant,
 Mirage, Precis, 3000GT

DESCRIPTION

All clutches are single disc type. Pressure plate assembly uses a diaphragm spring to engage pressure plate to clutch disc and flywheel. Most models use a hydraulic clutch system. Some 4-speed models use a cable clutch system.

ADJUSTMENTS & INSPECTION

CLUTCH BOOSTER

Booster Operation Inspection (Stealth & 3000GT AWD) – 1) Start engine and idle for 2 minutes. Turn engine off. Depress clutch pedal several times. If depressed pedal height gradually rises with successive pedal strokes, go to step **3)**.

2) If clutch pedal depressed height remains the same on each stroke, inspect booster check valve and vacuum hose. If check valve and vacuum hose are okay, replace booster.

3) Depress clutch pedal repeatedly until depressed height no longer changes. Depress and hold clutch pedal. Start engine. If pedal moves down slightly, go to next step. If pedal does not move when engine is started, inspect booster check valve and vacuum hose. If check valve and vacuum hose are okay, replace booster.

4) With engine running, depress and hold clutch pedal. Turn engine off. If pedal height does not change, booster is okay. If pedal height rises, inspect booster check valve and vacuum hose. If check valve and vacuum hose are okay, replace booster.

NOTE: Check valve is press fit into vacuum hose. DO NOT remove check valve from vacuum hose. If check valve is faulty, replace check valve and vacuum hose as an assembly.

Check Valve & Vacuum Hose Inspection (Stealth & 3000GT AWD) – Remove booster vacuum hose from manifold and air line. Ensure air flows in manifold direction only. Ensure vacuum hose has no cracks or splits. Replace if necessary.

CLUTCH BOOSTER PUSH ROD

Push Rod Clearance Adjustment (Stealth & 3000GT AWD) – Check and adjust clearance between back of clutch master cylinder and clutch booster push rod. *See Fig. 1.* Dimension "A" should be .0083-.0181" (.210-.460 mm). Rotate push rod to adjust clearance. After adjusting push rod clearance, adjust pedal height and bleed hydraulic system.

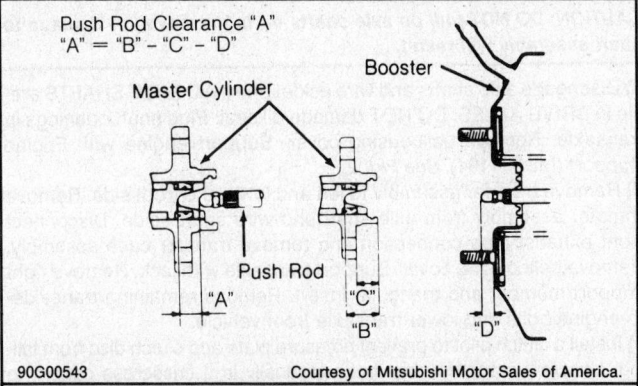

90G00543   Courtesy of Mitsubishi Motor Sales of America.

Fig. 1: Adjusting Clutch Booster Push Rod Clearance (Stealth & 3000GT AWD)

CLUTCH PEDAL HEIGHT & FREE PLAY

NOTE: Clutch pedal height is not adjustable on cable-operated clutch system.

Pedal Adjustment (Cable Clutch) – 1) Measure clutch pedal height. See CLUTCH PEDAL SPECIFICATIONS table. If clutch pedal height is not within specification, check pedal bracket for damage or deformation. Repair or replace as necessary.

2) Depress clutch pedal and check depressed height when clutch is disengaged. See CLUTCH PEDAL SPECIFICATIONS table. If depressed height is not as specified, repair clutch assembly as necessary.

3) Check clutch pedal free play. See CLUTCH PEDAL SPECIFICATIONS table. Rotate outer cable adjusting nut at floor board to adjust clutch pedal free play.

CLUTCH PEDAL SPECIFICATIONS

Application	In. (mm)
Colt, Mirage & Summit	
Free Play	
4-Speed (Cable Clutch)	.79-1.18 (20-30)
5-Speed (Hydraulic Clutch)	.24-.51 (6-13)
Pedal Height	
Pedal Depressed [1]	
4-Speed (Cable Clutch)	3.15 (80)
5-Speed (Hydraulic Clutch)	2.8 (70)
Pedal Released	6.6-6.7 (168-171)
Colt Vista, Expo & Summit Wagon	
Free Play	.24-.51 (6-13)
Pedal Height	
Pedal Depressed [1]	1.77 (45)
Pedal Released	7.68-7.87 (195-200)
Eclipse & Galant	
Free Play	.24-.51 (6-13)
Pedal Height	
Pedal Depressed [1]	2.2 (56)
Pedal Released	7.0-7.1 (178-181)
Precis	
Free Play	.24-.51 (6-13)
Pedal Height	
Pedal Depressed [1]	1.57 (40)
Pedal Released	7.0 (178)
Stealth & 3000GT	
Free Play	.24-.51 (6-13)
Pedal Height	
Pedal Depressed [1]	2.2 (56)
Pedal Released	7.0-7.2 (178-183)

[1] – Specification given is minimum distance.

Pedal Adjustment (Hydraulic Clutch) – 1) Loosen adjusting bolt or clutch pedal switch lock nut located at upper end of clutch pedal. Rotate adjusting bolt or switch until correct pedal released height is obtained. See CLUTCH PEDAL SPECIFICATIONS table.

2) Depress clutch pedal and check depressed height when clutch is disengaged. See CLUTCH PEDAL SPECIFICATIONS table. If measurement is not as specified, readjust clutch pedal.

3) Check clutch pedal free play. See CLUTCH PEDAL SPECIFICATIONS table. If clutch pedal free play and pedal height are okay and system fails to operate, defective system components exist.

REMOVAL & INSTALLATION

CLUTCH ASSEMBLY

Removal (Colt, Colt Vista 2WD, Expo 2WD, Mirage, Summit & Summit Wagon 2WD) – 1) Remove battery, battery tray and air cleaner assembly. Drain transaxle oil. On Colt, Mirage and Summit, disconnect tension rod located above transaxle mounting bracket.

2) On all models, disconnect control cables, speedometer cable and electrical connections at transaxle. Remove clutch release cylinder with line connected and wire aside.

3) Remove starter motor, with harness connected, and wire aside. Support transaxle. Remove upper transaxle-to-engine bolts and transaxle mounting bracket bolt. Loosen, but do not remove, nuts on ball joints and tie rod ends. Using Remover (MB991113), separate ball joints and tie rod ends from steering knuckles. Remove nuts and remove ball joints and tie rod ends.

1994 CLUTCHES
FWD & AWD (Cont.)

CAUTION: DO NOT pull on axle shafts during removal, or damage to shaft assembly will result.

4) Disengage axle shafts and wire aside. See FWD AXLE SHAFTS article in DRIVE AXLES. DO NOT damage oil seal. Plug shaft openings in transaxle.

CAUTION: Ensure a pad is inserted between engine support and front deck. Ensure that hood weatherstrip is not caught between front deck and pad.

5) Remove bellhousing cover. Support engine with Engine Support (MB991191). *See Fig. 2.* Remove remaining transaxle-to-engine bolts. Remove transaxle assembly. Insert a clutch pilot to prevent pressure plate and clutch disc from dropping during removal.

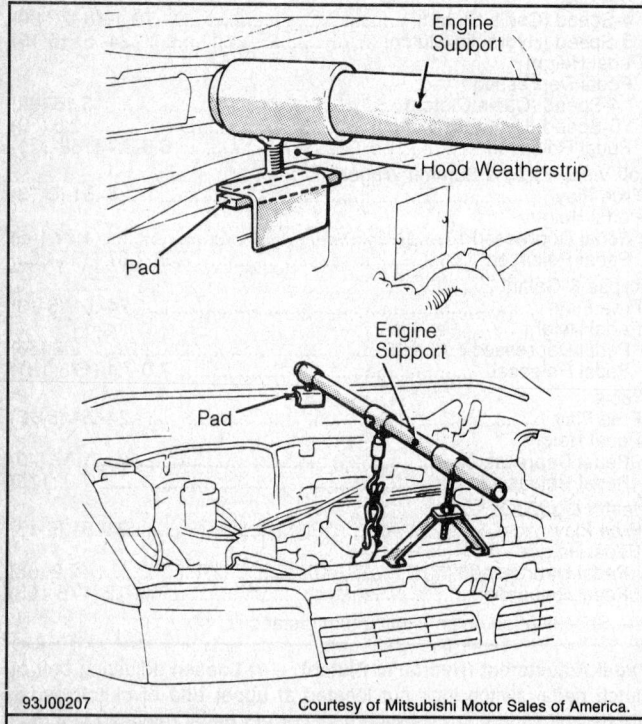

Fig. 2: Supporting Engine For Clutch Removal

6) Diagonally loosen pressure plate bolts to avoid warping pressure plate flange during removal. Remove pressure plate and clutch disc. *See Fig. 3.*

Inspection – 1) Check release bearing and release fork for damage or wear. DO NOT clean bearing assembly in solvent. Inspect hydraulic system components for fluid leakage and cylinder dust boot for cracks or deterioration.

2) Inspect pressure plate surface for wear, cracks, and/or discoloration. Check clutch disc rivets and replace assembly if loose. Measure diaphragm spring ends for wear and uneven height. Replace assembly if height difference between fingers exceeds .02" (.5 mm).

3) Check facing of clutch disc for loose rivets, uneven contact, deterioration, seizure or oil saturation. Measure distance from clutch disc surface to head of rivet. Replace clutch disc if distance is less than .012" (.30 mm). Replace worn or defective components as necessary.

CAUTION: Install clutch disc with manufacturer's stamp mark (located near hub of clutch disc) toward pressure plate.

Installation – 1) Using clutch pilot, install pressure plate and clutch disc. Tighten bolts evenly in a crisscross pattern to specification. See TORQUE SPECIFICATIONS.

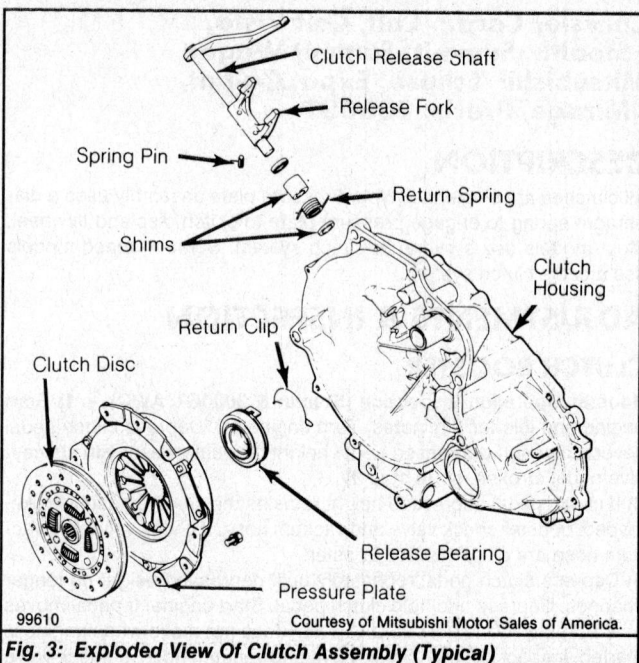

Fig. 3: Exploded View Of Clutch Assembly (Typical)

2) Clean release bearing sliding surface. Apply multipurpose grease to release bearing sliding surface. Apply a light amount of grease to input shaft splines. DO NOT allow grease or dirt on clutch disc or pressure plate surfaces.

3) To install remaining components, reverse removal procedure. Refill all fluids to proper levels. Adjust all control cables, clutch pedal height and free play. See CLUTCH PEDAL HEIGHT & FREE PLAY under ADJUSTMENTS & INSPECTION.

Removal (Colt Vista AWD, Expo AWD & Summit Wagon AWD) – 1) Remove battery, battery tray and air cleaner assembly. Drain transaxle oil.

2) Disconnect control cables, speedometer cable and electrical connections at transaxle. Remove clutch release cylinder with line connected and wire aside.

3) Remove starter motor, with harness connected, and wire aside. Support transaxle. Remove upper transaxle-to-engine bolts and transaxle mounting bracket bolt. Loosen, but do not remove, nuts on ball joints and tie rod ends. Using Remover (MB991113), seperate ball joints and tie rod ends from steering knuckles. Remove nuts and remove ball joints and tie rod ends.

CAUTION: DO NOT pull on axle shafts during removal, or damage to shaft assembly will result.

4) Disengage axle shafts and wire aside. See FWD AXLE SHAFTS article in DRIVE AXLES. DO NOT damage oil seal. Plug shaft openings in transaxle. Remove bellhousing cover. Support engine with Engine Support (MB991191). *See Fig. 2.*

5) Remove transfer assembly to left and lower the front side. Remove transfer assembly from axle shaft and wire shaft aside. Disconnect front exhaust pipe connection and remove transfer case assembly. Remove bellhousing cover. Support transaxle with jack. Remove right support member and triangular insert. Remove remaining transaxle-to-engine bolts and lower transaxle from vehicle.

6) Install a clutch pilot to prevent pressure plate and clutch disc from falling. Unscrew pressure plate bolts gradually in a crisscross pattern to prevent warpage and remove pressure plate and clutch disc. *See Fig. 3.*

Inspection – 1) Check release bearing and release fork for damage or wear. DO NOT clean bearing assembly in solvent. Inspect hydraulic system components for fluid leakage. Inspect cylinder dust boot for cracks or deterioration.

2) Inspect pressure plate surface for wear, cracks, and/or discoloration. Check clutch disc rivets and replace assembly if loose. Measure diaphragm spring ends for wear and uneven height. Replace assembly if height difference between fingers exceeds .02" (.5 mm).

3) Check facing of clutch disc for loose rivets, uneven contact, deterioration, seizure or oil saturation. Measure distance from clutch disc surface to head of rivet. Replace clutch disc if distance is less than .012" (.30 mm). Replace worn or defective components as necessary.

CAUTION: Install clutch disc with manufacturer's stamp mark (located near hub of clutch disc) toward pressure plate.

Installation – 1) Using a pilot, install clutch disc and pressure plate. Tighten bolts evenly in a crisscross pattern to specification. See TORQUE SPECIFICATIONS.

2) Clean release bearing sliding surface. Apply multipurpose grease to release bearing sliding surface. Apply a light amount of grease to input shaft splines. DO NOT allow grease or dirt on clutch disc or pressure plate surfaces.

3) Reverse removal procedure to install transaxle. Tighten engine mount bolts with engine weight applied on engine mounts. See TORQUE SPECIFICATIONS.

4) Refill all fluids to proper levels. Adjust all control cables, clutch pedal height and free play. See CLUTCH PEDAL HEIGHT & FREE PLAY under ADJUSTMENTS & INSPECTION.

Removal (Eclipse & Galant) – 1) Drain transaxle. Remove battery and tray. Remove air cleaner and air intake hoses. Remove autocruise control actuator and bracket (if equipped). Disconnect speedometer cable, control cables and electrical connections at transaxle.

2) Without disconnecting fluid line, remove clutch release cylinder with fluid line support bracket and wire aside. Disconnect back-up light harness and starter motor wiring. Remove starter motor. Remove upper transaxle-to-engine bolts.

3) Remove transaxle mount bracket. Raise and support vehicle. Remove front wheels and engine undercover. On models with anti-lock brakes, remove speed sensor. Disconnect tie rod ends, and disengage axle shafts and support aside. See FWD AXLE SHAFTS article in DRIVE AXLES.

4) On AWD models, move transfer assembly to left and lower the front side. Remove transfer assembly from axle shaft and wire shaft aside. Disconnect front exhaust pipe connection and remove transfer case assembly. On all models, remove bellhousing cover. Support transaxle with jack. On AWD models, remove right support member and triangular insert.

5) On all models, remove remaining transaxle-to-engine bolts. Remove transaxle mount insulator bolt. Slide transaxle assembly to right and lower unit from vehicle.

6) Insert a clutch pilot to prevent pressure plate and clutch disc from dropping. Diagonally loosen pressure plate bolts to avoid warping pressure plate flange during removal. Remove pressure plate and clutch disc. *See Fig. 3.*

Inspection – 1) Check release bearing and release fork for damage or wear. DO NOT clean bearing assembly in solvent. Inspect hydraulic system components for fluid leakage. Inspect cylinder dust boot for cracks or deterioration.

2) Inspect pressure plate surface for wear, cracks, and/or discoloration. Check clutch disc rivets and replace assembly if loose. Measure diaphragm spring ends for wear and uneven height. Replace assembly if height difference between fingers exceeds .02" (.5 mm).

3) Check facing of clutch disc for loose rivets, uneven contact, deterioration, seizure or oil saturation. Measure distance from clutch disc surface to head of rivet. Replace clutch disc if distance is less than .012" (.30 mm). Replace worn or defective components as necessary.

CAUTION: Install clutch disc with manufacturer's stamp mark (located near hub of clutch disc) toward pressure plate.

Installation – 1) Using clutch pilot, install pressure plate and clutch disc. Tighten bolts evenly in a crisscross pattern to specification. See TORQUE SPECIFICATIONS.

2) Clean release bearing sliding surface. Apply multipurpose grease to release bearing sliding surface. Apply a light amount of grease to input shaft splines. DO NOT allow grease or dirt on clutch disc or pressure plate surfaces.

3) To install remaining components, reverse removal procedure. Refill all fluids to proper levels. Adjust all control cables, clutch pedal height and free play. See CLUTCH PEDAL HEIGHT & FREE PLAY under ADJUSTMENTS & INSPECTION.

Removal (Precis) – 1) Drain transaxle fluid. Remove clutch release cylinder. Remove air cleaner assembly. Disconnect select and shift cables. Disconnect speedometer cable and clutch cable. Disconnect back-up light harness and starter motor wiring. Remove starter motor.

2) Remove all upper transaxle-to-engine bolts and bracket bolt. Raise and support vehicle. Remove front wheels and engine undercovers. Disconnect tie rod ends and lower ball joints.

3) Disengage axle shafts and support aside. See FWD AXLE SHAFTS article in DRIVE AXLES. Remove bellhousing cover. Support transaxle with jack. Remove remaining transaxle-to-engine bolts. Remove transaxle mount insulator bolt.

4) Slide transaxle assembly to right and lower unit from vehicle. Insert a clutch pilot to prevent pressure plate and clutch disc from dropping. Diagonally loosen pressure plate bolts to avoid warping pressure plate flange during removal. Remove pressure plate and clutch disc. *See Fig. 3.*

Inspection – 1) Check release bearing and release fork for damage or wear. DO NOT clean bearing assembly in solvent. Inspect clutch cable for or signs of fraying. Check cable for rough movement.

2) Inspect pressure plate surface for wear, cracks, and/or discoloration. Check clutch disc rivets and replace assembly if loose. Measure diaphragm spring ends for wear and uneven height. Replace assembly if height difference between fingers exceeds .02" (.5 mm).

3) Check facing of clutch disc for loose rivets, uneven contact, deterioration, seizure or oil saturation. Measure distance from clutch disc surface to head of rivet. Replace clutch disc if measurement is less than .012" (.30 mm). Replace worn or defective components as necessary.

CAUTION: Install clutch disc with manufacturer's stamp mark (located near hub of clutch disc) toward pressure plate.

Installation – 1) Using clutch pilot, install pressure plate and clutch disc. Tighten bolts evenly in a crisscross pattern to specification. See TORQUE SPECIFICATIONS.

2) Clean release bearing sliding surface. Apply multipurpose grease to release bearing sliding surface. Apply a light amount of grease to input shaft splines. DO NOT allow grease or dirt on clutch disc or pressure plate surfaces.

3) To install remaining components, reverse removal procedure. Refill all fluids to proper level. Adjust all control cables, clutch pedal height and free play. See CLUTCH PEDAL HEIGHT & FREE PLAY under ADJUSTMENTS & INSPECTION.

Removal (Stealth & 3000GT) – 1) Remove both inner fender splash shields. On AWD models, remove air cleaner cover, air hoses and vacuum pipe. On all models, remove air cleaner, intake hose, battery, battery tray and washer tank.

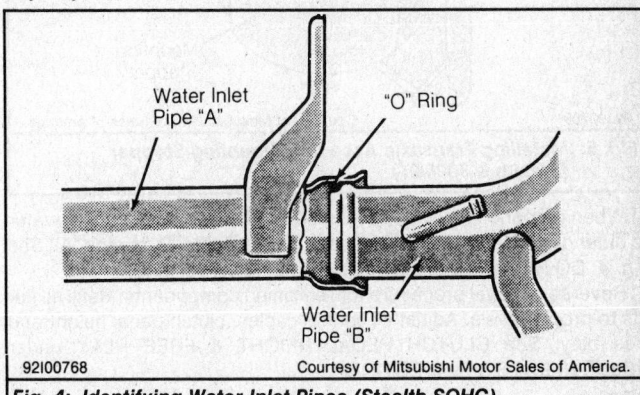

92I00768   Courtesy of Mitsubishi Motor Sales of America.

Fig. 4: Identifying Water Inlet Pipes (Stealth SOHC)

2) On Stealth SOHC, disconnect lower radiator hose and water inlet pipe "B". *See Fig. 4.* On all models, disconnect transaxle control cables and speedometer cable.

3) Remove clutch tube bracket and disconnect clutch release cylinder (including clutch damper assembly on FWD models) and wire aside. Support transaxle assembly with jack and disconnect transaxle mount. Remove mount, bracket, plug and stoppers.

4) Remove transaxle assembly upper coupling bolts. Disconnect tie rod ends and lower arm ball joints. Remove right support member, starter cover (if equipped) and starter.

5) Remove left side bearing bracket mounting bolts and pry left axle shaft from transaxle. Wire left axle shaft and inner shaft assembly aside. Pry right axle shaft from transaxle and wire aside.

6) Remove front bank side and rear bank side transaxle stays. Support transaxle assembly with a transmission jack. Remove transaxle assembly lower coupling bolts and lower transaxle from vehicle.

7) Insert a clutch pilot to prevent pressure plate and clutch disc from falling. Loosen pressure plate bolts diagonally to avoid warping pressure plate flange. Remove pressure plate and clutch disc. *See Fig. 3.*

Inspection – 1) Check release bearing and release fork for damage or wear. DO NOT clean bearing assembly in solvent. Inspect hydraulic system components for fluid leakage. Inspect cylinder dust boot for cracks or deterioration.

2) Inspect pressure plate surface for wear, cracks, and/or discoloration. Check clutch disc rivets and replace assembly if loose. Measure diaphragm spring ends for wear and uneven height. Replace assembly if height difference between fingers exceeds .02" (.5 mm).

3) Check facing of clutch disc for loose rivets, uneven contact, deterioration, seizure or oil saturation. Measure distance from clutch disc surface to head of rivet. Replace clutch disc if distance is less than .012" (.30 mm). Replace worn or defective components as necessary.

CAUTION: Install clutch disc with manufacturer's stamp mark (located near hub of clutch disc) toward pressure plate.

Installation – 1) Using clutch pilot, install pressure plate and clutch disc. Tighten bolts evenly in a crisscross pattern to specification. See TORQUE SPECIFICATIONS.

2) Clean release bearing sliding surface. Apply multipurpose grease to release bearing sliding surface. Apply a light amount of grease to input shaft splines. DO NOT allow grease or dirt on clutch disc or pressure plate surfaces.

3) To install remaining components, reverse removal procedure. Install mounting stoppers as shown in illustration. *See Fig. 5.*

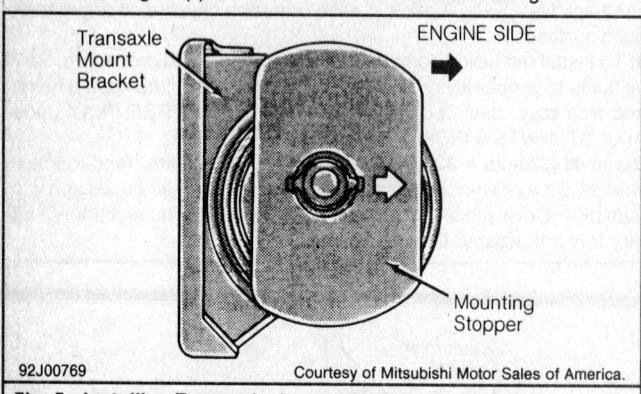

Fig. 5: Installing Transaxle Assembly Mounting Stopper (Stealth & 3000GT)

4) When reconnecting water inlet pipe on Stealth SOHC, apply water to outer circumference of "O" ring and connect pipe "B" to pipe "A". *See Fig. 4.* DO NOT allow engine oil to contaminate "O" ring.

5) Reverse removal procedure for remaining components. Refill all fluids to proper levels. Adjust all control cables, clutch pedal height and free play. See CLUTCH PEDAL HEIGHT & FREE PLAY under ADJUSTMENTS & INSPECTION.

CLUTCH BOOSTER

CAUTION: Wait at least 60 seconds after disconnecting negative battery cable before removing air bag module mounting nuts. Supplemental Restraint System (SRS) retains enough voltage for a short period after power disruption to deploy air bag.

Removal (Stealth & 3000GT AWD) – 1) After setting steering wheel and front wheels to straight-ahead position, remove ignition key. Disconnect negative battery cable. Wait at least 60 seconds and then remove air bag module mounting nut from back of steering wheel. Pull air bag module forward.

CAUTION: When disconnecting air bag module-clock spring connector, take care not to apply excessive force.

2) When disconnecting clock spring connector from air bag module, press air bag's lock toward outer side to spread it open. Using a screwdriver, pry gently to remove connector. *See Fig. 6.* Remove air bag module. Store air bag module, with pad cover face up, in a clean, dry place.

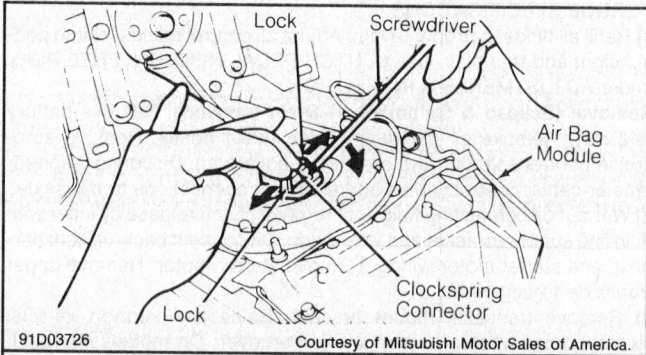

Fig. 6: Disconnecting Clockspring Connector (Stealth & 3000GT)

3) Using puller, remove steering wheel. DO NOT hammer on steering wheel to remove it. Remove column covers and knee protector. Remove lap cooler duct and foot shower duct.

4) Remove column switch assembly, key interlock cable and slide lever. Remove steering column assembly. Remove brake master cylinder and brake booster.

5) Disconnect clutch master cylinder from clutch pedal support bracket. *See Fig. 7.* Remove all clevis pins and yoke. Remove clutch pedal shaft and clutch pedal. Remove bushing, spacer and lever assembly. Remove clutch booster support bracket and clutch booster.

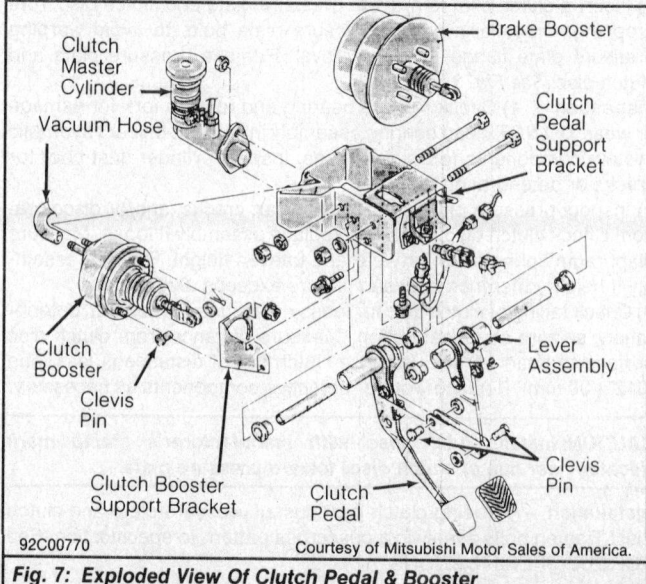

Fig. 7: Exploded View Of Clutch Pedal & Booster (Stealth & 3000GT AWD)

Installation – 1) To install, reverse removal procedure. Before installing clutch booster, adjust clutch booster push rod. See CLUTCH BOOSTER PUSH ROD under ADJUSTMENTS & INSPECTION.

2) Before installing brake booster, adjust brake booster push rod in similar fashion as clutch booster push rod. *See Fig. 1.* Dimension "A" for brake booster push rod is .026-.033" (.66-.84 mm). Bleed brake system.

3) Reverse removal procedure for remaining components. Before installing steering wheel, line up NEUTRAL mark on clockspring with mating mark on outer housing. Reconnect negative battery cable after installation is complete. Adjust clutch pedal height and free play. See CLUTCH PEDAL HEIGHT & FREE PLAY under ADJUSTMENTS & INSPECTION.

4) Turn ignition on from passenger's seat. SRS warning light in instrument cluster should illuminate for approximately 7 seconds and then go out. If SRS warning light fails to come on, remains on, or flashes, a problem exists in SRS. SRS should be serviced as soon as possible.

CLUTCH MASTER CYLINDER

Removal & Installation (Hydraulic Clutch) – 1) Drain master cylinder. Disconnect external reservoir (if equipped). Remove cotter pin, washer and clevis pin. Disconnect push rod from clutch pedal. Remove hydraulic line at clutch master cylinder and plug.

2) Remove retaining nuts and clutch master cylinder. To install, reverse removal procedure. Apply grease to clevis pin before installation. Bleed clutch system.

CLUTCH RELEASE CYLINDER

Removal & Installation (Hydraulic Clutch) – 1) Remove and plug hydraulic line at release cylinder. Remove clip and clevis pin attaching push rod to clutch release arm (if equipped). Remove cylinder-to-transaxle bolts and remove clutch release cylinder.

2) To install, reverse removal procedure. Apply grease to clevis pin or push rod-to-release shaft contact area. Bleed clutch system.

OVERHAUL

CLUTCH MASTER CYLINDER

Disassembly – Remove piston stop ring, damper and push rod assembly. Remove piston assembly. Note position of reservoir band for reassembly reference and remove reservoir. *See Fig. 8.*

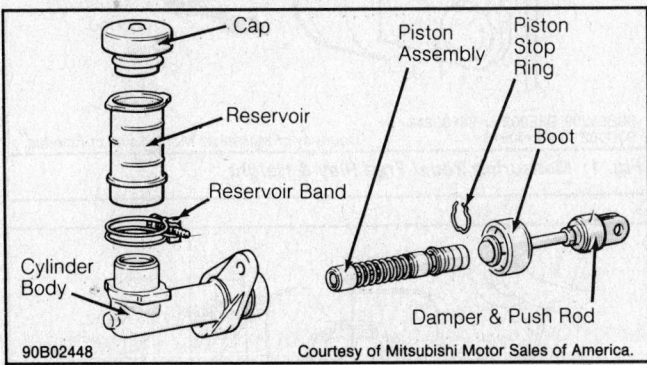

90B02448   Courtesy of Mitsubishi Motor Sales of America.

Fig. 8: Exploded View Of Clutch Master Cylinder (Typical)

Inspection & Reassembly – Inspect components for rust, scoring or damage. Replace damaged component(s). Apply DOT 3 brake fluid to components during reassembly. To reassemble, reverse disassembly procedure. Ensure piston moves freely in bore.

CLUTCH RELEASE CYLINDER

Disassembly – Remove valve plate and spring. *See Fig. 9.* Remove push rod and boot. Cover piston assembly opening with a rag. Slowly apply air pressure to hydraulic line opening to force piston from body.

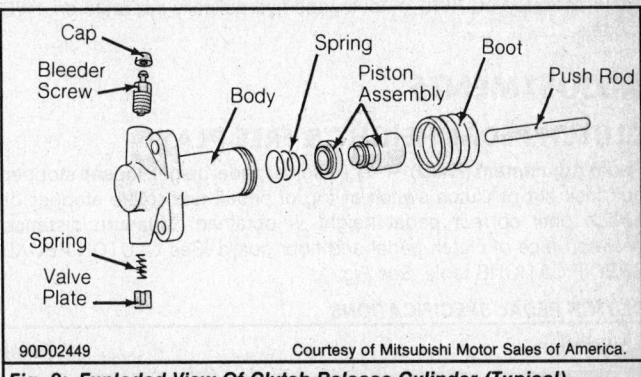

90D02449   Courtesy of Mitsubishi Motor Sales of America.

Fig. 9: Exploded View Of Clutch Release Cylinder (Typical)

Inspection & Reassembly – Inspect components for rust, scoring or damage. Replace damaged component(s). Apply DOT 3 brake fluid to components during reassembly. To reassemble, reverse disassembly procedure. Ensure piston moves freely in bore.

TORQUE SPECIFICATIONS
TORQUE SPECIFICATIONS

Application	Ft. Lbs. (N.m)
Clutch Booster Mounting Nuts	
Stealth & 3000GT (AWD)	[1]
Engine Mount-To-Transaxle	
Colt, Eclipse, Galant, Mirage & Summit	
8-mm Bolt	[1]
10-mm Bolt	22-25 (30-34)
12-mm Bolt	32-39 (43-53)
Colt Vista, Expo & Summit Wagon	
2WD	32-39 (43-53)
AWD	
8-mm Bolt	22-25 (30-34)
10-mm Bolt	31-40 (42-54)
Precis	32-41 (43-56)
Stealth & 3000GT	
Upper Mounting Bolt	54 (73)
Lower Mounting Bolt	65 (88)
Flywheel-To-Crankshaft Bolt	
Stealth & 3000GT	55 (75)
All Others	94-101 (127-137)
Fulcrum Bolt	25-30 (34-41)
Pressure Plate-To-Flywheel Bolt	11-15 (15-20)
Transfer Case-To-Transaxle Bolt	
Stealth & 3000GT	64 (87)
All Others	40-43 (54-58)
Wheel Lug Nut	
Colt Vista, Expo & Summit Wagon	
Aluminum Wheel	65-80 (88-109)
Steel Wheel	50-57 (68-77)
Eclipse, Stealth & 3000GT	89-103 (120-140)
All Others	65-80 (88-109)

[1] – Tighten to 84-108 INCH lbs. (9.5-12.2 N.m).

1994 CLUTCHES RWD & 4WD

Mitsubishi: Montero, Pickup

DESCRIPTION

All models use diaphragm spring, single-disc type clutches. Clutch is cable-operated on RWD models, and hydraulically operated on 4WD models.

ADJUSTMENTS

CLUTCH PEDAL HEIGHT & FREE PLAY

Pedal Adjustment (RWD) – **1)** To adjust pedal height, loosen stopper bolt lock nut or clutch switch at top of pedal, and rotate stopper or switch until correct pedal height is obtained. Measure distance between face of clutch pedal and floor board. See CLUTCH PEDAL SPECIFICATIONS table. *See Fig. 1.*

CLUTCH PEDAL SPECIFICATIONS

Application	In. (mm)
Montero	
Free Play	.24-.51 (6-13)
Pedal Height	
Pedal Depressed [1]	1.4 (35)
Pedal Released	7.3-7.5 (185-190)
Pickup	
2.4L	
Free Play	.8-1.4 (20-35)
Pedal Height	
Pedal Depressed [1]	2.4 (60)
Pedal Released	6.5-6.7 (166-171)
3.0L	
Free Play	.31-.67 (8-17)
Pedal Height	
Pedal Depressed [1]	2.4 (60)
Pedal Released	6.5-6.7 (166-171)

[1] – Specification given is minimum distance.

2) Measure clutch pedal free play. See CLUTCH PEDAL SPECIFICATIONS table. *See Fig. 1.* If pedal free play adjustment is necessary, pull clutch cable housing toward engine compartment. Rotate cable adjusting nut until .12-.16" (3.0-4.0 mm) clearance is obtained between adjusting nut and insulator holder. *See Fig. 2.*
3) After making adjustments, depress pedal several times and hold down. Measure distance between face of clutch pedal and floor board. If depressed pedal height is less than specification, check clutch components for damage and deformation. See CLUTCH PEDAL SPECIFICATIONS table.

Pedal Adjustment (4WD) – **1)** To adjust pedal height, loosen lock nut and rotate pedal stop bolt or switch at top of pedal assembly until correct pedal height is obtained. Measure distance between face of clutch pedal and floor board. See CLUTCH PEDAL SPECIFICATIONS table. *See Fig. 1.*
2) Measure clutch pedal free play. *See Fig. 1.* See CLUTCH PEDAL SPECIFICATIONS table. If pedal free play needs to be adjusted, loosen lock nut on master cylinder push rod and rotate push rod to obtain correct free play. See CLUTCH PEDAL SPECIFICATIONS table. Tighten lock nut. *See Fig. 1.*
3) After making adjustments, depress pedal several times and hold down. Measure distance between face of clutch pedal and floor board. If depressed pedal height is not as specified, bleed system and inspect hydraulic and clutch components. See CLUTCH PEDAL SPECIFICATIONS table.

INTERLOCK SWITCH

Interlock Switch Adjustment – **1)** Check and adjust pedal height and free play. See CLUTCH PEDAL HEIGHT & FREE PLAY. *See Fig. 1.* Measure clutch pedal full stroke. Full stroke should be 5.72" (145 mm). If full stroke is out of tolerance, adjust by turning push rod. *See Fig. 3.*
2) Measure clearance "A" with clutch pedal fully depressed (full stroke). *See Fig. 3.* Clearance "A" should be .177-.217" (4.5-5.5 mm). If clearance is out of tolerance, adjust by loosening interlock switch lock nut and turning interlock switch in appropriate direction. When clearance "A" is correct, tighten lock nut to 115 INCH lbs. (13 N.m).

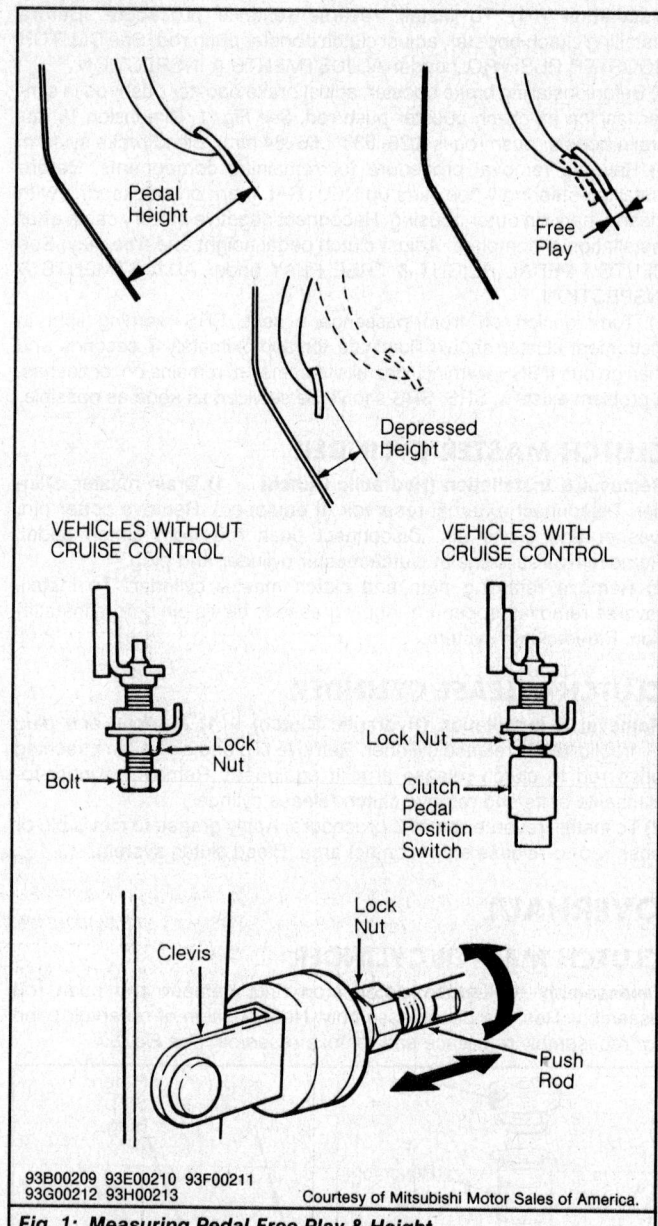

93B00209 93E00210 93F00211
93G00212 93H00213

Courtesy of Mitsubishi Motor Sales of America.

Fig. 1: Measuring Pedal Free Play & Height

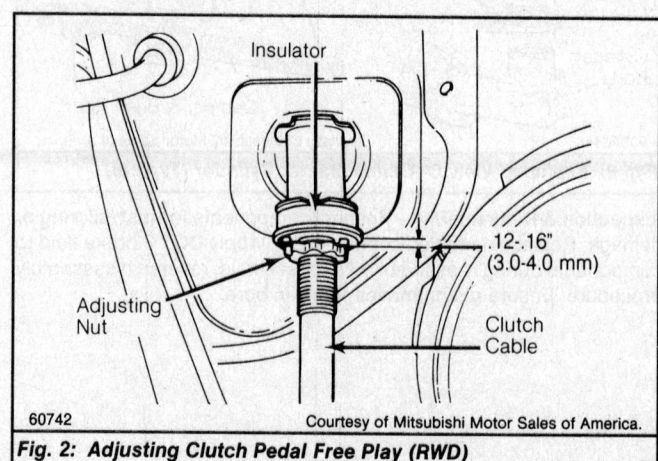

60742

Courtesy of Mitsubishi Motor Sales of America.

Fig. 2: Adjusting Clutch Pedal Free Play (RWD)

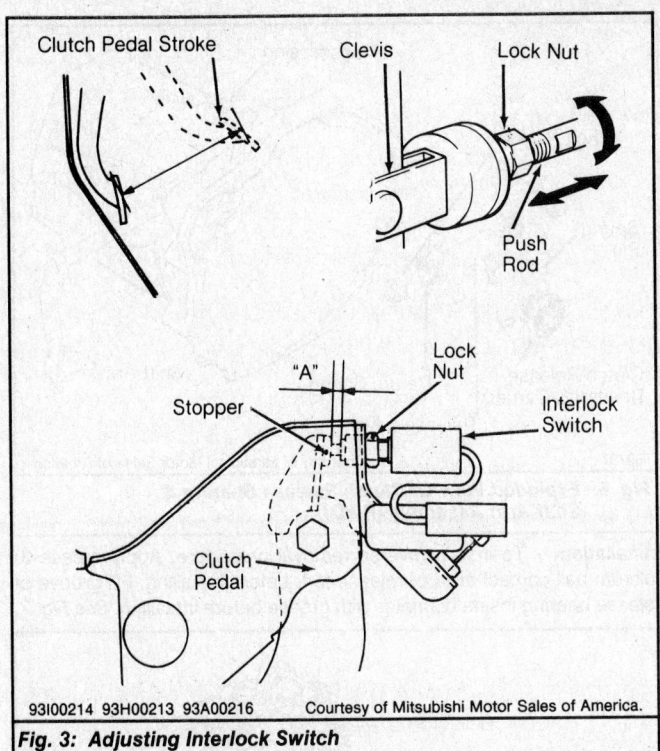

Fig. 3: Adjusting Interlock Switch

REMOVAL & INSTALLATION

CLUTCH ASSEMBLY

Removal (4WD) – **1)** Remove switch panel from rear console. Remove suspension control switch or hole cover. Disconnect rear console harness connector. Remove side panel. Remove rear console assembly. Remove shift lever knob(s). Remove floor console harness connector. Remove front console assembly.

2) Move transmission lever to neutral position and transfer lever to 4H (4WD high range) position on Montero or 2H (RWD high range) on Pickup. Remove control lever boot retainer and boot. Remove transmission and transfer control lever assemblies. Remove control lever bushing (transmission), gaskets and stopper plates.

3) Raise and support vehicle. Remove skid plate and front exhaust pipe. Drain transmission and transfer case fluid. Index mark front and rear drive shaft flanges. Remove front and rear drive shafts.

4) Remove drive shaft dust seals. Disconnect HI/LO and 2WD/4WD detection switch connectors. Disconnect back-up light switch connector. Disconnect center differential lock detection switch connector. Disconnect center differential lock operation switch connector. Disconnect 4WD operation detection switch. Disconnect speedometer cable. Remove clutch slave cylinder heat shield. Remove clutch slave cylinder (without disconnecting hydraulic line) and wire aside. Remove starter and starter cover. Remove heat shield and both transmission stays and then bellhousing lower cover.

5) Support transmission with transmission jack. Remove transfer case roll stopper and bracket. Remove crossmember and engine mounting rear insulator. Remove transfer case protector bracket and mass damper. Remove remaining bellhousing bolts. Pull toward rear of vehicle to free transmission input shaft from clutch. Lower transmission/transfer case from vehicle.

6) Insert a clutch pilot to prevent pressure plate and clutch disc from dropping. Diagonally loosen pressure plate bolts to avoid warping pressure plate flange during removal. Remove pressure plate and clutch disc. See Fig. 4.

Inspection – **1)** Check release bearing and release fork for damage or wear. DO NOT clean bearing assembly in solvent. Inspect hydraulic system components for fluid leakage. Inspect cylinder dust boot for cracks or deterioration.

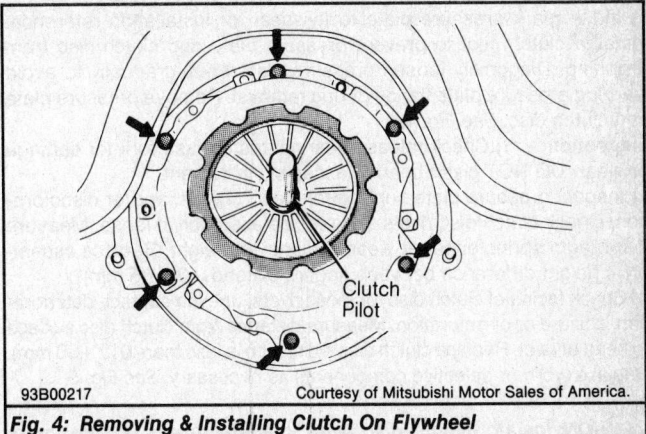

Fig. 4: Removing & Installing Clutch On Flywheel

2) Inspect pressure plate surface for wear, cracks, and/or discoloration. Check clutch disc rivets and replace assembly if loose. Measure diaphragm spring ends for wear and uneven height. Replace assembly if height difference between fingers exceeds .02" (.5 mm).

3) Check facing of clutch disc for loose rivets, uneven contact, deterioration, seizure or oil saturation. Measure depth from clutch disc surface to head of rivet. Replace clutch disc if measurement is less than .012" (.30 mm). See Fig. 5. Replace worn or defective components as necessary.

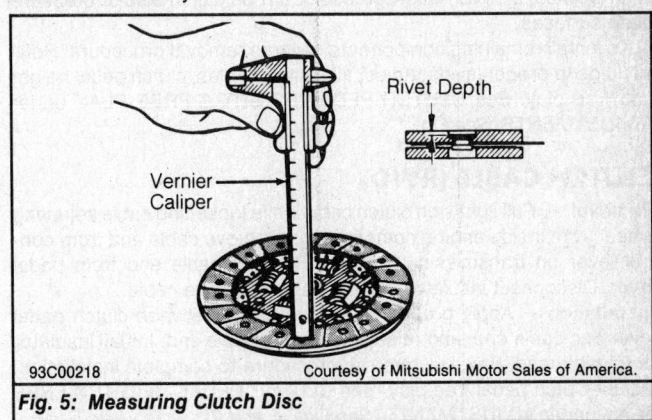

Fig. 5: Measuring Clutch Disc

CAUTION: Install clutch disc with manufacturer's stamp mark (located near hub of clutch disc) toward pressure plate.

Installation – **1)** Using clutch pilot, install pressure plate and clutch disc. Tighten bolts evenly in a crisscross pattern to specification. See TORQUE SPECIFICATIONS.

2) Clean release bearing sliding surface. Apply a light coating of multipurpose grease to release bearing sliding surface. Apply a very light coating of grease to input shaft splines. DO NOT allow grease or dirt on clutch disc or pressure plate surfaces.

3) To install remaining components, reverse removal procedure. Refill all fluids to proper levels. Adjust all control cables, clutch pedal height and free play. See CLUTCH PEDAL HEIGHT & FREE PLAY under ADJUSTMENTS. See Fig. 1.

Removal (RWD) – **1)** Disconnect negative battery cable. Remove shift knob, dust cover retaining plate, gaskets, stopper plate and control lever assembly. Raise and support vehicle.

2) Remove front exhaust pipe. drain transmission oil. Index mark drive shaft flange and remove drive shaft.

3) Disconnect back-up light switch connector, speedometer cable connection and exhaust pipe mounting bracket. Remove lower bellhousing cover. Disconnect clutch cable from clutch lever.

4) Support transmission with jack. Remove rear engine mount nuts and bolts from transmission. Remove crossmember with rear engine mount. Remove remaining bellhousing bolts, move transmission toward rear and lower from vehicle.

5) Index mark pressure plate to flywheel for installation reference. Install a clutch pilot to prevent pressure plate and clutch disc from dropping. Diagonally loosen pressure plate bolts gradually to avoid warping pressure plate flange during removal. Remove pressure plate and clutch disc. *See Fig. 4.*

Inspection – 1) Check release bearing and release fork for damage or wear. DO NOT clean bearing assembly in solvent.

2) Inspect pressure plate surface for wear, cracks, and/or discoloration. Check clutch disc rivets and replace assembly if loose. Measure diaphragm spring ends for wear and uneven height. Replace assembly if height difference between fingers exceeds .02" (.5 mm).

3) Check facing of clutch disc for loose rivets, uneven contact, deterioration, seizure or oil saturation. Measure distance from clutch disc surface to head of rivet. Replace clutch disc if distance is less than .012" (.30 mm). Replace worn or defective components as necessary. *See Fig. 5.*

CAUTION: Install clutch disc with manufacturer's stamp mark (located near hub of clutch disc) toward pressure plate.

Installation – 1) Using clutch pilot, install pressure plate and clutch disc. If reusing pressure plate, ensure index marks are aligned. Tighten bolts evenly in a crisscross pattern to specification. See TORQUE SPECIFICATIONS. *See Fig. 4.*

2) Clean release bearing sliding surface. DO NOT clean release bearing with solvent. Apply a light coat of multipurpose grease to release bearing sliding surface. Apply a very light coating of grease to input shaft splines. DO NOT allow grease or dirt on clutch disc or pressure plate surfaces.

3) To install remaining components, reverse removal procedure. Refill all fluids to proper levels. Adjust all control cables, clutch pedal height and free play. See CLUTCH PEDAL HEIGHT & FREE PLAY under ADJUSTMENTS. *See Fig. 1.*

CLUTCH CABLE (RWD)

Removal – Pull lightly on clutch cable while loosening cable adjusting wheel from inside engine compartment. Remove cable end from control lever on transmission housing. Remove cable end from pedal lever. Disconnect insulator from cable and remove cable.

Installation – Apply grease to contact areas between clutch pedal lever and cable end, and release lever and cable end. Install insulator onto cable end. Reverse removal procedure to complete installation. Adjust clutch pedal free play. See CLUTCH PEDAL HEIGHT & FREE PLAY under ADJUSTMENTS. *See Figs. 1 and 2.*

CLUTCH RELEASE BEARING & SHIFT ARM OR RELEASE FORK

Removal (RWD) – 1) Remove transmission. See CLUTCH ASSEMBLY under REMOVAL & INSTALLATION. Remove return clips, release bearing and carrier. Use a punch to remove shift arm spring pin and release lever assembly. Remove shift arm, felt packing and 2 return springs. *See Fig. 6.*

2) Ensure release bearing turns freely and smoothly under light load. Replace bearing if noise, roughness or dryness is present. DO NOT clean bearing in solvent. Use shop towel or compressed air only.

Installation – 1) Insert lever and shaft into left side of transmission case. Place shift arm, felt packing and return springs on shaft assembly. Apply grease to inside of bushing and oil seal lips. Apply oil to felt packing.

2) Align shift arm pin and control shaft pin holes. Drive spring pins into position, with slit area upward. Reverse removal procedure to complete installation. Check pedal height and free play. Adjust if necessary. See CLUTCH PEDAL HEIGHT & FREE PLAY under ADJUSTMENTS.

Removal (4WD) – 1) Remove transmission. See CLUTCH ASSEMBLY under REMOVAL & INSTALLATION. Remove return spring or clips, and remove release bearing.

2) Slide release fork toward outside of transmission and disengage from fulcrum ball. DO NOT slide release fork toward inside of case, or damage to fulcrum ball clip will result. Remove release fork boot.

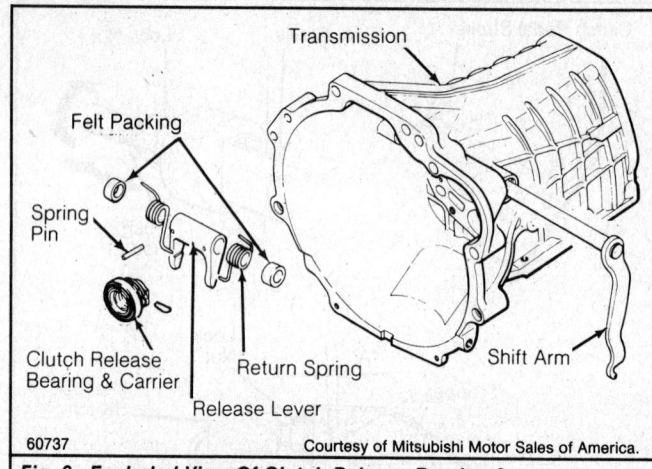

60737   Courtesy of Mitsubishi Motor Sales of America.

Fig. 6: Exploded View Of Clutch Release Bearing & Shift Arm Assembly (RWD)

Installation – To install, reverse removal procedure. Apply grease to fulcrum ball contact area of release fork before installing. Fill groove of release bearing inside diameter with grease before installing. *See Fig. 7.*

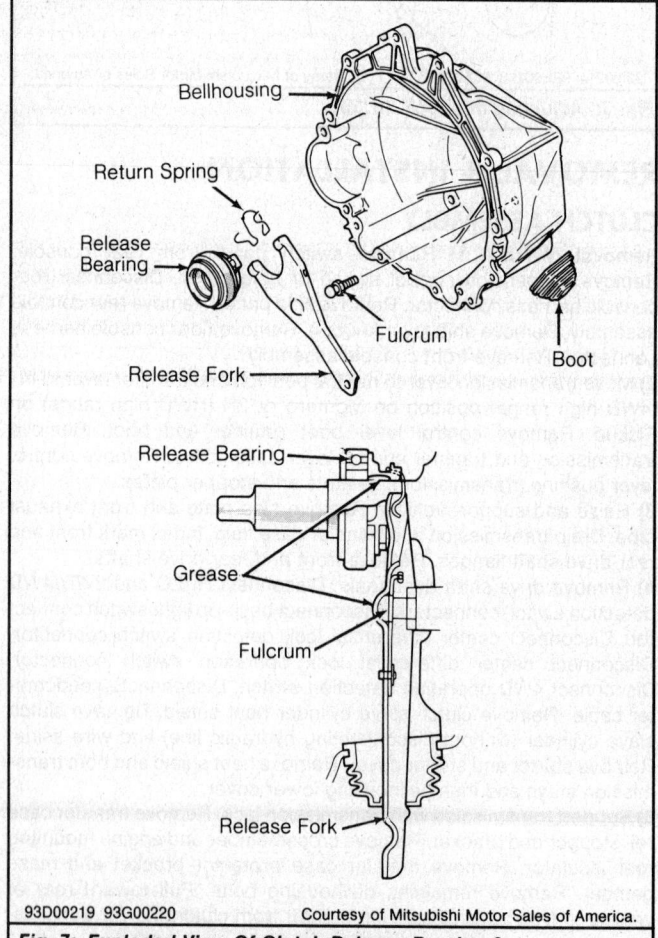

93D00219 93G00220   Courtesy of Mitsubishi Motor Sales of America.

Fig. 7: Exploded View Of Clutch Release Bearing & Shift Arm Assembly (4WD)

CLUTCH MASTER CYLINDER (4WD)

Removal & Installation – 1) Drain master cylinder. Remove cotter pin, washer and clevis pin. Disconnect push rod from clutch pedal. Remove and plug hydraulic line at clutch master cylinder.

2) Remove retaining nuts, clutch master cylinder and gasket. To install, reverse removal procedure. Apply grease to clevis pin before installing. Fill reservoir and bleed clutch system.

CLUTCH RELEASE CYLINDER (4WD)

Removal & Installation – Remove and plug hydraulic line at release cylinder. Remove cylinder-to-transmission bolts. Remove clutch release cylinder. To install, reverse removal procedure. Apply grease to push rod-to-release fork contact area. Bleed clutch system.

OVERHAUL

CLUTCH MASTER CYLINDER (4WD)

Disassembly – Remove piston stop ring, damper and push rod assembly. *See Fig. 8.* Remove piston assembly. Note position of reservoir band for reassembly reference. Remove reservoir.

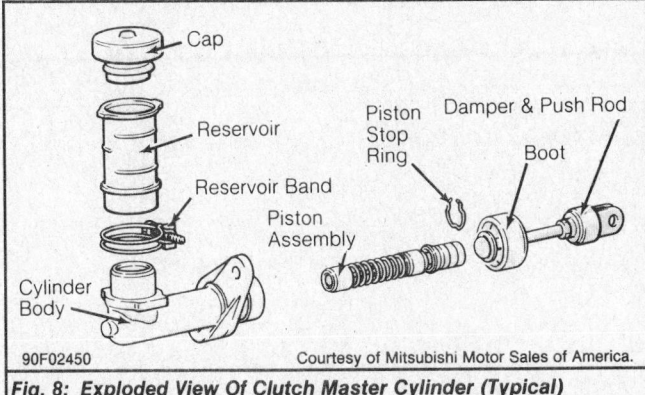

Fig. 8: *Exploded View Of Clutch Master Cylinder (Typical)*

90F02450   Courtesy of Mitsubishi Motor Sales of America.

Inspection & Reassembly – Inspect components for corrosion, scoring or damage. Replace if necessary. Apply DOT 3 brake fluid to components during reassembly. To reassemble, reverse disassembly procedure. Ensure piston moves freely in bore.

CLUTCH RELEASE CYLINDER (4WD)

Disassembly – Remove valve plate and spring. *See Fig. 9.* Remove push rod and boot. Cover piston assembly opening with a rag. Slowly apply air pressure to hydraulic line opening to force piston from body.

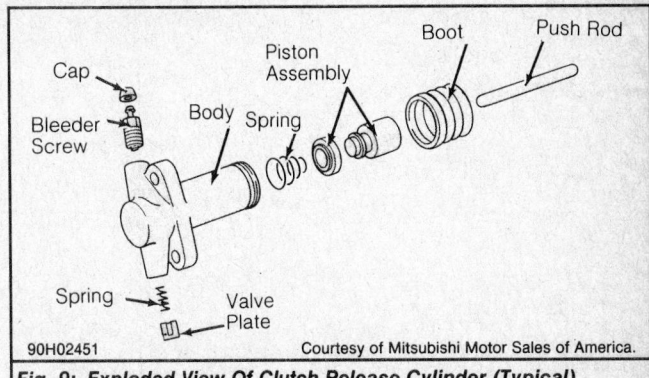

90H02451   Courtesy of Mitsubishi Motor Sales of America.

Fig. 9: *Exploded View Of Clutch Release Cylinder (Typical)*

Inspection & Reassembly – Inspect components for corrosion, scoring or damage. Replace if necessary. Apply DOT 3 brake fluid to components during reassembly. To reassemble, reverse disassembly procedure. Ensure piston moves freely in bore.

TORQUE SPECIFICATIONS

TORQUE SPECIFICATIONS

Application	Ft. Lbs. (N.m)
Flexhose-To-Release Cylinder Bolt	14-18 (19-24)
Flywheel Bolt	
2.4L Engines	94-101 (127-137)
3.0L Engines	53-55 (72-75)
Fulcrum Ball	22-30 (30-41)
Gearshift-To-Transfer Case Bolt	11-15 (15-20)
Hydraulic Line-To-Master Cylinder	10-12 (14-16)
Pressure Plate Bolt	11-15 (15-20)
Release Cylinder-To-Transmission Bolt	22-30 (30-41)
Transmission-To-Engine Bolt	
2.4L Engines	
8 x 25 mm & 8 x 55 mm	15-20 (20-27)
10 x 40 mm & 10 x 65 mm	31-40 (42-54)
10 x 60 mm	20-25 (27-34)
3.0L Engines	
10 x 35 mm	24-36 (33-49)
10 x 40 mm	22-30 (30-41)
10 x 55 mm	20-25 (27-34)
12 x 35 mm, 12 x 40 mm & 12 x 50 mm	47-61 (64-83)
12 x 55 mm	58-72 (79-98)

Chrysler Corp.: Colt, Colt Vista, Stealth, Summit, Summit Wagon
Mitsubishi: Diamante, Eclipse, Expo, Galant, Mirage, Precis, 3000GT

DESCRIPTION & OPERATION

Power from transaxle is transferred to driving wheels by 2 axle shafts. Both axle shafts use Constant Velocity (CV) joints at inner and outer ends. CV joints are enclosed in CV boots, and connected by an intermediate shaft. Intermediate shaft is splined on both ends.

Retaining rings retain intermediate shaft in both inner and outer CV joints. A retaining ring retains inner CV joint stub in differential side gear. Outer CV joint stub is splined into wheel hub, and secured by a spindle nut. On some models, left axle has a dynamic damper to reduce vibration. See DYNAMIC DAMPER INSTALLATION SPECIFICATIONS table.

TROUBLE SHOOTING

NOTE: See TROUBLE SHOOTING article in GENERAL INFORMATION.

BAND & BOOT IDENTIFICATION

Band identification numbers are stamped on inside edge of band. *See Fig. 1.* Boot identification numbers are stamped on largest ridge of boot. See BAND & BOOT APPLICATION table.

NOTE: The following are possible types of Constant Velocity (CV) joints used on axle shaft: Birfield Joint (BJ), Double Offset Joint (DOJ), Rzeppa Joint (RJ) and Tripod Joint (TJ). Determine type of CV joint used prior to disassembly. See AXLE SHAFT SPECIFICATIONS table. Note type of boot and location prior to removal. See BAND & BOOT APPLICATION table. Install a NEW retaining ring each time axle shaft is removed from transaxle.

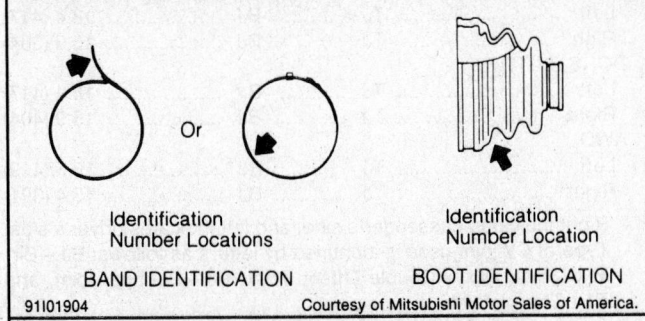

Identification Number Locations

Identification Number Location

BAND IDENTIFICATION

BOOT IDENTIFICATION

91I01904   Courtesy of Mitsubishi Motor Sales of America.

Fig. 1: Locating Band & Boot Identification Numbers

REMOVAL, DISASSEMBLY, REASSEMBLY & INSTALLATION

AXLE SHAFT

CAUTION: DO NOT place vehicle weight on hub assembly with axle shaft removed.

Removal – 1) Note type and location of CV joint prior to removal. See AXLE SHAFT SPECIFICATIONS table. Remove cotter pin, and loosen axle shaft nut with brakes applied. Raise and support vehicle. Remove front wheels. Remove axle shaft nut and washer. Remove brake caliper assembly, and support with wire. Support control arm.
2) Remove speed sensor and/or height sensor (if equipped). Remove ball joint stud nut, and separate ball joint from control arm. Disconnect tie rod end from steering knuckle. Disconnect stabilizer bar and strut bar from control arm (if equipped).

BAND & BOOT APPLICATION

Application	Large Band	Small Band	Boot
Colt, Mirage & Summit	[1]	[1]	[1]
Colt Vista, Expo & Summit Wagon	[1]	[1]	[1]
Diamante			
BJ	20-15	20-22	[1]
TJ	20-75	20-72	[1]
Eclipse			
FWD			
BJ-TJ Type Axle			
1.8L			
BJ	20-113	20-146	17-249 #BJ87L
TJ	20-110	20-146	17-261 #TJ87
2.0L			
BJ	20-75	20-111	17-31 #BJ92L
TJ	20-12	20-111	17-55 #TJ92
AWD			
BJ	20-113	20-146	17-249 #BJ87L
TJ	20-110	20-146	17-261 #TJ87
Galant			
BJ	[1]	[1]	[1]
TJ	[1]	[1]	[1]
Precis	[1]	[1]	[1]
Stealth & 3000GT			
FWD			
SOHC			
BJ	[1]	[1]	[1]
TJ	20-131	20-72	[1]
DOHC			
BJ	[1]	[1]	[1]
TJ	20-131L	20-72	[1]
AWD			
BJ	[1]	[1]	[1]
TJ	20-131	20-72	[1]

[1] – Boots and bands are packaged as a kit. Kits are broken down by type of joint. No specifications or identification numbers given by manufacturer.

CAUTION: DO NOT pull on axle shafts during removal, or damage to shaft assembly will result.

3) Attach puller to hub and press axle shaft off hub. Swing hub and steering knuckle assembly aside. On left axles without intermediate shaft, pry axle shafts from transaxle using pry bar. DO NOT damage oil seals.
4) On left axles with intermediate shaft, place screwdriver between center bearing and axle shaft. Pry axle shaft from center bearing. Remove center bearing bolts. Place pry bar between transaxle case and intermediate shaft. Pry intermediate shaft from transaxle.
5) On Eclipse, Galant, Stealth and 3000GT AWD models, remove center bearing bolts from left axle with intermediate shaft. Using soft-faced hammer, tap lightly on Tripod Joint (TJ) case, and remove axle shaft from transaxle. *See Fig. 2.*

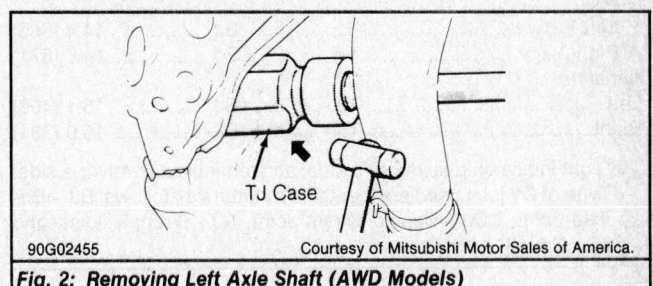

TJ Case

90G02455   Courtesy of Mitsubishi Motor Sales of America.

Fig. 2: Removing Left Axle Shaft (AWD Models)

1994 DRIVE AXLES
FWD Axle Shafts (Cont.)

Installation – Position dynamic damper properly on axle shaft (if equipped). See DYNAMIC DAMPER. To complete installation, reverse removal procedure. *See Fig. 3.* On all models, when installing axle shaft nut, washer must be installed with chamfered edge (raised side) toward axle shaft nut. Tighten axle shaft nut to specification. See TORQUE SPECIFICATIONS.

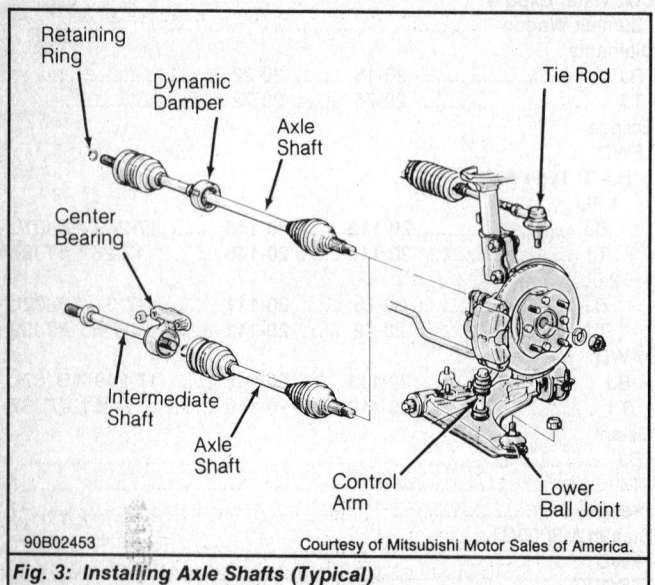

90B02453   Courtesy of Mitsubishi Motor Sales of America.

Fig. 3: Installing Axle Shafts (Typical)

AXLE SHAFT SPECIFICATIONS

Application [1]	[2] Inner Joint	[2] Outer Joint	Length In. (mm)
Colt, Mirage & Summit			
1.5L			
Left	TJ	BJ Or RJ	27.5 (698)
Right	TJ	RJ	14.9 (407)
1.8L			
Left	TJ	BJ Or RJ	27.5 (698)
Right	TJ	RJ	14.4 (365)
Colt Vista, Expo & Summit Wagon (1.8L)			
FWD			
Left	TJ	RJ	27.9 (709)
Right	TJ	RJ	14.5 (368)
4WD			
Left	DOJ	BJ	14.6 (371)
Right	DOJ	BJ	14.8 (377)
Colt Vista, Expo & Summit Wagon (2.4L)			
FWD (A/T)			
Left	TJ	BJ	27.7 (703)
Right	TJ	BJ	14.6 (371)
FWD (M/T)			
Left	TJ	BJ	27.8 (706)
Right	TJ	BJ	14.5 (368)
4WD			
Left	TJ	BJ	14.4 (366)
Right	TJ	BJ	14.6 (371)
Diamante			
Left	TJ	BJ	16.1 (409)
Right	TJ	BJ	15.0 (381)

[1] – Right indicates passenger's side, and left indicates driver's side.

[2] – Type of CV joint used are identified by letters as follows: BJ – Birfield Joint, DOJ – Double Offset Joint, RJ – Rzeppa Joint, and TJ – Tripod Joint.

AXLE SHAFT SPECIFICATIONS (Cont.)

Application [1]	[2] Inner Joint	[2] Outer Joint	Length In. (mm)
Eclipse			
FWD			
1.8L			
Left	TJ	BJ	27.9 (709)
Right	TJ	BJ	14.5 (368)
2.0L (A/T Turbo)			
Left	TJ	BJ	27.6 (701)
Right	TJ	BJ	14.5 (368)
2.0L (All Others)			
Left	TJ	BJ	27.8 (706)
Right	TJ	BJ	14.4 (366)
AWD (A/T)			
Left	TJ	BJ	14.4 (366)
Right	TJ	BJ	14.6 (371)
AWD (M/T)			
Left	TJ	BJ	14.5 (368)
Right	TJ	BJ	14.5 (368)
Galant			
Left	TJ	BJ	N/A
Right	TJ	BJ	N/A
Precis			
Left	DOJ	BJ	26.1 (663)
Right	DOJ	BJ	14.6 (371)
Stealth & 3000GT			
FWD			
SOHC (A/T)			
Left	TJ	BJ	16.5 (419)
Right	TJ	BJ	15.5 (394)
SOHC (M/T)			
Left	TJ	BJ	16.5 (419)
Right	TJ	BJ	16.0 (406)
DOHC (A/T)			
Left	TJ	BJ	16.4 (417)
Right	TJ	BJ	15.5 (394)
DOHC (M/T)			
Left	TJ	BJ	16.4 (417)
Right	TJ	BJ	15.9 (404)
AWD			
Left	TJ	BJ	16.5 (419)
Right	TJ	BJ	15.4 (391)

[1] – Right indicates passenger's side, and left indicates driver's side.

[2] – Type of CV joint used is identified by letters as follows: BJ – Birfield Joint, DOJ – Double Offset Joint, RJ – Rzeppa Joint, and TJ – Tripod Joint.

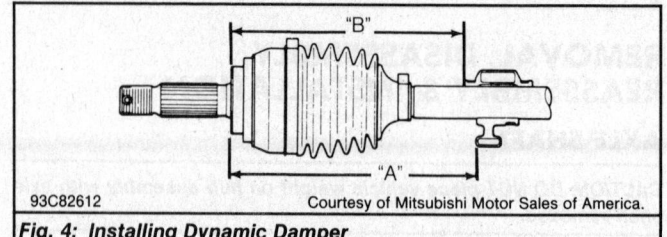

93C82612   Courtesy of Mitsubishi Motor Sales of America.

Fig. 4: Installing Dynamic Damper

DYNAMIC DAMPER

Dynamic damper must be properly positioned on axle shaft. Position damper so proper distance exists between damper and end of boot with axle shaft in a straight position. *See Fig. 4.* Distance must be within specification. See DYNAMIC DAMPER INSTALLATION SPECIFICATIONS table.

DYNAMIC DAMPER INSTALLATION SPECIFICATIONS

Application	[1] Damper-To-Boot End Distance In. (mm)
Colt, Mirage & Summit (1.5L)	
A/T	13.70-13.94 (348-354)
M/T	18.82-19.06 (434-439)
Colt, Mirage & Summit (1.8L)	
Left (M/T)	14.25-14.49 (362-368)
Right (A/T)	7.77-8.01 (197-203)
Colt Vista, Expo & Summit Wagon (FWD)	
1.8L	
Left [2]	16.89-17.13 (429-435)
Right [3]	7.77-8.01 (197-203)
2.4L	
Left [3]	14.25-14.49 (362-368)
Right [3]	7.72-7.96 (197-203)
Colt Vista, Expo & Summit Wagon (AWD)	
1.8L & 2.4L	
Both Sides [3]	7.72-7.96 (197-203)
Galant	
Left [2]	14.25-14.49 (362-368)
Right [2]	8.58-8.82 (218-224)
Precis [3]	15.0 (381)

[1] – Ensure axle shaft is in straight position.
[2] – Measure at width "A".
[3] – Measure at width "B".

INTERMEDIATE SHAFT

Disassembly – On Colt Vista, Eclipse, Expo, Stealth, Summit and 3000GT AWD models, press intermediate shaft and bearing assembly from TJ case with Intermediate Shaft Remover (MB991248 or MD998801). On all models, press out intermediate shaft from center bearing assembly with Bearing Puller (MB990810-01). Remove center bearing from bracket with appropriate bearing remover. *See Fig. 5.*

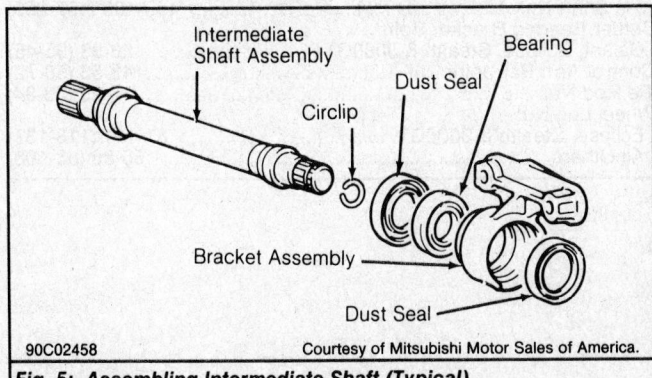

90C02458   Courtesy of Mitsubishi Motor Sales of America.

Fig. 5: Assembling Intermediate Shaft (Typical)

Reassembly – Grease center bearing and inside center bearing bracket. Press bearing into bearing bracket assembly with appropriate bearing installer. Press dust seals into bearing with handle and installer. Lubricate assembly with grease. Press intermediate shaft into center bearing assembly.

BIRFIELD JOINT (BJ) & RZEPPA JOINT (RJ) ASSEMBLY

Disassembly – Note type of boot and location prior to removal. See BAND & BOOT IDENTIFICATION. DO NOT disassemble BJ or RJ type assemblies. Only CV boot may be replaced. To remove boot, wrap splined area of axle shaft with tape. Remove band and boot.
Reassembly – Ensure proper boot is installed. See BAND & BOOT APPLICATION table. Apply proper amount of grease to joint and inside of boot. See AXLE SHAFT LUBRICATION SPECIFICATIONS table. Tighten bands on boots with axle shaft in straight position.

AXLE SHAFT LUBRICATION SPECIFICATIONS

Application	Ozs. (g)
Colt, Mirage & Summit	
Outer Boot	[1]
TJ Boot	
Inner-RJ Type Axle	4.4 (125)
Inner-BJ Type Axle	3.4 (95)
Colt Vista, Expo & Summit Wagon	
1.8L	
FWD	
Inner Boot	3.9 (110)
Outer Boot	[1]
4WD	
Inner Boot	3.2 (90)
Outer Boot	[1]
2.4L	
AWD	
Inner Boot	3.7 (105)
Outer Boot	[1]
FWD	
Inner Case	4.2 (120)
Outer Boot	[1]
Diamante	
Inner Boot	5.3 (150)
Outer Boot	[1]
Eclipse	
Inner Boot	
1.8L	3.7 (105)
2.0L	
Except AWD	4.2 (120)
AWD	3.7 (105)
Outer Boot	
1.8L	3.4 (95)
2.0L	
Except AWD	3.9 (110)
AWD	3.4 (95)
Galant	
BJ Boot	4.2 (120)
TJ Boot	4.2 (120)
Precis	
Inner Boot	2.1-3.2 (59-90)
Outer Boot	3.5-4.9 (90-125)
Stealth & 3000GT	
Outer Boot	[1]
Inner Boot	
SOHC	5.3 (151)
DOHC & AWD	5.6 (160)

[1] – Apply same amount of grease as removed. No specification available from manufacturer.

DOUBLE OFFSET JOINT (DOJ) ASSEMBLY

Disassembly – **1)** Note type of boot and location prior to removal. See BAND & BOOT IDENTIFICATION. Remove bands and boot from DOJ housing. *See Fig. 6.* Remove circlip and remove DOJ housing.
2) Place reference marks on axle shaft, DOJ inner race and DOJ outer race for reassembly reference. Remove snap ring. Remove DOJ cage, balls and DOJ inner race. Wrap splined area of axle shaft with tape, and remove boot.

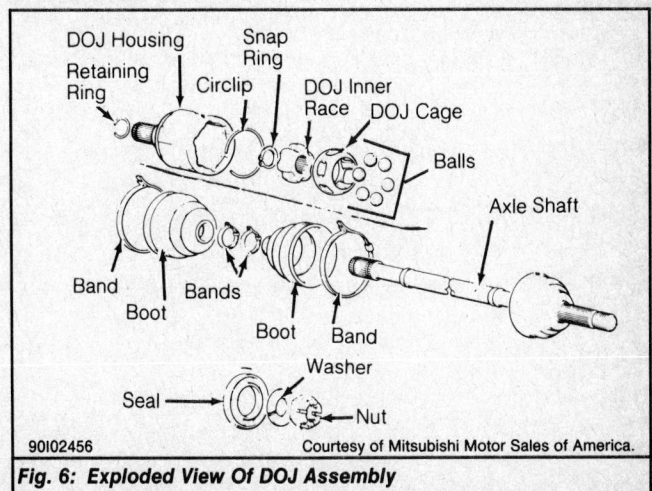

90I02456   Courtesy of Mitsubishi Motor Sales of America.

Fig. 6: Exploded View Of DOJ Assembly

Reassembly – 1) To reassemble, reverse disassembly procedure. Ensure reference marks are aligned on DOJ inner race and axle shaft. Apply one half of proper lubricant amount in balls and inner race, and other half in DOJ boot. See AXLE SHAFT LUBRICATION SPECIFICATIONS table.

2) Install boot and bands. Tighten bands with axle shaft in straight position. Position boots so bands are positioned at specified distance and secure. See DOJ BAND INSTALLATION SPECIFICATIONS table.

DOJ BAND INSTALLATION SPECIFICATIONS

Application	Distance Between Bands In. (mm)
Colt Vista, Expo & Summit Wagon 4WD	3.42-3.66 (87.0-93.0)
Precis	2.96-3.04 (75.1-77.2)

TRIPOD JOINT (TJ) ASSEMBLY

Disassembly – 1) Note type of boot and location prior to removal. See BAND & BOOT APPLICATION table. Remove bands and boot from TJ case. See Fig. 7. Place reference mark on TJ case and spider assembly. Pull axle shaft and spider assembly from TJ case.

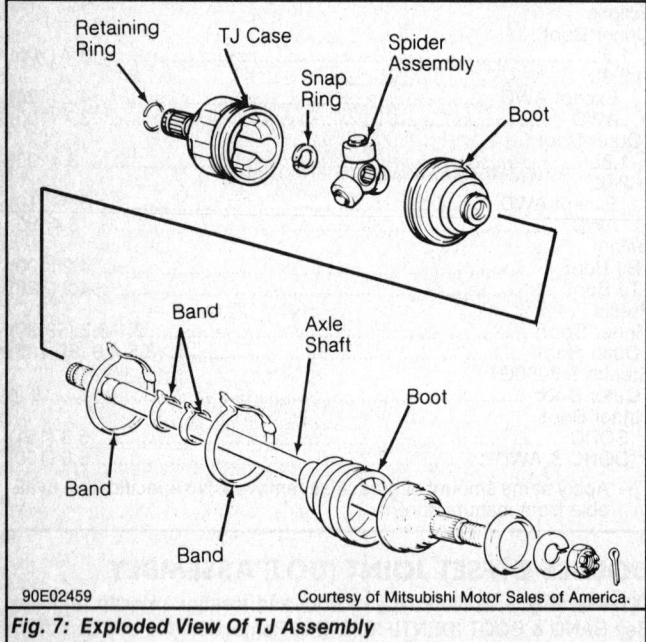

Fig. 7: Exploded View Of TJ Assembly

90E02459   Courtesy of Mitsubishi Motor Sales of America.

2) Remove snap ring and pull spider assembly from axle shaft. Clean, but DO NOT disassemble spider assembly. Wrap splined area of axle shaft with tape, and remove boot. Dynamic damper (if equipped) and outer boots can be serviced at this time.

Reassembly – 1) To reassemble, reverse disassembly procedure. Use new snap ring to retain spider assembly. Ensure reference marks are aligned on spider assembly and TJ case. Using proper lubricant, apply one half of grease in TJ case and other half TJ boot. See AXLE SHAFT LUBRICATION SPECIFICATIONS table.

2) Install boot and bands. Tighten bands on boots with axle shaft in straight position. Position boots so bands are positioned at specified distance and secure. See TJ BAND INSTALLATION SPECIFICATIONS table.

TJ BAND INSTALLATION SPECIFICATIONS

Application	Distance Between Bands In. (mm)
Colt, Mirage & Summit	3.23-3.47 (82.0-88.1)
Colt Vista, Expo & Summit Wagon	
1.8L	3.11-3.35 (79.0-85.0)
2.4L	
FWD	3.03-3.27 (77.0-83.0)
4WD	3.23-3.47 (82.0-88.1)
Diamante	2.83-3.07 (72.0-78.0)
Eclipse	
Left Axle Shaft	
FWD	
1.8L	2.83-3.07 (72.0-78.0)
2.0L	3.03-3.27 (77.0-83.0)
AWD	3.23-3.47 (82.0-88.1)
Right Axle Shaft	
FWD	
1.8L	3.23-3.47 (82.0-88.1)
2.0L	3.03-3.27 (77.0-83.0)
AWD	3.23-3.47 (82.0-88.1)
Galant	3.03-3.27 (77.0-83.0)

TORQUE SPECIFICATIONS
TORQUE SPECIFICATIONS

Application	Ft. Lbs. (N.m)
Axle Shaft Nut	145-188 (197-255)
Center Bearing Bracket Bolt	
Galant, Eclipse, Stealth & 3000GT	26-33 (35-45)
Control Arm Ball Joint Nut	43-53 (58-72)
Tie Rod Nut	17-25 (23-34)
Wheel Lug Nut	
Eclipse, Stealth & 3000GT	87-101 (118-137)
All Others	65-80 (88-108)

**Chrysler Corp.: Colt Vista, Stealth,
Summit Wagon
Mitsubishi: Eclipse, Expo, 3000GT**

NOTE: Information in this article applies only to AWD models with independent rear suspension. For other models, see appropriate DIFFERENTIALS & AXLE SHAFTS article.

DESCRIPTION & OPERATION

Power from differential is transferred to rear wheels by 2 axle shafts. Both axle shafts use CV joints at inner and outer ends. CV joints are enclosed in CV boots, and are connected by an interconnecting shaft. Interconnecting shaft is splined on both ends. A retaining ring retains inner CV joint in differential side gear. Outer CV joint is attached to stub axle shaft.

TROUBLE SHOOTING

NOTE: See TROUBLE SHOOTING article in GENERAL INFORMATION.

BAND & BOOT IDENTIFICATION

Band identification numbers are stamped on inside edge of band. *See Fig. 1.* Boot identification numbers are stamped on the largest ridge of boot. See BAND & BOOT APPLICATION table.

NOTE: The following are possible types of Constant Velocity (CV) joints used on axle shaft: Birfield Joint (BJ), Double Offset Joint (DOJ) and Tripod Joint (TJ). Determine type of CV joint used prior to disassembly. Note type of boot and location prior to removal. See BAND & BOOT APPLICATION table. Install a NEW retaining ring each time axle shaft is removed from differential side gear.

BAND & BOOT APPLICATION

Application	Identification Numbers
Colt Vista, Expo & Summit Wagon	
BJ	
Large Band	20-110
Small Band	[1]
Boot	[1]
DOJ	
Large Band	20-82
Small Band	[1]
Boot	[1]
Eclipse	
BJ	
Large Band	20-113
Small Band	20-146
Boot	17-314 #BJ87
TJ	
Large Band	20-10
Small Band	20-146
Boot	17-261 #BJ87
Stealth & 3000GT	
BJ	
Large Band	20-74
Small Band	[2]
Boot	[1]
TJ	
Large Band	20-75
Small Band	[1]
Boot	[1]

[1] – Boots and bands are packaged as a kit. Kits are broken down by type of joint. No identification numbers given by manufacturer.
[2] – Left axle shaft band is White. Right axle shaft band is Blue.

REMOVAL, DISASSEMBLY, REASSEMBLY & INSTALLATION

AXLE SHAFT

CAUTION: DO NOT place vehicle weight on hub assembly with axle shaft removed.

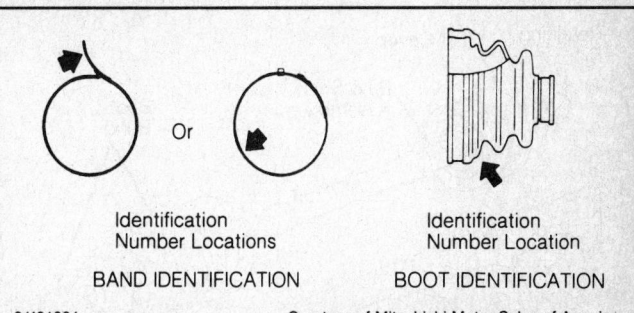

BAND IDENTIFICATION — Identification Number Locations

BOOT IDENTIFICATION — Identification Number Location

91I01904   Courtesy of Mitsubishi Motor Sales of America.

Fig. 1: Locating Band & Boot Identification Numbers

Removal & Installation (Colt Vista, Expo & Summit Wagon) – 1) Raise and support vehicle. Remove wheels. Remove side flange-to-differential bolts and separate axle shaft.
2) Remove brake drum or caliper and rotor. Remove speed sensor ring (if equipped). Remove axle shaft nut and washer. Attach puller to hub and press axle shaft from hub. To install, reverse removal procedure.

Removal & Installation (Eclipse, Stealth & 3000GT) – 1) Raise and support vehicle. Unbolt axle shaft from stub axle shaft. Pry axle shaft from differential using flat-blade screwdriver. Ensure seal is not damaged by axle shaft splines during removal. Remove oil seal from differential carrier (if necessary).
2) To install, reverse removal procedure. Using Seal Installer (C-3893), install oil seal in differential. Coat seal lip with grease. Install new retaining clip on axle shaft. Install axle shaft in differential carrier. Install companion flange bolts.

NOTE: Always replace retaining clip when axle shaft has been removed.

DOUBLE OFFSET JOINT (DOJ) ASSEMBLY

NOTE: BJ and shaft assembly cannot be disassembled. DO NOT attempt to disassemble.

Disassembly (Colt Vista, Expo & Summit Wagon) – 1) Remove axle shaft. Note type of band and boot location prior to removal. See BAND & BOOT IDENTIFICATION. Remove bands and boot from DOJ housing. Remove circlip and remove DOJ housing. *See Fig. 2.*
2) Place reference marks on axle shaft, DOJ inner race and DOJ outer race for reassembly reference. Remove snap ring. Remove DOJ cage, balls and DOJ inner race. Wrap splined area of axle shaft with tape, and remove boot.

Reassembly – 1) To reassemble, reverse disassembly procedure. Ensure reference marks are aligned on DOJ inner race and axle shaft. Apply one half of proper lubricant amount to balls and inner race, and other half in DOJ boot. See DOUBLE OFFSET JOINT (DOJ) ASSEMBLY SPECIFICATIONS table.
2) Install boot and bands. Tighten large band with axle shaft in straight position. Position boots so bands are positioned at specified distance and tighten small band. *See Fig. 3.* See DOUBLE OFFSET JOINT (DOJ) ASSEMBLY SPECIFICATIONS table. Install axle shaft.

DOUBLE OFFSET JOINT (DOJ) ASSEMBLY SPECIFICATIONS

Application	In. (mm)
Axle Shaft Dimensions	
Colt Vista, Expo & Summit Wagon	
Length (Both Shafts)	
With ABS	18.62 (473)
Without ABS	19.60 (498)
DOJ Boot Length	
Colt Vista, Expo & Summit Wagon	2.72-3.18 (69-81)

TRIPOD JOINT (TJ) ASSEMBLY

NOTE: BJ and shaft assembly cannot be disassembled. DO NOT attempt to disassemble.

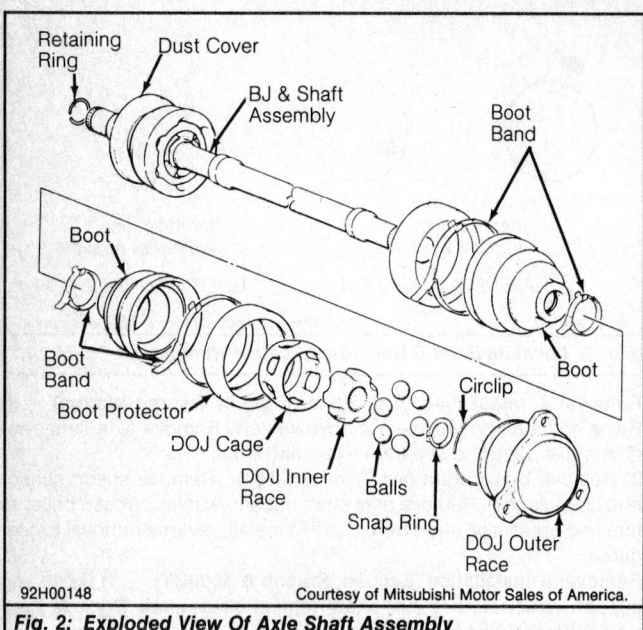

Fig. 2: Exploded View Of Axle Shaft Assembly (Colt Vista, Expo & Summit Wagon)

Disassembly (Eclipse, Stealth & 3000GT) – Remove axle shaft. Remove boot bands from inner CV joint (TJ). Scribe alignment marks (for reassembly reference) on shaft, TJ case and spider assembly. Remove TJ case, snap ring and spider assembly. Remove boot bands from outer CV joint (BJ). Wrap axle shaft splines with tape and remove CV boots. *See Fig. 4.*

Reassembly – 1) To reassemble, reverse disassembly procedure. If reusing BJ and shaft assembly, pack BJ with specified quantity of CV joint grease. See TRIPOD JOINT (TJ) ASSEMBLY SPECIFICATIONS table. Install CV joint boots and clamps on axle shaft. Lubricate and assemble TJ.

2) Align reference marks made during disassembly and install TJ assembly. Install snap ring. Pack TJ and boot with specified quantity of CV joint grease. See TRIPOD JOINT (TJ) ASSEMBLY SPECIFICATIONS table.

3) Tighten large CV boot band in straight position. Set CV boot length to specification. *See Fig. 3.* See TRIPOD JOINT (TJ) ASSEMBLY SPECIFICATIONS table. Tighten small CV boot band. Install axle shaft.

TRIPOD JOINT (TJ) ASSEMBLY SPECIFICATIONS

Application	In. (mm)
Drive Axle Shaft Dimensions	
Eclipse	
Length (Both Shafts)	15.2 (385)
Stealth & 3000GT	
Length (Both Shafts)	15.6 (396.2)
TJ Boot Length	
Eclipse	2.90-3.14 (74-80)
Stealth & 3000GT	3.23-3.47 (82-88)
CV Joint Grease Capacity	**Ozs. (g)**
Eclipse	
Both Joints	[1] 3.7 (105)
Stealth & 3000GT	
TJ	[1] 4.8 (135)

[1] – Split grease equally between boot and joint.

STUB AXLE SHAFTS

End Play Check (Eclipse, Stealth & 3000GT) – Place dial indicator stem on rear axle flange near lug nut. Check stub axle shaft end play. If end play is greater than .031" (.8 mm), check torque of companion flange nut. See TORQUE SPECIFICATIONS. If torque is as specified, replace inner and outer bearings.

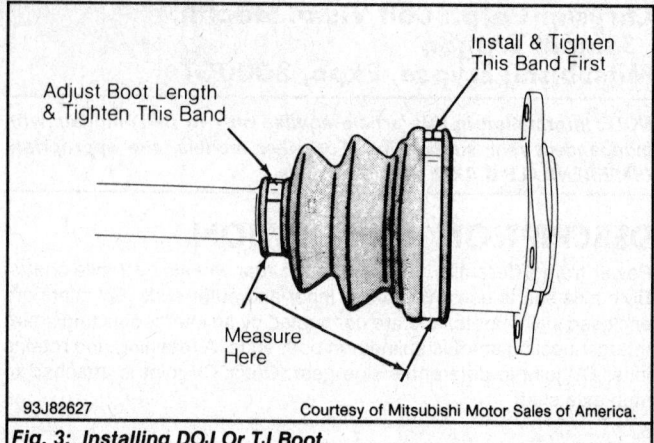

Fig. 3: Installing DOJ Or TJ Boot

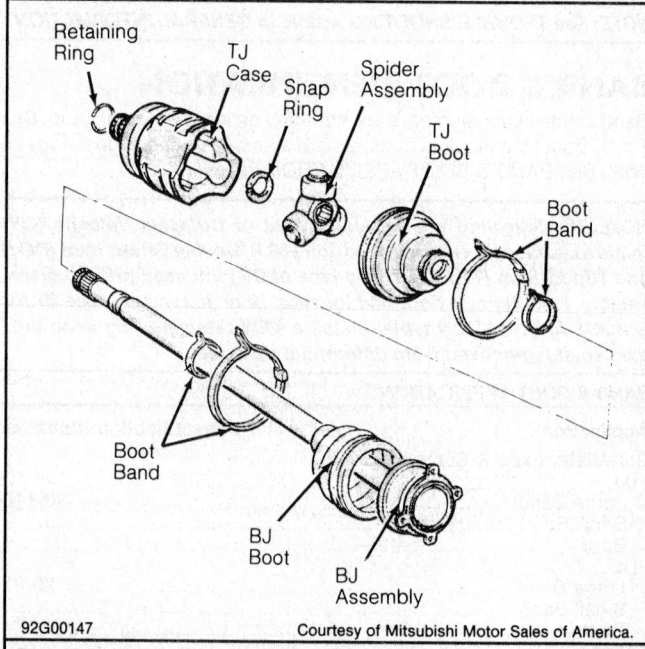

Fig. 4: Exploded View Of Axle Shaft Assembly (Eclipse, Stealth & 3000GT)

Removal – 1) Raise and support vehicle on safety stands. Remove rear wheels. Remove rear speed sensor (if equipped). *See Fig. 5.* Disconnect parking brake cable from rear brake caliper assembly. Remove rear caliper assembly and rotor. Support caliper assembly away from work area with wire.

2) Scribe index marks on flange yoke and companion flange. Remove axle shaft mounting bolts. Remove self-locking nut with Nut Remover/Installer (MB990767-01). Separate axle from flange.

3) Remove axle shaft from trailing arm using Slide Hammer (MB990211-01) and Adapter (MB990241-01). Slide hammer attachment fits on outboard end of axle shaft flange.

NOTE: When removing axle shaft spline, DO NOT damage oil seal.

Disassembly – Remove rear speed sensor rotor (if equipped). *See Fig. 5.* Remove outer bearing and dust cover from axle shaft. Remove axle shaft. Remove oil seal using Handle (MB990938-01) and Seal Remover/Installer (MB990928-01). Remove inner bearing.

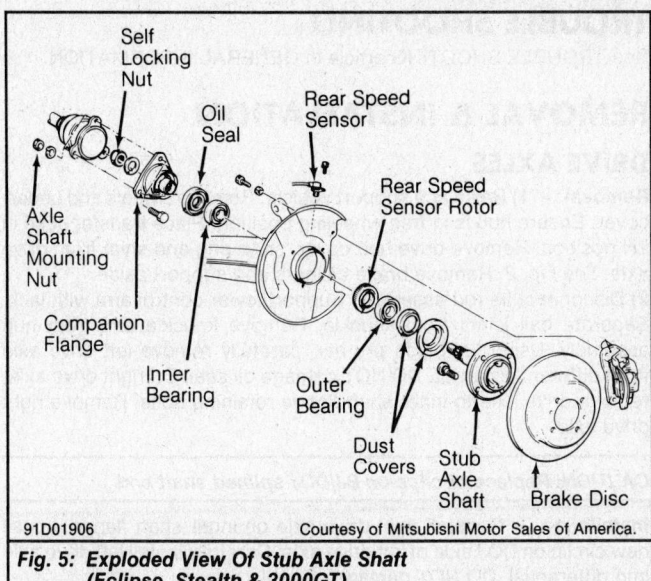

Self
Locking
Nut

Oil
Seal

Rear Speed
Sensor

Rear Speed
Sensor Rotor

Axle
Shaft
Mounting
Nut

Companion
Flange

Inner
Bearing

Outer
Bearing

Dust
Covers

Stub
Axle
Shaft

Brake Disc

91D01906   Courtesy of Mitsubishi Motor Sales of America.

**Fig. 5: Exploded View Of Stub Axle Shaft
(Eclipse, Stealth & 3000GT)**

Inspection – Check companion flange for wear or damage. Check dust cover for deformation or damage. Check wheel bearings for burning, discoloration or rough rotation. Check axle shaft for cracking, wear or damage. Check oil seal for cracking or damage.

Reassembly & Installation – **1)** To reassemble and install, reverse disassembly and removal procedures. When installing inner bearing, use Handle (MB990938-01) and Seal Remover/Installer (MB990931-01). Use Seal Installer (MB990799-01) to install oil seal and dust cover. **2)** Tighten all components to specification. See TORQUE SPECIFICATIONS. Ensure axle shaft end play is within service limit.

TORQUE SPECIFICATIONS

TORQUE SPECIFICATIONS

Application	Ft. Lbs. (N.m)
Colt Vista, Expo & Summit Wagon	
Axle Shaft Nut	145-188 (197-255)
Companion Flange-To-Axle Shaft Nut	40-47 (54-64)
Wheel Lug Nut	65-80 (88-108)
Eclipse	
Axle Flange-To-Axle Shaft Flange Bolt	40-47 (54-64)
Brake Caliper Bolt	36-43 (49-58)
Companion Flange Nut	116-159 (157-216)
Wheel Lug Nut	87-101 (118-137)
Stealth & 3000GT	
Axle Flange-To-Axle Shaft Flange Bolt	40-47 (54-64)
Brake Caliper Bolt	36-43 (49-58)
Companion Flange Nut	
Non-Turbo	137 (186)
Turbo	188-217 (255-294)
Wheel Lug Nut	87-101 (118-137)

	INCH Lbs. (N.m)
Rear Speed Sensor Bolts	84-120 (9-14)

1994 DRIVE AXLES
Differentials & Axle Shafts – Front

Mitsubishi: Montero, Pickup 4WD

DESCRIPTION & OPERATION

Front axle assembly consists of differential carrier, housing tube, inner shaft and drive axles. *See Fig. 1.* A full-floating axle design is used. Drive axles are flexible assemblies made up of inner and outer CV joints. Birfield Joints (BJ) and Double Offset Joints (DOJ) are used at opposite ends of each drive axle.

AXLE RATIO & IDENTIFICATION

AXLE RATIO SPECIFICATIONS

Application	Ratio
Montero	
LT31X10.50R15 Tire	4.88:1
P235/75R15 Tire	4.63:1
Pickup	4.22:1

LUBRICATION

CAPACITY

DIFFERENTIAL FLUID CAPACITY

Application	Specification
Montero	2.6 Pts. (1.2L)
Pickup	2.3 Pts. (1.1L)

FLUID TYPE

All models use fluid type SAE 80W-90/API GL-5.

TROUBLE SHOOTING

See TROUBLE SHOOTING article in GENERAL INFORMATION.

REMOVAL & INSTALLATION

DRIVE AXLES

Removal – 1) Raise and support vehicle. Remove wheels and undercover. Ensure hub is in free-wheeling position. Place transfer case in 2H position. Remove drive hub cover, snap ring and shim from drive axle. *See Fig. 2.* Remove brake calipers and support aside.
2) Disconnect tie rod assembly. Support lower control arm with jack. Separate ball joints from knuckle. Remove knuckle and front hub assembly. Using flat-blade pry bar, carefully remove left drive axle from differential carrier. DO NOT damage oil seal. On right drive axle, remove drive axle-to-inner shaft flange retaining bolts. Remove right drive axle.

CAUTION: *Replace circlips on BJ/DOJ splined shaft end.*

Installation – 1) Install right drive axle on inner shaft flange. Install new circlip on DOJ side of left drive axle. Carefully install left drive axle into differential. DO NOT damage oil seal.
2) Reinstall knuckle with front hub assembly. To complete installation, reverse removal procedure. Install shim and snap ring. Check axle end play. *See Fig. 3.* End play should be .016-.028" (.4-.7 mm) on Montero, .008-.020" (.2-.5 mm) on Pickup. If end play is not within specification, install correct shim.

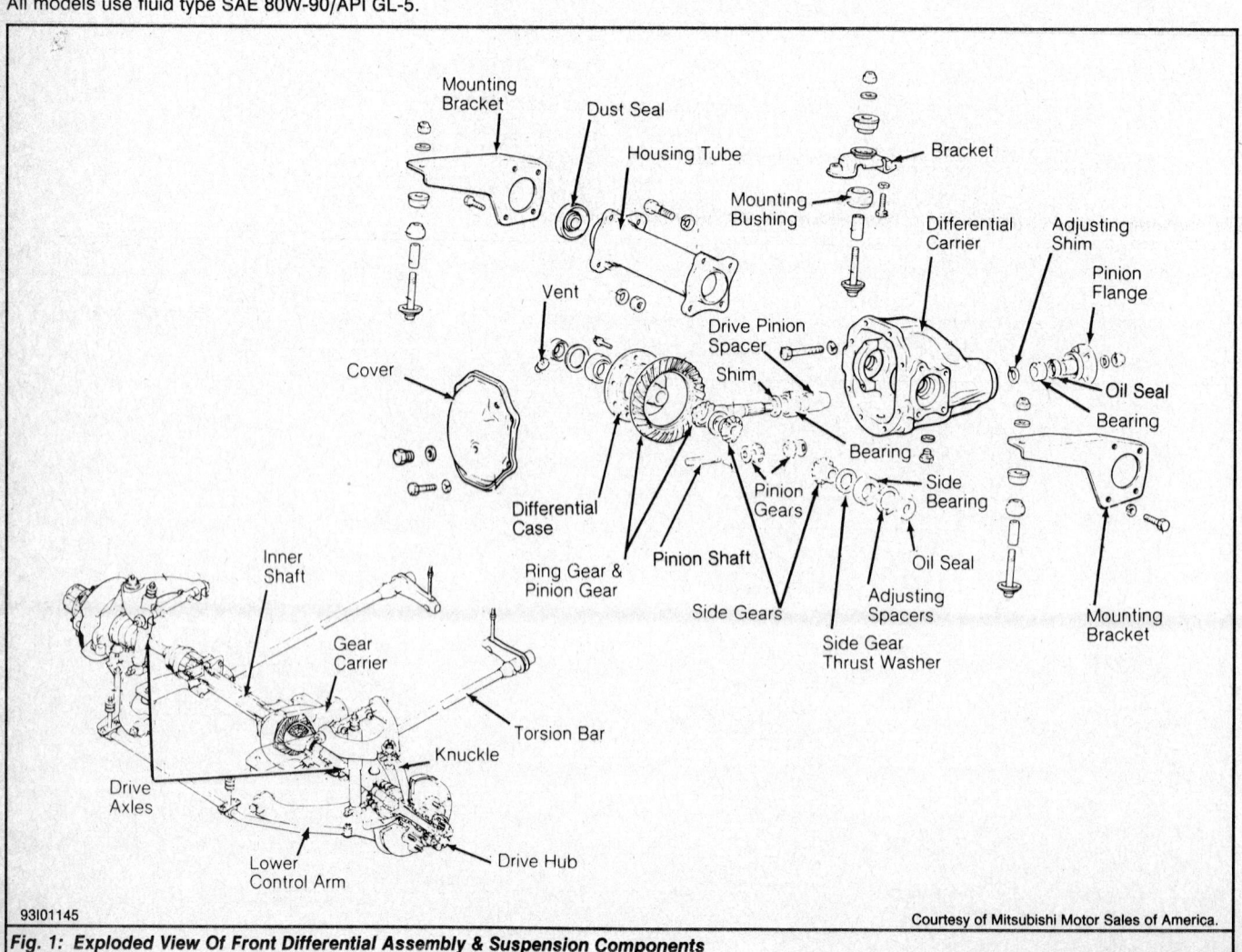

93I01145

Courtesy of Mitsubishi Motor Sales of America.

Fig. 1: Exploded View Of Front Differential Assembly & Suspension Components

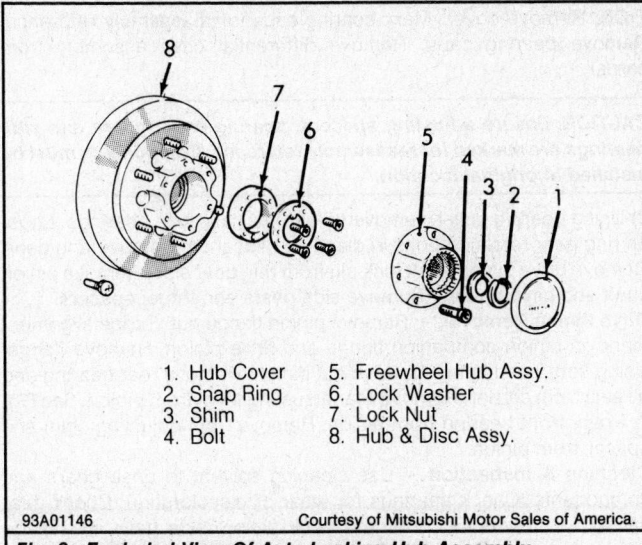

1. Hub Cover
2. Snap Ring
3. Shim
4. Bolt
5. Freewheel Hub Assy.
6. Lock Washer
7. Lock Nut
8. Hub & Disc Assy.

93A01146   Courtesy of Mitsubishi Motor Sales of America.

Fig. 2: Exploded View Of Auto-Locking Hub Assembly (Pickup Shown, Montero Similar)

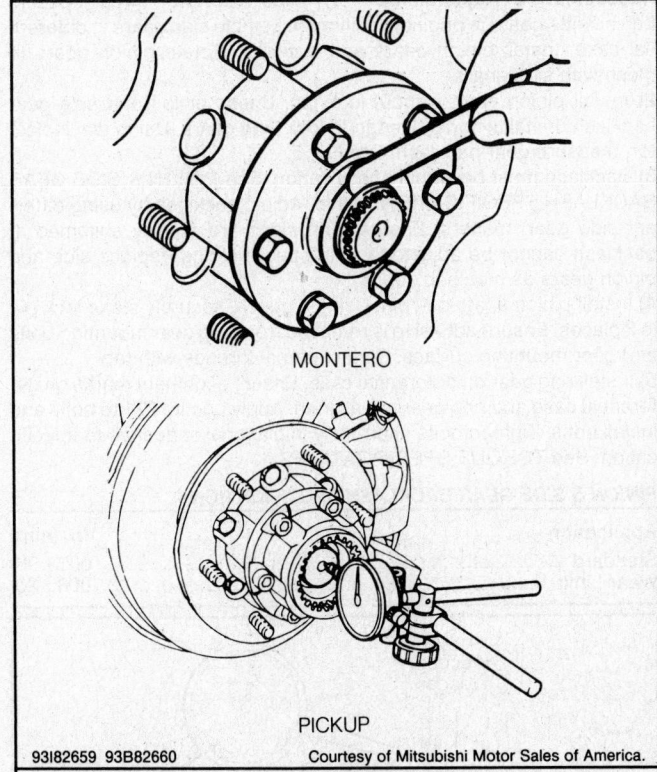

MONTERO

PICKUP

93I82659 93B82660   Courtesy of Mitsubishi Motor Sales of America.

Fig. 3: Measuring Axle Shaft End Play

DIFFERENTIAL CARRIER ASSEMBLY

Removal – **1)** Raise and support vehicle. Drain gear oil. Support differential carrier. Remove drive axles and inner shaft. See DRIVE AXLES and INNER SHAFT & BEARING under REMOVAL & INSTALLATION. Place alignment mark on drive shaft and pinion companion flange for reassembly reference.

2) Remove drive shaft. Remove differential mounting brackets at differential and frame. See Fig. 1. Disconnect front crossmember from frame. Remove differential carrier assembly and front crossmember. Remove differential carrier from front crossmember.

Installation – To install, reverse removal procedure. Align marks on drive shaft and pinion companion flange.

INNER SHAFT & BEARING

Removal – Remove right drive axle. See DRIVE AXLES under REMOVAL & INSTALLATION. Using slide hammer, remove inner shaft from differential carrier. If dust seal replacement is required, pry dust seal from housing tube assembly using a screwdriver. See Fig. 1. To remove bearing, bend outer area of dust cover inward on inner shaft. Press shaft out of bearing. Remove dust cover from shaft.

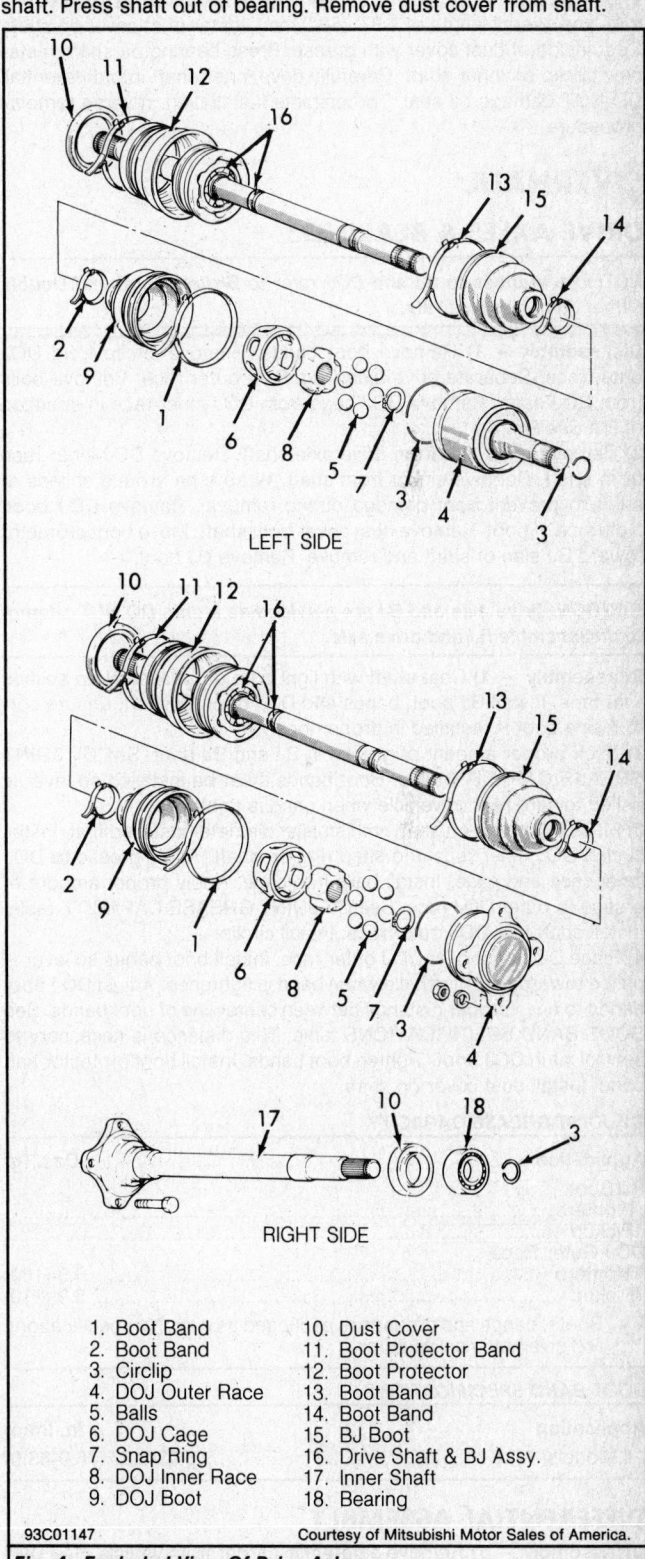

LEFT SIDE

RIGHT SIDE

1. Boot Band
2. Boot Band
3. Circlip
4. DOJ Outer Race
5. Balls
6. DOJ Cage
7. Snap Ring
8. DOJ Inner Race
9. DOJ Boot
10. Dust Cover
11. Boot Protector Band
12. Boot Protector
13. Boot Band
14. Boot Band
15. BJ Boot
16. Drive Shaft & BJ Assy.
17. Inner Shaft
18. Bearing

93C01147   Courtesy of Mitsubishi Motor Sales of America.

Fig. 4: Exploded View Of Drive Axles

Inspection – Inspect inner shaft for damaged splines or threads. Inspect bearing for roughness or damage.

Installation – **1)** Install housing tube. Using Seal Installer (MB990955) and Handle (C-4171), install new dust seal in housing tube. Dust seal must be even with housing tube. Coat seal lip with grease.

2) Using a pipe with O.D. of 2.95" (74.3 mm), wall thickness of .16" (4.0 mm) and overall length of 1.97" (50.0 mm), install dust cover on shaft. Coat inside of dust cover with grease. Press bearing on shaft. Install new circlip on inner shaft. Carefully drive inner shaft into differential. DO NOT damage oil seal. To complete installation, reverse removal procedure.

OVERHAUL

DRIVE AXLES & BEARINGS

NOTE: References to BJ and DOJ refer to Birfield Joint and Double Offset Joint, respectively.

Disassembly – **1)** Remove boot bands. Remove circlip from DOJ outer race. Separate drive axle from DOJ outer race. Remove balls from DOJ cage. Remove DOJ cage from DOJ inner race in direction of BJ. *See Fig. 4.*

2) Remove snap ring from drive axle shaft. Remove DOJ inner race from shaft. Remove circlip from shaft. Wrap tape around splines of shaft to prevent boot damage during removal. Remove DOJ boot. Note size of boot. Remove dust cover from shaft. Move boot protector toward BJ side of shaft and remove. Remove BJ boot.

CAUTION: Drive axle and BJ are serviced as a unit. DO NOT attempt to disassemble BJ and drive axle.

Reassembly – **1)** Coat shaft with light coat of grease. Wrap splines with tape. Install BJ boot, bands and DOJ boot on shaft. Ensure correct size boot is installed in proper location.

2) Pack proper amount of grease in BJ and BJ boot. See CV JOINT GREASE CAPACITY table. Boot bands must be installed so lever is pulled toward rear of vehicle when band is tightened.

3) Place DOJ cage on shaft with smaller diameter installed first. Install circlip, DOJ inner race and snap ring on shaft. Apply grease to DOJ inner race and cage. Install balls into cage. Apply proper amount of grease to outer DOJ race. See CV JOINT GREASE CAPACITY table. Install shaft into DOJ outer race. Install circlip.

4) Place DOJ boot over DOJ outer race. Install boot bands so lever is pulled toward rear of vehicle when band is tightened. Adjust DOJ boot bands to have proper distance between center line of boot bands. See BOOT BAND SPECIFICATIONS table. This distance is necessary to control air in DOJ boot. Tighten boot bands. Install boot protector and band. Install dust cover on shaft.

CV JOINT GREASE CAPACITY

Application	Ozs. (g)
BJ Boot	
Montero	1
Pickup	1
DOJ Outer Race	
Montero	3.5 (100)
Pickup	3.9 (110)

1 – Boots, bands and grease are packaged as a kit. No specifications are given by manufacturer.

BOOT BAND SPECIFICATIONS

Application	In. (mm)
All Models	3.03-3.27 (76.9-83.0)

DIFFERENTIAL ASSEMBLY

Disassembly – **1)** Remove differential carrier from vehicle. See DIFFERENTIAL CARRIER ASSEMBLY under REMOVAL & INSTALLATION. Remove cover. Mark bearing caps for reassembly reference. Remove bearing caps. Remove differential case assembly from carrier.

CAUTION: Ensure adjusting spacers, bearing caps, gears and side bearings are marked for reassembly reference. Components must be installed in original location.

2) Using bearing puller, remove differential case side bearings. Loosen ring gear retaining bolts in diagonal sequence. Remove ring gear. Remove drive pinion shaft lock pin from ring gear side. Remove pinion shaft and pinion gears. Remove side gears and thrust spacers.

Drive Pinion Removal – Remove pinion flange nut. Scribe alignment mark on pinion companion flange and drive pinion. Remove flange. Using soft-faced hammer, drive out pinion. Remove rear bearing and oil seal from carrier. Remove rear adjusting shim from pinion. *See Fig. 1.* Press front bearing from pinion. Remove front adjusting shim and spacer from pinion.

Cleaning & Inspection – Use cleaning solvent to rinse gears and components. Check bearings for wear or discoloration. Check gear carrier for cracks or damage. Check pinion, side gear and flange splines for excessive wear. Check ring gear, pinion and side gears for wear or damage. Replace components as necessary.

Reassembly & Adjustments – **1)** Place side gear thrust spacers behind side gears in original position. Assemble side gears in differential case. Install pinion gears and washers. Rotate pinion gears to mesh with side gears.

2) Install pinion shaft without lock pin. Check pinion and side gear backlash. Install wooden wedge to lock side gears. Using dial indicator, measure gear backlash. *See Fig. 5.*

3) Backlash must be within specification. See PINION & SIDE GEAR BACKLASH SPECIFICATIONS table. Adjust backlash by using different side gear spacers. Ensure both sides are equally shimmed. If backlash cannot be adjusted within specifications, replace side and pinion gears as matched set.

4) Install pinion shaft lock pin. Using a punch, securely stake lock pin in 2 places. Ensure adhesive is removed from ring gear mounting bolts and gear mounting surface. Clean internal threads with tap.

5) Install ring gear on differential case. Ensure alignment marks on differential case and ring gear are aligned. Apply Loctite 271 to bolts and install bolts. Tighten bolts alternately in diagonal sequence to specification. See TORQUE SPECIFICATIONS.

PINION & SIDE GEAR BACKLASH SPECIFICATIONS

Application	In. (mm)
Standard	.003 (.08)
Wear Limit	.008 (.20)

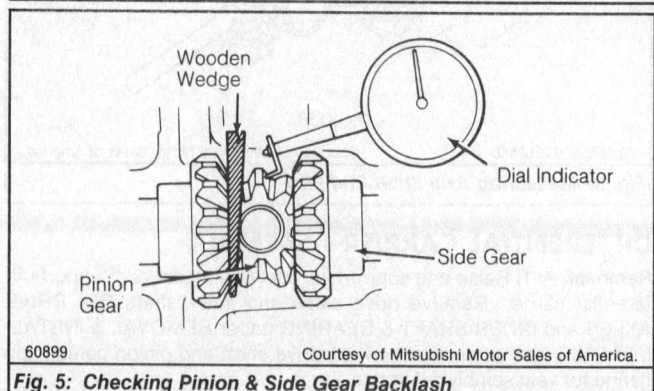

60899   Courtesy of Mitsubishi Motor Sales of America.

Fig. 5: Checking Pinion & Side Gear Backlash

Drive Pinion Depth – **1)** Install pinion bearing races in carrier housing. Ensure races are fully seated. Install Pinion Height Gauge (MB990901-01) with pinion bearings. *See Fig. 6.* DO NOT install oil seal.

2) Using INCH-lb. torque wrench, measure pinion rotating torque. Gradually tighten pinion height gauge to increase rotating torque to proper specification. See PINION ROTATING TORQUE SPECIFICATIONS table. Install Cylinder Gauge (MB990903-01). Ensure flat areas are aligned and gauge contacts carrier bearing bores firmly. See Fig. 6.

3) Select adjusting shim with same thickness as gap between cylinder gauge and pinion height gauge. Use minimum amount of adjusting shims. Install selected adjusting shims between drive pinion gear and rear drive pinion bearing. Using Bearing Installer (MB990802-01), install rear pinion bearing.

PINION ROTATING TORQUE SPECIFICATIONS

Application	INCH Lbs. (N.m)
Oil Seal Not Installed	
With Lubrication	1.3-2.2 (.15-.25)
Without Lubrication	2.6-4.3 (.30-.50)
Oil Seal Installed	
With Lubrication	3.1-3.9 (.35-.45)
Without Lubrication	4.3-6.1 (.50-.70)

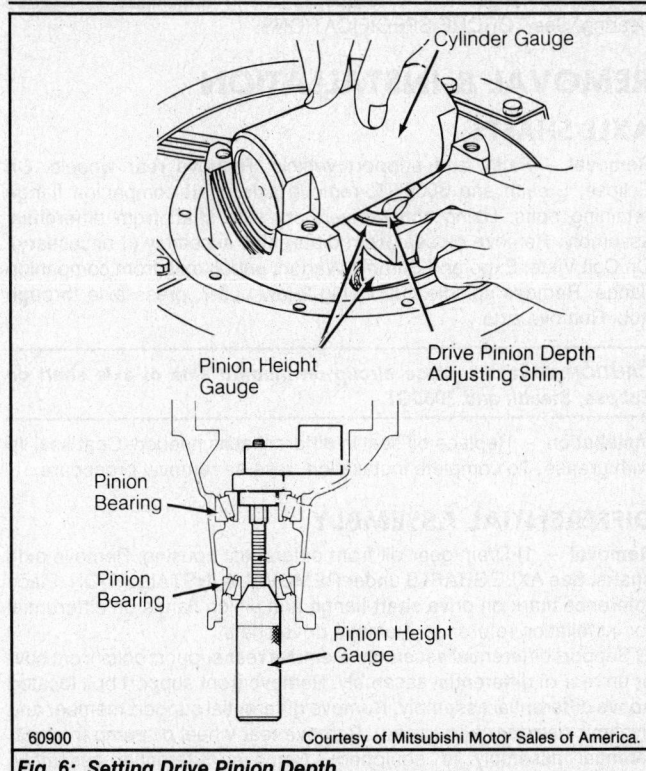

Cylinder Gauge

Pinion Height Gauge

Drive Pinion Depth Adjusting Shim

Pinion Bearing

Pinion Bearing

Pinion Height Gauge

60900   Courtesy of Mitsubishi Motor Sales of America.

Fig. 6: Setting Drive Pinion Depth

Drive Pinion Preload – 1) Install drive pinion in differential carrier. Install spacer, pinion front shim(s) and front pinion bearing. DO NOT install oil seal at this time. Install pinion companion flange, washer and retaining nut. Tighten nut to 137 ft. lbs. (190 N.m).

2) Using INCH-lb. torque wrench, check pinion rotating torque without pinion oil seal. See PINION ROTATING TORQUE SPECIFICATIONS table. Adjust rotating torque by replacing drive pinion front shims or spacer. Once correct rotating torque is obtained, install oil seal. Coat seal lip with grease.

3) Install pinion flange so alignment marks are correct. Apply light coat of grease to flange washer contact area. Install new retaining nut. Check pinion rotating torque with pinion oil seal installed. Rotating torque must be within specification. See PINION ROTATING TORQUE SPECIFICATIONS table.

Side Bearing Installation – 1) Using Bearing Installer (MB990802-01), install bearings on differential case. Select 2 side bearing adjusting shims thinner than those removed. Shims must be equal in thickness on both sides. Install shims on each side of case assembly. Install case assembly in differential carrier housing.

2) Push case assembly fully to one side of carrier. Using 2 feeler gauges (feeler gauges 180 degrees opposed), measure clearance between carrier and side bearing. Remove shims from one side of differential carrier.

3) Measure thickness of shims removed. Add .002" (.05 mm) to 50% of measured clearance and then add thickness measurement of removed shim. This is thickness of new shim that should be installed on each side of case. Install equal thickness shims on each side of case assembly.

NOTE: Ensure zero clearance exists between gear carrier and adjusting shim.

4) Install side bearing shims and differential case assembly in differential carrier. Using brass drift, tap shims to fit them to side bearing outer race. Install bearing caps. Tighten bolts to specification. See TORQUE SPECIFICATIONS. Check ring gear backlash.

Ring Gear Backlash – 1) Lock drive pinion in place. Using dial indicator, check ring gear backlash at heel of ring gear tooth. Measure at 4 locations of ring gear. Gear backlash should be .004-.006" (.10-.15 mm).

2) If backlash is not within specification, change side bearing adjusting shims and recheck backlash. See GEAR TOOTH CONTACT PATTERNS article in GENERAL INFORMATION. Check gear tooth contact using Prussion Blue.

CAUTION: When changing shims, total thickness of all shims must remain constant to ensure correct bearing preload.

Ring Gear Runout – Using dial indicator, measure runout at back side of ring gear. Runout should be .002" (.05 mm). If runout is excessive, change ring gear-to-differential case mounting position. Ensure ring gear mounting bolts are tightened to correct specification. Recheck runout. Install cover and gasket.

TORQUE SPECIFICATIONS
TORQUE SPECIFICATIONS

Application	Ft. Lbs. (N.m)
Brake Caliper Bolt	58-72 (79-98)
Carrier-To-Housing Tube Bolt	58-72 (79-98)
Cover Bolt	11-16 (15-22)
Drain Plug	43-51 (58-69)
Drive Shaft Flange Bolt	36-43 (49-58)
Fill Plug	29-43 (39-58)
Front Crossmember Bolt	72-87 (98-118)
Hub Cover Bolt	13-25 (18-34)
Knuckle-To-Ball Joint Nut	
Upper	43-65 (58-88)
Lower	87-130 (118-176)
Mounting Bracket-To-Frame Bolt	58-80 (79-108)
Mounting Bracket-To-Housing Tube Bolt	58-72 (79-98)
Pinion Flange Nut	137-159 (186-220)
Right Drive Axle-To-Inner Shaft Bolt	36-43 (49-58)
Ring Gear-To-Case Bolt	58-65 (79-88)
Side Bearing Cap Bolt	40-47 (54-64)
Tie Rod-To-Knuckle Nut	33 (45)
Wheel Lug Nuts	
Montero	72-87 (98-118)
Pickup	87-101 (118-137)

	INCH Lbs. (N.m)
Undercover-To-Frame Bolts (Montero)	84-108 (9.5-12.2)

1994 DRIVE AXLES
Differentials & Axle Shafts – Rear Integral

**Chrysler Corp.: Colt Vista AWD,
Stealth AWD, Summit Wagon AWD
Mitsubishi: Eclipse AWD, Expo AWD,
3000GT AWD**

DESCRIPTION

On All-Wheel Drive (AWD) models, the rear axle features an integral housing. Differential consists of hypoid reduction gears and straight bevel differential gears. Limited slip differential is available.

NOTE: Vehicle references in this article refer to AWD models only.

AXLE RATIO & IDENTIFICATION

Ratio is determined by dividing number of ring gear teeth by number of drive pinion teeth.

AXLE RATIO SPECIFICATIONS

Application	Ratio
Colt Vista, Expo & Summit Wagon	
Automatic Transaxle	
1.8L	3.55:1
2.4L	3.31:1
Manual Transaxle	
1.8L	2.85:1
2.4L	3.55:1
Eclipse	
Automatic Transaxle	3.31:1
Manual Transaxle	3.55:1
Stealth & 3000GT	3.55:1

LUBRICATION

CAPACITY

Gear oil capacity is 1.48 pts. (.7L) for Colt Vista, Eclipse, Expo and Summit Wagon. For Stealth and 3000GT, gear oil capacity is 2.4 pts. (1.1L).

FLUID TYPE

Use SAE 80W-90 API GL-5 hypoid gear oil. For limited slip differentials, add Hypoid Gear Oil Additive Friction Modifier (4318058). For temperatures less than -30°F (-34°C), use SAE 75W.

TROUBLE SHOOTING

See TROUBLE SHOOTING article in GENERAL INFORMATION.

TESTING & PRE-INSPECTION

AXLE SHAFT END PLAY

1) Raise and support vehicle. Remove tire and wheel assembly. Remove caliper and disc rotor or brake drum. Using dial indicator, check axle shaft end play. End play should not exceed .031" (.78 mm) for Eclipse, Stealth and 3000GT. On Colt Vista, Expo and Summit Wagon, end play should not exceed .002" (.05 mm).
2) If end play is not within specification, check torque of axle shaft nut. If torque is within specification, replace bearing. See TORQUE SPECIFICATIONS.

AXLE BACKLASH

1) Raise and support rear axle. Place transaxle in Neutral. Apply parking brake. Rotate drive shaft clockwise. Place reference marks on drive shaft flange dust cover and differential housing.
2) Rotate drive shaft counterclockwise, and measure distance between reference marks. Differential must be removed and backlash adjusted if distance exceeds .2" (5 mm). See DIFFERENTIAL ASSEMBLY under OVERHAUL.

LIMITED SLIP DIFFERENTIAL VISCOUS UNIT

1) Block front wheels. Place transaxle in Neutral. Release parking brake. Raise rear wheels off ground. Disconnect drive shaft from differential assembly.
2) Slowly turn one wheel counterclockwise. Observe direction of rotation on opposite wheel. Wheels should turn in same direction. If wheels rotate in opposite direction, differential must be removed and viscous unit replaced.

WHEEL BEARING ROTATING RESISTANCE

Eclipse, Stealth & 3000GT – 1) Remove axle shaft from companion flange. See AXLE SHAFTS under REMOVAL & INSTALLATION. On vehicles with rear disc brake, remove caliper assembly. On vehicles with rear drum brake, remove drum. On all models, attach a spring scale to hub bolt. Pull scale at right angle to hub bolt, and measure wheel bearing rotating resistance.
2) Rotating resistance should be 2.6 lbs. (1.2 kg) or less. If rotating resistance is greater than specification, check torque of axle shaft companion flange nut. If torque is within specification, replace bearing. See TORQUE SPECIFICATIONS.

REMOVAL & INSTALLATION

AXLE SHAFTS

Removal – Raise and support vehicle. Remove rear wheels. On Eclipse, Stealth and 3000GT, remove axle shaft companion flange retaining bolts. Using screwdriver, pry axle shaft from differential assembly. Remove oil seal from differential assembly (if necessary). On Colt Vista, Expo and Summit Wagon, unbolt axle from companion flange. Remove spindle nut. Using 2-jaw puller, press axle through hub. Remove axle.

CAUTION: Always replace circlip on inboard side of axle shaft on Eclipse, Stealth and 3000GT.

Installation – Replace oil seal in differential as needed. Coat seal lip with grease. To complete installation, reverse removal procedure.

DIFFERENTIAL ASSEMBLY

Removal – 1) Drain gear oil from differential housing. Remove axle shafts. See AXLE SHAFTS under REMOVAL & INSTALLATION. Place reference mark on drive shaft flange and pinion flange on differential for installation reference. Remove drive shaft.
2) Support differential assembly. Remove rear support bolts from cover on rear of differential assembly. Remove front support bolt located above differential assembly. Remove differential support member and dynamic damper (if equipped). Remove rear wheel oil pump from differential assembly (if equipped). Remove differential assembly. Remove vent plug (if equipped).
Installation – To install, reverse removal procedure. Apply semi-drying sealant to mating surfaces of cover and vent plug (if equipped). Fill differential when finished. See CAPACITY and FLUID TYPE under LUBRICATION.

DRIVE SHAFT

Removal & Installation – Place reference marks on drive shaft flange and pinion flange for installation reference. Remove drive shaft. To install, reverse removal procedure. Coat front yoke with oil before installation. Ensure reference marks align.

OVERHAUL

DIFFERENTIAL ASSEMBLY

NOTE: For overhaul procedures of limited slip differential carrier assemblies, see DISASSEMBLY & INSPECTION (STEALTH & 3000GT).

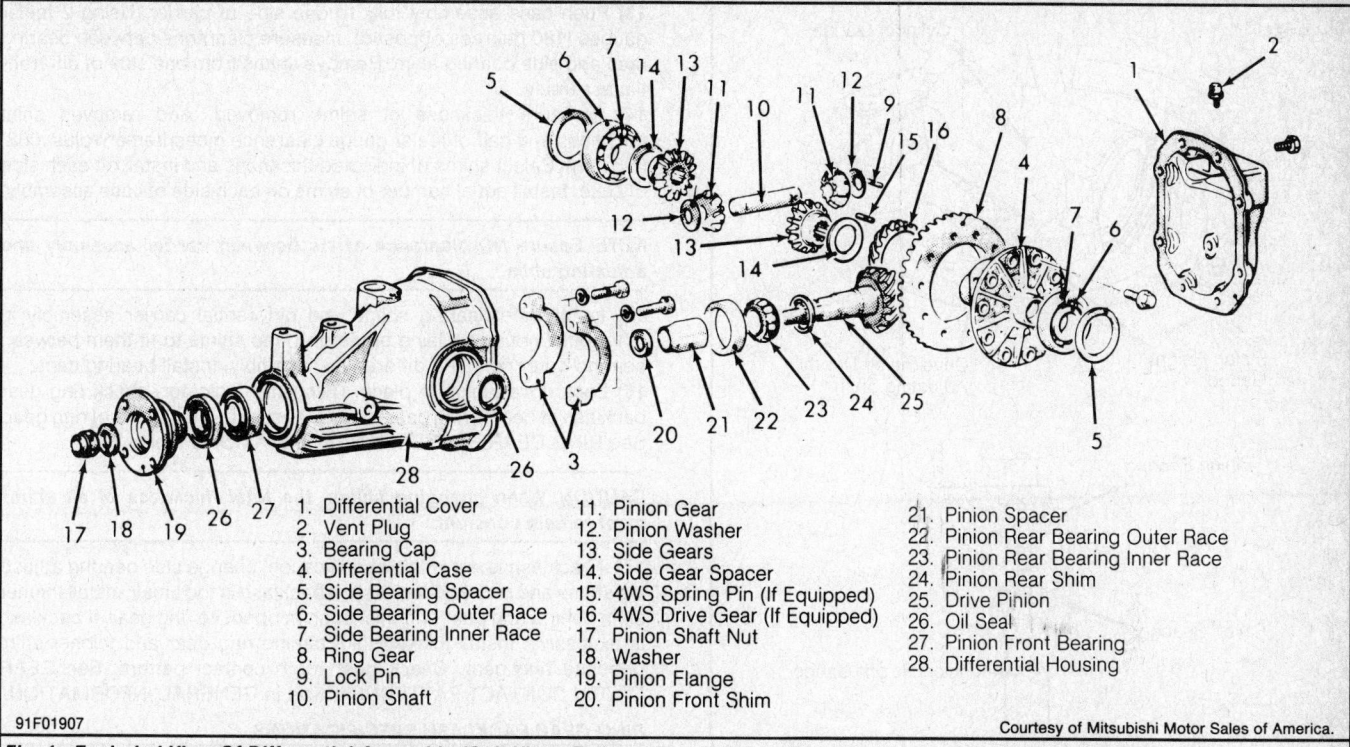

1. Differential Cover
2. Vent Plug
3. Bearing Cap
4. Differential Case
5. Side Bearing Spacer
6. Side Bearing Outer Race
7. Side Bearing Inner Race
8. Ring Gear
9. Lock Pin
10. Pinion Shaft
11. Pinion Gear
12. Pinion Washer
13. Side Gears
14. Side Gear Spacer
15. 4WS Spring Pin (If Equipped)
16. 4WS Drive Gear (If Equipped)
17. Pinion Shaft Nut
18. Washer
19. Pinion Flange
20. Pinion Front Shim
21. Pinion Spacer
22. Pinion Rear Bearing Outer Race
23. Pinion Rear Bearing Inner Race
24. Pinion Rear Shim
25. Drive Pinion
26. Oil Seal
27. Pinion Front Bearing
28. Differential Housing

91F01907

Courtesy of Mitsubishi Motor Sales of America.

Fig. 1: Exploded View Of Differential Assembly (Colt Vista, Eclipse, Expo & Summit Wagon Shown; Stealth & 3000GT Are Similar)

Disassembly & Inspection (Colt Vista, Eclipse, Expo & Summit Wagon) – 1) Remove differential assembly from vehicle. See DIFFERENTIAL ASSEMBLY under REMOVAL & INSTALLATION. Remove cover.

2) Mark bearing caps for location. Remove bearing caps. Remove differential carrier assembly from differential housing. DO NOT drop or damage side bearing outer races. Mark location of side bearing spacers and side bearings. See Fig. 1.

CAUTION: Mark location of side bearing spacers, bearing caps and side bearings. Components must be installed in original position.

3) Using bearing puller, remove differential carrier side bearings. Place alignment marks on ring gear and differential case. Loosen ring gear retaining bolts in diagonal sequence. Remove ring gear.

4) Drive out pinion shaft lock pin. Remove differential pinion shaft and pinion gears. Remove pinion side gears and thrust spacers. Mark components for reassembly reference. See Fig. 1.

5) Remove drive pinion companion flange retaining nut. Scribe alignment marks on drive pinion and companion flange for reassembly reference. Using soft-faced hammer, drive out pinion. Remove front adjusting shim and spacer from pinion.

6) Using bearing puller, remove rear bearing from drive pinion. Remove rear adjusting shim from pinion. Remove oil seal and bearing races from differential assembly. Check components for wear or damage; replace if necessary. Check bearings for discoloration or flaking. Check carrier for cracks.

Reassembly & Adjustment – 1) Install thrust spacers, pinion washers and pinion gears in differential carrier. Install pinion shaft without lock pin. Install wooden wedge to lock side gears. See Fig. 2. Using dial indicator, measure pinion and side gear backlash.

2) Backlash must be within specification. See PINION & SIDE GEAR BACKLASH SPECIFICATIONS table. Adjust backlash by using different side gear spacers. Ensure both sides are equally shimmed.

PINION & SIDE GEAR BACKLASH SPECIFICATIONS

Application	In. (mm)
Standard	.003 (.08)
Wear Limit	.008 (.20)

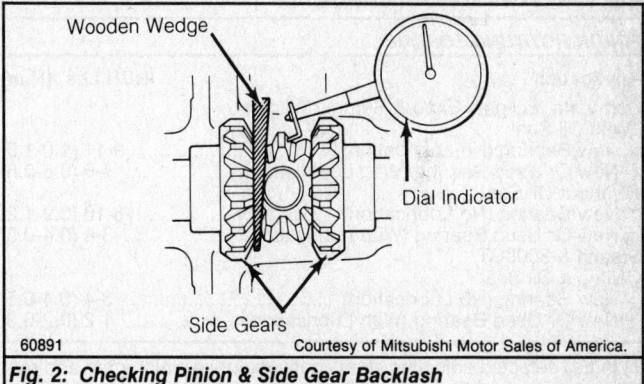

60891

Courtesy of Mitsubishi Motor Sales of America.

Fig. 2: Checking Pinion & Side Gear Backlash

3) Install front and rear pinion bearing outer races. Adjust pinion depth. Ensure races are fully seated.

NOTE: Pinion height gauges may vary. Follow gauge manufacturer instructions during assembly. Apply a light coat of grease to mating surface of washer located on front of pinion height gauge, near front pinion bearing.

4) Install pinion height gauge and pinion bearings using Pinion Height Gauge (MB990836). See Fig. 3. DO NOT install oil seal. Using torque wrench, measure pinion rotating torque.

5) Gradually tighten pinion height gauge to increase rotating torque to specification. See PINION ROTATING TORQUE table. Install Cylinder Gauge (MB990392) in side bearing seats.

6) Ensure flat areas align, and gauge contacts side bearing seat firmly. Select adjusting shim with same thickness as gap between cylinder gauge and pinion height gauge. Use minimum amount of adjusting shims. Install selected adjusting shims between drive pinion gear and rear pinion bearing. See Fig. 3. Using bearing installer, install rear pinion bearing.

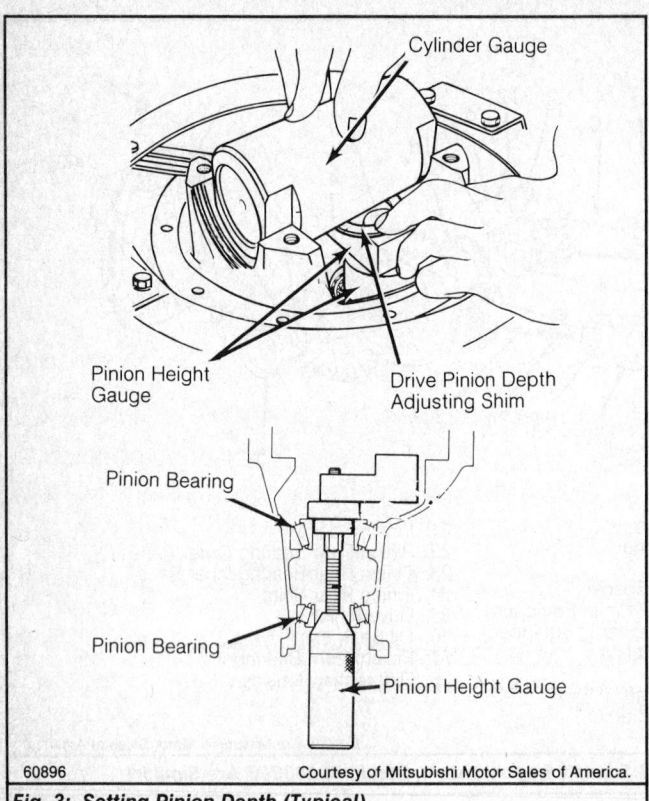

Fig. 3: Setting Pinion Depth (Typical)

PINION ROTATING TORQUE

Application	INCH Lbs. (N.m)
Colt Vista, Eclipse, Expo & Summit Wagon	
With Oil Seal	
New Bearing (No Lubrication)	9-11 (1.0-1.3)
New Or Used Bearing (With Lubrication)	4-5 (0.5-0.6)
Without Oil Seal	
New Bearing (No Lubrication)	8-10 (0.9-1.2)
New Or Used Bearing (With Lubrication)	3-4 (0.4-0.5)
Stealth & 3000GT	
Without Oil Seal	
New Bearing (No Lubrication)	3-4 (0.4-0.5)
New Or Used Bearing (With Lubrication)	1-2 (0.2-0.3)

7) Install selected adjusting shims between drive pinion gear and rear drive pinion bearing. See Fig. 1. Install rear pinion bearing. Install drive pinion in differential housing. Install spacer, pinion front shim and front pinion bearing. DO NOT install oil seal.

8) Install companion flange, washer and retaining nut. Tighten retaining nut to specification. See TORQUE SPECIFICATIONS. Check pinion rotating torque. See PINION ROTATING TORQUE table. Adjust rotating torque by replacing drive pinion front shims or spacer.

9) Once correct rotating torque is obtained, remove companion flange and install oil seal. Coat seal lip with grease. Install drive pinion assembly and companion flange so alignment marks are correct. Apply light coat of grease to companion flange washer contact area. Install new retaining nut and tighten to specification. See TORQUE SPECIFICATIONS.

10) Check pinion rotating torque. See PINION ROTATING TORQUE table. If preload is not within specification, remove oil seal and start preload procedure again.

11) Install pinion shaft lock pin from back side of ring gear. Securely stake pin in 2 places. Install ring gear on differential case. Align marks on differential case and ring gear. Apply Loctite 271 to bolts. Install bolts and alternately tighten to specification in diagonal sequence. See TORQUE SPECIFICATIONS.

12) Press side bearing onto differential case. Install differential carrier into differential housing. Select 2 side bearing adjusting shims thinner than those removed. Shims thickness on both sides must be equal. Install shims on each side of case assembly.

13) Push case assembly fully to one side of carrier. Using 2 feeler gauges (180 degrees opposed), measure clearance between bearing race and side bearing shim. Remove shims from one side of differential assembly.

14) Measure thickness of shims removed. Add removed shim thickness and half of feeler gauge clearance measurement plus .002" (.05 mm). Select shims of indicated thickness and install on each side of case. Install equal number of shims on each side of case assembly.

NOTE: Ensure NO clearance exists between carrier assembly and adjusting shim.

15) Install side bearing shims and differential carrier assembly in differential housing. Using brass drift, tap shims to fit them between bearing outer race and differential assembly. Install bearing caps.

16) Lock drive pinion in place. Using dial indicator, check ring gear backlash at heel of ring gear tooth. Measure at 4 locations of ring gear. See RING GEAR BACKLASH SPECIFICATIONS table.

CAUTION: When changing shims, the total thickness of all shims must remain constant.

17) If backlash is not within specification, change side bearing adjusting shims and recheck backlash. If backlash is too small, install thinner shim behind ring gear and thicker shim opposite ring gear. If backlash is excessive, install thicker shim behind ring gear and thinner shim opposite ring gear. Check gear tooth contact pattern. See GEAR TOOTH CONTACT PATTERNS article in GENERAL INFORMATION.

RING GEAR BACKLASH SPECIFICATIONS

Application	In. (mm)
All Models	.004-.006 (.10-.15)

Ring Gear Runout – Using dial indicator, measure runout at back side of ring gear. Runout must be within .002" (.05 mm). If runout is excessive, change ring gear-to-differential case mounting position. Recheck runout.

Disassembly & Inspection (Stealth & 3000GT) – 1) Remove side bearing snap rings. Using Side Bearing Nut Remover (MB991367) with Adapter (MB991385), remove side bearing lock nut. Use a press to remove side bearing outer races. Remove differential carrier assembly from differential housing.

2) Remove spring pin and 4-Wheel Steering (4WS) drive gear. Place alignment marks on ring gear and differential case. Loosen ring gear retaining bolts in diagonal sequence. Remove ring gear.

NOTE: For drive pinion disassembly and reassembly procedures, see DISASSEMBLY & INSPECTION (COLT VISTA, ECLIPSE, EXPO & SUMMIT WAGON) under OVERHAUL.

3) Remove screws and differential case cover. See Fig. 4. Mark left thrust washer and remove. Remove viscous unit. Remove pinion mate washers and pinion mates. Remove differential pinion shaft. Remove right side gear and thrust washer. Check components for unusual wear, heat damage or other damage. Replace if necessary.

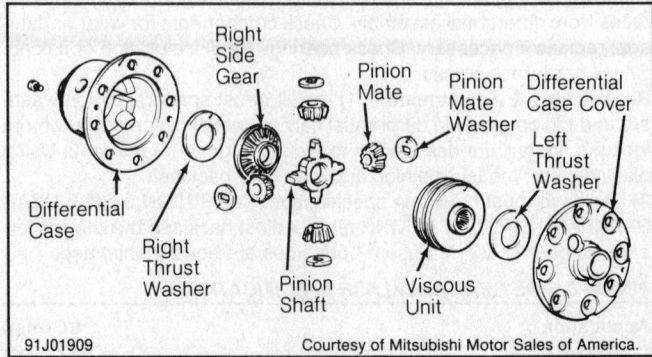

Fig. 4: Exploded View Of Limited Slip Differential

NOTE: Thrust washers are of different thickness. Ensure thrust washers are installed in original position during reassembly.

Reassembly – 1) Ensure all LSD carrier assembly components are in good condition. If differential side gear and/or pinion mate gear need replacement, they must be replaced as matched set including viscous unit. Thoroughly clean all components in unleaded gasoline to remove oil and grease.

2) Reassemble differential unit, and temporarily secure cover with screws. Clamp differential case in a vise. Insert 2 feeler gauges of .0012" (.03 mm) thickness at opposite positions in differential case between case and right thrust washer. *See Fig. 5.*

CAUTION: DO NOT insert feeler gauge in oil groove of differential case.

3) Insert Side Gear Holder (MB991294) into spline part of differential side gear, and ensure side gear rotates. *See Fig. 5.* Replace .0012" (.03 mm) feeler gauges with .0035" (.09 mm) feeler gauges. Check if side gear rotates. If side gear no longer rotates, backlash of differential gear is normal. If side gear rotates, install a different size left thrust washer and retest.

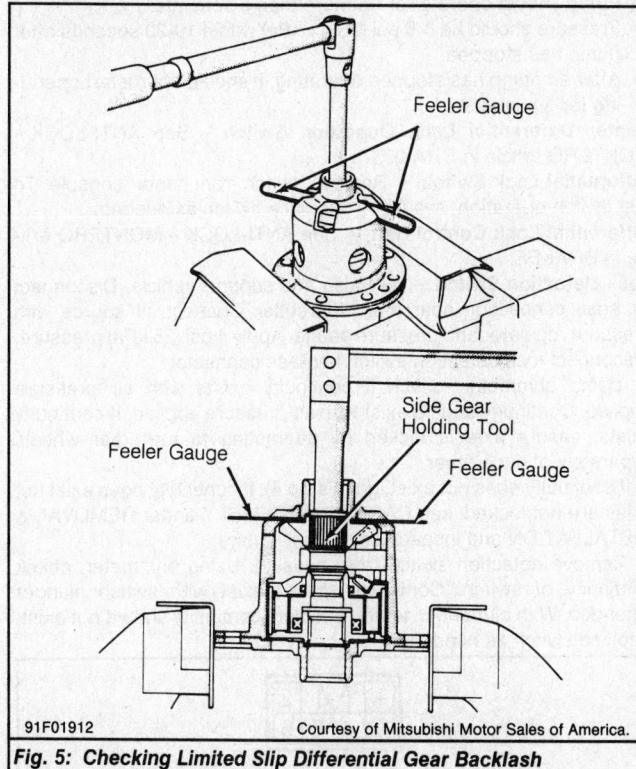

91F01912   Courtesy of Mitsubishi Motor Sales of America.

Fig. 5: Checking Limited Slip Differential Gear Backlash

4) Tighten differential case halve screws. Mount ring gear to carrier assembly. Ensure reference mark is aligned. Tighten bolts in crisscross sequence. Install spring pin and 4-Wheel Steering (4WS) drive gear (if applicable). Press on carrier assembly side bearings. Install carrier assembly in housing.

5) Install side bearing outer races and bearing nuts. Tighten side bearing lock nut until nut just contacts race. Bearing races should be seated against bearing with zero preload.

6) Lock drive pinion in place. Using dial indicator, check ring gear backlash at heel of ring gear tooth. Measure at 4 locations of ring gear. See RING GEAR BACKLASH SPECIFICATIONS table.

7) If backlash is not within specification, change side bearing lock nut preload by loosening one bearing lock nut while tightening the opposite lock nut an equal amount until backlash is correct.

8) To adjust carrier side bearing preload, tighten both lock nuts half the distance between adjacent lock nut holes using side bearing nut remover. Install snap rings. Check gear tooth contact pattern. See GEAR TOOTH CONTACT PATTERNS article in GENERAL INFORMATION.

TORQUE SPECIFICATIONS

TORQUE SPECIFICATIONS (COLT VISTA, EXPO & SUMMIT WAGON)

Application	Ft. Lbs. (N.m)
Axle Shaft Installation Nut	145-188 (200-255)
Bearing Cap Bolt	25-29 (34-39)
Cover Bolt	26 (35)
Differential Assembly-To-Crossmember Bolt	72-87 (98-118)
Drain Plug	43-50 (58-68)
Drive Shaft-To-Axle Shaft Companion Flange Bolt	40-47 (54-64)
Filler Plug	36 (49)
Pinion Flange Nut	137 (186)
Propeller Shaft-To-Pinion Flange Bolt	43-65 (58-88)
Ring Gear Bolt	58-65 (79-88)

	INCH Lbs. (N.m)
Speed Sensor Bolt (If Equipped)	108 (12)

TORQUE SPECIFICATIONS (ECLIPSE)

Application	Ft. Lbs. (N.m)
Axle Shaft Installation Nut	116-159 (157-216)
Bearing Cap Bolt	29-43 (39-58)
Brake Assembly Installation Bolt	36-43 (49-58)
Cover Bolt	22-30 (30-41)
Differential Assembly-To-Crossmember Bolt	72-87 (98-118)
Differential Assembly-To-Drive Shaft Bolt	22-25 (30-34)
Differential Assembly-To-Dynamic Damper Bolt	58-72 (79-98)
Drain Plug	43-50 (58-68)
Drive Shaft-To-Axle Shaft Companion Flange Bolt	40-47 (54-64)
Filler Plug	29-43 (39-58)
Pinion Flange Nut	116-159 (157-216)
Ring Gear Bolt	58-65 (79-88)

	INCH Lbs. (N.m)
Speed Sensor Bolt (If Equipped)	84-120 (9-14)

TORQUE SPECIFICATIONS (STEALTH & 3000GT)

Application	Ft. Lbs. (N.m)
Axle Shaft Installation Nut	
Non-Turbo	137 (186)
Turbo	188-217 (255-294)
Brake Assembly Installation Bolt	36-43 (49-58)
Cover Bolt	26 (35)
Differential Assembly Support Bolt	65 (88)
Differential Assembly-To-Drive Shaft Bolt	22-25 (30-34)
Differential Crossmember-To-Frame Bolt	65 (88)
Drain Plug	43-50 (58-68)
Drive Shaft-To-Axle Shaft Companion Flange Bolt	40-47 (54-64)
Filler Plug	36 (49)
Pinion Flange Nut	137 (186)
Rear Oil Pump Bolt	17 (23)
Ring Gear Bolt	58-65 (79-88)

	INCH Lbs. (N.m)
Speed Sensor Bolt (If Equipped)	108 (12)

1994 DRIVE AXLES
Differentials & Axle Shafts – Rear Non-Integral

Mitsubishi: Montero, Pickup

DESCRIPTION

Rear axle features a rigid banjo-type housing with semi-floating axle shafts. Differential consists of hypoid reduction gears and straight bevel differential gears. Limited Slip Differential (LSD) is available on Montero RS (w/o ABS) and Pickup 4WD. Locking rear differential is available on Montero SR model.

AXLE RATIO & IDENTIFICATION

Ratio is determined by dividing number of ring gear teeth by number of drive pinion teeth.

AXLE RATIO SPECIFICATIONS

Application	Ratio
Montero	
LT31X10.50R15 Tire	4.88:1
P235/75R15 Tire	4.63:1
Pickup	
2WD	3.91:1
4WD	4.22:1

LUBRICATION

CAPACITY

REAR AXLE GEAR OIL CAPACITY

Application	Pts. (L)
Montero	
Conventional & Locking	5.5 (2.6)
Limited Slip	6.8 (3.2)
Pickup	
Conventional	
2WD	3.2 (1.5)
4WD	5.5 (2.6)
Limited Slip Differential	5.5 (2.6)

FLUID TYPE

Conventional differentials use SAE 80W or SAE 90W API GL-5. Limited slip differentials use Mitsubishi Gear Oil (8149630 EX), or Mopar Gear Oil (4318058) and Mopar Friction Modifier (4318060).

TROUBLE SHOOTING

See TROUBLE SHOOTING article in GENERAL INFORMATION.

TESTING & INSPECTION

AXLE SHAFT END PLAY

Pickup – Using dial indicator, check axle shaft end play. End play should be .002-.008" (.05-.20 mm). If end play is not within specification, change shims to obtain correct end play. See AXLE SHAFT under REMOVAL & INSTALLATION.

Montero – Using dial indicator, check axle shaft end play. End play should be .010" (.25 mm). If end play is not within specification, replace axle bearing. See AXLE SHAFT under OVERHAUL.

AXLE TOTAL BACKLASH

1) Raise and support rear axle. Place transmission in Neutral. Apply parking brake. Rotate drive shaft clockwise. Place reference marks on pinion dust cover and differential housing.
2) Rotate drive shaft counterclockwise, and measure distance between reference marks. Differential must be removed and backlash adjusted if distance exceeds 0.2" (5 mm). See RING GEAR BACKLASH procedure under DIFFERENTIAL ASSEMBLY (LIMITIED SLIP) under OVERHAUL.

LIMITED SLIP DIFFERENTIAL PRELOAD

1) Place transmission in Neutral. Block front wheels. Raise one rear wheel off ground and remove wheel. Release parking brake.

2) Using torque wrench and axle puller adapter, measure starting torque while rotating wheel in forward direction. See Fig. 1. Differential must be repaired if torque is less than 18 ft. lbs. (25 N.m).

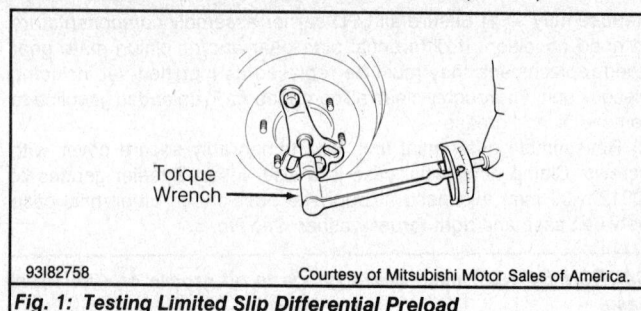

93182758   Courtesy of Mitsubishi Motor Sales of America.

Fig. 1: Testing Limited Slip Differential Preload

LOCKING DIFFERENTIAL

Air Pump – Connect air pressure gauge in-line to air hose from air pump. Air pump is located in right storage area, under rear seat. Connect battery voltage to air pump (positive lead to Red wire). The air pump is operating correctly when the following sequences occur;
- Pump should operate for no more than 5 seconds.
- Pressure should be 4-6 psi (28-41 kPa) within 10-20 seconds after pump has stopped.
- After air pump has stopped operating, it should not restart operating for 5 minutes.

Center Differential Lock Operation Switch – See ANTI-LOCK – MONTERO article in BRAKES.

Differential Lock Switch – Remove switch from center console. To test switch operation, see Fig. 2. Replace switch as needed.

Differential Lock Control Unit – See ANTI-LOCK – MONTERO article in BRAKES.

Lock Detection Switch – 1) Raise and support vehicle. Disconnect air hose connection near rear differential. Connect air source with pressure regulator and pressure gauge. Apply 4 psi (25 kPa) pressure. Disconnect lock detection switch harness connector.
2) Using ohmmeter, check if continuity exists with air pressure applied. Continuity should exist with air pressure applied. If continuity exists, ensure axle is locked by attempting to turn rear wheels separately of each other.
3) If continuity does not exist, go to step 4). If continuity does exist but axles are not locked, see CARRIER ASSEMBLY under REMOVAL & INSTALLATION and inspect locking assembly.
4) Remove detection switch from housing. Using ohmmeter, check continuity of switch. Continuity should exist with switch plunger extended. With plunger in neutral position, continuity should not exist. Replace switch as needed.

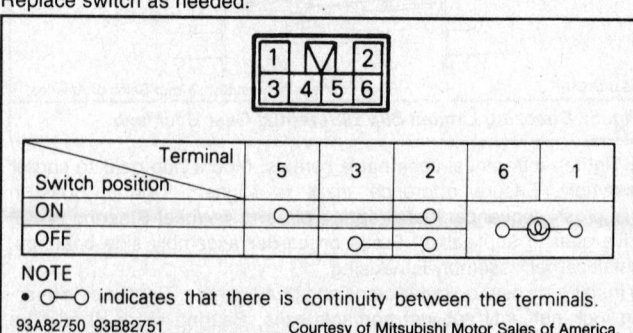

			Terminal				
Switch position			5	3	2	6	1
ON			○———————○				
OFF				○———————○		○—○—○	

NOTE
- ○—○ indicates that there is continuity between the terminals.

93A82750 93B82751   Courtesy of Mitsubishi Motor Sales of America.

Fig. 2: Checking Differential Lock Switch Continuity

REMOVAL & INSTALLATION

AXLE SHAFT

Removal (Montero) – Block front wheels. Raise and support rear axle housing. Remove brake caliper and rotor. See Fig. 3. Remove parking brake cable attaching bolts. Remove connection for parking brake cable end from rear brake assembly. Remove ABS speed sensor (if equipped). Unbolt backing plate with bearing housing from rear axle housing. Using Puller (MB990241) and Slide Hammer (MB990211), remove axle assembly. DO NOT damage oil seal. Remove "O" ring. Replace if necessary.

Installation – Install new oil seal in axle housing as needed. To install axle assembly, reverse removal procedure.

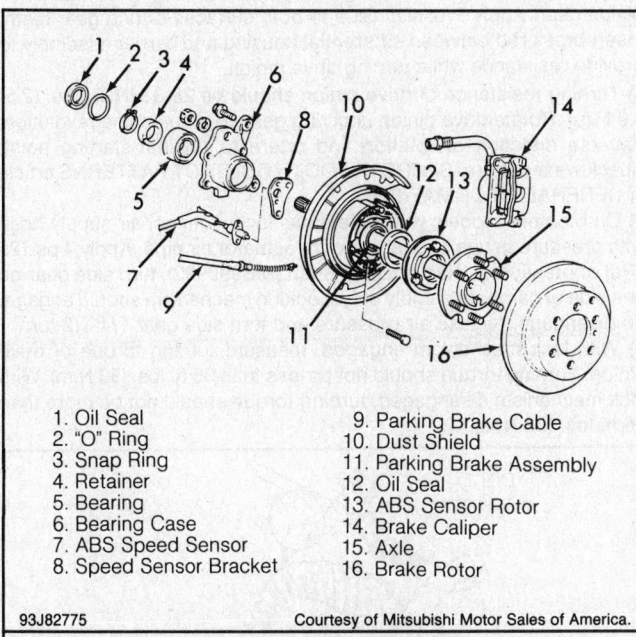

1. Oil Seal	9. Parking Brake Cable
2. "O" Ring	10. Dust Shield
3. Snap Ring	11. Parking Brake Assembly
4. Retainer	12. Oil Seal
5. Bearing	13. ABS Sensor Rotor
6. Bearing Case	14. Brake Caliper
7. ABS Speed Sensor	15. Axle
8. Speed Sensor Bracket	16. Brake Rotor

93J82775   Courtesy of Mitsubishi Motor Sales of America.

Fig. 3: Exploded View Of Axle Shaft (Montero)

Removal (Pickup) – **1)** Block front wheels. Raise and support rear axle housing. Remove brake drum. *See Fig. 4*. Remove parking brake cable attaching bolts. Remove connection for parking brake cable end from rear brake assembly. Drain brake fluid from bleeder screw at left side of rear brake, and disconnect brake tubes.

2) Remove flange nuts and rear axle shaft assembly. Use Puller (MB990241) and Slide Hammer (MB990211) if necessary. DO NOT damage oil seal. Remove shim(s) and "O" ring. Replace if necessary.

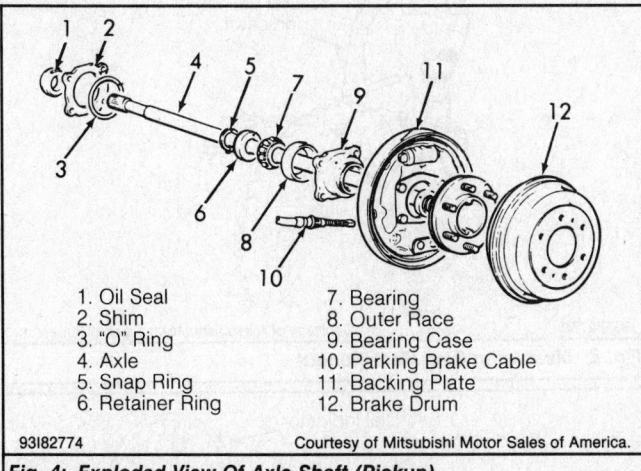

1. Oil Seal	7. Bearing
2. Shim	8. Outer Race
3. "O" Ring	9. Bearing Case
4. Axle	10. Parking Brake Cable
5. Snap Ring	11. Backing Plate
6. Retainer Ring	12. Brake Drum

93J82774   Courtesy of Mitsubishi Motor Sales of America.

Fig. 4: Exploded View Of Axle Shaft (Pickup)

Installation – **1)** Insert new "O" ring and shim of .04" (1.0 mm) thickness into left side axle housing. Install left axle shaft assembly into axle housing, and tighten nuts to specification. See TORQUE SPECIFICATIONS.

2) Install right axle shaft assembly into axle housing without shim or "O" ring. Temporarily tighten nuts in diagonal sequence to 51.6 INCH lbs. (5.8 N.m) in 2 stages. Measure clearance between bearing case of right axle and rear axle housing end with feeler gauge.

3) Select shims equal to sum of measured clearance plus .002-.008" (.05-.20 mm). Remove right axle shaft, and install selected shim(s) and "O" ring into right axle housing end. Install right axle shaft assembly into rear axle housing. Tighten nuts in diagonal sequence to specification. See TORQUE SPECIFICATIONS.

4) Using dial indicator, check end play of axle shaft. End play should be .002-.008" (.05-.20 mm). If end play is not within specification, change shim(s) to obtain correct end play. Reverse removal procedure to install remaining components. Adjust parking brake, and bleed brake system.

CARRIER ASSEMBLY

Removal – Raise and support vehicle. Drain gear oil. Mark drive shaft flange-to-pinion flange position. Remove drive shaft. Remove axle shafts. See AXLE SHAFT under REMOVAL & INSTALLATION. Support differential carrier with jack. Remove differential carrier retaining nuts. Remove differential carrier.

Inspection – Check for leaks at vent plug, differential carrier companion flange and where carrier joins axle housing.

Installation – Apply sealant to axle housing surface. To install, reverse removal procedure. Align marks on drive shaft and pinion flange.

DRIVE SHAFT

Removal – Make match marks on drive shaft yoke flange and pinion flange. Remove bolts and drive shaft from vehicle.

Installation – To install, reverse removal procedure. Ensure match marks are aligned. Tighten bolts to specification. See TORQUE SPECIFICATIONS.

OVERHAUL

AXLE SHAFT

Removal – **1)** Secure axle shaft assembly in a vise, and remove one retainer bolt from backing plate. Push bearing case completely to side of dust cover. Place adhesive tape around edge of bearing case at retainer bolt hole to prevent damage.

CAUTION: DO NOT damage bearing case or axle shaft when grinding or chiseling retainer ring.

---

2) Secure axle shaft, and grind retainer ring until retainer ring wall thickness is .04-.06" (1.0-1.5 mm) on axle shaft side and .08" (2.0 mm) on bearing side. *See Fig. 5*.

3) Change angle of grind, and remove remaining .08" (2.0 mm) of retainer ring wall on bearing side. *See Fig. 5*. Using a chisel, cut retainer ring. Remove ring. DO NOT damage axle shaft.

4) Install Puller (MB990787-01) to remove bearing case from axle shaft. *See Fig. 6*. Rotate nuts with equal force to remove wheel bearing. Remove bearing outer race using a hammer and drift. Remove oil seal from axle housing using a slide hammer and hook.

Inspection – Inspect bearings for roughness, pitting or damage. Inspect axle shaft for damaged splines or flange. Inspect bearing case for cracks or damage.

Installation – **1)** Apply Multipurpose Grease (SAE J310) to oil seal, oil seal cavity and contact surfaces. Install oil seal using seal driver. Press new oil seal into bearing case until it is flush with face of bearing case. Install backing plate and bearing case.

2) Apply grease to external surfaces of bearing outer race. Press bearing outer race into bearing case. Install bearing on axle shaft. Install rear brake assembly with bearing case onto axle. On Montero, install inner bearing on axle. On all models, install new retainer ring. Do not exceed 22,046 lbs. (100,00 N) on Montero, 17,637 lbs. (80,000 N) on Pickup when pressing on retainer ring. Install new snap ring.

3) Using a feeler gauge, measure clearance between snap ring and new retainer ring. Clearance should be less than .007" (.17 mm). If clearance exceeds specification, install correct snap ring. See SNAP RING THICKNESS SPECIFICATION table.

CHRYSLER/MITSU.
7-18

1994 DRIVE AXLES
Differentials & Axle Shafts – Rear Non-Integral (Cont.)

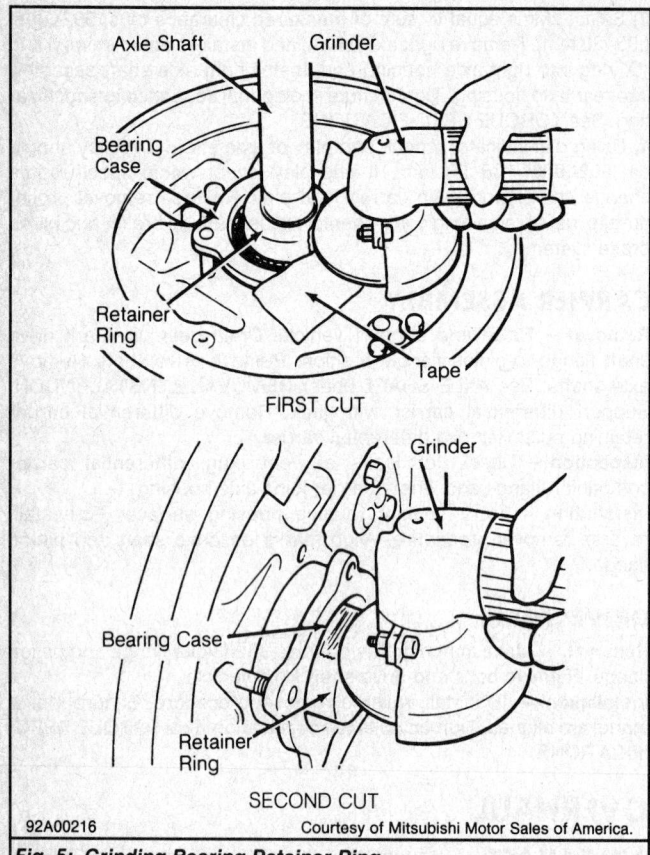

Fig. 5: Grinding Bearing Retainer Ring

92A00216   Courtesy of Mitsubishi Motor Sales of America.

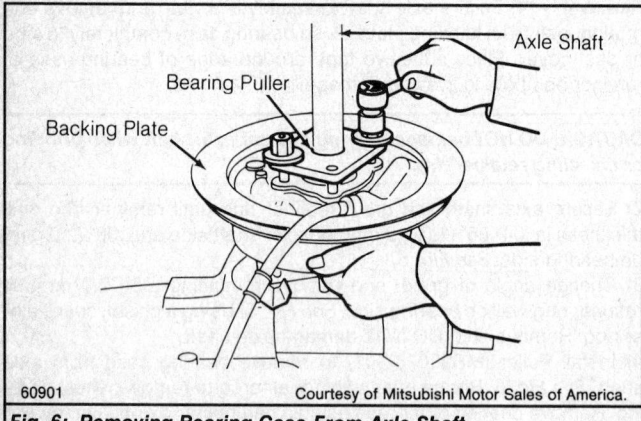

60901   Courtesy of Mitsubishi Motor Sales of America.

Fig. 6: Removing Bearing Case From Axle Shaft

SNAP RING THICKNESS SPECIFICATION

Thickness In. (mm)	Color
.060 (1.52)	Red
.067 (1.70)	Purple
.073 (1.85)	Blue
.079 (2.01)	Yellow
.085 (2.16)	Neutral

DIFFERENTIAL ASSEMBLY (CONVENTIONAL)

Pre-Disassembly Inspection – 1) Secure differential assembly in appropriate holder. Secure drive pinion from turning. Mount dial indicator on case and check ring gear backlash at 4 positions. *See Fig. 7.* Backlash should be .004-.006" (.10-.16 mm) on Pickup 2WD models, .005-.007" (.13-.18 mm) on Montero and Pickup 4WD models.

2) Remount dial indicator and measure ring gear runout. *See Fig. 8.* On all models, runout should not exceed .002" (.05 mm). Remount dial indicator and measure pinion gear backlash on models without limited slip differential. *See Fig. 9.* Secure side gear from turning with wedge. Backlash should be .0004-.0030" (.010-.080 mm) on Pickup 2WD models, 0-.003" (0-.08 mm) on Montero and Pickup 4WD models. On all models, pinion gear backlash service limit is .008" (.20 mm).

3) Check gear tooth contact pattern between ring gear and drive pinion gear. Apply Prussian Blue to both surfaces of ring gear teeth. Insert brass rod between differential housing and carrier assembly to provide resistance while turning drive pinion.

4) Turning resistance of drive pinion should be 28-33 INCH lbs. (2.5-3.0 N.m). Rotate drive pinion until ring gear completes one revolution. Reverse direction of rotation and return to original starting point. Check wear pattern. See GEAR TOOTH CONTACT PATTERNS article in GENERAL INFORMATION.

5) On Montero models with differential lock, connect air supply hose with pressure gauge and regulator to actuator air pipe. Apply 4 psi (25 kPa) of pressure. Using Adapter Shaft (MB990992), turn side gear on one side of carrier assembly only. Locking mechanism should engage. To disengage, release air pressure and turn side gear 1/4-1/2 turn.

6) With lock mechanism engaged, measure turning torque of drive pinion. Turning torque should not be less than 36 ft. lbs. (50 N.m). With lock mechanism disengaged, turning torque should not be more than 36 ft. lbs. (50 N.m).

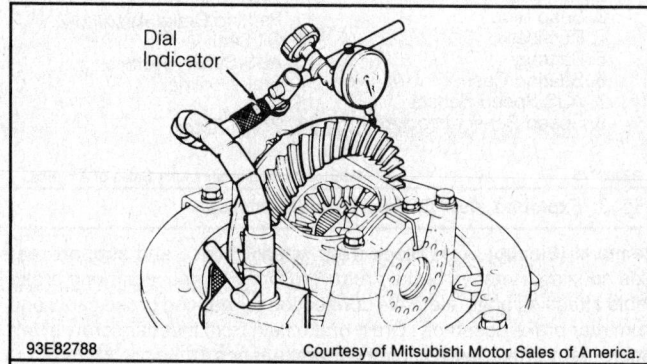

93E82788   Courtesy of Mitsubishi Motor Sales of America.

Fig. 7: Measuring Ring Gear Backlash

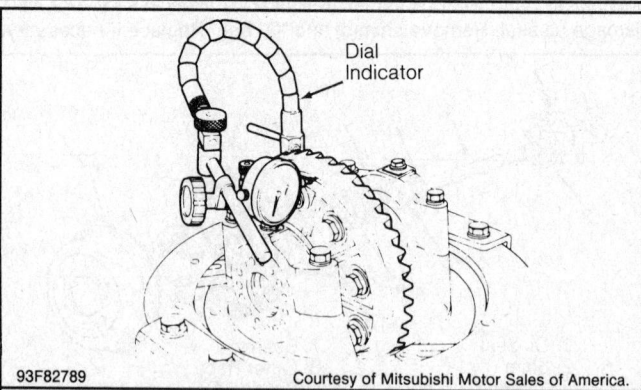

93F82789   Courtesy of Mitsubishi Motor Sales of America.

Fig. 8: Measuring Ring Gear Runout

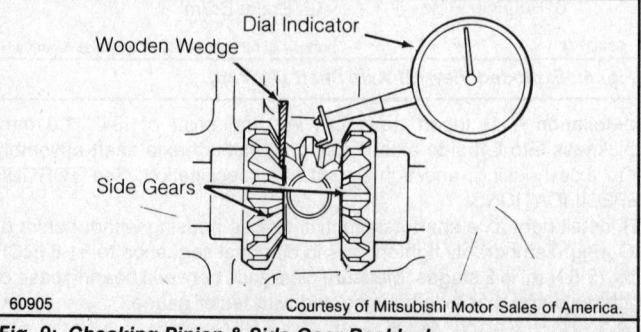

60905   Courtesy of Mitsubishi Motor Sales of America.

Fig. 9: Checking Pinion & Side Gear Backlash

1994 DRIVE AXLES
Differentials & Axle Shafts – Rear Non-Integral (Cont.)

CHRYSLER/MITSU.
7-19

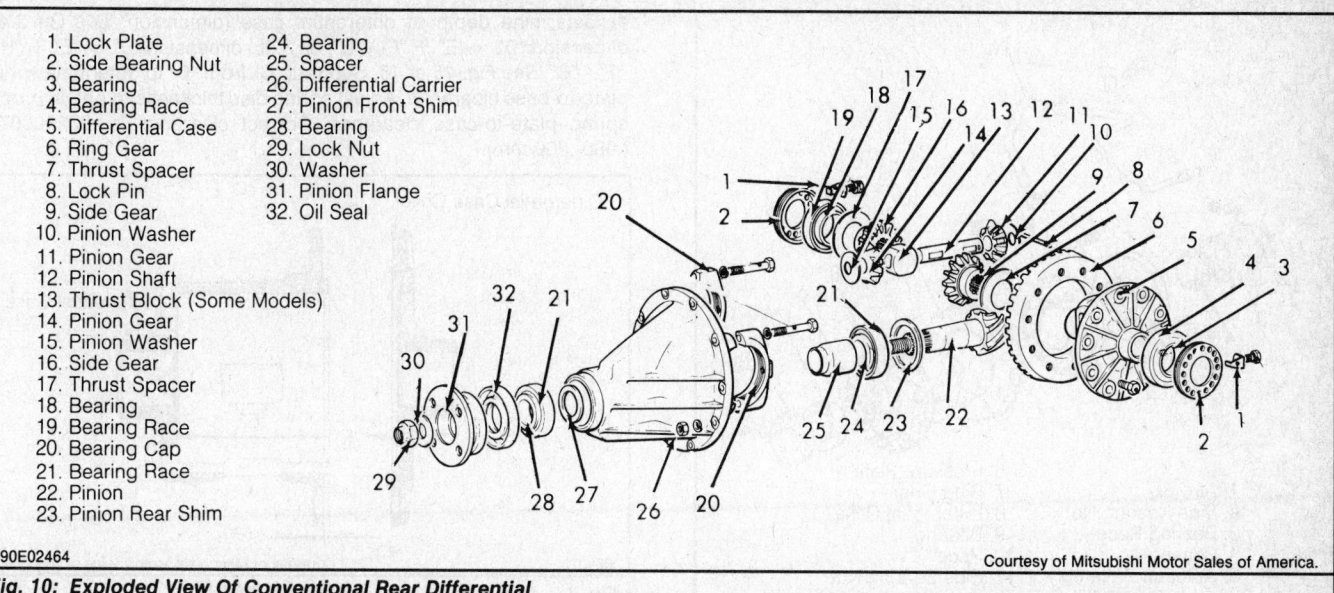

1. Lock Plate
2. Side Bearing Nut
3. Bearing
4. Bearing Race
5. Differential Case
6. Ring Gear
7. Thrust Spacer
8. Lock Pin
9. Side Gear
10. Pinion Washer
11. Pinion Gear
12. Pinion Shaft
13. Thrust Block (Some Models)
14. Pinion Gear
15. Pinion Washer
16. Side Gear
17. Thrust Spacer
18. Bearing
19. Bearing Race
20. Bearing Cap
21. Bearing Race
22. Pinion
23. Pinion Rear Shim
24. Bearing
25. Spacer
26. Differential Carrier
27. Pinion Front Shim
28. Bearing
29. Lock Nut
30. Washer
31. Pinion Flange
32. Oil Seal

90E02464

Courtesy of Mitsubishi Motor Sales of America.

Fig. 10: Exploded View Of Conventional Rear Differential

NOTE: See DIFFERENTIAL ASSEMBLY (LIMITED SLIP) for carrier assembly and drive pinion installation.

Carrier Assembly & Drive Pinion Removal – 1) Remove differential carrier from axle housing. Remove lock plates. Mark location of side bearing nuts for reassembly. Remove side bearing nuts. *See Fig. 10.* Mark location of bearing caps for reassembly. Remove bearing caps. Remove differential carrier assembly from differential housing.
2) Secure drive pinion companion flange from turning. Remove companion flange retaining nut. Scribe alignment marks on drive pinion and companion flange for reassembly. Using soft-faced hammer, drive pinion out of housing. Remove front adjusting shim and spacer from pinion.
3) Using bearing splitter and press, remove rear bearing from pinion. Remove rear adjusting shim from drive pinion. Remove oil seal and bearing races from differential housing.
Disassembly (Carrier Assembly) – 1) Using bearing splitter and press, remove differential case side bearings. Place alignment marks on ring gear and differential case for reassembly. Loosen ring gear bolts in diagonal sequence. Remove ring gear.
2) Remove pinion shaft lock pin from differential carrier. Remove differential pinion shaft and thrust block (if equipped). Remove pinion gears and washers. Remove side gears and thrust spacers. Mark components for reassembly reference.
Inspection – Wash parts in clean solvent and dry with compressed air. Inspect bearings for discoloration and/or flaking. Check all gears for irregular wear or damage. Ring gear and drive pinion must be replaced as matched set. Side gears and pinion gears must be replaced as matched set.
Reassembly & Adjustment – 1) Install thrust spacers, side gears, pinion washers and pinion gears in differential case. DO NOT install thrust block (if equipped) at this time.
2) Install pinion shaft without lock pin. Check pinion and side gear backlash. Install wooden wedge to lock side gears. *See Fig. 9.* Using dial indicator, measure gear backlash. Backlash should be .0004-.0030" (.010-.080 mm). Service limit is .008" (.20 mm).
3) Adjust backlash by using different side gear spacers. Ensure both sides are equally shimmed. Install thrust block (if equipped) once correct backlash is obtained. Install pinion shaft lock pin from ring gear side of carrier housing. Securely stake pin in 2 places. Ensure adhesive is removed from ring gear mounting bolts and gear mounting surface. Clean internal threads with tap.
4) Ensure alignment marks on differential case and ring gear align. Apply Loctite 271 to bolts, and install ring gear on differential case. Tighten bolts in diagonal sequence to specification. See TORQUE SPECIFICATIONS. Using appropriate adapter, press on carrier side bearings.

DIFFERENTIAL ASSEMBLY (LIMITED SLIP)

NOTE: Manufacturer does not provide disassembly or reassembly procedures for locking type differential. See Figs. 12 and 13 for exploded views of assembly.

NOTE: See PRE-DISASSEMBLY INSPECTION under DIFFERENTIAL ASSEMBLY (CONVENTIONAL) before disassembling carrier assembly. For carrier assembly and drive pinion removal, see DIFFERENTIAL ASSEMBLY (CONVENTIONAL).

Disassembly – 1) Once ring gear is removed, loosen carrier housing screws in diagonal pattern. Separate cases and remove components. *See Fig. 11.* Maintain parts in order of disassembly. Clean all parts in new solvent.
2) Inspect condition of friction and spring plates and friction discs. Replace disc and/or plates if worn or heat damaged. Distortion of discs will cause incorrect clutch pressure. Scratches, nicks or burrs on components can be repaired with an oil stone.
3) Discs must be flat and free of distortion. Check discs on surface plate with dial indicator. Maximum warpage of friction plate or disc is .003" (.08 mm). Inspect thickness of discs and plates. Thickness limit between discs and plates is .004" (.10 mm).

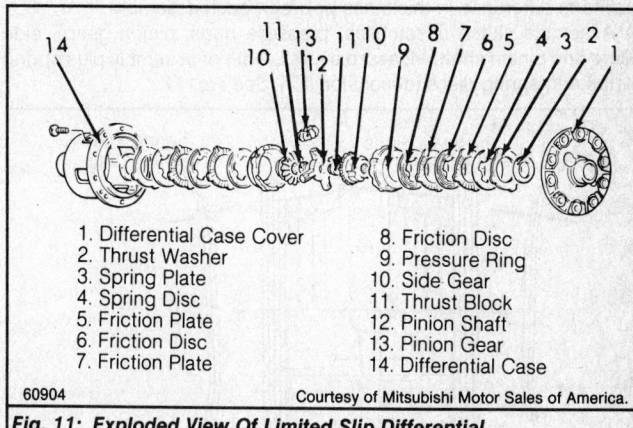

1. Differential Case Cover
2. Thrust Washer
3. Spring Plate
4. Spring Disc
5. Friction Plate
6. Friction Disc
7. Friction Plate
8. Friction Disc
9. Pressure Ring
10. Side Gear
11. Thrust Block
12. Pinion Shaft
13. Pinion Gear
14. Differential Case

60904

Courtesy of Mitsubishi Motor Sales of America.

Fig. 11: Exploded View Of Limited Slip Differential

Reassembly – 1) Arrange friction plates and discs of each side of differential. Measure each assembly thickness. Assembled discs and plates should not exceed a difference of .002" (.05 mm). Replace discs or plates as needed.

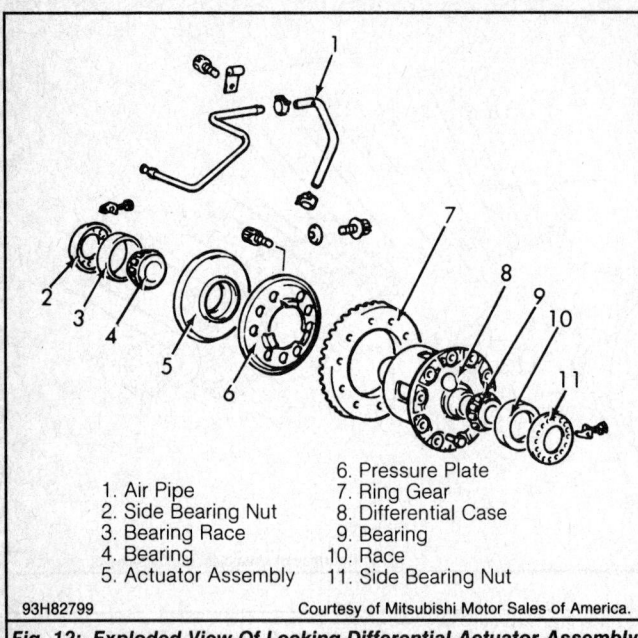

1. Air Pipe
2. Side Bearing Nut
3. Bearing Race
4. Bearing
5. Actuator Assembly
6. Pressure Plate
7. Ring Gear
8. Differential Case
9. Bearing
10. Race
11. Side Bearing Nut

93H82799　　Courtesy of Mitsubishi Motor Sales of America.

Fig. 12: Exploded View Of Locking Differential Actuator Assembly

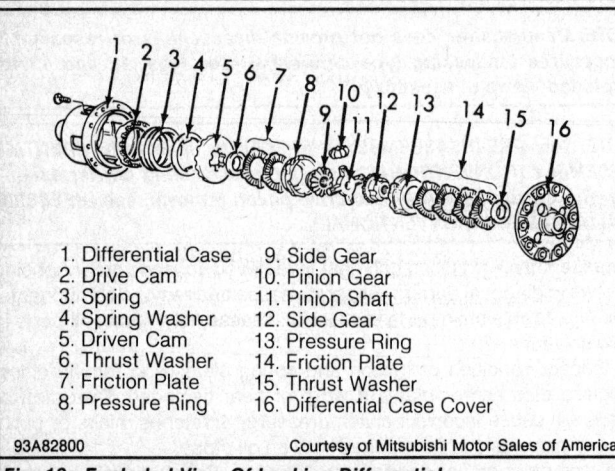

1. Differential Case
2. Drive Cam
3. Spring
4. Spring Washer
5. Driven Cam
6. Thrust Washer
7. Friction Plate
8. Pressure Ring
9. Side Gear
10. Pinion Gear
11. Pinion Shaft
12. Side Gear
13. Pressure Ring
14. Friction Plate
15. Thrust Washer
16. Differential Case Cover

93A82800　　Courtesy of Mitsubishi Motor Sales of America.

Fig. 13: Exploded View Of Locking Differential

2) Assemble one spring plate and one spring disc on each side. Measure assembly thickness. Assemble disc and plates to obtain minimum difference in thickness between each assembly.

3) Assemble clutch assemblies, pressure rings, pinion gears, side gears and pinion shaft. Measure overall width of assembly plus spring plates and spring discs (dimension "C"). See Fig. 14.

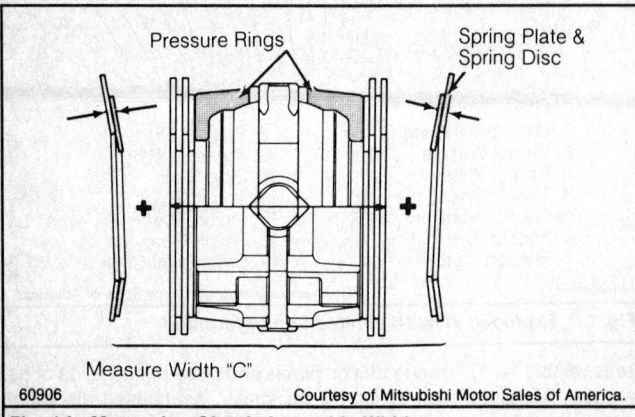

60906　　Courtesy of Mitsubishi Motor Sales of America.

Fig. 14: Measuring Clutch Assembly Width

4) Determine depth of differential case (dimension "D"). On 2.4L, dimension "D" = "E" + "F" - "G"; on 3.0L, dimension "D" = "E" + "H" - "F" - "G". See Fig. 15 or 16. Subtract "C" from "D" to determine spring plate-to-case clearance. Adjust spring disc thickness to obtain proper spring plate-to-case clearance. Correct clearance is .0024-.0079" (.060-.200 mm).

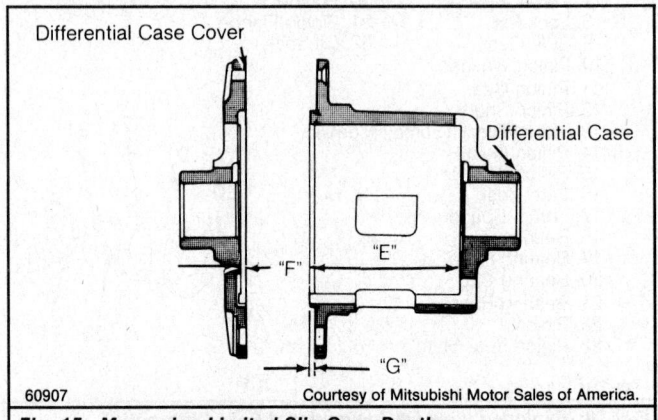

60907　　Courtesy of Mitsubishi Motor Sales of America.

Fig. 15: Measuring Limited Slip Case Depth (Pickup – 2.4L)

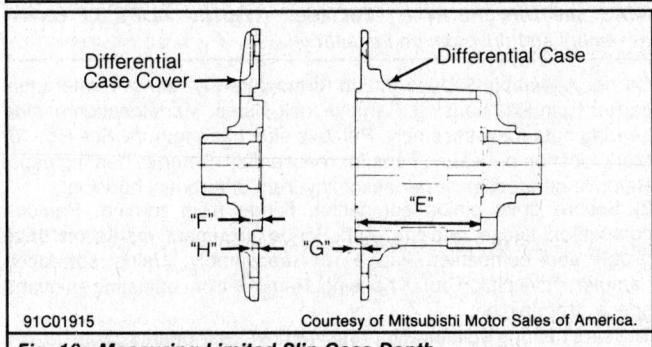

91C01915　　Courtesy of Mitsubishi Motor Sales of America.

Fig. 16: Measuring Limited Slip Case Depth (Montero & Pickup – 3.0L)

5) Remove spring plates, spring discs, friction plates and friction disc from pressure rings. Mark components for location. Install thrust washers on each end of pressure rings. See Fig. 17.

6) Measure clearance from end of thrust washer to rear face of pressure ring. Clearance should be .002" (.05 mm) or less. If clearance is not as specified, select proper thickness thrust washers to obtain correct clearance.

7) Once correct thrust washers are determined, install thrust washers on pressure rings. Squeeze pressure rings together, and measure width (dimension "H") from end of thrust washer to remaining thrust washer. See Fig. 17.

8) Determine distance between thrust washer surfaces when differential case is assembled (dimension "I"). Dimension "I" = "J" + "K" + "L". Dimension "J" is the same as dimension "D" in step **4)**.

9) Subtract "H" from "I". This is the clearance between thrust washer and differential case. Correct clearance is .002-.008" (.05-.20 mm). If clearance is not within specification, change thrust washer to obtain correct clearance.

10) Apply gear oil and friction modifier to all components. Install components in differential case. Ensure assembly order and direction of clutch components are correct. See Fig. 18.

11) Install differential case cover with reference marks aligned. Tighten screws to specification in several steps. See TORQUE SPECIFICATIONS. Ensure cases contact each other completely when fully assembled. Check for incorrect clutch assembly if gap exists.

12) Using Clutch Plate Preload Tool (MB990988), Shaft (MB990989) and torque wrench, measure starting torque. See Fig. 19. Rotate unit slightly before measuring starting torque.

1994 DRIVE AXLES
Differentials & Axle Shafts – Rear Non-Integral (Cont.)

CHRYSLER/MITSU.
7-21

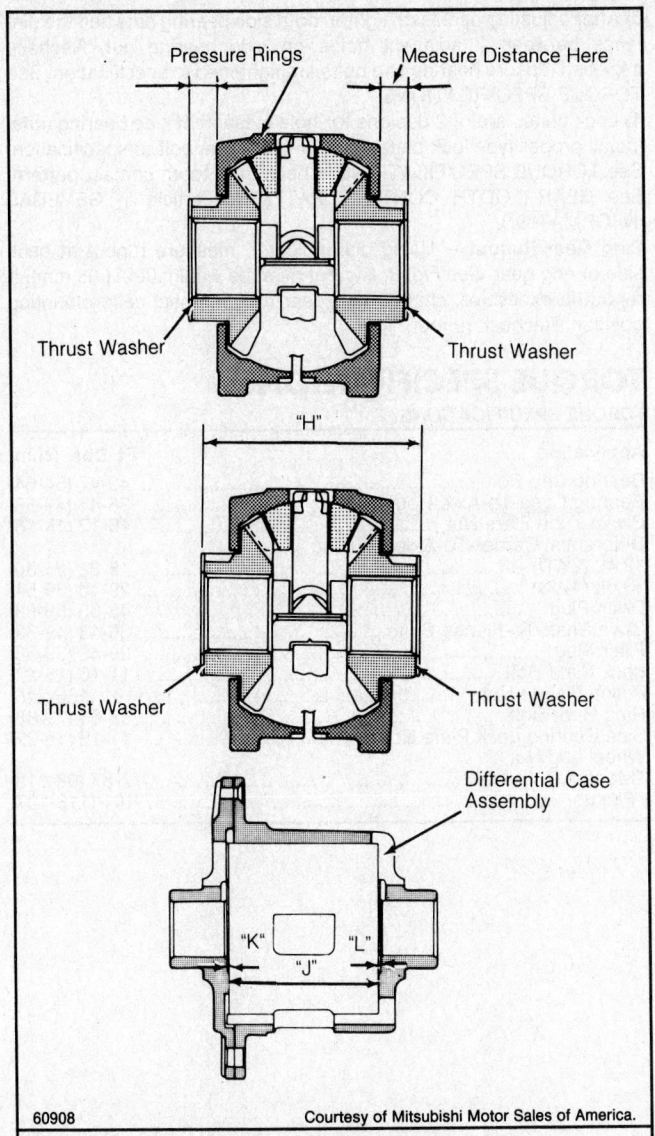

Fig. 17: *Measuring Thrust Washer Clearance*

60908   Courtesy of Mitsubishi Motor Sales of America.

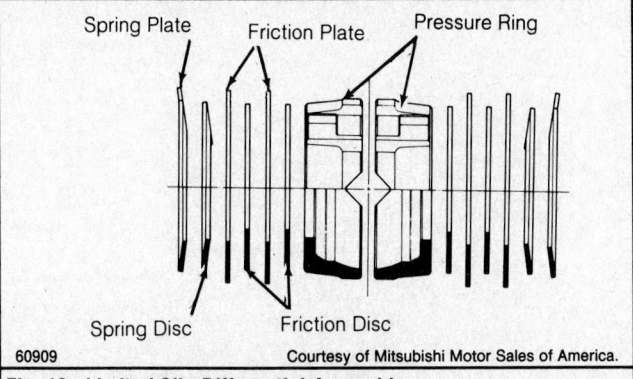

Fig. 18: *Limited Slip Differential Assembly*

60909   Courtesy of Mitsubishi Motor Sales of America.

13) Ensure starting torque is within specification. See STARTING TORQUE table. Ensure adhesive is removed from ring gear mounting bolts and gear mounting surface. Clean internal threads with tap.
14) Ensure alignment marks on differential case and ring gear align. Apply Loctite 271 to bolts, and install ring gear on differential case. Tighten bolts in diagonal sequence to specification. See TORQUE SPECIFICATIONS.

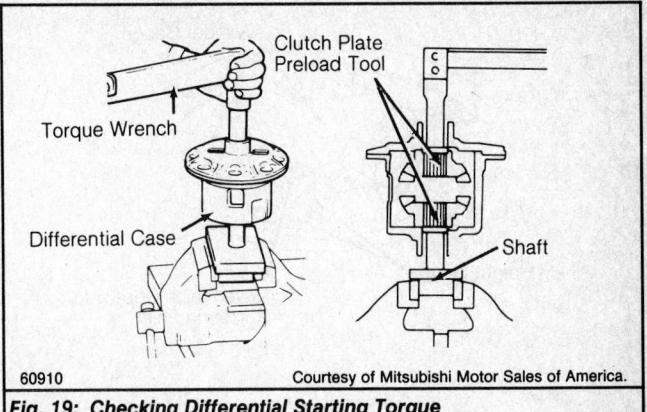

Fig. 19: *Checking Differential Starting Torque*

60910   Courtesy of Mitsubishi Motor Sales of America.

STARTING TORQUE

Application	Ft. Lbs. (N.m)
Used Clutch Plates	29-54 (40-75)
New Clutch Plates	18-54 (25-75)

Carrier Assembly & Drive Pinion Installation – 1) Install pinion bearing races in differential housing. Ensure races are fully seated. Install Pinion Height Gauge (MB990901) and pinion bearings. *See Fig. 20.* DO NOT install oil seal.
2) Using torque wrench, measure pinion rotating torque. Gradually tighten pinion height gauge to increase rotating torque. See PINION ROTATING TORQUE SPECIFICATIONS table.

PINION ROTATING TORQUE SPECIFICATIONS

Application	INCH Lbs. (N.m)
Oil Seal Not Installed	
With Lubrication	3.5-4.3 (.4-.5)
Without Lubrication	5.2-7.8 (.6-.9)
Oil Seal Installed	
With Lubrication	5.6-6.5 (.65-.75)
Without Lubrication	7.4-10.0 (.85-1.15)

3) Install cylinder gauge in side bearing seats. Ensure flat areas align, and gauge contacts side bearing seat firmly. *See Fig. 20.* Select adjusting shim with same thickness as gap between cylinder gauge and pinion height gauge.
4) Use minimum amount of adjusting shims. Install selected adjusting shims between drive pinion gear and rear pinion bearing. *See Fig. 20.* Using bearing installer and press, install rear pinion bearing.
5) Install drive pinion in differential housing. Install spacer, pinion front shim(s) and front pinion bearing. DO NOT install oil seal. Install pinion companion flange, washer and retaining nut. Tighten nut to specification. See TORQUE SPECIFICATIONS.
6) Check pinion rotating torque. See PINION ROTATING TORQUE SPECIFICATIONS table. Adjust rotating torque by replacing drive pinion front shims or spacer. Once correct rotating torque is obtained, install oil seal. Coat seal lip with grease. Install pinion companion flange so alignment marks are correct. Apply light coat of grease to contact area of pinion flange washer.
7) Install new retaining nut. Recheck pinion rotating torque. Ensure rotating torque is within specification. Press side bearings onto differential case. Install outer races. Install differential carrier into differential housing. Align bearing cap index marks, and snug carrier cap bolts. Ensure outer races and bearing caps are installed in original location.
8) Install side bearing nuts. Tighten bearing cap bolts to specification. See TORQUE SPECIFICATIONS. Tighten bearing nuts until bearing outer races are seated against bearings. Adjust ring gear backlash.
Ring Gear Backlash – 1) Secure drive pinion in place. Using dial indicator, check ring gear backlash at heel of ring gear tooth. *See Fig. 7.* Measure at 4 locations of ring gear. Gear backlash must be within specification. Backlash should be .004-.006" (.10-.16 mm) on Pickup 2WD models, .005-.007" (.13-.18 mm) on Montero and Pickup 4WD.

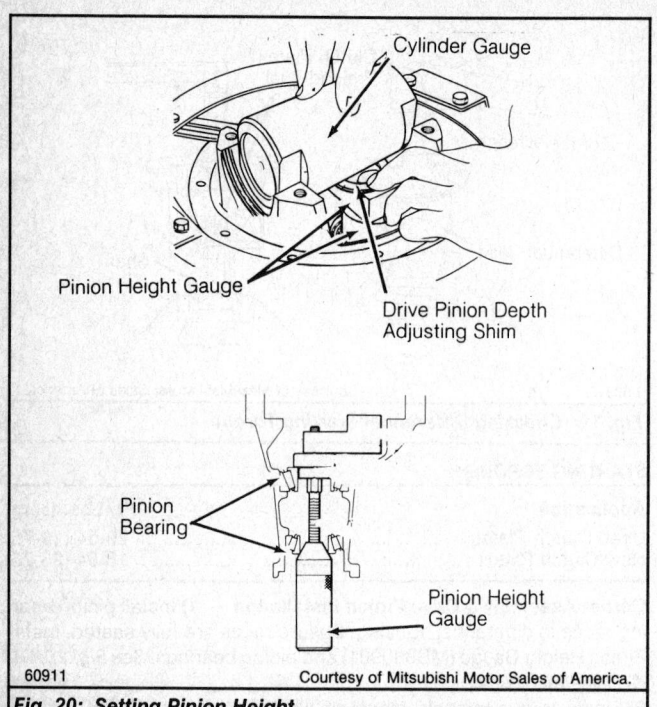

Fig. 20: Setting Pinion Height

60911   Courtesy of Mitsubishi Motor Sales of America.

Labels in figure: Cylinder Gauge; Pinion Height Gauge; Drive Pinion Depth Adjusting Shim; Pinion Bearing; Pinion Height Gauge

2) If backlash is less than specification, loosen side bearing nut at back of ring gear, and tighten side bearing nut on tooth side of ring gear by same amount. If backlash exceeds specification, loosen side bearing nut at tooth side of ring gear, and tighten side bearing nut at back of ring gear by same amount.

3) After adjusting backlash, tighten both side bearing nuts half the distance between 2 adjacent holes on side bearing nut. Recheck backlash. Ensure bearing cap bolts are tightened to specification. See TORQUE SPECIFICATIONS.

4) Lock plates are of 2 designs for hole location of side bearing nuts. Install proper type lock plate. Tighten lock plate bolt to specification. See TORQUE SPECIFICATIONS. Check gear tooth contact pattern. See GEAR TOOTH CONTACT PATTERNS article in GENERAL INFORMATION.

Ring Gear Runout – Using dial indicator, measure runout at back side of ring gear. *See Fig. 8.* Runout must be within .002" (.05 mm). If runout is excessive, change ring gear-to-differential case mounting position. Recheck runout.

TORQUE SPECIFICATIONS
TORQUE SPECIFICATIONS

Application	Ft. Lbs. (N.m)
Bearing Cap Bolt	40-47 (54-64)
Bearing Case-To-Axle Housing Bolt	36-43 (49-58)
Brake Tube Flare Nut	10-12 (14-16)
Differential Carrier-To-Axle Housing Nut	
2.4L (2WD)	18-22 (24-30)
3.0L (4WD)	29-40 (39-54)
Drain Plug	43-50 (58-68)
Drive Shaft-To-Flange Bolt	36-43 (49-58)
Filler Plug	29-43 (39-58)
Lock Plate Bolt	11-16 (15-22)
Pinion Flange Nut	137-181 (186-245)
Ring Gear Bolt	58-65 (79-88)
Side Bearing Lock Plate Bolts	11-16 (15-22)
Wheel Lug Nut	
Montero	72-87 (98-118)
Pickup	87-101 (118-137)

Mitsubishi: Montero, Pickup

DESCRIPTION

Montero is equipped with an automatic locking clutch. Locking clutch engages, providing full time AWD operation, when 4WD (4H) is selected at transfer case, at speeds up to 62 MPH. Selecting center differential lock position (4HLc or 4HLLc), while in AWD at 4 MPH or less, provides 4WD operation. Center differential lock disengages when 4H or 2H are selected. Locking clutch disengages when 2H is selected.

On Pickup, automatic locking hubs are engaged by rotational force of axle shaft when 4WD is selected at transfer case. Locking hubs disengage when 2WD is selected or vehicle is driven in Reverse. Cams, brakes and springs are used to lock or unlock locking hubs.

Engagement is accomplished through gears and spring actions within hub. When hub is locked, hub brake engages inner hub, which is connected to axle shaft by inner splines of hub. Hub brake is connected to hub body by outer splines.

REMOVAL & INSTALLATION

AUTOMATIC LOCKING HUBS

Removal & Installation (Montero) – 1) Remove right side inner shaft for automatic locking clutch removal. See INNER SHAFT & BEARING in DIFFERENTIALS & AXLE SHAFTS – FRONT article. With inner shaft removed, remove locking clutch engage switch. *See Fig. 1.*

2) Remove 4 inner shaft tube-to-differential mounting bracket bolts. Pivot differential mounting bracket. Remove 4 inner shaft tube-to-differential carrier assembly mounting bolts. Pull inner shaft tube and automatic locking clutch out of differential carrier assembly.

3) To install, reverse removal procedure. Tighten inner shaft tube bolts to 65 ft. lbs. (90 N.m) and locking clutch engage switch to 26 ft. lbs. (36 N.m).

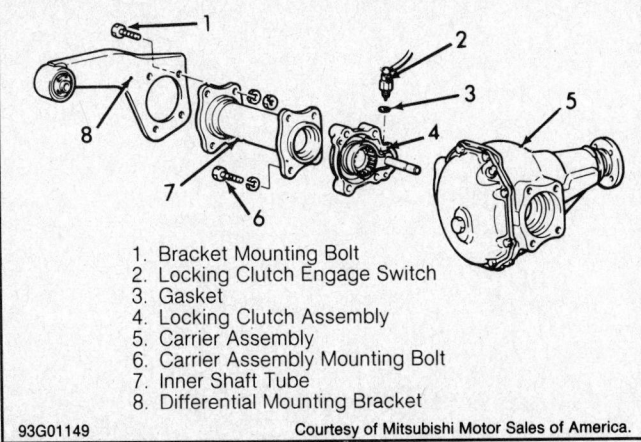

1. Bracket Mounting Bolt
2. Locking Clutch Engage Switch
3. Gasket
4. Locking Clutch Assembly
5. Carrier Assembly
6. Carrier Assembly Mounting Bolt
7. Inner Shaft Tube
8. Differential Mounting Bracket

93G01149   Courtesy of Mitsubishi Motor Sales of America.

Fig. 1: Removing Automatic Locking Clutch (Montero)

Removal (Pickup) – 1) Hub must be unlocked. To unlock hub, place transfer case lever in 2H position, and move vehicle in Reverse approximately 4-6 feet.

2) Remove cover from locking hub. If hub cover cannot be loosened by hand, wrap shop towel around cover, and use an oil filter wrench to loosen cover.

3) Raise and support vehicle. Remove wheel assembly. Using snap ring pliers, remove snap ring and shim from end of axle. Remove locking hub retaining bolts. Remove locking hub.

Installation – 1) To install, reverse removal procedure. Apply sealant to contact areas between locking hub assembly and rotor assembly. DO NOT apply sealant on outer areas of rotor assembly, toward brake contact areas.

2) Align locking hub assembly key with steering knuckle keyway. Loosely install locking hub assembly on rotor assembly. Ensure locking hub assembly fully contacts rotor assembly.

3) Install locking hub retaining bolts and tighten to 36-43 ft. lbs. (49-58 N.m). Using spring scale attached to wheel stud, measure turning resistance required to rotate hub assembly.

4) Turning resistance should not exceed 3.1 lbs. (1.4 kg). If turning resistance exceeds specification, check for incorrect installation of locking hub assembly or components.

5) Install shim and snap ring on drive axle. Rotate drive axle until maximum end play is obtained. Using a dial indicator, check drive axle end play.

6) Drive axle end play should be .008-.020" (.20-.51 mm). If axle end play is not within specification, adjust end play by changing axle shaft shim. Install hub cover. Tighten hub cover bolts to 13-25 ft. lbs. (18-34 N.m).

OVERHAUL

NOTE: Locking clutch overhaul procedure for Montero is not available from manufacturer. See Fig. 2 for exploded view of locking clutch.

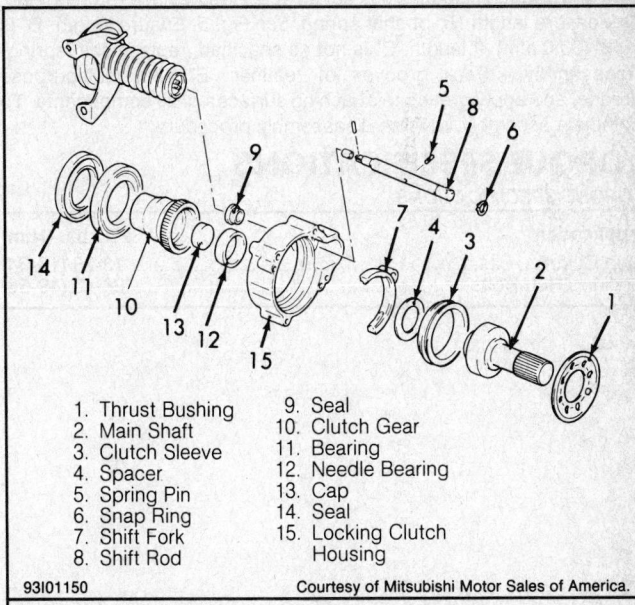

1. Thrust Bushing
2. Main Shaft
3. Clutch Sleeve
4. Spacer
5. Spring Pin
6. Snap Ring
7. Shift Fork
8. Shift Rod
9. Seal
10. Clutch Gear
11. Bearing
12. Needle Bearing
13. Cap
14. Seal
15. Locking Clutch Housing

93I01150   Courtesy of Mitsubishi Motor Sales of America.

Fig. 2: Exploded View Of Locking Clutch (Montero)

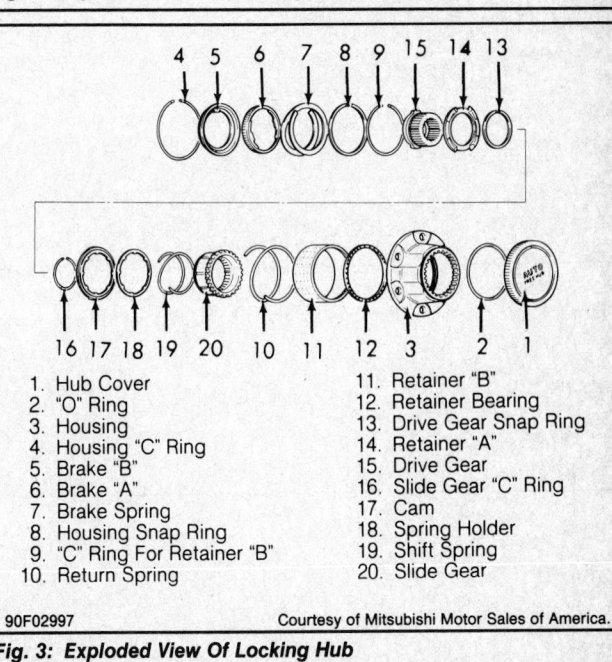

1. Hub Cover
2. "O" Ring
3. Housing
4. Housing "C" Ring
5. Brake "B"
6. Brake "A"
7. Brake Spring
8. Housing Snap Ring
9. "C" Ring For Retainer "B"
10. Return Spring
11. Retainer "B"
12. Retainer Bearing
13. Drive Gear Snap Ring
14. Retainer "A"
15. Drive Gear
16. Slide Gear "C" Ring
17. Cam
18. Spring Holder
19. Shift Spring
20. Slide Gear

90F02997   Courtesy of Mitsubishi Motor Sales of America.

Fig. 3: Exploded View Of Locking Hub

Disassembly (Pickup) – 1) Remove locking hub. AUTOMATIC LOCKING HUBS under REMOVAL & INSTALLATION. Push brake "B" in hub housing, and remove housing "C" ring. *See Fig. 3.* Using Adapter (MB990811-01), lightly press drive gear assembly, and remove "C" ring from retainer "B". Slowly release drive gear assembly.

2) Remove drive gear assembly, slide gear assembly and return spring. Remove slide gear "C" ring. Remove shift spring.

Inspection – 1) Check drive gear and slide gear splines for damage. Check cam portion of retainer "A" for wear or damage. Check cam for wear and damage. Check slide gear and housing tooth surfaces for damage. Check retainer "B" and housing contact surfaces for wear and damage.

2) Check brake assembly thickness. *See Fig. 4.* Assemble brake "A" and brake "B". Using slide calipers, measure thickness of assembled brake at both brake "A" lugs.

3) Standard thickness is .413" (10.49 mm). Minimum thickness is .378" (9.60 mm). If measured thickness is less than minimum thickness, replace brake "A" and brake "B".

4) Measure length "A" of return spring. *See Fig. 5.* Ensure length "A" is 1.38" (35.1 mm). If length "A" is not as specified, replace return spring.

5) Measure length "B" of shift spring. *See Fig. 5.* Ensure length "B" is 1.18" (30.0 mm). If length "B" is not as specified, replace shift spring.

Reassembly – Pack grooves of retainer "B" with multipurpose grease, and apply grease to attaching surfaces of all components. To complete assembly, reverse disassembly procedure.

TORQUE SPECIFICATIONS

TORQUE SPECIFICATIONS

Application	Ft. Lbs. (N.m)
Hub Cover	13-25 (18-34)
Locking Hub Bolts	36-43 (49-58)

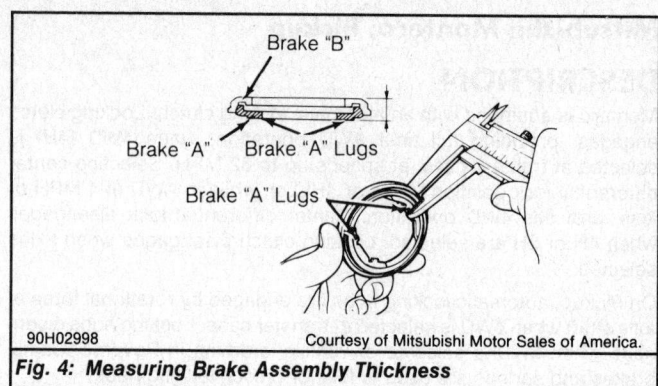

Fig. 4: *Measuring Brake Assembly Thickness*

Courtesy of Mitsubishi Motor Sales of America.

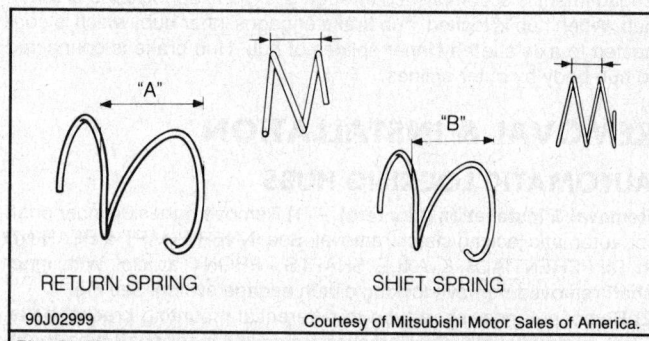

Fig. 5: *Measuring Lengths Of Return Spring & Shift Spring*

Courtesy of Mitsubishi Motor Sales of America.

1994 BRAKES
Disc & Drum – Except Precis

Chrysler Motors: Colt, Colt Vista, Stealth, Summit, Summit Wagon
Mitsubishi: Diamante, Eclipse, Expo, Galant, Mirage, Montero, Pickup, 3000GT

INTRODUCTION

This article contains information on repair and service of basic hydraulic brake system. If vehicle is equipped with anti-lock brakes, also see appropriate ANTI-LOCK article. For information on Precis, see DISC & DRUM – PRECIS article.

DESCRIPTION

Brake system consists of a master cylinder, vacuum power brake unit, proportioning valve and self-adjusting assembly. Expo, Montero and Pickup have a Load-Sensing Proportioning Valve (LSPV). All models are equipped with front disc brakes and either rear disc or drum brakes. Parking brake assembly activates rear brakes.

BLEEDING BRAKE SYSTEM

BLEEDING PROCEDURES

Bleed brakes whenever hydraulic lines are opened or pedal feels spongy. Bleed system in appropriate sequence. See BRAKE LINE BLEEDING SEQUENCE table. On all models except Montero and Pickup, bleed system with engine running.

BRAKE LINE BLEEDING SEQUENCE

Application	Sequence
Colt Vista, Expo & Summit Wagon	LR, RF, RR, LF
Colt, Diamante, Eclipse, Galant, Mirage, Stealth, Summit & 3000GT	RR, LF, LR, RF
Montero	RR, LR, LSPV, RF, LF
Pickup	RR, LSPV, RF, LF

ADJUSTMENTS

BRAKE PEDAL HEIGHT & FREE PLAY

1) Separate connector from stoplight switch, and loosen lock nut. Position switch so it does not contact brake pedal arm. Adjust brake pedal height by rotating master cylinder push rod (yoke, if equipped) until distance from top of brake pedal, with pedal released, is within specification. See BRAKE PEDAL SPECIFICATIONS table.

2) DO NOT depress push rod. Tighten lock nut, and ensure brake pedal height is within specification. Start engine to evacuate brake booster chamber. Stop engine, and apply brake several times to remove vacuum from brake booster.

3) Using hand pressure, depress brake pedal to measure free play before resistance is felt. Free play distance for all models is .12-.31" (3.0-7.9 mm). If distance is not within specification, bleed system and check for misadjusted brakes.

BRAKE PEDAL SPECIFICATIONS

Application	Pedal Height In. (mm)
Colt, Mirage & Summit	6.6-6.7 (168-170)
Diamante, Eclipse & Galant	6.9-7.1 (175-180)
Colt Vista, Expo & Summit Wagon	7.7-7.9 (196-201)
Montero	7.3-7.7 (185-196)
Pickup	6.5 (165)
Stealth & 3000GT	7.0-7.2 (178-183)

LOAD-SENSING PROPORTIONING VALVE (LSPV)

Expo – Park vehicle on level surface. Remove excess weight from vehicle. Measure spring length. If spring length is not within specification, adjust turnbuckle until correct length is obtained. See LOAD-SENSING SPRING LENGTH table. See Fig. 1.

Montero & Pickup – Park vehicle on level surface. Remove excess weight from vehicle. Ensure lever is not against stopper bolt. Check spring length. If spring length is not within specification, adjust cable or support until correct length is obtained. See LOAD-SENSING SPRING LENGTH table. See Fig. 2.

LOAD-SENSING SPRING LENGTH

Application	In. (mm)
Expo	3.3-3.4 (84-86)
Montero	8.8-9.0 (224-229)
Pickup	7.0-7.1 (178-180)

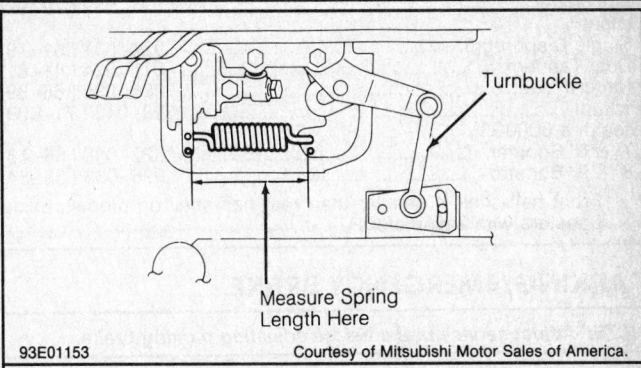

93E01153   Courtesy of Mitsubishi Motor Sales of America.

Fig. 1: Adjusting Load-Sensing Proportioning Valve Spring (Expo)

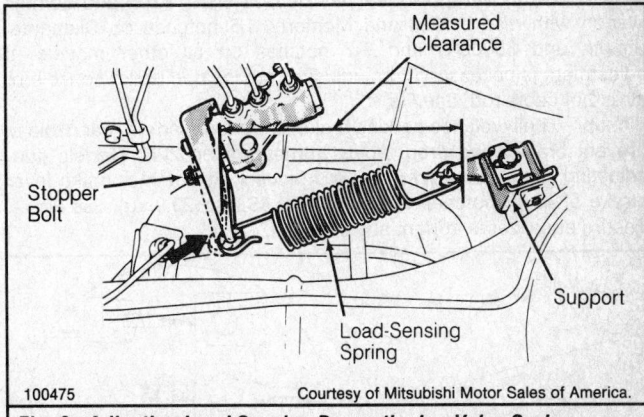

100475   Courtesy of Mitsubishi Motor Sales of America.

Fig. 2: Adjusting Load-Sensing Proportioning Valve Spring (Montero & Pickup)

MASTER CYLINDER PUSH ROD

Check and adjust clearance between back of master cylinder piston and master cylinder push rod. See Fig. 3. See PUSH ROD CLEARANCE SPECIFICATIONS table. After adjusting push rod clearance, adjust pedal height and bleed brake system.

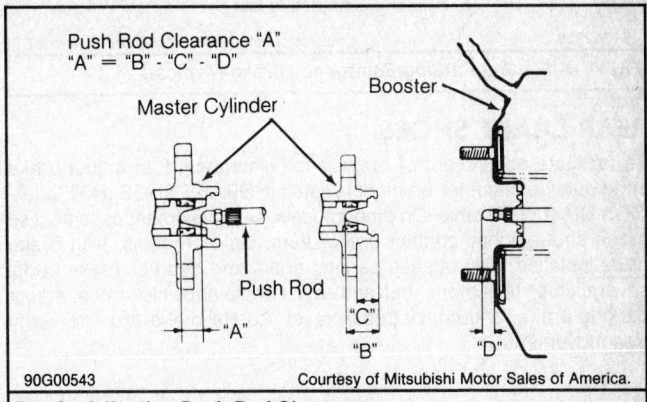

90G00543   Courtesy of Mitsubishi Motor Sales of America.

Fig. 3: Adjusting Push Rod Clearance

PUSH ROD CLEARANCE SPECIFICATIONS

Application [1]	In. (mm)
Colt, Mirage & Summit	
7" Booster	.020-.028 (.51-.71)
8" Booster	.024-.031 (.61-.79)
Diamante	.026-.033 (.66-.84)
Eclipse	
7" & 8" Booster	.020-.028 (.51-.71)
9" Booster	.031-.039 (.79-.99)
Colt Vista, Expo & Summit Wagon	
7" & 8" Booster	.020-.028 (.51-.71)
8" Booster	.024-.031 (.61-.79)
9" Booster	.031-.039 (.79-.99)
Galant	
Single Diaphragm	.024-.031 (.61-.79)
Dual Tandem	.016-.024 (.41-.61)
Montero	.026-.035 (.66-.89)
Pickup	.028-.043 (.71-1.09)
Stealth & 3000GT	
7" & 8" Booster	.022-.030 (.56-.76)
8" & 9" Booster	.026-.033 (.66-.84)

[1] – Front half-shell is smaller than rear half-shell on models using boosters with 2 diameters.

PARKING/EMERGENCY BRAKE

NOTE: Adjust service brake before adjusting parking brake.

Except Pickup – Start engine, and apply brake pedal. Pull parking brake lever with a force of 44-45 lbs. (20.0-20.4 kg). Parking brake lever should move up 4-6 notches on Colt Vista, Expo and Summit Wagon with disc brakes and Montero, 3-5 notches on Diamante, Stealth and 3000GT, and 5-7 notches on all other models. If adjustment is necessary, turn adjusting nut located under console or at end of cable rod. *See Fig. 4.*

Pickup – Fully release parking brake, and allow slack in rear cable to prevent brake shoe drag. Adjust turnbuckle on 2WD models (turn adjusting nut on equalizer on 4WD models) to obtain a brake lever stroke of 16-17 notches with a force of 66 lbs. (29.9 kg). *See Fig. 4.* Ensure equalizer is at right angle to joint.

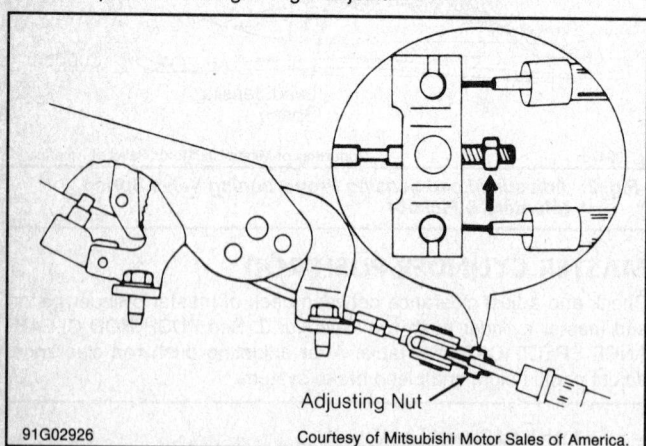

91G02926   Courtesy of Mitsubishi Motor Sales of America.

Fig. 4: Adjusting Parking/Emergency Brake (Typical)

REAR BRAKE SHOES

To facilitate adjustment of brake shoe clearance, first adjust brake shoe outside diameter on models listed in BRAKE SHOE INSTALLATION DIAMETER table. On other models, set adjustment assembly so brake shoes lightly contact brake drum. On all models, with brake drum installed, fully release parking brake and depress brake pedal several times to center shoes and adjust brake shoe clearance. Adjust parking brake, and check pedal travel. Rotate brake drum to verify free movement.

BRAKE SHOE INSTALLATION DIAMETER

Application	In. (mm)
Colt, Mirage & Summit	7.06-7.07 (179.3-179.6)
Pickup	9.97-9.98 (253.2-253.5)

STOPLIGHT SWITCH

Loosen lock nut, and adjust switch-to-pedal arm clearance to .02-.04" (0.5-1.0 mm). Tighten lock nut. DO NOT depress master cylinder push rod during stoplight switch adjustment.

TESTING

POWER BRAKE UNIT

Check Valve Inspection – Remove vacuum hose from power brake unit. On Colt, Mirage and Summit, remove check valve from hose; check valve and hose are a unit on all other models. Using a vacuum pump, ensure airflow is in direction of intake manifold only.

System Check – 1) Run engine for 2 minutes. Shut engine off, and depress brake pedal several times with normal pressure. If pedal height gradually becomes higher with successive applications, power brake unit is okay. If pedal height remains steady, power brake unit is faulty.

2) With engine stopped, depress brake pedal repeatedly until pedal height no longer falls. Hold brake pedal down, and start engine. If pedal moves downward slightly, power brake unit is okay. If pedal height does not change, power brake unit is faulty.

3) With engine running, press and hold brake pedal. Shut off engine. Hold brake pedal for 30 seconds. Brake pedal height should not change. If pedal height falls, power brake unit is faulty.

LOAD-SENSING PROPORTIONING VALVE (LSPV)

Expo, Montero & Pickup – 1) Before diagnosing Load-Sensing Proportioning Valve (LSPV), ensure all other brake components are operating properly. When all other brake system components are determined to be okay, ensure LSPV spring length is within specification. *See Fig. 1 or 2.* See LOAD-SENSING PROPORTIONING VALVE (LSPV) under ADJUSTMENTS.

2) After spring length is determined to be within specification, connect pressure gauges to input and output ports of LSPV. *See Fig. 5 or 6.* Bleed brake system. See BLEEDING BRAKE SYSTEM.

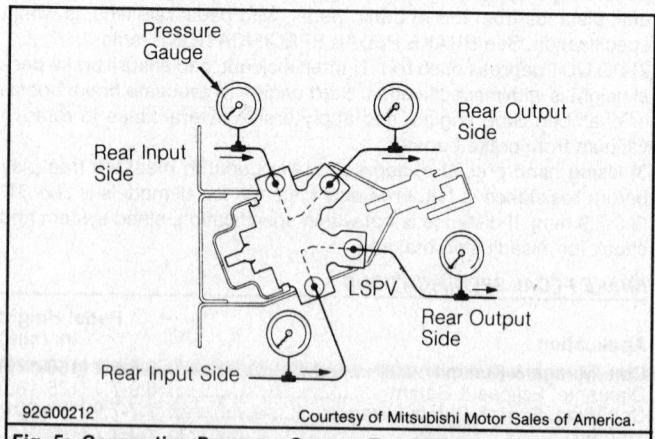

92G00212   Courtesy of Mitsubishi Motor Sales of America.

Fig. 5: Connecting Pressure Gauges To LSPV (Expo)

3) On Expo, loosen turnbuckle to relieve spring tension. *See Fig. 1.* Slowly depress brake pedal and check readings on pressure gauges (Test 1). See LSPV PRESSURE SPECIFICATIONS table. Tighten turnbuckle until spring length is 4.00" (101.6 mm). Slowly depress brake pedal and check readings on pressure gauges (Test 2). If fluid pressure is not within specification, replace LSPV assembly.

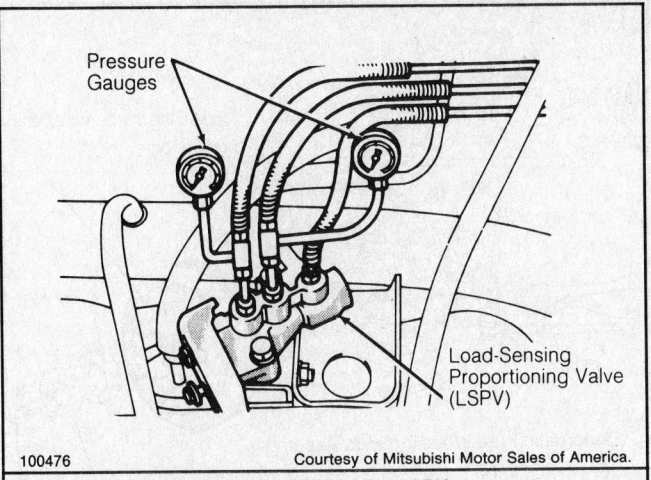

Fig. 6: Connecting Pressure Gauges To LSPV (Montero & Pickup)

4) On Montero, disconnect spring at support and pull spring and lever toward support until spring length is 8.9" (226 mm). See Fig. 2. Without depressing brake pedal, check readings on pressure gauges (Test 1). See LSPV PRESSURE SPECIFICATIONS table. Push lever away from support until spring length is 10.1" (257 mm). Without depressing brake pedal, check readings on pressure gauges (Test 2). If fluid pressure is not within specification, replace LSPV assembly.

5) On Pickup, remove load-sensing spring. See Fig. 2. Slowly depress brake pedal. Check readings on pressure gauges (Test 1). See LSPV PRESSURE SPECIFICATIONS table. Install load-sensing spring. Load weight into rear of vehicle until measured spring length is 7.0" (178 mm) with lever pressed in slightly.

6) Slowly depress brake pedal. Check readings on pressure gauges (Test 2). See LSPV PRESSURE SPECIFICATIONS table. If fluid pressure is not within specification, replace LSPV assembly.

LSPV PRESSURE SPECIFICATIONS

Application	Inlet Pressure psi (kg/cm²)	Outlet Pressure psi (kg/cm²)
Expo		
Turnbuckle Loosened		
Test 1	1066 (75)	455-526 (32-37)
Test 2	1994 (140)	888-1002 (62-70)
Turnbuckle Tightened	1994 (140)	1571-1813 (110-127)
Montero		
LSPV Spring Pulled		
Test 1	1422 (100)	873-1002 (61-70)
Test 2	2560 (180)	1129-1314 (79-92)
LSPV Lever Pushed	2560 (180)	[1] 1863-2148 (131-151)
Pickup		
LSPV Spring Removed		
Test 1	853 (60)	242-327 (17-23)
Test 2	1994 (140)	370-540 (26-38)
LSPV Spring Installed	1994 (140)	[2] 299-583 (21-41)

[1] – Maximum side-to-side pressure differential is 57 psi (4 kg/cm²).
[2] – On vehicles with both 2WD and heavy-duty suspension, outlet pressure is 526-697 psi (37-49 kg/cm²).

PROPORTIONING VALVE (NON-LOAD-SENSING)

Pressure Test (Colt, Colt Vista, Diamante, Eclipse, Expo, Galant, Mirage, Stealth, Summit, Summit Wagon & 3000GT) –
1) Connect pressure gauges to input and output ports of proportioning valve. See Fig. 7. Bleed brake system. See BLEEDING BRAKE SYSTEM.
2) Slowly depress brake pedal. Check readings on pressure gauges. Ensure output pressure begins to drop relative to input pressure at specified pressure range (split point). See SPLIT POINT PRESSURE SPECIFICATIONS table.

3) Continue depressing brake pedal, and check readings on pressure gauges. See PROPORTIONING VALVE PRESSURE SPECIFICATIONS table. If fluid pressures or split point are not within specification, replace proportioning valve.

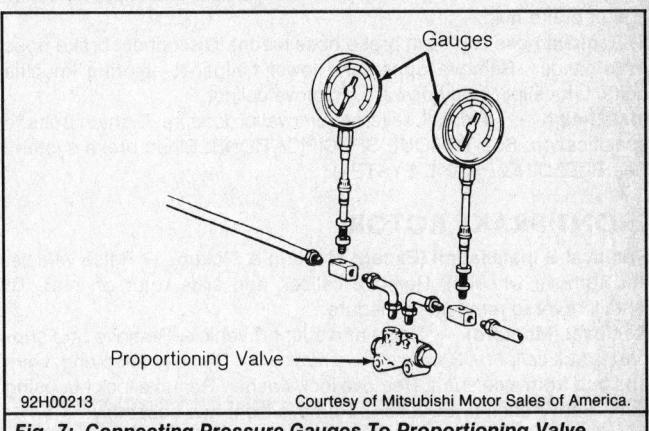

Fig. 7: Connecting Pressure Gauges To Proportioning Valve (Typical)

SPLIT POINT PRESSURE SPECIFICATIONS

Application	psi (kg/cm²)
Colt, Mirage & Summit	
Hatchback	348-420 (25-30)
Sedan	420-491 (30-35)
Diamante, Stealth & 3000GT	533-604 (38-43)
Eclipse	
2WD	561-633 (39-45)
4WD	491-561 (35-39)
Galant	462-533 (33-38)
Colt Vista, Expo & Summit Wagon	462-533 (33-38)

PROPORTIONING VALVE PRESSURE SPECIFICATIONS

Application	Inlet Pressure psi (kg/cm²)	[1] Outlet Pressure psi (kg/cm²)
Colt, Mirage & Summit		
Hatchback	953 (67)	519-590 (37-42)
Sedan	1024 (72)	590-661 (42-47)
Diamante	1138 (80)	676-747 (48-53)
Eclipse		
2WD	1163 (82)	739-811 (52-57)
4WD	1095 (77)	661-739 (47-52)
Galant	996 (70)	604 (43)
Stealth & 3000GT	1138 (80)	739-811 (52-57)
Colt Vista, Expo & Summit Wagon	1067 (75)	676 (48)

[1] – Maximum side-to-side pressure differential is 57 psi (4 kg/cm²).

REMOVAL & INSTALLATION

FRONT DISC BRAKE PADS

CAUTION: DO NOT remove or contaminate special grease coating on lock pins.

Removal – 1) Raise and support vehicle. Remove front wheel(s). Remove lower lock pin or sleeve bolt. See Fig. 16. Lift caliper body upward.
2) Support caliper aside. Remove shim(s), shim holder (if equipped), anti-squeak shim and pad assembly from support mounting. Remove pad clips.
Installation – If installing new pads, compress piston to bottom of bore. Install retaining clips, pad assembly, shim(s), shim holder (if equipped) and anti-squeak shim onto support mounting. Start engine. Depress brake pedal several times to expand caliper piston. Check brake fluid level.

FRONT BRAKE CALIPER

Removal – 1) Raise and support vehicle. Remove front wheel(s). Separate rubber flexhose from hydraulic line at brake hose mount, located on strut housing. Secure end of hydraulic line to prevent spillage of brake fluid.

2) Remove hose clip from brake hose mount. Disconnect brake hose from caliper. Remove upper and lower caliper-to-steering knuckle bolts. Lift caliper body upward. Remove caliper.

Installation – To install, reverse removal procedure. Tighten bolts to specification. See TORQUE SPECIFICATIONS. Bleed brake system. See BLEEDING BRAKE SYSTEM.

FRONT BRAKE ROTOR

Removal & Installation (Except Montero & Pickup) – Raise vehicle, and remove wheel(s). Remove caliper, and slide rotor off hub. To install, reverse removal procedure.

Removal (Montero) – Raise and support vehicle. Remove and support brake calipers. Remove drive hub cover. Remove snap ring, shim and hub from axle shaft. Remove lock washer. Remove lock nut using Lock Nut Wrench (MB990954). Remove front hub assembly.

Installation – 1) Install front hub assembly. Install lock nut, and tighten it to 119 ft. lbs. (165 N.m). Loosen lock nut, and retighten it to 18 ft. lbs. (24 N.m). Loosen lock nut 30-40 degrees. Reverse removal procedure for remaining components.

2) After installation is complete, check axle shaft-to-hub clearance. Using feeler gauge, clearance should be .016-.028" (.4-.7 mm). Use appropriate shim to obtain correct clearance. Shim is located behind snap ring on end of axle shaft. Install shim, and recheck clearance.

Removal (Pickup 2WD) – Raise and support vehicle. Remove front caliper. Remove hub (dust) cap, cotter pin and nut. Remove washer and outer wheel bearing. Remove front hub assembly. Remove bolts attaching rotor to front hub, and separate assemblies.

Installation – To install, reverse removal procedure. Tighten wheel bearings to 22 ft. lbs. (30 N.m). Loosen nut, and then retighten it to 72 INCH lbs. (8 N.m). Install cotter pin. If pin does not align, loosen nut a maximum of 30 degrees as needed.

Removal (Pickup 4WD) – Raise and support vehicle. Remove and support brake calipers. Place hub in free-wheeling position. Remove drive hub cover using an oil filter wrench and protective cloth. Remove snap ring, shim and free-wheeling hub from axle shaft. See Fig. 8. Remove lock washer. Remove lock nut using Lock Nut Wrench (MB990954). Remove front hub assembly.

Installation – 1) Install front hub assembly. Install lock nut, and tighten it to 94-145 ft. lbs. (127-197 N.m). Loosen lock nut, and retighten it to 18 ft. lbs. (24 N.m). Loosen lock nut 30-40 degrees. Reverse removal procedure for remaining components.

2) After installation is complete, check axle shaft end play. Adjust end play to .008-.020" (.2-.5 mm). Rotate axle shaft forward and rearward until maximum end play is obtained.

3) If adjusting axle shaft end play, use proper shim to obtain desired end play. Shim is located behind snap ring on end of axle shaft. Install shim, and recheck axle end play.

PARKING BRAKE SHOES

Removal (Colt, Colt Vista, Diamante, Expo, Mirage, Montero & Summit Wagon) – 1) Raise and support vehicle. Remove rear wheel(s). Disconnect rear speed sensor. Remove rear disc brake calipers and rotors. On all models except Montero, remove hub cap, flange nut and washer. See Fig. 9.

2) Remove rear hub/bearing assembly. On all models, remove adjusting wheel spring. Remove shoe hold-down cup, spring and pin. Note how shoe-to-anchor spring is installed, and then remove adjuster and shoe-to-anchor spring. Remove strut and return spring. Remove clip and shoe and lining assembly.

CAUTION: Shoe-to-anchor spring must be installed correctly for proper functioning of parking brakes.

Installation – 1) To install, reverse removal procedure. When installing shoe-to-anchor spring, ensure spring is installed correctly.

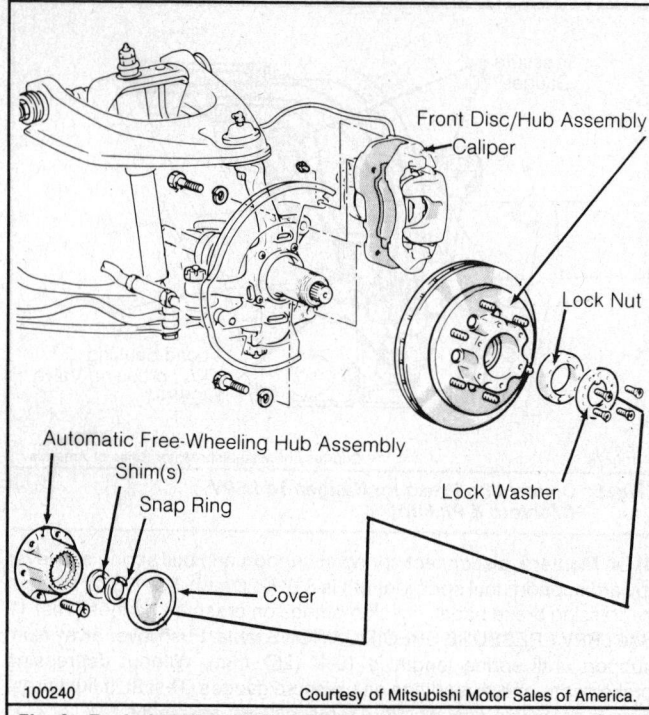

Fig. 8: Exploded View Of Front Brake Assembly (Pickup 4WD)

100240 — Courtesy of Mitsubishi Motor Sales of America.

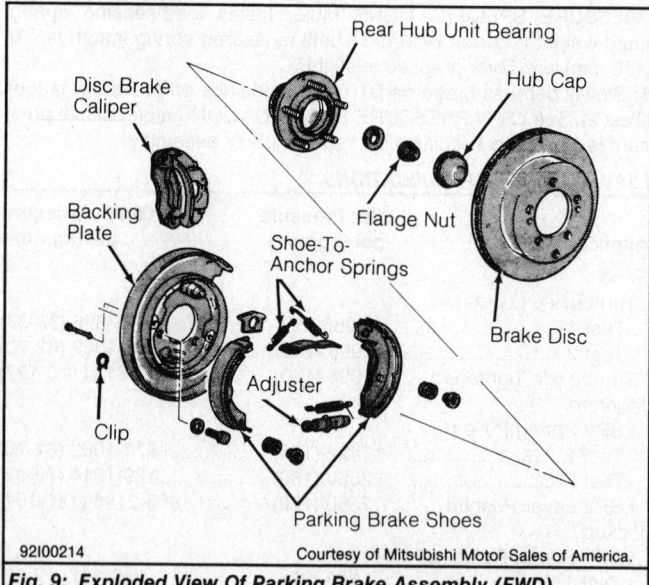

Fig. 9: Exploded View Of Parking Brake Assembly (FWD)

92I00214 — Courtesy of Mitsubishi Motor Sales of America.

When installing adjuster, install left adjuster with adjusting bolt facing vehicle front and right adjuster with adjusting bolt facing vehicle rear.

2) On all models except Montero, after tightening flange nut, align spindle indentation and crimp nut. On all models, after installing speed sensor, ensure gap between rotor teeth and sensor pole piece is .008-.028" (0.20-0.71 mm).

Removal (Stealth & 3000GT) – 1) Raise and support vehicle. Remove rear wheel(s). Disconnect rear speed sensor. Remove rear disc brake calipers and rotors. Disconnect axle from companion flange.

2) Secure hub with Holder (MB990767). Remove companion flange nut and flange. Using puller, remove hub. Remove adjusting wheel spring. Remove shoe hold-down cup, spring and pin. Note how shoe-to-anchor spring is installed, and then remove adjuster and shoe-to-anchor spring. Remove strut and return spring. Remove clip and shoe and lining assembly.

CAUTION: Shoe-to-anchor spring must be installed correctly for proper functioning of parking brakes.

Installation – To install, reverse removal procedure. When installing shoe-to-anchor spring, ensure spring is installed correctly. When installing adjuster, install left adjuster with adjusting bolt facing vehicle front and right adjuster with adjusting bolt facing vehicle rear. Tighten companion flange nut to 188-217 ft. lbs. (260-300 N.m).

REAR DISC BRAKE PADS

NOTE: Replace inner and outer pads at same time.

Removal – Raise and support vehicle. Remove rear wheel(s), and disconnect parking brake cable. Remove lower lock pin bolt. Lift caliper body upward. Using a wire, support caliper from underbody. Remove inner shim(s), anti-squeak shim and pad assembly from support mounting. Remove pad clips.

Installation – Rotate piston to align notches in piston projection on back of pads (if equipped). Install retaining clips, pad assembly, inner shim(s) and anti-squeak shim onto support mounting. Lower caliper body, and install lock pin.

REAR BRAKE CALIPER

Removal – Raise and support vehicle. Remove rear wheel(s). Disconnect parking brake cable connection. Disconnect brake hose from caliper. Secure end of hydraulic line to prevent spillage of brake fluid. Remove upper and lower caliper mounting bolts. Lift caliper body upward. Remove caliper.

Installation – To install, reverse removal procedure. Tighten bolts to specification. See TORQUE SPECIFICATIONS. Bleed brake system. See BLEEDING BRAKE SYSTEM.

REAR BRAKE ROTOR

Removal & Installation – Raise and support vehicle. Remove rear caliper and rotor. To install, reverse removal procedure.

REAR BRAKE DRUM & SHOES

Removal (Colt, Colt Vista, Expo, Galant, Mirage, Summit & Summit Wagon) – **1)** Raise and support vehicle. Remove rear hub (dust) cap and nut. *See Fig. 10.* On type No. 1 drums, remove outer wheel bearing and hub/brake drum assembly. On type No. 2 drums, remove brake drum assembly. On both brake types, remove shoe retainer spring, shoe-to-shoe spring and shoe hold-down spring.

2) Disconnect parking brake cable from lever. Remove brake shoes with adjuster spring as an assembly, and separate adjuster spring from brake shoes. Remove parking brake lever snap ring, and disengage lever from brake shoe.

Installation – **1)** To install, reverse removal procedure. Apply Lubriplate to backing plate bosses, adjuster assembly threads and parking brake lever pin.

2) Set adjustment assembly so brake shoes lightly contact brake drum. See REAR BRAKE SHOES under ADJUSTMENTS. Depress brake pedal to center shoes, and check pedal travel. Rotate brake drum to ensure free movement.

Removal (Pickup) – **1)** Raise and support vehicle. Remove wheel and brake drum. Remove shoe return spring and brake shoe adjuster. *See Fig. 11.* Remove adjusting spring, shoe retaining spring and shoe hold-down pins.

2) Remove shoe and lining assembly with parking brake lever. Remove cable from parking lever. Remove parking brake lever snap ring, and disengage lever from brake shoe.

Installation – **1)** To install, reverse removal procedure. Apply Lubriplate to backing plate bosses, adjuster assembly threads and parking brake lever pin.

2) Set adjustment assembly so brake shoes lightly contact brake drum. See REAR BRAKE SHOES under ADJUSTMENTS. Depress brake pedal to center shoes, and check pedal travel. Rotate brake drum to ensure free movement.

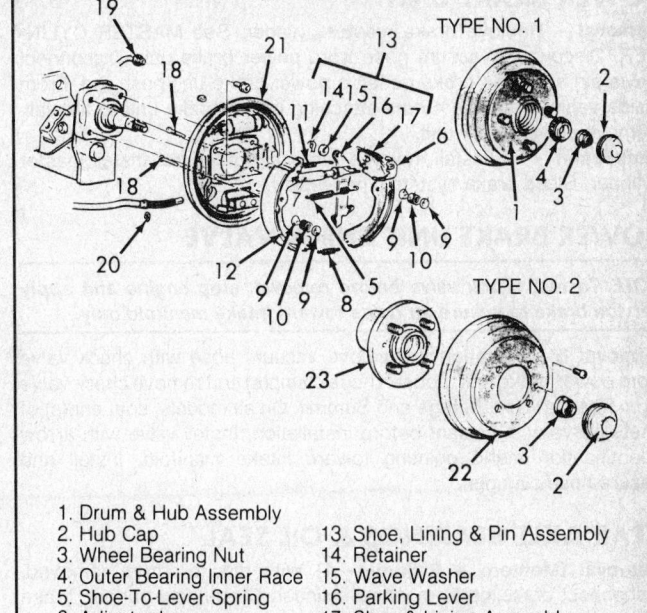

1. Drum & Hub Assembly
2. Hub Cap
3. Wheel Bearing Nut
4. Outer Bearing Inner Race
5. Shoe-To-Lever Spring
6. Adjuster Lever
7. Auto Adjuster Assembly
8. Retainer Spring
9. Shoe Hold-Down Cups
10. Shoe Hold-Down Springs
11. Shoe-To-Shoe Springs
12. Shoe & Lining Assembly
13. Shoe, Lining & Pin Assembly
14. Retainer
15. Wave Washer
16. Parking Lever
17. Shoe & Lining Assembly
18. Shoe Hold-Down Pins
19. Brake Tube
20. Snap Ring
21. Backing Plate
22. Drum
23. Hub Assembly

93J01155   Courtesy of Mitsubishi Motor Sales of America.

Fig. 10: Exploded View Of Rear Brake Assembly (FWD)

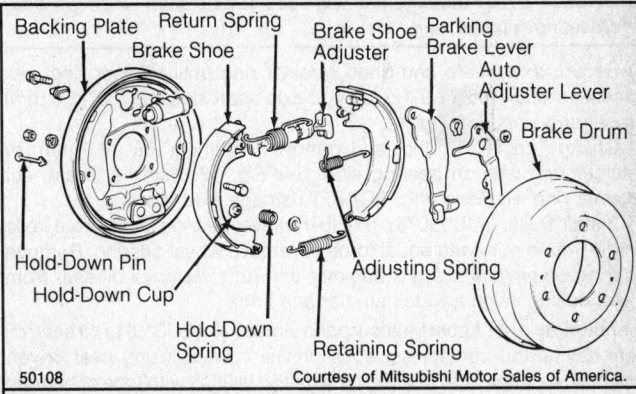

50108   Courtesy of Mitsubishi Motor Sales of America.

Fig. 11: Exploded View Of Rear Brake Assembly (Pickup)

WHEEL CYLINDERS

Removal & Installation – Raise and support vehicle. Remove rear brake drum and shoes. See REAR BRAKE DRUM & SHOES. Remove wheel cylinder and seal assembly. To install, reverse removal procedure. Bleed brakes. See BLEEDING BRAKE SYSTEM.

MASTER CYLINDER

Removal – Drain brake fluid from master cylinder. Remove sensor connector (if equipped). Disconnect brakelines from master cylinder, and install plugs to prevent brake fluid spillage. Remove master cylinder from booster unit, and separate reservoirs from housing (if necessary).

Installation – To install, reverse removal procedure. Before installation, check and adjust clearance between back of master cylinder piston and power brake push rod. See MASTER CYLINDER PUSH ROD under ADJUSTMENTS. After installation, adjust pedal height. See BRAKE PEDAL HEIGHT & FREE PLAY under ADJUSTMENTS. Bleed brake system.

POWER BRAKE UNIT

Removal – Remove brake master cylinder. See MASTER CYLINDER. Disconnect vacuum hose from power brake unit. Disconnect clevis pin attaching brake pedal to power brake unit push rod. From inside vehicle, remove 4 nuts attaching power brake unit to firewall. Remove power brake unit.

Installation – To install, reverse removal procedure. Install master cylinder. Bleed brake system if necessary.

POWER BRAKE UNIT CHECK VALVE

NOTE: To test check valve before removal, stop engine and apply service brake to ensure air flows toward intake manifold only.

Removal & Installation – Remove vacuum hose with check valve from power brake unit. Loosen hose clamp(s) and remove check valve from hose on Colt, Mirage and Summit. On all models, coat end(s) of check valve with sealant before installation. Install valve with arrow (identification mark) pointing toward intake manifold. Install and secure hose clamp(s).

REAR AXLE BEARINGS & OIL SEAL

Removal (Montero & Pickup) – **1)** With disc or drum removed, disconnect brakeline from wheel cylinder. Disconnect parking brake cable end, and remove cable attaching bolts. Remove brake backing plate, bearing case and axle shaft as an assembly. If axle shaft binds, use slide hammer and puller to remove.

2) Remove shims, "O" ring and snap ring. Retain shims for installation. Secure axle shaft assembly in a vise, and remove one retainer bolt from backing plate. Push bearing case completely to side of dust cover. Place adhesive tape around edge of bearing case at retainer bolt hole to prevent damage.

CAUTION: DO NOT damage bearing case or axle shaft when grinding or chiseling retainer ring.

3) Secure axle shaft, and grind retainer ring until retainer ring wall thickness is .04-.06" (1.0-1.5 mm) on axle shaft side and .08" (2.0 mm) on bearing side. *See Fig. 12.*

4) Change angle of grind, and remove remaining .08" (2.0 mm) of retainer ring wall on bearing side. *See Fig. 12.* Using a chisel, cut retainer ring. Remove ring. DO NOT damage axle shaft.

5) Install Puller (MB990787-01) to remove bearing case from axle shaft. Rotate nuts with equal force to remove wheel bearing. Remove bearing outer race using a hammer and drift. Remove oil seal from axle housing using a slide hammer and hook.

Installation – **1)** Apply Multipurpose Grease (SAE J310) to oil seal, oil seal cavity and contact surfaces. Install oil seal using seal driver. Press new oil seal into bearing case until it is flush with face of bearing case. Install backing plate and bearing case.

2) Apply grease to external surfaces of bearing outer race. Press bearing outer race into bearing case. Install rear brake assembly and bearing case. Pack bearing case and axle threads with grease. Install new retainer ring and snap ring.

3) Using a feeler gauge, measure clearance between snap ring and new retainer ring. Clearance should be less than .0065" (.166 mm). If clearance exceeds specification, install a new snap ring to bring clearance to specification. See SNAP RING THICKNESS SPECIFICATION table.

SNAP RING THICKNESS SPECIFICATION

Thickness In. (mm)	Color
.060 (1.52)	Red
.067 (1.70)	Purple
.073 (1.85)	Blue
.079 (2.01)	Yellow
.085 (2.16)	Neutral

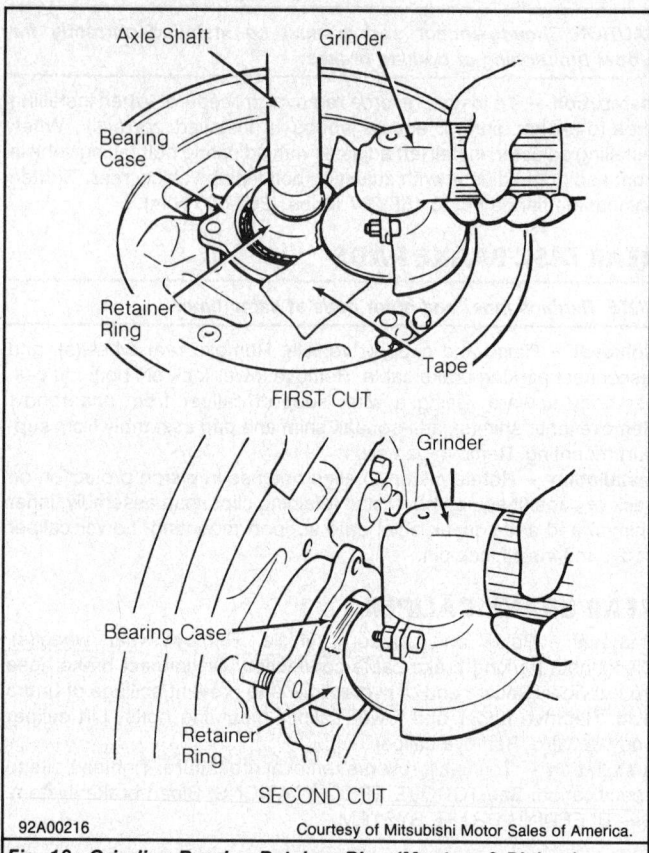

FIRST CUT — Axle Shaft, Grinder, Bearing Case, Retainer Ring, Tape

SECOND CUT — Grinder, Bearing Case, Retainer Ring

92A00216   Courtesy of Mitsubishi Motor Sales of America.

Fig. 12: Grinding Bearing Retainer Ring (Montero & Pickup)

4) Adjust clearance between bearing case and rear axle by inserting .04" (1.0 mm) shim and "O" ring into left rear axle housing. Apply semi-drying sealant to mating surface of bearing case. Install left axle shaft into rear housing, and tighten nuts diagonally to 36-43 ft. lbs. (49-58 N.m).

5) Install right axle shaft without shims and "O" ring. Temporarily tighten axle shaft nuts to about 53 INCH lbs. (6 N.m). Using a feeler gauge, measure clearance between bearing case and rear axle housing.

6) Remove right axle shaft. Install shims to equal bearing case-to-axle housing clearance plus .002-.008" (.05-.20 mm). Install "O" ring to right rear axle housing. Apply sealant to mating surface of bearing case.

7) Install axle into housing, tightening nuts diagonally to 36-43 ft. lbs. (49-58 N.m). Check axle shaft for .002-.008" (.05-.20 mm) end play using dial indicator. If end play is not within specification, change shims to obtain correct end play. To install remaining components, reverse removal procedure. Adjust parking brake, and bleed brake system. See BLEEDING BRAKE SYSTEM.

REAR AXLE HUB BEARINGS

NOTE: Rear hub bearings are not serviceable on Diamante, Eclipse, Galant and Stealth (FWD) models.

Removal & Installation (Colt, Colt Vista, Expo, Mirage, Summit & Summit Wagon) – **1)** Raise and support vehicle. Remove rear hub (dust) cap and nut. *See Fig. 10.* Remove brake drum and hub assembly. Press inner bearing and race out of hub assembly.

2) To install, reverse removal procedure. Press inner bearing and seal into hub assembly. Tighten wheel bearing nut to specification. See WHEEL BEARING NUT SPECIFICATIONS table. Rotate brake drum to ensure free movement.

WHEEL BEARING NUT SPECIFICATIONS

Application	Ft. Lbs. (N.m)
Colt, Mirage & Summit	130 (180)
Colt Vista, Eclipse & Summit Wagon	145-188 (197-255)
Diamante, Expo & Stealth (FWD)	166 (225)

OVERHAUL

NOTE: For exploded views of front disc brake calipers, see Figs. 13 and 14. For exploded views of rear brake calipers, see Figs. 16 and 17. For exploded view of master cylinder, see Fig. 15.

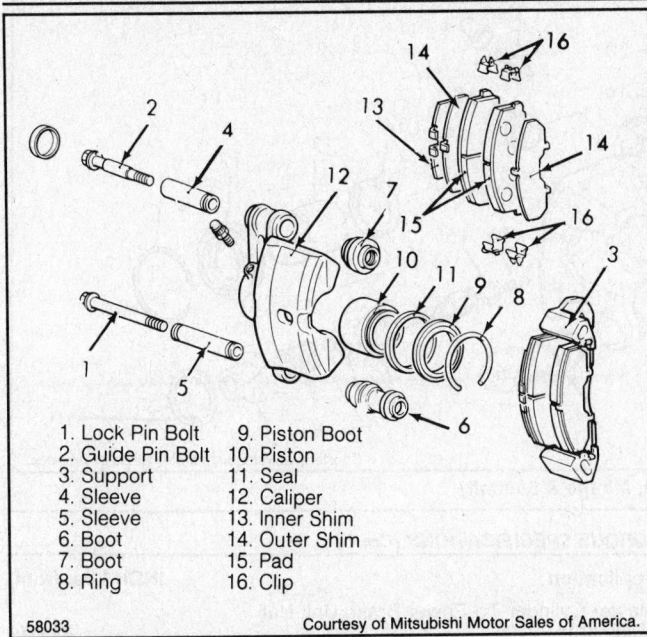

1. Lock Pin Bolt
2. Guide Pin Bolt
3. Support
4. Sleeve
5. Sleeve
6. Boot
7. Boot
8. Ring
9. Piston Boot
10. Piston
11. Seal
12. Caliper
13. Inner Shim
14. Outer Shim
15. Pad
16. Clip

58033   Courtesy of Mitsubishi Motor Sales of America.

Fig. 13: Exploded View Of Front Disc Brake Assembly (Typical Single Piston)

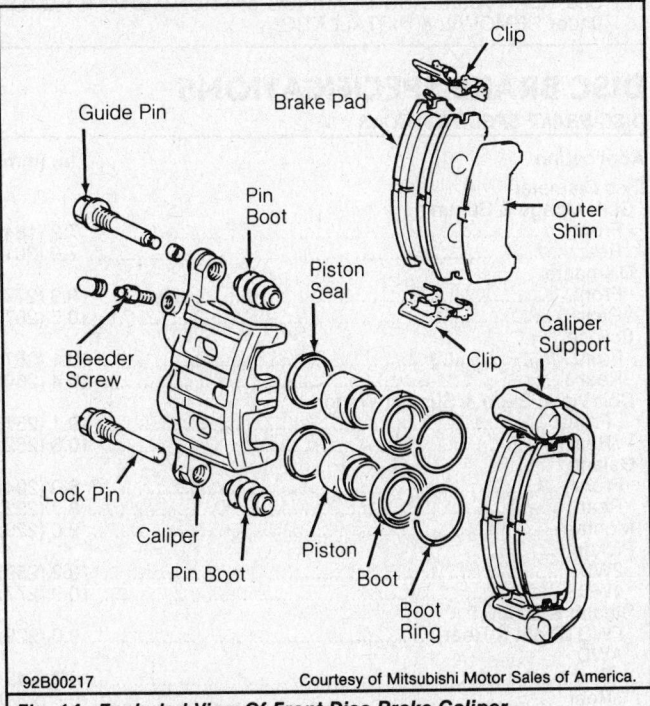

92B00217   Courtesy of Mitsubishi Motor Sales of America.

Fig. 14: Exploded View Of Front Disc Brake Caliper (Typical Dual Piston)

1. Reservoir Bolt
2. Nipple Or Reservoir
3. Seal
4. Stopper Bolt
5. Gasket
6. Master Cylinder
7. Secondary Piston
8. Primary Piston
9. Snap Ring

58045   Courtesy of Mitsubishi Motor Sales of America.

Fig. 15: Exploded View Of Master Cylinder (Typical)

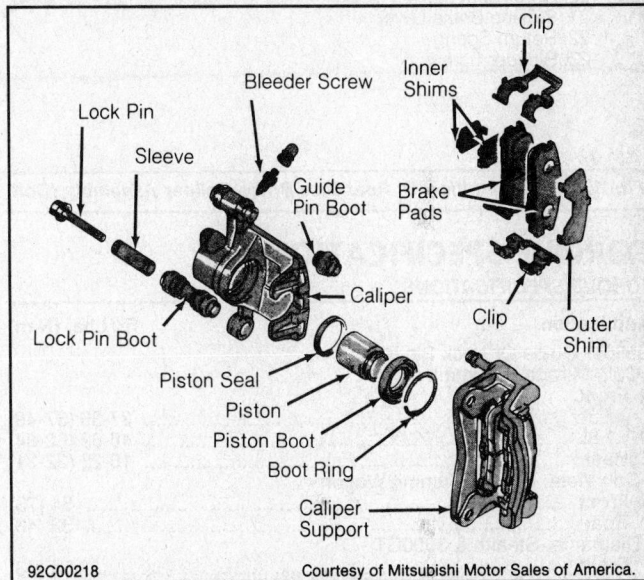

92C00218   Courtesy of Mitsubishi Motor Sales of America.

Fig. 16: Exploded View Of Rear Disc Brake Caliper Assembly (Diamante, Galant, Montero, Stealth & 3000GT)

1994 BRAKES
Disc & Drum – Except Precis (Cont.)

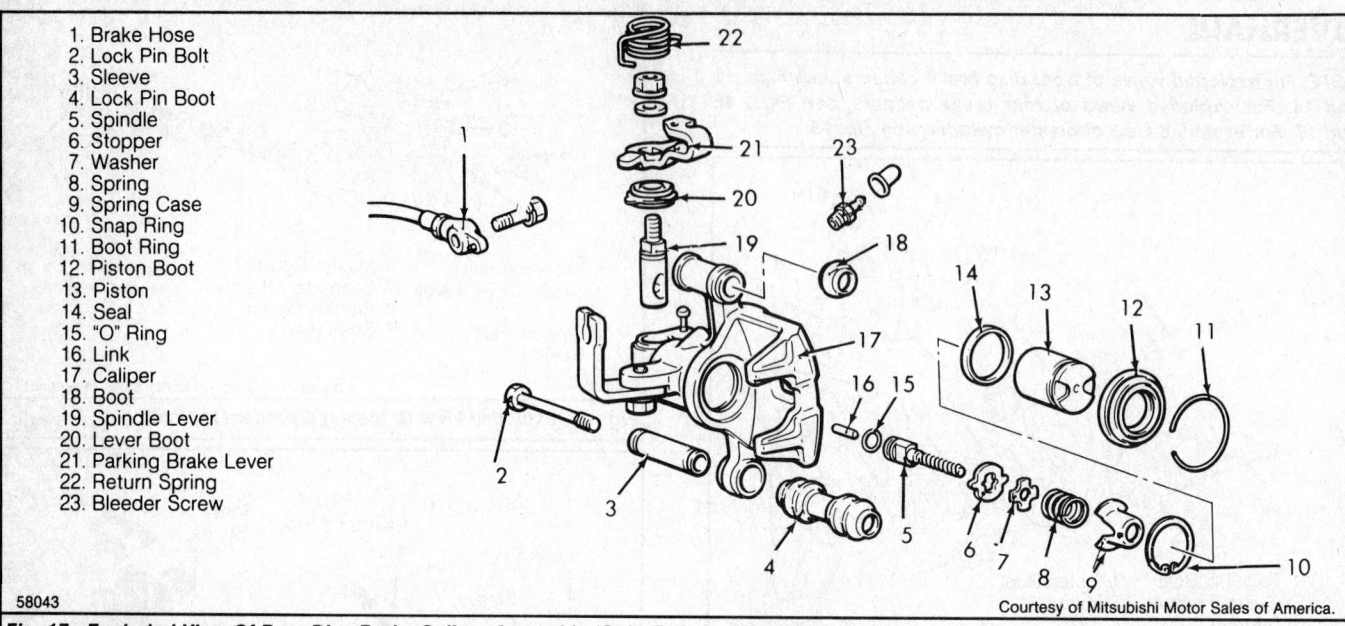

1. Brake Hose
2. Lock Pin Bolt
3. Sleeve
4. Lock Pin Boot
5. Spindle
6. Stopper
7. Washer
8. Spring
9. Spring Case
10. Snap Ring
11. Boot Ring
12. Piston Boot
13. Piston
14. Seal
15. "O" Ring
16. Link
17. Caliper
18. Boot
19. Spindle Lever
20. Lever Boot
21. Parking Brake Lever
22. Return Spring
23. Bleeder Screw

58043

Courtesy of Mitsubishi Motor Sales of America.

Fig. 17: Exploded View Of Rear Disc Brake Caliper Assembly (Colt, Eclipse, Mirage & Summit)

TORQUE SPECIFICATIONS
TORQUE SPECIFICATIONS

Application	Ft. Lbs. (N.m)
Caliper Guide Or Lock Pin Bolt	
Colt, Mirage & Summit	
Front	
1.5L	27-36 (37-49)
1.8L	46-62 (62-84)
Rear	16-23 (22-31)
Colt Vista, Expo & Summit Wagon	
Front	54 (73)
Rear	32 (43)
Diamante, Stealth & 3000GT	
Front	54 (73)
Rear	20 (27)
Eclipse & Galant	46-62 (62-84)
Expo	54 (73)
Montero	54 (73)
Pickup	
Guide Pin Bolt	29-36 (39-49)
Lock Pin Bolt	23-30 (31-41)
Caliper Mounting Bolts	
Except Expo, Montero & Pickup	
Front	58-72 (79-98)
Rear	36-43 (49-58)
Expo	65 (88)
Montero & Pickup	65 (88)
Companion Flange Nut	
Eclipse 4WD	116-159 (157-216)
Front Wheel Bearing Nut	
FWD	144-188 (195-254)
RWD & 4WD	[1]
Hub/Bearing Bolt	60 (81)
Locking or Full-Time Hub Bolt	36-43 (49-60)
Rear Wheel Bearing Nut	
Except Colt, Mirage & Summit	[1]
Colt, Mirage & Summit	108-145 (146-197)
Rotor-To-Hub Bolts Or Nuts	
Except Pickup 2WD	36-43 (49-60)
Pickup 2WD	34-38 (46-52)
Wheel Lug Nut	
Colt, Colt Vista, Diamante, Expo,	
Galant, Mirage, Summit & Summit Wagon	65-80 (88-108)
Eclipse, Pickup, Stealth & 3000GT	87-101 (118-137)
Montero	72-87 (98-118)

[1] – See REAR AXLE HUB BEARINGS or FRONT BRAKE ROTOR under REMOVAL & INSTALLATION.

TORQUE SPECIFICATIONS (Cont.)

Application	INCH Lbs. (N.m)
Master Cylinder-To-Power Brake Unit Nut	
Diamante	84 (10)
Stealth & 3000GT	120 (14)
Except Diamante, Stealth & 3000GT	72-108 (8-12)

[1] – See REAR AXLE HUB BEARINGS or FRONT BRAKE ROTOR under REMOVAL & INSTALLATION.

DISC BRAKE SPECIFICATIONS
DISC BRAKE SPECIFICATIONS

Application	In. (mm)
Disc Diameter	
Colt, Mirage & Summit	
Front	7.2 (184)
Rear	7.9 (201)
Diamante	
Front	10.9 (277)
Rear	10.5 (267)
Eclipse	
Front	10.1 (257)
Rear	10.4 (264)
Colt Vista, Expo & Summit Wagon	
Front	10.1 (257)
Rear	10.3 (262)
Galant	
Front	8.0 (204)
Rear	8.7 (222)
Montero	9.0 (229)
Pickup	
2WD	10.2 (259)
4WD	10.9 (277)
Stealth & 3000GT	
FWD (Front & Rear)	9.0 (229)
AWD	
Front	9.8 (249)
Rear	9.4 (239)
Lateral Runout	
Colt Vista, Diamante, Eclipse, Expo,	
Galant & Summit Wagon	.003 (.08)
All Other Models	.006 (.15)
Parallelism	[1]

[1] – Information is not available from manufacturer.

DISC BRAKE SPECIFICATIONS (Cont.)

Application	In. (mm)
Original Thickness	
Colt, Mirage & Summit	
Solid Disc	.51 (12.9)
Ventilated Disc	.71 (18.0)
Diamante	
Front	.94 (24)
Rear	.71 (18.0)
Colt Vista, Eclipse, Expo & Summit Wagon	
Front	.94 (24)
Rear	.39 (9.9)
Galant	
Front	.94 (24)
Rear	.39 (10)
Montero	
Front	.94 (24)
Rear	.71 (18)
Pickup	.87 (22.1)
Stealth & 3000GT	
Front	
FWD	.94 (24)
AWD	1.18 (30.0)
Rear	
FWD	.71 (18)
AWD	.79 (20.1)
Master Cylinder Diameter	
Colt, Mirage & Summit	
With ABS	.938 (23.83)
Without ABS	.813 (20.65)
Diamante	1.000 (25.40)
Eclipse	
Non-Turbo (w/o ABS)	.875 (22.23)
Turbo (w/ ABS)	1.000 (25.40)
Colt Vista, Expo, Montero,	
Pickup & Summit Wagon	.938 (23.83)
Galant	
With ABS	1.000 (25.40)
Without ABS	.938 (23.83)
Stealth & 3000GT	[1]
Minimum Refinish Thickness	
Colt, Mirage & Summit	
Front	
Solid	.45 (11.4)
Vented	.65 (16.5)
Rear	.33 (8.4)
Colt Vista, Expo &	
Summit Wagon	.94 (23.9)
Diamante	
Front	.88 (22.4)
Rear	.65 (16.5)
Eclipse	
Front	.88 (22.4)
Rear	.33 (8.4)
Galant	
Front	.88 (22.4)
Rear	.33 (8.4)
Montero	
Front	.88 (22.4)
Rear	.65 (16.5)
Pickup	.80 (20.3)
Stealth & 3000GT	
Front	
FWD	.88 (22.4)
AWD	1.12 (28.5)
Rear	
FWD	.65 (16.5)
AWD	.72 (18.3)
Discard Thickness	[1]

[1] – Information is not available from manufacturer.

DRUM BRAKE SPECIFICATIONS

DRUM BRAKE SPECIFICATIONS

Application	In. (mm)
Drum Diameter	
Colt, Mirage & Summit	
1.5L	7.1 (180)
1.8L	8.0 (203)
Colt Vista, Expo & Summit Wagon	
8" Drum	8.0 (203)
9" Drum	9.0 (229)
Galant	9.0 (229)
Pickup	10.0 (254)
Drum Width	[1]
Master Cylinder Diameter	[2]
Maximum Refinish Diameter	
Colt, Mirage & Summit	
1.5L	7.2 (183)
1.8L	8.1 (206)
Colt Vista, Expo & Summit Wagon	
8" Drum	8.1 (206)
9" Drum	9.1 (231)
Galant	9.1 (231)
Pickup	10.1 (257)
Wheel Cylinder Diameter	
Colt, Mirage & Summit	.750 (19.10)
Colt Vista, Expo & Summit Wagon	[1]
Galant	.750 (19.10)
Pickup	
2WD	.937 (23.80)
4WD	.875 (22.23)
Drum Discard Diameter	[1]

[1] – Information is not available from manufacturer.
[2] – See DISC BRAKE SPECIFICATIONS table under DISC BRAKE SPECIFICATIONS.

1994 BRAKES
Disc & Drum – Precis

DESCRIPTION & OPERATION

Brake system is hydraulically-operated using a master cylinder with a single reservoir and 2 outlets. A vacuum power brake unit is used. A proportioning valve is used to control braking action. Brake system is self-adjusting. Pad lining thickness wear limit indicators will begin squealing when pad thickness is .080" (2.0 mm).

BLEEDING BRAKE SYSTEM

BLEEDING PROCEDURE

Bleed brakes whenever hydraulic lines are opened or pedal feels spongy. Bleed system in order as shown in BRAKE LINE BLEEDING SEQUENCE table.

BRAKE LINE BLEEDING SEQUENCE

Application	Sequence
Precis	LR, RF, RR, LF

ADJUSTMENTS

BRAKE PEDAL HEIGHT & FREE PLAY

1) Measure pedal height from upper surface of floor board to top of brake pedal. *See Fig. 1.* See PEDAL HEIGHT & FREE PLAY SPECIFICATIONS table. To adjust pedal height, loosen stoplight switch and push rod lock nut. Adjust power brake unit push rod until specified pedal height is obtained. Tighten lock nut.

2) Adjust stoplight switch until clearance between brake pedal arm and stoplight switch is .02-.04" (.5-1.0 mm). Tighten lock nut. With engine off, depress brake pedal 2-3 times to exhaust power brake unit vacuum. Check brake pedal free play. See PEDAL HEIGHT & FREE PLAY SPECIFICATIONS table. If free play is not to specification, adjust stoplight switch until specified clearance is obtained.

3) Start engine. Apply brake pedal with 110 lbs. (50 kg) force. See PEDAL HEIGHT & FREE PLAY SPECIFICATIONS table. If clearance is not to specification, check brake shoe adjustment, push rod-to-master cylinder clearance and for fluid leaks or air in system.

PEDAL HEIGHT & FREE PLAY SPECIFICATIONS

Application	In. (mm)
Pedal Height	
Pedal Released ("A")	6.417-6.614 (163-168)
Pedal Depressed (Minimum)	2.76 (70)
Pedal Free Play	.12-.31 (3-8)

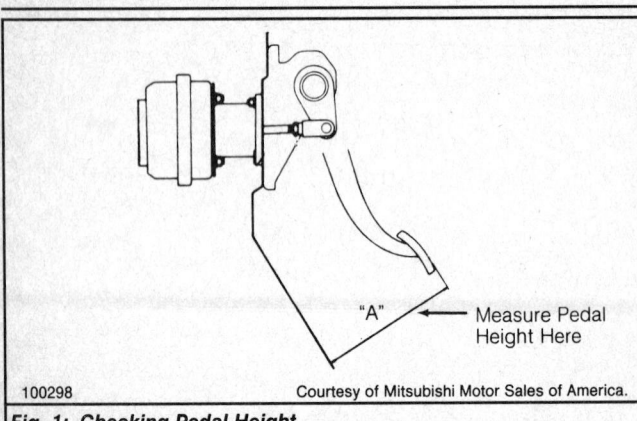

Fig. 1: Checking Pedal Height

PARKING/EMERGENCY BRAKE

NOTE: Ensure cables are not too tight. If cables are adjusted too tight, automatic shoe adjuster will not function.

1) Properly adjusted parking brake lever stroke should be 6-7 notches (clicks) at 44 lbs. (20 kg). If stroke is not as specified, remove console box, and release brake lever. Adjust cable adjusting nut, allowing enough slack in cables to prevent brake shoe drag. *See Fig. 2.*

2) Loosen parking brake switch mounting bolt. Adjust switch until indicator light goes out when brake lever is fully released, and light comes on when lever is pulled one notch. Ensure rear brakes do not drag with brake lever released.

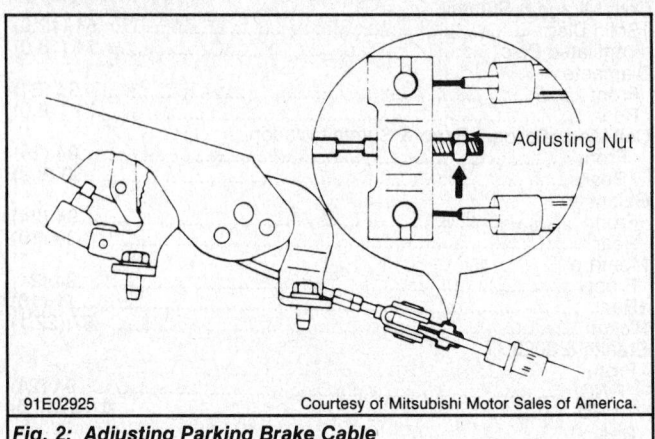

Fig. 2: Adjusting Parking Brake Cable

STOPLIGHT SWITCH

For stoplight switch adjustment procedure, see BRAKE PEDAL HEIGHT & FREE PLAY.

TESTING

POWER BRAKE UNIT

1) Run engine for 1-2 minutes. Turn ignition off. Depress brake pedal several times with normal pressure. If pedal depresses fully first time but gradually depresses less during successive pedal applications, go to next step. If pedal height remains unchanged during successive pedal applications, booster is defective.

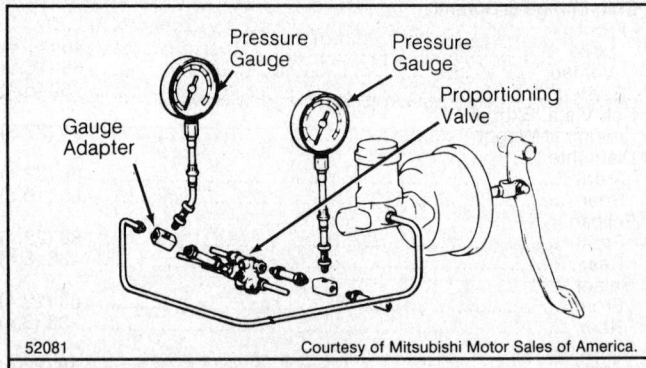

Fig. 3: Testing Proportioning Valve

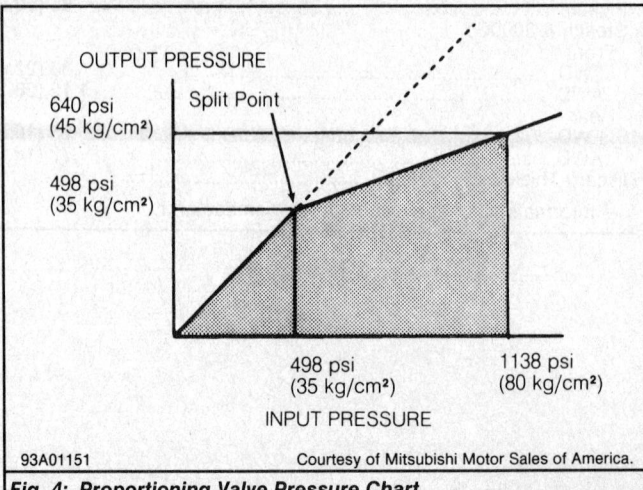

Fig. 4: Proportioning Valve Pressure Chart

2) With engine off, depress pedal several times using equal pedal pressure to ensure pedal height does not change. Depress and hold brake pedal and start engine. If pedal moves down slightly, go to next step. If pedal height does not change, booster is defective.

3) With engine running, depress brake pedal and turn ignition off. Hold pedal depressed for 30 seconds. If pedal height does not change, booster is okay. If pedal rises, check for defective booster, check valve or vacuum hose.

POWER BRAKE UNIT CHECK VALVE

1) Disconnect vacuum hose on booster side of check valve. Place finger over check valve. Start engine. If vacuum exists, go to next step. If vacuum does not exist, replace check valve.

2) Remove check valve, and apply vacuum to booster side of check valve. Valve should hold vacuum in this direction. If vacuum is not held, replace check valve.

PROPORTIONING VALVE FUNCTION TEST

1) Attach 2 pressure gauges, each measuring at least 2000 psi (140.6 kg/cm²), to input and output sides of proportioning valve. *See Fig. 3.* After installing gauges, bleed brake system before testing.

2) Measure input and output pressure with brakes applied. At split point, output pressure begins to drop relative to input pressure. *See Fig. 4.* If measured pressures are within range, proportioning valve is okay. If measured pressures are not within range, replace proportioning valve. DO NOT disassemble proportioning valve.

NOTE: Bleed brake system after gauges are removed and testing is completed.

REMOVAL & INSTALLATION

FRONT DISC BRAKE PADS

Removal & Installation – Raise and support vehicle. Remove front wheel. Remove lower guide pin bolt. *See Fig. 5.* Rotate caliper upward, and wire aside. Remove disc pads, shims and springs. To install, reverse removal procedure. Using Piston Expander (09581-11000), press piston back into caliper bore. Install disc pads, shims and springs. Depress brake pedal several times to expand caliper piston.

FRONT BRAKE CALIPER

Removal & Installation – Raise and support vehicle. Remove front wheel. Disconnect brake hose. Plug all fluid openings. Remove lower guide pin bolt. *See Fig. 5.* Rotate caliper upward and slide caliper from guide pin bolt. To install, reverse removal procedure. Bleed brake system.

FRONT BRAKE ROTOR

Removal – **1)** Raise and support vehicle. Remove wheels. Remove caliper assembly. Remove torque plate from knuckle. *See Fig. 5.* Remove ball joint and strut bar from lower arm. Remove axle shaft nut. Remove axle shaft using Puller (MB990241-01). Ensure spacer does not fall out of place.

2) Disconnect tie rod from knuckle. Remove knuckle, hub and rotor as an assembly. Mount steering knuckle in a soft-jawed vise. Install Remover/Installer (09517-21500) in hub and steering knuckle. Install Puller (MB991056) on steering knuckle. Separate hub from steering knuckle. Remove rotor from hub.

Installation – Install rotor on hub. Press hub into knuckle. Install new inner oil seal. Slide axle shaft into position. Install knuckle assembly by reversing removal procedure. Tighten nuts and bolts to specification. See TORQUE SPECIFICATIONS.

REAR BRAKE DRUM, BEARINGS & OIL SEAL

Removal – Raise and support vehicle. Remove rear wheels. Remove grease cap. Remove self-locking nut and outer wheel bearing. Remove brake drum. To remove oil seal, pry out seal using a flat-blade screwdriver. Remove inner bearing. Remove bearing races from drum using a brass drift.

Installation – **1)** To install, reverse removal procedure. Install a new self-locking nut, and tighten to specification. See TORQUE SPECIFICATIONS table at end of article.

2) Check wheel bearing end play. If end play exceeds .0043" (.11 mm), retighten self-locking nut, and check end play again. If end play remains out of specification, replace wheel bearing. Fill grease cap with grease, and install.

REAR BRAKE SHOES

Removal – **1)** Raise and support vehicle. Remove brake drum, bearings and oil seal. Remove automatic adjuster spring and adjuster lever. *See Fig. 6.*

2) Spread shoes and remove adjuster strut. Remove shoe-to-shoe spring and shoe hold-down spring. Remove parking brake cable at lever. Remove brake shoes. Replace brake shoes if lining thickness is .04" (1.0 mm) or less.

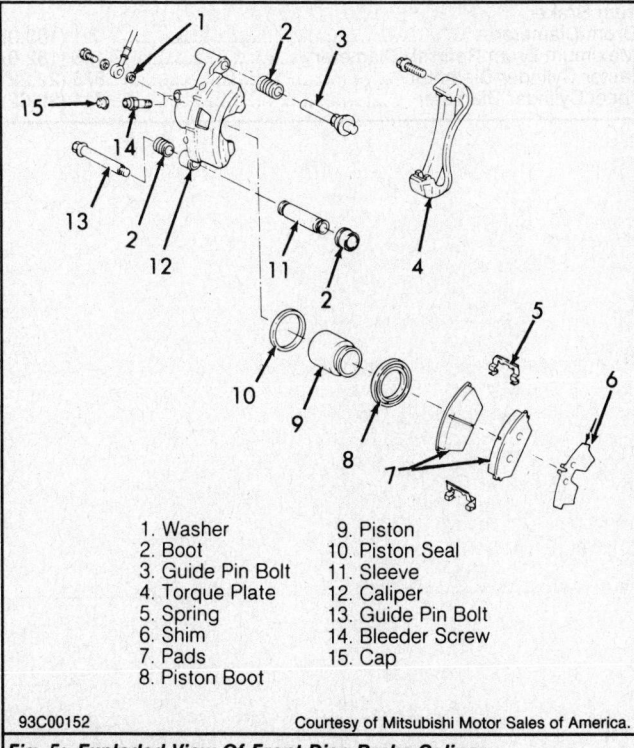

1. Washer
2. Boot
3. Guide Pin Bolt
4. Torque Plate
5. Spring
6. Shim
7. Pads
8. Piston Boot
9. Piston
10. Piston Seal
11. Sleeve
12. Caliper
13. Guide Pin Bolt
14. Bleeder Screw
15. Cap

93C00152   Courtesy of Mitsubishi Motor Sales of America.

Fig. 5: Exploded View Of Front Disc Brake Caliper

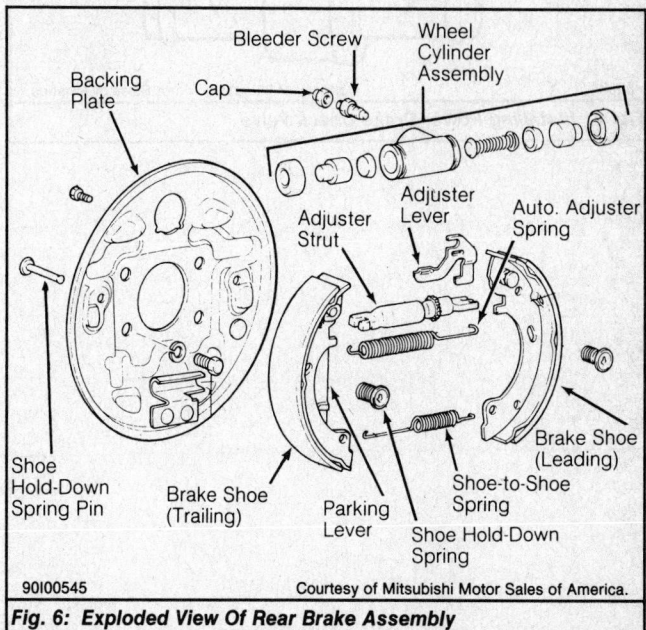

90I00545   Courtesy of Mitsubishi Motor Sales of America.

Fig. 6: Exploded View Of Rear Brake Assembly

Installation – 1) To install, reverse removal procedure. Apply Lubriplate to 6 shoe contact points, adjuster assembly and parking brake attachment.

2) Rotate adjuster strut to preset shoe clearance. Install brake drum. Apply and release parking brake. Depress and release brake pedal to adjust shoe clearance. Adjust parking brake and warning light (if necessary).

MASTER CYLINDER

Removal – Remove fluid level sensor harness connector. Disconnect brake lines from master cylinder. Plug all lines. Remove master cylinder from power brake unit. *See Fig. 7.* Separate reservoir from housing. Drain fluid from reservoir.

Installation – To install master cylinder, reverse removal procedure. After installation, adjust pedal height. Bleed brake system.

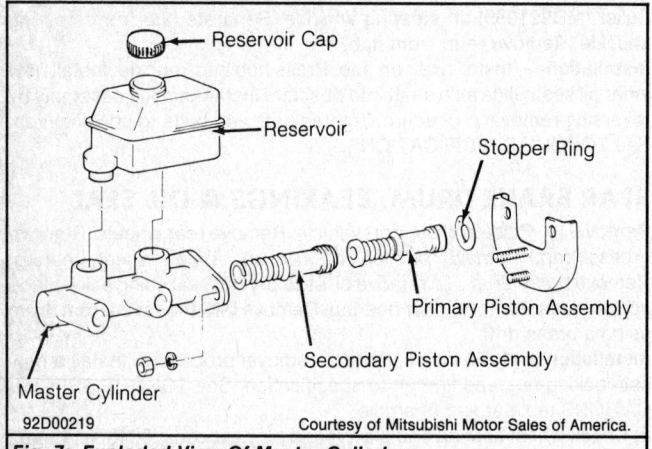

92D00219   Courtesy of Mitsubishi Motor Sales of America.

Fig. 7: Exploded View Of Master Cylinder

POWER BRAKE UNIT CHECK VALVE

Removal & Installation – Remove hose clamps from both ends of check valve. Remove check valve clamp. Remove check valve. To install, coat both ends of check valve with sealer. Install check valve with arrow pointing toward intake manifold side. *See Fig. 8.* Install check valve clamp and vacuum hoses. Secure hose clamps.

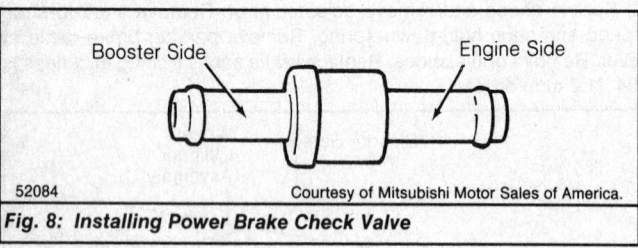

52084   Courtesy of Mitsubishi Motor Sales of America.

Fig. 8: Installing Power Brake Check Valve

POWER BRAKE UNIT

Removal & Installation – Remove master cylinder. Disconnect vacuum hose from power brake unit. From inside vehicle, disconnect brake pedal and operating rod of power brake unit. Remove 4 nuts attaching power brake unit to firewall. Remove power brake unit. To install, reverse removal procedure. Bleed brake system.

OVERHAUL

NOTE: For exploded view of front disc brake caliper, see Fig. 5.

TORQUE SPECIFICATIONS
TORQUE SPECIFICATIONS

Application	Ft. Lbs. (N.m)
Backing Plate Mounting Bolts	37-44 (50-60)
Caliper Lower Guide Pin Bolt	16-24 (22-32)
Caliper-To-Knuckle Bolt	48-55 (65-75)
Caliper Upper Guide Pin Bolt	26-33 (35-45)
Front Hub Nut	145-188 (197-255)
Rear Hub Self-Locking Nut	108-145 (146-197)
Torque Plate Mounting Bolt	47-54 (64-74)
Wheel Lug Nut	65-80 (88-108)

	INCH Lbs. (N.m)
Bleeder Screw	62-80 (7-9)
Brake Booster Mounting Nut	71-108 (8-12)
Brake Hose	71-108 (8-12)
Brake Line Flare Nut	71-108 (8-12)
Master Cylinder-To-Power Brake Unit Nut	71-108 (8-12)
Proportioning Valve Mounting Bolt	71-108 (8-12)
Wheel Cylinder Mounting Bolt	53-97 (6-11)

DISC & DRUM BRAKE SPECIFICATIONS
DISC & DRUM BRAKE SPECIFICATIONS

Application	In. (mm)
Disc Brake	
Disc Diameter	9.53 (242)
Discard Thickness	.665 (16.89)
Lateral Runout	.006 (.15)
Minimum Refinish Thickness	.670 (17.00)
Original Thickness	.750 (19.00)
Drum Brake	
Drum Diameter	7.1 (180.0)
Maximum Drum Refinish Diameter	7.165 (182.0)
Master Cylinder Diameter	.875 (22.22)
Wheel Cylinder Diameter	.811 (20.62)

Chrysler Corp.: Colt, Colt Vista,
 Stealth, Summit, Summit Wagon
Mitsubishi: Diamante, Eclipse,
 Expo, Mirage, 3000GT

DESCRIPTION

The Anti-Lock Brake System (ABS) is designed to prevent wheel lock-up during heavy braking. This allows operator to maintain steering control while stopping vehicle in shortest distance possible. Major components are hydraulic unit, wheel speed sensors, "G" force sensor (all-wheel drive vehicles), Electronic Control Unit (ECU) and ANTI-LOCK warning light. ABS has a self-diagnostic system to indicate a system malfunction and for use in system trouble shooting.

NOTE: For more information on brake system, see DISC & DRUM – EXCEPT PRECIS article.

OPERATION

Each wheel sensor sends an AC electrical signal to the Electronic Control Unit (ECU). The ECU translates this information as wheel speed. When any decelerating wheel speed rate is determined to be excessive in comparison to other monitored wheels, the hydraulic unit cycles hydraulic brake pressure to each wheel to equalize speed of all wheels. ABS turns itself off when vehicle reaches 4 MPH. Minor lock-up may occur at this point.

With engine running and vehicle speed greater than 4 MPH, pump motor will operate for a short period of time and may be heard inside vehicle. During pump motor operation, ABS system is completing a self-check. During ABS system operation, a pulsing brake pedal and vibration in steering wheel and vehicle body may be experienced. These conditions are normal.

CAUTION: See ANTI-LOCK BRAKE SAFETY PRECAUTIONS article in GENERAL INFORMATION.

BLEEDING BRAKE SYSTEM

CAUTION: When adding brake fluid, ensure filter is properly fitted on reserve tank.

ABS system is bled using conventional method. Manually bleed system using foot method with an assistant. For bleeding order see BRAKE LINE BLEEDING SEQUENCE table. Ensure all air is removed from brake system. Refill brake fluid reservoir after bleeding procedure is complete.

BRAKE LINE BLEEDING SEQUENCE

Application	Sequence
Colt Vista, Expo & Summit Wagon	LR, RF, RR, LF
Colt, Diamante, Eclipse	
Mirage, Stealth, Summit Wagon & 3000GT	RR, LF, LR, RF

ADJUSTMENTS

NOTE: For adjustment information for brake pedal height, free play, parking brake and stoplight switch, see DISC & DRUM – EXCEPT PRECIS article.

WHEEL SPEED SENSOR

Sensor-To-Rotor Gap Adjustment – 1) Raise and support vehicle. Remove tire and wheel assembly. Inspect sensor pole piece for damage. Repair if necessary. If sensor pole piece is okay, check wheel speed sensor-to-rotor gap.
2) Using a feeler gauge, check clearance between speed sensor pole and rotor tooth surface. *See Fig. 1.* See WHEEL SPEED SENSOR-TO-ROTOR GAP SPECIFICATIONS table. If clearance is not within specification, loosen sensor mounting bolt. Adjust sensor position until clearance is within specification. Tighten sensor mounting bolt.

WHEEL SPEED SENSOR-TO-ROTOR GAP SPECIFICATIONS [1]

Application	In. (mm)
Colt, Mirage & Summit	
Rear	.012-.035 (.3-.9)
Colt Vista, Expo & Summit Wagon	
FWD	.008-.028 (.2-.7)
AWD	.012-.035 (.3-.9)
Diamante, Stealth & 3000GT	
Front	.012-.035 (.3-.9)
Rear	.008-.028 (.2-.7)
Eclipse	.012-.035 (.3-.9)

[1] – Front sensor-to-rotor gap specifications are not provided for Colt, Mirage and Summit.

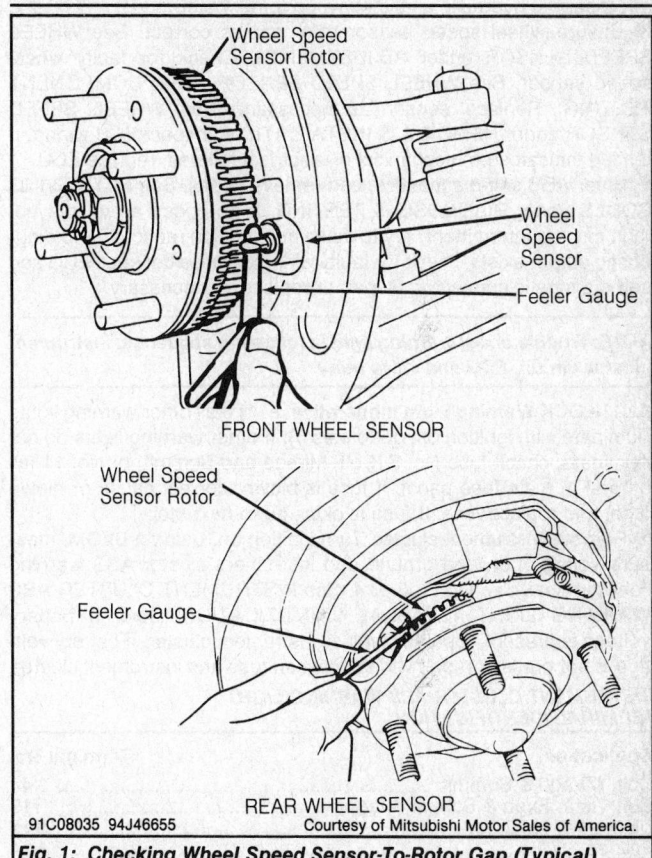

FRONT WHEEL SENSOR

REAR WHEEL SENSOR

91C08035 94J46655   Courtesy of Mitsubishi Motor Sales of America.

Fig. 1: Checking Wheel Speed Sensor-To-Rotor Gap (Typical)

TROUBLE SHOOTING

NOTE: If after all testing procedures have been completed system is not functioning properly, substitute ABS ECU with known good unit and retest.

ANTI-LOCK WARNING LIGHT

1) Turn ignition on. ANTI-LOCK warning light should blink twice (4 times on AWD models), and then go out. Turn ignition switch to START position. Warning light should come on and stay on.
2) When ignition switch is turned from START to ON position, warning light should blink twice (4 times on AWD models) and then go out. If warning light functions as specified, go step **3)**. If warning light does not function as specified, see appropriate trouble shooting test:

- ANTI-LOCK WARNING LIGHT INOPERATIVE.
- IGNITION SWITCH IN ON POSITION, WARNING LIGHT REMAINS ON.
- IGNITION SWITCH IN START POSITION, WARNING LIGHT INOPERATIVE.
- IGNITION SWITCH IN ON POSITION, WARNING LIGHT BLINKS ONCE. IN START POSITION, WARNING LIGHT STAYS ON. WHEN IGNITION SWITCH IS CYCLED FROM START TO ON POSITION, WARNING LIGHT BLINKS ONCE.

- IGNITION SWITCH IN ON POSITION, WARNING LIGHT BLINKS TWICE AND REMAINS OFF.
- WARNING LIGHT SWITCHES OFF ONE SECOND AFTER IGNITION SWITCH IS TURNED TO ON POSITION.

3) Test drive vehicle. If ABS light does not come on at low speed, go to next step. If ABS light comes on at low speed, motor relay, solenoid valve or wheel speed sensor malfunction is indicated. Go to step **6)**. If insufficient braking force or ABS malfunction exists, go to next step. If none of above symptoms exist, go to step **6)**.

4) Check conventional brake system components for proper operation. Check for mechanical lock of hydraulic unit solenoid valve. Check for plugged hydraulic line in hydraulic unit. Repair or replace as necessary. If hydraulic unit is okay, go to next step.

5) Ensure wheel speed sensor rotor gap is correct. See WHEEL SPEED SENSOR under ADJUSTMENTS. Check for faulty wheel speed sensor. See WHEEL SPEED SENSOR under COMPONENT TESTING. Replace sensor as necessary. See WHEEL SPEED SENSOR under REMOVAL & INSTALLATION. Inspect ECU wiring. If testing indicates no mechanical or electrical failures, replace ECU.

6) Enter ABS self-diagnostics, and retrieve codes. See RETRIEVING CODES under DIAGNOSIS & TESTING. If no codes are displayed, fault may be intermittent. Try to make malfunction reoccur. If no diagnostic output exists, check for faulty wiring harness between ECU and self-diagnostic connector. Repair or replace as necessary.

NOTE: *Trouble shoot warning light in following sequence: instrument cluster circuit, ECU and valve relay.*

ANTI-LOCK Warning Light Inoperative – **1)** If all other warning lights illuminate with ignition on, go to step **3)**. If other warning lights do not illuminate, check fuse No. 3 (Colt, Mirage and Summit) or No. 11 (all others) in main fuse panel. If fuse is blown, correct cause of blown fuse, and replace fuse. If fuse is okay, go to next step.

2) Remove instrument cluster. Turn ignition on. Using a DVOM, measure voltage between ground and instrument cluster ABS warning light terminal. *See Fig. 2, 3 or 4.* See INSTRUMENT CLUSTER ABS WARNING LIGHT TERMINAL IDENTIFICATION table. If battery voltage is present, repair or replace instrument cluster. If battery voltage is not present, repair wiring between fuse and instrument cluster.

INSTRUMENT CLUSTER ABS WARNING LIGHT TERMINAL IDENTIFICATION

Application	Terminal No.
Colt, Mirage & Summit	[1] 44
Colt Vista, Expo & Summit Wagon	[2] 113
Diamante	[2] 115
Eclipse	[3] 14
Stealth & 3000GT	[3] 59

[1] – See Fig. 2.
[2] – See Fig. 3.
[3] – See Fig. 4.

3) Turn ignition off. Check for faulty warning light bulb. Replace bulb as necessary. If bulb is okay, check for continuity between appropriate instrument cluster connector terminals:
- Colt, Mirage and Summit: No. 22 and 44
- Colt Vista, Expo and Summit Wagon: No. 113 and 17.
- Diamante: No. 101 and 115.
- Eclipse: No. 14 and 58.
- Stealth and 3000GT: No. 58 and 59.

If continuity is not present, clean and/or repair connector terminals. If continuity is present, go to next step.

4) To check ECU, turn ignition off. Remove ECU connector. Turn ignition on. Measure voltage between terminal No. 21 (Diamante) or No. 25 (all others) and ground. *See Fig. 5, 6 or 7.* If battery voltage is not present, repair circuit between warning light and ECU. If battery voltage is present, replace ECU.

5) To check valve relay, see HYDRAULIC UNIT RELAYS under COMPONENT TESTING. If relay is okay, remove harness connector. Turn ignition on. On Diamante, measure voltage between terminal No. 101 (single wire connector) and ground. On Colt, Mirage and Summit,

measure voltage between Green/Blue wire (8-pin connector) and ground.

6) On all other models except Colt, Mirage and Summit, measure voltage between terminal No. 8 and ground. *See Fig. 12.* On all vehicles, if battery voltage is present, go to next step. If battery voltage is not present, repair circuit between ANTI-LOCK warning light and hydraulic unit. See WIRING DIAGRAMS.

7) Turn ignition off. Check for continuity between terminal No. 1 (Colt, Diamante, Mirage & Summit) or No. 9 (all other models) and ground. *See Fig. 7.* If continuity does not exist, repair circuit between hydraulic unit and ground. If continuity exists, replace relay valve.

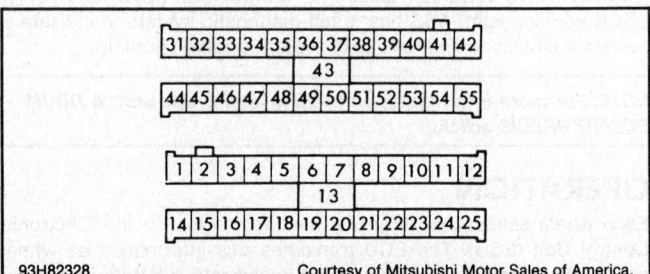

Fig. 2: **Instrument Cluster Terminals (Colt, Mirage & Summit)**

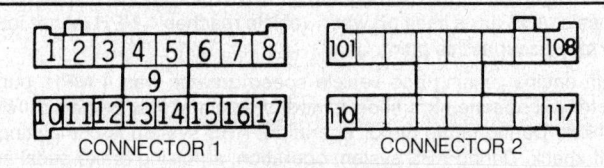

Fig. 3: **Instrument Cluster Terminals (Colt Vista, Diamante, Expo & Summit Wagon)**

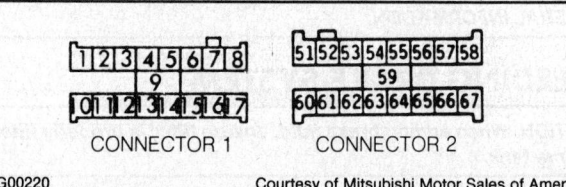

Fig. 4: **Instrument Cluster Terminals (Eclipse, Stealth & 3000GT)**

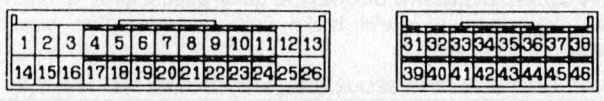

Fig. 5: **ECU Terminals (Colt, Mirage & Summit)**

Fig. 6: **ECU Terminals (Colt Vista, Eclipse, Expo, Stealth, Summit Wagon & 3000GT)**

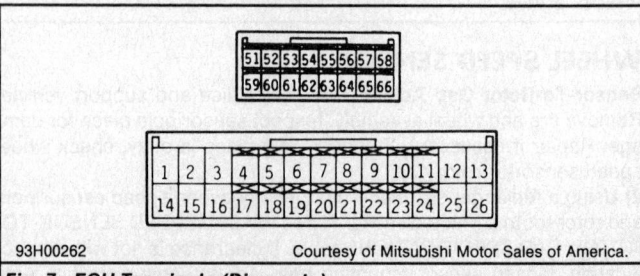

Fig. 7: **ECU Terminals (Diamante)**

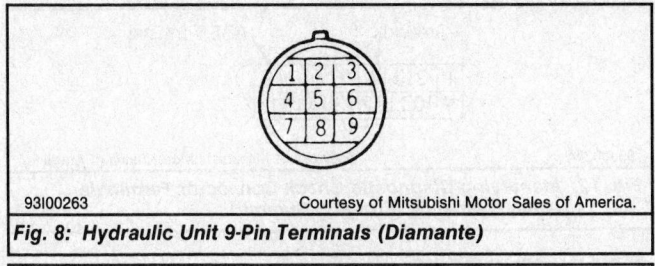

Fig. 8: Hydraulic Unit 9-Pin Terminals (Diamante)

Fig. 9: Hydraulic Unit Terminals (Colt Vista, Eclipse, Expo, Stealth, Summit Wagon & 3000GT)

Fig. 10: Hydraulic Unit Terminals (Colt, Mirage & Summit)

Ignition Switch In ON Position, Warning Light Remains On – 1) Enter ABS self-diagnostics. See RETRIEVING CODES under DIAGNOSIS & TESTING. If diagnostic output exists, go to step 9). If no diagnostic output exists, connect Multi-Use Tester (MUT) to another electronic control system. Refer to tester instruction manual.

2) If MUT can communicate with another electronic control system, go to next step. If MUT cannot communicate with another electronic control system, tester is malfunctioning. Inspect diagnostic connector for damaged terminals and correct hook-up. Repair as necessary. If diagnostic connector is okay, replace MUT.

3) Check fuse No. 15 (Colt, Mirage and Summit), No. 2 (Diamante) or No. 3 (all other models) in main fuse panel. If fuse is okay, go to next step. If fuse is blown, correct cause of blown fuse, and replace fuse.

4) On Diamante, go to step 6). On all models except Diamante, turn ignition on. ABS power relay should energize. Listen if power relay makes a click noise. See ABS POWER RELAY LOCATION table. If no click noise is heard, go to next step. If click noise is heard, go to step 7).

ABS POWER RELAY LOCATION

Application	Location
Colt, Mirage & Summit	Front Of P/S Reservoir
Colt Vista, Expo & Summit Wagon	In Relay Box
Eclipse	Behind RR Quarter Panel
Stealth & 3000GT	Engine Compartment Relay Box

5) Remove and test ABS power relay. See ABS POWER RELAY under REMOVAL & INSTALLATION and COMPONENT TESTING. Replace relay if faulty.

6) On all models, disconnect ECU wiring harness connector. Turn ignition on. Measure voltage between terminal No. 5 (Colt, Diamante, Mirage and Summit) or No. 18 (all others), and ground. *See Fig. 5, 6 or 7.* If battery voltage is present, go to next step. If battery voltage is not present, repair open circuit between power relay and ECU.

7) On Diamante models, go to next step. On all other models, check for continuity between ground and terminals No. 12 and 25 (Colt, Mirage and Summit), No. 9 and/or No.20 (check continuity with terminal No. 20 on FWD models) or No. 34 (all other models). If continuity exists, go to next step. If continuity does not exist in any circuit, check for open in ground circuit. Repair or replace wiring harness as necessary.

8) On all models, check continuity between data link connector and ECU. See DATA LINK-TO-ECU TERMINAL IDENTIFICATION table. If no continuity exists check for open between ECU and diagnostic connector. Inspect and repair wiring as necessary.

DATA LINK-TO-ECU TERMINAL IDENTIFICATION

Application	Data Link Terminal No.	Wire Color	[1] ECU Terminal No.
Colt, Mirage & Summit	4	YEL/RED	22
	10	[2] PNK/BLU	9
Colt Vista, Expo & Summit Wagon	4	YEL/RED	23
	10	GRN/WHT	24
Diamante	4	BRN	22
	10	GRN/RED	9
Eclipse	4	YEL/RED	23
	10	[3] PNK	24
Stealth & 3000GT	4	YEL/RED	23
	10	PNK	24

[1] – See Fig. 5, 6 or 7.
[2] – Wire color at data link connector is Light Green/White.
[3] – Wire color at data link connector is White.

9) Check for trouble codes. See TROUBLE CODE DEFINITION under DIAGNOSIS & TESTING. If no trouble code(s) is present, go to next step. If any trouble codes are present, see appropriate CODE under DIAGNOSIS & TESTING.

10) Disconnect ECU connector. If warning light is no longer illuminated, replace ECU. If warning light is still illuminated, disconnect hydraulic unit connector.

11) If warning light is still illuminated, repair harness or replace instrument cluster. If warning light is no longer illuminated, test valve relay. See HYDRAULIC UNIT RELAYS under COMPONENT TESTING. Replace valve relay if defective. If valve relay is okay, replace hydraulic unit.

Ignition Switch In START Position, Warning Light Inoperative (Colt, Diamante, Mirage & Summit) – 1) Remove valve relay from hydraulic unit. Inspect connector terminals, and repair if necessary. Test valve relay. See HYDRAULIC UNIT RELAYS under COMPONENT TESTING. Replace relay as needed.

2) Turn ignition on. Measure voltage between valve relay wiring harness connector terminal No. 3 and ground. *See Fig. 23.* If battery voltage is present, go to next step. If battery voltage is not present, repair circuit or diode between ABS warning light and valve relay.

3) Using an ohmmeter, check for continuity between valve relay terminal No. 1 and ground. If continuity exists, replace valve relay. If no continuity exists, repair circuit between valve relay and ground.

Ignition Switch In START Position, Warning Light Inoperative (Except Colt, Diamante, Mirage & Summit) – 1) On Eclipse, Stealth and 3000GT, remove ABS power relay fuse (No. 3) from junction block. On all models, disconnect hydraulic unit 10-pin connector. Turn ignition on. Using a DVOM, measure voltage between terminal No. 8 (Green/Red wire) and ground. *See Fig. 9.* If battery voltage is present, go to next step. If battery voltage is not present, repair circuit between ABS warning light and hydraulic unit.

2) Using an ohmmeter, check for continuity between terminal No. 9 and ground. If continuity exists, go to next step. If no continuity exists, repair hydraulic unit circuit.

3) Check for continuity between hydraulic unit connector terminals No. 8 and 9. If continuity exists, go to next step. If no continuity exists, replace valve relay.

4) Remove valve relay from hydraulic unit. Check for continuity between relay terminals No. 87a and 30. *See Fig. 24.* If no continuity exists, replace valve relay. If continuity exists, hydraulic unit wiring harness is faulty. Replace hydraulic unit.

Ignition Switch In ON Position, Warning Light Blinks Once. In START Position, Warning Light Stays On. When Ignition Switch Is Cycled From START To ON Position, Warning Light Blinks Once (Except Colt, Diamante, Mirage & Summit) – 1) Disconnect hydraulic unit wiring harness connector. Disconnect ECU wiring harness connector. Inspect connector terminals and repair as necessary.

2) Turn ignition on. Measure voltage between ECU connector terminal No. 25 and ground. *See Fig. 6.* If battery voltage is not present, repair open or shorted circuit between ABS warning light and ECU. If battery voltage is present, replace faulty ECU.

Ignition Switch In ON Position, Warning Light Blinks Twice And Remains Off (Colt, Diamante, Mirage & Summit) – 1) Remove hydraulic unit wiring harness connector. Disconnect ECU wiring harness connector. Inspect connector terminals and repair as necessary.

2) Turn ignition on. Measure voltage between terminal No. 21 and ground. *See Fig. 5 or 7.* If battery voltage is not present, repair open or shorted circuit between ABS warning light and ECU. If battery voltage is present, replace faulty ECU.

Warning Light Switches Off One Second After Ignition Switch Is Turned To ON Position (Colt, Diamante, Mirage & Summit) – Disconnect ECU wiring harness connector. Inspect connector terminals and repair as necessary. Turn ignition on. Measure voltage between ECU connector terminal No. 41 (Colt, Mirage and Summit) or No. 61 (Diamante) and ground. *See Fig. 5 or 7.* If battery voltage is not present, repair open or shorted circuit between alternator "L" terminal and ECU. If battery voltage is present, replace faulty ECU.

DIAGNOSIS & TESTING

RETRIEVING CODES

Scan Tool (All Models) – 1) With ignition off, connect Multi-Use Tester (MB991341) and ROM pack (MB991423) to self-diagnostic connector, located under driver side of dash, and to cigarette lighter socket. *See Fig. 11.* Stealth and 3000GT vehicles may require Adapter Harness (MB991377).

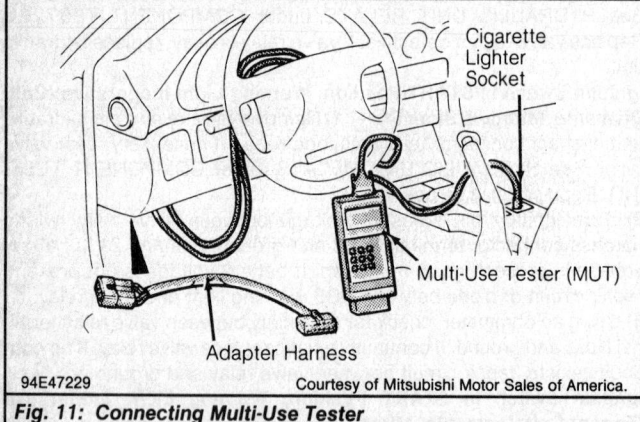

94E47229 Courtesy of Mitsubishi Motor Sales of America.

Fig. 11: Connecting Multi-Use Tester
(Stealth & 3000GT Are Shown; Others Are Similar)

2) Turn ignition on. ABS warning light should come on as ABS goes into self-diagnostic mode. Read and record all diagnostic output (trouble) codes from ECU memory. Refer to Multi-Use Tester (MUT) instructions for specific trouble code retrieval procedure.

3) After all trouble codes have been retrieved and recorded, clear codes from ECU memory. Refer to Multi-Use Tester (MUT) instructions for specific trouble code clearing instructions. See TROUBLE CODE DEFINITION and appropriate CODE under DIAGNOSIS & TESTING for servicing procedure.

4) If trouble codes cannot be cleared, ECU is currently detecting a malfunction. If codes can be cleared, problem is either intermittent or only appears while driving.

Voltmeter (Colt, Diamante, Mirage & Summit) – 1) To retrieve stored trouble codes, locate diagnostic connector under left side of dash. Turn ignition off. Connect analog voltmeter between diagnostic terminal and ground terminal of diagnostic connector. *See Fig. 12.* Start engine.

2) Stored trouble codes will be indicated by sweeps of voltmeter needle. Long sweeps indicate first digit of code; short sweeps indicate second digit of code. If more than one fault is present, lowest number code will be given first. After trouble code has been retrieved, test indicated component and/or related circuit (if necessary).

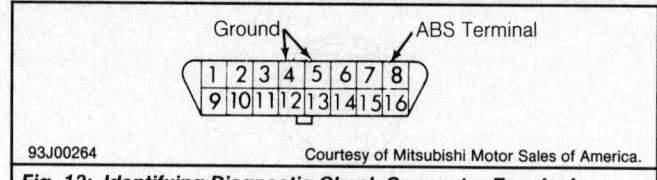

93J00264 Courtesy of Mitsubishi Motor Sales of America.

Fig. 12: Identifying Diagnostic Check Connector Terminals (Colt, Diamante, Mirage & Summit)

CLEARING CODES

(Colt, Diamante, Mirage & Summit) – To erase one code, locate diagnostic code erasure connector. On Colt, Mirage and Summit, connector is located behind ashtray. On Diamante, *see Fig. 13.* Using jumper wire, connect code erasure connector terminals. Turn ignition on. ABS warning light should come on. After 3 seconds, turn ignition off. Disconnect jumper wire. Turn ignition on. To erase more than one code, repeat procedure.

(All Other Models) – To erase code(s) with scan tester, follow tester instructions.

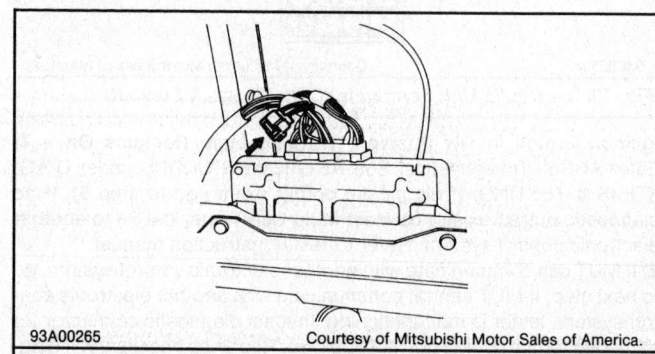

93A00265 Courtesy of Mitsubishi Motor Sales of America.

Fig. 13: Locating Diagnostic Code Erasure Connector (Diamante)

TROUBLE CODE DEFINITION
TROUBLE CODES (COLT, MIRAGE & SUMMIT)

Code	[1] System Affected
11	Right Front Wheel Speed Sensor (Open)
12	Left Front Wheel Speed Sensor (Open)
13	Right Rear Wheel Speed Sensor (Open)
14	Left Rear Wheel Speed Sensor (Open)
15	Speed Sensor Output Signal Fault
16	Low Battery Voltage
21	Right Front Wheel Speed Sensor (Short)
22	Left Front Wheel Speed Sensor (Short)
23	Right Rear Wheel Speed Sensor (Short)
24	Left Rear Wheel Speed Sensor (Short)
25	Failure Of Both Rear Wheel Sensors
31	Right Front Wheel Speed Sensor Rotor
32	Left Front Wheel Speed Sensor Rotor
33	Right Rear Wheel Speed Sensor Rotor
34	Left Rear Wheel Speed Sensor Rotor
35	Low Alternator Voltage
41	Right Front Solenoid Valve
42	Left Front Solenoid Valve
43	Right Rear Solenoid Valve
44	Left Rear Solenoid Valve
51-52	Valve Relay
53-54	Motor Relay
55	Faulty Hydraulic Control Motor
62	Miscellaneous Failures
63	ECU Failure

[1] – See appropriate CODE under DIAGNOSIS & TESTING.

TROUBLE CODES (DIAMANTE)

Code	[1] System Affected
11	Right Front Wheel Speed Sensor (Open)
12	Left Front Wheel Speed Sensor (Open)
13	Right Rear Wheel Speed Sensor (Open)
14	Left Rear Wheel Speed Sensor (Open)
15	Speed Sensor Output Signal Fault
16	Low/High Battery Voltage
21	Right Front Wheel Speed Sensor (Short)
22	Left Front Wheel Speed Sensor (Short)
23	Right Rear Wheel Speed Sensor (Short)
24	Left Rear Wheel Speed Sensor (Short)
25	Failure Of Both Rear Wheel Sensors
31, 32	Wheel Speed Sensor Rotor
35	Low Alternator "L" Terminal Voltage
37	Low Pressure Warning Switch Voltage
41-46	Solenoid Valve Circuit
51	Valve Relay Failure Or Short
52	Valve Relay Failure
53	Low Voltage To Motor Relay
54	Motor Relay Failure Or Short
61	Hydraulic Unit
62	Miscellaneous Failures
63	Faulty ECU

[1] – See appropriate CODE under DIAGNOSIS & TESTING.

TROUBLE CODES (ALL OTHER MODELS)

Code	[1] System Affected
11	Left Front Wheel Speed Sensor
12	Right Front Wheel Speed Sensor
13	Left Rear Wheel Speed Sensor
14	Right Rear Wheel Speed Sensor
15	Speed Sensor Output Signal Fault
21	"G" Force Sensor (AWD)
22	Stoplight Switch Circuit
41	Left Front Solenoid Valve
42	Right Front Solenoid Valve
43	Rear Solenoid Valve
51	Valve Relay
52	Motor Relay
55	Faulty ECU

[1] – See appropriate CODE under DIAGNOSIS & TESTING.

CODE 11, 12, 13 OR 14: FAULTY WHEEL SPEED SENSOR INPUT

NOTE: If after all testing procedures have been completed system is not functioning properly, substitute ABS ECU with known good unit and retest.

(Colt, Diamante, Mirage & Summit) – Trouble code will set if ECU detects wheel speed sensor has open circuit. Check continuity of circuit between ECU and sensor. See WIRING DIAGRAMS. Repair as needed. Inspect condition of speed sensors. See WHEEL SPEED SENSOR under COMPONENT TESTING.

NOTE: If after all testing procedures have been completed system is not functioning properly, substitute ABS ECU with known good unit and retest.

(All Other Models) – 1) Trouble code will set if ECU detects wheel speed sensor has no input signal. Trouble code will also set if wheel sensor voltage output is low while driving vehicle.
2) Inspect condition of sensor rotor. Damaged rotor teeth can set code. Inspect wheel sensor wiring harness for open or poor connection. See WIRING DIAGRAMS. Repair or replace if necessary. If no open circuit or poor connection is found, go to next step.
3) Test wheel speed sensor. See WHEEL SPEED SENSOR under COMPONENT TESTING. Replace wheel sensor as necessary. Ensure wheel speed sensor-to-rotor gap is within specification. See WHEEL SPEED SENSOR under ADJUSTMENTS.

CODE 15: FAULTY WHEEL SPEED SENSOR OUTPUT

NOTE: If after all testing procedures have been completed system is not functioning properly, substitute ABS ECU with known good unit and retest.

1) This code normally is set when Codes 11-14 are set. Test each sensor. See WHEEL SPEED SENSOR under COMPONENT TESTING. If all sensor voltages and resistances are within specification, go to next step. If any sensor is malfunctioning, replace sensor. See WHEEL SPEED SENSOR under REMOVAL & INSTALLATION.
2) Check each wheel speed sensor-to-rotor gap. See WHEEL SPEED SENSOR under ADJUSTMENTS. If all gaps are within specification, go to next step. If any gaps are not within specification, adjust sensor-to-rotor gap.
3) Inspect all wheel speed sensor rotors for damaged and missing teeth. Replace any damaged rotors. Using an oscilloscope, check waveform patterns. See Fig. 14. If all rotors are okay, replace ECU and road test vehicle. Ensure trouble code does not reset.

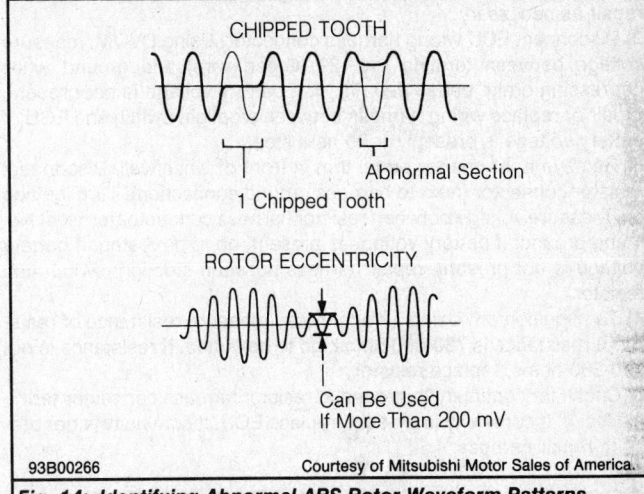

CHIPPED TOOTH

Abnormal Section

1 Chipped Tooth

ROTOR ECCENTRICITY

Can Be Used
If More Than 200 mV

93B00266   Courtesy of Mitsubishi Motor Sales of America.

Fig. 14: Identifying Abnormal ABS Rotor Waveform Patterns

CODE 16: ECU POWER VOLTAGE

(Colt, Diamante, Mirage & Summit) — Start engine. Using DVOM, measure voltage between ECU terminal No. 5 (backprobe) and ground. If 10 volts or more is present, replace ECU. If less than 10 volts is present, check fuse (No. 5 - Colt, Mirage and Summit; No. 2 - Diamante) contacts and ECU connector. Repair as necessary. If fuse contacts and ECU connector are okay, replace faulty ECU.

CODE 21, 22, 23 OR 24: FAULTY WHEEL SPEED SENSOR OUTPUT

(Colt, Diamante, Mirage & Summit) – 1) Trouble code will set if ECU detects wheel speed sensor has no output signal. Trouble code will also set if wheel sensor voltage output is low while driving vehicle.
2) Inspect condition of sensor rotor. Damage to rotor teeth can set code. Inspect wheel sensor wiring harness for poor connection. See WIRING DIAGRAMS. Repair or replace if necessary. If no short circuit or poor connection is found, go to next step.
3) Test wheel speed sensor. See WHEEL SPEED SENSOR under COMPONENT TESTING. Replace wheel sensor as necessary. Ensure wheel speed sensor-to-rotor gap is within specification. See WHEEL SPEED SENSOR under ADJUSTMENTS.

CODE 21: "G" FORCE SENSOR CIRCUIT

(AWD Models) – 1) Test "G" force sensor. See "G" FORCE SENSOR under COMPONENT TESTING. If sensor is okay, go to next step. If sensor is faulty, replace sensor. See "G" FORCE SENSOR (AWD) under REMOVAL & INSTALLATION.

2) Disconnect ECU wiring harness connector. Turn ignition on. Using a DVOM, measure voltage between terminal No. 6 and ground. *See Fig. 6.* If battery voltage is not present, repair or replace wiring harness between "G" force sensor and ECU. If battery voltage is present, "G" force sensor circuit is okay. Replace faulty ECU.

CODE 22: STOPLIGHT SWITCH CIRCUIT

(Colt Vista, Eclipse FWD, Expo, Stealth FWD, Summit Wagon & 3000GT FWD) – 1) Check if stoplights are functioning correctly. If stoplights function correctly, go to next step. If stoplights do not function correctly, check stoplight circuit and repair as necessary.
2) Ensure ignition is off. Disconnect ECU wiring harness connector. Using DVOM, measure voltage between terminal No. 29 (Green wire) and ground while depressing brake pedal. *See Fig. 6.* If battery voltage is not present, repair or replace wiring harness between stoplight switch and ECU. If battery voltage is present, stoplight switch circuit is okay. Replace faulty ECU.
(Eclipse AWD, Stealth AWD & 3000GT AWD) – 1) Check if stoplights are functioning correctly. If stoplights function correctly, go to next step. If stoplights do not function correctly, check stoplight circuit and repair as necessary.
2) Disconnect ECU wiring harness connector. Using DVOM, measure voltage between terminal No. 29 (Green wire) and ground while depressing brake pedal. *See Fig. 6.* If battery voltage is not present, repair or replace wiring harness between stoplight switch and ECU. If battery voltage is present, go to next step.
3) Remove right quarter panel trim in front of wheelwell. Disconnect resistor connector (next to harness ground connection). Turn ignition on. Measure voltage between resistor harness connector terminal No. 1 and ground. If battery voltage is present, go to next step. If battery voltage is not present, repair harness between stoplight switch and resistor.
4) Turn ignition off. Using an ohmmeter, measure resistance of resistor. If resistance is 780-860 ohms, go to next step. If resistance is not 780-860 ohms, replace resistor.
5) Check for continuity to ground at resistor harness connector terminal No. 2. If continuity is present, replace ECU. If continuity is not present, repair harness.

CODE 25: MALFUNCTION OF BOTH REAR WHEEL SENSORS

NOTE: If after all testing procedures have been completed system is not functioning properly, substitute ABS ECU with known good unit and retest.

(Colt, Diamante, Mirage & Summit) – Code is set when no signal is output from both rear wheel sensors. Code can also set if vehicle rear wheels are prevented from turning (stuck situation) when front wheels are turning. Conduct testing procedures from CODE 11, 12, 13 OR 14.

CODE 31, 32, 33 OR 34: DAMAGED WHEEL SPEED SENSOR ROTOR

NOTE: If after all testing procedures have been completed system is not functioning properly, substitute ABS ECU with known good unit and retest.

(Colt, Diamante, Mirage & Summit) – Inspect condition of wheel speed sensor and rotor. Damaged components or incorrect sensor-to-rotor gap can set code. See WHEEL SPEED SENSOR in ADJUSTMENTS. Check for excessive hub runout or defective bearing.

CODE 35: LOW ALTERNATOR "L" TERMINAL VOLTAGE

(Colt, Diamante, Mirage & Summit) – Remove ECU connector. Inspect for damage and repair as necessary. Turn ignition on. Using DVOM, measure voltage between terminal No. 41 (Colt, Mirage and Summit) or terminal No. 61 (Diamante) and vehicle ground. *See Fig. 5*

or 7. If 7 volts or more is present, replace ECU. If less than 7 volts is present, inspect and repair wiring harness between ECU connector and alternator. If wiring harness is okay, inspect alternator. Replace as needed.

CODE 37: LOW HYDRAULIC PRESSURE

(Diamante) – This code will set if hydraulic unit pressure is less than correct operating pressure. If pressure increases to correct operating pressure, code will be erased. If pressure does not increase to correct operating pressure within 35 seconds, Code 37 will be erased and Code 61 will be set. See CODE 61.

CODE 41, 42, 43 OR 44: SOLENOID VALVE CIRCUIT

(Colt, Mirage & Summit) – 1) Disconnect hydraulic unit connector. Using ohmmeter, measure resistance between terminals No. 1 and 3, 2 and 4, 5 and 7, and 6 and 8. *See Fig. 10.*
2) Resistance of each circuit should be 3100-3340 ohms. If resistance is correct, go to next step. If resistance is not correct, replace faulty hydraulic unit. See HYDRAULIC UNIT under REMOVAL & INSTALLATION.
3) Connect hydraulic unit connector. Disconnect ECU wiring harness connector. Measure resistance between hydraulic unit connector terminals and ECU connector terminals. *See Fig. 5.* See HYDRAULIC UNIT-TO-ECU CIRCUIT IDENTIFICATION table.
4) Resistance should be 3100-3340 ohms. If resistance is not within specification, repair circuit not within specification. If all resistance tests are within specification, solenoid valve circuit is okay. Replace faulty ECU.

HYDRAULIC UNIT-TO-ECU CIRCUIT IDENTIFICATION

Hydraulic Unit Terminal No.	Wire Color	ECU Terminal No.
1	Blue/Yellow	2
2	Orange	1
5	Yellow/Green	15
6	Yellow/Black	14

CODE 41, 42, 43, 44, 45 OR 46 SOLENOID VALVE CIRCUIT

(Diamante) – 1) Disconnect hydraulic unit 1-pin connector and 9-pin connector. Using ohmmeter, measure resistance between 1-pin component connector and hydraulic unit terminals No. 2, 3, 5, 6, 8 and 9. *See Fig. 8.*
2) Resistance of each circuit should be 2800-3400 ohms. If resistance is correct, go to next step. If resistance is not correct, replace faulty hydraulic unit. See HYDRAULIC UNIT under REMOVAL & INSTALLATION.
3) Connect hydraulic unit 9-pin connector. Disconnect ECU wiring harness connector. Measure resistance between hydraulic unit 1-pin connector and specified ECU connector terminals. *See Fig. 7.* See HYDRAULIC UNIT-TO-ECU CIRCUIT IDENTIFICATION table.
4) Resistance should be 2800-3400 ohms. If resistance is not within specification, repair circuit not within specification. If all resistance tests are within specification, solenoid valve circuit is okay. Replace faulty ECU.

HYDRAULIC UNIT-TO-ECU CIRCUIT IDENTIFICATION

Hydraulic Unit	ECU Terminal No. (Wire Color)
1-Pin Terminal	1 (Blue/White)
1-Pin Terminal	2 (Red/Black)
1-Pin Terminal	3 (Red/White)
1-Pin Terminal	14 (Blue/Black)
1-Pin Terminal	15 (Yellow/Black)
1-Pin Terminal	16 (Yellow/Red)

CODE 41, 42 OR 43: SOLENOID VALVE CIRCUIT (AWD)

(All Other Models) – **1)** Disconnect hydraulic unit 10-pin connector. Using ohmmeter, measure resistance between component connector terminal No. 8 and terminals No. 3 and 5. See Fig. 9.

2) Resistance should be 1000-1300 ohms. Check continuity between terminals No. 7 and 8. If resistance is within specification and continuity is present, go to next step. If resistance is not within specification and continuity is not present, replace faulty hydraulic unit. See HYDRAULIC UNIT under REMOVAL & INSTALLATION.

3) Disconnect ECU wiring harness connector. Measure resistance between hydraulic unit component connector terminal No. 8 and ECU harness connector terminals No. 17 and 35. See Fig. 6.

4) Resistance should be 1000-1300 ohms. Check continuity between hydraulic unit terminal No. 8 and ECU terminal No. 22. If resistance is not within specification, repair or replace wiring harness. If all resistance tests are within specification and continuity is present, replace ECU. If resistance is not within specification between hydraulic unit and/or continuity is not present, inspect and repair circuit as needed.

Solenoid Valve Circuit (FWD) – **1)** Disconnect hydraulic unit 10-pin connector. Using ohmmeter, measure resistance between component connector terminal No. 8 and terminals No. 3, 5 and 6. See Fig. 9.

2) Resistance should be 1000-1300 ohms. Check continuity between terminals No. 7 and 8. If resistance is within specification and continuity is present, go to next step. If resistance is not within specification and continuity is not present, replace faulty hydraulic unit. See HYDRAULIC UNIT under REMOVAL & INSTALLATION.

3) Disconnect ECU wiring harness connector. Measure resistance between hydraulic unit component connector terminal No. 8 and ECU harness connector terminals No. 1, 17 and 19. See Fig. 6.

4) Resistance should be 1000-1300 ohms. Check continuity between hydraulic unit terminal No. 8 and ECU terminal No. 22. If resistance is not within specification, repair or replace wiring harness. If all resistance tests are within specification and continuity is present, replace ECU. If resistance is not within specification between hydraulic unit and/or continuity is not present, inspect and repair circuit(s) as needed.

CODE 51: VALVE RELAY CIRCUIT

(Colt, Diamante, Mirage & Summit) – **1)** Remove and test valve relay. See HYDRAULIC UNIT RELAYS under COMPONENT TESTING. Replace relay if faulty. If relay is okay, reinstall valve relay and go to next step.

2) Remove ECU 26-pin connector. Using an ohmmeter, measure resistance between ECU connector terminal No. 8 and ground. See Figs. 5 and 7. If resistance is infinite, replace ECU. If resistance is not infinite, repair short between ECU connector and valve relay.

(All Other Models) – **1)** Remove and test valve relay. See HYDRAULIC UNIT RELAYS under COMPONENT TESTING. Replace relay if faulty. If relay is okay, reinstall valve relay and go to next step.

2) Turn ignition on. Disconnect hydraulic unit 2-pin connector. Measure voltage between terminal No. 52 and ground. See Fig. 15. If battery voltage is not present, repair harness between fusible link (No. 7, Yellow) and hydraulic unit 2-pin connector. If battery voltage is present, go to next step.

3) Turn ignition off. Using ohmmeter, check for continuity between hydraulic unit connector terminals No. 7 and 8. See Fig. 9. If continuity is present, go to next step. If continuity is not present, replace hydraulic unit.

4) Connect hydraulic unit connector. Disconnect ECU connector. Using ohmmeter, measure resistance between ECU connector terminals No. 2 and 27. Resistance should be 60-120 ohms. If resistance is okay, go to next step. If resistance is not within specification, repair wiring harness between hydraulic unit and ECU.

6) Turn ignition on. Measure voltage between ECU connector terminal No. 22 and ground. If battery voltage is not present, repair or replace faulty wiring harness between hydraulic unit and ECU. If battery voltage is present, replace faulty ECU.

93C00267   Courtesy of Mitsubishi Motor Sales of America.

Fig. 15: Hydraulic Unit Connector (Colt Vista, Eclipse, Expo, Stealth, Summit, Summit Wagon & 3000GT)

CODE 52 OR 53: MOTOR RELAY CIRCUIT

(Colt, Diamante, Mirage & Summit) – **1)** Check Yellow 60-amp fusible link No. 9 (Colt, Mirage and Summit) or No. 6 (Diamante), located in fuse block next to battery. If fusible link is blown, repair short circuit and replace fuse. If fuse is okay, remove connectors from solenoid valve, motor relay and valve relay. Inspect connectors for damage and repair if necessary. If connectors are okay, go to next step.

2) Measure voltage between valve relay wiring harness connector terminal No. 6 and ground. See Fig. 16. If battery voltage is not present, repair circuit between 60-amp fusible link and valve relay. If battery voltage is present, go to next step.

93D00268   Courtesy of Mitsubishi Motor Sales of America.

Fig. 16: Identifying Valve Relay Connector Terminals (Colt, Diamante, Mirage & Summit)

3) Turn ignition on. Measure voltage between valve relay wiring harness connector terminal No. 2 and ground. If battery voltage is not present, repair circuit between fuse No. 15 (Colt, Mirage and Summit) or No. 2 (Diamante), and valve relay. If battery voltage is present, go to next step.

4) Remove and test valve relay. See HYDRAULIC UNIT RELAYS under COMPONENT TESTING. Replace relay if faulty. If relay is okay, reinstall valve relay and go to next step.

5) Disconnect ECU connector. Turn ignition on. Measure voltage between ECU connector terminal No. 8 and ground. See Fig. 5 or 7. If battery voltage is present, go to next step. If battery voltage is not present, repair harness between valve relay and ECU connector.

6) Turn ignition off. Locate diode in valve relay White/Black wire. See Fig. 17. Using an ohmmeter, ensure diode resistance is infinite in one direction only. Replace diode if necessary. If diode is okay, go to next step.

7) Remove motor relay. Inspect terminals and repair if necessary. If terminals are okay, turn ignition on. Measure voltage between motor relay wiring harness connector terminal No. 3 (Red/Black wire on Colt, Mirage and Summit) or terminal No. 5 (White/Yellow wire on Diamante) and ground. If battery voltage is present, go to next step. If battery voltage is not present, repair wiring harness between 60-amp fusible link and motor relay.

8) Remove motor relay and valve relay. On Diamante, check for continuity between motor relay wiring harness terminal No. 3 (White/Black) and valve relay wiring harness terminal No. 3 (White/Black wire). If continuity is present, go to step **10)**. If continuity is not present, repair White/Black wire between motor relay and valve relay.

9) On Colt, Mirage and Summit, check for continuity between motor relay wiring harness terminal No. 2 (Green/Blue wire) and valve relay wiring harness terminal No. 3 (Green/Blue wire). If continuity is present, go to next step. If continuity is not present, repair Green/Blue wire between motor relay and valve relay.

10) Remove and test motor relay. See HYDRAULIC UNIT RELAYS under COMPONENT TESTING. Replace motor relay as needed. Install motor relay. Disconnect ECU connector. Turn ignition on. Measure voltage between ECU wiring harness connector terminal No. 7 and ground. See Fig. 5 or 7.

11) If battery voltage is not present, repair wiring harness between motor relay connector terminal No. 4 (Green/Black wire on Colt, Mirage and Summit) or terminal No. 1 (Blue/White wire on Diamante) and ECU connector terminal No. 7.

12) If battery voltage is present, check for short circuit between motor relay connector terminal No. 1 (Red/Yellow wire on Colt, Mirage and Summit) or No. 4 (White/Black wire on Diamante), and ECU connector terminal No. 13. If circuit is okay, replace faulty ECU.

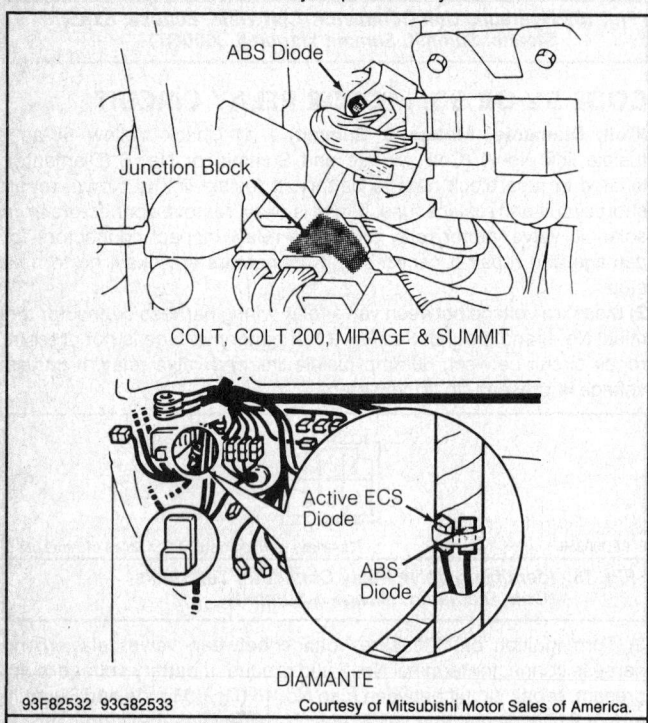

Fig. 17: Locating ABS Diode

(All Other Models) – **1)** Check if hydraulic unit motor operates when vehicle speed exceeds 4 MPH. If motor does not operate, go to next step. If motor operates, check for short in harness. Repair as needed. Remove and test motor relay. See HYDRAULIC UNIT RELAYS under COMPONENT TESTING. If relay is okay, go to next step. Replace relay if faulty.

2) Check pump motor ground connection. Ensure ground wire has a clean, tight connection. Repair if necessary. If ground connection is okay, go to next step.

3) Install motor relay. Disconnect 2-pin connector. *See Fig. 13.* Measure voltage between terminal No. 51 and ground. If battery voltage is present, go to next step. If battery voltage is not present, repair harness between fusible link and hydraulic unit 2-pin connector.

4) Connect hydraulic unit wiring harness. Disconnect ECU wiring harness connector. Using an ohmmeter, measure resistance between ECU harness connector terminals No. 2 and 26. *See Fig. 6.* Resistance should be 30-60 ohms. If resistance is not within specification, inspect and repair wiring harness between hydraulic unit and ECU. If resistance is within specification on Eclipse models, replace faulty ECU. If resistance is within specification on Colt Vista, Expo, Stealth, Summit, Summit Wagon and 3000GT models, go to next step.

6) Using an ohmmeter, measure resistance between ECU harness connector terminal No. 5 and ground. Resistance should be .1-.3 ohm. If resistance is not within specification, repair or replace wiring harness between hydraulic unit and ECU. If resistance is within specification, replace faulty ECU.

CODE 54: MOTOR RELAY

(Colt, Diamante, Mirage & Summit) – **1)** Turn ignition off. Remove motor relay connector. Inspect connector terminals for damage and repair if necessary. If connector terminals are okay, measure resistance between terminal No. 1 (Red/Yellow wire on Colt, Mirage and Summit) or terminal No. 4 (White/Black wire on Diamante), and ground. If resistance is .5-1.5 ohms, go to next step. If resistance is not .5-1.5 ohms, repair open or shorted short circuit between motor relay connector and hydraulic unit. If circuit is okay, replace hydraulic unit.

2) Remove ECU connector. Using an ohmmeter, measure resistance between ECU connector terminal No. 7 and ground. If zero ohms is present, replace ECU. If resistance is not zero ohms, repair short circuit in wiring harness between motor relay and ECU connector.

CODE 55: FAULTY HYDRAULIC UNIT MOTOR

(Colt, Mirage & Summit) – Code is normally set with Codes 52 and 53. Perform testing under CODES 52 and 53. Ensure hydraulic unit motor operates. Replace motor as needed.

CODE 55: FAULTY ECU

(Except Colt, Diamante, Mirage & Summit) – If Code 55 is present, replace faulty ECU.

CODE 61: HYDRAULIC UNIT)

NOTE: If after all testing procedures have been completed system is not functioning properly, substitute ABS ECU with known good unit and retest.

(Diamante – **1)** Start engine and allow to idle for 2 minutes. Stop engine. Repeat procedure 10 times. Bleed brake system. See BLEEDING BRAKE SYSTEM. If Code 61 is no longer present, system is okay and testing is complete. If Code 61 is still present, go to next step.

2) Remove hydraulic unit 9-pin connector. *See Fig. 8.* Inspect connector terminals and repair if necessary. Remove ECU connector. *See Fig. 7.* Check for continuity between ECU connector terminal No. 52 and hydraulic unit connector terminal No. 7. Check for continuity between ECU connector terminal No. 53 and hydraulic unit connector terminal No. 4. If continuity is not present, repair circuit. If continuity is present, replace hydraulic unit.

CODE 62: MISCELLANEOUS FAILURES

(Colt, Diamante, Mirage & Summit) – **1)** Code 62 indicates a problem with wheel speed sensor(s) or a faulty hydraulic unit. A false Code 62 may be set, however, if vehicle is driven for long periods on snow or ice, left and right tires are different sizes, or brakes are dragging.

2) Test each wheel speed sensor. See WHEEL SPEED SENSOR under COMPONENT TESTING. If all sensor voltages and resistances are within specification, go to next step. If any sensor is malfunctioning, replace sensor. See WHEEL SPEED SENSOR under REMOVAL & INSTALLATION.

3) Check each wheel speed sensor-to-rotor gap. See WHEEL SPEED SENSOR under ADJUSTMENTS. If all gaps are within specification, go to next step. If any gaps are not within specification, adjust sensor-to-rotor gap.

4) Inspect all wheel speed sensor rotors for damaged and missing teeth. Replace any damaged rotors. Using an oscilloscope, check waveform patterns and output voltage. *See Fig. 14.* Output voltage should be 0.2 volt (200 mV). If all rotors and wheel speed sensors are okay, go to next step.

5) If after all testing procedures have been completed system is not functioning properly, substitute ABS ECU with known good unit and retest. If Code 62 does not reset, replace original ECU. If Code 62 does reset, replace hydraulic unit.

CODE 63: FAULTY ECU

(Colt, Diamante, Mirage & Summit) – If Code 63 is present, replace faulty ECU.

COMPONENT TESTING

ABS POWER RELAY

Colt Vista, Eclipse, Expo & Summit Wagon – **1)** Remove ABS power relay. See ABS POWER RELAY under REMOVAL & INSTALLATION. Disconnect relay connector. Using an ohmmeter, check for continuity between terminals No. 1 and 3. *See Fig. 18.* If continuity exists, replace relay.

2) If no continuity exists, check for continuity between terminals No. 2 and 4. If continuity exists, go to next step. If no continuity exists, replace relay.

3) Apply battery voltage to terminal No. 2, and ground terminal No. 4. Check for continuity between terminals No. 1 and 3. If continuity exists, relay is okay. If continuity does not exist, replace relay.

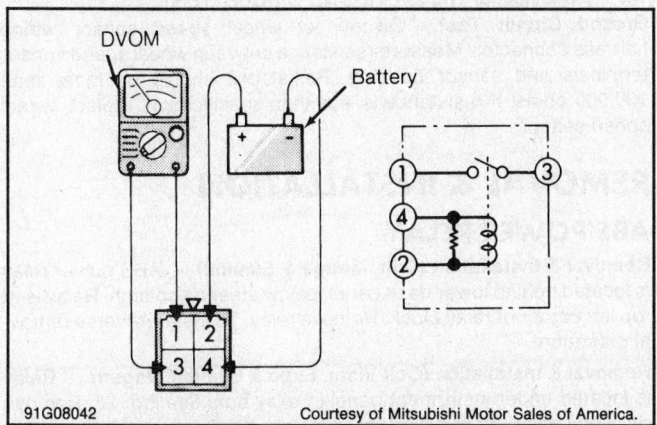

Fig. 18: Testing ABS Power Relay (Except Stealth & 3000GT) & Testing Motor Relay (Colt, Mirage & Summit)

Stealth & 3000GT – 1) Remove ABS power relay from relay box in engine compartment. Using an ohmmeter, check for continuity between relay terminals No. 1 and 3. *See Fig. 19.* If continuity exists, replace relay.

2) If no continuity exists, check for continuity between relay terminals No. 4 and 5. If no continuity exists, go to next step. If continuity exists, replace relay.

3) Apply battery voltage to relay terminal No. 1, and ground relay terminal No. 3. Check for continuity between terminals No. 4 and 5. If continuity exists, relay is okay. If continuity does not exist, replace relay.

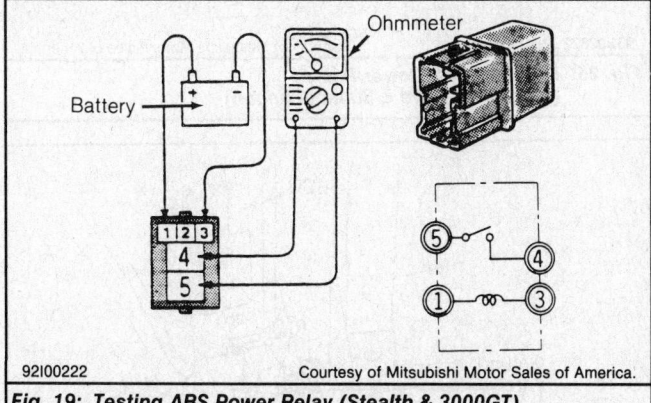

Fig. 19: Testing ABS Power Relay (Stealth & 3000GT)

"G" FORCE SENSOR

All-Wheel Drive (AWD) Models – 1) Remove "G" force sensor. See "G" FORCE SENSOR (AWD) under REMOVAL & INSTALLATION. Place sensor on level surface. Using an ohmmeter, check continuity between sensor terminals. If continuity exists, go to next step. If continuity does not exist, replace sensor.

2) Check for continuity between sensor terminals while slowly tilting sensor in direction of forward vehicle travel. *See Fig. 20.* No continuity should exist when sensor angle is 30 degrees or greater. If no continuity exists, go to next step. If continuity exists, replace sensor.

3) Check for continuity between sensor terminals while slowly tilting sensor in direction of reverse vehicle travel. *See Fig. 20.* No continuity should exist when sensor angle is 30 degrees or greater. If continuity exists, replace sensor.

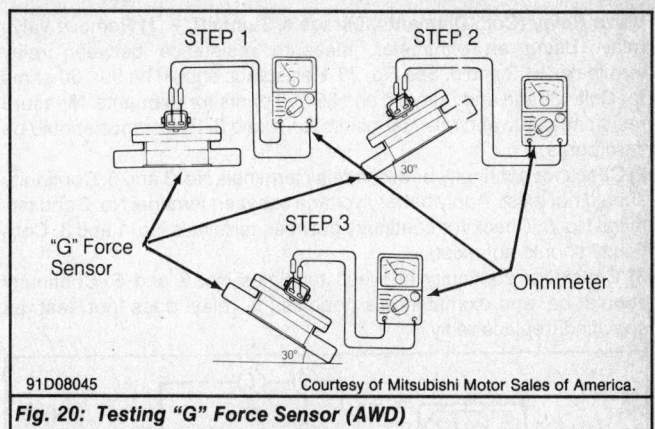

Fig. 20: Testing "G" Force Sensor (AWD)

HYDRAULIC UNIT RELAYS

Motor Relay (Colt, Mirage & Summit) – 1) Remove motor relay. Using an ohmmeter, measure resistance between relay terminals No. 2 and 4. *See Fig. 18.* Resistance should be 90-110 ohms. Check for continuity between relay terminals No. 1 and 3. Continuity should not exist.

2) Apply battery voltage between relay terminals No. 2 and No. 4. Check for continuity between terminals No. 1 and 3. Continuity should be zero ohms. If relay does not test as specified, replace relay.

Motor Relay (Colt Vista, Eclipse, Expo, Stealth, Summit Wagon & 3000GT) – 1) Remove motor relay. Using an ohmmeter, measure resistance between relay terminals No. 85 and 86. *See Fig. 21.* Resistance should be 72-88 ohms for Colt Vista, Expo and Summit Wagon models and 30-60 ohms for Eclipse, Stealth and 3000GT models. Check for continuity between relay terminals No. 30 and 87. Continuity should not exist.

2) Apply battery voltage to relay terminal No. 85, and ground terminal No. 86. Check for continuity between terminals No. 30 and 87. Continuity should exist. If relay does not test as specified, replace relay.

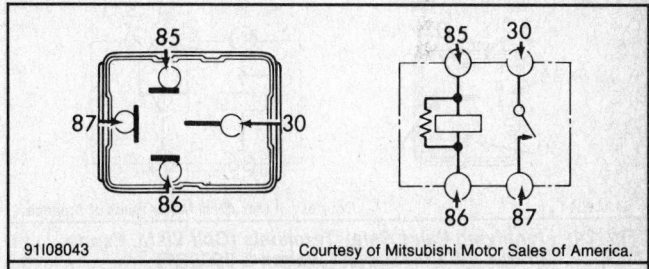

Fig. 21: Identifying Motor Relay Terminals (Colt Vista, Eclipse, Expo, Stealth, Summit Wagon & 3000GT)

Motor Relay (Diamante) – 1) Remove motor relay. Using an ohmmeter, measure resistance between relay terminals No. 1 and 3. *See Fig. 22.* Resistance should be 49-99 ohms. Check for continuity between relay terminals No. 4 and 5. Continuity should not exist.

2) Apply battery voltage between relay terminals No. 1 and No. 3. Check for continuity between terminals No. 4 and 5. Continuity should be zero ohms. If relay does not test as specified, replace relay.

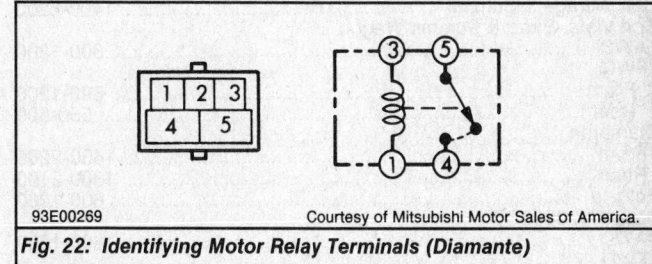

Fig. 22: Identifying Motor Relay Terminals (Diamante)

Valve Relay (Colt, Diamante, Mirage & Summit) – **1)** Remove valve relay. Using an ohmmeter, measure resistance between relay terminals No. 2 and 5. See Fig. 23. Resistance should be 90-100 ohms for Colt, Mirage and Summit, and 55-105 ohms for Diamante. Measure resistance between relay terminals No. 1 and 3. Resistance should be zero ohms.

2) Check for continuity between relay terminals No. 3 and 6. Continuity should not exist. Apply battery voltage between terminal No. 2 and terminal No. 5. Check for continuity between terminals No. 1 and 3. Continuity should not exist.

3) Check for continuity between terminals No. 3 and 6. Continuity should be approximately zero ohms. If relay does not test as specified, replace relay.

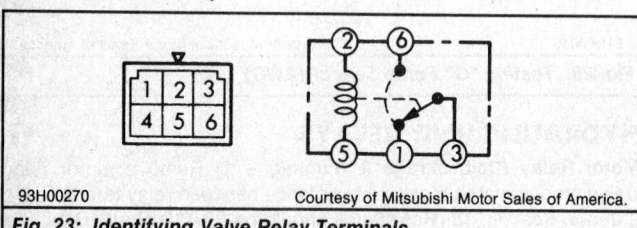

93H00270   Courtesy of Mitsubishi Motor Sales of America.
Fig. 23: Identifying Valve Relay Terminals (Colt, Diamante, Mirage & Summit)

Valve Relay (Colt Vista, Eclipse, Expo, Stealth, Summit Wagon & 3000GT) – **1)** Remove valve relay. Using an ohmmeter, measure resistance between relay terminals No. 85 and 86. See Fig. 24. Resistance should be 60-120 ohms.

2) Check for continuity between relay terminals No. 30 and 87a. Continuity should exist. Check for continuity between relay terminals No. 30 and 87. Continuity should not exist.

3) Apply battery voltage to relay terminal No. 85, and ground terminal No. 86. Check for continuity between terminals No. 30 and 87. Continuity should exist. Check for continuity between terminals No. 30 and 87a. Continuity should not exist. If relay does not test as specified, replace relay.

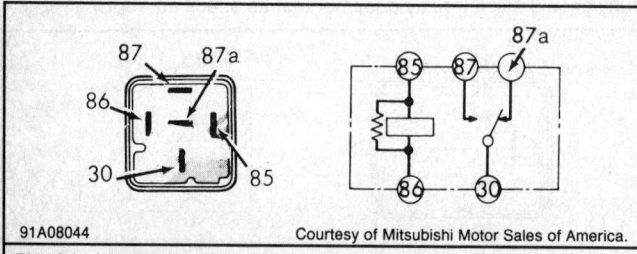

91A08044   Courtesy of Mitsubishi Motor Sales of America.
Fig. 24: Identifying Valve Relay Terminals (Colt Vista, Expo, Mirage, Stealth, Summit Wagon & 3000GT)

WHEEL SPEED SENSOR

Sensor Resistance Test – **1)** Before testing sensor resistance, ensure pole piece-to-wheel speed sensor tip is clean. Check wheel sensor pole piece for damage. If pole piece is damaged, replace sensor.

WHEEL SPEED SENSOR RESISTANCE SPECIFICATIONS

Application	Ohms
Colt, Mirage & Summit	1400-2200
Colt Vista, Expo & Summit Wagon	
AWD	800-1200
FWD	
Front	800-1200
Rear	550-800
Diamante	
Front	1400-2200
Rear	1300-2100
Eclipse	800-1200
Stealth & 3000GT	
AWD	800-1200
FWD	
Front	800-1200
Rear	600-800

2) Disconnect sensor connector. Inspect sensor wiring harness for broken and pinched wires. Repair or replace as necessary. Using an ohmmeter, measure sensor resistance at wiring connector. See WHEEL SPEED SENSOR RESISTANCE SPECIFICATIONS table. If resistance is not within specification, replace sensor. If resistance is within specification, go to GROUND CIRCUIT TEST.

Ground Circuit Test – Disconnect wheel speed sensor wiring harness connector. Measure resistance between wheel speed sensor terminals and sensor housing. Resistance should be more than 100,000 ohms. If resistance is less than specification, replace wheel speed sensor.

REMOVAL & INSTALLATION

ABS POWER RELAY

Removal & Installation (Colt, Mirage & Summit) – ABS power relay is located behind lower dash panel, below steering column. Relay is at top left corner of relay block. Remove relay. To install, reverse removal procedure.

Removal & Installation (Colt Vista, Expo & Summit Wagon) – Relay is located under instrument panel in relay box. See Fig. 25. Remove relay box cover. Remove relay. To install, reverse removal procedure.

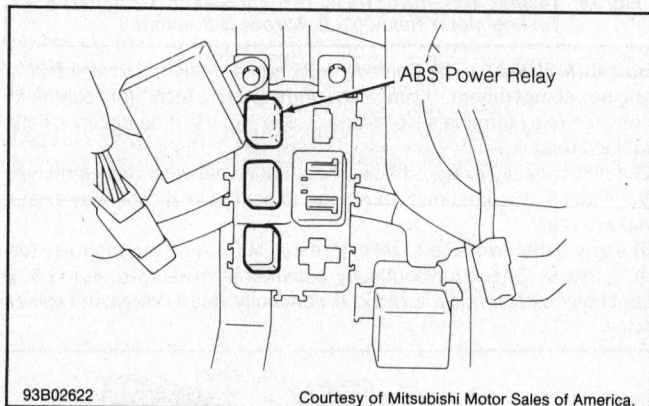

93B02622   Courtesy of Mitsubishi Motor Sales of America.
Fig. 25: Locating ABS Power Relay (Colt Vista, Expo & Summit Wagon)

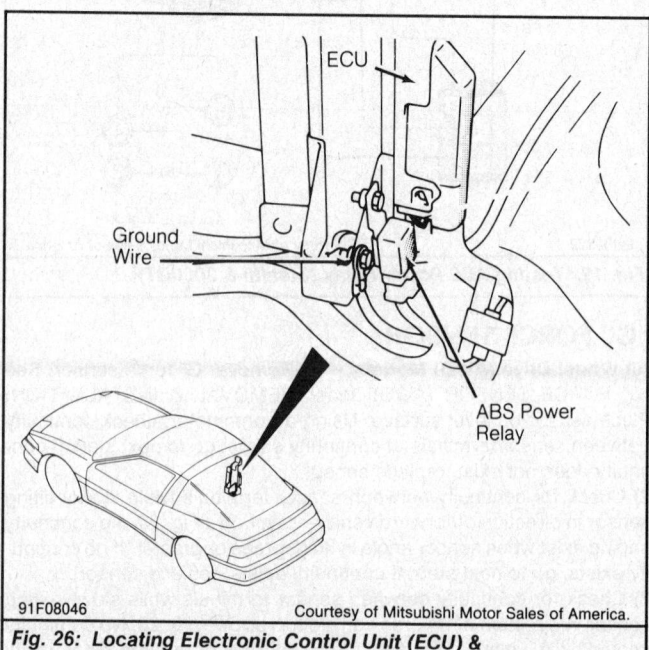

91F08046   Courtesy of Mitsubishi Motor Sales of America.
Fig. 26: Locating Electronic Control Unit (ECU) & ABS Power Relay (Eclipse)

Removal & Installation (Eclipse) – 1) ABS power relay is located near ECU, behind right rear quarter panel trim. *See Fig. 26.* Power relay is mounted to ECU bracket. Disconnect negative battery cable. Remove rear seat. Remove scuff plate.

2) Remove quarter panel mounting screws and trim clip. Carefully remove quarter panel trim. Disconnect relay connector, and remove relay. To install, reverse removal procedure.

Removal & Installation (Stealth & 3000GT) – ABS power relay is located in engine compartment relay box. *See Fig. 27.* Remove relay box cover. Remove relay. To install, reverse removal procedure.

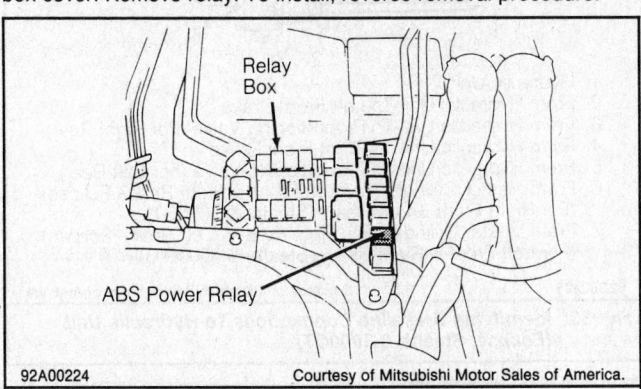

Fig. 27: Locating ABS Power Relay (Stealth & 3000GT)

ELECTRONIC CONTROL UNIT (ECU)

Removal & Installation (Colt, Colt Vista, Expo, Mirage, Summit & Summit Wagon) – Remove center console. ABS ECU is located in front of center console, below center dash. Disconnect negative battery cable. Disconnect harness connectors and remove ECU. To install, reverse removal procedure.

Removal & Installation (Diamante) – 1) ECU is located behind left rear quarter panel trim in trunk. *See Fig. 28.* Disconnect negative battery cable. Remove quarter panel mounting screws and trim clip.

2) Carefully remove quarter panel trim. Disconnect ECU wiring harness connector. Remove ECU mounting bolts/nuts and ECU. To install, reverse removal procedure.

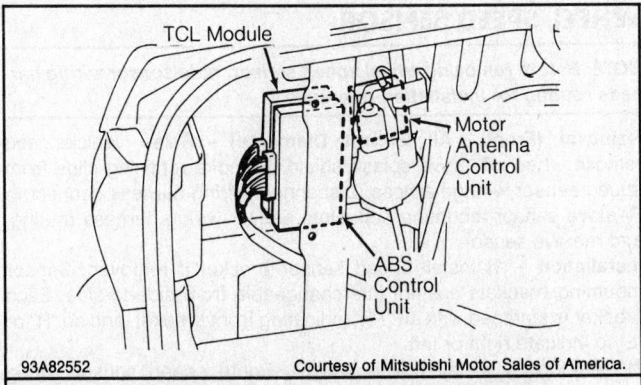

Fig. 28: Locating ABS Electronic Control Unit (Diamante)

Removal & Installation (Eclipse) – 1) ECU is located behind right rear quarter panel trim. *See Fig. 26.* Disconnect negative battery cable. Remove rear seat. Remove scuff plate. Remove quarter panel mounting screws and trim clip.

2) Carefully remove quarter panel trim. Disconnect ECU wiring harness connector. Remove ECU mounting bolts/nuts and ECU. To install, reverse removal procedure.

Removal & Installation (Stealth & 3000GT) – 1) ECU is located behind right rear quarter panel trim, next to stereo speaker. Disconnect negative battery cable. Remove rear seat cushion and seatback. Remove quarter panel mounting screws and trim clip.

2) Carefully remove quarter panel trim. Disconnect ECU wiring harness connector. Remove ECU mounting bolts/nuts and ECU. To install, reverse removal procedure.

"G" FORCE SENSOR (AWD)

Removal & Installation (Eclipse) – Sensor is located underneath rear seat. *See Fig. 29.* Remove rear seat. Disconnect sensor wiring harness connector. Remove sensor. To install, reverse removal procedure.

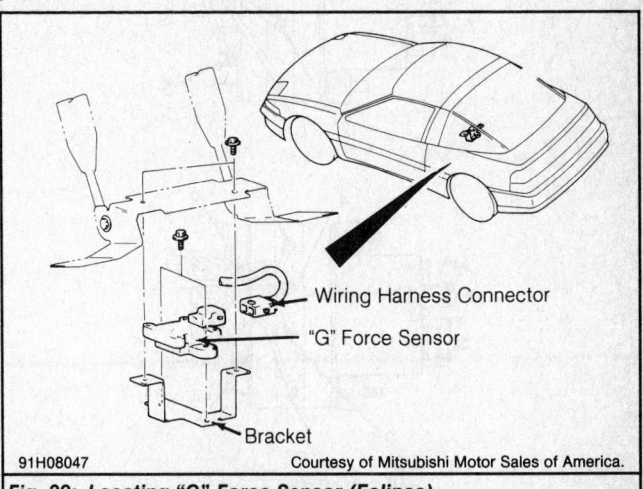

Fig. 29: Locating "G" Force Sensor (Eclipse)

Removal & Installation (Colt Vista, Expo, Stealth, Summit Wagon & 3000GT) – Remove center console assembly. Disconnect electrical connector. Remove mounting bolts. Remove sensor from vehicle. To install, reverse removal procedure.

HYDRAULIC UNIT

CAUTION: DO NOT turn hydraulic unit upside down or lay unit on its side. DO NOT drop hydraulic unit. DO NOT disassemble unit. Replace hydraulic unit as an assembly. If unit is replaced, slowly release safety plug to release internal gas.

Removal & Installation (Colt, Mirage & Summit) – Remove left front inner fender to access hydraulic unit. Remove mounting bracket and A/C relay box. Disconnect brakelines and harness connectors. *See Fig. 30.* Remove hydraulic unit. To install, reverse removal procedure. Ensure brakelines are correctly installed.

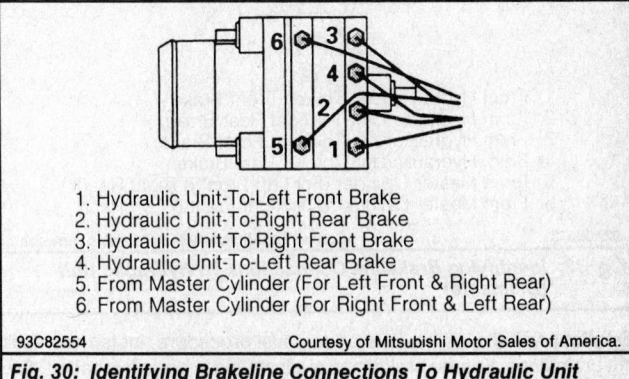

1. Hydraulic Unit-To-Left Front Brake
2. Hydraulic Unit-To-Right Rear Brake
3. Hydraulic Unit-To-Right Front Brake
4. Hydraulic Unit-To-Left Rear Brake
5. From Master Cylinder (For Left Front & Right Rear)
6. From Master Cylinder (For Right Front & Left Rear)

Fig. 30: Identifying Brakeline Connections To Hydraulic Unit (Colt, Mirage & Summit)

Removal & Installation (Colt Vista, Expo & Summit Wagon) – Remove dust cover and oil reservoir. Disconnect electrical connector. Disconnect brakelines. Remove hydraulic unit. To install, reverse removal procedure. Ensure brakelines are correctly installed. *See Fig. 31.*

Removal (Diamante) – 1) Remove hydraulic unit connectors, connector bracket and clip. Disconnect hydraulic lines. Remove A/C pressure clamp bolt.

2) Remove condensor tank and bracket. Disconnect 4-wheel steering connector. Push hydraulic unit backward until clear of A/C lines. Remove hydraulic unit and bracket.

1994 BRAKES
Anti-Lock – Except Galant, Montero & Pickup (Cont.)

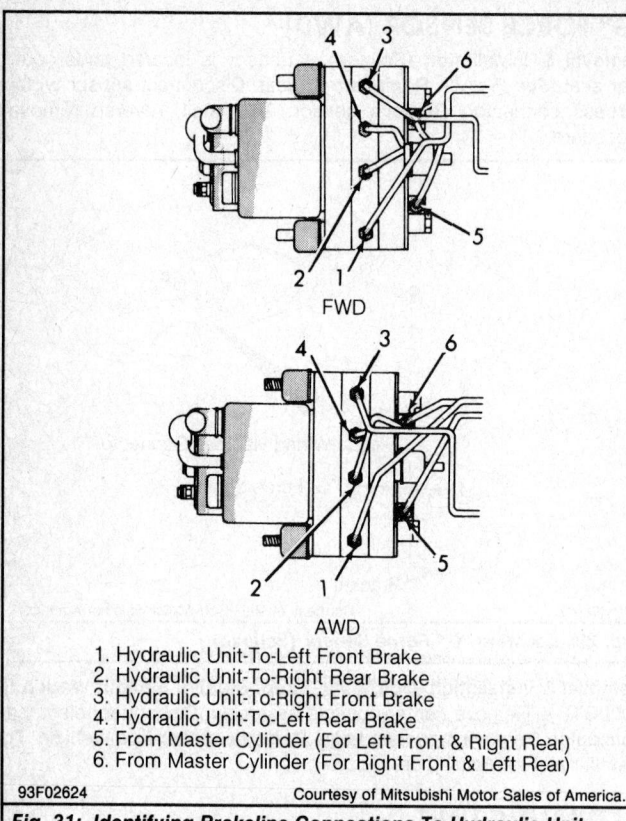

FWD

AWD

1. Hydraulic Unit-To-Left Front Brake
2. Hydraulic Unit-To-Right Rear Brake
3. Hydraulic Unit-To-Right Front Brake
4. Hydraulic Unit-To-Left Rear Brake
5. From Master Cylinder (For Left Front & Right Rear)
6. From Master Cylinder (For Right Front & Left Rear)

93F02624   Courtesy of Mitsubishi Motor Sales of America.

Fig. 31: Identifying Brakeline Connections To Hydraulic Unit (Colt Vista, Expo & Summit Wagon)

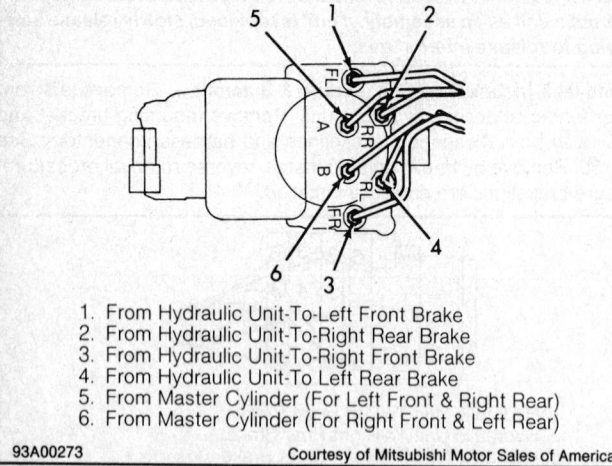

1. From Hydraulic Unit-To-Left Front Brake
2. From Hydraulic Unit-To-Right Rear Brake
3. From Hydraulic Unit-To-Right Front Brake
4. From Hydraulic Unit-To Left Rear Brake
5. From Master Cylinder (For Left Front & Right Rear)
6. From Master Cylinder (For Right Front & Left Rear)

93A00273   Courtesy of Mitsubishi Motor Sales of America.

Fig. 32: Identifying Brakeline Connections To Hydraulic Unit (Diamante)

Installation – To install, reverse removal procedure. Install hydraulic unit brakelines. Ensure brakelines are installed in correct location. *See Fig. 32.* Bleed brake system. See BLEEDING BRAKE SYSTEM.

Removal (Eclipse) – 1) On turbo models, remove air pipe between intercooler and throttle body. On all models, remove brakelines from hydraulic unit. Remove relay box cover.

2) Disconnect ground wire and wiring harness connectors from hydraulic unit. Remove hydraulic unit retaining nuts. Carefully remove hydraulic unit.

Installation – To install, reverse removal procedure. Install hydraulic unit brakelines. Ensure brakelines are installed in correct location. *See Fig. 33.* Bleed brake system. See BLEEDING BRAKE SYSTEM.

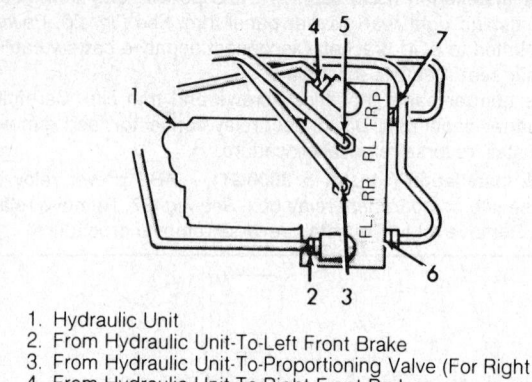

1. Hydraulic Unit
2. From Hydraulic Unit-To-Left Front Brake
3. From Hydraulic Unit-To-Proportioning Valve (For Right Rear)
4. From Hydraulic Unit-To-Right Front Brake
5. From Hydraulic Unit-To-Proportioning Valve (For Left Rear)
6. From Master Cylinder (For Left Front & Right Rear – Eclipse) (For Right Front & Left Rear – Stealth & 3000GT)
7. From Master Cylinder (For Right Front & Left Rear – Eclipse) (For Left Front & Right Rear – Stealth & 3000GT)

92B00225   Courtesy of Mitsubishi Motor Sales of America.

Fig. 33: Identifying Brakeline Connections To Hydraulic Unit (Eclipse, Stealth & 3000GT)

Removal (Stealth & 3000GT) – 1) Remove splash shield. Drain brake fluid. Remove relay box, leaving harness attached. Remove air duct. Remove brakelines from hydraulic unit.

2) Disconnect ground wire and wiring harness connectors from hydraulic unit. Remove bracket bolt and hydraulic unit retaining nuts. Carefully remove hydraulic unit.

CAUTION: DO NOT turn hydraulic unit upside down or lay unit on its side. Unit may be damaged if dropped or subjected to impact shocks. Replace hydraulic unit as an assembly. DO NOT disassemble unit.

Installation – To install, reverse removal procedure. Install hydraulic unit brakelines. Ensure brakelines are installed in correct location. *See Fig. 33.* Bleed brake system. See BLEEDING BRAKE SYSTEM.

WHEEL SPEED SENSOR

NOTE: Before removing wheel speed sensor, note sensor wiring harness routing for installation reference.

Removal (Front – All Except Diamante) – Raise vehicle, and remove wheel. Remove splash shield. Remove retaining clips from speed sensor wiring harness. Disconnect wiring harness connector. Remove sensor mounting bolt. Note sensor wiring harness routing, and remove sensor.

Installation – 1) Install speed sensor bracket if removed. Sensor mounting brackets are not interchangeable from side-to-side. Each bracket is stamped with an "FR" indicating front bracket, and an "R" or "L" to indicate right or left.

2) Temporarily install speed sensor. Route speed sensor wiring harness in its original location, and ensure no twist exists in harness. Adjust wheel speed sensor-to-rotor gap. See WHEEL SPEED SENSOR under ADJUSTMENTS. To complete installation, reverse removal procedure.

Removal (Rear – All Except Diamante) – Raise vehicle, and remove wheel. Remove splash shield. Remove retaining clips and band from speed sensor wiring harness. Disconnect wiring harness connector. Remove sensor mounting bolt. Note sensor wiring harness routing, and remove sensor.

Installation – 1) Install sensor bracket if removed. Sensor mounting brackets are not interchangeable from side-to-side. Each bracket is stamped with an "R" or "L" to indicate right or left.

2) Temporarily install speed sensor. Route speed sensor wiring harness in its original location, and ensure no twist exists in harness. Ensure sensor harness is not in contact with trailing arm.

3) On FWD vehicles, adjust wheel speed sensor-to-rotor gap. See WHEEL SPEED SENSOR under ADJUSTMENTS. On all models, reverse removal procedure to complete installation.

Removal & Installation (Diamante) – Unplug wheel sensor connector. Remove bolts attaching sensor. Remove wheel sensor from vehicle. To install, reverse removal procedure. Sensors are not interchangeable. Adjust wheel speed sensor-to-rotor gap. See WHEEL SPEED SENSOR under ADJUSTMENTS. To complete installation, reverse removal procedure.

WHEEL SENSOR ROTOR

NOTE: *For more information on front or rear brake assembly, see DISC & DRUM – EXCEPT PRECIS article.*

Removal & Installation – Remove brake disc. Remove disc assembly. Remove wheel bearings. Remove axle hub. Remove bolts attaching sensor rotor to hub assembly. To install, reverse removal procedure.

OVERHAUL

HYDRAULIC UNIT

DO NOT attempt to overhaul or disassemble hydraulic unit. If hydraulic unit is defective, replace entire assembly.

TORQUE SPECIFICATIONS

TORQUE SPECIFICATIONS

Application	Ft. Lbs. (N.m)
Front Bearing Nut	144-188 (195-255)
Front Brake Caliper Bolts	58-72 (78-97)
Hydraulic Unit Mounting Bolts	13-18 (18-24)
Rear Bearing Nut	
AWD	[1] 116-159 (157-215)
FWD Disc	[1] 144-188 (195-255)
FWD Drum	[2]
Rear Brake Caliper Bolts	36-43 (48-58)
Rear Drive Shaft-To-Companion Flange (AWD)	40-47 (54-64)
Wheel Lug Nuts	
Diamante, Expo, Galant, Summit, Summit Wagon & Vista Wagon	65-80 (88-108)
Eclipse, Stealth & 3000GT	87-101 (118-137)

	INCH Lbs. (N.m)
Bleeder Screw	60-84 (7-9)
Flared Brakeline Nuts	120-144 (14-16)
Front Sensor Rotor Mounting Bolts	84-120 (9-14)
"G" Force Sensor Mounting Bolts	
Colt Vista, Expo, Eclipse & Summit Wagon	84-120 (9-14)
Stealth & 3000GT	48 (5.4)
Wheel Speed Sensor Bolt	84-120 (9-14)

[1] – Install a new nut.
[2] – Tighten bearing to 14 ft. lbs. (19 N.m). Back off bearing nut, and tighten to 84 INCH lbs. (9 N.m).

1994 BRAKES
Anti-Lock – Except Galant, Montero & Pickup (Cont.)

WIRING DIAGRAMS

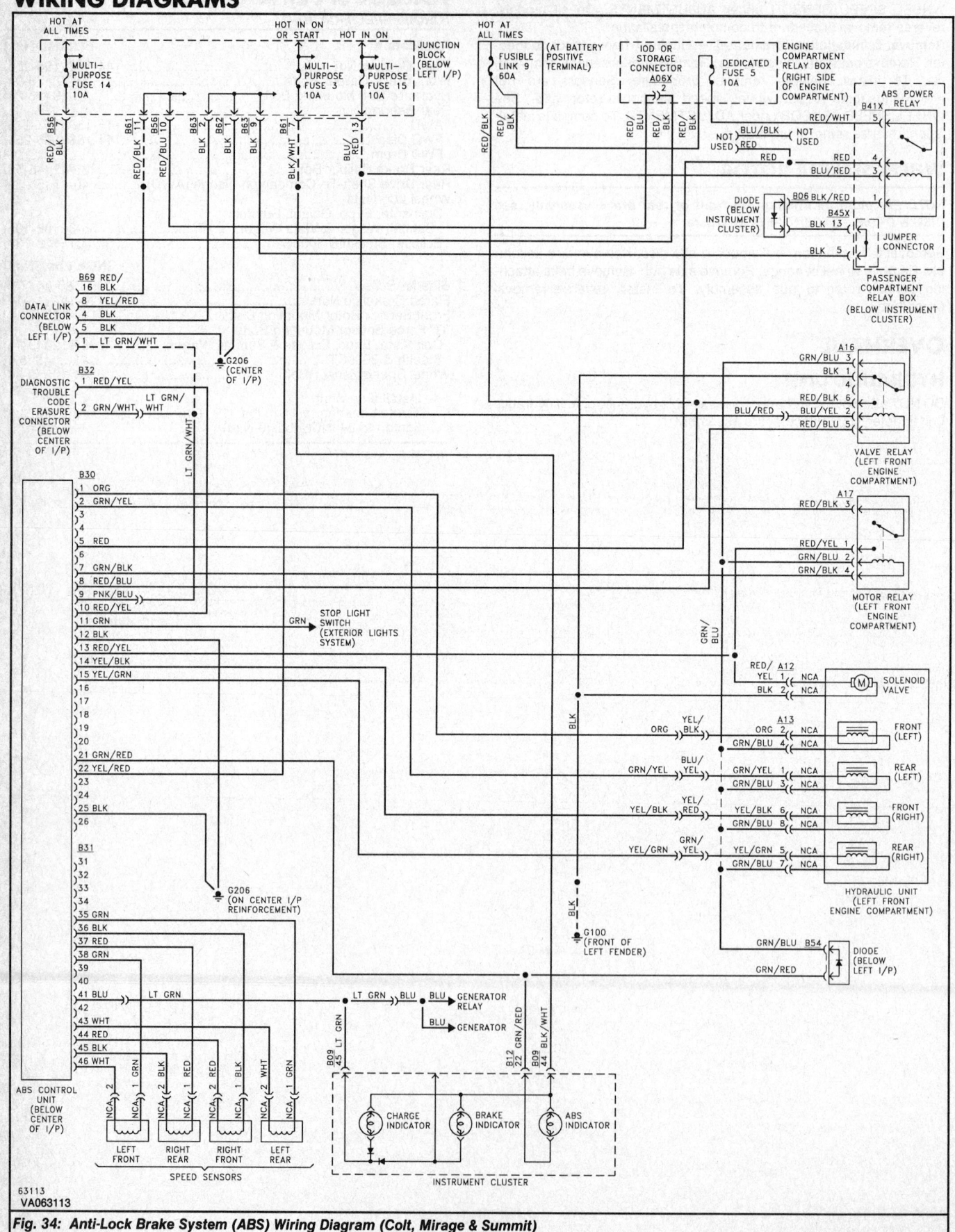

Fig. 34: Anti-Lock Brake System (ABS) Wiring Diagram (Colt, Mirage & Summit)

63113
VA063113

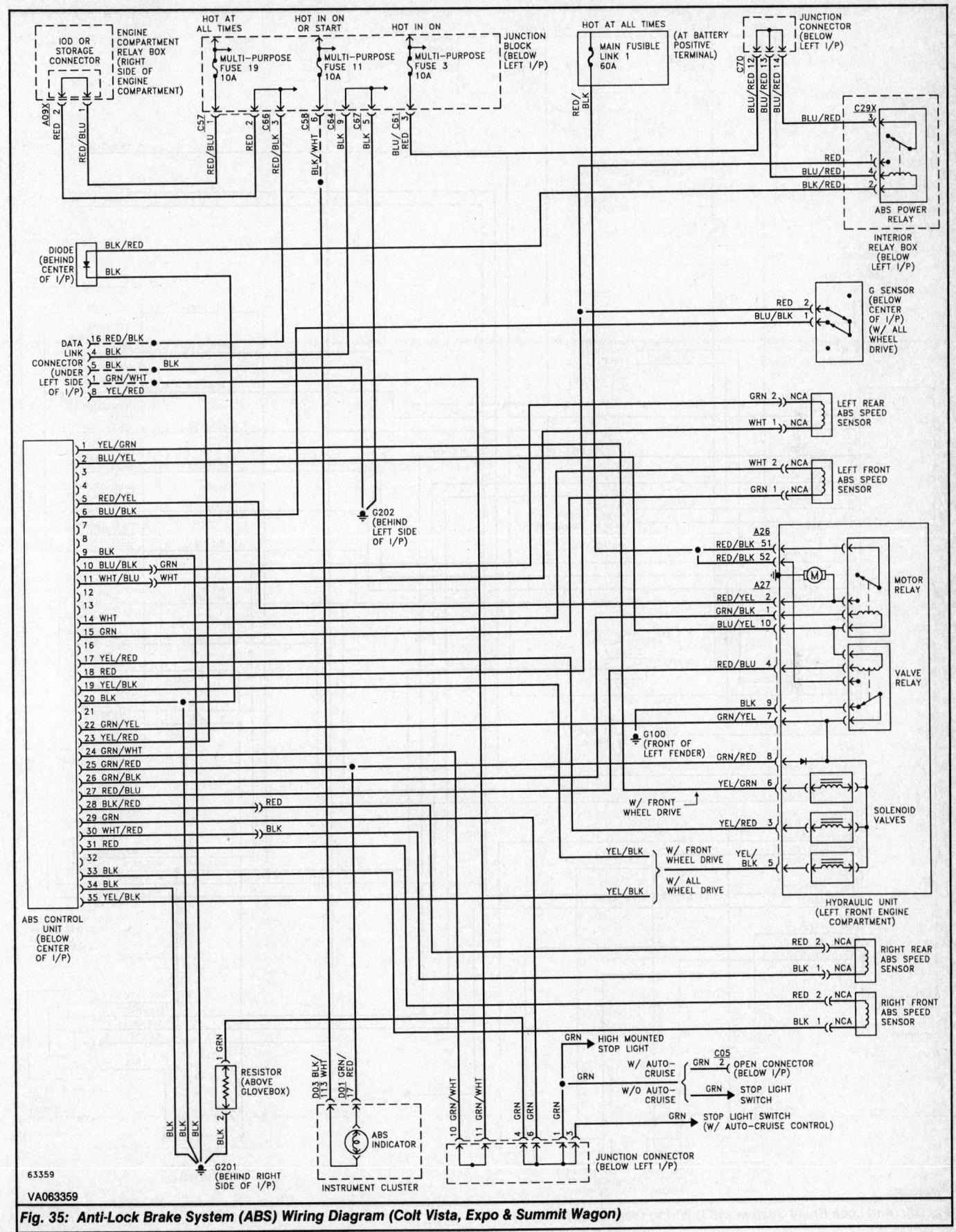

Fig. 35: Anti-Lock Brake System (ABS) Wiring Diagram (Colt Vista, Expo & Summit Wagon)

63359

VA063359

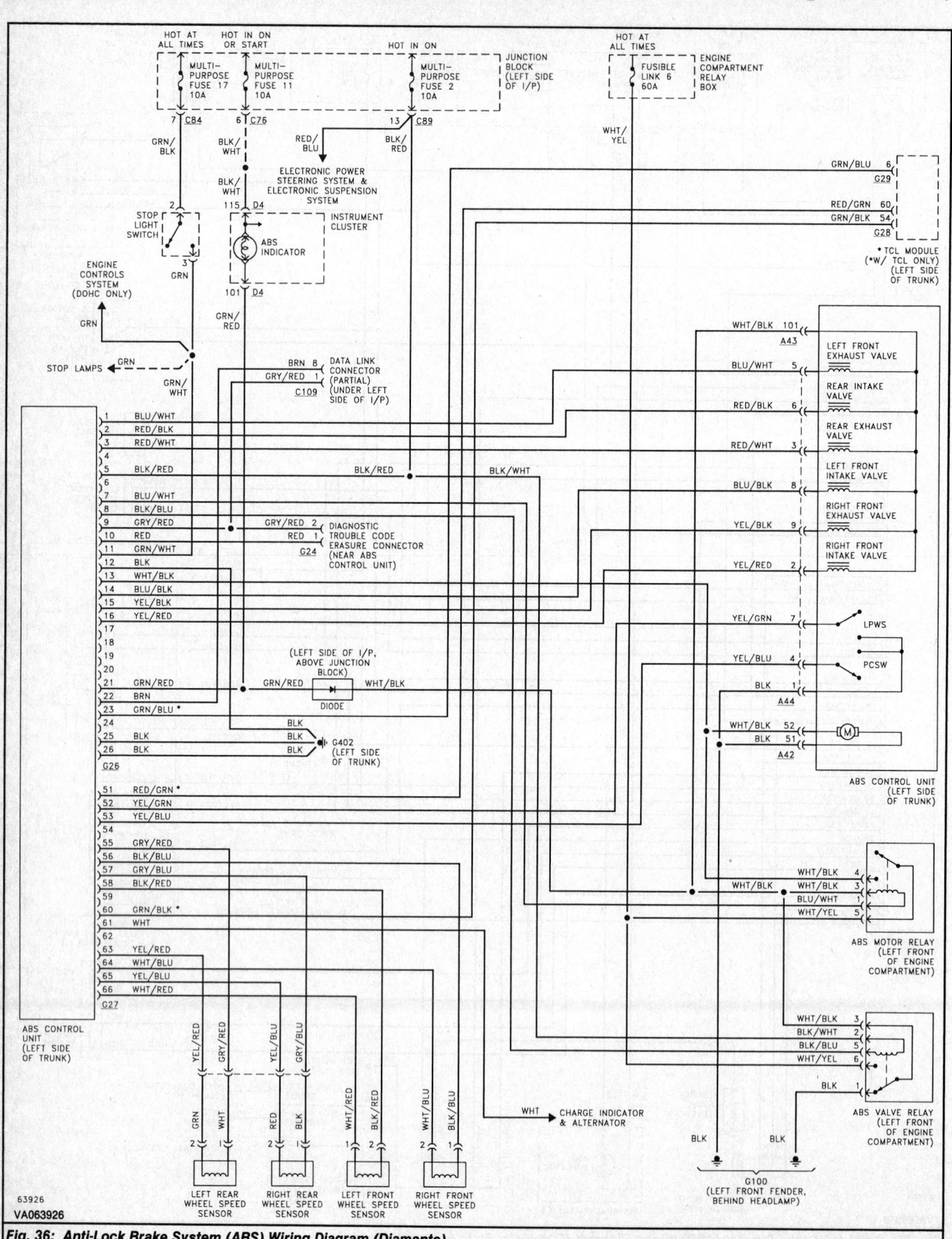

Fig. 36: Anti-Lock Brake System (ABS) Wiring Diagram (Diamante)

63926
VA063926

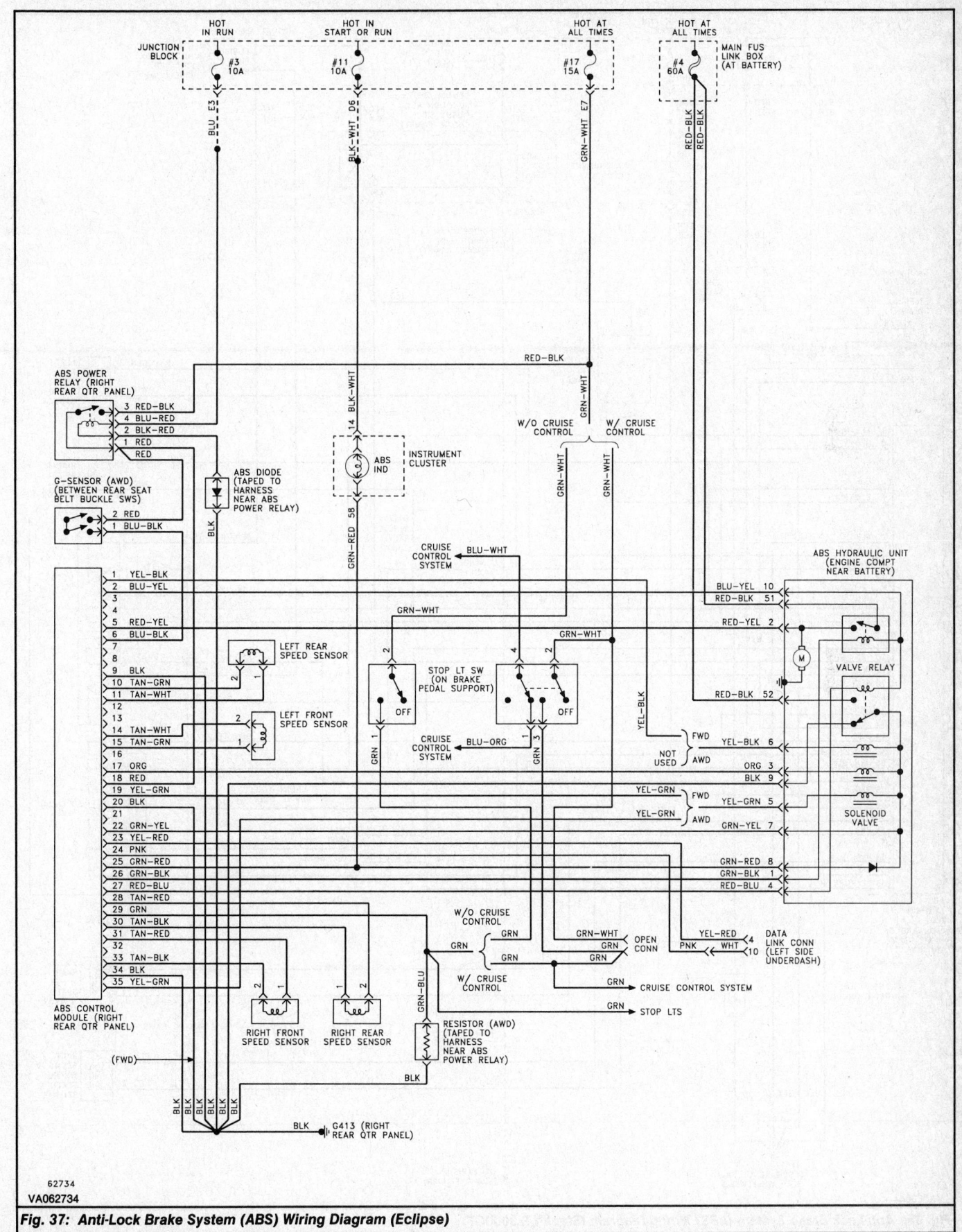

Fig. 37: Anti-Lock Brake System (ABS) Wiring Diagram (Eclipse)

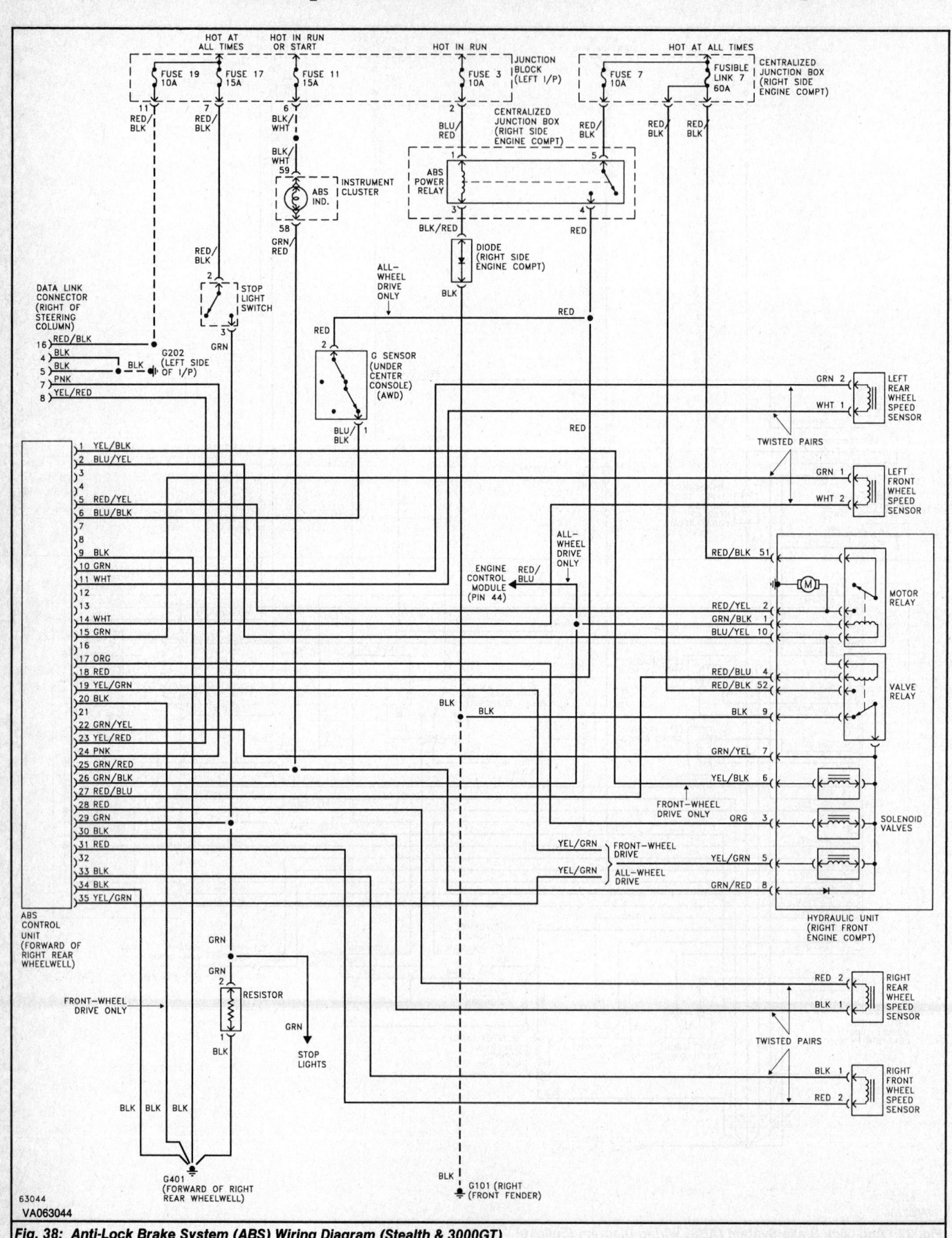

Fig. 38: *Anti-Lock Brake System (ABS) Wiring Diagram (Stealth & 3000GT)*

63044
VA063044

DESCRIPTION

The Anti-Lock Brake System (ABS) is designed to prevent wheel lock-up during heavy braking. This allows operator to maintain steering control while stopping vehicle in shortest distance possible. Major components are hydraulic unit, wheel speed sensors, pedal stroke sensor, Electronic Control Unit (ECU) and ANTI-LOCK warning light. ABS has a self-diagnostic system to indicate a system malfunction and for use in system trouble shooting.

NOTE: For more information on brake system, see DISC & DRUM – EXCEPT PRECIS article.

OPERATION

Each wheel sensor sends an AC electrical signal to the Electronic Control Unit (ECU). The ECU translates this information as wheel speed. When any decelerating wheel speed rate is determined to be excessive in comparison to other monitored wheels, the hydraulic unit cycles hydraulic brake pressure to each wheel to equalize speed of all wheels. ABS turns itself off when vehicle reaches 4 MPH. Minor lock-up may occur at this point.

With engine running and vehicle speed greater than 4 MPH, pump motor will operate for a short period of time and may be heard inside vehicle. During pump motor operation, ABS system is completing a self-check. During ABS system operation, a pulsing brake pedal and vibration in steering wheel and vehicle body may be experienced. These conditions are normal.

CAUTION: See ANTI-LOCK BRAKE SAFETY PRECAUTIONS article in GENERAL INFORMATION.

BLEEDING BRAKE SYSTEM

CAUTION: When adding brake fluid, ensure filter is properly fitted on reserve tank.

ABS system is bled using conventional method. Manually bleed system using foot method with an assistant. For bleeding order, see BRAKE LINE BLEEDING SEQUENCE table. Ensure all air is removed from brake system. Refill brake fluid reservoir after bleeding procedure is complete.

BRAKE LINE BLEEDING SEQUENCE

Application	Sequence
Galant	RR, LF, LR, RF

ADJUSTMENTS

NOTE: For adjustment information for brake pedal height, free play, parking brake and stoplight switch, see DISC & DRUM – EXCEPT PRECIS article.

WHEEL SPEED SENSOR

NOTE: Galant wheel speed sensor to not adjustable. Clearance between sensor mounting surface and rotor outside surface should be 1.11-1.12" (28.2-28.5 mm).

TROUBLE SHOOTING

NOTE: If system is not functioning properly after all testing procedures have been completed, substitute ABS ECU with known good unit and retest.

ANTI-LOCK WARNING LIGHT

1) Turn ignition on. ANTI-LOCK warning light should illuminate. Turn ignition switch to START position. Warning light should flash once (approximately one second) and go out.

2) If warning light functions as specified, go step **3)**. If warning light does not function as specified, see appropriate trouble shooting test:
- ANTI-LOCK WARNING LIGHT INOPERATIVE.
- ENGINE RUNNING, ANTI-LOCK WARNING LIGHT REMAINS ON.
- IGNITION SWITCH IN ON POSITION, WARNING LIGHT STAYS ON FOR APPROXIMATELY ONE SECOND, THEN SWITCHES OFF.
- IGNITION SWITCH TURNED TO START POSITION, WARNING LIGHT SWITCHES OFF (DOES NOT BLINK ONCE).

to next step. If ABS light comes on at low speed, motor relay, solenoid valve or wheel speed sensor malfunction is indicated. Go to step **6)**. If insufficient braking force or ABS malfunction exists, go to next step. If none of above symptoms exist, go to step **6)**.

4) Check conventional brake system components for proper operation. Check for mechanical lock of hydraulic unit solenoid valve. Check for plugged hydraulic line in hydraulic unit. Repair or replace as necessary. If hydraulic unit is okay, go to next step.

5) Check for faulty wheel speed sensor. See WHEEL SPEED SENSOR under COMPONENT TESTING. Replace sensor as necessary. See WHEEL SPEED SENSOR under REMOVAL & INSTALLATION. Inspect ECU wiring. If testing indicates no mechanical or electrical failures, replace ECU.

6) Enter ABS self-diagnostics, and retrieve codes. See RETRIEVING CODES under SELF-DIAGNOSTIC SYSTEM. If no codes are displayed, fault may be intermittent. Try to make malfunction reoccur. If no diagnostic output exists, check for faulty wiring harness between ECU and self-diagnostic connector. Repair or replace as necessary.

ANTI-LOCK Warning Light Inoperative – **1)** If all other warning lights illuminate with ignition on, go to step **3)**. If other warning lights do not illuminate, check fuse No. 8 in main fuse panel. If fuse is blown, correct cause of blown fuse, and replace fuse. If fuse is okay, go to next step.

2) Remove instrument cluster. Turn ignition on. Using a DVOM, measure voltage between ground and instrument cluster ABS warning light terminal No. 24. *See Fig. 1.* If battery voltage is present, repair or replace instrument cluster. If battery voltage is not present, repair wiring between fuse and instrument cluster.

3) Turn ignition off. Check for faulty warning light bulb. Replace bulb as necessary. If bulb is okay, check for continuity between instrument cluster connector terminals No. 24 and 37. If not continuity is present, clean and/or repair connector terminals. If continuity is present, go to next step.

4) To check ECU, turn ignition off. Remove ECU connector C-65. Turn ignition on. Measure voltage between terminal No. 39 and ground. *See Fig. 2.* If battery voltage is not present, repair circuit between warning light and ECU. If battery voltage is present, replace ECU.

5) To check valve relay, see HYDRAULIC UNIT RELAYS under COMPONENT TESTING. If relay is okay, remove harness connector. Turn ignition on. Measure voltage between terminal No. 31 (Green/Yellow wire, square 2-pin connector) and ground.

6) If battery voltage is present, go to next step. If battery voltage is not present, repair circuit between ANTI-LOCK warning light and hydraulic unit. See WIRING DIAGRAM.

7) Turn ignition off. Disconnect hydraulic unit round 2-pin connector. Check for continuity between terminal No. 21 and ground (Black wire, round 2-pin connector). If continuity does not exist, repair circuit between hydraulic unit and ground. If continuity exists, replace hydraulic unit.

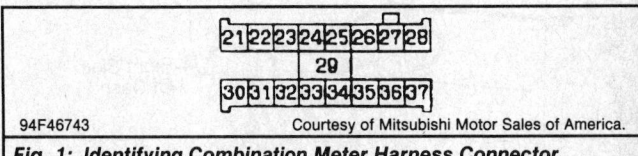

94F46743   Courtesy of Mitsubishi Motor Sales of America.

Fig. 1: Identifying Combination Meter Harness Connector Terminals

Engine Running, Anti-Lock Warning Light Remains On – **1)** Turn ignition off. Disconnect ECU harness connector C-65. Restart engine. If light is no longer on, replace ECU and retest. If light remains on, turn ignition off.

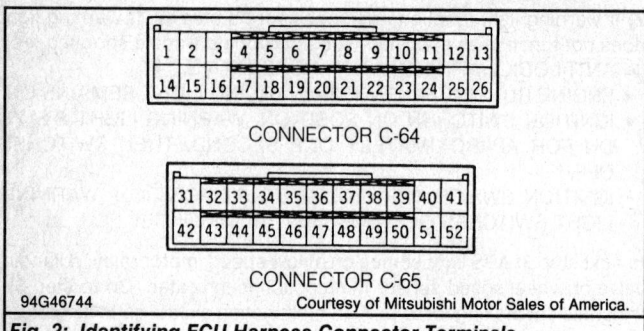

CONNECTOR C-64

CONNECTOR C-65

94G46744
Courtesy of Mitsubishi Motor Sales of America.

Fig. 2: Identifying ECU Harness Connector Terminals

2) Disconnect combination meter harness connector. Start and run engine. If light remains on, replace combination meter. If warning light goes out, check continuity between ECU harness connector terminal No. 39 and ground. *See Fig. 2.*

3) If continuity is present, inspect and repair circuit between ECU and combination meter as needed. If continuity does not exist, system is okay. Reconnect all components and retest system.

Ignition Switch In On Position, Warning Light Stays On For Approximately One Second, Then Switches Off – 1) Turn ignition off. Disconnect ECU harness connector C-65. Start and run engine. Using DVOM, measure voltage between ECU harness connector terminal No. 38 and ground. If voltage is less than 7 volts, go to step **3)**. If voltage is more than 7 volts, go to next step.

2) Inspect ECU harness connector. Repair as needed. If connector is okay, reconnect harness connector and retrieve codes. See RETRIEVING CODES under SELF-DIAGNOSTIC SYSTEM.

3) Measure voltage between generator "L" terminal (White wire) and ground. If voltage is less than 7 volts, replace generator. If voltage is more than 7 volts, turn ignition off. Disconnect generator harness connector. Using ohmmeter, check continuity between generator "L" terminal (White wire) and ECU harness connector C-65 terminal No. 38.

4) If continuity does not exist, inspect and repair circuit as needed. If continuity does exist, connect all components and retrieve codes. See RETRIEVING CODES under SELF-DIAGNOSTIC SYSTEM.

Ignition Switch Turned To Start Position, Warning Light Switches Off (Does Not Blink Once) – 1) Turn ignition off. Remove ABS valve relay. Inspect relay. See HYDRAULIC UNIT RELAYS under COMPONENT TESTING. Replace as needed. If relay is okay, disconnect ECU harness connector C-65.

2) Turn ignition on. Using DVOM, measure voltage between relay receptacle terminal No. 3 (Green/Yellow wire) and ground. If battery voltage is present, inspect and repair ABS valve relay ground circuit (terminal No. 1, Black wire). See WIRING DIAGRAM. If battery voltage is not present, go to next step.

3) Disconnect diode. *See Fig. 3.* Using ohmmeter, check for continuity in one direction of current flow only. Replace as needed. Check continuity between ABS valve relay receptacle terminal No. 3 (Green/Yellow wire) and diode Green/Yellow wire. *See Fig. 4.*

4) If continuity does not exist, inspect and repair circuit as needed. If continuity does exist, check continuity between combination meter terminal No. 37 and diode Green/Red wire. *See Fig. 2.* Inspect and repair as needed.

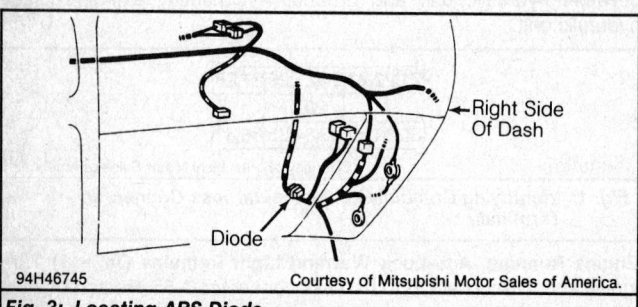

Right Side Of Dash

Diode

94H46745
Courtesy of Mitsubishi Motor Sales of America.

Fig. 3: Locating ABS Diode

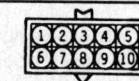

91C08040
Courtesy of Mitsubishi Motor Sales of America.

Fig. 4: Identifying Hydraulic Unit 10-Pin Harness Connector

SELF DIAGNOSTIC SYSTEM
RETRIEVING CODES

Using Scan Tester – 1) With ignition off, connect Multi-Use Tester II (MB991502) with ROM pack to self-diagnostic connector, located under right side of driver's dash.

2) Turn ignition on. ABS warning light should come on as ABS goes into self-diagnostic mode. Read and record all diagnostic output (trouble) codes from ECU memory. Refer to Multi-Use Tester II (MUT-II) instructions for specific trouble code retrieval procedure.

3) After all trouble codes have been retrieved and recorded, clear codes from ECU memory. Refer to tester instructions for specific trouble code clearing instructions. See TROUBLE CODE DEFINITION chart.

4) If trouble codes cannot be cleared, ECU is currently detecting a malfunction. If codes can be cleared, problem is either intermittent or only appears while driving.

Without Using Scan Tester – 1) Turn ignition on and depress brake pedal within 3 seconds and release. Continue to depress and release brake pedal once per second for 9 more cycles.

2) If trouble codes are stored in ECU memory, ABS indicator light will begin to flash intermittently. Long flashes represent tens; short flashes represent ones. For example, 4 long flashes and 3 short flashes indicate Code 43. If 2 or more codes are stored, lowest number will be displayed first.

3) After recording trouble code(s), perform necessary testing. See DIAGNOSTIC TESTING. If no codes are stored, ABS indicator light will flash constantly.

TROUBLE CODE DEFINITION
TROUBLE CODES

Code	[1] System Affected
11	Right Front Wheel Speed Sensor (Open)
12	Left Front Wheel Speed Sensor (Open)
13	Right Rear Wheel Speed Sensor (Open)
14	Left Rear Wheel Speed Sensor (Open)
16	Low Battery Voltage
21	Right Front Wheel Speed Sensor (Short)
22	Left Front Wheel Speed Sensor (Short)
23	Right Rear Wheel Speed Sensor (Short)
24	Left Rear Wheel Speed Sensor (Short)
25	Right Front Wheel Speed Sensor (Excessive Gap)
26	Left Front Wheel Speed Sensor (Excessive Gap)
27	Right Rear Wheel Speed Sensor (Excessive Gap)
28	Left Rear Wheel Speed Sensor (Excessive Gap)
31	Pedal Stroke Sensor
32	Pedal Stroke Sensor
33	Brakelight Switch
34	Pedal Stroke Sensor & Pump System
35	Right Front Wheel Speed Sensor (High Speed Input)
36	Left Front Wheel Speed Sensor (High Speed Input)
37	Right Rear Wheel Speed Sensor (High Speed Input)
38	Left Rear Wheel Speed Sensor (High Speed Input)
41	Right Front Solenoid Valve (Inside)
42	Left Front Solenoid Valve (Inside)
43	Right Rear Solenoid Valve (Inside)
44	Left Rear Solenoid Valve (Inside)
45	Right Front Solenoid Valve (Outside)
46	Left Front Solenoid Valve (Outside)
47	Right Rear Solenoid Valve (Outside)
48	Left Rear Solenoid Valve (Outside)
51-52	Valve Relay
53-54	Motor Relay

[1] – See appropriate CODE under DIAGNOSTIC TESTING.

CLEARING CODES

To erase code(s) with scan tester, follow tester instructions. To erase codes without scan tester, disconnect negative battery cable for at least 10 seconds.

DIAGNOSTIC TESTING

CODE 11, 12, 13 OR 14:
WHEEL SPEED SENSOR OPEN CIRCUIT

NOTE: Codes 11, 12, 13 & 14 are displayed when sensor with open circuit is identified.

1) Inspect condition of suspected speed sensor. Ensure tip of speed sensor is clean. Disconnect sensor harness connector. Using ohmmeter, measure resistance between harness connector terminals. If resistance is 1000-1200 ohms, go to next step. If resistance is not within specification, replace sensor and retest.
2) Trouble code will set if ECU detects wheel speed sensor(s) has open circuit. Check continuity of circuit between ECU and sensor. See WIRING DIAGRAM. Repair wiring as needed.

CODE 16: LOW BATTERY VOLTAGE

NOTE: Code 16 is output when ABS ECU power supply voltage is not within standard. If supply voltage returns to normal, trouble code will be erased.

1) Start engine. Using DVOM, measure voltage between ECU terminal No. 12 (backprobe) and ground. *See Fig. 2.* If 10 volts or more is present, replace ECU. If less than 10 volts is present, check fuse No. 13.
2) If fuse is okay, check continuity between fuse No. 13 receptacle (Blue wire) and ECU harness connector terminal No. 12. Repair wiring as needed. If circuit is okay, inspect charging system. Repair charging system as needed.

CODE 21, 22, 23 OR 24:
WHEEL SPEED SENSOR SHORT CIRCUIT

NOTE: Codes 21, 22, 23 & 24 are displayed when sensor with short circuit is identified.

1) Inspect condition of suspected speed sensor. Ensure tip of speed sensor is free of contaminates. Disconnect sensor harness connector. Using ohmmeter, measure resistance between each harness connector terminal and outside or sensor. If resistance is 100 k/ohms or greater, go to next step. If resistance is not within specification, replace sensor and retest.
2) Trouble code will set if ECU detects wheel speed sensor(s) has short circuit. Check continuity of circuit between ECU and sensor, and ground. See WIRING DIAGRAM. Repair wiring as needed. If all suspected circuits are okay, replace ABS ECU and retest.

CODE 25, 26, 27 OR 28:
EXCESSIVE WHEEL SPEED SENSOR GAP

NOTE: Codes 25, 26, 27 & 28 are displayed when detection speed of wheel speed sensor is below standard value.

1) Inspect condition of suspected speed sensor. Ensure tip of speed sensor is clean. Disconnect suspect sensor(s) harness connector. Using DVOM, measure voltage between each harness connector terminals while rotating wheel at 30-60 RPM. If pulse voltage is 70 mV or greater, go to next step. If voltage is not within specification, replace sensor and retest.
2) Trouble code will set if ECU does not detect voltage pulses from wheel speed sensor(s). Check continuity of circuit between ECU and sensor. See WIRING DIAGRAM. Repair wiring as needed. If all suspected circuits are okay, replace ABS ECU and retest.

CODE 31: PEDAL STROKE SENSOR (PSS)

NOTE: Code 31 is output if pedal stroke sensor supply voltage or input voltage is not within standard value.

1) Disconnect PSS harness connector (3-pin). PSS is incorporated in brakelight switch. Turn ignition on. Using DVOM, measure voltage between PSS harness connector terminal No. 3 (Blue/Red wire) and ground. *See Fig. 5.* If voltage is 4.6-5.4 volts, go to step **3)**. If voltage is 5.4 volts or more, replace ABS ECU and retest system.
2) If voltage is 4.6 volts or less, turn ignition off. Disconnect ABS ECU harness connector C-65. Using ohmmeter, check continuity between ABS ECU harness connector terminal No. 32 and PSS harness connector terminal No. 3 (Blue/Red wire). *See Fig. 2.* If continuity does not exist, inspect and repair circuit. If continuity exists, replace ECU and retest.
3) Turn ignition off. Connect PSS harness connector. Turn ignition on. Backprobing ABS ECU harness connector C-64, measure voltage between ECU harness connector terminal No. 7 and ground. If voltage is .47-4.53 volts, replace ABS ECU and retest.
4) If voltage is .47 volts or less, turn ignition off. Disconnect PSS and ABS ECU harness connectors. Check continuity between PSS harness connector terminal No. 2 (Blue/Black wire) and ECU harness connector (C-64) terminal No. 7. If continuity does not exist, inspect and repair circuit as needed.
5) If continuity exists, check continuity of ground circuit. See WIRING DIAGRAM. Repair wiring as needed. If continuity exists, check operation of PSS. See PEDAL STROKE SENSOR under COMPONENT TESTING. Replace as needed. If PSS is okay, replace ABS ECU and retest.

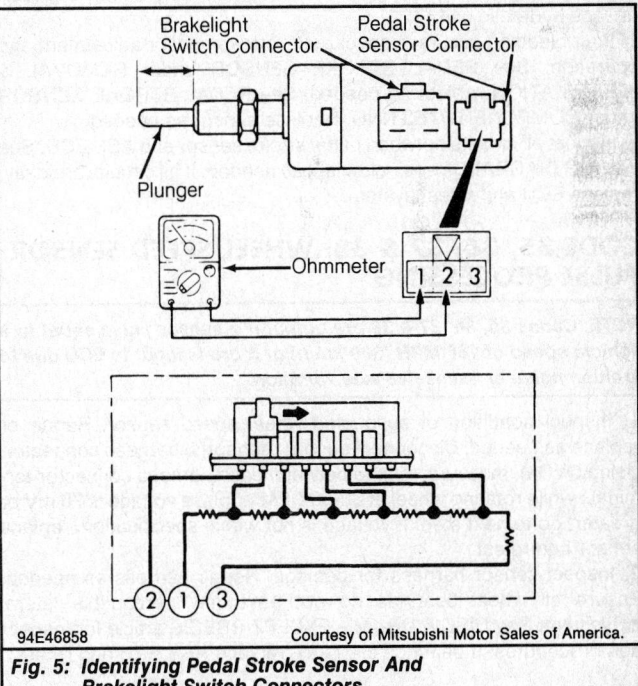

94E46858   Courtesy of Mitsubishi Motor Sales of America.

Fig. 5: Identifying Pedal Stroke Sensor And Brakelight Switch Connectors

CODE 32: PEDAL STROKE SENSOR (PSS)

NOTE: Code 32 is output if vehicle acceleration (or deceleration) is above specified value with respect to pedal stroke sensor input voltage for at least 10 seconds or more. Code will also be output if input voltage is above specified value for 15 seconds or more.

1) Inspect PSS installation. See PEDAL STROKE SENSOR under REMOVAL & INSTALLATION. Adjust as needed. Inspect PSS operation. See PEDAL STROKE SENSOR under COMPONENT TESTING. Replace sensor as needed.

2) Ensure ignition is off. Disconnect ABS ECU harness connector C-64. Using ohmmeter, check continuity between harness connector terminal No. 7 and ground. If continuity does not exist, repair circuit as needed. See WIRING DIAGRAM. If continuity exists, replace ECU and retest system.

CODE 33: BRAKELIGHT SWITCH CIRCUIT

NOTE: Code 33 is output if an open circuit is detected when brakelight switch is on for 15 minutes or more. Code will also be output if a short circuit is detected.

1) Check if brakelights are functioning correctly. If brakelights function correctly, go to next step. If brakelights do not function correctly, check brakelight circuit and repair as needed.
2) Ensure ignition is off. Disconnect ABS ECU harness connector C-64. Using DVOM, measure voltage between terminal No. 4 and ground while depressing brake pedal. If battery voltage is not present, repair or replace wiring harness between brakelight switch and ECU. If battery voltage is present, brakelight switch circuit is okay. Replace faulty ECU and retest.

CODE 34: PEDAL STROKE SENSOR & PUMP SYSTEM

NOTE: Code 34 is output if a motor pump ON instruction has been given but output voltage of pedal stroke sensor does not change.

1) Connect scan tester. Perform actuator test No. 5. Refer to tester instructions for actuator test procedure. Determine if hydraulic unit air bleeds during brake pedal operation. If air bleeding does not occur, replace hydraulic unit.
2) If air bleeding occurs, inspect pedal stroke sensor adjustment and operation. See PEDAL STROKE SENSOR under REMOVAL & INSTALLATION. Adjust as needed. See PEDAL STROKE SENSOR under COMPONENT TESTING. Replace sensor as needed.
3) Inspect all circuits between pedal stroke sensor and ABS ECU. See WIRING DIAGRAM. Repair circuit(s) as needed. If all circuits are okay, replace ECU and retest system.

CODE 35, 36, 37 & 38: WHEEL SPEED SENSOR PULSE PROCESSING

NOTE: Codes 35, 36, 37 & 38 are output if a sensor pulse equal to a vehicle speed of 186 MPH (300 km/h) or more is input to ECU due to ignition noise or excessive axle vibration.

1) Inspect condition of suspected wheel speed sensor. Repair or replace as needed. Disconnect suspect sensor(s) harness connector. Using DVOM, measure voltage between each harness connector terminals while rotating wheel at 30-60 RPM. If pulse voltage is 70 mV or greater, go to next step. If voltage is not within specification, replace sensor and retest.
2) Inspect sensor harness for damage. Repair harness as needed. Ensure all wheel bearings do not have any perceptible lateral movement. See DISC & DRUM – EXCEPT PRECIS article for inspection procedures. If bearings are okay, replace ABS ECU and retest.

CODE 41-48: SOLENOID VALVE

NOTE: Codes 41-48 will be output if the ABS ECU detects a short or open in solenoid valve harness or solenoid coil.

1) Ensure ignition is off. Disconnect hydraulic unit 10-pin and 2-pin (square connector) harness connectors. Using ohmmeter, measure resistance between terminals No. 31 and 32 of 2-pin component connector and each terminal of 10-pin component connector except terminals No. 5 and 10. *See Fig. 4.*
2) If resistance of any circuit is not 5.5-6.5 ohms, replace hydraulic unit and retest. See HYDRAULIC UNIT under REMOVAL & INSTALLATION. If resistance is within specification, go to next step.

3) Disconnect ABS ECU harness connector. Check continuity of circuits between ECU and hydraulic unit. See WIRING DIAGRAM. If continuity does not exist in any circuit, inspect and repair suspected circuit(s) as needed.
4) If continuity exists in all circuits, turn ignition on. Using DVOM, measure voltage between ECU harness connector terminal No. 43 and ground. *See Fig. 2.* If battery voltage is present, replace ABS ECU and retest.
5) If battery voltage is not present, inspect and repair power supply circuit from fuse No. 8 and ECU terminal No. 43, including in-line diode. *See Fig. 3.* See WIRING DIAGRAM.

CODE 51: VALVE RELAY ALWAYS OFF

1) Remove and test valve relay. See HYDRAULIC UNIT RELAYS under COMPONENT TESTING. Replace relay if faulty. If relay is okay, measure voltage between relay receptacle terminal No. 6 and ground. *See Fig. 6.* If battery voltage is present, go to step **3)**.
2) If battery voltage is not present, check condition of fuse No. 1. Replace fuse as needed. If fuse is okay, inspect and repair circuit between fuse No. 1 and relay receptacle terminal No. 6.
3) Install valve relay. Ensure ignition is off. Disconnect ABS ECU harness connector. Turn ignition on. Measure voltage between ECU harness connector terminal No. 13 and ground. *See Fig. 2.* If battery voltage is present, go to step **5)**.
4) If battery voltage is not present, turn ignition off. Remove valve relay. Using ohmmeter, check continuity between relay receptacle terminal No. 5 and ECU terminal No. 13. If continuity does not exist, inspect and repair circuit as needed. If continuity exists, inspect and repair circuit between fuse No. 13 and relay receptacle No. 2.
5) Measure voltage between ECU harness connector terminal No. 43 and ground. If battery voltage is present, replace ABS ECU and retest. If battery voltage is not present, inspect and repair circuit between ECU terminal No. 43 and relay receptacle terminal No. 3. See WIRING DIAGRAM.

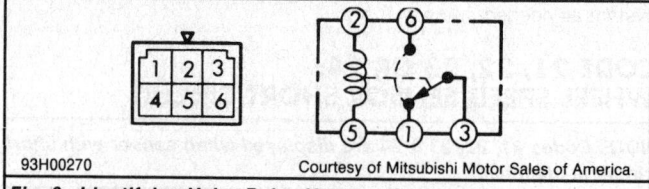

93H00270　　　Courtesy of Mitsubishi Motor Sales of America.
Fig. 6: Identifying Valve Relay Harness Connector

CODE 52: VALVE RELAY ALWAYS ON

1) Remove and test valve relay. See HYDRAULIC UNIT RELAYS under COMPONENT TESTING. Replace relay if faulty. If relay is okay, ensure ignition is off. Disconnect ABS ECU harness connector.
2) Turn ignition on. Measure voltage between ECU harness connector terminal No. 13 and ground. *See Fig. 2.* If battery voltage is present, replace ABS ECU and retest. If battery voltage is not present, inspect and repair circuit between ECU terminal No. 13 and relay receptacle No. 5.

CODE 53: MOTOR RELAY ALWAYS OFF

1) Connect scan tester. Perform actuator tests No. 1-5. Refer to tester instructions for actuator test procedure. If hydraulic unit motor can be heard operating during each actuator test, go to step **5)**.
2) If motor can not be heard during specific actuator test(s), remove and test motor relay. See HYDRAULIC UNIT RELAYS under COMPONENT TESTING. Replace relay if faulty. If relay is okay, measure voltage between relay receptacle terminal No. 5 and ground. *See Fig. 7.*
3) If battery voltage is present, go to next step. If battery voltage is not present, inspect fusible link No. 4 (Red). Replace fusible link as needed. If fusible link is okay, inspect and repair circuit between fusible link and relay receptacle No. 5.
4) Ensure ignition is off. Disconnect ABS ECU harness connector. Measure voltage between ECU harness connector terminal No. 31 and ground. *See Fig. 2.* If voltage is present, replace ABS ECU and retest. If voltage is not present, inspect and repair circuit between ECU terminal No. 31 and relay receptacle terminal No. 1.

5) Disconnect hydraulic unit 10-pin connector. Measure resistance between component connector terminals No. 5 and 10. *See Fig. 4.* If resistance is 10-13 ohms, go to next step. If resistance is not within specification, replace hydraulic unit.

6) Ensure ignition is off. Disconnect ABS ECU harness connector. Check continuity between hydraulic unit harness connector terminal No. 5 and ECU harness connector terminal No. 33.

7) Check continuity between hydraulic unit harness connector terminal No. 10 and ECU harness connector terminal No. 44. If continuity exists in both circuits, replace ABS ECU and retest system. If continuity does not exist, inspect and repair circuit(s) as needed.

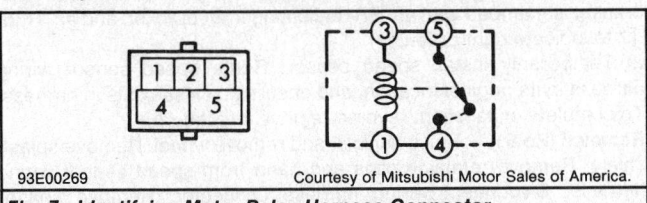

Fig. 7: Identifying Motor Relay Harness Connector

CODE 54: MOTOR RELAY ALWAYS ON

NOTE: Code 54 may output if hydraulic motor sensor is registering motor revolutions due to noise interference, even though motor relay is off.

1) Turn ignition switch to ON position. Monitor operation of hydraulic unit motor. Turn ignition off. If motor ceases to operate, replace ABS ECU and retest. If motor continues to operate, remove motor relay and inspect. See HYDRAULIC UNIT RELAYS under COMPONENT TESTING. Replace relay if faulty.

2) If relay is okay, turn ignition off. Disconnect ABS ECU harness connector. Check continuity between relay receptacle terminal No. 1 and ECU harness connector terminal No. 31. *See Fig. 2.* If continuity does not exist, inspect and repair circuit as needed. If continuity exists, replace ABS ECU and retest.

COMPONENT TESTING

HYDRAULIC UNIT RELAYS

NOTE: Relays are mounted next to hydraulic unit, see Fig. 8.

Motor Relay – 1) Remove motor relay. Using an ohmmeter, measure resistance between relay terminals No. 1 and 3. *See Fig. 7.* Resistance should be 49-99 ohms. Check for continuity between relay terminals No. 4 and 5. Continuity should not exist.

2) Apply battery voltage between relay terminal No. 1 and terminal No. 3. Check for continuity between terminals No. 4 and 5. Continuity should be zero ohms. If relay does not test as specified, replace relay.

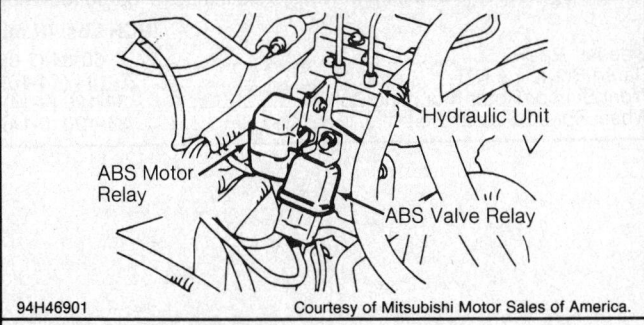

Fig. 8: Locating ABS Relays

Valve Relay – 1) Remove valve relay. Using an ohmmeter, measure resistance between relay terminals No. 2 and 5. *See Fig. 6.* Resistance should be 55-105 ohms. Measure resistance between relay terminals No. 1 and 3. Resistance should be zero ohms.

2) Check for continuity between relay terminals No. 3 and 6. Continuity should not exist. Apply battery voltage between terminal No. 2 and terminal No. 5. Check for continuity between terminals No. 1 and 3. Continuity should not exist.

3) Check for continuity between terminals No. 3 and 6. Continuity should be approximately zero ohms. If relay does not test as specified, replace relay.

PEDAL STROKE SENSOR/BRAKELIGHT SWITCH

1) Ensure plunger of sensor moves smoothly. Using ohmmeter, measure resistance of sensor in specified positions. *See Fig. 5.* See PEDAL STROKE SENSOR RESISTANCE SPECIFICATIONS table. Replace sensor if resistance measurements are not within specification.

2) Continuity should exist when brakelight switch plunger extended. No continuity should exist when plunger is depressed. Replace as needed.

PEDAL STROKE SENSOR RESISTANCE SPECIFICATIONS

Plunger Position In. (mm)	Ohms
.14-.18 (3.5-4.5)	237-261
.26-.30 (6.7-7.7)	414-458
.39-.43 (9.8-1-.8)	535-591
.51-.55 (12.9-13.9)	655-725
.63-.67 (16-17)	770-858
.69-.73 (17.5-18.5)	980-1084

WHEEL SPEED SENSOR

Sensor Resistance Test – 1) Before testing sensor resistance, ensure pole piece-to-wheel speed sensor tip is clean. Check wheel sensor pole piece for damage. If pole piece is damaged, replace sensor.

2) Disconnect sensor connector. Inspect sensor wiring harness for broken and pinched wires. Repair or replace harness as necessary. Using an ohmmeter, measure sensor resistance at wiring connector. See WHEEL SPEED SENSOR RESISTANCE SPECIFICATIONS table. If resistance is not within specification, replace sensor. If resistance is within specification, go to GROUND CIRCUIT TEST.

WHEEL SPEED SENSOR RESISTANCE SPECIFICATIONS

Application	Ohms
Galant	1000-1200

Ground Circuit Test – Disconnect wheel speed sensor wiring harness connector. Measure resistance between wheel speed sensor terminals and sensor housing. Resistance should be more than 100,000 ohms. If resistance is less than specification, replace wheel speed sensor.

REMOVAL & INSTALLATION

ELECTRONIC CONTROL UNIT (ECU)

Remove dash panel under glove compartment. Remove passenger threshold scuff plate. Remove right kick panel. Ensure ignition is off. Disconnect ABS ECU harness connectors. Remove ECU. *See Fig. 9.* To install, reverse removal procedures.

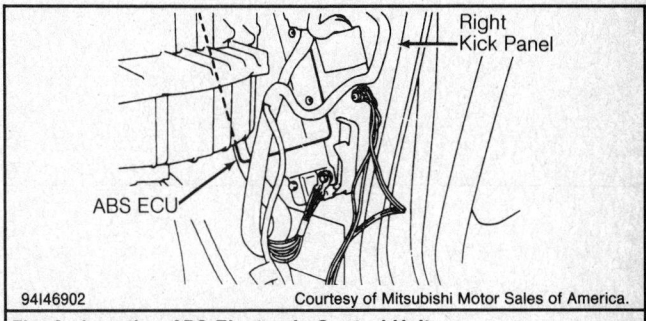

Fig. 9: Locating ABS Electronic Control Unit

1994 BRAKES
Anti-Lock – Galant (Cont.)

HYDRAULIC UNIT

CAUTION: DO NOT turn hydraulic unit upside down or lay unit on its side. DO NOT drop hydraulic unit. DO NOT disassemble unit. Replace hydraulic unit as an assembly. If unit is replaced, slowly release safety plug to release internal gas.

Removal & Installation – Remove air intake hose. Remove mounting bracket and relays. Disconnect brakelines and harness connectors. Remove hydraulic unit. To install, reverse removal procedure. Ensure brakelines are correctly installed. *See Fig. 10.*

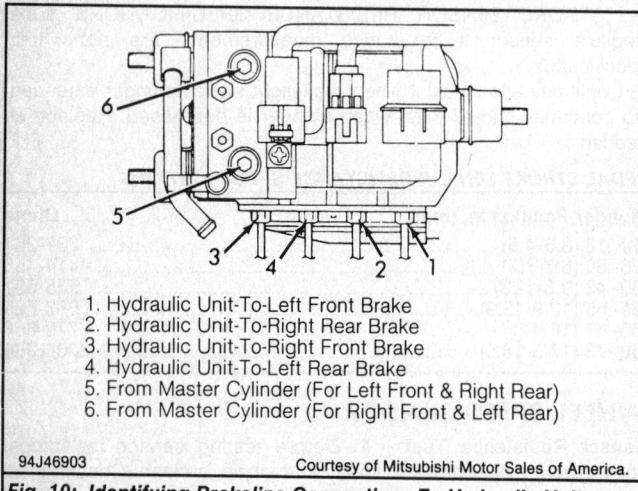

1. Hydraulic Unit-To-Left Front Brake
2. Hydraulic Unit-To-Right Rear Brake
3. Hydraulic Unit-To-Right Front Brake
4. Hydraulic Unit-To-Left Rear Brake
5. From Master Cylinder (For Left Front & Right Rear)
6. From Master Cylinder (For Right Front & Left Rear)

94J46903   Courtesy of Mitsubishi Motor Sales of America.

Fig. 10: Identifying Brakeline Connections To Hydraulic Unit

PEDAL STROKE SENSOR

Removal – Disconnect sensor electrical connectors. Unbolt and remove sensor.
Installation – Ensure brake pedal is correctly adjusted. Distance from floor to brake pedal should be 6.9-7.1" (175-180 mm). Install sensor until clearance between threaded end of sensor and brake pedal is .020-.039" (.5-1.0 mm). *See Fig. 11.* Ensure sensor connectors are facing right side of vehicle. Tighten lock nut.

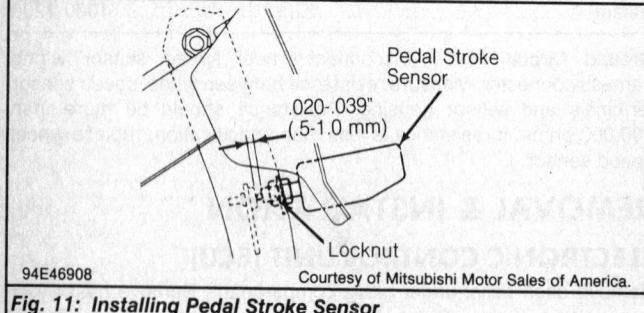

Pedal Stroke Sensor

.020-.039"
(.5-1.0 mm)

Locknut

94E46908   Courtesy of Mitsubishi Motor Sales of America.

Fig. 11: Installing Pedal Stroke Sensor

WHEEL SPEED SENSOR

NOTE: Before removing wheel speed sensor, note sensor wiring harness routing for installation reference.

Removal (Front) – Raise vehicle, and remove wheel. Remove splash shield. Remove retaining clips from speed sensor wiring harness. Disconnect wiring harness connector. Remove sensor mounting bolt. Note sensor wiring harness routing, and remove sensor.
Installation – 1) Install speed sensor bracket if removed. Sensor mounting brackets are not interchangeable from side-to-side. Each bracket is stamped with an "FR" indicating front bracket, and an "R" or "L" to indicate right or left.
2) Temporarily install speed sensor. Route speed sensor wiring harness in its original location, and ensure no twist exists in harness. To complete installation, reverse removal procedure.
Removal (Rear) – Raise vehicle, and remove wheel. Remove splash shield. Remove retaining clips and band from speed sensor wiring harness. Disconnect wiring harness connector. Remove sensor mounting bolt. Note sensor wiring harness routing, and remove sensor.
Installation – 1) Install sensor bracket if removed. Sensor mounting brackets are not interchangeable from side-to-side. Each bracket is stamped with an "R" or "L" to indicate right or left.
2) Temporarily install speed sensor. Route speed sensor wiring harness in its original location, and ensure no twist exists in harness. Ensure sensor harness is not in contact with trailing arm. Reverse removal procedure to complete installation.

WHEEL SENSOR ROTOR

NOTE: For more information on front or rear brake assembly, see DISC & DRUM – EXCEPT PRECIS article.

Removal & Installation – Remove brake disc. Remove disc assembly. Remove wheel bearings. Remove axle hub. Remove bolts attaching sensor rotor to hub assembly. To install, reverse removal procedure.

OVERHAUL
HYDRAULIC UNIT

DO NOT attempt to overhaul or disassemble hydraulic unit. If hydraulic unit is defective, replace entire assembly.

TORQUE SPECIFICATIONS
TORQUE SPECIFICATIONS

Application	Ft. Lbs. (N.m)
Hydraulic Unit Mounting Bolts	13-18 (18-24)
Wheel Lug Nuts	65-80 (88-108)

	INCH Lbs. (N.m)
Bleeder Screw	60-84 (7-9)
Flared Brakeline Nuts	120-144 (14-16)
Front Sensor Rotor Mounting Bolts	84-120 (9-14)
Wheel Speed Sensor Bolt	84-120 (9-14)

WIRING DIAGRAM

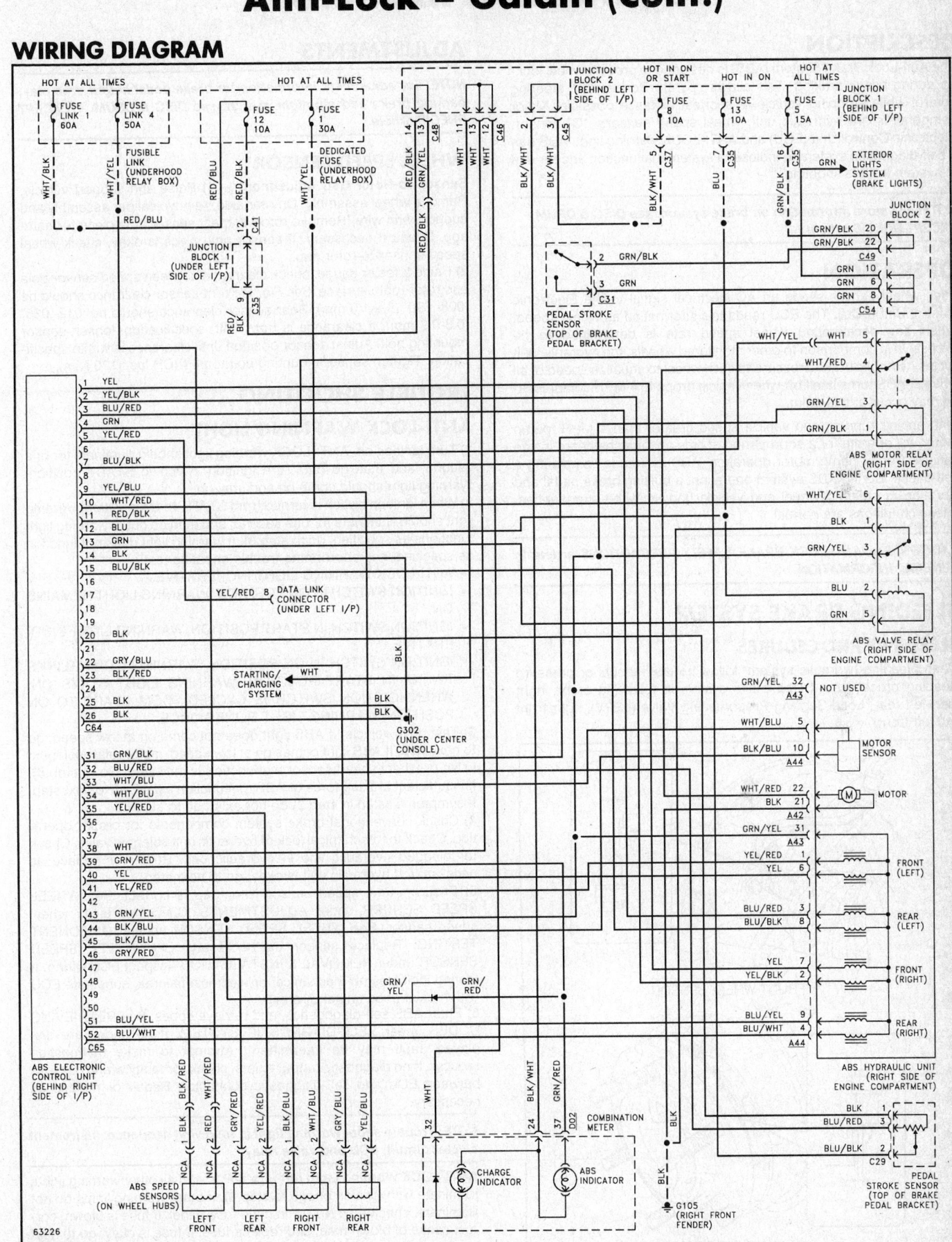

Fig. 12: Anti-Lock Brake System (ABS) Wiring Diagram (Galant)

1994 BRAKES
Anti-Lock – Montero

DESCRIPTION

The Anti-Lock Brake System (ABS) is designed to prevent wheel lock-up during heavy braking. This allows operator to maintain steering control while stopping vehicle in shortest distance possible. Major components are hydraulic unit, wheel speed sensors, "G" sensor, Electronic Control Unit (ECU) and ANTI-LOCK warning light. ABS has a self-diagnostic system to indicate a system malfunction and for use in system trouble shooting.

NOTE: For more information on brake system, see DISC & DRUM – EXCEPT PRECIS article.

OPERATION

Each wheel sensor sends an AC electrical signal to the Electronic Control Unit (ECU). The ECU reads this information as wheel speed. When any decelerating wheel speed rate is determined to be excessive in comparison to other monitored wheels, the hydraulic unit cycles hydraulic brake pressure to each wheel to equalize speed of all wheels. ABS turns itself off when vehicle drops to 4 MPH. Minor lock-up may occur at this point.

With engine running and vehicle speed greater than 4 MPH, pump motor will operate for a short period of time and may be heard inside vehicle. During pump motor operation, ABS system is completing a self-check. During ABS system operation, a pulsing brake pedal and vibration in steering wheel and vehicle body may be experienced. These conditions are normal.

CAUTION: See ANTI-LOCK BRAKE SAFETY PRECAUTIONS article in GENERAL INFORMATION.

BLEEDING BRAKE SYSTEM

BLEEDING PROCEDURES

When bleeding hydraulic system, follow normal manual or pressure bleeding procedures. Bleed brake system in following order: right rear, left rear, Load-Sensing Proportioning Valve (LSPV), right front and left front.

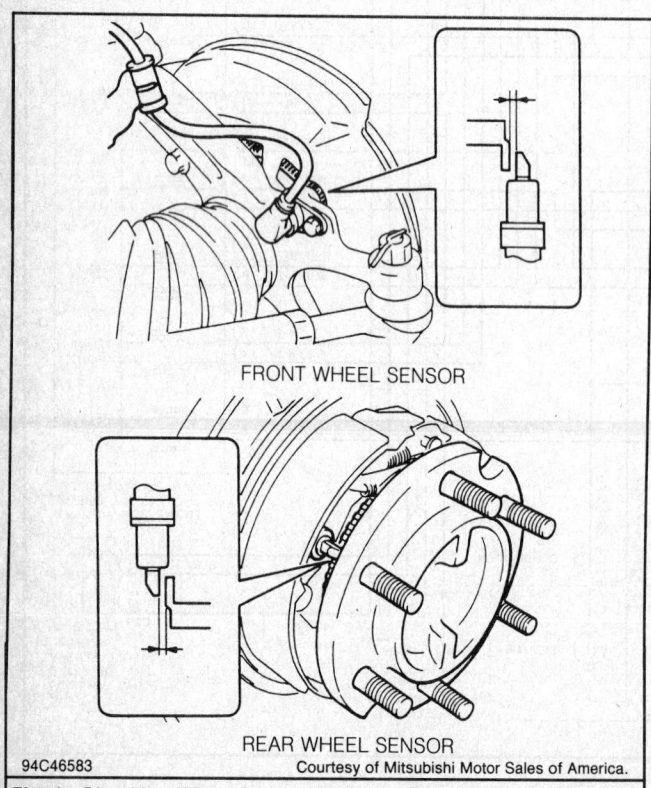

FRONT WHEEL SENSOR

REAR WHEEL SENSOR

94C46583   Courtesy of Mitsubishi Motor Sales of America.

Fig. 1: Checking Wheel Speed Sensor-To-Rotor Gap

ADJUSTMENTS

NOTE: For adjustment information for brake pedal height, free play, parking brake and stoplight switch, see DISC & DRUM – EXCEPT PRECIS article.

WHEEL SPEED SENSOR

Sensor-To-Rotor Gap Adjustment – 1) Raise and support vehicle. Remove wheel assembly. On rear axle, remove caliper assembly and support with wire. Remove rotor. Inspect sensor pole piece for damage. Repair if necessary. If sensor pole piece is okay, check wheel speed sensor-to-rotor gap.

2) Using a feeler gauge, check clearance between speed sensor pole and rotor tooth surface. See Fig. 1. Front sensor clearance should be .008-.390" (0.2-1.0 mm). Rear sensor clearance should be .012-.035" (0.3-0.9 mm). If clearance is not within specification, loosen sensor mounting bolt. Adjust sensor position until clearance is within specification. Tighten sensor mounting bolt to 84 INCH lbs. (120 N.m).

TROUBLE SHOOTING

ANTI-LOCK WARNING LIGHT

1) Turn ignition on. ANTI-LOCK warning light should illuminate for one second, and then go out. Turn ignition switch to START position. Warning light should come on and stay on.

2) When ignition switch is turned from START to ON position, warning light should illuminate for one second, and then go out. If warning light functions as specified, go to step 3). If warning light does not function as specified, see appropriate trouble shooting test:
- ANTI-LOCK WARNING LIGHT INOPERATIVE.
- IGNITION SWITCH IN ON POSITION, WARNING LIGHT REMAINS ON.
- IGNITION SWITCH IN START POSITION, WARNING LIGHT INOPERATIVE.
- IGNITION SWITCH IN ON POSITION, WARNING LIGHT BLINKS TWICE. IN START POSITION, WARNING LIGHT STAYS ON. WHEN IGNITION SWITCH IS CYCLED FROM START TO ON POSITION, WARNING LIGHT BLINKS ONCE.

3) Test drive vehicle. If ABS light does not come on at low speed, go to next step. If ABS light comes on at low speed, motor relay, solenoid valve or wheel speed sensor malfunction is indicated. Go to step 6). If insufficient braking force or ABS malfunction exists, go to next step. If symptoms listed in step 2) do not exist, go to step 6).

4) Check conventional brake system components for proper operation. Check for mechanical lock of hydraulic unit solenoid valve. Check for plugged hydraulic line in hydraulic unit. Repair or replace as necessary. If hydraulic unit is okay, go to next step.

5) Ensure wheel speed sensor rotor gap is correct. See WHEEL SPEED SENSOR under ADJUSTMENTS. Check for faulty wheel speed sensor. See WHEEL SPEED SENSOR under COMPONENT TESTING. Replace sensor as necessary. See WHEEL SPEED SENSOR under REMOVAL & INSTALLATION. Inspect ECU wiring. If testing indicates no mechanical or electrical failures, substitute ECU with known good unit and retest.

6) Enter ABS self-diagnostics, and retrieve codes. See RETRIEVING CODES under SELF-DIAGNOSTIC SYSTEM. If no codes are displayed, fault may be intermittent. Attempt to make malfunction reoccur. If no diagnostic output exists, check for faulty wiring harness between ECU and self-diagnostic connector. Repair or replace as necessary.

NOTE: Trouble shoot warning light in following sequence: instrument cluster circuit, ECU and valve relay.

ANTI-LOCK Warning Light Inoperative – 1) If all other warning lights illuminate with ignition on, go to step 3). If other warning lights do not illuminate, check fuse No. 11 in main fuse panel. If fuse is blown, correct cause of blown fuse, and replace fuse. If fuse is okay, go to next step.

2) Remove instrument cluster. Turn ignition on. Using DVOM, measure voltage between vehicle ground and instrument cluster ABS

warning light terminal No. 107. *See Fig. 2.* If battery voltage is present, repair or replace instrument cluster. If battery voltage is not present, repair wire harness between junction block and instrument cluster.

3) Turn ignition off. Check for faulty warning light bulb. Replace bulb as necessary. If bulb is okay, using an ohmmeter, check for continuity between instrument cluster connector terminals No. 107 and 158. *See Fig. 2.* If continuity exists, clean and/or repair connector terminals. If connector terminals are okay, check for open circuit to ECU and valve relay. See WIRING DIAGRAM. Go to steps **4)** and **5)**. If continuity does not exist, replace instrument cluster.

4) To check ECU, turn ignition off. Remove ECU connector. ECU is located on right rear wheelwell. *See Fig. 17.* Turn ignition on. Measure voltage between terminal No. 13 and vehicle ground. *See Fig. 3.* If battery voltage is not present, repair circuit between warning light and ECU. If battery voltage is present, substitute ECU with known good unit and retest.

5) To check valve relay, see HYDRAULIC UNIT RELAYS under COMPONENT TESTING. If relay is okay, remove hydraulic unit connector. Turn ignition on. Measure voltage between terminal No. 8 and vehicle ground. *See Fig. 4.* If battery voltage is present, go to next step. If battery voltage is not present, repair circuit between ABS warning light and hydraulic unit.

6) Turn ignition off. Check for continuity between terminal No. 9 and vehicle ground. If continuity does not exist, repair circuit between hydraulic unit and vehicle ground. If continuity exists, check for continuity between terminals No. 8 and 9. If continuity exists, check for defective connector. If continuity does not exist, replace hydraulic unit.

Ignition Switch In ON Position, Warning Light Remains On (ECU Power Circuit) – 1) Enter ABS self-diagnostics. See RETRIEVING CODES under SELF-DIAGNOSTIC SYSTEM. If diagnostic output exists, go to step **9)**. If no diagnostic output exists, connect Multi-Use Tester II (MUT-II) to another electronic control system.

2) If MUT-II can communicate with another electronic control system, go to next step. If MUT-II cannot communicate with another electronic control system, tester is malfunctioning. Inspect diagnostic connector for damaged terminals and correct hook-up. Repair as necessary. If diagnostic connector is okay, replace MUT-II.

3) Check fuse No. 7 in main fuse panel. If fuse is okay, go to next step. If fuse is blown, correct cause of blown fuse, and replace fuse.

4) Disconnect ECU wiring harness connector. Turn ignition on. Measure voltage between terminal No. 6 and vehicle ground. *See Fig. 3.* If battery voltage is present, go to next step. If battery voltage is not present, repair open circuit between fuse No. 7 and ECU.

5) Check for continuity between vehicle ground and terminals No. 9, 10, 11 and 112. If continuity exists, go to next step. If continuity does not exist in any circuit, check for open in vehicle ground circuit. Repair or replace wiring harness as necessary.

6) Check for continuity between terminal No. 14 of ECU connector and terminal No. 8 of diagnostic connector. Also check for continuity between terminal No. 15 of ECU connector and terminal No. 1 of diagnostic connector. *See Fig. 5.* If continuity does not exist, check for open between ECU and diagnostic connector. Repair as necessary. If continuity exists, replace ECU and go to next step.

7) Check for trouble codes. See TROUBLE CODE DEFINITION under SELF-DIAGNOSTIC SYSTEM. If no trouble codes are present, repeat testing. If any trouble codes are present, see appropriate CODE under TESTING.

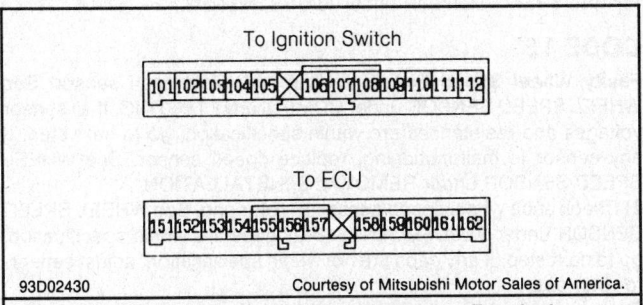

To Ignition Switch

To ECU

93D02430 — Courtesy of Mitsubishi Motor Sales of America.

Fig. 2: Identifying Instrument Cluster Connector Terminals

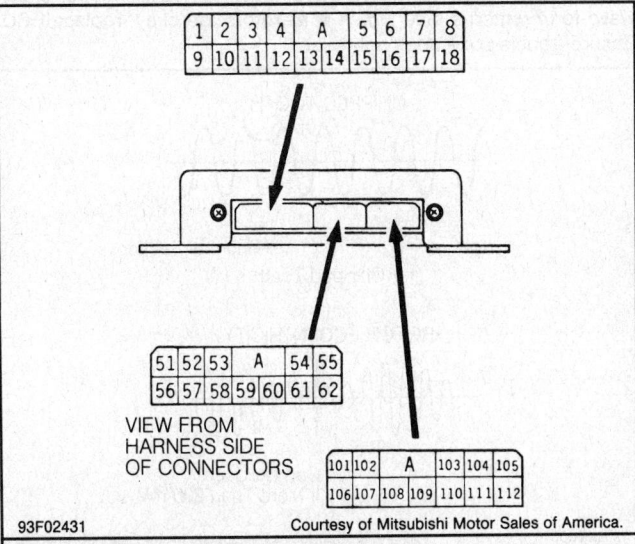

VIEW FROM HARNESS SIDE OF CONNECTORS

93F02431 — Courtesy of Mitsubishi Motor Sales of America.

Fig. 3: Identifying ECU Connector Terminals

93B02434 — Courtesy of Mitsubishi Motor Sales of America.

Fig. 4: Identifying Hydraulic Unit 10-Pin Connector Terminals

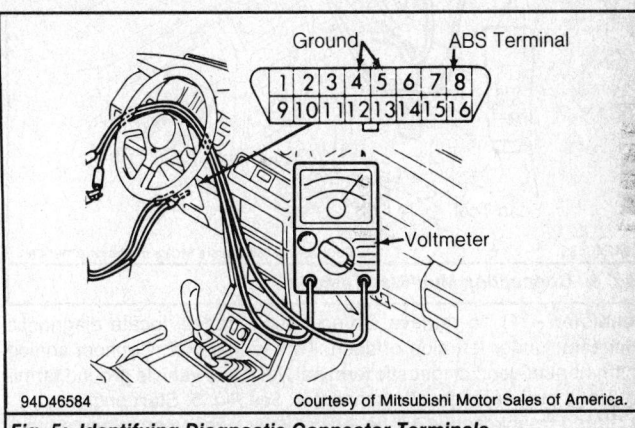

Ground   ABS Terminal

Voltmeter

94D46584 — Courtesy of Mitsubishi Motor Sales of America.

Fig. 5: Identifying Diagnostic Connector Terminals

Ignition Switch In START Position, Warning Light Inoperative – 1) Remove fuse No. 7 from junction block. Disconnect hydraulic unit 10-pin connector. Turn ignition on. Using DVOM, measure voltage between hydraulic unit harness connector terminal No. 8 and vehicle ground. *See Fig. 4.* If battery voltage is present, go to next step. If battery voltage is not present, repair circuit between ABS warning light and hydraulic unit.

2) Using ohmmeter, check for continuity between terminal No. 9 and vehicle ground. If continuity exists, go to next step. If continuity does not exist, repair hydraulic unit circuit.

3) Check continuity between hydraulic unit connector terminals No. 8 and 9. If continuity exists, go to next step. If continuity does not exist, replace valve relay.

4) Remove valve relay from hydraulic unit. Check for continuity between relay terminals No. 87a and 30. *See Fig. 14.* If continuity does not exist, replace valve relay. If continuity exists, hydraulic unit wiring harness is faulty. Replace hydraulic unit.

Ignition Switch In ON Position, Warning Light Blinks Twice. In START Position, Warning Light Stays On. When Ignition Switch Is Cycled From START To ON Position, Warning Light Blinks Once – 1) Disconnect hydraulic unit wiring harness connector. Disconnect ECU wiring harness connector. Inspect connector terminals and repair as necessary.

2) Turn ignition on. Measure voltage between ECU connector terminal No. 13 and vehicle ground. *See Fig. 3.* If battery voltage is not present, repair open or shorted circuit between ABS warning light and ECU. If battery voltage is present, substitute ECU with known good unit and retest.

SELF-DIAGNOSTIC SYSTEM

RETRIEVING CODES

Scan Tool – 1) With ignition off, connect Multi-Use Tester (MB991502) and ROM Pack to diagnostic connector, located under driver's side of dash, and to cigarette lighter socket. *See Fig. 6.*

2) Turn ignition on. ABS warning light should come on as ABS goes into self-diagnostic mode. Read and record all diagnostic output (trouble) codes from ECU memory. Refer to Multi-Use Tester II (MUT-II) instructions for specific trouble code retrieval procedure.

3) After all trouble codes have been retrieved and recorded, clear codes from ECU memory. Refer to Multi-Use Tester II (MUT-II) instructions for specific trouble code clearing instructions. See TROUBLE CODE DEFINITION SELF-DIAGNOSTIC SYSTEM. See appropriate CODE under TESTING.

4) If trouble codes cannot be cleared, ECU is currently detecting a malfunction. If codes can be cleared, problem is either intermittent or only appears while driving.

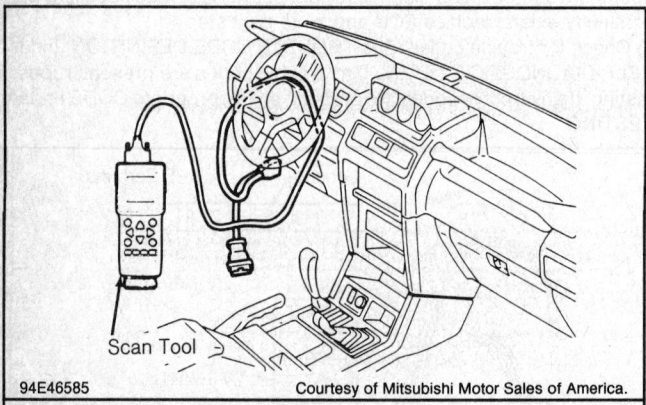

94E46585   Courtesy of Mitsubishi Motor Sales of America.
Fig. 6: Connecting Multi-Use Tester II

Voltmeter – 1) To retrieve stored trouble codes, locate diagnostic connector under left side of dash. Turn ignition off. Connect analog voltmeter between diagnostic terminal No. 8 and vehicle ground terminal No. 4 or 5 of diagnostic connector. *See Fig. 5.* Start engine.

2) Stored trouble codes will be indicated by sweeps of voltmeter needle. Long sweeps indicate first digit of code; short sweeps indicate second digit of code. If more than one fault is present, lowest number code will be given first. After trouble code has been retrieved, test indicated component and/or related circuit (if necessary). See TROUBLE CODE DEFINITION under SELF-DIAGNOSTIC SYSTEM. See appropriate code under TESTING.

CLEARING TROUBLE CODES

To clear trouble codes after repairs, disconnect negative battery cable for at least 10 seconds. Reconnect battery cable and repeat RETRIEVING CODES to confirm that malfunction has been corrected.

TROUBLE CODE DEFINITION

TROUBLE CODES

Code	¹ System Affected
11	Right Front Wheel Sensor (Open)
12	Left Front Wheel Sensor (Open)
13	Right Rear Wheel Sensor (Open)
14	Left Rear Wheel Sensor (Open)
15	Sensor Output Signal Fault
16	ECU Power Voltage
21	Right Front Wheel Sensor (Short)

¹ – See appropriate CODE under TESTING.

TROUBLE CODES (Cont.)

Code	¹ System Affected
22	Left Front Wheel Sensor (Short)
23	Right Rear Wheel Sensor (Short)
24	Left Rear Wheel Sensor (Short)
25-27	4WD Power Circuit Fault
31	"G" Sensor Power Voltage
32	"G" Sensor Output Voltage
33	Stoplight Switch Circuit
41, 43, or 45	Solenoid Valve Circuit
51	Valve Relay
53	Motor Relay
63	Faulty ECU
64	Faulty ECU

¹ – See appropriate CODE under TESTING.

TESTING

CODE 11, 12, 13 OR 14

Faulty Wheel Speed Sensor Input – 1) Trouble code will set if ECU detects wheel speed sensor has no input signal. Trouble code will also set if wheel sensor voltage output is low while driving vehicle.

2) Inspect wheel sensor wiring harness for open or poor connection. See WIRING DIAGRAM. Repair or replace if necessary. If no open circuit or poor connection is found, go to next step.

3) Test wheel speed sensor. See WHEEL SPEED SENSOR under COMPONENT TESTING. Replace speed sensor as necessary. Ensure wheel speed sensor-to-rotor gap is within specification. See WHEEL SPEED SENSOR under ADJUSTMENTS.

CODE 15

Faulty Wheel Speed Sensor Output – 1) Test each sensor. See WHEEL SPEED SENSOR under COMPONENT TESTING. If all sensor voltages and resistances are within specification, go to next step. If any sensor is malfunctioning, replace speed sensor. See WHEEL SPEED SENSOR under REMOVAL & INSTALLATION.

2) Check each wheel speed sensor-to-rotor gap. See WHEEL SPEED SENSOR under ADJUSTMENTS. If all gaps are within specification, go to next step. If any gaps are not within specification, adjust sensor-to-rotor gap.

3) Inspect all wheel speed sensor rotors for damaged and missing teeth. Replace any damaged rotors. Using an oscilloscope, check wave-form patterns. *See Fig. 7.* If all rotors are okay, replace ECU. Ensure trouble code does not reset.

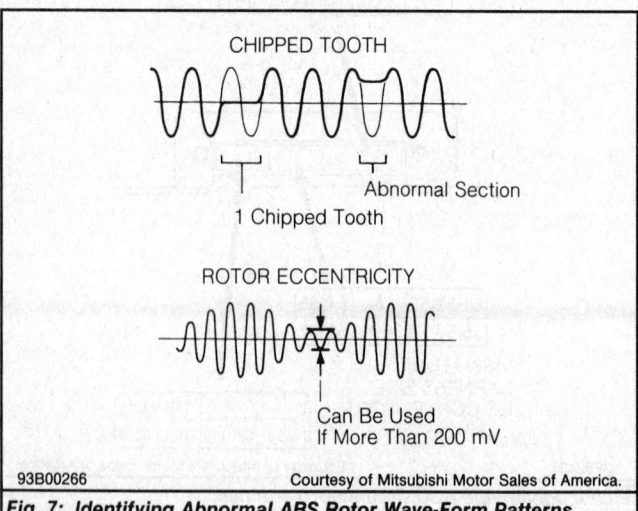

93B00266   Courtesy of Mitsubishi Motor Sales of America.
Fig. 7: Identifying Abnormal ABS Rotor Wave-Form Patterns

CODE 16

ECU Power Voltage – Start engine. Measure voltage between ECU terminal No. 6 and vehicle ground. *See Fig. 3.* If less than 10 volts is present, check fuse contacts and ECU connector. If 10 volts or more is present, measure voltage between ECU terminal No. 62 and vehicle ground. If less than 10 volts is present, check fuse contacts and ECU connector. If fuse contacts and ECU connector are okay, substitute ECU with known good unit and retest.

CODE 21, 22, 23 OR 24

Faulty Wheel Speed Sensor Output – 1) Test each sensor. See WHEEL SPEED SENSOR under COMPONENT TESTING. If all sensor voltages and resistances are within specification, go to next step. If any sensor is malfunctioning, replace sensor. See WHEEL SPEED SENSOR under REMOVAL & INSTALLATION.

2) Remove ECU connector. Check wheel speed circuit at ECU connector. *See Fig. 3*. See ECU CONNECTOR TERMINAL RESISTANCE SPECIFICATION table. If resistance values are not as specified, repair wiring harness. If resistance values are within specifications, go to next step.

3) Check each wheel speed sensor-to-rotor gap. See WHEEL SPEED SENSOR under ADJUSTMENTS. If all gaps are within specification, go to next step. If any gaps are not within specification, adjust sensor-to-rotor gap.

4) Inspect all wheel speed sensor rotors for damaged and missing teeth. Replace any damaged rotors. Using an oscilloscope, check wave-form patterns and output voltage. *See Fig. 8*. Output voltage should be 0.2 volt (200 mV). If all rotors and wheel speed sensors are okay, substitute ECU with known good unit and retest.

ECU CONNECTOR TERMINAL RESISTANCE SPECIFICATION

Application	ECU Terminals No.	Ohms
LF Wheel Speed Sensor	52 & 57	900-1100
RF Wheel Speed Sensor	51 & 56	900-1100
LR Wheel Speed Sensor	8 & 18	1300-2100
RR Wheel Speed Sensor	53 & 58	1300-2100

CODE 25

Free Wheel Engage Switch Circuit – 1) Start engine. Ensure center differential indicator light operates correctly when transfer shift lever is moved to desired 4WD positions. If indicator light operates correctly, go to step **3)**. If indicator light does not operate correctly, go to next step.

2) Turn engine off. Check wiring harness between 4WD indicator control unit, located behind radio, and free wheel engage switch, located on right side of front differential housing near carrier assembly. If circuit is okay, replace 4WD indicator control unit.

3) Disconnect ECU connector. Turn ignition on. Using DVOM, check voltage between terminal No. 55 and vehicle ground. *See Fig. 3*. In 2WD, battery voltage should exist. Battery voltage should not exist in 4WD. If voltage is as described, substitute ECU with known good unit and retest. See ELECTRONIC CONTROL UNIT (ECU) under REMOVAL & INSTALLATION. If voltage is not as described, repair harness between ECU and free wheel engage switch.

CODE 26

Center Differential Lock Switch Circuit – 1) Start engine. Ensure center differential indicator light operates correctly when transfer shift lever is moved to desired 4WD positions. If indicator light does not operate correctly, go to step **3)**. If indicator light operates correctly, disconnect ECU connector. Using DVOM, check voltage between terminal No. 107 and vehicle ground. *See Fig. 3*.

2) When center differential is locked, battery voltage should not be present. When center differential is unlocked, battery voltage should be present. If voltage is as described, substitute ECU with known good unit and retest. If voltage is not as described, repair wiring harness between ECU and center differential lock detection switch. *See Fig. 8*. Lock switch can be identified by Brown connector.

3) If no indicator lights illuminate, repair 4WD indicator power circuit, or check for faulty 4WD indicator control unit. See 4WD CONTROL UNIT under COMPONENT TESTING. If center differential light illuminates, regardless of position of transfer shift lever, check the following:

- Check for short in center differential lock switch circuit.
- Check for faulty center differential lock switch.
- Check for short in ECU circuit or faulty ECU.
- Check for short in indicator control unit circuit or faulty 4WD indicator control unit.

Repair wiring harness or replace component as necessary.

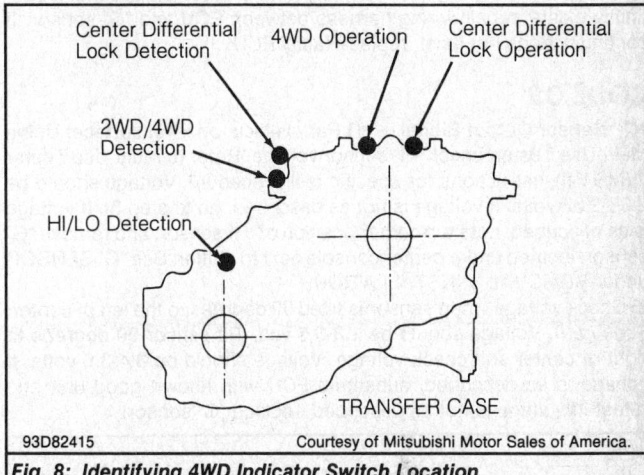

Fig. 8: Identifying 4WD Indicator Switch Location

NOTE: When checking for short in ECU circuit, remove ECU connector and ensure 4WD indicator light operates correctly. If 4WD indicator light operates correctly, replace faulty ECU. If 4WD indicator light does not operate correctly, replace faulty 4WD indicator control unit.

4) If center differential light does not illuminate with transfer shift lever in "4H" position, repair wiring harness between 4WD indicator control unit, and center differential lock switch. Check for faulty 4WD indicator control unit.

5) If front wheel indicator light does not illuminate with transfer shift lever in "4H" position, repair wiring harness between 4WD indicator control unit and free wheel engage switch. Check vehicle ground wire at engage switch. Check for faulty free wheel engage switch.

CODE 27

Rear Differential Lock Circuit (With Differential Lock) – 1) Start engine. Ensure rear differential indicator light illuminates when top of rear differential lock switch, (located below radio) is pushed. If indicator light illuminates, go to next step. If indicator light does not illuminate, turn engine off. Check wiring harness between rear differential lock control unit and rear differential lock switch. Check rear differential lock control unit power circuit. See REAR DIFFERENTIAL CONTROL UNIT under COMPONENT TESTING. If circuit is okay, replace rear differential lock control unit.

2) Disconnect ECU connector. Turn ignition on. Using DVOM, check voltage between terminal No. 108 and vehicle ground. *See Fig. 3*. When rear differential is locked, battery voltage should not be present. When rear differential is unlocked, battery voltage should be present. If voltage is as described, substitute ECU with known good unit and retest. If voltage is not as described, repair wiring harness between ECU and rear differential lock switch.

Rear Differential Without Differential Lock – Check fuse No. 18 in main fuse block. Replace if necessary. Disconnect ECU connector. Turn ignition on. Using DVOM, check voltage at terminal No. 108 and vehicle ground. *See Fig. 3*. If battery voltage is present, substitute ECU with known good unit and retest. If battery voltage is not present, check for open circuit between ECU and fuse block. Repair wiring harness as necessary.

CODE 31

"G" Sensor Power Voltage – 1) If Code 31 is present, and Code 32 is not present, substitute ECU with known good unit and retest. If

Code 31 and Code 32 are both present, disconnect "G" sensor wiring harness connector. "G" sensor is located under center console. See Fig. 18. Turn ignition to ACC switch position. Using ohmmeter, check continuity between "G" sensor harness connector terminal No. 1 (Blue wire) and vehicle ground. If continuity does not exist, replace "G" sensor. If continuity exists, disconnect ECU connector.

2) Check continuity between terminal No. 1 and vehicle ground. If continuity exists, repair wiring harness between ECU and "G" sensor. If continuity does not exist, replace faulty ECU.

CODE 32

"G" Sensor Output Signal – 1) Park vehicle on level surface. Using Multi-Use Tester, check "G" sensor voltage. Refer to Multi-Use Tester II (MUT-II) instructions for specific test procedure. Voltage should be 2.38-2.62 volts. If voltage is not as described, go to step 3). If voltage is as described, note top center position of "G" sensor, and remove "G" sensor, located under center console next to shifter. See "G" SENSOR under REMOVAL & INSTALLATION.

2) Check voltage when sensor is tilted 90 degrees to the left of center. See Fig. 9. Voltage should be 1.3-3.6 volt. Tilt sensor 90 degrees to right of center and check voltage. Voltage should be 3.4-3.6 volts. If voltage is as described, substitute ECU with known good unit and retest. If voltage is not as described, replace "G" sensor.

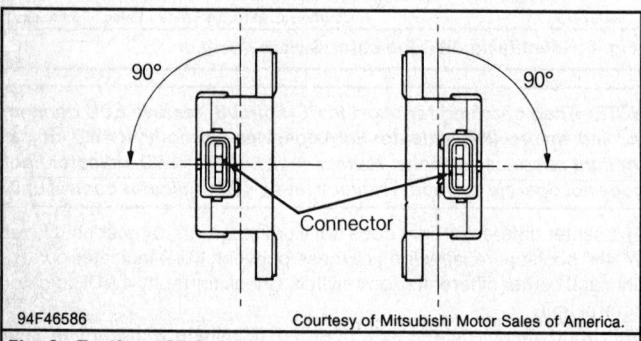

90°   90°

Connector

94F46586   Courtesy of Mitsubishi Motor Sales of America.

Fig. 9: Testing "G" Sensor

3) If "G" sensor voltage is less than 0.5 volt, go to next step. If "G" sensor voltage is more than 4.5 volts, go to step 9). If "G" sensor voltage is 0.3-4.7 volts, check for poor vehicle ground connection (loose mounting bolt) at sensor. Repair as necessary. If connection is okay, replace "G" sensor.

4) Start engine. Disconnect "G" sensor harness connector. Using DVOM, measure voltage between sensor harness connector terminal No. 1 (Blue wire) and ground. If battery voltage is not present, inspect and repair circuit between terminal No. 1 and fuse No. 7.

5) If battery voltage is present, connect sensor harness connector. Backprobe sensor harness connector terminal No. 3 (Black/Red wire). Measure voltage between terminal No. 3 and ground. Ensure vehicle is on level surface.

6) If voltage is 2.38-2.62 volts, go to step 8). If voltage is not 2.38-2.62, turn ignition to switch ACC position. Disconnect "G" sensor connector. Using ohmmeter, check resistance between terminal No. 3 (Blue/White) and vehicle ground. Resistance should be 500 ohms or more. If resistance is within specification, replace "G" sensor.

7) If resistance is not 500 ohms or more, turn ignition off. Disconnect "G" sensor and ECU connectors. Check continuity between terminal No. 3 and vehicle ground. If continuity does not exist, substitute ECU with known good unit and retest. If continuity exists, repair wiring harness between ECU and "G" sensor.

8) Turn ignition on. Using DVOM, check voltage at ECU terminal No. 110 and vehicle ground. See Fig. 3. Voltage should be 2.38-2.62 volts. If voltage is within specification, substitute ECU with known good unit and retest. If voltage is not 2.38-2.62 volts, repair wiring harness between ECU and "G" sensor.

9) Disconnect "G" sensor connector. Using ohmmeter, check continuity between terminal No. 2 (Blue/White) and vehicle ground. If continuity exists, replace "G" sensor. If continuity does not exist, check continuity between ECU terminal No. 111 and vehicle ground. If conti-

nuity exists, repair wiring harness between ECU and "G" sensor. If continuity does not exist, substitute ECU with known good unit and retest.

CODE 33

Stoplight Switch Circuit – 1) Check if stoplights are functioning correctly. If stoplights function correctly, go to next step. If stoplights do not function correctly, check stoplight circuit and repair as necessary.

2) Disconnect ECU connector. Using DVOM, measure voltage between terminal No. 109 and vehicle ground while depressing brake pedal. See Fig. 3. If battery voltage is not present, repair or replace wiring harness between stoplight switch and ECU. See WIRING DIAGRAM. If battery voltage is present, stoplight switch circuit is okay. Replace ECU.

CODE 41, 43 OR 45

Solenoid Valve Circuit – 1) Disconnect hydraulic unit 10-pin connector. Using ohmmeter, measure resistance between hydraulic unit terminal No. 7 and terminals No. 3, 5 and 6. See Fig. 4.

2) Resistance should be 1000-1300 ohms. If resistance is within specification, go to next step. If resistance is not within specification, replace faulty hydraulic unit. See HYDRAULIC UNIT under REMOVAL & INSTALLATION.

3) Connect hydraulic unit 10-pin connector. Disconnect ECU wiring harness connector. Measure resistance between ECU terminal No. 62 and terminals No. 1, 2 and 3. See Fig. 3.

4) Resistance should be 1000-1300 ohms. If resistance is not within specification, repair or replace wiring harness. If all resistance tests are within specification, solenoid valve circuit is okay. Replace ECU.

CODE 51

Valve Relay Circuit – 1) Remove and test valve relay. See HYDRAULIC UNIT RELAYS under COMPONENT TESTING. Replace relay if faulty. If relay is okay, reinstall valve relay and go to next step.

2) Check pump motor, and repair if necessary. Turn ignition on. Disconnect hydraulic unit 2-pin connector. Measure voltage between terminal No. 52 and vehicle ground. See Fig. 10.

3) If battery voltage is not present, repair wiring harness between fusible link and hydraulic unit 2-pin connector. If battery voltage is present, turn ignition off. Using ohmmeter, check for continuity between hydraulic unit 10-pin connector terminals No. 7 and 8. See Fig. 4. If continuity exists, go to next step. If continuity does not exist, repair or replace hydraulic unit.

4) Connect hydraulic unit connector. Disconnect ECU connector. Using ohmmeter, measure resistance between ECU connector terminals No. 4 and 5. See Fig. 3. Resistance should be 60-120 ohms. If resistance is within specification, go to next step. If resistance is not within specification, repair wiring harness between hydraulic unit and ECU.

5) Turn ignition on. Measure voltage between ECU connector terminal No. 62 and vehicle ground. If battery voltage is not present, repair or replace faulty wiring harness between hydraulic unit and ECU. If battery voltage is present, replace faulty ECU.

51 52

93C00267   Courtesy of Mitsubishi Motor Sales of America.

Fig. 10: Identifying Hydraulic Unit 2-Pin Connector

CODE 53

Motor Relay Circuit – 1) Using MUT-II, perform hydraulic unit actuator test. If motor is not operating, go to next step. If motor is still operating, repair or replace wiring harness between hydraulic unit and ECU.

2) Remove and test motor relay. See HYDRAULIC UNIT RELAYS under COMPONENT TESTING. If relay is okay, go to next step. Replace relay if faulty.

3) Check pump motor vehicle ground connection. Ensure vehicle ground wire has a clean, tight connection. Repair ground connection if necessary. If vehicle ground connection is okay, go to next step.

4) Install motor relay. Turn ignition on. Disconnect hydraulic unit 2-pin connector. Measure voltage between terminal No. 51 and vehicle ground. See Fig. 9. If battery voltage is present, go to next step. If battery voltage is not present, repair harness between fusible link and hydraulic unit 2-pin connector.

5) Connect hydraulic unit wiring harness. Disconnect ECU wiring harness connector. Using ohmmeter, measure resistance between ECU harness connector terminals No. 5 and 12. See Fig. 3. Resistance should be 30-60 ohms. If resistance is not within specification, repair or replace wiring harness between hydraulic unit and ECU. If resistance is within specification, go to next step.

6) Using ohmmeter, measure resistance between ECU connector terminal No. 106 and vehicle ground. Resistance should be .1-.3 ohm. If resistance is not within specification, repair or replace wiring harness between hydraulic unit and ECU. If resistance is within specification, replace faulty ECU.

CODE 63 OR 64

If Code 63 or Code 64 is present, replace faulty ECU.

COMPONENT TESTING

4WD CONTROL UNIT

Remove radio and remove 4WD control unit. Disconnect control unit harness connector. Backprobe harness connector. Measure voltage between each individual terminal and ground terminal No. 8 (Black wire). See Figs. 11 and 12. If after all tests have been completed system is not operating properly, substitute 4WD control unit with known good unit and retest.

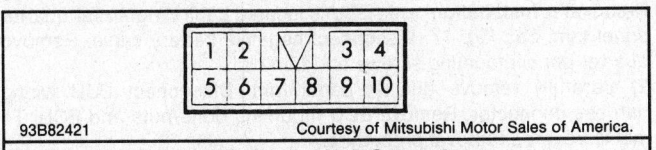

93B82421   Courtesy of Mitsubishi Motor Sales of America.

Fig. 11: Identifying 4WD Control Unit Connector

4WD INDICATOR SWITCHES

All switches are mounted to transfer case. See Fig. 8. Switches use single harness lead and ground to transfer case. See 4WD INDICATOR SWITCH CONTINUITY CHECK table. Ensure all appropriate grounding straps are connected to vehicle body or frame.

4WD INDICATOR SWITCH CONTINUITY CHECK

Switch [1]	Transfer Control Lever Position	Specification
Center Differential Lock Detection Switch	4H	No Continuity
	4HLc	Continuity
Center Differential Lock Operation Detection Switch	4H	No Continuity
	4HLc	Continuity
4WD Operation Detection Switch	2H	No Continuity
	4H	Continuity
HI/LO Detection Switch	4HLc	Continuity
	N	No Continuity
	4LLc	Continuity
2WD/4WD Detection Switch	2H	Continuity
	4H	No Continuity

[1] – See Fig. 8 for switch location.

HYDRAULIC UNIT RELAYS

Motor Relay – 1) Remove motor relay. Using ohmmeter, measure resistance between relay terminals No. 85 and 86. See Fig. 13. Resistance should be 30-60 ohms. Check for continuity between relay terminals No. 30 and 87. Continuity should not exist.

2) Apply battery voltage to relay terminal No. 85, and vehicle ground terminal No. 86. Check for continuity between terminals No. 30 and 87. Continuity should exist. If relay does not test as specified, replace relay.

	Terminal ID.	Function/Description	Voltage Value (DC Volts Unless Otherwise Specified)
Yellow/Blue	1	HI/LO Detection Switch	KOEO – 9-11 Volts With Transfer In "N" KOEO – 0 Volt In "4HLc" Or "4LLc"
Blue/Orange	2	4WD Operation Detection Switch	KOEO – 9-11 Volts In "2H" KOEO – 0 Volt "4H"
Blue/Yellow	3	Ignition Switch (IG2)	Ignition Off – 0 Volt Ignition On – Battery Voltage
Blue/Green	4	Center Differential Lock Indicator Light	KOEO – Battery Voltage With Transfer In "4H" KOEO – 0-1.5 Volts With Transfer In "4HLc"
Blue/White	5	Center Differential Lock Detection Switch	KOEO – 9-11 Volts With Transfer In "4H" KOEO – 0 Volt With Transfer In "4HLc"
Yellow/Green	6	Free Wheel Engage Switch	KOEO – 9-11 Volts With Vehicle in 2WD KOEO – 0 Volt With Vehicle in 4WD
Yellow/Blue	7	Center Differential Lock Operation Detection Switch	KOEO – 9-11 Volts With Transfer In "4H" KOEO – 0 Volt With Transfer In "4HLc"
Yellow/Black	9	Rear Wheel Indicator Light	KOEO – 0 Volt With Transfer In "N" KOEO – 9-11 Volts In "4HLc" Or "4LLc"
Yellow/Red	10	Front Wheel Indicator Light	KOEO – 0 Volt With Vehicle In 2WD KOEO – 9-11 Volts With Vehicle In 4WD

93C82422   Courtesy of Mitsubishi Motor Sales of America.

Fig. 12: 4WD Control Unit Pin Voltage Chart

1994 BRAKES
Anti-Lock – Montero (Cont.)

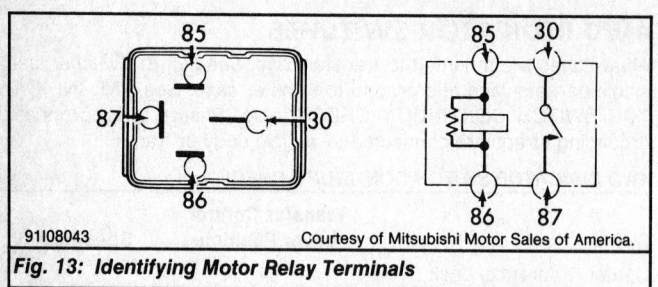

91I08043   Courtesy of Mitsubishi Motor Sales of America.

Fig. 13: Identifying Motor Relay Terminals

Valve Relay – 1) Remove valve relay. Using ohmmeter, measure resistance between relay terminals No. 85 and 86. *See Fig. 14.* Resistance should be 60-120 ohms.

2) Check for continuity between relay terminals No. 30 and 87a. Continuity should exist. Check for continuity between relay terminals No. 30 and 87. Continuity should not exist.

3) Apply battery voltage to relay terminal No. 85, and vehicle ground terminal No. 86. Check for continuity between terminals No. 30 and 87. Continuity should exist. Check for continuity between terminals No. 30

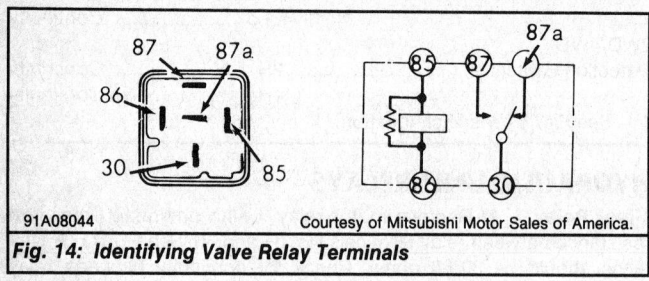

91A08044   Courtesy of Mitsubishi Motor Sales of America.

Fig. 14: Identifying Valve Relay Terminals

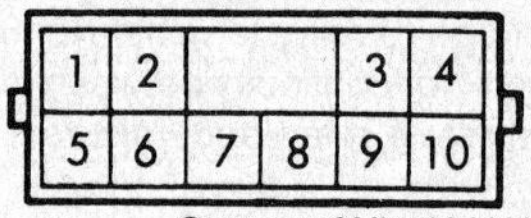

```
┌───────────────────────┐
│  ┌──┬──┐    ┌──┬──┐   │
│  │ 1│ 2│    │ 3│ 4│   │
│  ├──┼──┼──┬──┼──┼──┤   │
│  │ 5│ 6│ 7│ 8│ 9│10│   │
│  └──┴──┴──┴──┴──┴──┘   │
└───────────────────────┘
```

93D82423   Courtesy of Mitsubishi Motor Sales of America.

Fig. 15: Identifying Rear Differential Control Unit Connector

and 87a. Continuity should not exist. If relay does not test as specified, replace relay.

REAR DIFFERENTIAL CONTROL UNIT

Remove rear seat and remove rear differential control unit. Do not disconnect control unit harness connector. Backprobe harness connector. Measure voltage between each individual terminal and ground terminal No. 6 (Black wire). *See Figs. 15 and 16.* If after all tests have been completed system is not operating properly, substitute rear differential control unit with known good unit and retest.

WHEEL SPEED SENSOR

Sensor Resistance Test – 1) Before testing sensor resistance, ensure pole piece-to-wheel speed sensor tip is clean. Check wheel sensor pole piece for damage. If pole piece is damaged, replace sensor.

2) Disconnect sensor connector. Inspect sensor wiring harness for broken and pinched wires. Repair or replace harness as necessary. Using ohmmeter, measure sensor resistance at wiring connector. Front sensor resistance should be 900-1100 ohms. Rear resistance should be 1300-2100 ohms. If resistance is not within specification, replace sensor. If resistance is within specification, go to GROUND CIRCUIT TEST.

Ground Circuit Test – Disconnect wheel speed sensor wiring harness connector. Measure resistance between wheel speed sensor terminals and sensor housing. Resistance should be more than 100,000 ohms. If resistance is less than specification, replace wheel speed sensor.

REMOVAL & INSTALLATION

ELECTRONIC CONTROL UNIT (ECU)

Removal & Installation – 1) ECU is located behind right rear quarter panel trim. *See Fig. 17.* Disconnect negative battery cable. Remove quarter panel mounting screws and trim clip.

2) Carefully remove quarter panel trim. Disconnect ECU wiring harness connector. Remove ECU mounting bolts/nuts and ECU. To install, reverse removal procedure.

	Terminal ID.	Function/Description	Voltage Value (DC Volts Unless Otherwise Specified)
Blue/Red	1	Rear Differential Lock Switch (OFF)	KOEO – Battery Voltage With Transfer In "N"
Yellow/White	2	Vehicle Speed Sensor	KOER – 5 Volts With Wheels Rotating
Blue/Yellow	3	Ignition Switch (IG1)	Ignition Off – 0 Volt / Ignition On – Battery Voltage
Red	4	Rear Differential Lock Air Pump	KOEO – Battery Voltage When Pumping Air / KOEO – 0 Volt When Releasing Air
Blue/White	5	Center Differential Lock Switch	KOEO – Battery Voltage With Transfer Unlocked / KOEO – 0 Volt With Transfer Locked
Red/Blue	8	Rear Differential Lock Detection Switch	KOEO – Bat. Voltage/Differential Unlocked / KOEO – 0 Volt With Differential Locked
Blue/Yellow	9	Rear Differential Lock Switch (ON)	KOEO – 0 Volt
Red/Yellow	10	Rear Differential Lock Indicator Light	KOEO – 0 Volt With Differential Locked / KOEO – Battery Voltage With Differential Locked

93E82424   Courtesy of Mitsubishi Motor Sales of America.

Fig. 16: Rear Differential Control Unit Pin Voltage Chart

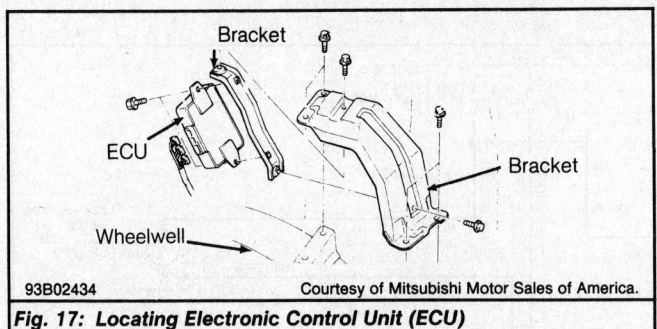

93B02434   Courtesy of Mitsubishi Motor Sales of America.

Fig. 17: Locating Electronic Control Unit (ECU)

"G" SENSOR

CAUTION: DO NOT turn "G" sensor upside-down or lay unit on its side. DO NOT drop "G" sensor. DO NOT disassemble unit. Replace "G" sensor as an assembly.

Removal & Installation – Sensor is located under center console, near shifter. *See Fig. 18.* Remove center console assembly. Disconnect sensor wiring harness connector. Remove sensor. To install, reverse removal procedure. Tighten bolts to 80 INCH lbs. (12 N.m).

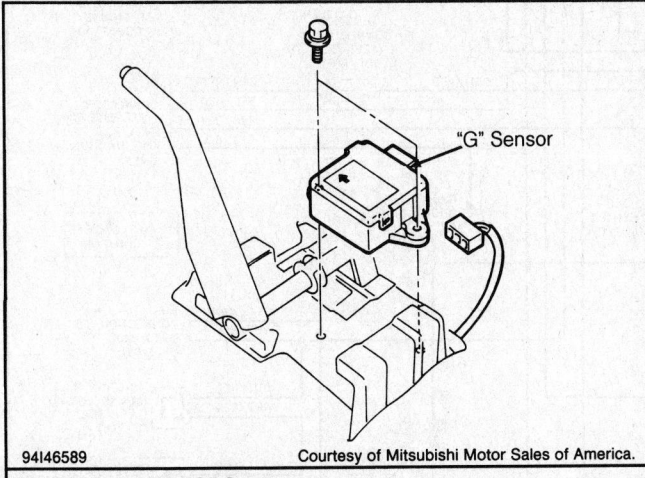

94I46589   Courtesy of Mitsubishi Motor Sales of America.

Fig. 18: Locating "G" Sensor

HYDRAULIC UNIT

Removal – Remove brakelines from hydraulic unit. Remove relay box cover. *See Fig. 19.* Disconnect vehicle ground wire and wiring harness connectors from hydraulic unit. Remove hydraulic unit retaining nuts. Carefully remove hydraulic unit.
Installation – To install, reverse removal procedure. Install hydraulic unit brakelines. Ensure brakelines are installed in correct location. Bleed brake system. See BLEEDING BRAKE SYSTEM.

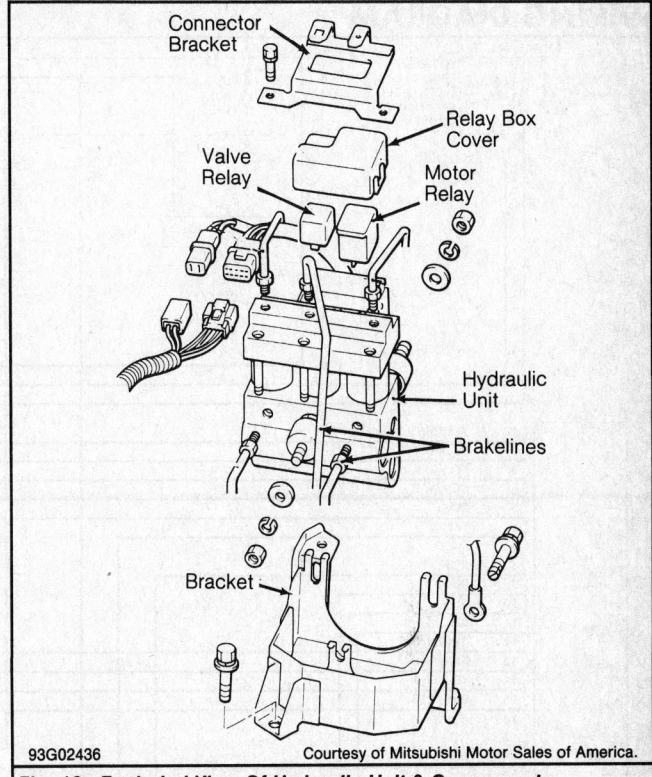

93G02436   Courtesy of Mitsubishi Motor Sales of America.

Fig. 19: Exploded View Of Hydraulic Unit & Components

WHEEL SPEED SENSOR

Removal & Installation – Unplug wheel sensor connector. Remove sensor bolts. Remove speed sensor from vehicle. To install, reverse removal procedure. Sensors are not interchangeable. Adjust wheel speed sensor-to-rotor gap. See WHEEL SPEED SENSOR under ADJUSTMENTS. To complete installation, reverse removal procedure.

WHEEL SENSOR ROTOR

Removal & Installation – Remove brake disc. Remove disc assembly. Remove wheel bearings. Remove axle hub. Remove bolts attaching sensor rotor to hub assembly. To install, reverse removal procedure.

OVERHAUL

HYDRAULIC UNIT

DO NOT attempt to overhaul or disassemble hydraulic unit. If hydraulic unit is defective, replace entire assembly.

TORQUE SPECIFICATIONS

TORQUE SPECIFICATIONS

Application	INCH Lbs. (N.m)
"G" Sensor Mounting Bolt	80 (12)
Wheel Speed Sensor Bolt	84-120 (9-14)

1994 BRAKES
Anti-Lock – Montero (Cont.)

WIRING DIAGRAM

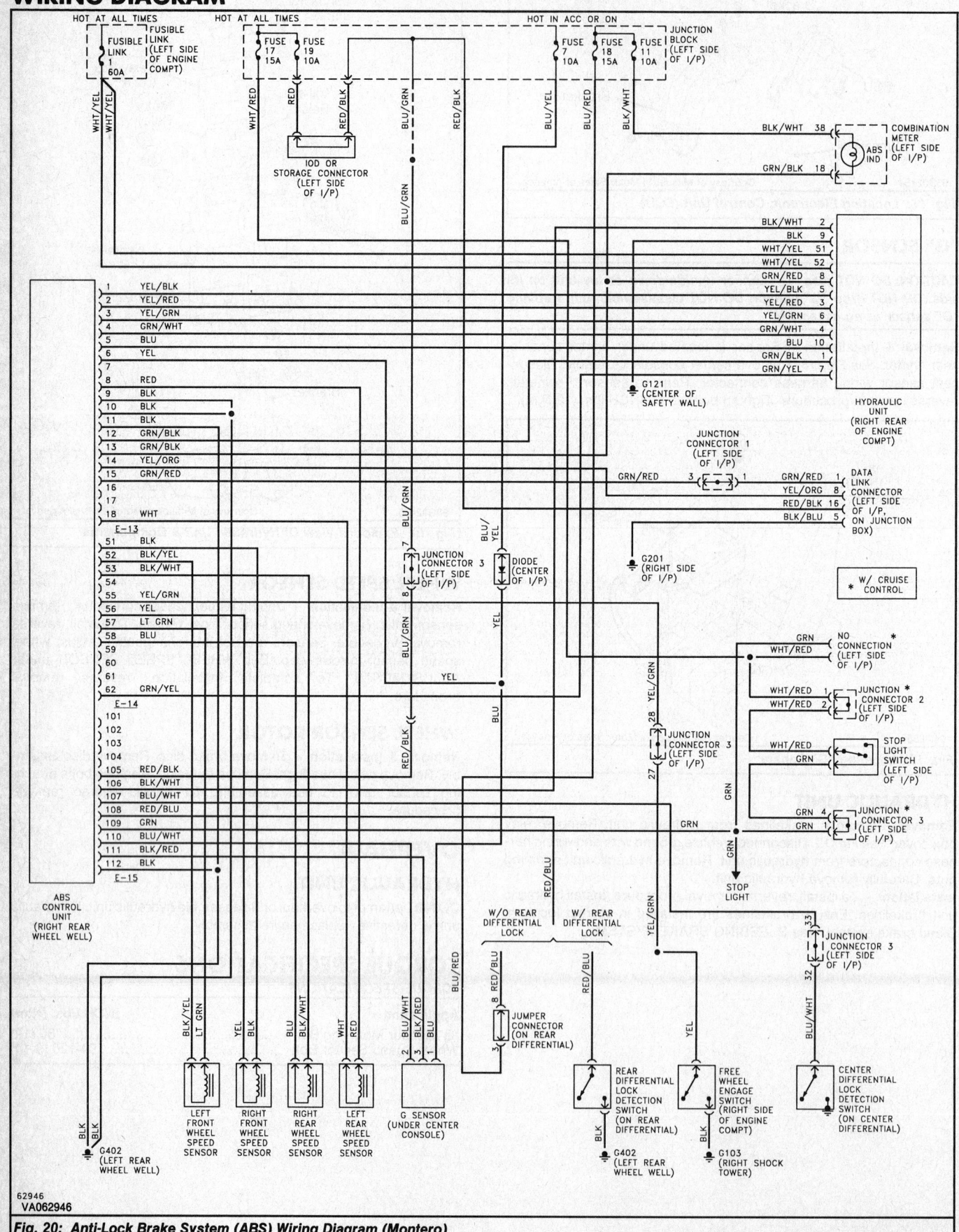

Fig. 20: Anti-Lock Brake System (ABS) Wiring Diagram (Montero)

DESCRIPTION

The Rear Wheel Anti-Lock (RWAL) brake system is designed to control braking force of rear wheels. This serves to eliminate wheel lock and maintain directional stability during hard brake application. System consists of a wheel speed sensor (mounted in rear differential), modulator valve, "G"-force sensor, RWAL control unit, ANTI-LOCK warning light and connecting wiring harness.

Constant power is supplied to terminal No. 1 of the RWAL control unit through fuse No. 1. Ignition power is supplied to control unit through fuse No. 20 when ignition switch is in the ON position. Ignition power is supplied to the ANTI-LOCK warning light through fuse No. 7 when ignition switch is in the ON position.

System also has a self-diagnostic function, which enables technician to quickly trouble shoot system by monitoring stored RWAL trouble codes. See RETRIEVING CODES under SELF-DIAGNOSTIC SYSTEM.

NOTE: For more information on brake system, see DISC & DRUM – EXCEPT PRECIS article in BRAKES.

OPERATION

The RWAL control unit continuously monitors brakelight switch input, as well as wheel speed and "G"-force sensor input signals, to determine control of the modulator valve and ANTI-LOCK warning light. Control unit is located under center of instrument panel, behind "G"-force sensor.

If RWAL control unit detects a malfunction in the RWAL system, control unit will turn on ANTI-LOCK warning light by providing a ground circuit at terminal No. 8 of control unit. When a malfunction code is stored and ANTI-LOCK warning light is illuminated, control unit will disable anti-lock function. During this time, system will function as a normal hydraulic brake system. When system returns to normal, control unit will enable anti-lock function.

CAUTION: See ANTI-LOCK BRAKE SAFETY PRECAUTIONS article in GENERAL INFORMATION.

MODULATOR VALVE

Based upon wheel speed input signals, RWAL control unit regulates hydraulic brake pressure to both rear wheels. Under normal conditions, RWAL system functions like a conventional brake system.

Normal wheel speed-to-acceleration/deceleration braking is programmed into RWAL control unit memory. If the difference between optimum braking rear wheel speed and actual braking rear wheel speed exceeds programmed limits, RWAL system will enter anti-lock mode.

Modulator consists of a release valve which dumps pressure and a hold valve which maintains rear wheel hydraulic pressure. During anti-lock mode, pressure in rear wheel hydraulic circuit is regulated by control unit through the modulator valve. This prevents rear wheel lock, while providing maximum stopping and directional stability.

During anti-lock operation (hard brake application), a series of rapid pulsations (caused by the fluctuating of the modulator valve) may be felt at the brake pedal. These pulsations, in conjunction with a "clicking" or "buzzing" noise, are considered normal during anti-lock operation and will cease when normal braking is resumed or vehicle comes to a complete stop.

WHEEL SPEED SENSOR

The 2-wire rear wheel speed sensor is mounted in the rear differential carrier. Sensor transmits wheel speed information to the RWAL control unit. This low AC voltage signal is generated through magnetic induction when a toothed exciter ring inside the differential passes the stationary magnetic coil of the sensor. This voltage signal increases in both frequency and amplitude as rear wheel speed increases.

BLEEDING BRAKE SYSTEM

BLEEDING PROCEDURES

When bleeding hydraulic system, follow normal manual or pressure bleeding procedures. Bleed brake system in following order: right rear, left rear, Load-Sensing Proportioning Valve (LSPV), right front and left front.

ADJUSTMENTS

For adjustment information on load-sensing proportioning valve (LSPV), parking brake, pedal free play, pedal height, pedal travel and brakelight switch, see DISC & DRUM – EXCEPT PRECIS article in BRAKES.

COMPONENT LOCATION

COMPONENT LOCATION

Component	Location
Electronic Control Unit	Behind "G" Sensor
"G" Sensor	Below Dash, Behind Center Console
Modulator Valve	Right, Middle Of Frame
Speed Sensor	Differential Carrier Housing

TROUBLE SHOOTING

NOTE: To trouble shoot electronic portion of RWAL system, see RETRIEVING CODES. To trouble shoot hydraulic portion of system, see DISC & DRUM – EXCEPT PRECIS article in BRAKES.

ANTI-LOCK WARNING LIGHT

1) Warning light illuminates (continuously) when there is a system malfunction or low system voltage. When ignition is on, warning light should illuminate for approximately 2 seconds and go out (circuit self-check).

2) If warning light will not illuminate, check condition of fuses No. 1, 7 and 20. Replace as needed. If fuses are okay, check condition of warning light bulb. Remove instrument cluster and inspect. Replace as needed.

3) If bulb is okay, check continuity of bulb receptacle circuit. Using ohmmeter, backprobe White/Blue wire (10-pin harness connector) and White/Red wire (12-pin connector). If continuity exists, go to next step. If continuity does not exist, replace instrument panel.

4) Disconnect instrument cluster 12-pin connector. Turn ignition on. Using ohmmeter, measure voltage between White/Red wire and vehicle ground. If voltage is less than battery voltage, inspect and repair circuit as needed. If voltage is battery voltage, go to next step.

5) Turn ignition off. Disconnect 10-pin instrument cluster harness connector. Disconnect ECU harness connector. ECU is located under dash, behind center console.

6) Check continuity between instrument cluster harness 10-pin connector White/Blue wire and ECU harness connector terminal No. 8. *See Fig. 1.* If continuity does not exist, inspect and repair circuit as needed. If continuity exists, go to next step.

7) Check continuity of ECU ground circuits. Using ohmmeter, check continuity between ECU terminals No. 9 and 10, and vehicle ground. *See Fig. 1.* If continuity does not exist, inspect and repair circuit as needed. If continuity does exist, substitute ECU with known good unit and retest.

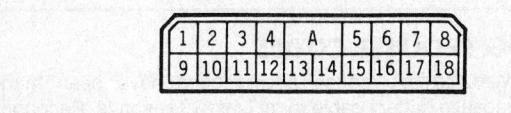

93E82440   Courtesy of Mitsubishi Motor Sales of America.

Fig. 1: Identifying RWAL Electronic Control Unit Connector

1994 BRAKES
Anti-Lock – Pickup (Cont.)

SELF-DIAGNOSTIC SYSTEM

RETRIEVING CODES

Scan Tool – 1) With ignition off, connect Multi-Use Tester II (MB991341) and ROM Pack to diagnostic connector, located under driver's side of dash, and to cigarette lighter socket.

2) Turn ignition on. RWAL warning light should come on as RWAL goes into self-diagnostic mode. Read and record all diagnostic output (trouble) codes from ECU memory. Refer to Multi-Use Tester II (MUT-II) instructions for specific trouble code retrieval procedure.

3) After all trouble codes have been retrieved and recorded, clear codes from ECU memory by disconnecting battery for at least 10 seconds. See RWAL TROUBLE CODES table and appropriate CODE under DIAGNOSTIC TESTING for servicing procedure.

Voltmeter – 1) To retrieve stored trouble codes, locate diagnostic connector under left side of dash. Turn ignition off. Connect analog voltmeter between diagnostic terminal and vehicle ground terminal of diagnostic connector. See Fig. 2. Turn ignition on.

2) Stored trouble codes will be indicated by sweeps of voltmeter needle. Long sweeps indicate first digit of code; short sweeps indicate second digit of code. If more than one fault is present, lowest number code will be given first. After trouble code has been retrieved, test indicated component and/or related circuit (if necessary). See RWAL TROUBLE CODES table and appropriate CODE under DIAGNOSTIC TESTING for servicing procedure.

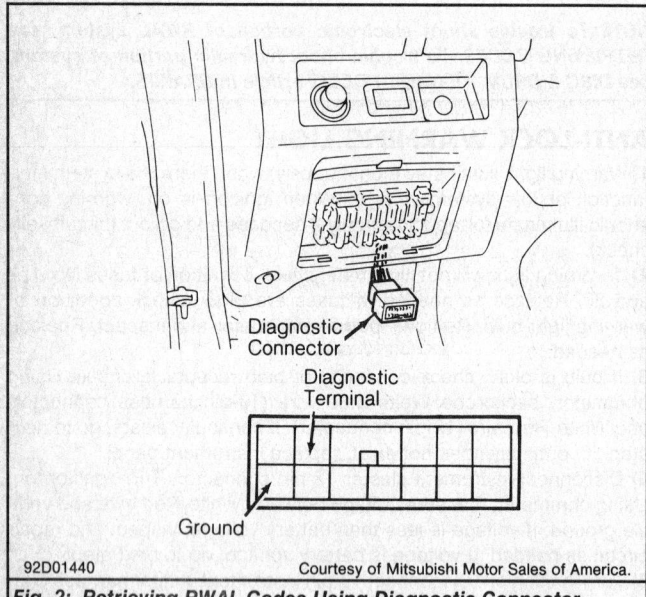

Diagnostic Connector

Diagnostic Terminal

Ground

92D01440   Courtesy of Mitsubishi Motor Sales of America.

Fig. 2: Retrieving RWAL Codes Using Diagnostic Connector

RWAL TROUBLE CODES

Code [1]	Condition/Circuit
15	Wheel Speed Sensor Circuit (Open Or Short)
16	Loss Of Battery Voltage
21	"G"-Force Sensor Circuit (Open Or Short)
22	Brakelight Switch Circuit
41, 42	Modulator Valve Circuit (Open Or Short)
55 [2]	Electronic Control Unit (ECU)

[1] – Continuous short sweeps of voltmeter needle indicate no faults are stored.
[2] – Replace ECU.

CLEARING TROUBLE CODES

To clear RWAL trouble codes after repairs have been made, disconnect negative battery cable for at least 10 seconds. Reconnect battery cable and repeat RETRIEVING CODES to confirm that failure has been corrected.

DIAGNOSTIC TESTING

CODE 15: WHEEL SPEED SENSOR

1) Disconnect speed sensor harness connector. Using ohmmeter, check resistance between sensor terminals. Resistance should be 420-520 ohms. Check resistance between sensor terminals and sensor body. Resistance should be greater than 100,000 ohms. Replace sensor as needed. If measurements are within specification, go to next step.

2) Check continuity between speed sensor and ECU. Disconnect ECU harness connector. Connect jumper wire between speed sensor harness connector terminal No. 1 (Black wire) and vehicle ground. Using ohmmeter, check continuity between ECU terminal No. 14 and vehicle ground. See Fig. 1. If continuity does not exist, inspect and repair circuit as needed.

3) Connect jumper wire between speed sensor harness connector terminal No. 2 (Red wire) and vehicle ground. Check continuity between ECU terminal No. 13 and vehicle ground. See Fig. 1. If continuity does not exist, inspect and repair circuit as needed.

4) If after all tests have been completed system still does not function properly, substitute ECU with known good unit and retest system.

CODE 16: POWER SUPPLY

1) Disconnect ECU harness connector. Turn ignition on. Using DVOM, measure voltage between ECU harness connector terminals No. 1 and 2 and vehicle ground. See Fig. 1. Voltage should be battery voltage. If voltage is not within specification, inspect and repair circuits between fuses No. 1 and 20 and ECU.

2) Conduct performance test on alternator. Ensure output is 13.9-14.9 volts at 68°F (20°C). Repair charging system as needed. If after all tests have been completed system still does not function properly, substitute ECU with known good unit and retest system.

CODE 21: "G" SENSOR

1) Disconnect "G" sensor connector. Connect positive lead of a 7.0-7.5 voltage supply (dry cell batteries) to terminal No. 1 of sensor. See Fig. 3.

2) Connect negative lead of voltage supply to terminal No. 3 of sensor. Connect voltmeter between terminal No. 2 and case of sensor. With sensor in normal level position, voltage should be 1.1-1.5 volts. With sensor turned 90 degrees (bracket up), voltage reading should be 4.6-5.0 volts. If voltage reading is not as indicated, replace "G" sensor.

3) Check continuity between "G" sensor and ECU. See "G" SENSOR HARNESS CONTINUITY CHECK table. Inspect and repair circuits as needed. If after all tests have been completed system still does not function properly, substitute ECU with known good unit and retest system.

"G" SENSOR HARNESS CONTINUITY CHECK

ECU [1] Terminal No.	Wire Color	[2] "G" Sensor Terminal No.
5	Black	3
6	White	2
16	Black/White	1

[1] – See Fig. 1.
[2] – See Fig. 3.

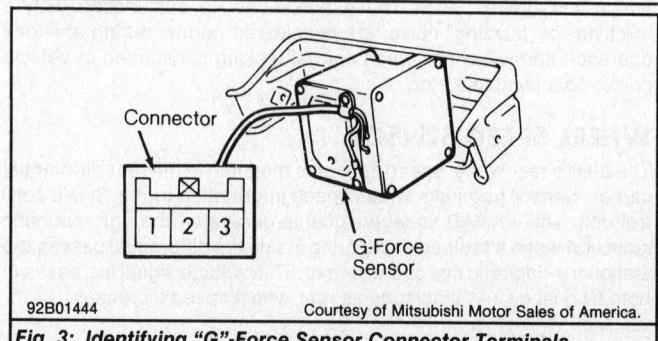

Connector

1   2   3

G-Force Sensor

92B01444   Courtesy of Mitsubishi Motor Sales of America.

Fig. 3: Identifying "G"-Force Sensor Connector Terminals

CODE 22: BRAKELIGHT SWITCH

1) Disconnect brakelight switch connector. On models with cruise control, connect ohmmeter across switch terminals "A" and "B". *See Fig. 4*. On models without cruise control, connect ohmmeter across switch terminals.

2) With brake pedal depressed (plunger extended), continuity should exist between switch terminals. With brake pedal released (plunger retracted), continuity should not exist.

3) If Code 22 is stored and brakelight switch tests okay, check continuity between brakelight switch (Green wire) and terminal No. 18 of ECU. Inspect and repair circuit as needed.

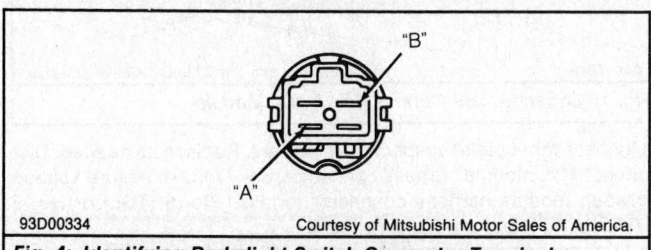

93D00334   Courtesy of Mitsubishi Motor Sales of America.

Fig. 4: Identifying Brakelight Switch Connector Terminals (Models Equipped With Cruise Control)

CODE 41 & 42: MODULATOR VALVE

1) Disconnect modulator valve harness connector. Check resistance of hold valve solenoid winding between terminals No. 3 and 4 of modulator valve. *See Fig. 5*. Resistance should be 5 ohms.

2) Check resistance of release valve solenoid winding between modulator valve terminals No. 1 and 2. Resistance should be 4.3 ohms. If resistance values are not within specification, replace modulator valve as an assembly.

3) Check continuity between modulator valve and ECU. Disconnect ECU harness connector. Connect jumper wire between modulator valve terminal No. 2 (White/Green wire) and vehicle ground. Using ohmmeter, check continuity between ECU harness connector terminal No. 4 and vehicle ground.

4) Move jumper wire to between modulator valve terminal No. 4 (White/Blue wire) and vehicle ground. Check continuity between ECU harness connector terminal No. 3 and vehicle ground. *See Fig. 1*. If continuity does not exist, inspect and repair circuits as needed.

5) Using ohmmeter, check continuity between modulator valve harness connector terminals No. 1 and 3 (Black wire) and ground. If continuity does not exist, inspect and repair circuits as needed. If after all tests have been completed system still does not function properly, substitute ECU with known good unit and retest system.

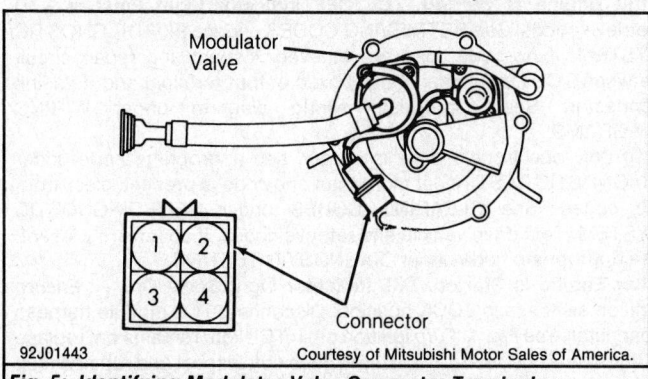

92J01443   Courtesy of Mitsubishi Motor Sales of America.

Fig. 5: Identifying Modulator Valve Connector Terminals

REMOVAL & INSTALLATION

Removal and installation procedures are not available from manufacturer.

TORQUE SPECIFICATIONS

TORQUE SPECIFICATIONS

Application	Ft. Lbs. (N.m)
Modulator Flare Nuts	9-12 (13-17)

WIRING DIAGRAM

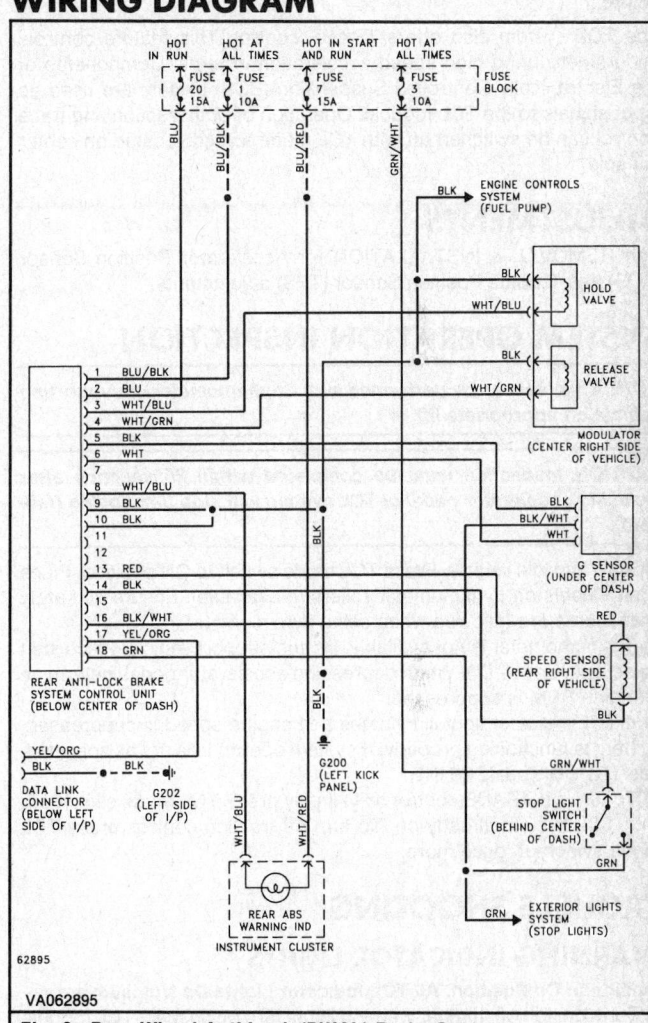

Fig. 6: Rear Wheel Anti-Lock (RWAL) Brake System Wiring Diagram (Pickup)

1994 BRAKES
Traction Control System

Diamante

DESCRIPTION & OPERATION

The Traction Control (TCL) system utilizes information from many on-vehicle systems to limit front wheel slippage under acceleration due to lack of front wheel traction. Traction is controlled by limiting engine power, (vehicle brakes are not used). A vacuum-operated diaphragm (actuator) is connected to throttle linkage and limits throttle valve opening. When front wheel slippage is detected by Anti-Lock Braking System (ABS) wheel speed sensors, a signal is sent from ABS module to TCL module, then to Engine Control Module (ECM), controlling actuator.

The TCL system also offers TRACE control. This feature controls understeer during high speed acceleration in turns. Components of the Electronically Controlled Suspension (ECS) system are used as input signals to the TCL module. Operation of both traction and trace control can be switched off with TCL mode switch, located on center console.

ADJUSTMENTS

See REMOVAL & INSTALLATION for Accelerator Position Sensor (APS) and Throttle Position Sensor (TPS) adjustments.

SYSTEM OPERATION INSPECTION

NOTE: This test can be performed with a dynamometer or supporting vehicle on appropriate lift.

CAUTION: Inspection must be completed within 20 seconds after pressing accelerator pedal or TCL system will stop functioning (fail-safe).

1) Start and idle vehicle. Press TCL mode switch to ON position. Place front wheels on dynamometer rollers (if available). Ensure all safety procedures are followed when using dynamometer.
2) If dynamometer is not available, lift and support vehicle. Place shift selector in drive ("D"). When depressing accelerator pedal, determine if engine RPM is suppressed.
3) If TCL indicator light illuminates and engine speed is suppressed, system is functioning properly. If system operation is not as specified, see TROUBLE SHOOTING.
4) To turn off TRACE control only, lightly press TCL mode switch off, with TCL system already on. To turn off traction control, press TCL mode switch off once more.

TROUBLE SHOOTING

WARNING INDICATOR LIGHTS

Ignition In On Position, All TCL Indicator Lights Do Not Illuminate –
1) Turn ignition on. If other warning lights turn on, inspect TCL module harness connection. *See Fig. 1.* Repair harness as needed. If TCL module harness connection is okay, inspect TCL indicator light bulbs. Replace bulbs as needed.
2) If other warning lights do not illuminate, inspect fuse No. 11. Replace fuse as needed. If fuse No. 11 is okay, inspect power supply circuit between fuse No. 11 and combination meter. See appropriate wiring diagram under WIRING DIAGRAMS.

Ignition In On Position, TCL OFF, TCL Or TRACE OFF Indicator Light Does Not Illuminate – **1)** Turn ignition on. If only TCL OFF light is illuminated, turn ignition switch to LOCK position. If another TCL warning light other than TCL OFF light is illuminated, go to **3)**. Disconnect TCL module harness connector. *See Fig. 1.*
2) Using DVOM, measure voltage between TCL module harness connector terminal No. 2 and ground. *See Fig. 2.* If voltage is not present, inspect and repair circuit between MFI relay and TCL module as needed. See appropriate wiring diagram under WIRING DIAGRAMS. If voltage is present, replace TCL module and retest.

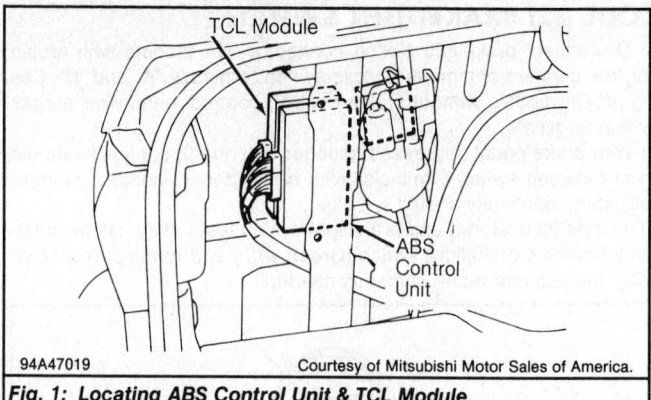
94A47019   Courtesy of Mitsubishi Motor Sales of America.
Fig. 1: Locating ABS Control Unit & TCL Module

3) Inspect light bulb of suspect warning light. Replace as needed. Disconnect TCL module harness connector. *See Fig. 1.* Measure voltage between module harness connector terminal No. 8 (TCL) or No. 5 (TRACE OFF), and ground. *See Fig. 2.*
4) If battery voltage is present, replace TCL module and retest. If battery voltage is not present, inspect and repair circuit between module and combination meter. See appropriate wiring diagram under WIRING DIAGRAMS.

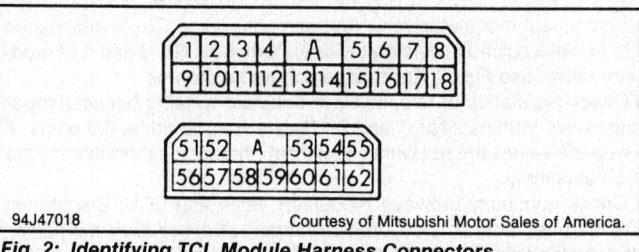
94J47018   Courtesy of Mitsubishi Motor Sales of America.
Fig. 2: Identifying TCL Module Harness Connectors

After Engine Is Started, Only TCL OFF Indicator Light Remains Illuminated – 1) Retrieve codes. See RETRIEVING CODES under SELF-DIAGNOSTIC SYSTEM. If codes are present, see appropriate code under DIAGNOSTIC TESTING. If no codes are present, turn ignition switch to LOCK position.
2) Disconnect TCL module harness connector. *See Fig. 1.* If TCL OFF indicator light goes out, replace TCL module and retest. If TCL OFF light remains illuminated, inspect and repair circuit between indicator light and TCL module for short. See appropriate wiring diagram under WIRING DIAGRAMS.

After Engine Is Started, TCL OFF Indicator Light Flashes – 1) Retrieve codes. See RETRIEVING CODES under SELF-DIAGNOSTIC SYSTEM. If no codes can be retrieved, inspect and repair circuit between TCL module serial/diagnostic output terminal and data link connector. See appropriate wiring diagram under WIRING DIAGRAMS.
2) If only one trouble code is output, see appropriate code under DIAGNOSTIC TESTING. If more than one code is present, clear trouble codes. See CLEARING CODES under SELF-DIAGNOSTIC SYSTEM. Test drive vehicle and retrieve codes. If codes are present, see appropriate code under DIAGNOSTIC TESTING.

After Engine Is Started, TCL Indicator Light Stays On. – Ensure ignition switch is in LOCK position. Disconnect TCL module harness connector. *See Fig. 1.* Turn ignition on. If TCL light remains on, replace TCL module and retest. If TCL light goes out, inspect and repair circuit between TCL light and module for short. *See Fig. 2.* See appropriate wiring diagram in WIRING DIAGRAMS.

With Engine Idling, TRACE OFF & TCL OFF Indicator Lights Do Not Alternate When TCL Switch Is Turned Off – 1) Start and idle engine. Press TCL mode switch to OFF position. Using DVOM, backprobe TCL module harness connector. *See Fig. 2.* Measure voltage between module harness connector terminal No. 13 and ground.
2) If battery voltage is present, replace TCL module and retest. If battery voltage is not present, turn ignition switch to LOCK position. Dis-

connect TCL module harness connector. Using ohmmeter, check continuity between module harness connector terminals No. 2 and 4. Press TCL mode switch and monitor ohmmeter.

3) If continuity exists, inspect and repair circuit between TCL mode switch terminal No. 2 and module harness connector terminal No. 13. *See Fig. 3*. If continuity does not exist, replace TCL mode switch.

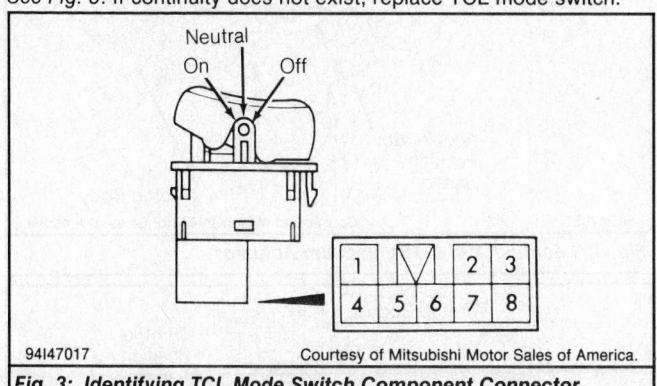

Fig. 3: Identifying TCL Mode Switch Component Connector

94I47017   Courtesy of Mitsubishi Motor Sales of America.

TCL OFF Indicator Light Is Normal When Vehicle Is Idling, But Illuminates When Vehicle Is Moving – 1) Retrieve codes. See RETRIEVING CODES under SELF-DIAGNOSTIC SYSTEM. If no codes can be retrieved, inspect and repair circuit between TCL module serial/diagnostic output terminal and data link connector. See appropriate wiring diagram under WIRING DIAGRAMS.

2) If only one trouble code is output, see appropriate code under DIAGNOSTIC TESTING. If more than one code is present, clear trouble codes. See CLEARING CODES under SELF-DIAGNOSTIC SYSTEM. Test drive vehicle and retrieve codes. If codes are present, see appropriate code under DIAGNOSTIC TESTING.

SELF-DIAGNOSTIC SYSTEM

INTRODUCTION

The first step in diagnosing any problem is verifying the customer's complaint with a test drive under the conditions the problem reportedly occurred. Before entering self-diagnostics, perform a careful and complete visual inspection. Most problems result from mechanical breakdowns (throttle linkage), poor electrical connections or damaged/misrouted vacuum hoses. To verify vacuum hose routing and connections, see appropriate VACUUM DIAGRAMS article in ENGINE PERFORMANCE.

SYSTEM DIAGNOSIS

System diagnosis can be accomplished using an appropriate scan tester or a voltmeter. See RETRIEVING CODES. The TCL module monitors several different inputs. If an abnormal input signal occurs, a trouble code is stored in TCL module memory and assigned a trouble code number. Each circuit has its own trouble code number and message. A specific trouble code indicates a particular system failure, but does not indicate that cause of failure is necessarily within system.

A trouble code does not condemn any specific component; it simply points out a probable malfunctioning area. If a trouble code is set, the TCL module will turn on TCL warning light.

SERVICE PRECAUTIONS

- Ensure vehicle has a fully charged battery and functional charging system.
- Visually inspect connectors and circuit wiring being worked on.
- DO NOT disconnect battery or specific module unless instructed to. This will erase any trouble codes stored.
- DO NOT cause short circuits when performing electrical tests. This will set additional trouble codes, making diagnosis of original problem more difficult.
- When vehicle has multiple trouble codes, always repair lowest number trouble code first.

RETRIEVING CODES

NOTE: Code retrieval is identified by system.

Traction Control System Using Scan Tester – 1) With ignition off, connect Multi-Use Tester II (MB991502) with ROM pack to both self-diagnostic connectors, located under right side of driver's dash.

2) Turn ignition on. Read and record all diagnostic output (trouble) codes from module memory. Refer to Multi-Use Tester II (MUT-II) instructions for specific trouble code retrieval procedure.

3) After all trouble codes have been retrieved and recorded, clear codes from ECU memory. Refer to tester instructions for specific trouble code clearing instructions. See TROUBLE CODE DEFINITION chart.

4) If trouble codes cannot be cleared, module is currently detecting a malfunction. If codes can be cleared, problem is either intermittent or only appears while driving.

Traction Control System Using Voltmeter – 1) Start and idle vehicle engine. Connect analog voltmeter negative lead to Data Link Connector (DLC) ground terminal and positive lead to terminal No. 55. *See Fig. 4*.

2) If trouble codes are stored in TCL module memory, voltmeter needle will begin to pulse. Long pulses represent tens; short pulses represent ones. For example, 4 long pulses and 3 short pulses indicate Code 43. If 2 or more codes are stored, lowest number will be displayed first.

3) After recording trouble code(s), perform necessary testing. See DIAGNOSTIC TESTING. If no codes are stored, voltmeter needle will pulse constantly.

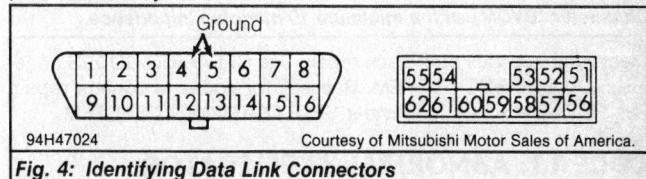

94H47024   Courtesy of Mitsubishi Motor Sales of America.

Fig. 4: Identifying Data Link Connectors

Automatic Transmission Using Scan Tester – 1) With ignition off, connect Multi-Use Tester II (MB991502) with ROM pack to self-diagnostic connector, located under right side of driver's dash.

2) Turn ignition on. Read and record all diagnostic output (trouble) codes from module memory. Refer to Multi-Use Tester II (MUT-II) instructions for specific trouble code retrieval procedure.

3) After all trouble codes have been retrieved and recorded, clear codes from ECU memory. Refer to tester instructions for specific trouble code clearing instructions.

4) If trouble codes cannot be cleared, module is currently detecting a malfunction. If codes can be cleared, problem is either intermittent or only appears while driving.

Automatic Transmission Using Voltmeter – 1) Ensure ignition is off. Connect analog voltmeter negative lead to Data Link Connector (DLC) ground terminal and positive lead to terminal No. 6. *See Fig. 4*.

2) If trouble codes are stored in TCL module memory, voltmeter needle will begin to pulse. Long pulses represent tens; short pulses represent ones. For example, 4 long pulses and 3 short pulses indicate Code 43. If 2 or more codes are stored, lowest number will be displayed first.

3) After recording trouble code(s), perform necessary testing. See appropriate MITCHELL® TRANSMISSION SERVICE & REPAIR MANUAL, IMPORTED CARS, LIGHT TRUCKS & VANS. If no codes are stored, voltmeter needle will pulse constantly.

CLEARING CODES

To erase code(s) with scan tester, follow tester instructions. To erase codes without scan tester, disconnect negative battery cable for at least 10 seconds.

TROUBLE CODE DEFINITION

TROUBLE CODES

Code	[1] Probable Cause
11	Abnormal Accelerator Position Output
12	Open Signal Wire-Shift Control Solenoid Valve "A"
13	Open Signal Wire-Shift Control Solenoid Valve "B"
14	Accelerator Or Throttle Position Sensor Failure
15	TCL Switch Failure
16	Decrease Of TCL Module Power Supply Voltage
17	Open In IG2 Signal Circuit
21	Front Wheel Speed Sensor Open Circuit
22	ABS 1 (ABS Fail) Signal Open Circuit Or ABS Failure
23	Left Rear Wheel Speed Sensor Open Circuit
24	Right Rear Wheel Speed Sensor Open Circuit
25	Temporary Failure Of Both Rear Wheel Speed Sensors
26	Simultaneous Failure Of Both Rear Wheel Speed Sensors
31-33	Steering Wheel Sensor Open Circuit
34	Steering Wheel Sensor ST-1 Or ST-2 Failure
35	Steering Wheel Sensor ST-N Failure
41	Abnormal Signal Output To Engine Control Module
42	Engine Control Module Throttle System Failure
43	Malfunction Indicator Light Illuminated

[1] – See appropriate CODE under DIAGNOSTIC TESTING.

DIAGNOSTIC TESTING

CAUTION: Ensure ignition switch is in LOCK position when performing resistance or continuity tests.

NOTE: Perform all resistance and voltage tests using a Digital Volt-Ohmmeter (DVOM) with a minimum 10-megohm impedance.

Clear trouble codes after each repair. See CLEARING CODES under SELF-DIAGNOSTIC SYSTEM. Recheck for codes to confirm repair. See RETRIEVING CODES under SELF-DIAGNOSTIC SYSTEM.

CODE 11: ABNORMAL ACCELERATOR POSITION OUTPUT

NOTE: Code 11 will output if Accelerator Position Sensor (APS) output voltage becomes less than .2 volts due to open or shorted APS circuit.

1) Retrieve electronically controlled automatic transmission trouble codes. See RETRIEVING CODES under SELF-DIAGNOSTIC SYSTEM. If Codes 11 and 12 are not present, go to step **8)**. If Codes 11 and/or 12 are present, retrieve engine self-diagnostic trouble codes, see RETRIEVING CODES under appropriate SELF-DIAGNOSTICS article in ENGINE PERFORMANCE.

2) If Code 14 is present, go to step **8)**. If Code 14 is not present, disconnect APS and Throttle Position Sensor (TPS) harness connectors. *See Figs. 5 and 6.* Turn ignition on.

3) Using DVOM, measure voltage between TPS harness connector terminal No. 1 and ground. *See Fig. 7.* If voltage is 4-5 volts, replace TPS and retest. See THROTTLE POSITION SENSOR (TPS) under REMOVAL & INSTALLATION. If voltage is not within specification, go to next step.

4) Turn ignition off. Disconnect Engine Control Module (ECM) harness connectors. *See Fig. 8.* Turn ignition on. Measure voltage between ECM harness connector terminal No. 61 (Federal models) or terminal No. 81 (California models), and ground. *See Fig. 9.*

5) If voltage is 4-5 volts, inspect and repair circuit between ECM and TPS. See appropriate wiring diagram under WIRING DIAGRAMS. Go to next step. If voltage is not within specification, replace ECM and go to next step.

6) Turn ignition off. Connect APS and TPS harness connectors. Disconnect TCL module. *See Fig. 1.* Turn ignition on. Measure voltage between TCL module harness connector terminal No. 59 and ground. *See Fig. 2.* If voltage is .2 volt or more, replace TCL module and retest.

7) If voltage is less than 2 volts, inspect and repair circuit between TCL module harness connector terminal No. 59 and APS harness connector terminal No. 3. Clear codes and retest.

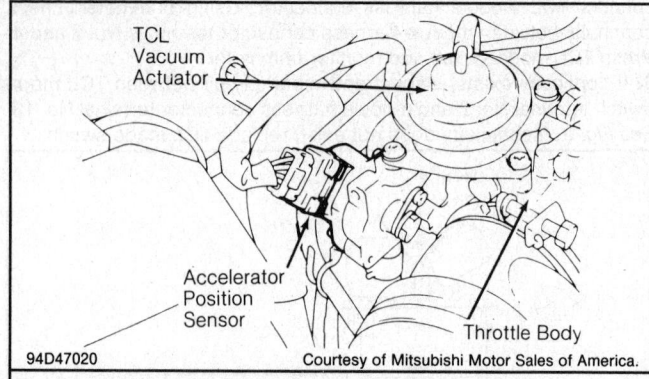

94D47020 Courtesy of Mitsubishi Motor Sales of America.

Fig. 5: Locating APS & TCL Vacuum Actuator

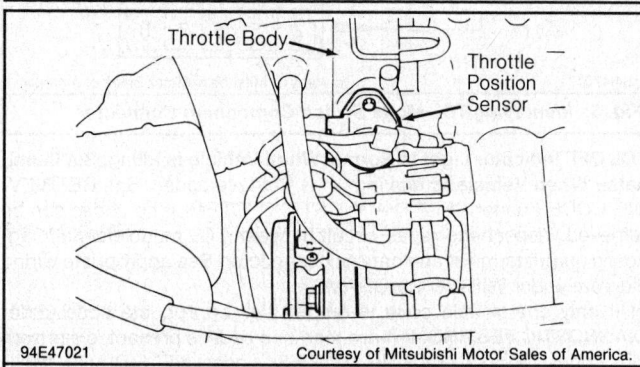

94E47021 Courtesy of Mitsubishi Motor Sales of America.

Fig. 6: Locating TPS

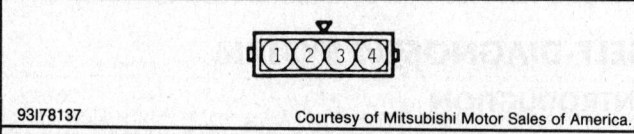

93I78137 Courtesy of Mitsubishi Motor Sales of America.

Fig. 7: Identifying APS & TPS Harness Connector

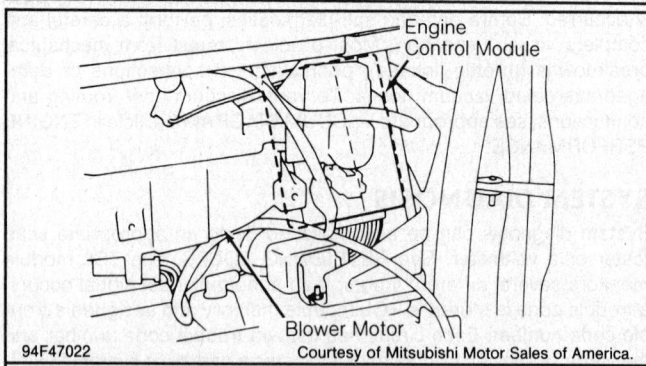

94F47022 Courtesy of Mitsubishi Motor Sales of America.

Fig. 8: Locating Engine Control Module

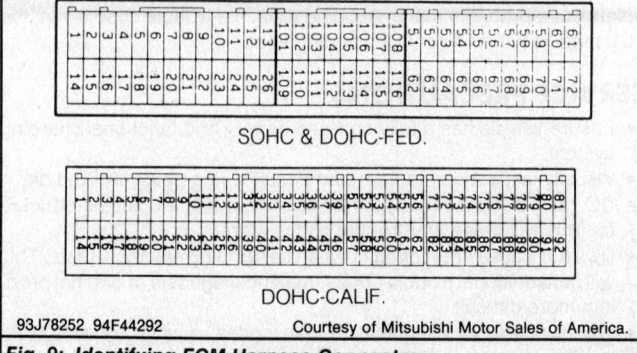

SOHC & DOHC-FED.

DOHC-CALIF.

93J78252 94F44292 Courtesy of Mitsubishi Motor Sales of America.

Fig. 9: Identifying ECM Harness Connectors

8) Disconnect APS and Throttle Position Sensor (TPS) harness connectors. *See Figs. 5 and 6.* Turn ignition on. Using DVOM, measure voltage between APS harness connector terminal No. 4 and ground. *See Fig. 7.*

9) If voltage is not 4-5 volts, inspect and repair circuit between APS harness connector terminal No. 4 and Engine Control Module (ECM) terminal No. 61 (Federal models) or terminal No. 81 (California models). See appropriate wiring diagram under WIRING DIAGRAMS.

10) If voltage is 4-5 volts, turn ignition to LOCK position. Using ohmmeter, measure resistance between APS component connector terminals No. 3 and 4. *See Fig. 7.* Depress accelerator pedal slowly to floor while monitoring ohmmeter.

11) If resistance increases from zero ohms to 3.5-6.5 ohms smoothly as pedal is depressed, go to next step. If resistance is not within specification, or resistance value changes erratically, replace APS and retest. See ACCELERATOR POSITION SENSOR (APS) under REMOVAL & INSTALLATION.

12) Turn ignition off. Connect APS and TPS harness connectors. Disconnect TCL module. Turn ignition on. Measure voltage between TCL module harness connector terminal No. 59 and ground. *See Fig. 2.* If voltage is .2 volt or more, replace TCL module and retest.

13) If voltage is less than 2 volts, inspect and repair circuit between TCL module harness connector terminal No. 59 and APS harness connector terminal No. 3. Clear codes and retest.

CODE 12 & 13: OPEN SIGNAL WIRE-SHIFT CONTROL SOLENOID VALVE "A" OR "B"

NOTE: Codes 12 and 13 are output when an open circuit is detected between the TCL module and Shift Control Solenoid Valve (SCSV) "A" or "B". A short in the Park/Neutral Position (PNP) switch may also set code(s).

1) Ensure ignition is off. Disconnect TCL module harness connector. *See Fig. 1.* Turn ignition on. Move shift selector to "L" position. Using DVOM, measure voltage between TCL module harness connector terminal No. 4 (SCSV "A"), or terminal No. 12 (SCSV "B"), and ground. *See Fig. 2.*

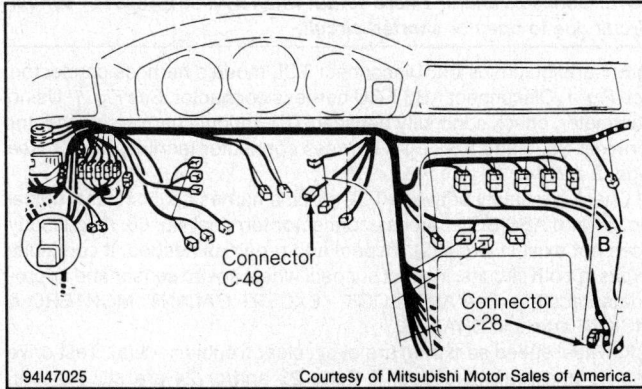

94I47025   Courtesy of Mitsubishi Motor Sales of America.

Fig. 10: Locating Intermediate Harness Connectors C-28 & C-48

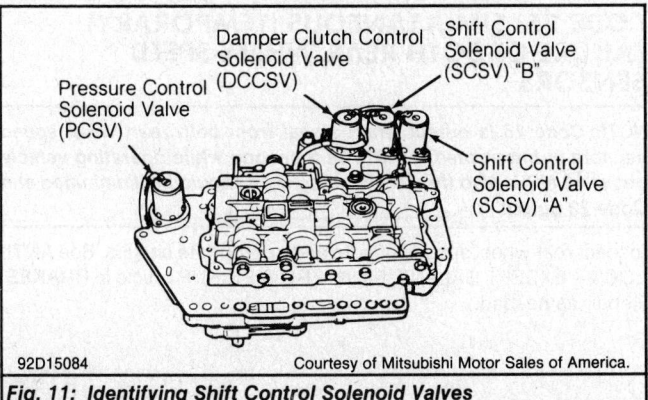

92D15084   Courtesy of Mitsubishi Motor Sales of America.

Fig. 11: Identifying Shift Control Solenoid Valves

2) If battery voltage is present, replace TCL module and retest. If battery voltage is not present, disconnect intermediate connector C-28, located behind center of dash, right of radio. *See Fig. 10.*

3) Measure voltage between terminal No. 8 (SCSV "A"), or terminal No. 5 (SCSV "B"), and ground. *See Fig. 2.* If battery voltage is not present, inspect and repair circuit(s) between TCL module and connector C-28 as needed. See appropriate wiring diagram in WIRING DIAGRAMS.

4) If battery voltage is present, turn ignition to ACC position. Lift and support vehicle. Remove transmission pan drain plug and drain fluid into appropriate container. Remove transmission pan.

5) Disconnect SCSV "A" and "B" harness connector. *See Fig. 11.* Connect jumper wire to intermediate connector C-28 terminals No. 5 and 8, and ground. Check continuity between SCSV 4-pin harness connector terminals No. 3 and 4, and ground.

6) If continuity does not exist, inspect and repair circuit(s) as needed. See appropriate wiring diagram in WIRING DIAGRAMS. If continuity exists in both circuits, replace suspect SCSV according to original trouble code.

CODE 14: ACCELERATOR OR THROTTLE POSITION SENSOR FAILURE

NOTE: Code 14 is output when initial difference between Accelerator Position Sensor (APS) and Throttle Position Sensor (TPS) is 20 degrees or greater due to open circuit.

1) Ensure ignition is off. Disconnect APS harness connector. *See Fig. 5.* Using ohmmeter, measure resistance between APS component terminals No. 3 and 4. Depress accelerator pedal slowly to floor while monitoring ohmmeter.

2) If resistance increases from zero ohms to 3.5-6.5 ohms smoothly as pedal is depressed, replace TPS. See THROTTLE POSITION SENSOR (TPS) under REMOVAL & INSTALLATION. If resistance is not within specification, or resistance value changes erratically, replace APS and retest. See ACCELERATOR POSITION SENSOR (APS) under REMOVAL & INSTALLATION.

CODE 15: TCL SWITCH FAILURE

NOTE: Code 15 is output when an ON signal is input simultaneously from both ON and OFF positions of switch due to internal short

Disconnect TCL switch harness connector. Inspect switch operation. See TCL SWITCH under COMPONENT TESTING. Replace switch as needed. If switch is okay, check continuity of circuits between TCL module and switch. Inspect and repair circuits as needed. If continuity exists in both circuits, replace TCL module and retest.

CODE 16: DECREASE OF TCL MODULE POWER SUPPLY VOLTAGE

NOTE: Code 16 is output when the TCL module power supply voltage is not within specification. If voltage returns to normal, code will be erased.

CAUTION: Ensure vehicle battery is fully charged and charging system is operating properly. A correct diagnosis cannot be achieved if battery voltage drops during testing.

1) Start and idle engine. Using DVOM, backprobe TCL module connector. *See Fig. 1.* Measure voltage between module connector terminal No. 2 (Red/Black wire) and ground. *See Fig. 2.*

2) If battery voltage is present, replace TCL module and retest. If battery voltage is not present, inspect circuit between fusible link No. 7 (Blue) and MFI relay. See appropriate wiring diagram in WIRING DIAGRAMS.

3) If circuit and fuses are okay, turn ignition off. Disconnect TCL module harness connector and inspect. Repair as needed. If connector is okay, no faults exist. Clear codes and retest system.

CODE 17: OPEN IG2 SIGNAL CIRCUIT

NOTE: Code 17 is output when engine is operating at 450 RPM or more, and IG2 power supply voltage is not being received by TCL module due to open or shorted circuit.

1) Ensure ignition is off. Disconnect TCL module harness connector. *See Fig. 1.* Turn ignition on. Using DVOM, measure voltage between module harness connector terminal No. 3 and ground. *See Fig. 2.*
2) If battery voltage is present, replace TCL module and retest. If battery voltage is not present, inspect No. 7 fuse. Replace as needed. If fuse is okay, inspect and repair circuit between fuse No. 7 and TCL module harness connector. See appropriate wiring diagram in WIRING DIAGRAMS.

CODE 21: FRONT WHEEL SPEED SENSOR OPEN CIRCUIT

NOTE: Code 21 is output if speed signal of front wheel has differed from rear wheel by 5 MPH or more, due to open circuit.

1) Retrieve electronically controlled automatic transmission trouble codes. See RETRIEVING CODES under SELF-DIAGNOSTIC SYSTEM. If code 32 is output, see appropriate MITCHELL® TRANSMISSION SERVICE & REPAIR MANUAL, IMPORTED CARS, LIGHT TRUCKS & VANS. If code 32 is not output, turn ignition off.
2) Disconnect TCL module harness connector. *See Fig. 1.* Disconnect transmission control module harness connector. *See Fig. 12.* Using ohmmeter, check continuity between TCL module harness connector terminal No. 55 and transmission control module harness connector terminal No. 10. *See Figs. 2 and 13.*
3) If continuity does not exist, inspect and repair circuit as needed. See appropriate wiring diagram in WIRING DIAGRAMS. If continuity exists, check for continuity between circuit and vehicle ground. If continuity exists, inspect and repair circuit for short to ground. If continuity does not exist, replace automatic transmission control unit. See AUTOMATIC TRANSMISSION CONTROL UNIT under REMOVAL & INSTALLATION.

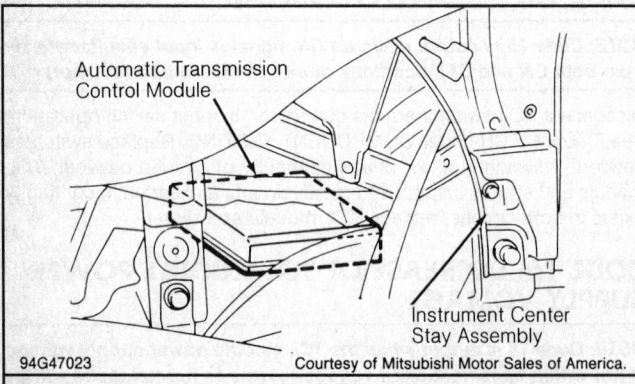

94G47023   Courtesy of Mitsubishi Motor Sales of America.

Fig. 12: Locating Automatic Transmission Control Module

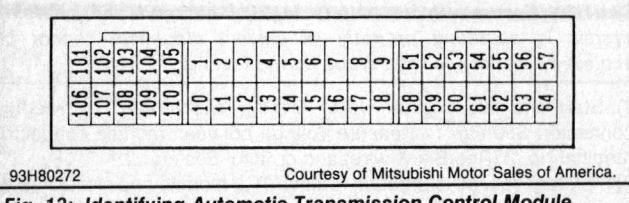

93H80272   Courtesy of Mitsubishi Motor Sales of America.

Fig. 13: Identifying Automatic Transmission Control Module Harness Connector

CODE 22: ABS (ABS FAIL) SIGNAL OPEN CIRCUIT OR ABS FAILURE

NOTE: With ignition switch in ON position, Code 22 is output when TCL OFF indicator light is on while ABS ECU is operating and ABS warning light is on.

1) Start and run engine. If ABS warning light is on, further diagnostic testing of ABS system is required. See ANTI-LOCK – EXCEPT GALANT, MONTERO & PICKUP article in BRAKES. If ABS light is off, turn ignition off. Disconnect TCL module harness connector. *See Fig. 1.* Disconnect ABS ECU harness connector. *See Fig. 1.*
2) Using ohmmeter, check continuity between TCL module harness connector terminal No. 60 and ABS ECU harness connector terminal No. 51. *See Figs. 2 and 14.*
3) If continuity does not exist, inspect and repair circuit as needed. See appropriate wiring diagram in WIRING DIAGRAMS. If continuity exists, check for continuity between circuit and vehicle ground. If continuity exists, inspect and repair circuit for short to ground. If continuity does not exist, replace TCL module. See TCL MODULE under REMOVAL & INSTALLATION.

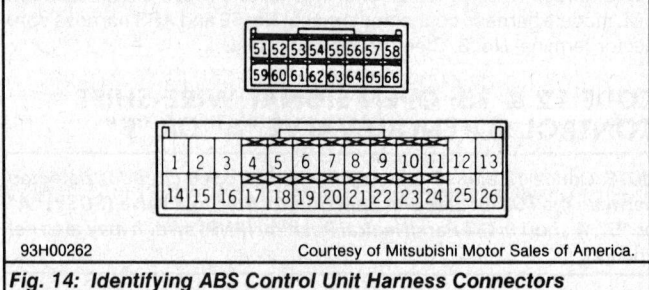

93H00262   Courtesy of Mitsubishi Motor Sales of America.

Fig. 14: Identifying ABS Control Unit Harness Connectors

CODE 23 & 24: LEFT & RIGHT REAR WHEEL SPEED SENSOR OPEN CIRCUIT

NOTE: Codes 23 and/or 24 are output when a pulse is input by sensor circuit due to open or shorted circuit.

1) Ensure ignition is off. Disconnect TCL module harness connector. *See Fig. 1.* Disconnect ABS ECU harness connector. *See Fig. 1.* Using ohmmeter, check continuity between TCL module harness connector terminal No. 6 and ABS ECU harness connector terminal No. 23. *See Figs. 2 and 14.*
2) Check continuity between TCL module harness connector terminal No. 54 and ABS ECU harness connector terminal No. 60. If continuity does not exist in circuit(s), inspect and repair as needed. If continuity exists in both circuits, inspect suspect wheel speed sensor and appropriate circuit(s). See ANTI-LOCK – EXCEPT GALANT, MONTERO & PICKUP article in BRAKES.
3) If wheel speed sensor(s) are okay, clear trouble code(s). Test drive vehicle and retrieve codes. If Code 23 and/or 24 are still present, replace TCL module and retest.

CODE 25: SIMULTANEOUS (TEMPORARY) FAILURE OF BOTH REAR WHEEL SPEED SENSORS

NOTE: Code 25 is output when signal from both rear wheel speed sensors is interrupted for .015 of a second while operating vehicle above 12 MPH. Also the ABS warning light should be illuminated and Code 22 output.

Inspect rear wheel speed sensors and appropriate circuits. See ANTI-LOCK – EXCEPT GALANT, MONTERO & PICKUP article in BRAKES. Repair as needed.

CODE 26: SIMULTANEOUS FAILURE OF BOTH REAR WHEEL SPEED SENSORS

NOTE: Code 26 is output when a failure is detected in rear wheel sensor. Rear wheels are stationary for 20 seconds or more while traction control is operating.

If code was set due to front wheel slippage of 20 seconds or more (i.e. vehicle operation on lift), clear codes and retest. If code 26 is still present, perform testing for Codes 23 & 24.

CODE 31-33: STEERING WHEEL SENSOR OPEN CIRCUIT

1) Ensure ignition is off. Disconnect Electronically Controlled Suspension (ECS) control unit (if equipped). *See Fig. 15.* Turn ignition on. Using DVOM, backprobe TCL module unit connector. Measure voltage between TCL module connector terminals No. 18, 56 and 57. If 4-5 volts is not present in each circuit, replace TCL module and retest.

2) If voltage measured in each circuit is 4-5 volts, backprobe connector C-48 (18-pin) at lower end of steering column. *See Figs. 10 and 16.* Measure voltage between connector terminals No. 7, 8 and 17. If 4-5 volts is not present in each circuit, inspect and repair suspect circuit(s) between intermediate connector C-48 and TCL module.

3) If voltage measured in each circuit is 4-5 volts, turn ignition switch to LOCK position. On vehicles equipped with ECS, disconnect connector C-48. Connect jumper wire between ECS control unit harness connector G-13 terminal No. 116 and ground. *See Fig. 17.* Check continuity between C-48 connector (steering wheel sensor side) terminal No. 2 (Black wire) and ground. *See Fig. 16.*

4) If continuity exists, replace steering wheel sensor. See STEERING WHEEL SENSOR under REMOVAL & INSTALLATION. If continuity does not exist, inspect and repair circuit between ECS control unit and steering wheel sensor. See appropriate wiring diagram in WIRING DIAGRAMS.

5) On vehicles without ECS, disconnect connector C-48. *See Fig. 10.* Disconnect TCL module harness connector. Connect jumper wire between TCL module harness connector terminal No. 58 and ground. Check continuity between C-48 connector (steering wheel sensor side) terminal No. 2 (Blue wire) and ground.

6) If continuity exists, replace steering wheel sensor. See STEERING WHEEL SENSOR under REMOVAL & INSTALLATION. If continuity does not exist, inspect and rep module and steering wheel sensor. See appropriate wiring diagram in WIRING DIAGRAMS.

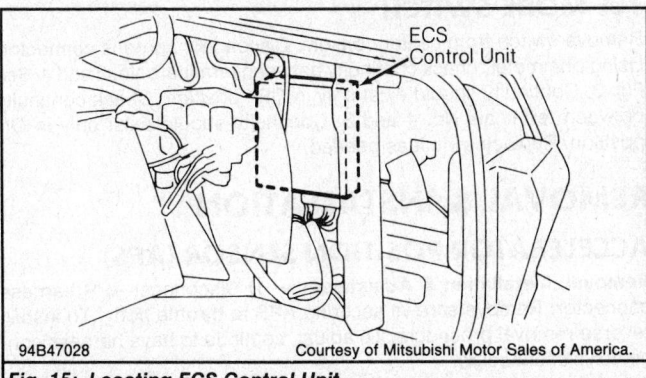

94B47028   Courtesy of Mitsubishi Motor Sales of America.

Fig. 15: Locating ECS Control Unit

94J47026   Courtesy of Mitsubishi Motor Sales of America.

Fig. 16: Identifying Intermediate Connector C-48 Terminals

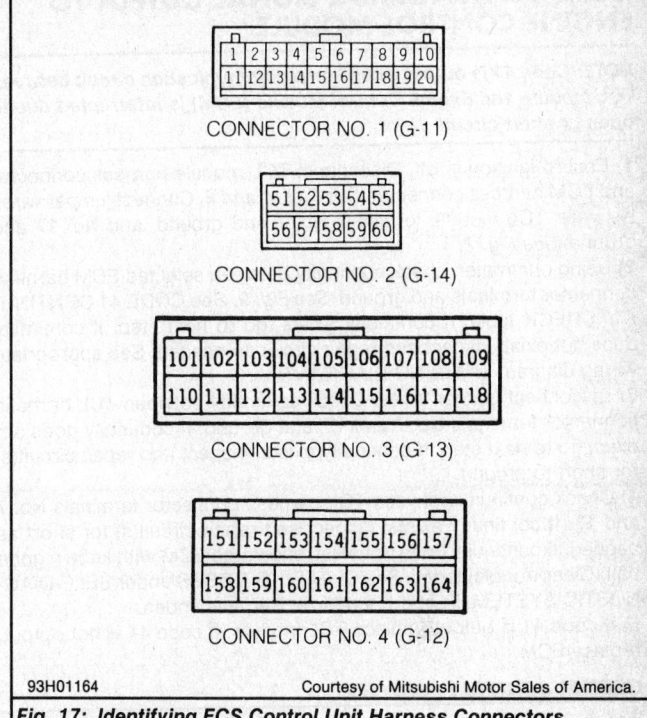

93H01164   Courtesy of Mitsubishi Motor Sales of America.

Fig. 17: Identifying ECS Control Unit Harness Connectors

CODE 34: STEERING WHEEL SENSOR ST-1 OR ST-2 FAILURE

NOTE: Code 34 may be output if vehicle tires are not equal size.

1) Disconnect steering wheel sensor harness connector C-48. *See Fig. 10.* Turn ignition on. Using DVOM, measure voltage between steering wheel sensor harness connector C-48 terminal No. 10 and ground. *See Fig. 16.* If voltage is 4-5 volts, replace steering wheel sensor. See STEERING WHEEL SENSOR under REMOVAL & INSTALLATION.

2) If voltage is not 4-5 volts on vehicles with Electronic Controlled Suspension (ECS), inspect and repair circuit between ECS control unit and steering wheel sensor. See appropriate wiring diagram in WIRING DIAGRAMS. If circuit is okay, replace ECS control unit and retest. *See Fig. 15.*

3) If voltage is not 4-5 volts on vehicles without ECS, inspect and repair circuit between TCL module and steering wheel sensor. See appropriate wiring diagram in WIRING DIAGRAMS. If circuit is okay, replace TCL module and retest. *See Fig. 1.*

CODE 35: STEERING WHEEL SENSOR ST-N FAILURE

1) Clear trouble codes. See CLEARING CODES under SELF-DIAGNOSTIC SYSTEM. Test drive vehicle. Retrieve codes. If Code 34 is not output, replace steering wheel sensor. See STEERING WHEEL SENSOR under REMOVAL & INSTALLATION. If Code 34 is not output on vehicles with Electronic Controlled Suspension (ECS), inspect and repair circuits between ECS control unit and steering wheel sensor. See appropriate wiring diagram in WIRING DIAGRAMS. If circuits are okay, replace ECS control unit and retest. *See Fig. 15.*

2) If Code 34 is not output on vehicles without ECS, inspect and repair circuits between TCL module and steering wheel sensor. See appropriate wiring diagram in WIRING DIAGRAMS. If circuits are okay, replace TCL module and retest. *See Fig. 1.*

CODE 41: ABNORMAL SIGNAL OUTPUT TO ENGINE CONTROL MODULE

NOTE: Code 41 is output when serial communication circuit between TCL module and Engine Control Module (ECM) is interrupted due to open or short circuit.

1) Ensure ignition is off. Disconnect TCL module harness connector and ECM harness connector. *See Figs. 1 and 8.* Connect jumper wires between TCL module terminals No. 7 and ground, and No. 17 and ground. *See Fig. 2.*
2) Using ohmmeter, check continuity between selected ECM harness connector terminals and ground. *See Fig. 9.* See CODE 41 CONTINUITY CHECK table. If continuity exists, go to next step. If continuity does not exist, inspect and repair circuit as needed. See appropriate wiring diagram in WIRING DIAGRAMS.
3) Disconnect jumper wires. Check continuity between TCL harness connector terminals No. 7 and 17, and ground. If continuity does not exist, go to next step. If continuity exists, inspect and repair circuit(s) for short to ground.
4) Check continuity between TCL harness connector terminals No. 7 and 17. If continuity exists, inspect and repair circuit(s) for short as needed. If continuity does not exist, substitute ECM with known good unit. Clear trouble codes. See CLEARING CODES under SELF-DIAGNOSTIC SYSTEM. Test drive vehicle. Retrieve codes.
5) If code 41 is output, replace TCL module. If code 41 is not output, replace ECM.

CODE 41 CONTINUITY CHECK

TCL Terminal No. [1]	[2] ECM Terminal No.
California Vehicles	
7	21
17	20
Federal Vehicles	
7	53
7	59

[1] – See Fig. 2.
[2] – See Fig. 9.

CODE 42: ENGINE CONTROL MODULE THROTTLE SYSTEM FAILURE

See SELF-DIAGNOSTICS article in ENGINE PERFORMANCE.

CODE 43: MALFUNCTION INDICATOR LIGHT ILLUMINATED

See SELF-DIAGNOSTICS article in ENGINE PERFORMANCE.

COMPONENT TESTING

STEERING WHEEL SENSOR

See ELECTRONIC – DIAMANTE article in SUSPENSION.

TCL VACUUM ACTUATOR

1) Remove vacuum hose from actuator and connect vacuum pump with vacuum tee. *See Fig. 18.* Perform test under SYSTEM OPERATION INSPECTION. As throttle pedal is depressed, vacuum should increase to 5.9 in. Hg. Once system has operated for 20 seconds, vacuum should decrease to zero in. Hg.
2) If system vacuum is within specifications, but engine speed does not decrease, manually apply vacuum to actuator and check operation. Replace components as needed.

TCL VACUUM SOLENOID

NOTE: For component location, see Fig. 19.

See SELF-DIAGNOSTICS article in ENGINE PERFORMANCE.

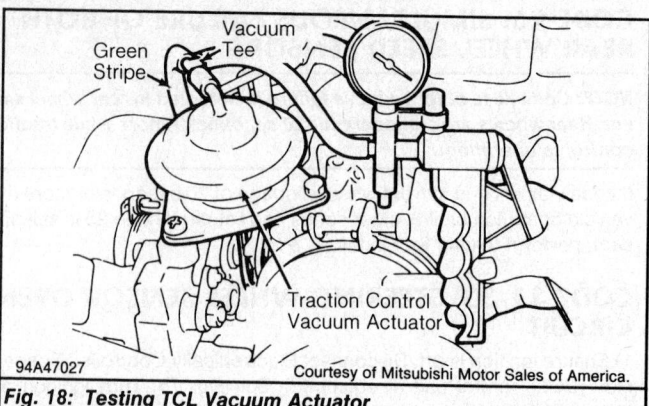

94A47027   Courtesy of Mitsubishi Motor Sales of America.
Fig. 18: Testing TCL Vacuum Actuator

TCL VENTILATION SOLENOID

NOTE: For component location, see Fig. 19.

See SELF-DIAGNOSTICS article in ENGINE PERFORMANCE.

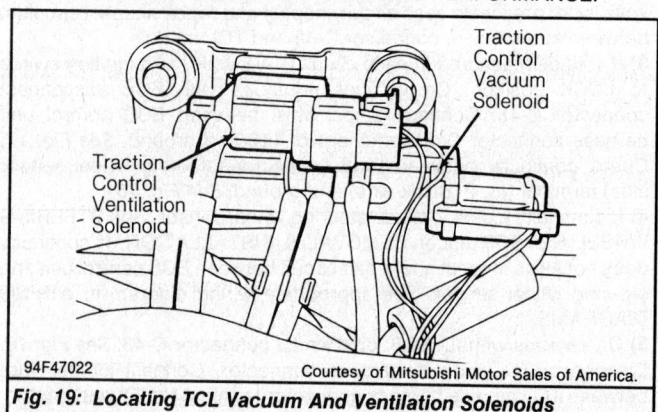

94F47022   Courtesy of Mitsubishi Motor Sales of America.
Fig. 19: Locating TCL Vacuum And Ventilation Solenoids

WHEEL SPEED SENSOR

See ANTI-LOCK – EXCEPT GALANT, MONTERO & PICKUP article in BRAKES.

TCL MODE SWITCH

Remove switch from center console. Disconnect harness connector. Using ohmmeter, check continuity between terminals No. 2 and 4. *See Fig. 3.* Continuity should exist only in OFF position. Check continuity between terminals No. 4 and 8. Continuity should exist only in ON position. Replace switch as needed.

REMOVAL & INSTALLATION

ACCELERATOR POSITION SENSOR (APS)

Removal, Installation & Adjustment – 1) Disconnect APS harness connector. Remove screws securing APS to throttle body. To install, reverse removal procedure. To adjust, continue to have harness connector disconnected.
2) Using ohmmeter, measure resistance between APS terminals No. 1 and No. 2. *See Fig. 7.* Insert .020" (.50 mm) feeler gauge between accelerator lever and throttle lever.
3) Loosen APS mounting screws and rotate APS fully counterclockwise. Ensure there is continuity between terminals No. 1 and No. 2. Rotate APS clockwise until there is no continuity and tighten screws to specification. See TORQUE SPECIFICATIONS.

STEERING WHEEL SENSOR

For removal and installation procedures, see ELECTRONIC – DIAMANTE article in SUSPENSION.

THROTTLE POSITION SENSOR (TPS)

NOTE: Ensure basic idle speed is set to specification before adjusting TPS. See ON-VEHICLE ADJUSTMENTS article in ENGINE PERFORMANCE. Perform all adjustments with engine at normal operating temperature, front wheels in straight-ahead position, cooling fan and all accessories off, and transmission in Park or Neutral.

Removal, Installation & Adjustment – 1) Disconnect TPS harness connector. Remove screws securing TPS to throttle body. To install, reverse removal procedure. To adjust, continue to have harness connector disconnected.

2) Using ohmmeter, measure resistance between TPS terminals No. 3 and No. 4. *See Fig. 7.* Insert .025" (.65 mm) feeler gauge between fixed speed adjusting screw and throttle lever.

3) Loosen TPS mounting screws and rotate TPS fully clockwise. Ensure there is continuity between terminals No. 3 and No. 4. Rotate TPS counterclockwise until there is no continuity and tighten screws to specification. See TORQUE SPECIFICATIONS.

TORQUE SPECIFICATIONS

TORQUE SPECIFICATIONS

Application	INCH Lbs. (N.m)
APS Switch Screws	13-20 (1.5-2.5)
TPS Switch Screws	13-20 (1.5-2.5)
Transmission Pan Bolt	89-108 (10-12)

WIRING DIAGRAMS

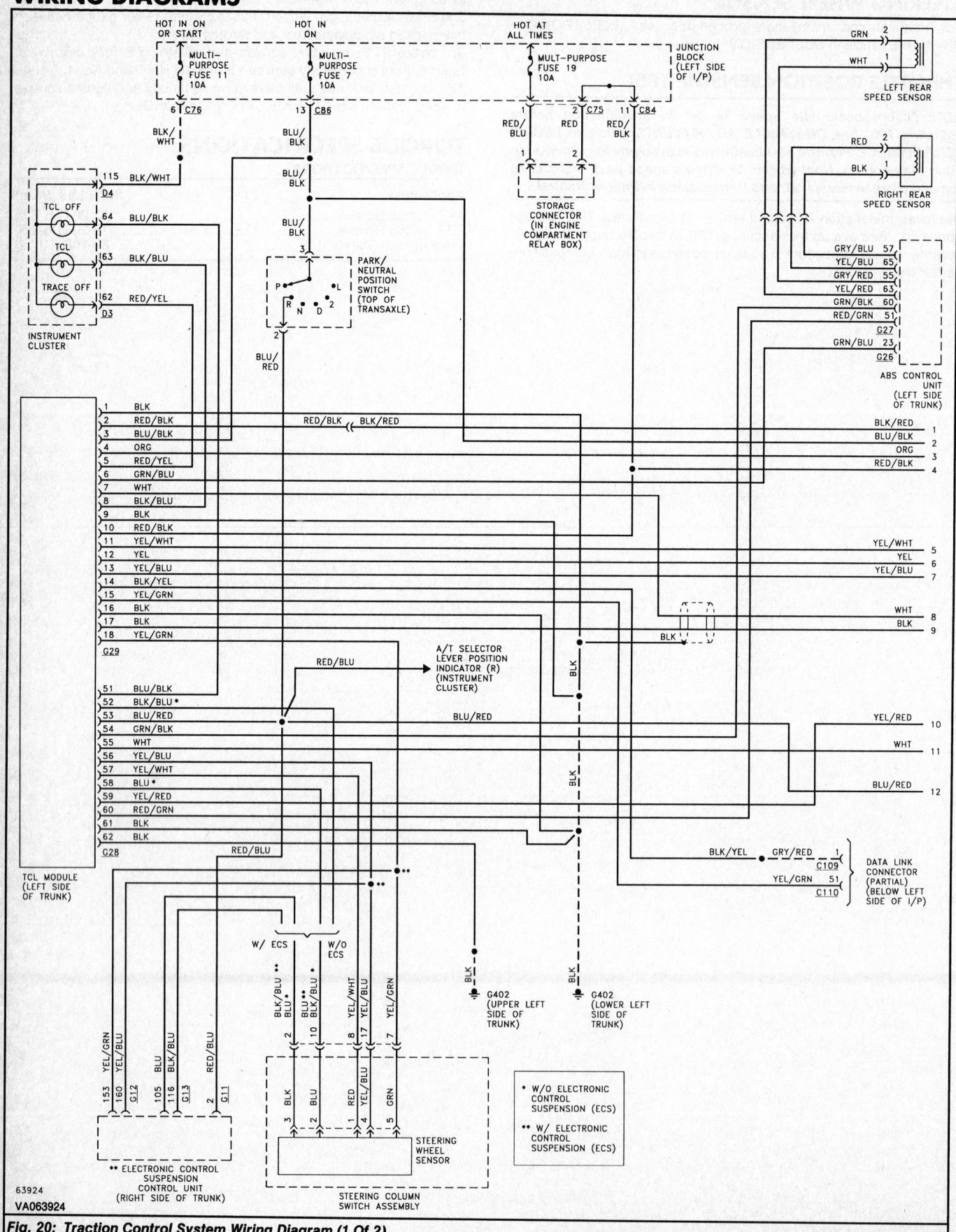

Fig. 20: Traction Control System Wiring Diagram (1 Of 2)

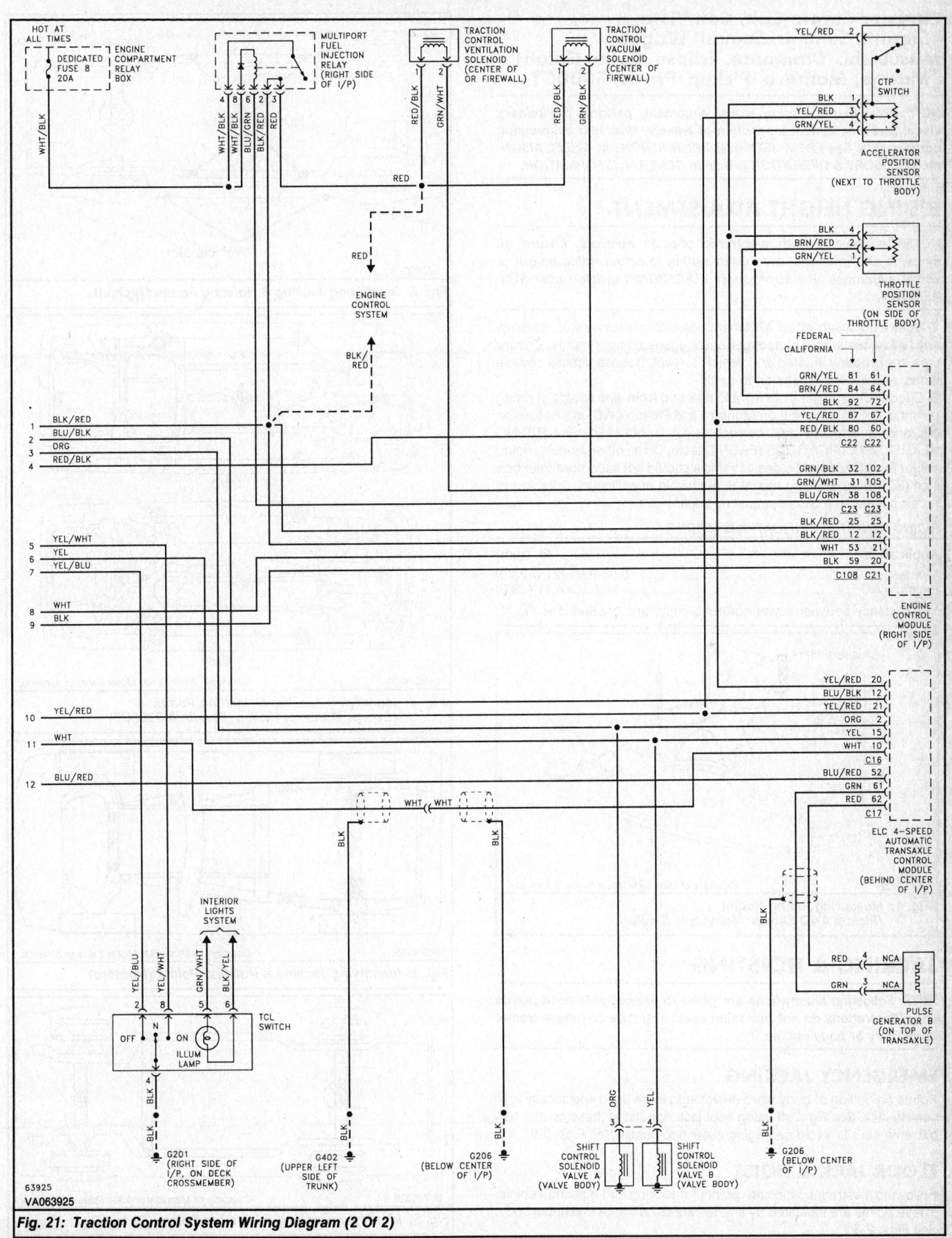

Fig. 21: Traction Control System Wiring Diagram (2 Of 2)

63925

VA063925

1994 WHEEL ALIGNMENT
Specifications & Procedures

**Chrysler Corp.: Colt, Colt Vista, Stealth, Summit, Summit Wagon
Mitsubishi: Diamante, Eclipse, Expo, Galant, Mirage, Montero, Pickup, Precis, 3000GT**

NOTE: Prior to performing wheel alignment, perform preliminary visual and mechanical inspection of wheels, tires and suspension components. See PRE-ALIGNMENT INSTRUCTIONS in WHEEL ALIGN-MENT THEORY & OPERATION article in GENERAL INFORMATION.

RIDING HEIGHT ADJUSTMENT

NOTE: On vehicles with electronic chassis controls, ensure all systems are functional before attempting to adjust riding height or wheel alignment. See appropriate ELECTRONIC article under SUS-PENSION.

1) Before adjusting wheel alignment, visually inspect vehicle. Remove any heavy items from passenger and luggage compartments. Ensure tires are properly inflated and vehicle is level. Bounce vehicle several times, and allow suspension to settle.
2) Check riding height from front to rear and from side to side. If riding height is not as specified on Montero and Pickup 4WD, adjust torsion bar anchor arm nut until correct height is obtained. See RIDING HEIGHT SPECIFICATIONS (FRONT) table. On all other models, riding height for left and right sides of vehicle should not vary more than one inch (25.4 mm). If riding height is not within specification, check and repair suspension before adjusting alignment.

RIDING HEIGHT SPECIFICATIONS (FRONT)

Application	[1] In. (mm)
Montero	0.83-0.91 (21.0-23.0)
Pickup 4WD	3.11 (79.0)

[1] – Distance between lower control bumper and bracket. *See Fig. 1.*

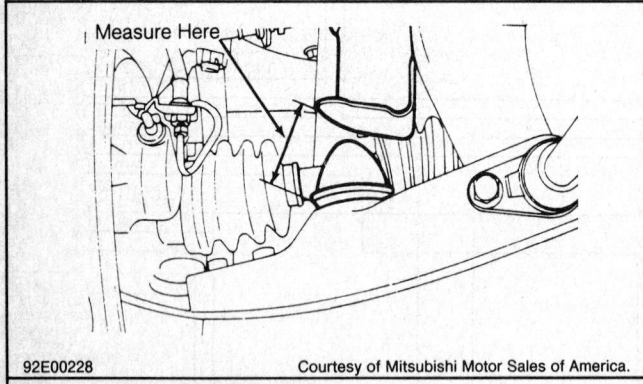

**Fig. 1: Measuring Riding Height
(Pickup 4WD Shown; Montero Is Similar)**

JACKING & HOISTING

NOTE: Following illustrations are given to provide reference points only. Illustrations do not represent exact structure of vehicle frame, underbody or body outline.

EMERGENCY JACKING

Points on outline of body were designated to be used specifically with vehicle jack. *See Fig. 2.* If using floor jack or hoist at these points, use extreme care to avoid damaging outer body shell. *See Figs. 3-6.*

FLOOR JACK & HOIST

Following illustrations indicate points for jacking and hoisting vehicle. These points are indicated by shaded areas on frame and underbody. *See Figs. 2-6.*

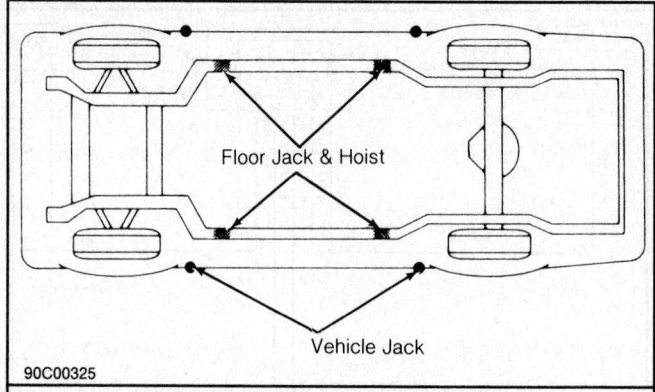

Fig. 2: Identifying Jacking & Hoisting Points (Typical)

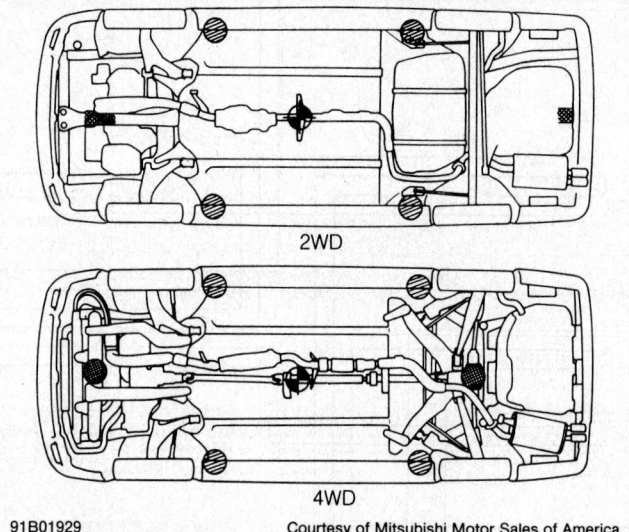

Courtesy of Mitsubishi Motor Sales of America.

**Fig. 3: Identifying Jacking & Hoisting Points
(Except Montero, Pickup, Stealth & 3000GT)**

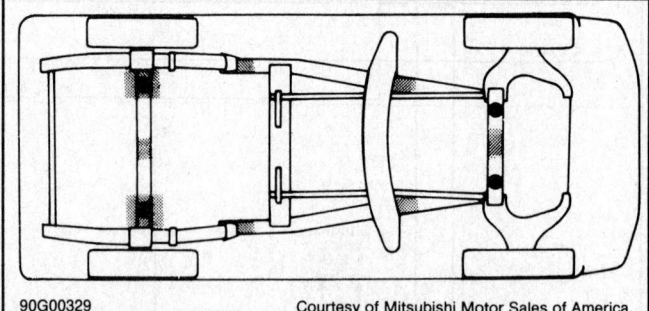

Courtesy of Mitsubishi Motor Sales of America.

Fig. 4: Identifying Jacking & Hoisting Points (Montero)

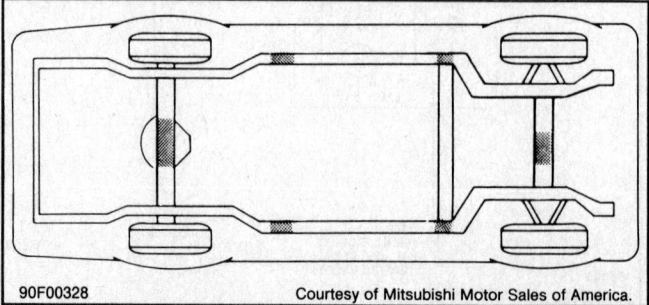

Courtesy of Mitsubishi Motor Sales of America.

Fig. 5: Identifying Jacking & Hoisting Points (Pickup)

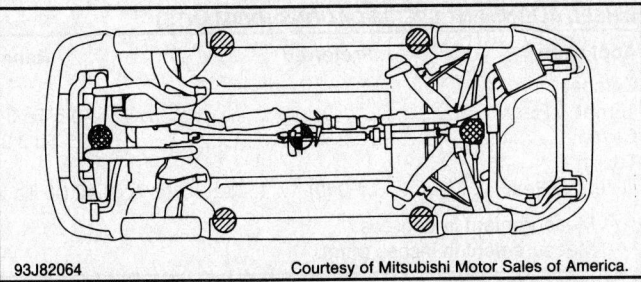

Fig. 6: Identifying Jacking & Hoisting Points (Stealth & 3000GT AWD Shown; FWD Is Similar)

WHEEL ALIGNMENT PROCEDURES

CAMBER ADJUSTMENT

Except Montero, Pickup, Stealth & 3000GT – Camber is preset and cannot be adjusted. Check camber. See appropriate WHEEL ALIGNMENT SPECIFICATIONS table. If camber is not within specification, replace damaged or bent parts.

Montero & Pickup – 1) Check camber. See appropriate WHEEL ALIGNMENT SPECIFICATIONS table. If camber is not within specification, remove shock absorber mounting nut and lock nut.

CAUTION: Difference in shim thickness between front and rear must not exceed .16" (4.0 mm). DO NOT use more than 3 shims at one location.

---

2) Compress shock absorber, and loosen upper arm mounting bolts and nuts. Adjust camber by increasing or decreasing shims between upper arm shaft and crossmember. *See Fig. 7.*

Stealth & 3000GT – Check camber. See WHEEL ALIGNMENT SPECIFICATIONS (STEALTH & 3000GT) table. If camber is not within specification, loosen eccentric cam nut. Rotate eccentric cam bolt to obtain correct camber. *See Fig. 8.* Each marking represents a change of .12-.25 degree of camber.

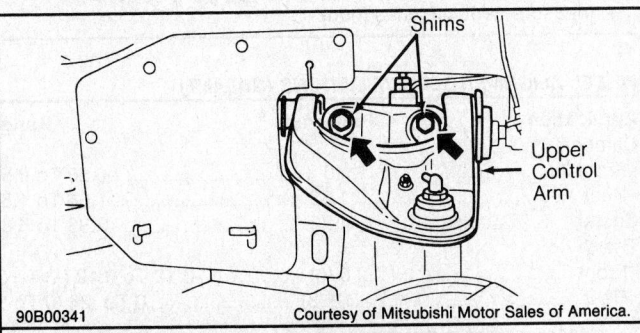

Fig. 7: Adjusting Camber & Caster (Pickup Shown; Montero Camber Adjustment Is Similar)

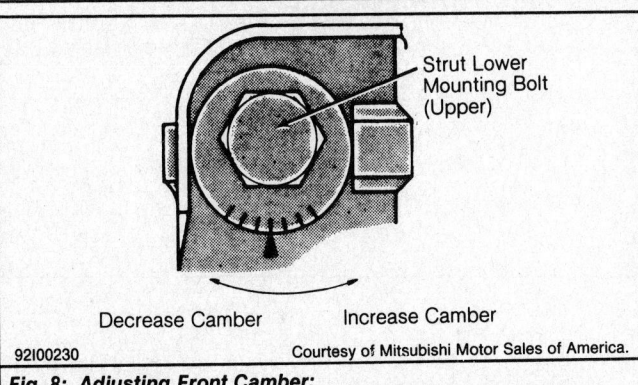

Fig. 8: Adjusting Front Camber; Adjusting Rear Camber Is Similar (Stealth & 3000GT)

CASTER ADJUSTMENT

Except Montero & Pickup – Check caster. See appropriate WHEEL ALIGNMENT SPECIFICATIONS table. If caster is not within specification, replace damaged or bent parts.

Montero & Pickup – 1) Check caster. See WHEEL ALIGNMENT SPECIFICATIONS (MONTERO, & PICKUP) table. If caster is not within specification, remove shock absorber mounting nut and lock nut.

CAUTION: Difference in shim thickness between front and rear must not exceed .16" (4.0 mm). DO NOT use more than 3 shims at one location.

---

2) Compress shock absorber, and loosen upper arm mounting bolts and nuts. Adjust caster by increasing or decreasing shims between upper arm shaft and crossmember. *See Fig. 7.*

TOE-IN ADJUSTMENT

Front – Check front toe-in. See appropriate WHEEL ALIGNMENT SPECIFICATIONS table. If front toe-in is not within specification, remove clips. Turn tie rods or turnbuckles same amount, but in opposite directions. Recheck front toe-in.

Rear (Except Galant, Stealth & 3000GT) – Check rear toe-in. See appropriate WHEEL ALIGNMENT SPECIFICATIONS table. If rear toe-in is not within specification, replace damaged or bent parts.

Rear (Galant, Stealth FWD & 3000GT FWD) – Check rear toe-in. See WHEEL ALIGNMENT SPECIFICATIONS (STEALTH & 3000GT) table. If rear toe-in is not within specification, loosen both assist link eccentric cam nuts. Turn assist link eccentric cam bolts equal amount to obtain correct rear toe-in. *See Fig. 9.*

Rear (Stealth AWD & 3000GT AWD) – Check rear toe-in. See WHEEL ALIGNMENT SPECIFICATIONS (STEALTH & 3000GT) table. If rear toe-in is not within specification, loosen both trailing arm eccentric cam nuts. Turn trailing arm eccentric cam bolts equal amount to obtain correct rear toe-in. *See Fig. 10.*

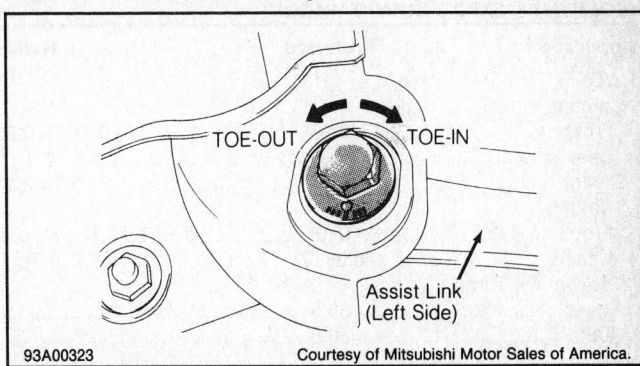

Fig. 9: Adjusting Rear Toe-In (Stealth FWD & 3000GT FWD)

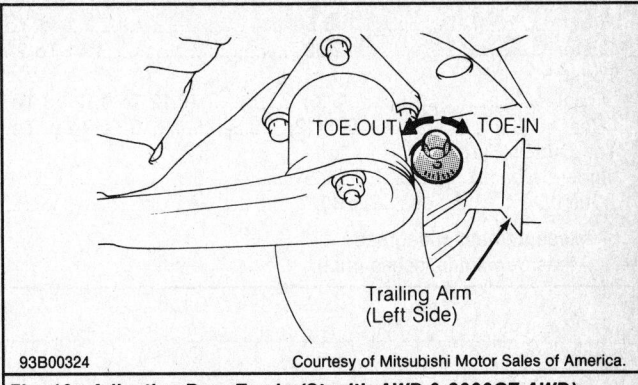

Fig. 10: Adjusting Rear Toe-In (Stealth AWD & 3000GT AWD)

1994 WHEEL ALIGNMENT
Specifications & Procedures (Cont.)

TORQUE SPECIFICATIONS

TORQUE SPECIFICATIONS

Application	Ft. Lbs. (N.m)
Shock Absorber-To-Crossmember Nut	
Montero & Pickup	10-13 (14-18)
Shock Absorber-To-Lower Arm Bolt	
Montero	11-16 (15-22)
Pickup	10 (14)
Upper Arm Shaft To Crossmember Nut	
Montero & Pickup	72-87 (98-118)
Wheel Lug Nut	
Eclipse, Pickup, Stealth & 3000GT	87-101 (118-137)
Montero	72-87 (98-118)
All Other Models	65-80 (90-110)

WHEEL ALIGNMENT SPECIFICATIONS

WHEEL ALIGNMENT SPECIFICATIONS (COLT, MIRAGE & SUMMIT)

Application	Preferred	Range
Camber [1]		
Front	0	-0.5 To 0.5
Rear	-0.67	-1.17 To -0.17
Caster [1]	2.25	
Toe-In [2]		
Front	0 (0)	-0.12 To 0.12 (-3 To 3)
Rear	0.12 (3)	0.04 To 0.2 (1 To 5)
Toe-Out On Turns [1]		
Inner	37.18	
Outer	31	

[1] – Measurement in degrees.
[2] – Measurement in inches (mm).

WHEEL ALIGNMENT SPECIFICATIONS (COLT VISTA, EXPO & SUMMIT WAGON)

Application	Preferred	Range
FWD		
Camber [1]		
Front	0.33	-0.17 To 0.83
Rear	-0.5	-1 To 0
Caster [1]	2.17	1.5 To 2.83
Toe-In [2]		
Front	0 (0)	-0.12 To 0.12 (-3 To 3)
Rear	0.08 (2)	0 To 0.2 (0 To 5)
Toe-Out On Turns [1]		
Inner	36.5	
Outer	30.5	
4WD		
Camber [1]		
Front	0.67	0.17 To 11.17
Rear	-0.5	-1 To 0
Caster [1]	2.08	1.41 To 2.75
Toe-In [2]		
Front	0 (0)	-0.12 To 0.12 (-3 To 3)
Rear	0.08 (2)	0 To 0.2 (0 To 5)
Toe-Out On Turns [1]		
Inner	36.5	
Outer	30.7	

[1] – Measurement in degrees.
[2] – Measurement in inches (mm).

WHEEL ALIGNMENT SPECIFICATIONS (DIAMANTE)

Application	Preferred	Range
Camber [1]		
Front & Rear	0	-0.5 To 0.5
Caster [1]	2.75	2.25 To 3.35
Toe-In [2]		
Front & Rear	0 (0)	-0.12 To 0.12 (-3 To 3)

[1] – Measurement in degrees.
[2] – Measurement in inches (mm).

WHEEL ALIGNMENT SPECIFICATIONS (ECLIPSE)

Application	Preferred	Range
1.8L		
Camber [1]		
Front	0.23	-0.27 To 0.73
Rear	-0.75	-1.25 To -0.25
Caster [1]	2.33	1.83 To 2.83
Toe-In [2]		
Front & Rear	0 (0)	-0.12 To 0.12 (-3 To 3)
2.0L		
FWD		
Camber [1]		
Front	0.08	-0.03 To 0.11
Rear	-0.75	-1.25 To -0.25
Caster [1]	2.4	1.9 To 2.9
Toe-In [2]		
Front & Rear	0 (0)	-0.12 To 0.12 (-3 To 3)
AWD		
Camber [1]		
Front	0.17	-0.33 To 0.67
Rear	-1.55	-2.05 To -1.05
Caster [1]	2.3	1.8 To 2.8
Toe-In [2]		
Front	0 (0)	-0.12 To 0.12 (-3 To 3)
Rear	0.14 (3)	-0.02 To 0.26 (0.5 To 6.5)

[1] – Measurement in degrees.
[2] – Measurement in inches (mm).

WHEEL ALIGNMENT SPECIFICATIONS (GALANT)

Application	Preferred	Range
Camber [1]		
Front	0	-0.50 To 0.50
Rear	1.33	-.66 To 1.83
Caster [1]	4.33	2.83 To 5.83
Toe-In [2]		
Front	0 (0)	-0.12 To 0.12 (-3 To 3)
Rear	.12 (3)	0 To .24 (0 To 6)

[1] – Measurement in degrees.
[2] – Measurement in inches (mm).

WHEEL ALIGNMENT SPECIFICATIONS (MONTERO)

Application	Preferred	Range
Camber [1]		
Front	0.67	0.17 To 1.17
Rear	0	
Caster [1]	3	2 To 4
Toe-In [2]		
Front	0.14 (3.5)	0 To 0.28 (0 To 7)
Rear	0	
Toe-Out On Turns [1]		
Inner	21.93	
Outer	20	

[1] – Measurement in degrees.
[2] – Measurement in inches (mm).

WHEEL ALIGNMENT SPECIFICATIONS (PICKUP)

Application	Preferred	Range
2WD		
Camber (Front) [1]	0.67	0.17 To 1.17
Caster [1]	2.5	1.5 To 3.5
Toe-In [2]		
Front	0.22 (5.5)	0.08 To 0.35 (2 To 9)
Rear	0	
4WD		
Camber (Front) [1]	1	0.5 To 1.5
Caster [1]	2	1 To 3
Toe-In [2]		
Front	0.22 (5.5)	0.08 To 0.35 (2 To 9)
Rear	0	

[1] – Measurement in degrees.
[2] – Measurement in inches (mm).

WHEEL ALIGNMENT SPECIFICATIONS (PRECIS)

Application	Preferred	Range
Camber [1]		
Front	0	-0.5 To 0.5
Rear	-0.67	
Caster [1]		
With P/S	1.67	1.17 To 2.17
Without P/S	1.03	0.53 To 1.53
Toe-In [2]		
Front	0.04 (1)	-0.08 To 0.16 (-2 To 4)
Rear	0.06 (1.5)	-012 To 0.23 (3 To 6)
Toe-Out On Turns [1]		
Inner	37.4	
Outer	31.52	

[1] – Measurement in degrees.
[2] – Measurement in inches (mm).

WHEEL ALIGNMENT SPECIFICATIONS (STEALTH & 3000GT)

Application	Preferred	Range
Camber [1]		
Front	0	-0.5 To 0.5
Rear (FWD)	0	-0.5 To 0.5
Rear (AWD)	-0.17	-0.67 To 0.33
Caster [1]	3.92	3.42 To 4.42
Toe-In [2]		
Front	0 (0)	-0.12 To 0.12 (-3 To 3)
Rear	0.01 (0.5)	-0.08 To 0.1 (-2 To 3)
Toe-Out On Turns [1]		
Inner	33.75	
Outer	28.35	

[1] – Measurement in degrees.
[2] – Measurement in inches (mm).

1994 SUSPENSION
Front – FWD

Chrysler Corp: Colt, Colt Vista, Stealth, Summit, Summit Wagon
Mitsubishi: Diamante, Eclipse, Expo, Galant, Mirage, Precis, 3000GT

DESCRIPTION

Front suspension consists of a MacPherson hydraulic strut assembly, steering knuckle, control arm, ball joint and stabilizer bar. *See Fig. 1 and 2.*

On Diamante, Stealth and 3000GT models equipped with Electronically Controlled Suspension (ECS), hydraulic struts are electronically controlled. For testing and diagnosis information on electronically controlled suspension, see appropriate ELECTRONIC article in SUSPENSION.

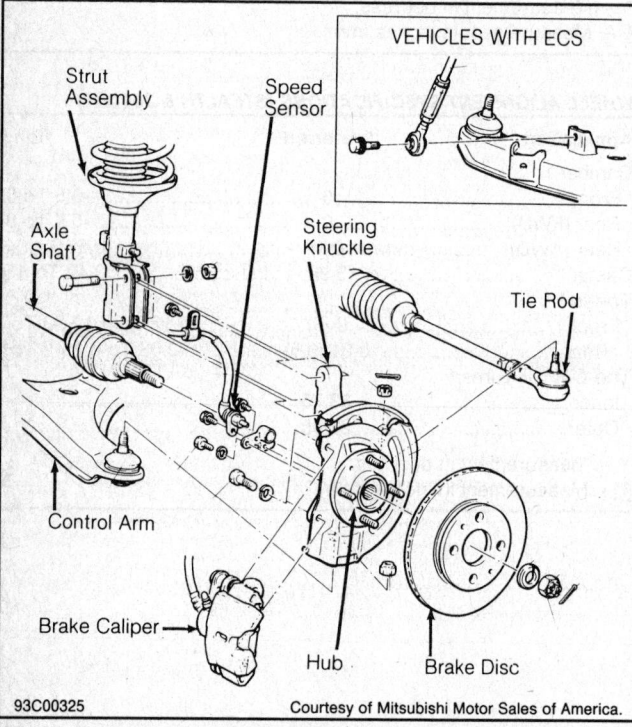

93C00325   Courtesy of Mitsubishi Motor Sales of America.

Fig. 1: Exploded View Of Front Suspension (Except Galant)

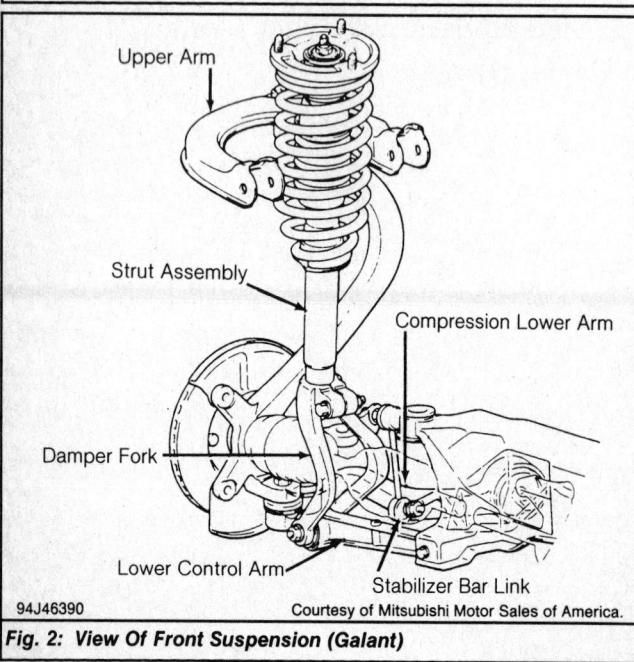

94J46390   Courtesy of Mitsubishi Motor Sales of America.

Fig. 2: View Of Front Suspension (Galant)

ADJUSTMENTS & INSPECTION

WHEEL ALIGNMENT
SPECIFICATIONS & PROCEDURES

NOTE: See SPECIFICATIONS & PROCEDURES article in WHEEL ALIGNMENT.

WHEEL BEARING

Axial Play Inspection – 1) Wheel bearings are not adjustable. To inspect bearings, raise and support vehicle. Remove wheel assembly. Remove brake caliper. Remove brake disc from hub (if necessary).
2) Attach dial indicator at right angle to hub. Move hub in and out, and measure axial play. Check bearings or hub assembly if movement exceeds specification. See WHEEL BEARING AXIAL PLAY SPECIFICATIONS table.

WHEEL BEARING AXIAL PLAY SPECIFICATIONS

Application	In. (mm)
Colt Vista, Diamante, Expo, Galant, Stealth, Summit Wagon & 3000GT	.002 (.05)
Precis	.004 (.10)
All Others	.008 (.20)

BALL JOINT CHECKING

Upper Control Arm Ball Joint – 1) Raise and support vehicle. Remove wheel. Loosen ball joint nut. Using Steering Linkage Puller (MB991113-01), separate ball joint from steering knuckle. Install nut on ball joint stud. Move stud from side-to-side. Replace ball joint if side play is present.
2) Using INCH-lb. torque wrench, rotate ball joint and note starting torque. Replace ball joint if roughness is felt when rotating ball joint or if starting torque exceeds specification. See BALL JOINT STARTING TORQUE SPECIFICATIONS table.

Lower Control Arm Ball Joint, Compression Arm Ball Joint & Stabilizer Link Ball Joint – 1) Raise and support vehicle. Remove wheel. Disconnect stabilizer bar from control arm (if needed). Loosen ball joint nut. Using Steering Linkage Puller (MB991113-01), separate ball joint from steering knuckle. Install nut on ball joint stud. Move stud from side-to-side. Replace ball joint if side play is present.
2) Using INCH-lb. torque wrench, rotate ball joint and note starting torque. Replace ball joint if roughness is felt when rotating ball joint or if starting torque exceeds specification. See BALL JOINT STARTING TORQUE SPECIFICATIONS table.

BALL JOINT STARTING TORQUE SPECIFICATIONS

Application	INCH Lbs. (N.m)
Control Arm Ball Joint	
Colt, Mirage & Summit	9-56 (1.0-6.5)
Colt Vista, Expo & Summit Wagon	17-78 (2-9)
Diamante	87-190 (10-21.5)
Eclipse	26-87 (3-10)
Galant	
Compression Ball Joint	4-22 (.5-2.5)
Lower Ball Joint	9-30 (1.0-3.5)
Upper Ball Joint	4-13 (.5-1.5)
Precis	26-52 (3-5.9)
Stealth & 3000GT	86-191 (9.7-21.6)
Stabilizer Link Ball Joint	
Galant	4-13 (.5-1.5)
All Others	15-28 (1.7-3.2)

REMOVAL & INSTALLATION

COMPRESSION ARM & BALL JOINT

Removal – Raise and support vehicle. Remove wheel(s). Loosen ball joint nut. Using Steering Linkage Puller (MB991113-01), separate ball joint from steering knuckle. Remove compression arm bushing mounting bolts. Remove control arm.

Inspection – 1) Check ball joint dust cover for damage. Check control arm for bending and cracks. Check ball joints. See BALL JOINT CHECKING under ADJUSTMENTS & INSPECTION. Replace ball joint if defective.

2) Inspect compression arm bushing for cracks and deterioration. Replace arm if bushing if damaged. If ball joint dust cover replacement is necessary, remove dust cover from ball joint. Apply grease to lip and inside of dust cover. Install dust cover using Dust Cover Installer (MB990800). See DUST COVER INSTALLER APPLICATION table. Ensure dust cover is fully seated.

LOWER CONTROL ARM & BALL JOINT

Removal – 1) Raise and support vehicle. Remove wheel(s). Disconnect stabilizer bar from control arm (if necessary). Loosen ball joint nut. Using Steering Linkage Puller (MB991113-01), separate ball joint from steering knuckle.

2) Remove control arm bushing or clamp (if equipped). Loosen control arm mounting nuts. On Galant, unbolt damper fork from lower control arm. On all models, remove control arm. On Precis, remove ball joint from control arm.

Inspection – 1) Check ball joint dust cover for damage. Check control arm for bending and cracks. Check ball joints. See BALL JOINT CHECKING under ADJUSTMENTS & INSPECTION. Replace ball joint if defective.

2) Inspect control arm bushings for cracks and deterioration. Replace bushings if damaged. See LOWER CONTROL ARM BUSHINGS under REMOVAL & INSTALLATION.

3) If ball joint dust cover replacement is necessary, remove dust cover from ball joint. Apply grease to lip and inside of dust cover. Install dust cover using dust cover installer. See DUST COVER INSTALLER APPLICATION table. Ensure dust cover is fully seated.

DUST COVER INSTALLER APPLICATION

Application	Dust Cover Installer
Colt, Colt Vista, Expo, Summit & Summit Wagon	MB990800
Diamante, Stealth & 3000GT	MB990799-01
Eclipse, Galant & Mirage	MB990800-01
Precis	09545-21100

Installation – 1) Install control arm to crossmember. Ensure control arm is not twisted. Install control arm mounting bolt, bushings and clamp (if equipped). Connect stabilizer bar to control arm (as necessary).

2) To complete installation, reverse removal procedure. Install new self-locking nuts (if used). Lower vehicle and tighten all bolts to specification. See TORQUE SPECIFICATIONS.

LOWER CONTROL ARM BUSHINGS

Removal (Colt, Colt Vista, Expo, Summit & Summit Wagon) – Remove control arm. Apply soapy water solution between control arm bushing and shaft. Pry upward on bushing to remove.

Installation – Apply soapy water to control arm shaft and replacement bushing. Install bushing on control arm shaft, with locator pin located within 72-78 degrees of control arm center. See Fig. 3. Using press and wood block, press bushing on control arm until clearance between bushing and control arm is .04-.12" (1-3 mm).

CAUTION: Ensure press load does not exceed 1100 lbs. (490 kg) when installing control arm bushing.

Removal & Installation (Diamante, Eclipse, Galant, Mirage, Precis, Stealth & 3000GT) – Information is not available from manufacturer.

STABILIZER BAR

Removal (Colt, Mirage & Summit) – 1) Raise and support vehicle. Disconnect tie rod end from steering knuckle. Disconnect rear crossmember bolts. Remove rear roll stopper mounting bolts.

2) Pull roll stopper forward. Remove stabilizer link mounting nuts. Remove stabilizer link, cups and bushings (if equipped).

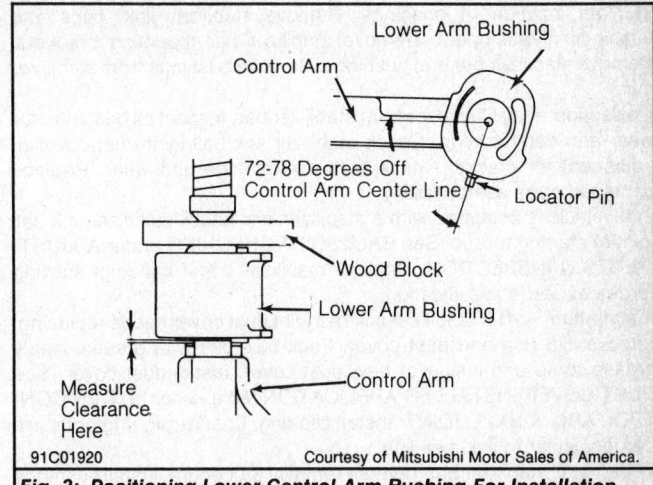

Fig. 3: Positioning Lower Control Arm Bushing For Installation

3) Note location of brackets and bushings. Remove stabilizer bar mounting bolts and brackets. Remove stabilizer bar and bushings. Remove bushings from stabilizer bar.

Inspection – 1) Check for bent or damaged stabilizer bar. Inspect all bushings for wear and deterioration. Check stabilizer link ball joint dust cover for cracks. Replace damaged parts as necessary.

2) Check stabilizer link ball joint(s) starting torque. See BALL JOINT CHECKING under ADJUSTMENTS & INSPECTION. Replace stabilizer link if ball joint starting torque exceeds specification.

NOTE: Replace self-locking nuts (if used). Tighten stabilizer bar bolts to specification with vehicle at normal riding height. See TORQUE SPECIFICATIONS.

Installation – 1) If stabilizer link ball joint dust cover needs replacing, remove clip ring and dust cover. Pack ball joint with grease. Apply grease to lip and inside of new dust cover. Install dust cover. See DUST COVER INSTALLER APPLICATION table under LOWER CONTROL ARM & BALL JOINT. Install clip ring. Ensure clip ring ends are perpendicular to link axis line.

2) To complete installation, reverse removal procedure. Stabilizer bar brackets are marked "R" for right and "L" for left. Install bushings securely in brackets.

3) Position left stabilizer bushing so bushing is on marked area of stabilizer bar and approximately 0.2" (5.1 mm) from inside edge of marked area. See Fig. 5.

4) Tighten stabilizer link nuts until distance from end of bolt to nut is .87" (22 mm). See Fig. 4. Lower vehicle and tighten remaining stabilizer bar fasteners to specification. See TORQUE SPECIFICATIONS.

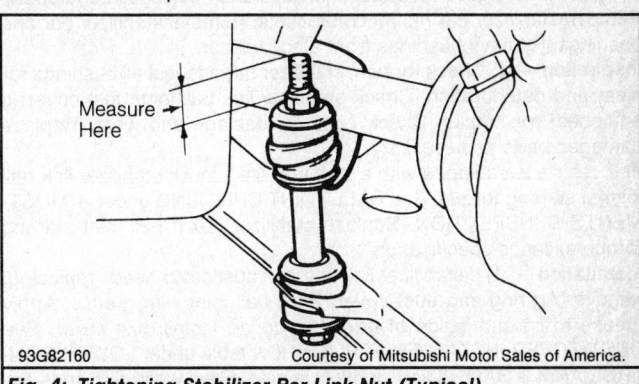

Fig. 4: Tightening Stabilizer Bar Link Nut (Typical)

Removal (Colt Vista, Expo & Summit Wagon) – 1) Raise and support vehicle. On FWD models, remove tie rod end. On AWD models, remove front exhaust pipe. On all models, disconnect stabilizer link.

2) Note location of bushings. Remove stabilizer link, cups and bushings (if equipped). Remove stabilizer bar mounting brackets. Remove stabilizer bar and bushings. Remove bushings from stabilizer bar.

Inspection – 1) Check for bent stabilizer bar. Inspect all bushings for wear and deterioration. Check stabilizer link ball joint dust cover (if equipped) for cracks. Check bolts for damage and wear. Replace damaged parts as necessary.

2) If vehicle is equipped with a stabilizer link, check stabilizer link ball joint(s) starting torque. See BALL JOINT CHECKING under ADJUST-MENTS & INSPECTION. Replace stabilizer link if ball joint starting torque exceeds specification.

Installation – 1) If stabilizer link ball joint dust cover needs replacing, remove clip ring and dust cover. Pack ball joint with grease. Apply grease to lip and inside of new dust cover. Install dust cover. See DUST COVER INSTALLER APPLICATION table under LOWER CONTROL ARM & BALL JOINT. Install clip ring. Ensure clip ring ends are perpendicular to link axis line.

2) To install stabilizer bar, reverse removal procedure. Install bushings securely in brackets. On Expo FWD, position stabilizer bushing so bushing is on marked area of stabilizer bar and .27" (7 mm) from inside edge of marked area. See Fig. 4.

3) Tighten stabilizer bar-to-lower control arm mounting nuts until distance from end of bolt to nut is .3-.4" (8-10 mm). On all models, tighten all stabilizer bar fasteners to specification. See TORQUE SPECIFICATIONS.

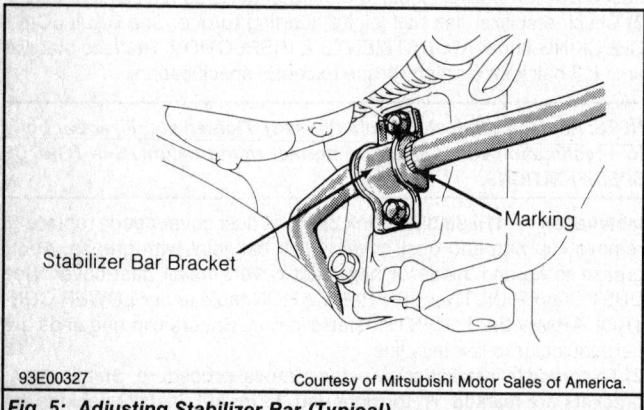

Stabilizer Bar Bracket

Marking

93E00327   Courtesy of Mitsubishi Motor Sales of America.

Fig. 5: Adjusting Stabilizer Bar (Typical)

Removal (Diamante & Eclipse) – 1) Raise and support vehicle. On FWD models, remove front exhaust pipe and disconnect centermember(s). On AWD models, remove left crossmember, transfer case and bracket.

2) On all models, remove stabilizer link mounting nuts. Note location of bushings. Remove stabilizer link, cups and bushings (if equipped). Remove stabilizer bar mounting brackets. Remove stabilizer bar and bushings. Remove bushings from stabilizer bar.

Inspection – 1) Check for bent stabilizer bar. Inspect all bushings for wear and deterioration. Check stabilizer link ball joint dust cover (if equipped) for cracks. Check bolts for damage and wear. Replace damaged parts as necessary.

2) If vehicle is equipped with a stabilizer link, check stabilizer link ball joint(s) starting torque. See BALL JOINT CHECKING under ADJUST-MENTS & INSPECTION. Replace stabilizer link if ball joint starting torque exceeds specification.

Installation – 1) If stabilizer link ball joint dust cover needs replacing, remove clip ring and dust cover. Pack ball joint with grease. Apply grease to lip and inside of new dust cover. Install dust cover. See DUST COVER INSTALLER APPLICATION table under LOWER CONTROL ARM & BALL JOINT. Install clip ring. Ensure clip ring ends are perpendicular to link axis line.

2) To install stabilizer bar, reverse removal procedure. Install bushings securely in brackets. On Eclipse and Galant, position stabilizer brackets so they are inside marked area of stabilizer bar.

3) On Eclipse and Galant models, tighten stabilizer bar link nuts until the distance from end of bolt to nut is .63-.70" (16.0-17.8 mm). On all models, tighten all stabilizer bar fasteners with vehicle at normal riding height. See TORQUE SPECIFICATIONS.

Removal & Installation (Galant) – Raise and support vehicle. Remove front wheels. Disconnect stabilizer bar from link. Unbolt frame mount bracket from crossmember. Remove stabilizer bar. To install, reverse removal procedure. Tighten bolts to specification. See TORQUE SPECIFICATIONS.

Inspection – Check for bent or damaged stabilizer bar. Check all rubber parts for cracks and wear. Check bolts for damage and wear. Replace damaged parts as necessary.

Removal (Precis) – 1) Raise and support vehicle. Disconnect tie rod end from steering knuckle. Remove rear roll stopper assembly mounting bolts. Pull rear roll bracket assembly forward. DO NOT disconnect centermember.

2) Remove stabilizer links. Using gearbox access opening, remove stabilizer bar bracket nuts. Remove stabilizer bar brackets. Remove stabilizer bar. Separate brackets, and remove bushings from bar.

Inspection – Check for bent or damaged stabilizer bar. Check all rubber parts for cracks and wear. Check bolts for damage and wear. Replace damaged parts as necessary.

Installation – To install, reverse removal procedure. Install brackets in original positions. Install bushings securely in brackets. Tighten stabilizer bar-to-lower control arm mounting nuts until distance from end of bolt to nut is .95-1.0" (24-26 mm). See Fig. 3. Tighten all bolts and nuts to specification. See TORQUE SPECIFICATIONS.

Removal (Stealth & 3000GT) – 1) Raise and support vehicle. Remove transfer case and bracket. Remove stabilizer links.

2) Note location of brackets and bushings. Remove stabilizer bar mounting brackets. Remove stabilizer bar and bushings.

Inspection – 1) Check for bent or damaged stabilizer bar. Inspect all bushings for wear and deterioration. Check stabilizer link ball joint dust cover for cracks. Replace damaged parts as necessary.

2) Check stabilizer link ball joint(s) starting torque. See BALL JOINT CHECKING under ADJUSTMENTS & INSPECTION. Replace stabilizer link if ball joint starting torque exceeds specification.

Installation – 1) If stabilizer link ball joint dust cover needs replacing, remove clip ring and dust cover. Pack ball joint with grease. Apply grease to lip and inside of new dust cover. Install dust cover. See DUST COVER INSTALLER APPLICATION table under LOWER CONTROL ARM & BALL JOINT. Install clip ring. Ensure clip ring ends are perpendicular to link axis line.

2) To install stabilizer bar, reverse removal procedure. Position stabilizer brackets so they are inside marked area of stabilizer bar. See Fig. 4. Tighten all fasteners to specification. See TORQUE SPECIFICATIONS.

STEERING KNUCKLE

Removal – 1) Remove cotter pin, and loosen axle shaft nut. Raise and support vehicle. Remove wheel assembly. Remove axle shaft nut. Remove brake caliper, and wire aside. Do not allow caliper to hang from brake hose.

2) Remove brake disc from hub (if possible). Remove front speed sensor (if equipped). Disconnect stabilizer bar from control arm (as necessary). Support control arm. Disconnect damper fork (if equipped). Disconnect lower ball joint and tie rod end from steering knuckle. Disconnect compression arm ball joint (if equipped). Install puller on hub.

3) Tighten puller, and separate axle shaft from hub. On Galant models, unbolt and separate upper ball joint from knuckle. On all other models, separate steering knuckle from strut. Remove knuckle/hub assembly from vehicle. Separate hub from steering knuckle (if required). See WHEEL BEARINGS under REMOVAL & INSTALLATION.

Installation – To install, reverse removal procedure. Install washer on axle shaft, with raised area toward axle shaft nut. Tighten bolts to specification. See TORQUE SPECIFICATIONS. Tighten axle shaft nut to specification with vehicle on ground.

STRUT ASSEMBLY

Removal (Galant) – 1) Raise and support vehicle. Remove front wheels. Support lower control arms. Remove strut assembly-to-damper fork pinch bolt.

2) Place punch mark on a upper strut mounting stud and on inner fender adjacent to stud for reassembly reference. Remove upper strut mounting nuts. Remove strut assembly.

Installation – To install, reverse removal procedure. Ensure strut assembly and damper fork mating surfaces are clean. Tighten fasteners to specification. See TORQUE SPECIFICATIONS.

Removal (Except Galant) – 1) Raise and support vehicle. Remove front wheels. Separate brake hose bracket and speed sensor bracket (if equipped) from strut. Support lower control arms. Remove strut assembly-to-steering knuckle bolts.

2) On Diamante, Stealth and 3000GT with ECS, remove ECS connector and cap from top of strut. On all models, place punch mark on a upper strut mounting stud and on inner fender adjacent to stud for reassembly reference. Remove upper strut mounting nuts. Remove strut assembly carefully to avoid damaging actuator on struts (if equipped).

Installation – To install, reverse removal procedure. Ensure strut assembly and steering knuckle mating surfaces are clean. Tighten fasteners to specification. See TORQUE SPECIFICATIONS.

WHEEL BEARINGS

CAUTION: DO NOT use hammer to remove hub. Bearings may be damaged during removal.

Removal (Precis) – 1) Remove steering knuckle and hub assembly. See STEERING KNUCKLE under REMOVAL & INSTALLATION. Install Hub Remover/Installer (09517-21500) in hub and steering knuckle. See Fig. 6.

2) Install Knuckle Bridge (MB991056) on steering knuckle. Separate hub from steering knuckle. See Fig. 6. Remove brake disc from hub. Using bearing puller, remove bearing inner race from hub. See Fig. 7.

3) Remove seal from steering knuckle. Using drift and hammer, remove bearing races from steering knuckle. If either race needs replacing, replace both races as a set.

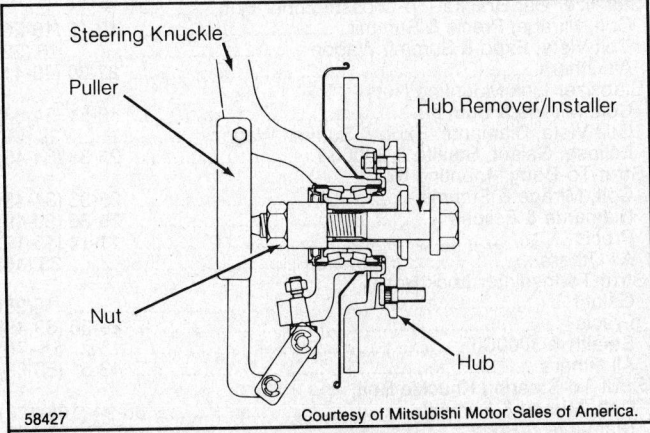

Fig. 6: Removing Hub From Steering Knuckle

Installation – 1) Use handle and appropriate race installer and base. Install bearing races. Ensure races are fully seated. Install brake disc on hub. Tighten bolts to specification. See TORQUE SPECIFICATIONS. Pack wheel bearings with grease. Install outer bearing onto knuckle.

2) Apply grease to seal lip and hub contact surface. Install outer seal in steering knuckle using seal installer. Install outer seal until seal is even with steering knuckle end surface.

3) Install inner bearing in steering knuckle. Using Hub Remover/Installer (09517-21500), mount hub on steering knuckle. See Fig. 8. Tighten axle shaft nut to 144-188 ft. lbs. (195-255 N.m).

4) Rotate hub to seat bearing. Using an INCH-lb. torque wrench, measure hub starting torque. Starting torque should be 11 INCH lbs.

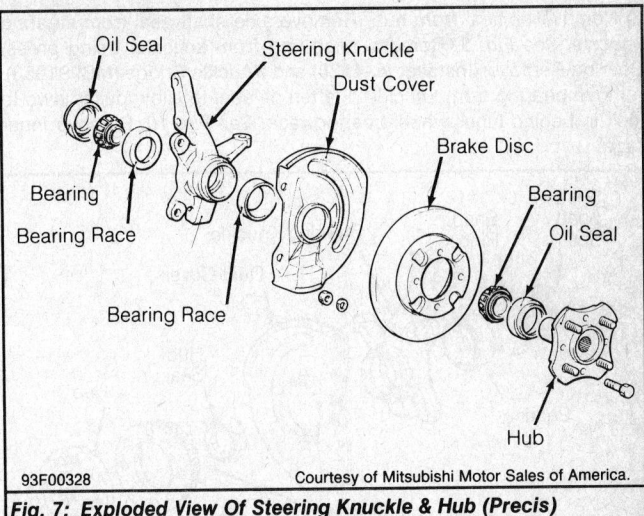

Fig. 7: Exploded View Of Steering Knuckle & Hub (Precis)

(1.2 N.m) or less. See Fig. 8. Check axial play. See WHEEL BEARING AXIAL PLAY SPECIFICATIONS table under ADJUSTMENTS & INSPECTION.

5) If axial play exceeds specification, check assembly procedure. Install inner seal until seal contacts bearing outer race. Coat seal lip surface with grease. Reverse removal procedure to install remaining components.

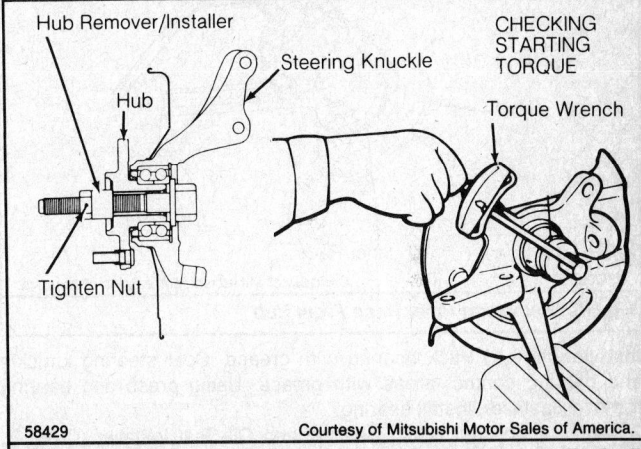

Fig. 8: Installing Hub & Checking Bearing Starting Torque (Typical)

Removal (Galant, Stealth & 3000GT AWD) – Raise and support vehicle. Remove wheel assembly. Remove axle shaft nut cotter pin. Apply brakes and remove axle shaft nut and washer. Remove brake caliper and support with wire. Remove brake disc. Unbolt and remove hub/bearing assembly.

Inspection – Check hub for cracks and spline for wear. Rotate hub and check for binding or rough rotation. Install Remover/Installer (MB990998) in hub/bearing assembly. Tighten nut to 145-188 ft. lbs. (200-260 N.m). Using an INCH-lb. torque wrench, measure hub/bearing starting torque. See Fig. 8. Starting torque should be 16 INCH lbs. (1.8 N.m). Replace hub/bearing assembly if starting torque is not within specification.

Installation – To install, reverse disassembly procedure. Tighten axle shaft nut to 166 ft. lbs. (230 N.m) with brakes applied. Install new cotter pin.

Removal (Except Galant, Precis, Stealth & 3000GT AWD) – 1) Remove steering knuckle. See STEERING KNUCKLE under REMOVAL & INSTALLATION. Secure steering knuckle in vise. Using Hub Remover/Installer (MB990998) and Puller (MB991056), separate hub from knuckle. See Fig. 6.

1994 SUSPENSION
Front – FWD (Cont.)

2) Remove oil seal from hub. Remove axle shaft seal from steering knuckle. *See Fig. 9.* Remove snap ring from knuckle. Using press, Bearing Remover/Installer (C-4628) and Knuckle Bridge (MB991056), remove bearing from knuckle. Flatten oil seal to allow puller jaws to lock in behind inner wheel bearing race. *See Fig. 10.* Remove inner race.

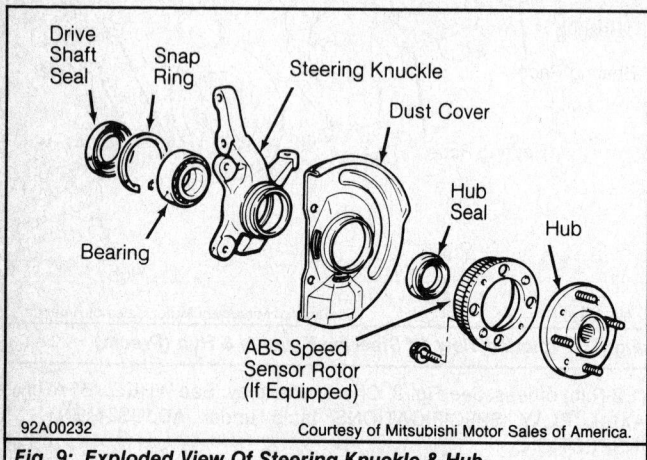

92A00232   Courtesy of Mitsubishi Motor Sales of America.

Fig. 9: Exploded View Of Steering Knuckle & Hub (Except Precis, Stealth & 3000GT AWD)

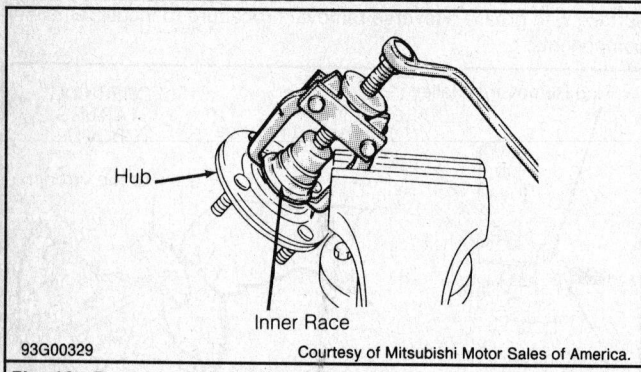

93G00329   Courtesy of Mitsubishi Motor Sales of America.

Fig. 10: Removing Inner Race From Hub

Installation – 1) Pack bearing with grease. Coat steering knuckle and bearing contact areas with grease. Using press and bearing remover/installer, install bearing.

2) Install snap ring. Using Bearing and Oil Seal Installer (C-3893), install hub seal until seal is even with steering knuckle surface. Apply grease to hub seal lip. Place hub on steering knuckle.

3) Using Hub Remover/Installer (MB990998), install hub on steering knuckle. Tighten nut to 144-188 ft. lbs. (195-255 N.m). Rotate hub to seat bearing. Using an INCH-lb. torque wrench, measure bearing starting torque. *See Fig. 8.*

4) Starting torque should be 16 INCH lbs. (1.8 N.m) or less. Rotation roughness must not be felt. Install steering knuckle in vise. Install dial indicator, with stem resting against hub surface. Check hub axial play.

5) Hub axial play should not exceed specification. See WHEEL BEARING AXIAL PLAY SPECIFICATIONS table under ADJUSTMENTS & INSPECTION. If starting torque or hub axial play are not to specifications, check component installation. Remove hub remover/installer.

6) Apply grease to bearing and inside of steering knuckle. Using Seal Installer (C-3972-A) and Handle (C-4171), install axle shaft seal until seal contacts snap ring. To complete installation, reverse removal procedure.

TORQUE SPECIFICATIONS
TORQUE SPECIFICATIONS

Application	Ft. Lbs. (N.m)
Axle Shaft Nut	144-188 (195-255)
Ball Joint-To-Control Arm Bolt (Precis)	69-87 (94-118)
Brake Disc-To-Hub Nut	36-43 (49-58)
Caliper Assembly-To-Knuckle Bolts	
Colt, Colt Vista, Expo, Galant,	
Mirage, Summit & Summit Wagon	65 (88)
Precis	43-52 (58-71)
All Others	58-72 (79-98)
Centermember Rear Mounting Bolt Or Nut	
Colt, Mirage, Precis & Summit	43-58 (58-79)
Eclipse	58-72 (79-98)
Compression Arm Ball Joint Nut	43-51 (58-70)
Compression Arm Mounting Bolt	60 (81)
Damper Fork Pinch Bolt	75 (102)
Damper Fork-To-Lower Control Arm Bolt	64 (87)
Exhaust Pipe-To-Manifold Bolts (Eclipse)	
Non-Turbo	22-29 (30-39)
Turbo	29-43 (39-58)
Hub/Bearing-To-Knuckle	
Galant	65 (88)
All Others	76 (105)
Lower Ball Joint-To-Knuckle Nut	
Colt Vista, Expo & Summit Wagon	49 (66)
All Others	43-52 (58-71)
Lower Control Arm Bushing Bracket-To-Body Bolt	
Colt, Mirage, Precis & Summit	43-58 (58-79)
Colt Vista, Diamante,	
Expo & Summit Wagon	51 (70)
Eclipse, Stealth & 3000GT	
Short Bolt [1]	58-72 (79-98)
Long (Clamp Mounting) Bolt	72-87 (98-118)
Lower Control Arm Bushing Bracket-To-Body	
Self-Locking Nut	
Eclipse, Galant, Stealth & 3000GT	25-34 (34-46)
Lower Control Arm-To-Crossmember Bolt [1]	
Diamante, Eclipse & Galant	72-87 (98-118)
All Others	78 (106)
Lug Nut	
Eclipse, Stealth & 3000GT	87-101 (118-137)
All Others	65-80 (88-108)
Roll Stopper Mounting Bolts	
Front	22-29 (30-39)
Rear	33-43 (45-58)
Stabilizer Bar Bracket-To-Crossmember Bolt	
Colt, Mirage, Precis & Summit	12-19 (16-26)
Colt Vista, Expo & Summit Wagon	16 (22)
All Others	22-30 (30-41)
Stabilizer Link Mounting Nuts	
Colt, Mirage & Summit	40-51 (54-68)
Colt Vista, Diamante, Expo & Summit Wagon	29 (39)
Eclipse, Galant, Stealth & 3000GT	25-33 (34-45)
Strut-To-Body Mounting Nut	
Colt, Mirage & Summit	25-33 (34-45)
Diamante & Eclipse	29-36 (39-49)
Precis	11-14 (15-19)
All Others	33 (45)
Strut-To-Insulator Lock Nut	
Galant	18 (25)
Precis	29-36 (39-49)
Stealth & 3000GT	56 (78)
All Others	43-51 (58-69)
Strut-To-Steering Knuckle Bolt	
Colt, Mirage & Summit	80-94 (108-127)
Diamante & Precis	65-76 (88-103)
Eclipse	80-101 (108-137)
Stealth & 3000GT	65-76 (88-103)
All Others	78 (108)
Tie Rod-To-Knuckle Nut	
Colt, Mirage, Precis & Summit	11-25 (15-34)
Galant	17-25 (23-34)
All Others	21 (29)
Upper Ball Joint Nut	20 (27)
Upper Control Arm Shaft-To-Body Mounting Nut	62 (84)
Upper Control Arm Pivot Bolt	41 (57)

[1] – Fastener should be temporarily tightened, and then fully tightened when installation is completed and vehicle is unladen.

DESCRIPTION

Independent front suspension combines double wishbone and coil spring construction. The components used in this system are upper control arm, lower control arm, coil spring, shock absorber, steering knuckle, strut rod and stabilizer bar. *See Fig. 1.*

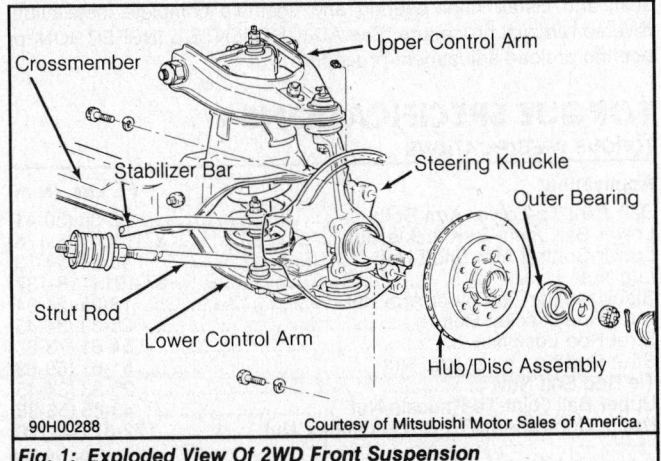

90H00288   Courtesy of Mitsubishi Motor Sales of America.

Fig. 1: Exploded View Of 2WD Front Suspension

ADJUSTMENTS & INSPECTION

BALL JOINT CHECKING

Lower Ball Joint – Secure ball joint. Measure vertical movement of ball joint. Replace ball joint if vertical movement is greater than .020" (.5 mm).
Upper Ball Joint – Secure ball joint. Using an INCH-lb. torque wrench, check upper ball joint starting torque. Starting torque should be 7-30 INCH lbs. (0.8-3.5 N.m). Replace ball joint if starting torque is not within specification. Replace snap ring if loose on dust cover.

WHEEL ALIGNMENT
SPECIFICATIONS & PROCEDURES

NOTE: See SPECIFICATIONS & PROCEDURES article in WHEEL ALIGNMENT.

WHEEL BEARING

Bearing Adjustment – Remove cotter pin. While turning hub, tighten castle nut to 22 ft. lbs. (29 N.m) to seat bearings. Rotate nut counterclockwise (loosen) and retighten to 72 INCH lbs. (8 N.m). Install cotter pin. Loosen castle nut if slots do no align with hole in spindle. DO NOT loosen nut more than 30 degrees to accommodate cotter pin. Repeat procedure if hole and slot cannot be aligned within 30 degrees. Replace bearing if worn.

REMOVAL & INSTALLATION

LOWER CONTROL ARM, BALL JOINT & COIL SPRING

Removal – 1) Raise and support vehicle. Remove wheel assembly. Loosen strut rod adjusting nut at frame. Disconnect stabilizer bar and strut rod from control arm. Remove shock absorber.
2) Compress coil spring with Spring Compressor (MB990792-01). Remove lower ball joint-to-steering knuckle cotter pin and castle nut. Separate lower ball joint from knuckle. Remove coil spring. Remove lower control arm pivot shaft. Remove lower control arm. Remove ball joint-to-control arm nuts. Remove ball joint from control arm.
Inspection – Inspect control arm and coil spring for cracks or damage. Check ball joint. See BALL JOINT CHECKING under ADJUSTMENTS & INSPECTION.
Installation – To install, reverse removal procedure. Tighten lower control arm shaft nut with vehicle on ground. See TORQUE SPECIFICATIONS.

UPPER CONTROL ARM

Removal – 1) Remove wheel assembly. Remove shock absorber. Compress coil spring with Spring Compressor (MB990792-01). Remove upper ball joint-to-steering knuckle castle nut.
2) Separate knuckle from ball joint using a ball joint separator fork. Remove upper control arm shaft-to-crossmember bolts. Note position of alignment shims for installation. Remove control arm and ball joint. Remove dust cover retaining ring and dust cover. Check ball joint. See BALL JOINT CHECKING under ADJUSTMENTS & INSPECTION.
Installation – To install components, reverse removal procedure. Ensure alignment shims are installed in original position. Tighten all fasteners to specification. See TORQUE SPECIFICATIONS. Check wheel alignment. See SPECIFICATIONS & PROCEDURES article in WHEEL ALIGNMENT.

STABILIZER BAR

Removal & Installation – Remove skid plate (if equipped). Remove bump stopper. Remove stabilizer link nuts and bushing. Disconnect stabilizer bar bracket from frame. Remove stabilizer bar. To install, reverse removal procedure. Ensure stabilizer link bolt protrudes .87-.94" (22-24 mm) from bottom of locking nut. *See Fig. 2.*

STRUT ROD

Removal & Installation – Remove strut rod and bump stopper from lower control arm. Remove strut rod lock nut and outer bushing from frame bracket. Remove strut rod and bracket from frame. Note position of strut rod bushings. *See Fig. 3.* To install, reverse removal procedure. Tighten bolts to specification. See TORQUE SPECIFICATIONS.

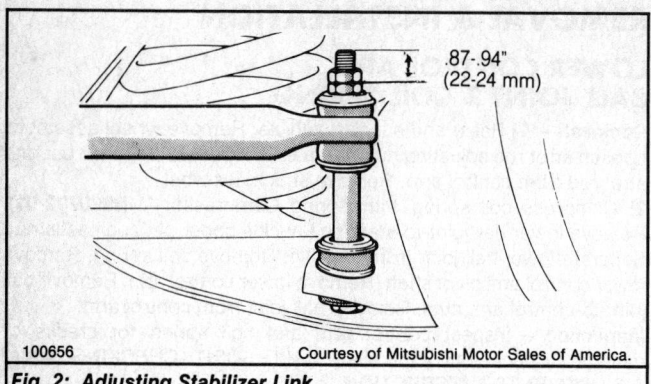

.87-.94"
(22-24 mm)

100656   Courtesy of Mitsubishi Motor Sales of America.

Fig. 2: Adjusting Stabilizer Link

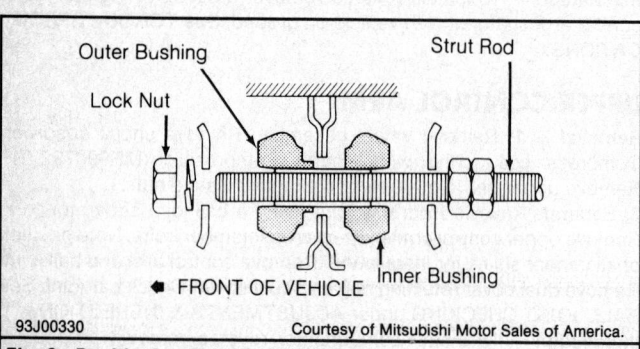

Outer Bushing   Strut Rod

Lock Nut

Inner Bushing

◀ FRONT OF VEHICLE

93J00330   Courtesy of Mitsubishi Motor Sales of America.

Fig. 3: Positioning Strut Rod Bushing

WHEEL BEARING

Removal – 1) Raise and support vehicle. Remove wheel. Remove caliper assembly and set aside. Remove dust cap, cotter pin, castle nut, washer and outer bearing.

2) Remove rotor and hub assembly from spindle. Remove oil seal from back side of hub. Remove inner bearing. Use brass drift to drive races outward from hub.

Installation – Clean and pack both bearings with grease. Using race driver, install inner and outer race in hub. Lightly grease lip of grease seal, and install inner bearing and seal. To complete installation, reverse removal procedure. See ADJUSTMENTS & INSPECTION for bearing preload adjustment procedure.

TORQUE SPECIFICATIONS
TORQUE SPECIFICATIONS

Application	Ft. Lbs. (N.m)
Ball Joint-To-Lower Arm Bolts	22-30 (30-41)
Lower Ball Joint-To-Knuckle Nut	87-130 (118-176)
Lower Control Arm Shaft Nut	[1] 40-54 (54-73)
Lug Nut	87-101 (118-137)
Stabilizer Bar-To-Lower Arm Nut	18-25 (24-34)
Strut Rod Bracket Bolt	25-33 (34-45)
Strut Rod Lock Nut	[1] 54-61 (73-83)
Strut Rod-To-Lower Arm Nut	51-61 (69-83)
Tie Rod End Nut	25-33 (34-45)
Upper Ball Joint-To-Knuckle Nut	43-65 (58-88)
Upper Control Arm-To-Crossmember Nut	72-87 (98-118)

	INCH Lbs. (N.m)
Shock Absorber-To-Crossmember Nut	108-156 (12-17)
Shock Absorber-To-Lower Control Arm Bolt	84-120 (9-14)

[1] – Tighten to specification with vehicle on ground and unladen.

DESCRIPTION

Independent front suspension used double wishbone construction with torsion bar. Components used with this system include upper control arm, lower control arm, shock absorber, stabilizer bar and steering knuckle. *See Fig. 1.*

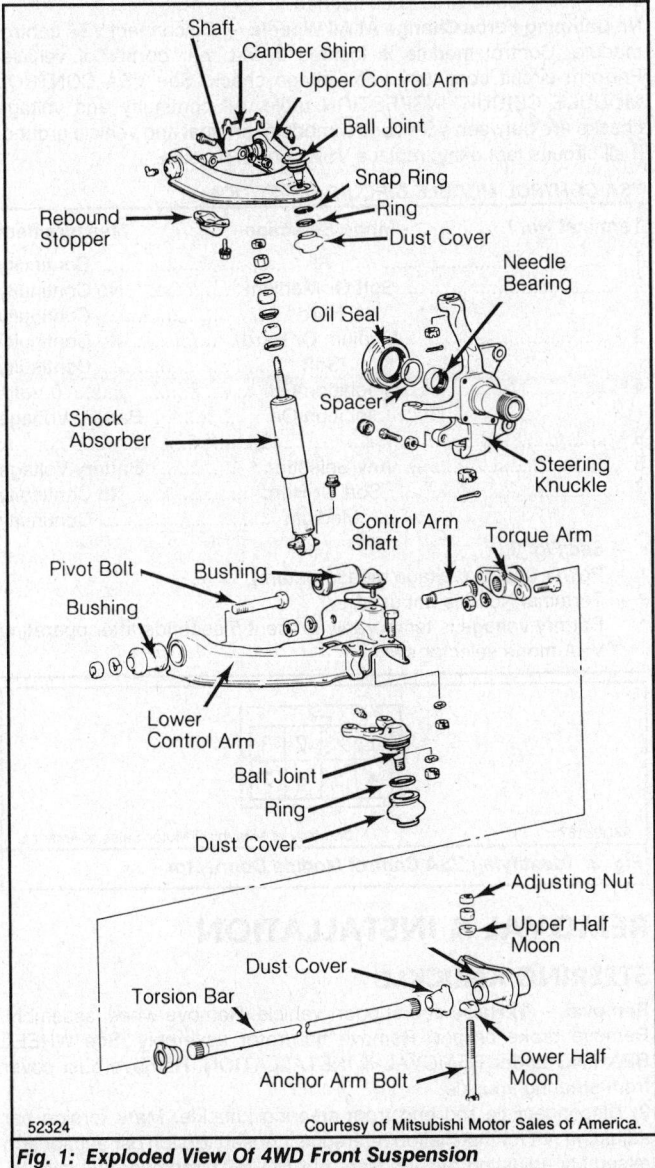

52324   Courtesy of Mitsubishi Motor Sales of America.

Fig. 1: Exploded View Of 4WD Front Suspension

ADJUSTMENTS & INSPECTION

WHEEL ALIGNMENT SPECIFICATIONS & PROCEDURES

NOTE: See SPECIFICATIONS & PROCEDURES article in WHEEL ALIGNMENT.

WHEEL BEARING

Preload – 1) Remove locking hub assembly. See LOCKING HUB under REMOVAL & INSTALLATION. Remove lock washer screws. Remove lock washer. *See Fig. 2.* Remove brake caliper.
2) Using Socket (MB990954-01) and torque wrench, rotate front hub while tightening lock nut to 95-145 ft. lbs. (130-200 N.m). Loosen nut. Retighten nut to 18 ft. lbs. (24 N.m).

3) Loosen nut 30-40 degrees. Install lock washer. If lock washer hole is not aligned with lock nut hole, lock nut may be rotated up to 20 degrees to obtain alignment. After setting preload, check hub turning resistance and axial play.
Hub Turning Resistance & Axial Play – 1) Using dial indicator, check front hub axial play. Axial play should be .002" (.05 mm) or less. Using INCH-lb. torque wrench or spring scale attached to wheel stud, measure hub turning resistance. Turning resistance should be 1-4 lbs. (0.45-1.80 kg) if measured using spring scale or 2.6-11.3 INCH lbs. (0.3-1.3 N.m) if measured using torque wrench.
2) Adjust wheel bearing so turning resistance and axial play are within specification. If turning resistance and axial play cannot be adjusted to specification, check wheel bearing condition and installation.
Drive Axle End Play – Install drive axle shim and snap ring. *See Fig. 2.* Measure clearance between shim and snap ring. If clearance is not .016-.028" (.40-.70 mm) on Montero or .008-.020" (20-50 mm) on Pickup, replace shim to bring clearance into specification.

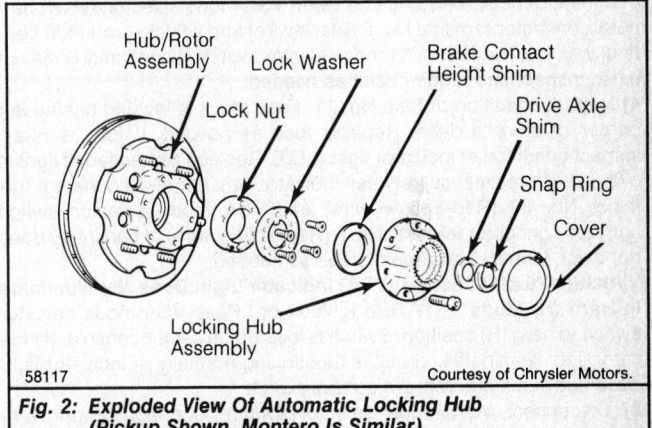

58117   Courtesy of Chrysler Motors.

Fig. 2: Exploded View Of Automatic Locking Hub (Pickup Shown, Montero Is Similar)

BALL JOINT CHECKING

Lower Ball Joint – Place ball joint in soft-jawed vise. Install dial indicator with stem resting on end of ball joint stud. Measure ball joint stud end play. Replace ball joint if end play exceeds .02" (.5 mm). For ball joint replacement, see LOWER BALL JOINT under REMOVAL & INSTALLATION.
Upper Ball Joint – 1) Disconnect ball joint from steering knuckle. Place nut on ball joint stud. Using INCH-lb. torque wrench, measure starting torque required to rotate ball joint stud.
2) Starting torque should be 7-30 INCH lbs. (0.8-3.4 N.m). Replace ball joint if starting torque is not within specification. For ball joint replacement, see UPPER BALL JOINT under REMOVAL & INSTALLATION.

TROUBLE SHOOTING

VARIABLE SHOCK ABSORBERS

Variable Shock Absorber (VSA) Indicator Light Does Not Illuminate In Soft (S) Mode – 1) Turn ignition on. Push VSA mode selector switch to soft (S) position. Switch is located on center console. If indicator light illuminates, circuit is functioning normally. If indicator light does not illuminate, remove control switch.
2) Disconnect VSA mode selector switch. Connect jumper wire between VSA mode selector switch harness connector terminal No. 4 (Red/Green wire) and vehicle ground. If indicator light illuminates, go to next step. If light does not illuminate, go to step **4)**.
3) Check continuity of VSA mode selector switch ground circuit. Using ohmmeter, check resistance between VSA mode selector switch harness connector terminal No. 2 (Black wire) and vehicle ground. If continuity exists, replace VSA mode selector switch. If continuity does not exist, inspect and repair circuit as needed.

4) Inspect condition of fuse No. 11. Fuse block is located behind left corner of driver's dash. Replace fuse as needed. If fuse is okay, inspect condition of indicator light (LED). Replace as needed. If light is okay, check resistance between indicator light harness connector terminal No. 84 (Red/Green wire) and VSA mode selector switch harness connector terminal No. 4 (Red/Green wire). If continuity does not exist, inspect and repair circuit as needed.

Variable Shock Absorber (VSA) Indicator Light Does Not Illuminate In Medium (M) Mode – 1) Turn ignition on. Push VSA mode selector switch to medium (M) position. Switch is located on center console. If indicator light illuminates, circuit is functioning normally. If indicator light does not illuminate, remove control switch.

2) Disconnect VSA mode selector switch. Connect jumper wire between VSA mode selector switch harness connector terminal No. 5 (Red/Yellow wire) and vehicle ground. If indicator light illuminates, go to next step. If light does not illuminate, go to step **4)**.

3) Check continuity of VSA mode selector switch ground circuit. Using ohmmeter, check resistance between VSA mode selector switch harness connector terminal No. 2 (Black wire) and vehicle ground. If continuity exists, replace VSA mode selector switch. If continuity does not exist, inspect and repair circuit as needed.

4) Inspect condition of fuse No. 11. Fuse block is located behind left corner of driver's dash. Replace fuse as needed. If fuse is okay, inspect condition of indicator light (LED). Replace as needed. If light is okay, check resistance between indicator light harness connector terminal No. 83 (Red/Yellow wire) and VSA mode selector switch harness connector terminal No. 5 (Red/Yellow wire). If continuity does not exist, inspect and repair circuit as needed.

Variable Shock Absorber (VSA) Indicator Light Does Not Illuminate In Hard (H) Mode – 1) Turn ignition on. Push VSA mode selector switch to hard (H) position. Switch is located on center console. If indicator light illuminates, circuit is functioning normally. If indicator light does not illuminate, remove control switch.

2) Disconnect VSA mode selector switch. Connect jumper wire between VSA mode selector switch harness connector terminal No. 6 (Red wire) and vehicle ground. If indicator light illuminates, go to next step. If light does not illuminate, go to step **4)**.

3) Check continuity of VSA mode selector switch ground circuit. Using ohmmeter, check resistance between VSA mode selector switch harness connector terminal No. 2 (Black wire) and vehicle ground. If continuity exists, replace VSA mode selector switch. If continuity does not exist, inspect and repair circuit as needed.

4) Inspect condition of fuse No. 11. Fuse block is located behind left corner of driver's dash. Replace fuse as needed. If fuse is okay, inspect condition of indicator light (LED). Replace as needed. If light is okay, check resistance between indicator light harness connector terminal No. 82 (Red wire) and VSA mode selector switch harness connector terminal No. 6 (Red wire). If continuity does not exist, inspect and repair circuit as needed.

NOTE: If damping force does not change for all shock absorbers, malfunction of wiring harness should be diagnosed first.

Damping Force Does Not Change With Mode Selector Switch Change – 1) Turn ignition on. Have an assistant conduct a bounce test on each corner of vehicle as VSA mode selector switch is changed between each mode. If damping force does not change on a individual shock absorber, disconnect and remove actuator from malfunctioning shock.

2) Swap actuator with known good actuator from other shock and inspect system operation. Replace actuator if malfunction of shock appears at other wheel. If initial shock absorber still does not function properly, remove actuator.

3) Turn control rod of shock absorber. Replace shock absorber, if rod does not turn easily without binding. If rod turns freely, disconnect actuator harness connector.

4) Using DVOM, measure voltage between actuator harness connector terminal No. 1 (Blue wire) and vehicle ground. If battery voltage does not exist, inspect condition of fuse No. 7. Fuse block is located behind left corner of driver's dash. Replace fuse as needed. If fuse is

okay, inspect and repair power supply circuit between VSA control unit and actuator harness connector. VSA control unit is located in left rear corner of vehicle. See WIRING DIAGRAM.

5) Replace VSA control unit if power supply circuit is okay. Check continuity of remaining ground circuits. See WIRING DIAGRAM . Inspect and repair ground circuits as needed.

No Damping Force Change At All Wheels – Disconnect VSA control module. Control module is located in left rear corner of vehicle. Perform circuit continuity and voltage check. See VSA CONTROL MODULE CIRCUIT INSPECTION table. All continuity and voltage checks are between VSA control module terminal and vehicle ground. If all circuits test okay, replace VSA control module.

VSA CONTROL MODULE CIRCUIT INSPECTION

Terminal No. [1]	Mode Selection	Measurement
1	All	Continuity
2	Soft Or Medium	No Continuity
	Hard	Continuity
3	Medium Or Hard	No Continuity
	Soft	Continuity
4 [2]	Ignition Off	0 Volts
	Ignition On	Battery Voltage
5 [3]		
6	Any Selection [4]	Battery Voltage
7	Soft Or Hard	No Continuity
	Medium	Continuity

[1] – See Fig. 3.
[2] – Power supply (voltage measurement).
[3] – Terminal No. 5 is not used.
[4] – Battery voltage is temporarily present 5 seconds after operating VSA mode selector switch.

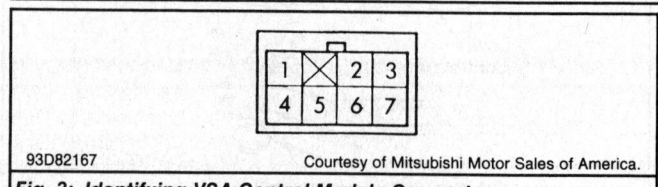

93D82167   Courtesy of Mitsubishi Motor Sales of America.

Fig. 3: Identifying VSA Control Module Connector

REMOVAL & INSTALLATION

STEERING KNUCKLE

Removal – 1) Raise and support vehicle. Remove wheel assembly. Remove brake caliper. Remove hub/rotor assembly. See WHEEL BEARING under REMOVAL & INSTALLATION. Remove dust cover from steering knuckle.

2) Disconnect tie rod end from steering knuckle. Mark torsion bar adjusting nut for installation reference. Loosen torsion bar anchor arm assembly adjusting nut. Loosen, but DO NOT remove, ball joint-to-steering knuckle nuts.

3) Using ball joint separator, separate ball joints from steering knuckle. Detach upper and lower ball joints from steering knuckle. Remove steering knuckle from axle shaft. Remove oil seal and spacer from steering knuckle.

Inspection – Inspect steering knuckle for cracks. Inspect spindle for wear and heat damage.

Installation – 1) If needle bearing needs replacement, drive bearing from steering knuckle. Use Bearing Driver (MB990956-01) and Handle (MB9909938-01) to install NEW needle bearing until it is even with steering knuckle end face.

NOTE: DO NOT reuse steering knuckle needle bearing if it is removed.

2) Lubricate bearing roller surface and spacer-to-steering knuckle contact areas. Install spacer with chamfered side toward inside of vehicle. Using Seal Installer (MB990985-01) and handle, install seal in steering knuckle until seal is even with steering knuckle end face.

Apply grease to seal lip area and inside of seal. To complete installation, reverse removal procedure. Tighten bolts to specification. See TORQUE SPECIFICATIONS.

LOCKING HUB

Removal (Pickup) – 1) Place hub in FREE position by shifting transfer case lever to 2H position and moving vehicle in Reverse 4-7 feet. Remove cover from locking hub. If necessary, wrap shop towel around cover and use an oil filter wrench to loosen cover.

2) Raise and support vehicle. Remove wheel assembly. Using snap ring pliers, remove snap ring and shim from end of axle shaft. *See Fig. 2.* Remove locking hub retaining bolts and locking hub assembly.

Installation – 1) Set wheel bearing preload. See WHEEL BEARING under ADJUSTMENTS & INSPECTION. Using spring scale attached to wheel stud, measure and record turning resistance required to rotate hub/rotor assembly before installing locking hub.

2) Align locking hub assembly key area with steering knuckle spindle keyway area. Loosely install locking hub assembly on hub/rotor assembly. Ensure locking hub assembly fully contacts hub/rotor assembly.

3) Install locking hub retaining bolts. Tighten bolts to specification. See TORQUE SPECIFICATIONS. Using spring scale attached to wheel stud, measure turning resistance required to rotate hub/rotor assembly.

4) Subtract turning resistance measured in step **1)** from turning resistance measured in step **3)** (after installing locking hub). If difference exceeds 3.1 lbs. (14 N), check for incorrect installation of locking hub assembly or components. Reverse removal procedure to complete installation.

LOWER BALL JOINT

Removal – 1) Raise and support vehicle. Remove skid plate (if equipped). Remove wheel assembly. Mark torsion bar adjusting nut for reassembly reference. Release torsion bar tension.

2) Loosen, but DO NOT remove, lower ball joint stud nut. Using ball joint separator, separate ball joint from steering knuckle. Remove ball joint stud nut. Remove ball joint-to-lower control arm bolts. Remove ball joint.

Installation – Lubricate ball joint. Reverse removal procedure to complete installation. Tighten bolts to specification. See TORQUE SPECIFICATIONS.

LOWER CONTROL ARM

Removal – 1) Raise and support vehicle. Remove wheel assembly. Remove front skid plate and undercover (if equipped). Remove torsion bar. See TORSION BAR. Remove stabilizer bar bolt from control arm.

2) Remove shock absorber-to-control arm bolts. Loosen, but DO NOT remove, lower ball joint-to-steering knuckle nut. Using ball joint fork, separate lower ball joint from steering knuckle.

3) Remove ball joint stud nut from steering knuckle. Remove control arm shaft. *See Fig. 1.* Remove torque arm. Remove lower control arm pivot bolt. Remove lower control arm.

Inspection – 1) Inspect control arm for cracks and deformation. Check ball joints. See BALL JOINT CHECKING under ADJUSTMENTS & INSPECTION.

2) Inspect ball joint dust covers for damage. Replace damaged dust covers. Inspect control arm bushing and frame bracket bushing for damage. Replace bushings if necessary.

NOTE: Differential carrier may require detachment in order to replace left bracket bushing.

3) On Pickup, install Bushing Remover/Installer (MB990958-01) in frame bracket bushing if bushing needs replacement. *See Fig. 4.* Tighten bushing remover/installer bolt until bushing is removed. Reverse bushing remover/installer to install bushing.

4) Use press and Bushing Remover/Installer (MB990883-01) if control arm bushing needs replacement. Press bushing from control arm. *See Fig. 5.*

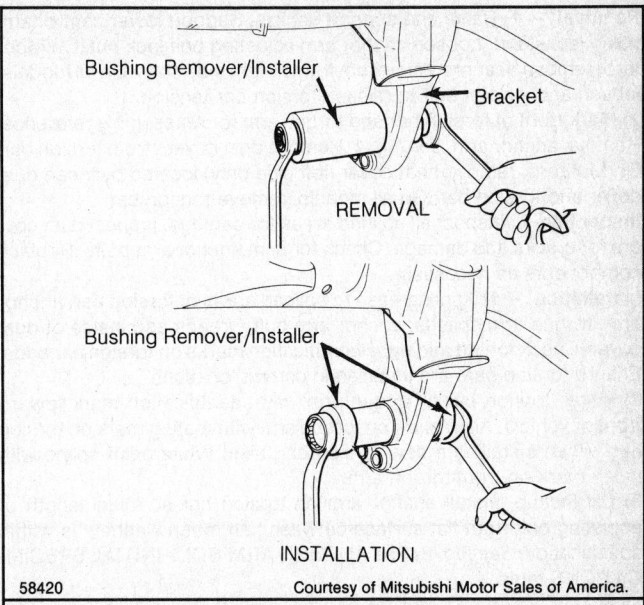

Fig. 4: Replacing Bracket Bushing (Pickup)

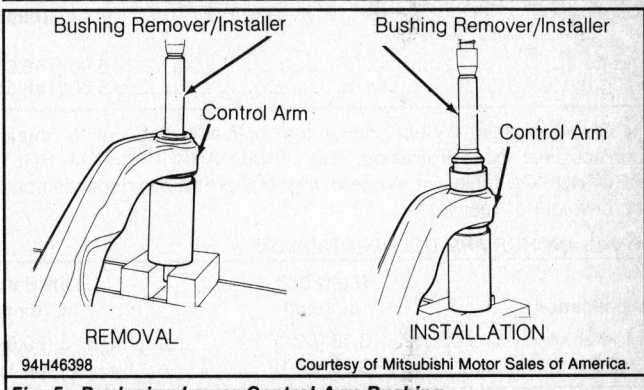

Fig. 5: Replacing Lower Control Arm Bushing

5) Coat bushing and control arm with soapy solution. Using press and bushing remover/installer, press bushing into control arm. Position bushing so distance from bushing to control arm is equal at both ends.

NOTE: Tighten lower control arm shaft and pivot bolt to specification with vehicle at normal operating height.

Installation – To install, reverse removal procedure. Tighten bolts to specification. See TORQUE SPECIFICATIONS. Tighten lower control arm shaft and pivot bolt to specification with vehicle at normal operating height.

STABILIZER BAR

Removal – Remove skid plate (if equipped). Remove stabilizer bar bolt from lower control arm. Remove stabilizer bar clamp-to-hanger bolts. Remove stabilizer bar and bushings. Remove stabilizer bar-to-frame hangers (if necessary).

Installation – 1) To install, reverse removal procedure. Install stabilizer bar-to-frame hangers and stabilizer bar-to-control arm bolt using new nuts.

2) Tighten hanger-to-frame nut and stabilizer bar-to-control arm nut until distance from threaded end of bolt to nut is .16-.20" (4.0-5.0 mm) for Montero and .31-.35" (8.0-9.0 mm) for Pickup.

TORSION BAR

NOTE: Mark torsion bar and anchor arm location for reassembly reference before removing.

Removal – 1) Raise and support vehicle. Support lower control arm using jackstand. Loosen anchor arm adjusting bolt lock nut. On Montero, remove heat protector from frame (right side only). On all models, loosen anchor arm bolt to release torsion bar tension.

2) Mark front of torsion bar and torque arm for reassembly reference. Remove anchor arm. See Fig. 1. Remove dust covers from torsion bar. On Montero, remove heat cover (left side only) located between dust cover and torsion bar. On all models, remove torsion bar.

Inspection – Inspect all splined areas for damage. Inspect dust covers for cracks and damage. Check for bent anchor arm bolts. Replace components as necessary.

Installation – 1) Apply grease to splined areas of torsion bar, anchor arm, torque arm splines, anchor arm bolt threads and inside of dust cover. Check for left and right identification marks on torsion bar ends. Ensure torsion bars are installed in correct locations.

2) Install torsion bar in torque arm, with identification mark toward front of vehicle. Align mark on torque arm with mating mark on torsion bar. When installing a new torsion bar, align White paint spline with index mark on front torque arm.

3) On Pickup, install anchor arm on torsion bar so initial length of adjusting bolt from flat surface between half moon washers is within specification. See Fig. 6. See ANCHOR ARM BOLT INITIAL SPECIFICATIONS table.

ANCHOR ARM BOLT INITIAL SPECIFICATIONS

Application	In. (mm)
Pickup	
Left	5.90 (149.0)
Right	5.80 (148.5)

4) On all models, tighten anchor arm bolt adjusting nut to obtain correct final bolt protrusion. See FINAL ANCHOR ARM BOLT PROTRUSION table. On Montero, final bolt protrusion depends upon curb weight of vehicle.

FINAL ANCHOR ARM BOLT PROTRUSION

Application	Right Bolt In. (mm)	Left Bolt In. (mm)
Montero	3.15 (80.0)	3.15 (80.0)
Pickup	3.39 (86.1)	3.94 (100.1)

5) To complete installation, reverse removal procedure. Tighten bolts to specification. See TORQUE SPECIFICATIONS table at end of article. Check riding height and front wheel alignment. See SPECIFICATIONS & PROCEDURES article in WHEEL ALIGNMENT.

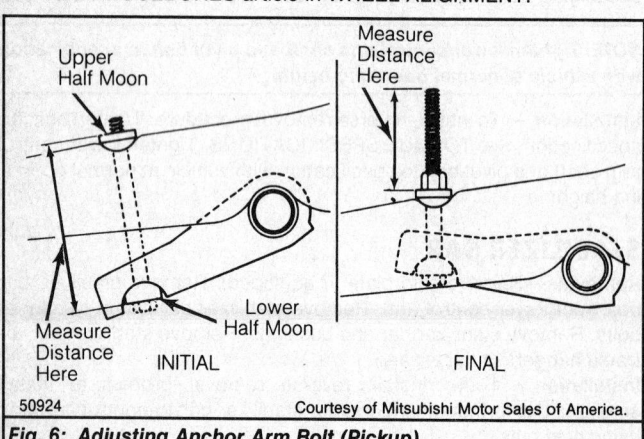

Fig. 6: Adjusting Anchor Arm Bolt (Pickup)

UPPER BALL JOINT

NOTE: On Pickup, replace upper control arm if ball joint is defective.

Removal (Montero) – 1) Raise and support vehicle. Remove wheel assembly. Mark torsion bar adjusting nut for reassembly reference. Release torsion bar tension. Loosen, but DO NOT remove, upper ball joint-to-steering knuckle nut.

2) Using ball joint separator, separate ball joint from steering knuckle. Remove ball joint nut from steering knuckle. Remove ball joint-to-upper control arm bolts. Remove ball joint.

Installation – Lubricate ball joint. Reverse removal procedure to complete installation. Tighten bolts to specification. See TORQUE SPECIFICATIONS.

UPPER CONTROL ARM

Removal – 1) Support lower control arm using jackstand. Remove wheel assembly. Mark anchor arm bolt for reassembly reference. Loosen anchor arm bolt to release torsion bar tension. Disconnect and plug brake hose at frame mount bracket.

2) Remove cotter pin from ball joint stud. Loosen, but DO NOT remove, ball joint stud nut. Using ball joint fork, loosen ball joint from steering knuckle. Remove ball joint stud nut. Remove rebound stopper and brake hose support from control arm.

3) Remove ABS sensor bracket (if equipped). Remove upper control arm mounting bolts and shim(s). Note direction of bolt installation and locations of camber adjustment shims. Remove control arm. If clearance is inadequate for control arm removal, remove shock absorber.

Inspection – Inspect control arm for cracks and deformation. Check ball joints. See BALL JOINT CHECKING under ADJUSTMENTS & INSPECTION. Inspect ball joint dust cover for damage, and replace cover as necessary.

Installation – 1) To install, reverse removal procedure. On Pickup, install control arm bolts from inside of control arm shaft, with nuts against frame; on Montero, install control arm bolts from outside of frame, with nuts against control arm.

2) Ensure alignment shims are placed in original locations. On Pickup, install shock absorber (if removed) with White paint mark on lower end of shock facing outside of vehicle.

3) Tighten shock absorber upper nut to end of threads, and install lock nut. On Montero, tighten shock absorber upper nut until distance from end of threads to nut is .04-.08" (1.0-2.0 mm). Install lock nut.

4) On all models, tighten bolts to specification. See TORQUE SPECIFICATIONS. Bleed brakes. Adjust anchor arm bolt to proper torsion bar setting. See TORSION BAR under REMOVAL & INSTALLATION. Check wheel alignment, and adjust it if necessary. See SPECIFICATIONS & PROCEDURES article in WHEEL ALIGNMENT.

WHEEL BEARING

Removal – 1) Raise and support vehicle. Remove wheel assembly. Remove brake caliper assembly. Remove locking hub. See LOCKING HUB.

2) Remove lock washer. Using Socket (MB990954-01), remove lock nut. Remove front hub assembly from steering knuckle. Remove oil seal and bearings from hub. If bearing races need to be replaced, drive bearing races from hub using brass drift and hammer.

Installation – 1) Lubricate bearings. Install bearing races in hub. Ensure bearing races are fully seated. To complete installation, reverse removal procedure. Adjust wheel bearings. See WHEEL BEARING under ADJUSTMENTS & INSPECTION.

2) Install seal in hub using Seal Installer (MB990955-01). Install seal until it is even with hub surface. Apply sealant to locking hub-to-front hub contact surface. On Montero, apply sealant to front hub-to-cover surface.

TORQUE SPECIFICATIONS

TORQUE SPECIFICATIONS

Application	Ft. Lbs. (N.m)
Anchor Arm Bolt Lock Nut	29-36 (39-49)
Automatic Hub Cover	13-25 (18-34)
Ball Joint Nut	
Lower	87-130 (118-176)
Upper	43-65 (58-88)
Ball Joint-To-Lower Control Arm Bolt	39-54 (53-73)
Caliper Bolt	58-72 (79-98)
Control Arm-To-Frame Bolt/Nut	
Lower	[1] 101-116 (137-157)
Upper	72-87 (98-118)
Locking Hub-To-Hub/Rotor Bolt	36-43 (49-58)
Manual Hub Cover Bolt	10 (14)
Shock Absorber Lower Mount Bolt	
Montero	11-16 (15-22)
Pickup	10 (14)
Shock Absorber Shaft Nut	10-13 (14-18)
Tie Rod Nut	33 (45)
Torque Arm Nut	69-87 (94-118)
	INCH Lbs. (N.m)
Stabilizer Bar Clamp Bolt	84-108 (8-12)

[1] – Tighten with vehicle at normal operating height.

1994 SUSPENSION
Front – Montero & Pickup – 4WD (Cont.)

WIRING DIAGRAM

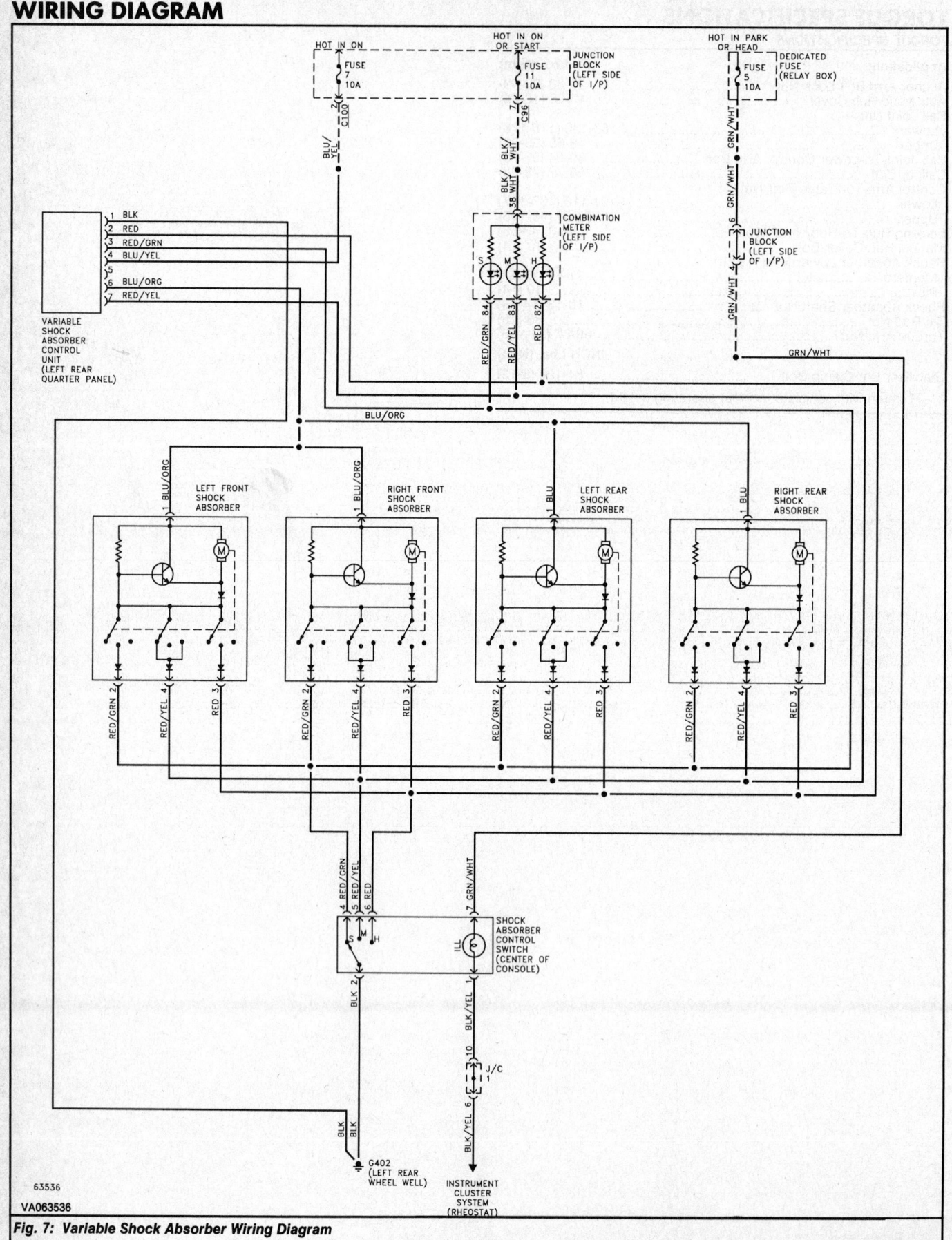

63536

VA063536

Fig. 7: Variable Shock Absorber Wiring Diagram

**Chrysler Corp: Colt, Colt Vista,
Stealth, Summit, Summit Wagon
Mitsubishi: Diamante, Eclipse, Expo,
Galant, Mirage, Precis, 3000GT**

DESCRIPTION

NOTE: Diamante, Stealth and 3000GT may be equipped with Electronically Controlled Suspension (ECS). The suspension remains the same, but it is electronically controlled. For testing and diagnosis information on electronically controlled suspension, see appropriate ELECTRONIC article in SUSPENSION.

Colt, Eclipse FWD, Mirage & Summit – Rear suspension system is a 3-link type with "U"-shaped torsion axle beam. *See Fig. 1.*

Diamante, Stealth FWD & 3000GT FWD – Rear suspension system is multi-link type with hydraulic shock absorbers, coil springs and stabilizer bar. *See Fig. 2.*

Eclipse AWD, Stealth AWD & 3000GT AWD – Rear suspension system is an independent, double-wishbone type. System consists of upper and lower suspension arms, shock absorbers, coil springs and stabilizer bar. *See Fig. 3.*

Galant – Rear multi-link suspension incorporates an upper A-arm, lower trailing link and 2 lower split level lateral links. Rear strut assembly is connected to knuckle. Rear stabilizer bar is available as an option. *See Fig. 4.*

Colt Vista FWD, Expo FWD & Summit Wagon FWD – Rear suspension is an independent trailing arm type. System consists of low profile coil springs, suspension arms and shock absorbers. *See Fig. 5.*

Colt Vista AWD, Expo AWD & Summit Wagon AWD – Rear suspension is an independent trailing arm type. System consists of low profile coil springs, suspension arms, shock absorbers and a stabilizer bar. *See Fig. 6.*

Precis – Rear suspension is an independent trailing arm type, consisting of an integral axle, suspension arms, shock absorbers, coil springs and stabilizer bar. *See Fig. 7.* Torsion bar is located inside axle beam and is not removable.

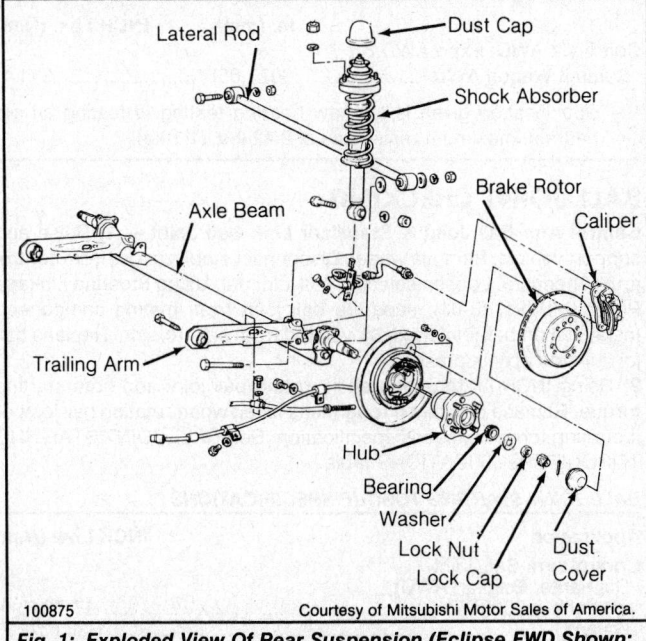

Fig. 1: Exploded View Of Rear Suspension (Eclipse FWD Shown; Colt, Mirage & Summit Are Similar)

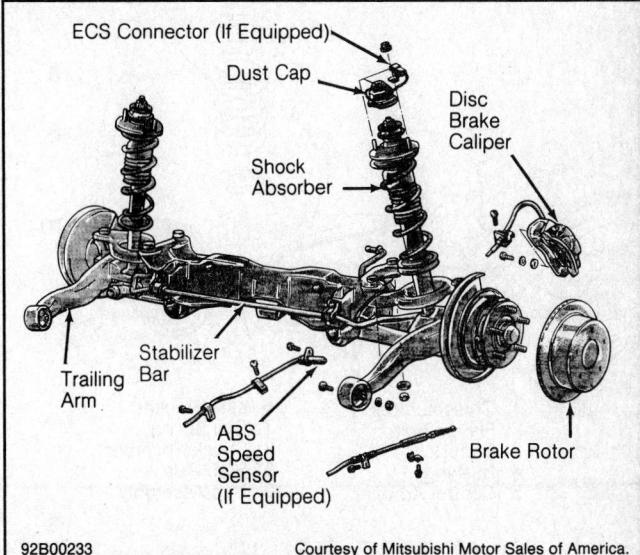

Fig. 2: Exploded View Of Rear Suspension (Diamante, Stealth FWD & 3000GT FWD)

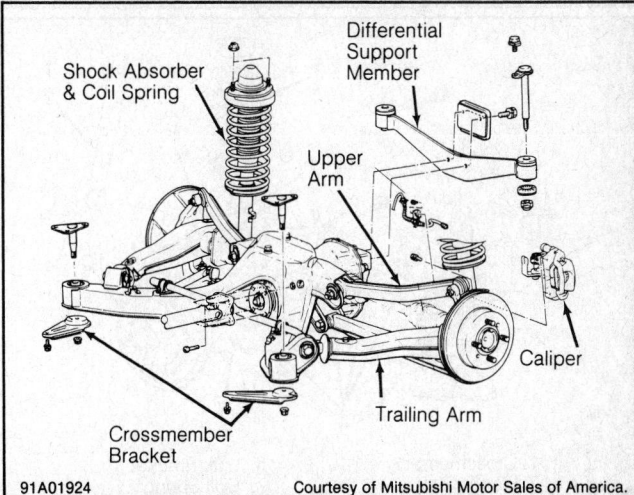

Fig. 3: Exploded View Of Rear Suspension (Eclipse AWD Shown, Stealth AWD & 3000GT AWD Are Similar)

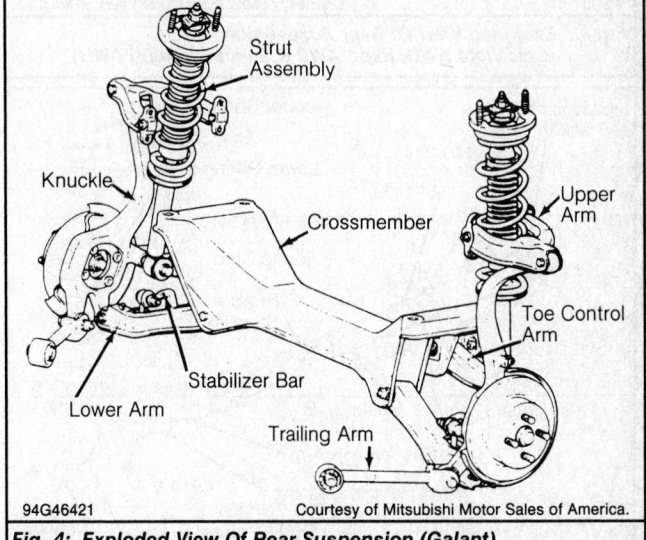

Fig. 4: Exploded View Of Rear Suspension (Galant)

1994 SUSPENSION
Rear – AWD & FWD (Cont.)

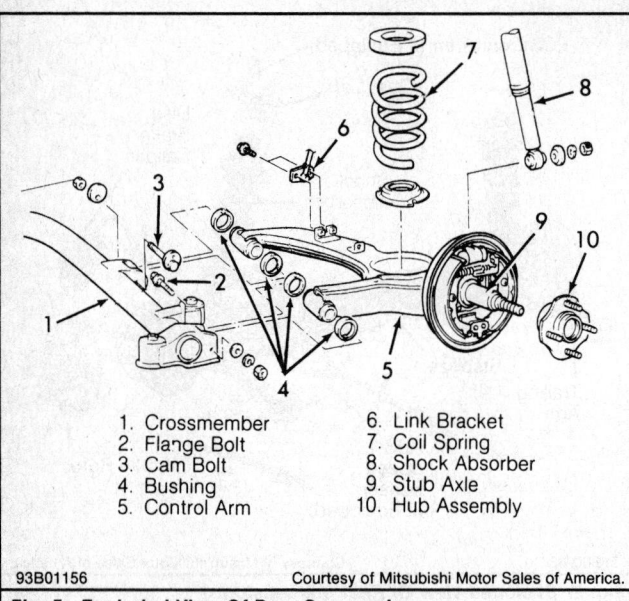

1. Crossmember
2. Flange Bolt
3. Cam Bolt
4. Bushing
5. Control Arm
6. Link Bracket
7. Coil Spring
8. Shock Absorber
9. Stub Axle
10. Hub Assembly

93B01156   Courtesy of Mitsubishi Motor Sales of America.

Fig. 5: Exploded View Of Rear Suspension (Colt Vista FWD, Expo FWD, Summit Wagon FWD)

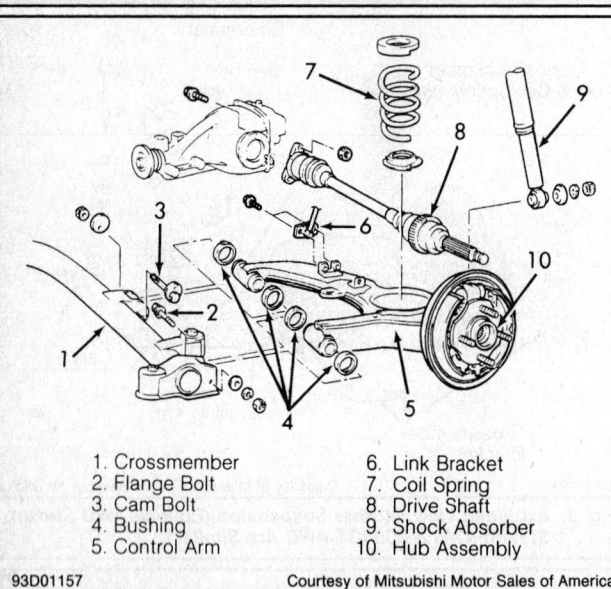

1. Crossmember
2. Flange Bolt
3. Cam Bolt
4. Bushing
5. Control Arm
6. Link Bracket
7. Coil Spring
8. Drive Shaft
9. Shock Absorber
10. Hub Assembly

93D01157   Courtesy of Mitsubishi Motor Sales of America.

Fig. 6: Exploded View Of Rear Suspension (Colt Vista AWD, Expo AWD & Summit Wagon AWD)

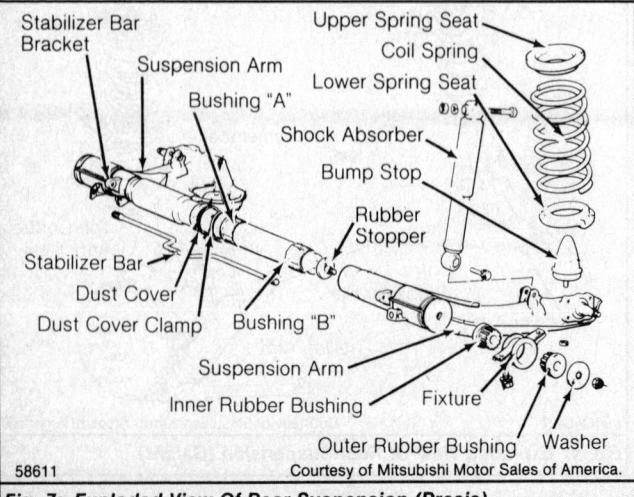

Stabilizer Bar Bracket
Suspension Arm
Bushing "A"
Stabilizer Bar
Dust Cover
Dust Cover Clamp
Bushing "B"
Suspension Arm
Inner Rubber Bushing
Outer Rubber Bushing
Upper Spring Seat
Coil Spring
Lower Spring Seat
Shock Absorber
Bump Stop
Rubber Stopper
Fixture
Washer

58611   Courtesy of Mitsubishi Motor Sales of America.

Fig. 7: Exploded View Of Rear Suspension (Precis)

ADJUSTMENTS & INSPECTION

WHEEL ALIGNMENT
SPECIFICATIONS & PROCEDURES

NOTE: See SPECIFICATIONS & PROCEDURES article in WHEEL ALIGNMENT.

WHEEL BEARING

1) Raise and support vehicle. Remove rear wheel assembly. Remove brake disc or drum if necessary. Measure axle shaft end play using dial indicator. See AXIAL END PLAY & ROTARY SLIDING RESISTANCE SPECIFICATIONS table.

2) If end play exceeds limit, retighten wheel bearing nut or companion flange nut (if equipped) to specification. See appropriate TORQUE SPECIFICATIONS table. DO NOT back off wheel bearing nut more than 15 degrees to align cotter pin holes (if equipped). Recheck end play. If end play exceeds limit, replace wheel bearings.

3) Check rotary sliding resistance. Attach a spring scale to hub bolt. Measure rotary sliding resistance by pulling spring scale at a 90-degree angle to hub bolt. Note measurement when hub begins to rotate. See AXIAL END PLAY & ROTARY SLIDING RESISTANCE SPECIFICATIONS table. If resistance exceeds limit, remove and inspect wheel bearings. Replace wheel bearings as needed.

AXIAL END PLAY & ROTARY SLIDING RESISTANCE SPECIFICATIONS

Application	End Play In. (mm)	Rotary Resistance Lbs. (kg)
Colt, Mirage & Summit	.008 (.20)	4.9 (2.2)
Colt Vista FWD, Expo FWD, Galant & Summit Wagon FWD	.002 (.05)	4.0 (1.8)
Eclipse FWD	.004 (.10)	7.0 (3.1)
Eclipse AWD, Stealth AWD & 3000GT AWD	.031 (.79)	2.6 (1.2)
Stealth FWD & 3000GT FWD	.002 (.05)	7.0 (3.1)
Precis	.004 (.10)	4.8 (2.1)

	In. (mm)	INCH Lbs. (N.m)
Colt Vista AWD, Expo AWD & Summit Wagon AWD	.002 (.05)	9 (1.1)

¹ – Specification given is for new bearing testing. If testing an old bearing, maximum resistance is 2.42 lbs. (1.1 kg).

BALL JOINT CHECKING

Control Arm Ball Joint & Stabilizer Link Ball Joint – 1) Raise and support vehicle. Remove wheel. Disconnect stabilizer bar from control arm (if needed). Loosen selected ball joint nut. Using Steering Linkage Puller (MB991113-01), separate ball joint from mating component. Install nut on ball joint stud. Move stud from side-to-side. Replace ball joint if side play is present.

2) Using INCH-lb. torque wrench, rotate ball joint and note starting torque. Replace ball joint if roughness is felt when rotating ball joint or if starting torque exceeds specification. See BALL JOINT STARTING TORQUE SPECIFICATIONS table.

BALL JOINT STARTING TORQUE SPECIFICATIONS

Application	INCH Lbs. (N.m)
Control Arm Ball Joint	
Diamante, Eclipse (AWD), Stealth & 3000GT	17-78 (2-9)
Galant	1-23 (.1-2.7)
Stabilizer Link Ball Joint	
Galant	4-13 (.5-1.5)
All Others	15-28 (1.7-3.2)

REMOVAL & INSTALLATION

REAR SUSPENSION ASSEMBLY

Removal (Colt, Eclipse FWD, Diamante, Mirage, Stealth FWD, Summit & 3000GT FWD) – 1) On all models except Eclipse, remove trunk side trim. On Eclipse FWD, remove hole cover. On all models, raise and support vehicle. Remove wheel assembly.

2) On models equipped with disc brakes, remove caliper and disc assembly. *See Fig. 1 or 2.* On all models, remove cotter pin, lock cap, lock nut, washer and outer bearing (components vary between applications). Remove hub assembly or brake drum assembly (depending on application). Remove dust cover (if equipped).

3) Disconnect and remove rear speed sensor (if equipped). Disconnect parking brake cable from brake assembly and torsion axle and arm assembly. Remove brake assembly. Disconnect brake hose. Remove brake hose bracket from torsion axle and arm assembly.

4) Remove dust cap from top of shock assembly. *See Fig. 1 or 2.* On all models, slightly raise torsion axle and arm assembly using a floor jack. Remove upper and lower shock absorber mounting nuts. Remove shock absorber. Disconnect lateral rod from body. Remove trailing arm bolts. Lower jack, and remove rear suspension assembly from vehicle.

Inspection – Check axle beam, lateral rod and trailing arm for deformation and damage. Check rubber bushings for deterioration, cracks and unusual wear.

Installation – 1) If trailing arm bushing needs replacing, remove bushing using Bushing Press (MB991045 for Colt, Diamante, Mirage, Stealth, Summit and 3000GT; MB991159 for Eclipse FWD). Remove lateral rod bushing using Driver (MB990947-01) and Adapters (MB990847-01 and MB990845-01).

2) Press in new arm bushing from beveled side of housing. Ensure slots in bushing face front-to-rear. Press in new lateral rod bushing using driver. Ensure bushing protrudes equally on both sides.

3) To complete installation, reverse removal procedure. Bleed brakes, and check wheel bearings. See WHEEL BEARING under ADJUSTMENTS & INSPECTION. Tighten all fasteners to specification. See TORQUE SPECIFICATIONS (FWD) table. Check wheel alignment.

Removal (Colt Vista, Eclipse AWD, Expo, Stealth AWD, Summit Wagon & 3000GT AWD) – 1) On Colt Vista, Eclipse, Expo and Summit Wagon, remove shock/strut access cover. On Stealth and 3000GT, remove trunk room trim. On all models, remove center exhaust pipe and main muffler.

2) Remove shock absorber upper mounting nuts. On vehicles with electronically controlled suspension, disconnect electrical connector and remove cap from top of shock.

3) On all models, remove brake tube bracket bolt. Disconnect parking brake. Remove caliper lock pin. Rotate caliper upward, and remove caliper assembly and brake disc. Secure caliper assembly aside using wire. Cover guide pin with cloth.

4) On Stealth and 3000GT with 4-wheel steering, disconnect pressure tubes, feed, suction and return lines. Remove power cylinder tie rod coupling nut. On models with anti-lock brakes, disconnect electrical harness connectors.

5) On all models, mark drive shaft flange and differential flange for installation reference. Disconnect drive shaft, and secure it using wire. Support differential using transmission jack, and remove self-locking nuts.

6) Remove differential support member. Remove crossmember bracket. Lower transmission jack slightly, and remove parking brake cable and rear speed sensor bolts. Remove cable band. Remove rear speed sensor connector and "O" ring (if equipped).

CAUTION: Ensure drive shaft does not bend excessively. Due to weight being handled, 3 people are required to lower suspension assembly.

---

7) Move suspension assembly toward rear of vehicle, and slowly lower suspension assembly. DO NOT contact stabilizer bar and drive shaft. Support lower arm using a wooden block to protect dust shield.

Inspection – Check crossmember for cracks and other damage. Inspect all components for damage and unusual wear. Replace components as necessary.

Installation – To install, reverse removal procedure. Ensure reference marks align when installing drive shaft. Tighten all suspension fasteners to specification with vehicle on ground and suspension unloaded. See appropriate TORQUE SPECIFICATIONS table. Check wheel alignment. See SPECIFICATIONS & PROCEDURES article in WHEEL ALIGNMENT.

Removal (Galant) – 1) Remove rear seat to access upper strut mounting nuts. Mark upper strut mounting stud and body for reassembly reference. Remove nuts. Raise and support vehicle. Remove disc brake caliper (if equipped). Support caliper with wire. Do not allow caliper to hang from brake hose.

2) Remove brake drum or disc. Disconnect parking brake cable. Disconnect and plug hydraulic brake hose (drum brake equipped). Remove rear ABS sensor connector. Unbolt upper arm brackets from frame. Remove frame grommet to access trailing arm front bolt. Disconnect trailing arm.

3) Remove center exhaust pipe. Support crossmember with transmission jack. Remove nuts connecting rear suspension crossmember to body. Lower rear suspension assembly.

Inspection – Check all components from damage or cracking. Replace as needed.

Installation – Install rear suspension assembly in reverse order of disassembly. Tighten bolts to specification. See appropriate TORQUE SPECIFICATIONS table. On vehicles with drum brakes, bleed brake system. On all vehicles, ensure parking brake is correctly adjusted. Inspect rear wheel alignment. See SPECIFICATIONS & PROCEDURES article in WHEEL ALIGNMENT.

Removal (Precis) – 1) Drain brake fluid. Raise and support vehicle. Remove wheel assembly. Remove brake drum and wheel bearings. Disconnect brakelines and parking brake cable. Remove brake assembly. Remove muffler and pipe.

2) Raise suspension slightly using floor jack. Disconnect shock absorbers from suspension arms. *See Fig. 7.* Lower suspension enough to remove coil springs and seats. Remove fixture-to-body bolts. Remove suspension assembly.

Disassembly – 1) Scribe alignment marks on fixture-to-suspension arm position for reassembly reference. Scribe mark on stabilizer bar in alignment with punch mark on stabilizer bar bracket for reassembly reference.

2) Remove fixture retaining nuts at both ends of suspension arm. Remove fixtures and rubber bushings. Note position of rubber bushings. Remove dust cover clamp, and slide dust cover toward right suspension arm. DO NOT damage dust cover.

3) Separate suspension into right and left arms. Remove stabilizer bar. *See Fig. 7.* Remove rubber stoppers. Using a screwdriver and hammer, drive out bushing "A" from left suspension arm. Drive bushing "B" from left suspension arm.

Inspection – Check for bent or damaged suspension arm, dust cover, rubber stopper and damaged or worn bushings. Replace components as necessary.

Reassembly – 1) If dust cover is replaced, slide new dust cover up to stopper on right suspension arm. Apply grease to outside of right suspension arm. Using right suspension arm, install rubber stopper into left suspension arm.

2) Apply grease to outer surfaces of bushings "A" and "B". Using Bushing Installer (MB990780) and Handle (MB990779), install bushing "B" until bushing bottoms in arm. Install bushing "A" using bushing installer. Install stabilizer bar. Slowly push suspension arms together, and wipe away excess grease.

3) Ensure stabilizer bar mark aligns with punch mark on stabilizer bar bracket. Install inner and outer rubber bushings, fixtures and washers. DO NOT apply grease to bushings or shaft threads.

4) Ensure toothed side of washer faces bushing and cutout area of fixture faces forward. Install fixtures and suspension arm in original positions. Align marks scribed during disassembly. Install nuts.

5) Tighten nuts to specification with vehicle at normal operating height and no load. See TORQUE SPECIFICATIONS (FWD) table. Pack dust cover with grease, and secure using new clamp.

Installation – 1) To install, reverse removal procedure. Check upper and lower spring seats for proper installation. Tighten bolts to specification. See TORQUE SPECIFICATIONS (FWD) table.

2) Tighten suspension arm nuts and shock absorber bolts to specification with vehicle at normal operating height and no load. Check wheel bearings (if required). See WHEEL BEARING under ADJUSTMENTS & INSPECTION. Bleed and adjust brakes. Check wheel alignment. See SPECIFICATIONS & PROCEDURES article in WHEEL ALIGNMENT.

SHOCK & STRUT ASSEMBLIES

Removal (Except Precis) – 1) On Colt, Mirage and Summit hatchback models, remove trunk side trim. On Diamante, Eclipse, Stealth and 3000GT, remove trunk side trim or shock/strut access cover. On Colt Vista, Expo and Summit Wagon, remove shock/strut access cover. On Galant, remove rear seat.

2) On all models, raise and support vehicle. Remove wheel assembly. Support lower arm assembly using jackstands. On models with electronically controlled suspension, disconnect electrical connector from top of shock and remove actuator.

CAUTION: On models with spring assisted shock absorbers, DO NOT remove center strut rod nut until spring is compressed.

---

3) On all models, remove dust cap from top of shock assembly. Raise lower arm assembly using a jack. Remove mounting nuts, and disconnect upper strut mount from body. Disconnect shock from lower arm or knuckle assembly. Lower jack, and remove shock assembly from vehicle.

Inspection – Check shock for oil leakage, abnormal noise and poor function. Check coil spring for bending and weakness. Check rubber parts for deterioration and cracks. Check suspension arm and spindle for cracks and deformation.

Installation – To install, reverse removal procedure. Tighten all fasteners to specification. See appropriate TORQUE SPECIFICATIONS table. Check wheel alignment. See SPECIFICATIONS & PROCEDURES article in WHEEL ALIGNMENT.

Removal (Precis) – Support suspension arm using jack. Remove lower shock absorber mounting bolt (if necessary, remove brake assembly). Lower jack slowly, and remove coil springs and seats. Remove upper shock absorber mounting bolts, and remove shock.

Inspection – Check shocks for oil leakage, abnormal noise and poor damping performance. Check coil springs for bending and weakness. Check rubber parts for deterioration and cracks. Check suspension arm and spindle for cracks and deformation.

Installation – To install, reverse removal procedure. Tighten all fasteners to specification. See TORQUE SPECIFICATIONS (FWD) table.

STABILIZER BAR

Removal (Colt Vista AWD, Diamante, Eclipse AWD, Expo AWD, Galant, Stealth, Summit Wagon AWD & 3000GT AWD) – 1) Raise and support vehicle. Support rear suspension assembly using a transmission jack. Remove self-locking nuts and crossmember brackets. Remove bracket bolt for parking brake cable and speed sensor cable (if equipped).

2) Remove stabilizer bar bracket and bushings. Remove stabilizer link nut. Remove lower joint cups and stabilizer rubber (if applicable). Remove stabilizer link-to-stabilizer bar nut, and remove stabilizer link. Lower transmission jack slightly, and remove stabilizer bar.

Inspection – 1) Check bushings for wear and deterioration. Check stabilizer bar, stabilizer link and all bolts for damage and wear. Check ball joint dust cover for cracks. Replace components as necessary.

2) If replacing ball joint dust cover, remove clip ring and dust cover. Pack new dust cover with grease. Wrap stud threads using vinyl tape, and install dust cover. Secure cover using clip ring.

3) Check stabilizer link ball joint starting torque. Deflect ball joint stud from side to side several times. Install 2 nuts on ball joint. Measure ball joint starting torque using INCH-lb. torque wrench.

4) Starting torque should be 15-28 INCH lbs. (1.7-3.2 N.m). If starting torque exceeds specification, replace link. If ball joint starting torque is less than specification, ball joint may be reused unless it has drag and excessive play.

Installation – To install, reverse removal procedure. When installing stabilizer link, hold link using wrench and tighten nut until distance from end of bolt to edge of nut is within specification. See STABILIZER LINK SPECIFICATIONS table. Tighten all remaining fasteners to specification. See appropriate TORQUE SPECIFICATIONS table.

STABILIZER LINK SPECIFICATIONS

Application	Distance In. (mm)
Colt Vista AWD, Expo AWD & Summit Wagon AWD	.98-1.06 (24.9-26.9)
Diamante, Stealth & 3000GT	.20-.28 (5.1-7.1)
Eclipse AWD	.35-.43 (8.9-11.0)

Removal & Installation (Precis) – See REAR SUSPENSION ASSEMBLY.

TRAILING ARM

Removal (Diamante, Eclipse AWD, Stealth AWD & 3000GT AWD) – 1) Disconnect parking brake cable end. Remove bracket for parking brake cable and speed sensor cable (if equipped). Remove rear brake assembly, and suspend caliper using wire. Remove brake disc.

2) Disconnect axle shaft from axle shaft companion flange. Hold hub using Yoke Holder (MB990767-01), and remove companion flange-to-axle shaft nut. Remove companion flange. Remove rear speed sensor and "O" ring (if equipped). Loosen upper and lower arm ball joint nuts, and disconnect ball joints.

3) Remove trailing arm installation nut and bolt. Disconnect shock absorber from trailing arm. Remove trailing arm. Check trailing arm and bushing for cracks, deterioration and wear. Replace components as necessary.

Disassembly – 1) Using Bushing Arbor (MB990849) and Base (MB990646), remove bushing. Remove connecting rod bolt and nut. Install Rod Remover/Installer (MB991254) on trailing arm.

2) Apply lubricant to sliding areas marked "A" in figure. *See Fig. 8.* Install bolt "B" to trailing arm at point shown. Turn threaded shaft "C" on remover/installer to remove connecting rod.

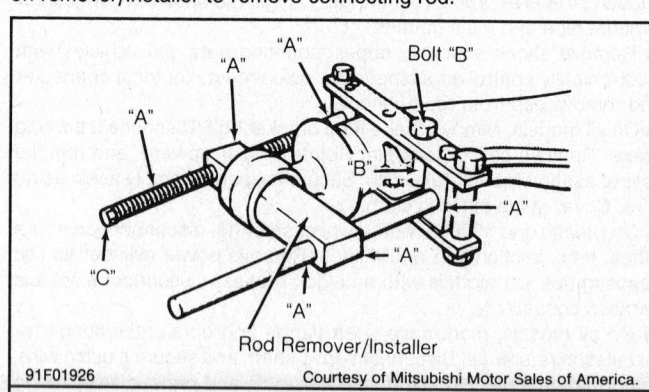

91F01926   Courtesy of Mitsubishi Motor Sales of America.

Fig. 8: *Removing Connecting Rod From Front Trailing Arm (Diamante, Eclipse AWD, Stealth AWD & 3000GT AWD)*

Reassembly – If trailing arm bushing needs replacement, use bushing arbor and base to install new bushing. Press fit bushing until bushing outer pipe edge is flush with lower arm pipe edge. To complete reassembly, reverse disassembly procedure. Apply soapy water to rubber portion of connecting rod.

Installation – To install trailing arm, reverse removal procedure. Tighten all fasteners to specification. See appropriate TORQUE SPECIFICATIONS table. Check wheel alignment. See SPECIFICATIONS & PROCEDURES article in WHEEL ALIGNMENT.

UPPER & LOWER ARMS

NOTE: Coil springs have color marks for spring identification and load classification. When replacing springs, ensure markings are correct for appropriate vehicle.

Removal (Diamante, Eclipse AWD, Stealth AWD & 3000GT AWD) – Loosen upper arm ball joint nut, and disconnect upper arm ball joint. Remove upper arm bolt and arm. Loosen lower arm ball joint nut, and disconnect lower arm ball joint. Hold stabilizer link using a wrench, and remove stabilizer link nut. Disconnect link from lower arm. Remove lower arm bolt, and remove lower arm.

Inspection – 1) Check bushing for wear and deterioration. Check upper and lower arms for bends and breakage. Check ball joint dust covers for cracks. Check all bolts for wear and damage. Replace components as necessary.

2) Check ball joint starting torque. Deflect ball joint stud side to side several times. Install 2 nuts on ball joint. Using INCH-lb. torque wrench, measure ball joint starting torque. Starting torque should be 17-78 INCH lbs. (2-9 N.m). If starting torque exceeds specification, replace arm. If ball joint starting torque is less than specification, ball joint may be reused unless it has drag and excessive play.

Installation – 1) If ball joint dust cover needs replacement, remove dust cover and apply grease to lip and inside of new dust cover. Install dust cover using Installer (MB990800). Ensure dust cover is fully seated.

2) If lower arm bushing needs replacement, use Bushing Arbor (MB991246), Bushing Ring (MB991245) and Base (MB990847) to remove and install bushing. Press fit bushing until bushing outer edge is flush with lower arm edge.

3) To complete installation, reverse removal procedure. When installing stabilizer link, hold link using a wrench and tighten nut until distance from end of bolt to edge of nut is as specified. See STABILIZER LINK SPECIFICATIONS table under STABILIZER BAR. Tighten upper and lower arm nuts to specification. See appropriate TORQUE SPECIFICATIONS table. Check wheel alignment. See SPECIFICATIONS & PROCEDURES article in WHEEL ALIGNMENT.

Removal (Colt Vista, Expo & Summit Wagon) – 1) Support lower arm using floor jack. Remove shock absorber from lower arm. *See Fig. 4 or 5.* Scribe mark coil spring and lower arm for installation reference. Slowly lower jack to remove tension from coil spring, and remove coil spring. Remove stabilizer bar (AWD models). See STABILIZER BAR. Remove brake drum or caliper assembly and disc. Remove hub assembly.

2) Remove parking brake cable end. Remove parking brake cable bracket from lower arm. Scribe mark lower arm cam bolts for installation reference. Remove crossmember-to-lower arm flange and cam bolts. Remove lower arm from vehicle.

Inspection – Check lower arm for deformation and deterioration. Check all bolts for condition and straightness. Check spring seats for cracks and wear. Check bushings for cracking and deterioration.

Disassembly – If lower arm bushings need replacement, scribe mark lower arm-to-old bushing slit. Insert a chisel between bushing and arm, and remove bushing.

Reassembly – Align slit on new bushing with scribe mark on arm, and install bushing. Press fit bushing until outer edge is flush with lower arm edge.

Installation – To install control arms, reverse removal procedure. When installing stabilizer link (AWD models), hold link using a wrench and tighten nut until distance from end of bolt to edge of nut is within specification. See STABILIZER LINK SPECIFICATIONS table under STABILIZER BAR. Tighten all nuts and bolts to specification. See appropriate TORQUE SPECIFICATIONS table. Check wheel alignment. See SPECIFICATIONS & PROCEDURES article in WHEEL ALIGNMENT.

WHEEL BEARING

NOTE: Intergral hub/bearing unit is used only on Galant. Follow instructions for Disc or Drum Brakes – FWD. Hub/bearing assembly is attached to knuckle with 4 bolts.

Removal (Disc Brakes – FWD) – 1) Raise and support vehicle. Remove wheel assembly. Remove speed sensor (if equipped). Disconnect parking brake cable and brake hose. Remove tube bracket. Remove brake disc and caliper assembly.

2) Support caliper aside. Remove hub cap, wheel bearing nut and washer (if equipped). Remove rear hub assembly. Replace rear hub assembly as unit. Separate speed sensor rotor (if equipped).

Installation – To install, reverse removal procedure. Tighten wheel bearing nut to specification. See TORQUE SPECIFICATIONS (FWD) table. Check wheel bearings. See WHEEL BEARING under ADJUSTMENTS & INSPECTION.

Removal (Disc Brakes – AWD) – 1) Raise and support vehicle. Remove wheel assembly. Remove speed sensor (if equipped). Remove brake caliper assembly and brake disc. Separate companion flange from axle shaft. Remove companion flange nut and washer.

2) Remove companion flange and axle shaft assembly. Remove rear speed sensor rotor (if equipped). Remove outer bearing and dust cover from axle shaft. Remove inner bearing and oil seal using Driver (MB990938-01) and Adapter (MB990928-01).

Installation – To install, reverse removal procedure. Install inner bearing using Driver (MB990938-01) and Adapter (MB990931-01). Use Seal Installer (MB990799-01) for oil seal and dust cover. Press outer bearing onto axle shaft. Check wheel bearings. See WHEEL BEARING under ADJUSTMENTS & INSPECTION.

Removal (Drum Brakes – FWD) – Raise and support vehicle. Remove wheel assembly. Remove hub cap. Remove wheel bearing nut or cotter pin, lock cap, lock nut and tongued washer (components vary among models). Remove outer wheel bearing race. Remove hub assembly or brake drum. Remove inner oil seal and bearing. Remove bearing races using a brass drift.

Installation – To install, reverse removal procedure. Replace hub assembly with integral bearings as unit. Install races using Driver (MB990938-01) and Adapter (MB990926-01 or MB990928-01). Install oil seal using driver and Adapter (MB990929-01 or MB990938-01). Check wheel bearings. See WHEEL BEARING under ADJUSTMENTS & INSPECTION.

Removal (Drum Brakes – AWD) – 1) Raise and support vehicle. Remove wheel and brake drum. Remove axle shaft from axle shaft companion flange. Hold axle shaft using Axle Holder (MB990767), and remove companion flange retaining nut. Remove companion flange. Using slide hammer, remove axle shaft.

2) Using Bearing Puller/Installer (MB990560) and hydraulic press, remove outer wheel bearing and dust cover from axle shaft. If necessary, remove inner arm to access inner bearing. See REAR SUSPENSION ASSEMBLY under REMOVAL & INSTALLATION. Remove oil seal from inside of inner arm. Using Bearing Remover/Installer (C-3893), remove inner bearing from arm.

Installation – 1) Using Bearing Remover/Installer (C-3893), install inner bearing in arm. Using Seal Installer (MB990799), install seal in inner arm, with concave side facing outward.

2) Coat seal lip with grease. Install dust cover. If backing plate was removed, apply semi-drying sealant to flange area of inner arm. Install backing plate. Tighten bolts to specification. See TORQUE SPECIFICATIONS (AWD) table.

3) Using Dust Cover Installer (MB990799), install dust cover on axle shaft. Concave side of dust cover must face splined end of axle shaft. Using bearing puller/installer and press, install bearing on axle shaft, with seal surface facing toward flange side of axle shaft.

4) Install axle shaft in inner arm. Install companion flange and new flange nut. Using axle holder, tighten nut to specification. See TORQUE SPECIFICATIONS (AWD) table. Check axle shaft end play. See WHEEL BEARING under ADJUSTMENTS & INSPECTION. To complete installation, reverse removal procedure.

TORQUE SPECIFICATIONS

TORQUE SPECIFICATIONS (FWD)

Application	Ft. Lbs. (N.m)
Backing Plate-To-Arm Bolt	
Except Precis	36-43 (49-58)
Precis	22-29 (30-39)
Ball Joint Nut (All Styles)	21 (28)
Caliper Bolt	36-43 (49-58)
Fixture-To-Body Bolt (Precis) [1]	65-79 (88-107)
Hub/Bearing-To-Knuckle Bolt	54-65 (74-88)
Lateral Rod [1]	
Eclipse	
Axle Beam Side	72-87 (98-118)
Body Side	58-72 (79-98)
Except Eclipse	58-72 (79-98)
Lower Arm-To-Crossmember Nut [1]	65-80 (88-109)
Lower Arm-To-Knuckle Nut	72 (98)
Shock Absorber-To-Arm Nut Or Bolt [1]	
Except Precis	58-72 (79-98)
Precis	47-58 (64-79)
Shock Absorber-To-Body Bolt Or Nut [1]	
Colt, Mirage & Summit	18-25 (25-34)
Colt Vista, Diamante, Eclipse, Expo, Stealth, Summit Wagon & 3000GT	29-36 (39-49)
Galant	32 (44)
Precis	47-58 (64-79)
Shock Absorber-To-Insulator Nut	14-18 (19-25)
Stabilizer Bar Frame Bracket Bolt	7-10 (9-14)
Stabilizer Link Ball Joint Nut	28 (39)
Suspension Arm End Nut (Precis) [1]	65-80 (88-109)
Toe Control Arm-To-Crossmember Nut [1]	65-80 (88-109)
Trailing Arm-To-Frame Bolt [1]	
Colt, Galant, Mirage & Summit	94-108 (127-146)
Diamante, Stealth & 3000GT	101-116 (137-157)
Eclipse	72-87 (98-118)
Trailing Arm-To-Knuckle Nut [1]	87-101 (118-137)
Upper Arm-To-Knuckle Nut [1]	72 (98)
Upper Arm Frame Bracket Nut	28 (39)
Upper Arm-To-Frame Bracket [1]	41 (57)
Wheel Bearing Nut	
Colt, Mirage & Summit	108-145 (146-197)
Diamante, Stealth & 3000GT	181 (245)
Eclipse (With Disc Brakes)	144-188 (195-260)
Colt Vista, Expo & Summit Wagon	166 (230)
Precis	
Step 1	14 (19)
Step 2	[2] 0 (0)
Step 3	7 (9)

	INCH Lbs. (N.m)
Brakeline Nut	106-142 (12-16)
Dust Shield Bolt	89-124 (10-14)
Hub Assembly-To-Speed Sensor Rotor Bolts	89-124 (10-14)
Load Sensing Proportioning Valve Bracket Nut	89-124 (10-14)
Speed Sensor Bolts	89-124 (10-14)

[1] – Tighten with vehicle at normal operating height and no load.
[2] – Loosen nut to specification.

TORQUE SPECIFICATIONS (AWD)

Application	Ft. Lbs. (N.m)
Axle Shaft-To-Axle Shaft Flange Nut	40-47 (54-64)
Axle Shaft End Nut	145-188 (197-260)
Axle Shaft-To-Differential Nut	22-25 (30-34)
Brake Assembly Bolt	36-43 (49-58)
Brake Tube Bracket-To-Shock Absorber Bolt	12-19 (16-26)
Center Exhaust Pipe-To-Front Pipe Bolt	22-29 (30-39)
Companion Flange-To-Hub Nut	
Eclipse	116-159 (157-216)
Stealth & 3000GT	188-217 (260-300)
Crossmember Bracket-To-Body Bolt	51-61 (69-83)
Crossmember Bracket-To-Crossmember Bolt	80-94 (109-127)
Differential Carrier-To-Support Member Bolt	58-72 (79-98)
Differential Support-To-Body Nut	80-94 (109-127)
Lower Arm Ball Joint Nut	
Eclipse	43-52 (58-71)
Stealth & 3000GT	54-64 (73-87)
Lower Arm-To-Crossmember Nut [1]	
Except Stealth & 3000GT	65-80 (88-109)
Stealth & 3000GT	101-116 (137-157)
Muffler-To-Pipe Bolt	
Except Stealth & 3000GT	29-36 (39-49)
Stealth & 3000GT	22-29 (30-39)
Shock Absorber-To-Arm Bolt	65-80 (88-109)
Shock Absorber-To-Body Nut	29-36 (39-49)
Stabilizer Link-To-Stabilizer Bar Nut	25-33 (34-45)
Tie Rod End Nut	42 (58)
Trailing Arm-To-Crossmember Nut [1]	
Eclipse	101-116 (137-157)
Stealth & 3000GT	145-174 (197-236)
Upper Arm Ball Joint Nut	
Eclipse	43-52 (58-71)
Stealth & 3000GT	54-64 (73-87)
Upper Arm-To-Crossmember Nut [1]	101-116 (137-157)

	INCH Lbs. (N.m)
Speed Sensor Bolts	89-124 (10-14)
Stabilizer Bar Bracket Bolt	89-124 (10-14)

[1] – Tighten with vehicle at normal operating height and no load.

DESCRIPTION

The Electronically Controlled Suspension (ECS) uses compressed air to adjust vehicle height and ride characteristics while automatically compensating for loads and driving conditions.

The system has 3 driving heights (low, high and extra high), and 4 operational modes (soft, medium-soft, medium-firm and firm). This system also has a manual override option, enabling driver to select sport mode. In sport mode, suspension characteristics are automatically set to medium-firm or firm, depending on road conditions.

WARNING: Diamante is equipped with a Supplemental Restraint System (SRS) that includes an air bag located in steering column. Use caution when working around steering column. Ensure battery is disconnected before attempting any repair. DO NOT apply electrical power to any component on steering column without disconnecting air bag module (air bag could deploy).

OPERATION

System airflow is controlled by air compressor, solenoids, sensors, air springs and control module. *See Fig. 1.* Each coil spring is reinforced with an air spring. Air suspension leveling system operates by regulating pressure in air springs to maintain vehicle height at a predetermined level.

The suspension height is monitored by height sensors mounted in front and rear. The damping system works simultaneously with valves located inside strut housing to govern strut damping characteristics. Vehicle roll in turns is controlled by a "G" sensor located in front of engine compartment.

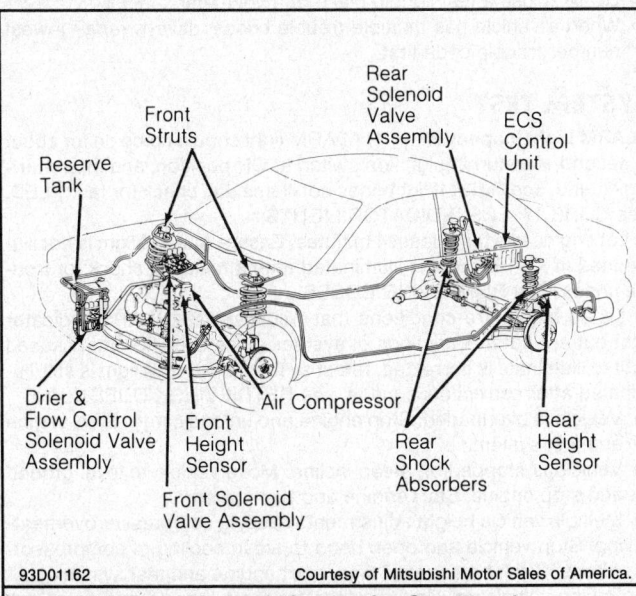

93D01162   Courtesy of Mitsubishi Motor Sales of America.

Fig. 1: Identifying Electronic Suspension Components

DISABLING & ACTIVATING AIR BAG SYSTEM

WARNING: Wait at least 60 seconds after disconnecting negative battery cable before servicing SRS. System reserve capacitor maintains SRS voltage for about 60 seconds after battery is disconnected. Servicing SRS before 60-second period may cause accidental air bag deployment and possible personal injury.

To disable system, turn ignition switch to OFF position. Disconnect and isolate negative battery cable end. Wait at least 60 seconds. To activate system, reconnect negative battery cable.

AIR BAG SERVICE PRECAUTIONS

The following precautions should be observed when working with SRS:

- Disable SRS before servicing any SRS or steering column component. Failure to do this may result in accidental air bag deployment and possible personal injury. See DISABLING & ACTIVATING AIR BAG SYSTEM.
- Wait at least 60 SECONDS after disabling air bag system. SRS system retains enough voltage, for a short time after system is disabled, to deploy air bag.
- Always wear safety glasses when servicing or handling an air bag.
- DO NOT expose air bag module and clockspring to temperatures greater than 200°F (93°C).
- When placing a live air bag on a bench or other surface, always face air bag and trim cover up, away from surface. This will reduce motion of module if air bag accidentally deploys.
- After air bag deploys, air bag surface may contain deposits of sodium hydroxide, which irritate skin. Always wear safety glasses, rubber gloves and long-sleeved shirt during clean-up. Wash hands using mild soap and water. Follow correct clean-up and disposal procedures.
- Because of critical system operating requirements, DO NOT service any SRS components. Repairs are only made by replacing defective part(s).
- DO NOT allow any electrical source near inflator on the back of air bag module.
- When carrying live air bag module, trim cover should be pointed away from body to minimize injury in case of accidental air bag deployment.
- If SRS is not fully functional for any reason, DO NOT drive vehicle until system is repaired and is fully functional. DO NOT remove bulbs, modules, sensors or other components, or in any way disable system from operating normally. If SRS is not functional, park vehicle until repairs are made.

ADJUSTMENTS

HEIGHT SENSOR RODS

Rod Length Adjustment – 1) Inspect for bent or damaged height sensor rod. Measure actuating rod length. *See Fig. 2.* Adjust height sensor rod length to specification. See HEIGHT SENSOR ROD LENGTH SPECIFICATIONS table.
2) Ensure adjusting sleeve is centered on threaded portion of height sensor rod. Tighten adjusting sleeve lock nuts to 84 INCH lbs. (10 N.m). Vehicle height is raised by lengthening height sensor rods and lowered by shortening height sensor rods.

HEIGHT SENSOR ROD LENGTH SPECIFICATIONS

Application	In. (mm)
Front Actuating Rod	10.5-10.6 (267-269)
Rear Actuating Rod	5.3-5.4 (135-137)

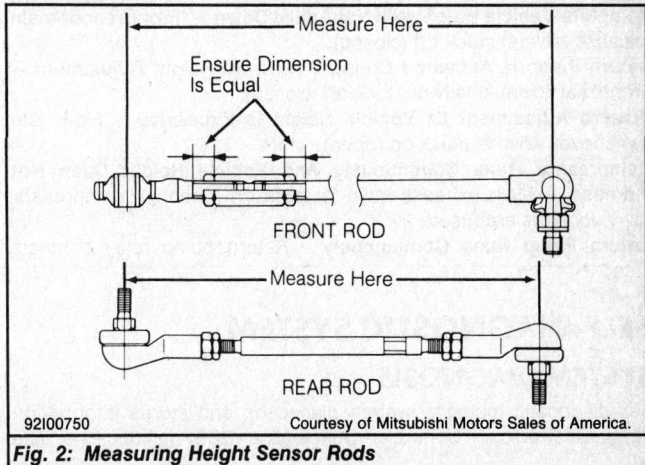

92I00750   Courtesy of Mitsubishi Motors Sales of America.

Fig. 2: Measuring Height Sensor Rods

VEHICLE HEIGHT

Vehicle Height Check – **1)** With vehicle unloaded, start engine and let idle for 3 minutes. Measure distance from top of wheelwell to center of axle for right front and left rear wheels. *See Fig. 3.* If vehicle height is not within specification, loosen turnbuckles on front and rear height sensor rods. Adjust height sensor rods to obtain correct vehicle riding height. See VEHICLE RIDING HEIGHT table. *See Fig. 3.*

2) Adjustments to vehicle height must be made with engine idling. After vehicle height is adjusted, ensure ALARM indicator light is off, indicating vehicle height adjustment is complete. For proper height sensor rod lengths, see HEIGHT SENSOR RODS under ADJUSTMENTS.

VEHICLE RIDING HEIGHT

Application	In. (mm)
Dimension A (Right Front)	15.4-15.8 (391-401)
Dimension B (Left Rear)	14.3-14.6 (363-371)

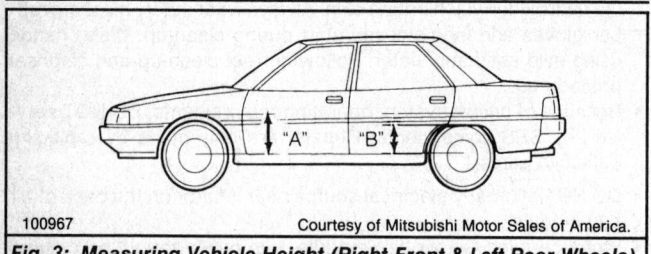

100967   Courtesy of Mitsubishi Motor Sales of America.

Fig. 3: Measuring Vehicle Height (Right Front & Left Rear Wheels)

TROUBLE SHOOTING

SYMPTOM DIAGNOSIS

Ensure all trouble codes are retrieved, repaired and cleared before preceding with symptom diagnosis. See RETRIEVING CODES and CLEARING CODES under SELF-DIAGNOSTIC SYSTEM. Mechanical components may malfunction due to corrosion or freezing caused by moisture penetration.

Height Decreases When Vehicle Is Parked – Check for air line and/or connections leakage and air valve(s) worn valve seat.

Vehicle Corner (LF, RF, LR & RR) Height Increases After Rolling Control – Air valve(s) is stuck on (closed).

Vehicle Corner (LF, RF, LR & RR) Height Decreases After Rolling Control – Air valve(s) is stuck on (open).

Vehicle Front Height Increases After Rolling Control – Front air supply valve is stuck on (open).

Vehicle Rear Height Increases After Rolling Control – Rear air supply valve is stuck on (open).

Vehicle Front Height Decreases After Rolling Control Or Vehicle Height Will Not Increase – Front air supply valve is stuck off (closed).

Vehicle Rear Height Decreases After Rolling Control Or Vehicle Height Will Not Increase – Rear air supply valve is stuck off (closed).

Complete Vehicle Height Will Not Adjust Down – Front/rear or main exhaust valve(s) stuck off (closed).

Return Pump Is Activated During Downward Height Adjustment – Front/rear exhaust valves stuck off (closed).

Upward Adjustment Of Vehicle Height Is Excessive – Flow rate switchover valve is stuck on (open).

Compressor Runs Continuously And Vehicle Height Does Not Increase – Main exhaust valve is stuck on (open) or compressor relay contacts are fused.

Return Pump Runs Continuously – Return pump relay contacts fused.

SELF-DIAGNOSTIC SYSTEM

SYSTEM DIAGNOSIS

Self-diagnostic memory system diagnoses and stores information about Electronically Controlled Suspension (ECS) malfunctions. The system has a fail-safe mode, which terminates ECS control to maintain driving stability when a malfunction is detected.

Self-diagnostic system warns driver of abnormal condition by illuminating ALARM light. *See Fig. 4.* Not all functions are monitored by diagnostic system, so not all malfunctions are detected.

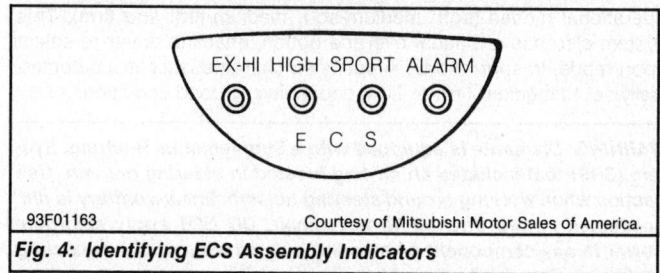

93F01163   Courtesy of Mitsubishi Motor Sales of America.

Fig. 4: Identifying ECS Assembly Indicators

SERVICE PRECAUTIONS

Before proceeding with diagnosis, following precautions must be observed:

- Ensure vehicle has a fully charged battery and functional charging system.
- Visually inspect connectors and circuit wiring being worked on.
- DO NOT disconnect battery or ECS control unit unless instructed by specific test. This will erase any trouble codes stored in control unit memory.
- DO NOT cause short circuits when performing electrical tests. This may set additional trouble codes, making diagnosis of original problem more difficult.
- DO NOT use a test light in place of a voltmeter.
- When a vehicle has multiple trouble codes, always repair lowest number trouble code first.

SYSTEM TEST

ALARM Light Inspection – **1)** ALARM light should come on for about .5 second after turning ignition switch to ON position, and after starting engine. *See Fig. 4.* If light does not illuminate, check for faulty LED. See CODE 17: ECS INDICATOR LIGHTS.

2) Let engine idle for at least 4 minutes. Ensure ALARM light is not illuminated. If ALARM light is illuminated after 4 minutes, check for trouble codes. See RETRIEVING CODES.

3) Listed below are conditions that will illuminate ALARM indicator light but are not malfunctions of system. Once condition that caused light to illuminate is corrected, retest system. If ALARM light is still illuminated after correction is made, see RETRIEVING CODES.

- Vehicle is overloaded. Stop engine and unload cargo. Start engine and test system.
- Vehicle is stopped on steep incline. Move vehicle to level ground and stop engine. Start engine and test system.
- Multiple vehicle height adjustments causing compressor overheating. Stop vehicle and open hood to aid in cooling of compressor. After sufficient amount of time, start engine and test system.
- Driving vehicle on winding roads for more than 18 minutes. Stop engine and allow return pump to cool down. After sufficient amount of time, start engine and test system.

RETRIEVING CODES

NOTE: Certain self-diagnostic testing and diagnostic procedures require Multi-Use Tester II (MB991341), ROM pack (MB991466) and supporting documentation. See Fig. 8. For testing and diagnostic procedures not requiring tester and documentation, begin by retrieving trouble code(s) using an analog voltmeter, and then test appropriate circuit or component for faults.

1) Turn ignition on. Connect an analog voltmeter to self-diagnostic connector located below driver's side of dash. Connect positive probe to diagnostic output terminal, and connect negative probe to ground terminal. *See Fig. 5.*

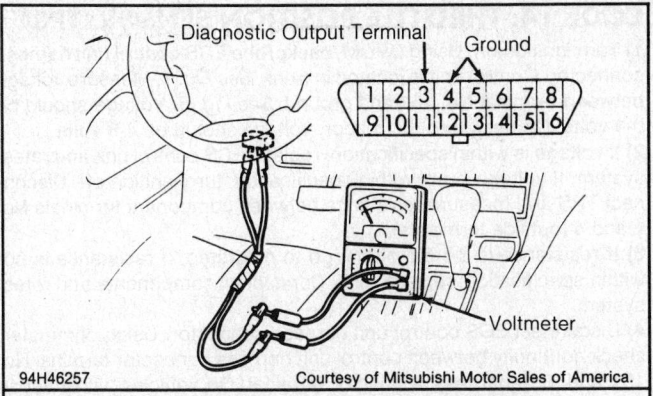

94H46257   Courtesy of Mitsubishi Motor Sales of America.

Fig. 5: Identifying Self-Diagnostic Connector Terminals

2) Voltage signals generated are read as needle sweeps. The needle sweep range is 0-12 volts. Longer duration pulses are recorded as the tens digit of code, and shorter duration pulses are recorded as ones digit of code. Codes are separated by a pause.

3) Record needle sweep pattern or output code(s). If 2 or more trouble codes are stored, lowest number code will be indicated first. See TROUBLE CODE IDENTIFICATION table. After repairs have been completed, erase trouble codes. See CLEARING CODES. Check for any other stored trouble codes.

TROUBLE CODE IDENTIFICATION

Code	Description
11	"G" Sensor
12	Generator "L" Terminal
13	Low-Pressure Switch
14	Throttle Position Sensor (TPS)
15	High-Pressure Switch
17	ECS Indicator Lights
18	Headlight Switch Circuit
21	Steering Wheel Sensor
22	Front Height Sensor
23	Rear Height Sensor
24	Vehicle Speed Sensor (VSS)
25	Rear Pressure Sensor
26	Brake Light Switch
31	Park/Neutral Position (PNP) Switch
33	Door Switch
34	Closed Throttle Position Switch
41	Damping Force Switching Actuator
42	ECS Power Supply Circuit
43	Compressor
44	Return Pump
45	Exhaust Valve
46	Flow-Rate Switchover Valve
47	Front/Rear Exhaust Valve
51	Front Or Rear Air Supply Valve
52	Left Front/Right Front Valves
53	Left Rear/Right Rear Valves
54	Vehicle Height Adjustments Do Not Stop
55	Compressor Operates Continuously
56	Return Pump Operates Continuously

CLEARING CODES

Turn ignition off. Disconnect negative battery cable for at least 10 seconds. Reconnect cable. Reset clock and radio memory. To stabilize engine controls, start engine and allow it to idle for at least 5 minutes under the following conditions:
- Steering wheel in neutral position
- All accessories in OFF position
- Transaxle selector set to "N" or "P" position on A/T models, or "N" on M/T models.

DIAGNOSTIC TESTS

CAUTION: Ensure ignition switch is in OFF position when performing resistance tests.

NOTE: Perform all resistance and voltage tests using a Digital Volt-Ohmmeter (DVOM) with a minimum 10-megohm impedance, unless stated otherwise in test procedures.

NOTE: For wire color identification at ECS control unit terminals, see ECS CONTROL UNIT under COMPONENT TESTS.

Clear trouble codes after each repair. See CLEARING CODES under SELF-DIAGNOSTIC SYSTEM. Recheck for codes to confirm repair. See RETRIEVING CODES under SELF-DIAGNOSTIC SYSTEM.

CODE 11: "G" SENSOR

1) Ensure vehicle is on level surface. Vehicle should be horizontal (no lean). Visually inspect condition of "G" sensor. Sensor consists of an iron core suspended in silicone oil. If any leakage is detected, replace sensor. Inspect sensor mounting surface for damage. Sensor should be upright. Repair as needed.

2) Turn ignition on. Using DVOM, backprobe ECS control unit. Control unit is located in trunk. *See Fig. 1.* Measure voltage between terminal No. 114 and ground. *See Fig. 6.* If voltage is 7-7.6 volts, go to next step. If voltage is not within specification, replace ECS control unit and retest.

3) Measure voltage between control unit terminal No. 108 and ground. If voltage 1.9-3.1 volts, replace control unit and retest. If voltage is not within specification, go to next step.

4) Turn ignition off. Disconnect ECS control unit harness connector. Disconnect "G" sensor harness connector. Using ohmmeter, check continuity between control unit harness connector terminal No. 114 and sensor harness connector terminal No. 1 (Red/Black wire).

5) If continuity does not exist, inspect and repair circuit as needed. Connect all components and retest. If continuity exists, connect ECS control unit harness connector. Check continuity between sensor harness connector terminal No. 3 (Black wire) and ground. If continuity does not exist, inspect and repair circuit as needed.

6) Disconnect ECS control unit harness connector. Check continuity between control unit harness connector terminal No. 108 and sensor harness connector terminal No. 2 (Green/Orange wire). If continuity exists, replace "G" sensor. If continuity does not exist, inspect and repair circuit as needed. Connect all components and retest.

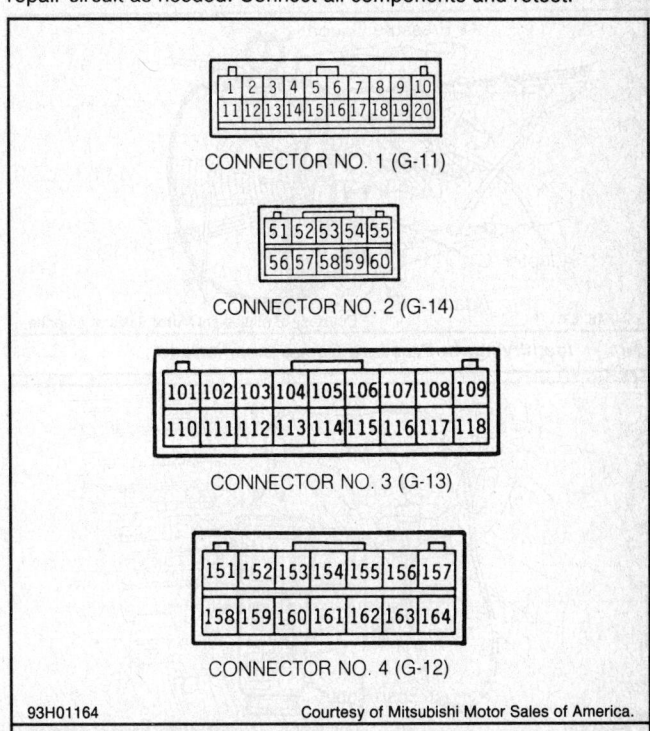

93H01164   Courtesy of Mitsubishi Motor Sales of America.

Fig. 6: Identifying ECS Control Unit Connector Terminals

1994 SUSPENSION
Electronic – Diamante (Cont.)

CODE 12: GENERATOR "L" TERMINAL

1) Start and run engine. Using DVOM, backprobe ECS control unit harness connector. Control unit is located in trunk. *See Fig. 1*. Measure voltage between terminal No. 152 and ground. *See Fig. 6*. If 13-15 volts is present, replace ECS control unit.

2) If voltage is not 13-15 volts, measure voltage between generator harness connector terminal No. 2 (White wire) and ground. If 13-15 volts is present, inspect and repair circuit between generator and control unit as needed. If voltage is not within specification, replace generator. Connect all components and retest.

CODE 13: LOW-PRESSURE SWITCH

1) The low-pressure switch operates between 10-20 psi (70-140 kPa). Remove joint "H" of blue marked air tube (left front valve) of front solenoid valve assembly. Connect Air Pressure Gauge (MB991075) with Adapters "C" (MB991075) and "E" (MB991226). *See Fig. 7*. Connect scan tester. *See Fig. 8*.

2) Start engine and wait until compressor discontinues operating. Input simulated vehicle speed of 2 MPH or greater. Conduct actuator test No. 9 or 10 with scan tester. This will increase pressure in low-pressure tank. As tank pressure increases, monitor air pressure gauge. Return pump should turn off when pressure reaches 16-24 psi (110-170 kPa).

3) Conduct actuator test No. 6 with scan tester. This will decrease pressure in low-pressure tank. Return pump should turn on when pressure reaches 6-14 psi (40-100 kPa). If return pump does not operate within specification, disconnect ECS control unit harness connector, located in trunk. *See Fig. 1*.

4) Using ohmmeter, check continuity between low-pressure switch harness connector terminal No. 2 (Black/White wire) and control unit harness connector terminal No. 118. If continuity does not exist, inspect and repair circuit as needed. Connect control unit harness connector.

5) Check continuity between switch harness connector terminal No. 3 (Black wire) and ground. If continuity does not exist, inspect and repair circuit as needed. If continuity exists in both circuits, replace low-pressure switch. Retest system to verify repair. If system is still at fault, inspect return pump. See CODE 44: RETURN PUMP. If return pump tests okay, replace ECS control unit and retest.

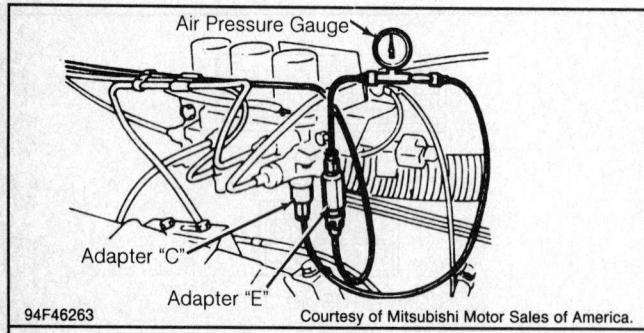

94F46263   Courtesy of Mitsubishi Motor Sales of America.

Fig. 7: Identifying Air Pressure Gauge Installation

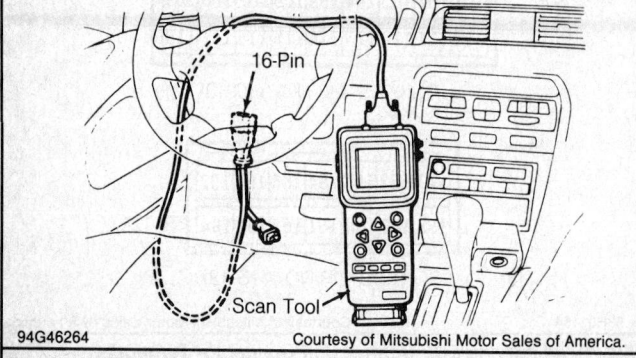

94G46264   Courtesy of Mitsubishi Motor Sales of America.

Fig. 8: Identifying Scan Tester

CODE 14: THROTTLE POSITION SENSOR (TPS)

1) Turn ignition on. Using DVOM, backprobe ECS control unit harness connector. Control unit is located in trunk. *See Fig. 1*. Measure voltage between terminal No. 151 and ground. *See Fig. 6*. Voltage should be 0-1 volts. Depress throttle to floor, voltage should be 4-8 volts.

2) If voltage is within specification, replace ECS control unit and retest system. If voltage is not within specification, turn ignition off. Disconnect TPS and measure resistance between component terminals No. 1 and 4 (outside terminals).

3) If resistance is 3.5-6.5 ohms, go to next step. If resistance is not within specification, replace TPS. Connect all components and retest system.

4) Disconnect ECS control unit harness connector. Using ohmmeter, check continuity between control unit harness connector terminal No. 151 and TPS harness connector terminal. On vehicles with traction control, connect to terminal No. 3 (Yellow/Red wire).

5) On vehicles without traction control, connect to terminal No. 2 (Brown/Red wire). Inspect and repair circuit as needed. Connect all components and retest system.

CODE 15: HIGH-PRESSURE SWITCH

1) The high-pressure switch operates between 108-128 psi (760-900 kPa). Remove joint "A" of Yellow marked air tube (front air supply valves) of front solenoid valve assembly. Connect Air Pressure Gauge (MB991075) with Adapter "E" (MB991226). Ensure shutoff valve of gauge is closed.

2) Start engine and wait until compressor discontinues operating. As tank pressure increases, monitor air pressure gauge. Compressor should turn off when pressure reaches 128 psi (900 kPa) or greater.

3) Slowly open pressure gauge shutoff valve. This will decrease pressure in high-pressure tank. Compressor should turn on when pressure reaches 101-115 psi (710-810 kPa). If return pump does not operate within specification, disconnect ECS control unit harness connector, located in trunk. *See Fig. 1*.

4) Using ohmmeter, check continuity between high-pressure switch harness connector terminal No. 1 (Black/Yellow wire) and control unit harness connector terminal No. 159. If continuity does not exist, inspect and repair circuit as needed. Connect control unit harness connector.

5) Check continuity between switch harness connector terminal No. 3 (Black wire) and ground. If continuity does not exist, inspect and repair circuit as needed. If continuity exists in both circuits, replace low-pressure switch. Retest system to verify repair. If system is still at fault, inspect compressor. See COMPONENT TESTS. If compressor tests okay, replace ECS control unit and retest.

CODE 17: ECS INDICATOR LIGHTS

1) Inspect fuse No. 11. Replace as needed. Ensure ignition is off. Disconnect ECS control unit harness connector. Turn ignition on. Using jumper wire, ground appropriate indicator light terminal and determine if light illuminates. See ECS CONTROL UNIT INDICATOR LIGHT CIRCUIT IDENTIFICATION table.

ECS CONTROL UNIT INDICATOR LIGHT CIRCUIT IDENTIFICATION [1]

Application	Terminal No.
EX-HI	6
HIGH	7
SPORT	8
ALARM	10

[1] – See Fig. 6.

2) If any indicator light does not illuminate, replace indicator light assembly. If all lights function properly, check continuity between ECS harness connector terminal No. 18 and ground. Ensure ECS mode switch is in SPORT position. If continuity exists, go to step **5)**. If continuity does not exist, go to next step.

3) Disconnect ECS mode switch harness connector. Check continuity between switch harness connector terminal No. 6 (Red/Black wire) and control unit harness connector terminal No. 18. If continuity does not exist, inspect and repair circuit as needed.

4) If continuity exists, check continuity between switch harness connector terminal No. 3 (Black wire) and ground. If continuity does not exist, repair circuit as needed. If continuity exists, replace ECS mode switch.

5) Check continuity between ECS harness connector terminal No. 20 and ground. Ensure ECS mode switch is in HIGH position. If continuity exists, replace ECS control unit. Connect all components and retest system. If continuity does not exist, go to next step.

6) Disconnect ECS mode switch harness connector. Check continuity between switch harness connector terminal No. 2 (Red/Green wire) and control unit harness connector terminal No. 20. If continuity does not exist, inspect and repair circuit as needed.

7) If continuity exists, check continuity between switch harness connector terminal No. 3 (Black wire) and ground. If continuity does not exist, repair circuit as needed. If continuity exists, replace ECS mode switch.

CODE 18: HEADLIGHT SWITCH CIRCUIT

1) Inspect fuse No. 3. Battery voltage is conducted through fuse with headlight switch on. Replace fuse as needed. Turn ignition switch and headlight switch on. Using DVOM, backprobe ECS control unit terminal No. 19. See Fig. 6.

2) If battery voltage is present, replace ECS control unit and retest. If battery voltage is not present, turn ignition switch and headlight switch off. Disconnect control unit harness connector.

3) Using ohmmeter, check continuity between fuse receptacle negative terminal (Yellow/Red wire) and control unit terminal No. 19. Repair circuit as needed.

CODE 21: STEERING WHEEL SENSOR

WARNING: Wait at least 60 seconds after disconnecting negative battery cable before servicing SRS. System reserve capacitor maintains SRS voltage for about 60 seconds after battery is disconnected. Servicing SRS before 60-second period may cause accidental air bag deployment and possible personal injury.

NOTE: Steering wheel angular velocity sensor is an electronic unit using photo-couplers. Clean hands and working environment are recommended to avoid contaminating this component.

1) Turn ignition on. Disconnect steering wheel sensor harness connector. See Fig. 9. See STEERING WHEEL ANGULAR VELOCITY SENSOR under REMOVAL & INSTALLATION. Using DVOM, measure voltage between sensor harness connector terminal No. 2 (Blue wire) and ground. If 4-8 volts is present, go to 3). If 4-8 volts is not present, go to next step.

2) Turn ignition off. Disconnect ECS control unit harness connector. Using ohmmeter, check continuity between control unit harness connector terminal No. 105 and sensor harness connector terminal No. 2. See Fig. 6. If continuity exists, replace control unit and retest. If continuity does not exist, inspect and repair circuit as needed.

3) Turn ignition off. Using ohmmeter, check continuity between sensor harness connector terminal No. 3 (Black wire) and ground. If continuity exists, go to step 5). If continuity does not exist, disconnect ECS control unit harness connector.

4) Check continuity between control unit harness connector terminal No. 116 and sensor harness connector terminal No. 3 (Black wire). If continuity exists, replace control unit and retest. If continuity does not exist, inspect and repair circuit as needed.

5) Connect steering wheel sensor harness connector. Turn ignition on. Backprobe control unit harness connector between terminal No. 153 and ground, using analog voltmeter. Turn steering wheel back and forth. Voltmeter pointer should pulse between 0-4 volts. Move positive lead of voltmeter to terminal No. 160 and repeat test.

6) If either circuit did not operate to specification, go to next step. If both circuits are okay, replace control unit and retest.

7) Turn ignition off. Disconnect sensor harness connector. Using ohmmeter, check continuity between control unit harness connector terminal No. 153 and sensor harness connector terminal No. 5 (Green wire).

If continuity does not exist, inspect and repair circuit as needed. Repeat step 5). If continuity exists, go to next step.

8) Check continuity between control unit harness connector terminal No. 160 and sensor harness connector terminal No. 4 (Yellow/Blue wire). If continuity does not exist, inspect and repair circuit as needed. Repeat step 5). If continuity exists, replace steering wheel sensor and retest.

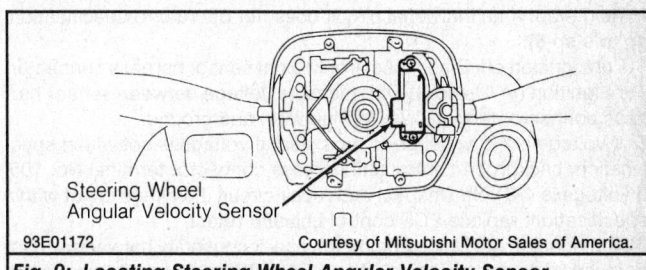

Fig. 9: Locating Steering Wheel Angular Velocity Sensor

CODE 22: FRONT HEIGHT SENSOR

1) Turn ignition on. Using analog voltmeter, backprobe ECS control unit harness connector. Connect voltmeter between harness connector terminal No. 154 and ground. See Fig. 6. Cycle front of vehicle up and down while monitoring voltmeter.

2) As front end of vehicle cycles, voltmeter needle should pulse from zero volts to 4-8 volts. Move voltmeter positive lead to control unit terminals No. 155, 156, then 157. Repeat test procedure for each circuit.

3) If needle pulses are observed for each circuit, replace control unit and retest system. If no needle pulses are observed for any circuit, go to next step. If an individual circuit does not operate to specification, go to step 8).

4) Turn ignition off. Disconnect front height sensor harness connector. Turn ignition on. Using DVOM, measure voltage between sensor harness connector terminal No. 6 (Blue wire) and ground.

5) If voltage is 4-8 volts, go to next step. If voltage is not within specification, backprobe control unit harness connector terminal No. 105. If voltage is 4-8 volts, inspect and repair circuit. If voltage is not within specification, replace control unit and retest.

6) Turn ignition off. Using ohmmeter, check continuity between sensor harness connector terminal No. 4 (Black/Blue wire) and ground. If continuity exists, replace front height sensor and retest. If continuity does not exist, backprobe ECS control unit harness connector terminal No. 116.

7) If continuity to ground is present, inspect and repair circuit between control unit and sensor. If continuity does not exist, replace ECS control unit and retest.

8) Turn ignition off. Disconnect control unit and front height sensor harness connector. Using ohmmeter, check continuity of suspected circuit. For sensor harness connector terminal identification, see FRONT HEIGHT SENSOR-TO-ECS CONTROL UNIT TERMINAL IDENTIFICATION table.

FRONT HEIGHT SENSOR-TO-ECS CONTROL UNIT TERMINAL IDENTIFICATION [1]

ECS Control Unit Terminal No.	Front Height Sensor Terminal No.	Wire Color
154	3	Green
155	2	Green/Black
156	1	Green/White
157	5	Green/Orange

[1] – For ECS control unit harness connector terminal identification, see Fig. 6.

9) If continuity does not exist, inspect and repair circuit as needed. If continuity exists, replace height sensor and retest system.

CODE 23: REAR HEIGHT SENSOR

1) Turn ignition on. Using analog voltmeter, backprobe ECS control unit harness connector. Connect voltmeter between harness connector terminal No. 161 and ground. *See Fig. 6.* Cycle rear of vehicle up and down while monitoring voltmeter.

2) As rear end of vehicle cycles, voltmeter needle should pulse from zero volts to 4-8 volts. Move voltmeter positive lead to control unit terminals No. 162, then 163. Repeat test procedure for each circuit.

3) If needle pulses are observed for each circuit, replace control unit and retest system. If no needle pulses are observed for any circuit, go to next step. If an individual circuit does not operate to specification, go to step **8)**.

4) Turn ignition off. Disconnect front height sensor harness connector. Turn ignition on. Using DVOM, measure voltage between sensor harness connector terminal No. 6 (Blue wire) and ground.

5) If voltage is 4-8 volts, go to next step. If voltage is not within specification, backprobe control unit harness connector terminal No. 105. If voltage is 4-8 volts, inspect and repair circuit. If voltage is not within specification, replace ECS control unit and retest.

6) Turn ignition off. Using ohmmeter, check continuity between sensor harness connector terminal No. 4 (Black/Blue wire) and ground. If continuity exists, replace front height sensor and retest. If continuity does not exist, backprobe ECS control unit harness connector terminal No. 116.

7) If continuity to ground is present, inspect and repair circuit between control unit and sensor. If continuity does not exist, replace ECS control unit and retest.

8) Turn ignition off. Disconnect control unit harness connector. Using ohmmeter, check continuity between harness connector terminals No. 116 and 164. If continuity exists, go to next step. If continuity does not exist, replace height sensor and retest.

9) Disconnect front height sensor harness connector. Using ohmmeter, check continuity of suspected circuit from test in step **3)**. For sensor harness connector terminal identification, see REAR HEIGHT SENSOR-TO-ECS CONTROL UNIT TERMINAL IDENTIFICATION table.

10) If continuity does not exist, inspect and repair circuit as needed. If continuity exists, replace height sensor and retest system.

REAR HEIGHT SENSOR-TO-ECS CONTROL UNIT TERMINAL IDENTIFICATION [1]

ECS Control Unit Terminal No.	Front Height Sensor Terminal No.	Wire Color
161	3	Yellow
162	2	Yellow/Black
163	1	Yellow/White

[1] – For ECS control unit harness connector terminal identification, *see Fig. 6.*

CODE 24: VEHICLE SPEED SENSOR

1) Ensure ignition is off. Disconnect ECS control unit harness connector. Control unit is located in trunk. *See Fig. 1.* Lift and support vehicle until wheels are off ground. Using an analog voltmeter, measure voltage between ECS control unit harness connector terminal No. 158 and ground while turning front wheels. *See Fig. 6.*

2) If voltmeter displays full sweep pulses of pointer, VSS is operating properly. Replace ECS control unit and retest. If voltmeter shows no pointer fluctuation, remove combination meter. VSS is located in combination meter. Removal and installation of instrument panel is basically and unbolt and bolt-on procedure.

3) Remove combination meter harness connector. Turn ignition on. Using DVOM, measure voltage between combination meter harness connector terminal No. 9 and ground. *See Fig. 10.* Voltage should be 7-9 volts. If voltage is not within specification, inspect and repair circuit between combination meter and ECS control unit.

4) If voltage is within specification, turn ignition off. Check continuity between combination meter harness connector terminal No. 13 and ground. If continuity does not exist, inspect and repair circuit as needed. If continuity does exist, disassemble combination meter and replace speedometer. Reconnect all components and retest system to verify repair.

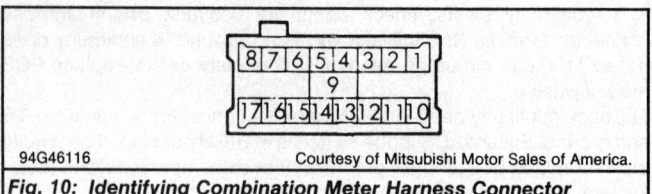

Fig. 10: Identifying Combination Meter Harness Connector

94G46116   Courtesy of Mitsubishi Motor Sales of America.

CODE 25: REAR PRESSURE SENSOR

1) Turn ignition on. Using DVOM, backprobe ECS control unit. Control unit is located in trunk. *See Fig. 1.* Measure voltage between control unit harness connector terminal No. 117 and ground. *See Fig. 6.* Voltage should range from .5-4.5 volts, depending on load in vehicle (rear air spring pressure).

2) If voltage is within specification, replace ECS control unit and retest. If voltage is not within specification, turn ignition off. Disconnect control unit harness connector. Using ohmmeter, measure resistance between control unit harness connector terminals No. 105 and 115.

3) If resistance is 3.5-7.0 k/ohms, go to step **5)**. If resistance not within specification, disconnect rear solenoid valve assembly harness connector. Solenoid assembly is located next to control unit. Measure resistance between solenoid harness connector terminals No. 6 (Blue wire) and No. 8 (Black wire).

4) If resistance is 3.5-7.0 k/ohms, inspect and repair circuits between rear solenoid valve assembly and ECS control unit. If resistance is not within specification, replace rear pressure sensor and retest system.

5) Measure resistance between control unit harness connector terminals No. 115 and 117. If resistance is 0-5 k/ohms, pressure sensor is functioning properly. Check all harness connections. Check for possible air leaks and retest system.

6) If resistance is not within specification, disconnect rear solenoid valve assembly harness connector and measure resistance between terminals No. 7 (Yellow/Blue wire) and No. 8 (Black wire).

7) If resistance is not 0-5 k/ohms, replace pressure sensor. If resistance is within specification, inspect and repair circuit between control unit harness connector terminal No. 117 and solenoid harness connector terminal No. 7. Connect all components and retest system.

CODE 26: BRAKELIGHT SWITCH

1) Inspect fuse No. 17. Replace as needed. Turn ignition on. Using DVOM, backprobe ECS control unit. Control unit is located in trunk. *See Fig. 1.* Measure voltage between control unit harness connector terminal No. 13 and ground. *See Fig. 6.*

2) With brake pedal not depressed, battery voltage should be present. Depress brake pedal. Voltage should drop to zero volts. If voltage is within specification, replace ECS control unit and retest system.

3) If voltage is not within specification, turn ignition off. Disconnect brakelight switch harness connector. Turn ignition on. Measure voltage between switch harness connector terminal No. 2 (Green/Black wire) and ground. If battery voltage is not present, inspect and repair circuit between brakelight switch and fuse No. 17.

4) If battery voltage is present, turn ignition off. Using ohmmeter, check continuity between switch component terminals No. 2 (Green/Black wire) and No. 3 (Green wire). Continuity should exist with brake pedal depressed.

5) If switch operates as specified, inspect and repair circuit between brakelight switch and ECS control unit. If switch does not operate as specified, replace switch and retest system.

CODE 31: PARK/NEUTRAL POSITION (PNP) SWITCH

1) Inspect fuse No. 7. Replace as needed. Turn ignition on. Using DVOM, backprobe ECS control unit. Control unit is located in trunk. *See Fig. 1.* Move shift lever to Reverse "R" position. Measure voltage between control unit terminal No. 2 and vehicle ground. *See Fig. 6.*

2) If battery voltage is present, replace ECS control unit and retest. If battery voltage is not present, disconnect PNP harness connector. Measure voltage between PNP harness connector terminal No. 3 and ground. *See Fig. 11.*

3) If battery voltage is not present, inspect and repair circuit between fuse No. 7 and PNP switch. If battery voltage is present, turn ignition off. Disconnect ECS control unit harness connector. Using ohmmeter, check continuity between control unit harness connector terminal No. 2 and PNP harness connector terminal No. 2.

4) If continuity does not exist, inspect and repair circuit as needed. If continuity exists, replace PNP switch and retest system. See REMOVAL & INSTALLATION.

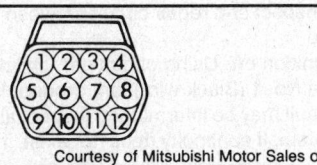

94I44600   Courtesy of Mitsubishi Motor Sales of America.

Fig. 11: Identifying PNP Switch Harness Connector

CODE 33: DOOR SWITCH

1) Turn ignition on. Using DVOM, backprobe ECS control unit harness connector. Measure voltage between terminal No. 4 and ground. If battery voltage is present, go to next step. If battery voltage is not present, replace control unit and retest system.

2) While monitoring voltage, open and close each vehicle door. When door is open, voltage should drop to zero and return to battery voltage when door is closed. If voltage is as specified, system is operating properly. Check for poor harness connections and retest.

3) If voltage is not as specified for all door switches, inspect circuit between ECS control unit and sub-circuit harness connector terminal No. 5 (Green/Red wire). Sub-circuit connector (22-pin) is located under carpet next to passenger side center door pillar.

4) If voltage is not as specified for individual door switch(es), remove suspected door switch. Using ohmmeter, check continuity between switch terminal No. 1 (Green/Red wire) and switch mounting surface.

5) Depress and release switch button. Ohmmeter continuity reading should pulse. Replace switch as needed. If switch tests okay, inspect and repair circuit between switch and ECS control unit.

CODE 34: CLOSED THROTTLE POSITION SWITCH

1) Turn ignition on. Using DVOM, backprobe ECS control unit. Control unit is located in trunk. See Fig. 1. Measure voltage between control unit harness connector terminal No. 12 and ground.

2) With throttle pedal not depressed, 4-8 volts should be present. Depress throttle pedal. Voltage should drop to zero volts. If voltage is within specification, replace ECS control unit and retest system.

3) If voltage is not within specification, turn ignition off. Disconnect Throttle Position Sensor (TPS) harness connector. Using ohmmeter, check continuity between specified component terminals. For terminal identification, see CLOSED THROTTLE POSITION SENSOR TERMINAL IDENTIFICATION table.

CLOSED THROTTLE POSITION SENSOR TERMINAL IDENTIFICATION

Terminal No.	Wire Color
With Traction Control	
1	Blue
2	Yellow/Blue
Without Traction Control	
3	Yellow/Blue
4	Blue

4) Continuity should exist with throttle closed. With throttle open, continuity should not exist. If closed throttle position switch operates as specified, go to next step. Replace TPS if switch does not operate as specified. See REMOVAL & INSTALLATION. Connect all components and retest.

5) Inspect and repair circuit between TPS and ECS control unit. If circuit is okay, Engine Control Module (ECM) may be at fault. See appropriate SELF-DIAGNOSTICS article in ENGINE PERFORMANCE.

CODE 41: DAMPING FORCE SWITCHING ACTUATOR

NOTE: Damping force switching actuators are located on top of strut assemblies.

1) Ensure ignition is off. Disconnect ECS control unit. Using ohmmeter, measure resistance between control unit harness connector terminals No. 51 and 56, then between terminals No. 52 and 57. Resistance should be 6.1-6.7 ohms.

2) If either resistance is not within specification, go to step **4)**. If resistances are within specification, actuator stepper motor coils are okay. Connect control unit harness connector. Using scan tester, perform actuator tests 01, 02, 03 and 04. Monitor each damping actuator during each test. If actuator can be heard operating, component is okay.

3) If all actuators are heard operating during each test, system is functioning properly. Trouble code may be set due to intermittent problem. Check all harness connections. If one or more actuators do not operate properly, replace ECS control unit and retest.

4) Ensure ignition is off. Disconnect ECS control unit. Check continuity of all circuits suspected of short or open. For circuit identification, see WIRING DIAGRAM. Inspect and repair circuits as needed. Once faulty circuit(s) are repaired, conduct actuator testing explained in step **2)**.

CODE 42: ECS POWER SUPPLY CIRCUIT

1) Inspect fuses No. 2, 13 and 19. Replace fuses as needed. Using DVOM, backprobe ECS control unit terminal No. 55. Control unit is located in trunk. See Figs. 1 and 6. Turn ignition on. If battery voltage is present, go to step **7)**. If battery voltage is not present, go to next step.

2) Turn ignition off. Remove and inspect ECS power relay. See Fig. 12. See RELAYS under COMPONENT TESTS. Replace as needed. If relay is okay, turn ignition on. Measure voltage between ECS power relay receptacle terminal No. 4 and ground. See Fig. 13.

3) If battery voltage is present, go to next step. If battery voltage is not present, inspect and repair circuit between fuse No. 2 and relay receptacle.

4) Turn ignition off. Using ohmmeter, check continuity between relay receptacle terminal No. 2 and ground. See Fig. 13. If continuity is not present, inspect and repair circuit as needed.

5) Using DVOM, measure voltage between ECS power relay receptacle No. 3 and ground. If battery voltage is present, go to next step. If battery voltage is not present, inspect and repair circuit between fuse No. 13 and relay receptacle.

6) Disconnect control unit harness connector. Using ohmmeter, check continuity between relay receptacle terminal No. 1 and control unit harness connector terminal No. 55. See Fig. 6. If continuity exists, go to next step. If continuity does not exist, inspect and repair circuit as needed.

7) Ensure ignition is on. Backprobe ECS control unit terminal No. 58. If battery voltage is present, go to step **12)**. If battery voltage is not present, turn ignition off. Remove and inspect solenoid valve power relay. See RELAYS under COMPONENT TESTS. Replace relay as needed.

8) If relay tests okay, measure voltage between relay receptacle terminals No. 3 and 4, and ground. If battery voltage is present, go to next step. If battery voltage is not present, inspect and repair circuits between relay receptacle and fuse No. 2.

9) Turn ignition off. Disconnect control unit harness connector. Using ohmmeter, check continuity between control unit harness connector terminal No. 58 and relay receptacle terminal No. 1. See Figs. 6 and 13.

10) If continuity does not exist, inspect and repair circuit as needed. If continuity exists, check continuity between control unit harness connector terminal No. 106 and relay receptacle terminal No. 2.

11) If continuity does not exist, inspect and repair circuit as needed. If continuity exists, ECS control unit may be at fault or ECS is in fail-safe mode. If ECS system is in fail-safe mode, relay ground signal will be disabled. Ensure all trouble codes other than Code 42 (if present) are repaired first. Erase codes, see CLEARING CODES. If Code 42 is reset after retrieving codes, substitute ECS control unit with known good control unit and retest.

12) With ECS control unit harness connector disconnected, measure voltage between terminal No. 60 and ground. If battery voltage is not present, inspect and repair circuit between fuse No. 19 and terminal No. 60. If battery voltage is present, replace ECS control unit.

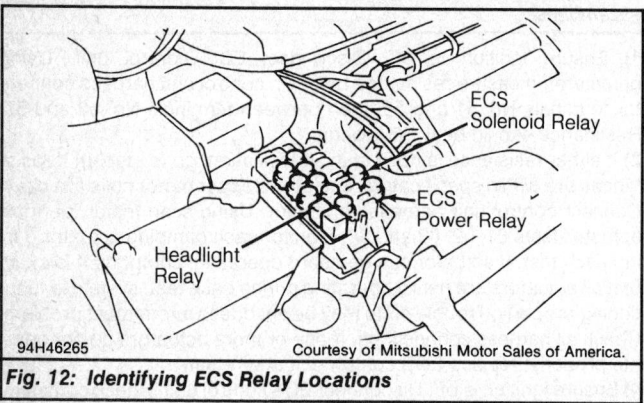

94H46265   Courtesy of Mitsubishi Motor Sales of America.

Fig. 12: Identifying ECS Relay Locations

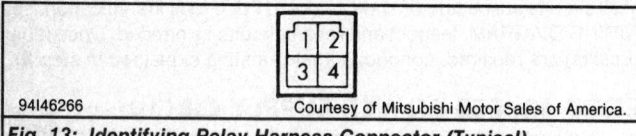

94I46266   Courtesy of Mitsubishi Motor Sales of America.

Fig. 13: Identifying Relay Harness Connector (Typical)

CODE 43: COMPRESSOR

1) Ensure ignition is off. Connect scan tester and perform actuator test 05. Compressor should operate for 3 seconds. If compressor operates as specified, problem may be intermittent. Inspect all harness connections and retest.

2) If compressor does not operate as specified, turn ignition off. Bleed off system pressure until air pressure is less than 108 PSI (760 kPa). See CODE 15. Using DVOM, backprobe ECS control unit harness connector. Control unit is located in trunk. See Fig. 1.

3) Turn ignition on. Measure voltage between control unit harness connector terminal No. 103 and ground. If battery voltage is not present, replace ECS control unit and retest. If battery voltage is present, disconnect compressor harness connector.

4) Measure voltage between compressor harness connector terminal No. 1 (Red/White wire) and ground (harness connector terminal No. 2, Black wire). If battery voltage is present, replace compressor. See REMOVAL & INSTALLATION. If battery voltage is not present, inspect compressor relay. See RELAYS under COMPONENT TESTS.

5) Replace relay as needed. If relay tests okay, measure voltage between relay receptacle terminal No. 3 (White/Blue wire) and ground. If battery voltage is present, go to next step. If battery voltage is not present, inspect and repair circuit between ECS control unit and relay receptacle.

6) Turn ignition off. Using ohmmeter, check continuity between relay receptacle No. 1 (Black wire) and ground. If continuity exists, system is okay. Fault may be intermittent. Inspect all harness connections and retest system. If continuity does not exist, inspect and repair circuit as needed.

CODE 44: RETURN PUMP

1) Ensure ignition is off. Connect scan tester and perform actuator test 06. Return pump should operate for 3 seconds. If return pump operates as specified, problem may be intermittent. Inspect all harness connections and retest.

2) If return pump does not operate as specified, turn ignition off. Connect air pressure gauge. See CODE 13. Ensure low pressure tank pressure is at least 20 psi (140 kPa). Using DVOM, backprobe ECS control unit harness connector. Control unit is located in trunk. See Fig. 1.

3) Turn ignition on. Measure voltage between control unit harness connector terminal No. 112 and ground. If battery voltage is not present, replace ECS control unit and retest. If battery voltage is present, disconnect return pump harness connector.

4) Measure voltage between return pump harness connector terminal No. 1 (Red wire) and ground (harness connector terminal No. 2, Black wire). If battery voltage is present, replace return pump. If battery voltage is not present, inspect return pump relay. See RELAYS under COMPONENT TESTS.

5) Replace relay as needed. If relay tests okay, measure voltage between relay receptacle terminal No. 3 (White/Red wire) and ground. If battery voltage is present, go to next step. If battery voltage is not present, inspect and repair circuit between ECS control unit and relay receptacle.

6) Turn ignition off. Using ohmmeter, check continuity between relay receptacle No. 1 (Black wire) and ground. If continuity exists, system is okay. Fault may be intermittent. Inspect all harness connections and retest system. If continuity does not exist, inspect and repair circuit as needed.

CODE 45: EXHAUST VALVE

1) Ensure ignition is off. Connect scan tester and perform actuator test 07. Exhaust valve should operate. If exhaust valve operates as specified, problem may be intermittent. Inspect all harness connections and retest.

2) If exhaust valve does not operate, backprobe ECS control unit using DVOM. Measure voltage between control unit harness connector terminal No. 111 and ground. Repeat actuator test 07. If battery voltage is present, go to next step. If battery voltage is not present, replace control unit and retest.

3) Turn ignition off. Disconnect control unit harness connector. Using ohmmeter, measure resistance between control unit harness connector terminal No. 111 and ground. If resistance is 14-16 ohms, go to step 7). If resistance is not 14-16 ohms, go to next step.

4) Disconnect exhaust valve harness connector. Measure resistance between exhaust valve component terminals. If resistance is 14-16 ohms, go to step 7). If resistance is not within specification, go to next step.

5) Check continuity between control unit harness connector terminal No. 111 and exhaust valve harness connector terminal No. 2 (Red/Yellow wire). If continuity exists, go to next step. If continuity does not exist, inspect and repair circuit as needed.

6) Check continuity between exhaust valve harness connector terminal No. 1 (Black wire) and ground. If continuity does not exist, inspect and repair circuit as needed. If continuity does exist, go to next step.

7) Connect a alternate battery voltage source to exhaust valve component connector. Connect positive lead to terminal No. 2 (Red/Yellow wire). If valve operates, fault may be intermittent. Inspect all harness connectors and retest. Replace valve if it fails to operate.

CODE 46: FLOW-RATE SWITCHOVER VALVE

1) Ensure ignition is off. Connect scan tester and perform actuator test 07. Switchover valve should operate. If switchover valve operates as specified, problem may be intermittent. Inspect all harness connections and retest.

2) If valve fails to operate, turn ignition off. Using DVOM, backprobe ECS control unit harness connector. Control unit is located in trunk. See Fig. 1. Measure voltage between control unit harness connector terminal No. 102 and ground. See Fig. 6. Repeat test in step 1).

3) If battery voltage is not present, replace control unit and retest. If battery voltage is present, turn ignition off. Disconnect control unit harness connector. Using ohmmeter, measure resistance between control unit harness connector terminal No. 102 and ground.

4) If resistance is 8.5-13.5 ohms, component is okay. If component is suspected of fault, check switchover valve. See SOLENOID VALVE ASSEMBLIES under COMPONENT TESTS. If resistance is not 8.5-13.5 ohms, disconnect valve harness connector.

5) Check continuity between ECS control unit harness connector terminal No. 102 and valve harness connector terminal No. 2 (White/Blue wire). If continuity exists, go to next step. If continuity does not exist, inspect and repair circuit as needed. Connect all components and retest.

6) Check continuity between valve harness connector terminal No. 1 (Black wire) and ground. If continuity does not exist, inspect and repair circuit as needed. If continuity does exist, solenoid valve may be faulty. Check switchover valve. See SOLENOID VALVE ASSEMBLIES under COMPONENT TESTS. Replace as needed and retest system.

CODE 47: FRONT/REAR EXHAUST VALVE

1) Ensure ignition is off. Connect scan tester and perform actuator test 07, 09 and 10. Exhaust valves should operate. If exhaust valves operate as specified, problem may be intermittent. Inspect all harness connections and retest.

2) If valves fail to operate, turn ignition off. Using DVOM, backprobe ECS control unit harness connector. Control unit is located in trunk. *See Fig. 1.* Measure voltage between control unit harness connector terminal No. 104 and ground, then terminal No. 113 and ground. *See Fig. 6.* Repeat test in step 1).

3) If battery voltage is not present in either circuit, replace control unit and retest. If battery voltage is present, turn ignition off. Disconnect control unit harness connector. Using ohmmeter, measure resistance between control unit harness connector terminal No. 104 and ground, then terminal No. 113 and ground.

4) If resistances are 8.5-13.5 ohms, component is okay. If component is suspected of fault, check front/rear exhaust valve. See SOLENOID VALVE ASSEMBLIES under COMPONENT TESTS. If resistance is not 8.5-13.5 ohms, disconnect valve harness connector.

5) Check continuity between ECS control unit harness connector terminal No. 104 and valve harness connector terminal No. 3 (White/Red wire) for front exhaust valve. Check continuity between ECS control unit harness connector terminal No. 113 and valve harness connector terminal No. 4 (White/Green wire) for rear exhaust valve.

6) If continuity exists in both circuits, go to next step. If continuity does not exist in either circuit, inspect and repair faulty circuit as needed. Connect all components and retest. Check continuity between valve harness connector terminal No. 1 (Black wire) and ground. If continuity does not exist, inspect and repair circuit as needed. If continuity does exist, solenoid valve may be faulty. Check front/rear exhaust valves. See SOLENOID VALVE ASSEMBLIES under COMPONENT TESTS. Replace as needed and retest system.

CODE 51: FRONT OR REAR AIR SUPPLY VALVE

NOTE: Code 51 may be set for either front or rear air supply valve.

Front Air Supply Valve – 1) Ensure ignition is off. Connect scan tester and perform actuator test 08, 09 and 10. Air supply valve should operate. If valve operates as specified, problem may be intermittent. Inspect all harness connections and retest.

2) If valve fails to operate, turn ignition off. Using DVOM, backprobe ECS control unit harness connector. Control unit is located in trunk. *See Fig. 1.* Measure voltage between control unit harness connector terminal No. 101 and ground. *See Fig. 6.* Repeat test in step 1).

3) If battery voltage is not present, replace control unit and retest. If battery voltage is present, turn ignition off. Disconnect control unit harness connector. Using ohmmeter, measure resistance between control unit harness connector terminal No. 101 and ground.

4) If resistance is 8.5-13.5 ohms, component is okay. If component is suspected of fault, check front air supply valve. See SOLENOID VALVE ASSEMBLIES under COMPONENT TESTS. If resistance is not 8.5-13.5 ohms, disconnect valve harness connector.

5) Check continuity between ECS control unit harness connector terminal No. 101 and valve harness connector terminal No. 2 (Light Green/White wire). If continuity exists, go to next step. If continuity does not exist, inspect and repair circuit as needed. Connect all components and retest.

6) Check continuity between valve harness connector terminal No. 1 (Black wire) and ground. If continuity does not exist, inspect and repair circuit as needed. If continuity does exist, solenoid valve may be faulty. Check air supply valve. See SOLENOID VALVE ASSEMBLIES under COMPONENT TESTS. Replace valve as needed and retest system.

Rear Air Supply Valve – 1) Ensure ignition is off. Connect scan tester and perform actuator test 08, 09 and 10. Air supply valve should oper-

ate. If valve operates as specified, problem may be intermittent. Inspect all harness connections and retest.

2) If valve fails to operate, turn ignition off. Using DVOM, backprobe ECS control unit harness connector. Control unit is located in trunk. *See Fig. 1.* Measure voltage between control unit harness connector terminal No. 101 and ground. *See Fig. 6.* Repeat test in step 1).

3) If battery voltage is not present, replace control unit and retest. If battery voltage is present, turn ignition off. Disconnect control unit harness connector. Using ohmmeter, measure resistance between control unit harness connector terminal No. 110 and ground.

4) If resistance is 8.5-13.5 ohms, component is okay. If component is suspected of fault, check front air supply valve. See SOLENOID VALVE ASSEMBLIES under COMPONENT TESTS. If resistance is not 8.5-13.5 ohms, disconnect valve harness connector.

5) Check continuity between ECS control unit harness connector terminal No. 110 and valve harness connector terminal No. 2 (Red/White wire). If continuity exists, go to next step. If continuity does not exist, inspect and repair circuit as needed. Connect all components and retest.

6) Check continuity between valve harness connector terminal No. 1 (Black wire) and ground. If continuity does not exist, inspect and repair circuit as needed. If continuity does exist, solenoid valve may be faulty. Check air supply valve. See SOLENOID VALVE ASSEMBLIES under COMPONENT TESTS. Replace valve as needed and retest system.

CODE 52: LEFT FRONT/RIGHT FRONT VALVES

1) Ensure ignition is off. Connect scan tester and perform actuator test 07, 09 and 10. Exhaust valves should operate. If valves operate as specified, problem may be intermittent. Inspect all harness connections and retest.

2) If valves fail to operate, turn ignition off. Using DVOM, backprobe ECS control unit harness connector. Control unit is located in trunk. *See Fig. 1.* Measure voltage between control unit harness connector terminal No. 53 and ground, then terminal No. 54 and ground. *See Fig. 6.* Repeat test in step 1).

3) If battery voltage is not present in either circuit, replace control unit and retest. If battery voltage is present, turn ignition off. Disconnect control unit harness connector. Using ohmmeter, measure resistance between control unit harness connector terminal No. 53 and ground, then terminal No. 54 and ground.

4) If resistances is 8.5-13.5 ohms, component is okay. If component is suspected of fault, check left front/right front valve. See SOLENOID VALVE ASSEMBLIES under COMPONENT TESTS. If resistances are not 8.5-13.5 ohms, disconnect valve harness connector.

5) Check continuity between ECS control unit harness connector terminal No. 53 and valve harness connector terminal No. 3 (Light Green/Blue wire) for left front valve. Check continuity between ECS control unit harness connector terminal No. 54 and valve harness connector terminal No. 4 (Light Green/Green wire) for right front valve.

6) If continuity exists in both circuits, go to next step. If continuity does not exist in either circuit, inspect and repair faulty circuit as needed. Connect all components and retest. Check continuity between valve harness connector terminal No. 1 (Black wire) and ground. If continuity does not exist, inspect and repair circuit as needed. If continuity does exist, solenoid valve may be faulty. Check left front/right front valves. See SOLENOID VALVE ASSEMBLIES under COMPONENT TESTS. Replace as needed and retest system.

CODE 53: LEFT REAR/RIGHT REAR VALVES

1) Ensure ignition is off. Connect scan tester and perform actuator test 07, 09 and 10. Exhaust valves should operate. If valves operate as specified, problem may be intermittent. Inspect all harness connections and retest.

2) If valves fail to operate, turn ignition off. Using DVOM, backprobe ECS control unit harness connector. Control unit is located in trunk. *See Fig. 1.* Measure voltage between control unit harness connector terminal No. 107 and ground, then terminal No. 109 and ground. *See Fig. 6.* Repeat test in step 1).

3) If battery voltage is not present in either circuit, replace control unit and retest. If battery voltage is present, turn ignition off. Disconnect control unit harness connector. Using ohmmeter, measure resistance

between control unit harness connector terminal No. 107 and ground, then terminal No. 109 and ground.

4) If resistances is 8.5-13.5 ohms, component is okay. If component is suspected of fault, check left rear/right rear valve. See SOLENOID VALVE ASSEMBLIES under COMPONENT TESTS. If resistances are not 8.5-13.5 ohms, disconnect valve harness connector.

5) Check continuity between ECS control unit harness connector terminal No. 109 and valve harness connector terminal No. 3 (Red/Blue wire) for left rear valve. Check continuity between ECS control unit harness connector terminal No. 107 and valve harness connector terminal No. 4 (Red/Green wire) for right rear valve.

6) If continuity exists in both circuits, go to next step. If continuity does not exist in either circuit, inspect and repair faulty circuit as needed. Connect all components and retest. Check continuity between valve harness connector terminal No. 1 (Black wire) and ground. If continuity does not exist, inspect and repair circuit as needed. If continuity does exist, solenoid valve may be faulty. Check left rear/right rear valves. See SOLENOID VALVE ASSEMBLIES under COMPONENT TESTS. Replace as needed and retest system.

CODE 54: VEHICLE HEIGHT ADJUSTMENTS DO NOT STOP

1) Ensure vehicle is not overloaded. Unload vehicle as needed and retest. Check both height sensor adjustments. See ADJUSTMENTS. If vehicle sensors are correctly adjusted, see Codes 22 and 23. Also see HEIGHT SENSORS under COMPONENT TESTS.

2) Inspect condition of air spring. If vehicle has been lifted, then lowered quickly, damage to air spring diaphragm (folding) may have occurred. Can solenoids be heard operating. Solenoid valves may be leaking (worn valve seat) causing constant adjustment.

3) If solenoids are operating, check air pressure measurement. See Code 15. If pressure measurement is greater than 135 psi (950 kPa) and high-pressure switch is okay, air line clogs or poor system harness connections may cause fault. Repair as needed.

CODE 55: COMPRESSOR OPERATES CONTINUOUSLY

Determine if compressor is functioning correctly. See CODE 43. Repair as needed. Determine if air pressure is correct. See CODE 13 and CODE 14. Repair as needed.

CODE 56: RETURN PUMP OPERATES CONTINUOUSLY

Check for air leakage from any air supply valve. Repair as needed.

COMPONENT TESTS

AIR COMPRESSOR & EXHAUST VALVE

Function Test – 1) Remove air compressor. See AIR COMPRESSOR under REMOVAL & INSTALLATION. Using Air Pressure Gauge (MB991075) and Adapter ("C"), connect air compressor to gauge side of tool.

2) Apply battery voltage between air compressor terminals No. 1 and 2. *See Fig. 14.* Check pressure relief valve operation. Pressure relief valve should operate at 142-185 psi (10.0-13.0 kg/cm²).

3) Remove compressor from gauge. With air pressure held, apply battery voltage between terminals No. 3 and 4. *See Fig. 14.* Ensure a click is heard and air pressure is slowly released.

4) If pressure relief valve does not function as described, or there is a malfunction of exhaust solenoid valve, replace air compressor.

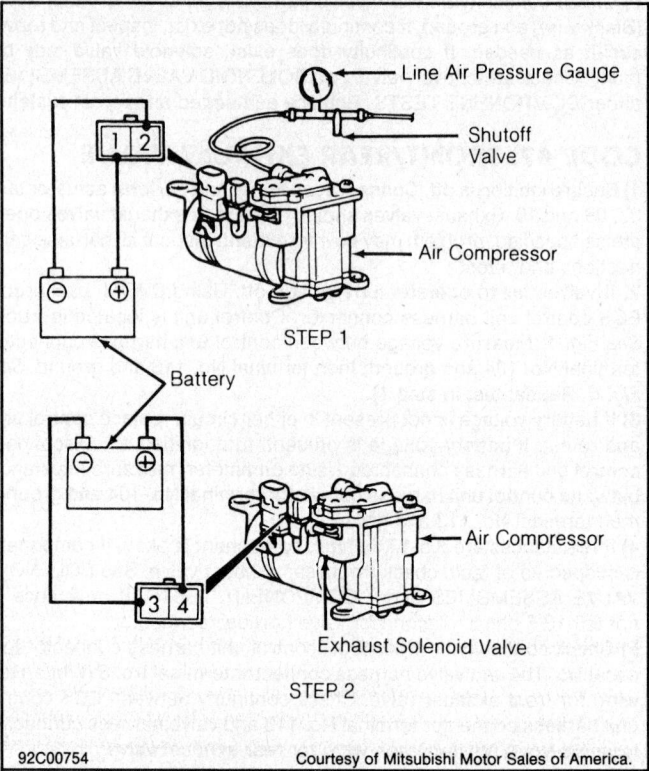

Fig. 14: Testing Air Compressor

ECS CONTROL UNIT

NOTE: Unless stated otherwise in testing procedures, perform all voltage tests using a Digital Volt-Ohmmeter (DVOM) with a minimum 10-megohm input impedance. Voltage readings may vary slightly due to battery condition or charging rate.

Pin Voltage Checks – 1) Pin voltage charts are supplied to reduce diagnostic time. Checking pin voltages at the ECS control unit connector determines whether it is receiving and transmitting proper voltage signals. Diagnostic charts may also help determine if control unit harness is shorted or open.

CAUTION: Shorting positive DVOM lead between connector terminal and ground could damage vehicle wiring, sensor and control unit.

2) If necessary, remove control unit to access harness connector. See REMOVAL & INSTALLATION for control unit location. Using DVOM, backprobe terminals with positive lead. Connect negative lead to control unit ground terminal. See appropriate chart for identification of ground terminal. *See Figs. 15 and 16.*

3) All measurements are applicable to vehicle at normal operating temperature at sea level. Unless otherwise noted, ignition switch is in ON position with engine off. Also, engine is idling when specification requires engine running. Ensure transmission shift selector is in Neutral or Park (as applicable). If DVOM displays measurement that is not within specification, see SELF-DIAGNOSTIC SYSTEM.

	Terminal ID.	Function/Description	Voltage Value (DC Volts Unless Otherwise Specified)
Red/Blue	1	BLANK	N/A
	2	Park/Neutral Position Switch	Battery Voltage In Reverse
Green/Red	3	BLANK	N/A
	4	Door Switch Signal	Battery Voltage With Doors Closed
Green	5	BLANK	N/A
Red/White	6	EX-HI Indicator Light Signal	Not Available
Red/Yellow	7	HIGH Indicator Light Signal	Not Available
Gray/Red	8	SPORT Indicator Light Signal	Not Available
Yellow/Green	9	Service Data Switching Signal	3-5 Volts With DLC Disconnected
	10	ALARM Indicator Light Signal	Not Available
Brown	11	BLANK	N/A
Green/White	12	Closed Throttle Position Switch Signal	4-8 Volts With Throttle Depressed
Yellow/Blue	13	Stop Light Switch Signal	Battery Voltage With Switch Off
	14	Service Data Output Signal	0-Battery Voltage, Fluctuates
	15	BLANK	N/A
	16	BLANK	N/A
Red/Green	17	BLANK	N/A
Yellow/Red	18	Mode Switch Signal	Not Available
Red/Black	19	Headlight Switch Signal	Battery Voltage With Headlight Switch On
Yellow	20	Mode Switch Signal	Not Available
Green	51	Damping Force Switching Actuator	Not Available
Lt. Green/Blue	52	Damping Force Switching Actuator	Not Available
Lt. Green/Green	53	Left Front Valve Signal	Battery Voltage With Valve On (Open)
Blue/Red	54	Right Front Valve Signal	Battery Voltage With Valves On (Open)
Blue	55	Ignition Power Supply Voltage	Battery Voltage With Ignition On
Black	56	Damping Force Switching Actuator	Not Available
Red/Black	57	Damping Force Switching Actuator	Not Available
Black	58	Solenoid Valve Power Relay Output Signal	Battery Voltage, Normal System Operation [1]
Orange	59	Ground	Not Applicable
	60	Battery Supply Voltage	Battery Voltage, Constant

[1] – System is not in fail-safe mode.

94D46261

Fig. 15: Pin Voltage Chart (1 Of 2)

1994 SUSPENSION
Electronic – Diamante (Cont.)

	Terminal ID.	Function/Description	Voltage Value (DC Volts Unless Otherwise Specified)
Lt. Green/White	101	Front Air Supply Valve Signal	Battery Voltage With Valves On (Open)
White/Blue	102	Flow Rate Switchover Valve	Battery Voltage With Valve On
White/Black	103	Compressor Relay Activation Signal	Battery Voltage With Relay On
White/Red	104	Front Exhaust Valve Signal	Battery Voltage With Valves On (Open)
Blue	105	Sensor Power Supply (5V)	4-8 Volts, Constant
Blue/Black	106	Solenoid Valve Power Relay Drive Signal	Battery Voltage With Relay Off
Red/Green	107	Right Rear Valve Signal	Battery Voltage With Valve On (Open)
Green/Orange	108	G-Sensor Output Signal	1.9-3.1 Volts With Vehicle Stopped
Red/Blue	109	Left Rear Valve Signal	Battery Voltage With Valve On (Open)
Red/White	110	Rear Air Supply Valve Signal	Battery Voltage With Valve On (Open)
Red/Yellow	111	Exhaust Solenoid Valve	Battery Voltage With Valve On (Open)
White/Red	112	Return Pump Relay Activation Signal	Battery Voltage With Pump Relay On
White/Green	113	Rear Exhaust Valve Signal	Battery Voltage With Valves On (Open)
Red/Black	114	G-Sensor Power Sensor	7-7.6 Volts, Control Unit Activated
Black	115	Sensor Ground	Not Applicable
Black/Blue	116	Sensor Ground	Not Applicable
Yellow/Black	117	Rear Air Spring Pressure	.5-4.5 Volts As Pressure Increases
Black/White	118	Low Pressure Tank Pressure Signal	4-8 Volts With Low Pressure Switch Off
Green/White	151	Throttle Position Sensor	0-1 Volts With KOER [1]
White	152	Generator "L" Terminal	Battery Voltage With KOER [1]
Yellow/Green	153	Steering Wheel Sensor "A"	3-4 With Photo-Interruptor Off
Green	154	Front Vehicle Height Signal	4-8 Volts With Photo-Interruptor Off
Green/Black	155	Front Vehicle Height Signal	4-8 Volts With Photo-Interruptor Off
Green/White	156	Front Vehicle Height Signal	4-8 Volts With Photo-Interruptor Off
Green/Orange	157	Front Vehicle Height Signal	4-8 Volts With Photo-Interruptor Off
Yellow/White	158	Vehicle Speed Sensor	0-9 Volts With Sensor Rotating
Black/Yellow	159	High Pressure Switch	4-8 Volts With High Pressure Switch Off
Yellow/Blue	160	Steering Wheel Sensor "B"	3-4 Volts With Photo-Interrupter Off
Yellow	161	Rear Vehicle Height Signal	4-8 Volts With Photo-Interruptor Off
Yellow/Black	162	Rear Vehicle Height Signal	4-8 Volts With Photo-Interruptor Off
Yellow/White	163	Rear Vehicle Height Signal	4-8 Volts With Photo-Interruptor Off
Yellow/Green	164	Rear Vehicle Height Signal	0 Volts, Constant

[1] – KOER – Key On, Engine Running.

94E46262

Fig. 16: Pin Voltage Chart (2 Of 2)

"G" SENSOR

See CODE 11: "G" SENSOR under DIAGNOSTIC TESTS.

HEIGHT SENSORS

Turn ignition on. Check voltage of height sensor terminals. Check voltage between specified terminals and ground. Ensure voltages are as specified. See appropriate HEIGHT SENSOR TERMINAL VOLTAGE table. See Figs. 17 and 18.

FRONT HEIGHT SENSOR TERMINAL VOLTAGE

Vehicle Height	Sensor Link Position	Volts
Maximum Level		
Terminals No. 1 & 3	1	0-.5
Terminals No. 2 & 5	1	4.5-5.0
Higher Than HIGH		
Terminals No. 1, 3 & 5	2	0-.5
Terminal No. 2	2	4.5-5.0
HIGH (Target Height)		
Terminals No. 1 & 5	3	0-.5
Terminals No. 2 & 3	3	4.5-5.0
Higher Than NORMAL		
Terminals No. 1, 2 & 5	4	0-.5
Terminal No. 3	4	4.5-5.0
NORMAL (Target Height)		
Terminal No. 1	5	4.5-5.0
Terminals No. 2, 3 & 5	5	0-.5
Lower Than NORMAL		
Terminal No. 1	6	4.5-5.0
Terminals No. 2, 3 & 5	6	0-.5
LOW (Target Height)		
Terminals No. 1 & 2	7	4.5-5.0
Terminals No. 3 & 5	7	0-.5
Lower Than LOW		
Terminals No. 1, 2 & 3	8	4.5-5.0
Terminal No. 5	8	0-.5
Minimum Level		
Terminals No. 1, 2, 3 & 5	9	4.5-5.0

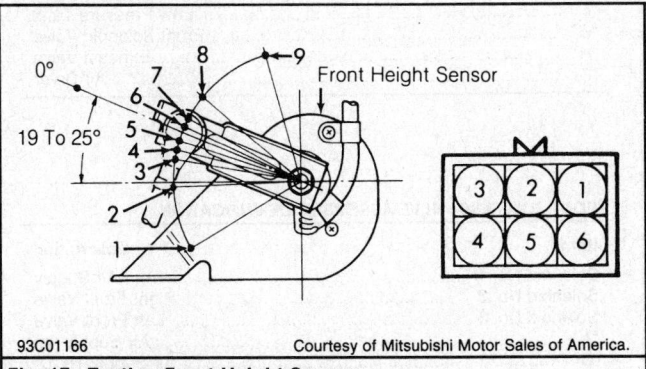

93C01166   Courtesy of Mitsubishi Motor Sales of America.

Fig. 17: Testing Front Height Sensor

REAR HEIGHT SENSOR TERMINAL VOLTAGE

Vehicle Height	Sensor Link Position	Volts
Higher Than HIGH		
Terminals No. 1 & 3	1	0-.5
Terminal No. 2	1	4.5-5.0
HIGH (Target Height)		
Terminal No. 1	2	0-.5
Terminals No. 2 & 3	2	4.5-5.0
Higher Than NORMAL		
Terminals No. 1 & 2	3	0-.5
Terminal No. 3	3	4.5-5.0
NORMAL (Target Height)		
Terminals No. 1, 2 & 3	4	0-.5
Lower Than NORMAL		
Terminal No. 1	5	4.5-5.0
Terminals No. 2 & 3	5	0-.5
LOW (Target Height)		
Terminals No. 1 & 2	6	4.5-5.0
Terminal No. 3	6	0-.5
Lower Than LOW		
Terminals No. 1, 2 & 3	7	4.5-5.0

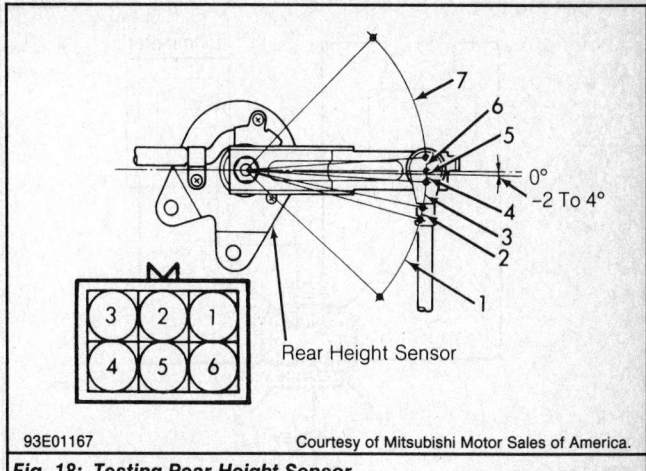

93E01167   Courtesy of Mitsubishi Motor Sales of America.

Fig. 18: Testing Rear Height Sensor

HIGH-PRESSURE SWITCH

See CODE 15: HIGH-PRESSURE SWITCH under DIAGNOSTIC TESTS.

LOW-PRESSURE SWITCH

See CODE 13: LOW-PRESSURE SWITCH under DIAGNOSTIC TESTS.

REAR PRESSURE SENSOR

See CODE 25: REAR PRESSURE SENSOR under DIAGNOSTIC TESTS.

RELAYS

Air Compressor Relay, ECS Power Relay, Return Pump Relay & Solenoid Valve Power Relay Tests – 1) Remove appropriate relay. *See Figs. 12 and 19.* Connect an ohmmeter between relay terminals No. 3 and 4. *See Figs. 20-22.* Continuity should not be present. Connect battery positive to relay terminal No. 1, and ground relay terminal No. 2.

2) Continuity should be present between relay terminals No. 3 and 4. Disconnect battery voltage. Check continuity between terminals No. 1 and 2. Continuity should be present. Replace relay if continuity is not as specified.

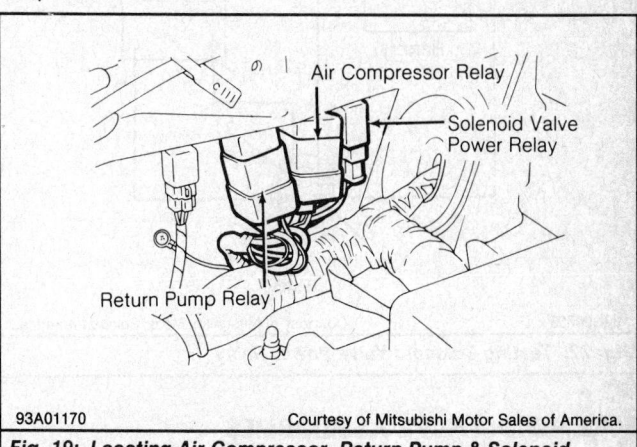

93A01170   Courtesy of Mitsubishi Motor Sales of America.

Fig. 19: Locating Air Compressor, Return Pump & Solenoid Valve Power Relays

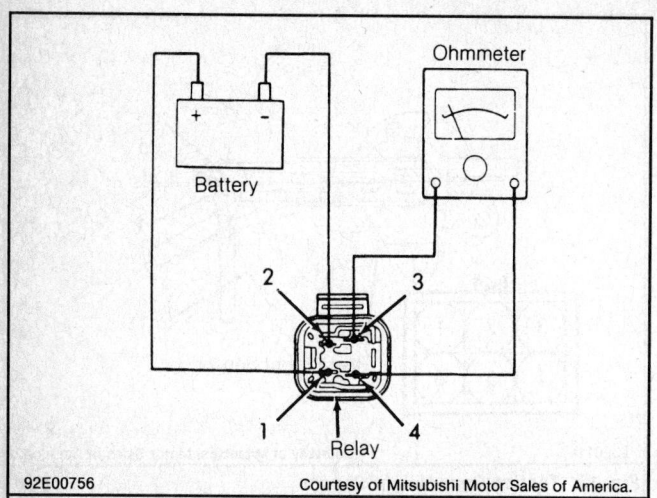

Fig. 20: Testing Air Compressor & Return Pump Relays

92E00756   Courtesy of Mitsubishi Motor Sales of America.

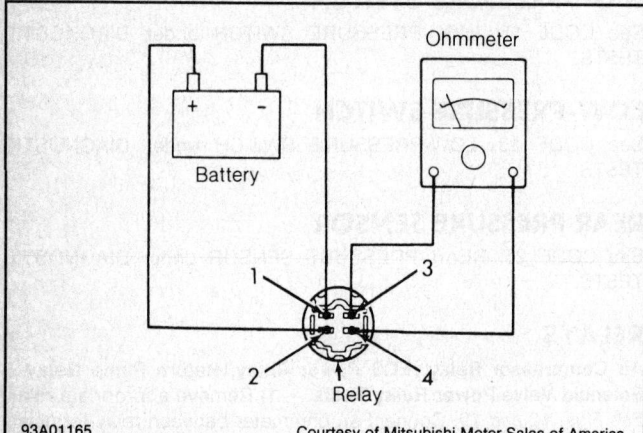

Fig. 21: Testing ECS Power Relay

93A01165   Courtesy of Mitsubishi Motor Sales of America.

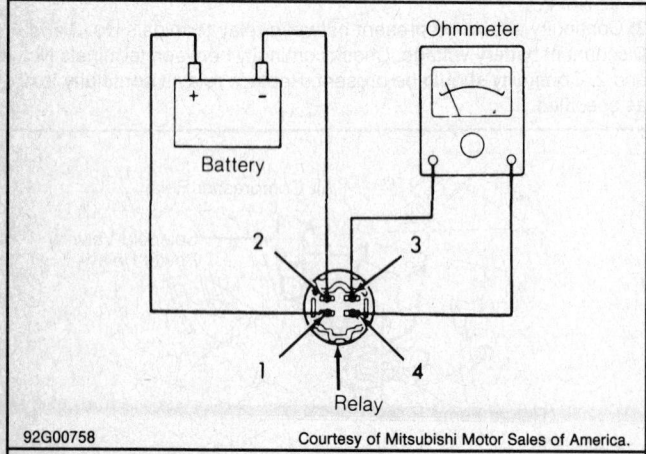

Fig. 22: Testing Solenoid Valve Power Relay

92G00758   Courtesy of Mitsubishi Motor Sales of America.

SOLENOID VALVE ASSEMBLIES

Flow Control Solenoid Valve Assembly Test – 1) Apply air pressure at port "A". See Fig. 23. Apply battery voltage to assembly terminal No. 2, and ground assembly terminal No. 1. If solenoid clicks, and air volume from ports "B" and "C" increases, go to next step. If there is no click, or air volume does not increase, replace defective solenoid valve No. 1.

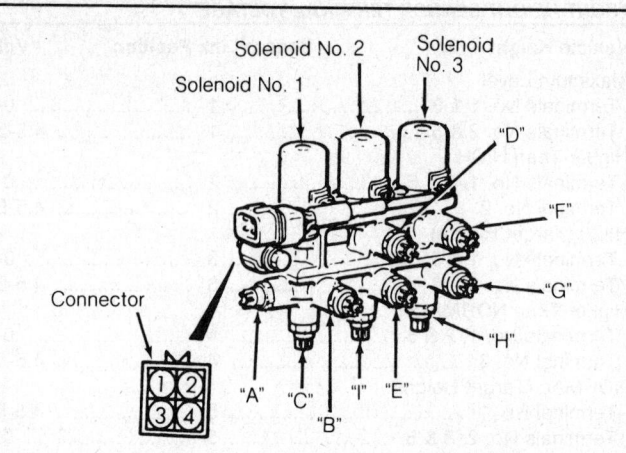

FLOW CONTROL SOLENOID VALVE ASSEMBLY IDENTIFICATION

Item	Description
Solenoid No. 1	Flow Rate Switchover Valve
Solenoid No. 2	Rear Exhaust Valve
Solenoid No. 3	Front Exhaust Valve
"A"	Air Supply (High Pressure Tank)
"B"	Front Air Supply Valve
"C"	Rear Air Supply Valve (Dryer)
"D"	Low Pressure Tank
"E"	Rear Solenoid Valve
"F"	Low Pressure Tank
"G"	Front Solenoid Valve
"H"	Exhaust Valve
"I"	Air Dryer

FRONT SOLENOID VALVE ASSEMBLY IDENTIFICATION

Item	Description
Solenoid No. 1	Front Air Supply
Solenoid No. 2	Right Front Valve
Solenoid No. 3	Left Front Valve
"A"	Air Supply (In)
"B"	Air Supply To "D"
"C"	Air Supply To "F"
"D"	Air Supply From "B"
"E"	Air Supply (Out)
"F"	Air Supply From "C"
"G"	Air Supply (Out)
"H"	Exhaust Valve

92H00759   Courtesy of Mitsubishi Motor Sales of America.

Fig. 23: Identifying Test Points For Flow Control & Front Solenoid Valve Assemblies

2) Apply air pressure to port "E". See Fig. 23. Air should flow from port "D". Apply battery voltage to assembly terminal No. 3, and ground assembly terminal No. 1. If solenoid clicks, and airflow switches from port "D" to port "I", go to next step. If there is no click, or airflow does not change, replace defective solenoid valve No. 2.

3) Apply air pressure to port "G". Air should flow from port "F". Apply battery voltage to assembly terminal No. 4, and ground assembly terminal No. 1. If solenoid clicks, and airflow switches from port "F" to port "H", go to next step. If there is no click, or airflow does not change, replace defective solenoid valve No. 3.

4) Apply air pressure to port "C". If air exits from port "B", replace defective check valve. If air does not exit from port "B", go to next step.

5) Apply 142 psi air pressure to port "B" with ports "A" and "C" plugged. *See Fig. 23.* Apply soap and water solution to solenoid. *See Fig. 24.* If there is no air leakage, solenoid valve seal is operating properly. If air leaks, replace defective solenoid valve seal. Repeat test for ports "H" and "I".

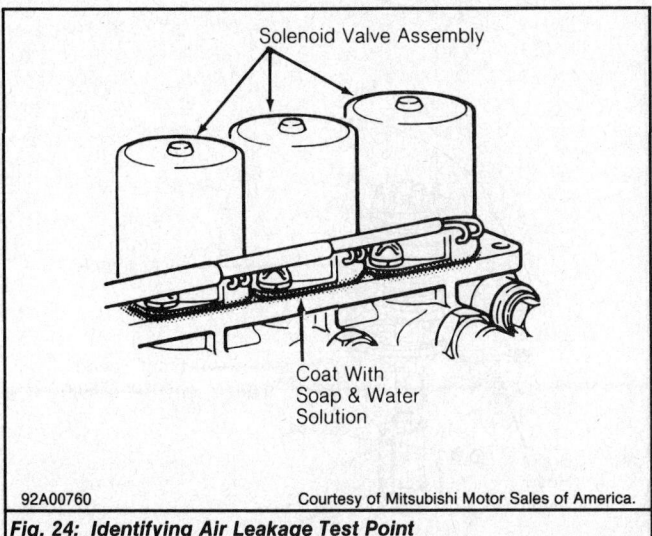

92A00760   Courtesy of Mitsubishi Motor Sales of America.

Fig. 24: Identifying Air Leakage Test Point

Front Solenoid Valve Assembly Test – 1) Apply air pressure at port "A". *See Fig. 23.* Apply battery voltage to assembly terminal No. 2, and ground assembly terminal No. 1. If solenoid clicks, and air volume from ports "B" and "C" increases, go to next step. If solenoid does not click, or air volume does not increase, replace defective solenoid valve No. 1.

2) Apply air pressure to port "E". Air should flow from port "D". Apply battery voltage to assembly terminal No. 3, and ground assembly terminal No. 1. If solenoid clicks, and airflow switches from port "D" to port "H", go to next step. If there is no click, or airflow does not change, replace defective solenoid valve No. 2.

3) Apply air pressure to port "G". *See Fig. 23.* Air should flow from port "F". Apply battery voltage to assembly terminal No. 4, and ground assembly terminal No. 1. If solenoid clicks, and airflow switches from port "F" to port "H", go to next step. If there is no click, or airflow does not change, replace defective solenoid valve No. 3.

4) Apply battery voltage to assembly terminal No. 2, and ground assembly terminal No. 1. Apply air pressure to port "B", and plug port "C". If air exits from port "A", replace defective check valve. If air does not exit from port "A", go to next step.

5) Apply 142 psi air pressure to port "B". *See Fig. 23.* Apply soap and water solution to solenoid. *See Fig. 24.* If there is no air leakage, solenoid valve seal is operating properly. If air leaks, replace defective solenoid valve seal. Repeat test for port "H".

Rear Solenoid Valve Assembly – 1) Apply air pressure at port "A". *See Fig. 25.* Apply battery voltage to assembly terminal No. 2, and ground assembly terminal No. 1. If solenoid clicks, and air exits from ports "B" and "C", go to next step. If there is no click, or air does not exit from ports "B" and "C", replace defective solenoid valve No. 1.

2) Apply air pressure to port "E". Air should flow from port "D". Apply battery voltage to assembly terminal No. 3, and ground assembly terminal No. 1. If solenoid clicks, and airflow switches from port "D" to port "H", go to next step. If there is no click, or airflow does not change, replace defective solenoid valve No. 2.

3) Apply air pressure to port "G". *See Fig. 25.* Air should flow from port "F". Apply battery voltage to assembly terminal No. 4, and ground assembly terminal No. 1. If solenoid clicks, and airflow switches from port "F" to port "H", go to next step. If there is no click, or airflow does not change, replace defective solenoid valve No. 3.

4) Apply 142 psi air pressure in port "A". Apply soap and water solution to solenoid. *See Fig. 24.* If there is no air leakage, solenoid valve seal is operating properly. If air leaks, replace defective solenoid valve seal. Repeat test for port "H".

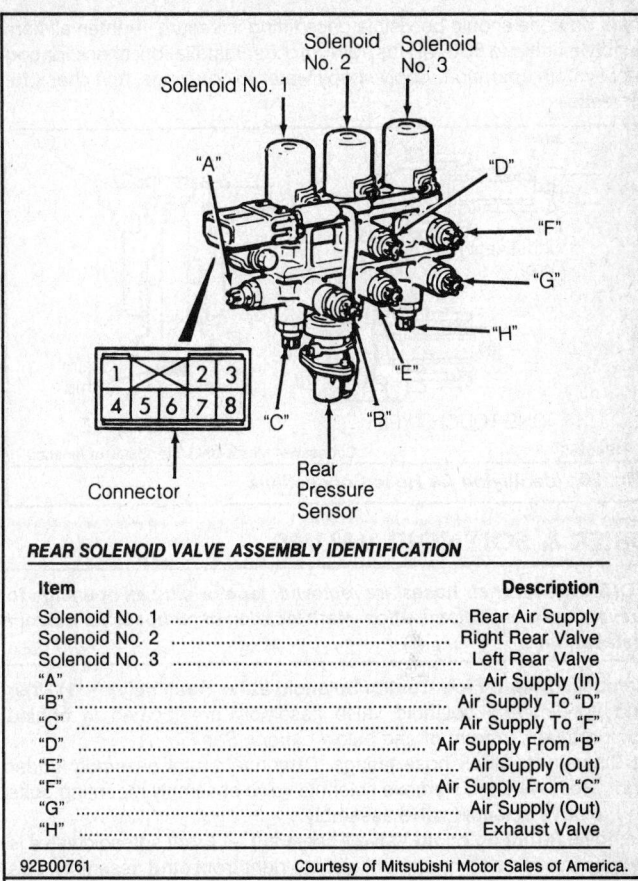

REAR SOLENOID VALVE ASSEMBLY IDENTIFICATION

Item	Description
Solenoid No. 1	Rear Air Supply
Solenoid No. 2	Right Rear Valve
Solenoid No. 3	Left Rear Valve
"A"	Air Supply (In)
"B"	Air Supply To "D"
"C"	Air Supply To "F"
"D"	Air Supply From "B"
"E"	Air Supply (Out)
"F"	Air Supply From "C"
"G"	Air Supply (Out)
"H"	Exhaust Valve

92B00761   Courtesy of Mitsubishi Motor Sales of America.

Fig. 25: Identifying Test Points For Rear Solenoid Valve Assembly

STEERING WHEEL ANGULAR VELOCITY SENSOR

See CODE 21: STEERING WHEEL SENSOR under DIAGNOSTIC TESTS.

VEHICLE SPEED SENSOR

See CODE 24: VEHICLE SPEED SENSOR under DIAGNOSTIC TESTS.

REMOVAL & INSTALLATION

AIR COMPRESSOR

Removal – Remove air cleaner and air intake hose. Remove air hose from compressor and tape openings to prevent contamination. Disconnect wiring harness connectors. Remove compressor mounting bolts and mounting rubber. Remove air compressor.

Installation – To install, reverse removal procedure. Tighten air hose fitting to 80 INCH lbs. (9 N.m). Use new "O" rings on air hoses. Ensure electrical harness connector is fully seated. Apply soap and water solution to fittings to check for air leaks.

AIR HOSES

NOTE: When replacing hoses attached to wiring harnesses, leave old hose in place and install new hose alongside harness.

Removal & Installation – When servicing air hoses, verify part number and use a new connector and "O" ring. One-Touch style connectors require Special Disassembly Tool (MB991229). Ensure corresponding paint marks match before installation of air hoses. *See Fig. 26.* On flare nut style fittings, push air hose until fully seated. Paint mark on hose should be visible once fitting is secure. Tighten all flare nut style fitting to 80 INCH lbs. (9 N.m). After installation, check for correct system operation. Apply soapy water to couplings, and check for air leaks.

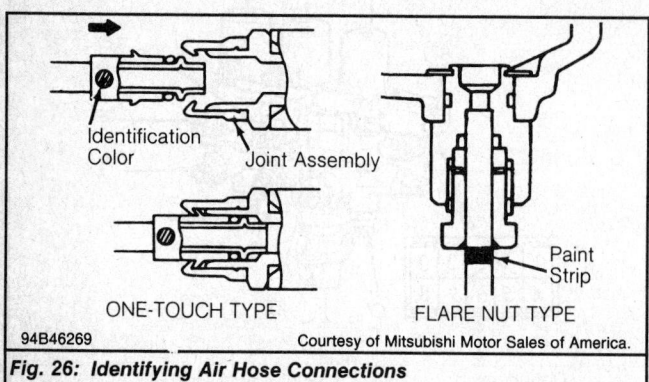

94B46269   Courtesy of Mitsubishi Motor Sales of America.

Fig. 26: Identifying Air Hose Connections

DRIER & SOLENOID VALVES

NOTE: Whenever air hoses are removed, tape or plug all openings to prevent system contamination. Mark location of air hoses for correct installation.

Removal (Drier & Flow Control Solenoid Valve Assembly) – 1) Drier and flow control solenoid valve assembly are located in engine compartment, in front of and below battery. *See Fig. 1.*
2) Disconnect all air hose fittings. Disconnect joint assembly under drier. Remove drier. Remove solenoid valve assembly mounting bolts and remove solenoid valve assembly.
Removal (Front Solenoid Valve Assembly) – Front solenoid valve is located in engine compartment, next to right front strut assembly. *See Fig. 1.* Disconnect all air hose fittings. Remove solenoid valve assembly mounting bolts, and remove solenoid assembly from firewall.
Removal (Rear Solenoid Valve Assembly) – Rear solenoid valve is located next to right rear strut assembly. *See Fig. 1.* Remove right side of trunk trim panel for access. Disconnect all air hoses. Label air hoses for installation reference. Remove solenoid valve mounting bolts, and separate unit from body.
Installation (Solenoid Valve Assemblies & Drier) – 1) To install, reverse removal procedure. Tighten valve assembly mounting bolts and air hose flare nut style fittings to 80 INCH lbs. (9 N.m). Drier and solenoid valve assemblies require no additional adjustment.
2) Handle air hoses carefully to prevent bending or damage. Use new "O" rings, and ensure hoses are attached to correct fitting. Start engine to verify correct operation. Use soapy water to check for air leaks on connections.

ECS CONTROL UNIT

Removal & Installation – Remove trunk right side trim panel. Ensure ignition is off. Disconnect ECS control unit wiring harness connector. *See Fig. 1.* Remove ECS control unit mounting bolts. Carefully separate control unit from vehicle body. Handle control unit carefully. To install, reverse removal procedure.

FRONT STRUT ASSEMBLY

NOTE: Support steering knuckle with wire to prevent axle shaft and brake hose stress. Keep air hose connections plugged during disassembly to prevent system contamination.

Removal – 1) Raise and support vehicle. Remove front wheels. Disconnect front height sensor actuating rod from right lower control arm. Separate brake hose bracket from strut. Support lower control arms. Remove 2 bolts at strut assembly and knuckle.
2) Remove dust cap from top of strut. Remove air hose connection and electrical harness connection. Remove actuator. Note strut insulator position, and remove upper strut mounting nuts. Remove strut assembly. *See Fig. 27.*

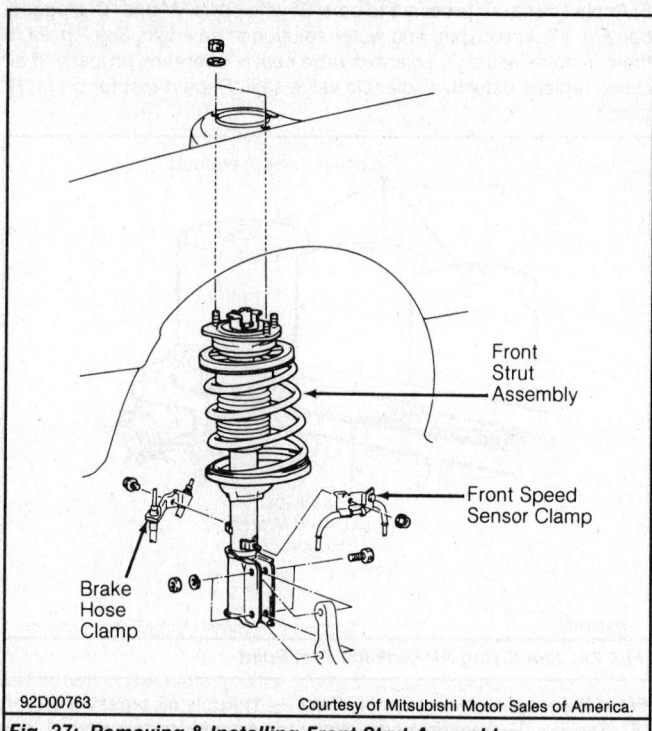

92D00763   Courtesy of Mitsubishi Motor Sales of America.

Fig. 27: Removing & Installing Front Strut Assembly

Installation – 1) To install, reverse removal procedure. Ensure strut insulator is installed correctly. Install air hoses using new "O" rings. Tighten air hose fittings to 84 INCH lbs. (10 N.m). Tighten front axle nut to 145-188 ft. lbs. (196-255 N.m).
2) Before lowering vehicle, start engine and press vehicle height switch (HIGH switch) for 2 seconds or more. This will supply air to strut and prevent double folding of air spring diaphragm.
3) Turn ignition off, and lower vehicle. Start engine, and verify correct system operation. Use soapy water to inspect for air leaks. If system does not function properly and a folded diaphragm is suspected, see DIAPHRAGM CHECK.
Diaphragm Check – 1) Lift front of vehicle. Visually inspect or feel diaphragm. *See Fig. 28.* If diaphragm is folded, lift front of vehicle, allowing front wheels to hang free.

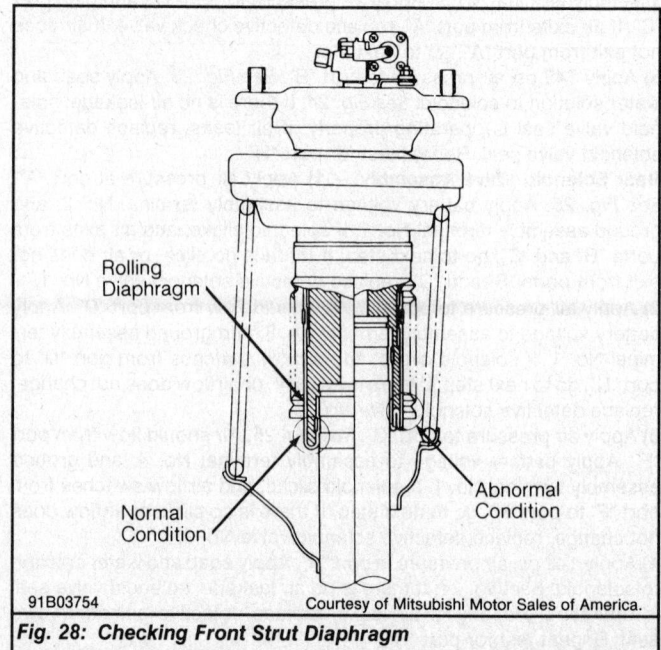

91B03754   Courtesy of Mitsubishi Motor Sales of America.

Fig. 28: Checking Front Strut Diaphragm

2) Disconnect front height sensor actuating rod. Start engine. Move front height sensor actuating rod to activate system. If this fails to return diaphragm to normal position, disconnect air hose from front strut assembly.

3) Supply air to each strut assembly to return diaphragm to normal position. *See Fig. 28.* If diaphragm still fails to return to normal position, apply soap and water to diaphragm to help diaphragm move when air is applied to strut.

4) Install air hoses and height sensor actuating rod as necessary. Lower vehicle SLOWLY to avoid folding diaphragm again. Ensure ECS system functions normally.

HEIGHT SENSORS

Removal (Front) – Remove air compressor. See AIR COMPRESSOR under REMOVAL & INSTALLATION. Detach front height sensor rod from lower (control) arm. *See Fig. 29.* Separate sensor wiring connector. Remove mounting screws and height sensor.

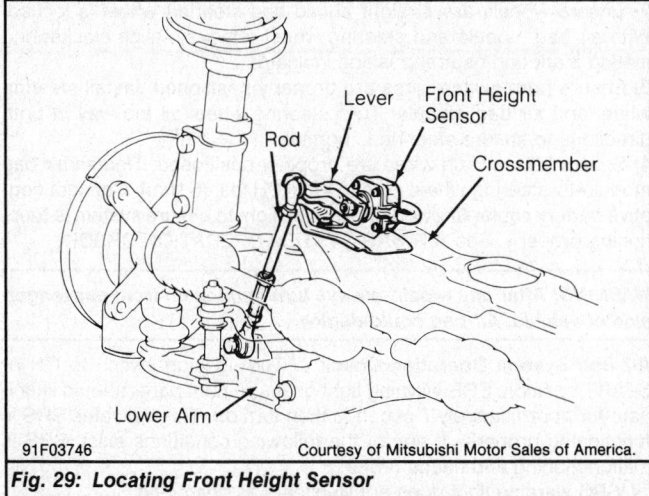

Fig. 29: *Locating Front Height Sensor*

Removal (Rear) – Disconnect rear height sensor rod from lower control arm and rear height sensor. *See Fig. 30.* Disconnect wiring connector. Remove mounting screws and rear height sensor.

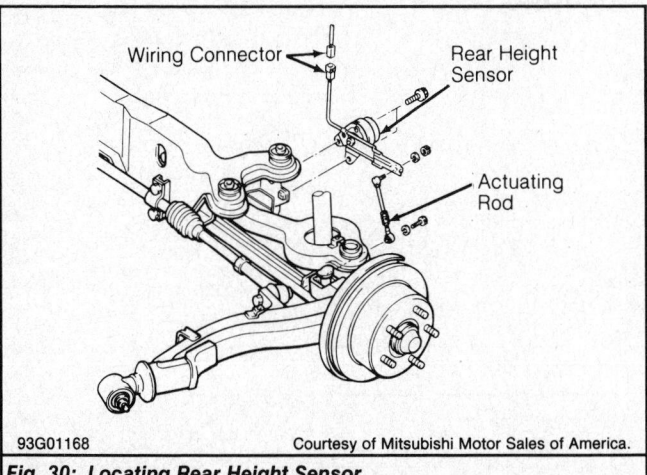

Fig. 30: *Locating Rear Height Sensor*

Installation (Front & Rear) – **1)** Inspect for bent or damaged actuating rod. Adjust actuating rod length to specification. See HEIGHT SENSOR RODS under ADJUSTMENTS. Tighten actuating rod lock nuts to 16 ft. lbs. (22 N.m).

2) Ensure actuating rod swivel is at rocking center. *See Fig. 31.* Attach wiring connector to sensor. To complete installation, reverse removal procedure. Start engine, and verify correct system operation.

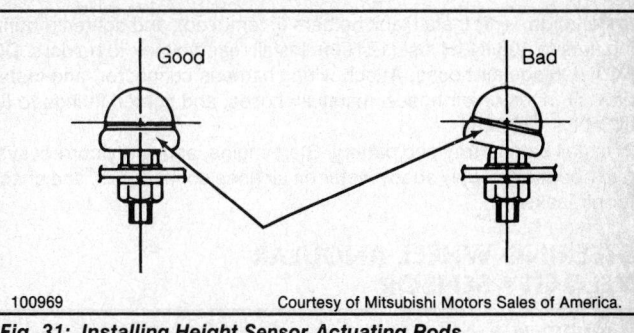

Fig. 31: *Installing Height Sensor Actuating Rods*

REAR SHOCK ABSORBER ASSEMBLY

Removal – **1)** Lift and support vehicle. Remove rear wheels. Remove trunk room side trim to access actuator and upper mounting nuts. Disconnect air hose and harness connector from actuator.

2) Remove actuator from actuator bracket. Disconnect height sensor rod from lateral rod. Using a jack, lift rear axle slightly. Remove shock absorber assembly upper mounting nuts and lower mounting bolt. Remove shock absorber assembly. *See Fig. 32.*

CAUTION: DO NOT let rear axle drop low enough to damage brake hoses or rear height sensor.

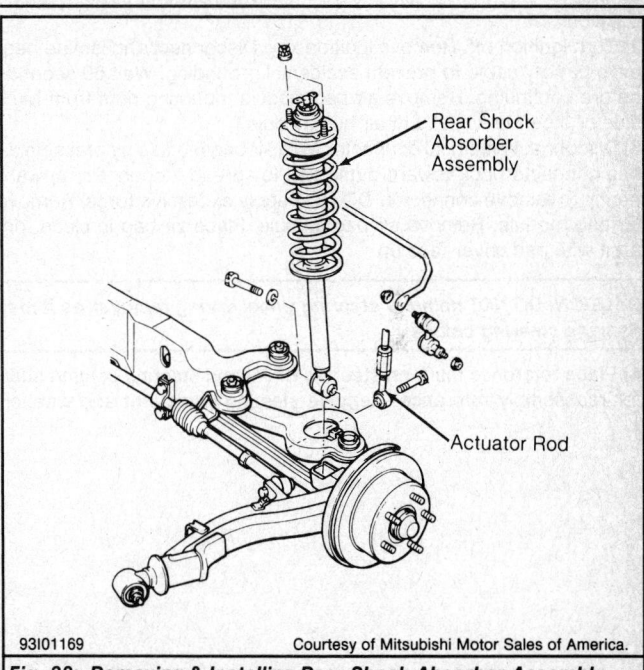

Fig. 32: *Removing & Installing Rear Shock Absorber Assembly*

Installation – **1)** To install, reverse removal procedure. Before installing air hose, apply rubber grease to new "O" ring. Tighten upper mounting nuts to 33 ft. lbs. (45 N.m). Tighten air hose fitting to 84 INCH lbs. (10 N.m).

2) Before lowering vehicle, start engine and press vehicle height switch (HIGH switch) for 2 seconds or more. This will supply air to strut, and prevent double folding of air spring diaphragm.

3) Turn ignition off and lower vehicle. Start engine, and verify correct system operation. Use soapy water to check for air leaks.

RESERVE TANK

Removal – Remove air intake shield panel. Remove battery and battery tray. Disconnect electrical harness connectors and air hoses. Tape air hose fittings closed to prevent system contamination. Ensure air hoses do not bend or contact hot engine surfaces. Remove reserve tank from holders. Remove holders if necessary.

Installation – 1) Install tank holders (if removed), and tighten mounting nuts to 108 INCH lbs. (12 N.m). Install reserve tank to holders. DO NOT damage air hoses. Attach wiring harness connector, and install new "O" rings on air hoses. Install air hoses, and tighten fittings to 84 INCH lbs. (10 N.m).

2) Install battery tray and battery. Start engine, and verify correct system operation. Apply soapy water on air hose connections, and check for air leaks.

STEERING WHEEL ANGULAR VELOCITY SENSOR

WARNING: Wait at least 60 seconds after disconnecting negative battery cable before servicing SRS. System reserve capacitor maintains SRS voltage for about 60 seconds after battery is disconnected. Servicing SRS before 60-second period may cause accidental air bag deployment and possible personal injury.

NOTE: Steering wheel angular velocity sensor is an electronic unit using photo-couplers. Clean hands and working environment are recommended to avoid contaminating this component.

Removal – 1) Before proceeding, follow air bag service precautions. See AIR BAG SERVICE PRECAUTIONS. Disable SRS. See DISABLING & ACTIVATING AIR BAG SYSTEM. Air bag module is mounted on face of steering wheel. Ensure front wheels are in straight-ahead position.

2) Turn ignition off. Remove ignition key. Disconnect and isolate negative battery cable to prevent accidental grounding. Wait 60 seconds before continuing. Remove air bag module mounting nuts from back side of steering wheel. Lift air bag module.

3) Disconnect electrical connector from air bag module by pressing air bag connector lock toward outer side to spread it open. Pry upward gently to remove connector. DO NOT apply excessive force. Remove air bag module. Remove air bag module. Place air bag in clean, dry area with pad cover face up.

CAUTION: DO NOT hammer steering wheel during removal, as it may damage steering column.

4) Place reference mark on steering wheel and steering column shaft for reassembly reference. Remove steering wheel nut and washer.

Using steering wheel puller, remove steering wheel. Remove steering column covers.

5) Clockspring is located behind steering wheel. Remove rear console assembly. Using a screwdriver, push in SRS Diagnostic Unit (SDU) lock spring to unlock wiring connector lock lever. Disconnect 2-pin Red clockspring connector at SDU. Remove knee protector. Remove screws attaching clockspring. Remove clockspring.

6) Disconnect steering wheel angular velocity sensor wiring connectors. Remove column switch. Remove sensor from steering column.

Installation – 1) To install, gently position sensor in steering column. DO NOT bend or contaminate slit plate. Install mounting screws and wire connector. Reverse removal procedure to install remaining components.

CAUTION: If rotating part of clockspring is not properly centered with steering column and front wheels, clockspring failure will result. The following procedure must be used to center clockspring.

2) Ensure wheels are straight ahead and steering wheel is locked. With air bag module and steering wheel removed, align clockspring mating mark and neutral position indicator.

3) Ensure horn switch wires are properly positioned. Install steering wheel and air bag module. Turn steering wheel all the way in both directions to ensure steering is normal.

4) Ensure horn switch wires are properly positioned. Tighten air bag module-to-steering wheel nuts to 48 INCH lbs. (5 N.m). Connect negative battery cable. Check SRS warning light to ensure system is functioning properly. See AIR BAG SYSTEM OPERATION CHECK.

WARNING: After any repair, always turn ignition on from passenger-side of vehicle. Air bag could deploy.

Air Bag System Operation Check – Turn ignition switch to ON or START position. SRS warning light on instrument panel should illuminate for approximately 7 seconds then turn off. This indicates SRS is functioning properly. If any of the following conditions exist, SRS is malfunctioning and needs repair.

- SRS warning light does not illuminate as described.
- SRS warning light stays on for more than 7 seconds.
- SRS warning light illuminates while driving.

If SRS warning light does not illuminate as described, SRS system is malfunctioning.

WIRING DIAGRAMS

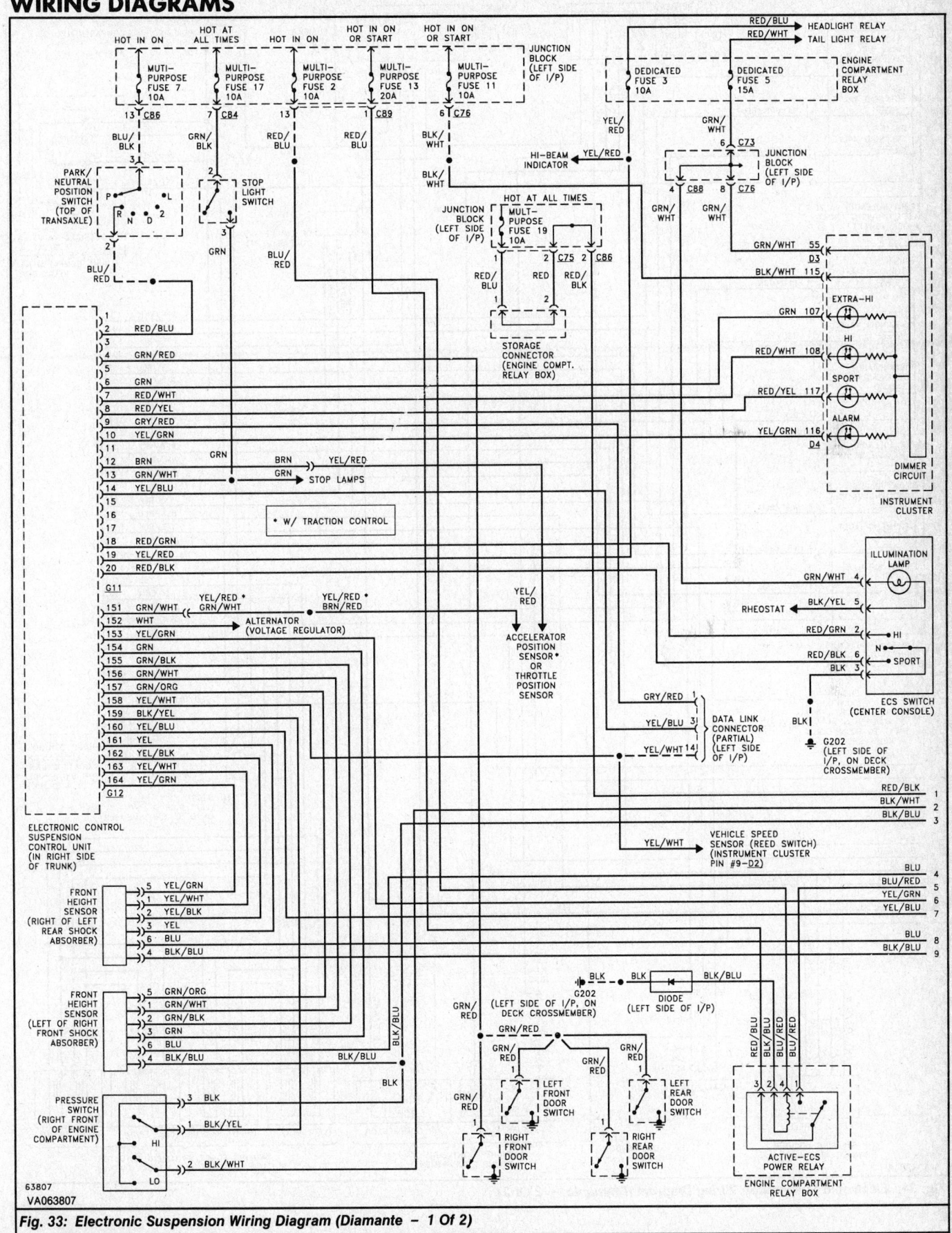

Fig. 33: Electronic Suspension Wiring Diagram (Diamante – 1 Of 2)

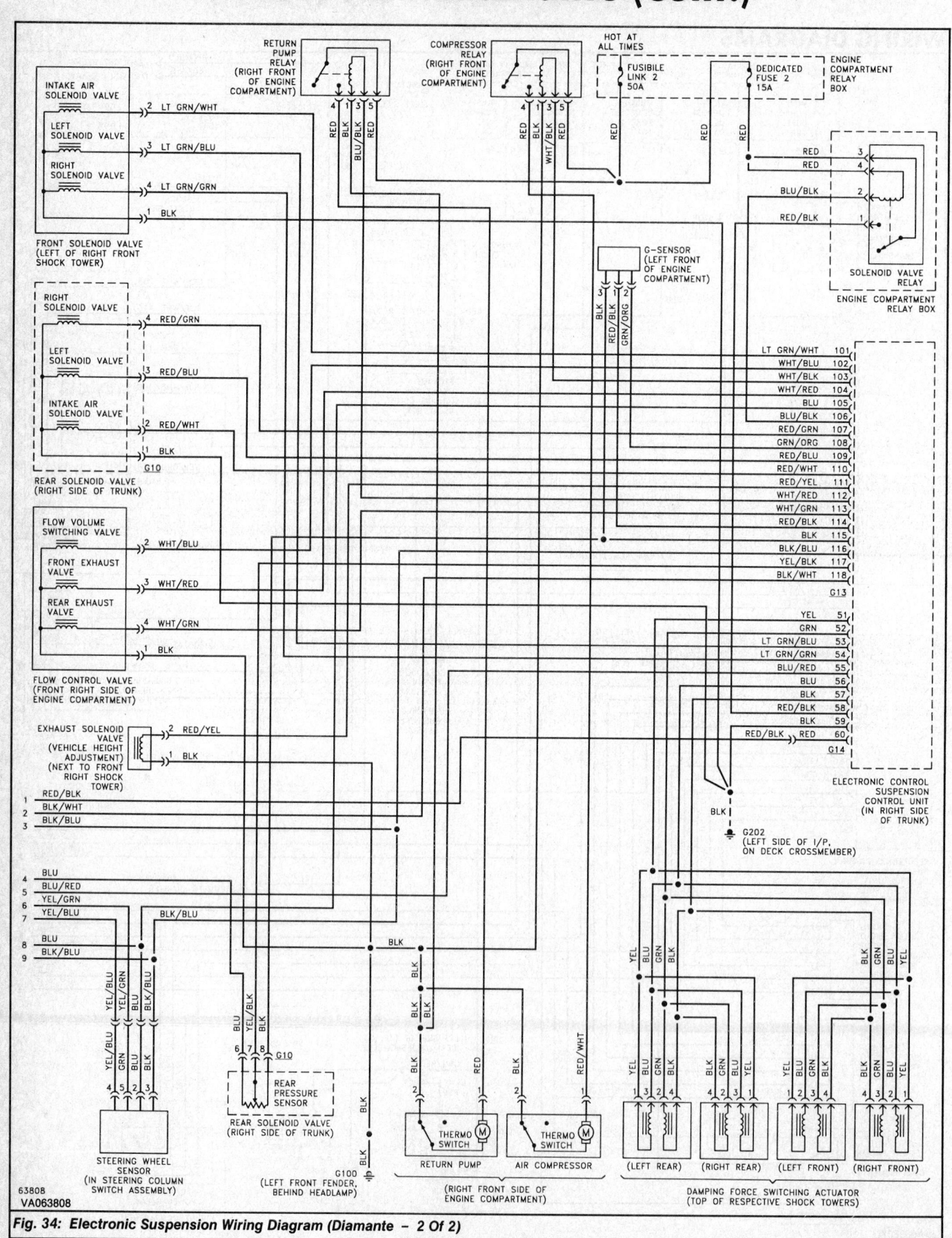

Fig. 34: Electronic Suspension Wiring Diagram (Diamante - 2 Of 2)

VA063808
63808

DESCRIPTION

Electronically Controlled Suspension (ECS) is designed to improve vehicle ride characteristics while automatically compensating for driving conditions. System controls shock absorber damping through electronic valve (actuator) control of shock absorbers.

Using ECS switch on dash, driver can manually select damping characteristics for regular driving by selecting either TOUR mode (soft damping) or SPORT mode (hard damping). Shock absorber damping is automatically firmed up under braking (anti-dive function), quick acceleration (anti-squat function) or hard cornering (anti-roll function).

ECS control unit is equipped with self-diagnostic function which monitors several circuits and alerts driver when a malfunction is detected.

WARNING: Stealth and 3000GT are equipped with a Supplemental Restraint System (SRS) that includes an air bag, located in steering column. Use caution when working around steering column. Ensure battery is disconnected before attempting any repair. DO NOT apply electrical power to any component on steering column without disconnecting air bag module (air bag could deploy).

OPERATION

ECS control unit uses inputs from ECS switch, "G" sensor, shock absorber actuator position detection switches, vehicle speed sensor, throttle position sensor, stoplight switch and steering wheel angular velocity sensor. The control unit uses these inputs to determine proper valving for the specific ride characteristics. Valving inside strut housing governs strut dampening characteristics.

ECS switch is used to manually select basic ride characteristics. The "G" sensor detects pitching, bouncing and rough road. Steering wheel angular velocity sensor, located in steering column, detects how fast the steering wheel is being turned.

DISABLING & ACTIVATING AIR BAG SYSTEM

WARNING: Wait at least 60 seconds after disconnecting negative battery cable before servicing SRS. System reserve capacitor maintains SRS voltage for about 60 seconds after battery is disconnected. Servicing SRS before 60-second period may cause accidental air bag deployment and possible personal injury.

To disable system, turn ignition switch to OFF position. Disconnect and isolate negative battery cable end. Wait at least 60 seconds. To activate system, reconnect negative battery cable.

AIR BAG SERVICE PRECAUTIONS

The following precautions should be observed when working with SRS:

- Disable SRS before servicing any SRS or steering column component. Failure to do this may result in accidental air bag deployment and possible personal injury. See DISABLING & ACTIVATING AIR BAG SYSTEM.
- Wait at least 60 SECONDS after disabling air bag system. SRS system retains enough voltage, for a short time after system is disabled, to deploy air bag.
- After repairs, always turn ignition on from passenger-side of vehicle in case of accidental air bag deployment. Ensure SRS warning light is working properly and no system faults are indicated.
- Always wear safety glasses when servicing or handling an air bag.
- DO NOT expose air bag module and clockspring to temperatures greater than 200°F (93°C).
- When placing a live air bag on a bench or other surface, always face air bag and trim cover up, away from surface. This will reduce motion of module if air bag accidentally deploys.

- After air bag deploys, air bag surface may contain deposits of sodium hydroxide, which irritate skin. Always wear safety glasses, rubber gloves and long-sleeved shirt during clean-up. Wash hands using mild soap and water. Follow correct clean-up and disposal procedures.
- Because of critical system operating requirements, DO NOT service any SRS components. Repairs are only made by replacing defective part(s).
- DO NOT allow any electrical source near inflator on the back of air bag module.
- When carrying live air bag module, trim cover should be pointed away from body to minimize injury in case of accidental air bag deployment.
- If SRS is not fully functional for any reason, DO NOT drive vehicle until system is repaired and is fully functional. DO NOT remove bulbs, modules, sensors or other components, or in any way disable system from operating normally. If SRS is not functional, park vehicle until repairs are made.

SELF-DIAGNOSTIC SYSTEM

SYSTEM DIAGNOSIS

Self-diagnostic system diagnoses and stores Electronically Controlled Suspension (ECS) malfunction data. ECS control unit monitors system circuits and stores a trouble code if a malfunction is detected. When a malfunction is detected, self-diagnostic system alerts driver by flashing TOUR SPORT light on dash. Self-diagnostic system has a fail-safe mode which terminates ECS control to maintain driving stability when a malfunction is detected in a monitored circuit.

SERVICE PRECAUTIONS

Before proceeding with diagnosis, following precautions must be observed:

- Ensure vehicle has a fully charged battery and functional charging system.
- Visually inspect connectors and circuit wiring being worked on.
- DO NOT disconnect battery or ECS control unit unless instructed by specific test. This will erase any trouble codes stored in control unit memory.
- DO NOT cause short circuits when performing electrical tests. This may set additional trouble codes, making diagnosis of original problem more difficult.
- DO NOT use a test light in place of a voltmeter.
- When a vehicle has multiple trouble codes, always repair lowest number trouble code first.

RETRIEVING CODES

NOTE: If no codes are present or ECS indicator does not light, proceed to SYSTEM TESTS (NO CODES).

Turn ignition on. ECS indicator should light either TOUR or SPORT mode. If ECS indicator light flashes, a malfunction has been detected and a trouble code has been stored. If indicator lights but does not flash, ECS system is okay.

NOTE: Trouble codes can be retrieved using either Multi-Use Tester II (MB991501) or voltmeter. Use Multi-Use Tester II (MUT-II) to check service data and conduct actuator tests.

Retrieving Codes Using Scan Tester – 1) Connect scan tester to ECS self-diagnostic connector. *See Fig. 1.* Refer to instructions for MUT operation, and check for self-diagnostic (trouble) codes.
2) Record trouble codes. If 2 or more trouble codes are stored, lowest number code will be indicated first. Proceed to appropriate code test for diagnosis and servicing procedure. See DIAGNOSTIC TESTS.

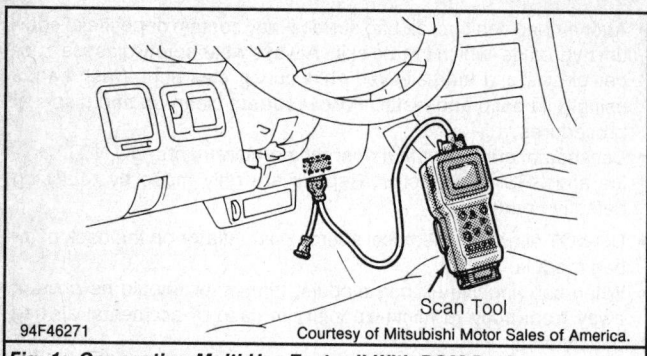

Scan Tool

94F46271   Courtesy of Mitsubishi Motor Sales of America.

Fig. 1: Connecting Multi-Use Tester II With ROM Pack

Retrieving Codes Using Voltmeter – 1) With ignition off, connect voltmeter positive probe to terminal No. 3 of self-diagnostic connector, located under right side of dash. See Fig. 2. Connect voltmeter negative probe to terminal No. 4 or 5 of self-diagnostic connector.

2) Turn ignition on. Voltage signals generated are read as needle sweeps. The needle sweep range is 0-12 volts. Longer duration pulses are recorded as the tens digit of code, and shorter duration pulses are recorded as ones digit of code. Codes are separated by a pause.

3) Read and record self-diagnostic (trouble) codes on basis of deflection of voltmeter needle. See TROUBLE CODE IDENTIFICATION table. Proceed to appropriate CODE test for diagnosis and servicing procedure. If 2 or more trouble codes are stored, lowest number code will be indicated first. After repairs are complete, erase trouble codes. See CLEARING CODES.

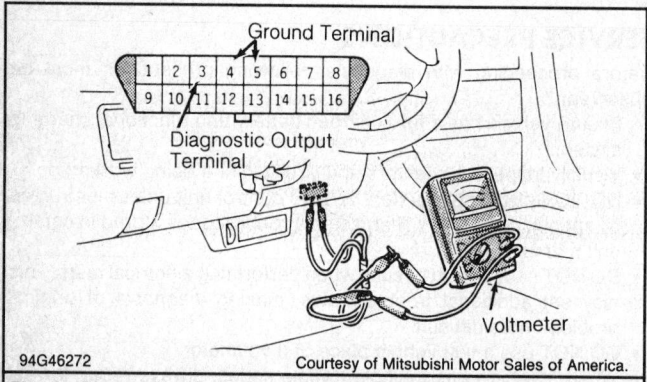

Ground Terminal

Diagnostic Output Terminal

Voltmeter

94G46272   Courtesy of Mitsubishi Motor Sales of America.

Fig. 2: Connecting Voltmeter To Self-Diagnostic Connector

TROUBLE CODE IDENTIFICATION

Code	Description
11	"G" Sensor
14	Throttle Position Sensor (TPS)
21	Steering Wheel Sensor
24	Vehicle Speed Sensor (VSS)
26	Brakelight Switch
61	Right Front Strut Actuator
62	Left Front Strut Actuator
63	Right Rear Strut Actuator
64	Left Rear Strut Actuator

CLEARING CODES

If using scan tester, refer to tester instructions. If using voltmeter, turn ignition off. Disconnect negative battery cable for at least 10 seconds. Reconnect battery cable. If code is not cleared and faults are not present, control unit will automatically clear codes after 60 ignition cycles.

DIAGNOSTIC TESTS

CODE 11: "G" SENSOR

1) Using scan tester, access service data for "G" sensor. With vehicle in stationary condition, voltage measurement should be 2-3 volts.

While bouncing vehicle, voltage should fluctuate near 2.5 volts. If "G" sensor passes testing, go to next step. If "G" sensor fails testing, go to step 5).

2) Select TOUR mode using ECS switch. Using scan tester, check service data for items No. 61, 62, 63 and 64 (actuator indicators). All service data indications should be SOFT.

3) Remove "G" sensor. See "G" SENSOR under REMOVAL & INSTALLATION. Reconnect "G" sensor to harness connector. Turn ignition on. Slowly shake sensor up and down at about one cycle per second while observing scan tester service data indication for each actuator.

4) Each actuator indication should be HARD while shaking "G" sensor and should switch back to SOFT when sensor is held stationary. If each actuator indication tests as specified, "G" sensor circuit is okay. If any actuator indications do not test as specified, replace ECS control unit. See REMOVAL & INSTALLATION.

5) Disconnect "G" sensor connector. Turn ignition on. Using voltmeter, measure voltage between "G" sensor harness connector terminal No. 1 (Green/Red wire) and ground. Reading should be 5 volts. Using ohmmeter, check for continuity between "G" sensor harness connector terminal No. 3 (Black wire) and ground. Continuity should be present. If measurements are not within specification, go to step 6). If measurements are within specification, go to step 7).

6) Turn ignition off. Check for continuity between "G" sensor harness connector terminal No. 1 (Green/Red wire) and ECS control unit harness connector terminal No. 54 (Green/Red wire). See Fig. 3. Check for continuity between "G" sensor harness connector terminal No. 3 (Black wire) and ECS control unit harness connector terminal No. 57 (Black wire). If continuity does not exist, inspect and repair harness. If continuity does exist, replace ECS control unit.

7) Turn ignition off. Check for continuity between "G" sensor harness connector terminal No. 2 (Green/Brown wire) and ECS control unit harness connector terminal No. 61 (Green/Brown wire). See Fig. 3. If continuity is does not exist, inspect and repair harness. If continuity does exist, install a known good "G" sensor. Recheck for Code 11. If Code 11 is reset, replace ECS control unit. If Code 11 is not reset, replace "G" sensor.

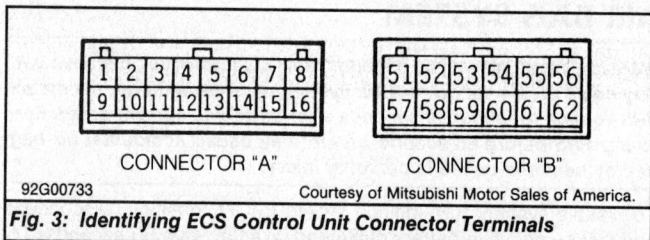

CONNECTOR "A"   CONNECTOR "B"

92G00733   Courtesy of Mitsubishi Motor Sales of America.

Fig. 3: Identifying ECS Control Unit Connector Terminals

CODE 14: THROTTLE POSITION SENSOR

Using scan tester, access Throttle Position Sensor (TPS) test. With TPS fully closed, voltage should be .3-1.0 volt. Slowly press down on accelerator pedal. TPS voltage should smoothly increase to 4.5-5.5 volts with throttle fully open. Replace TPS if it does not test as specified.

CODE 21: STEERING WHEEL ANGULAR VELOCITY SENSOR

1) Using scan tester, check service data for steering wheel angular velocity sensor. Monitor ST1 and ST2 readings. Scan tester should display oscillating ON and OFF signals when turning steering wheel clockwise and counterclockwise. If steering wheel angular velocity sensor passes test, go to next step. If steering wheel angular velocity sensor fails test, go to step 5).

2) Raise and support front of vehicle. Place steering wheel in straight-ahead position. Select TOUR mode using ECS switch. Using scan tester, enter a simulated vehicle speed of 62 MPH (100 KM/H). Check service data indications for items No. 61, 62, 63 and 64 (actuator indications). All service data indications should be SOFT.

3) While monitoring service data indication for item No. 61, turn steering wheel sharply clockwise or counterclockwise 90 degrees from straight-ahead position. Service data indication should switch from

SOFT to MEDIUM or HARD in approximately 0.3 second. Service data indication should return to SOFT about one second after steering wheel is held stationary. Repeat this step for items No. 62, 63 and 64.

4) If all service data indications respond as specified, ECS system is okay. If any service data indications do not respond as specified, replace ECS control unit. Disconnect steering wheel angular velocity sensor connector. See STEERING WHEEL ANGULAR VELOCITY SENSOR under REMOVAL & INSTALLATION.

5) Turn ignition on. Measure voltage between ground and steering wheel angular velocity sensor harness connector terminals No. 2 (Green/Blue wire), No. 3 (Green/Black wire) and No. 4 (Green/Red wire). Voltage should be 5 volts at each terminal. If voltage is within specification, go to step **8)**.

6) If voltage is not within specification, turn ignition off. Check continuity between sensor terminal No. 2 and ECS control unit terminal No. 56, sensor terminal No. 3 and control unit terminal No. 55 and sensor terminal No. 4 and control unit terminal No. 54. See Fig. 3. Inspect and repair harness as necessary. If harness is okay, replace ECS control unit.

7) Check for continuity between steering wheel angular velocity sensor harness connector terminal No. 1 (Black wire) and ground. If continuity does not exist, go to next step.

8) Check for continuity between steering wheel angular velocity sensor harness connector terminal No. 1 (Black wire) and ECS control unit harness connector terminal No. 57 (Black wire). See Fig. 3.

9) If continuity is present, replace ECS control unit. If continuity is not present, repair Black wire between steering wheel angular velocity sensor and ECS harness connector.

10) Replace steering wheel angular velocity sensor with a known good sensor. Recheck for Code 21. If Code 21 is reset, replace ECS control unit. If Code 21 is not reset, replace steering wheel angular velocity sensor.

CODE 24: VEHICLE SPEED SENSOR (VSS)

Non-Turbo – 1) Using scan tester, access service data for vehicle speed sensor. Raise and support vehicle. Start and operate vehicle. Monitor speedometer. Speedometer reading should match scan tester reading. If vehicle speed sensor passes test, go to next step. If vehicle speed sensor service fails test, go to step **4)**.

2) Select TOUR mode using ECS switch. While monitoring service data indication for item No. 61, vary simulated vehicle speed using scan tester. See HIGH SPEED SENSITIVITY CONTROL TEST SPECIFICATIONS table. Repeat this step for items No. 62, 63 and 64.

HIGH SPEED SENSITIVITY CONTROL TEST SPECIFICATIONS

Simulated Vehicle Speed Change	Scan Tester Service Data Indication Change
Accelerate From 80 MPH To 81 MPH	From SOFT To MEDIUM
Decelerate From 75 MPH To 74 MPH	From MEDIUM To SOFT

3) If high speed sensitivity control passes test, ECS system is okay. If high speed sensitivity control fails test, replace ECS control unit.

4) Remove knee protector, steering column covers and meter bezel. Remove instrument cluster, and disconnect combination meter harness connector. Check for continuity between combination meter harness connector terminal No. 109 (Yellow/White wire) and ECS control unit harness connector terminal No. 53 (Yellow/White wire). See Figs. 3 and 4.

5) Check for continuity between combination meter harness connector terminal No. 64 (Black wire) and ground. See Fig. 4. Repair wiring harness if continuity does not exist. If continuity exists, go to next step.

6) Test vehicle speed sensor. See VEHICLE SPEED SENSOR under COMPONENT TESTING. If vehicle speed sensor is okay, replace ECS control unit. If vehicle speed sensor is faulty, replace combination meter.

Turbo – 1) Using scan tester, access service data for Vehicle Speed Sensor (VSS). Raise and support vehicle. Start and operate vehicle. Monitor speedometer. Speedometer reading should match scan tester reading. If vehicle speed sensor passes test, go to next step. If vehicle speed sensor service fails test, go to step **4)**.

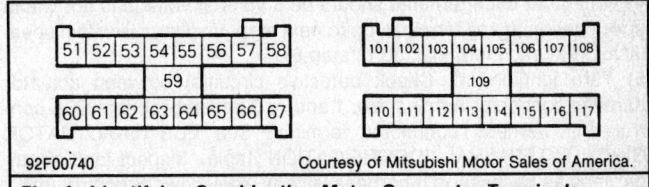

Fig. 4: Identifying Combination Meter Connector Terminals (Connectors D-04 & D-05)

Courtesy of Mitsubishi Motor Sales of America.

2) Select TOUR mode using ECS switch. While monitoring service data indication for item No. 61, vary simulated vehicle speed using scan tester. See HIGH SPEED SENSITIVITY CONTROL TEST SPECIFICATIONS table under CODE 24. Repeat this step for items No. 62, 63 and 64.

3) If high speed sensitivity control tests okay, speed sensor circuit is functioning properly. If any high speed sensitivity control fails tests, replace ECS control unit.

4) Remove knee protector, steering column covers and meter bezel. Remove instrument cluster, and separate speed sensor connector from cluster. Using an ohmmeter, check for continuity between vehicle speed sensor harness connector terminal No. 2 (Black wire) and ground. If continuity exists, go to next step. If continuity does not exist, repair wiring harness.

5) Turn ignition on. Using voltmeter, measure voltage between vehicle speed sensor harness connector terminal No. 1 (Black/White wire) and ground. If battery voltage is present, go to next step. If battery voltage is not present, inspect and repair wiring harness.

6) Turn ignition off. Check for continuity between vehicle speed sensor harness connector terminal No. 3 (Yellow wire) and ECS control unit harness connector terminal No. 53 (Yellow/White wire). See Fig. 4.

7) If continuity does not exist, inspect and repair harness. If continuity exists, test vehicle speed sensor. See VEHICLE SPEED SENSOR under COMPONENT TESTING. If vehicle speed sensor is okay, replace ECS control unit. Replace vehicle speed sensor if it is faulty.

CODE 26: BRAKE LIGHT SWITCH

Using scan tester, access stoplight switch test. Scan tester should display ON with brake pedal depressed, and OFF with brake pedal released. Replace switch is it does not operate within specification.

CODE 61, 62, 63 OR 64: STRUT ACTUATORS

1) Identify malfunctioning actuator or actuator circuit according to output trouble code. See TROUBLE CODE ACTUATOR IDENTIFICATION table. Using scan tester, access actuator testing. When TOUR mode is selected, scan tester should display SOFT for each actuator. When SPORT is selected, scan tester should display HARD for each actuator.

TROUBLE CODE ACTUATOR IDENTIFICATION

Trouble Code	Related Actuator Circuit
61	Right Front
62	Left Front
63	Right Rear
64	Left Rear

2) If actuator scan tester data test as specified, actuator is okay. If actuator scan tester data indications do not test as specified, go to next step.

3) Remove cap from top of shock absorber associated with diagnostic trouble code. Turn ignition on. Measure voltage between ground and actuator harness connector terminals No. 1 and 3. See Fig. 5.

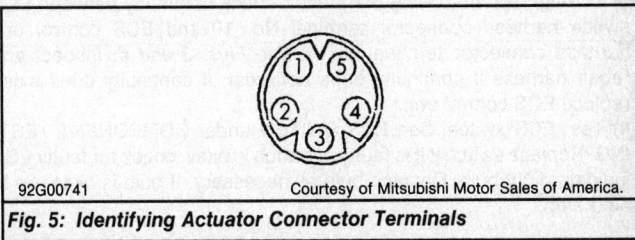

Fig. 5: Identifying Actuator Connector Terminals

Courtesy of Mitsubishi Motor Sales of America.

4) Voltage at each terminal should be 5 volts. If voltage is not within specification at any terminal, go to next step. If voltage is within specification at each terminal, go to step **6)**.

5) Turn ignition off. Check defective circuit(s) between actuator harness connector terminal No. 1 and/or 3 and appropriate ECS control unit harness connector terminal. See ECS-TO-ACTUATOR CIRCUIT TERMINAL IDENTIFICATION table. Inspect and repair harness as necessary. If harness is okay, replace ECS control unit.

ECS-TO-ACTUATOR CIRCUIT TERMINAL IDENTIFICATION

Actuator Connector Terminal No. [1]	ECS Control Unit Connector [2] Terminal No.
Front Right Actuator	
1	7
3	6
5	5
Front Left Actuator	
1	10
3	9
5	8
Rear Right Actuator	
1	3
3	2
5	11
Rear Left Actuator	
1	16
3	15
5	14

[1] – See Fig. 5.
[2] – See Fig. 3.

6) Using ohmmeter, check for continuity between ground and actuator harness connector terminals No. 2 and 4 (Black wires). See Fig. 5. If continuity exists at both terminals, go to next step. If continuity does not exist at either terminal, inspect repair appropriate circuit.

7) Turn ignition on. Using scan tester, energize appropriate actuator while measuring voltage between ground and actuator harness connector terminal No. 5. See Fig. 5. Refer to scan tester manufacturer instructions for specific procedure.

8) Voltage should be zero volts normally and jump to 9 volts during forced activation (drive) of actuator. If actuator does not test as specified, go to next step. If actuator passes test, go to step **10)**.

9) Turn ignition off. Check continuity between appropriate actuator harness connector terminal No. 5 and appropriate ECS control unit harness connector terminal. See ECS-TO-ACTUATOR CIRCUIT TERMINAL IDENTIFICATION table. Inspect and repair harness as necessary. If harness is okay, replace ECS control unit.

10) Replace malfunctioning strut assembly (and actuator) with a known good unit. Recheck for self-diagnostic trouble codes. If original trouble code is reset, replace ECS control unit. If original trouble code is not reset, replace strut assembly.

SYSTEM TESTS (NO CODES)

ECS INDICATOR LIGHT DOES NOT CHANGE WHEN ECS SWITCH IS OPERATED

1) Remove ECS switch. See ECS SWITCH under REMOVAL & INSTALLATION. Check for continuity between ground and ECS switch harness connector terminal No. 11 (Black wire). See Fig. 6. If continuity exists, go to next step. If continuity does not exist, repair Black wire between connector terminal No. 11 and ground.

2) Turn ignition on. Measure voltage between ground and ECS switch harness connector terminal No. 10 (Red/Black wire). See Fig. 6. If voltage is not 5 volts, go to next step. If voltage is 5 volts, go to step **4)**.

3) Turn ignition off. Using ohmmeter, check continuity between ECS switch harness connector terminal No. 10 and ECS control unit harness connector terminal No. 1. See Figs. 3 and 6. Inspect and repair harness if continuity does not exist. If continuity does exist, replace ECS control unit.

4) Test ECS switch. See ECS SWITCH under COMPONENT TESTING. Replace switch if it is faulty. If switch is okay, check for faulty ECS indicator light bulb. Replace bulb as necessary. If bulb is okay, go to next step.

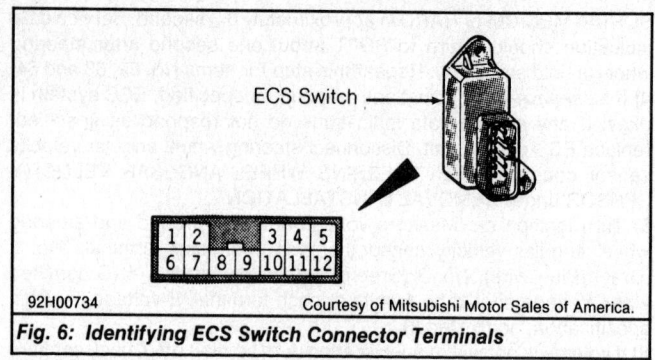

Fig. 6: Identifying ECS Switch Connector Terminals

5) Using ohmmeter, check for continuity between combination meter harness connector terminal No. 10 (White/Orange wire) and ECS control unit harness connector terminal No. 2 (White/Orange wire). See Figs. 3 and 7. Inspect and repair harness if continuity does not exist. If continuity does exist, go to next step.

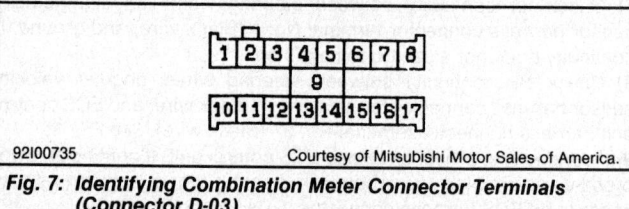

Fig. 7: Identifying Combination Meter Connector Terminals (Connector D-03)

6) Check for continuity between combination meter harness connector terminal No. 11 (White/Black wire) and ECS control unit harness connector terminal No. 3 (White/Black wire). See Figs. 3 and 7. Inspect and repair harness if continuity does not exist. If continuity does not exist, go to next step.

7) Check for continuity between ground and combination meter harness connector terminal No. 2 (Black/Yellow wire). See Fig. 7. Inspect and repair harness if continuity is not present. If continuity does exist, go to next step.

8) Replace combination meter with a known good unit. Check ECS indicator light operation. If ECS indicator light operates correctly, replace combination meter. If ECS indicator light still does not operate correctly, replace ECS control unit.

ANTI-DIVE CONTROL STOPS OPERATING

1) Using scan tester, access service data on stoplight switch. See CODE 26 under DIAGNOSTIC TESTS. If stoplight switch is functioning properly, go to next step. If stoplight switch is malfunctioning, go to step **5)**.

2) Select TOUR mode using ECS switch. Using scan tester, enter a simulated vehicle speed of 62 MPH. Refer to scan tester instructions for specific procedure. Using scan tester, ensure service data indication for items No. 61, 62, 63 and 64 is SOFT.

3) While monitoring service data indication for item No. 61, depress brake pedal and reduce simulated speed from scan tester. Service data indication should change to HARD until simulated vehicle speed falls below 50 MPH; indication should then change to SOFT. Repeat this step for service data items No. 62, 63 and 64.

4) If any service data items do not test as specified, replace ECS control unit. If all service data items test as specified, anti-dive control is functioning properly.

5) Turn ignition on. Depress brake pedal. Ensure stoplight comes on. If stoplight does not come on, go to step **7)**. If stoplight comes on, check continuity between stoplight switch harness connector terminal No. 3 (Green wire) and ECS control unit harness connector terminal No. 58 (Green wire). See Fig. 3.

6) If continuity exists, replace ECS control unit. If continuity does not exist, repair harness between stoplight switch and ECS control unit.

7) Disconnect stoplight switch harness connector. Measure voltage between ground and stoplight switch harness connector terminal No. 2 (Red/Black wire). If battery voltage is present, go to next step. If battery voltage is not present, repair harness.

8) Remove and test stoplight switch. See BRAKELIGHT SWITCH under COMPONENT TESTING. If stoplight switch is okay, replace ECS control unit. If stoplight switch is faulty, replace stoplight switch.

ANTI-SQUAT CONTROL STOPS OPERATING

1) Using scan tester, access data on Throttle Position Sensor (TPS). See CODE 14 under DIAGNOSTIC TESTS. If TPS tests okay, go to next step. If TPS is malfunctioning, go to step **7)**.

2) Select TOUR mode using ECS switch. Using scan tester, enter a simulated vehicle speed of 19 MPH. Refer to scan tester instructions for specific procedure. Using scan tester, ensure service data indication for items No. 61, 62, 63 and 64 is SOFT.

3) While monitoring service data indication for item No. 61, quickly depress accelerator pedal. Service data indication should change to HARD for a second and then change to MEDIUM. Release accelerator pedal. Service data indication should change to SOFT.

4) Increase simulated speed from scan tester to 37 MPH. Quickly depress accelerator pedal again. Service data indication should change to MEDIUM. Release accelerator pedal. Service data indication should change to SOFT.

5) Increase simulated speed from scan tester to 56 MPH. Quickly depress accelerator pedal again. Service data indication should remain at SOFT for a second and then change to MEDIUM. Release accelerator pedal. Service data indication should change to SOFT.

6) Repeat steps 3)-5) for scan tester items No. 62, 63 and 64. If any service data item does not test as specified, replace ECS control unit. If all service data items test as specified, anti-squat control is functioning properly.

7) Start engine. If CHECK ENGINE light comes on and stays on, go to step **9)**. If CHECK ENGINE light does not stay on, check continuity between TPS harness connector terminal No. 2 (Brown/Red wire) and ECS control unit harness connector terminal No. 59 (Brown/Red wire). See Fig. 3.

8) If continuity does not exist, repair harness. If continuity does exist, test TPS. See THROTTLE POSITION SENSOR under COMPONENT TESTING. If TPS is okay, replace ECS control unit. If TPS is faulty, replace TPS.

9) Disconnect TPS harness connector. Turn ignition on. Measure voltage between ground and TPS harness connector terminal No. 1 (Green/Yellow wire). If 5 volts are present, go to next step. If 5 volts are not present, check Green/Yellow wire between TPS connector terminal No. 1 and engine control unit connector terminal No. 61. Inspect and repair wire as necessary. If wire is okay, replace ECM.

10) Using an ohmmeter, check continuity between TPS harness connector terminal No. 4 (Black wire) and ground. If continuity exists, replace TPS. If continuity does not exist, check Black wire between TPS connector terminal No. 4 and engine control unit connector terminal No. 72. Repair wire as necessary. If wire is okay, replace ECM.

COMPONENT TESTING

ACTUATOR

Damping Force Check – Turn ignition on. Select TOUR mode using ECS switch. Push vehicle up and down at each corner of vehicle. Select SPORT mode using ECS switch. Push vehicle at same points and ensure damping force is stiffer than first check.

Operating Sound Check – Turn ignition on. Listen at top of each shock absorber while an assistant switches suspension modes by pressing ECS switch. Actuators should be heard each time ECS switch is pressed.

ECS CONTROL UNIT POWER SUPPLY & GROUND CIRCUIT

Ground Circuit Inspection – **1)** Disconnect ECS control unit harness connector. Using an ohmmeter, check continuity between harness connector terminal No. 52 (Black wire) and ground. See Fig. 3.

2) If continuity exists, ground circuit is okay. If continuity does not exist, repair Black wire between ECS control unit harness connector and ground connection on chassis below rear glass latch point.

Power Circuit Inspection – **1)** Disconnect ECS control unit harness connector. Turn ignition on. Using a voltmeter, measure voltage between harness connector terminal No. 51 (Blue/Red wire) and ground. See Fig. 3.

2) If battery voltage is present, go to next step. If battery voltage is not present, check fuse No. 3 in passenger compartment fuse box. Replace fuse if it is blown. If fuse is okay, check Blue/Red wire between ECS control unit harness connector and fuse No. 3. Repair wiring as necessary.

3) Using a voltmeter, measure voltage between harness connector terminal No. 62 (Red/Black wire) and ground. See Fig. 3. If battery voltage is present, power circuits are okay. If battery voltage is not present, go to next step.

4) Check fuse No. 19 in passenger compartment fuse box. Replace blown fuse. If fuse is okay, check Red/Black wire between ECS control unit harness connector and junction block. Repair wire as necessary.

ECS SWITCH

Continuity Test – Using an ohmmeter, check for continuity between appropriate switch terminals with ECS switch in ON and OFF positions. See ECS SWITCH CONTINUITY TEST SPECIFICATIONS table.

ECS SWITCH CONTINUITY TEST SPECIFICATIONS

Application	Continuity Between Terminals No.
ECS Switch Position	
ON	3 & 4; 10 & 11
OFF	3 & 4

BRAKELIGHT SWITCH

Continuity Test – Remove brakelight switch. Using an ohmmeter, check continuity between brakelight switch terminals No. 2 and 3. See Fig. 8. Continuity should exist. Continuity should not exist when brakelight switch plunger is depressed at least .16" (4.0 mm). Replace switch if continuity does not change as specified.

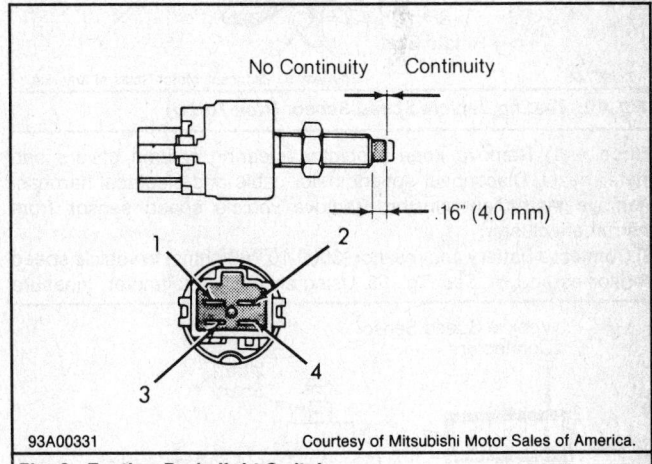

93A00331   Courtesy of Mitsubishi Motor Sales of America.

Fig. 8: Testing Brakelight Switch

THROTTLE POSITION SENSOR

Resistance Test – **1)** Disconnect Throttle Position Sensor (TPS). Using an ohmmeter, measure resistance between TPS terminals No. 1 and 4. See Fig. 9. If resistance is 3500-6500 ohms, go to next step. If resistance is not 3500-6500 ohms, replace TPS.

2) Measure resistance between TPS terminals No. 2 and 4 while slowly moving throttle plate. If resistance varies in direct relation to throttle plate position, TPS is okay. If resistance does not vary in direct relation to throttle plate position, replace TPS.

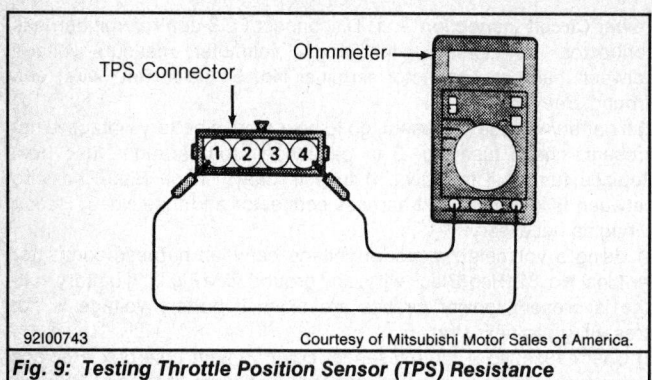

Fig. 9: *Testing Throttle Position Sensor (TPS) Resistance*

VEHICLE SPEED SENSOR

Non-Turbo – 1) Remove knee protector, steering column covers and meter bezel. Disconnect speedometer cable and electrical harness. Remove instrument cluster.

2) Using an ohmmeter, check circuit continuity between reed switch (speedometer) terminal and ground terminal of combination meter. *See Fig. 10.* Rotate speedometer input shaft and ensure continuity pulses on and off 4 times per shaft revolution. Replace combination meter if continuity does not pulse with shaft rotation.

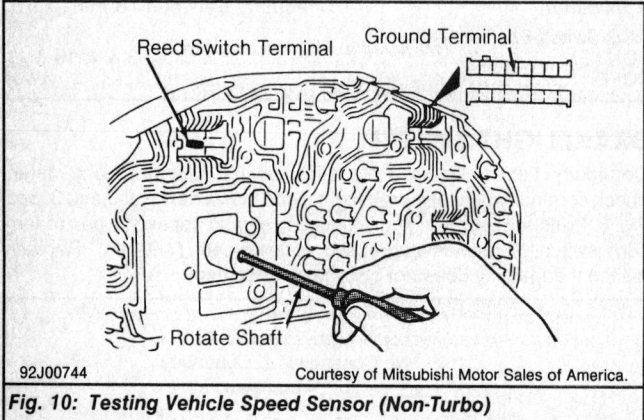

Fig. 10: *Testing Vehicle Speed Sensor (Non-Turbo)*

Turbo – 1) Remove knee protector, steering column covers and meter bezel. Disconnect speedometer cable and electrical harness. Remove instrument cluster. Remove vehicle speed sensor from instrument cluster.

2) Connect a battery and resistor (3000-10,000 ohms) to vehicle speed sensor as shown. *See Fig. 11.* Using an analog voltmeter, measure

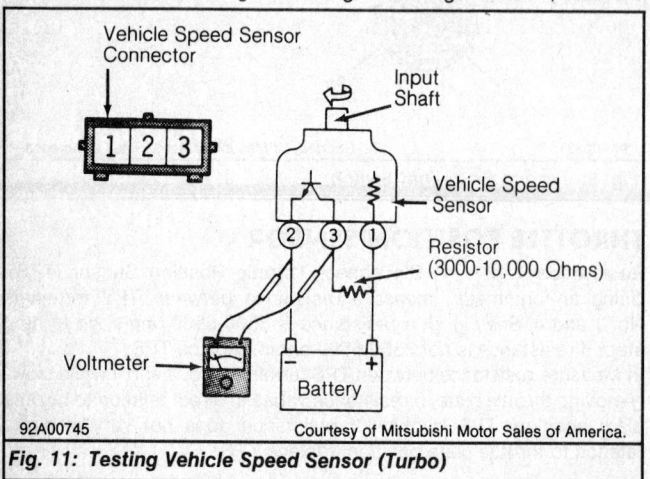

Fig. 11: *Testing Vehicle Speed Sensor (Turbo)*

voltage between sensor terminals No. 2 and 3. Rotate speed sensor input shaft and ensure voltage pulses 4 times per shaft revolution. Replace vehicle speed sensor if voltage does not pulse as specified.

REMOVAL & INSTALLATION

ECS CONTROL UNIT

Removal & Installation – Remove luggage compartment right cargo floor box. *See Fig. 12.* Remove ECS control unit lid. Disconnect harness connectors, and remove ECS control unit. To install, reverse removal procedure.

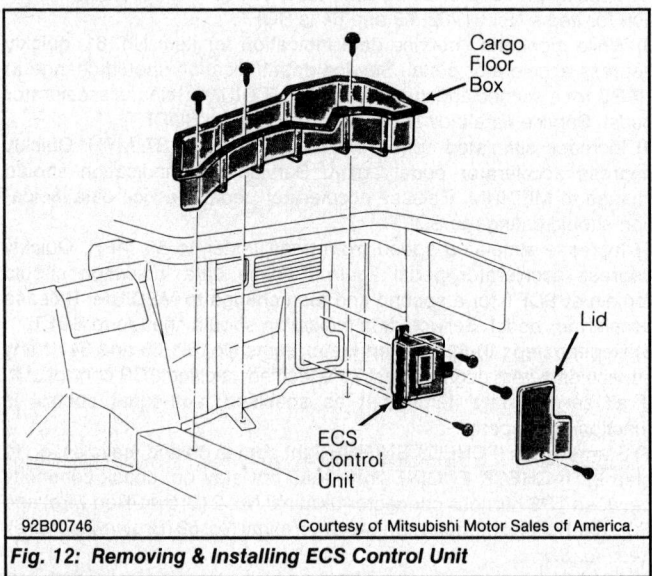

Fig. 12: *Removing & Installing ECS Control Unit*

ECS SWITCH

Removal & Installation – Remove lower knee protector and steering column covers. Remove meter bezel. Remove ECS switch from meter bezel. To install, reverse removal procedure.

"G" SENSOR

Removal – "G" sensor is located under driver's seat. *See Fig. 13.* Remove seat headrest. Remove seat anchor covers and front mounting nuts. Remove seat rear mounting bolts. Disconnect harness connectors (if equipped). Remove seat assembly. Remove "G" sensor.

Installation – 1) Install "G" sensor. When installing seat assembly, ensure slide rail adjuster is locked at both sides and rails are in same relative positions.

2) Install seat assembly. Temporarily tighten fasteners in following order: front outboard nut, front inboard nut, rear outboard bolt and rear inboard bolt. Tighten nuts to 22 ft. lbs. (30 N.m) and bolts to 33 ft. lbs. (45 N.m). Reverse removal procedure for remaining components.

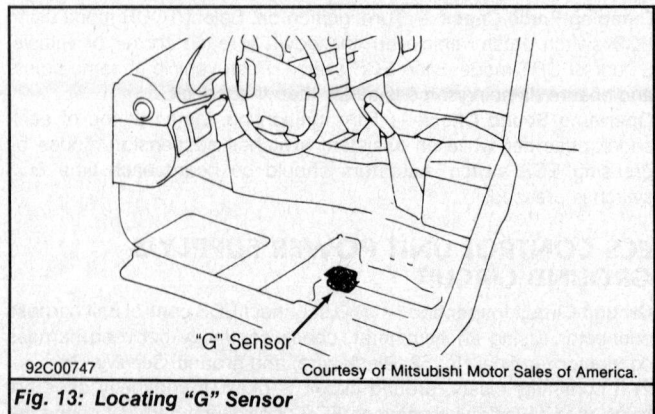

Fig. 13: *Locating "G" Sensor*

STEERING WHEEL ANGULAR VELOCITY SENSOR

WARNING: *Wait at least 60 seconds after disconnecting negative battery cable before servicing SRS. System reserve capacitor maintains SRS voltage for about 60 seconds after battery is disconnected. Servicing SRS before 60-second period may cause accidental air bag deployment and possible personal injury.*

NOTE: *Steering wheel angular velocity sensor is an electronic unit using photo-couplers. Clean hands and working environment are recommended to avoid contaminating this component.*

Removal – 1) Before proceeding, follow air bag service precautions. See AIR BAG SERVICE PRECAUTIONS. Disable SRS. See DISABLING & ACTIVATING AIR BAG SYSTEM. Ensure front wheels are in straight-ahead position.
2) Turn ignition off. Remove ignition key. Disconnect and isolate negative battery cable to prevent accidental grounding. Wait 60 seconds before continuing. Remove air bag module mounting nuts from back side of steering wheel. Lift air bag module.
3) Disconnect electrical connector from air bag module by pressing air bag connector lock toward outer side to spread it open. Pry upward gently to remove connector. *See Fig. 14.* DO NOT apply excessive force. Remove air bag module. Remove air bag module. Place air bag in clean, dry area with pad cover face up.

CAUTION: *DO NOT hammer steering wheel during removal, as it may damage steering column.*

4) Place reference mark on steering wheel and steering column shaft for reassembly reference. Remove steering wheel nut and washer. Using steering wheel puller, remove steering wheel. Remove steering column covers.
5) Clockspring is located behind steering wheel. Remove rear console assembly. Using a screwdriver, push in SRS Diagnostic Unit (SDU) lock spring to unlock wiring connector lock lever. Disconnect 2-pin Red clockspring connector at SDU. Remove knee protector. Remove screws attaching clockspring. Remove clockspring.

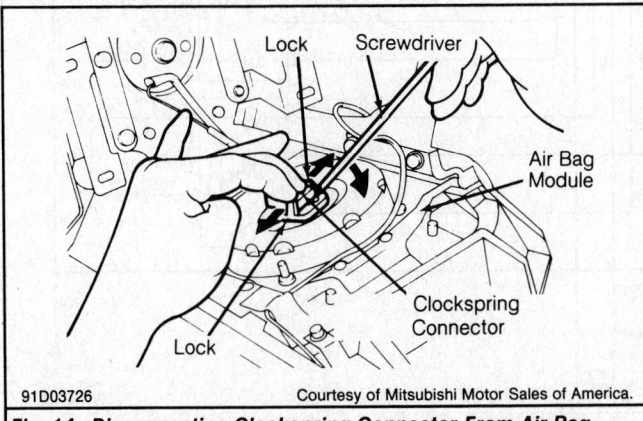

91D03726   Courtesy of Mitsubishi Motor Sales of America.
Fig. 14: Disconnecting Clockspring Connector From Air Bag

6) Disconnect steering wheel angular velocity sensor wiring connectors. *See Fig. 15.* Remove column switch. Remove sensor from steering column.
Installation – 1) To install, gently position sensor in steering column. DO NOT bend or contaminate slit plate. Install mounting screws and wire connector. Reverse removal procedure to install remaining components.

CAUTION: *If rotating part of clockspring is not properly centered with steering column and front wheels, clockspring failure will result. The following procedure must be used to center clockspring.*

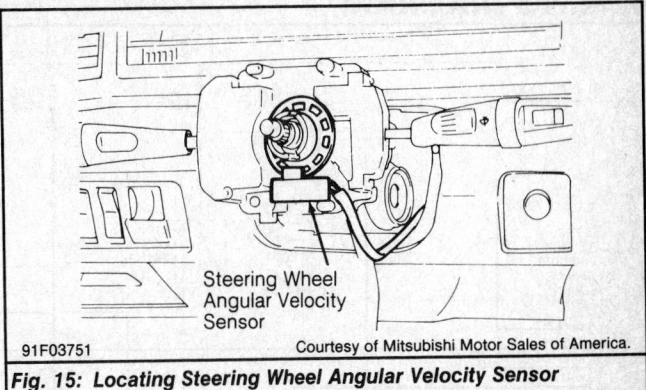

91F03751   Courtesy of Mitsubishi Motor Sales of America.
Fig. 15: Locating Steering Wheel Angular Velocity Sensor

2) Ensure wheels are straight ahead and steering wheel is locked. With air bag module and steering wheel removed, align clockspring mating mark and NEUTRAL position mark. *See Fig. 16.*
3) Ensure horn switch wires are properly positioned. Install steering wheel and air bag module. Turn steering wheel all the way in both directions to ensure steering is normal.
4) Ensure horn switch wires are properly positioned. Tighten air bag module-to-steering wheel nuts to 48 INCH lbs. (5 N.m). Connect negative battery cable. Check SRS warning light to ensure system is functioning properly. See AIR BAG SYSTEM OPERATION CHECK.

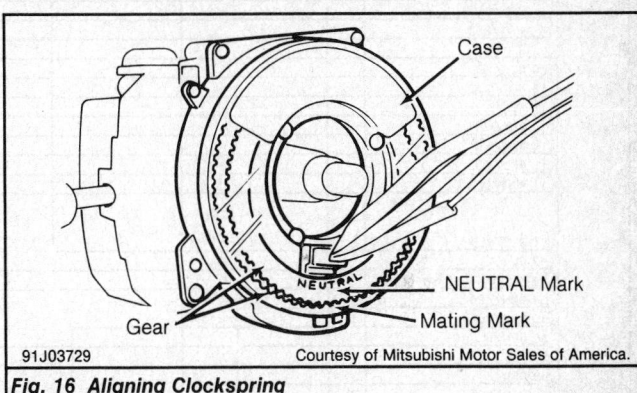

91J03729   Courtesy of Mitsubishi Motor Sales of America.
Fig. 16 Aligning Clockspring

WARNING: *After any repair, always turn ignition on from passenger-side of vehicle. Air bag could deploy.*

Air Bag System Operation Check – Turn ignition switch to ON or START position. SRS warning light on instrument panel should illuminate for approximately 7 seconds then turn off. This indicates SRS is functioning properly. If any of the following conditions exist, SRS is malfunctioning and needs repair.
- SRS warning light does not illuminate as described.
- SRS warning light stays on for more than 7 seconds.
- SRS warning light illuminates while driving.

If SRS warning light does not illuminate as described, SRS is malfunctioning.

STRUT ASSEMBLY

NOTE: *For removal and installation information, see FRONT – FWD article or REAR – AWD & FWD article.*

1994 SUSPENSION
Electronic – Stealth & 3000GT (Cont.)

WIRING DIAGRAM

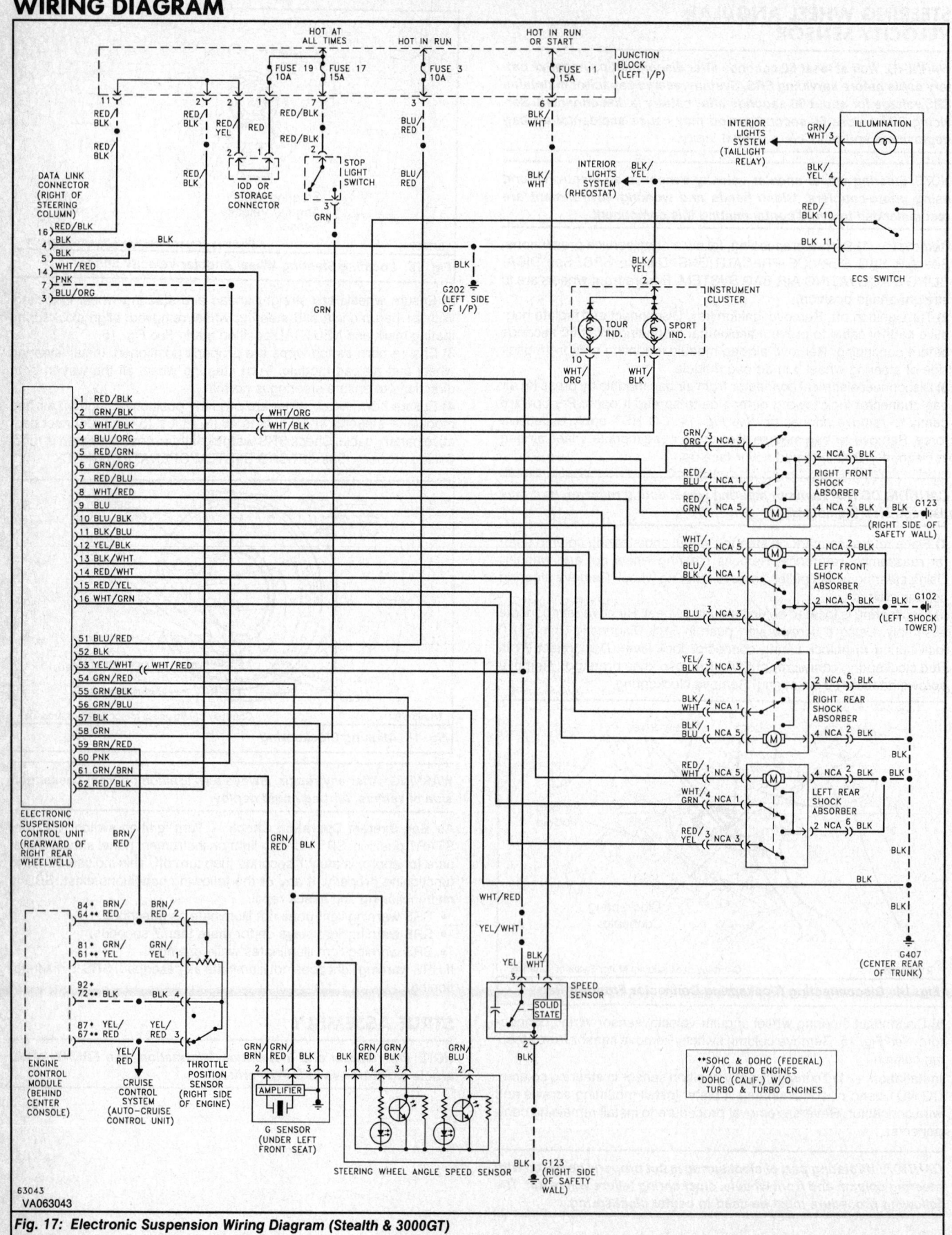

Fig. 17: Electronic Suspension Wiring Diagram (Stealth & 3000GT)

63043
VA063043

Chrysler Corp.: Colt, Colt Vista,
Stealth, Summit, Summit Wagon
Mitsubishi: Diamante, Eclipse, Expo,
Galant, Mirage, Precis, 3000GT

DESCRIPTION & OPERATION

The steering system consists of solid steering shaft with a lower joint assembly. Diamante, Stealth and 3000GT models are equipped with a Supplemental Restraint System (SRS) that includes an air bag and clockspring located in the steering column.

WARNING: Diamante, Stealth and 3000GT are equipped with a Supplemental Restraint System (SRS) that includes an air bag located in steering column. Use caution when working around steering column. Ensure battery is disconnected before attempting any repair. DO NOT apply electrical power to any component on steering column without disconnecting air bag module (air bag could deploy).

NOTE: For information on air bag DIAGNOSIS & TESTING or DISPOSAL PROCEDURES, see MITCHELL® AIR BAG SERVICE & REPAIR MANUAL, DOMESTIC & IMPORTED MODELS.

DISABLING & ACTIVATING AIR BAG SYSTEM

WARNING: Wait at least 60 seconds after disconnecting negative battery cable before servicing SRS. System reserve capacitor maintains SRS voltage for about 60 seconds after battery is disconnected. Servicing SRS before 60-second period may cause accidental air bag deployment and possible personal injury.

To disable system, turn ignition switch to OFF position. Disconnect and isolate negative battery cable end. Wait at least 60 seconds. To activate system, reconnect negative battery cable. For air bag servicing information not covered in this article, see AIR BAG RESTRAINT SYSTEM article in ACCESSORIES & EQUIPMENT.

AIR BAG SERVICE PRECAUTIONS

The following precautions should be observed when working with SRS:

- Disable SRS before servicing any SRS or steering column component. Failure to do this may result in accidental air bag deployment and possible personal injury. See DISABLING & ACTIVATING AIR BAG SYSTEM.
- Wait at least 60 SECONDS after disabling air bag system. SRS system retains enough voltage, for a short time after system is disabled, to deploy air bag.
- After repairs, always turn ignition on from passenger-side of vehicle in case of accidental air bag deployment. Ensure SRS warning light is working properly and no system faults are indicated.
- Always wear safety glasses when servicing or handling an air bag.
- DO NOT expose air bag module and clockspring to temperatures greater than 200°F (93°C).
- When placing a live air bag on a bench or other surface, always face air bag and trim cover up, away from surface. This will reduce motion of module if air bag accidentally deploys.
- After air bag deploys, air bag surface may contain deposits of sodium hydroxide, which irritate skin. Always wear safety glasses, rubber gloves and long-sleeved shirt during clean-up. Wash hands using mild soap and water. Follow correct clean-up and disposal procedures.
- Because of critical system operating requirements, DO NOT service any SRS components. Repairs are only made by replacing defective part(s).
- DO NOT allow any electrical source near inflator on the back of air bag module.

- When carrying live air bag module, trim cover should be pointed away from body to minimize injury in case of accidental air bag deployment.
- If SRS is not fully functional for any reason, DO NOT drive vehicle until system is repaired and is fully functional. DO NOT remove bulbs, modules, sensors or other components, or in any way disable system from operating normally. If SRS is not functional, park vehicle until repairs are made.

REMOVAL & INSTALLATION

STEERING WHEEL & AIR BAG

Removal – 1) Before proceeding, follow air bag service precautions. See AIR BAG SERVICE PRECAUTIONS. Disable SRS. See DISABLING & ACTIVATING AIR BAG SYSTEM.
2) Air bag module is mounted on face of steering wheel. *See Fig. 1.* Ensure wheels are straight ahead and steering wheel is locked. Remove air bag module-to-steering wheel nuts from back side of steering wheel.
3) Lift air bag module. Disconnect electrical connector from air bag module by pressing air bag connector lock toward outside to spread it open. *See Fig. 2.* Pry upward gently to remove connector. DO NOT apply excessive force. Remove air bag module.
4) Place reference mark on steering wheel and steering column shaft for installation reference. Remove steering wheel nut and washer. Using steering wheel puller, remove steering wheel.

CAUTION: DO NOT hammer on steering wheel during removal, as it may damage steering column.

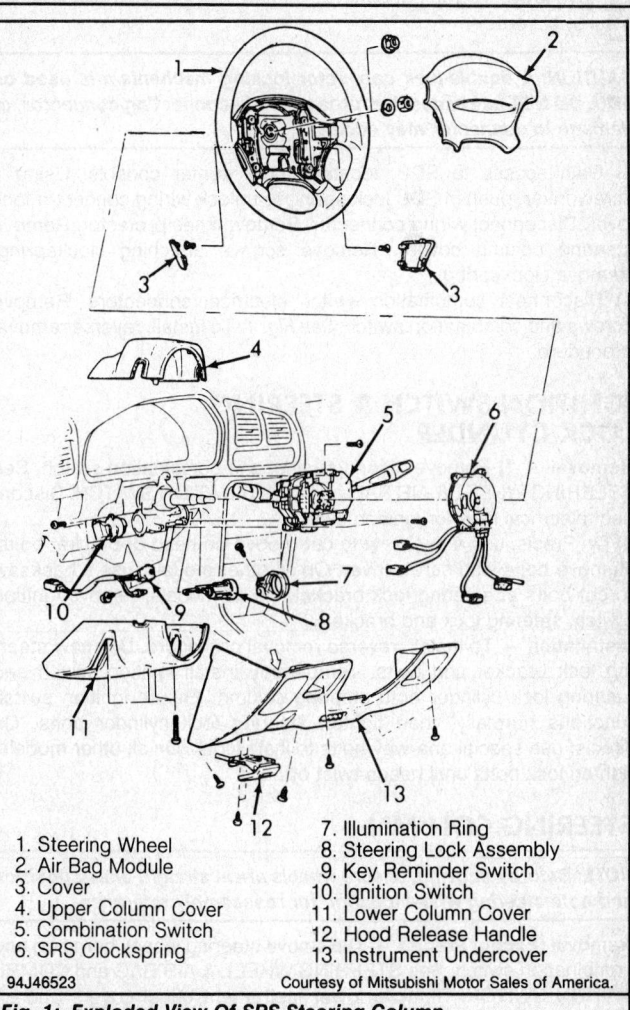

1. Steering Wheel
2. Air Bag Module
3. Cover
4. Upper Column Cover
5. Combination Switch
6. SRS Clockspring
7. Illumination Ring
8. Steering Lock Assembly
9. Key Reminder Switch
10. Ignition Switch
11. Lower Column Cover
12. Hood Release Handle
13. Instrument Undercover

94J46523
Courtesy of Mitsubishi Motor Sales of America.

Fig. 1: Exploded View Of SRS Steering Column Components (Typical)

Installation – To install, reverse removal procedure. Ensure reference marks are aligned. Tighten steering wheel nut to specification. See TORQUE SPECIFICATIONS.

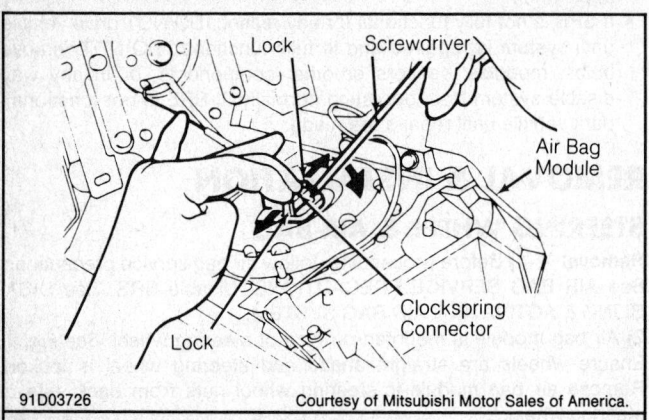

91D03726   Courtesy of Mitsubishi Motor Sales of America.

Fig. 2: Disconnecting Clockspring Connector

COMBINATION SWITCH

CAUTION: When installing steering wheel, if rotating part of clockspring is not properly centered with steering column and front wheels, clockspring failure will result.

Removal & Installation – **1)** Remove steering wheel and air bag. See STEERING WHEEL & AIR BAG under REMOVAL & INSTALLATION. Remove lower instrument panel cover (if equipped). Remove steering column covers.

CAUTION: A double-lock connector locking mechanism is used on SDU. DO NOT use excessive force when disconnecting connector, or damage to connector may occur.

2) Gain access to SDU, located under center console. Using a screwdriver, push in SDU lock spring to unlock wiring connector lock lever. Disconnect wiring connector. Remove knee protector. Remove steering column covers. Remove screws attaching clockspring. Remove clockspring.

3) Disconnect combination switch electrical connectors. Remove screws and combination switch. *See Fig. 1.* To install, reverse removal procedure.

IGNITION SWITCH & STEERING LOCK CYLINDER

Removal – **1)** Remove steering wheel and combination switch. See STEERING WHEEL & AIR BAG and COMBINATION SWITCH. Disconnect electrical lead for ignition switch.

2) On Precis, use a hacksaw to cut groove on head of bracket bolts. Remove bolts with screwdriver. On all other models, use a hacksaw to cut bolts at steering lock bracket. On all models, remove ignition switch, steering lock and bracket.

Installation – To install, reverse removal procedure. Use new steering lock bracket and bolts. Temporarily install ignition switch and steering lock cylinder onto steering column. Ensure ignition switch functions normally, then tighten steering lock cylinder bolts. On Precis, use special one-way bolts to install lock. On all other models, tighten lock bolts until heads twist off.

STEERING COLUMN

NOTE: Before removing, ensure wheels are in straight-ahead position and note steering wheel location for reassembly reference.

Removal (Except Precis) – **1)** Remove steering wheel, horn pad and combination switch. See STEERING WHEEL & AIR BAG and COMBINATION SWITCH. Remove lower instrument panel covers and air ducts. Disconnect all electrical connectors to steering column.

2) Remove key interlock cable and slide lever (if equipped). Remove coupling bolt at steering gear. Remove cover bolts or retaining band. Remove steering column bracket bolts. Remove steering column assembly.

Installation – To install, reverse removal procedure. Ensure coupling is installed on steering gear so steering wheel will be centered.

Removal (Precis) – **1)** Remove steering wheel, horn pad and combination switch. See STEERING WHEEL & AIR BAG and COMBINATION SWITCH. Remove lower crash pad, and disconnect rheostat connector. Remove column shroud. Disconnect all electrical connectors to steering column.

CAUTION: Note direction and location of installed lower joint assembly before removing. Ensure joint assembly is installed correctly, as joints at ends of shaft are of different length. See Fig. 3.

---

2) Remove coupling bolt at bottom of lower joint assembly. Remove steering column support bracket bolts. Remove steering column assembly. Remove lower joint assembly from steering shaft.

Installation – **1)** Connect lower joint assembly upper joint to steering shaft. Ensure joint is installed in correct direction. *See Fig. 3.* Align lower joint assembly to steering gear pinion, and temporarily tighten lower joint bolt.

2) Install lower joint assembly on steering gear so steering wheel is centered. Attach steering column brackets to dash. Tighten lower bolt of lower joint assembly. Tighten column bracket bolts. To install remaining components, reverse removal procedure.

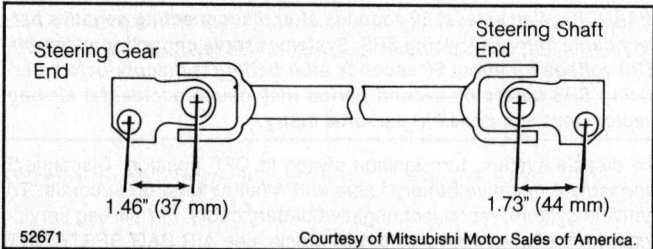

52671   Courtesy of Mitsubishi Motor Sales of America.

Fig. 3: Installing Lower Joint Assembly (Precis)

OVERHAUL

STEERING COLUMN

Disassembly – Remove steering column. See STEERING COLUMN under REMOVAL & INSTALLATION. Remove joint assembly. Remove boot, cover and bearing. Remove snap ring, stopper and spacer. If removing steering lock, cut retaining screws with hacksaw. Remove steering lock and bracket. *See Fig. 4.*

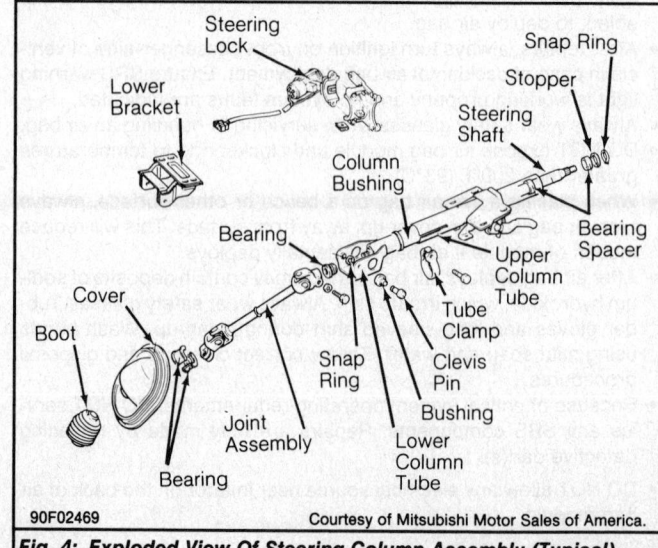

90F02469   Courtesy of Mitsubishi Motor Sales of America.

Fig. 4: Exploded View Of Steering Column Assembly (Typical)

CAUTION: If steering lock is removed, use new steering lock bracket and bolts when reassembling steering lock.

Reassembly – 1) To reassemble, reverse disassembly procedure. Align steering lock with column boss. Ensure steering lock is operational. On all models except Precis, tighten steering lock bracket bolt until bolt head breaks off.

2) Apply multipurpose grease to bearing spacer and lower column tube-to-shaft contact areas. Install cover on joint assembly. Fill inside of bearing with multi-purpose grease. Install bearing on joint assembly. Wrap tape around circumference of bearing approximately 1 1/2 times. Press bearings into cover.

TORQUE SPECIFICATIONS
TORQUE SPECIFICATIONS

Application	Ft. Lbs. (N.m)
Joint Clamp Bolt	11-14 (14-19)
Steering Wheel Nut	25-33 (34-45)
	INCH Lbs. (N.m)
Air Bag Module Nuts	48 (5)
Column Bracket Bolt	84-120 (10-14)
Dust Cover Bolt	36-50 (4-6)

1994 STEERING
Steering Columns – RWD

Mitsubishi: Montero, Pickup

DESCRIPTION & OPERATION

Steering column consists of a collapsible steering shaft with lower joint assembly.

REMOVAL & INSTALLATION

STEERING WHEEL

WARNING: Wait at least 60 seconds after disconnecting negative battery cable before servicing SRS. System reserve capacitor maintains SRS voltage for about 60 seconds after battery is disconnected. Servicing SRS before 60-second period may cause accidental air bag deployment and possible personal injury.

CAUTION: Montero is equipped with an air bag Supplemental Restraint System (SRS). For steering wheel removal and installation information, see AIR BAG RESTRAINT SYSTEM article in ACCESSORIES & EQUIPMENT.

Removal (Pickup) – Remove screws retaining horn pad. Remove horn pad. Place reference mark on steering wheel and steering column shaft for installation reference. Remove steering wheel nut and washer. Using steering wheel puller, remove steering wheel.

CAUTION: DO NOT hammer on steering wheel during servicing, as it may damage steering column.

Installation – To install, reverse removal procedure. Ensure reference marks are aligned. Tighten steering wheel nut to specification. See TORQUE SPECIFICATIONS.

COMBINATION SWITCH

Removal & Installation – On Pickup, remove horn pad and steering wheel. On Montero, remove air bag and steering wheel. See STEERING WHEEL under REMOVAL & INSTALLATION. On Montero, remove instrument lower cover and lower heater duct. On all models, remove upper and lower steering column covers. Disconnect combination switch electrical connectors. Remove screws and combination switch. To install, reverse removal procedure.

IGNITION SWITCH

Removal & Installation (Montero) – **1)** Remove lower instrument cover and heater duct (if equipped). Remove upper and lower steering column covers. Disconnect harness connector from ignition switch. Insert ignition key into cylinder and turn key to ACC position.
2) Using small punch or awl, press down on lock pin, located in cylinder lock housing. Remove ignition switch assembly. To install, reverse removal procedure.
Removal & Installation (Pickup) – **1)** Remove upper and lower steering column covers. Disconnect harness connector from ignition switch. Using hacksaw, cut slots in bolt heads of lock assembly. Using screwdriver, remove bolts and lock assembly.
2) To install, reverse removal procedure. Tighten new bolts until heads of bolts sheer off.

STEERING COLUMN

WARNING: Failure to follow air bag service precautions may result in air bag deployment and personal injury. See AIR BAG RESTRAINT SYSTEM article in ACCESSORIES & EQUIPMENT. Follow all service precautions before attempting repairs. After component replacement, perform a system operational check to ensure proper system operation.

CAUTION: Applying excessive pressure or causing impact to steering shaft during service may cause column to collapse. Before removing steering column, ensure wheels are in straight-ahead position. Note steering wheel location for installation reference.

Removal – **1)** Remove steering wheel and combination switch (if necessary). See STEERING WHEEL under REMOVAL & INSTALLATION.
2) Remove air ducts and lower instrument panel covers (if equipped). Disconnect all electrical connections. Disconnect brake pedal return spring (if equipped). On Pickup, disconnect gearshift control cable.
3) On all models, remove bolts for dust cover at firewall. Remove bolt from clamp at steering gear. DO NOT separate lower steering shaft from steering column (if equipped). Remove steering column bolts and remove steering column.
Installation – To install, reverse removal procedure. Apply sealant to dust cover bolts before installing. Tighten bolts to specification. See TORQUE SPECIFICATIONS.

OVERHAUL

STEERING COLUMN

WARNING: Failure to follow air bag service precautions may result in air bag deployment and personal injury. See AIR BAG RESTRAINT SYSTEM article in ACCESSORIES & EQUIPMENT. Follow all service precautions before attempting repairs. After component replacement, perform a system operational check to ensure proper system operation.

NOTE: Montero steering column is not repairable. See below for joint assembly and steering lock removal and installation.

Disassembly (Montero) – Remove steering column from vehicle. See STEERING COLUMN under REMOVAL & INSTALLATION. Remove clamp bolt from joint assembly. *See Fig. 1.* Remove assembly. Remove lower boot, upper boot and dust cover from joint assembly. To remove steering lock, use a hacksaw to cut bolts at steering lock bracket side. Remove steering lock and bracket.

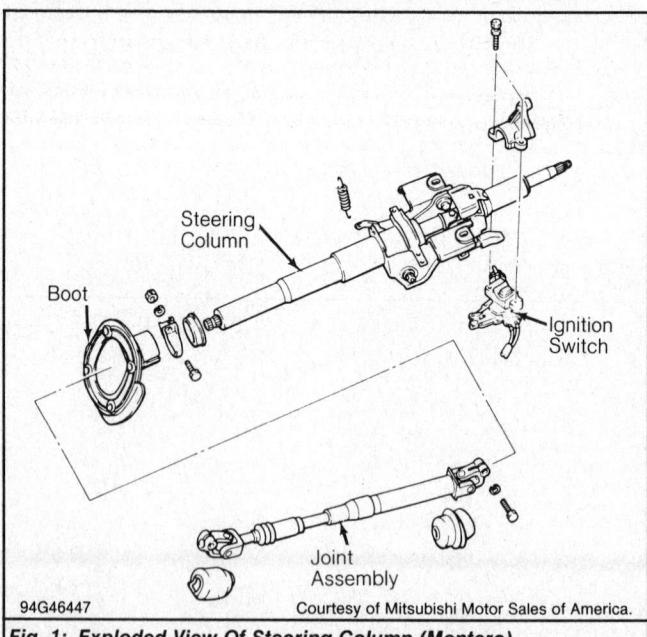

Steering Column

Boot

Ignition Switch

Joint Assembly

94G46447   Courtesy of Mitsubishi Motor Sales of America.

Fig. 1: Exploded View Of Steering Column (Montero)

Reassembly – **1)** To reassemble, reverse disassembly procedure. Install upper boot on joint assembly. Install lower boot and dust cover on joint assembly. Leave boots on shafts without assembling them to universal joint.
2) Apply multipurpose grease to universal joints of joint assembly. When installing upper boot, lower boot and dust cover, ensure arrows on boots align with slit area on yoke. Align steering lock with column boss. Ensure steering lock is operational. Tighten bolt until bolt head breaks off.

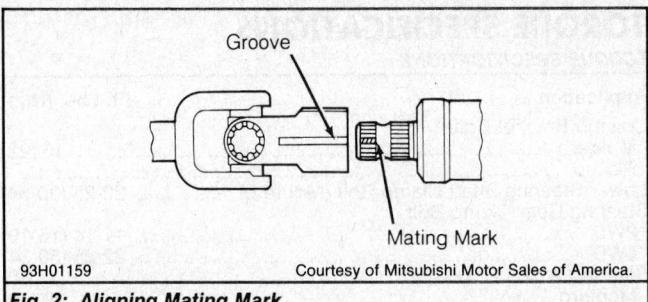

93H01159
Courtesy of Mitsubishi Motor Sales of America.

Fig. 2: Aligning Mating Mark

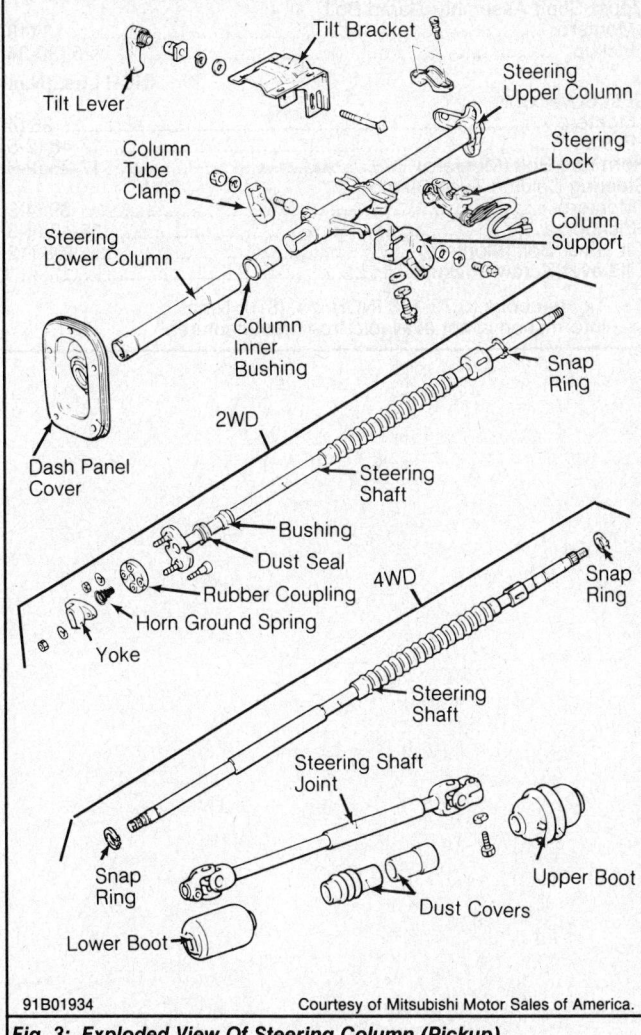

91B01934
Courtesy of Mitsubishi Motor Sales of America.

Fig. 3: Exploded View Of Steering Column (Pickup)

3) Assemble upper steering column with lower joint assembly. Ensure mating mark on lower steering shaft aligns with yoke groove in upper steering shaft. *See Fig. 2.* Apply thread sealant to bolts and nuts of lower steering column.

Disassembly (Pickup) – 1) Remove steering column from vehicle. See STEERING COLUMN under REMOVAL & INSTALLATION. On A/T models, remove gearshift assembly. Disconnect shift indicator. Disconnect link assembly.

2) Remove boot and cotter pin. Disconnect overdrive switch connector. Remove nut and guide bolt at bottom of gearshift lever. Remove gearshift lever guide bolt and gearshift assembly. Ensure gearshift assembly does not bind in detent plate. Remove steel ball, ball support and spring.

3) On all models, remove tilt lever, tilt lever bolt, tilt lever screw and tilt bracket. *See Fig. 3.* To remove steering lock, cut a slot in retaining screws with hacksaw. Remove screws using screwdriver. Remove steering lock and bracket. Remove dash panel cover.

4) To remove steering support, cut a groove in bolt head with a hacksaw. Use screwdriver to remove bolt. Remove column tube clamp, column inner bushing, and lower column. Remove snap ring(s). Remove steering shaft assembly.

5) On 2WD models, remove yoke, horn ground spring, steering coupling, rubber coupling, and steering shaft. Remove dust cover and clamp. On 4WD models, remove lower joint from steering shaft. Remove lower joint boots and dust covers.

Inspection – Check for worn or damaged bushings, dust seals, bearings and tilt bracket. Check joint bearing and steering shaft for wear. Replace components if necessary.

Reassembly – 1) To reassemble, reverse disassembly procedure. Apply grease to dust cover grommet. On 2WD models, apply grease to both ends of horn ground spring and to inner surface of bushing before installing.

2) On 4WD models, install upper boot on steering shaft. Install lower boot and dust cover on lower steering shaft joint. Leave boots on shafts without assembling them to universal joint. Install upper and lower boots and dust cover. Ensure arrows on boots align with slit area on yoke.

3) On all models, align steering lock with column boss. Ensure steering lock is operational. Tighten bolt until bolt head breaks off. Apply grease to tilt lever screw before installing.

4) Install tilt lever fully onto tilt lever screw. Install tilt lever into tilt lever bolt. Tilt lever is threaded in the opposite direction. Before installing tilt lever, ensure tilt lever screw end contacts tilt bracket stopper plate.

5) Ensure steering column locks in proper positions. *See Fig. 4.* If steering column fails to lock in proper positions, adjust position of tilt lever screw end.

6) On A/T models, apply grease to bushing (located in end of gearshift) and all gearshift contact areas before installing. On all models, tighten steering column tube clamp bolt to specification. See TORQUE SPECIFICATIONS.

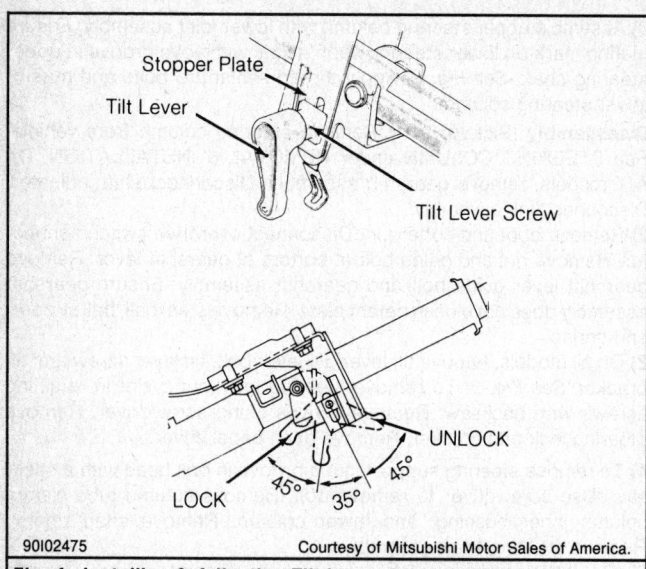

Stopper Plate

Tilt Lever

Tilt Lever Screw

UNLOCK

LOCK

45° 35° 45°

90I02475

Courtesy of Mitsubishi Motor Sales of America.

Fig. 4: Installing & Adjusting Tilt Lever Assembly (Pickup)

TORQUE SPECIFICATIONS
TORQUE SPECIFICATIONS

Application	Ft. Lbs. (N.m)
Column Bracket Bolts	
Montero	16 (22)
Pickup	1
Lower Steering Shaft Clamp Bolt (Montero)	22-25 (30-34)
Steering Gear Clamp Bolt	
2WD	11-14 (15-19)
4WD	22-25 (30-34)
Steering Wheel Nut	
Montero	29 (40)
Pickup	25-33 (34-45)
Upper Column Side Bolt (Montero)	17 (23)
Upper Shaft Assembly Clamp Bolt	
Montero	13 (18)
Pickup	22-25 (30-34)
	INCH Lbs. (N.m)
Dust Cover Bolt	
Montero	36 (4)
Pickup	17-48 (2-5)
Horn Pad Bolt (Montero)	17-26 (2-3)
Steering Column Tube Clamp	
Montero	39 (4.5)
Pickup	36-48 (4-5)
Tilt Lever Bolt (Montero)	108 (12)
Tilt Lever Screw (Pickup)	2

1 – Tighten bolts to 72-108 INCH lbs. (8-12 N.m).
2 – Information is not available from manufacturer.

Chrysler Corp.: Colt, Summit
Mitsubishi: Eclipse, Mirage, Precis

DESCRIPTION

Steering gear is a rack and pinion type. *See Fig. 1.* Steering gear is connected to steering knuckles by tie rods. A flexible coupling connects steering column to steering gear pinion shaft.

ADJUSTMENTS

Adjustments are made during reassembly procedure of overhaul. See OVERHAUL.

REMOVAL & INSTALLATION

STEERING GEAR

Removal – 1) Disconnect negative battery cable. Raise and support vehicle. Remove front wheels. Remove dust cover bolts (if equipped). Remove steering column "U" joint-to-pinion shaft clamp bolt(s). Clamp bolt is accessible from inside of vehicle.

2) Remove tie rod end cotter pins and castle nuts. Using a tie rod end puller, separate tie rods from steering knuckles. On Eclipse, remove stabilizer bar bracket, front engine roll stopper (motor mount) bolts, centermember rear mounting bolts and front exhaust pipe.

3) On all models, remove steering gear mounting clamp bolts. Remove steering gear. DO NOT damage rubber boots. Remove mounting bushings, and note their locations for installation reference. To remove rack on Eclipse, move rack completely right and remove it from centermember. While tilting rack down, move rack left and remove it.

Installation – To install, reverse removal procedure. Tighten bolts and nuts to specifications. See TORQUE SPECIFICATIONS. Check and adjust toe-in. See SPECIFICATIONS & PROCEDURES article in WHEEL ALIGNMENT.

OVERHAUL

STEERING GEAR

Disassembly – 1) Mount steering gear in a soft-jawed vise. Remove tie rod end assemblies. Remove adjusting plug lock nut. *See Fig. 1.* Remove rack or yoke adjusting screw (plug), plunger spring, rubber cushion and rack support from housing.

2) Pry pinion shaft oil seal from housing. Remove pinion bearing snap ring from housing. Remove pinion bearing with pinion shaft.

3) On Precis, remove bearing snap ring from pinion shaft. On all other models, remove lock nut and top cover. Using an appropriate sleeve and press, remove bearing from pinion shaft. Remove bellows boot retaining clamps. Remove bellows boots.

4) Using chisel, unstake right (opposite pinion shaft) rack end tab washer. Move rack completely toward pinion shaft side housing. Using a copper or brass plate to protect rack teeth, place exposed end of rack in vise.

5) Loosen tie rod ball joint. Remove tie rod from rack. Pulling toward side of pinion shaft, remove rack from housing. *See Fig. 2.*

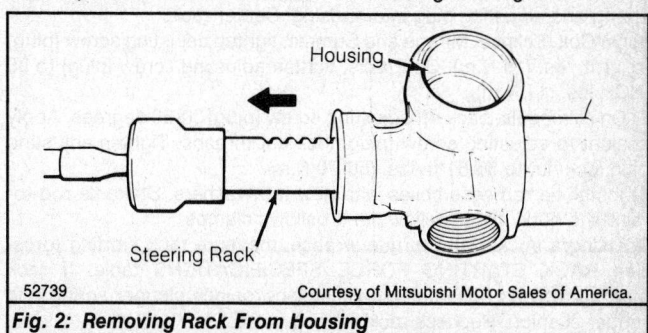

52739

Courtesy of Mitsubishi Motor Sales of America.

Fig. 2: Removing Rack From Housing

Inspection – 1) Check steering housing rubber mounts for deterioration and cracking. Inspect rack bushing for excessive play. Check for damage to rack teeth, pinion shaft teeth and pinion shaft splines.

2) Inspect bushing and seal mating surfaces for scratching and scoring. Check housing for cracks and dents. Inspect all rotating surfaces for wear. Replace components as necessary.

Reassembly – 1) Clean all components in solvent. Always use new seals. Using an appropriate sleeve and press, install pinion shaft bearing onto pinion shaft.

2) Install bearing snap ring to pinion shaft. Grease rack, pinion shaft, bushing, needle bearing and other sliding surfaces. DO NOT cover air passages in housing bushing with grease.

3) Install rack into housing from pinion shaft side of housing. Install pinion shaft into housing while meshing pinion shaft with rack teeth.

4) Ensure rack is properly centered. Measure travel of rack at each end of housing. If travel is not equal, remove pinion shaft. Center rack, and install pinion shaft. Select and install snap ring. To minimize pinion shaft axial play on Precis, refer to SNAP RING THICKNESS COLOR CODING (PRECIS) table.

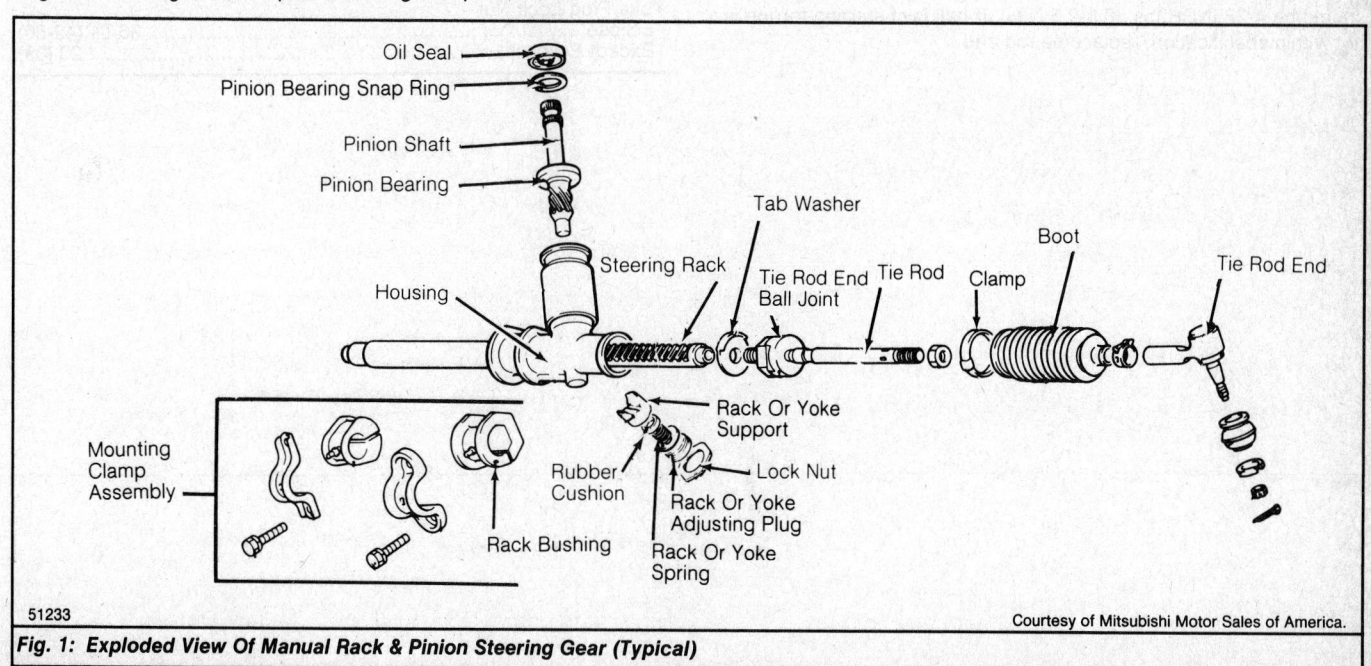

51233

Courtesy of Mitsubishi Motor Sales of America.

Fig. 1: Exploded View Of Manual Rack & Pinion Steering Gear (Typical)

SNAP RING THICKNESS COLOR CODING (PRECIS)

Color Code	In. (mm)
Blue	.063 (1.59)
White	.066 (1.66)
Yellow	.069 (1.74)

5) On all models, install pinion shaft top cover and locking nut. Tighten nut to specification. See TORQUE SPECIFICATIONS. Grease oil seal lip and oil seal-to-housing mating surface. Install oil seal into housing. Grease rack support. Install rack support, rubber cushion, plunger spring and adjusting plug into housing. Center rack.

6) On Colt, Eclipse, Mirage and Summit, tighten adjusting screw (plug) to 11 ft. lbs. (15 N.m). On Precis, tighten adjusting screw (plug) to 96 INCH lbs. (11 N.m).

7) On all models, back off adjusting screw (plug) 30-60 degrees. Apply sealant to adjusting screw (plug) lock nut threads. Tighten adjusting plug lock nut to 36-51 ft. lbs. (50-70 N.m).

8) Install tie rod assemblies with new tab washers. Stake tie rod-to-rack end nuts. Install bellows and bellows clamps.

9) Using a socket and torque wrench, measure rack starting force. See RACK STARTING FORCE SPECIFICATIONS table. If rack starting force is not within specification, replace plunger spring and rubber cushion. Recheck rack starting force.

RACK STARTING FORCE SPECIFICATIONS

Application	INCH Lbs. (N.m)
Colt, Mirage & Summit	3-12 (0.3-1.4)
Eclipse	
0-90 Degrees	5-11 (0.6-1.3)
90-650 Degrees	2-9 (0.2-1.0)
Precis	4-10 (0.4-1.1)

TIE ROD ASSEMBLY

Disassembly – **1)** Mount steering gear in a soft-jawed vise. Remove boot clamps and boots. Using a chisel, unstake left tie rod. Move tie rod completely right. Place rack in soft-jawed vise. Loosen tie rod end nut. See Fig. 1.

2) Remove left tie rod from rack. Repeat procedure for right tie rod, moving rack left and loosening end nut.

Inspection – **1)** Inspect ball joints for pitting and wear. Check for damaged or deformed tie rod. Check boots for cracks and cuts.

2) On Colt, Eclipse, Mirage and Summit, check for ball stud axial deflection. Deflection should be less than .06" (1.5 mm). Replace tie rod end if ball stud axial deflection is greater than specification.

3) On all models, check ball stud starting torque. Starting torque should be 4-22 INCH lbs. (0.5-2.5 N.m). If ball joint starting torque is not within specification, replace tie rod end.

Reassembly – Install tie rod end ball joint to rack. Tighten tie rod ball joint-to-rack nut to specification. See TORQUE SPECIFICATIONS. Install boots and boot clamps. Adjust tie rod end lock nuts until distance between bellows and lock nut is as specified. See Fig. 3. See TIE ROD LOCK NUT INSTALLATION SPECIFICATIONS table.

TIE ROD LOCK NUT INSTALLATION SPECIFICATIONS

Application	[1] In. (mm)
Colt, Mirage & Summit	7.2 (183)
Eclipse	7.2-7.3 (183-185)
Precis	7.1 (180)

[1] – Distance between bellows and lock nut.

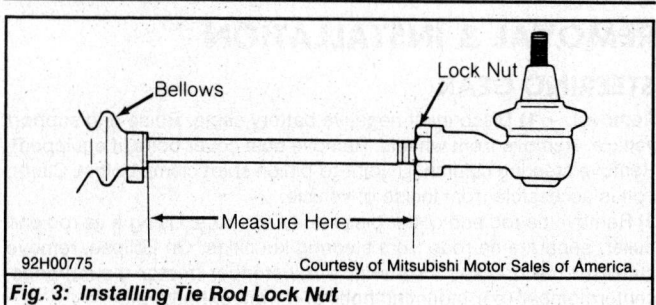

92H00775   Courtesy of Mitsubishi Motor Sales of America.

Fig. 3: Installing Tie Rod Lock Nut

TORQUE SPECIFICATIONS
TORQUE SPECIFICATIONS

Application	Ft. Lbs. (N.m)
Pinion Shaft Top Cover Lock Nut	
Eclipse	36-51 (49-69)
Except Eclipse	43 (60)
Steering Gear Mounting Bracket Bolt	
Eclipse	43-58 (60-79)
Except Eclipse	51 (69)
Tie Rod Ball Joint-To-Rack Nut	
Eclipse	58-72 (79-98)
Except Eclipse	65 (88)
Tie Rod End Castle Nut	
Eclipse	17-25 (23-34)
Except Eclipse	11-25 (15-34)
Tie Rod End Lock Nut	
Colt, Mirage & Summit	30 (42)
Eclipse & Precis	36-40 (49-54)
"U" Joint-To-Pinion Shaft Clamp Bolt	
Colt, Mirage & Summit	11-17 (15-23)
Eclipse & Precis	11-14 (15-19)
Yoke Plug Lock Nut	
Eclipse	36-51 (49-69)
Except Eclipse	29 (39)

**Chrysler Corp.: Colt, Colt Vista,
Stealth, Summit, Summit Wagon
Mitsubishi: Diamante, Eclipse, Expo,
Galant, Mirage, Precis, 3000GT**

DESCRIPTION & OPERATION

Power-assisted rack and pinion steering system consists of a vane pump, flow control valve and an oil reservoir. Belt-driven vane pump supplies fluid through hoses to flow control valve. Flow control valve regulates fluid pressure to assist rack and pinion steering gear.

On some Diamante and Galant models, steering force is controlled electronically. See appropriate ELECTRONIC POWER STEERING article. On Stealth and 3000GT models with 4-Wheel Steering (4WS), a rear oil pump, flow control valve and power cylinder are included in power-assisted steering system.

LUBRICATION

CAPACITY

On 4WS models, fluid capacity is approximately 1.6 qts. (1.5L). On all other models, fluid capacity is approximately .95 qt. (.9L).

FLUID TYPE

Use Dexron or Dexron-II ATF type fluid.

FLUID LEVEL CHECK

Start engine, and let it idle. Turn steering wheel several times to bring steering fluid to normal operating temperature. Turn steering wheel left and right several times while checking fluid for foaming and clouding. Fluid level should be between MIN and MAX marks on filler cap dipstick. Fill to MAX mark with Dexron or Dexron-II ATF.

HYDRAULIC SYSTEM BLEEDING

CAUTION: DO NOT hold steering wheel to left or right lock for longer than 10 seconds, or oil pump damage may occur.

WARNING: Use caution when bleeding system on 4WS models. All 4 wheels will be rotating during testing.

All Models (Front Steering) – 1) Lift and support vehicle. Disconnect coil high tension wire. Crank engine 10-15 seconds while turning steering wheel left and right. Connect coil high tension wire. Start engine, and let it idle. Turn steering wheel left and right until no air bubbles appear in oil reservoir.

2) Check fluid level, and ensure fluid is not milky. Turn steering wheel left and right, and ensure fluid level does not change. If fluid level changes more than .25" (6.3 mm) or if pump is noisy, fill with fluid to MAX mark on dipstick again. Repeat procedure until air bubbles are no longer present in fluid and fluid level stabilizes.

4WS (Rear System) – 1) Bleed air from power steering system. See ALL MODELS. Have an assistant enter vehicle. Raise and support vehicle. Start engine, and let it idle. Loosen bleed screw on left side of rear control valve, and install a bleed hose to bleed screw.

2) Have assistant turn steering wheel to full left position, and then immediately return wheel halfway. Ensure air and fluid is discharged from hose. Repeat step several times. Ensure all air has been bled from system. Repeat step for right side bleed screw, turning steering wheel to full right position, and then immediately returning wheel halfway.

3) Turn engine off. Loosen bleed screws on power cylinder. Install a bleed hose to power cylinder bleed screws. Have assistant start engine and run vehicle to 43-50 MPH to circulate fluid. Reduce vehicle speed to 19-25 MPH, and maintain speed while turning steering wheel to full left and right positions.

4) When steering wheel is turned to full left or right positions, pressure will rise and air will circulate through bleed hose. Ensure air is discharged into oil reservoir. Repeat step several times until all air has been bled from system.

ADJUSTMENTS
POWER STEERING PUMP BELT
BELT ADJUSTMENT

Application	[1] Deflection New Belt – In. (mm)	[1] Deflection Used Belt – In. (mm)
Colt, Mirage & Summit		
1.5L	.16-.22 (4.0-5.5)	.22-.30 (5.5-7.6)
1.8L		
With A/C	.22-.24 (5.5-6.0)	.27-.30 (6.8-7.6)
W/O A/C	.30-.35 (7.6-9.0)	.37-.45 (9.5-11.5)
Colt Vista, Expo & Summit Wagon		
1.8L	.30-.35 (7.6-9.0)	.37-.45 (9.5-11.5)
2.4L	.18-.26 (4.5-6.6)	.24-.35 (6.0-9.0)
Diamante SOHC		
Alternator & P/S	.15-.19 (3.8-4.8)	.23-.31 (5.8-7.8)
DOHC		
P/S	.30-.35 (7.6-9.0)	.41-.49 (10.5-12.5)
Eclipse		
1.8L	.23-.35 (5.8-9.0)	[2]
2.0L	.23-.35 (5.8-9.0)	[2]
Galant		
P/S	.18-.22 (4.5-5.5)	.26-.30 (6.6-7.6)
Precis	.28-.39 (7.1-10.0)	[2]
Stealth SOHC		
Alternator & P/S	.15-.19 (3.8-4.8)	.23-.31 (5.8-7.8)
DOHC		
P/S	.29-.35 (7.3-9.0)	.41-.49 (10.5-12.5)
3000GT	.29-.35 (7.3-9.0)	.41-.49 (10.5-12.5)

[1] – With 22 lbs. (10 kg) pressure applied midway on belt run.
[2] – Information is not available from manufacturer.

PINION ROTATING FORCE

NOTE: Pinion rotating force procedure is performed with rack and pinion assembly off vehicle and supported in soft-jawed vise.

Except Precis – Using adapter and torque wrench, measure rotating force while turning pinion gear through one complete rotation within 4-6 seconds. See PINION ROTATING FORCE SPECIFICATIONS and PINION ROTATING FORCE ADAPTER tables. If rotating force is not within specification, adjust end plug (rack support cover), and recheck rotating force. Tighten locking nut to 36-51 ft. lbs. (49-69 N.m).

Precis – Center rack, and attach end plug (rack support cover) to rack housing. Tighten end plug to 96 INCH lbs. (11 N.m) using torque wrench and adapter. See PINION ROTATING FORCE SPECIFICATIONS and PINION ROTATING FORCE ADAPTER tables. Loosen end plug 30-60 degrees, and tighten locking nut to 36-51 ft. lbs. (49-69 N.m).

PINION ROTATING FORCE SPECIFICATIONS

Application	INCH Lbs. (N.m)
Except Colt, Diamante, Mirage & Summit	5-11 (.6-1.3)
Diamante	6-10.4 (.7-1.2)
Colt, Mirage & Summit	5-12 (.6-1.4)

PINION ROTATING FORCE ADAPTER

Application	Tool No.
Except Precis	CT-1108 Or MB991006
Precis	09565-11100

TESTING

HYDRAULIC SYSTEM PRESSURE TEST

CAUTION: DO NOT leave valve on pressure gauge closed longer than 10 seconds, or damage to oil pump will result.

1) Disconnect pressure hose from oil pump. Install Pressure Gauge (MB990662-01). *See Fig. 1.* Bleed air from system. See HYDRAULIC SYSTEM BLEEDING. Start engine, and let it idle. Turn steering wheel several times until temperature reaches 122°F (50°C). Set engine idle speed to 1000 RPM.
2) Close and open valve to measure oil pump pressure. Replace pump if pressure is not within specification. See OIL PUMP PRESSURE SPECIFICATIONS table. Install pressure hose. Bleed system.

OIL PUMP PRESSURE SPECIFICATIONS

Application	psi (kg/cm²)
Valve Closed	
Except Colt, Galant, Mirage, Precis & Summit	1067-1166 (75-82)
Colt, Mirage & Summit	1351-1451 (95-102)
Galant	1209-1309 (83-90)
Precis	923 (65)
Valve Open	
All Models	114-142 (8-10)

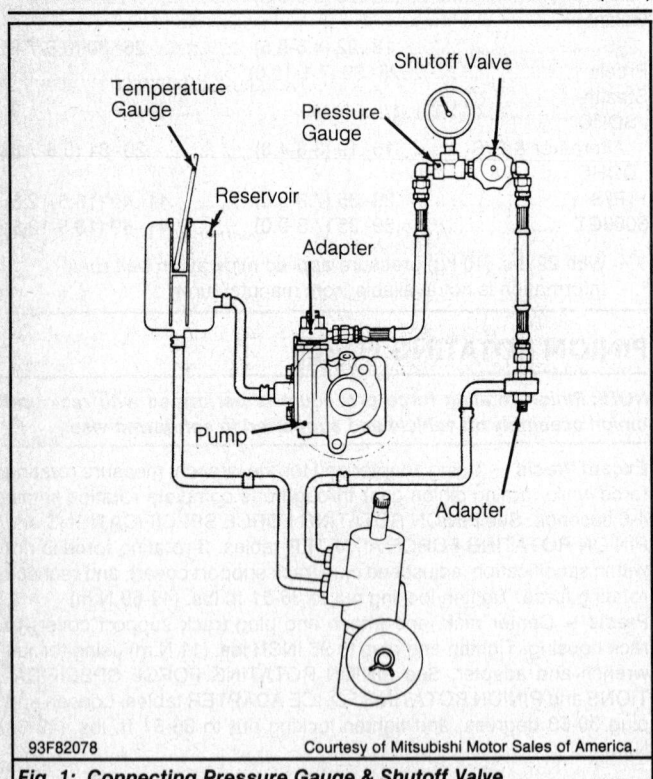

Fig. 1: *Connecting Pressure Gauge & Shutoff Valve*

STEERING WHEEL TURNING FORCE

Place vehicle on level surface with steering wheel in straight-ahead position. Attach a spring scale to steering wheel. With engine running at idle, measure turning force by turning steering wheel left and right within a range of 1 1/2 turns. See STEERING WHEEL TURNING FORCE table.

STEERING WHEEL TURNING FORCE

Application	Lbs. (kg)
Except Diamante & Precis	8 (3.6)
Diamante	7 (3.2)
Precis	9 (4.1)

REMOVAL & INSTALLATION

CAUTION: On vehicles equipped with Supplemental Restraint System (SRS), ensure steering wheel is straight ahead and locked (key removed from ignition switch) before removing steering rack and pinion, to prevent damage to clockspring.

POWER STEERING PUMP

Removal & Installation – Disconnect pressure and suction hoses from pump. Drain fluid into container. Remove oil pump mounting bolts, belt and oil pump. Remove reservoir hoses and retaining bolts. Remove reservoir. To install, reverse removal procedure. Fill and bleed system. See HYDRAULIC SYSTEM BLEEDING.

POWER RACK & PINION

Removal & Installation (Colt, Mirage, Precis & Summit) – **1)** Raise and support vehicle. Pull back dust shield (if equipped), and remove coupling bolt from pinion shaft joint. Disconnect hydraulic lines from steering gear, and remove "O" rings. Drain fluid.
2) Remove tie rod end cotter pins and nuts. Using Puller (MB991113), separate tie rod ends from steering knuckles. Remove rack housing mounting clamp assemblies. Remove power rack and pinion assembly. To install, reverse removal procedure. Fill and bleed system. Check wheel alignment.
Removal & Installation (Colt Vista, Expo & Summit Wagon) – **1)** Raise and support vehicle. Remove dust shield bolts. Remove coupling bolt from pinion shaft joint. Disconnect hydraulic lines from steering gear. Drain fluid.
2) Remove tie rod end cotter pins and nuts. Using a tie rod puller, separate tie rod ends from steering knuckles. Remove rear mounting bolts from center crossmember. Remove long bolt from engine mount attached to center crossmember. Remove crossmember.
3) On FWD models, remove stabilizer bar. On AWD models, remove crossmember support bracket, located on left side of transaxle. *See Fig. 2.* On all models, remove rack housing mounting clamp assemblies. Remove power rack and pinion assembly.
4) To install, reverse removal procedure. Fill and bleed system. Check wheel alignment.

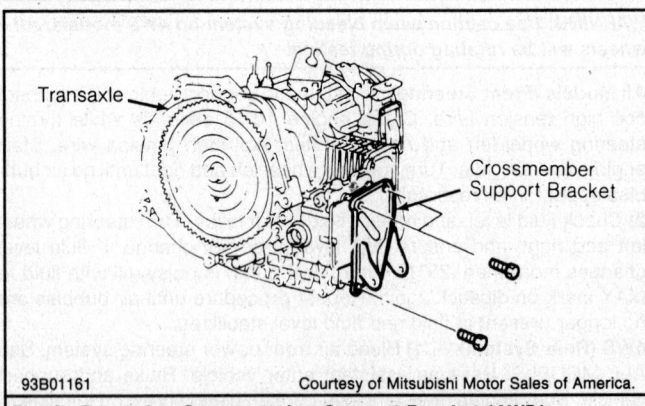

Fig. 2: *Removing Crossmember Support Bracket (AWD)*

Removal & Installation (Diamante, Stealth & 3000GT) – **1)** Raise and support vehicle. Remove coupling bolt from pinion shaft joint. Remove hydraulic lines from steering gear. Drain fluid. Remove tie rod end cotter pins and nuts. Using Puller (MB991113), separate tie rods from steering knuckles. Remove left and right crossmember.
2) Remove front exhaust pipe mounting nuts and lower pipe. On AWD vehicles, remove bolts from transfer assembly, and remove transfer assembly from transaxle. Remove and support drive shaft from transfer assembly. Remove stabilizer bar (if necessary).
3) Remove power rack and pinion assembly by moving assembly completely to right and off crossmember. Tilt power rack and pinion assembly downward, and remove from left side.

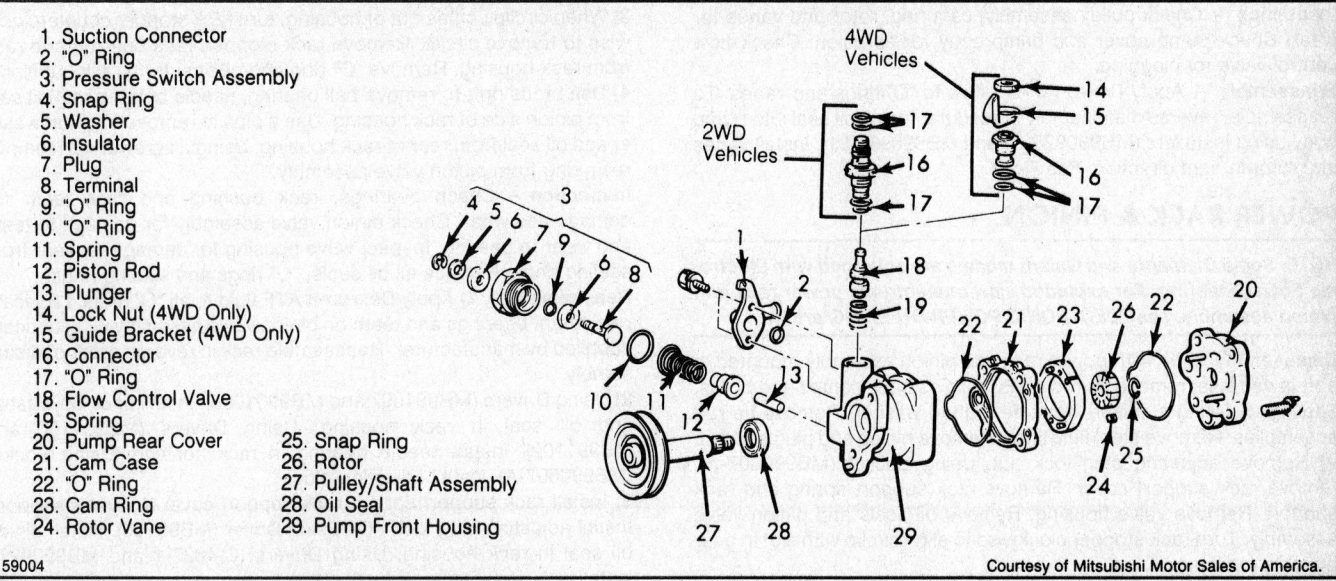

1. Suction Connector
2. "O" Ring
3. Pressure Switch Assembly
4. Snap Ring
5. Washer
6. Insulator
7. Plug
8. Terminal
9. "O" Ring
10. "O" Ring
11. Spring
12. Piston Rod
13. Plunger
14. Lock Nut (4WD Only)
15. Guide Bracket (4WD Only)
16. Connector
17. "O" Ring
18. Flow Control Valve
19. Spring
20. Pump Rear Cover
21. Cam Case
22. "O" Ring
23. Cam Ring
24. Rotor Vane
25. Snap Ring
26. Rotor
27. Pulley/Shaft Assembly
28. Oil Seal
29. Pump Front Housing

59004

Courtesy of Mitsubishi Motor Sales of America.

Fig. 3: Exploded View Of Power Steering Pump (Typical)

4) To install, reverse removal procedure. Fill and bleed system. Check wheel alignment. See SPECIFICATIONS & PROCEDURES article in WHEEL ALIGNMENT.

Removal & Installation (Eclipse) – 1) Raise and support vehicle. Remove coupling bolt from pinion shaft joint. Remove hydraulic lines from steering gear. Drain fluid. On Galant with electronic power steering, disconnect solenoid valve connector.

2) Remove tie rod end cotter pins and nuts. Using Puller (MB991113), separate tie rods from steering knuckles. Remove rear mounting bolts from center crossmember. Remove long bolt from engine mount attached to center crossmember.

3) Remove exhaust pipe mounting nuts and lower pipe. On AWD models, remove bolts, and remove transfer assembly from transaxle. Remove and support drive shaft from transfer assembly. Remove stabilizer bar (if necessary).

4) Remove rack housing mounting clamp assemblies. Remove rack and pinion assembly by moving assembly completely to right and off crossmember. Tilt power rack and pinion assembly downward, and remove from left side.

5) To install, reverse removal procedure. Fill and bleed system. Check wheel alignment. See SPECIFICATIONS & PROCEDURES article in WHEEL ALIGNMENT.

Removal & Installation (Galant) – 1) Raise and support vehicle. Remove front wheels. Disconnect stabilizer bar from link. Unbolt frame mount bracket from crossmember. Remove stabilizer bar. Remove coupling bolt from pinion shaft joint. Disconnect EPS harness connector (if equipped). Remove hydraulic lines from steering gear. Drain fluid.

2) Remove tie rod end cotter pins and nuts. Using Puller (MB991113), separate tie rods from steering knuckles. Remove both crossmember stays (crossmember reinforcement brackets). Remove rear mounting bolts from center crossmember. Remove long bolt from engine mount attached to center crossmember.

3) Remove rack housing mounting clamp assemblies. Unbolt compression lower control arm and support with wire. Do not allow arm to be supported by ball joint. Remove rack and pinion assembly by moving assembly completely to left and off crossmember. To install, reverse removal procedure. Ensure steering is straight ahead. Fill and bleed system. Check wheel alignment. See SPECIFICATIONS & PROCEDURES article in WHEEL ALIGNMENT.

REAR OIL PUMP

Removal & Installation (4WS) – 1) Raise and support vehicle. Remove muffler. Support differential case using transmission jack. Remove rear strut assembly lower mounting bolts. Remove crossmember brackets at front of suspension.

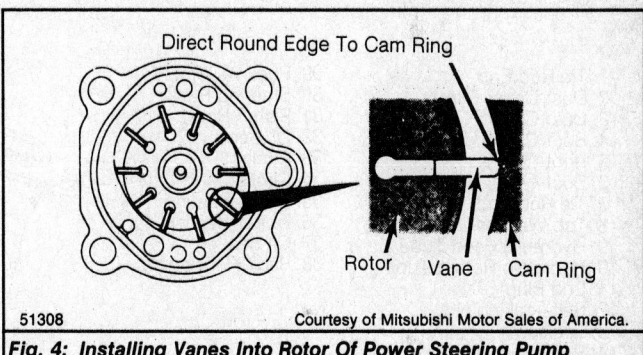

Direct Round Edge To Cam Ring

Rotor Vane Cam Ring

51308

Courtesy of Mitsubishi Motor Sales of America.

Fig. 4: Installing Vanes Into Rotor Of Power Steering Pump

2) Remove crossmember mounting nuts on differential (rear) side of suspension. Disconnect pressure and suction hoses from rear oil pump. Drain fluid. Slightly lower rear suspension. Remove rear oil pump. To install, reverse removal procedure. Fill and bleed system.

POWER CYLINDER

Removal & Installation (4WS) – 1) Raise and support vehicle. Remove muffler. Support differential case using transmission jack. Remove rear strut assembly lower mounting bolts. Remove crossmember brackets at front of suspension.

2) Remove crossmember mounting nuts on differential (rear) side of suspension. Disconnect pressure hoses and "O" rings from power cylinder. Drain fluid. Slightly lower rear suspension. Remove tie rod nuts and power cylinder mounting bracket bolts. Remove power cylinder. To install, reverse removal procedure. Fill and bleed system. Check wheel alignment.

OVERHAUL

POWER STEERING PUMP

NOTE: Manufacturer does not supply information on rear oil pump overhaul.

Disassembly – 1) Remove pump rear cover, cam ring, "O" rings and vanes from rotor. *See Fig. 3.* Remove snap ring from pulley assembly. Remove rotor.

2) Tap pulley assembly using plastic hammer to remove it from pump body. Remove suction connector and oil seal from pump body. Remove connector, flow control valve and spring from pump body.

Inspection – Check pulley assembly, cam ring, rotor and vanes for wear. Check pump cover and pump body for abrasion. Check flow control valve for clogging.

Reassembly – Apply Dexron-II ATF fluid to "O" rings and vanes. To reassemble, reverse disassembly procedure. Install oil seal into pump body using Installers (MB990925-01 and MB990938-01). Install vanes into rotor in right direction. See Fig. 4.

POWER RACK & PINION

NOTE: Some Diamante and Galant models are equipped with Electronic Power Steering. For exploded view of electronic power rack and pinion assembly, see ELECTRONIC POWER STEERING article.

Disassembly – **1)** With power rack and pinion assembly mounted in soft-jawed vise, remove tie rod ends, bellows boot clamps and boots. See Fig. 5. Using a chisel, move tie rod tab washer. Remove tie rod assemblies. Remove steel fluid lines. Remove pinion end plug and nut.
2) Remove adjusting plug lock nut. Using Socket (MB990607-A), remove rack support cover. Remove rack support spring and rack support. Remove valve housing. Remove oil seals and pinion valve assembly. Turn rack stopper clockwise to align circlip with slot in gear housing for removal.

3) When circlip comes out of housing, turn rack stopper counterclockwise to remove circlip. Remove rack stopper, rack bushing and rack from rack housing. Remove "O" ring and oil seal from rack bushing.
4) Use brass drift to remove ball bearing, needle bearing and oil seal from pinion side of rack housing. Use a pipe to remove back-up washer and oil seal from rear of rack housing. Using a screwdriver, remove resin ring from pinion valve assembly.

Inspection – Check bearings, rack bushing and rack teeth for damage and wear. Check pinion valve assembly for damage to teeth and wear to bearing. Inspect valve housing for damage or wear from sealing rings. Replace all oil seals, "O" rings and sealing rings.

Reassembly – **1)** Apply Dexron-II ATF fluid to all "O" rings. Lubricate rack teeth, bearings and teeth on pinion valve assembly with lubricant supplied by manufacturer. Reassemble rack in reverse order of disassembly.
2) Using Drivers (MB991097 and MB9901098), install back-up washer and oil seal in rack housing. Using Drivers (MB991100 and MB991102), install needle bearing in rack housing. Using Socket (MB990607-A), install adjusting plug.
3) Install rack support spring, rack support cover and rack support. Install adjusting plug lock nut. Using Driver (MB99100), install pinion oil seal in rack housing. Using Drivers (C-4637-1 and MB990927), install "O" ring into rack bushing. Adjust pinion rotating force. See PINION ROTATING FORCE under ADJUSTMENTS.

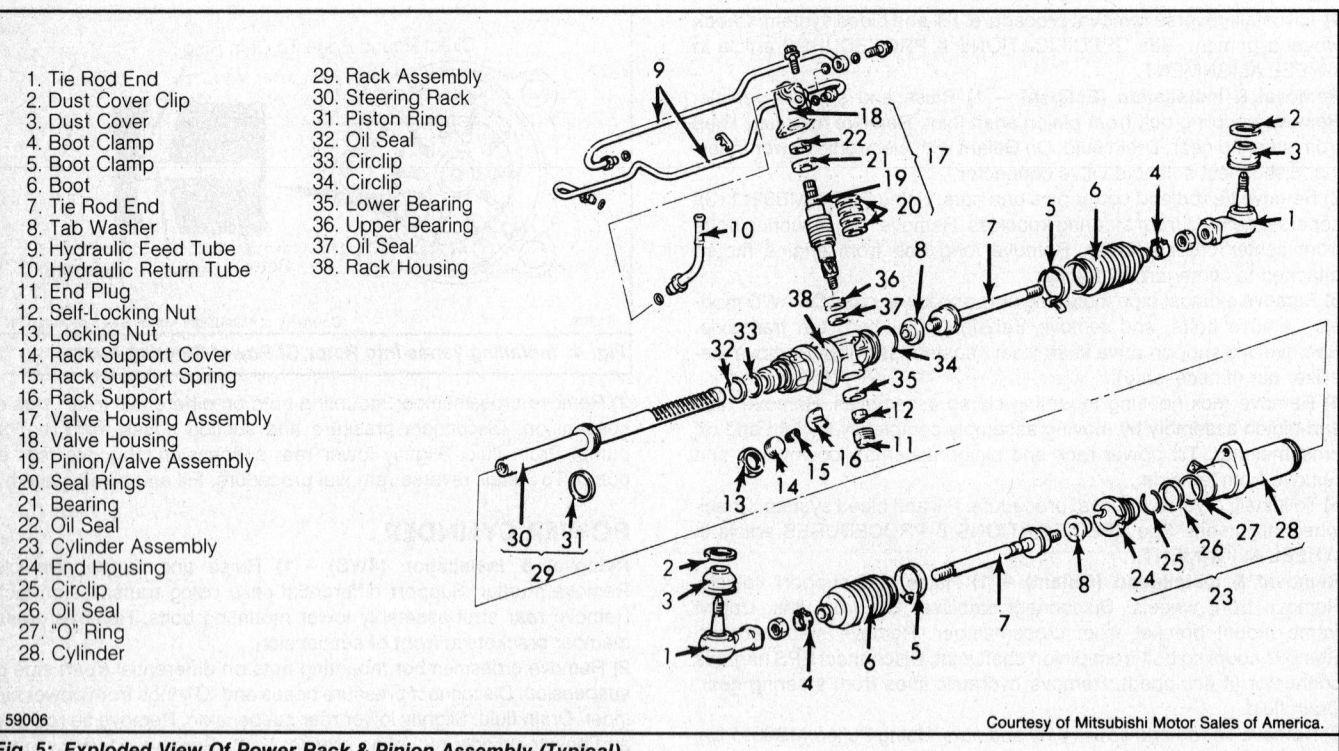

1. Tie Rod End	29. Rack Assembly
2. Dust Cover Clip	30. Steering Rack
3. Dust Cover	31. Piston Ring
4. Boot Clamp	32. Oil Seal
5. Boot Clamp	33. Circlip
6. Boot	34. Circlip
7. Tie Rod End	35. Lower Bearing
8. Tab Washer	36. Upper Bearing
9. Hydraulic Feed Tube	37. Oil Seal
10. Hydraulic Return Tube	38. Rack Housing
11. End Plug	
12. Self-Locking Nut	
13. Locking Nut	
14. Rack Support Cover	
15. Rack Support Spring	
16. Rack Support	
17. Valve Housing Assembly	
18. Valve Housing	
19. Pinion/Valve Assembly	
20. Seal Rings	
21. Bearing	
22. Oil Seal	
23. Cylinder Assembly	
24. End Housing	
25. Circlip	
26. Oil Seal	
27. "O" Ring	
28. Cylinder	

59006   Courtesy of Mitsubishi Motor Sales of America.

Fig. 5: Exploded View Of Power Rack & Pinion Assembly (Typical)

TORQUE SPECIFICATIONS

TORQUE SPECIFICATIONS

Application	Ft. Lbs. (N.m)
Centermember Mounting Bolt	58-65 (78-88)
Crossmember Bracket Bolt	56 (78)
Crossmember Bracket Nut	84-94 (110-130)
Crossmember Mounting Nut	84-94 (110-130)
Coupling-To-Pinion Shaft Joint Bolt	
Colt, Mirage & Summit	11-17 (15-24)
Colt Vista, Diamante, Expo, Mirage,	
Stealth, Summit Wagon & 3000GT	13 (18)
Eclipse, Galant & Precis	11-14 (15-20)
Exhaust Pipe Nuts	
Eclipse	22-29 (30-40)
Stealth & 3000GT	36 (50)
Power Cylinder Mounting Bolt	30 (42)
Power Steering Pump	
Cover Bolts	
Colt, Eclipse, Galant, Mirage & Summit	13-16 (18-22)
Colt Vista, Expo,	
Stealth, Summit Wagon & 3000GT	14 (20)
Diamante	16 (22)
Precis	24-31 (33-43)
Mounting Bolts	
Colt, Eclipse, Galant, Mirage & Summit	18-24 (25-33)
Colt Vista, Expo & Summit Wagon	29 (40)
Diamante	16 (22)
Precis	14 (20)
Stealth & 3000GT	31 (43)

TORQUE SPECIFICATIONS (Cont.)

Application	Ft. Lbs. (N.m)
Pressure Hose-To-Pump Nut	
Colt, Eclipse, Galant, Mirage & Summit	10-15 (14-21)
Colt Vista, Expo & Summit Wagon	13 (18)
Diamante & Stealth	17 (24)
Precis	12-17 (16-24)
Rack Mounting Bolt	
Colt, Eclipse, Galant, Precis & Summit	43-58 (60-78)
Colt Vista, Diamante, Expo, Mirage	
Stealth, Summit Wagon & 3000GT	51 (70)
Rack Support Lock Nut	36-51 (50-70)
Strut Assembly Lower Mounting Bolt	72 (100)
Tie Rod End-To-Steering Knuckle	
Colt, Mirage, Precis & Summit	11-25 (15-34)
Colt Vista, Expo & Summit Wagon	21 (29)
Diamante & Stealth	36 (50)
Eclipse & Galant	17-25 (24-34)
Tie Rod Lock Nut	
Colt, Mirage & Summit	25-36 (34-50)
Diamante, Eclipse, Galant, Precis,	
Stealth & 3000GT	36-40 (50-54)
Colt Vista, Expo & Summit Wagon	38 (53)
Tie Rod-To-Rack	
Colt, Eclipse, Galant, Precis & Summit	58-72 (80-100)
Colt Vista, Diamante, Expo,	
Stealth, Summit Wagon & 3000GT	65 (90)
Transfer Assembly Bolts	
Eclipse	43-58 (60-80)
Stealth & 3000GT	64 (88)

1994 STEERING
Manual Recirculating Ball

Mitsubishi: Pickup

DESCRIPTION & OPERATION

STEERING GEAR

Steering system is a variable ratio, recirculating ball type. Variable ratio minimizes gear ratio in straight-ahead position, resulting in high on-center stability. Gear ratio increases as wheel is turned from center, allowing easy turning.

STEERING LINKAGE

Linkage consists of an idler arm, relay rod and adjustable tie rods. Components are connected to steering knuckles by ball joints. Linkage assembly is connected to steering gear by pitman arm.

LUBRICATION

FLUID TYPE

Fluid type is SAE 90 gear oil.

FLUID LEVEL CHECK

Remove breather plug. Check oil level through breather hole. *See Fig. 1.* Proper level from hole is 1.4" (35 mm). Fluid capacity is .50 pt. (.2L).

ADJUSTMENTS

Adjustments are made during reassembly procedure. See STEERING GEAR under OVERHAUL.

REMOVAL & INSTALLATION

IDLER ARM

Removal – Remove idler arm-to-bracket lock nut. Using Puller (C-3894-A), separate relay rod from idler arm. Remove idler arm bracket-to-frame bolts and nuts. Remove idler arm.
Inspection – Check idler arm bushings for damage or wear. Check idler arm ball stud for looseness.
Installation – 1) Apply multipurpose grease to inside surface of bushing and idler arm support shaft. Insert bushing in idler arm. Insert idler arm support in idler arm.
2) Install washer (knurled side toward bushing) and new lock nut. Tighten lock nut to 29-43 ft. lbs. (29-58 N.m). Place idler arm assembly in vise. Using a spring gauge, measure turning resistance.
3) Turning resistance should be 26-78 INCH lbs. (2.9-8.8 N.m). If turning resistance is not within specification, loosen or tighten lock nut to obtain proper resistance. Install idler arm bracket-to-frame bolts and nuts. Install relay rod-to-idler arm. See TORQUE SPECIFICATIONS.

RELAY ROD

Removal – Remove tie rod ends. See TIE ROD ASSEMBLY under REMOVAL & INSTALLATION. Remove cotter pins and castle nuts from idler arm and pitman arm. Using Puller (C-3894-A), separate relay rod from idler arm and pitman arm.
Installation – To install relay rod, reverse removal procedure. Ensure dust covers are well greased and lower edge of covers are coated with packing sealer. Tighten relay rod-to-idler arm and relay rod-to-pitman arm castle nuts to specification. See TORQUE SPECIFICATIONS.

STEERING GEAR & PITMAN ARM

Removal – 1) Remove "U" joint-to-pinion shaft clamp bolt. Disconnect steering shaft from pinion shaft. Raise and support vehicle.
2) Remove cotter pin and pitman arm-to-steering gear nut. Using Puller (C-3894-A), separate relay rod from pitman arm. Remove steering gear-to-frame bolts and nuts. Remove steering gear.
3) Remove pitman arm-to-steering gear nut and lock washer. *See Fig. 1.* Mark pitman arm-to-steering gear relation for installation reference. Using Puller (CT-1106), remove pitman arm from steering gear.

Installation – 1) Align marks made during removal, and install pitman arm. Install lock washer and nut, and tighten to specification. See TORQUE SPECIFICATIONS. Install steering shaft to pinion shaft.
2) Mount steering gear to frame. Tighten steering gear-to-frame bolts and "U" joint-to-pinion shaft clamp bolt. Install relay rod on pitman arm, and tighten relay rod-to-pitman arm castle nut. Install new cotter pin.

TIE ROD ASSEMBLY

Removal – Remove cotter pins and castle nuts from ball joints at steering knuckle and relay rod end. Using a tie rod puller, separate tie rod ends from knuckle and relay rod end. Loosen tie rod adjusting sleeve lock nuts and unscrew tie rod ends.
Inspection – Check tie rod ends for damage and ball studs for looseness. Measure ball stud starting torque. See TIE ROD BALL STUD STARTING TORQUE table. If ball stud starting torque exceeds specification, replace tie rod.

TIE ROD BALL STUD STARTING TORQUE

Application	INCH Lbs. (N.m)
2WD	4-13 (.45-1.47)
4WD	9-26 (1.01-2.94)

Installation – 1) Install "O" ring on ball socket. Grease inside of tie rod end dust cover. Coat lower edge of cup with packing sealer. Install tie rod ends to adjusting sleeves.

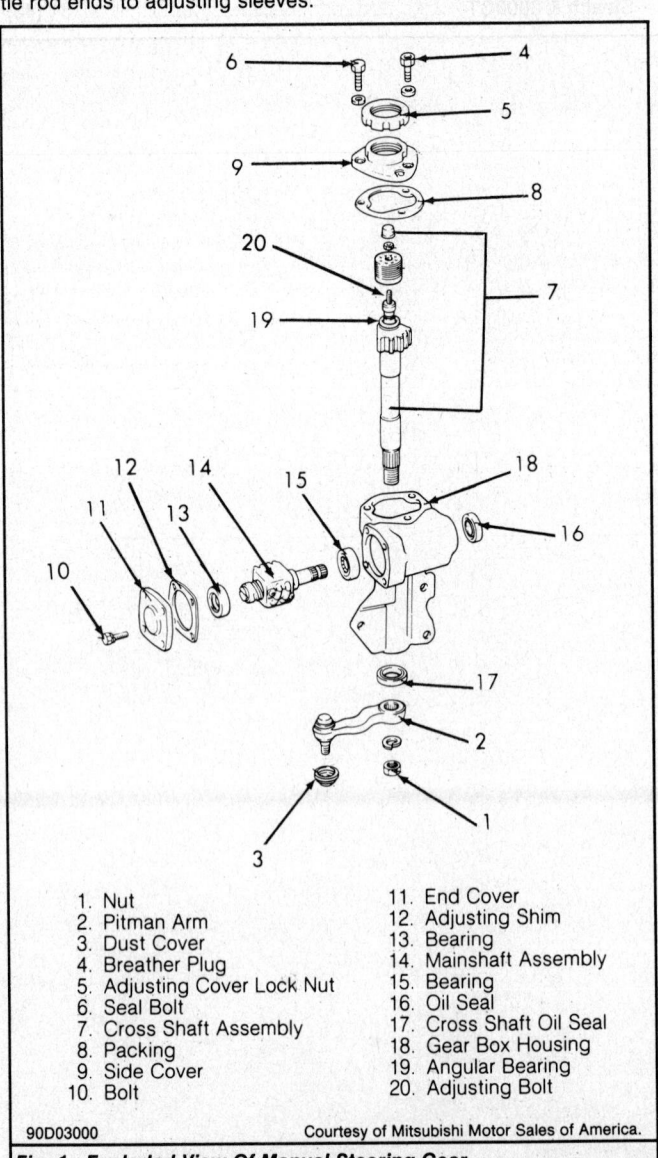

1. Nut
2. Pitman Arm
3. Dust Cover
4. Breather Plug
5. Adjusting Cover Lock Nut
6. Seal Bolt
7. Cross Shaft Assembly
8. Packing
9. Side Cover
10. Bolt
11. End Cover
12. Adjusting Shim
13. Bearing
14. Mainshaft Assembly
15. Bearing
16. Oil Seal
17. Cross Shaft Oil Seal
18. Gear Box Housing
19. Angular Bearing
20. Adjusting Bolt

90D03000   Courtesy of Mitsubishi Motor Sales of America.

Fig. 1: Exploded View Of Manual Steering Gear

Chrysler Corp.: Colt, Colt Vista,
Stealth, Summit, Summit Wagon
Mitsubishi: Diamante, Eclipse, Expo, Galant,
Mirage, Montero, Pickup, Precis, 3000GT

IDENTIFICATION

AUTOMATIC TRANSMISSION APPLICATIONS

Model	Transmission/Transaxle
Chrysler Corp.	
Colt & Summit	
1.5L	Model F3A21 Transaxle
1.8L	Model F4A22 Transaxle
Colt Vista & Summit Wagon	
FWD	
1.8L	Model F4A22 Transaxle
2.4L	Model F4A23 Transaxle
AWD	
1.8L	Model W4A32 Transaxle
2.4L	Model W4A32 Transaxle
Stealth	Model F4A33 Transaxle
Mitsubishi	
Diamante	Model F4A33 Transaxle
Eclipse	
1.8 & 2.0L	Model F4A22 Transaxle
2.0L Turbo	Model F4A33 Transaxle
AWD	Model W4A33 Transaxle
Expo	
FWD	
1.8L	Model F4A22 Transaxle
2.4L	Model F4A23 Transaxle
AWD	
1.8L	Model W4A32 Transaxle
2.4L	Model W4A32 Transaxle
Galant	
SOHC	Model F4A23 Transaxle
DOHC	Model F4A33 Transaxle
Mirage	
1.5L	Model F3A21 Transaxle
1.8L	Model F4A22 Transaxle
Montero	
3.0L	Model V4AW2 Transmission
3.5L	Model V4AW3 Transmission
Pickup	
RWD & 4WD	Model R4AC1 Transmission
Precis	Model KM176 Transaxle
3000GT	Model F4A33 Transaxle

LUBRICATION

SERVICE INTERVALS

Transaxle/Transmission – Check fluid level every 12 months or 15,000 miles. Change fluid and filter every 30,000 miles. If vehicle is operated under severe conditions, change fluid more often. If severe darkening of fluid and strong odor are noted, bands should also be adjusted.

Transfer Case – On 4WD and AWD models, change transfer case fluid every 30,000 miles.

CHECKING FLUID LEVEL

Transaxle/Transmission – 1) Park vehicle on level area. Ensure oil is at normal operating temperature, parking brake is engaged, and engine is at idle. Move gear selector through each position, stopping briefly at each selection.
2) Place gear selector in Neutral, and clean area around dipstick tube. Ensure fluid level is between lower and upper marks, but never over upper mark, in HOT range. Add or drain fluid if necessary.

CAUTION: If severe darkening of fluid and strong odor are noted, change fluid and filter, and adjust bands.

Transfer Case (Stealth & 3000GT) – Lubricant level should be approximately .5" (13 mm) below fill hole on side of transfer case.
Transfer Case (All Others) – Lubricant level should be to bottom of fill hole on side of transfer case.

RECOMMENDED FLUID

Transaxle/Transmission – Use Chrysler Plus/Mitsubishi Plus ATF, Dexron or Dexron-II ATF.
Transfer Cases – Use SAE 75W-85 gear oil with API GL-4 rating or higher.

FLUID CAPACITIES

TRANSAXLE/TRANSMISSION REFILL CAPACITIES

Application	Refill Qts. (L)	Dry Fill Qts. (L)
Colt, Mirage & Summit	4.8 (4.5)	6.3 (6.0)
Colt Vista, Expo & Summit Wagon	4.8 (4.5)	6.4 (6.1)
Diamante, Stealth & 3000GT	4.8 (4.5)	7.9 (7.5)
Eclipse		
F4A22	4.2 (4.0)	6.4 (6.1)
F4A33 & W4A33	6.4 (6.1)	7.4 (7.0)
Galant		
SOHC	¹ 4.8 (4.5)	6.3 (6.0)
DOHC	¹ 4.8 (4.5)	7.9 (7.5)
Montero		
3.0L	5.8 (5.5)	7.6 (7.2)
3.5L	5.8 (5.5)	9.0 (8.5)
Pickup	¹ 4.2 (4.0)	7.4 (7.0)
Precis	4.8 (4.5)	6.4 (6.1)

¹ – Idle engine in Neutral, then add fluid to bring level between notches at "H" mark.

TRANSFER CASE REFILL CAPACITIES

Application	Pts. (L)
Colt Vista, Eclipse, Expo & Summit Wagon	1.3 (0.6)
Montero	4.9 (2.3)
Pickup	4.6 (2.2)
Stealth & 3000GT	.6 (.3)

DRAINING & REFILLING

NOTE: Although manufacturer recommends changing only fluid, the oil filter/screen may also require replacement. If replacing oil filter/screen, note length and location of all bolts.

Transaxle (Except Montero & Pickup) – 1) Remove drain plug(s), and drain fluid. See Fig. 1. Some models may contain a drain plug located in housing below axle shaft, in oil pan. Remove oil pan. Remove oil filter/screen if necessary.
2) If oil filter/screen is replaced, tighten bolts to specification. See TORQUE SPECIFICATIONS. Clean oil pan, replace gasket, and install oil pan. Tighten oil pan bolts and drain plug to specification. See TORQUE SPECIFICATIONS. Ensure dipstick hole area is clean, and pour approximately 4.2 qts. (4.0L) of Dexron-II fluid into dipstick hole.
3) Operate engine at idle for 2 minutes. Shift transaxle to each position, ending in Neutral. Add sufficient fluid to reach lower mark. After reaching normal operating temperature, fluid should be between upper and lower marks of HOT range on dipstick.

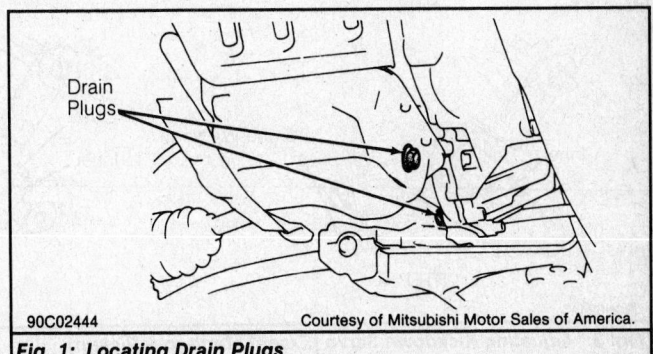

90C02444   Courtesy of Mitsubishi Motor Sales of America.

Fig. 1: Locating Drain Plugs

Transmission (Montero & Pickup) – 1) Remove drain plug (if equipped) from transmission pan, and allow fluid to drain. On models without drain plug, oil pan must be removed to drain fluid. Remove oil filter/screen if necessary.

2) If oil filter/screen is replaced, tighten bolts to specification. See TORQUE SPECIFICATIONS. Clean oil pan, replace gasket, and install oil pan. Tighten oil pan bolts and drain plug to specification. See TORQUE SPECIFICATIONS. Fill transmission, through filler tube, with 5.3 qts. (5.0L) of Dexron-II ATF on Montero, or 2.0 qts. (1.9L) on all others. Start engine, and allow to idle for 2 minutes.

3) Shift transmission into each position, ending in Neutral. Check fluid level with engine running at idle. If necessary, add sufficient fluid to bring level to lower mark of dipstick. Recheck fluid level after transmission is at normal operating temperature.

Transfer Case – Drain plug is located on bottom of transfer case. Change drain plug gasket whenever fluid is changed. On Stealth and 3000GT, lubricant level should be approximately .5" (13 mm) below fill hole on side of transfer case. On all other models, lubricant level should be at bottom of fill hole on side of transfer case.

ADJUSTMENTS

KICKDOWN BAND

Pickup – 1) Locate kickdown band adjusting screw on left side of transmission case. Loosen lock nut, and back off 5 turns. Ensure adjusting screw turns freely in transmission case.

2) Using torque wrench, tighten adjusting screw to 72 INCH lbs. (8 N.m). Back off adjusting screw 2 7/8 turns. Hold adjusting screw in this position, and tighten lock nut to 30 ft. lbs. (41 N.m).

LOW-REVERSE BAND

Pickup – 1) Raise vehicle, drain transmission, and remove oil pan. Loosen adjusting screw lock nut, and back off nut 5 turns. Ensure adjusting screw turns freely in lever.

2) Using torque wrench, tighten band adjusting screw to 30 INCH lbs. (3.5 N.m). Back off adjusting screw 6 turns. Hold adjusting screw in this position, and tighten lock nut to 25 ft. lbs. (34 N.m).

3) Reinstall oil pan using new gasket. Tighten pan bolts to 150 INCH lbs. (17 N.m). Refill transmission with specified fluid.

KICKDOWN SERVO

Except Montero & Pickup – 1) Remove all dirt and grease around kickdown servo switch. Remove snap ring and kickdown servo switch.

2) To prevent servo piston from turning, install Adapter (MD998915) and Kickdown Servo Wrench (MD998914) so tab of wrench engages with notch of piston. *See Fig. 2.*

CAUTION: DO NOT push servo piston inward while installing adapter and servo wrench. Install adapter in brake pressure port by hand ONLY. DO NOT use wrench to tighten adapter.

3) Loosen lock nut to "V" channel of adjuster rod. *See Fig. 2.* Tighten inner section of Kickdown Service Adjustment Assembly (MD998916) until it contacts lock nut.

4) Install outer section of kickdown service adjustment assembly on lock nut. Rotate outer section to left and inner section to right to contact lock nut with inner section.

5) Using an INCH-lb. torque wrench on inner section, tighten inner section to 86 INCH lbs. (9.8 N.m), and then loosen inner section. Tighten inner section to 43 INCH lbs. (4.9 N.m).

CAUTION: Before tightening lock nut with torque wrench, tighten it by hand until it contacts piston. If torque wrench is used initially, lock nut and adjustment rod may rotate together.

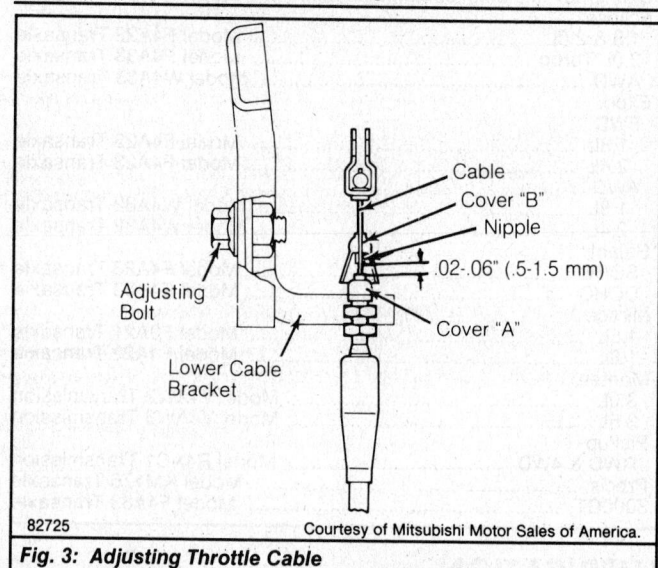

82725   Courtesy of Mitsubishi Motor Sales of America.

**Fig. 3: Adjusting Throttle Cable
(Colt, Mirage & Summit – Model F3A21)**

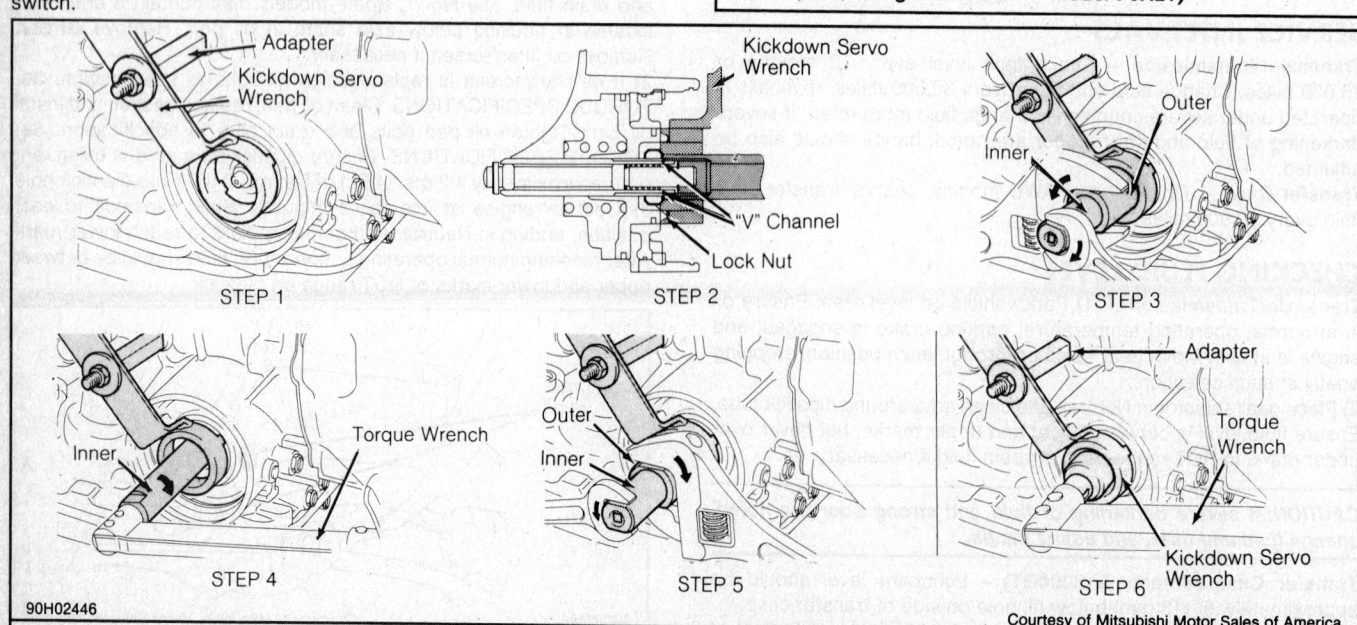

90H02446   Courtesy of Mitsubishi Motor Sales of America.

Fig. 2: Adjusting Kickdown Servo (Except Montero & Pickup)

6) Back off outer section 2-2 3/4 turns. Rotate outer section to right and inner section to left until inner section is free of lock nut. Tighten lock nut by hand until it contacts piston. Using torque wrench, tighten lock nut to 18-23 ft. lbs. (25-32 N.m).

7) Remove adapter and kickdown servo wrench. Install new "O" ring in groove around switch. Install switch and snap ring.

TRANSMISSION THROTTLE CONTROL

Colt, Mirage & Summit (Model F3A21) – **1)** Ensure throttle lever is in curb idle position. Engine must be at normal operating temperature.

2) Raise cover "B" of throttle cable upward to expose nipple. See Fig. 3. Loosen lower cable bracket mounting bolt. Move lower cable bracket until distance between nipple and top of cover "A" on throttle cable is .02-.06" (.5-1.5 mm).

3) Tighten lower cable bracket mounting bolt to 108-126 INCH lbs. (12-14 N.m). With throttle lever in wide open throttle position, pull cable upward to ensure some cable free play exists.

CAUTION: On Pickup, always adjust throttle control cable whenever idle is adjusted.

Pickup – **1)** Ensure engine idle is adjusted correctly. Ensure throttle lever and throttle cable bracket are not bent. Pull lightly on inner throttle cable.

2) While in closed throttle position, measure gap between inner cable stopper and outer cable housing. Adjust cable as necessary to obtain a gap of .031-.059" (.79-1.50 mm). See Fig. 4 (STEP 1).

3) While holding throttle in wide open position, pull on inner throttle cable. Adjust bellcrank as necessary to obtain a gap of 1.46-1.50" (37.08-38.10 mm) between inner cable stopper and outer cable. See Fig. 4 (STEP 2).

4) With throttle fully closed, recheck gap between inner cable stopper and outer cable housing. Gap should be .031-.059" (.79-1.50 mm). See Fig. 4 (STEP 3). While holding throttle in wide open position, pull on inner throttle cable. Check for a gap of 1.30-1.38" (33.02-35.05 mm).

Montero – Ensure throttle lever and throttle cable bracket are not bent. Ensure distance between inner cable stopper end and dust cover is 0-.04" (0-1.0 mm). See Fig. 5.

SHIFT LINKAGE

Montero – Loosen swivel nut on transmission control rod. See Fig. 6. Ensure shift and transmission levers are both in Neutral. Tighten swivel nut.

Except Montero – Adjust shift cable at transaxle/transmission end of cable. Place shift lever in Neutral. Ensure shift lever and neutral safety switch are in Neutral position. If cable was replaced, ensure

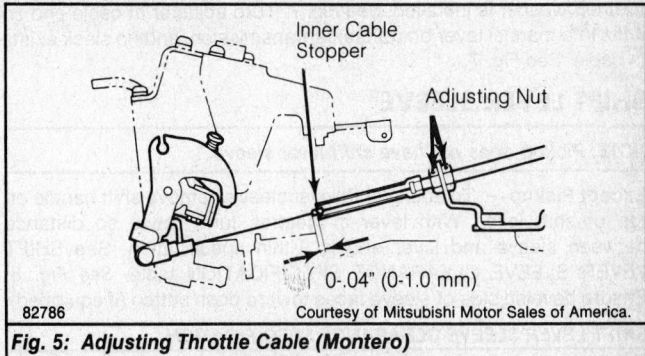

Fig. 5: Adjusting Throttle Cable (Montero)

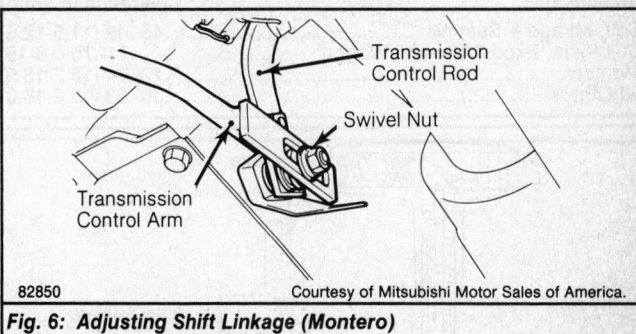

Fig. 6: Adjusting Shift Linkage (Montero)

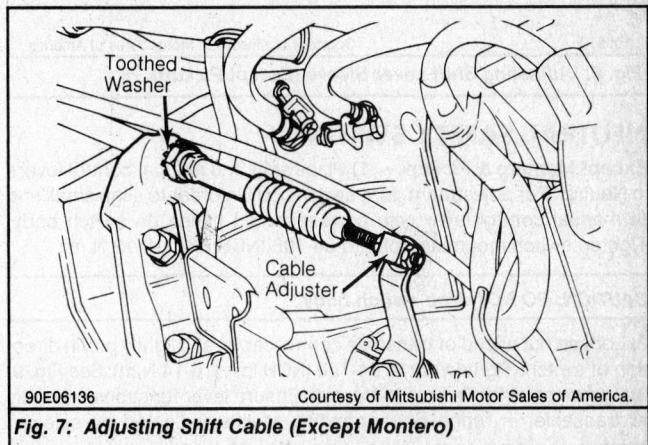

Fig. 7: Adjusting Shift Cable (Except Montero)

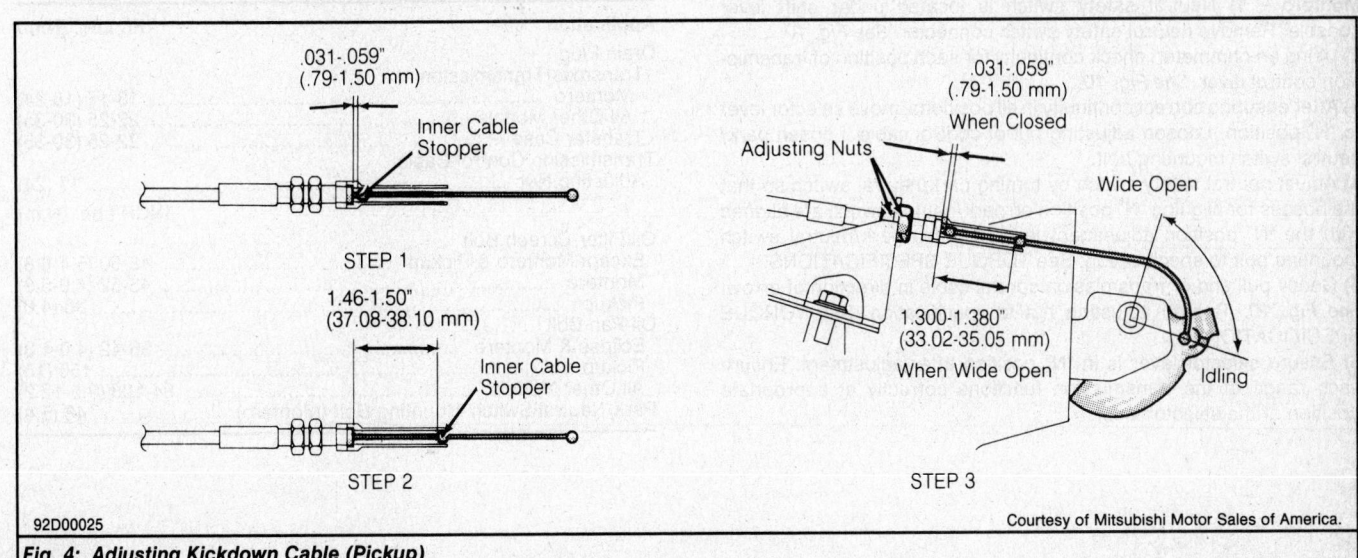

Fig. 4: Adjusting Kickdown Cable (Pickup)

toothed washer is installed. *See Fig. 7.* Turn adjuster at cable end so it fits into manual lever on transaxle/transmission, and no slack exists in cable. *See Fig. 7.*

SHIFT LEVER SLEEVE

NOTE: Pickup does not have shift lever sleeve.

Except Pickup – To adjust shift lever sleeve, remove shift handle on top of shift lever. With lever in Neutral, turn sleeve so distance between sleeve and lever end is within specification. See SHIFT LEVER SLEEVE CLEARANCE SPECIFICATION table. *See Fig. 8.* Ensure beveled side of sleeve faces toward push button (if equipped).

SHIFT LEVER SLEEVE CLEARANCE SPECIFICATION

Application	Clearance In. (mm)
Colt, Mirage & Summit	.45-.49 (11.5-12.5)
Colt Vista, Expo & Summit Wagon	.71-.75 (18-19)
Montero	.72-.74 (18.2-18.9)
All Others	.60-.63 (15.2-16.0)

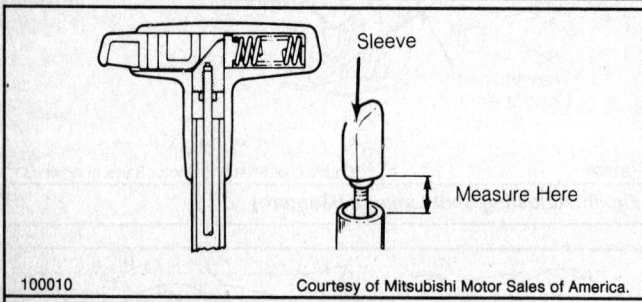

100010   Courtesy of Mitsubishi Motor Sales of America.

Fig. 8: Adjusting Shift Lever Sleeve (Except Pickup)

NEUTRAL SAFETY SWITCH

Except Montero & Pickup – **1)** Place shift and manual control levers in Neutral. For adjustment, turn switch body in order to align small end of manual control lever with corresponding flange on switch body. Tighten switch mounting bolts to 84-108 INCH lbs. (10-12 N.m).

CAUTION: DO NOT drop switch body.

2) Loosen nut at end of transaxle control cable, and lightly pull in direction of switch. Tighten nut to 84-120 INCH lbs. (10-14 N.m). *See Fig. 9.*
3) Ensure selector lever is in Neutral. Ensure lever functions correctly at transaxle, in range corresponding to that indicated by selector lever.
Montero – **1)** Neutral safety switch is located under shift lever console. Remove neutral safety switch connector. *See Fig. 10.*
2) Using an ohmmeter, check continuity for each position of transmission control lever. *See Fig. 10.*
3) After ensuring correct continuity in all positions, move selector lever to "N" position. Loosen adjusting nut of control cable. Loosen park/neutral switch mounting bolt.
4) Adjust neutral safety switch by turning park/neutral switch so that the bosses for aligning "N" position on park/neutral switch are aligned with the "N" position adjustment lever. Tighten park/neutral switch mounting bolt to specification. See TORQUE SPECIFICATIONS.
5) Gently pull end of transmission control cable in direction of arrow. *See Fig. 10.* Tighten adjusting nut to specification. See TORQUE SPECIFICATIONS.
6) Ensure selector lever is in "N" position after adjustment. Ensure each range of the transmission functions correctly at appropriate position of the selector lever.

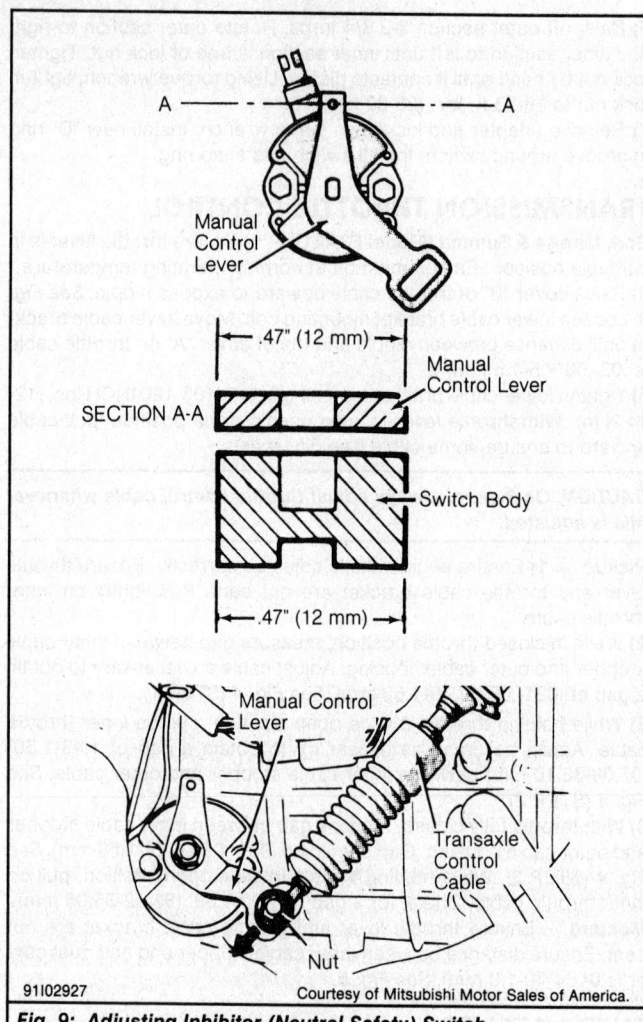

91I02927   Courtesy of Mitsubishi Motor Sales of America.

Fig. 9: Adjusting Inhibitor (Neutral Safety) Switch (Except Montero & Pickup)

Pickup – Neutral safety switch is part of transmission-mounted neutral safety/back-up light switch assembly, and is nonadjustable.

TORQUE SPECIFICATIONS
TORQUE SPECIFICATIONS

Application	Ft. Lbs. (N.m)
Drain Plug	
Transaxle/Transmission	
Montero	13-17 (18-24)
All Other Models	22-25 (30-35)
Transfer Case	22-25 (30-35)
Transmission Control Cable	
Adjusting Nut	17 (24)

	INCH Lbs. (N.m)
Oil Filter/Screen Bolt	
Except Montero & Pickup	48-60 (5.4-6.8)
Montero	43-52 (4.9-5.9)
Pickup	36 (4.0)
Oil Pan Bolt	
Eclipse & Montero	36-42 (4.0-4.8)
Pickup	156 (18)
All Other Models	84-108 (9.5-12.2)
Park/Neutral Switch Mounting Bolt (Montero)	48 (5.4)

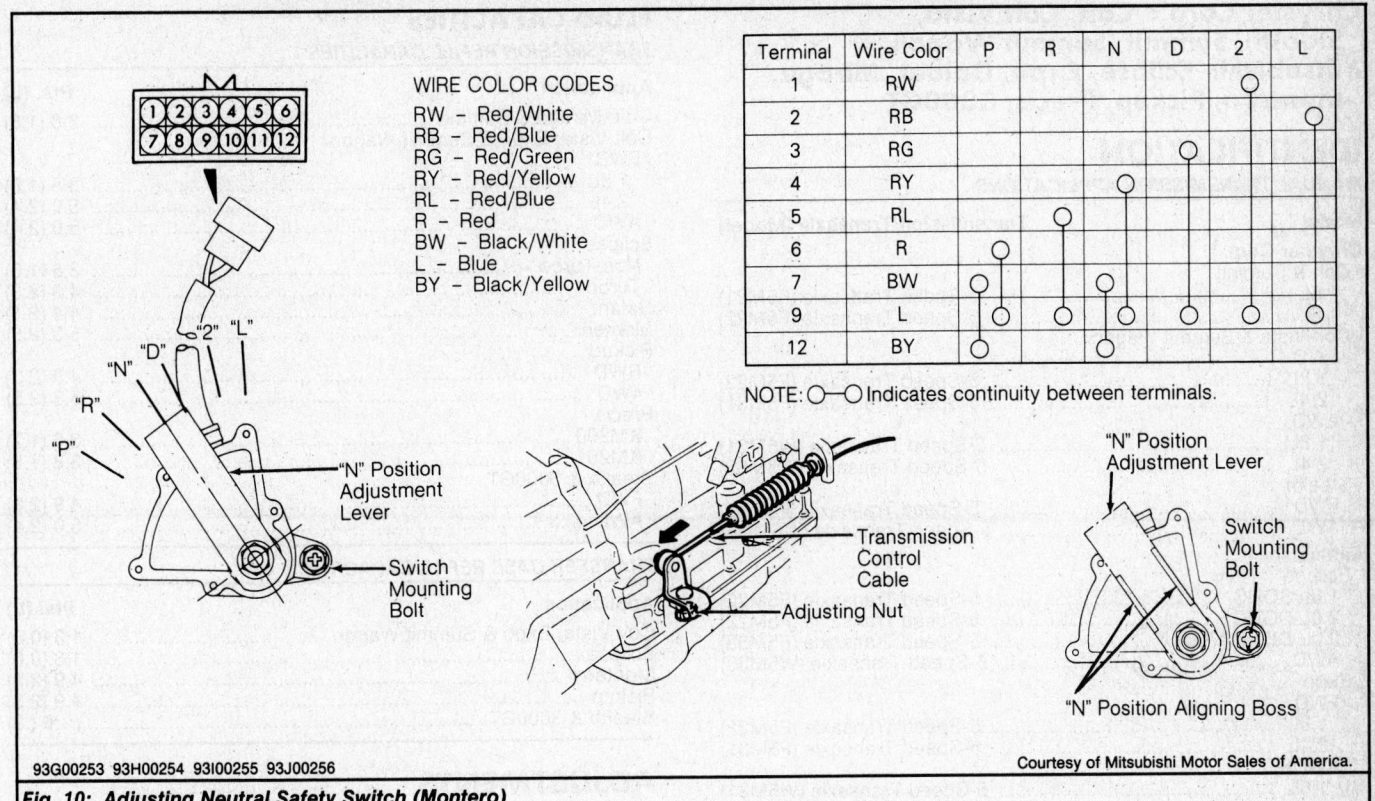

WIRE COLOR CODES
RW – Red/White
RB – Red/Blue
RG – Red/Green
RY – Red/Yellow
RL – Red/Blue
R – Red
BW – Black/White
L – Blue
BY – Black/Yellow

Terminal	Wire Color	P	R	N	D	2	L
1	RW					●	
2	RB						●
3	RG				●		
4	RY			●			
5	RL		●				
6	R	●					
7	BW	●		●			
9	L	●	●	●	●	●	●
12	BY	●		●			

NOTE: ○—○ Indicates continuity between terminals.

Fig. 10: Adjusting Neutral Safety Switch (Montero)

93G00253 93H00254 93I00255 93J00256

Courtesy of Mitsubishi Motor Sales of America.

1994 TRANSMISSION SERVICING
Manual Transmission

**Chrysler Corp.: Colt, Colt Vista,
Stealth, Summit, Summit Wagon
Mitsubishi: Eclipse, Expo, Galant, Mirage,
Montero, Pickup, Precis, 3000GT**

IDENTIFICATION
MANUAL TRANSMISSION APPLICATIONS

Model	Transmission/Transaxle (Model)
Chrysler Corp.	
Colt & Summit	
1.5L	5-Speed Transaxle (F5M21)
1.8L	5-Speed Transaxle (F5M22)
Colt Vista & Summit Wagon	
FWD	
1.8L	5-Speed Transaxle (F5M22)
2.4L	5-Speed Transaxle (F5M31)
AWD	
1.8L	5-Speed Transaxle (W5M31)
2.4L	5-Speed Transaxle (W5M33)
Stealth	
FWD	5-Speed Transaxle (F5M33)
AWD	5-Speed Transaxle (W5MG1)
Mitsubishi	
Eclipse	
1.8L SOHC	5-Speed Transaxle (F5M22)
2.0L DOHC	5-Speed Transaxle (F5M22)
2.0L DOHC (Turbo)	5-Speed Transaxle (F5M33)
AWD	5-Speed Transaxle (W5M33)
Expo	
FWD	
1.8L	5-Speed Transaxle (F5M22)
2.4L	5-Speed Transaxle (F5M31)
AWD	
1.8L	5-Speed Transaxle (W5M31)
2.4L	5-Speed Transaxle (W5M33)
Galant	5-Speed Transaxle (F5M31)
Mirage	
1.5L	5-Speed Transaxle (F5M21)
1.8L	5-Speed Transaxle (F5M22)
Montero	5-Speed Transmission (V5MT1)
Pickup	
RWD	5-Speed Transmission (R5M21)
4WD	5-Speed Transmission (V5MT1)
Precis	4-Speed Transaxle (KM200)
	5-Speed Transaxle (KM201)
3000GT	
FWD	5-Speed Transaxle (F5M33)
AWD	5-Speed Transaxle (W5MG1)

LUBRICATION

SERVICE INTERVALS

Check transaxle/transmission and transfer case fluid level every 30,000 miles. Change fluid at 30,000 miles if operated under severe conditions.

CHECKING FLUID LEVEL

Transaxle/Transmission – Check fluid level at fill hole on side of transaxle or transmission. Lubricant must be at bottom of fill hole.
Transfer Case (Stealth & 3000GT) – Transfer case contains separate drain and fill plugs. Lubricant should be .5" (13 mm) from bottom of fill hole.
Transfer Case (Except Stealth & 3000GT) – Transfer case contains separate drain and fill plugs. Lubricant must be at bottom of fill hole.

RECOMMENDED FLUID

Transaxle/Transmission – Use API classification GL-4 or higher SAE 75W-85W gear oil.
Transfer Case – Use API classification GL-4 or higher SAE 75W-85W gear oil.

FLUID CAPACITIES
TRANSMISSION REFILL CAPACITIES

Application	Pts. (L)
Colt, Mirage & Summit	3.8 (1.8)
Colt Vista, Expo & Summit Wagon	
FWD	
1.8L	3.8 (1.8)
2.4L	5.0 (2.4)
AWD	5.0 (2.4)
Eclipse	
Non-Turbo	3.8 (1.8)
Turbo	4.9 (2.3)
Galant	4.4 (2.1)
Montero	5.3 (2.5)
Pickup	
RWD	4.9 (2.3)
4WD	5.3 (2.5)
Precis	
KM200	3.6 (1.7)
KM201	3.8 (1.8)
Stealth & 3000GT	
FWD	4.9 (2.3)
AWD	5.0 (2.4)

TRANSFER CASE REFILL CAPACITIES

Application	Pts. (L)
Colt Vista, Expo & Summit Wagon	1.3 (0.6)
Eclipse	1.3 (0.6)
Montero	4.9 (2.3)
Pickup	4.9 (2.3)
Stealth & 3000GT	.6 (.3)

ADJUSTMENTS

SELECT CABLE

1) Place transaxle side shift lever in Neutral. This will also place transaxle side select lever in Neutral. *See Fig. 1.*
2) Loosen selector cable adjuster nuts (inside of vehicle). *See Fig. 2.* With select lever in Neutral, adjust select cable end until eye fits easily over select lever pin. Tighten adjuster nuts.

SHIFT CABLE & GEARSHIFT LEVER

1) With transaxle select lever in Neutral, move gearshift lever into 4th gear. It may be necessary to depress clutch pedal.
2) Loosen shift cable adjuster nuts (inside of vehicle). Disconnect cable end from shift lever pin. Tilt gearshift lever into 4th gear position until it touches stopper. *See Fig. 3.* Hold lever in this position, and adjust shift lever cable until it aligns with shift lever pin.
3) Move shift lever between 3rd, Neutral and 4th gear positions. Shift lever-to-stopper clearances should be equal on both sides of lever. *See Fig. 3.* If clearances "A" and "B" are not equal, readjust shift cable. Road test vehicle to ensure proper adjustment and smooth shifting.

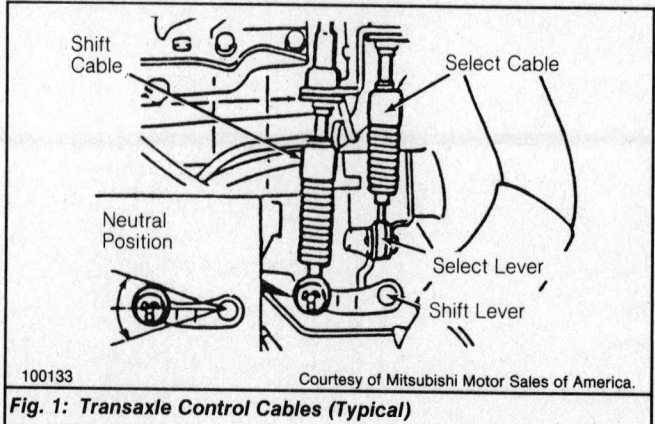

100133   Courtesy of Mitsubishi Motor Sales of America.

Fig. 1: Transaxle Control Cables (Typical)

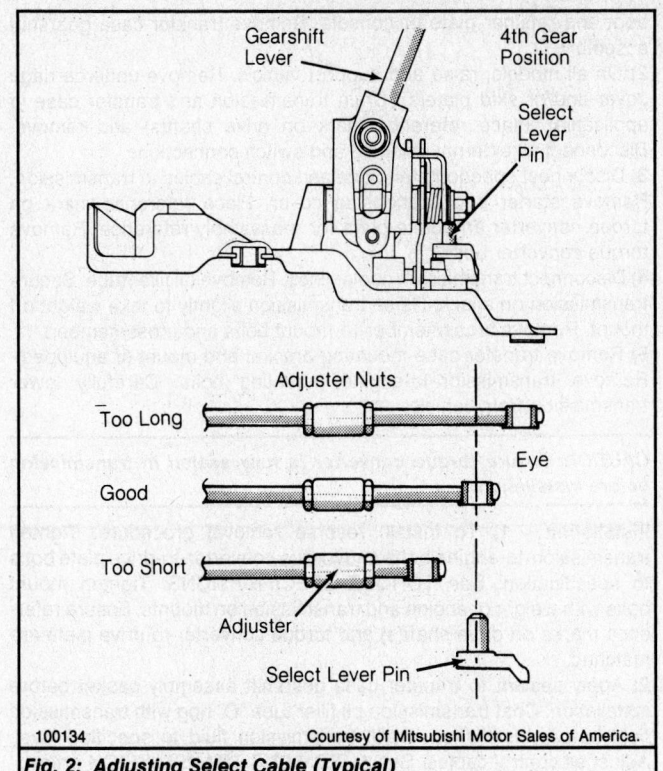

Fig. 2: Adjusting Select Cable (Typical)

100134   Courtesy of Mitsubishi Motor Sales of America.

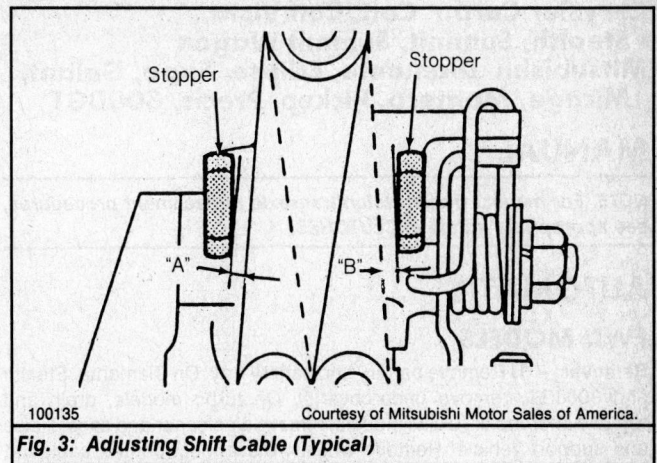

100135   Courtesy of Mitsubishi Motor Sales of America.

Fig. 3: Adjusting Shift Cable (Typical)

TORQUE SPECIFICATIONS

TORQUE SPECIFICATIONS

Application	Ft. Lbs. (N.m)
Drain Plug & Filler Plug	
Except Montero & Pickup	22-25 (30-34)
Montero & Pickup	
RWD	22-25 (30-34)
4WD	40-61 (54-83)

1994 TRANSMISSION SERVICING
Transmission Removal & Installation

**Chrysler Corp.: Colt, Colt Vista,
Stealth, Summit, Summit Wagon
Mitsubishi: Diamante, Eclipse, Expo, Galant,
Mirage, Montero, Pickup, Precis, 3000GT**

MANUAL

NOTE: For manual transmission/transaxle replacement procedures, see appropriate article in CLUTCHES.

AUTOMATIC

FWD MODELS

Removal – 1) Remove battery and battery tray. On Diamante, Stealth and 3000GT, remove undercover(s). On turbo models, drain and remove intercooler. On all models, remove air cleaner and case. Raise and support vehicle. Remove wheels. Disconnect control cables at transaxle. Drain transaxle fluid.

2) On Mirage 1.8L, disconnect tension rod. On all models, disconnect neutral safety switch connector, oil cooler hoses and electrical connectors from transaxle. Disconnect speedometer cable and throttle control cable (if equipped). Remove starter motor.

3) On models equipped with electronically controlled suspension, remove air compressor and bracket. Disconnect front height sensor rod at lower control arm.

4) On all models, remove upper transaxle-to-engine bolts. Remove engine undercover (if equipped). Remove axle shafts. See FWD AXLE SHAFTS article in DRIVE AXLES. Separate lower control arms from struts for access to axle shafts (if necessary).

5) Remove front exhaust pipe (if necessary). On Eclipse AWD, Stealth and 3000GT, remove right member and gusset. On AWD models, separate transfer assembly from transaxle. Reference mark transfer assembly-to-drive shaft and remove transfer assembly.

6) On all models, remove transmission inspection (dust) cover. Place index mark on torque converter and drive plate for reassembly reference. Remove torque converter-to-drive plate bolts. Push torque converter away from engine into transaxle.

7) On all 4-cylinder models, support engine. On all models, support transaxle with jack. Remove transaxle mounts bolts, mounting brackets and remaining transaxle-to-engine bolts. Slide transaxle assembly to right and lower to remove.

CAUTION: Ensure torque converter is fully seated in transaxle before installation. Always install new snap rings on inner constant velocity joints.

Installation – 1) To install, reverse removal procedure. Tighten transaxle-to-engine bolts and torque converter-to-drive plate bolts to specification. See TORQUE SPECIFICATIONS.

2) Ensure reference marks on torque converter-to-drive plate and transfer assembly-to-drive shaft align. Tighten mounting bolts with weight of engine and transaxle on mounts. Refill transaxle fluid to specified level. Adjust all control cables. See AUTOMATIC TRANSMISSION article.

RWD MODELS

Removal – 1) Disconnect negative battery cable. Remove front exhaust pipe. On Montero, remove transfer case shift lever knob, dust boot and retainer plate or console. Remove transfer case gearshift assembly.

2) On all models, raise and support vehicle. Remove undercarriage cover and/or skid plate(s). Drain transmission and transfer case (if applicable). Place reference mark on drive shaft(s) and remove. Disconnect all external solenoid and switch connections.

3) Disconnect speedometer cable and control cables at transmission. Remove starter and bellhousing cover. Place reference mark on torque converter and drive plate for reassembly reference. Remove torque converter bolts.

4) Disconnect transmission cooler lines. Remove oil filler tube. Secure transmission on a jack. Raise transmission slightly to take weight off mount. Remove crossmember-to-mount bolts and crossmember.

5) Remove transfer case mounting bracket and mount (if equipped). Remove transmission-to-engine mounting bolts. Carefully lower transmission from vehicle.

CAUTION: Ensure torque converter is fully seated in transmission before installation.

Installation – 1) To install, reverse removal procedure. Tighten transmission-to-engine bolts and torque converter-to-drive plate bolts to specification. See TORQUE SPECIFICATIONS. Tighten mount bolts with weight of engine and transmission on mounts. Ensure reference marks on drive shaft(s) and torque converter-to-drive plate are matched.

2) Apply sealant to transfer case gearshift assembly gasket before installation. Coat transmission oil filler tube "O" ring with transmission fluid before installation. Refill transmission fluid to specified level. Adjust all control cables. See AUTOMATIC TRANSMISSION article.

TORQUE SPECIFICATIONS

TORQUE SPECIFICATIONS

Applications	Ft. Lbs. (N.m)
FWD Models	
Torque Converter-To-Drive Plate Bolt	
Precis	53-55 (72-76)
All Others	34-38 (46-52)
Transaxle-To-Engine Block Bolt	
8-mm Bolt	[1]
10-mm Bolt	22-25 (30-34)
12-mm Bolt	31-40 (42-54)
Upper Coupling Bolts (Diamante, Stealth & 3000GT)	54 (73)
Lower Coupling Bolts (Diamante, Stealth & 3000GT)	65 (88)
RWD Models	
Torque Converter-To-Drive Plate Bolt	
Montero	25-30 (34-41)
Pickup	33-38 (45-52)
Transmission-To-Engine Block Bolt	
Montero	
10 x 40-mm Bolt	22-30 (30-41)
12 x 40-mm Bolt	47-61 (64-83)
12 x 55-mm Bolt	58-72 (79-98)
Pickup	
10 x 16-mm Bolt	22-30 (30-41)
10 x 50-mm Bolt	31-40 (42-54)
10 x 70-mm Bolt	31-40 (42-54)

[1] – Tighten to 84-108 INCH lbs. (10-12 N.m).

1994 FORD MOTOR CO. CONTENTS

ENGINE PERFORMANCE

ENGINE PERFORMANCE (Cont.)

1994 FORD MOTOR CO. CONTENTS (Cont.)

1994 FORD MOTOR CO. CONTENTS (Cont.)

1994 ENGINE PERFORMANCE
Ford Motor Co. Introduction

1994 MODEL COVERAGE

MODEL	BODY CODE	ENGINE	ENGINE ID [1]	FUEL SYSTEM	IGNITION SYSTEM
Aspire	05, 06, 07	1.3L	H	SFI	Magnetic
Capri	01	1.6L	Z	MFI	Magnetic
	03	1.6L	6 [2]	MFI Turbo	Magnetic

[1] – See eighth character of Vehicle Identification Number.
[2] – XR2 model is turbocharged and intercooled.

VIN DEFINITION

KNJPT06H9P6100000
① ② ③ ④ ⑤ ⑥ ⑦ ⑧ ⑨ ⑩ ⑪ ⑫ ⑬ ⑭ ⑮ ⑯ ⑰

- ①②③ Indicates Nation of Origin.
- ④ Indicates Restraint System.
- ⑤ Indicates Carline Code.
- ⑥⑦ Indicates Body Type.
- ⑧ **Indicates Engine.**
- ⑨ Indicates Check Digit.
- ⑩ **Indicates Model Year.**
- ⑪ Indicates Assembly Plant.
- ⑫⑬⑭⑮⑯⑰ Indicates Serial Number.

MODEL YEAR VIN CODE APPLICATION

VIN Code	Model Year
N	1992
P	1993
R	1994

Emission Applications

1994 FORD MOTOR CO.

Model, Engine & Fuel System	Emission Control Systems & Devices
Aspire 1.3L 4-Cyl. MFI	**PCV, EVAP, TWC, FR, SPK, O2S, CEC,** EGR-CVS, EVAP-CPCS, EVAP-CPCV, SPK-CC
Capri 1.6L 4-Cyl. MFI Turbo & Non-Turbo	**PCV, EVAP, TWC, FR, SPK, O2S, CEC,** EVAP-CPCS, EVAP-CPCV, VA

NOTE: For quick reference, major emission control systems and devices are listed in bold type; components and other related devices are listed in light type.

CEC – Computerized Engine Controls
EGR-CVS – EGR Control/Vent Solenoid
EVAP – Fuel Evaporative System
EVAP-CPCS – EVAP Canister Purge Control Solenoid
EVAP-CPCV – EVAP Canister Purge Control Valve
FR – Fill Pipe Restrictor

O2S – Oxygen Sensor
PCV – Positive Crankcase Ventilation
PFI – Port Fuel Injection
SPK – Spark Controls
SPK-CC – SPK Computer Controlled
TWC – Three-Way Catalyst
VA – Vacuum Advance

1994 ENGINE PERFORMANCE
Service & Adjustment Specifications

Aspire, Capri

INTRODUCTION

Use this article to quickly find specifications related to servicing and on-vehicle adjustments. This is a quick-reference article to use when you are familiar with an adjustment procedure and only need a specification.

CAPACITIES

BATTERY SPECIFICATIONS

Application	Amp Hr. Rating
Aspire & Capri	50

FLUID CAPACITIES

Application	Qts. (L)
Aspire	
Automatic Transaxle (Mercon)	6.0 (5.7)
Cooling System	
With A/C	6.3 (6.0)
Without A/C	5.8 (5.5)
Crankcase (Includes Filter)	3.6 (3.4)
Manual Transaxle (Mercon)	2.6 (2.5)
Capri	
Automatic Transaxle (Mercon)	6.7 (6.3)
Cooling System	
Non-Turbo	5.3 (5.0)
Turbo	6.3 (6.0)
Crankcase (Includes Filter)	
Non-Turbo	3.5 (3.3)
Turbo	3.7 (3.5)
Manual Transaxle	
Non-Turbo (SAE 75W-90)	2.8 (2.7)
Turbo (Mercon)	3.5 (3.4)

QUICK-SERVICE

SERVICE INTERVALS & SPECIFICATIONS

REPLACEMENT INTERVALS

Component	Interval (Miles)
Aspire & Capri	
Air Filter	30,000
Camshaft Timing Belt	60,000
Coolant	30,000
Fuel Filter	60,000
Oil & Filter	5000
Spark Plugs	[1] 30,000

[1] – 15,000 miles on Turbo models.

BELT ADJUSTMENTS
Tension in Lbs. (kg) Using Strand Tension Gauge

Application	New Belt	Used Belt
Aspire		
Air Conditioner	110-132 (50-60)	95-110 (43-50)
Alternator	86-104 (39-47)	68-860 (31-39)
Power Steering	110-132 (50-60)	95-110 (43-50)
Capri		
Air Conditioner	110-132 (50-60)	110-132 (50-60)
Alternator	110-132 (50-60)	110-132 (50-60)

MECHANICAL CHECKS

ENGINE COMPRESSION

Measure engine compression at speed with engine at normal operating temperature, all spark plugs removed, and throttle wide open.

COMPRESSION SPECIFICATIONS

Application	Specification
Compression Ratio	
Aspire	9.7:1
Capri	[1]
Compression Pressure	[2]

[1] – Information is not available from manufacturer.
[2] – Lowest cylinder compression reading should not be less than 75 percent of highest cylinder compression reading.

VALVE CLEARANCE

NOTE: All models are equipped with hydraulic lash adjusters. No adjustments are required.

IGNITION SYSTEM

IGNITION COIL

IGNITION COIL RESISTANCE

Application	Primary (Ohms)	Secondary (Ohms)
Aspire	0.5-0.7	20,000-31,000
Capri	0.8-1.6	6000-30,000

CRANKSHAFT POSITION (CKP) SENSOR

CRANKSHAFT POSITION (CKP) SENSOR RESISTANCE

Application	Ohms
Aspire	[1]
Capri	[2]

[1] – Cannot be measured. If defective, distributor must be replaced.
[2] – Equipped with Cylinder Identification (CID) sensor. Resistance is not specified by manufacturer.

HIGH TENSION WIRE RESISTANCE

HIGH TENSION WIRE RESISTANCE

Application	Ohms
Coil Wire & Spark Plug Wires	4000-7000 Per Foot

SPARK PLUGS

SPARK PLUG TYPE

Application	Motorcraft
Aspire	AGS32C
Capri	
Non-Turbo	AGSP42C
Turbo	AGSP32C

SPARK PLUG SPECIFICATIONS

Application	Gap In. (mm)	Torque Ft. Lbs. (N.m)
All	0.039-0.043 (1.0-1.1)	10-17 (14-23)

FIRING ORDER

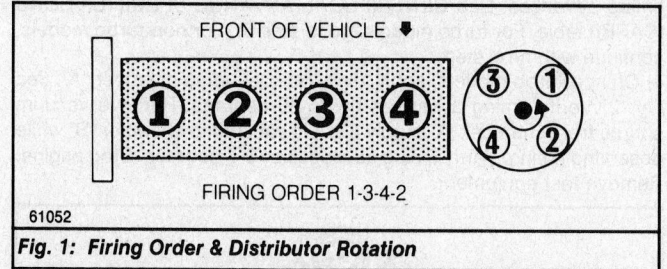

FRONT OF VEHICLE ↓

FIRING ORDER 1-3-4-2

61052

Fig. 1: Firing Order & Distributor Rotation

IGNITION TIMING

IGNITION TIMING (Degrees BTDC @ RPM)

Application	Auto. Trans.	Man. Trans.
Aspire	9-11 @ 700-800	9-11 @ 650-750
Capri Non-Turbo	1-3 @ 800-900	1-3 @ 800-900
Capri Turbo	11-13 @ 800-900	11-13 @ 800-900

FUEL SYSTEM

FUEL PUMP

NOTE: Fuel pump performance is a measurement of fuel pressure and volume availability, not regulated fuel pressure.

Application	Pressure psi (kg/cm²)	Min. Vol. In 10 Sec. Ozs. (cc)
Aspire	50 (3.5) Minimum	5.5 (167)
Capri	64-85 (4.5-6.0)	5.5 (167)

REGULATED FUEL PRESSURE

Application	At Idle psi (kg/cm²)
Aspire	[1] 30-38 (2.1-2.7)
Capri	[1] 27-34 (1.9-2.4)

[1] – Pressure regulator maintains fuel pressure at a constant 36.3 psi (2.6 kg/cm²) higher than intake manifold pressure.

INJECTOR RESISTANCE

INJECTOR RESISTANCE

Application	Ohms
Aspire & Capri	12-16

IDLE SPEED

IDLE SPEED SPECIFICATIONS [1]

Application	Auto. Trans.	Man. Trans.
Aspire	700-800-870	650-750
Capri	800-900	800-900

[1] – With jumper wire connected between Self-Test Input (STI) terminal and ground.

THROTTLE POSITION (TP) SWITCH

NOTE: On Aspire, TP switch is preset at factory. No adjustment is required.

TP SWITCH ADJUSTMENT (CAPRI)

Test Condition [1]	Continuity Between [2] IDL-TL	Continuity Between [2] PSW-TL
0.02" (0.5 mm)	Yes	No
0.03" (0.7 mm)	No	No
Wide Open Throttle	No	Yes

[1] – Insert specified feeler gauge between throttle adjustment screw and stop lever.
[2] – Throttle position switch terminals.

1994 ENGINE PERFORMANCE
On-Vehicle Adjustments

Aspire, Capri

ENGINE MECHANICAL

Before performing any on-vehicle adjustments to fuel or ignition systems, ensure engine mechanical condition is okay.

VALVE CLEARANCE

NOTE: All models are equipped with hydraulic lash adjusters. No adjustments are required.

IGNITION TIMING

Aspire – 1) Set automatic transmission lever to Park position, or manual transmission lever to Neutral position. Start and warm engine to normal operating temperature. Connect timing light. Turn off all accessories.

2) Connect jumper wire between Self-Test Input (STI) terminal and ground. See Fig. 1. If timing marks on crankshaft pulley and index pointer are not aligned, go to next step. If timing is as specified, no adjustment is required.

3) Loosen distributor bolts. Rotate distributor until timing marks are aligned. Tighten bolts to 14-18 ft. lbs. (19-25 N.m). Recheck timing. Readjust as necessary. Disconnect jumper wire and timing light.

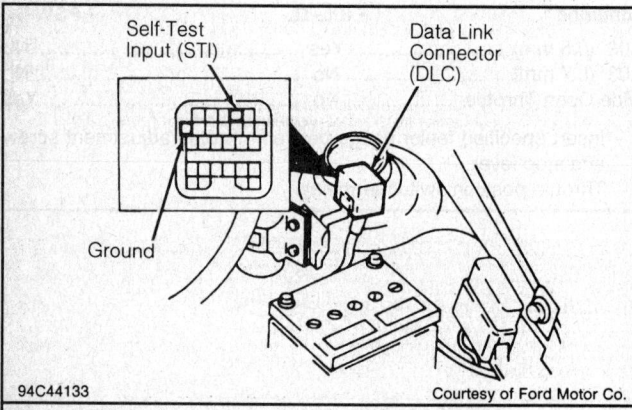

94C44133   Courtesy of Ford Motor Co.

Fig. 1: Identifying Self-Test Input Terminal (Aspire)

Capri – 1) Set automatic transmission lever to Park position, or manual transmission lever to Neutral position. Disconnect and plug hoses attached to diaphragm on distributor. Connect tachometer and timing light. Turn off all electrical loads.

2) Warm engine to operating temperature. Ensure idle speed is set to specification. See IDLE SPEED & MIXTURE. Determine initial timing. See IGNITION TIMING table. If base timing is not correct, loosen distributor mounting bolts. Rotate distributor until marks align. Tighten bolts to 14-18 ft. lbs. (19-25 N.m).

IGNITION TIMING (Degrees BTDC @ RPM)

Application	Auto. Trans.	Man. Trans.
Non-Turbo	1-3 @ 800-900	1-3 @ 800-900
Turbo	11-13 @ 800-900	11-13 @ 800-900

CENTRIFUGAL ADVANCE SPECIFICATIONS (CAPRI)

Application	Degrees BTDC
Non-Turbo	
1500 RPM	0
3000 RPM	21
5000 RPM	25
Turbo	
1200 RPM	0
3500 RPM	12
5500 RPM	18

3) Increase engine RPM while observing timing marks. Verify ignition timing advances. See CENTRIFUGAL ADVANCE SPECIFICATIONS (CAPRI) table. For turbo models, go to step **5)**. For non-turbo models, continue with next step.

4) On non-turbo models, apply 16 in. Hg vacuum to chamber "A". See Fig. 2. Verify timing advances by 26-30 degrees. Remove vacuum source from chamber "A". Apply 8 in. Hg vacuum to chamber "B" while observing timing. Verify timing advances by 3-7 degrees. Stop engine. Remove test equipment.

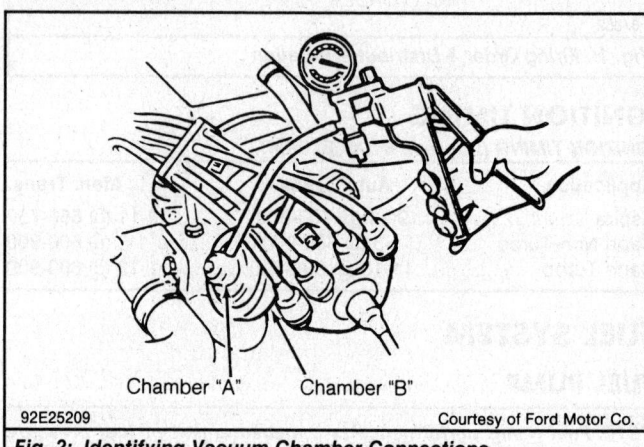

Chamber "A"   Chamber "B"

92E25209   Courtesy of Ford Motor Co.

Fig. 2: Identifying Vacuum Chamber Connections (Capri Non-Turbo)

5) On turbo models, apply 20 in. Hg vacuum to advance diaphragm. Verify timing advances by 13-17 degrees. Disconnect vacuum source. Apply 8 psi (0.6 kg/cm²) pressure to advance diaphragm. Verify timing retards by 3-7 degrees. Stop engine. Remove test equipment.

IDLE SPEED & MIXTURE

NOTE: Idle mixture is controlled by PCM and is not adjustable.

IDLE SPEED

Aspire – 1) Ensure ignition timing is set to specification. See IGNITION TIMING. Turn off all accessories. Set automatic transmission lever to Park position, or manual transmission lever to Neutral position. Set parking brake.

2) Connect tachometer to engine. Warm engine to normal operating temperature. Connect a jumper wire between STI test connector and ground. See Fig. 1.

3) Locate Idle Speed Control By-Pass Air (ISC-BPA) valve on intake manifold. Remove cap, and adjust idle speed to 650-750 RPM (manual transmission) or 700-800 RPM (automatic transmission) by rotating idle air adjust screw on ISC-BPA valve. See Fig. 3. Remove jumper wire.

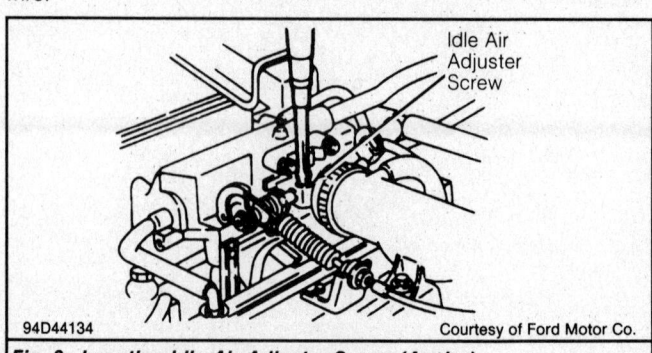

Idle Air Adjuster Screw

94D44134   Courtesy of Ford Motor Co.

Fig. 3: Locating Idle Air Adjuster Screw (Aspire)

Capri – 1) Turn off all accessories. Set automatic transmission lever to Park position, or manual transmission lever to Neutral position. Set parking brake. Connect tachometer to engine. Warm engine to normal operating temperature. Connect a jumper wire between single-wire STI test connector and ground. *See Fig. 4.*

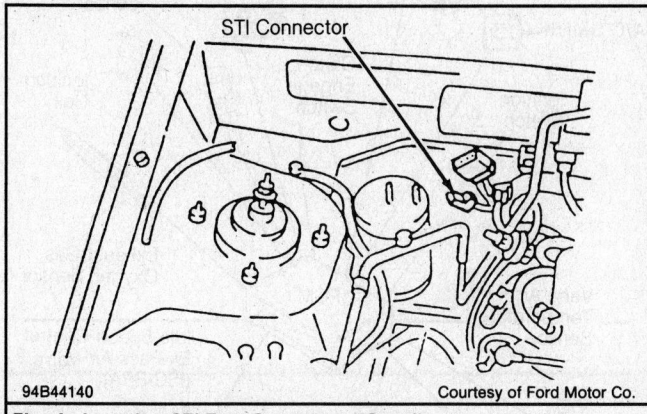

| 94B44140 | Courtesy of Ford Motor Co. |

Fig. 4: Locating STI Test Connector (Capri)

2) Locate Idle Speed Control By-Pass Air (ISC-BPA) valve on throttle body. Remove cap, and adjust idle speed to 800-900 RPM by rotating idle air adjust screw on ISC-BPA valve. *See Fig. 5.* Remove jumper wire.

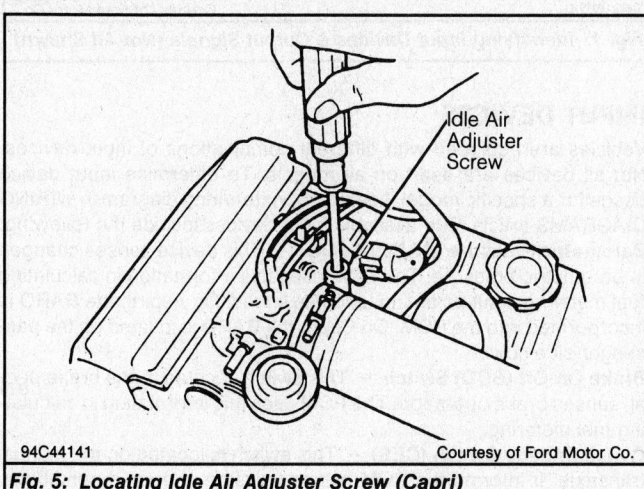

| 94C44141 | Courtesy of Ford Motor Co. |

Fig. 5: Locating Idle Air Adjuster Screw (Capri)

THROTTLE POSITION (TP) SENSOR/SWITCH

Aspire – 1) Unplug TP sensor connector. Connect ohmmeter between terminals "A" and "B" (upper terminals) on TP sensor. Move throttle lever to full open position. Resistance should be approximately 5 ohms.

2) Move throttle lever to full closed position. Resistance should be less than one ohm. If resistance is not as specified, go to next step. If resistance is as specified, no adjustment is required.

3) Loosen TP sensor screws. With throttle lever in closed position, rotate TP sensor until resistance is less than one ohm. Tighten screws. Move throttle lever to full open position. Resistance should be approximately 5 ohms. Replace throttle body if TP sensor cannot be adjusted to specification.

Capri – 1) Ensure idle speed and ignition timing are adjusted to specification. Stop engine. Disconnect negative battery cable.

CAUTION: DO NOT tamper with throttle stop screw at throttle lever. Doing so may result in damage to throttle body.

---

2) Unplug Throttle Position (TP) switch connector at throttle body. Insert 0.028" in. (0.7 mm) feeler gauge between throttle stop screw and stop lever. Check for continuity between terminals "B" and "D" on TP switch connector. *See Fig. 6.*

3) To adjust, loosen TP switch attaching screws. Insert a 0.020" (0.5 mm) feeler gauge between throttle stop screw and stop lever. Rotate TP switch until continuity exists. Insert a 0.028" (0.7 mm) feeler gauge between stop screw and stop lever. Continuity should not exist. Repeat adjustment as necessary.

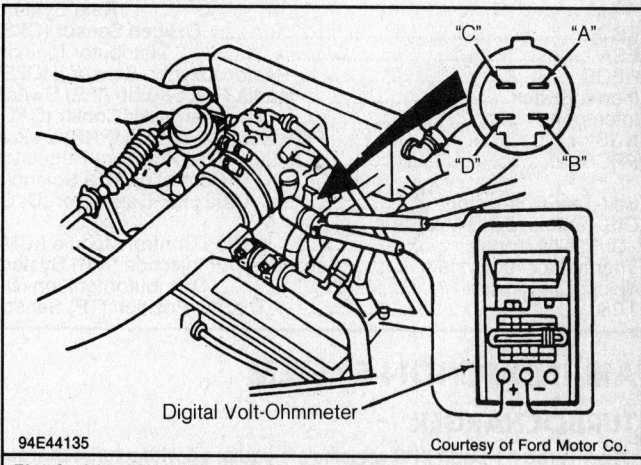

| 94E44135 | Courtesy of Ford Motor Co. |

Fig. 6: Identifying Throttle Position (TP) Switch Connector Terminals (Capri)

1994 ENGINE PERFORMANCE
Theory & Operation

Aspire, Capri

INTRODUCTION

This article covers basic description and operation of engine performance-related systems and components. Read this article before diagnosing vehicles or systems with which you are not completely familiar.

NOTE: The CHECK ENGINE light, located in the instrument cluster, is referred to as Malfunction Indicator Light (MIL) in this article.

TERMINOLOGY

Because of Federal government requirements, manufacturers may use names and acronyms for systems and components different from those used in previous years. The following table will help eliminate confusion when dealing with these components and systems. Only relevant components and systems whose names have changed from current Ford Motor Co. terminology have been listed. See REVISED TERMINOLOGY table.

REVISED TERMINOLOGY

1992 & Earlier	1994
BP SENSOR	Barometric Pressure (BARO) Sensor
CHECK ENGINE Light	Malfunction Indicator Light (MIL)
Camshaft Sensor	Camshaft Position (CMP) Sensor
CPS	Crankshaft Position (CKP) Sensor
DIS	Electronic Ignition (EI) Low Data Rate System
ECA	Powertrain Control Module (PCM)
EDIS	Electronic Ignition (EI) High Data Rate System
EGO	Oxygen Sensor (O2S)
ESA	Distributor Ignition
HEGO	Heated Oxygen Sensor (HO2S)
Inertia Switch	Inertia Fuel Shutoff (IFS) Switch
Intercooler	Charge Air Cooler (CAC)
NGS	Park/Neutral Position (PNP) Switch
PRCS	Fuel Pressure Regulator Control (FPRC) Solenoid
Self-Test Connector	Data Link Connector (DLC)
DIS Module, EDIS Module Or TFI-IV Module	Ignition Control Module (ICM)
Thermactor Air System	Secondary Air Injection (AIR) System
Thick Film Ignition-IV	Distributor Ignition (DI)
TPS	Throttle Position (TP) Sensor

AIR INDUCTION SYSTEM

TURBOCHARGER

Capri Turbo – Capri XR2 vehicles are equipped with a turbocharger. Turbocharger system includes an integral wastegate and a Charge Air Cooler (CAC) mounted next to the radiator. A gauge on the instrument panel displays boost. A buzzer warns of overboost.

COMPUTERIZED ENGINE CONTROLS

A Powertrain Control Module (PCM) receives and processes signals from various sensors and switches. *See Fig. 1.* From these it generates signals which control ignition timing, fuel injection functions, and various emission control devices. The PCM has system diagnostic capabilities, and will store trouble codes for use by service technicians.

POWERTRAIN CONTROL MODULE (PCM)

The PCM is located under the instrument panel on the driver's side. It receives and processes data from sensors, switches, and other components. The PCM generates output signals to control fuel injection, spark timing, other engine functions, and emission systems.

NOTE: Components are grouped into 2 categories. The first category is INPUT DEVICES, which control or produce voltage signals monitored by the control unit. The second category is OUTPUT SIGNALS, which are components controlled by the control unit.

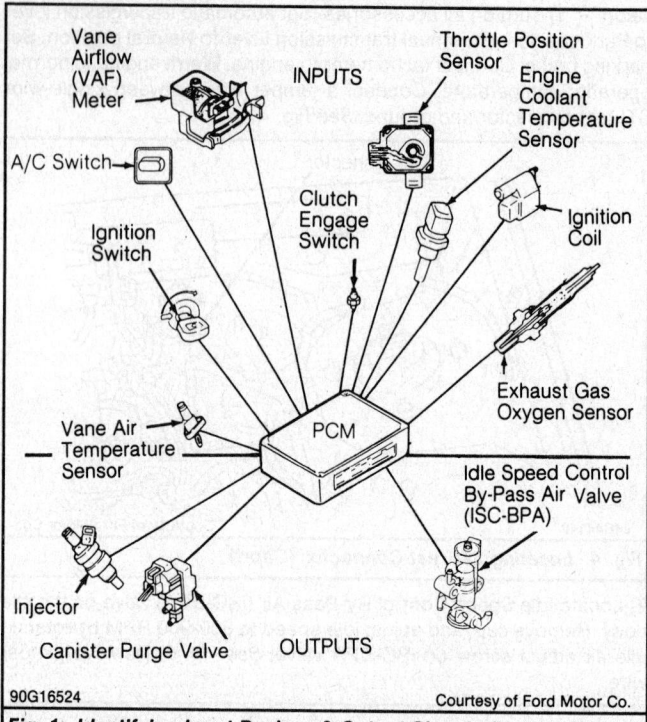

Fig. 1: Identifying Input Devices & Output Signals (Not All Shown)

Courtesy of Ford Motor Co.

INPUT DEVICES

Vehicles are equipped with different combinations of input devices. Not all devices are used on all models. To determine input device usage for a specific model, see appropriate wiring diagram in WIRING DIAGRAMS article. The available input devices include the following:

Barometric Pressure (BARO) Sensor – This device senses changes in barometric pressure. The PCM uses this information in calculating fuel metering, ignition timing, and idle speed. On Aspire, the BARO is incorporated into the PCM. On Capri, the BARO is located on the passenger-side cowl.

Brake On-Off (BOO) Switch – This switch, located at the brake pedal, senses brake operation. The PCM uses this information in calculating fuel metering.

Clutch Engage Switch (CES) – This switch is located on the manual transaxle. It informs the PCM of transmission operating conditions. The PCM uses this signal for idle speed control and canister purge valve operation.

Crankshaft Position (CKP) Sensor (Aspire) – This sensor is located within the distributor. It sends engine RPM and crankshaft position data to the PCM. The PCM uses this signal for calculating fuel metering, ignition timing, idle speed control, and canister purge valve operation.

Cylinder Identification (CID) Sensor (Capri) – This sensor is located within the distributor. It provides crankshaft position data to the PCM for calculating fuel metering and ignition timing.

Electrical Load Switches – Blower control, cooling fan, rear window defroster, air conditioning, and headlight switches all send signals to the PCM. The PCM uses these signals for idle speed control.

Engine Coolant Temperature (ECT) Sensor – This sensor is threaded into the intake manifold. It sends coolant temperature data to the PCM. The PCM uses this signal for calculating fuel metering, idle speed control, and canister purge valve operation.

Mass Airflow (MAF) Meter – This sensor is located within the air cleaner housing. It sends intake airflow data to the PCM. The PCM uses this signal for calculating fuel metering.

Oxygen Sensor (O2S) – This sensor is threaded into the exhaust manifold. It senses oxygen concentration in the exhaust gas. The PCM uses this signal for calculating fuel metering, idle speed control, and canister purge valve operation.

1994 ENGINE PERFORMANCE
Theory & Operation (Cont.)

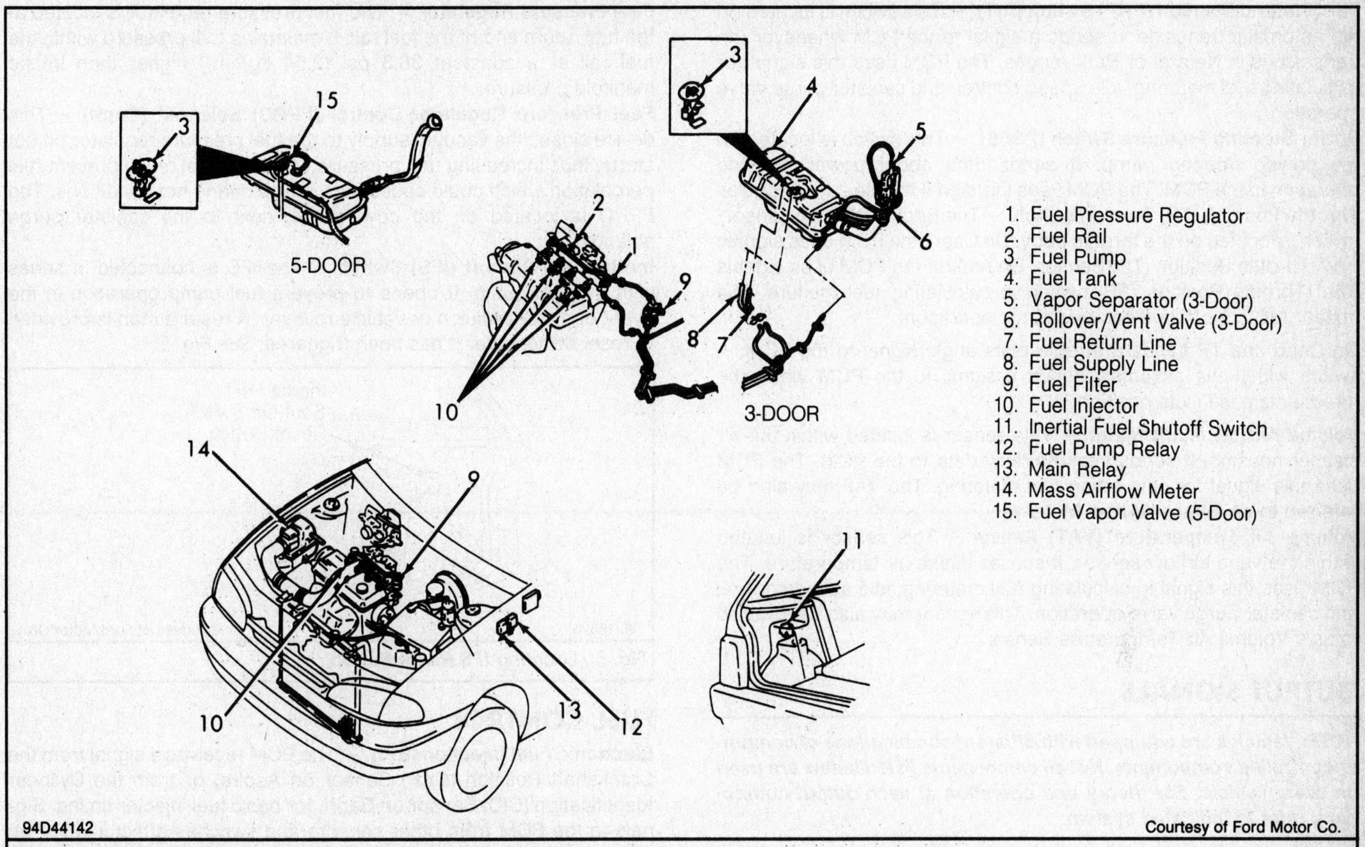
5-DOOR
3-DOOR
1. Fuel Pressure Regulator
2. Fuel Rail
3. Fuel Pump
4. Fuel Tank
5. Vapor Separator (3-Door)
6. Rollover/Vent Valve (3-Door)
7. Fuel Return Line
8. Fuel Supply Line
9. Fuel Filter
10. Fuel Injector
11. Inertial Fuel Shutoff Switch
12. Fuel Pump Relay
13. Main Relay
14. Mass Airflow Meter
15. Fuel Vapor Valve (5-Door)
94D44142
Courtesy of Ford Motor Co.

Fig. 2: Locating Fuel Delivery System Components (Aspire)

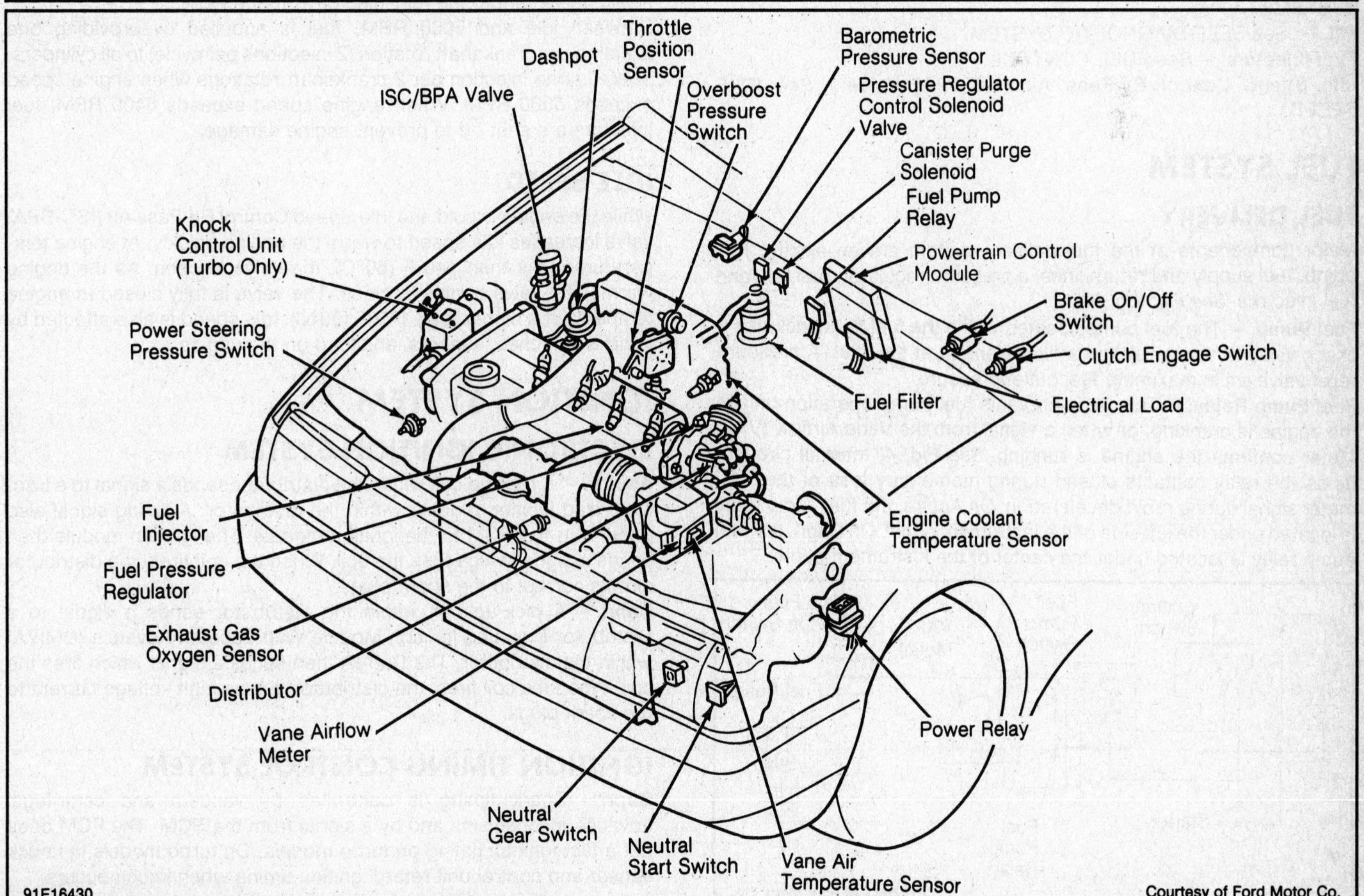
Dashpot
Throttle Position Sensor
ISC/BPA Valve
Overboost Pressure Switch
Barometric Pressure Sensor
Pressure Regulator Control Solenoid Valve
Canister Purge Solenoid
Fuel Pump Relay
Powertrain Control Module
Knock Control Unit (Turbo Only)
Brake On/Off Switch
Clutch Engage Switch
Power Steering Pressure Switch
Fuel Filter
Electrical Load
Fuel Injector
Engine Coolant Temperature Sensor
Fuel Pressure Regulator
Exhaust Gas Oxygen Sensor
Distributor
Vane Airflow Meter
Power Relay
Neutral Gear Switch
Neutral Start Switch
Vane Air Temperature Sensor
91E16430
Courtesy of Ford Motor Co.

Fig. 3: Locating Fuel Delivery System Components (Capri)

Park/Neutral Position (PNP) Switch (A/T) – This switch is located on the automatic transaxle. It sends a signal to the PCM whenever the transaxle is in Neutral or Park ranges. The PCM uses this signal for calculating fuel metering, idle speed control, and canister purge valve operation.

Power Steering Pressure Switch (PSPS) – This switch is located on the power steering pump. It sends data about power steering operation to the PCM. The PCM uses this signal for idle speed control.

Throttle Position (TP) Sensor/Switch – The throttle position sensor/switch is located on the throttle body. On Capri, the PCM uses signals from Throttle Position (TP) Sensor. On Aspire, the PCM uses signals from Throttle Position (TP) switch in calculating fuel mixture, idle speed, A/C cut-off, and canister purge operation.

On Capri, the TP sends a throttle plate angle signal to the PCM. A switch within the assembly sends a signal to the PCM when the throttle plate is in idle position.

Volume Airflow (VAF) Meter – This sensor is located within the air cleaner housing. It sends intake airflow data to the PCM. The PCM uses this signal for calculating fuel metering. The VAF may also be referred to as a Vane Airflow Meter.

Volume Air Temperature (VAT) Sensor – This sensor is located within the vane airflow sensor. It senses intake air temperature. The PCM uses this signal in calculating fuel metering, idle speed control, and canister purge valve operation. This sensor may also be referred to as a Volume Air Temperature Sensor.

OUTPUT SIGNALS

NOTE: Vehicles are equipped with different combinations of computer-controlled components. Not all components listed below are used on every vehicle. For theory and operation of each output component, refer to indicated system.

Canister Purge Control Solenoid (EVAP-CPCS) – See EMISSION SYSTEMS.

MIL – See SELF-DIAGNOSTIC SYSTEM.

Fuel Injectors – See FUEL CONTROL.

Idle Speed Control By-Pass Air (ISC-BPA) Valve – See IDLE SPEED.

FUEL SYSTEM

FUEL DELIVERY

Major components of the fuel delivery system are an electric fuel pump, fuel supply and return lines, a pressure regulator, fuel rail, and fuel injectors. *See Fig. 2 or 3.*

Fuel Pump – The fuel pump, located within the fuel tank, includes a check valve at the outlet and a filter element at the inlet. A pressure relief valve limits maximum fuel outlet pressure.

Fuel Pump Relay – This relay prevents fuel pump operation unless the engine is cranking, or when a signal from the Vane Airflow (VAF) Meter confirms the engine is running. *See Fig. 4.* Internal circuitry holds the relay contacts closed during momentary loss of the VAF meter signal during rapid deceleration. On Aspire, the fuel pump relay is located under the left side of the instrument panel. On Capri, the fuel pump relay is located under the center of the instrument panel.

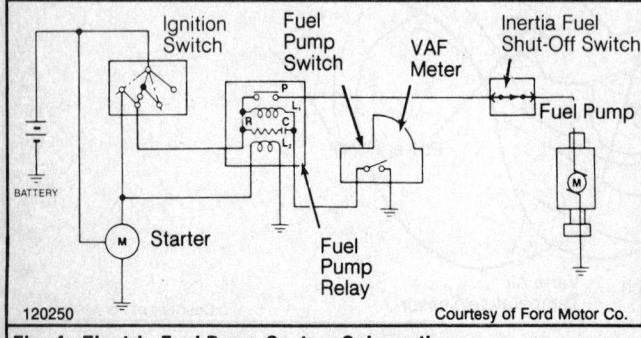

120250   Courtesy of Ford Motor Co.

Fig. 4: Electric Fuel Pump System Schematic

Fuel Pressure Regulator – The fuel pressure regulator is located at the fuel return end of the fuel rail. It maintains fuel pressure within the fuel rail at a constant 36.3 psi (2.54 kg/cm²) higher than intake manifold pressure.

Fuel Pressure Regulator Control (FPRC) Solenoid (Capri) – This device closes the vacuum supply to the fuel pressure regulator on hot starts, thus increasing fuel pressure within the fuel rail to prevent fuel percolation which could cause hard starts during hot conditions. The FPRC is located on the cowl panel, next to the canister purge solenoid.

Inertia Fuel Shutoff (IFS) Switch – The IFS is connected in series with the fuel pump. It opens to prevent fuel pump operation in the event of major collision or vehicle rollover. A reset button is provided to reset switch after it has been triggered. *See Fig. 5.*

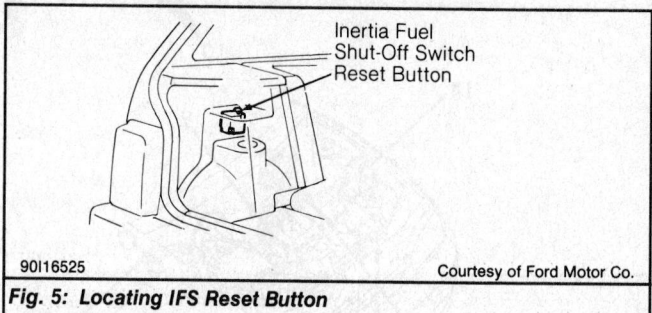

Inertia Fuel
Shut-Off Switch
Reset Button

90116525   Courtesy of Ford Motor Co.

Fig. 5: Locating IFS Reset Button

FUEL CONTROL

Electronic Fuel Injection (EFI) – The PCM receives a signal from the Crankshaft Position (CKP) Sensor on Aspire, or from the Cylinder Identification (CID) Sensor on Capri, for basic fuel injector timing. Signals to the PCM from other sensors and switches affect injector-on time. The amount of fuel injected is determined by duration of the electronic pulse sent to the fuel injector from the PCM.

Between idle and 5000 RPM, fuel is supplied by providing one injection per crankshaft rotation (2 injections per cycle) to all cylinders. There is one injection per 2 crankshaft rotations when engine speed exceeds 5000 RPM. When engine speed exceeds 6400 RPM, fuel injectors are shut off to prevent engine damage.

IDLE SPEED

While the engine is cold, the Idle Speed Control By-Pass Air (ISC-BPA) valve increases idle speed to warm the engine quickly. At engine temperatures less than 140°F (60°C), the valve is open. As the engine warms, the valve begins to close. The valve is fully closed at engine temperatures higher than 140°F (60°C). Idle speed is also affected by various switches, sensors, and load on the engine.

IGNITION SYSTEM

ELECTRONIC IGNITION SYSTEM

Aspire – A pick-up coil within the distributor sends a signal to a transistorized ignition module within the distributor. A timing signal also goes from the PCM to the ignition module. The ignition module then sends a signal which fires the coil. When the coil fires, the distributor directs current to the spark plugs.

Capri – A pick-up coil within the distributor sends a signal to a Distributor-Mounted Ignition Module With Vacuum Advance (DMIVA) within the distributor. The DMIVA then sends a signal which fires the coil. When the coil fires, the distributor directs high voltage current to the spark plugs.

IGNITION TIMING CONTROL SYSTEM

Capri – Spark timing is controlled by vacuum and centrifugal advance mechanisms and by a signal from the PCM. The PCM does not affect ignition timing on turbo models. On turbo models, a knock sensor and control unit retard ignition timing when knock occurs.

Aspire – The PCM generates a spark timing signal from data received from the barometric pressure sensor, crankshaft position sensor, and vane airflow meter. This signal goes to the ignition module. The ignition module then sends a signal to fire the coil.

High Altitude Spark Advance Correction – A barometric pressure sensor is incorporated into the PCM on Aspire, and is a separate component on Capri. At high altitudes, the PCM sends a signal to the ignition module to advance ignition timing. This feature is not used on turbo models.

Knock Sensor (Capri Turbo) – A Knock Sensor (KS) generates a signal when knock occurs. A control unit processes this signal and then sends it to the ignition module to retard spark timing. The KS is located in the engine block, near the oil pressure switch.

Knock Control Unit (Capri Turbo) – The knock control unit filters normal engine vibration signals from the KS, then sends a signal to the ignition module to retard spark timing. This unit is located on right side of engine compartment.

EMISSION SYSTEMS

DECELERATION SYSTEM (DASHPOT)

The deceleration control system closes the throttle plate gradually during deceleration. The dashpot prevents engine stalling on deceleration, and provides a smooth transition from deceleration to sudden acceleration.

EVAPORATIVE SYSTEM

Carbon Canister – The carbon canister stores vapors from the fuel tank until they are purged and burned in the engine. The carbon canister is located on the right side of the engine compartment near the cowl panel.

Canister Purge Control Solenoid – This component is connected between the carbon canister and intake manifold. When the PCM sends a signal to the solenoid to open, fuel vapors in the carbon canister are drawn into the engine. This solenoid is part of the canister purge control valve.

Canister Purge Control Valve – This valve opens to purge vapors from the carbon canister into the engine intake system.

Rollover Vent Valve – This valve, located in front of the fuel tank, blocks the vapor line in the event of vehicle rollover.

CATALYTIC CONVERTER

The catalytic converter is in the exhaust system, between the exhaust manifold and the muffler. It converts certain exhaust gases and pollutants into harmless substances.

PCV VALVE

The Positive Crankcase Ventilation (PCV) valve, located in the valve cover, controls the flow of blow-by gas from the crankcase to the intake manifold.

SELF-DIAGNOSTIC SYSTEM

NOTE: For additional information and operating procedures for the self-diagnostic system, refer to SELF-DIAGNOSTICS article.

NOTE: The CHECK ENGINE light, located in the instrument cluster, is referred to as Malfunction Indicator Light (MIL) in this article.

The PCM monitors its inputs and outputs. When it detects a malfunction, it sets a code in the PCM and sends a signal to the Malfunction Indicator Light (MIL). The light (MIL) remains on until the malfunction is repaired. Trouble codes may be accessed at the Self-Test Output (STO) and Self-Test Input (STI) connectors, located near the battery.

If a sensor fails, the PCM will use a substitute value in its calculations to permit continued engine operation. In this condition, the vehicle will run, but driveability may be poor. Intermittent failures may result in the MIL flickering or going out after the fault goes away. The corresponding trouble code, however, will be stored in the PCM. If the fault does not recur, the related code will be erased from PCM memory.

MALFUNCTION INDICATOR LIGHT (MIL)

Hard failures cause the MIL warning light to come on and remain on until the malfunction is repaired. If the warning light comes on and stays on during vehicle operation, determine and correct the cause of the malfunction.

Aspire, Capri

INTRODUCTION

The following diagnostic steps will help prevent overlooking a simple problem. This is also where to begin diagnosis for a no-start condition.

The first step in diagnosing any driveability problem is verifying the customer's complaint with a test drive under the conditions the problem reportedly occurred.

Before entering self-diagnostics, perform a careful and complete visual inspection. Most engine control problems result from mechanical breakdowns, poor electrical connections, or damaged/misrouted vacuum hoses. Before condemning the computerized system, perform each test listed in this article.

NOTE: *Perform all voltage tests with a Digital Volt-Ohmmeter (DVOM) with minimum 10-megohm input impedance, unless stated otherwise in test procedure.*

PRELIMINARY INSPECTION & ADJUSTMENTS

VISUAL INSPECTION

Perform a visual inspection. Look for chafed, stretched, cut, or pinched wiring. Ensure electrical connections fit tightly and are not corroded. Ensure vacuum hoses are properly routed and are not cut or pinched. If necessary, see VACUUM DIAGRAMS article to verify routing and connections. Inspect air induction system for possible leaks.

MECHANICAL INSPECTION

Compression – Engine mechanical condition can be checked with a compression gauge, vacuum gauge, or engine analyzer. See engine analyzer instruction manual for specific instructions. Lowest compression reading must not be less than 75 percent of highest reading.

CAUTION: *DO NOT use ignition switch during compression tests on vehicles with fuel injection. Fuel injectors are triggered by ignition switch during cranking mode. Use a remote starter to crank engine to prevent fire hazard and contamination of catalytic converter and engine oiling system.*

Exhaust System Backpressure – Exhaust system backpressure can be checked with a vacuum gauge or a 0-5 psi pressure gauge. If a pressure gauge is used, remove Oxygen Sensor (O2S). Connect gauge to O2S port. Start and run engine at 2500 RPM. If backpressure is more than 2 psi, exhaust system is plugged.

If a vacuum gauge is used, connect it to intake manifold vacuum port. Start engine. Observe vacuum gauge. Open throttle part way and hold steady. If vacuum gauge drops slowly after stabilizing, inspect exhaust system for a restriction.

FUEL SYSTEM

FUEL PRESSURE

WARNING: *ALWAYS relieve fuel pressure before disconnecting any fuel injection system component. DO NOT allow fuel to contact engine or electrical components.*

Fuel Pressure Release (Aspire) – Start engine. Unplug fuel pump relay connector, located behind left side of instrument panel. Allow engine to stall. Fuel pressure is now relieved.
Fuel Pressure Release (Capri) – Remove rear seat cushion. Start engine. Unplug fuel pump connector. Run engine until it stalls. Fuel pressure is now relieved.

Fuel Pressure Check – 1) Connect fuel pressure gauge between fuel filter and fuel rail. Open main valve and close drain valve. Locate fuel pump test connector in engine compartment. On Aspire, test connector is terminal No. 22 of Data Link Connector, located behind battery, at left shock tower. See Fig. 1. On Capri, test connector is located at right rear of engine compartment. See Fig. 2.

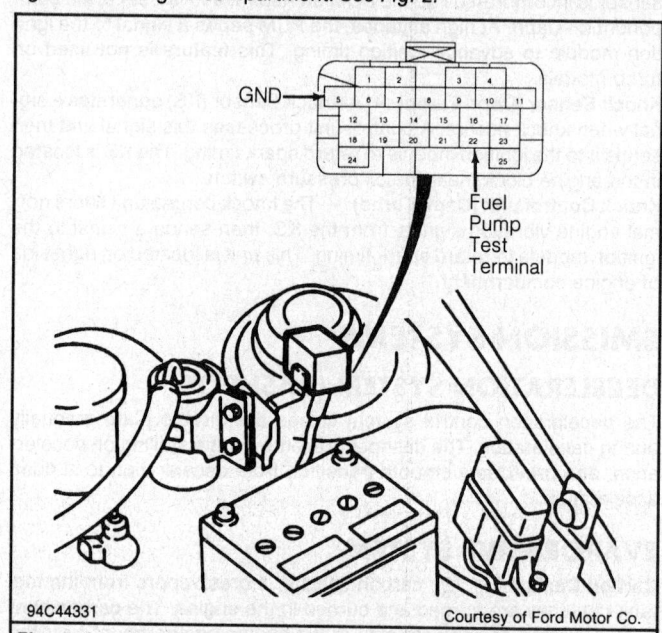

GND

Fuel Pump Test Terminal

94C44331   Courtesy of Ford Motor Co.
Fig. 1: Locating Fuel Pump Test Connector (Aspire)

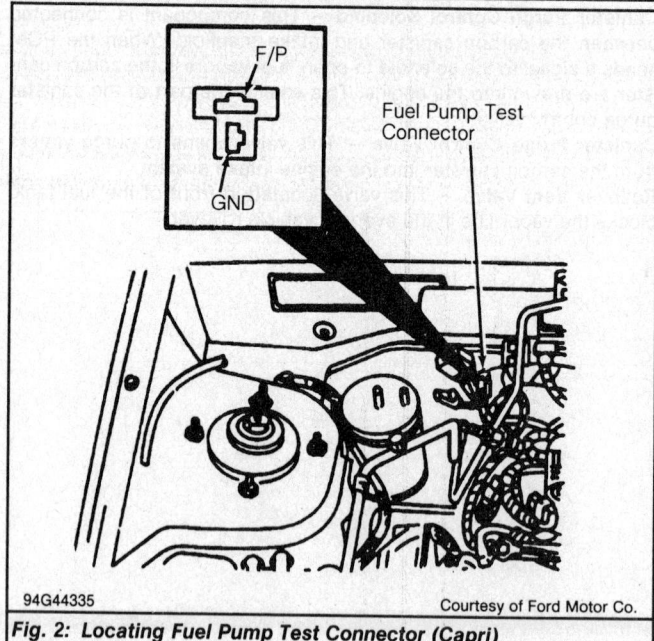

F/P

Fuel Pump Test Connector

GND

94G44335   Courtesy of Ford Motor Co.
Fig. 2: Locating Fuel Pump Test Connector (Capri)

2) Connect jumper wire between fuel pump test terminals. Turn ignition on. If pump does not run, check fuel pump circuit. If possible, start engine. Measure and record fuel pressure. See REGULATED FUEL PRESSURE table. Disconnect vacuum from pressure regulator. Turn engine off. Wait 5 minutes. Verify residual pressure is at least 21 psi (1.5 kg/cm²).
3) Operate fuel pump by reconnecting jumper wire at fuel pump test connector. Check fuel pump performance. Pinch hose between pressure gauge and fuel filter. Do not hold longer than necessary to measure pressure. See FUEL PUMP PERFORMANCE table. If pump does not meet specifications, inspect fuel pump circuit, fuel pump, fuel tank, and fuel filter.

REGULATED FUEL PRESSURE

Application	At Idle psi (kg/cm²)
Aspire	¹ 30-38 (2.1-2.7)
Capri	¹ 28-31 (2.0-2.2)

¹ – Pressure regulator maintains fuel pressure at a constant 36.3 psi 2.54 kg/cm²) higher than intake manifold pressure.

FUEL PUMP PERFORMANCE

Application	Pressure psi (kg/cm²)	Min. Vol. In 10 Sec. Ozs. (cc)
Aspire	50 (3.5)	5.5 (167)
Capri	64-85 (4.5-6.0)	5.5 (167)

Fuel Pump Circuit (Aspire) – 1) Turn ignition on. Connect jumper wire between fuel pump test connector terminal and ground. Test connector is terminal No. 22 of Data Link Connector, located behind battery, at left shock tower. *See Fig. 1.* Turn ignition on to activate fuel pump.

2) Listen for fuel pump sound. If there is no sound, inspect main fuse, inertia switch (located at left rear of passenger compartment), fuel pump relay, fuel pump, and all electrical connections.

Fuel Pump Circuit (Capri) – 1) Turn ignition on. Connect jumper wire between fuel pump test connector terminal and ground. Fuel pump test connector is located at right rear of engine compartment. *See Fig. 2.* Turn on ignition to activate fuel pump.

2) Listen for fuel pump sound. If there is no sound, inspect main fuse, inertia switch (located at left rear corner of luggage compartment), fuel pump relay, fuel pump, and all electrical connections.

Fuel Pump Relay (Aspire) – Remove fuel pump relay, located under left side of instrument panel. Continuity should not exist between terminals "A" and "C". *See Fig. 3.* Using fused jumper wires, apply 12 volts to relay terminals "E" and "F". Continuity should exist between terminals "A" and "C". Replace relay if operation is not as specified.

Fuel Pump Relay (Capri) – Remove fuel pump relay, located below center of instrument panel, under PCM. Continuity should not exist between terminals "A" and "C". *See Fig. 3.* Using fused jumper wires, apply 12 volts to relay terminals "B" and "C". Continuity should exist between terminals "A" and "C". Replace relay if operation is not as specified.

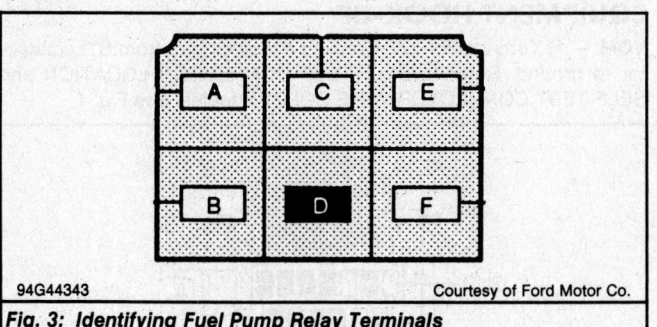

94G44343   Courtesy of Ford Motor Co.

Fig. 3: Identifying Fuel Pump Relay Terminals

IGNITION CHECKS

Firing Order – Inspect spark plug wiring routing. Firing order is 1-3-4-2.

Spark – 1) Crank engine. Check for a strong Blue spark at each spark plug wire by using a high output spark tester. Verify resistance of each spark plug wire is 4000-7000 ohms per foot.

2) Unplug and inspect all related ignition system connectors and harness. Clean or repair as necessary, and recheck spark. If still no spark, go to IGNITION COIL POWER SOURCE.

Ignition Coil Power Source – Unplug connector at ignition coil. Turn ignition on. Measure voltage between primary wire on harness connector and ground. Wire is Blue on Aspire; Black/White on Capri. If battery voltage does not exist, inspect battery feed, ignition switch, and fusible links. If battery voltage exists, go to IGNITION COIL RESISTANCE.

Ignition Coil Resistance – Measure resistance between primary terminals of coil. Measure resistance between positive primary terminal and high voltage terminal. See IGNITION COIL RESISTANCE table. Insulation resistance between coil case and primary positive terminal should be infinite. Replace coil if resistance measurements are not within specification.

IGNITION COIL RESISTANCE

Application	Primary (Ohms)	Secondary (Ohms)
Aspire	0.5-0.7	20,000-31,000
Capri	0.8-1.6	6000-30,000

IDLE SPEED & IGNITION TIMING

Ensure idle speed and ignition timing are set to specification. For adjustment procedures, see ON-VEHICLE ADJUSTMENTS article.

SUMMARY

If no faults were found while performing BASIC DIAGNOSTIC PROCEDURES, proceed to SELF-DIAGNOSTICS article. If no hard codes are found in self-diagnostics, proceed to TROUBLE SHOOTING – NO CODES article for diagnosis by symptom (ROUGH IDLE, NO START, etc.) or diagnostic procedures for intermittent problems.

1994 ENGINE PERFORMANCE
Self-Diagnostics

Aspire, Capri

INTRODUCTION

If no faults were found while performing BASIC DIAGNOSTIC PROCEDURES, proceed with self-diagnostics. If no fault codes, or only pass codes, are displayed after entering self-diagnostics, proceed to TROUBLE SHOOTING – NO CODES article for diagnosis by symptom (i.e., ROUGH IDLE, NO START, etc.).

This article uses many abbreviations for devices, signal names, and wire colors. See SELF-DIAGNOSTICS ABBREVIATIONS table. Abbreviations for wire colors in individual PINPOINT TEST diagrams are as follows:

- BLK – Black
- BLU – Blue
- BRN – Brown
- GRN – Green
- LT GRN – Light Green

- ORG – Orange
- PNK – Pink
- RED – Red
- WHT – White
- YEL – Yellow

SELF-DIAGNOSTICS ABBREVIATIONS

Application	Abbreviation
A/C Relay	ACR
Analog Volt-Ohmmeter	VOM
Barometric Pressure Sensor	BARO
Blower Motor Control	BLMT
Boost Pressure Switch	BPS
Brake ON/OFF Switch	BOO
Breakout Box	BOB
Canister Purge Control Solenoid	CANP
Clutch Cycling Pressure	CCPS
Clutch Pedal Position	CPP
Condenser Fan Relay	CFAN
Crankshaft Position Sensor	CKP
Cylinder Identification Sensor	CID
Data Link Connector	DLC
Defroster Switch	DEF
Digital Volt-Ohmmeter	DVOM
Electric Load Control Unit	ELU
Engine Coolant Temperature Sensor	ECT
Fuel Pressure Regulator Control Solenoid	FPRC
Fuel Pump Relay	FPR
Headlight Switch	HDLP
High Pressure Switch	HPS
Idle	IDL
Idle Speed Control	ISC
Ignition Diagnostic Monitor	IDM
Ignition Switch	VST
Intake Air Temperature Sensor	IAT
Keep Alive Power	KAPWR
Key On Engine Off	KOEO
Key On Engine Running	KOER
Knock Control	KC
Malfunction Indicator Light	MIL
Mass Airflow Meter	MAF
New Generation Star Scan Tester	NGS
Oxygen Sensor	O2S
Park/Neutral Position	PNP
Power & Ground Connections	PGC
Power Steering Switch	PSP
Powertrain Control Module	PCM
Relay Output Check	ROC
Reference Voltage & Signal Return	VREF
Self-Test Input	STI
Self-Test Output	STO
Signal Return	SIGRTN
Solenoid Controlled By Ground	SCG
Switch Monitor Lamp	SML
Switch To Ground	STG
Switch To Power	STP
Throttle Position Sensor	TP
Transmission Control Module	TCM
Volume Airflow Meter	VAF
Vehicle Power	VPWR
Vehicle Speed Sensor	VSS

SELF-DIAGNOSTIC SYSTEM

Hard Failures – Hard failures cause Malfunction Indicator Light (MIL) to come on and remain on until problem is repaired. If MIL comes on and remains on (light may flash) during vehicle operation, cause of malfunction must be determined by using diagnostic (code) charts. If a sensor fails, PCM will use a substitute value in its calculations to permit continued engine operation. In this condition (limp-in mode), vehicle will run but driveability will not be optimum.

Intermittent Failures – Intermittent failures may cause MIL to flicker or come on and go off after intermittent defect goes away. Corresponding trouble code, however, will be retained in PCM memory. If related defect does not reoccur within a certain time, related trouble code will be erased from PCM memory. Intermittent failures may be caused by a sensor, connector, or wiring. See INTERMITTENTS in TROUBLE SHOOTING – NO CODES article.

VISUAL CHECK & VEHICLE PREPARATION

Before connecting any equipment to diagnose electronic engine control system, perform following preparatory procedures:

- Verify condition of air cleaner and air ducts.
- Inspect all vacuum hoses for leaks, restrictions, or improper routing.
- Inspect electrical system for corrosion, bent or broken pins, loose wires or terminals, or improper routing.
- Inspect PCM, sensors, and actuators for physical damage.
- Check engine oil and coolant level.
- Observe all necessary safety precautions to prevent personal injury or vehicle damage.
- Set parking brake. Position shift lever into Park for automatic transmissions, or Neutral for manual transmissions. Do not move shift lever during test unless specifically directed.
- Turn off all lights and accessories. Ensure vehicle doors are closed when measuring voltage or resistance.
- Start engine. Run at idle until upper radiator hose is hot and pressurized and engine is off fast idle. Inspect for leaks around exhaust manifold, exhaust gas oxygen sensor, and vacuum hose connections.
- Turn ignition off. Service items as required. Go to EQUIPMENT HOOK-UP.

EQUIPMENT HOOK-UP

VOM – 1) Turn ignition off. Connect a jumper wire from STI connector to ground. Refer to SELF-TEST CONNECTOR LOCATION and SELF-TEST CONNECTOR WIRE COLORS tables. See Fig. 1.

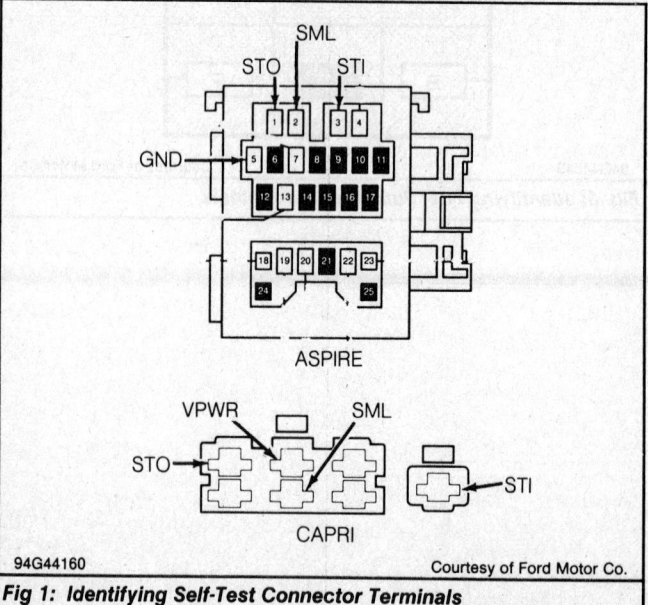

94G44160   Courtesy of Ford Motor Co.

Fig 1: Identifying Self-Test Connector Terminals

2) Connect VOM between STO terminal and engine ground. Set VOM to measure 0-20 volts DC.

MIL – Connect jumper wire between STI connector and ground.

NGS Or Super Star II Tester – Connect instrument according to manufacturer's instructions.

SELF-TEST CONNECTOR LOCATION

Application	Location
Aspire	LR Corner Engine Compartment
Capri	RR Corner Engine Compartment

SELF-TEST CONNECTOR WIRE COLORS

Circuit	Wire Color
Aspire	
PCM STO	White/Black
SML	Blue/Black
STI	Blue
Capri	
SML	Black/Blue
STI	Yellow
STO	Green/Black

RETRIEVING CODES

Reading Service Codes – Engine control system communicates malfunctions to technician through service codes. These service codes are 2-digit numbers representing a particular defect. Service codes are transmitted through STO connector.

Service codes are displayed as timed pulses, and may be read with a VOM, NGS, or Super Star II tester. VOM displays codes by needle sweeps. See Fig. 2.

Turn ignition off. Follow all procedures of EQUIPMENT HOOK-UP. Engine should be at normal operating temperature.

VOM – Disconnect and reconnect jumper wire from STI terminal to ground. Turn ignition on. Record displayed codes. Erase codes, then repeat test procedure to verify all codes are currently valid. See ERASING CODES & RETESTING. Service only those codes which appear during retest. Refer to TROUBLE CODE IDENTIFICATION table to find appropriate pinpoint test.

MIL – Turn ignition on. Connect jumper wire between STI connector and ground. Observe MIL, and record pulses to determine codes stored.

NOTE: If MIL flashes continuously prior to connecting test equipment, go to PINPOINT TEST STI.

NGS Or Super Star II Tester – Follow manufacturer's instructions to retrieve codes.

ERASING CODES & RETESTING

Erasing codes and retesting will give an indication of whether codes are hard or intermittent defects. Hard codes reset immediately and will be displayed during retest.

Disconnect negative battery cable. Press brake pedal for 5-10 seconds. Turn off NGS or Super Star II tester. Reconnect battery. Perform tests under RETRIEVING CODES to again display and record codes.

CLEARING CODES

Clearing Codes Procedure – Disconnect negative battery cable. Press brake pedal for 5-10 seconds. Turn off VOM or Super Star II tester. Reconnect battery.

QUICK TESTS

KEY ON, ENGINE OFF (KOEO) SELF-TEST

NOTE: Do not move throttle during KOEO self-test.

1) This is a test of electronic engine control system, conducted with power (voltage) applied and engine not running. Enter self-test. Record all codes displayed.

2) Erase codes. Repeat self-test. Diagnose only codes occurring during repeat self-test. See TROUBLE CODE IDENTIFICATION table. If no codes are present, proceed to KEY ON, ENGINE RUNNING (KOER) SELF-TEST.

KEY ON, ENGINE RUNNING (KOER) SELF-TEST

NOTE: It is necessary to clear codes in memory before performing this test. Do not move throttle during test.

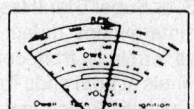 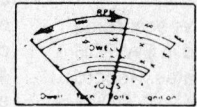

1 NEEDLE PULSE (SWEEP) + 1 NEEDLE PULSE (SWEEP) = 2 NEEDLE PULSES (SWEEPS) FOR 1ST DIGIT

1.6-SECOND PULSE BETWEEN DIGITS

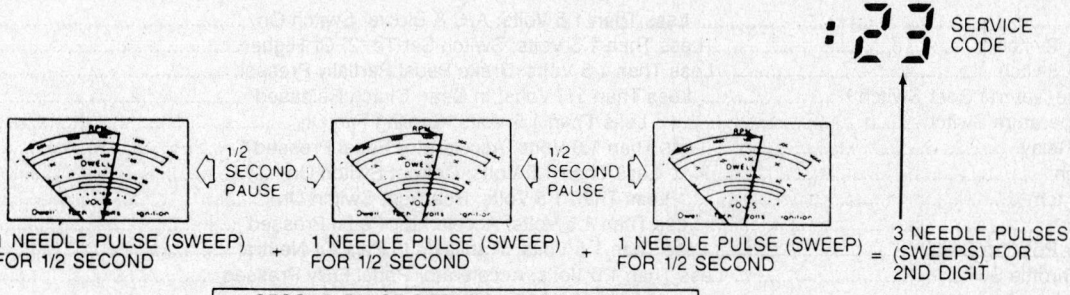

:23 SERVICE CODE

1 NEEDLE PULSE (SWEEP) FOR 1/2 SECOND + 1/2 SECOND PAUSE + 1 NEEDLE PULSE (SWEEP) FOR 1/2 SECOND + 1/2 SECOND PAUSE + 1 NEEDLE PULSE (SWEEP) FOR 1/2 SECOND = 3 NEEDLE PULSES (SWEEPS) FOR 2ND DIGIT

4-SECOND PAUSE BETWEEN SERVICE CODES, WHEN MORE THAN ONE CODE IS INDICATED

90H16532

Courtesy of Ford Motor Co.

Fig. 2: Reading Service Codes With VOM

1994 ENGINE PERFORMANCE
Self-Diagnostics (Cont.)

TROUBLE CODE IDENTIFICATION

TROUBLE CODE IDENTIFICATION

Service Code	Fault	Circuit & Pinpoint Test
01 [2]	Ignition Diagnostic Monitor	IDM
02 [1]	Crankshaft Position Sensor	CKP
03 [2]	Cylinder Identification Sensor	CID
06 [1]	Vehicle Speed Sensor	VSS
08 [1]	Mass Airflow Meter	MAF
08 [2]	Volume Airflow Meter	VAF
09	Engine Coolant Temperature Sensor	ECT
10	Intake Air Temperature Sensor	IAT
12 [2]	Throttle Position Sensor	TP
14	Barometric Pressure Sensor	BARO
15	Oxygen Sensor	O2S
16 [1]	Exhaust Gas Recirculation Valve Position Sensor	EVP
17	Oxygen Sensor	O2S
25 [2]	Fuel Pressure Regulator Control Solenoid	SCG
26 [2]	Canister Purge Control Solenoid	SCG
34	Idle Speed Control	ISC
Codes Not Listed	Power & Ground Connections	PGC

[1] – Aspire only.
[2] – Capri only.

1) Deactivate self-test. Start and run engine at 2000 RPM for 2 minutes to warm up O2S. Turn off engine and wait 10 seconds.
2) Restart engine, and activate self-test. Record all service codes displayed. See TROUBLE CODE IDENTIFICATION table. If no codes are present, proceed to SWITCH MONITOR TEST.

SWITCH MONITOR TEST

NOTE: All switches must be tested individually. Allowing a switch to remain on while testing another will lead to false test results.

This test procedure checks input signals received by ECA from individual switches. Use following procedure to perform switch monitor test:

- Turn engine off and allow it to cool.
- Turn all accessories off.
- Deactivate self-test.
- Ensure transmission lever is in Neutral or Park.
- Turn ignition on.

NGS Or Super Star II Tester – Connect and operate tester according to manufacturer's instructions. Operate each switch listed in SWITCH MONITOR TEST table. Note output as each switch operates. Record test results.
VOM – **1)** Ground STI connector. Connect VOM positive lead to SML terminal on self-test connector. Connect negative lead to ground. *See Fig. 1.*

SWITCH MONITOR TEST

2) Operate each switch listed in SWITCH MONITOR TEST table. Note output on VOM as each switch is operated. Go to specified PINPOINT TEST if any switch does not meet specification.

NOTE: Do not move throttle, clutch, or transmission range selector lever unless so directed.

WIGGLE TEST

Inspecting Circuitry – **1)** Visually inspect suspected sensor, switch, or solenoid. Enter WIGGLE TEST if using NGS or Super Star II tester. If using VOM, connect it to STO terminal on self-test connector, and ground STI self-test connector terminal. Lightly tap suspected sensor, switch, or solenoid.
2) Push and pull on suspected sensor, switch, or solenoid connector, but do not unplug it. Test and wiggle harness vigorously, working in small sections, from suspected device toward dash panel, and from dash panel to PCM.
3) If VOM, NGS, or Super Star II tester does not display a positive indication of an intermittent defect, carefully disconnect suspected device. Remove terminals from connector.
4) Inspect terminals at both ends for corrosion, bad crimps, or improperly seated terminals. Reconnect after inspection. Unplug harness from PCM.
5) Inspect PCM and harness connector terminals for corrosion, bad crimps, or improperly seated terminals. If VOM does not indicate any intermittent defect, reconnect wiring and erase codes.

SWITCH MONITOR TEST

Switch	VOM Indication/Condition	[1] Pinpoint Test
A/C Switch	Less Than 1.5 Volts; A/C & Blower Switch On	STG
Blower Motor Switch	Less Than 1.5 Volts; Switch Set To "2" Or Higher	[2] STG
Brake On/Off Switch	Less Than 1.5 Volts; Brake Pedal Partially Pressed	STP
Clutch Engage/Neutral Gear Switch [3]	Less Than 1.5 Volts; In Gear, Clutch Released	STG
Coolant Temperature Switch	Less Than 1.5 Volts; Cooling Fan On	[2] STP
Cooling Fan Relay	Less Than 1.5 Volts; Accelerator Pedal Pressed [4]	ROC
Defrost Switch	Less Than 1.5 Volts; Defrost Switch On	STP
Headlight Switch	Less Than 1.5 Volts; Headlight Switch On	STP
Idle Switch	Less Than 1.5 Volts; Accelerator Pedal Pressed	[2] STG
Manual Lever Position Switch	Less Than 1.5 Volts; Transaxle In Park Or Neutral	STP
Wide Open Throttle Switch [5]	Less Than 1.5 Volts; Accelerator Pedal Fully Pressed	STG

[1] – Proceed to specified PINPOINT TEST if indication is incorrect.
[2] – On Capri, go to PINPOINT TEST ELU.
[3] – Not applicable to vehicles with A/T.
[4] – Fan should operate.
[5] – Except Capri non-turbo.

SUMMARY

If no hard codes, or only pass codes, exist and driveability symptoms or intermittent codes still exist, proceed to TROUBLE SHOOTING – NO CODES article for diagnosis by symptom (i.e., ROUGH IDLE, NO START, etc.) or intermittent diagnostic procedures.

PINPOINT TESTS

NOTE: Following tests and illustrations are courtesy of Ford Motor Co. Complete EEC system wiring diagrams may be found in WIRING DIAGRAMS article.

HOW TO USE PINPOINT TESTS

NOTE: Inspect all wiring, harnesses, connectors, and components for damage, overheating, shorting, or looseness. If any defect is found, repair as necessary before proceeding to any PINPOINT TEST.

1) Do not perform any PINPOINT TEST unless directed by a QUICK TESTS procedure. Repair all non-EEC related defects. Follow each test step in order until defect is found. DO NOT replace any part unless so directed. When more than one service code exists, start with first code displayed.

2) PINPOINT TESTS require that electrical circuits are okay before replacing sensors or any other components. Always test circuits for continuity between sensor and PCM. Test all circuits for shorts to voltage, opens, or shorts to ground. VREF and VPWR circuits should be tested with KOEO or as specified in PINPOINT TESTS.

3) DO NOT measure voltage or resistance at PCM, or connect any test light unless specified in test procedure. DO NOT pierce wiring. Isolate both ends of a circuit and turn ignition off before testing for shorts or continuity, unless otherwise specified.

4) Disconnect solenoids and switches before testing for circuit continuity or energizing solenoids.

5) An open is defined as any resistance greater than 10,000 ohms unless otherwise specified.

6) To help diagnose circuits to PCM, turn ignition off and disconnect PCM harness. Connect BOB between PCM and PCM harness to perform circuit and pinpoint tests.

PCM LOCATION

On Aspire, PCM is located behind left side of instrument panel. On Capri, PCM is located below center of instrument panel.

PINPOINT TEST IDM
IGNITION DIAGNOSTIC MONITOR

NOTE: Enter this test only when Code 01 is displayed during QUICK TESTS procedure or when directed here from another PINPOINT TEST.

94C44307

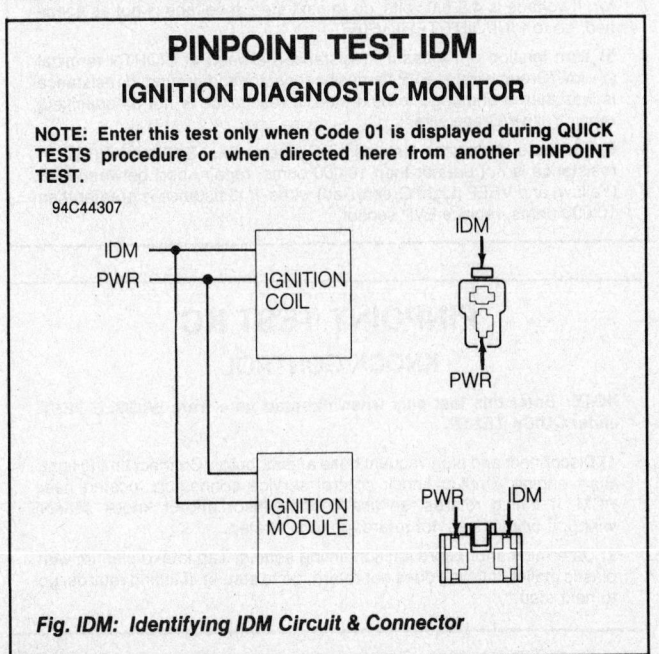

Fig. IDM: Identifying IDM Circuit & Connector

PINPOINT TEST IDM (Cont.)

IDM CIRCUIT PIN IDENTIFICATION

Circuit	PCM Pin	BOB Pin	Wire Color
Capri			
IDM	1M	6	YEL/BLU
PWR	[1]	[1]	BLK/WHT

[1] – Circuits are part of vehicle harness, and are not connected to PCM.

Capri – 1) Connect spark tester between coil secondary wire and ground. Crank engine several times, leaving ignition on between cranking periods. If continuous sparks do not jump tester gap, go to step **3)**. If continuous sparks jump tester gap, go to next step.

2) Turn ignition off. Connect BOB. Leave PCM disconnected. Connect test light between BOB pins IDM and VPWR. Crank engine several times. If test light flashes each time engine cranks, IDM circuit is okay. Return to QUICK TESTS if directed here from there. If test light does not flash, repair IDM wire between ECA and coil.

3) Unplug connector from ignition coil. Connect test light between coil IDM wire and PWR wire. Crank engine several times, leaving ignition on between cranking periods. If test light does not flash continuously, go to step **5)**. If test light flashes continuously, go to next step.

4) Turn ignition on. Measure voltage between coil harness PWR wire and ground. If voltage is greater than 10 volts, replace coil. If voltage is less than 10 volts, repair wire between ignition switch and coil.

5) Unplug connector from ignition module. Connect a jumper wire between PWR wire on ignition module harness connector and mating terminal on ignition module. Leave IDM wire disconnected. Connect test light between IDM terminal on ignition module and PWR wire. Crank engine several times, leaving ignition on between cranking periods. If test light flashes each time engine cranks, repair wire between ignition module IDM wire and coil. If test light does not flash, go to next step.

6) Unplug connector from ignition module. Measure voltage between ignition module PWR wire and ground. If voltage is not higher than 10 volts, repair PWR wire from ignition switch. If voltage is higher than 10 volts, go to next step.

7) Turn ignition off. Unplug ignition module connector. Turn ignition on. Connect test light between ignition module PWR wire and ignition module GND wire. Turn ignition on. If test light glows, replace ignition module. If test light does not glow, repair ignition module ground wire.

PINPOINT TEST CID
CYLINDER IDENTIFICATION SENSOR

NOTE: Enter this test only when Code 03 is displayed during QUICK TESTS procedure, or when directed here from another PINPOINT TEST.

92D25208

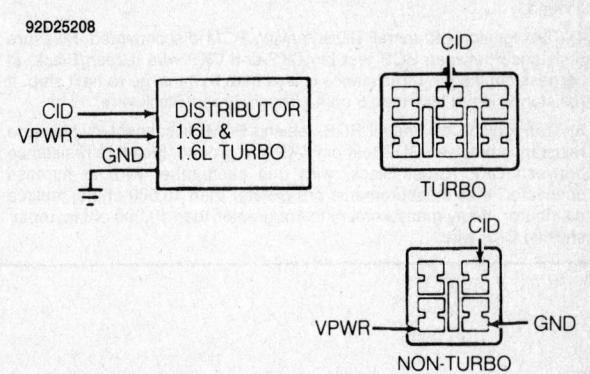

Fig. CID: Identifying CID Circuit & Connectors

CID CIRCUIT PIN IDENTIFICATION

Circuit	PCM Pin	BOB Pin	Wire Color
CID	1N	34	YEL

PINPOINT TEST CID (Cont.)

1) Turn ignition off. Install BOB, leaving PCM disconnected. Unplug distributor connector. Measure resistance between BOB pin No. 34 and CID terminal on distributor harness connector. Repair Yellow wire between PCM and distributor if resistance is greater than 5 ohms. If resistance is less than 5 ohms, go to next step.

2) Turn ignition on. Measure voltage between distributor VPWR and GND wires. If voltage is greater than 10 volts, replace CID sensor. If voltage is not greater than 10 volts, repair distributor GND wire.

PINPOINT TEST CKP

CRANKSHAFT POSITION SENSOR

NOTE: Enter this test only when Code 02 is displayed during QUICK TESTS procedure or when directed here from another PINPOINT TEST.

94H44161

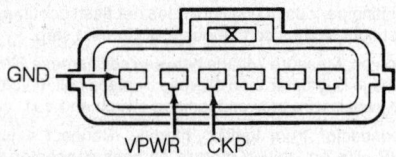

Fig. CKP: *Identifying CKP Circuit & Connector*

CKP CIRCUIT PIN IDENTIFICATION

Circuit	PCM Pin	BOB Pin	Wire Color
CKP	2E	56	GRN/BLK
GND	2C	16	BLK/LT GRN
VPWR	1B	37, 57	YEL/WHT

1) Turn ignition off. Install BOB. Reconnect PCM. Measure voltage at BOB test pin CKP while bumping starter. If voltage does not alternate between about zero and 5 volts, go to next step. If voltage alternates as specified, CKP circuit is okay. Return to QUICK TESTS if sent here from there; otherwise temporarily substitute known good PCM and repeat test to check for improvement.

2) Turn ignition off. Unplug 6-pin distributor connector. Turn ignition on. Measure voltage on VPWR (Yellow/Black) wire at harness connector. If voltage is greater than 10 volts, go to next step. If voltage is not greater than 10 volts, repair VPWR wire to distributor.

3) Turn ignition off. Measure resistance between GND (Black) wire at harness connector and ground. If resistance is less than 5 ohms, go to next step. If resistance is not less than 5 ohms, repair Black wire to ground.

4) Turn ignition off. Install BOB, leaving PCM disconnected. Measure resistance between BOB test pin CKP and CKP wire (Green/Black) at harness connector. If resistance is less than 5 ohms, go to next step. If resistance is not less than 5 ohms, repair Green/Black wire.

5) Turn ignition off. Install BOB, leaving PCM disconnected. Measure resistance between BOB test pin CKP and ground. Measure resistance between CKP (Green/Black) wire and each other wire at harness connector. If all measurements are greater than 10,000 ohms, replace distributor. If any measurement is not greater than 10,000 ohms, repair shorted CKP wire.

PINPOINT TEST EVP

EXHAUST GAS RECIRCULATION VALVE POSITION (EVP) SENSOR

NOTE: Enter this test only when Code 16 is displayed during QUICK TESTS procedure or when directed here from another PINPOINT TEST.

94D44167

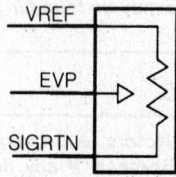 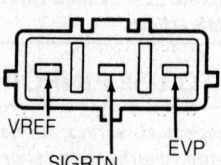

Fig. EVP: *Identifying EVP Circuit & Connector*

EVP CIRCUIT PIN IDENTIFICATION

Circuit	PCM Pin	BOB Pin	Wire Color
EVP	2J	6	YEL
SIGRTN	2D	46	LT YEL/GRN
VREF	2K	26	LT GRN/RED

1) Inspect hoses and connections between intake manifold and EGR valve. If all appears okay, go to next step. Repair hoses or connections as necessary.

2) Turn ignition off. Connect vacuum gauge between EGR valve and vacuum hose going to EGR valve. Start engine. Warm engine to normal operating temperature. Observe vacuum gauge while assistant drives vehicle. If gauge indicates about 5 in. Hg at normal cruise, and zero in. Hg at idle, deceleration, and high speed, go to next step. If gauge indicates otherwise, inspect hoses for leaks, damage, or obstructions. If hoses are okay, repair EGR system.

3) Turn ignition off. Install BOB, leaving PCM connected. Connect vacuum tester to EGR valve vacuum port. Turn ignition on. Measure voltage between BOB test pins EVP and SIGRTN while applying vacuum to EGR valve. If voltage does not increases smoothly from approximately 0.8 volt at zero vacuum to approximately 5.0 volts at 5.9 in. Hg., go to next step. If voltage is as specified, EVP circuit is okay. Return to QUICK TESTS if sent here from there; otherwise temporarily substitute known good PCM and retest.

4) Turn ignition off. Unplug EVP connector. Turn ignition on. Measure voltage at VREF terminal (Light Green/Red wire) at EVP harness connector. If voltage is 4.5-5.0 volts, go to next step. If voltage is not as specified, go to PINPOINT TEST VREF.

5) Turn ignition off. Measure resistance between at SIGRTN terminal (Yellow/Green wire) at EVP harness connector and ground. If resistance is less than 5 ohms, go to next step. If resistance is not as specified, repair Yellow/Green wire.

6) Measure resistance between BOB test pins EVP and VREF. If resistance is not greater than 10,000 ohms, repair short between EVP (Yellow) and VREF (Light Green/Red) wires. If resistance is greater than 10,000 ohms, replace EVP sensor.

PINPOINT TEST KC

KNOCK CONTROL

NOTE: Enter this test only when directed here from WIGGLE TEST under QUICK TESTS.

1) Disconnect and plug vacuum hose at distributor. Connect timing light. Start engine. Unplug knock control service connector, located near PCM. If timing retards, service knock sensor and/or knock sensor wiring. If timing does not retard, go to next step.

2) Determine and record ignition timing setting. Tap intake plenum with plastic mallet. If timing does not retard, go to step 4). If timing retards, go to next step.

PINPOINT TEST KC (Cont.)

93A78097

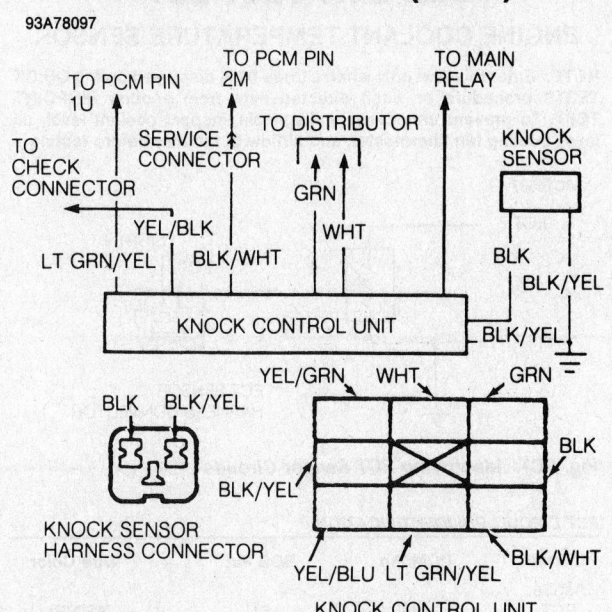

Fig. KC: Identifying KC Circuit & Connectors

3) Plug in knock control service connector, located near PCM. Determine and record ignition timing setting. Tap intake plenum with plastic mallet. If timing does not retard, knock control unit is okay. Go to next step. If timing retards, replace knock control unit.

4) Turn ignition off. Unplug knock control service connector, located near PCM. Install a known good knock sensor. Start engine. Tap intake plenum with plastic mallet. If timing retards, replace knock sensor. If timing does not retard, go to next step.

5) Inspect VPWR and GND (Yellow/Green and Black/Yellow wires respectively) to knock control unit for shorts or open circuits. Service wires as necessary. If wires are okay, replace knock control unit.

PINPOINT TEST MAF

MASS AIRFLOW METER

NOTE: Enter this test only when Code 08 is displayed during QUICK TESTS procedure or when directed here from another PINPOINT TEST.

94A44164

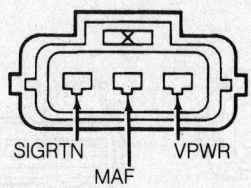

Fig. MAF: Identifying MAF Circuit & Connectors

MAF CIRCUIT PIN IDENTIFICATION

Circuit	PCM Pin	BOB Pin	Wire Color
MAF	2Q	27	GRN/BLK
SIGRTN	2C	16	BLK/LT GRN
VPWR	1B	37, 57	YEL/WHT

1) Turn ignition off. Connect BOB. Reconnect PCM. Turn ignition on. Measure voltage between BOB test pins MAF and SIGRTN, first with engine off, then with engine running. If voltage is not 1.0-1.5 volts with off, and 1.5-5.0 volts with engine running, go to next step. If voltage is as specified, MAF circuit is okay. Return to QUICK TESTS if sent here from there; otherwise temporarily substitute known good PCM and retest.

2) Turn ignition off. Unplug PCM connectors. Unplug MAF sensor connector, located between air cleaner and throttle body. Measure resistance between BOB test pin MAF and MAF terminal (Green/Black wire) on harness connector. If resistance is less than 5 ohms, go to next step. If resistance is not as specified, repair open Green/Black wire.

3) Measure resistance between BOB test pin MAF and ground. Measure resistance between BOB test pin MAF and BOB test pin VPWR. If both measurements are greater than 10,000 ohms, go to next step. If either measurement is not as specified, repair shorted MAF (Green/Black) wire.

4) Turn ignition on. Check for battery voltage at VPWR terminal (Yellow/White wire) at MAF harness connector. If battery voltage exists, go to next step. If battery voltage does not exist, go to PINPOINT TEST VPWR. If VPWR is okay, repair shorted Yellow/White wire.

5) Turn ignition off. Measure resistance between MAF harness connector SIGRTN terminal (Black/Light Green wire) and ground. If resistance is less than 5 ohms, replace MAF sensor. If resistance is not less than 5 ohms, repair Black/Light Green wire.

PINPOINT TEST VSS

VEHICLE SPEED SENSOR

NOTE: Enter this test only when Code 06 is displayed during QUICK TESTS procedure or when directed here from another PINPOINT TEST.

94G44194

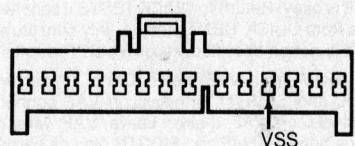

Fig. VSS: Identifying VSS Circuit & Connectors

VSS CIRCUIT PIN IDENTIFICATION

Circuit	PCM Pin	BOB Pin	Wire Color
VSS	1M	21	GRN/RED

1) Turn ignition off. Install BOB. Disconnect speedometer cable at transaxle. Turn ignition on. Measure voltage at BOB test pin while rotating speedometer cable. If voltage does not cycle between zero and 5 volts, go to next step. If voltage cycles as specified, VSS circuit is okay; return to diagnostic routine.

2) Turn ignition off. Unplug PCM connectors. Unplug 14-pin instrument cluster connector. Measure resistance of VSS wire (Green/Red) wire between BOB test pin VSS and instrument cluster harness connector. If resistance is less than 5 ohms, go to next step. If resistance is not as specified, repair open VSS wire.

3) Measure resistance of VSS wire (Green/Red) wire between BOB test pin VSS and ground. If resistance is not less than 10,000 ohms, repair shorted VSS wire. If resistance is as specified, measure voltage at BOB test pin VSS. If voltage is not zero, service VSS.

PINPOINT TEST VAF
VOLUME AIRFLOW METER

NOTE: Enter this test only when a Code 08 is displayed during QUICK TESTS procedure, or when directed here from another PINPOINT TEST. To avoid unnecessary diagnostic time, inspect for unmetered air leaks between VAF meter and throttle body. This test is intended to diagnose only VAF and VREF circuits.

94C44323

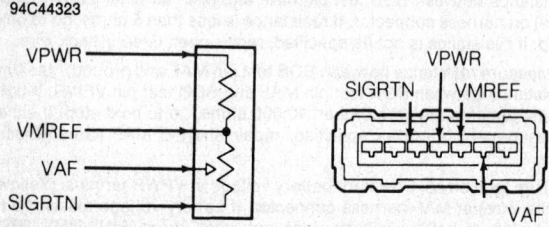

Fig. VAF: Identifying VAF Meter Circuits

VAF CIRCUIT PIN IDENTIFICATION

Circuit	PCM Pin	BOB Pin	Wire Color
Capri			
SIGRTN	2C	46	BLU/YEL
VAF	2E	43	LT GRN/BLK
VMREF	2B	18	LT GRN/RED
VPWR	3I	37	YEL/GRN

Capri – 1) Turn ignition off. Install BOB. Turn ignition on. Measure voltage between VAF and SIGRTN pins while moving vane in VAF meter. Voltage should be as specified in VAF METER VOLTAGE table. If voltage is as specified, go to next step. If voltage is not as specified, go to step 3).

2) Measure voltage between VMREF and SIGRTN test pins. If voltage is 7-9 volts, circuit is okay. Return to QUICK TESTS if sent here from there. If not sent here from QUICK TESTS, temporarily substitute known good PCM. If voltage is not as specified, repair VMREF wire to VAF.

3) Unplug connector from VAF meter. Using jumper wires, connect VPWR, VMREF, and SIGRTN terminals on VAF connector to corresponding terminals on VAF meter. Leave VAF wire disconnected. Measure voltage between VAF and SIGRTN pins on harness connector while moving vane in VAF meter. Voltage should be as specified in VAF METER VOLTAGE table. If voltage is as specified, go to next step. If voltage is as specified, repair VAF wire to PCM.

VAF METER VOLTAGE

Door Position	Volts
1/8 Open	3.24
1/4 Open	5.60
3/8 Open	5.62
1/2 Open	5.83
5/8 Open	6.02
3/4 Open	6.57
7/8 Open	7.46
Full Open	7.87

4) Unplug connector from VAF. Using jumper wires, connect VPWR and SIGRTN terminals on VAF connector to corresponding terminals on VAF meter. Leave VAF and VMREF wires disconnected. Measure voltage between VAF terminal at VAF meter, and SIGRTN pin at harness connector while moving vane in VAF meter. Voltage should be as specified in VAF METER VOLTAGE table. If voltage is not as specified, go to next step. If voltage is as specified, repair VMREF wire to PCM.

5) Unplug connector from VAF meter. Turn ignition on. Measure voltage between SIGRTN and VPWR wires. If voltage is more than 10 volts, replace VAF meter. If voltage is not more than 10 volts, go to next step.

6) Unplug VAF meter connector. Turn ignition on. Measure voltage between VAF meter VPWR wire and ground. If voltage is more than 10 volts, repair VAF wire to PCM. If voltage is not more than 10 volts, go to PINPOINT TEST VPWR.

PINPOINT TEST ECT
ENGINE COOLANT TEMPERATURE SENSOR

NOTE: Enter this test only when a Code 09 is displayed during QUICK TESTS procedure or when directed here from another PINPOINT TEST. To prevent unnecessary diagnosis, inspect coolant level, oil level, cooling fan, thermostat, and airflow to radiator before testing.

90C16537

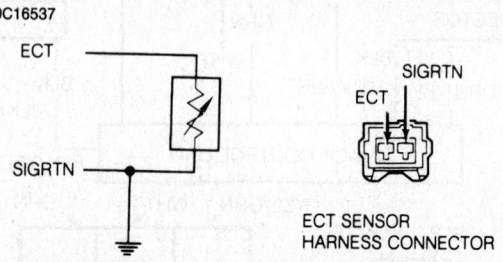

Fig. ECT: Identifying ECT Sensor Circuits

ECT CIRCUIT PIN IDENTIFICATION

Circuit	PCM Pin	BOB Pin	Wire Color
Aspire			
ECT	2H	51	RED/BLU
SIGRTN	2D	46	YEL/GRN
Capri			
ECT	2I	7	BLU/RED
SIGRTN	2C	46	BLU/YEL

1) Start and run engine until coolant temperature reaches 176°F (80°C). Turn ignition off. Install BOB. Leave PCM disconnected. Measure resistacne between BOB test pins ECT and SIGRTN. If resistance is not 250-350 ohms, go to next step. If resistance is as specified, ECT circuit is okay.

2) Unplug ECT sensor, threaded into intake manifold. Inspect ECT wire (Red/Blue or Blue/Red) between ECT and PCM for shorts or opens. If wire is okay, go to next step. Repair ECT wire as necessary.

3) Inspect SIGRTN wire (Yellow/Green or Blue/Yellow) between ECT and PCM for opens. Repair SIGRTN wire as necessary. If wire is okay, replace ECT sensor.

PINPOINT TEST IAT
INTAKE AIR TEMPERATURE SENSOR

NOTE: Enter this test only when a Code 10 is displayed during QUICK TESTS procedure or when directed here from another PINPOINT TEST.

94B44306

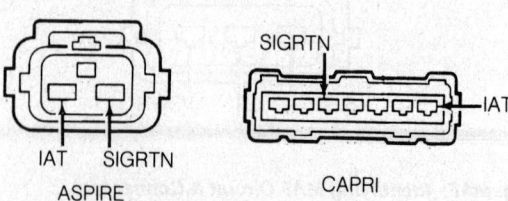

Fig. IAT: Identifying IAT Circuits

1) Turn ignition off. Install BOB, leaving PCM disconnected. Measure ambient temperature at IAT, located in air cleaner on Aspire, or in VAF on Capri. Measure resistance between IAT and SIGRTN test pins. Compare resistance to specifications in appropriate IAT SENSOR RESISTANCE table. If resistance is not within specification, go to next step. If resistance is within specification, IAT circuit is okay.

PINPOINT TEST IAT (Cont.)

IAT CIRCUIT PIN IDENTIFICATION

Circuit	PCM Pin	BOB Pin	Wire Color
Aspire			
IAT	2L	27	GRN/RED
SIGRTN	2D	46	YEL/GRN
Capri			
IAT	2J	25	BRN/YEL
SIGRTN	2C	46	BLU/YEL

IAT SENSOR RESISTANCE – ASPIRE

Temperature °F (°C)	Ohms
32 (0)	72,100-79,400
55 (13)	54,300-58,600
77 (25)	29,700-36,300
110 (43)	17,900-19,300
185 (85)	3300-3700

IAT SENSOR RESISTANCE – CAPRI

Temperature °F (°C)	Ohms
-4 (-20)	10,000-20,000
32 (0)	4000-7000
68 (20)	2000-3000
104 (40)	900-1300
140 (60)	400-700

2) Unplug IAT connector on Aspire, or VAF connector on Capri. Inspect IAT wire for continuity between IAT wire at connector and IAT terminal at BOB. If resistance is less than 5 ohms, go to next step. Repair wire as necessary.

3) Inspect IAT wire for shorts to ground. If resistance to ground is not less than 10,000 ohms, go to next step. Repair wire as necessary.

4) Inspect SIGRTN wire for continuity between SIGRTN wire at connector and SIGRTN terminal at BOB. If resistance is less than 5 ohms, replace IAT. Repair wire as necessary.

PINPOINT TEST TP
THROTTLE POSITION SENSOR

NOTE: Enter this test only when a Code 12 is displayed during QUICK TESTS procedure or when directed here from another PINPOINT TEST.

94G44210

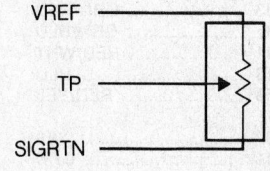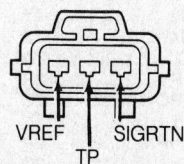

ASPIRE

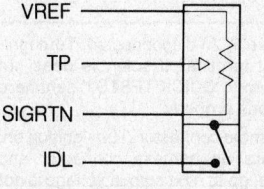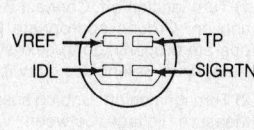

CAPRI

Fig. TP: Identifying TP Circuits

PINPOINT TEST TP (Cont.)

TP CIRCUIT PIN IDENTIFICATION

Circuit	PCM Pin	BOB Pin	Wire Color
Aspire			
TP	2M	47	LT GRN/WHT
SIGRTN	2D	46	YEL/GRN
VREF	2K	26	LT GRN/RED
Capri			
IDL	1E	28	GRN/ORG
SIGRTN	2C	46, 49	BLU/YEL
TP	2G	47	ORG
VREF	2A	26	WHT/BLK

1) Turn ignition off. Install BOB. Turn ignition on. Measure voltage between BOB test pins TP and SIGRTN while opening throttle. Compare voltage to specification in appropriate TP SENSOR OUTPUT VOLTAGE table. If output voltage is not within specification, go to next step.

TP SENSOR OUTPUT VOLTAGE – ASPIRE

Throttle Opening	[1] Voltage
1/4	0.5
1/2	2.75
3/4	3.88
Full Open	5.0

[1] – Voltage may differ by 15 percent.

TP SENSOR OUTPUT VOLTAGE – CAPRI

Throttle Opening	[1] Voltage
1/8	1.00
1/4	1.60
3/8	2.37
1/2	2.74
5/8	3.15
3/4	3.43
7/8	3.60
Full Open	4.02

[1] – Voltage may differ by 15 percent.

2) Turn ignition off. Unplug TP sensor connector at throttle body. Turn ignition on. Measure voltage between VREF wire on TP harness connector and ground. If voltage is 4-5 volts, go to next step. If voltage is not 4-5 as specified, go to PINPOINT TEST VREF.

3) Turn ignition off. Install BOB, leaving PCM disconnected. Inspect TP wire for continuity or shorts to ground. If wire is okay, replace TP sensor. Repair wire as necessary.

PINPOINT TEST BARO
BAROMETRIC PRESSURE SENSOR

NOTE: Enter this procedure only when a Code 14 is displayed during QUICK TESTS procedure or when directed here from another PINPOINT TEST. To prevent unnecessary replacement of components, note following non-EEC items may be at fault: unusually high or low atmospheric pressure, blocked vacuum lines, or basic mechanical engine components.

Aspire – BARO sensor is incorporated into PCM; it cannot be checked or serviced separately. If Code 14 is set and cannot be cleared, replace PCM.

Capri – Turn ignition off. Connect BOB. Remove dust cover from BARO sensor, located on passenger side cowl. Turn ignition on. Connect vacuum pump to BARO sensor. Measure voltage between pins BARO and SIGRTN on BOB while applying vacuum to BARO sensor. See BAROMETRIC PRESSURE SENSOR OUTPUT VOLTAGE table. Replace BARO sensor if voltage is not as specified.

PINPOINT TEST BARO (Cont.)

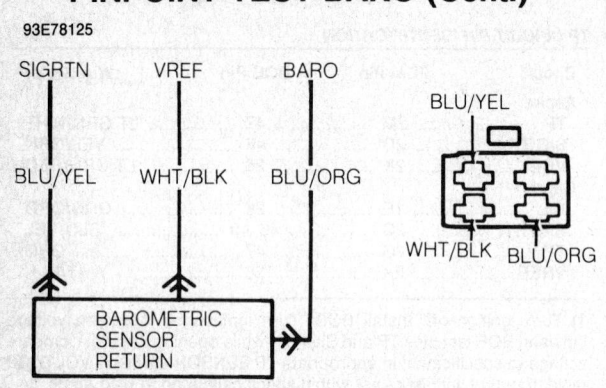

Fig. BARO: Identifying BARO Sensor Circuits

BAROMETRIC PRESSURE SENSOR OUTPUT VOLTAGE

Vacuum (In. Hg)	[1] Voltage
0	3.84
5	3.36
10	2.66
15	1.93
20	1.26
25	.58

[1] – Voltage may differ by 15 percent.

PINPOINT TEST O2S

OXYGEN SENSOR

NOTE: Enter this test only when a Code 15 (lean) or Code 17 (rich) is displayed during QUICK TESTS procedure.

O2S CIRCUIT PIN IDENTIFICATION

Circuit	PCM Pin	BOB Pin	Wire Color
Aspire			
O2S	2N	29	WHT
Capri			
O2S	2D	29	BLK

1) Warm engine to operating temperature, and let idle. Unplug O2S. Measure voltage between O2S connector (sensor side) and ground. With engine at idle, voltage should fluctuate between 0.2-0.8 volt.

2) Increase and decrease engine speed while reading voltmeter. When engine speed is decreasing, voltage should decrease. When engine speed is increasing, voltage should increase. If voltage is within specification, go to next step. If voltage is not within specification, replace O2S.

3) With ignition off, install BOB. Leave PCM disconnected. Unplug O2S connector. Measure continuity between O2S test pin and O2S connector wire. If continuity exists, O2S circuit is okay. Return to QUICK TESTS if sent here from there. If not sent here from QUICK TESTS, replace PCM. If voltage is not as specified, repair VMREF wire to VAF. If continuity does not exist, service PCM sensor wire to PCM.

PINPOINT TEST SCG

SOLENOID CONTROLLED BY GROUND

NOTE: Enter this test only when a Code 25 is displayed during QUICK TESTS procedure or when directed here from another PINPOINT TEST.

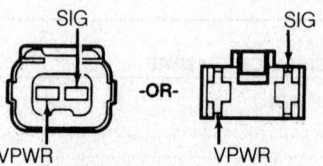

TYPICAL CONNECTORS

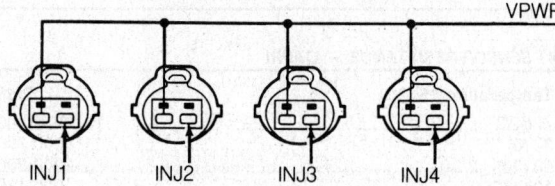

ASPIRE FUEL INJECTORS

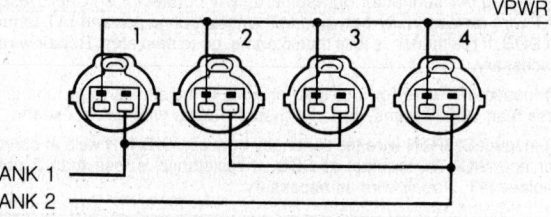

CAPRI FUEL INJECTORS

Fig. SCG: Identifying SCG Circuits & Connectors

SCG CIRCUIT PIN IDENTIFICATION

Circuit	PCM Pin	BOB Pin	Wire Color
Aspire			
CANP	2X	31	RED/BLU
INJ1	2U	58	GRN/YEL
INJ2	2V	59	GRN/BLK
INJ3	2Y	33	GRN/RED
INJ4	2Z	8	GRN/BLU
IAC	2W	41	RED/WHT
EGRV	2R	13	BLU
EGRC	2S	53	RED/YEL
Capri			
CANP	2P	32	YEL
IAC	2Q	41	GRN
FPRC	2K	31	BRN
BANK1	3E	58	YEL
BANK2	3C	59	YEL/BLK

1) Turn ignition off. Connect BOB. Leave PCM disconnected. Turn ignition on. Ground appropriate BOB test terminal. If solenoid does not operate properly, go to next step. Return to QUICK TESTS if sent here from there. Solenoid is okay if it functions properly.

2) Turn ignition off. Unplug suspect solenoid connector. Turn ignition on. Measure voltage between VPWR wire on harness connector and ground. If voltage is higher than 10 volts, go to next step. If voltage is not as specified, go to PINPOINT TEST VPWR.

3) Inspect wire to solenoid for shorts or open circuit. Repair wire as necessary. If wire is okay, replace solenoid.

PINPOINT TEST PGC
POWER & GROUND CONNECTIONS

NOTE: Enter this test only when directed here from QUICK TESTS or another PINPOINT TEST.

PGC CIRCUIT PIN IDENTIFICATION

Circuit	PCM Pin	BOB Pin	Wire Color
Aspire			
GND	2A	39, 40, 44, 60	BLK/ORG
GND	2B	20	BLK/ORG
GND	2C	16	BLK/ORG
KAPWR	1A	1	[1] BLU/RED
MT/AT [2]	1G	36	[3] BLK
Capri			
GND	2R	49	BLK
GND	3A	20	BLK
GND	3G	40	BLK
KAPWR	3J	1	[1] BLU/RED
MT/AT [2]	2RT	43	[3] BLK

[1] – Battery voltage.
[2] – Manual transmission only.
[3] – Ground.

1) Turn ignition off. Install BOB, leaving PCM disconnected. Turn ignition on. Measure voltage at BOB pin in question. Compare voltage to specification in PGC CIRCUIT PIN IDENTIFICATION table. If voltage is to specification, go to next step. If voltage is not to specification, repair wire in question.

2) Measure resistance between ground and BOB pin in question. If any measurement is greater than 5 ohms, repair associated wire to ground. If resistance is not greater than 5 ohms, return to PINPOINT TEST VREF if sent here from there, and temporarily substitute known good PCM. If not sent here from PINPOINT TEST VREF, return to diagnostic routine.

PINPOINT TEST STI
SELF-TEST INPUT

NOTE: Enter this test only when sent here from RETRIEVING CODES under SELF-DIAGNOSTIC SYSTEM.

STI CIRCUIT PIN IDENTIFICATION

Circuit	PCM Pin	BOB Pin	Wire Color
Aspire			
STI	1K	48	BLU
Capri			
STI	1W	48	YEL

Turn ignition off. Install BOB, leaving PCM disconnected. Inspect STI wire for shorts or opens. Repair as necessary. If STI wire is okay, go to PINPOINT TEST STO.

PINPOINT TEST STO
SELF-TEST OUTPUT

NOTE: Enter this test only when codes cannot be retrieved or when directed by PINPOINT TEST STI.

STO CIRCUIT PIN IDENTIFICATION

Circuit	PCM Pin	BOB Pin	Wire Color
Aspire			
STO	1F	17	WHT/BLK
Capri			
STO	1B	17	GRN/BLK

PINPOINT TEST STO (Cont.)

94144329

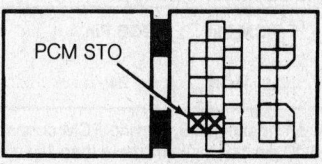

DATA LINK CONNECTOR (ASPIRE)

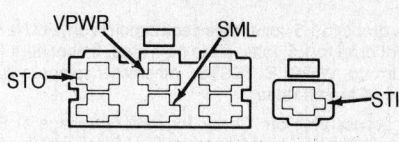

DATA LINK CONNECTOR (CAPRI)

Fig. STO: Identifying STI & STO Circuits & Connector

1) Turn ignition off. Install BOB, leaving PCM disconnected. Measure resistance between STO test pin and STO terminal of DLC. If resistance is less than 5 ohms, go to next step. If resistance is greater than 5 ohms, repair circuit between PCM and self-test connector.

2) Measure resistance between STO test pin and ground. If resistance is less than 10,000 ohms, repair shorted STO wire. Turn ignition on. Measure voltage between STO test pin and ground. If voltage is not zero, go to PINPOINT TEST PGC.

PINPOINT TEST ELU
ELECTRONIC LOAD CONTROL UNIT

NOTE: This test is for Capri models only. Enter this test only when directed here from QUICK TESTS.

93D78124

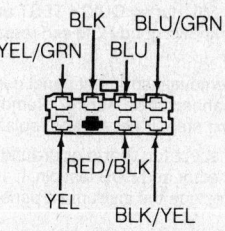

Fig. ELU: Identifying ELU Circuit & Connector

1994 ENGINE PERFORMANCE
Self-Diagnostics (Cont.)

PINPOINT TEST ELU (Cont.)

ELU CIRCUIT PIN IDENTIFICATION

Switch	PCM Pin	BOB Pin	Wire Color
Capri			
ELU	1L	24	BLU

1) Turn ignition off. Install BOB, leaving PCM connected. Turn ignition on. Voltage at BOB pin 11 should be more than 10 volts with all accessories off. Measure voltage at BOB pin 11 while turning each load circuit on and off: defroster, headlamps, blower speed to position 4, and cooling fan.

2) If voltage drops to 1.5 volts while each circuit is on, ELU is okay. If voltage does not drop to 1.5 volts, go to next step. If sent here from QUICK TEST, return to WIGGLE TESTS; otherwise temporarily substitute known good PCM and retest.

3) Turn all accessories off. Check for battery voltage at ELU Yellow/Green wire with ignition on. Inspect the ELU Black wire for continuity to ground. If conditions are as specified, go to next step. If conditions are not as specified, inspect and repair circuits as required.

4) Turn ignition off. Unplug ELU connector. Measure voltage and resistance on appropriate circuits. See ELU SWITCH OPERATION table. If all switch circuits are as specified, temporarily substitute known good PCM and retest. If switch circuits are not as specified, inspect and repair circuits as required.

ELU SWITCH OPERATION

Application	Specification
Defroster Switch [1]	
On	More Than 10 Volts
Off	Less Than 5 Volts
Headlamps [1]	
On	More Than 10 Volts
Off	Less Than 5 Volts
Cooling Fan [1]	
On	Less Than 1.5 Volts
Off	More Than 10 Volts
Blower Fan [2]	
On 2, 3, Or 4 Position	Less Than 5 Ohms
On 1 Or Off Position	More Than 10,000 Ohms

[1] – With ignition on.
[2] – With ignition off.

PINPOINT TEST MIL

MALFUNCTION INDICATOR LIGHT

NOTE: Enter this test only when directed here from QUICK TESTS.

MIL CIRCUIT PIN IDENTIFICATION

Switch	PCM Pin	BOB Pin	Wire Color
Aspire			
MIL	1E	15	BLU
Capri			
MIL	1A	51	YEL/BLK

1) Turn ignition off. Install BOB, leaving PCM disconnected. Turn ignition on. Ground BOB test pin. If MIL light comes on, MIL circuit is okay. If codes do not flash on MIL during QUICK TEST or MIL never comes on, temporarily substitute known good PCM and retest. If MIL light stays off, go to next step.

2) Turn ignition off. Remove instrument panel connector (8-pin connector on Capri; 14-pin connector on Aspire). Remove and inspect bulb. If bulb is okay, go to next step. If necessary, replace bulb.

3) Turn ignition off. Inspect for shorts or grounds in MIL wire between instrument panel connector and BOB test pin. If any defects exist, repair wire. If wire is okay, replace the instrument panel printed circuit board.

PINPOINT TEST ROC

RELAY OUTPUT CHECK

NOTE: Enter this test only when directed here from WIGGLE TEST under QUICK TESTS.

WAC CIRCUIT PIN IDENTIFICATION

Switch	PCM Pin	BOB Pin	Wire Color
Aspire			
ACR	1J	54	BLU/ORG
FPR	1H	55	WHT/YEL
CFAN	2P	45	LT GRN
Capri			
ACR	1F	30	WHT

1) Turn ignition off. Install BOB, leaving PCM connected. Turn ignition on. Ground appropriate test pin at BOB. Listen for clicking from suspect relay. If relay does not click, go to next step. If relay clicks, ROC is okay. If sent here from QUICK TEST, return to WIGGLE TESTS; otherwise temporarily substitute known good PCM and retest.

2) Turn ignition off. Inspect for shorts or grounds in wire between appropriate relay connector and BOB test pin. Repair wire as necessary. If no problems are found, go to next step.

3) Turn ignition off. Disconnect suspect relay. Turn ignition on. Measure voltage at power terminal of relay connector. If voltage is more than 10 volts, replace relay. If voltage is less than 10 volts, repair power wire.

PINPOINT TEST STG

SWITCH TO GROUND

NOTE: Enter this test only when directed here from QUICK TESTS or another PINPOINT TEST.

STG CIRCUIT PIN IDENTIFICATION

Switch	PCM Pin	BOB Pin	Wire Color
Aspire			
PSP	1P	19	BLU/YEL
CCPS	1Q	10	GRN/WHT
HPS [1]	2I	50	BLU
BLMT	1R	22	ORG/BLU
PNP/CPP	1V	43	GRN/BLK
IDL	1N	18	RED
Capri			
PSP	1K	19	GRN/RED
PNP/CPP	1G	8	RED/BLU
IDL	1E	28	GRN/ORG
BPS [2]	2L	12	LT GRN/BLK

[1] – Output voltage should always be 5 volts regardless of switch position.
[2] – Turbo only.

1) Turn ignition off. Install BOB, leaving PCM connected. Measure voltage between BOB test pin for switch in question and ground. Exercise switch. With switch open, voltage should be greater than 10 volts. With switch closed, voltage should be zero. If switch output is not as specified, go to next step. If switch output is as specified, switch is okay.

2) Unplug PCM connectors. Unplug switch in question. Inspect wire between switch and BOB for shorts or open circuits. If wire is okay, go to next step. Repair wire as necessary.

3) Inspect for open circuit in wire between switch in question and ground. Repair wire as necessary. If wire is okay, replace switch.

PINPOINT TEST STP

SWITCH TO POWER

NOTE: Enter this test only when directed here from QUICK TESTS.

1) Turn ignition off. Install BOB, leaving PCM disconnected. Turn ignition on. Cycle switch in question. Measure voltage between switch BOB test pin and ground. If voltage is not as specified, go to next step. If voltage is approximately as specified, switch is okay. If sent here from SWITCH MONITOR TEST in QUICK TESTS, temporarily substitute known good PCM and retest. If sent here from elsewhere in QUICK TESTS, return to QUICK TESTS.

PINPOINT TEST STP (Cont.)

STP CIRCUIT PIN IDENTIFICATION

Switch	PCM Pin	BOB Pin	Wire Color
Aspire			
BOO	1O	¹ 2	GRN
DEF	1L	¹ 42	BLK/RED
HDLP	1U	¹ 28	RED/GRN
VST	1C	² 25	BLK/WHT
Capri			
BOO	1J	¹ 3	WHT/GRN
VST	3B	² 5	BLK/RED

¹ – Battery voltage with switch closed.
² – Approximately 9 volts while cranking engine.

2) Turn ignition off. Unplug switch connector. Turn ignition on. Check for battery voltage at harness connector PWR wire for the switch in question. If battery voltage exists, go to next step. If battery voltage does not exist, repair open PWR wire to switch.

3) Measure resistance between switch terminals. Operate switch. If resistance is less than 5 ohms with switch closed and greater than 10,000 ohms with switch open, switch is okay. If sent here from SWITCH MONITOR TEST in QUICK TESTS, return to QUICK TESTS. If resistance is not as specified, replace switch.

PINPOINT TEST VPWR

VEHICLE POWER

NOTE: Enter this test only when directed here from another PINPOINT TEST. To prevent replacement of good components, note following non-EEC components may be faulty: ignition switch, alternator, battery cables, ground straps, or voltage regulator. This test is intended to diagnose only PCM, wiring harness circuits, and battery voltage.

90A16535

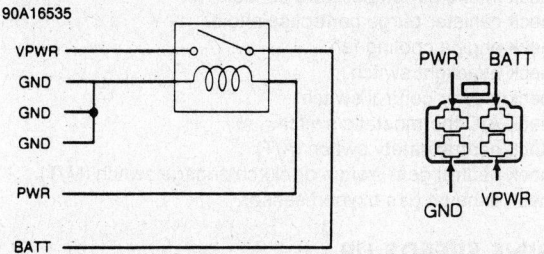

Fig. VPWR: Identifying VPWR Circuit & Connector

VPWR CIRCUIT PIN IDENTIFICATION

Circuit	PCM Pin	BOB Pin	Wire Color
Aspire			
GND	2A	39, 40, 44, 60	BLK/ORG
GND	2B	20	BLK/ORG
GND	2C	16	BLK/LT GRN
VPWR	1B	37, 57	YEL/WHT
Capri			
GND	2R	49	BLK
GND	3A	20	BLK
GND	3G	40	BLK
VPWR	3I	37	YEL/GRN

1) Turn ignition off. Install BOB, leaving PCM disconnected. Turn ignition on. Measure voltage between VPWR test pin and battery ground. If voltage is greater than 10 volts, go to next step. If voltage is not greater than 10 volts, go to step **3)**.

2) Turn ignition off. Measure resistance of each wire between BOB GND test pins and ground. Repair any wire with resistance not less than 5 ohms. If resistance is less than 5 ohms for each wire, VPWR circuit is okay. Return to the PINPOINT TEST that sent you here.

3) Turn ignition off. Remove main relay. On Aspire, main relay is located behind instrument panel, on left side. On Capri, relay is located on left side of engine compartment. Measure resistance between BOB test pin VPWR and main relay harness connector. If resistance is less than 5 ohms, go to next step. Repair VPWR wire if resistance is not less than 5 ohms.

PINPOINT TEST VPWR (Cont.)

4) Inspect GND wire for continuity between main relay harness connector and ground. If wire is okay, go to next step. Repair wire as necessary.

5) Measure voltage between main relay harness connector BATT wire and ground. If voltage is greater than 10 volts, go to next step. If voltage is not greater than 10 volts, repair BATT wire from battery to harness connector.

6) Measure voltage between harness connector PWR wire and ground. If voltage is not greater than 10 volts, repair PWR wire from ignition switch to harness connector. If voltage is greater than 10 volts, replace main relay.

PINPOINT TEST VREF

REFERENCE VOLTAGE & SIGNAL RETURN

NOTE: Enter this test only when directed from another PINPOINT TEST.

94G44285

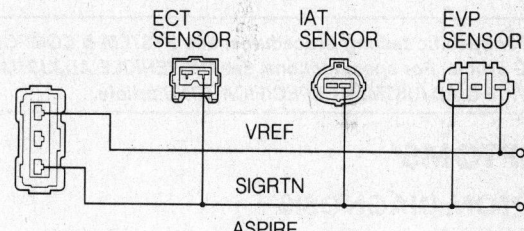

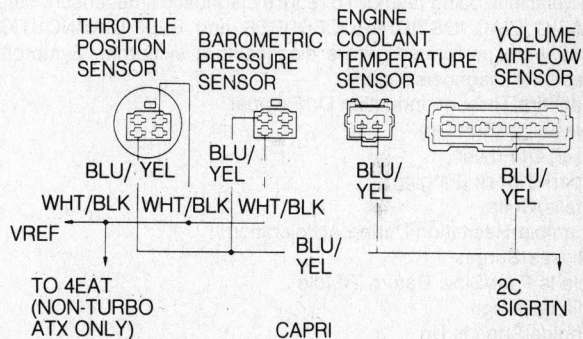

Fig. VREF: Identifying VREF Circuit & Connector

VREF CIRCUIT PIN IDENTIFICATION

Circuit	PCM Pin	BOB Pin	Wire Color
Aspire			
SIGRTN	2A	26, 49	YEL/GRN
VREF	2K	26	LT GRN/RED
Capri			
SIGRTN	2C	46	BLU/YEL
VREF	2A	26	WHT/BLK

1) Turn ignition off. Install BOB, leaving PCM connected. Turn ignition on. Measure voltage between BOB test pins VREF and SIGRTN. If voltage is 4.5-5.5 volts, go to next step. If voltage is not as specified, go to PINPOINT TEST VPWR. If VPWR is okay, temporarily substitute known good PCM and retest.

2) Unplug BARO, EVP, TP, and VAF connectors. Turn ignition on. Measure voltage at VREF terminal at each connector. If voltage is zero volts, go to next step. If voltage is 4.5-5.5 volts, VREF circuit is okay; return to QUICK TESTS. If battery voltage exists, repair short to voltage.

3) Turn ignition off. Disconnect PCM. Measure resistance between VREF terminal at each sensor harness connector and appropriate BOB test pin. If resistance of each wire is less than 5 ohms, go to next step. Repair any wire as necessary.

4) On Capri with A/T, unplug TCM, located behind instrument panel, above glove box. Measure resistance between BOB test pin VREF and ground. If resistance is not greater than 10,000 ohm, repair VREF wire.

1994 ENGINE PERFORMANCE
Trouble Shooting – No Codes

Aspire, Capri

INTRODUCTION

Before diagnosing symptoms or intermittent faults, perform steps in BASIC DIAGNOSTIC PROCEDURES and SELF-DIAGNOSTICS articles. Use this article to diagnose driveability problems existing when a hard fault code is not present.

NOTE: Some driveability problems may have been corrected by manufacturer with a revised computer calibration chip or computer control unit. Check with manufacturer for latest chip or computer application.

Symptom checks can direct the technician to malfunctioning component(s) for further diagnosis. A symptom should lead to a specific component, system test, or adjustment.

Use intermittent test procedures to locate driveability problems which do not occur when the vehicle is being tested. These test procedures should also be used if a soft (intermittent) trouble code was present but no problem was found during self-diagnostic testing.

NOTE: For specific testing procedures, see SYSTEM & COMPONENT TESTING article. For specifications, see ON-VEHICLE ADJUSTMENTS or SERVICE & ADJUSTMENT SPECIFICATIONS article.

SYMPTOMS

SYMPTOM DIAGNOSIS

Symptom checks cannot be used properly unless problem occurs while vehicle is being tested. To reduce diagnostic time, ensure steps in BASIC DIAGNOSTIC PROCEDURES and SELF-DIAGNOSTICS articles were performed before diagnosing a symptom. Symptoms available for diagnosis include:

- Backfire Through Induction Or Exhaust
- Dieseling (Run-On)
- Lack Of Power
- Spark Knock (Pinging)
- Stalls/Quits
- Stumble/Hesitation During Acceleration
- Misses/Surges
- Idle Is Fast/Slow Return To Idle
- Idle Is Rough
- Engine Speeds Up
- Cranks Normally/No Start
- Cranks Normally/Slow To Start
- Poor Fuel Economy
- Exhaust Smoke/Odor
- Fuel Odor/Leaks
- Fails Emission Test

BACKFIRE THROUGH INDUCTION OR EXHAUST

- Check volume airflow meter or mass airflow meter.
- Check idle speed control solenoid.

DIESELING (RUN-ON)

- Check idle speed control solenoid.

LACK OF POWER

- Check volume airflow meter or mass airflow meter.
- Check throttle position switch.
- Check exhaust gas oxygen sensor.
- Check A/C switch.

SPARK KNOCK (PINGING)

- Verify ignition timing is correct.
- Check volume airflow meter or mass airflow meter.

STALLS/QUITS

- Check volume airflow meter or mass airflow meter.
- Check idle speed control solenoid.
- Check pressure regulator control solenoid.
- Check exhaust gas oxygen sensor.
- Check engine coolant temperature sensor.

STUMBLE/HESITATION DURING ACCELERATION

- Check throttle position switch.
- Check volume airflow meter or mass airflow meter.
- Check canister purge control solenoid.
- Check heated exhaust gas oxygen sensor.
- Check A/C Wide Open Throttle (WAC) relay (Festiva).
- Check A/C thermostatic switch.

MISSES/SURGES

- Check exhaust gas oxygen sensor.
- Check throttle position switch.
- Check volume airflow meter or mass airflow meter.
- Check engine coolant temperature sensor.

IDLE IS FAST/SLOW RETURN TO IDLE

- Check idle speed control solenoid.
- Check by-pass air control valve.
- Check engine coolant temperature sensor.

IDLE IS ROUGH

- Check idle speed control solenoid.
- Check by-pass air control valve.
- Check throttle position switch.
- Check volume airflow meter or mass airflow meter.
- Check intake air temperature sensor.
- Check canister purge control solenoid.
- Check engine cooling fan.
- Check headlight switch.
- Check blower control switch.
- Check A/C thermostatic switch.
- Check neutral safety switch (A/T).
- Check neutral gear switch or clutch engage switch (M/T).
- Check exhaust gas oxygen sensor.

ENGINE SPEEDS UP

- Check idle speed control solenoid.
- Check exhaust gas oxygen sensor.
- Check by-pass air control valve.

CRANKS NORMALLY/NO START

- Enssure secondary ignition spark is present.
- Ensure fuel pressure is within specification.
- Check volume airflow meter or mass airflow meter.
- Check engine coolant temperature sensor.

CRANKS NORMALLY/SLOW TO START

- Check ignition module.
- Check engine coolant temperature sensor.
- Check volume airflow meter or mass airflow meter.
- Check evaporative emission control components.

POOR FUEL ECONOMY

- Ensure intake air is not restricted.
- Ensure fuel pressure is within specification.
- Check ignition module.
- Check canister purge control solenoid.
- Check intake air temperature sensor.
- Check volume airflow meter or mass airflow meter.
- Check exhaust gas oxygen sensor.

EXHAUST SMOKE/ODOR

- Check intake air temperature sensor.
- Check volume airflow meter or mass airflow meter.
- Check exhaust gas oxygen sensor.

FUEL ODOR/LEAKS

- Check evaporative emission control components.
- Check rollover vent valve.
- Check by-pass air control valve.

FAILS EMISSION TEST

- Check canister purge control solenoid.
- Check pressure regulator control solenoid.
- Check exhaust gas oxygen sensor.
- Check by-pass air control valve.

INTERMITTENTS

INTERMITTENT PROBLEM DIAGNOSIS

Intermittent fault testing requires duplicating circuit or component failure to identify problem. These procedures may lead to computer setting a fault code (on some systems) which may help in diagnosis.

If problem vehicle does not produce fault codes, monitor voltage or resistance values with a DVOM while attempting to reproduce conditions causing intermittent fault. A status change on DVOM indicates a fault has been located.

Use a DVOM to pinpoint faults. When monitoring voltage, ensure ignition switch is in ON position or engine is running. Ensure ignition switch is in OFF position or negative battery cable is disconnected when monitoring circuit resistance. Status changes on DVOM during test procedures indicate area of fault.

TEST PROCEDURES

Intermittent Simulation – To reproduce conditions creating an intermittent fault, use following methods:
- Lightly vibrate component.
- Heat component.
- Wiggle or bend wiring harness.
- Spray component with water mist.
- Remove/apply vacuum source.

Monitor circuit/component voltage or resistance while simulating intermittent. If engine is running, monitor for self-diagnostic codes. Use test results to identify a faulty component or circuit.

1994 ENGINE PERFORMANCE
System & Component Testing

Aspire, Capri

INTRODUCTION

Before testing separate components or systems, perform procedures in BASIC DIAGNOSTIC PROCEDURES article. Since many computer-controlled and monitored components set a trouble code if they malfunction, also perform procedures in SELF-DIAGNOSTICS article.

NOTE: Testing individual components does not isolate shorts or opens. Perform all voltage tests with a Digital Volt-Ohmmeter (DVOM) with minimum 10-megohm input impedance, unless stated otherwise in test procedure. Use ohmmeter and Breakout Box (BOB – 007-00033) to isolate wiring harness shorts or opens.

AIR INDUCTION SYSTEMS

TURBOCHARGERS

Wastegate Actuator – Disconnect air hose from wastegate actuator. Apply 7.0-8.6 psi (0.5-0.6 kg/cm²) regulated air pressure to wastegate inlet fitting. Replace turbocharger if wastegate actuator rod does not move.

COMPUTERIZED ENGINE CONTROLS

POWERTRAIN CONTROL MODULE (PCM)

Ground Circuits – Turn ignition off. Connect BOB, leaving PCM disconnected. Measure resistance between each specified BOB pin and ground. See PCM GROUND CIRCUIT RESISTANCE table. Repair indicated PCM ground circuit if resistance is greater than 5 ohms.

PCM GROUND CIRCUIT RESISTANCE

PCM Pin	BOB Pin	Wire Color
Aspire		
1G [1]	36	Black
2A	39, 40, 44, 60	Black/Orange
2B	20	Black/Orange
2C	16	Black/Orange
Capri		
1V [1]	44	Black
2R	49	Black
3A	20	Black
3G	40	Black

[1] – Manual transmission only.

Power Circuits – Turn ignition off. Connect BOB, leaving PCM disconnected. Turn ignition on. Repair indicated PCM power circuit if battery voltage does not appear on specified BOB pin. See PCM POWER CIRCUIT RESISTANCE table.

PCM POWER CIRCUIT RESISTANCE

PCM Pin	BOB Pin	Wire Color
Aspire		
1A	1	Blue/Red
1B	37, 57	Yellow/White
Capri		
3I	37	Yellow/Green
3J	1	Black/Red

ENGINE SENSORS & SWITCHES

Inspect each component and all related wiring for any looseness or damage. Make all resistance and voltage measurements using Breakout Box (BOB) unless specified otherwise.

Barometric Pressure (BARO) Sensor (Aspire) – This unit is part of PCM, and cannot be checked or serviced. If a Code 14 is set and cannot be cleared, replace PCM.

Barometric Pressure (BARO) Sensor (Capri) – Connect BOB. Remove dust cover from BARO sensor, located on passenger side cowl. Turn ignition on. Connect vacuum pump to BARO sensor. Measure voltage between pins BP and SIGRTN on BOB while applying vacuum to BARO sensor. See BAROMETRIC PRESSURE SENSOR OUTPUT VOLTAGE table. Replace BARO sensor if voltage is not as specified.

BAROMETRIC PRESSURE SENSOR OUTPUT VOLTAGE

Vacuum – In. Hg	[1] Volts
0	3.84
5	3.36
10	2.66
15	1.93
20	1.26
25	0.58

[1] – Voltage may differ by plus or minus 15 percent.

Brake On-Off (BOO) Switch – Unplug connector from BOO switch at brake pedal. Connect ohmmeter to switch terminals. With pedal released, ohmmeter should indicate no continuity. Ohmmeter should indicate continuity with pedal pressed.

Clutch Engage Switch (CES) – Unplug connector from CES switch at clutch pedal. Connect ohmmeter to switch terminals. With pedal released, ohmmeter should indicate continuity. Ohmmeter should indicate no continuity with pedal pressed.

Crankshaft Position (CKP) Sensor (Aspire) – 1) Turn ignition off. Install BOB. Reconnect PCM. Measure voltage at BOB test pin CKP while bumping starter. If voltage does not alternate between about zero and 5 volts, go to next step. If voltage does not alternate as specified, go to next step. If voltage alternates as specified, CKP circuit is okay.

2) Turn ignition off. Unplug 6-pin distributor connector. Turn ignition on. Measure voltage on VPWR (Yellow/Black) wire at harness connector. If voltage is greater than 10 volts, go to next step. If voltage is not greater than 10 volts, repair VPWR wire to distributor.

3) Turn ignition off. Measure resistance between GND (Black) wire at harness connector and ground. If resistance is less than 5 ohms, go to next step. If resistance is not less than 5 ohms, repair Black wire to ground.

4) Turn ignition off. Install BOB, leaving PCM disconnected. Measure resistance between BOB test pin CKP and CKP wire (Green/Black) at harness connector. If resistance is less than 5 ohms, go to next step. If resistance is not less than 5 ohms, repair Green/Black wire.

5) Turn ignition off. Install BOB, leaving PCM disconnected. Measure resistance between BOB test pin CKP and ground. Measure resistance between CKP (Green/Black) wire and each other wire at harness connector. If all measurements are greater than 10,000 ohms, replace distributor. If any measurement is not greater than 10,000 ohms, repair shorted CKP wire.

Cylinder Identification (CID) Sensor (Capri) – Turn ignition off. Connect BOB, leaving ECA connected. Turn ignition on, but DO NOT start engine. Measure voltage at BOB test pin No. 34 (Yellow wire). Voltage should be less than one volt or more than 10 volts. Start engine and run at idle. Voltage should be 3-5 volts. Replace CID sensor if voltage is not as specified.

Engine Coolant Temperature (ECT) Sensor – 1) Remove ECT sensor. ECT sensor is threaded into top right front of engine on Aspire, and on underside of intake manifold on Capri. Place ECT sensor and thermometer into container of coolant.

2) Connect ohmmeter to coolant temperature sensor terminals. Cool and heat container. Measure resistance at specified temperatures. See ENGINE COOLANT TEMPERATURE SENSOR RESISTANCE table. Replace ECT sensor if resistance is not within specification.

ENGINE COOLANT TEMPERATURE SENSOR RESISTANCE

Temperature – °F (°C)	Ohms
-4 (-20)	14,600-17,800
68 (20)	2200-2700
176 (80)	250-350

Oxygen (O₂) Sensor – With engine at normal operating temperature, unplug connector from O₂ sensor. Measure voltage between O₂ sensor terminal and ground. Voltage should increase with increasing engine speed, and decrease with decreasing engine speed. Voltage at idle should fluctuate within a range of 0.2-0.8 volt.

NOTE: A steady voltage of more than 0.55 volt indicates a continuously rich condition. A steady voltage of less than 0.55 volt indicates a continuously lean condition.

Idle Switch (Capri) – Unplug connector from throttle position sensor on throttle body. Connect ohmmeter to switch terminals IDL and ground (Green/Orange and Blue/Yellow wires on mating connector). Resistance must be less than 5 ohms with throttle in idle position, and more than 10,000 ohms at WOT position.

Knock Sensor (Capri Turbo) – Disconnect vacuum hose at distributor. Connect timing light. Start engine. Determine and record ignition timing. Tap intake plenum with a plastic mallet. Knock sensor is okay if timing retards. If timing does not retard, check associated circuitry and components. See TIMING CONTROL SYSTEMS under IGNITION SYSTEM.

Park/Neutral Position (PNP) Switch (M/T) – **1)** Unplug PNP switch connector, located at transmission. Set shift lever to Neutral position. Resistance across switch should be infinite.

2) Set shift lever to any other gear. Resistance across switch terminals should be zero ohms. If necessary, replace switch.

Power Steering Pressure Switch – **1)** Start and idle engine. Remove connector from switch, located at steering gear. Connect ohmmeter to switch terminals. Turn steering wheel from side to side while observing ohmmeter.

2) Replace power steering switch if continuity does not exist with front wheels turned, or if continuity exists with wheels straight ahead.

Throttle Position (TP) Sensor (Aspire) – **1)** Turn ignition off. Install BOB. Turn ignition on. Measure voltage between BOB test pins TP and SIGRTN while opening throttle. Compare voltage to specification in appropriate TP SENSOR OUTPUT VOLTAGE table. Replace TP sensor if output voltage is not within specification.

TP SENSOR OUTPUT VOLTAGE (ASPIRE)

Throttle Opening	[1] Voltage
1/4	0.5
1/2	2.75
3/4	3.88
Full Open	5.0

[1] – Voltage may differ by 15 percent.

Throttle Position (TP) Sensor (Capri) – Unplug connector from TP sensor, located on VAF meter. Connect ohmmeter to sensor terminals TP and SIGRTN (Orange and Blue/Yellow wires on mating connector). Measure resistance at each throttle opening specified in THROTTLE POSITION (TP) SENSOR RESISTANCE (CAPRI) table. Replace sensor if resistance is not within specification.

THROTTLE POSITION (TP) SENSOR RESISTANCE (CAPRI)

Throttle Opening	[1] Ohms
1/8	989
1/4	1104
3/8	1278
1/2	1462
5/8	1480
3/4	1459
7/8	1144
Fully Open	1072

[1] – Resistance may differ by plus or minus 15 percent.

Volume Airflow Meter (Capri) – **1)** Inspect all wiring, harnesses, connectors, and components for evidence of damage, overheating, shorting, or looseness. If any defect exists, repair as necessary.

2) Inspect Volume Airflow Meter (VAF) for damage. Ensure measuring plate moves smoothly. Turn ignition off. Install BOB. Turn ignition on. Measure voltage between BOB test pins VAF and SIGRTN. Voltage must be as specified in VOLUME AIRFLOW METER VOLTAGE table.

VOLUME AIRFLOW METER VOLTAGE

Opening	[1] Volts
Fully Closed	0.5-1.5
1/8	0.59
1/4	1.19
3/8	1.78
1/2	2.38
5/8	2.97
3/4	3.56
7/8	4.16
Fully Open	4.5-5.0

[1] – Voltage may differ by plus or minus 15 percent.

INTAKE AIR TEMPERATURE (IAT)

1) Turn ignition off. Install BOB, leaving PCM disconnected. Measure ambient temperature at IAT, located in air cleaner on Aspire, or in VAF on Capri. Measure resistance between IAT and SIGRTN test pins. Compare resistance to specifications in appropriate IAT SENSOR RESISTANCE table. If resistance is not within specification, replace IAT sensor. If resistance is within specification, VAT circuit is okay.

IAT SENSOR RESISTANCE (ASPIRE)

Temperature °F (°C)	Ohms
32 (0)	72,100-79,400
55 (13)	54,300-58,600
77 (25)	29,700-36,300
110 (43)	17,900-19,300
185 (85)	3300-3700

IAT SENSOR RESISTANCE (CAPRI)

Temperature °F (°C)	Ohms
-4 (-20)	10,000-20,000
32 (0)	4000-7000
68 (20)	2000-3000
104 (40)	900-1300
140 (60)	400-700

MODULES, RELAYS & SOLENOIDS

MODULES

Ignition Module – See IGNITION SYSTEM.

RELAYS

A/C Clutch Relay – See MISCELLANEOUS CONTROLS.
Cooling Fan Relay – See MISCELLANEOUS CONTROLS.

SOLENOIDS

Canister Purge Control Solenoid – See FUEL EVAPORATION.
Fuel Pressure Regulator Control Solenoid – See FUEL DELIVERY under FUEL SYSTEM.
Idle Speed Control (ISC) Solenoid – This solenoid is part of the Idle Speed Control By-Pass Air (ISC-BPA) valve. See IDLE CONTROL SYSTEM.

FUEL SYSTEM

FUEL DELIVERY

Fuel Pressure Regulator – **1)** Measure fuel pressure. See FUEL PRESSURE in BASIC DIAGNOSTIC PROCEDURES article. Stop engine. With fuel pressure tester still installed, measure fuel pressure after 5 minutes. If fuel pressure is greater than 21 psi (1.5 kg/cm²) after 5 minutes, go to next step. If fuel pressure does not remain higher than 21 psi (1.5 kg/cm²), fuel pressure regulator, fuel pump, or fuel injectors may be defective.

2) Connect vacuum tester to vacuum fitting on fuel pressure regulator and apply 20 in. Hg. Replace fuel pressure regulator if vacuum does not hold. Reinstall fuel pressure regulator.

3) Start engine. Measure fuel pressure. If fuel pressure is higher than specification, inspect for engine vacuum leaks, damage to fuel pressure regulator housing, or a restricted fuel return line. Replace fuel pressure regulator if no problems exist.

Fuel Pressure Regulator Control (FPRC) Solenoid (Capri) – 1) Locate FPRC solenoid on cowl panel, next to canister purge solenoid. Unplug FPRC connector. Remove both vacuum lines. Plug one vacuum port. Apply vacuum to remaining port. Replace FPRC solenoid if it does not hold vacuum.

2) Connect 12-volt power to FPRC terminals. If vacuum drops to zero, FPRC solenoid is okay. Replace FPRC solenoid if vacuum does not drop to zero.

FUEL CONTROL

Fuel Injectors – Using stethoscope, listen for clicking at each injector with engine running. If no clicking sound occurs, measure injector resistance. Replace injector if resistance is not 12-16 ohms. If injector resistance is okay, inspect related circuits for 12 volt source and connection to PCM. Repair or replace circuits as necessary.

IDLE CONTROL SYSTEM

Idle Speed Control By-Pass Air (ISC-BPA) Valve - 1) Remove ISC-BPA valve from engine. Connect a hose from a hot water tap to coolant inlet nipple on ISC-BPA valve. Blow through valve air port. Note resistance to airflow.

2) Supply hot water to ISC-BPA valve. Blow through valve again. If resistance to airflow does not increase when valve is hot, replace ISC-BPA valve.

3) Apply 12 volts to solenoid terminals. If solenoid does not click, replace ISC-BPA valve. Measure resistance across IAC terminals. If resistance is not 6-14 ohms, replace ISC-BPA valve.

IGNITION SYSTEM

NOTE: For basic ignition checks, see BASIC DIAGNOSTIC PROCEDURES article.

TIMING CONTROL SYSTEMS

Advance Components (Capri) – Ignition advance is controlled by a centrifugal advance mechanism within the distributor, and by a vacuum advance mechanism. See IGNITION TIMING in ON-VEHICLE ADJUSTMENTS article. If centrifugal advance is not within specification, service distributor. See CENTRIFUGAL ADVANCE SPECIFICATIONS table. Replace vacuum advance unit if vacuum advance is not within specification. See IGNITION TIMING table. Also see IGNITION TIMING in ON-VEHICLE ADJUSTMENTS article.

CENTRIFUGAL ADVANCE SPECIFICATIONS

Application	Degrees BTDC
Non-Turbo	
1500 RPM	0
3500 RPM	21
5500 RPM	25
Turbo	
1200 RPM	0
3500 RPM	12
5500 RPM	18

Advance Components (Aspire) – Ignition timing advance is controlled by the PCM.

Retard Components (Capri Turbo) – Positive pressure to the vacuum advance cylinder on the distributor retards ignition timing. The Powertrain Control Module (PCM) also retards ignition timing when it receives a signal from Knock Sensor (KS) and related circuitry.

1) Disconnect and plug hoses at distributor. Connect timing light. Start engine. Determine and record ignition timing. Tap intake plenum with plastic mallet while monitoring ignition timing. If timing retards, Knock Control (KC) circuitry is okay. If timing does not retard, go to next step.

2) Unplug KC sensor service connector, located near PCM. Tap intake plenum with plastic mallet while observing ignition timing. If timing retards, go to step **4)**. If timing retards, go to next step.

3) Reconnect KC service connector. Tap intake plenum with plastic mallet while monitoring ignition timing. If ignition timing retards, replace knock controller. If ignition timing does not retard, go to next step.

4) Unplug KC service connector. Temporarily install known good knock sensor. Tap intake plenum with plastic mallet while monitoring ignition timing. If ignition timing retards, replace knock sensor. If ignition timing does not retard, go to next step.

5) Turn ignition off. Connect BOB. Ensure vehicle power (VPWR) and ground wires to knock sensor are okay. Check all knock sensor wiring for shorts or opens. If wiring is okay, replace knock sensor.

EMISSION SYSTEMS & SUB-SYSTEMS

FUEL EVAPORATION

Canister Purge Control Solenoid – 1) Disconnect vacuum hoses from solenoid. Solenoid is located near center of firewall. *See Fig. 1.* Blow through port "A". No air should flow from port "B".

2) Unplug 2-wire connector from solenoid. Connect 12 volts to one terminal. Ground the other terminal of solenoid. Blow through port "A". Air should flow through port "B". Replace canister purge control solenoid if performance is not as specified.

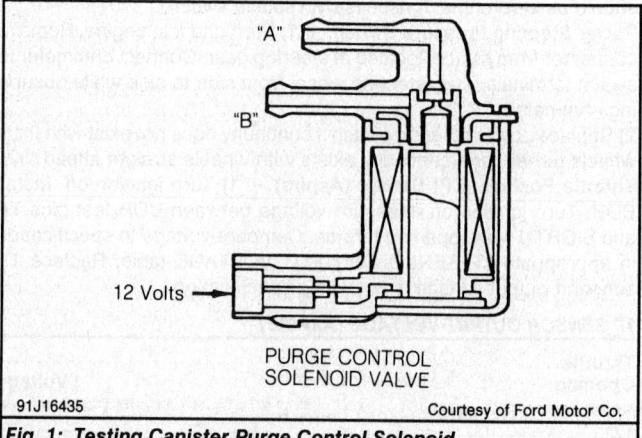

91J16435   Courtesy of Ford Motor Co.

Fig. 1: Testing Canister Purge Control Solenoid

Carbon Canister – 1) Start and warm engine to operating temperature. Stop engine. Remove carbon canister. Carbon canister is located at right rear corner of engine compartment.

2) Inspect carbon canister for presence of liquid fuel. Blow into air vent, and check for air exiting from fuel vapor inlet. Replace carbon canister if it contains fuel, or if air does not pass freely through it.

POSITIVE CRANKCASE VENTILATION (PCV)

Idle engine until it is warm. Remove fresh air hose at inlet end. Plug nipple immediately to prevent stalling. Verify presence of vacuum at inlet end of hose. If there is no vacuum, replace PCV valve, or service hoses or loose oil dipstick.

THROTTLE CONTROLS

Dashpot – Disconnect PCV valve. Remove resonance chamber. Push dashpot rod inward, then release it. Replace dashpot if rod does not go inward slowly and return quickly.

MISCELLANEOUS CONTROLS

NOTE: Although some of the controlled devices listed here are not technically engine performance components, they can affect driveability if they malfunction.

A/C CLUTCH

A/C Clutch Relay – See appropriate circuit test in SELF-DIAGNOSTICS article.

Aspire, Capri

INTRODUCTION

NOTE: Unless stated otherwise in testing procedures, perform all voltage tests with a Digital Volt-Ohmmeter (DVOM) with minimum 10-megohm input impedance. Voltage readings may differ slightly because of battery condition or charging rate.

Pin voltage charts are supplied to reduce diagnostic time. Checking pin voltages at the Powertrain Control Module (PCM) determines whether it is receiving and transmitting proper voltage signals. Charts may also help determine if PCM wiring harness is shorted or open.

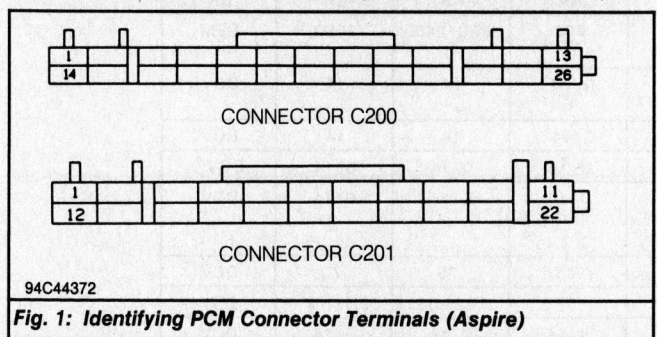

Fig. 1: Identifying PCM Connector Terminals (Aspire)

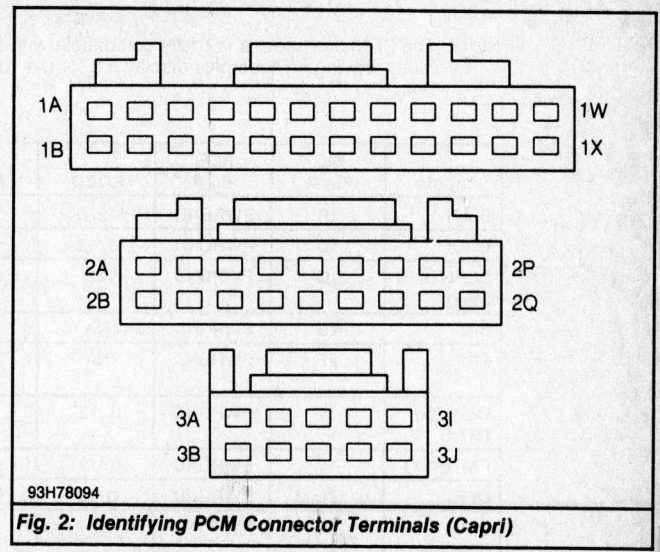

Fig. 2: Identifying PCM Connector Terminals (Capri)

NOTE: For additional pin voltage information, see appropriate trouble code information in SELF-DIAGNOSTICS article.

1994 ENGINE PERFORMANCE
Pin Voltage Charts (Cont.)

NOTE: The PCM on Aspire is not fully compatible with the EEC-IV monitor. Some inputs and outputs register faulty readings. These pins display NA for pin voltages. These pins may be monitored with a breakout box.

Inputs	SIG Pin #	REF. Pin #	KOEO	Units	Hot Idle	30 MPH	55 MPH	Units
BLMT [1]	1R	PWRGND	12/0	DCV	14/0	14/0	14/0	DCV
BOO	1O	PWRGND	0/12	DCV	0/14	0	0	DCV
CCPS (A/C Only) [2]	1Q	PWRGND	12	DCV	14/0	14/0	14/0	DCV
CID	2G	PWRGND	NA	NA	NA	NA	NA	NA
CKP	2E	PWRGND	NA	DCV	700	1800/2400 [3]	3000	RPM
CPP/PNP (MTX)	1V	PWRGND	0/12 [4]	RPM	0/14 [4]	14	14	DCV
PNP (ATX)	1V	PWRGND	0/12 [5]	DCV	0/14 [5]	14	14	DCV
DEF	1L	PWRGND	0/12	DCV [6]	0/14	0/14	0/14	DCV [6]
DRL (Canada Only)	1I	PWRGND	0/12	DCV	0/14	0/14	0/14	DCV
ECT	2H	SIGRTN	2.7-4.4 [7]	DCV	.75	.75	.70	DCV
EVP	2J	PWRGND	.66	DCV	.67	1.32/.63 [3]	2.1/.72 [3]	DCV
HDLR	1U	PWRGND	0/12	DCV	0/14	0/14	0/14	DCV
HPS (A/C Only) [2]	2I	PWRGND	12	DCV	14/0	14/0	14/0	DCV
IAT	2L	SIGRTN	2.5 [7]	DCV	2.83	3.21	3.50	DCV
IDL	1N	PWRGND	0/12 [8]	DCV	0	14	14	DCV
MAF	2O	PWRGND	1-1.5	DCV	2.0	2.6	2.8	DCV
O2S	2N	PWRGND	0	DCV	.2-.8	.2-.65	.2-.6	DCV
PSP (ATX)	1P	PWRGND	12	DCV	14	14	14	DCV
STI	1K	PWRGND	12	DCV	14	14	14	DCV
TP	2M	PWRGND	.5-4.2 [9]	DCV	.52	.72	1.12/.55 [3]	DCV
VSS	1M	PWRGND	NA [10]	DCV	NA [10]	NA [10]	NA [10]	DCV
VST	1C	PWRGND	0/10 [11]	DCV	0	0	0	DCV

Reference values shown may differ by plus or minus 20% depending on operating conditions and other factors.

[1] – Zero volts with blower switch off and position 1; battery voltage at positions 2 and 3.
[2] – Zero volts with A/C off; battery voltage at positions 2 and 3.
[3] – Automatic transmission/manual transmission.
[4] – Zero volts in Neutral or with clutch pressed; battery voltage otherwise.
[5] – 0.5 volt in Park or Neutral; battery voltage otherwise.
[6] – Use manual DC volts setting.
[7] – At 68°F (20°C).
[8] – 0.5 volt with accelerator pedal released; 12 volts with pedal at WOT.
[9] – 0.5 volt with accelerator pedal released; 12 volts with pedal at WOT.
[10] – Alternates between 0 and 5 volts as vehicle is rolled.
[11] – 10 volts with engine cranking; zero volts with switch in RUN position.

94B44413

Courtesy of Ford Motor Co.

Fig. 3: Checking PCM Pin Voltages – 1 Of 2 (Aspire)

NOTE: The PCM on Aspire is not fully compatible with the EEC-IV monitor. Some inputs and outputs register faulty readings. These pins display NA for pin voltages. These pins may be monitored with a breakout box.

Outputs	SIG Pin #	REF. Pin #	KOEO	Units	Hot Idle	30 MPH	55 MPH	Units
ACR (A/C Only) [1]	1J	PWRGND	12	DCV	14/0	14/0	14/0	DCV
CANP	2X	PWRGND	12	DCV	14	9.5	4.4	DCV
CFAN (A/C Only)	2P	PWRGND	12	DCV	14	14	14	DCV
CFR	1S	PWRGND	12	DCV	14	14	14	DCV
EGRC	2S	PWRGND	12	DCV	14	14	14	DCV
EGRV	2R	PWRGND	12	DCV [2]	14	14	14	DCV [2]
FPR	1H	PWRGND	12	DCV	0	0	0	DCV
IAC	2W	PWRGND	9	DCV	10.25	6.80	6.65	DCV
ICM	2F	PWRGND	0	DCV	.20	.31	.49	DCV
INJ1	2U	PWRGND	NA	mSEC	4.5	6.3/4.8 [3]	8.2/7.0 [3]	mSEC
INJ2	2V	PWRGND	NA	mSEC	4.5	6.3/4.8 [3]	8.2/7.0 [3]	mSEC
INJ3	2Y	PWRGND	NA	NA	NA	NA	NA	NA
INJ4	2Z	PWRGND	NA	NA	NA	NA	NA	NA
MIL	1E	PWRGND	0/12 [4]	DCV	14	14	14	DCV
SIL (MTX)	1T	PWRGND	12	DCV	14	0/14 [5]	0/14 [5]	DCV
SML	1D	PWRGND	12	DCV	0/14 [6]	0/14 [6]	0/14 [6]	DCV
STO	1F	PWRGND	12	DCV	14	14	14	DCV
VREF	2K	PWRGND	5	DCV	5	5	5	DCV

Reference values shown may differ by plus or minus 20% depending on operating conditions and other factors.

[1] – Zero volts with A/C off; battery voltage at positions 2 and 3.
[2] – Use manual DC volts setting.
[3] – Automatic transmission/manual transmission.
[4] – Zero volts with MIL on; battery voltage with MIL off.
[5] – Zero volts with shift indicator light on; battery voltage with light off.
[6] – Zero volts with light on; battery voltage with light off.

94J44411

Courtesy of Ford Motor Co.

Fig. 4: Checking PCM Pin Voltages – 2 Of 2 (Aspire)

1994 ENGINE PERFORMANCE
Pin Voltage Charts (Cont.)

Inputs	SIG Pin #	REF. Pin #	KOEO	Units	Hot Idle	30 MPH	55 MPH	Units
TP	2G	SIGRTN	0.5	DCV	0.5	0.6	0.8	DCV
VAF	2E	SIGRTN	1.8	DCV	6.7	8	8.2	DCV
ECT	2I	SIGRTN	2.5	DCV	0.4	0.5	0.5	DCV
BARO	2H	SIGRTN	3.9	DCV	3.9	3.9	3.8	DCV
IAT	2J	PWRGND	2.4	DCV	3	3	3	DCV
IDL	1E	PWRGND	0	DCV	0	12.6	12.4	DCV
PNP/CPP	1G	PWRGND	12	DCV	14	14	14	DCV
BOO	1J	PWRGND	0/12[1]	DCV[1]	0/12	0	0	DCV[1]
PSP	1K	PWRGND	12	DCV	14	14	14	DCV
IDM	1M	PWRGND	N/A	RPM	850-1050	2650-2700	3125-3175	RPM
O2S	2D	PWRGND	N/A	DCV	0.8	0.5	0.6	DCV

[1] – 12 volts with pedal pressed; zero volts with pedal released.

Outputs	SIG Pin #	REF. Pin #	KOEO	Units	Hot Idle	30 MPH	55 MPH	Units
BANK 1	3E	PWRGND	N/A	mSEC	3.9	5.8	7.1	mSEC
BANK 2	3C	PWRGND	N/A	mSEC	3.9	5.9	7.1	mSEC
CANP	2P	PWRGND	12	DCV[1]	14.3[2]	14[2]	14[2]	DCV[1]
IAC	2Q	PWRGND	7	DCV	10	9.7	9.8	DCV
FPRC	2K	PWRGND	12	DCV	14	14.3	14	DCV
STO	1B	PWRGND	0.7	DCV	14	14	13.8	DCV
MIL	1A	PWRGND	1.6	DCV	13.2	14	13.8	DCV

Reference values shown may differ by plus or minus 20% depending on operating conditions and other factors.

[1] – Test in manual DC volts.
[2] – Voltage may be lower while purging occurs.

94F44409

Courtesy of Ford Motor Co.

Fig. 5: Checking PCM Pin Voltages (Capri Non-Turbo)

Inputs	SIG Pin #	REF. Pin #	KOEO	Units	Hot Idle	30 MPH	55 MPH	Units
TP	2G	SIGRTN	0.4	DCV	0.36	0.5	0.67	DCV
VAF	2E	SIGRTN	2	DCV	5.5	7.4	8.1	DCV
ECT	2I	SIGRTN	2.5	DCV	0.4	0.5	0.5	DCV
BARO	2H	SIGRTN	3.9	DCV	3.8	3.8	3.8	DCV
IAT	2J	PWRGND	2.2	DCV	2.3	2.6	2.7	DCV
IDL	1E	PWRGND	0	DCV	0	13.9	13.9	DCV
PNP/CPP	1G	PWRGND	12	DCV	14	14	14	DCV
BOO	1J	PWRGND	0/12	DCV[1]	0/12	0	0	DCV[1]
PSP	1K	PWRGND	12	DCV	13.6	13.7	13.7	DCV
KCU	2M	PWRGND	12	DCV	12	12	12	DCV
IDM	1M	PWRGND	N/A	RPM	800-900	2640-2680	3120-3160	RPM
O2S	2D	PWRGND	N/A	DCV	0	0.5	0.5	DCV

[1] – 12 volts with pedal pressed; zero volts with pedal released.

Outputs	SIG Pin #	REF. Pin #	KOEO	Units	Hot Idle	30 MPH	55 MPH	Units
BANK 1	3E	PWRGND	N/A	mSEC	3.4	3.5	4.3	mSEC
BANK 2	3C	PWRGND	N/A	mSEC	3.4	3.5	3.5	mSEC
CANP	2P	PWRGND	12	DCV[1]	14.3[2]	14[2]	14[2]	DCV[1]
IAC	2Q	PWRGND	7.5	DCV	7.6	9.4	9.6	DCV
FPRC	2K	PWRGND	12	DCV	14	14	14	DCV
STO	1B	PWRGND	0.71	DCV	13.5	13.5	13.5	DCV
MIL	1A	PWRGND	1.6	DCV	13.6	13.7	13.6	DCV

Reference values shown may differ by plus or minus 20% depending on operating conditions and other factors.

[1] – Test in manual DC volts.
[2] – Voltage may be lower while purging occurs.

94I44410

Courtesy of Ford Motor Co.

Fig. 6: Checking PCM Pin Voltages (Capri Turbo)

1994 ENGINE PERFORMANCE
Sensor Operating Range Charts

Aspire, Capri

INTRODUCTION

Sensor operating range information can help determine if a sensor is out of calibration. An out-of-calibration sensor may not set a trouble code, but it may cause driveability problems.

NOTE: Unless stated otherwise in test procedure, perform all voltage tests using a Digital Volt-Ohmmeter (DVOM) with a minimum 10-megohm input impedance.

NOTE: On Aspire, BARO sensor cannot be tested or serviced separately. If a Code 14 is set and cannot be cleared, PCM must be replaced.

BAROMETRIC PRESSURE SENSOR OUTPUT VOLTAGE [1]

Vacuum – In. Hg.	[2] Volts
0	3.84
5	3.36
10	2.66
15	1.93
20	1.26
25	0.58

[1] – Measure voltage between breakout box test pins BP and SIGRTN.
[2] – Voltage may differ by plus or minus 15 percent.

ENGINE COOLANT TEMPERATURE SENSOR RESISTANCE [1]

Temperature – °F (°C)	Ohms
–4 (–20)	14,600-17,800
68 (20)	2200-2700
176 (80)	290-350

[1] – Measure resistance between breakout box test pins ECT and SIGRTN.

IGNITION DIAGNOSTIC MONITOR VOLTAGE [1]

RPM	Volts
500	1.103
1000	1.257
1500	1.542
2000	1.768
2500	2.06
3000	2.15
3500	2.26
4000	2.50
4500	2.47
5000	2.40

[1] – Measure voltage between breakout box test pins IDM and VPWR.

TP SENSOR OUTPUT VOLTAGE – ASPIRE

Throttle Opening	[1] Voltage
1/4	0.50
1/2	2.75
3/4	3.88
Full Open	5.0

[1] – Voltage may differ by 15 percent.

TP SENSOR OUTPUT VOLTAGE – CAPRI

Throttle Opening	[1] Voltage
1/8	1.00
1/4	1.60
3/8	2.37
1/2	2.74
5/8	3.15
3/4	3.43
7/8	3.60
Full Open	4.02

[1] – Voltage may differ by 15 percent.

VOLUME AIRFLOW METER VOLTAGE (CAPRI) [1]

Door Opening	[2] Volts
1/8	3.24
1/4	5.60
3/8	5.62
1/2	5.83
5/8	6.02
3/4	6.57
7/8	7.46
Fully Open	7.87

[1] – Measure voltage between breakout box test pins VAF and SIGRTN.
[2] – Voltage may differ by plus or minus 15 percent.

IAT SENSOR RESISTANCE – ASPIRE [1]

Temperature °F (°C)	[2] Ohms
32 (0)	72,100-79,400
55 (13)	54,300-58,600
77 (25)	29,700-36,300
110 (43)	17,900-19,300
185 (85)	3300-3700

[1] – Measure resistance between breakout box test pins IAT and SIGRTN.
[2] – Resistance may differ by plus or minus 15 percent.

IAT SENSOR RESISTANCE – CAPRI [1]

Temperature °F (°C)	[2] Ohms
-4 (-20)	10,000-20,000
32 (0)	4000-7000
68 (20)	2000-3000
104 (40)	900-1300
140 (60)	400-700

[1] – Measure resistance between breakout box test pins IAT and SIGRTN.
[2] – Resistance may differ by plus or minus 15 percent.

Aspire, Capri

INTRODUCTION

This article contains underhood views or schematics of vacuum hose routing. Use these vacuum diagrams during the visual inspection in BASIC DIAGNOSTIC PROCEDURES article. This will assist in identifying improperly routed vacuum hoses which cause driveability and/or computer-indicated malfunctions.

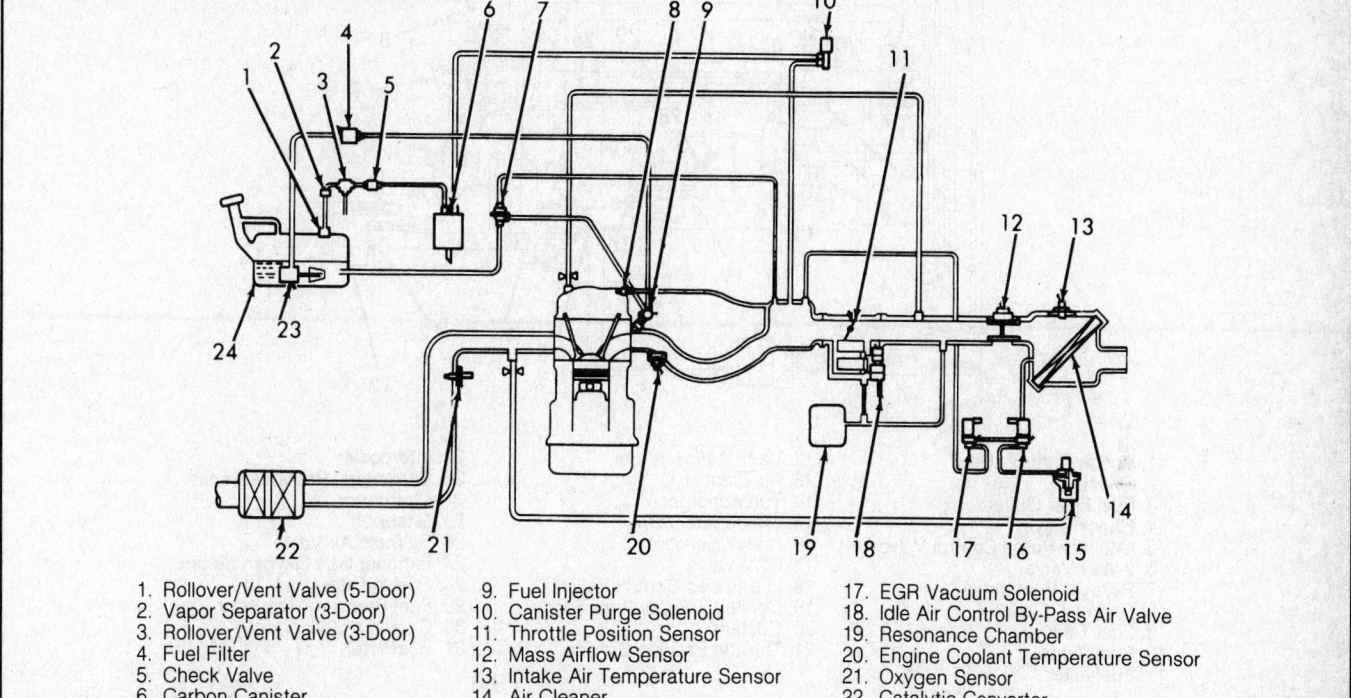

1. Rollover/Vent Valve (5-Door)	9. Fuel Injector	17. EGR Vacuum Solenoid
2. Vapor Separator (3-Door)	10. Canister Purge Solenoid	18. Idle Air Control By-Pass Air Valve
3. Rollover/Vent Valve (3-Door)	11. Throttle Position Sensor	19. Resonance Chamber
4. Fuel Filter	12. Mass Airflow Sensor	20. Engine Coolant Temperature Sensor
5. Check Valve	13. Intake Air Temperature Sensor	21. Oxygen Sensor
6. Carbon Canister	14. Air Cleaner	22. Catalytic Converter
7. Fuel Pressure Regulator	15. EGR Control Valve	23. Fuel Pump
8. PCV Valve	16. EGR Vent Solenoid	24. Fuel Tank

94G44418

Courtesy of Ford Motor Co.

Fig. 1: Vacuum Diagram (Aspire)

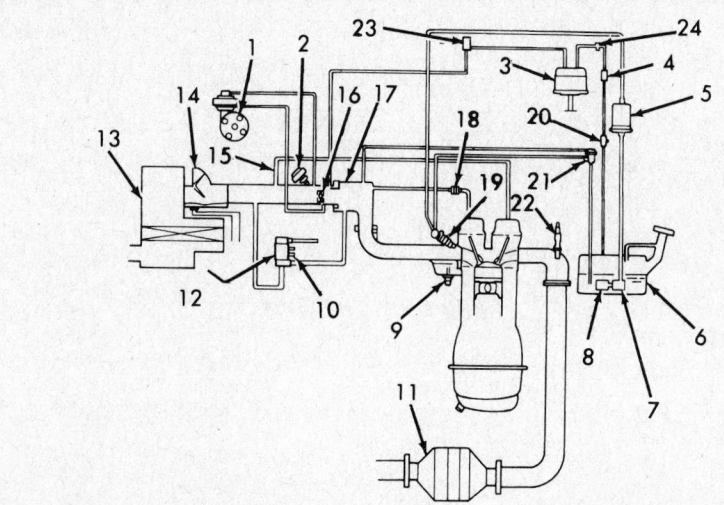

1. Distributor	9. Coolant Temperature Sensor	17. Surge Tank
2. Dashpot	10. Coolant	18. PCV Valve
3. Charcoal Canister	11. Catalytic Converter	19. Fuel Injector
4. 2-Way Valve	12. Idle Speed Control Valve	20. Rollover Vent Valve
5. Fuel Filter Outlet	13. Air Cleaner	21. Fuel Pressure Regulator
6. Fuel Tank	14. Vane Airflow Meter	22. Exhaust Gas Oxygen Sensor
7. Fuel Pump	15. Orifice	23. Canister Purge Control Solenoid Valve
8. Fuel Filter	16. Throttle Position Sensor	24. Restrictor

92C25215

Courtesy of Ford Motor Co.

Fig. 2: Vacuum Diagram (Capri 1.6L Non-Turbo)

1994 ENGINE PERFORMANCE
Vacuum Diagrams (Cont.)

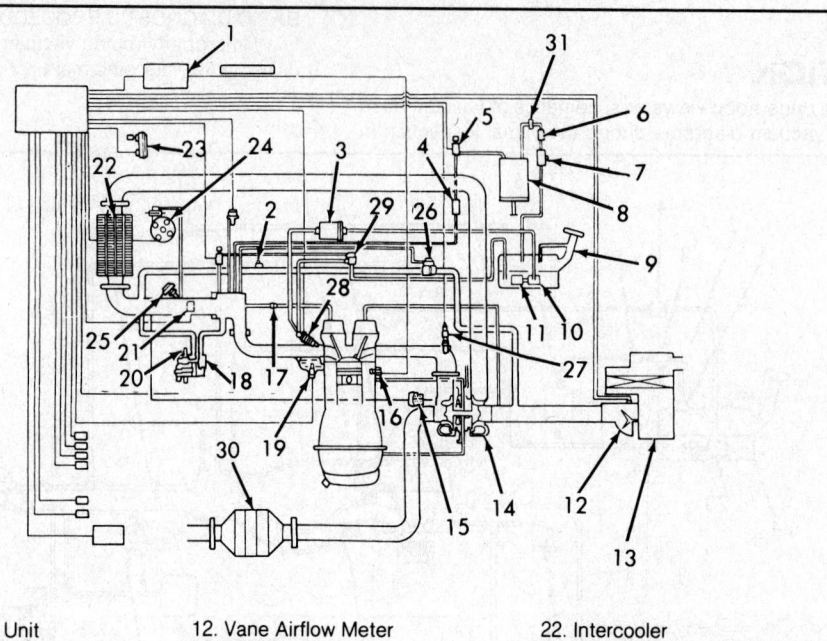

1. Knock Control Unit	12. Vane Airflow Meter	22. Intercooler
2. Orifice	13. Air Cleaner	23. Barometric Pressure Sensor
3. Fuel Filter Outlet	14. Turbocharger	24. Distributor
4. Check Valve	15. Wastegate Valve	25. Dashpot
5. Canister Purge Control Valve	16. Knock Sensor	26. By-Pass Air Valve
6. 2-Way Valve	17. PCV Valve	27. Exhaust Gas Oxygen Sensor
7. Rollover Vent Valve	18. Idle Speed Control Valve	28. Fuel Injector
8. Charcoal Canister	19. Coolant Temperature Sensor	29. Fuel Pressure Regulator
9. Fuel Tank	20. Coolant	30. Catalytic Converter
10. Fuel Pump	21. Throttle Position Sensor	31. Restrictor
11. Fuel Filter		

92D25216

Courtesy of Ford Motor Co.

Fig. 3: Vacuum Diagram (Capri 1.6L Turbo)

Aspire, Capri

INTRODUCTION

Removal, overhaul, and installation procedures are covered in this article. If component removal and installation is primarily an unbolt and bolt-on procedure, only a torque specification may be furnished.

IGNITION SYSTEM

DISTRIBUTOR

Removal – Disconnect negative battery cable. Disconnect vacuum hoses (if equipped). Disconnect coil wire (if equipped). Remove retaining screws and distributor cap. Unplug electrical connectors. Mark distributor housing and cylinder head for reassembly reference. Remove distributor and "O" ring.

Installation – To install, reverse removal procedure. Install new "O" ring. Insert and rotate distributor until drive tangs engage camshaft slots. See Fig. 1, 2, or 3. Check ignition timing and adjust as necessary.

NOTE: Distributor on Aspire cannot be disassembled for service. It must be replaced as an assembly if internal components are defective.

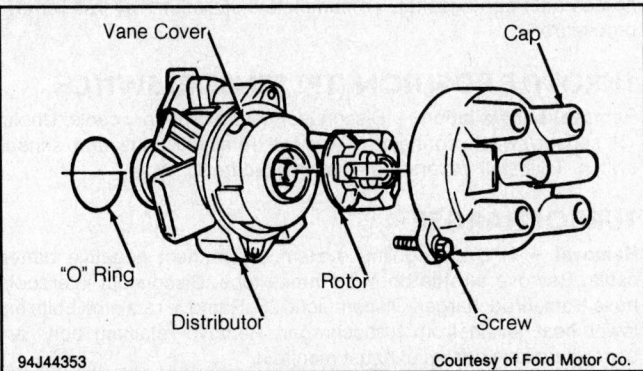

94J44353   Courtesy of Ford Motor Co.

Fig. 1: Exploded View Of Distributor (Aspire)

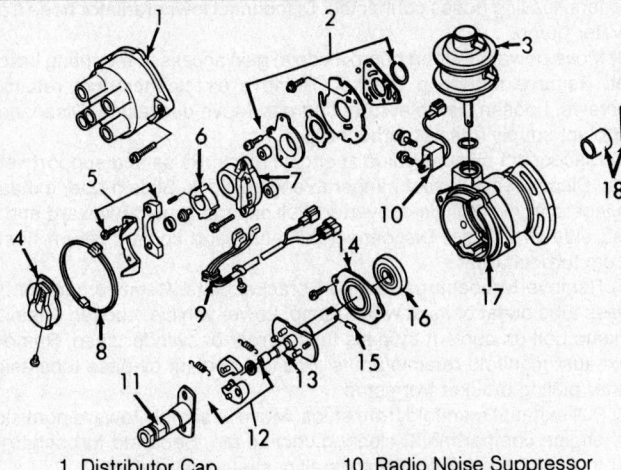

1. Distributor Cap
2. Breaker Plate
3. Vacuum Control Unit
4. Rotor
5. Pick-Up Unit
6. Armature
7. Igniter Assembly
8. Gasket
9. Harness Assembly
10. Radio Noise Suppressor
11. Upper Shaft
12. Mechanical Advance
13. Lower Shaft
14. Plate
15. Roll Pin
16. Bearing
17. Housing
18. Drive Assembly

91A16667   Courtesy of Ford Motor Co.

Fig. 2: Exploded View Of Distributor (Capri Non-Turbo)

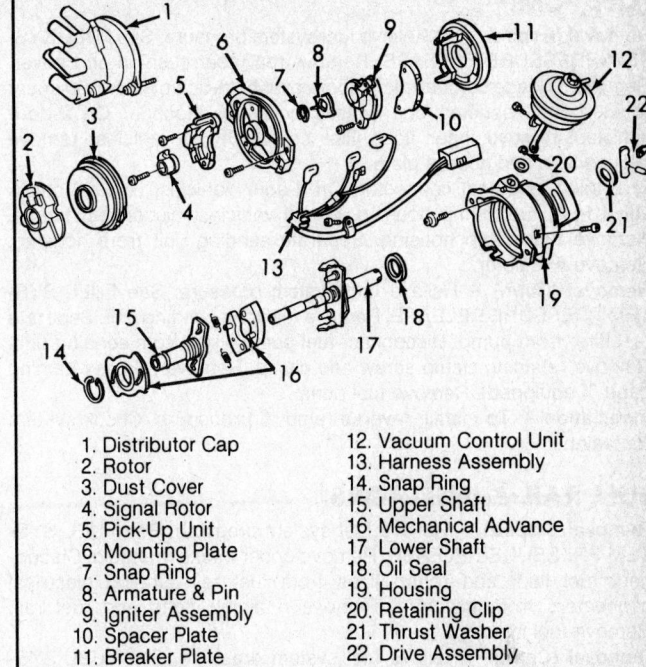

1. Distributor Cap
2. Rotor
3. Dust Cover
4. Signal Rotor
5. Pick-Up Unit
6. Mounting Plate
7. Snap Ring
8. Armature & Pin
9. Igniter Assembly
10. Spacer Plate
11. Breaker Plate
12. Vacuum Control Unit
13. Harness Assembly
14. Snap Ring
15. Upper Shaft
16. Mechanical Advance
17. Lower Shaft
18. Oil Seal
19. Housing
20. Retaining Clip
21. Thrust Washer
22. Drive Assembly

91B16668   Courtesy of Ford Motor Co.

Fig. 3: Exploded View Of Distributor (Capri Turbo)

POWERTRAIN CONTROL MODULE (PCM)

NOTE: Electronic modules are sensitive to static electric charges. Damage may result if they are exposed to these charges. Follow all handling precautions when removing or installing the PCM.

Removal & Installation (Aspire) – PCM is located under left side of instrument panel. Disconnect negative battery cable. Remove retaining nuts. Move anti-lock brake module aside (if equipped). Pull PCM downward for access. Unplug PCM harness connectors. To install, reverse removal procedure.

Removal & Installation (Capri) – PCM is located below center of instrument panel. Disconnect negative battery cable. Disengage push-pin retainers by pulling back on front edges of both center carpet panels. Remove carpet panel retaining screws and panels. Unplug PCM harness connectors. Remove mounting bolts and PCM. To install, reverse removal procedure.

FUEL SYSTEM

WARNING: ALWAYS relieve fuel pressure before disconnecting any fuel injection-related component. DO NOT allow fuel to contact engine or electrical components.

FUEL SYSTEM PRESSURE RELEASE

WARNING: ALWAYS relieve fuel pressure before disconnecting any fuel injection system component. DO NOT allow fuel to contact engine or electrical components.

Fuel Pressure Release (Aspire) – Start engine. Unplug fuel pump relay connector, located behind left side of instrument panel. Allow engine to stall. Fuel pressure is now relieved.

Fuel Pressure Release (Capri) – Remove rear seat cushion. Start engine. Unplug fuel pump connector. Run engine until it stalls. Fuel pressure is now relieved.

FUEL PUMP

Removal (Aspire) – **1)** Relieve fuel system pressure. See FUEL SYSTEM PRESSURE RELEASE. Remove rear seat cushion and cover. Remove luggage compartment floor cover hold-down pins. Fold cover forward until sending unit access cover is exposed. On 2-door vehicles, remove inner floor filler cover. On all vehicles, remove ground lead and access plate.

2) Unplug electrical connector. On 4-door vehicles, remove check valve from fuel pump housing. On all vehicles, disconnect hoses. Remove fuel pump housing. Separate sending unit from housing. Remove fuel pump.

Removal (Capri) – Relieve fuel system pressure. See FUEL SYSTEM PRESSURE RELEASE. Remove fuel tank sending unit. Separate fuel filter from pump. Disconnect fuel pump wires from sending unit. Remove retaining clamp screw and clamp. Remove rubber retaining band (if equipped). Remove fuel pump.

Installation – To install, reverse removal procedure. Check system for leaks.

FUEL RAIL & INJECTORS

Removal (Aspire) – Relieve fuel system pressure. See FUEL SYSTEM PRESSURE RELEASE. Remove upper intake manifold. Disconnect fuel inlet and return lines from fuel rail. Unplug electrical connectors from injectors. Remove retaining bolts and fuel rail. Remove fuel injectors.

Removal (Capri) – Relieve fuel system pressure. See FUEL SYSTEM PRESSURE RELEASE. Remove throttle body. See THROTTLE BODY. See INTAKE PLENUM. Disconnect fuel inlet and return lines from fuel rail. Unplug electrical connectors from injectors. Remove pressure regulator. *See Fig. 4.* Remove retaining bolts and fuel rail. Remove fuel injectors.

Installation – Lubricate NEW "O" rings with engine oil, and install onto fuel injectors. Install fuel injectors into cylinder head. Install fuel rail and retaining bolts. To complete installation, reverse removal procedure. Inspect system for leaks.

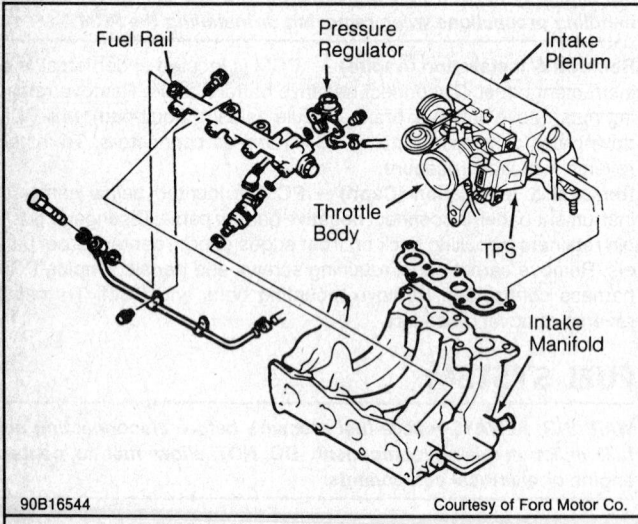

Fig. 4: Exploded View Of Fuel Control System (Capri)

INTAKE PLENUM

Removal (Capri) – Drain radiator. Remove negative battery cable. Disconnect throttle cable. Separate air duct from throttle body. Unplug TP sensor/switch connector. Mark coolant and vacuum hoses for reassembly reference. Disconnect hoses from throttle body. Remove retaining bolts and intake plenum. *See Fig. 4.*

NOTE: To prevent dust and dirt from entering intake manifold ports, cover ports with clean cloth after removing intake plenum.

Installation – To install, reverse removal procedure. Use NEW gasket. Tighten bolts to specification. See TORQUE SPECIFICATIONS table.

OXYGEN SENSOR (O2S)

Removal & Installation – O2S is threaded into exhaust pipe just below exhaust header. It is equipped with a permanent pigtail which must not be damaged. Sensor may be difficult to remove when engine temperature is less than 120° (48°C). Always use anti-seize compound on threads before installation.

THROTTLE BODY

NOTE: Clean throttle body exterior before removal.

Removal & Installation (Aspire) – Drain radiator. Disconnect negative battery cable. Remove air cleaner intake duct. Disconnect throttle cable. Unplug electrical connector. Remove throttle body.

Removal & Installation (Capri) – Drain radiator. Disconnect negative battery cable. Remove resonance chamber. Disconnect throttle cable. Remove air duct. Mark coolant and vacuum hoses for reassembly reference. Disconnect hoses from throttle body. Disconnect TP sensor/switch connector. Remove retaining bolts and throttle body. Install new throttle body gasket. To complete installation, reverse removal procedure.

THROTTLE POSITION (TP) SENSOR/SWITCH

Removal & Installation – Disconnect negative battery cable. Unplug TP sensor/switch connector. Remove retaining bolts and sensor/switch. To install, reverse removal procedure.

TURBOCHARGER

Removal – **1)** Drain cooling system. Disconnect negative battery cable. Remove throttle body air intake tube. Disconnect intercooler hose from turbocharger. Disconnect O2S. Remove retaining bolts and lower heat shield from turbocharger. Remove retaining bolts and upper heat shield from exhaust manifold.

2) Remove retaining bolts and side heat shield from turbocharger. Remove power steering belt. Remove power steering pump fasteners, leaving hoses connected. Disconnect lower radiator hose from water pump.

3) Move power steering pump aside to gain access to mounting bracket. Remove mounting bracket. Remove air cleaner duct retaining screws. Loosen clamp at turbocharger. Move duct aside. Disconnect coolant supply hose at turbocharger.

4) Disconnect oil supply line at engine block. Raise and support vehicle. Disconnect exhaust hanger at engine block. Slide rubber exhaust hangers from catalytic converter. Pull exhaust pipe downward and to left side of vehicle. Disconnect oil return and coolant return hoses from turbocharger.

5) Remove turbocharger support bracket bolts. Remove coolant by-pass tube outlet bolts at water pump. Lower vehicle. Loosen retaining clamp bolt on coolant by-pass tube at rear of cylinder head. Remove exhaust manifold retaining nuts. Position coolant by-pass tube aside after pulling bracket from stud.

6) Pull exhaust manifold from studs. Move assembly toward right side of engine compartment, clearing cooling fan. Separate turbocharger from exhaust manifold. Remove all gaskets and sealant.

CAUTION: Before installing turbocharger, put 0.8 oz. (25 ml) engine oil into turbocharger oil inlet port.

Installation – **1)** Install turbocharger onto exhaust manifold, using new gasket. Install turbocharger and exhaust manifold assembly onto cylinder head, using new gasket. Install coolant by-pass tube bracket. Install exhaust manifold nuts.

2) Tighten heater tube clamp bolt. Raise and support vehicle. Install coolant by-pass tube bolts. Install turbocharger support bracket retaining bolts. Connect coolant return and oil return hoses to turbocharger. Install exhaust pipe onto turbocharger. Tighten nuts and washers by hand. Install exhaust hanger.

3) Slide rubber exhaust hangers onto catalytic converter. Tighten exhaust pipe nuts and washers. Lower vehicle. Connect oil supply line to engine block. Connect oil supply line to turbocharger. Tighten bolts and nuts to specification. See TORQUE SPECIFICATIONS. To complete installation, reverse removal procedure.

MASS AIRFLOW (MAF) METER

Removal & Installation (Aspire) – Disconnect negative battery cable. Unplug MAF and IAT electrical connectors. Loosen clamp, then separate air intake tube from MAF sensor. Disconnect vacuum hose. Remove upper air cleaner. Remove MAF sensor. To install, reverse removal procedurre.

VOLUME AIRFLOW (VAF) METER

Removal – **1)** Disconnect primary and secondary wires from coil. On all, disconnect VAF wire harness connector. Remove air duct.

2) Remove air cleaner cover. Remove attaching bolt and nuts. Remove vane airflow meter.

Installation – To install, reverse removal procedure. Position new gasket over VAF mounting studs. Tighten bolts and nuts to specification. See TORQUE SPECIFICATIONS.

NOTE: For all on-vehicle adjustments not covered in this article, see ON-VEHICLE ADJUSTMENTS article.

TORQUE SPECIFICATIONS
TORQUE SPECIFICATIONS

Application	Ft. Lbs. (N.m)
Coolant By-Pass Tube Outlet Bolts	14-19 (19-26)
Distributor Mounting Bolts	14-19 (19-26)
Exhaust Manifold Nuts	29-42 (39-57)
Exhaust Pipe Nuts	18-25 (24-34)
Fuel Line-To-Fuel Filter Bolt	18-25 (24-34)
Fuel Rail Retaining Bolt	14-19 (19-26)
Heat Shield Bolts	14-19 (19-26)
Intake Plenum Bolts/Nuts	11-16 (15-22)
Oil Supply Line-To-Turbocharger Bolt	12-17 (16-23)
Oxygen Sensor (O2S)	22-36 (30-49)
Power Steering Pump Bracket Bolts/Nut	35-48 (47-65)
Throttle Body Bolt/Nuts	12-17 (16-23)
Turbocharger Mounting Nuts	20-25 (27-34)
Turbocharger Support Bracket Bolts	32-45 (43-61)

	INCH Lbs. (N.m)
Barometric Pressure (BARO) Sensor Nut	54-84 (6-9)
MAF Sensor Bolts	54-88 (8-10)
Oil Supply Line Bolt	104-156 (12-18)
VAF Meter Nuts	104-156 (12-18)

1994 ENGINE PERFORMANCE
Wiring Diagrams

Aspire, Capri

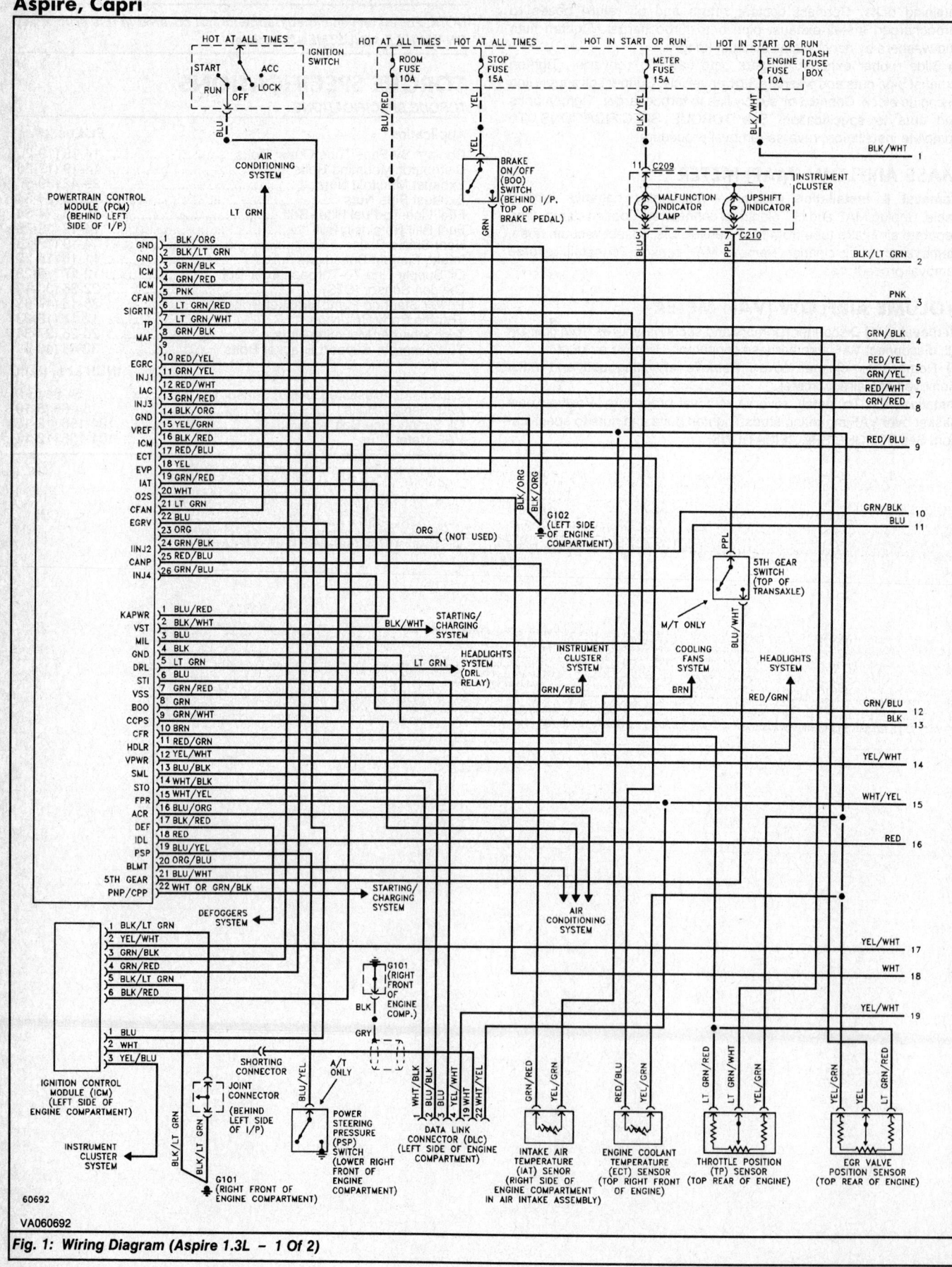

Fig. 1: Wiring Diagram (Aspire 1.3L - 1 Of 2)

60692

VA060692

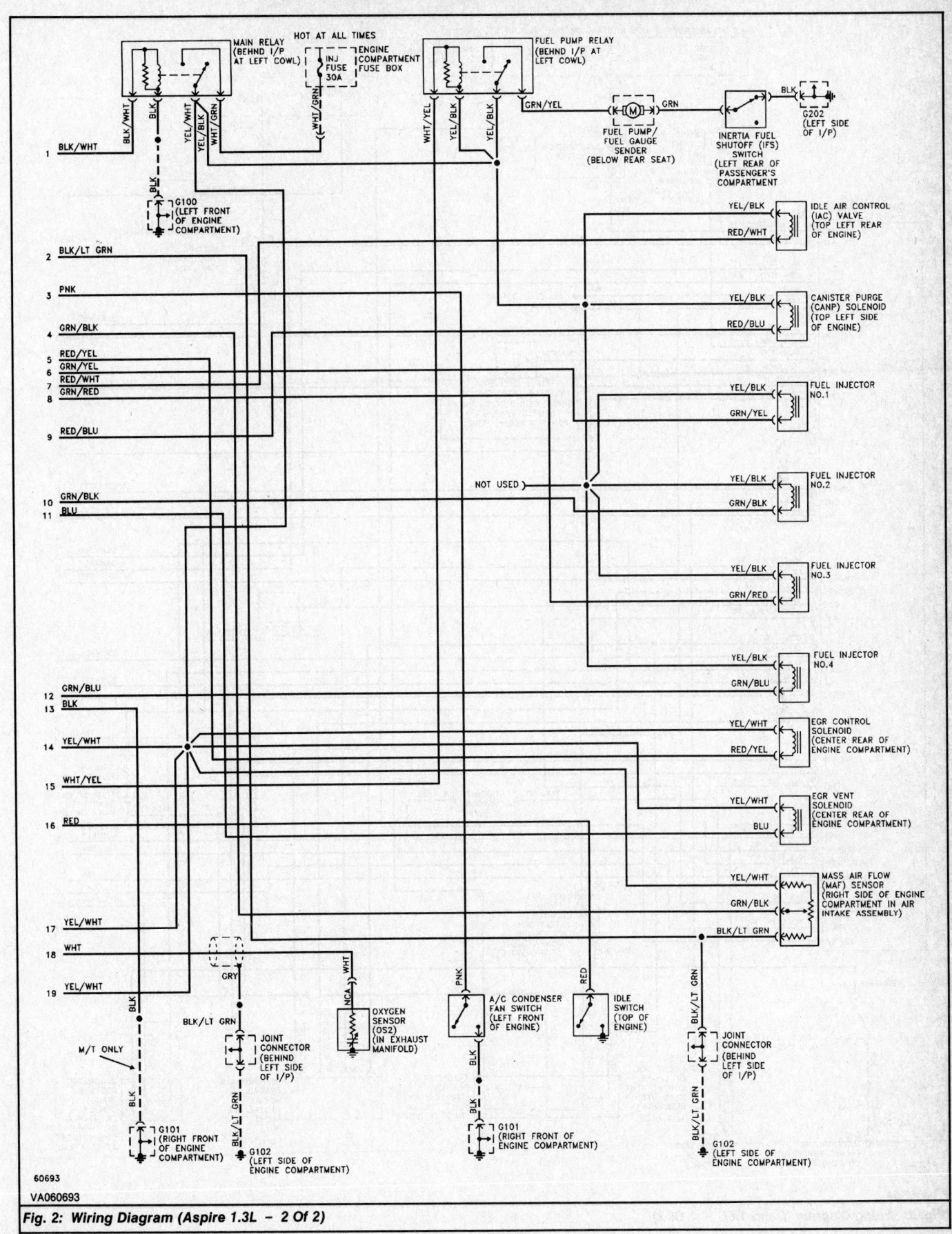

Fig. 2: Wiring Diagram (Aspire 1.3L – 2 Of 2)

60693

VA060693

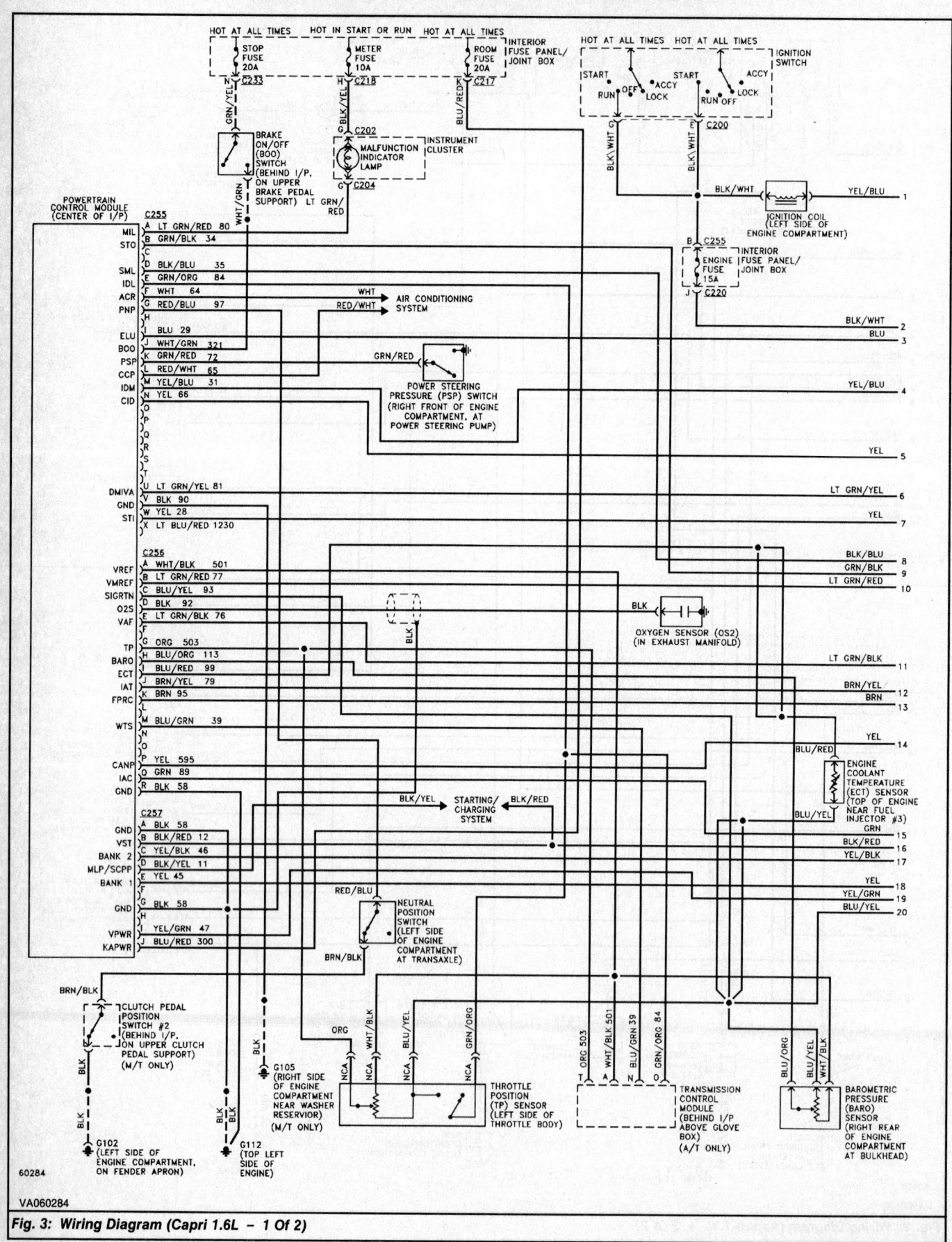

Fig. 3: Wiring Diagram (Capri 1.6L – 1 Of 2)

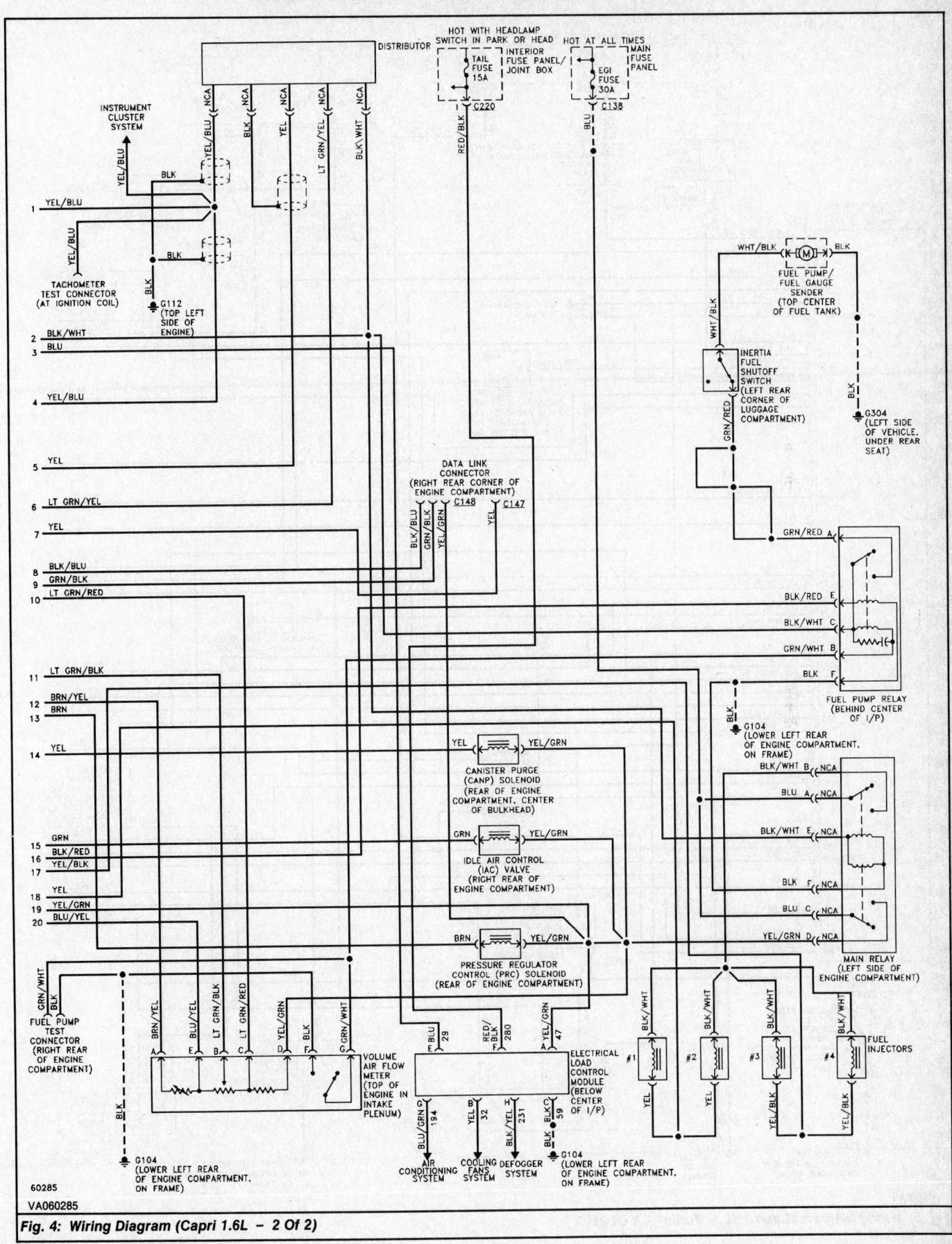

Fig. 4: Wiring Diagram (Capri 1.6L – 2 Of 2)

60285

VA060285

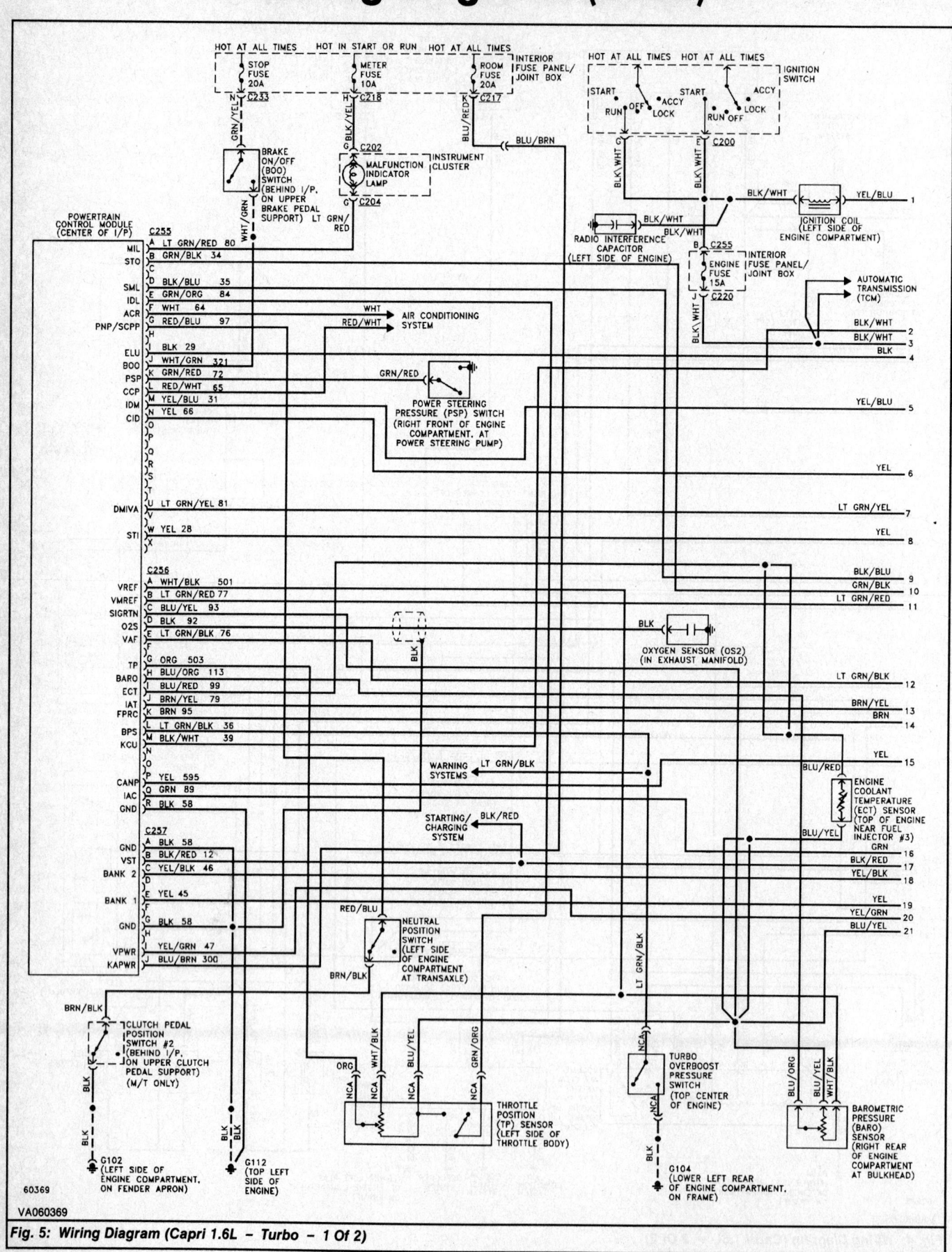

Fig. 5: Wiring Diagram (Capri 1.6L – Turbo – 1 Of 2)

VA060369

60369

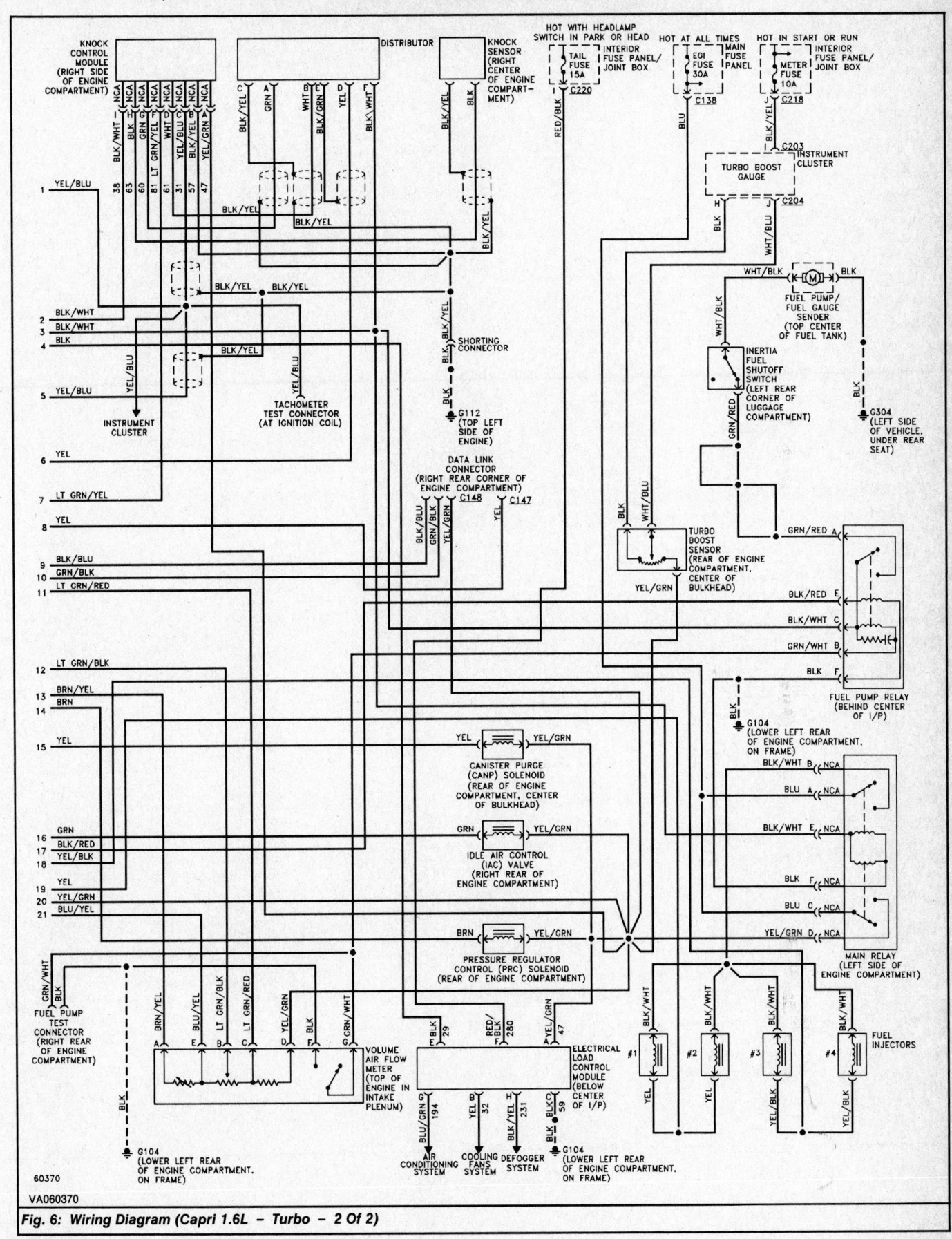

Fig. 6: Wiring Diagram (Capri 1.6L - Turbo - 2 Of 2)

DESCRIPTION

This alternator is a 3-phase, self-rectifying type unit, with 6 rectifier diodes, a diode trio, and an integral regulator. A charge indicator light on the instrument panel warns of charging system malfunctions.

TROUBLE SHOOTING

NOTE: See TROUBLE SHOOTING article in GENERAL INFORMATION.

ADJUSTMENTS

BELT TENSION

BELT ADJUSTMENTS
Using Belt Tension Gauge Or Deflection Method

Application	Tension Lbs. (Kg)	[1] Deflection In. (mm)
Air Conditioner		
New [2]	110-132 (50-60)	0.31-0.35 (8-9)
Used [3]	95-110 (43-50)	0.35-0.40 (9-10)
Alternator		
New [2]	86-104 (39-47)	0.31-0.35 (8-9)
Used [3]	82-115 (37-52)	.35-0.40 (9-10)
Power Steering		
New [2]	110-132 (50-60)	0.31-0.35 (8-9)
Used [3]	95-110 (43-50)	0.35-0.40 (9-10)

[1] – With 22 lbs. (10 kg) pressure at center of longest accessible span.
[2] – New belts have not been run.
[3] – Used belts have been run more than 10 minutes.

ON-VEHICLE TESTING

NOTE: Before testing, inspect alternator wiring harness connections and drive belt tension. Service as necessary. Ensure battery is charged and in good condition. Ensure battery cables and engine ground cable are clean and tight. Wait at least 30 seconds after starting engine before measuring voltage.

ALTERNATOR OUTPUT

CAUTION: DO NOT start engine with "L" and "S" terminals disconnected from alternator. DO NOT allow "L" terminal to contact ground while engine is running. See Fig. 1.

No-Load Test – **1)** Turn headlights on for 15 seconds, then turn them off. Connect DVOM to battery terminals. Measure and record battery voltage.

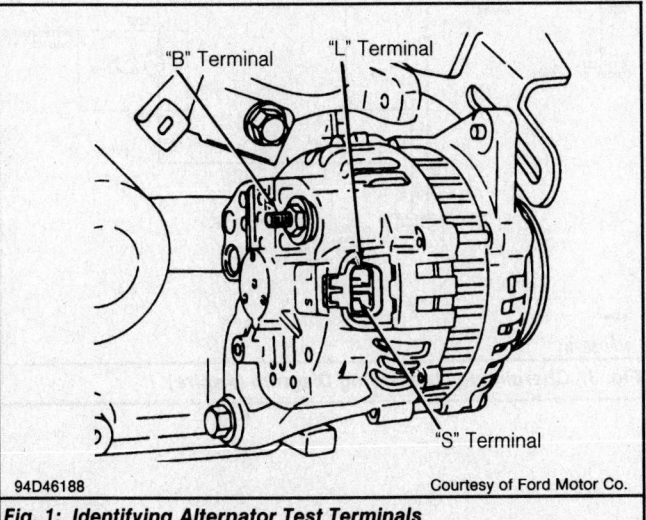

94D46188   Courtesy of Ford Motor Co.

Fig. 1: Identifying Alternator Test Terminals

2) Start engine and run at 1500 RPM with no electrical load on engine. Voltage should be 14.1-14.7 volts. If voltage is as specified, charging system is okay. If voltage increase is less than 2.5 volts higher than that measured in step **1)**, go to LOAD TEST. If voltage increase is more than 2.5 volts higher than that measured in step **1)**, repair or replace alternator.

Load Test – With engine running, turn on air conditioner. Set blower to high speed. Turn on high beam headlights. Increase engine speed to 2000 RPM. Voltage should stabilize at least 0.5 volt higher than that measured in step **1)** of NO-LOAD TEST. If voltage increase is as specified, alternator is okay. If voltage increase is not as specified, repair or replace alternator.

BENCH TESTING

CAUTION: Hold tip of 200-watt soldering iron against rear housing bearing recess for 3 to 4 minutes before attempting to disassemble alternator.

ROTOR

Measure resistance between rotor slip rings. If resistance is not 3-4 ohms, replace rotor. Check for continuity between individual slip rings and rotor shaft. If continuity exists, rotor or slip ring is grounded. Replace rotor. Inspect condition and color of slip rings. If dark or grooved, polish in a lathe with fine sandpaper.

STATOR

Inspect for continuity between stator coil leads and stator core. Replace stator if continuity exists. Continuity should exist between each pair of stator leads. If there is no continuity, replace stator. If burn spots are evident on stator laminations, replace stator.

BRUSHES

Inspect brushes. Replace brushes if worn to wear limit line. Use a spring pressure gauge to push each NEW brush into its holder until 0.08-0.12" (2-3 mm) projects from holder. Spring force should be about 13 ozs. If spring force is not as specified, replace brush spring.

RECTIFIER

1) Disconnect stator leads from rectifier. Measure resistance between each positive rectifier terminal and positive heat sink. Transpose ohmmeter leads and repeat measurement. Resistance should be high for one set of measurements, and low for the other set of measurements. Replace rectifier if resistance is not as specified.
2) Repeat step **1)** for negative diodes and negative heat sink. Replace rectifier if resistance is not as specified.

DIODE TRIO

Measure resistance between each diode trio input terminal (P_1, P_2, and P_3) and output terminal ("L"). Transpose ohmmeter leads and repeat measurement. Resistance should be very high for one set of measurements, and low for the other set of measurements. Replace diode trio if resistance is not as specified.

BEARINGS

Inspect bearings for noise, looseness, or poor lubrication. Inspect grease seals for cuts, cracks, or other deterioration. Replace bearings as necessary.

OVERHAUL

NOTE: Use illustration for exploded view of alternator. See Fig. 2.

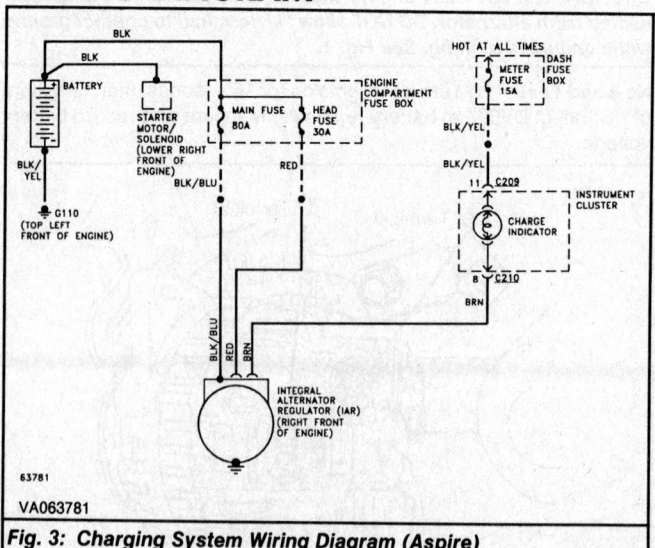

1994 ELECTRICAL
Alternators & Regulators – Aspire (Cont.)

1. Rotor
2. Bearing
3. Nut
4. Insulator
5. Rear Housing
6. Rectifier
7. Screw
8. Regulator
9. Shield
10. Screw
11. Stator
12. Screw
13. Screw
14. Nut
15. Lock Washer
16. Pulley
17. Front Housing
18. Bearing
19. Retainer
20. Spacer

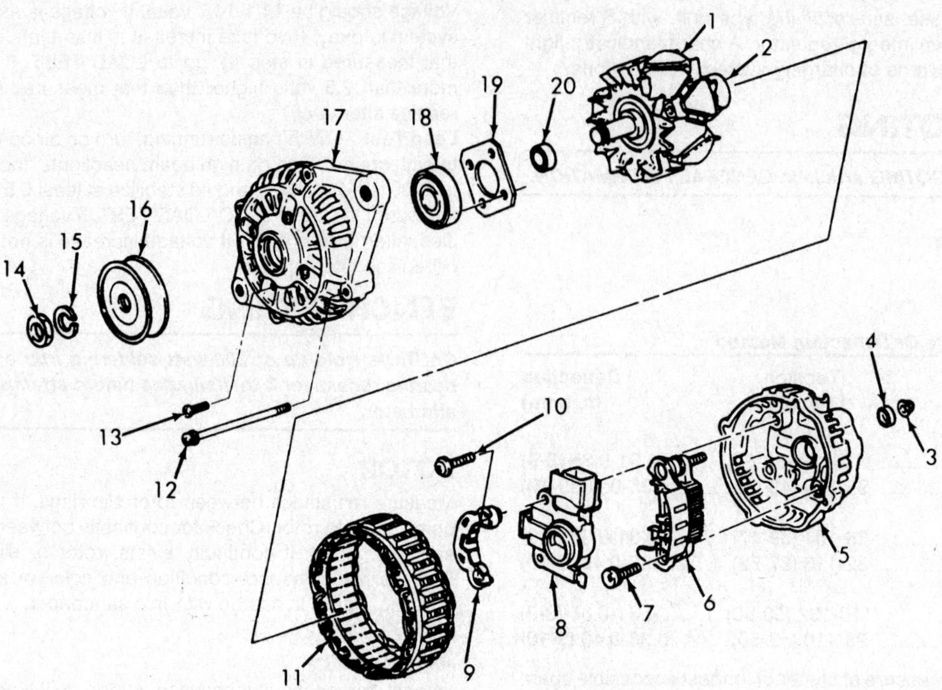

94E46189

Courtesy of Ford Motor Co.

Fig. 2: Exploded View Of Mitsubishi Alternator

TORQUE SPECIFICATIONS

TORQUE SPECIFICATIONS

Application	Ft. Lbs. (N.m)
Alternator Adjustment Bolt	14-18 (19-25)
Alternator Mount Bolt	27-46 (37-62)
Idler Pulley Attaching Nut	23-34 (31-46)
Power Steering Pump Adjustment Lock Nut	27-38 (37-52)
Power Steering Pump Mounting Bolt	27-40 (37-54)

WIRING DIAGRAM

VA063781

Fig. 3: Charging System Wiring Diagram (Aspire)

DESCRIPTION

The Mitsubishi alternator is a conventional 3-phase, self-rectifying unit, which includes a rectifier and integral regulator. A charge indicator light on the instrument panel warns of charging system malfunctions.

ADJUSTMENTS

BELT TENSION

BELT ADJUSTMENTS
Using Belt Tension Gauge Or Deflection Method

Application	Tension Lbs. (Kg)	[1] Deflection In. (mm)
A/C, Alternator & P/S		
New [2]	110-132 (50-60)	0.31-0.35 (8-9)
Used [3]	110-132 (50-60)	0.35-0.39 (9-10)

[1] – With 22 lbs. (10 kg) pressure on the longest unsupported span.
[2] – New belts (no run time).
[3] – Used belts (run time more than 10 minutes).

TROUBLE SHOOTING

NOTE: See TROUBLE SHOOTING article in GENERAL INFORMATION.

ON-VEHICLE TESTING

NOTE: Before testing, inspect alternator wiring harness connections and drive belt tension. Service as necessary. Ensure battery is charged and in good condition. Ensure battery cables and engine ground cable are clean and tight. Wait at least 30 seconds after starting engine before measuring voltage.

ALTERNATOR OUTPUT TEST

CAUTION: DO NOT ground "B+" terminal.

1) Start engine and observe charge indicator light. If indicator light does not go out, go to step **2)**. If indicator light does go out, turn engine off, go to step **5)**.
2) Set ignition switch to ON position with engine off. Measure voltage at each terminal. See ALTERNATOR TERMINAL VOLTAGE table. *See Fig. 1.*
3) With engine running at normal curb idle, again measure alternator terminal voltages. See ALTERNATOR TERMINAL VOLTAGE table.

ALTERNATOR TERMINAL VOLTAGE

Alternator Terminal	Ign. ON/Eng. OFF Volts	Engine At Idle Volts
B+	Approximately 12	14.1-14.7
"L"	Aprroximately 1	14.1-14.7
"S"	Approximately 12	14.1-14.7

4) Inspect wiring harness between battery and B+ terminal if voltage check is okay. Inspect remaining charging system wiring if voltages are less than specification. If wiring harness is okay, repair or replace alternator. *See Fig. 2.*
5) Disconnect negative battery terminal. Disconnect harness connector from alternator B+ terminal. Connect positive lead of Rotunda Starting and Charging Tester (078-00005 VAT40) to alternator B+ terminal. Connect negative lead to disconnected harnes B+ terminal. Set tester to ammeter function. *See Fig. 2.* Reconnect negative battery terminal.
6) Connect tachometer to engine. With engine running and all accessories and lights on, press brake pedal. With engine speed of 2500-3000 RPM, alternator output should be 70 amps or more. If alternator output is not as specified, recheck belt tension. If belt tension is okay, repair or replace alternator.

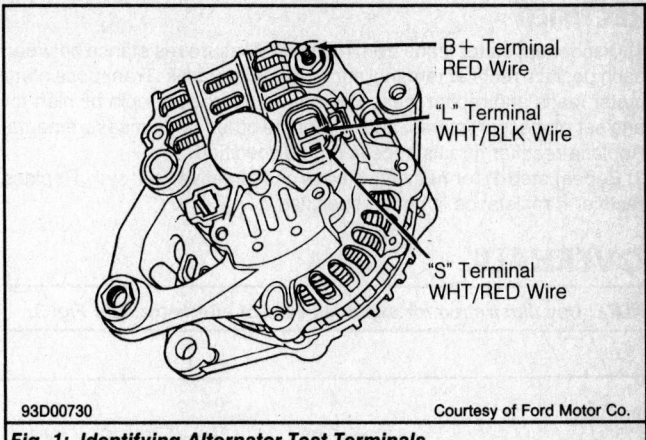

Fig. 1: Identifying Alternator Test Terminals

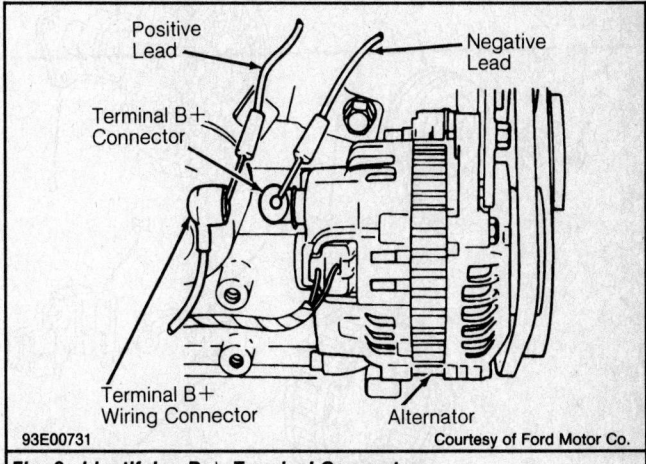

Fig. 2: Identifying B + Terminal Connectors

BENCH TESTING

CAUTION: Hold tip of 200-watt soldering iron against rear housing bearing recess for 3 to 4 minutes before attempting to disassemble alternator.

ROTOR

Inspect rotor for stripped threads or damage at pulley end. Inspect for scored bearing surfaces, scuff marks on the pole fingers, or dirty or contaminated slip rings. Measure resistance across rotor slip rings. If resistance is not 2-6 ohms, replace rotor. Measure insulation resistance between individual slip rings and rotor shaft. If continuity exists, rotor windings are grounded. Replace rotor.

STATOR

1) Inspect stator for burned or discolored windings, scuff marks on the inside of stator frame, or damage to stator frame. Measure insulation resistance between stator leads and stator frame. Replace stator if continuity exists.
2) Check for continuity between each pair of stator leads. Replace stator if continuity does not exist for each measurement. An internal short between adjacent stator windings may not be detectable. If alternator fails to produce rated output, stator windings may be shorted. If readings are not normal, replace stator.

BRUSHES

Inspect brushes for burn spots or discoloration caused by arcing. Replace brushes if worn to wear limit line. Install new brushes so that wear limit line is 0.08-0.12" (2-3 mm) from brush holder.

RECTIFIER

1) Disconnect stator leads from rectifier. Measure resistance between each positive rectifier terminal and positive heat sink. Transpose ohmmeter leads and repeat measurement. Resistance should be high for one set of measurements, and low for the other set of measurements. Replace rectifier if resistance is not as specified.

2) Repeat step **1)** for negative diodes and negative heat sink. Replace rectifier if resistance is not as specified.

OVERHAUL

NOTE: Use illustration for exploded view of alternator. See Fig. 3.

TORQUE SPECIFICATIONS

Application	Ft. Lbs. (N.m)
Alternator Adjustment Bolt	28-39 (38-53)
Alternator Fan Nut	36-65 (49-88)
Alternator Mount Bolt	14-15 (19-21)
Power Steering Pump Adjustment Lock Nut	32-45 (43-61)

Application	INCH Lbs. (N.m)
Alternator Through Bolts	36-59 (4.1-6.7)
Bearing Plate Retainer Screws	25-40 (2.8-4.5)
Brush Holder Mounting Screws	20-30 (2.3-3.4)
Rectifier Screws	25-35 (2.8-4.0)
Voltage Regulator Screws	25-35 (2.8-4.0)

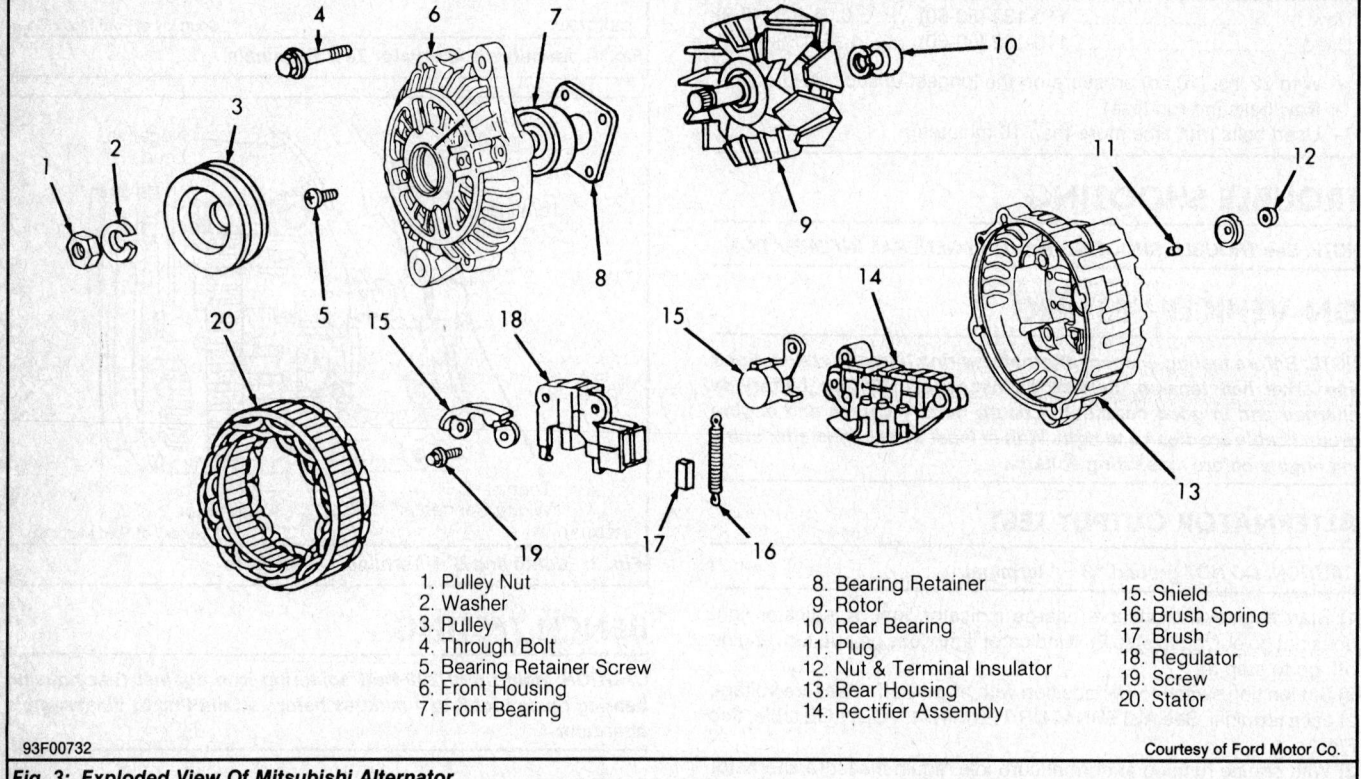

1. Pulley Nut	8. Bearing Retainer	15. Shield
2. Washer	9. Rotor	16. Brush Spring
3. Pulley	10. Rear Bearing	17. Brush
4. Through Bolt	11. Plug	18. Regulator
5. Bearing Retainer Screw	12. Nut & Terminal Insulator	19. Screw
6. Front Housing	13. Rear Housing	20. Stator
7. Front Bearing	14. Rectifier Assembly	

93F00732

Courtesy of Ford Motor Co.

Fig. 3: Exploded View Of Mitsubishi Alternator

WIRING DIAGRAM

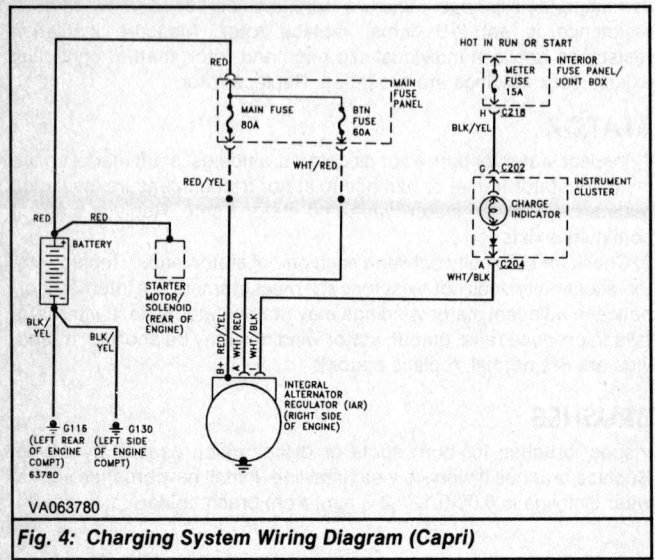

VA063780

Fig. 4: Charging System Wiring Diagram (Capri)

Aspire, Capri

DESCRIPTION

Starters on Aspire and Capri are conventional direct drive units with integral solenoids. When the starter is energized, the starter solenoid engages the starter pinion with the flywheel ring gear.

TROUBLE SHOOTING

ENGINE CRANKS SLOWLY

Undercharged battery. Loose or corroded cable connections. Defective starter.

ENGINE WILL NOT CRANK

Undercharged battery. Defective ignition switch. Defective clutch engage switch (M/T) or neutral safety switch (A/T). Loose or corroded cable connections. Defective starter, starter drive, or flywheel ring gear. Faulty circuit grounds.

STARTER SPINS BUT ENGINE DOES NOT CRANK

Defective flywheel ring gear and/or starter drive pinion.

ENGINE STARTS WITH CLUTCH ENGAGED (M/T)

Defective clutch engage switch of switch adjustment (adjust or replace).

ENGINE STARTS IN SHIFT POSITIONS OTHER THAN PARK OR NEUTRAL (A/T)

Defective neutral safety switch or switch adjustment (adjust or replace).

ON-VEHICLE TESTING

PRELIMINARY TEST

Ensure battery is fully charged and is in good condition. If starter will not crank engine with fully charged battery, proceed with the following test.

1) Connect positive voltmeter lead of DVOM to "S" terminal on starter solenoid. Connect negative lead to starter housing.

2) Set ignition switch to START position, and observe voltmeter. If voltage at terminal "S" is greater than 8 volts, starter or circuit malfunction is indicated. See VOLTAGE DROP TEST and STARTER GROUND CIRCUIT TEST.

3) If voltage is less than 8 volts at starter solenoid terminal "S", malfunction in circuit to terminal "S" is indicated. Proceed to the following tests.

NOTE: If the solenoid is extremely hot, it may not function even though voltage at the "S" terminal is 8 volts or more. Allow solenoid to cool and retest.

IGNITION SWITCH TEST

1) Locate ignition switch connector under dash. Using a 12-volt test light or voltmeter, check for battery voltage on Black/White wire (Capri) or Blue wire (Aspire) when ignition switch is turned to RUN or ON position. This will verify proper operation of ignition switch.

NOTE: Leave ignition switch connector in place during this test.

2) If there is no voltage at this wire, problem is either ignition switch or circuit between battery and ignition switch.

CLUTCH ENGAGE SWITCH (M/T) TEST

Unplug clutch engage switch from main wiring harness. Check for continuity across switch terminals. Continuity should exist when switch plunger is pushed in, and should not exist when switch plunger is released. If clutch engage switch does not operate as specified, replace switch.

NEUTRAL SAFETY SWITCH (A/T) TEST

Aspire – 1) Unplug manual lever position switch connector, located at top of transaxle. Check for continuity between switch terminals No. 1 and No. 3 (White and Black/White wires on mating connector). *See Fig. 1.*

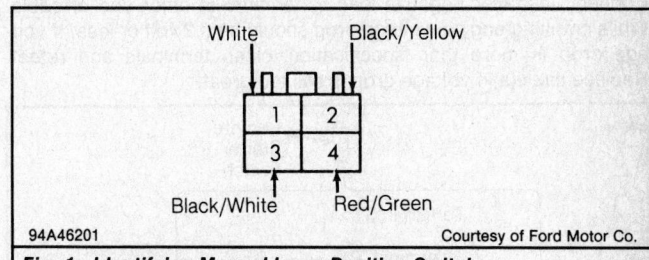

Fig. 1: Identifying Manual Lever Position Switch Connector Terminals (Aspire)

2) Set transaxle selector lever to Park or Neutral position. Continuity should exist.

3) Set transaxle selector lever to any position except Park or Neutral. Continuity should not exist. If park/neutral switch does not operate as specified, replace switch.

Capri – Unplug neutral safety switch from main wiring harness. Check for continuity between switch terminals "A" and "B". *See Fig. 2.* Set transmission shift selector to Park or Neutral position. Continuity should exist between terminals "A" and "B". Continuity should not exist in any other transmission shift selector position. If switch does not operate as specified, replace switch.

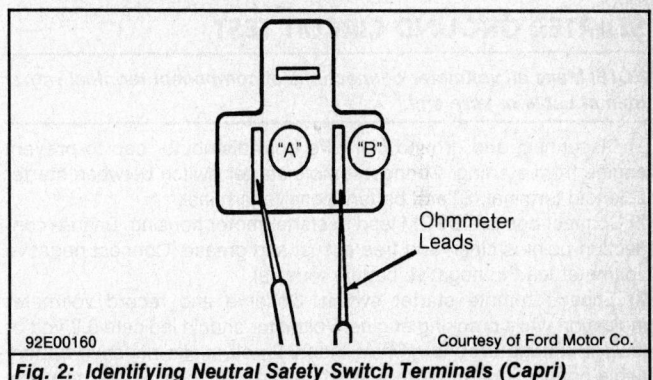

Fig. 2: Identifying Neutral Safety Switch Terminals (Capri)

VOLTAGE DROP TEST

NOTE: Make all voltmeter connections at component terminal rather than at cable or wire end.

1) Disconnect and ground coil wire from distributor cap to prevent engine from starting. Connect remote starter switch between starter solenoid terminal "S" and battery positive terminal. *See Fig. 3.*

2) Connect positive DVOM lead to battery positive terminal. Connect negative lead to starter solenoid terminal "M".

3) Engage remote starter switch. Observe voltmeter. Voltmeter indication should be less than 0.5 volt. If voltage at terminal "M" is greater than 0.5 volt, connect negative voltmeter lead to solenoid terminal "B", and repeat test.

4) If voltage at terminal "B" is less than 0.5 volt, inspect solenoid cable connections and solenoid contacts for problem.

5) Clean solenoid terminals "B", "M", and "S", and repeat steps 1) through 4). If voltmeter still indicates greater than 0.5 volt at terminal "M" and less than 0.5 volt at terminal "B", solenoid contacts are defective.

6) If voltmeter indicates greater than 0.5 volt at terminal "B", clean cables and connections at solenoid. Repeat test. If voltmeter still indi-

cates greater than 0.5 volt, check for poor positive battery cable connection or defective cable. Repair or replace as necessary.

7) To locate excessive voltage drop, move negative voltmeter lead toward battery, and repeat test for each connection point. When high voltmeter indication no longer exists, last connection point is defective.

8) Cable resistance also can be checked in the following way: Connect positive lead of voltmeter to cable end nearest battery positive. Connect voltmeter negative lead to terminal at other end of cable. While cranking engine, voltage drop should be 0.2 volt or less. If voltage drop is more than specification, clean terminals and retest. Replace cable(s) if voltage drop is still too great.

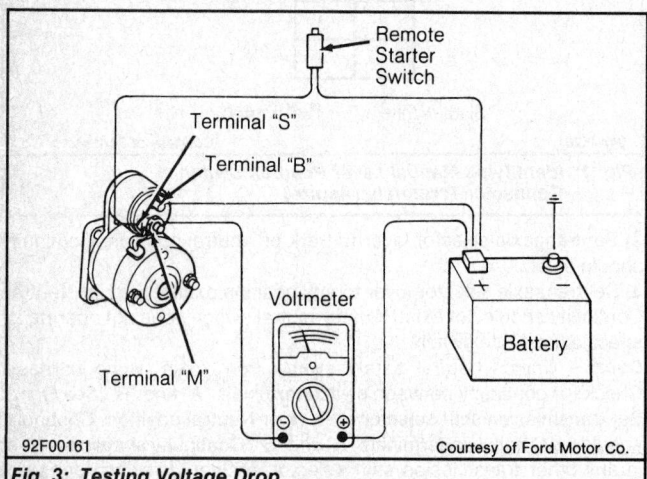

92F00161   Courtesy of Ford Motor Co.
Fig. 3: Testing Voltage Drop

STARTER GROUND CIRCUIT TEST

NOTE: Make all voltmeter connections at component terminal rather than at cable or wire end.

1) Disconnect and ground coil wire from distributor cap to prevent engine from starting. Connect remote starter switch between starter solenoid terminal "S" and battery positive terminal.

2) Connect positive DVOM lead to starter motor housing. Ensure connection point is clean and free of rust and grease. Connect negative voltmeter lead to negative battery terminal.

3) Engage remote starter switch. Observe and record voltmeter indication while cranking engine. Voltmeter should indicate 0.2 volt or less. If voltage drop is greater than 0.2 volt, clean negative battery cable connections at battery and body connections. Retest to verify problem has been corrected.

4) If voltage drop is still excessive, replace negative battery cable(s) as necessary. If battery cables test okay, but starter still cranks slowly or not at all, remove and repair starter motor.

BENCH TESTING

STARTER NO-LOAD TEST

Remove starter. Place starter on bench. Connect a fully charged 12-volt battery, voltmeter, ammeter, and remote starter switch to starter. *See Fig. 4.* Engage remote starter switch. Starter should rotate smoothly. Voltage should be greater, and current draw is less than specifications at 5000 RPM (minimum). See NO-LOAD TEST SPECIFICATIONS table. If voltage and/or current is not within specifications, disassemble starter and determine cause.

NO-LOAD TEST SPECIFICATIONS

Application	Maximum Amps	Minimum Volts
Aspire & Capri	60	11.5

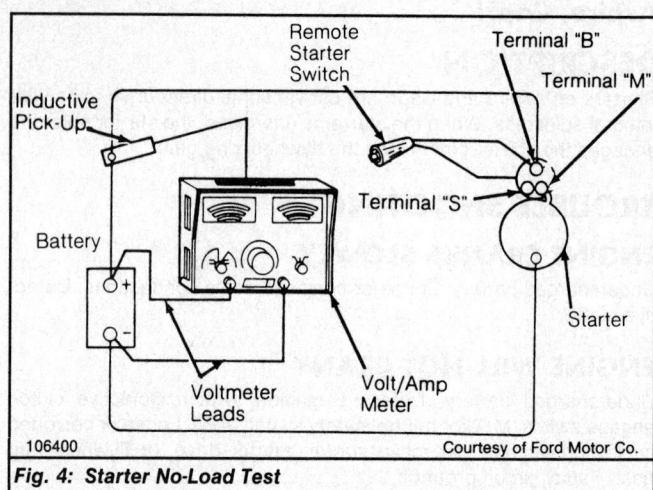

106400   Courtesy of Ford Motor Co.
Fig. 4: Starter No-Load Test

PINION GAP ADJUSTMENT TEST

1) Disconnect field lead from terminal "M" of solenoid to prevent starter from operating. *See Fig. 5.* Connect jumper wire from 12-volt battery positive terminal to terminal "S" of solenoid.

2) Connect another jumper wire from negative battery terminal to terminal "M" of solenoid. Solenoid should energize when battery is connected, extending out drive pinion. With drive pinion extended, measure pinion gap between drive pinion and collar. Gap should be 0.02-0.08" (0.5-2.0 mm).

NOTE: DO NOT engage solenoid for longer than 10 seconds. If test must be repeated, wait at least 3 minutes between tests to allow solenoid to cool.

3) Add or subtract shims between solenoid and end housing to achieve proper pinion depth gap. Install field lead to terminal "M" of solenoid. Install nut and tighten to 71-106 INCH lbs. (8-12 N.m).

SOLENOID TEST

Disconnect wiring and cables from solenoid. Check for continuity between terminal "M" and body of starter solenoid. Continuity should exist. If continuity does not exist, replace solenoid.

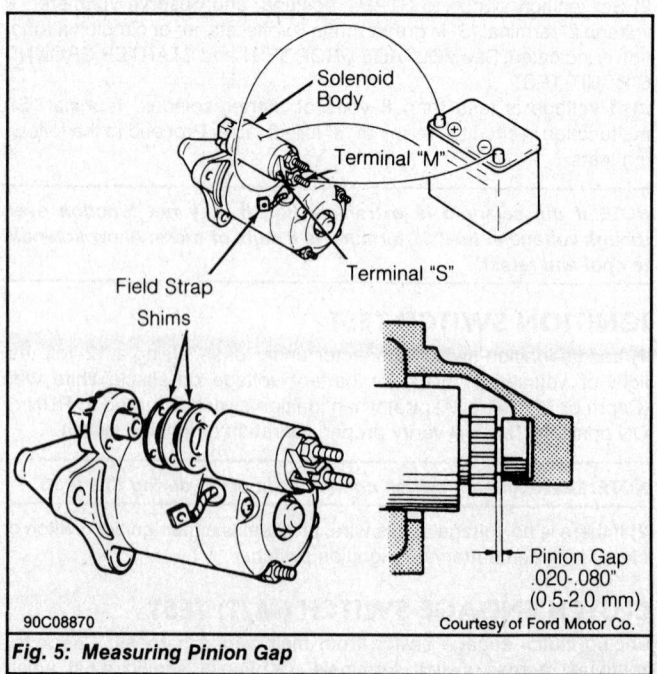

90C08870   Courtesy of Ford Motor Co.
Fig. 5: Measuring Pinion Gap

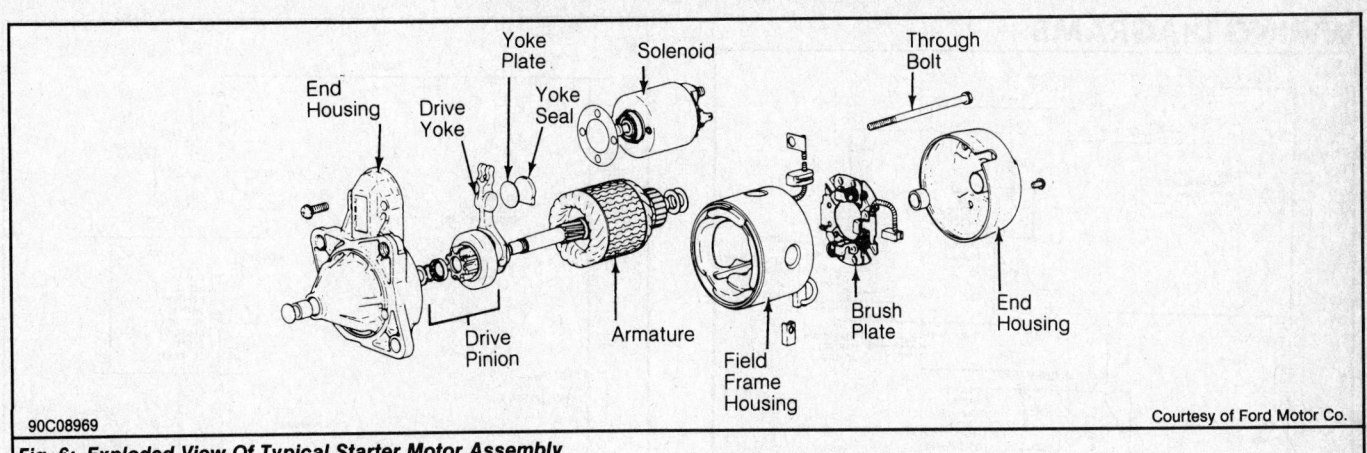

90C08969

Courtesy of Ford Motor Co.

Fig. 6: Exploded View Of Typical Starter Motor Assembly

ARMATURE TEST

1) Place armature in growler. Turn on growler and hold a piece of hacksaw blade over armature. Slowly rotate armature. If hacksaw blade is attracted to core or if it vibrates, replace armature.

2) Remove armature from growler. Measure insulation resistance between commutator and core. If continuity exists, replace armature. Measure insulation resistance between commutator and shaft. If continuity exists, replace armature.

3) Inspect for continuity between each commutator segment. If an open exists between any 2 segments, replace armature.

COMMUTATOR TEST

1) Clean and polish commutator with No. 400 grit sandpaper (if required). If surface is scored, out of round, or pitted, turn commutator on a lathe.

2) Maximum commutator runout and minimum diameter of commutator must not exceed specification after turning. See STARTER MOTOR SPECIFICATIONS table.

3) Commutator mica undercut depth should be 0.02-0.03" (0.5-0.8 mm). If undercut depth is not within specification, undercut to standard depth.

BRUSH & SPRING TEST

1) Connect ohmmeter between positive brush holder and negative brush holder. If ohmmeter indicates continuity, replace brush holder assembly.

2) Measure brush length. See STARTER MOTOR SPECIFICATIONS table. If brush length is less than specification, replace brushes.

3) Measure spring tension. Spring tension should be 2.2-4.4 lbs. (1-2 kg). Ensure brushes move freely in holders.

FIELD COIL TEST

1) Connect ohmmeter between field lead and soldered portion of brush lead. If continuity does not exist, repair or replace field coil.

2) Test field coil for shorts to ground by connecting ohmmeter between field lead and starter housing. If continuity exists, repair or replace field coil.

OVERHAUL

NOTE: *Use illustration for exploded view of starter. See Fig. 6.*

STARTER MOTOR SPECIFICATIONS

STARTER MOTOR SPECIFICATIONS

Application	Specification
Brush Length	
Minimum	0.45" (11.5 mm)
New	0.67" (17 mm)
Brush Spring Force	2.2-4.3 Lbs. (1-2 kg)
Commutator	
Runout	0.002" (0.05 mm)
Minimum Diameter	1.22" (31.0 mm)
Segment Depth	0.02-0.03" (0.5-0.8 mm)
Pinion Gap	0.02-0.08" (0.5-2.0 mm)

TORQUE SPECIFICATIONS

TORQUE SPECIFICATIONS

Application	Ft. Lbs. (N.m)
Starter Motor Mounting Bolts	23-34 (31-46)

	INCH Lbs. (N.m)
Solenoid Retaining Screws	36-66 (4.1-7.5)
Terminal Nuts	71-106 (8-12)
Through Bolts	53-71 (6-8)

1994 ELECTRICAL
Starters (Cont.)

WIRING DIAGRAMS

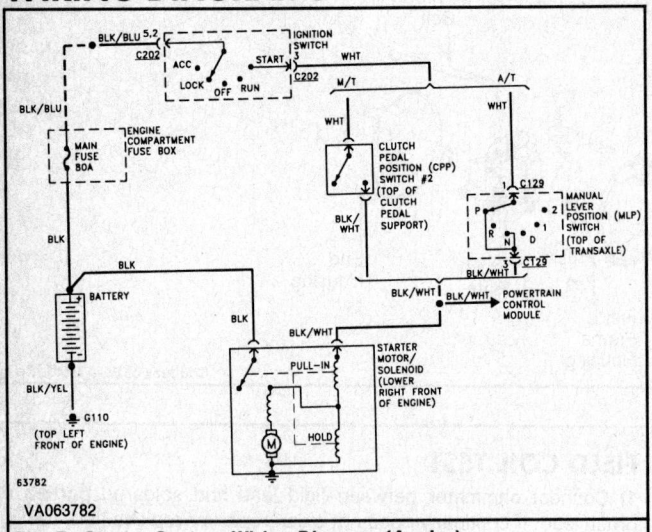

Fig. 7: Starter System Wiring Diagram (Aspire)

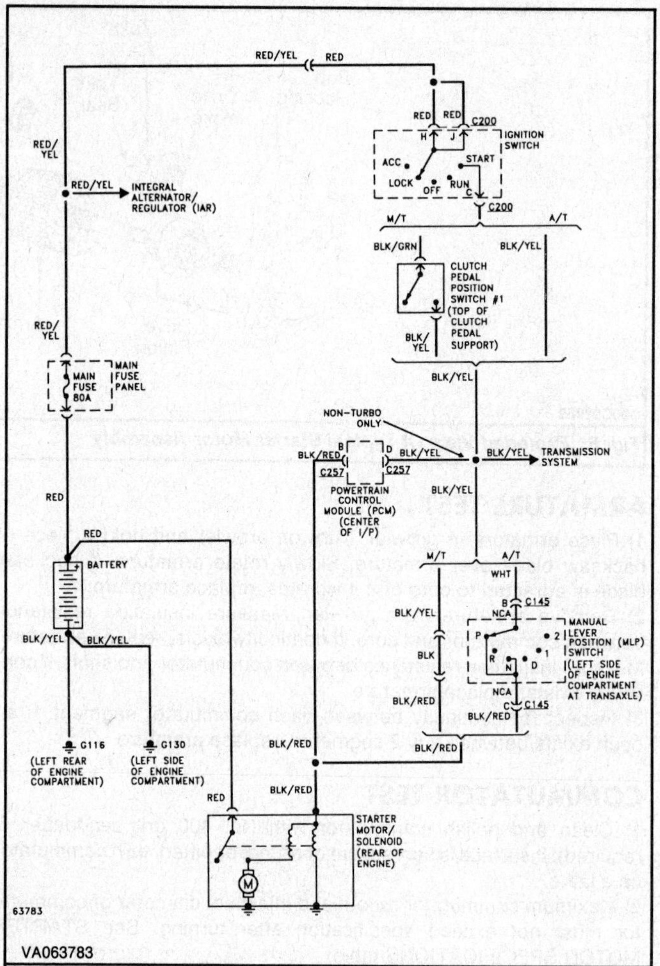

Fig. 8: Starter System Wiring Diagram (Capri)

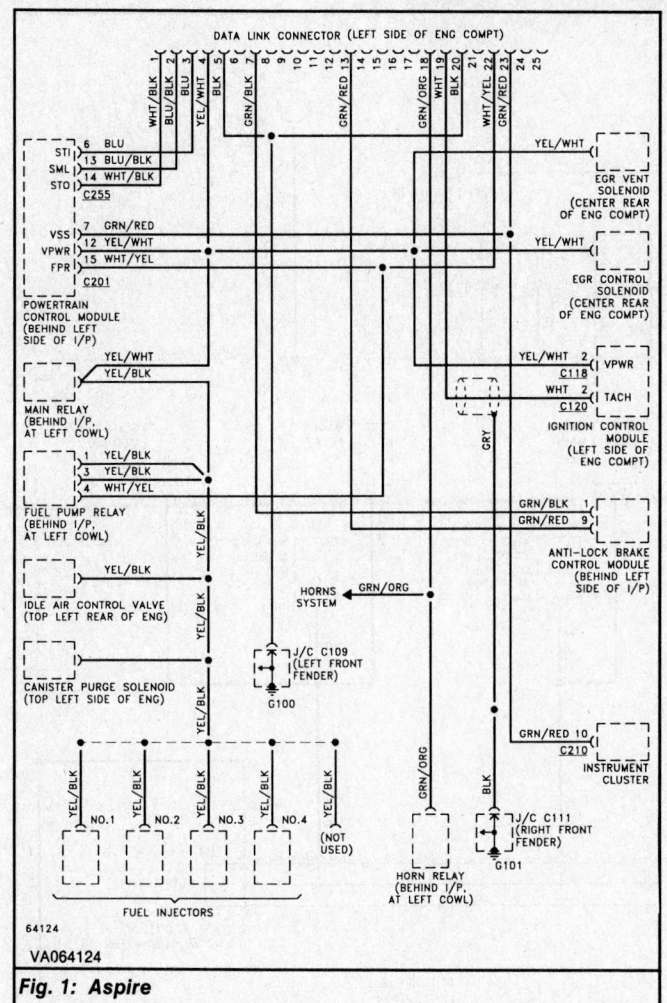

Fig. 1: Aspire

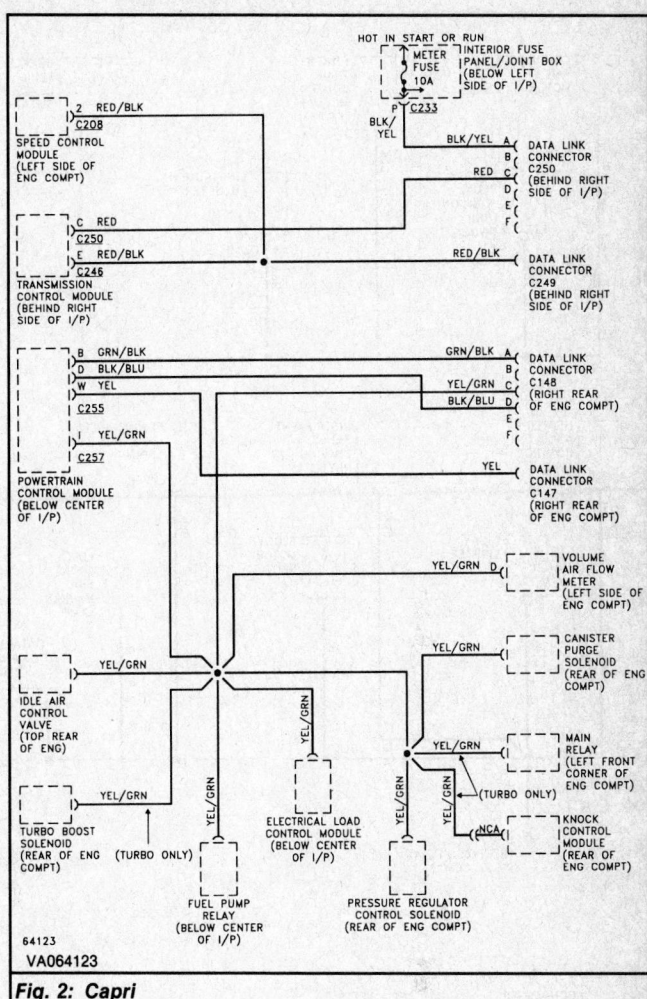

Fig. 2: Capri

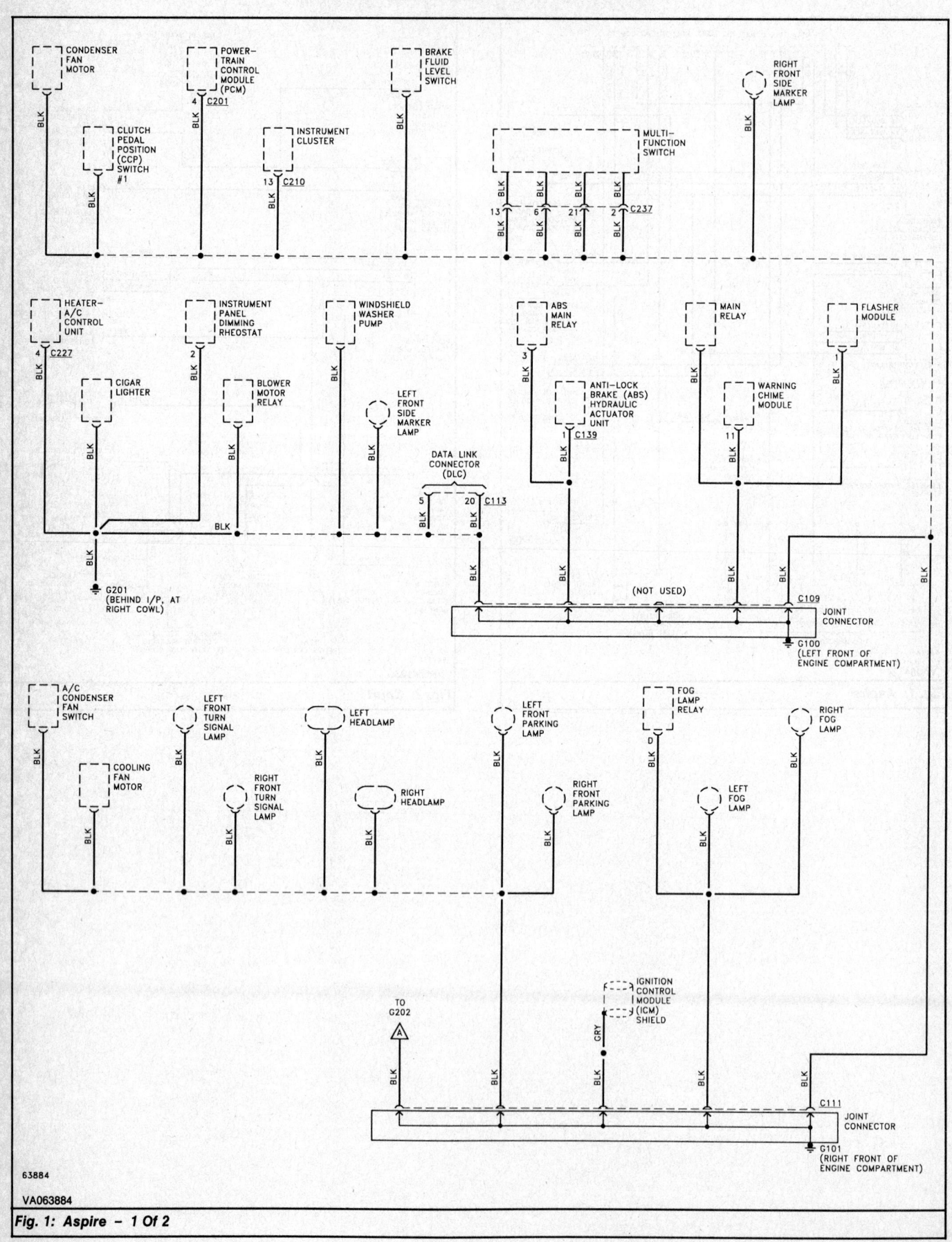

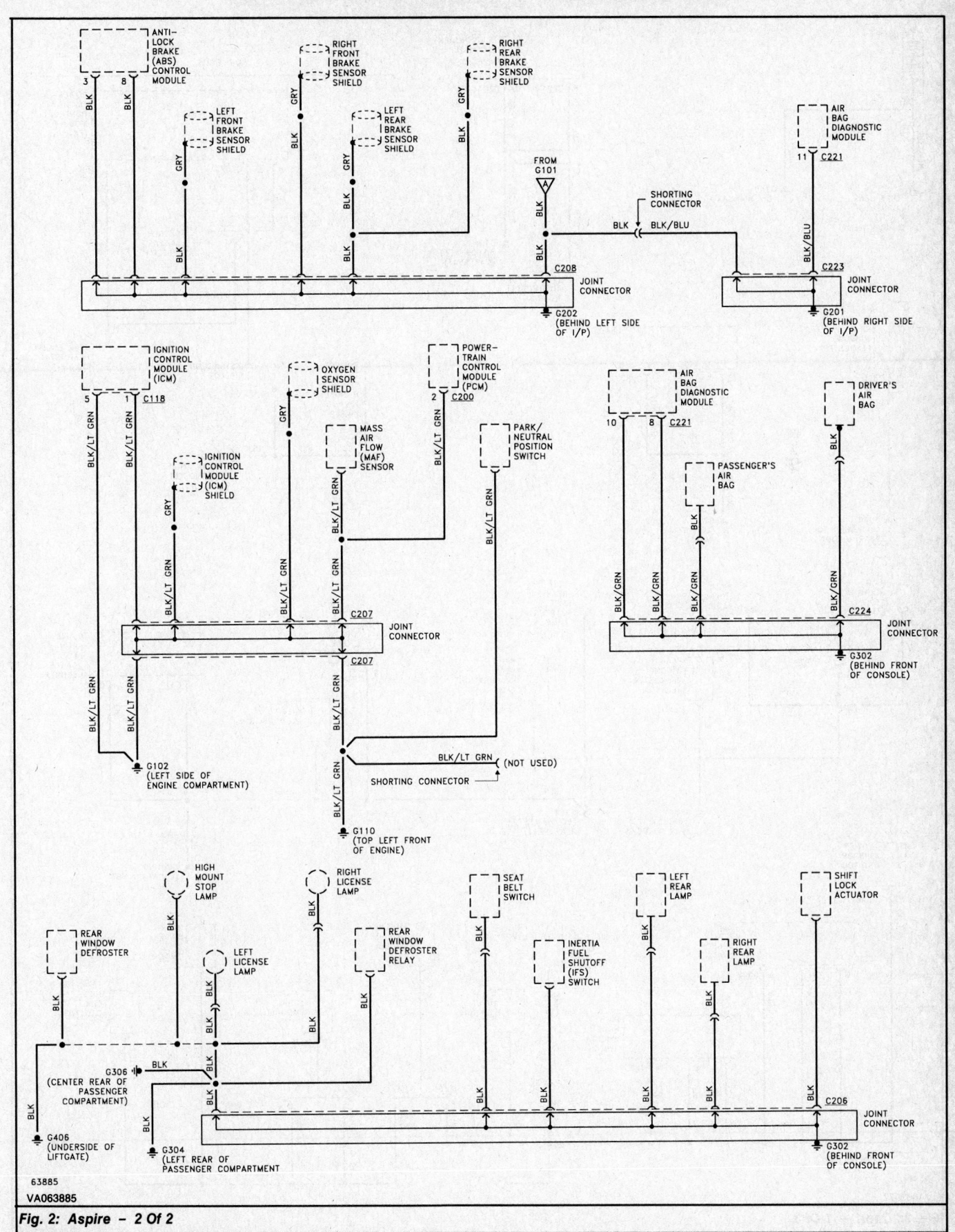

Fig. 2: Aspire - 2 Of 2

63885
VA063885

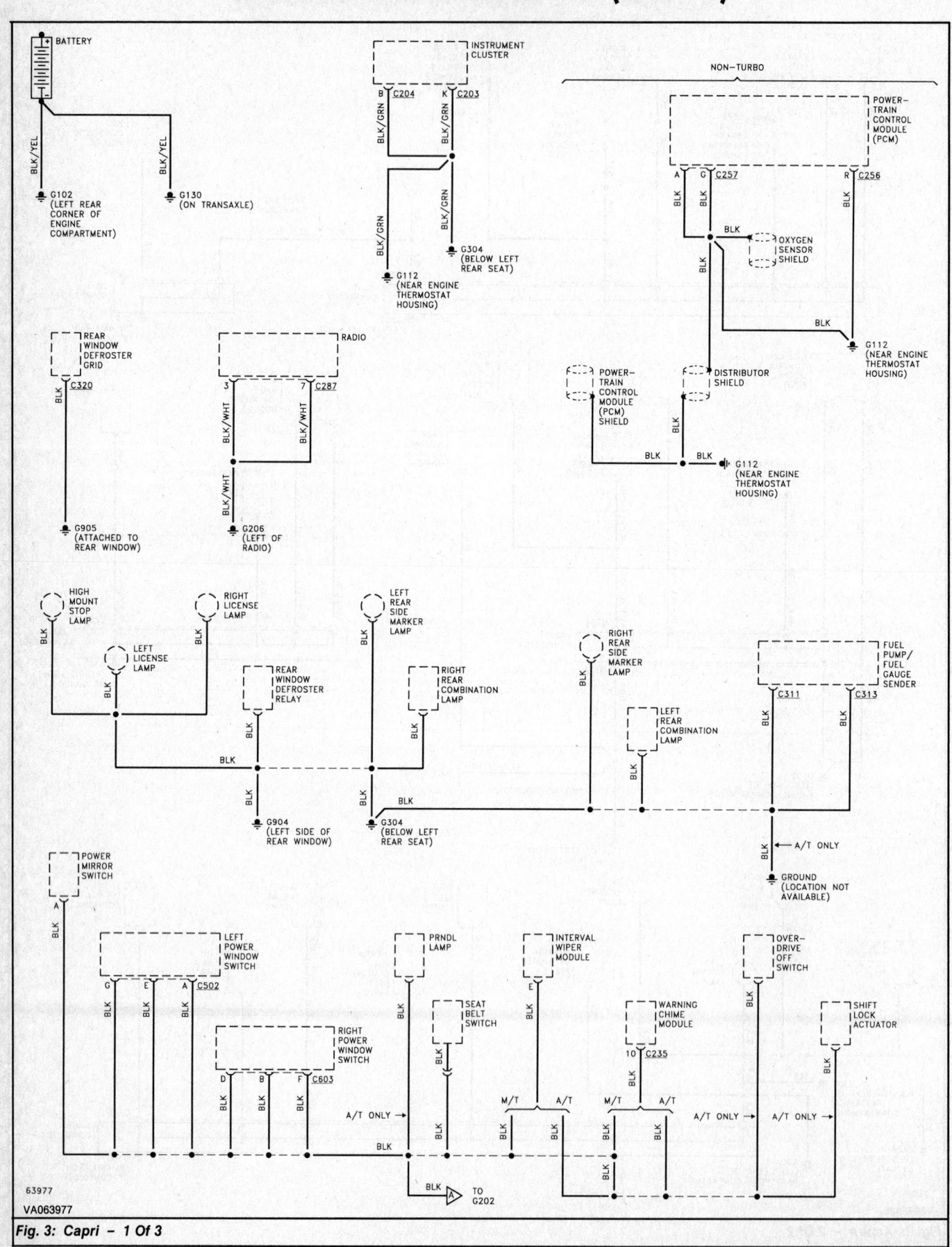

63977
VA063977

Fig. 3: Capri - 1 Of 3

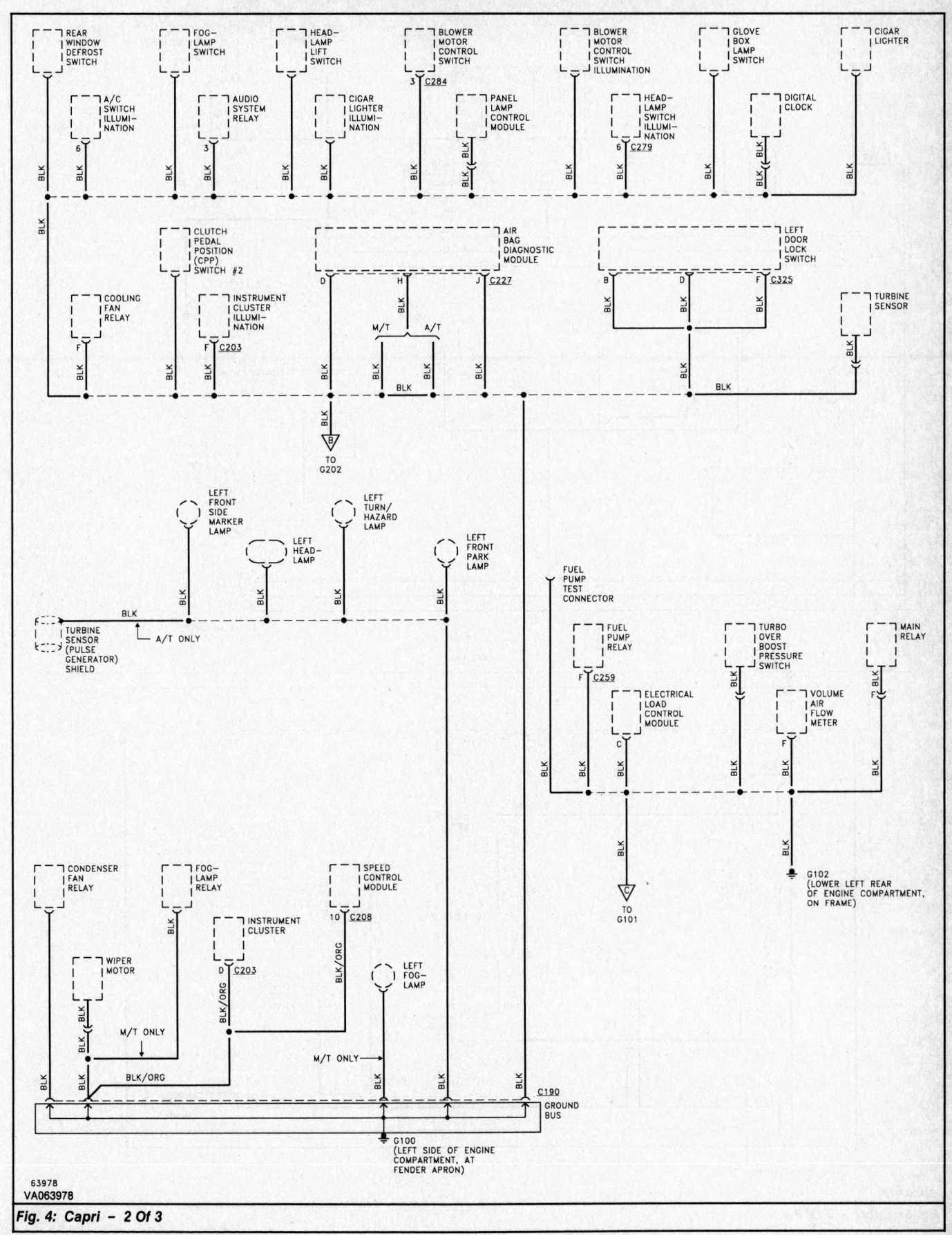

63978
VA063978

Fig. 4: Capri – 2 Of 3

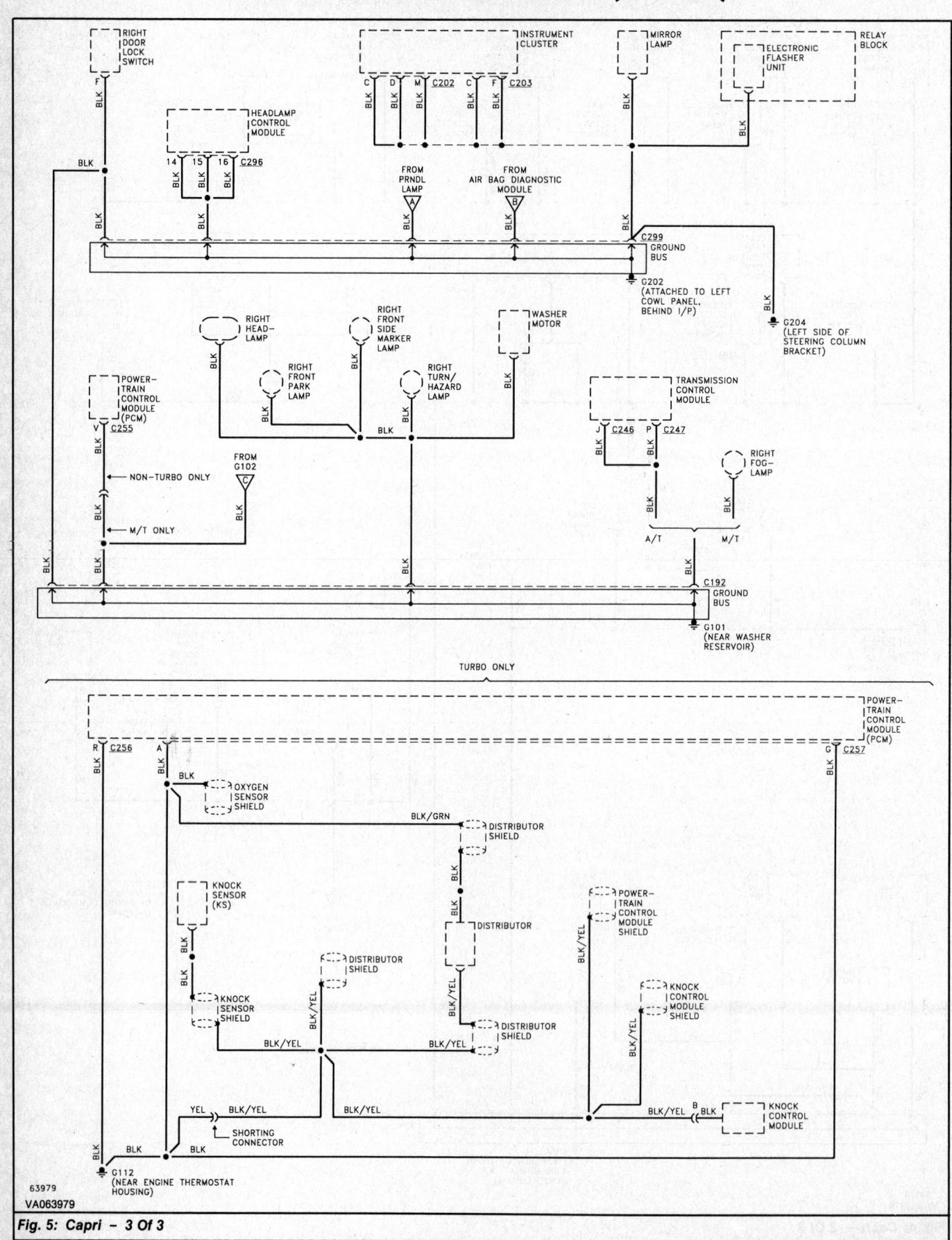

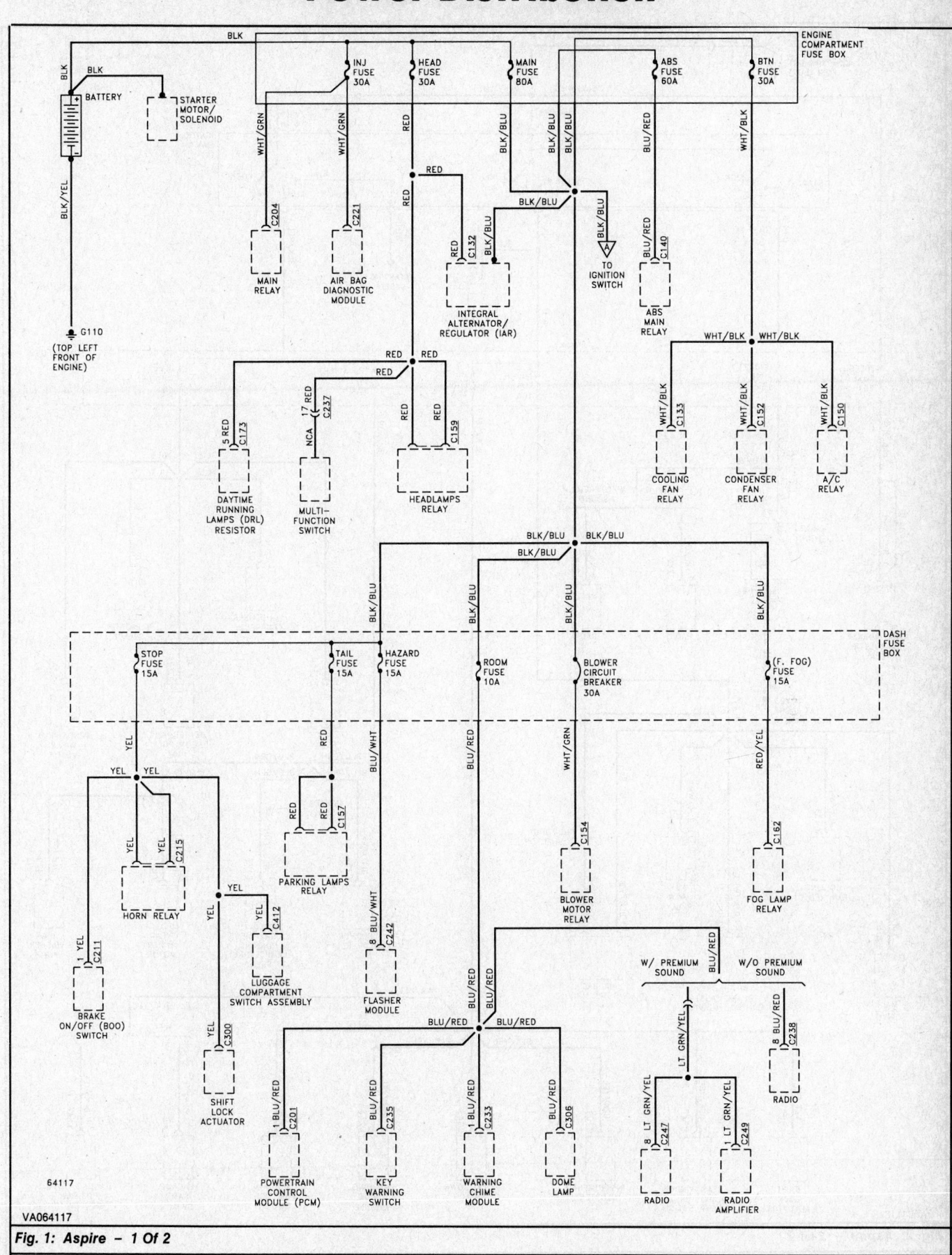

64117

VA064117

Fig. 1: Aspire – 1 Of 2

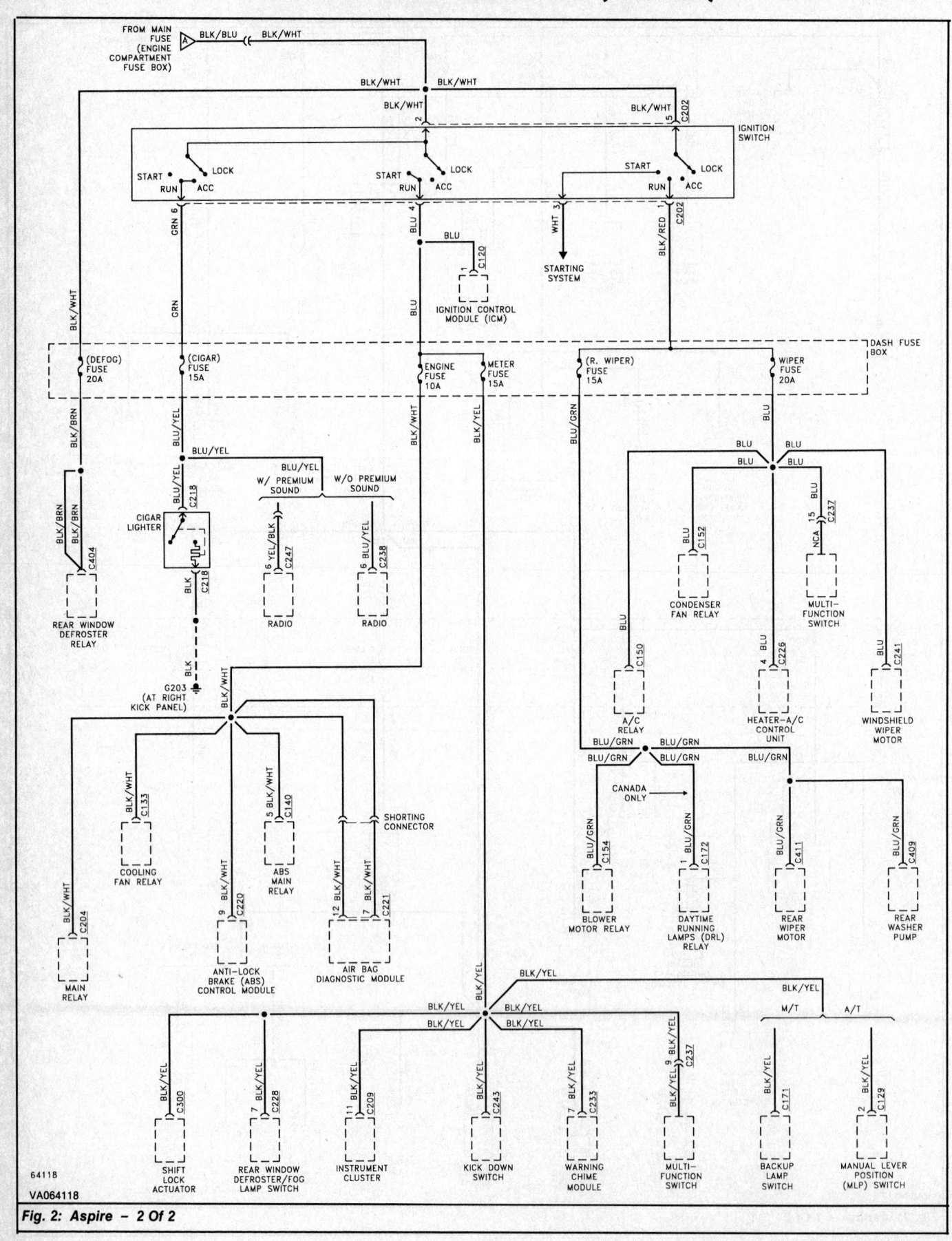

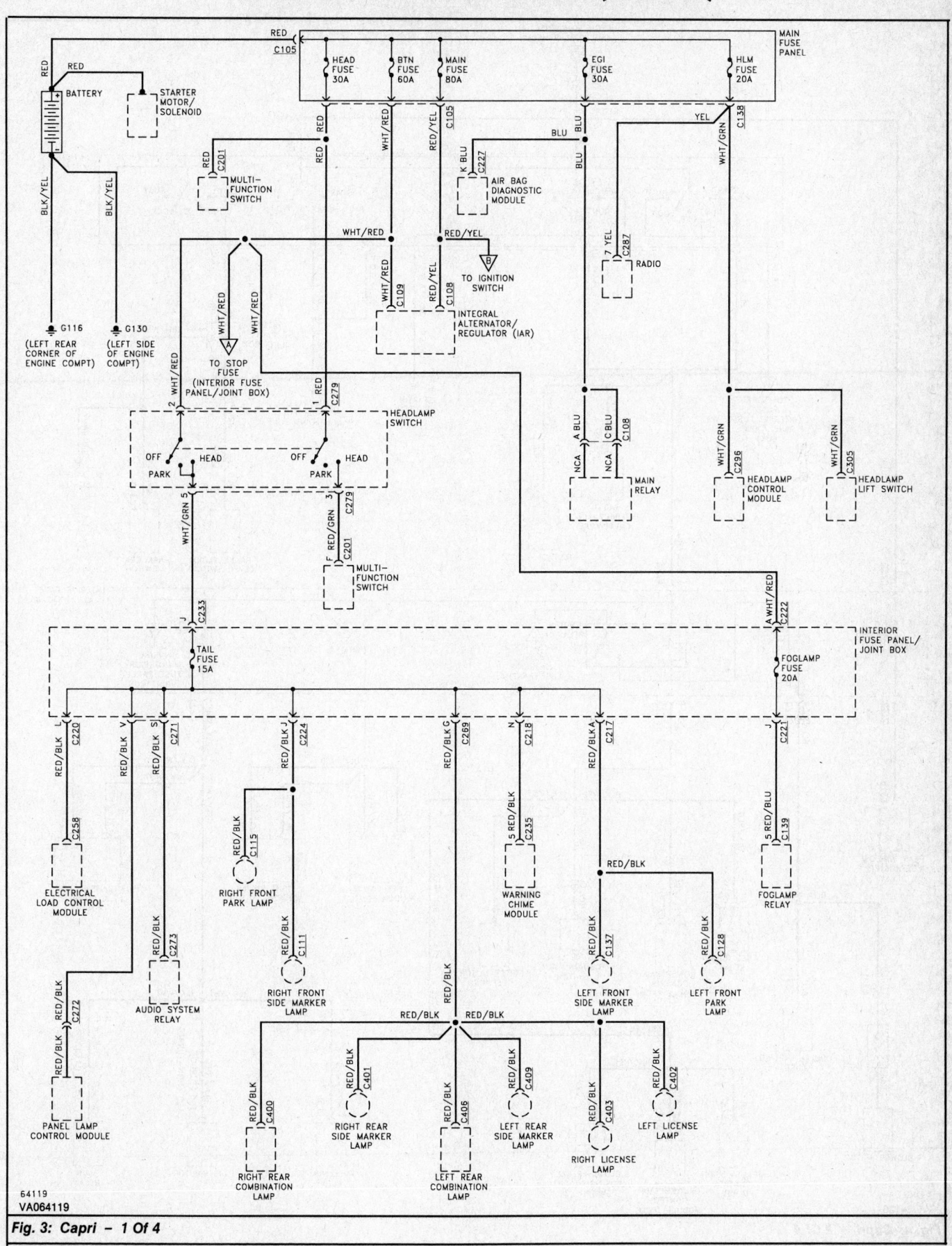

64119

VA064119

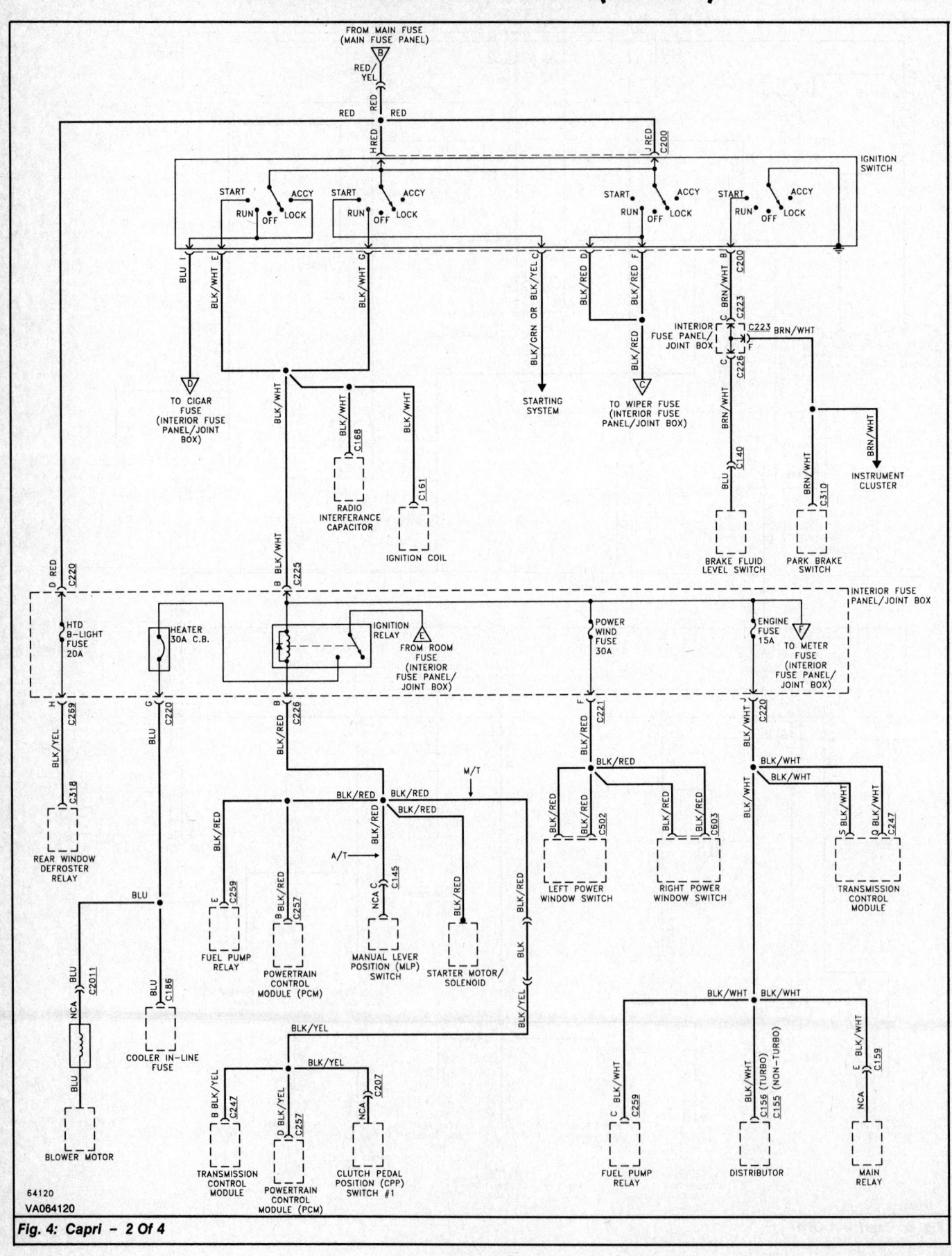

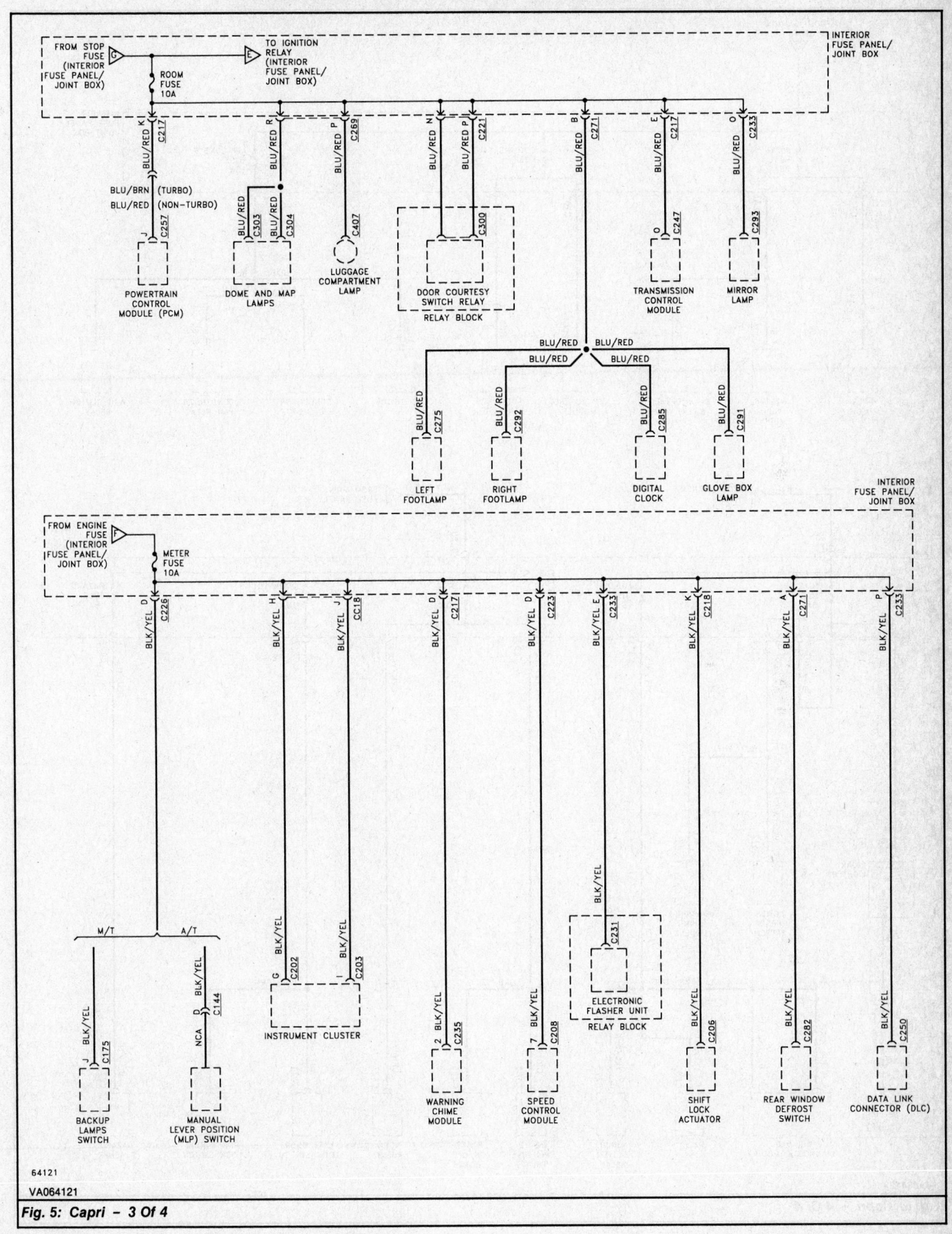

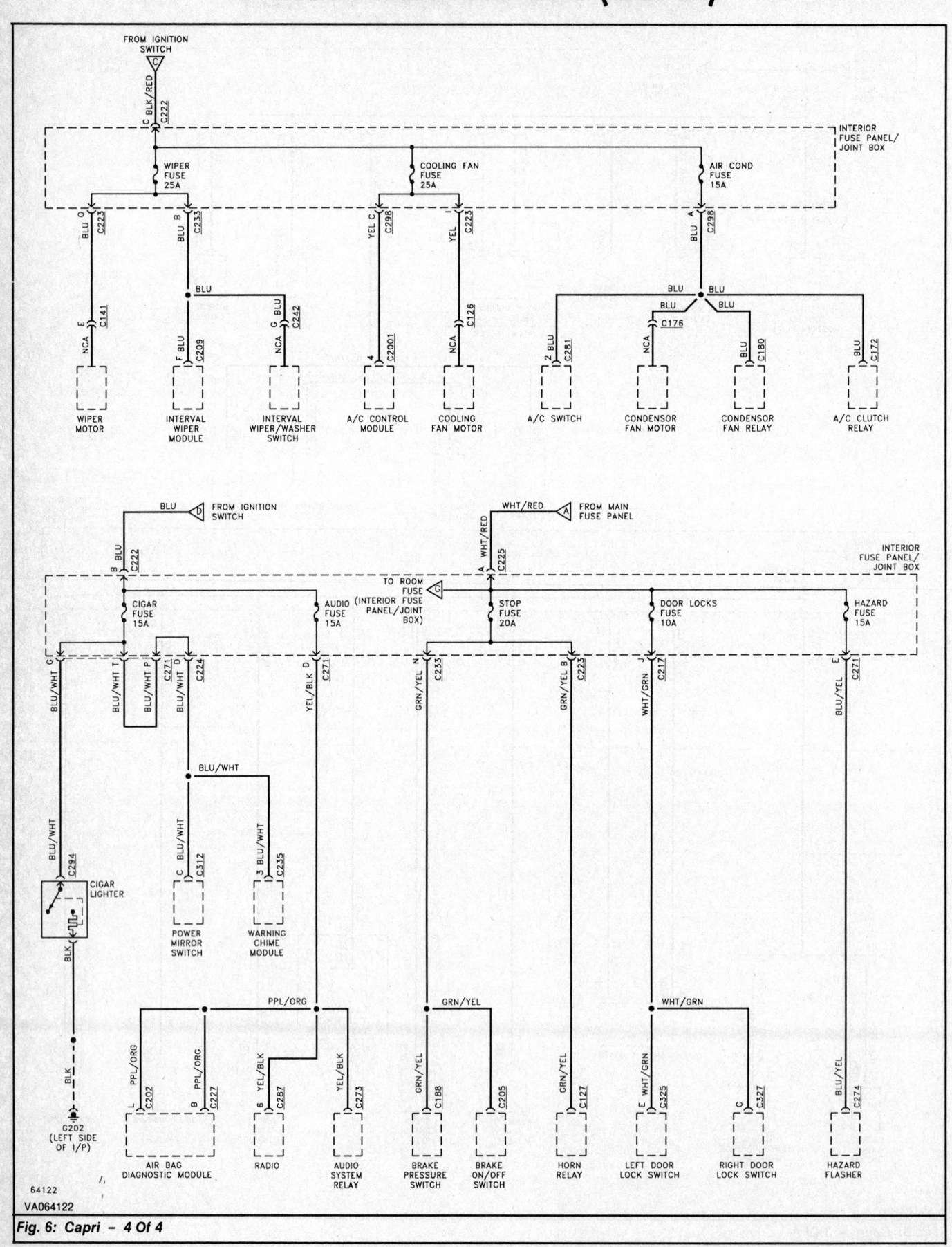

Aspire, Capri

WARNING: To avoid injury from an accidental air bag deployment, read and carefully follow all WARNINGS and SERVICE PRECAUTIONS.

NOTE: For information on air bag DIAGNOSIS & TESTING or DISPOSAL PROCEDURES, see the MITCHELL® AIR BAG SERVICE & REPAIR MANUAL, DOMESTIC & IMPORTED MODELS.

IDENTIFICATION

All models are equipped with air bags for driver and front passenger. The words Supplemental Restraint System or SRS may be embossed on the steering wheel hub. A label denoting that vehicle is equipped with air bags is affixed to driver's sun visor.

DESCRIPTION & OPERATION

The Supplemental Restraint System (SRS) is designed to provide increased accident protection for driver and passenger by deploying air bags in a front end collision. The air bags, stored in the steering wheel module and in the instrument panel above the glove box, deploy about 40 milliseconds after the impact sensors close. The SRS is designed to be used with 3-point safety belts.

During a front end collision, the front impact sensor(s) internal balls are thrown forward. The balls complete an electrical circuit which ignites the inflator to deploy the air bags. At least 2 sensors, one safing impact sensor and one front impact sensor, must activate simultaneously to inflate the air bags.

SRS includes following major components: diagnostic monitor, driver-side air bag module, passenger-side air bag module, SRS readiness light (AIR BAG warning light), front impact and safing sensors, ignitor assemblies (part of air bag modules), clockspring, and associated wiring harnesses. *See Figs. 1 and 2.*

BACK-UP POWER SUPPLY

Back-up power supply is located inside the diagnostic monitor. If battery or battery cables are damaged in a collision before impact sensors close the circuit, back-up power supply will deploy air bags. Back-up power supply will hold a deployment charge for approximately one minute after battery is disconnected.

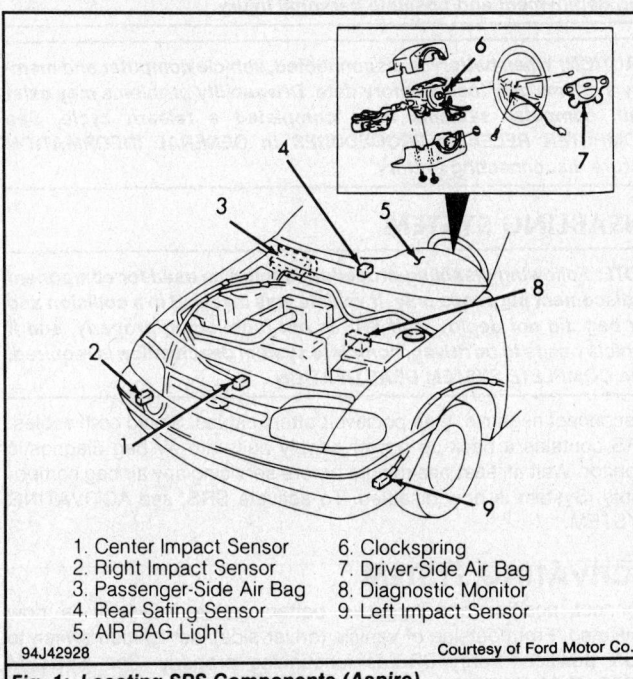

1. Center Impact Sensor
2. Right Impact Sensor
3. Passenger-Side Air Bag
4. Rear Safing Sensor
5. AIR BAG Light
6. Clockspring
7. Driver-Side Air Bag
8. Diagnostic Monitor
9. Left Impact Sensor

94J42928   Courtesy of Ford Motor Co.

Fig. 1: Locating SRS Components (Aspire)

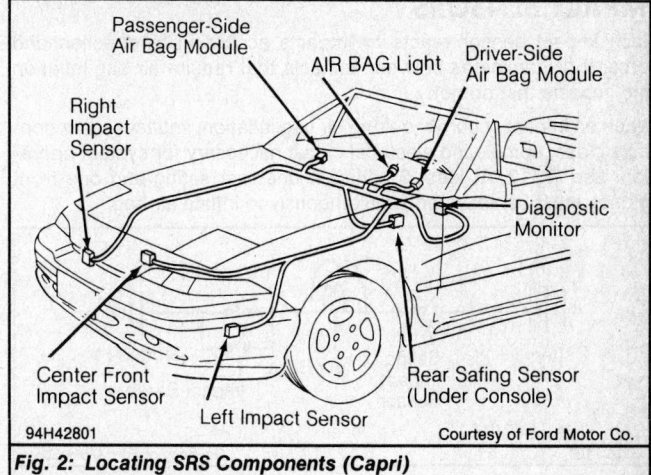

94H42801   Courtesy of Ford Motor Co.

Fig. 2: Locating SRS Components (Capri)

CLOCKSPRING

The steering column contains a clockspring assembly which transmits electrical signals from steering column wiring harness to driver-side air bag module. Clockspring is mounted between steering column and steering wheel.

DIAGNOSTIC MONITOR

Diagnostic monitor contains a microcomputer which monitors electrical system components and connections. Diagnostic monitor performs a self-check of system circuits each time ignition is turned on. Monitor also energizes SRS readiness light (AIR BAG warning light) during initial system self-check, and whenever a fault is detected. The faults are translated into coded flashes displayed by AIR BAG warning light.

If a system fault exists and/or AIR BAG warning light is malfunctioning, a tone will sound, indicating need for service. See TONE GENERATOR. Diagnostic monitor can also disarm SRS if certain faults occur.

DRIVER-SIDE AIR BAG MODULE

Driver-side air bag module is mounted on front face of steering wheel, encased in steering wheel trim cover. When front impact sensors close, signaling an impact, the ignitor causes ignition of inflator gas generant. This ignition reaction produces nitrogen gas, which inflates air bag.

When air bag deploys, tear seams molded into trim cover separate, allowing inflation of the air bag. Driver-side air bag module is not serviceable and must be replaced as a complete assembly.

PASSENGER-SIDE AIR BAG MODULE

Passenger-side air bag module is mounted in right side of instrument panel, above glove box. When a front impact sensor and rear safing impact sensor close, signaling an impact, the air bag ignitors cause ignition of inflator gas generant.

Since passenger-side air bag is larger than driver-side air bag, inflator contains more gas generant in a different configuration to produce more gas. When air bag is activated, instrument panel trim cover tears at seams and hinges aside during deployment. Passenger-side air bag module is serviced only as a complete assembly.

ELECTRICAL SYSTEM

SRS is powered directly from battery, and can function with ignition switch in any position. System can also function when driver-side and passenger-side seats are unoccupied. The 3 main functions performed by electrical subsystem are detecting an impact, switching electric power to ignitors for air bags, and monitoring readiness of SRS.

IMPACT SENSORS

Each impact sensor reacts to impacts according to direction and force. It discriminates between impacts that require air bag inflation and impacts that do not.

When an impact occurs requiring air bag inflation, impact sensor contacts close, completing electrical circuit necessary for system operation. See Fig. 3. At least 2 sensors, one rear safing and one front impact, must be activated simultaneously to inflate air bag.

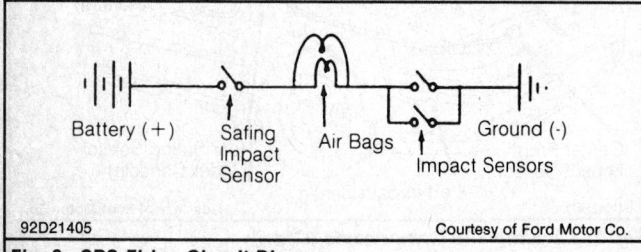

| 92D21405 | Courtesy of Ford Motor Co. |

Fig. 3: SRS Firing Circuit Diagram

On Aspire, there are 4 impact sensors. Three front impact sensors, and one rear safing sensor. The center impact sensor is mounted on radiator support, directly behind center of front bumper. One impact sensor is located below each of the front fenders on left and right bumper cover supports. Safing sensor is mounted on bulkhead behind center of instrument panel. See Fig. 1.

On Capri, there are 4 impact sensors. One dual impact safing sensor (center impact sensor), 2 impact sensors, and one rear safing sensor. The center impact sensor is mounted on radiator support, directly behind center of front bumper. One impact sensor is located below each front headlight. Rear safing sensor is located under center console, behind parking brake handle.

TONE GENERATOR

AIR BAG warning light is the primary means of determining SRS condition. However, a series of 5 sets of 5 tones, indicating system requires service, will sound if AIR BAG warning light is out and a fault occurs in the system. Unless serviced, SRS may not function properly in an accident.

SYSTEM OPERATION CHECK

1) When checking SRS operation, and at completion of each diagnostic test, check for faults in SRS. To check system, set ignition switch to RUN position. If AIR BAG warning light glows for 4-8 seconds and then goes out, SRS is functioning properly.
2) If a fault code is detected in SRS during initial system check, AIR BAG warning light will fail to light, stay on continuously, or flash a code sequence. If AIR BAG warning light flashes, indicating a fault in system, count number of flashes after fault code has cycled twice. Number of flashes represents a code number used to diagnose SRS.
3) If a system fault code exists and AIR BAG warning light fails to light, an audible tone will occur, indicating AIR BAG warning light is out and service is required. See TONE GENERATOR.

SERVICE PRECAUTIONS

These precautions should be observed when working with SRS:
- Disable SRS before servicing any SRS or steering column components. Failure to do so may result in accidental air bag deployment and personal injury. See DISABLING & ACTIVATING AIR BAG SYSTEM.
- Wait one minute after disabling SRS before working on vehicle. Back-up power supply holds a deployment charge for approximately one minute after positive battery cable is disconnected. Servicing SRS before one minute may cause accidental air bag deployment and possible personal injury.
- Because of critical system operating requirements, DO NOT service impact sensors, clockspring, diagnostic monitor, or air bag modules. Repairs are made by replacement only.

- Always wear safety glasses whenever servicing a vehicle equipped with an air bag or when handling an air bag.
- When carrying a live air bag module, point air bag module and trim cover away from your body. Doing so minimizes chance of injury in event of accidental deployment.
- When placing a live air bag module on a bench or other surface, always face air bag module and trim cover upward, away from surface. This will reduce motion of module if it is accidentally deployed.
- After deployment, air bag surface may contain deposits of sodium hydroxide, which may irritate skin. Sodium hydroxide is a product of gas generant combustion. Always wear gloves and safety glasses when handling a deployed air bag. Wash your hands with mild soap and water.
- If scrapping a vehicle with an undeployed air bag module, air bag must be deployed.
- If a part is replaced and new part does not correct condition, reinstall original part and perform diagnostic procedure again.
- Never probe connectors on air bag module. Doing so may cause air bag deployment and/or personal injury.
- Instruction to disconnect or unplug always refers to connectors. DO NOT remove component from vehicle if instructed to disconnect.
- After any servicing, verify AIR BAG warning light does not indicate any fault codes. See SYSTEM OPERATION CHECK.
- Replace air bag module if trim cover (deployment door) is marred or damaged. DO NOT repaint trim cover; paint may degrade cover material. Replace air bag module as necessary.

DISABLING & ACTIVATING AIR BAG SYSTEM

DISABLING SYSTEM

WARNING: Wait one minute after disabling SRS before working on vehicle. Back-up power supply holds a deployment charge for approximately one minute after positive battery cable is disconnected. Servicing SRS before one minute may cause accidental air bag deployment and possible personal injury.

CAUTION: When battery is disconnected, vehicle computer and memory systems may lose memory data. Driveability problems may exist until computer systems have completed a relearn cycle. See COMPUTER RELEARN PROCEDURES in GENERAL INFORMATION before disconnecting battery.

DISABLING SYSTEM

NOTE: Following disabling procedure should be used for component replacement purposes only. If vehicle was involved in a collision and air bag did not deploy or if SRS is not functioning properly, and if vehicle needs to be driven, complete system deactivation is required. See COMPLETE SYSTEM DEACTIVATION.

Disconnect negative, then positive battery cables. Shield both cables. SRS contains a back-up power supply built into air bag diagnostic monitor. Wait at least one minute before servicing any air bag components. System is now disabled. To activate SRS, see ACTIVATING SYSTEM.

ACTIVATING SYSTEM

Connect positive and negative battery cables. System is now activated. From outside of vehicle (driver side), set ignition switch to RUN position. Verify SRS is functioning properly. See SYSTEM OPERATION CHECK.

COMPLETE SYSTEM REACTIVATION

WARNING: Back-up power supply will hold a deployment charge for approximately one minute after positive battery cable is disconnected. Servicing SRS before one minute may cause accidental air bag deployment and possible personal injury. Always deactivate driver-side and passenger-side air bag modules before attempting any service procedures.

NOTE: Complete system deactivation sequence is required for following situations:
* *Vehicle was involved in a collision, air bags did not deploy, and vehicle needs to be driven.*
* *SRS is not functioning properly and vehicle needs to be driven.*
* *Diagnosis and testing purposes.*

1) Disconnect negative and positive battery cables. Wait at least one minute to deplete charge in back-up power supply. Remove driver-side air bag module. See DRIVER-SIDE AIR BAG MODULE under REMOVAL & INSTALLATION.
2) Connect Air Bag Simulator (105-00010) to clockspring. *See Fig. 4.* Remove passenger-side air bag module. See PASSENGER-SIDE AIR BAG MODULE under REMOVAL & INSTALLATION. Connect air bag simulator to passenger-side wiring harness. Connect positive and negative battery cables. To reactivate SRS, see COMPLETE SYSTEM REACTIVATION.

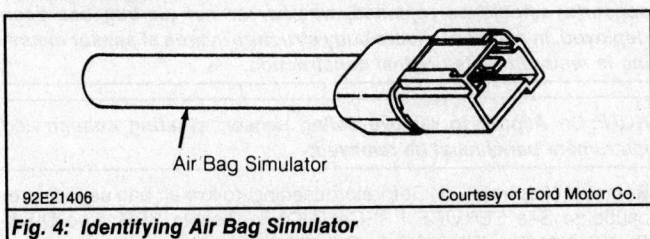

92E21406   Courtesy of Ford Motor Co.

Air Bag Simulator

Fig. 4: Identifying Air Bag Simulator

COMPLETE SYSTEM REACTIVATION

Disconnect negative and positive battery cables. Remove air bag simulators. Install air bag modules. Install nuts and washers. Tighten to specification. See TORQUE SPECIFICATIONS. Reconnect positive and negative battery cables. System is now reactivated. Verify SRS is functioning properly. See SYSTEM OPERATION CHECK.

REMOVAL & INSTALLATION

WARNING: Failure to follow air bag service precautions may result in air bag deployment and personal injury. See SERVICE PRECAUTIONS. After component replacement, verify proper system operation. See SYSTEM OPERATION CHECK.

CAUTION: When battery is disconnected, vehicle computer and memory systems may lose memory data. Driveability problems may exist until computer systems have completed a relearn cycle. See COMPUTER RELEARN PROCEDURES in GENERAL INFORMATION before disconnecting battery.

CLOCKSPRING

Removal – 1) Before proceeding, follow air bag service procedures. See SERVICE PRECAUTIONS. Disable SRS. See DISABLING & ACTIVATING AIR BAG SYSTEM.

CAUTION: When removing steering wheel, DO NOT use a knock-off type steering wheel puller, or strike steering wheel or shaft with a hammer. A sudden impact could damage bearing or collapse steering column.

2) Remove driver-side air bag module. See DRIVER-SIDE AIR BAG MODULE. Position front wheels straight ahead, with steering column shaft alignment mark at 12 o'clock position. Remove steering wheel. See STEERING WHEEL.
3) Remove instrument panel moldings and trim panels as necessary for access to lower steering column shroud. Remove steering column lower shroud.
4) Unplug clockspring wiring harness. Apply 2 strips of tape across clockspring stator and rotor to prevent accidental rotation. *See Fig. 5.* Remove retaining screws. Lift clockspring from steering column.

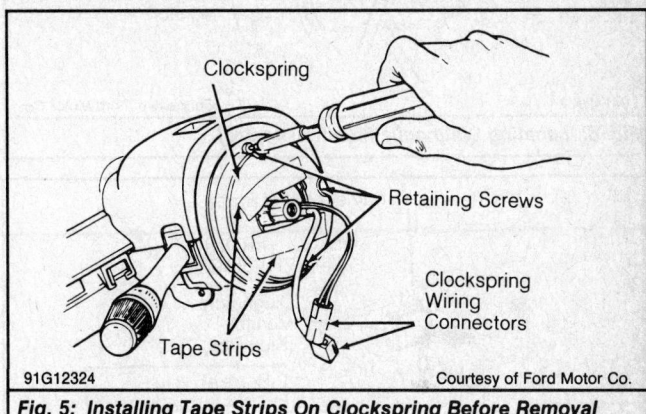

Clockspring

Retaining Screws

Clockspring Wiring Connectors

Tape Strips

91G12324   Courtesy of Ford Motor Co.

Fig. 5: Installing Tape Strips On Clockspring Before Removal (Typical)

NOTE: Service replacement clockspring will contain a Red plastic locking insert to prevent rotation. DO NOT remove insert until clockspring is securely installed.

Installation – 1) Position front wheels straight ahead, with steering column shaft alignment mark at 12 o'clock position. Align clockspring to column shaft and mounting bosses. Slide clockspring onto shaft. Tighten screws to specification. See TORQUE SPECIFICATIONS.
2) Remove tape strips. If new clockspring is being installed, remove Red plastic locking insert. Route clockspring wiring down through column and connect to column wiring harness. Install steering column lower shroud and lower instrument panel cover. Install moldings.
3) Install steering wheel and driver-side air bag module. Activate SRS. Verify system is functioning properly. See SYSTEM OPERATION CHECK.

DIAGNOSTIC MONITOR

Removal & Installation (Aspire) – 1) Before proceeding, follow air bag service precautions. See SERVICE PRECAUTIONS. Disable SRS. See DISABLING & ACTIVATING AIR BAG SYSTEM.
2) Diagnostic monitor has a Blue casing, and is located behind radio and shift panel console. *See Fig. 6.* Remove ashtray from rear of shift console. Remove screw from ashtray opening in console.
3) Apply parking brake. Remove parking brake access cover. Remove parking brake console panel. Remove gear selector knob/handle. Remove shift console mounting screws.
4) Raise shift console. Unplug harness connectors as necessary. Remove shift console. Unplug diagnostic monitor connectors. Remove diagnostic monitor.
5) To install, reverse removal procedure. Activate SRS. Verify system is functioning properly. See SYSTEM OPERATION CHECK.
Removal & Installation (Capri) – 1) Before proceeding, follow air bag service precautions. See SERVICE PRECAUTIONS. Disable SRS. See DISABLING & ACTIVATING AIR BAG SYSTEM.
2) Diagnostic monitor has a Blue casing, and is mounted on upper instrument panel brace, behind fuse panel. *See Fig. 7.* Press monitor retaining tabs and pull monitor downward. Unplug connector. Remove monitor.
3) To install, reverse removal procedure. Activate SRS. Verify system is functioning properly. See SYSTEM OPERATION CHECK.

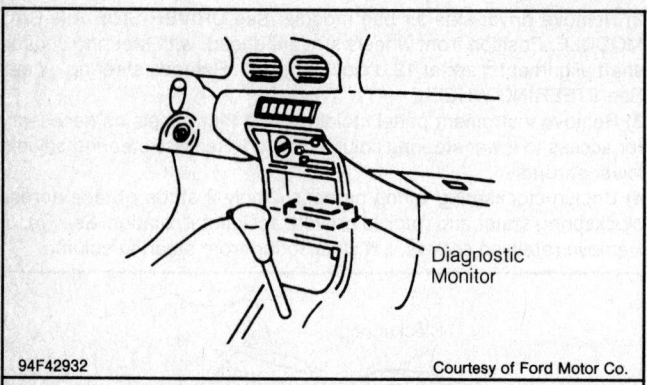

94F42932   Courtesy of Ford Motor Co.
Fig. 6: Locating Diagnostic Monitor (Aspire)

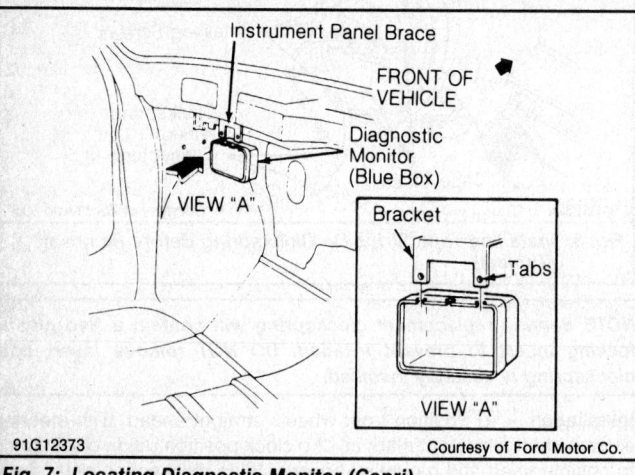

91G12373   Courtesy of Ford Motor Co.
Fig. 7: Locating Diagnostic Monitor (Capri)

FRONT IMPACT SENSORS

NOTE: Vehicle sensor orientation is critical for proper system operation. If a vehicle equipped with SRS is involved in a crash, and fenders or grille area have been damaged, inspect sensor mounting brackets for deformation. If damaged, system should be deactivated to ensure air bag does not deploy. See COMPLETE SYSTEM DEACTIVATION under DISABLING & ACTIVATING AIR BAG SYSTEM. Damaged sensor(s) should be replaced, whether or not air bag has been deployed. In addition, ensure body structure in area of sensor mounting is restored to its original construction.

Removal (Aspire) – **1)** Before proceeding, follow air bag service precautions. See SERVICE PRECAUTIONS. Disable SRS. See DISABLING & ACTIVATING AIR BAG SYSTEM.
2) Center impact sensor is mounted on radiator support, directly behind center of front bumper. One impact sensor is located below each of the front fenders on left and right bumper cover supports.
3) To remove center impact sensor, unplug center impact sensor connector. Remove bolts and sensor. To remove left or right impact sensor, raise and support vehicle. Remove wheel and tire.
4) Remove front fender splash shield. Disengage impact sensor wiring harness from fender apron clip. Unplug sensor connector. Remove sensor.
Installation – Install sensor with arrow pointing toward front of vehicle. Tighten sensor bolts to specification. See TORQUE SPECIFICATIONS. To complete installation, reverse removal procedure. Activate SRS. Verify system is functioning properly. See SYSTEM OPERATION CHECK.
Removal (Capri) – **1)** Before proceeding, follow air bag service precautions. See SERVICE PRECAUTIONS. Disable SRS. See DISABLING & ACTIVATING AIR BAG SYSTEM. Center front sensor is mounted on radiator support, directly behind center of front bumper.

2) Front impact sensors are attached to left and right tow bracket on inner fender panel, below headlight. Unplug foglight connectors.
3) Remove bumper side reinforcement plate retaining screws located inside front of left and right front fenders. Remove bumper retaining nuts from foglight cavities.
4) With assistant, carefully slide bumper forward to remove from vehicle. Unplug sensor connector. Disengage all wiring retainers. Remove sensor.
5) To remove front impact sensor, raise headlights with service switch. Remove headlight bezel and splash shield. Remove wiring connector retaining clip from apron under headlight. Unplug sensor connector. Remove sensor.
Installation – Install sensor with top arrow pointing toward front of vehicle. Tighten sensor bolts to specification. See TORQUE SPECIFICATIONS. To complete installation, reverse removal procedure. Activate SRS. Verify system is functioning properly. See SYSTEM OPERATION CHECK.

REAR SAFING SENSOR

NOTE: Vehicle sensor orientation is critical for proper system operation. If a vehicle equipped with SRS is involved in a collision, and fenders or grille area have been damaged, inspect sensor mounting brackets for deformation. If damaged, system should be deactivated to ensure air bag does not deploy. See COMPLETE SYSTEM DEACTIVATION under DISABLING & ACTIVATING AIR BAG SYSTEM. Damaged sensor(s) should be replaced, whether or not air bag has been deployed. In addition, ensure body structure in area of sensor mounting is restored to its original construction.

NOTE: On Aspire, to remove safing sensor, steering column and instrument panel must be removed.

Removal (Aspire) – **1)** Before proceeding, follow air bag service precautions. See SERVICE PRECAUTIONS. Disable SRS. See DISABLING & ACTIVATING AIR BAG SYSTEM.
2) Rear safing sensor is located in center of defroster duct, against bulkhead. *See Fig. 8.* Remove driver-side air bag. See DRIVER-SIDE AIR BAG. Remove steering wheel. See STEERING WHEEL. Remove turn signal and wiper switches. Remove ignition switch.
3) Remove steering column shaft lower pinch bolt. Remove lower steering column mounting bracket nuts. Remove upper steering column mounting bracket bolts. Mark lower steering column shaft and gear input shaft coupling for reassembly reference. Remove steering column.
4) Remove instrument cluster. *See Fig. 9.* Remove instrument panel finish panel. Push interior fuse block forward, but do not remove. Remove ashtray from rear of shift console. Remove screw from ashtray opening in console.
5) Apply parking brake. Remove parking brake access cover. Remove parking brake console panel. Remove transmission gear selector knob/handle. Remove shift console mounting screws.
6) Raise shift console to unplug connectors as necessary. Remove shift console. Unplug diagnostic monitor connectors. Remove diagnostic monitor. Remove A/C heater control mounting screws.
7) Disengage control cables. Remove A/C heater control. Open glove box. Remove passenger-side air bag module. See PASSENGER-SIDE AIR BAG. Remove instrument panel access covers. Remove instrument panel lower mounting bolts.
8) Loosen hood release lock nut. Remove cable. Carefully pull instrument panel out far enough for access to connectors. Unplug connectors as necessary. Remove instrument panel. Remove defroster duct. Unplug safing sensor connector. Remove sensor.
Installation – **1)** Connect sensor to wiring harness. Position sensor with top arrow pointing toward front of vehicle. Tighten retaining nuts to specification. See TORQUE SPECIFICATIONS.
2) To complete installation, reverse removal procedure. Activate SRS. Verify system is functioning properly. See SYSTEM OPERATION CHECK.

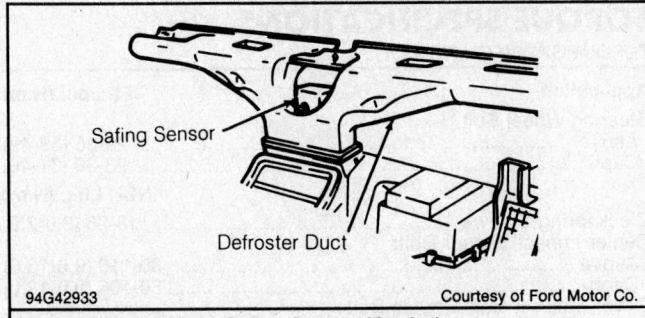

Fig. 8: Locating Rear Safing Sensor (Aspire)

94G42933   Courtesy of Ford Motor Co.

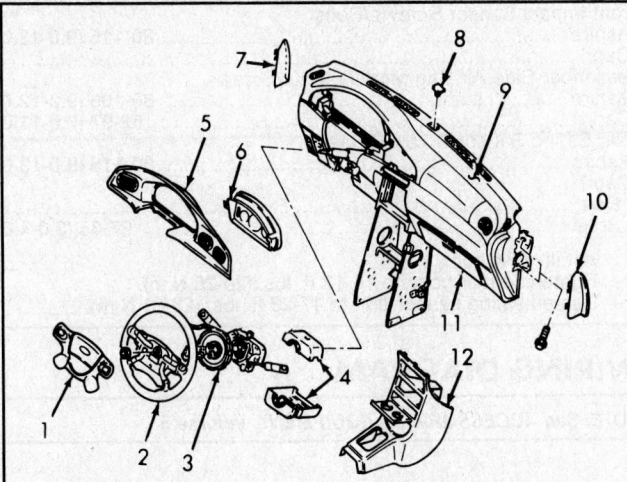

1. Driver-Side Air Bag
2. Steering Wheel
3. Clockspring
4. Steering Column Shroud
5. Instrument Panel Finish Panel
6. Instrument Cluster
7. Access Cover
8. Access Cover
9. Instrument Panel
10. Access Cover
11. Glove Box
12. Shift Console

94H42934   Courtesy of Ford Motor Co.

Fig. 9: Exploded View Of Instrument Panel (Aspire)

Removal (Capri) – 1) Before proceeding, follow air bag service precautions. See SERVICE PRECAUTIONS. Disable SRS. See DISABLING & ACTIVATING AIR BAG SYSTEM.

2) Rear safing sensor is located under center console, behind parking brake handle assembly. See Fig. 10. Slide both seats fully forward. Remove 2 side screws near rear of console. Slide both seats fully rearward.

3) Remove 2 screws retaining rear console to shifter console. Raise parking brake lever as far as possible. Raise rear of console and pull backwards to remove console front eyelet tabs from shifter console.

4) Remove mirror switch by pressing side tabs and prying upward on switch. Unplug mirror switch connector. Remove console from between seats. Remove sensor retaining screw and bolt. Unplug sensor connector. Remove sensor.

Installation – 1) Connect sensor to wiring harness. Position sensor onto bracket, with sensor top arrow pointing toward front of vehicle. Install retaining bolt and screw, and tighten to specification. See TORQUE SPECIFICATIONS.

2) To complete installation, reverse removal procedure. Activate SRS. Verify system is functioning properly. See SYSTEM OPERATION CHECK.

DRIVER-SIDE AIR BAG MODULE

Removal – 1) Before proceeding, follow air bag service precautions. See SERVICE PRECAUTIONS. Disable SRS. See DISABLING & ACTIVATING AIR BAG SYSTEM.

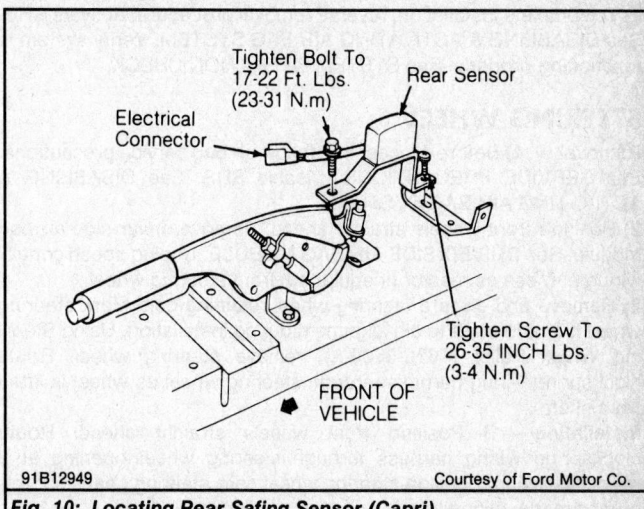

Fig. 10: Locating Rear Safing Sensor (Capri)

91B12949   Courtesy of Ford Motor Co.

2) Remove nuts/bolts and washers retaining air bag module to steering wheel. See Fig. 11. Unplug air bag module wiring connector from clockspring connector. Unplug speed control connector, if necessary. Remove air bag module.

Installation – Connect air bag module wiring connector to clockspring connector. Position air bag module to steering wheel and secure with nut and washer assemblies. Tighten air bag module nuts/bolts to specification. See TORQUE SPECIFICATIONS. Activate SRS. Ensure system is functioning properly. See SYSTEM OPERATION CHECK.

PASSENGER-SIDE AIR BAG MODULE

Removal (Aspire) – 1) Before proceeding, follow air bag service precautions. See SERVICE PRECAUTIONS. Disable SRS. See DISABLING & ACTIVATING AIR BAG SYSTEM. Remove glove box.

2) Working through glove box opening, remove air bag module mounting bolts. Remove passenger-side air bag module. Unplug air bag module connectors.

Installation – To install, reverse removal procedure. Activate SRS. Verify system is functioning properly. See SYSTEM OPERATION CHECK.

Removal (Capri) – 1) Before proceeding, follow air bag service precautions. See SERVICE PRECAUTIONS. Disable SRS. See DISABLING & ACTIVATING AIR BAG SYSTEM. Remove glove box.

2) Remove bypass airflow tube (to heater ducts). Remove vent tube. Unplug air bag module wiring harness connector. Remove air bag module.

Installation – 1) Insert air bag module into space in instrument panel. Install and tighten air bag module mounting bolts to specification. See TORQUE SPECIFICATIONS.

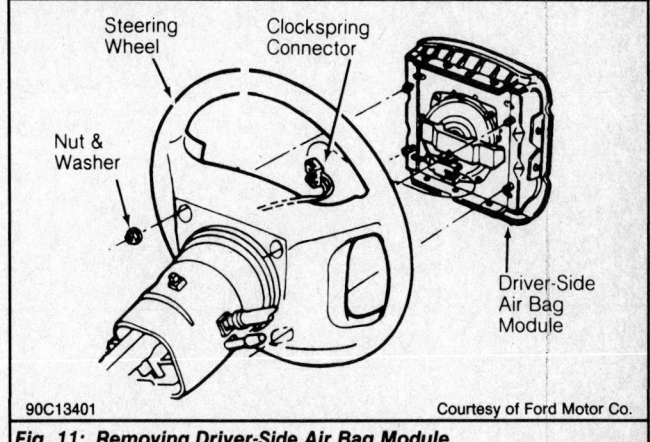

Fig. 11: Removing Driver-Side Air Bag Module

90C13401   Courtesy of Ford Motor Co.

2) To complete installation, reverse removal procedure. Activate SRS. See DISABLING & ACTIVATING AIR BAG SYSTEM. Verify system is functioning properly. See SYSTEM OPERATION CHECK.

STEERING WHEEL

Removal – 1) Before proceeding, follow air bag service precautions. See SERVICE PRECAUTIONS. Disable SRS. See DISABLING & ACTIVATING AIR BAG SYSTEM.

2) Position front wheels straight ahead. Remove driver-side air bag module. See DRIVER-SIDE AIR BAG MODULE. Unplug speed control wiring harness connector (if equipped) from steering wheel.

3) Remove and discard steering wheel retaining bolt. Mark steering wheel hub and shaft to aid alignment during installation. Using Steering Wheel Puller (T67L-3600-A), remove steering wheel. Route clockspring wiring harness through steering wheel as wheel is lifted from shaft.

Installation – 1) Position front wheels straight ahead. Route clockspring wiring harness through steering wheel opening at 3 o'clock position. Position steering wheel onto steering shaft with reference marks aligned.

2) Ensure air bag clockspring wire is not pinched when positioning steering wheel. Install NEW steering wheel retaining bolt and tighten to specification. See TORQUE SPECIFICATIONS. Connect speed control wiring harness. Secure connector into clip.

3) Install driver-side air bag module. See DRIVER-SIDE AIR BAG MODULE. Activate SRS. Verify system is functioning properly. See SYSTEM OPERATION CHECK.

TORQUE SPECIFICATIONS
TORQUE SPECIFICATIONS

Application	Ft. Lbs. (N.m)
Steering Wheel Bolt [1]	
Aspire	29-36 (39-49)
Capri	23-33 (31-45)
	INCH Lbs. (N.m)
Clockspring Screws	18-26 (2.0-2.9)
Center Impact Sensor Bolts	
Aspire	80-115 (9.0-13.0)
Capri	80-106 (9.0-12.0)
Driver-Side Air Bag Module Bolts	
Aspire	80-115 (9.0-13.0)
Capri	18-27 (2.0-3.0)
Front Impact Sensor Screws/Bolts	
Aspire	80-115 (9.0-13.0)
Capri	[2]
Passenger-Side Air Bag Module Bolts/Screws	
Aspire	80-106 (9.0-12.0)
Capri	62-97 (7.0-11.0)
Rear Safing Sensor Screws/Nuts	
Aspire	80-115 (9.0-13.0)
Capri	
Bolt	[3]
Screw	27-35 (3.0-4.0)

[1] – Install NEW bolt.
[2] – Tighten sensor bolts to 15-18 ft. lbs. (20-25 N.m).
[3] – Tighten safing sensor bolt to 17-23 ft. lbs. (23-31 N.m).

WIRING DIAGRAM

NOTE: See ACCESSORIES & EQUIPMENT, Volume 5.

Capri

DESCRIPTION & OPERATION

Speed (cruise) control system is designed to maintain constant speeds greater than 30 MPH. System will disengage when OFF button, clutch, or brake pedal is pressed.

Major components of speed control system are operator controls, throttle actuator, and electronic control unit. Operator controls are located in steering wheel. Speed control module (throttle actuator) is located in engine compartment.

Clutch and brake switches are mounted on their respective pedals. A brake pressure switch is connected to brakeline, in engine compartment. Electronic speed sensor is located at instrument cluster.

CONTROL SWITCHES

Speed control buttons are in center of steering wheel. To set speed, press and release ON button, then press and release SET ACCELERATOR (SET ACL) button. Vehicle should maintain chosen speed. To reduce speed, press COAST (CST) button until lower speed is reached, then release button. To increase speed, press SET ACL button until higher speed is reached, then release button.

Speed control can be turned off by pressing OFF button or by stepping on brake or clutch pedals. To resume speed after braking or shifting, press RESUME (RSM) button for about one second. If speed control was turned off, accelerate to desired speed, then press and release SET ACL button.

TROUBLE SHOOTING

See appropriate procedure under DIAGNOSIS & TESTING.

ADJUSTMENTS

SPEED CONTROL CABLE

1) To adjust cable, make adjustment shim. See Fig. 1. Adjustment shim should be 0.078" (2.0 mm) thick, with a slotted opening 0.50" (13 mm) wide.

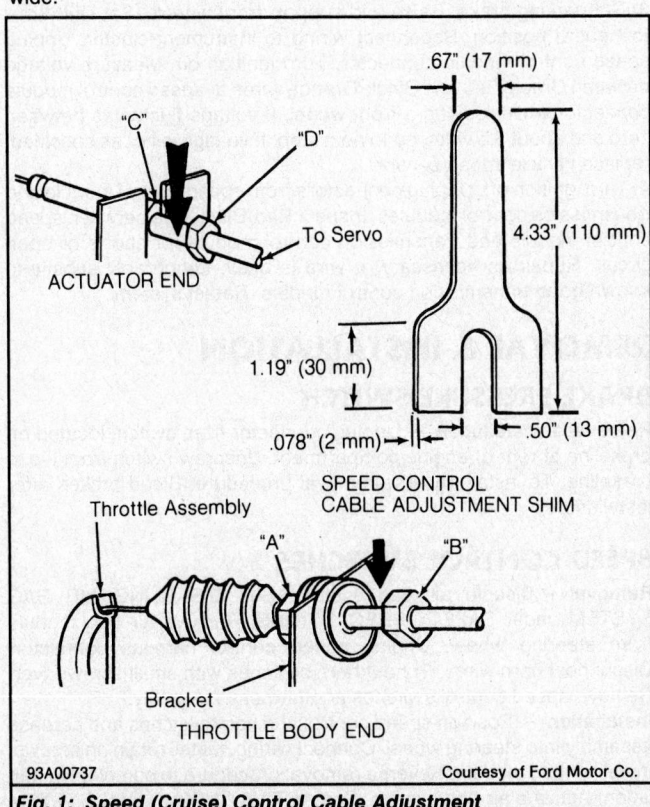

SPEED CONTROL CABLE ADJUSTMENT SHIM

.67" (17 mm)

4.33" (110 mm)

1.19" (30 mm)

.078" (2 mm) → | | ← .50" (13 mm)

"C" "D"

To Servo

ACTUATOR END

Throttle Assembly

"A" "B"

Bracket

THROTTLE BODY END

93A00737   Courtesy of Ford Motor Co.

Fig. 1: Speed (Cruise) Control Cable Adjustment

2) Adjust cable at throttle body first. Disconnect cable from cruise control actuator. Loosen cable retaining nuts on bracket at valve cover. Insert adjustment shim between bracket and nut "B". Tighten both nuts to remove all cable slack. Loosen nut "A" only enough to remove adjustment shim. Retighten nut "A" without moving nut "B".

3) After throttle body end of cable has been adjusted, adjust cable at actuator. Loosen both nuts at bracket. Insert adjustment shim between bracket and nut "D". Tighten both nuts to remove all slack at throttle body end of cable. Loosen nut "C" only enough to remove adjustment shim. Retighten nut "C" without moving nut "D".

CLUTCH SWITCH

Adjust clutch switch by adjusting clutch pedal height. Clutch pedal height is corrected by adjusting clutch stop bolt. Measure distance from center of clutch pedal to lower dash panel (footwell front area). Pedal height should be 8.44-8.64" (214.5-219.5 mm). Loosen stop bolt lock nut and rotate stop bolt if necessary.

STOPLIGHT SWITCH

Ensure brake pedal height is correct and fully returned. See DISC & DRUM article in BRAKES. Measure distance between stoplight switch screw and brake pedal rubber pad. Distance should be 0.08" (2 mm). Loosen switch lock nut, and rotate switch to make adjustment.

SAFETY PRECAUTIONS

CAUTION: Vehicle is equipped with Supplemental Restraint System (SRS). Observe all safety precautions. The air bag system is powered directly from the battery. Before any repairs are performed, disconnect and shield battery cables. Wait at least one minute BEFORE servicing ANY air bag component. Use caution when working near steering column. Air bag could accidently deploy at any time.

DISABLING AIR BAG SYSTEM

NOTE: The following disabling sequence is ONLY for component removal and replacement purposes.

To disable SRS, disconnect negative, then positive battery cable. Wait one minute. System is now disabled.

ACTIVATING AIR BAG SYSTEM

To activate SRS, reconnect positive, then negative battery cable. From passenger's side of vehicle, turn ignition on. System is now activated. Observe AIR BAG light to verify system is functioning properly.

NOTE: For information on air bag DIAGNOSIS & TESTING or DISPOSAL PROCEDURES, see MITCHELL® AIR BAG SERVICE & REPAIR MANUAL, DOMESTIC & IMPORTED MODELS.

DIAGNOSIS & TESTING

SPEED CONTROL INOPERATIVE

1) With ignition off, inspect STOP and METER fuses. Replace failed fuses. Turn ignition on. If fuse(s) fail again, go to next step. If fuses do not fail, go to step 3).

2) With ignition off, locate and unplug interior fuse block connectors. Measure resistance between Green/Yellow wire and ground, and between Black/Yellow wire and ground. If resistance is less than 5 ohms, repair short circuit in wire(s). If resistance is more than 5 ohms, go to next step.

3) Locate speed control unit. Turn ignition on. Measure voltage on Black/Yellow wire at speed control unit. If battery voltage exists, go to next step. If battery voltage does not exist, repair Black/Yellow wire.

4) Turn ignition off. Unplug speed control module connector. Unplug stoplight switch connector. Measure resistance of White/Green wire between stoplight switch and speed control module. Measure resistance between Green/White wire and ground. If resistance is not

greater than 5 ohms between connectors, and is greater than 10,000 ohms to ground, go to next step. If resistance is not as specified, repair Green/White wire.

5) Unplug brake pressure switch connector, located on brakeline at lower rear of engine compartment. Turn ignition on. Measure voltage on Green/Yellow wire at connector. If battery voltage exists, go to next step. If battery voltage does not exist, repair Green/Yellow wire.

6) Reconnect brake pressure switch. Measure voltage on Green/Black wire at switch connector. If battery voltage exists, go to next step. If battery voltage does not exist, replace brake pressure switch.

7) Unplug speed control module connector. Turn ignition on. Measure voltage on Green/Black wire at connector. If battery voltage exists, go to next step. If battery voltage does not exist, repair Green/Black wire.

8) Unplug horn relay connector. Measure voltage on Green/Yellow wire at harness connector. If battery voltage exists, go to next step. If battery voltage does not exist, repair Green/Yellow wire.

9) Reconnect wiring harness to horn relay. Measure voltage on Green/Black wire at harness connector. If battery voltage exists, go to next step. If battery voltage does not exist, replace horn relay.

10) Disconnect wiring at speed control switch. Measure voltage on Green/Black wire at switch connector. If battery voltage exists, go to next step. If battery voltage does not exist, repair Green/Black wire.

11) Unplug speed control switch connector. Measure resistance between specified clockspring terminal pairs with each switch pressed. See SPEED CONTROL SWITCH TEST table. If resistance is approximately as specified, go to next step. If resistance is not as specified, replace speed control switch.

SPEED CONTROL SWITCH TEST

Position	Terminals	Resistance
ON	GRN/BLK – BLU/WHT	Less Than 5
OFF	BLU/WHT – GRN/WHT	Less Than 5
SET/ACL	BLU/WHT – GRN/WHT	680
CST	BLU/WHT – GRN/WHT	120
RSM	BLU/WHT – GRN/WHT	2200

12) Turn ignition off. Unplug speed control module connector. Unplug speed control switch connector. Measure resistance of Black/White and Green/White wires between speed control switch and speed control module. Measure resistance between the same wires and ground. If resistance is not greater than 5 ohms between connectors, and is greater than 10,000 ohms to ground, go to next step. If resistance is not as specified, repair appropriate wire.

13) Turn ignition off. Unplug speed control module connector. Measure resistance of Black/Orange wire at harness connector and ground. If resistance is less than 5 ohms, go to TRANSAXLE DOES NOT OPERATE NORMALLY WITH SPEED CONTROL ENGAGED (4EAT ONLY). If resistance is not as specified, repair Black/Orange wire.

SPEED FLUCTUATES

1) Drive vehicle, leaving speed control disengaged. If speed does not fluctuate, go to next step. If speed fluctuates, service engine as necessary.

2) Inspect speed control actuator, throttle linkage, and throttle plate for sticking or binding. Inspect all brackets for looseness. If all is okay, go to next step. Service as necessary.

3) Unplug vehicle speed sensor connector, located at instrument cluster. Measure resistance between sensor terminals. If resistance is not 200-300 ohms, replace sensor. If resistance is as specified, inspect and repair associated wiring as necessary.

SPEED CONTROL DOES NOT DISENGAGE WHEN BRAKES ARE APPLIED

1) Unplug stoplight switch connector, located at brake pedal lever. Measure voltage on Green/Yellow wire at switch connector. If battery voltage exists, go to next step. If battery voltage does not exist, repair Green/Yellow wire to fuse panel.

2) Reconnect wiring to stoplight switch. Press brake pedal. Measure voltage on White/Green wire at switch connector. If battery voltage exists, go to SPEED CONTROL DOES NOT DISENGAGE WHEN CLUTCH IS RELEASED for M/T models, or SPEED CONTROL INOPERATIVE for A/T models. If battery voltage does not exist, replace stoplight switch.

SPEED CONTROL DOES NOT DISENGAGE WHEN CLUTCH IS RELEASED

1) Unplug clutch switch connector, located at clutch pedal lever. Press brake pedal. Measure voltage on White/Green wire at switch connector. If battery voltage exists, go to next step. If battery voltage does not exist, repair White/Green wire from stoplight switch.

2) Reconnect wiring to clutch switch. Press brake pedal. Measure voltage on Green wire at switch connector. If battery voltage exists, go to next step. If battery voltage does not exist, replace clutch switch.

3) Turn ignition off. Unplug speed control module connector. Unplug clutch switch connector. Measure resistance of Green wire between clutch switch and speed control module. Measure resistance between Green wire and ground. If resistance is not greater than 5 ohms between connectors, and is greater than 10,000 ohms to ground, go to SPEED CONTROL INOPERATIVE. If resistance is not as specified, repair Green wire.

TRANSAXLE DOES NOT OPERATE NORMALLY WITH SPEED CONTROL ENGAGED (4EAT ONLY)

1) Turn ignition off. Unplug 10-pin instrument cluster connector. Unplug transaxle control module connector, located behind instrument panel, above glove box. Measure resistance of Green/Red wire between instrument cluster and transmission control module. Measure resistance of Green/Red wire and ground. If resistance is not greater than 5 ohms between connectors, and is greater than 10,000 ohms to ground, go to next step. If resistance is not as specified, repair Green/Red wire.

2) Measure resistance between Black wire at harness connector and ground. If resistance is less than 5 ohms, go to next step. If resistance is not as specified, repair Black wire.

3) Set parking brake. Raise and support front wheels. Set shift lever to Neutral position. Reconnect wiring to instrument cluster. Unplug speed control module connector. Turn ignition on. Measure voltage between Green/Red and Black/Orange wires at speed control module connector while rotating a front wheel. If voltage fluctuates between zero and about 5.5 volts, go to next step. If voltage is not as specified, replace vehicle speed sensor.

4) Turn ignition off. Unplug connectors from speed control module and transmission control modules. Inspect Red/Black wire between speed control module and transmission control module for shorts or open circuit. Repair as necessary. If wire is okay, temporarily substitute known good transmission control module. Retest system.

REMOVAL & INSTALLATION
BRAKE PRESSURE SWITCH

Removal & Installation – Unplug connector from switch, located on brakeline at rear of engine compartment. Unscrew switch from tee in brakeline. To install, reverse removal procedure. Bleed brakes after installation.

SPEED CONTROL SWITCHES

Removal – Disable air bag system. See DISABLING AIR BAG SYSTEM under SAFETY PRECAUTIONS. Remove air bag module from steering wheel. Unplug speed control harness connector. Disconnect horn wires. Pry out horn switches with small screwdriver. Remove speed control switches and harness assembly.

Installation – Position speed control and horn switches and harness assembly into steering wheel. Connect wiring. Install retaining screws. Install air bag module. Reverse removal procedure to complete installation. Activate air bag system. See ACTIVATING AIR BAG SYSTEM under SAFETY PRECAUTIONS.

SPEED CONTROL MODULE

Removal – Unplug harness connector. Remove retaining screws. Disengage cable by pressing locking arm and rotating cable cap counterclockwise. *See Fig. 2.* Pry locking arm springs slightly while pushing cable end from pulley slot. *See Fig. 3.*

Installation – Install speed control module. Install cable end into pulley slot. Insert cable cap locking tabs into slots. Rotate cap clockwise until cap locking arm engages locking tab. Connect wiring. Adjust cable. See SPEED CONTROL CABLE under ADJUSTMENTS. Check for proper speed control operation.

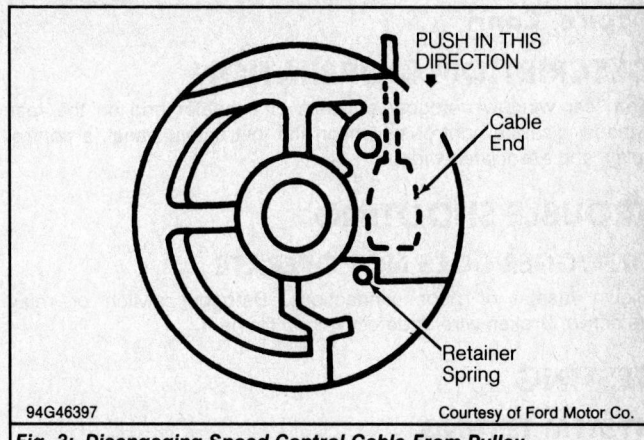

Fig. 3: Disengaging Speed Control Cable From Pulley

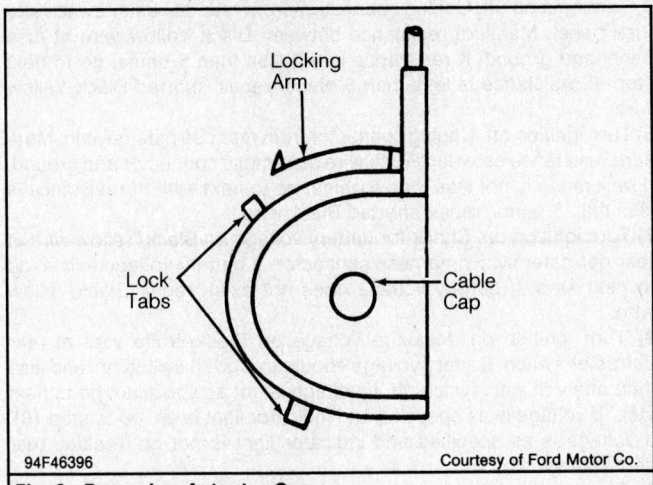

Fig. 2: Removing Actuator Cap

STOPLIGHT & CLUTCH SWITCHES

Removal – Unplug electrical connector. Remove switch retaining nuts. Remove switch from pedal bracket.

Installation – To install, reverse removal procedure. Adjust switches. See CLUTCH SWITCH or STOPLIGHT SWITCH under ADJUSTMENTS.

TORQUE SPECIFICATIONS

TORQUE SPECIFICATIONS

Applications	INCH Lbs. (N.m)
Brake Pressure Switch	71-97 (8-11)
Speed Control Module Bolts	71-106 (8-12)

WIRING DIAGRAM

NOTE: See ACCESSORIES & EQUIPMENT, Volume 5.

Aspire, Capri

DESCRIPTION & OPERATION

The rear window defogger consists of a heater grid on the rear window glass, a control switch on the instrument panel, a control relay, and associated wiring.

TROUBLE SHOOTING

DEFOGGER DOES NOT OPERATE

Blown fuse(s) or poor connections. Defogger switch or relay defective. Broken wire or defective grid filament.

TESTING

SYSTEM TESTING

Aspire – **1)** Turn ignition off. Inspect METER and DEFOG fuses. If either fuse has failed, go to next step. If both fuses are okay, go to step **4)**.

2) Replace defective fuse. Turn ignition on. If either fuse fails again, go to next step. If neither fuse fails, go to step **4)**.

3) Turn ignition off. Remove METER and DEFOG fuses. Unplug connector from fog light/rear window defroster switch and defogger relay, located at right rear of passenger compartment. Measure resistance between lower terminal of METER fuse and ground. Repeat measurement at DEFOG fuse terminal. Repair Black/Yellow or Black/Brown wire as appropriate if either measurement is less than 10,000 ohms.

4) Turn ignition off. Install METER and DEFOG fuses. Unplug connector from fog light/rear window defroster switch. Turn ignition on. Check for voltage on Black/Blue wire at harness connector. If battery voltage exists, go to next step. If battery voltage does not exist, repair Black/Blue wire.

5) Turn ignition off. Unplug connectors from rear window grid. Turn ignition on. Check for voltage on Black/Blue wire at harness connector. If battery voltage does not exist, go to next step. If battery voltage exists, go to step **11)**.

6) Turn ignition off. Turn rear window defroster off. Unplug connector from fog light/rear window defroster switch. Measure resistance between switch terminals for Black/Yellow and Black/Red wires. Turn rear window defroster on. Resistance should be less than 5 ohms with switch on, and more than 10,000 ohms with switch off. Replace switch if resistance is not as specified.

7) Turn ignition off. Unplug connector from rear defroster relay. Connect battery voltage to Black/Red and Black/Brown wire terminals of relay. Measure voltage on Black/Blue wire terminal on relay. With terminal for Black wire grounded, battery voltage should exist. With terminal for Black wire open, voltage should be less than one volt. Replace relay if operation is not as specified.

8) Turn ignition off. Unplug connector from rear defroster relay. Measure voltage on Black/Brown wire at relay connector. If battery voltage exists, go to next step. If battery voltage does not exist, repair Black/Brown wire.

9) Turn ignition off. Unplug connector from rear defroster relay. Measure resistance of Black wire between relay connector and ground. If resistance is less than 5 ohms, go to next step. If resistance is not less than 5 ohms, repair Black wire.

10) Turn ignition off. Reconnect fog light/rear window defroster switch. Unplug connector from rear defroster relay. Turn ignition on. Turn rear window defroster off, then on. Measure voltage on Black/Red wire at rear defroster relay connector. Battery voltage should exist with switch on, and less than one volt with switch off. If voltage is as specified, repair Black/Blue wire between relay and rear window. If voltage is not as specified, repair Black/Red wire.

11) Turn ignition off. Unplug connector from rear window. Measure resistance of Black wire between harness connector and ground. If resistance is less than 5 ohms, service window grid. See FILAMENT TESTING. If resistance is not less than 5 ohms, repair Black wire.

Capri – **1)** Turn ignition on. Turn on rear window defroster. If defroster does not work at all, go to next step. If rear window defroster works in some places but not in others, go to FILAMENT TESTING.

2) Turn ignition on. Turn on rear window defroster. Observe indicator light. If light is not on, go to next step. If light is on, go to step **6)**.

3) Inspect METER fuse. If fuse has failed, go to next step. If fuse is okay, go to step **6)**.

4) Turn ignition off. Replace METER fuse. Turn ignition on. Turn on rear window defroster. If fuse fails, go to next step. If fuse does not fail, go to step **6)**.

5) Turn ignition off. Unplug connectors from rear defroster switch and fuse panel. Measure resistance between Black/Yellow wire at fuse panel and ground. If resistance is not less than 5 ohms, go to next step. If resistance is less than 5 ohms, repair shorted Black/Yellow wire.

6) Turn ignition off. Unplug connector from rear defroster switch. Measure resistance between Black wire at harness connector and ground. If resistance is not less than 5 ohms, go to next step. If resistance is less than 5 ohms, repair shorted Black wire.

7) Turn ignition on. Check for battery voltage on Black/Yellow wire at rear defroster switch harness connector. If battery voltage exists, go to next step. If battery voltage does not exist, repair Black/Yellow wire.

8) Turn ignition on. Measure voltage on Black/White wire at rear defroster switch. Battery voltage should exist with switch on, and less than one volt with switch off. If voltage is not as specified, go to next step. If voltage is as specified and indicator light is on, go to step **10)**. If voltage is as specified and indicator light is not on, replace rear defroster switch.

9) Turn ignition off. Unplug rear window defroster switch. Measure resistance between Black/White and Black/Yellow wire terminals on switch. Resistance should be less than 5 ohms with switch on, and more than 10,000 ohms with switch off. Replace switch if resistance is not as specified.

10) Turn ignition on. Measure voltage on Black/White wire at defroster relay, located at left rear of luggage compartment. Battery voltage should exist with defroster switch on, and less than one volt with switch off. If voltage is as specified, go to next step. If voltage is not as specified, repair Black/White wire.

11) Unplug connector from rear defroster relay. Measure resistance between Black wire at harness connector and ground. If resistance is less than 5 ohms, go to next step. If resistance is not less than 5 ohms, repair open Black wire.

12) Measure voltage on Black/Yellow wire at defroster relay. If battery voltage exists, battery voltage exists, go to step **14)**. If voltage is not as specified, go to next step.

13) Inspect HTD B-LIGHT fuse. If fuse is okay, repair open Black/Yellow wire. Replace fuse if it has failed. If fuse fails again, inspect for shorted Black/Yellow wire. Repair as necessary.

14) Unplug defroster relay. Connect battery voltage to relay terminal for Black/White wire terminal. Connect Black wire terminal to ground. Measure resistance between Black/Yellow wire terminals. If resistance is less than 5 ohms, go to next step. Replace relay if resistance is not as specified.

15) Reconnect all wiring. Turn ignition on. Turn rear window defroster on. Measure voltage at Black/Blue wire at rear window defroster grid connector. If battery voltage exists, go to next step. If battery voltage does not exist, repair Black/Blue wire.

16) Turn ignition off. Unplug connector from rear window. Measure resistance of Black wire between harness connector and ground. If resistance is less than 5 ohms, service window grid. See FILAMENT TESTING. If resistance is not less than 5 ohms, repair Black wire.

FILAMENT TESTING

1) To locate breaks in grid filaments, touch positive lead of voltmeter to middle portion of each filament. Connect negative ground lead to ground. Turn ignition and rear defogger switches on.

2) If grid wire is okay, voltage will be 5-7 volts. If grid is broken toward ground side, voltage will be high (11-13 volts). If grid filament is broken toward power supply, voltage will be low (0-1 volt). To locate break, move positive lead along wire until meter needle moves abruptly. To repair grid filament, see GRID FILAMENT REPAIR.

GRID FILAMENT REPAIR

Use razor blade to remove protective covering from damaged area. Once damaged area is exposed, clean area of broken grid line with alcohol. Place tape along both sides of grid line to be repaired. See Fig. 1. Thoroughly mix small amount of Repair Agent (Dupont Paste No. 4817). Apply repair agent to grid line break area, overlapping both lines. After a couple of minutes, carefully remove tape from line edges. DO NOT touch repaired area for 24 hours.

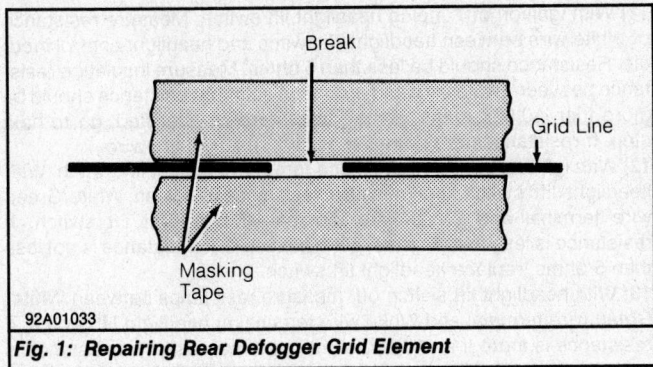

Fig. 1: Repairing Rear Defogger Grid Element

REMOVAL & INSTALLATION

REAR DEFOGGER SWITCH

Removal & Installation (Aspire) – Disconnect negative battery cable. Using a small screwdriver, press retaining tabs at top and bottom of switch inward. Unplug connector. To install, reverse removal procedure.

Removal & Installation (Capri) – 1) Disconnect negative battery cable. Pull out center storage compartment. Remove nuts, lower screws, and heater/radio bezel. Pull outward and remove trim covers, one located on each side of steering column.

2) Remove instrument panel bezel retaining screws. Pull instrument bezel from dash. Unplug rear defogger switch connector. Press tangs on both sides of switch to remove switch. To install, reverse removal procedure.

WIRING DIAGRAMS

NOTE: See ACCESSORIES & EQUIPMENT, Volume 5.

Capri

DESCRIPTION & OPERATION

Headlights are raised and lowered by an electric motor. Headlight assemblies raise automatically when headlights are turned on; they retract, after a slight delay, when headlights are turned off.

Headlight lift switch, located on console, is used to raise and lower headlights without turning them on. This switch allows service of headlights, and can be used to prevent lights from freezing closed in winter climates.

A manual control knob, located under a rubber boot, is provided at rear of each headlight. Knobs are provided to operate each motor manually in the event of system failure.

NOTE: DO NOT raise or lower headlights manually if electrical power is available.

ADJUSTMENTS

HEADLIGHT DOORS

Headlight linkage and assembly is preset at factory to meet clearance requirement between turn signal light and headlight. If linkage needs adjustment, headlight carrier hinges and motor carrier assembly must be replaced with linkage.

TROUBLE SHOOTING

Inspect for damaged mechanical components and headlight door blockage.

Inspect electrical components for:
- Blown Fuses
- Damage To Wiring Harness
- Loose Or Corroded Connectors
- Defective Bulbs

Shake wiring harness. Look for obvious signs of shorts, opens, or damage.

TESTING

1) Inspect 20-amp HLM fuse. If fuse has failed, go to next step. If fuse is okay, go to step 4).
2) Replace 20-amp HLM fuse. If fuse fails again, go to next step. If fuse does not fail, go to step 4).
3) With key off, unplug headlight lift switch, radio, and headlight control module connectors. Unplug main fuse panel connector. Measure resistance between White/Green wire at main fuse panel connector and ground. If resistance is less than 5 ohms, repair the White/Green wire. If resistance is not less than 5 ohms, go to next step.
4) Reconnect wiring to fuse panel. Measure voltage on White/Green wire at headlight control module. If battery voltage exists, go to next step. If battery voltage does not exist, repair White/Green wire.
5) With headlights on, measure and record voltage on Red/Black wire at headlight control module. With high beams on, measure and record voltage on Red/White wire at headlight control module. If battery voltage exists on both wires, go to next step. If battery voltage does not exist, repair wire(s) in question.
6) With ignition off, measure resistance between Black wire at headlight control module and ground. If resistance is less than 5 ohms, go to next step. If resistance is not less than 5 ohms, repair Black wire.
7) Measure resistance of Brown, Red, Black, White, and Green wires between headlight control module and left headlight door motor. If

resistances are less than 5 ohms, go to next step. If resistance(s) are not less than 5 ohms, repair wire(s) in question.
8) Measure resistance of Brown, Red, Black, White, and Green wires between headlight control module and right headlight door motor. If resistances are less than 5 ohms, go to next step. If resistance(s) are not less than 5 ohms, repair wire(s) in question.
9) With headlights off, unplug headlight door motor connectors. Apply 12 volts to Brown wire at headlight door motor connector. Ground Green wire at headlight door motor connector. Headlight door should open. Transpose connections. Door should close. If headlight door opens and closes, go to next step. If headlight door does not open and close, replace headlight door motor(s).
10) Measure voltage on White/Green wire at headlight lift switch. If battery voltage exists, go to next step. If battery voltage does not exist, repair White/Green wire.
11) With ignition off, unplug headlight lift switch. Measure resistance of White wire between headlight lift switch and headlight control module. Resistance should be less than 5 ohms. Measure insulation resistance between White wire and ground. Insulation resistance should be more than 10,000 ohms. If resistances are as specified, go to next step. If resistances are not as specified, repair White wire.
12) With ignition off, disconnect and remove headlight lift switch. With headlight lift switch on, measure resistance between White/Green wire terminal and White wire terminal at headlight lift switch. If resistance is less than 5 ohms, go to next step. If resistance is not less than 5 ohms, replace headlight lift switch.
13) With headlight lift switch off, measure resistance between White/Green wire terminal and White wire terminal at headlight lift switch. If resistance is more than 10,000 ohms, go to next step. If resistance is not more than 10,000 ohms, replace headlight lift switch.
14) Reconnect headlight control module, headlight door motors, and headlight lift switch. Turn headlights on. If headlight doors open, return to TROUBLE SHOOTING and step 1). If headlight doors do not open, replace headlight control module. Turn headlights off. If headlight doors close, return to TROUBLE SHOOTING and step 1). If headlight doors do not close, replace headlight control module.

REMOVAL & INSTALLATION

CAUTION: When battery is disconnected, vehicle computer and memory systems may lose memory data. Driveability problems may exist until computer systems have completed a relearn cycle. See COMPUTER RELEARN PROCEDURES article in GENERAL INFORMATION before disconnecting battery.

CONTROL MODULE

Removal & Installation – Control module is located in center of instrument panel below radio. Manufacturer gives no removal and installation procedure.

HEADLIGHT DOOR ASSEMBLY

Removal & Installation – 1) Raise headlights to normal operating position by turning headlight motor switch on. Remove 4 screws and washers retaining outer bezel enclosing entire headlight assembly. Remove bezel. Remove headlight retainer screws. Remove headlight. Unplug connector.

NOTE: DO NOT disturb headlight adjuster screws.

2) Remove windshield washer reservoir or coolant reservoir, depending on which headlight assembly requires service. Remove screws and cover from headlight assembly.

CAUTION: *Headlight assembly cover is painted to match body color. Use care to prevent damage during removal and installation.*

3) Remove bolts retaining headlight assembly to body. Unplug connector from motor. Remove headlight assembly. For installation, reverse removal procedure. Check operation and aim of headlights.

CAUTION: *DO NOT adjust linkage to motor.*

WIRING DIAGRAM

NOTE: See ACCESSORIES & EQUIPMENT, Volume 5.

HEADLIGHT DOOR MOTOR

Removal & Installation – Remove headlight assembly. See HEADLIGHT DOOR ASSEMBLY. Remove nut retaining linkage to motor. Remove retaining bolts and motor. When installing, tighten retaining bolts to 27-44 INCH lbs. (3-5 N.m). When connecting linkage, tighten nut to 71-88 INCH lbs. (8-10 N.m). To complete installation, reverse removal procedure. Check operation and aim of headlights.

CAUTION: *DO NOT adjust linkage to motor.*

Aspire, Capri

DESCRIPTION & OPERATION

Instrument panel on Aspire includes a speedometer, fuel gauge, and coolant temperature gauge. Instrument panel is equipped with indicator/warning lights for charging system, oil pressure, seat belt, rear defogger, turn signals, high beam, air bag, and brakes. A CHECK ENGINE light comes on if a computerized engine control fault occurs while the engine is running.

Instrument panel on Capri includes a voltmeter, speedometer, tachometer, and gauges for fuel, water temperature, and oil pressure. A boost gauge is incorporated into tachometer on turbo models. Instrument panel is equipped with indicator/warning lights for charging system, air bag, manual shift, seat belt, turn signals, high beam, and brakes. A CHECK ENGINE light comes on if a computerized engine control fault occurs while the engine is running.

CAUTION: These vehicles are equipped with Supplemental Restraint System (SRS). Observe appropriate safety precautions. Air bag system is powered directly from battery and back-up power supply. Before any repairs are performed, disconnect and shield battery ground cable. Wait at least one minute before servicing ANY air bag component. Use caution when working near steering column. Air bag could accidently deploy at any time.

TROUBLE SHOOTING

NOTE: Check for continuity between chassis ground and Black wire of instrument panel connector, especially if fault exists in more than one gauge circuit. See appropriate wiring diagram in WIRING DIAGRAMS. Inspect fuses. Inspect wiring harness for damage, shorts, opens, and loose or corroded connections. Inspect for damage to audio system relay or illumination lamps. If problem is not evident, follow appropriate trouble shooting procedures.

FUEL GAUGE

Fuel Gauge Always Indicates Empty – If fuel gauge always indicates empty, check these items:
- Check fuel gauge for open or damaged wires.
- Check for open ground at fuel gauge sending unit.
- Check for defective fuel sending unit.
- Check for defective fuel gauge.
- Check for blown METER fuse in fuse panel.
- Check for open in Black/Yellow power feed wire from fuse panel to instrument panel.
- Check for fuel tank float full of fuel (sunk). Check arm adjustment.

Fuel Gauge Always Indicates Full – If fuel gauge indicates full, check these items:
- Check for fuel gauge Yellow wire shorted to ground.
- Check for defective fuel sending unit.
- Check for defective fuel gauge.

Fuel Gauge Inaccurate – If fuel gauge is inaccurate, check these items:
- Check for loose or corroded wire connections.
- Check for defective fuel sending unit.

TEMPERATURE GAUGE

Temperature Gauge Always Indicates Cold – If temperature gauge always indicates cold, check these items:
- Check temperature gauge for open wire.
- Check for defective temperature sender.
- Check for defective temperature gauge.
- Check for failed METER fuse.
- Check for open in Black/Yellow power feed wire from fuse panel to instrument panel.

Temperature Gauge Always Indicates Hot – If temperature gauge always indicates hot, check these items:
- Check for temperature gauge wire (Yellow/White) shorted to ground.

- Check for defective temperature sender.
- Check for defective temperature gauge.

Temperature Gauge Inaccurate – If temperature gauge is inaccurate, check these items:
- Check for faulty (loose or corroded) wire connections.
- Check for defective temperature sender.
- Check for Yellow/White wire continuity.

SPEEDOMETER

Speedometer Does Not Operate – If speedometer does not operate, check these items:
- Check for broken speedometer drive cable.
- Check for broken drive gear in transmission.
- Check for poor cable connections.
- Check for defective speedometer head.

Speedometer Needle Wavers – If speedometer needle wavers, check these items:
- Check for binding speedometer drive cable.
- Check for missing teeth on drive gear in transmission.
- Check for defective speedometer head.

Speedometer Does Not Indicate Correct Vehicle Speed – If speedometer does not indicate correct vehicle speed, check these items:
- Check for incorrect size tires.
- Check for improper tire inflation.
- Check for defective speedometer head.

Speedometer Is Noisy – If speedometer makes noise, check these items:
- Check for proper lubrication in cable.
- Check for binding cable.
- Check for damage to speedometer.

TACHOMETER

Tachometer Does Not Work, But All Other Gauges Work Properly – If tachometer does not work, but all other gauges function properly, check these items:
- Check for defective tachometer.
- Check for open Yellow/Black tachometer signal wire from ignition coil to instrument panel (Capri), or open Yellow/Blue wire from ignition control module to instrument panel (Aspire).
- Check for faulty Black ground wire to instrument panel.
- Check for failed METER fuse.

Tachometer & All Gauges Do Not Function – If tachometer and all other gauges do not function properly, check these items:
- Check for failed METER fuse.
- Check for open in Black/Yellow wire from fuse panel to instrument panel and Black/White wire from ignition switch to fuse panel.

Tachometer Indicates Low – If tachometer indication is lower than normal, check these items:
- Check for defective tachometer.
- Check for faulty Black ground wire at instrument panel.

TURBO BOOST GAUGE (CAPRI)

Turbo Boost Gauge Always Indicates Low – If turbo boost gauge always indicates low, check these items:
- Check boost gauge for open or damaged wires.
- Check for defective boost sensing unit.
- Check for defective boost gauge.
- Check for failed METER fuse.
- Check for loose or corroded connections.

Turbo Boost Gauge Always Indicates High – If turbo boost gauge always indicates high, check these items:
- Check for damaged White/Black signal wire.
- Check for defective boost sensing unit.
- Check for defective boost gauge.

Turbo Boost Gauge Inaccurate – If turbo boost gauge is inaccurate, check these items:
- Check for loose or corroded connections.
- Check for defective boost sensing unit.
- Check for defective boost gauge.

TESTING

FUEL GAUGE SENDING UNIT TEST

NOTE: Inspect fuel tank for distortion or damage. If distorted or damaged, repair or replace tank before testing.

Aspire – Remove fuel gauge sending unit from tank. See FUEL SENDING UNIT under REMOVAL & INSTALLATION. Measure resistance between Yellow/White and Black/Yellow wire terminals of sending unit connectors as float arm is positioned as shown in illustration. *See Fig 1.* If resistance is not as specified in illustration, replace sending unit.

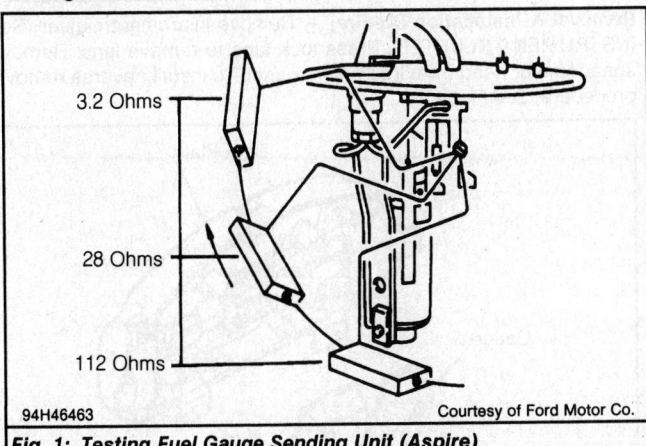

3.2 Ohms

28 Ohms

112 Ohms

94H46463   Courtesy of Ford Motor Co.

Fig. 1: Testing Fuel Gauge Sending Unit (Aspire)

Capri – Remove rear seat cushion. Unplug fuel pump/fuel gauge sending unit electrical connector at access cover. Turn ignition on. Fuel gauge should indicate empty. Using a jumper wire, connect Yellow fuel gauge wire of harness connector to ground. Fuel gauge should indicate full. If not, test fuel gauge. See FUEL GAUGE TEST. If fuel gauge operates as specified, replace fuel gauge sending unit.

FUEL GAUGE TEST

Aspire – Connect Rotunda Gauge System Tester (021-00055) between Yellow wire at fuel tank sending unit connector and ground. Set tester to resistances shown in FUEL GAUGE TEST (ASPIRE) table. Observe gauge at each setting for 2 minutes. Replace gauge if indications are not as specified. *See Fig. 2.*

FUEL GAUGE TEST (ASPIRE)

Gauge Needle Position [1]	Resistance Setting Ohms
Full Position (Up)	6.5
Half-Full Position (Middle)	About 32.5
Empty Position (Down)	95

[1] – Allowable error is twice width of needle.

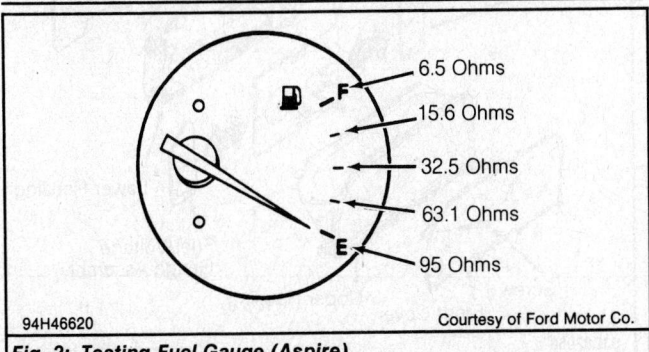

6.5 Ohms

15.6 Ohms

32.5 Ohms

63.1 Ohms

95 Ohms

94H46620   Courtesy of Ford Motor Co.

Fig. 2: Testing Fuel Gauge (Aspire)

Capri – Ground Yellow wire at instrument cluster connector. Fuel gauge should indicate full. With 12 volts applied to Yellow wire at instrument cluster connector, fuel gauge should indicate empty. Replace gauge if indications are not as specified.

OIL PRESSURE GAUGE TEST

Capri – **1)** Unplug connector from oil pressure sending unit, located on right side of engine block. Turn ignition on. Oil pressure gauge should indicate low. Install jumper wire between Yellow/Red wire of oil pressure sending unit harness connector and ground. Oil pressure gauge should indicate high. Connect Rotunda Gauge System Tester (021-00038) to Yellow/Red wire. Set tester to resistance values specified in TESTING OIL PRESSURE GAUGE (CAPRI) table.
2) If oil pressure gauge operates as specified, replace sending unit. If gauge does not operate as specified, inspect instrument panel power and ground circuits.

TESTING OIL PRESSURE GAUGE (CAPRI)

Needle Position (psi) [1]	Resistance Setting Ohms
Up Position (120)	0
Three Quarter Position (90)	15
Middle Position (60)	32
Down Position (0)	210

[1] – Allowable error is twice width of needle.

OIL PRESSURE WARNING LIGHT TEST

Light Stays On With Engine Running (Aspire) – **1)** Turn ignition on. Disconnect Yellow/Red wire from oil pressure switch, located at upper right front of engine. Light should go off. If light stays on, repair short in Yellow/Red wire between instrument cluster and oil pressure switch.
2) Reconnect wire to switch. Light should be on with ignition on. If light does not go off when engine is started, check engine for low oil pressure. If oil pressure is okay, check oil pressure switch for faulty operation.
Oil Light Will Not Go On With Ignition On (Aspire) – Ground Yellow/Red wire at instrument panel connector. Turn ignition on. If light goes on, repair Yellow/Red wire between oil pressure switch and indicator light, or replace defective oil pressure switch. If light does not come on, replace bulb. If bulb is okay, check instrument panel ground circuit.

TEMPERATURE GAUGE TEST

Aspire – **1)** Unplug coolant temperature sensor, located at upper right front of engine. Connect one lead of Rotunda Gauge System Tester (021-00055) to Yellow wire at coolant temperature sending unit. Connect other tester lead to ground. Set tester to 16 ohms. Turn ignition on.
2) After one minute, gauge should indicate hot (H). Set tester to 180.5 ohms. After one minute, gauge should indicate cold (C). If gauge indications are okay, check Yellow/White wire at instrument cluster connector for a short or open. If wire is okay, test temperature sending unit. See TEMPERATURE SENDING UNIT TEST.
Capri – **1)** Unplug connector from temperature sending unit, located at front of cylinder head. Connect one lead of Rotunda Gauge System Tester (021-00055) to Yellow/Black wire which was removed. Connect other tester lead to ground. Set tester to 18 ohms, turn ignition switch on, and observe temperature gauge. Gauge should indicate 250°F.
2) Set tester to 60 ohms. Gauge should indicate 175°F. Set tester to 223 ohms. Gauge should indicate 100°F. If gauge indicates within 2 needle widths of specified temperature, gauge is functioning properly. If indications are not as specified, replace gauge.

TEMPERATURE SENDING UNIT TEST

Aspire – Remove coolant temperature sending unit from engine. Place sending unit in container of oil. Measure resistance between sending unit terminal and case. Heat oil to 122°F (50°C). Resistance should be 90-154 ohms. Heat oil to 239°F (115°C). Resistance should be 24-28 ohms. If resistance is not as specified, replace sending unit.
Capri – Remove sending unit from engine. Place sending unit in container of water. Heat water to 176°F (80°C). Measure resistance between sending unit terminal and case. Resistance should be 49.3-57.7 ohms. If resistance is not as specified, replace sending unit.

TURBO BOOST GAUGE & SENSOR TEST

Capri – 1) Unplug 3-pin boost sensor electrical connector, located on right side of firewall. Turn ignition on. Measure voltage between Yellow/Green and Black wires. Battery voltage should exist. If voltage is as specified, go to next step. If voltage is not as specified, repair Yellow/Green or Black wires as necessary.

2) Remove instrument cluster. See INSTRUMENT CLUSTER under REMOVAL & INSTALLATION. With boost sensor disconnected, measure resistance of White/Black wire between instrument panel and boost sensor harness connector. If resistance is less than 5 ohms, go to next step. If resistance is not less than 5 ohms, repair White/Black wire.

3) Ground White/Black wire at boost gauge. Boost gauge should indicate low. Apply 12 volts to White/Black wire at boost gauge. Boost gauge should indicate high. If boost gauge operates as specified, go to next step. If boost gauge does not operate as specified, replace boost gauge.

4) Reconnect instrument panel wiring. With ignition on and boost sensor disconnected, connect jumper wire between Yellow/Green and White/Black wires of boost sensor harness connector. Boost gauge should indicate high. If boost gauge indicates high, replace boost sensor. If boost gauge does not indicate high, go to TROUBLE SHOOTING for other possible causes.

REMOVAL & INSTALLATION

INSTRUMENT CLUSTER

Removal & Installation (Aspire) – 1) Disconnect negative battery cable. Remove instrument panel insert. Disconnect speedometer cable at transaxle. Remove instrument cluster screws.

2) Pull instrument cluster away from panel. Reach behind instrument panel. Press lock tab on speedometer cable and pull it out from instrument cluster. Press lock tabs to release electrical connectors from rear of panel. Remove instrument cluster. To install, reverse removal procedure.

Removal & Installation (Capri) – 1) Disconnect negative battery cable. Remove heater/radio bezel. Pull outward to remove trim covers located on both sides of steering column. Remove retaining screws and carefully pull instrument panel bezel partially away from dash. Unplug electrical connectors from clock and switches in bezel. Remove instrument panel bezel. *See Fig. 3.*

2) Disconnect speedometer cable from transaxle. Remove instrument panel retaining screws. Slide instrument panel outward. Press lock tab to release speedometer cable from instrument cluster. Unplug electrical connectors. Remove instrument cluster. To install instrument panel, reverse removal procedure.

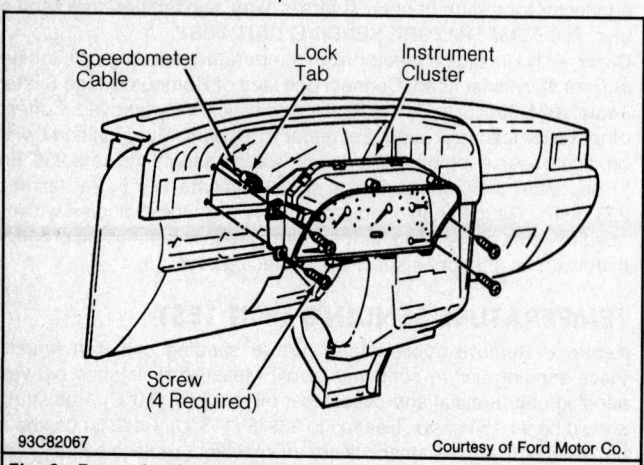

93C82067   Courtesy of Ford Motor Co.

Fig. 3: Removing Instrument Panel (Capri)

INDICATOR LIGHTS

Removal & Installation – Remove instrument cluster panel for access. See INSTRUMENT CLUSTER. To remove bulb, rotate bulb holders counterclockwise to disengage from printed circuit board. Twist bulb counterclockwise to remove from holder. To install bulb, reverse removal procedure. Install instrument panel. Test lights.

SPEEDOMETER

NOTE: Federal law requires that a label stating odometer has been repaired or replaced be affixed to any vehicle that has had its odometer repaired, replaced, or set to zero.

Removal & Installation (Aspire) – Remove instrument cluster. See INSTRUMENT CLUSTER. Press lock tabs to remove lens. Remove speedometer head from instrument panel. To install, reverse removal procedure. *See Fig. 4.*

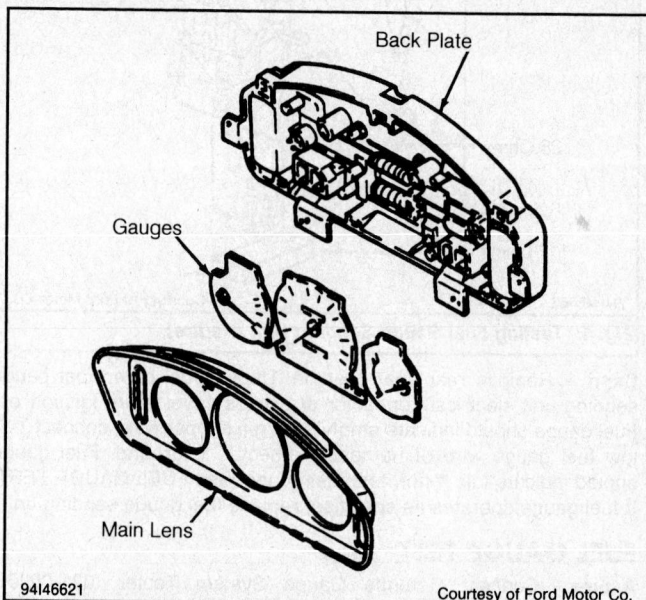

94I46621   Courtesy of Ford Motor Co.

Fig. 4: Exploded View Of Instrument Cluster (Aspire)

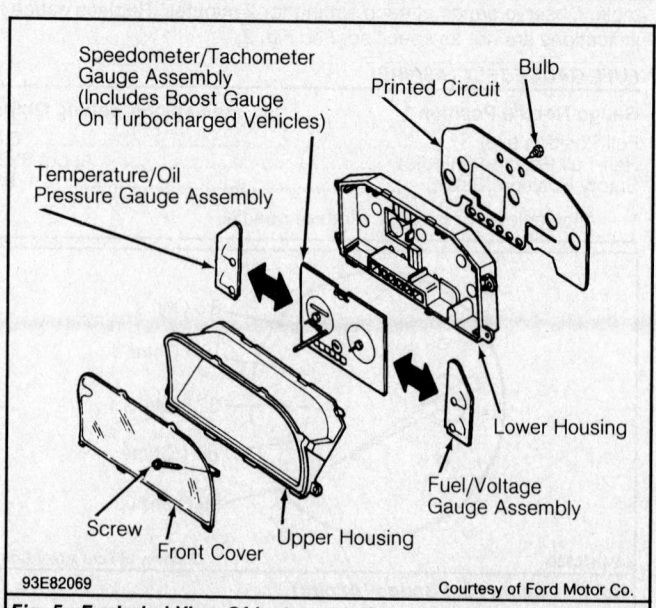

93E82069   Courtesy of Ford Motor Co.

Fig. 5: Exploded View Of Instrument Cluster (Capri)

Removal & Installation (Capri) – Disconnect negative battery cable. Disconnect speedometer cable at transaxle. Remove instrument cluster. See INSTRUMENT CLUSTER. Disassemble instrument cluster. Remove speedometer module from instrument panel. To install, apply a 3/16" (4.6 mm) ball of Silicone Damping Grease (D7AZ-19A331-A) into drive hole of speedometer head. To complete installation, reverse removal procedure. *See Figs. 3 and 5.*

SPEED SENSOR

On vehicles equipped with cruise control, a speed sensor is mounted in speedometer head. If replacement is necessary, speedometer head must be replaced. See SPEEDOMETER.

FUEL GAUGE

Removal & Installation – Remove instrument cluster. See INSTRUMENT CLUSTER. Remove fuel gauge. To install gauge, reverse removal procedure. On Capri, replace fuel gauge/voltmeter as an assembly.

FUEL SENDING UNIT

Removal & Installation (Aspire) – **1)** Start engine. Unplug fuel pump relay, located behind left side of instrument panel. Relieve fuel pressure by running engine until it stalls. Turn ignition off.
2) Remove rear seat cushion. Fold luggage compartment floor cover forward to expose access plate. On 2-door models, remove nuts and bolts from filler cover. On all models, remove sending unit access plate. Unplug connector.
3) On 4-door vehicles, separate check valve from bracket. On all models, disconnect and plug hoses. Remove fuel pump and sending unit as an assembly. To install, reverse removal procedure.

Removal & Installation (Capri) – **1)** Remove rear seat cushion. Remove access plate. Unplug sending unit wiring and fuel pump electrical connector.
2) Relieve relieve fuel pressure by starting and running engine until it stalls. Turn ignition off. Disconnect and plug fuel lines at sending unit. Remove sending unit. To install, reverse removal procedure.

TACHOMETER

CAUTION: Tachometer is calibrated at factory. Rough handling could disturb calibration.

Removal & Installation – Remove instrument cluster. See INSTRUMENT CLUSTER. Disassemble cluster to remove tachometer. To install, reverse removal procedure. On Capri, tachometer/speedometer/boost gauge must be replaced as an assembly.

TEMPERATURE GAUGE

Removal & Installation – Remove instrument cluster. See INSTRUMENT CLUSTER. Disassemble instrument cluster to remove temperature gauge. On Capri, replace temperature/oil pressure gauge as an assembly. To install gauge, reverse removal procedure.

TEMPERATURE SENDING UNIT

Removal – Unplug sending unit wire, located on upper right front of engine (Aspire) or cylinder head (Capri). Remove radiator cap to relieve cooling system pressure. Position drain pan below sending unit. Unscrew temperature sending unit.
Installation – To install, apply Pipe Sealant With Teflon (D8AZ-19554-A) to threads of sending unit. Reverse removal procedure to complete installation. Fill cooling system to proper level. Start engine. Check for coolant leaks at sending unit.

WIRING DIAGRAMS

NOTE: See ACCESSORIES & EQUIPMENT, Volume 5.

1994 ACCESSORIES & EQUIPMENT
Power Door Locks

Capri

DESCRIPTION & OPERATION

A control switch is mounted on each door trim panel. An actuator in each door operates the door lock linkage. In the event of system failure, manual door locks override electrical operation.

TROUBLE SHOOTING

Door Locks Inoperative – Go to SYSTEM TEST, step **1)**.
Door Locks Work From Only One Switch – Go to SYSTEM TEST, step **4)**.
Only One Door Lock Works – Go to SYSTEM TEST, step **4)**.

TESTING

Before performing any testing, inspect for binding or frozen locks, damaged actuators, or damaged switches. Inspect for failed DOOR LOCK or TAIL LAMP fuses, damaged wiring, or loose or corroded connections. Correct any obvious defects before proceeding.

SYSTEM TEST

1) Inspect DOOR LOCK fuse. If fuse has failed, go to next step. If fuse is okay, go to step **4)**.
2) Replace DOOR LOCK fuse. Turn ignition on. If fuse fails again, go to next step. If fuse does not fail, go to step **4)**.
3) Turn ignition off. Unplug connectors from both door switches. Unplug connector from fuse panel. Inspect White/Green wire at fuse panel for short to ground. If wire is okay, go to next step. If wire is not okay, repair wire as necessary.
4) Reconnect wiring to fuse panel if necessary. Unplug connectors from door switches. Turn ignition on. Check for battery voltage on White/Green wire at each door switch harness connector. If battery voltage exists, go to next step. If voltage is not as specified, repair White/Green wire as necessary.

Switch Position	Wire Terminals	Resistance In Ohms
Lock	W/GN	Greater than 10,000
Lock	BK (Pin 2A)	Less than 5
Lock	BK (Pin 7A)	Greater than 10,000
Unlock	W/GN	Less than 5
Unlock	BK (Pin 2A)	Greater than 10,000
Unlock	BK (Pin 7A)	Greater than 10,000
Rest	W/GN	Greater than 10,000
Rest	BK (Pin 2A)	Less than 5
Rest	BK (Pin 7A)	Greater than 10,000

MEASURED FROM PINK/LIGHT GREEN WIRE TERMINAL

Switch Position	Wire Terminals	Resistance In Ohms
Lock	W/GN	Less than 5
Lock	BK (Pin 2A)	Greater than 10,000
Lock	BK (Pin 7A)	Greater than 10,000
Unlock	W/GN	Greater than 10,000
Unlock	BK (Pin 2A)	Greater than 10,000
Unlock	BK (Pin 7A)	Less than 5
Rest	W/GN	Greater than 10,000
Rest	BK (Pin 2A)	Greater than 10,000
Rest	BK (Pin 7A)	Less than 5

MEASURED FROM PINK/YELLOW WIRE TERMINAL

94H46505   Courtesy of Ford Motor Co.
Fig. 1: Testing Left Door Lock Switch

5) Turn ignition off. Measure resistance between Black wire and ground at each switch harness connector. If resistance is less than 5 ohms for each wire, go to next step. Repair appropriate Black wire if resistance is not as specified.
6) Unplug left door lock switch. Measure resistance between Pink/Light Green wire terminal on switch and specified wire terminals, then repeat with Pink/Yellow wire terminal. See Fig. 1. Replace switch if measurements are not as specified.
7) Unplug right door lock switch. Measure resistance between Pink/Black wire terminal on switch and specified wire terminals, then repeat with Pink/Orange wire terminal. See Fig. 2. Replace switch if measurements are not as specified.

Switch Position	Wire Terminals	Resistance In Ohms
Lock	W/GN	Greater than 10,000
Lock	PK/LG (Pin 2B)	Less than 5
Lock	PK/Y (Pin 7B)	Greater than 10,000
Unlock	W/GN	Less than 5
Unlock	PK/LG (Pin 2B)	Greater than 10,000
Unlock	PK/Y (Pin 7B)	Greater than 10,000
Rest	W/GN	Greater than 10,000
Rest	PK/LG (Pin 2B)	Less than 5
Rest	PK/Y (Pin 7B)	Greater than 10,000

MEASURED FROM PINK/BLACK WIRE TERMINAL

Switch Position	Wire Terminals	Resistance In Ohms
Lock	W/GN	Less than 5
Lock	PK/LG (Pin 2B)	Greater than 10,000
Lock	PK/Y (Pin 7B)	Greater than 10,000
Unlock	W/GN	Greater than 10,000
Unlock	PK/LG (Pin 2B)	Greater than 10,000
Unlock	PK/Y (Pin 7B)	Less than 5
Rest	W/GN	Greater than 10,000
Rest	PK/LG (Pin 2B)	Greater than 10,000
Rest	PK/Y (Pin 7B)	Less than 5

MEASURED FROM PINK/ORANGE WIRE TERMINAL

94I46506   Courtesy of Ford Motor Co.
Fig. 2: Testing Right Door Switch

8) Turn ignition off. Measure resistance of Pink/Light Green and Pink/Yellow wires between left and right switch harness connectors. Measure resistance to ground of same wires. If resistance between connectors is less than 5 ohms, and resistance to ground is greater than 10,000 ohms for each wire, go to next step. If resistance is not as specified, repair appropriate wire.
9) Unplug right switch connector, leaving left switch connected. Unplug both door lock actuators. Measure resistance of Pink/Black and Pink Orange wires between right switch harness connector and both actuator connectors. Measure resistance to ground of same wires. If resistance between connectors is less than 5 ohms, and resistance to ground is greater than 10,000 ohms for each wire, replace appropriate door lock actuator. If resistance is not as specified, repair appropriate wire.

REMOVAL & INSTALLATION

CAUTION: When battery is disconnected, vehicle computer and memory systems may lose memory data. Driveability problems may exist until computer systems have completed a relearn cycle. See COMPUTER RELEARN PROCEDURES article in GENERAL INFORMATION before disconnecting battery.

DOOR LOCK ACTUATORS

Removal & Installation – Remove door trim panel and watershield. Unplug door lock switch. Remove window rear guide if necessary. Remove door lock actuator. To install, reverse removal procedure.

DOOR LOCK SWITCHES

Removal & Installation – Remove door trim panel. Remove retaining screws. Unplug connector. Remove switch. To install, reverse removal procedure.

WIRING DIAGRAM

NOTE: See ACCESSORIES & EQUIPMENT, Volume 5.

Capri

DESCRIPTION & OPERATION

Electric remote control side view mirrors are used on both sides of vehicle. A remote control switch is located in floor console. Both mirrors are spring loaded to swing away under minor impact.

WARNING: Objects seen in right mirror are closer than they appear. Right hand mirror should not be used to estimate distances of following vehicles when changing lanes.

TROUBLE SHOOTING

1) Inspect mirror system components for:
- Damaged Mirrors
- Damaged Remote Control Switch
- Blown Fuse
- Damaged Wiring Harness
- Loose Or Corroded Connections

2) Flex harness and connectors at control switch and mirrors. Look for obvious signs of opens or shorts.

3) Operate power mirror switch and determine condition. If mirrors do not operate at all, go to step **1)** under TESTING. If mirrors do not operate properly, go to step **6)** under TESTING.

TESTING

1) If the 15-amp CIGAR fuse is okay, go to step **4)**. If fuse is not okay, go to next step.

2) Replace 15-amp CIGAR fuse and turn ignition on. If fuse fails again, go to next step. If fuse does not fail, go to step **4)**.

3) Unplug interior fuse panel connector. Disconnect remote control mirror switch. Measure resistance between Blue/White wire at fuse panel connector and ground. If resistance is less than 5 ohms, repair Blue/White wire. If resistance is more than 5 ohms, go to step **4)**.

4) Disconnect remote control mirror switch. With ignition on, measure voltage on Blue/White wire at remote control mirror switch connector. If voltage is more than 10 volts, go to next step. If voltage is less than 10 volts, repair Blue/White wire between interior fuse panel and remote control mirror switch.

5) If resistance between Black wire at remote control mirror switch and ground is less than 5 ohms, go to next step. If resistance is more than 5 ohms, repair Black wire.

6) Measure voltages at remote control mirror switch as specified in SWITCH POSITION VOLTAGES (SWITCH CONNECTOR) table. If voltages are correct, go to next step. If voltages are not as specified, replace remote control mirror switch.

SWITCH POSITION VOLTAGES (SWITCH CONNECTOR)

Switch Position	Wire Color	Volts
Right Mirror Up	LT GRN/BLK	12
Right Mirror Up	BRN	0
Right Mirror Down	LT GRN/BLK	0
Right Mirror Down	BRN	12
Right Mirror Left	BRN/BLK	12
Right Mirror Left	BRN	0
Right Mirror Right	BRN/BLK	0
Right Mirror Right	BRN	12
Left Mirror Up	LT GRN/YEL	12
Left Mirror Up	BRN	0
Left Mirror Down	LT GRN/YEL	0
Left Mirror Down	BRN	12
Left Mirror Left	BRN/YEL	12
Left Mirror Left	BRN	0
Left Mirror Right	BRN/YEL	0
Left Mirror Right	BRN	12

7) Locate remote control mirror motor connectors. Operate switch. Measure voltages at remote control mirror motors as specified in SWITCH POSITION VOLTAGES (MOTOR CONNECTOR) table. If voltages are as specified, replace mirror motor(s). If voltages are not as specified, repair appropriate wire(s).

SWITCH POSITION VOLTAGES (MOTOR CONNECTOR)

Switch Position	Wire Color	Volts
Left Mirror Up	LT GRN/YEL	12
Left Mirror Up	BRN	0
Left Mirror Down	LT/GRN/YEL	0
Left Mirror Down	BRN	12
Left Mirror Left	BRN/YEL	12
Left Mirror Left	BRN	0
Left Mirror Right	BRN/YEL	0
Left Mirror Right	BRN	12
Right Mirror Up	LT GRN/BLK	12
Right Mirror Up	BRN	0
Right Mirror Down	LT GRN/BLK	0
Right Mirror Down	BRN	12
Right Mirror Left	BRN/BLK	12
Right Mirror Left	BRN	0
Right Mirror Right	BRN/BLK	0
Right Mirror Right	BRN	12

REMOVAL & INSTALLATION

POWER MIRROR SWITCH

Removal & Installation – Insert a small, flat tool at notch and gently pry out switch. Remove connector and switch. To install, reverse removal procedure. *See Fig. 1.*

NOTE: When installing power mirror switch, ensure switch LEFT/RIGHT orientation is correct.

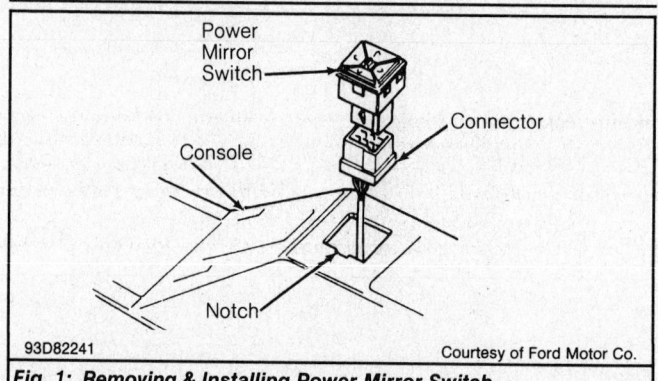

93D82241   Courtesy of Ford Motor Co.

Fig. 1: Removing & Installing Power Mirror Switch

POWER MIRROR ASSEMBLY

Removal & Installation – Remove trim cover, nut, and bezel. Remove lock nut, washer, and mirror assembly. Unplug connector from mirror. To install, reverse removal procedure. Ensure gasket is in position. Position wiring to avoid interference. *See Fig. 2.*

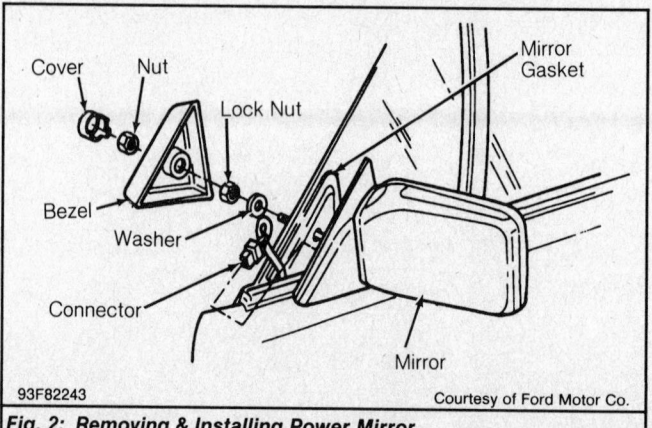

93F82243   Courtesy of Ford Motor Co.

Fig. 2: Removing & Installing Power Mirror

Aspire, Capri

SAFETY PRECAUTIONS

CAUTION: These vehicles are equipped with Supplemental Restraint System (SRS). Observe appropriate safety precautions. Air bag system is powered directly from battery and back-up power supply. Before any repairs are performed, disconnect and shield battery ground cable. Wait at least one minute before servicing ANY air bag component. Use caution when working near steering column. Air bag could accidently deploy at any time.

DISABLING & ACTIVATING AIR BAG SYSTEM

DISABLING AIR BAG SYSTEM

NOTE: The following disabling procedure is ONLY for component removal and replacement purposes.

To disable SRS, disconnect negative, then positive battery cable. Wait one minute. System is now disabled.

ACTIVATING AIR BAG SYSTEM

To activate SRS, reconnect positive, then negative battery cable. From passenger's side of vehicle, turn ignition on. System is now activated. Observe AIR BAG light to verify system is functioning properly.

NOTE: For information on air bag DIAGNOSIS & TESTING or DISPOSAL PROCEDURES, see MITCHELL® AIR BAG SERVICE & REPAIR MANUAL, DOMESTIC & IMPORTED MODELS.

TESTING

HAZARD WARNING SWITCH & TURN SIGNAL SWITCH

Aspire – 1) Remove steering column covers to gain access to turn signal/hazard switch connectors. Turn ignition on. Using a 12-volt test light, check for battery voltage at Black/Yellow wire at turn signal switch connector. If battery voltage exists, go to next step. If battery voltage does not exist, inspect METER fuse or Black/Yellow wire between fuse panel and turn signal switch.
2) Set turn signal switch to right turn position. Battery voltage should exist on Yellow wire at turn signal switch connector. If battery voltage exists, go to next step. Replace turn signal switch if battery voltage does not exist.
3) Set turn signal switch to left turn position. Battery voltage should exist on Green wire at turn signal switch connector. If battery voltage exists, turn signal switch is okay. Replace turn signal switch if battery voltage does not exist.
4) Unplug connector from multifunction switch. With hazard flasher set to OFF position, continuity should not exist between switch terminals for Orange and Black wires. With hazard flasher switch in ON position, continuity should exist. Replace switch if continuity is not as specified.

Capri – 1) Remove steering column covers. Turn ignition on. Check for battery voltage at Green/Red and Green/Yellow wires at turn signal/hazard switch connectors. If battery voltage exist, go to next step. If battery voltage does not exist, inspect METER and HAZARD fuses. Also check hazard and turn signal flasher and replace as necessary.
2) Set turn signal switch to right turn position. Connect test light to both Green/White wires at switch connector. Test light should flash on and off.

3) Set turn signal switch to left turn position. Connect test light to both Green/Black wires at switch connector. Test light should flash on and off. If turn signal/hazard switch does not function as specified, replace switch.

HEADLIGHT SWITCH

Aspire – Disconnect headlight switch. Set switch to position indicated in table. Check for continuity between switch terminals that correspond to wire colors listed. See HEADLIGHT SWITCH CONTINUITY TEST (ASPIRE) table. If switch does not function as indicated, replace switch.

HEADLIGHT SWITCH CONTINUITY TEST (ASPIRE)

Switch Position	Wire Color	Continuity
Flash	RED/BLK To RED/WHT	Yes
Low	RED/GRN To RED/BLK	Yes
High	RED/GRN To RED/WHT	Yes
PARK	RED/WHT To BLK	Yes
HEADLIGHT	RED/BLU To BLK	Yes
Off	BLK To All	No

Capri – 1) Remove instrument panel bezel to gain access to switch connector. See HEADLIGHT SWITCH under REMOVAL & INSTALLATION. Unplug headlight switch connector. Measure voltage between Red and Red/White wires of headlight switch harness connector and ground. If battery voltage exists, go to next step. If battery voltage does not exist, inspect HEAD and MAIN fuses and Red and Red/White wires between switch and fuse block.
2) Press headlight switch to first position. Check for continuity between switch terminals that correspond to Red and Red/Green wires of harness connector. Continuity should not exist. If continuity exists, replace switch.
3) Press headlight switch to second position. Check for continuity between switch terminals that correspond to Red and Red/Green wires of harness connector. Continuity should exist. If switch does not function as described, replace headlight switch. If switch functions as described but headlights do not work, go to next step.
4) Remove steering column covers to gain access to flash-to-pass switch connector. Set switch to position indicated in table. Test for battery voltage between indicated wire terminals and ground. See HEADLIGHT SWITCH TEST (CAPRI) table. If switch does not function as indicated, replace switch.

HEADLIGHT SWITCH TEST (CAPRI)

Switch Position	Wire Color	Voltage
Off		
Headlights Off	RED	Battery
	All Other Wires	0
Headlights On	RED, RED/GRN, RED/BLK	Battery
	All Other Wires	0
On		
Headlights Off	RED, RED/WHT	Battery
	All Other Wires	0
Headlights On	RED, RED/GRN, RED/WHT	Battery
	All Other Wires	0

IGNITION SWITCH

Aspire – Remove lower steering column cover to gain access to ignition switch connector. Unplug ignition switch connector. Test for continuity between terminals listed in table at specified switch positions. If continuity is not as specified, replace ignition switch. See IGNITION SWITCH CONTINUITY (ASPIRE) table. *See Fig. 1.*

IGNITION SWITCH CONTINUITY (ASPIRE)

Terminal	Position	Continuity
Black/White – Green	OFF	No
	ACC	Yes
	ON	Yes
	START	No
Black/White – Black/Red	OFF	No
	ACC	No
	ON	Yes
	START	No
Black/White – Blue	OFF	No
	ACC	No
	ON	Yes
	START	Yes
Black/White – White	OFF	No
	ACC	No
	ON	No
	START	Yes

Capri – Remove lower steering column cover to gain access to ignition switch connector. Check for continuity between terminals indicated in table. See IGNITION SWITCH CONTINUITY (CAPRI) table. Continuity should not exist between any terminal and chassis ground in any switch position except proof circuit in START position. *See Fig. 2.*

IGNITION SWITCH CONTINUITY (CAPRI)

Switch Position	Continuity Should Exist Only Between Circuits
ACC	37, 297
LOCK	No Continuity
OFF	No Continuity
RUN	37, 16, 687, 297
START	977, 162 (Chassis Ground), 37, 32, 262

NOTE: *Circuit pairs No. 37, 687, and 297 are connected together inside ignition switch.*

WIPER SWITCH

For testing information on wiper switch, see WIPER/WASHER SYSTEMS article.

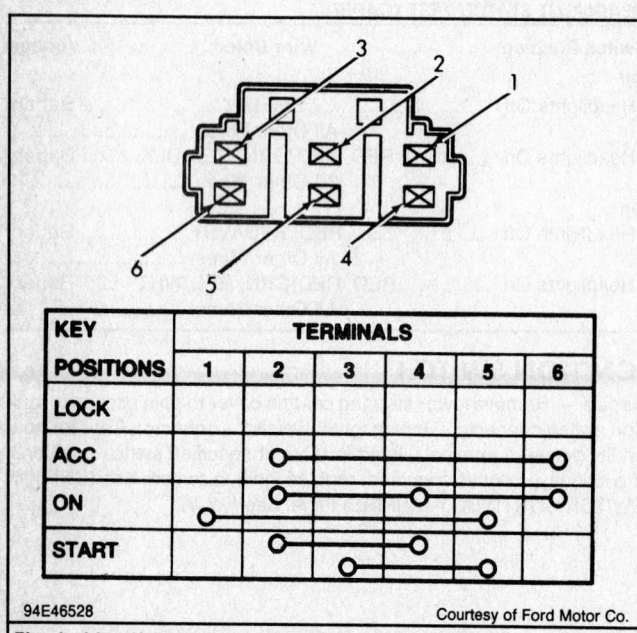

KEY POSITIONS	TERMINALS					
	1	2	3	4	5	6
LOCK						
ACC		O—————O				O
ON	O	O—————O		O—————O		O
START	O		O—————O		O	

94E46528   Courtesy of Ford Motor Co.

Fig. 1: Identifying Ignition Switch Terminals (Aspire)

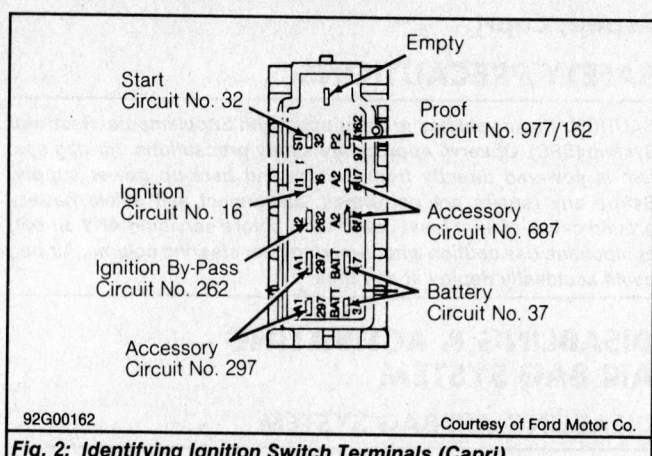

92G00162   Courtesy of Ford Motor Co.

Fig. 2: Identifying Ignition Switch Terminals (Capri)

REMOVAL & INSTALLATION

CAUTION: These vehicles are equipped with Supplemental Restraint System (SRS). Observe appropriate safety precautions. Air bag system is powered directly from battery and back-up power supply. See DISABLING & ACTIVATING AIR BAG SYSTEM. Use caution when working near steering column. Air bag could accidently deploy at any time.

STEERING WHEEL & HORN PAD

CAUTION: When removing steering wheel, DO NOT use a knock-off type steering wheel puller, or strike steering wheel or shaft with a hammer. A sudden impact could damage bearing, or collapse the steering column, requiring replacement of column.

CAUTION: Remove steering wheel carefully to avoid damaging clockspring wiring or air bag module connector, or accidentally rotating clockspring. After steering wheel removal, tape clockspring in position to prevent damage and to keep it from being rotated accidentally.

Removal – 1) Before proceeding, see SAFETY PRECAUTIONS. Disable SRS. See DISABLING & ACTIVATING AIR BAG SYSTEM.
2) Position front wheels straight ahead. Remove driver-side air bag module. Unplug speed control wiring harness connector (if equipped) from steering wheel.
3) Remove and discard steering wheel retaining bolt. Mark steering wheel hub and shaft to aid alignment during installation. Using Steering Wheel Puller (T67L-3600-A), remove steering wheel. Route clockspring wiring harness through steering wheel as wheel is lifted from shaft.
Installation – 1) Position front wheels straight ahead. Route clockspring wiring harness through steering wheel opening at 3 o'clock position. Position steering wheel onto steering shaft with reference marks aligned.
2) Ensure air bag clockspring wire is not pinched when positioning steering wheel. Install NEW steering wheel retaining bolt and tighten to specification. See TORQUE SPECIFICATIONS. Connect speed control wiring harness. Secure connector into clip.
3) Install driver-side air bag module. Activate SRS. Verify system is functioning properly.

COMBINATION SWITCH

Removal & Installation (Aspire) – 1) Before proceeding, see SAFETY PRECAUTIONS. Disable SRS. See DISABLING & ACTIVATING AIR BAG SYSTEM.
2) Remove steering wheel. See STEERING WHEEL & HORN PAD. Remove column shroud halves. Apply strips of tape across air bag clockspring rotor and stator to prevent rotation. Remove clockspring.

3) Remove combination switch screws. Unplug connectors. Remove switch. To install, reveres removal procedure. Install NEW steering wheel bolt and tighten to specification. See TORQUE SPECIFICATIONS.

Removal (Capri) – 1) Before proceeding, see SAFETY PRECAUTIONS. Disable SRS. See DISABLING & ACTIVATING AIR BAG SYSTEM. Remove lower steering column cover. Remove center access panel and trim cover under steering column. Remove left side defroster connector tube. Remove steering column upper retaining bolts. Column will pivot downward and rest on instrument panel brace.

CAUTION: Ensure no wiring is pinched beneath steering column when lowered.

---

2) Remove retaining screws and switch. Grasp switch and lever. Pull lever from of switch. Unplug switch electrical connectors. Remove switch.

Installation – Align key with slot. Install lever into switch assembly. Position switch onto steering column. Install retaining screws. To complete installation, reverse removal procedure.

HEADLIGHT SWITCH

Removal & Installation (Aspire) – See COMBINATION SWITCH under REMOVAL & INSTALLATION.

Removal & Installation (Capri) – 1) Headlight located on left side of instrument panel bezel. Disconnect negative battery cable. Pull out center storage compartment. Remove upper screws, lower screws, and heater/radio bezel. Pull outward to remove trim covers located on both sides of steering column.

2) Remove retaining screws. Carefully pull instrument panel bezel partially away from dash. Unplug headlight switch connector. Press tangs on both sides of switch and pull outward to remove switch from bezel. To install, reverse removal procedure.

IGNITION SWITCH & LOCK CYLINDER

Removal & Installation (Aspire) – Before proceeding, see SAFETY PRECAUTIONS. Disable SRS. See DISABLING & ACTIVATING AIR BAG SYSTEM. Remove steering column shroud. Remove ignition switch. Unplug connector. To Install, reverse removal procedure.

Removal (Capri) – 1) Disconnect negative battery cable. Remove lower steering column cover. Remove center access panel and trim cover under steering column. Remove left side defroster connector tube. Remove steering column upper retaining bolts. Column will pivot downward and rest on instrument panel brace.

CAUTION: Ensure no wiring is pinched beneath steering column when it is lowered.

---

2) With ignition key inserted in lock assembly, rotate tumbler while pressing release pin with an appropriate punch. Pull tumbler assembly from housing. Remove upper column cover. Remove column lock shield. Unplug ignition switch connector. Remove retaining screws and switch.

Installation – Position ignition switch onto column lock assembly. Fit actuator pin of lock assembly into slot in ignition switch. To complete installation, reverse removal procedure.

TURN SIGNAL SWITCH

See COMBINATION SWITCH under REMOVAL & INSTALLATION.

WIPER SWITCH

Removal & installation (Aspire) – See COMBINATION SWITCH under REMOVAL & INSTALLATION.

Removal & Installation (Capri) – Remove center trim panel and lower steering column cover. Disconnect wiper switch connector and pull wiring from routing clip. Grasp switch and lever firmly. Pull out to remove. To install, reverse removal procedure.

TORQUE SPECIFICATIONS

TORQUE SPECIFICATIONS

Application	Ft. Lbs. (N.m)
Column Lock Shield Screw & Nut	11-14 (15-19)
Ignition Lock Housing Bolt	12-13 (16-18)
Steering Wheel Bolt (Capri)	23-33 (31-45)
Steering Wheel Nut (Aspire)	29-36 (39-49)
Upper Column Retaining Bolts	17-23 (23-31)
	INCH Lbs. (N.m)
Ignition Switch Screw	50-70 (5.6-7.9)
Driver's Air Bag Module Nuts	35-53 (4-6)

WIRING DIAGRAMS

NOTE: See ACCESSORIES & EQUIPMENT, Volume 5.

Aspire, Capri

DESCRIPTION & OPERATION

Aspire and Capri are equipped with 2-speed wipers. An optional intermittent system is available. Aspire rear wiper uses a single-speed wiper motor. Washer systems for both front and rear washers use pumps mounted near fluid reservoirs.

SAFETY PRECAUTIONS

CAUTION: These vehicles are equipped with Supplemental Restraint System (SRS). Observe appropriate safety precautions. Air bag system is powered directly from battery and back-up power supply. Before any repairs are performed, disconnect and shield battery ground cable. Wait at least one minute before servicing ANY air bag component. Use caution when working near steering column. Air bag could accidently deploy at any time.

DISABLING & ACTIVATING AIR BAG SYSTEM

DISABLING AIR BAG SYSTEM

NOTE: The following disabling sequence is ONLY for component removal and replacement purposes.

To disable SRS, disconnect negative, then positive battery cable. Wait one minute. System is now disabled.

ACTIVATING AIR BAG SYSTEM

To activate SRS, reconnect positive, then negative battery cable. From passenger's side of vehicle, turn ignition on. System is now activated. Observe AIR BAG light to verify system is functioning properly.

NOTE: For information on air bag DIAGNOSIS & TESTING or DISPOSAL PROCEDURES, see MITCHELL® AIR BAG SERVICE & REPAIR MANUAL, DOMESTIC & IMPORTED MODELS.

ADJUSTMENTS

WIPER ARM ADJUSTMENT

Remove wiper arm and blade assemblies from pivot shafts. Turn wipers on. Allow wiper motor to cycle 2 to 3 times. Park motor. Reinstall wiper arm and blade assemblies with tips of wiper blades at specified distance from lower edge of windshield. See WIPER BLADE ADJUSTMENT SPECIFICATIONS table. Tighten wiper arm retaining nut to 89-124 INCH lbs. (10-14 N.m).

WIPER BLADE ADJUSTMENT SPECIFICATIONS

Application	Specification
Aspire	
Both Sides	1.2" (30 mm)
Rear	[1] 3.15" (80 mm)
Capri	
Driver Side	1.0" (25 mm)
Passenger Side	1.3" (32 mm)

[1] – From left edge of liftgate window.

TESTING

FRONT WIPER MOTOR TEST

Aspire – 1) Turn ignition off. Unplug wiper motor connector. Using fused jumper wire, apply 12 volts to terminal No. 2 of wiper motor. *See Fig. 1.* Motor should run at low speed.

2) Disconnect jumper wire, then apply 12 volts to terminal No. 1 of wiper motor. Motor should run at high speed.

3) Measure resistance between motor terminals No. 3 and 4. With motor in park position, resistance should be less than 5 ohms. With motor in any but park position, resistance should be more than 10,000 ohms. Replace motor if it does not perform as specified.

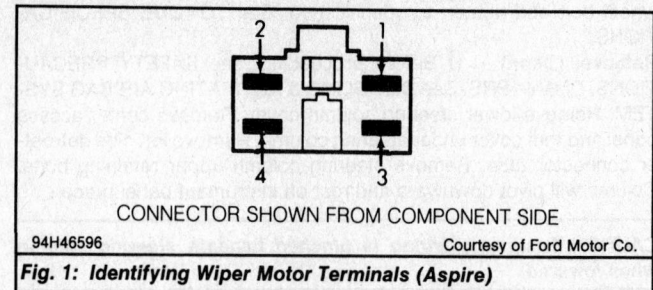

CONNECTOR SHOWN FROM COMPONENT SIDE

94H46596   Courtesy of Ford Motor Co.

Fig. 1: Identifying Wiper Motor Terminals (Aspire)

Capri – 1) Inspect WIPER fuse in interior fuse block and replace if necessary. Perform FRONT INTERVAL WIPE MODULE TEST. If wiper/washer switch and interval module are operating properly, unplug wiper motor connector. Turn ignition on. Set wiper/washer switch to HIGH position. Measure voltage at Blue/Red and Blue wires at wiper motor harness connector.

2) If battery voltage does not exist, inspect Blue/Red or Blue wire for open circuit. If battery voltage exists, Inspect Black ground wire at wiper motor harness connector for an open circuit. Repair as necessary. If Black ground wire is okay, replace wiper motor.

FRONT INTERVAL WIPE MODULE TEST

Capri – 1) Inspect WIPER fuse. Replace if necessary. Perform FRONT WIPER/WASHER SWITCH TEST. Locate interval wipe module connector, located below instrument panel, near console. Set wiper switch to OFF position.

2) Turn ignition on. Measure voltage on Blue/White and Blue/Black wires of module connector. No voltage should exist. Set wiper switch to LOW position. Measure voltage on Blue/White and Blue/Black wires of module connector. Battery voltage should exist.

3) Set wiper switch to HIGH position. Measure voltage on Blue/White, Blue/Black, and Blue/Red wires at module connector. Battery voltage should exist. Set wiper switch to INT position. Measure voltage on Blue/White and Blue/Black wires of module connector. Battery voltage should exist during each cycle. If module does not perform as specified, replace module.

Festiva – Information is not available from manufacturer.

FRONT WIPER/WASHER SWITCH TEST

Aspire – Remove steering column cover. Unplug wiper/washer switch. Test for continuity between specified terminals with wiper switch set to positions listed in table. See FRONT WIPER/WASHER SWITCH TEST (ASPIRE) table. *See Fig. 2.* Replace switch if continuity is not as specified.

FRONT WIPER/WASHER SWITCH TEST (ASPIRE)

Position	Terminals
OFF	1 – 5
INT	1 – 5
LOW	5 – 15
HIGH	4 – 15
MIST	4 – 15
WASH	3 – 15

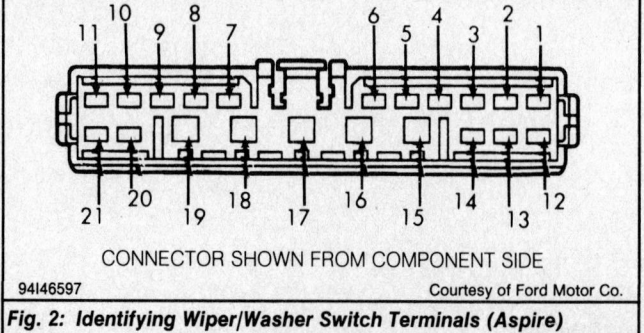

CONNECTOR SHOWN FROM COMPONENT SIDE

94I46597   Courtesy of Ford Motor Co.

Fig. 2: Identifying Wiper/Washer Switch Terminals (Aspire)

Capri – Remove lower steering column cover to gain access to wiper switch connector. Check for continuity between terminals listed in table at specified switch positions. See FRONT WIPER/WASHER SWITCH CONTINUITY (CAPRI) table. See Fig. 3. If continuity is not as specified, replace wiper/washer switch.

FRONT WIPER/WASHER SWITCH CONTINUITY (CAPRI)

Terminal	Position	Continuity
BLU – BLU/ORG	Pull Washer Lever	Yes
	Release Washer Lever	No
BLU – BRN/WHT	Intermittent	Yes
	All Other Positions	No
BLU – GRN	Low	Yes
	High	Yes
	All Other Positions	No
BLU – BLU/RED	High	Yes
	All Other Positions	No
ORG – YEL/RED	Rotate INT Control Knob	[1]

[1] – Ohmmeter should indicate smoothly increasing resistance from 420-880 ohms (minimum) to 7000-13,000 ohms (maximum).

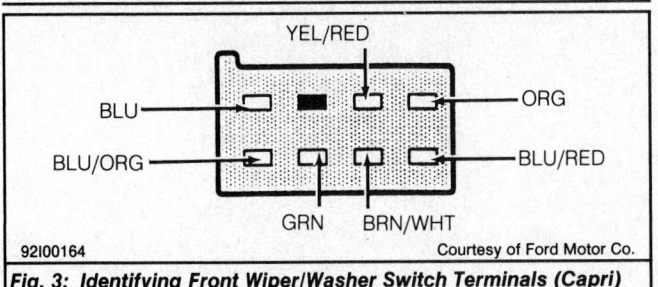

92I00164   Courtesy of Ford Motor Co.

Fig. 3: Identifying Front Wiper/Washer Switch Terminals (Capri)

WASHER MOTOR TEST

Remove washer fluid reservoir. Remove washer motor from reservoir. Connect fused jumper wire between washer motor terminal that corresponds to Blue/Orange wire (Blue/Green wire on Aspire rear washer motor) and battery positive terminal. Connect other washer motor terminal to ground. If washer motor does not run smoothly, replace motor.

REAR WIPER MOTOR TEST

Aspire – Turn ignition off. Unplug rear wiper motor connector. Using fused jumper wire, apply 12 volts to terminal that corresponds to Blue/Green wire of wiper motor. Connect motor terminal that corresponds to Black/Blue wire to ground. Motor should run smoothly. Replace motor if it does not perform as specified.

REAR WIPER/WASHER SWITCH TEST

Aspire – Remove steering column cover. Unplug wiper/washer switch. Test for continuity between specified terminals with rear wiper/washer switch set to positions listed in table. See REAR WIPER/WASHER SWITCH TEST (ASPIRE) table. See Fig. 2. Replace switch if continuity is not as specified.

REAR WIPER/WASHER SWITCH TEST (ASPIRE)

Position	Terminals
WASH	12 – 13
WIPE	13 – 14

REAR WASHER MOTOR TEST

See FRONT/REAR WASHER MOTOR TEST under TESTING.

REMOVAL & INSTALLATION

CAUTION: These vehicles are equipped with Supplemental Restraint System (SRS). Observe appropriate safety precautions. Air bag system is powered directly from battery and back-up power supply. See DISABLING & ACTIVATING AIR BAG SYSTEM. Use caution when working near steering column. Air bag could accidently deploy at any time.

FRONT WIPER MOTOR

Removal & Installation (Aspire) – Disconnect negative battery cable. Unplug wiper motor connector. Remove EGR solenoid valve bracket nuts. Slide vacuum fitting and cap from access plate. Remove access panel nuts. Loosen wiper motor bolts.
2) Pull wiper motor and access panel away from bulkhead. Disengage wiper linkage pivot from motor output arm. Separate motor from access panel. To install, reverse removal procedure.
Removal (Capri) – Disconnect negative battery cable. Gently pry linkage from ball socket at wiper motor arm. Unplug wiper motor connector. Remove mounting bolts and rubber insulators. Remove wiper motor.

NOTE: Disengage linkage from wiper motor arm ball socket, not by removing nut and wiper motor arm. This will eliminate need to adjust relationship between wiper motor and linkage. Replacement motors are supplied with arm attached.

Installation – Position wiper motor onto bulkhead. Install insulators. Tighten mounting screws to 62-89 INCH lbs. (7-10 N.m). Reverse removal procedure to complete installation. Check wipers for proper operation.

FRONT WIPER/WASHER SWITCH

Removal & Installation (Aspire) – **1)** Before proceeding, see SAFETY PRECAUTIONS. Disable SRS. See DISABLING & ACTIVATING AIR BAG SYSTEM.
2) Remove steering wheel. Remove column shroud halves. Apply strips of tape across air bag clockspring rotor and stator to prevent rotation. Remove clockspring.
3) Remove combination switch screws. Unplug connectors. Remove switch. To install, reveres removal procedure. Install NEW steering wheel bolt and tighten to specification. See TORQUE SPECIFICATIONS.
Removal & Installation (Capri) – Remove center trim panel and access cover under steering column. Remove lower steering column shroud. Unplug wiper/washer switch connector. Disengage wiring from routing clip. Firmly grasp switch and lever. Remove switch. To install, reverse removal procedure.

FRONT WASHER MOTOR & RESERVOIR

Removal & Installation (Aspire) – **1)** Disconnect negative battery cable. Remove filler neck. Raise and support vehicle. Remove coolant expansion reservoir. Remove left front wheel. Remove front fender splash shield. Remove front splash shield.
2) Remove reservoir. Disconnect washer pump fluid lines. Unplug connector. Remove reservoir. Separate pump from reservoir. To install, reverse removal procedure.
Removal & Installation (Capri) – Drain reservoir if necessary. Remove bolts securing reservoir to inner fender. Unplug washer pump motor connector. Disconnect fluid lines. Remove reservoir. To install, reverse removal procedure.

REAR WIPER MOTOR

Removal & Installation (Aspire) – Disconnect negative battery cable. Remove rear wiper pivot arm. Remove rear wiper pivot shaft cap, cowl nuts, and spacer. Remove motor cover. Remove liftgate trim panel. Unplug connector. Remove rear wiper motor. To install, reverse removal procedure.

1994 ACCESSORIES & EQUIPMENT
Wiper/Washer Systems (Cont.)

REAR WASHER MOTOR & RESERVOIR

Removal & Installation (Aspire) – Disconnect negative battery cable. Remove right luggage compartment side cover. Remove rear quarter trim panel. Remove reservoir mounting bolts. Separate hose from wiring duct. Unplug washer pump connector. Disconnect fluid lines. Remove reservoir. To install, reverse removal procedure.

TORQUE SPECIFICATIONS
TORQUE SPECIFICATIONS

Application	Ft. Lbs. (N.m)
Steering Wheel Nut (Aspire) [1]	29-36 (39-49)

	INCH Lbs. (N.m)
Front Wiper Arm Retaining Nut	89-124 (10-14)
Front Wiper Motor Mounting Bolts	62-89 (7-10)
Rear Outer Bushing Retaining Nut	27-44 (3-5)
Rear Wiper Arm Nut	44-84 (5-9.5)
Rear Wiper Motor Mounting Bolts	71-97 (8-11)

[1] – Install NEW bolt.

WIRING DIAGRAMS

NOTE: See ACCESSORIES & EQUIPMENT, Volume 5.

Aspire, Capri

NOTE: For repair procedures not covered in this article, see ENGINE OVERHAUL PROCEDURES article in GENERAL INFORMATION.

ENGINE IDENTIFICATION

Engine can be identified by Vehicle Identification Number (VIN) on metal tab attached to instrument panel. Tab is close to windshield on driver's side, and is visible through windshield. VIN has 17 characters. The 8th character identifies engine.

ENGINE IDENTIFICATION CODE (8TH VIN CHARACTER)

Engine	Code
Aspire	
1.3L SOHC SFI	H
Capri	
1.6L DOHC PFI	Z
1.6L DOHC PFI Turbo	6

ADJUSTMENTS

VALVE ARRANGEMENT

Intake Manifold Side – Intake valves.
Exhaust Manifold Side – Exhaust valves.

VALVE CLEARANCE ADJUSTMENT

Hydraulic lifters are used. Adjustment is not necessary.

REMOVAL & INSTALLATION

NOTE: For reassembly reference, label all electrical connectors, vacuum hoses, and fuel lines before removal. Also place mating marks on engine hood and other major assemblies before removal.

FUEL PRESSURE RELEASE

Aspire – Start engine. Unplug fuel pump relay connector, located behind left side of instrument panel. Allow engine to stall. Fuel pressure is now relieved.
Capri – Remove rear seat. Remove fuel pump access panel. Unplug fuel pump electrical connector. Start and idle engine until it dies. Turn ignition off.

ENGINE

NOTE: When removing engine mounts, mark and note location and position to ensure proper installation. Engine and transaxle are removed as an assembly.

Removal (Aspire) – **1)** Release fuel pressure. See FUEL PRESSURE RELEASE. Remove battery and battery tray. Discharge A/C system, using approved refrigerant recovery/recycling equipment. Mark hood and hinges for installation reference. Remove hood. Drain coolant. Remove air cleaner and intake duct. Remove radiator and fan.
2) Disconnect accelerator cable from throttle body. Remove accelerator shaft bracket. Disconnect speedometer cable at transaxle. Mark and disconnect fuel lines. Plug fuel lines. Disconnect heater and radiator hoses. Remove brake booster vacuum hose. On A/T models, disconnect vacuum modulator and governor hoses.
3) On all vehicles, unplug all engine and transmission connectors. Disconnect all engine and transmission grounds. Remove and plug power steering lines (if equipped).
4) On A/T models, remove shift lever-to-manual shaft bolt. Remove shift cable and bracket from transaxle. On M/T models, disconnect clutch control cable. On all models, loosen front wheel bolts.
5) Raise and support vehicle. Drain engine oil and transmission fluid. Remove front wheels. Remove right front splash shield. Remove lower arm clamp bolts and nuts. Pull lower arms downward, separating lower arms from knuckles. Remove drive shafts and joints. Install Dif-

ferential Plugs (T87C-7025-C) into differential side gears. See FWD AXLE SHAFTS article in DRIVE AXLES.
6) On M/T models, disconnect shift control rod. On all models, remove power steering pump (if equipped). Remove A/C compressor (if equipped). On M/T models, disconnect gearshift rod and gearshift stabilizer bar. Remove exhaust pipe. Remove starter. Remove front and rear transaxle support insulator support nuts. Remove muffler pipe bracket.
7) Remove front and rear transmission case brackets. Remove engine rear plate. On A/T models, remove torque converter nuts. On all models, lower vehicle. Disconnect vacuum lines from intake manifold and fuel vapor canister.
8) Attach engine sling to lifting eyes. Remove slack from chain. Disconnect any remaining wiring or hoses from engine and transaxle. Remove engine support insulator bolt. Lift engine and transaxle from engine. Separate engine and transaxle.
Removal (Capri) – **1)** Release fuel pressure. See FUEL PRESSURE RELEASE. Discharge A/C system, using approved refrigerant recovery/recycling equipment. Disconnect and remove battery, battery tray, and battery tray support bracket.
2) Release wiring harness retaining straps from battery support tray. Disconnect windshield washer supply hose between fluid reservoir and hood. Mark hinge locations for installation reference. Remove hood.
3) Disconnect intake air tube and wiring to ignition coil and vane airflow meter. Remove air cleaner/vane airflow meter assembly. Remove air cleaner support brackets. Disconnect intercooler hoses from turbocharger (if equipped).
4) Drain engine coolant. Remove radiator. Disconnect accelerator cable, and remove retaining bracket from cam cover. Position cable to one side.
5) Disconnect and plug fuel lines at fuel filter and pressure regulator. Disconnect power brake booster hose from manifold. Disconnect heater hoses at heater core tubes. Label and remove vacuum hoses located at throttle body.
6) On turbo models, disconnect clutch cable and remove support bracket and cable from transmission. On non-turbo models, disconnect clutch slave hydraulic line. On A/T models, remove transaxle cooler lines.
7) On all models, disconnect starter wiring at starter. Remove harness from locating strap on bracket. Disconnect alternator wiring. Disconnect wiring from engine coolant sensors located on rear of engine block. Remove ground connection at bracket on thermostat cover. Disconnect oxygen sensor wire, main wiring harness connector, TPS connector (turbocharged only), knock sensor connector, distributor wiring, and transaxle wiring. Disconnect ground wire and strap at front of engine, and reinstall lifting eye.
8) Remove engine oil dipstick and retaining clip. Remove power steering pump from mounting bracket. Remove power steering pump mounting bracket. With hoses attached, position pump aside. Remove upper A/C compressor bolts (if equipped).
9) Raise and support vehicle. Drain engine oil and cooling system. On vehicles with air conditioning, remove lower A/C compressor mounting bolts, and position compressor aside.

CAUTION: Do not allow A/C compressor to hang by hoses. Support compressor aside with mechanic's wire.

---

10) Remove front wheels. Remove front ball joints-to-steering knuckle retaining bolts. Remove splash guards. Drain transmission oil. Separate drive shafts from differential. Remove front exhaust pipe bracket. Disconnect front exhaust pipe from exhaust manifold or turbocharger (if equipped).
11) Remove frame support bar-to-engine support bolt. Loosen right control arm bolt, and pivot support bar downward. Disengage rubber exhaust hangers behind catalytic converter. Allow exhaust system to hang down 6 inches, and support system with mechanic's wire. Unbolt shift linkage and stabilizer bar at transaxle. Remove nuts from front and rear engine mounts. Lower vehicle.

12) Attach hoist to lift eyes. Support engine weight with hoist. Remove right engine mount through-bolt. Raise engine off mounts and slightly pivot engine/transaxle assembly. Unplug oil pressure sensor wiring. Disconnect starter/alternator wiring harness from engine. Carefully lift engine/transaxle assembly, turning assembly while raising to avoid interference with other components.

Installation (All Models) – 1) Install engine in reverse order of removal. Attach hoist to engine/transaxle assembly. Position in vehicle. Tighten nuts and bolts to specification. See TORQUE SPECIFICATIONS.

2) To complete installation, reinstall hoses and electrical connectors. See TORQUE SPECIFICATIONS. Refill engine, transaxle, and power steering fluids to proper levels. Charge A/C system. Start engine and check for leaks and proper fluid levels.

INTAKE MANIFOLD

Removal (Aspire) – Relieve fuel pressure. See FUEL PRESSURE RELEASE. Disconnect negative battery cable. Drain cooling system. Remove intake manifold bracket. Disconnect throttle cable. Remove air duct. Mark and disconnect vacuum hoses, fuel hoses, and wiring. Remove intake manifold bolts. Remove intake manifold and gasket.

Installation – Clean all gasket mating surfaces. Ensure surface is free of burrs, scratches, and cracks. Replace all gaskets. Position gasket and manifold to cylinder head. Install bolts and tighten to specification. See TORQUE SPECIFICATIONS. Reinstall hoses and wires. Connect accelerator cable and battery cable. Refill cooling system.

Removal (Capri) – 1) Disconnect negative battery cable. Release fuel pressure. See FUEL PRESSURE RELEASE under REMOVAL & INSTALLATION. Drain cooling system. Disconnect intercooler tube and/or air intake tube. Disconnect air by-pass hoses. Disconnect main engine harness and TP sensor connectors. Disconnect vacuum hoses from throttle body.

2) Disconnect fuel lines from fuel filter and pressure regulator. Disconnect throttle cable. Disconnect hoses from Idle Air Control (IAC) valve. Remove IAC valve retaining nut and bolt. Remove intake manifold retaining nuts and bolts from support bracket and cylinder head. Remove intake manifold and throttle body.

Installation – 1) Install new intake manifold gasket, ensuring coolant passage openings align with openings in cylinder head and manifold. Install intake manifold. Tighten retaining nut and bolts and support bracket bolts to specification. See TORQUE SPECIFICATIONS.

2) Install IAC valve. Connect air hoses. Connect throttle cable. Connect fuel lines to fuel filters and pressure regulator. Connect engine wiring. Connect vacuum lines to throttle body. Install intake air tube. Connect intercooler tube and/or intake air tube. Connect air by-pass hoses. Fill cooling system. Connect negative battery cable. Start engine. Check for fluid leaks and correct operation.

EXHAUST MANIFOLD

Removal (Aspire) – Raise and support vehicle. Remove exhaust pipe nuts at exhaust manifold. Remove muffler pipe bracket bolts. Lower vehicle. Remove duct between air cleaner and intake manifold. Remove exhaust manifold heat shield. Remove O_2 sensor. Remove exhaust manifold.

Installation – Position new gaskets onto cylinder head and exhaust pipe. Install exhaust manifold and nuts. To complete installation, reverse removal procedure. Tighten all bolts and nuts to specification. See TORQUE SPECIFICATIONS.

Removal (Capri Non-Turbo) – Remove intake air tube. Remove front exhaust pipe-to-exhaust manifold retaining nuts. Remove exhaust support bracket (if equipped). Remove heat shield. Disconnect O_2 sensor electrical connector. Remove exhaust manifold.

Installation – Install exhaust manifold gaskets. Install heavier gasket first. Install exhaust manifold. Connect O_2 sensor wiring. Install manifold heat shield. Install intake air tube. Connect front exhaust pipe to intake manifold and tighten retaining nuts to specification. Install exhaust support bracket, if removed. Tighten bolts and nuts to specification. See TORQUE SPECIFICATIONS. Start engine and check for leaks.

Removal (Capri Turbo) – 1) Disconnect negative battery cable. Drain cooling system. Remove throttle body air intake tube. Disconnect intercooler hose from turbocharger, and position both intercooler hoses aside. Remove O_2 sensor connector from its retaining clip, and disconnect O_2 sensor. Remove lower heat shield and then upper heat shield. Remove turbocharger side heat shield.

NOTE: Feed O_2 sensor wire and guide through upper heat shield.

2) Remove power steering pump (leave hoses attached) and lay aside. Disconnect lower radiator hose from water pump. Position power steering pump aside for access to mounting bracket retaining bolts and nut. Remove power steering pump bracket. Disconnect air cleaner duct and position it aside. Disconnect coolant return hose at turbocharger. Remove bolt and brass sealing washers from oil supply line at engine block.

3) Raise vehicle. Remove retaining nuts and washers from exhaust pipe flange. Remove 2 bolts retaining exhaust hangers to engine block. Slide off rubber exhaust hangers at catalytic converter. Pull exhaust pipe downward and to left side of vehicle. Disconnect oil return hose at turbocharger. Disconnect coolant return hose at turbocharger. Remove 2 retaining bolts from turbocharger support bracket. Remove 2 bolts retaining coolant by-pass tube outlet to water pump. Lower vehicle.

4) Loosen retaining clamp bolt on coolant by-pass tube at rear of cylinder head. Remove retaining nuts from exhaust manifold. Pull coolant by-pass tube bracket from exhaust stud, and position tube aside. Grasp manifold, pull from studs, and work assembly from vehicle. Separate turbocharger from exhaust manifold.

NOTE: When reinstalling turbocharger, thoroughly remove all gaskets and sealant. Use new gaskets. Add 0.85 oz. (25 cc) of engine oil into turbocharger oil passage. Turbocharger mounting nuts are of special quality. Ensure correct nuts are used for installation.

Installation – To install, reverse removal procedure. Observe the following installation notes: Remove oil supply line from turbocharger. Position new (2-piece) exhaust gasket onto cylinder head with heavy gasket installed first. Position one brass washer on each side of oil line fitting. Tighten bolts and nuts to specification. See TORQUE SPECIFICATIONS.

NOTE: If turbocharger was replaced, before starting engine, disconnect ignition coil and crank engine for 20 seconds. Connect ignition coil. Start and run engine at idle for 30 seconds. Check for leaks.

CYLINDER HEAD

Removal (Aspire) – 1) Release fuel pressure. See FUEL PRESSURE RELEASE. Disconnect battery ground cable. Drain cooling system. Mark distributor and head for installation reference. Remove distributor. Remove valve cover. Remove exhaust manifold. See EXHAUST MANIFOLD. Remove intake manifold. See INTAKE MANIFOLD. Remove timing belt. See TIMING BELT.

NOTE: If original timing belt is to be reused, mark direction of rotation for installation reference.

2) Unplug harness connectors. Remove engine ground strap. Remove front and rear engine lifting hooks. Remove upper radiator hose, by-pass hose, and bracket. Remove bolts and cylinder head.

Inspection – Thoroughly clean mating surfaces of cylinder head and block. Inspect cylinder head for cracks, nicks, burrs, or other defects. Measure warpage over entire gasket area. If warpage exceeds 0.006" (0.15 mm), resurface cylinder head and/or block gasket surface.

Installation – 1) Position ace new head gasket properly onto block. See Fig. 1. Carefully set lace cylinder head into position. Install and tighten cylinder head bolts in sequence, in 2 stages. See Fig. 2. See TORQUE SPECIFICATIONS.

2) Tighten rocker arm shaft bolts to specification in sequence shown. See Fig. 3. To complete installation, reverse removal procedure.

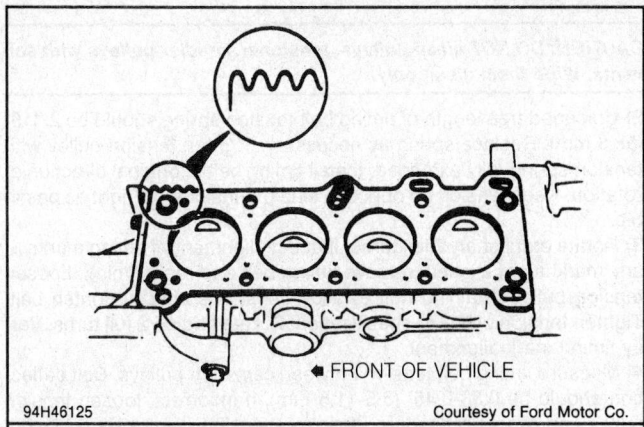

Fig. 1: Installing Head Gasket (Aspire)

← FRONT OF VEHICLE

94H46125   Courtesy of Ford Motor Co.

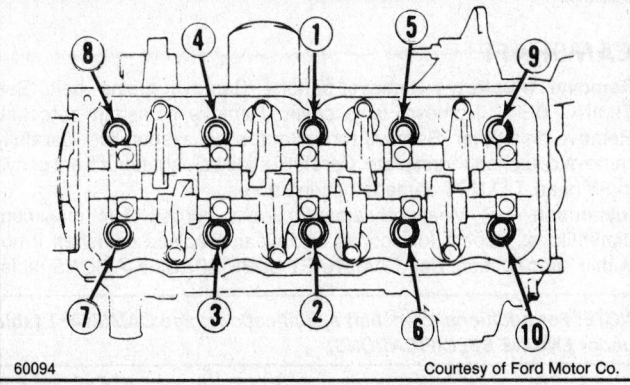

60094   Courtesy of Ford Motor Co.

Fig. 2: Installing Cylinder Head Bolts (Aspire)

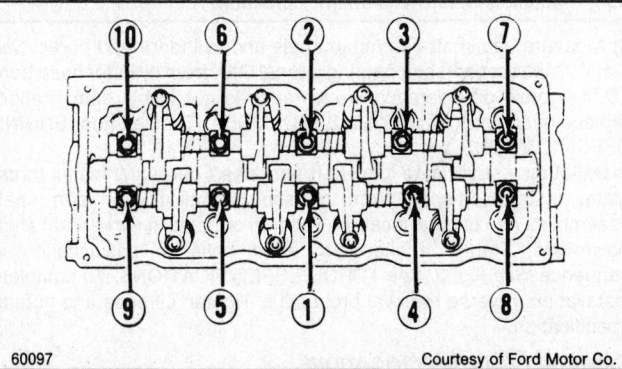

60097   Courtesy of Ford Motor Co.

Fig. 3: Rocker Arm Shaft Tightening Sequence (Aspire)

Removal (Capri) – 1) Release fuel pressure. See FUEL PRESSURE RELEASE. Drain cooling system. Disconnect negative battery cable. Disconnect intake air duct from throttle body. Disconnect air by-pass hoses. Remove spark plug wires and retainers. Disconnect intake air duct from air cleaner. Disconnect coolant hose from thermostat cover. Disconnect vacuum hoses and coolant hoses from throttle body and intake manifold.

2) Disconnect throttle cable. Remove throttle cable retaining brackets and cable. Disconnect fuel lines at fuel filter and pressure regulator. Unplug main harness connector. Unplug O_2 sensor connector. Remove ground connection retaining screw at bracket. Disconnect intercooler tubes from turbocharger (if equipped). Remove ground wire and strap retaining bolts at front sides of cylinder head.

3) Remove timing belt. See TIMING BELT. On turbocharged models, remove exhaust manifold and turbocharger as an assembly. See EXHAUST MANIFOLD. On non-turbo models, disconnect front exhaust pipe from exhaust manifold. Remove intake manifold support upper retaining bolts.

4) On all models, remove cylinder head cover. Remove cylinder head and intake manifold as an assembly. Separate intake manifold from cylinder head if necessary.

Installation – 1) Position new (2-piece) exhaust gasket onto cylinder head with heavy gasket installed first. Install exhaust manifold. Install intake manifold to head using new gasket. Tighten all manifold nuts to specification. See TORQUE SPECIFICATIONS.

NOTE: Ensure coolant passage openings in gasket align with manifold and cylinder head.

2) Thoroughly clean gasket surfaces of head and block. Place new head gasket onto cylinder block. Carefully place cylinder head onto block. Tighten cylinder head in sequence and in 2 stages to correct specification. *See Fig. 4.* To complete installation, reverse removal procedure. See TORQUE SPECIFICATIONS.

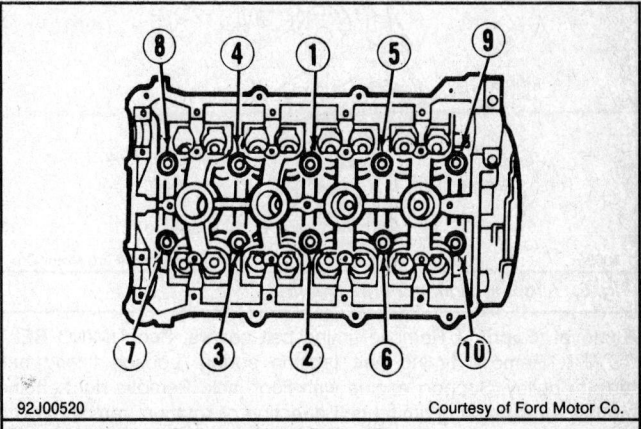

92J00520   Courtesy of Ford Motor Co.

Fig. 4: Installing Cylinder Head Bolts (Capri)

FRONT COVER & OIL SEAL

Removal & Installation – Front cover is the housing for the oil pump. See OIL PUMP under ENGINE OILING.

TIMING BELT COVER

Removal & Installation (Aspire) – Remove accessory belts. Remove water pump pulley. Remove crankshaft pulley. Remove bolts retaining upper and lower cover halves to engine front. Remove both covers. To install, reverse removal procedure. Tighten nuts and drive belts to specification. See TORQUE SPECIFICATIONS.

Removal & Installation (Capri) – Raise and support vehicle. Remove right front tire and wheel assembly. Remove right front splash guard. Lower vehicle. Remove spark plugs and set No. 1 cylinder to TDC of compression stroke. Remove accessory drive belts. Remove dipstick. Remove water pump pulley. Remove crankshaft pulley, damper and baffle plate. Remove upper timing belt cover. Remove center and lower timing belt covers. To install, reverse removal procedure. Tighten nuts and bolts to specification. See TORQUE SPECIFICATIONS.

TIMING BELT

NOTE: Always rotate engine in direction of normal operation. Rotating crankshaft backwards may cause belt to jump timing.

Removal (Aspire) – Remove timing belt covers. See TIMING BELT COVER. Mark timing belt direction of rotation for installation reference. Remove timing belt tensioner pulley bolt. Remove tensioner pulley, spring, and spring cover. Remove timing belt.

CAUTION: Never twist, turn inside out, or bend timing belt. Keep belt away from grease and oil.

Installation – Ensure timing belt and sprockets are clean and not worn or damaged. Align crankshaft and camshaft timing marks. *See*

Fig. 5. Position belt onto sprockets, in original running direction. Install timing belt tensioner spring, spring cover, and pulley. To complete installation, reverse removal procedure. Tighten all bolts and nuts to specification. See TORQUE SPECIFICATIONS.

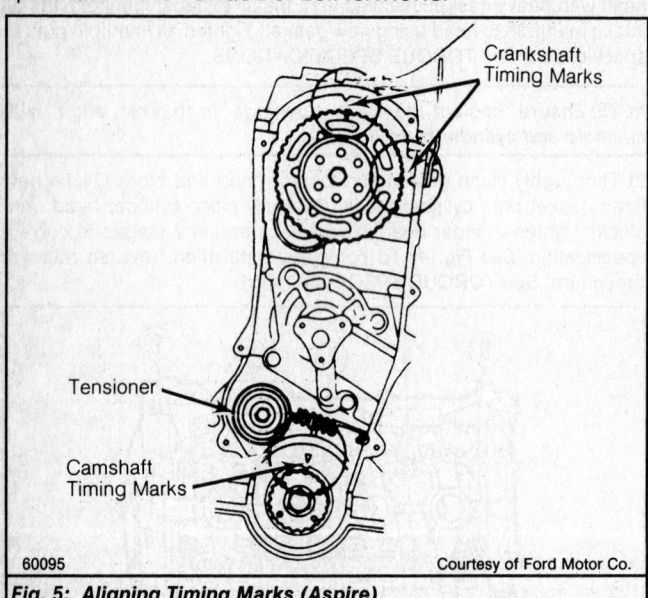

60095   Courtesy of Ford Motor Co.

Fig. 5: Aligning Timing Marks (Aspire)

Removal (Capri) – Remove timing belt covers. See TIMING BELT COVER. Remove timing belt tension spring. Loosen timing belt tension pulley. Support engine with floor jack. Remove right engine mount. After marking timing belt direction of rotation, remove timing belt.

Installation – 1) Inspect timing belt for wear, tears, peeling, cracks, or hardening. Ensure sprockets, tensioner, and idler pulleys are clean and not worn, deformed, or damaged. Align timing marks on camshafts and crankshaft. Intake cam should have letter "I" aligned with arrow on belt cover. Exhaust cam should have letter "E" aligned with arrow on belt cover. Crankshaft key should align with arrow. *See Fig. 6.*

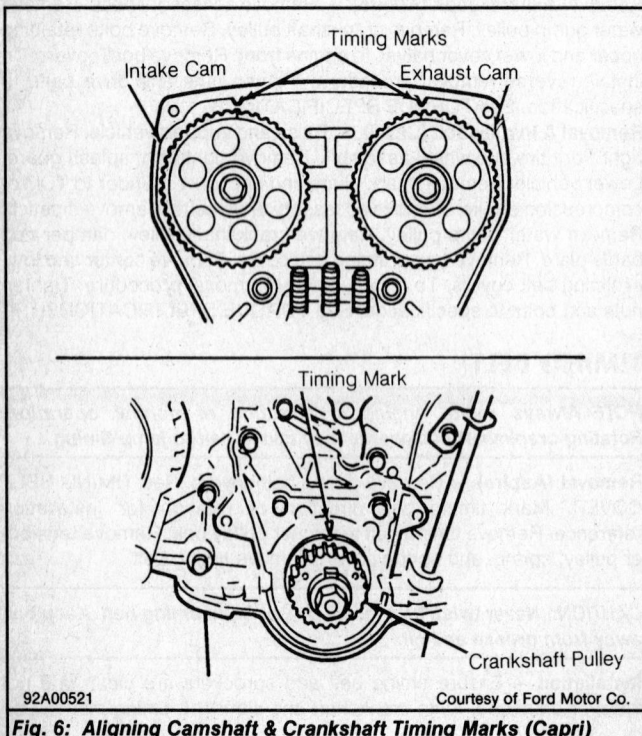

92A00521   Courtesy of Ford Motor Co.

Fig. 6: Aligning Camshaft & Crankshaft Timing Marks (Capri)

CAUTION: DO NOT clean pulleys, tensioner, or idler pulleys with solvents. Wipe them clean only.

2) Unloaded free length of timing belt tension spring should be 2.315" (58.8 mm). Replace spring as necessary. Tighten tension pulley with tension spring fully extended. Install timing belt in original direction of rotation. Keep tension on opposite side of tensioner as tight as possible.

3) Rotate crankshaft 2 full turns. Inspect alignment of timing marks. If any mark is not aligned, remove timing belt and reset timing. Loosen tension pulley retaining bolt to allow tension spring to tighten belt. Tighten tension pulley to specification. Rotate engine 2 full turns. Verify timing mark alignment.

4) Measure timing belt tension between camshaft pulleys. Belt deflection should be 0.33-0.45" (8.5-11.5 mm). If incorrect, loosen tension pulley and repeat procedure. If correct tension cannot be achieved, replace tension spring. To complete installation, reverse removal procedure.

CAMSHAFT

Removal (Aspire) – Remove battery. Remove timing belt. See TIMING BELT. Remove valve cover. Remove camshaft sprocket. Remove distributor. Remove rocker arm shaft assemblies. Carefully remove camshaft thrust plate. Carefully slide camshaft out front of cylinder head. DO NOT damage bearing bores.

Inspection – 1) Measure camshaft lobes across their maximum dimensions. Inspect for scoring and wear. Replace camshaft if not within specification. See CAMSHAFT LOBE SPECIFICATIONS table.

NOTE: For additional camshaft specifications, see CAMSHAFT table under ENGINE SPECIFICATIONS.

NOTE: Camshaft bearings are not replaceable. If not within specification, replace cylinder head and/or camshaft.

2) Measure camshaft bearing journals and cylinder head bores. *See Fig. 7.* Subtract camshaft bearing journal O.D. from cylinder head bore I.D. to obtain oil clearance. If clearance is not within specification, replace head and/or camshaft. See CAMSHAFT table under ENGINE SPECIFICATIONS.

Installation – Lubricate camshaft and insert carefully. Install thrust plate. Install camshaft front oil seal. Install rocker arm shaft assemblies into original location. Position oil holes in rocker arm shaft downward. Tighten rocker arm shaft bolts to specification in sequence. *See Fig. 3.* See TORQUE SPECIFICATIONS. To complete installation, reverse removal procedure. Tighten all bolts and nuts to specification.

CAMSHAFT LOBE SPECIFICATIONS

Application	Standard Height In. (mm)	Wear Limit In. (mm)
Lobe Height		
1.3L	1.4332-1.4371 (36.403-36.503)	1.4273 (36.253)
1.6L	1.6098 (40.888)	1.5944 (40.498)

Removal (Capri) – 1) Disconnect battery ground terminal. Disconnect air by-pass hoses. Remove intake air duct. Disconnect throttle cable. Remove throttle cable retaining brackets. Remove cam cover. Remove timing belt. See TIMING BELT.

2) Hold camshaft with wrench while removing pulley retaining bolt. Remove camshaft pulley(s). Remove seal plate. Remove camshaft seal with Seal Remover (T78P-3504-N). If removing intake cam, remove distributor.

3) Note numerical and directional markings on camshaft bearing caps for installation reference. Remove bearing cap bolts alternately and gradually to prevent overstressing camshaft. Remove camshaft.

Inspection – 1) Measure camshaft lobes across their maximum dimensions. Inspect for scoring and wear. Replace camshaft if not within specification. See CAMSHAFT table under ENGINE SPECIFICATIONS.

NOTE: For additional camshaft specifications, see CAMSHAFT table under ENGINE SPECIFICATIONS.

NOTE: Camshaft bearings are not replaceable. If not within specification, replace cylinder head and/or camshaft.

2) Measure camshaft bearing journals and cylinder head bores (with bearing caps in place and tightened to specification). See Fig. 7. Subtract camshaft bearing journal O.D. from cylinder head bore I.D. to obtain oil clearance. If clearance is not within specification, replace head and/or camshaft. See CAMSHAFT table under ENGINE SPECIFICATIONS.

Installation – 1) Lubricate camshaft bearings with engine oil. Position camshaft(s) in cylinder head. Ensure all tappets are in place. Install intake cam with the "I" mark straight up and exhaust cam with the "E" mark straight up. Install bearing caps according to numbers and arrows. Arrows must point toward front of engine. Tighten retaining bolts gradually and in sequence to specification *See Fig. 8.* See TORQUE SPECIFICATIONS.

2) Install timing belt in original running direction. To complete installation, reverse removal procedure. Start engine and check for leaks and proper operation.

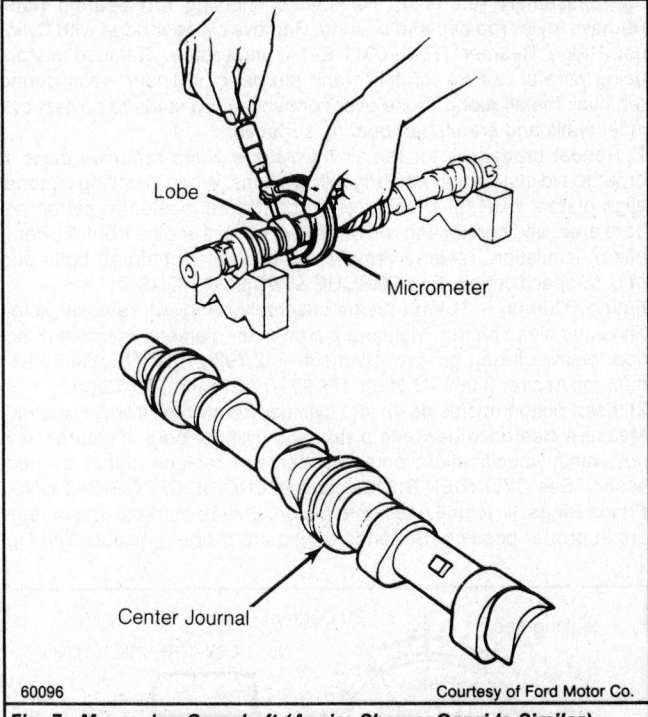

Fig. 7: Measuring Camshaft (Aspire Shown; Capri Is Similar)

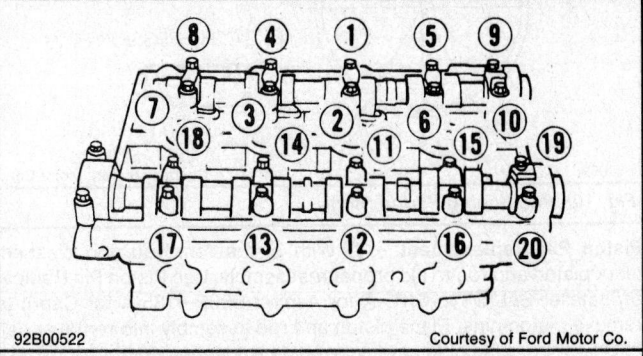

Fig. 8: Cam Bearing Cap Tightening Sequence (Capri)

CAMSHAFT END PLAY

1) Measure camshaft end play with thrust plate in position. Install dial indicator, with plunger on camshaft center. Pry camshaft fully to rear. Zero dial indicator.
2) Pry camshaft fully forward. Read dial indicator. Standard end play for Aspire is 0.002-0.007" (0.05-0.18 mm), with a limit of 0.008" (0.20 mm). Standard end play for Capri is 0.0028-0.0075" (0.07-0.19 mm), with a limit of 0.008" (0.20 mm). If end play exceeds specification on Aspire engines, replace thrust plate and again measure end play. If end play exceeds specification on Capri engines, replace camshaft and/or cylinder head.

CAMSHAFT OIL SEAL

Removal & Installation – See CAMSHAFT under REMOVAL & INSTALLATION.

REAR MAIN BEARING OIL SEAL

Removal (Aspire) – Remove transaxle. See TRANSMISSION REMOVAL & INSTALLATION article in TRANSMISSION SERVICING. Remove flywheel or flexplate. Remove rear engine plate (if equipped). Remove rear main bearing oil seal retainer. Press out rear main bearing oil seal.

Installation – Clean seal surface in retainer. Lubricate oil seal inside and outside. Install seal retainer. Install seal into retainer with hollow side of seal facing engine. Using Rear Main Seal Installer (T87C-6701-A), install rear main bearing oil seal. Flywheel bolts may be used to press seal installer and seal into cover plate. Install seal retainer and cover plate. If necessary, trim excess gasket material from seal retainer. Tighten plate bolts to 71-97 INCH lbs. (8-11 N.m). Install flywheel or flexplate and transaxle.

Removal (Capri) – Remove transaxle. See TRANSMISSION REMOVAL & INSTALLATION article in TRANSMISSION SERVICING. Remove clutch cover and disc (if equipped). Remove flywheel or flexplate. Remove rear seal with Seal Remover (T78P-3504-N).

Installation – Lubricate oil seal lip with engine oil. Using Rear Main Seal Installer (T87C-6701-A) and Screw Set (T90P-6701-AH), install rear main bearing oil seal. To complete installation, install flywheel or flexplate. Apply Threadlock/Sealer (E0AZ-19554/ESE-M4G204A) to flywheel retaining bolts. Tighten bolts to specification. See TORQUE SPECIFICATIONS. Install clutch (if equipped) and transaxle.

WATER PUMP

Removal & Installation (Aspire) – Remove timing belt. See TIMING BELT. Drain cooling system. Remove A/C compressor (if equipped). Remove water pump inlet bolts. Remove water pump. Clean gasket mounting surface, replace gasket, and coat with gasket sealer. Tighten bolts to specification. See TORQUE SPECIFICATIONS. Refill cooling system. Warm engine and check for leaks.

Removal (Capri) – 1) Remove timing belt. See TIMING BELT. Drain cooling system. Remove timing belt tensioner and idler pulleys. Remove oil dipstick bracket retaining bolt.
2) Remove power steering pump from bracket, leaving hoses attached. Remove power steering pump bracket. Position power steering pump to one side. Remove water pump outlet. Remove water pump.

NOTE: Raise engine slightly with floor jack, if necessary, to gain clearance for water pump removal.

Installation – Clean all gasket surfaces. Transfer rubber belt cover seal to new water pump (if necessary). To complete installation, reverse removal procedure. Fill cooling system. Start engine and check for leaks and proper system function.

OIL PAN

Removal (Aspire) – Disconnect battery ground cable. Raise and support vehicle. Drain engine oil. Remove exhaust pipe. Remove oil pan.

Installation – Thoroughly clean gasket surfaces. Apply sealer to gasket surfaces. See Fig. 9. Tighten oil pan bolts. See TORQUE SPECIFICATIONS. To complete installation, reverse removal procedure. Add engine oil to proper level. Start engine and check for leaks.

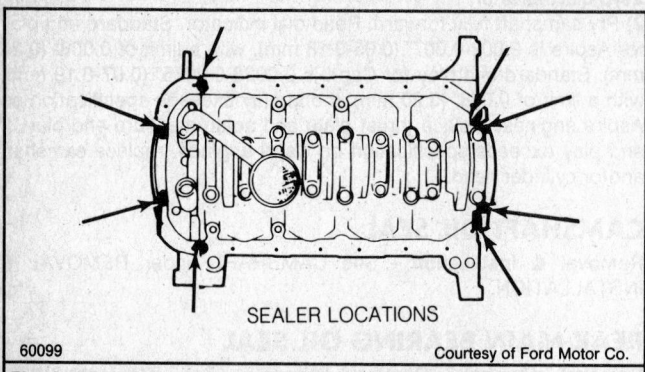

SEALER LOCATIONS

60099   Courtesy of Ford Motor Co.

Fig. 9: Identifying Oil Pan Sealing Points (Aspire)

Removal (Capri) – 1) Raise and support vehicle. Drain engine oil. Remove frame brace retaining bolt. Loosen right "A" arm front bolt, and pivot brace downward. Disconnect front exhaust pipe from exhaust manifold (or turbocharger). Remove exhaust pipe bracket retaining bolts. Loosen rubber exhaust hangers at catalytic converter.
2) Allow exhaust pipe to hang by mechanic's wire. Disconnect turbocharger oil return hose (if equipped). Remove oil pan retaining bolts. Carefully pry oil pan loose from cylinder block. Remove front and rear oil pan seals.
Installation – 1) Clean pan and block gasket surfaces. Apply Gasket Sealant (E8AZ-19562-A) to new front and rear pan seals. Install seals onto cylinder block. Apply Gasket Sealant (E3AZ-19562-A) to oil pan gasket surface. Install oil pan. Tighten pan bolts to specification. See TORQUE SPECIFICATIONS.
2) To complete installation, reverse removal procedure. Lower vehicle. Fill with oil and start engine. Check for oil leaks.

OVERHAUL

CYLINDER HEAD

Valve Springs – Inspect valve springs for cracks or damage. Measure valve springs squareness and free length. Replace spring if either measurement is out of specification. See VALVES & VALVE SPRINGS table under ENGINE SPECIFICATIONS.
Valve Stem Installed Height – Measure protruding length of each valve stem. See VALVE STEM INSTALLED HEIGHT table. If length is at service limit, use valve spring shims to bring measurement within range of acceptable limit. If length is greater than service limit, replace valve seat or cylinder head.

VALVE STEM INSTALLED HEIGHT

Application	In. (mm)
Aspire	
New	1.520-1.539 (38.6-39.1)
Acceptable Limit	1.539-1.579 (39.2-40.1)
Service Limit	1.579 (40.1)
Capri	
New	1.713 (43.5)
Acceptable Limit	1.713-1.732 (43.5-44)
Service Limit	1.772 (45)

NOTE: For additional valve specifications, see VALVES & VALVE SPRINGS table under ENGINE SPECIFICATIONS.

Valve Guides – Remove cylinder head, camshaft(s), and valves. Measure valve stem-to-guide oil clearance. If clearance exceeds specification, replace valve guides and/or valves. See CYLINDER HEAD table under ENGINE SPECIFICATIONS.

VALVE TRAIN INSPECTION

Camshaft (Capri) – Remove cam cover. Remove camshaft(s). Keep components in order of removal to aid reassembly to original position. To install, reverse removal procedure.
Rocker Arm Shaft Assembly (Aspire) – Remove valve cover. Keep components in order of removal to aid reassembly to original position. Remove rocker arm shaft retaining bolts and rocker arm shaft assembly. To install, reverse removal procedure.
Valve Lash Adjusters (Aspire) – Warm engine to normal operating temperature. Remove valve cover. Inspect hydraulic lash adjuster operation by pushing each rocker arm down by hand. If rocker arm moves downward, replace hydraulic lash adjuster. Adjustment on valve lash adjusters is not necessary.
Valve Lash Adjusters (Capri) – Inspect friction surfaces for wear and damage. Hold bucket body (each adjuster) and press between thumb and forefinger. If plunger moves, replace hydraulic lash adjuster. Adjustment on valve lash adjusters is not necessary.

CYLINDER BLOCK ASSEMBLY

Piston & Rod Assembly – 1) Remove cylinder head. See CYLINDER HEAD under REMOVAL & INSTALLATION. Remove oil pan. See OIL PAN under REMOVAL & INSTALLATION. Mark connecting rod caps for reassembly reference. Remove connecting rod bearing nuts. Remove lower rod cap and bearing. Remove cylinder ridge with Cylinder Ridge Reamer (T64L-6011-EA) if necessary. Remove piston, being careful not to scratch crank journal or cylinder walls during removal. Install rubber hose over connecting rod studs to protect cylinder walls and crankshaft bearing surfaces.
2) Repeat procedure for remaining pistons. Keep removed parts in order to aid installation into original positions. When installing pistons, align piston mark "F" (Aspire) or notch (Capri) located at piston pin bore area, and connecting rod oil groove toward engine front. To complete installation, reverse removal procedure. Tighten all bolts and nuts to specification. See TORQUE SPECIFICATIONS.
Fitting Pistons – 1) With piston assembly removed, remove piston rings and clean piston. Measure piston outer diameter in thrust direction, below oil ring groove. Diameter is 2.793-2.794" (70.954-70.974 mm) for Aspire; 3.0690-3.0698" (77.954-77.974 mm) for Capri.
2) Insert piston upside down into cylinder from which it was removed. Measure clearance between piston and cylinder bore. If clearance is not within specification, bore cylinder and replace piston as necessary. See CYLINDER BLOCK table in ENGINE SPECIFICATIONS.
Piston Rings – Install rings onto piston. Ensure marked side of rings are in proper position. Set ends of rings to proper position. See Fig. 10.

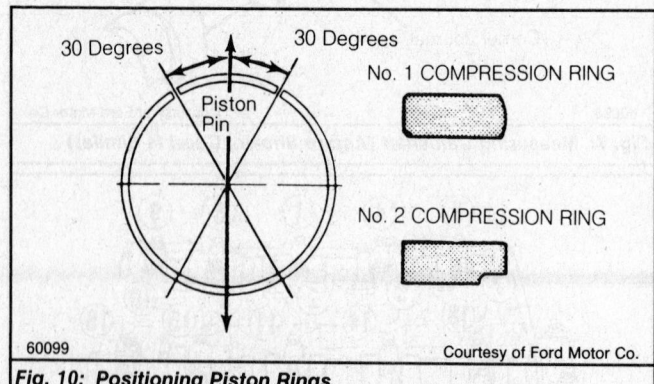

30 Degrees   30 Degrees

No. 1 COMPRESSION RING

Piston Pin

No. 2 COMPRESSION RING

60099   Courtesy of Ford Motor Co.

Fig. 10: Positioning Piston Rings

Piston Pin Replacement – 1) With piston removed and cleaned, mark piston and rod to aid proper reassembly. Use Piston Pin Remover/Installer Set (D81L-6135-A for Aspire; D90P-6135-A for Capri) to remove piston pins. Place piston and rod assembly into remover set.
2) On Aspire, assemble anvil, tube guide, and threaded plug onto base and press plates of an arbor press. Press out piston pin. On Capri, remove piston pin retaining clips. Place piston into piston pin remover/installer set. Drive piston pin out with hammer. Keep all removed com-

ponents together for reassembly. Remove piston and rod from remover/installer set. Remove piston rings and inspect.

3) Measure piston pin O.D. in 4 places 90 degrees apart. Measure I.D. of piston pin bore and rod pin bore in 4 places 90 degrees apart. Replace components if not within specifications. See PISTONS, PINS & RINGS table under ENGINE SPECIFICATIONS.

4) If measurements of rod, piston and pin are within specification, reassemble, using piston pin assembly set. Assemble with connecting rod oil groove on side of piston marked with "F" or with notch. Lubricate pin with engine oil before reassembly. With piston reassembled, rod should fall by its own weight with piston held horizontally. Repeat procedure for remaining pistons.

NOTE: Installation pressure for piston pins should be 1100-3300 lbs. (500-1500 kg).

Rod Bearings – Inspect rod bearing for abnormal wear. Inspect crankshaft journal. Measure rod bearing clearance with Plastigage. Machine or replace as necessary. See CRANKSHAFT, MAIN & CONNECTING ROD BEARINGS table under ENGINE SPECIFICATIONS.

Crankshaft & Main Bearings – 1) Remove oil pan. See OIL PAN under REMOVAL & INSTALLATION. Mark main bearing caps to aid in installation to original location and position.

NOTE: If replacing bearing inserts with engine in vehicle, remove one bearing at a time for measurement or replacement.

---

2) Remove main bearing cap bolts. Remove cap and lower bearing insert. Use bearing remover or bent cotter pin to remove upper bearing insert. Insert bearing remover in journal lubrication hole. Rotate crankshaft in normal direction of operation only. Repeat procedure for remaining main bearings.

3) Inspect bearings for abnormal wear. Inspect crankshaft for grooves, scratches, or pitting. Use Plastigage to measure main bearing clearance. Always keep at least 2 main bearings and caps tight during clearance measurement. See CRANKSHAFT, MAIN & CONNECTING ROD BEARINGS table under ENGINE SPECIFICATIONS.

4) Lubricate and install new bearings into cap and block. Match bearing tangs with notch in cap and block. Position cap in its proper location and position. Install and tighten cap bolts to specification. See TORQUE SPECIFICATIONS. Repeat procedure for remaining main bearings.

Crankshaft End Play – Tighten main bearing caps in sequence and to specification. Rotate crankshaft by hand. If it will not turn by hand, remove bearing cap and find source of interference. Measure crankshaft end play with dial indicator. End play should be 0.003-0.011" (0.08-0.28 mm). Service limit is 0.012" (0.30 mm). If end play is not within specification, replace thrust bearings as necessary or replace crankshaft.

Cylinder Block – 1) Using straightedge and feeler gauge, measure warpage of cylinder head surface of cylinder block. Warpage must not exceed 0.006" (0.15 mm). If warpage exceeds specification, cylinder block surface can be machined a maximum of 0.008" (0.20 mm).

2) Inspect cylinder bore for wear, out-of-round, taper, and piston fit. See CYLINDER BORE SPECIFICATIONS table. Oversize pistons are available in 0.010" (0.25 mm) and 0.020" (0.50 mm) sizes.

CYLINDER BORE SPECIFICATIONS

Application	In. (mm)
Cylinder Diameter	
Standard Bore	
Aspire	2.7953-2.7960 (71.000-71.019)
Capri	3.0709-3.0716 (78.000-78.019)
Maximum Bore	
Aspire	2.8020 (71.17)
Capri	3.0905-3.0913 (78.500-78.519)
Maximum Out-Of-Round & Taper	0.0007 (0.019)
Piston-To-Bore Clearance	0.006 (0.15)

ENGINE OILING

ENGINE LUBRICATION SYSTEM

Oil pump is driven directly by crankshaft. The oil pump draws oil from the oil pan. Oil is then filtered and routed throughout engine. Turbocharged engines have oil spray nozzles mounted in the cylinder block. Oil is sprayed up inside pistons to aid in cooling and prevent detonation.

Crankcase Capacity – On Aspire, crankcase capacity is 3.2 qts. (3.0L) without filter change, and 3.6 qts. (3.4L) with filter change. On Capri non-turbo engine, capacity is 3.2 qts (3.0L) without filter and 3.5 qts. (3.3L) with filter. On Capri turbo, total capacity is 3.7 qts. (3.5L).

Normal Oil Pressure (Hot) – On Aspire, oil pressure should be 28-43 psi (2.0-3.0 kg/cm²) at 1000 RPM, and 43-57 psi (3.0-4.0 kg/cm²) at 3000 RPM. On Capri, oil pressure should be 43-48 psi (3.0-3.4 kg/cm²) at 3000 RPM.

Pressure Regulator Valve – Pressure regulator valve is located in oil pump body, and is nonadjustable.

OIL PUMP

Removal – 1) Remove oil pan, pick-up tube and screen, timing belt, and crankshaft sprocket. Remove front engine cover. Remove bolts retaining pump cover to back side of front cover housing.

2) Remove pump cover and inner and outer gears. Pry out front seal from front cover. Remove cotter pin. Remove pressure regulator retainer, spring, and valve.

Inspection – Disassemble oil pump. Clean all parts. Measure pressure spring free length. Measure inner-to-outer rotor clearance. Measure outer rotor-to-pump housing clearance. Measure end play clearance between pump cover and rotor. Replace parts not within specification. See OIL PUMP SPECIFICATIONS table.

OIL PUMP SPECIFICATIONS

Application	In. (mm)
Inner Gear Tooth Tip-To-Outer Gear	
Aspire	0.0078 (0.198)
Capri	[1] 0.0008-0.0063 (0.02-0.16)
Outer Gear-To-Housing	
Aspire	0.0087 (0.22)
Capri	[2] 0.0035-0.0071 (0.09-0.18)
End Play	
Aspire	0.0055 (0.14)
Capri	[3]
Pressure Spring Free Length	
Aspire	[4]
Capri	1.791 (45.5)

[1] – If measurement exceeds 0.0079" (0.20 mm), replace rotors or pump.

[2] – If measurement exceeds 0.0087" (0.22 mm), replace rotors or pump.

[3] – If measurement exceeds 0.0055" (0.14 mm), replace rotors or pump.

[4] – Specification not available for Aspire.

Installation – 1) Install pressure regulator valve, spring, retainer, and new cotter pin. Press a new seal into front cover housing. Install outer and inner gears into housing. Install pump cover. Coat bolts with Loctite and tighten to specification. See TORQUE SPECIFICATIONS.

2) Install new gasket and front cover housing. Install new gasket, pick-up tube, and screen. Tighten all bolts and nuts to specification. To complete installation, reverse removal procedure.

TORQUE SPECIFICATIONS

Application	Ft. Lbs. (N.m)
"A" Arm Front Bolt	72-86 (97-117)
A/C Compressor Bolt	29-40 (39-54)
Camshaft Pulley Bolt	37-45 (49-61)
Connecting Rod Nut	
Stage 1	11-13 (15-18)
Stage 2	
Aspire	22-25 (30-34)
Capri	35-38 (47-52)
Crankshaft Pulley Bolts	10-13 (12-17)
Crankshaft Sprocket Bolt	80-87 (108-118)
Crossmember-To-Body Bolt	
Aspire	47-66 (64-89)
Capri	27-37 (35-50)
Cylinder Head Bolt	
Aspire	
Stage 1	35-40 (50-60)
Stage 2	56-60 (76-81)
Capri	
Stage 1	15-25 (20-34)
Stage 2	56-60 (76-81)
Distributor Mounting Bolts (Aspire)	14-18 (19-25)
Engine Mount Body Bracket (Capri)	15-20 (20-28)
Engine To Transaxle	
Aspire	
Automatic	41-59 (55-80)
Manual	47-66 (64-89)
Capri	
Automatic (Front)	28-38 (37-52)
Automatic (Upper)	41-59 (55-80)
Manual (Lower)	28-38 (37-52)
Manual (Upper)	66-86 (89-117)
Exhaust Manifold-To-Cylinder Head	
Aspire	12-17 (16-23)
Capri	29-42 (39-57)
Exhaust Bracket	32-45 (43-61)
Exhaust Pipe-To-Manifold	
Aspire	29-42 (39-57)
Capri	
Non-Turbo	23-34 (31-46)
Turbo	18-23 (24-32)
Flywheel/Flexplate Bolt	71-76 (96-103)
Front Engine Mount Nut	
Aspire	32-38 (43-52)
Capri	48-65 (64-89)
Heat Shield	12-17 (16-24)
Hood Hinge Bolt	15-20 (20-28)
Heater Tube	32-45 (43-61)
Intake Manifold Bracket	32-45 (43-61)
Intake Manifold-To-Cylinder Head	
Aspire	14-20 (19-27)
Capri	14-18 (19-25)
Main Bearing Cap Bolts	40-44 (54-59)
O₂ Sensor	27-33 (37-45)
Oil Pump Cover Bolt	14-18 (19-25)
Power Steering Pump Bracket	35-49 (47-66)
Power Steering Adjuster Nut	27-38 (37-52)
Power Steering Pivot Bolt	23-34 (31-46)
Pulse Air Tube Nut	23-34 (31-46)
Rear Engine Mount Nut	
Aspire	21-34 (28-46)
Capri	24-34 (32-47)
Rear Engine Mount Bolt (Capri)	28-38 (37-52)
Rocker Arm Shaft Bolts	16-21 (22-28)

TORQUE SPECIFICATIONS (Cont.)

Application	Ft. Lbs. (N.m)
Side Engine Mount Nuts	
Aspire	29-40 (39-54)
Capri	
Right Side	45-62 (60-85)
Left Side	33-48 (45-65)
Spark Plug	11-17 (15-23)
Thermostat Housing Bolt	14-22 (19-30)
Timing Belt Tensioner Adjuster Bolt	
Aspire	14-19 (19-26)
Capri	28-38 (37-52)
Turbo Support Bracket-To-Exhaust Pipe	32-45 (43-61)
Turbo Oil Supply Tube-To-Engine Block	12-18 (16-24)
Turbo-To-Manifold	20-25 (27-33)
Water Outlet Bolt	14-22 (19-30)
Water Pump Pulley Bolts (Aspire)	36-45 (49-61)
Water Pump-To-Block	14-19 (19-26)
Wheels	66-89 (90-120)

Application	INCH Lbs. (N.m)
Camshaft Bearing Cap Bolt	97-124 (11-14)
Camshaft Cover	71-97 (8-11)
Camshaft Thrust Plate Bolt	71-106 (8-12)
Flywheel Cover Bolts	61-87 (7-10)
Front Cover Housing Bolt	71-97 (8-11)
Oil Pan Bolt	
Aspire	71-80 (8-9)
Capri	71-97 (8-11)
Oil Pressure Sender	106-159 (12-18)
Oil Pump Cover Bolt (Aspire)	89-133 (10-15)
Oil Spray Nozzle Bolts (Capri Turbo)	106-159 (12-18)
Pickup Tube-To-Oil Pump Bolt	71-97 (8-11)
Radiator Fan Bracket	71-97 (8-11)
Rear Cover Plate Bolt	71-97 (8-11)
Temperature Sender	44-89 (5-10)
Timing Belt Cover Bolt	71-97 (8-11)
Turbo Oil Supply Tube Banjo Bolt	106-159 (12-18)
Valve Cover Bolt	44-79 (5-9)
Water Pump Pulley Bolts (Capri)	71-97 (8-11)

ENGINE SPECIFICATIONS

GENERAL SPECIFICATIONS

Application	Specification
Displacement	
Aspire	80.8 Cu. In. (1.3L)
Capri	97.4 Cu. In. (1.6L)
Bore	
Aspire	2.80" (71.0 mm)
Capri	3.07" (78 mm)
Stroke	3.29" (83.6 mm)
Compression Ratio	
Aspire	9.7:1
Capri	¹
Fuel System	PFI
Horsepower @ RPM	
Aspire	58 @ 5000
Capri	
Non-Turbo	100 @ 5750
Turbo	132 @ 6000
Torque Ft. Lbs. @ RPM	
Aspire	73 @ 3000
Capri	
Non-Turbo	95 @ 5500
Turbo	136 @ 3000

¹ – Information is not available from manufacturer.

CRANKSHAFT, MAIN & CONNECTING ROD BEARINGS

Application	In. (mm)
Crankshaft	
End Play	0.003-0.011 (0.08-0.28)
Service (Maximum)	0.0118 (0.30)
Main Bearings	
Journal Diameter	1.9661-1.9668 (49.938-49.956)
Undersized Bearing	
0.010" (0.25 mm) Standard	1.9562-1.9569 (49.688-49.706)
Undersize Minimum	1.954 (49.64)
0.20" (0.50 mm) Standard	1.9464-1.9471 (49.438-49.456)
Undersize Minimum	1.944 (49.39)
Journal Out-Of-Round	0.0019 (0.05)
Journal Taper	0.0019 (0.05)
Oil Clearance	0.0009-0.0017 (0.024-0.042)
Connecting Rod Bearings	
Journal Diameter	
Aspire	1.5724-1.5731 (39.939-39.957)
Capri	1.7693-1.7699 (44.940-44.956)
Journal Out-Of-Round	0.002 (0.05)
Journal Taper	0.002 (0.05)
Oil Clearance	0.0011-0.0027 (0.028-0.068)

CONNECTING RODS

Application	In. (mm)
Bore Diameter	
Pin Bore	
Aspire	0.7854-0.7859 (19.948-19.961)
Capri	0.7875-0.7880 (20.003-20.014)
Crankpin Bore	1.8897-1.8904 (48.000-48.016)
Center-To-Center Length	5.230-5.234 (132.85-132.95)
Maximum Bend & Twist [1]	
Aspire	0.0016 (0.04)
Capri	0.0078 (0.198)
Side Play Maximum	0.012 (0.30)

[1] – Per 3.94" (100 mm) of length.

CAMSHAFT

Application	In. (mm)
End Play	[1] 0.0028-0.0075 (0.05-0.18)
Journal Diameter	
Aspire	
No. 1 & 3	1.7103-1.7112 (43.440-43.456)
No. 2	1.7091-1.7100 (43.410-43.435)
Capri (All Journals)	1.0213-1.0222 (25.940-25.965)
Journal Runout	0.0012 (0.03)
Lobe Height	
Aspire	[2] 1.4331-1.4371 (36.403-36.503)
Capri	[3][4] 1.6098 (40.888)
Oil Clearance	
Aspire	
No. 1 & 3 Journals	[5] 0.0014-0.0033 (0.035-0.085)
No. 2 Journal	[5] 0.0026-0.0045 (0.065-0.115)
Capri (All Journals)	[5] 0.0014-0.0032 (0.035-0.081)

[1] – End play limit is 0.008" (0.20 mm).
[2] – Wear limit is 1.4272" (36.253 mm).
[3] – Wear limit is 1.5940" (40.489 mm).
[4] – Minimum lobe height is 1.6019" (40.688 mm)
[5] – Maximum clearance is 0.0059" (0.150 mm).

PISTONS, PINS & RINGS

Application	In. (mm)
Pistons	
Clearance (Maximum)	0.006 (0.15)
Diameter	
Aspire	[1] 2.793-2.794 (70.954-70.974)
Capri	3.0690-3.0698 (77.954-77.974)
0.001" (0.25 mm) Oversize	3.0789-3.0797 (78.204-78.224)
0.002" (0.50 mm) Oversize	3.0887-3.0895 (78.454-78.474)
Pins	
Outside Diameter	
Aspire	0.7864-0.7866 (19.974-19.980)
Capri	0.7869-0.7871 (19.987-19.993)
Inside Diameter	0.524 (13.309)
Pin-To-Piston Fit	
Aspire	0.0003-0.0005 (0.0076-0.0127)
Capri	0.0002-0.0005 (0.005-0.013)
Pin-To-Rod Fit [2]	
Aspire	[3] 0-0.001 (0-0.026)
Capri	0.0004-0011 (0.010-0.027)
Piston Ring Groove Width (Thickness)	
Aspire	
Compression (Top)	0.0602-0.0608 (1.530-1.545)
Compression (Second)	0.0598-0.0604 (1.520-1.535)
Oil	0.1583-0.1591 (4.020-4.040)
Capri	
Compression (Top)	0.0598-0.0604 (1.520-1.535)
Compression (Second)	0.0598-0.0604 (1.520-1.535)
Oil	0.1583-0.1591 (4.020-4.040)
Piston Rings	
Aspire	
Ring Width (Thickness)	
Compression (Top & Second)	0.0579-0.0587 (1.47-1.49)
Side Clearance	
Compression (Top & Second)	0.001-0.003 (0.03-0.065)
Oil Ring	Snug Fit
Ring Gap	
Compression (Top & Second)	0.006-0.012 (0.15-0.30)
Oil (Steel Rail)	0.008-0.028 (0.20-0.70)
Limit	0.039 (1.0)
Capri	
Ring Width (Thickness)	
Compression (Top & Second)	0.0579-0.0587 (1.47-1.49)
Oil	0.1580-0.1588 (4.015-4.035)
Side Clearance	
Compression (Top & Second)	0.0012-0.0026 (0.03-0.065)
Oil Ring	0.0012-0.0026 (0.03-0.065)
Limit	0.0059 (0.15)
Ring Gap	
Compression (Top)	0.008-0.0157 (0.20-0.40)
Compression (Second)	0.0059-0.0118 (0.15-0.30)
Oil	0.008-0.028 (0.20-0.70)

[1] – Measured 0.65" (16.5 mm) below oil ring groove.
[2] – This is a negative clearance (interference fit).
[3] – Installation pressure should be 1100-3300 lbs. (500-1500 kg).

CYLINDER BLOCK

Application	In. (mm)
Cylinder Bore	
Standard Diameter	
Aspire	2.7953-2.7961 (71.00-71.02)
Limit	2.8020 (71.17)
Capri	3.0709-3.0716 (78.000-78.019)
.0010" (0.25 mm) Oversize	3.0807-3.0815 (78.250-78.269)
.0020" (0.50 mm) Oversize	3.0905-3.0913 (78.500-78.519)
Maximum Taper	0.0007 (0.019)
Maximum Out-Of-Round	0.0007 (0.019)
Maximum Deck Warpage	0.006 (0.15)
Maximum Resurface Grinding	0.008 (0.20)

1994 ENGINES
1.3L & 1.6L 4-Cylinder (Cont.)

VALVES & VALVE SPRINGS

Application	Specification
Intake Valves	
Face Angle	45°
Valve Head Diameter	
Aspire	[1]
Capri	1.217-1.224" (30.90-31.10 mm)
Minimum Margin Thickness	
Aspire	
Intake	0.04 (1.0)
Exhaust	0.05 (1.3)
Capri	
Intake	0.020" (0.50 mm)
Exhaust	0.020" (0.50 mm)
Stem Diameter	
Aspire	0.2744-0.2750" (6.970-6.985 mm)
Capri	0.2350-0.2356" (5.970-5.985 mm)
Exhaust Valves	
Face Angle	45°
Valve Head Diameter	
Aspire	[1]
Capri	1.028-1.035" (26.1-26.3 mm)
Minimum Margin Thickness	
Aspire	0.039" (1.0 mm)
Capri	0.020" (0.5 mm)
Stem Diameter	
Aspire	0.2742-0.2748" (6.965-6.980 mm)
Capri	0.2348-0.2354" (5.965-5.980 mm)
Valve Springs	
Free Length	
Aspire	1.717" (43.6 mm)
Capri	1.858" (47.2 mm)
Minimum	1.803" (45.8 mm)
Out-Of-Square	
Aspire	0.059" (1.50 mm)
Capri	0.063" (1.60 mm)

[1] – Information is not available from manufacturer.

CYLINDER HEAD

Application	Specification
Maximum Warpage	0.006" (0.15 mm)
Valve Seats	
Intake Valve	
Seat Angle	45°
Seat Width	
Aspire	0.043-0.067" (1.10-1.70 mm)
Capri	0.0315-0.0551" (0.80-1.40 mm)
Maximum Seat Runout	0.0016" (0.04 mm)
Exhaust Valve	
Seat Angle	45°
Seat Width	
Aspire	0.043-0.067" (1.10-1.70 mm)
Capri	0.0315-0.0551" (0.80-1.40 mm)
Maximum Seat Runout	0.0016" (0.04 mm)
Valve Guides	
Intake Valve	
Valve Guide I.D.	
Aspire	0.276-0.277" (7.01-7.03 mm)
Capri	0.2366-0.2374" (6.01-6.03 mm)
Valve Stem-To-Guide Oil Clearance	
Aspire	Maximum Service Limit 0.008" (0.20 mm)
Capri	0.0010-0.0024" (0.025-0.060 mm)
Exhaust Valve	
Valve Guide I.D.	
Aspire	0.276-0.277" (7.01-7.03 mm)
Capri	0.2366-0.2374" (6.01-6.03 mm)
Valve Stem-To-Guide Oil Clearance	
Aspire	Maximum Service Limit 0.008" (0.20 mm)
Capri	0.0012-0.0026" (0.300-0.650 mm)

Aspire, Capri

SPECIFICATIONS

BELT ADJUSTMENT

BELT TENSION ADJUSTMENT SPECIFICATIONS
Using Belt Tension Gauge Or Deflection Method [1]

Application	Tension Lbs. (kg)	Deflection In. (mm)
Aspire		
A/C		
New Belt [2]	110-132 (50-60)	0.28-0.35 (7-9)
Used Belt [3]	95-110 (43-50)	0.35-0.43 (9-11)
Alternator & P/S		
New Belt [2]	110-132 (50-60)	0.31-0.35 (8-9)
Used Belt [3]	95-110 (43-50)	0.35-0.39 (9-10)
Capri		
A/C, Alternator & P/S		
New Belt [2]	110-132 (50-60)	0.31-0.35 (8-9)
Used Belt [3]	110-132 (50-60)	0.35-0.39 (9-10)

[1] – Positioned on the longest accessible span with 22 lbs. (10 kg) pressure applied.
[2] – New belts have not been run.
[3] – Used belts have been run 10 minutes or more.

COOLING SYSTEM SPECIFICATIONS

COOLING SYSTEM SPECIFICATIONS

Application	Specification
Coolant Capacity	
Aspire	5.3 Qts. (5.0L)
Capri	
Non-Turbo	5.3 Qts. (5.0L)
Turbo	6.3 Qts. (6.0L)
Coolant Replacement Interval	Every 36 Months
Pressure Cap	
Aspire	11-15 psi
Capri	15-19 psi
Thermostat Opens	
Aspire	188-193°F (87-89°C)
Capri [1]	
Main Valve	196-199°F (91-93°C)
Subvalve	190-194°F (88-90°C)

[1] – Dual-stage thermostat.

ELECTRIC COOLING FAN

DESCRIPTION

Capri – Power for the cooling fan is provided by the COOLING fuse. Cooling fan is activated when ground is supplied for fan motor. Ground may be supplied by A/C cooling fan relay (if equipped) or cooling fan relay, located in the left front corner of engine compartment. When cooling fan relay is energized, relay contacts are open. When cooling fan relay is not energized, relay contacts are closed, providing ground through closed contacts to activate cooling fan.

Cooling fan relay is energized when coolant temperature switch is closed. This occurs when coolant temperature is less than 212°F (100°C). At temperatures higher than 212°F (100°C), coolant temperature switch opens and cooling fan relay is de-energized, closing relay contacts and energizing cooling fan.

When ECA senses A/C request, it energizes A/C cooling fan relay by providing a ground for relay coil at PCM. Power for the A/C cooling fan relay is provided by the HEATER fuse. When A/C cooling fan relay is energized, it opens the power circuit for the cooling fan relay.

CAUTION: Stay clear of cooling fan at all times. Because it is electric and temperature sensitive, it may start at any time, even though engine is not running.

Aspire – Power for cooling fan is provided by the COOLING FAN fuse. Cooling fan is activated when power is supplied to the fan motor, through the cooling fan relay, located in the left front corner of engine compartment. Cooling fan relay coil power is supplied through the ENGINE fuse in the underdash fuse panel.

The PCM grounds the cooling fan relay coil when it determines the need for cooling fan operation. When the relay operates, it provides power to the cooling fan motor.

TROUBLE SHOOTING

Cooling Fan Does Not Operate Or Operates Erratically – If cooling fan does not run at any time, or operates erratically, check the following items to help locate fault:
- Check power fuse.
- Check cooling fan relay.
- Check coolant temperature switch (if equipped).
- Check cooling fan wiring.
- Check cooling fan motor.
- Check A/C cooling fan relay.

Cooling Fan Runs Continuously – If cooling fan runs continuously, check the following items to help locate fault:
- Check cooling fan relay.
- Check coolant temperature switch.
- Check cooling fan wiring.
- Check cooling fan motor (Capri only).
- Check for engine overheating.
- Check A/C cooling fan relay.

Cooling Fan Does Not Run With A/C On – If cooling fan does not run with A/C on, check the following items to help isolate fault:
- Check A/C cooling fan relay (if equipped).
- Check cooling fan wiring.

TESTING

Voltage Supply (Aspire) – 1) Unplug cooling fan relay connector. Check for voltage at White/Black wire terminal of connector. If battery voltage does not exist, inspect for blown COOLING FAN fuse in engine compartment fuse panel. Also inspect for open in Yellow wire between cooling fan and relay.

2) Turn ignition on. Check for battery voltage at Black/White wire terminal of connector. If battery voltage does not exist, inspect for blown ENGINE fuse in underdash fuse panel. Inspect for open in Brown wire between cooling fan relay and PCM.

Voltage Supply (Capri) – 1) Unplug cooling fan motor connector. Turn ignition on. Check for voltage at Yellow wire terminal of connector. If voltage battery voltage does not exist, inspect for blown COOLING fuse. Also inspect for open in Yellow wire between cooling fan and fuse.

2) Unplug cooling fan relay connector. Cooling fan relay is located in the left front corner of engine compartment. Turn ignition on. Check for battery voltage at Yellow wire terminal of connector. If battery voltage does not exist, inspect for blown HEATER fuse. Inspect for open in Yellow or Yellow/Green wire between cooling fan relay and fuse.

3) Unplug A/C cooling fan relay connector. A/C relay is located in the left rear corner of engine compartment, on firewall. Relay may be identified by wire colors to relay connector. See appropriate WIRING DIAGRAM.

4) Turn ignition on. Check for battery voltage at Blue wire terminal of connector. If battery voltage does not exist, inspect for blown HEATER fuse or open in Blue wire between A/C cooling fan relay and fuse. **Ground Circuit (Capri)** – Turn ignition off. Unplug connectors from cooling fan and A/C cooling fan relays. Inspect for continuity between ground and Black wire terminal of relay connectors. If continuity does not exist, repair Black ground wire.

Cooling Fan Relay (Capri) – Unplug cooling fan relay connector. Apply battery voltage and ground to Yellow and Green/Red wire terminals of relay. Check for continuity between Yellow/Green and Black wire terminals of relay. Continuity should not exist while relay is energized. With no voltage to relay coil, continuity should exist.

A/C Cooling Fan Relay (Capri) – Unplug A/C relay connector. Apply battery voltage and ground to Blue and White wire terminals of relay. Check for continuity between Blue and Red wire terminals of relay. Continuity should not exist while relay is energized. When relay is not energized, continuity should exist.

Coolant Temperature Switch (Capri) – 1) Unplug connector from coolant temperature switch, located near thermostat housing. With coolant temperature less than 200°F (93°C), continuity should exist between ground and coolant temperature switch.

2) Start and warm engine until coolant temperature reaches 212°F (100°C). Check for continuity between ground and coolant temperature switch terminal. Continuity should not exist. If continuity is not as specified, replace switch.

Fan Motor – Unplug fan motor wire connector. Apply ground and battery voltage to motor connector. Fan should run. On all vehicles, replace fan motor if it does not run.

Harness & Circuit Check – Turn ignition off. Unplug harness connectors of the following components: PCM, cooling fan motor, coolant temperature switch, cooling fan relay, and A/C cooling fan relay. Check for continuity and shorts on the related harness leads of each connector.

WIRING DIAGRAMS

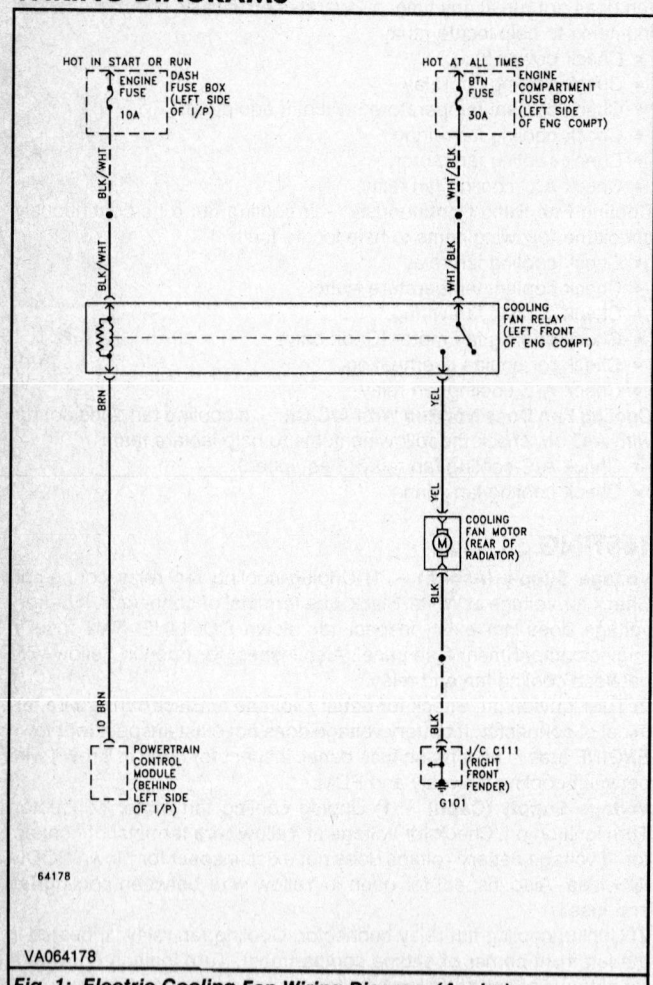

Fig. 1: Electric Cooling Fan Wiring Diagram (Aspire)

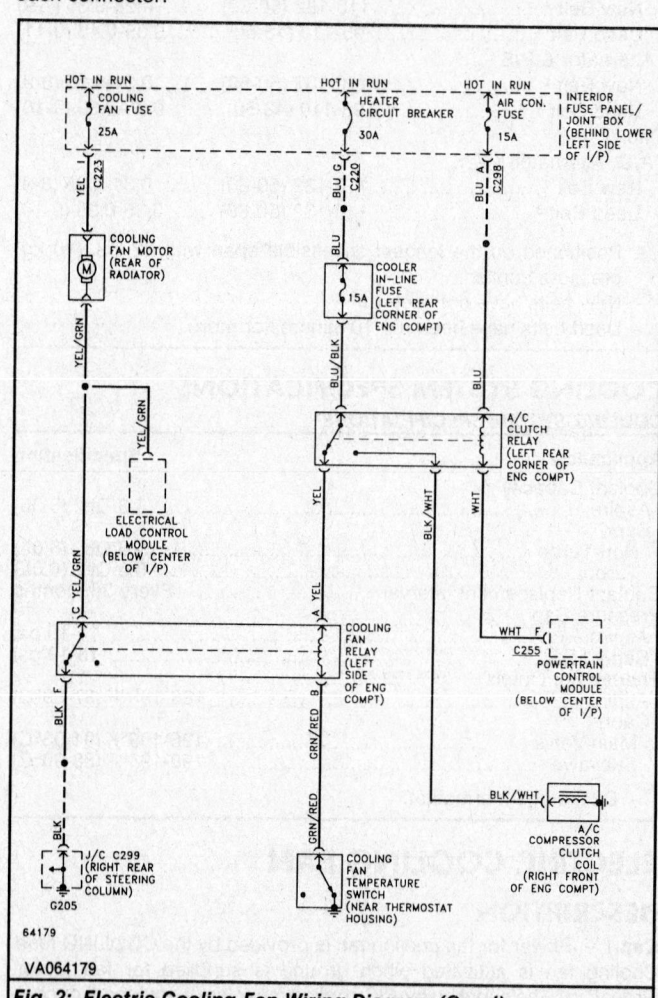

Fig. 2: Electric Cooling Fan Wiring Diagram (Capri)

Aspire, Capri

DESCRIPTION

The clutch is single-disc type, with a diaphragm spring. On Aspire and Capri turbo, clutch is controlled by a mechanical release system consisting of a clutch pedal, cable, release lever, and release bearing. On Capri non-turbo, clutch is controlled by a hydraulic release system consisting of a clutch pedal, master cylinder, slave cylinder, release lever, and release bearing.

ADJUSTMENTS

CLUTCH PEDAL FREE PLAY

1) Measure clutch pedal travel from engaged position to first indication of clutch release. See Fig. 1. Free play must be within specifications. See CLUTCH PEDAL SPECIFICATIONS table.

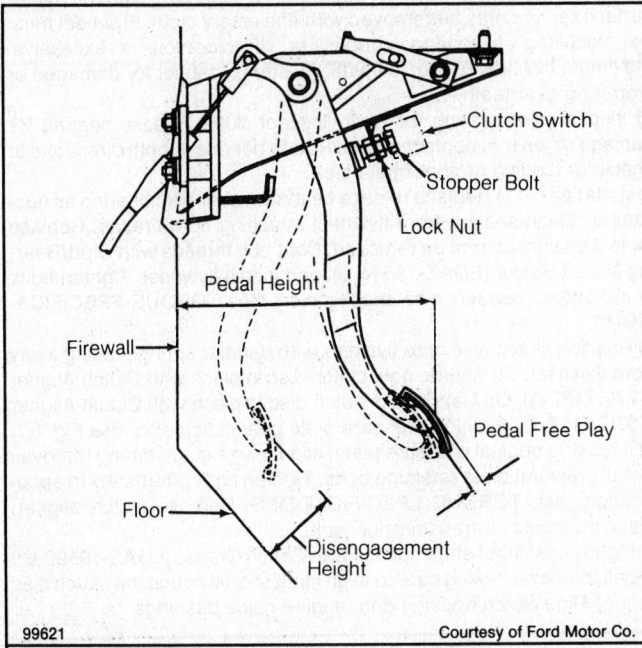

99621   Courtesy of Ford Motor Co.

Fig. 1: Adjusting Clutch Pedal
(Capri Turbo Shown; Aspire & Capri Non-Turbo Similar)

2) On Aspire and Capri turbo, if free play is not within specification, rotate clutch cable adjustment nut at release lever to obtain specified pedal free play. See Fig. 2.
3) On Capri non-turbo, loosen master cylinder push rod lock nut. Rotate adjuster nut in direction required to achieve specified free play. If satisfactory adjustment cannot be obtained, repair or replace clutch components as necessary.

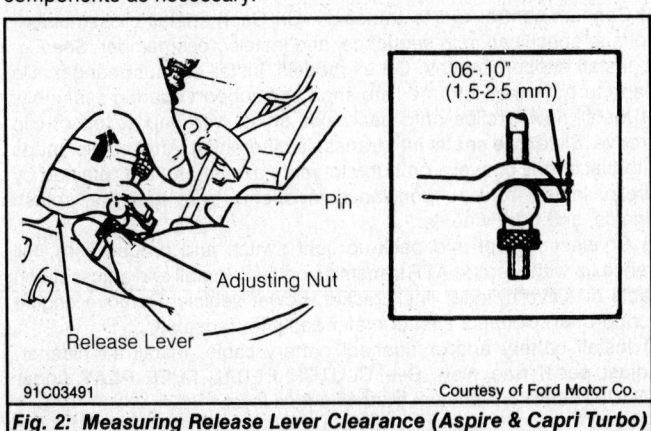

91C03491   Courtesy of Ford Motor Co.

Fig. 2: Measuring Release Lever Clearance (Aspire & Capri Turbo)

CLUTCH PEDAL SPECIFICATIONS

Application	In. (mm)
Aspire	
Pedal Height	8.1 (205)
Free Play	0.35-0.59 (9-15)
Release Lever-To-Pin	0.06-0.10 (1.5-2.5)
Disengagement Height	2.9 (74)
Capri	
Pedal Height	
Non-Turbo	9.02-9.21 (229-234)
Turbo	8.4-8.6 (214-219)
Free Play	
Non-Turbo	0.02-0.12 (0.6-3.0)
Turbo	0.35-0.59 (9-15)
Release Lever-To-Pin (Turbo)	0.06-0.10 (1.5-2.5)

CLUTCH PEDAL HEIGHT

1) On Aspire and Capri turbo, disconnect clutch cable from release lever at transaxle. On Capri non-turbo, disconnect clutch master cylinder push rod. On all models, move carpet and insulation out of way. Measure distance from upper center of pedal to firewall. See Fig. 1. If not within specifications, inspect pedal mounting for wear or damage. See CLUTCH PEDAL SPECIFICATIONS table.
2) If adjustment is required, remove instrument panel bracket and air duct. Loosen clutch pedal switch lock nut. Rotate switch until correct clutch pedal height is obtained.
3) On Aspire and Capri turbo, install clutch cable at transaxle. On Capri non-turbo, install master cylinder push rod. On all models, recheck pedal height. If connecting clutch cable changes pedal height, inspect cable for improper routing, binding, or adjustment. If connecting push rod changes pedal height, inspect for proper push rod adjustment. Install carpet and insulation to complete adjustment.

REMOVAL & INSTALLATION

CLUTCH ASSEMBLY

Removal (Aspire) – 1) Raise and support vehicle. Remove axle shafts. See FWD AXLE SHAFTS article in DRIVE AXLES. Unplug electrical connectors. Remove clutch cable adjuster nut. Disengage clutch cable at clutch release shaft. Pull cable through clutch cable bracket.
2) Disconnect ground strap at transaxle. Remove starter. Disconnect speedometer cable. Remove upper transaxle bolts from bellhousing. Install Engine Support Bar (D88L-6000-A)

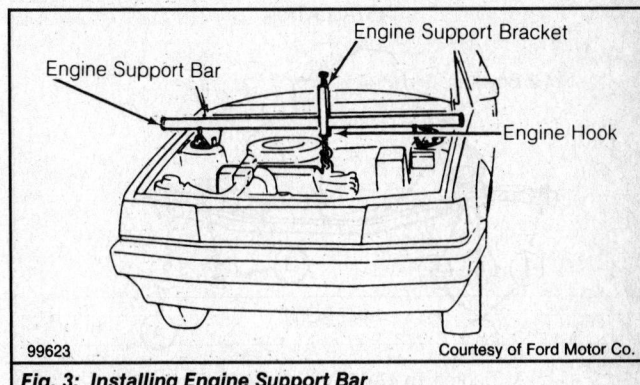

99623   Courtesy of Ford Motor Co.

Fig. 3: Installing Engine Support Bar
(Capri Turbo Shown; Others Similar)

3) Raise and support vehicle. Remove shift rod adjuster sleeve. Remove stabilizer bar nut, lock washer, and flat washer. Disengage stabilizer bar from control rod and support bar stud. Remove bolts from case rear bracket and case front bracket. Remove brackets.
4) Remove support insulator nuts from rear engine support. Remove rear engine support. Position transmission jack under transaxle. Secure transaxle to jack. Remove transaxle retaining bolts. Pull transaxle away from engine. Lower transaxle from vehicle.
5) If reusing pressure plate, mark pressure plate-to-flywheel position for installation reference. Remove pressure plate bolts evenly. See

Fig. 5. To avoid dropping clutch assembly while removing bolts, install clutch aligner. Remove pressure plate, clutch disc, and clutch aligner. Remove flywheel. Remove pilot bearing from flywheel if it is to be replaced.

Removal (Capri) – **1)** Disconnect negative battery cable. On non-turbo, remove battery, air cleaner assembly, and clutch slave hydraulic line retaining bracket and cylinder. On turbo, loosen clutch cable adjuster nut. Disengage cable from release lever.

2) On turbo, remove air intake by-pass valve mounting nut. On all models, remove starter. Disconnect back-up light switch and neutral switch. Disconnect ground cable/strap and supporting brackets. Disconnect speedometer cable from transaxle.

3) Attach Engine Support Bar (D88L-6000-A) to engine hanger. *See Fig. 3.* Remove top transaxle-to-engine bolts. Raise vehicle. Remove bolt and nut retaining shift rod to input shift rail. Drain transaxle fluid. Remove all support brackets attached to transaxle. Remove front wheels.

4) Remove engine splash shields. Remove front stabilizer bar. Disengage right and left side axle shafts from transaxle. Support axle shafts out of the way. On turbo, remove intermediate shaft and support bearing assembly. See FWD AXLE SHAFTS article in DRIVE AXLES.

5) Remove 2 front crossmember braces and brace to "A" arm support bolts. Remove exhaust hanger from crossmember. Remove crossmember bolts in sequence, and remove crossmember. *See Fig. 4.* Remove transaxle end plate bolts.

NOTE: Loosen & Tighten Crossmember Bolts In Numbered Sequence Shown.

REMOVAL

⑤ ① ② ③ ④

◄ FRONT

INSTALLATION

No. 2 Bracket

① ④ ⑤ Ⓑ ③ ②
Ⓐ Ⓐ

◄ FRONT

A: Tighten To 47-66 Ft. Lbs. (64-89 N.m)
B: Tighten To 20-46 Ft. Lbs. (27-62 N.m)

93H00734   Courtesy of Ford Motor Co.

Fig. 4: Removing & Installing Crossmember (Capri)

6) Place transmission jack under transaxle, ensuring it is secure. Remove remaining flywheel housing bolts. Lower transaxle by loosening engine bracket bar hook bolt. Pull transaxle away from engine. Lower transaxle from vehicle.

CAUTION: DO NOT allow oil or grease to contact clutch disc face or mating surfaces. Handle disc by edges. DO NOT touch face.

7) If reusing pressure plate, mark pressure plate-to-flywheel position for installation reference. Remove pressure plate bolts evenly. *See Fig. 5.* To avoid dropping clutch assembly while removing bolts, install clutch aligner. Remove pressure plate, clutch disc, and clutch aligner. Remove flywheel. Remove pilot bearing from flywheel, if it is to be replaced.

Inspection – **1)** Inspect pressure plate surfaces for scoring, cracks, or discoloration. Remove minor scratches or discoloration with fine emery cloth. Inspect pressure plate diaphragm spring fingers for discoloration, scoring, or broken or bent segments. All spring ends must be of the same height.

2) Inspect clutch disc lining surface for hardening or presence of oil. Inspect for worn clutch disc lining. Inspect for loose lining rivets. Measure depth of rivet heads. Minimum allowable rivet depth is 0.012" (0.3 mm). Inspect for wear or rust on splines. Rust may be removed with emery cloth.

3) Inspect flywheel surface for marks, scoring, or discoloration. Minor surface repairs may be removed with fine emery cloth. Flywheel must be machined if scoring, runout, or discoloration is excessive. Maximum flywheel runout is 0.008" (0.2 mm). Inspect for damaged or worn ring gear teeth.

4) Inspect pilot bearing for wear. Inspect clutch release bearing for damage or wear at contact points. Rotate bearing in both directions to check for binding or abnormal noise.

Installation – **1)** Replace release bearing and/or pilot bearing as necessary. Clean sealant from flywheel attaching bolt threads. Replace bolts if sealant cannot be removed. Coat bolt threads with Stud/Bearing Mount Sealer (EOAZ-19554-B), and install flywheel. Tighten bolts in a diagonal sequence to specification. See TORQUE SPECIFICATIONS.

2) Position clutch disc onto flywheel with damper springs facing away from flywheel. On Aspire, hold clutch disc in place with Clutch Aligner (T77F-7137-A). On Capri, hold clutch disc in place with Clutch Aligner (T87C-7137-A). Position pressure plate over clutch disc. *See Fig. 5.*

3) If reusing original pressure plate, align marks made during removal. Install pressure plate retaining bolts. Tighten bolts alternately to specification. See TORQUE SPECIFICATIONS. Remove clutch aligner. Place transaxle on transmission jack.

4) Lightly coat input shaft splines with Clutch Grease (C1AZ-19590-B). Install transaxle, taking care to align input shaft through the clutch disc spline. Align clutch housing onto engine guide bushings.

CAUTION: Transaxle aluminum alloy construction requires precise tightening of mounting bolts. Torque specifications must be strictly adhered to. See TORQUE SPECIFICATIONS.

5) Install transaxle lower attaching bolts and tighten to specification. Using transaxle jack, raise transaxle to correct height. Tighten engine bracket bar hook. Install front engine mount and bracket and tighten to specification. Install starter and lower mounting bolts. On Capri non-turbo, install slave cylinder. Slide extension bar onto transaxle bracket.

6) Connect control rod to transaxle. On Capri, install crossmember bolts to specification in sequence, and install crossmember. *See Fig. 4.* Install support braces. On all models, install exhaust hanger. On Capri turbo, install intermediate shaft and support bearing assembly.

7) Install new circlips onto each axle shaft, with gap at top of clip groove. Slide axle shafts into transaxle differential. After circlip snaps into place, pull outward on hubs to verify axle shafts are retained by circlip. Install front suspension components, wire harness, splash shields, and front wheels.

8) Connect neutral and back-up light switch and ground wire. Fill transaxle with Mercon ATF transmission fluid. Install and adjust clutch cable or slave cylinder line bracket. Lower vehicle. Remove engine support bar. Connect speedometer cable to transaxle.

9) Install battery and/or connect battery cable. Install air cleaner. Adjust pedal free play. See CLUTCH PEDAL FREE PLAY under ADJUSTMENTS. Recheck transaxle fluid level.

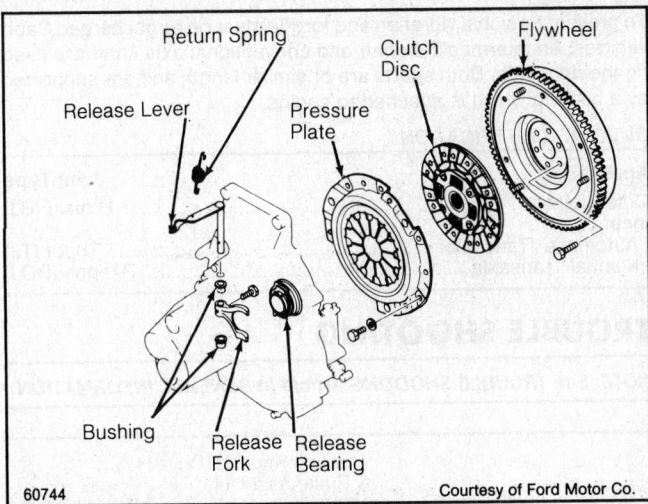

Fig. 5: Exploded View Of Clutch Assembly

60744 — Courtesy of Ford Motor Co.

CLUTCH RELEASE BEARING & FORK

NOTE: The clutch release bearing is pre-lubricated and permanently sealed. DO NOT clean release bearing in solvent.

Removal – Remove transaxle. Remove release lever bolt and slide release bearing off. *See Fig. 5.* Remove release lever shaft and release lever.

Inspection – Inspect release bearing for roughness, sticking, or noise. Inspect release lever and transaxle front bearing retainer for wear or damage. Ensure bearing slides smoothly on transaxle input shaft. Inspect release lever shaft for bent, worn, or damaged condition. Inspect all mating surfaces for wear or damage. Replace worn or defective components.

Installation – Apply light film of grease to transmission front bearing retainer lever-to-bearing surfaces and release lever contact surface. Align bolt hole in release lever and shaft. Apply Stud/Bearing Sealant (E0AZ-19554-B) to release lever bolt. Fill grease groove in release bearing hub. Remove any excess grease. Install release lever return spring. To complete installation, reverse removal procedure.

PILOT BEARING

NOTE: DO NOT remove pilot bearing unless necessary.

Removal & Installation – Remove transaxle, pressure plate, clutch disc, and flywheel. Drive pilot bearing with flywheel with a driver that makes full contact with bearing outer race. Reverse procedure for installation.

CLUTCH MASTER CYLINDER

Removal & Installation (Capri Non-Turbo) – **1)** Disconnect battery cables. Remove battery. Remove wiper motor. Disconnect hydraulic line fitting at bracket on transaxle case. Drain fluid. Reconnect fitting after fluid has drained. Disconnect hydraulic line from clutch master cylinder.

2) Remove master cylinder. To install, reverse removal procedure. Tighten master cylinder nuts to 14-19 ft. lbs. (19-26 N.m). Fill reservoir. Bleed system. Recheck clutch pedal height. See CLUTCH PEDAL FREE PLAY and CLUTCH PEDAL HEIGHT under ADJUSTMENTS.

CLUTCH RELEASE CYLINDER

Removal & Installation (Capri Non-Turbo) – Disconnect and plug hydraulic line. Remove bolts retaining slave cylinder to bellhousing. Remove slave cylinder. To install, reverse removal procedure. Tighten slave cylinder bolts to 12-17 ft. lbs. (16-23 N.m). Fill reservoir and bleed system.

CLUTCH CABLE

Removal & Installation (Aspire & Capri Turbo) – **1)** Disconnect clutch cable from release lever. Remove nuts retaining clutch cable at firewall. Unhook clutch cable at clutch pedal.

2) Remove clutch cable from engine compartment side. To install, apply lithium grease to pedal cable hook and joint between release lever and pin. Reverse removal procedure to complete installation. *See Fig. 2.*

OVERHAUL

NOTE: Manufacturer does not provide overhaul information for clutch master cylinder and clutch release cylinder.

TORQUE SPECIFICATIONS

TORQUE SPECIFICATIONS

Application	Ft. Lbs. (N.m)
Clutch Cable Bracket Nuts	12-17 (16-23)
Clutch Pedal Push Rod Lock Nut	9-13 (12-17)
Clutch Pedal Through Bolt Nut	15-26 (20-35)
Crossmember	
"A" Bolts	47-66 (64-90)
"B" Bolt	21-34 (28-46)
Crossmember Brace (Front)	23-34 (31-46)
Crossmember Brace	69-86 (93-117)
Engine Mount Bolt (No. 2)	33-48 (45-65)
Engine-To-Transaxle	46-66 (63-90)
Flywheel Housing-To-Engine Bolt	46-66 (63-90)
Flywheel-To-Crankshaft Bolt	
Aspire	71-76 (96-103)
Capri	71-76 (96-103)
Front Engine Mount (Capri)	27-38 (37-52)
Front Wheel Lug Nut	66-89 (90-120)
Lower Ball Joint Pinch Bolt	32-40 (43-54)
Master Cylinder Retaining Nuts	14-19 (19-26)
Pressure Plate-To-Flywheel Bolt	13-20 (17-27)
Rear Engine Cover-To-Housing Bolt	27-38 (37-52)
Rear Mount-To-Transmission Bolt	50-70 (68-95)
Rear Transmission Mount-To-Body Bolt	25-35 (34-48)
Release Fork Attaching Bolt	26-30 (35-41)
Slave Cylinder Retaining Bolts	12-17 (16-23)
Stabilizer Bracket-To-Body Bolt	33-41 (45-56)
Starter Motor-To-Mount Bolt	23-34 (31-46)
Transaxle Drain Plug	29-40 (39-54)
	INCH Lbs. (N.m)
Release Lever Bolt	71-97 (8-11)
Speedometer Drive Gear Bolt	69-106 (7.8-12)

1994 DRIVE AXLES
FWD Axle Shafts

Aspire, Capri

DESCRIPTION & OPERATION

Axle shafts transfer power from transaxle to drive wheels. All axle shafts consist of a shaft with a flexible Constant Velocity (CV) joint at each end. Inner CV joint is coupled to transaxle by splines. Outer CV joint is splined to hub assembly and secured by axle shaft nut.

Three different types of axle shaft CV joints are used: Double Offset Joint (DOJ) or Rzeppa type, Birfield Joint (BJ), and Tripot Joint (TJ).

CV joint boots protect CV joints by maintaining proper lubrication and preventing contaminants from entering joint. Boots must be replaced when signs of leakage or cracks exist. Inner CV joint may be disassembled and serviced. Outer CV joint boot may be replaced, but outer Birfield CV joint must NOT be disassembled. It must be replaced as an assembly, if faulty.

To prevent torsional vibration and torque steer on turbocharged Capri vehicles, an intermediate shaft and conventional axle shaft are used on the right side. Both shafts are of similar length and are supported by a bearing which is attached to engine.

CV JOINT IDENTIFICATION

Application	Joint Type
Outer Joint	Birfield (BJ)
Inner Joint	
Automatic Transaxle	Tripot (TJ)
Manual Transaxle	Rzeppa (DOJ)

TROUBLE SHOOTING

NOTE: See TROUBLE SHOOTING article in GENERAL INFORMATION.

PRYING AXLE SHAFT FROM DIFFERENTIAL

REMOVING AXLE SHAFT FROM STEERING KNUCKLE & DRIVE HUB

90B01076

Fig. 1: Removing & Installing Axle Shafts

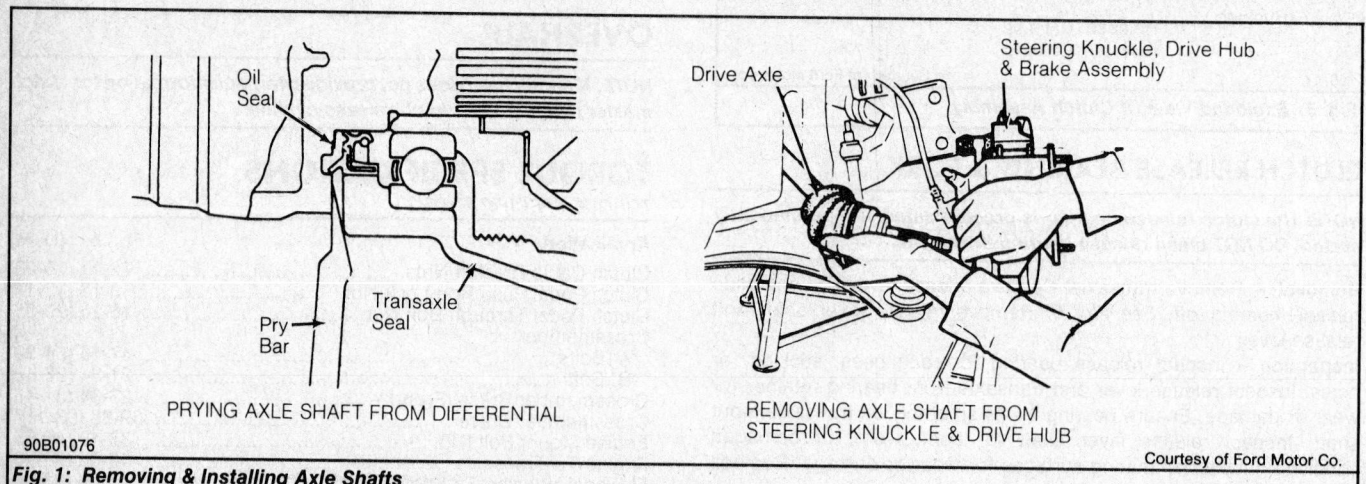

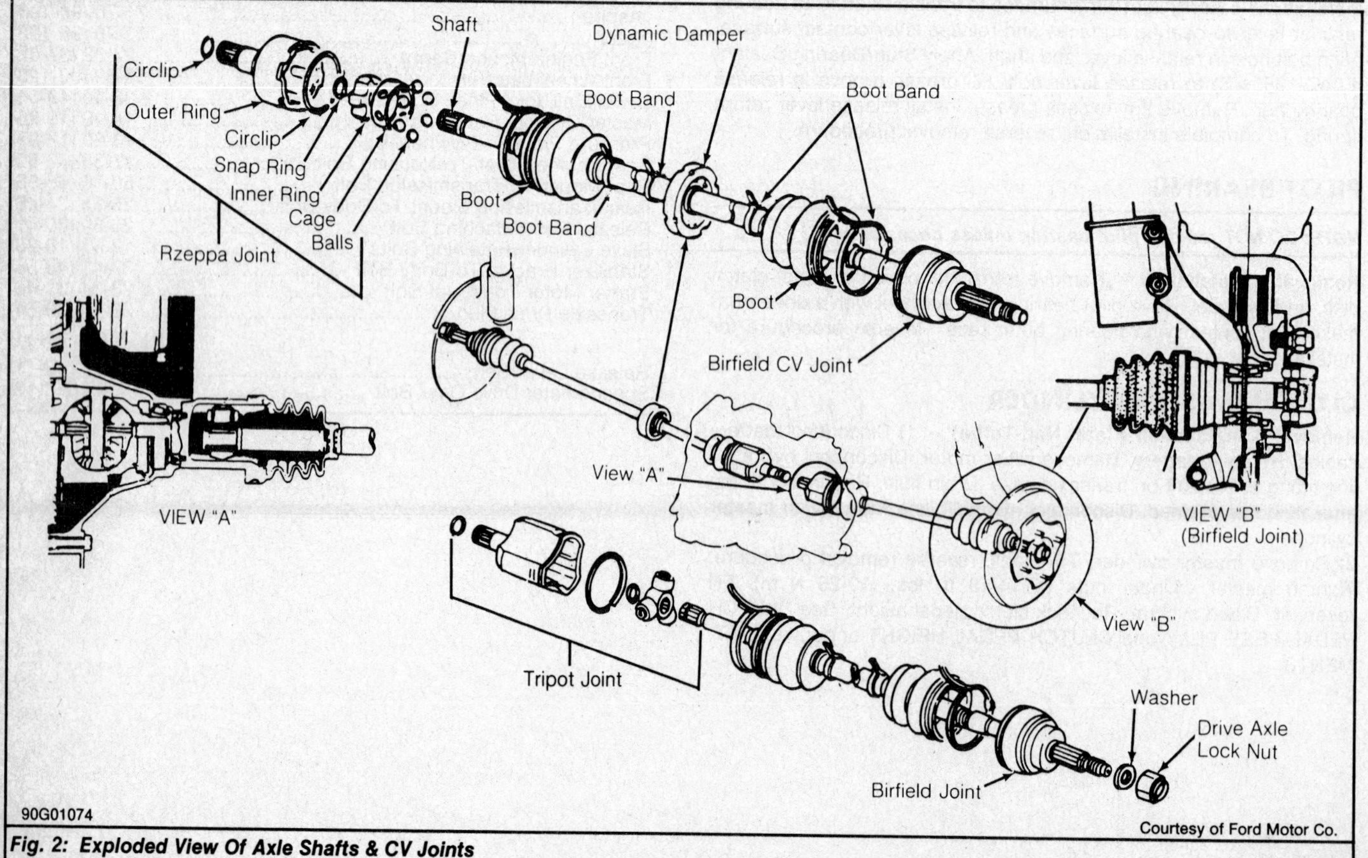

Fig. 2: Exploded View Of Axle Shafts & CV Joints

90G01074

REMOVAL, DISASSEMBLY, REASSEMBLY & INSTALLATION

FWD AXLE SHAFTS

Removal (Aspire) – **1)** Raise and support vehicle. Drain transaxle fluid. Remove front wheels. Loosen front axle hub retainer nut, leaving nut on shaft. Remove joint clamp bolt and nut. Separate ball joint from knuckle by prying downward on lower arm.

CAUTION: Separate axle shaft from transaxle gradually. If shaft is yanked from transaxle, the differential oil seal may be damaged.

2) Pry drive shaft and joint from transaxle. Remove hub retainer nut and washer. Discard retainer nut.

CAUTION: Take care not to damage transaxle oil seal while removing drive shaft from wheel hub.

3) Remove axle shaft from wheel hub. If difficult to remove, use hammer and brass drift to tap axle from drive hub. Remove and discard drive shaft bearing circlip. Plug transaxle openings with Plugs (T87C-7025-C). Remove axle shaft assembly from vehicle.
Removal (Capri) – **1)** Raise and support vehicle. Remove lower underbody splash shields. Drain transaxle fluid. Remove front wheels. Loosen axle shaft lock nut. Remove stabilizer bar-to-control arm attaching nuts, bolt, washers, and bushings. Remove joint clamp bolt from lower control arm. Pry downward to separate steering knuckle from ball joint, taking care not to damage ball joint dust boot.
2) On Capri turbo, remove bolts securing intermediate shaft bearing bracket to engine. On all models, slowly pry axle shaft from transaxle. Axle is held into transaxle by a circlip fitted to the end of the axle. Remove axle shaft from wheel hub. If difficult to remove, use axle puller to separate axle from drive hub. Remove axle shaft from transaxle. Plug transaxle openings with Plugs (T87C-7025-C). Remove axle shaft assembly from vehicle. *See Fig. 1.*

CAUTION: Damage to CV joint will occur if a hammer is used to separate axle shaft from wheel hub.

Disassembly (Rzeppa/DOJ Type) – **1)** Label and remove CV joint boot. Mark alignment of axle shaft to outer race of CV joint. Remove circlip and outer bearing race housing. Mark alignment of inner race to shaft. Remove inner snap ring. Remove cage assembly. *See Fig. 2.*

2) Pry ball bearings from bearing cage. Mark alignment of bearing cage to inner race. Rotate inner race about 30 degrees and remove from cage assembly. If necessary, remove remaining boot.

NOTE: Inspect old grease for contamination by rubbing between fingers. Any gritty feeling indicates contaminated CV joint. If joint is contaminated, disassemble, clean, and inspect thoroughly.

NOTE: On Aspire, assemble axle shafts to dimensions shown. See Fig. 3.

Reassembly (Rzeppa/DOJ Type) – **1)** Apply Grease (E43Z-19590-A) to all areas of CV joint during reassembly. Reverse disassembly procedure for reassembly, noting alignment marks made during disassembly. Ensure chamfer on bearing cage faces snap ring. Lubricate outer race housing with 1.4-2.1 ounces (40-60 g) of grease.
2) Install right side dynamic damper (if equipped) at a distance of 18.99-19.27" (482.5-489.5 mm) from outboard end of axle shaft. Installed length of CV boot should be 3.5" (90 mm). *See Fig. 4.*
Disassembly (Tripot Type) – Remove boot clamp and boot. Paint an alignment mark of axle shaft to outer race of CV joint. Remove circlip and outer bearing race housing. Mark alignment of inner race to shaft. Remove snap ring. Remove tripot assembly with a soft brass drift and hammer. *See Fig. 2.*
Reassembly (Tripot Type) – Apply Grease (E43Z-19590-A) to all areas of CV joint during reassembly. Reverse removal procedure, noting alignment marks made during disassembly. Ensure chamfer on bearing cage faces snap ring. Lubricate outer race housing with 3.5 ounces (100 g) of grease. Installed length of CV boot should be 3.5" (90 mm). *See Fig. 4.*

NOTE: Always install NEW cotter pin, washer, and suspension lock nuts.

Installation (All Models) – **1)** To install axle shaft, reverse removal procedure. Always install a NEW retaining circlip. Inspect seals at both ends of axle shaft. If necessary, replace seals prior to installation. Lubricate transaxle seal lip with transaxle oil. *See Fig. 1.*
2) After installing axle shaft into transaxle, pull axle shaft outward by hand to ensure proper engagement of retaining circlip and snap ring. Install axle shaft into wheel hub. Align suspension alignment marks and tighten nuts.

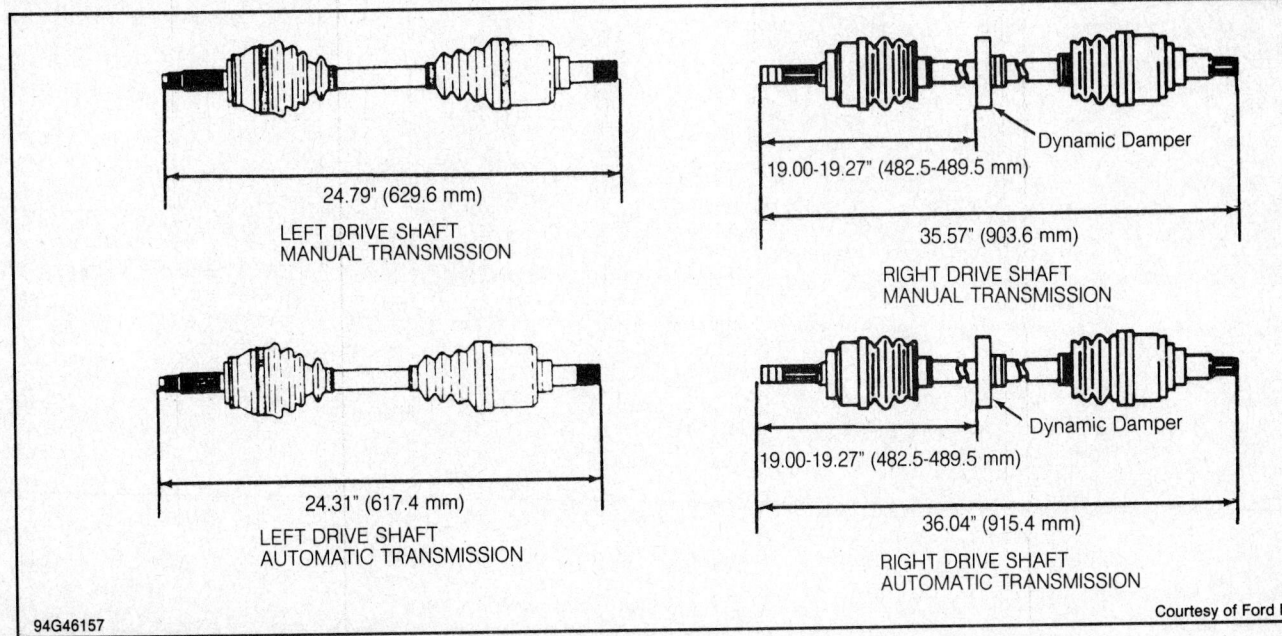

24.79" (629.6 mm)
LEFT DRIVE SHAFT
MANUAL TRANSMISSION

24.31" (617.4 mm)
LEFT DRIVE SHAFT
AUTOMATIC TRANSMISSION

Dynamic Damper
19.00-19.27" (482.5-489.5 mm)
35.57" (903.6 mm)
RIGHT DRIVE SHAFT
MANUAL TRANSMISSION

Dynamic Damper
19.00-19.27" (482.5-489.5 mm)
36.04" (915.4 mm)
RIGHT DRIVE SHAFT
AUTOMATIC TRANSMISSION

Courtesy of Ford Motor Co.

94G46157

Fig. 3: Assembling Axle Shafts (Aspire)

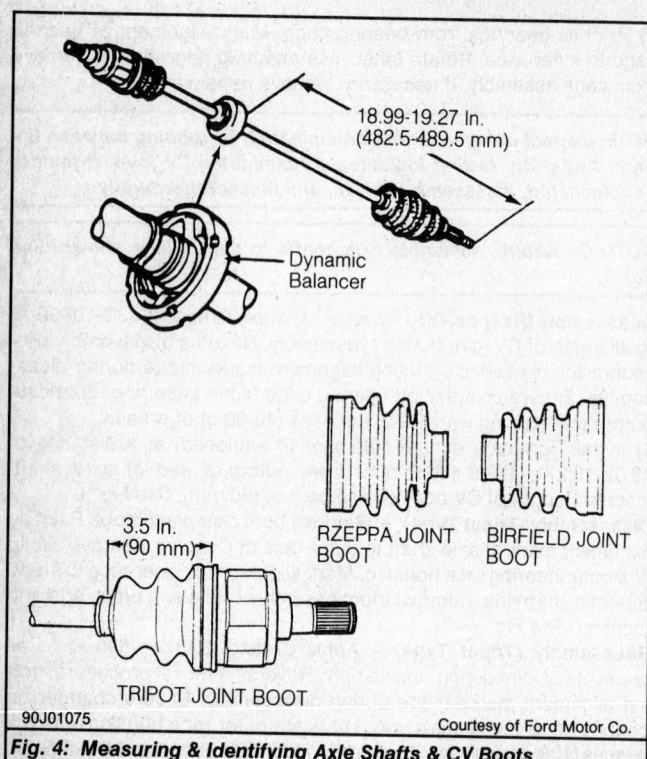

Fig. 4: Measuring & Identifying Axle Shafts & CV Boots

18.99-19.27 In. (482.5-489.5 mm)

Dynamic Balancer

3.5 In. (90 mm)

RZEPPA JOINT BOOT

BIRFIELD JOINT BOOT

TRIPOT JOINT BOOT

90J01075

Courtesy of Ford Motor Co.

INTERMEDIATE SHAFT

Removal – Remove intermediate shaft and axle shaft as an assembly. See FWD AXLE SHAFTS under REMOVAL, DISASSEMBLY, REASSEMBLY & INSTALLATION.

Disassembly – Separate intermediate shaft from axle shaft. Remove circlip from intermediate shaft. Press bearing and bracket from shaft assembly. See Fig. 5. Press bearing from bracket. Inspect bracket for damage or wear. Replace if necessary.

Reassembly – Press NEW bearing into bracket and install NEW seals. Install bearing and bracket assembly onto intermediate shaft. Install NEW circlip. Assemble intermediate shaft and axle shaft.

Installation – Install intermediate shaft and axle shaft as an assembly. See FWD AXLE SHAFTS under REMOVAL, DISASSEMBLY, REASSEMBLY & INSTALLATION.

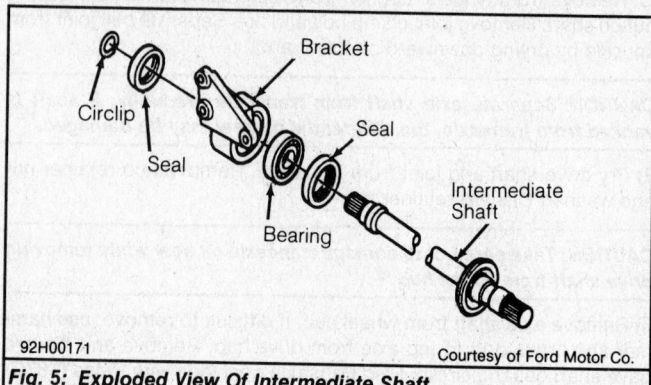

Fig. 5: Exploded View Of Intermediate Shaft

Bracket
Circlip
Seal
Seal
Bearing
Seal
Intermediate Shaft

92H00171

Courtesy of Ford Motor Co.

TORQUE SPECIFICATIONS

TORQUE SPECIFICATIONS

Application	Ft. Lbs. (N.m)
Axle Nut [1]	116-173 (157-235)
Ball Joint Pinch Bolt	32-40 (43-54)
Caliper Retaining Bolt	29-36 (39-49)
Stabilizer Bar Bracket Nut	40-50 (54-68)
Stabilizer Link Bolt	9-13 (12-18)
Steering Knuckle-To-Strut Bolt	69-86 (93-117)
Tie Rod End Nut	21-32 (29-44)
Wheel Lug Nuts	66-89 (90-120)

[1] – Stake locking flange on nut into axle slot.

Aspire, Capri

DESCRIPTION & OPERATION

On Capri, vehicle braking is provided by front and rear disc brakes. Front and rear brakes are a full-floating, single-piston design. Rear caliper houses a self-adjusting parking brake. Brake line routing has been diagonally split; left front to right rear, and right front to left rear.

On Aspire, vehicle braking is provided by front disc brakes and rear drum brakes. Rear brakes are self-energizing and self-adjusting. Front brakes are a full-floating, single-piston design with caliper attached to steering knuckle.

BLEEDING BRAKE SYSTEM

MANUAL BLEEDING PROCEDURE

1) Bleed vacuum from power brake unit by pressing brake pedal several times. Fill master cylinder with clean brake fluid. Install clear vinyl bleeder hose onto first bleeder screw to be serviced. See BRAKELINE BLEEDING SEQUENCE table. Place other end of hose in clean transparent container.

2) If master cylinder is known or suspected to contain air, it must be bled first. To bleed master cylinder, loosen front brakeline fitting. Press brake pedal to end of travel and tighten fitting. Release brake pedal slowly. Repeat process on rear brakeline, repeating until all air is removed from master cylinder. Keep brake fluid reservoir covered and full at all times. Rinse spillage from all surfaces with water.

3) Partially fill container with clean brake fluid. Open bleeder screw about 3/4 turn. Slowly press brake pedal through its full travel. Close bleeder screw and release pedal. Repeat procedure until flow of brake fluid is clear, with no sign of air bubbles. Proceed to next bleeder screw in sequence and repeat procedure.

BRAKELINE BLEEDING SEQUENCE

Application	Sequence
Aspire	RR, LR, RF & LF
Capri	RR, LR, RF & LF

NOTE: *Check fluid level in master cylinder frequently during bleeding sequence.*

PRESSURE BLEEDING PROCEDURE

1) Exhaust vacuum from power brake unit by pressing brake pedal several times. Fill master cylinder with clean brake fluid. Ensure pressure bleeder is at least half full and charged to 10-30 psi. Connect pressure bleeder to master cylinder according to manufacturer's instructions. Open valve on bleeder tank.

2) Install clear vinyl bleeder hose onto first bleeder screw to be serviced. See BRAKELINE BLEEDING SEQUENCE table. Place other end of hose in clean transparent container. Partially fill container with clean brake fluid.

3) Open bleeder screw 3/4 of a turn. Allow fluid to run until flow of fluid is clear and shows no signs of air bubbles. Proceed to next bleeder screw in sequence and repeat procedure. Close valve on bleeder tank and remove pressure bleeder from master cylinder. Fill master cylinder with clean brake fluid. Clean all spillage.

ADJUSTMENTS

BRAKE PEDAL HEIGHT

Aspire – 1) Move carpet and insulation away from firewall and brake pedal. Measure distance horizontally between upper center of brake pedal pad and firewall. Distance should be 8.03-8.23" (204-209 mm).

2) If pedal height is incorrect, inspect pedal assembly for missing, worn or damaged bushings, or for loose attaching bolts. If pedal height is still not within specifications, check brake pedal, booster or master cylinder for correct and/or correctly installed parts. If all appears okay, go to next step.

3) Loosen Brake On/Off (BOO) switch lock nuts. Move BOO switch to rear until it no longer contacts pedal.

4) Loosen brake booster push rod lock unit. Rotate push rod until brake pedal height is within specification. Hold push rod and tighten lock nut.

5) Unplug BOO switch connector. Connect ohmmeter across switch terminals. Move switch toward brake pedal lever until ohmmeter indicates continuity.

6) Carefully move switch away from lever until ohmmeter indicates no continuity. Rotate switch 1/2 additional turn toward brake pedal lever. Tighten lock nuts.

Capri – 1) Move carpet and insulation away from floor board and brake pedal. With engine running, use Brake Pedal Effort Gauge (021-00001) to apply 132 lbs. (60 kg) of force to brake pedal. Measure distance from upper surface of brake pedal pad to floor. If distance is less than 3.27" (83 mm), inspect pedal assembly for missing, worn, or damaged bushings, or for loose attaching bolts.

2) Verify that floor board is not distorted and pedal is not bent. If pedal height is still not within specifications, inspect brake pedal, booster, or master cylinder for correct and/or incorrectly installed parts. Check for air in hydraulic system.

BRAKE PEDAL FREE PLAY

Aspire – Pump brake pedal several times to bleed vacuum from power brake booster. Gently move brake pedal back and forth by hand and measure play before resistance is felt. Free play should be 0.16-0.28" (4-7 mm). If free play is not within specifications, adjust length of brake pedal push rod.

Capri – 1) Release parking brake. Fill master cylinder. Using Brake Pedal Effort Gauge (021-00001), apply 110 lbs. (50 kg) force to pedal. Measure distance from top of brake pedal to six o'clock position of steering wheel.

2) Apply 5 lbs. (2.3 kg) force to brake pedal and measure pedal travel. Pedal travel should be 0.16-0.27" (4-7 mm). If pedal free play travel is not as specified, inspect pedal assembly for missing or worn bushings, or for bent or loose attaching bolts. There may also be air in hydraulic system. See BLEEDING BRAKE SYSTEM.

POWER BRAKE UNIT PUSH ROD

Aspire – This adjustment is normally required only when master cylinder is replaced. Remove master cylinder. See MASTER BRAKE CYLINDER under REMOVAL & INSTALLATION. Position Adjustment Gauge (T87C-2500-A) onto master cylinder. Loosen set screw on gauge. Position gauge plunger against bottom of primary piston. See Fig. 1. Invert gauge and position onto power booster. Observe clearance between gauge and power booster push rod. Adjust push rod length until clearance is zero.

Capri – Power brake push rod length is not adjustable.

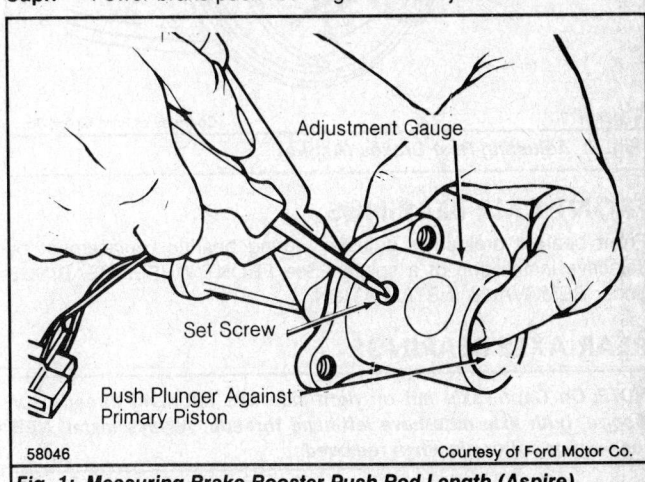

Adjustment Gauge

Set Screw

Push Plunger Against Primary Piston

58046

Courtesy of Ford Motor Co.

Fig. 1: *Measuring Brake Booster Push Rod Length (Aspire)*

PARKING/EMERGENCY BRAKE

Aspire – 1) Release parking brake. Remove parking brake console access cover. Remove locking clip from cable adjuster nut. Raise and support rear of vehicle. Tighten parking brake adjuster until slight drag is felt when rotating wheels.

2) Loosen adjuster in small increments until drag is eliminated. As parking brake lever is pulled upward, parking brake should lock rear wheels in 11-16 notches. Verify brake warning light operates when parking brake lever is raised.

Capri – 1) Release parking brake. Remove parking brake console. Loosen parking brake cable lock nut. Loosen or tighten adjustment nut so parking brake begins to apply when lever is pulled up 5 notches and is fully applied at 7-11 notches.

2) Using Spring Scale (T74P-3504-Y), measure force required to apply parking brake. A properly operating system will require 44 lb. (97 kg) of force to fully apply parking brakes. Tighten lock nut. Ensure brakes do not drag when parking brake lever is released. Verify brake warning light operates when parking brake lever is raised.

REAR BRAKE SHOES

NOTE: Rear brakes adjust themselves automatically as the vehicle is driven. Manual brake adjustment is necessary only after brake service, or if the adjuster has malfunctioned.

Aspire – 1) Remove rear brake drums and hold-down springs. See REAR BRAKE SHOES under REMOVAL & INSTALLATION. Apply small amount of Grease (ESA-M1C172-A) to shoe pads. Install hold-down springs.

2) Measure brake drum inside diameter with brake drum gauge. Measure diameter across brake shoes. Insert screwdriver into brake adjuster quadrant. *See Fig. 2.* Adjust shoes and linings to the same diameter as brake drum.

3) Install brake drum and wheel. Tighten nuts and bolts to specification. See TORQUE SPECIFICATIONS. Make final adjustment by applying brakes several times while driving vehicle forward and reverse.

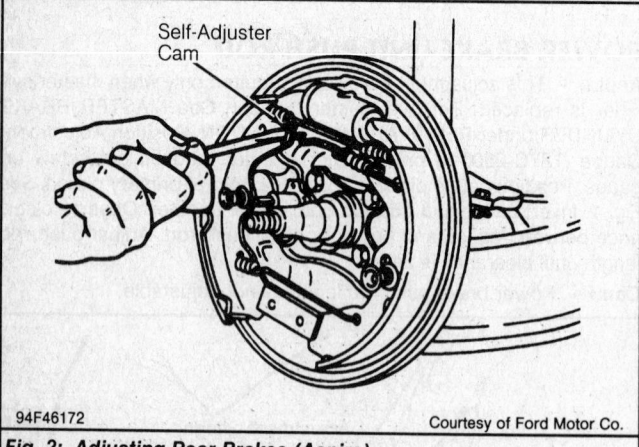

Self-Adjuster Cam

94F46172   Courtesy of Ford Motor Co.

Fig. 2: Adjusting Rear Brakes (Aspire)

FRONT AXLE BEARINGS

Front bearing preload is adjusted during bearing replacement by selective installation of a spacer. See FRONT WHEEL BEARINGS under REMOVAL & INSTALLATION.

REAR AXLE BEARINGS

NOTE: On Capri, axle nut on right side has left-hand threads. On Aspire, both axle nuts have left-hand threads. Always install NEW lock nut or cotter pin when removed.

Aspire – See REAR WHEEL BEARINGS under REMOVAL & INSTALLATION.

Capri – With bearings installed, tighten NEW lock nut to 18-22 ft. lbs. (24-30 N . m) while rotating wheel. Slightly loosen lock nut so it can be turned by hand. Install a lug nut into axle hub. Attach an INCH-lb. torque wrench to lug nut at 12 o'clock position. Measure bearing pre-load. Tighten lock nut until bearing preload, including seal drag, is 3.5-6.5 INCH lbs. (0.4-0.74 N . m). Stake NEW lock nut into notch on spindle, or install NEW cotter pin.

TESTING

POWER BRAKE UNIT

NOTE: Inspect all vacuum hoses for holes, collapsed areas, and secure connections. Ensure all unused vacuum ports are capped.

Functional Test – 1) Check master cylinder fluid level. Inspect hydraulic system for leaks. Set shifter lever to Neutral or Park position, turn ignition off, and apply parking brake. Pump brake pedal several times to eliminate vacuum from system, then press and hold pedal in down position.

2) Start and idle engine. If vacuum system is functioning properly, pedal will move downward under constant foot pressure. If no pedal motion occurs, vacuum booster is not functioning properly. Go to next step.

3) Run engine for at least one minute. Turn ignition off. Press brake pedal several times. Booster is okay if pedal stroke is long at first and becomes shorter with each stroke. If stroke does not shorten, inspect for a damaged, restricted, or improperly connected check valve vacuum hose. Repair and recheck. Go to next step.

4) Restart engine. Press and hold pedal down. Turn ignition off and wait 30 seconds. Booster is okay if pedal height remains unchanged. If pedal height changes, inspect for damaged, restricted, or improperly connected check valve or vacuum hose. Go to next step.

5) Connect pressure gauge to master cylinder output line. Connect vacuum gauge to booster. Connect Brake Pedal Effort Gauge (021-00001) to brake pedal. Bleed air from pressure gauge. Start engine. When vacuum gauge indicates 19.7 in. Hg, turn ignition off. Observe vacuum gauge for 15 seconds. Booster is okay if vacuum gauge indicates 18.7-19.7 in. Hg. If vacuum gauge indicates less than 18.7 in. Hg, go to next step.

6) Restart engine. Apply and hold 44 lbs. (20 kg) force to brake pedal. When vacuum gauge indicates 19.7 in. Hg, turn ignition off. Observe vacuum gauge for 15 seconds. Booster is okay if vacuum gauge indicates 18.7-19.7 in. Hg. If vacuum gauge indicates less than 18.7 in. Hg, go to next step.

7) With engine stopped and vacuum gauge at zero, observe pressure gauge. Apply 44 lbs. (20 kg) force to brake pedal. Observe pressure gauge. Booster is okay if pressure gauge indicates 256 psi (18 kg/cm²).

8) Release brake pedal. Start engine. When vacuum gauge indicates 19.7 in. Hg, apply 44 lbs. (20 kg) force to brake pedal. Booster is okay if pressure gauge indicates 768 psi (54 kg/cm²).

Diagnosis – If booster does not function properly, see TROUBLE SHOOTING article in GENERAL INFORMATION.

CHECK VALVE

1) On Aspire, check valve is integral with vacuum hose between power booster and intake manifold. On Capri, check valve is located on power brake booster.

2) To test valve, disconnect check valve vacuum hose from manifold. Alternately apply vacuum and pressure to hose. Air should flow only toward engine. If pressure by-passes check valve or if check valve blocks vacuum, replace hose and check valve.

REMOVAL & INSTALLATION

FRONT BRAKE CALIPER & PADS

Removal & Installation (Aspire) – 1) Remove approximately 1/3 of brake fluid from master cylinder reservoir. Raise and support front of vehicle. Remove wheels. Use "C" clamp to force piston into bore approximately 0.13" (3 mm). Remove anti-rattle clip and anti-rattle spring. Remove caliper pins. Remove brake pads and shims. DO NOT discard shims from inner brake pad.

2) To install brake caliper and pads, reverse removal procedure. Apply grease supplied with brake pad set to back of inner brake pad and both sides of inner shim. Install brake pad shims behind inner brake pads.

Removal & Installation (Capri) – 1) Raise and support front of vehicle. Remove wheels. Remove brake pad pin retainer spring. Remove brake pad pins. Remove brake pads and shims. Mark shims so they can be reinstalled in their original position. DO NOT discard shims from inner brake pad.

2) Remove anchor plate clips from anchor plate. Label anchor plate clip location for installation to original locations. Remove flex hose-to-caliper banjo bolt. Remove caliper retaining bolts and caliper.

3) To install, reverse removal procedure. Install brake pad shims behind inner brake pad. Install anchor plate clips in original locations. Install calipers with bleed screws in upward position to ensure proper bleeding of air.

FRONT BRAKE ROTOR

Removal (Aspire) – Remove front brake caliper. See FRONT BRAKE CALIPER & PADS. Remove rotor screws. Remove rotor. To install, reverse removal procedure.

Removal (Capri) – 1) Raise and support front of vehicle. Remove wheel. Unstake drive shaft nut tab. Remove and discard drive shaft nut. Separate tie rod end from knuckle.

2) Disconnect brake hose from strut (if necessary). Remove brake caliper from knuckle, and wire out of way. Remove nuts and bolts holding ball joint and strut to knuckle assembly.

3) Remove knuckle assembly from ball joint and drive shaft. If binding occurs, use a dual-jawed puller to force knuckle assembly from drive axle shaft.

NOTE: Hub and rotor are a matched and balanced assembly. Before removing rotor, locate paint or etch mark indicating proper hub-to-rotor alignment. If marks are not visible, mark hub and rotor for assembly alignment. Failure to properly align hub and rotor can result in an imbalance condition.

---

4) Using a puller, separate knuckle from wheel hub. Retain original outer bearing preload spacer to maintain bearing preload setting. If replacing bearing, install appropriate spacer to adjust bearing preload (if necessary). See FRONT WHEEL BEARINGS under REMOVAL & INSTALLATION. Scribe match marks on hub and rotor. Remove rotor bolts. Separate hub from rotor.

Installation – Align reference marks. Install rotor onto hub. Tighten bolts to 33-40 ft. lbs. (45-54 N.m). Press knuckle and preload spacer into wheel hub. To complete installation, reverse removal procedure. Tighten NEW axle shaft lock nut to 117-175 ft. lbs. (159-237 N.m).

REAR BRAKE CALIPER & PADS

Removal (Capri) – 1) Raise and support vehicle. Remove wheel. Remove parking brake return spring. Loosen parking brake cable housing adjuster nut. Disengage cable housing from bracket on lower control arm. Loosen parking brake cable bracket bolt. Disengage brake cable from caliper.

2) Remove lower caliper retaining bolt. Pivot caliper upward on upper caliper guide pin. Remove brake pad retaining spring, pads, and shims. Label anchor plate clip location for installation reference. If replacing rear brake pads only, reverse removal procedure to install. If removing caliper, go to next step.

3) Remove attaching clip from brake flex hose. Remove flex hose banjo bolt from caliper. Discard copper washers. Remove lower caliper retaining bolt. Using a cold chisel, remove upper caliper guide pin dust cap. Remove upper caliper guide pin. Lift caliper from rotor.

Installation – 1) To install, install brake pads and shims into caliper anchor plate. Remove upper guide pin and lower guide pin bushing from caliper. Remove guide pin and guide pin bushing dust boots.

Lubricate upper guide pin and lower guide pin bushing with Disc Brake Caliper Slide Grease (D7AZ-19590-A).

2) To complete installation, reverse removal procedure. To install caliper over new brake pads, it may be necessary to rotate caliper piston into caliper bore. Use NEW copper washers on flex hose. Bleed brakes, then pump brake pedal several times to seat pads.

REAR BRAKE ROTOR

Removal & Installation (Capri) – See REAR WHEEL BEARINGS under REMOVAL & INSTALLATION.

REAR BRAKE SHOES

Removal & Installation (Aspire) – 1) Raise and support vehicle. Release parking brake. Remove wheel. Remove hub grease cap. Remove nut cover. Unstake and remove axle nut (left-hand thread). Discard cotter pin. Remove brake drum, washer, outer bearing cone, and roller.

2) Remove hold-down springs and pins. Remove retracting springs. Remove shoes from backing plate. To install, reverse removal procedure. Apply brake grease to all shoe contact points on backing plate. See REAR BRAKE SHOES under ADJUSTMENTS.

REAR WHEEL CYLINDER

Removal & Installation (Aspire) – Remove rear brake shoes. Disconnect brakeline from wheel cylinder. Remove wheel cylinder. To install, reverse removal procedure. Bleed brake system.

MASTER BRAKE CYLINDER

Removal – Pump brake pedal several times to bleed vacuum from power booster. Disconnect low fluid level sensor wiring (if equipped). Drain some brake fluid from reservoir. Disconnect brakelines from master cylinder. Cap lines and master cylinder ports. Remove attaching nuts and master cylinder.

Installation – To install, reverse removal procedure. Tighten mounting nuts to 84-144 INCH lbs. (10-16 N.m). Fill master cylinder to proper level. Bleed hydraulic system (if necessary). On Capri, check stoplight switch adjustment. On Aspire, check push rod adjustment. See BRAKE PEDAL FREE PLAY under ADJUSTMENTS.

POWER BRAKE UNIT

Removal & Installation – Pump brake pedal several times to bleed vacuum from power booster. On Capri, remove battery. On all models, remove master cylinder. Disconnect vacuum line. Remove clevis pin at brake pedal. Remove power brake unit. To install, reverse removal procedure. Tighten mounting nuts to 14-19 ft. lbs. (19-26 N.m).

FRONT WHEEL BEARINGS

Removal – 1) Raise and support vehicle. Remove wheel. Raise staked edge of hub retainer flange. Remove and discard axle nut.

2) Remove brake hose clip at shock bracket. Remove anti-lock sensor (if equipped). Remove tie rod end nut. Separate tie rod end from knuckle.

3) Remove caliper bolts. Separate caliper from rotor. Suspend caliper out of work area with wire. Remove rotor screws and rotor.

4) Remove bolt and nut located at point where lower arm ball joint connects to front knuckle. Separate lower arm ball joint from lower arm. Remove spring and shock bracket bolts.

5) Remove knuckle and wheel hub assembly from drive shaft. Separate hub from knuckle with Puller (T87C-1104-A) and Hub Remover (T92C-1104-AH). Retain outer bearing retainer washer for use during reassembly. Press outer bearing cone and roller from shaft. Remove and discard inner and outer oil seals.

6) Pull bearing races from bores with Puller (T77F-1102-A) and slide hammer. If necessary, remove and discard rotor shield.

Adjustment – 1) Install Spacer Selector (T87-1104-B). *See Fig. 3.* Clamp bolt head in vise. Tighten nut in stages to 36 ft. lbs. (49 N.m), 72 ft. lbs. (98 N.m), 108 ft. lbs. (147 N.m), and 145 ft. lbs. (196 N.m). After tightening nut to each torque, seat bearings by rotating knuckle.

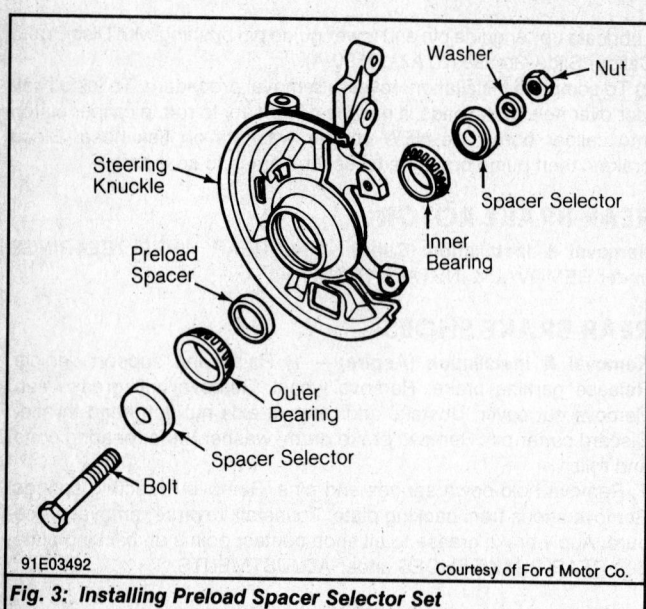

91E03492   Courtesy of Ford Motor Co.

Fig. 3: Installing Preload Spacer Selector Set

2) Remove knuckle and Spacer Selector from vise. Clamp knuckle in vise, in area of spring and shock mount.

NOTE: *Read torque wrench just as spacer selector starts to rotate.*

---

3) Using INCH-lb. torque wrench, measure torque to rotate spacer selector. If torque is 2.2-16 INCH lbs. (0.25-1.8 N.m), outer bearing retainer is of correct thickness. If torque is less than specified, install a thinner retainer washer. If torque is more than specified, install a thicker retainer washer.

4) Bearing spacers are available in various thicknesses. See PRELOAD SPACER table. Changing spacer thickness one number changes bearing preload 1.8-3.5 INCH lbs. (0.2-0.4 N.m). Install appropriate spacer to adjust preload to specification. Remove preload spacer selector set.

PRELOAD SPACER

Stamped Mark On Spacer	In. (mm)
1	0.2474 (6.285)
2	0.2490 (6.325)
3	0.2506 (6.365)
4	0.2522 (6.405)
5	0.2537 (6.445)
6	0.2553 (6.485)
7	0.2569 (6.525)
8	0.2585 (6.565)
9	0.2600 (6.605)
10	0.2616 (6.645)
11	0.2632 (6.685)
12	0.2648 (6.725)
13	0.2663 (6.765)
14	0.2679 (6.805)
15	0.2695 (6.845)
16	0.2711 (6.885)
17	0.2726 (6.925)
18	0.2742 (6.965)
19	0.2758 (7.005)
20	0.2774 (7.045)
21	0.2789 (7.085)

Installation – 1) Lubricate bearings with wheel bearing grease. Pack hub with grease in area of ends of rollers. Install inner bearing into steering knuckle. Install NEW inner bearing grease seal. Drive seal into place with seal installer.

2) Install original outer wheel bearing preload spacer (or spacer selected during preload adjustment procedure) into steering knuckle bore. Install outer wheel bearing into steering knuckle bore.

3) Liberally lubricate lip of NEW outer grease seal with grease. Drive seal into steering knuckle bore. Install brake rotor onto axle hub. Tighten bolts to 33-40 ft. lbs. (45-54 N.m). Position rotor/hub assembly into steering knuckle, and press assembly into place with adapter from spacer selector set. To complete installation, reverse removal procedure.

REAR WHEEL BEARINGS

Removal & Installation (Aspire) – 1) Raise and support rear axle. Remove wheel. Remove wheel bearing dust cap. Remove cotter pin, nut cover, and nut. Discard cotter pin.

2) Remove brake drum, washer, and bearings as an assembly. Remove outer cone, roller, and washer. Pry out and discard inner grease seal. Remove inner bearing. Mark bearings for installation reference if they are to be reinstalled.

3) Lubricate bearings with wheel bearing grease. Pack hub with grease in area of ends of rollers. Install inner bearing. Install NEW inner bearing grease seal. Drive seal into place with seal installer. To complete installation, reverse removal procedure. Adjust rear wheel bearing preload. See REAR AXLE BEARINGS under ADJUSTMENTS.

Removal & Installation (Capri) – 1) Raise and support rear axle. Remove wheel. Remove wheel bearing dust cap. Remove rear brake caliper. See REAR BRAKE CALIPER & PADS under REMOVAL & INSTALLATION. Carefully unstake rear axle lock nut, taking care not to damage threads on axle spindle. Remove and discard axle nut.

NOTE: *Axle lock nut on right side has left-hand threads. Always install NEW nut upon reassembly.*

---

2) Remove rotor/hub assembly. DO NOT allow outer wheel bearing to fall from hub. Remove inner bearing grease seal. Remove inner bearing. To install rear bearings, reverse removal procedure. Adjust rear wheel bearing preload. See REAR AXLE BEARINGS under ADJUSTMENTS.

OVERHAUL

NOTE: *See Figs. 4-10 for exploded views of brake assemblies and components.*

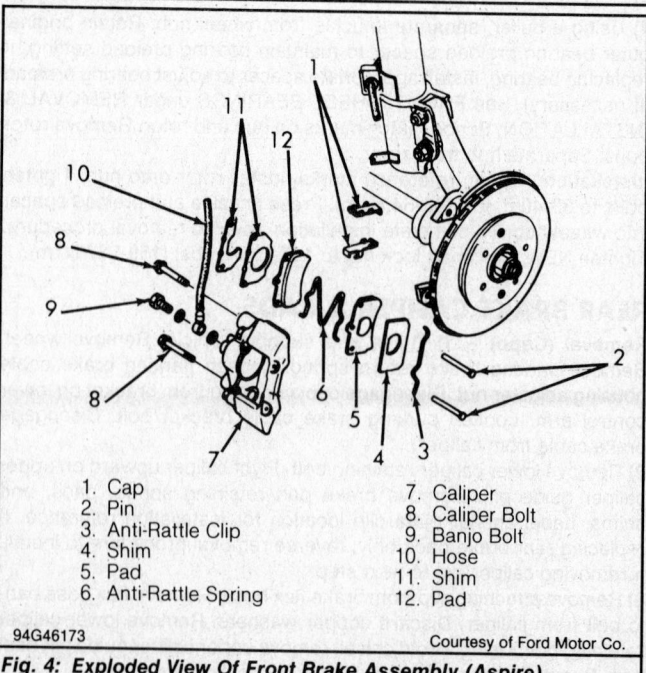

1. Cap	7. Caliper
2. Pin	8. Caliper Bolt
3. Anti-Rattle Clip	9. Banjo Bolt
4. Shim	10. Hose
5. Pad	11. Shim
6. Anti-Rattle Spring	12. Pad

94G46173   Courtesy of Ford Motor Co.

Fig. 4: Exploded View Of Front Brake Assembly (Aspire)

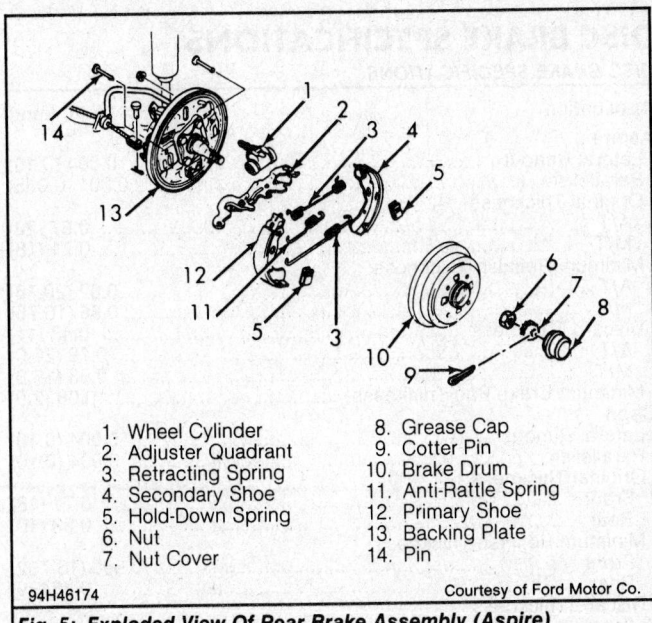

1. Wheel Cylinder
2. Adjuster Quadrant
3. Retracting Spring
4. Secondary Shoe
5. Hold-Down Spring
6. Nut
7. Nut Cover
8. Grease Cap
9. Cotter Pin
10. Brake Drum
11. Anti-Rattle Spring
12. Primary Shoe
13. Backing Plate
14. Pin

94H46174

Courtesy of Ford Motor Co.

Fig. 5: Exploded View Of Rear Brake Assembly (Aspire)

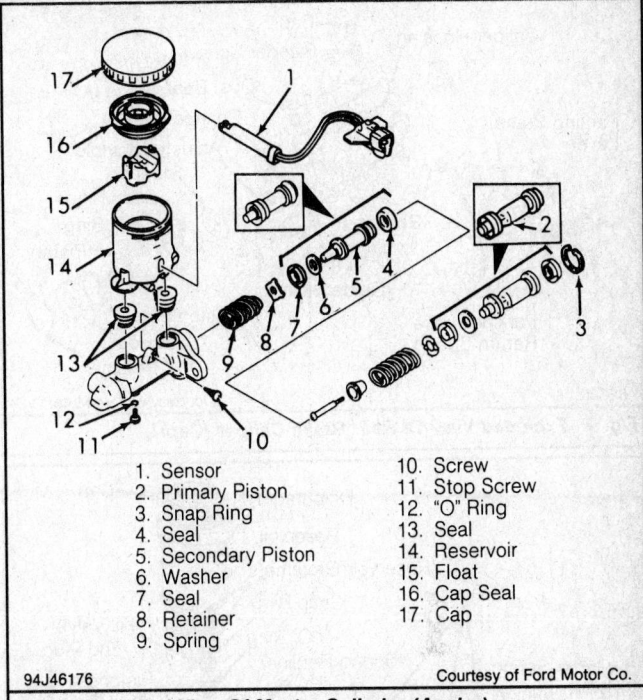

1. Sensor
2. Primary Piston
3. Snap Ring
4. Seal
5. Secondary Piston
6. Washer
7. Seal
8. Retainer
9. Spring
10. Screw
11. Stop Screw
12. "O" Ring
13. Seal
14. Reservoir
15. Float
16. Cap Seal
17. Cap

94J46176

Courtesy of Ford Motor Co.

Fig. 7: Exploded View Of Master Cylinder (Aspire)

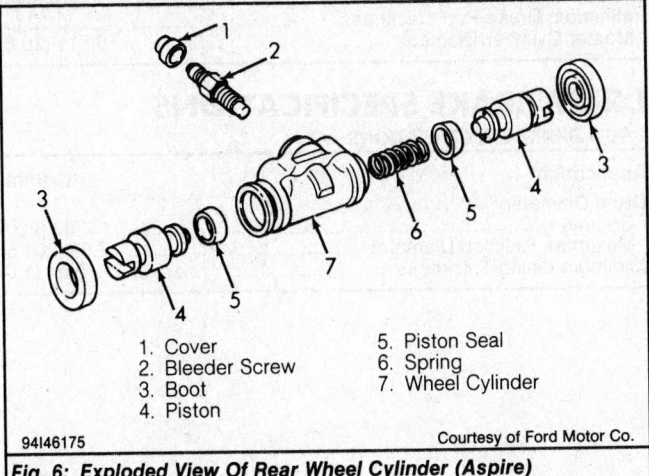

1. Cover
2. Bleeder Screw
3. Boot
4. Piston
5. Piston Seal
6. Spring
7. Wheel Cylinder

94I46175

Courtesy of Ford Motor Co.

Fig. 6: Exploded View Of Rear Wheel Cylinder (Aspire)

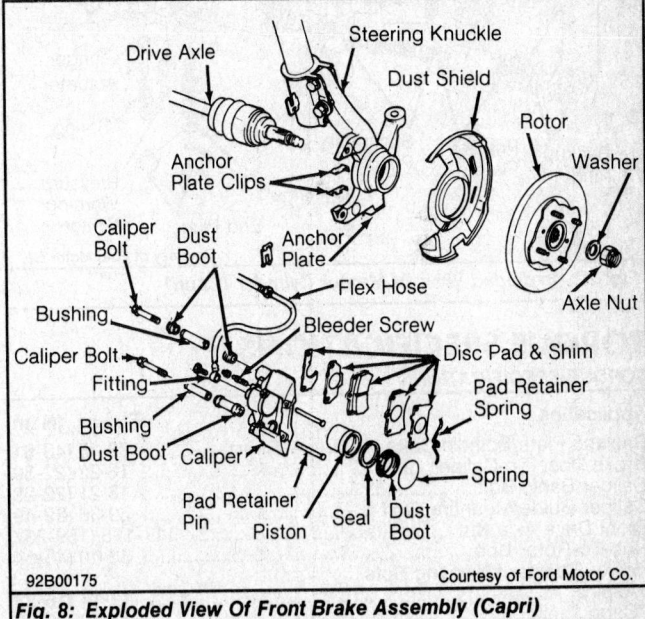

92B00175

Courtesy of Ford Motor Co.

Fig. 8: Exploded View Of Front Brake Assembly (Capri)

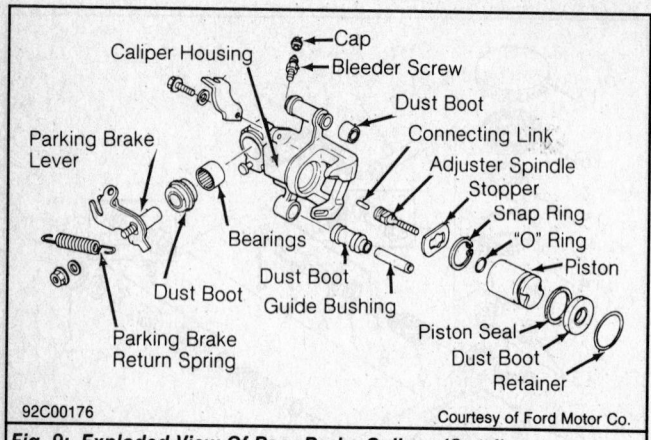

Fig. 9: Exploded View Of Rear Brake Caliper (Capri)

92C00176   Courtesy of Ford Motor Co.

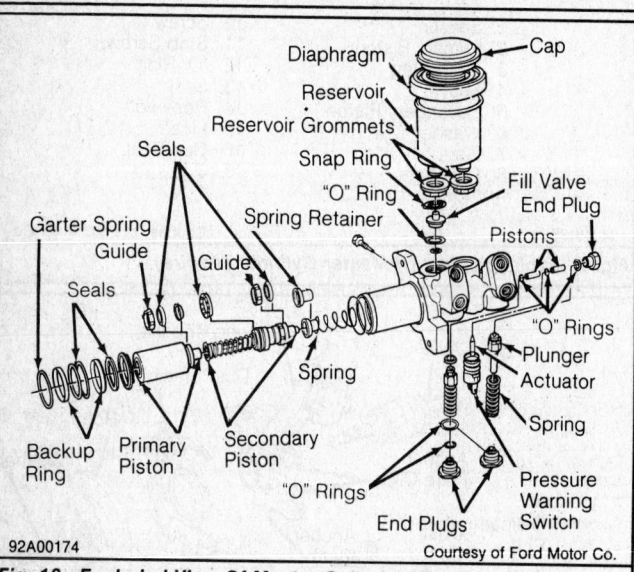

Fig. 10: Exploded View Of Master Cylinder (Capri)

92A00174   Courtesy of Ford Motor Co.

DISC BRAKE SPECIFICATIONS
DISC BRAKE SPECIFICATIONS

Application	In. (mm)
Aspire	
Lateral Runout	0.004 (0.10)
Parallelism	0.001 (0.025)
Original Thickness	
A/T	0.87 (22)
M/T	0.71 (18)
Minimum Refinish Thickness	
A/T	0.82 (20.76)
M/T	0.66 (16.76)
Discard Thickness	0.43 (11)
A/T	0.79 (20.0)
M/T	0.63 (16.0)
Minimum Brake Pad Thickness	0.08 (2.0)
Capri	
Lateral Runout	0.004 (0.10)
Parallelism	0.004 (0.10)
Original Thickness	
Front	0.71 (18)
Rear	0.39 (10)
Minimum Refinish Thickness	
Front	0.660 (16.762)
Rear	0.354 (9)
Discard Thickness	
Front	0.63 (16)
Rear	0.35 (9)
Minimum Brake Pad Thickness	0.12 (3)
Master Cylinder Diameter	0.811 (20.6)

DRUM BRAKE SPECIFICATIONS
DRUM BRAKE SPECIFICATIONS

Application	In. (mm)
Drum Diameter	
Original	7.87 (200)
Maximum Refinish Diameter	7.93 (201.5)
Minimum Lining Thickness	0.04 (1.0)

TORQUE SPECIFICATIONS
TORQUE SPECIFICATIONS

Application	Ft. Lbs. (N.m)
Backing Plate/Spindle Bolts (Aspire – Rear)	32-45 (43-61)
Brake Hose-To-Caliper	16-22 (22-30)
Caliper Banjo Bolt	16-21 (22-29)
Caliper Guide/Mounting Bolt	29-36 (39-49)
Front Drive Axle Nut	117-175 (159-237)
Hub-To-Rotor Bolt	33-40 (45-54)
Power Booster Mounting Nuts	
Aspire	12-17 (16-23)
Capri	14-19 (19-26)
Rear Axle Nut	[1]
Rear Strut/Spindle (Capri – Rear)	69-86 (93-117)
Rotor-To-Hub Bolts	33-40 (45-54)
Steering Knuckle-To-Control Arm	32-40 (43-54)
Steering Knuckle-To-Strut	69-86 (93-117)
Steering Knuckle-To-Tie Rod	21-33 (29-44)
Wheel Lug Nut	65-87 (88-118)
	INCH Lbs. (N.m)
Master Cylinder-To-Booster Nut	89-142 (10-16)
Wheel Cylinder Mounting Bolt	89-106 (10-12)

[1] – See REAR AXLE BEARINGS under ADJUSTMENTS.

Aspire

DESCRIPTION

The Anti-Lock Brake System (ABS) operates by modulating hydraulic pressure to individual brakes when one or more wheels approaches a slip condition. When necessary, the ABS module sends appropriate signals to solenoid valves in the hydraulic actuator. These valves control flow to the appropriate caliper or wheel cylinder to prevent further lock-up. *See Fig. 1.*

NOTE: For more information on brake system, see appropriate DISC & DRUM article.

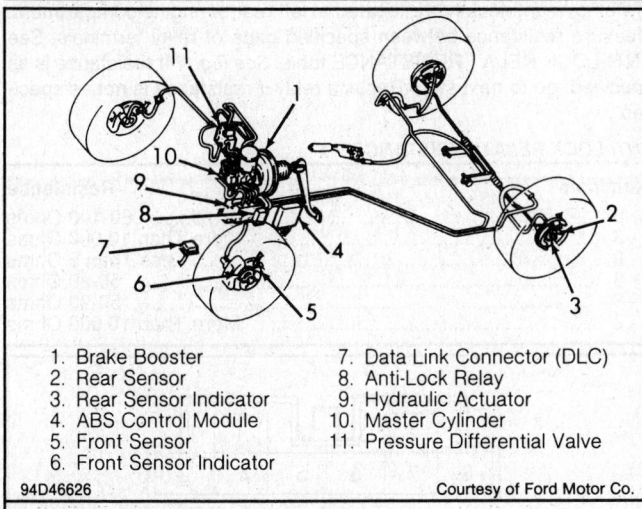

1. Brake Booster
2. Rear Sensor
3. Rear Sensor Indicator
4. ABS Control Module
5. Front Sensor
6. Front Sensor Indicator
7. Data Link Connector (DLC)
8. Anti-Lock Relay
9. Hydraulic Actuator
10. Master Cylinder
11. Pressure Differential Valve

94D46626   Courtesy of Ford Motor Co.

Fig. 1: Identifying ABS Components

OPERATION

HYDRAULIC ACTUATOR

Active components of the hydraulic actuator are a motor, pumps, and valves. When the control module senses impending wheel lock-up, it sends a signal to the appropriate valve within the hydraulic actuator to reduce pressure to the associated brake. The hydraulic actuator is located to the left of and below the master cylinder.

WHEEL SENSORS

Each wheel is equipped with a variable reluctance speed sensor. The wheel sensors send wheel speed signals to the ABS module.

ABS MODULE

The ABS module continuously monitors signals from the wheel cylinders. When it detects impending lock-up, it sends a signal to the hydraulic actuator to reduce pressure to the appropriate brake. The ABS module has self-diagnostic capabilities, and will store any trouble code it detects. When a code is stored in memory, the ANTI-LOCK warning light on the instrument panel will come on. The ABS module is located behind left side of instrument panel.

CAUTION: See ANTI-LOCK BRAKE SAFETY PRECAUTIONS article in GENERAL INFORMATION.

BLEEDING BRAKE SYSTEM

See appropriate DISC & DRUM article.

ADJUSTMENTS

See appropriate DISC & DRUM article.

TROUBLE SHOOTING

See DIAGNOSIS & TESTING.

ANTI-LOCK WARNING LIGHT

See DIAGNOSIS & TESTING.

DIAGNOSIS & TESTING

ABS FUNCTION TEST

1) Inspect system for sufficient fluid, leaks, or damaged components. Inspect fuses and wiring. Service as necessary. Drive vehicle to verify fault exists.

2) Apply parking brake. Shift transaxle into Park (A/T) or Neutral (M/T). Block drive wheels. Turn off all electrical loads.

3) Turn ignition on. Observe ANTI-LOCK LIGHT. If ANTI-LOCK light stays on, go to next step. If light does not come on, inspect METER fuse and light circuit, then go to PINPOINT TEST G. If light flashes continuously, check for short between pin TBS and ground at Data Link Connector (DLC), located near battery. If light comes on for about 1.5 seconds and then goes out, go to PINPOINT TEST F.

4) Start engine. Drive vehicle. If ANTI-LOCK warning light comes on, an ABS failure exists. If codes are to retrieved with Super STAR tester, go to step **5)**. If codes are to be retrieved with a VOM, go to step **6)**. If warning light does not come on, but ABS problems exist, go to PINPOINT TEST H.

6) Turn ignition off. Locate DLC. *See Fig. 2.* Connect Super STAR tester. Retrieve codes, following manufacturer's instructions.

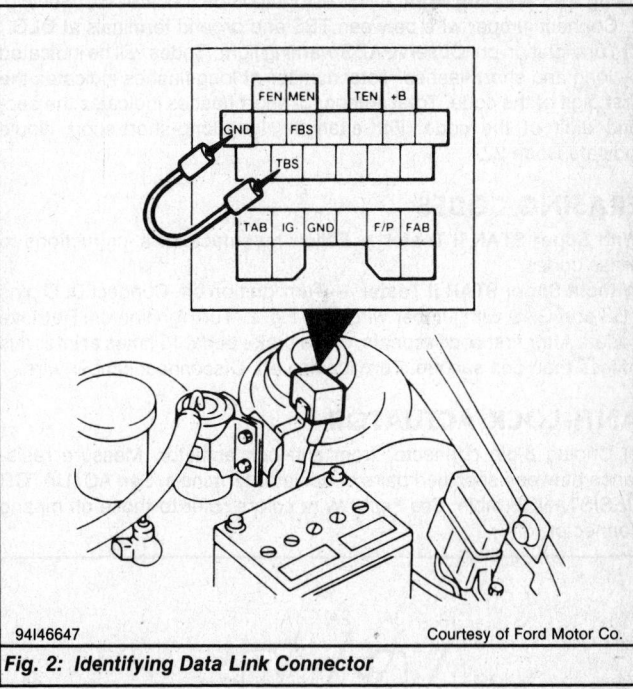

94I46647   Courtesy of Ford Motor Co.

Fig. 2: Identifying Data Link Connector

7) Turn ignition off. Connect jumper wire between TBS and ground terminals at DLC. Connect analog voltmeter between terminals FBS and GND terminals at DLC.

8) Turn ignition on. If using Super STAR tester, wait 2 seconds before turning tester on. Observe ANTI-LOCK warning light. If it flashes briefly, then goes out, ABS system is okay. If it remains on, record and erase codes, then retrieve and record codes again. See RETRIEVING CODES and ERASING CODES. If any codes still exist, go to next step. If warning light flashes codes, retrieve and record codes, then go to next step.

9) Erase codes. See ERASING CODES. Repeat step **5)** or **6)** as appropriate. With ignition on, tap, wiggle, and move suspected sensor and wiring harness. If any code resets, see ABS CODE IDENTIFICATION table for appropriate action. If no code sets, operation is normal. If intermittent condition cannot be duplicated, inspect all connections carefully.

ABS CODE IDENTIFICATION

Code Number	PINPOINT TEST
11	A
12	A
13	A
14	A
15	B
22	C
51	D
53	E
61	Replace ABS Module
No Code [1]	F

[1] – ABS warning light remains on.

RETRIEVING CODES

Using Super STAR II Tester – Follow manufacturer's instructions to retrieve codes.

Using VOM – 1) Turn ignition off. Locate Data Link Connector (DLC). *See Fig. 2.* Connect jumper wire between TBS and ground terminals at DLC. Connect analog voltmeter between FBS and ground terminals at DLC.

2) Turn ignition on. Codes will be indicated by long and short VOM needle sweeps. Total number of long sweeps indicates the first digit of the code. Total number of short sweeps indicates the second digit of the code. For example, long-long-short-short indicates Code 22.

Using ABS Warning Light – 1) Turn ignition off. Locate DLC. *See Fig. 2.* Connect jumper wire between TBS and ground terminals at DLC.

2) Turn ignition on. Observe ABS warning light. Codes will be indicated by long and short flashes. Total number of long flashes indicates the first digit of the code. Total number of short flashes indicates the second digit of the code. For example, long-long-short-short would indicate Code 22.

ERASING CODES

With Super STAR II Tester – Follow manufacturer's instructions to erase codes.

Without Super STAR II Tester – Turn ignition off. Connect DLC pins TBS and GND with jumper wire. *See Fig. 2.* Turn ignition on. Retrieve codes. After first code repeats, press brake pedal 10 times at intervals of less than one second. Turn ignition off. Disconnect jumper wire.

ANTI-LOCK ACTUATOR

1) Unplug 8-pin connector from anti-lock actuator. Measure resistance between specified pairs of actuator terminals. See ACTUATOR RESISTANCE table. *See Fig. 3* Wire colors refer to those on mating connector.

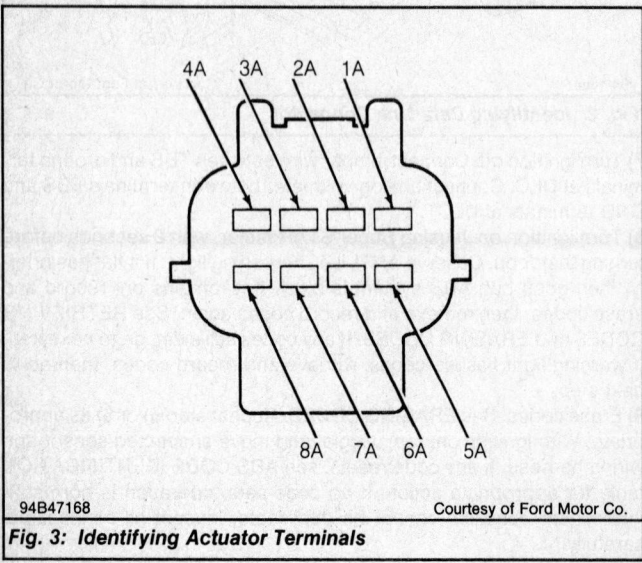

94B47168   Courtesy of Ford Motor Co.

Fig. 3: Identifying Actuator Terminals

2) If all resistances are approximately 3 ohms, return to appropriate PINPOINT TEST. Replace actuator if any resistance is not approximately 3 ohms.

ACTUATOR RESISTANCE

Terminals	Wire Colors
4 - 5	60-100 Ohms
1A - 3A	Yellow/White & Yellow/Green
5A - 7A	Yellow/White & Blue/Orange
2A - 4A	Yellow/White & Brown
6A - 8A	Yellow/White & Black/Yellow

ANTI-LOCK RELAY

1) Remove anti-lock relay, located at left rear of engine compartment. Measure resistance between specified pairs of relay terminals. See ANTI-LOCK RELAY RESISTANCE table. *See Fig. 4* If resistance is as specified, go to next step. Replace relay if resistance is not as specified.

ANTI-LOCK RELAY RESISTANCE

Terminals	Resistance
4 - 5	60-100 Ohms
1 - 3	More Than 10,000 Ohms
3 - 6	Less Than 5 Ohms
6 - 8	50-90 Ohms
3 - 8	50-90 Ohms
1 - 2	More Than 10,000 Ohms

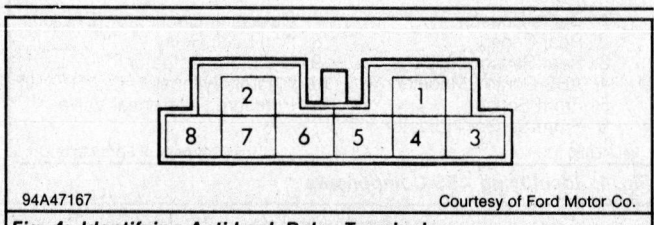

94A47167   Courtesy of Ford Motor Co.

Fig. 4: Identifying Anti-Lock Relay Terminals

2) Connect battery voltage to relay terminal No. 5. Connect terminal No. 4. to ground. Resistance between terminals No. 1 and No. 6 should be less than 5 ohms. Resistance between terminals No. 3 and No. 6 should be more than 10,000 ohms. If resistance is as specified, go to next step. Replace relay if resistance is not as specified.

3) Connect battery voltage to relay terminal No. 7. Connect terminal No. 8 to ground. Resistance between terminals No. 1 and No. 2 should be less than 5 ohms. If resistance is as specified, go to next step. Replace relay if resistance is not as specified.

4) Disconnect jumper wires from relay. Set DVOM to diode check mode. With positive lead of DVOM connected to relay terminal No. 7, and negative lead connected to terminal No. 6, continuity should exist. Transpose DVOM leads. Continuity should not exist. Replace relay if continuity is not as specified.

CONTINUOUS TEST

1) Connect Super Star II tester, or connect jumper wire to retrieve codes. See RETRIEVING CODES. If using Super Star II tester, set controls so that speaker is on.

2) Tap, move, and wiggle suspected sensor or harness, working in short sections from sensor to instrument cluster, and to ABS control module. Drive vehicle, if necessary. If any codes set, repair only the codes set during this test.

3) If no code sets, operation is normal. Turn off ignition. Inspect all wiring and connectors for faulty crimps, splices, corrosion, or improperly seated terminals. Repair as necessary.

WHEEL SPEED SENSORS

See DIAGNOSIS & TESTING.

PINPOINT TESTS

PINPOINT TEST A

ANTI-LOCK SENSORS

1) Inspect all wiring, brakelines, and other ABS components for visible physical deterioration or damage. If all is okay, go to next step. Make any necessary repairs.

2) Turn ignition off. Unplug connector from ABS control module, located behind left side of instrument panel. Measure resistance between ground and Yellow/Green, Green, White, and Yellow wires at harness connector. If any measurement is less than 10,000 ohms, repair shorted wire. If wire is okay, test appropriate wheel speed sensor for short to ground. See WIRING DIAGRAM.

3) Measure resistance between the following pairs of wires at harness connector: White and Red, Yellow and Orange, Yellow/Green and Yellow/Blue, and Green and Blue. If all measurements are 1600-2000 ohms, go to step **5)**. If any measurement is not 1600-2000 ohms, go to next step.

4) Unplug connector from appropriate wheel speed sensor. Measure sensor resistance between sensor terminals. If resistance is 1600-2000 ohms, repair appropriate wire between sensor and control module. If resistance is not 1600-2000 ohms, replace sensor. Measure resistance between either sensor terminal and ground. If resistance is less than 10,000 ohms, go to next step. If resistance is not less than 10,000 ohms, replace sensor.

5) Measure AC voltage between the following pairs of wires at harness connector while spinning appropriate wheel at approximately 50 RPM. Left front wheel: White and Red wires. Right front wheel: Yellow and Orange wires. Left rear wheel: Yellow/Green and Yellow/Blue wires. Right rear wheel: Green and Blue wires. If all measurements are 0.25-3.0 volts, go to step **7)**. If any measurement is not as specified, go to next step.

6) Remove appropriate wheel. Inspect for damage to sensor, or objects sticking to sensor. Ensure sensor bolt torque is 12-17 ft. lbs. (16-23 N.m). Verify clearance between sensor and toothed rotor is 0.012-0.043". If all is okay, replace sensor. If conditions are not as specified, replace components as appropriate.

7) Press brake pedal. If stoplights operate, go to next step. If stoplights do not operate, repair as necessary.

8) Unplug ABS control module connector. Turn ignition on. Measure voltage on Green wire at module harness connector. With brake pedal pressed, battery voltage should exist. With brake pedal released, voltage should be 0-2 volts. Repair Green wire between stoplight switch and ABS control module if voltage is not as specified.

PINPOINT TEST B

ANTI-LOCK SENSOR OPEN CIRCUIT

Drive vehicle at 6 MPH (10 KM/H). Retrieve codes. If Code 11, 12, or 13 appears, go to PINPOINT TEST A. If no code appears, go to CONTINUOUS TEST. If Code 15 appears, substitute known good ABS control module and repeat this test.

PINPOINT TEST C

SOLENOID VALVE

1) Inspect all wiring, brakelines, and other ABS components for visible physical deterioration or damage. If all is okay, go to next step. Make any necessary repairs.

2) Turn ignition on. Measure voltage on Yellow/White wire at ABS control module, leaving connector attached to module. If battery voltage exists, go to next step. If battery voltage does not exist, repair Yellow/White wire between anti-lock relay and module.

3) Turn ignition off. Unplug connector from ABS control module. Measure resistance between Yellow/White wire and the following wires: Yellow/Green wire (left front), Blue/Orange wire (right front), Brown wire (left rear), and Black/Yellow wire (right rear). If any measurement is not about 3 ohms, go to ANTI-LOCK ACTUATOR under DIAGNOSIS & TESTING. If measurements are as specified, go to PINPOINT TEST H.

PINPOINT TEST D

FAIL-SAFE RELAY

1) Inspect all wiring, brakelines, and other ABS components for visible physical deterioration or damage. If all is okay, go to next step. Make any necessary repairs.

2) Inspect ABS fuse in main fuse junction panel. Inspect METER fuse in interior fuse panel. If fuses are okay, go to next step. Replace fuses as necessary.

3) Turn ignition off. Unplug ABS control module. Turn ignition on. Temporarily ground Black/Blue wire at harness connector. If relay clicks, go to next step. If relay does not click, inspect Black/Blue wire for open between anti-lock relay and ABS control module. Repair wire if necessary. If wire is okay, go to step **6)**.

4) Turn ignition on. Temporarily ground Black/Blue wire at harness connector. Observe ANTI-LOCK warning light. If light is not on, go to next step. If light is on, go to step **6)**.

5) Turn ignition on. Temporarily ground Black/Blue wire at harness connector. Measure voltage on Yellow/White wire at harness connector. If battery voltage does not exist, go to next step. If battery voltage exists and you were not directed here from PINPOINT TEST E, go to PINPOINT TEST G. Return to PINPOINT TEST E if directed here from there.

6) Go to ANTI-LOCK RELAY under DIAGNOSIS & TESTING. If anti-lock relay is okay, repair Yellow/White wire between anti-lock relay and ABS control module. Replace relay if defective.

PINPOINT TEST E

MOTOR AND MOTOR RELAY

CAUTION: While performing this test, DO NOT allow motor to run for longer than 2 seconds.

1) Perform PINPOINT TEST D. If fail-safe relay is okay, go to next step. Replace fail-safe relay if defective.

2) Inspect all wiring, brakelines, and other ABS components for visible physical deterioration or damage. If all is okay, go to next step. Make any necessary repairs.

3) Turn ignition off. Unplug ABS control module connector. Turn ignition on. Temporarily ground Black/Blue wire at harness connector. Temporarily ground Blue/Red wire at harness connector for no longer than 2 seconds. If relay does not click and motor does not operate, go to next step. If relay clicks but motor does not operate, go to step **5)**. If relay clicks and motor operates, go to step **8)**.

4) Go to ANTI-LOCK RELAY under DIAGNOSIS & TESTING. If anti-lock relay is okay, go to next step. Replace relay if it is defective.

5) Turn ignition off. Unplug 2-pin motor connector from anti-lock actuator. Measure resistance between Red/Yellow and Black motor wires. If resistance is less than one ohm, go to next step. If resistance is not less than one ohm, replace actuator.

6) Using fused jumper wire, apply battery voltage to Red/Yellow wire at motor connector. Temporarily ground Black wire at motor connector for no longer than 2 seconds. If motor runs, go to next step. If motor does not run, replace actuator.

7) Disconnect jumper wires. Measure resistance between Black wire at motor harness connector and ground. If resistance is less than 5 ohms, repair Red/Yellow wire between anti-lock relay and anti-lock actuator. If resistance is not less than 5 ohms, repair Black wire to ground.

8) Turn ignition off. Connect wiring to anti-lock actuator. Unplug connector from ABS control module. Measure resistance between Red/Yellow wire at harness connector and ground. If resistance is less than one ohm, go to PINPOINT TEST G. If resistance is not less than one ohm, repair Red/Yellow wire between ABS control module and anti-lock actuator.

PINPOINT TEST F

GENERATOR

1) Measure voltage at battery terminals. If voltage is at least 11.5 volts, go to next step. If voltage is less than specified, charge or replace battery as necessary.

2) Turn ignition on. Measure voltage by backprobing Black/White wire terminal at ABS control module. Battery voltage should exist. Turn ignition off. Again measure voltage. No voltage should exist. If voltages are as specified, go to next step. If voltages are not as specified, repair Black/White wire between fuse panel and control module.

3) Start and idle engine. Measure voltage at Brown wire at alternator. Voltage should be about 13-14 volts. With ignition on and engine not running, voltage should be about one volt. If voltage is as specified, go to next step. If voltage is not as specified, repair or replace alternator.

4) Start and idle engine. Measure voltage at Brown wire at ABS module connector. Battery voltage should exist. With ignition on and engine not running, voltage should be about one volt. If voltage is as specified, go to PINPOINT TEST G. If voltage is not as specified, repair Brown wire between alternator and ABS control module.

PINPOINT TEST G
WARNING INDICATOR

1) Turn ignition off. Unplug ABS control module connector. Turn ignition on. If ANTI-LOCK warning light comes on, go to next step. If warning light does not come on, inspect METER fuse and bulb. If fuse and bulb are okay, repair Black/Yellow wire between instrument cluster and anti-lock relay.

2) With ABS control module disconnected, turn ignition on. Unplug anti-lock relay. If warning light goes out, go to next step. If warning light does not go out, repair grounded Pink wire between instrument cluster and anti-lock relay.

3) Leave ABS control module and anti-lock relay disconnected. Turn ignition on. Connect Blue/Yellow wire at anti-lock relay to ground, then repeat Blue/Yellow at ABS module to ground. If ANTI-LOCK warning light comes on for both connections, go to next step. If light does not come on at all, inspect METER fuse, bulb, or Blue/Yellow wires. Repair as necessary. If light comes on when only one Blue/Yellow wire is grounded, repair the other Blue/Yellow wire.

4) Turn ignition off. Leave ABS module disconnected. Measure resistance of Black wire between harness connector and ground. If resistance is less than 5 ohms, replace ABS control module. If resistance is not less than 5 ohms, repair Black wire to ground.

PINPOINT TEST H
HYDRAULIC SYSTEM

NOTE: An assistant is necessary to perform this test

1) Inspect all wiring, brakelines, and other ABS components for visible physical deterioration or damage. If all is okay, go to next step. Make any necessary repairs.

2) Raise and support vehicle. Set transaxle to Neutral range. Release parking brake. Ensure brakes do not drag. Locate Data Link Connector (DLC) at left side of engine compartment. Connect jumper wire between DLC terminals TBS and GND. Press brake pedal. Ensure that wheels do not rotate. With brakes still applied, turn ignition on. Attempt to rotate each wheel in turn. If pressure is released within 0.5 second, and wheel rotates when pressure reduction occurs. *See Fig. H*

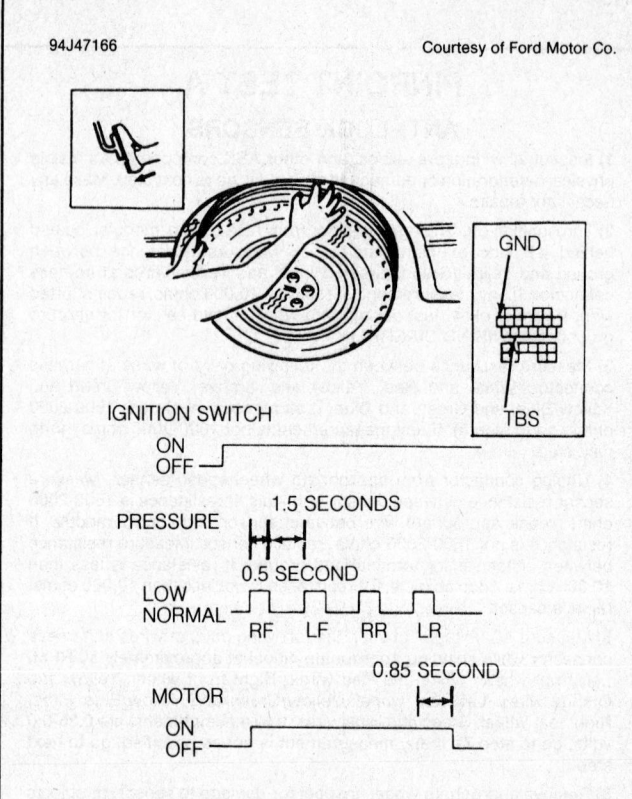

Fig. H: Testing Anti-Lock Brakes

If pressure reduction occurs properly, ABS system is functioning normally. Return to PINPOINT TEST A if directed here from there. Return to PINPOINT TEST C if directed here from there. If pressure reduction does not occur, inspect hydraulic system and all ABS wiring. If okay, replace ABS control module.

REMOVAL & INSTALLATION

ABS CONTROL MODULE

Removal & Installation – Disconnect negative battery cable. Unplug connectors. Remove module. To install, reverse removal procedure.

HYDRAULIC ACTUATOR

Removal & Installation – Remove battery. Separate connectors from bracket. Unplug connectors. Note brakeline routing for assembly reference. Disconnect brakelines. Remove actuator. To install, reverse removal procedure. Tighten brakeline fittings to 10-15 ft. lbs. (16-23 N.m). Bleed brakes. See appropriate DISK & DRUM article.

WHEEL SPEED SENSOR

Removal & Installation (Front) – 1) Disconnect negative battery cable. Unplug sensor connector. Disengage grommet. Raise and support vehicle.

2) Remove wheel and tire. Remove harness support bolts. Remove sensor bolts. Remove sensor. To install, reverse removal procedure. Tighten sensor bolts to 12-17 ft. lbs. (16-23 N.m).

Removal & Installation (Rear) – 1) Disconnect negative battery cable. Remove quarter trim panel. Unplug sensor connector. Disengage grommet. Raise and support vehicle.

2) Remove wheel and tire. Remove brake drum. Remove harness bolts. Remove sensor bolts. Remove sensor. To install, reverse removal procedure. Tighten sensor bolts to 12-17 ft. lbs. (16-23 N.m).

TORQUE SPECIFICATIONS

TORQUE SPECIFICATIONS

Application	Ft. Lbs. (N.m)
Actuator Nuts	14-16 (19-22)
Brakeline Fitting	10-15 (13-21)
Wheel Sensor Bolt	12-17 (16-23)
Wheel Lug Nuts	65-87 (88-118)

WIRING DIAGRAM

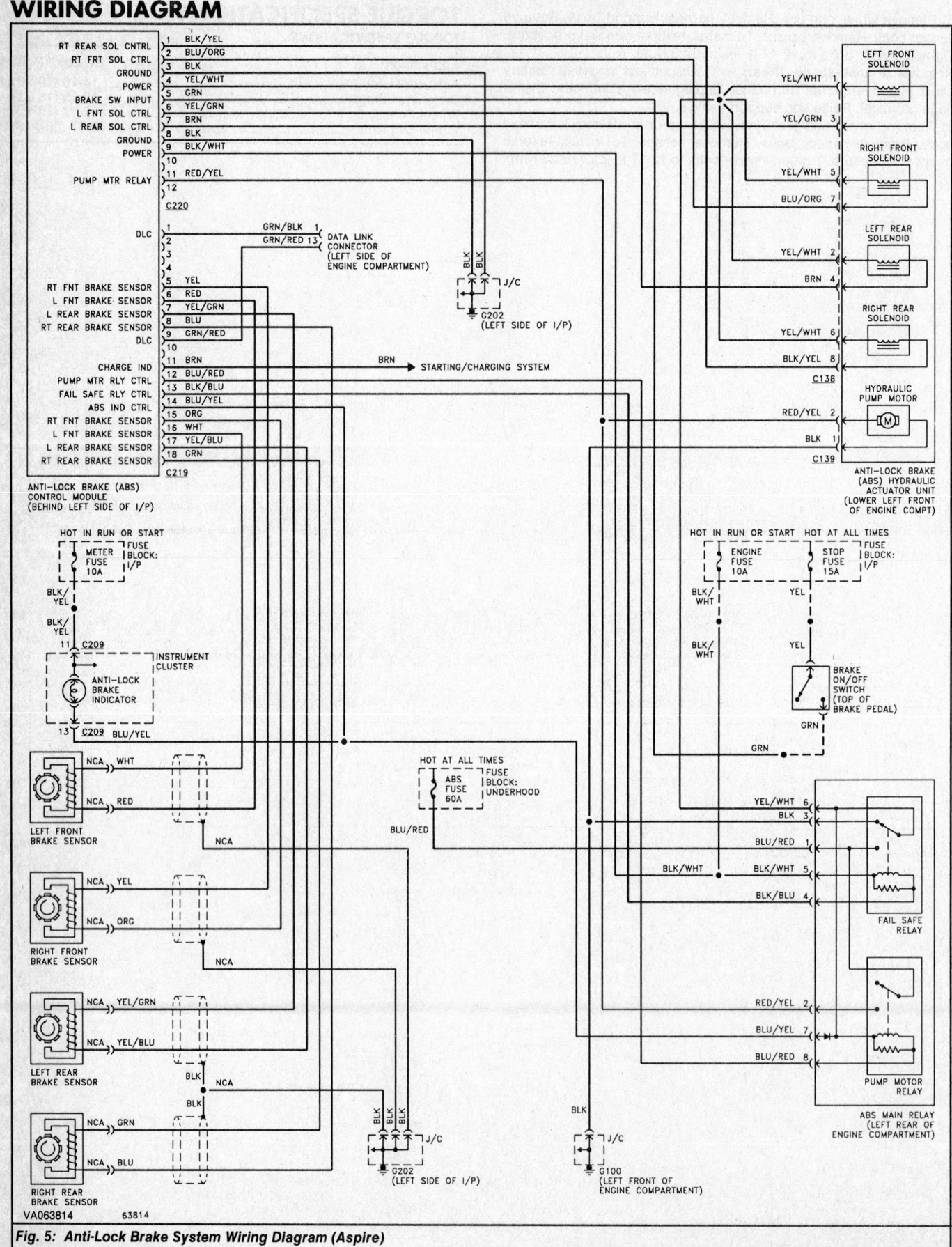

Fig. 5: Anti-Lock Brake System Wiring Diagram (Aspire)

VA063814   63814

Aspire, Capri

NOTE: *Prior to performing wheel alignment, perform preliminary visual and mechanical inspection of wheels, tires and suspension components. See PRE-ALIGNMENT INSTRUCTIONS in WHEEL ALIGNMENT THEORY & OPERATION article in GENERAL INFORMATION.*

RIDING HEIGHT ADJUSTMENT

Aspire – 1) Check tire pressure and adjust as necessary. Ensure wheel bearing play is correct. Place vehicle on level ground. Remove any unusually heavy items before checking suspension.
2) Measure height from highest point of fender cutout to wheel center. *See Fig. 1.* Compare left and right side measurements at both front and rear. Side-to-side variation should not exceed 0.4" (10 mm). If riding height is not within specification, check for spring damage or sag.

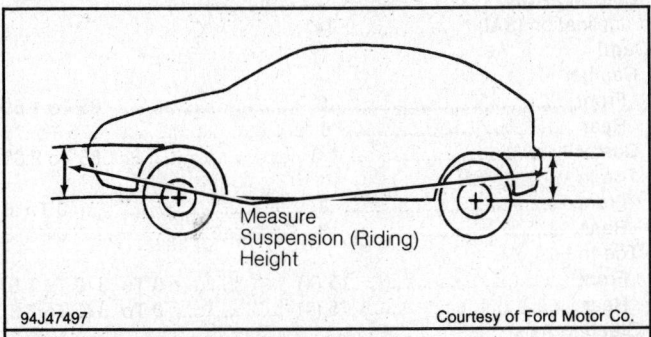

94J47497   Courtesy of Ford Motor Co.

Fig. 1: Measuring Riding Height (Aspire)

Capri – 1) Before adjusting alignment, check riding height. Riding height must be checked with vehicle on level floor and tires properly inflated. Bounce vehicle several times and allow suspension to settle.
2) Visually inspect vehicle for signs of abnormal height from front to rear or side to side. Check passenger and luggage compartments for extra heavy items and remove if present. If riding height is not within specification, check, repair or replace suspension components. Riding height between left and right side of vehicle should vary less than 1" (25.4 mm).

JACKING & HOISTING

FLOOR JACK

Aspire – When using floor jack other than jack supplied with vehicle, place jack at points indicated in illustration. *See Fig. 2.* Use two safety stands on each side of vehicle body once vehicle has been raised with jack.
Capri – When using floor jack other than jack supplied with vehicle, place jack at front of engine mount member and center of rear crossmember. Use two safety stands on each side of vehicle body once vehicle has been raised with jack.

HOIST

Aspire & Capri – When using frame-contact hoist, adapters should be placed at all four contact points shown in illustration. *See Fig. 2.* Position adapter so they are centered on the contact points. When using a twin-post hoist, place lifting pads on side sills of vehicle body.

EMERGENCY JACKING

CAUTION: *Service jack is intended for EMERGENCY use only. Under no circumstances should vehicle ever be lifted by front or rear control arms, half-shafts or CV joints, or trailing links. Severe damage to vehicle could result.*

ALIGNMENT PROCEDURES

NOTE: *Where possible, rear alignment corrections should be made before front corrections are made.*

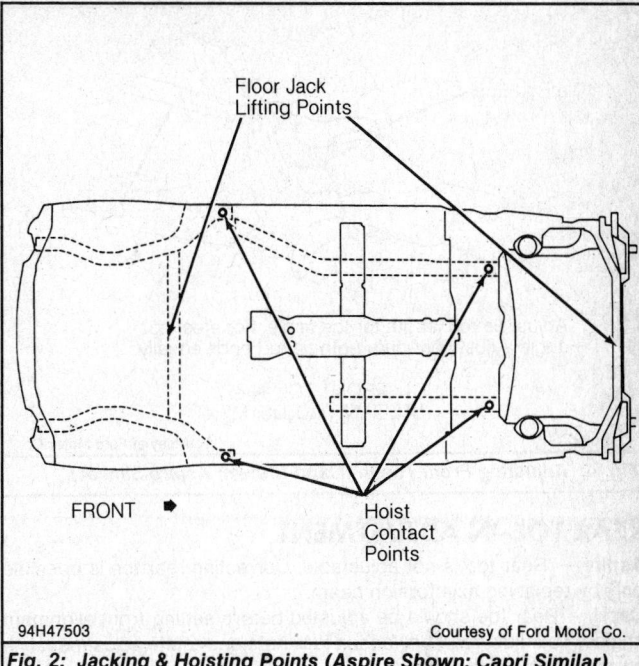

94H47503   Courtesy of Ford Motor Co.

Fig. 2: Jacking & Hoisting Points (Aspire Shown; Capri Similar)

CASTER ADJUSTMENT

Caster is permanently set at factory and is not adjustable. Caster should be checked however as a possible cause of suspension problem.

CAMBER ADJUSTMENT

Aspire – Adjustment information is not available from manufacturer.
Capri – To adjust camber, raise vehicle and remove front wheel. Remove 4 top strut mounting nuts and lower strut. Rotate strut bearing 180 degrees. *see Fig. 3.* This will change camber approximately 1/2 degree. Bounce vehicle 3 or more times to normalize wheel position, and recheck camber setting.

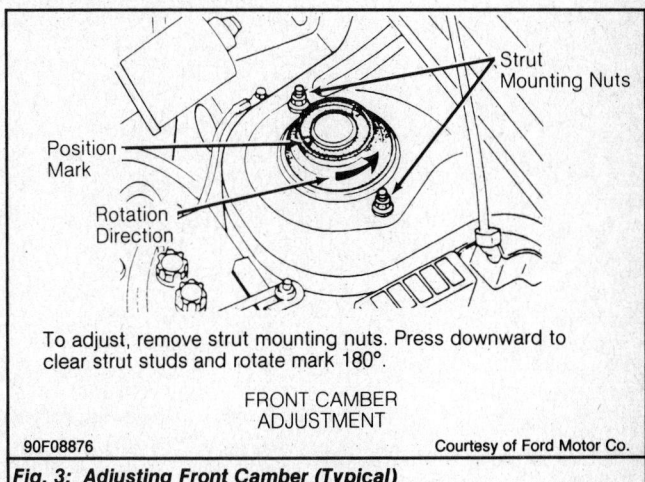

To adjust, remove strut mounting nuts. Press downward to clear strut studs and rotate mark 180°.

FRONT CAMBER ADJUSTMENT

90F08876   Courtesy of Ford Motor Co.

Fig. 3: Adjusting Front Camber (Typical)

FRONT TOE-IN ADJUSTMENT

Aspire – Front toe-in is adjusted by turning tie rods equally until adjustment is correct. Additional information is not available from manufacturer.
Capri – Center and lock steering wheel. Loosen tie rod end jam nuts. Release steering gear boot clips and ensure boots do not twist when tie rods are turned. *See Fig. 4.* Turn both tie rods equally until adjustment is correct. Tighten jam nuts to specification and install boot clips.

1994 WHEEL ALIGNMENT
Specifications & Procedures (Cont.)

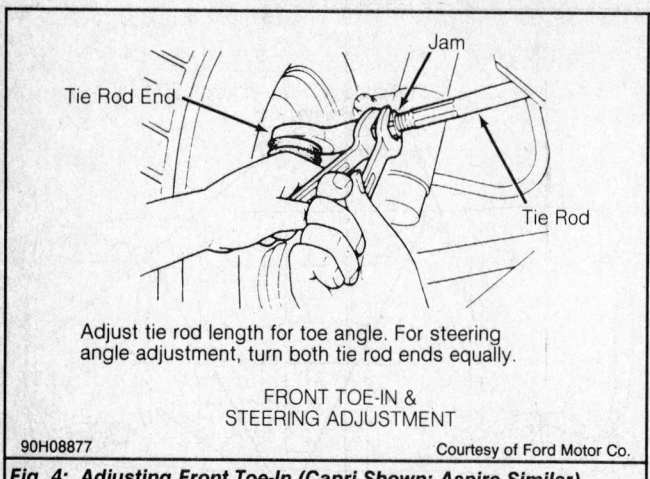

Adjust tie rod length for toe angle. For steering angle adjustment, turn both tie rod ends equally.

FRONT TOE-IN &
STEERING ADJUSTMENT

90H08877   Courtesy of Ford Motor Co.

Fig. 4: Adjusting Front Toe-In (Capri Shown; Aspire Similar)

REAR TOE-IN ADJUSTMENT

Aspire – Rear toe is not adjustable. Correcting rear toe is possible only by replacing axle torsion beam.
Capri – Rear toe should be adjusted before setting front alignment angles. To adjust rear toe, loosen lock nuts and rotate adjustment link on rear control arms.

TORQUE SPECIFICATIONS
TORQUE SPECIFICATIONS

Application	Ft. Lbs. (N.m)
Strut Upper Mounting Nuts	
Aspire	34-46 (46-62)
Capri	17-21 (23-29)
Tie Rod Jamb Nut	
Aspire	22-37 (30-50)
Capri	
Front	26-30 (35-40)
Rear	41-47 (55-64)
Wheel Lug Nuts	66-87 (89-118)

WHEEL ALIGNMENT SPECIFICATIONS
WHEEL ALIGNMENT SPECIFICATIONS

Application	Preferred	Range
Aspire		
Camber [1]		
Front	.83	.08 To 1.58
Rear	.25	-1 To .5
Caster [1]	1.67	.92 To 2.42
Toe-In [1]		
Front	.28	.04 To .52
Rear	.24	0 To .48
Toe-In [2]		
Front	.14 (3.5)	.02 To .26 (.5 To 6.5)
Rear	.12 (3)	0 To .24 (0 To 6)
Steering Axis		
Inclination (SAI) [1]	14	
Capri		
Camber [1]		
Front	.8	.05 To 1.55
Rear	0	-.75 To .75
Caster [1]	1.6	.85 To 2.35
Toe-In [1]		
Front	.3	0 To .6
Rear	.3	0 To .6
Toe-In [2]		
Front	.15 (4)	0 To .3 (0 To 7.5)
Rear	.15 (4)	0 To .3 (0 To 7.5)
Steering Axis		
Inclination (SAI) [1]	12.36	

[1] – Measurement in degrees.
[2] – Measurement in inches (mm).

Aspire, Capri

DESCRIPTION

Front suspension system uses MacPherson struts. Upper ends of struts are attached to shock towers, and lower ends are attached to steering knuckle. Steering knuckle attaches to lower control arm at ball joint. Lower control arm is attached to chassis. Sway is controlled by a stabilizer bar. *See Figs. 1 and 2.*

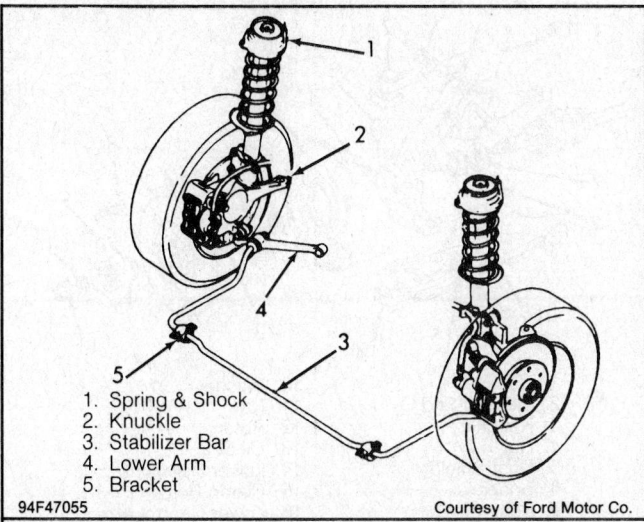

1. Spring & Shock
2. Knuckle
3. Stabilizer Bar
4. Lower Arm
5. Bracket

94F47055   Courtesy of Ford Motor Co.

Fig. 1: Identifying Front Suspension Components (Aspire)

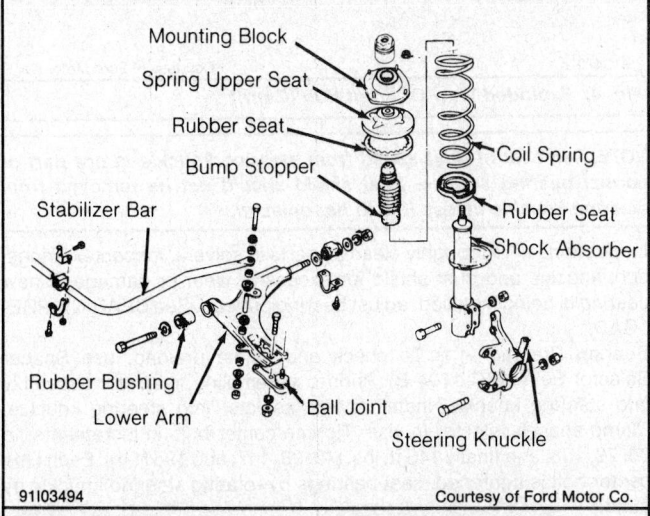

91I03494   Courtesy of Ford Motor Co.

Fig. 2: Identifying Front Suspension Components (Capri)

ADJUSTMENTS & INSPECTION

WHEEL ALIGNMENT
SPECIFICATIONS & PROCEDURES

NOTE: See SPECIFICATIONS & PROCEDURES article in WHEEL ALIGNMENT.

WHEEL BEARINGS

Wheel bearing preload is maintained by a selective spacer in steering knuckle, between inner and outer hub bearings. For adjustment procedures and inspection, see WHEEL BEARING under REMOVAL & INSTALLATION.

BALL JOINT CHECKING

Raise and support vehicle until tire is just clear of ground. Move wheel vertically while inspecting for play. If play exists between steering knuckle and control arm, replace ball joint. If play exists but ball joint is okay, wheel bearings should be checked for wear and correct preload. Replace wheel bearing if necessary.

REMOVAL & INSTALLATION

STABILIZER BAR

Removal (Aspire) – Raise and support vehicle. Remove stabilizer bar brackets. Remove insulators. Remove cotter pins and stabilizer bar nuts at front suspension lower arms. Remove rear washers and bushings. Pull stabilizer bar forward to remove.
Installation – 1) Install bushings and washers onto stabilizer bar. Insert stabilizer ends into lower arms. Position rear half of bushings and washers onto stabilizer bar ends. Install nuts finger tight.
2) Install insulators onto crossbar with split side forward, next to White locating marks. Install brackets. Tighten nuts to specification. See TORQUE SPECIFICATIONS. Install NEW cotter pins.
Removal & Installation (Capri) – 1) Remove stabilizer bar-to-control arm attaching bolts, nuts, washers, and bushings. Remove stabilizer frame mounting brackets. Remove split bushings from stabilizer bar.
2) To install, reverse removal procedure. Tighten frame mounting nuts to 32-39 ft. lbs. (44-55 N.m). Tighten stabilizer bar to control arm link until 0.43" (10.8 mm) of threads extend beyond nut.

STRUT ASSEMBLY & COIL SPRING

Removal – 1) Raise and support front of vehicle so struts are fully extended. Remove front wheels. Remove brake line clip from strut lower mounting bracket. Disengage brakeline. Mark strut mounting block and strut tower for reassembly reference.
2) Remove 2 bolts retaining strut lower bracket to steering knuckle. Working from inside engine compartment, remove nuts retaining strut mounting block in strut tower. Disengage strut lower bracket from steering knuckle. Lower strut from vehicle.
Disassembly & Reassembly – 1) Compress spring to unload strut. Pry out mounting block cap. Remove strut upper nut and lock washer.
2) Remove strut mounting block and spacer plate. Remove washer, bearing seal, and bearing from strut rod. Remove spring upper seat, seat insulator and coil spring. Remove jounce bumper and dust shield. Reverse disassembly procedure to install coil spring and reassemble strut. Tighten strut rod nut to 40-50 ft. lbs. (54-67 N.m) on Aspire, or 22-27 ft. lbs. (29-36 N.m) on Capri.
Installation – 1) Install spacer onto strut. Position strut into strut tower, with reference marks aligned. Install and tighten nuts on upper mounting block studs. Tighten nuts to 34-46 ft. lbs. (46-63 N.m) on Aspire, or 17-22 ft. lbs. (23-29 N.m) on Capri.
2) Install steering knuckle into strut lower bracket. To complete installation, reverse removal procedure. Tighten bolts and nuts to 69-86 ft. lbs. (93-117 N.m) on all models.

HUB & KNUCKLE ASSEMBLY

Removal – 1) Raise and support vehicle. Remove wheel. Apply brakes to prevent hub from rotating. Remove and discard drive axle lock nut.

NOTE: See ACCESSORIES & EQUIPMENT supplement. Always use a NEW drive axle lock nut when servicing hub or drive axle.

2) Remove clip which secures brake hose to strut bracket. Separate tie rod end from steering knuckle. Remove brake caliper and wire aside. Do not allow caliper to hang by brake hose.
3) Remove clamp bolt and nut where lower control arm ball joint connects to steering knuckle. On Capri, remove stabilizer link.
4) On all models, pry lower control arm downward. Separate ball joint from steering knuckle. Remove bolts attaching steering knuckle between flanges of strut bracket. Slide hub/knuckle assembly from end of drive axle. If binding occurs or hub is frozen to drive axle, use a hub puller to press axle from hub.

Installation – 1) Apply a thin coat of SAE 30 oil to drive axle splines. Slide hub/knuckle assembly onto drive axle. Stop at area where uppermost arm of steering knuckle seats into strut bracket. Install and tighten strut bracket nuts and bolts to 69-86 ft. lbs. (93-117 N.m).
2) To complete installation, reverse removal procedure. Tighten ball joint pinch bolt to 32-40 ft. lbs. (43-54 N.m). Tighten caliper bolts to 29-36 ft. lbs. (39-49 N.m). Install and tighten NEW drive axle lock nut to 116-174 ft. lbs. (157-235 N.m). Stake NEW axle lock nut into shaft groove. Tighten tie rod nut to 22-33 ft. lbs. (29-44 N.m). Install NEW cotter pin.

CAUTION: If lock nut flange cracks, even slightly, during staking process, it must be replaced.

WHEEL BEARING

Removal (Aspire) – 1) Remove front hub. See HUB & KNUCKLE ASSEMBLY. Separate hub from knuckle with Knuckle Puller (T87C-1104-A) and Hub/Bearing Remover(T92C-1104-AH).

NOTE: The outer bearing retainer is preselected to provide correct bearing preload. Save it for use during reassembly.

2) Remove outer bearing retainer washer. Using a press and bearing splitter, remove outer bearing cone. Remove and discard inner oil seal. Remove inner bearing cone. Remove and discard inner oil seal. Remove races. *See Fig. 3.*

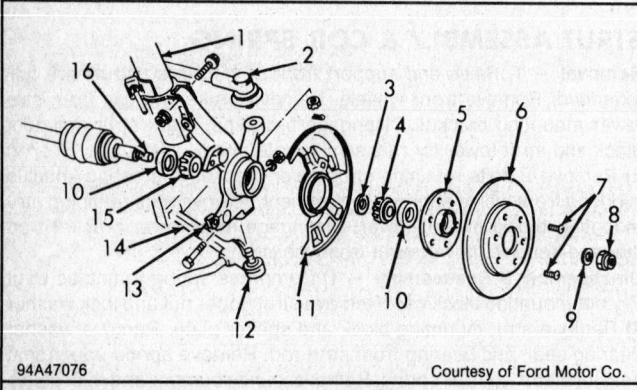

94A47076   Courtesy of Ford Motor Co.
Fig. 3: Exploded View Of Front Hub (Aspire)

Installation – 1) Drive races into knuckle. Pack inner and outer bearing cones with grease meeting specification ESA-M1C75-B. Pack hub in area of ends of rollers. Install inner cone into knuckle bore so that it rests in level position. Lubricate lip of NEW inner oil seal. Form grease into a strip, concentrated along edges of inner oil seal lip. Tap inner oil seal into place.
2) Install original outer bearing spacer, or spacer selected from bearing preload procedure, into knuckle bore. See BEARING PRELOAD. Lubricate lip of NEW inner oil seal. Form grease into a strip, concentrated along edges of inner oil seal lip. Tap outer oil seal into place.
3) Install knuckle and hub. See HUB & KNUCKLE ASSEMBLY. Using spacer from Spacer Selector (T87C-1104-B), position hub/rotor assembly into knuckle bore, then press into position.
Removal (Capri) – 1) Remove hub and knuckle assembly. See HUB & KNUCKLE ASSEMBLY under REMOVAL & INSTALLATION. Using Knuckle Puller (T87C-1104-A), or a press and bearing puller, remove drive hub/rotor assembly from steering knuckle/dust shield assembly. *See Fig. 4.*
2) Remove bearing preload spacer from hub. Spacer is preselected to provide correct bearing preload. Ensure correct spacer is installed during reassembly. Clamp hub/rotor assembly in a vise. Scribe alignment marks on hub and rotor for reassembly reference.

3) Remove rotor. Use Bearing Splitter (D84L-1123-A), Shaft Protector (D80L-625-2), and a press, or Bearing Puller (D80L-927-A) and Puller Attachment (D84L-1123-A) to remove outer bearing from wheel hub. Remove and discard outer and inner grease seals. Using Bearing Puller (T77F-1102-A) and Slide Hammer (T-50T-100-A), remove races from steering knuckle.

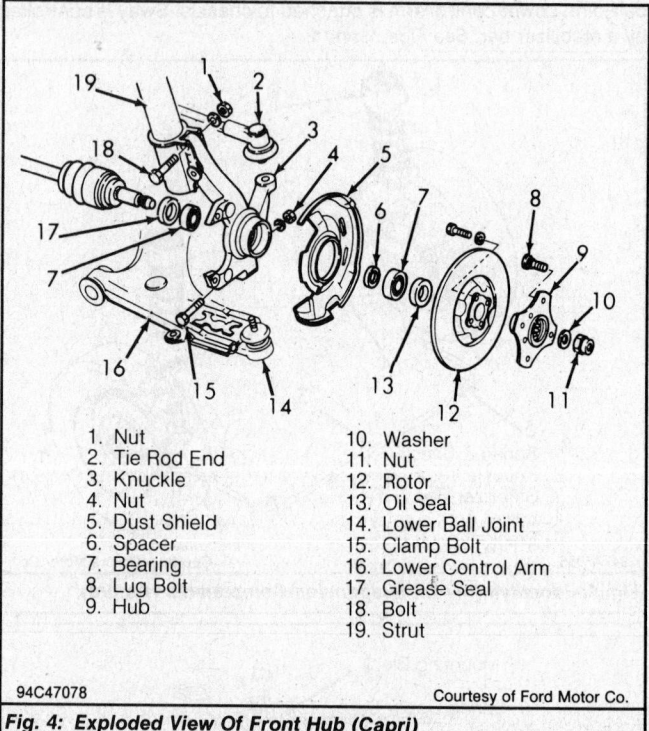

1. Nut	10. Washer
2. Tie Rod End	11. Nut
3. Knuckle	12. Rotor
4. Nut	13. Oil Seal
5. Dust Shield	14. Lower Ball Joint
6. Spacer	15. Clamp Bolt
7. Bearing	16. Lower Control Arm
8. Lug Bolt	17. Grease Seal
9. Hub	18. Bolt
	19. Strut

94C47078   Courtesy of Ford Motor Co.
Fig. 4: Exploded View Of Front Hub (Capri)

NOTE: Removal of dust shield from steering knuckle is not part of normal bearing service. Dust shield should not be removed from steering knuckle unless it is to be replaced.

Inspection – Thoroughly clean all parts in solvent. Inspect bearings, hub, knuckle and dust shield for excessive wear or damage. If new bearing is being installed, adjust bearing preload. See BEARING PRELOAD.
Bearing Preload – 1) To check and adjust preload, use Spacer Selector Set (T87C-1104-B). Prior to assembling hub/rotor assembly into steering knuckle, install spacer selector into steering knuckle. Clamp spacer selector in vise. Tighten center bolt, in increments, to 36, 72, 108, and finally 145 ft. lbs. (49, 98, 147, and 196 N.m). Each time center bolt is tightened, seat bearings by rotating steering knuckle by hand.
2) Reinstall steering knuckle in vise, clamping it where shock absorber mounts. Using an INCH-lb. torque wrench, measure torque required to rotate center bolt. Measure torque just as wrench starts to rotate.
3) Spacer thickness is correct if torque wrench indicates 2.2-16 INCH lbs. (0.25-1.8 N.m). If required torque is less than 2.2 INCH lbs. (0.25 N.m), install a thinner spacer. If required torque greater than 16 INCH lbs. (1.8 N.m), install a thicker spacer.
4) Bearing spacers are available in 21 thicknesses in 0.0016" (0.040 mm) increments. Spacer No. 1 is thinnest, and No. 21 is thickest. See PRELOAD SPACER AVAILABILITY (CAPRI) table. Changing spacer thickness by one size will change bearing preload by 1.8-3.5 INCH lbs. (0.2-0.4 N.m). Install appropriate spacer to adjust preload to specification. Remove spacer selector set.

PRELOAD SPACER AVAILABILITY (CAPRI)

Stamped Mark On pacer	In. (mm)
1	0.2474 (6.285)
2	0.2490 (6.325)
3	0.2506 (6.365)
4	0.2522 (6.405)
5	0.2537 (6.445)
6	0.2553 (6.485)
7	0.2569 (6.525)
8	0.2585 (6.565)
9	0.2600 (6.605)
10	0.2616 (6.645)
11	0.2632 (6.685)
12	0.2648 (6.725)
13	0.2663 (6.765)
14	0.2679 (6.805)
15	0.2695 (6.845)
16	0.2711 (6.885)
17	0.2726 (6.925)
18	0.2742 (6.965)
19	0.2758 (7.005)
20	0.2774 (7.045)
21	0.2789 (7.085)

Installation – 1) Using Bearing Cup Replacer (D79P-1202-A) and Handle (T80T-4000-W), install bearing races into steering knuckle. Lubricate bearing races and bearing. Install inner bearing into steering knuckle. Lubricate seal lips. Install inner bearing seal into knuckle. Install original bearing preload spacer, or spacer selected during bearing preload adjustment procedure. Position outer bearing into knuckle. Install outer seal. Install hub onto rotor, aligning reference marks made during removal. Install rotor.

2) Using a press and adapter from Spacer Selector Set (T87C-1104-B), install knuckle onto hub. To complete installation, reverse removal procedure.

LOWER CONTROL ARM

Removal (Aspire) – 1) Raise and support vehicle. Remove wheel and tire. Remove lower arm-to-chassis bolt and washer. Remove ball joint bolt. Remove stabilizer bar nut. Discard cotter pin. Remove stabilizer bar bushing.

2) Pull lower arm downward, prying ball joint stud from knuckle. Disengage lower arm from stabilizer bar. Remove lower arm.

Installation – 1) Install NEW mounting bolt bushing if necessary. Position stabilizer bar washer and bushing onto stabilizer bar. Position lower arm over stabilizer bar. Raise lower arm inner end into pivot bracket. Finger-tighten bolt to hold it in place. Position ball joint stud into knuckle bore. Install ball joint bolt and nut.

2) Install stabilizer bar bushing, washer and nut. Tighten to specification. See TORQUE SPECIFICATIONS. Install NEW cotter pin. Tighten lower arm-to-chassis bolt to specification. Tighten ball joint nut to specification. Install wheel and tire. Lower vehicle.

Removal & Installation (Capri) – 1) Raise and support vehicle. Remove wheel. Disconnect stabilizer bar from control arm. Remove ball joint clamp bolt. Remove control arm front mount bolt. Remove control arm rear bracket and mount bolts. Remove control arm.

2) To install, reverse removal procedure. Tighten rear bracket bolt to 44-54 ft. lbs. (59-74 N.m). Tighten control arm rear nut to 55-69 ft. lbs. (75-93 N.m). Tighten control arm front bolt to 69-86 ft. lbs. (93-117 N.m). Tighten ball joint clamp to 32-40 ft. lbs. (43-54 N.m).

BALL JOINT

Removal & Installation (Capri) – Raise and support vehicle. Remove wheel. Remove ball joint clamp bolt from steering knuckle. Pry lower control arm downward to separate it from steering knuckle. Remove ball joint retaining bolts. Pry ball joint from control arm. To install, reverse removal procedure. Tighten ball joint bolts to 69-86 ft. lbs. (93-117 N.m).

LOWER CONTROL ARM BUSHING

Removal & Installation (Aspire) – Remove control arm from vehicle. See LOWER CONTROL ARM & BALL JOINT. Use Bushing Receiver Cup (T88C-5493-E), Bushing Pilot (T81P-5493-B2) and "C" Clamp Assembly (T74P-3044-A1) to remove control arm bushing. To install, press bushing into control arm with same tools used for removal. Install control arm.

Removal & Installation (Capri) – Remove control arm from vehicle. See LOWER CONTROL ARM. Use Bushing Receiver Cup (T87C-5493-B1), Bushing Driver (T87C-5493-B2) and vise to remove control arm bushing. To install, press bushing into control arm with same tools used for removal. Install control arm.

NOTE: Insert bushing quickly and smoothly. Bushing should only be distorted for a short time.

TORQUE SPECIFICATIONS
TORQUE SPECIFICATIONS

Application	Ft. Lbs. (N.m)
Aspire	
Axle Nut	116-174 (157-236)
Ball Joint Retainer Nut	32-40 (43-54)
Ball Joint Stud Nut	22-32 (29-43)
Caliper Bolts	29-36 (39-49)
Control Arm Pivot Bolt	32-40 (43-54)
Stabilizer Bar Nuts	47-57 (64-77)
Stabilizer Mounting Bracket Nuts	40-50 (54-68)
Steering Knuckle-To-Strut	69-86 (93-117)
Wheel Lug Nut	65-88 (90-120)
Capri	
Ball Joint Pinch Bolt	32-40 (43-54)
Brake Rotor-To-Hub	33-40 (44-54)
Caliper Bolts	29-36 (39-49)
Ball Joint Bolt	69-86 (93-117)
Control Arm Bracket Bolt	44-54 (59-74)
Control Arm Front Bolt	69-86 (93-117)
Control Arm Rear Bolt	55-69 (75-93)
Drive Axle Nut	116-174 (157-236)
Shock Absorber Bolt-To-Knuckle	69-72 (93-97)
Stabilizer Bracket Nuts	40-50 (54-68)
Steering Knuckle-To-Strut	69-86 (93-117)
Steering Knuckle-To-Tie Rod	22-33 (29-44)
Strut Assembly-To-Strut Tower	17-22 (23-29)
Strut Rod Nut	22-27 (29-36)
Wheel Lug Nut	65-88 (90-120)

Aspire, Capri

DESCRIPTION

Rear suspension on Aspire is semi-independent, with a torsion beam axle which also operates as a stabilizer bar, and MacPherson struts. On Capri, rear suspension is fully independent, with trailing arms, lower control arms, and MacPherson struts. *See Fig. 1 or 2.*

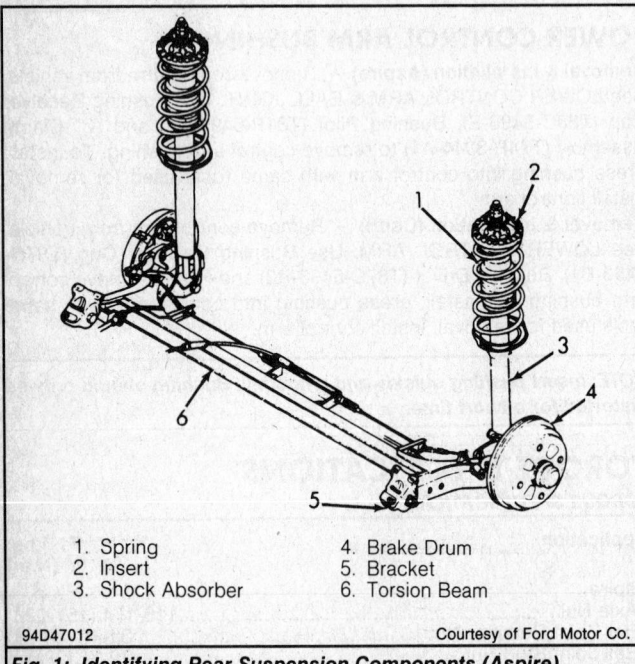

1. Spring
2. Insert
3. Shock Absorber
4. Brake Drum
5. Bracket
6. Torsion Beam

94D47012   Courtesy of Ford Motor Co.

Fig. 1: Identifying Rear Suspension Components (Aspire)

Crossmember
Lower Control Arm
Stabilizer Link Bushings
Lateral Link
Lower Control Arm
Rear Stabilizer Bar (MTX Only)
Trailing Arm
Stabilizer Link

94E47013   Courtesy of Ford Motor Co.

Fig. 2: Identifying Rear Suspension Components (Capri)

ADJUSTMENTS & INSPECTION

WHEEL BEARING

1) Raise and support vehicle. Release parking brake. Remove wheel and dust cap. Rotate brake drum to verify there is no brake drag. Remove bearing nut. On Capri, discard lock nut.

NOTE: On Capri, lock nut on right side has left-hand threads. Always install NEW lock nut on Capri, or NEW cotter pin on Aspire.

2) On all models, tighten nut to 18-21 ft. lbs. (25-29 N.m) while rotating brake drum. After tightening, loosen nut until it can be rotated by hand. Measure and record seal drag with an INCH-lb. torque wrench attached to lug nut at 12 o'clock position. Seal drag torque must be added to specified wheel bearing torque.

3) Add seal drag torque to specified preload. As an example, if seal drag is 2.2 INCH lbs. (0.25 N.m) and specified bearing preload torque is 1.3-4.3 INCH lbs. (0.15-0.49 N.m), total bearing preload should be 3.5-6.5 INCH lbs. (0.40-0.73 N.m). Specified wheel bearing torque is 23-75 INCH lbs. (2.6-8.5 N.m) for Aspire, and 1.3-4.3 INCH lbs. (0.15-0.49 N.m) for Capri.

4) Tighten lock nut by hand. Rotate brake drum with torque wrench. Continue to tighten lock nut slowly until preload torque is within specification. Install NEW cotter pin (Aspire) or lock nut (Capri). To complete adjustment, reverse disassembly procedure.

REMOVAL & INSTALLATION

WHEEL BEARING

Removal (Aspire) – 1) Raise and support vehicle. Remove wheel and tire. Remove dust cap. Remove cotter pin, nut cover, and nut. Discard cotter pin. Remove brake drum, washer, and bearings as an assembly.

2) Remove outer bearing cone and washer. Pry out and discard inner oil seal. Remove inner bearing cone. If necessary, pull bearing races from brake drum with Puller (T77F-1102-A) and Slide Hammer (T50T-100-A).

Installation – 1) Tap inner race into place with Cup Replacer (T77F-1202-A) and Handle (T80T-4000-W). Tap outer race into place with Cup Replacer (T77F-1217-A) and Handle (T80T-4000-W).

2) Pack bearings and hubs in area at ends of rollers with grease meeting Ford specification ESA-M1C75-B. Install bearings and grease seals. Adjust bearing preload. See WHEEL BEARING under ADJUSTMENTS. To complete installation, reverse removal procedure.

Removal (Capri) – 1) Raise and support vehicle. Release parking brake. Remove wheel and tire. Remove dust cap. Raise staked portion of lock nut. Remove and discard lock nut.

NOTE: Lock nut on right side has left-hand threads. Lock nut on left side has right-hand threads.

2) Remove brake drum, hub, and bearing as an assembly. Pry grease seal from hub. Remove inner bearing. If necessary, tap races from brake drum with brass drift.

Installation – Tap races into place with brass drift. Pack bearings and hubs in area of ends of rollers with grease meeting Ford specification ESA-M1C75-B. Install bearings and grease seals. Adjust bearing preload. See WHEEL BEARING under ADJUSTMENTS. To complete installation, reverse removal procedure.

SPINDLE

Removal & Installation (Aspire) – 1) Raise and support vehicle. Remove brake drum. *See Fig. 3.* Remove anti-lock sensor (if equipped). Support torsion beam to unload suspension. Remove shock absorber bolt. Remove torsion beam support.

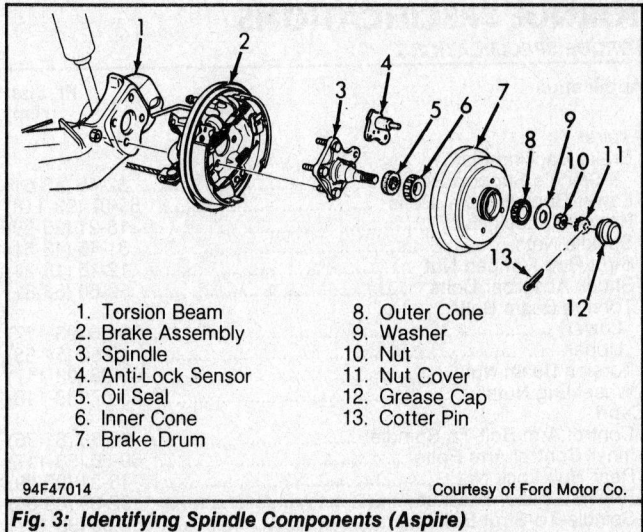

1. Torsion Beam
2. Brake Assembly
3. Spindle
4. Anti-Lock Sensor
5. Oil Seal
6. Inner Cone
7. Brake Drum
8. Outer Cone
9. Washer
10. Nut
11. Nut Cover
12. Grease Cap
13. Cotter Pin

94F47014   Courtesy of Ford Motor Co.

Fig. 3: Identifying Spindle Components (Aspire)

NOTE: The hex heads on the outboard side of the brake backing plate appear to be spindle nuts; actually they are serrated studs. DO NOT attempt to remove them. The spindle nuts are on the inboard side of the torsion beam arms.

2) Remove spindle nuts. Support backing plate with wire. Remove spindle. To install, reverse removal procedure.

Removal & Installation (Capri) – Raise and support vehicle. Remove wheel, caliper, and rotor. Loosen spindle-to-strut nuts. Loosen outer control arm bolt and nut. Remove spindle bolts and control arm bolt. Remove spindle. To install, reverse removal procedure.

STRUTS

CAUTION: On Aspire, DO NOT have left and right struts removed simultaneously. If both must be removed, complete installation on one side before removing the other.

Removal (Aspire) – Remove luggage compartment side cover. Remove shock absorber cap, jam nut, and flanged nut. Remove bushing washer and upper bushing. Raise and support vehicle. Remove lower shock absorber bolt from torsion beam arm. Pull strut assembly downward to remove. *See Fig. 4.*

Installation – 1) Guide shock absorber rod through hole in tower. Align hole in lower end of shock absorber with hole in torsion beam. Install and finger-tighten bolt. Lower vehicle.
2) From inside vehicle, install upper bushing, bushing washer, and flanged nut. Hold rod. Tighten flanged nut to specification. Install jam nut and shock absorber cap. Reverse removal procedure to complete installation. Tighten bolts to specification. See TORQUE SPECIFICATIONS.

Removal & Installation (Capri) – 1) Remove wheel, caliper, antimoan bracket, and brake drum. Loosen trailing arm bolt and spindle-to-strut bolts, then remove them. Mark strut rubber mounting bracket for installation reference.
2) From inside vehicle, remove strut retaining nuts. Compress coil spring. Remove rod nut. Remove rubber mounting bracket, upper spring seat, lower spring seat, and rubber spring seat.
3) Slowly release and remove spring compressor. Remove spring, dust boot, and rebound bumpers. *See Fig. 4.* To install, reverse removal procedure.

Inspection – Inspect jounce bumper, spring seat insulator, and strut rod bushings for wear or damage. Replace strut if it is leaking.

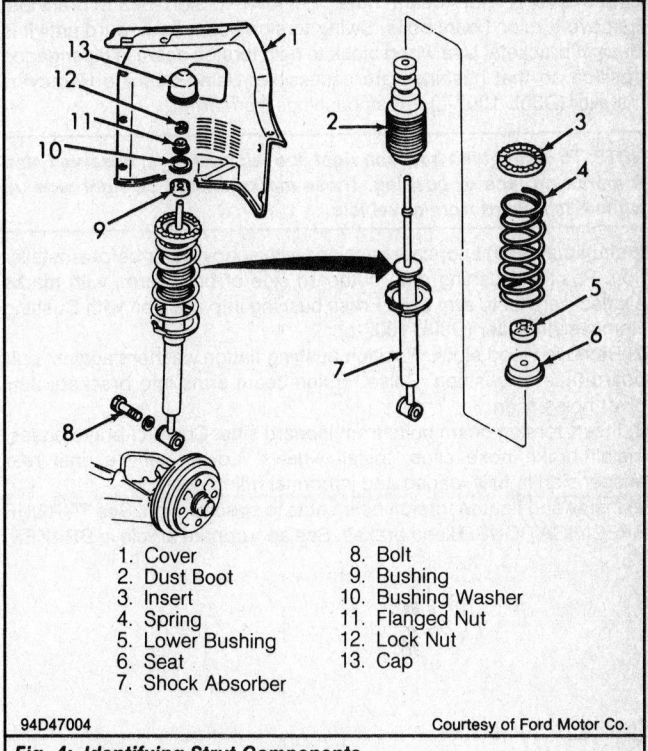

1. Cover
2. Dust Boot
3. Insert
4. Spring
5. Lower Bushing
6. Seat
7. Shock Absorber
8. Bolt
9. Bushing
10. Bushing Washer
11. Flanged Nut
12. Lock Nut
13. Cap

94D47004   Courtesy of Ford Motor Co.

Fig. 4: Identifying Strut Components (Aspire Shown; Capri Is Similar)

TORSION BEAM

Removal (Aspire) – 1) Raise and support vehicle. Remove wheels and tires. Remove spindles. See SPINDLE. Disconnect brake hoses. Disconnect parking brake cables. Disengage brake cable and conduit from torsion beam.
2) Release brake adjuster hole covers. Pull anti-lock sensors through backing plate. Remove backing plates and brake assemblies. Remove torsion beam nuts and bolts. Remove torsion beam.

Installation – 1) If removed, install torsion beam brackets with washers, lock washers, and bolts. Leave bolts loose at this time.
2) If installing new torsion beam, install bushings. See TORSION BEAM BUSHINGS. Install bushing flange washers. Position torsion beam arms into brackets. Align bolt holes, then install bolts and lock washers. Leave nuts loose.
3) Install backing plates. Route anti-lock sensor wires through backing plates. Secure brake shoes. Install spindles. See SPINDLE. Install parking brake cable and conduit. Connect parking brake cables to levers. Connect brake hoses.
4) To complete installation, reverse removal procedure. Lower vehicle to load suspension. Tighten torsion beam nuts to specification. See TORQUE SPECIFICATIONS.
5) Check rear suspension alignment by locating and marking underbody at a point equally distant from inner right and left torsion beam bolts. From this point, measure distance to centers of left and right shock absorber bolts. If distances are not equal within 0.2 (5 mm), shift torsion bar brackets as necessary to center suspension.
6) When centered, tighten upper and lower torsion beam bolts to specification. See TORQUE SPECIFICATIONS. Bleed brakes. See appropriate article in BRAKES.

TORSION BEAM BUSHINGS

Aspire – 1) Raise and support vehicle with rear struts fully extended. Remove wheels. Remove right brake hose support bracket. Disconnect rear brake hose. Remove left brake hose clip. Disconnect hose at crossmember.

2) Remove torsion beam nuts. Remove torsion beam brackets. Remove torsion beam bolts. Swing torsion beam downward until it is clear of brackets. Use wood block to hold torsion beam in disengaged position so that bushings are accessible. Using Bushing Remover/ Installer (D80L-1002-L), press bushings from arms.

NOTE: *To distinguish between right and left bushings, observe F and R marks on face of bushing. These marks should be right side up when F is toward front of vehicle.*

Installation – 1) Lubricate bushings with soapy water before installation. Position bushing onto outboard side of beam arm, with marks aligned parallel to arm axis. Press bushing into position with Bushing Remover/Installer (D80L-1002-L).

2) Remove wood block. Position bushing flange washers against outboard face of bushing. Raise torsion beam arms into brackets until pivot holes align.

3) Insert torsion beam bolts from inboard side. Connect brake hoses. Install brake hose clips. Install wheels. Lower vehicle until rear suspension is fully loaded and in normal riding position.

4) Install and tighten torsion beam nuts to specification. See TORQUE SPECIFICATIONS. Bleed brakes. See appropriate article in BRAKES.

TORQUE SPECIFICATIONS
TORQUE SPECIFICATIONS

Application	Ft. Lbs. (N.m)
Aspire	
Brake Backing Plate	
& Spindle Support Bolts	32-45 (43-61)
Lower Body Bracket Bolts	69-87 (93-118)
Rear Hub Lock Nut	18-21 (25-29)
Spindle Nuts	31-45 (43-61)
Strut Rod Flanged Nut	12-18 (16-24)
Shock Absorber Bolts	50-60 (68-81)
Torsion Beam Bolts	
Lower	69-86 (93-117)
Upper	40-50 (54-68)
Torsion Beam Nuts	69-86 (93-117)
Wheel Lug Nuts	65-87 (88-118)
Capri	
Control Arm Bolt-To-Spindle	45-55 (61-75)
Inner Control Arm Bolts	69-86 (93-117)
Rear Hub Lock Nut	18-21 (25-29)
Rear Stabilizer Bracket	32-39 (43-55)
Spindle-To-Strut Bolts	69-86 (93-117)
Strut Rod Flanged Nut	40-50 (54-68)
Strut-To-Strut Tower	17-22 (23-29)
Wheel Bearing Lock Nut	18-21 (25-29)
Wheel Lug Nuts	67-88 (90-120)

Aspire, Capri

DESCRIPTION & OPERATION

The steering column assembly consists of a steering shaft, steering shaft tube, upper and lower bearings, mounting brackets, ignition lock, combination switch, and universal joints. The steering column and shaft are designed to collapse under heavy load. *See Fig. 1 or 2.*

CAUTION: All models are equipped with Supplemental Restraint System (SRS). Observe safety precautions. The air bag system is powered directly from the battery and back-up power supply. Before any repairs are performed, disconnect and shield battery ground cable. Wait at least one minute before servicing any air bag component. Use caution when working near steering column. Air bag could accidently deploy at any time.

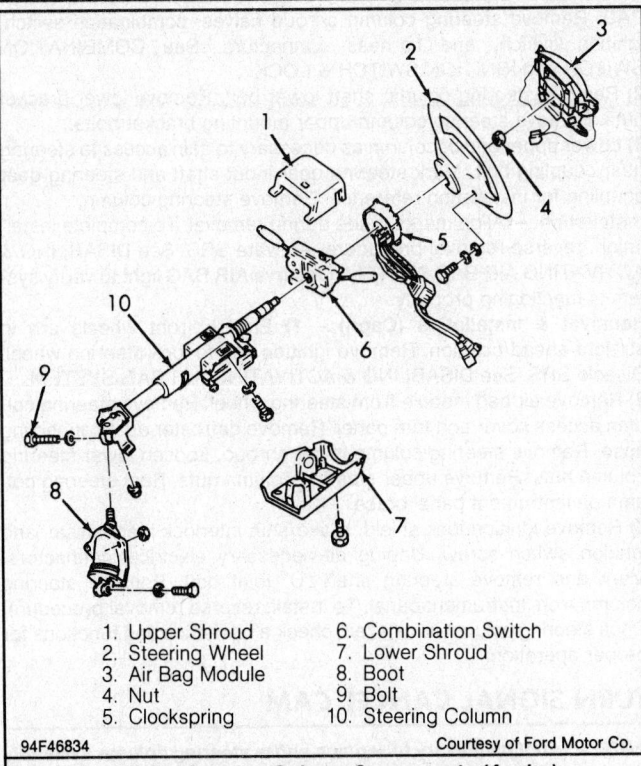

1. Upper Shroud
2. Steering Wheel
3. Air Bag Module
4. Nut
5. Clockspring
6. Combination Switch
7. Lower Shroud
8. Boot
9. Bolt
10. Steering Column

94F46834   Courtesy of Ford Motor Co.

Fig. 1: Identifying Steering Column Components (Aspire)

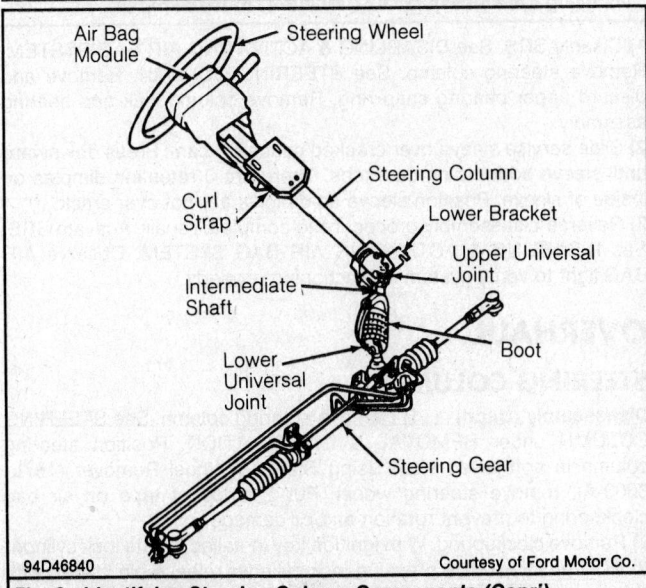

94D46840   Courtesy of Ford Motor Co.

Fig. 2: Identifying Steering Column Components (Capri)

DISABLING & ACTIVATING AIR BAG SYSTEM

DISABLING AIR BAG SYSTEM

Disconnect negative battery cable. Wait one minute. System is now disabled.

ACTIVATING AIR BAG SYSTEM

To activate SRS, reconnect negative battery cable. From passenger's side of vehicle, set ignition switch to RUN position. System is now activated. Observe AIR BAG light to verify system is functioning properly.

NOTE: For information on air bag DIAGNOSIS & TESTING or DISPOSAL PROCEDURES, see MITCHELL® AIR BAG SERVICE & REPAIR MANUAL, DOMESTIC & IMPORTED MODELS.

REMOVAL & INSTALLATION

STEERING WHEEL & HORN PAD

CAUTION: When removing steering wheel, DO NOT use a knock-off type steering wheel puller, or strike the steering wheel or shaft with hammer. A sudden impact could damage bearing, or collapse the steering column, requiring replacement of column.

CAUTION: Remove steering wheel carefully to avoid damaging clockspring wiring or air bag module connector, or accidentally rotating clockspring. After steering wheel removal, tape clockspring in position to prevent rotation and/or damage.

Removal (Aspire) – Disable SRS. See DISABLING & ACTIVATING AIR BAG SYSTEM. Ensure front wheels are in straight-ahead position. Remove air bag module bolts. Unplug connectors. Mark steering wheel and steering shaft for reassembly reference. Using Steering Wheel Remover (T67L-3600-A), remove steering wheel.

Installation – To install, reverse removal procedure. Connect air bag module wiring. Install air bag module. Tighten air bag module nuts to specification. See TORQUE SPECIFICATIONS. Activate SRS. See DISABLING & ACTIVATING AIR BAG SYSTEM. Observe AIR BAG light to verify system is functioning properly.

Removal (Capri) – 1) Disable SRS. See DISABLING & ACTIVATING AIR BAG SYSTEM. Ensure front wheels are in straight-ahead position. From rear of steering wheel, remove nuts and washers securing air bag module to steering wheel. Unplug air bag module-to-clockspring connector.

2) Remove air bag module. Place air bag module out of the way with pad facing upward. Unplug horn and cruise control (if equipped) connectors from steering wheel. Scribe marks on steering shaft and steering wheel hub for installation reference. Loosen steering wheel retaining bolt 4-6 turns. Use Steering Wheel Remover (T67L-3600-A) to remove steering wheel.

Installation – 1) Ensure front wheels are in straight-ahead position. Route clockspring wiring harness through steering wheel opening. Position steering wheel onto steering shaft with reference marks aligned.

2) Ensure clockspring wiring is not pinched when installing steering wheel. Install and tighten NEW steering wheel nut to specification. See TORQUE SPECIFICATIONS. Connect horn and cruise control (if equipped) wiring.

3) Connect air bag module wiring. Install air bag module. Tighten air bag module nuts to specification. See TORQUE SPECIFICATIONS. Activate SRS. See DISABLING & ACTIVATING AIR BAG SYSTEM. Observe AIR BAG light to verify system is functioning properly.

COMBINATION SWITCH

Removal & Installation (Aspire) – 1) Disable SRS. See DISABLING & ACTIVATING AIR BAG SYSTEM. Remove steering wheel. See STEERING WHEEL. Remove steering column shroud halves. Apply 2 strips of tape across clockspring rotor and stator to prevent rotation.

2) Remove clockspring from steering shaft. Remove clockspring ground screw. Remove clockspring. Remove combination switch screws. Unplug connectors. Remove combination switch.
Installation – To install, reverse removal procedure. Activate SRS. See DISABLING & ACTIVATING AIR BAG SYSTEM. Observe AIR BAG light to verify system is functioning properly.
Removal & Installation (Capri) – Disable SRS. See DISABLING & ACTIVATING AIR BAG SYSTEM. Remove upper steering column bolts. Steering column will rest on instrument panel bracket. Remove combination switch. Pull lever firmly from switch. Release wiring harness clip. Unplug connectors. To install, reverse removal procedure. Check combination switch for proper operation.

IGNITION SWITCH & LOCK

Removal & Installation (Aspire) – **1)** Disable SRS. See DISABLING & ACTIVATING AIR BAG SYSTEM. Remove steering wheel. See STEERING WHEEL & HORN PAD. Remove steering column shroud halves. Remove screws and ignition switch. Unplug connectors.
2) To install, reverse removal procedure. Activate SRS. See DISABLING & ACTIVATING AIR BAG SYSTEM. Observe AIR BAG light to verify system is functioning properly.
Removal & Installation (Capri) – **1)** Disable SRS. See DISABLING & ACTIVATING AIR BAG SYSTEM. Remove steering wheel. See STEERING WHEEL & HORN PAD. Remove center access panel and trim panel under steering wheel. Remove left side defroster connector tube.
2) Remove upper steering column bolts. Lower steering column onto instrument panel brace. With ignition key inserted, rotate lock cylinder while pressing release pin (located at base of lock cylinder housing) with 1/8" (3 mm) drift. Pull lock cylinder from ignition lock housing. If lock cylinder will not rotate, see NON-FUNCTIONING IGNITION LOCK (CAPRI).
3) Remove column lock shield. Unplug switch harness connector. Remove ignition switch. *See Fig. 3.*
4) Install ignition switch onto column lock assembly. Ensure actuator pin of lock assembly fits into ignition switch slot. To complete installation, reverse removal procedure.

NOTE: Use NON-FUNCTIONING IGNITION LOCK replacement procedure only when ignition lock is inoperative and the lock cylinder will not rotate.

Non-Functioning Ignition Lock (Capri) – **1)** Remove lower steering column shroud. With a 1/8" drill bit, drill out retaining pin, no deeper than 1/2" (12.7 mm). With a chisel and hammer, using sharp blows at base of cap, carefully remove ignition lock cylinder cap. With a 3/8" drill bit, drill out center of key slot no deeper than 1 3/4" (44 mm), or until lock cylinder breaks away from base of lock cylinder.

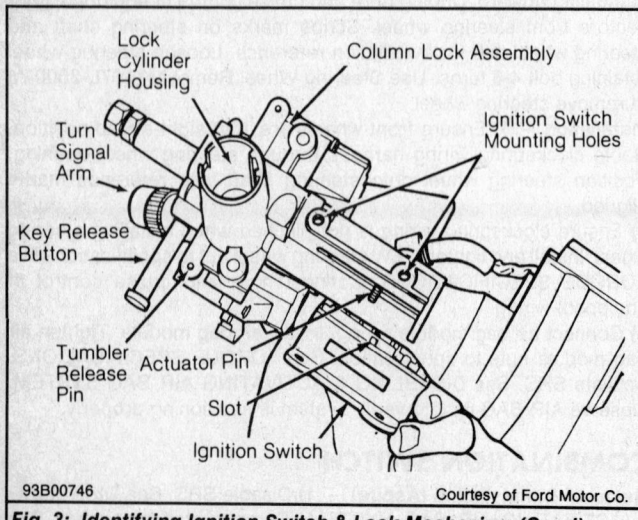

Lock Cylinder Housing
Column Lock Assembly
Ignition Switch Mounting Holes
Turn Signal Arm
Key Release Button
Tumbler Release Pin
Actuator Pin
Slot
Ignition Switch
93B00746
Courtesy of Ford Motor Co.
Fig. 3: Identifying Ignition Switch & Lock Mechanism (Capri)

2) Remove lock cylinder. Clean drill shavings from lock cylinder housing. Remove snap ring washer and steering column lock gear. Replace lock cylinder housing if damaged. Install new lock cylinder and key into housing. Check operation. To complete installation, reverse removal procedure.

STEERING COLUMN

CAUTION: Steering column is not repairable, and must be replaced if damaged or collapsed. Replace fasteners as necessary with approved fasteners of the same part number. Torque values must be used as specified during assembly to ensure proper function of parts. See TORQUE SPECIFICATIONS.

Removal (Aspire) – **1)** Disable SRS. See DISABLING & ACTIVATING AIR BAG SYSTEM. Ensure front wheels are in straight-ahead position. Remove steering wheel. See STEERING WHEEL & HORN PAD. Remove steering column shroud halves, combination switch, ignition switch, and harness connectors. See COMBINATION SWITCH and IGNITION SWITCH & LOCK.
2) Remove steering column shaft lower bolt. Remove lower bracket nuts. Remove steering column upper mounting bracket bolts.
3) Lower upper end of column as necessary to gain access to steering gear coupling bolt. Mark steering gear input shaft and steering gear coupling for installation reference. Remove steering column.
Installation – Align marks made during removal. To complete installation, reverse removal procedure. Activate SRS. See DISABLING & ACTIVATING AIR BAG SYSTEM. Observe AIR BAG light to verify system is functioning properly.
Removal & Installation (Capri) – **1)** Ensure front wheels are in straight-ahead position. Remove ignition key to lock steering wheel. Disable SRS. See DISABLING & ACTIVATING AIR BAG SYSTEM.
2) Remove air bag module from steering wheel. Remove steering column access cover and trim panel. Remove defroster duct connecting hose. Remove steering column lower shroud. Loosen lower steering column nuts. Remove upper steering column nuts. Rest steering column on instrument panel brace.
3) Remove ignition lock shield, brake/shift interlock mechanism, and ignition switch screw. Unplug all necessary electrical connectors. Mark and remove steering shaft "U" joint bolt. Remove steering column from instrument panel. To install, reverse removal procedure. Once steering column is installed, check all switches and functions for proper operation.

TURN SIGNAL CANCEL CAM

NOTE: It is not necessary to replace entire steering column assembly in case of cracked turn signal cancel cam. Use Turn Signal Cancelling Cam Sleeve (E1AZ-13B368-A) to make repair.

1) Disable SRS. See DISABLING & ACTIVATING AIR BAG SYSTEM. Remove steering column. See STEERING COLUMN. Remove and discard upper bearing snap ring. Remove column lock and bearing assembly.
2) Slide service sleeve over cracked canceling cam. Press downward until sleeve bottoms on cam tabs. There are 3 retention dimples on inside of sleeve. Position sleeve so dimples are not over crack.
3) Reverse disassembly procedure to complete repair. Activate SRS. See DISABLING & ACTIVATING AIR BAG SYSTEM. Observe AIR BAG light to verify system is functioning properly.

OVERHAUL

STEERING COLUMN

Disassembly (Capri) – **1)** Remove steering column. See STEERING COLUMN under REMOVAL & INSTALLATION. Position steering column in soft-jawed vise. Using Steering Wheel Remover (T67L-3600-A), remove steering wheel. Put 2 strips of tape on air bag clockspring to prevent rotation and/or damage.
2) Remove clockspring. With ignition key installed, rotate lock cylinder to RUN position while pressing lock cylinder release pin inward with

1/8" drift. Remove lock cylinder and upper column shroud. Remove key warning switch.

3) Remove bearing plate. Remove and discard snap ring located at top end of steering column. Remove multifunction switch. Remove column lock and upper bearing with bearing puller. *See Fig. 4.*

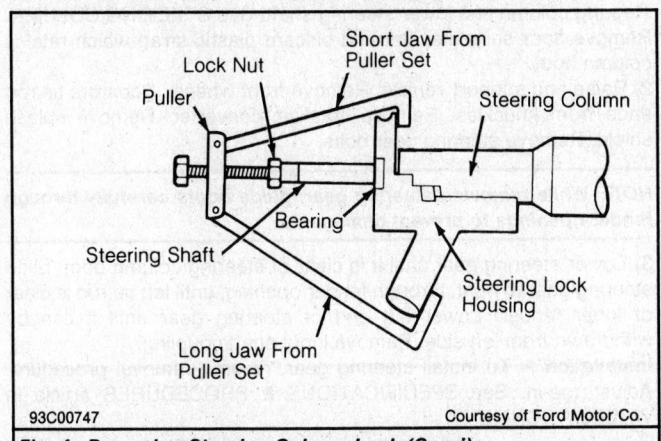

93C00747   Courtesy of Ford Motor Co.

Fig. 4: Removing Steering Column Lock (Capri)

Inspection – If steering shaft shear pins break during housing or bearing removal, the complete shaft and column must be replaced. To determine if pins have sheared, measure steering shaft from top end of shaft to center of "U" joint bearing. If length is less than 24.80" (630 mm) or greater than 24.88" (632 mm), pins have sheared. If pins have sheared, replace steering shaft and column assembly.

Reassembly – **1)** Install steering column lock and upper bearing. Tighten bolts to 12-20 ft. lbs. (16-28 N.m). Stake upper shaft serration diameter enough to ensure an interference fit between bearing and steering column upper shaft.

2) Position bearing and insulator as far down steering column upper shaft as possible. To seat bearing and insulator, put a piece of pipe approximately 1 1/2" long by 3/4" inside diameter over end of steering shaft. Install flat washer and steering wheel nut over pipe. Tighten until bearing is seated. *See Fig. 5.* Install NEW snap ring.

3) Install combination switch, bearing retaining plate, and key warning sensor. Install upper column shroud. Install lock cylinder by rotating it and pressing release pin. Install air bag clockspring. Remove tape strips. Tighten steering wheel nut to 23-33 ft. lbs. (31-45 N.m). Secure curl strap with retaining clips. Install steering column.

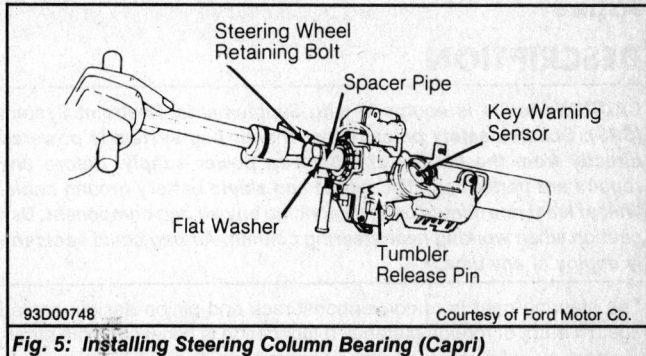

93D00748   Courtesy of Ford Motor Co.

Fig. 5: Installing Steering Column Bearing (Capri)

Disassembly & Reassembly (Aspire) – Disassembly of steering column is not recommended by manufacturer. If any components are defective, replace steering column.

Inspection – Measure steering shaft for signs of collapse. Steering shaft length should be 23.6" (598 mm). If length is not within specification, replace steering column. Inspect for steering shaft side play. If side play exceeds 0.03" (0.75 mm), replace steering column.

TORQUE SPECIFICATIONS
TORQUE SPECIFICATIONS

Application	Ft. Lbs. (N.m)
Aspire	
Steering Column Attaching Bolt	13-19 (18-26)
Steering Wheel Nut	29-36 (39-49)
"U" Joint Bolt	14-19 (19-26)
Capri	
Ignition Lock Housing Bolt	12-21 (16-28)
Ignition Lock Shield Bolt	14-18 (19-25)
Steering Column Bolt	17-23 (23-31)
Steering Column Bracket Nut & Bolt	14-18 (19-25)
Steering Column Nut	17-23 (23-31)
Steering Wheel Nut	23-33 (31-45)
"U" Joint Bolt	14-19 (19-26)

	INCH Lbs. (N.m)
Air Bag Module	
Aspire	80-115 (9-13)
Capri	35-53 (4-6)

Aspire

DESCRIPTION

CAUTION: Aspire is equipped with Supplemental Restraint System (SRS). Observe safety precautions. The air bag system is powered directly from the battery and back-up power supply. Before any repairs are performed, disconnect and shield battery ground cable. Wait at least one minute before servicing any air bag component. Use caution when working near steering column. Air bag could accidently deploy at any time.

The steering gear is of conventional rack and pinion design, sealed against entry of foreign material. If lubrication is necessary, the steering gear must be removed and disassembled. *See Fig 1.*

ADJUSTMENTS

No routine adjustments are necessary. All adjustments are made at time of overhaul.

REMOVAL & INSTALLATION

STEERING GEAR

1) Disconnect negative battery cable. Mark lower steering column shaft and steering gear input shaft for installation reference. Remove steering column and lower steering shaft. See STEERING COLUMN. Remove floor set plate. Cut and discard plastic strap which retains column boot.

2) Raise and support vehicle. Remove front wheels. Separate tie rod ends from knuckles. Remove catalytic converter. Remove splash shield. Remove steering gear bolts.

NOTE: While removing steering gear, guide boots carefully through fender openings to prevent damage.

3) Lower steering gear until it is clear of steering column boot. Slide steering gear to right, through fender opening, until left tie rod is clear of inner fender. Lower left end of steering gear until it can be withdrawn from left side. Remove input shaft coupling.

Installation – To install steering gear, reverse removal procedure. Adjust toe-in. See SPECIFICATIONS & PROCEDURES article in WHEEL ALIGNMENT.

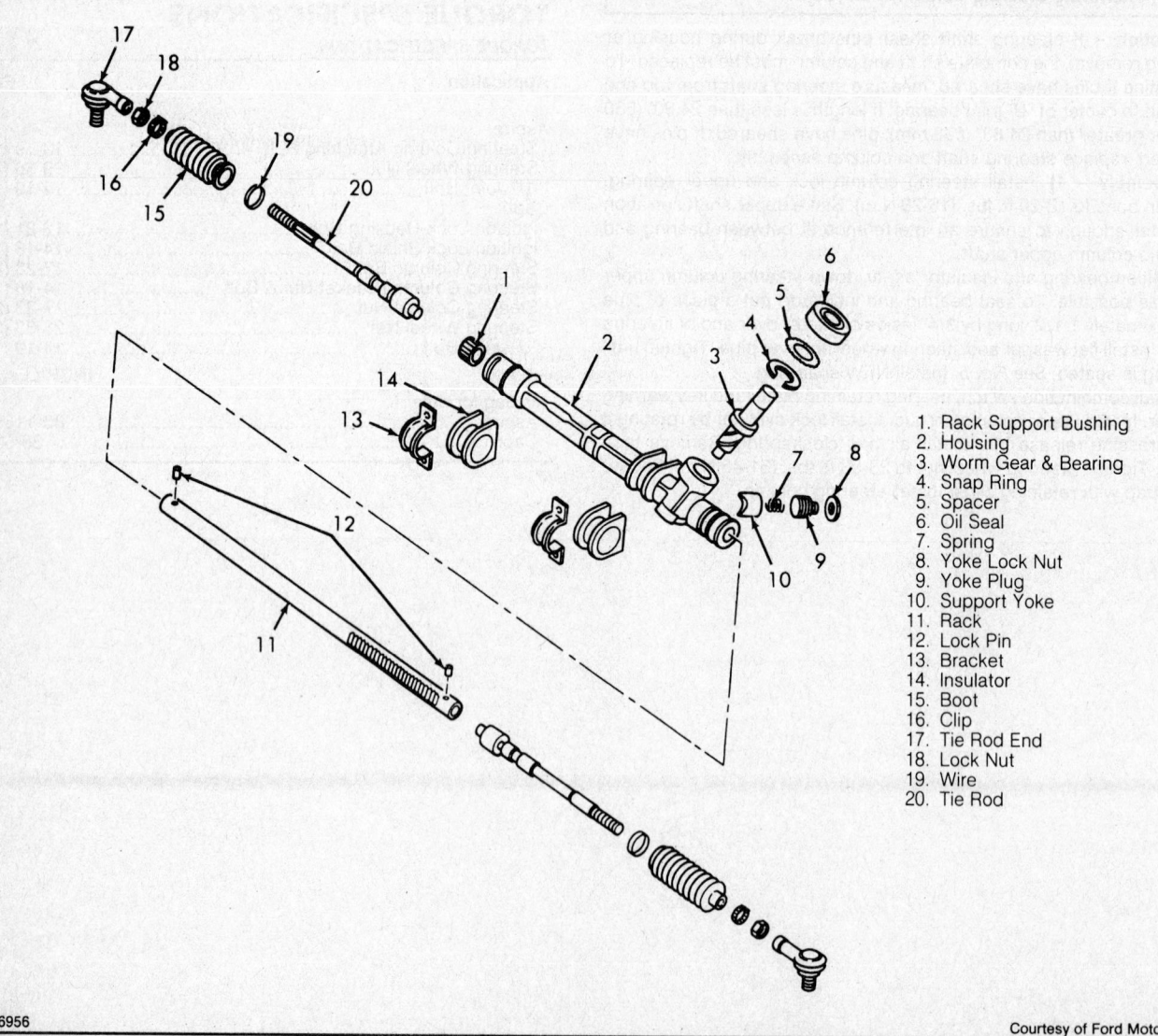

1. Rack Support Bushing
2. Housing
3. Worm Gear & Bearing
4. Snap Ring
5. Spacer
6. Oil Seal
7. Spring
8. Yoke Lock Nut
9. Yoke Plug
10. Support Yoke
11. Rack
12. Lock Pin
13. Bracket
14. Insulator
15. Boot
16. Clip
17. Tie Rod End
18. Lock Nut
19. Wire
20. Tie Rod

94D46956

Courtesy of Ford Motor Co.

Fig. 1: Exploded View Of Manual Steering Gear

STEERING COLUMN

Removal – 1) Remove steering wheel. Remove turn signal, windshield wiper, and ignition switches. See STEERING COLUMN article. Remove lower bolt from lower steering column shaft. Remove steering column bracket nuts and bolts.

NOTE: When free, upper end of steering column may be lowered for access to shaft coupling at lower end.

---

2) Note orientation of shaft coupling. Mark shaft coupling and shafts for installation reference. Remove steering column.
Installation – To install, reverse removal procedure. Align reference marks. Take care to install shaft coupling the way it came out.

OVERHAUL

STEERING GEAR

Disassembly – 1) Remove steering gear. See STEERING GEAR under REMOVAL & INSTALLATION. Remove mounting brackets and insulators. *See Fig. 1.* Mark tie rod ends and tie rods for assembly reference, then remove. Remove boots. Remove lock pins from both ends of rack.
2) Extend rack from either end of housing. Clamp rack in soft-jawed vise. Unscrew tie rods. Remove yoke lock nut, yoke plug, spring, and yoke.
3) Pry oil seal from housing. Remove spacer. Remove snap ring. Use Valve Body Puller (T78P-3504-B) to remove worm gear and bearing. Remove rack by pulling it out from left end of housing. DO NOT remove it through right end.
4) If worm gear and bearing are to be replaced, remove with Puller (D80L-100-L). If necessary, remove rack support bushing by pressing lock tabs and extracting bushing with Puller (D80L-100-L).
Inspection – Inspect all parts for wear or damage. Using dial indicator and "V" blocks, measure rack runout. Replace rack if runout exceeds 0.004" (0.1 mm). Replace rack support bushing if rack fits loosely. Inspect tie rod ends for smooth operation. Replace parts as necessary.
Assembly – 1) Clean all parts. Lubricate rack teeth, worm gear teeth, and steering gear housing with grease meeting Ford specification ESA-M1C75-B. Pack upper and lower worm gear bearings. Take care not to plug vent holes with grease. Lubricate oil seal lips, support yoke, and rack.
2) Lubricate rack support bushing with lithium grease. Install rack support bushing into right end of housing, engaging lock tabs with lock slots.
3) If replacing worm gear lower bearing, start it into position with worm gear. Complete installation with a wooden dowel or bushing driver.
4) Install rack from left end of housing, with rack teeth facing worm gear. Position rack with left end extending 2.4" (62 mm) from end of housing. *See Fig. 2.*

5) Install worm gear so that when bearing is seated, its clamp bolt notch faces 35-55 degrees clockwise from left. Install snap ring, spacer, and oil seal. *See Fig. 2.*

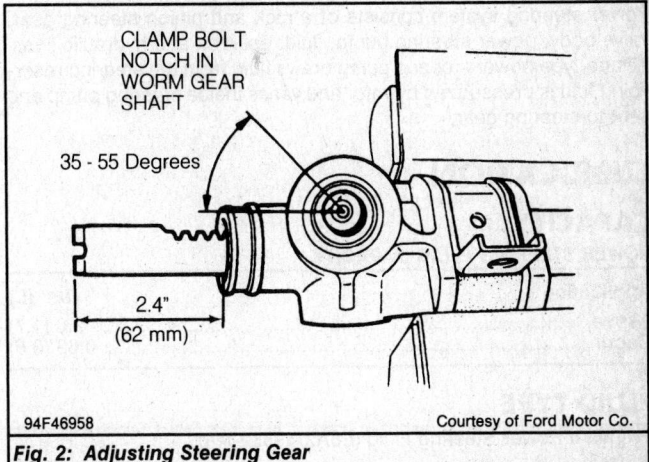

CLAMP BOLT
NOTCH IN
WORM GEAR
SHAFT

35 - 55 Degrees

2.4"
(62 mm)

94F46958   Courtesy of Ford Motor Co.

Fig. 2: Adjusting Steering Gear

6) Wrap worm gear serrations with plastic tape to protect oil seal during installation. Apply grease to tape. Install oil seal. Remove tape.
7) Install tie rods. Install lock pins. Install boots. Install tie rod ends. Position rack so that tie rods are equally extended. Lubricate yoke. Install yoke and spring. Apply sealant to yoke plug threads. Tighten yoke plug to 80-97 INCH lbs. (9-11 N.m).
8) Slowly cycle rack back and forth 5 times through 90 percent of its travel. Position rack so tie rods are equally extended. Loosen yoke plug. Tighten yoke plug to 22-30 INCH lbs. (2.5-3.4 N.m).
9) Using spring scale, measure force required to rotate input shaft 180 degrees. Rotate input shaft to position which required maximum rotating force. Tighten yoke plug to 48 INCH lbs. (5.4 N.m), then back it off 5-35 degrees. Install and tighten yoke plug lock nut to specification without allowing yoke plug to rotate. See TORQUE SPECIFICATIONS.

TORQUE SPECIFICATIONS
TORQUE SPECIFICATIONS

Application	Ft. Lbs. (N.m)
Steering Gear Bolts	27-38 (37-52)
Tie Rod End Castle Nut	31-42 (42-57)
Tie Rod End Jam Nut	25-37 (34-50)
Wheel Lugs	65-87 (88-118)
Yoke Plug Lock Nut	29-36 (39-49)

Aspire, Capri

DESCRIPTION & OPERATION

Power steering system consists of a rack and pinion steering gear, valve body, power steering pump, fluid reservoir and hydraulic lines. A vane-type power steering pump draws fluid from the steering reservoir. Fluid is pressurized by rotor and vanes inside steering pump and sent to steering gear.

LUBRICATION

CAPACITY

POWER STEERING FLUID CAPACITY

Application	Qts. (L)
Aspire	2.0 (1.7)
Capri	0.63 (0.6)

FLUID TYPE

Premium Power Steering Fluid (E6AZ-19582-AA).

FLUID LEVEL CHECK

Check fluid level before engine is started, while fluid is still cool. Remove reservoir cap from steering pump. Fluid should be between the "L" and "H" marks on dipstick. If fluid is needed, fill to the "L" mark on dipstick.

Run engine until warm. Rotate steering wheel fully in both directions about 10 times. Return steering to straight-ahead position. Shut engine off. Fluid level should be between "L"and "H" marks. Add fluid if necessary.

HYDRAULIC SYSTEM BLEEDING

1) Raise and support front of vehicle. Fill reservoir to specified level. With ignition coil wire disconnected, crank engine and add fluid to steering pump until fluid level remains constant. While cranking engine, rotate steering wheel from lock to lock. Recheck and add fluid as necessary.
2) Start and idle engine for several minutes. Rotate steering wheel completely from lock to lock several times. Check fluid level. Add fluid as necessary. Continue this procedure until there is no bubbling or decrease in fluid level.

ADJUSTMENTS

POWER STEERING PUMP BELT

On Aspire, remove air duct and air cleaner. On all models, loosen steering pump pivot bolt and adjuster bolt lock nut. Using Belt Tension Gauge (021-0028A), fit gauge to longest available belt span. Adjust belt to specification. See BELT TENSION SPECIFICATIONS table. Tighten adjuster bolt lock nut to 32-45 ft. lbs. (43-61 N.m) on Capri, or 27-40 ft. lbs. (37-54 N.m) on Aspire.

BELT TENSION SPECIFICATIONS

Application	[1] Deflection In. (mm)	Gauge Tension Lbs. (kg)
New Belt		
Aspire & Capri	10.31-0.35 (8-9)	110-132 (50-60)
Used Belt		
Aspire	0.35-0.39 (9-10)	95-110 (43-50)
Capri	0.31-0.35 (8-9)	110-132 (50-60)

[1] – Apply about 22 lbs. (10 kg) pressure.

REMOVAL & INSTALLATION

POWER STEERING PUMP

Removal (Aspire) – Remove air duct and air cleaner. Unplug connector from switch on power steering pump. Disconnect and plug hoses. Loosen mounting bolts. Back off tension adjuster bolt. Loosen tensioner shaft. Remove tensioner bolt. Remove drive belt. Remove pivot bolt and power steering pump.

Removal (Capri) – 1) Remove right radiator support and brace. Remove pump drive belt. Disconnect intercooler outlet hose at throttle intake (if equipped). Remove ground wire from engine lifting eye.

2) Remove and plug pressure and return hoses. Disconnect wire from pressure switch. Remove adjuster screw, nut, and block from pump bracket. Remove power steering pump pivot bolt. Remove bracket bolts and pump.

Installation (Aspire & Capri) – To install pump, reverse removal procedure. Adjust power steering pump belt tension. See POWER STEERING PUMP BELT under ADJUSTMENTS. Tighten all nuts and bolts to specification. See TORQUE SPECIFICATIONS. Add power steering fluid. Bleed air from system and check for leaks. See HYDRAULIC SYSTEM BLEEDING under LUBRICATION.

STEERING GEAR

Removal (Aspire) – 1) Disconnect negative battery cable. Remove steering column boot retainer. Pry up boot. Remove steering gear input shaft coupling bolt. Raise and support vehicle.

2) Remove power steering hose bracket. Disconnect and plug hydraulic lines. Remove front wheels. Separate tie rod ends from knuckles. Remove small front fender splash shield. Disconnect exhaust pipe. Lower exhaust system.

3) Mark tie rods, tie rod ends and lock nuts for installation reference. Remove tie rod ends. Remove mounting bracket bolts. Remove steering gear by sliding it to right.

Installation – Position steering gear in its mounting position. Align steering gear input shaft and steering shaft. Install shaft coupling, leaving bolt loose. Install steering gear mounting brackets. Tighten coupling bolt to 13-19 ft. lbs. (18-26 N.m). To complete installation, reverse removal procedure. Fill system with fluid. Bleed system. See HYDRAULIC SYSTEM BLEEDING under LUBRICATION.

Removal (Capri) – 1) Disconnect negative battery cable. Cut plastic wire tie on dust boot. Pull dust boot back to expose intermediate shaft lower "U" joint. Mark and loosen lower "U" joint. Disconnect and plug hydraulic lines. Loosen front wheel lug nuts.

2) Raise and support vehicle. Remove front wheels. Separate tie rod ends from steering knuckles. Remove splash shields.

3) Mark tie rod end and tie rod for installation reference. Remove right tie rod end. Remove steering gear bolts and washers. Slide steering gear to left, then pull right tie rod through fender opening. Remove steering gear by sliding it to right.

Installation – 1) Position steering gear in its mounting position. Attach intermediate shaft to steering gear pinion. Tighten clamp bolt to 13-19 ft. lbs. (18-26 N.m). Guide intermediate shaft into steering column hole. Lower vehicle.

2) Lift steering gear and align intermediate shaft with "U" joint. Install clamp bolt. Raise vehicle. Install and tighten steering gear bolts to specification. See TORQUE SPECIFICATIONS. Install right tie rod end, aligning marks made during removal. Attach tie rod ends to steering knuckles. Install and tighten tie rod end nuts to specification. See TORQUE SPECIFICATIONS. Install NEW tie rod end cotter pins.

3) Connect catalytic converter to inlet pipe. Tighten nuts to 23-34 ft. lbs. (31-46 N.m). Install splash shields. Install front wheels. Lower vehicle.

4) Connect fluid lines. On Capri, replace copper washers on banjo fitting. Connect negative battery cable. Add power steering fluid. Bleed air from system. See HYDRAULIC SYSTEM BLEEDING under LUBRICATION. Inspect for leaks.

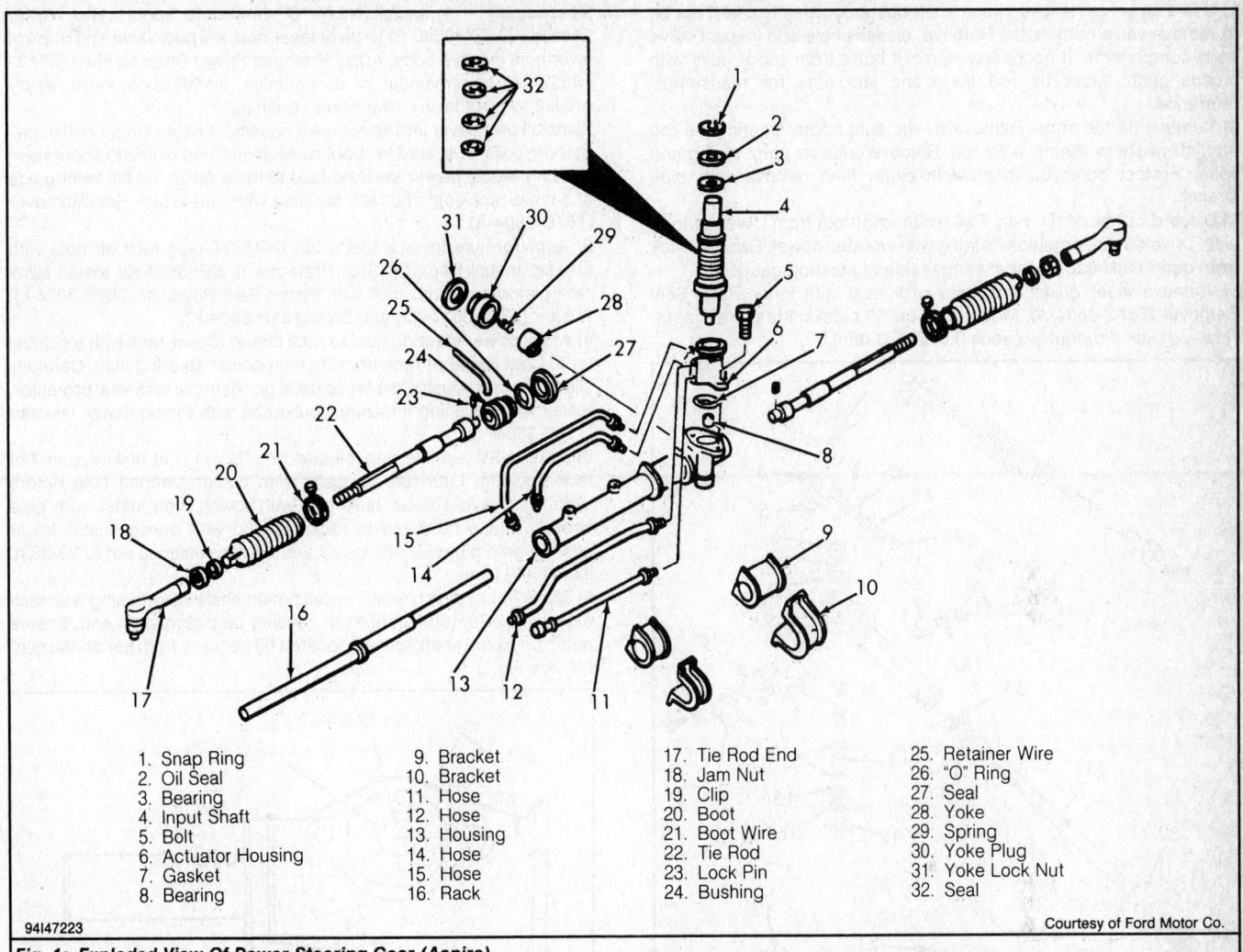

1. Snap Ring	9. Bracket	17. Tie Rod End	25. Retainer Wire
2. Oil Seal	10. Bracket	18. Jam Nut	26. "O" Ring
3. Bearing	11. Hose	19. Clip	27. Seal
4. Input Shaft	12. Hose	20. Boot	28. Yoke
5. Bolt	13. Housing	21. Boot Wire	29. Spring
6. Actuator Housing	14. Hose	22. Tie Rod	30. Yoke Plug
7. Gasket	15. Hose	23. Lock Pin	31. Yoke Lock Nut
8. Bearing	16. Rack	24. Bushing	32. Seal

94147223

Courtesy of Ford Motor Co.

Fig. 1: Exploded View Of Power Steering Gear (Aspire)

OVERHAUL

STEERING GEAR

Disassembly (Aspire) – 1) Remove steering gear. See STEERING GEAR under REMOVAL & INSTALLATION. Clamp steering gear in soft-jawed vise. Loosen yoke lock nut. *See Fig. 1.* Remove yoke plug and lock nut. Remove spring. Remove yoke.

2) Remove pinion gear snap ring. Using Pin Remover (T87P3504N), remove actuator oil seal. Remove hose retainer bolt. Remove actuator housing, input shaft and control valve as an assembly. Remove shims (if present).

3) Remove valve body gasket. Clamp actuator housing and control valve assembly into soft-jawed vise. Tap input shaft with rubber mallet to remove shaft and control valve. Remove seals from control valve. Press bearing from actuator housing.

4) Remove mounting brackets and insulators. Remove pressure lines. Use Torque Adapter (T88C3504CH) to rotate rack bushing until hooked end of retainer wire aligns with slot in housing. Pry retainer wire from slot. Rotate bushing. Remove retainer wire.

5) Remove rack from right side of housing. Remove bushing and "O" ring from rack. Use Oil Seal Remover ((T87P3504A) to remove oil seal. Use Puller (D80L100A) and Collet (D80L100L) to remove lower bearing.

Reassembly – 1) Tap lower bearing into place. Tap oil seal into housing with seal lip toward seal driver. Using Seal Replacer (T81P3504L) and Sizer (T81P3504K), install "O" ring.

2) Install Protector (T81P3504N) over end of steering gear rack to protect bushing. Install bushing onto rack. Install Rack Oil Seal Protector (T87P3504H) over rack. Install rack together with oil seal protector into housing. Remove oil seal protector.

3) Insert retainer wire through slot and into bushing hole. Use Adapter (T88C3504CH) to install retainer wire. Install hoses, insulators and brackets.

4) Slide Mandrel (T81P3504M1) over shaft and control. Install first seal into groove with Pusher (T81P3504M2). Compress seal with Sizer (T81P3504M3). Install Spacer (T81P3504M4). Install and compress second seal. Install 2 more spacers, then install and compress third seal.

5) Turn second spacer around so small ends face each other. Install fourth seal. Insert and fully seat shaft and control assembly into housing. Install valve body gasket into housing.

6) If actuator housing, steering gear housing, or control assembly have been replaced, adjust actuator. See ACTUATOR ADJUSTMENT. If none of those components have been replaced, install shims that were removed earlier.

7) Position actuator housing and control assembly onto housing. Install hose retainer bolts. Use Torque Adapter (T90C3504EH) to install bearing, if removed. Install oil seal. Install snap ring.

8) Adjust yoke preload. See YOKE PRELOAD ADJUSTMENT. Reverse disassembly procedure to complete assembly.

Disassembly (Capri) – 1) Remove steering gear. See STEERING GEAR under REMOVAL & INSTALLATION. Clamp steering gear in soft-jawed vise. Remove hydraulic lines. *See Fig. 2.* Remove mount brackets and rubber mount bushings. Remove brass tubing seats with a self-tapping screw and 2 screwdrivers.

2) Use a chisel to remove pinion shaft dust boot. Use No. 40 Torx bit to remove valve body bolts. Remove, disassemble and inspect valve body components. If necessary, remove burrs from spool valve with crocus cloth. Mark tie rod ends and jam nuts for reassembly reference.

3) Remove tie rod ends. Remove tie rod dust boots. Uncrimp tie rod end tab washers. Remove tie rod. Remove adjuster plug, spring and yoke. Protect outer bulkhead with cloth, then remove with pipe wrench.

4) Discard bulkhead "O" ring. Pull pinion shaft out from lower bearing side. Drive out upper pinion bearing with wooden dowel. Remove rack from outer bulkhead end (passenger side of steering gear).

5) Remove inner guide and inner rack seal with Inner Rack Seal Remover (T87C-3504-A). Mount rack on "V" blocks. Measure runout. Replace rack if runout exceeds 0.012" (0.3 mm).

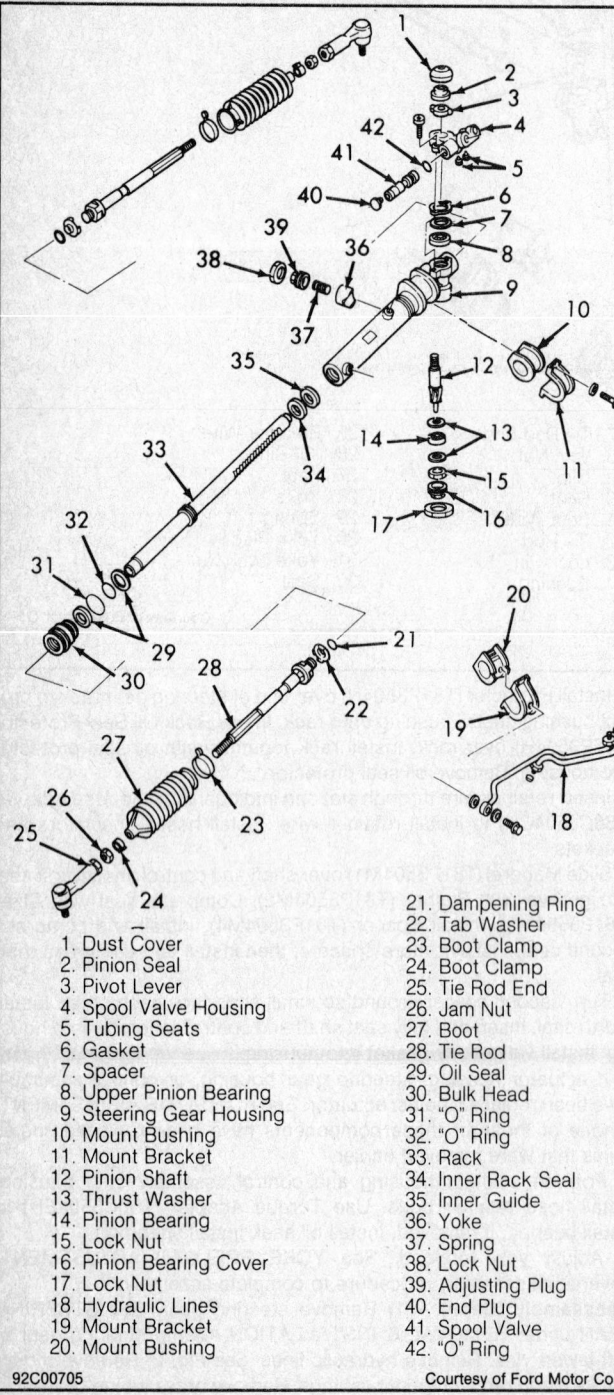

1. Dust Cover
2. Pinion Seal
3. Pivot Lever
4. Spool Valve Housing
5. Tubing Seats
6. Gasket
7. Spacer
8. Upper Pinion Bearing
9. Steering Gear Housing
10. Mount Bushing
11. Mount Bracket
12. Pinion Shaft
13. Thrust Washer
14. Pinion Bearing
15. Lock Nut
16. Pinion Bearing Cover
17. Lock Nut
18. Hydraulic Lines
19. Mount Bracket
20. Mount Bushing
21. Dampening Ring
22. Tab Washer
23. Boot Clamp
24. Boot Clamp
25. Tie Rod End
26. Jam Nut
27. Boot
28. Tie Rod
29. Oil Seal
30. Bulk Head
31. "O" Ring
32. "O" Ring
33. Rack
34. Inner Rack Seal
35. Inner Guide
36. Yoke
37. Spring
38. Lock Nut
39. Adjusting Plug
40. End Plug
41. Spool Valve
42. "O" Ring

92C00705   Courtesy of Ford Motor Co.

Fig. 2: Exploded View Of Power Steering Gear (Capri)

Reassembly – 1) Install NEW "O" ring onto spool valve. Apply Grease (C1AZ-19590-E) to pivot lever hole in spool valve and to pivot lever hole in valve body. Apply Premium Power Steering Fluid (E6AZ-19582-AA) to remainder of spool valve. Install spool valve. Apply grease to pivot lever/collar and to bushing.

2) Install pivot lever into spool valve housing. Ensure longer end of pivot lever/collar is seated in spool valve. Install end plug into spool valve housing. Apply power steering fluid to inner guide. Install inner guide and inner rack seal into rack housing with Inner Rack Seal Remover (T87C-3504-A).

3) Apply grease to rack teeth, but DO NOT plug rack air hole with grease. Install Rack Oil Seal Protector (D83P-3504-K). Install NEW rack piston seal onto rack with Piston Seal Replacer (T81P-3504-L), Pusher (T75L-3517-A2) and Sizer (T81P-3504-K).

4) Apply power steering fluid to rack piston. Cover rack with electrical tape. Coat inside of rack housing with power steering fluid. Carefully slide rack into housing, as far as it will go. Remove rack seal protector. Install NEW bushing into outer bulkhead with Pinion Cover Installer (T18P-3504-Y).

5) Install NEW sealing ring, oil seal and "O" rings at bulkhead end of rack housing. Lubricate all parts with power steering fluid before installation. Wrap outer bulkhead with towel, then install with pipe wrench. Stake bulkhead to rack housing with punch. Install lower bearing onto pinion shaft. Install and tighten retaining nut to 29-36 ft. lbs. (39-49 N.m).

6) Stake nut to pinion shaft. Install pinion shaft into housing with rack extending 2.70" (68.7 mm) from housing on pinion shaft end. Ensure notch on pinion shaft spline is located 60 degrees from horizontal center. *See Fig. 3.*

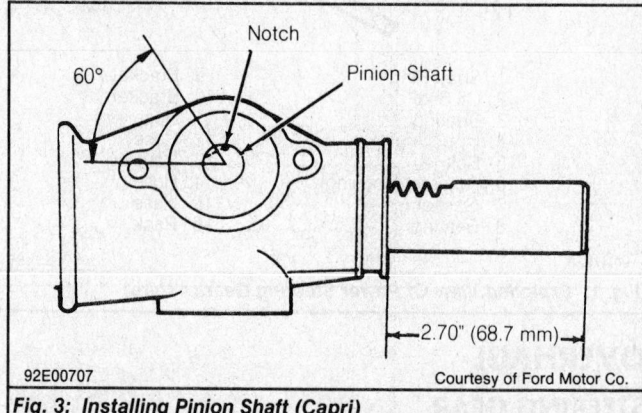

92E00707   Courtesy of Ford Motor Co.

Fig. 3: Installing Pinion Shaft (Capri)

7) Grease upper pinion bearing. Install into housing with Upper Pinion Seal Replacer (T78P-3504-D). Tighten pinion bearing cover to 44-80 INCH lbs. (5-9 N.m), then loosen 10-20 degrees. Tighten lock nut to 29-36 ft. lbs. (39-49 N.m).

8) Using a NEW gasket, install valve body. Install yoke, spring, yoke plug and lock nut. Tighten cover to 40-49 INCH lbs. (4.5-5.5 N.m). Loosen cover 45 degrees. Measure pinion rotating torque with INCH-lb. torque wrench and Pinion Adapter (T87C-3504-C).

9) Pinion rotating torque should be 5.3-13.3 INCH lbs. (0.6-1.5 N.m). If pinion rotating torque is not within specification, loosen or tighten adjuster plug as necessary. After pinion rotating torque is adjusted to specification, tighten lock nut to 29-36 ft. lbs. (39-49 N.m). Mount steering gear in soft-jawed vise. Install damper ring, washer and tie rod.

10) Tighten tie rod to 44-59 ft. lbs. (60-80 N.m). Stake tab washer in 2 places. Position damper ring into washer. Install remaining damper ring, washer and tie rod. Install dust boots.

11) Install tie rod ends, aligning marks made during disassembly. Wrap electrical tape around and apply grease to pinion shaft. Apply grease to lips of pinion shaft seal. Install pinion shaft seal with Pinion Bearing Replacer (T78P-3504-D).

12) Remove tape from pinion shaft. Install support brackets and rubber bushings. Install hydraulic lines and NEW copper sealing rings onto each banjo fitting.

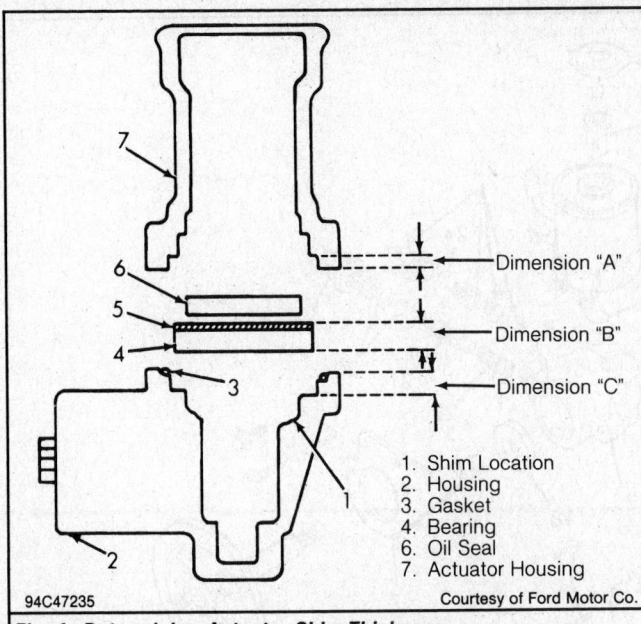

1994 STEERING
Power Rack & Pinion (Cont.)

7
6
5
4
3
Dimension "A"
Dimension "B"
Dimension "C"
1
2
1. Shim Location
2. Housing
3. Gasket
4. Bearing
6. Oil Seal
7. Actuator Housing
94C47235
Courtesy of Ford Motor Co.

Fig. 4: Determining Actuator Shim Thickness

ACTUATOR ADJUSTMENT

1) Measure dimensions "A", "B", and "C". *See Fig. 4.* Determine required shim thickness by adding dimensions "A" and "B", then subtracting dimension "C". Shims are available in 0.002" (0.05 mm) thickness. Always round up or down to nearest whole number.

2) For example if required thickness is 0.17 mm, divide 0.17 by 0.02, then round off to nearest whole number, which is 3. Therefore, 3 shims would be required.

YOKE PRELOAD ADJUSTMENT

1) Install rack yoke. Install spring. Apply sealant to yoke plug threads and lock nut. Install yoke plug. Tighten yoke plug to 22-29 ft. lbs. (29-39 N.m), then loosen it.

2) Install Gauge (T90C3504CH) over yoke plug. Loosen and tighten yoke plug to 43 INCH lbs. (4.9 N.m) 3 times. Scribe yoke plug at 0-degree mark of gauge. Loosen yoke plug until scribe mark aligns with 67.5-degree mark on gauge.

3) Measure rotating torque of shaft. If rotating torque is not 7.0-11.3 INCH lbs. (0.8-1.3 N.m), repeat adjustment procedure.

POWER STEERING PUMP

Disassembly (Aspire) – 1) Secure pump in a soft-jawed vise. Remove support bracket. Remove supply tubes and "O" ring. Remove switch, spring, plunger and "O" ring.

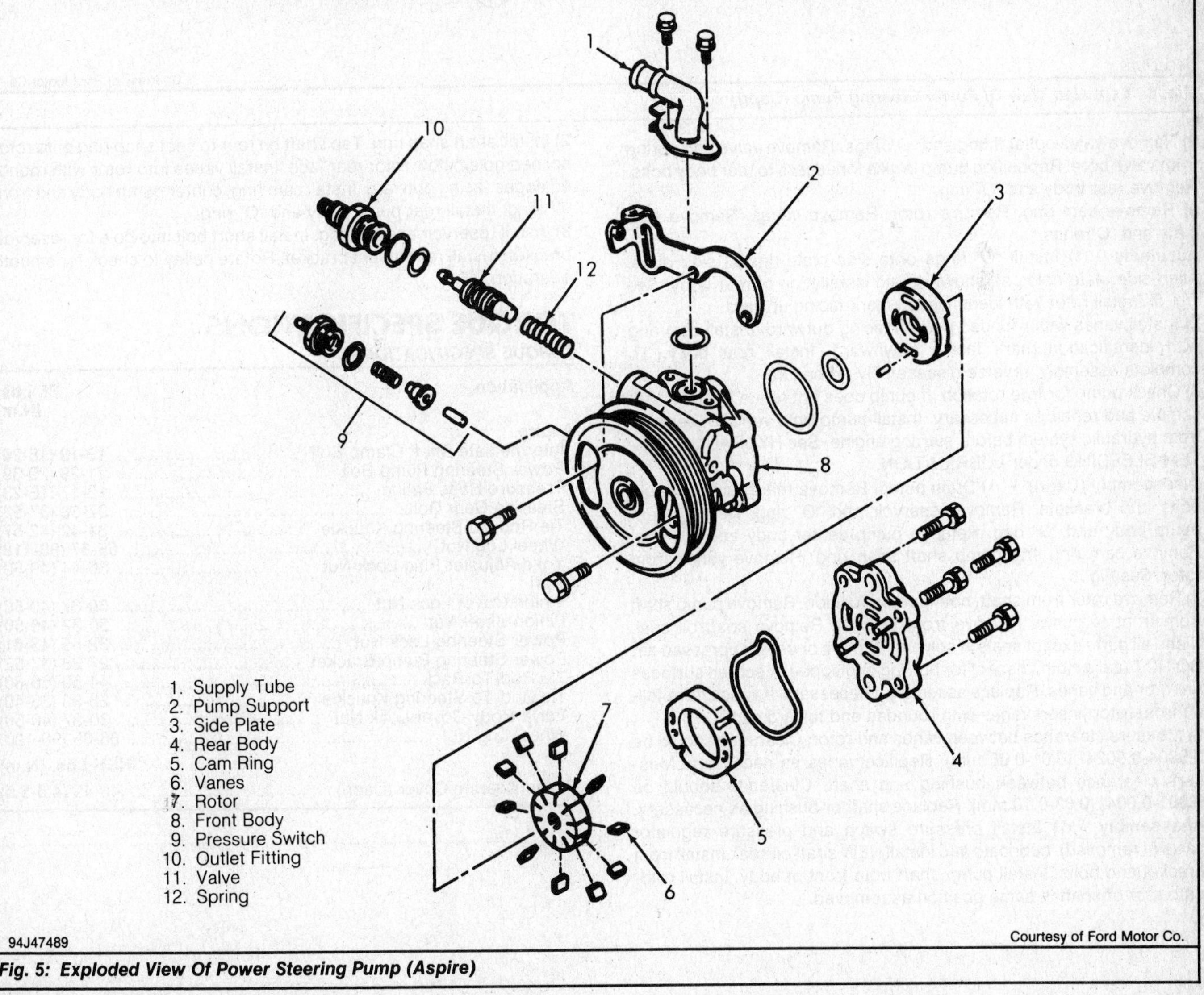

1
2
3
4
5
6
7
8
9
10
11
12
1. Supply Tube
2. Pump Support
3. Side Plate
4. Rear Body
5. Cam Ring
6. Vanes
7. Rotor
8. Front Body
9. Pressure Switch
10. Outlet Fitting
11. Valve
12. Spring
94J47489
Courtesy of Ford Motor Co.

Fig. 5: Exploded View Of Power Steering Pump (Aspire)

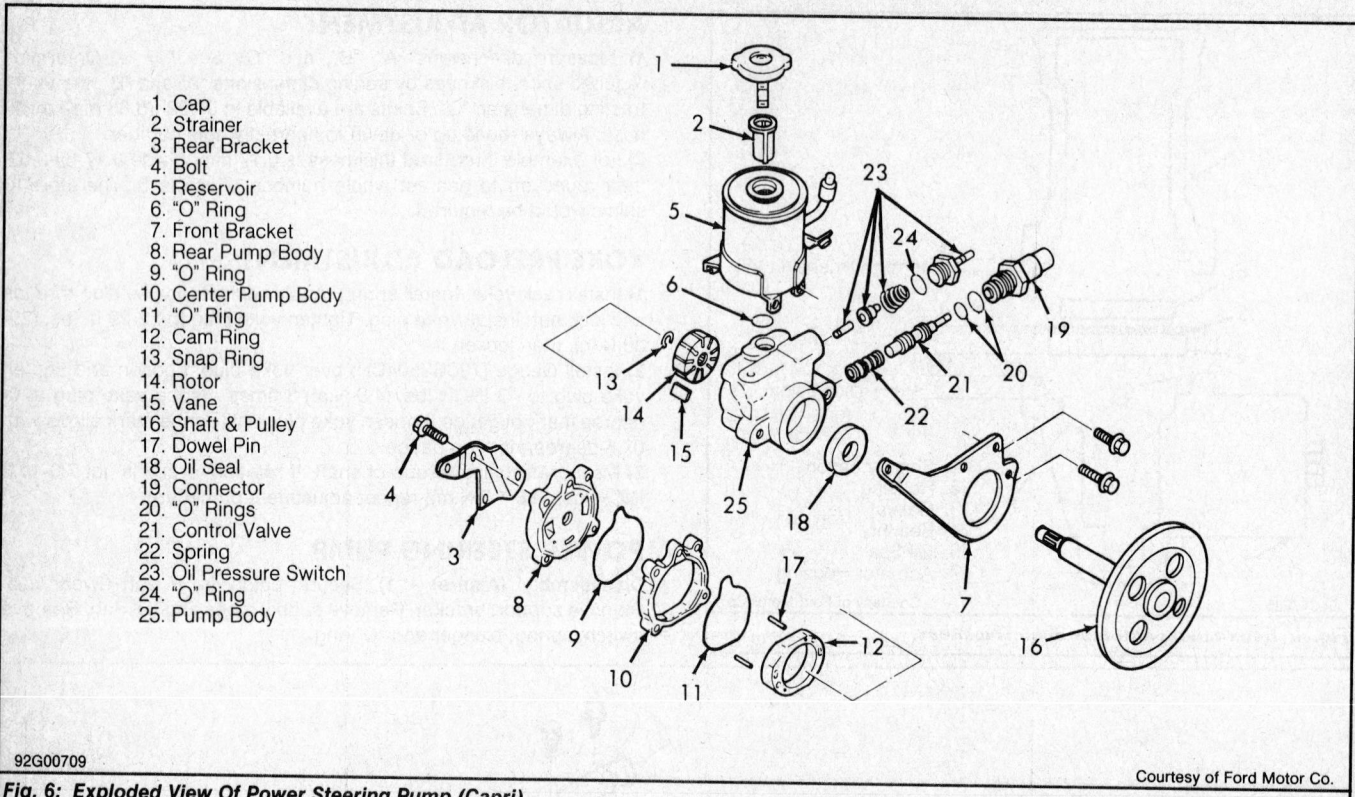

1. Cap
2. Strainer
3. Rear Bracket
4. Bolt
5. Reservoir
6. "O" Ring
7. Front Bracket
8. Rear Pump Body
9. "O" Ring
10. Center Pump Body
11. "O" Ring
12. Cam Ring
13. Snap Ring
14. Rotor
15. Vane
16. Shaft & Pulley
17. Dowel Pin
18. Oil Seal
19. Connector
20. "O" Rings
21. Control Valve
22. Spring
23. Oil Pressure Switch
24. "O" Ring
25. Pump Body

92G00709

Courtesy of Ford Motor Co.

Fig. 6: Exploded View Of Power Steering Pump (Capri)

2) Remove valve outlet fitting and "O" rings. Remove valve and spring from valve bore. Reposition pump in vise for access to rear body bolts. Remove rear body and "O" ring.

3) Remove cam ring. Remove rotor. Remove vanes. Remove side plate and "O" rings.

Assembly – 1) Install "O" rings onto side plate. Install side plate. Align side plate holes as shown to aid installation of rear body. See Fig. 5. Install rotor with identification mark facing upward.

2) Install vanes with rounded portion facing outward. Install cam ring with identification mark facing downward. Install rear body. To complete assembly, reverse disassembly procedure.

3) Check pump for free rotation. If pump does not rotate freely, disassemble and repair as necessary. Install pump onto vehicle. Bleed air from hydraulic system before starting engine. See HYDRAULIC SYSTEM BLEEDING under LUBRICATION.

Disassembly (Capri) – 1) Drain pump. Remove rear bracket, mount bolts and brackets. Remove reservoir and "O" ring. Remove rear pump body and "O" ring. Remove pump center body and "O" ring. Remove cam ring and pump shaft snap ring. Remove vanes from rotor. See Fig. 6.

2) Remove rotor from shaft, noting rotor position. Remove pump shaft from front of pump. Remove front bracket. Remove shaft oil seal. Clean all parts except seals in solvent. Drip dry or use compressed air; DO NOT use a cloth. Inspect for burring or chipped or scored surfaces on rotor and vanes. Replace assembly if necessary. If vanes have fallen from rotor, insert vanes with rounded end toward cam.

3) Measure clearance between vanes and rotor. Clearance should be 0.0004-0.0024" (0.01-0.06 mm). Replace vanes as necessary. Measure clearance between bushing and shaft. Clearance should be 0.001-0.004" (0.03-0.10 mm). Replace shaft or bushing as necessary.

Reassembly – 1) Install pressure switch and pressure regulator valve (if removed). Lubricate and install NEW shaft oil seal. Install front bracket and bolts. Install pump shaft from front of body. Install rotor onto rear of shaft in same position as removed.

2) Install shaft snap ring. Tap shaft on rear to seat snap ring onto rotor splined hole below rotor rear face. Install vanes into rotor with rounded edges facing outward. Install cam ring, center pump body and front "O" ring. Install rear pump body and "O" ring.

3) Install reservoir and "O" ring. Install short bolt into hole for reservoir bracket. Install rear mount bracket. Rotate pulley to check for smooth operation.

TORQUE SPECIFICATIONS
TORQUE SPECIFICATIONS

Application	Ft. Lbs. (N.m)
Aspire	
Intermediate Shaft Clamp Bolt	13-19 (18-26)
Power Steering Pump Bolt	21-29 (29-39)
Pressure Hose Fitting	12-17 (16-23)
Steering Gear Bolts	27-38 (37-52)
Tie Rod-To-Steering Knuckle	31-42 (42-57)
Wheel Lug Nut	65-87 (88-118)
Yoke Adjuster Plug Lock Nut	36-44 (49-59)
Capri	
Pinion Cover Lock Nut	30-37 (40-50)
Pinion Shaft Nut	30-37 (40-50)
Power Steering Lock Nut	32-45 (43-61)
Power Steering Pump Bracket	27-38 (37-52)
Tie Rod-To-Rack	44-59 (60-80)
Tie Rod-To-Steering Knuckle	26-30 (35-40)
Valve Body Cover Lock Nut	30-37 (40-50)
Wheel Lug Nut	66-89 (90-120)
	INCH Lbs. (N.m)
Pinion Bearing Cover (Capri)	40-49 (4.5-5.5)

Aspire, Capri

IDENTIFICATION

AUTOMATIC TRANSMISSION APPLICATIONS

Model	Transmission
Aspire	FLC
Capri	4EAT

LUBRICATION

SERVICE INTERVALS

Check fluid level at every engine oil change. Fluid and filter changes, or band adjustments are not required under normal operation. Under severe operating conditions, change fluid every 30 months or 30,000 miles. On Aspire, adjust band when fluid is changed.

CHECKING FLUID LEVEL

With transmission at normal operating temperature, park vehicle on level surface. Apply parking brake. Run engine at idle. Run gearshift lever through all positions, ending in Park. With engine running, fluid level should be between "F" and "L" marks. DO NOT overfill.

RECOMMENDED FLUID

Use Mercon ATF.

FLUID CAPACITIES

NOTE: *Capacities given are approximate refill amounts that apply to overhaul situation. Correct fluid level should be determined by mark on dipstick.*

TRANSMISSION REFILL CAPACITIES

Application	Qts. (L)
Aspire	5.6 (5.3)
Capri	6.0 (5.7)

DRAINING & REFILLING

1) Remove undercover and side cover, if necessary, to gain access to transaxle oil pan. Remove drain plug. Drain fluid. Remove oil pan. Discard gasket. Clean or replace filter screen as necessary. On Aspire, tighten screen bolts to 27-35 INCH lbs. (3-4 N.m). On Capri, tighten screen bolts to 71-97 INCH lbs. (8-11 N.m).

CAUTION: *DO NOT use any type of gasket sealer or RTV on oil pan gasket. DO NOT overtighten.*

2) Install oil pan bolts. On Aspire, tighten bolts to 44-71 INCH lbs. (5-8 N.m). On Capri, tighten bolts to 71-97 INCH lbs. (8-11 N.m). On all models, install drain plug with NEW washer. Tighten plug to 29-40 ft. lbs. (39-54 N.m).

3) Install undercover and side cover. Add about 3 qts. of Mercon ATF through dipstick tube. DO NOT overfill. Run engine to normal operating temperature and check fluid level. Adjust as necessary.

ADJUSTMENTS

NEUTRAL SAFETY SWITCH

Neutral safety switch is threaded into transaxle case. Adjustment is not necessary.

SHIFT CONTROL CABLE

CAUTION: *After completing linkage adjustments, verify neutral safety switch operates properly. With parking brake and service brakes applied, try to start engine in each gear position. Engine must crank only when gearshift lever is in Neutral and Park.*

Aspire – 1) Disconnect negative battery cable. Remove shift console. Set shift lever to Park position. Remove shift lever knob and lock nut. Remove shift quadrant attaching screws.
2) Loosen transmission shift cable bracket bolts. Adjust shift cable and bracket at control lever to desired position. Check shift cable and bracket at transaxle lever for adjustment.
3) Lightly press selector cam to verify clearances are within specification. See Fig. 1. Verify guide plate and guide pin are within specification when control lever is set to Neutral and Drive positions. Readjust cable and bracket as necessary.

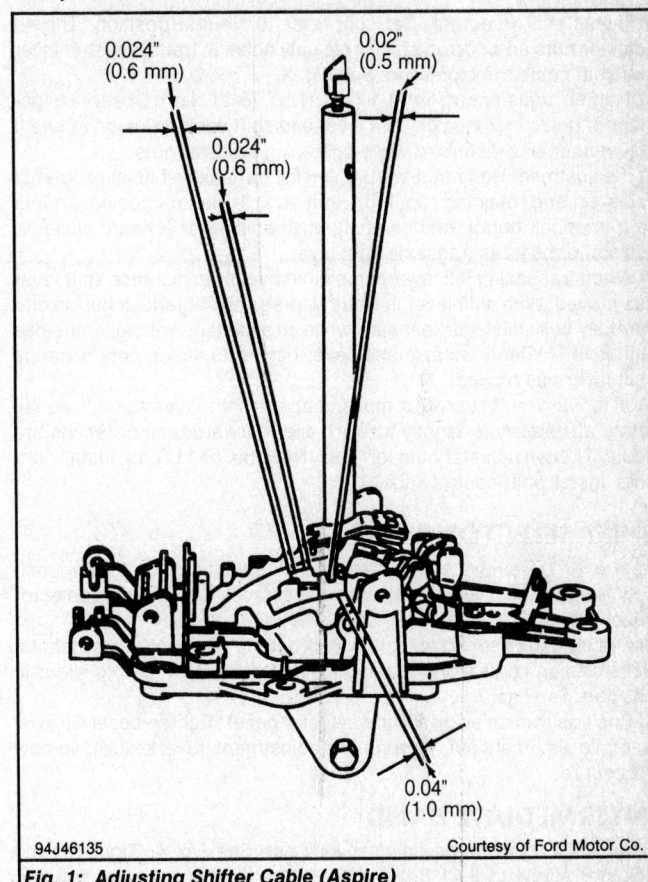

94J46135   Courtesy of Ford Motor Co.

Fig. 1: Adjusting Shifter Cable (Aspire)

Capri – 1) Set shift lever to Neutral position. Remove spring clip and pin attaching shift cable trunnion to transaxle shift lever. Rotate transaxle shift lever fully counterclockwise to Park position, then rotate transaxle shift lever clockwise 2 detents to Neutral position.

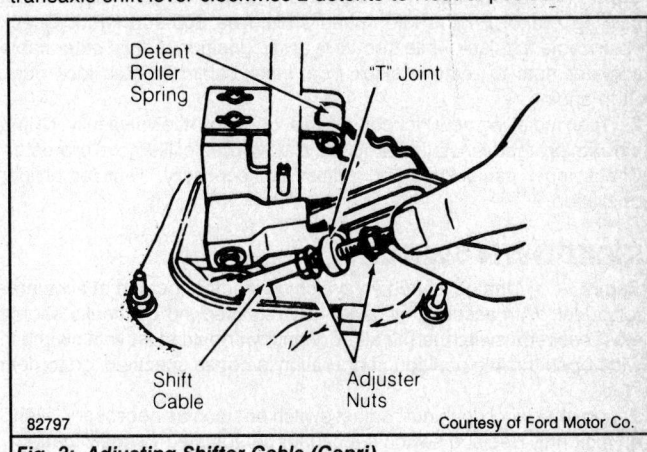

82797   Courtesy of Ford Motor Co.

Fig. 2: Adjusting Shifter Cable (Capri)

2) While rotating lever, position it between ends of shift cable trunnion. If hole in transaxle shift lever aligns with hole in shift cable trunnion, shift control cable is properly adjusted. If holes do not align, go to next step. If holes do align, go to step **5)**.

3) Loosen lock nut and unscrew shift knob. Raise ashtray receptacle. Disconnect wiring. Remove shift quadrant. Loosen adjuster nuts on shift cable. Set shift lever to Park position. Observe position of detent spring roller. If spring roller is not centered in Park detent, loosen attaching screws and move detent spring forward or backward to center spring roller.

4) Install shift quadrant. Set shift lever to Neutral position. Thread adjuster nuts up or down shift cable until holes in transaxle shift lever and shift cable trunnion align. *See Fig. 2.*

5) Tighten adjuster nuts to 71-97 INCH lbs. (8-11 N.m). Observe alignment of holes in transaxle shift lever and shift cable trunnion to see if adjustment was disturbed while tightening adjuster nuts.

6) If adjustment was not disturbed, install transaxle shift lever-to-shift cable pin and retaining clip. With shift lever in Neutral position, press shift interlock button and carefully push shift lever forward while an assistant observes transaxle shift lever.

7) When transaxle shift lever begins to move, note distance shift lever has moved. With shift lever in Neutral, press shift interlock button and carefully pull shift lever rearward while an assistant watches transaxle shift lever. When transaxle shift lever begins to move, note distance shift lever has moved.

8) If forward and rearward movements of shift lever are not equal, rotate adjuster nuts slightly forward and rearward until distances are equal. Tighten adjuster nuts to 71-97 INCH lbs. (8-11 N.m). Install console. Install shift control knob.

SHIFT SELECTOR BEZEL

Aspire – 1) Remove shift console panel. Set shift lever to Park position. Remove shift lever knob and knob screws. Remove shift selector bezel.

2) Ensure detent spring roller is in Park detent. Align holes in slider and transmission control dial bezel. Install alignment pin to hold slider in position. *See Fig. 3.*

3) Position transmission control selector bezel. Tighten bezel screws. Remove alignment pin. To complete adjustment, reverse disassembly procedure.

INTERMEDIATE BAND

Aspire – Loosen band adjuster lock nut. *See Fig. 4.* Tighten band adjuster screw to 9-11 ft. lbs. (12-15 N.m). Back off band adjuster screw exactly 3 turns. Hold band adjuster screw in position while tightening lock nut to 41-59 ft. lbs. (55-80 N.m).

KICKDOWN CABLE

Capri – 1) Set shifter in Park position. Start and warm engine. Set parking brake. Engine idle speed should be 800-900 RPM. Check inner cable for slack while throttle is at idle position. Adjust outer cable adjuster nuts to remove slack from inner cable. Tighten lock nuts. Stop engine.

2) When installing new kickdown cable, open throttle valve fully. Crimp pin with protector installed around kickdown cable. Remove protector. Check inner cable for slack. Adjust as necessary. Test for proper operation.

KICKDOWN SWITCH

Aspire – 1) Unplug kickdown switch connector, located at accelerator pedal. With accelerator pedal fully released, no continuity should exist between switch terminals. Continuity should exist with switch in wide open throttle position. If operation is not as specified, go to next step.

2) Loosen switch lock nut. Adjust switch position as necessary. Tighten lock nut. Replace switch if it cannot be adjusted to specification.

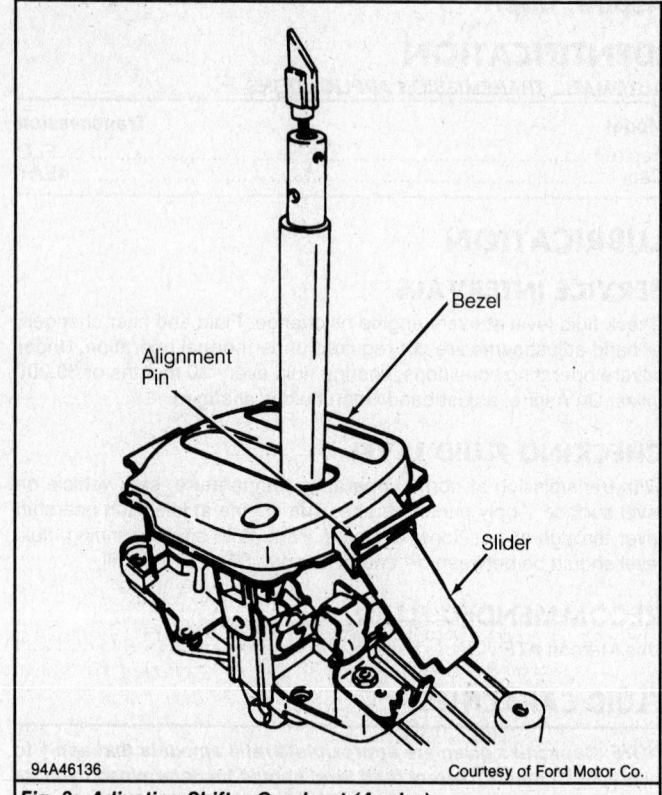

94A46136   Courtesy of Ford Motor Co.

Fig. 3: Adjusting Shifter Quadrant (Aspire)

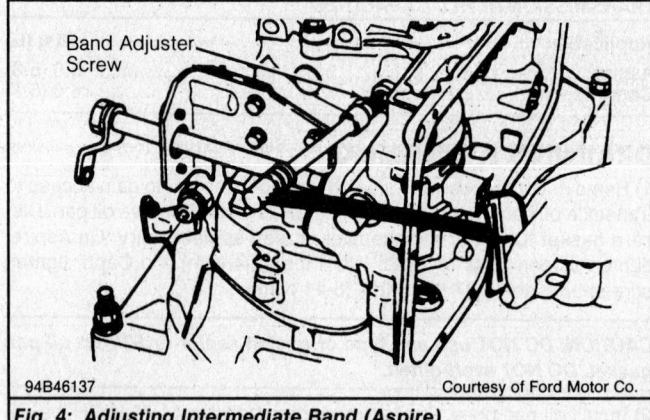

94B46137   Courtesy of Ford Motor Co.

Fig. 4: Adjusting Intermediate Band (Aspire)

Aspire, Festiva

IDENTIFICATION

FORD MANUAL TRANSAXLE APPLICATIONS

Model	Transaxle
Aspire	5-Speed Transaxle
Capri	
Non-Turbo	F2 5-Speed Transaxle
Turbo	G 5-Speed Transaxle

LUBRICATION

SERVICE INTERVALS

Inspect fluid level each year. No fluid change interval is recommended.

CHECKING FLUID LEVEL

1) Place vehicle on level surface. Slide protective boot up speedometer cable. Disconnect speedometer cable from drive gear at transaxle. Remove speedometer drive gear from transaxle. Carefully remove "O" ring from gear sleeve and wipe sleeve clean.

2) Use marks on gear sleeve to confirm fluid level. On Aspire full/low mark is about half way up gear shaft. On Capri full/low mark is just above lower drive gear. Add fluid, as needed, through speedometer driven gear hole.

3) Inspect "O" ring. Reinstall or replace as needed. Install speedometer driven gear. Tighten mounting bolt to 69-104 INCH lbs. (7.8-12 N.m).

RECOMMENDED FLUID

Use Motorcraft MERCON ATF E6AZ-19582B (ESR-M2C163-A2).

FLUID CAPACITIES

TRANSAXLE REFILL CAPACITIES

Application	Qts. (L)
Aspire	2.6 (2.5)
Capri	3.4 (3.2)

ADJUSTMENTS

GEARSHIFT LINKAGE

No external linkage or selector adjustments are provided or necessary under normal operation.

Aspire, Capri

MANUAL

NOTE: For manual transmission/transaxle replacement procedures, see FWD article in CLUTCHES.

AUTOMATIC

Removal (Aspire) – 1) Disconnect negative battery cable. Disengage shift linkage from manual shaft. Remove shift cable and bracket. Disconnect speedometer cable from transaxle. Unplug connectors located next to governor.

2) Disconnect transaxle vacuum and vent hoses. Disconnect ground wire from transaxle. Remove starter. Remove coolant pipe retaining bracket, located below distributor cap. Remove 2 upper bellhousing bolts. Support engine with Engine Support Bar (D87L-6000-A). *See Fig. 1.* Raise and support vehicle. Remove front wheels. Drain transaxle fluid.

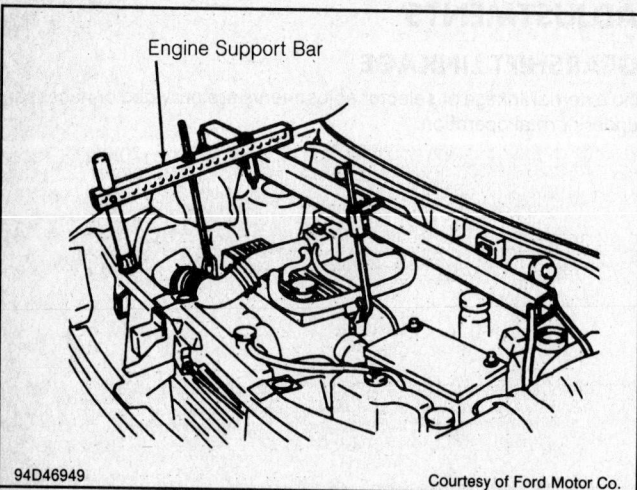

Engine Support Bar

94D46949   Courtesy of Ford Motor Co.

Fig. 1: Engine Support Bar (Aspire Shown; Capri Is Similar)

3) Remove fender splash shields. Remove stabilizer bar brackets. Remove lower control arm clamp bolts and nuts. Pull lower control arms downward, separating lower control arms from knuckle.

4) Separate tie rod ends from knuckles. Remove front axle shafts. See FWD AXLE SHAFTS article in DRIVE AXLES. Remove front and rear transaxle support insulator nuts. Remove rear engine support. Remove front transaxle support insulator.

5) Remove front transaxle support bracket. Remove rear transaxle support bracket and insulator. Remove intake manifold support brace. Remove transaxle-to-engine brace. Remove torque converter cover. Remove torque converter bolts.

6) Mark oil cooler tubes and hoses for reassembly reference. Disconnect oil cooler hoses. Position transaxle jack. Secure transaxle to jack. Remove bellhousing bolts. Remove transaxle.

Installation – 1) Position transaxle into vehicle. Install and tighten bellhousing bolts to 47-66 ft. lbs. (64-89 N.m). Remove transmission jack. Install starter. Install and tighten torque converter bolts to 25-36 ft. lbs. (34-49 N.m).

2) Install flywheel cover. Tighten bolts to 71-97 INCH lbs. (8-11 N.m). Install transaxle-to-engine supports. Tighten bolts to 27-38 ft. lbs. (37-52 N.m). Install intake manifold support. Tighten bolts to 27-38 ft. lbs. (37-52 N.m).

3) Install case rear bracket and front support bracket. Tighten bolts to 27-38 ft. lbs. (37-52 N.m). Leave transaxle front support bracket through-bolt loose.

4) Install rear engine support. Install and tighten rebound insulator bolts to 47-66 ft. lbs. (64-89 N.m). Tighten front support through-bolt to 69-83 ft. lbs. (93-113 N.m).

5) Install and tighten front support insulator nuts to 32-38 ft. lbs. (43-52 N.m). Install and tighten rear support insulator nuts to 21-34 ft. lbs. (28-46 N.m).

6) Remove differential plugs. Install axle shafts. Connect oil cooler hoses. Connect tie rod ends to knuckles. Tighten nuts to 26-29 ft. lbs. (35-40 N.m). Install NEW cotter pins.

7) Connect lower arm ball joints to knuckles. Tighten clamp bolts to 40-50 ft. lbs. (54-68 N.m). Install stabilizer bar brackets. Tighten mounting nuts to 32-38 ft. lbs. (43-52 N.m).

8) Install splash shield. Install front wheels. Lower vehicle. Remove engine support bar. Connect shift cable to transaxle. Install shift lever onto manual shaft. Tighten nut to 32-47 ft. lbs. (44-64 N.m).

CAUTION: DO NOT tighten manual shaft bolt with power wrench. Damage to transaxle may result.

9) Connect transaxle vacuum hose. Connect transaxle wiring. Connect ground wire to transaxle. Connect speedometer cable to transaxle. Connect negative battery cable. Add specified transaxle fluid. Start engine and check for leaks and proper fluid level.

Removal (Capri) – 1) Disconnect and remove battery. Remove air cleaner. Disconnect speedometer cable from transaxle. With transaxle in Park range, disengage shift cable from neutral safety switch. Remove shift cable retaining bolts. Disconnect kickdown cable from throttle body. Unplug transaxle electrical connectors next to governor.

2) Remove dipstick bracket and ground wire. Remove upper starter bolts. Remove upper intake manifold support bolts. Remove heater by-pass tube bracket. Remove transaxle-to-engine upper mount bolts. Install Engine Support Bar (D88L-6000-A). *See Fig. 1.*

3) Raise vehicle. Drain transaxle fluid. Disconnect oil cooler hoses. Remove lower intake manifold support bolts. Disconnect starter wiring. Remove front wheels and splash shields. Separate ball joints from control arms. Remove left control arm retaining bolt. Loosen right control arm bolt.

4) Remove frame brace-to-crossmember bolts. Remove front and rear transaxle mount bolts. Remove crossmember braces and crossmember. Remove left drive axle. Disconnect right drive axle from transaxle. Install Differential Plugs (T88C-7025-AH).

CAUTION: Misalignment of differential side gears could result if differential plugs are not installed.

5) Remove torque converter cover plate. Remove front and rear transaxle mounts. Remove exhaust manifold support mount. Lower vehicle. Lower, but DO NOT remove, engine/transaxle assembly from support bar. Raise vehicle. Remove torque converter bolts. Secure transaxle to jack with chains. Remove lower transaxle-to-engine bolts. Remove transaxle.

CAUTION: Raise transaxle slowly, taking care that dipstick tube clears battery tray.

Installation – 1) Install NEW circlips onto inner CV joint shafts. Position transaxle into vehicle, while aligning torque converter studs to drive plate. Install and tighten lower engine-to-transaxle bolts to 46-66 ft. lbs. (63-89 N.m). Install and tighten torque converter bolts to 32-45 ft. lbs. (43-61 N.m). Remove transaxle jack. Lower vehicle.

CAUTION: Take care not to damage A/C (if equipped) or other components while raising engine/transaxle into position.

2) Raise engine/transaxle assembly into position with support bar. Raise vehicle. Install and tighten transaxle rear mount to 49-69 ft. lbs. (67-93 N.m). Install and tighten exhaust manifold support nuts to 14-18 ft. lbs. (19-25 N.m).

3) Install torque converter cover plate. Align gusset plates, then install and tighten bolts to 27-38 ft. lbs. (37-52 N.m). Position crossmember onto transaxle mounts. Loosely install nuts onto rear transaxle mount stud first, then front studs. Install and tighten crossmember brace bolts to 27-40 ft. lbs. (36-54 N.m). Tighten transaxle mount nuts to 21-33 ft. lbs. (28-46 N.m).

4) Install axle shafts. Tighten NEW retaining nuts to 116-173 ft. lbs. (157-235 N.m). Pull outward on shafts to verify proper seating. Position shift cable. Tighten shift cable lower mounting bolt to 71-97 INCH lbs. (8-11 N.m).

5) With crossmember and frame braces installed, tighten bolts to 27-40 ft. lbs. (36-54 N.m). Install and tighten control arm bolts to 69-86 ft. lbs. (93-117 N.m). Install ball joints. Tighten pinch bolts to 32-40 ft. lbs. (43-54 N.m).

6) Install splash shields. Install lower starter mounting bolts loosely. Connect starter wiring. Loosely install intake manifold bracket bolts. Install and tighten wheel nuts to 66-89 ft. lbs. (90-120 N.m). Lower vehicle.

7) Install and tighten upper transaxle to engine retaining bolts to 46-66 ft. lbs. (63-89 N.m). Remove engine support bar. Install heater by-pass tube bracket. Install and tighten remaining intake manifold support bolts to 23-34 ft. lbs. (31-46 N.m). Install and tighten remaining starter mounting bolts to 23-34 ft. lbs. (31-46 N.m).

8) Position ground wire. Install dipstick tube retaining bolt. Reconnect oil cooler hoses with NEW seals. Tighten to 12-18 ft. lbs. (16-24 N.m). Route and connect shift cable to neutral safety switch. Tighten shift cable retainer and neutral safety switch nut to 71-97 INCH lbs. (8-11 N.m). Connect kickdown cable to throttle housing. Connect transaxle wiring and speedometer cable. Install air cleaner and battery.

9) Fill transaxle to specification. See AUTOMATIC TRANSMISSION article in TRANSMISSION SERVICING. Run engine to warm transaxle fluid. Check transaxle for proper operation and fluid level.

TORQUE SPECIFICATIONS

TORQUE SPECIFICATIONS

Applications	Ft. Lbs. (N.m)
Aspire	
Bellhousing Bolts	47-66 (64-89)
Case Rear Bracket	27-38 (37-52)
Clamp Bolt	40-50 (54-68)
Front Support Through-Bolt	69-83 (93-113)
Front Support Insulator Nuts	32-38 (43-52)
Front Transaxle Support Bolts	28-38 (38-52)
Intake Manifold Support Bolts	27-38 (37-52)
Manual Shaft Bolt	32-47 (44-64)
Rear Rebound Insulator Bolts	47-66 (64-89)
Rear Support Insulator Nut	21-34 (28-46)
Rebound Insulator Bolt	47-66 (64-89)
Tie Rod End Nut	26-29 (35-40)
Stabilizer Bar Bracket Nuts	32-38 (43-52)
Starter Motor	23-34 (31-46)
Torque Converter Nuts	25-36 (34-49)
Transaxle-To-Engine Bolts	27-38 (37-52)
Wheel Hub Bolts	65-87 (88-118)
Capri	
Axle Shaft Nuts	116-173 (157-235)
Ball Joint Pinch Bolts	32-40 (43-54)
Control Arm Bolts	69-86 (93-117)
Crossmember Brace Bolts	27-40 (36-54)
Crossmember Nut	55-69 (75-93)
Drain Plug	29-40 (39-54)
Exhaust Manifold Nut	23-34 (31-46)
Exhaust Manifold Support Nuts	14-18 (19-25)
Exhaust Manifold-To-Transaxle Mount Bolt	46-69 (63-93)
Front & Rear Transaxle Mount Bolts	27-40 (36-54)
Front & Rear Transaxle Mount Nuts	21-34 (28-46)
Gusset Plate-To-Transaxle	27-38 (37-52)
Intake Manifold Support Bolts	23-34 (31-46)
Oil Cooler Line	12-18 (16-24)
Right Transaxle Mount	27-40 (36-54)
Starter Motor	23-34 (31-46)
Throttle Cable Bracket	14-19 (19-26)
Torque Converter Bolt	32-45 (43-61)
Transaxle Rear Mount	49-69 (67-93)
Transaxle-To-Engine	46-66 (63-89)
Wheel Lug Nuts	66-89 (90-120)

	INCH Lbs. (N.m)
Flywheel Cover Bolt	
Aspire	71-97 (8-11)
Capri	62-89 (7-10)
Line Pressure Plug	44-89 (5-10)
Shift Cable Retainer Bolts	71-97 (8-11)

1994 GEO CONTENTS

1994 MODEL COVERAGE

MODEL	BODY CODE	ENGINE	ENGINE VIN CODE [1]	FUEL SYSTEM	IGNITION SYSTEM
Metro	M	1.0L SOHC	6	TBI	[2] Magnetic
Prizm	S	1.6L DOHC [3]	6	MFI	[2] Magnetic
Prizm LSi	S	1.8L DOHC [4]	8	MFI	[2] Magnetic
Tracker	J	1.6L SOHC	U [5]	TBI	[2] Magnetic
Tracker	J	1.6L SOHC	6 [6]	MFI	[2] Magnetic

[1] – Engine may be identified by eighth digit of Vehicle Identification Number (VIN).
[2] – Spark control system is controlled by Engine Control Module (ECM) or Powertrain Control Module (PCM).
[3] – This is the 4A-FE engine.
[4] – This is the 7A-FE engine.
[5] – Federal emissions.
[6] – California emissions.

VIN DEFINITION

2C1MR2466RZ700001

① Indicates Nation Of Origin.
② Indicates Manufacturer.
③ Indicates Division (Exc. Tracker)
③ Indicates Vehicle Make And Type (Tracker).
④⑤ Indicates Vehicle Line (Exc. Tracker).
④ Indicates Gross Vehicle Weight (Tracker).
⑤ Indicates Series Or Chassis Type (Tracker).
⑥ Indicates Body Style (Exc. Tracker).
⑥ Indicates Load Capacity (Tracker).
⑦ Indicates Restraint System (Exc. Tracker).
⑦ Indicates Body Style (Tracker).
⑧ **Indicates Engine Type and Make.**
⑨ Indicates Check Digit.
⑩ **Indicates Model Year.**
⑪ Indicates Assembly Plant.
⑫-⑰ Indicates Plant Sequential Number.

MODEL YEAR VIN CODE APPLICATION

VIN Code	Model Year
M	1991
N	1992
P	1993
R	1994

ENGINE CODE LOCATION

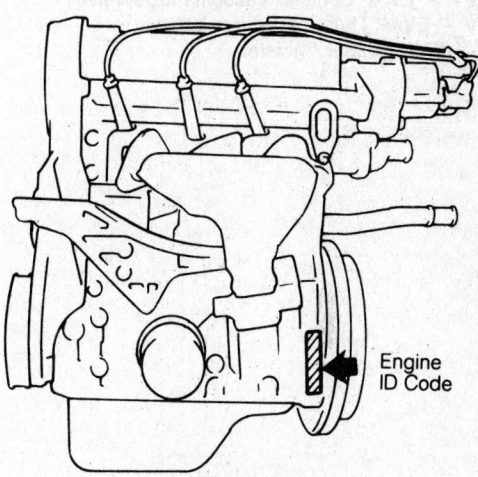

Engine ID Code

1.0L 3-CYLINDER (4-CYLINDER MODELS SIMILAR)

121559   Courtesy of General Motors Corp.

1994 ENGINE PERFORMANCE
Emission Applications

1994 GEO

Model, Engine & Fuel System	Emission Control Systems & Devices

Metro
1.0L 3-Cyl. TBI .... **PCV, EVAP, TWC, FR, EGR,** [1] **EFE, SPK,** [1] **HO2S,** [2] **O2S, MIL,**
[1] EVAP-CSPV, [2] EVAP-CVPV, [2] EVAP-TVV, EVAP-VC, EGR-VM, EGR-SVV, SPK-CC

Prizm
1.6L 4-Cyl. MFI .... **PCV, EVAP, TWC, FR,** [1] **EGR, SPK, O2S,** [1] **SUB-O2S, MIL,**
EVAP-VC, EVAP-TVV, [1] EGR-VM, [1] EGR-SVV, [1] EGR-TS, SPK-CC

Prizm LSi
1.8L 4-Cyl. MFI .... **PCV, EVAP, TWC, FR,** [1] **EGR, SPK, O2S,** [1] **SUB-O2S, MIL,**
EVAP-VC, EVAP-TVV, [1] EGR-VM, [1] EGR-SVV, [1] EGR-TS, SPK-CC

Tracker
1.6L 4-Cyl. [3] .... **PCV, EVAP, TWC, FR, EGR, SPK, HO2S, MIL,**
EVAP-VC, EVAP-CSPV, EGR-VM, EGR-SVV, EGR-TS, SPK-CC

[1] – California emissions only.
[2] – Federal emissions only.
[3] – Federal engine uses 8-valves with TBI (RPO LS5). California and New York engine uses 16-valves with MFI (RPO L01).

> **NOTE:** For quick reference, major emission control systems and devices are listed in bold type; components and other related devices are listed in light type.

EFE – Early Fuel Evaporation
EGR – Exhaust Gas Recirculation
EGR-SVV – EGR Solenoid Vacuum Valve
EGR-TS – EGR Temperature Sensor
EGR-VM – EGR Vacuum Modulator
EVAP – Fuel Evaporative System
EVAP-CSPV – EVAP Canister Solenoid Purge Valve
EVAP-CVPV – EVAP Canister Vacuum Purge Valve
EVAP-TVV – EVAP Thermal Vacuum Valve
EVAP-VC – EVAP Vapor Canister

FR – Fillpipe Restrictor
HO2S – Heated Oxygen Sensor
MFI – Multiport Fuel Injection
MIL – Malfunction Indicator Light
O2S – Oxygen Sensor
PCV – Positive Crankcase Ventilation
SPK – Spark Controls
TBI – Throttle Body Injection
SPK-CC – SPK Computer Controlled
TWC – Three-Way Catalytic Converter
SUB-O2S – Sub-Oxygen Sensor

Metro, Prizm, Tracker

INTRODUCTION

Use this article to quickly find specifications related to servicing and on-vehicle adjustments. This is a quick-reference article to use when you are familiar with an adjustment procedure and only need a specification.

NOTE: *Metro is equipped with standard or upgraded emission systems. Standard emission systems include all XFi models and base models with automatic transaxle and Federal emissions. Upgraded emission systems include base models with manual transaxle, and base models with automatic transaxle and California emissions. Refer to emission label for correct identification.*

CAPACITIES

BATTERY SPECIFICATIONS

Application	Cold Crank Amps @ 0°F (-18°C)	Reserve Capacity Minutes
Metro	390	50
Prizm & Prizm LSi	310	90
Tracker	500	75

FLUID CAPACITIES

Application	Qts. (L)
Crankcase (Includes Filter) [1]	
Metro	3.7 (3.5)
Prizm (4A-FE Engine)	3.2 (3.0)
Prizm LSi (7A-FE Engine)	3.9 (3.7)
Tracker	4.5 (4.2)
Cooling System (Includes Heater)	
Metro	
A/T	4.2 (4.0)
M/T	4.1 (3.9)
Prizm & Prizm LSi	6.7 (6.3)
Tracker	
A/T	5.5 (5.2)
M/T	5.6 (5.3)
Automatic Transaxle/Transmission (Dexron-IIE)	
Metro	5.2 (4.9)
Prizm & Prizm LSi	
3-Speed	2.6 (2.5)
4-Speed (Includes Differential)	3.5 (3.3)
Tracker	3.0 (2.8)
Manual Transaxle/Transmission [2]	
Metro	2.5 (2.4)
Prizm & Prizm LSi	2.7 (2.6)
Tracker	
2WD	1.8 (1.7)
4WD	1.6 (1.5)
Differential	
Prizm & Prizm LSi (Dexron-IIE)	
3-Speed A/T Models	1.5 (1.4)
Tracker [3]	
Front	1.2 (1.1)
Rear	2.3 (2.2)
Transfer Case [2]	
Tracker	1.8 (1.7)

[1] – Use engine oil with API rating of SG or SH.
[2] – Use synthetic 75W-90 GL-4 gear lubricant.
[3] – Use synthetic gear lubricant (GM 12345836).

QUICK-SERVICE

SERVICE INTERVALS & SPECIFICATIONS

REPLACEMENT INTERVALS [1]

Component	Miles
Metro	
Air Filter	30,000
Coolant	30,000
Fuel Filter	30,000
Ignition Wires	60,000
Oil & Filter	7500
Spark Plug	30,000
Timing Belt	60,000
Transaxle Lubricant	
A/T	100,000
M/T	30,000
Prizm & Prizm LSi	
Air Filter	30,000
Coolant	[2]
Oil & Filter	7500
Spark Plug	30,000
Timing Belt	60,000
Transaxle Lubricant	
A/T	[3]
M/T	[3]
Valve Clearance Adjustment	60,000
Tracker	
Air Filter	30,000
EVAP Canister	100,000
Coolant	30,000
Drive Axle Lubricant	[4]
Fuel Filter	30,000
Ignition Wires & Distributor Cap	60,000
Oil & Filter	7500
Heated Oxygen Sensor (HO2S)	80,000
PCV Valve	50,000
Spark Plug	30,000
Timing Belt	60,000
Transfer Case	[4]
Transmission Lubricant	
A/T	[5] 100,000
M/T	[4]

[1] – Under normal driving conditions.
[2] – Change at 45,000 miles and then every 30,000 miles thereafter.
[3] – Check fluid every 15,000 miles. Fluid does not require changing unless contaminated.
[4] – Change at 7500 miles and then every 30,000 miles thereafter.
[5] – Replace A/T cooler hose every 45,000 miles.

BELT ADJUSTMENT

Application	[1] Belt Deflection
Metro	
A/C Compressor	
New Belt	.20-.25" (5.1-6.4 mm)
Used Belt [2]	.31-.39" (7.9-9.9 mm)
Alternator	
New Belt	.20-.27" (5.1-7.0 mm)
Used Belt [2]	.24-.31" (6.1-8.0 mm)
Water Pump	.25-.32" (6.4-8.1 mm)
Prizm & Prizm LSi	
A/C Compressor	
New Belt	.24-.28" (6.1-7.1 mm)
Used Belt [2]	.33-.37" (8.5-9.5 mm)
Alternator	
New Belt	.20-.32" (5.1-8.1 mm)
Used Belt [2]	.24-.35" (6.1-8.9 mm)
P/S Pump	.20-.32" (5.1-8.1 mm)
Tracker	
A/C Compressor	.24-.25" (5.1-6.4 mm)
Alternator/Water Pump	
New Belt	.20-.27" (6.1-6.9 mm)
Used Belt [2]	.24-.31" (6.1-7.9 mm)
P/S Pump	.24-.35" (6.1-8.9 mm)

[1] – Deflection is with 22 lbs. (10 kg) pressure applied midway on longest belt run.
[2] – Used belt is a belt in operation for more than 5 minutes.
[3] – Belt tension is checked with belt tension gauge.

BELT ADJUSTMENT (Cont.)

Application Prizm & Prizm LSi	[3] Belt Tension
Alternator	
New Belt	141-182 lbs. (64-82 kg)
Used Belt [2]	111-152 lbs. (50-69 kg)
P/S Pump	
New Belt	100-150 lbs. (45-68 kg)
Used Belt [2]	60-121 lbs. (27-55 kg)

[1] – Deflection is with 22 lbs. (10 kg) pressure applied midway on longest belt run.
[2] – Used belt is a belt in operation for more than 5 minutes.
[3] – Belt tension is checked with belt tension gauge.

MECHANICAL CHECKS

ENGINE COMPRESSION

Check engine compression with engine at normal operating temperature at specified cranking speed, with all spark plugs removed and throttle wide open.

COMPRESSION SPECIFICATIONS

Application	Specification
Compression Ratio	
Metro	9.5:1
Prizm & Prizm LSi	9.5:1
Tracker	
MFI	9.5:1
TBI	8.9:1
Normal Compression Pressure	
Metro	[1] 199 psi (14.0 kg/cm²)
Prizm & Prizm LSi	[2] 191 psi (13.4 kg/cm²)
Tracker	[1] 199 psi (14.0 kg/cm²)
Minimum Compression Pressure	
Metro	[1] 156 psi (11.0 kg/cm²)
Prizm & Prizm LSi	[2] 142 psi (10.0 kg/cm²)
Tracker	[1] 170 psi (12.0 kg/cm²)
Maximum Variation Between Cylinders	14 psi (1.0 kg/cm²)

[1] – Checked at 400 RPM.
[2] – Checked at 250 RPM.

VALVE CLEARANCE

VALVE CLEARANCE SPECIFICATIONS

Application	In. (mm)
Metro	[1]
Prizm & Prizm LSi	
Intake	[2] .006-.010 (.15-.25)
Exhaust	[2] .010-.014 (.25-.35)
Tracker	
MFI (16-valve)	
Intake & Exhaust	[2] .0051-.0067 (.13-.17)
Intake & Exhaust	[3] .0067-.0081 (.17-.21)
TBI (8-valve)	
Intake	[2] .0051-.0067 (.13-.17)
Exhaust	[2] .0063-.0075 (.16-.190)
Intake	[3] .0091-.0106 (.23-.27)
Exhaust	[3] .0102-.0114 (.26-.29)

[1] – Clearance is automatically adjusted by hydraulic lash adjuster.
[2] – Adjustments made with engine cold 77°F (25°C).
[3] – Adjustments made with engine hot 154°F (68°C).

IGNITION SYSTEM

IGNITION COIL
IGNITION COIL RESISTANCE – Ohms @ 68°F (20°C)

Application	Primary	Secondary
Metro		
Standard	1.33-1.65	22,100-29,900
Upgraded	1.08-1.32	22,100-29,900
Prizm & Prizm LSi		
Cold [1]	1.11-1.75	9000-15,700
Hot [2]	1.41-2.05	11,400-18,400
Tracker	1.08-1.32	22,100-29,900

[1] – Temperatures between 14-104°F (–10-50°C)
[2] – Temperatures between 104-212°F (50-100°C)

DISTRIBUTOR SENSORS
PICK-UP COIL AIR GAP [1]

Application	Clearance In. (mm)
Except Tracker	.008-.016 (.20-.41)
Tracker	[2]

[1] – This may also be referred to as Camshaft Position (CMP) sensor on some models.
[2] – Information is not available from manufacturer.

PICK-UP COIL RESISTANCE [1] – Ohms @ 68°F (20°C)

Application	Ohms
Metro	140-180
Prizm & Prizm LSi	[2]
Tracker	[3]

[1] – This may also be referred to as Camshaft Position (CMP) sensor on some models.
[2] – Resistance between terminals No. 2 and 5 should be 370-550 ohms cold and 475-650 ohms hot. Resistance between terminals No. 3 and 6 should be 185-275 ohms cold and 240-325 ohms hot.
[3] – Information is not available from manufacturer.

HIGH TENSION WIRE RESISTANCE
HIGH TENSION WIRE RESISTANCE

Application	Ohms
All Models	3000-6700 Per Foot

SPARK PLUGS
SPARK PLUG TYPE

A/C	Nippondenso	NGK
Metro		
R42XLS	W20EPR-U11	BPR6ES-11
Prizm & Prizm LSi		
N/A	K16R-U	BKR5EYA
Tracker		
MFI		
FR2LS	K20PR-U	BKR6E
TBI		
N/A	W16EXR-U	BPR5ES

SPARK PLUG SPECIFICATIONS

Application	Gap In. (mm)	Torque Ft. Lbs. (N.m)
Metro	.039-.043 (1.0-1.1)	21 (28)
Prizm & Prizm LSi	.031 (0.79)	13 (18)
Tracker	.028 (0.71)	21 (28)

FIRING ORDER & TIMING MARKS

NOTE: For firing order and distributor rotations, see Figs. 1-3. To locate ignition timing mark, see Figs. 4-6.

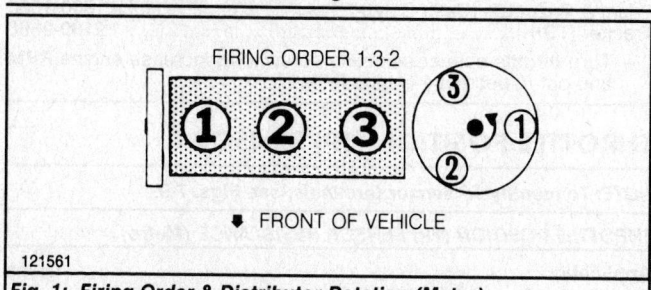

121561

Fig. 1: Firing Order & Distributor Rotation (Metro)

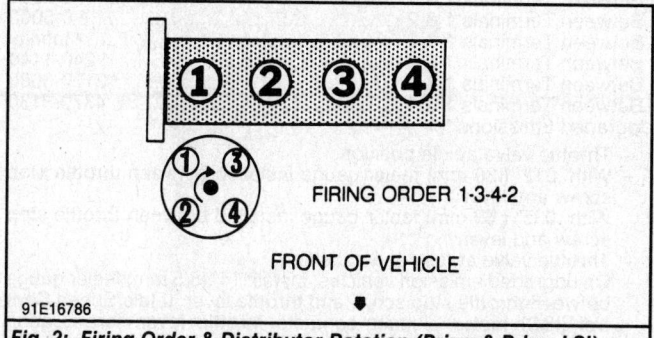

91E16786

Fig. 2: Firing Order & Distributor Rotation (Prizm & Prizm LSi)

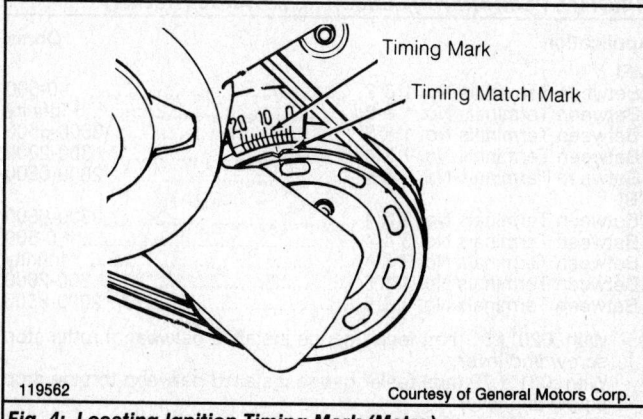

91F16787

Fig. 3: Firing Order & Distributor Rotation (Tracker)

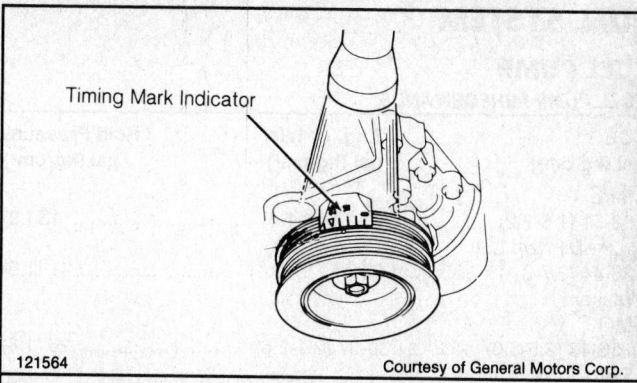

119562   Courtesy of General Motors Corp.

Fig. 4: Locating Ignition Timing Mark (Metro)

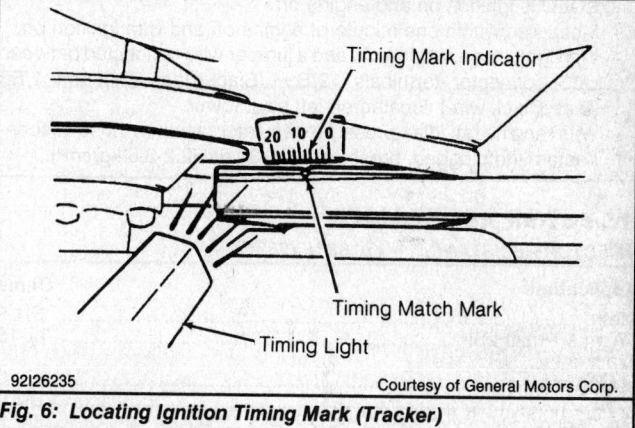

121564   Courtesy of General Motors Corp.

Fig. 5: Locating Ignition Timing Mark (Prizm & Prizm LSi)

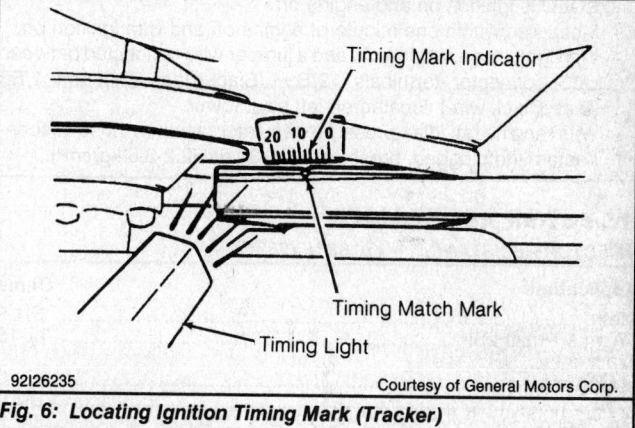

92I26235   Courtesy of General Motors Corp.

Fig. 6: Locating Ignition Timing Mark (Tracker)

IGNITION TIMING

IGNITION TIMING SPECIFICATIONS (Degrees BTDC @ RPM) [1]

Application	Man. Trans.	Auto. Trans.
Metro	[2] 4-6 @ 750-850	[2] 4-6 @ 800-900
Prizm & Prizm LSi	[3] 10 @ 650-750	[3] 10 @ 650-750
Tracker	[4] 5 @ 800	[4] 5 @ 800
Tracker	[5] 8 @ 800	[5] 8 @ 800

[1] – If specification differs from emission label, use specification listed on emission label.

[2] – With jumper wire installed between 6-pin duty check data link connector terminals "D" (Black wire) and "E" (Purple/Green wire), located behind left strut tower.

[3] – With jumper wire installed between Black 23-pin data link connector terminals E1 (Brown wire) and TE1 (Blue/White wire), located on left strut tower.

[4] – On MFI equipped vehicle, with jumper wire installed between 6-pin duty check data link connector terminals No. 4 (Black wire) and No. 5 (Blue/Red wire), located between right strut tower and battery.

[5] – On TBI-equipped vehicle, with jumper wire installed between 4-pin duty check data link connector terminals "C" (Black wire) and "D" (Blue/Red wire), located between right strut tower and battery.

FUEL SYSTEM

FUEL PUMP

FUEL PUMP PERFORMANCE

KOEO [1] psi (kg/cm²)	Eng. @ Idle psi (kg/cm²)	[2] Hold Pressure psi (kg/cm²)
Metro		
23-31 (1.6-2.2)	13-20 (.9-1.4)	13 (.9)
Prizm & Prizm LSi		
38-44 (2.7-3.1) [3]	[4] 38-44 (2.7-3.1)	21 (1.5)
Tracker		
MFI		
36-43 (2.5-3.0)	30-37 (2.1-2.6)	26 (1.8)
TBI		
34-41 (2.4-2.9)	34-41 (2.4-2.9)	25 (1.7)

[1] – KOEO is ignition on and engine off.

[2] – Measured within one minute of engine off and with ignition on.

[3] – With ignition on, engine off, and a jumper wire connected between DLC connector terminals 12/B+ (Black/Red wire) and 1/FP (Blue/Black wire), located on left strut tower.

[4] – With engine at idle, pressure regulator vacuum hose disconnected and plugged, pressure is 31-37 psi (2.2-2.6 kg/cm²).

INJECTOR RESISTANCE

INJECTOR RESISTANCE – @ 68°F (20°C)

Application	Ohms
Metro	.5-1.5
Prizm & Prizm LSi	12-15
Tracker	
MFI	[1]
TBI	1.0-2.0

[1] – Injector resistance not provided by manufacturer.

IDLE SPEED

IDLE SPEED SPECIFICATIONS [1][2]

Application	Idle RPM A/C Off	Idle RPM A/C On
Metro Standard		
XFi	[3] 650-750	[3] 850-950
Base A/T	[3] 800-900	[3] 850-950
Base M/T	[3] 750-850	[3] 850-950
Metro Upgraded		
A/T	[4] 800-900	N/A
M/T	[4] 750-850	N/A
Prizm & Prizm LSi	[4]	[4]
Tracker [5]	750-850	[6]

[1] – If specification differs from emission label, use specification listed on emission label.

[2] – Check using Tech 1 connected to Data Link Connector (DLC) with engine warm, accessories off and transaxle in Neutral (M/T) or Park (A/T).

[3] – Idle Speed Control (ISC) duty is 25-35% with A/C off and 15-25% with A/C on.

[4] – Idle speed is computer controlled and is not adjustable.

[5] – Idle speed is checked with Tech 1 and a jumper wire connected between duty check data link connector terminal No. 2 (Blue/Yellow wire), diagnostic request, and terminal No. 3 (TBI) or No. 4 (MFI), (Black wire) ground.

[6] – Idle speed should be 950-1050 RPM in Neutral or Park, and 750-850 RPM in Drive, Reverse or any other forward gear.

THROTTLE OPENER

THROTTLE OPENER ADJUSTMENT

Application	RPM
Prizm & Prizm LSi (Calif. Only)	1300-1500
Tracker (TBI)	[1] 2100-2300

[1] – Turn throttle opener adjusting screw in to increase engine RPM and out to decrease engine RPM.

THROTTLE POSITION (TP) SENSOR

NOTE: To identify TP sensor terminals, see Figs. 7-9.

THROTTLE POSITION (TP) SENSOR RESISTANCE (Metro)

Application	Ohms
Standard Emissions	
Between Terminals 1 & 2	[1] 0-5000
Between Terminals 1 & 2	[2] 0-5000
Between Terminals 1 & 2	[3] Infinity
Between Terminals 1 & 3	[1] 240-1140
Between Terminals 1 & 3	[4] 3170-6600
Between Terminals 1 & 4	4370-8130
Upgraded Emissions [5]	

[1] – Throttle valve at idle position.

[2] – With .012" (.30 mm) feeler gauge installed between throttle stop screw and lever.

[3] – With .035" (.89 mm) feeler gauge installed between throttle stop screw and lever.

[4] – Throttle valve at fully open position.

[5] – On upgraded emission vehicles, install .14" (3.5 mm) feeler gauge between throttle stop screw and throttle lever. If Idle Speed Control (ISC) motor plunger contacts throttle lever screw, bring engine to operating temperature. Using a Tech 1 connected to DLC, ensure TP sensor voltage is .98-1.02 volts. Adjust or replace TP sensor as necessary.

THROTTLE POSITION (TP) SENSOR RESISTANCE (Prizm & Prizm LSi)

Application	Ohms
Between Terminals E2 & IDL	[1] 0-2300
Between Terminals E2 & IDL	[2] Infinity
Between Terminals E2 & VC	4000-8500
Between Terminals E2 & VTA	[3] 200-6000
Between Terminals E2 & VTA	[4] 3300-10,000

[1] – With .016" (.40 mm) feeler gauge installed between throttle stop screw and lever.

[2] – With .035" (.89 mm) feeler gauge installed between throttle stop screw and lever.

[3] – With zero clearance between throttle stop screw and lever.

[4] – Throttle valve at fully open position.

THROTTLE POSITION (TP) SENSOR RESISTANCE (Tracker)

Application	Ohms
MFI	
Between Terminals No. 1 & 2	[1] 0-500
Between Terminals No. 1 & 2	[2] Infinity
Between Terminals No. 1 & 3	3500-6500
Between Terminals No. 1 & 4	[3][5] 300-2000
Between Terminals No. 1 & 4	[4][5] 2000-6500
TBI	
Between Terminals No. 2 & 4	3500-6500
Between Terminals No. 3 & 4	[6] 0-500
Between Terminals No. 3 & 4	[7] Infinity
Between Terminals No. 4 & 5	[3][5][8] 300-2000
Between Terminals No. 4 & 5	[4][5] 2000-6500

[1] – With .020" (.51 mm) feeler gauge installed between throttle stop screw and lever.

[2] – With .031" (.79 mm) feeler gauge installed between throttle stop screw and lever.

[3] – Throttle valve at idle position.

[4] – Throttle valve at fully open position.

[5] – There should be more than 2000 ohms resistance in TP sensor between idle position and fully open position.

[6] – With .012" (.30 mm) feeler gauge installed between throttle stop screw and lever.

[7] – With .022" (.56 mm) feeler gauge installed between throttle stop screw and lever.

[8] – When checking resistance at idle position, apply 19.7 in. Hg vacuum to throttle opener to move throttle valve to idle position.

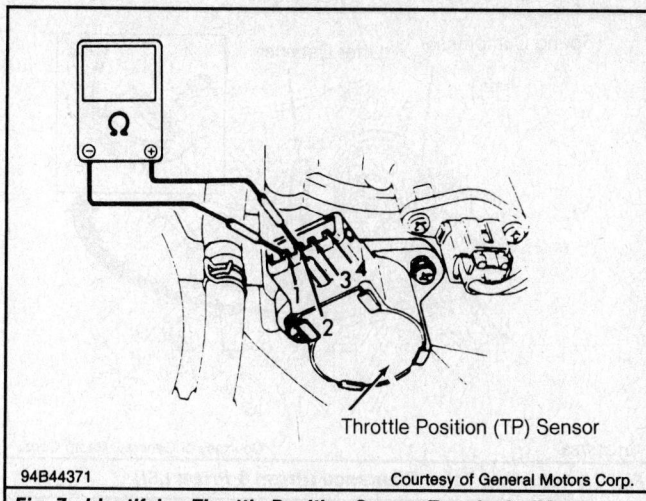

94B44371   Courtesy of General Motors Corp.

Fig. 7: Identifying Throttle Position Sensor Terminals (Metro – Standard Emissions Shown; Tracker – MFI Is Similar)

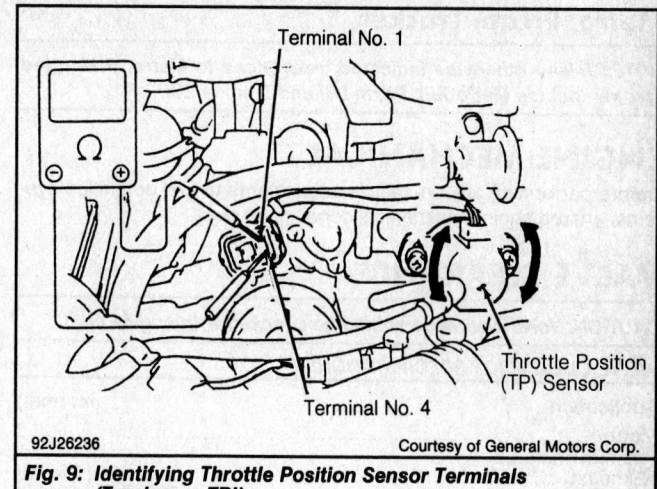

92J26236   Courtesy of General Motors Corp.

Fig. 9: Identifying Throttle Position Sensor Terminals (Tracker – TBI)

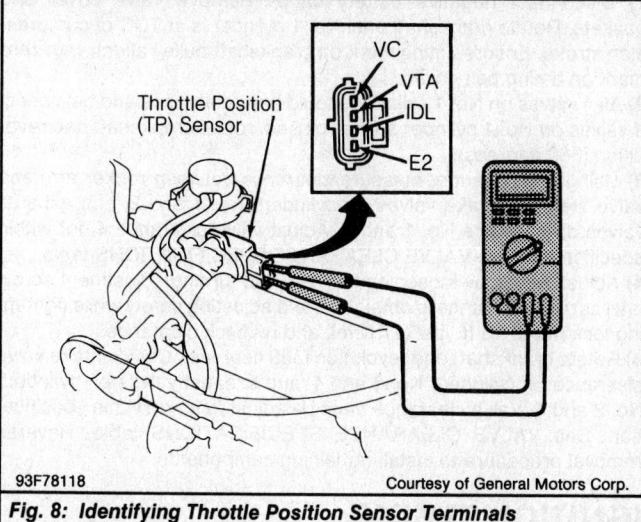

93F78118   Courtesy of General Motors Corp.

Fig. 8: Identifying Throttle Position Sensor Terminals (Prizm & Prizm LSi)

1994 ENGINE PERFORMANCE
On-Vehicle Adjustments

Metro, Prizm, Tracker

NOTE: Unless otherwise indicated, references to Metro, Prizm and Tracker include Metro XFi, Prizm LSi and Tracker LSi.

ENGINE MECHANICAL

Before performing any on-vehicle adjustments to fuel or ignition systems, ensure engine mechanical condition is okay.

VALVE CLEARANCE

CAUTION: Valve clearance should be checked with engine cold.

VALVE CLEARANCE SPECIFICATIONS

Application	In. (mm)
Metro .... [1]	
Prizm & Prizm LSi	
Exhaust .... [2] .010-.014 (.25-.35)	
Intake .... [2] .006-.010 (.15-.25)	
Tracker	
Exhaust .... [2] [3]	
Intake .... [2] .005-.007 (.13-.18)	

[1] – Clearance is automatically adjusted by hydraulic lash adjuster.
[2] – Adjustments made with engine cold.
[3] – Valve clearance should be .006-.008 (.15-.20) on TBI (Federal) and .005-.007 (.13-.18) on MFI (Calif. & New York).

METRO

Hydraulic lash adjusters are used. No adjustment is required.

PRIZM & PRIZM LSI

1) Disconnect negative battery cable. Remove valve cover and gaskets. Rotate crankshaft until No. 1 cylinder is at TDC of compression stroke. Ensure timing mark on crankshaft pulley aligns with zero mark on timing belt cover.
2) Valves on No. 1 cylinder should have clearance and be closed. If both valves on No. 1 cylinder are not closed, rotate crankshaft one revolution (360 degrees).
3) Using feeler gauge, measure and record clearance between camshaft lobe and adjuster shim on intake valves of cylinders No. 1 and 2, and exhaust valves of cylinders No. 1 and 3. Adjust valve clearance if not within specification. See VALVE CLEARANCE SPECIFICATIONS table.
4) Rotate crankshaft one revolution (360 degrees). Check clearance on intake valves of cylinders No. 3 and 4, and exhaust valves of cylinders No. 2 and 4. Adjust valve clearance if not within specification. See VALVE CLEARANCE SPECIFICATIONS table.
5) To adjust valve clearance, rotate crankshaft until camshaft lobe is pointing upward, away from adjuster shim. Install Spring Compressor (J-39871-1) between camshaft and adjuster shim to push lifter downward. *See Fig. 1.*
6) Insert Lifter Detainer (J-39871-2) between camshaft and lifter. Ensure bottom edge of lifter detainer is positioned on lifter, not on adjuster shim. *See Fig. 1.* This will hold lifter away from camshaft.
7) Remove spring compressor. Using small screwdriver and magnet, remove adjuster shim. Replacement adjuster shim thickness can be determined by using adjuster shim charts. *See Figs. 2 and 3.* Adjuster shim thickness can also be determined by using following formula:
N = T + A
- N = Thickness of adjuster shim required.
- T = Thickness of adjuster shim removed.
- A = Measured clearance minus valve clearance specification.
8) To install NEW adjuster shim, depress valve spring using spring compressor. Install adjuster shim. Remove lifter detainer and spring compressor.
9) Ensure valve clearance is within specification. To install remaining components, reverse removal procedure.

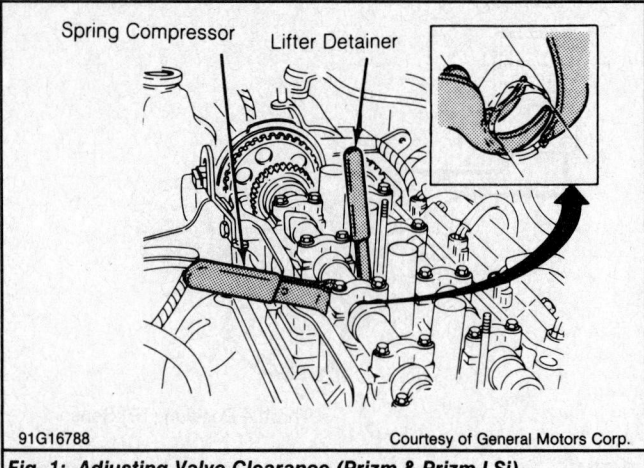

91G16788   Courtesy of General Motors Corp.

Fig. 1: Adjusting Valve Clearance (Prizm & Prizm LSi)

TRACKER

1) Disconnect negative battery cable. Remove valve cover and gaskets. Rotate crankshaft until No. 1 cylinder is at TDC of compression stroke. Ensure timing mark on crankshaft pulley aligns with zero mark on timing belt cover.
2) All 4 valves on No. 1 cylinder should have clearance and be closed. If valves on No. 1 cylinder are not closed, rotate crankshaft one revolution (360 degrees).
3) Using feeler gauge, measure clearance between rocker arm and valve stem on intake valves on cylinders No. 1 and 2, and exhaust valves on cylinders No. 1 and 3. Adjust valve clearance if not within specification. See VALVE CLEARANCE SPECIFICATIONS table.
4) Adjust valves by loosening lock nut and turning adjustment screw until correct clearance is obtained. Hold adjusting screw while tightening lock nut to 13 ft. lbs. (17 N.m), and recheck clearance.
5) Rotate crankshaft one revolution (360 degrees). Check intake valve clearance on cylinders No. 3 and 4, and exhaust valves on cylinders No. 2 and 4. Valve clearance must be adjusted if not within specification. See VALVE CLEARANCE SPECIFICATIONS table. Reverse removal procedure to install remaining components.

IGNITION TIMING

IGNITION TIMING SPECIFICATIONS (Degrees BTDC @ RPM) [1]

Application	Man. Trans.	Auto. Trans.
Metro	[2] 5 @ [3]	[2] 5 @ [3]
Tracker		
TBI (Federal)	[4] 8 @ 800	[4] 8 @ 800
MFI (Calif. & New York)	[5] 5 @ 800	[5] 5 @ 800

[1] – If specification differs from emission label, use specification listed on emission label.
[2] – With jumper wire installed between terminals "D" (Black wire) and "E" (Purple/Green wire) of duty check data link connector, located on left strut tower.
[3] – Specified idle. See emission label located on vehicle.
[4] – With jumper wire installed between terminals "C" (Black wire) and "D" (Blue/Red wire) of duty check data link connector, located near front of battery tray.
[5] – With jumper wire installed between terminals No. 4 (Black wire) and No. 5 (Blue/Red wire) of duty check data link connector, located near front of battery tray.

METRO

1) Warm engine to normal operating temperature. Turn engine off but keep ignition on for 5 seconds. Restart engine, and raise engine speed to 2000 RPM for 5 minutes. Return to idle. Ensure all accessories are off and idle speed is within specification. Adjust idle speed first if it is not within specification. See IDLE SPEED under IDLE SPEED & MIXTURE.

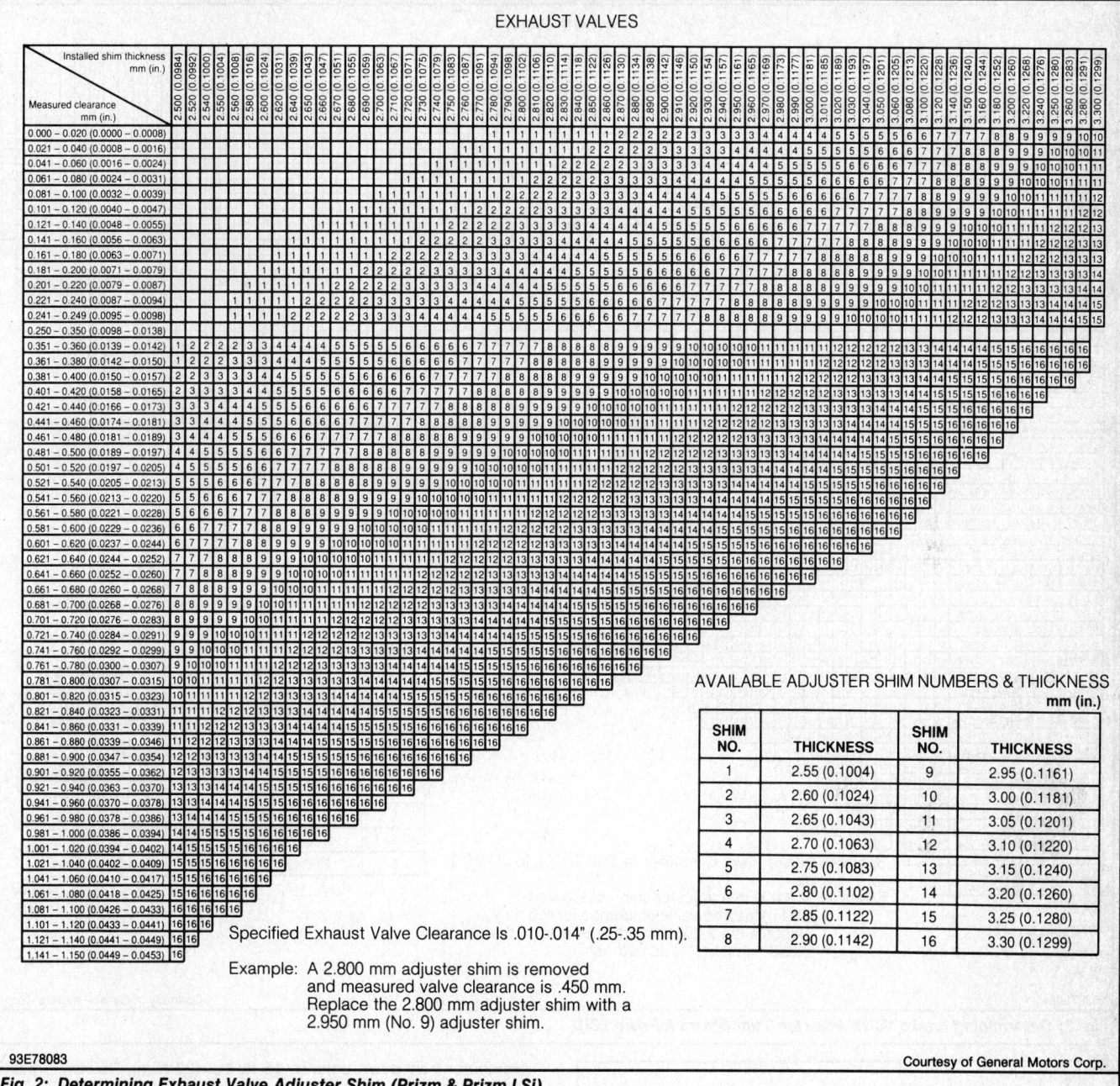

Fig. 2: Determining Exhaust Valve Adjuster Shim (Prizm & Prizm LSi)

2) Connect timing light to No. 1 spark plug wire. Remove cap from duty check Data Link Connector (DLC), located in rear corner of engine compartment near left strut tower. Connect a jumper wire between terminals "D" (Black wire) and "E" (Purple/Green wire) of duty check DLC. See Fig. 4.

3) Check timing mark alignment on crankshaft pulley with timing marks on timing belt cover. Ignition timing must be within specification. See IGNITION TIMING SPECIFICATIONS table.

4) If ignition timing is not as specified, loosen distributor hold-down flange bolts, and rotate distributor to obtain correct ignition timing. Tighten distributor hold-down flange bolts to 11 ft. lbs. (15 N.m). Recheck ignition timing.

5) Turn engine off. Remove jumper wire, and install cap on duty check DLC. Remove test equipment.

PRIZM

1) Warm engine to normal operating temperature. Turn engine off. Remove cover from Data Link Connector (DLC) located on left strut tower. Connect a tachometer to battery and terminal No. 19/IG (Black wire) of DLC. See Fig. 5.

CAUTION: DO NOT ground terminal No. 19/IG in Data Link Connector (DLC). Grounding this terminal could result in ignitor or ignition coil damage.

2) Start engine. Ensure all accessories are off. With transaxle in Neutral, ensure idle speed is 650-750 RPM. If idle speed is not as specified, see IDLE SPEED under IDLE SPEED & MIXTURE.

3) Turn engine off. Connect timing light to No. 1 spark plug wire. Install jumper wire between terminals No. 3/E1 (Brown wire) and No. 8/TE1 (Blue/White wire) of DLC. See Fig. 5.

1994 ENGINE PERFORMANCE
On-Vehicle Adjustments (Cont.)

INTAKE VALVES

Measured clearance mm (in.) \ Installed shim thickness mm (in.)	2.500 (0.0984)	2.520 (0.0992)	2.540 (0.1000)	2.550 (0.1004)	2.560 (0.1008)	2.580 (0.1016)	2.600 (0.1024)	2.620 (0.1031)	2.640 (0.1039)	2.650 (0.1043)	2.660 (0.1047)	2.670 (0.1051)	2.680 (0.1055)	2.690 (0.1059)	2.700 (0.1063)	2.710 (0.1067)	2.720 (0.1071)	2.730 (0.1075)	2.740 (0.1079)	2.750 (0.1083)	2.760 (0.1087)	2.770 (0.1091)	2.780 (0.1094)	2.790 (0.1098)	2.800 (0.1102)	2.810 (0.1106)	2.820 (0.1110)	2.830 (0.1114)	2.840 (0.1118)	2.850 (0.1122)	2.860 (0.1126)	2.870 (0.1130)	2.880 (0.1134)	2.890 (0.1138)	2.900 (0.1142)	2.910 (0.1146)	2.920 (0.1150)	2.930 (0.1154)	2.940 (0.1157)	2.950 (0.1161)	2.960 (0.1165)	2.970 (0.1169)	2.980 (0.1173)	2.990 (0.1177)	3.000 (0.1181)	3.010 (0.1185)	3.020 (0.1189)	3.030 (0.1193)	3.040 (0.1197)	3.050 (0.1201)	3.060 (0.1205)	3.080 (0.1213)	3.100 (0.1220)	3.120 (0.1228)	3.140 (0.1236)	3.150 (0.1240)	3.160 (0.1244)	3.180 (0.1252)	3.200 (0.1260)	3.220 (0.1268)	3.240 (0.1276)	3.250 (0.1280)	3.260 (0.1283)	3.280 (0.1291)	3.300 (0.1299)
0.000 – 0.020 (0.0000 – 0.0008)													1	1	1	1	1	1	1	1	1	2	2	2	2	2	3	3	3	3	3	4	4	4	4	4	5	5	5	5	5	6	6	6	6	6	7	7	7	7	7	8	8	9	9	9	9	10	10	11	11	11	11	12	12
0.021 – 0.040 (0.0008 – 0.0016)											1	1	1	1	1	1	1	1	1	2	2	2	2	2	3	3	3	3	3	4	4	4	4	4	5	5	5	5	5	6	6	6	6	6	7	7	7	7	8	8	8	8	9	9	9	10	10	10	11	11	11	12	12	12	13
0.041 – 0.060 (0.0016 – 0.0024)									1	1	1	1	1	1	1	1	1	2	2	2	2	2	3	3	3	3	3	4	4	4	4	4	5	5	5	5	5	6	6	6	6	6	7	7	7	7	7	8	8	8	8	9	9	9	10	10	10	11	11	11	12	12	12	13	13
0.061 – 0.080 (0.0024 – 0.0031)								1	1	1	1	1	1	1	1	2	2	2	2	2	3	3	3	3	3	4	4	4	4	4	5	5	5	5	5	6	6	6	6	6	7	7	7	7	7	8	8	8	8	8	9	9	9	10	10	10	11	11	11	12	12	12	13	13	13
0.081 – 0.100 (0.0032 – 0.0039)							1	1	1	1	1	1	1	2	2	2	2	2	3	3	3	3	3	4	4	4	4	4	5	5	5	5	5	6	6	6	6	6	7	7	7	7	7	8	8	8	8	8	9	9	9	9	10	10	11	11	11	11	12	12	13	13	13	13	14
0.101 – 0.120 (0.0040 – 0.0047)						1	1	1	1	1	1	2	2	2	2	2	3	3	3	3	3	4	4	4	4	4	5	5	5	5	5	6	6	6	6	6	7	7	7	7	7	8	8	8	8	8	9	9	9	9	9	10	10	11	11	11	11	12	12	13	13	13	13	14	14
0.121 – 0.140 (0.0048 – 0.0055)					1	1	1	1	1	2	2	2	2	2	3	3	3	3	3	4	4	4	4	4	5	5	5	5	5	6	6	6	6	6	7	7	7	7	7	8	8	8	8	8	9	9	9	9	9	10	10	10	11	11	11	12	12	12	13	13	13	14	14	14	15
0.141 – 0.149 (0.0056 – 0.0059)					1	1	1	1	2	2	2	2	3	3	3	3	3	4	4	4	4	4	5	5	5	5	5	6	6	6	6	6	7	7	7	7	7	8	8	8	8	8	9	9	9	9	9	10	10	10	10	11	11	11	12	12	12	13	13	13	14	14	14	15	15
0.150 – 0.250 (0.0059 – 0.0098)																																																																	
0.251 – 0.260 (0.0099 – 0.0102)	1	2	2	2	2	3	3	4	4	4	4	5	5	5	5	5	6	6	6	6	6	7	7	7	7	7	8	8	8	8	8	9	9	9	9	9	10	10	10	10	10	11	11	11	11	11	12	12	12	12	12	13	13	14	14	14	14	15	15	16	16	16	16	16	
0.261 – 0.280 (0.0103 – 0.0110)	1	2	2	2	3	3	3	4	4	4	5	5	5	5	5	6	6	6	6	6	7	7	7	7	7	8	8	8	8	8	9	9	9	9	9	10	10	10	10	10	11	11	11	11	11	12	12	12	12	12	13	13	13	14	14	14	15	15	15	16	16	16	16	16	
0.281 – 0.300 (0.0111 – 0.0118)	2	2	3	3	3	3	4	4	5	5	5	5	5	6	6	6	6	6	7	7	7	7	7	8	8	8	8	8	9	9	9	9	9	10	10	10	10	10	11	11	11	11	11	12	12	12	12	12	13	13	13	13	14	14	15	15	15	15	16	16	16	16	16		
0.301 – 0.320 (0.0119 – 0.0126)	2	3	3	3	3	4	4	5	5	5	5	6	6	6	6	6	7	7	7	7	7	8	8	8	8	8	9	9	9	9	9	10	10	10	10	10	11	11	11	11	11	12	12	12	12	12	13	13	13	13	13	14	14	15	15	15	15	16	16	16	16				
0.321 – 0.340 (0.0126 – 0.0134)	3	3	3	4	4	4	5	5	5	6	6	6	6	6	7	7	7	7	7	8	8	8	8	8	9	9	9	9	9	10	10	10	10	10	11	11	11	11	11	12	12	12	12	12	13	13	13	13	13	14	14	14	15	15	15	16	16	16	16	16					
0.341 – 0.360 (0.0134 – 0.0142)	3	3	4	4	4	5	5	5	6	6	6	6	7	7	7	7	7	8	8	8	8	8	9	9	9	9	9	10	10	10	10	10	11	11	11	11	11	12	12	12	12	12	13	13	13	13	13	14	14	14	14	15	15	15	16	16	16	16	16						
0.361 – 0.380 (0.0142 – 0.0150)	3	4	4	4	5	5	5	6	6	6	7	7	7	7	7	8	8	8	8	8	9	9	9	9	9	10	10	10	10	10	11	11	11	11	11	12	12	12	12	12	13	13	13	13	13	14	14	14	14	14	15	15	15	16	16	16	16	16							
0.381 – 0.400 (0.0150 – 0.0157)	4	4	5	5	5	5	6	6	7	7	7	7	7	8	8	8	8	8	9	9	9	9	9	10	10	10	10	10	11	11	11	11	11	12	12	12	12	12	13	13	13	13	13	14	14	14	14	14	15	15	15	15	16	16	16	16	16								
0.401 – 0.420 (0.0158 – 0.0165)	4	5	5	5	5	6	6	7	7	7	7	8	8	8	8	8	9	9	9	9	9	10	10	10	10	10	11	11	11	11	11	12	12	12	12	12	13	13	13	13	13	14	14	14	14	14	15	15	15	15	15	16	16	16	16										
0.421 – 0.440 (0.0166 – 0.0173)	5	5	5	6	6	6	7	7	7	8	8	8	8	8	9	9	9	9	9	10	10	10	10	10	11	11	11	11	11	12	12	12	12	12	13	13	13	13	13	14	14	14	14	14	15	15	15	15	15	16	16	16	16	16											
0.441 – 0.460 (0.0174 – 0.0181)	5	5	6	6	6	7	7	7	8	8	8	8	9	9	9	9	9	10	10	10	10	10	11	11	11	11	11	12	12	12	12	12	13	13	13	13	13	14	14	14	14	14	15	15	15	15	15	16	16	16	16	16	16												
0.461 – 0.480 (0.0181 – 0.0189)	5	6	6	6	7	7	7	8	8	8	9	9	9	9	9	10	10	10	10	10	11	11	11	11	11	12	12	12	12	12	13	13	13	13	13	14	14	14	14	14	15	15	15	15	15	16	16	16	16	16	16	16													
0.481 – 0.500 (0.0189 – 0.0197)	6	6	7	7	7	7	8	8	9	9	9	9	9	10	10	10	10	10	11	11	11	11	11	12	12	12	12	12	13	13	13	13	13	14	14	14	14	14	15	15	15	15	15	16	16	16	16	16	16	16	16														
0.501 – 0.520 (0.0197 – 0.0205)	6	7	7	7	7	8	8	9	9	9	9	10	10	10	10	10	11	11	11	11	11	12	12	12	12	12	13	13	13	13	13	14	14	14	14	14	15	15	15	15	15	16	16	16	16	16	16	16	16																
0.521 – 0.540 (0.0205 – 0.0213)	7	7	7	8	8	8	9	9	9	10	10	10	10	10	11	11	11	11	11	12	12	12	12	12	13	13	13	13	13	14	14	14	14	14	15	15	15	15	15	16	16	16	16	16	16	16	16																		
0.541 – 0.560 (0.0213 – 0.0220)	7	7	8	8	8	9	9	9	10	10	10	10	11	11	11	11	11	12	12	12	12	12	13	13	13	13	13	14	14	14	14	14	15	15	15	15	15	16	16	16	16	16	16	16	16																				
0.561 – 0.580 (0.0221 – 0.0228)	7	8	8	8	9	9	9	10	10	10	11	11	11	11	11	12	12	12	12	12	13	13	13	13	13	14	14	14	14	14	15	15	15	15	15	16	16	16	16	16	16	16	16																						
0.581 – 0.600 (0.0229 – 0.0236)	8	8	9	9	9	9	10	10	11	11	11	11	11	12	12	12	12	12	13	13	13	13	13	14	14	14	14	14	15	15	15	15	15	16	16	16	16	16	16	16	16																								
0.601 – 0.620 (0.0237 – 0.0244)	8	9	9	9	9	10	10	11	11	11	11	12	12	12	12	12	13	13	13	13	13	14	14	14	14	14	15	15	15	15	15	16	16	16	16	16	16	16	16																										
0.621 – 0.640 (0.0244 – 0.0252)	9	9	9	10	10	10	11	11	11	12	12	12	12	12	13	13	13	13	13	14	14	14	14	14	15	15	15	15	15	16	16	16	16	16	16	16	16																												
0.641 – 0.660 (0.0252 – 0.0260)	9	9	10	10	10	11	11	11	12	12	12	12	13	13	13	13	13	14	14	14	14	14	15	15	15	15	15	16	16	16	16	16	16	16	16																														
0.661 – 0.680 (0.0260 – 0.0268)	9	10	10	10	11	11	11	12	12	12	13	13	13	13	13	14	14	14	14	14	15	15	15	15	15	16	16	16	16	16	16	16	16																																
0.681 – 0.700 (0.0268 – 0.0276)	10	10	11	11	11	11	12	12	13	13	13	13	13	14	14	14	14	14	15	15	15	15	15	16	16	16	16	16	16	16	16																																		
0.701 – 0.720 (0.0276 – 0.0283)	10	11	11	11	11	12	12	13	13	13	13	14	14	14	14	14	15	15	15	15	15	16	16	16	16	16	16	16	16																																				
0.721 – 0.740 (0.0284 – 0.0291)	11	11	11	12	12	12	13	13	13	14	14	14	14	14	15	15	15	15	15	16	16	16	16	16	16	16	16																																						
0.741 – 0.760 (0.0292 – 0.0299)	11	11	12	12	12	13	13	13	14	14	14	14	15	15	15	15	15	16	16	16	16	16	16	16	16																																								
0.761 – 0.780 (0.0300 – 0.0307)	11	12	12	12	13	13	13	14	14	14	15	15	15	15	15	16	16	16	16	16	16	16	16																																										
0.781 – 0.800 (0.0307 – 0.0315)	12	12	13	13	13	13	14	14	15	15	15	15	15	16	16	16	16	16	16	16	16																																												
0.801 – 0.820 (0.0315 – 0.0323)	12	13	13	13	13	14	14	15	15	15	15	16	16	16	16	16	16	16	16																																														
0.821 – 0.840 (0.0323 – 0.0331)	13	13	13	14	14	14	15	15	15	16	16	16	16	16	16	16	16																																																
0.841 – 0.860 (0.0331 – 0.0339)	13	13	14	14	14	15	15	15	16	16	16	16	16	16	16																																																		
0.861 – 0.880 (0.0339 – 0.0346)	13	14	14	14	15	15	15	16	16	16	16	16	16																																																				
0.881 – 0.900 (0.0347 – 0.0354)	14	14	15	15	15	15	16	16	16	16	16																																																							
0.901 – 0.920 (0.0355 – 0.0362)	14	15	15	15	15	16	16	16	16																																																									
0.921 – 0.940 (0.0363 – 0.0370)	15	15	15	16	16	16	16	16																																																										
0.941 – 0.960 (0.0370 – 0.0378)	15	15	16	16	16	16	16																																																											
0.961 – 0.980 (0.0378 – 0.0386)	15	16	16	16	16	16																																																												
0.981 – 1.000 (0.0386 – 0.0394)	16	16	16	16	16																																																													
1.001 – 1.020 (0.0394 – 0.0402)	16	16	16																																																															
1.021 – 1.040 (0.0402 – 0.0409)	16	16																																																																	
1.041 – 1.050 (0.0410 – 0.0413)	16																																																																		

Specified Intake Valve Clearance Is .006-.010" (.15-.25 mm).

Example: A 2.800 mm adjuster shim is removed and measured valve clearance is .450 mm. Replace the 2.800 mm adjuster shim with a 3.050 mm (No. 11) adjuster shim.

AVAILABLE ADJUSTER SHIM NUMBERS & THICKNESS mm (in.)

SHIM NO.	THICKNESS	SHIM NO.	THICKNESS
1	2.55 (0.1004)	9	2.95 (0.1161)
2	2.60 (0.1024)	10	3.00 (0.1181)
3	2.65 (0.1043)	11	3.05 (0.1201)
4	2.70 (0.1063)	12	3.10 (0.1220)
5	2.75 (0.1083)	13	3.15 (0.1240)
6	2.80 (0.1102)	14	3.20 (0.1260)
7	2.85 (0.1122)	15	3.25 (0.1280)
8	2.90 (0.1142)	16	3.30 (0.1299)

93F78084 Courtesy of General Motors Corp.

Fig. 3: Determining Intake Valve Adjuster Shim (Prizm & Prizm LSi)

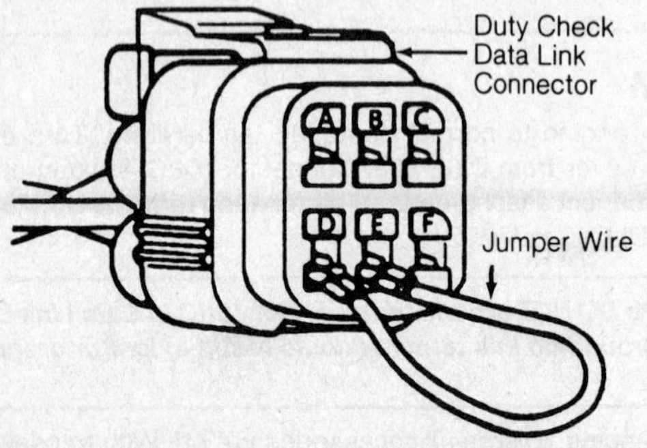
Duty Check
Data Link
Connector
A
B
C
D
E
F
Jumper Wire

93G78085 Courtesy of General Motors Corp.

Fig. 4: Identifying Duty Check DLC Terminals (Metro)

4) Start engine and check timing mark alignment on crankshaft pulley with timing marks on timing belt cover. Notch on crankshaft pulley should line up at 10 degrees BTDC on timing indicator.

5) If adjustment is required, loosen distributor hold-down bolts and rotate distributor until a 10-degree BTDC reading is obtained. Tighten distributor hold-down bolts to 15 ft. lbs. (20 N.m). Recheck ignition timing.

6) Turn engine off. Remove jumper wire from DLC. Recheck timing. Ignition timing should be varying between 5 degrees and 15 degrees BTDC. Remove timing light.

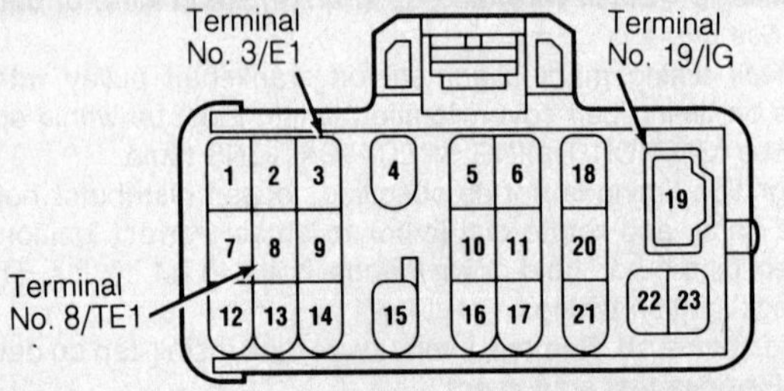
Terminal
No. 3/E1
Terminal
No. 19/IG
Terminal
No. 8/TE1
1
2
3
4
5
6
18
19
7
8
9
10
11
20
12
13
14
15
16
17
21
22
23

93H78086 Courtesy of General Motors Corp.

Fig. 5: Identifying DLC Terminals (Prizm & Prizm LSi)

TRACKER

1) Warm engine to normal operating temperature. Turn engine off, but keep ignition on for 5 seconds. Restart engine, and raise engine speed to 2000 RPM for 5 minutes. Return to idle. Ensure all accessories are off and idle speed is within specification. Adjust idle speed first if it is not within specification. See IDLE SPEED under IDLE SPEED & MIXTURE.

2) Connect timing light to No. 1 spark plug wire. Remove cap from duty check Data Link Connector (DLC), located near fusible link box, by battery. On TBI (Federal), connect a jumper wire between terminals "C" (Black wire) and "D" (Blue/Red wire) of duty check DLC. *See Fig. 6.* On MFI (Calif. and New York), connect a jumper wire between terminals No. 4 (Black wire) and No. 5 (Blue/Red wire) of duty check DLC. *See Fig. 6.*

3) On all models, check timing mark alignment on crankshaft pulley with timing marks on timing belt cover. Ignition timing must be within specification. See IGNITION TIMING SPECIFICATIONS table.

4) If ignition timing is not as specified, loosen distributor hold-down flange bolts, and rotate distributor to obtain correct ignition timing. Tighten distributor hold-down flange bolts to 15 ft. lbs. (20 N.m). Recheck ignition timing.

5) Turn engine off. Remove jumper wire and install cap on duty check DLC. Remove test equipment.

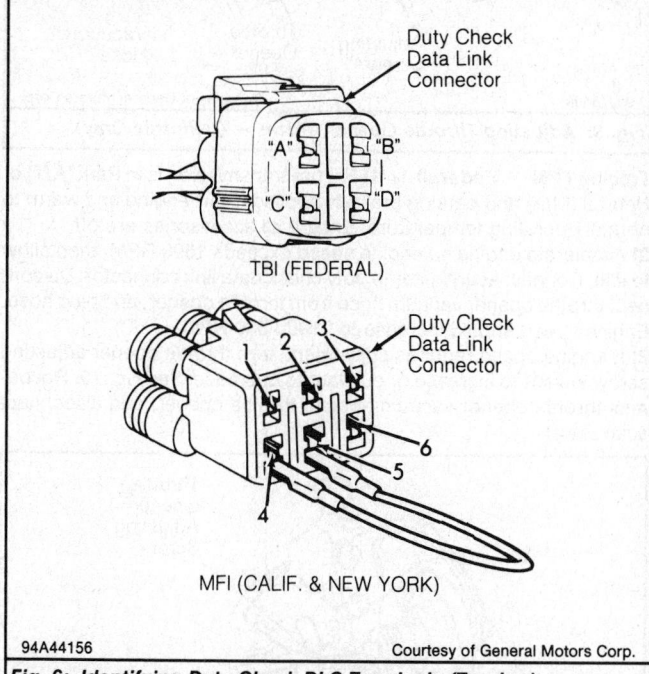

Fig. 6: Identifying Duty Check DLC Terminals (Tracker)

IDLE SPEED & MIXTURE

NOTE: Air/fuel mixture is controlled by the Engine Control Module (ECM)/Powertrain Control Module (PCM) and is not adjustable.

IDLE SPEED

Metro – 1) Place transaxle in Park (A/T) or Neutral (M/T) and apply parking brake. Ensure throttle cable has at least .12-.20" (3.1-5.1 mm) of slack in cable. Adjust throttle cable slack (if necessary).

2) Ensure all emission hoses and air cleaner are properly installed. Ensure ignition timing is within specification. See IGNITION TIMING. Ensure all accessories are off. Start engine and warm to normal operating temperature. Connect scan tester to Data Link Connector (DLC). Ensure idle speed is within specification. See IDLE SPEED SPECIFICATIONS table.

NOTE: On models equipped with upgraded emissions, if idle speed is not as specified, inspect Idle Speed Control (ISC) system. DO NOT manually adjust idle speed. Damage to ISC system may occur.

3) On standard emissions, if idle speed requires adjustment, remove cover from idle speed adjusting screw. Turn idle speed adjusting screw inward to decrease idle speed or outward to increase idle speed. *See Fig. 7.*

4) On A/C-equipped models with standard emissions, turn A/C to low speed. With A/C operating, idle speed should be within specification. See A/C IDLE SPEED SPECIFICATIONS table.

5) If idle speed requires adjustment, rotate adjustment screw on A/C Solenoid Vacuum (SV) valve to obtain correct idle speed. *See Fig. 7.* A/C SV valve is mounted on firewall, right of ignition coil.

6) On all models, turn engine off. Install idle speed adjusting screw cover (if removed), and remove scan tester.

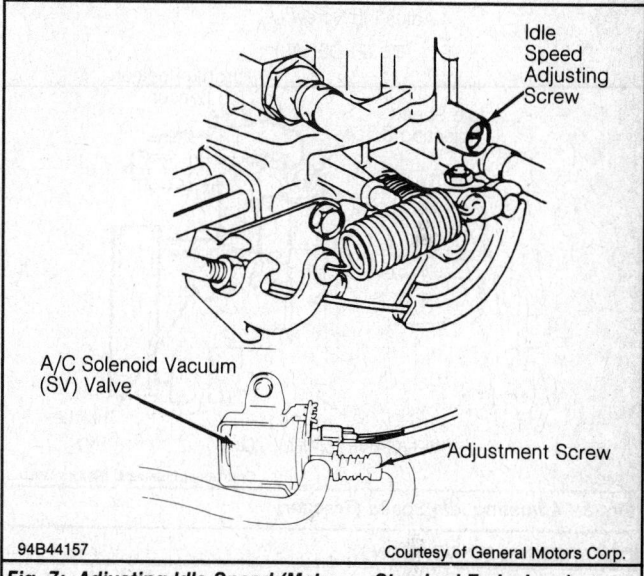

Fig. 7: Adjusting Idle Speed (Metro – Standard Emissions)

Prizm & Prizm LSi – Idle speed adjustment is controlled by the Engine Control Module (ECM)/Powertrain Control Module (PCM). ECM/PCM controls idle speed with the Idle Air Control (IAC) valve. No adjustment is required. Check IAC valve as necessary.

Tracker – 1) Place transaxle in Park (A/T) or Neutral (M/T) and apply parking brake. Ensure throttle cable has at least .4-.6" (10.-15. mm) of slack in cable. Adjust throttle cable slack (if necessary).

2) Ensure all emission hoses, electrical connections and air cleaner are properly installed. Ensure ignition timing is within specification. See IGNITION TIMING. Ensure all accessories are off. Remove cover from idle speed adjusting screw.

3) Start engine and warm to normal operating temperature. Accelerate engine so engine speed exceeds 1500 RPM, then allow to idle. Connect scan tester to duty check Data Link Connector (DLC). On TBI (Federal), connect a jumper wire between duty check DLC terminals "B" (Blue/Yellow wire), located near fusible link box by the battery, and ground. *See Fig. 6.*

4) On MFI (Calif. and New York), connect a jumper wire between duty check DLC terminals No. 2 (Blue/Yellow wire) and No. 4 (Black wire), located near fusible link box by the battery. *See Fig. 6.* On all models, idle speed should be within specification. See IDLE SPEED SPECIFICATIONS table.

5) If idle speed requires adjustment, turn idle speed adjusting screw to obtain correct idle speed. *See Fig. 8.*

6) On A/C-equipped models, turn A/C to low speed. With A/C operating, idle speed should be within specification. See A/C IDLE SPEED SPECIFICATIONS table.

7) If idle speed requires adjustment, turn idle speed adjusting screw to obtain correct idle speed. *See Fig. 8.*

8) On all models, turn engine off. Remove jumper wire from duty check DLC. Install idle speed adjusting screw cover (if removed), and remove scan tester.

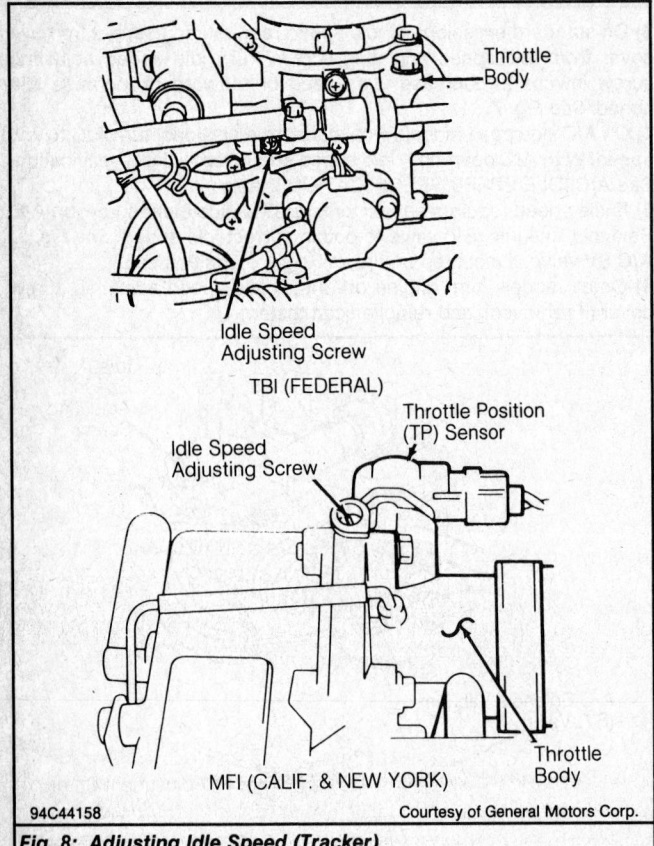

Throttle Body

Idle Speed Adjusting Screw

TBI (FEDERAL)

Throttle Position (TP) Sensor

Idle Speed Adjusting Screw

Throttle Body

MFI (CALIF. & NEW YORK)

94C44158   Courtesy of General Motors Corp.

Fig. 8: Adjusting Idle Speed (Tracker)

IDLE SPEED SPECIFICATIONS [1]

Application	RPM
Metro	
A/T	[2][3] 800-900
M/T	[2][3] 750-850
Metro XFi	[2] 650-750
Prizm & Prizm LSi	[4]
Tracker	[2][5] 750-850

[1] – If specification differs from emission label, use specification listed on emission label.
[2] – With transaxle/transmission in Neutral (M/T) or Park (A/T).
[3] – If equipped with upgraded emissions, idle speed is computer controlled and is not adjustable. Check Idle Speed Control (ISC) system if not within specification.
[4] – Idle speed is computer controlled and is not adjustable.
[5] – Idle speed checked with duty check data link connector grounded.

A/C IDLE SPEED SPECIFICATIONS

Application	[1] RPM
Metro [2]	850-950
Tracker	
A/T	[3]
M/T	950-1050

[1] – Transaxle/transmission in Neutral (M/T) or in Park (A/T).
[2] – A/C Solenoid Vacuum (SV) valve is used for maintaining idle speed during A/C operation.
[3] – Idle speed should be 950-1050 RPM in Neutral or Park, and 750-850 RPM in Drive, Reverse or any other forward gear.

THROTTLE OPENER

Prizm (California Only) – 1) Start engine and warm to normal operating temperature. Connect tachometer to battery and terminal No. 19/IG (Black wire) of data link connector. See Fig. 5.

2) Disconnect throttle opener vacuum hose from throttle opener, and plug hose. Maintain engine speed at 2500 RPM. Release throttle lever, and ensure throttle opener is set with engine speed at 1300-1500 RPM and radiator fan motor off. If throttle opener does not set, replace throttle opener.

3) If throttle opener setting speed requires adjustment, turn adjusting screw clockwise to increase engine speed or counterclockwise to decrease engine speed. See Fig. 9. Reconnect throttle opener vacuum hose to throttle opener and disconnect tachometer.

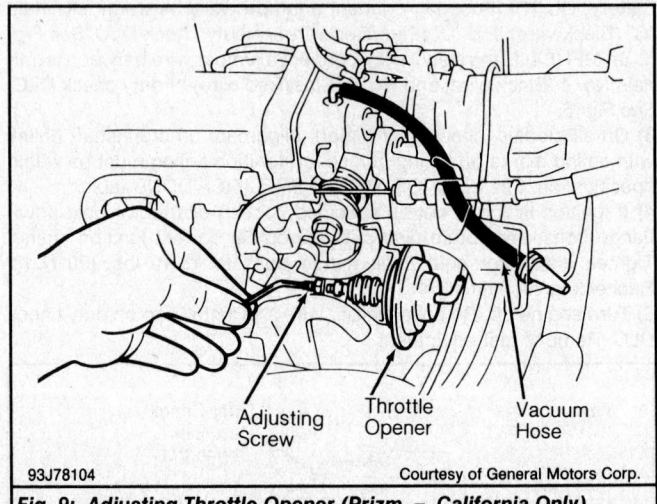

Adjusting Screw

Throttle Opener

Vacuum Hose

93J78104   Courtesy of General Motors Corp.

Fig. 9: Adjusting Throttle Opener (Prizm – California Only)

Tracker (TBI – Federal) – 1) Ensure transmission is in Park (A/T) or Neutral (M/T) and parking brake is applied. Start engine and warm to normal operating temperature. Ensure all accessories are off.

2) Accelerate engine so engine speed exceeds 1500 RPM, then allow to idle. Connect scan tester to duty check data link connector. Disconnect throttle opener vacuum hose from throttle opener, and plug hose. Engine speed should increase to 2100-2300 RPM.

3) If engine speed requires adjustment, turn throttle opener adjusting screw inward to increase or outward to decrease. See Fig. 10. Reconnect throttle opener vacuum hose to throttle opener, and disconnect scan tester.

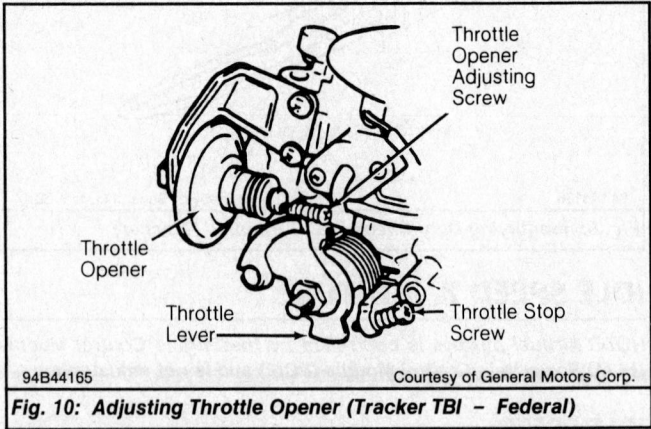

Throttle Opener Adjusting Screw

Throttle Opener

Throttle Lever

Throttle Stop Screw

94B44165   Courtesy of General Motors Corp.

Fig. 10: Adjusting Throttle Opener (Tracker TBI – Federal)

THROTTLE POSITION (TP) SENSOR
INSPECTION

NOTE: Perform all testing procedures with engine at normal operating temperature.

Metro (Standard Emissions) – 1) Disconnect negative battery cable. Remove air cleaner. Disconnect electrical connector from TP sensor. Loosen TP sensor retaining screws.

2) To check proper TP sensor operation, using ohmmeter, check resistance or continuity with selected feeler gauge thickness between throttle lever and stop screw. *See Figs. 11 and 12.* See THROTTLE POSITION (TP) SENSOR RESISTANCE table.

3) If TP sensor resistances are not as specified, adjust or replace TP sensor. See METRO (STANDARD EMISSIONS) procedure under ADJUSTMENTS. Once properly adjusted, reconnect electrical connector and install air cleaner.

Metro (Upgraded Emissions) – 1) Disconnect negative battery cable. Remove air cleaner. Disconnect electrical connector from TP sensor. Loosen TP sensor retaining screws. Check if Idle Speed Control (ISC) motor plunger is contacting throttle lever screw.

2) If ISC motor plunger is contacting throttle lever screw, bring engine to normal operating temperature. To check proper TP sensor operation, connect scan tester to DLC and turn ignition on. Insert a .14" (3.5 mm) feeler gauge between throttle lever and stop screw. *See Fig. 11.* Observe voltage on scan tester.

3) If TP sensor voltage is not .98-1.02 volts, adjust or replace TP sensor. See METRO (UPGRADED EMISSIONS) procedure under ADJUSTMENTS. Once properly adjusted, reconnect electrical connector and install air cleaner.

Prizm & Prizm LSi – 1) Disconnect negative battery cable. Disconnect electrical connector from TP sensor. Loosen TP sensor retaining screws.

2) To check proper TP sensor operation, using ohmmeter, check resistance or continuity with selected feeler gauge thickness between throttle lever and stop screw. *See Figs. 13 and 14.* See THROTTLE POSITION (TP) SENSOR RESISTANCE table.

3) If TP sensor resistances are not as specified, adjust or replace TP sensor. See PRIZM procedure under ADJUSTMENTS. Once properly adjusted, reconnect electrical connector.

Tracker – 1) Disconnect negative battery cable. Disconnect electrical connector from TP sensor. Loosen TP sensor retaining screws.

2) To check proper TP sensor operation, using ohmmeter, check resistance or continuity with selected feeler gauge thickness between throttle lever and stop screw. *See Figs. 10 and 15.* See THROTTLE POSITION (TP) SENSOR RESISTANCE table.

3) If TP sensor resistances are not as specified, adjust or replace TP sensor. See TRACKER procedure under ADJUSTMENTS. Once properly adjusted, reconnect electrical connector.

ADJUSTMENTS

NOTE: Perform all testing procedures with engine at normal operating temperature.

CAUTION: DO NOT use throttle stop screw to adjust throttle position sensor.

Metro (Standard Emissions) – 1) Disconnect negative battery cable. Remove air cleaner. Disconnect electrical connector from TP sensor. Loosen TP sensor retaining screws. Insert a .012" (.30 mm) feeler gauge between throttle lever and stop screw. *See Fig. 11.* Connect ohmmeter between TP sensor terminals No. 1 and 2. *See Fig. 12.*

2) Rotate throttle position sensor fully clockwise, then slowly rotate counterclockwise until ohmmeter indicates continuity. Hold TP sensor and tighten retaining screws to 18 INCH lbs. (2 N.m). Remove feeler gauge. Ohmmeter should still indicate continuity.

3) Insert a .035" (.89 mm) feeler gauge between throttle lever and stop screw. Ohmmeter should indicate no continuity. Remove feeler gauge. Reconnect electrical connector and install air cleaner.

Metro (Upgraded Emissions) – 1) Disconnect negative battery cable. Remove air cleaner. Disconnect electrical connector from TP sensor. Loosen TP sensor retaining screws. Check if Idle Speed Control (ISC) motor plunger is contacting throttle lever screw.

2) If ISC motor plunger is contacting throttle lever screw, bring engine to normal operating temperature. Connect scan tester to DLC and turn ignition on. Insert a .14" (3.5 mm) feeler gauge between throttle lever and stop screw. *See Fig. 11.* Observe voltage on scan tester.

THROTTLE POSITION (TP) SENSOR RESISTANCE

Application	Ohms
Metro (Standard Emissions)	
Between Terminals 1 & 2 [1]	0-5000
Between Terminals 1 & 2 [2]	Infinity
Between Terminals 1 & 2 [3]	0-5000
Between Terminals 1 & 3 [3]	240-1140
Between Terminals 1 & 3 [4]	3170-6600
Between Terminals 1 & 4	4370-8130
Prizm & Prizm LSi	
Between Terminals E2 & IDL [5]	0-2300
Between Terminals E2 & IDL [2]	Infinity
Between Terminals E2 & VC	4000-8500
Between Terminals E2 & VTA [6]	200-6000
Between Terminals E2 & VTA [4]	3300-10,000
Tracker (TBI – Federal)	
Between Terminals 2 & 4	3500-6500
Between Terminals 3 & 4 [1]	0-500
Between Terminals 3 & 4 [7]	Infinity
Between Terminals 4 & 5 [3]	300-2000
Between Terminals 4 & 5 [4]	2000-6500
Tracker (MFI – Calif. & New York)	
Between Terminals 1 & 3	3500-6500
Between Terminals 1 & 2 [8]	0-500
Between Terminals 1 & 2 [9]	Infinity
Between Terminals 1 & 4 [3]	300-2000
Between Terminals 1 & 4 [4]	2000-6500

[1] – With .012" (.30 mm) feeler gauge installed between throttle stop screw and lever.
[2] – With .035" (.89 mm) feeler gauge installed between throttle stop screw and lever.
[3] – Throttle valve at idle position.
[4] – Throttle valve at fully open position.
[5] – With .016" (.40 mm) feeler gauge installed between throttle stop screw and lever.
[6] – With zero clearance between throttle stop screw and lever.
[7] – With .022" (.56 mm) feeler gauge installed between throttle stop screw and lever.
[8] – With .020" (.50 mm) feeler gauge installed between throttle stop screw and lever.
[9] – With .031" (.80 mm) feeler gauge installed between throttle stop screw and lever.

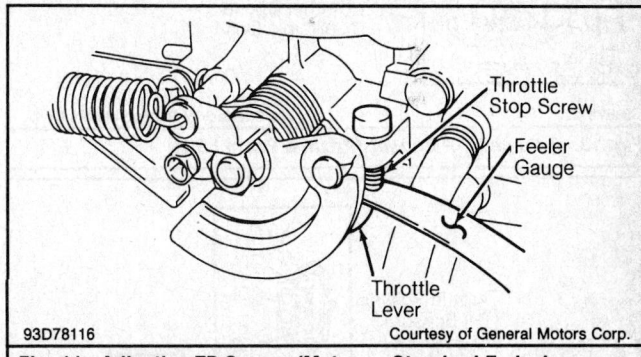

93D78116   Courtesy of General Motors Corp.

Fig. 11: Adjusting TP Sensor (Metro – Standard Emissions Shown; Upgraded Emissions Similar)

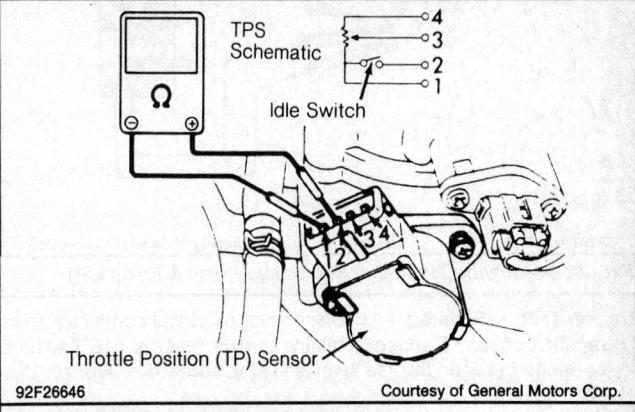

92F26646   Courtesy of General Motors Corp.

Fig. 12: Identifying TP Sensor Terminals (Metro – Standard Emissions)

3) If TP sensor voltage is not .98-1.02 volts, rotate TP sensor until voltage is as specified. Remove feeler gauge. Reconnect electrical connector and install air cleaner.

Prizm & Prizm LSi – 1) Disconnect electrical connector from TP sensor. Loosen TP sensor retaining screws. Insert a .016" (.40 mm) feeler gauge between throttle lever and stop screw. *See Fig. 13.* On models equipped with throttle opener (California only), disconnect throttle opener vacuum hose from throttle body, and apply vacuum to hose. Connect ohmmeter between TP sensor terminals IDL and E2. *See Fig. 14.*

2) Rotate throttle position sensor fully clockwise, then slowly rotate counterclockwise until ohmmeter indicates continuity. Hold TP sensor and tighten retaining screws. Remove feeler gauge. Ohmmeter should still indicate continuity.

3) Insert a .035" (.89 mm) feeler gauge between throttle lever and stop screw. Ohmmeter should indicate no continuity. Remove feeler gauge. Reconnect electrical connector, and reconnect throttle opener vacuum hose to throttle body (if removed).

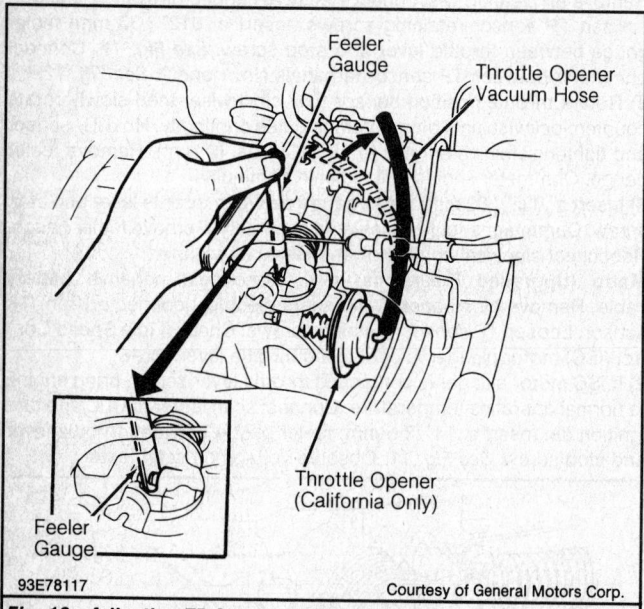

Feeler Gauge

Throttle Opener Vacuum Hose

Throttle Opener (California Only)

Feeler Gauge

93E78117

Courtesy of General Motors Corp.

Fig. 13: Adjusting TP Sensor (Prizm & Prizm LSi)

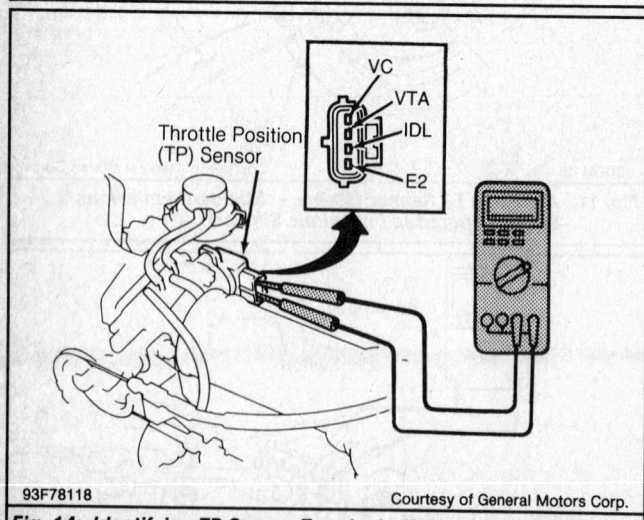

VC

VTA

IDL

E2

Throttle Position (TP) Sensor

93F78118

Courtesy of General Motors Corp.

Fig. 14: Identifying TP Sensor Terminals (Prizm & Prizm LSi)

Tracker (TBI – Federal) – 1) Disconnect electrical connector from TP sensor. Loosen TP sensor retaining screws. Insert a .016" (.40 mm) feeler gauge between throttle lever and stop screw. *See Fig. 10.* Dis-

connect throttle opener vacuum hose from throttle opener solenoid vacuum valve and apply 16-20 in. Hg vacuum to throttle opener. Connect ohmmeter between TP sensor terminals No. 1 and 4. *See Fig. 15.*

2) Rotate throttle position sensor fully clockwise, then slowly rotate counterclockwise until ohmmeter indicates 12-18 ohms. Hold TP sensor and tighten retaining screws to 31 INCH lbs. (3.5 N.m). Remove feeler gauge. Ohmmeter should still indicate continuity.

3) Insert a .035" (.89 mm) feeler gauge between throttle lever and stop screw. Ohmmeter should indicate no continuity. Remove feeler gauge. Reconnect electrical connector, and reconnect throttle opener vacuum hose to throttle opener solenoid vacuum valve.

Tracker (MFI – Calif. & New York) – 1) Disconnect electrical connector from TP sensor. Loosen TP sensor retaining screws. Insert a .026" (.65 mm) feeler gauge between throttle lever and stop screw. *See Fig. 10.* Connect ohmmeter between TP sensor terminals No. 1 and 2. *See Fig. 15.*

2) Rotate throttle position sensor fully counterclockwise, then slowly rotate clockwise until position where ohmmeter changes from continuity to no continuity. Hold TP sensor and tighten retaining screws to 23-38 INCH lbs. (2.5-4.5 N.m). Remove feeler gauge. Ohmmeter should still indicate continuity.

3) Insert a .037" (.80 mm) feeler gauge between throttle lever and stop screw. Ohmmeter should indicate no continuity. Remove feeler gauge.

4) Insert a .020" (.50 mm) feeler gauge between throttle lever and stop screw. Ohmmeter should indicate continuity. Remove feeler gauge. Reconnect electrical connector.

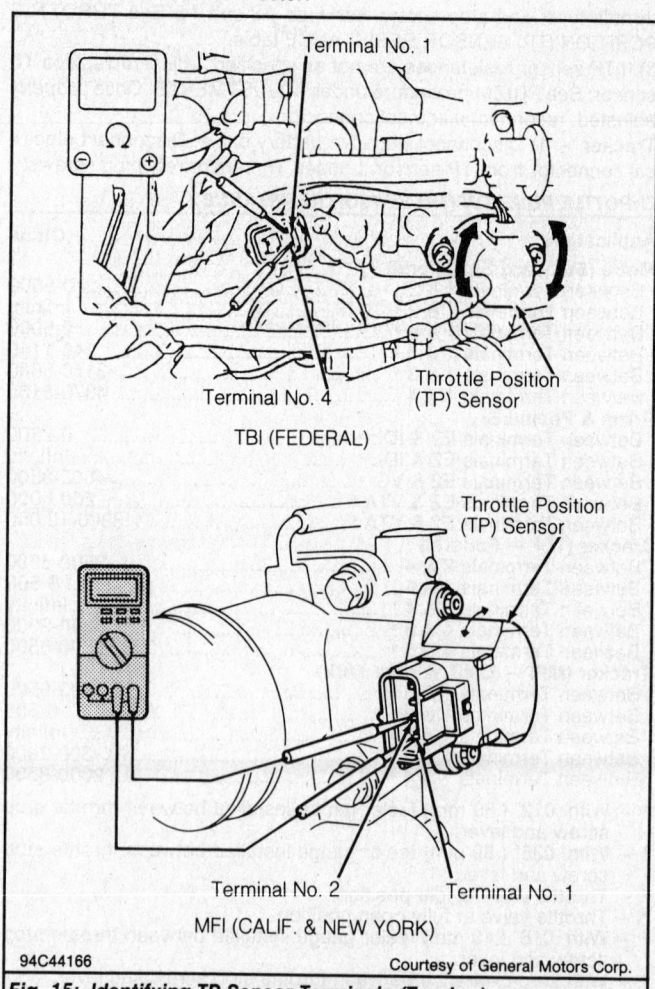

Terminal No. 1

Terminal No. 4

Throttle Position (TP) Sensor

TBI (FEDERAL)

Throttle Position (TP) Sensor

Terminal No. 2

Terminal No. 1

MFI (CALIF. & NEW YORK)

94C44166

Courtesy of General Motors Corp.

Fig. 15: Identifying TP Sensor Terminals (Tracker)

Metro, Prizm, Tracker

INTRODUCTION

This article covers basic description and operation of engine performance-related systems and components. Read this article before diagnosing vehicles or systems with which you are not completely familiar.

NOTE: Some states in the Northeast have adopted California emission standards. Refer to Underhood Vehicle Emissions Control Information Label for specific emission specifications and setting procedures.

NOTE: Metro is equipped with standard or upgraded emission systems. Standard emission systems include all XFi models and base models with automatic transaxle and Federal emissions. Upgraded emission systems include base models with manual transaxle and base models with automatic transaxle and California emissions. Refer to Underhood Vehicle Emissions Control Information Label for specific emission specifications and setting procedures.

COMPUTERIZED ENGINE CONTROLS

Fuel injection system is Throttle Body Injection (TBI) on Metro and Tracker (Federal). Multiport Fuel Injection (MFI) is used on Prizm and Tracker (California and New York). The electronic fuel injection engine control system monitors vehicle operating conditions through input signals and regulates air/fuel mixture and other engine control operations by output signals. This lowers exhaust emissions while maintaining fuel economy and driveability.

The control systems have a fail-safe mechanism. If a fault occurs while driving, the system will substitute calculated signals and/or pre-programmed values. Driving performance will be affected, but vehicle may still be driven. These systems have a self-diagnostic feature capable of recognizing a system fault and storing a related trouble code in memory for future retrieval and diagnosis.

ENGINE CONTROL MODULE (ECM)

NOTE: ECM is also known as Powertrain Control Module (PCM). All references to ECM include PCM unless specified otherwise.

NOTE: For ECM locations, see ECM LOCATION table.

Metro – Power for ECM is supplied through the FI fuse, located in fuse/relay block. The ECM distributes power or controls ground of various sensors, switches and solenoids for engine control.
Prizm – Power for ECM is supplied through the EFI F-HTR fuse, located in fuse/relay block. The ECM distributes power or controls ground of various sensors, switches and solenoids for engine control.
Tracker – Power for ECM is supplied through the FI fuse, located in fuse block. The ECM distributes power or controls ground of various sensor, switches and solenoids for engine control.

ECM LOCATION

Application	Location
Metro	Underneath Dash, Behind Left Side
Prizm	Behind Center Console, Under Heater Case
Tracker	Under Left Side Of Dash, Left Of Steering Column

NOTE: Components are grouped into 2 categories. The first category is INPUT DEVICES, which are components that control or produce voltage signals monitored by the ECM. The second category is OUTPUT SIGNALS, which are components controlled by the ECM.

INPUT DEVICES

Vehicles are equipped with different combinations of input devices. Not all devices are used on all models. To determine the input device usage on a specific model, see appropriate wiring diagram in WIRING DIAGRAMS article. The available input signals include the following:
A/C Signal – On models with A/C, a signal is sent to the ECM when A/C is operating. ECM uses this signal with other inputs to determine engine idle speed and fuel mixture.
Camshaft Position (CMP) Sensor – CMP sensor is a signal generator (pick-up coil and magnet) and a signal rotor. CMP sensor is located in the distributor housing. A pulsing signal is sent to ECM, where it is used to calculate engine speed. On Metro, signal is also used as input to determine energizing of fuel injector.
Crank Signal – Engine start signal, sent from starter circuit, is used by ECM to determine when engine is cranking. On Metro, ECM uses crank signal to control fuel pump and injector. On Prizm, ECM/PCM uses signal to control injection time of fuel injectors. On Tracker, ECM uses signal to calculate fuel injection timing, Idle Air Control (IAC) valve and throttle opener solenoid vacuum valve.
EGR Temperature Sensor (Prizm – California & Tracker) – The EGR temperature sensor is located at base of EGR valve. A 5-volt reference voltage is supplied and monitored by ECM. Sensor resistance is converted to a temperature reading by ECM. Sensor resistance changes with respect to exhaust gas temperature. When exhaust gas temperature is high, resistance is low. When exhaust gas temperature is low, resistance is high. ECM uses this information to control EGR Solenoid Vacuum (EGR-SV) valve which controls EGR function.
Electrical Load Signal (Metro) – ECM monitors a signal from diode module to determine electrical load caused by cooling fan, blower motor, rear defogger, stoplights or headlights. When voltage decreases below a specified value, ECM increases idle speed using either Idle Air Control (IAC) valve (standard emissions) or Idle Speed Control (ISC) Motor (upgraded emissions). As voltage increases, ECM readjusts the idle speed.
Engine Coolant Temperature (ECT) Sensor – Engine Coolant Temperature (ECT) sensor monitors coolant temperature. A 5-volt reference voltage is supplied and monitored by ECM. Sensor resistance, which changes according to coolant temperature, is converted to a temperature reading by ECM. High coolant temperature causes low resistance and low coolant temperature causes high resistance. The ECM uses this information for fuel control, timing, air management, idle speed and closed loop fuel control.
Heated Oxygen (HO2S) Sensor (Metro – Upgraded Emissions & Tracker) – HO2S is mounted in exhaust manifold in front of 3-way catalytic converter. HO2S produces .1-.9 volts under normal operating temperatures greater than 600°F (316°C). ECM uses HO2S voltage to determine exhaust gas oxygen concentration during engine operation. Low voltage indicates a lean exhaust mixture and a higher voltage indicates a rich exhaust mixture. HO2S works similar to a non-heated sensor, except HO2S is heated to operating temperatures during engine operation.
Ignition Signal (Tracker) – Ignition system circuit sends a signal to ECM. ECM detects status of ignition coil and uses signal for controlling various circuits and devices.
Intake Air Temperature (IAT) Sensor – Intake air temperature sensor measures intake manifold air temperature. The IAT sensor resistance changes with respect to temperature. High air temperature decreases IAT sensor resistance. Low air temperature increases IAT sensor resistance.

Sensor resistance modifies a reference voltage that is supplied and monitored by ECM. The ECM uses this information to control output signals to the fuel injectors. For IAT sensor locations, see INTAKE AIR TEMPERATURE SENSOR (IAT) LOCATION table.

INTAKE AIR TEMPERATURE SENSOR (IAT) LOCATION

Application	Location
Metro	Left Side Of Air Cleaner Assembly
Prizm	Inside Air Cleaner Assembly
Tracker	On Air Intake Manifold

Knock Sensor (Prizm 1.8L) – Knock sensor, located in rear of cylinder block, sends a variable AC voltage signal to PCM depending on engine detonation. PCM uses this signal to determine if ignition timing should be retarded.

Manifold Absolute Pressure (MAP) Sensor (Except Tracker – California) – MAP sensor is connected to ECM by a wiring harness and to engine by a manifold vacuum hose. ECM supplies a 5-volt reference signal, a bias voltage and a ground to MAP sensor. MAP sensor voltage varies according to changes in engine load and engine RPM (manifold vacuum). Low voltage signal indicates low manifold pressure and high voltage indicates high manifold pressure. ECM uses voltage signal to control fuel volume available.

On Prizm, MAP sensor is used to measure barometric pressure, which allows ECM to automatically adjust for different altitudes and to control ignition timing.

Oxygen (O2S) Sensor (Metro – Standard Emission & Prism) – O2S is mounted in exhaust manifold or exhaust pipe in front of 3-way catalytic converter. O2S generates voltage according to oxygen content in exhaust gases. Voltage will vary from .1 volts (lean condition) to as high as .9 volts (rich condition).

Sensor will not generate a voltage signal until it reaches an operating temperature greater than 600°F (316°C). Sensor sends voltage signal to ECM, which uses it to obtain correct emissions by adjusting air/fuel ratio. Until sensor is warmed up, ECM adjusts air/fuel mixture based upon preprogrammed ECM memory (Open Loop Operation).

Park/Neutral Switch (Tracker A/T) – On A/T applications, ECM monitors switch position and receives a voltage signal when transmission is in Park or Neutral positions. ECM uses this input signal to help control fuel injector time and Idle Air Control (IAC) valve operation.

NOTE: On Metro A/T, gear position signal is received from Transaxle Control Module (TCM). See TCM GEAR SIGNAL (METRO A/T).

Power Steering Pressure (PSP) Switch (Tracker) – PSP switch is located in power steering pump housing. PSP switch indicates to the ECM when power steering pressure is applied. ECM uses this signal to control Idle Air Control (IAC) valve to increase engine idle speed.

Sub-Oxygen (Sub-O2S) Sensor (Prizm – California) – Sub-O2S is mounted in exhaust system, after warm-up Three-Way Catalytic Converter (TWC). Sub-O2S sensor rechecks oxygen level in exhaust after TWC and sends reference signal to ECM. This provides a more precise fuel injector control.

System Voltage (Metro) – Fuel injector is driven by its solenoid coil based upon the ECM output signal. There is a delay between the ECM signal and valve action when no fuel is provided. This delay, known as ineffective injection time, depends on system voltage. ECM takes voltage information to compensate for fuel injection time.

TCM Gear Signal (Metro A/T) – On A/T equipped vehicles, ECM monitors a voltage signal sent from Transaxle Control Module (TCM) when transaxle is in any position except Park or Neutral. ECM uses this input signal to help control fuel injector and Idle Air Control (IAC) valve (Standard Emissions) or Idle Speed Control (ISC) motor (Upgraded Emissions).

Throttle Position (TP) Sensor – ECM supplies TP sensor with a 5-volt reference signal. TP sensor contains a potentiometer and idle switch. TP sensor sends an output signal to ECM corresponding to opening of throttle valve and idle switch signal (when throttle is in idle position).

ECM uses these signals to control air/fuel ratio during acceleration, deceleration and idling. These signals are also used to determine idle speed. On Metro A/T, ECM sends a signal to TCM for automatic transaxle control.

Vehicle Speed Sensor (Metro & Tracker) – Vehicle Speed Sensor (VSS) consists of a reed switch built into speedometer head. On Metro, ECM applies 12-volts to VSS. On Tracker, ECM applies 5-volts to VSS. As speedometer cable rotates, the reed switch closes the circuit to ground 4 times per revolution. As vehicle speed increases, frequency of ground pulses increase. This pulse is sent to ECM and used to calculate vehicle speed.

Vehicle Speed Sensor (Prizm) – Vehicle Speed Sensor (VSS) is an electronic relay mounted on transaxle. As transaxle rotates VSS, voltage pulses are provided to speedometer. The speedometer converts the vehicle speed input into a wave form and provides ECM and cruise control module (if equipped) with its own vehicle speed input. This pulse is converted by ECM and interpreted as vehicle speed.

OUTPUT SIGNALS

NOTE: Vehicles are equipped with various combinations of computer-controlled components. Not all components listed are used on every vehicle. For theory and operation on each output component, refer to the system indicated after component.

A/C Solenoid Vacuum (SV) Valve – See IDLE SPEED under FUEL SYSTEM.

Circuit Opening Relay – See FUEL DELIVERY under FUEL SYSTEM.

Distributor Igniter – See IGNITION SYSTEM.

ECM Main Relay – See FUEL DELIVERY under FUEL SYSTEM.

EFI F-HTR Relay – See FUEL DELIVERY under FUEL SYSTEM.

EGR Solenoid Vacuum (EGR-SV) Valve – See EXHAUST GAS RECIRCULATION (EGR) under EMISSION SYSTEMS.

EVAP Canister Purge Control Solenoid – See FUEL EVAPORATIVE SYSTEM (EVAP) under EMISSION SYSTEMS.

FI Main Relay – See FUEL DELIVERY under FUEL SYSTEM.

Fuel-Cut System – See FUEL CONTROL under FUEL SYSTEM.

Fuel Injector – See FUEL CONTROL under FUEL SYSTEM.

Fuel Pump Relay – See FUEL DELIVERY under FUEL SYSTEM.

Idle Air Control (IAC) Valve – See IDLE SPEED under FUEL SYSTEM.

Idle Speed Control (ISC) Motor – See IDLE SPEED under FUEL SYSTEM.

Main Relay – See FUEL DELIVERY under FUEL SYSTEM.

Malfunction Indicator Light (MIL) – See SELF-DIAGNOSTIC SYSTEM.

Shift Indicator Light – See TRANSMISSION CONTROL under MISCELLANEOUS CONTROLS.

Throttle Opener Solenoid Vacuum Valve – See IDLE SPEED under FUEL SYSTEM.

Throttle Position Sensor Output Signal – See TRANSMISSION CONTROL under MISCELLANEOUS CONTROLS.

Transmission Torque Converter Clutch (TCC) Relay – See TRANSMISSION CONTROL under MISCELLANEOUS CONTROLS.

Transmission Torque Converter Clutch (TCC) Solenoid – See TRANSMISSION CONTROL under MISCELLANEOUS CONTROLS.

FUEL SYSTEM

FUEL DELIVERY

Circuit Opening Relay (Prizm) – Circuit opening relay is located behind center console of instrument panel. Relay is mounted on bracket attached to the ECM/PCM.

During cranking, a signal from ignition switch closes the contacts in circuit opening relay to energize fuel pump and pressurize fuel system. Once engine is started, ECM/PCM controls circuit opening relay and fuel pump remains on. Fuel pump will operate as long as engine is cranking or running and ECM is receiving ignition reference pulses. If no ignition references are received, ECM/PCM will shut off fuel pump.

EFI F-HTR Relay (Prizm) – The EFI F-HTR relay is located in fuse/relay block on left front side of engine compartment. When ignition is turned on, EFI F-HTR relay supplies voltage to circuit opening relay. The ECM grounds the circuit opening relay and operates the fuel pump.

FI Main Relay (Metro) – FI main relay is located in fuse/relay block on left side of engine compartment, near the battery. FI main relay supplies voltage to fuel pump relay when ignition is turned on. ECM grounds fuel pump relay, and power is then supplied to fuel pump.

Fuel pump will operate as long as engine is cranking or running and ECM is receiving ignition reference pulses. If no ignition references are received, ECM will shut off fuel pump.

Fuel Pump – Electric fuel pump is located in the fuel tank. Fuel pump delivers fuel to fuel injectors where system pressure is controlled by fuel pressure regulator. Fuel pump contains an internal check valve to maintain pressure in fuel lines after fuel pump is turned off.

Fuel Pump Relay (Metro) – Fuel pump relay is located in fuse/relay block on left side of engine compartment, near battery. When ignition is turned on, fuel pump relay receives voltage from FI main relay. ECM grounds fuel pump relay, and power is then supplied to fuel pump.

Fuel pump will operate as long as engine is cranking or running and ECM is receiving ignition reference pulses. If no ignition references are received, ECM will shut off fuel pump.

Fuel Pump Relay (Tracker) – Fuel pump relay is mounted on the ECM, located under left side of instrument panel, near kick panel. When ignition is turned on, ECM grounds main relay and provides voltage to pump relay. ECM will ground fuel pump relay and provide power to fuel pump.

Fuel pump will operate as long as engine is cranking or running and ECM is receiving ignition reference pulses. If no ignition references are received, ECM will shut off fuel pump.

Fuel Pressure Regulator – Regulator is a spring/vacuum-operated, diaphragm-type relief valve which maintains a regulated fuel pressure under all conditions. When manifold vacuum is high (low fuel requirements), diaphragm is drawn in, counteracting spring pressure. In this condition, excess fuel is routed back to fuel tank. When manifold vacuum drops (engine load), spring pressure overcomes vacuum, closing off fuel tank return line. This maintains pressure and volume to fuel injectors.

Main Relay (Tracker) – Main relay is mounted on ECM, located under left side of instrument panel, near kick panel. When ignition is turned on, ECM grounds main relay and provides voltage to fuel pump relay. ECM grounds fuel pump relay, and power is then supplied to the fuel pump.

FUEL CONTROL

Battery Voltage Signal – ECM monitors battery voltage. A drop in battery voltage directly affects fuel injector pulse width. As battery voltage drops, pulse width decreases, causing a leaner air/fuel mixture. ECM compensates by increasing pulse width to provide richer mixture.

Fuel-Cut System (Metro & Tracker) – The fuel-cut system will stop fuel injection during deceleration to prevent unburned gases from being exhausted. Fuel-cut system will also deactivate injectors when engine speed exceeds 7000 RPM (Metro) or 6800 RPM (Tracker). This prevents engine damage due to excessive engine speed. As engine speed drops to less than 6800 RPM (Metro) or 6500 RPM (Tracker), fuel injection will once again occur.

Fuel-Cut System (Prizm) – ECM/PCM controls fuel injection based on signals from TP sensor and MAP sensor. During sudden deceleration ECM/PCM fuel-cut system will stop fuel injection to prevent unburned gases from being exhausted. Fuel injection operation will be stopped when throttle is at idle position and engine speed is 3500 RPM or more. Fuel injection operation will resume when engine speed is less than 1400 RPM.

Fuel Injector – When fuel injector(s) receive system voltage whenever ignition switch is in ON or START position. Fuel injector(s) are energized through a ground path provided by ECM. This opens fuel injector, allowing pressurized fuel to flow through injector and into intake manifold or cylinder. Air/fuel mixtures are controlled by fuel injector pulse width (ON time). ECM determines proper pulse width based upon input signals from various sensors and switches.

Fuel injection timing is determined by ECM based upon RPM signals received from Camshaft Position (CMP) sensor, Throttle Position (TP) sensor and Engine Coolant Temperature (ECT) sensor.

IDLE SPEED

A/C Solenoid Vacuum (SV) Valve – When A/C is operated, ECM receives an idle-up signal from A/C amplifier and controls A/C SV operation. The A/C SV supplies a certain amount of by-pass air to create a lean condition. ECM uses this signal to adjust air/fuel mixture and increase engine speed to prevent stalling.

Electrical Load Idle-Up Signal (Metro) – ECM monitors a signal from diode module to determine electrical load caused by cooling fan, blower motor, rear defogger, stoplights or headlights. When voltage decreases below a specified value, ECM increases idle speed. Idle speed is controlled by using Idle Air Control (IAC) valve (standard emissions) or Idle Speed Control (ISC) motor (upgraded emissions). As voltage increases, ECM readjusts idle speed.

Fast Idle Air Valve (Metro – Standard Emissions & Tracker) – Fast idle air valve is used to increase idle speed. On Metro (Standard Emissions) and Tracker (Federal emissions), when engine coolant is less than 140°F (60°C) intake air is increased and engine idle speed increases. On Tracker (California), when engine coolant is less than 158°F (70°C) intake air is increased and engine idle speed increases. Engine coolant temperature alters fast idle air valve thermowax to increase or decrease air into the intake manifold.

When coolant temperature is less than specified, fast idle air valve thermowax contracts, causing valve to open by spring pressure, allowing air into intake manifold. This increased airflow increases idle speed. As coolant temperature increases, fast idle air valve thermowax expands, allowing valve to close off airflow, causing idle speed to decrease. When engine coolant temperature is greater than specified coolant temperature, valve fully closes and normal idle speed is obtained.

Idle Air Control (IAC) Valve (Metro – Standard Emissions, Prizm & Tracker) – IAC valve is located on left side of engine, below air cleaner (Metro), on bottom of throttle body (Prizm), or on right side of throttle body (Tracker). IAC valve by-passes air around throttle valve directly into intake manifold. Air is allowed to pass through IAC valve when it is energized by ECM. IAC valve is energized whenever idle speed drops to less than desired RPM due to engine load (i.e., electrical, P/S, A/T in Drive, etc.).

IAC valve is also energized each time engine is started and during periods of deceleration to compensate for rich mixtures caused by a fully closed throttle.

Idle Speed Control (ISC) Motor (Metro – Upgraded Emissions) – ISC motor is located at rear of Throttle Body assembly. ISC motor is used to control throttle valve opening through a signal from ECM. ISC motor has a DC motor, gears, a plunger and an idle switch. When plunger is in contact with throttle lever screw, idle switch sends an ON signal to ECM. When plunger is not in contact with throttle screw, idle switch sends an OFF signal to ECM.

CAUTION: ISC motor and throttle lever screw are not adjustable and are factory preset. Removing or disassembling ISC motor may cause damage to ISC motor and/or throttle valve.

Throttle Opener Control System (Prizm – California) – Throttle opener is located on front of throttle body. When engine is running and vacuum is applied to throttle opener, throttle opener will retract, allowing throttle lever to move and lowering idle speed. Throttle opener is fully extended when engine is first started. Throttle lever and valve are slightly open, increasing engine idle speed.

Throttle Opener Control System (Tracker – Federal) – When vehicle is first started, ECM activates a Throttle Opener Solenoid Vacuum (TOSV) valve, which supplies vacuum to the throttle opener. The ECM controls TOSV valve according to ignition signal, starter signal and signal from Engine Coolant Temperature (ECT) sensor. The TOSV valve is activated for .2-35 seconds after engine starts, depending on ECT sensor.

Energizing the TOSV valve opens a vacuum passage between TOSV valve filter and throttle opener, and closes the manifold vacuum passage. When vacuum passage is closed, diaphragm spring pushes on throttle linkage, increasing throttle opening.

Once vehicle starts, ECM de-energizes the TOSV valve, allowing manifold vacuum to pass through TOSV valve to throttle opener diaphragm. Diaphragm will retract, allowing throttle linkage to return to normal base idle position.

IGNITION SYSTEM

ELECTRONIC IGNITION SYSTEM

Metro – Ignition system circuit consists of a battery, distributor, ignition switch, spark plugs, igniter, and primary and secondary wiring. An Ignition Control (IC) system is used that is monitored and controlled by the ECM. An ignition noise suppressor condenser and noise suppressor filter, are used. Noise suppressor filter provides ignition signal for tachometer (if equipped).

Distributor uses a signal generator (signal rotor and pick-up coil/Camshaft Position (CMP) sensor) and rotor to produce reference signals for the ECM. All spark timing changes within distributor are performed electronically by ECM.

Ignition coil power is provided through 20-amp IG fuse located in fuse/relay block, below left side of instrument panel. Fuse receives power when ignition is turned on.

Ground circuit for ignition coil is regulated by the ECM through igniter. On vehicles with standard emission system, igniter is located inside ECM. On upgraded emission system, igniter is located under ignition coil and mounted on right side of firewall in engine compartment. As rotating signal rotor passes pole piece of pick-up coil/CMP sensor, a reference signal is sent to ECM. ECM uses this signal to determine when to signal igniter to open ground circuit for primary ignition.

When igniter opens ground circuit for primary ignition, magnetic field around ignition coil windings collapses, producing an induced high voltage surge used to operate the spark plugs. Igniter sends a signal back to ECM to confirm primary ignition circuit operation was completed.

Prizm – Ignition system circuit consists of a battery, distributor, ignition switch, spark plugs, igniter, and primary and secondary wiring. An Ignition Control (IC) system is used that is monitored and controlled by the ECM/PCM. An ignition noise suppressor condenser is also used.

Distributor uses a signal generator (signal rotor and pick-up coil/Camshaft Position (CMP) sensor) and rotor to produce reference signals to the ECM/PCM. Ignition coil and igniter are mounted inside distributor. Power for ignition coil is provided through the ignition switch. As rotating signal rotor passes pole piece of pick-up coil/CMP sensor, a reference signal is sent to the ECM/PCM. ECM/PCM uses this signal to determine when to signal igniter to open ground circuit for primary ignition.

When igniter opens ground circuit for primary ignition, magnetic field around ignition coil windings collapses, producing an induced high voltage surge used to operate the spark plugs. Igniter sends a signal back to ECM to confirm primary ignition circuit operation was completed.

Tracker – Ignition system circuit consists of a battery, distributor, ignition switch, spark plugs, igniter, and primary and secondary wiring. An Ignition Control (IC) system is used that is monitored and controlled by the ECM. An ignition noise suppressor condenser and noise suppressor filter are used. Noise suppressor filter provides ignition signal for tachometer (if equipped).

Distributor uses a signal generator (signal rotor and pick-up coil/Camshaft Position (CMP) sensor) to produce ignition pulses through externally mounted igniter. Igniter is located under ignition coil and mounted on right side of firewall in engine compartment.

Power for ignition coil and igniter is provided through 15-amp IG-COIL METER fuse, located in fuse block below left side of steering column. Fuse receives power when ignition is turned on. Ground circuit for ignition coil is regulated by ECM through igniter.

As rotating signal rotor passes pole piece of pick-up coil/CMP sensor, a reference signal is sent to ECM, which uses this signal to determine when to signal igniter to open ground circuit for primary ignition. When

igniter opens ground circuit for primary ignition, magnetic field around ignition coil windings collapses, producing an induced high voltage surge used to operate the spark plugs.

IGNITION TIMING CONTROL SYSTEM

Ignition Timing Advance Control – ECM (Metro and Tracker) or ECM/PCM (Prizm) controls ignition timing based upon various sensor input signals.

EMISSION SYSTEMS

EXHAUST GAS RECIRCULATION (EGR)

An Exhaust Gas Recirculation (EGR) system is used to lower oxides of nitrogen (NOx) exhaust gas emissions. The EGR system introduces exhaust gases into intake system. Exhaust gases are noncombustible gases which, when combined with the incoming air/fuel mixture, lowers peak combustion chamber temperatures.

The EGR valve receives ported vacuum signal from an ECM regulated EGR Solenoid Vacuum (SV) Valve. Various inputs to ECM are used to determine EGR operation. On California Prizm and Tracker, EGR valve operation is monitored by ECM through signal from EGR temperature (EGRT) sensor. EGRT sensor monitors exhaust gas temperature. If abnormal temperature exists, Malfunction Indicator Light (MIL) will be activated.

On all models, vacuum signal to EGR valve is further controlled by a vacuum modulator located in the vacuum line between the EGR-SV and EGR valve.

Under low driving speeds and light load conditions, vacuum modulator diaphragm is pushed downward and opens vacuum modulator. This allows air to enter modulator from the outside, reducing vacuum supply to EGR valve. The EGR valve closes slightly, reducing amount of recirculated exhaust gases.

Under high driving speeds and heavy load conditions, vacuum modulator diaphragm is pushed upward, closing vacuum modulator. This increases vacuum supply to EGR valve and valve opens slightly, increasing amount of recirculated exhaust gases.

Under following conditions, ECM does not allow EGR operation:
• A/T is in lock-up condition (Tracker).
• Barometric pressure is low at high altitude (Tracker – Federal).
• Coolant temperature is low.
• Engine is operating under heavy load.
• Engine running and vehicle stopped (Tracker – California).
• Engine speed exceeds 6000 RPM (Tracker – Federal).
• Intake manifold pressure is low (Metro).
• Throttle valve is at idle position.

EGR Temperature (EGRT) Sensor (California – Prizm & Tracker) – EGR temperature sensor resistance changes with respect to exhaust gas temperature. High exhaust gas temperature decreases sensor resistance. Low exhaust gas temperature increases sensor resistance. A reference voltage, supplied and monitored by ECM, is modified by sensor resistance. ECM uses this information to determine EGR operation. ECM will turn MIL on if there is a EGR system malfunction.

FUEL EVAPORATIVE SYSTEM (EVAP)

Metro (Standard Emissions) – Fuel tank vapors flow through an in-line Tank Pressure Control (TPC) valve from fuel tank to charcoal canister. TPC valve maintains constant pressure in the fuel tank. When pressure exceeds specification, fuel tank vapors flow to charcoal canister. If fuel tank pressure becomes negative, TPC valve allows air to flow into tank. Charcoal canister retains vapors until ported vacuum is applied to EVAP Solenoid Purge (SP) valve causing valve to open, allowing fuel vapors to enter intake manifold. Ported vacuum will only be applied to EVAP-SP valve when engine is running and at operating temperature and throttle valve is not in idle position.

Ported vacuum is applied to EVAP-SP through EVAP Thermal Vacuum Valve (TVV) which is located in bottom of intake manifold. When engine coolant reaches specified temperature, EVAP-TVV opens, allowing air to flow through valve and into intake manifold. This airflow opens canister purge control valve and allows fuel vapors to flow from carbon canister into intake manifold.

Metro (Upgraded Emissions) – Fuel tank vapors flow through an in-line Tank Pressure Control (TPC) valve from fuel tank to charcoal canister. TPC valve maintains constant pressure in the fuel tank. When pressure exceeds specification, fuel tank vapors flow to charcoal canister. If fuel tank pressure becomes negative, TPC valve allows air to flow into tank.

EVAP charcoal canister retains vapors until ECM energizes EVAP Solenoid Purge (SP) valve and opens vacuum passage, allowing fuel vapors to enter intake manifold. ECM will energize EVAP-SP valve and open vacuum passage when engine speed is greater than 2000 RPM, engine is at operating temperature, throttle valve is not in idle position and engine load is within specifications.

Prizm – Fuel tank vapors are stored in EVAP charcoal canister. A check valve in fuel tank cap maintains constant pressure in the fuel tank. When fuel tank pressure exceeds specified pressure, fuel tank vapors flow to EVAP charcoal canister. EVAP charcoal canister retains vapors until EVAP Thermal Vacuum Valve (TVV) opens in accordance with engine conditions, allowing fuel vapors to be drawn into intake manifold.

EVAP TVV is mounted in bottom of intake manifold. When engine coolant reaches specified temperature, EVAP-TVV opens, allowing air to flow through valve and into intake manifold. This airflow opens canister purge control valve and allows fuel vapors to flow from carbon canister into intake manifold. EVAP-TVV will only be opened with engine running and at normal operating temperature.

Tracker – Fuel tank vapors flow through an in-line Tank Pressure Control (TPC) valve from fuel tank to charcoal canister. TPC valve maintains constant pressure in the fuel tank. When pressure exceeds specified pressure, fuel tank vapors flow to EVAP charcoal canister. If fuel tank pressure becomes negative, TPC valve allows air to flow into tank.

EVAP charcoal canister retains vapors until ECM provides a ground to EVAP Solenoid Purge (SP) valve and opens vacuum passage, allowing fuel vapors to be drawn into intake manifold. ECM will energize EVAP-SP valve and open vacuum passage when engine speed is greater than 1500 RPM, engine is at an operating temperature greater than 140°F (60°C), vehicle speed is greater than 15 MPH, and throttle valve is not in idle position. If engine coolant temperature is not greater than 140°F (60°C), ECM will interrupt ground to EVAP-SP valve and cancel vacuum passage from EVAP canister and intake manifold.

POSITIVE CRANKCASE VENTILATION (PCV)

Positive Crankcase Ventilation (PCV) system circulates crankcase blow-by gases (hydrocarbons) into air induction system rather than allowing them to escape to the atmosphere. Crankcase gases are mixed with air/fuel mixture. Crankcase ventilation system uses a PCV valve which prevents hydrocarbon fumes from collecting in intake manifold when engine is not running.

When engine is above idle and manifold vacuum is high, PCV valve allows crankcase fumes to be drawn into intake manifold. The PCV valve is a metered orifice type on Prizm. Metro and Tracker use a check valve.

SELF-DIAGNOSTIC SYSTEM

MALFUNCTION INDICATOR LIGHT (MIL)

NOTE: MIL is also known as the CHECK ENGINE light.

All vehicles are equipped with MIL, located on instrument panel. Light will glow when ignition is turned on and engine is not running. Light should go out when engine is started. When MIL remains on or flashes with engine running, the self-diagnostic system has detected a problem. If problem goes away, light will go out after 10 seconds, but a trouble code will remain stored in the ECM memory. For additional information, see SELF-DIAGNOSTICS article.

MISCELLANEOUS CONTROLS

TRANSMISSION CONTROL

Transmission Torque Converter Clutch (TCC) Relay (Tracker A/T) – TCC relay is located in right corner of engine compartment on fusible link box. Battery voltage is supplied to TCC relay on Blue/Black wire from the main relay. Main relay is mounted on ECM, located under left side of instrument panel, near kick panel.

Based on signals from TP sensor (throttle valve open 7-62 degrees), ignition coil and Engine Coolant Temperature (ECT) sensor (coolant temperature is greater than 140°F), ECM will ground TCC relay. If brake switch is closed, voltage will be provided through contacts of TCC relay, to fluid pressure switch on transmission. When fluid pressure switch closes (fluid pressure less than 60 psi), voltage will be applied to TCC solenoid to allow torque converter lock-up.

Transaxle Torque Converter Clutch (TCC) Solenoid (Prizm A/T) – TCC solenoid is used to engage lock-up clutch. The PCM will apply or remove system voltage to turn the solenoid on or off to control hydraulic pressure to lock-up relay valve within the transaxle. If PCM determines a failure in either shift solenoid No. 1 or No. 2, PCM will not turn on solenoid, preventing lock-up.

For the converter clutch to apply, transaxle internal fluid pressure must be correct and PCM must energize solenoid. The PCM uses coolant temperature, throttle position, vehicle speed and stoplight switch to determine when to control TCC solenoid.

Shift Indicator Light (Metro M/T) – ECM controls shift indicator light to indicate shift point to obtain maximum fuel economy based on engine speed and load. ECM will activate shift indicator light when following conditions are present:

- Engine is not idling or under heavy load.
- Engine speed is greater than 1500 RPM.
- Vehicle speed is greater than 3 MPH.

NOTE: Engine speed for shift indicator light operation may vary with intake manifold pressure and coolant temperature.

1994 ENGINE PERFORMANCE
Basic Diagnostic Procedures

Metro, Prizm, Tracker

INTRODUCTION

NOTE: Perform all voltage tests with a Digital Volt-Ohmmeter (DVOM) with a minimum 10-megohm input impedance, unless stated otherwise in test procedure.

The following diagnostic steps will help prevent overlooking a simple problem. This is also where to begin diagnosis for a no-start condition. The first step in diagnosing any driveability problem is verifying the customer's complaint with a test drive under the conditions the problem reportedly occurred.

Before entering self-diagnostics, perform a careful and complete visual inspection. Most engine control problems result from mechanical breakdowns, poor electrical connections or damaged/misrouted vacuum hoses. Before condemning the computerized system, perform each test listed in this article.

TERMINOLOGY

Due to federal government requirements, manufacturers may use names and acronyms for systems and components different than those used in previous years. The following table will help eliminate confusion when dealing with these components and systems. Only relevant components and systems whose names have changed from current General Motors Corp. terminology have been listed.

SAE TERMINOLOGY

Former Name Or Acronym	New Name Or Acronym
ALDL	Data Link Connector (DLC)
CHECK ENGINE Light	Malfunction Indicator Light (MIL)
CTS	Engine Coolant Temp. (ECT) Sensor
Diagnostic Circuit Check	On-Board Diagnostic (OBD) System Check
ESC System	Knock Sensor (KS) System
EST System	Ignition Control (IC) System
MAT Sensor	Intake Air Temperature (IAT) Sensor
Park/Neutral (P/N) Switch	Park/Neutral Position (PNP) Switch
Port Fuel Injection	Multiport Fuel Injection (MFI)
Scan Data	Scan Tester (ST) Data
SERVICE ENGINE SOON Light	Malfunction Indicator Light (MIL)
Thermostatic Air Cleaner (TAC)	Air Cleaner (ACL)
Throttle Position Sensor (TPS)	Throttle Position (TP) Sensor
Throttle Position Switch	Closed Throttle Position (CTP) Switch
Throttle Position Switch	Wide Open Throttle (WOT) Switch
Viscous Converter Clutch (VCC)	Torque Converter Clutch (TCC)

¹ – Text includes old and new terminology. This is a representative listing.

PRELIMINARY INSPECTION & ADJUSTMENTS

NOTE: Following procedures describe how to check individual systems. For a no-start condition, see DIAGNOSTIC CHARTS.

VISUAL INSPECTION

Visually inspect all electrical wiring, looking for chafed, stretched, cut or pinched wiring. Ensure electrical connectors fit tightly and are not corroded. Ensure vacuum hoses are properly routed and are not pinched or cut. See VACUUM DIAGRAMS article to verify routing and connections (if necessary). Inspect air induction system for possible vacuum leaks.

MECHANICAL INSPECTION

CAUTION: DO NOT use ignition switch during compression tests on fuel injected vehicles. Use a remote starter to crank engine. Fuel injectors on many models are triggered by ignition switch during cranking mode, which can create a fire hazard or contaminate engine oiling system.

Compression – Check engine mechanical condition using a compression gauge, vacuum gauge or engine analyzer. See engine analyzer manual for specific instructions. See COMPRESSION SPECIFICATIONS table.

COMPRESSION SPECIFICATIONS

Application	Specification
Compression Ratio	
Metro, Prizm & Prizm LSi	9.5:1
Tracker	8.9:1
Normal Compression Pressure	
Metro & Tracker	199 psi (1372.1 kPa)
Prizm & Prizm LSi	191 psi (1316.9 kPa)
Minimum Compression Pressure	
Metro	156 psi (1075.6 kPa)
Prizm & Prizm LSi	142 psi (979.1 kPa)
Tracker	170 psi (1172.2 kPa)
Maximum Variation Between Cylinders	14 psi (96.5 kPa)

Exhaust System Backpressure – Exhaust system can be checked using a vacuum or pressure gauge. If using a pressure gauge, remove O_2 sensor or air injection check valve (if equipped). Connect a 1-10 psi pressure gauge. Operate engine at 2500 RPM. If exhaust system backpressure is greater than 2 psi, exhaust system or catalytic converter is plugged.

If using a vacuum gauge, connect vacuum gauge hose to intake manifold vacuum port. Start engine. Observe vacuum gauge. Open throttle part way and hold steady. If vacuum gauge reading slowly drops after stabilizing, check exhaust system for restriction.

FUEL SYSTEM

WARNING: Always relieve fuel pressure before disconnecting any fuel injection-related component. DO NOT allow fuel to contact engine or electrical components.

FUEL PRESSURE RELEASE

Metro – 1) Loosen fuel tank cap to release fuel tank pressure. Remove cover from fuse/relay block located in left front corner of engine compartment, behind battery. Remove coolant reservoir from bracket. Remove fuse/relay block retaining screws. From underneath fuse/relay block, release 2 locking tabs of fuel pump relay. *See Fig. 1.*
2) Remove fuel pump relay from fuse/relay block. Disconnect electrical connector from fuel pump relay. Start engine. Idle engine until it dies. Crank engine for about 10 seconds to ensure residual fuel line pressure is released. Turn ignition off. Install fuel pump relay and remaining components.

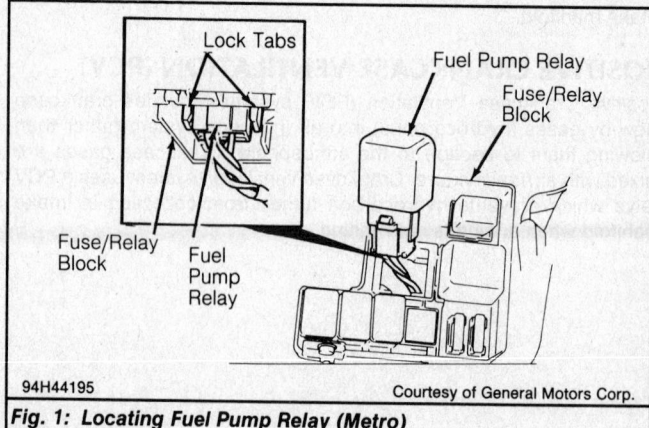

94H44195   Courtesy of General Motors Corp.

Fig. 1: Locating Fuel Pump Relay (Metro)

Prizm & Prizm LSi – Loosen fuel tank cap to release fuel tank pressure. Disconnect electrical connector on circuit opening relay attached to ECM, located under radio in instrument panel center console. Start engine. Idle engine until it dies. Crank engine for about 10 seconds to ensure residual fuel line pressure is released. Turn ignition off. Install circuit opening relay and remaining components.

Tracker – 1) Loosen fuel tank cap to release fuel tank pressure. Disconnect electrical connector from fuel pump relay. Fuel pump relay is mounted on ECM, located under left side of dash, near kick panel. *See Fig. 2.*

2) Start engine. Idle engine until it dies. Crank engine for about 10 seconds to ensure residual fuel line pressure is released. Turn ignition off. Install fuel pump relay and remaining components.

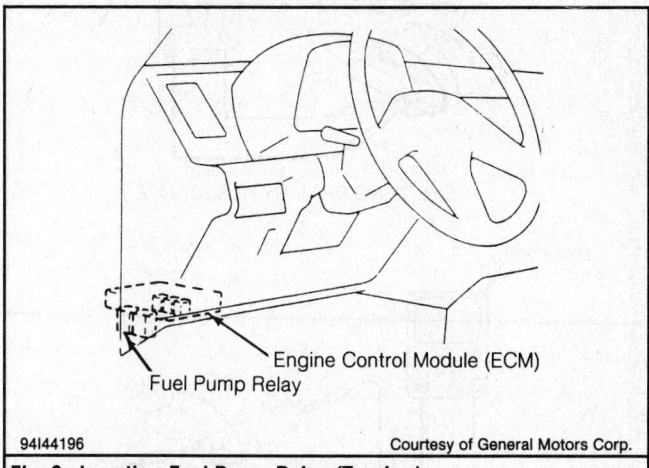

94I44196   Courtesy of General Motors Corp.

Fig. 2: Locating Fuel Pump Relay (Tracker)

FUEL PRESSURE

NOTE: For fuel pump specifications, see FUEL PUMP PERFORMANCE table.

Metro – Release fuel pressure. See FUEL PRESSURE RELEASE. Disconnect negative battery cable. Remove air cleaner assembly. Remove fuel inlet hose from throttle body. Install Fuel Pressure Gauge (J-34730-1) and Adapter (J-34730-75). *See Fig. 3.* Reconnect negative battery cable. Check fuel pressure. *See Figs. 13 and 14, or 18 and 19.* Release fuel pressure. Remove fuel pressure gauge.

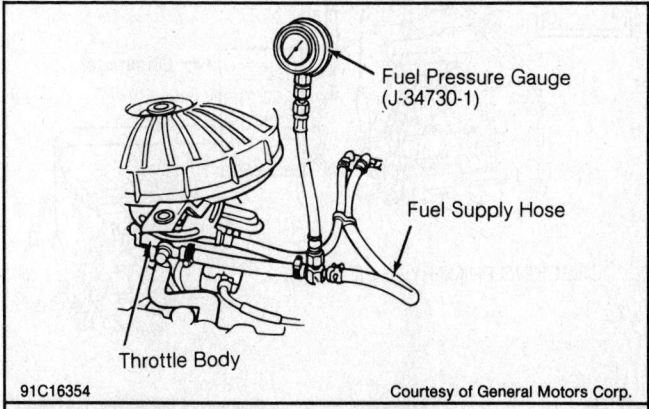

91C16354   Courtesy of General Motors Corp.

Fig. 3: Installing Fuel Pressure Gauge (Metro)

Prizm & Prizm LSi – 1) Release fuel pressure. See FUEL PRESSURE RELEASE. Disconnect negative battery cable. Remove bolt and fuel inlet hose from fuel rail.

2) Install Adapter (J-39802) with gaskets and fuel inlet hose to to fuel rail. *See Fig. 4.* Tighten adapter retaining bolt to 22 ft. lbs. (29 N.m). Install Fuel Pressure Gauge (J-34730-1A) to adapter.

3) Reconnect negative battery cable. Turn ignition on. Connect jumper wire between Data Link Connector (DLC) terminals B+ (Black/Red wire) and FP (Blue/Black wire). DLC is located on left strut tower. Check fuel pressure. *See Fig. 23 or 27.* Release fuel pressure. Remove fuel pressure gauge. Remove jumper wire from DLC.

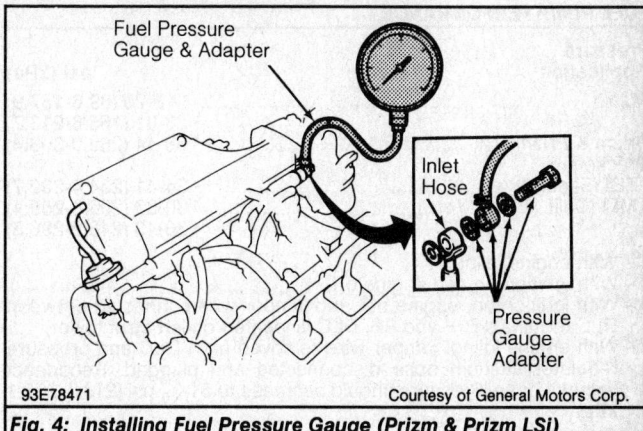

93E78471   Courtesy of General Motors Corp.

Fig. 4: Installing Fuel Pressure Gauge (Prizm & Prizm LSi)

Tracker (TBI – Federal) – Release fuel pressure. See FUEL PRESSURE RELEASE. Disconnect negative battery cable. Raise and support vehicle. Install Fuel Pressure Gauge (J-34730-1) and Adapter (J-37746) to fuel filter inlet. *See Fig. 5.* Fuel filter is located on right side of frame, above rear differential. Reconnect negative battery cable. Check fuel pressure. *See Figs. 31 and 32.* Release fuel pressure. Remove fuel pressure gauge.

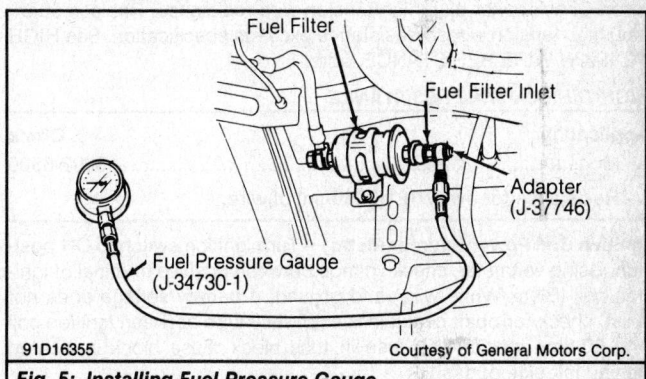

91D16355   Courtesy of General Motors Corp.

Fig. 5: Installing Fuel Pressure Gauge (Tracker TBI – Federal)

Tracker (MFI – Calif. & New York) – Release fuel pressure. See FUEL PRESSURE RELEASE. Disconnect negative battery cable. Remove fuel plug bolt from fuel rail located below fuel pressure regulator. Install Fuel Pressure Gauge (J-34730-1) and Adapter (J-41041) to fuel rail. *See Fig. 6.* Reconnect negative battery cable. Check fuel pressure. *See Figs. 38, 39 and 40.* Release fuel pressure. Remove fuel pressure gauge.

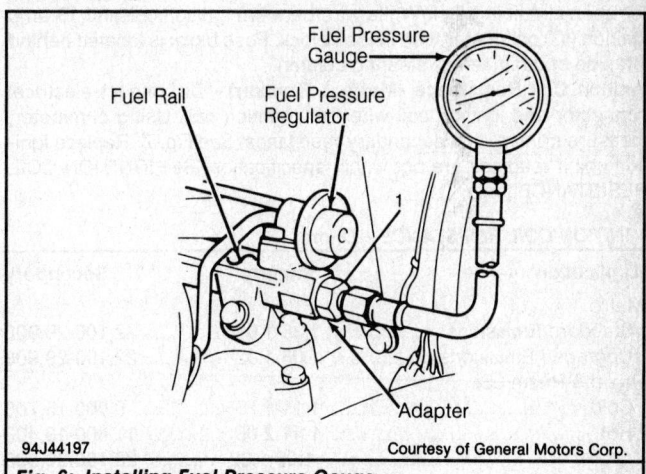

94J44197   Courtesy of General Motors Corp.

Fig. 6: Installing Fuel Pressure Gauge (Tracker MFI – Calif. & New York)

FUEL PUMP PERFORMANCE

Pressure Application	psi (kPa)
Metro	[1] 13-20 (89.6-137.9)
	[2] 23-31 (158.6-213.7)
Prizm & Prizm LSi	[3] [4] 38-44 (262.0-303.4)
Tracker	
TBI (Federal)	[1] [2] 34-41 (234.4-282.7)
MFI (Calif. & New York)	[1] 30-37 (206.9-255.1)
	[2] 36-43 (248.2-296.5)

[1] – With engine idling.
[2] – With ignition on and engine off.
[3] – With ignition on, engine off, and jumper wire connected between DLC terminals B+ and FP. DLC is located on left strut tower.
[4] – With engine idling, jumper wire removed from DLC and pressure regulator vacuum hose disconnected and plugged. Reconnect vacuum hose. Pressure should decrease to 31-37 psi (213.7-255.1 kPa).

IGNITION CHECKS

NOTE: For a no-start condition, see DIAGNOSTIC CHARTS.

Spark – Crank engine, checking for a strong Blue spark at coil wire and each spark plug wire using Spark Tester (ST-125). If spark exists on some plugs, check for defective distributor cap and defective rotor. Check spark plug high tension wire resistance. Replace spark plug high tension wires if resistance exceeds specification. See HIGH TENSION WIRE RESISTANCE table.

HIGH TENSION WIRE RESISTANCE

Application	Ohms
All Models	[1] 3000-6500

[1] – Resistance for every 12" (305 mm) of wire.

Ignition Coil Power Source (Metro) – Turn ignition switch to ON position. Using voltmeter, check voltage between positive terminal of ignition coil (Black/White wire) and ground. If battery voltage does not exist, check for open circuit in Black/White wire between ignition coil and 20-amp ignition (IG) fuse in fuse block. Fuse block is located behind left side of dash.

Ignition Coil Power Source (Prizm & Prizm LSi) – Ignition coil is located in distributor. Disconnect electrical connector from distributor. Turn ignition on. Using voltmeter, check voltage between Black/Orange wire of distributor connector and ground. If battery voltage does not exist, check for open circuit in Black/Orange wire between distributor connector and ignition switch.

Ignition Coil Power Source (Tracker) – Turn ignition on. Using voltmeter, check voltage between positive terminal of ignition coil (Black/White wire) and ground. If battery voltage does not exist, check for open circuit in Black/White wire between ignition coil and 15-amp ignition (IG) coil/meter fuse in fuse block. Fuse block is located behind left side of dash, left of steering column.

Ignition Coil Resistance (Metro & Tracker) – Disconnect electrical connector and ignition coil wire from ignition coil. Using ohmmeter, measure primary and secondary resistance. See Fig. 7. Replace ignition coil if readings are not within specification. See IGNITION COIL RESISTANCE table.

IGNITION COIL RESISTANCE – Ohms

Application	Primary	Secondary
Metro		
Standard Emissions	1.35-1.65	22,100-29,900
Upgraded Emissions	1.08-1.32	22,100-29,900
Prizm & Prizm LSi		
Cold	1.11-1.75	9,000-15,700
Hot	1.41-2.05	11,400-18,400
Tracker	[1] 1.08-1.32	[1] 22,100-29,900

[1] – Ohms @ 68°F (20°C)

Ignition Coil Resistance (Prizm & Prizm LSi) – Remove distributor cap, rotor and dust cover. Using an ohmmeter, measure primary and secondary resistance. See Fig. 8. Replace ignition coil if readings are not within specification. See IGNITION COIL RESISTANCE table.

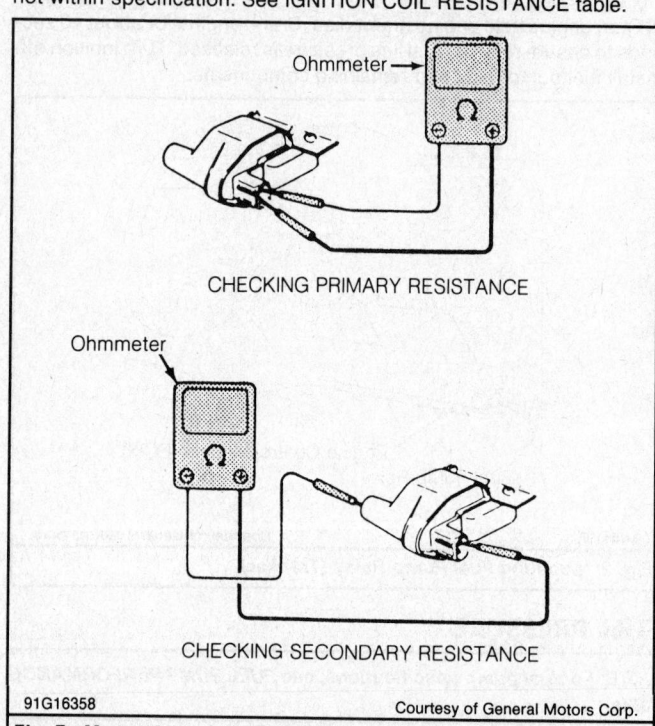

CHECKING PRIMARY RESISTANCE

CHECKING SECONDARY RESISTANCE

91G16358   Courtesy of General Motors Corp.

Fig. 7: Measuring Ignition Coil Resistance (Metro & Tracker)

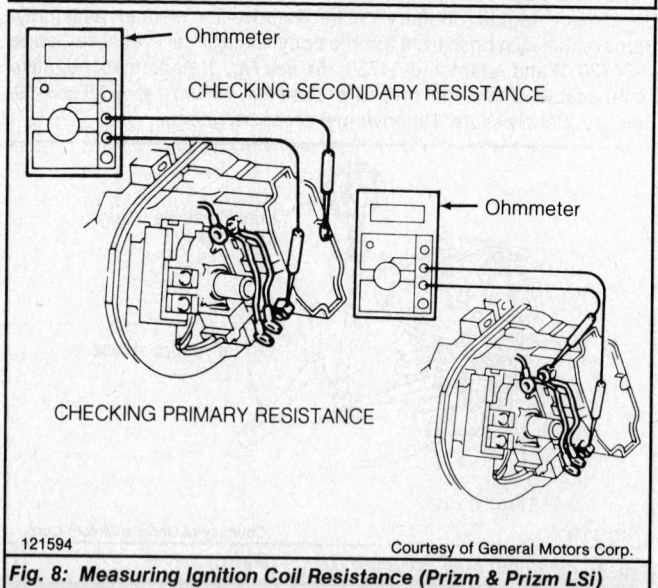

CHECKING SECONDARY RESISTANCE

CHECKING PRIMARY RESISTANCE

121594   Courtesy of General Motors Corp.

Fig. 8: Measuring Ignition Coil Resistance (Prizm & Prizm LSi)

Noise Filter/Condenser (Metro & Tracker) – 1) Disconnect negative battery cable. Disconnect electrical connector from noise filter/condenser. Noise filter/condenser is located below ignition coil.
2) Using ohmmeter, measure resistance between terminals "A" and "B" of noise filter/condenser. See Fig. 9. If resistance is not about 2200 ohms, replace noise filter/condenser.
3) Using ohmmeter, check continuity between terminals "A" and "B" of noise filter/condenser. If continuity exists, replace filter/condenser.
Signal Rotor/Camshaft Position (CMP) Sensor – Measure signal rotor/CMP sensor air gap. If gap is not .008-.016" (.20-.40 mm), adjust or replace distributor. Check signal rotor/CMP resistance. See SYSTEM & COMPONENT TESTING article.

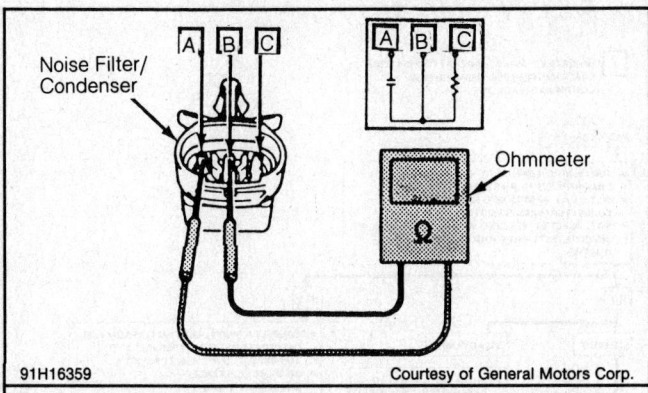

91H16359   Courtesy of General Motors Corp.

Fig. 9: Identifying Noise/Filter Condenser Connector Terminals (Metro & Tracker)

IDLE SPEED & IGNITION TIMING

Ensure idle speed and base ignition timing are set to specification. For adjustment procedures, see ON-VEHICLE ADJUSTMENTS article.

SUMMARY

If no faults were found while performing BASIC DIAGNOSTIC PROCEDURES, go to SELF-DIAGNOSTICS article. If no hard codes are found in self-diagnostics, go to TROUBLE SHOOTING – NO CODES article for diagnosis by symptom (i.e., ROUGH IDLE, NO START, etc.) or intermittent diagnostic procedures.

DIAGNOSTIC CHARTS
DIAGNOSTIC CHARTS DIRECTORY

Application [1]	Fig. No.
Metro (Standard Emissions)	10-14
Metro (Upgraded Emissions)	15-19
Prizm Except LSi	20-23
Prizm LSi	24-27
Tracker (TBI – Federal)	28-32
Tracker (MFI – Calif. & New York)	33-40

[1] – Before using diagnostic charts, perform appropriate On-Board Diagnostic (OBD) System Check chart to determine starting point. See SELF-DIAGNOSTICS article.

METRO (STANDARD EMISSIONS) CHART A1-3, ENGINE CRANKS BUT WILL NOT RUN

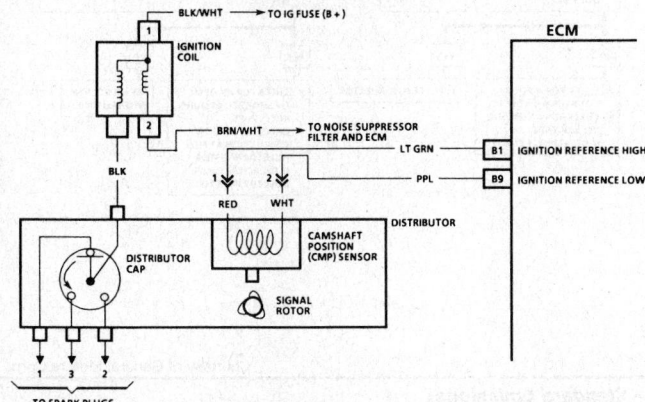

Before using this chart, ensure battery condition, engine cranking speed and fuel quantity are okay.

When ignition switch is in ON or START position, battery voltage is applied to ignition coil. If ignition coil's primary coil is being toggled to ground by ECM, a high voltage is induced in secondary windings of ignition coil and is applied through distributor to spark plugs.

NOTE: Test numbers refer to numbers on diagnostic chart.

1) Checks if diagnostic trouble codes are stored in ECM memory.
2) Checks for spark at ignition coil.
3) Checks for spark at distributor.
4) Checks for spark at spark plugs.

DIAGNOSTIC AIDS

Water or foreign material in fuel can cause a no-start condition during freezing weather. Engine may start after 5-6 minutes in a heated shop. Problem may not reoccur until vehicle is parked overnight in freezing temperatures.

Low fuel pressure can result in very lean air/fuel ratio. Fouled or damaged spark plugs will also cause "engine cranks but will not run" condition.

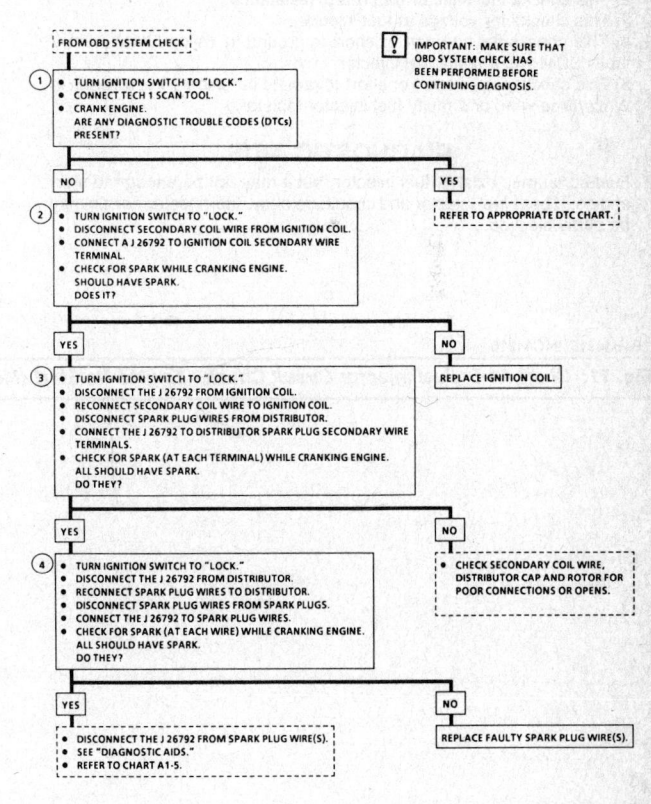

94J44213 94A44214   Courtesy of General Motors Corp.

Fig. 10: Chart A1-3, Engine Cranks But Will Not Run (Metro – Standard Emissions)

**METRO (STANDARD EMISSIONS)
CHART A1-5, FUEL INJECTOR CIRCUIT
CHECK (ENGINE NO-START)**

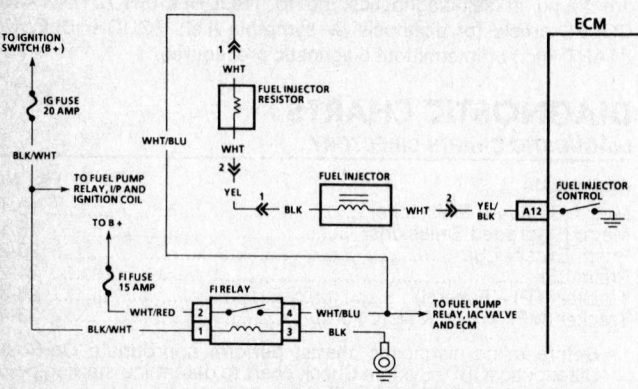

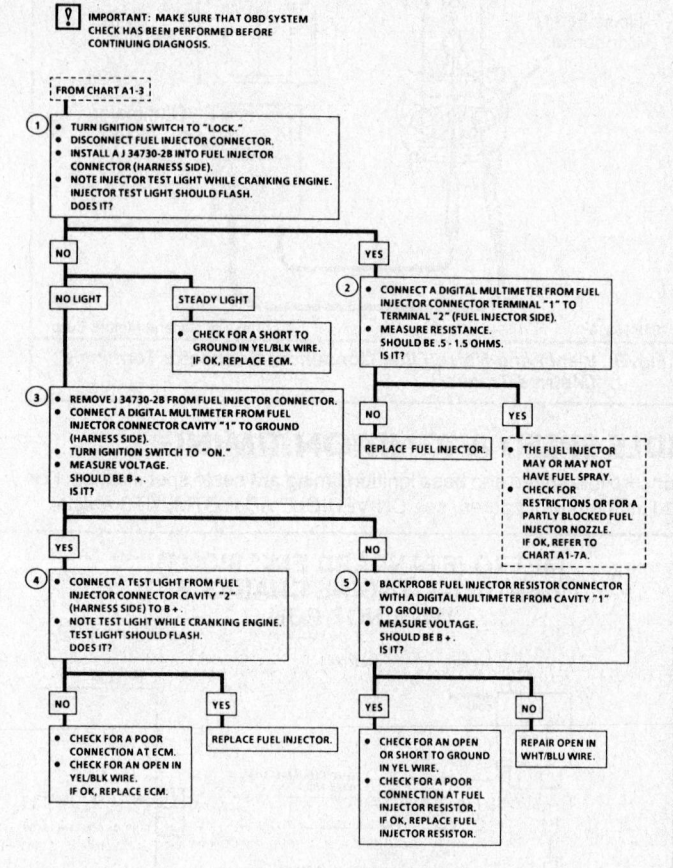

When solenoid coil of fuel injector is energized by ECM, it will activate fuel injector plunger and pressurized fuel will be injected into throttle body. Fuel pump will operate as long as engine is cranking and ECM is receiving ignition reference pulses. If ECM does not receive reference pulses, fuel pump will stop after 3 seconds.

NOTE: Test numbers refer to numbers on diagnostic chart.

1) Checks to see if ECM is controlling fuel injector signals.
2) This checks fuel injector for correct resistance.
3) This checks for voltage at fuel injector.
4) This checks for an open or short to ground in Yellow/Black wire, a faulty ECM and a faulty fuel injector.
5) This checks for an open or short to ground in Yellow wire, an open in White/Blue wire, or a faulty fuel injector resistor.

DIAGNOSTIC AIDS

Fuel spray may exist at fuel injector, but it may not be enough to start engine. If both fuel injector and circuit are okay, fuel injector nozzle may be partly blocked.

94B44215 94C44216

Fig. 11: Chart A1-5, Fuel Injector Circuit Check – Engine No-Start (Metro – Standard Emissions)

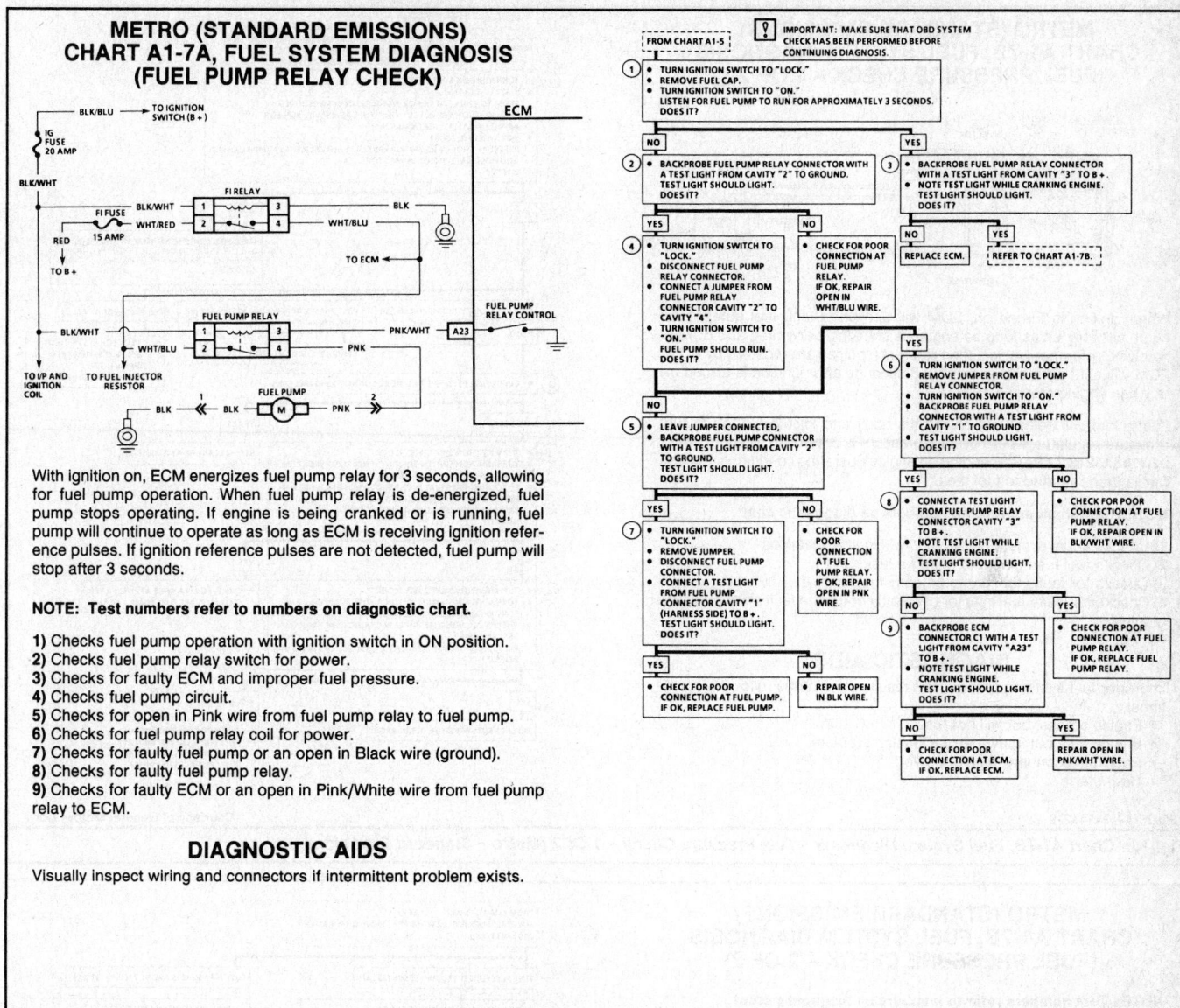

**METRO (STANDARD EMISSIONS)
CHART A1-7A, FUEL SYSTEM DIAGNOSIS
(FUEL PUMP RELAY CHECK)**

With ignition on, ECM energizes fuel pump relay for 3 seconds, allowing for fuel pump operation. When fuel pump relay is de-energized, fuel pump stops operating. If engine is being cranked or is running, fuel pump will continue to operate as long as ECM is receiving ignition reference pulses. If ignition reference pulses are not detected, fuel pump will stop after 3 seconds.

NOTE: Test numbers refer to numbers on diagnostic chart.

1) Checks fuel pump operation with ignition switch in ON position.
2) Checks fuel pump relay switch for power.
3) Checks for faulty ECM and improper fuel pressure.
4) Checks fuel pump circuit.
5) Checks for open in Pink wire from fuel pump relay to fuel pump.
6) Checks for fuel pump relay coil for power.
7) Checks for faulty fuel pump or an open in Black wire (ground).
8) Checks for faulty fuel pump relay.
9) Checks for faulty ECM or an open in Pink/White wire from fuel pump relay to ECM.

DIAGNOSTIC AIDS

Visually inspect wiring and connectors if intermittent problem exists.

94D44217 94E44218

Fig. 12: Chart A1-7A, Fuel System Diagnosis – Fuel Pump Relay Check (Metro – Standard Emissions)

METRO (STANDARD EMISSIONS)
CHART A1-7B, FUEL SYSTEM DIAGNOSIS
(FUEL PRESSURE CHECK – 1 OF 2)

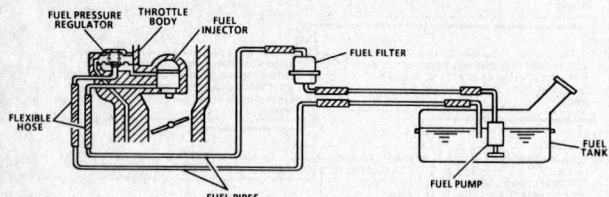

When ignition is turned on, ECM will turn on in-tank fuel pump. Fuel pump will stay on as long as engine is cranking or running and ECM is receiving reference pulses. If no reference pulses are received by ECM, ECM will shut off fuel pump about 3 seconds after ignition is turned on or when engine stops.

Fuel pump will deliver fuel to throttle body and injectors, then to fuel pressure regulator, where system pressure is controlled to about 23-31 psi (158.6-213.7 kPa) depending on engine operating conditions. Excess fuel is then returned to fuel tank.

NOTE: Test numbers refer to numbers on diagnostic chart.

1) Checks if fuel system pressure is within specifications.
2) Checks fuel feed pipe and hose for leaks.
3) Checks for faulty fuel pump or leaky fuel filter.
4) Checks for leaky fuel injector or throttle body or a faulty fuel pressure regulator.

DIAGNOSTIC AIDS
Improper fuel system pressure can result in one of the following conditions:
- Engine cranks, but will not run.
- Engine cuts out, may feel like ignition problem.
- Poor fuel economy, loss of power.
- Hard starts.

92J26244 94F44219

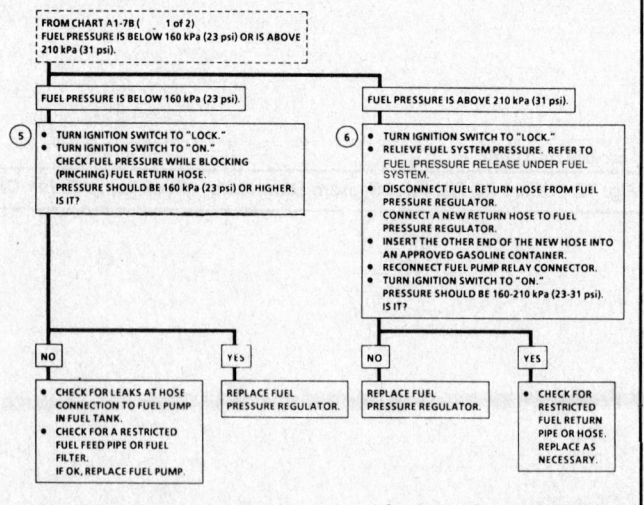

Courtesy of General Motors Corp.

Fig. 13: Chart A1-7B, Fuel System Diagnosis – Fuel Pressure Check – 1 Of 2 (Metro – Standard Emissions)

METRO (STANDARD EMISSIONS)
CHART A1-7B, FUEL SYSTEM DIAGNOSIS
(FUEL PRESSURE CHECK – 2 OF 2)

NOTE: Test numbers refer to numbers on diagnostic chart.

5) Checks for restricted fuel feed pipe, restricted fuel filter or a faulty fuel pressure regulator.
6) Determines if a restricted fuel return pipe or faulty fuel pressure regulator exists.

FROM CHART A1-7B (1 of 2)
FUEL PRESSURE IS BELOW 160 kPa (23 psi) OR IS ABOVE 210 kPa (31 psi).

FUEL PRESSURE IS BELOW 160 kPa (23 psi).

5) • TURN IGNITION SWITCH TO "LOCK."
• TURN IGNITION SWITCH TO "ON."
CHECK FUEL PRESSURE WHILE BLOCKING (PINCHING) FUEL RETURN HOSE.
PRESSURE SHOULD BE 160 kPa (23 psi) OR HIGHER.
IS IT?

FUEL PRESSURE IS ABOVE 210 kPa (31 psi).

6) • TURN IGNITION SWITCH TO "LOCK." REFER TO FUEL PRESSURE RELEASE UNDER FUEL SYSTEM.
• DISCONNECT FUEL RETURN HOSE FROM FUEL PRESSURE REGULATOR.
• CONNECT A NEW RETURN HOSE TO FUEL PRESSURE REGULATOR.
• INSERT THE OTHER END OF THE NEW HOSE INTO AN APPROVED GASOLINE CONTAINER.
• RECONNECT FUEL PUMP RELAY CONNECTOR.
• TURN IGNITION SWITCH TO "ON."
PRESSURE SHOULD BE 160-210 kPa (23-31 psi).
IS IT?

NO
• CHECK FOR LEAKS AT HOSE CONNECTION TO FUEL PUMP IN FUEL TANK.
• CHECK FOR A RESTRICTED FUEL FEED PIPE OR FUEL FILTER.
IF OK, REPLACE FUEL PUMP.

YES
• REPLACE FUEL PRESSURE REGULATOR.

NO
• REPLACE FUEL PRESSURE REGULATOR.

YES
• CHECK FOR RESTRICTED FUEL RETURN PIPE OR HOSE. REPLACE AS NECESSARY.

94I44220

Courtesy of General Motors Corp.

Fig. 14: Chart A1-7B, Fuel System Diagnosis – Fuel Pressure Check – 2 Of 2 (Metro – Standard Emissions)

METRO (UPGRADED EMISSIONS) CHART A2-3, ENGINE CRANKS BUT WILL NOT RUN

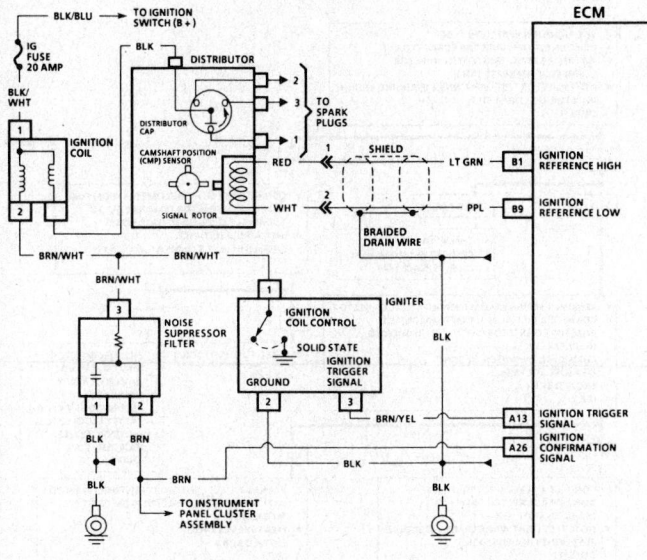

Before using this chart, ensure battery condition, engine cranking speed and fuel quantity are okay.

When ignition switch is in ON or START position, battery voltage is applied to ignition coil. If ignition coil's primary coil is being toggled to ground by the ignitor, a high voltage is induced in secondary windings of ignition coil and is applied through distributor to spark plugs.

NOTE: Test numbers refer to numbers on diagnostic chart.

1) Checks if diagnostic trouble codes are stored in ECM memory.
2) Checks for spark at ignition coil.
3) Checks for spark at distributor.
4) Checks for spark at spark plugs.

94J44221 94A44222

DIAGNOSTIC AIDS

Water or foreign material in fuel can cause a no-start condition during freezing weather. Engine may start after 5-6 minutes in a heated shop. Problem may not reoccur until vehicle is parked overnight in freezing temperatures.

Low fuel pressure can result in very lean air/fuel ratio. Fouled or damaged spark plugs will also cause "engine cranks but will not run" condition.

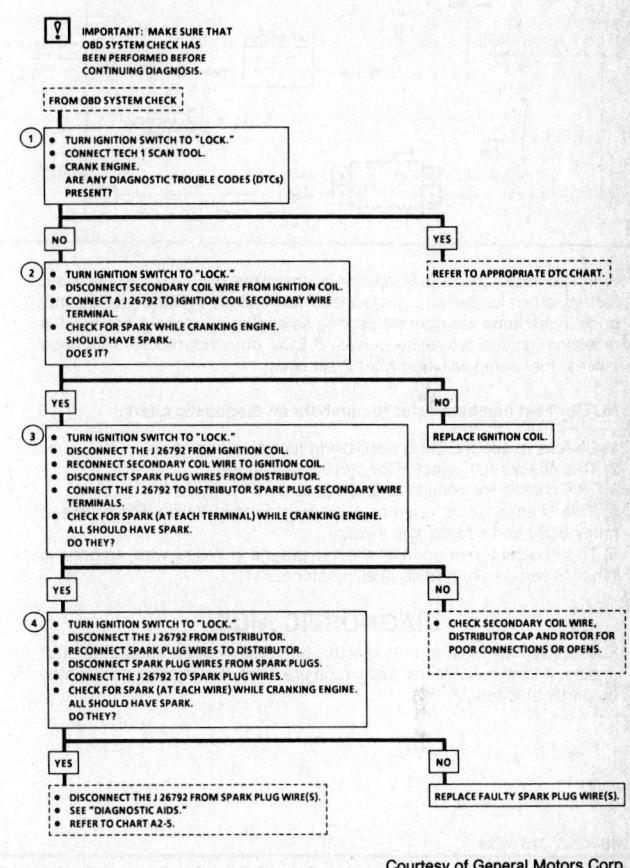

Courtesy of General Motors Corp.

Fig. 15: Chart A2-3, Engine Cranks But Will Not Run (Metro – Upgraded Emissions)

METRO (UPGRADED EMISSIONS)
CHART A2-5, FUEL INJECTOR CIRCUIT
CHECK (ENGINE NO-START)

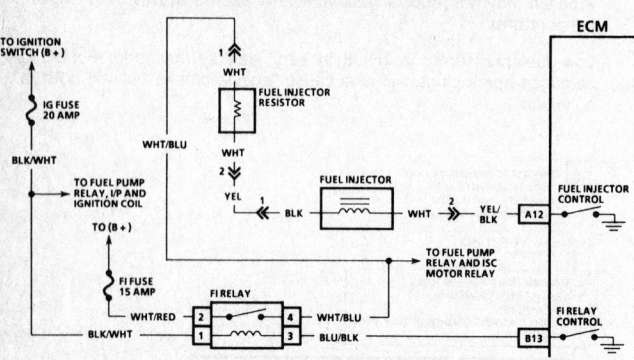

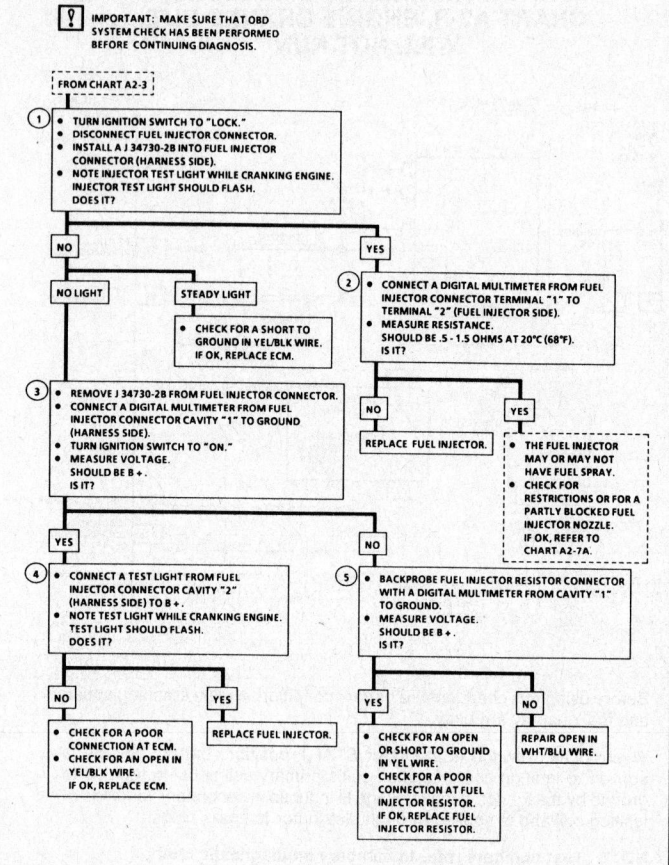

When solenoid coil of fuel injector is energized by ECM, it will activate fuel injector plunger and pressurized fuel will be injected into throttle body. Fuel pump will operate as long as engine is cranking and ECM is receiving ignition reference pulses. If ECM does not receive reference pulses, fuel pump will stop after 2 seconds.

NOTE: Test numbers refer to numbers on diagnostic chart.

1) Checks to see if ECM is controlling fuel injector signals.
2) This checks fuel injector for correct resistance.
3) This checks for voltage at fuel injector.
4) This checks for an open or short to ground in Yellow/Black wire, a faulty ECM and a faulty fuel injector.
5) This checks for an open or short to ground in Yellow wire, an open in White/Blue wire, or a faulty fuel injector resistor.

DIAGNOSTIC AIDS

Fuel spray may exist at fuel injector, but it may not be enough to start engine. If both fuel injector and circuit are okay, fuel injector nozzle may be partly blocked.

94B44223 94C44224

Fig. 16: Chart A2-5, Fuel Injector Circuit Check – Engine No-Start (Metro – Upgraded Emissions)

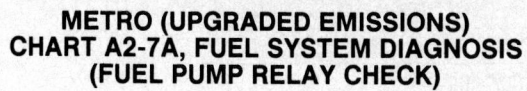

METRO (UPGRADED EMISSIONS)
CHART A2-7A, FUEL SYSTEM DIAGNOSIS
(FUEL PUMP RELAY CHECK)

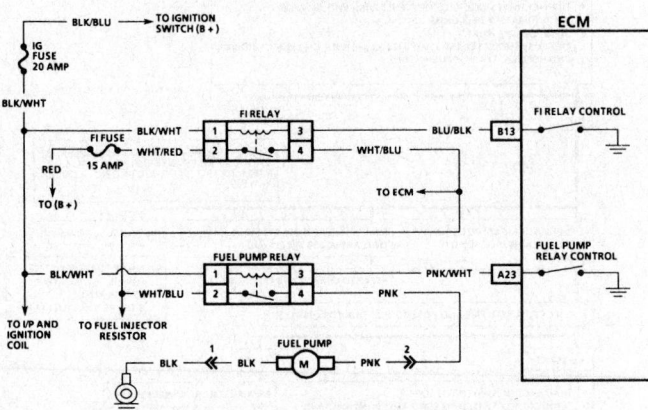

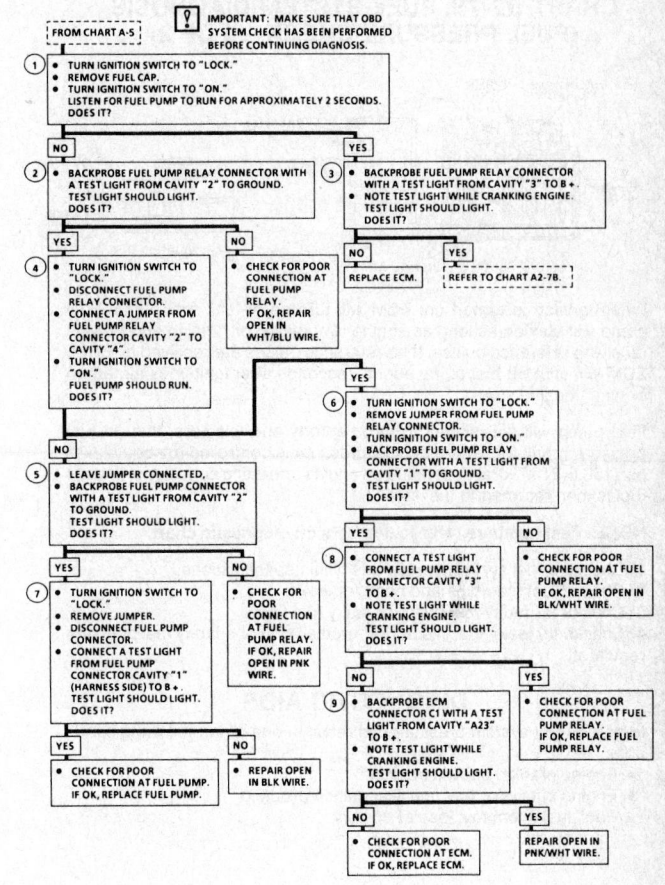

With ignition on, ECM energizes fuel pump relay for 2 seconds, allowing for fuel pump operation. When fuel pump relay is de-energized, fuel pump stops operating. If engine is being cranked or is running, fuel pump will continue to operate as long as ECM is receiving ignition reference pulses. If ignition reference pulses are not detected, fuel pump will stop after 2 seconds.

NOTE: Test numbers refer to numbers on diagnostic chart.

1) Checks fuel pump operation with ignition switch in ON position.
2) Checks fuel pump relay switch for power.
3) Checks for faulty ECM and improper fuel pressure.
4) Checks fuel pump circuit.
5) Checks for open in Pink wire from fuel pump relay to fuel pump.
6) Checks for fuel pump relay coil for power.
7) Checks for faulty fuel pump or an open in Black wire (ground).
8) Checks for faulty fuel pump relay.
9) Checks for faulty ECM or an open in Pink/White wire from fuel pump relay to ECM.

DIAGNOSTIC AIDS

Visually inspect wiring and connectors if intermittent problem exists.

94D44225 94E44226

Courtesy of General Motors Corp.

Fig. 17: Chart A2-7A, Fuel System Diagnosis – Fuel Pump Relay Check (Metro – Upgraded Emissions)

METRO (UPGRADED EMISSIONS)
CHART A2-7B, FUEL SYSTEM DIAGNOSIS
(FUEL PRESSURE CHECK – 1 OF 2)

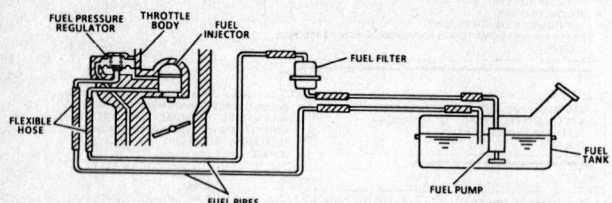

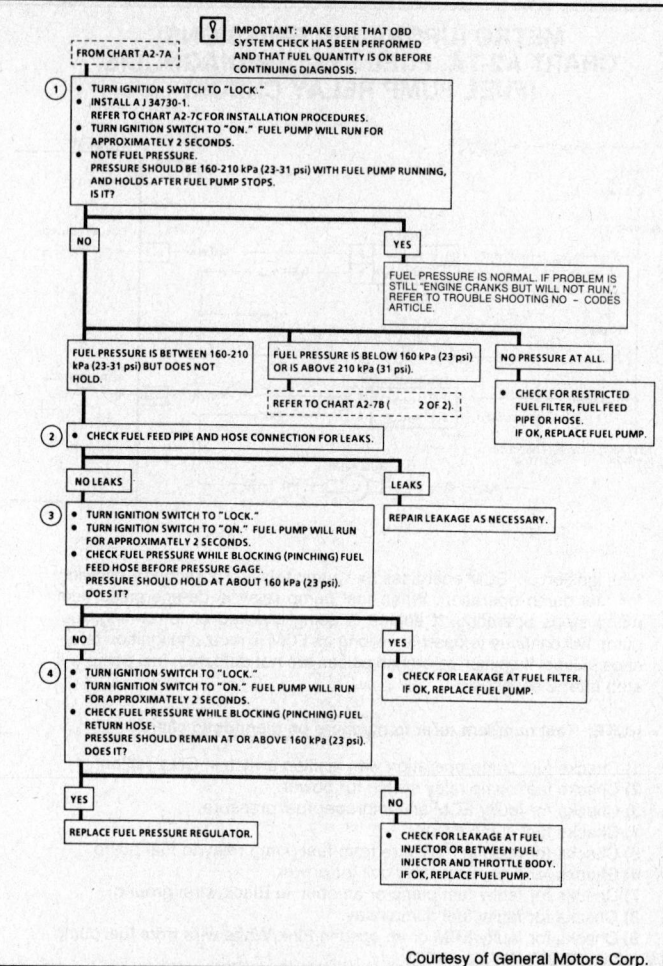

When ignition is turned on, ECM will turn on in-tank fuel pump. Fuel pump will stay on as long as engine is cranking or running and ECM is receiving reference pulses. If no reference pulses are received by ECM, ECM will shut off fuel pump about 2 seconds after ignition is turned on or when engine stops.

Fuel pump will deliver fuel to throttle body and injectors, then to fuel pressure regulator, where system pressure is controlled to about 23-31 psi (158.6-213.7 kPa) depending on engine operating conditions. Excess fuel is then returned to fuel tank.

NOTE: Test numbers refer to numbers on diagnostic chart.

1) Checks if fuel system pressure is within specifications.
2) Checks fuel feed pipe and hose for leaks.
3) Checks for faulty fuel pump or leaky fuel filter.
4) Checks for leaky fuel injector or throttle body or a faulty fuel pressure regulator.

DIAGNOSTIC AIDS

Improper fuel system pressure can result in one of the following conditions:
- Engine cranks, but will not run.
- Engine cuts out, may feel like ignition problem.
- Poor fuel economy, loss of power.
- Hard starts.

92J26244 94F44227

Courtesy of General Motors Corp.

Fig. 18: Chart A2-7B, Fuel System Diagnosis – Fuel Pressure Check – 1 Of 2 (Metro – Upgraded Emissions)

METRO (UPGRADED EMISSIONS)
CHART A2-7B, FUEL SYSTEM DIAGNOSIS
(FUEL PRESSURE CHECK – 2 OF 2)

NOTE: Test numbers refer to numbers on diagnostic chart.

5) Checks for restricted fuel feed pipe, restricted fuel filter or a faulty fuel pressure regulator.
6) Determines if a restricted fuel return pipe or faulty fuel pressure regulator exists.

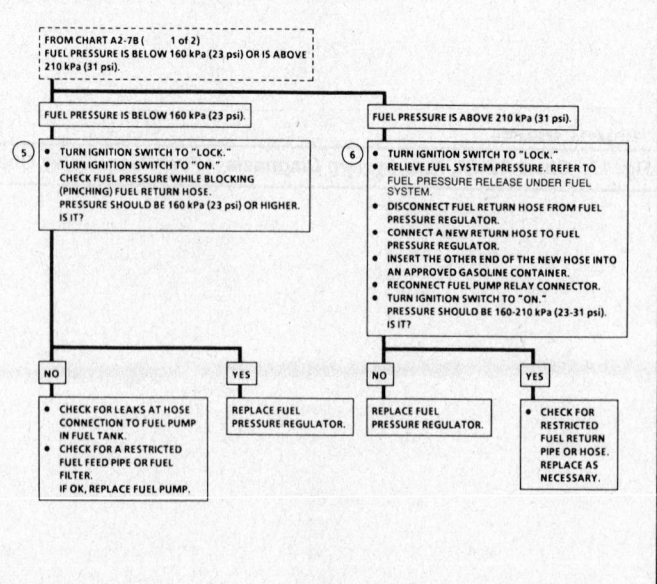

94G44228

Courtesy of General Motors Corp.

Fig. 19: Chart A2-7B, Fuel System Diagnosis – Fuel Pressure Check – 2 Of 2 (Metro – Upgraded Emissions)

PRIZM EXCEPT LSi
CHART A1-3, ENGINE CRANKS BUT WILL NOT RUN

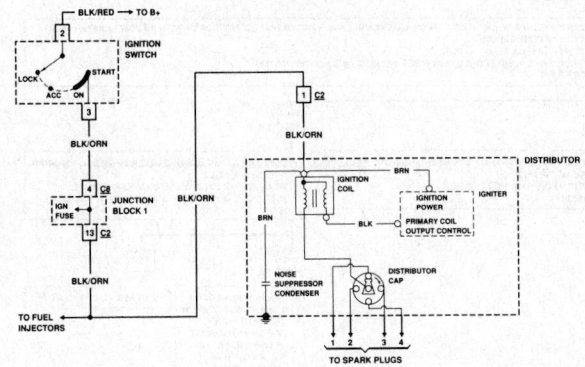

When ignition switch is turned to ON or START position, voltage is applied to ignition coil and to ignitor (inside distributor). Ignitor controls ground circuit of ignition coil. When ignitor receives power and an ignition firing input, it toggles ground path to ignition coil on and off, inducing a high voltage in secondary winding of coil. This induced voltage is then applied through distributor cap to each spark plug.

NOTE: Test numbers refer to numbers on diagnostic chart.

1) Checks for spark at distributor cap.
2) Checks for faulty spark plug wires or misadjusted signal rotor air gap.

93D78405 93E78406

DIAGNOSTIC AIDS

Water or foreign material in fuel can cause a no-start or a lack of power condition. Low fuel pressure, a restricted fuel filter or fuel injectors may cause a no-start condition. Refer to CHART A1-5 for fuel injector circuit test.

An intermittent may be caused by a poor connection, rubbed-through wire insulation, or a wire broken inside insulation. Inspect harness connectors for backed-out terminals, improper mating, broken locks, improperly formed or damaged terminals, and poor terminal-to-wire connections before replacing components.

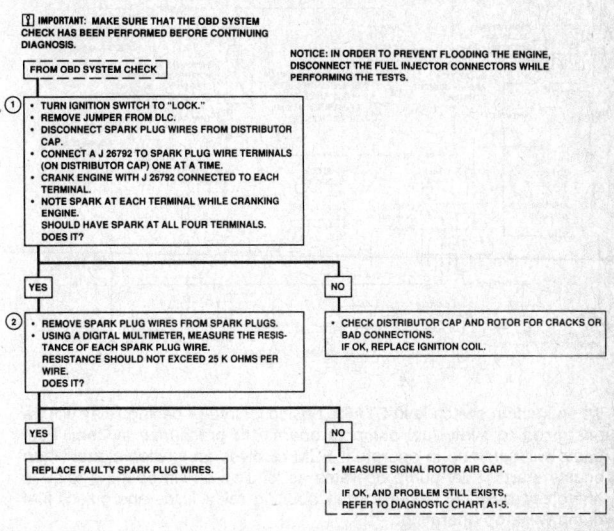

Courtesy of General Motors Corp.

Fig. 20: Chart A1-3, Engine Cranks But Will Not Run (Prizm Except LSi)

PRIZM EXCEPT LSi
CHART A1-5, FUEL INJECTOR CIRCUIT CHECK (ENGINE NO-START)

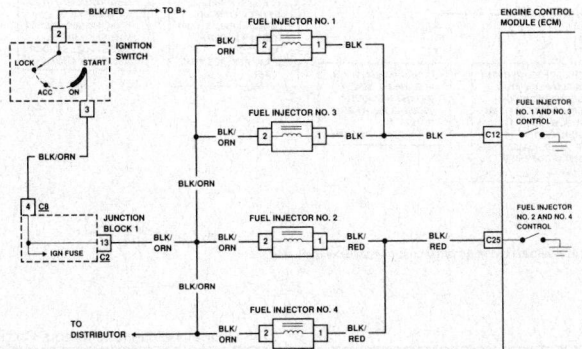

When ignition switch is turned to ON or START position (engine running), ECM will energize/de-energize fuel injector solenoid coil. With coil energized, a plunger is activated, allowing pressurized fuel to be sprayed through fuel injectors into combustion chamber where it is mixed with air from intake manifold, thus creating proper air/fuel mixture needed for combustion.

NOTE: Test numbers refer to numbers on diagnostic chart.

1) Checks if ECM is controlling ground path to fuel injectors.
2) Checks resistance of fuel injectors.
3) Checks for open or short to ground in Black or Black/Red wire between fuel injectors and ECM, or for faulty fuel injectors or ECM.

93F78407 93G78408

DIAGNOSTIC AIDS

Fuel spray may exist at fuel injectors, but it may not be enough to start engine. If fuel injectors and their circuits are okay, and fuel spray is detected, fuel injector nozzle may be partly blocked or restricted. See CHART A1-7A for circuit opening relay check.

An intermittent may be caused by a poor connection, rubbed-through wire insulation, or a wire broken inside insulation. Inspect harness connectors for backed-out terminals, improper mating, broken locks, improperly formed or damaged terminals, and poor terminal-to-wire connections before replacing components.

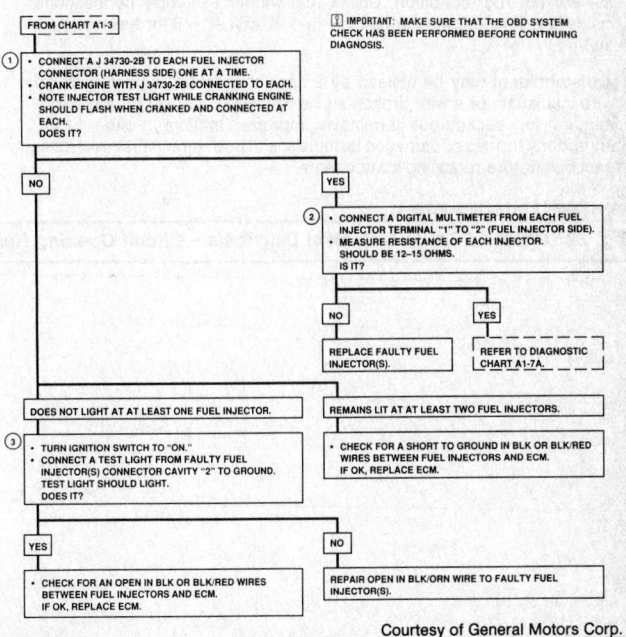

Courtesy of General Motors Corp.

Fig. 21: Chart A1-5, Fuel Injector Circuit Check – Engine No-Start (Prizm Except LSi)

PRIZM EXCEPT LSi
CHART A1-7A, FUEL SYSTEM DIAGNOSIS
(CIRCUIT OPENING RELAY CHECK)

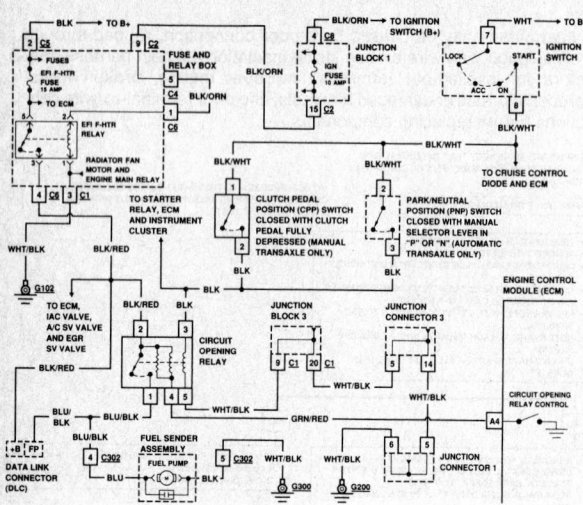

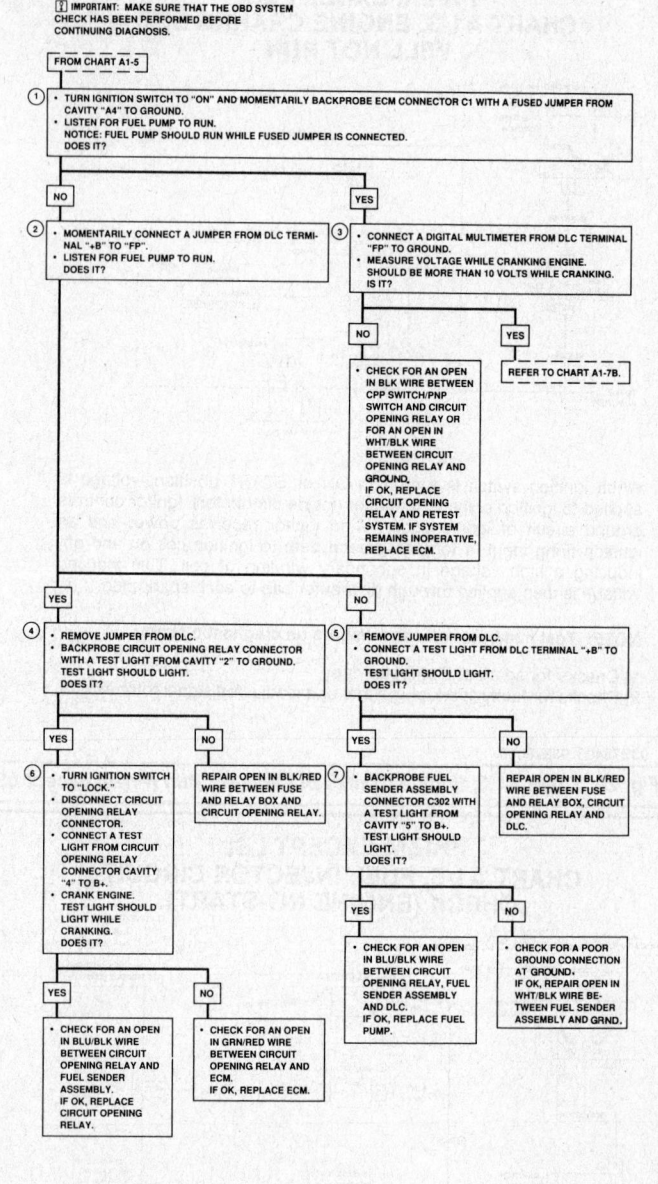

When ignition switch is in START position, circuit opening relay will be energized to allow fuel pump to operate to pressurize system. Fuel pump will continue to operate if ECM receives an ignition signal when engine starts. Fuel pump operates as long as circuit opening relay is energized by ECM. When circuit opening relay is de-energized, fuel pump will stop operating.

NOTE: Test numbers refer to numbers on diagnostic chart.

1) Checks for normal fuel pump operation.
2) Checks if fuel pump will run when DLC terminals B+ and FP are jumpered together.
3) Checks fuel pump operation while ignition signal is present at ECM.
4) Checks for an open in Black/Red wire to circuit opening relay.
5) Checks for an open in Black/Red wire to DLC.
6) Checks for an open Blue/Black or Green/Red wire, a faulty ECM, or a faulty circuit opening relay.
7) Checks for open White/Black or Blue/Black wire, or faulty fuel pump.

DIAGNOSTIC AIDS

A restricted or leaking fuel feed pipe or hose will cause an "engine cranks but will not run" condition. Check fuel sender assembly connections inside fuel tank for poor connection. See CHART A1-7B for fuel pressure test.

An intermittent may be caused by a poor connection, rubbed-through wire insulation, or a wire broken inside insulation. Inspect harness connectors for backed-out terminals, improper mating, broken locks, improperly formed or damaged terminals, and poor terminal-to-wire connections before replacing components.

93H78409 93A78410 93B78411

Courtesy of General Motors Corp.

Fig. 22: Chart A1-7A, Fuel System Diagnosis – Circuit Opening Relay Check (Prizm Except LSi)

PRIZM EXCEPT LSi
CHART A1-7B, FUEL SYSTEM DIAGNOSIS (FUEL PRESSURE CHECK)

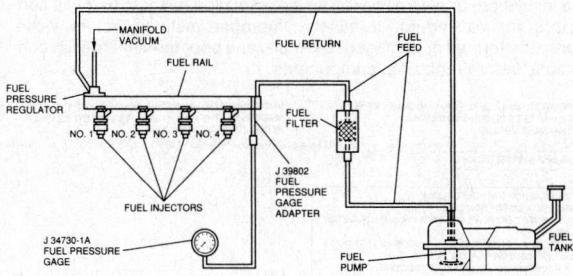

When ignition switch is turned to START position, circuit opening relay will be energized to allow fuel pump to operate to pressurize system. Fuel pump will continue to operate if ECM receives an ignition signal when engine starts. Fuel pump operates as long as circuit opening relay is energized by ECM. When circuit opening relay is de-energized, fuel pump will stop operating. Fuel pump delivers fuel to fuel rail where pressure is maintained by fuel pressure regulator at 41 psi (282.7 kPa) more than pressure inside intake manifold. Excess fuel is returned to fuel tank through a return pipe and hoses.

NOTE: Test numbers refer to numbers on diagnostic chart.

1) Measures fuel pressure with ignition switch in ON position.
2) Determines if fuel pressure is normal.
3) Checks for leaking fuel pressure regulator.
4) Checks for plugged fuel injectors.
5) Checks for leaking fuel injectors or a leaking fuel pump.
6) Checks for a leaking fuel pressure regulator or fuel pump

DIAGNOSTIC AIDS

Check for leakage around all fuel hose/pipe connections. A plugged fuel injector could be the cause of a hard/no-start condition or loss of power/ poor fuel economy. Refer to TROUBLE SHOOTING NO-CODES article for mechanical checks and inspections if fuel spray and pressure is normal.

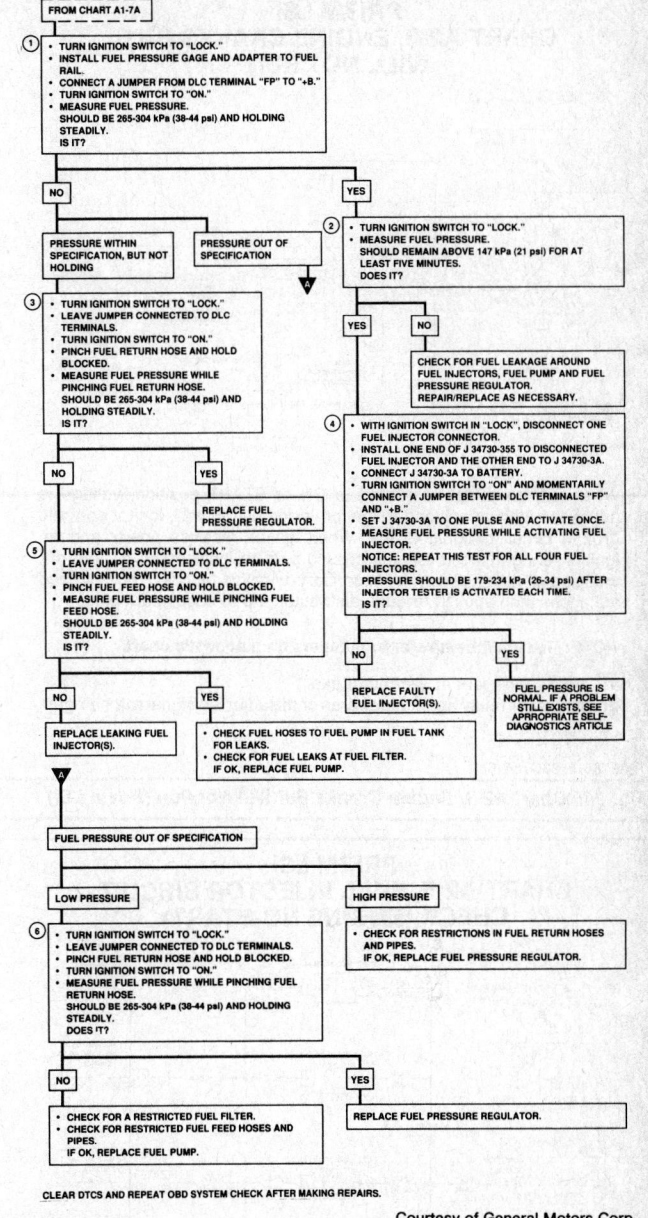

93C78412 93D78413 93E78414

Courtesy of General Motors Corp.

Fig. 23: Chart A1-7B, Fuel System Diagnosis – Fuel Pressure Check (Prizm Except LSi)

PRIZM LSi
CHART A2-3, ENGINE CRANKS BUT WILL NOT RUN

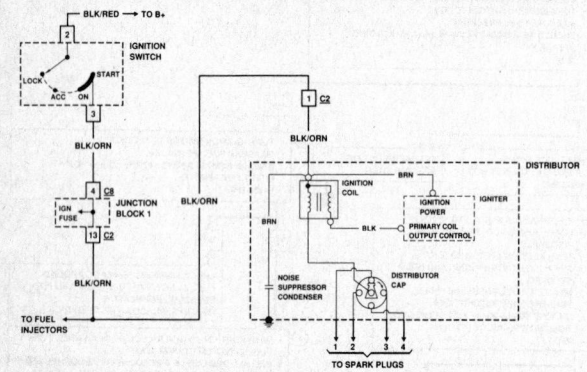

When ignition switch is turned to ON or START position, voltage is applied to ignition coil and to ignitor (inside distributor). Ignitor controls ground circuit of ignition coil. When ignitor receives power and an ignition firing input, it toggles ground path to ignition coil on and off, inducing a high voltage in secondary winding of coil. This induced voltage is then applied through distributor cap to each spark plug.

NOTE: Test numbers refer to numbers on diagnostic chart.

1) Checks for spark at distributor cap.
2) Checks for faulty spark plug wires or misadjusted signal rotor air gap.

93F78415 93G78416

DIAGNOSTIC AIDS

Water or foreign material in fuel can cause no-start or lack of power condition. Low fuel pressure or restricted fuel filter or injectors may cause no-start condition. Refer to CHART A2-5 for fuel injector circuit test.

An intermittent may be caused by a poor connection, rubbed-through wire insulation, or a wire broken inside insulation. Inspect harness connectors for backed-out terminals, improper mating, broken locks, improperly formed or damaged terminals, and poor terminal-to-wire connections before replacing. components

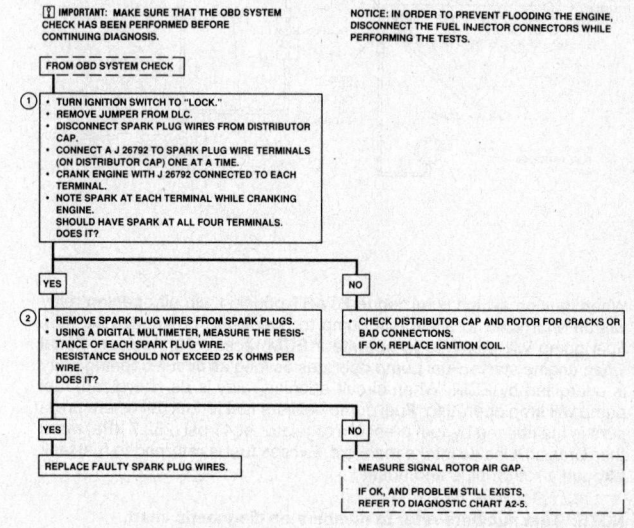

Courtesy of General Motors Corp.

Fig. 24: Chart A2-3, Engine Cranks But Will Not Run (Prizm LSi)

PRIZM LSi
CHART A2-5, FUEL INJECTOR CIRCUIT CHECK (ENGINE NO-START)

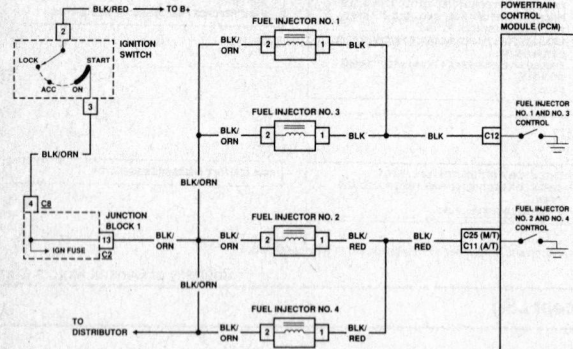

With ignition switch in ON or START position (engine running), PCM will energize/de-energize fuel injector solenoid coil. With coil energized, a plunger is activated, allowing pressurized fuel to be sprayed through fuel injectors into combustion chamber where it is mixed with air from intake manifold, creating proper air/fuel mixture needed for combustion.

NOTE: Test numbers refer to numbers on diagnostic chart.

1) Checks if PCM is controlling ground path of fuel injectors.
2) Checks resistance of fuel injectors.
3) Checks for an open or short to ground in Black or Black/Red wire between fuel injectors and PCM, or for faulty fuel injectors or PCM.

DIAGNOSTIC AIDS

Fuel spray may exist at fuel injectors, but it may not be enough to start engine. If fuel injectors and their circuit are okay, and fuel spray is detected, fuel injector nozzle may be partly blocked or restricted. See CHART A2-7A for circuit opening relay check.

93H78417 93I78418

An intermittent may be caused by a poor connection, rubbed-through wire insulation, or a wire broken inside insulation. Inspect harness connectors for backed-out terminals, improper mating, broken locks, improperly formed or damaged terminals, and poor terminal-to-wire connections before replacing components.

Courtesy of General Motors Corp.

Fig. 25: Chart A2-5, Fuel Injector Circuit Check – Engine No-Start (Prizm LSi)

PRIZM LSi
CHART A2-7A, FUEL SYSTEM DIAGNOSIS
(CIRCUIT OPENING RELAY CHECK)

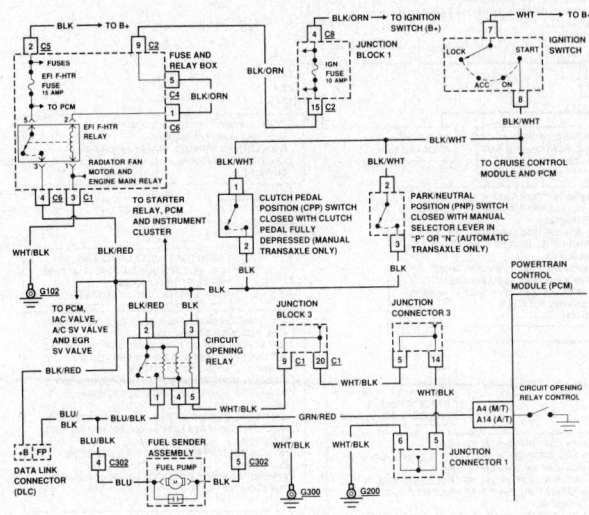

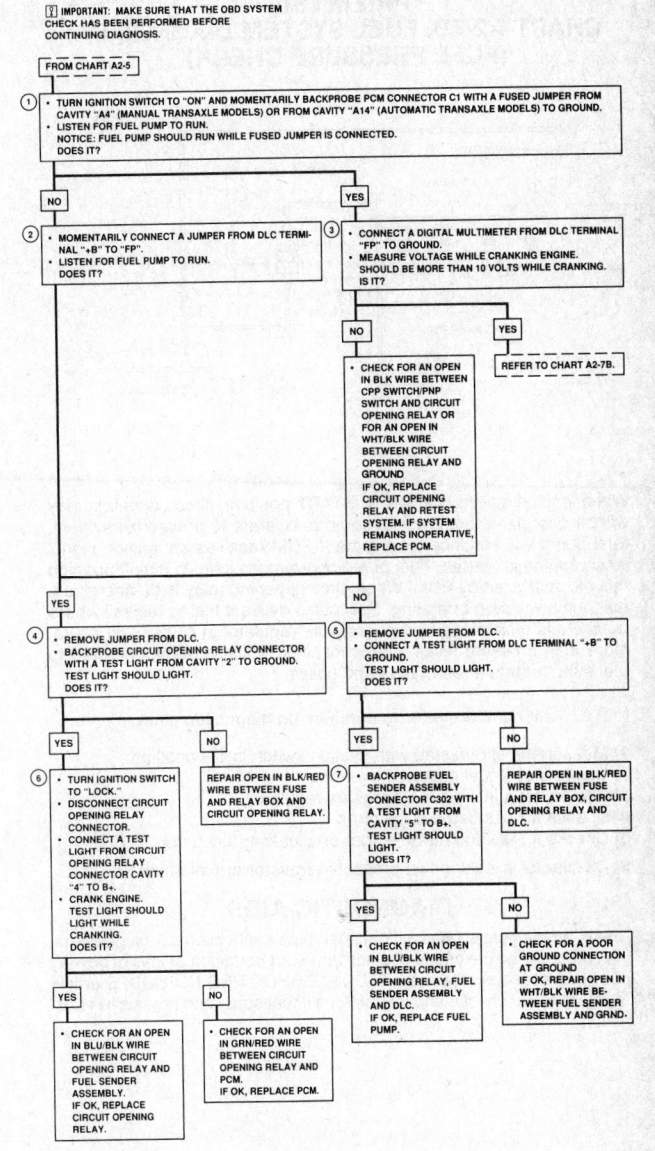

When ignition switch is turned to START position, circuit opening relay will be energized to allow fuel pump to operate to pressurize system. Fuel pump will continue to operate if PCM receives an ignition signal when engine starts. Fuel pump operates as long as circuit opening relay is energized by PCM. When circuit opening relay is de-energized, fuel pump will stop operating.

NOTE: Test numbers refer to numbers on diagnostic chart.

1) Checks for normal fuel pump operation.
2) Checks if fuel pump will run when DLC terminals B+ and FP are jumpered together.
3) Checks fuel pump operation while ignition signal is present at PCM.
4) Checks for an open in Black/Red wire to circuit opening relay.
5) Checks for an open in Black/Red wire to DLC.
6) Checks for an open Blue/Black or Green/Red wire, a faulty PCM, or a faulty circuit opening relay.
7) Checks for open White/Black or Blue/Black wire, or faulty fuel pump.

DIAGNOSTIC AIDS

A restricted or leaking fuel feed pipe or hose will cause an "engine cranks but will not run" condition. Check fuel sender assembly connections inside fuel tank for poor connection. See CHART A2-7B for fuel system pressure test.

An intermittent may be caused by a poor connection, rubbed-through wire insulation, or a wire broken inside insulation. Inspect harness connectors for backed-out terminals, improper mating, broken locks, improperly formed or damaged terminals, and poor terminal-to-wire connections before replacing components.

93J78419 93C78420 93B78478

CLEAR DTCs AND REPEAT OBD SYSTEM CHECK AFTER MAKING REPAIRS.

Courtesy of General Motors Corp.

Fig. 26: Chart A2-7A, Fuel System Diagnosis – Circuit Opening Relay Check (Prizm LSi)

PRIZM LSi
CHART A2-7B, FUEL SYSTEM DIAGNOSIS
(FUEL PRESSURE CHECK)

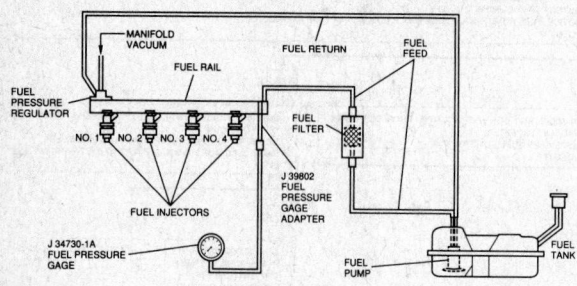

When ignition switch is in ON or START position, circuit opening relay will be energized to allow fuel pump to operate to pressurize system. Fuel pump will continue to operate if PCM receives an ignition signal when engine is started. Fuel pump operates as long as circuit opening relay is energized by PCM. When circuit opening relay is de-energized, fuel pump will stop operating. Fuel pump delivers fuel to fuel rail where pressure is maintained by fuel pressure regulator at 41 psi (282.7 kPa) more than pressure inside intake manifold. Excess fuel is returned to fuel tank through a return pipe and hoses.

NOTE: Test numbers refer to numbers on diagnostic chart.

1) Measures fuel pressure with ignition switch in ON position.
2) Determines if fuel pressure is normal.
3) Checks for a leaking fuel pressure regulator.
4) Checks for plugged fuel injectors.
5) Checks for leaking fuel injectors or a leaking fuel pump.
6) Checks for a leaking fuel pressure regulator or fuel pump

DIAGNOSTIC AIDS

Check for leakage around all fuel hose/pipe connections. A plugged fuel injector could be the cause of a hard/no-start condition or loss of power/poor fuel economy. Refer to TROUBLE SHOOTING NO-CODES article for mechanical checks and inspections if fuel spray and pressure is normal.

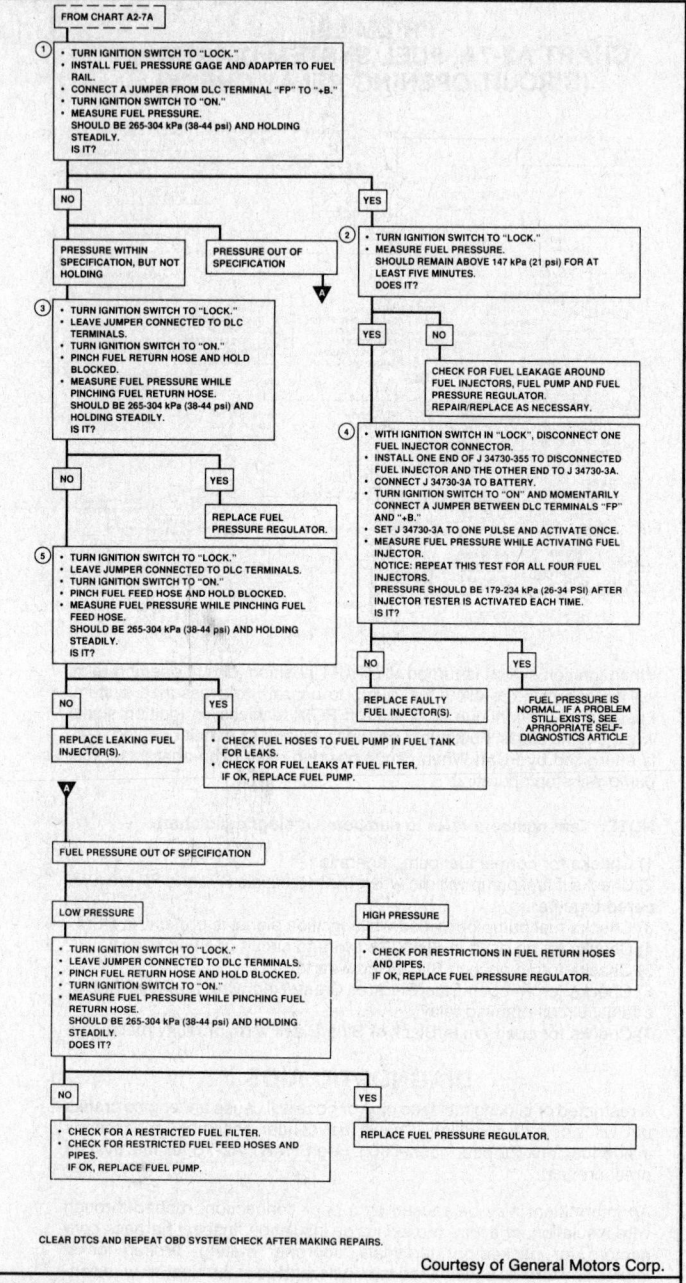

93D78421 93E78422 93F78423

Courtesy of General Motors Corp.

Fig. 27: Chart A2-7B, Fuel System Diagnosis – Fuel Pressure Check (Prizm LSi)

TRACKER (TBI – FEDERAL)
CHART A-3, ENGINE CRANKS BUT
WILL NOT RUN

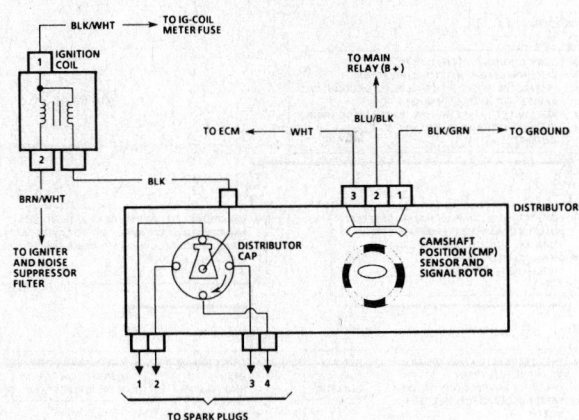

Before using this chart, ensure battery condition, engine cranking speed and fuel quality are okay.

When ignition switch is turned to ON or START position, main relay applies battery voltage to ignition coil. If ignition coil's primary coil is being toggled to ground through ignitor, sending a signal to ECM, a high voltage is induced in secondary windings of ignition coil and is applied through distributor to spark plugs.

NOTE: Test numbers refer to numbers on diagnostic chart.

1) Checks if diagnostic trouble codes are stored in ECM memory.
2) Checks for spark at ignition coil.
3) Checks for spark at distributor.
4) Checks for spark at spark plugs.

DIAGNOSTIC AIDS

Water or foreign material in fuel can cause no-start condition during freezing weather. Engine may start after 5-6 minutes in heated shop. Problem may not reoccur until vehicle is parked overnight in freezing temperature. Low fuel pressure can result in a very lean air/fuel ratio. Fouled or damaged spark plugs will also cause a "engine cranks but will not run" condition.

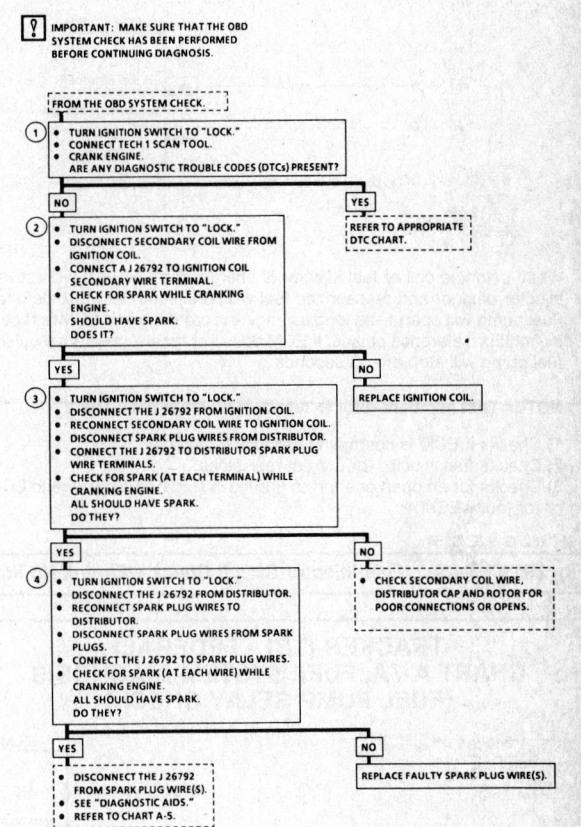

94H44286 94I44287

Courtesy of General Motors Corp.

Fig. 28: Chart A-3, Engine Cranks But Will Not Run (Tracker – TBI – Federal)

TRACKER (TBI – FEDERAL)
CHART A-5, FUEL INJECTOR CIRCUIT CHECK (ENGINE NO-START)

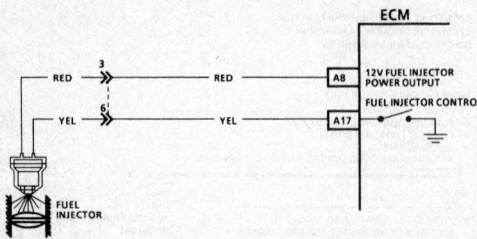

When solenoid coil of fuel injector is energized by ECM, it will activate injector plunger and pressurized fuel will be injected into throttle body. Fuel pump will operate as long as engine is cranking and ECM is receiving ignition reference pulses. If ECM does not receive reference pulses, fuel pump will stop after 3 seconds.

NOTE: Test numbers refer to numbers on diagnostic chart.

1) Checks if ECM is controlling fuel injector signals.
2) Checks fuel injector for correct resistance.
3) Checks for an open or short to ground in Red or Yellow wire to ECM, or for faulty ECM.

92D26263 92E26264

DIAGNOSTIC AIDS

Fuel spray may be present at injector, but may not be enough to start engine. If both fuel injector and related circuits are okay, check for a partially blocked injector nozzle.

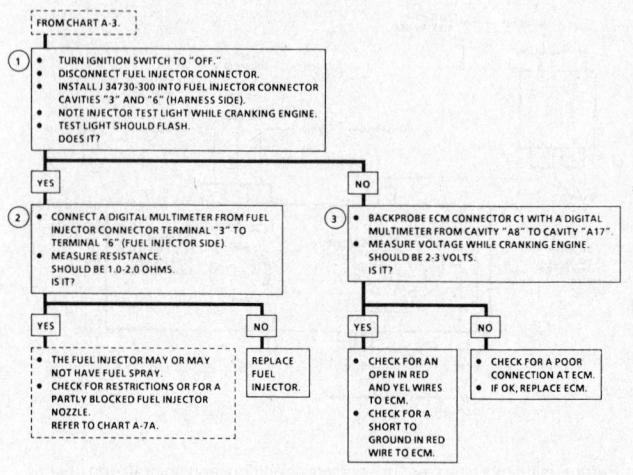

Courtesy of General Motors Corp.

Fig. 29: Chart A-5, Fuel Injector Circuit Check – Engine No-Start (Tracker – TBI – Federal)

TRACKER (TBI – FEDERAL)
CHART A-7A, FUEL SYSTEM DIAGNOSIS (FUEL PUMP RELAY CHECK)

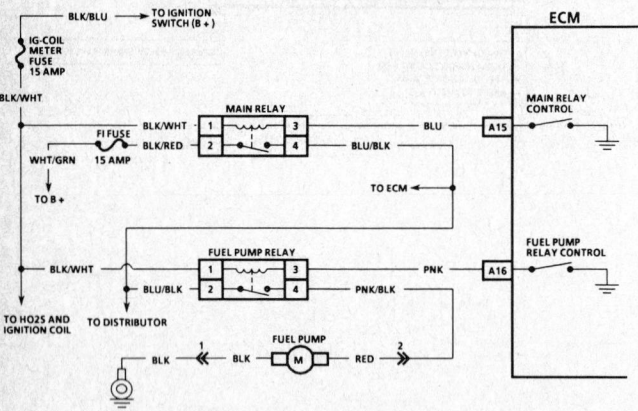

When ignition is turned on, ECM energizes fuel pump relay for 3 seconds, allowing fuel pump operation. When fuel pump relay is de-energized, fuel pump stops operating. If engine is being cranked or is running, fuel pump will continue to operate as long as ECM is receiving ignition reference pulses. If ignition reference pulses are not detected, fuel pump will stop after 3 seconds.

NOTE: Test numbers refer to numbers on diagnostic chart.

1) Checks fuel pump operation with ignition on.
2) Checks fuel pump relay switch for power.
3) Checks for faulty ECM or improper fuel pressure.
4) Checks fuel pump circuit.
5) Checks for open in Pink/Black wire.
6) Checks fuel pump relay coil for power.
7) Checks for a faulty fuel pump or an open in Black wire.
8) Checks for faulty fuel pump relay.
9) Checks for faulty ECM and an open in Pink wire.

DIAGNOSTIC AIDS
Visually inspect wiring and connectors if intermittent problem exists.

94J44288 92G26266

Courtesy of General Motors Corp.

Fig. 30: Chart A-7A, Fuel System Diagnosis – Fuel Pump Relay Check (Tracker – TBI – Federal)

TRACKER (TBI – FEDERAL)
CHART A-7B, FUEL SYSTEM DIAGNOSIS
(FUEL PRESSURE CHECK – 1 OF 2)

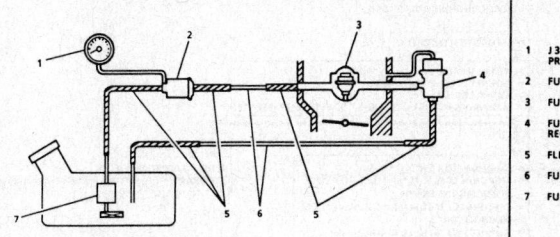

1. J 34730-1 FUEL PRESSURE GAGE
2. FUEL FILTER
3. FUEL INJECTOR
4. FUEL PRESSURE REGULATOR
5. FLEXIBLE HOSE
6. FUEL PIPES
7. FUEL PUMP

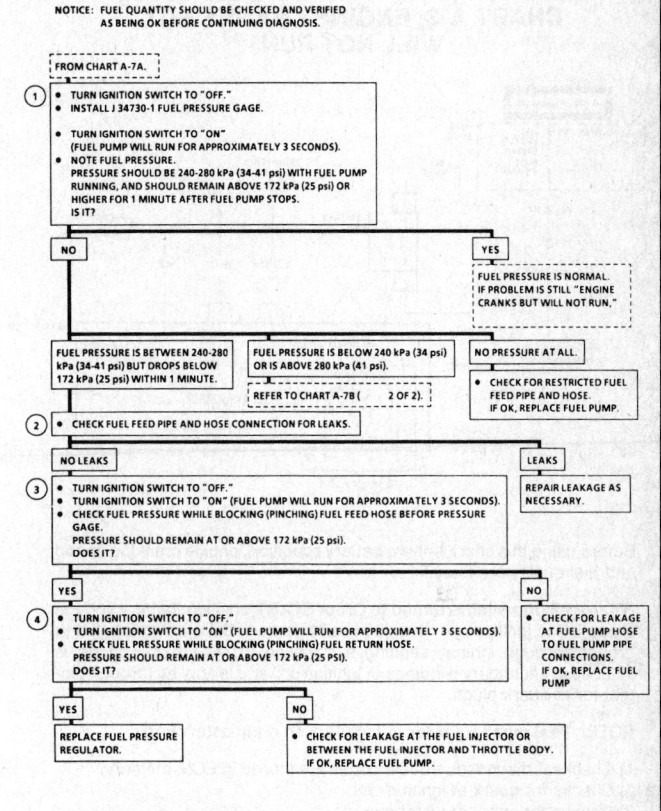

When ignition is turned on, ECM energizes fuel pump relay for 3 seconds, allowing fuel pump operation. If engine is being cranked or is running, fuel pump will continue to operate as long as ECM is receiving ignition reference pulses. If ignition reference pulses are not detected, fuel pump will stop after 3 seconds.

Fuel pump delivers fuel through fuel filter to fuel injector and fuel pressure regulator, where system pressure is controlled at 34-41 psi (234.4-282.7 kPa). Excess fuel returns to fuel tank through fuel return pipe.

NOTE: Test numbers refer to numbers on diagnostic chart.

1) Checks if fuel pressure is within specification.
2) Checks fuel feed pipe and hose for leaks.
3) Checks for faulty fuel pump and faulty fuel pressure regulator.
4) Checks for leaky fuel injector, throttle body or for a faulty fuel pressure regulator.

DIAGNOSTIC AIDS

Improper fuel system pressure can result in one of the following conditions:
- Engine cranks, but will not run.
- Engine cuts out, may feel like ignition problem.
- Poor fuel economy, loss of power.
- Hard starts.

92H26267 92I26268

Courtesy of General Motors Corp.

Fig. 31: Chart A-7B, Fuel System Diagnosis – Fuel Pressure Check – 1 Of 2 (Tracker – TBI – Federal)

TRACKER (TBI – FEDERAL)
CHART A-7B, FUEL SYSTEM DIAGNOSIS
(FUEL PRESSURE CHECK – 2 OF 2)

NOTE: Test numbers refer to numbers on diagnostic chart.

5) Checks for leaks at fuel pump hose connections, faulty fuel pump or a faulty fuel pressure regulator.
6) Checks for restricted fuel feed pipe, faulty fuel filter or restricted fuel return pipe.

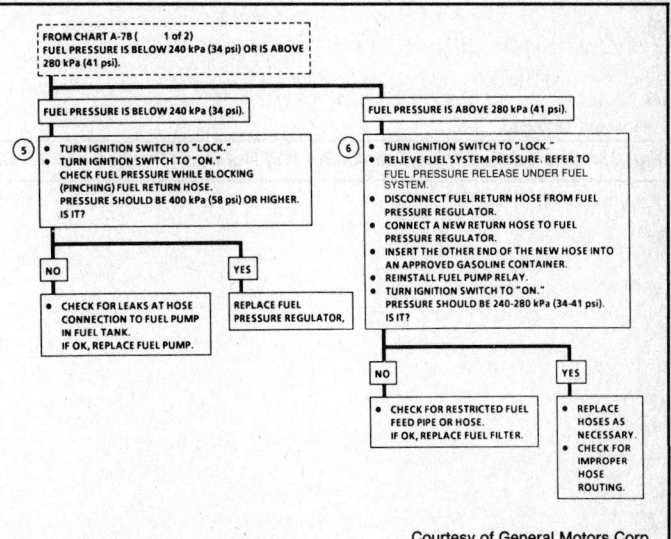

94A44289

Courtesy of General Motors Corp.

Fig. 32: Chart A-7B, Fuel System Diagnosis – Fuel Pressure Check – 2 Of 2 (Tracker – TBI – Federal)

**TRACKER (MFI – CALIF. & NEW YORK)
CHART A-3, ENGINE CRANKS BUT
WILL NOT RUN**

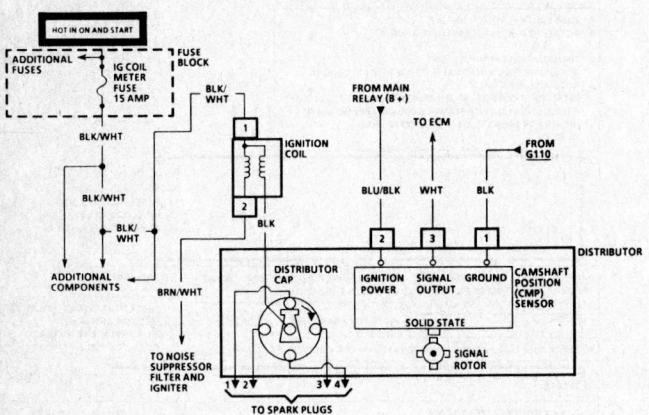

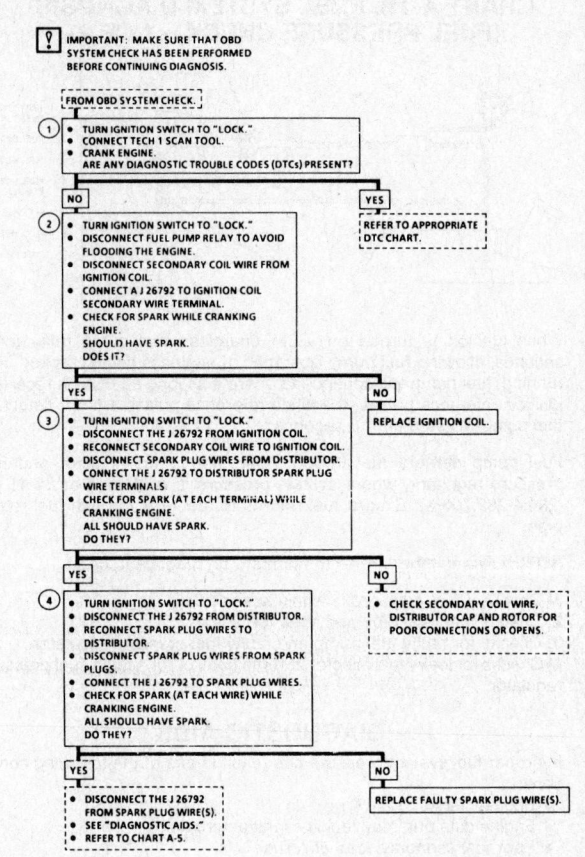

Before using this chart, ensure battery condition, engine cranking speed and fuel quality are okay.

When ignition switch is turned to ON or START position, battery voltage is applied to ignition coil. If ignition coil's primary coil is being toggled to ground through ignitor, sending a signal to ECM, a high voltage is induced in secondary windings of ignition coil and is applied through distributor to spark plugs.

NOTE: Test numbers refer to numbers on diagnostic chart.

1) Checks if diagnostic trouble codes are stored in ECM memory.
2) Checks for spark at ignition coil.
3) Checks for spark at distributor.
4) Checks for spark at spark plugs.

DIAGNOSTIC AIDS

Water or foreign material in fuel can cause no-start condition during freezing weather. Engine may start after 5-6 minutes in heated shop. Problem may not reoccur until vehicle is parked overnight in freezing temperature. Low fuel pressure can result in a very lean air/fuel ratio. Fouled or damaged spark plugs will also cause a "engine cranks but will not run" condition.

94D44290 94E44291

Courtesy of General Motors Corp.

Fig. 33: Chart A-3, Engine Cranks But Will Not Run (Tracker – MFI – Calif. & New York)

TRACKER (MFI – CALIF. & NEW YORK) CHART A-5, FUEL INJECTOR CIRCUIT CHECK (ENGINE NO-START – 1 OF 3)

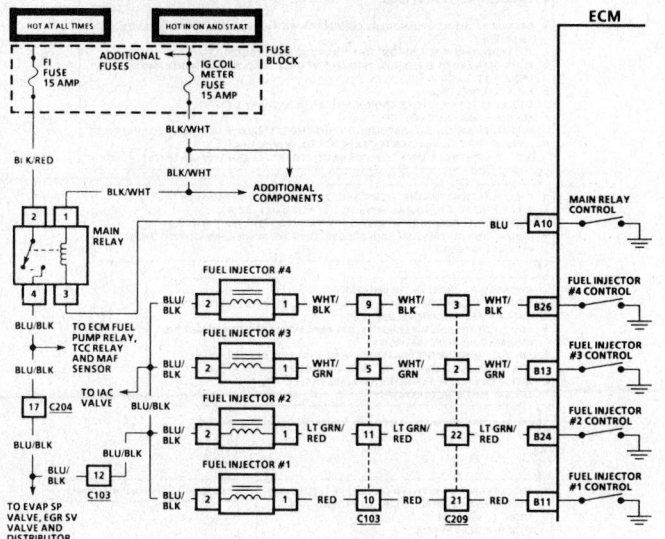

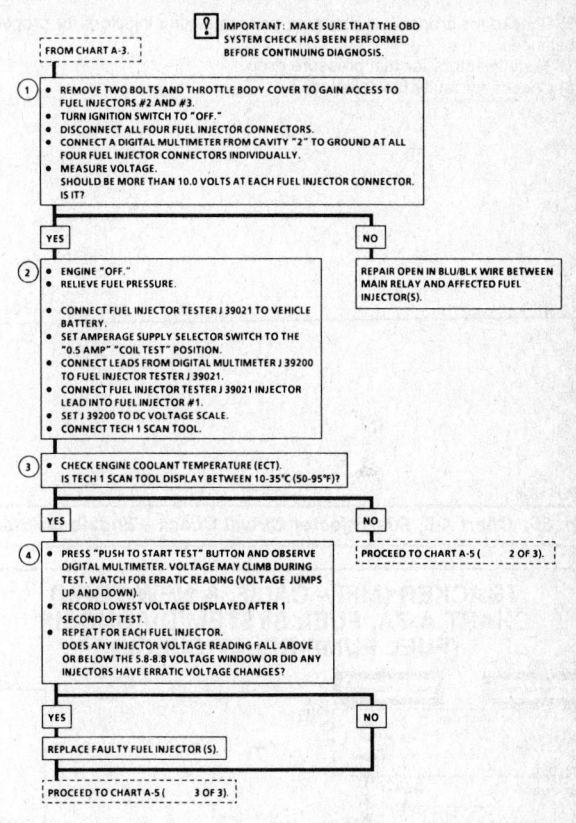

DIAGNOSTIC AIDS

An intermittent may be caused by a poor connection, rubbed-through wire insulation, or a wire broken inside insulation. Inspect harness connectors for backed-out terminals, improper mating, broken locks, improperly formed or damaged terminals, and poor terminal-to-wire connections before replacing components.

When solenoid coil of fuel injector is energized by ECM, it will activate injector plunger and pressurized fuel will be injected into each combustion chamber. Fuel pump will operate as long as engine is cranking and ECM is receiving ignition reference pulses. If ECM does not receive reference pulses, fuel pump will stop after 3 seconds.

NOTE: Test numbers refer to numbers on diagnostic chart.

1) Checks for an open in Blue/Black wires between fuel injectors and ECM.
2) Sets up the fuel injector tester (J-39021).
3) Checks engine coolant temperature for proper test conditions.
4) Checks for faulty fuel injectors when engine coolant temperature is between 50-90°F (10-35°C).

94G44293 94H44294

Courtesy of General Motors Corp.

Fig. 34: Chart A-5, Fuel Injector Circuit Check – Engine No-Start – 1 OF 3 (Tracker – MFI – Calif. & New York)

TRACKER (MFI – CALIF. & NEW YORK) CHART A-5, FUEL INJECTOR CIRCUIT CHECK (ENGINE NO-START – 2 OF 3)

NOTE: Test numbers refer to numbers on diagnostic chart.

5) Checks for faulty fuel injectors when engine coolant temperature is greater than or less than 50-90°F (10-35°C).

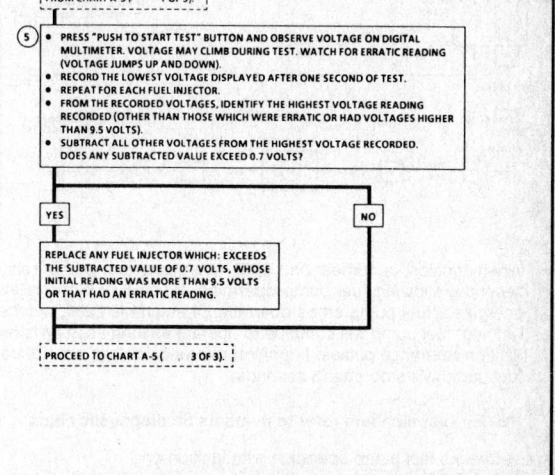

94I44295

Courtesy of General Motors Corp.

Fig. 35: Chart A-5, Fuel Injector Circuit Check – Engine No-Start – 2 OF 3 (Tracker – MFI – Calif. & New York)

TRACKER (MFI – CALIF. & NEW YORK)
CHART A-5, FUEL INJECTOR CIRCUIT
CHECK (ENGINE NO-START – 3 OF 3)

NOTE: Test numbers refer to numbers on diagnostic chart.

6) Checks for proper fuel pressure prior to testing injectors for proper balance.
7) Tests injectors for fuel pressure drop.
8) Checks for faulty fuel injectors.

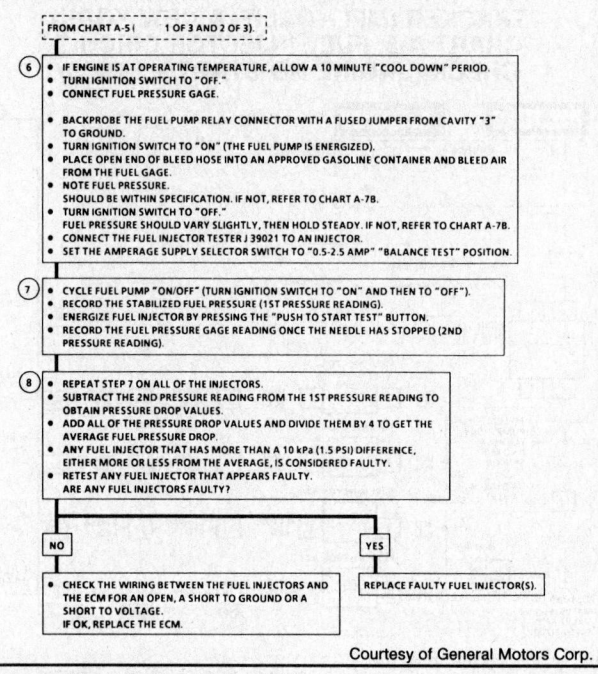

94J44296

Courtesy of General Motors Corp.

Fig. 36: Chart A-5, Fuel Injector Circuit Check – Engine No-Start – 3 OF 3 (Tracker – MFI – Calif. & New York)

TRACKER (MFI – CALIF. & NEW YORK)
CHART A-7A, FUEL SYSTEM DIAGNOSIS
(FUEL PUMP RELAY CHECK)

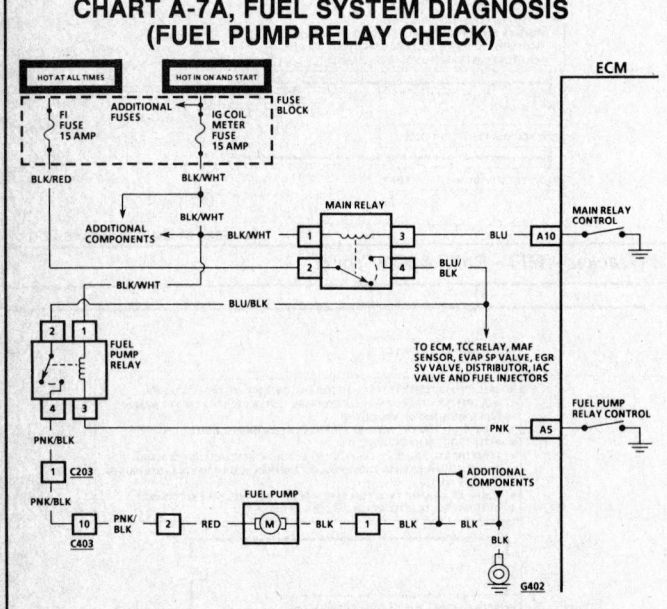

DIAGNOSTIC AIDS
Visually inspect wiring and connectors if intermittent problem exists.

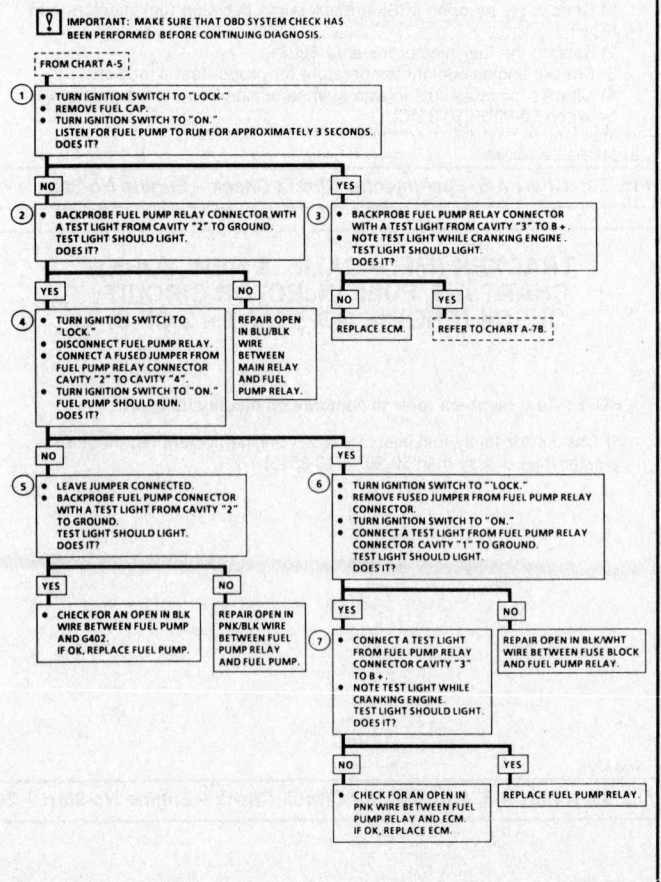

When ignition is turned on, ECM energizes fuel pump relay for 3 seconds, allowing fuel pump operation. When fuel pump relay is de-energized, fuel pump stops operating. If engine is being cranked or is running, fuel pump will continue to operate as long as ECM is receiving ignition reference pulses. If ignition reference pulses are not detected, fuel pump will stop after 3 seconds.

NOTE: Test numbers refer to numbers on diagnostic chart.

1) Checks fuel pump operation with ignition on.
2) Checks fuel pump relay switch for power.
3) Checks for faulty ECM.
4) Checks fuel pump circuit.
5) Checks for open in Pink/Black or Black wires and for faulty fuel pump.
6) Checks fuel pump relay coil for power.
7) Checks for a faulty fuel pump relay, faulty ECM, or an open in Pink

94A44297 94B44298

Courtesy of General Motors Corp.

Fig. 37: Chart A-7A, Fuel System Diagnosis – Fuel Pump Relay Check (Tracker – MFI – Calif. & New York)

TRACKER (MFI – CALIF. & NEW YORK) CHART A-7B, FUEL SYSTEM DIAGNOSIS (FUEL PRESSURE CHECK – 1 OF 3)

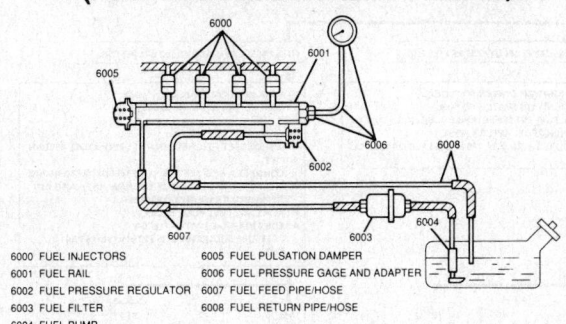

6000 FUEL INJECTORS
6001 FUEL RAIL
6002 FUEL PRESSURE REGULATOR
6003 FUEL FILTER
6004 FUEL PUMP
6005 FUEL PULSATION DAMPER
6006 FUEL PRESSURE GAGE AND ADAPTER
6007 FUEL FEED PIPE/HOSE
6008 FUEL RETURN PIPE/HOSE

When ignition is turned on, ECM energizes fuel pump relay for 3 seconds, allowing fuel pump operation. If engine is being cranked or is running, fuel pump will continue to operate as long as ECM is receiving ignition reference pulses. If ignition reference pulses are not detected, fuel pump will stop after 3 seconds.

Fuel pump delivers fuel through fuel filter to fuel injector and fuel pressure regulator, where system pressure is controlled at 36-43 psi (248.2-296.5 kPa). Excess fuel returns to fuel tank through fuel return pipe.

NOTE: Test numbers refer to numbers on diagnostic chart.

1) Checks if fuel pressure is within specification with engine not running.
2) Checks if fuel pressure is within specification with engine idling.
3) Checks for restricted fuel feed pipe, faulty fuel pump or faulty fuel pressure regulator.

DIAGNOSTIC AIDS

Improper fuel system pressure can result in one of the following conditions:

- Engine cranks, but will not run.
- Engine cuts out, may feel like ignition problem.
- Poor fuel economy, loss of power.
- Hard starts.

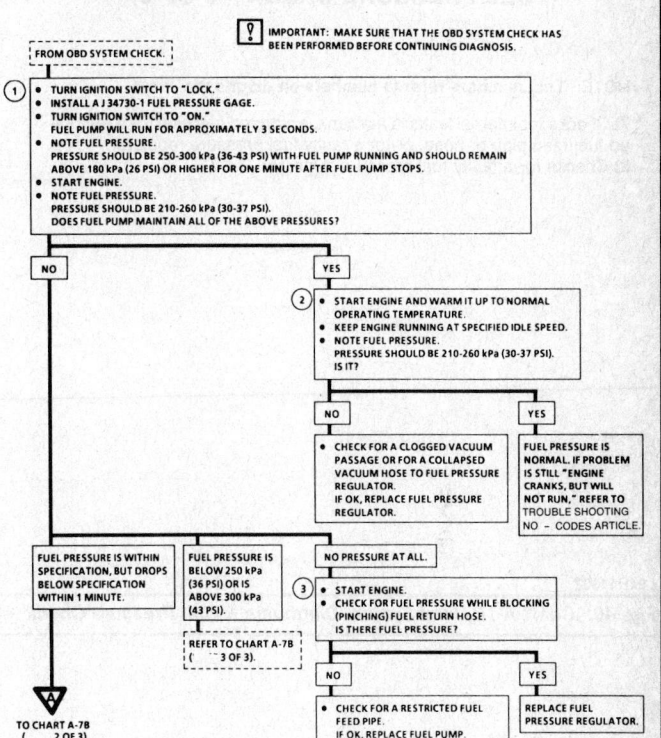

94C44299 94F44300

Courtesy of General Motors Corp.

Fig. 38: Chart A-7B, Fuel System Diagnosis – Fuel Pressure Check – 1 Of 3 (Tracker – MFI – Calif. & New York)

TRACKER (MFI – CALIF. & NEW YORK) CHART A-7B, FUEL SYSTEM DIAGNOSIS (FUEL PRESSURE CHECK – 2 OF 3)

NOTE: Test numbers refer to numbers on diagnostic chart.

4) Checks for leaks at fuel feed pipe and hose connections.
5) Checks for leaks at fuel pump hose-to-fuel pump pipe connections or for a faulty fuel pump.
6) Checks for leakage at fuel injector, a faulty fuel pump or faulty fuel pressure regulator.

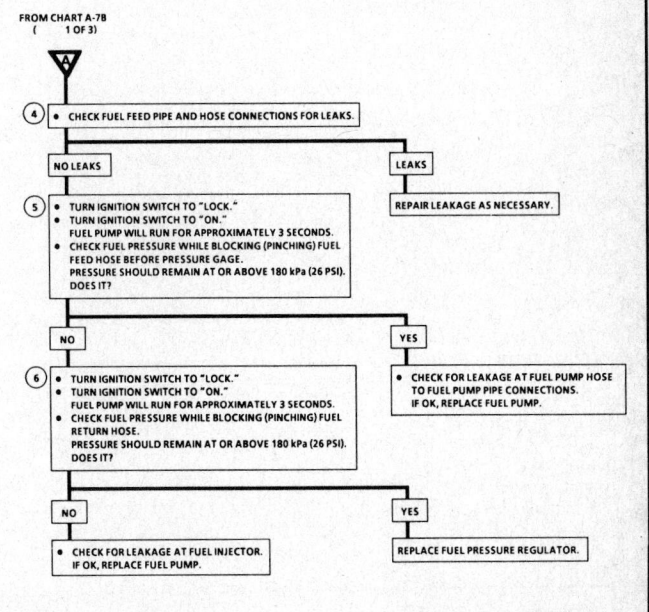

94G44301

Courtesy of General Motors Corp.

Fig. 39: Chart A-7B, Fuel System Diagnosis – Fuel Pressure Check – 2 Of 3 (Tracker – MFI – Calif. & New York)

**TRACKER (MFI – CALIF. & NEW YORK)
CHART A-7B, FUEL SYSTEM DIAGNOSIS
(FUEL PRESSURE CHECK – 3 OF 3)**

NOTE: Test numbers refer to numbers on diagnostic chart.

7) Checks for internal leaks in fuel tank, a clogged fuel filter, or a restricted fuel feed pipe or hose, or for a faulty fuel pressure regulator.
8) Checks for a faulty fuel pressure regulator.

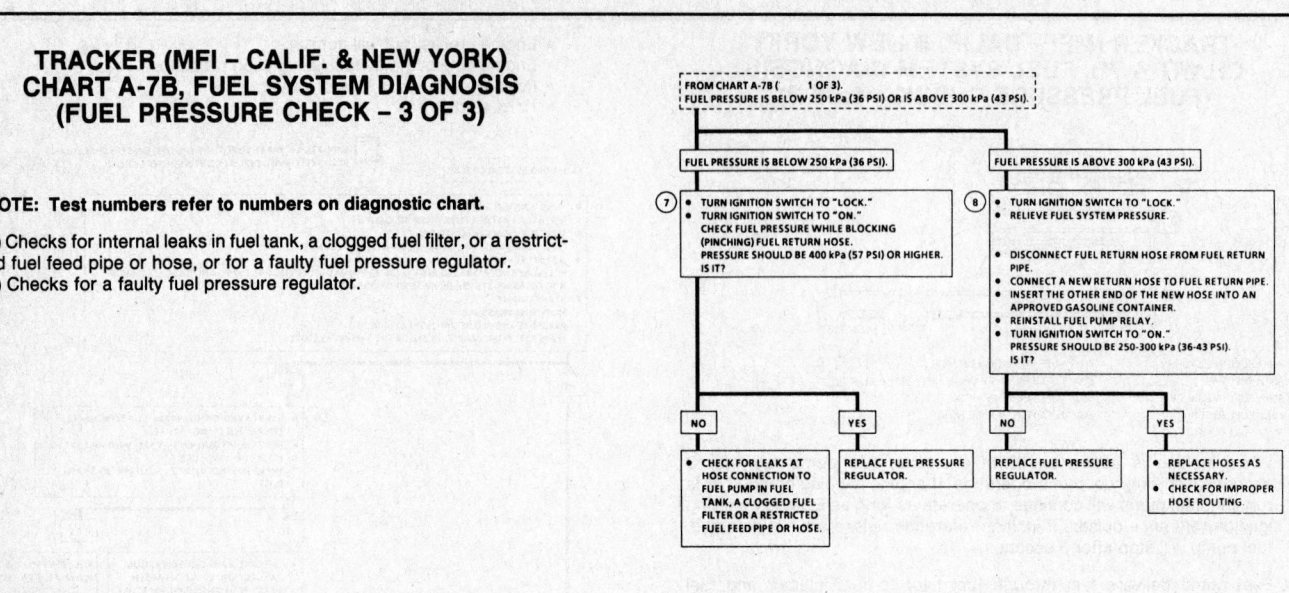

94H44302   Courtesy of General Motors Corp.

Fig. 40: Chart A-7B, Fuel System Diagnosis – Fuel Pressure Check – 3 Of 3 (Tracker – MFI – Calif. & New York)

Metro, Prizm, Tracker

INTRODUCTION

Most engine control problems result from mechanical failures, poor electrical connections or damaged vacuum hoses. Before condemning the computer system, perform checks and inspections covered in BASIC DIAGNOSTIC PROCEDURES article. Failure to do so may result in lost diagnostic time.

If no faults were found while performing BASIC DIAGNOSTIC PROCEDURES, proceed with DIAGNOSTIC PROCEDURE. If no fault codes or only a non-running Code 12 is present and driveability problems exist, proceed to TROUBLE SHOOTING – NO CODES article for diagnosis by symptom (i.e., ROUGH IDLE, NO START, etc.). If only intermittent codes are present, see INTERMITTENTS in TROUBLE SHOOTING – NO CODES article.

TERMINOLOGY

Due to Federal government requirements, manufacturers may use names and acronyms for systems and components different than those used in previous years. The following table will help eliminate confusion when dealing with these components and systems. Only relevant components and systems whose names have changed from current General Motors Corp. terminology have been listed.

SAE TERMINOLOGY

Former Name Or Acronym	New Name Or Acronym
ALDL	Data Link Connector (DLC)
CHECK ENGINE Light	Malfunction Indicator Light (MIL)
CTS	Engine Coolant Temp. (ECT) Sensor
Diagnostic Circuit Check	On-Board Diagnostic (OBD) System Check
ESC System	Knock Sensor (KS) System
EST System	Ignition Control (IC) System
MAT Sensor	Intake Air Temperature (IAT) Sensor
Park/Neutral (P/N) Switch	Park/Neutral Position (PNP) Switch
Port Fuel Injection	Multiport Fuel Injection
Scan Data	Scan Tester (ST) Data
SERVICE ENGINE SOON Light	Malfunction Indicator Light (MIL)
Thermostatic Air Cleaner (TAC)	Air Cleaner (ACL)
Throttle Position Sensor (TPS)	Throttle Position (TP) Sensor
Throttle Position Switch	Closed Throttle Position (CTP) Switch
Throttle Position Switch	Wide Open Throttle (WOT) Switch
Viscous Converter Clutch (VCC)	Torque Converter Clutch (TCC)

SELF-DIAGNOSTIC SYSTEM

SELF-DIAGNOSTICS DIRECTORY

Prizm LSi uses a Powertrain Control Module (PCM). All other models use a Engine Control Module (ECM). All references to ECM include PCM unless specified otherwise.

The ECM is equipped with a self-diagnostic system, which detects system failures or abnormalities. When a malfunction occurs, ECM will illuminate the CHECK ENGINE light located on instrument cluster. This light is also referred to as the Malfunction Indicator Light (MIL). When malfunction is detected and MIL is turned on, a corresponding trouble code will be stored in ECM memory. To retrieve stored codes, see READING TROUBLE CODES or RETRIEVING CODES (NON-SCAN). Malfunctions are recorded as HARD FAILURES or as INTERMITTENT FAILURES.

Hard Failures – Hard failures cause MIL to illuminate and remain on until the malfunction is repaired. If light comes on and remains on (light may flash) during vehicle operation, cause must be found using diagnostic code charts. If a sensor fails, ECM will use a substitute value in its calculations to continue engine operation. In this condition, vehicle is functional, but loss of good driveability will most likely occur.

Intermittent Failures – Intermittent failures cause MIL to flicker or illuminate and go out about 10 seconds after the intermittent fault goes away. The corresponding trouble code, however, will be retained in ECM memory. If related fault does not reoccur within 50 engine restarts, it will be erased from ECM memory. Intermittent failures may be caused by faulty sensor, connector or wiring. See INTERMITTENTS in TROUBLE SHOOTING – NO CODES article.

DIAGNOSTIC PROCEDURE

Diagnosis of the computerized engine control system should be performed in the following order:

1) Ensure all engine systems not related to the computer are operating properly. DO NOT proceed with testing unless all other problems have been repaired. Perform on-board diagnostic system check chart before using trouble code charts.

2) If trouble codes were displayed (other than Code 12), determine whether codes are hard or intermittent. Hard codes cause Malfunction Indicator Light (MIL) to illuminate continuously with engine running. For diagnosing hard codes, proceed to appropriate diagnostic code chart. For diagnosing intermittent codes, proceed to INTERMITTENTS in TROUBLE SHOOTING – NO CODES article.

3) If trouble codes were not displayed and a driveability problem exists, refer to SYMPTOMS in TROUBLE SHOOTING – NO CODES article. From there you will be sent to the appropriate area in SYSTEM & COMPONENT TESTING article.

4) After repairs are made, clear trouble codes, confirm closed loop operation and ensure MIL is not illuminated.

RETRIEVING CODES (NON-SCAN)

All vehicles are equipped with a Malfunction Indicator Light (MIL), located on instrument cluster. Light comes on, as a bulb check, when ignition switch is turned to ON position and engine is not running. Light should not flash at this time and should go out when engine is started.

If MIL remains on or flashes with engine running, self-diagnostic system has detected a problem. If problem goes away, light will go out after 10 seconds, but a fault code will be stored in ECM memory.

Metro & Tracker – All trouble codes except Code 41 (ignition signal circuit) are stored in ECM memory. Code 41 is erased from memory as soon as ignition is turned off. In order to detect an active Code 41, connect a scan tester to Data Link Connector (DLC). Crank engine for 3 seconds, and leave ignition switch in ON position. If ignition switch is turned to OFF position, a hard or active Code 41 will be lost.

Prizm & Prizm LSi – All trouble codes except Code 16 (PCM control signal on Prizm LSi), Code 43 (crank signal) and Code 51 (switch condition signal) are stored in ECM memory. Codes 16, 43 and 51 are erased from memory as soon as ignition is turned off. To detect an active Code 16, 43 or 51, turn ignition switch to ON position (engine off) with diagnostic request terminal TE1 in Data Link Connector (DLC) grounded. See Fig. 2. DLC is located on left shock tower. If ignition switch is turned to OFF position at any time during this procedure, a hard or active Code 16, 43 or 51 will be lost.

READING TROUBLE CODES

Metro – 1) Perform on-board diagnostic system check before diagnosing vehicle using self-diagnostic system. See appropriate ON-BOARD DIAGNOSTIC (OBD) SYSTEM CHECK chart under DIAGNOSTIC CODE CHARTS.

2) Fault codes can be retrieved using a scan tester connected to Data Link Connector (DLC) or by counting flashes of Malfunction Indicator Light (MIL) after grounding either DIAG SW connector in fuse block or diagnostic request terminal in duty check data link connector, located on left side of firewall. See Fig. 1.

3) To retrieve code(s) using DIAG SW connector in fuse block, remove spare fuse from fuse block and insert into DIAG SW connector terminal. See Fig. 1. Turn ignition on and observe MIL to read fault code(s). Proceed to appropriate chart(s) under DIAGNOSTIC CODE CHARTS to diagnose fault codes. See SELF-DIAGNOSTICS DIRECTORY table.

4) To retrieve code(s) using the duty check data link connector, connect jumper wire between duty check data link connector terminals No. 2 and 4. *See Fig. 1.* Turn ignition on and observe MIL to read fault code(s). If fault codes are stored, code will flash 3 times, starting with the lowest code. Proceed to appropriate chart(s) under DIAGNOSTIC CODE CHARTS to diagnose fault codes. See SELF-DIAGNOSTICS DIRECTORY table.

5) If no fault codes are stored, MIL will flash Code 12, indicating ECM diagnostic system is operating.

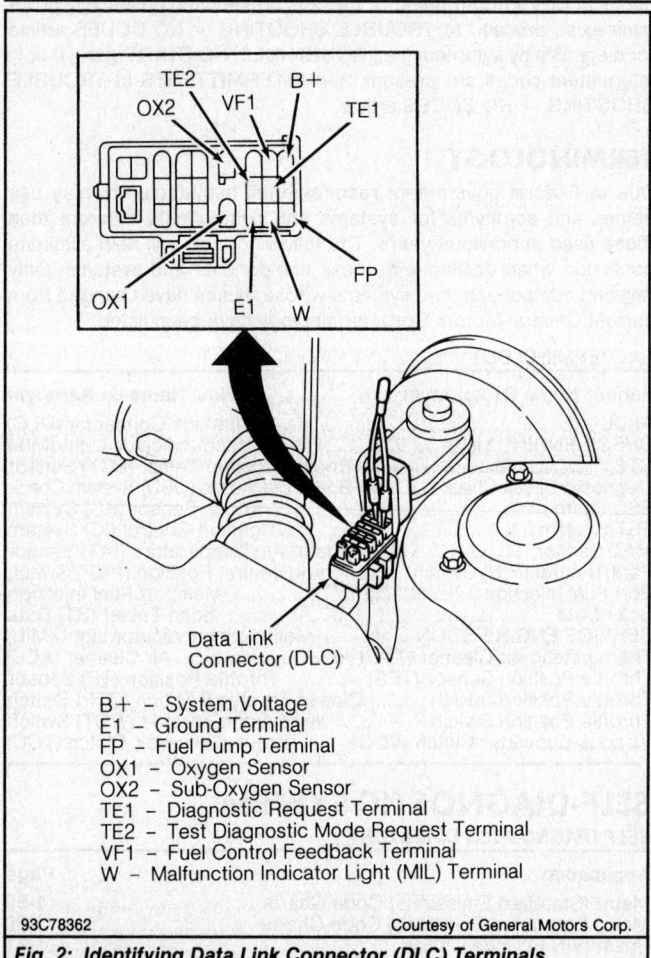

Fuel Injector Resistor

1. Blank
2. Diagnostic Request Terminal
3. Diagnostic Output Terminal
4. Ground Terminal
5. Test Switch Terminal
6. Duty Check Terminal

93B78361   Courtesy of General Motors Corp.

Fig. 1: Locating & Identifying Data Link Connectors (Metro)

Prizm & Prizm LSi – 1) Perform on-board diagnostic system check before diagnosing vehicle using self-diagnostic system. See appropriate ON-BOARD DIAGNOSTIC (OBD) SYSTEM CHECK chart under DIAGNOSTIC CODE CHARTS.

2) Ensure ignition is off. Using a jumper wire, connect between Data Link Connector (DLC) terminals TE1 and E1. *See Fig. 2.* DLC is located on left strut tower. Turn ignition on and observe Malfunction Indicator Light (MIL) to read fault code(s). If fault codes are stored, code will flash 3 times starting with the lowest code. Proceed to appropriate chart(s) under DIAGNOSTIC CODE CHARTS to diagnose fault codes. See SELF-DIAGNOSTICS DIRECTORY table.

3) If no fault codes are stored, remove jumper wire from DLC terminal TE1. Turn ignition switch to LOCK position. Reconnect jumper wire between DLC terminals TE2 and E1. *See Fig. 2.* Turn ignition on. MIL will flash on and off rapidly.

4) Start and run engine until normal operating temperature is obtained. Test drive vehicle at condition at which problem occured. With ignition still on, connect jumper wire between Data Link Connector (DLC) terminals TE1 and E1, and observe MIL. Code(s) will flash if present. Proceed to appropriate chart(s) under DIAGNOSTIC CODE CHARTS to diagnose fault codes. See SELF-DIAGNOSTICS DIRECTORY table.

5) If fault codes are not present, ECM and wiring are okay. Proceed to INTERMITTENTS in TROUBLE SHOOTING – NO CODES article.

NOTE: Test diagnostic mode will not function if DLC terminal TE2 is grounded with ignition switch in any other position than LOCK. When in test diagnostic mode, Code 42 will set if vehicle is not driven above 3 MPH, and Code 43 will set if engine is not cranked. This is considered normal. Code 51 will set if acelerator pedal depressed off the idle position for 3 seconds, gear selector in Park or Neutral (A/T), or if A/C is on (if equipped). Systems are properly functioning if Code 51 sets under these conditions.

Data Link Connector (DLC)

B+ – System Voltage
E1 – Ground Terminal
FP – Fuel Pump Terminal
OX1 – Oxygen Sensor
OX2 – Sub-Oxygen Sensor
TE1 – Diagnostic Request Terminal
TE2 – Test Diagnostic Mode Request Terminal
VF1 – Fuel Control Feedback Terminal
W – Malfunction Indicator Light (MIL) Terminal

93C78362   Courtesy of General Motors Corp.

Fig. 2: Identifying Data Link Connector (DLC) Terminals (Prizm & Prizm LSi)

Tracker – 1) Perform on-board diagnostic system check before diagnosing vehicle using self-diagnostic system. See appropriate ON-BOARD DIAGNOSTIC (OBD) SYSTEM CHECK chart under DIAGNOSTIC CODE CHARTS.

2) Fault code(s) can be retrieved using a scan tester connected to Data Link Connector (DLC) or by counting flashes of Malfunction Indicator Light (MIL) after grounding the diagnostic request terminal in the duty check data link connector, located near battery. *See Fig. 3.*

3) Turn ignition off. Using a jumper wire, connect between duty check data link connector terminals No. 2 and 3 (TBI – Federal) or No. 2 and 4 (MFI – Calif. and New York). Turn ignition on and observe MIL to read fault codes. If fault codes are stored, code will flash 3 times starting with the lowest code. Proceed to appropriate charts under DIAGNOSTIC CODE CHARTS to diagnose fault codes. See SELF-DIAGNOSTICS DIRECTORY table.

4) If no fault codes are stored, MIL will flash Code 12, indicating ECM diagnostic system is operating.

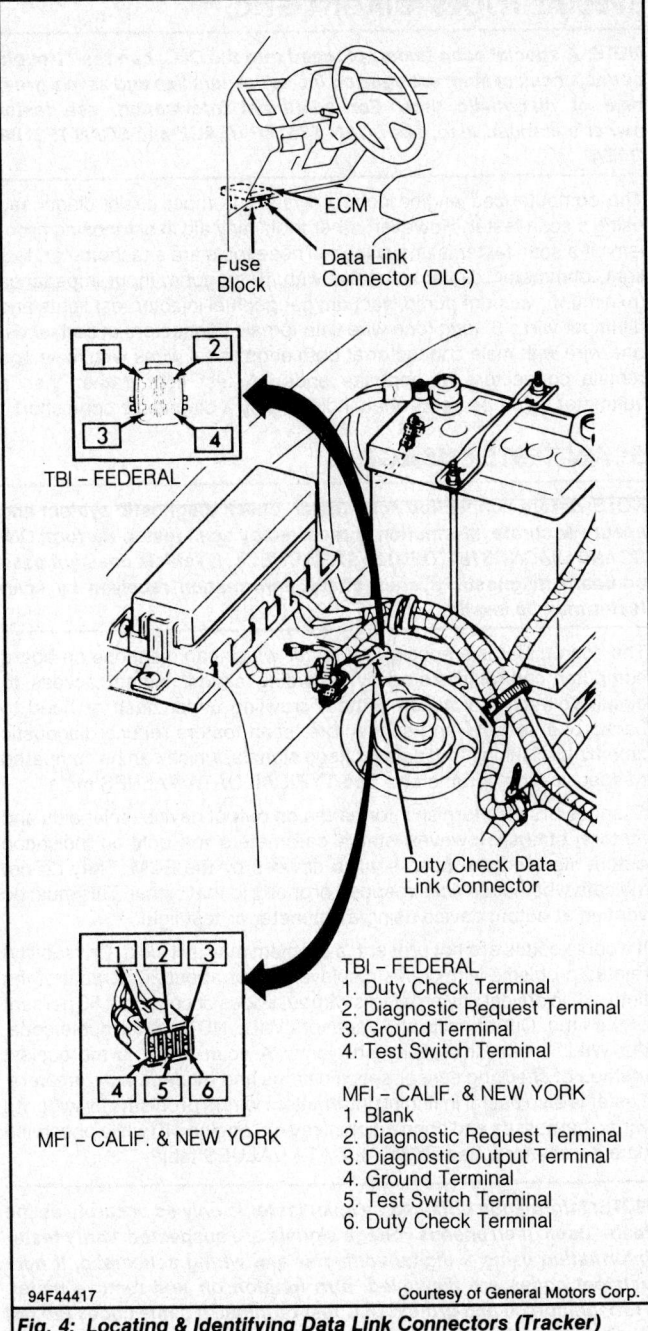

94F44417   Courtesy of General Motors Corp.

Fig. 4: Locating & Identifying Data Link Connectors (Tracker)

TBI – FEDERAL
1. Duty Check Terminal
2. Diagnostic Request Terminal
3. Ground Terminal
4. Test Switch Terminal

MFI – CALIF. & NEW YORK
1. Blank
2. Diagnostic Request Terminal
3. Diagnostic Output Terminal
4. Ground Terminal
5. Test Switch Terminal
6. Duty Check Terminal

TROUBLE CODE DEFINITIONS

NOTE: Trouble codes will be recorded at various operating times. Some codes require sensor or switch operation for 5 seconds and others may require longer under certain conditions. Some codes may not set in a service bay operational mode.

TROUBLE CODE IDENTIFICATION (METRO)

Code	Circuit Affected	Probable Cause
13	Oxygen Sensor	Signal Voltage Does Not Change
14	Coolant Temp. Sensor	Low Temp. Indicated
15	Coolant Temp. Sensor	High Temp. Indicated
21	Throttle Position Sensor	Signal Voltage High
22	Throttle Position Sensor	Signal Voltage Low
23	Intake Air Temp. Sensor	Low Temp. Indicated
24	Vehicle Speed Sensor	No Speedometer
25	Intake Air Temp. Sensor	High Temp. Indicated
31	MAP Sensor	Low Voltage Input, Low Vacuum
32	MAP Sensor	High Voltage Input, High Vacuum
41	Ignition Signal	No Signal
42	Camshaft Position Sensor	No Signal For 2 Seconds
46 [1]	Idle Speed Control Motor	ISC Motor Inoperative
51	EGR System	EGR SV Valve Inoperative

[1] – Upgraded emissions only.

TROUBLE CODE IDENTIFICATION (PRIZM & PRIZM LSi)

Code	Circuit Affected	Probable Cause
12	No RPM Signal	No Signal
13	No RPM Signal	No Signal
14	Ignition Signal	No Signal
16 [1]	PCM Control Signal	PCM Failure
21	Oxygen Sensor	Open/Short Circuit
22	Coolant Temp. Sensor	Open/Short Circuit
24	Intake Air Temp. Sensor	Open/Short Circuit
25	Oxygen Sensor	Lean Exhaust Indicated
26	Oxygen Sensor	Rich Exhaust Indicated
27 [2]	Sub-Oxygen Sensor	Open/Short Circuit
31	MAP Sensor	Open/Short Circuit
41	Throttle Position Sensor	Open/Short Circuit
42	Vehicle Speed Sensor	Open/Short Circuit
43	Crank Signal	No Signal
51	Switch Condition Signal	No Signal
52 [1]	Knock Sensor	Open/Short Circuit
71 [2]	EGR System	Out Of Calibration

[1] – Prizm LSi (VIN 8) only.
[2] – California models only.

TROUBLE CODE IDENTIFICATION (TRACKER)

Code	Circuit Affected	Probable Cause
13	Heated Oxygen Sensor	Open Circuit
14	Coolant Temp. Sensor	Low Temp. Indicated
15	Coolant Temp. Sensor	High Temp. Indicated
21	Throttle Position Sensor	Signal Voltage High
22	Throttle Position Sensor	Signal Voltage Low
23	Intake Air Temp. Sensor	Low Temp. Indicated
24	Vehicle Speed Sensor	Incorrect Signal Voltage
25	Intake Air Temp. Sensor	High Temp. Indicated
31 [1]	MAP Sensor	High Voltage Input, High Vacuum
32 [1]	MAP Sensor	Low Voltage Input, Low Vacuum
33 [2]	MAF Sensor	High Current Input
34 [2]	MAF Sensor	Low Current Input
41	Ignition Signal	No Signal
42	Camshaft Position Sensor	No Signal For 2-3 Seconds
44	Idle Switch	Open/Misadjusted
45	Idle Switch	Grounded/Misadjusted
51	EGR System	Out Of Calibration
52 [2]	Fuel System	Fuel Leakage Detected
53 [1]	Ground	Circuit Open
53 [2]	ECM Failure	Failure Detected

[1] – TBI (Federal) models only.
[2] – MFI (Calif. & New York) models only.

CLEARING CODES

Metro – Turn ignition switch to OFF position. Remove TAIL fuse in passenger compartment fuse block or 40-amp fusible link (Green) in underhood fuse/relay block (located on front of left inner fender panel) for at least 30 seconds. ECM fault code memory is now clear. Install TAIL fuse or 40-amp fusible link (Green). If 40-amp fusible link is removed to clear ECM memory, clock and radio memory will also be erased.

Prizm & Prizm LSi – Turn ignition switch to OFF position. Disconnect negative battery cable, or remove EFI F-HTR fuse in underhood fuse/relay block, for at least 30 seconds. ECM fault code memory is now clear. Connect negative battery cable or install EFI F-HTR fuse. If negative battery terminal is removed to clear ECM memory, clock and radio memory will also be erased.

Tracker – Turn ignition switch to OFF position. Remove TAIL/DOME fuse in passenger compartment fuse block or 40-amp fusible link (Green) in underhood fuse/relay block (located on rear of right inner fender panel) for at least 30 seconds. ECM fault code memory is now clear. Install TAIL/DOME fuse or 40-amp fusible link (Green). If 40-amp fusible link is removed to clear ECM memory, clock and radio memory will also be erased.

ECM LOCATIONS
ECM LOCATION

Application	Location
Metro & Tracker	Behind Left Side Of Dash
Prizm & Prizm LSi [1]	Behind Center of Dash

[1] – Prizm LSi uses a Powertrain Control Module (PCM).

DIAGNOSTIC MATERIALS

Diagnostic Aids – Diagnostic aids (located in many trouble code charts) are provided as additional tips to help with diagnosis when inspected circuit is okay.

SPECIAL TOOLS (DIAGNOSTIC)

NOTE: *A special scan tester, plugged into the DLC, can read trouble codes, check system voltages on the serial data line and save a great deal of diagnostic time. For additional information, see tester owner's manual. Also, see SCAN TESTER USAGE and SCAN TESTER DATA.*

The computerized engine control system is most easily diagnosed using a scan tester. However, other tools may aid in diagnosing problems if a scan tester is unavailable. These tools are a tachometer, test light, ohmmeter, digital voltmeter with 10-megohm input impedance (minimum), vacuum pump, vacuum gauge, fuel injector test lights and 6 jumper wires 6" long (one wire with female connectors at both ends, one wire with male connector at both ends and 4 wires with male and female connectors at opposite ends). A test light, rather than a voltmeter, must be used when indicated by a diagnostic code chart.

SCAN TESTER USAGE

NOTE: *Before connecting scan tester, check diagnostic system and ensure accurate information is received by scan tester. Perform ON-BOARD DIAGNOSTIC (OBD) SYSTEM CHECK. If vehicle does not pass on-board diagnostic system check, information received by scan tester may be invalid.*

The scan tester is a specialized tester which can diagnose on-board computer control systems by providing almost instant access to circuit voltage information without crawling under dash or hood to backprobe sensors and connectors. scan testers reduce diagnostic time by furnishing input data (voltage signals) which can be compared to specification parameters. See TYPICAL DATA VALUES table.

Scan testers also furnish information on output device (solenoids and motors) status. However, status parameters are only an indication output signals have been sent to devices by the ECM. They do not indicate whether devices respond properly to that signal. This must be verified at output device using a voltmeter or test light.

If trouble codes are not present, a problem may still exist. Driveability-related problems with codes displayed occur about 20 percent of the time, while driveability problems without codes occur about 80 percent of the time. Out-of-calibration sensors WILL NOT set a trouble code, but WILL cause driveability problems. A scan tester is the easiest method of checking sensor specifications and other data parameters. Tester is also useful in finding intermittent wiring problems by wiggling wiring harnesses and connections (key on, engine off) while observing data parameters. See TYPICAL DATA VALUES table.

NOTE: *Information obtained by scan tester is only as accurate as the tester itself. If erroneous voltage signals are suspected, verify tester information using a digital voltmeter and wiring schematic. If non-existent codes are displayed, turn ignition off and remove tester. Turn ignition on and ground DLC test terminal. If same codes are not flashed by Malfunction Indicator Light (MIL) as were indicated by scan tester, tester cannot be used on vehicle and information obtained by it will not be guaranteed accurate.*

SCAN TESTER DATA

NOTE: Information contained in the following table is typical of readings taken on vehicle with engine idling, upper radiator hose hot, throttle closed, transmission in Park or Neutral, closed loop status achieved and all accessories off (except as noted in tables). Not all devices and systems are used on all models. For additional information, see tester owner's manual.

NOTE: On Prizm and Prizm LSi, typical data values information is not available from manufacturer.

TYPICAL DATA VALUES (Metro)

Tester Position	Units Measured	Nominal Data Value
A/C Switch	On/Off	Off
BARO [1]	Volts/kPa	3.68 (100)
Desired Idle	RPM	ECM Controls (Varies)
EGR Solenoid	On/Off	Off
Electrical Load	On/Off	[2] Off
Eng. Coolant Temp.	°F (°C)	176-201 (80-94)
Engine Speed	RPM	800-900
Fuel EVAP Purge [1]	On/Off	Off
IAC/ISC Duty [1]	%	10-50
Idle Switch	On/Off	On
Injector Pulse Width	Mil/Sec	1.0-1.7
Intake Air Temp.	°F (°C)	[3] 68-95 (20-35)
ISC Duty [4]	%	10-50
L.T. Fuel Trim	Counts	119-131
MAP	Volts/kPa	1.32-1.90 (34-42)
MPH	MPH	0
O₂ [5]	Millivolts	10-900
O₂ Activation	Act/Deact	Activate
Park/Neutral Pos	P/N/RDL	P/N (A/T) RDL (M/T)
Power Steerg Sw	On/Off	Off
Power Steer VSV [4]	On/Off	Off
Rich/Lean Stat	Rich/Lean	Switches
Spark Advance	°	20-28
S.T. Fuel Trim	Counts	113-143
System Voltage	Volts	14.0-14.5
Throttle Angle	°	0
Throttle Position	Volts	.45-.65

[1] – Upgraded emissions only.
[2] – On when radiator fan motor cycles on.
[3] – Varies with ambient temperature.
[4] – Standard emissions only.
[5] – Heated O₂ on upgraded emissions.

TYPICAL DATA VALUES (Tracker)

Tester Position	Units Measured	Nominal Data Value
A/C Request [1]	Yes/No	No
A/C Switch [2]	On/Off	Off
BARO [1]	Volts/kPa	4.00 (98)
Charging EFF1 [2]	%	10
Desired Idle	RPM	ECM Controls (Varies)
EGR Gas Temp.	°F (°C)	140-145 (60-65)
EGR Solenoid	On/Off	Off
Eng. Coolant Temp.	°F (°C)	176-194 (80-90)
Engine Speed	RPM	750-850
Fuel EVAP Purge [2]	%	0
Fuel EVAP VSV [1]	On/Off	Off
Fuel Pump [2]	On/Off	On
HO2S	Millivolts	10-900
Idle Switch	On/Off	On
Injector Pulse Width	Mil/Sec	1.1-1.6
Intake Air Temp. [1]	°F (°C)	149-167 (65-75)
ISC Adjust Monit	%	0
ISC Air Flow	L/Min	25-40
L.T. Fuel Trim	Counts	118
MAP	Volts/kPa	1.56 (39)
Mass Air Flow [2]	g/S	3.1
MPH	MPH	0
O₂ Activation [2]	Act/Deact	Activate
Park/Neutral Pos	P/N/RDL	P/N (A/T) RDL (M/T)
Power Steerg Sw	On/Off	Off
Rich/Lean Stat	Rich/Lean	Switches
Spark Advance	°	5-15
S.T. Fuel Trim	Counts	127
System Voltage	Volts	14.0-14.5
Throt Open Sol [1]	On/Off	Off
Throttle Angle	°	0
Throttle Position	Volts	.85-.95
Time From Start [1]	Sec	Counts 0-510

[1] – TBI (Federal) only.
[2] – MFI (Calif. & New York) only.

SUMMARY

If no hard fault codes are present, driveability symptoms exist or intermittent codes exist, proceed to TROUBLE SHOOTING – NO CODES article for diagnosis by symptom (i.e., ROUGH IDLE, NO START, etc.) or intermittent diagnostic procedures.

NOTE: The following diagnostic mini-schematics are supplied courtesy of General Motors Corp.

DIAGNOSTIC CODE CHARTS
METRO (STANDARD EMISSIONS) CODE CHARTS

ON-BOARD DIAGNOSTIC (OBD) SYSTEM CHECK (METRO STANDARD EMISSIONS)

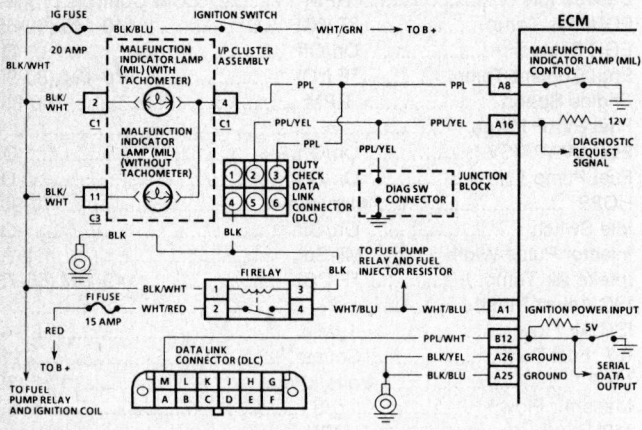

On-board diagnostic system check is an organized approach in identifying a problem created by an electronic engine system malfunction. It must be the starting point for any driveability complaint diagnosis, because it directs the service technician to the next logical step in diagnosing a complaint. Understanding the chart and using it correctly will reduce diagnostic time and prevent unnecessary replacement of good parts.

NOTE: Test numbers refer to test numbers on diagnostic chart.

1) Checks Malfunction Indicator Light (MIL) operation.
2) Checks if ECM's self-diagnostic mode is operating.
3) Checks if ECM's serial data output is operating.
4) Checks if engine will start.
5) Checks for any codes that are stored in ECM memory with engine running.

6) Checks for any codes that are stored in ECM memory with engine off. If no codes are set and engine won't start, go to appropriate CHART A1-3 in BASIC DIAGNOSTIC PROCEDURES article.
7) Compares ECM's control data to typical data values.
8) Checks if code(s) are intermittent problems.

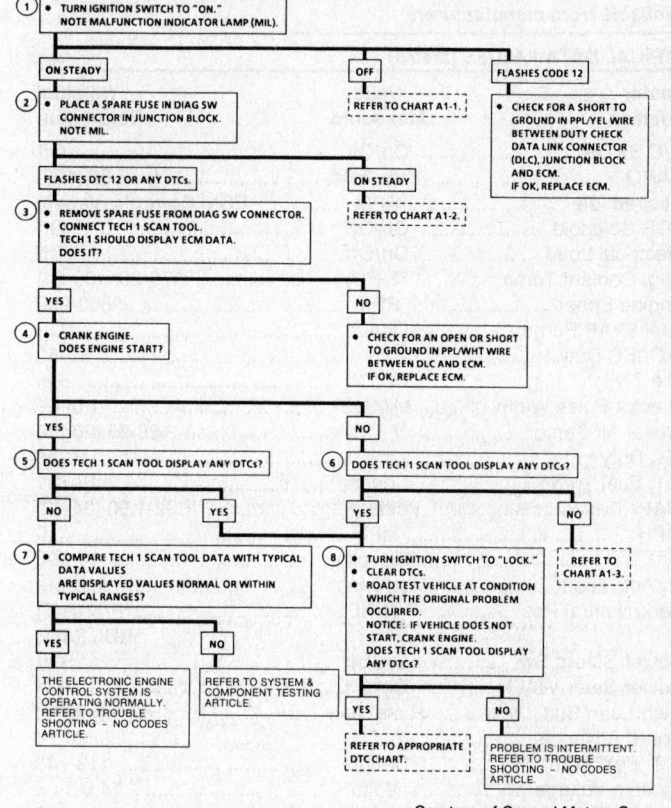

94D44431 94E44432

Courtesy of General Motors Corp.

CHART A1-1,
NO MALFUNCTION INDICATOR LIGHT (MIL)
(METRO STANDARD EMISSIONS)

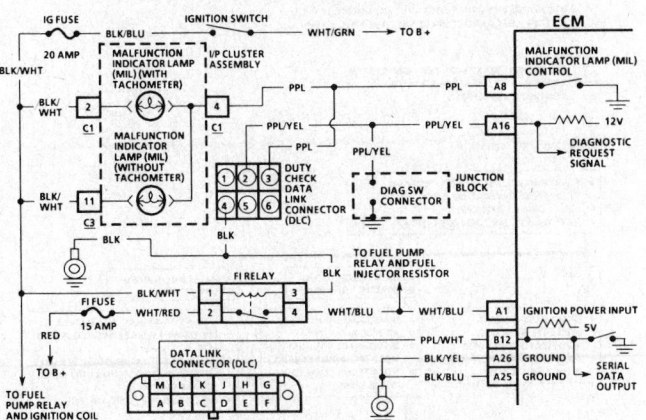

Malfunction Indicator Light (MIL) should remain on when ignition switch is in ON position and engine is not running. Battery voltage is applied to indicator bulb. ECM controls indicator bulb and turns it on by providing a ground path through Purple wire to ECM.

NOTE: Test numbers refer to test numbers on diagnostic chart.

1) Checks if ECM is receiving power.
2) Checks if ECM is faulty.
3) Checks for open in White/Blue wire between Fuel Injection (FI) relay and ECM.
4) Checks if ECM has a good ground.
5) Checks for open in Black/White wire to instrument cluster, and Purple wire to ECM.
6) Checks if Fuel Injection (FI) relay switch is receiving power.
7) Checks if Fuel Injection (FI) relay coil is receiving power.
8) Checks if Fuel Injection (FI) relay or ECM is faulty, or circuit is open in Black wire between Fuel Injection (FI) relay and ground.

94D44431 94F44433

DIAGNOSTIC AIDS
Check connectors for contamination, corrosion or for bent terminals.

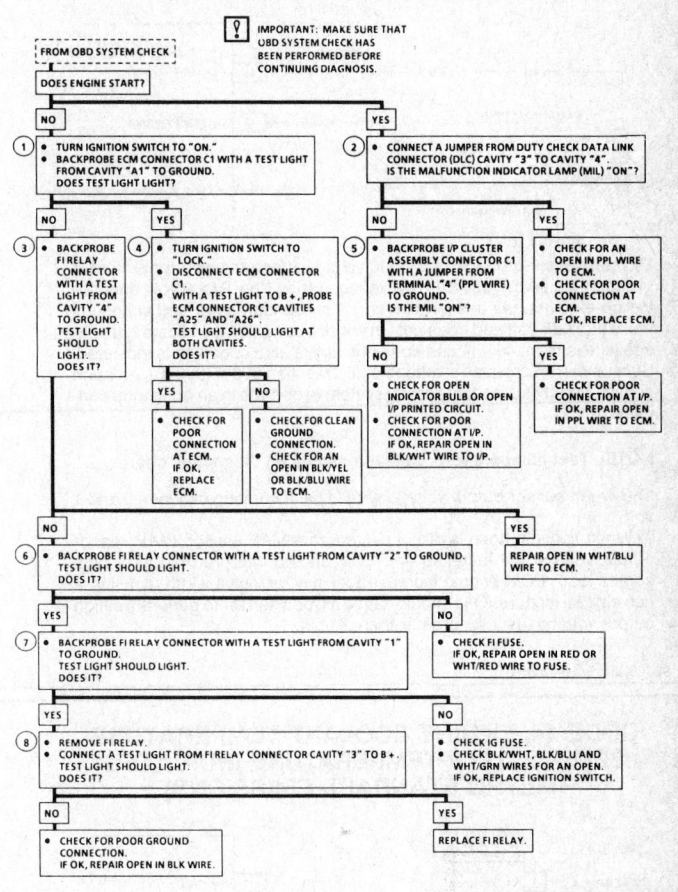

Courtesy of General Motors Corp.

CHART A1-2, WON'T FLASH CODE 12
OR ANY CODES, OR MALFUNCTION
INDICATOR LIGHT (MIL) ON STEADY
(METRO STANDARD EMISSIONS)

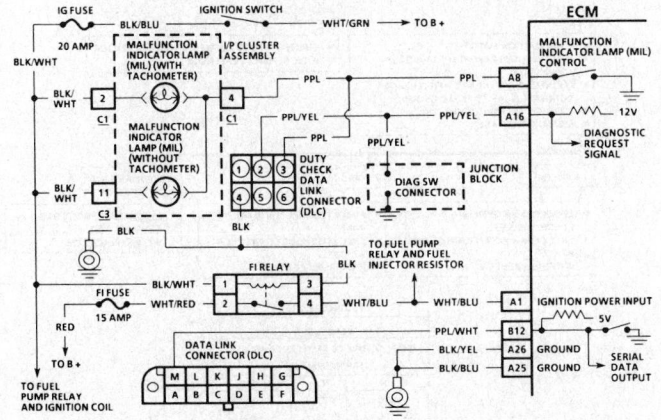

Malfunction Indicator Light (MIL) will flash trouble codes when either diagnostic request terminal in duty check data link connector or DIAG SW connector in junction block is grounded.

94D44431 94G44434

NOTE: Test numbers refer to test numbers on diagnostic chart.

1) Checks for a grounded light circuit.
2) Checks if problem is an open in diagnostic request terminal circuit or a faulty ECM.

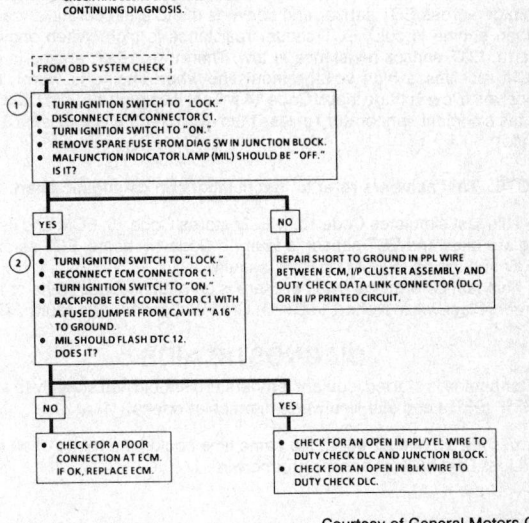

Courtesy of General Motors Corp.

CODE 13, OXYGEN SENSOR, SIGNAL VOLTAGE DOES NOT CHANGE (METRO STANDARD EMISSIONS)

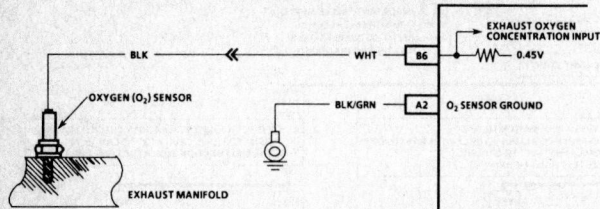

Oxygen sensor produces a varying voltage after exhaust temperature is greater than 600°F (360°C). This voltage varies from 0 to .9 volt, depending on exhaust gas oxygen content. After sensor is hot and voltage is more than .45 volt and does not vary, a rich condition is indicated. If voltage is less than .45 volt and does not vary, a lean condition is indicated. Sensor will not produce a voltage until it reaches 600°F (360°C). An open sensor circuit causes fuel control system to operate in an open loop condition.

NOTE: Test numbers refer to test numbers on diagnostic chart.

1) Oxygen sensor output voltage should be fluctuating between 0 and 1 volt.
2) When vacuum hose is disconnected from MAP sensor, MAP sensor output voltage will increase and ECM should interpret this as a high engine load. ECM should increase fuel injector pulse width, causing a rich air/fuel mixture. This should cause oxygen sensor to generate a high output voltage (usually, greater than .9 volt).

92J26277 94H44435

DIAGNOSTIC AIDS

Normal oxygen sensor voltage will vary from 0 to .9 volt. A loose or intermittent oxygen sensor ground can set a Code 13. Oxygen sensor ground is located on lower right rear of intake manifold.

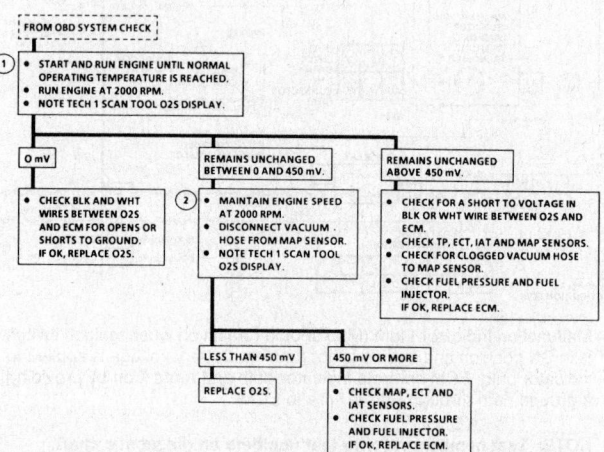

Courtesy of General Motors Corp.

CODE 14, ENGINE COOLANT TEMPERATURE SENSOR, LOW TEMPERATURE INDICATED (METRO STANDARD EMISSIONS)

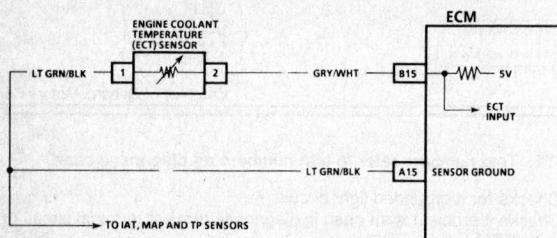

Engine Coolant Temperature (ECT) sensor is a thermistor in series with a fixed resistor in ECM. ECM applies 5 volts to sensor. ECM monitors voltage across ECT sensor and converts it into a temperature reading. When engine is cold, ECT sensor resistance is high. When engine is warm, ECT sensor resistance is low. Therefore, when engine is cold, ECM receives a high voltage input and when engine is warm, ECM receives a low voltage input. Code 14 will set if voltage input at ECM indicates a coolant temperature of less than –54°F (–48°C) for at least 3 seconds.

NOTE: Test numbers refer to test numbers on diagnostic chart.

1) This test simulates Code 15. If ECM stores Code 15, ECM and its wiring are okay and ECT sensor is faulty. If Code 14 resets, ECT sensor is okay and wiring to ECM or ECM is faulty.
2) This test determines whether there is an open in Gray/White or Light Green/Black wire, a short to B+ in Gray/White wire, or a faulty ECM.

DIAGNOSTIC AIDS

After engine is started, coolant temperature should rise steadily to about 203°F (95°C) and stabilize when thermostat opens.

Codes 14, 23 and 32 set at the same time could be a result of an open in Light Green/Black sensor ground wire.

94I44436 94J44437

When replacing ECT sensor, check TEMPERATURE TO RESISTANCE VALUES table at various temperature levels to evaluate the possibility of a "shifted" (mis-scaled) sensor. A "shifted" sensor could result in driveability complaints.

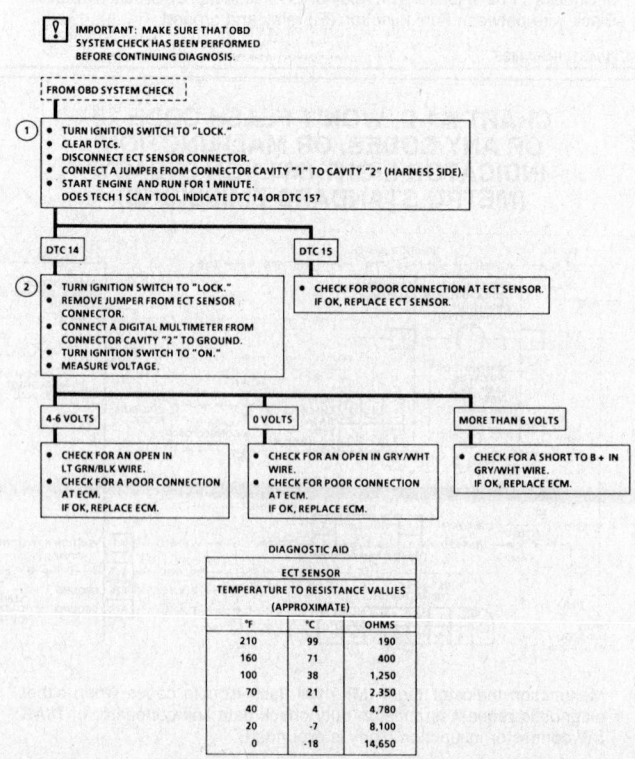

ECT SENSOR		
TEMPERATURE TO RESISTANCE VALUES (APPROXIMATE)		
°F	°C	OHMS
210	99	190
160	71	400
100	38	1,250
70	21	2,350
40	4	4,780
20	-7	8,100
0	-18	14,650

"AFTER REPAIRS," CONFIRM "CLOSED LOOP" OPERATION, NO DTCs AND NO MALFUNCTION INDICATOR LAMP (MIL).

Courtesy of General Motors Corp.

CODE 15, ENGINE COOLANT TEMPERATURE SENSOR, HIGH TEMPERATURE INDICATED (METRO STANDARD EMISSIONS)

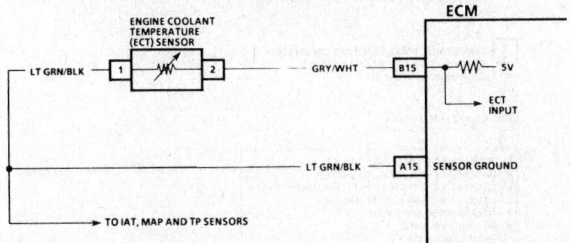

Engine Coolant Temperature (ECT) sensor is a thermistor in series with a fixed resistor in ECM. ECM applies 5 volts to sensor. ECM monitors voltage across ECT sensor and converts it into a temperature reading. When engine is cold, ECT sensor resistance is high. When engine is warm, ECT sensor resistance is low. Therefore, when engine is cold, ECM receives a high voltage input and when engine is warm, ECM receives a low voltage input. Code 15 will set if voltage input at ECM indicates a coolant temperature of greater than 276°F (136°C) for at least 3 seconds.

NOTE: Test number refers to number on diagnostic chart.

1) This test simulates Code 14. If ECM sets Code 14, ECM and its wiring are okay and ECT sensor is faulty. If Code 15 resets, ECT sensor is okay and wiring to ECM or ECM is faulty.

DIAGNOSTIC AIDS

After engine is started, coolant temperature should rise steadily to about 203°F (95°C) and stabilize when thermostat opens.

94I44436 94A44438

Ensure engine is not overheating and has not been subjected to conditions which would create an overheating condition (i.e., overload, trailer towing, hilly terrain, heavy stop and go traffic, etc.). When replacing ECT sensor, check TEMPERATURE TO RESISTANCE VALUES table at various temperature levels to evaluate the possibility of a "shifted" (mis-scaled) sensor. A "shifted" sensor could result in driveability complaints.

> **IMPORTANT: MAKE SURE THAT OBD SYSTEM CHECK HAS BEEN PERFORMED BEFORE CONTINUING DIAGNOSIS.**

FROM OBD SYSTEM CHECK

1
- TURN IGNITION SWITCH TO "LOCK."
- CLEAR DTCs.
- DISCONNECT ECT SENSOR CONNECTOR.
- START AND RUN ENGINE FOR 1 MINUTE.
- DOES TECH 1 SCAN TOOL INDICATE DTC 14 OR DTC 15?

DTC 14
- REPLACE ECT SENSOR.

DTC 15
- CHECK FOR SHORT TO GROUND IN GRY/WHT WIRE. IF OK, REPLACE ECM.

DIAGNOSTIC AID

ECT SENSOR		
TEMPERATURE TO RESISTANCE VALUES (APPROXIMATE)		
°F	°C	OHMS
210	99	190
160	71	400
100	38	1,250
70	21	2,350
40	4	4,780
20	-7	8,100
0	-18	14,650

"AFTER REPAIRS," CONFIRM "CLOSED LOOP" OPERATION, NO DTCs AND NO MALFUNCTION INDICATOR LAMP (MIL).

Courtesy of General Motors Corp.

CODE 21, THROTTLE POSITION (TP) SENSOR, SIGNAL VOLTAGE HIGH (METRO STANDARD EMISSIONS)

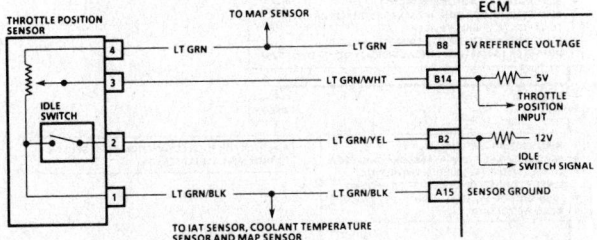

Throttle Position (TP) sensor resistance changes along with throttle valve position. ECM provides a 5-volt reference voltage to TP sensor. ECM reads voltage across sensor and converts it into a throttle position. When TP sensor resistance decreases, indicating throttle valve opening is increasing to WOT, voltage being monitored at ECM increases. When sensor resistance increases, indicating throttle valve opening is decreasing to idle, voltage being monitored at ECM decreases. Code 21 will set when high voltage input at ECM was indicated for 2 seconds with engine running at idle.

NOTE: Test numbers refer to test numbers on diagnostic chart.

1) Checks for open or short to B+ in Light Green/White wire or a faulty ECM.
2) Checks for open or short to B+ in Light Green wire or a faulty ECM.
3) Checks for a faulty ECM, or a misadjusted or faulty TP sensor.

DIAGNOSTIC AIDS

See ON-VEHICLE ADJUSTMENTS article for TP sensor adjustment. Codes 21 and 22 set at the same time could be the result of an open Light Green wire between ECM and TP sensor.

92G26282 94B44439

> **IMPORTANT: MAKE SURE THAT OBD SYSTEM CHECK HAS BEEN PERFORMED BEFORE CONTINUING DIAGNOSIS.**

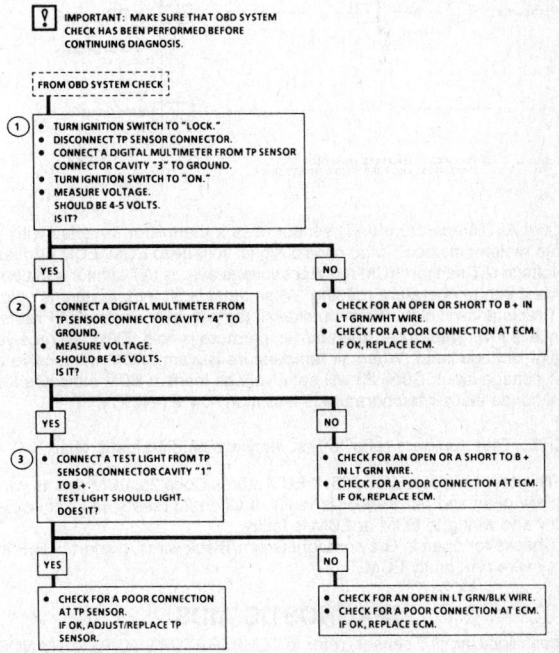

FROM OBD SYSTEM CHECK

1
- TURN IGNITION SWITCH TO "LOCK."
- DISCONNECT TP SENSOR CONNECTOR.
- CONNECT A DIGITAL MULTIMETER FROM TP SENSOR CONNECTOR CAVITY "3" TO GROUND.
- TURN IGNITION SWITCH TO "ON."
- MEASURE VOLTAGE.
- SHOULD BE 4-5 VOLTS.
- IS IT?

YES / **NO**
- NO: CHECK FOR AN OPEN OR SHORT TO B+ IN LT GRN/WHT WIRE.
- CHECK FOR A POOR CONNECTION AT ECM. IF OK, REPLACE ECM.

2
- CONNECT A DIGITAL MULTIMETER FROM TP SENSOR CONNECTOR CAVITY "4" TO GROUND.
- MEASURE VOLTAGE.
- SHOULD BE 4-6 VOLTS.
- IS IT?

YES / **NO**
- NO: CHECK FOR AN OPEN OR A SHORT TO B+ IN LT GRN WIRE.
- CHECK FOR A POOR CONNECTION AT ECM. IF OK, REPLACE ECM.

3
- CONNECT A TEST LIGHT FROM TP SENSOR CONNECTOR CAVITY "1" TO B+.
- TEST LIGHT SHOULD LIGHT.
- DOES IT?

YES / **NO**
- YES: CHECK FOR A POOR CONNECTION AT TP SENSOR. IF OK, ADJUST/REPLACE TP SENSOR.
- NO: CHECK FOR AN OPEN IN LT GRN/BLK WIRE.
- CHECK FOR A POOR CONNECTION AT ECM. IF OK, REPLACE ECM.

"AFTER REPAIRS," CONFIRM "CLOSED LOOP" OPERATION, NO DTCs AND NO MALFUNCTION INDICATOR LAMP (MIL).

Courtesy of General Motors Corp.

CODE 22, THROTTLE POSITION (TP) SENSOR, SIGNAL VOLTAGE LOW (METRO STANDARD EMISSIONS)

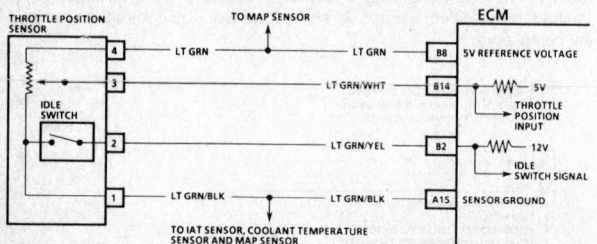

Throttle Position (TP) sensor resistance changes along with throttle valve position. ECM provides a 5-volt reference voltage to TP sensor. ECM reads voltage across sensor and converts it into a throttle position. When TP sensor resistance decreases, indicating throttle valve opening is increasing to WOT, voltage being monitored at ECM increases. When sensor resistance increases, indicating throttle valve opening is decreasing to idle, voltage being monitored at ECM decreases. Code 22 will set when low voltage input at ECM was indicated for 2 seconds with engine running off idle.

NOTE: Test numbers refer to test numbers on diagnostic chart.

1) Measures TP sensor signal voltage at sensor. Checks for short to ground in Light Green/White wire.
2) Checks for reference voltage from ECM.

92G26282 94E44440

DIAGNOSTIC AIDS

See ON-VEHICLE ADJUSTMENTS article for TP sensor adjustment. Codes 21 and 22 set at the same time could be the result of an open Light Green wire between ECM and TP sensor.

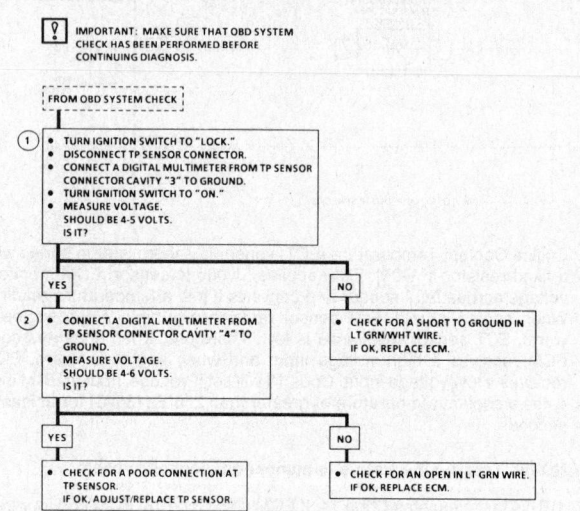

"AFTER REPAIRS," CONFIRM "CLOSED LOOP" OPERATION, NO DTCs AND NO MALFUNCTION INDICATOR LAMP (MIL).

Courtesy of General Motors Corp.

CODE 23, INTAKE AIR TEMPERATURE SENSOR, LOW TEMPERATURE INDICATED (METRO STANDARD EMISSIONS)

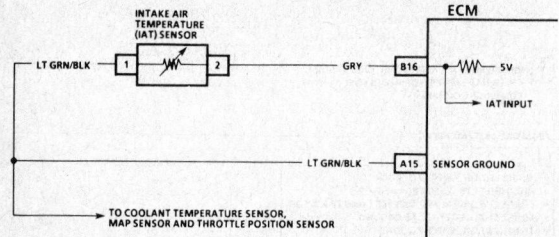

Intake Air Temperature (IAT) sensor uses a thermistor in series with a fixed resistor inside ECM to control signal voltage to ECM. ECM applies 5 volts to IAT sensor. ECM monitors voltage across IAT sensor and converts it into temperature reading. When outside air temperature is cold, IAT resistance is high. When outside air temperature is warm, IAT resistance is low. Therefore, when air temperature is cold, ECM will receive a high voltage input. When air temperature is warm, ECM will receive a low voltage input. Code 23 will set if voltage input at ECM indicates for 3 seconds that air temperature is less than –54°F (–48°C).

NOTE: Test numbers refer to test numbers on diagnostic chart.

1) This test simulates Code 25. If ECM stores Code 25, ECM and its wiring are okay and IAT sensor is faulty. If Code 23 resets, IAT sensor is okay and wiring to ECM or ECM is faulty.
2) Checks for open in Gray or Light Green/Black wires, a short to B+ in Gray wire or a faulty ECM.

DIAGNOSTIC AIDS

When replacing IAT sensor, refer to TEMPERATURE TO RESISTANCE VALUES table at various temperature levels to evaluate the possibility of a "shifted" (mis-scaled) sensor. A "shifted" sensor could result in poor driveability complaints. For additional IAT sensor specifications, refer to SYSTEM & COMPONENT TESTING article.

92J26285 94F44441

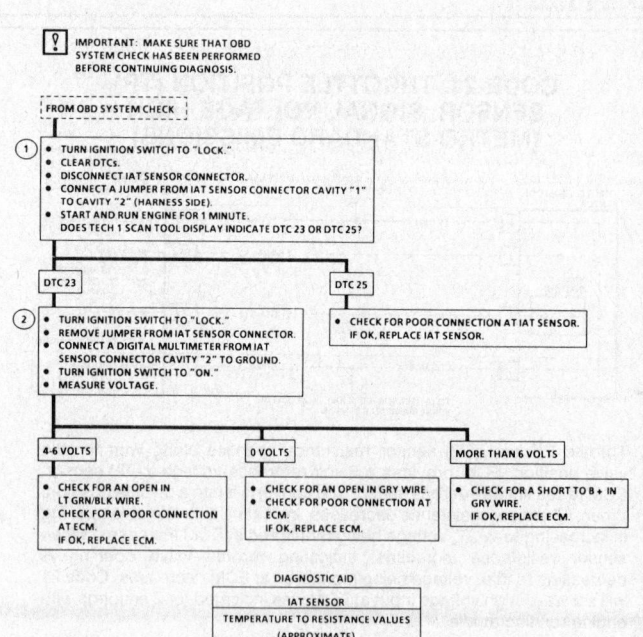

DIAGNOSTIC AID		
IAT SENSOR		
TEMPERATURE TO RESISTANCE VALUES (APPROXIMATE)		
°F	°C	OHMS
210	99	190
160	71	400
100	38	1,250
70	21	2,350
40	4	4,780
20	-7	8,100
0	-18	14,650

"AFTER REPAIRS," CONFIRM "CLOSED LOOP" OPERATION, NO DTCs AND NO MALFUNCTION INDICATOR LAMP (MIL).

Courtesy of General Motors Corp.

CODE 24, VEHICLE SPEED SENSOR
(METRO STANDARD EMISSIONS)

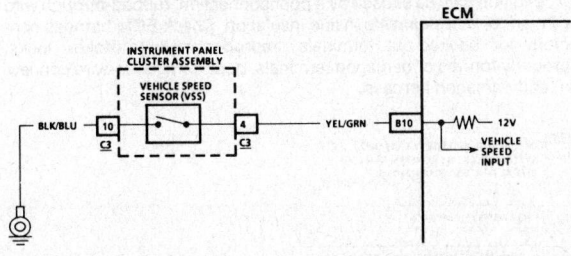

ECM supplies a B+ signal to Vehicle Speed Sensor (VSS). While vehicle is moving, a reed switch inside VSS will open and close, toggling B+ signal high and low. ECM then converts this toggled high/low voltage into a vehicle speed that is displayed as MPH/KPH. Code 24 will set if a constant voltage signal (high or low) is detected at ECM for at least 4 seconds, with engine running and vehicle moving.

NOTE: Test numbers refer to test numbers on diagnostic chart.

1) Checks if problem is intermittent.
2) If VSS is not receiving 12 volts from ECM, Code 24 will set. Checks for open in Yellow/Green wire or a faulty ECM.
3) Checks for a poor ground connection, an open in Black/Blue wire or a faulty VSS.

DIAGNOSTIC AIDS

If speedometer cable is binding, Code 24 can be set. Ensure that speedometer cable is free from restrictions and has a secure connection to instrument cluster. If problem is intermittent, refer to TROUBLE SHOOTING – NO CODES article.

92I26573 94G44442

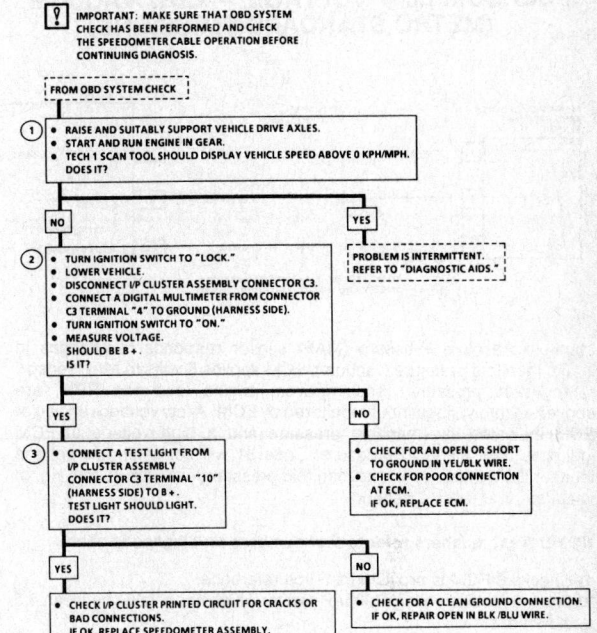

Courtesy of General Motors Corp.

CODE 25, INTAKE AIR TEMPERATURE SENSOR, HIGH TEMPERATURE INDICATED
(METRO STANDARD EMISSIONS)

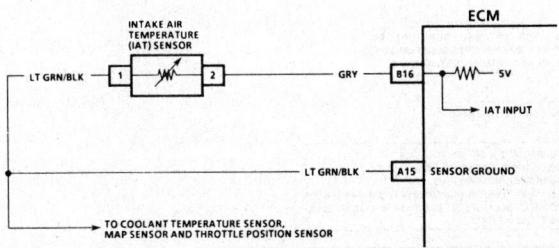

Intake Air Temperature (IAT) sensor uses a thermistor in series with a fixed resistor inside ECM to control signal voltage to ECM. ECM applies 5 volts to IAT sensor. ECM monitors voltage across IAT sensor and converts it into temperature reading. When outside air temperature is cold, IAT resistance is high. When outside air temperature is warm, IAT resistance is low. Therefore, when air temperature is cold, ECM will receive a high voltage input. When air temperature is warm, ECM will receive a low voltage input. Code 25 will set if voltage input at ECM indicates an air temperature of greater than 277°F (136°C) for at least 3 seconds.

NOTE: Test numbers refer to test numbers on diagnostic chart.

1) This test simulates Code 23. If ECM stores Code 23, ECM and its wiring are okay and IAT sensor is faulty. If Code 25 resets, IAT sensor is okay and wiring to ECM or ECM is faulty.

DIAGNOSTIC AIDS

When replacing IAT sensor, refer to TEMPERATURE TO RESISTANCE VALUES table at various temperature levels to evaluate the possibility of a "shifted" (mis-scaled) sensor. A "shifted" sensor could result in poor driveability complaints. For additional IAT sensor specifications, refer to SYSTEM & COMPONENT TESTING article.

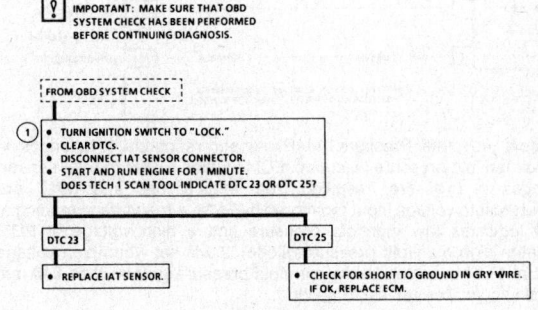

IAT SENSOR		
TEMPERATURE TO RESISTANCE VALUES (APPROXIMATE)		
°F	°C	OHMS
210	99	190
160	71	400
100	38	1,250
70	21	2,350
40	4	4,780
20	-7	8,100
0	-18	14,650

"AFTER REPAIRS," CONFIRM "CLOSED LOOP" OPERATION, NO DTCs AND NO MALFUNCTION INDICATOR LAMP (MIL).

92J26285 94H44443

Courtesy of General Motors Corp.

CODE 31, MANIFOLD ABSOLUTE PRESSURE SENSOR, LOW VOLTAGE – LOW VACUUM (METRO STANDARD EMISSIONS)

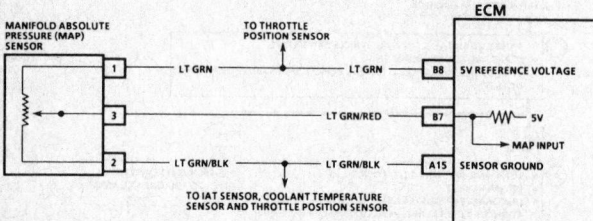

Manifold Absolute Pressure (MAP) sensor responds to changes in intake manifold pressure (vacuum). ECM applies 5 volts to MAP sensor. Changes in pressure, resulting from engine load and RPM, are converted into voltage input monitored by ECM. A low voltage reading at ECM indicates low manifold pressure and a high voltage at ECM indicates high manifold pressure. Code 31 will set when low voltage input at ECM indicates intake manifold pressure less than 40 mm Hg. of vacuum for at least .2 second.

NOTE: Test numbers refer to test numbers on diagnostic chart.

1) Checks if ECM is providing a 5-volt reference.
2) Checks for bias voltage to MAP sensor which has a value between 4.5 and 4.9 volts.

DIAGNOSTIC AIDS

Check for blocked or pinched vacuum hose to MAP sensor. An intermittent condition may be caused by a poor connection, rubbed-through wire insulation, or a broken wire inside insulation. Check ECM harness connectors for backed-out terminals, improper mating, broken locks, improperly formed or damaged terminals, poor terminal-to-wire connection, and damaged harness.

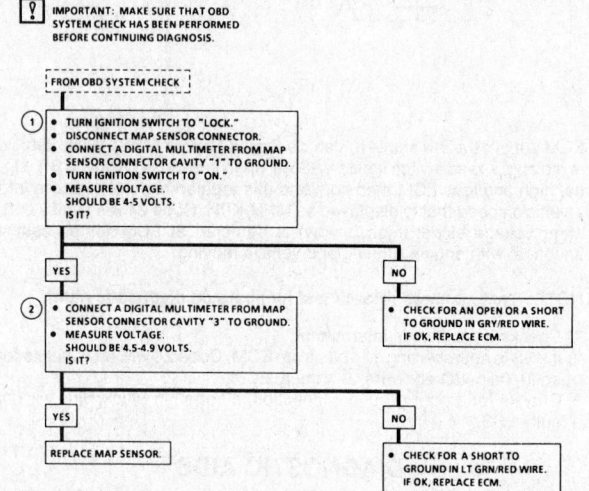

"AFTER REPAIRS," CONFIRM "CLOSED LOOP" OPERATION, NO DTCs AND NO MALFUNCTION INDICATOR LAMP (MIL).

92B26576 94I44444   Courtesy of General Motors Corp.

CODE 32, MANIFOLD ABSOLUTE PRESSURE SENSOR, HIGH VOLTAGE – HIGH VACUUM (METRO STANDARD EMISSIONS)

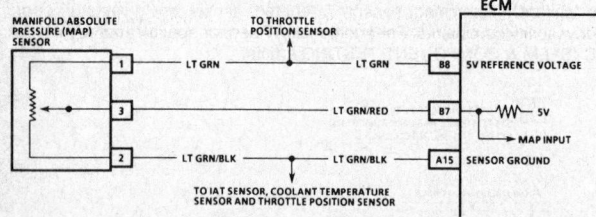

Manifold Absolute Pressure (MAP) sensor responds to changes in intake manifold pressure (vacuum). ECM applies 5 volts to MAP sensor. Changes in pressure, resulting from engine load and RPM, are converted into voltage input monitored by ECM. A low voltage reading at ECM indicates low manifold pressure and a high voltage at ECM indicates high manifold pressure. Code 32 will set when high voltage input at ECM indicates intake manifold pressure greater than 840 mm Hg. of vacuum for at least .2 second.

NOTE: Test numbers refer to test numbers on diagnostic chart.

1) Checks for open or short to voltage in Light Green/Red wire or a faulty ECM. Under normal conditions Light Green/Red wire should have an available voltage of less than 5 volts. A short to 5 volts or B+ will set Code 32.
2) Checks for open in Light Green/Black wire, poor connection at MAP sensor or ECM, and a faulty MAP sensor or ECM.

DIAGNOSTIC AIDS

Check for leaking vacuum hose to MAP sensor. An intermittent condition may be caused by a poor connection, rubbed-through wire insulation, or a broken wire inside insulation. Check ECM harness connectors for backed-out terminals, improper mating, broken locks, improperly formed or damaged terminals, poor terminal-to-wire connection, and damaged harness.

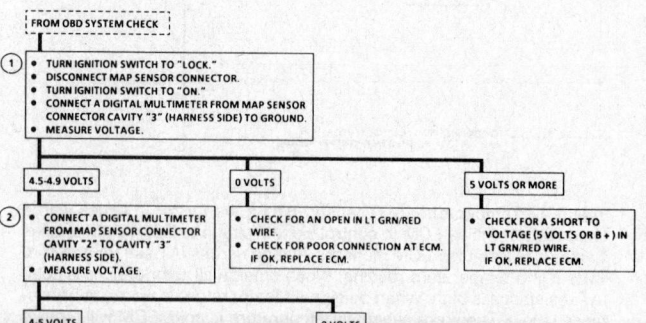

"AFTER REPAIRS," CONFIRM "CLOSED LOOP" OPERATION, NO DTCs AND NO MALFUNCTION INDICATOR LAMP (MIL).

92B26576 94J44445   Courtesy of General Motors Corp.

CODE 41, IGNITION SIGNAL CIRCUIT, (METRO STANDARD EMISSIONS)

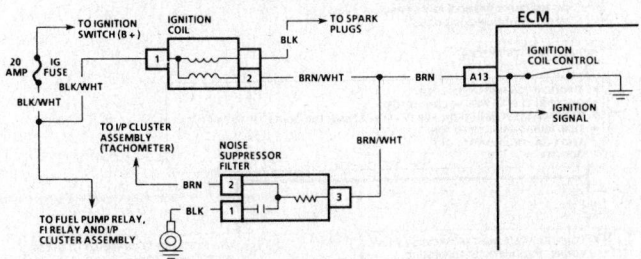

ECM receives ignition signal when ignition switch is turned to ON position. When ignition is in START position, this signal is toggled on and off through ECM. As this signal is toggled on and off, it induces a voltage in secondary coil of ignition coil. This induced voltage is then used to fire spark plugs. Code 41 will set if toggled ignition signal is not present at ECM within 3 seconds of cranking.

NOTE: Test numbers refer to test numbers on diagnostic chart.

1) Checks for power at ignition coil.
2) Checks for poor connection or a faulty ignition coil.
3) Checks for poor connection or a faulty ECM.
4) Checks for faulty noise suppressor filter.
5) Checks for open or short circuit to ground in wires between ignition coil, noise suppressor filter and ECM.

DIAGNOSTIC AIDS

An intermittent condition may be caused by a poor connection, rubbed-through wire insulation, or a broken wire inside insulation. Check ECM harness connectors for backed-out terminals, improper mating, broken locks, improperly formed or damaged terminals, poor terminal-to-wire connection, and damaged harness.

94A44446 94B44447

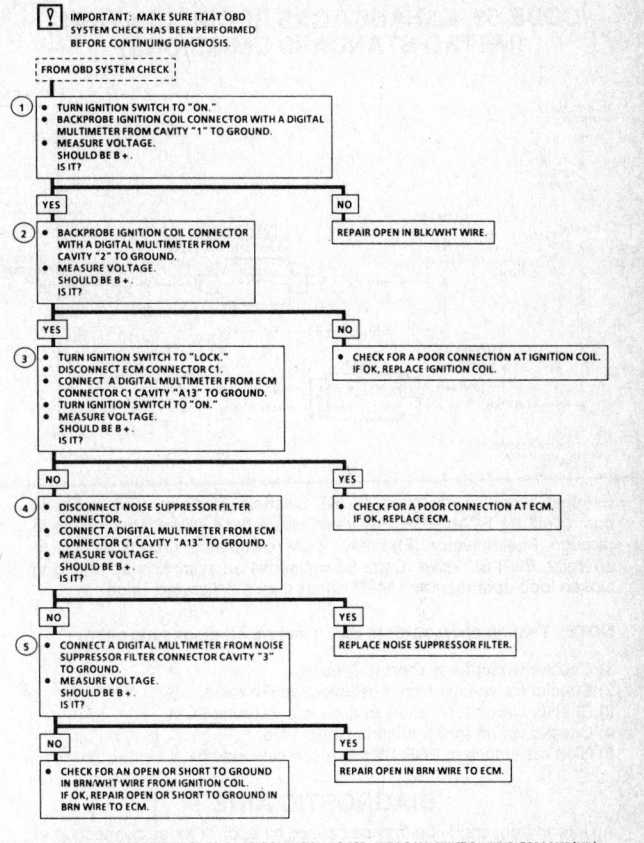

"AFTER REPAIRS," CONFIRM "CLOSED LOOP" OPERATION, NO DTCs AND NO MALFUNCTION INDICATOR LAMP (MIL).

Courtesy of General Motors Corp.

CODE 42, CAMSHAFT POSITION SENSOR CIRCUIT, NO SIGNAL FOR 2 SECONDS (METRO STANDARD EMISSIONS)

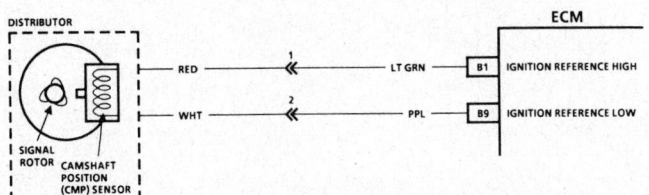

When distributor shaft rotates, a fluctuating magnetic field is generated due to changes in air gap between Camshaft Position (CMP) sensor and distributor shaft signal rotor. As a result, a small AC voltage is induced in CMP sensor. This ignition reference signal is sent to ECM on ECM terminals B1 and B9. ECM monitors AC voltage between these terminals. ECM uses this signal in determining when to fire ignition coil and fuel injector. Code 42 will set when ignition reference signal is not present at ECM for 2 seconds.

NOTE: Test numbers refer to test numbers on diagnostic chart.

1) Checks Camshaft Position (CMP) sensor resistance.
2) Checks for a proper AC signal voltage being produced. When distributor shaft turns, CMP sensor acts as an AC voltage signal generator.
3) Checks if proper AC signal voltage is getting through to ECM.

93H78391 94C44448

DIAGNOSTIC AIDS

A loose or damaged CMP sensor could cause an intermittent code. A misaligned CMP sensor or improper air gap could also set a Code 42 or an intermittent "engine cranks but won't run" condition. For CMP sensor specifications, refer to SYSTEM & COMPONENT TESTING article.

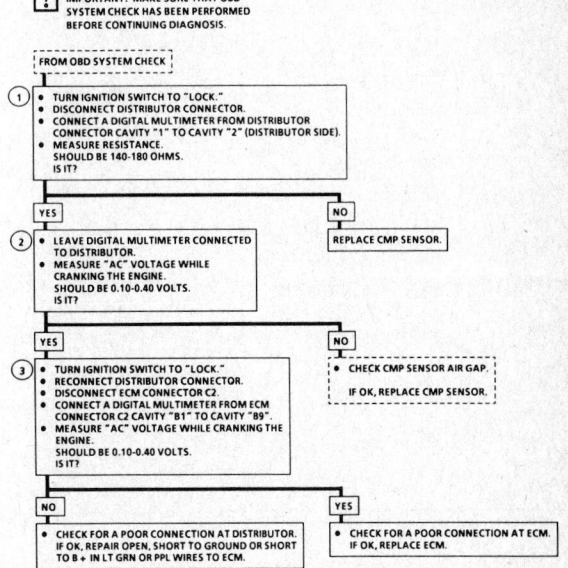

"AFTER REPAIRS," CONFIRM "CLOSED LOOP" OPERATION, NO DTCs AND NO MALFUNCTION INDICATOR LAMP (MIL).

Courtesy of General Motors Corp.

CODE 51, EXHAUST GAS RECIRCULATION
(METRO STANDARD EMISSIONS)

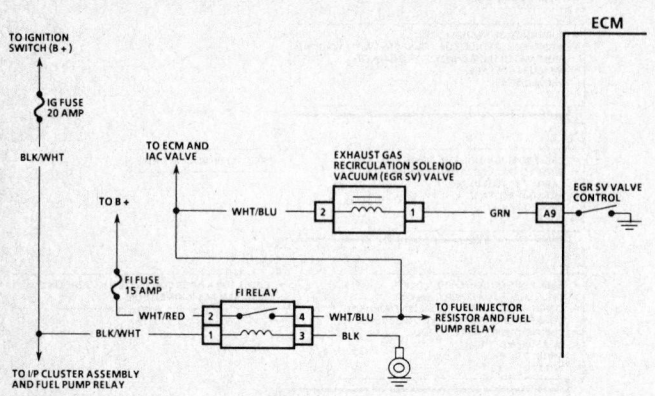

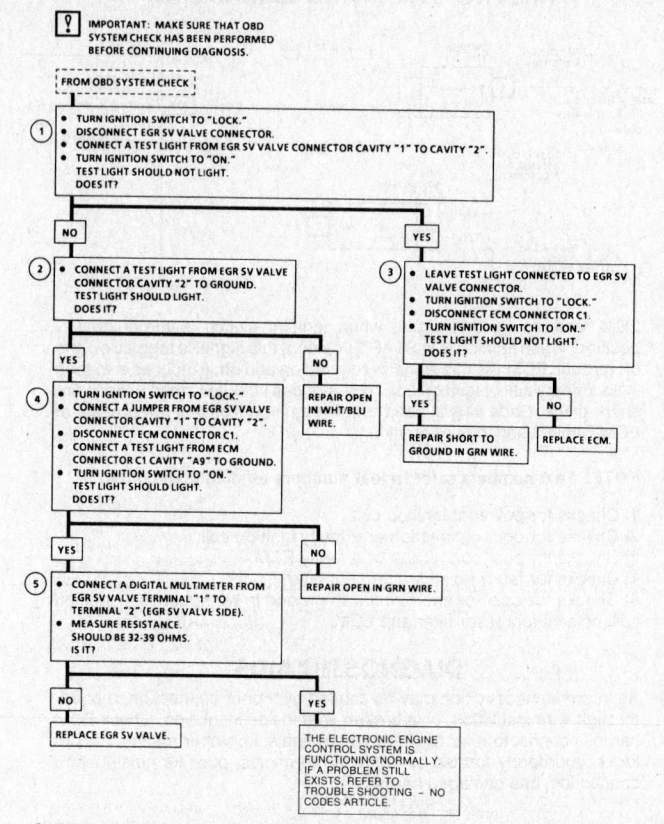

Exhaust Gas Recirculation (EGR) Solenoid Vacuum (SV) valve is controlled by ECM. EGR SV valve is supplied with battery voltage through Fuel Injector (FI) relay. ECM completes ground circuit to energize EGR SV valve. Code 51 will set when system is operating in closed loop operation and MAP is less than a calibrated value.

NOTE: Test numbers refer to test numbers on diagnostic chart.

1) Checks circuit for a short to ground.
2) Checks for voltage from Fuel Injection (FI) relay.
3) Checks circuit for a short to ground or a faulty ECM.
4) Checks circuit for an open in Green wire.
5) High resistance in EGR SV valve can set Code 51.

DIAGNOSTIC AIDS

An intermittent condition may be caused by poor or loose connection at ECM. This could cause a code to be falsely set. Check all throttle body vacuum hoses and EGR valve. Check MAP sensor vacuum hose for leaks or restrictions. ECM will periodically turn off the EGR SV valve when EGR is enabled in closed loop operation. Code 51 will set if corresponding manifold pressure change is less than a calibrated value, determining that a fault exists in the EGR system.

93J78393   94D44449

METRO (UPGRADED EMISSIONS) CODE CHARTS

ON-BOARD DIAGNOSTIC (OBD) SYSTEM CHECK (METRO UPGRADED EMISSIONS)

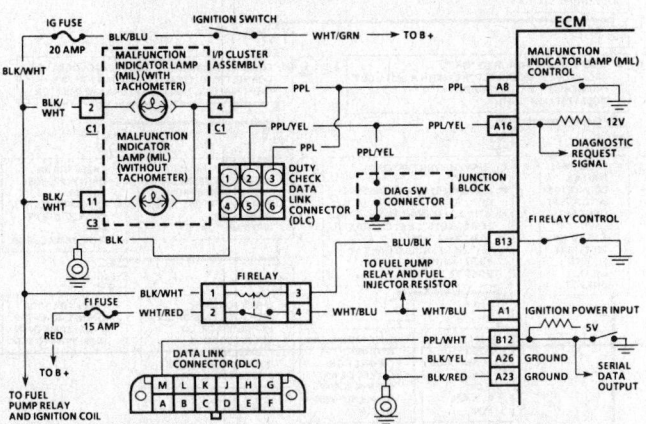

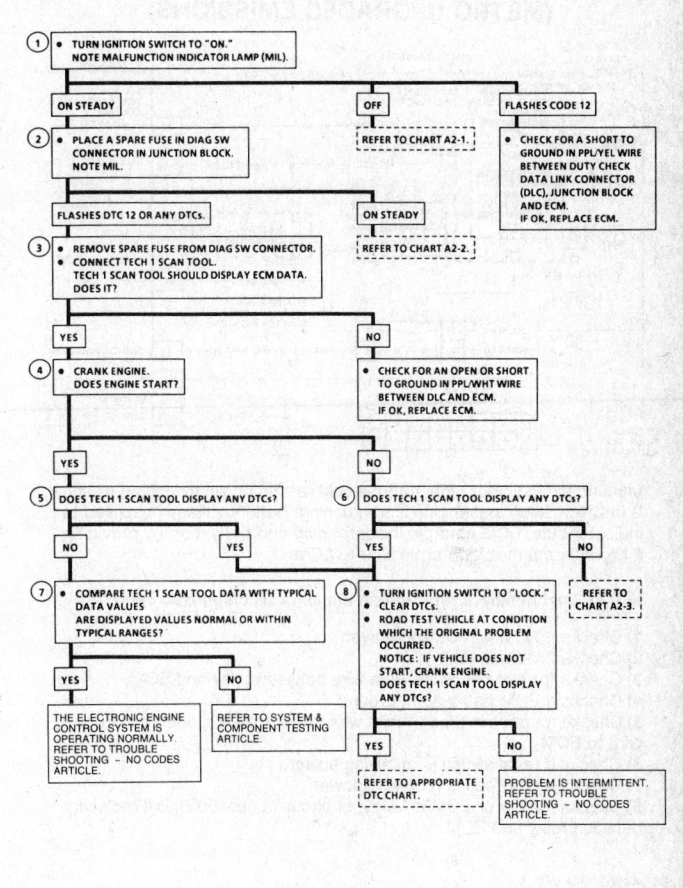

On-board diagnostic system check is an organized approach in identifying a problem created by an electronic engine system malfunction. It must be the starting point for any driveability complaint diagnosis, because it directs the service technician to the next logical step in diagnosing a complaint. Understanding the chart and using it correctly will reduce diagnostic time and prevent unnecessary replacement of good parts.

NOTE: Test numbers refer to test numbers on diagnostic chart.

1) Checks Malfunction Indicator Light (MIL) operation.
2) Checks if ECM's self-diagnostic mode is operating.
3) Checks if ECM's serial data output is operating.
4) Checks if engine will start.
5) Checks for any codes that are stored in ECM memory with engine running.
6) Checks for any codes that are stored in ECM memory with engine off. If no codes are set and engine won't start, go to appropriate CHART A2-3 in BASIC DIAGNOSTIC PROCEDURES article.
7) Compares ECM's control data to typical data values.
8) Checks if code(s) are intermittent problems.

94D44852 94E44853

Courtesy of General Motors Corp.

CHART A2-1,
NO MALFUNCTION INDICATOR LIGHT (MIL)
(METRO UPGRADED EMISSIONS)

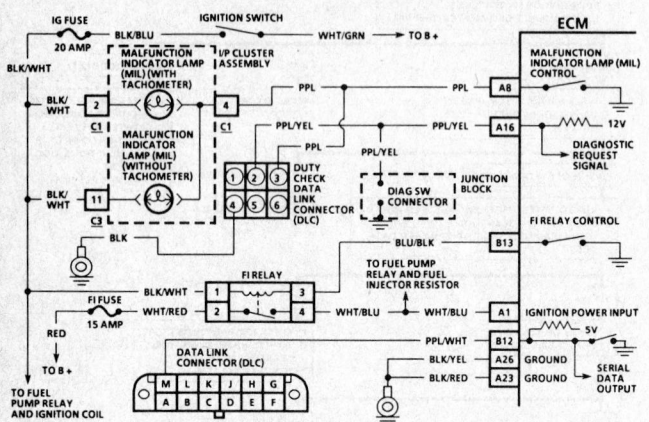

DIAGNOSTIC AIDS
Check connectors for contamination, corrosion or for bent terminals.

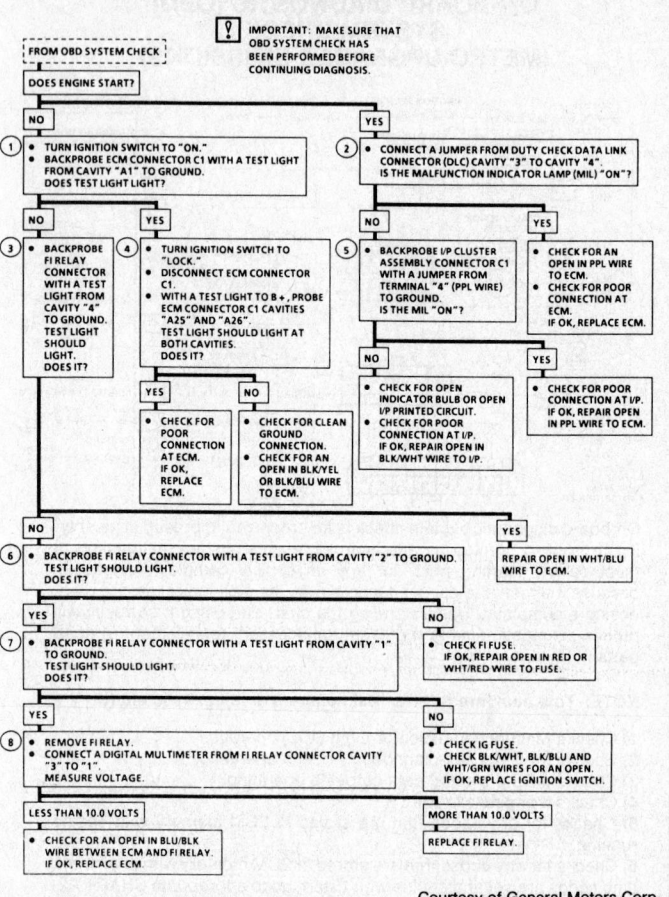

Malfunction Indicator Light (MIL) should remain on when ignition switch is in ON position and engine is not running. Battery voltage is applied to indicator bulb. ECM controls indicator bulb and turns it on by providing a ground path through Purple wire to ECM.

NOTE: Test numbers refer to test numbers on diagnostic chart.

1) Checks if ECM is receiving power.
2) Checks if ECM is faulty.
3) Checks for open in White/Blue wire between relay and ECM.
4) Checks if ECM has a good ground.
5) Checks for open in Black/White wire to instrument cluster, and Purple wire to ECM.
6) Checks if relay switch is receiving power.
7) Checks if relay coil is receiving power.
8) Checks if relay or ECM is faulty, or circuit is open in Blue/Black wire between relay and ECM.

94D44852 94F44854

Courtesy of General Motors Corp.

CHART A2-2, WON'T FLASH CODE 12
OR ANY CODES, OR MALFUNCTION
INDICATOR LIGHT (MIL) ON STEADY
(METRO UPGRADED EMISSIONS)

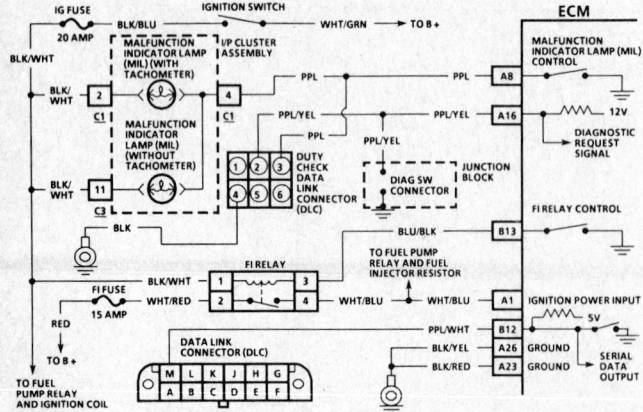

NOTE: Test numbers refer to test numbers on diagnostic chart.

1) Checks for a grounded light circuit.
2) Checks if problem is an open in diagnostic request terminal circuit or a faulty ECM.

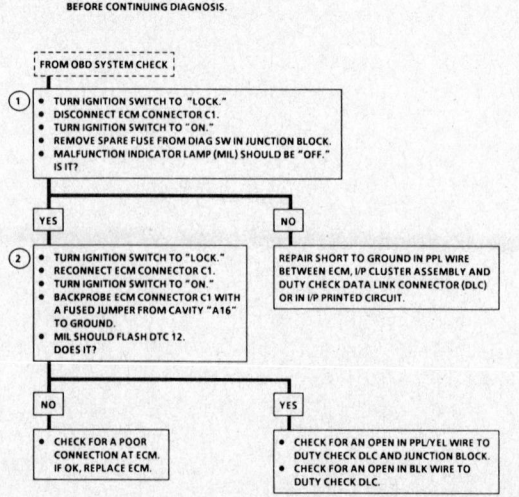

Malfunction Indicator Light (MIL) will flash trouble codes when either diagnostic request terminal in duty check data link connector or DIAG SW connector in junction block is grounded.

94D44852 94G44855

Courtesy of General Motors Corp.

CODE 13, HEATED OXYGEN SENSOR, SIGNAL VOLTAGE DOES NOT CHANGE (METRO UPGRADED EMISSIONS)

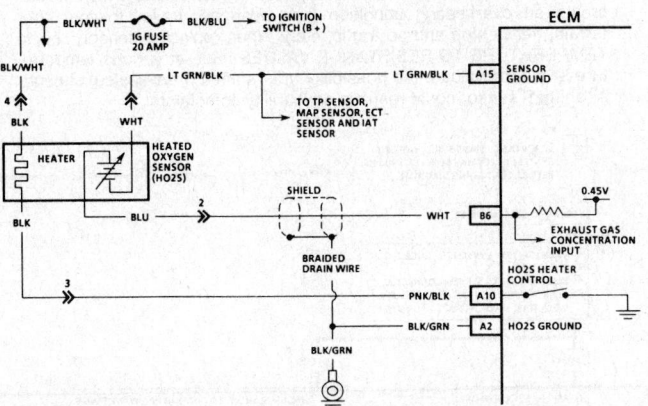

Heated Oxygen Sensor (HO2S) produces a varying voltage after exhaust temperature is greater than 600°F (360°C). This voltage varies from 0 to .9 volt, depending on exhaust gas oxygen content. After sensor is hot and voltage is more than .45 volt and does not vary, a rich condition is indicated. If voltage is less than .45 volt and does not vary, a lean condition is indicated. Sensor will not produce a voltage until it reaches 600°F (360°C). An open sensor circuit causes fuel control system to operate in an open loop condition.

NOTE: Test numbers refer to test numbers on diagnostic chart.

1) Sensor output voltage should be fluctuating between 0 and 1 volt.
2) When vacuum hose is disconnected from MAP sensor, MAP sensor output voltage will increase and ECM should interpret this as a high engine load. ECM should increase fuel injector pulse width, causing a rich air/fuel mixture. This should cause sensor to generate a high output voltage (usually, greater than .9 volt).

94H44856 94I44857

DIAGNOSTIC AIDS

Normal sensor voltage will vary from 0 to .9 volt. A loose or intermittent sensor ground can set a Code 13. Sensor ground is located on lower right rear of intake manifold.

* IF DTC 13 AND ANY OTHER DTCs ARE SET IN MEMORY TOGETHER, CHECK AND CORRECT THE OTHER DTC(s) FIRST.

IMPORTANT: MAKE SURE THAT OBD SYSTEM CHECK HAS BEEN PERFORMED BEFORE CONTINUING DIAGNOSIS.

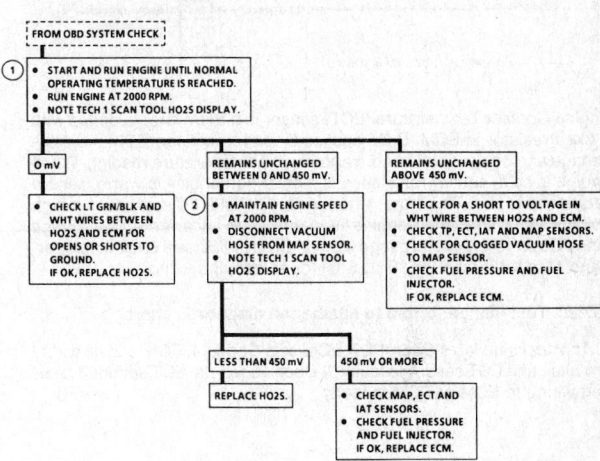

"AFTER REPAIRS," CONFIRM "CLOSED LOOP" OPERATION, NO DTCs AND NO MALFUNCTION INDICATOR LAMP (MIL).

Courtesy of General Motors Corp.

CODE 14, ENGINE COOLANT TEMPERATURE SENSOR, LOW TEMPERATURE INDICATED (METRO UPGRADED EMISSIONS)

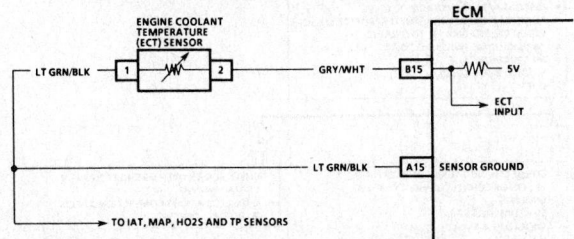

Engine Coolant Temperature (ECT) sensor is a thermistor in series with a fixed resistor in ECM. ECM applies 5 volts to sensor. ECM monitors voltage across sensor and converts it into a temperature reading. When engine is cold, sensor resistance is high. When engine is warm, sensor resistance is low. Therefore, when engine is cold, ECM receives a high voltage input and when engine is warm, ECM receives a low voltage input. Code 14 will set if voltage input at ECM indicates a coolant temperature of less than −54°F (−48°C) for at least 3 seconds.

NOTE: Test numbers refer to test numbers on diagnostic chart.

1) This test simulates Code 15. If ECM stores Code 15, ECM and its wiring is okay and sensor is faulty. If Code 14 resets, sensor is okay and wiring to ECM or ECM is faulty.
2) This test determines whether there is an open in Gray/White or Light Green/Black wire, a short to B+ in Gray/White wire, or a faulty ECM.

DIAGNOSTIC AIDS

After engine is started, coolant temperature should rise steadily to about 203°F (95°C) and stabilize when thermostat opens. Codes 14, 23 and 32 set at the same time could be a result of an open in Light Green/Black

94J44858 94A44859

sensor ground wire. When replacing sensor, check TEMPERATURE TO RESISTANCE VALUES table at various temperature levels to evaluate the possibility of a "shifted" (mis-scaled) sensor. A "shifted" sensor could result in driveability complaints.

DIAGNOSTIC AID		
ECT SENSOR		
TEMPERATURE TO RESISTANCE VALUES (APPROXIMATE)		
°F	°C	OHMS
210	99	190
160	71	400
100	38	1,250
70	21	2,350
40	4	4,780
20	-7	8,100
0	-18	14,650

IMPORTANT: MAKE SURE THAT OBD SYSTEM CIRCUIT CHECK HAS BEEN PERFORMED BEFORE CONTINUING DIAGNOSIS.

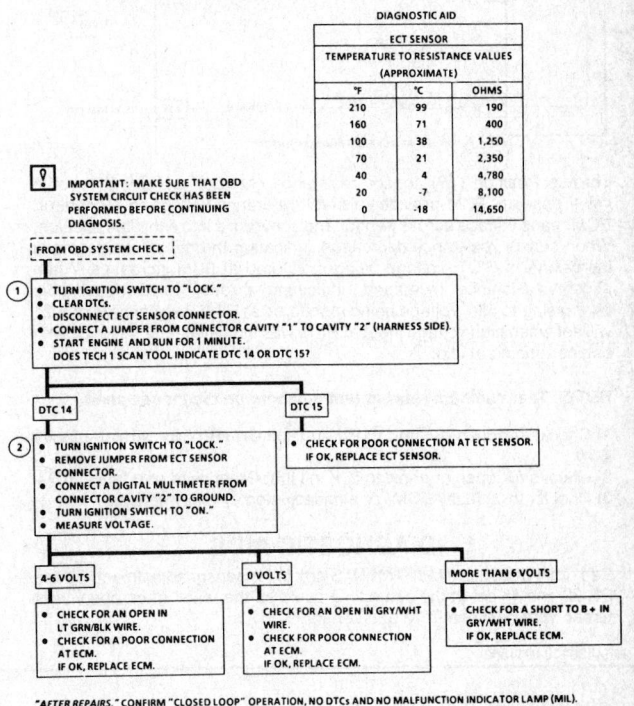

"AFTER REPAIRS," CONFIRM "CLOSED LOOP" OPERATION, NO DTCs AND NO MALFUNCTION INDICATOR LAMP (MIL).

Courtesy of General Motors Corp.

CODE 15, ENGINE COOLANT TEMPERATURE SENSOR, HIGH TEMPERATURE INDICATED (METRO UPGRADED EMISSIONS)

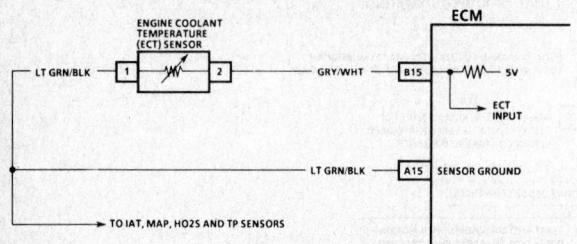

Engine Coolant Temperature (ECT) sensor is a thermistor in series with a fixed resistor in ECM. ECM applies 5 volts to sensor. ECM monitors voltage across sensor and converts it into a temperature reading. When engine is cold, sensor resistance is high. When engine is warm, sensor resistance is low. Therefore, when engine is cold, ECM receives a high voltage input and when engine is warm, ECM receives a low voltage input. Code 15 will set if voltage input at ECM indicates a coolant temperature of greater than 276°F (136°C) for at least 3 seconds.

NOTE: Test number refers to number on diagnostic chart.

1) This test simulates Code 14. If ECM sets Code 14, ECM and its wiring are okay and ECT sensor is faulty. If Code 15 resets, ECT sensor is okay and wiring to ECM or ECM is faulty.

DIAGNOSTIC AIDS

After engine is started, coolant temperature should rise steadily to about 203°F (95°C) and stabilize when thermostat opens. Ensure engine is not overheating and has not been subjected to conditions which would create an overheating condition (i.e., overload, trailer towing, hilly terrain, heavy stop and go traffic, etc.). When replacing sensor, check TEMPERATURE TO RESISTANCE VALUES table at various temperature levels to evaluate the possibility of a "shifted" (mis-scaled) sensor. A "shifted" sensor could result in driveability complaints.

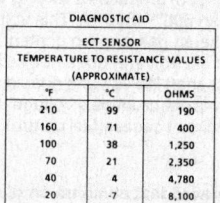

IMPORTANT: MAKE SURE THAT OBD SYSTEM CHECK HAS BEEN PERFORMED BEFORE CONTINUING DIAGNOSIS.

FROM OBD SYSTEM CHECK

1) • TURN IGNITION SWITCH TO "LOCK."
   • CLEAR DTCs.
   • DISCONNECT ECT SENSOR CONNECTOR.
   • START AND RUN ENGINE FOR 1 MINUTE.
     DOES TECH 1 INDICATE DTC 14 OR DTC 15?

DTC 14
• REPLACE ECT SENSOR.

DTC 15
• CHECK FOR SHORT TO GROUND IN GRY/WHT WIRE. IF OK, REPLACE ECM.

DIAGNOSTIC AID

| ECT SENSOR | | |
| TEMPERATURE TO RESISTANCE VALUES (APPROXIMATE) | | |
°F	°C	OHMS
210	99	190
160	71	400
100	38	1,250
70	21	2,350
40	4	4,780
20	-7	8,100
0	-18	14,650

"AFTER REPAIRS," CONFIRM "CLOSED LOOP" OPERATION, NO DTCs AND NO MALFUNCTION INDICATOR LAMP (MIL).

94J44858 94D44860

Courtesy of General Motors Corp.

CODE 21, THROTTLE POSITION SENSOR, SIGNAL VOLTAGE HIGH (METRO UPGRADED EMISSIONS)

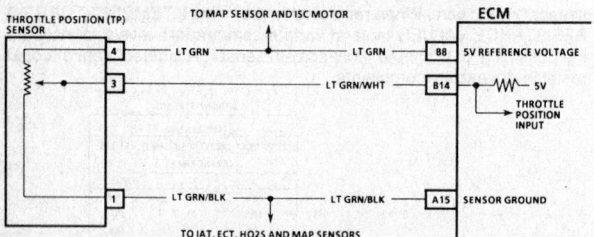

Throttle Position (TP) sensor resistance changes along with throttle valve position. ECM provides a 5-volt reference voltage to TP sensor. ECM reads voltage across sensor and converts it into a throttle position. When sensor resistance decreases, indicating throttle valve opening is increasing to WOT, voltage being monitored at ECM increases. When sensor resistance increases, indicating throttle valve opening is decreasing to idle, voltage being monitored at ECM decreases. Code 21 will set when high voltage input at ECM was indicated for 2 seconds with engine running at idle.

NOTE: Test numbers refer to test numbers on diagnostic chart.

1) Checks for open or short to B+ in Light Green/White wire or a faulty ECM.
2) Checks for open or short to B+ in Light Green wire or a faulty ECM.
3) Checks for a faulty ECM, or a misadjusted or faulty sensor.

DIAGNOSTIC AIDS

See ON-VEHICLE ADJUSTMENTS article for sensor adjustment. Codes 21, 22 and 46 set at the same time could be the result of an open Light Green wire between ECM and sensor.

IMPORTANT: MAKE SURE THAT OBD SYSTEM CHECK HAS BEEN PERFORMED BEFORE CONTINUING DIAGNOSIS.

FROM OBD SYSTEM CHECK

1) • TURN IGNITION SWITCH TO "LOCK."
   • DISCONNECT TP SENSOR CONNECTOR.
   • CONNECT A DIGITAL MULTIMETER FROM TP SENSOR CONNECTOR CAVITY "3" TO GROUND.
   • TURN IGNITION SWITCH TO "ON."
   • MEASURE VOLTAGE.
     SHOULD BE 4-5 VOLTS.
     IS IT?

YES

NO
• CHECK FOR AN OPEN OR SHORT TO B+ IN LT GRN/WHT WIRE.
• CHECK FOR A POOR CONNECTION AT ECM. IF OK, REPLACE ECM.

2) • CONNECT A DIGITAL MULTIMETER FROM TP SENSOR CONNECTOR CAVITY "4" TO GROUND.
   • MEASURE VOLTAGE.
     SHOULD BE 4-6 VOLTS.
     IS IT?

YES

NO
• CHECK FOR AN OPEN OR A SHORT TO B+ IN LT GRN WIRE.
• CHECK FOR A POOR CONNECTION AT ECM. IF OK, REPLACE ECM.

3) • CONNECT A TEST LIGHT FROM TP SENSOR CONNECTOR CAVITY "1" TO B+.
   • TEST LIGHT SHOULD LIGHT.
     DOES IT?

YES
• CHECK FOR A POOR CONNECTION AT TP SENSOR. IF OK, ADJUST/REPLACE TP SENSOR.

NO
• CHECK FOR AN OPEN IN LT GRN/BLK WIRE.
• CHECK FOR A POOR CONNECTION AT ECM. IF OK, REPLACE ECM.

"AFTER REPAIRS," CONFIRM "CLOSED LOOP" OPERATION, NO DTCs AND NO MALFUNCTION INDICATOR LAMP (MIL).

94E44861 94F44862

Courtesy of General Motors Corp.

CODE 22, THROTTLE POSITION SENSOR, SIGNAL VOLTAGE LOW (METRO UPGRADED EMISSIONS)

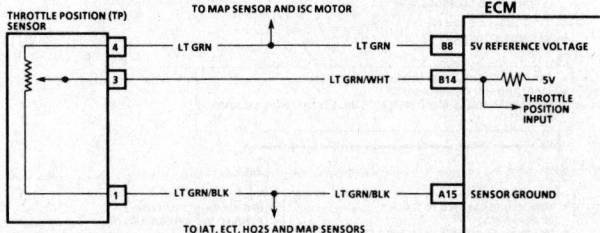

Throttle Position (TP) sensor resistance changes along with throttle valve position. ECM provides a 5-volt reference voltage to sensor. ECM reads voltage across sensor and converts it into a throttle position. When sensor resistance decreases, indicating throttle valve opening is increasing to WOT, voltage being monitored at ECM increases. When sensor resistance increases, indicating throttle valve opening is decreasing to idle, voltage being monitored at ECM decreases. Code 22 will set when low voltage input at ECM was indicated for 2 seconds with engine running off idle.

NOTE: Test numbers refer to test numbers on diagnostic chart.

1) Measures TP sensor signal voltage at sensor. Checks for short to ground in Light Green/White wire.
2) Checks for reference voltage from ECM.

94E44861 94G44863

DIAGNOSTIC AIDS

See ON-VEHICLE ADJUSTMENTS article for sensor adjustment. Codes 21, 22 and 46 set at the same time could be the result of an open Light Green wire between ECM and sensor.

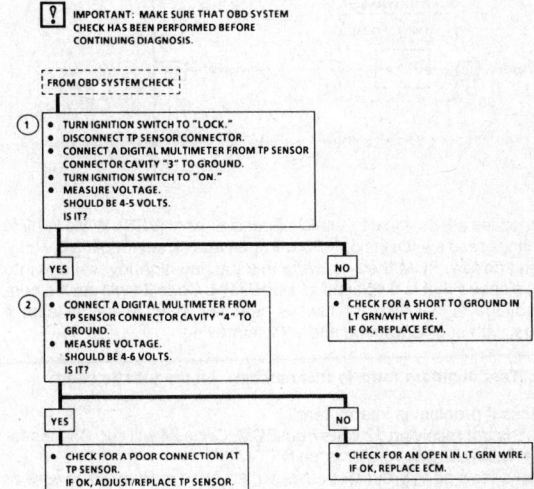

"AFTER REPAIRS," CONFIRM "CLOSED LOOP" OPERATION, NO DTCs AND NO MALFUNCTION INDICATOR LAMP (MIL).

Courtesy of General Motors Corp.

CODE 23, INTAKE AIR TEMPERATURE SENSOR, LOW TEMPERATURE INDICATED (METRO UPGRADED EMISSIONS)

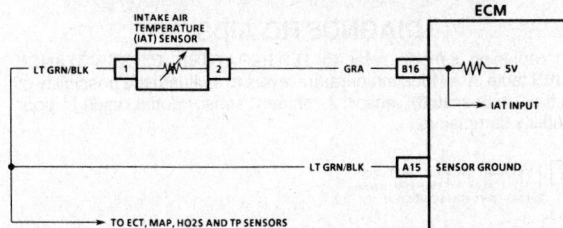

Intake Air Temperature (IAT) sensor uses a thermistor in series with a fixed resistor inside ECM to control signal voltage inside ECM. ECM applies 5 volts to IAT sensor. ECM monitors voltage across sensor and converts it into temperature reading. When outside air temperature is cold, sensor resistance is high. When outside air temperature is warm, sensor resistance is low. Therefore, when air temperature is cold, ECM will receive a high voltage input. When air temperature is warm, ECM will receive a low voltage input. Code 23 will set if voltage input at ECM indicates for 3 seconds that air temperature is less than –54°F (–48°C).

NOTE: Test numbers refer to test numbers on diagnostic chart.

1) This test simulates Code 25. If ECM stores Code 25, ECM and its wiring are okay and IAT sensor is faulty. If Code 23 resets, sensor is okay and wiring to ECM or ECM is faulty.
2) Checks for open in Gray or Light Green/Black wires, a short to B+ in Gray wire or a faulty ECM.

DIAGNOSTIC AIDS

When replacing IAT sensor, refer to TEMPERATURE TO RESISTANCE VALUES table at various temperature levels to evaluate the possibility of a "shifted" (mis-scaled) sensor. A "shifted" sensor could result in poor driveability complaints.

94H44864 94I44865

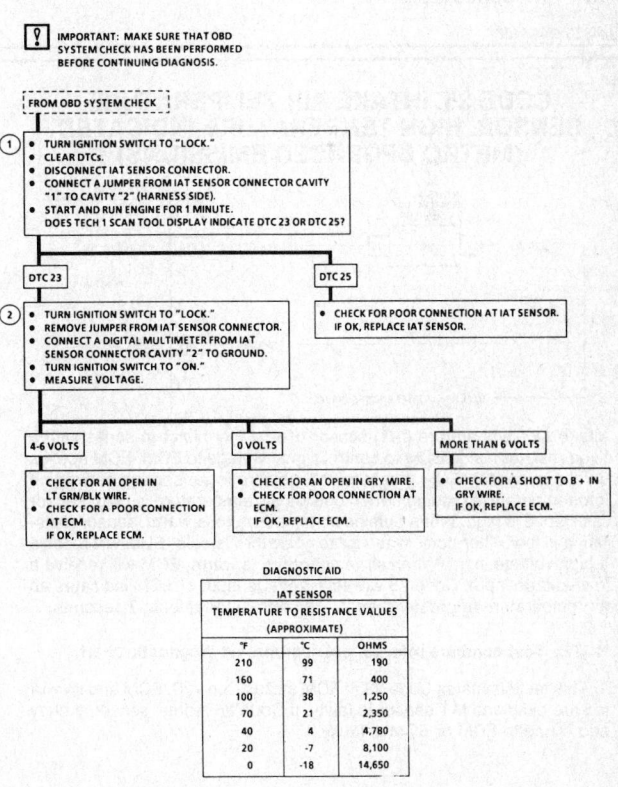

IAT SENSOR TEMPERATURE TO RESISTANCE VALUES (APPROXIMATE)		
°F	°C	OHMS
210	99	190
160	71	400
100	38	1,250
70	21	2,350
40	4	4,780
20	-7	8,100
0	-18	14,650

"AFTER REPAIRS," CONFIRM "CLOSED LOOP" OPERATION, NO DTCs AND NO MALFUNCTION INDICATOR LAMP (MIL).

Courtesy of General Motors Corp.

CODE 24, VEHICLE SPEED SENSOR
(METRO UPGRADED EMISSIONS)

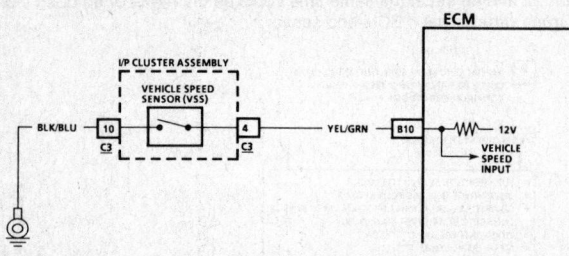

ECM supplies a B+ signal to Vehicle Speed Sensor (VSS). While vehicle is moving, a reed switch inside VSS will open and close, toggling B+ signal high and low. ECM then converts this toggled high/low voltage into a vehicle speed that is displayed as MPH/KPH. Code 24 will set if a constant voltage signal (high or low) is detected at ECM for at least 4 seconds, with engine running and vehicle moving.

NOTE: Test numbers refer to test numbers on diagnostic chart.

1) Checks if problem is intermittent.
2) If VSS is not receiving 12 volts from ECM, Code 24 will set. Checks for open in Yellow/Green wire or a faulty ECM.
3) Checks for a poor ground connection, an open in Black/Blue wire or a faulty VSS.

DIAGNOSTIC AIDS

If speedometer cable is binding, Code 24 can be set. Ensure that speedometer cable is free from restrictions and has a secure connection to instrument cluster. If problem is intermittent, refer to TROUBLE SHOOTING – NO CODES article.

94J44866 94A44867

IMPORTANT: MAKE SURE THAT OBD SYSTEM CHECK HAS BEEN PERFORMED AND CHECK THE SPEEDOMETER CABLE OPERATION BEFORE CONTINUING DIAGNOSIS.

FROM OBD SYSTEM CHECK

1. • RAISE AND SUITABLY SUPPORT VEHICLE DRIVE AXLES.
   • START AND RUN ENGINE IN GEAR.
   • TECH 1 SCAN TOOL SHOULD DISPLAY VEHICLE SPEED ABOVE 0 KPH/MPH. DOES IT?

NO

YES

2. • TURN IGNITION SWITCH TO "LOCK."
   • LOWER VEHICLE.
   • DISCONNECT I/P CLUSTER ASSEMBLY CONNECTOR C3.
   • CONNECT A DIGITAL MULTIMETER FROM CONNECTOR C3 TERMINAL "4" TO GROUND (HARNESS SIDE).
   • TURN IGNITION SWITCH TO "ON."
   • MEASURE VOLTAGE. SHOULD BE B+. IS IT?

PROBLEM IS INTERMITTENT. REFER TO "DIAGNOSTIC AIDS."

YES

NO

3. • CONNECT A TEST LIGHT FROM I/P CLUSTER ASSEMBLY CONNECTOR C3 TERMINAL "10" (HARNESS SIDE) TO B+. TEST LIGHT SHOULD LIGHT. DOES IT?

• CHECK FOR AN OPEN OR SHORT TO GROUND IN YEL/BLK WIRE.
• CHECK FOR POOR CONNECTION AT ECM. IF OK, REPLACE ECM.

YES

NO

• CHECK I/P CLUSTER PRINTED CIRCUIT FOR CRACKS OR BAD CONNECTIONS. IF OK, REPLACE SPEEDOMETER ASSEMBLY.

• CHECK FOR A CLEAN GROUND CONNECTION. IF OK, REPAIR OPEN IN BLK /BLU WIRE.

"AFTER REPAIRS," CONFIRM "CLOSED LOOP" OPERATION, NO DTCs AND NO MALFUNCTION INDICATOR LAMP (MIL).

Courtesy of General Motors Corp.

CODE 25, INTAKE AIR TEMPERATURE
SENSOR, HIGH TEMPERATURE INDICATED
(METRO UPGRADED EMISSIONS)

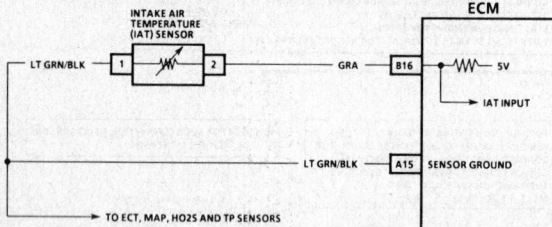

Intake Air Temperature (IAT) sensor uses a thermistor in series with a fixed resistor inside ECM to control signal voltage to ECM. ECM applies 5 volts to sensor. ECM monitors voltage across sensor and converts it into temperature reading. When outside air temperature is cold, sensor resistance is high. When outside air temperature is warm, sensor resistance is low. Therefore, when air temperature is cold, ECM will receive a high voltage input. When air temperature is warm, ECM will receive a low voltage input. Code 25 will set if voltage input at ECM indicates an air temperature of greater than 277°F (136°C) for at least 3 seconds.

NOTE: Test numbers refer to test numbers on diagnostic chart.

1) This test simulates Code 23. If ECM stores Code 23, ECM and its wiring are okay and IAT sensor is faulty. If Code 25 resets, sensor is okay and wiring to ECM or ECM is faulty.

94H44864 94B44868

DIAGNOSTIC AIDS

When replacing sensor, refer to TEMPERATURE TO RESISTANCE VALUES table at various temperature levels to evaluate the possibility of a "shifted" (mis-scaled) sensor. A "shifted" sensor could result in poor driveability complaints.

IMPORTANT: MAKE SURE THAT OBD SYSTEM CHECK HAS BEEN PERFORMED BEFORE CONTINUING DIAGNOSIS.

FROM OBD SYSTEM CHECK

1. • TURN IGNITION SWITCH TO "LOCK."
   • CLEAR DTCs.
   • DISCONNECT IAT SENSOR CONNECTOR.
   • START AND RUN ENGINE FOR 1 MINUTE. DOES TECH 1 SCAN TOOL INDICATE DTC 23 OR DTC 25?

DTC 23

DTC 25

• REPLACE IAT SENSOR.

• CHECK FOR SHORT TO GROUND IN GRY WIRE. IF OK, REPLACE ECM.

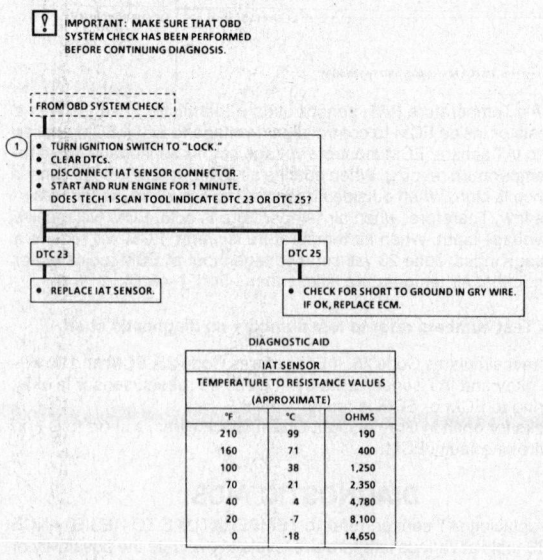

DIAGNOSTIC AID

IAT SENSOR		
TEMPERATURE TO RESISTANCE VALUES		
(APPROXIMATE)		
°F	°C	OHMS
210	99	190
160	71	400
100	38	1,250
70	21	2,350
40	4	4,780
20	-7	8,100
0	-18	14,650

"AFTER REPAIRS," CONFIRM "CLOSED LOOP" OPERATION, NO DTCs AND NO MALFUNCTION INDICATOR LAMP (MIL).

Courtesy of General Motors Corp.

CODE 31, MANIFOLD ABSOLUTE PRESSURE SENSOR, LOW VOLTAGE – LOW VACUUM (METRO UPGRADED EMISSIONS)

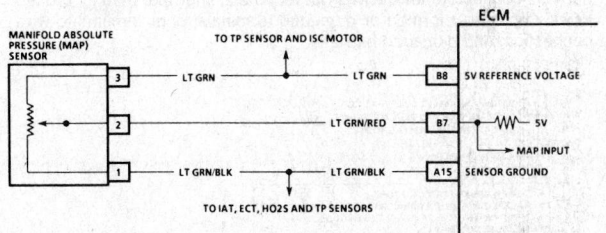

MAP sensor responds to changes in intake manifold pressure (vacuum). ECM applies 5 volts to MAP sensor. Changes in pressure, resulting from engine load and RPM, are converted into voltage input monitored by ECM. A low voltage reading at ECM indicates low manifold pressure and a high voltage at ECM indicates high manifold pressure. Code 31 will set when low voltage input at ECM indicates intake manifold pressure less than –27 mm Hg. of vacuum for at least .2 second.

NOTE: Test numbers refer to test numbers on diagnostic chart.

1) Checks if ECM is providing a 5-volt reference.
2) Checks for bias voltage to MAP sensor which has a value between 4.5 and 4.9 volts.

94C44869 94F44870

DIAGNOSTIC AIDS

Check for blocked or pinched vacuum hose to MAP sensor. An intermittent condition may be caused by a poor connection, rubbed-through wire insulation, or a broken wire inside insulation. Check ECM harness connectors for backed-out terminals, improper mating, broken locks, improperly formed or damaged terminals, poor terminal-to-wire connection, and damaged harness.

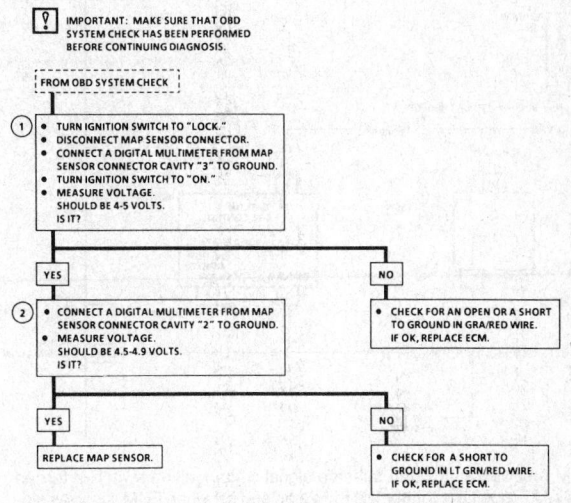

"AFTER REPAIRS," CONFIRM "CLOSED LOOP" OPERATION, NO DTCs AND NO MALFUNCTION INDICATOR LAMP (MIL).

Courtesy of General Motors Corp.

CODE 32, MANIFOLD ABSOLUTE PRESSURE SENSOR, HIGH VOLTAGE – HIGH VACUUM (METRO UPGRADED EMISSIONS)

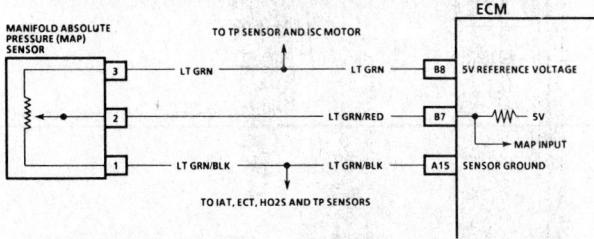

MAP sensor responds to changes in intake manifold pressure (vacuum). ECM applies 5 volts to MAP sensor. Changes in pressure, resulting from engine load and RPM, are converted into voltage input monitored by ECM. A low voltage reading at ECM indicates low manifold pressure and a high voltage at ECM indicates high manifold pressure. Code 32 will set when high voltage input at ECM indicates intake manifold pressure greater than 974 mm Hg. of vacuum for at least .2 second.

NOTE: Test numbers refer to test numbers on diagnostic chart.

1) Checks for open or short to voltage in Light Green/Red wire or a faulty ECM. Under normal conditions Light Green/Red wire should have an available voltage of less than 5 volts. A short to 5 volts or B+ will set Code 32.
2) Checks for open in Light Green/Black wire, poor connection at MAP sensor or ECM, and a faulty MAP sensor or ECM.

94C44869 94G44871

DIAGNOSTIC AIDS

Check for leaking vacuum hose to MAP sensor. An intermittent condition may be caused by a poor connection, rubbed-through wire insulation, or a broken wire inside insulation. Check ECM harness connectors for backed-out terminals, improper mating, broken locks, improperly formed or damaged terminals, poor terminal-to-wire connection, and damaged harness.

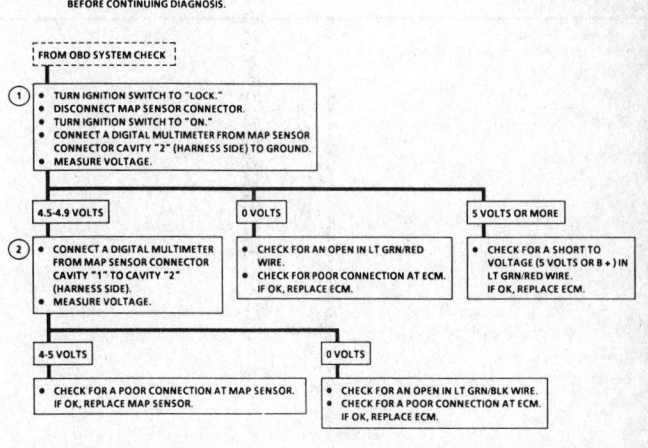

"AFTER REPAIRS," CONFIRM "CLOSED LOOP" OPERATION, NO DTCs AND NO MALFUNCTION INDICATOR LAMP (MIL).

Courtesy of General Motors Corp.

CODE 41, NO IGNITION SIGNAL, (1 OF 2) (METRO UPGRADED EMISSIONS)

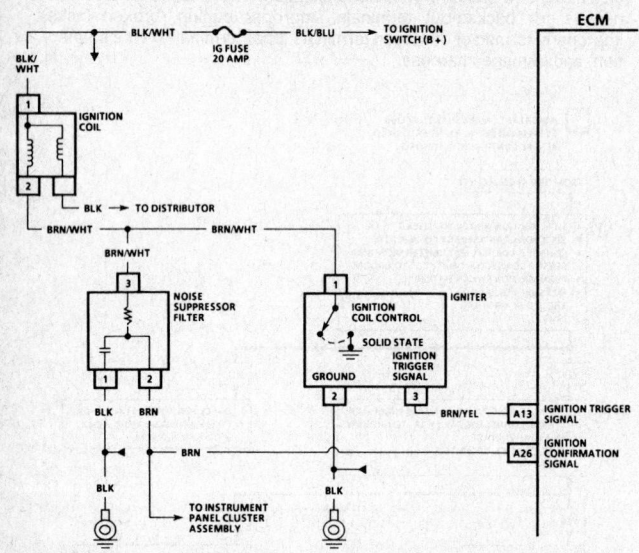

ECM receives an ignition fail-safe signal when ignition switch is turned to START position. Igniter will toggle on and off when ECM receives signal. As igniter is toggled on and off, so is the primary windings if the ignition coil, thus inducing a voltage into secondary windings of ignition coil. This induced voltage is then used to fire spark plugs. Code 41 will set if toggled ignition fail-safe signal is not present at ECM within 3 seconds of cranking.

NOTE: Test numbers refer to test numbers on diagnostic chart.

1) Checks for power at ignition coil.
2) Checks for open or short circuit to ground in wires between ignition coil, noise suppressor filter and igniter, or a faulty ignition coil.
3) Checks for faulty noise suppressor filter.
4) Checks for faulty noise suppressor filter.
5) Checks for open or short circuit to ground in Brown/White or Brown wires.

DIAGNOSTIC AIDS

An intermittent condition may be caused by a poor connection, rubbed-through wire insulation, or a broken wire inside insulation. Check ECM harness connectors for backed-out terminals, improper mating, broken locks, improperly formed or damaged terminals, poor terminal-to-wire connection, and damaged harness.

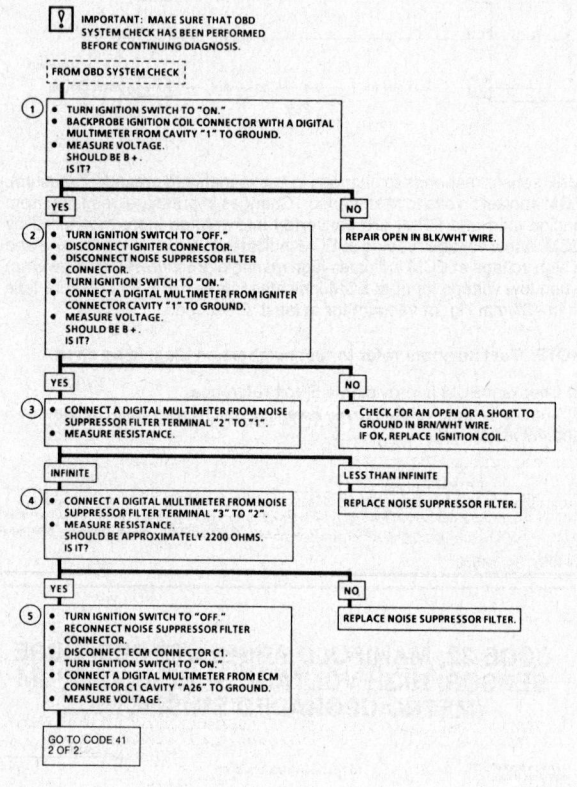

94I44872 94I44873

Courtesy of General Motors Corp.

CODE 41, NO IGNITION SIGNAL,
(2 OF 2)
(METRO UPGRADED EMISSIONS)

NOTE: Test numbers refer to test numbers on diagnostic chart.

6) Checks for open in Black wire.
7) Checks for faulty Brown/Yellow wire, igniter or ECM.

DIAGNOSTIC AIDS

An intermittent condition may be caused by a poor connection, rubbed-through wire insulation, or a broken wire inside insulation. Check ECM harness connectors for backed-out terminals, improper mating, broken locks, improperly formed or damaged terminals, poor terminal-to-wire connection, and damaged harness.

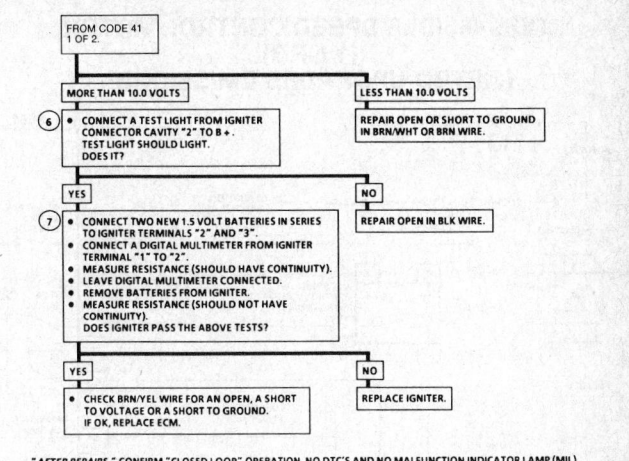

FROM CODE 41
1 OF 2.

| MORE THAN 10.0 VOLTS | | LESS THAN 10.0 VOLTS |

6) • CONNECT A TEST LIGHT FROM IGNITER CONNECTOR CAVITY "2" TO B + . TEST LIGHT SHOULD LIGHT. DOES IT?

REPAIR OPEN OR SHORT TO GROUND IN BRN/WHT OR BRN WIRE.

YES / NO

7) • CONNECT TWO NEW 1.5 VOLT BATTERIES IN SERIES TO IGNITER TERMINALS "2" AND "3".
• CONNECT A DIGITAL MULTIMETER FROM IGNITER TERMINAL "1" TO "2".
• MEASURE RESISTANCE (SHOULD HAVE CONTINUITY).
• LEAVE DIGITAL MULTIMETER CONNECTED.
• REMOVE BATTERIES FROM IGNITER.
• MEASURE RESISTANCE (SHOULD NOT HAVE CONTINUITY).
DOES IGNITER PASS THE ABOVE TESTS?

REPAIR OPEN IN BLK WIRE.

YES / NO

• CHECK BRN/YEL WIRE FOR AN OPEN, A SHORT TO VOLTAGE OR A SHORT TO GROUND. IF OK, REPLACE ECM.

REPLACE IGNITER.

"AFTER REPAIRS," CONFIRM "CLOSED LOOP" OPERATION, NO DTC'S AND NO MALFUNCTION INDICATOR LAMP (MIL).

94J44874

Courtesy of General Motors Corp.

CODE 42, CAMSHAFT POSITION SENSOR,
NO SIGNAL FOR 2 SECONDS
(METRO UPGRADED EMISSIONS)

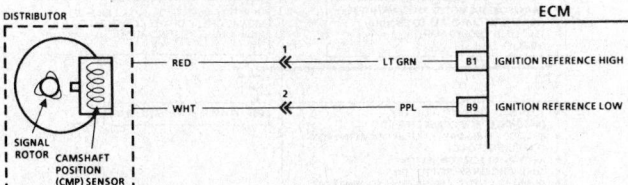

DISTRIBUTOR

ECM

RED —— 1 —— LT GRN — B1 — IGNITION REFERENCE HIGH

WHT —— 2 —— PPL — B9 — IGNITION REFERENCE LOW

SIGNAL ROTOR   CAMSHAFT POSITION (CMP) SENSOR

When distributor shaft rotates, a fluctuating magnetic field is generated due to changes in air gap between Camshaft Position (CMP) sensor and distributor shaft signal rotor. As a result, a small AC voltage is induced in CMP sensor. This ignition reference signal is sent to ECM on ECM terminals B1 and B9. ECM monitors AC voltage between these terminals. ECM uses this signal in determining when to fire ignition coil and fuel injector. Code 42 will set when ignition reference signal is not present at ECM for 2 seconds while engine is cranking.

NOTE: Test numbers refer to test numbers on diagnostic chart.

1) Checks Camshaft Position (CMP) sensor resistance.
2) Checks for a proper AC signal voltage being produced. When distributor shaft turns, CMP sensor acts as an AC voltage signal generator.
3) Checks if proper AC signal voltage is getting through to ECM.

DIAGNOSTIC AIDS

A loose or damaged CMP sensor could cause an intermittent code. A misaligned CMP sensor or improper air gap could also set a Code 42 or an intermittent "engine cranks but won't run" condition. For sensor specifications, refer to SYSTEM & COMPONENT TESTING article.

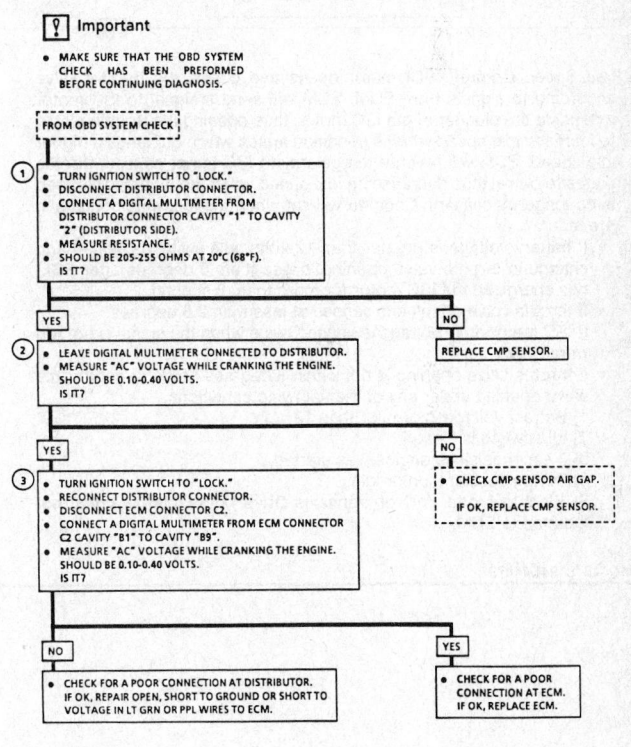

Important

• MAKE SURE THAT THE OBD SYSTEM CHECK HAS BEEN PREFORMED BEFORE CONTINUING DIAGNOSIS.

FROM OBD SYSTEM CHECK

1) • TURN IGNITION SWITCH TO "LOCK."
• DISCONNECT DISTRIBUTOR CONNECTOR.
• CONNECT A DIGITAL MULTIMETER FROM DISTRIBUTOR CONNECTOR CAVITY "1" TO CAVITY "2" (DISTRIBUTOR SIDE).
• MEASURE RESISTANCE.
• SHOULD BE 205-255 OHMS AT 20°C (68°F). IS IT?

YES / NO

REPLACE CMP SENSOR.

2) • LEAVE DIGITAL MULTIMETER CONNECTED TO DISTRIBUTOR.
• MEASURE "AC" VOLTAGE WHILE CRANKING THE ENGINE. SHOULD BE 0.10-0.40 VOLTS. IS IT?

YES / NO

• CHECK CMP SENSOR AIR GAP.
IF OK, REPLACE CMP SENSOR.

3) • TURN IGNITION SWITCH TO "LOCK."
• RECONNECT DISTRIBUTOR CONNECTOR.
• DISCONNECT ECM CONNECTOR C2.
• CONNECT A DIGITAL MULTIMETER FROM ECM CONNECTOR C2 CAVITY "B1" TO CAVITY "B9".
• MEASURE "AC" VOLTAGE WHILE CRANKING THE ENGINE. SHOULD BE 0.10-0.40 VOLTS. IS IT?

NO / YES

• CHECK FOR A POOR CONNECTION AT DISTRIBUTOR. IF OK, REPAIR OPEN, SHORT TO GROUND OR SHORT TO VOLTAGE IN LT GRN OR PPL WIRES TO ECM.

• CHECK FOR A POOR CONNECTION AT ECM. IF OK, REPLACE ECM.

94A44875 94C44877

Courtesy of General Motors Corp.

CODE 46, IDLE SPEED CONTROL MOTOR, (1 OF 3) (METRO UPGRADED EMISSIONS)

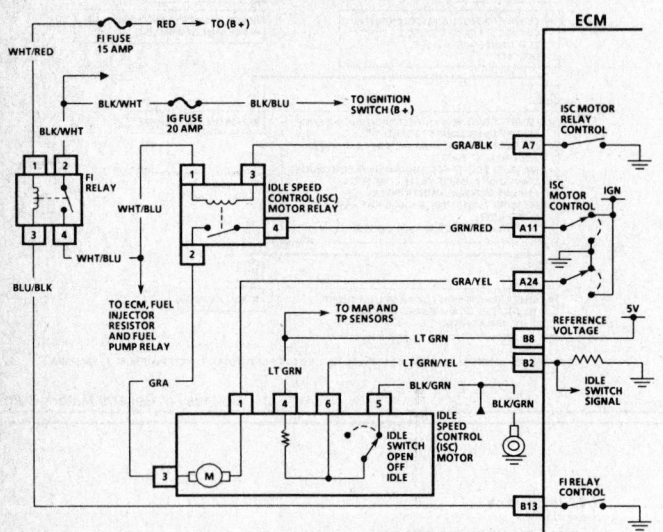

Idle Speed Control (ISC) motor opens and closes the throttle valve according to signals from ECM. ECM will send a signal to ISC motor extending the plunger of the ISC motor, thus opening the throttle plates to increase idle speed when a condition arises which demands a higher idle speed. ECM will reverse the polarity to ISC motor causing throttle plates to close, thus decreaseing idle speed when the higher idle speed is no longer necessary. Code 46 will set when the following conditions are met.

- If battery voltage is greater than 12 volts, idle switch is closed and change in throttle valve opening is less than .3 degrees after ECM has energized the ISC motor for more than .8 second.
- If throttle valve opening is sensed at less than 2.5 degrees.
- If ISC motor drive voltage is sensed twice when the signal is not fed from ECM.
- If throttle valve opening is not within 3 degrees of the target throttle valve opening under any of the following conditions.
  1) Battery voltage is greater than 12 volts.
  2) Idle switch is closed.
  3) 3 seconds since engine was started.
  4) During deceleration or idle.
  5) Electrical load, A/C or transaxle Drive range idle-up signal not inputted to ECM.

94D44878 94E44879

NOTE: Test numbers refer to test numbers on diagnostic chart.

1) Checks electrical load idle-up circuit.
2) Checks for open in White/Blue wire.
3) Checks for open in Gray/Black wire or for faulty ISC motor relay.
4) Checks for open, short to ground or short to voltage in Green/Red, Gray or Gray/Yellow wires, or for faulty ISC motor.

DIAGNOSTIC AIDS

An intermittent condition may be caused by a poor connection, rubbed-through wire insulation, or a broken wire inside insulation. Check ECM harness connectors for backed-out terminals, improper mating, broken locks, improperly formed or damaged terminals, poor terminal-to-wire connection, and damaged harness. Codes 21, 22 and 46 set at the same time could be the result of an open Light Green wire.

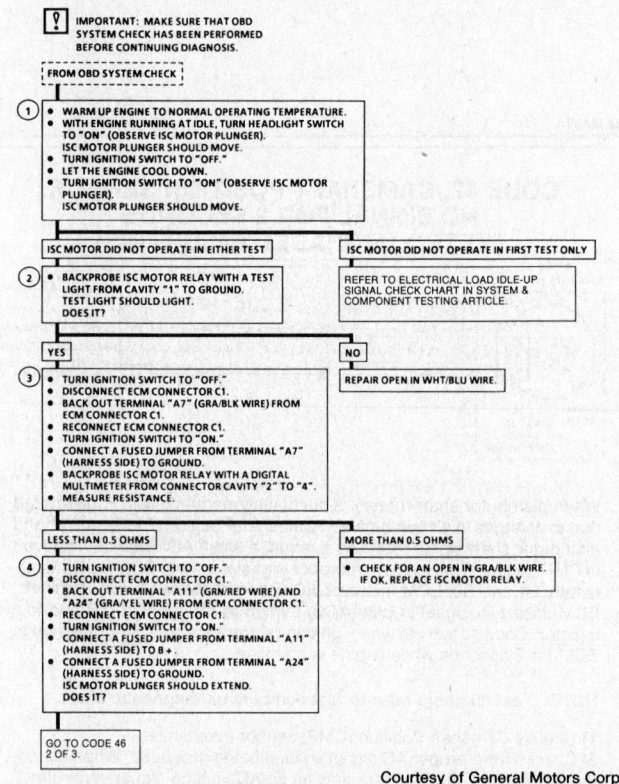

CODE 46, IDLE SPEED CONTROL MOTOR
(2 OF 3)
(METRO UPGRADED EMISSIONS)

NOTE: Test numbers refer to test numbers on diagnostic chart.

5) Checks for open, short to ground or short to voltage in Green/Red, Gray or Gray/Yellow wires, or for faulty ISC motor.
6) Checks for open in Black/Green wire.
7) Checks for open, short to ground or short to voltage in Light Green wire, or for faulty ECM.

DIAGNOSTIC AIDS

An intermittent condition may be caused by a poor connection, rubbed-through wire insulation, or a broken wire inside insulation. Check ECM harness connectors for backed-out terminals, improper mating, broken locks, improperly formed or damaged terminals, poor terminal-to-wire connection, and damaged harness. Codes 21, 22 and 46 set at the same time could be the result of an open Light Green wire.

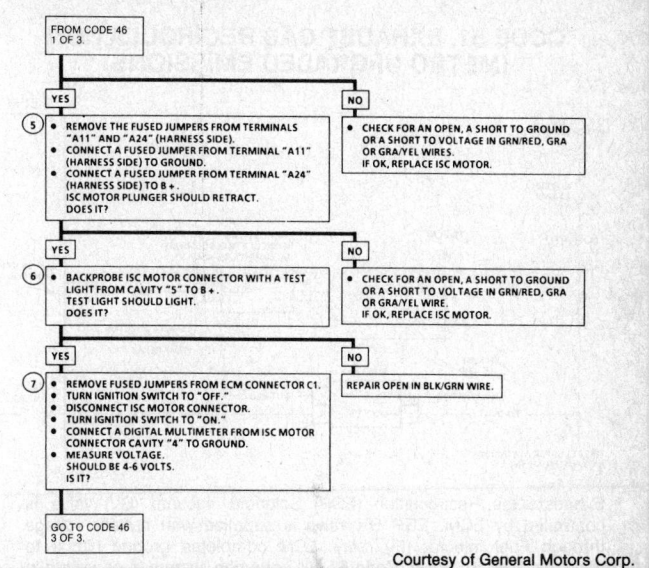

94H44880

Courtesy of General Motors Corp.

CODE 46, IDLE SPEED CONTROL MOTOR
(3 OF 3)
(METRO UPGRADED EMISSIONS)

NOTE: Test numbers refer to test numbers on diagnostic chart.

8) Checks for short to voltage in Light Green/Yellow wire, or for faulty ISC motor.
9) Checks for open, short to ground or short to voltage in Light Green/Yellow wire, or faulty ISC motor or ECM.

DIAGNOSTIC AIDS

An intermittent condition may be caused by a poor connection, rubbed-through wire insulation, or a broken wire inside insulation. Check ECM harness connectors for backed-out terminals, improper mating, broken locks, improperly formed or damaged terminals, poor terminal-to-wire connection, and damaged harness. Codes 21, 22 and 46 set at the same time could be the result of an open Light Green wire.

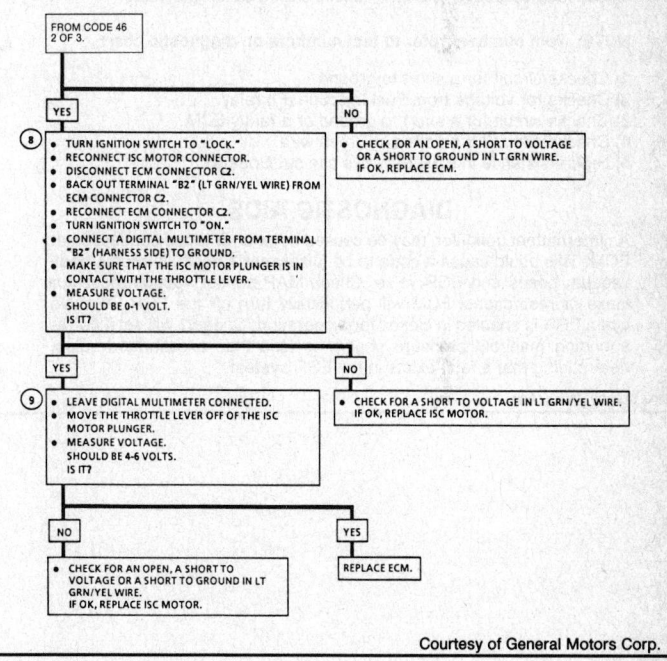

94I44881

Courtesy of General Motors Corp.

CODE 51, EXHAUST GAS RECIRCULATION (METRO UPGRADED EMISSIONS)

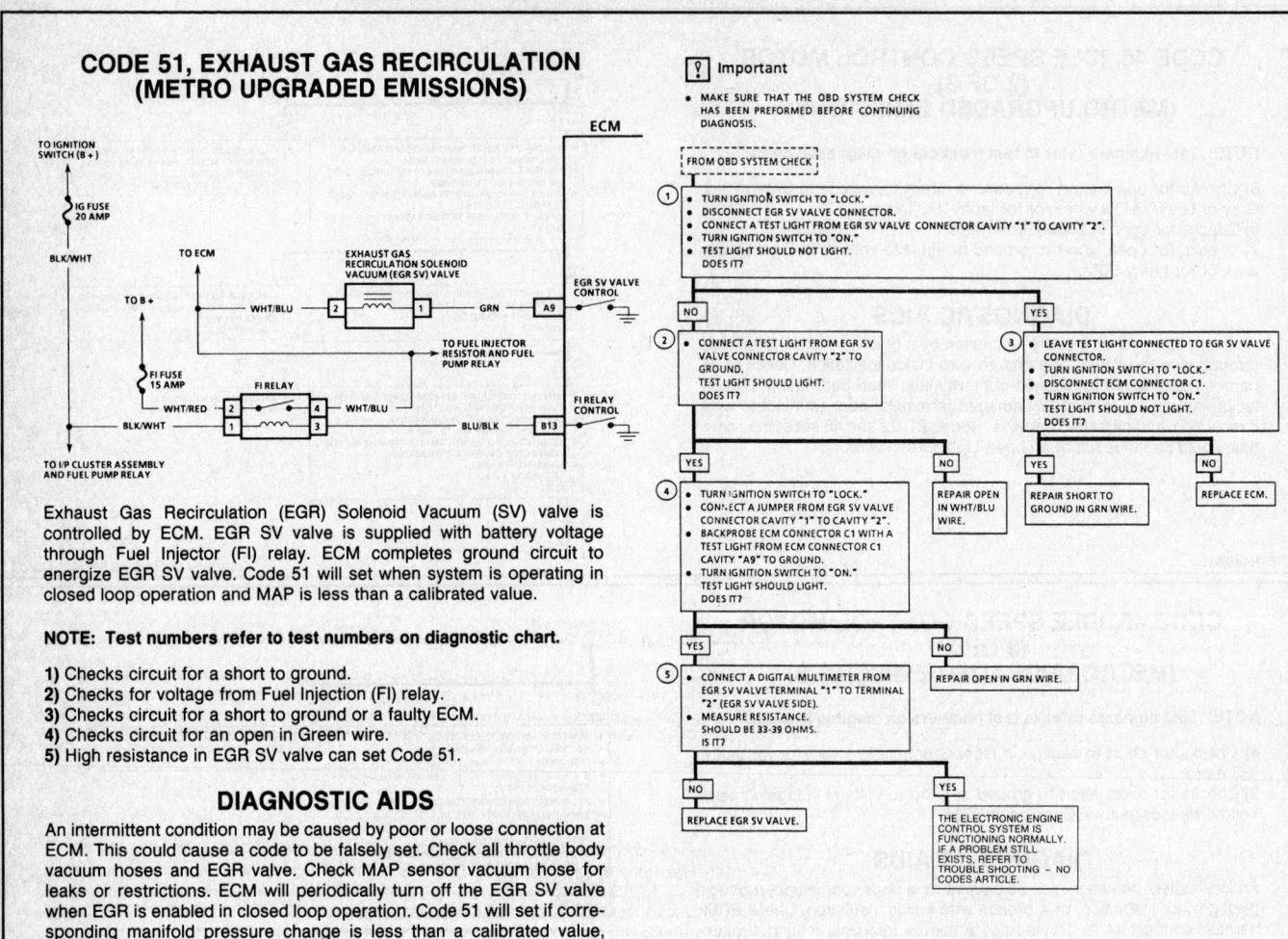

Exhaust Gas Recirculation (EGR) Solenoid Vacuum (SV) valve is controlled by ECM. EGR SV valve is supplied with battery voltage through Fuel Injector (FI) relay. ECM completes ground circuit to energize EGR SV valve. Code 51 will set when system is operating in closed loop operation and MAP is less than a calibrated value.

NOTE: Test numbers refer to test numbers on diagnostic chart.

1) Checks circuit for a short to ground.
2) Checks for voltage from Fuel Injection (FI) relay.
3) Checks circuit for a short to ground or a faulty ECM.
4) Checks circuit for an open in Green wire.
5) High resistance in EGR SV valve can set Code 51.

DIAGNOSTIC AIDS

An intermittent condition may be caused by poor or loose connection at ECM. This could cause a code to be falsely set. Check all throttle body vacuum hoses and EGR valve. Check MAP sensor vacuum hose for leaks or restrictions. ECM will periodically turn off the EGR SV valve when EGR is enabled in closed loop operation. Code 51 will set if corresponding manifold pressure change is less than a calibrated value, determining that a fault exists in the EGR system.

94J44882 94A44883

Courtesy of General Motors Corp.

PRIZM (VIN 6) CODE CHARTS

ON-BOARD DIAGNOSTIC (OBD) SYSTEM CHECK (1 OF 2) (PRIZM)

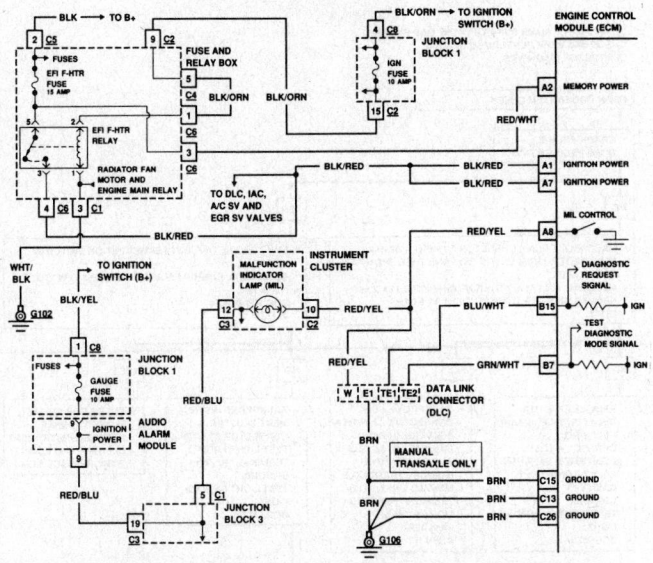

On-board diagnostic system check is an organized approach in identifying a problem created by an electronic engine system malfunction. It must be the starting point for any driveability complaint diagnosis, because it directs the service technician to the next logical step in diagnosing a complaint. Understanding the chart and using it correctly will reduce diagnostic time and prevent unnecessary replacement of good parts.

NOTE: Test numbers refer to test numbers on diagnostic chart.

1) Checks Malfunction Indicator Light (MIL) operation with ignition switch in ON position.
2) Checks if ECM's normal diagnostic mode is operating.
3) Checks if ECM's test diagnostic mode is operating.
4) Checks if engine will start.

93J78377 94C44455

5) Checks for any codes that are stored in ECM's memory with engine running.
6) Checks for any codes that are stored in ECM's memory with engine off. If no other codes than Code 42 are set and engine won't start, go to appropriate CHART A1-3 in BASIC DIAGNOSTIC PROCEDURES article.

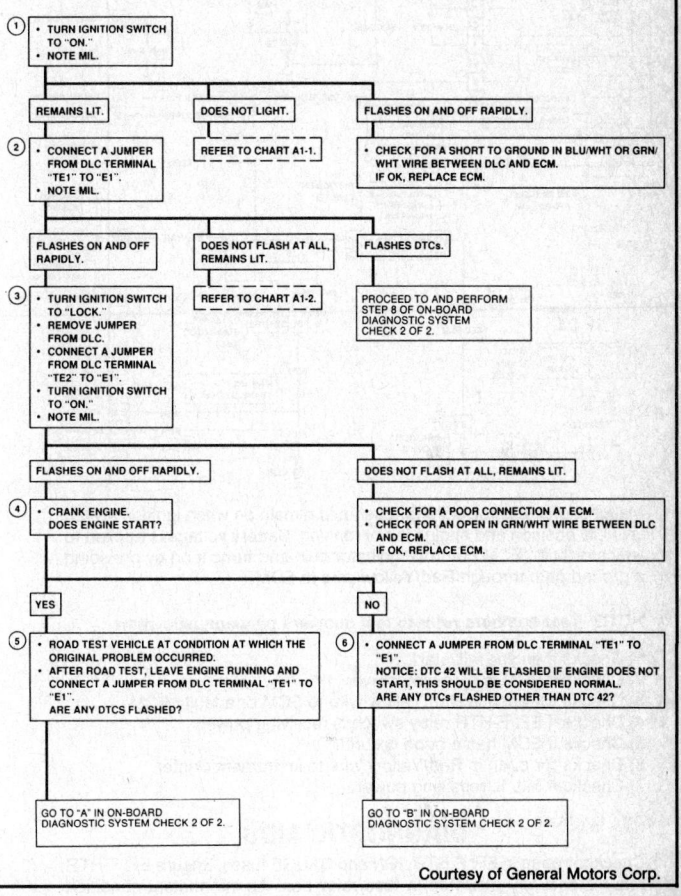

ON-BOARD DIAGNOSTIC (OBD) SYSTEM CHECK (2 OF 2) (PRIZM)

NOTE: Test numbers refer to test numbers on diagnostic chart.

7) Checks if Code 51 (Switch Condition Signal) is functioning.
8) This step checks if code(s) are intermittent problems.

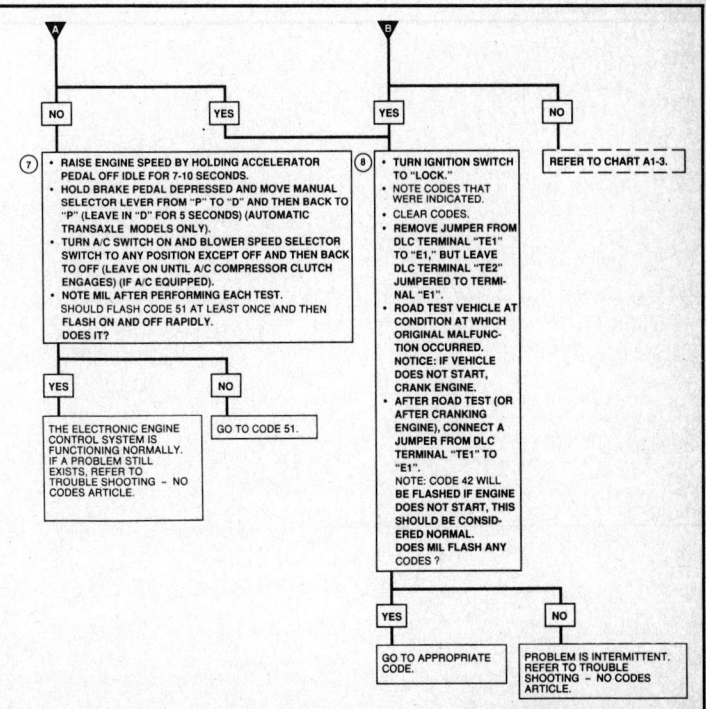

93A78808

**CHART A1-1, NO MALFUNCTION INDICATOR LIGHT (1 OF 2)
(PRIZM)**

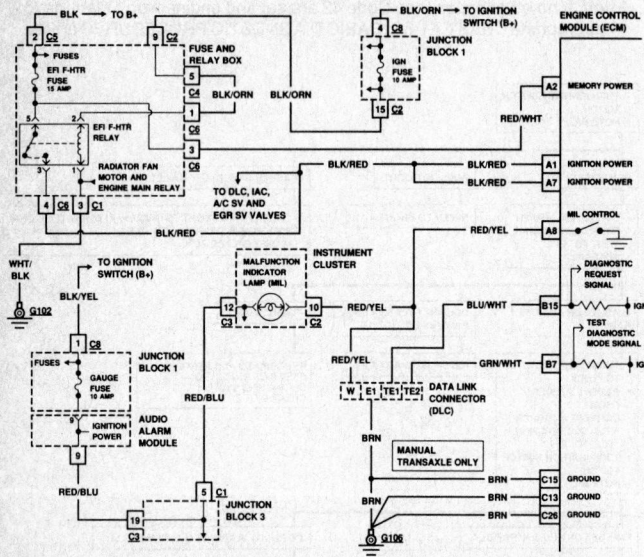

may be caused by poor connection, rubbed-through insulation, or a broken wire inside insulation. Check ECM harness connectors for backed-out terminals, improper mating, broken locks, improperly formed or damaged terminals, and poor terminal-to-wire connections before component replacement.

Malfunction Indicator Light (MIL) should remain on when ignition switch is in ON position and engine is not running. Battery voltage is applied to indicator bulb. ECM controls indicator bulb and turns it on by providing a ground path through Red/Yellow wire to ECM.

NOTE: Test numbers refer to test numbers on diagnostic chart.

1) Checks if engine will start.
2) Checks if ECM is receiving power.
3) Checks for open in Red/Yellow wire to ECM or a faulty ECM.
4) Checks if EFI F-HTR relay switch is receiving power.
5) Checks if ECM has a good ground.
6) Checks for open in Red/Yellow wire to instrument cluster.
7) Checks if MIL is receiving power.

DIAGNOSTIC AIDS

Check for open in EFI F-HTR, IGN and GAUGE fuses. Ensure EFI F-HTR relay is securely mounted in fuse/relay box. An intermittent condition

93J78377 94D44456

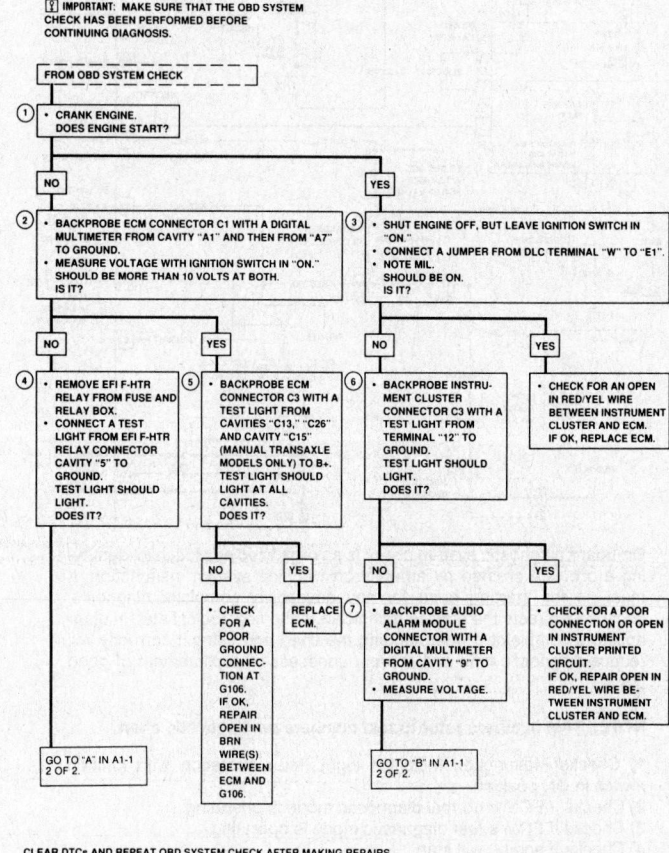

CLEAR DTCs AND REPEAT OBD SYSTEM CHECK AFTER MAKING REPAIRS.

Courtesy of General Motors Corp.

CHART A1-1, NO MALFUNCTION INDICATOR LIGHT (2 OF 2) (PRIZM)

NOTE: Test numbers refer to test numbers on diagnostic chart.

8) Checks if EFI F-HTR relay coil is receiving power.
9) Checks for open in EFI F-HTR ground wire.
10) Checks for open in Black/Orange wire between junction block No. 1 and fuse/relay box or a faulty junction block No. 1.

DIAGNOSTIC AIDS

Check for open in EFI F-HTR, IGN and GAUGE fuses. Ensure EFI F-HTR relay is securely mounted in fuse/relay box. An intermittent condition may be caused by poor connection, rubbed-through insulation, or a broken wire inside insulation. Check ECM harness connectors for backed-out terminals, improper mating, broken locks, improperly formed or damaged terminals, and poor terminal-to-wire connections before component replacement.

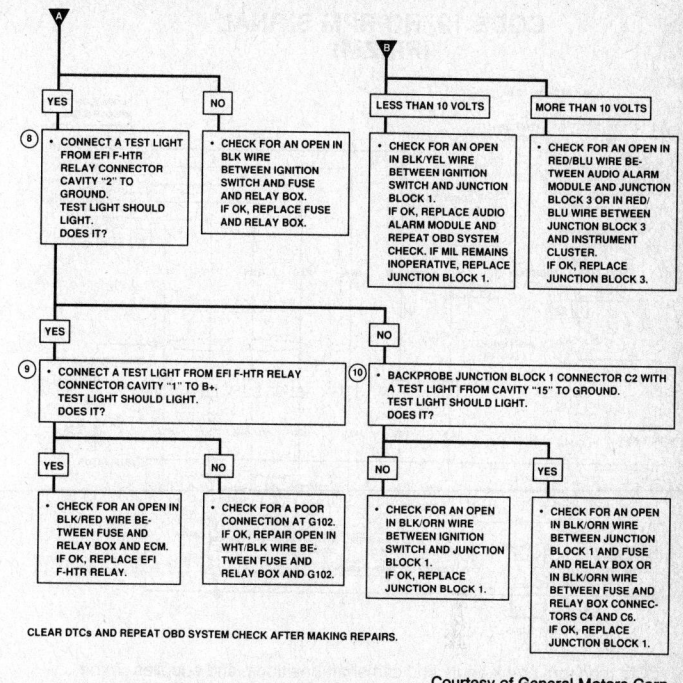

CLEAR DTCs AND REPEAT OBD SYSTEM CHECK AFTER MAKING REPAIRS.

94E44457

Courtesy of General Motors Corp.

CHART A1-2, MALFUNCTION INDICATOR LIGHT WON'T FLASH ANY CODES, OR ON STEADY (PRIZM)

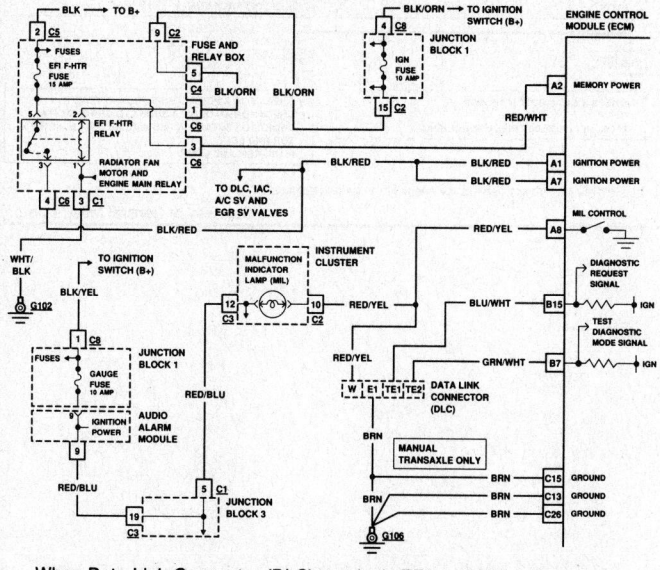

When Data Link Connector (DLC) terminals TE1 and E1 are jumpered, Malfunction Indicator Light (MIL) will flash codes that are in ECM's memory.

NOTE: Test numbers refer to test numbers on diagnostic chart.

1) Checks for short to ground in Red/Yellow wire.
2) Checks for open in Blue/White wire (diagnostic request terminal).
3) Checks for open in Brown ground wire to DLC or a faulty ECM.

93J78377 94F44458

DIAGNOSTIC AIDS

An intermittent condition may be caused by poor connection, rubbed-through insulation, or a broken wire inside insulation. Check ECM harness connectors for backed-out terminals, improper mating, broken locks, improperly formed or damaged terminals, and poor terminal-to-wire connections before component replacement.

IMPORTANT: MAKE SURE THAT THE OBD SYSTEM CHECK HAS BEEN PERFORMED BEFORE CONTINUING DIAGNOSIS.

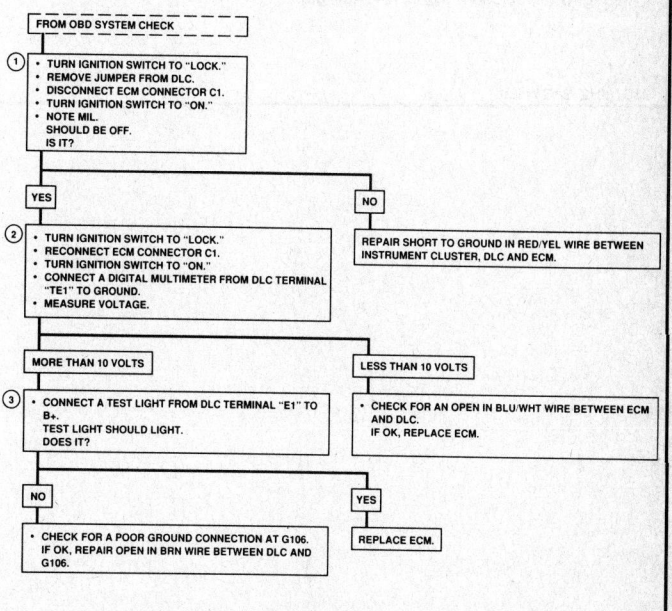

CLEAR DTCs AND REPEAT OBD SYSTEM CHECK AFTER MAKING REPAIRS.

Courtesy of General Motors Corp.

CODE 12, NO RPM SIGNAL (PRIZM)

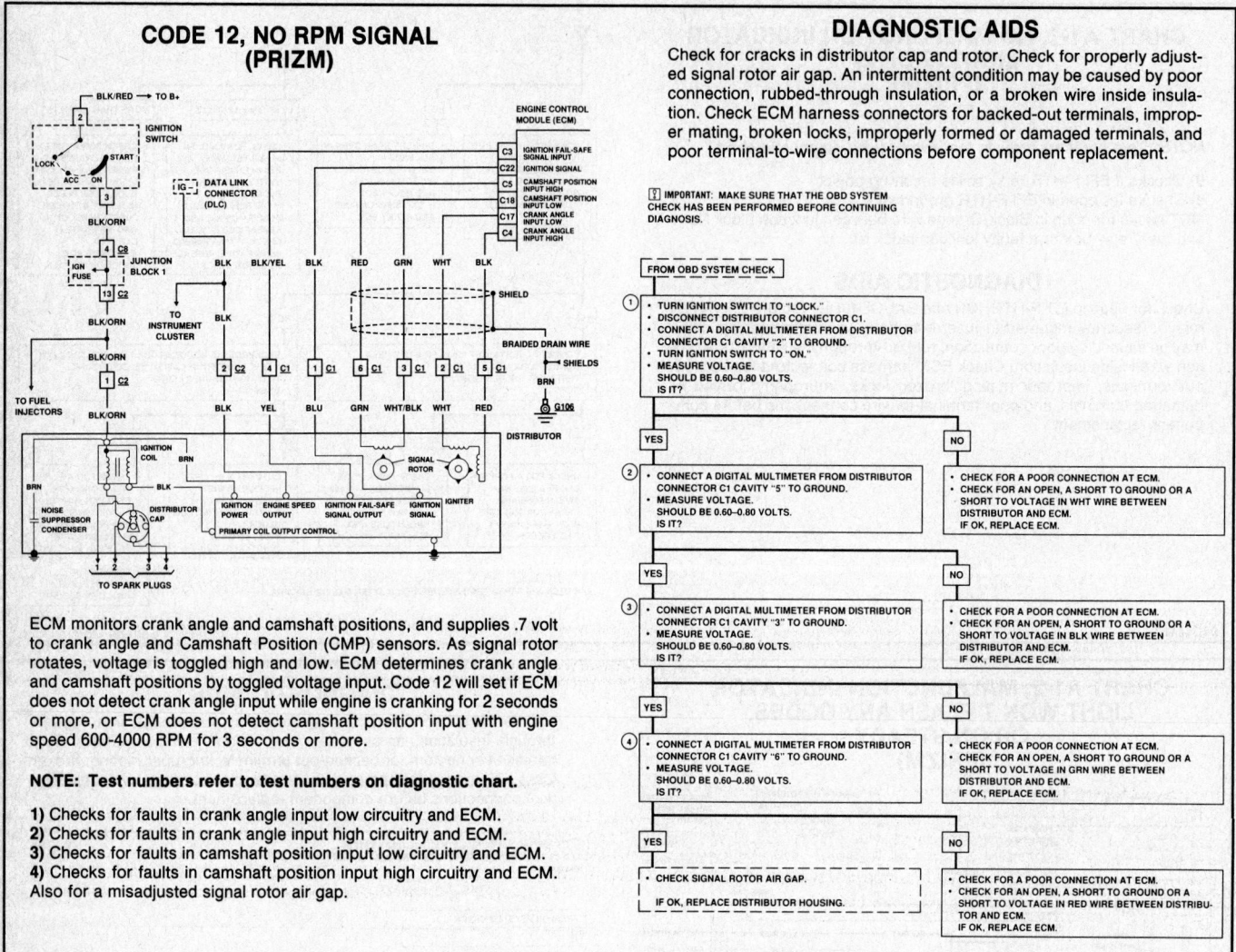

ECM monitors crank angle and camshaft positions, and supplies .7 volt to crank angle and Camshaft Position (CMP) sensors. As signal rotor rotates, voltage is toggled high and low. ECM determines crank angle and camshaft positions by toggled voltage input. Code 12 will set if ECM does not detect crank angle input while engine is cranking for 2 seconds or more, or ECM does not detect camshaft position input with engine speed 600-4000 RPM for 3 seconds or more.

NOTE: Test numbers refer to test numbers on diagnostic chart.

1) Checks for faults in crank angle input low circuitry and ECM.
2) Checks for faults in crank angle input high circuitry and ECM.
3) Checks for faults in camshaft position input low circuitry and ECM.
4) Checks for faults in camshaft position input high circuitry and ECM. Also for a misadjusted signal rotor air gap.

DIAGNOSTIC AIDS

Check for cracks in distributor cap and rotor. Check for properly adjusted signal rotor air gap. An intermittent condition may be caused by poor connection, rubbed-through insulation, or a broken wire inside insulation. Check ECM harness connectors for backed-out terminals, improper mating, broken locks, improperly formed or damaged terminals, and poor terminal-to-wire connections before component replacement.

IMPORTANT: MAKE SURE THAT THE OBD SYSTEM CHECK HAS BEEN PERFORMED BEFORE CONTINUING DIAGNOSIS.

FROM OBD SYSTEM CHECK

1) • TURN IGNITION SWITCH TO "LOCK."
   • DISCONNECT DISTRIBUTOR CONNECTOR C1.
   • CONNECT A DIGITAL MULTIMETER FROM DISTRIBUTOR CONNECTOR C1 CAVITY "2" TO GROUND.
   • TURN IGNITION SWITCH TO "ON."
   • MEASURE VOLTAGE.
   SHOULD BE 0.60–0.80 VOLTS.
   IS IT?

YES →
2) • CONNECT A DIGITAL MULTIMETER FROM DISTRIBUTOR CONNECTOR C1 CAVITY "5" TO GROUND.
   • MEASURE VOLTAGE.
   SHOULD BE 0.60–0.80 VOLTS.
   IS IT?

NO →
• CHECK FOR A POOR CONNECTION AT ECM.
• CHECK FOR AN OPEN, A SHORT TO GROUND OR A SHORT TO VOLTAGE IN WHT WIRE BETWEEN DISTRIBUTOR AND ECM.
IF OK, REPLACE ECM.

YES →
3) • CONNECT A DIGITAL MULTIMETER FROM DISTRIBUTOR CONNECTOR C1 CAVITY "3" TO GROUND.
   • MEASURE VOLTAGE.
   SHOULD BE 0.60–0.80 VOLTS.
   IS IT?

NO →
• CHECK FOR A POOR CONNECTION AT ECM.
• CHECK FOR AN OPEN, A SHORT TO GROUND OR A SHORT TO VOLTAGE IN BLK WIRE BETWEEN DISTRIBUTOR AND ECM.
IF OK, REPLACE ECM.

YES →
4) • CONNECT A DIGITAL MULTIMETER FROM DISTRIBUTOR CONNECTOR C1 CAVITY "6" TO GROUND.
   • MEASURE VOLTAGE.
   SHOULD BE 0.60–0.80 VOLTS.
   IS IT?

NO →
• CHECK FOR A POOR CONNECTION AT ECM.
• CHECK FOR AN OPEN, A SHORT TO GROUND OR A SHORT TO VOLTAGE IN GRN WIRE BETWEEN DISTRIBUTOR AND ECM.
IF OK, REPLACE ECM.

YES →
• CHECK SIGNAL ROTOR AIR GAP.
IF OK, REPLACE DISTRIBUTOR HOUSING.

NO →
• CHECK FOR A POOR CONNECTION AT ECM.
• CHECK FOR AN OPEN, A SHORT TO GROUND OR A SHORT TO VOLTAGE IN RED WIRE BETWEEN DISTRIBUTOR AND ECM.
IF OK, REPLACE ECM.

CLEAR DTCs AND REPEAT OBD SYSTEM CHECK AFTER MAKING REPAIRS.

93G78812 94G44459

Courtesy of General Motors Corp.

CODE 13, NO RPM SIGNAL (PRIZM)

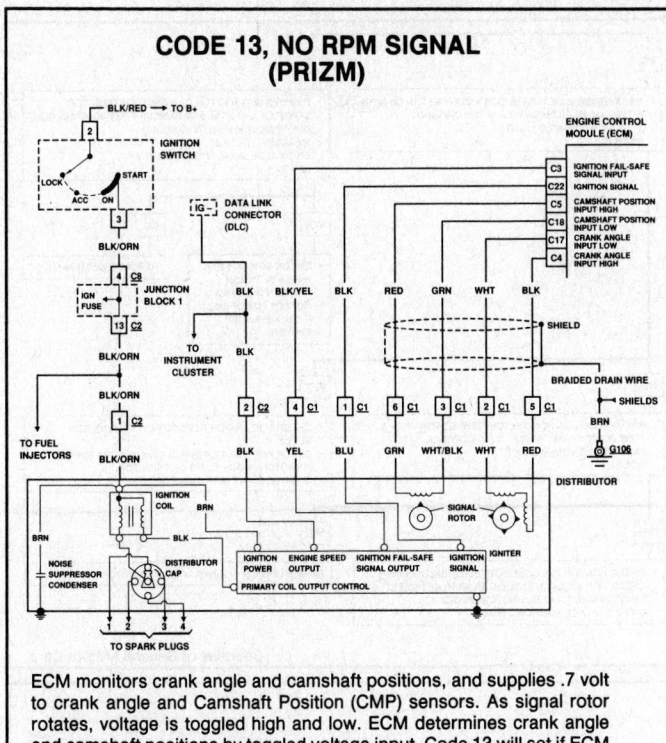

ECM monitors crank angle and camshaft positions, and supplies .7 volt to crank angle and Camshaft Position (CMP) sensors. As signal rotor rotates, voltage is toggled high and low. ECM determines crank angle and camshaft positions by toggled voltage input. Code 13 will set if ECM does not detect crank angle input with engine speed greater than 1500 RPM for .3 second or more.

NOTE: Test numbers refer to test numbers on diagnostic chart.

93G78812 94J44460

1) Checks for faults in crank angle input low circuitry and ECM.
2) Checks for faults in crank angle input high circuitry and ECM. Also for a misadjusted signal rotor air gap.

DIAGNOSTIC AIDS

Check for cracks in distributor cap and rotor. Check for properly adjusted signal rotor air gap. An intermittent condition may be caused by poor connection, rubbed-through insulation, or a broken wire inside insulation. Check ECM harness connectors for backed-out terminals, improper mating, broken locks, improperly formed or damaged terminals, and poor terminal-to-wire connections before component replacement.

☑ **IMPORTANT:** MAKE SURE THAT THE OBD SYSTEM CHECK HAS BEEN PERFORMED BEFORE CONTINUING DIAGNOSIS.

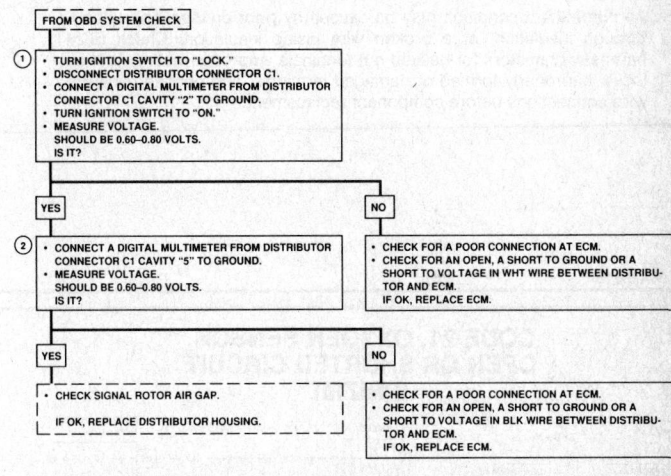

CLEAR DTCs AND REPEAT OBD SYSTEM CHECK AFTER MAKING REPAIRS.

Courtesy of General Motors Corp.

CODE 14, NO IGNITION SIGNAL, (1 OF 2) (PRIZM)

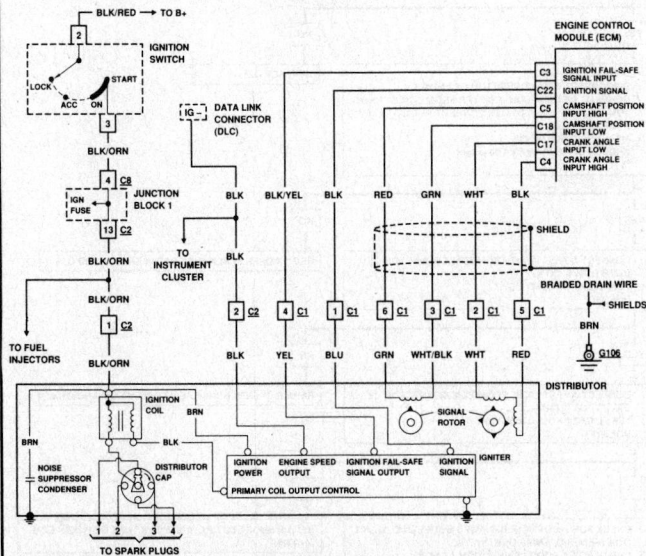

Igniter receives 5 volts from ECM. Igniter processes voltage then returns voltage to ECM as a ignition fail-safe signal. ECM also receives a .7 volt ignition signal when starter is being cranked. ECM uses these signals to pulse injectors. Code 14 will set if ignition fail-safe signal is not present 4 successive times during cranking.

NOTE: Test numbers refer to test numbers on diagnostic chart.

1) Checks for 5-volt signal from ECM.
2) Verifies .10-2 volt signal from ECM.
3) Checks for power to distributor.

93G78812 94A44461

DIAGNOSTIC AIDS

An intermittent condition may be caused by poor connection, rubbed-through insulation, or a broken wire inside insulation. Check ECM harness connectors for backed-out terminals, improper mating, broken locks, improperly formed or damaged terminals, and poor terminal-to-wire connections before component replacement.

☑ **IMPORTANT:** MAKE SURE THAT THE OBD SYSTEM CHECK HAS BEEN PERFORMED BEFORE CONTINUING DIAGNOSIS.

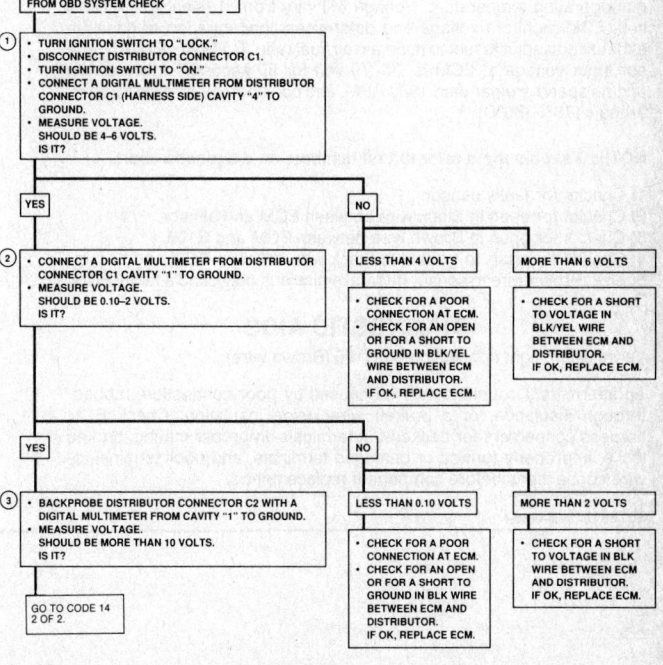

CLEAR DTCs AND REPEAT OBD SYSTEM CHECK AFTER MAKING REPAIRS.

Courtesy of General Motors Corp.

CODE 14, NO IGNITION SIGNAL, (2 OF 2) (PRIZM)

NOTE: Test numbers refer to test numbers on diagnostic chart.

4) Checks for open in Black/Orange wire between junction block No. 1 and distributor or a faulty junction block No. 1.
5) Checks for open in power feed to igniter, or a faulty ignition coil or igniter.
6) Checks for open in Red/Black or Black/Orange wires to ignition switch and a faulty ignition switch.

DIAGNOSTIC AIDS

An intermittent condition may be caused by poor connection, rubbed-through insulation, or a broken wire inside insulation. Check ECM harness connectors for backed-out terminals, improper mating, broken locks, improperly formed or damaged terminals, and poor terminal-to-wire connections before component replacement.

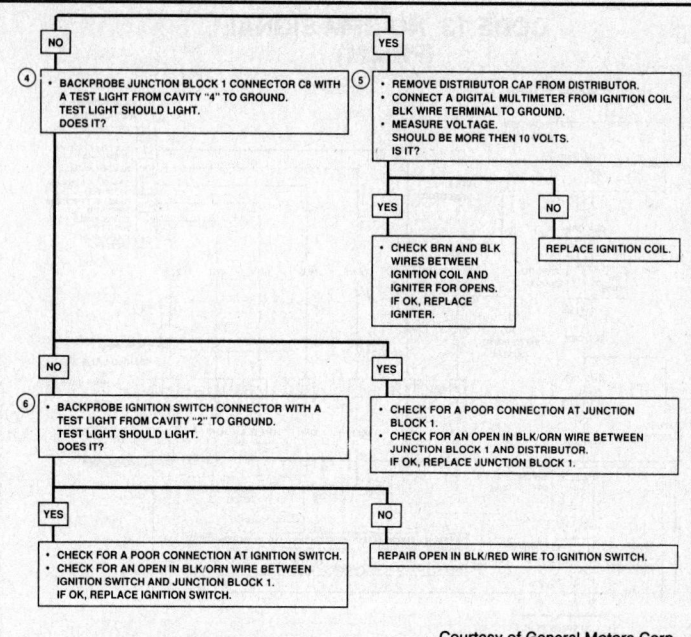

93A78816

Courtesy of General Motors Corp.

CODE 21, OXYGEN SENSOR, OPEN OR SHORTED CIRCUIT (PRIZM)

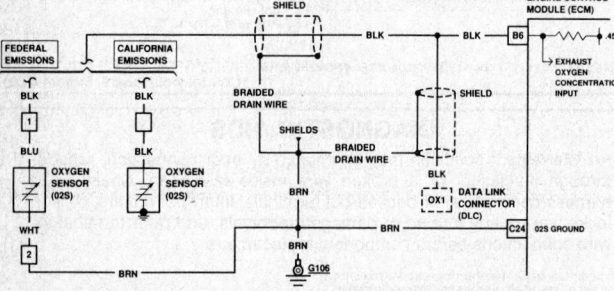

Oxygen (O_2) sensor produces a varying voltage as engine reaches normal operating temperature. Voltage will vary from .1 (lean) to 1.0 (rich) volt. ECM monitors voltage and determines concentration of gases in exhaust and adjusts fuel to maintain air/fuel ratio. Code 21 will set if sensor input voltage at ECM is .35-.70 volt for 60 seconds or more with engine speed greater than 1500 RPM, and coolant temperature is greater than 176°F (80°C).

NOTE: Test numbers refer to test numbers on diagnostic chart.

1) Checks for faulty sensor.
2) Checks for open in Black wire between ECM and sensor.
3) Checks for open in Brown wire between ECM and G106.
4) Checks for short to ground in Black wire between ECM and sensor, open in Brown wire to sensor (federal emissions only), and a faulty ECM.

DIAGNOSTIC AIDS

Verify clean, tight connection on G106 (Brown wire).

An intermittent condition may be caused by poor connection, rubbed-through insulation, or a broken wire inside insulation. Check ECM harness connectors for backed-out terminals, improper mating, broken locks, improperly formed or damaged terminals, and poor terminal-to-wire connections before component replacement.

IMPORTANT: MAKE SURE THAT THE OBD SYSTEM CHECK HAS BEEN PERFORMED BEFORE CONTINUING DIAGNOSIS.

```
FROM OBD SYSTEM CHECK

1) • DISCONNECT O2S CONNECTOR.
   • START AND RUN ENGINE AT 1,500 RPM FOR 1 MINUTE
     OR UNTIL NORMAL OPERATING TEMPERATURE IS
     ATTAINED.
   • CONNECT A DIGITAL MULTIMETER FROM O2S CONNEC-
     TOR TERMINAL "1" (O2S SIDE) TO GROUND.
   • MEASURE VOLTAGE.
     SHOULD BE BETWEEN 0.80 AND 0.95 VOLTS.
     IS IT?

   YES → 2)              NO → REPLACE O2S.

2) • SHUT ENGINE OFF.
   • DISCONNECT ECM CONNECTOR C2 AND C3.
   • CONNECT A DIGITAL MULTIMETER FROM ECM CONNEC-
     TOR C2 CAVITY "B6" TO O2S CONNECTOR CAVITY "1"
     (HARNESS SIDE).
   • MEASURE RESISTANCE.
     SHOULD BE LESS THAN 0.50 OHMS.
     IS IT?

   YES → 3)              NO → REPAIR OPEN IN BLK WIRE BETWEEN ECM AND O2S.

3) • CONNECT A TEST LIGHT FROM ECM CONNECTOR C3
     CAVITY "C24" TO B+.
     TEST LIGHT SHOULD LIGHT.
     DOES IT?

   YES → 4)              NO → REPAIR OPEN IN BRN WIRE BETWEEN ECM AND G106.

4) • CONNECT A TEST LIGHT FROM ECM CONNECTOR C2
     CAVITY "B6" TO B+.
     TEST LIGHT SHOULD NOT LIGHT.
     DOES IT?

   NO                    YES → REPAIR SHORT TO GROUND IN BLK WIRE BETWEEN ECM AND O2S.
   ↓
   • CHECK FOR AN OPEN IN BRN WIRE BETWEEN O2S AND
     G106 (FEDERAL EMISSIONS ONLY).
   • CHECK FOR A POOR CONNECTION AT ECM.
     IF OK, REPLACE ECM.
```

CLEAR DTCs AND REPEAT OBD SYSTEM CHECK AFTER MAKING REPAIRS.

93B78817 94B44462

Courtesy of General Motors Corp.

CODE 22, ENGINE COOLANT TEMPERATURE SENSOR, OPEN OR SHORTED CIRCUIT (PRIZM)

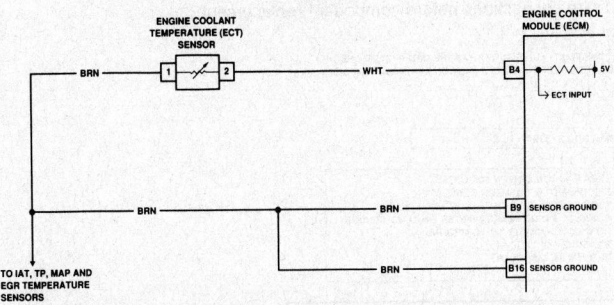

Engine Coolant Temperature (ECT) sensor is a thermistor in series with a fixed resistor in ECM. ECM applies 5 volts to sensor. ECM monitors voltage across ECT sensor and converts it into a temperature reading. When engine is cold, ECT sensor resistance is high. When engine is warm, ECT sensor resistance is low. Therefore, when engine is cold, ECM receives a high voltage input and when engine is warm, ECM receives a low voltage input. Code 22 will set if voltage input at ECM indicates either a very low or very high engine coolant temperature for at least .5 second.

NOTE: Test numbers refer to test numbers on diagnostic chart.

1) Checks for open or short to ground in White wire between ECM and ECT sensor or a faulty ECM.
2) Checks for open in Brown wire between ECM and ECT sensor or a faulty ECM.
3) Determines if problem is a faulty ECT sensor or ECM.

DIAGNOSTIC AIDS

Ensure engine is not overheating and has not been subjected to conditions which would create an overheating condition (i.e., overload, trailer towing, hilly terrain, heavy stop and go traffic, etc.). When replacing ECT sensor, check TEMPERATURE TO RESISTANCE VALUES table. A "shifted" (mis-scaled) sensor could result in poor driveability complaints. If Codes 24, 31 and 41 are also set, problem is open in sensor ground circuit. An intermittent condition may be caused by poor con-

nection, rubbed-through insulation, or a broken wire inside insulation. Check ECM harness connectors for backed-out terminals, improper mating, broken locks, improperly formed or damaged terminals, and poor terminal-to-wire connections before component replacement.

> ☐ IMPORTANT: MAKE SURE THAT THE OBD SYSTEM CHECK HAS BEEN PERFORMED BEFORE CONTINUING DIAGNOSIS.

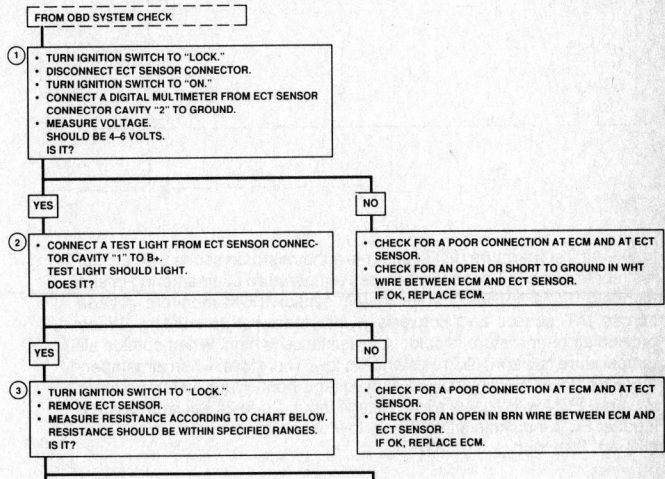

DIAGNOSTIC AID		
ECT SENSOR		
TEMPERATURE TO RESISTANCE VALUES		
TEMPERATURE		RESISTANCE
-20°C	-4°F	10 – 20 K OHMS
0°C	32°F	4 – 7 K OHMS
20°C	68°F	2 – 3 K OHMS
40°C	104°F	0.9 – 1.3 K OHMS
60°C	140°F	0.4 – 0.7 K OHMS
80°C	176°F	0.2 – 0.4 K OHMS

CLEAR DTCs AND REPEAT OBD SYSTEM CHECK AFTER MAKING REPAIRS.

93D78819 94C44463

Courtesy of General Motors Corp.

CODE 24, INTAKE AIR TEMPERATURE SENSOR, OPEN OR SHORTED CIRCUIT (PRIZM)

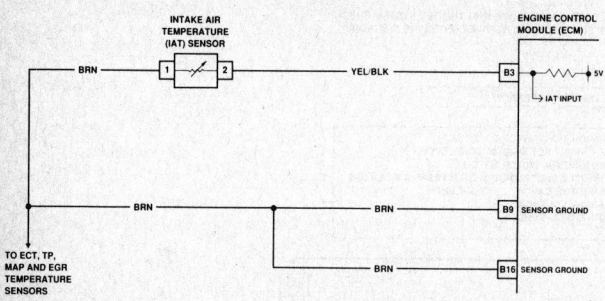

Intake Air Temperature (IAT) sensor is a thermistor in series with a fixed resistor in ECM. IAT sensor measures temperature of air entering intake manifold. ECM applies 5 volts to IAT sensor. ECM monitors voltage across IAT sensor and converts it into temperature reading. When outside air temperature is cold, IAT resistance is high. When outside air temperature is warm, IAT resistance is low. Therefore, when air temperature is cold, ECM will receive a high voltage input. When air temperature is warm, ECM will receive a low voltage input. Code 24 will set if voltage input at ECM indicates either a very low or very high air temperature for at least .5 second.

NOTE: Test numbers refer to test numbers on diagnostic chart.

1) Checks for open or short to ground in Yellow/Black wire between ECM and IAT sensor, and a faulty ECM.
2) Checks for open in Brown wire between ECM and IAT sensor, and a faulty ECM.
3) Determines if problem is a faulty IAT sensor or ECM.

DIAGNOSTIC AIDS

When replacing IAT sensor, check TEMPERATURE TO RESISTANCE VALUES table. A "shifted" (mis-scaled) sensor could result in poor drive-ability complaints. If Codes 22, 31 and 41 are also set, problem is open in sensor ground circuit.

An intermittent condition may be caused by poor connection, rubbed-through insulation, or a broken wire inside insulation. Check ECM harness connectors for backed-out terminals, improper mating, broken locks, improperly formed or damaged terminals, and poor terminal-to-wire connections before component replacement.

IMPORTANT: MAKE SURE THAT THE OBD SYSTEM CHECK HAS BEEN PERFORMED BEFORE CONTINUING DIAGNOSIS.

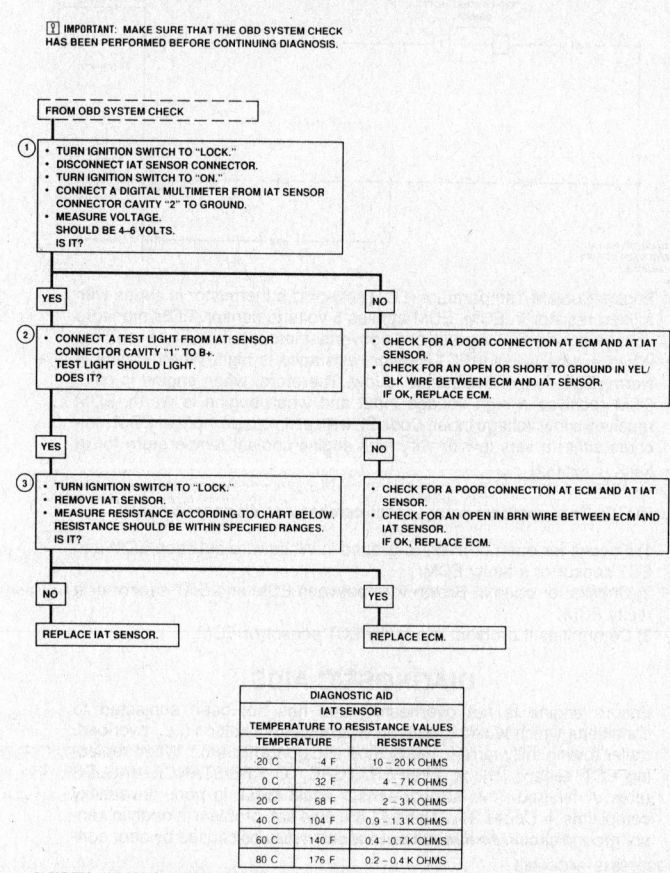

DIAGNOSTIC AID		
IAT SENSOR		
TEMPERATURE TO RESISTANCE VALUES		
TEMPERATURE		RESISTANCE
20 C	4 F	10 – 20 K OHMS
0 C	32 F	4 – 7 K OHMS
20 C	68 F	2 – 3 K OHMS
40 C	104 F	0.9 – 1.3 K OHMS
60 C	140 F	0.4 – 0.7 K OHMS
80 C	176 F	0.2 – 0.4 K OHMS

CLEAR DTCS AND REPEAT OBD SYSTEM CHECK AFTER MAKING REPAIRS.

CODE 25, OXYGEN SENSOR, LEAN EXHAUST INDICATED (PRIZM)

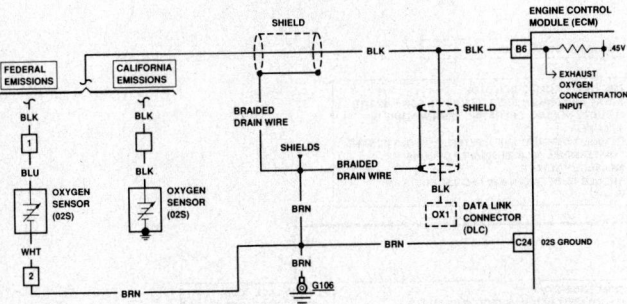

Oxygen (O₂) sensor produces a varying voltage as engine reaches normal operating temperature. Voltage will vary from .1 (lean) to 1.0 (rich) volt. ECM monitors voltage and determines concentration of gases in exhaust and adjusts fuel to maintain air/fuel ratio. Code 25 will set if sensor input voltage at ECM is less than .45 volt for 90 seconds or more with sensor warm and engine speed greater than 1500 RPM, vehicle speed is less than 60 MPH, and engine coolant temperature is greater than 122°F (50°C). Code 25 will also set if engine speed varies more than 15 RPM over preceding crank angle period for 30 seconds while idling with engine coolant temperature greater than 122°F (50°C).

NOTE: Test numbers refer to test numbers on diagnostic chart.

1) Checks for faulty sensor.
2) Checks for open in Black wire between ECM and sensor.
3) Checks for open in Brown wire between ECM and G106.
4) Checks for short to ground in Black wire between ECM and sensor, open in Brown wire to sensor (federal emissions only), and a faulty ECM.

DIAGNOSTIC AIDS

Verify clean, tight connection on G106 (Brown wire). A lean air/fuel condition may be caused by contaminated fuel, low fuel pressure or vacuum and exhaust leaks. An intermittent condition may be caused by poor connection, rubbed-through insulation, or a broken wire inside insulation.

93B78817 94E44465

Check ECM harness connectors for backed-out terminals, improper mating, broken locks, improperly formed or damaged terminals, and poor terminal-to-wire connections before component replacement.

IMPORTANT: MAKE SURE THAT THE OBD SYSTEM CHECK HAS BEEN PERFORMED BEFORE CONTINUING DIAGNOSIS.

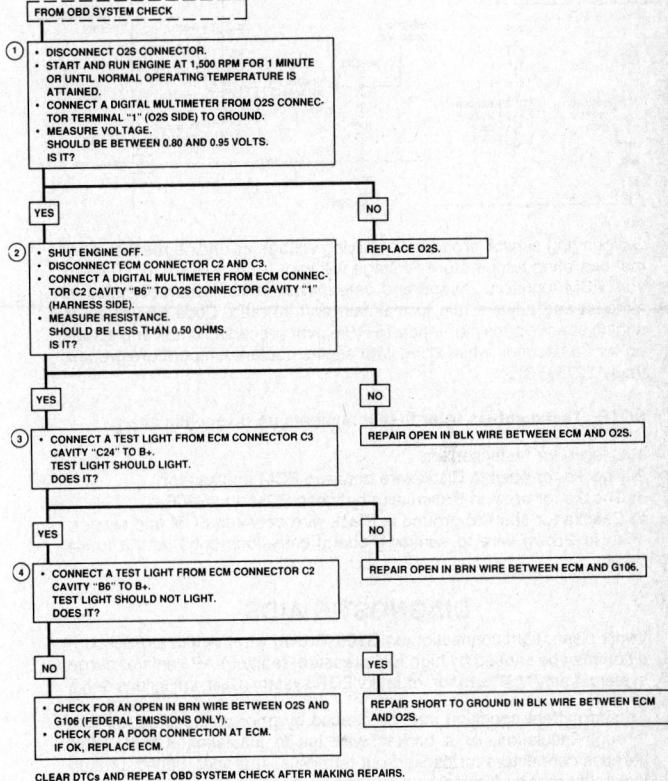

CLEAR DTCs AND REPEAT OBD SYSTEM CHECK AFTER MAKING REPAIRS.

Courtesy of General Motors Corp.

CODE 26, OXYGEN SENSOR, RICH EXHAUST INDICATED (PRIZM)

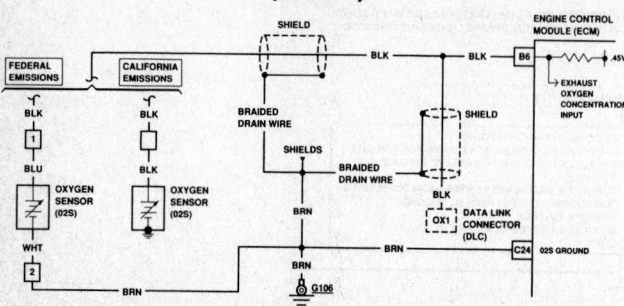

Oxygen (O₂) sensor produces a varying voltage as engine reaches normal operating temperature. Voltage will vary from .1 (lean) to 1.0 (rich) volt. ECM monitors voltage and determines concentration of gases in exhaust and adjusts fuel to maintain air/fuel ratio. Code 26 will set if engine speed varies more than 15 RPM over preceding crank angle period for 30 seconds while idling with engine coolant temperature greater than 122°F (50°C).

NOTE: Test numbers refer to test numbers on diagnostic chart.

1) Checks for faulty sensor.
2) Checks for open in Black wire between ECM and sensor.
3) Checks for open in Brown wire between ECM and G106.
4) Checks for short to ground in Black wire between ECM and sensor, open in Brown wire to sensor (Federal emissions only), and a faulty ECM.

DIAGNOSTIC AIDS

Verify clean, tight connection on G106 (Brown wire). A rich air/fuel condition may be caused by high fuel pressure, faulty EVAP canister purge system, faulty MAP sensor, or faulty EGR system (Calif. emissions only).

An intermittent condition may be caused by poor connection, rubbed-through insulation, or a broken wire inside insulation. Check ECM harness connectors for backed-out terminals, improper mating, broken locks, improperly formed or damaged terminals, and poor terminal-to-wire connections before component replacement.

? IMPORTANT: MAKE SURE THAT THE OBD SYSTEM CHECK HAS BEEN PERFORMED BEFORE CONTINUING DIAGNOSIS.

FROM OBD SYSTEM CHECK

1. • DISCONNECT O2S CONNECTOR.
   • START AND RUN ENGINE AT 1,500 RPM FOR 1 MINUTE OR UNTIL NORMAL OPERATING TEMPERATURE IS ATTAINED.
   • CONNECT A DIGITAL MULTIMETER FROM O2S CONNECTOR TERMINAL "1" (O2S SIDE) TO GROUND.
   • MEASURE VOLTAGE.
     SHOULD BE BETWEEN 0.80 AND 0.95 VOLTS.
     IS IT?

   YES → | NO → REPLACE O2S.

2. • SHUT ENGINE OFF.
   • DISCONNECT ECM CONNECTOR C2 AND C3.
   • CONNECT A DIGITAL MULTIMETER FROM ECM CONNECTOR C2 CAVITY "B6" TO O2S CONNECTOR CAVITY "1" (HARNESS SIDE).
   • MEASURE RESISTANCE.
     SHOULD BE LESS THAN 0.50 OHMS.
     IS IT?

   YES → | NO → REPAIR OPEN IN BLK WIRE BETWEEN ECM AND O2S.

3. • CONNECT A TEST LIGHT FROM ECM CONNECTOR C3 CAVITY "C24" TO B+.
     TEST LIGHT SHOULD LIGHT.
     DOES IT?

   YES → | NO → REPAIR OPEN IN BRN WIRE BETWEEN ECM AND G106.

4. • CONNECT A TEST LIGHT FROM ECM CONNECTOR C2 CAVITY "B6" TO B+.
     TEST LIGHT SHOULD NOT LIGHT.
     DOES IT?

   NO → | YES → REPAIR SHORT TO GROUND IN BLK WIRE BETWEEN ECM AND O2S.

• CHECK FOR AN OPEN IN BRN WIRE BETWEEN O2S AND G106 (FEDERAL EMISSIONS ONLY).
• CHECK FOR A POOR CONNECTION AT ECM.
  IF OK, REPLACE ECM.

CLEAR DTCs AND REPEAT OBD SYSTEM CHECK AFTER MAKING REPAIRS.

CODE 27, SUB-OXYGEN SENSOR, OPEN OR SHORTED CIRCUIT (PRIZM – CALIF. EMISSIONS)

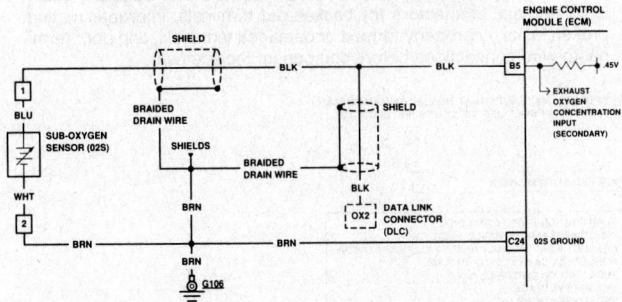

Sub-oxygen (O_2) sensor produces a varying voltage as engine reaches normal operating temperature. Voltage will vary from .1 (lean) to 1.0 (rich) volt. ECM monitors voltage and determines concentration of gases in exhaust after converter. ECM uses this input and Oxygen (O_2) sensor input, and adjusts fuel to maintain air/fuel ratio. Code 27 will set when engine is at operating temperature and engine is off idle for 2 seconds or more with sensor input at ECM .45 volt or more, and sub-O_2 sensor input at ECM .45 volt or less.

NOTE: Test numbers refer to test numbers on diagnostic chart.

1) Checks for faulty sub-O_2 sensor.
2) Checks for open in Black wire between ECM and sub-O_2 sensor.
3) Checks for open in Brown wire between ECM and G106.
4) Checks for short to ground in Black wire between ECM and sub-O_2 sensor, open in Brown wire to sub-O_2 sensor, and a faulty ECM.

DIAGNOSTIC AIDS

Verify clean, tight connection on G106 (Brown wire).

An intermittent condition may be caused by poor connection, rubbed-through insulation, or a broken wire inside insulation. Check ECM harness connectors for backed-out terminals, improper mating, broken locks, improperly formed or damaged terminals, and poor terminal-to-wire connections before component replacement.

93J78823 94G44467

IMPORTANT: MAKE SURE THAT THE OBD SYSTEM CHECK HAS BEEN PERFORMED BEFORE CONTINUING DIAGNOSIS.

FROM OBD SYSTEM CHECK

1) • START AND RUN ENGINE AT 1,500 RPM FOR 1 MINUTE OR UNTIL NORMAL OPERATING TEMPERATURE IS ATTAINED.
• RAISE AND SUITABLY SUPPORT VEHICLE.
• DISCONNECT SUB-O2S CONNECTOR.
• CONNECT A DIGITAL MULTIMETER FROM SUB-O2S CONNECTOR TERMINAL "1" (SUB-O2S SIDE) TO GROUND.
• MEASURE VOLTAGE.
SHOULD BE BETWEEN 0.80 AND 0.95 VOLTS.
IS IT?

YES → NO → REPLACE SUB-O2S.

2) • LOWER VEHICLE.
• SHUT ENGINE OFF.
• DISCONNECT ECM CONNECTOR C2 AND C3.
• CONNECT A DIGITAL MULTIMETER FROM ECM CONNECTOR C2 CAVITY "B5" TO SUB-O2S CONNECTOR CAVITY "1" (HARNESS SIDE).
• MEASURE RESISTANCE.
SHOULD BE LESS THAN 0.50 OHMS.
IS IT?

YES → NO → REPAIR OPEN IN BLK WIRE BETWEEN ECM AND SUB-O2S.

3) • CONNECT A TEST LIGHT FROM ECM CONNECTOR C3 CAVITY "C24" TO B+.
TEST LIGHT SHOULD LIGHT.
DOES IT?

YES → NO → REPAIR OPEN IN BRN WIRE BETWEEN ECM AND G106.

4) • CONNECT A TEST LIGHT FROM ECM CONNECTOR C2 CAVITY "B5" TO B+.
TEST LIGHT SHOULD NOT LIGHT.
DOES IT?

NO → YES → REPAIR SHORT TO GROUND IN BLK WIRE BETWEEN ECM AND SUB-O2S.

• CHECK FOR AN OPEN IN BRN WIRE BETWEEN SUB-O2S AND G106.
• CHECK FOR A POOR CONNECTION AT ECM. IF OK, REPLACE ECM.

CLEAR DTCs AND REPEAT OBD SYSTEM CHECK AFTER MAKING REPAIRS.

CODE 31, MANIFOLD ABSOLUTE PRESSURE SENSOR, OPEN OR SHORTED CIRCUIT (PRIZM)

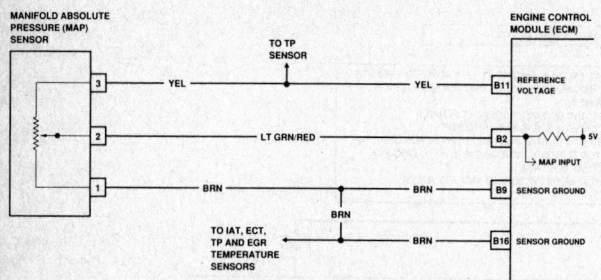

MAP sensor responds to changes in manifold pressure (vacuum). MAP sensor consists of a semi-conductor type pressure converting element which converts a pressure change into an electrical change and an electrical circuit which amplifies and corrects electrical change. ECM applies 5 volts to MAP sensor.

Changes in pressure, resulting from engine load and RPM, are converted into voltage input monitored by ECM. A low voltage input at ECM indicates low manifold pressure and a high voltage input at ECM indicates high manifold pressure. Code 31 will set if voltage input at ECM indicates either very low or very high manifold pressure for at least .5 second.

NOTE: Test numbers refer to test numbers on diagnostic chart.

1) Checks for open or short to ground in Yellow wire between ECM and MAP sensor.
2) Checks for open in Light Green/Red wire between ECM and MAP sensor.
3) Checks for open in Brown wire between ECM and MAP sensor, and a faulty ECM or MAP sensor.

93B78825 94H44468

DIAGNOSTIC AIDS

If Codes 22, 24 and 41 are also set, problem is open in sensor ground circuit. An intermittent condition may be caused by poor connection, rubbed-through insulation, or a broken wire inside insulation. Check ECM harness connectors for backed-out terminals, improper mating, broken locks, improperly formed or damaged terminals, and poor terminal-to-wire connections before component replacement.

☐ IMPORTANT: MAKE SURE THAT THE OBD SYSTEM CHECK HAS BEEN PERFORMED BEFORE CONTINUING DIAGNOSIS.

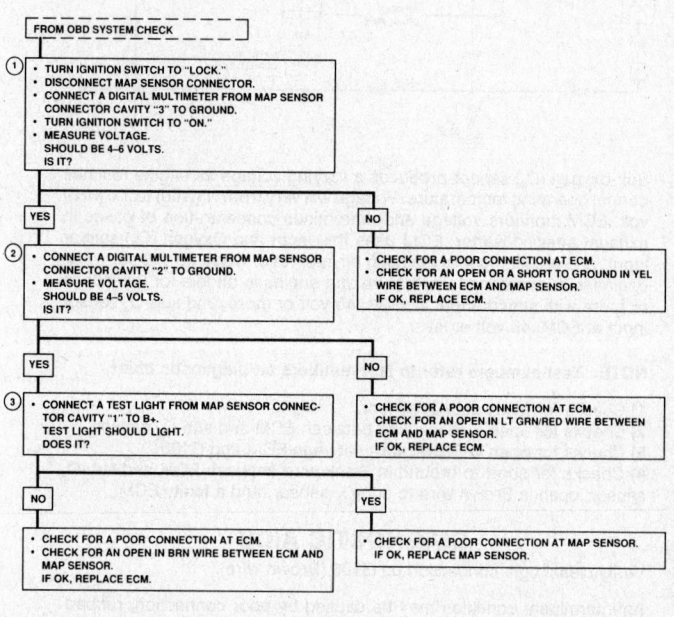

CLEAR DTCs AND REPEAT OBD SYSTEM CHECK AFTER MAKING REPAIRS.

Courtesy of General Motors Corp.

CODE 41, THROTTLE POSITION SENSOR, OPEN OR SHORTED CIRCUIT (PRIZM)

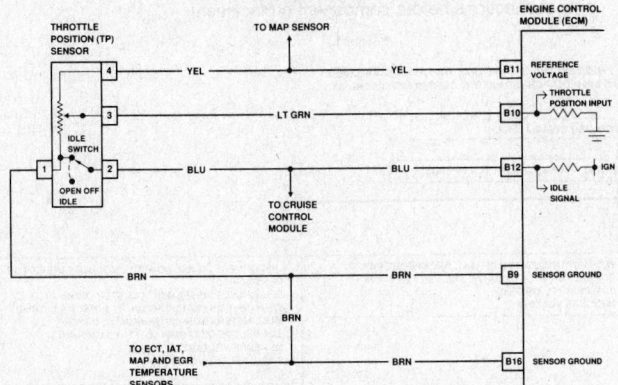

Throttle Position (TP) sensor consists of a contact point (idle switch) and a potentiometer, and is connected to throttle valve shaft on throttle body. TP sensor detects throttle valve opening. Idle switch detects throttle opening and turns on during idle. Fully opened throttle is detected by potentiometer.

ECM provides a 5-volt reference voltage to TP sensor and as brush moves over resistance according to throttle valve opening, output voltage varies accordingly. ECM monitors on/off signal and sensor output voltage, and uses these to detect throttle valve opening. Code 41 will set if throttle position input at ECM indicates Wide Open Throttle (WOT) with engine idling for at least .5 second, or if throttle position input at ECM indicates and idle signal with engine off idle for at least .5 second.

NOTE: Test numbers refer to test numbers on diagnostic chart.

1) Checks for a fault in Yellow wire between ECM and TP sensor.
2) Checks for open in Brown wire between ECM and TP sensor.
3) Checks for a fault in Light Green wire between ECM and TP sensor, a faulty ECM, or a misadjusted or faulty TP sensor.

93D78827 94I44469

DIAGNOSTIC AIDS

Check for properly adjusted TP sensor before replacement of TP sensor. If Codes 22, 24 and 31 are also set, problem is open in sensor ground circuit. An intermittent condition may be caused by poor connection, rubbed-through insulation, or a broken wire inside insulation. Check ECM harness connectors for backed-out terminals, improper mating, broken locks, improperly formed or damaged terminals, and poor terminal-to-wire connections before component replacement.

IMPORTANT: MAKE SURE THAT THE OBD SYSTEM CHECK HAS BEEN PERFORMED BEFORE CONTINUING DIAGNOSIS.

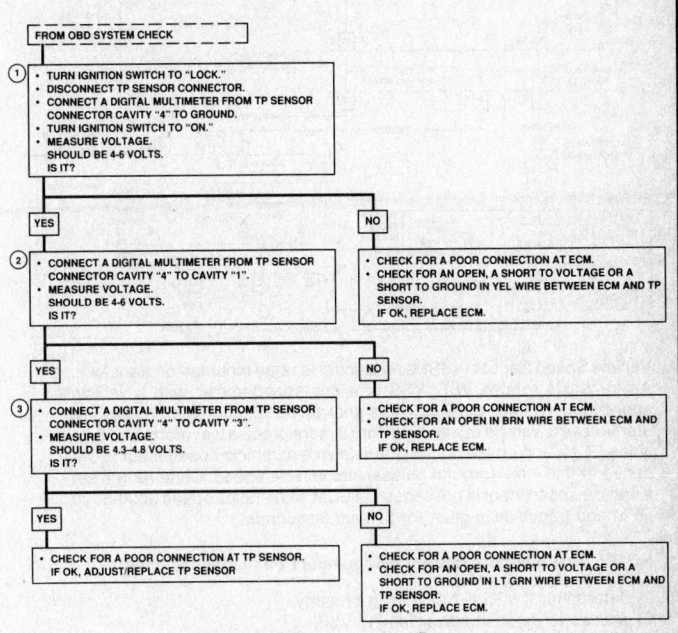

CLEAR DTCs AND REPEAT OBD SYSTEM CHECK AFTER MAKING REPAIRS.

Courtesy of General Motors Corp.

CODE 42, VEHICLE SPEED SENSOR CIRCUIT, OPEN OR SHORTED CIRCUIT (1 OF 2) (PRIZM)

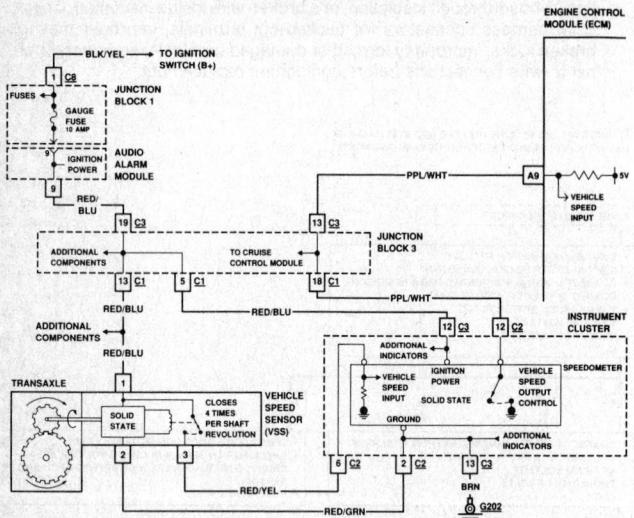

Vehicle Speed Sensor (VSS) is an electronic relay mounted on transaxle. As transaxle rotates VSS, VSS provides speedometer with a vehicle speed input (voltage pulses). This signal drives speedometer. Speedometer converts vehicle speed input into a more precise waveform and provides ECM, and cruise control module with a vehicle speed input. ECM converts this input (ground pulses) into vehicle speed. Code 42 will set if vehicle speed input is not sensed at ECM with engine speed 3000-5000 RPM and transaxle in gear, for at least 8 seconds.

NOTE: Test numbers refer to test numbers on diagnostic chart.

1) Determines if VSS is functioning properly.
2) Checks for open in power feed to VSS.
3) Checks for open or short in ECM speed input circuit or a faulty ECM.
4) Determines if ECM or speedometer is faulty.

DIAGNOSTIC AIDS

Verify clean, tight connection on G202 (Brown wire).

93F78829 94B44470

An intermittent condition may be caused by poor connection, rubbed-through insulation, or a broken wire inside insulation. Check ECM harness connectors for backed-out terminals, improper mating, broken locks, improperly formed or damaged terminals, and poor terminal-to-wire connections before component replacement.

IMPORTANT: MAKE SURE THAT THE OBD SYSTEM CHECK HAS BEEN PERFORMED BEFORE CONTINUING DIAGNOSIS.

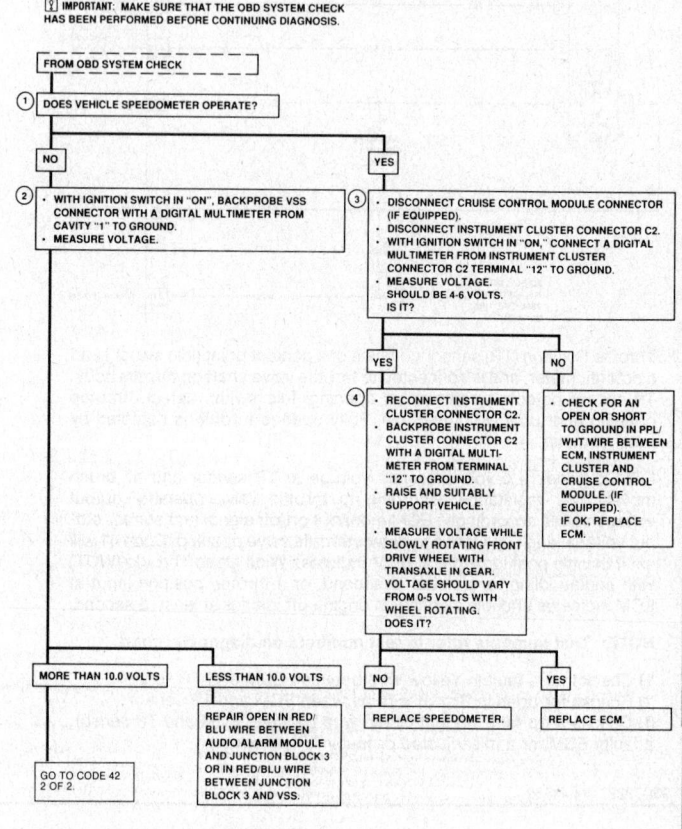

CLEAR DTCs AND REPEAT OBD SYSTEM CHECK AFTER MAKING REPAIRS.

Courtesy of General Motors Corp.

CODE 42, VEHICLE SPEED SENSOR CIRCUIT, OPEN OR SHORTED CIRCUIT (2 OF 2) (PRIZM)

NOTE: Test numbers refer to test numbers on diagnostic chart.

5) Checks for open in ground to VSS.
6) Checks for open in power feed to speedometer.
7) Determines if VSS or speedometer is faulty.

DIAGNOSTIC AIDS

Verify clean, tight connection on G202 (Brown wire).

An intermittent condition may be caused by poor connection, rubbed-through insulation, or a broken wire inside insulation. Check ECM harness connectors for backed-out terminals, improper mating, broken locks, improperly formed or damaged terminals, and poor terminal-to-wire connections before component replacement.

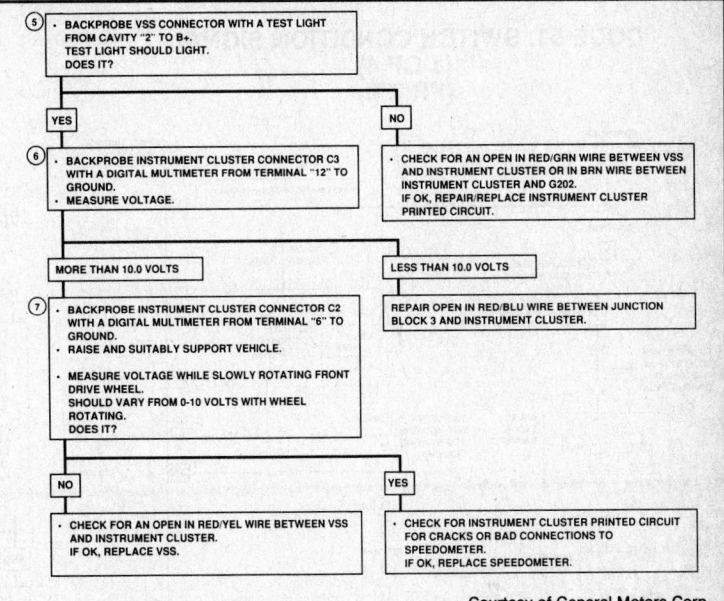

93J78831

Courtesy of General Motors Corp.

CODE 43, CRANK SIGNAL, NO SIGNAL (PRIZM)

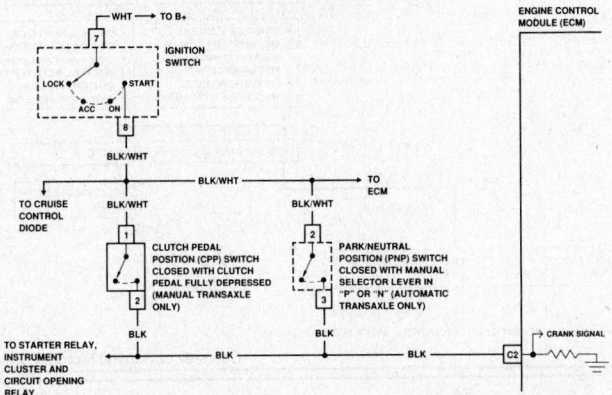

ECM receives a signal when ignition switch is in START position. ECM uses this signal, along with others, to determine injection time of fuel injectors. If signal is not detected during ignition, ECM will still allow engine to start, but Code 43 will set. Code 43 will set when crank signal is not detected at ECM during ignition.

NOTE: Test numbers refer to test numbers on diagnostic chart.

1) Checks for open in Black wire between Clutch Pedal Position (CPP) switch (M/T) or Park/Neutral Position (PNP) switch (A/T) and ECM, or a faulty ECM.

DIAGNOSTIC AIDS

An intermittent condition may be caused by poor connection, rubbed-through insulation, or a broken wire inside insulation. Check ECM harness connectors for backed-out terminals, improper mating, broken locks, improperly formed or damaged terminals, and poor terminal-to-wire connections before component replacement.

IMPORTANT: MAKE SURE THAT THE OBD SYSTEM CHECK HAS BEEN PERFORMED BEFORE CONTINUING DIAGNOSIS.

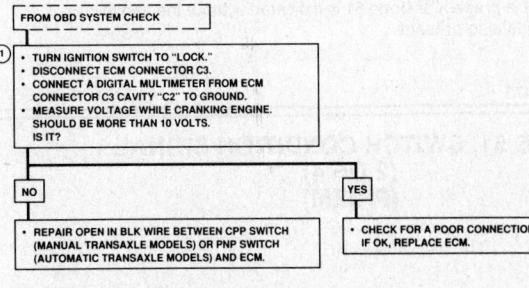

CLEAR DTCs AND REPEAT OBD SYSTEM CHECK AFTER MAKING REPAIRS.

93A78832 94C44471

Courtesy of General Motors Corp.

CODE 51, SWITCH CONDITION SIGNAL
(1 OF 4)
(PRIZM)

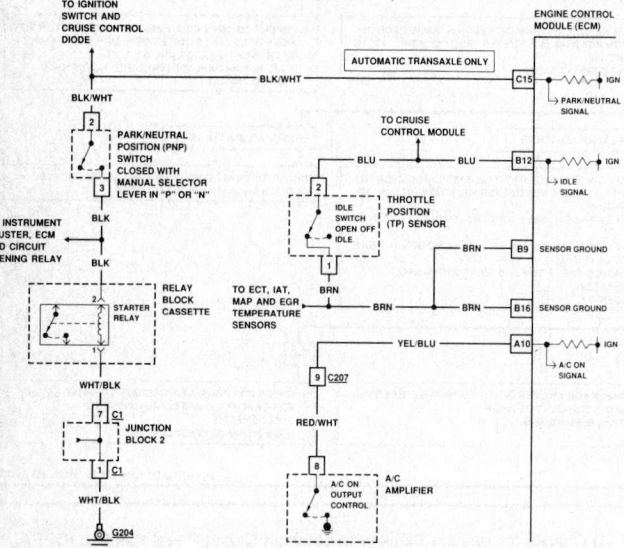

ECM receives a signal when the following occurs:
- Accelerator pedal is depressed (indicating throttle lever is in off idle position).
- Vehicle is equipped with A/C and A/C switch is depressed with blower speed selector in any position except OFF (indicating A/C operation has been requested).
- Vehicle is equipped with A/T and selector lever is in Reverse or any forward gear (indicating transaxle is in gear other than Park or Neutral).

Code 51 indicates that above systems are functioning normally. If Code 51 is not indicated with accelerator depressed, A/C is on or with gear selector lever in Reverse or any forward gear (excluding Park or Neutral) with Data Link Connector (DLC) terminals TE2 and TE1 jumpered to ground, a fault is present. If Code 51 is indicated without the above conditions, a fault is also present.

93C78834 94D44472

NOTE: Test numbers refer to test numbers on diagnostic chart.

1) Determines if systems are functioning normally in test diagnostic mode.
2) Checks if TP sensor circuit is operating normally.
3) Checks for short to ground in A/C circuit, open in PNP switch circuit, open in TP sensor circuit, or a faulty ECM or A/C amplifier.

IMPORTANT: MAKE SURE THAT THE OBD SYSTEM CHECK HAS BEEN PERFORMED BEFORE CONTINUING DIAGNOSIS.

FROM OBD SYSTEM CHECK

① • TURN IGNITION SWITCH TO "LOCK."
• CLEAR DTCs.
• CONNECT A JUMPER FROM DLC TERMINAL "TE2" TO TERMINAL "E1".
• TURN IGNITION SWITCH TO "ON."
  MIL SHOULD BE FLASHING ON AND OFF RAPIDLY.
• START AND ROAD TEST VEHICLE FOR 1 MINUTE ABOVE 16 KPH (10 MPH).
• LEAVE ENGINE RUNNING AT IDLE.
• CONNECT A JUMPER FROM DLC TERMINAL "TE1" TO TERMINAL "E1".
• NOTE MIL.
  SHOULD FLASH ON AND OFF RAPIDLY, NOT DTC 51. DOES IT?

YES → ② • HOLD ACCELERATOR PEDAL DEPRESSED OFF IDLE FOR 7-10 SECONDS.
• NOTE MIL.
  SHOULD FLASH DTC 51 AT LEAST ONCE AND THEN FLASH ON AND OFF RAPIDLY. DOES IT?

NO, FLASHES DTC 51 → ③ • SHUT ENGINE OFF, BUT LEAVE IGNITION SWITCH IN "ON."
• DISCONNECT TP SENSOR CONNECTOR.
• CONNECT A DIGITAL MULTIMETER FROM TP SENSOR CONNECTOR CAVITY "2" TO GROUND.
• MEASURE VOLTAGE.

MORE THAN 10 VOLTS | **LESS THAN 10 VOLTS**

MORE THAN 10 VOLTS:
• CONNECT A DIGITAL MULTIMETER FROM TP SENSOR TERMINAL "1" TO TERMINAL "2" (TP SENSOR SIDE).
• MEASURE RESISTANCE.

LESS THAN 10 VOLTS:
• CHECK FOR A POOR CONNECTION AT ECM.
• CHECK FOR AN OPEN IN BLU WIRE BETWEEN TP SENSOR AND ECM. IF OK, REPLACE ECM.

LESS THAN INFINITE | **INFINITE**

INFINITE:
ADJUST/REPLACE TP SENSOR.

GO TO "A" IN CODE 51 2 OF 4. | GO TO "B" IN CODE 51 2 OF 4.

CLEAR DTCs AND REPEAT OBD SYSTEM CHECK AFTER MAKING REPAIRS.

Courtesy of General Motors Corp.

CODE 51, SWITCH CONDITION SIGNAL
(2 OF 4)
(PRIZM)

A **B**

IS VEHICLE EQUIPPED WITH A/C OR AUTOMATIC TRANSAXLE?

YES **NO**

NO: REPLACE ECM.

YES:
• IF VEHICLE IS EQUIPPED WITH AN AUTOMATIC TRANSAXLE ONLY, CHECK FOR A POOR CONNECTION AT ECM, AND FOR AN OPEN IN BLK/WHT WIRE BETWEEN ECM AND PNP SWITCH. IF OK, REPLACE ECM.
• IF VEHICLE IS EQUIPPED WITH A/C ONLY, DISCONNECT A/C AMPLIFIER CONNECTOR. CONNECT A DIGITAL MULTIMETER FROM A/C AMPLIFIER CONNECTOR CAVITY "8" TO GROUND. MEASURE VOLTAGE. IF VOLTAGE IS MORE THAN 10 VOLTS, REPLACE A/C AMPLIFIER. IF VOLTAGE IS LESS THAN 10 VOLTS, CHECK FOR A SHORT TO GROUND IN YEL/BLU OR RED/WHT BETWEEN ECM AND A/C AMPLIFIER. IF OK, REPLACE ECM.
• IF VEHICLE IS EQUIPPED WITH BOTH A/C AND AN AUTOMATIC TRANSAXLE, TURN IGNITION SWITCH TO "LOCK." RECONNECT TP SENSOR CONNECTOR AND DISCONNECT A/C AMPLIFIER CONNECTOR. REMOVE JUMPER FROM DLC TERMINAL "TE1" BUT LEAVE TERMINAL "TE2" JUMPERED. TURN IGNITION SWITCH TO "ON" AND THEN CONNECT A JUMPER FROM DLC TERMINAL "TE1" TO "E1."
NOTICE: MIL WILL FLASH CODE 42 AND CODE 43, THIS SHOULD BE CONSIDERED NORMAL.
DOES MIL FLASH CODE 51 ?

YES **NO**

NO: REPLACE A/C AMPLIFIER

YES:
• CHECK FOR AN OPEN IN BLK/WHT WIRE BETWEEN ECM AND PNP SWITCH OR FOR A SHORT TO GROUND IN YEL/BLU AND RED/WHT BETWEEN ECM AND A/C AMPLIFIER. IF OK, REPLACE ECM.

GO TO "A" IN CODE 51 3 OF 4.

93E78836

Courtesy of General Motors Corp.

CODE 51, SWITCH CONDITION SIGNAL
(3 OF 4)
(PRIZM)

NOTE: Test numbers refer to test numbers on diagnostic chart.

4) Checks for short to ground in TP sensor circuit, or a faulty TP sensor or ECM.
5) Checks for short to ground in PNP switch circuit.
6) Determines whether system is functioning normally or if there is a problem in A/C circuit.

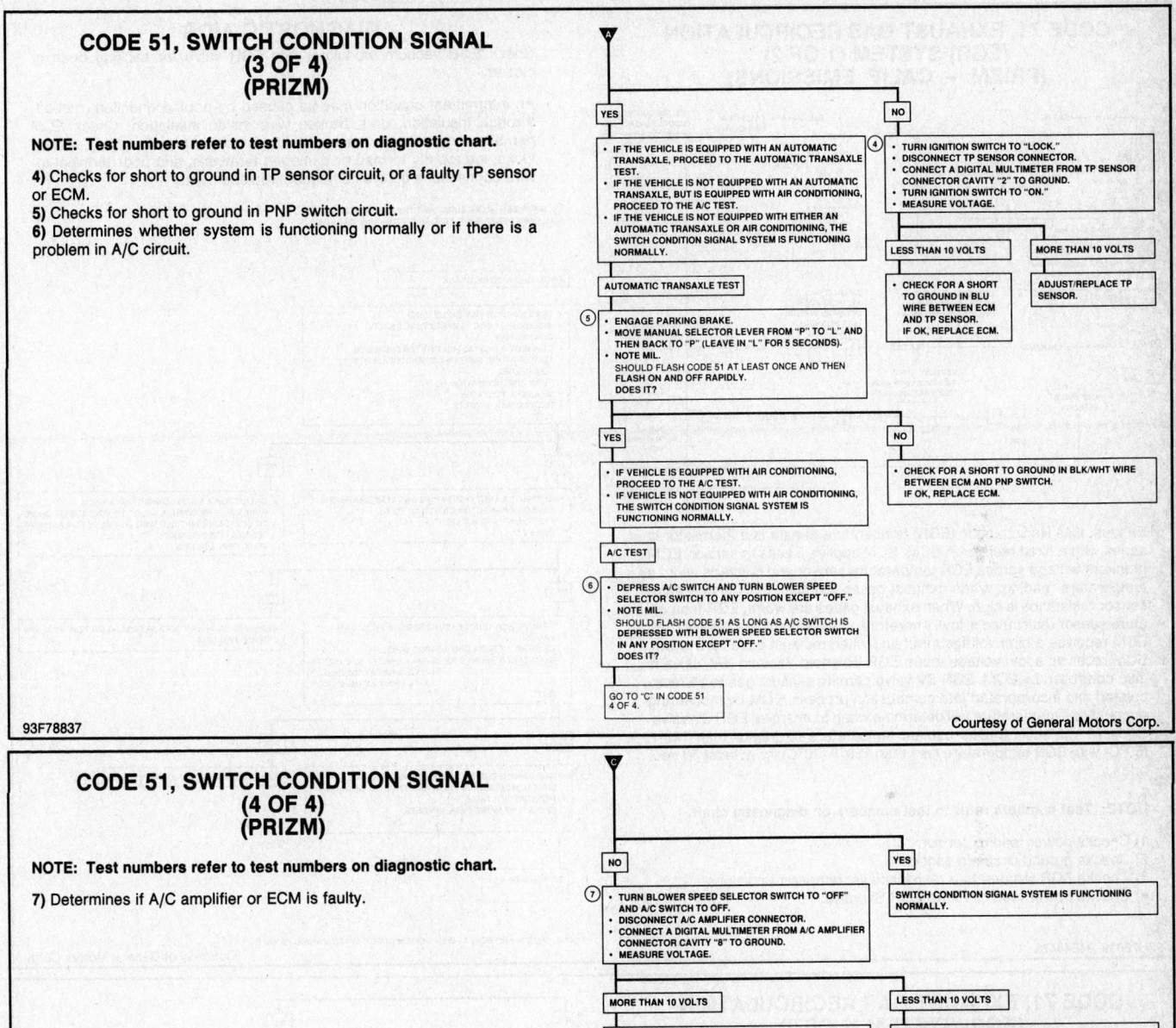

93F78837

Courtesy of General Motors Corp.

CODE 51, SWITCH CONDITION SIGNAL
(4 OF 4)
(PRIZM)

NOTE: Test numbers refer to test numbers on diagnostic chart.

7) Determines if A/C amplifier or ECM is faulty.

93G78838

Courtesy of General Motors Corp.

CODE 71, EXHAUST GAS RECIRCULATION (EGR) SYSTEM (1 OF 2) (PRIZM – CALIF. EMISSIONS)

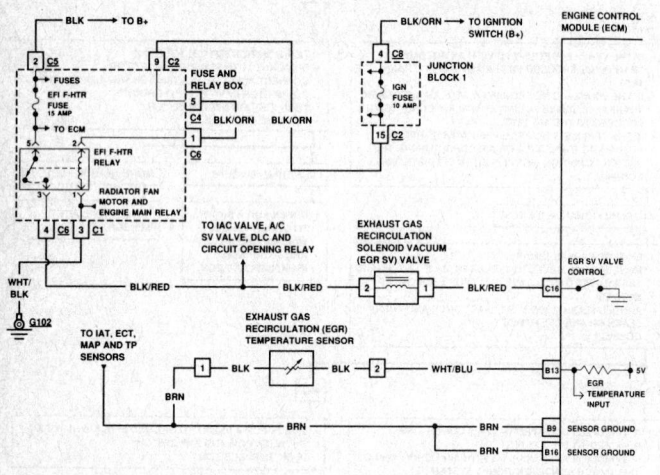

Exhaust Gas Recirculation (EGR) temperature sensor is a thermistor in series with a fixed resistor in ECM. ECM applies 5 volts to sensor. ECM monitors voltage across EGR temperature sensor and converts it into a temperature reading. When exhaust gases are cold, EGR temperature sensor resistance is high. When exhaust gases are warm, EGR temperature sensor resistance is low. Therefore, when exhaust gases are cold, ECM receives a high voltage input and when exhaust gases are warm, ECM receives a low voltage input. EGR Solenoid Vacuum (SV) valve is also controlled by ECM. EGR SV valve permits exhaust gas to be recirculated and incorporated into combustion process. ECM by monitoring exhaust gas temperature will determine when to energize EGR SV valve. Code 71 will set if engine coolant temperature is greater than 140°F (60°C) with EGR temperature less than 158°F (70°C) for at least 50 seconds.

NOTE: Test numbers refer to test numbers on diagnostic chart.

1) Checks power feed to sensor.
2) Checks ground circuit to sensor.
3) Checks EGR temperature resistance vs. temperature values.
4) Checks power feed circuit to EGR SV valve.

93H78839 94E44473

DIAGNOSTIC AIDS

Check EGR vacuum modulator and EGR valve for sticking open or closed.

An intermittent condition may be caused by poor connection, rubbed-through insulation, or a broken wire inside insulation. Check ECM harness connectors for backed-out terminals, improper mating, broken locks, improperly formed or damaged terminals, and poor terminal-to-wire connections before component replacement.

IMPORTANT: MAKE SURE THAT THE OBD SYSTEM CHECK HAS BEEN PERFORMED BEFORE CONTINUING DIAGNOSIS.

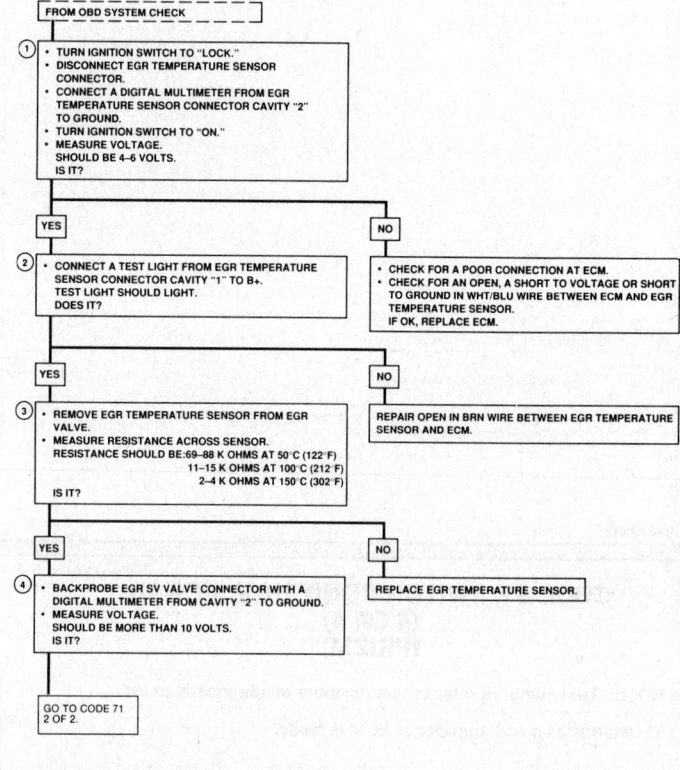

CLEAR DTCs AND REPEAT OBD SYSTEM CHECK AFTER MAKING REPAIRS.

Courtesy of General Motors Corp.

CODE 71, EXHAUST GAS RECIRCULATION (EGR) SYSTEM (2 OF 2) (PRIZM – CALIF. EMISSIONS)

NOTE: Test numbers refer to test numbers on diagnostic chart.

5) Checks for a faulty EGR SV valve, mechanical checks and a faulty ECM.

DIAGNOSTIC AIDS

Check EGR vacuum modulator and EGR valve for sticking open or closed.

An intermittent condition may be caused by poor connection, rubbed-through insulation, or a broken wire inside insulation. Check ECM harness connectors for backed-out terminals, improper mating, broken locks, improperly formed or damaged terminals, and poor terminal-to-wire connections before component replacement.

94F44474

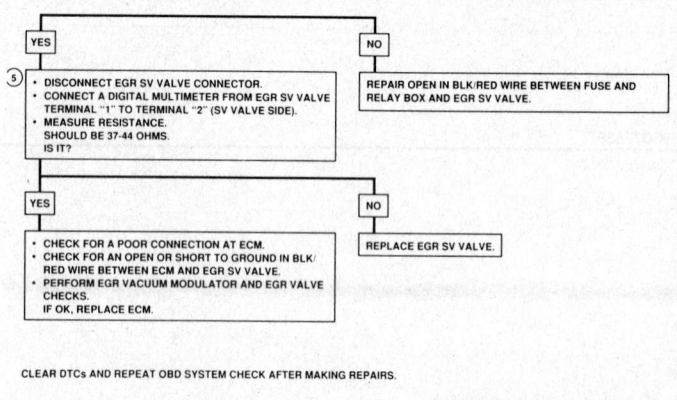

CLEAR DTCs AND REPEAT OBD SYSTEM CHECK AFTER MAKING REPAIRS.

Courtesy of General Motors Corp.

PRIZM LSi (VIN 8) CODE CHARTS

ON-BOARD DIAGNOSTIC (OBD) SYSTEM CHECK (1 OF 2) (PRIZM LSi)

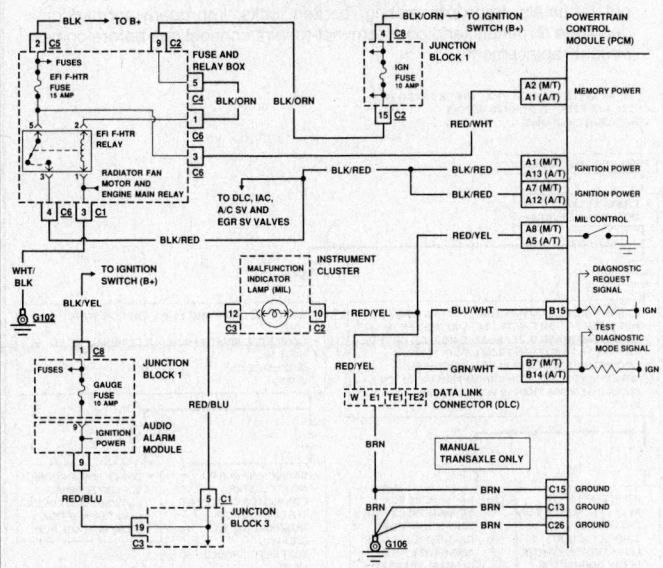

On-board diagnostic system check is an organized approach in identifying a problem created by an electronic engine system malfunction. It must be the starting point for any driveability complaint diagnosis, because it directs the service technician to the next logical step in diagnosing a complaint. Understanding the chart and using it correctly will reduce diagnostic time and prevent unnecessary replacement of good parts.

NOTE: Test numbers refer to test numbers on diagnostic chart.

1) Checks Malfunction Indicator Light (MIL) operation with ignition switch in ON position.
2) Checks if PCM's normal diagnostic mode is operating.
3) Checks if PCM's test diagnostic mode is operating.
4) Checks if engine will start.

93G79109 94A44511

5) Checks for any codes that are stored in PCM's memory with engine running.
6) Checks for any codes that are stored in PCM's memory with engine off. If no other codes than Code 42 are set and engine won't start, go to appropriate CHART A2-3 in BASIC DIAGNOSTIC PROCEDURES article.

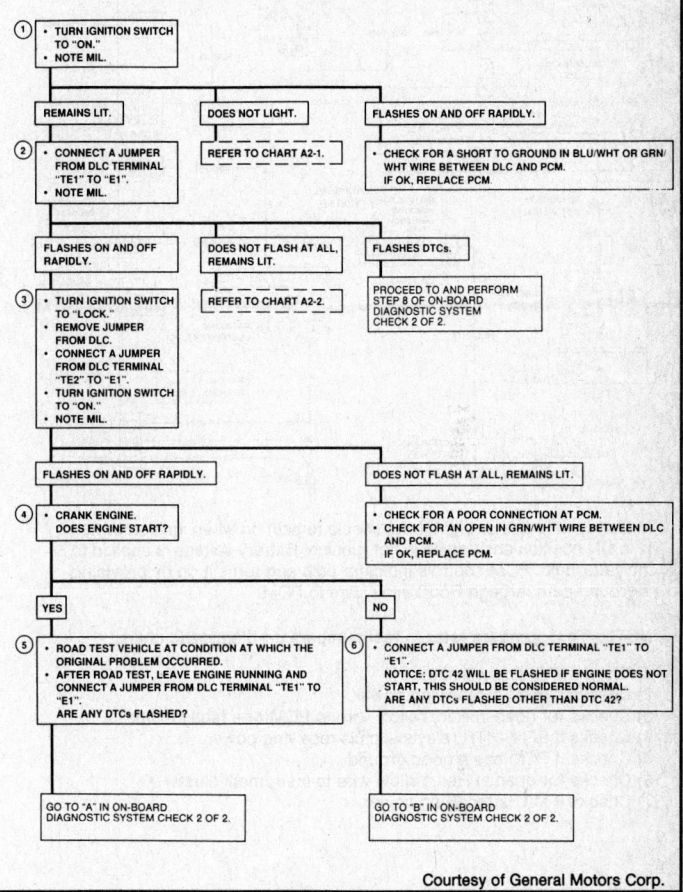

Courtesy of General Motors Corp.

ON-BOARD DIAGNOSTIC (OBD) SYSTEM CHECK (2 OF 2) (PRIZM LSi)

NOTE: Test numbers refer to test numbers on diagnostic chart.

7) Checks if Code 51 (Switch Condition Signal) is functioning.
8) Checks if code(s) are intermittent problems.

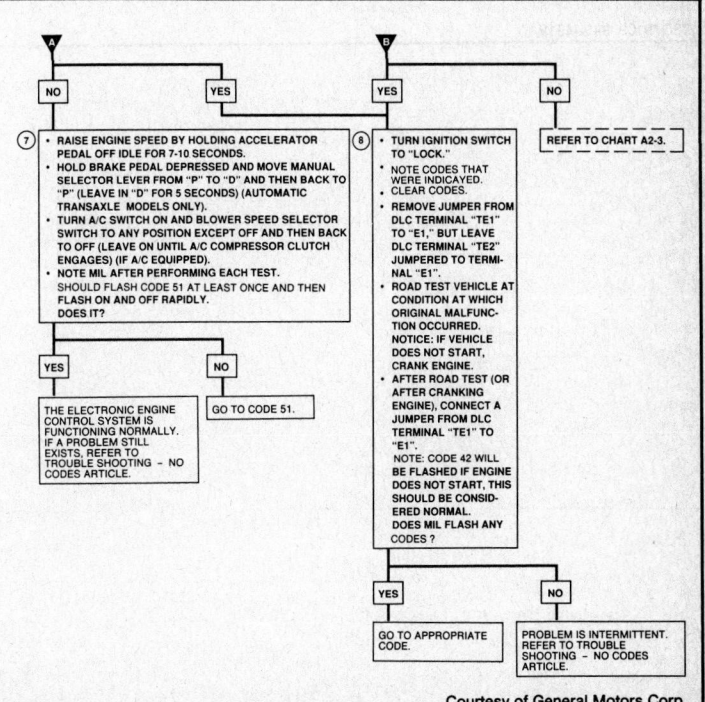

93A79111

Courtesy of General Motors Corp.

CHART A2-1, NO MALFUNCTION INDICATOR LIGHT (1 OF 2) (PRIZM LSi)

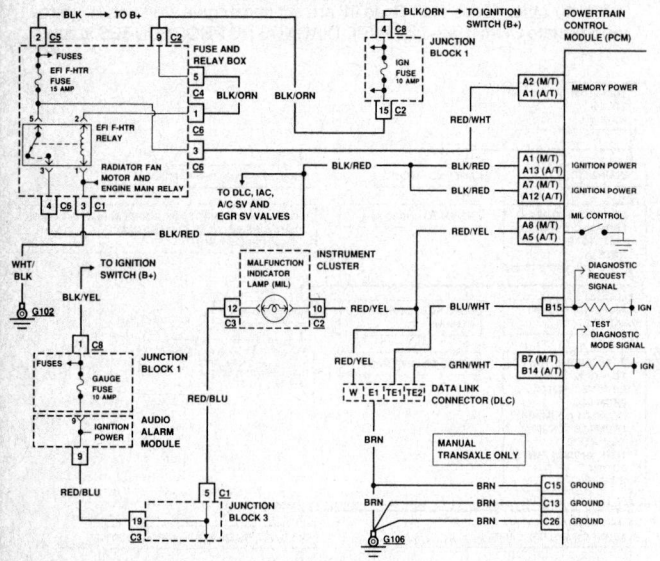

Malfunction Indicator Light (MIL) should remain on when ignition switch is in ON position and engine is not running. Battery voltage is applied to indicator bulb. PCM controls indicator bulb and turns it on by providing a ground path through Red/Yellow wire to PCM.

NOTE: Test numbers refer to test numbers on diagnostic chart.

1) Checks if engine will start.
2) Checks if PCM is receiving power.
3) Checks for open in Red/Yellow wire to PCM or a faulty PCM.
4) Checks if EFI F-HTR relay switch is receiving power.
5) Checks if PCM has a good ground.
6) Checks for open in Red/Yellow wire to instrument cluster.
7) Checks if MIL is receiving power.

DIAGNOSTIC AIDS

Check for open in EFI F-HTR, IGN and GAUGE fuses. Ensure EFI F-HTR relay is securely mounted in fuse/relay box. An intermittent condition may be caused by poor connection, rubbed-through insulation, or a broken wire inside insulation. Check PCM harness connectors for backed-out terminals, improper mating, broken locks, improperly formed or damaged terminals, and poor terminal-to-wire connections before component replacement.

IMPORTANT: MAKE SURE THAT THE OBD SYSTEM CHECK HAS BEEN PERFORMED BEFORE CONTINUING DIAGNOSIS.

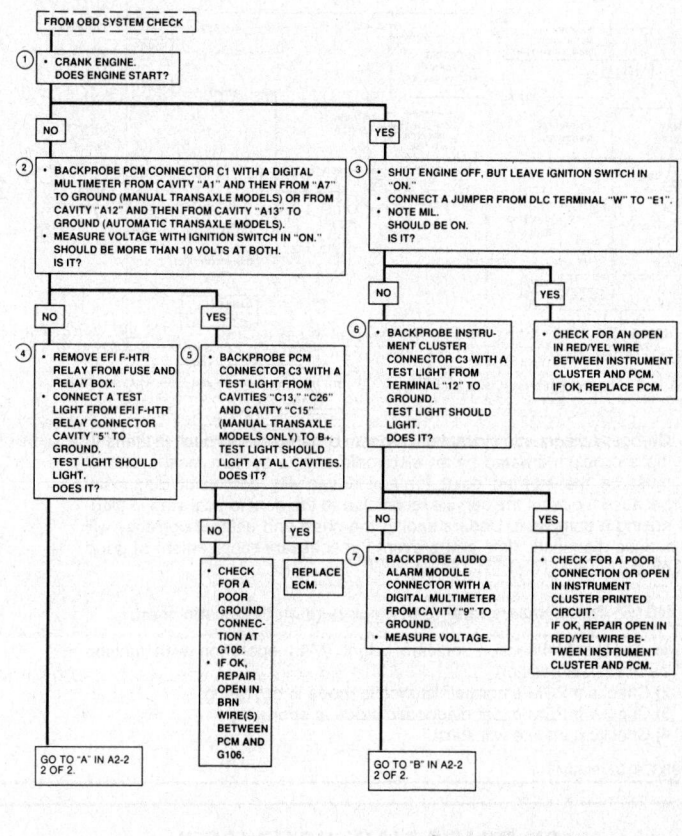

CHART A2-1, NO MALFUNCTION INDICATOR LIGHT (2 OF 2) (PRIZM LSi)

NOTE: Test numbers refer to test numbers on diagnostic chart.

8) Checks if EFI F-HTR relay coil is receiving power.
9) Checks for open in EFI F-HTR ground wire.
10) Checks for open in Black/Orange wire between junction block 1 and fuse/relay box or a faulty junction block 1.

DIAGNOSTIC AIDS

Check for open in EFI F-HTR, IGN and GAUGE fuses. Ensure EFI F-HTR relay is securely mounted in fuse/relay box. An intermittent condition may be caused by poor connection, rubbed-through insulation, or a broken wire inside insulation. Check PCM harness connectors for backed-out terminals, improper mating, broken locks, improperly formed or damaged terminals, and poor terminal-to-wire connections before component replacement.

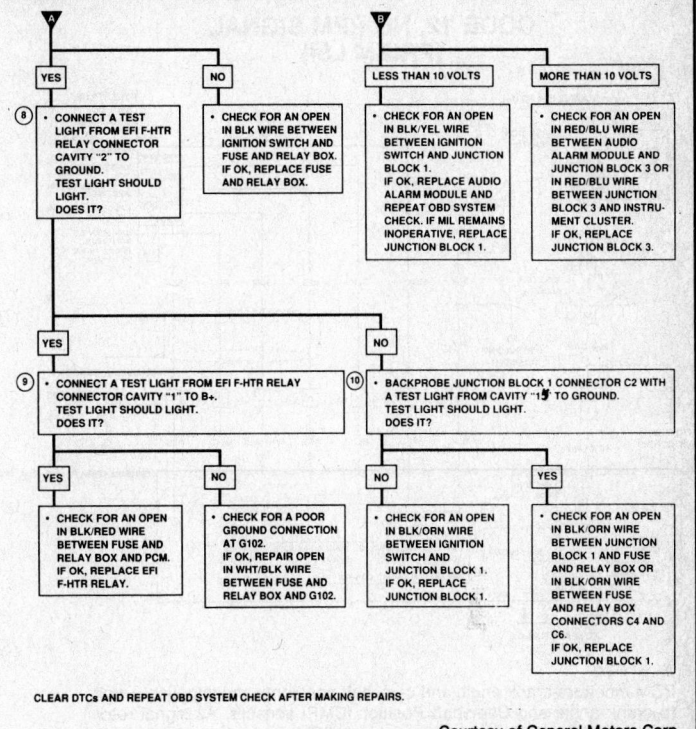

CLEAR DTCs AND REPEAT OBD SYSTEM CHECK AFTER MAKING REPAIRS.

94C44513

Courtesy of General Motors Corp.

CHART A2-2, MALFUNCTION INDICATOR LIGHT (MIL) WON'T FLASH ANY CODES, ON STEADY (PRIZM LSi)

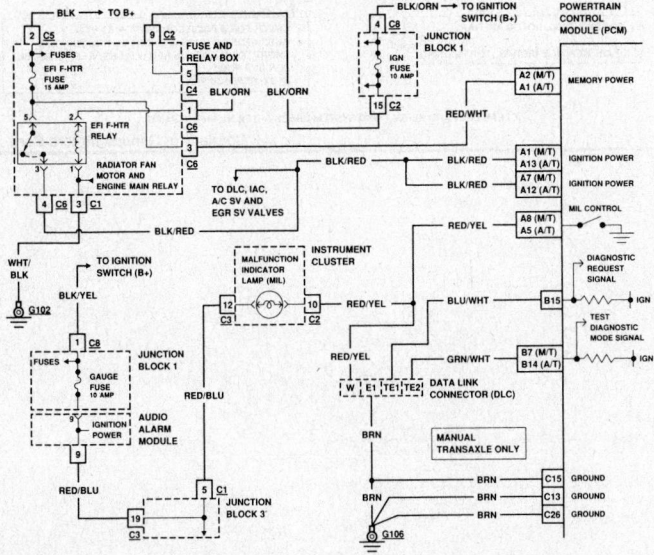

When Data Link Connector (DLC) terminals TE1 and E1 are jumpered, Malfunction Indicator Light (MIL) will flash codes that are in PCM's memory.

NOTE: Test numbers refer to test numbers on diagnostic chart.

1) Checks for short to ground in Red/Yellow wire.
2) Checks for open in Blue/White wire (diagnostic request terminal).
3) Checks for open in Brown ground wire to DLC or a faulty PCM.

DIAGNOSTIC AIDS

An intermittent condition may be caused by poor connection, rubbed-through insulation, or a broken wire inside insulation. Check PCM harness connectors for backed-out terminals, improper mating, broken locks, improperly formed or damaged terminals, and poor terminal-to-wire connections before component replacement.

CLEAR DTCs AND REPEAT OBD SYSTEM CHECK AFTER MAKING REPAIRS.

93G79109 94D44514

Courtesy of General Motors Corp.

CODE 12, NO RPM SIGNAL (PRIZM LSi)

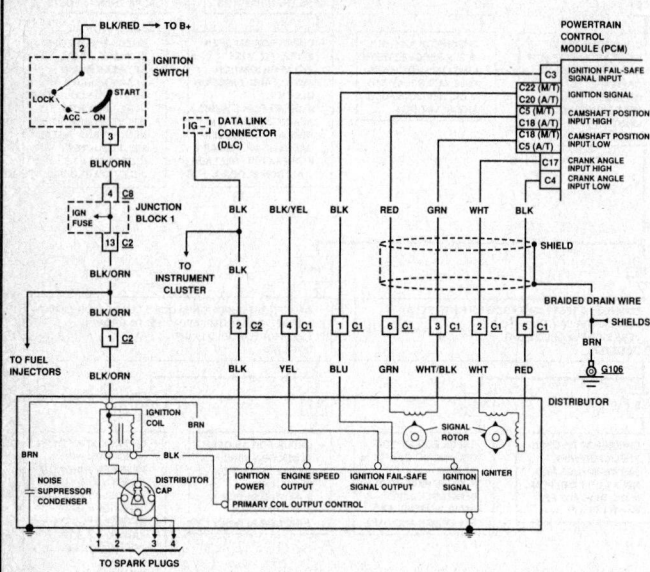

PCM monitors crank angle and camshaft positions, and supplies .7 volt to crank angle and Camshaft Position (CMP) sensors. As signal rotor rotates, voltage is toggled high and low. PCM determines crank angle and camshaft positions by toggled voltage input. Code 12 will set if PCM does not detect crank angle input while engine is cranking for 2 seconds or more, or PCM does not detect camshaft position input with engine speed 600-4000 RPM for 3 seconds or more.

NOTE: Test numbers refer to test numbers on diagnostic chart.

1) Checks for faults in crank angle input low circuitry and PCM.
2) Checks for faults in crank angle input high circuitry and PCM.
3) Checks for faults in camshaft position input low circuitry and PCM.
4) Checks for faults in camshaft position input high circuitry and PCM. Also for a misadjusted signal rotor air gap.

93E79115 94E44515

DIAGNOSTIC AIDS

Check for cracks in distributor cap and rotor. Check for properly adjusted signal rotor air gap. An intermittent condition may be caused by poor connection, rubbed-through insulation, or a broken wire inside insulation. Check PCM harness connectors for backed-out terminals, improper mating, broken locks, improperly formed or damaged terminals, and poor terminal-to-wire connections before component replacement.

⟨Y⟩ IMPORTANT: MAKE SURE THAT THE OBD SYSTEM CHECK HAS BEEN PERFORMED BEFORE CONTINUING DIAGNOSIS.

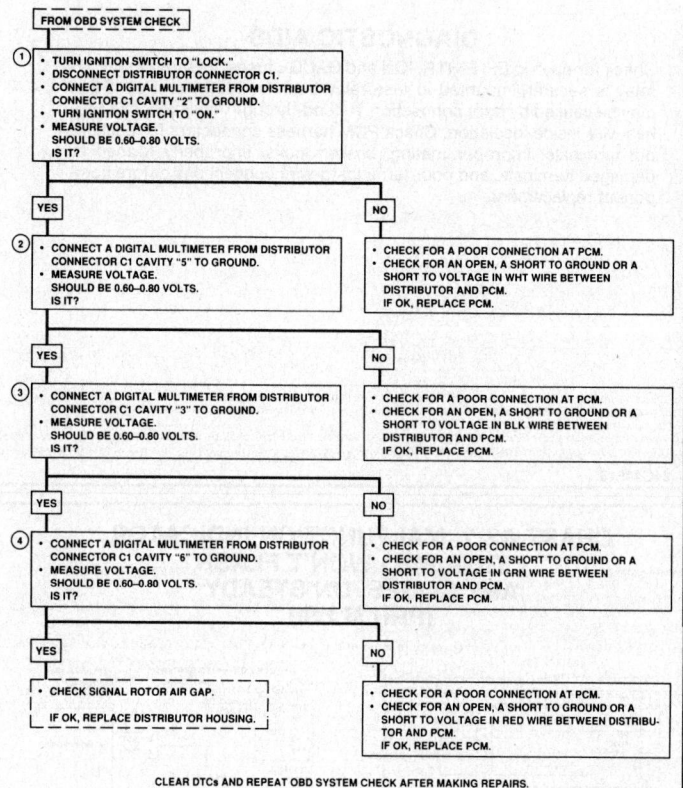

CLEAR DTCs AND REPEAT OBD SYSTEM CHECK AFTER MAKING REPAIRS.

Courtesy of General Motors Corp.

CODE 13, NO RPM SIGNAL (PRIZM LSi)

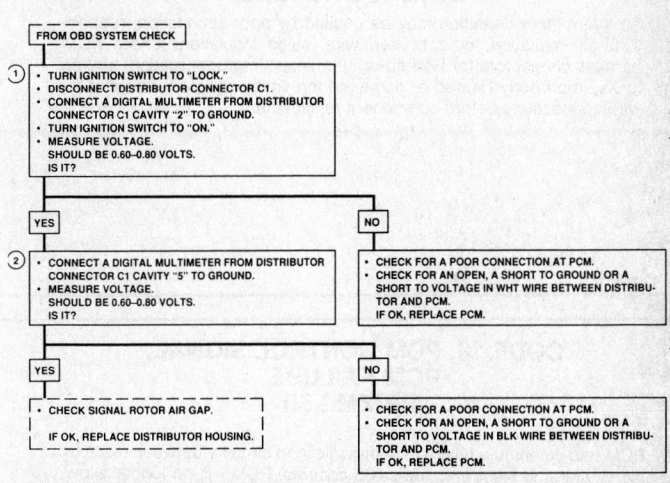

PCM monitors crank angle and camshaft positions, and supplies .7 volt to crank angle and Camshaft Position (CMP) sensors. As signal rotor rotates, voltage is toggled high and low. PCM determines crank angle and camshaft positions by toggled voltage input. Code 13 will set if PCM does not detect crank angle input with engine speed greater than 1500 RPM for .3 second or more.

NOTE: Test numbers refer to test numbers on diagnostic chart.

93E79115 94F44516

1) Checks for faults in crank angle input low circuitry and PCM.
2) Checks for faults in crank angle input high circuitry and PCM. Also for a misadjusted signal rotor air gap.

DIAGNOSTIC AIDS

Check for cracks in distributor cap and rotor. Check for properly adjusted signal rotor air gap. An intermittent condition may be caused by poor connection, rubbed-through insulation, or a broken wire inside insulation. Check PCM harness connectors for backed-out terminals, improper mating, broken locks, improperly formed or damaged terminals, and poor terminal-to-wire connections before component replacement.

IMPORTANT: MAKE SURE THAT THE OBD SYSTEM CHECK HAS BEEN PERFORMED BEFORE CONTINUING DIAGNOSIS.

FROM OBD SYSTEM CHECK

1) • TURN IGNITION SWITCH TO "LOCK."
   • DISCONNECT DISTRIBUTOR CONNECTOR C1.
   • CONNECT A DIGITAL MULTIMETER FROM DISTRIBUTOR CONNECTOR C1 CAVITY "2" TO GROUND.
   • TURN IGNITION SWITCH TO "ON."
   • MEASURE VOLTAGE.
     SHOULD BE 0.60–0.80 VOLTS.
     IS IT?

YES → 2)
NO → • CHECK FOR A POOR CONNECTION AT PCM.
• CHECK FOR AN OPEN, A SHORT TO GROUND OR A SHORT TO VOLTAGE IN WHT WIRE BETWEEN DISTRIBUTOR AND PCM.
IF OK, REPLACE PCM.

2) • CONNECT A DIGITAL MULTIMETER FROM DISTRIBUTOR CONNECTOR C1 CAVITY "5" TO GROUND.
   • MEASURE VOLTAGE.
     SHOULD BE 0.60–0.80 VOLTS.
     IS IT?

YES → • CHECK SIGNAL ROTOR AIR GAP.
IF OK, REPLACE DISTRIBUTOR HOUSING.
NO → • CHECK FOR A POOR CONNECTION AT PCM.
• CHECK FOR AN OPEN, A SHORT TO GROUND OR A SHORT TO VOLTAGE IN BLK WIRE BETWEEN DISTRIBUTOR AND PCM.
IF OK, REPLACE PCM.

CLEAR DTCs AND REPEAT OBD SYSTEM CHECK AFTER MAKING REPAIRS.

Courtesy of General Motors Corp.

CODE 14, NO IGNITION SIGNAL, (1 OF 2) (PRIZM LSi)

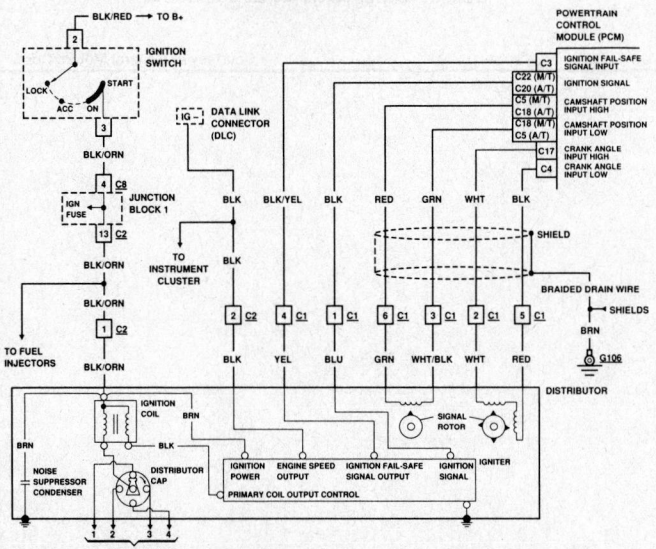

Igniter receives 5 volts from PCM. Igniter processes voltage then returns voltage to PCM as a ignition fail-safe signal. PCM also receives a .7 volt ignition signal when starter is being cranked. PCM uses these signals to pulse injectors. Code 14 will set if ignition fail-safe signal is not present 4 successive times during cranking.

NOTE: Test numbers refer to test numbers on diagnostic chart.

1) Checks for 5-volt signal from PCM.
2) Verifies .10-2 volt signal from PCM.
3) Checks for power to distributor.

93E79115 94G44517

DIAGNOSTIC AIDS

An intermittent condition may be caused by poor connection, rubbed-through insulation, or a broken wire inside insulation. Check PCM harness connectors for backed-out terminals, improper mating, broken locks, improperly formed or damaged terminals, and poor terminal-to-wire connections before component replacement.

IMPORTANT: MAKE SURE THAT THE OBD SYSTEM CHECK HAS BEEN PERFORMED BEFORE CONTINUING DIAGNOSIS.

FROM OBD SYSTEM CHECK

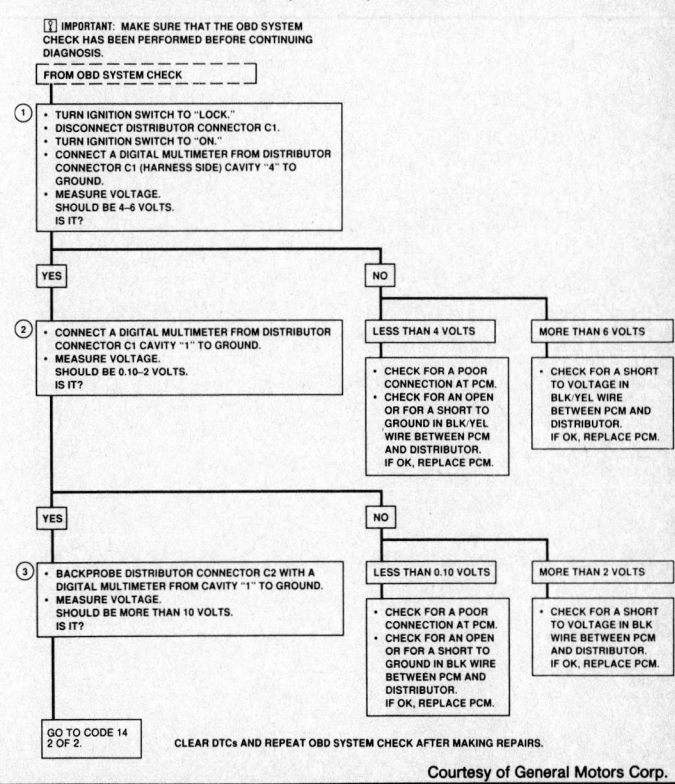

CLEAR DTCs AND REPEAT OBD SYSTEM CHECK AFTER MAKING REPAIRS.

Courtesy of General Motors Corp.

CODE 14, NO IGNITION SIGNAL, (2 OF 2) (PRIZM LSi)

NOTE: Test numbers refer to test numbers on diagnostic chart.

4) Checks for open in Black/Orange wire between junction block No. 1 and distributor or a faulty junction block No. 1.
5) Checks for open in power feed to igniter, or a faulty ignition coil or igniter.
6) Checks for open in Red/Black or Black/Orange wires to ignition switch and a faulty ignition switch.

DIAGNOSTIC AIDS

An intermittent condition may be caused by poor connection, rubbed-through insulation, or a broken wire inside insulation. Check PCM harness connectors for backed-out terminals, improper mating, broken locks, improperly formed or damaged terminals, and poor terminal-to-wire connections before component replacement.

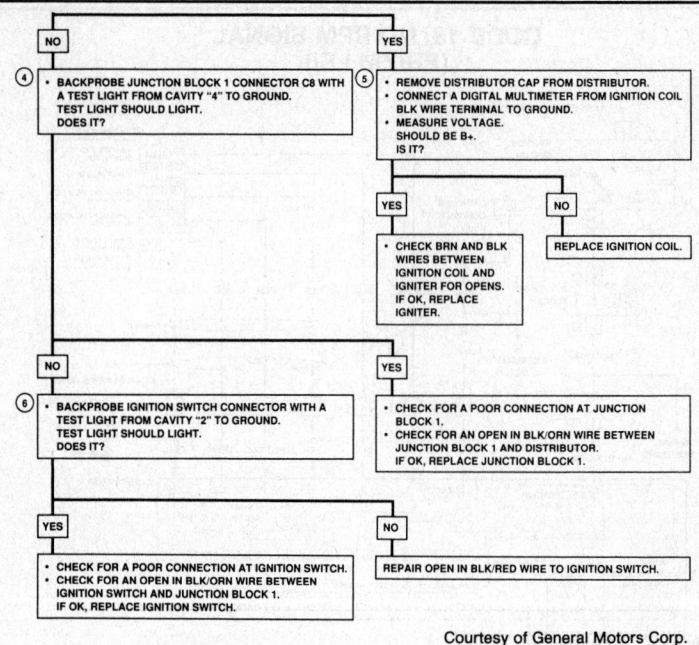

93I79119

Courtesy of General Motors Corp.

CODE 16, PCM CONTROL SIGNAL, PCM FAILURE (PRIZM LSi)

PCM has detected a failure in communication circuitry between electronic engine and electronic transaxle controls. PCM will no longer allow transaxle to go into a Torque Converter Clutch (TCC) lock-up condition. Replace PCM if Code 16 is set.

⚠ IMPORTANT: MAKE SURE THAT THE OBD SYSTEM CHECK HAS BEEN PERFORMED BEFORE CONTINUING DIAGNOSIS.

```
FROM OBD SYSTEM CHECK
```
- PCM COMMUNICATION CIRCUITRY BETWEEN ELECTRONIC ENGINE AND ELECTRONIC TRANSAXLE CONTROLS HAS DETECTED A FAILURE.
- REPLACE PCM.

CLEAR DTCs AND REPEAT OBD SYSTEM CHECK AFTER MAKING REPAIRS.

94H44518

Courtesy of General Motors Corp.

CODE 21, OXYGEN SENSOR CIRCUIT, OPEN OR SHORTED CIRCUIT (PRIZM LSi)

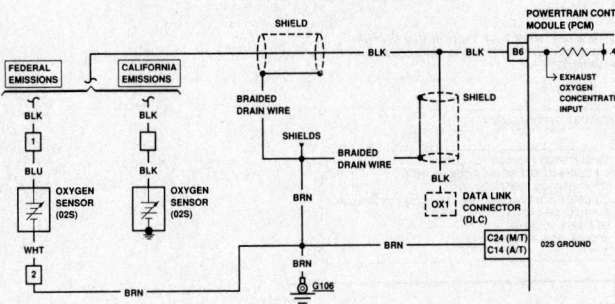

Oxygen (O₂) sensor produces a varying voltage as engine reaches normal operating temperature. Voltage will vary from .1 (lean)-1.0 (rich) volt. PCM monitors voltage and determines concentration of gases in exhaust and adjusts fuel to maintain air/fuel ratio. Code 21 will set if O₂ sensor input voltage at PCM is .35-.70 volt for 60 seconds or more with engine speed greater than 1500 RPM, and coolant temperature is greater than 176°F (80°C).

NOTE: Test numbers refer to test numbers on diagnostic chart.

1) Checks for faulty O₂ sensor.
2) Checks for open in Black wire between PCM and O₂ sensor.
3) Checks for open in Brown wire between PCM and G106.
4) Checks for short to ground in Black wire between PCM and O₂ sensor, open in Brown wire to O₂ sensor (federal emissions only), and a faulty PCM.

DIAGNOSTIC AIDS

Verify clean, tight connection on G106 (Brown wire). An intermittent condition may be caused by poor connection, rubbed-through insulation, or a broken wire inside insulation. Check PCM harness connectors for backed-out terminals, improper mating, broken locks, improperly formed or damaged terminals, and poor terminal-to-wire connections before component replacement.

93C79121 94I44519

⚠ IMPORTANT: MAKE SURE THAT THE OBD SYSTEM CHECK HAS BEEN PERFORMED BEFORE CONTINUING DIAGNOSIS.

FROM OBD SYSTEM CHECK

1) • DISCONNECT O2S CONNECTOR.
   • START AND RUN ENGINE AT 1,500 RPM FOR 1 MINUTE OR UNTIL NORMAL OPERATING TEMPERATURE IS ATTAINED.
   • CONNECT A DIGITAL MULTIMETER FROM O2S CONNECTOR TERMINAL "1" (O2S SIDE) TO GROUND.
   • MEASURE VOLTAGE.
   SHOULD BE BETWEEN 0.80 AND 0.95 VOLTS.
   IS IT?

   YES → | NO → REPLACE O2S.

2) • SHUT ENGINE OFF.
   • DISCONNECT PCM CONNECTOR C2 AND C3.
   • CONNECT A DIGITAL MULTIMETER FROM PCM CONNECTOR C2 CAVITY "B6" TO O2S CONNECTOR CAVITY "1" (HARNESS SIDE).
   • MEASURE RESISTANCE.
   SHOULD BE LESS THAN 0.50 OHMS.
   IS IT?

   YES → | NO → REPAIR OPEN IN BLK WIRE BETWEEN PCM AND O2S.

3) • CONNECT A TEST LIGHT FROM PCM CONNECTOR C3 CAVITY "C24" (MANUAL TRANSAXLE MODELS) OR FROM CAVITY "C14" (AUTOMATIC TRANSAXLE MODELS) TO B+.
   TEST LIGHT SHOULD LIGHT.
   DOES IT?

   YES → | NO → REPAIR OPEN IN BRN WIRE BETWEEN PCM AND G106.

4) • CONNECT A TEST LIGHT FROM PCM CONNECTOR C2 CAVITY "B6" TO B+.
   TEST LIGHT SHOULD NOT LIGHT.
   DOES IT?

   NO → | YES →

   | CHECK FOR AN OPEN IN BRN WIRE BETWEEN O2S AND G106 (FEDERAL EMISSIONS ONLY). • CHECK FOR A POOR CONNECTION AT PCM. IF OK, REPLACE PCM. | REPAIR SHORT TO GROUND IN BLK WIRE BETWEEN PCM AND O2S. |

CLEAR DTCs AND REPEAT OBD SYSTEM CHECK AFTER MAKING REPAIRS.

Courtesy of General Motors Corp.

CODE 22, ENGINE COOLANT TEMPERATURE SENSOR, OPEN OR SHORTED CIRCUIT (PRIZM LSi)

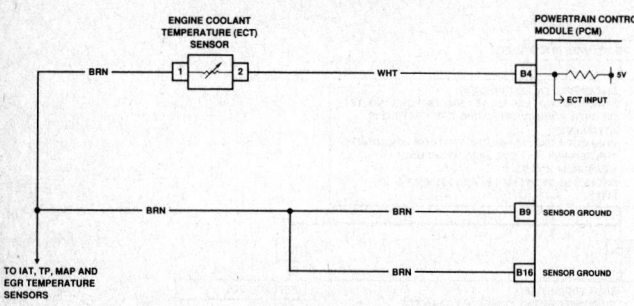

Engine Coolant Temperature (ECT) sensor is a thermistor in series with a fixed resistor in PCM. PCM applies 5 volts to sensor. PCM monitors voltage across ECT sensor and converts it into a temperature reading. When engine is cold, ECT sensor resistance is high. When engine is warm, ECT sensor resistance is low. Therefore, when engine is cold, PCM receives a high voltage input and when engine is warm, PCM receives a low voltage input. Code 22 will set if voltage input at PCM indicates either a very low or very high engine coolant temperature for at least .5 second.

NOTE: Test numbers refer to test numbers on diagnostic chart.

1) Checks for open or short to ground in White wire between PCM and ECT sensor or a faulty PCM.
2) Checks for open in Brown wire between PCM and ECT sensor or a faulty PCM.
3) Determines if problem is a faulty ECT sensor or PCM.

DIAGNOSTIC AIDS

Ensure engine is not overheating and has not been subjected to conditions which would create an overheating condition (i.e., overload, trailer towing, hilly terrain, heavy stop and go traffic, etc.). When replacing ECT sensor, check TEMPERATURE TO RESISTANCE VALUES table. A "shifted" (mis-scaled) sensor could result in poor driveability complaints. If Codes 24, 31 and 41 are also set, problem is open in sensor ground circuit. An intermittent condition may be caused by poor con-

nection, rubbed-through insulation, or a broken wire inside insulation. Check PCM harness connectors for backed-out terminals, improper mating, broken locks, improperly formed or damaged terminals, and poor terminal-to-wire connections before component replacement.

IMPORTANT: MAKE SURE THAT THE OBD SYSTEM CHECK HAS BEEN PERFORMED BEFORE CONTINUING DIAGNOSIS.

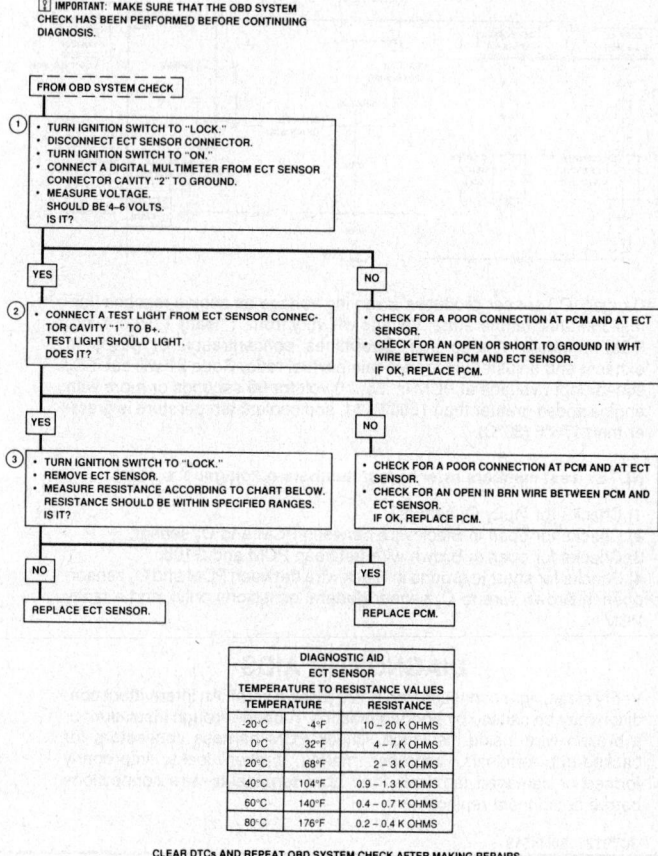

DIAGNOSTIC AID	
ECT SENSOR	
TEMPERATURE TO RESISTANCE VALUES	
TEMPERATURE	RESISTANCE
-20°C -4°F	10 – 20 K OHMS
0°C 32°F	4 – 7 K OHMS
20°C 68°F	2 – 3 K OHMS
40°C 104°F	0.9 – 1.3 K OHMS
60°C 140°F	0.4 – 0.7 K OHMS
80°C 176°F	0.2 – 0.4 K OHMS

CLEAR DTCs AND REPEAT OBD SYSTEM CHECK AFTER MAKING REPAIRS.

93E79123 94B44520

CODE 24, INTAKE AIR TEMPERATURE SENSOR, OPEN OR SHORTED CIRCUIT (PRIZM LSi)

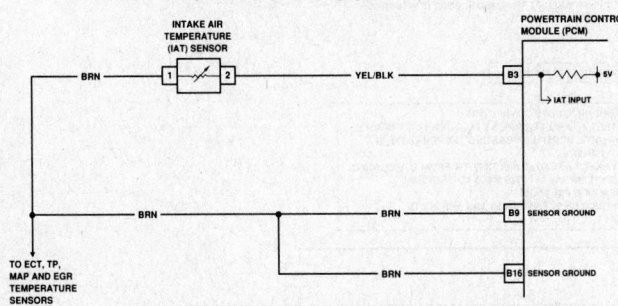

Intake Air Temperature (IAT) sensor is a thermistor in series with a fixed resistor in PCM. IAT sensor measures temperature of air entering intake manifold. PCM applies 5 volts to IAT sensor. PCM monitors voltage across IAT sensor and converts it into temperature reading. When outside air temperature is cold, IAT resistance is high. When outside air temperature is warm, IAT resistance is low. Therefore, when air temperature is cold, PCM will receive a high voltage input. When air temperature is warm, PCM will receive a low voltage input. Code 24 will set if voltage input at PCM indicates either a very low or very high air temperature for at least .5 second.

NOTE: Test numbers refer to test numbers on diagnostic chart.

1) Checks for open or short to ground in Yellow/Black wire between PCM and IAT sensor, and a faulty PCM.
2) Checks for open in Brown wire between PCM and IAT sensor, and a faulty PCM.
3) Determines if problem is a faulty IAT sensor or PCM.

DIAGNOSTIC AIDS

When replacing IAT sensor, check TEMPERATURE TO RESISTANCE VALUES table. A "shifted" (mis-scaled) sensor could result in poor drive-ability complaints. If Codes 22, 31 and 41 are also set, problem is open in sensor ground circuit. An intermittent condition may be caused by poor connection, rubbed-through insulation, or a broken wire inside insulation. Check PCM harness connectors for backed-out terminals, improper mating, broken locks, improperly formed or damaged terminals, and poor terminal-to-wire connections before component replacement.

⚠ IMPORTANT: MAKE SURE THAT THE OBD SYSTEM CHECK HAS BEEN PERFORMED BEFORE CONTINUING DIAGNOSIS.

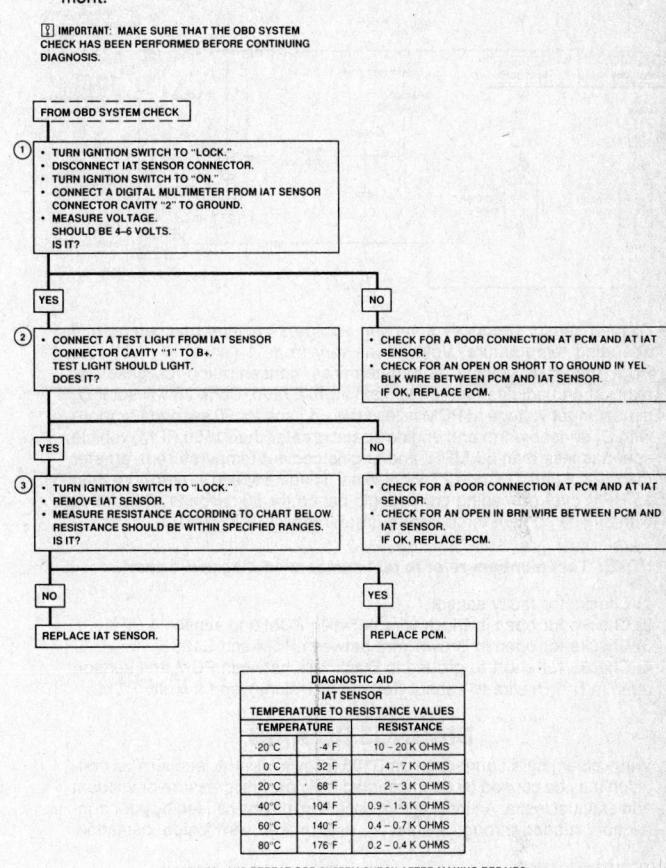

DIAGNOSTIC AID		
IAT SENSOR		
TEMPERATURE TO RESISTANCE VALUES		
TEMPERATURE		RESISTANCE
-20°C	-4 F	10 – 20 K OHMS
0°C	32 F	4 – 7 K OHMS
20°C	68 F	2 – 3 K OHMS
40°C	104 F	0.9 – 1.3 K OHMS
60°C	140 F	0.4 – 0.7 K OHMS
80°C	176 F	0.2 – 0.4 K OHMS

CLEAR DTCs AND REPEAT OBD SYSTEM CHECK AFTER MAKING REPAIRS.

93G79125 94C44521

Courtesy of General Motors Corp.

CODE 25, OXYGEN SENSOR, LEAN EXHAUST INDICATED (PRIZM LSi)

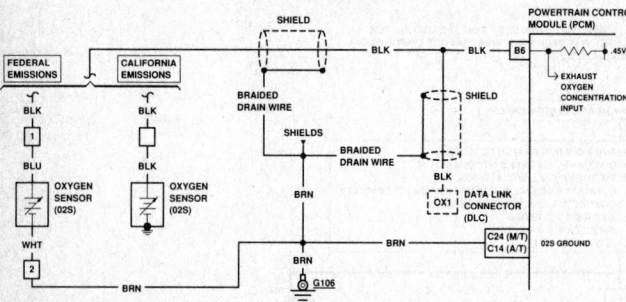

Oxygen sensor produces a varying voltage as engine reaches normal operating temperature. Voltage will vary from .1 (lean)-1.0 (rich) volt. PCM monitors voltage and determines concentration of gases in exhaust and adjusts fuel to maintain air/fuel ratio. Code 25 will set if O_2 sensor input voltage at PCM is less than .45 volt for 90 seconds or more with O_2 sensor warm and engine speed greater than 1500 RPM, vehicle speed is less than 60 MPH, and engine coolant temperature is greater than 122°F (50°C). Code 25 will also set if engine speed varies more than 15 RPM over preceding crank angle period for 30 seconds while idling with engine coolant temperature greater than 122°F (50°C).

NOTE: Test numbers refer to test numbers on diagnostic chart.

1) Checks for faulty sensor.
2) Checks for open in Black wire between PCM and sensor.
3) Checks for open in Brown wire between PCM and G106.
4) Checks for short to ground in Black wire between PCM and sensor, open in Brown wire to sensor (federal emissions), and a faulty PCM.

DIAGNOSTIC AIDS

Verify clean, tight connection on G106 (Brown wire). A lean air/fuel condition may be caused by contaminated fuel, low fuel pressure or vacuum and exhaust leaks. An intermittent condition may be caused by poor connection, rubbed-through insulation, or a broken wire inside insulation.

Check PCM harness connectors for backed-out terminals, improper mating, broken locks, improperly formed or damaged terminals, and poor terminal-to-wire connections before component replacement.

Y IMPORTANT: MAKE SURE THAT THE OBD SYSTEM CHECK HAS BEEN PERFORMED BEFORE CONTINUING DIAGNOSIS.

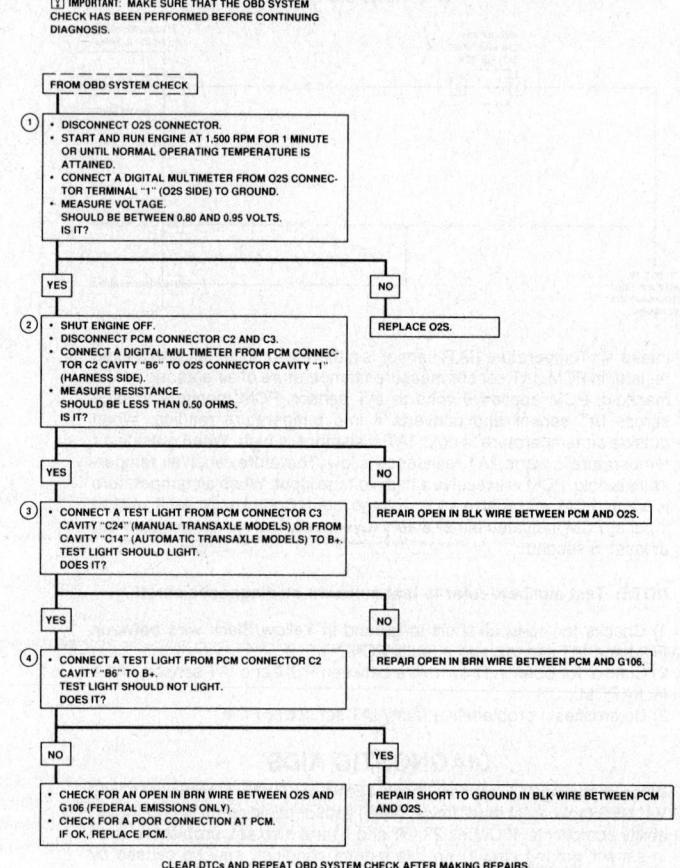

CLEAR DTCs AND REPEAT OBD SYSTEM CHECK AFTER MAKING REPAIRS.

93C79121 94D44522

CODE 26, OXYGEN SENSOR, RICH EXHAUST INDICATED (PRIZM LSi)

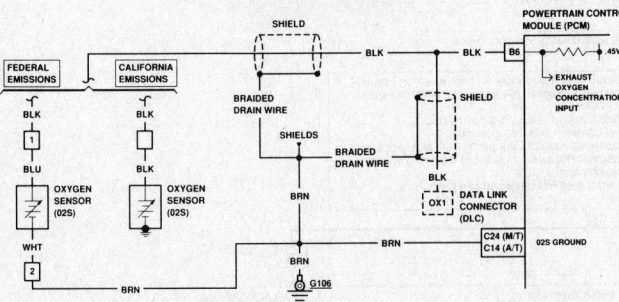

Oxygen sensor produces a varying voltage as engine reaches normal operating temperature. Voltage will vary from .1 (lean) to 1.0 (rich) volt. PCM monitors voltage and determines concentration of gases in exhaust and adjusts fuel to maintain air/fuel ratio. Code 26 will set if engine speed varies more than 15 RPM over preceding crank angle period for 30 seconds while idling with engine coolant temperature greater than 122°F (50°C).

NOTE: Test numbers refer to test numbers on diagnostic chart.

1) Checks for faulty sensor.
2) Checks for open in Black wire between PCM and sensor.
3) Checks for open in Brown wire between PCM and G106.
4) Checks for short to ground in Black wire between PCM and sensor, open in Brown wire to sensor (Federal emissions), and a faulty PCM.

DIAGNOSTIC AIDS

Verify clean, tight connection on G106 (Brown wire). A rich air/fuel condition may be caused by high fuel pressure, faulty EVAP canister purge system, faulty MAP sensor, or faulty EGR system (Calif. emissions). An intermittent condition may be caused by poor connection, rubbed-through insulation, or a broken wire inside insulation. Check PCM harness connectors for backed-out terminals, improper mating, broken locks, improperly formed or damaged terminals, and poor terminal-to-wire connections before component replacement.

93C79121 94E44523

⚠ IMPORTANT: MAKE SURE THAT THE OBD SYSTEM CHECK HAS BEEN PERFORMED BEFORE CONTINUING DIAGNOSIS.

FROM OBD SYSTEM CHECK

①
- DISCONNECT O2S CONNECTOR.
- START AND RUN ENGINE AT 1,500 RPM FOR 1 MINUTE OR UNTIL NORMAL OPERATING TEMPERATURE IS ATTAINED.
- CONNECT A DIGITAL MULTIMETER FROM O2S CONNECTOR TERMINAL "1" (O2S SIDE) TO GROUND.
- MEASURE VOLTAGE.
SHOULD BE BETWEEN 0.80 AND 0.95 VOLTS.
IS IT?

YES → (down) NO → REPLACE O2S.

②
- SHUT ENGINE OFF.
- DISCONNECT PCM CONNECTOR C2 AND C3.
- CONNECT A DIGITAL MULTIMETER FROM PCM CONNECTOR C2 CAVITY "B6" TO O2S CONNECTOR CAVITY "1" (HARNESS SIDE).
- MEASURE RESISTANCE.
SHOULD BE LESS THAN 0.50 OHMS.
IS IT?

YES → (down) NO → REPAIR OPEN IN BLK WIRE BETWEEN PCM AND O2S.

③
- CONNECT A TEST LIGHT FROM PCM CONNECTOR C3 CAVITY "C24" (MANUAL TRANSAXLE MODELS) OR FROM CAVITY "C14" (AUTOMATIC TRANSAXLE MODELS) TO B+.
TEST LIGHT SHOULD LIGHT.
DOES IT?

YES → (down) NO → REPAIR OPEN IN BRN WIRE BETWEEN PCM AND G106.

④
- CONNECT A TEST LIGHT FROM PCM CONNECTOR C2 CAVITY "B6" TO B+.
TEST LIGHT SHOULD NOT LIGHT.
DOES IT?

NO → CHECK FOR AN OPEN IN BRN WIRE BETWEEN O2S AND G106 (FEDERAL EMISSIONS ONLY).
- CHECK FOR A POOR CONNECTION AT PCM.
IF OK, REPLACE PCM.

YES → REPAIR SHORT TO GROUND IN BLK WIRE BETWEEN PCM AND O2S.

CLEAR DTCs AND REPEAT OBD SYSTEM CHECK AFTER MAKING REPAIRS.

CODE 27, SUB-OXYGEN SENSOR, OPEN OR SHORTED CIRCUIT (PRIZM LSi – CALIF. EMISSIONS)

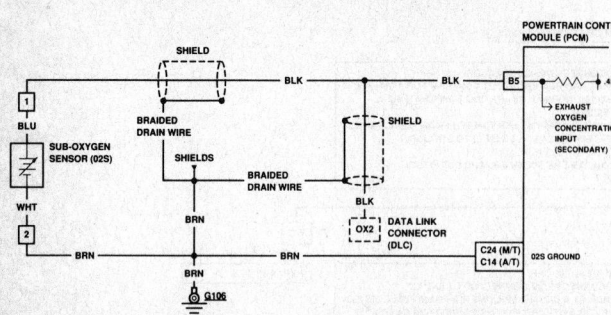

Sub-oxygen sensor produces a varying voltage as engine reaches normal operating temperature. Voltage will vary from .1 (lean) to 1.0 (rich) volt. PCM monitors voltage and determines concentration of gases in exhaust after converter. PCM uses this input and Oxygen (O_2) sensor input, and adjusts fuel to maintain air/fuel ratio. Code 27 will set when engine is at operating temperature and engine is off idle for 2 seconds or more with O_2 sensor input at PCM .45 volt or more, and sub-O_2 sensor input at PCM .45 volt or less.

NOTE: Test numbers refer to test numbers on diagnostic chart.

1) Checks for faulty sub-O_2 sensor.
2) Checks for open in Black wire between PCM and sub-O_2 sensor.
3) Checks for open in Brown wire between PCM and G106.
4) Checks for short to ground in Black wire between PCM and sub-O_2 sensor, open in Brown wire to sub-O_2 sensor, and a faulty PCM.

DIAGNOSTIC AIDS

Verify clean, tight connection on G106 (Brown wire). An intermittent condition may be caused by poor connection, rubbed-through insulation, or a broken wire inside insulation. Check PCM harness connectors for backed-out terminals, improper mating, broken locks, improperly formed or damaged terminals, and poor terminal-to-wire connections before component replacement.

93I79127 94F44524

⚠ **IMPORTANT:** MAKE SURE THAT THE DIAGNOSTIC CIRCUIT CHECK HAS BEEN PERFORMED BEFORE CONTINUING DIAGNOSIS.

FROM DIAGNOSTIC CIRCUIT CHECK

① • START AND RUN ENGINE AT 1,500 RPM FOR 1 MINUTE OR UNTIL NORMAL OPERATING TEMPERATURE IS ATTAINED.
• RAISE AND SUITABLY SUPPORT VEHICLE.
• DISCONNECT SUB-O2S CONNECTOR.
• CONNECT A DIGITAL MULTIMETER FROM SUB-O2S CONNECTOR TERMINAL "1" (SUB-O2S SIDE) TO GROUND.
• MEASURE VOLTAGE.
SHOULD BE BETWEEN 0.80 AND 0.95 VOLTS.
IS IT?

YES → **NO** → REPLACE SUB-O2S.

② • LOWER VEHICLE.
• SHUT ENGINE OFF.
• DISCONNECT PCM CONNECTOR C2 AND C3.
• CONNECT A DIGITAL MULTIMETER FROM PCM CONNECTOR C2 CAVITY "B5" TO SUB-O2S CONNECTOR CAVITY "1" (HARNESS SIDE).
• MEASURE RESISTANCE.
SHOULD BE LESS THAN 0.50 OHMS.
IS IT?

YES → **NO** → REPAIR OPEN IN BLK WIRE BETWEEN PCM AND SUB-O2S.

③ • CONNECT A TEST LIGHT FROM PCM CONNECTOR C3 CAVITY "C24" (MANUAL TRANSAXLE MODELS) OR FROM "C14" (AUTOMATIC TRANSAXLE MODELS) TO B+.
TEST LIGHT SHOULD LIGHT.
DOES IT?

YES → **NO** → REPAIR OPEN IN BRN WIRE BETWEEN PCM AND G106.

④ • CONNECT A TEST LIGHT FROM PCM CONNECTOR C2 CAVITY "B5" TO B+.
TEST LIGHT SHOULD NOT LIGHT.
DOES IT?

NO → **YES** → REPAIR SHORT TO GROUND IN BLK WIRE BETWEEN PCM AND SUB-O2S.

• CHECK FOR AN OPEN IN BRN WIRE BETWEEN SUB-O2S AND G106.
• CHECK FOR A POOR CONNECTION AT PCM.
IF OK, REPLACE PCM.

CLEAR DTCs AND REPEAT OBD SYSTEM CHECK AFTER MAKING REPAIRS.

Courtesy of General Motors Corp.

CODE 31, MANIFOLD ABSOLUTE PRESSURE SENSOR, OPEN OR SHORTED CIRCUIT (PRIZM LSi)

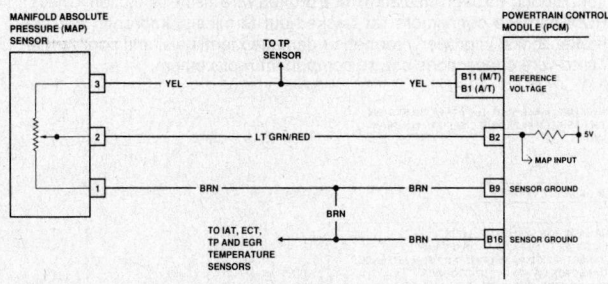

MAP sensor responds to changes in intake manifold pressure (vacuum). MAP sensor consists of a semi-conductor type pressure converting element which converts a pressure change into an electrical change and an electrical circuit which amplifies and corrects electrical change. PCM applies 5 volts to MAP sensor. Changes in pressure, resulting from engine load and RPM, are converted into voltage input monitored by PCM. A low voltage input at PCM indicates low manifold pressure and a high voltage input at PCM indicates high manifold pressure. Code 31 will set if voltage input at PCM indicates either very low or very high manifold pressure for at least .5 second.

NOTE: Test numbers refer to test numbers on diagnostic chart.

1) Checks for open or short to ground in Yellow wire between PCM and MAP sensor.
2) Checks for open in Light Green/Red wire between PCM and MAP sensor.
3) Checks for open in Brown wire between PCM and MAP sensor, and a faulty PCM or MAP sensor.

DIAGNOSTIC AIDS

If Codes 22, 24 and 41 are also set, problem is open in sensor ground circuit. An intermittent condition may be caused by poor connection, rubbed-through insulation, or a broken wire inside insulation. Check PCM harness connectors for backed-out terminals, improper mating, broken locks, improperly formed or damaged terminals, and poor terminal-to-wire connections before component replacement.

IMPORTANT: MAKE SURE THAT THE OBD SYSTEM CHECK HAS BEEN PERFORMED BEFORE CONTINUING DIAGNOSIS.

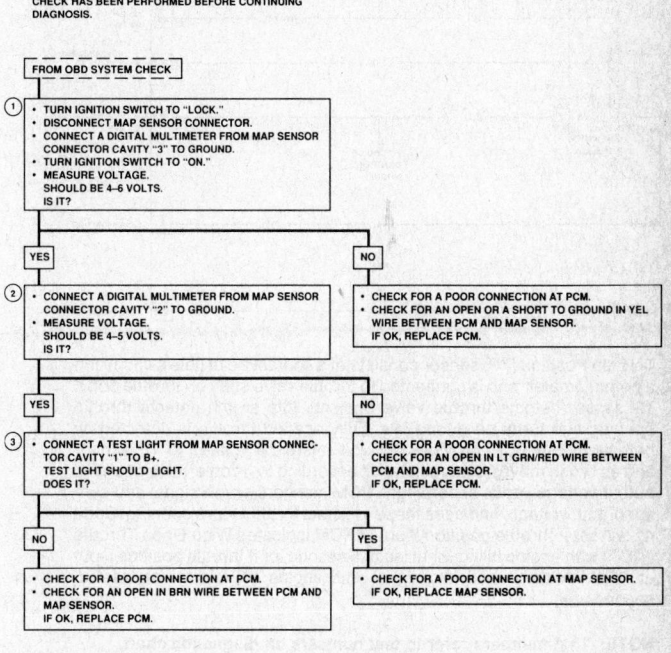

CLEAR DTCs AND REPEAT OBD SYSTEM CHECK AFTER MAKING REPAIRS.

93A79129 94G44525

Courtesy of General Motors Corp.

CODE 41, THROTTLE POSITION (TP) SENSOR, OPEN OR SHORTED CIRCUIT (PRIZM LSi)

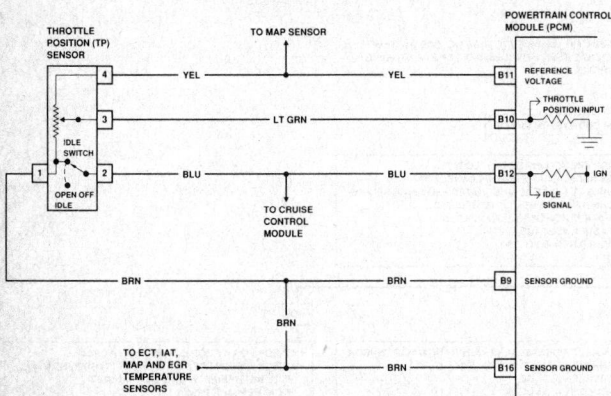

Throttle Position (TP) sensor consists of a contact point (idle switch) and a potentiometer, and is connected to throttle valve shaft on throttle body. TP sensor detects throttle valve opening. Idle switch detects throttle opening and turns on during idle. Fully opened throttle is detected by potentiometer. PCM provides a 5-volt reference voltage to TP sensor and as brush moves over resistance according to throttle valve opening, output voltage varies accordingly. PCM monitors on/off signal and sensor output voltage, and uses these to detect throttle valve opening. Code 41 will set if throttle position input at PCM indicates Wide Open Throttle (WOT) with engine idling for at least .5 second, or if throttle position input at PCM indicates and idle signal with engine off idle for at least .5 second.

NOTE: Test numbers refer to test numbers on diagnostic chart.

1) Checks for a fault in Yellow wire between PCM and TP sensor.
2) Checks for open in Brown wire between PCM and TP sensor.
3) Checks for a fault in Light Green wire between PCM and TP sensor, a faulty PCM, or a misadjusted or faulty TP sensor.

93E79131 94H44526

DIAGNOSTIC AIDS

Check for properly adjusted TP sensor before replacement of TP sensor. If Codes 22, 24 and 31 are also set, problem is open in sensor ground circuit. An intermittent condition may be caused by poor connection, rubbed-through insulation, or a broken wire inside insulation. Check PCM harness connectors for backed-out terminals, improper mating, broken locks, improperly formed or damaged terminals, and poor terminal-to-wire connections before component replacement.

⚠ IMPORTANT: MAKE SURE THAT THE OBD SYSTEM CHECK HAS BEEN PERFORMED BEFORE CONTINUING DIAGNOSIS.

FROM OBD SYSTEM CHECK

① • TURN IGNITION SWITCH TO "LOCK."
• DISCONNECT TP SENSOR CONNECTOR.
• CONNECT A DIGITAL MULTIMETER FROM TP SENSOR CONNECTOR CAVITY "4" TO GROUND.
• TURN IGNITION SWITCH TO "ON."
• MEASURE VOLTAGE.
SHOULD BE 4–6 VOLTS.
IS IT?

YES → **NO**

② • CONNECT A DIGITAL MULTIMETER FROM TP SENSOR CONNECTOR CAVITY "4" TO CAVITY "1".
• MEASURE VOLTAGE.
SHOULD BE 4–6 VOLTS.
IS IT?

NO:
• CHECK FOR A POOR CONNECTION AT PCM.
• CHECK FOR AN OPEN, A SHORT TO VOLTAGE OR A SHORT TO GROUND IN YEL WIRE BETWEEN PCM AND TP SENSOR.
IF OK, REPLACE PCM.

YES → **NO**

③ • CONNECT A DIGITAL MULTIMETER FROM TP SENSOR CONNECTOR CAVITY "4" TO CAVITY "3".
• MEASURE VOLTAGE.
SHOULD BE 4.3–4.8 VOLTS.
IS IT?

NO:
• CHECK FOR A POOR CONNECTION AT PCM.
• CHECK FOR AN OPEN IN BRN WIRE BETWEEN PCM AND TP SENSOR.
IF OK, REPLACE PCM.

YES → **NO**

YES:
• CHECK FOR A POOR CONNECTION AT TP SENSOR.
IF OK, ADJUST/REPLACE TP SENSOR.

NO:
• CHECK FOR A POOR CONNECTION AT PCM.
• CHECK FOR AN OPEN, A SHORT TO VOLTAGE OR A SHORT TO GROUND IN LT GRN WIRE BETWEEN PCM AND TP SENSOR.
IF OK, REPLACE PCM.

CLEAR DTCs AND REPEAT OBD SYSTEM CHECK AFTER MAKING REPAIRS.

Courtesy of General Motors Corp.

CODE 42, VEHICLE SPEED SENSOR, OPEN OR SHORTED CIRCUIT (1 OF 2) (PRIZM LSi)

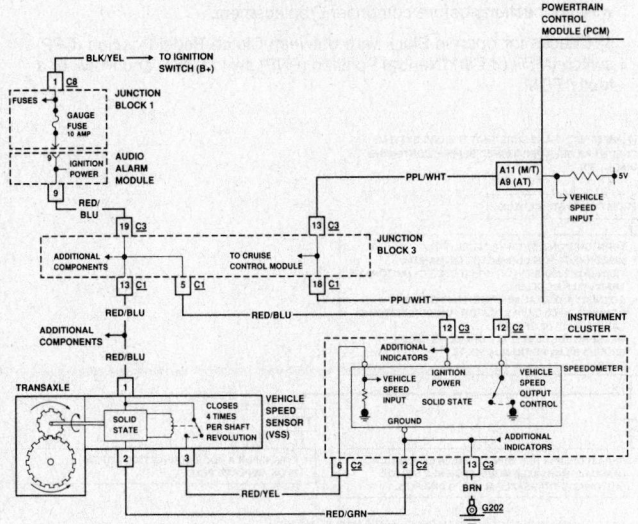

Vehicle Speed Sensor (VSS) is an electronic relay mounted on transaxle. As transaxle rotates VSS, VSS provides speedometer with a vehicle speed input (voltage pulses). This signal drives speedometer. Speedometer converts vehicle speed input into a more precise waveform and provides PCM, and cruise control module with a vehicle speed input. PCM converts this input (ground pulses) into vehicle speed. Code 42 will set if vehicle speed input is not sensed at PCM with engine speed 3000-5000 RPM and transaxle in gear, for at least 8 seconds.

NOTE: Test numbers refer to test numbers on diagnostic chart.

1) Determines if VSS is functioning properly.
2) Checks for open in power feed to VSS.
3) Checks for open or short in PCM speed input circuit or a faulty PCM.
4) Determines if PCM or speedometer is faulty.

93G79133 94I44527

DIAGNOSTIC AIDS

Verify clean, tight connection on G202 (Brown wire). An intermittent condition may be caused by poor connection, rubbed-through insulation, or a broken wire inside insulation. Check PCM harness connectors for backed-out terminals, improper mating, broken locks, improperly formed or damaged terminals, and poor terminal-to-wire connections before component replacement.

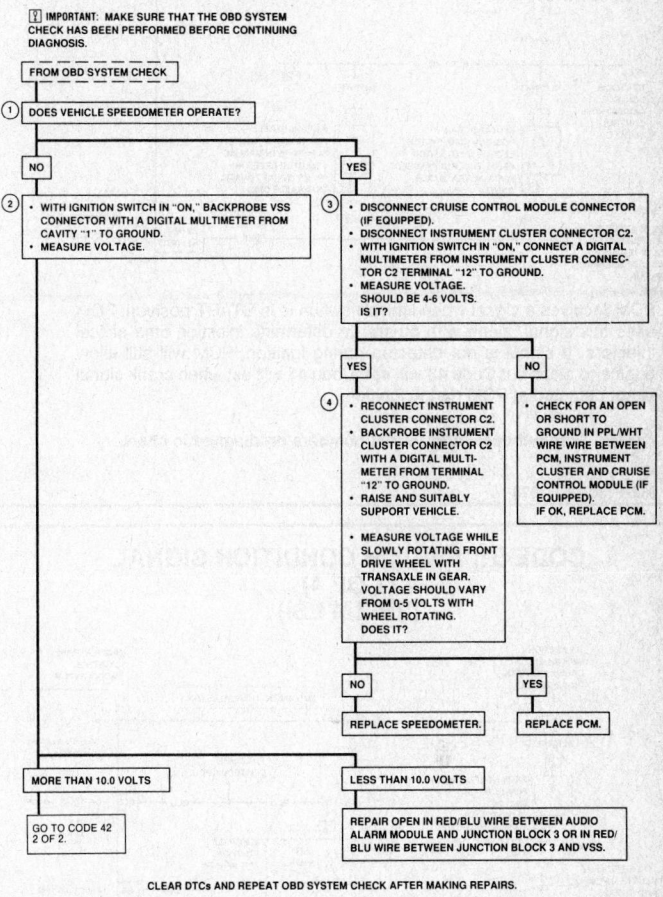

CLEAR DTCs AND REPEAT OBD SYSTEM CHECK AFTER MAKING REPAIRS.

Courtesy of General Motors Corp.

CODE 42, VEHICLE SPEED SENSOR, OPEN OR SHORTED CIRCUIT (2 OF 2) (PRIZM LSi)

NOTE: Test numbers refer to test numbers on diagnostic chart.

5) Checks for open in ground to VSS.
6) Checks for open in power feed to speedometer.
7) Determines if VSS or speedometer is faulty.

DIAGNOSTIC AIDS

Verify clean, tight connection on G202 (Brown wire). An intermittent condition may be caused by poor connection, rubbed-through insulation, or a broken wire inside insulation. Check PCM harness connectors for backed-out terminals, improper mating, broken locks, improperly formed or damaged terminals, and poor terminal-to-wire connections before component replacement.

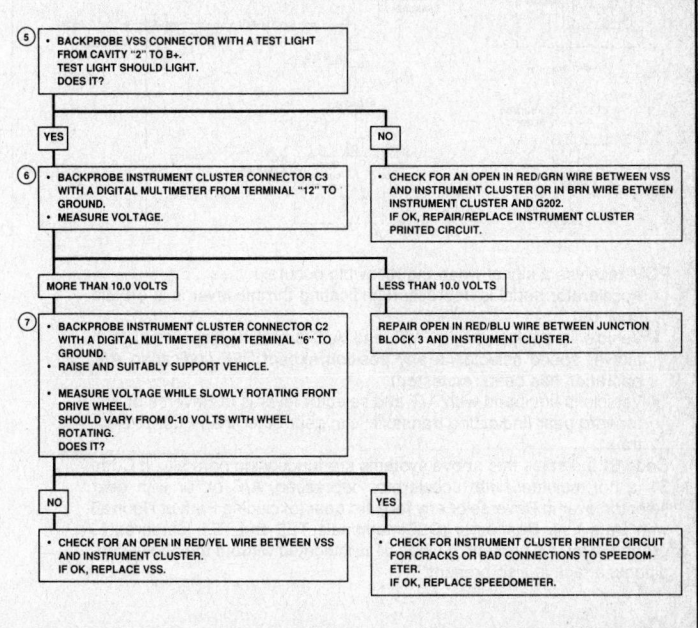

93I79135

Courtesy of General Motors Corp.

CODE 43, NO CRANK SIGNAL
(PRIZM LSi)

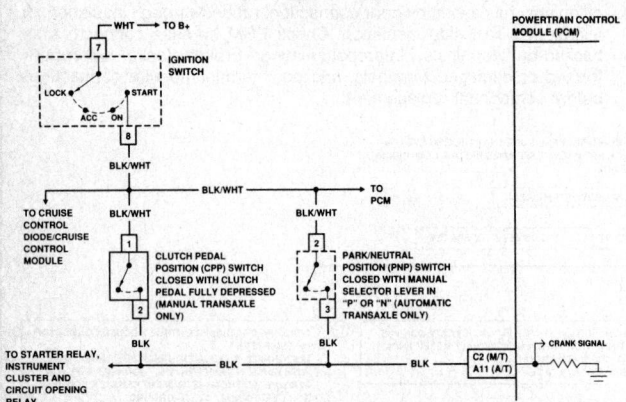

PCM receives a signal when ignition switch is in START position. PCM uses this signal, along with others, to determine injection time of fuel injectors. If signal is not detected during ignition, PCM will still allow engine to start, but Code 43 will set. Code 43 will set when crank signal is not detected at PCM during ignition.

NOTE: Test numbers refer to test numbers on diagnostic chart.

93J79136 94J44528

DIAGNOSTIC AIDS

An intermittent condition may be caused by poor connection, rubbed-through insulation, or a broken wire inside insulation. Check PCM harness connectors for backed-out terminals, improper mating, broken locks, improperly formed or damaged terminals, and poor terminal-to-wire connections before component replacement.

1) Checks for open in Black wire between Clutch Pedal Position (CPP) switch (M/T) or Park/Neutral Position (PNP) switch (A/T) and PCM, or a faulty PCM.

IMPORTANT: MAKE SURE THAT THE OBD SYSTEM CHECK HAS BEEN PERFORMED BEFORE CONTINUING DIAGNOSIS.

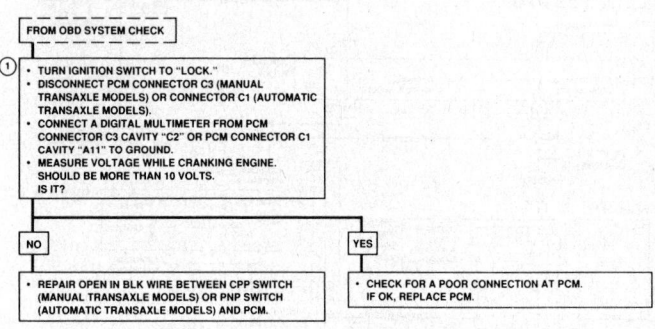

CLEAR DTCs AND REPEAT OBD SYSTEM CHECK AFTER MAKING REPAIRS.

Courtesy of General Motors Corp.

CODE 51, SWITCH CONDITION SIGNAL
(1 OF 4)
(PRIZM LSi)

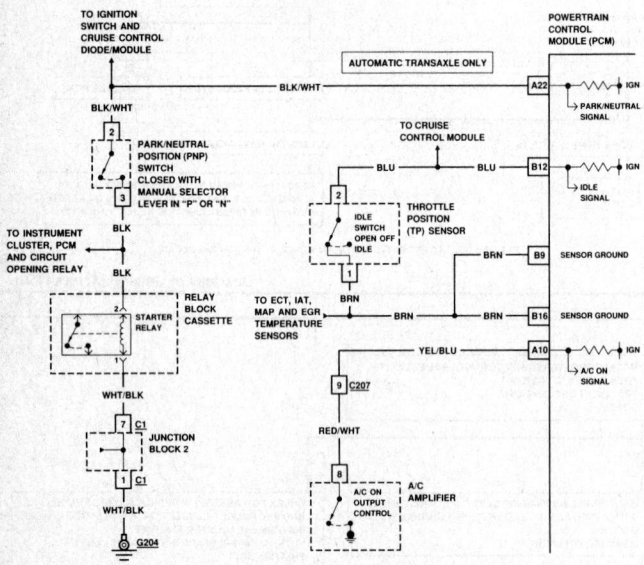

PCM receives a signal when the following occurs:
- Accelerator pedal is depressed (indicating throttle lever is in off idle position).
- Vehicle is equipped with A/C and A/C switch is depressed with blower speed selector in any position except OFF (indicating A/C operation has been requested).
- Vehicle is equipped with A/T and selector lever is in Reverse or any forward gear (indicating transaxle is in gear other than Park or Neutral).

Code 51 indicates that above systems are functioning normally. If Code 51 is not indicated with accelerator depressed, A/C on or with gear selector lever in Reverse or any forward gear (excluding Park or Neutral) with Data Link Connector (DLC) terminals TE2 and TE1 jumpered to ground, a fault is present. If Code 51 is indicated without the above conditions, a fault is also present.

93B79138 94A44529

NOTE: Test numbers refer to test numbers on diagnostic chart.

1) Determines if systems are functioning normally in test diagnostic mode.
2) Checks if TP sensor circuit is operating normally.
3) Checks for short to ground in A/C circuit, open in PNP switch circuit, open in TP sensor circuit, or a faulty PCM or A/C amplifier.

IMPORTANT: MAKE SURE THAT THE OBD SYSTEM CHECK HAS BEEN PERFORMED BEFORE CONTINUING DIAGNOSIS.

FROM OBD SYSTEM CHECK

① • TURN IGNITION SWITCH TO "LOCK."
• CLEAR DTCs.
• CONNECT A JUMPER FROM DLC TERMINAL "TE2" TO TERMINAL "E1".
• TURN IGNITION SWITCH TO "ON."
  MIL SHOULD BE FLASHING ON AND OFF RAPIDLY.
• START AND ROAD TEST VEHICLE FOR 1 MINUTE ABOVE 16 KPH (10 MPH).
• LEAVE ENGINE RUNNING AT IDLE.
• CONNECT A JUMPER FROM DLC TERMINAL "TE1" TO TERMINAL "E1".
• NOTE MIL.
  SHOULD FLASH ON AND OFF RAPIDLY, NOT DTC 51.
  DOES IT?

YES

② • HOLD ACCELERATOR PEDAL DEPRESSED OFF IDLE FOR 7-10 SECONDS.
• NOTE MIL.
  SHOULD FLASH DTC 51 AT LEAST ONCE AND THEN FLASH ON AND OFF RAPIDLY.
  DOES IT?

NO, FLASHES DTC 51

③ • SHUT ENGINE OFF, BUT LEAVE IGNITION SWITCH IN "ON."
• DISCONNECT TP SENSOR CONNECTOR.
• CONNECT A DIGITAL MULTIMETER FROM TP SENSOR CONNECTOR CAVITY "2" TO GROUND.
• MEASURE VOLTAGE.

MORE THAN 10 VOLTS

• CONNECT A DIGITAL MULTIMETER FROM TP SENSOR TERMINAL "1" TO TERMINAL "2" (TP SENSOR SIDE).
• MEASURE RESISTANCE.

LESS THAN 10 VOLTS

• CHECK FOR A POOR CONNECTION AT PCM.
• CHECK FOR AN OPEN IN BLU WIRE BETWEEN TP SENSOR AND PCM.
  IF OK, REPLACE PCM.

LESS THAN INFINITE

INFINITE

ADJUST/REPLACE TP SENSOR.

GO TO "A" IN CODE 51 2 OF 4.

GO TO "B" IN CODE 51 2 OF 4.

CLEAR DTCs AND REPEAT OBD SYSTEM CHECK AFTER MAKING REPAIRS.

Courtesy of General Motors Corp.

CODE 51, SWITCH CONDITION SIGNAL
(2 OF 4)
(PRIZM LSi)

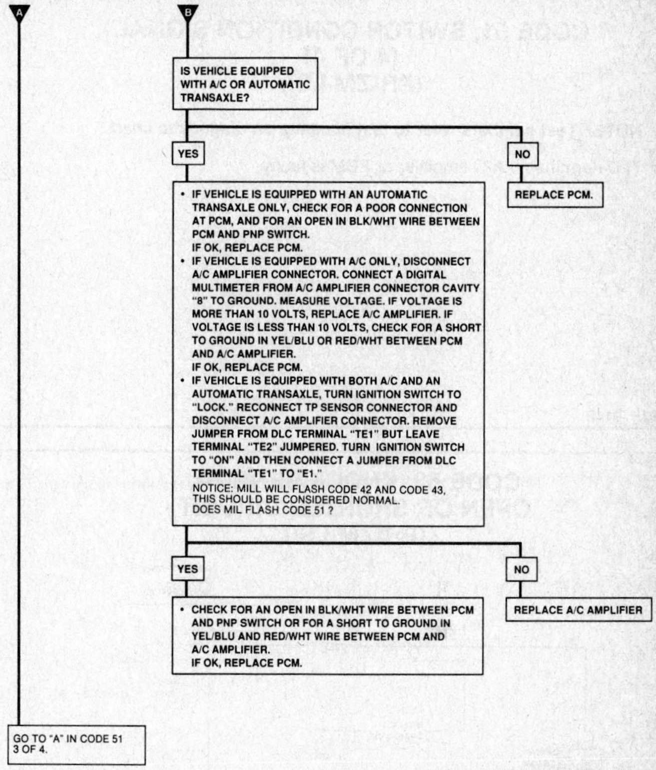

A

B

IS VEHICLE EQUIPPED WITH A/C OR AUTOMATIC TRANSAXLE?

YES

NO

- IF VEHICLE IS EQUIPPED WITH AN AUTOMATIC TRANSAXLE ONLY, CHECK FOR A POOR CONNECTION AT PCM, AND FOR AN OPEN IN BLK/WHT WIRE BETWEEN PCM AND PNP SWITCH.
  IF OK, REPLACE PCM.
- IF VEHICLE IS EQUIPPED WITH A/C ONLY, DISCONNECT A/C AMPLIFIER CONNECTOR. CONNECT A DIGITAL MULTIMETER FROM A/C AMPLIFIER CONNECTOR CAVITY "8" TO GROUND. MEASURE VOLTAGE. IF VOLTAGE IS MORE THAN 10 VOLTS, REPLACE A/C AMPLIFIER. IF VOLTAGE IS LESS THAN 10 VOLTS, CHECK FOR A SHORT TO GROUND IN YEL/BLU OR RED/WHT BETWEEN PCM AND A/C AMPLIFIER.
  IF OK, REPLACE PCM.
- IF VEHICLE IS EQUIPPED WITH BOTH A/C AND AN AUTOMATIC TRANSAXLE, TURN IGNITION SWITCH TO "LOCK." RECONNECT TP SENSOR CONNECTOR AND DISCONNECT A/C AMPLIFIER CONNECTOR. REMOVE JUMPER FROM DLC TERMINAL "TE1" BUT LEAVE TERMINAL "TE2" JUMPERED. TURN IGNITION SWITCH TO "ON" AND THEN CONNECT A JUMPER FROM DLC TERMINAL "TE1" TO E1."
  NOTICE: MILL WILL FLASH CODE 42 AND CODE 43. THIS SHOULD BE CONSIDERED NORMAL.
  DOES MIL FLASH CODE 51 ?

REPLACE PCM.

YES

NO

- CHECK FOR AN OPEN IN BLK/WHT WIRE BETWEEN PCM AND PNP SWITCH OR FOR A SHORT TO GROUND IN YEL/BLU AND RED/WHT WIRE BETWEEN PCM AND A/C AMPLIFIER.
  IF OK, REPLACE PCM.

REPLACE A/C AMPLIFIER

GO TO "A" IN CODE 51 3 OF 4.

93F79140

Courtesy of General Motors Corp.

CODE 51, SWITCH CONDITION SIGNAL
(3 OF 4)
(PRIZM LSi)

NOTE: Test numbers refer to test numbers on diagnostic chart.

4) Checks for short to ground in TP sensor circuit, or a faulty TP sensor or PCM.
5) Checks for short to ground in PNP switch circuit.
6) Determines whether system is functioning normally or if there is a problem in A/C circuit.

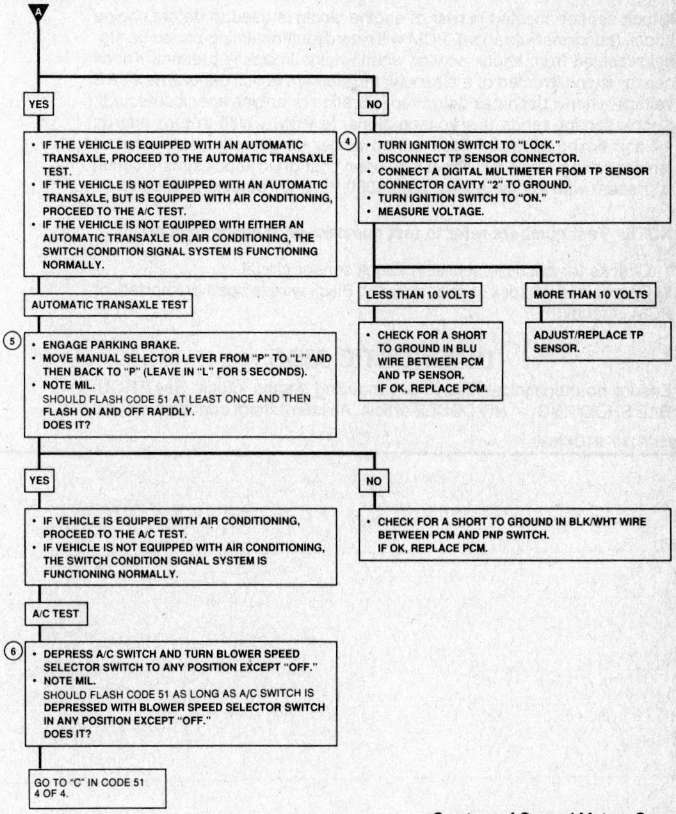

A

YES

NO

- IF THE VEHICLE IS EQUIPPED WITH AN AUTOMATIC TRANSAXLE, PROCEED TO THE AUTOMATIC TRANSAXLE TEST.
- IF THE VEHICLE IS NOT EQUIPPED WITH AN AUTOMATIC TRANSAXLE, BUT IS EQUIPPED WITH AIR CONDITIONING, PROCEED TO THE A/C TEST.
- IF THE VEHICLE IS NOT EQUIPPED WITH EITHER AN AUTOMATIC TRANSAXLE OR AIR CONDITIONING, THE SWITCH CONDITION SIGNAL SYSTEM IS FUNCTIONING NORMALLY.

④
- TURN IGNITION SWITCH TO "LOCK."
- DISCONNECT TP SENSOR CONNECTOR.
- CONNECT A DIGITAL MULTIMETER FROM TP SENSOR CONNECTOR CAVITY "2" TO GROUND.
- TURN IGNITION SWITCH TO "ON."
- MEASURE VOLTAGE.

AUTOMATIC TRANSAXLE TEST

LESS THAN 10 VOLTS

MORE THAN 10 VOLTS

⑤
- ENGAGE PARKING BRAKE.
- MOVE MANUAL SELECTOR LEVER FROM "P" TO "L" AND THEN BACK TO "P" (LEAVE IN "L" FOR 5 SECONDS).
- NOTE MIL.
  SHOULD FLASH CODE 51 AT LEAST ONCE AND THEN FLASH ON AND OFF RAPIDLY.
  DOES IT?

- CHECK FOR A SHORT TO GROUND IN BLU WIRE BETWEEN PCM AND TP SENSOR.
  IF OK, REPLACE PCM.

ADJUST/REPLACE TP SENSOR.

YES

NO

- IF VEHICLE IS EQUIPPED WITH AIR CONDITIONING, PROCEED TO THE A/C TEST.
- IF VEHICLE IS NOT EQUIPPED WITH AIR CONDITIONING, THE SWITCH CONDITION SIGNAL SYSTEM IS FUNCTIONING NORMALLY.

- CHECK FOR A SHORT TO GROUND IN BLK/WHT WIRE BETWEEN PCM AND PNP SWITCH.
  IF OK, REPLACE PCM.

A/C TEST

⑥
- DEPRESS A/C SWITCH AND TURN BLOWER SPEED SELECTOR SWITCH TO ANY POSITION EXCEPT "OFF."
- NOTE MIL.
  SHOULD FLASH CODE 51 AS LONG AS A/C SWITCH IS DEPRESSED WITH BLOWER SPEED SELECTOR SWITCH IN ANY POSITION EXCEPT "OFF."
  DOES IT?

GO TO "C" IN CODE 51 4 OF 4.

93G79141

Courtesy of General Motors Corp.

CODE 51, SWITCH CONDITION SIGNAL
(4 OF 4)
(PRIZM LSi)

NOTE: Test numbers refer to test numbers on diagnostic chart.

7) Determines if A/C amplifier or PCM is faulty.

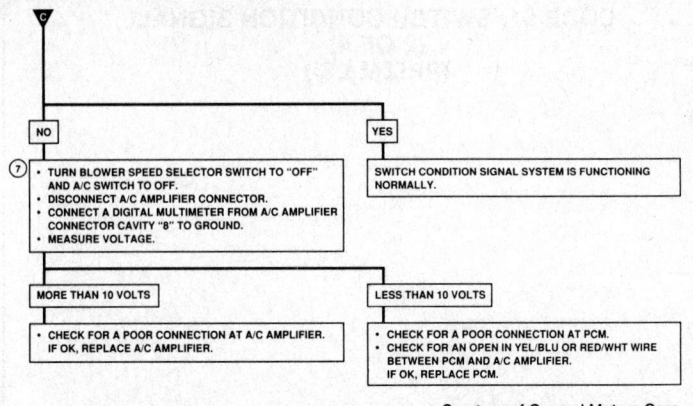

7)	• TURN BLOWER SPEED SELECTOR SWITCH TO "OFF" AND A/C SWITCH TO OFF. • DISCONNECT A/C AMPLIFIER CONNECTOR. • CONNECT A DIGITAL MULTIMETER FROM A/C AMPLIFIER CONNECTOR CAVITY "8" TO GROUND. • MEASURE VOLTAGE.

NO → ... YES → SWITCH CONDITION SIGNAL SYSTEM IS FUNCTIONING NORMALLY.

MORE THAN 10 VOLTS
• CHECK FOR A POOR CONNECTION AT A/C AMPLIFIER. IF OK, REPLACE A/C AMPLIFIER.

LESS THAN 10 VOLTS
• CHECK FOR A POOR CONNECTION AT PCM.
• CHECK FOR AN OPEN IN YEL/BLU OR RED/WHT WIRE BETWEEN PCM AND A/C AMPLIFIER. IF OK, REPLACE PCM.

93H79142   Courtesy of General Motors Corp.

CODE 52, KNOCK SENSOR,
OPEN OR SHORTED CIRCUIT
(PRIZM LSi)

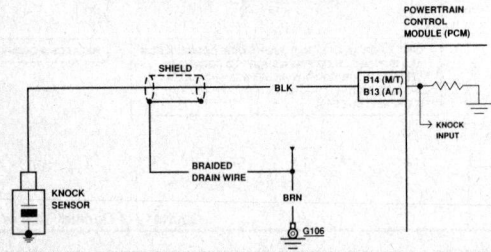

Knock sensor (located in rear of engine block) is used to detect engine knock (abnormal vibration). PCM will retard ignition timing based on signal received from knock sensor when engine knock is present. Knock sensor is constructed of a piezoelectric element which generates an AC voltage when it becomes deformed (vibration or engine knock detected). Knock sensor sends this voltage signal to PCM which in turn retards ignition timing. Engine knock will no longer be detected with reduced ignition timing. Code 52 will set if an open or short in knock sensor circuit is present with engine speed 1200-6000 RPM for at least .5 second.

NOTE: Test numbers refer to test numbers on diagnostic chart.

1) Checks for possible shorts in knock sensor circuit.
2) Determines if knock sensor is faulty, Black wire is open or shorted, or PCM is faulty.

DIAGNOSTIC AIDS

Ensure no mechanical failures are inducing engine knock. See TROUBLE SHOOTING – NO CODES article. An intermittent condition may be

caused by poor connection, rubbed-through insulation, or a broken wire inside insulation. Check PCM harness connectors for backed-out terminals, improper mating, broken locks, improperly formed or damaged terminals, and poor terminal-to-wire connections before component replacement.

⚠ IMPORTANT: MAKE SURE THAT THE OBD SYSTEM CHECK HAS BEEN PERFORMED BEFORE CONTINUING DIAGNOSIS.

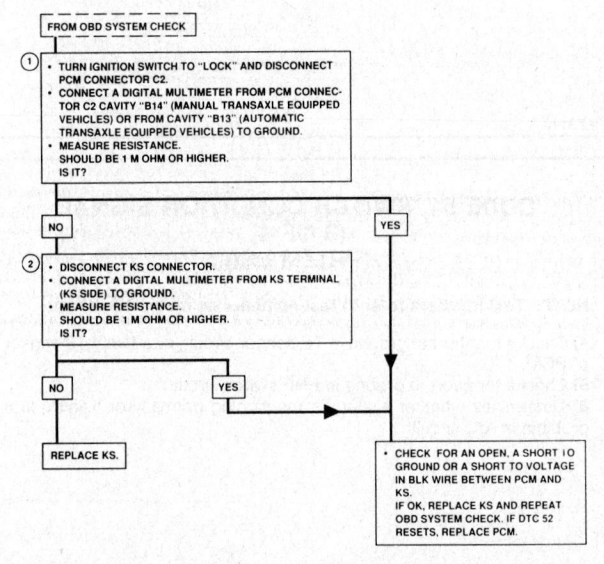

FROM OBD SYSTEM CHECK

1) • TURN IGNITION SWITCH TO "LOCK" AND DISCONNECT PCM CONNECTOR C2.
• CONNECT A DIGITAL MULTIMETER FROM PCM CONNECTOR C2 CAVITY "B14" (MANUAL TRANSAXLE EQUIPPED VEHICLES) OR FROM CAVITY "B13" (AUTOMATIC TRANSAXLE EQUIPPED VEHICLES) TO GROUND.
• MEASURE RESISTANCE. SHOULD BE 1 M OHM OR HIGHER. IS IT?

NO → ... YES

2) • DISCONNECT KS CONNECTOR.
• CONNECT A DIGITAL MULTIMETER FROM KS TERMINAL (KS SIDE) TO GROUND.
• MEASURE RESISTANCE. SHOULD BE 1 M OHM OR HIGHER. IS IT?

NO → REPLACE KS.   YES

• CHECK FOR AN OPEN, A SHORT TO GROUND OR A SHORT TO VOLTAGE IN BLK WIRE BETWEEN PCM AND KS.
IF OK, REPLACE KS AND REPEAT OBD SYSTEM CHECK. IF DTC 52 RESETS, REPLACE PCM.

CLEAR DTCs AND REPEAT OBD SYSTEM CHECK AFTER MAKING REPAIRS.

93I79143 94D44530   Courtesy of General Motors Corp.

CODE 71, EXHAUST GAS RECIRCULATION (EGR) SYSTEM (1 OF 2) (PRIZM LSi – CALIF. EMISSIONS)

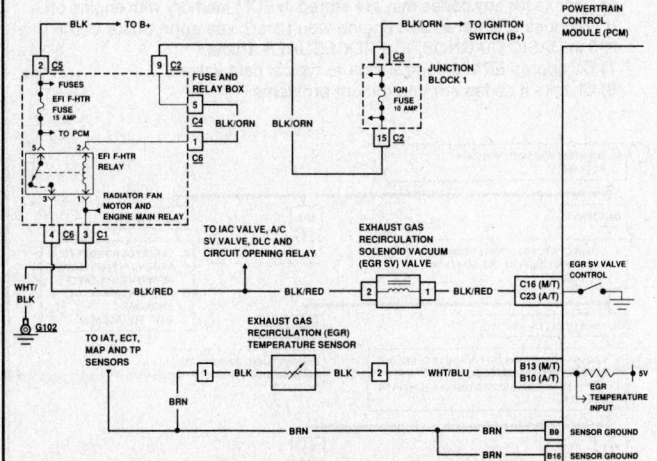

Exhaust Gas Recirculation (EGR) temperature sensor is a thermistor in series with a fixed resistor in PCM. PCM applies 5 volts to sensor. PCM monitors voltage across EGR temperature sensor and converts it into a temperature reading. When exhaust gases are cold, EGR temperature sensor resistance is high. When exhaust gases are warm, EGR temperature sensor resistance is low. Therefore, when exhaust gases are cold, PCM receives a high voltage input and when exhaust gases are warm, PCM receives a low voltage input. EGR Solenoid Vacuum (SV) valve is also controlled by PCM. EGR SV valve permits exhaust gas to be recirculated and incorporated into combustion process. PCM by monitoring exhaust gas temperature will determine when to energize EGR SV valve. Code 71 will set if engine coolant temperature is greater than 140°F (60°C) with EGR temperature less than 158°F (70°C) for at least 50 seconds.

NOTE: Test numbers refer to test numbers on diagnostic chart.

1) Checks power feed to sensor.
2) Checks ground circuit to sensor.
3) Checks EGR temperature resistance vs. temperature values.
4) Checks power feed circuit to EGR SV valve.

93A79145 94E44531

DIAGNOSTIC AIDS

Check EGR vacuum modulator and EGR valve for sticking open or closed. An intermittent condition may be caused by poor connection, rubbed-through insulation, or a broken wire inside insulation. Check PCM harness connectors for backed-out terminals, improper mating, broken locks, improperly formed or damaged terminals, and poor terminal-to-wire connections before component replacement.

⚠ IMPORTANT: MAKE SURE THAT THE OBD SYSTEM CHECK HAS BEEN PERFORMED BEFORE CONTINUING DIAGNOSIS.

FROM OBD SYSTEM CHECK

1)
- TURN IGNITION SWITCH TO "LOCK."
- DISCONNECT EGR TEMPERATURE SENSOR CONNECTOR.
- CONNECT A DIGITAL MULTIMETER FROM EGR TEMPERATURE SENSOR CONNECTOR CAVITY "2" TO GROUND.
- TURN IGNITION SWITCH TO "ON."
- MEASURE VOLTAGE.
  SHOULD BE 4–6 VOLTS.
  IS IT?

YES → **NO** →
- CHECK FOR A POOR CONNECTION AT PCM.
- CHECK FOR AN OPEN, A SHORT TO VOLTAGE OR SHORT TO GROUND IN WHT/BLU WIRE BETWEEN PCM AND EGR TEMPERATURE SENSOR.
  IF OK, REPLACE PCM.

2)
- CONNECT A TEST LIGHT FROM EGR TEMPERATURE SENSOR CONNECTOR CAVITY "1" TO B+.
  TEST LIGHT SHOULD LIGHT.
  DOES IT?

YES → **NO** →
REPAIR OPEN IN BRN WIRE BETWEEN EGR TEMPERATURE SENSOR AND PCM.

3)
- REMOVE EGR TEMPERATURE SENSOR FROM EGR VALVE.
- MEASURE RESISTANCE ACROSS SENSOR.
  RESISTANCE SHOULD BE: 69–88 K OHMS AT 50 C (122°F)
  11–15 K OHMS AT 100°C (212°F)
  2–4 K OHMS AT 150°C (302°F)
  IS IT?

YES → **NO** →
REPLACE EGR TEMPERATURE SENSOR.

4)
- BACKPROBE EGR SV VALVE CONNECTOR WITH A DIGITAL MULTIMETER FROM CAVITY "2" TO GROUND.
- MEASURE VOLTAGE.
  SHOULD BE MORE THAN 10 VOLTS.
  IS IT?

GO TO CODE 71 2 OF 2.

CLEAR DTCs AND REPEAT OBD SYSTEM CHECK AFTER MAKING REPAIRS.

Courtesy of General Motors Corp.

CODE 71, EXHAUST GAS RECIRCULATION (EGR) SYSTEM (2 OF 2) (PRIZM LSi – CALIF. EMISSIONS)

NOTE: Test numbers refer to test numbers on diagnostic chart.

5) Checks for a faulty EGR SV valve, mechanical checks and a faulty PCM.

DIAGNOSTIC AIDS

Check EGR vacuum modulator and EGR valve for sticking open or closed. An intermittent condition may be caused by poor connection, rubbed-through insulation, or a broken wire inside insulation. Check PCM harness connectors for backed-out terminals, improper mating, broken locks, improperly formed or damaged terminals, and poor terminal-to-wire connections before component replacement.

94F44532

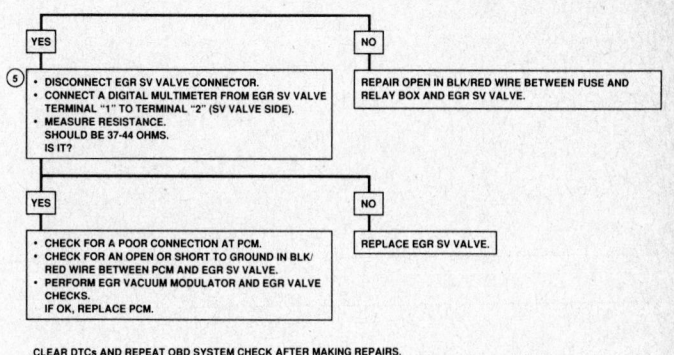

YES → **NO** →
REPAIR OPEN IN BLK/RED WIRE BETWEEN FUSE AND RELAY BOX AND EGR SV VALVE.

5)
- DISCONNECT EGR SV VALVE CONNECTOR.
- CONNECT A DIGITAL MULTIMETER FROM EGR SV VALVE TERMINAL "1" TO TERMINAL "2" (SV VALVE SIDE).
- MEASURE RESISTANCE.
  SHOULD BE 37-44 OHMS.
  IS IT?

YES → **NO** →
REPLACE EGR SV VALVE.

- CHECK FOR A POOR CONNECTION AT PCM.
- CHECK FOR AN OPEN OR SHORT TO GROUND IN BLK/RED WIRE BETWEEN PCM AND EGR SV VALVE.
- PERFORM EGR VACUUM MODULATOR AND EGR VALVE CHECKS.
  IF OK, REPLACE PCM.

CLEAR DTCs AND REPEAT OBD SYSTEM CHECK AFTER MAKING REPAIRS.

Courtesy of General Motors Corp.

1994 ENGINE PERFORMANCE
Self-Diagnostics (Cont.)

TRACKER (MFI – CALIF. & NEW YORK) CODE CHARTS

ON-BOARD DIAGNOSTIC (OBD) SYSTEM CHECK (TRACKER – MFI CALIF. & NEW YORK)

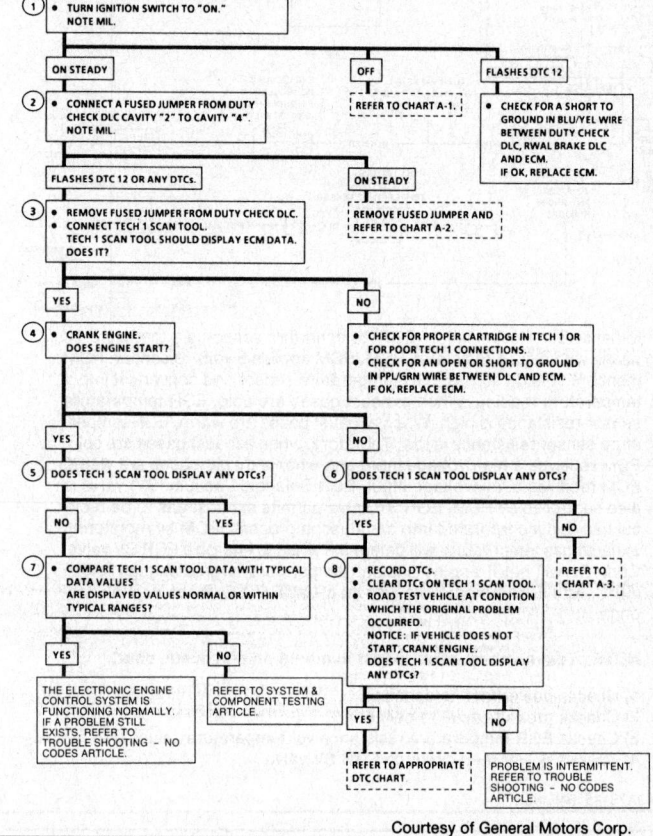

On-board diagnostic system check is an organized approach in identifying a problem created by an electronic engine system malfunction. It must be the starting point for any driveability complaint diagnosis, because it directs the service technician to the next logical step in diagnosing a complaint. Understanding the chart and using it correctly will reduce diagnostic time and prevent unnecessary replacement of good parts.

NOTE: Test numbers refer to test numbers on diagnostic chart.

1) Checks Malfunction Indicator Light (MIL) operation.
2) Checks if ECM's self-diagnostic mode is operating.
3) Checks if ECM's serial data output is operating.
4) Checks if engine will start.
5) Checks for any codes that are stored in ECM memory with engine running.
6) Checks for any codes that are stored in ECM memory with engine off. If no codes are stored and engine won't start, see appropriate CHART A-3 in BASIC DIAGNOSTIC PROCEDURES article.
7) Compares ECM's control data to typical data values.
8) Checks if codes are intermittent problems.

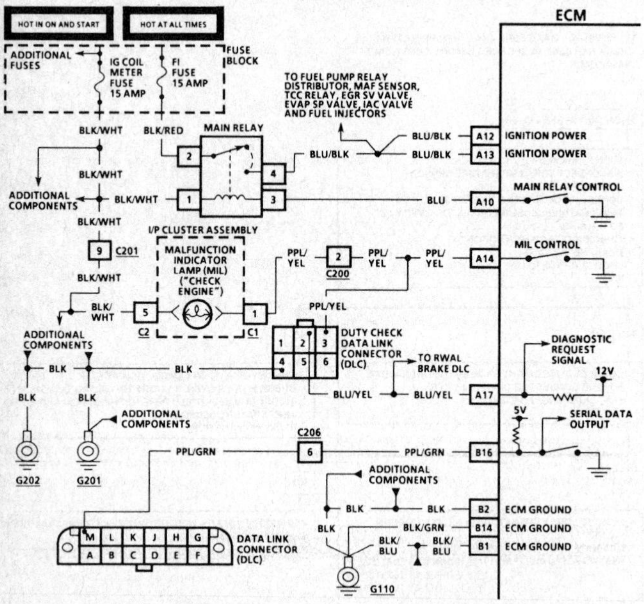

94I44931 94J44932

Courtesy of General Motors Corp.

CHART A-1,
NO MALFUNCTION INDICATOR LIGHT (MIL)
(TRACKER – MFI CALIF. & NEW YORK)

6) Checks if main relay switch is receiving power.
7) Checks if main relay coil is receiving power.
8) Checks if main relay or ECM is faulty, or for open in Blue wire between main relay and ECM.

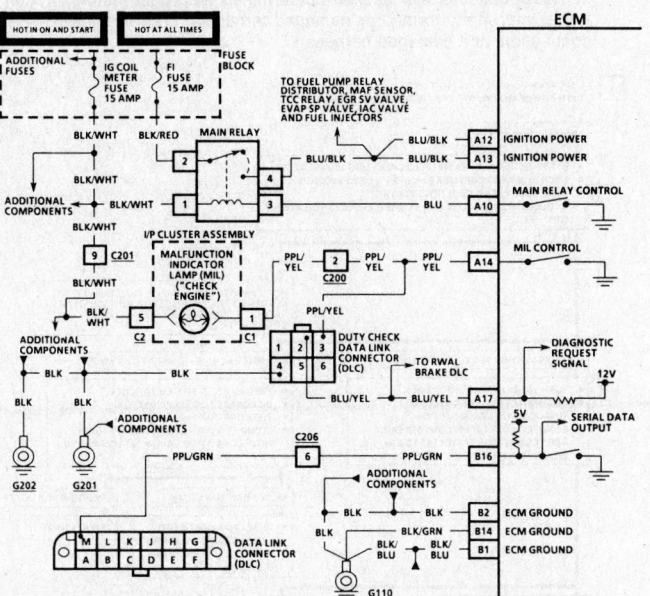

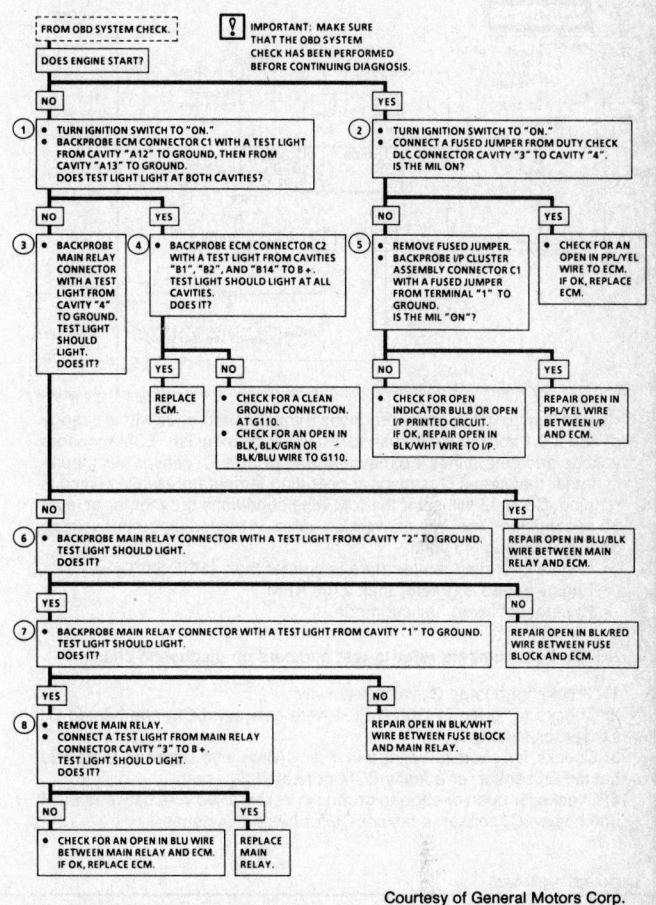

Malfunction Indicator Light (MIL) should remain on when ignition switch is in ON position and engine is not running. Battery voltage is applied to indicator bulb. ECM controls indicator bulb and turns it on by providing a ground path through Purple/Yellow wire to ECM.

NOTE: Test numbers refer to test numbers on diagnostic chart.

1) Checks if ECM is receiving power.
2) Checks if ECM is faulty.
3) Checks for open in Blue/Black wire between main relay and ECM.
4) Checks if ECM has a good ground.
5) Checks for open in Black/White wire to instrument cluster, and Purple/Yellow wire to ECM.

94I44931 94A44933

Courtesy of General Motors Corp.

CHART A-2, WON'T FLASH CODE 12
OR ANY CODES, OR MALFUNCTION
INDICATOR LIGHT (MIL) ON STEADY
(TRACKER – MFI CALIF. & NEW YORK)

Malfunction Indicator Light (MIL) will flash trouble codes when diagnostic request terminal in duty check data link connector is grounded.

NOTE: Test numbers refer to test numbers on diagnostic chart.

1) Checks for a short to ground in Purple/Yellow wire.
2) Checks for a faulty ECM or open in Blue/Yellow and Black wires to duty check data link connector.

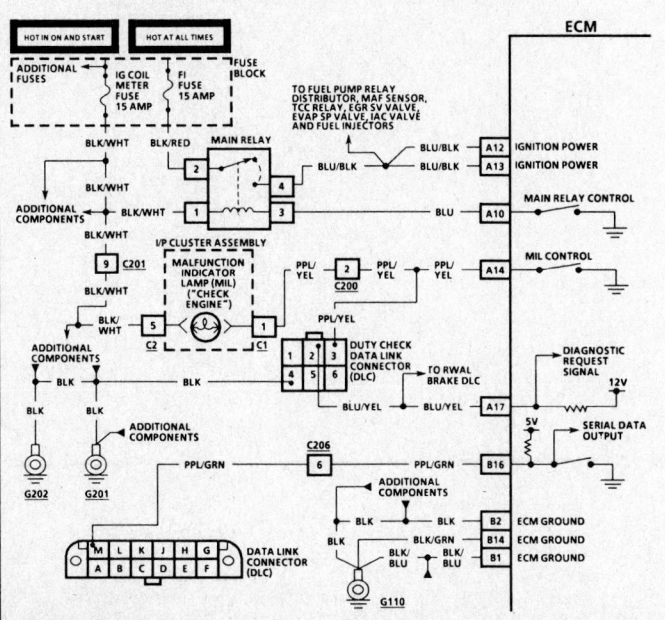

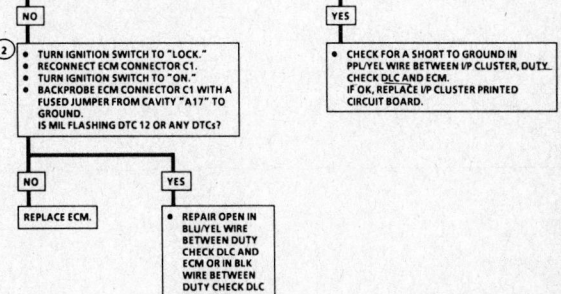

94I44931 94B44934

Courtesy of General Motors Corp.

CODE 13, HEATED OXYGEN SENSOR CIRCUIT, OPEN CIRCUIT
(TRACKER – MFI CALIF. & NEW YORK)

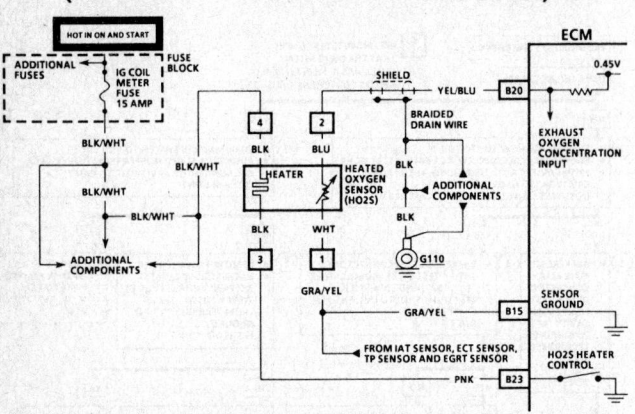

Heated Oxygen (O_2) sensor produces a voltage that varies within a range of about 0.1 volt (lean exhaust) to 1.0 volt (rich exhaust). ECM monitors voltage and determines if exhaust is lean or rich. O_2 sensor has a built-in heater that keeps O_2 sensor at operating temperature while engine is running. Code 13 will set if the following conditions are met for at least 30 seconds and the A/D conversion value of heated O_2 output voltage does not exceed .45 volt.

- Engine operating temperature is greater than 158°F (70°C).
- Engine speed is greater than 2100 RPM.
- Has not achieved fuel cut mode.

NOTE: Test numbers refer to test numbers on diagnostic chart.

1) Checks for heated O_2 voltage activity.
2) Checks for open in Gray/Yellow wire between ECM and heated O_2 sensor, or a faulty ECM.
3) Checks for short to voltage in Yellow/Blue wire between ECM and heated O_2 sensor, or a faulty ECM or heated O_2 sensor.
4) Checks for open or short to ground in Yellow/Blue wire between ECM and heated O_2 sensor, a faulty ECM or heated O_2 sensor.

94C44935 94D44936

DIAGNOSTIC AIDS

An intermittent condition may be caused by a poor connection, rubbed-through wire insulation, or a broken wire inside insulation. Check ECM harness connectors for backed-out terminals, improper mating, broken locks, improperly formed or damaged terminals, poor terminal-to-wire connection, and damaged harness.

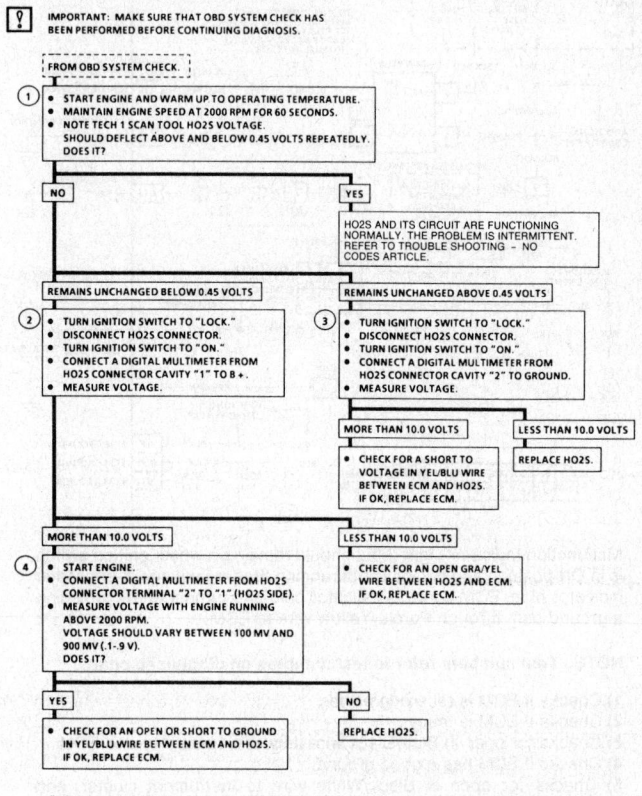

"AFTER REPAIRS," CONFIRM "CLOSED LOOP" OPERATION, NO DTCs AND NO MALFUNCTION INDICATOR LAMP (MIL).

Courtesy of General Motors Corp.

CODE 14, ENGINE COOLANT TEMPERATURE SENSOR, LOW TEMPERATURE INDICATED (TRACKER – MFI CALIF. & NEW YORK)

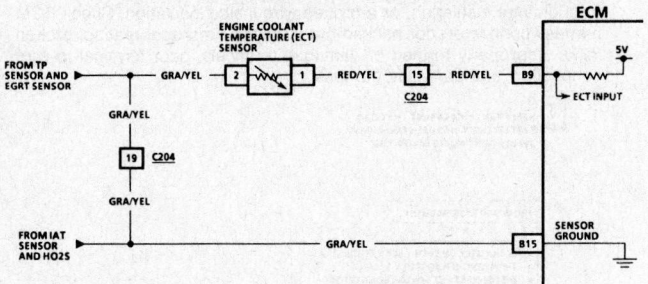

Engine Coolant Temperature (ECT) sensor is a thermistor in series with a fixed resistor in ECM. ECM applies and monitors 5 volts to sensor. ECM monitors voltage across ECT sensor and converts it into a temperature reading. When engine is cold, sensor resistance is high. When engine is warm, sensor resistance is low. Therefore, when engine is cold, ECM receives a high voltage input and when engine is warm, ECM receives a low voltage input. Code 14 will set when voltage input at ECM indicates coolant temperature less than –54°F (–48°C) for at least 5 seconds.

NOTE: Test numbers refer to test numbers on diagnostic chart.

1) This test simulates Code 15. If ECM stores Code 15, ECM and its wiring are okay and ECT sensor is faulty. If Code 14 resets, ECT sensor is okay and wiring to ECM or ECM is faulty.

2) This test determines whether an open exists in Red/Yellow or Gray/Yellow wires, a short to B+ exists in Red/Yellow wire or ECM is faulty.

DIAGNOSTIC AIDS

After engine is started, coolant temperature should rise steadily to about 203°F (95°C) and then stabilize when thermostat opens. If Codes 13, 14, 21, 23 and 44 are stored at same time, an open could exist in Gray/Yellow wire. When replacing ECT sensor, refer to TEMPERATURE TO RESISTANCE VALUES table at various temperature levels to evaluate the possibility of a "shifted" (mis-scaled) sensor.

94E44937 94F44938

A "shifted" sensor could result in poor driveability complaints. An intermittent condition may be caused by a poor connection, rubbed-through wire insulation, or a broken wire inside insulation. Check ECM harness connectors for backed-out terminals, improper mating, broken locks, improperly formed or damaged terminals, poor terminal-to-wire connection, and damaged harness.

> **IMPORTANT: MAKE SURE THAT OBD SYSTEM CHECK HAS BEEN PERFORMED BEFORE CONTINUING DIAGNOSIS.**

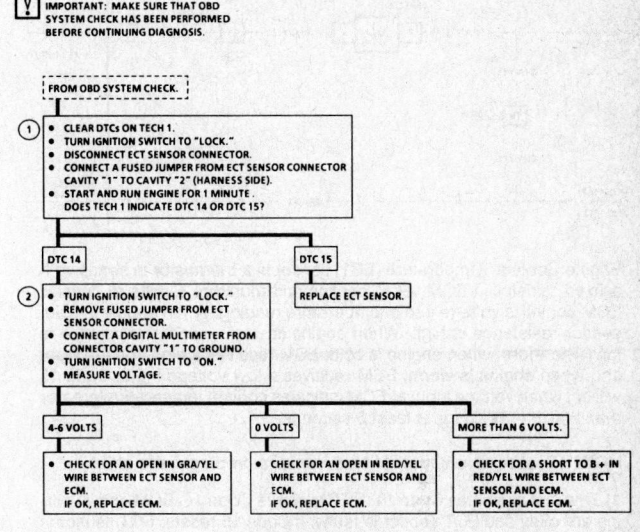

DIAGNOSTIC AID

ECT SENSOR		
TEMPERATURE TO RESISTANCE VALUES (APPROXIMATE)		
°F	°C	OHMS
210	99	190
160	71	400
100	38	1,250
70	21	2,350
40	4	4,780
20	-7	8,100
0	-18	14,650

"AFTER REPAIRS," CONFIRM "CLOSED LOOP" OPERATION, NO DTCs AND NO MALFUNCTION INDICATOR LAMP (MIL).

Courtesy of General Motors Corp.

CODE 15, ENGINE COOLANT TEMPERATURE SENSOR, HIGH TEMPERATURE INDICATED (TRACKER – MFI CALIF. & NEW YORK)

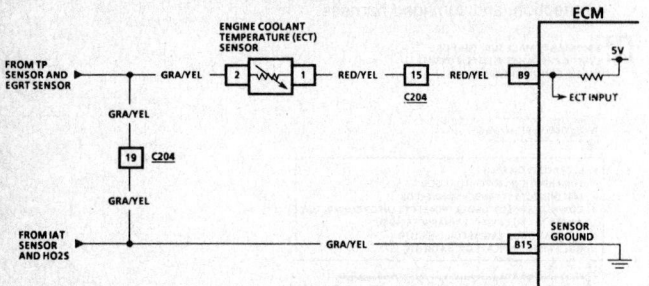
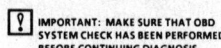

Engine Coolant Temperature (ECT) sensor is a thermistor in series with a fixed resistor in ECM. ECM applies and monitors 5 volts to sensor. ECM converts voltage into a temperature reading. When engine is cold, sensor resistance is high. When engine is warm, sensor resistance is low. Therefore, when engine is cold, ECM receives a high voltage input and when engine is warm, ECM receives a low voltage input. Code 15 will set when voltage input at ECM indicates coolant temperature greater than 280°F (138°C) for at least 5 seconds.

NOTE: Test numbers refer to test numbers on diagnostic chart.

1) This test simulates Code 14. If ECM stores Code 14, ECM and its wiring are okay and ECT sensor is faulty. If Code 15 resets, ECT sensor is okay and wiring to ECM or ECM is faulty.

DIAGNOSTIC AIDS

After engine is started, coolant temperature should rise steadily to about 203°F (95°C) and then stabilize when thermostat opens. Ensure engine is not overheating and has not been subjected to conditions which would create an overheating condition (i.e., overload, trailer towing, hilly terrain, heavy stop and go traffic, etc.). When replacing ECT sensor, ref-

er to TEMPERATURE TO RESISTANCE VALUES table at various temperature levels to evaluate the possibility of a "shifted" (mis-scaled) sensor.

A "shifted" sensor could result in poor driveability complaints. An intermittent condition may be caused by a poor connection, rubbed-through wire insulation, or a broken wire inside insulation. Check ECM harness connectors for backed-out terminals, improper mating, broken locks, improperly formed or damaged terminals, poor terminal-to-wire connection, and damaged harness.

IMPORTANT: MAKE SURE THAT OBD SYSTEM CHECK HAS BEEN PERFORMED BEFORE CONTINUING DIAGNOSIS.

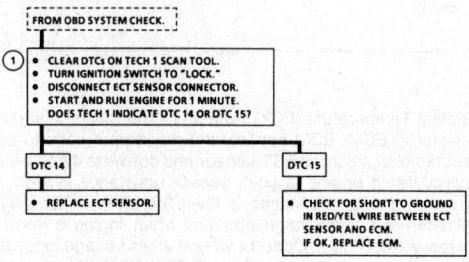

ECT SENSOR		
TEMPERATURE TO RESISTANCE VALUES (APPROXIMATE)		
°F	°C	OHMS
210	99	190
160	71	400
100	38	1,250
70	21	2,350
40	4	4,780
20	-7	8,100
0	-18	14,650

"AFTER REPAIRS," CONFIRM "CLOSED LOOP" OPERATION, NO DTCs AND NO MALFUNCTION INDICATOR LAMP (MIL).

94E44937 94G44939

Courtesy of General Motors Corp.

CODE 21, THROTTLE POSITION (TP) SENSOR, SIGNAL VOLTAGE HIGH (TRACKER – MFI CALIF. & NEW YORK)

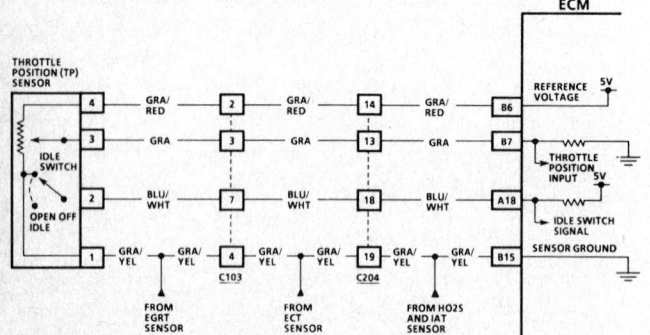
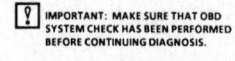

Throttle Position (TP) sensor consists of a potentiometer that changes resistance with throttle valve position. ECM provides a 5-volt reference voltage to TP sensor. ECM reads voltage across TP sensor and converts voltage into throttle position. When TP sensor resistance decreases, throttle valve opening increases to Wide Open Throttle (WOT) and voltage monitored by ECM increases. When TP sensor resistance increases, throttle valve opening decreases to idle and voltage monitored by ECM decreases. Code 21 will set when high voltage input at ECM is indicated with engine running at idle for at least 5 seconds.

NOTE: Test numbers refer to test numbers on diagnostic chart.

1) With TP sensor disconnected, voltage input at ECM should go low if ECM and its wiring are okay. If voltage input remains high, short to voltage is present in Gray wire between ECM and TP sensor, or ECM is faulty.

DIAGNOSTIC AIDS

A misadjusted TP sensor can cause a false Code 21 or 22 to set. For additional TP sensor specifications, refer to SYSTEM & COMPONENT TESTING article. An intermittent condition may be caused by a poor connection, rubbed-through wire insulation, or a broken wire inside insulation. Check ECM harness connectors for backed-out terminals, improper mating, broken locks, improperly formed or damaged terminals, poor terminal-to-wire connection, and damaged harness.

IMPORTANT: MAKE SURE THAT OBD SYSTEM CHECK HAS BEEN PERFORMED BEFORE CONTINUING DIAGNOSIS.

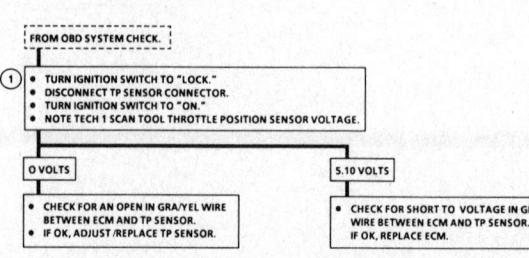

"AFTER REPAIRS," CONFIRM "CLOSED LOOP" OPERATION, NO DTCs AND NO MALFUNCTION INDICATOR LAMP (MIL).

94J44940 94A44941

Courtesy of General Motors Corp.

CODE 22, THROTTLE POSITION (TP) SENSOR, SIGNAL VOLTAGE LOW (TRACKER – MFI CALIF. & NEW YORK)

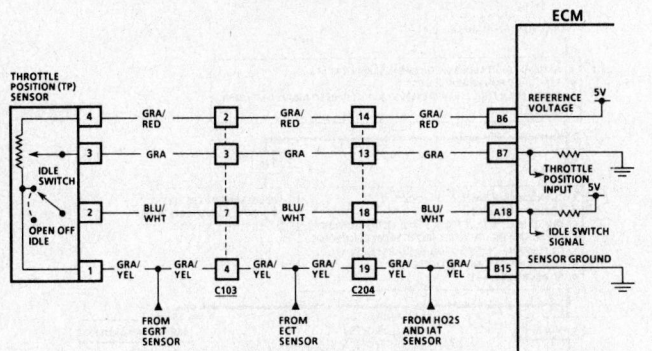

Throttle Position (TP) sensor consists of a potentiometer that changes resistance with throttle valve position. ECM provides a 5-volt reference voltage to TP sensor. ECM reads voltage across TP sensor and converts voltage into throttle position. When TP sensor resistance decreases, throttle valve opening increases to Wide Open Throttle (WOT) and voltage monitored by ECM increases. When TP sensor resistance increases, throttle valve opening decreases to idle and voltage monitored by ECM decreases. Code 22 will set when low voltage input at ECM is indicated with engine running at idle for at least 5 seconds.

NOTE: Test numbers refer to test numbers on diagnostic chart.

1) By connecting a jumper between TP sensor cavities, voltage input at ECM should be high, indicating a faulty TP sensor. If voltage input is low, problem is in ECM or ECM wiring.
2) Checks for open or short to ground in Gray and Gray/Red wires between ECM and TP sensor, and a faulty ECM.

94J44940 94B44942

DIAGNOSTIC AIDS

A misadjusted TP sensor can cause a false Code 21 or 22 to set. For additional TP sensor specifications, refer to SYSTEM & COMPONENT TESTING article. An intermittent condition may be caused by a poor connection, rubbed-through wire insulation, or a broken wire inside insulation. Check ECM harness connectors for backed-out terminals, improper mating, broken locks, improperly formed or damaged terminals, poor terminal-to-wire connection, and damaged harness.

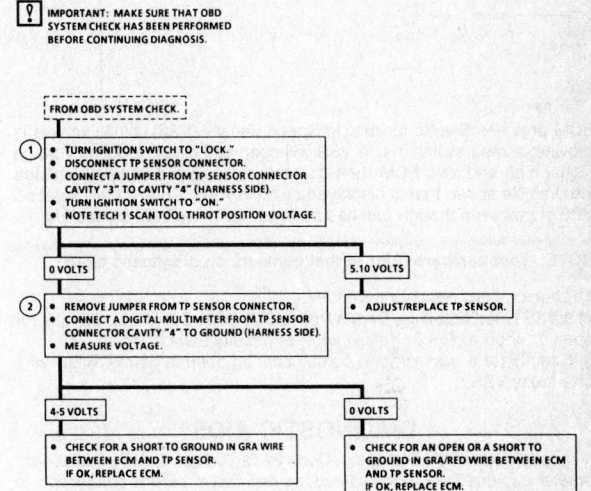

Courtesy of General Motors Corp.

CODE 23, INTAKE AIR TEMPERATURE SENSOR, LOW TEMPERATURE INDICATED (TRACKER – MFI CALIF. & NEW YORK)

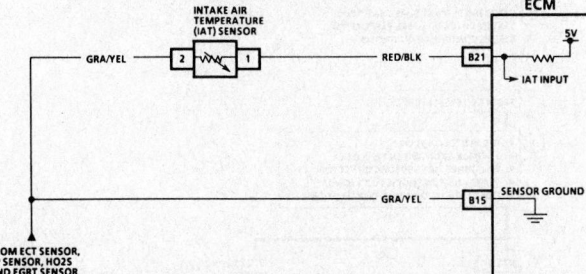

Intake Air Temperature (IAT) sensor is a thermistor in series with a fixed resistor in ECM. ECM applies and monitors 5 volts to sensor. ECM monitors voltage across IAT sensor and converts it into a temperature reading. When outside air temperature is cold, sensor resistance is high. When outside air temperature is warm, sensor resistance is low. Therefore, when air temperature is cold, ECM receives a high voltage input and when air temperature is warm, ECM receives a low voltage input. Code 23 will set when voltage input at ECM indicates air temperature less than –52°F (–47°C) for at least 5 seconds.

NOTE: Test numbers refer to test numbers on diagnostic chart.

1) This test simulates Code 25. If ECM stores Code 25, ECM and its wiring are okay, and IAT sensor is faulty. If Code 23 resets, IAT sensor is okay, and wiring is to ECM or ECM is faulty.
2) Checks for open in Red/Black or Gray/Yellow wires, a short to B+ in Red/Black wire or a faulty ECM.

DIAGNOSTIC AIDS

Codes 21 and 23 stored at the same time could be the result of an open in Gray/Yellow wire. When replacing IAT sensor, refer to TEMPERATURE TO RESISTANCE VALUES table at various temperature levels to evaluate the possibility of a "shifted" (mis-scaled) sensor. A "shifted" sensor could result in poor driveability complaints. An intermittent condition may be caused by a poor connection, rubbed-through wire insulation, or a broken wire inside insulation. Check ECM harness connectors for backed-out terminals, improper mating, broken locks, improperly formed or damaged terminals, poor terminal-to-wire connection, and damaged harness.

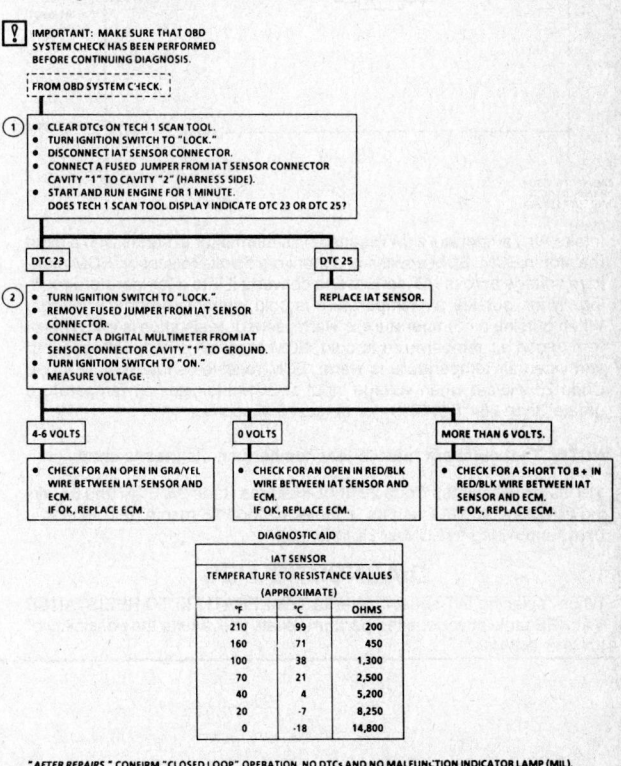

IAT SENSOR		
TEMPERATURE TO RESISTANCE VALUES (APPROXIMATE)		
°F	°C	OHMS
210	99	200
160	71	450
100	38	1,300
70	21	2,500
40	4	5,200
20	-7	8,250
0	-18	14,800

"AFTER REPAIRS," CONFIRM "CLOSED LOOP" OPERATION, NO DTCs AND NO MALFUNCTION INDICATOR LAMP (MIL).

Courtesy of General Motors Corp.

94C44943 94D44944

CODE 24, VEHICLE SPEED SENSOR
(TRACKER – MFI CALIF. & NEW YORK)

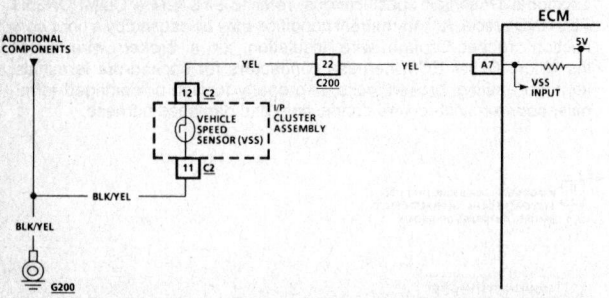

ECM provides 5 volts to Vehicle Speed Sensor (VSS). While vehicle is moving, a reed switch inside VSS will open and close, toggling voltage signal high and low. ECM then converts this toggled high/low voltage into vehicle speed that is displayed as MPH/KPH. Code 24 will set if no VSS signal even though fuel has been cut for more than 5 seconds.

NOTE: Test numbers refer to test numbers on diagnostic chart.

1) Checks if problem is intermittent.
2) If VSS is not receiving 5 volts from ECM, Code 24 will set. Checks for open or short to B+ in Yellow wire, or a faulty ECM.
3) Checks for a poor ground connection, an open in Black/Yellow wire or a faulty VSS.

DIAGNOSTIC AIDS

If speedometer cable is binding, Code 24 can be set. Ensure that speedometer cable is free from restrictions and has a secure connection to instrument cluster. If problem is intermittent, refer to TROUBLE SHOOTING – NO CODES article.

94E44945 94F44946

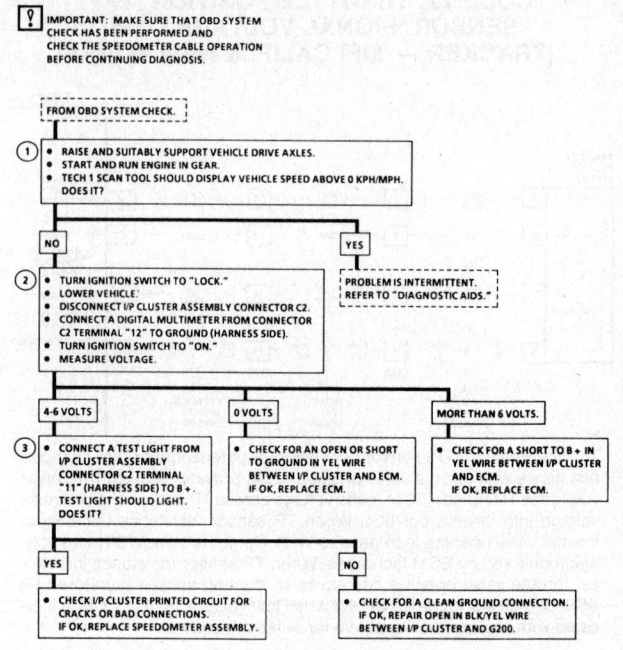

"AFTER REPAIRS," CONFIRM "CLOSED LOOP" OPERATION, NO DTCs AND NO MALFUNCTION INDICATOR LAMP (MIL).

Courtesy of General Motors Corp.

CODE 25, INTAKE AIR TEMPERATURE
SENSOR, HIGH TEMPERATURE INDICATED
(TRACKER – MFI CALIF. & NEW YORK)

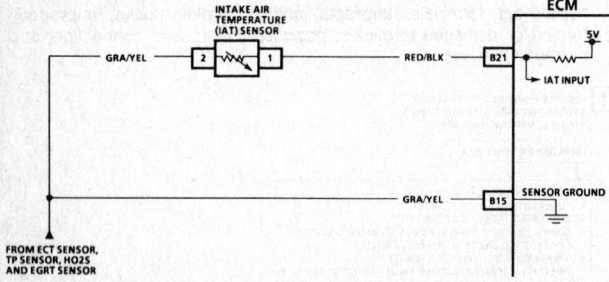

Intake Air Temperature (IAT) sensor is a thermistor in series with a fixed resistor in ECM. ECM applies and monitors 5 volts to sensor. ECM monitors voltage across IAT sensor and converts it into a temperature reading. When outside air temperature is cold, sensor resistance is high. When outside air temperature is warm, sensor resistance is low. Therefore, when air temperature is cold, ECM receives a high voltage input and when air temperature is warm, ECM receives a low voltage input. Code 25 will set when voltage input at ECM indicates air temperature greater than 284°F (140°C) for at least 5 seconds.

NOTE: Test numbers refer to test numbers on diagnostic chart.

1) This test simulates Code 23. If ECM stores Code 23, ECM and its wiring are okay, and IAT sensor is faulty. If Code 25 resets, IAT sensor is okay, and wiring to ECM or ECM is faulty.

DIAGNOSTIC AIDS

When replacing IAT sensor, refer to TEMPERATURE TO RESISTANCE VALUES table at various temperature levels to evaluate the possibility of

94C44943 94G44947

a "shifted" (mis-scaled) sensor. A "shifted" sensor could result in poor driveability complaints. An intermittent condition may be caused by a poor connection, rubbed-through wire insulation, or a broken wire inside insulation. Check ECM harness connectors for backed-out terminals, improper mating, broken locks, improperly formed or damaged terminals, poor terminal-to-wire connection, and damaged harness.

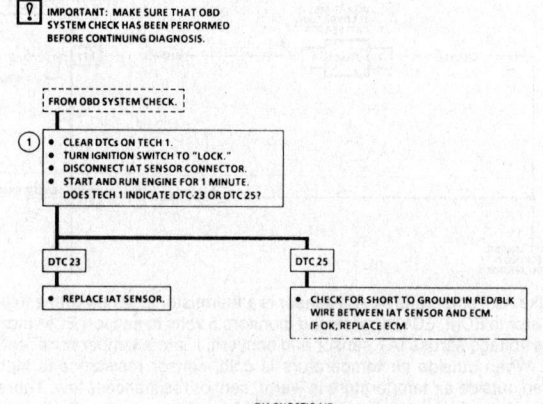

DIAGNOSTIC AID

IAT SENSOR		
TEMPERATURE TO RESISTANCE VALUES (APPROXIMATE)		
°F	°C	OHMS
210	99	200
160	71	450
100	38	1,300
70	21	2,500
40	4	5,200
20	-7	8,250
0	-18	14,800

"AFTER REPAIRS," CONFIRM "CLOSED LOOP" OPERATION, NO DTCs AND NO MALFUNCTION INDICATOR LAMP (MIL).

Courtesy of General Motors Corp.

CODE 33, MASS AIRFLOW SENSOR HIGH CURRENT INPUT
(TRACKER – MFI CALIF. & NEW YORK)

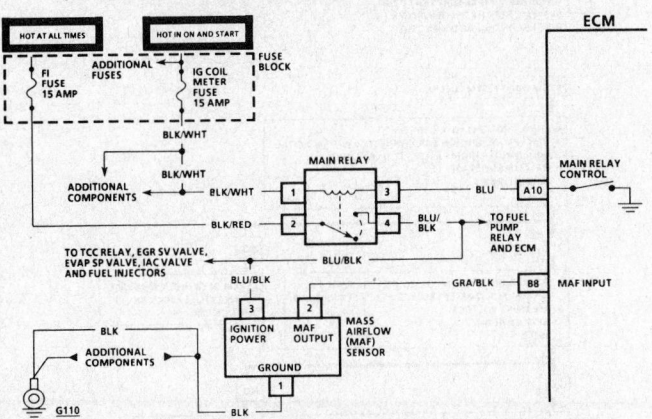

MAF sensor measures the amount of air which passes through it in a given amount of time. ECM controls fuel delivery by using this information to determine the operating condition of the engine. A large quantity of air movement indicates acceleration, while a small quantity indicates deceleration or idle. As amount of air entering sensor increases, sensor signal current to ECM also increases. As airflow decreases, sensor signal current to ECM decreases. MAF sensor is located between air intake tube and air cleaner in left front of engine compartment. Code 33 will set MAF sensor output current is higher than 4.9 milliamps for more than 100 milliseconds.

NOTE: Test numbers refer to test numbers on diagnostic chart.

1) Checks for a faulty MAF sensor circuit without engine running.
2) Checks for a faulty MAF sensor or ECM.
3) Checks for open in Black wire between MAF sensor and G110.
4) Checks for a faulty MAF sensor or ECM, and a short to voltage in Gray/Black wire between ECM and MAF sensor.

94H44948 94I44949

DIAGNOSTIC AIDS

An intermittent condition may be caused by a poor connection, rubbed-through wire insulation, or a broken wire inside insulation. Check ECM harness connectors for backed-out terminals, improper mating, broken locks, improperly formed or damaged terminals, poor terminal-to-wire connection, and damaged harness.

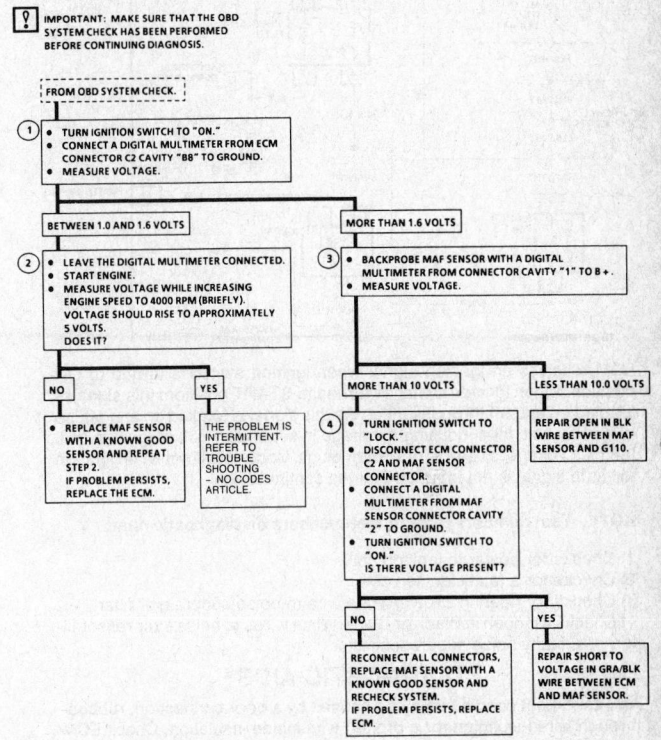

"AFTER REPAIRS," CONFIRM "CLOSED LOOP" OPERATION, NO DTCs AND NO MALFUNCTION INDICATOR LAMP (MIL).

Courtesy of General Motors Corp.

CODE 34, MASS AIRFLOW SENSOR LOW CURRENT INPUT
(TRACKER – MFI CALIF. & NEW YORK)

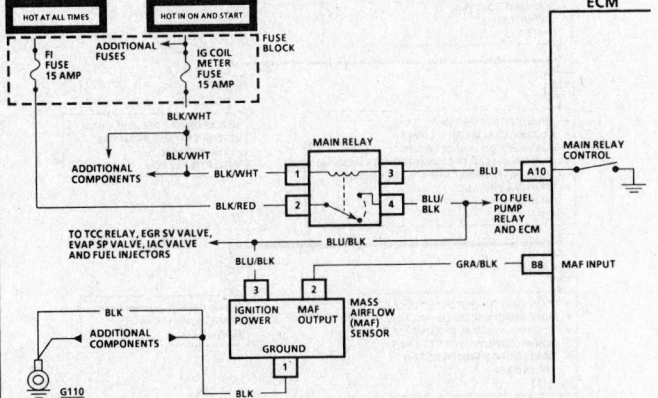

MAF sensor measures the amount of air which passes through it in a given amount of time. ECM controls fuel delivery by using this information to determine the operating condition of the engine. A large quantity of air movement indicates acceleration, while a small quantity indicates deceleration or idle. As amount of air entering sensor increases, sensor signal current to ECM also increases. As air flow decreases, sensor signal current to ECM decreases. MAF sensor is located between air intake tube and air cleaner in left front of engine compartment. Code 34 will set MAF sensor output current is higher than .65 milliamps for more than 100 milliseconds.

NOTE: Test numbers refer to test numbers on diagnostic chart.

1) Checks for open in Blue/Black wire between MAF sensor and main relay.
2) Checks for open in Gray/Black wire between MAF sensor and ECM, and a faulty MAF sensor or ECM.

DIAGNOSTIC AIDS

An intermittent condition may be caused by a poor connection, rubbed-through wire insulation, or a broken wire inside insulation. Check ECM harness connectors for backed-out terminals, improper mating, broken locks, improperly formed or damaged terminals, poor terminal-to-wire connection, and damaged harness.

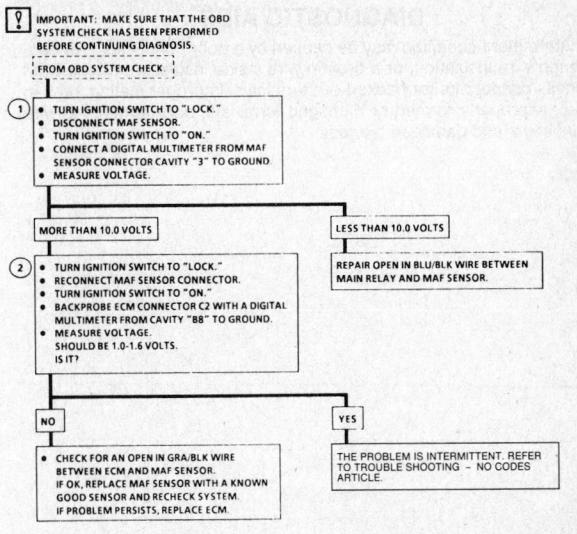

94H44948 94C44950

Courtesy of General Motors Corp.

CODE 41, NO IGNITION SIGNAL,
(1 OF 2)
(TRACKER – MFI CALIF. & NEW YORK)

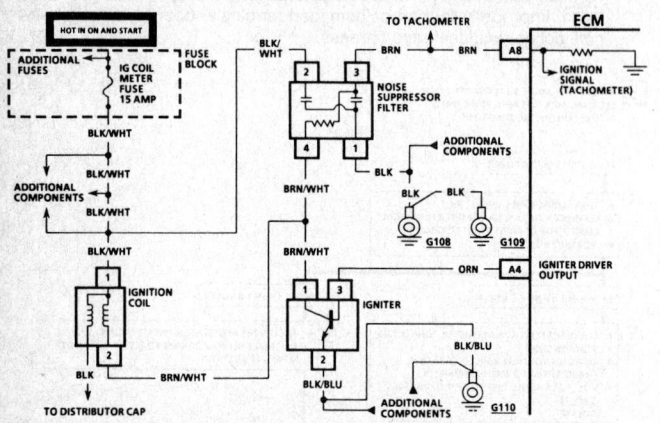

ECM receives an ignition signal when ignition switch is turned to ON position. When ignition switch is turned to START position, this signal is toggled on and off through igniter. As this signal is toggled on and off, so is ignition coil, thus inducing a voltage in secondary coil of ignition coil. Induced voltage is used to fire spark plugs. Code 41 will set when ignition fail-safe signal is not inputted 6 times continuously.

NOTE: Test numbers refer to test numbers on diagnostic chart.

1) Checks for power to ignition coil.
2) Checks for a faulty ignition coil.
3) Checks for open in Brown/White wire to noise suppressor filter.
4) Checks for open in Black or Black/White wires to noise suppressor filter, or a faulty noise suppressor filter.

DIAGNOSTIC AIDS

An intermittent condition may be caused by a poor connection, rubbed-through wire insulation, or a broken wire inside insulation. Check ECM

94D44951 94E44952

harness connectors for backed-out terminals, improper mating, broken locks, improperly formed or damaged terminals, poor terminal-to-wire connection, and damaged harness.

💡 IMPORTANT: MAKE SURE THAT OBD SYSTEM CHECK HAS BEEN PERFORMED BEFORE CONTINUING DIAGNOSIS.

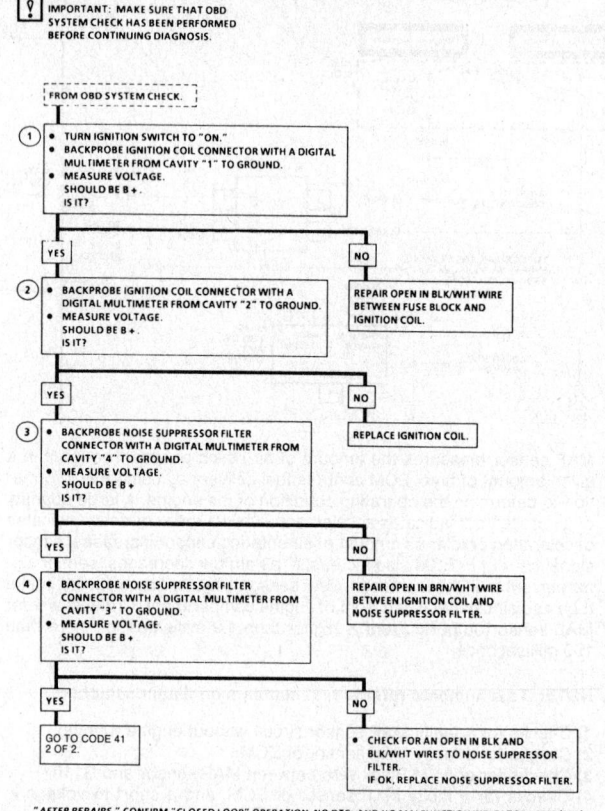

"AFTER REPAIRS," CONFIRM "CLOSED LOOP" OPERATION, NO DTCs AND NO MALFUNCTION INDICATOR LAMP (MIL).

Courtesy of General Motors Corp.

CODE 41, NO IGNITION SIGNAL,
(2 OF 2)
(TRACKER – MFI CALIF. & NEW YORK)

NOTE: Test numbers refer to test numbers on diagnostic chart.

5) Checks for open in Brown wire to ECM.
6) Checks for open in Brown/White to igniter.
7) Checks igniter for good ground.
8) Checks if ECM is toggling ignition signals. Either an open, a short to ground, or a faulty ECM or igniter.

DIAGNOSTIC AIDS

An intermittent condition may be caused by a poor connection, rubbed-through wire insulation, or a broken wire inside insulation. Check ECM harness connectors for backed-out terminals, improper mating, broken locks, improperly formed or damaged terminals, poor terminal-to-wire connection, and damaged harness.

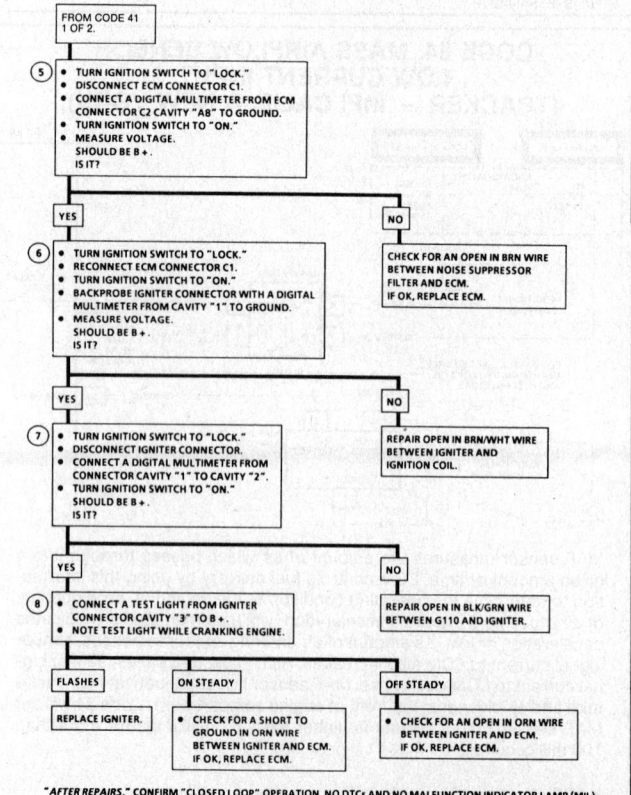

"AFTER REPAIRS," CONFIRM "CLOSED LOOP" OPERATION, NO DTCs AND NO MALFUNCTION INDICATOR LAMP (MIL).

94F44953

Courtesy of General Motors Corp.

CODE 42, CAMSHAFT POSITION SENSOR CIRCUIT, NO SIGNAL FOR 3 SECONDS (TRACKER – MFI CALIF. & NEW YORK)

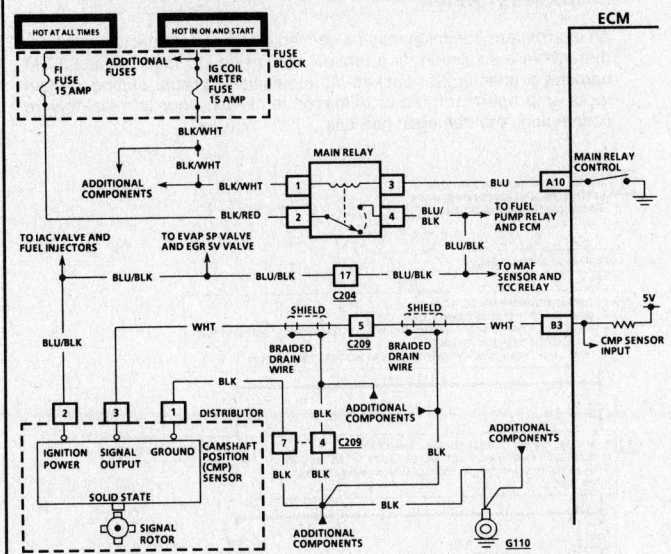

When distributor shaft rotates, a fluctuating magnetic field is generated due to changes in air gap between Camshaft Position (CMP) sensor and distributor shaft signal rotor. As a result, a reference voltage is induced in CMP sensor. This reference voltage is monitored by ECM to determine the crank angle input. ECM uses crank angle input to determine when to ground igniter, controlling ignition coil and ignition timing. Code 42 will set when CMP sensor signal input is not present at ECM for 3 seconds.

NOTE: Test numbers refer to test numbers on diagnostic chart.

1) Checks for open, short to ground, or short to voltage in White wire between ECM and distributor, or a faulty ECM.
2) Checks for open in Blue/Black wire between main relay and distributor.
3) Checks for open in Black wire between distributor and G110.
4) Checks for a faulty CMP sensor.

94G44954 94H44955

DIAGNOSTIC AIDS

A loose or damaged CMP sensor could cause an intermittent code. A misaligned CMP sensor or improper air gap could also set a Code 42 or an intermittent "engine cranks but won't run" condition. For CMP sensor specifications, refer to SYSTEM & COMPONENT TESTING article. An intermittent condition may be caused by a poor connection, rubbed-through wire insulation, or a broken wire inside insulation. Check ECM harness connectors for backed-out terminals, improper mating, broken locks, improperly formed or damaged terminals, poor terminal-to-wire connection, and damaged harness.

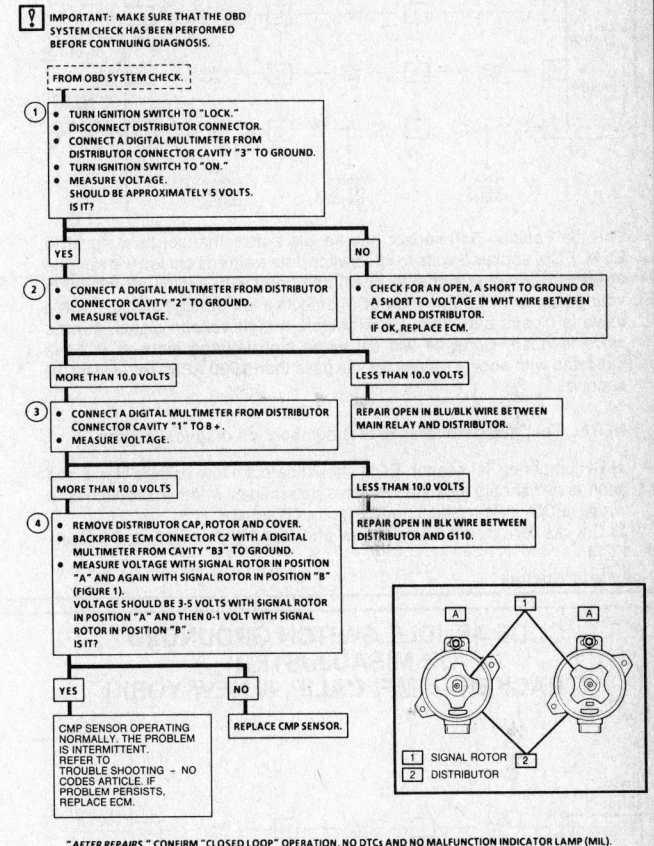

"AFTER REPAIRS," CONFIRM "CLOSED LOOP" OPERATION, NO DTCs AND NO MALFUNCTION INDICATOR LAMP (MIL).

Courtesy of General Motors Corp.

CODE 44, IDLE SWITCH OPEN
OR MISADJUSTED
(TRACKER – MFI CALIF. & NEW YORK)

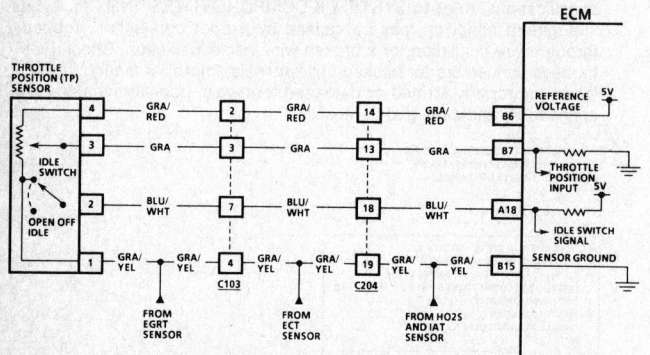

Throttle Position (TP) sensor has an idle switch that sends a signal to ECM. ECM applies 5 volts to idle switch. Idle switch is closed with engine at idle (low voltage signal at ECM) and open with engine off idle (high voltage signal at ECM). When ECM detects a low voltage signal, throttle valve is closed and when ECM detects a high voltage signal, throttle valve is open. Code 44 will set when high voltage input at ECM is indicated with engine running at idle (less than 1000 RPM) for at least 10 seconds.

NOTE: Test numbers refer to test numbers on diagnostic chart.

1) By jumpering TP sensor, ECM should detect a low voltage signal and scan tester should indicate ON. This determines whether problem is in wiring, ECM, or a misadjusted or faulty TP sensor.
2) Checks for open in Gray/Yellow and Blue/White wires, and a faulty ECM.

94J44940 94I44956

DIAGNOSTIC AIDS

A misadjusted TP sensor could cause Code 44 to set. Before replacing TP sensor, check TP sensor adjustment. Refer to ON-VEHICLE ADJUSTMENTS article.

An intermittent condition may be caused by a poor connection, rubbed-through wire insulation, or a broken wire inside insulation. Check ECM harness connectors for backed-out terminals, improper mating, broken locks, improperly formed or damaged terminals, poor terminal-to-wire connection, and damaged harness.

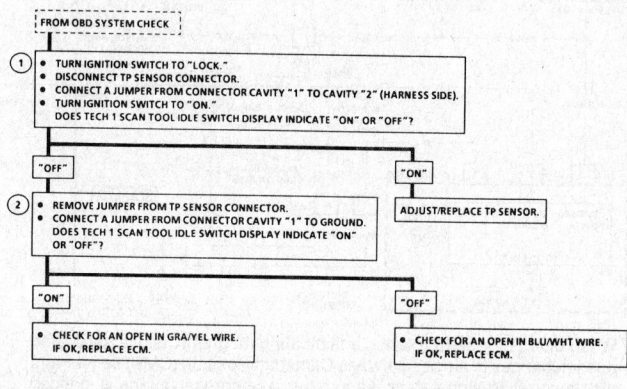

CODE 45, IDLE SWITCH GROUNDED
OR MISADJUSTED
(TRACKER – MFI CALIF. & NEW YORK)

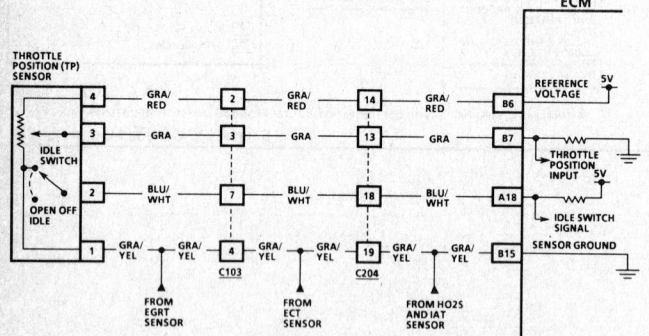

Throttle Position (TP) sensor has an idle switch that sends a signal to ECM. ECM applies 5 volts to idle switch. Idle switch is closed with engine at idle (low voltage signal at ECM) and open with engine off idle (high voltage signal at ECM). When ECM detects a low voltage signal, throttle valve is closed and when ECM detects a high voltage signal, throttle valve is open. Code 45 will set when larger than 30 degree throttle valve openning, or a charging efficiency greater than 40 percent and an engine speed greater than 2300 RPM with idle open, for at least 3 seconds.

NOTE: Test numbers refer to test numbers on diagnostic chart.

1) By disconnecting TP sensor, ECM should detect a high voltage signal and scan tester should indicate OFF. Checks for short to ground in Blue/White wire.

94J44940 94J44957

2) Checks for short to B+ in Gray/Red wire, or a misadjusted or faulty TP sensor.

DIAGNOSTIC AIDS

A misadjusted TP sensor could cause Code 45 to set. Before replacing TP sensor, check TP sensor adjustment. Refer to ON-VEHICLE ADJUSTMENTS article. An intermittent condition may be caused by a poor connection, rubbed-through wire insulation, or a broken wire inside insulation. Check ECM harness connectors for backed-out terminals, improper mating, broken locks, improperly formed or damaged terminals, poor terminal-to-wire connection, and damaged harness.

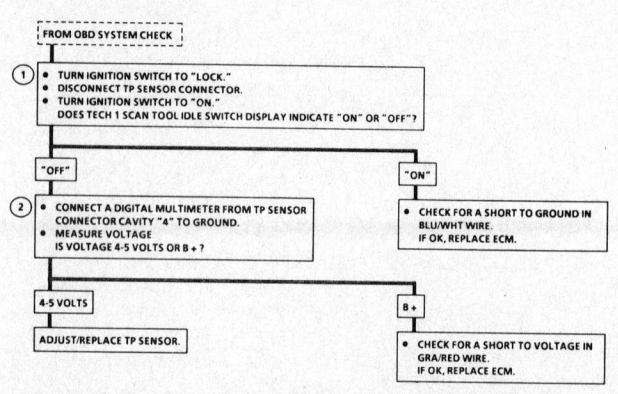

CODE 51, EXHAUST GAS RECIRCULATION (EGR) CIRCUIT
(TRACKER – MFI CALIF. & NEW YORK)

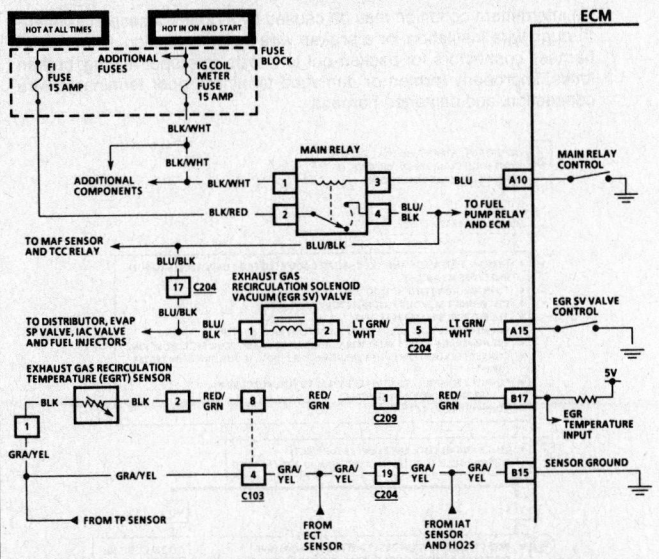

Exhaust Gas Recirculation (EGR) temperature sensor is mounted on top of EGR valve. EGR temperature sensor is a variable resistor that changes along with temperature of exhaust gases. ECM applies 5 volts to EGR temperature sensor and reads voltage across sensor. As exhaust gas temperature increases, sensor resistance decreases providing ECM with a low voltage input. When exhaust gas temperature decreases, sensor resistance increases providing ECM with a high voltage input. ECM calculates exhaust gas temperature by voltage inputs received. Code 51 will set when one of the 3 following conditions are met:

- EGR temperature less than 176°F (80°C) is sensed for 5 seconds when the following conditions are met simultaneously for 30 seconds.
  - Charging efficiency between 30 and 58 percent.
  - EGR Solenoid Vacuum (SV) valve off.
  - Engine coolant temperature is greater than 167°F (75°C).
  - Mass air flow rate between 10.2 and 28.2 g/sec.
- Engine coolant temperature less than 104°F (40°C) and exhaust gas temperature is greater than 428°F (220°C).
- EGR temperature less than 14°F (–10°C) is sensed for 3 seconds when engine coolant temperature has been greater than 158°F (70°C) for more than 80 seconds.

NOTE: Test numbers refer to test numbers on diagnostic chart.

94A44958 94B44959

1) Checks for proper EGR valve operation.
2) Checks for 5-volt reference to EGR temperature sensor.
3) Checks for short to voltage in Red/Green wire.
4) Checks for open Gray/Yellow wire, a faulty ECM or EGR temperature sensor.

DIAGNOSTIC AIDS

An intermittent condition may be caused by a poor connection, rubbed-through wire insulation, or a broken wire inside insulation. Check ECM harness connectors for backed-out terminals, improper mating, broken locks, improperly formed or damaged terminals, poor terminal-to-wire connection, and damaged harness.

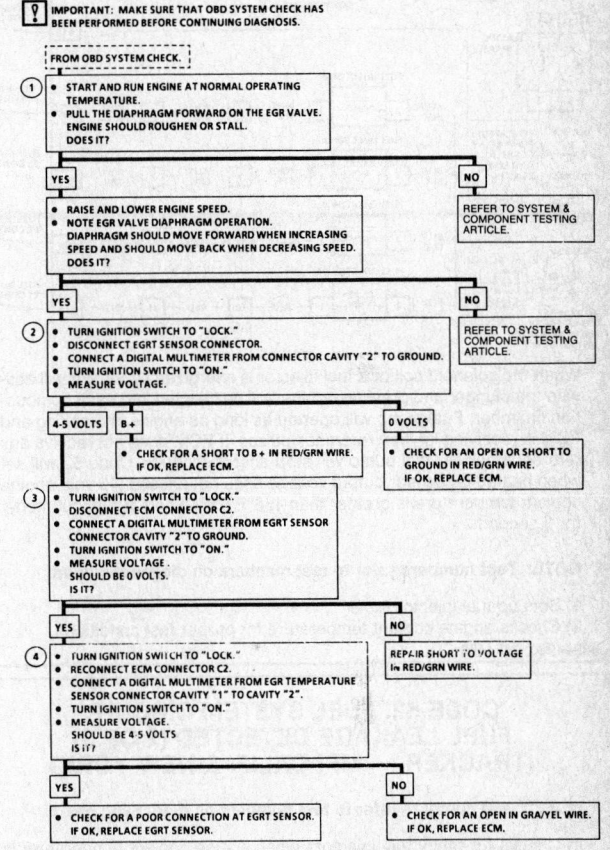

"AFTER REPAIRS," CONFIRM "CLOSED LOOP" OPERATION, NO DTCs AND NO MALFUNCTION INDICATOR LAMP (MIL).

Courtesy of General Motors Corp.

CODE 52, FUEL SYSTEM CIRCUIT, FUEL LEAKAGE DETECTED (1 OF 3) (TRACKER – MFI CALIF. & NEW YORK)

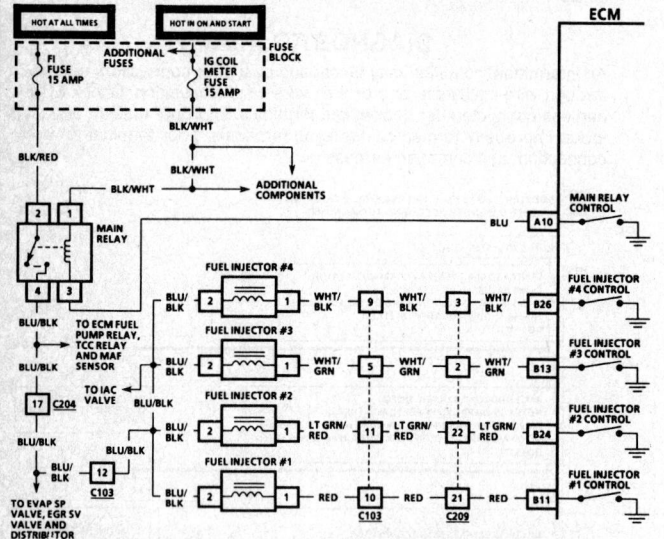

When the solenoid coil of a fuel injector is energized by ECM it will activate the plunger and pressurized fuel will be injected into each combustion chamber. Fuel pump will operate as long as engine is cranking and ECM is receiving ignition reference pulses. If ECM does not receive any reference pulses, fuel pump will stop after 3 seconds. Code 52 will set when heated O_2 sensor output voltage does not exceed .45 volt, engine coolant temperature is greater than 158°F (70°C) and at fuel cut mode, for 3 seconds.

NOTE: Test numbers refer to test numbers on diagnostic chart.

1) Sets up fuel injector tester.
2) Checks engine coolant temperature for proper test conditions.

94E44960 94F44961

3) Checks for faulty fuel injectors when engine coolant temperature is between 50 and 95°F (10-35°C).

DIAGNOSTIC AIDS

An intermittent condition may be caused by a poor connection, rubbed-through wire insulation, or a broken wire inside insulation. Check ECM harness connectors for backed-out terminals, improper mating, broken locks, improperly formed or damaged terminals, poor terminal-to-wire connection, and damaged harness.

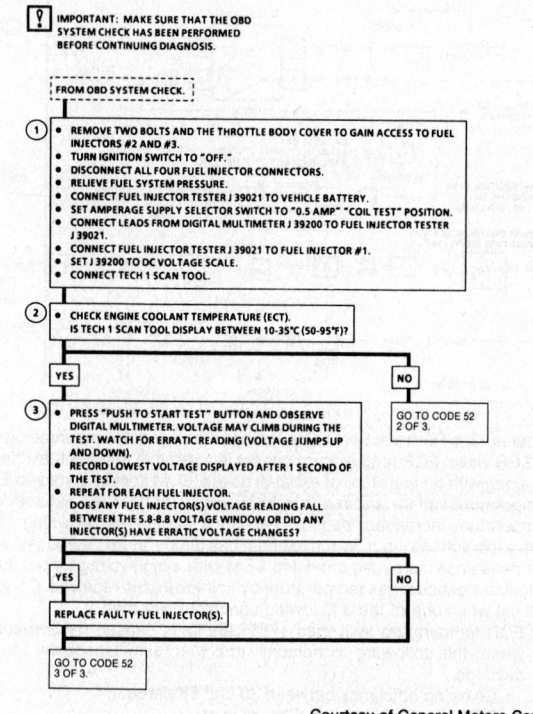

Courtesy of General Motors Corp.

CODE 52, FUEL SYSTEM CIRCUIT, FUEL LEAKAGE DETECTED (2 OF 3) (TRACKER – MFI CALIF. & NEW YORK)

NOTE: Test numbers refer to test numbers on diagnostic chart.

4) Checks for faulty fuel injectors when engine coolant temperature is greater than or less than 50-95°F (10-35°C).

DIAGNOSTIC AIDS

An intermittent condition may be caused by a poor connection, rubbed-through wire insulation, or a broken wire inside insulation. Check ECM harness connectors for backed-out terminals, improper mating, broken locks, improperly formed or damaged terminals, poor terminal-to-wire connection, and damaged harness.

94G44962

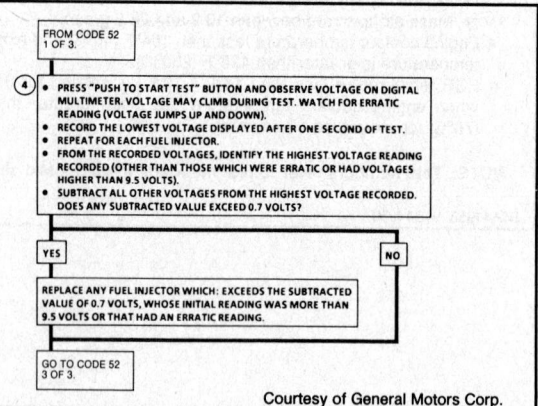

Courtesy of General Motors Corp.

CODE 52, FUEL SYSTEM CIRCUIT, FUEL LEAKAGE DETECTED (3 OF 3) (TRACKER – MFI CALIF. & NEW YORK)

NOTE: Test numbers refer to test numbers on diagnostic chart.

5) Checks for proper fuel pressure prior to testing injectors for proper balance.

6) Checks fuel injectors for proper fuel pressure drop.

7) Checks for faulty fuel injector(s).

DIAGNOSTIC AIDS

An intermittent condition may be caused by a poor connection, rubbed-through wire insulation, or a broken wire inside insulation. Check ECM harness connectors for backed-out terminals, improper mating, broken locks, improperly formed or damaged terminals, poor terminal-to-wire connection, and damaged harness.

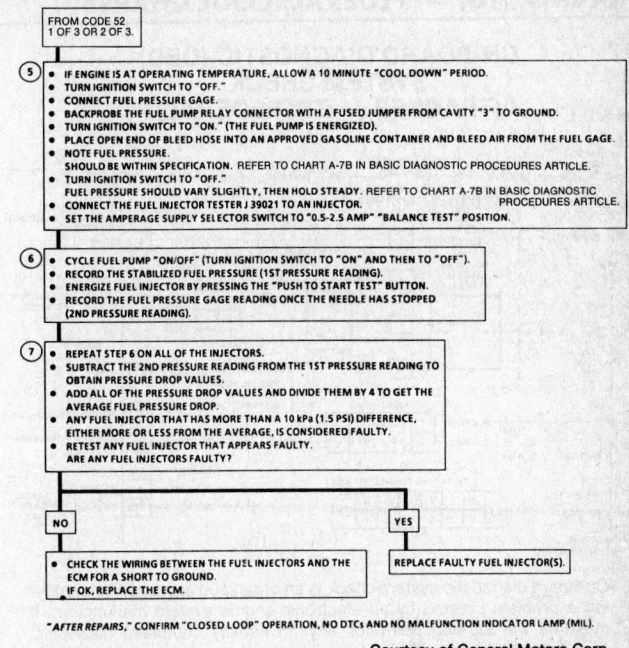

94H44963

Courtesy of General Motors Corp.

CODE 53, ECM FAILURE DETECTED (TRACKER – MFI CALIF. & NEW YORK)

ECM has detected a failure in the communication circuitry. If Code 53 is set, ECM must be replaced.

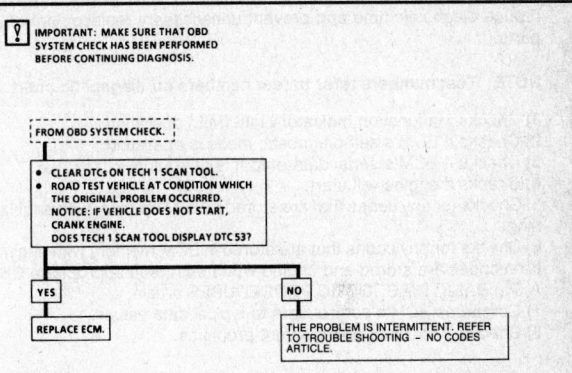

94I44964

Courtesy of General Motors Corp.

TRACKER (TBI – FEDERAL) CODE CHARTS

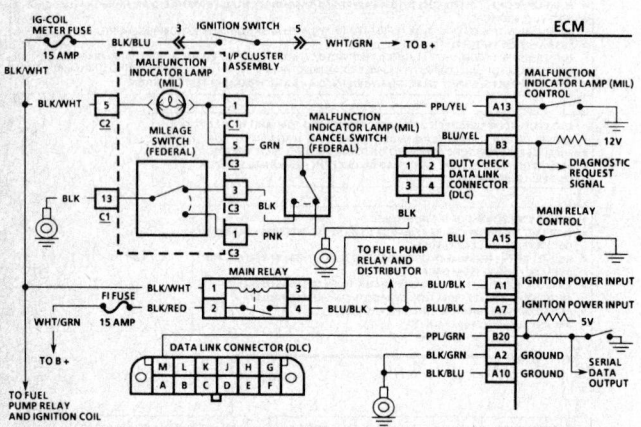

ON-BOARD DIAGNOSTIC (OBD)
SYSTEM CHECK
(TRACKER – TBI FEDERAL)

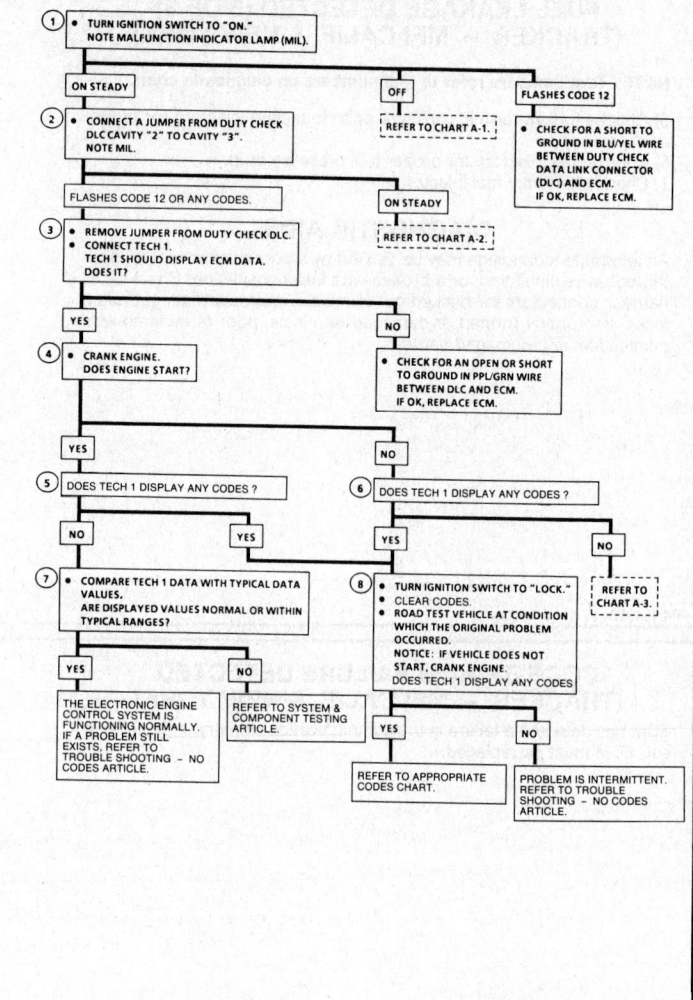

On-board diagnostic system check is an organized approach in identifying a problem created by an electronic engine system malfunction. It must be the starting point for any driveability complaint diagnosis, because it directs the service technician to the next logical step in diagnosing a complaint. Understanding the chart and using it correctly will reduce diagnostic time and prevent unnecessary replacement of good parts.

NOTE: Test numbers refer to test numbers on diagnostic chart.

1) Checks Malfunction Indicator Light (MIL) operation.
2) Checks if ECM's self-diagnostic mode is operating.
3) Checks if ECM's serial data output is operating.
4) Checks if engine will start.
5) Checks for any codes that are stored in ECM memory with engine running.
6) Checks for any codes that are stored in ECM memory with engine off.
If no codes are stored and engine won't start, see appropriate CHART A-3 in BASIC DIAGNOSTIC PROCEDURES article.
7) Compares ECM's control data to typical data values.
8) Checks if codes are intermittent problems.

94D44605 93F78951

CHART A-1,
NO MALFUNCTION INDICATOR LIGHT (MIL)
(TRACKER – TBI FEDERAL)

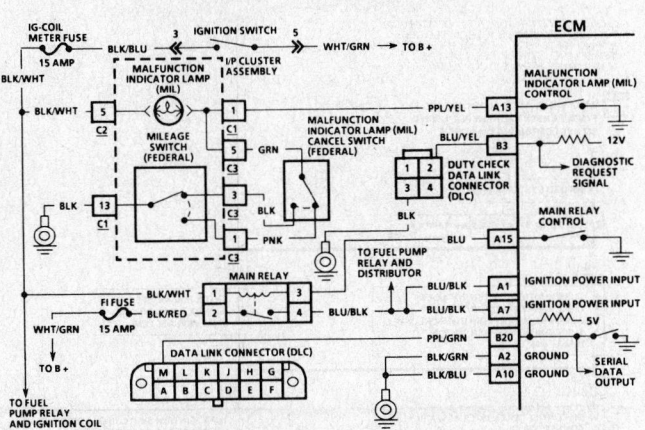

Malfunction Indicator Light (MIL) should remain on when ignition switch is in ON position and engine is not running. Battery voltage is applied to indicator bulb. ECM controls indicator bulb and turns it on by providing a ground path through Purple/Yellow wire to ECM.

NOTE: Test numbers refer to test numbers on diagnostic chart.

1) Checks if ECM is receiving power.
2) Checks if ECM is faulty.
3) Checks for open in Blue/Black wire between main relay and ECM.
4) Checks if ECM has a good ground.
5) Checks for open in Black/White wire to instrument cluster, and Purple/Yellow wire to ECM.
6) Checks if main relay switch is receiving power.
7) Checks if main relay coil is receiving power.
8) Checks if main relay or ECM is faulty, or for open in Blue wire between main relay and ECM.
9) Checks for a faulty ignition switch or open in Black/Blue or Black/White wires to IG-COIL METER fuse.

DIAGNOSTIC AIDS

Check connectors for contamination, corrosion or bent terminals.

94D44605 94E44606

Courtesy of General Motors Corp.

CHART A-2, WON'T FLASH CODE 12 OR ANY CODES, OR MALFUNCTION INDICATOR LIGHT (MIL) ON STEADY (TRACKER – TBI FEDERAL)

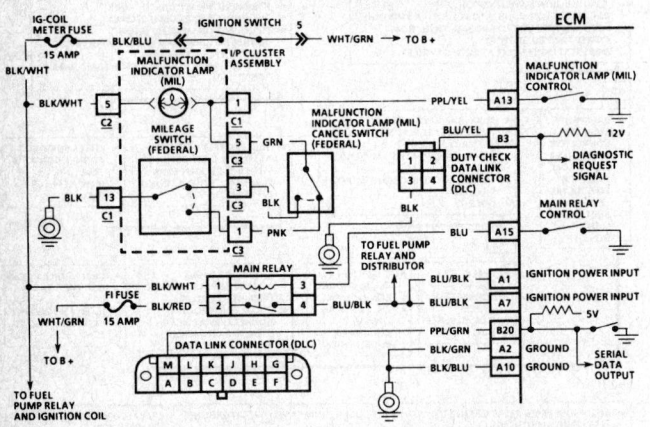

Malfunction Indicator Light (MIL) will flash trouble codes when diagnostic request terminal in duty check data link connector is grounded. MIL is also activated by a mileage switch at 50,000, 80,000 and 100,000 miles, alerting operator that vehicle is in need of regular maintenance service. Once service is performed, MIL cancel switch should be reset. Cancel switch is located behind instrument panel, attached to left speaker.

NOTE: Test numbers refer to test numbers on diagnostic chart.

1) Checks for a short to ground in Purple/Yellow wire.
2) Checks for a faulty ECM or open in Blue/Yellow and Black wires to duty check data link connector.
3) Checks for short to ground in instrument panel printed circuit.
4) Checks to see if MIL cancel switch or mileage switch is faulty.

94D44605 94F44607

DIAGNOSTIC AIDS

Ensure MIL cancel switch is reset after 50,000, 80,000 and 100,000 maintenance service has been completed for MIL to go out.

ENSURE ODOMETER DOES NOT INDICATE 50,000, 80,000 OR 100,000 MILES. IF ODOMETER DOES DISPLAY ANY ONE OF THESE MILAGES, PERFORM MAINTENANCE SERVICE. RESET MIL WHEN MAINTENANCE SERVICE IS COMPLETE.

IMPORTANT: MAKE SURE THAT THE OBD SYSTEM CHECK HAS BEEN PERFORMED BEFORE CONTINUING DIAGNOSIS.

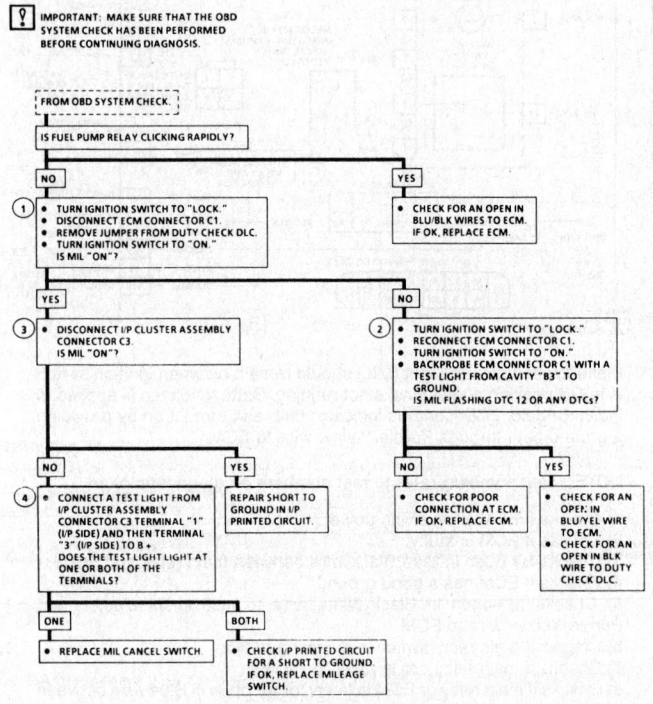

Courtesy of General Motors Corp.

CODE 13, HEATED OXYGEN SENSOR CIRCUIT, OPEN CIRCUIT (TRACKER – TBI FEDERAL)

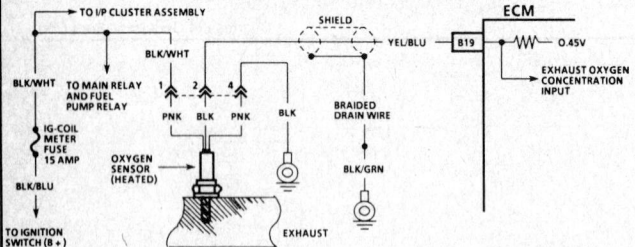

Heated Oxygen (O_2) sensor produces a voltage that varies within a range of about 0.1 volt (lean exhaust) to 1.0 volt (rich exhaust). ECM monitors voltage and determines if exhaust is lean or rich. O_2 sensor has a built-in heater that keeps O_2 sensor at operating temperature while engine is running. O_2 sensor is like an open circuit and produces no voltage when sensor temperature is less than 600°F (360°C), causing an open loop condition. Code 13 will set if the following conditions are met for at least 30 seconds.
- Engine operating temperature is greater than 158°F (70°C).
- Engine running for at least 2 minutes.
- Engine speed is greater than 260 RPM.
- MAP sensor pressure is greater than 350 mm Hg of vacuum.
- Heated O_2 sensor temperature less than 600°F (360°C).

NOTE: Test numbers refer to test numbers on diagnostic chart.

1) Checks for short to voltage in Yellow/Blue wire or a faulty ECM.
2) Checks for short to ground in Yellow/Blue wire, a faulty ECM or a faulty heated O_2 sensor.

92E26918 94G44608

DIAGNOSTIC AIDS

Normal heated O_2 sensor voltage is .1-.9 volt (varying) in closed loop operation. For additional heated O_2 sensor specifications, refer to SENSOR OPERATING RANGE CHARTS article.

IMPORTANT: MAKE SURE THAT THE OBD SYSTEM CHECK HAS BEEN PERFORMED BEFORE CONTINUING DIAGNOSIS.

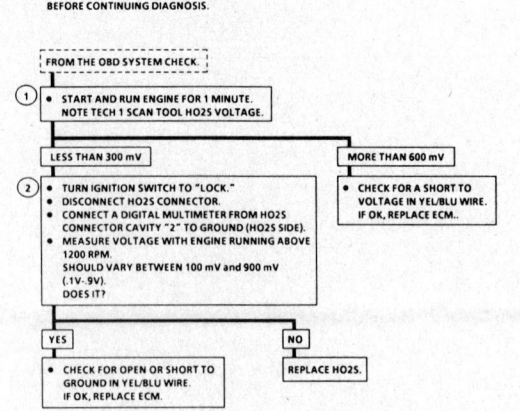

"AFTER REPAIRS," CONFIRM "CLOSED LOOP" OPERATION, NO DTCs AND NO MALFUNCTION INDICATOR LAMP (MIL).

Courtesy of General Motors Corp.

CODE 14, ENGINE COOLANT TEMPERATURE SENSOR, LOW TEMPERATURE INDICATED (TRACKER – TBI FEDERAL)

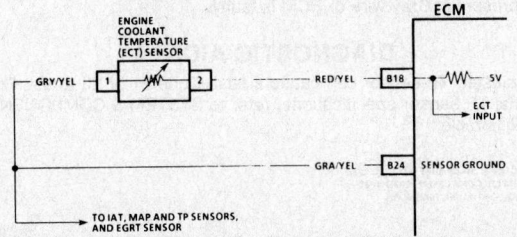

Engine Coolant Temperature (ECT) sensor is a thermistor in series with a fixed resistor in ECM. ECM applies and monitors 5 volts to sensor. ECM converts voltage into a temperature reading. When engine is cold, sensor resistance is high. When engine is warm, sensor resistance is low. Therefore, when engine is cold, ECM receives a high voltage input and when engine is warm, ECM receives a low voltage input. Code 14 will set when voltage input at ECM indicates coolant temperature less than –54°F (–48°C) for at least 5 seconds.

NOTE: Test numbers refer to test numbers on diagnostic chart.

1) This test simulates Code 15. If ECM stores Code 15, ECM and its wiring are okay and ECT sensor is faulty. If Code 14 resets, ECT sensor is okay and wiring to ECM or ECM is faulty.

2) This test determines whether an open exists in Red/Yellow or Gray/Yellow wires, a short to B+ exists in Red/Yellow wire or ECM is faulty.

DIAGNOSTIC AIDS

After engine is started, coolant temperature should rise steadily to about 203°F (95°C) and then stabilize when thermostat opens. If Codes 14 and 21 are stored at same time, an open could exist in Gray/Yellow wire. When replacing sensor, refer to TEMPERATURE TO RESISTANCE VALUES table at various temperature levels to evaluate the possibility of a "shifted" (mis-scaled) sensor. A "shifted" sensor could result in poor driveability complaints.

94H44609 94A44610

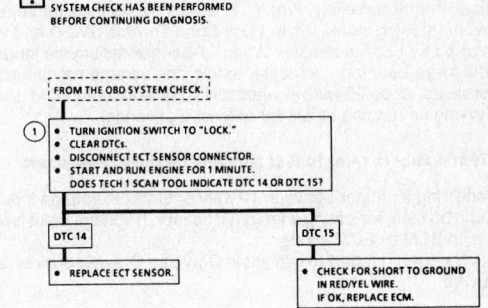

ECT SENSOR		
TEMPERATURE TO RESISTANCE VALUES (APPROXIMATE)		
°F	°C	OHMS
210	99	190
160	71	400
100	38	1,250
70	21	2,350
40	4	4,780
20	-7	8,100
0	-18	14,650

"AFTER REPAIRS," CONFIRM "CLOSED LOOP" OPERATION, NO DTCs AND NO MALFUNCTION INDICATOR LAMP (MIL).

Courtesy of General Motors Corp.

CODE 15, ENGINE COOLANT TEMPERATURE SENSOR, HIGH TEMPERATURE INDICATED (TRACKER – TBI FEDERAL)

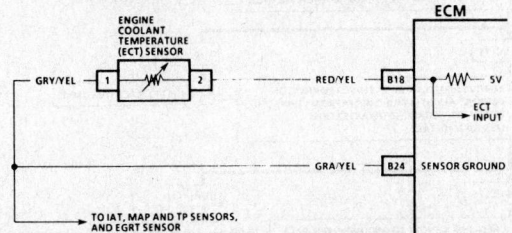

Engine Coolant Temperature (ECT) sensor is a thermistor in series with a fixed resistor in ECM. ECM applies and monitors 5 volts to sensor. ECM converts voltage into a temperature reading. When engine is cold, sensor resistance is high. When engine is warm, sensor resistance is low. Therefore, when engine is cold, ECM receives a high voltage input and when engine is warm, ECM receives a low voltage input. Code 15 will set when voltage input at ECM indicates coolant temperature greater than 284°F (140°C) for at least 5 seconds.

NOTE: Test numbers refer to test numbers on diagnostic chart.

1) This test simulates Code 14. If ECM stores Code 14, ECM and its wiring are okay and ECT sensor is faulty. If Code 15 resets, ECT sensor is okay and wiring to ECM or ECM is faulty.

DIAGNOSTIC AIDS

After engine is started, coolant temperature should rise steadily to about 203°F (95°C) and then stabilize when thermostat opens. Ensure engine is not overheating and has not been subjected to conditions which would create an overheating condition (i.e., overload, trailer towing, hilly terrain, heavy stop and go traffic, etc.). When replacing sensor, refer to TEMPERATURE TO RESISTANCE VALUES table at various temperature levels to evaluate the possibility of a "shifted" (mis-scaled) sensor. A "shifted" sensor could result in poor driveability complaints.

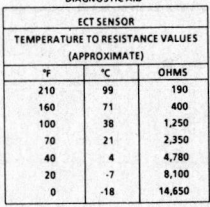

ECT SENSOR		
TEMPERATURE TO RESISTANCE VALUES (APPROXIMATE)		
°F	°C	OHMS
210	99	190
160	71	400
100	38	1,250
70	21	2,350
40	4	4,780
20	-7	8,100
0	-18	14,650

"AFTER REPAIRS," CONFIRM "CLOSED LOOP" OPERATION, NO DTCs AND NO MALFUNCTION INDICATOR LAMP (MIL).

Courtesy of General Motors Corp.

94H44609 94B44611

CODE 21, THROTTLE POSITION (TP) SENSOR, SIGNAL VOLTAGE HIGH (TRACKER – TBI FEDERAL)

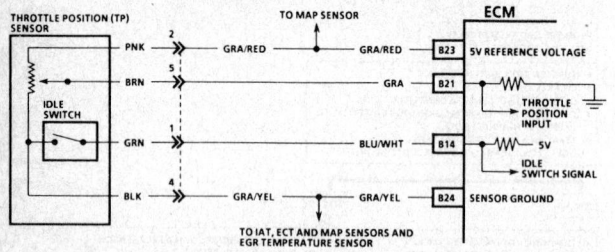

Throttle Position (TP) sensor consists of a potentiometer that changes resistance with throttle valve position. ECM provides a 5-volt reference voltage to TP sensor. ECM reads voltage across TP sensor and converts voltage into throttle position. When sensor resistance decreases, throttle valve opening increases to Wide Open Throttle (WOT) and voltage monitored by ECM increases. When TP sensor resistance increases, throttle valve opening decreases to idle and voltage monitored by ECM decreases. Code 21 will set when high voltage input at ECM is indicated with engine running at idle for at least 5 seconds.

94C44612 94D44613

NOTE: Test numbers refer to test numbers on diagnostic chart.

1) With TP sensor disconnected, voltage input at ECM should go low if ECM and its wiring are okay. If voltage input remains high, short to voltage is present in Gray wire or ECM is faulty.

DIAGNOSTIC AIDS

A misadjusted TP sensor can cause a false Code 21 or 22 to set. For additional TP sensor specifications, refer to SYSTEM & COMPONENT TESTING article.

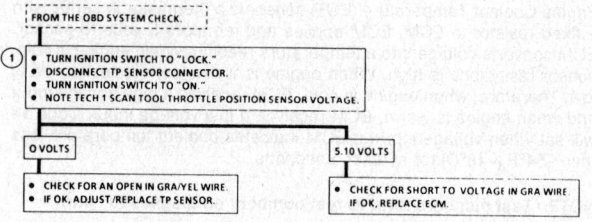

"AFTER REPAIRS," CONFIRM "CLOSED LOOP" OPERATION, NO DTCs AND NO MALFUNCTION INDICATOR LAMP (MIL)

Courtesy of General Motors Corp.

CODE 22, THROTTLE POSITION (TP) SENSOR, SIGNAL VOLTAGE LOW (TRACKER – TBI FEDERAL)

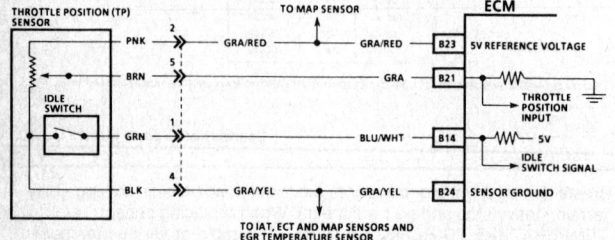

Throttle Position (TP) sensor consists of a potentiometer that changes resistance with throttle valve position. ECM provides a 5-volt reference voltage to TP sensor. ECM reads voltage across TP sensor and converts voltage into throttle position. When TP sensor resistance decreases, throttle valve opening increases to Wide Open Throttle (WOT) and voltage monitored by ECM increases. When TP sensor resistance increases, throttle valve opening decreases to idle and voltage monitored by ECM decreases. Code 22 will set when low voltage input at ECM is indicated with engine running at idle for at least 5 seconds.

NOTE: Test numbers refer to test numbers on diagnostic chart.

1) By connecting a jumper between TP sensor cavities, voltage input at ECM should be high, indicating a faulty TP sensor. If voltage input is low, problem is in ECM or ECM wiring.
2) Checks for open or short to ground in Gray and Gray/Red wires, and a faulty ECM.

94C44612 94E44614

DIAGNOSTIC AIDS

A misadjusted TP sensor can cause a false Code 21 or 22 to set. For additional TP sensor specifications, refer to SYSTEM & COMPONENT TESTING article. Codes 22 and 32 set at the same time could be the result of an open Gray/Red wire between ECM and TP sensor.

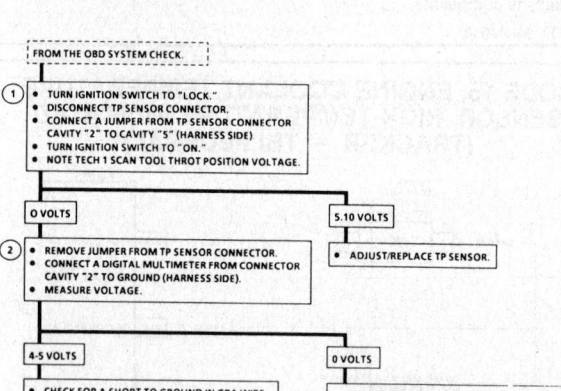

"AFTER REPAIRS," CONFIRM "CLOSED LOOP" OPERATION, NO DTCs AND NO MALFUNCTION INDICATOR LAMP (MIL)

Courtesy of General Motors Corp.

CODE 23, INTAKE AIR TEMPERATURE SENSOR, LOW TEMPERATURE INDICATED (TRACKER – TBI FEDERAL)

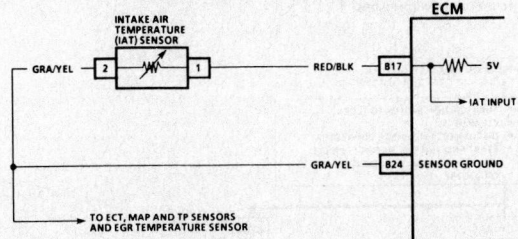

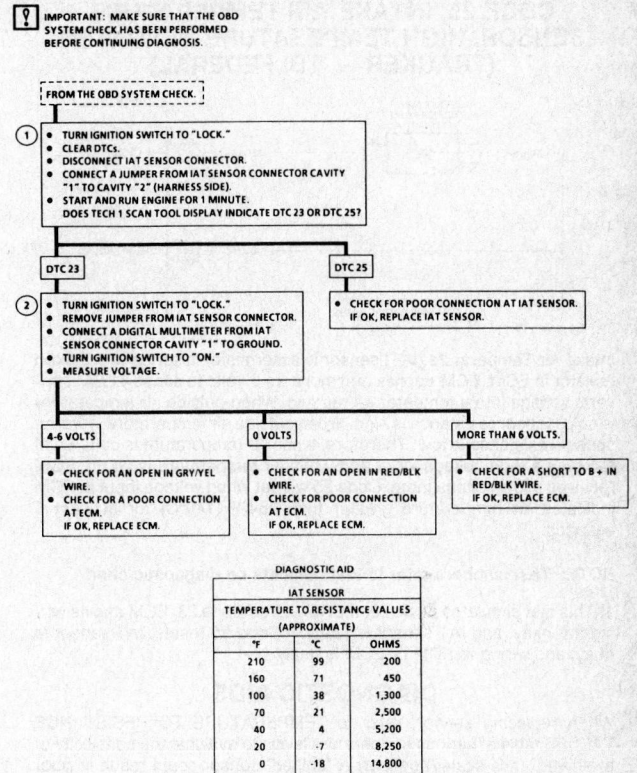

Intake Air Temperature (IAT) sensor is a thermistor in series with a fixed resistor in ECM. ECM applies 5 volts to sensor. ECM monitors voltage across IAT sensor and converts it into a temperature reading. When outside air temperature is cold, sensor resistance is high. When outside air temperature is warm, sensor resistance is low. Therefore, when air temperature is cold, ECM receives a high voltage input and when air temperature is warm, ECM receives a low voltage input. Code 23 will set when voltage input at ECM indicates air temperature less than –52°F (–47°C) for at least 5 seconds.

NOTE: Test numbers refer to test numbers on diagnostic chart.

1) This test simulates Code 25. If ECM stores Code 25, ECM and its wiring are okay, and IAT sensor is faulty. If Code 23 resets, IAT sensor is okay, and wiring to ECM or ECM is faulty.
2) Checks for open in Red/Black or Gray/Yellow wires, a short to B+ in Red/Black wire or a faulty ECM.

DIAGNOSTIC AIDS

Codes 21 and 23 stored at the same time could be the result of an open in Gray/Yellow wire. When replacing sensor, refer to TEMPERATURE TO RESISTANCE VALUES table at various temperature levels to evaluate the possibility of a "shifted" (mis-scaled) sensor. A "shifted" sensor could result in poor driveability complaints.

94F44615 94G44616

IAT SENSOR		
TEMPERATURE TO RESISTANCE VALUES (APPROXIMATE)		
°F	°C	OHMS
210	99	200
160	71	450
100	38	1,300
70	21	2,500
40	4	5,200
20	-7	8,250
0	-18	14,800

"AFTER REPAIRS," CONFIRM "CLOSED LOOP" OPERATION, NO DTCs AND NO MALFUNCTION INDICATOR LAMP (MIL).

Courtesy of General Motors Corp.

CODE 24, VEHICLE SPEED SENSOR (VSS) CIRCUIT (TRACKER – TBI FEDERAL)

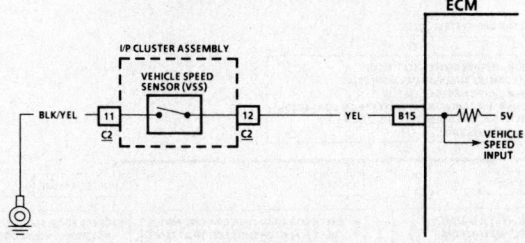

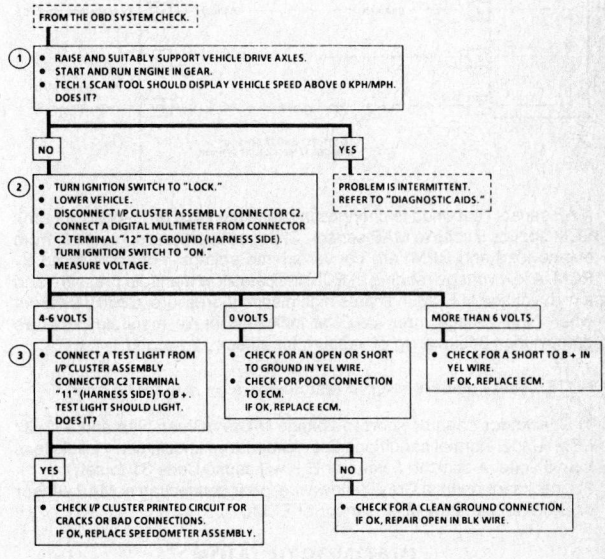

ECM provides 5 volts to Vehicle Speed Sensor (VSS). While vehicle is moving, a reed switch inside VSS will open and close, toggling voltage signal high and low. ECM then converts this toggled high/low voltage into vehicle speed that is displayed as MPH. Code 24 will set if a constant voltage signal (high or low) is detected at ECM for at least 4 seconds, with engine running and vehicle moving.

NOTE: Test numbers refer to test numbers on diagnostic chart.

1) Checks if problem is intermittent.
2) If VSS is not receiving 5 volts from ECM, Code 24 will set. Checks for open or short to B+ in Yellow wire, or a faulty ECM.
3) Checks for a poor ground connection, an open in Black/Yellow wire or a faulty VSS.

DIAGNOSTIC AIDS

If speedometer cable is binding, Code 24 can be set. Ensure that speedometer cable is free from restrictions and has a secure connection to instrument cluster. If problem is intermittent, refer to TROUBLE SHOOTING – NO CODES article.

94J44619 94C44620

"AFTER REPAIRS," CONFIRM "CLOSED LOOP" OPERATION, NO DTCs AND NO MALFUNCTION INDICATOR LAMP (MIL).

Courtesy of General Motors Corp.

CODE 25, INTAKE AIR TEMPERATURE SENSOR, HIGH TEMPERATURE INDICATED (TRACKER – TBI FEDERAL)

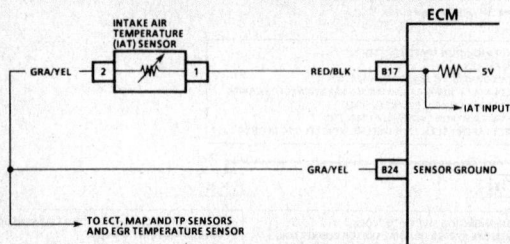

Intake Air Temperature (IAT) sensor is a thermistor in series with a fixed resistor in ECM. ECM applies and monitors 5 volts to sensor. ECM converts voltage into a temperature reading. When outside air temperature is cold, sensor resistance is high. When outside air temperature is warm, sensor resistance is low. Therefore, when air temperature is cold, ECM receives a high voltage input and when air temperature is warm, ECM receives a low voltage input. Code 25 will set when voltage input at ECM indicates air temperature greater than 284°F (140°C) for at least 5 seconds.

NOTE: Test numbers refer to test numbers on diagnostic chart.

1) This test simulates Code 23. If ECM stores Code 23, ECM and its wiring are okay, and IAT sensor is faulty. If Code 25 resets, IAT sensor is okay, and wiring to ECM or ECM is faulty.

DIAGNOSTIC AIDS

When replacing sensor, refer to TEMPERATURE TO RESISTANCE VALUES table at various temperature levels to evaluate the possibility of a "shifted" (mis-scaled) sensor. A "shifted" sensor could result in poor driveability complaints.

94F44615 94D44621

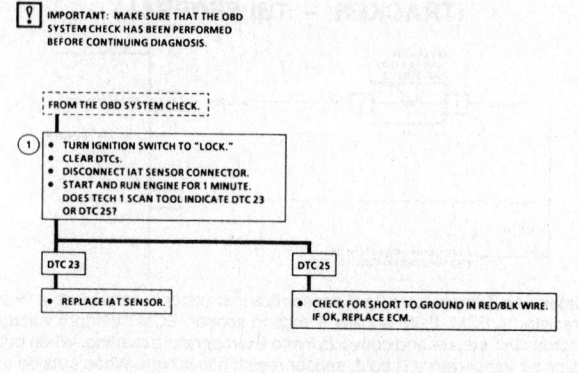

IAT SENSOR		
TEMPERATURE TO RESISTANCE VALUES		
(APPROXIMATE)		
°F	°C	OHMS
210	99	200
160	71	450
100	38	1,300
70	21	2,500
40	4	5,200
20	-7	8,250
0	-18	14,800

"AFTER REPAIRS," CONFIRM "CLOSED LOOP" OPERATION, NO DTCs AND NO MALFUNCTION INDICATOR LAMP (MIL).

Courtesy of General Motors Corp.

CODE 31, MANIFOLD ABSOLUTE PRESSURE SENSOR, HIGH VOLTAGE – HIGH VACUUM (TRACKER – TBI FEDERAL)

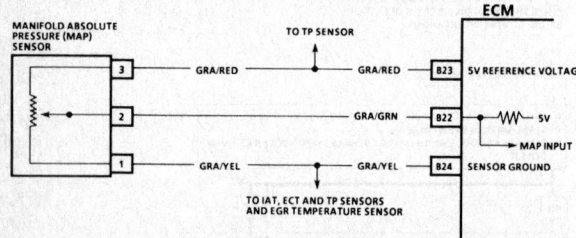

MAP sensor responds to changes in intake manifold pressure (vacuum). ECM applies 5 volts to MAP sensor. Changes in pressure, resulting from engine load and RPM, are converted into voltage input monitored by ECM. A low voltage reading at ECM indicates low manifold pressure and a high voltage at ECM indicates high manifold pressure. Code 31 will set when high voltage input at ECM indicates intake manifold pressure greater than 840 mm Hg of vacuum for at least .2 second.

NOTE: Test numbers refer to test numbers on diagnostic chart.

1) Checks for open or short to voltage in Gray/Green wire and a faulty ECM. Under normal conditions Gray/Green wire should carry a little less than 5 volts. A short to 5 volts or B+ will cause Code 31 to set.

2) Checks for open in Gray/Yellow wire, poor connection at MAP sensor or ECM, and a faulty MAP sensor or ECM.

DIAGNOSTIC AIDS

Check for leaking vacuum hose to MAP sensor. An intermittent condition may be caused by a poor connection, rubbed-through wire insulation, or a broken wire inside insulation. Check ECM harness connectors for backed-out terminals, improper mating, broken locks, improperly formed or damaged terminals, poor terminal-to-wire connection, and damaged harness.

94E44622 94F44623

Courtesy of General Motors Corp.

CODE 32, MANIFOLD ABSOLUTE PRESSURE SENSOR, LOW VOLTAGE – LOW VACUUM (TRACKER – TBI FEDERAL)

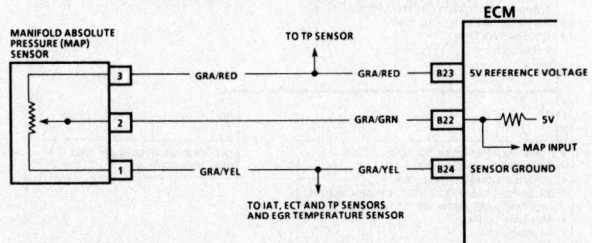

MAP sensor responds to changes in intake manifold pressure (vacuum). ECM applies 5 volts to MAP sensor. Changes in pressure, resulting from engine load and RPM, are converted into voltage input monitored by ECM. A low voltage reading at ECM indicates low manifold pressure and a high voltage at ECM indicates high manifold pressure. Code 32 will set when low voltage input at ECM indicates intake manifold pressure less than 40 mm Hg of vacuum for at least .2 second.

NOTE: Test numbers refer to test numbers on diagnostic chart.

1) Checks if ECM is providing a 5 volt reference.
2) Checks for bias voltage to MAP sensor which has a value between 4.5 and 4.9 volts.

94E44622 94G44624

DIAGNOSTIC AIDS

Check for blocked or pinched vacuum hose to MAP sensor. An intermittent condition may be caused by a poor connection, rubbed-through wire insulation, or a broken wire inside insulation. Check ECM harness connectors for backed-out terminals, improper mating, broken locks, improperly formed or damaged terminals, poor terminal-to-wire connection, and damaged harness. Codes 22 and 32 stored at the same time could be the result of an open in Gray/Red wire.

IMPORTANT: MAKE SURE THAT THE OBD SYSTEM CHECK HAS BEEN PERFORMED BEFORE CONTINUING DIAGNOSIS.

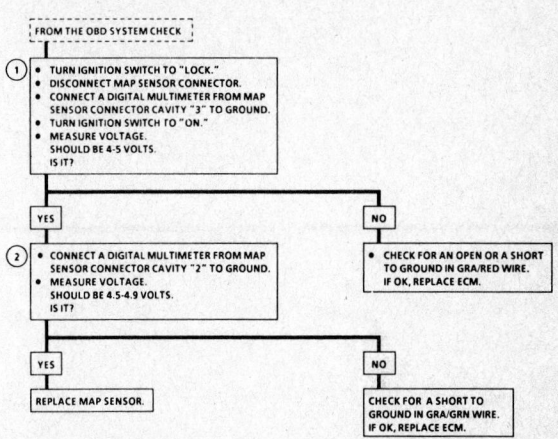

Courtesy of General Motors Corp.

CODE 41, NO IGNITION SIGNAL, (1 OF 2) (TRACKER – TBI FEDERAL)

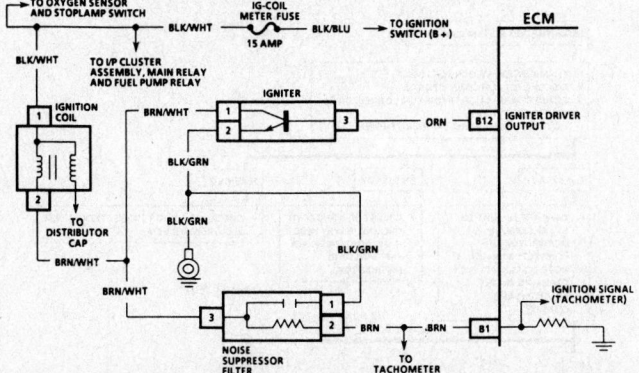

ECM receives an ignition signal when ignition switch is turned to ON position. When ignition switch is turned to START position, this signal is toggled on and off through igniter. As this signal is toggled on and off, so is ignition coil, thus inducing a voltage in secondary coil of ignition coil. Induced voltage is used to fire spark plugs. Code 41 will set when toggled ignition signal is not present at ECM within 3 seconds of cranking.

NOTE: Test numbers refer to test numbers on diagnostic chart.

1) Checks for power to ignition coil.
2) Checks for a poor connection or a faulty ignition coil.
3) Checks for open in Brown/White wire to noise suppressor filter.
4) Checks for a poor connection or a faulty noise suppressor filter.

DIAGNOSTIC AIDS

An intermittent condition may be caused by a poor connection, rubbed-through wire insulation, or a broken wire inside insulation. Check ECM harness connectors for backed-out terminals, improper mating, broken locks, improperly formed or damaged terminals, poor terminal-to-wire connection, and damaged harness.

92E26934 94H44625

IMPORTANT: MAKE SURE THAT THE OBD SYSTEM CHECK HAS BEEN PERFORMED BEFORE CONTINUING DIAGNOSIS.

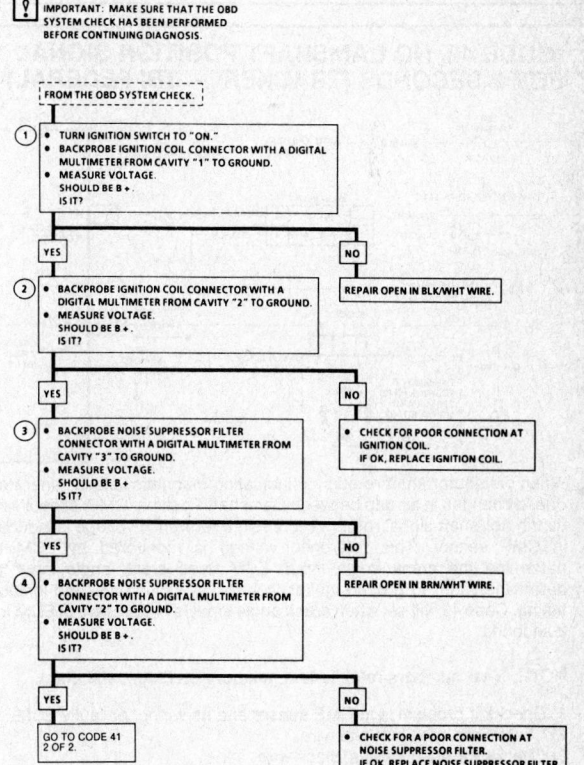

Courtesy of General Motors Corp.

CODE 41, NO IGNITION SIGNAL, (2 OF 2)
(TRACKER – TBI FEDERAL)

NOTE: Test numbers refer to test numbers on diagnostic chart.

5) Checks for open in Brown wire to ECM.
6) Checks for open in Brown/White to igniter.
7) Checks igniter for good ground.
8) Checks if ECM is toggling ignition signals. Either an open, a short to ground, or a faulty ECM or igniter.

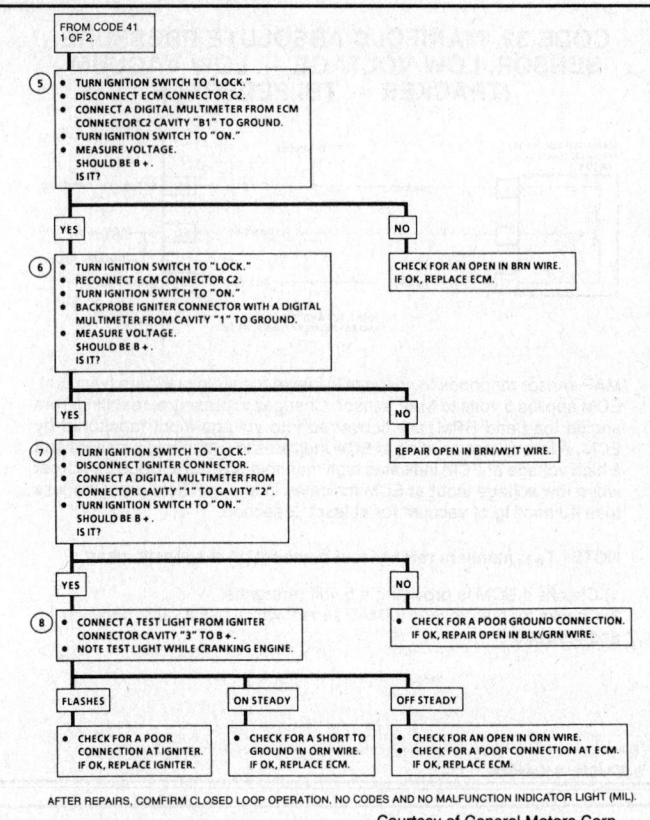

AFTER REPAIRS, COMFIRM CLOSED LOOP OPERATION, NO CODES AND NO MALFUNCTION INDICATOR LIGHT (MIL).

93C78966
Courtesy of General Motors Corp.

CODE 42, NO CAMSHAFT POSITION SIGNAL FOR 2 SECONDS (TRACKER – TBI FEDERAL)

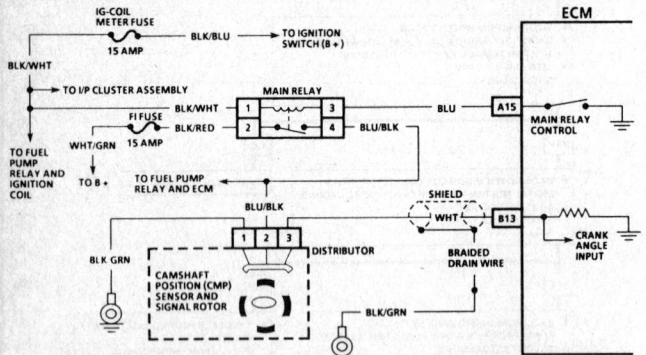

When distributor shaft rotates, a fluctuating magnetic field is generated due to changes in air gap between Camshaft Position (CMP) sensor and distributor shaft signal rotor. As a result, a reference voltage is induced in CMP sensor. This reference voltage is monitored by ECM to determine the crank angle input. ECM uses crank angle input to determine when to ground igniter, controlling ignition coil and ignition timing. Code 42 will set when crank angle input is not present at ECM for 2 seconds.

NOTE: Test numbers refer to test numbers on diagnostic chart.

1) Checks if problem is in CMP sensor and its wiring, or faulty ECM.
2) Checks for open in White wire.
3) Checks for open in Blue/Black wire.
4) Checks for poor ground connection and open Black/Green wire, or misadjusted or faulty CMP sensor.

DIAGNOSTIC AIDS

A loose or damaged CMP sensor could cause an intermittent code. A misaligned CMP sensor or improper air gap could also set a Code 42 or an intermittent "engine cranks but won't run" condition. For CMP sensor specifications, refer to SYSTEM & COMPONENT TESTING article.

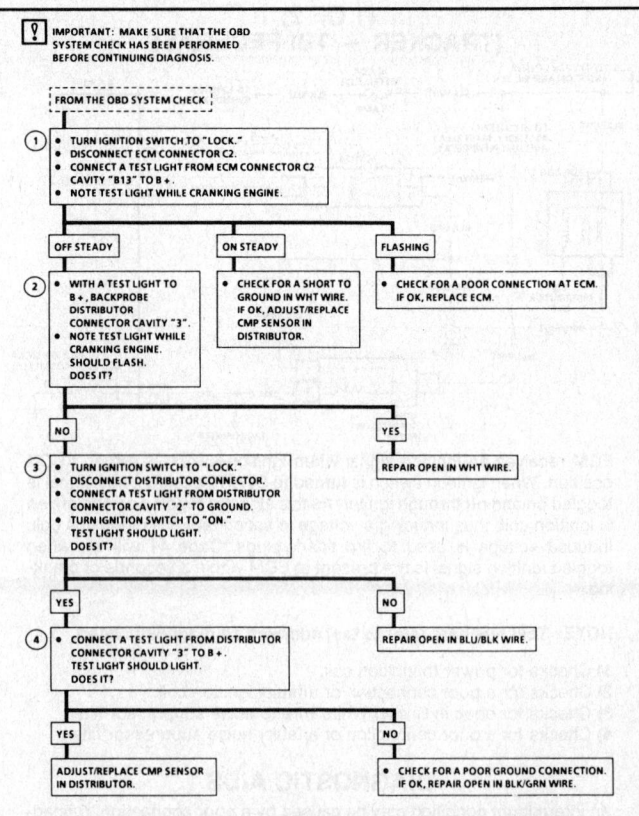

"AFTER REPAIRS," CONFIRM "CLOSED LOOP" OPERATION, NO DTCs AND NO MALFUNCTION INDICATOR LAMP (MIL).

94I44626 94J44627
Courtesy of General Motors Corp.

CODE 44, IDLE SWITCH OPEN OR MISADJUSTED (TRACKER – TBI FEDERAL)

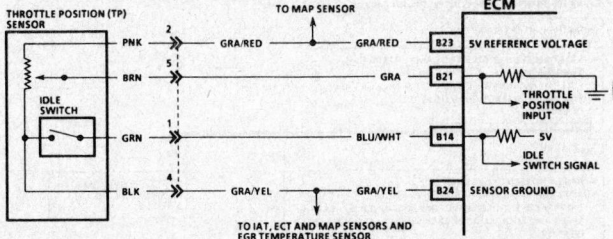
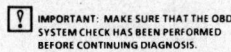

Throttle Position (TP) sensor has an idle switch that sends a signal to ECM. ECM applies 5 volts to idle switch. Idle switch is closed with engine at idle (low voltage signal at ECM) and open with engine off idle (high voltage signal at ECM). When ECM detects a low voltage signal, throttle valve is closed and when ECM detects a high voltage signal, throttle valve is open. Code 44 will set when high voltage input at ECM is indicated with engine running at idle (less than 1000 RPM) for at least 10 seconds.

NOTE: Test numbers refer to test numbers on diagnostic chart.

1) By jumpering TP sensor, ECM should detect a low voltage signal and scan tester should indicate ON. This determines whether problem is in wiring, ECM, or a misadjusted or faulty TP sensor.

2) Checks for open in Gray/Yellow and Blue/White wires, and a faulty ECM.

94C44612 94B44629

DIAGNOSTIC AIDS

A misadjusted TP sensor could cause Code 44 to set. Before replacing TP sensor, check TP sensor adjustment. Refer to ON-VEHICLE ADJUSTMENTS article.

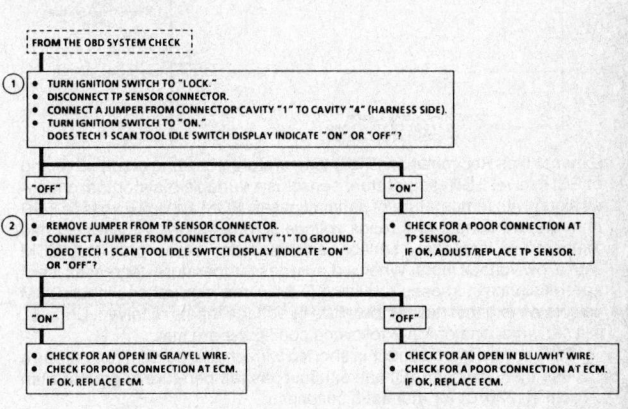

IMPORTANT: MAKE SURE THAT THE OBD SYSTEM CHECK HAS BEEN PERFORMED BEFORE CONTINUING DIAGNOSIS.

"AFTER REPAIRS," CONFIRM "CLOSED LOOP" OPERATION, NO DTCs AND NO MALFUNCTION INDICATOR LAMP (MIL).

Courtesy of General Motors Corp.

CODE 45, IDLE SWITCH GROUNDED OR MISADJUSTED (TRACKER – TBI FEDERAL)

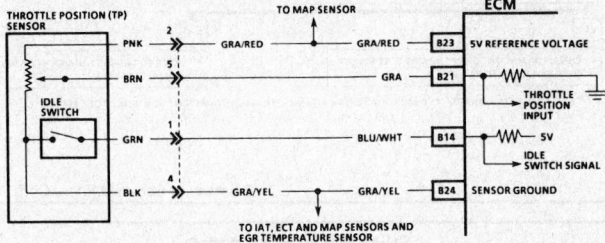

Throttle Position (TP) sensor has an idle switch that sends a signal to ECM. ECM applies 5 volts to idle switch. Idle switch is closed with engine at idle (low voltage signal at ECM) and open with engine off idle (high voltage signal at ECM). When ECM detects a low voltage signal, throttle valve is closed and when ECM detects a high voltage signal, throttle valve is open. Code 45 will set when low voltage input at ECM is indicated with engine running off idle (greater than 2900 RPM), and MAP sensor reading is greater than 320 mm Hg of vacuum, for at least 5 seconds.

NOTE: Test numbers refer to test numbers on diagnostic chart.

1) By disconnecting TP sensor, ECM should detect a high voltage signal and scan tester should indicate OFF. Checks for short to ground in Blue/White wire.

2) Checks for short to B+ in Gray/Red wire, or a misadjusted or faulty TP sensor.

94C44612 94E44630

DIAGNOSTIC AIDS

A misadjusted TP sensor could cause Code 45 to set. Before replacing TP sensor, check TP sensor adjustment. Refer to ON-VEHICLE ADJUSTMENTS article.

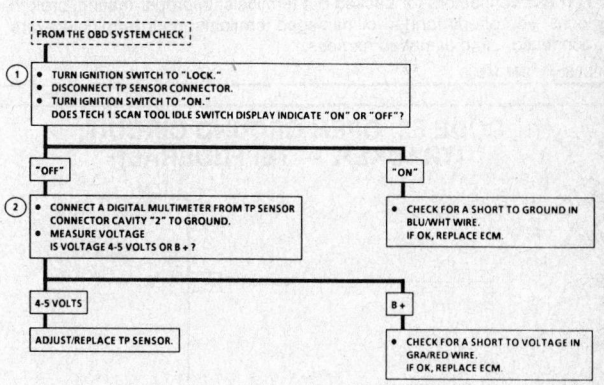

IMPORTANT: MAKE SURE THAT THE OBD SYSTEM CHECK HAS BEEN PERFORMED BEFORE CONTINUING DIAGNOSIS.

"AFTER REPAIRS," CONFIRM "CLOSED LOOP" OPERATION, NO DTCs AND NO MALFUNCTION INDICATOR LAMP (MIL).

Courtesy of General Motors Corp.

CODE 51, EXHAUST GAS RECIRCULATION CIRCUIT (TRACKER – TBI FEDERAL)

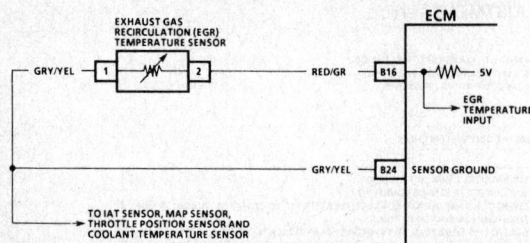

Exhaust Gas Recirculation (EGR) temperature sensor is mounted on top of EGR valve. EGR temperature sensor is a variable resistor that changes along with temperature of exhaust gases. ECM applies 5 volts to EGR temperature sensor and reads voltage across sensor. As exhaust gas temperature increases, sensor resistance decreases providing ECM with a low voltage input. When exhaust gas temperature decreases, sensor resistance increases providing ECM with a high voltage input. ECM calculates exhaust gas temperature by voltage inputs received. Code 51 will set when one of the 2 following conditions are met.

- EGR temperature sensor is shorted with engine coolant temperature less than 104°F (40°C) and exhaust gas temperature is greater than 428°F (220°C) for at least 3 seconds.
- EGR temperature sensor is open with engine coolant temperature greater than 158°F (70°C) and intake air temperature is greater than 122°F (50°C) for at least 80 seconds.

NOTE: Test numbers refer to test numbers on diagnostic chart.

1) Checks for proper EGR valve operation.
2) Checks for 5-volt reference to EGR temperature sensor.
3) Checks for short to voltage in Red/Green wire.
4) Checks for open Gray/Yellow wire, a faulty ECM or EGR temperature sensor.

DIAGNOSTIC AIDS

An intermittent condition may be caused by a poor connection, rubbed-through wire insulation, or a broken wire inside insulation. Check ECM harness connectors for backed-out terminals, improper mating, broken locks, improperly formed or damaged terminals, poor terminal-to-wire connection, and damaged harness.

92D26941 94A44636

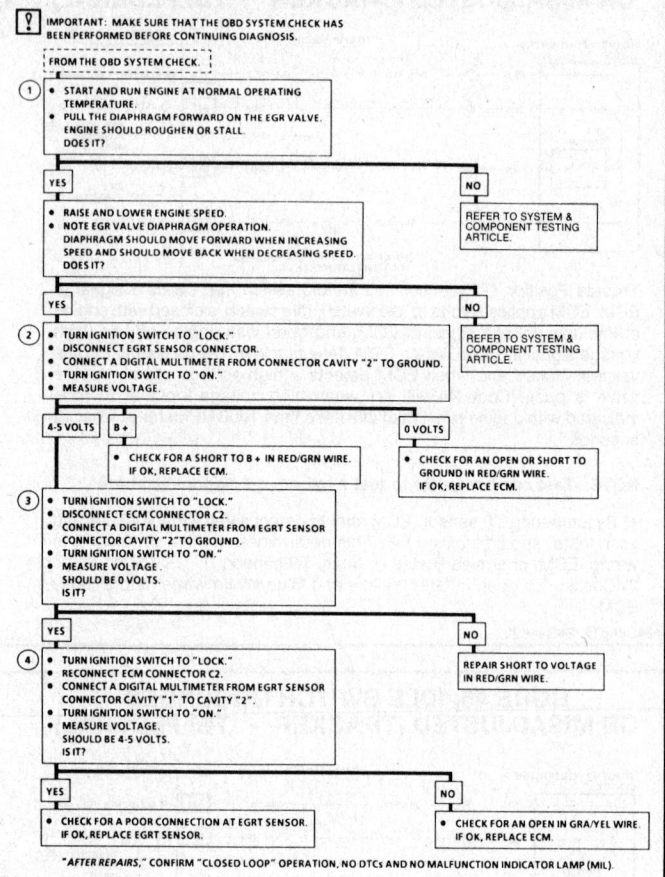

Courtesy of General Motors Corp.

CODE 53, OPEN GROUND CIRCUIT, (TRACKER – TBI FEDERAL)

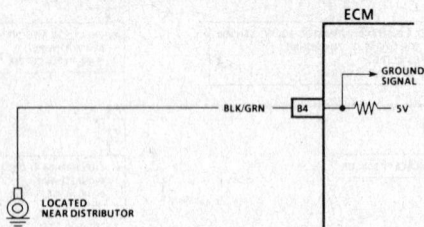

An additional ground is supplied to ECM. ECM supplies 5 volts to Black/Green wire through a fixed resistor. ECM expects voltage signal to be low. Code 53 will set when a high voltage signal is indicated at ECM for 3 seconds.

NOTE: Test numbers refer to test numbers on diagnostic chart.

1) Probing Black/Green wire cavity with test light to B+, checks for open in Black/Green wire, a poor ground connection or a faulty ECM.

DIAGNOSTIC AIDS

A poor ground connection could cause Code 53 to set. Ensure ground connection is clean and tight.

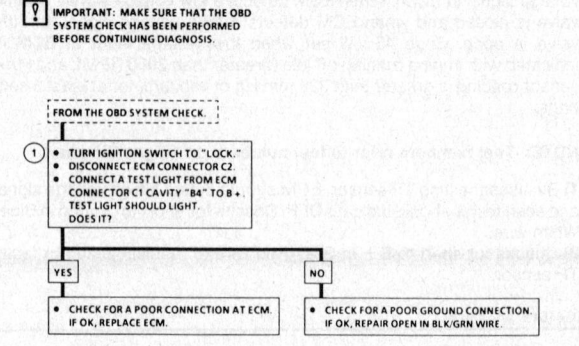

92F26943 94A44628

Courtesy of General Motors Corp.

Metro, Prizm, Tracker

INTRODUCTION

Before diagnosing symptoms or intermittent faults, perform steps in BASIC DIAGNOSTIC PROCEDURES and SELF-DIAGNOSTICS articles. Use this article to diagnose driveability problems existing when a hard fault code is not present or vehicle is not equipped with a self-diagnostic system.

NOTE: Some driveability problems may have been corrected by manufacturer with a revised computer calibration chip or computer control unit. Check with manufacturer for latest chip or computer application.

Symptom checks can direct the technician to malfunctioning component(s) for further diagnosis. A symptom should lead to a specific component, system test or an adjustment.

Use intermittent test procedures to locate driveability problems that DO NOT occur when the vehicle is being tested. These test procedures should also be used if a soft (intermittent) trouble code was present, but no problem was found during self-diagnostic testing.

NOTE: For specific testing procedures, see SYSTEM & COMPONENT TESTING article. For specifications, see ON-VEHICLE ADJUSTMENTS or SERVICE & ADJUSTMENT SPECIFICATIONS article.

SYMPTOMS

SYMPTOM DIAGNOSIS

Symptom checks cannot be used properly unless the problem occurs while the vehicle is being tested. To reduce diagnostic time, ensure steps in BASIC DIAGNOSTIC PROCEDURES and SELF-DIAGNOSTICS articles were performed before diagnosing a symptom. Symptoms available for diagnosis include the following:

- Hard Starting (Cranks Okay)
- Engine Surges And/Or Chuggles
- Lack Of Power, Sluggish Or Spongy
- Detonation/Spark Knock
- Hesitation, Sag Or Stumble
- Cuts Out, Misses
- Rough, Unstable Or Incorrect Idle
- Poor Fuel Economy
- Excessive Exhaust Emissions
- Engine Diesels
- Engine Backfires

NOTE: Systems and components listed under each symptom may not be applicable on all models.

HARD STARTING (CRANKS OKAY)

If vehicle cranks okay, but is difficult to start or starts and immediately dies, check the following items:
- Ensure sufficient secondary spark is available.
- Check distributor cap and spark plug wires.
- Check spark plugs.
- Ensure compression is within specifications.
- Ensure all fuses are okay.
- Check ignition coil resistance.
- Check vacuum hoses and switches for no vacuum leaks.
- Check fuel pump or circuit opening relay.
- Check fuel pressure.
- Check for contaminated fuel.
- Check for faulty in-tank fuel pump check valve, allowing fuel from lines to drain back to tank after engine has stopped.
- Check EGR valve and solenoid operation.
- Check air intake system for restriction.
- Ensure ignition and valve timing are correct.
- Ensure noise suppressor (if equipped) has correct resistance.

- Check distributor signal rotor air gap.
- Check for worn distributor shaft.
- Check Camshaft Position (CMP) sensor resistance and connections.
- Check Engine Coolant Temperature (ECT) sensor has correct resistance.
- Check operation of Idle Air Control (IAC) valve (if equipped).
- Check Mass Airflow (MAF) sensor.
- Check Manifold Absolute Pressure (MAP) sensor.
- Check Throttle Position (TP) sensor.
- Check for cracks or poor connections at throttle body.
- Check throttle shaft for sticking and throttle linkage for binding and misadjustment.

ENGINE SURGES AND/OR CHUGGLES

If engine power varies or vehicle feels like it is speeding up and slowing down during steady throttle operation, check the following items:
- Check vacuum hoses for leaks or kinks.
- Check for proper Torque Converter Clutch (TCC) operation.
- Check EGR valve and solenoid operation.
- Ensure correct speedometer operation.
- Check fuel pressure while condition exists.
- Check in-line fuel filter and replace if dirty or clogged.
- Check fuel for water contamination.
- Determine if condition is caused by a rich or lean system. Using Tech 1, measure O2S/HO2S output voltage while driving vehicle when condition exists. Voltage less than .45 volt, indicates a lean system. Voltage greater than .45 volt, indicates a rich system.
- Check O2S/HO2S operation and for RTV sealant or silicone contamination. Also check for sensor cracking or glycol contamination. This will cause a false high voltage signal to ECM. ECM will respond by reducing (leaner) air/fuel ratio.
- Verify ignition timing is correct.
- Ensure sufficient secondary spark is available.
- Check ECM ground connections.
- Check for faulty spark plugs.
- Check for defective spark plug wires.
- Check for restricted exhaust.
- Check charging system output. Repair charging system if voltage is not 12-16 volts.

LACK OF POWER, SLUGGISH OR SPONGY

If engine delivers less power than expected, or if there is little or no increase in speed when accelerator pedal is depressed, check the following items:
- A/C clutch disengages at full throttle (Metro and Tracker).
- Check throttle cable adjustment.
- Verify air intake or exhaust system is not restricted.
- Check for contaminated fuel.
- Check fuel pressure.
- Check in-line fuel filter and replace if dirty or clogged.
- Ensure sufficient secondary spark exists.
- Ensure ignition timing and controls are working properly.
- Check ECM ground connections.
- Check EGR valve and solenoid operation.
- Determine if condition is caused by a rich or lean system. Using Tech 1, measure O2S/HO2S output voltage while driving vehicle when condition exists. Voltage less than .45 volt, indicates a lean system. Voltage greater than .45 volt, indicates a rich system.
- Check O2S/HO2S operation and for RTV sealant or silicone contamination. Also check for sensor cracking or glycol contamination. This will cause a false high voltage signal to ECM. ECM will respond by reducing (leaner) air/fuel ratio.
- Check charging system output. Repair charging system if voltage is not 12-16 volts.
- Check Torque Converter Clutch (TCC) operation.
- Check for faulty spark plugs.
- Check for defective spark plug wires.
- Ensure valve timing and engine compression are okay.
- Check for worn camshaft.

DETONATION/SPARK KNOCK

If engine exhibits a mild-to-severe ping or knock (usually worse under acceleration), check the following items:

- Check for contaminated or poor quality fuel.
- Check fuel pressure.
- Ensure ignition timing and controls are working properly.
- Ensure spark plug application and gap is correct.
- Check EGR valve and solenoid operation.
- Check PCV valve operation.
- Determine if condition is caused by a rich or lean system. Using Tech 1, measure O2S/HO2S output voltage while driving vehicle when condition exists. Voltage less than .45 volt, indicates a lean system. Voltage greater than .45 volt, indicates a rich system.
- Check O2S/HO2S operation and for RTV sealant or silicone contamination. Also check for sensor cracking or glycol contamination. This will cause a false high voltage signal to ECM. ECM will respond by reducing (leaner) air/fuel ratio.
- Ensure transaxle/transmission shift points are correct.
- Check Torque Converter Clutch (TCC) operation.
- Ensure correct ECM application. Check with dealer for latest application information.
- Check for engine overheating.
- Check for restricted air flow or coolant flow through radiator.
- Check water pump drive belt adjustment.
- Check for correct thermostat and coolant solution.
- Check coolant temperature sensor.
- Check for incorrect or damaged basic engine parts such as camshaft, cylinder heads or pistons.
- Check for excessive carbon build-up on engine components.
- Check for excessive oil entering the engine.

HESITATION, SAG OR STUMBLE

If there is a momentary lack of throttle response, which may occur at any speed, or is most severe when moving off from a stop (vehicle stalls), check the following items:

- Check throttle position sensor/switch for sticking or misadjustment.
- Check Manifold Absolute Pressure (MAP) sensor operation.
- Check Mass Airflow (MAF) sensor response and accuracy.
- Check EGR valve and solenoid operation.
- Check for fouled spark plugs or defective spark plug wires.
- Check for defective ignition wiring or connections.
- Ensure ignition timing and controls are working properly.
- Check charging system output. Repair charging system if voltage is not 12-16 volts.
- Check fuel pressure.
- Check fuel for water contamination.
- Ensure correct ECM application. Check with dealer for latest application information.
- Check canister purge operation.
- Ensure engine warms to normal operating temperature.

CUTS OUT, MISSES

If exhaust has a steady spitting sound at idle or low speed. If a steady jerking exists as engine load increases and is not normally felt with engine speed greater than 1500 RPM or vehicle speed greater than 30 MPH, check the following items:

- With engine running and stabilized, using insulated pliers, remove spark plug wires one at a time. If there is about a 50 RPM drop on each cylinder, go to ROUGH, UNSTABLE OR INCORRECT IDLE. If there is no RPM drop or an excessive drop check for spark at suspect cylinder(s).
- Check for defective spark plugs, spark plug wires, distributor cap or rotor.
- Ensure spark plug wire resistance is 3000-6700 per foot.
- Check for defective ignition wiring or connections.

- Check fuel pressure.
- Check fuel for water contamination.
- Ensure fuel injectors driver wiring circuit at each injector is operating.
- Check valve clearance adjustment.
- Check for low compression.
- Ensure valve timing is okay.
- Check for damaged basic engine parts such as camshaft, valves, pistons etc.
- Check intake and exhaust manifold passage for casting flash.

ROUGH, UNSTABLE OR INCORRECT IDLE

If engine runs unevenly at idle (may shake) or if idle speed is incorrect or unstable (RPM varies, engine is hunting), check the following items:

- Ensure no vacuum leaks exist.
- Check PCV valve operation.
- Check ECM ground connections.
- Ensure base idle adjustment is correct.
- Verify vacuum hose routing is correct.
- Check for defective ignition system components.
- Ensure ignition timing and controls are working properly.
- Ensure all fuel injectors are operating correctly and not leaking.
- Clean fuel injectors.
- Check for fuel in vacuum hose to fuel pressure regulator.
- Check for low compression.
- Check for broken motor mounts.
- Determine if condition is caused by a rich or lean system. Using Tech 1, measure O2S/HO2S output voltage while driving vehicle when condition exists. Voltage less than .45 volt, indicates a lean system. Voltage greater than .45 volt, indicates a rich system.
- Check O2S/HO2S operation and for RTV sealant or silicone contamination. Also check for sensor cracking or glycol contamination. This will cause a false high voltage signal to ECM. ECM will respond by reducing (leaner) air/fuel ratio.
- Check EGR and solenoid operation (There should be no EGR operation at idle).
- Check air valve, IAC or ISC valve operation.
- Check MAP sensor operation.
- Check TP sensor for a sticking throttle shaft or binding throttle linkage.
- Check charging system output. Repair charging system if voltage is not 12-16 volts.
- Ensure correct ECM application. Check with dealer for latest application information.
- Check canister purge and PCV valve operation.
- Check for A/C signal to ECM when A/C is on.
- Check park/neutral switch operation.
- A/C system overcharged, pressure to high or faulty dual pressure switch.
- Check Engine Coolant Temperature (ECT) sensor.
- Check Mass Airflow (MAF) sensor.

POOR FUEL ECONOMY

If fuel economy is lower than expected during a road test, or has decreased since previous road tests, check the following items:

- Ensure air intake system is not restricted or leaking.
- Ensure ignition timing and controls are working properly.
- Check for faulty spark plugs or spark plug wires.
- Check for continuous A/C or Defroster operation.
- Ensure engine warms to normal operating temperature.
- Check for low compression.
- Check for restricted exhaust system.
- Check Torque Converter Clutch (TCC) operation.
- Check fuel pressure.
- Check engine coolant level and thermostat operation.
- Check for proper speedometer calibration.
- Verify brakes are not dragging.
- Check for faulty ECM.

EXCESSIVE EXHAUST EMISSIONS

If vehicle fails emission test or has excessive "rotten egg smell", check the following items:
- Check for defective oxygen sensor.
- Check for proper fuel filler cap.
- Check fuel pressure.
- Check for leaking fuel injector if vehicle is running rich.
- Check canister purge and PCV valve operation.
- Check throttle position sensor or switch if vehicle is running rich.
- Check Manifold Absolute Sensor (MAP) if vehicle is running rich.
- Check EGR operation.
- Check for vacuum leaks.
- Ensure ignition timing and controls are working properly.
- Check for faulty spark plugs or spark plug wires.
- Check for exhaust leaks.
- Check for excessive carbon build-up on engine components.
- Ensure engine warms to normal operating temperature.
- Ensure correct ECM application. Check with dealer for latest application information.
- Check for lead contaminated catalytic converter (look for removal of fuel filler neck restrictor).

ENGINE DIESELS, RUN-ON

If engine continues to run after ignition is turned off, check the following items:
- If engine runs smoothly, check ignition switch and adjustment.
- Check for leaking fuel injectors.
- Check throttle opener adjustment (Tracker – Federal).
- Check for excessive fuel additives (high percentage of alcohol).

ENGINE BACKFIRES

If fuel ignites in intake manifold or exhaust system and makes a loud popping noise, check the following items:
- Ensure sufficient secondary spark is available.
- Ensure ignition timing and controls are working properly.
- Check for faulty spark plugs, spark plug wires, distributor cap and rotor causing crossfire between spark plugs.
- Check for proper spark plug wire routing.
- Check for low compression (sticking or leaking valves).
- Ensure valve timing is correct.
- Check fuel pressure.
- Check EGR and solenoid operation.
- Check intake and exhaust manifolds for casting flash.

INTERMITTENTS

INTERMITTENT PROBLEM DIAGNOSIS

Most intermittent problems are caused by faulty electrical connection or wiring. Ensure connector halves and terminals are fully seated and not backed out. Ensure terminals are not damaged, properly formed and there is a firm terminal-to-wire connection.

DO NOT use Diagnostic Trouble Code (DTC) procedures to diagnosis intermittent problems. Intermittent fault testing requires duplicating circuit or component failure to identify the problem. These procedures may lead to the computer setting a fault code (on some systems) which may help in diagnosis.

If problem vehicle does not produce fault codes, road test vehicle and monitor voltage or resistance values using a DVOM or Tech 1. While attempting to reproduce conditions causing intermittent fault, a status change on DVOM or Tech 1 indicates a fault has been located.

Use a DVOM or Tech 1 to pinpoint faults. When monitoring voltage, ensure ignition switch is in ON position, or engine is running. Ensure ignition switch is in OFF position or negative battery cable is disconnected when monitoring circuit resistance. Status changes on DVOM or Tech 1 during test procedures indicate area or component of fault.

An intermittent MIL, and NO DTCs may be caused by electrical system interference from a defective relay, an ECM driven solenoid or a switch. These defective components can cause a sharp electrical surge during system operation. Improper installation of add-on electrical options, such as lights and radios, improper routing of ignition wires to close to spark plugs, ignition components and alternator can also cause an intermittent MIL.

TEST PROCEDURES

Intermittent Simulation – To reproduce the conditions creating an intermittent fault, use the following methods:
- Lightly vibrate component.
- Heat component.
- Wiggle or bend wiring harness.
- Spray component or wires with water mist.
- Remove/apply vacuum source.

Monitor circuit/component voltage or resistance while simulating intermittent. If engine is running, monitor for self-diagnostic codes. Use test results to identify a faulty component or circuit.

Metro, Prizm, Tracker

INTRODUCTION

NOTE: Testing individual components does not isolate shorts or opens. Unless stated otherwise in test procedure, perform all voltage tests using a Digital Volt-Ohmmeter (DVOM) with a minimum 10-megohm input impedance. Use ohmmeter to isolate wiring harness shorts or opens.

CAUTION: On Metro, Transaxle Control Module (TCM) on 3-speed automatic transaxle is mounted behind dash, on left side of steering column. DO NOT confuse this with ECM. ECM contains 26-pin and 16-pin connectors; TCM contains 10-pin and 14-pin connectors.

Before testing separate components or systems, perform procedures in BASIC DIAGNOSTIC PROCEDURES article. Since many computer-controlled and monitored components will set a diagnostic trouble code if they malfunction, it is also recommended that self-diagnostics be performed. See SELF-DIAGNOSTICS article.

TERMINOLOGY

Due to Federal government requirements, manufacturers may use names and acronyms for systems and components different than those used in previous years. The following table will help eliminate confusion when dealing with these components and systems. Only relevant components and systems whose names have changed from current General Motors Corp. terminology have been listed.

SAE TERMINOLOGY

Former Name Or Acronym	New Name Or Acronym
ALDL	Data Link Connector (DLC)
CHECK ENGINE Light	Malfunction Indicator Light (MIL)
CTS	Engine Coolant Temp. (ECT) Sensor
Diagnostic Circuit Check	On-Board Diagnostic (OBD) System Check
ESC System	Knock Sensor (KS) System
EST System	Ignition Control (IC) System
MAT Sensor	Intake Air Temperature (IAT) Sensor
Park/Neutral (P/N) Switch	Park/Neutral Position (PNP) Switch
Port Fuel Injection	Multiport Fuel Injection
Scan Data	Scan Tester (ST) Data
SERVICE ENGINE SOON Light	Malfunction Indicator Light (MIL)
Thermostatic Air Cleaner (TAC)	Air Cleaner (ACL)
Throttle Position Sensor (TPS)	Throttle Position (TP) Sensor
Throttle Position Switch	Closed Throttle Position (CTP) Switch
Throttle Position Switch	Wide Open Throttle (WOT) Switch
Viscous Converter Clutch (VCC)	Torque Converter Clutch (TCC)

COMPUTERIZED ENGINE CONTROLS

NOTE: Prizm LSi uses a Powertrain Control Module (PCM). All other models use an Engine Control Module (ECM). All references to ECM include PCM unless specified otherwise.

ENGINE CONTROL MODULE (ECM)

Ground Circuit Checks – 1) Using an ohmmeter, check ground circuits to ECM for continuity to ground. See appropriate wiring diagram in WIRING DIAGRAMS article to determine ECM ground terminals. Resistance to ground should be zero ohms. If reading is other than zero ohms, repair open circuit to ground.
2) Using a DVOM, touch negative voltmeter lead to a good ground. Touch positive voltmeter lead to each ground terminal. With vehicle running, voltmeter should indicate less than one volt. If voltmeter reading is greater than one volt, check for open, corrosion or loose connection on ground lead.
Power Circuit Checks – 1) Using a voltmeter, check for battery voltage between ECM constant battery power terminals and ground. See appropriate wiring diagram in WIRING DIAGRAMS article to determine ECM power terminals. If battery voltage is not present, check ECM power supply fuse. If fuse is okay, check for open in power supply or ECM wiring.

2) Turn ignition switch to ON position. Using a voltmeter, check for battery voltage between ECM ignition power terminals and ground. If battery voltage is not present, check power supply fuse(s). If fuse is okay, check for an open in wiring between fuse and ECM, or check for a defective ignition switch.
3) Connect voltmeter between ground and ECM start (crank) signal terminal. Turn ignition switch to the START position. Battery voltage should be present between ECM start terminal and ground ONLY when ignition switch is in START position. If voltage is not present, check fuse(s). If fuse is okay, check for an open in wiring between fuse and ECM, or check for a defective ignition switch.

ENGINE SENSORS & SWITCHES

NOTE: For additional sensor testing specifications, see SENSOR OPERATING RANGE CHARTS article.

Camshaft Position Sensor (Metro) – 1) A malfunction in the camshaft position sensor circuit will set diagnostic trouble Code 42. For testing procedures, see SELF-DIAGNOSTICS article. Use the following procedure to diagnose camshaft position sensor.
2) Ensure air gap measures .008-.016" (.2-.4 mm). Adjust as necessary. If air gap is okay, disconnect distributor 2-pin electrical connector. Using an ohmmeter, measure resistance between terminals of distributor connector. Resistance should be 140-180 ohms. If resistance is not as specified, replace camshaft position sensor.
Camshaft Position Sensor (Prizm & Prizm LSi) – 1) Ensure ignition is off. Remove rotor from distributor housing. Remove ignition coil dust cover and gasket from distributor housing. Remove 2 nuts and 4 wires from ignition coil terminals.
2) Remove 3 screws and 3 wires from igniter terminals. Remove 2 screws and igniter from distributor housing. Remove 2 connectors from harness retainer. Remove distributor wire from housing. Remove screw and noise suppressor condenser from housing.
3) Using ohmmeter, measure resistance of distributor connector C1, when cold (14-104°F; –10-50°C), between terminals No. 3 and 6. *See Fig. 1.* Camshaft Position (CMP) sensor resistance should be 185-275 ohms. If resistance is not as specified, replace distributor housing.
4) Measure resistance of distributor connector C1, when cold, between terminals No. 2 and 5. CMP sensor resistance should be 370-550 ohms. If resistance is not as specified, replace distributor housing.
5) Measure resistance of distributor connector C1, when hot (104-212°F; 50-100°C), between terminals No. 3 and 6. CMP sensor resistance should be 240-325 ohms. If resistance is not as specified, replace distributor housing.

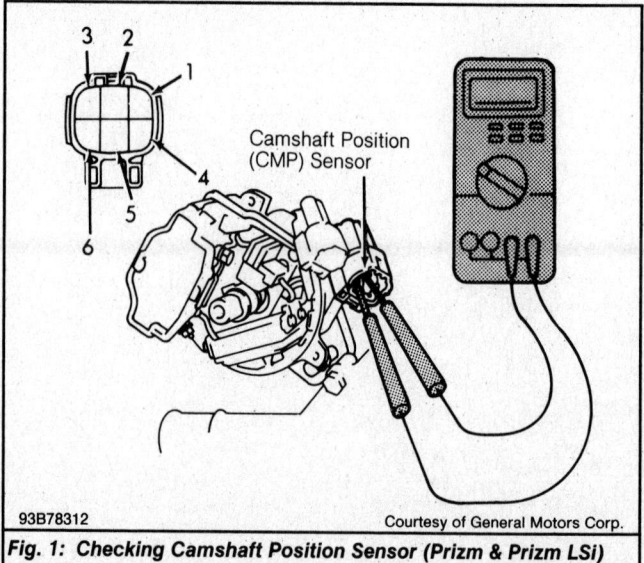

93B78312   Courtesy of General Motors Corp.

Fig. 1: Checking Camshaft Position Sensor (Prizm & Prizm LSi)

6) Measure resistance of distributor connector C1, when hot, between terminals No. 2 and 5. CMP sensor resistance should be 475-650 ohms. If resistance is not as specified, replace distributor housing.

7) Measure air gap between signal rotor and camshaft position sensor. Air gap should be .008-.016" (.2-.4 mm). If air gap is not as specified, replace distributor housing. When testing is complete, reverse disassembly procedure.

Camshaft Position Sensor – Hall Effect (Tracker – MFI Calif. & New York) – 1) A malfunction in the camshaft position sensor circuit will set diagnostic trouble Code 42. For testing procedures, see SELF-DIAGNOSTICS article. Use the following procedure to diagnose camshaft position sensor.

2) Turn ignition off. Remove distributor cap. Remove rotor and signal rotor cover from distributor housing. Using voltmeter, probe Yellow ECM 26-pin electrical connector C2 terminal No. 3 to ground. ECM is located behind left side of dash. Turn ignition on.

3) CMP sensor voltage with signal rotor inserted between Hall element and magnet (magnetic flux cut off) should be 3-5 volts. See Fig. 2. If voltage is as specified, go to next step. If voltage is not as specified, check for faulty wiring and ECM. If wiring and ECM are okay, replace distributor housing.

4) CMP sensor voltage without signal rotor inserted between Hall element and magnet (magnetic flux applied) should be 0-1 volt. See Fig. 2. If voltage is as specified, CMP sensor is okay. Turn ignition off and reverse disassembly procedure.

5) If voltage is not as specified, check for faulty wiring and ECM. If wiring and ECM are okay, replace distributor housing. When testing is complete, reverse disassembly procedure.

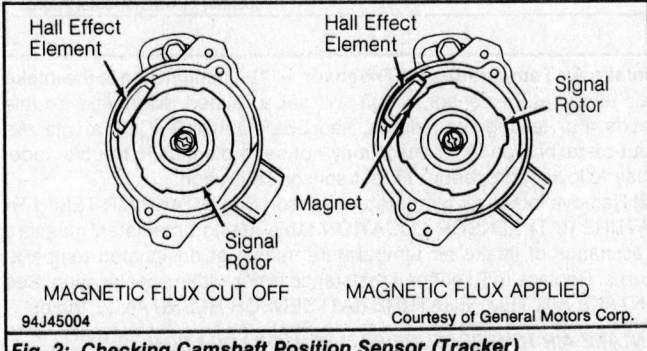

Fig. 2: Checking Camshaft Position Sensor (Tracker)

Camshaft Position Sensor – Hall Effect (Tracker – TBI Federal) – 1) A malfunction in the camshaft position sensor circuit will set diagnostic trouble Code 42. For testing procedures, see SELF-DIAGNOSTICS article. Use the following procedure to diagnose camshaft position sensor.

2) Ensure ignition is off. Disconnect ECM 24-pin electrical connector C2 (Yellow). ECM is located behind left side of dash. Remove distributor cap from distributor. Remove rotor and signal rotor cover from distributor housing.

3) Using voltmeter, probe ECM 17-pin electrical connector C1 (Green – still connected) terminal No. 1 to ECM 24-pin electrical connector C2 (Yellow – disconnected) terminal No. 13. See Fig. 3. Turn ignition on. Ensure Camshaft Position (CMP) sensor magnet is free from any metal particals.

4) CMP sensor voltage with signal rotor inserted between hall element and magnet (magnetic flux cut off) should fluctuate between 0-1 volt. See Fig. 2. If voltage is as specified, go to next step. If voltage is not as specified, check for faulty wiring and ECM. If wiring and ECM are okay, replace distributor housing.

5) CMP sensor voltage without signal rotor inserted between hall element and magnet (magnetic flux applied) should indicate battery voltage. See Fig. 2. If voltage is as specified, CMP sensor is okay. Turn ignition off and reverse disassembly procedure.

6) If voltage is not as specified, check for faulty wiring and ECM. If wiring and ECM are okay, replace distributor housing. When testing is complete, reverse disassembly procedure.

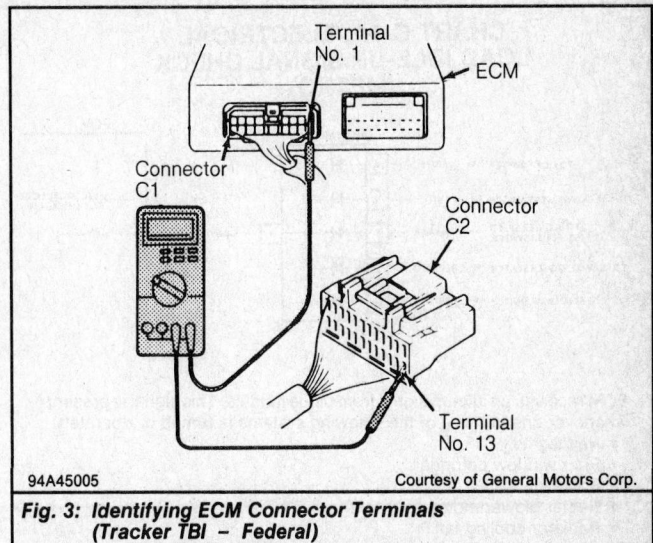

Fig. 3: Identifying ECM Connector Terminals (Tracker TBI – Federal)

EGR Temperature Sensor – See EXHAUST GAS RECIRCULATION under EMISSIONS SYSTEMS & SUB-SYSTEMS.

NOTE: Electrical load sensor may be referred to as diode module or diode.

Electrical Load Sensor (Metro, Prizm & Prizm LSi) – For location of electrical load sensor, see illustrations. See Figs. 4 and 5. To test electrical load sensor circuit, see illustrations. See Figs. 6 and 7.

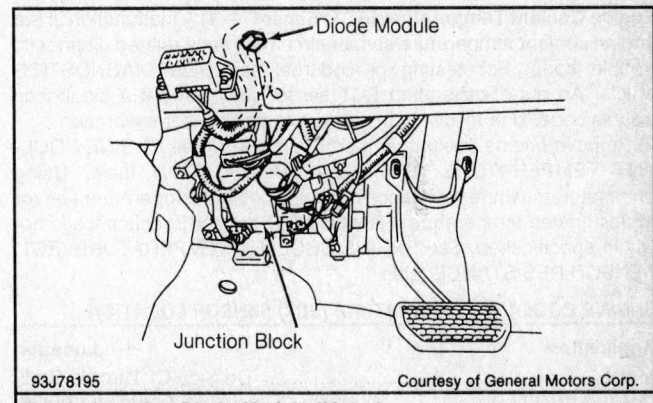

Fig. 4: Locating Diode Module (Metro)

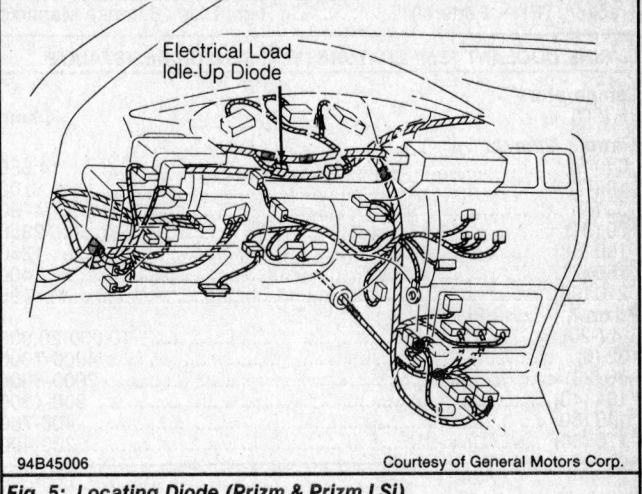

Fig. 5: Locating Diode (Prizm & Prizm LSi)

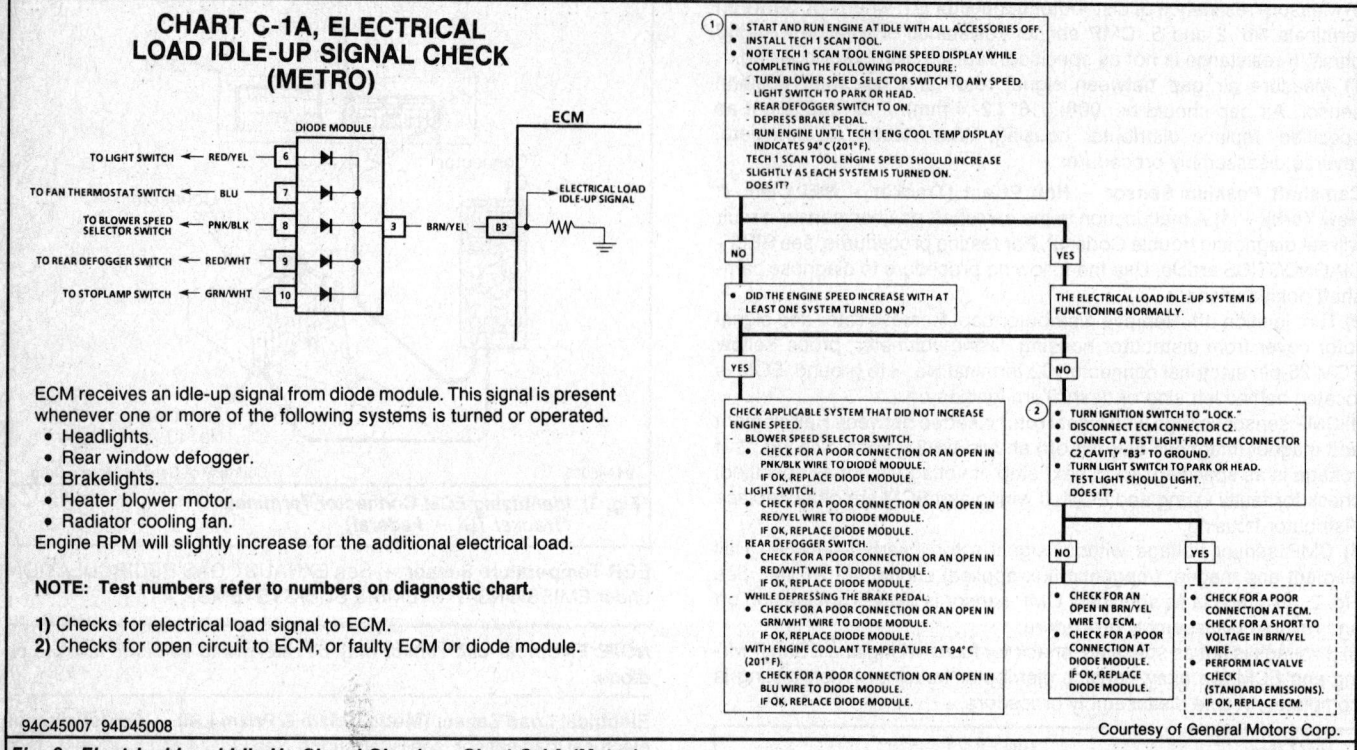

Fig. 6: Electrical Load Idle-Up Signal Check – Chart C-1A (Metro)

Engine Coolant Temperature (ECT) Sensor – 1) A malfunction in the engine coolant temperature sensor circuit will set a related diagnostic trouble code. For testing procedures, see SELF-DIAGNOSTICS article. An out-of-calibration ECT sensor may not set a diagnostic trouble code. Use following procedure to test sensor calibration.

2) Remove engine coolant temperature sensor. See ENGINE COOLANT TEMPERATURE (ECT) SENSOR LOCATION table. Using ohmmeter, measure resistance of engine coolant temperature sensor at designated temperatures. Replace ECT sensor if resistance is not within specification. See ENGINE COOLANT TEMPERATURE (ECT) SENSOR RESISTANCE table.

ENGINE COOLANT TEMPERATURE (ECT) SENSOR LOCATION

Application	Location
Metro	On Side Of Throttle Body
Prizm & Prizm LSi	On Left Side Of Engine, In Engine Coolant Housing
Tracker (MFI – Calif & New York)	In Thermostat Housing
Tracker (TBI – Federal)	On Right Side Of Intake Manifold

ENGINE COOLANT TEMPERATURE (ECT) SENSOR RESISTANCE

Temperature °F (°C)	Ohms
Metro & Tracker	
0 (-18)	14,650
19 (-7)	8100
39 (4)	4780
70 (21)	2350
100 (38)	1250
160 (71)	400
210 (99)	190
Prizm & Prizm LSi	
-4 (-20)	10,000-20,000
32 (0)	4000-7000
68 (20)	2000-3000
104 (40)	900-1300
140 (60)	400-700
176 (80)	200-400

Intake Air Temperature (IAT) Sensor – 1) A malfunction in the intake air temperature sensor circuit will set a related diagnostic trouble code. For testing procedures, see SELF-DIAGNOSTICS article. An out-of-calibration IAT sensor may not set a diagnostic trouble code. Use following procedure to test sensor calibration.

2) Remove intake air temperature sensor. See INTAKE AIR TEMPERATURE (IAT) SENSOR LOCATION table. Using ohmmeter, measure resistance of intake air temperature sensor at designated temperatures. Replace IAT sensor if resistance is not within specification. See INTAKE AIR TEMPERATURE (IAT) SENSOR RESISTANCE table.

INTAKE AIR TEMPERATURE (IAT) SENSOR LOCATION

Application	Location
Metro	In Air Cleaner Assembly
Prizm & Prizm LSi	In Air Cleaner Assembly
Tracker (MFI – Calif & New York)	In Air Cleaner Assembly
Tracker (TBI – Federal)	On Right Side Of Intake Manifold

INTAKE AIR TEMPERATURE (IAT) SENSOR RESISTANCE

Temperature °F (°C)	Ohms
Metro	
0 (-18)	14,650
19 (-7)	8100
39 (4)	4780
70 (21)	2350
100 (38)	1250
160 (71)	400
210 (99)	190
Prizm & Prizm LSi	
-4 (-20)	10,000-20,000
32 (0)	4000-7000
68 (20)	2000-3000
104 (40)	900-1300
140 (60)	400-700
176 (80)	200-400
Tracker	
0 (-18)	14,800
19 (-7)	8250
39 (4)	5200
70 (21)	2500
100 (38)	1300
160 (71)	450
210 (99)	200

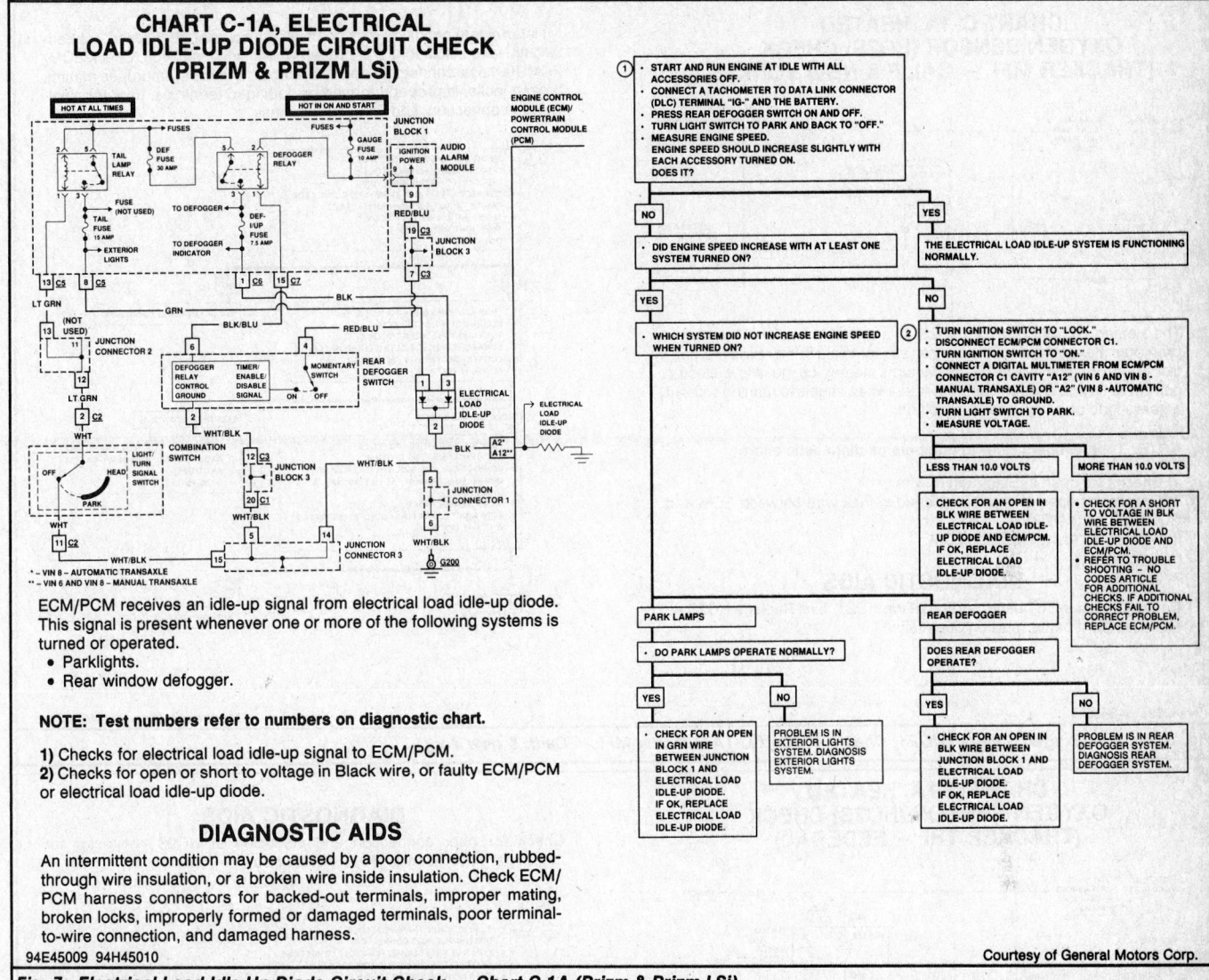

Fig. 7: Electrical Load Idle-Up Diode Circuit Check – Chart C-1A (Prizm & Prizm LSi)

Knock Sensor (Prizm LSi) – **1)** A malfunction in the knock sensor circuit will set diagnostic trouble Code 52. For testing procedures, see SELF-DIAGNOSTICS article. Use the following procedure to diagnose knock sensor.

2) Check knock sensor resistance using ohmmeter. Measure resistance between knock sensor terminal and ground. Knock sensor, located on rear of engine block, has Black wire connector. Replace sensor if resistance is not one megohm or higher.

3) To check knock sensor operation, remove connector from knock sensor. Connect DVOM between knock sensor terminal and ground. Adjust voltmeter to 200 millivolts on AC scale. Tap on engine block near knock sensor, and note reading. Replace knock sensor if no reading is obtained.

Manifold Absolute Pressure (MAP) Sensor (Except Tracker MFI – Calif & New York) – **1)** A malfunction in the manifold absolute pressure sensor circuit will set diagnostic trouble Codes 31 and/or 32. For testing procedures, see SELF-DIAGNOSTICS article. Use the following procedure to diagnose MAP sensor. If driveability problems exist, MAP sensor failure is suspected and no Codes 31 and/or 32 is set, disconnect MAP sensor connector. If driveability improves, replace MAP sensor.

2) MAP sensor is located on firewall. With ignition on, check supply voltage from ECM to MAP sensor on designated wire terminal. See MAP SENSOR WIRE TERMINAL IDENTIFICATION table. Reading should be approximately 5 volts.

3) Disconnect vacuum hose at MAP sensor. Install hand-held vacuum pump. Turn ignition on. Check signal voltage at designated wire terminal of MAP sensor. See MAP SENSOR WIRE TERMINAL IDENTIFICATION table.

4) Apply vacuum, and note change in signal voltage. As vacuum reading changes, signal voltage should change. Reading should be about 1-1.5 volts at high vacuum (idle position) to 4-4.5 volts at low vacuum (full throttle position).

MAP SENSOR WIRE TERMINAL IDENTIFICATION

Application	Supply Voltage Wire Color	Signal Voltage Wire Color
Metro	Light Green	Light Green/Red
Prizm & Prizm LSi	Yellow	Light Green/Red
Tracker		
TBI – Federal	Gray/Red	Gray/Green

Mass Airflow (MAF) Sensor (Tracker MFI – Calif. & New York) – A malfunction in the MAF sensor circuit will set diagnostic trouble Codes 33 and/or 34. For testing procedures, see SELF-DIAGNOSTICS article. If driveability problems exist, MAF sensor failure is suspected and no Codes 33 and/or 34 is set, disconnect MAF sensor connector. If driveability improves, replace MAF sensor.

CHART C-1A, HEATED OXYGEN SENSOR (HO2S) CHECK (TRACKER MFI – CALIF & NEW YORK)

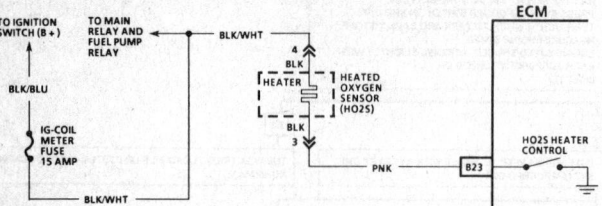

The Heated Oxygen Sensor (HO2S) has a built-in heater. This heater promotes the activation of the oxygen sensor to aid in improved fuel control during engine warm-up. ECM turns heater on (to allow electric current to flow to oxygen sensor heater) when engine is running without a heavy load or a high speed condition.

NOTE: Test numbers refer to numbers on diagnostic chart.

1) Checks for open in Black/White wire.
2) Checks for open or short to ground in Pink wire between ECM and HO2S, or faulty HO2S.
3) Checks for faulty HO2S or ECM.

DIAGNOSTIC AIDS

Codes can not set if heater portion of the HO2S fails. Replace HO2S as an assembly if heater portion does fail.

An intermittent condition may be caused by a poor connection, rubbed-through wire insulation, or a broken wire inside insulation. Check ECM/PCM harness connectors for backed-out terminals, improper mating, broken locks, improperly formed or damaged terminals, poor terminal-to-wire connection, and damaged harness.

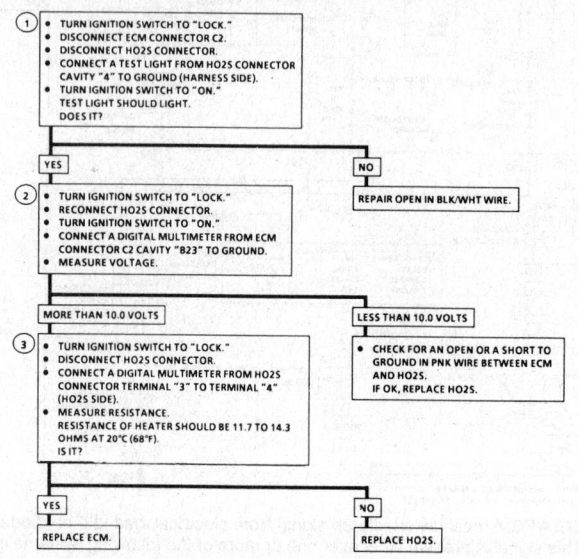

94A45088 94B45089

Courtesy of General Motors Corp.

Fig. 8: Heated Oxygen Sensor (HO2S) Check – Chart C-1A (Tracker MFI – Calif. & new York)

CHART C-1A, HEATED OXYGEN SENSOR (HO2S) CHECK (TRACKER TBI – FEDERAL)

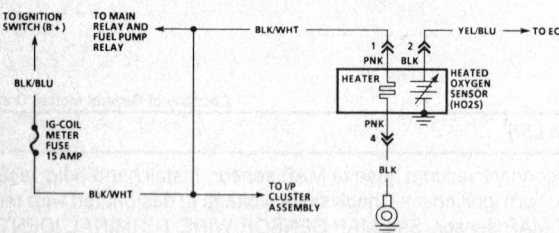

The Heated Oxygen Sensor (HO2S) has a built-in heater. This heater is operational whenever ignition switch is turned to ON position. The heater causes the HO2S to produce a voltage input to the ECM. This allows for better fuel control during engine warm-up. Codes can not set if heater portion of the HO2S fails. Replace HO2S as an assembly if heater portion does fail.

NOTE: Test numbers refer to numbers on diagnostic chart.

1) Checks for voltage on Black/White wire at HO2S.
2) Checks ground side of circuit to HO2S heater.
3) Checks heater element resistance. Resistance should be 3-5.5 ohms at 73°F (23°C).

DIAGNOSTIC AIDS

Check for poor connection and corrosion at HO2S connector for intermittent operation of HO2S heater cicuit.

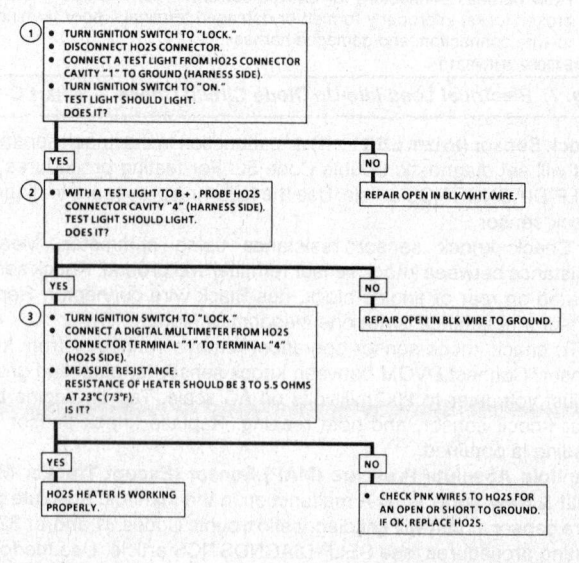

94E45090 94G45092

Courtesy of General Motors Corp.

Fig. 9: Heated Oxygen Sensor (HO2S) Check – Chart C-1A (Tracker TBI – Federal)

NOTE: For Heated Oxygen Sensor (HO2S) on Tracker, also see Figs. 8 and 9.

Oxygen (O₂) Sensor – 1) A malfunction in the oxygen sensor circuit will set a related diagnostic trouble code. For testing procedures, see SELF-DIAGNOSTICS article. Use following procedure to test oxygen sensor.

2) Start engine and warm to operating temperature. Disconnect oxygen sensor. Connect a DVOM between lead of oxygen sensor and ground. Place DVOM on the 2-volt scale. Voltmeter reading should increase to greater than .8 volt.

3) Using another DVOM on the 20-volt scale, connect voltmeter in series between the oxygen sensor wire from ECM and positive post of battery. Reading on voltmeter connected to oxygen sensor should decrease to a low voltage (less than .3 volt).

4) If a second DVOM is not available, install short jumper in oxygen sensor wire from ECM. Hold jumper in one hand and touch positive post of battery with other hand. This should cause oxygen sensor to produce less than .3 volt.

Sub-Oxygen Sensor (Prizm & Prizm LSi – California) – 1) A malfunction in the sub-oxygen sensor circuit will set diagnostic trouble Code 27. For testing procedures, see SELF-DIAGNOSTICS article. Use following procedure to test sub-oxygen sensor.

2) Start engine and warm to operating temperature. Disconnect sub-oxygen sensor. Connect a DVOM between lead of sub-oxygen sensor and ground. Place DVOM on the 2-volt scale. Voltmeter reading should increase to greater than .8 volt.

3) Using another DVOM on the 20-volt scale, connect voltmeter in series between the sub-oxygen sensor wire from ECM and positive post of battery. Reading on voltmeter connected to sub-oxygen sensor should decrease to a low voltage (less than .3 volt).

4) If a second DVOM is not available, install short jumper in sub-oxygen sensor wire from ECM. Hold jumper in one hand and touch positive post of battery with other hand. This should cause sub-oxygen sensor to produce less than .3 volt.

Park/Neutral Position Switch (Metro & Tracker) – Disconnect park/neutral position switch. Using ohmmeter, check for continuity between specified wires with gearshift in selected position. See PARK/NEUTRAL POSITION SWITCH CONTINUITY table. Continuity should exist between appropriate wires with gearshift in corresponding position as listed.

NOTE: On Metro A/T, ECM receives gear position signals from Transaxle Control Module (TCM). Park/neutral position switch provides gear position signal to TCM.

PARK/NEUTRAL POSITION SWITCH CONTINUITY

Gear Position	Wire Colors
Metro	
Park	Yellow & Blue/White
	Black & Blue/White
Reverse	Yellow & Red
	Black & Red
Neutral	Yellow & Blue
	Black & Blue
Drive	Yellow & Green
	Black & Green
2nd Gear	Yellow & Green/Red
	Black & Green/Red
Low	Yellow & Green/Blue
	Black & Green/Blue
Tracker	
Park Or Neutral	Black/Red & Black/Yellow

CHART C-1, POWER STEERING PRESSURE (PSP) SWITCH CHECK (TRACKER)

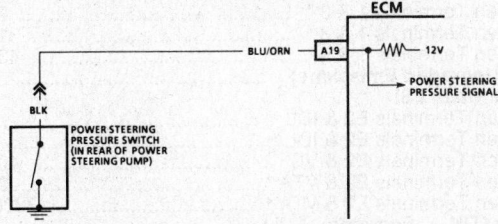

MFI – CALIF. & NEW YORK

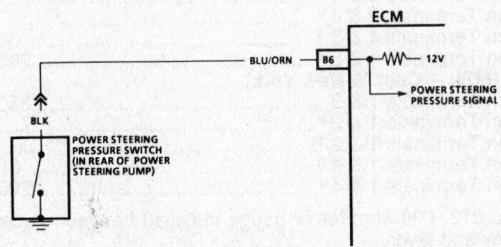

TBI – FEDERAL

The Power Steering Pressure (PSP) switch is normally open to ground, and ECM terminal will be near battery voltage. Turning the steering wheel increases power steering oil pressure and its load on an idling engine. Pressure switch will close before the load can cause an idle problem. Closing the switch causes ECM voltage signal to read less than one volt. ECM will increase idle air rate and prevent engine load stall.

NOTE: Test numbers refer to numbers on diagnostic chart.

94H45093 94I45094 94J45095

1) Checks for ECM signal voltage, and for open or short to ground in Blue/Orange wire.
2) Checks for poor ground at power steering pump and for faulty PSP switch.

DIAGNOSTIC AIDS

A pressure switch that will not close, or loss of ground at power steering pressure switch may cause engine to stop when power steering loads are high. A switch that will not open or a signal line shorted to ground may affect idle quality.

An intermittent condition may be caused by a poor connection, rubbed-through wire insulation, or a broken wire inside insulation. Check ECM/PCM harness connectors for backed-out terminals, improper mating, broken locks, improperly formed or damaged terminals, poor terminal-to-wire connection, and damaged harness.

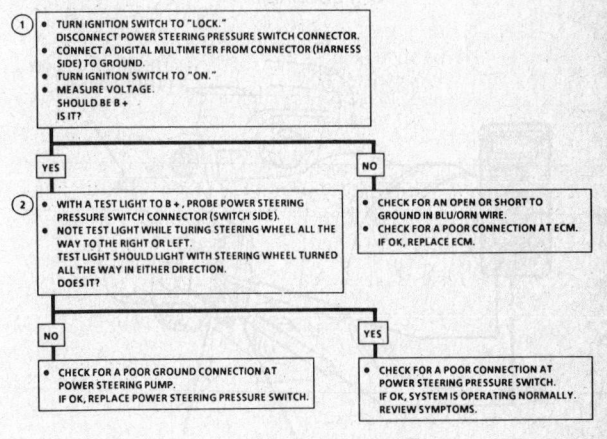

Courtesy of General Motors Corp.

Fig. 10: Power Steering Pressure (PSP) Switch Check – Chart C-1 (Tracker)

Power Steering Pressure Switch (Tracker) – Power steering pressure switch is located on power steering pump. To test power steering pressure switch circuit, see illustration. *See Fig. 10.*

NOTE: If power steering pressure switch fails to close, or open circuit in wiring exists between ECM and pressure switch, engine may stall when wheels are turned. If power steering pressure switch fails to open or short to ground exists in wiring between ECM and pressure switch, idle quality will be affected.

Throttle Position (TP) Sensor (Metro & Tracker) – 1) A malfunction in the throttle position sensor circuit will set diagnostic trouble Codes 21 and/or 22. For testing and adjusting procedures, see THROTTLE

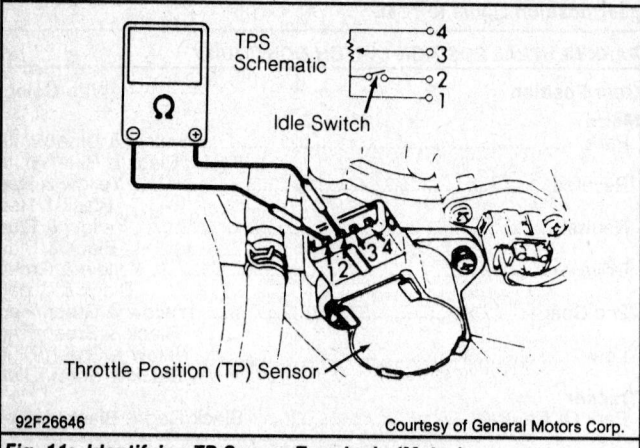

Fig. 11: Identifying TP Sensor Terminals (Metro)

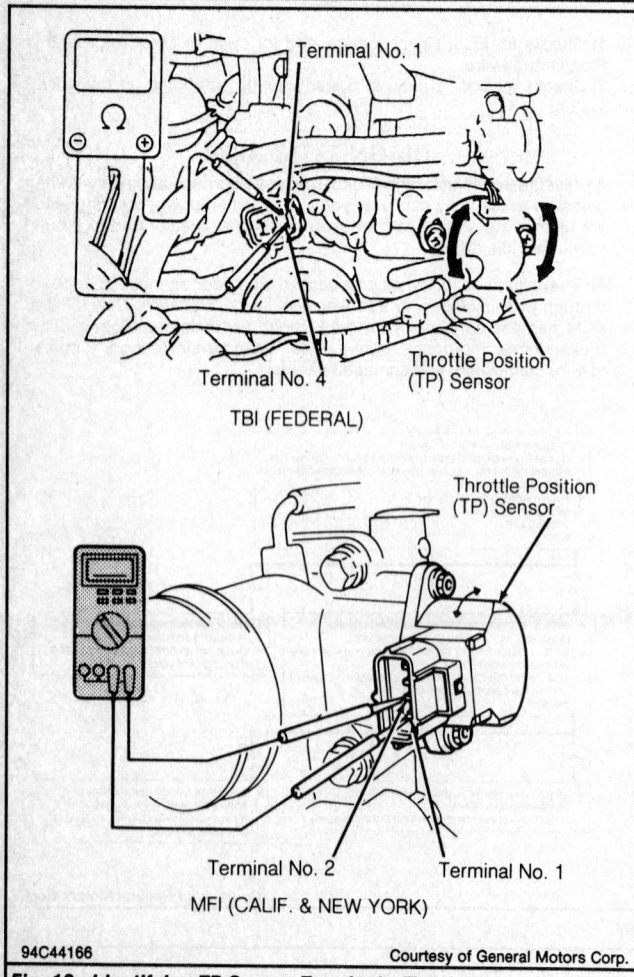

TBI (FEDERAL)

MFI (CALIF. & NEW YORK)

Fig. 12: Identifying TP Sensor Terminals (Tracker)

POSITION (TP) SENSOR in ON-VEHICLE ADJUSTMENTS article. Use the following procedure to diagnose TP sensor.
2) Using ohmmeter, measure resistance or continuity of throttle position sensor between designated terminals with selected feeler gauge thickness between throttle lever and stop screw. *See Fig. 11 or 12.* Adjust or replace TP sensor if resistance is not within specification. See THROTTLE POSITION (TP) SENSOR RESISTANCE table.

Throttle Position (TP) Sensor (Prizm & Prizm LSi) – 1) A malfunction in the throttle position sensor circuit will set diagnostic trouble Code

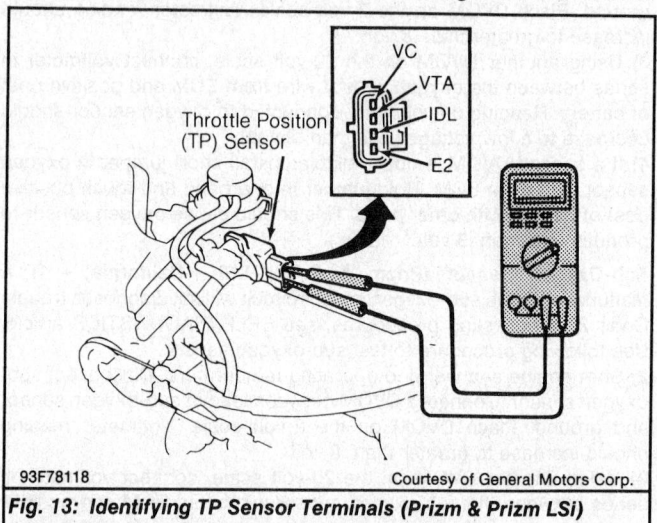

Fig. 13: Identifying TP Sensor Terminals (Prizm & Prizm LSi)

THROTTLE POSITION (TP) SENSOR RESISTANCE

Application	Ohms
Metro (Standard Emissions)	
Between Terminals 1 & 2 [1]	0-5000
Between Terminals 1 & 2 [2]	Infinity
Between Terminals 1 & 2 [3]	0-5000
Between Terminals 1 & 3 [3]	240-1140
Between Terminals 1 & 3 [4]	3170-6600
Between Terminals 1 & 4	4370-8130
Metro (Upgraded Emissions)	[5]
Prizm & Prizm LSi	
Between Terminals E2 & IDL [6]	0-2300
Between Terminals E2 & IDL [2]	Infinity
Between Terminals E2 & VC	4000-8500
Between Terminals E2 & VTA [7]	200-6000
Between Terminals E2 & VTA [4]	3300-10,000
Tracker (TBI – Federal)	
Between Terminals 2 & 4	3500-6500
Between Terminals 3 & 4 [1]	0-500
Between Terminals 3 & 4 [8]	Infinity
Between Terminals 4 & 5 [3]	300-2000
Between Terminals 4 & 5 [4]	2000-6500
Tracker (MFI – Calif. & New York)	
Between Terminals 1 & 3	3500-6500
Between Terminals 1 & 2 [9]	0-500
Between Terminals 1 & 2 [10]	Infinity
Between Terminals 1 & 4 [3]	300-2000
Between Terminals 1 & 4 [4]	2000-6500

[1] – With .012" (.30 mm) feeler gauge installed between throttle stop screw and lever.
[2] – With .035" (.89 mm) feeler gauge installed between throttle stop screw and lever.
[3] – Throttle valve at idle position.
[4] – Throttle valve at fully open position.
[5] – For information on TP sensor, see THROTTLE POSITION (TP) SENSOR in ON-VEHICLE ADJUSTMENTS article.
[6] – With .016" (.40 mm) feeler gauge installed between throttle stop screw and lever.
[7] – With zero clearance between throttle stop screw and lever.
[8] – With .022" (.56 mm) feeler gauge installed between throttle stop screw and lever.
[9] – With .020" (.50 mm) feeler gauge installed between throttle stop screw and lever.
[10] – With .031" (.80 mm) feeler gauge installed between throttle stop screw and lever.

41. For testing and adjusting procedures, see THROTTLE POSITION (TP) SENSOR in ON-VEHICLE ADJUSTMENTS article. Use the following procedure to diagnose TP sensor.

2) Using ohmmeter, measure resistance or continuity of throttle position sensor between designated terminals with selected feeler gauge thickness between throttle lever and stop screw. *See Fig. 13.* Adjust or replace TP sensor if resistance is not within specification. See THROTTLE POSITION (TP) SENSOR RESISTANCE table.

Vehicle Speed Sensor (Metro & Tracker) – Vehicle speed sensor is mounted in rear of instrument cluster. A malfunction in the vehicle speed sensor circuit will set diagnostic trouble Code 24. For testing procedures, see SELF-DIAGNOSTICS article. For identification of vehicle speed sensor terminals, see illustrations. *See Fig. 14 or 15.*

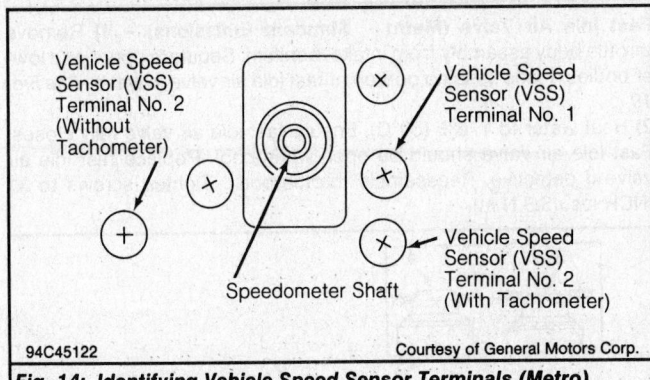

94C45122   Courtesy of General Motors Corp.

Fig. 14: Identifying Vehicle Speed Sensor Terminals (Metro)

91F17058   Courtesy of General Motors Corp.

Fig. 15: Identifying Vehicle Speed Sensor Terminals (Tracker)

Vehicle Speed Sensor (Prizm & Prizm LSi) – Vehicle speed sensor is mounted on transaxle. A malfunction in the vehicle speed sensor circuit will set diagnostic trouble Code 42. For testing procedures, see SELF-DIAGNOSTICS article.

MODULES, RELAYS & SOLENOIDS

MODULES

Diode Module Or Diode (Metro, Prizm & Prizm LSi) – Diode module or diode is also referred to as electrical load sensor. See ELECTRICAL LOAD SENSOR (METRO, PRIZM & PRIZM LSi) under ENGINE SENSORS & SWITCHES under COMPUTERIZED ENGINE CONTROLS.

RELAYS

Circuit Opening Relay (Prizm & Prizm LSi) – **1)** Circuit opening relay is located behind center of dash, near radio. To test circuit opening relay on Prizm, see CHART A1-7A, FUEL SYSTEM DIAGNOSIS (CIRCUIT OPENING RELAY CHECK) diagnostic chart in BASIC DIAGNOSTIC PROCEDURES article.

2) To test circuit opening relay on Prizm LSi, see CHART A2-7A, FUEL SYSTEM DIAGNOSIS (CIRCUIT OPENING RELAY CHECK) diagnostic chart in BASIC DIAGNOSTIC PROCEDURES article. For identification of Data Link Connector (DLC) terminals, see illustration. *See Fig. 16.*

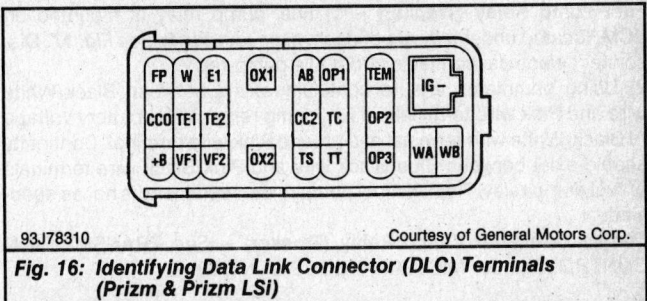

93J78310   Courtesy of General Motors Corp.

Fig. 16: Identifying Data Link Connector (DLC) Terminals (Prizm & Prizm LSi)

NOTE: EFI main relay may be referred to as main relay.

EFI F-HTR Relay (Prizm & Prizm LSi) – **1)** EFI F-HTR relay is located in fuse/relay block in left front side of engine compartment, left of air cleaner. Remove EFI F-HTR relay from fuse/relay block. Using ohmmeter, ensure continuity exists between Black/Orange wire and White/Black wire terminals of EFI F-HTR relay.

2) Apply battery voltage to Black/Orange wire terminal and ground White/Black wire terminal. Continuity should exist between Black/Red wire and Red/White wire terminals of EFI F-HTR relay. Replace EFI F-HTR relay if continuity is not as specified.

EFI Main Relay (Tracker) – **1)** EFI main relay is mounted on ECM, located under left side of dash, near kick panel. *See Fig. 17.* Disconnect electrical connector from EFI main relay.

2) Using ohmmeter, ensure continuity exists between Black/White wire and Blue wire terminals of EFI main relay. Apply battery voltage to Black/White wire terminal and ground Blue wire terminal. Continuity should exist between Black/Red wire and Blue/Black wire terminals of EFI main relay. Replace EFI main relay if continuity is not as specified.

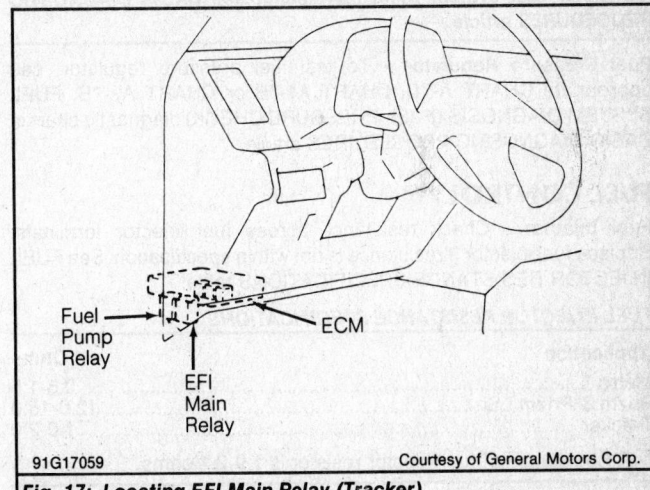

91G17059   Courtesy of General Motors Corp.

Fig. 17: Locating EFI Main Relay (Tracker)

FI Relay (Metro) – **1)** FI relay is located in fuse/relay block in left side of engine compartment, near battery. Remove FI relay from fuse/relay block. Using ohmmeter, ensure continuity exists between Black/White wire and Black or Blue/Black wire terminals of FI relay.

2) Apply battery voltage to Black/White wire terminal and ground Black wire terminal. Continuity should exist between White/Red wire and White/Blue wire terminals of FI relay. Replace FI relay if continuity is not as specified.

Fuel Pump Relay (Metro) – **1)** Fuel pump relay is located in fuse/relay box in left side of engine compartment, near battery. Remove fuel pump relay from fuse/relay box. Using an ohmmeter, ensure continuity exists between Black/White wire and Pink/White wire terminals of fuel pump relay.

2) Apply battery voltage to Black/White wire terminal and ground Pink/White wire terminal. Continuity should exist between White/Blue wire and Pink wire terminals of fuel pump relay. Replace fuel pump relay if continuity is not as specified.

Fuel Pump Relay (Tracker) – 1) Fuel pump relay is mounted on ECM, located under left side of dash, near kick panel. *See Fig. 17.* Disconnect electrical connector from fule pump relay.

2) Using ohmmeter, ensure continuity exists between Black/White wire and Pink wire terminals of fuel pump relay. Apply battery voltage to Black/White wire terminal and ground Pink wire terminal. Continuity should exist between Blue/Black wire and Pink/Black wire terminals of fuel pump relay. Replace fuel pump relay if continuity is not as specified.

Torque Converter Clutch Relay (Tracker) – See TRANSMISSION CONTROLS under MISCELLANEOUS CONTROLS.

SOLENOIDS

A/C Solenoid Vacuum (SV) Valve (Metro – Standard Emissions, Prizm & Prizm LSi) – See IDLE CONTROL SYSTEM.

Evaporative Emission Solenoid Purge (EVAP SP) Valve (Metro – Upgraded Emissions & Tracker) – See FUEL EVAPORATION under EMISSION SYSTEMS & SUB-SYSTEMS.

Exhaust Gas Recirculation Solenoid Vacuum (EGR SV) Valve – See EXHAUST GAS RECIRCULATION under EMISSION SYSTEMS & SUB-SYSTEMS.

Fuel Injector – See FUEL CONTROL.

Idle Air Control (IAC) Valve (Metro – Standard Emissions & Tracker) – See IDLE CONTROL SYSTEM.

Throttle Opener Solenoid Vacuum (TO SV) Valve (Prizm – Calif. & Tracker TBI – Federal) – See IDLE CONTROL SYSTEM.

FUEL SYSTEM

FUEL DELIVERY

NOTE: For fuel system pressure testing, see BASIC DIAGNOSTIC PROCEDURES article.

Fuel Pressure Regulator – To test fuel pressure regulator, see appropriate CHART A-7B, CHART A1-7B or CHART A2-7B, FUEL SYSTEM DIAGNOSIS (FUEL PRESSURE CHECK) diagnostic chart in BASIC DIAGNOSTIC PROCEDURES article.

FUEL CONTROL

Fuel Injector – Check resistance across fuel injector terminals. Replace fuel injector if resistance is not within specification. See FUEL INJECTOR RESISTANCE SPECIFICATIONS table.

FUEL INJECTOR RESISTANCE SPECIFICATIONS

Application	Ohms
Metro [1]	0.5-1.5
Prizm & Prizm LSi	12.0-15.0
Tracker	1.0-2.0

[1] – Resistance of fuel injector resistor is 1.9-2.1 ohms.

Fuel Pump Relay (Metro & Tracker) – See RELAYS under MODULES, RELAYS & SOLENOIDS.

Oxygen Sensor Heater (Tracker) – See ENGINE SENSORS & SWITCHES. **See Figs. 8 and 9.**

IDLE CONTROL SYSTEM

A/C Solenoid Vacuum (SV) Valve (Metro – Standard Emissions) – 1) A/C Solenoid Vacuum (SV) valve is mounted on firewall, to right of ignition coil. *See Fig. 18.* Install scan tester. Start and run engine. Turn A/C on and blower speed selector switch to any position except OFF. If engine speed increases slightly with A/C operation, A/C SV valve system is functioning normally.

2) If engine speed does not increase, backprobe A/C SV valve connector from cavity No. 2 to ground using a fused jumper. If engine speed increases, check for an open in Blue/Red wire. If wiring is okay, replace A/C amplifier. If engine speed does not increase, check for an open in Yellow wire. If wiring is okay, replace A/C SV valve.

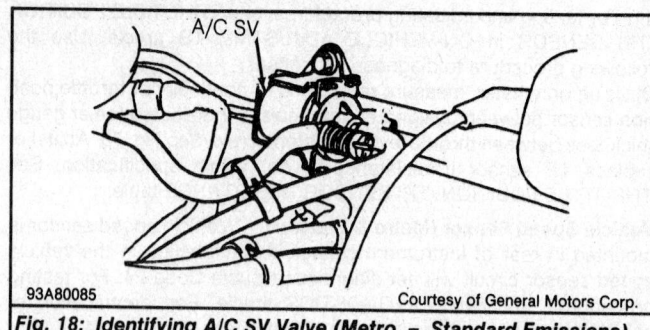

93A80085 — Courtesy of General Motors Corp.

Fig. 18: Identifying A/C SV Valve (Metro – Standard Emissions)

Fast Idle Air Valve (Metro – Standard Emissions) – 1) Remove throttle body assembly from intake manifold. Separate upper and lower bodies. Place sensing portion of fast idle air valve in water. *See Fig. 19.*

2) Heat water to 176°F (80°C). Ensure fast idle air valve fully closes. Fast idle air valve should be open when cool. Replace fast idle air valve if defective. Reassemble throttle body. Tighten screws to 31 INCH lbs. (3.5 N.m).

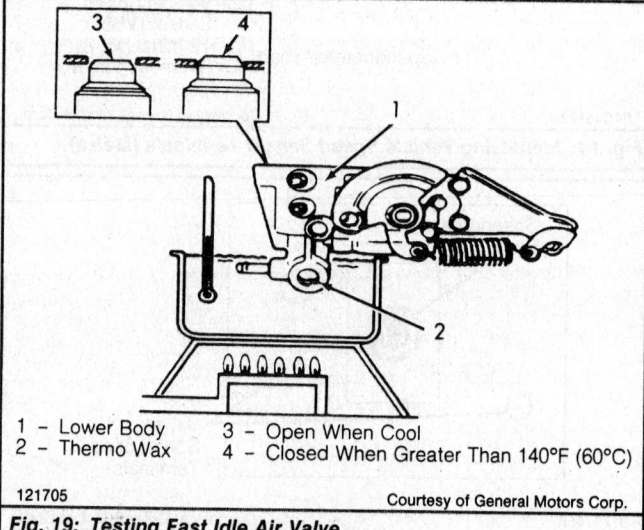

1 – Lower Body	3 – Open When Cool
2 – Thermo Wax	4 – Closed When Greater Than 140°F (60°C)

121705 — Courtesy of General Motors Corp.

Fig. 19: Testing Fast Idle Air Valve (Metro – Standard Emissions)

Fast Idle Air Valve (Tracker – TBI Federal) – 1) Fast idle air valve is located in lower body of throttle body. Remove fast idle air valve cap on throttle body. With engine temperature at 140°F (60°C) or less, ensure fast idle air valve is open. *See Fig. 20.*

2) Install fast idle air valve cap. Warm engine to normal operating temperature. Remove fast idle air valve cap. Inspect fast idle air valve. Fast idle air valve should be closed. Replace fast idle air valve if defective.

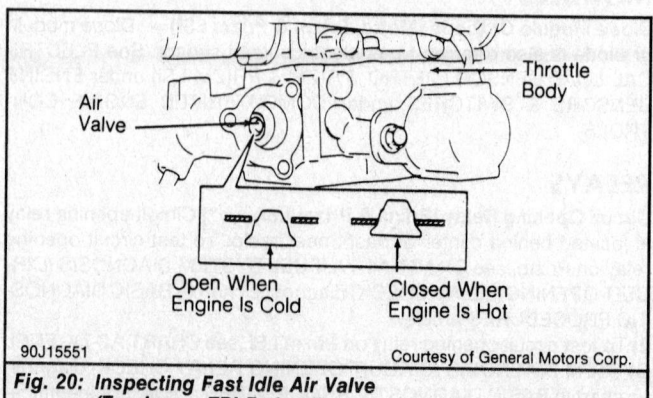

90J15551 — Courtesy of General Motors Corp.

Fig. 20: Inspecting Fast Idle Air Valve (Tracker – TBI Federal)

Idle Air Control (IAC) Valve (Metro) – **1)** Idle Air Control (IAC) valve is located below left side of air cleaner. IAC valve by-passes air around throttle valve and directly into intake manifold. Air is allowed to pass through IAC valve when valve is energized by ECM.

2) IAC valve is energized whenever idle speed drops to less than desired RPM due to engine load (i.e., electrical, P/S, A/T in Drive, etc.). IAC valve is energized each time engine is started and during periods of deceleration to compensate for rich mixtures caused by a fully closed throttle. Other information is not available from manufacturer.

Idle Air Control (IAC) Valve (Tracker) – **1)** With ignition off, disconnect electrical connector from Idle Air Control (IAC) valve. IAC valve is located on throttle body and contains a Blue/Black and Light Green/Black wire connector.

2) Turn ignition on. Using voltmeter, check for battery voltage at Blue/Black wire of electrical connector. Battery voltage should exist.

3) If battery voltage exists, go to next step. If battery voltage does not exist, check for open circuit in Blue/Black wire between IAC valve and EFI main relay. EFI main relay is mounted on ECM, located under left side of instrument panel, near kick panel. *See Fig. 17.*

4) Turn ignition off. Connect test light to battery voltage. Probe Light Green/Black wire. Turn ignition on. Light should glow momentarily.

5) If test light glows momentarily, go to next step. If test light stays on, check for short to ground in Light Green/Black wire between IAC valve and ECM. ECM is located under left side of instrument panel, near kick panel. If test light does not glow momentarily, check for open circuit in Light Green/Black wire between IAC valve and ECM. If circuit is not open, replace ECM.

6) Turn ignition off. Using ohmmeter, measure resistance between IAC valve terminals. Resistance should be 11-14 ohms at 68°F (20°C).

CAUTION: DO NOT apply battery voltage to IAC solenoid for more than one second. Allow 10 seconds between voltage applications to prevent valve damage.

7) If resistance is not as specified, replace IAC valve. If resistance is as specified, connect battery voltage to Blue/Black wire terminal and ground Light Green/Black wire terminal momentarily. A click should be heard to indicate valve operation. Replace IAC valve if a click is not heard. Reinstall electrical connector.

NOTE: Idle-up vacuum switching valve also may be referred to as Idle Speed Control (ISC) solenoid.

Idle-Up Vacuum Switching Valve (IVSV) (Prizm) – **1)** IVSV is located on end of intake manifold on Prizm except LSi or below mass airflow sensor on Prizm LSi. IVSV by-passes air into intake manifold on Prizm except LSi or around throttle valve of mass airflow sensor on Prizm LSi when it is activated by ECM.

2) IVSV is energized whenever idle speed drops to less than desired RPM due to engine load (i.e., electrical, P/S, A/T in Drive, etc.). Other information is not available from manufacturer.

Throttle Opener Solenoid Vacuum (TO SV) Valve (Prizm – Calif. & Tracker – TBI Federal) – For testing and adjusting procedures, see THROTTLE OPENER in ON-VEHICLE ADJUSTMENTS article.

IGNITION SYSTEM

NOTE: For basic ignition checks, see BASIC DIAGNOSTIC PROCEDURES article.

TIMING CONTROL SYSTEMS

Electronic Ignition Timing Advance (Metro XFi & Tracker) – Ignition timing is controlled by Electronic Control Module (ECM). Testing information is not supplied by manufacturer. If camshaft position sensor fails, a trouble code may be set. See SELF-DIAGNOSTICS article.

Electronic Ignition Timing Advance (Prizm) – Ignition timing is controlled by Electronic Control Module (ECM). Testing information is not supplied by manufacturer.

Electronic Ignition Timing Retard (Prizm LSi) – On Prizm LSi, a knock sensor, located in rear of cylinder block, sends a variable AC voltage signal to ECM depending on engine detonation. ECM uses this signal to determine if ignition timing should be retarded. Testing information is not supplied by manufacturer. If a fault occurs in retard circuit, a Code 52 will set in ECM memory. If a code is set, see SELF-DIAGNOSTICS article.

Mechanical Advance (Metro Without ESC) – Remove distributor cap. Turn rotor clockwise. Release rotor and observe movement. Rotor should smoothly return to full rest position. If mechanical advance performance is incorrect, replace distributor.

Vacuum Advance (Metro Without ESC) – **1)** Remove distributor cap. Disconnect vacuum hoses from vacuum advance unit on distributor. Using vacuum pump, apply 15 in. Hg of vacuum on outer vacuum advance unit while observing advance plate assembly.

2) Advance plate assembly should operate with a smooth movement and vacuum should not bleed off. Repeat procedure on inner vacuum advance unit. If vacuum advance unit does not operate correctly, replace vacuum advance unit.

EMISSION SYSTEMS & SUB-SYSTEMS

EXHAUST GAS RECIRCULATION

EGR Temperature Sensor (Prizm – Calif.) – EGR temperature sensor is located on right rear of engine near firewall. If EGR temperature sensor fails, Code 71 will be set in ECM memory. See SELF-DIAGNOSTICS article.

EGR Temperature Sensor (Tracker – Calif.) – EGR temperature sensor is located near EGR valve. Remove EGR temperature sensor. Immerse sensing portion of EGR temperature sensor in water. Heat water, and note EGR temperature sensor resistance at specified temperatures. See EGR TEMPERATURE SENSOR RESISTANCE table. Replace sensor if it is not within specification.

EGR TEMPERATURE SENSOR RESISTANCE

Temperature °F (°C)	Ohms
Prizm	
122 (50)	69,000-80,000
212 (100)	11,000-15,000
302 (150)	2000-4000
Tracker	
68 (20)	214,000-313,800
104 (40)	90,900-125,700
140 (60)	42,100-55,500
176 (80)	21,100-26,500
212 (100)	11,200-13,600

EGR System Check – **1)** With engine cool, grasp top of EGR valve and check for looseness. If looseness is felt, replace EGR valve.

WARNING: Wear gloves if EGR valve is hot.

2) Warm engine to normal operating temperature. Place finger on bottom of EGR valve diaphragm. Start engine. Increase engine speed. Note if EGR valve diaphragm moves. If diaphragm does not move, allow engine to idle. Disconnect vacuum hose from EGR valve. Apply 10 in. Hg of vacuum to valve. Vacuum should hold and engine should run rough or stall. If vacuum does not hold, go to step **4)**.

3) If engine ran rough or stalled and EGR valve held vacuum, check components controlling vacuum supply to EGR valve (i.e., EGR modulator, EGR solenoid vacuum valve, vacuum supply and hoses). Also, check ECM control of ground circuit to EGR solenoid vacuum valve and verify EGR solenoid vacuum valve has power when ignition is on. For wire colors and ECM terminal identification, see WIRING DIAGRAMS article.

4) If EGR valve did not hold vacuum, replace EGR valve. If engine did not run rough or stall, remove EGR valve and check for plugged EGR valve or EGR passages in intake/exhaust system. Clean or replace as necessary.

EGR Vacuum Supply – Locate EGR vacuum supply port on throttle body or intake manifold. Disconnect vacuum supply hose. Connect vacuum gauge to port. Start engine. Increase engine speed to 2000 RPM, and note vacuum reading. At least 10 in. Hg of vacuum should be obtained. If vacuum is low, check vacuum supply port for restriction (carbon, dirt, etc.).

EGR Modulator (Metro & Tracker) – 1) Remove EGR modulator. Plug one upper vacuum hose fitting while blowing air into other upper vacuum hose fitting. Air should pass through filter.

2) Connect vacuum pump to either upper vacuum hose fittings. Plug other upper vacuum hose fitting (exhaust gas pressure port). Blow air into bottom vacuum hose fitting while applying vacuum using vacuum pump. Vacuum should be obtained. Replace modulator if defective.

EGR Modulator (Prizm) – 1) Remove vacuum hoses from modulator. Plug modulator ports No. 2 and 3. *See Fig 21.* Blow into port No. 4. Air should pass from filter.

2) Connect hand-held vacuum pump to port No. 5. Plug ports No. 2 and 3. Blow air into port No. 4. Vacuum pump should not obtain vacuum. Replace EGR modulator if defective.

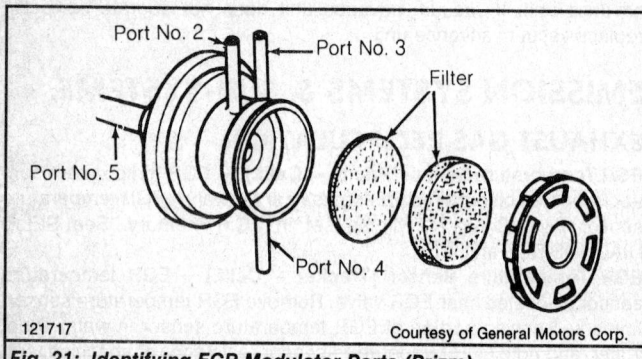

Fig. 21: Identifying EGR Modulator Ports (Prizm)

121717   Courtesy of General Motors Corp.

EGR Solenoid Vacuum (SV) Valve (Metro & Prizm) – 1) With ignition off, disconnect vacuum hoses and wiring from solenoid. For SV location, see EGR SOLENOID VACUUM (SV) VALVE LOCATION table. Using ohmmeter, ensure resistance between SV terminals is 33-39 ohms.

2) Blow air into port No. 1, ensuring air flows through filter only. *See Fig. 22 or 23.* Apply battery voltage and ground to SV terminals. With SV energized, blow air into port No. 1 to ensure air flows out port No. 2. Replace SV if defective.

3) Check ECM control of ground circuit to EGR SV valve. Ensure SV has voltage with ignition on. For wire colors and ECM terminal identification, see WIRING DIAGRAMS article.

EGR SOLENOID VACUUM (SV) VALVE LOCATION

Application	Location
Metro	[1] Forward Of Valve Cover
Prizm Except LSi	[2] Center Of Firewall
Prizm LSi	[3] Rear Of Engine, Near Mass Airflow Sensor
Tracker	[4] Forward Of Valve Cover

[1] – Connector has White/Blue and Green wires.
[2] – Connector has Black/Red and Black/Red wires.
[3] – Connector has White/Green and Black/Yellow wires.
[4] – Connector has Light Green/Red and Light Green/Yellow wires.

EGR Solenoid Vacuum (SV) Valve (Tracker) – 1) With ignition off, disconnect Green connector from ECM, located under left side of dash, near kick panel.

2) Disconnect electrical connector and vacuum hoses from SV. See EGR SOLENOID VACUUM (SV) VALVE LOCATION table. Turn ignition on. Using voltmeter, ensure battery voltage exists at terminal "A" of SV connector. *See Fig. 24.* If battery voltage does not exist, check for open circuit between SV and EFI main relay. EFI main relay is located near ECM. *See Fig. 17.*

3) Reconnect SV electrical connector. With ignition on, blow into port No. 1. Air should come out of port No. 2 only. If SV does not perform correctly, SV is defective or Light Green/Yellow wire is shorted to ground.

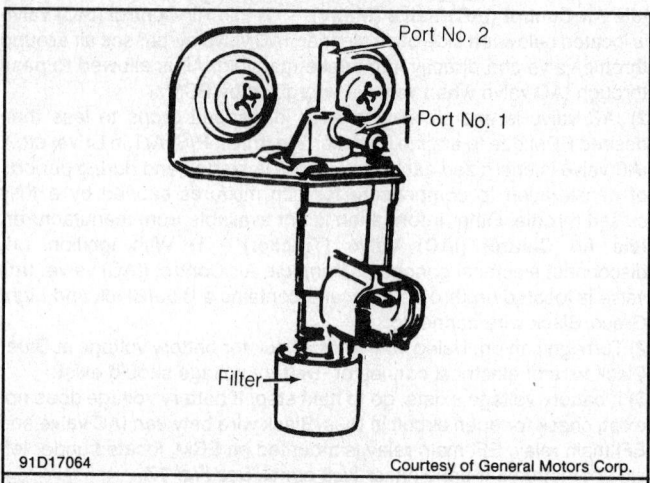

Fig. 22: Identifying EGR SV Ports (Metro)

91D17064   Courtesy of General Motors Corp.

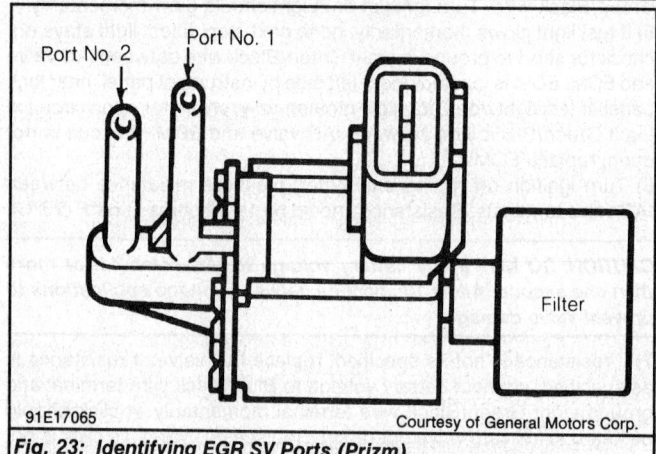

Fig. 23: Identifying EGR SV Ports (Prizm)

91E17065   Courtesy of General Motors Corp.

4) Turn ignition off. Using fused jumper wire, ground terminal G5 (Light Green/Yellow wire) on Green connector at ECM. Turn ignition on. With SV energized, blow air into port No. 1. Air should come out filter only. If air also comes out port No. 2, SV is defective or open circuit exists on Light Green/Yellow wire between ECM and SV.

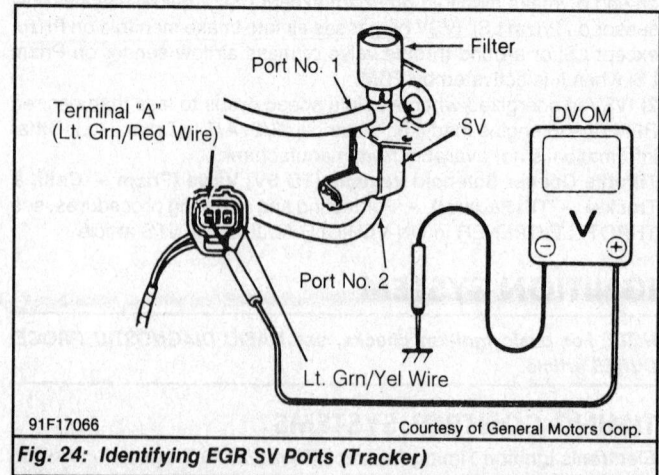

Fig. 24: Identifying EGR SV Ports (Tracker)

91F17066   Courtesy of General Motors Corp.

FUEL EVAPORATION

Fuel Evaporation Canister Check Valve (Metro – Standard Emissions) – While blowing into charcoal canister tank port, ensure air flows out air port (bottom of canister). *See Fig. 25.* While blowing air into purge port, air should not pass through air port. Apply 20 in. Hg of vacuum to TB port of canister valve. Blow air into purge port. Air should come out tank port. Replace check valve if defective.

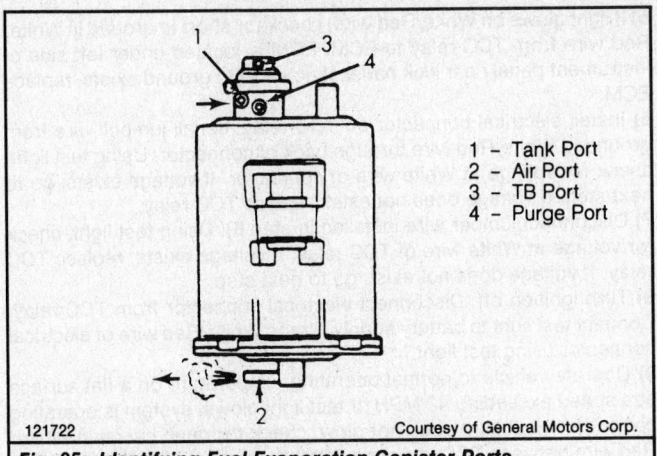

1 – Tank Port
2 – Air Port
3 – TB Port
4 – Purge Port

121722   Courtesy of General Motors Corp.

Fig. 25: Identifying Fuel Evaporation Canister Ports (Metro – Standard Emissions)

Fuel Evaporation Canister Check Valve (Prizm & Prizm LSi) – 1) With canister removed, blow into tank port of canister. Ensure air flows from purge port and air inlet (bottom of canister). See Fig. 26.

2) Blow into purge port. Air should not flow from any ports. Replace canister and check valve if they do not perform as indicated.

3) Apply 20 in. Hg of vacuum to vacuum signal line tube of canister valve while blowing air into purge tube. Air should come from throttle body tube. Replace canister if canister or check valve does not test as specified.

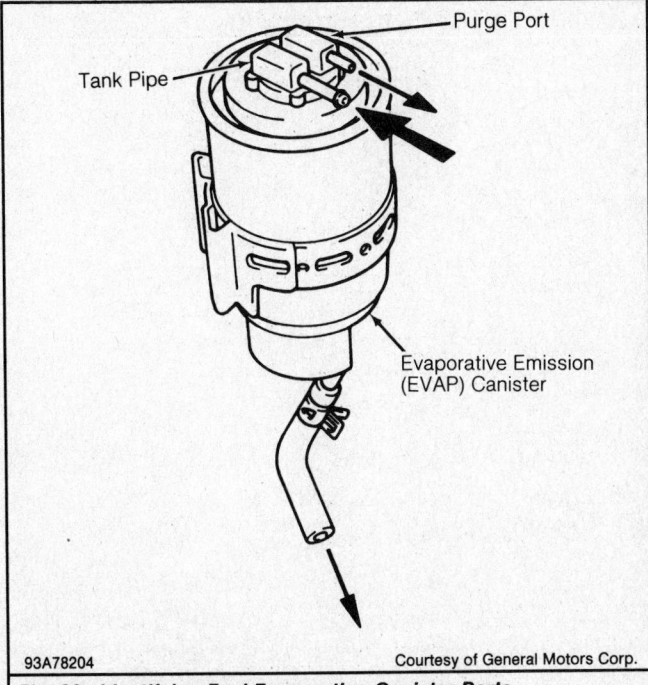

Purge Port

Tank Pipe

Evaporative Emission (EVAP) Canister

93A78204   Courtesy of General Motors Corp.

Fig. 26: Identifying Fuel Evaporation Canister Ports (Prizm & Prizm LSi)

Fuel Evaporation Canister (Tracker) – 1) Warm engine to normal operating temperature. Disconnect purge hose from canister. Place finger over end of disconnected hose to verify vacuum is not felt when engine is running at idle speed.

2) Ensure vacuum is felt when engine speed is increased to more than 1500 RPM. If check result is unsatisfactory, inspect vacuum passage, hoses, solenoid valve, wiring harness and ECM.

3) Disconnect vacuum hoses from canister. Flow through purge pipe and air pipe should not be restricted when air is blown into tank pipe.

4) When air is blown into purge pipe, air should not pass through air or tank pipe. If operation is not as described, replace charcoal canister.

Evaporative Emission Solenoid Purge (EVAP SP) Valve (Tracker) – 1) With ignition on and engine off, disconnect throttle body-to-EVAP SP valve hose at EVAP SP valve. EVAP SP valve is located on right side of engine compartment, near strut tower, and contains a Light Green/Red and Blue/Black wire connector.

2) Apply 10 in. Hg of vacuum on disconnected vacuum hose port on EVAP SP valve. EVAP SP valve should not hold vacuum.

3) If vacuum holds, go to next step. If vacuum does not hold, disconnect electrical connector at EVAP SP valve. Reapply vacuum to EVAP SP valve. If vacuum holds, replace EVAP SP valve. If vacuum does not hold, check for short to ground in Light Green/Red wire between EVAP SP valve and ECM. ECM is located under left side of dash, near kick panel.

4) With vacuum applied, ground Light Green/Red wire at EVAP SP valve electrical connector. If vacuum decreases, go to step 6). If vacuum does not decrease, disconnect electrical connector at EVAP SP valve. Connect test light to ground. Probe Blue/Black wire at electrical connector.

5) If test light glows, replace EVAP SP valve. If test light does not glow, check for open circuit in Blue/Black wire between EVAP SP valve and EFI main relay. EFI main relay is located near ECM. See Fig. 17.

6) Install vacuum gauge on vacuum hose to EVAP SP valve from throttle body. Start engine, and operate it at 2500 RPM. Momentarily increase engine speed, and then allow engine to idle. Ensure 10 in. Hg of vacuum is obtained.

7) If vacuum is okay, system is operating correctly. If low vacuum exists, check for damaged vacuum hoses and plugged vacuum passages.

Evaporation Emission Thermal Vacuum Valve (EVAP TVV) (Prizm & Prizm LSi) – 1) Disconnect negative battery cable. Drain engine coolant. Disconnect 2 vacuum hoses from EVAP TVV. Remove EVAP TVV from intake manifold.

2) Cool EVAP TVV in water to 95° F (35° C). Ensure air does not flow from upper to lower port. If air flows from upper to lower port, replace EVAP TVV.

3) Heat EVAP TVV in water to 129° F (54° C). Ensure air flows from upper to lower port. If air does not flow, replace EVAP TVV.

2-Way Check Valve (Metro) – Remove 2-way check valve, located in line from fuel tank to fuel evaporation canister. Blow air from Black side (fuel tank side) of check valve. Air should pass through check valve with slight resistance. Blow through Orange side (canister side) of check valve. Air should pass easily through check valve. If air passes easily from Black side or does not pass at all in both directions, replace check valve.

PCV Valve – Remove PCV valve from valve cover. Run engine at idle, placing thumb over end of hose to check for vacuum. If vacuum does not exist, check for plugged hoses or manifold port. Turn engine off. Remove PCV valve. Shake valve to ensure needle inside valve is free. Replace valve if needle is not free.

MISCELLANEOUS CONTROLS

NOTE: Although some controlled devices listed here are not technically engine performance components, they can affect driveability if they malfunction.

TRANSMISSION CONTROLS

Shift Indicator Light (Metro M/T) – 1) Turn ignition on and note shift indicator light. If shift indicator light is on, go to next step. If shift indicator light is off, go to step 3).

2) Turn ignition off. Disconnect ECM, located under left side of dash. Turn ignition on and note shift indicator light. If shift indicator light is off, ECM is faulty. If shift indicator light is on, check for short to ground in Light Blue wire between ECM and shift indicator light.

3) Turn ignition off. Disconnect electrical connectors at ECM, located under left side of dash. Turn ignition on. Install jumper wire between Light Blue wire of ECM connector and ground.

4) If shift indicator light is on, check for defective connection at ECM or for faulty ECM. If shift indicator light is off, check for defective bulb,

open in power supply circuit to shift indicator light and open in Light Blue wire from shift indicator light to ECM.

Torque Converter Clutch (TCC) Relay (Tracker A/T) – 1) TCC relay is located at right corner of engine compartment, on fusible link box, and contains a Green connector. With ignition on, disconnect TCC relay electrical connector.

2) Using test light connected to ground, check for voltage at White/Red and Blue/Black wires of electrical connector. If voltage exists at both wires, go to next step. If voltage does not exist, check for open or short to ground on defective circuit. White/Red wire goes from TCC relay to stoplight switch. Blue/Black wire goes from TCC relay to EFI main relay, located near ECM. *See Fig. 17.*

3) Connect test light to battery supply. Using test light, touch White/Red and White wires of TCC relay electrical connector. If light does not glow, go to step **6)**.

4) If light glows on White wire, check for short to ground in White wire from TCC relay to oil pressure switch at transmission. If no short to ground exists, replace oil pressure switch located inside transmission.

5) If light glows on White/Red wire, check for short to ground in White/Red wire from TCC relay to ECM. ECM is located under left side of instrument panel near kick panel. If no short to ground exists, replace ECM.

6) Install electrical connector on TCC relay. Install jumper wire from ground to White/Red wire through back of connector. Using test light, check for voltage at White wire of connector. If voltage exists, go to next step. If voltage does not exist, replace TCC relay.

7) Disconnect jumper wire installed in step **6)**. Using test light, check for voltage at White wire of TCC relay. If voltage exists, replace TCC relay. If voltage does not exist, go to next step.

8) Turn ignition off. Disconnect electrical connector from TCC relay. Connect test light to battery supply. Probe White/Red wire of electrical connector using test light.

9) Operate vehicle to normal operating temperature on a flat surface at a speed exceeding 42 MPH. If test light glows, system is operating correctly. If test light does not glow, check for open circuit in White/Red wire between TCC relay and ECM. If wiring is okay, replace ECM.

Metro, Prizm, Tracker

INTRODUCTION

Pin voltage charts are supplied to reduce diagnostic time. Checking pin voltages at Engine Control Module (ECM)/Powertrain Control Module (PCM) determines if it is receiving and transmitting proper voltage signals. Charts may also determine if ECM/PCM harness is shorted or open.

TERMINOLOGY

Due to Federal government requirements, manufacturers may use names and acronyms for systems and components different than those used in previous years. The following table will help eliminate confusion when dealing with these components and systems. Only relevant components and systems whose names have changed from current General Motors Corp. terminology have been listed.

A13	A12	A11	A10	A9	A8	A7	A6	A5	A4	A3	A2	A1
A26	A25	A24	A23	A22	A21	A20	A19	A18	A17	A16	A15	A14

BACKVIEW OF ECM CONNECTOR C1 (GRAY)

CAVITY/ PIN	WIRE COLOR	CIRCUIT	VOLTAGE	
			KEY "ON"	ENG. RUN
1/A1	WHT/BLU	IGNITION POWER INPUT	B +	B +
2/A2	BLK/GRN	O2S GROUND	0*	0*
3/A3	PPL/GRN	TEST SWITCH SIGNAL	B +	B +
4/A4	BLK/YEL	CRANK SIGNAL	0* (8)	0*
5/A5	BRN/BLK	THROTTLE POSITION OUTPUT CONTROL (AUTOMATIC TRANSAXLE)	0-10V (9)	0-10V (9)
6/A6	LT BLU	UPSHIFT INDICATOR CONTROL (MANUAL TRANSAXLE)	(11)	B +
7/A7	—	NOT USED	—	—
8/A8	PPL	MALFUNCTION INDICATOR LAMP (MIL) CONTROL	1-2V	B +
9/A9	GRN	EGR SV CONTROL	B +	B +
10/A10	RED/WHT	IAC VALVE CONTROL	1-1.5V	B +
11/A11	—	NOT USED	—	—
12/A12	YEL/BLK	FUEL INJECTOR CONTROL	B +	B +
13/A13	BRN	IGNITION COIL CONTROL	B +	B +
14/A14	WHT	MEMORY POWER INPUT	B +	B +
15/A15	LT GRN/BLK	SENSOR GROUND	0*	0*
16/A16	PPL/YEL	DIAGNOSTIC REQUEST SIGNAL	B +	B +
17/A17	—	NOT USED	—	—
18/A18	BRN/RED	THROTTLE POSITION OUTPUT CONTROL (AUTOMATIC TRANSAXLE)	0-10V (9)	0-10V (9)
19/A19	BRN/YEL	THROTTLE POSITION OUTPUT CONTROL (AUTOMATIC TRANSAXLE)	0-10V (9)	0-10V (9)
20/A20	—	NOT USED	—	—
21/A21	PPL/RED	DUTY CHECK OUTPUT	0*	0*
22/A22	—	NOT USED	—	—
23/A23	PNK/WHT	FUEL PUMP RELAY CONTROL	(3)	0*
24/A24	—	NOT USED	—	—
25/A25	BLK/BLU	ECM GROUND	0*	0*
26/A26	BLK/YEL	ECM GROUND	0*	0*

0* Less than .5 volts.
(1) Varies as front wheels rotate.
(2) 0 volts in "P" or "N"; B + otherwise.
(3) B + for first 2 seconds.
(4) B + with A/C switch "OFF" and 0 volts with A/C switch "ON."
(5) 0 volts at idle; B + otherwise.
(6) Varies with engine temperature.

(7) B + with light switch "ON" or with rear defogger "ON" or with blower motor "ON" or with radiator fan "ON" or with stoplamps "ON."
(8) Voltage present only during cranking.
(9) Varies with throttle position.
(10) Varies with ambient temperature.
(11) 1-2 volts with light switch "OFF" and 3-5 volts with light switch "ON."

Courtesy of General Motors Corp.

94C44356

Fig. 1: ECM Connector C1 Terminal Pin Voltages (Metro – Standard Emissions)

SAE TERMINOLOGY

Former Name Or Acronym	New Name Or Acronym
ALDL	Data Link Connector (DLC)
CHECK ENGINE Light	Malfunction Indicator Light (MIL)
CTS	Engine Coolant Temp. (ECT) Sensor
Diagnostic Circuit Check	On-Board Diagnostic (OBD) System Check
ESC System	Knock Sensor (KS) System
EST System	Ignition Control (IC) System
MAT Sensor	Intake Air Temperature (IAT) Sensor
Park/Neutral (P/N) Switch	Park/Neutral Position (PNP) Switch
Port Fuel Injection	Multiport Fuel Injection
Scan Data	Scan Tester (ST) Data
SERVICE ENGINE SOON Light	Malfunction Indicator Light (MIL)
Thermostatic Air Cleaner (TAC)	Air Cleaner (ACL)
Throttle Position Sensor (TPS)	Throttle Position (TP) Sensor
Throttle Position Switch	Closed Throttle Position (CTP) Switch
Throttle Position Switch	Wide Open Throttle (WOT) Switch
Viscous Converter Clutch (VCC)	Torque Converter Clutch (TCC)

NOTE: *All voltage tests should be performed using a Digital Volt-Ohmmeter (DVOM) with a minimum 10-megohm input impedance, unless stated otherwise in testing procedures. Voltage readings may vary slightly due to vehicle battery condition or charging rate.*

TEST CONDITIONS

ECM/PCM voltage charts are used with a DVOM to aid in diagnosis. Voltages may vary due to low battery charge or other reasons, but should be very close.

Following conditions must be met before testing:
- Engine at normal operating temperature.
- Engine idling for ENG. RUN column.
- Test terminal not grounded (except where noted).
- All voltages shown B+ indicate system voltage.

CAVITY/ PIN	WIRE COLOR	CIRCUIT	VOLTAGE KEY "ON"	VOLTAGE ENG. RUN
1/B1	LT GRN	IGNITION REFERENCE HIGH	.4-.8V	.4-.8V
2/B2	LT GRN/ YEL	IDLE SWITCH SIGNAL	(5)	(5)
3/B3	BRN/WHT	ELECTRICAL LOAD IDLE-UP SIGNAL	(7)	(7)
4/B4	BLU/RED	A/C IDLE-UP SIGNAL	(4)	(4)
5/B5	—	NOT USED	—	—
6/B6	WHT	EXHAUST OXYGEN CONCENTRATION INPUT	0*	.45-1V
7/B7	LT GRN/ RED	MAP INPUT	3-4V	1-2V
8/B8	LT GRN	REFERENCE VOLTAGE (5V)	4-5V	4-5V
9/B9	PPL	IGNITION REFERENCE LOW	.4-.8V	.4-.8V
10/B10	YEL/GRN	VEHICLE SPEED INPUT	0-12V (1)	0-12V (1)
11/B11	BRN/WHT	RD2L SIGNAL (AUTOMATIC TRANSAXLE)	0-12V (2)	0-12V (2)
12/B12	PPL/WHT	SERIAL DATA OUTPUT	4-5V	4-5V
13/B13	—	NOT USED	—	—
14/B14	LT GRN/ WHT	THROTTLE POSITION INPUT	.3-.6V (9)	.3-.6V (9)
15/B15	GRY/WHT	ECT INPUT	.4-.6V (6)	.4-.6V (6)
16/B16	GRY	IAT INPUT	1-3V (10)	1-3V (10)

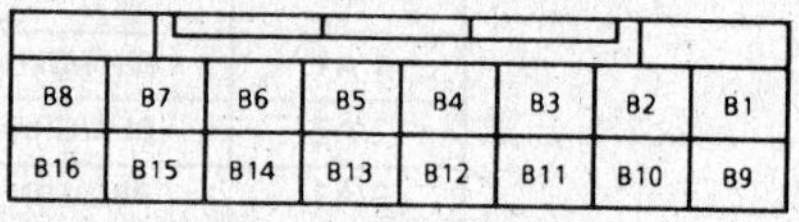

B8	B7	B6	B5	B4	B3	B2	B1
B16	B15	B14	B13	B12	B11	B10	B9

BACKVIEW OF ECM CONNECTOR C2 (GRAY)

0* Less than .5 volts.
(1) Varies as front wheels rotate.
(2) 0 volts in "P" or "N"; B+ otherwise.
(3) B+ for first 2 seconds.
(4) B+ with A/C switch "OFF" and 0 volts with A/C switch "ON."
(5) 0 volts at idle; B+ otherwise.
(6) Varies with engine temperature.
(7) B+ with light switch "ON" or with rear defogger "ON" or with blower motor "ON" or with radiator fan "ON" or with stoplamps "ON."
(8) Voltage present only during cranking.
(9) Varies with throttle position.
(10) Varies with ambient temperature.
(11) 1-2 volts with light switch "OFF" and 3-5 volts with light switch "ON."

94D44357

Courtesy of General Motors Corp.

Fig. 2: ECM Connector C2 Terminal Pin Voltages (Metro – Standard Emissions)

A13	A12	A11	A10	A9	A8	A7	A6	A5	A4	A3	A2	A1
A26	A25	A24	A23	A22	A21	A20	A19	A18	A17	A16	A15	A14

BACKVIEW OF ECM CONNECTOR C1 (GRAY)

CAVITY/ PIN	WIRE COLOR	CIRCUIT	VOLTAGE	
			KEY "ON"	ENG. RUN
1/A1	WHT/BLU	IGNITION POWER INPUT	B+	B+
2/A2	BLK/GRN	HO2S GROUND	0*	0*
3/A3	PPL/GRN	TEST SWITCH SIGNAL	B+	B+
4/A4	BLK/YEL	CRANK SIGNAL	0* (8)	0*
5/A5	BRN/BLK	THROTTLE POSITION OUTPUT CONTROL (AUTOMATIC TRANSAXLE)	0-10V (9)	0-10V (9)
6/A6	LT BLU	UPSHIFT INDICATOR CONTROL (MANUAL TRANSAXLE)	(11)	B+
7/A7	GRA/BLK	ISC MOTOR RELAY CONTROL	.4-1.0V	.4-1.0V
8/A8	PPL	MALFUNCTION INDICATOR LAMP (MIL) CONTROL	1-2V	B+
9/A9	GRN	EGR SV CONTROL	B+	B+
10/A10	PNK/BLK	HO2S HEATER CONTROL	B+	B+
11/A11	GRA/RED	ISC MOTOR CONTROL	0*	(14)
12/A12	YEL/BLK	FUEL INJECTOR CONTROL	B+	B+
13/A13	BRN/YEL	IGNITION TRIGGER SIGNAL	0*	.4-1.2V (13)
14/A14	WHT	MEMORY POWER INPUT	B+	B+
15/A15	LT GRN/BLK	SENSOR GROUND	0*	0*
16/A16	PPL/YEL	DIAGNOSTIC REQUEST SIGNAL	B+	B+
17/A17	PNK/WHT	FUEL PUMP RELAY CONTROL	(12)	.5-1.8V
18/A18	BRN/RED	THROTTLE POSITION OUTPUT CONTROL (AUTOMATIC TRANSAXLE)	0-10V (9)	0-10V (9)
19/A19	BRN/YEL	THROTTLE POSITION OUTPUT CONTROL (AUTOMATIC TRANSAXLE)	0-10V (9)	0-10V (9)
20/A20	RED/GRN	EVAP SP VALVE CONTROL	B+	B+
21/A21	PPL/RED	DUTY CHECK OUTPUT	0*	0*
22/A22	YEL/RED	EFE HEATER RELAY CONTROL	B+	B+
23/A23	BLK/RED	ECM GROUND	0*	0*
24/A24	GRA/YEL	ISC MOTOR CONTROL	0*	—
25/A25	BLK/BLU	ECM GROUND	0*	0*
26/A26	BRN	IGNITION CONFIRMATION SIGNAL	B+	B+

0* Less than .5 volts.
(1) Varies as front wheels rotate.
(2) 0 volts in "P" or "N"; B+ otherwise.
(3) B+ for first 2 seconds.
(4) B+ with A/C switch "OFF" and 0 volts with A/C switch "ON."
(5) 0 volts at idle; B+ otherwise.
(6) Varies with engine temperature.
(7) B+ with light switch "ON" or with rear defogger "ON" or with blower motor "ON" or with radiator fan "ON" or with stoplamps "ON."
(8) Voltage present only during cranking.
(9) Varies with throttle position.
(10) Varies with ambient temperature.
(11) 1-2 volts with light switch "OFF" and 3-5 volts with light switch "ON."
(12) 0.5-1.8 volts for 2 seconds after ignition switch "ON"; B+ otherwise.
(13) Varies with engine rpm.
(14) Momentarily B+ when ISC motor plunger extends.
(15) Momentarily B+ when ISC motor plunger retracts.

94I44360

Courtesy of General Motors Corp.

Fig. 3: ECM Connector C1 Terminal Pin Voltages (Metro – Upgraded Emissions)

CAVITY/ PIN	WIRE COLOR	CIRCUIT	VOLTAGE	
			KEY "ON"	ENG. RUN
1/B1	LT GRN	IGNITION REFERENCE HIGH	.4-.8V	.4-.8V
2/B2	LT GRN/ YEL	IDLE SWITCH SIGNAL	(5)	(5)
3/B3	BRN/YEL	ELECTRICAL LOAD IDLE-UP SIGNAL	(7)	(7)
4/B4	BLU/RED	A/C IDLE-UP SIGNAL	B+	(4)
5/B5	—	NOT USED	—	—
6/B6	WHT	EXHAUST OXYGEN CONCENTRATION INPUT	0*	.45-1V
7/B7	LT GRN/ RED	MAP INPUT	3-4V	1-2V
8/B8	LT GRN	REFERENCE VOLTAGE (5V)	4-5V	4-5V
9/B9	PPL	IGNITION REFERENCE LOW	.4-.8V	.4-.8V
10/B10	YEL/GRN	VEHICLE SPEED INPUT	0-12V (1)	0-12V (1)
11/B11	BRN/WHT	RD2L SIGNAL (AUTOMATIC TRANSAXLE)	0-12V (2)	0-12V (2)
12/B12	PPL/WHT	SERIAL DATA OUTPUT	4-5V	4-5V
13/B13	BLU/BLK	FI RELAY CONTROL	.4-1V	.4-1V
14/B14	LT GRN/ WHT	THROTTLE POSITION INPUT	.2-1.0V (9)	.2-1.0V (9)
15/B15	GRY/WHT	ECT INPUT	.4-.8V (6)	.4-.8V (6)
16/B16	GRY	IAT INPUT	2-2.7V (10)	2-2.7V (10)

94B44363

B8	B7	B6	B5	B4	B3	B2	B1
B16	B15	B14	B13	B12	B11	B10	B9

BACKVIEW OF ECM CONNECTOR C2 (GRAY)

0* Less than .5 volts.
(1) Varies as front wheels rotate.
(2) 0 volts in "P" or "N"; B+ otherwise.
(3) B+ for first 2 seconds.
(4) B+ with A/C switch "OFF" and 0 volts with A/C switch "ON."
(5) 0 volts at idle; 5 volts otherwise.
(6) Varies with engine temperature.
(7) B+ with light switch "ON" or with rear defogger "ON" or with blower motor "ON" or with radiator fan "ON" or with stoplamps "ON."
(8) Voltage present only during cranking.
(9) Varies with throttle position.
(10) Varies with ambient temperature.
(11) 1-2 volts with light switch "OFF" and 3-5 volts with light switch "ON."

Courtesy of General Motors Corp.

Fig. 4: ECM Connector C2 Terminal Pin Voltages (Metro – Upgraded Emissions)

CAVITY/ PIN	WIRE COLOR	CIRCUIT	VOLTAGE	
			KEY "ON"	ENG. RUN
1/A1	BLK/RED	IGNITION POWER	B+	B+
2/A2	RED/WHT	MEMORY POWER	B+	B+
3/A3	—	NOT USED	—	—
4/A4	GRN/RED	CIRCUIT OPENING RELAY CONTROL	(1)	0*
5/A5	—	NOT USED	—	—
6/A6	RED/YEL	A/C CUTOUT CONTROL	0*	0* (2)
7/A7	BLK/RED	IGNITION POWER	B+	B+
8/A8	RED/YEL	MIL CONTROL	0-1V	B+
9/A9	—	NOT USED	—	—
10/A10	YEL/BLU	A/C ON SIGNAL	B+(3)	B+(3)
11/A11	PPL/WHT	VEHICLE SPEED INPUT	0* (4)	2-3V VARIES
12/A12	BLK	ELECTRICAL LOAD IDLE-UP SIGNAL	0* (5)	0* (5)

93A78162

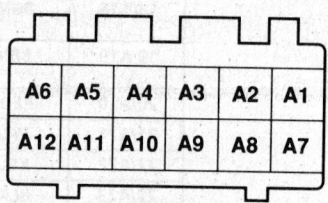

A6	A5	A4	A3	A2	A1
A12	A11	A10	A9	A8	A7

BACK VIEW OF ECM CONNECTOR C1 (GRAY)

0* LESS THAN 0.50 VOLTS
(1) 0 VOLTS FOR 3 SECONDS, THEN B+
(2) 5 TO 6 VOLTS WITH A/C SWITCH DEPRESSED
(3) 0 VOLTS WITH A/C SWITCH DEPRESSED
(4) VARIES FROM 0 TO 5V WITH FRONT WHEELS ROTATING
(5) B+ WITH LIGHT/TURN SIGNAL SWITCH IN PARK OR HEAD OR WITH DEFOGGER ON
(6) VARIES WITH INTAKE AIR TEMPERATURE
(7) VARIES WITH ENGINE COOLANT TEMPERATURE
(8) VARIES WITH THROTTLE LEVER POSITION
(9) 0 VOLTS AT IDLE; B+ OFF IDLE
(10) VARIES WITH EXHAUST GAS TEMPERATURE
(11) B+ WITH IGNITION SWITCH IN "START"
(12) 0 VOLTS IN "P" OR "N"; B+ IN "R", "D", "2" OR "L"
(13) VARIES CONSTANTLY WITH SYSTEM IN CLOSED LOOP

Courtesy of General Motors Corp.

Fig. 5: ECM Connector C1 Terminal Pin Voltages (Prizm VIN 6, 1.6L DOHC)

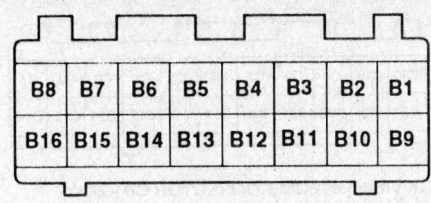

BACK VIEW OF ECM CONNECTOR C2 (GRAY)

CAVITY/ PIN	WIRE COLOR	CIRCUIT	VOLTAGE	
			KEY "ON"	ENG. RUN
1/B1	—	NOT USED	—	—
2/B2	LT GRN/RED	MAP INPUT	3-4V	1.1-1.8V
3/B3	YEL/BLK	IAT INPUT	1-3.5V (6)	1.5-2.5V (6)
4/B4	WHT	ECT INPUT	.5-3.5V (7)	1-2V (7)
5/B5	BLK	SECONDARY EXHAUST OXYGEN CONCENTRATION INPUT (CALIFORNIA ONLY)	0*	0-1V (13)
6/B6	BLK		0*	0-1V (13)
7/B7	GRN/WHT	TEST DIAGNOSTIC MODE SIGNAL	B+	B+
8/B8	RED/WHT	FUEL CONTROL FEEDBACK OUTPUT	0*	1.5-3.5V
9/B9	BRN	SENSOR GROUND	0*	0*
10/B10	LT GRN	THROTTLE POSITION INPUT	.5-4.5V (8)	.5-4.5V (8)
11/B11	YEL	REFERENCE VOLTAGE (5V)	5V	5V
12/B12	BLU	IDLE SIGNAL	(9)	(9)
13/B13	WHT/BLU	EGR TEMPERATURE INPUT (CALIFORNIA ONLY)	1-3.5V (10)	1.5-2.5V(10)
14/B14	—	NOT USED	—	—
15/B15	BLU/WHT	DIAGNOSTIC REQUEST SIGNAL	B+	B+
16/B16	BRN	SENSOR GROUND	0*	0*

0* LESS THAN 0.50 VOLTS
(1) 0 VOLTS FOR 3 SECONDS, THEN B+
(2) 5 TO 6 VOLTS WITH A/C SWITCH DEPRESSED
(3) 0 VOLTS WITH A/C SWITCH DEPRESSED
(4) VARIES FROM 0 TO 5V WITH FRONT WHEELS ROTATING
(5) B+ WITH LIGHT/TURN SIGNAL SWITCH IN PARK OR HEAD OR WITH DEFOGGER ON
(6) VARIES WITH INTAKE AIR TEMPERATURE
(7) VARIES WITH ENGINE COOLANT TEMPERATURE
(8) VARIES WITH THROTTLE LEVER POSITION
(9) 0 VOLTS AT IDLE; B+ OFF IDLE
(10) VARIES WITH EXHAUST GAS TEMPERATURE
(11) B+ WITH IGNITION SWITCH IN "START"
(12) 0 VOLTS IN "P" OR "N"; B+ IN "R", "D", "2" OR "L"
(13) VARIES CONSTANTLY WITH SYSTEM IN CLOSED LOOP

94E44366

Courtesy of General Motors Corp.

Fig. 6: ECM Connector C2 Terminal Pin Voltages (Prizm VIN 6, 1.6L DOHC)

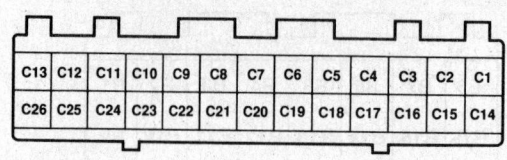

BACK VIEW OF ECM CONNECTOR C3 (GRAY)

CAVITY/ PIN	WIRE COLOR	CIRCUIT	VOLTAGE	
			KEY "ON"	ENG. RUN
1/C1	—	NOT USED	—	—
2/C2	BLK	CRANK SIGNAL	0* (11)	0* (11)
3/C3	BLK/YEL	IGNITION FAIL-SAFE SIGNAL INPUT	.56V	1.5V
4/C4	BLK	CRANK ANGLE INPUT HIGH	.69V	.69V
5/C5	RED	CAMSHAFT POSITION INPUT HIGH	.69V	.69V
6/C6	—	NOT USED	—	—
7/C7	—	NOT USED	—	—
8/C8	—	NOT USED	—	—
9/C9	BLK/WHT	IAC VALVE CLOSE CONTROL	.3-.7V	5-7V
10/C10	BLK/BLU	IAC VALVE OPEN CONTROL	B+	8-10V
11/C11	—	NOT USED	—	—
12/C12	BLK	FUEL INJECTOR NO. 1 AND NO. 3 CONTROL	B+	B+
13/C13	BRN	GROUND	0*	0*
14/C14	—	NOT USED	—	—
15/C15	BRN (M/T)	GROUND (M/T ONLY)	0*	0*
	BLK/WHT (A/T)	PARK/NEUTRAL POSITION SIGNAL (A/T ONLY)	(12)	(12)
16/C16	BLK/RED	EGR SV VALVE CONTROL (CALIFORNIA ONLY)	B+	B+
17/C17	WHT	CRANK ANGLE INPUT LOW	.69V	.69V
18/C18	GRN	CAMSHAFT POSITION INPUT LOW	.69V	.69V
19/C19	—	NOT USED	—	—
20/C20	—	NOT USED	—	—
21/C21	—	NOT USED	—	—
22/C22	BLK	IGNITION SIGNAL	0*	0-2V (8)
23/C23	WHT/RED	A/C SV VALVE CONTROL	B+	B+ (3)
24/C24	BRN	O2S GROUND	0*	0*
25/C25	BLK/RED	FUEL INJECTOR NO. 2 AND NO. 4 CONTROL	B+	B+
26/C26	BRN	GROUND	0*	0*

0* LESS THAN 0.50 VOLTS
(1) 0 VOLTS FOR 3 SECONDS, THEN B+
(2) 5 TO 6 VOLTS WITH A/C SWITCH DEPRESSED
(3) 0 VOLTS WITH A/C SWITCH DEPRESSED
(4) VARIES FROM 0 TO 5V WITH FRONT WHEELS ROTATING
(5) B+ WITH LIGHT/TURN SIGNAL SWITCH IN PARK
    OR HEAD OR WITH DEFOGGER ON

(6) VARIES WITH INTAKE AIR TEMPERATURE
(7) VARIES WITH ENGINE COOLANT TEMPERATURE
(8) VARIES WITH THROTTLE LEVER POSITION
(9) 0 VOLTS AT IDLE; B+ OFF IDLE
(10) VARIES WITH EXHAUST GAS TEMPERATURE
(11) B+ WITH IGNITION SWITCH IN "START"
(12) 0 VOLTS IN "P" OR "N"; B+ IN "R", "D", "2" OR "L"
(13) VARIES CONSTANTLY WITH SYSTEM IN CLOSED LOOP

93G78168

Courtesy of General Motors Corp.

Fig. 7: ECM Connector C3 Terminal Pin Voltages (Prizm VIN 6, 1.6L DOHC)

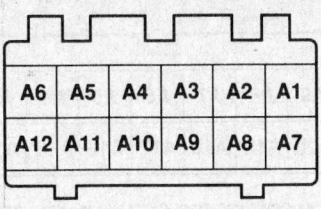

BACK VIEW OF PCM CONNECTOR C1 (MANUAL TRANSAXLE) (GRAY)

CAVITY/ PIN	WIRE COLOR	CIRCUIT	VOLTAGE	
			KEY "ON"	ENG. RUN
1/A1	BLK/RED	IGNITION POWER	B+	B+
2/A2	RED/WHT	MEMORY POWER	B+	B+
3/A3	—	NOT USED	—	—
4/A4	GRN/RED	CIRCUIT OPENING RELAY CONTROL	(7)	0*
5/A5	—	NOT USED	—	—
6/A6	RED/YEL	A/C CUTOUT CONTROL	0*	0* (8)
7/A7	BLK/RED	IGNITION POWER	B+	B+
8/A8	RED/YEL	MIL CONTROL	0-1V	B+
9/A9	—	NOT USED	—	—
10/A10	YEL/BLU	A/C ON SIGNAL	B+(5)	B+(5)
11/A11	PPL/WHT	VEHICLE SPEED INPUT	0* (4)	2-3V VARIES
12/A12	BLK	ELECTRICAL LOAD IDLE-UP SIGNAL	0* (1)	0* (1)

0* LESS THAN 0.50 VOLTS
(1) B+ WITH LIGHT/TURN SIGNAL SWITCH IN PARK OR HEAD OR WITH DEFOGGER ON
(2) B+ WITH BRAKE PEDAL DEPRESSED
(3) 0 VOLTS WITH OVERDRIVE SWITCH RELEASED; B+ WITH OVERDRIVE SWITCH DEPRESSED
(4) VARIES FROM 0 TO 5V WITH FRONT WHEELS ROTATING
(5) 0 VOLTS WITH A/C SWITCH DEPRESSED
(6) B+ WITH IGNITION SWITCH IN "START"
(7) 0 VOLTS FOR 3 SECONDS, THEN B+
(8) 5 TO 6 VOLTS WITH A/C SWITCH DEPRESSED
(9) 0 VOLTS IN "P" OR "N"; B+ IN "R", "D", "2" OR "L"

(10) VARIES WITH INTAKE AIR TEMPERATURE
(11) VARIES WITH ENGINE COOLANT TEMPERATURE
(12) VARIES WITH EXHAUST GAS TEMPERATURE
(13) VARIES WITH THROTTLE LEVER POSITION
(14) 0 VOLTS AT IDLE; B+ OFF IDLE
(15) B+ WITH MANUAL SELECTOR LEVER IN "2"
(16) B+ WITH MANUAL SELECTOR LEVER IN "L"
(17) B+ WITH MANUAL SELECTOR LEVER IN "R"
(18) VARIES CONSTANTLY WITH SYSTEM IN CLOSED LOOP
(19) B+ WITH VEHICLE IN TCC LOCKUP CONDITION
(20) B+ WITH TRANSAXLE IN 1st OR 2nd GEAR
(21) B+ WITH TRANSAXLE IN 2nd OR 3rd GEAR

93H78169

Courtesy of General Motors Corp.

Fig. 8: PCM Connector C1 Terminal Pin Voltages (Prizm VIN 8, 1.8L DOHC Manual Transaxle)

1994 ENGINE PERFORMANCE
Pin Voltage Charts (Cont.)

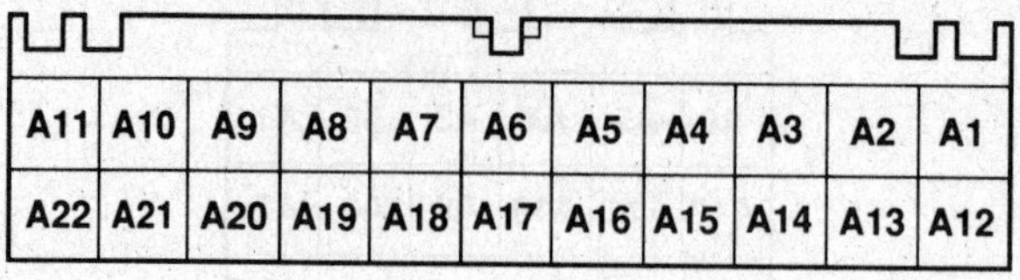

A11	A10	A9	A8	A7	A6	A5	A4	A3	A2	A1
A22	A21	A20	A19	A18	A17	A16	A15	A14	A13	A12

BACK VIEW OF PCM CONNECTOR C1 (AUTOMATIC TRANSAXLE) (GRAY)

CAVITY/ PIN	WIRE COLOR	CIRCUIT	VOLTAGE KEY "ON"	VOLTAGE ENG. RUN
1/A1	RED/WHT	MEMORY POWER	B+	B+
2/A2	BLK	ELECTRICAL LOAD IDLE-UP SIGNAL	0* (1)	0* (1)
3/A3	—	NOT USED		
4/A4	GRN/WHT	BRAKE SIGNAL	0* (2)	0* (2)
5/A5	RED/YEL	MIL CONTROL	0-1V	B+
6/A6	—	NOT USED	—	—
7/A7	LT GRN	O/D ON/OFF SIGNAL/"O/D OFF" DIAGNOSTIC OUTPUT CONTROL	(3)	(3)
8/A8	—	NOT USED	—	—
9/A9	PPL/WHT	VEHICLE SPEED INPUT	0* (4)	2-3V VARIES
10/A10	YEL/BLU	A/C ON SIGNAL	B+ (5)	B+ (5)
11/A11	BLK	CRANK SIGNAL	0* (6)	0* (6)
12/A12	BLK/RED	IGNITION POWER	B+	B+
13/A13	BLK/RED	IGNITION POWER	B+	B+
14/A14	GRN/RED	CIRCUIT OPENING RELAY CONTROL	(7)	0*
15/A15	—	NOT USED	—	—
16/A16	—	NOT USED	—	—
17/A17	—	NOT USED	—	—
18/A18	—	NOT USED	—	—
19/A19	—	NOT USED	—	—
20/A20	RED	O/D CUT SIGNAL	B+	B+
21/A21	RED/YEL	A/C CUTOUT CONTROL	0*	0* (8)
22/A22	BLK/YEL	PARK/NEUTRAL POSITION SIGNAL	(9)	(9)

0* LESS THAN 0.50 VOLTS
(1) B+ WITH LIGHT/TURN SIGNAL SWITCH IN PARK OR HEAD OR WITH DEFOGGER ON
(2) B+ WITH BRAKE PEDAL DEPRESSED
(3) 0 VOLTS WITH OVERDRIVE SWITCH RELEASED; B+ WITH OVERDRIVE SWITCH DEPRESSED
(4) VARIES FROM 0 TO 5V WITH FRONT WHEELS ROTATING
(5) 0 VOLTS WITH A/C SWITCH DEPRESSED
(6) B+ WITH IGNITION SWITCH IN "START"
(7) 0 VOLTS FOR 3 SECONDS, THEN B+
(8) 5 TO 6 VOLTS WITH A/C SWITCH DEPRESSED
(9) 0 VOLTS IN "P" OR "N"; B+ IN "R", "D", "2" OR "L"

(10) VARIES WITH INTAKE AIR TEMPERATURE
(11) VARIES WITH ENGINE COOLANT TEMPERATURE
(12) VARIES WITH EXHAUST GAS TEMPERATURE
(13) VARIES WITH THROTTLE LEVER POSITION
(14) 0 VOLTS AT IDLE; B+ OFF IDLE
(15) B+ WITH MANUAL SELECTOR LEVER IN "2"
(16) B+ WITH MANUAL SELECTOR LEVER IN "L"
(17) B+ WITH MANUAL SELECTOR LEVER IN "R"
(18) VARIES CONSTANTLY WITH SYSTEM IN CLOSED LOOP
(19) B+ WITH VEHICLE IN TCC LOCKUP CONDITION
(20) B+ WITH TRANSAXLE IN 1st OR 2nd GEAR
(21) B+ WITH TRANSAXLE IN 2nd OR 3rd GEAR

93A78170

Courtesy of General Motors Corp.

Fig. 9: PCM Connector C1 Terminal Pin Voltages (Prizm VIN 8, 1.8L DOHC Automatic Transaxle)

```
┌─┐     ┌─┐     ┌─┐
┘ └─────┘ └─────┘ └
```

| B8 | B7 | B6 | B5 | B4 | B3 | B2 | B1 |
| B16 | B15 | B14 | B13 | B12 | B11 | B10 | B9 |

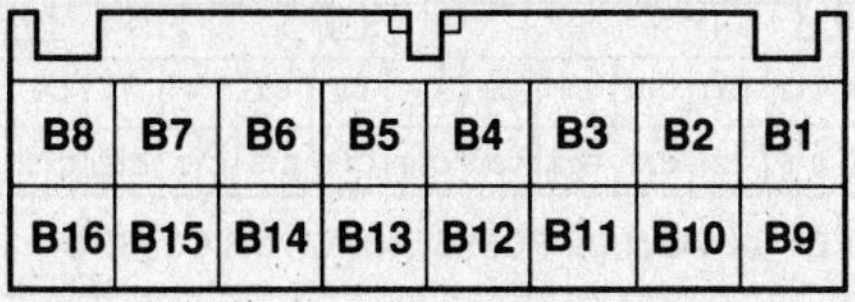

BACK VIEW OF PCM CONNECTOR C2 (GRAY)

CAVITY/ PIN	WIRE COLOR	CIRCUIT	VOLTAGE	
			KEY "ON"	ENG. RUN
1/B1	YEL	REFERENCE VOLTAGE (5V) (A/T ONLY)	4-6V	4-6V
2/B2	LT GRN/RED	MAP INPUT	3-4V	1.1-1.8V
3/B3	YEL/BLK	IAT INPUT	1-3.5V (10)	1.5-2.5V (10)
4/B4	WHT	ECT INPUT	.5-3.5V (11)	1-2V (11)
5/B5	BLK	EXHAUST OXYGEN CONCENTRATION INPUT (SECONDARY) (CALIFORNIA ONLY)	0*	0-1V (18)
6/B6	BLK	EXHAUST OXYGEN CONCENTRATION INPUT	0*	0-1V (18)
7/B7	GRN/WHT (M/T)	TEST DIAGNOSTIC MODE SIGNAL (M/T ONLY)	B+	B+
	BLK (A/T)	THROTTLE POSITION OUTPUT (A/T ONLY)	0*	(13)
8/B8	RED/WHT	FUEL CONTROL FEEDBACK OUTPUT	0*	1.5-3.5V
9/B9	BRN	SENSOR GROUND	0*	0*
10/B10	LT GRN (M/T)	THROTTLE POSITION INPUT (M/T ONLY)	.5-4.5V (13)	.5-4.5V (13)
	WHT/BLU (A/T)	EGR TEMPERATURE INPUT (CALIFORNIA A/T ONLY)	1-3.5V (12)	1.5-2.5V (12)
11/B11	YEL (M/T)	REFERENCE VOLTAGE (5V) (M/T ONLY)	4-6V	4-6V
	LT GRN (A/T)	THROTTLE POSITION INPUT (A/T ONLY)	.5-4.5V (13)	.5-4.5V (13)
12/B12	BLU	IDLE SIGNAL	(14)	(14)
13/B13	WHT/BLU (M/T)	EGR TEMPERATURE INPUT (CALIFORNIA M/T ONLY)	1-3.5V (12)	1.5-2.5V (12)
	BLK (A/T)	KNOCK INPUT	0*	0-.2V
14/B14	BLK (M/T)	KNOCK INPUT	0*	0-.2V
	GRN/WHT (A/T)	TEST DIAGNOSTIC MODE SIGNAL (A/T ONLY)	B+	B+
15/B15	BLU/WHT	DIAGNOSTIC REQUEST SIGNAL	B+	B+
16/B16	BRN	SENSOR GROUND	0*	0*

0* LESS THAN 0.50 VOLTS
(1) B+ WITH LIGHT/TURN SIGNAL SWITCH IN PARK OR HEAD OR WITH DEFOGGER ON
(2) B+ WITH BRAKE PEDAL DEPRESSED
(3) 0 VOLTS WITH OVERDRIVE SWITCH RELEASED; B+ WITH OVERDRIVE SWITCH DEPRESSED
(4) VARIES FROM 0 TO 5V WITH FRONT WHEELS ROTATING
(5) 0 VOLTS WITH A/C SWITCH DEPRESSED
(6) B+ WITH IGNITION SWITCH IN "START"
(7) 0 VOLTS FOR 3 SECONDS, THEN B+
(8) 5 TO 6 VOLTS WITH A/C SWITCH DEPRESSED
(9) 0 VOLTS IN "P" OR "N"; B+ IN "R", "D", "2" OR "L"

(10) VARIES WITH INTAKE AIR TEMPERATURE
(11) VARIES WITH ENGINE COOLANT TEMPERATURE
(12) VARIES WITH EXHAUST GAS TEMPERATURE
(13) VARIES WITH THROTTLE LEVER POSITION
(14) 0 VOLTS AT IDLE; B+ OFF IDLE
(15) B+ WITH MANUAL SELECTOR LEVER IN "2"
(16) B+ WITH MANUAL SELECTOR LEVER IN "L"
(17) B+ WITH MANUAL SELECTOR LEVER IN "R"
(18) VARIES CONSTANTLY WITH SYSTEM IN CLOSED LOOP
(19) B+ WITH VEHICLE IN TCC LOCKUP CONDITION
(20) B+ WITH TRANSAXLE IN 1st OR 2nd GEAR
(21) B+ WITH TRANSAXLE IN 2nd OR 3rd GEAR

93B78171

Courtesy of General Motors Corp.

Fig. 10: PCM Connector C2 Terminal Pin Voltages (Prizm VIN 8, 1.8L DOHC)

1994 ENGINE PERFORMANCE
Pin Voltage Charts (Cont.)

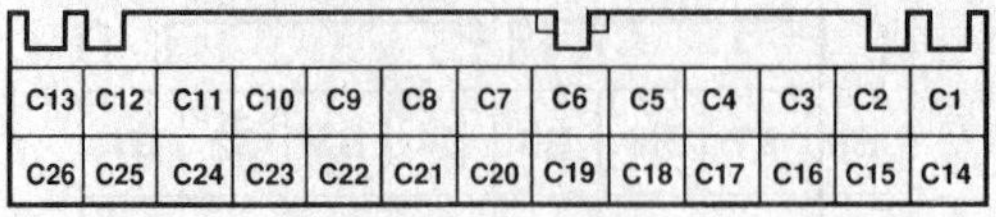

BACK VIEW OF PCM CONNECTOR C3 (GRAY)

CAVITY/ PIN	WIRE COLOR	CIRCUIT	VOLTAGE	
			KEY "ON"	ENG. RUN
1/C1	BLU/YEL	TCC SOLENOID CONTROL (A/T ONLY)	0*	0* (19)
2/C2	BLK (M/T)	CRANK SIGNAL (M/T ONLY)	0* (6)	0* (6)
	PPL (A/T)	SHIFT SOLENOID NO. 1 CONTROL (A/T ONLY)	0*	B+ (20)
3/C3	BLK/YEL	IGNITION FAIL-SAFE SIGNAL INPUT	.56V	1.5V
4/C4	BLK	CRANK ANGLE INPUT HIGH	.69V	.69V
5/C5	RED (M/T)	CAMSHAFT POSITION INPUT HIGH (M/T ONLY)	.69V	.69V
	GRN (A/T)	CAMSHAFT POSITION INPUT LOW (A/T ONLY)	.69V	.69V
6/C6	LT GRN/RED	2 POSITION SIGNAL (A/T ONLY)	0* (15)	0* (15)
7/C7	—	NOT USED	—	—
8/C8	—	NOT USED	—	—
9/C9	BLK/WHT	IAC VALVE CLOSE CONTROL	.3-.7V	5-7V
10/C10	BLK/BLU	IAC VALVE OPEN CONTROL	B+	8-10V
11/C11	BLK/RED	FUEL INJECTOR NO. 2 AND NO. 4 CONTROL (A/T ONLY)	B+	B+
12/C12	BLK	FUEL INJECTOR NO. 1 AND NO. 3 CONTROL	B+	B+
13/C13	BRN	GROUND	0*	0*
14/C14	BRN	O2S GROUND (A/T ONLY)	0*	0*
15/C15	BRN (M/T)	GROUND (M/T ONLY)	0*	0*
	BRN/YEL (A/T)	SHIFT SOLENOID NO. 2 CONTROL (A/T ONLY)	0*	0* (21)
16/C16	BLK/RED	EGR SV VALVE CONTROL (CALIFORNIA M/T ONLY)	B+	B+
17/C17	WHT	CRANK ANGLE INPUT LOW	.69V	.69V
18/C18	GRN (M/T)	CAMSHAFT POSITION INPUT LOW (M/T ONLY)	.69V	.69V
	RED (A/T)	CAMSHAFT POSITION INPUT HIGH (A/T ONLY)	.69V	.69V
19/C19	LT GRN	L POSITION SIGNAL (A/T ONLY)	0* (16)	0* (16)
20/C20	BLK	IGNITION SIGNAL (A/T ONLY)	0*	0-2V (13)
21/C21	WHT/RED	A/C SV VALVE CONTROL (A/T ONLY)	B+	B+ (5)
22/C22	BLK (M/T)	IGNITION SIGNAL (M/T ONLY)	0*	0-2V (13)
	RED/BLK (A/T)	R POSITION SIGNAL (A/T ONLY)	0* (17)	0* (17)
23/C23	WHT/RED (M/T)	A/C SV VALVE CONTROL (M/T ONLY)	B+	B+(5)
	BLK/RED (A/T)	EGR SV VALVE CONTROL (CALIFORNIA A/T ONLY)	B+	B+
24/C24	BRN	O2S GROUND (M/T ONLY)	0*	0*
25/C25	BLK/RED	FUEL INJECTOR NO. 2 AND NO. 4 CONTROL (M/T ONLY)	B+	B+
26/C26	BRN	GROUND	0*	0*

0* LESS THAN 0.50 VOLTS
(1) B+ WITH LIGHT/TURN SIGNAL SWITCH IN PARK OR HEAD OR WITH DEFOGGER ON
(2) B+ WITH BRAKE PEDAL DEPRESSED
(3) 0 VOLTS WITH OVERDRIVE SWITCH RELEASED; B+ WITH OVERDRIVE SWITCH DEPRESSED
(4) VARIES FROM 0 TO 5V WITH FRONT WHEELS ROTATING
(5) 0 VOLTS WITH A/C SWITCH DEPRESSED

(6) B+ WITH IGNITION SWITCH IN "START"
(7) 0 VOLTS FOR 3 SECONDS, THEN B+
(8) 5 TO 6 VOLTS WITH A/C SWITCH DEPRESSED
(9) 0 VOLTS IN "P" OR "N"; B+ IN "R", "D", "2" OR "L"
(10) VARIES WITH INTAKE AIR TEMPERATURE
(11) VARIES WITH ENGINE COOLANT TEMPERATURE
(12) VARIES WITH EXHAUST GAS TEMPERATURE
(13) VARIES WITH THROTTLE LEVER POSITION
(14) 0 VOLTS AT IDLE; B+ OFF IDLE

(15) B+ WITH MANUAL SELECTOR LEVER IN "2"
(16) B+ WITH MANUAL SELECTOR LEVER IN "L"
(17) B+ WITH MANUAL SELECTOR LEVER IN "R"
(18) VARIES CONSTANTLY WITH SYSTEM IN CLOSED LOOP
(19) B+ WITH VEHICLE IN TCC LOCKUP CONDITION
(20) B+ WITH TRANSAXLE IN 1st OR 2nd GEAR
(21) B+ WITH TRANSAXLE IN 2nd OR 3rd GEAR

93C78172

Fig. 11: PCM Connector C3 Terminal Pin Voltages (Prizm VIN 8, 1.8L DOHC)

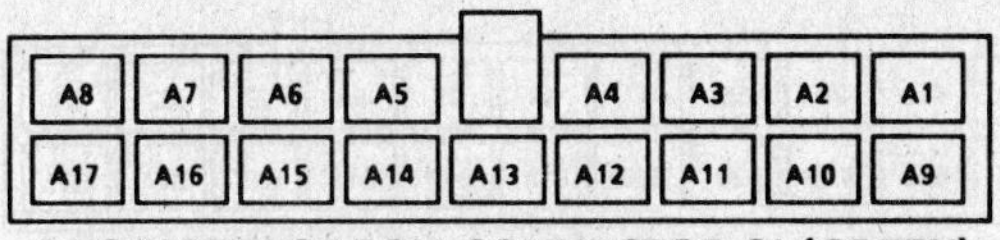

BACK VIEW OF ECM CONNECTOR C1 (GREEN)

Connector pins (top row, left to right): A8, A7, A6, A5, A4, A3, A2, A1

Connector pins (bottom row, left to right): A17, A16, A15, A14, A13, A12, A11, A10, A9

CAVITY/ PIN	WIRE COLOR	CIRCUIT	VOLTAGE KEY "ON"	VOLTAGE ENG. RUN
1/A1	BLU/BLK	IGNITION POWER INPUT	B +	B +
2/A2	BLK/GRN	GROUND	0*	0*
3/A3	—	NOT USED	—	—
4/A4	—	NOT USED	—	—
5/A5	LT GRN/ YEL	EGR SOLENOID VACUUM VALVE CONTROL	B +	B +
6/A6	LT GRN/ BLK	IAC VALVE CONTROL	B +	B +
7/A7	BLU/BLK	IGNITION POWER INPUT	B +	B +
8/A8	RED	FUEL INJECTOR POWER OUTPUT	0*	B +
9/A9	WHT	MEMORY POWER INPUT	B +	B +
10/A10	BLK/BLU	GROUND	0*	0*
11/A11	BLK/YEL	CRANK SIGNAL	0* (1)	0*
12/A12	BLK/RED	PARK/NEUTRAL SIGNAL (AUTOMATIC TRANSMISSION)	0* (2)	0* (2)
13/A13	PPL/YEL	MALFUNCTION INDICATOR LAMP (MIL) CONTROL	0*	B +
14/A14	LT GRN/ WHT	THROTTLE OPENER SOLENOID VACUUM VALVE CONTROL	B +	B +
15/A15	BLU	MAIN RELAY CONTROL	0.8V	0.8V
16/A16	PNK	FUEL PUMP RELAY CONTROL	B + (3)	0*
17/A17	YEL	FUEL INJECTOR CONTROL	0*	B +

*   Less than .5 volts.
(1) B + while cranking.
(2) B + in R, D, L, 2.
(3) 0V for 3 seconds.
(4) 0V with A/C "ON."
(5) 0V with wheels cramped.
(6) 0V with purge "ON."
(7) 5V off idle.
(8) Varies with vehicle speed.
(9) Varies with temperature.
(10) Varies with engine load.

94F44367

Courtesy of General Motors Corp.

Fig. 12: ECM Connector C1 Terminal Pin Voltages (Tracker – TBI Federal)

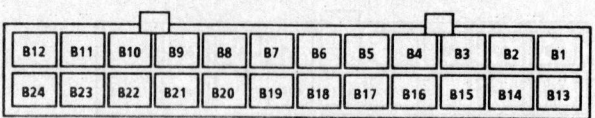

BACK VIEW OF ECM CONNECTOR C2 (YELLOW)

CAVITY/ PIN	WIRE COLOR	CIRCUIT	VOLTAGE	
			KEY "ON"	ENG. RUN
1/B1	BRN	IGNITION SIGNAL (TACHOMETER)	B +	B +
2/B2	YEL/BLK	A/C ON SIGNAL	B +	B + (4)
3/B3	BLU/YEL	DIAGNOSTIC REQUEST SIGNAL	B +	B +
4/B4	BLK/GRN	GROUND SIGNAL	0*	0*
5/B5	—	NOT USED	—	—
6/B6	BLU/ORN	POWER STEERING PRESSURE SIGNAL	B + (5)	B + (5)
7/B7	BLU/RED	TEST SWITCH SIGNAL	B +	B +
8/B8	LT GRN/ RED	EVAP SOLENOID PURGE VALVE CONTROL	B +	B + (6)
9/B9	PPL	DUTY CHECK OUTPUT	0*	0*
10/B10	—	NOT USED	—	—
11/B11	WHT/YEL	TCC RELAY CONTROL (AUTOMATIC TRANSMISSION)	B +	B +
12/B12	ORN	IGNITER DRIVER OUTPUT	0*	.2-.4V
13/B13	WHT	CRANK ANGLE INPUT	0*	1-2V
14/B14	BLU/WHT	IDLE SWITCH SIGNAL	5V	0*(7)
15/B15	YEL	VEHICLE SPEED INPUT	0-5V (8)	0-5V (8)
16/B16	RED/GRN	EGR TEMPERATURE INPUT	3-4.5V (9)	3-4.5V (9)
17/B17	RED/BLK	IAT INPUT	.5-3V (9)	.5-3V (9)
18/B18	RED/YEL	ECT INPUT	.5-3V (9)	.5-3V (9)
19/B19	YEL/BLU	EXHAUST OXYGEN CONCENTRATION INPUT	0*	0-.9V VARIES
20/B20	PPL/GRN	SERIAL DATA OUTPUT	5V	5V
21/B21	GRA	THROTTLE POSITION INPUT	.6-1.5V	.6-1.5V
22/B22	GRA/GRN	MAP INPUT	3-4V	1-5V (10)
23/B23	GRA/RED	REFERENCE VOLTAGE	5V	5V
24/B24	GRA/YEL	SENSOR GROUND	0*	0*

    *   Less than .5 volts.
 (1) B + while cranking.   (6) 0V with purge "ON."
 (2) B + in R, D, L, 2.   (7) 5V off idle.
 (3) 0V for 3 seconds.   (8) Varies with vehicle speed.
 (4) 0V with A/C "ON."   (9) Varies with temperature.
 (5) 0V with wheels cramped. (10) Varies with engine load.

94G44368

Fig. 13: ECM Connector C2 Terminal Pin Voltages (Tracker – TBI Federal)

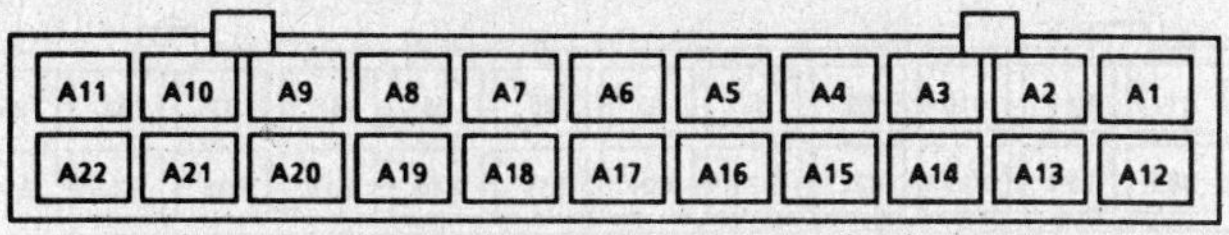

| A11 | A10 | A9 | A8 | A7 | A6 | A5 | A4 | A3 | A2 | A1 |
| A22 | A21 | A20 | A19 | A18 | A17 | A16 | A15 | A14 | A13 | A12 |

BACK VIEW OF ECM CONNECTOR C1 (YELLOW)

CAVITY/ PIN	WIRE COLOR	CIRCUIT	VOLTAGE	
			KEY "ON"	ENG. RUN
A1	WHT	MEMORY POWER	B +	B +
A2	BLK/YEL	CRANK SIGNAL	0* (1)	0* (1)
A3	PPL	DUTY CHECK OUTPUT	0	0
A4	ORN	IGNITER DRIVER OUTPUT	0	.5-2.0V (5)
A5	PNK	FUEL PUMP RELAY CONTROL	(2)	0*
A6	BLU/RED	TEST SWITCH SIGNAL	B +	B +
A7	YEL	VSS INPUT	(3)	(3)
A8	BRN	IGNITION SIGNAL (TACHOMETER)	B +	B +
A9	YEL/BLK	A/C ON SIGNAL	B +	B + (4)
A10	BLU	MAIN RELAY CONTROL	0*	0*
A11	—	NOT USED	—	—
A12	BLU/BLK	IGNITION POWER	B +	B +
A13	BLU/BLK	IGNITION POWER	B +	B +
A14	PPL/YEL	MIL CONTROL	0*	B +
A15	LT.GRN/ WHT	EGR SV VALVE CONTROL	B +	B + (10)
A16	WHT/YEL	TCC RELAY CONTROL (AUTOMATIC TRANSMISSION ONLY)	B +	B + (6)
A17	BLU/YEL	DIAGNOSTIC REQUEST SIGNAL	B +	B +
A18	BLU/WHT	IDLE SWITCH SIGNAL	0* (7)	0* (7)
A19	BLU/ORN	POWER STEERING PRESSURE SIGNAL	B + (8)	B + (8)
A20	—	NOT USED	—	—
A21	—	NOT USED	—	—
A22	BLK/RED	PARK/NEUTRAL SIGNAL (AUTOMATIC TRANSMISSION ONLY)	0* (9)	0* (9)

*   LESS THAN 0.5 VOLTS
(1) B + WITH IGNITION SWITCH IN "START"
(2) 0 VOLTS FOR 3 SECONDS, THEN B +
(3) VARIES BETWEEN 0-5 VOLTS WITH DRIVE WHEELS ROTATING
(4) 0 VOLTS WITH A/C ON
(5) VARIES WITH ENGINE RPM

(6) 0 VOLTS WITH TRANSMISSION IN GEAR, WITH VEHICLE SPEED AT 67 KM/H (42 MPH) ON FLAT SURFACE FOR 4 SECONDS OR MORE
(7) 4-6 VOLTS OFF IDLE
(8) 0 VOLTS WITH WHEELS CRAMPED
(9) B + WITH SELECTOR LEVER IN "R", "D", "2" or "L".
(10) WITH COLD ENGINE AT IDLE

94H44369

Courtesy of General Motors Corp.

Fig. 14: ECM Connector C1 Terminal Pin Voltages (Tracker – MFI Calif. & New York)

1994 ENGINE PERFORMANCE
Pin Voltage Charts (Cont.)

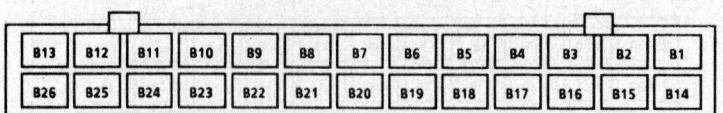

BACKVIEW OF ECM CONNECTOR C2 (YELLOW)

CAVITY/PIN	WIRE COLOR	CIRCUIT	VOLTAGE KEY "ON"	VOLTAGE ENG. RUN
B1	BLK/BLU	ECM GROUND-G110	0*	0*
B2	BLK	ECM GROUND-G110	0*	0*
B3	WHT	CMP SENSOR INPUT	5V	2.2V
B4	—	NOT USED	—	—
B5	—	NOT USED	—	—
B6	GRA/RED	REFERENCE VOLTAGE (5V)	4-6V	4-6V
B7	GRA	THROTTLE POSITION INPUT	.5-4.0V (5)	.5-4.0V (5)
B8	GRA/BLK	MAF INPUT	1.3V	2-3.1V (5)
B9	RED/YEL	ECT INPUT	.9V (10)	(10)
B10	—	NOT USED	—	—
B11	RED	FUEL INJECTOR #1 CONTROL	B +	B +
B12	LT. GRN/BLK	IAC VALVE CONTROL	B +	B + -0V (5)
B13	WHT/GRN	FUEL INJECTOR #3 CONTROL	B +	B +
B14	BLK/GRN	ECM GROUND-G110	0*	0*

CAVITY/PIN	WIRE COLOR	CIRCUIT	VOLTAGE KEY "ON"	VOLTAGE ENG. RUN
B15	GRA/YEL	SENSOR GROUND	0*	0*
B16	PPL/GRN	SERIAL DATA OUTPUT	4-6V	4-6V
B17	RED/GRN	EGR TEMPERATURE INPUT	3.5V (11)	(11)
B18	—	NOT USED	—	—
B19	—	NOT USED	—	—
B20	YEL/BLU	EXHAUST OXYGEN CONCENTRATION INPUT	0	.1-.9V
B21	RED/BLK	IAT INPUT	(12)	(12)
B22	—	NOT USED	—	—
B23	PNK	HO2S HEATER CONTROL	B +	0*
B24	LT.GRN/RED	FUEL INJECTOR #2 CONTROL	B +	B +
B25	LT.GRN/YEL	EVAP SP VALVE CONTROL	B +	B +
B26	WHT/BLK	FUEL INJECTOR #4 CONTROL	B +	B +

*   LESS THAN 0.5 VOLTS
(1) B + WITH IGNITION SWITCH IN "START"
(2) 0 VOLTS FOR 3 SECONDS, THEN B +
(3) VARIES BETWEEN 0-5 VOLTS WITH DRIVE WHEELS ROTATING
(4) 0 VOLTS WITH A/C ON
(5) VARIES WITH THROTTLE POSITION
(6) 0 VOLTS WITH TRANSMISSION IN GEAR, WITH VEHICLE SPEED AT 67 KM/H (42 MPH) ON FLAT SURFACE FOR 4 SECONDS OR MORE

(7) 4-6 VOLTS OFF IDLE
(8) 0 VOLTS WITH WHEELS CRAMPED
(9) B + WITH MANUAL SELECTOR LEVER IN "R", "D", "2" OR "L"
(10) VARIES WITH ENGINE COOLANT TEMPERATURE
(11) VARIES WITH EXHAUST GAS TEMPERATURE
(12) VARIES WITH AMBIENT TEMPERATURE

94A44370

Fig. 15: ECM Connector C2 Terminal Pin Voltages (Tracker – MFI Calif. & New York)

Metro, Prizm, Tracker

INTRODUCTION

Sensor operating range information can help determine if a sensor is out of calibration. An out-of-calibration sensor may not set a trouble code, but it may cause driveability problems.

NOTE: Unless stated otherwise in test procedure, perform all voltage tests using a Digital Volt-Ohmmeter (DVOM) with a minimum 10-megohm input impedance.

ENGINE COOLANT TEMPERATURE (ECT) SENSOR RESISTANCE

Temperature – °F (°C)	Ohms
Metro & Tracker	
0 (–18)	14,650
19 (–7)	8100
39 (4)	4780
70 (21)	2350
100 (38)	1250
160 (71)	400
210 (99)	190
Prizm & Prizm LSi	
–4 (–20)	10,000-20,000
32 (0)	4000-7000
68 (20)	2000-3000
104 (40)	900-1300
140 (60)	400-700
176 (80)	200-400

EGR TEMPERATURE SENSOR RESISTANCE

Temperature – °F (°C)	Ohms
Prizm & Prizm LSi	
122 (50)	69,000-88,000
212 (100)	11,000-15,000
302 (150)	2000-4000
Tracker	
68 (20)	214,000-313,800
104 (40)	90,900-125,700
140 (60)	42,100-55,500
176 (80)	21,100-26,500
212 (100)	11,200-13,600

INTAKE AIR TEMPERATURE (IAT) SENSOR RESISTANCE

Temperature – °F (°C)	Ohms
Metro	
0 (–18)	14,650
19 (–7)	8100
39 (4)	4780
70 (21)	2350
100 (38)	1250
160 (71)	400
210 (99)	190
Prizm & Prizm LSi	
–4 (–20)	10,000-20,000
32 (0)	4000-7000
68 (20)	2000-3000
104 (40)	900-1300
140 (60)	400-700
176 (80)	200-400
Tracker	
0 (–18)	14,800
19 (–7)	8250
39 (4)	5200
70 (21)	2500
100 (38)	1300
160 (71)	450
210 (99)	200

Manifold Absolute Pressure (MAP) Sensor – For information on MAP sensor, see ENGINE SENSORS & SWITCHES in SYSTEM & COMPONENT TESTING article.

OXYGEN SENSOR HEATER RESISTANCE

Application	Ohms
Metro (Upgraded Emissions)	[1]
Tracker	
MFI (Calif. & New York)	[2] 11.7-14.3
TBI (Federal)	[3] 3.0-5.5

[1] – A low resistance should be present.
[2] – With temperature of 68°F (20°C).
[3] – With temperature of 73°F (23°C).

THROTTLE POSITION (TP) SENSOR RESISTANCE

Application	Ohms
Metro (Standard Emissions)	
Between Terminals 1 & 2 [1]	0-5000
Between Terminals 1 & 2 [2]	Infinity
Between Terminals 1 & 2 [3]	0-5000
Between Terminals 1 & 3 [3]	240-1140
Between Terminals 1 & 3 [4]	3170-6600
Between Terminals 1 & 4	4370-8130
Metro (Upgraded Emissions)	[5]
Prizm & Prizm LSi	
Between Terminals E2 & IDL [6]	0-2300
Between Terminals E2 & IDL [2]	Infinity
Between Terminals E2 & VC	4000-8500
Between Terminals E2 & VTA [7]	200-6000
Between Terminals E2 & VTA [4]	3300-10,000
Tracker (TBI – Federal)	
Between Terminals 2 & 4	3500-6500
Between Terminals 3 & 4 [1]	0-500
Between Terminals 3 & 4 [8]	Infinity
Between Terminals 4 & 5 [3]	300-2000
Between Terminals 4 & 5 [4]	2000-6500
Tracker (MFI – Calif. & New York)	
Between Terminals 1 & 3	3500-6500
Between Terminals 1 & 2 [9]	0-500
Between Terminals 1 & 2 [10]	Infinity
Between Terminals 1 & 4 [3]	300-2000
Between Terminals 1 & 4 [4]	2000-6500

[1] – With .012" (.30 mm) feeler gauge installed between throttle stop screw and lever.
[2] – With .035" (.89 mm) feeler gauge installed between throttle stop screw and lever.
[3] – Throttle valve at idle position.
[4] – Throttle valve at fully open position.
[5] – For information on TP sensor, see THROTTLE POSITION (TP) SENSOR in ON-VEHICLE ADJUSTMENTS article.
[6] – With .016" (.40 mm) feeler gauge installed between throttle stop screw and lever.
[7] – With zero clearance between throttle stop screw and lever.
[8] – With .022" (.56 mm) feeler gauge installed between throttle stop screw and lever.
[9] – With .020" (.50 mm) feeler gauge installed between throttle stop screw and lever.
[10] – With .031" (.80 mm) feeler gauge installed between throttle stop screw and lever.

Vehicle Speed Sensor – For information on vehicle speed sensor, see ENGINE SENSORS & SWITCHES in SYSTEM & COMPONENT TESTING article.

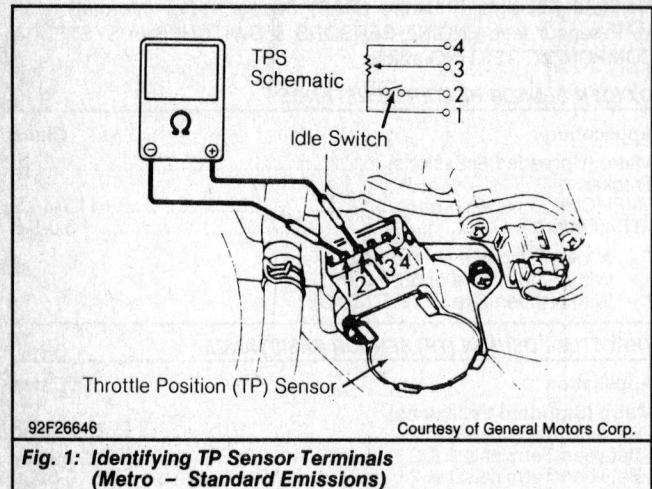

Fig. 1: Identifying TP Sensor Terminals (Metro – Standard Emissions)

92F26646   Courtesy of General Motors Corp.

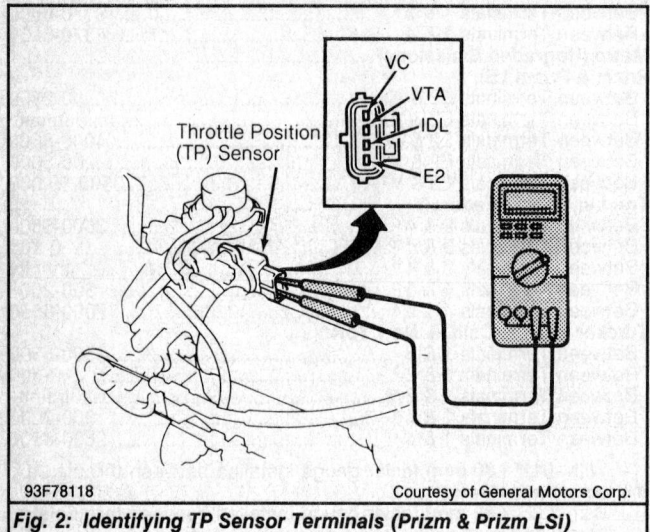

Fig. 2: Identifying TP Sensor Terminals (Prizm & Prizm LSi)

93F78118   Courtesy of General Motors Corp.

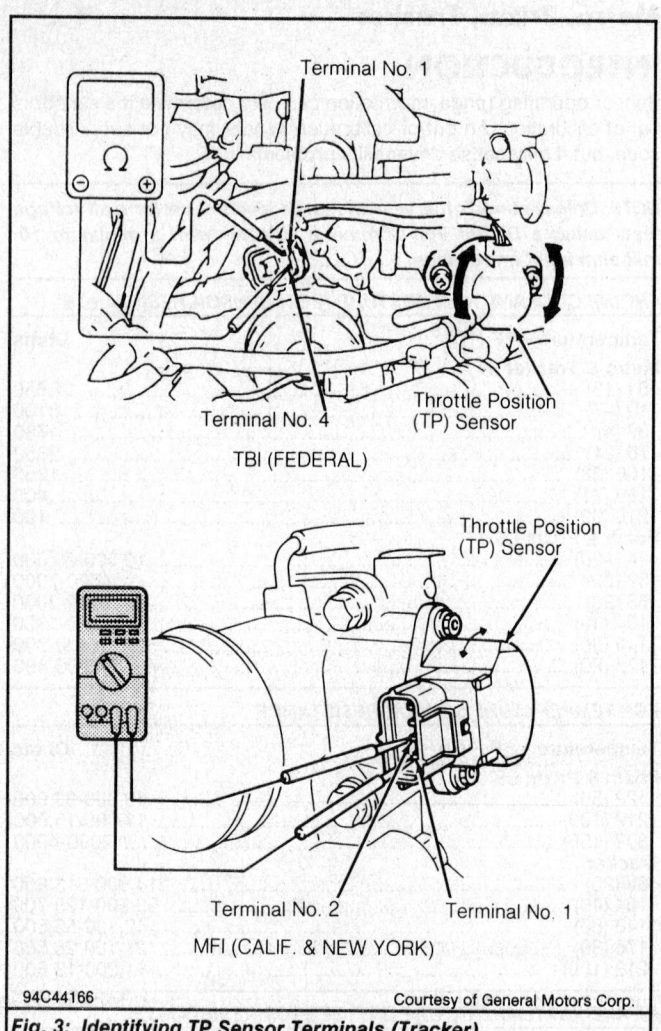

Fig. 3: Identifying TP Sensor Terminals (Tracker)

94C44166   Courtesy of General Motors Corp.

Metro, Prizm, Tracker

INTRODUCTION

This article contains underhood views of vacuum hose routing diagrams. Vacuum hose routing diagrams are located next to Vehicle Emission Control Information Label located in the engine compartment. Use vacuum hose routing diagrams during visual inspection in BASIC DIAGNOSTIC PROCEDURES article. This will assist in identifying improperly routed vacuum hoses which may cause driveability and/or computer-indicated malfunctions.

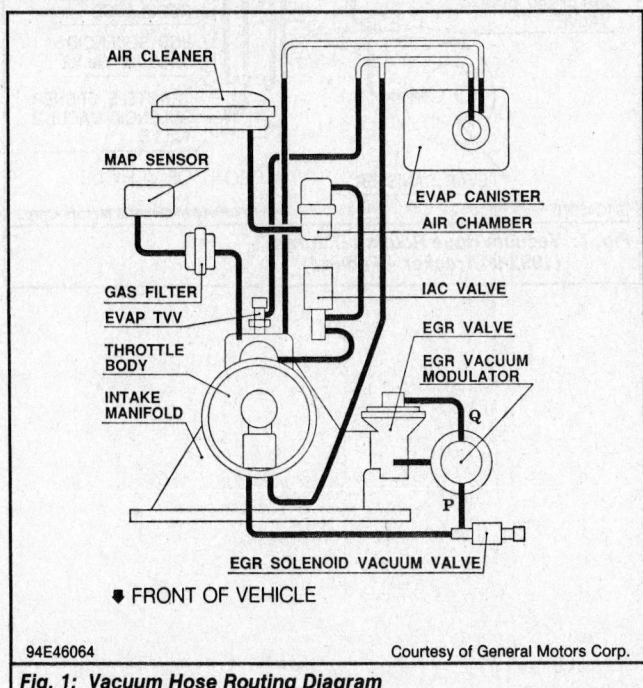

94E46064   Courtesy of General Motors Corp.

Fig. 1: Vacuum Hose Routing Diagram (1993 Metro – California; 1994 Metro – Standard Federal)

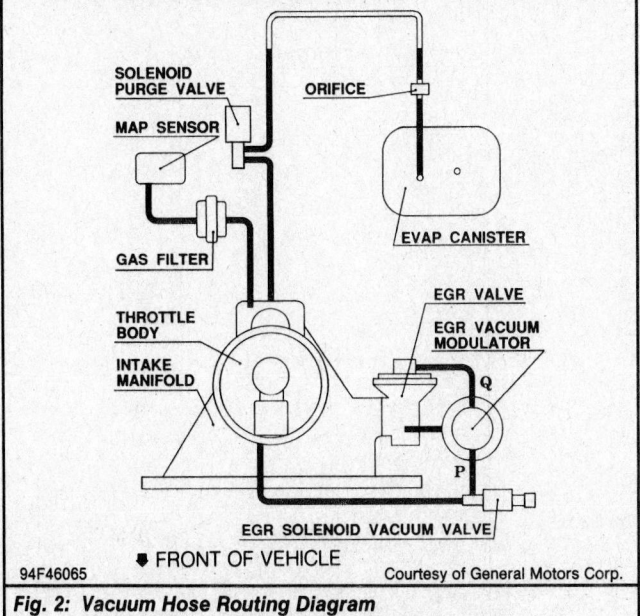

94F46065   Courtesy of General Motors Corp.

Fig. 2: Vacuum Hose Routing Diagram (1994 Metro – California & Upgraded Federal)

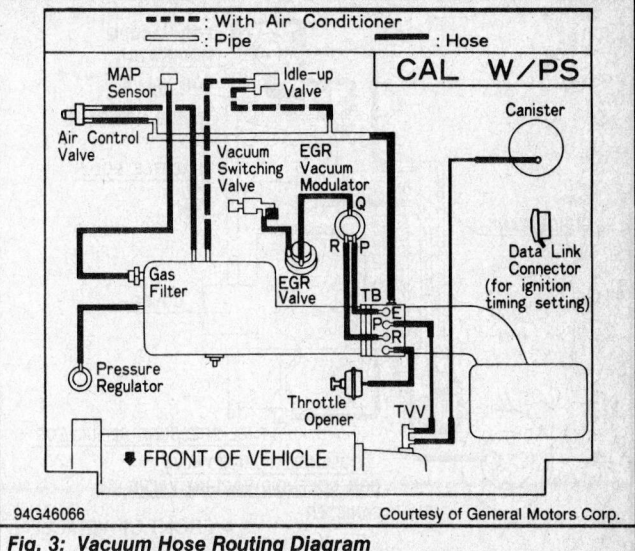

94G46066   Courtesy of General Motors Corp.

Fig. 3: Vacuum Hose Routing Diagram (1994 Prizm – California With Variable Ratio P/S)

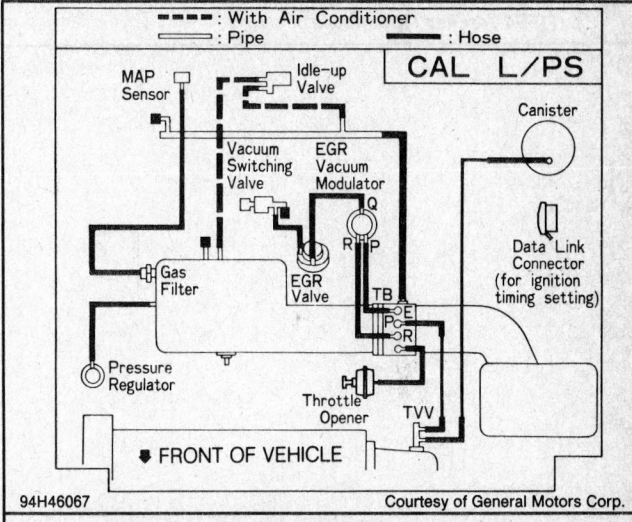

94H46067   Courtesy of General Motors Corp.

Fig. 4: Vacuum Hose Routing Diagram (1994 Prizm – California Except Variable Ratio P/S)

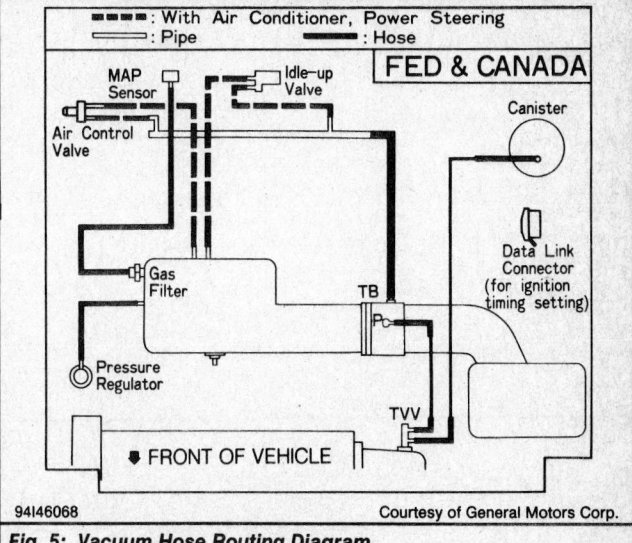

94I46068   Courtesy of General Motors Corp.

Fig. 5: Vacuum Hose Routing Diagram (1993-94 Prizm – Federal)

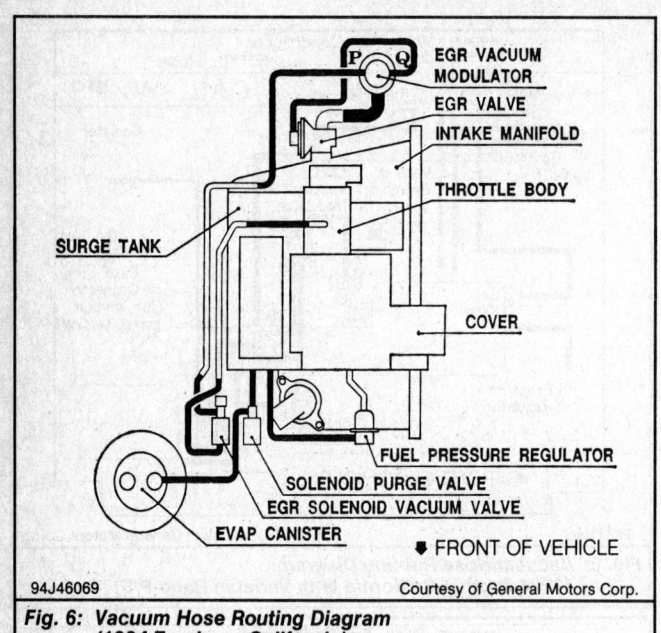

EGR VACUUM MODULATOR
EGR VALVE
INTAKE MANIFOLD
THROTTLE BODY
COVER
SURGE TANK
FUEL PRESSURE REGULATOR
SOLENOID PURGE VALVE
EGR SOLENOID VACUUM VALVE
EVAP CANISTER
⬇ FRONT OF VEHICLE

94J46069   Courtesy of General Motors Corp.

*Fig. 6: Vacuum Hose Routing Diagram
(1994 Tracker – California)*

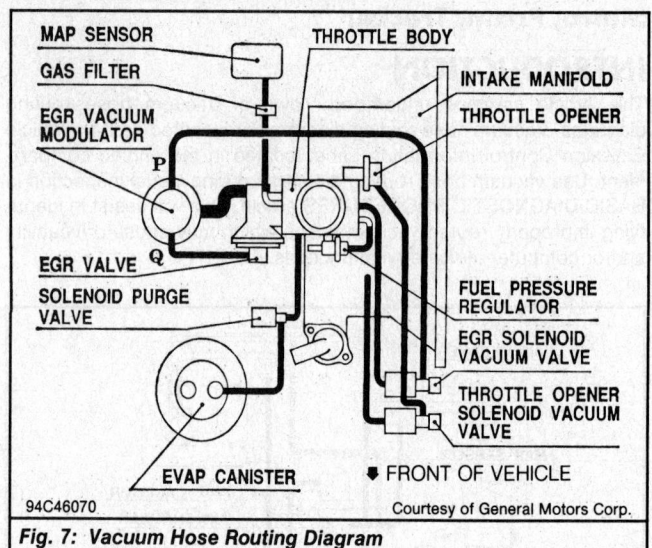

MAP SENSOR
GAS FILTER
THROTTLE BODY
EGR VACUUM MODULATOR
INTAKE MANIFOLD
THROTTLE OPENER
EGR VALVE
SOLENOID PURGE VALVE
FUEL PRESSURE REGULATOR
EGR SOLENOID VACUUM VALVE
THROTTLE OPENER SOLENOID VACUUM VALVE
EVAP CANISTER
⬇ FRONT OF VEHICLE

94C46070   Courtesy of General Motors Corp.

*Fig. 7: Vacuum Hose Routing Diagram
(1993-94 Tracker – Federal)*

Metro, Prizm, Tracker

INTRODUCTION

Removal, overhaul and installation procedures are covered in this article. If component removal and installation is primarily an unbolt and bolt on procedure, only a torque specification may be furnished.

CAUTION: When battery is disconnected, vehicle computer and memory systems may lose memory data. Driveability problems may exist until computer systems have completed a relearn cycle. See COMPUTER RELEARN PROCEDURES article in GENERAL INFORMATION before disconnecting battery.

IGNITION SYSTEM

DISTRIBUTOR

Removal & Installation – 1) Disconnect negative battery cable. Remove distributor cap. *See Figs. 1-3.* Mark distributor-to-engine position and distributor rotor-to-distributor housing position for installation reference. Remove distributor harness connector and hold-down bolt. Remove distributor.

2) DO NOT rotate crankshaft with distributor removed, or reference marks will be incorrect. To install distributor, use reference marks and reverse removal procedure.

Installing Distributor After Engine Has Been Rotated – 1) Rotate crankshaft until No. 1 piston is at TDC on compression stroke. Ensure timing marks on crankshaft pulley and timing cover are aligned to TDC position.

2) Align distributor drive mark with housing mark, or turn distributor rotor to No. 1 spark plug terminal on cap and install distributor. Start engine and set timing to specification. See IGNITION TIMING in ON-VEHICLE ADJUSTMENTS article.

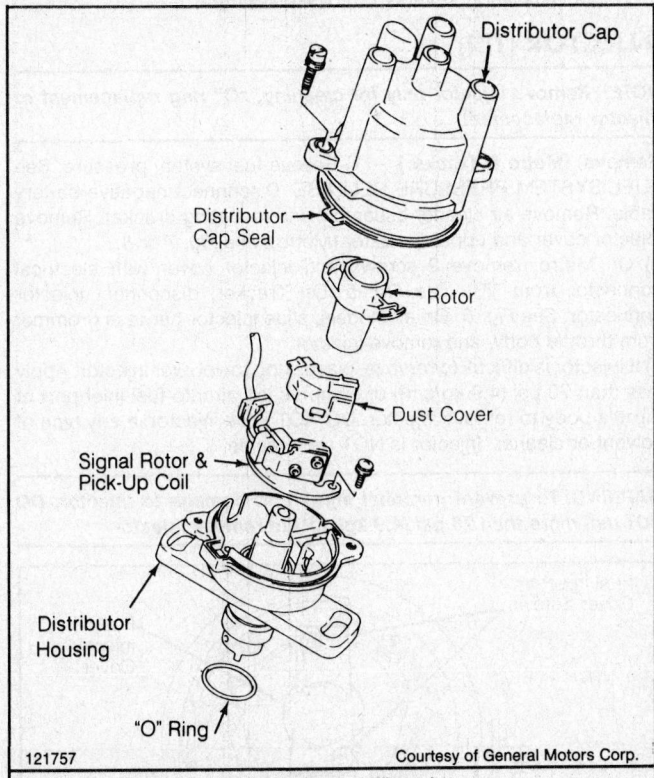

Fig. 1: Exploded View Of Distributor (Metro)

PICK-UP COIL/CAMSHAFT POSITION SENSOR

NOTE: *On Tracker, distributor housing components are not serviced separately. Distributor housing components must be serviced as a complete assembly. See Fig. 3.*

Removal & Installation (Metro & Prizm) – Remove distributor cap and rotor. Remove screws holding pick-up coil/Camshaft Position (CMP) sensor to base plate. Disconnect pick-up coil/CMP sensor connector, and remove pick-up coil/CMP sensor. To install, reverse removal procedure. Adjust air gap to specification. See PICK-UP COIL/CAMSHAFT POSITION SENSOR AIR GAP table.

PICK-UP COIL/CAMSHAFT POSITION SENSOR AIR GAP

Application	Clearance In. (mm)
Metro & Prizm	.008-.016 (.20-.41)

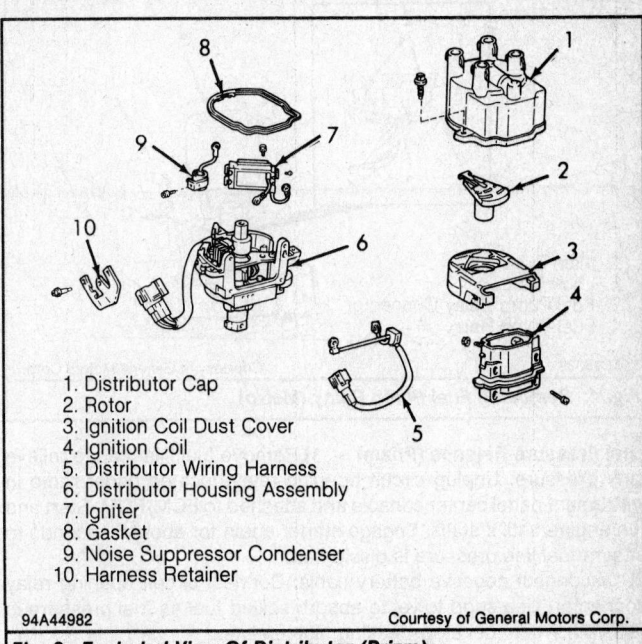

1. Distributor Cap
2. Rotor
3. Ignition Coil Dust Cover
4. Ignition Coil
5. Distributor Wiring Harness
6. Distributor Housing Assembly
7. Igniter
8. Gasket
9. Noise Suppressor Condenser
10. Harness Retainer

94A44982   Courtesy of General Motors Corp.

Fig. 2: Exploded View Of Distributor (Prizm)

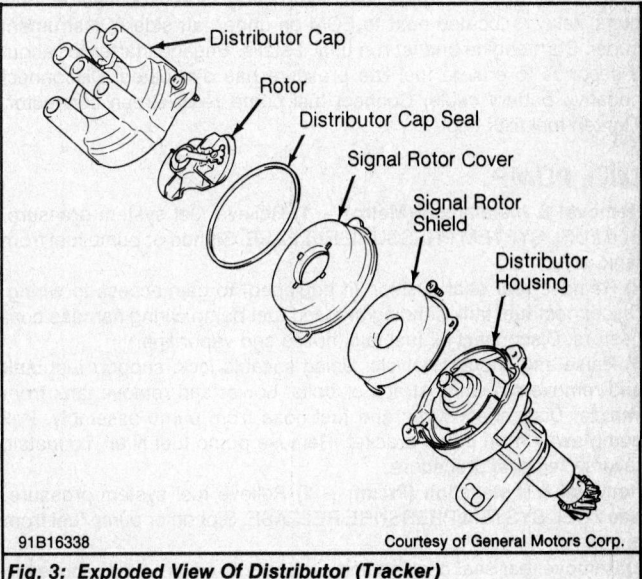

91B16338   Courtesy of General Motors Corp.

Fig. 3: Exploded View Of Distributor (Tracker)

FUEL SYSTEM

WARNING: ALWAYS relieve fuel pressure before disconnecting any fuel injection-related component. DO NOT allow fuel to contact engine or electrical components.

FUEL SYSTEM PRESSURE RELEASE

Fuel Pressure Release (Metro) – 1) Remove main fuse box cover and engine coolant reservoir from bracket. Remove main fuse box attaching screws. From underneath fuse box, release 2 locking tabs of fuel pump relay. See Fig. 4.

2) Disengage fuel pump relay from fuse box, and remove harness connector. Loosen fuel filler cap to relieve tank pressure. Start engine and idle until engine dies. Engage starter again for about 3 seconds to ensure fuel line pressure is dissipated. Turn ignition off. Install fuel pump relay and tighten fuel filler cap.

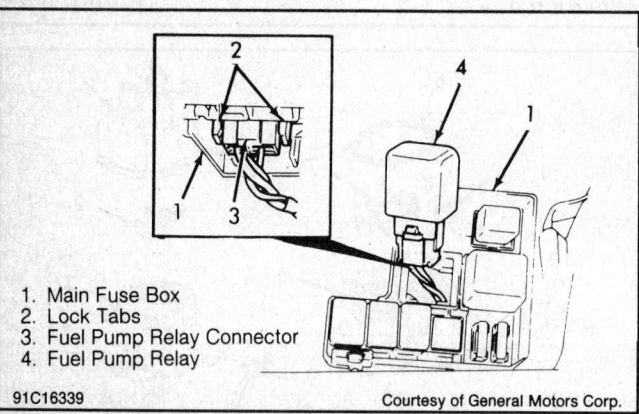

1. Main Fuse Box
2. Lock Tabs
3. Fuel Pump Relay Connector
4. Fuel Pump Relay

91C16339   Courtesy of General Motors Corp.

Fig. 4: Removing Fuel Pump Relay (Metro)

Fuel Pressure Release (Prizm) – 1) Remove fuel filler cap to relieve tank pressure. Unplug circuit opening relay, located under radio in instrument panel center console and attached to ECM/PCM. Start and run engine until it stalls. Engage starter again for about 3 seconds to ensure fuel line pressure is dissipated.

2) Disconnect negative battery cable. Connect circuit opening relay connector. Use shop towel to absorb spilled fuel as fuel pressure is relieved. When fuel stops leaking, tighten line.

Fuel Pressure Release (Tracker) – Remove fuel filler cap to relieve tank pressure. Disconnect fuel pump relay Green connector. Fuel pump relay is located next to ECM on under left side of instrument panel. Start engine and let run until it stalls. Engage starter for about 3 seconds to ensure fuel line pressure has dissipated. Disconnect negative battery cable. Connect fuel pump relay Green connector. Tighten fuel filler cap.

FUEL PUMP

Removal & Installation (Metro) – 1) Relieve fuel system pressure. See FUEL SYSTEM PRESSURE RELEASE. Siphon or pump fuel from tank.

2) Remove rear seat cushion (if equipped) to gain access to wiring. Disconnect fuel tank sending unit and fuel pump wiring harness connectors. Disconnect all fuel tank hoses and vapor line.

3) Raise and support vehicle. Using suitable jack, support fuel tank and remove mounting straps or bolts. Lower and remove tank from vehicle. Disconnect wires and fuel hose from pump assembly. Pull pump away from pump bracket. Remove pump fuel filter. To install, reverse removal procedure.

Removal & Installation (Prizm) – 1) Relieve fuel system pressure. See FUEL SYSTEM PRESSURE RELEASE. Siphon or pump fuel from tank.

2) Remove rear seat cushion and service hole cover to gain access to wiring and fuel hoses. Disconnect fuel tank sending unit and fuel pump wiring harness connectors. Disconnect all fuel tank hoses and vapor line.

3) Remove fuel tank sending unit through service hole. Remove fuel pump from fuel tank sending unit. To install, reverse removal procedure.

Removal & Installation (Tracker) – 1) Relieve fuel system pressure. See FUEL SYSTEM PRESSURE RELEASE. Siphon or pump fuel from tank. Raise and support vehicle. Remove crossmember from underbody. Disconnect fuel tank sending unit and fuel pump wiring harness connectors. Disconnect all fuel tank hoses and vapor line.

2) Using suitable jack, support fuel tank. Remove fuel tank mounting bolts. Lower and remove tank from vehicle. Remove fuel pump mounting bolts. Disconnect wires and fuel hose from pump assembly. Pull pump away from pump bracket. Remove pump fuel filter. To install, reverse removal procedure.

FUEL RAIL & INJECTORS (MFI)

Removal (Prizm) – 1) Clean area around injectors with carburetor cleaner and/or compressed air. Relieve fuel pressure. See FUEL SYSTEM PRESSURE RELEASE.

2) Remove PCV hoses from valve cover. Remove fuel pressure regulator, vacuum hose and fuel return hose. Disconnect injector electrical connectors. Disconnect cold start valve fuel line and fuel rail inlet line.

3) Wrap shop cloth around fuel fittings when disconnecting to collect excess fuel. Cover ends of components to keep dirt out and fuel in. Remove 2 fuel rail-to-cylinder head bolts. Remove fuel rail with injectors attached. Ensure injectors DO NOT fall out of fuel rail.

4) Remove 2 spacers from delivery pipe-to-cylinder head bolt locations. Remove insulators from injector bores. Remove "O" ring and grommet from end of each injector.

Inspection – Inspect all components for damage and replace as necessary.

NOTE: Replace injector "O" ring seals and pressure regulator when servicing injectors.

Installation – 1) Install NEW "O" ring and grommet on injectors. Lubricate new injector "O" rings with clean gasoline. Install insulators into injector bores. Install spacers at delivery pipe-to-cylinder head bolt locations.

2) Install fuel rail and tighten to specification. See TORQUE SPECIFICATIONS. Ensure injectors rotate smoothly in injector bore. If injectors are tight and will not rotate, loosen and reinstall injectors. To complete installation, reverse removal procedure.

INJECTOR (TBI)

NOTE: Remove injector only for cleaning, "O" ring replacement or injector replacement.

Removal (Metro & Tracker) – 1) Relieve fuel system pressure. See FUEL SYSTEM PRESSURE RELEASE. Disconnect negative battery cable. Remove air cleaner assembly and mounting bracket. Remove injector cover and upper insulator (Metro). See Fig. 7 or 8.

2) On Metro, remove 2 screws and injector cover with electrical connector from TBI. See Fig. 5. On Tracker, disconnect injector connector. See Fig. 6. On all models, slide injector harness grommet from throttle body, and remove injector.

3) If injector is difficult to remove, place shop towel over injector. Apply less than 70 psi (4.9 kg/cm²) of compressed air into fuel inlet port of throttle body to remove injector. DO NOT soak injector in any type of solvent or cleaner. Injector is NOT serviceable.

WARNING: To prevent personal injury and damage to injector, DO NOT use more than 70 psi (4.9 kg/cm²) to remove injector.

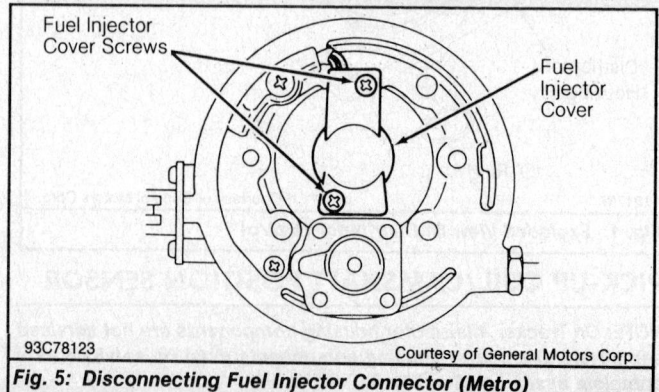

Fuel Injector Cover Screws

Fuel Injector Cover

93C78123   Courtesy of General Motors Corp.

Fig. 5: Disconnecting Fuel Injector Connector (Metro)

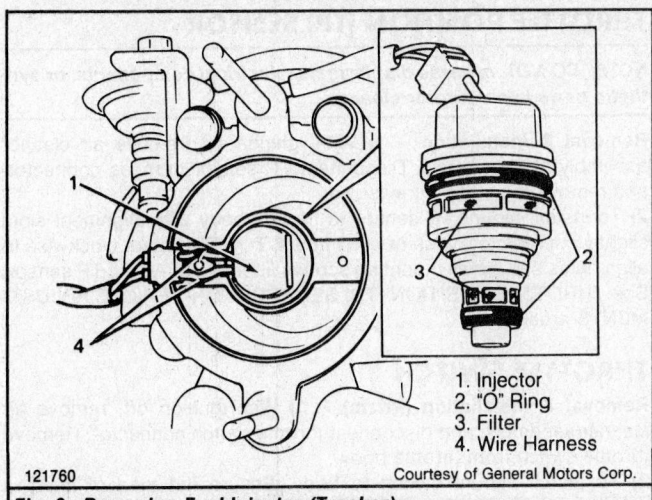

1. Injector
2. "O" Ring
3. Filter
4. Wire Harness

121760   Courtesy of General Motors Corp.

Fig. 6: Removing Fuel Injector (Tracker)

Installation – 1) Apply thin coat of fuel to NEW injector "O" rings. Install "O" rings on injector. Insert injector into throttle body. Carefully install injector wiring harness grommet to housing.

2) Install injector cover, and tighten mounting screws to specification. See TORQUE SPECIFICATIONS. To complete installation, reverse removal procedure. Pressurize fuel system, and check for leaks.

OXYGEN SENSOR (O2S)

Removal & Installation – 1) Oxygen sensor is mounted in exhaust manifold or exhaust pipe, below exhaust header. Sensor is equipped with a permanent pigtail which must be protected from damage when removing sensor. Ensure sensor is free of contaminants, but avoid using cleaning solvents of any type.

2) Sensor may be difficult to remove when engine temperature is less than 120°F (49°C). If O2S is difficult to remove, use rust penetrant to avoid possible damage to exhaust manifold threads. Discard O2S sensor if contaminated.

3) Always use anti-seize compound on threads before installing NEW sensor. New sensor comes pre-coated with anti-seize. DO NOT remove anti-seize from sensor. Tighten O2S to 30 ft. lbs. (41 N.m).

THROTTLE BODY (TBI)

Removal & Disassembly (Metro) – 1) Disconnect negative battery cable. Drain cooling system. Relieve fuel system pressure. See FUEL SYSTEM PRESSURE RELEASE.

2) Remove air cleaner assembly. Disconnect and label all wire connectors, vacuum hoses, fuel lines and cable linkages from throttle body. Unbolt and remove throttle body assembly from manifold. Remove fuel injector. See INJECTOR (TBI).

3) Disassemble throttle body except for fuel pressure regulator and air valve (these components are not serviceable). See Fig. 7. Blow out all passages with carburetor cleaner and compressed air. DO NOT immerse throttle body in water or cleaning solution, as component damage will result.

NOTE: Thoroughly clean parts with carburetor cleaner. DO NOT immerse diaphragms, electrical components, or synthetic parts in carburetor cleaner. Dry components with compressed air. Blow out all passages with compressed air. DO NOT use wire or pointed metal objects for cleaning. Inspect throttle body for cracks, warpage or scratches in sealing areas.

Reassembly & Installation – 1) To reassemble, reverse disassembly procedure. Tighten TBI body assembly screws to 31 INCH lbs. (3.5 N.m). To install, reverse removal procedure. Use new base gasket with no sealer.

2) Tighten throttle body-to-manifold bolts to 17 ft. lbs. (23 N.m). Refill cooling system. On automatic transaxle models, adjust Throttle Position (TP) sensor. See THROTTLE POSITION (TP) SENSOR in ON-VEHICLE ADJUSTMENTS article.

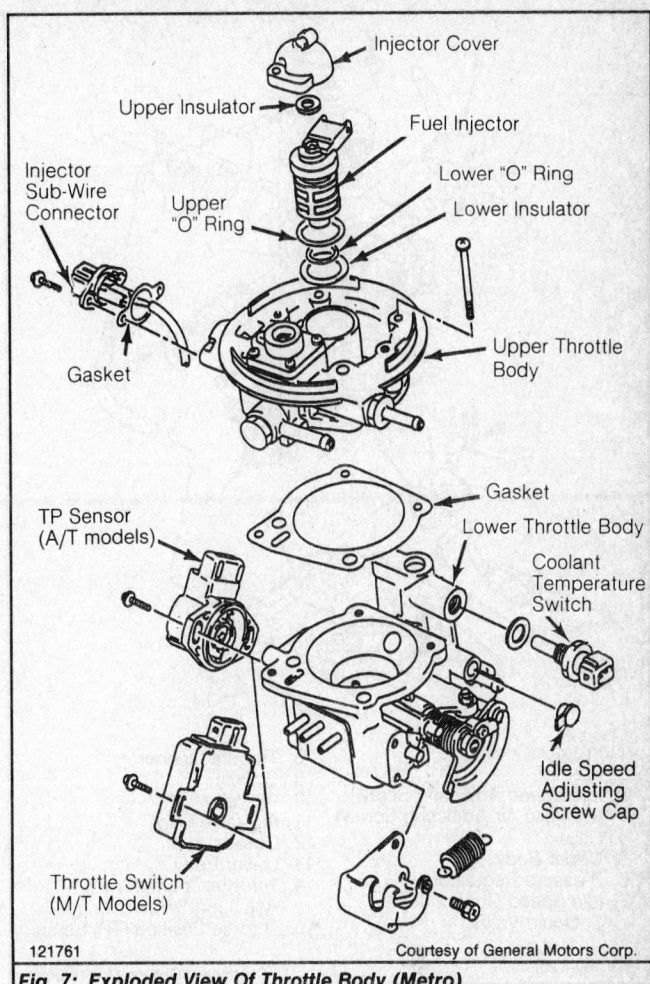

Injector Cover
Upper Insulator
Fuel Injector
Injector Sub-Wire Connector
Upper "O" Ring
Lower "O" Ring
Lower Insulator
Gasket
Upper Throttle Body
TP Sensor (A/T models)
Gasket
Lower Throttle Body
Coolant Temperature Switch
Idle Speed Adjusting Screw Cap
Throttle Switch (M/T Models)

121761   Courtesy of General Motors Corp.

Fig. 7: Exploded View Of Throttle Body (Metro)

3) On manual transaxle models, adjust throttle switch. See THROTTLE SWITCH in ON-VEHICLE ADJUSTMENTS article. Reconnect negative battery cable. Pressurize fuel system, and check for leaks.

Removal & Disassembly (Tracker) – 1) Drain cooling system. Relieve fuel pump pressure. See FUEL SYSTEM PRESSURE RELEASE. Disconnect negative battery cable. Remove air cleaner assembly and fuel lines. Disconnect and label all vacuum and coolant hoses, wire connectors and cable linkages from throttle body.

2) Remove 4 bolts retaining throttle body to intake manifold. Remove throttle body and discard gasket. Clean gasket mating surfaces. Remove fuel injector. See INJECTOR (TBI).

3) Remove Throttle Position (TP) sensor, fuel pressure regulator and Idle Speed Control (ISC) solenoid valve from throttle body. See Fig. 8. Remove attaching screws, and separate upper and lower throttle bodies.

4) DO NOT soak any electrical device or air valve in solvent or other cleaner. DO NOT use drills or wires to clean passage ways. Clean upper and lower passages with compressed air only.

Reassembly & Installation – 1) Assemble upper and lower throttle bodies with NEW gasket. Install and tighten 2 upper-to-lower throttle body attaching screws to 31 INCH lbs. (3.5 N.m). Install fuel pressure regulator with NEW "O" ring, and tighten mounting screws to 31 INCH lbs. (3.5 N.m).

2) Install ISC solenoid valve with NEW gasket, and tighten mounting screws to 31 INCH lbs. (3.5 N.m). Apply thin coat of gasoline to NEW injector "O" rings. Install "O" rings on injector. Insert injector into throttle body. Carefully install wiring harness to injector.

3) Install injector cover. Tighten screws to 31 INCH lbs. (3.5 N.m). Install TP sensor. Clamp wiring harness securely to side of throttle body. Adjust TP sensor. See THROTTLE POSITION (TP) SENSOR in ON-VEHICLE ADJUSTMENTS article. Install NEW throttle body base gasket on intake manifold. DO NOT use sealer or glue.

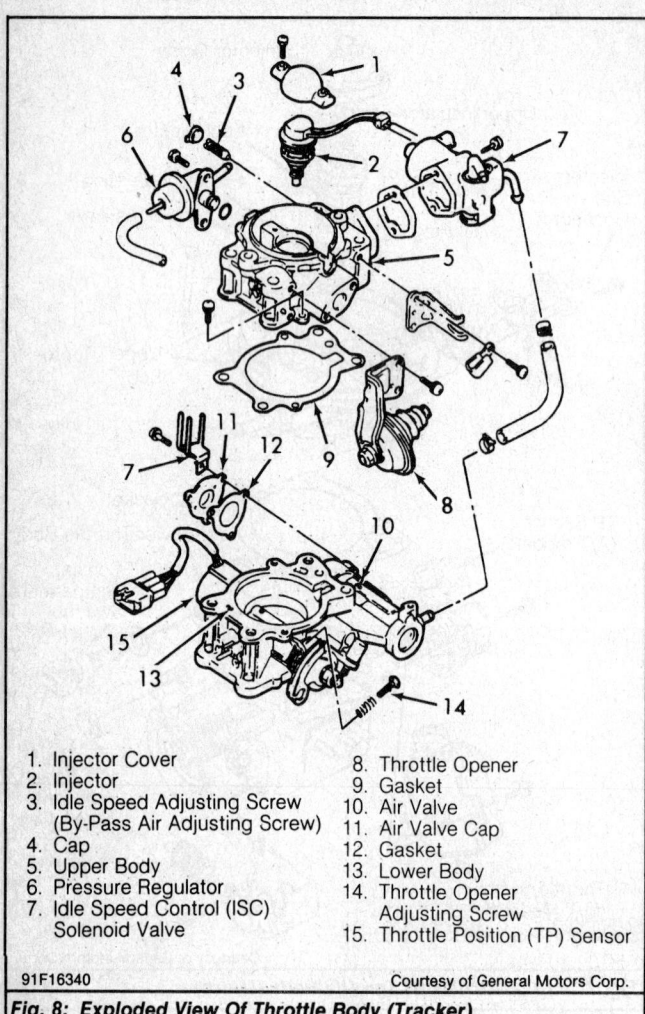

1. Injector Cover
2. Injector
3. Idle Speed Adjusting Screw (By-Pass Air Adjusting Screw)
4. Cap
5. Upper Body
6. Pressure Regulator
7. Idle Speed Control (ISC) Solenoid Valve
8. Throttle Opener
9. Gasket
10. Air Valve
11. Air Valve Cap
12. Gasket
13. Lower Body
14. Throttle Opener Adjusting Screw
15. Throttle Position (TP) Sensor

91F16340   Courtesy of General Motors Corp.

Fig. 8: Exploded View Of Throttle Body (Tracker)

4) Install throttle body and tighten to specification. See TORQUE SPECIFICATIONS. To complete installation, reverse removal procedure. Refill cooling system. Pressurize fuel system, and check for leaks.

THROTTLE BODY (PFI)

Removal & Installation (Prizm) – 1) Disconnect negative battery cable. Remove air cleaner assembly and air intake duct. Disconnect and label all vacuum hoses, wire connectors and cable linkages from throttle body.

2) Remove coolant hoses from throttle body. On all models, remove bolts retaining throttle body to intake chamber. Remove throttle body, and discard gasket. Clean gasket mating surfaces. DO NOT scratch mated sealing surfaces when removing old gasket material.

3) To install, reverse removal procedure. Use NEW gasket. DO NOT use sealer on gasket. Tighten 4 throttle body-to-intake chamber bolts to specification. See TORQUE SPECIFICATIONS. Refill cooling system.

THROTTLE POSITION (TP) SENSOR

NOTE: DO NOT immerse diaphragms, electrical components, or synthetic parts in carburetor cleaner.

Removal & Installation – 1) With ignition off, remove air cleaner assembly (if necessary). Disconnect TP sensor harness connector, and remove mounting screws.

2) To install, mount TP sensor to throttle body with alignment slots slightly counterclockwise of body holes. Turn TP sensor clockwise to align holes and install mounting screws finger tight. Adjust TP sensor. See THROTTLE POSITION (TP) SENSOR in ON-VEHICLE ADJUSTMENTS article.

THROTTLE SWITCH

Removal & Installation (Prizm) – 1) With ignition off, remove air cleaner assembly, and disconnect throttle switch connector. Remove throttle switch from throttle body.

2) To install, mount switch to body. Ensure flat tang of shaft is positioned into switch. Rotate switch counterclockwise until it stops, then turn switch clockwise to align switch slots with body holes. Install and tighten switch screws finger tight.

3) To adjust switch, see THROTTLE SWITCH in ON-VEHICLE ADJUSTMENTS article. Reconnect switch connector, and install air cleaner.

TORQUE SPECIFICATIONS
TORQUE SPECIFICATIONS

Application	Ft. Lbs. (N.m)
Metro	
ECM Bracket-To-Dash Board Support Bolts	11 (15)
Spark Plug	21 (28)
Throttle Body Mounting Bolt	17 (23)
Prizm	
Distributor Mounting Bolt	15 (20)
ECM/PCM Bracket	11 (15)
Fuel Filter Fittings	21 (28)
Fuel Rail-To-Cylinder Head Bolt	11 (15)
Fuel Tank Strap-To-Chassis Bolt	29 (39)
Spark Plug	21 (28)
Throttle Body Mounting Bolt	16 (22)
Tracker	
Distributor Mounting Bolt	11 (15)
ECM Bracket-To-Dash Board Support Bolts	15 (20)
Fuel Filter Fittings	26 (35)
Spark Plug	21 (28)
Throttle Body Mounting Bolt	13-20 (18-27)
	INCH Lbs. (N.m)
Metro	
Distributor Mounting Bolt	120 (13)
Injector Cover Screw	31 (3.5)
Prizm	
Cold Start Injector Mounting Bolt	82 (9.3)
Fuel Pump Bracket-To-Tank Mounting Screw	30 (3.0)
Pressure Regulator Mounting Bolt	74 (6.5)
Tracker	
Injector Cover Screw	31 (3.5)
Pressure Regulator Mounting Bolt	31 (3.5)

Metro, Prizm, Tracer

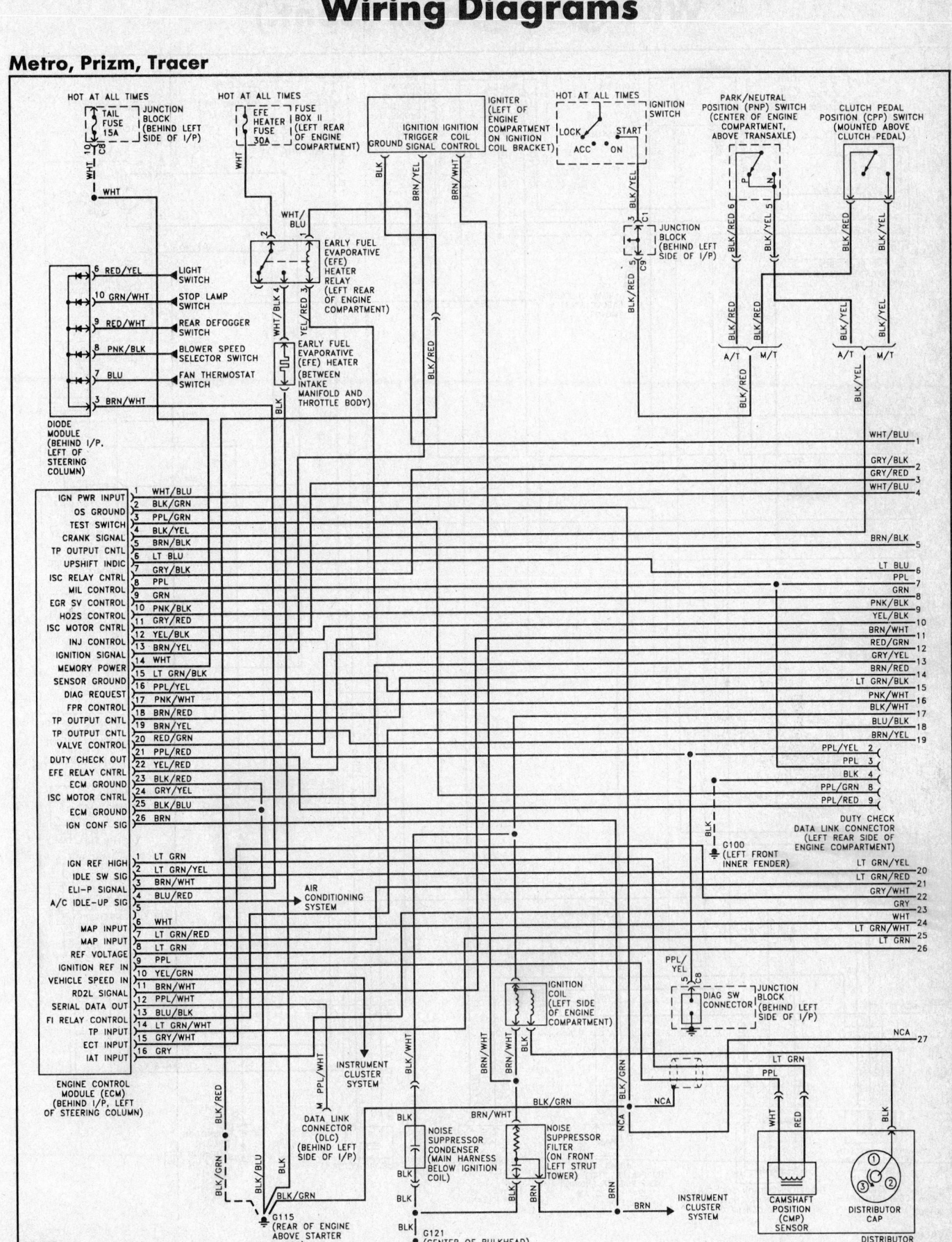

Fig. 1: Wiring Diagram (Metro 1.0L - California - 1 Of 2)

61908

VA061908

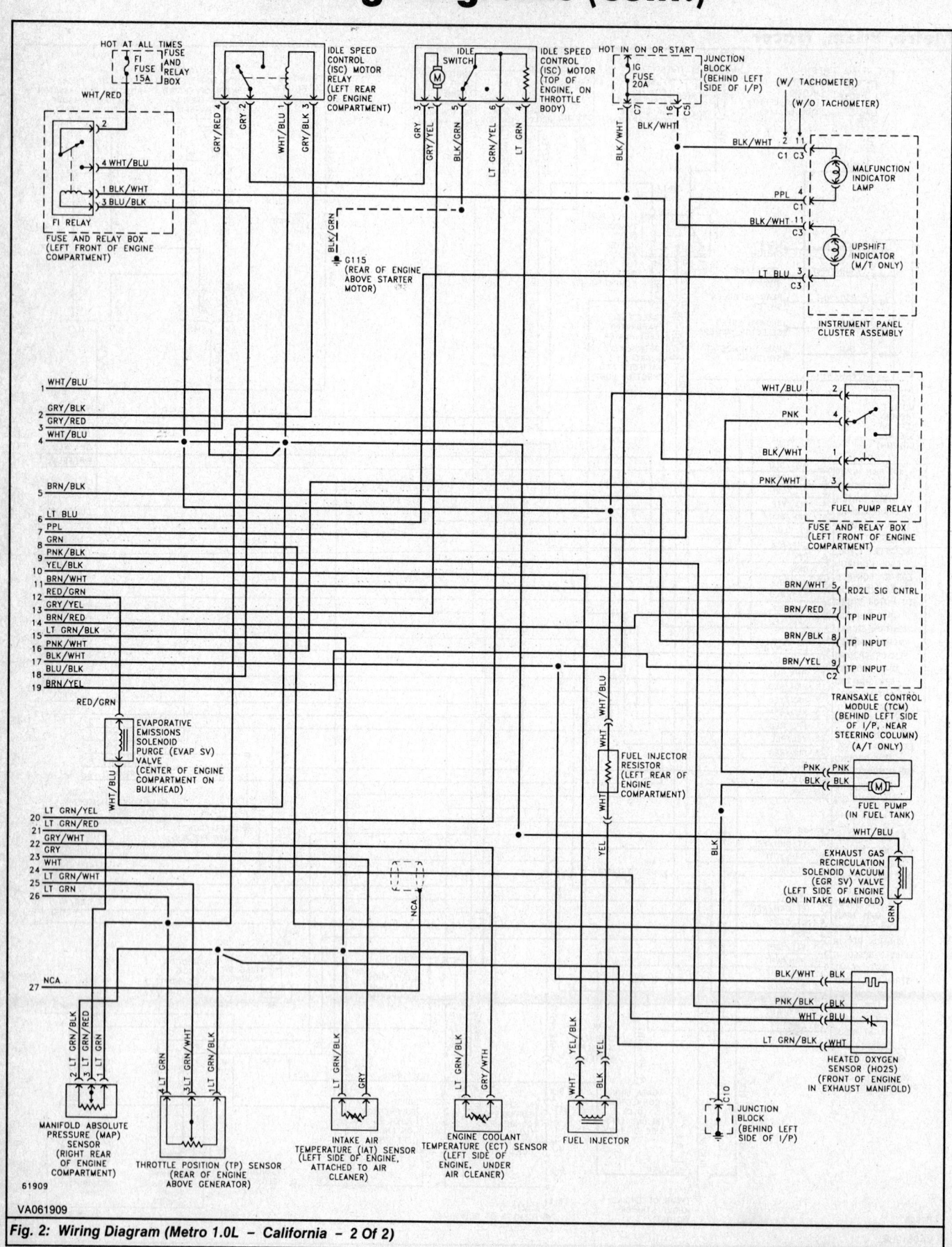

Fig. 2: Wiring Diagram (Metro 1.0L - California - 2 Of 2)

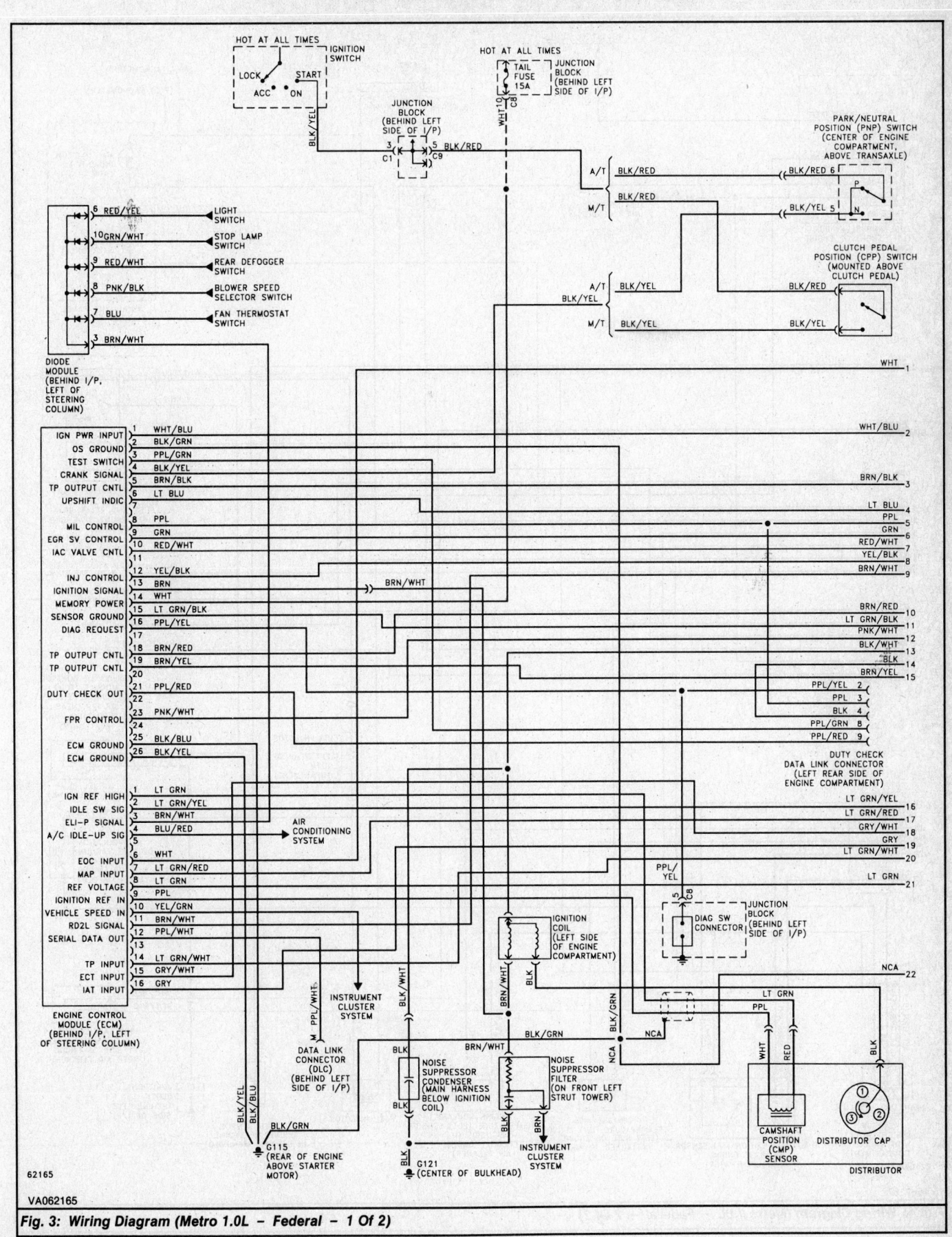

Fig. 3: Wiring Diagram (Metro 1.0L - Federal - 1 Of 2)

62165

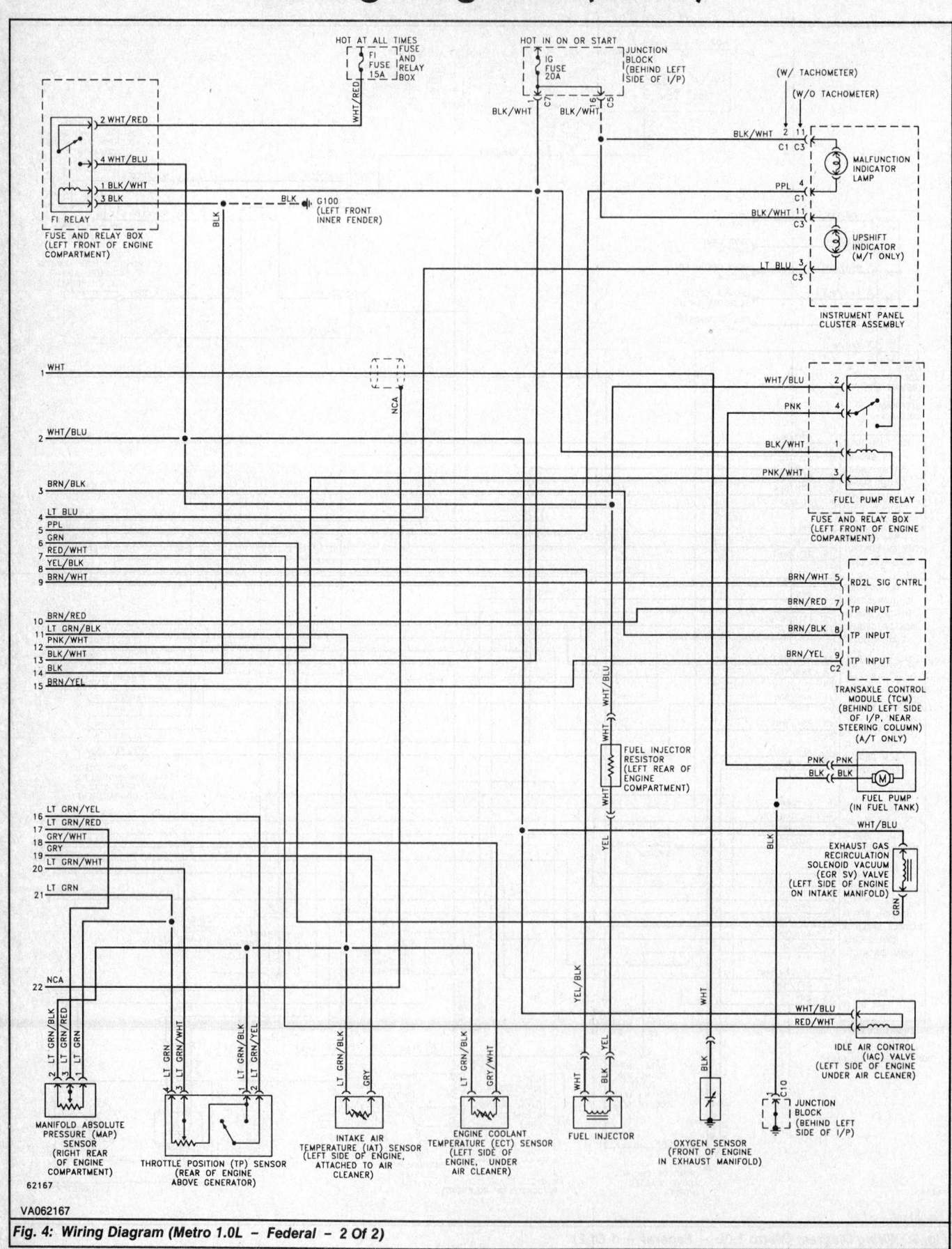

Fig. 4: Wiring Diagram (Metro 1.0L - Federal - 2 Of 2)

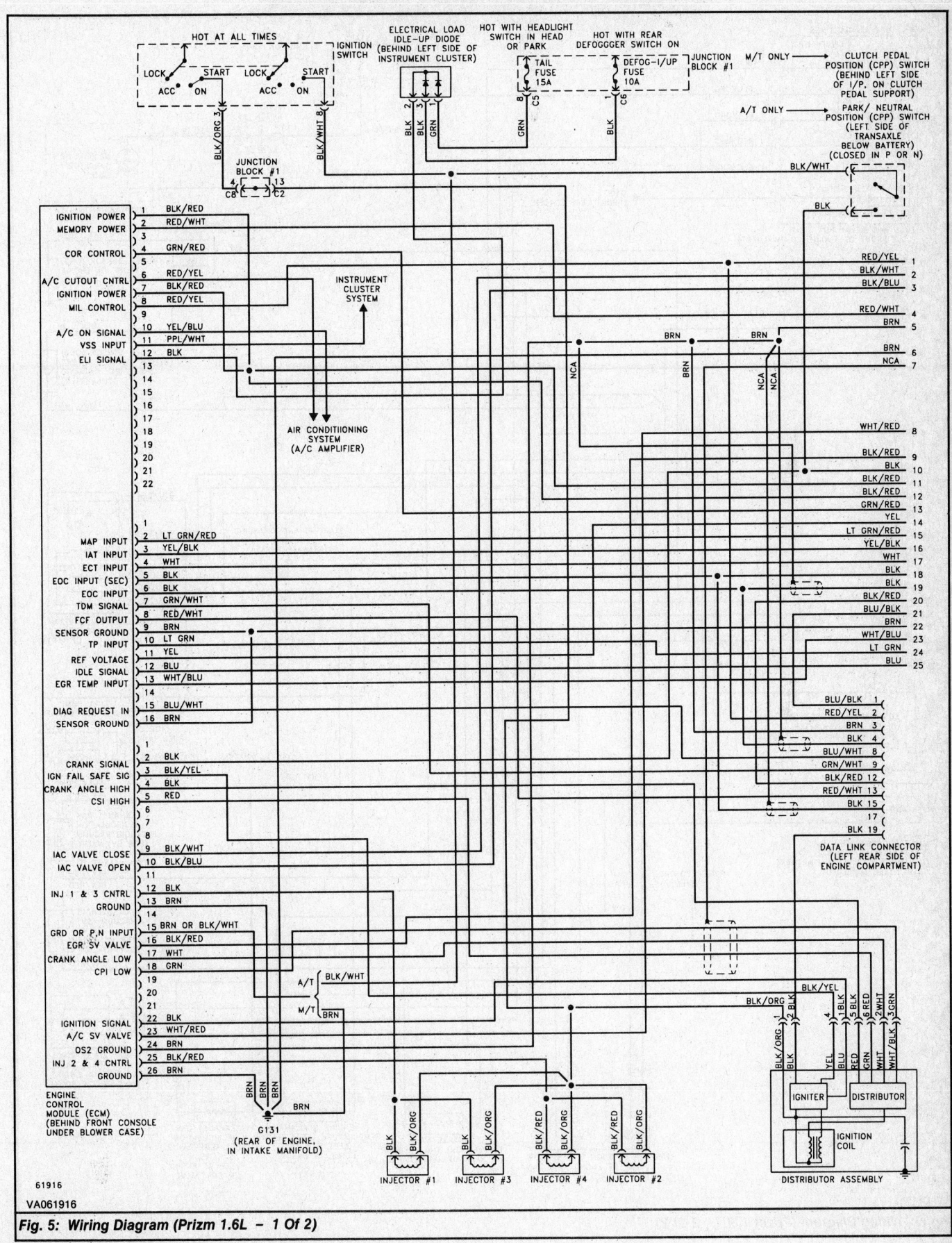

Fig. 5: *Wiring Diagram (Prizm 1.6L – 1 Of 2)*

61916

VA061916

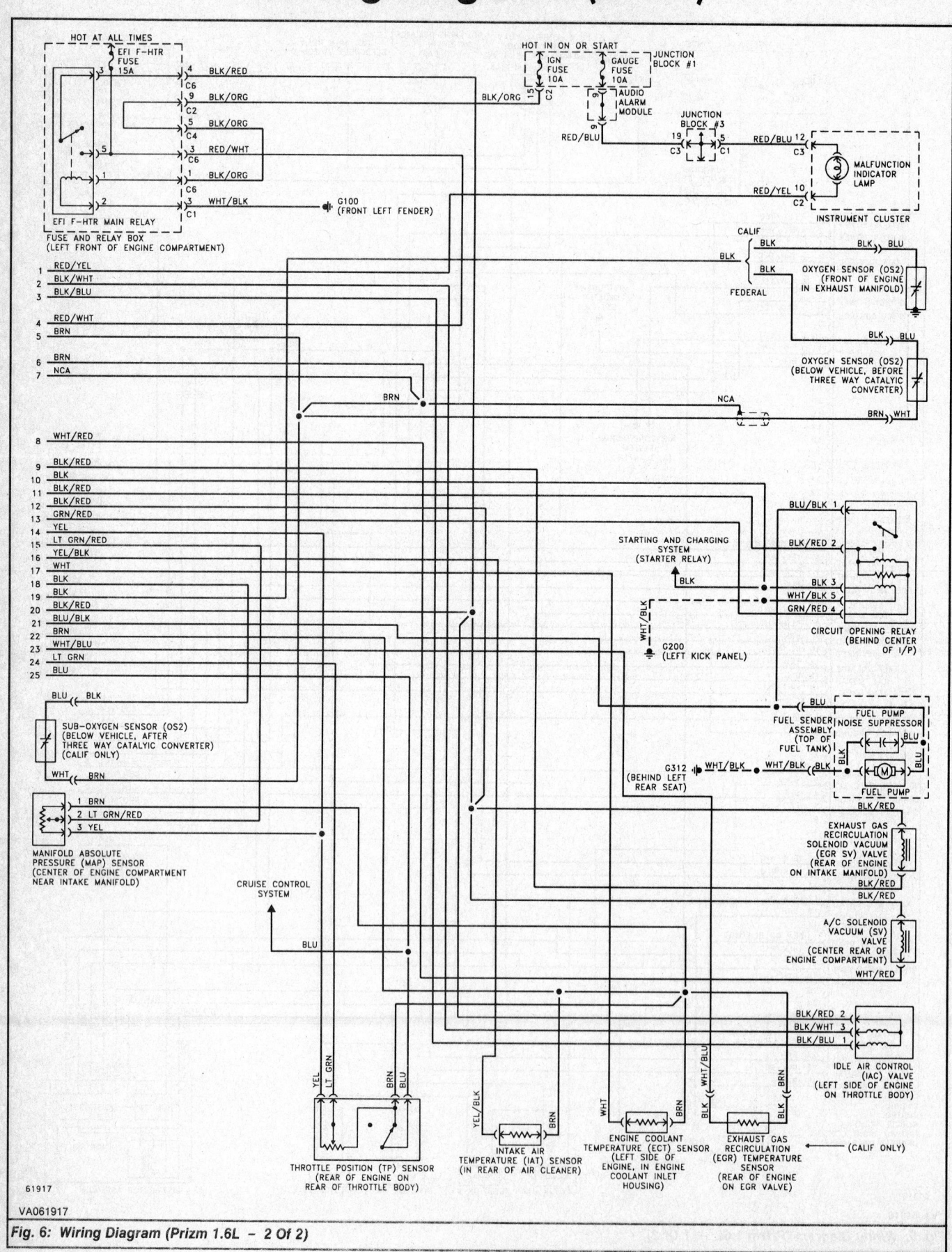

Fig. 6: Wiring Diagram (Prizm 1.6L - 2 Of 2)

VA061917

61917

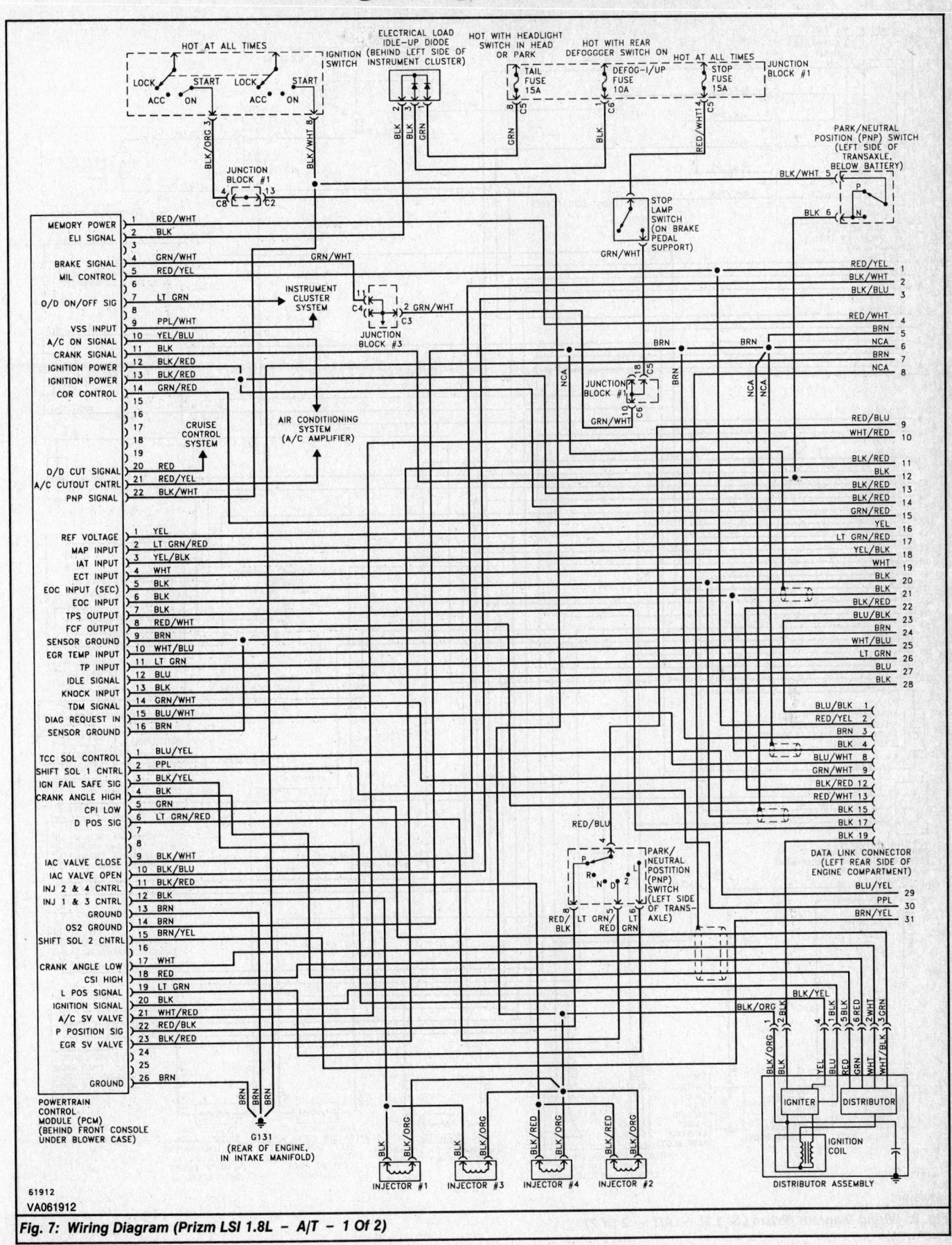

Fig. 7: Wiring Diagram (Prizm LSI 1.8L - A/T - 1 Of 2)

61912
VA061912

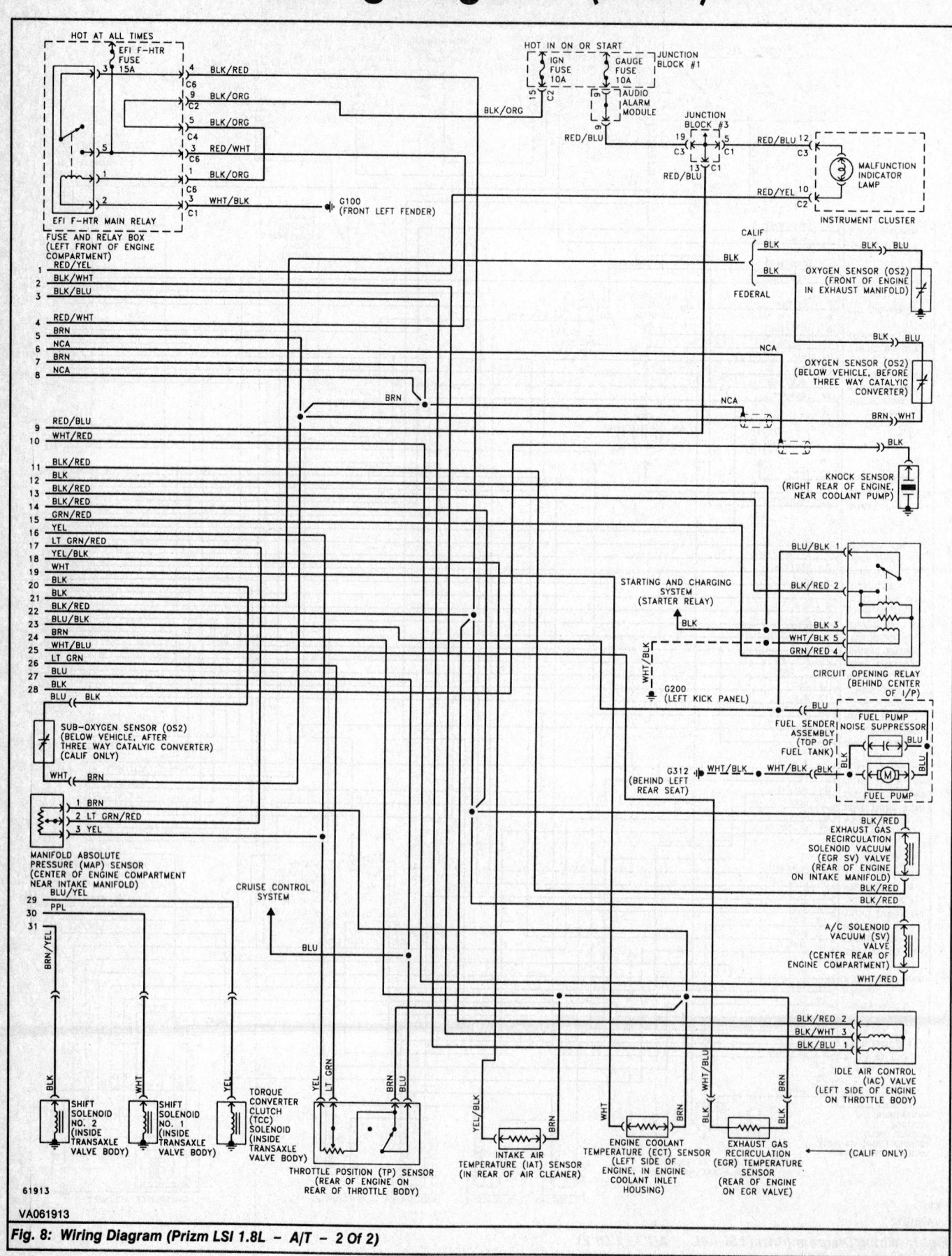

61913

VA061913

Fig. 8: Wiring Diagram (Prizm LSI 1.8L – A/T – 2 Of 2)

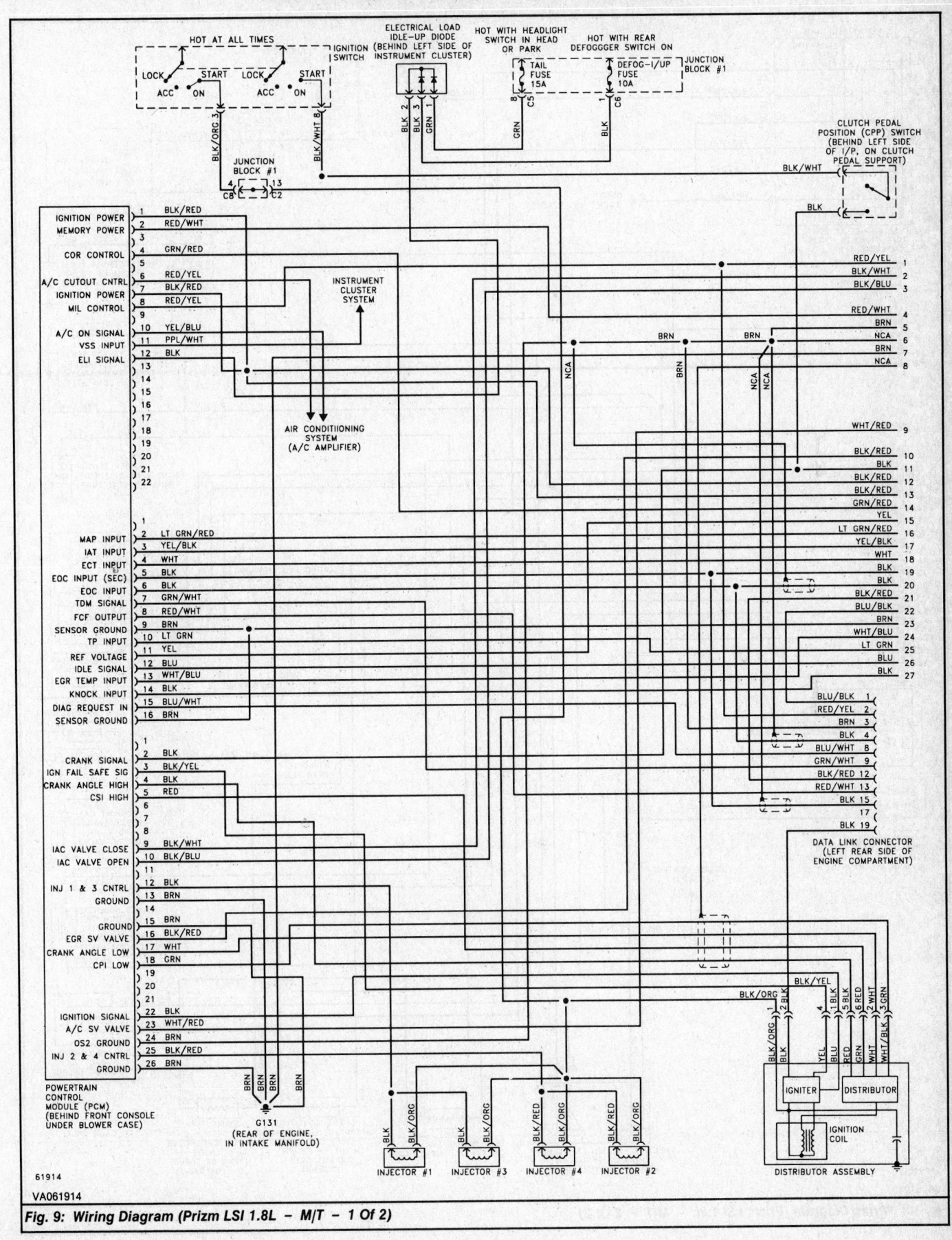

Fig. 9: Wiring Diagram (Prizm LSI 1.8L - M/T - 1 Of 2)

61914

VA061914

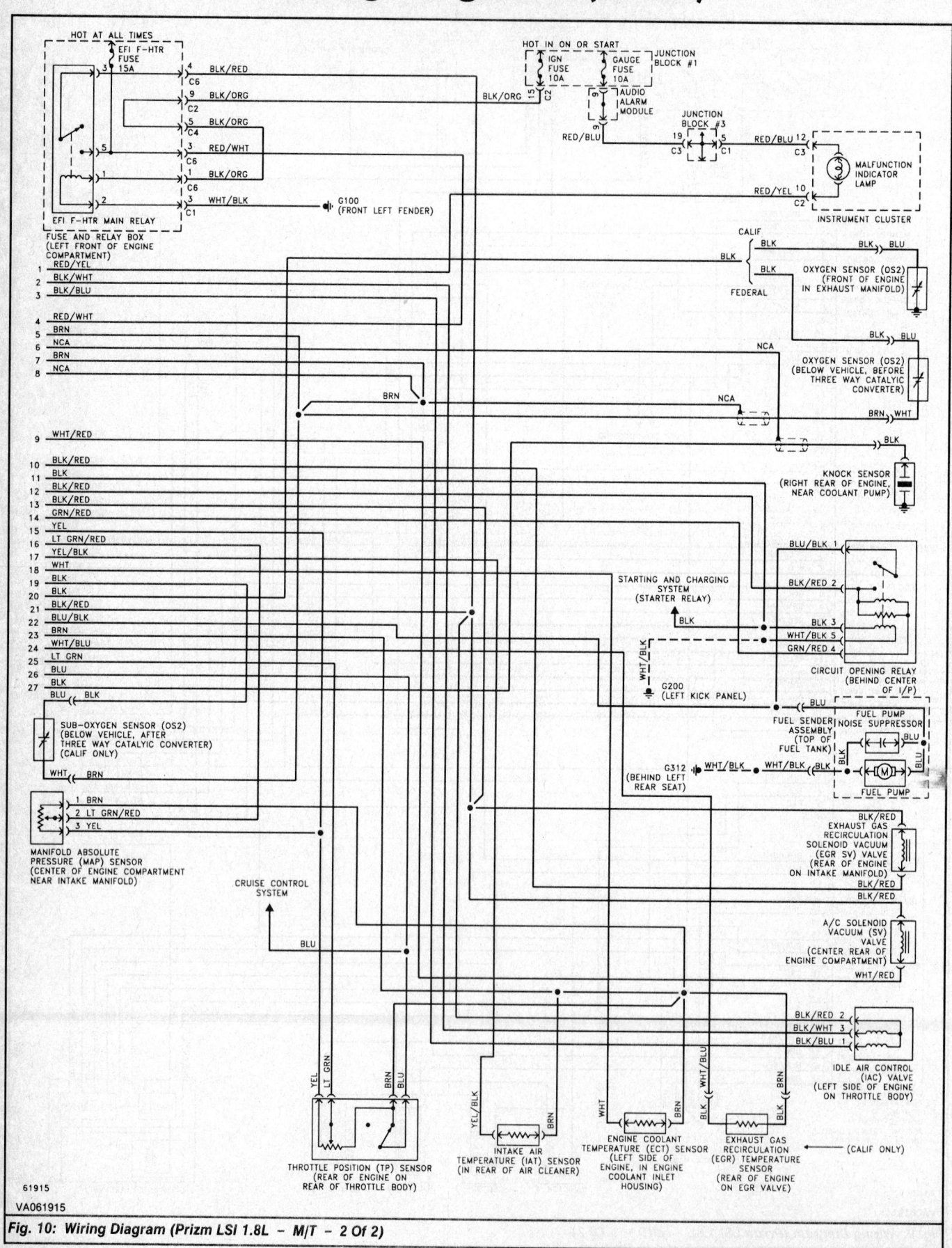

61915

VA061915

Fig. 10: Wiring Diagram (Prizm LSI 1.8L – M/T – 2 Of 2)

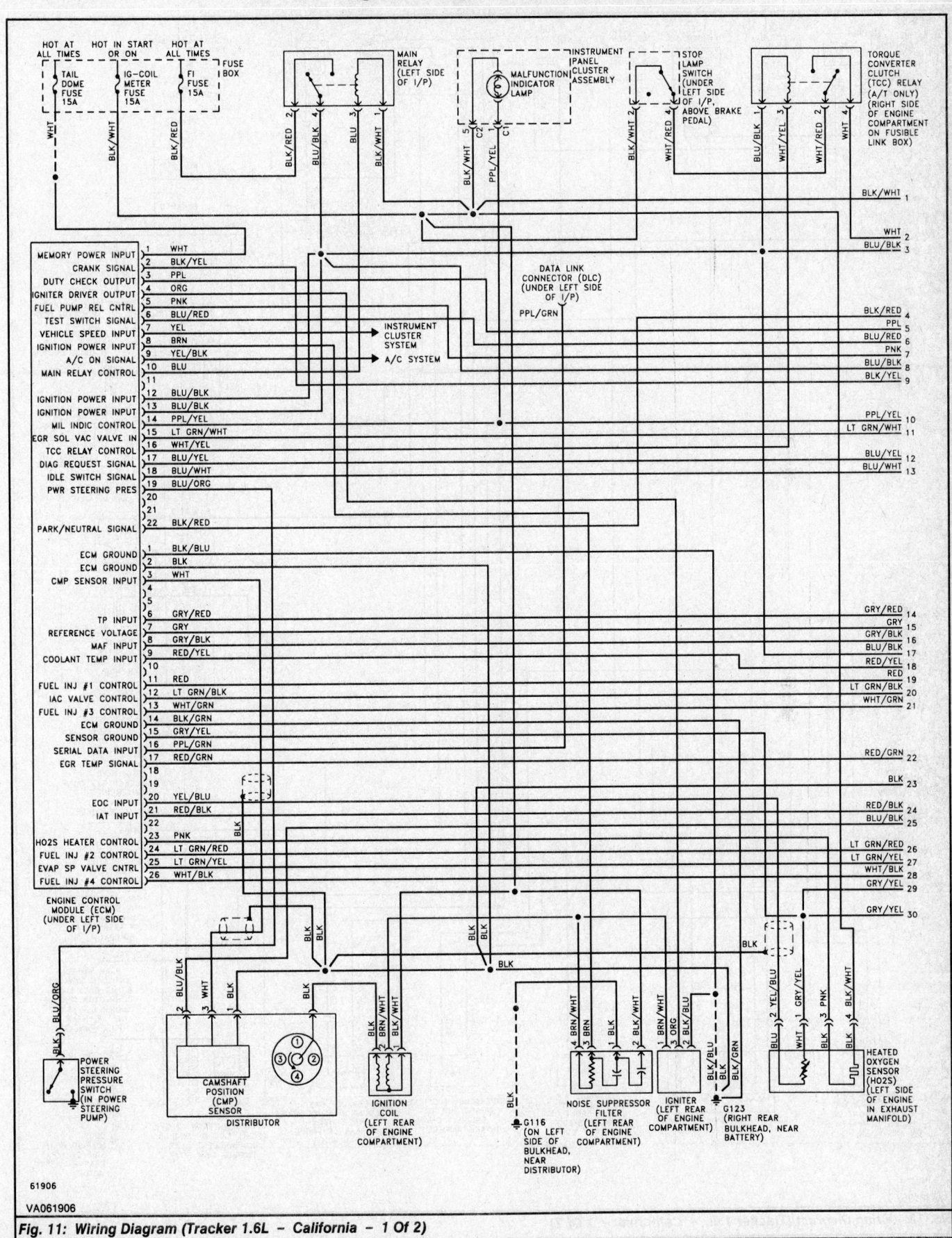

Fig. 11: Wiring Diagram (Tracker 1.6L – California – 1 Of 2)

61906

VA061906

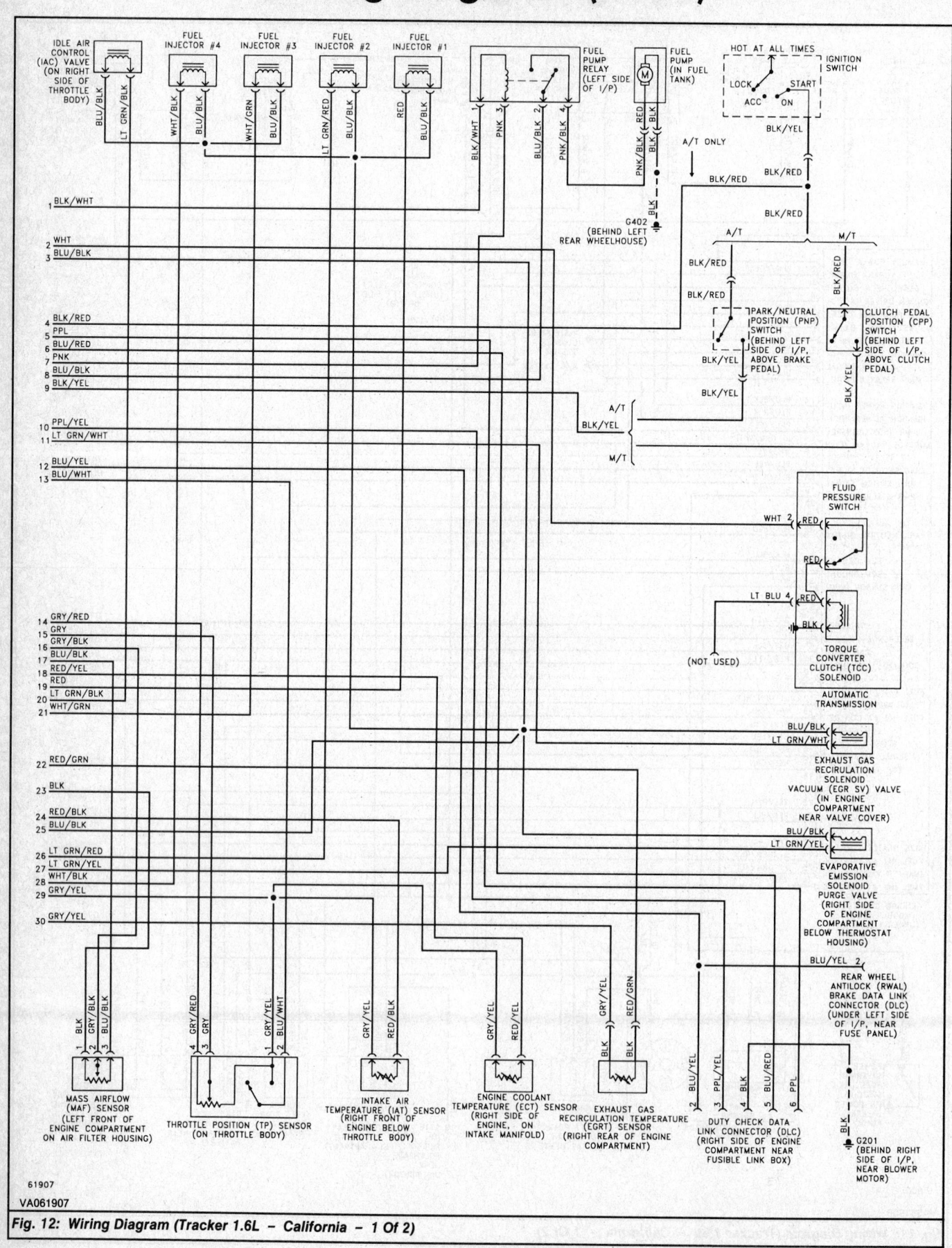

Fig. 12: Wiring Diagram (Tracker 1.6L - California - 1 Of 2)

61907
VA061907

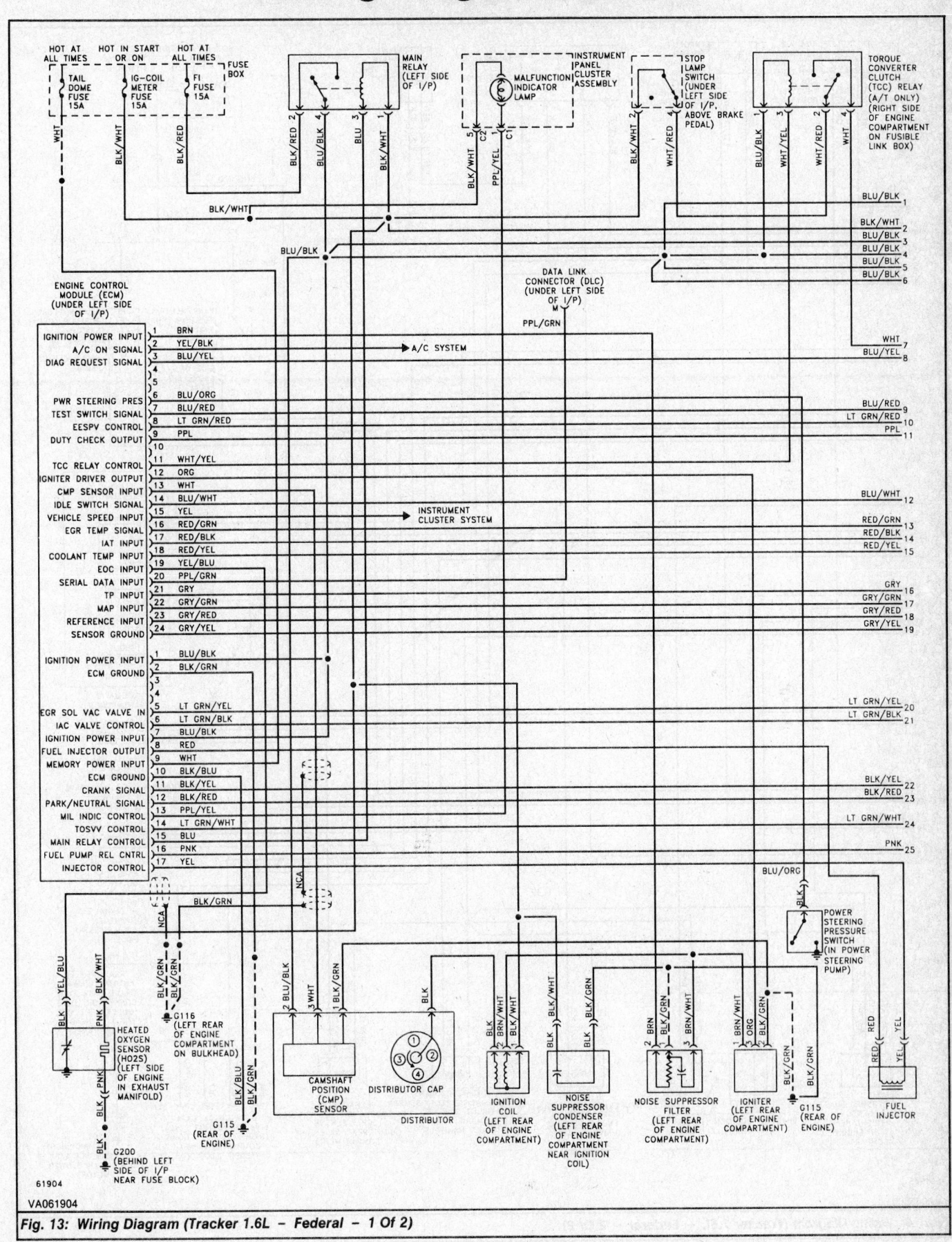

Fig. 13: Wiring Diagram (Tracker 1.6L - Federal - 1 Of 2)

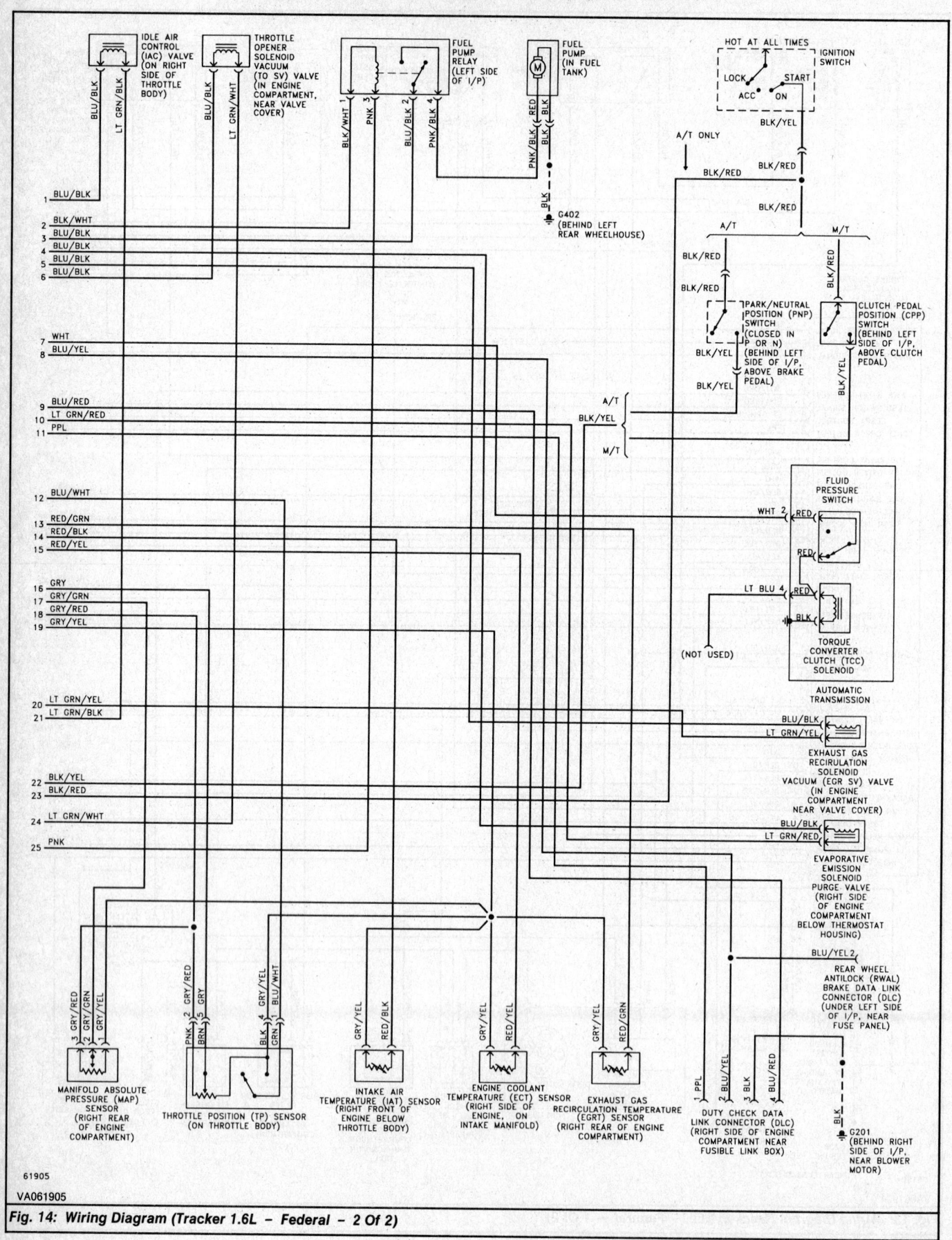

61905

VA061905

Fig. 14: *Wiring Diagram (Tracker 1.6L - Federal - 2 Of 2)*

DESCRIPTION

Metro models built in Japan (VIN J) are equipped with a Nippondenso 50-amp alternator with internal regulator. Metro models built in Canada (VIN 2) are equipped with a Mitsubishi 55-amp alternator with internal regulator. Both alternators are serviceable and can be repaired or overhauled.

The Integrated Circuit (IC) regulator is a solid state unit mounted inside alternator to rear end frame. Voltage regulator voltage cannot be adjusted.

Two brushes carry current through 2 slip rings to field coil mounted on rotor. Stator windings are assembled inside a laminated core forming part of alternator drive and frame assemblies.

A rectifier bridge containing 6 diodes is connected to stator windings. Two neutral diodes are also used to smooth out voltage fluctuations caused by varying alternator speeds. A capacitor (condenser), mounted in regulator, protects the rectifier bridge and neutral diodes. This capacitor also suppresses radio interference noise.

ADJUSTMENTS

BELT TENSION

ALTERNATOR BELT ADJUSTMENT

Application	Specification [1] Belt Deflection
New Belt	.20-.27" (5-7 mm)
Used Belt [2]	.24-.31" (6-8 mm)

[1] – Check belt with 22 lbs. (10 kg) pressure applied midway on longest belt run.
[2] – Belt operated for 15 minutes is considered used.

TROUBLE SHOOTING

NOTE: See TROUBLE SHOOTING article in GENERAL INFORMATION.

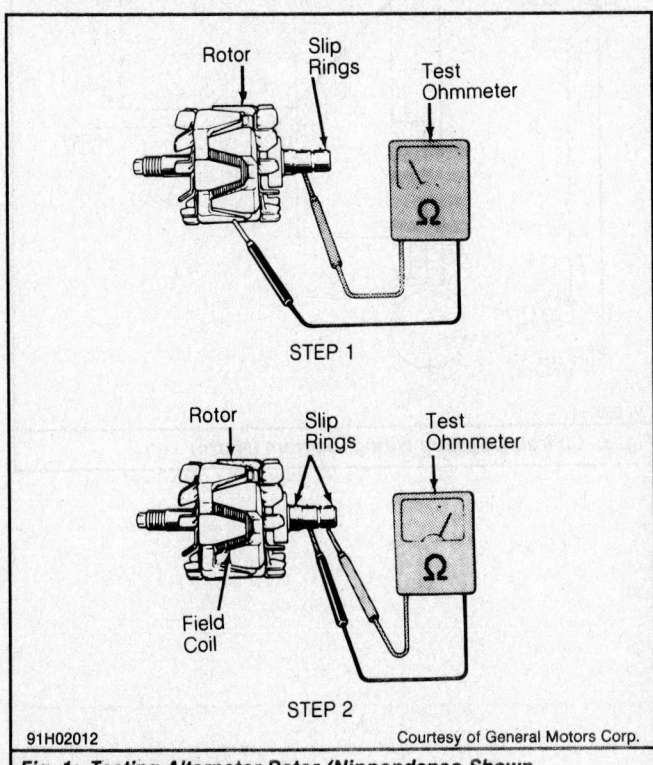

Fig. 1: Testing Alternator Rotor (Nippondenso Shown, Mitsubishi Similar)

91H02012   Courtesy of General Motors Corp.

ON-VEHICLE TESTING

SYSTEM OUTPUT TEST

1) Test battery and check alternator belt tension. Visually inspect related wiring connections. Turn ignition switch to OFF position. Disconnect negative battery cable. Disconnect alternator output wire from terminal "B". Using an ammeter, connect positive lead to terminal "B" and negative lead to disconnected alternator output wire.
2) Using a voltmeter, connect positive lead to alternator terminal "B" and negative lead to ground. Connect negative battery cable. Start engine. Turn headlights on high beam and heater switch to HIGH position. Using a screwdriver, ground alternator terminal "F". Increase engine speed to 2000 RPM and note maximum current output on ammeter.
3) If maximum current output is within about 10 amps of rated amp output (50 or 55 amps) and voltmeter reading is 13.5-16.0 volts, alternator is okay. If maximum current output is not within 10 amps of rated amp output and/or voltmeter reading is less than 13.5 volts, repair or replace alternator.

VOLTAGE REGULATOR TEST

1) Connect a fast battery charger to battery. Connect voltmeter to battery terminals.
2) Turn ignition switch to ON position. Slowly increase charger charging rate. Charge indicator light in vehicle should begin to dim when voltmeter reads 13.5-16.0 volts. If charge light does not dim at specified voltage, replace internal voltage regulator.

ROTOR TEST

1) Using an ohmmeter, measure resistance between rotor and slip rings. *See Fig. 1 (STEP 1).* If continuity exists, replace rotor.
2) Measure resistance between slip rings. *See Fig. 1 (STEP 2).* If resistance is not 2.8-3.0 ohms, replace rotor.

STATOR TEST

1) Using an ohmmeter, measure resistance between stator leads. *See Fig. 2 (STEP 1).* If resistance is greater than 5 ohms between stator leads, replace stator.
2) Check for continuity between stator leads and stator core. *See Fig. 2 (STEP 2).* If continuity exists, replace stator.

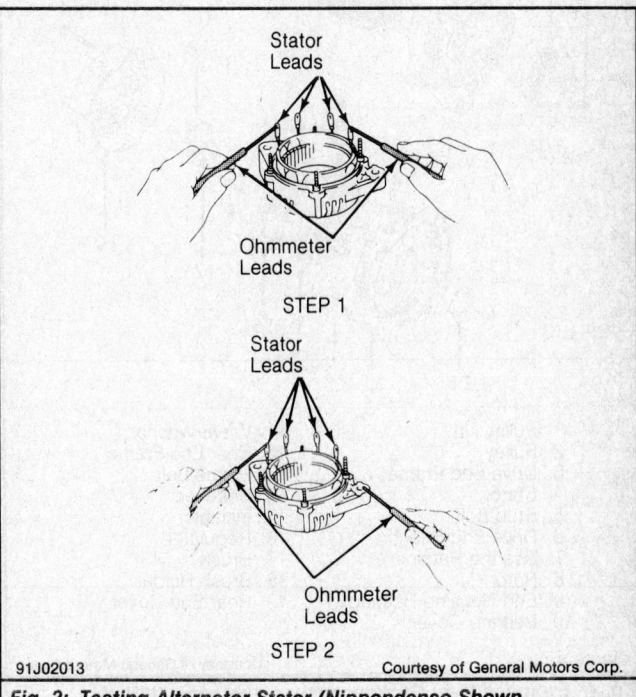

Fig. 2: Testing Alternator Stator (Nippondenso Shown, Mitsubishi Similar)

91J02013   Courtesy of General Motors Corp.

RECTIFIER TEST

1) With rectifier assembly on bench, contact diode plate using one ohmmeter probe and each diode lead using other probe. Note ohmmeter reading. Reverse probes, and repeat test for all diodes.
2) All diodes should show a low reading in one direction and no reading in opposite direction. If any rectifier diode is defective, replace rectifier assembly.

OVERHAUL

NOTE: For overhaul, see exploded view of alternator. See Fig. 3 or 4.

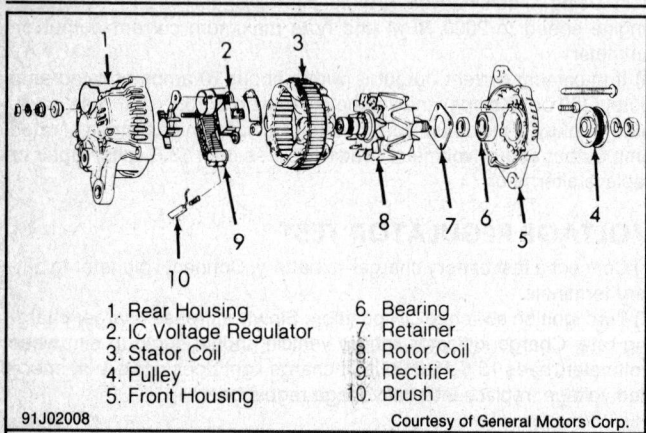

1. Rear Housing	6. Bearing
2. IC Voltage Regulator	7. Retainer
3. Stator Coil	8. Rotor Coil
4. Pulley	9. Rectifier
5. Front Housing	10. Brush

91J02008   Courtesy of General Motors Corp.

Fig. 3: Exploded View Of Mitsubishi Alternator (VIN 2)

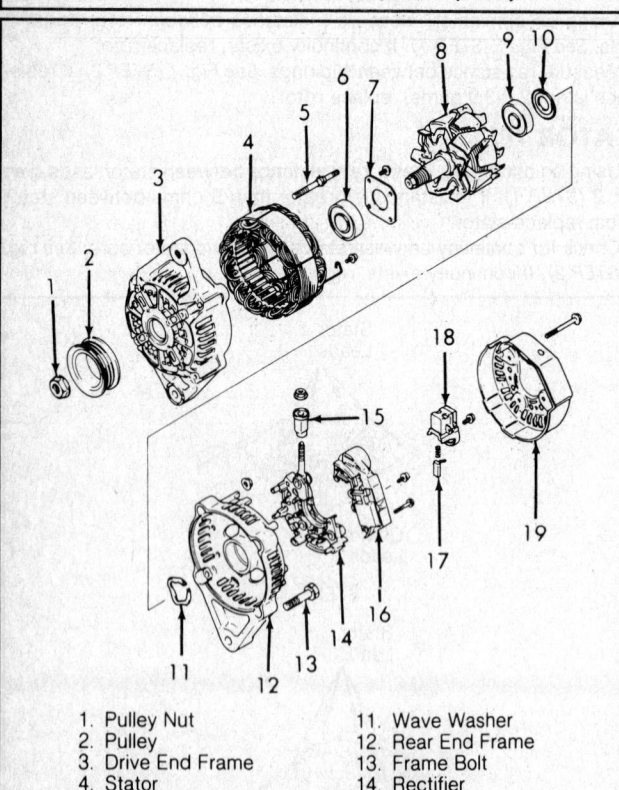

1. Pulley Nut	11. Wave Washer
2. Pulley	12. Rear End Frame
3. Drive End Frame	13. Frame Bolt
4. Stator	14. Rectifier
5. Stud Bolt	15. Insulator
6. Drive End Bearing	16. Regulator
7. Bearing Retainer	17. Brush
8. Rotor	18. Brush Holder
9. End Housing Bearing	19. Rear End Cover
10. Bearing Cover	

91B02014   Courtesy of General Motors Corp.

Fig. 4: Exploded View Of Nippondenso Alternator (VIN J)

TORQUE SPECIFICATIONS

TORQUE SPECIFICATIONS

Application	Ft. Lbs. (N.m)
Drive Belt Adjuster Bolt	17 (23)
Lower Pivot Bolt/Nut	17 (33)
Alternator Housing Bolts	22 (30)
Pulley Nut	48 (65)
Rectifier End Frame Nuts	15 (20)

	INCH Lbs. (N.m)
Alternator "B" Terminal Nut	44 (5)
Connector Nut	71 (8)
Stator Stud Bolts	71 (8)

WIRING DIAGRAM

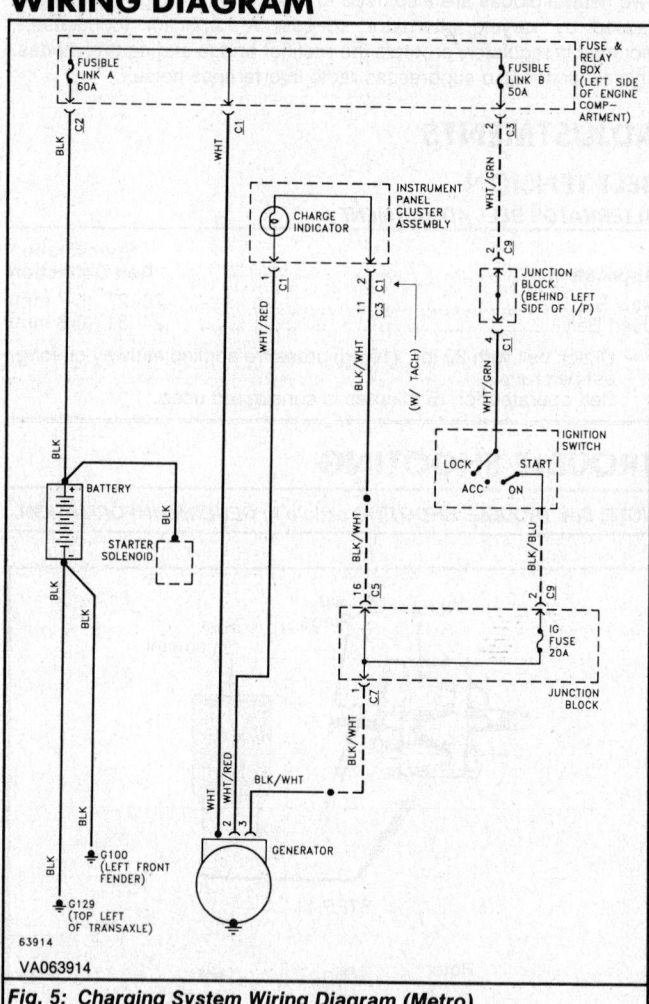

Fig. 5: Charging System Wiring Diagram (Metro)

DESCRIPTION

Prizm is equipped with 2 different Delco CS-121 alternators or a Nippondenso alternator. Delco alternators used on vehicles with VIN 8 (1.8L) with automatic transaxles have a maximum output of 77 amps. Delco alternators used on vehicles with VIN 6 (1.6L) or VIN 8 (1.8L) with manual transaxles, have a maximum output of 70 amps. Nippondenso alternators maximum output is 70 amps. Delco alternator is a non-serviceable type and must be replaced as a unit. Nippondenso alternator is serviceable and can be repaired or overhauled.

Both alternators use an internal voltage regulator. The Integrated Circuit (IC) regulator is a solid state unit mounted inside alternator to rear end frame. Voltage regulator voltage cannot be adjusted.

Two brushes carry current through 2 slip rings to field coil mounted on rotor. Stator windings are assembled inside a laminated core forming part of alternator drive and frame assemblies. A rectifier bridge containing 6 diodes (8 diodes in Nippondenso unit) is connected to stator windings.

ADJUSTMENTS

BELT TENSION

BELT ADJUSTMENT

Application	Specification [1] Belt Deflection
Alternator Belt	
New Belt	.20-.31" (5-8 mm)
Used Belt [2]	.24-.35" (6-9 mm)

[1] – Check belt with 22 lbs. (10 kg) pressure applied midway on longest belt run.
[2] – Belt operated for 15 minutes is considered used.

TROUBLE SHOOTING

NOTE: See TROUBLE SHOOTING article in GENERAL INFORMATION.

ON-VEHICLE TESTING

SYSTEM OUTPUT TEST

1) Test battery and check alternator belt tension. Visually inspect related wiring connections. Turn ignition switch to OFF position. Disconnect negative battery cable. Disconnect alternator output wire from terminal "B". Using an ammeter, connect positive ammeter lead to terminal "B" and negative lead to disconnected alternator output wire.
2) Using a voltmeter, connect positive voltmeter lead to alternator terminal "B" and negative lead to ground. Install tachometer. Connect negative battery cable. Start engine. Turn headlights on high beam and heater switch to HIGH position. Using a screwdriver, ground alternator terminal "F". Increase engine speed to 2000 RPM and note maximum current output on ammeter.
3) If maximum current output is within about 10 amps of rated amp output (70 or 77 amps) and voltmeter reading is 13.5-16.0 volts, alternator is okay. If maximum current output is not within 10 amps of rated amp output and/or voltmeter reading is less than 13.5 volts, repair or replace alternator.

VOLTAGE REGULATOR TEST

1) Connect a fast battery charger to battery. Connect voltmeter to battery terminals.
2) Turn ignition switch to ON position. Slowly increase charger charging rate. Charge indicator light in vehicle should begin to dim when voltmeter reads 13.5-16.0 volts. If charge light does not dim, replace internal voltage regulator.

BENCH TESTING

NOTE: Bench testing procedures apply to Nippondenso alternator only. Delco alternator is not serviceable, replace as a unit if faulty.

STATOR TEST

1) Using an ohmmeter, check stator leads for continuity. See Fig. 2 (STEP 1). If continuity does not exist between stator leads, replace drive end frame assembly.
2) Check for continuity between stator leads and stator core. See Fig. 2 (STEP 2). If continuity exists, replace drive end frame assembly.

ROTOR TEST

1) Using an ohmmeter, check for continuity between rotor and slip rings. See Fig. 1 (STEP 1). If continuity exists, replace rotor.
2) Check for continuity between slip rings. See Fig. 1 (STEP 2). If continuity does not exist and resistance is not 2.8-3.0 ohms, replace rotor.

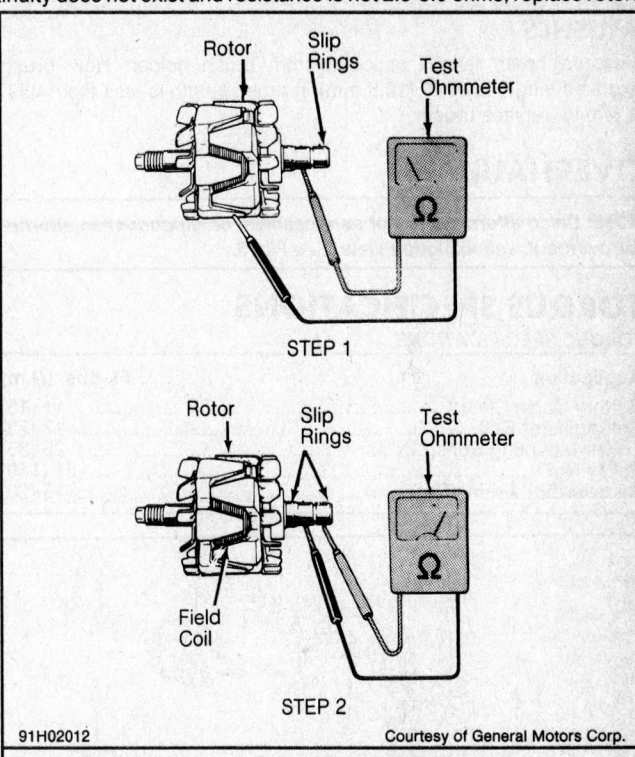

91H02012   Courtesy of General Motors Corp.

Fig. 1: Testing Alternator Rotor (Nippondenso)

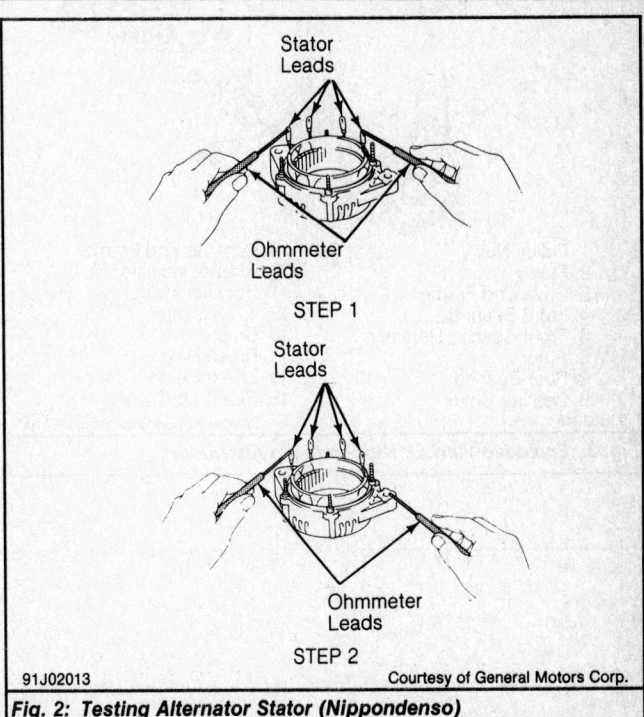

91J02013   Courtesy of General Motors Corp.

Fig. 2: Testing Alternator Stator (Nippondenso)

3) Measure diameter of both slip rings. If either slip ring diameter is less than .504" (12.8 mm), replace rotor. If slip rings are scored or rough, replace rotor.

RECTIFIER TEST

1) With rectifier assembly on bench, contact diode plate using one ohmmeter probe and each of 3 diode leads using other probe. Note ohmmeter reading. Reverse probes, and repeat test for all diodes.

2) All diodes should show a low resistance in one direction and no continuity in opposite direction. If any diode is defective, replace rectifier assembly.

BRUSHES

Measure brush length exposed from brush holder. New brush exposed length is .413" (10.5 mm). If brush length is less than .059" (1.5 mm), replace brush.

OVERHAUL

NOTE: Delco alternator is not serviceable. For Nippondenso alternator overhaul, see exploded view. See Fig. 3.

TORQUE SPECIFICATIONS

TORQUE SPECIFICATIONS

Application	Ft. Lbs. (N.m)
Battery Cable Clamp	11 (15)
Belt Adjuster Bolt	17 (23)
Lower Mounting Bolts & Nuts	26 (35)
Pulley Nut	81 (110)
Rectifier End Frame Nuts	15 (20)

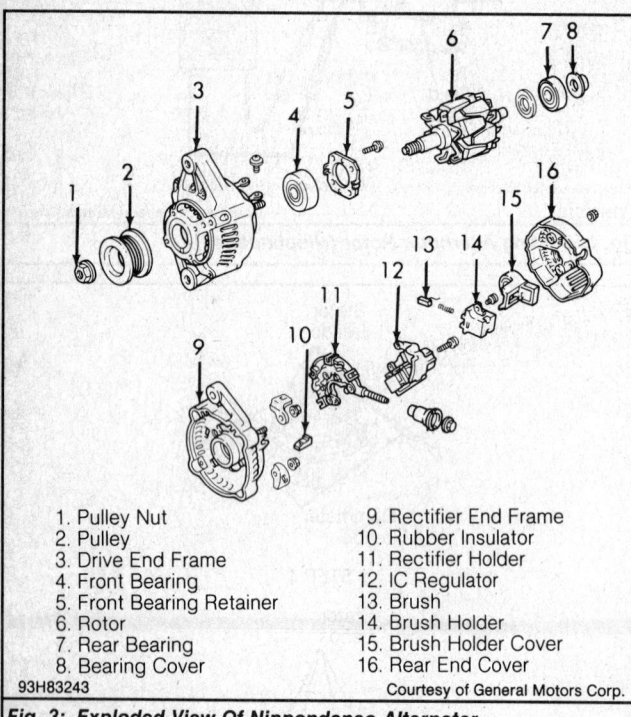

1. Pulley Nut
2. Pulley
3. Drive End Frame
4. Front Bearing
5. Front Bearing Retainer
6. Rotor
7. Rear Bearing
8. Bearing Cover
9. Rectifier End Frame
10. Rubber Insulator
11. Rectifier Holder
12. IC Regulator
13. Brush
14. Brush Holder
15. Brush Holder Cover
16. Rear End Cover

93H83243   Courtesy of General Motors Corp.

Fig. 3: Exploded View Of Nippondenso Alternator

WIRING DIAGRAM

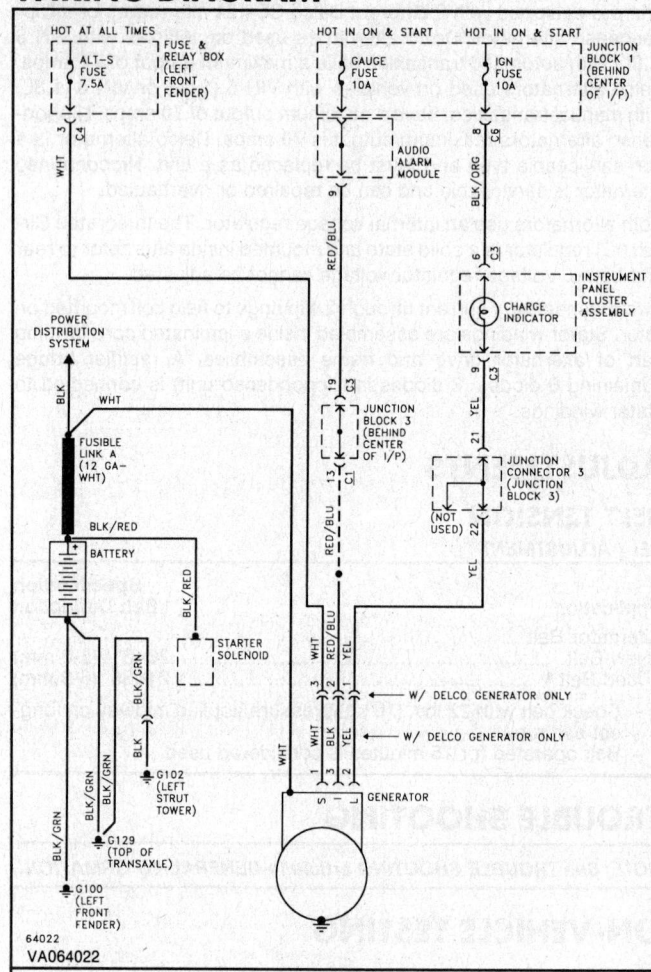

Fig. 4: Charging System Wiring Diagram (Prizm)

DESCRIPTION

All Tracker models are equipped with Mitsubishi 55-amp alternator with internal voltage regulator. The Integrated Circuit (IC) voltage regulator is a solid state unit mounted to rectifier end frame. Brushes carry current through 2 slip rings to field coil mounted on rotor. A rectifier bridge containing 6 diodes is connected to stator windings. Two neutral diodes are used to smooth out voltage fluctuations caused by varying alternator speeds. A capacitor (condenser), mounted in regulator, protects the rectifier bridge and neutral diodes. This capacitor also suppresses radio interference noise.

ADJUSTMENTS

BELT TENSION

BELT ADJUSTMENT

Application	[1] Belt Deflection In. (mm)
Alternator Belt	
New Belt	.20-.27" (5-7 mm)
Used Belt [2]	.24-.31" (6-8 mm)

[1] – Check belt with 22 lbs. (10 kg) pressure applied midway on longest belt run.
[2] – Belt operated for 15 minutes is considered used.

TROUBLE SHOOTING

NOTE: See TROUBLE SHOOTING article in GENERAL INFORMATION.

ON-VEHICLE TESTING

SYSTEM OUTPUT TEST

1) Turn ignition switch to OFF position. Disconnect negative battery cable. Disconnect alternator output wire from terminal "B". *See Fig. 1.* Using an ammeter, connect positive ammeter lead to terminal "B" and negative lead to disconnected alternator output wire.

2) Using a voltmeter, connect positive voltmeter lead to alternator terminal "B" and negative lead to ground. Install tachometer. Connect negative battery cable. Start engine. Turn headlights on high beam and heater switch to HIGH position. Using a screwdriver, ground alternator "F" terminal. Increase engine speed to 2000 RPM and note maximum current output on ammeter.

3) If maximum current output is within 10 amps of rated amp output (55 amps) and voltmeter reading is 13.5-16.0 volts, alternator is okay. If maximum current output is not within 10 amps of rated amp output and/or voltmeter reading is less than 13.5 volts, repair or replace alternator.

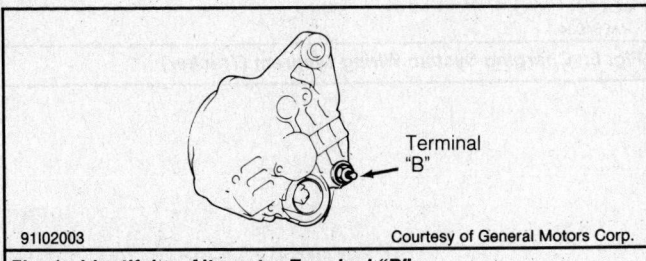

91I02003   Courtesy of General Motors Corp.

Fig. 1: Identifying Alternator Terminal "B"

VOLTAGE REGULATOR TEST

Connect voltmeter and a fast battery charger to battery. Turn ignition switch to ON position. Slowly increase charger charging rate. Charge indicator light in vehicle should begin to dim when voltmeter reads 13.5-16.0 volts. If charge indicator light does not dim, replace internal voltage regulator.

BENCH TESTING

ROTOR TEST

1) Using an ohmmeter, measure resistance between rotor and slip rings (STEP 1 in illustration). *See Fig. 2.* If resistance is less than 5 ohms, replace rotor.

2) Using an ohmmeter, measure resistance between slip rings (STEP 2 in illustration). *See Fig. 2.* If resistance is greater than 3.5 ohms, replace rotor.

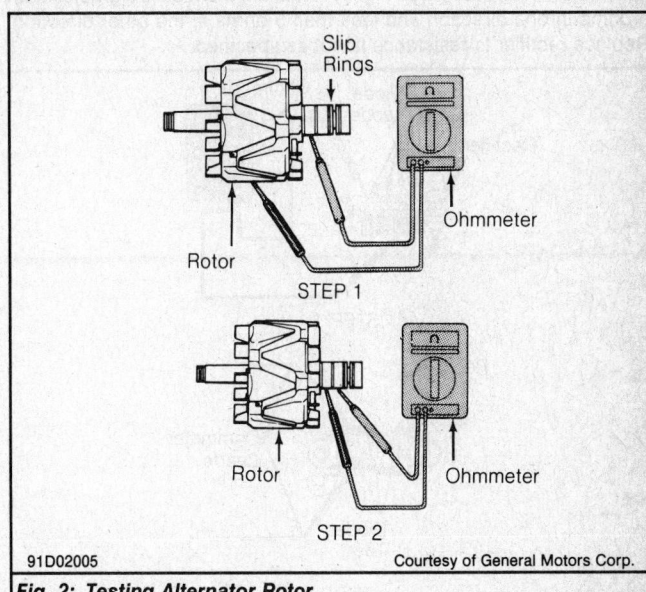

91D02005   Courtesy of General Motors Corp.

Fig. 2: Testing Alternator Rotor

STATOR TEST

1) Using an ohmmeter, measure resistance between stator leads (STEP 1 in illustration). *See Fig. 3.* If resistance is greater than 5 ohms for any measurement, replace stator.

2) Using an ohmmeter, measure resistance between each stator lead and stator core (STEP 2 in illustration). *See Fig. 3.* If resistance is less than 5 ohms, replace stator.

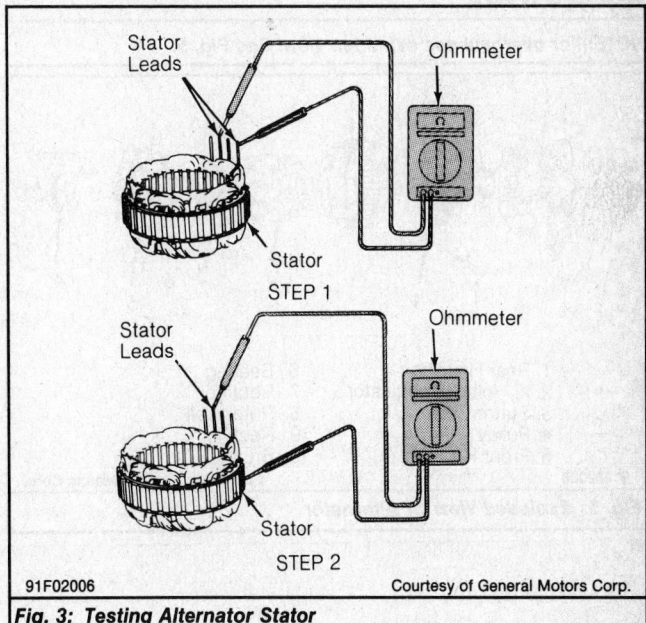

91F02006   Courtesy of General Motors Corp.

Fig. 3: Testing Alternator Stator

RECTIFIER TEST

1) Using an ohmmeter, measure resistance, between each diode lead and upper/lower rectifier bodies (STEP 1 in illustration). *See Fig. 4.* Check resistance in both directions by reversing ohmmeter leads. Resistance should be greater than 5 ohms in one direction and less than 5 ohms in the other direction. If resistance does not exist or exists in both directions, replace rectifier.

2) Using an ohmmeter, measure resistance between diode trio leads (STEP 2 in illustration). *See Fig. 4.* Resistance should be greater than 5 ohms in one direction and less than 5 ohms in the other direction. Replace rectifier is resistance is not as specified.

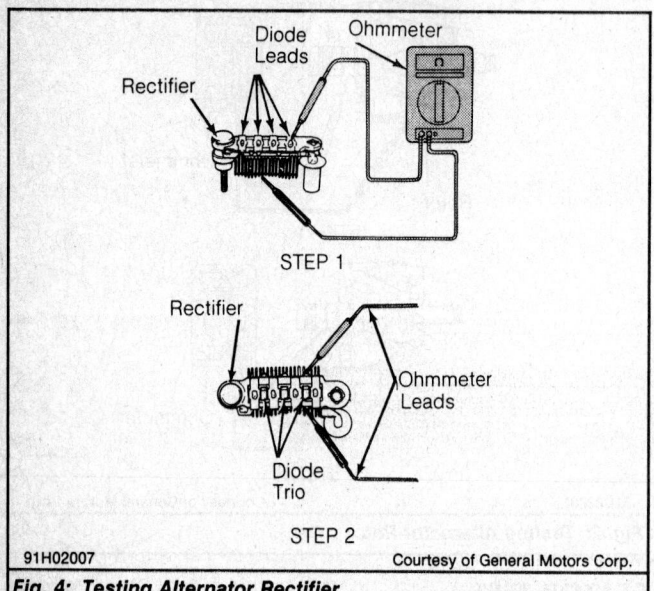

91H02007   Courtesy of General Motors Corp.

Fig. 4: Testing Alternator Rectifier

BRUSHES

Remove brush holder. Measure each brush from edge of brush holder at end of brush. Replace if brushes are not .08-.63" (2-16 mm).

OVERHAUL

NOTE: For overhaul see exploded view. See Fig. 5.

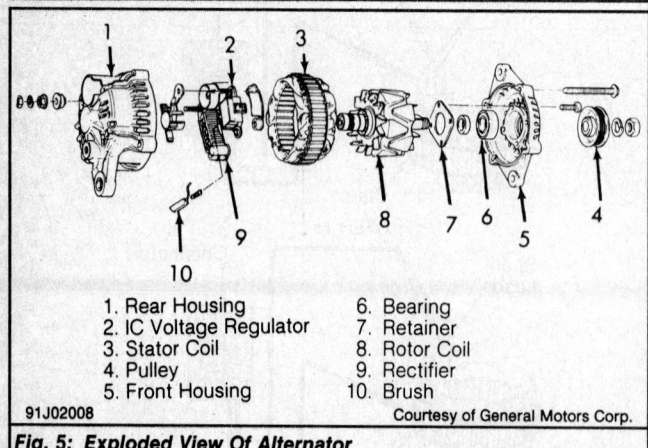

1. Rear Housing	6. Bearing
2. IC Voltage Regulator	7. Retainer
3. Stator Coil	8. Rotor Coil
4. Pulley	9. Rectifier
5. Front Housing	10. Brush

91J02008   Courtesy of General Motors Corp.

Fig. 5: Exploded View Of Alternator

TORQUE SPECIFICATIONS

TORQUE SPECIFICATIONS

Application	Ft. Lbs. (N.m)
Alternator Housing Bolts	10 (14)
Alternator Rectifier Nut	24 (33)
Drive Belt Adjusting Bolt	24 (33)
Lower Pivot Bolt/Nut	24 (33)
Upper Mounting Bolts/Nuts	20 (27)
Pulley Nut	48 (65)

WIRING DIAGRAM

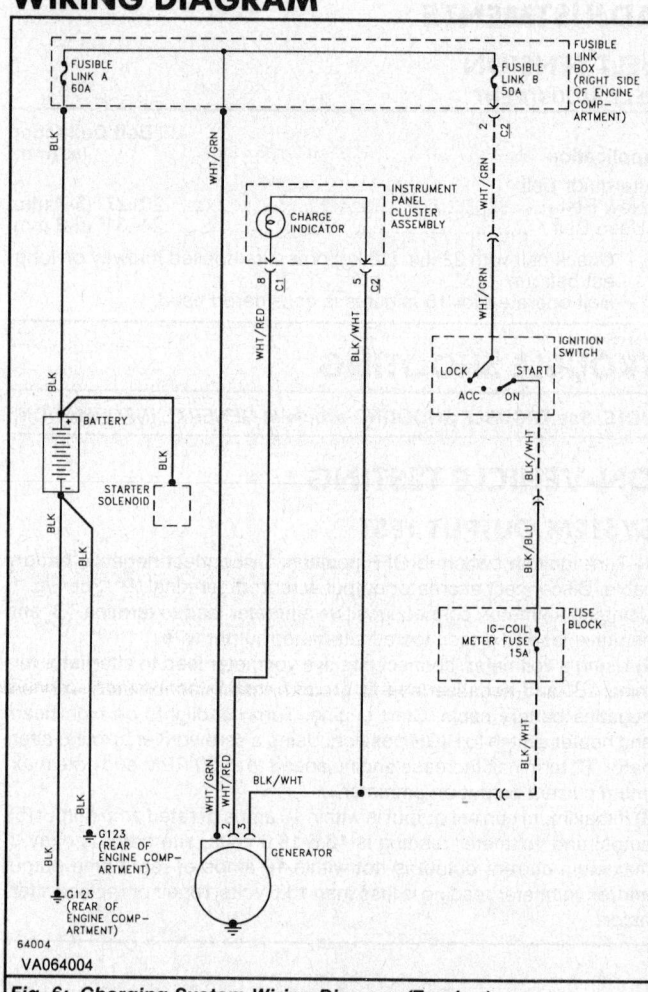

64004

VA064004

Fig. 6: Charging System Wiring Diagram (Tracker)

Metro (M/T)

DESCRIPTION

Metro models with manual transmission use 2 variations of the Nippondenso direct-drive starter depending on assembly plant location. Starters are identified by VIN J (Japan) or VIN 2 (Canada). Nippondenso direct drive starters are a conventional 12-volt, 4-brush-type. Starter solenoid attached to drive housing. When starter is energized, the starter solenoid engages starter pinion drive to flywheel ring gear. The overrunning clutch-pinion drive mounts directly on armature shaft drive end.

TROUBLE SHOOTING

NOTE: See TROUBLE SHOOTING article in GENERAL INFORMATION.

ON-VEHICLE TESTING

NOTE: Before testing, ensure battery is fully charged, battery cables and terminal ends are clean and tight, and engine grounds are good.

CRANKING TEST

1) With starter installed, connect voltmeter and ammeter to battery. See Fig. 1. Disconnect ignition coil secondary wire from distributor cap and attach to ground. Crank engine and observe meters.
2) On VIN J, current draw should be 270 amps at cranking voltage of 9.5 volts. On VIN 2, current draw should be 150 amps at cranking voltage of 9.0 volts. If readings are not as specified, replace starter.

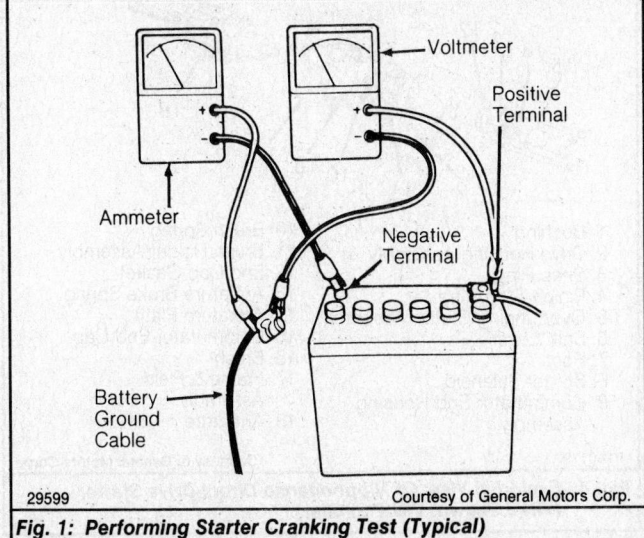

Fig. 1: Performing Starter Cranking Test (Typical)

CLUTCH START SWITCH

1) Clutch start switch, mounted to bracket above clutch pedal, completes start circuit when pedal is fully pressed. Switch is wired in series between ignition switch and starter solenoid.
2) Disconnect switch harness connector. Using ohmmeter, ensure continuity exists between switch connector terminals when clutch pedal is fully pressed. If continuity does not exist, adjust or replace switch.
3) Turn ignition switch to START position and fully press clutch pedal. Using test light, ensure switch has voltage on both connector terminals. Repair or replace if necessary.

BENCH TESTING

NO-LOAD TEST

1) Remove starter. Connect ammeter in series between starter and fully charged 12-volt battery. See Fig. 2.
2) Connect remote starter or jumper wire to battery and ST (start) terminal of solenoid. DO NOT crank starter longer than 5 seconds. On VIN J, current draw should be 42.5 amps at 11 volts. On VIN 2, current draw should be 60 amps at 11 volts. Ensure pinion gear extends quickly and completely.
3) Starter should spin smoothly. If starter does not operate as described, replace starter.

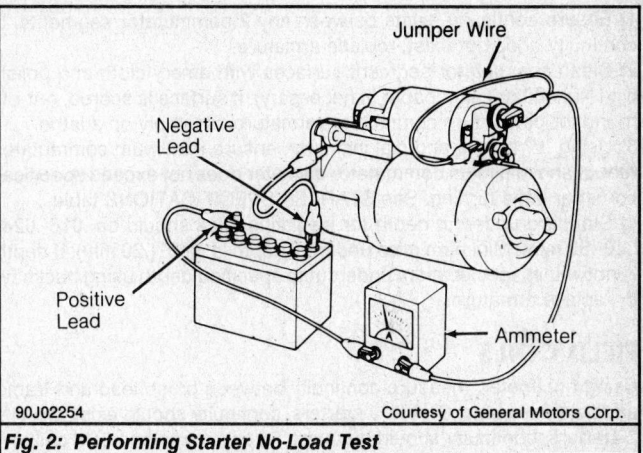

Fig. 2: Performing Starter No-Load Test

NOTE: Perform solenoid tests with starter assembled and field lead from starter disconnected at the solenoid.

CAUTION: DO NOT engage starter solenoid for more than 5 seconds during testing, or damage to coil winding may result.

SOLENOID TESTS

Solenoid Pull-In Coil Test – 1) Disconnect starter field lead from solenoid. Ensure field lead does not touch starter housing. See Fig. 3. Using 12-volt battery, connect negative battery lead to solenoid field lead terminal.
2) Connect another negative battery lead to starter housing. Connect positive battery lead to solenoid ST (start) terminal. Pinion gear should extend quickly and completely when solenoid is energized. If pinion gear does not operate as described, replace solenoid. If pinion gear operates as described, go to SOLENOID HOLD-IN COIL TEST and then PINION GEAR RETURN TEST.
Solenoid Hold-In Coil Test – After solenoid passes pull-in coil test, disconnect negative battery lead from solenoid field lead terminal. See Fig. 3. Pinion gear should remain extended. If pinion gear does not operate as described, replace solenoid. If pinion gear operates as described, go to PINION GEAR RETURN TEST.
Pinion Gear Return Test – Perform this test after solenoid passes pull-in coil test and hold-in coil test. With test leads still connected to starter, disconnect negative battery lead from starter housing. See Fig. 3. Pinion gear should retract smoothly. If pinion gear does not operate as described, replace solenoid and return spring.

ARMATURE TEST

1) Using ohmmeter, check continuity between commutator and armature core, and between commutator and shaft. Continuity should not exist. If continuity exists in either test, replace armature.
2) Ensure continuity exists between any 2 commutator segments. If continuity does not exist, replace armature.

BRUSHES & SPRINGS

1) Using ohmmeter, check continuity between positive and negative brush holders. Continuity should not exist. If continuity exists, replace shorted brush holder assembly.

2) Measure brush length. Brush length on Japanese produced models (VIN J) should be .42-.63" (10.7-16.0 mm). Brush length on Canadian produced models (VIN 2) should be .45-.67" (11.5-17.0 mm). Check brush springs for corrosion or damage. Ensure spring tension is sufficient to hold brushes against commutator. Ensure brushes move freely in holders.

COMMUTATOR TEST

1) Ensure continuity exists between any 2 commutator segments. If continuity does not exist, replace armature.

2) Clean commutator segment surfaces with emery cloth and polish with No. 400 grit sandpaper (if necessary). If surface is scored, out-of-round, or pitted, turn commutator/armature assembly on a lathe.

3) Using "V" blocks and dial indicator, ensure maximum commutator runout and minimum commutator diameter does not exceed specification after lathe turning. See STARTER SPECIFICATIONS table.

4) Standard undercut depth for insulating mica should be .016-.024" (.40-.60 mm). Minimum mica undercut depth is .008" (.20 mm). If depth is not within specification, undercut to specified depth using hacksaw or replace armature.

FIELD COILS

Using ohmmeter, measure continuity between brush lead and frame and field assembly. On VIN J starters, continuity should exist. On VIN 2 starters, continuity should not exist. Repair or replace field coil(s) if necessary.

OVERRUNNING CLUTCH-PINION GEAR

Ensure overrunning clutch-pinion gear assembly rotates freely in one direction and locks securely in opposite direction. Inspect pinion teeth for wear. Replace if necessary.

STARTER SPECIFICATIONS METRO M/T

Application	Specification
Brush Length	
VIN J	.42-.63" (10.7-16.0 mm)
VIN 2	.45-.67" (11.5-17.0 mm)
Commutator Insulation Depth	
Minimum Depth	.008" (.2 mm)
Standard Depth	
VIN 2	.016-.024" (.4-.6 mm)
Commutator Outside Diameter	
VIN J	1.1" (28 mm)
VIN 2	1.236-1.260" (31.4-32.0 mm)
Commutator Runout	.002-.016" (.05-.41 mm)
Starter Current Draw	
VIN J	
No-Load	42.5 Amps At 11 Volts
Load (60.2 INCH Lbs. Torque)	270 Amps At 9.5 Volts
Locked Rotor (112.4 INCH Lbs. Torque)	600 Amps At 7.7 Volts
VIN 2	
No-Load	60 Amps At 11.0 Volts
Load (23.9 INCH Lbs. Torque)	150 Amps At 9.0 Volts
Locked Rotor (76.1 INCH Lbs. Torque)	380 Amps At 5.0 Volts

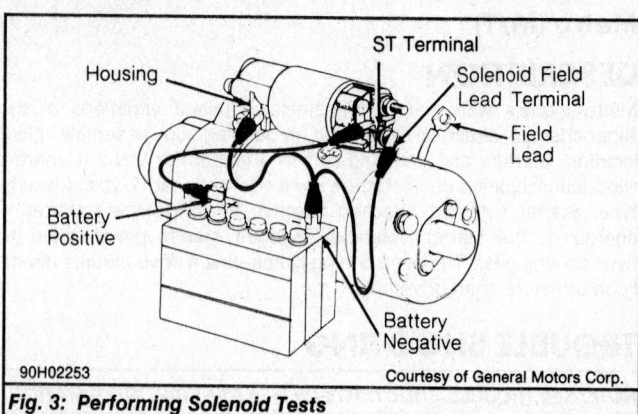

90H02253

Courtesy of General Motors Corp.

Fig. 3: Performing Solenoid Tests

OVERHAUL

NOTE: Use illustration for exploded view of starter. See Fig. 4.

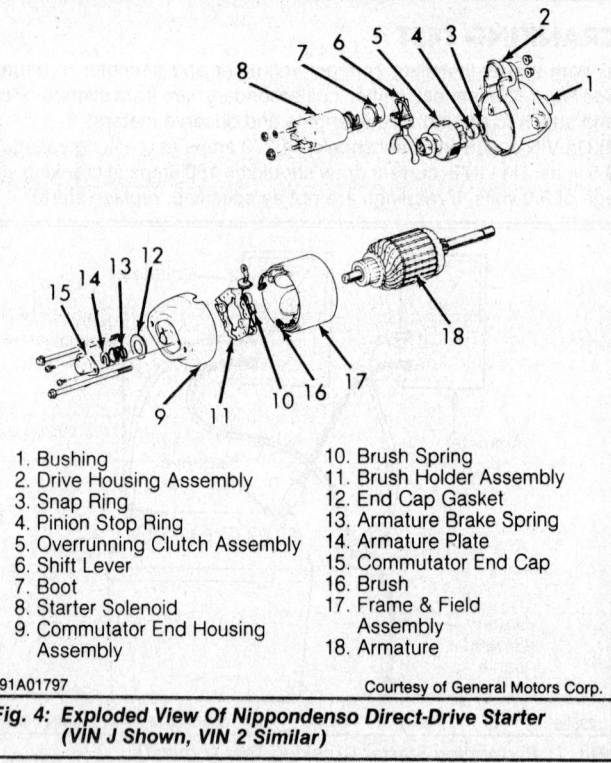

1. Bushing
2. Drive Housing Assembly
3. Snap Ring
4. Pinion Stop Ring
5. Overrunning Clutch Assembly
6. Shift Lever
7. Boot
8. Starter Solenoid
9. Commutator End Housing Assembly
10. Brush Spring
11. Brush Holder Assembly
12. End Cap Gasket
13. Armature Brake Spring
14. Armature Plate
15. Commutator End Cap
16. Brush
17. Frame & Field Assembly
18. Armature

91A01797

Courtesy of General Motors Corp.

Fig. 4: Exploded View Of Nippondenso Direct-Drive Starter (VIN J Shown, VIN 2 Similar)

TORQUE SPECIFICATIONS
TORQUE SPECIFICATIONS

Application	Ft. Lbs. (N.m)
Mounting Bolts	17 (23)

	INCH Lbs. (N.m)
Commutator End Housing Bolts	71 (8)
Solenoid Field Coil Lead Wire Nut	89 (10)
Solenoid Mounting Nuts	62 (7)

WIRING DIAGRAM

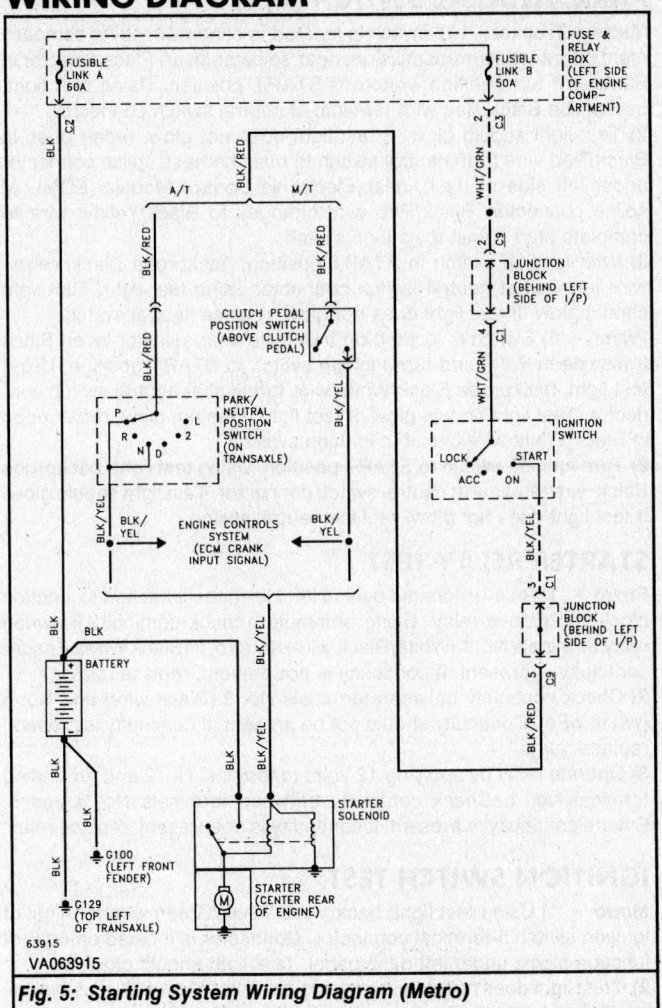

63915
VA063915

Fig. 5: Starting System Wiring Diagram (Metro)

Metro (A/T), Prizm, Tracker

DESCRIPTION

Nippondenso and Mitsubishi starters are solenoid-actuated gear reduction type. Starters are equipped with overrunning clutch/drive assembly. The brush holder assembly contains 4 brushes and springs in the commutator end of starter housing. The integral starter solenoid is attached to the drive housing. All vehicles use some type of clutch start (M/T) or neutral safety (A/T) switch incorporated within starter wiring circuit. Prizm using relays in starter wiring circuit.

ON-VEHICLE TESTING

NOTE: Before testing, ensure battery is fully charged, battery cables and terminal ends are clean and tight and engine grounds are good.

CRANKING TEST

1) Connect voltmeter and ammeter to battery. *See Fig. 1.* Ensure battery is fully charged. Disconnect ignition coil secondary wire from distributor cap, and attach it to ground. Crank engine, and observe meters.
2) Ensure cranking voltage more than 9.5 volts and current draw is less than 230 amps. If readings are not as specified, repair or replace starter.

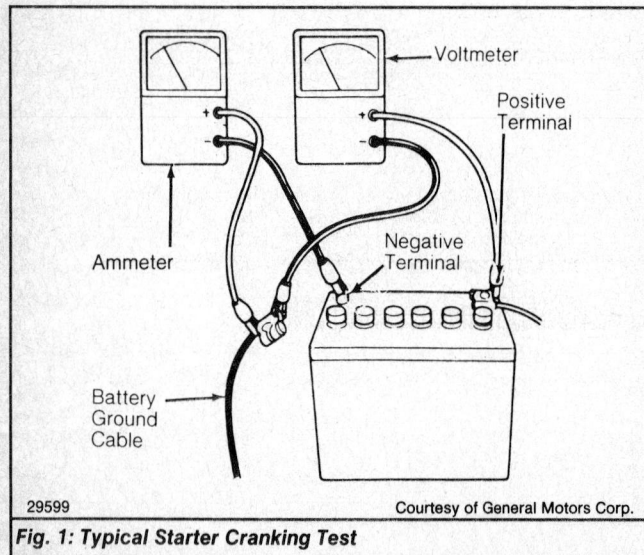

29599   Courtesy of General Motors Corp.

Fig. 1: Typical Starter Cranking Test

CIRCUIT TEST

If a no-start condition exists, touch test light to starter solenoid "S" terminal. Put gear selector in Park (A/T) or Neutral (M/T) position. On M/T, fully depress clutch pedal. On all models turn ignition switch to START position. If test light does not glow, check ignition switch, relays and wiring circuit. See appropriate relay and switch tests under ON-VEHICLE TESTING. If test light glows, check battery cable connections. If connections are okay, remove starter, and go to BENCH TESTING.

CLUTCH PEDAL POSITION SWITCH (M/T)

1) Switch is located above clutch pedal on bracket. Disconnect switch harness connector.
2) With clutch pedal fully depressed, using ohmmeter, check continuity between switch connector terminals. If continuity exists, check circuits between starter solenoid and clutch pedal switch, and battery and clutch pedal switch. If continuity is not present, adjust or replace switch as required.

PARK/NEUTRAL SWITCH (A/T)

Metro & Tracker – 1) Switch is located in center of engine compartment on transaxle/transmission, near selector lever. Place selector in Park, and turn ignition switch to START position. Using test light, backprobe Black/Red wire terminal at neutral switch connector.
2) Test light should glow. If test light does not glow, repair open in Black/Red wire from neutral switch to main harness splice connector under left side of dash, near Electronic Control Module (ECM). At splice connector, Black/Red wire changes to Black/Yellow wire to complete start circuit to ignition switch.
3) With ignition switch in START position, backprobe Black/Yellow wire terminal at neutral switch connector using test light. Test light should glow. If test light does not glow, replace neutral switch.
Prizm – 1) Switch is located on transaxle near selector lever. Place transaxle in Park, and turn ignition switch to START position. Using test light, backprobe Black/White wire terminal at neutral switch connector. Test light should glow. If test light does not glow, repair open in Black/White wire circuit to ignition switch.
2) Turn ignition switch to START position. Using test light, backprobe Black wire terminal at neutral switch connector. Test light should glow. If test light does not glow, replace neutral switch.

STARTER RELAY TEST

Prizm – 1) Relay is located behind left kick panel attached to junction block 1. Remove relay. Using ohmmeter, check continuity between relay terminals No. 1 (White/Black wire) and No. 2 (Black Wire). Ensure continuity is present. If continuity is not present, replace relay.
2) Check continuity between terminals No. 3 (Black wire) and No. 5 (White wire). Continuity should not be present. If continuity is present, replace relay.
3) Operate relay by applying 12 volts to terminal No. 2 and grounding terminal No. 1. Check continuity between terminals No. 3 and 5. Ensure continuity is present. If continuity is not present, replace relay.

IGNITION SWITCH TEST

Metro – 1) Using test light, backprobe White/Green wire terminal of ignition switch 5-terminal connector. Connector is located on right of junction block, under left dash panel. Test light should glow.
2) If test light does not glow, check fusible links "A" and "B". Fusible link box is located behind battery. Check for open in wiring circuit (White/Green wire) to ignition switch. See WIRING DIAGRAMS.
3) Turn ignition switch to START position. Using a test light, backprobe Black/Yellow wire terminal at ignition switch (start circuit) and Black/Blue wire terminal (ignition power circuit). Test light should glow. If test light does not glow at either terminal, replace ignition switch.
Prizm – 1) Using test light connected to ground, backprobe White wire terminal of ignition switch connector. Connector is located behind lower instrument panel. Test light should glow.
2) If test light does not glow, check fusible link AM1. Fuse and Relay box is located on positive battery cable. Check for open in wiring circuit to ignition switch. See WIRING DIAGRAMS.
3) Turn ignition switch to START position. Using a test light, backprobe Black/White wire terminal at ignition switch connector (start circuit). Test light should glow. If test light does not glow, replace ignition switch.
Tracker – 1) Using test light, backprobe White/Green wire terminal of ignition switch 7-terminal connector. Connector is located behind lower instrument panel, near steering column. Test light should glow.
2) If test light does not glow, check fusible link "B". Fusible link box is located on right inner fender. Check for open in White/Green wiring circuit to ignition switch. See WIRING DIAGRAMS.
3) Turn ignition switch to START position. Using a test light, backprobe Black/Yellow wire terminal (at ignition switch 7-terminal connector) to starter circuit. Test light should glow. If test light does not glow, replace ignition switch.

BENCH TESTING

NO-LOAD TEST

1) Remove starter. Connect ammeter in series with starter motor and fully charged 12-volt battery. *See Fig. 2.* Connect voltmeter to battery to observe voltage draw readings.

2) Connect remote starter or jumper wire to battery and starter terminal of solenoid. Crank starter for maximum of 5 seconds. Starter drive pinion should extend completely and quickly. Starter should spin rapidly and smoothly. See STARTER SPECIFICATIONS table for current draw specification. If current draw is not as specified, repair or replace starter.

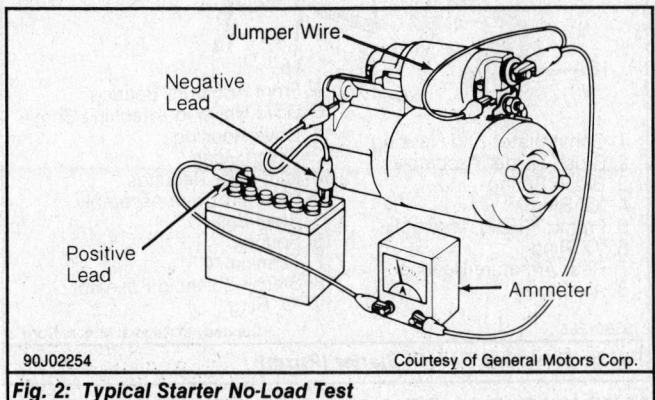

90J02254   Courtesy of General Motors Corp.

Fig. 2: Typical Starter No-Load Test

SOLENOID PULL-IN COIL TEST

NOTE: Perform the following solenoid tests with starter assembled and field lead disconnected from starter at solenoid.

CAUTION: DO NOT engage starter solenoid for longer than 5 seconds during testing or damage to coil winding may result.

1) Disconnect field lead from solenoid field lead (solenoid-to-starter wire) terminal. *See Fig. 3.* Ensure field lead does not touch starter housing. Connect negative lead of 12-volt battery to solenoid field lead terminal (terminal "C"). *See Fig. 3 or 6.*

2) Connect another negative battery lead to starter drive housing. Connect positive battery lead to solenoid ST terminal. *See Fig. 3.*

3) Pinion gear should extend quickly and completely when solenoid is energized. If pinion gear does not operate as indicated, replace solenoid.

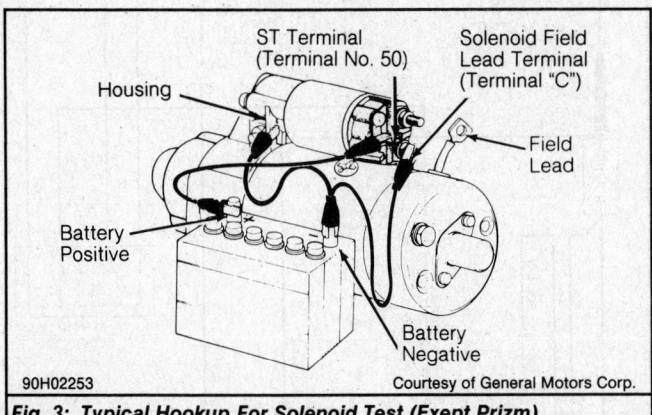

90H02253   Courtesy of General Motors Corp.

Fig. 3: Typical Hookup For Solenoid Test (Exept Prizm)

SOLENOID HOLD-IN COIL TEST

If pull-in coil tests okay, disconnect negative battery lead from solenoid field lead terminal (terminal "C"). Pinion gear should remain extended. If pinion gear does not operate as indicated, replace solenoid.

STARTER COMPONENT INSPECTION

Armature Coil – **1)** Using ohmmeter, check continuity between armature core and insulation between commutator segments. No continuity should be present. If continuity is not present, check armature for shorts using a growler. Replace armature as required.

2) Ensure continuity exists between segments on commutator. If continuity is not present between any 2 segments, replace armature.

Brushes & Springs – **1)** Measure brush length, and replace brushes if less than specification. See STARTER SPECIFICATIONS table. Check brush springs for corrosion or damage. Ensure spring tension is sufficient to press brushes against commutator.

2) Check condition of brush holders, spring clips and insulation between positive and negative holders. Repair or replace as required. Ensure brushes move freely in holders. Before installing new brushes, buff commutator end of brush using emery cloth.

Commutator – **1)** Using "V" blocks and dial indicator, check commutator runout (out-of-round). See STARTER SPECIFICATIONS table. Turn commutator/armature on lathe until runout (out-of-round) is within specification.

2) Check commutator diameter. Commutator should not be less than specification. See STARTER SPECIFICATIONS table.

Field Coil – Check field coils in housing for open circuits. Ensure continuity exists between field lead wire and field coil brush lead. If continuity is not present, replace field coil. Check field coils for short circuits. If shorts exist, replace defective field coil.

STARTER SPECIFICATIONS

Application	Specification
Brush Length	
Metro A/T (VIN J)	.35-.55" (9-14 mm)
Metro A/T (VIN 2)	.47-.69" (12-18 mm)
Prizm	.39-.61" (10-15 mm)
Tracker	.47-.69" (12-18 mm)
Commutator Insulation Depth	
Minimum Depth	.008" (.2 mm)
Standard Depth	
Metro (A/T VIN 2)	.020-.031" (.5-.8 mm)
Prizm	.024" (.6 mm)
Tracker	.020-.031" (.5-.8 mm)
Commutator Outside Diameter	
Metro (A/T VIN J)	1.1" (28 mm)
Metro (A/T VIN 2)	1.134-1.157" (28.8-29.4 mm)
Prizm	1.14-1.18" (28.9-30.0 mm)
Tracker	1.134-1.157" (28.8-29.4 mm)
Commutator Runout	.002-.016" (.05-.41 mm)
Starter Current Draw	
Metro (A/T VIN J)	
No-Load	75 Amps At 11.5 Volts
Load (67.3 INCH Lbs. Torque)	230 Amps At 8.7 Volts
Locked Rotor (75.2 INCH Lbs. Torque)	310 Amps At 2.5 Volts
Metro (A/T VIN 2)	
No-Load	75 Amps At 11.0 Volts
Load (80.5 INCH Lbs. Torque)	300 Amps At 7.7 Volts
Locked Rotor (13.7 Ft. Lbs. Torque)	780 Amps At 4.0 Volts
Prizm	
No-Load	60-90 Amps At 11.0 Volts
Tracker	
No-Load A/T	50 amps at 11.0 volts
No-Load M/T	90 amps at 11.0 volts
Load A/T(92.0 INCH Lbs. Torque)	300 Amps At 7.7 Volts
Load M/T(80.5 INCH Lbs. Torque)	300 Amps At 7.7 Volts
Locked Rotor A/T(18.8 Ft. Lbs. Torque)	980 Amps At 4.0 Volts
Locked Rotor M/T(13.8 Ft. Lbs. Torque)	780 Amps At 4.0 Volts

OVERHAUL

NOTE: Use illustration for exploded view of starters. See Figs. 4-6.

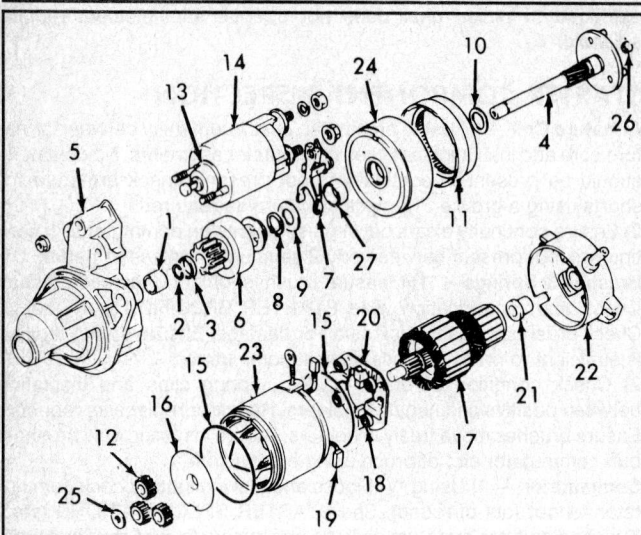

1. Needle Bearing
2. Snap Ring
3. Pinion Stop Ring
4. Planetary Carrier Shaft
5. Drive Housing Assembly
6. Overrunning Clutch Assembly
7. Shift Lever
8. "C" Clip
9. Washer
10. Washer
11. Internal Gear
12. Planetary Gear
13. Boot
14. Starter Solenoid
15. "O" Ring
16. Plate
17. Armature
18. Brush Spring
19. Brush
20. Brush Holder Assembly
21. Bushing
22. Commutator End Housing
23. Frame & Field Assembly
24. Center Bearing & Shock Absorber
25. Washer
26. Bushing
27. Bushing

90E08965   Courtesy of General Motors Corp.

Fig. 4: Exploded View Of Starter (Metro A/T VIN J)

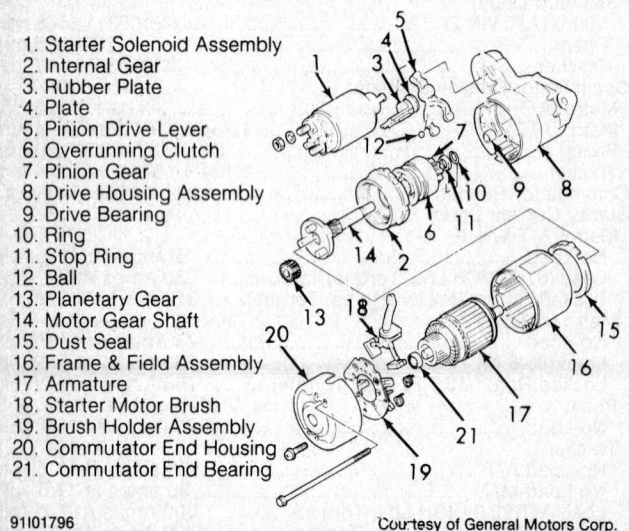

1. Starter Solenoid Assembly
2. Internal Gear
3. Rubber Plate
4. Plate
5. Pinion Drive Lever
6. Overrunning Clutch
7. Pinion Gear
8. Drive Housing Assembly
9. Drive Bearing
10. Ring
11. Stop Ring
12. Ball
13. Planetary Gear
14. Motor Gear Shaft
15. Dust Seal
16. Frame & Field Assembly
17. Armature
18. Starter Motor Brush
19. Brush Holder Assembly
20. Commutator End Housing
21. Commutator End Bearing

91I01796   Courtesy of General Motors Corp.

Fig. 5: Exploded View Of Starter (Metro A/T VIN 2 & Tracker)

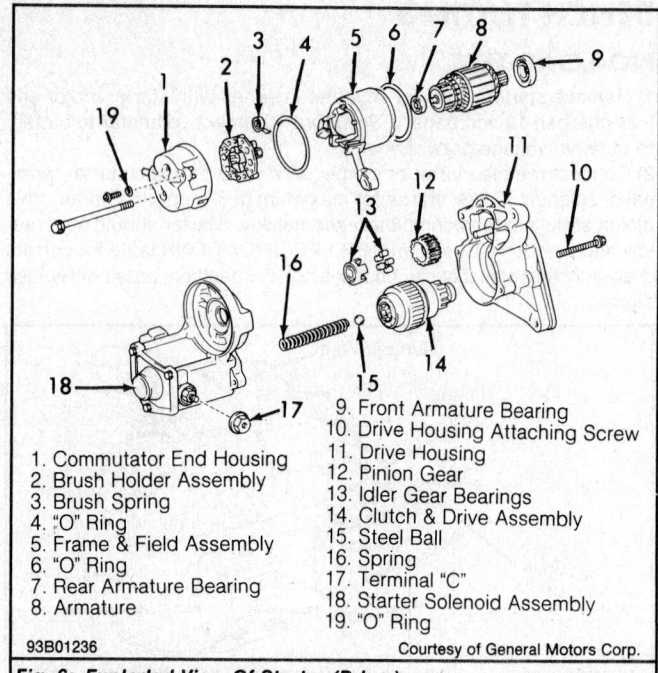

1. Commutator End Housing
2. Brush Holder Assembly
3. Brush Spring
4. "O" Ring
5. Frame & Field Assembly
6. "O" Ring
7. Rear Armature Bearing
8. Armature
9. Front Armature Bearing
10. Drive Housing Attaching Screw
11. Drive Housing
12. Pinion Gear
13. Idler Gear Bearings
14. Clutch & Drive Assembly
15. Steel Ball
16. Spring
17. Terminal "C"
18. Starter Solenoid Assembly
19. "O" Ring

93B01236   Courtesy of General Motors Corp.

Fig. 6: Exploded View Of Starter (Prizm)

WIRING DIAGRAMS

NOTE: For Metro starting system wiring diagram, see STARTERS – DIRECT DRIVE article.

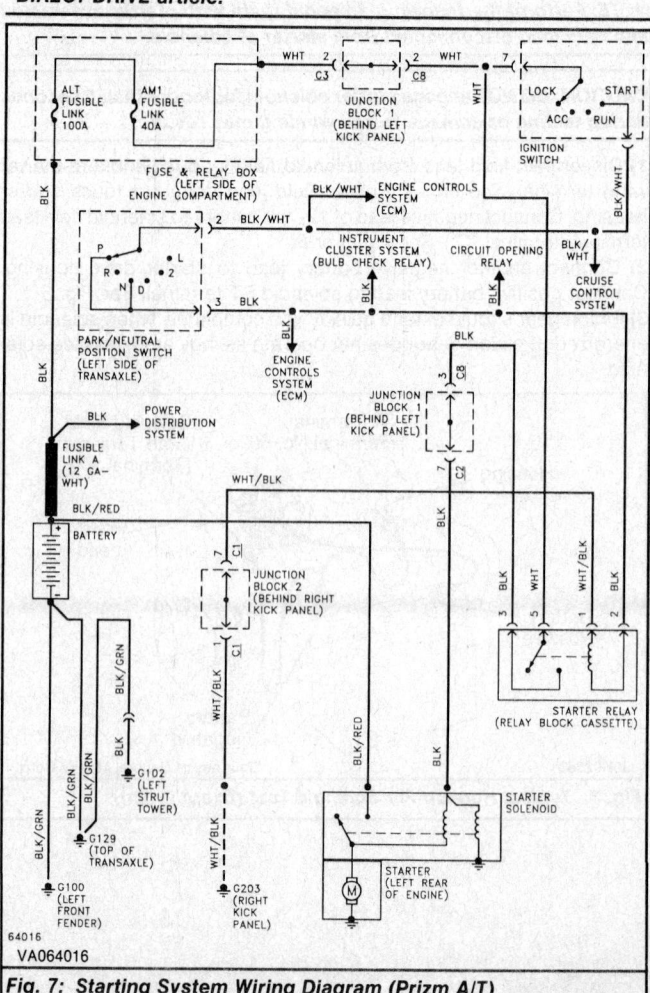

Fig. 7: Starting System Wiring Diagram (Prizm A/T)

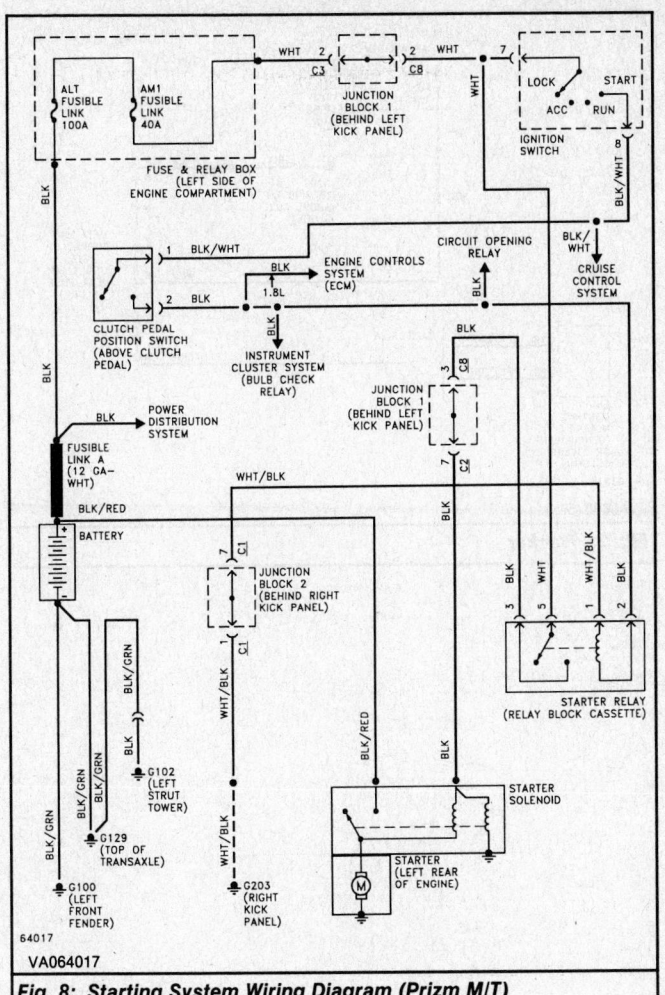

Fig. 8: Starting System Wiring Diagram (Prizm M/T)

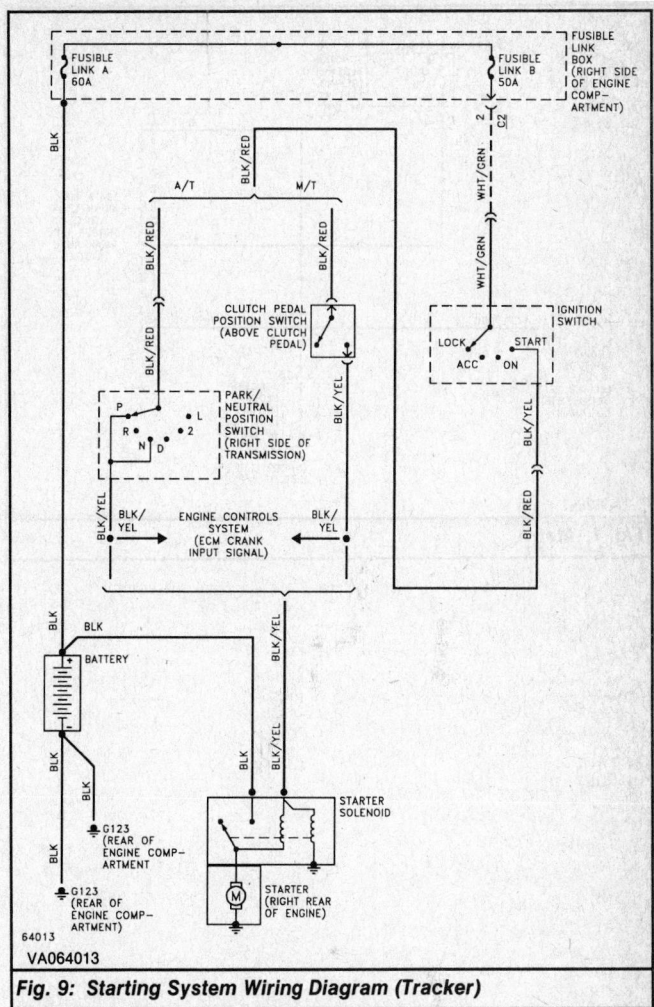

Fig. 9: Starting System Wiring Diagram (Tracker)

TORQUE SPECIFICATIONS

STARTER TORQUE SPECIFICATIONS

Model	Ft. Lbs. (N.m)
Commutator End Cover Bolts	
Tracker	22 (30)
Starter Mounting Bolts	
Metro (A/T)	17 (23)
Prizm	31 (42)
Tracker	22 (30)
Solenoid Field Coil Lead Wire Nut	
Tracker	11 (15)

	INCH Lbs (N.m)
Battery-To-Starter Terminal Nut	
Prizm	80 (9)
Commutator End Cover Bolts	
Metro	71 (8)
Solenoid Field Coil Lead Wire Nut	
Metro	89 (10)
Prizm	71 (8)
Starter Assembly Bolts	
Prizm	53 (6)

1994 WIRING DIAGRAMS
Data Link Connectors

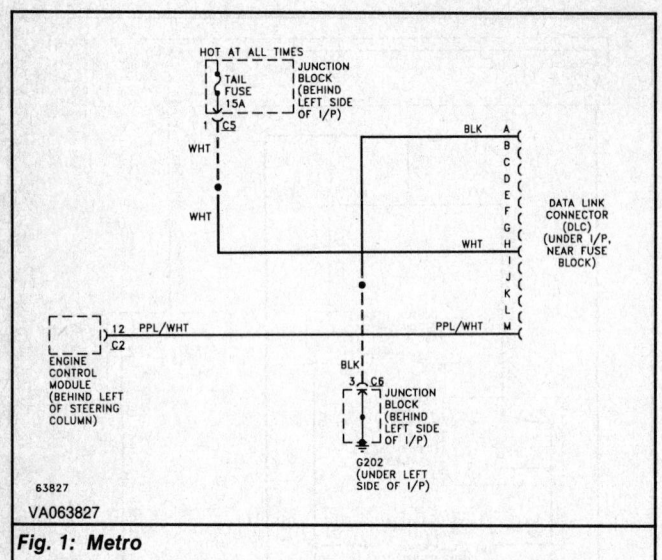

Fig. 1: Metro

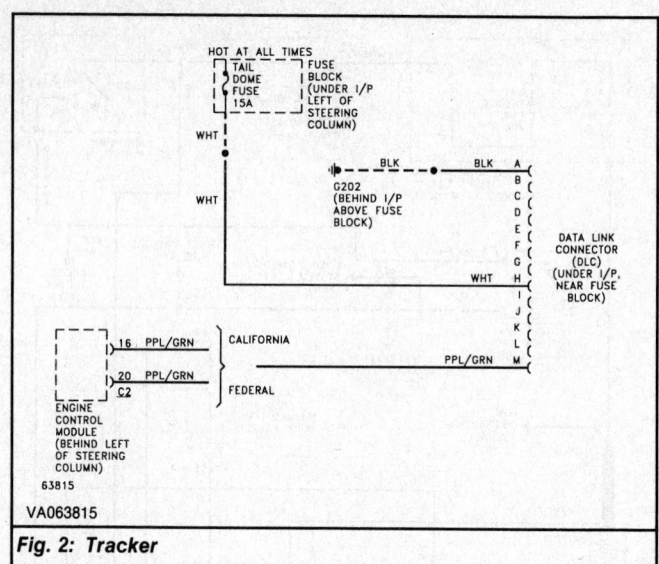

Fig. 2: Tracker

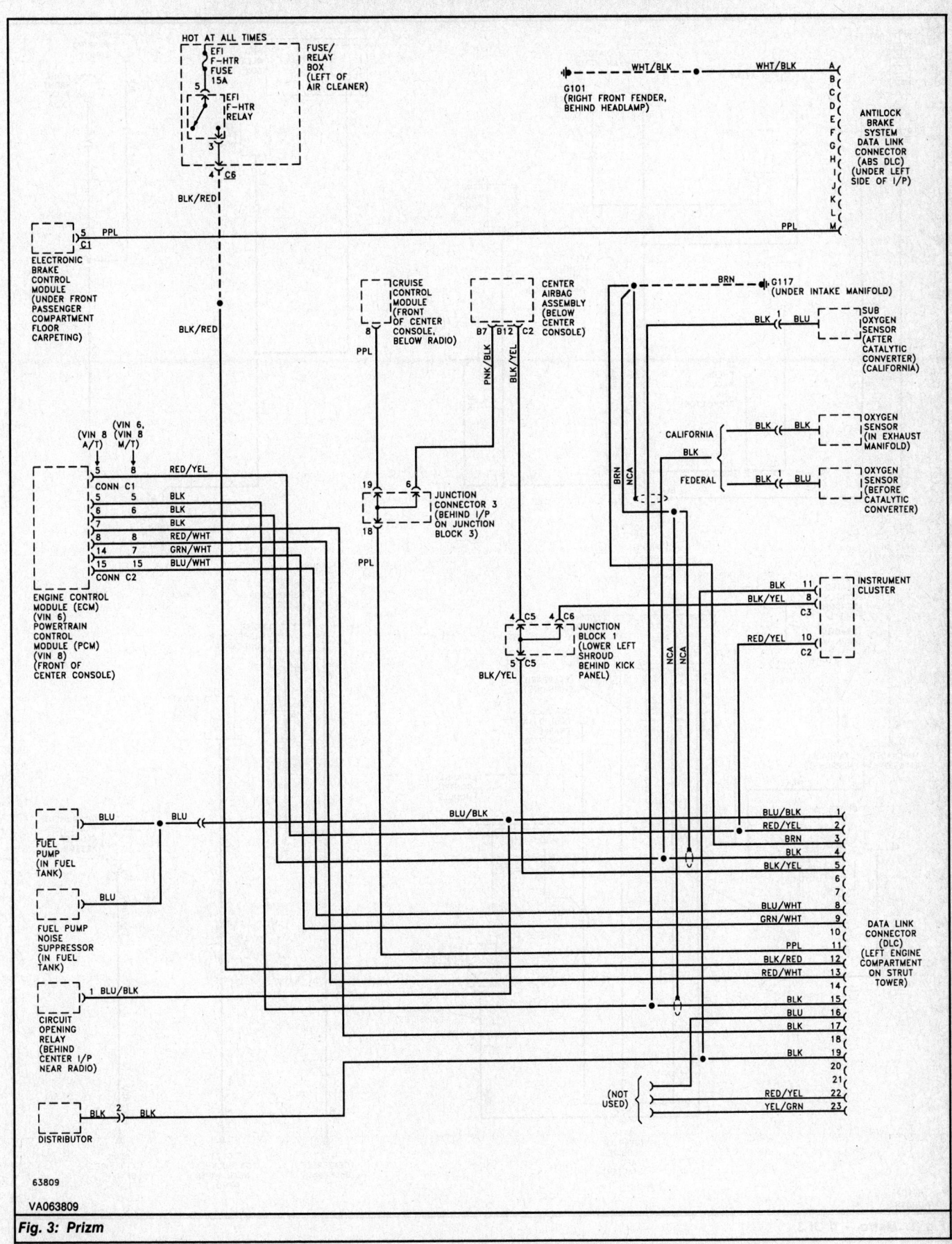

Fig. 3: Prizm

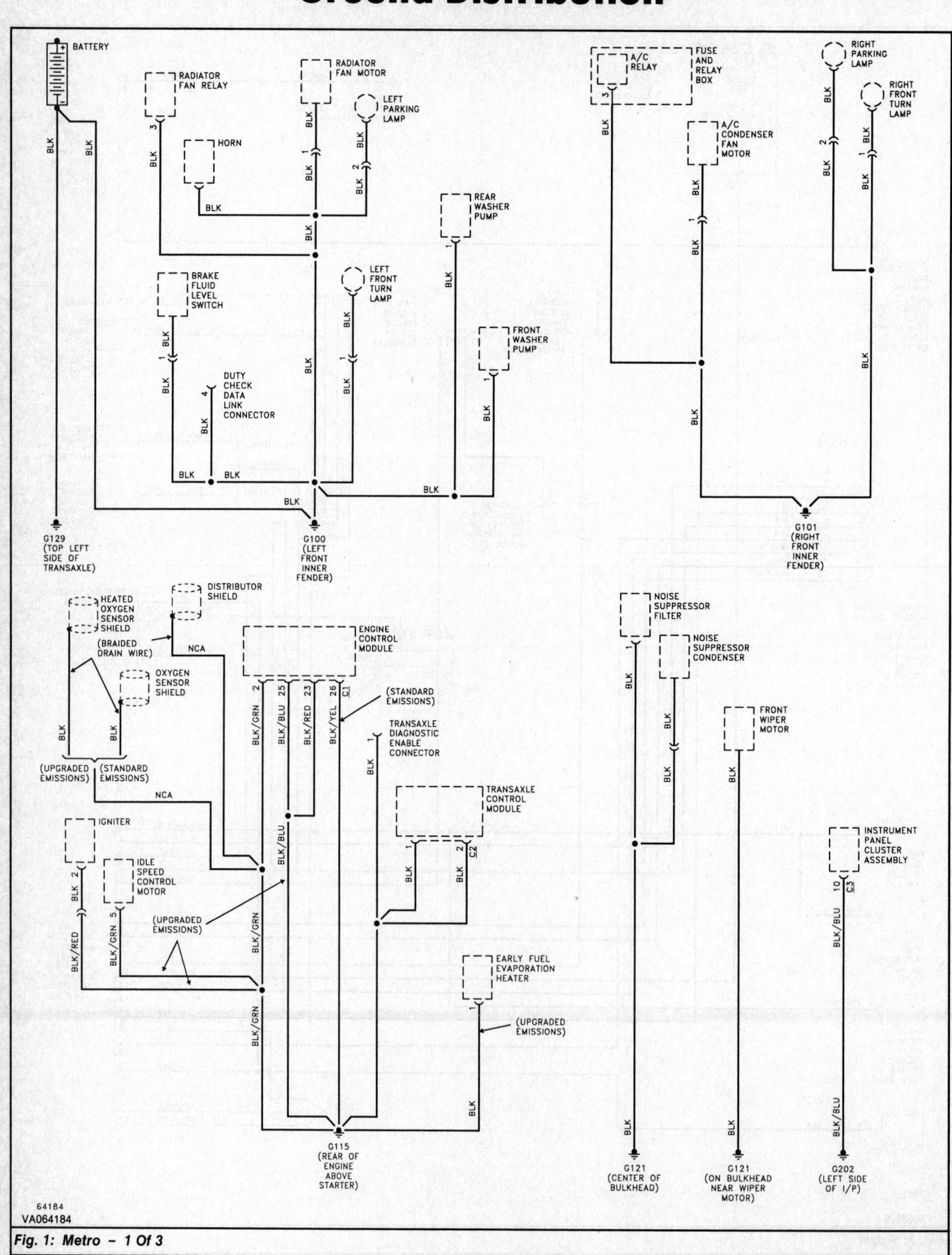

64184
VA064184

Fig. 1: Metro – 1 Of 3

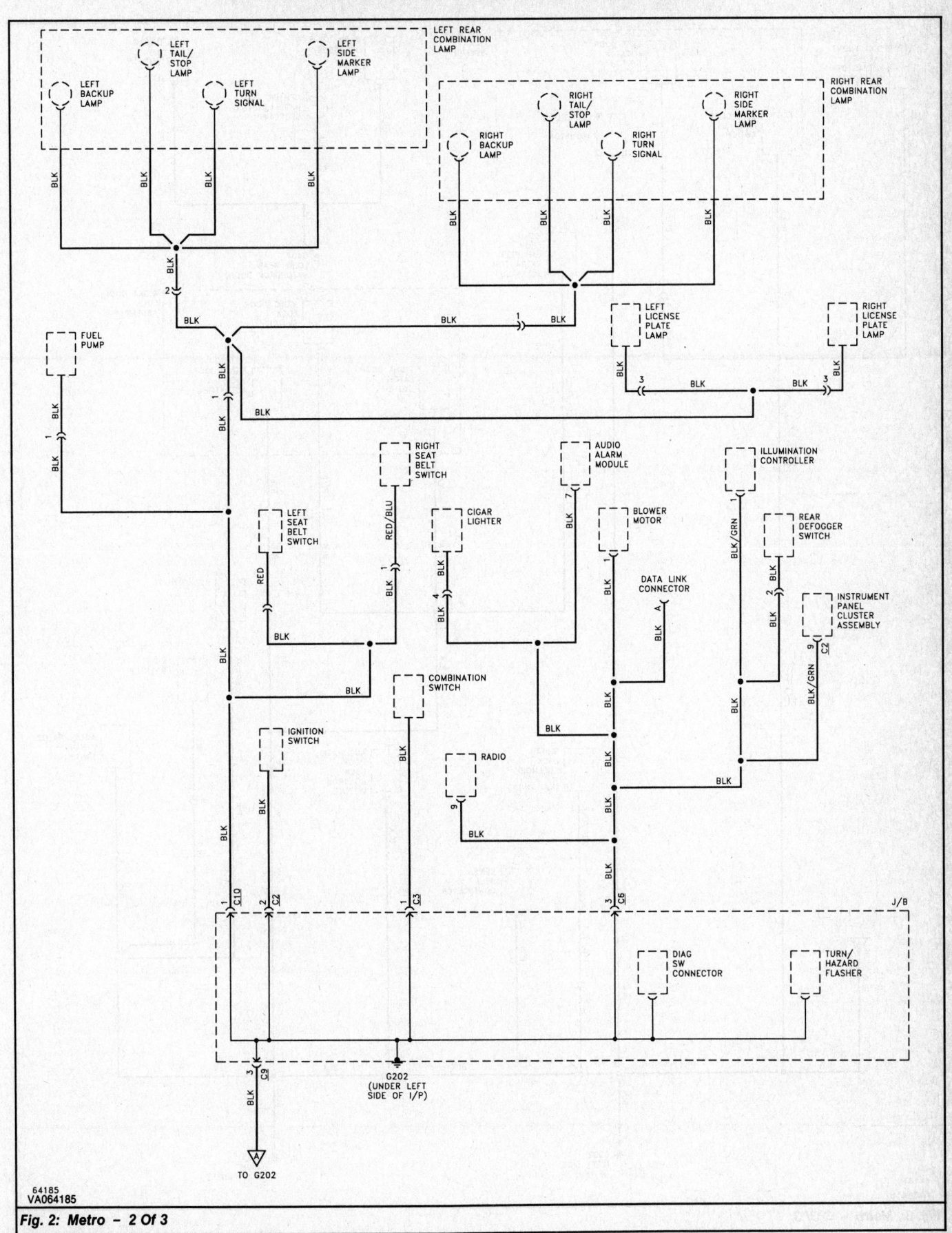

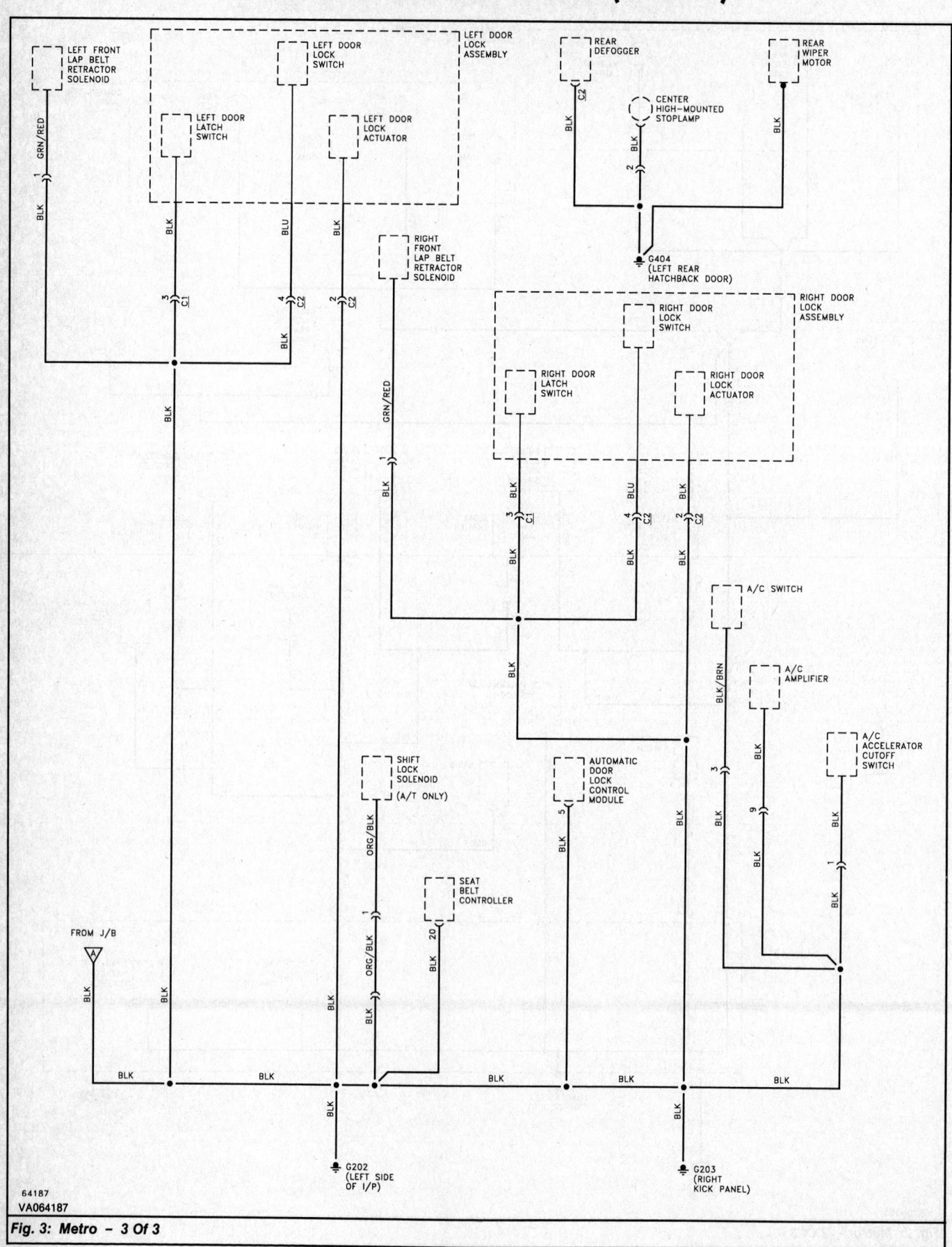

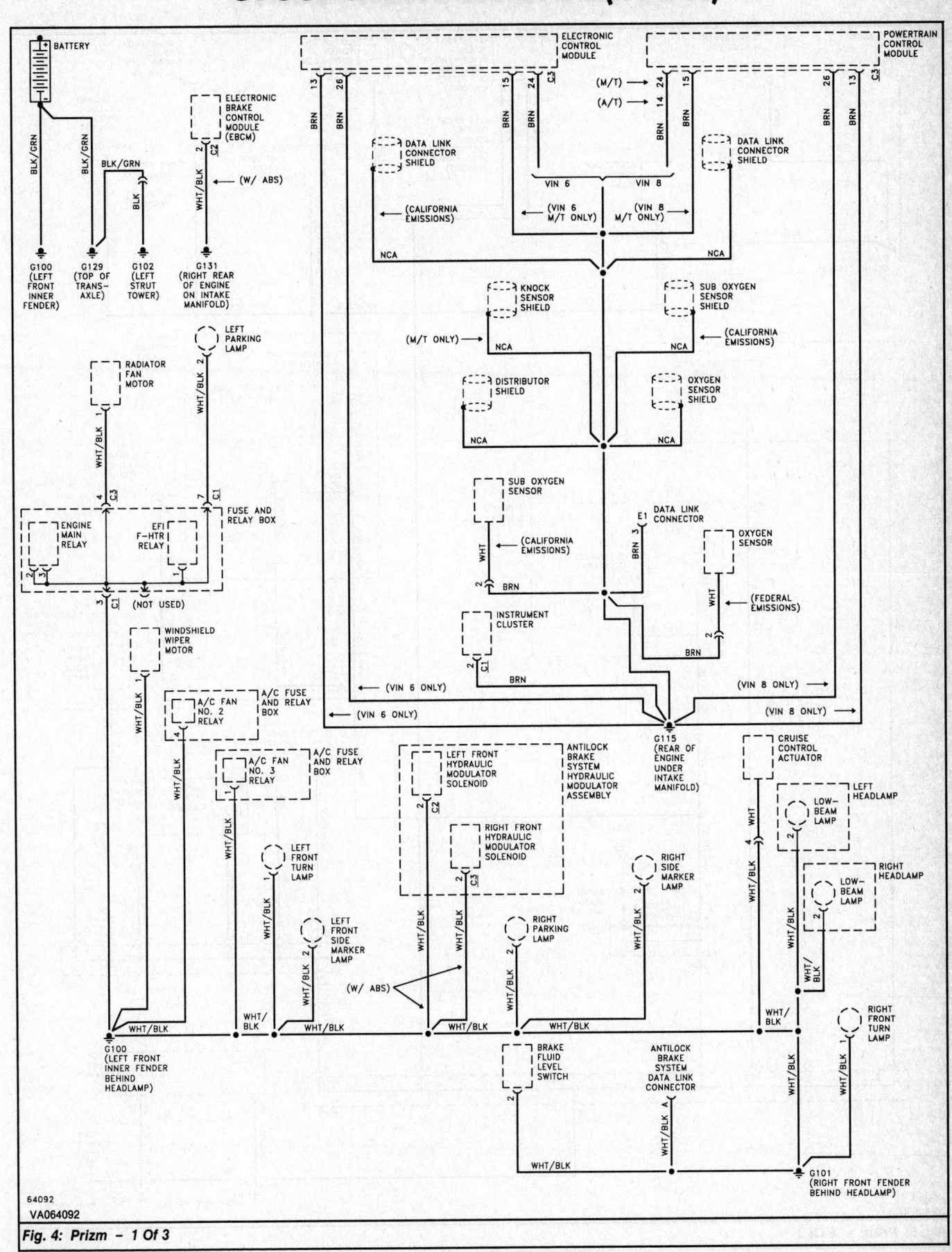

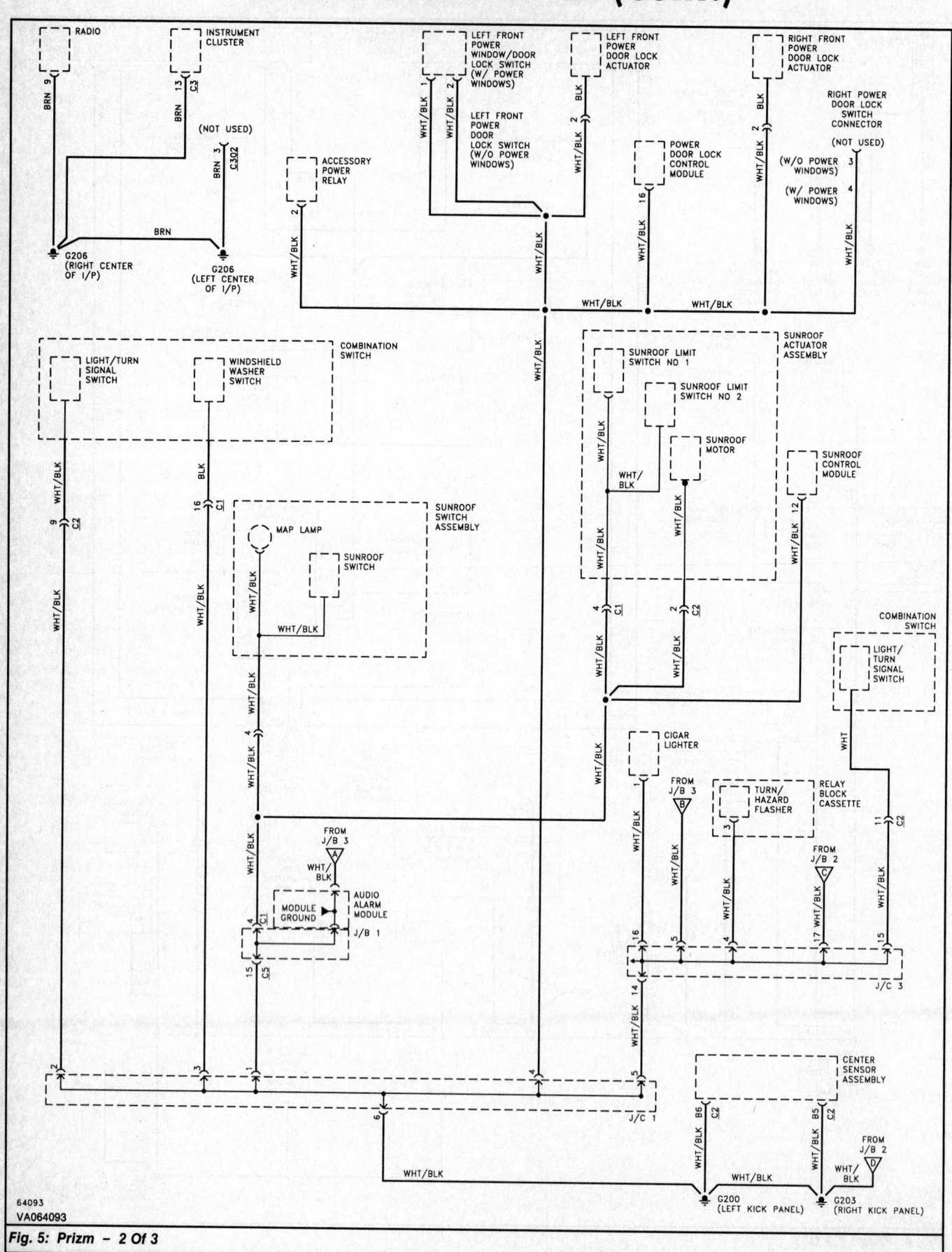

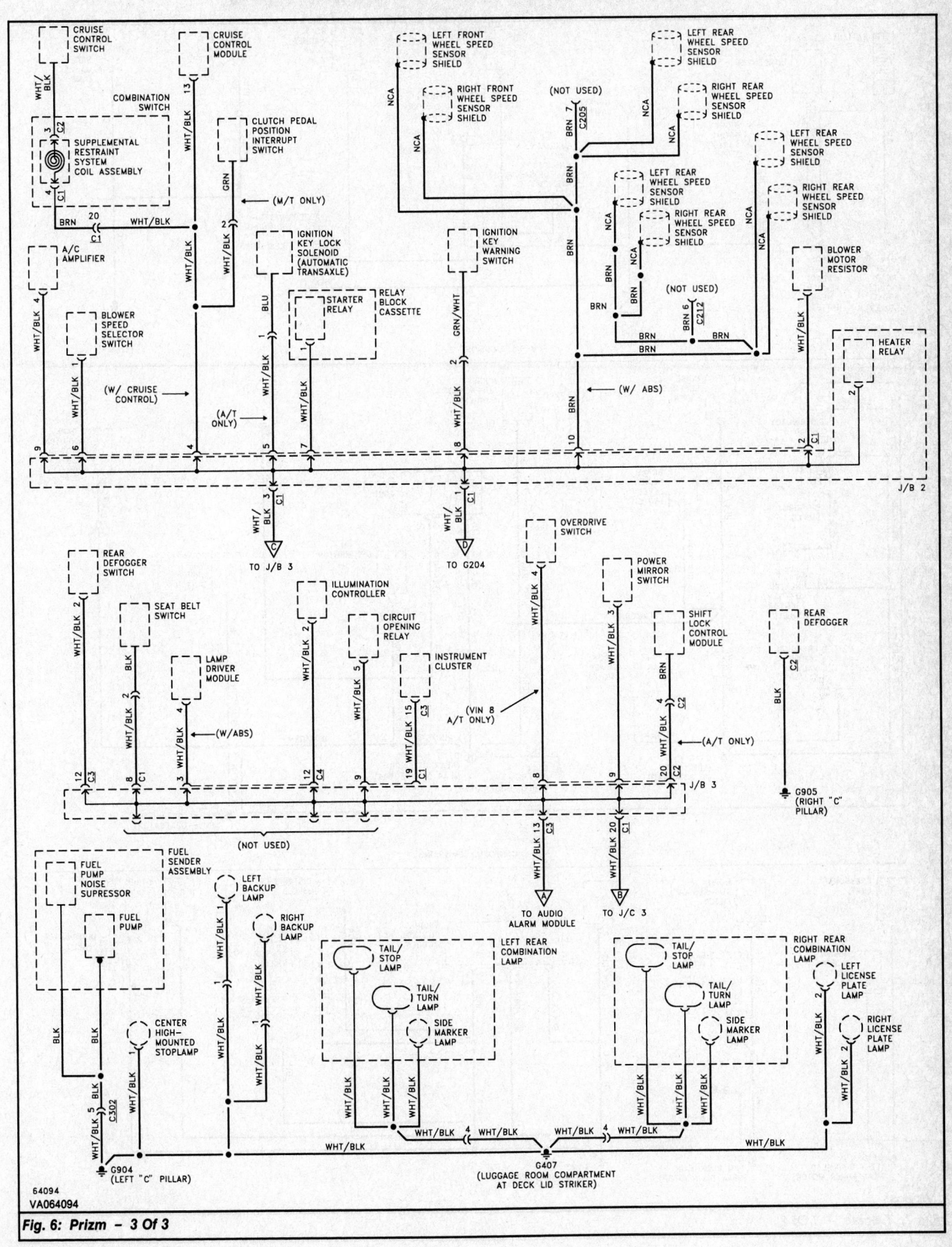

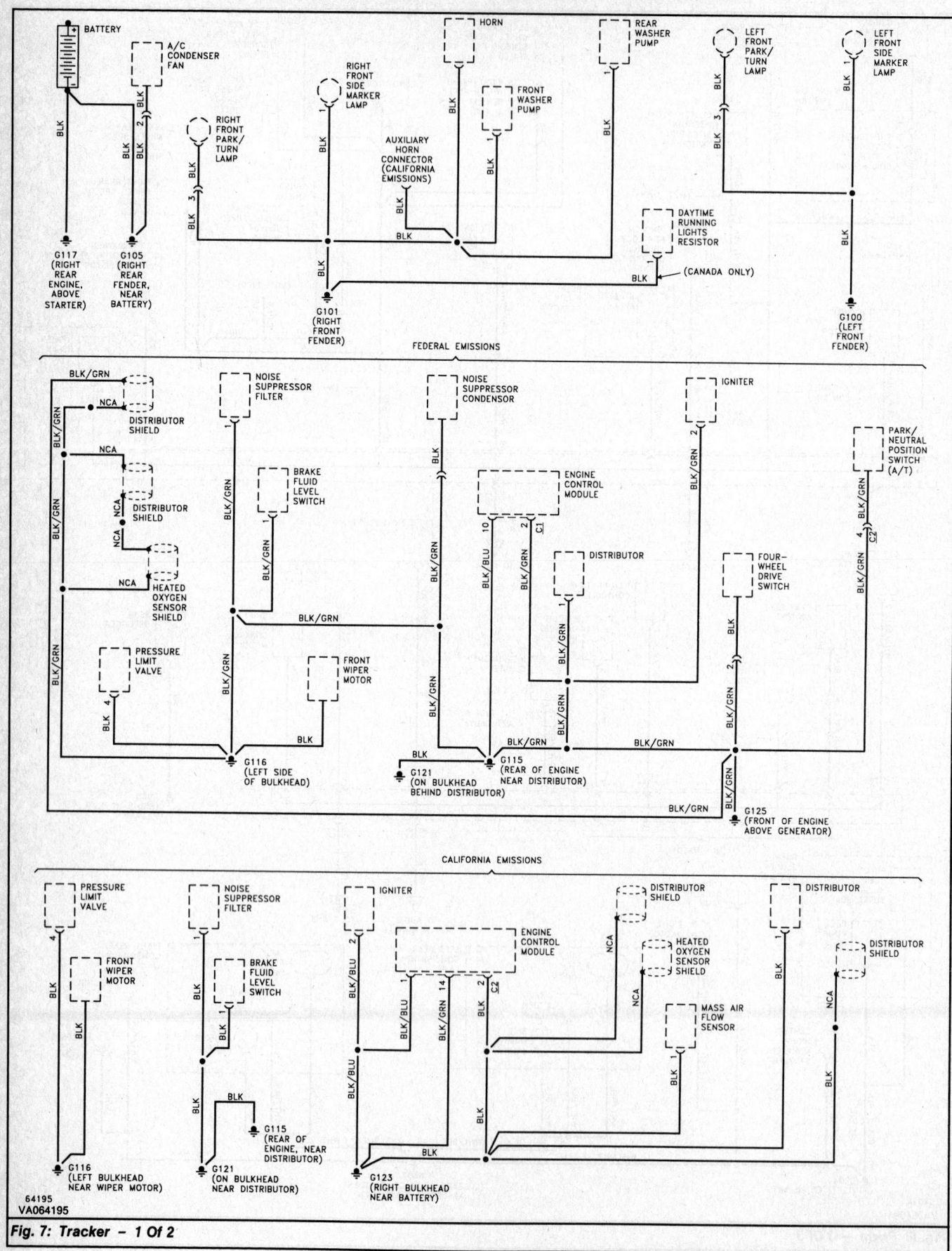

Fig. 7: Tracker - 1 Of 2

64195
VA064195

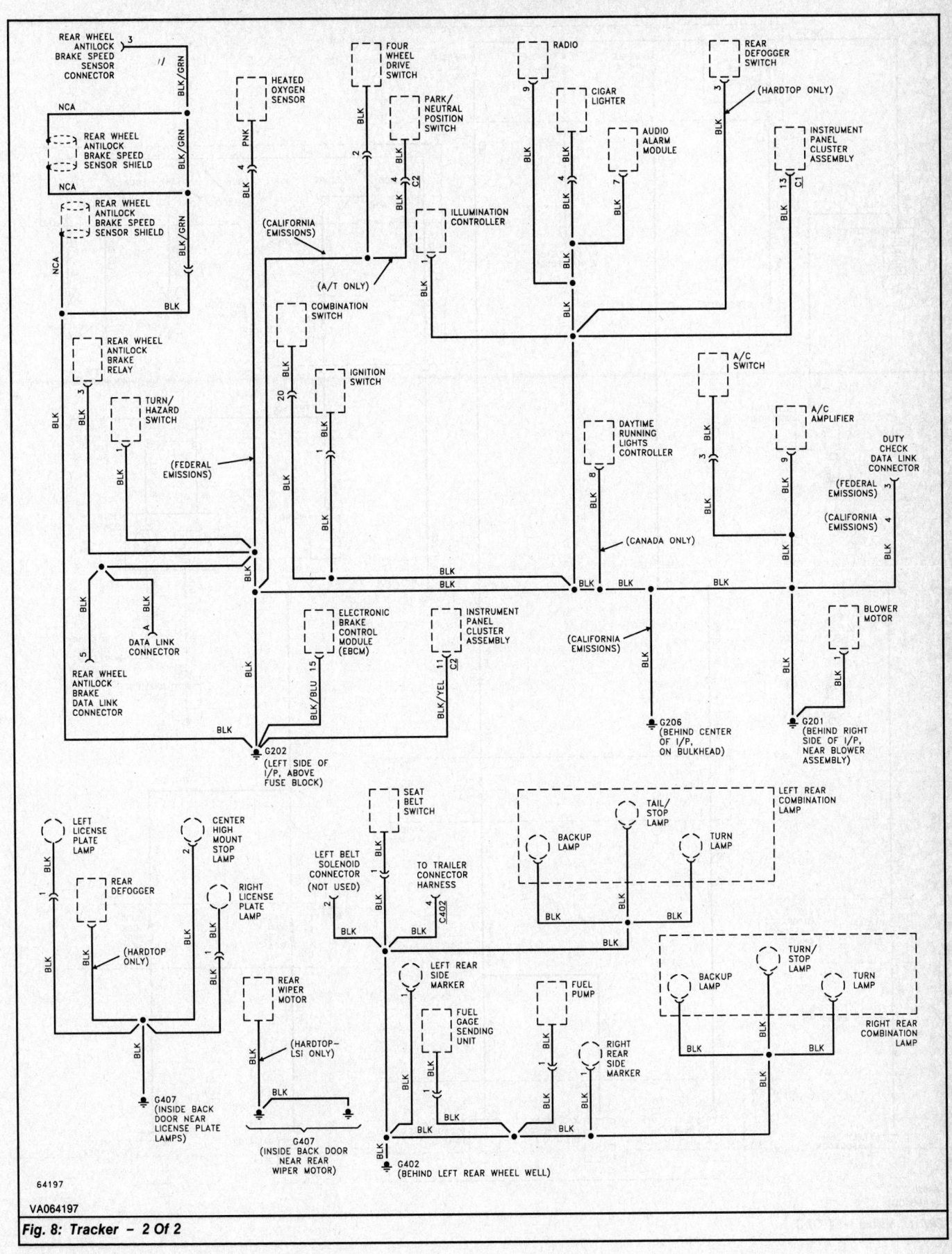

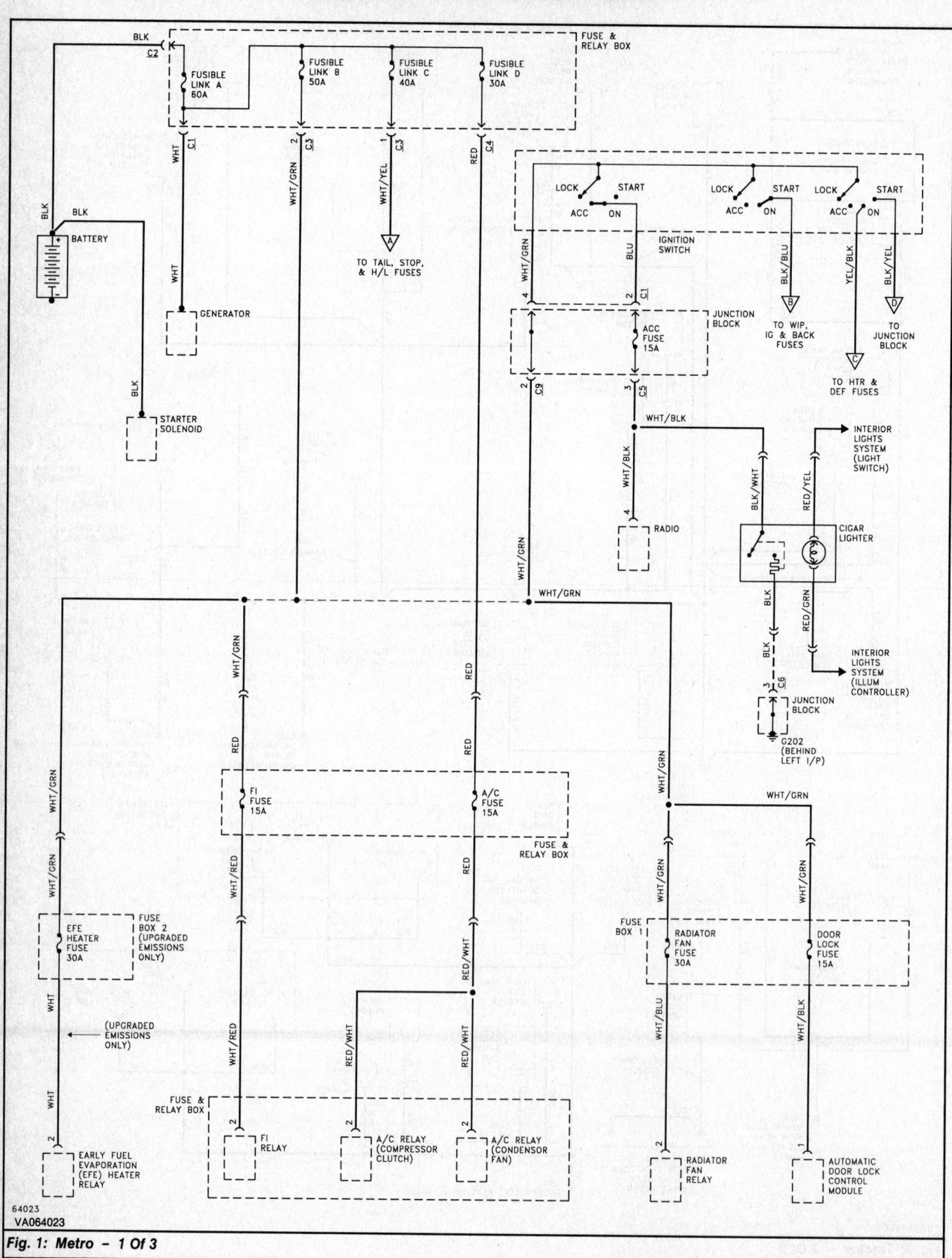

64023
VA064023

Fig. 1: Metro - 1 Of 3

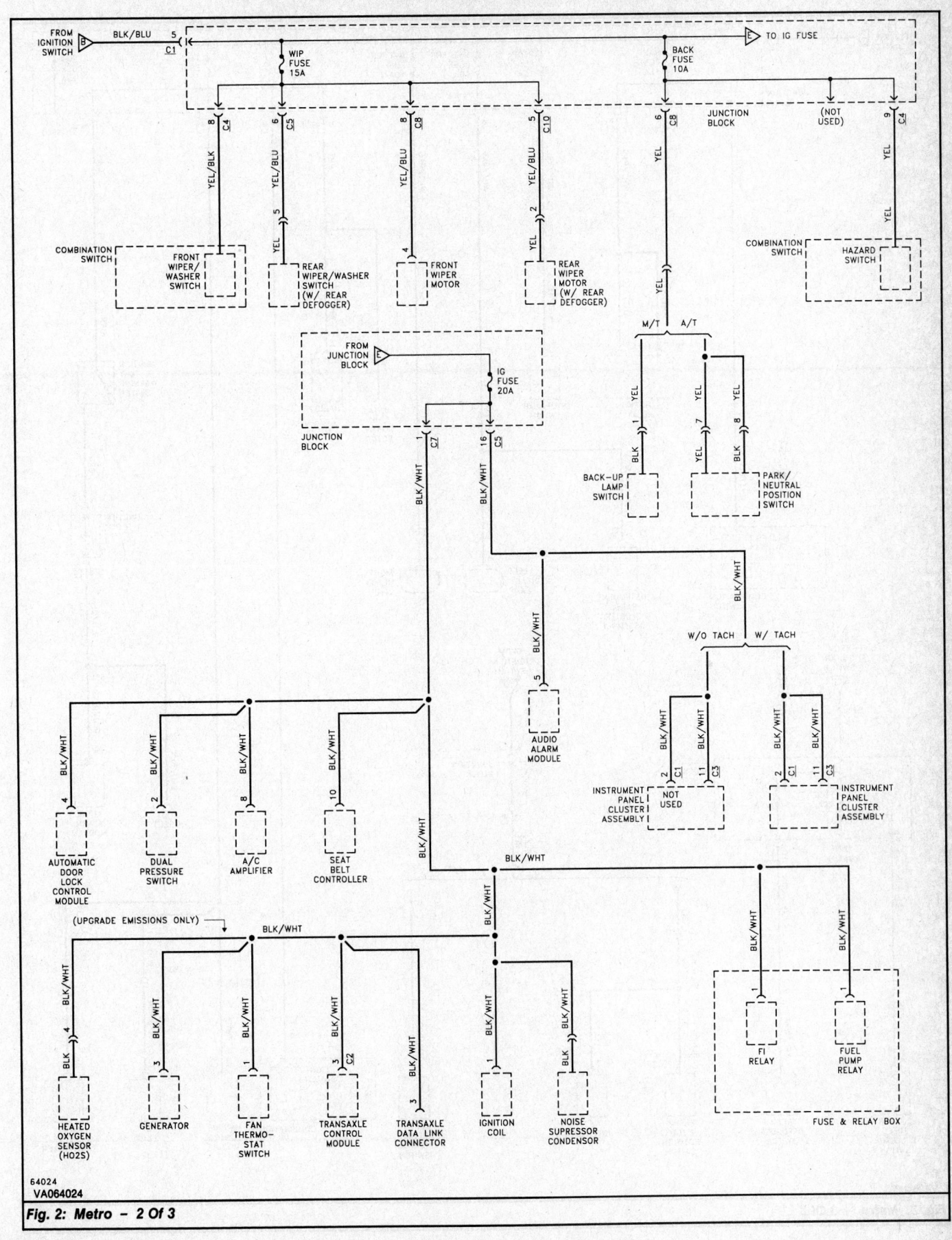

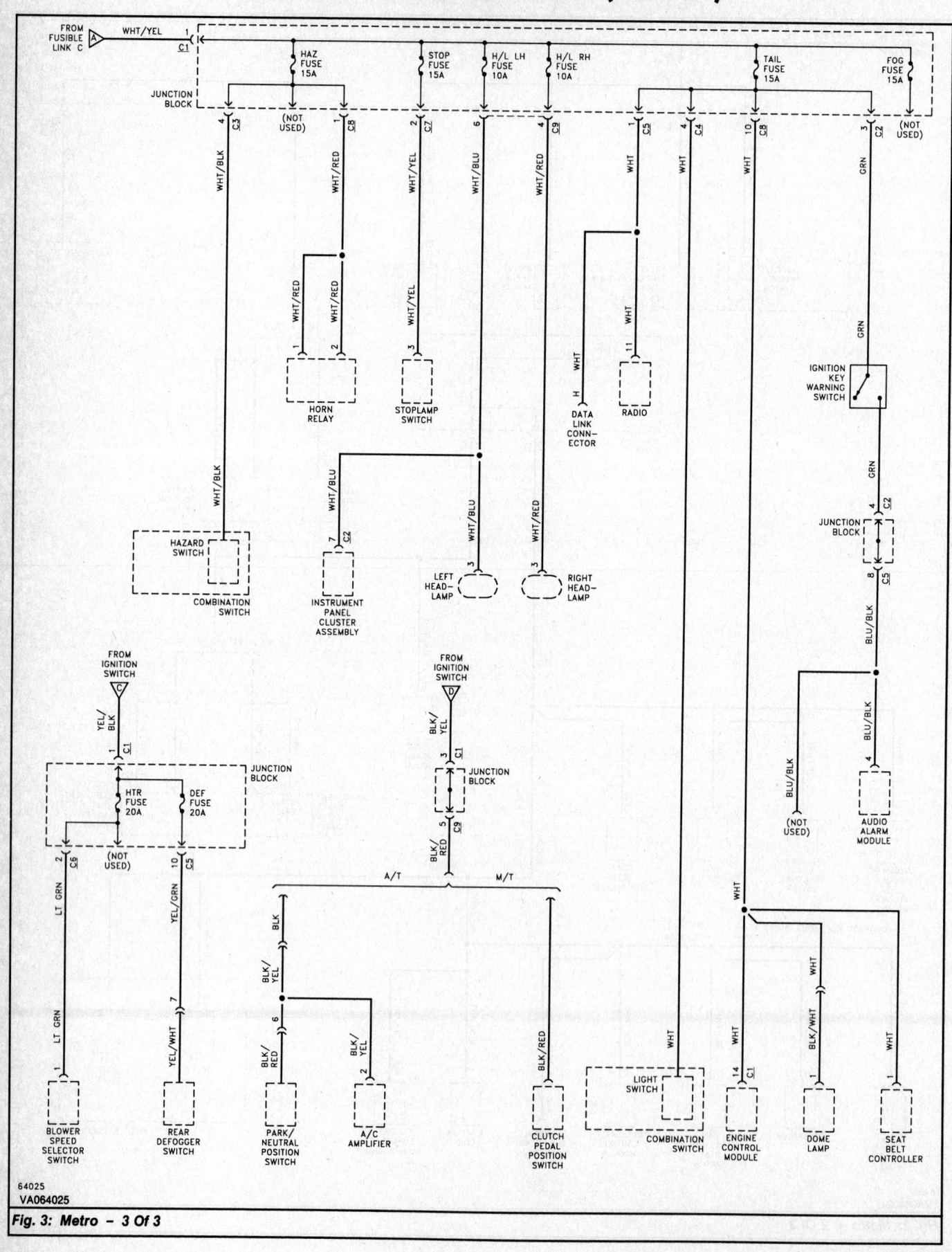

64025

VA064025

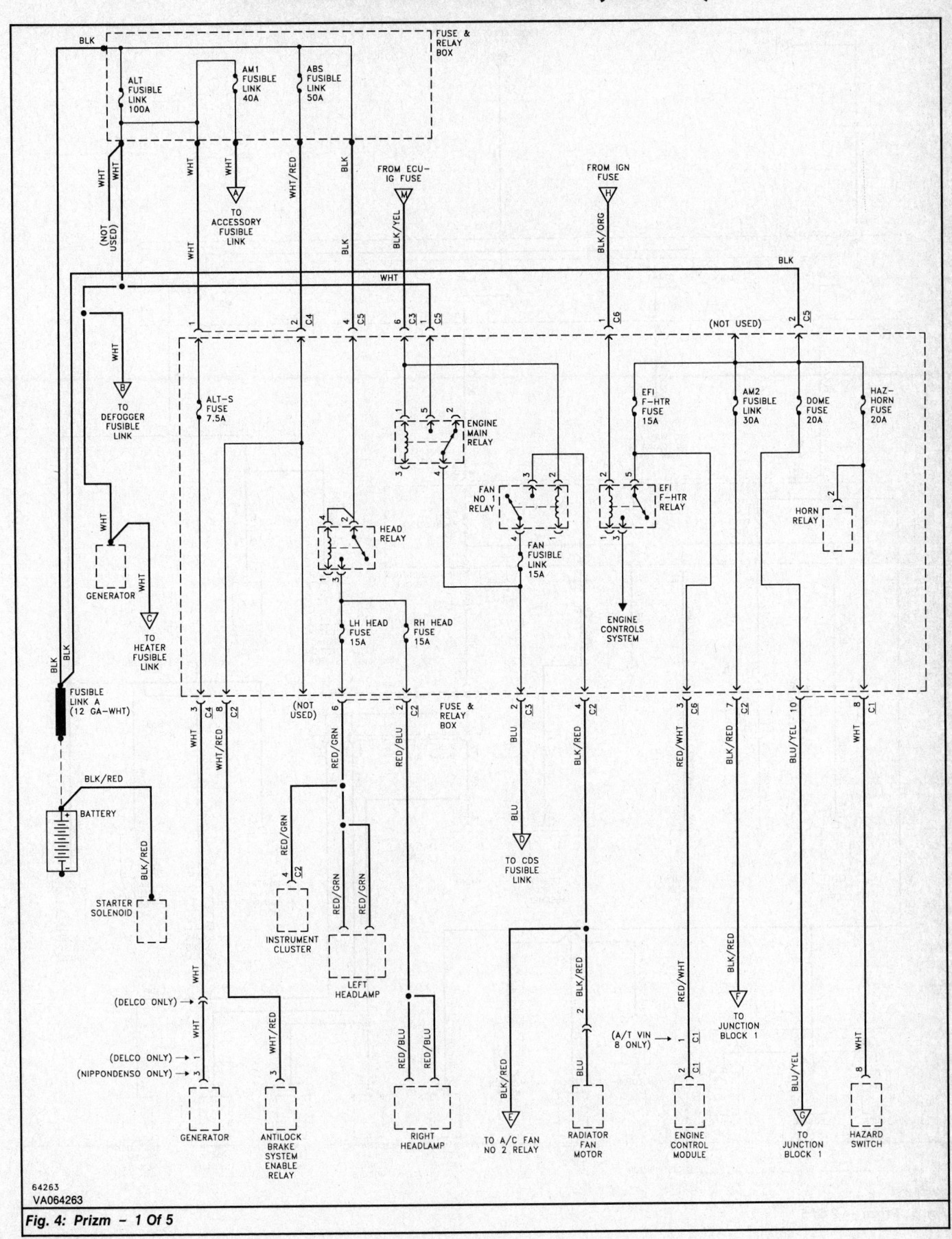

Fig. 4: Prizm - 1 Of 5

64263
VA064263

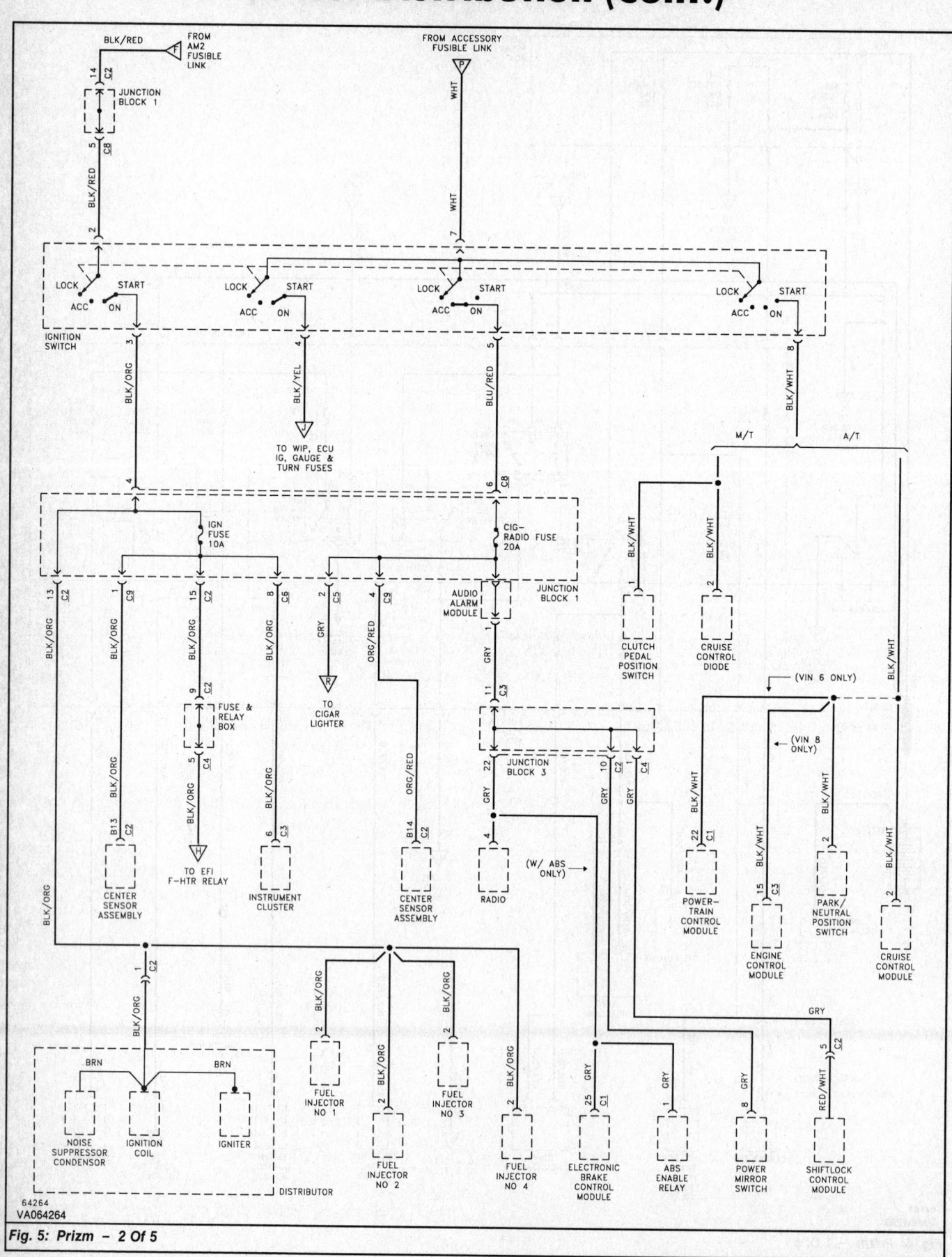

64264
VA064264

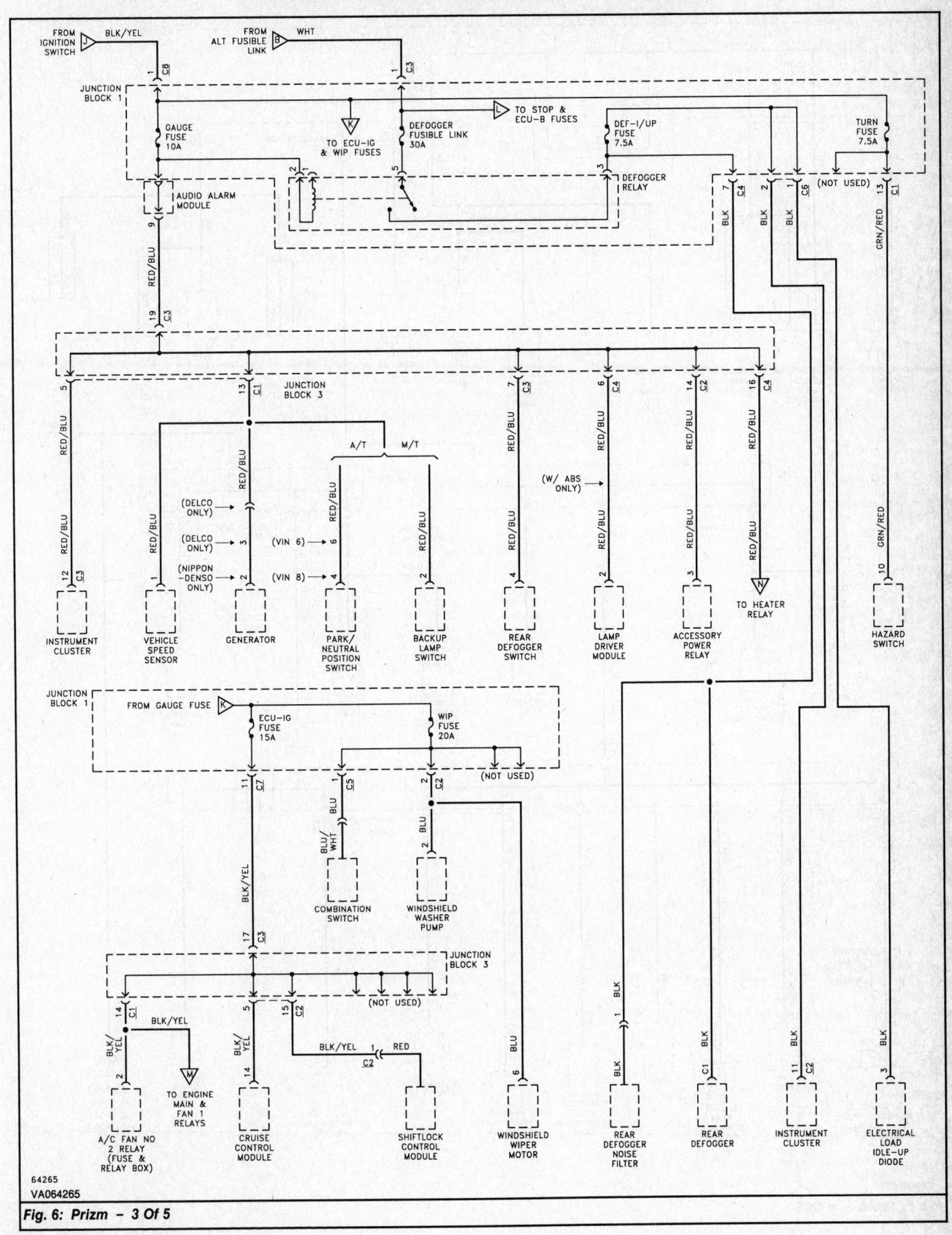

64265
VA064265

Fig. 6: Prizm – 3 Of 5

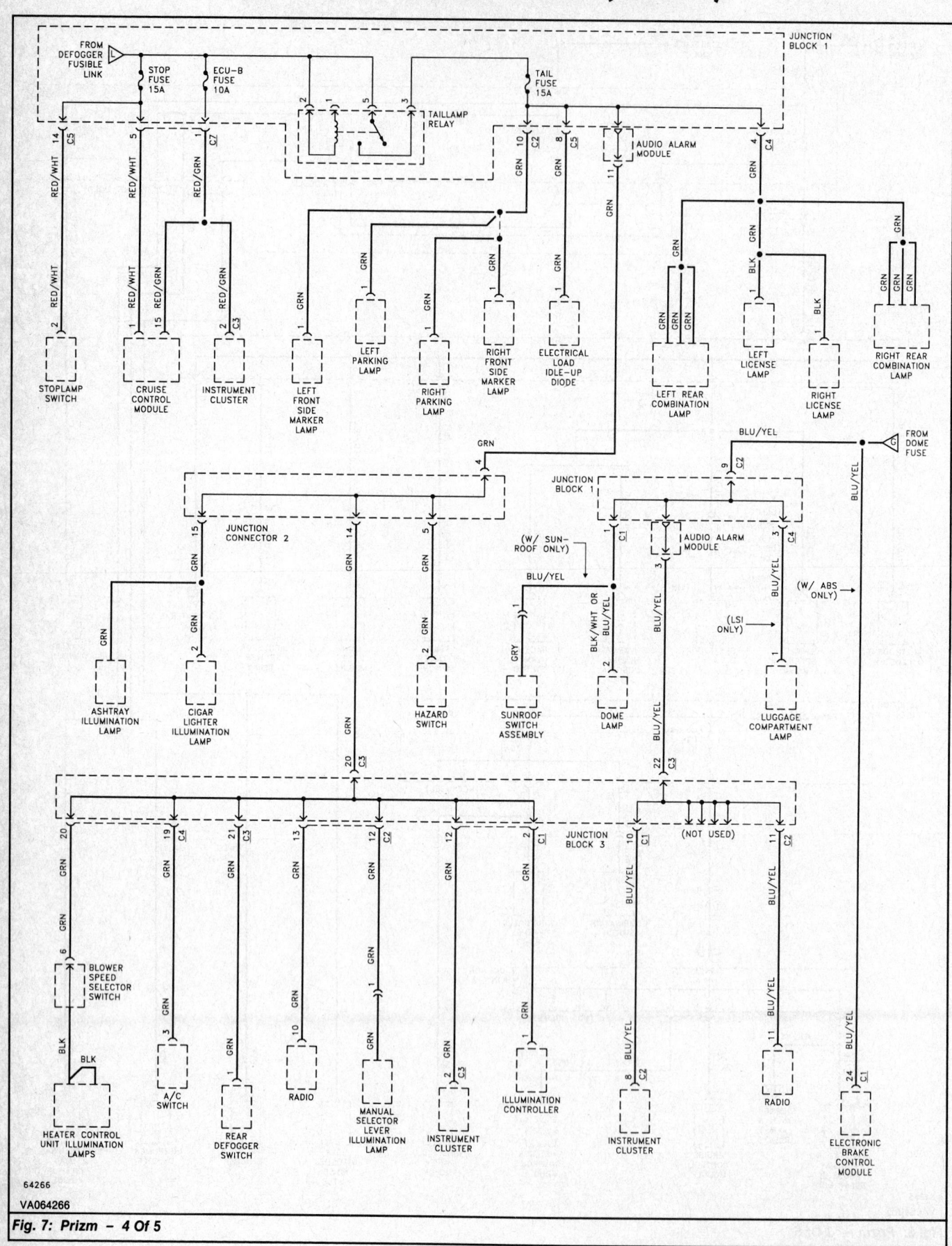

64266

VA064266

Fig. 7: Prizm – 4 Of 5

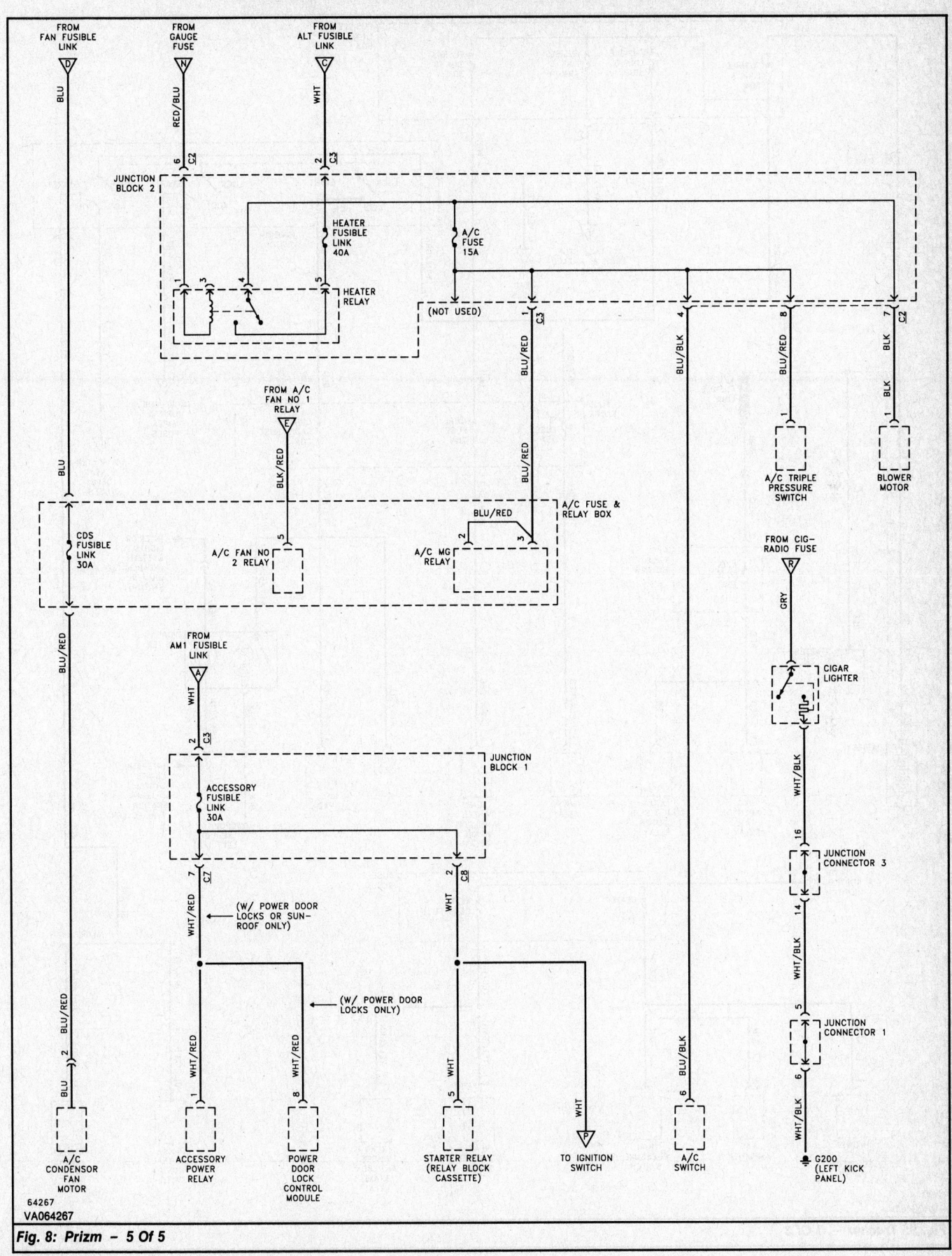

64267
VA064267

Fig. 8: Prizm - 5 Of 5

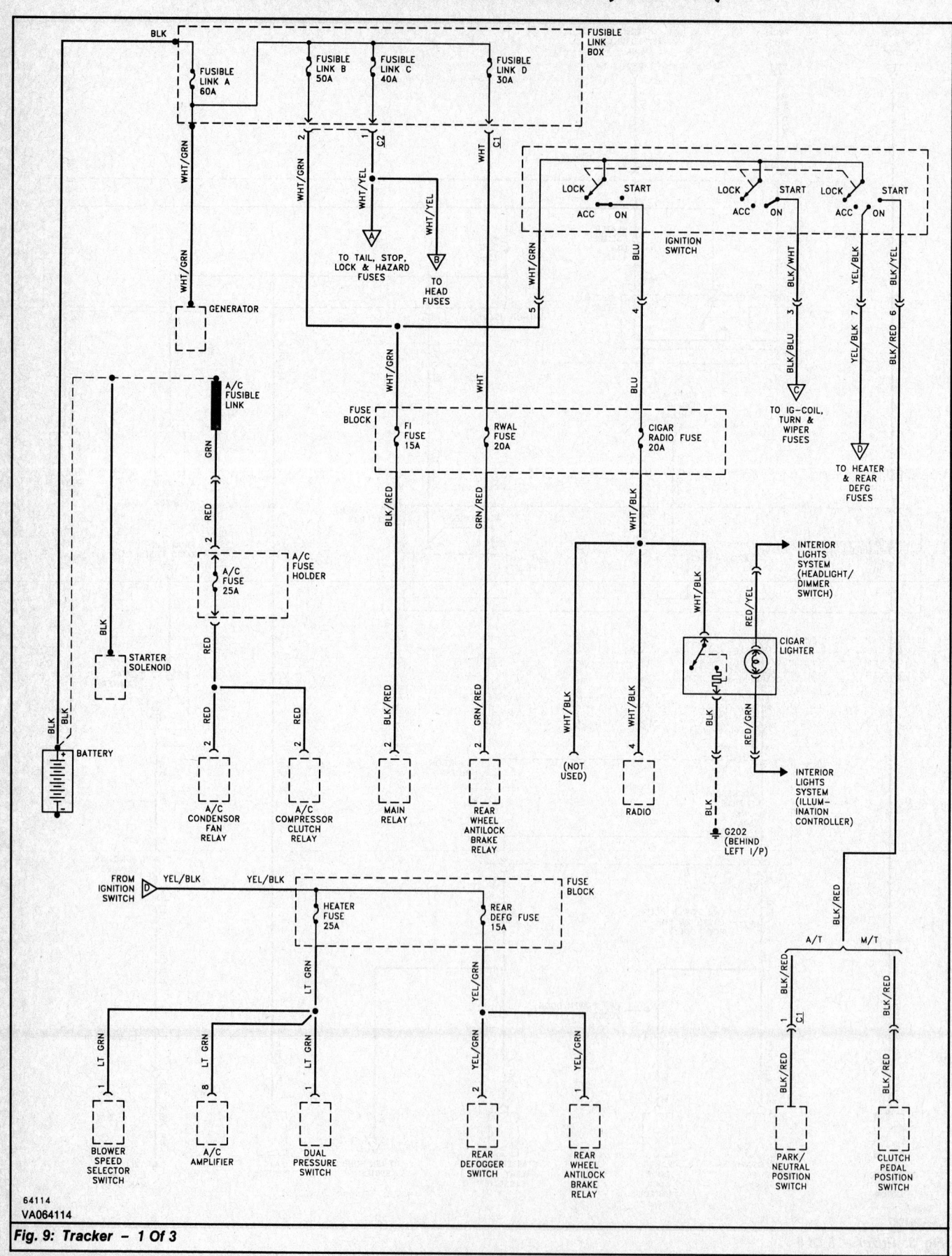

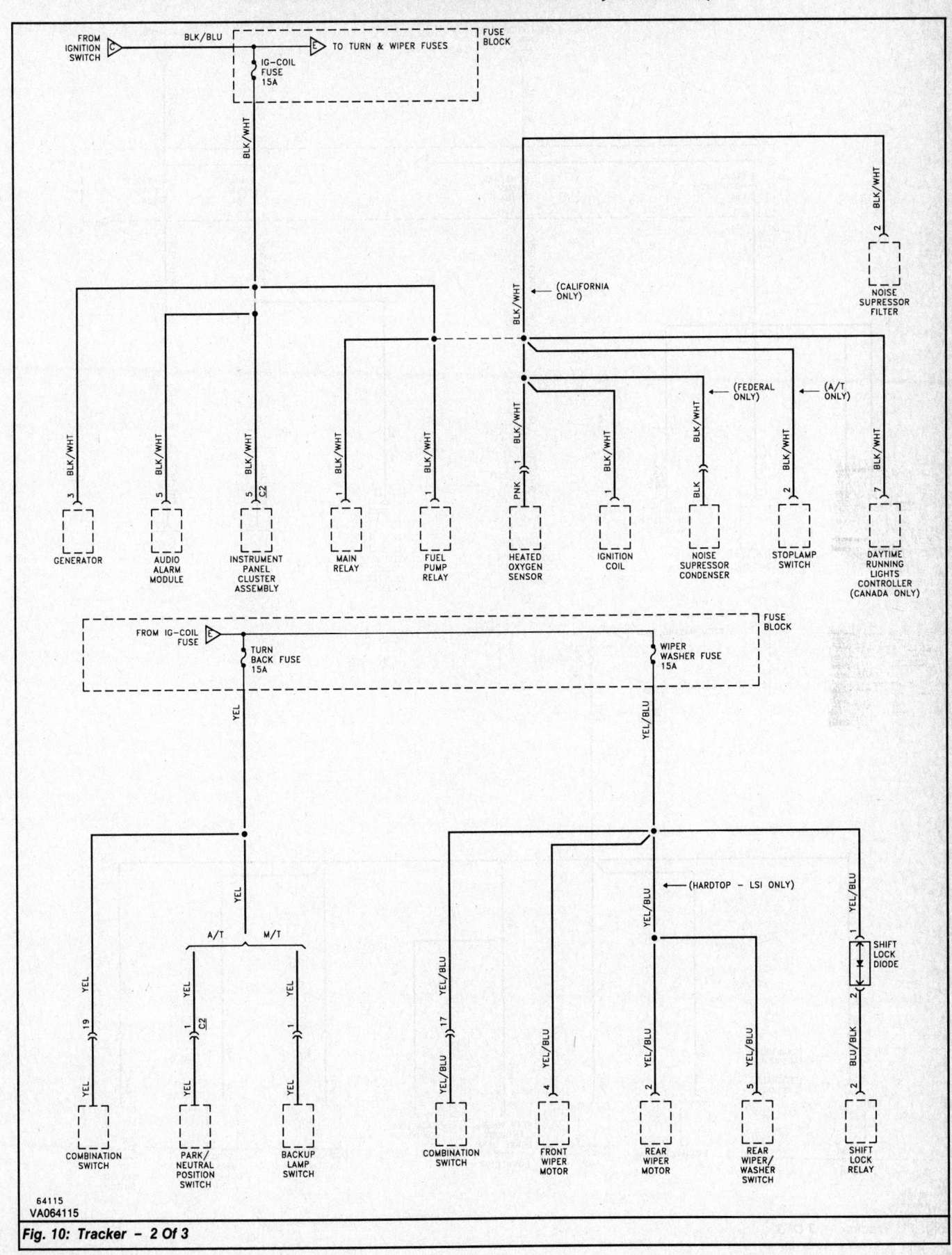

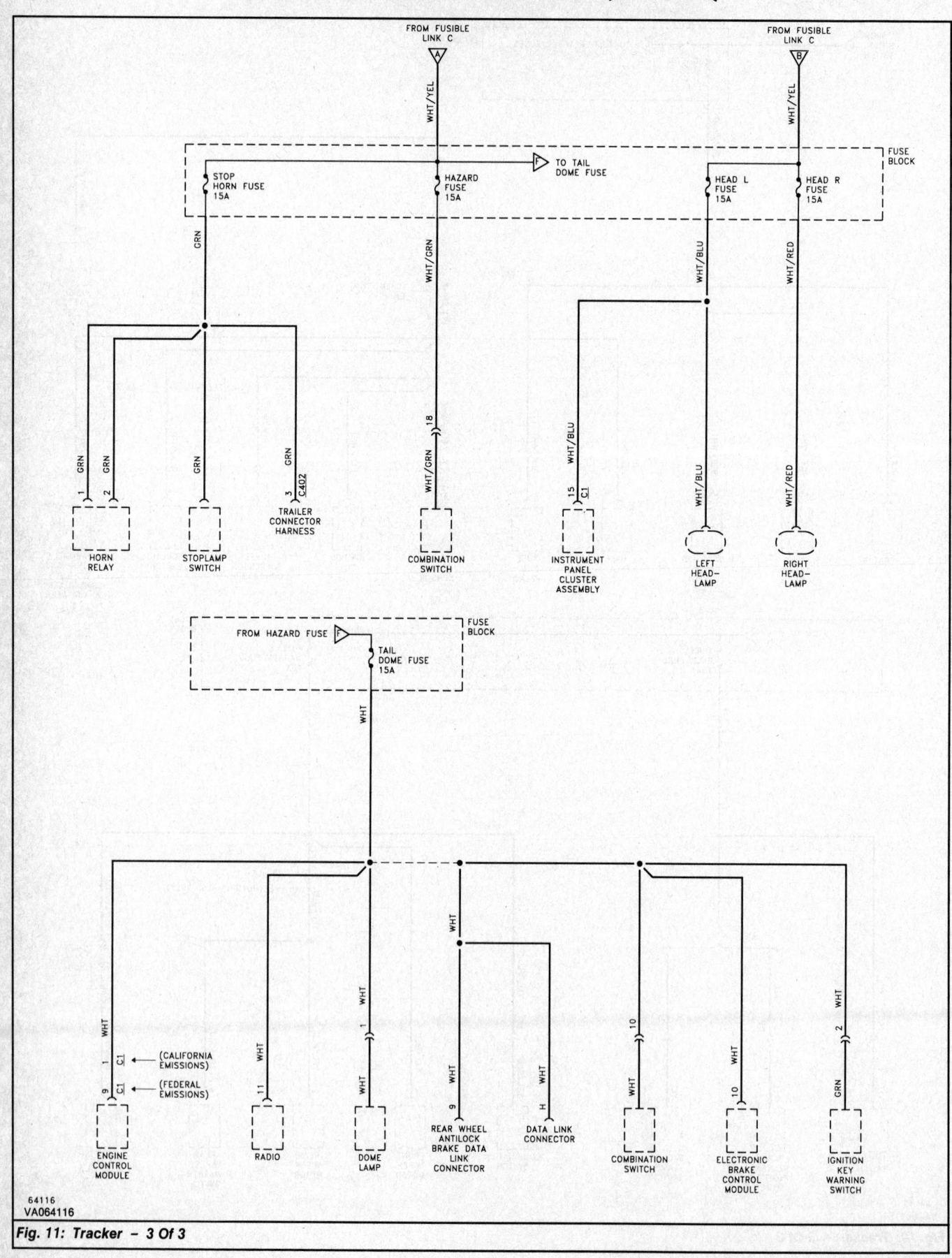

Prizm

WARNING: To avoid injury from accidental air bag deployment, read and carefully follow all WARNINGS and SERVICE PRECAUTIONS.

The main portions of the Supplemental Inflatable Restraint (SIR) system are the deployment loop and center sensor assembly. The main function of the deployment loop is to supply current through inflator modules which will cause deployment of air bags in the event of an accident severe enough to warrant deployment.

The main function of the center sensor assembly is to supply sufficient voltage to inflator modules, ensuring sufficient energy to deploy air bags for a few seconds if voltage is lost in an accident. A second function of the center sensor assembly is SIR diagnosis. If monitored voltages fall outside of expected limits, center sensor assembly will indicate a system fault by storing a malfunction code and illuminating AIR BAG indicator light.

SYSTEM OPERATION CHECK

NOTE: For information on air bag DIAGNOSIS & TESTING or DISPOSAL PROCEDURES, see the MITCHELL® AIR BAG SERVICE & REPAIR MANUAL, DOMESTIC & IMPORTED MODELS.

If system is functioning normally, AIR BAG indicator light should light steadily for about 6 seconds when ignition switch is first turned to ACC or ON position. SIR system faults are usually due to a disconnected/loose electrical connector caused by previous service on vehicle. Always check Yellow SIR connector at base of steering column and behind glove box. The following air bag system indicator light conditions can indicate a system failure:

- Light does not glow at all.
- Light comes on while vehicle is driven.
- Light continuously flashes.
- Light glows continuously and will not turn off.
- Light begins to flash trouble Codes.

SERVICE PRECAUTIONS

These precautions should be observed when working with SIR systems:

- Disable SIR system before servicing any SIR system or steering column component. Failure to do this could result in accidental air bag deployment and possible personal injury. See DISABLING & ACTIVATING AIR BAG SYSTEM.
- Wait about 2 minutes after disabling SIR system before servicing. System maintains SIR system voltage for about 2 minutes. Servicing SIR system before 2 minutes may cause accidental air bag deployment and possible personal injury.
- After repairs, ensure AIR BAG indicator light is working properly and no system faults are indicated. See SYSTEM OPERATION CHECK.
- Always wear safety glasses when servicing or handling an air bag.
- Inflator module must be stored in its original special container until used for service. It must be stored in a clean, dry place, away from sources of extreme heat, sparks or high electrical energy.
- When placing a live inflator module (air bag module) on a bench or other surface, always face air bag and trim cover up, away from surface. This will reduce motion of module if accidentally deployed.
- After deployment, air bag surface may contain deposits of sodium hydroxide, which can irritate skin. Always wear safety glasses, rubber gloves and long-sleeved shirt during clean-up, and wash hands using mild soap and water. Follow correct disposal procedures. See DISPOSAL PROCEDURES.
- At no time should any electrical source be allowed near inflator on back of inflator module.
- When carrying a live inflator module, trim cover should be pointed away from your body to minimize injury in case of accidental deployment.
- DO NOT probe a wire through insulator; this will damage it and eventually cause failure due to corrosion.

- When performing electrical tests, prevent accidental shorting of terminals. Such mistakes can damage fuses or components and may cause a second fault code to set, making diagnosis of original problem more difficult.
- When using diagnostic charts to diagnose SIR system, under no circumstances should a volt/ohmmeter, test light or any type of electrical equipment not specified by manufacturer be used.
- Air bag system is powered directly from battery and back-up power supply. Before servicing ANY system components or performing any wiring repairs, see DISABLING & ACTIVATING AIR BAG SYSTEM. After any servicing, ensure AIR BAG light does not indicate any faults still exist. See SYSTEM OPERATION CHECK.
- Because of critical operating requirements of system, DO NOT attempt to service sensors, clockspring, monitor, back-up power supply or air bag module. Corrections are made by replacement only.
- If SIR system is not fully functional for any reason, vehicle should not be driven until system is repaired. DO NOT remove bulbs, modules, sensors or other components or in any way disable system from operating normally. If SIR system is not functional, park vehicle until repairs can be made.

DISABLING & ACTIVATING AIR BAG SYSTEM

WARNING: Wait about 2 minutes after disabling SIR system before servicing. System maintains SIR system voltage for about 2 minutes. Servicing SIR system before 2 minutes may cause accidental air bag deployment and possible personal injury.

1) Ensure front wheels face straight ahead. Turn ignition switch to LOCK position. Remove IGN, CIG and RADIO fuses from junction block. *See Fig. 1.* Remove Connector Position Assurance (CPA) clip and disconnect Yellow 2-pin SIR lower steering column connector. *See Fig. 2.*

2) Open glove box door. Carefully pry off passenger inflator module connector retainer. *See Fig. 3.* Remove Connector Position Assurance (CPA) clip and disconnect Yellow 2-pin SIR passenger inflator module connector.

3) To activate SIR system, turn ignition switch to LOCK position. Connect 2-pin connector and CPA clip at base of steering column and behind glove box. Install IGN, CIG and RADIO fuses into junction block. Turn ignition switch to ACC or ON position and ensure air bag indicator illuminates steady for about 6 seconds, then turns off.

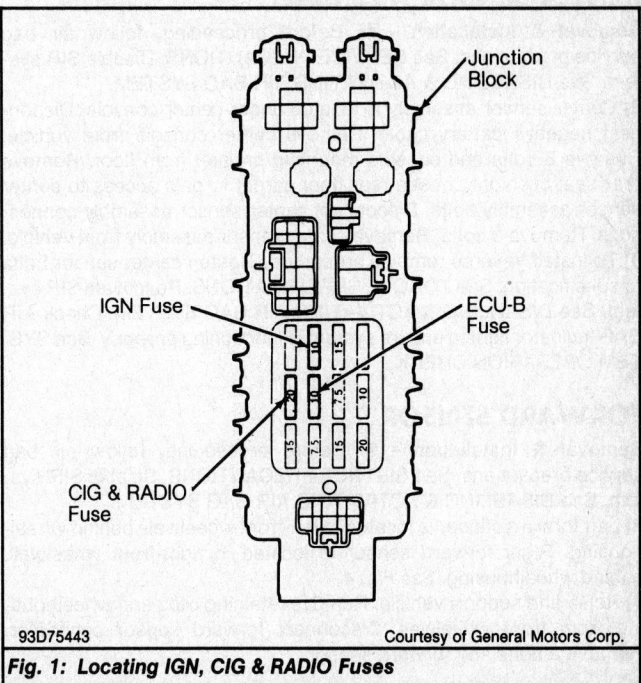

93D75443   Courtesy of General Motors Corp.

Fig. 1: Locating IGN, CIG & RADIO Fuses

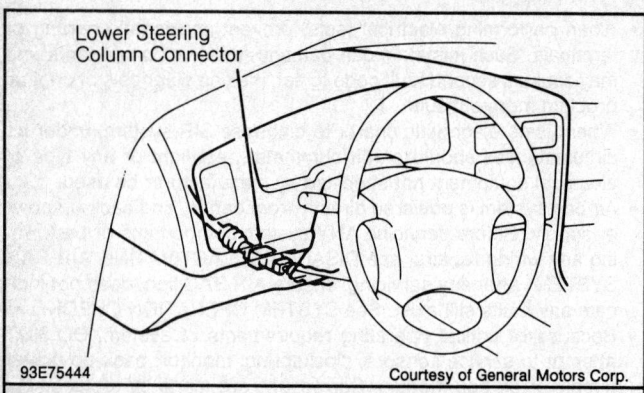

Lower Steering
Column Connector

93E75444   Courtesy of General Motors Corp.

Fig. 2: Locating 2-Pin Lower Steering Column Connector

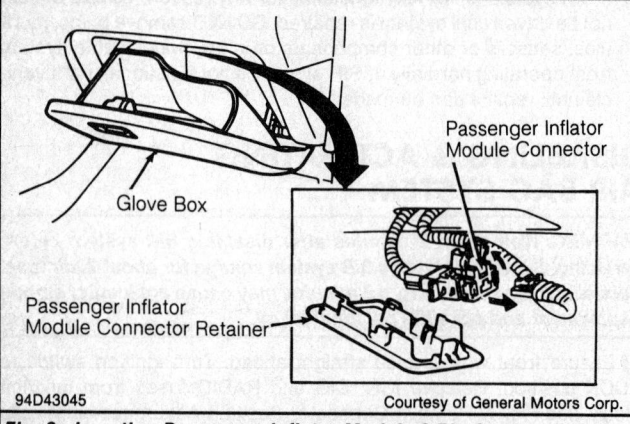

Glove Box

Passenger Inflator
Module Connector

Passenger Inflator
Module Connector Retainer

94D43045   Courtesy of General Motors Corp.

Fig. 3: Locating Passenger Inflator Module 2-Pin Connector

REMOVAL & INSTALLATION

WARNING: Failure to follow air bag service precautions may result in air bag deployment and personal injury. See SERVICE PRECAUTIONS. After component replacement, perform a system operational check to ensure proper system operation. See SYSTEM OPERATION CHECK.

CENTER SENSOR ASSEMBLY

Removal & Installation – 1) Before proceeding, follow air bag service precautions. See SERVICE PRECAUTIONS. Disable SIR system. See DISABLING & ACTIVATING AIR BAG SYSTEM.
2) Center sensor assembly is located under center console. Disconnect negative battery cable. Remove center console from vehicle. Remove 3 bolts and console mounting bracket from floor. Remove rear seat cushion. Loosen rear floor carpet to gain access to center sensor assembly bolts. Disconnect center sensor assembly connections. Remove 3 bolts. Remove center sensor assembly from vehicle.
3) To install, reverse removal procedure. Tighten center sensor bolts to specification. See TORQUE SPECIFICATIONS. Reactivate SIR system. See DISABLING & ACTIVATING AIR BAG SYSTEM. Check AIR BAG indicator light to ensure system is functioning properly. See SYSTEM OPERATION CHECK.

FORWARD SENSOR

Removal & Installation – 1) Before proceeding, follow air bag service precautions. See SERVICE PRECAUTIONS. Disable SIR system. See DISABLING & ACTIVATING AIR BAG SYSTEM.
2) Left forward sensor is located in left-front wheelwell, behind wheelhousing. Right forward sensor is located in right-front wheelwell, behind wheelhousing. See Fig. 4.
3) Raise and support vehicle. Remove retaining clips and wheelhousing from front wheelwell. Disconnect forward sensor connector. Remove 2 bolts and forward sensor.

4) To install, reverse removal procedure. Use NEW forward sensor bolts and tighten to specification. See TORQUE SPECIFICATIONS. Reactivate SIR system. See DISABLING & ACTIVATING AIR BAG SYSTEM. Check AIR BAG indicator light to ensure system is functioning properly. See SYSTEM OPERATION CHECK.

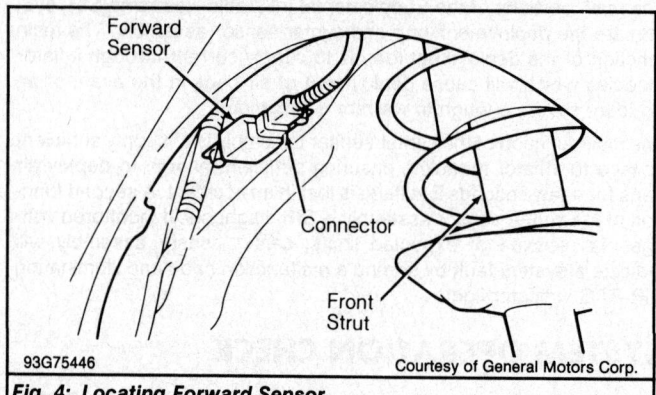

Forward
Sensor

Connector

Front
Strut

93G75446   Courtesy of General Motors Corp.

Fig. 4: Locating Forward Sensor

DRIVER INFLATOR MODULE

Removal – 1) Before proceeding, follow air bag service precautions. See SERVICE PRECAUTIONS. Disable SIR system. See DISABLING & ACTIVATING AIR BAG SYSTEM.
2) Driver inflator module is located on steering wheel hub. Ensure front wheels face straight ahead. Remove 2 side trim covers from steering column. Remove 2 Torx screws, Connector Position Assurance (CPA) clip and disconnect upper steering column electrical connector. Remove inflator module from steering wheel. See Fig. 5.

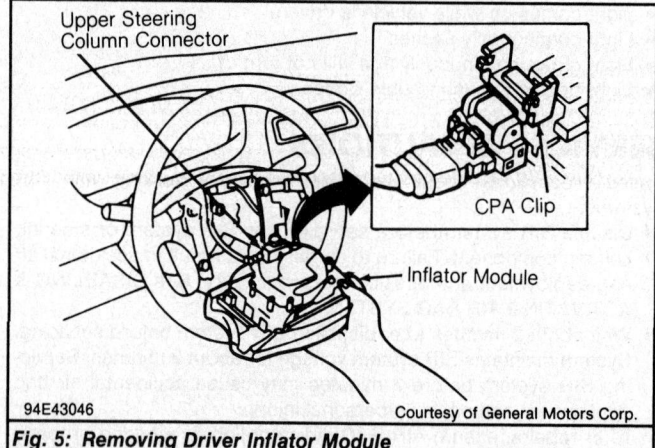

Upper Steering
Column Connector

CPA Clip

Inflator Module

94E43046   Courtesy of General Motors Corp.

Fig. 5: Removing Driver Inflator Module

Installation – 1) To install, reverse removal procedure. Tighten inflator module screws to specification. See TORQUE SPECIFICATIONS.
2) After all components are installed, reactivate SIR system. See DISABLING & ACTIVATING AIR BAG SYSTEM. Check AIR BAG indicator light to ensure system is functioning properly. See SYSTEM OPERATION CHECK.

PASSENGER INFLATOR MODULE

Removal – 1) Before proceeding, follow air bag service precautions. See SERVICE PRECAUTIONS. Disable SIR system. See DISABLING & ACTIVATING AIR BAG SYSTEM.
2) Passenger inflator module is located on right side of instrument panel. Remove plastic retaining nut and right-side kick panel. Remove 4 screws and 4 bolts retaining glove box to instrument panel. Remove 4 passenger inflator module-to-instrument panel bolts. Remove Connector Position Assurance (CPA) clip and disconnect electrical connector. Remove inflator module from instrument panel. See Fig. 6.

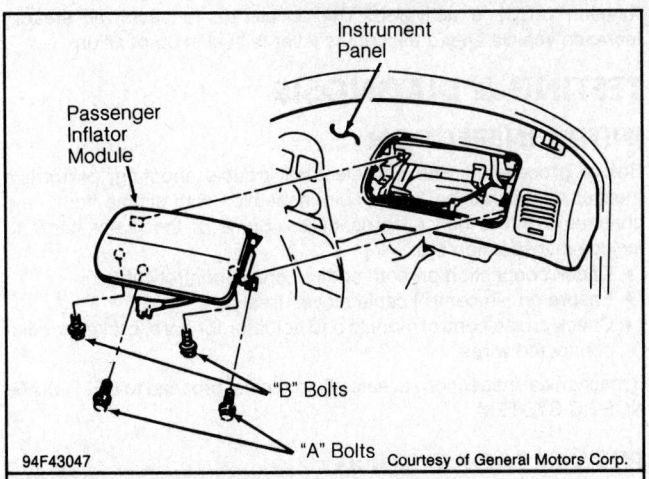

Fig. 6: Removing Passenger Inflator Module

Installation – 1) To install, reverse removal procedure. Tighten inflator module screws to specification. See TORQUE SPECIFICATIONS.
2) After all components are installed, reactivate SIR system. See DISABLING & ACTIVATING AIR BAG SYSTEM. Check AIR BAG indicator light to ensure system is functioning properly. See SYSTEM OPERATION CHECK.

SIR COIL

CAUTION: Failure to lock steering with front wheels in straight-ahead position could cause damage to SIR coil.

Removal – 1) Before proceeding, follow air bag service precautions. See SERVICE PRECAUTIONS. Disable SIR system. See DISABLING & ACTIVATING AIR BAG SYSTEM. SIR coil is located under steering wheel, in steering column. Remove steering wheel. See STEERING WHEEL.
2) Remove upper and lower steering column trim covers. Unclip and set aside left-front carpet retainer. Remove 2 screws and disconnect hood release lever from knee bolster. Remove 2 trim caps. Unbolt and remove knee bolster from instrument panel. Remove tape from SIR coil assembly harness from combination switch harness. Disconnect SIR coil electrical connector.
3) Mark SIR coil and steering shaft for reassembly reference. Remove screws and SIR coil.
Installation – Before installing SIR coil ensure coil is centered. See CENTERING SIR COIL ASSEMBLY. To install, reverse removal procedure. After all components are installed, reactivate SIR system. See DISABLING & ACTIVATING AIR BAG SYSTEM. Check AIR BAG indicator light to ensure system is functioning properly. See SYSTEM OPERATION CHECK.

STEERING WHEEL

CAUTION: Failure to lock steering with front wheels in straight-ahead position could cause damage to SIR coil.

Removal – 1) Before proceeding, follow air bag service precautions. See SERVICE PRECAUTIONS. Disable SIR system. See DISABLING & ACTIVATING AIR BAG SYSTEM.
2) Disconnect electrical connectors and remove inflator module. See INFLATOR MODULE. Remove steering wheel retaining nut. Mark

steering wheel and shaft for reassembly reference. Using proper steering wheel puller, remove steering wheel.
Installation – To install, reverse removal procedure. Ensure reference marks are aligned. Tighten steering wheel retaining nut to specification. See TORQUE SPECIFICATIONS. Reactivate SIR system. See DISABLING & ACTIVATING AIR BAG SYSTEM. Check AIR BAG indicator light to ensure system is functioning properly. See SYSTEM OPERATION CHECK.

ADJUSTMENTS

CENTERING SIR COIL ASSEMBLY

1) If coil assembly has been removed from steering column and is being reinstalled, go to step **2)**. New coil assemblies are supplied pre-centered.
2) Ensure front wheels face straight ahead when installing or removing a coil assembly. If coil is removed without wheels in straight-ahead position and steering wheel has not been moved, same coil can be reinstalled if coil hub also has not been rotated.
3) If coil may have been moved, gently turn SIR coil counterclockwise by hand until it reaches its stop. Turn SIR coil clockwise 3 turns and align Red alignment marks. Coil is now centered. *See Fig. 7.*

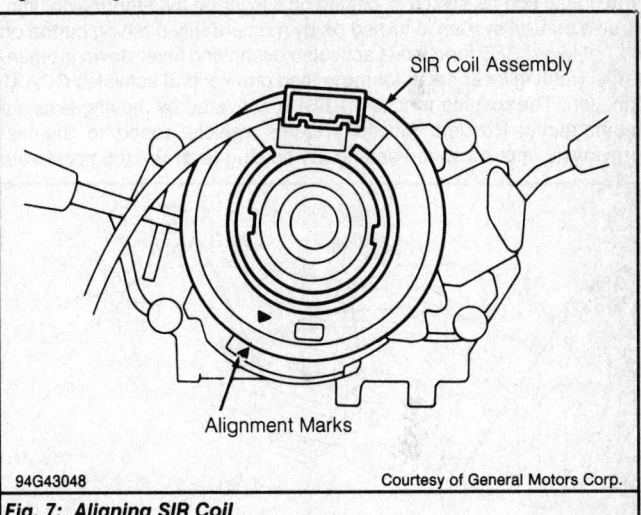

Fig. 7: Aligning SIR Coil

TORQUE SPECIFICATIONS

TORQUE SPECIFICATIONS

Application	Ft. Lbs. (N.m)
Forward Sensor Bolts	18 (24)
Glove Box Bolts	11 (15)
Inflator Module Bolt	
Passenger Side Bolt "B" [1]	15 (20)
Steering Column Bolts & Nuts	18 (24)
Steering Column Pinch Bolt	26 (35)
Steering Wheel Nut	25 (34)

	INCH Lbs. (N.m)
Center Sensor Assembly Bolts	115 (13)
Inflator Module Screw/Bolt	
Driver Side	78 (9)
Passenger Side Bolt "A" [1]	47 (5)
Knee Bolster Bolts	89 (10)

[1] – See Fig. 6.

WIRING DIAGRAM

NOTE: See ACCESSORIES & EQUIPMENT, Volume 5.

Prizm

DESCRIPTION

Main cruise control system components are the Cruise Control Module (CCM), actuator, cruise control switch, Vehicle Speed Sensor (VSS) and cancel switches. Several cancel switches are used to disengage cruise operation. The cancel switches are as follows: parking brake switch, brakelight switch, brake fluid level switch, cruise control switch, park/neutral switch (A/T) and Clutch Pedal Position (CPP) interrupt switch (M/T). *See Fig. 1.*

OPERATION

The CCM monitors vehicle speed and provides necessary commands to the actuator to maintain or change vehicle speed in response to inputs from cruise control switch. Cruise control operation is disengaged when one or more of the cancel switches closes. Upon receiving a cancel signal, CCM de-energizes a magnetic clutch inside cruise control actuator.

CRUISE CONTROL SWITCH

The cruise control switch is located on a lever on the steering column. Cruise control system is turned on by momentarily pushing button on end of lever. SET function is activated by moving lever down momentarily. Holding lever down for more than one second activates COAST function. The resume function (RES) is activated by moving lever up momentarily. Resume function returns vehicle speed to the last previously entered speed setting. By holding lever up, the accelerate

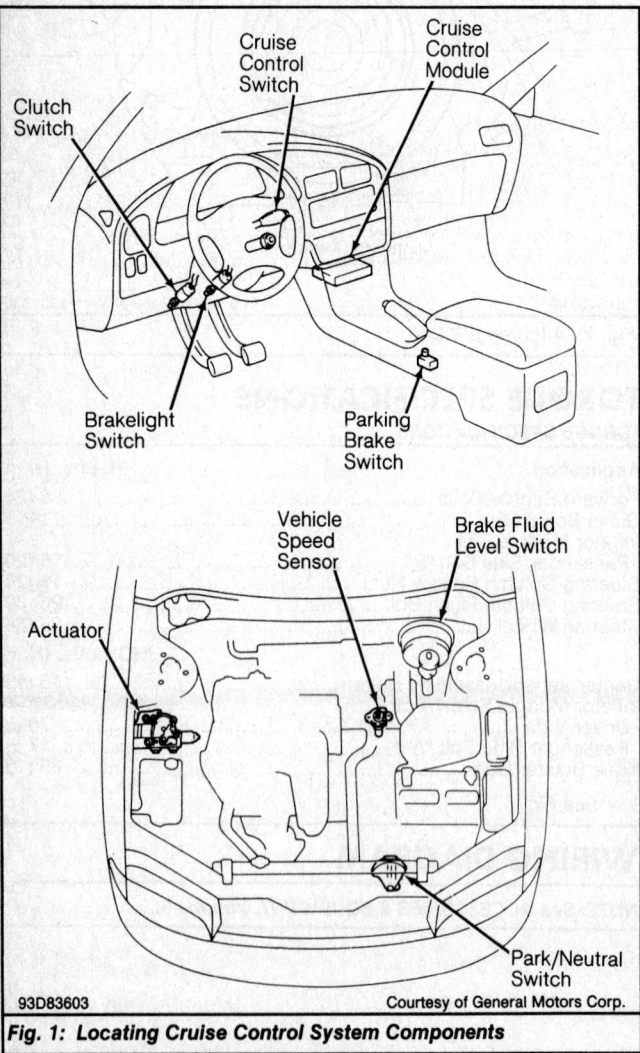

Fig. 1: Locating Cruise Control System Components

93D83603   Courtesy of General Motors Corp.

function (ACC) is activated. The accelerate function will steadily increase vehicle speed as long as lever is held in up position.

TESTING & DIAGNOSIS

INITIAL INSPECTION

Before proceeding with any electrical trouble shooting, perform a mechanical inspection first. Begin inspection with simple items and continue to more difficult procedures. Some of the major items to include in inspection are:

- Check connection on both ends of cruise control cable.
- Ensure cruise control cable moves freely.
- Check cruise control module and actuator for bare, broken, or disconnected wires.

If mechanical inspection reveals no problems, proceed to SELF-DIAGNOSTIC SYSTEM.

PIN VOLTAGE TESTING

Use the pin voltage chart to pinpoint a malfunctioning circuit. *See Fig. 3.* Test circuit voltages by backprobing Cruise Control Module (CCM) harness connector with a DVOM. *See Fig. 2.* All voltage tests are made with Black lead of DVOM grounded and ignition switch is is ON position. Voltages may vary slightly from specification, but a variance of 5 volts or more definitely indicates a circuit problem.

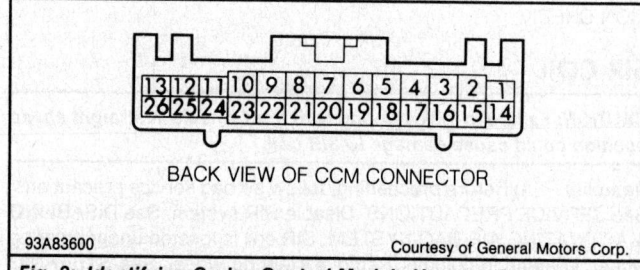

BACK VIEW OF CCM CONNECTOR

93A83600   Courtesy of General Motors Corp.

Fig. 2: Identifying Cruise Control Module Harness Connector Terminals

SELF-DIAGNOSTIC SYSTEM

The Cruise Control Module (CCM) has a self diagnostic capability. Using the cruise control switch and on-board diagnostic charts, a self-test can be performed which covers all switch signals and vehicle speed sensor signal. In addition to an on-board diagnostic test, Diagnostic Trouble Codes (DTCs) can be read through the CRUISE indicator light on instrument panel.

In many cases, when a system fault has been identified by the CCM, cruise operation will automatically be disabled and a DTC will be stored in memory. When this occurs, CRUISE indicator light will flash 5 times. Light will flash 5 times every time driver attempts to re-engage cruise control system.

RETRIEVING TROUBLE CODES

Diagnostic Trouble Codes (DTCs) are accessed by shorting 2 terminals of the Data Link Connector (DLC). The DLC is located in engine compartment just forward of master cylinder reservoir. To display stored codes, connect a jumper wire between terminal Tc and E1. *See Fig. 4.* The cruise indicator light will now steadily flash on and off, indicating no DTCs are stored, or display any stored codes by flashing a numbered sequence. If more than one code is stored, codes will be flashed sequentially from lowest to highest.

When reading DTCs, carefully read all codes and write them down. Continue reading codes until first code repeats. After recording any codes, clear codes from memory and test drive vehicle to verify symptom and see if any DTCs return. After any repairs or adjustments to the cruise system have been made, clear codes and repeat procedure.

CRUISE CONTROL SYSTEM VOLTAGE CHART

	Pin No.	Function/Description	Specified Voltage
Red/White	1	Battery Power	12 Volts
Black (M/T)	2	Clutch Pedal Switch Signal	Pedal Not Depressed – 12V Pedal Depressed – 0V
Black/White (A/T)	2	Park/Neutral Signal	In Drive – 12V In Park Or Neutral – 0V
Red/Black	3	Parking Brake/Brake Fluid Switch	Switch Open – 12V Switch Closed – 0V
White/Blue	4	Cruise On/Off Signal	ON/OFF Switch Depressed – 0V ON/OFF Switch Released – 12V
Green/Red	5	CRUISE Light Control	CRUISE Light Off – 12V CRUISE Light On – 0V
N/A	6	Not Used	
N/A	7	Not Used	
Purple	8	Diagnostic Request Signal	12V
Red	9	Overdrive Cut Cont.	12V
Green/Black	10	Magnetic Clutch Control	Cruise Control Disengaged – 0V Cruise Control Engaged – 12V
Red/Black	11	Actuator Motor Close Circuit	Close Side Activated – 12V
Red/Green	12	Actuator Motor Open Circuit	Open Side Activated – 12V
White/Black	13	Ground	0V
Black/Yellow	14	Ignition Power	12V
Red/Green	15	Memory Power	12V
Green/White	16	Brake Signal	Brake Pedal Depressed – 12V
N/A	17	Not Used	
Green/Black	18	Cruise Control Switch	RES/ACC Position – 0.7-2.5V SET/COAST Position – 2.4-4.6V CANCEL Position – 4.1-7.2V Switch Not In Use – 12V
N/A	19	Not Used	
Purple/White	20	Vehicle Speed Input	Varies With Speed – 0-5V
N/A	21	Not Used	
Brown/White	22	Shift Solenoid 2 Signal (A/T)	Transaxle In 2nd or 3rd – 12V
Blue	23	Idle Switch Signal	Switch Closed – 0V Switch Open – 12V
Blue/Orange	24	Reference Voltage	5V
Lt Green	25	Throttle Angle Input	Varies With Throttle Position
Blue/Red	26	Throttle Angle Sensor Ground	0V

94D46378

Fig. 3: Cruise Control System Pin Voltage Chart

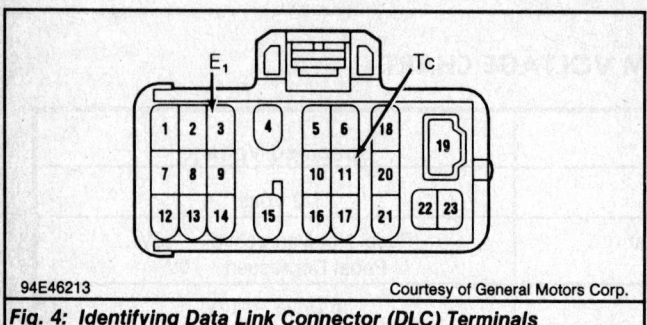

94E46213   Courtesy of General Motors Corp.

Fig. 4: Identifying Data Link Connector (DLC) Terminals

CLEARING TROUBLE CODES

To clear any stored DTCs, turn ignition switch to LOCK position. Remove STOP and ECU-B fuses from junction block 1 (behind left kick panel). Wait 30 seconds and reinstall fuses. Retrieve trouble codes to ensure all codes have been cleared. See RETRIEVING TROUBLE CODES.

TROUBLE CODE DEFINITIONS
TROUBLE CODE IDENTIFICATION

Code	Circuit Affected	Failure
11	Actuator DC Servo Motor	Short
12	Actuator Magnetic Clutch	Short
13	Actuator	Open
21	Vehicle Speed Sensor	Open Or Short
23	Vehicle Speed Sensor	Speed Signal 10 MPH Lower Than Set Speed
32	Cruise Control Switch	Short
34	Cruise Control Switch	Incorrect Voltage

REMOVAL & INSTALLATION

ACTUATOR

Removal & Installation – Disconnect negative battery cable. Remove actuator cover. Loosen cable lock nuts and remove cable from actuator. Disconnect electrical connector. Remove mounting bolts, actuator brackets and actuator from vehicle. To install, reverse removal procedure.

CRUISE CONTROL SWITCH

WARNING: Disable air bag system before servicing steering column components. Wait about 10 minutes after disabling SIR system before servicing. System maintains SIR system voltage for about 10 minutes. Servicing SIR system before 10 minutes may cause accidental air bag deployment and possible personal injury.

Removal – **1)** Disable air bag system. See AIR BAG RESTRAINT SYSTEM article. Remove air bag module from steering wheel. See AIR BAG RESTRAINT SYSTEM article.
2) Disconnect cruise control switch connector from SIR coil assembly. Remove Black wire from cruise control switch connector using a pick or terminal remover. Remove 3 screws and cruise control switch from steering wheel.

Installation – To install, reverse removal procedure. Activate air bag system and perform air bag system check to ensure system operation. See AIR BAG RESTRAINT SYSTEM article.

CRUISE CONTROL MODULE (CCM)

Removal – **1)** Disconnect negative battery cable. Move transmission selector to LOW position (A/T), or move gearshift to 4th gear and remove knob and boot (M/T).
2) Remove center console trim bezel. Disconnect electrical connectors from rear defogger switch, hazard switch and lighter at rear of center console. Remove center console tray.
3) Remove 4 screws and radio from center console. Remove 5 screws and rear console from vehicle. Remove transmission selector trim bezel (A/T). Remove 2 screws and center console from vehicle. Disconnect CCM electrical connector, remove mounting bolts and remove CCM from vehicle.
Installation – To install, reverse removal procedure. Tighten CCM mounting bolts to 89 INCH lbs. (10 N.m)

WIRING DIAGRAM

NOTE: See ACCESSORIES & EQUIPMENT, Volume 5.

DIAGNOSTIC CHARTS

Before performing electrical testing using diagnostic flow charts, ensure basic inspection of fuses, harness connectors and physical damage have been made. When using the following diagnostic flow charts to pinpoint a faulty component or circuit, start with ON-BOARD DIAGNOSTIC CHECK. The charts may also be used in conjunction with any Diagnostic Trouble Codes (DTCs) displayed from CRUISE indicator light.

ON-BOARD DIAGNOSTIC SYSTEM CHECK
(1 of 2)

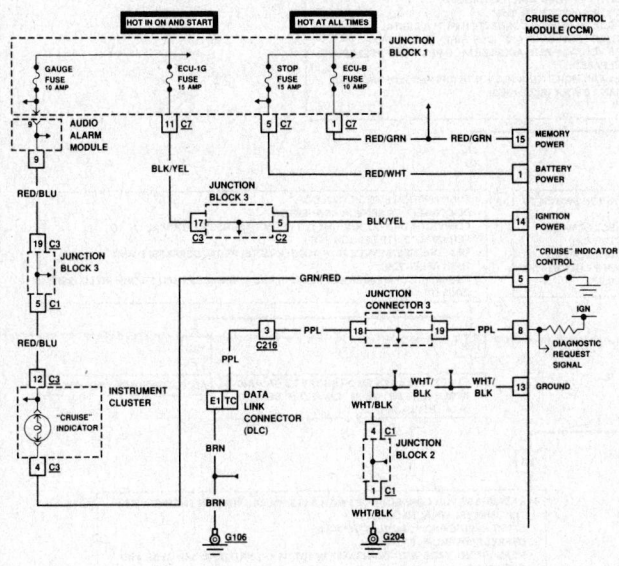

The on-board diagnostic system check is an organized approach in identifying a problem created by an electronic cruise control system malfunction. It must be the starting point for any cruise control electrical repair because it directs the service technician to the next logical step in diagnosing a complaint. Understanding the chart and using it correctly will reduce diagnostic time and prevent unnecessary replacement of good parts.

NOTE: Test numbers refer to numbers on diagnostic chart.

1) Checks CRUISE indicator light operation with ignition on.
2) Checks CRUISE indicator light and cruise operation and cruise ON/OFF switch circuit.
3) Checks SET/COAST switch circuit.
4) Checks RES/ACC switch circuit.
5) Checks clutch pedal/transaxle in gear signal circuit.
6) Checks all cancel switch circuits.
7) Checks VSS signal input greater than 25 MPH.

DIAGNOSTIC AIDS

Check ECU-IG fuse, STOP fuse and ECU-B fuse. An intermittent condition may be caused by rubbed-through insulation, or a wire broken inside insulation. Check harness connectors for backed-out or damaged terminals, improper mating or broken connector lock, before replacing component.

1
- TURN IGNITION SWITCH TO "ON."
- OBSERVE "CRUISE" INDICATOR.
  SHOULD BE OUT.
  IS IT?

| YES | REMAINS LIT | FLASHES |

REMAINS LIT:
- CHECK FOR SHORT TO GROUND IN GRN/RED WIRE BETWEEN INSTRUMENT CLUSTER AND CCM.
- CHECK FOR A SHORT TO GROUND IN INSTRUMENT CLUSTER PRINTED CIRCUIT. IF OK, REPLACE CCM.

FLASHES:
- CHECK FOR SHORT TO GROUND IN PPL WIRE BETWEEN DLC AND CCM OR IN JUNCTION CONNECTOR 3. IF OK, REPLACE CCM.

2
- PRESS "CRUISE ON-OFF" BUTTON.
- OBSERVE "CRUISE" INDICATOR.
  SHOULD BE LIT.
  IS IT?

YES | NO | FLASHES FIVE TIMES AND GOES OUT.

NO: REFER TO CHART 9B-1.

FLASHES FIVE TIMES AND GOES OUT: PROCEED DIRECTLY TO AND PERFORM STEP 12 OF THIS CHART

3
- TURN IGNITION SWITCH TO "LOCK."
- WAIT FIVE SECONDS.
- TURN IGNITION SWITCH TO "ON."
- MOVE CRUISE CONTROL SWITCH DOWN TO "SET/COAST" POSITION AND HOLD IT THERE.
- PRESS "CRUISE ON-OFF" BUTTON.
- OBSERVE "CRUISE" INDICATOR.
  SHOULD FLASH TWO TIMES, PAUSE ONE SECOND, FLASH TWO TIMES, PAUSE ONE SECOND, REPEAT...
  DOES IT?

YES | NO

NO: REFER TO CHART 9B-2.

4
- MOVE CRUISE CONTROL SWITCH UP TO "RES / ACC" POSITION AND HOLD IT THERE.
- OBSERVE "CRUISE" INDICATOR.
  SHOULD FLASH THREE TIMES, PAUSE ONE SECOND, FLASH THREE TIMES, PAUSE ONE SECOND, REPEAT...
  DOES IT?

YES | NO

NO: REFER TO CHART 9B-3.

5
- RAISE VEHICLE DRIVE WHEELS.
- NOTICE: DO NOT PERFORM THIS TEST WITHOUT SUPPORTING THE LOWER CONTROL ARMS SO THAT THE DRIVE AXLES ARE IN A NORMAL HORIZONTAL POSITION.
- START AND RUN ENGINE AT IDLE IN GEAR.
- OBSERVE "CRUISE" INDICATOR.
  SHOULD BE LIT.
  IS IT?

YES | NO

NO: REFER TO CHART 9B-4A.

6
- OBSERVE "CRUISE" INDICATOR WHILE PERFORMING THE FOLLOWING SWITCH TESTS ONE AT A TIME:
  - DEPRESS BRAKE PEDAL.
  - PULL CRUISE CONTROL SWITCH BACK TO THE "CANCEL" POSITION.
  - ENGAGE PARKING BRAKE.
  - REMOVE BRAKE FLUID RESERVOIR CAP AND MANUALLY HOLD FLOAT DOWN.
  - MOVE MANUAL SELECTOR LEVER TO "N" AND BACK TO "D" (A/T ONLY).
  - DEPRESS CLUTCH PEDAL (M/T ONLY).
  "CRUISE" INDICATOR SHOULD GO OUT WHILE EACH TEST IS PERFORMED AND RELIGHT AFTER EACH TEST. DOES IT FOR ALL TESTS?

YES | NO

NO: "CRUISE" INDICATOR DID NOT GO OUT WITH:
- BRAKE PEDAL DEPRESSED, REFER TO CHART 9B-5A.
- CRUISE CONTROL SWITCH PULLED BACK TO "CANCEL," REFER TO CHART 9B-5B.
- PARKING BRAKE ENGAGED/BRAKE FLUID RESERVOIR FLOAT HELD DOWN, REFER TO CHART 9B-5C.
- MANUAL SELECTOR LEVER IN "N" (AUTOMATIC TRANSAXLE), REFER TO CHART 9B-5D.
- CLUCH PEDAL DEPRESSED (MANUAL TRANSAXLE), REFER TO CHART 9B-5E.
- ALL CANCEL TESTS, REPLACE CCM.

7
- ACCELERATE ENGINE UNTIL SPEEDOMETER REGISTERS 40 KM/H (25 MPH) OR ABOVE.
- OBSERVE "CRUISE" INDICATOR.
  SHOULD FLASH ON AND OFF RAPIDLY.
  DOES IT?

YES | NO

NO: REFER TO DTC 21 CHART

YES ▽
9

Continued
On Next
Page

ON-BOARD DIAGNOSTIC SYSTEM CHECK
(2 of 2)

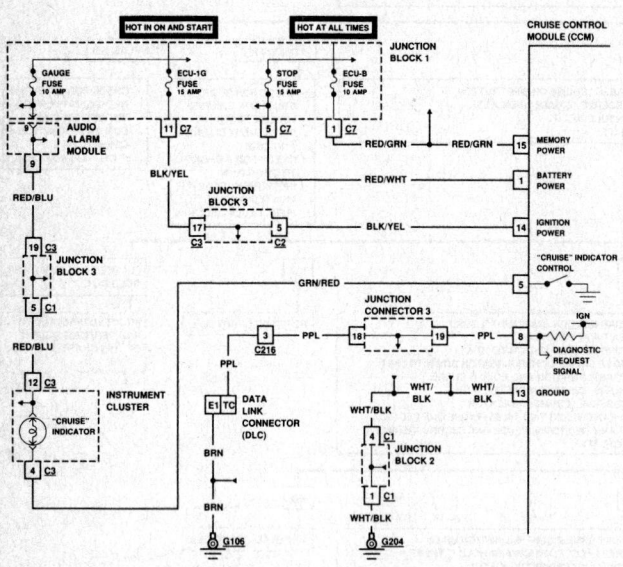

The on-board diagnostic system check is an organized approach in identifying a problem created by an electronic cruise control system malfunction. It must be the starting point for any cruise control electrical repair because it directs the service technician to the next logical step in diagnosing a complaint. Understanding the chart and using it correctly will reduce diagnostic time and prevent unnecessary replacement of good parts.

NOTE: Test numbers refer to numbers on diagnostic chart.

8) Checks throttle position sensor idle switch circuit.
9) Checks for an open or short to ground in Blue wire.
10) Checks for proper actuation of shift solenoid No. 2.
11) Checks for trouble codes.
12) Checks for open in Brown/Yellow wire.
13) Checks for open or short to ground in Red wire.
14) Checks for faulty Cruise Control Module (CCM).

DIAGNOSTIC AIDS

Check ECU-IG fuse, STOP fuse and ECU-B fuse. An intermittent condition may be caused by rubbed-through insulation, or a wire broken inside insulation. Check harness connectors for backed-out or damaged terminals, improper mating or broken connector lock, before replacing component.

B

8)
- TURN IGNITION SWITCH TO "LOCK."
- DISCONNECT ECM/PCM CONNECTOR C2.
- BACKPROBE TP SENSOR CONNECTOR WITH A FUSED JUMPER FROM CAVITY "1" (BRN WIRE) TO GROUND.
- TURN IGNITION SWITCH TO "ON."
- BACKPROBE TP SENSOR CONNECTOR WITH A DIGITAL MULTIMETER FROM CAVITY "2" (BLU WIRE) TO GROUND.
- MEASURE VOLTAGE WITH ACCELERATOR PEDAL DEPRESSED AND THEN RELEASED.
  SHOULD READ MORE THAN 10.0 VOLTS (DEPRESSED) AND THEN, LESS THAN 1.0 VOLT (RELEASED).
  DOES IT?

YES | **NO**

YES:
- TURN IGNITION SWITCH TO "LOCK."
- RECONNECT ECM/PCM CONNECTOR C2.
- IS VEHICLE EQUIPPED WITH A VIN 8 - AUTOMATIC TRANSAXLE?

9)
- TURN IGNITION SWITCH TO "LOCK."
- DISCONNECT TP SENSOR CONNECTOR.
- CONNECT A DIGITAL MULTIMETER FROM TP SENSOR TERMINAL "1" TO TERMINAL "2" (TP SENSOR SIDE).
- MEASURE RESISTANCE WITH ACCELERATOR PEDAL DEPRESSED AND THEN RELEASED.
  SHOULD READ INFINITE (DEPRESSED) AND THEN, LESS THAN 1.0 OHM (RELEASED).
  DOES IT?

YES | **NO**

YES:
- CHECK FOR AN OPEN OR SHORT TO GROUND IN BLU WIRE BETWEEN CCM AND TP SENSOR. IF OK, REPLACE CCM.

NO:
- ADJUST/REPLACE TP SENSOR.

NO | **YES**

10)
- BACKPROBE PCM CONNECTOR C3 WITH A DIGITAL MULTIMETER FROM CAVITY "15" (BRN/YEL WIRE) TO GROUND.
- START ENGINE AND ROAD TEST VEHICLE.
- DEPRESS "OVERDRIVE" SWITCH.
- MEASURE VOLTAGE WITH TRANSAXLE IN 1ST GEAR, 2ND GEAR, 3RD GEAR AND OVERDRIVE.
  SHOULD READ 0.0 VOLTS (1ST GEAR), MORE THAN 10.0 VOLTS (2ND GEAR), MORE THAN 10.0 VOLTS (3RD GEAR) AND 0.0 VOLTS (OVERDRIVE).
  DOES IT?

YES | **NO**

NO:
- SEE APPROPRIATE MITCHELL® TRANSMISSION SERVICE & REPAIR MANUAL.

11)
- TURN IGNITION SWITCH TO "LOCK."
- WAIT TEN SECONDS AND THEN TURN IGNITION SWITCH TO "ON."
- CONNECT A JUMPER FROM DLC TERMINAL "Tc" TO "E1."
- OBSERVE "CRUISE" INDICATOR.

12)
- BACKPROBE CCM CONNECTOR WITH A DIGITAL MULTIMETER FROM CAVITY "22" (BRN/WHT WIRE) TO GROUND.
- MEASURE VOLTAGE WITH TRANSAXLE IN 2ND GEAR.

MORE THAN 10.0 VOLTS | **LESS THAN 10.0 VOLTS**

13)
- TURN IGNITION SWITCH TO "LOCK."
- DISCONNECT CCM CONNECTOR.
- CONNECT A DIGITAL MULTIMETER FROM CCM CONNECTOR CAVITY "9" (RED WIRE) TO GROUND.
- TURN IGNITION SWITCH TO "ON."
- MEASURE VOLTAGE.

LESS THAN 10.0 VOLTS:
- CHECK FOR OPEN IN BRN/YEL WIRE BETWEEN CCM & PCM. IF OKAY, SEE APPROPRIATE MITCHELL® TRANSMISSION SERVICE & REPAIR MANUAL.

MORE THAN 10.0 VOLTS | **LESS THAN 10.0 VOLTS**

14)
- TURN IGNITION SWITCH TO "LOCK."
- RECONNECT CCM CONNECTOR.
- CONNECT A DIGITAL MULTIMETER FROM CCM CONNECTOR CAVITY "9" (RED WIRE) TO GROUND.
- ROAD TEST VEHICLE.
- MEASURE VOLTAGE WHILE DRIVING VEHICLE UP A STEEP GRADE WITH TRANSAXLE IN OVERDRIVE AND CRUISE CONTROL ENGAGED.

LESS THAN 10.0 VOLTS:
- CHECK FOR AN OPEN OR A SHORT TO GROUND IN RED WIRE BETWEEN CCM AND PCM. IF OK, REPLACE PCM.

LESS THAN 1.0 VOLT | **MORE THAN 1.0 VOLT**

LESS THAN 1.0 VOLT:
- DOES TRANSAXLE SHIFT OUT OF OVERDRIVE?

MORE THAN 1.0 VOLT:
- REPLACE CCM.

YES | **NO**

YES:
- PROCEED TO AND PERFORM STEP 11 OF THIS CHART.

NO:
- SEE APPROPRIATE MITCHELL® TRANSMISSION SERVICE & REPAIR MANUAL.

FLASHES ON AND OFF RAPIDLY | **FLASHES DTCs** | **REMAINS LIT, DOES NOT FLASH**

FLASHES ON AND OFF RAPIDLY:
THE ELECTRONIC CRUISE CONTROL SYSTEM IS FUNCTIONING NORMALLY. PROBLEM COULD BE INTERMITTENT– REFER TO DIAGNOSTIC AIDS. IF A PROBLEM STILL EXISTS, CHECK THE CRUISE CONTROL CABLE CONNECTIONS AND ACCELERATOR BRACKET/LEVER ASSEMBLY FOR BINDING OR IMPROPER ADJUSTMENT.

FLASHES DTCs:
REFER TO APPROPRIATE DTC CHART.

REMAINS LIT, DOES NOT FLASH:
- CHECK FOR AN OPEN IN PPL WIRE BETWEEN CCM AND DLC OR IN BRN WIRE BETWEEN DLC AND G106. IF OK, REPLACE CCM.

CHART 9B-1
CRUISE INDICATOR LIGHT DOES NOT GLOW
(1 of 2)

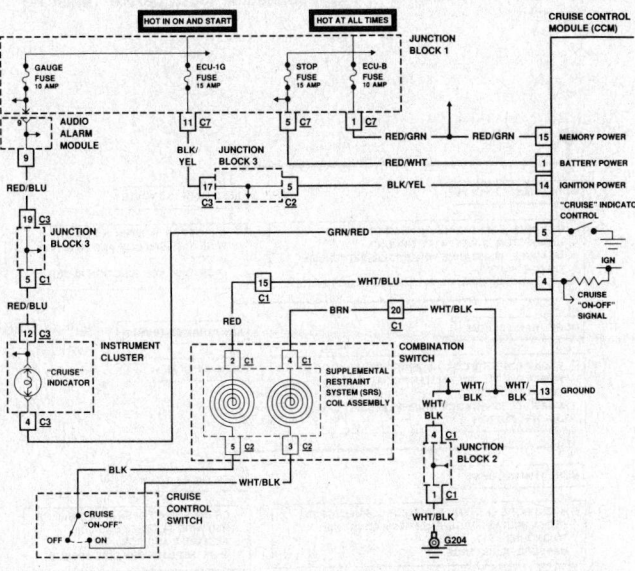

Voltage is supplied to CRUISE indicator light through GAUGE fuse whenever ignition switch is in ON position. A ground is provided to CRUISE indicator light when CCM receives an on signal from cruise control switch.

NOTE: Test numbers refer to numbers on diagnostic chart.

1) Checks for voltage through CRUISE indictor light to CCM.
2) Checks CCM ground circuit.
3) Checks for voltage to cruise indicator light.
4) Checks for ignition voltage at CCM.
5) Determines if fault is in wiring to instrument cluster.
6) Determines if fault is in wiring or in junction block 1 or 3.
7) Checks CCM memory power circuit.
8) Checks CCM battery power circuit.

DIAGNOSTIC AIDS

Check ECU-IG fuse, STOP fuse and ECU-B fuse. An intermittent condition may be caused by rubbed-through insulation, or a wire broken inside insulation. Check harness connectors for backed-out or damaged terminals, improper mating or broken connector lock, before replacing component.

IMPORTANT: MAKE SURE THAT CCM OBD SYSTEM CHECK HAS BEEN PERFORMED BEFORE CONTINUING DIAGNOSIS.

FROM CCM OBD SYSTEM CHECK.

① • TURN IGNITION SWITCH TO "LOCK."
• DISCONNECT CCM CONNECTOR.
• CONNECT A DIGITAL MULTIMETER FROM CCM CONNECTOR CAVITY "5" TO GROUND.
• TURN IGNITION SWITCH TO "ON."
• MEASURE VOLTAGE.

MORE THAN 10.0 VOLTS

② • CONNECT A DIGITAL MULTIMETER FROM CCM CONNECTOR CAVITY "13" TO B+.
• MEASURE VOLTAGE.

MORE THAN 10.0 VOLTS

④ • CONNECT A DIGITAL MULTIMETER FROM CCM CONNECTOR CAVITY "14" TO GROUND.
• MEASURE VOLTAGE.

LESS THAN 10.0 VOLTS

• CHECK FOR AN OPEN IN WHT/BLK WIRE BETWEEN CCM AND G204. IF OK, REPLACE JUNCTION BLOCK 2.

LESS THAN 10.0 VOLTS

③ • BACKPROBE INSTRUMENT CLUSTER CONNECTOR C3 WITH A DIGITAL MULTIMETER FROM TERMINAL "12" TO GROUND.
• MEASURE VOLTAGE.

LESS THAN 10.0 VOLTS

⑤ • BACKPROBE AUDIO ALARM MODULE CONNECTOR WITH A DIGITAL MULTIMETER FROM CAVITY "9" TO GROUND.
• MEASURE VOLTAGE.

MORE THAN 10.0 VOLTS

• CHECK FOR AN OPEN IN GRN/RED WIRE BETWEEN INSTRUMENT CLUSTER AND CCM OR FOR AN OPEN IN INSTRUMENT CLUSTER PRINTED CIRCUIT. IF OK, REPLACE "CRUISE" INDICATOR BULB.

LESS THAN 10.0 VOLTS

REPLACE AUDIO ALARM MODULE AND RETEST SYSTEM. IF SYSTEM REMAINS INOPERATIVE, REPLACE JUNCTION BLOCK 1.

MORE THAN 10.0 VOLTS

• CHECK FOR AN OPEN IN RED/BLU WIRE BETWEEN AUDIO ALARM MODULE AND INSTRUMENT CLUSTER. IF OK, REPLACE JUNCTION BLOCK 3.

MORE THAN 10.0 VOLTS

LESS THAN 10.0 VOLTS

⑥ • BACKPROBE JUNCTION BLOCK 3 CONNECTOR C3 WITH A DIGITAL MULTIMETER FROM CAVITY "17" TO GROUND.
• MEASURE VOLTAGE.

LESS THAN 10.0 VOLTS

• CHECK FOR AN OPEN IN BLK/YEL WIRE BETWEEN JUNCTION BLOCK 1 AND 3. IF OK, REPLACE JUNCTION BLOCK 1.

MORE THAN 10.0 VOLTS

• CHECK FOR AN OPEN IN BLK/YEL WIRE BETWEEN JUNCTION BLOCK 3 AND CCM. IF OK, REPLACE JUNCTION BLOCK 3.

⑦ • CONNECT A DIGITAL MULTIMETER FROM CCM CONNECTOR CAVITY "15" TO GROUND.
• MEASURE VOLTAGE.

MORE THAN 10.0 VOLTS

LESS THAN 10.0 VOLTS

• CHECK FOR AN OPEN IN RED/GRN WIRE BETWEEN JUNCTION BLOCK 1 AND CCM. IF OK, REPLACE JUNCTION BLOCK 1.

⑧ • CONNECT A DIGITAL MULTIMETER FROM CCM CONNECTOR CAVITY "1" TO GROUND.
• MEASURE VOLTAGE.

B

**Continued
On Next
Page**

CHART 9B-1
CRUISE INDICATOR LIGHT DOES NOT GLOW
(2 of 2)

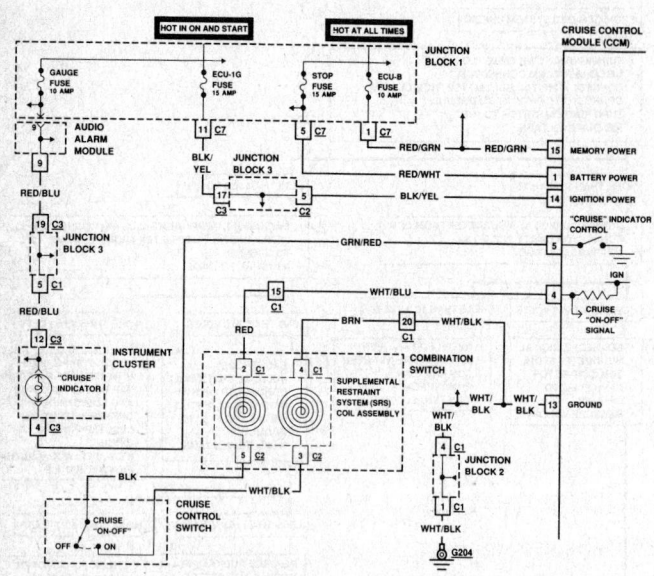

Voltage is supplied to CRUISE indicator light through GAUGE fuse whenever ignition switch is in ON position. A ground is provided to CRUISE indicator light when CCM receives an on signal from cruise control switch.

NOTE: Test numbers refer to numbers on diagnostic chart.

9) Checks CCM cruise on/off circuit.
10) Checks for an open White/Blue or Red wire and for a faulty Supplemental Restraint System (SRS) coil assembly.
11) Checks for open Brown or White/Black wire, faulty cruise control switch or faulty SRS coil assembly.

93D83645 93G83648

DIAGNOSTIC AIDS

Check ECU-IG fuse, STOP fuse and ECU-B fuse. An intermittent condition may be caused by rubbed-through insulation, or a wire broken inside insulation. Check harness connectors for backed-out or damaged terminals, improper mating or broken connector lock, before replacing component.

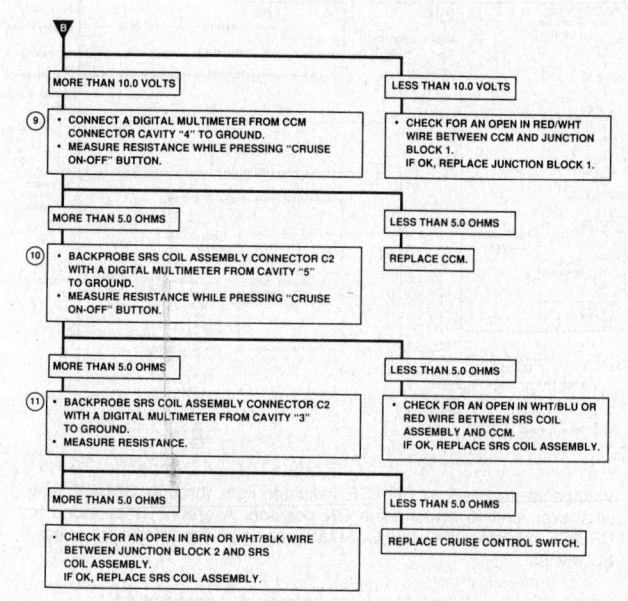

Courtesy of General Motors Corp.

CHART 9B-2, CRUISE INDICATOR LIGHT DOES NOT FLASH, SET/COAST TEST

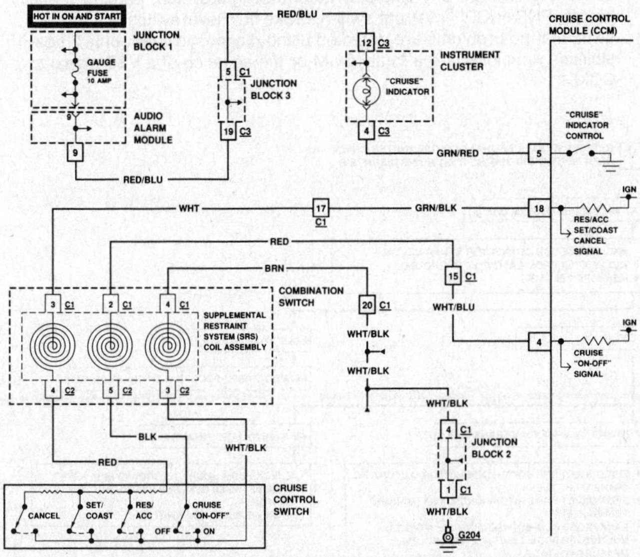

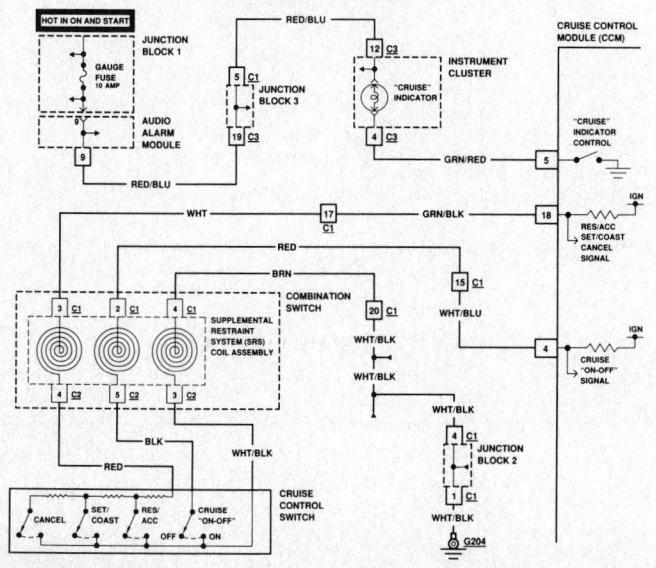

IMPORTANT: BE SURE THAT CCM OBD SYSTEM CHECK HAS BEEN PERFORMED BEFORE CONTINUING DIAGNOSIS.

FROM CCM OBD SYSTEM CHECK.

1)
- TURN IGNITION SWITCH TO "LOCK."
- DISCONNECT CCM CONNECTOR.
- TURN IGNITION SWITCH TO "ON."
- CONNECT A DIGITAL MULTIMETER FROM CCM CONNECTOR CAVITY "18" TO GROUND.
- MEASURE RESISTANCE WITH CRUISE CONTROL SWITCH IN RELEASED POSITION.

INFINITE

2)
- LEAVE DIGITAL MULTIMETER CONNECTED.
- MOVE CRUISE CONTROL SWITCH DOWN TO "SET/COAST" POSITION AND HOLD.
- MEASURE RESISTANCE. SHOULD BE APPROXIMATELY 200 OHMS. IS IT?

LESS THAN INFINITE

3)
- LEAVE DIGITAL MULTIMETER CONNECTED.
- DISCONNECT SRS COIL ASSEMBLY CONNECTOR C2.
- MEASURE RESISTANCE FROM CCM CONNECTOR CAVITY "18" TO GROUND.

LESS THAN INFINITE
- CHECK FOR A SHORT TO GROUND IN WHT OR GRN/BLK WIRE BETWEEN SRS COIL ASSEMBLY AND CCM. IF OK, REPLACE SRS COIL ASSEMBLY.

INFINITE
- REPLACE CRUISE CONTROL SWITCH.

NO

4)
- DISCONNECT SRS COIL ASSEMBLY CONNECTOR C2.
- BACKPROBE SRS COIL ASSEMBLY CONNECTOR C2 WITH A DIGITAL MULTIMETER FROM CAVITY "3" TO CAVITY "4".
- MOVE CRUISE CONTROL SWITCH DOWN TO THE "SET/COAST" POSITION AND HOLD.
- MEASURE RESISTANCE. SHOULD BE APPROXIMATELY 200 OHMS. IS IT?

YES
- REPLACE CCM.

YES
- CHECK FOR AN OPEN IN WHT OR GRN/BLK WIRE BETWEEN SRS COIL ASSEMBLY AND CCM. IF OK, REPLACE SRS COIL ASSEMBLY.

NO
- REPLACE CRUISE CONTROL SWITCH.

When cruise control switch is moved to SET/COAST position and ON/OFF switch is pressed, CCM enters a self-diagnostic check mode. During this test, CCM checks set/coast circuit. If circuit is okay, CRUISE indicator light flashes 2 times every second.

NOTE: Test numbers refer to numbers on diagnostic chart.

1) Checks circuit to CCM for shorts.
2) Checks for set/coast signal to CCM.
3) Checks for shorts in set/coast circuit.
4) Checks for faulty wiring in set/coast circuit.

DIAGNOSTIC AIDS

An intermittent condition may be caused by rubbed-through insulation, or a wire broken inside insulation. Check harness connectors for backed-out or damaged terminals, improper mating or broken connector lock, before replacing component.

93H83649 93C83651 93D83652

Courtesy of General Motors Corp.

CHART 9B-3, CRUISE INDICATOR LIGHT DOES NOT FLASH, RES/ACC TEST

When cruise control switch is moved to RES/ACC position and ON/OFF switch is pressed, CCM enters a self-diagnostic check mode. During this test, CCM checks RES/ACC circuit. If circuit is okay, CRUISE indicator light flashes 3 times every second.

NOTE: Test numbers refer to numbers on diagnostic chart.

1) Checks for faulty RES/ACC switch circuit or faulty CCM.

DIAGNOSTIC AIDS

An intermittent condition may be caused by rubbed-through insulation, or a wire broken inside insulation. Check harness connectors for backed-out or damaged terminals, improper mating or broken connector lock, before replacing component.

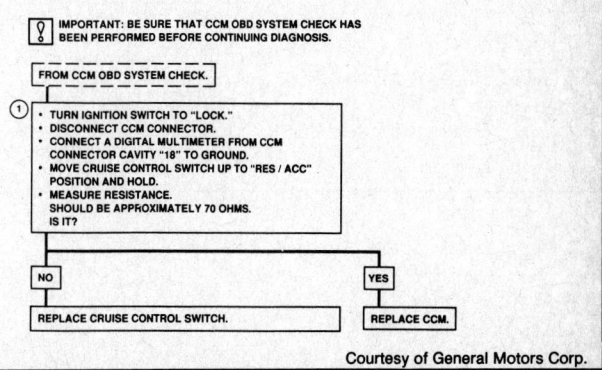

IMPORTANT: BE SURE THAT CCM OBD SYSTEM CHECK HAS BEEN PERFORMED BEFORE CONTINUING DIAGNOSIS.

FROM CCM OBD SYSTEM CHECK.

1)
- TURN IGNITION SWITCH TO "LOCK."
- DISCONNECT CCM CONNECTOR.
- CONNECT A DIGITAL MULTIMETER FROM CCM CONNECTOR CAVITY "18" TO GROUND.
- MOVE CRUISE CONTROL SWITCH UP TO "RES/ACC" POSITION AND HOLD.
- MEASURE RESISTANCE. SHOULD BE APPROXIMATELY 70 OHMS. IS IT?

NO
- REPLACE CRUISE CONTROL SWITCH.

YES
- REPLACE CCM.

93E83653 93F83654

Courtesy of General Motors Corp.

CHART 9B-4A
CRUISE INDICATOR LIGHT DOES NOT GLOW DURING CANCEL TEST

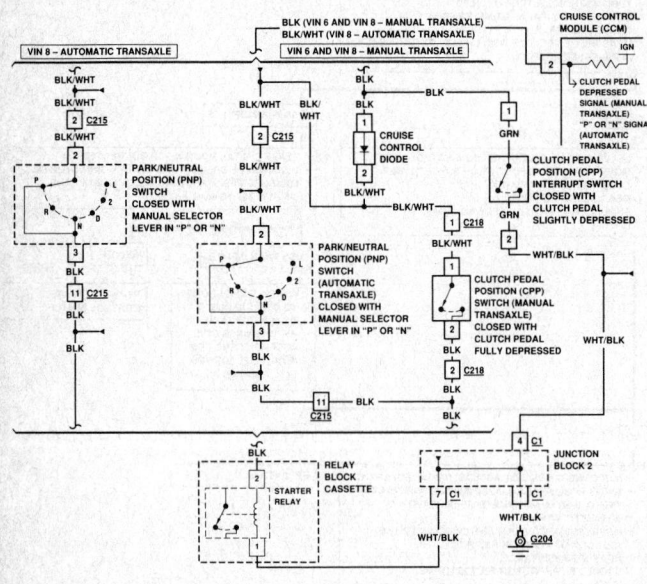

CCM lights CRUISE indicator light when CCM senses wheels turning and all cancel switches open.

NOTE: Test numbers refer to numbers on diagnostic chart.

1) Checks CCM clutch pedal depressed signal (M/T), or park/neutral signal (A/T).
2) Checks for faulty Park/Neutral Position (PNP) switch (A/T), or Clutch Pedal Position (CPP) switch (M/T).
3) Checks for short to ground in Black wire or faulty CPP interrupt switch (M/T).

DIAGNOSTIC AIDS

To light CRUISE indicator light during this portion of testing, CCM needs to sense a vehicle speed input from Vehicle Speed Sensor (VSS) and no cancel signal from any cancel switch (stoplight switch, parking brake switch, PNP or CPP interrupt switch, brake fluid level switch or CANCEL switch). If no problems are detected using diagnostic chart, only 2 possibilities remaining are a faulty CCM or the absence of a VSS signal to CCM.

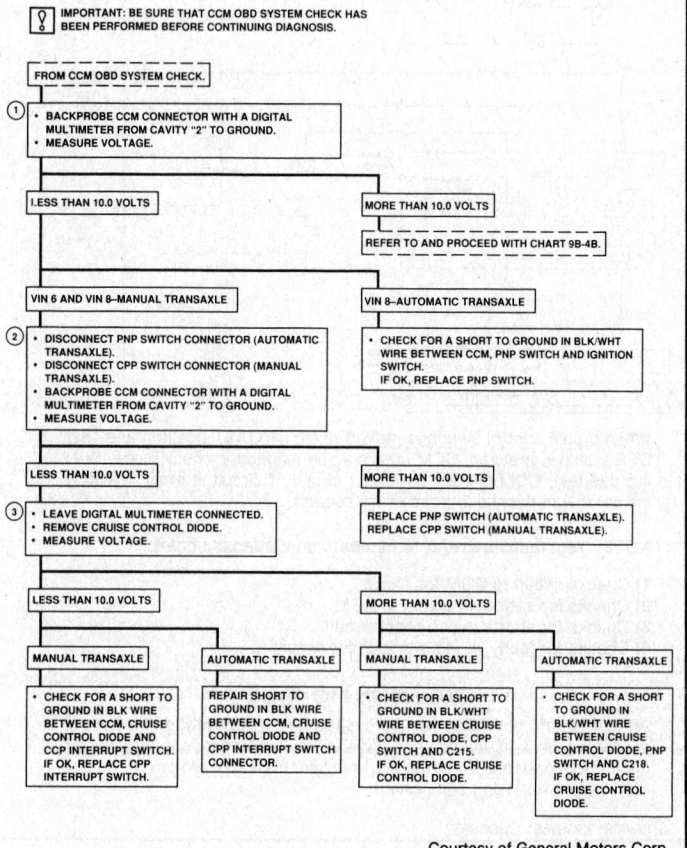

93G83655 93H83656

Courtesy of General Motors Corp.

CHART 9B-4B
CRUISE INDICATOR LIGHT DOES NOT GLOW DURING CANCEL TEST

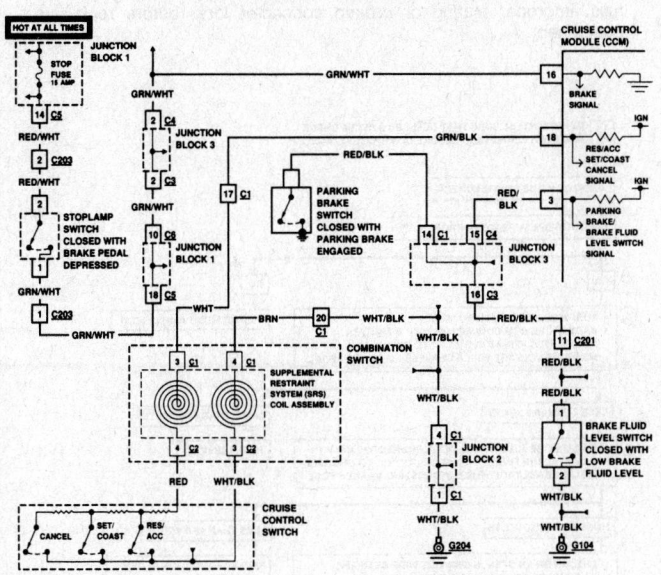

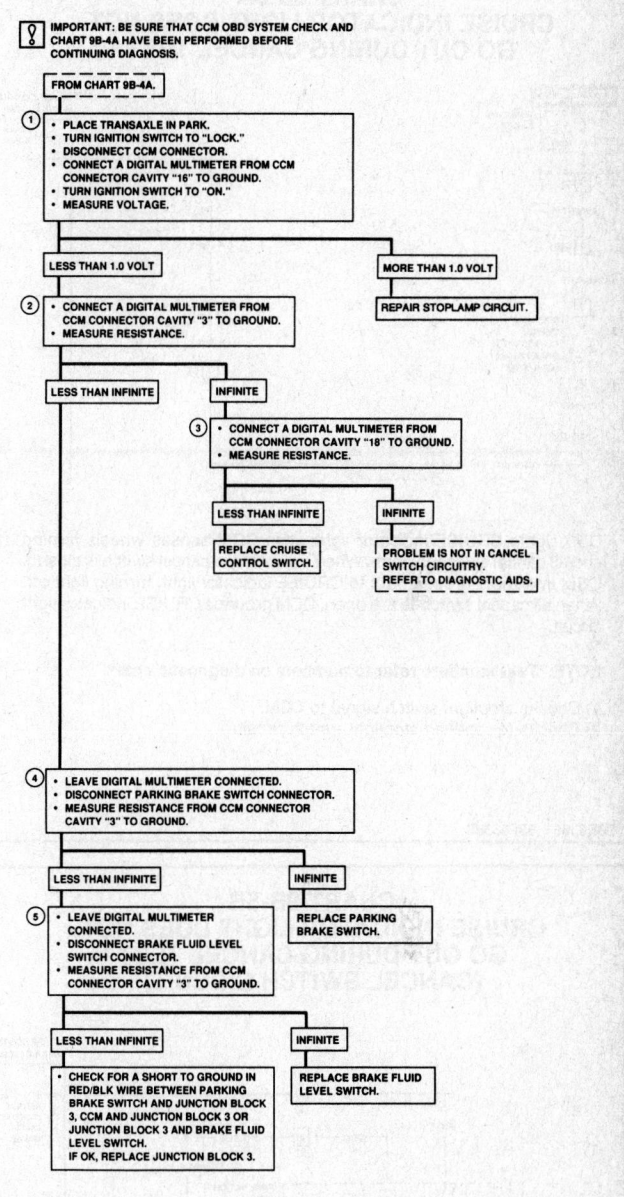

CCM lights CRUISE indicator light when CCM senses wheels turning and all cancel switches open.

NOTE: Test numbers refer to numbers on diagnostic chart.

1) Checks for voltage signal from stoplight switch circuit.
2) Checks for parking brake/brake fluid level switch signal.
3) Determines if fault is cruise control switch or in VSS circuit.
4) Checks for faulty parking brake switch.
5) Checks for short to ground in Red/Black wire or faulty brake fluid level switch.

DIAGNOSTIC AIDS

To light CRUISE indicator light during this portion of testing, CCM needs to sense a vehicle speed input from Vehicle Speed Sensor (VSS) and no cancel signal from any cancel switch (stoplight switch, parking brake switch, PNP or CPP interrupt switch, brake fluid level switch or CANCEL switch). If no problems are detected using diagnostic chart, only 2 possibilities remaining are a faulty CCM or the absence of a VSS signal to CCM. Proceed to DTC 21 chart and perform all testing within DTC 21 diagnostic chart. If all tests in DTC 21 chart appear normal, replace CCM.

93I83657 93J83658 93A83659

CHART 9B-5A
CRUISE INDICATOR LIGHT DOES NOT
GO OUT DURING CANCEL TEST

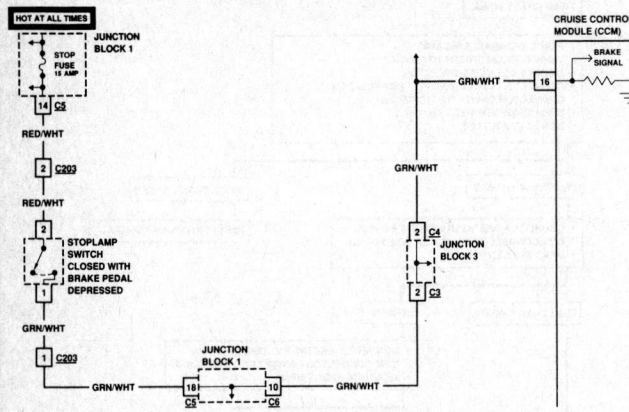

DIAGNOSTIC AIDS

Ensure vehicle stoplights function normally. An intermittent condition may be caused by rubbed-through insulation, or a wire broken inside insulation. Check harness connectors for backed-out or damaged terminals, improper mating or broken connector lock, before replacing component.

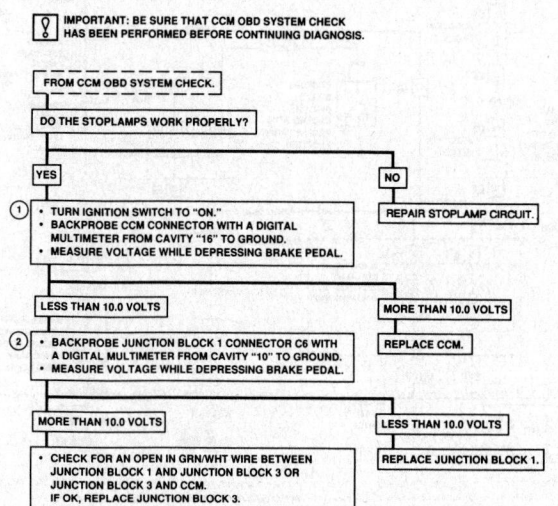

CCM lights CRUISE indicator light when CCM senses wheels turning and all cancel switches open. When one or more cancel switch is closed, CCM interrupts ground path to CRUISE indicator light, turning light off. When all cancel switches are open, CCM grounds CRUISE indicator light circuit.

NOTE: Test numbers refer to numbers on diagnostic chart.

1) Checks stoplight switch signal to CCM.
2) Checks for open in stoplight switch circuit.

93E83661 93F83662

Courtesy of General Motors Corp.

CHART 9B-5B
CRUISE INDICATOR LIGHT DOES NOT
GO OUT DURING CANCEL TEST
(CANCEL SWITCH CIRCUIT)

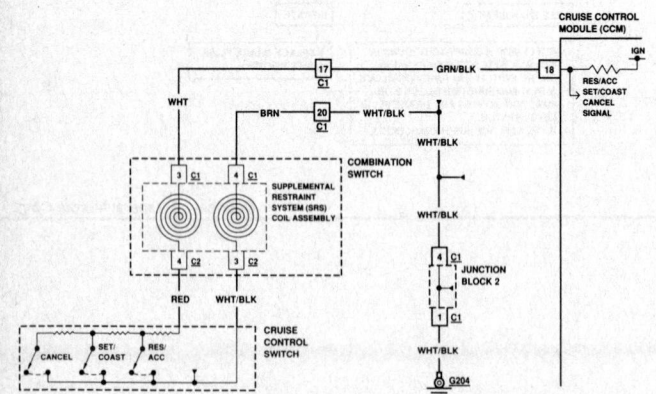

NOTE: Test numbers refer to numbers on diagnostic chart.

1) Determines if cruise control switch or CCM is faulty.

DIAGNOSTIC AIDS

An intermittent condition may be caused by rubbed-through insulation, or a wire broken inside insulation. Check harness connectors for backed-out or damaged terminals, improper mating or broken connector lock, before replacing component.

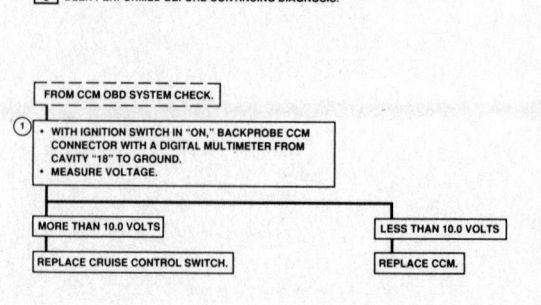

CCM lights CRUISE indicator light when CCM senses wheels turning and all cancel switches open. When one or more cancel switch is closed, CCM interrupts ground path to CRUISE indicator light, turning light off. When all cancel switches are open, CCM grounds CRUISE indicator light circuit.

93I83665 93J83666

Courtesy of General Motors Corp.

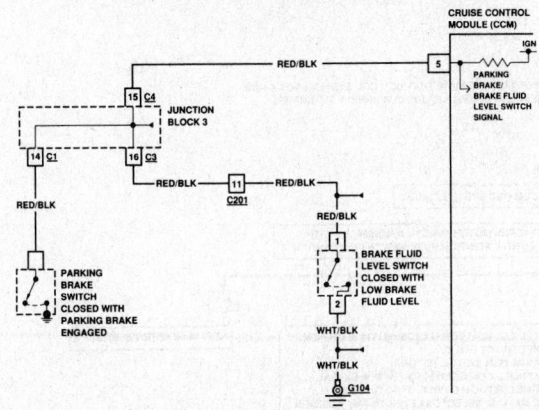

**CHART 9B-5C
CRUISE INDICATOR LIGHT DOES NOT
GO OUT DURING CANCEL TEST
(PARKING BRAKE CIRCUIT)**

IMPORTANT: BE SURE THAT THE CCM OBD SYSTEM CHECK HAS BEEN PERFORMED BEFORE CONTINUING DIAGNOSIS.

FROM CCM OBD SYSTEM CHECK.

1. • REMOVE GAUGE FUSE FROM JUNCTION BLOCK 1.
   • WITH IGNITION SWITCH IN "ON" BACKPROBE CCM CONNECTOR WITH A DIGITAL MULTIMETER FROM CAVITY "5" TO GROUND.
   • MEASURE VOLTAGE.

MORE THAN 10.0 VOLTS | **LESS THAN 10.0 VOLTS** → **REPLACE CCM.**

2. • TURN IGNITION SWITCH TO "LOCK."
   • DISCONNECT PARKING BRAKE SWITCH CONNECTOR.
   • CONNECT A DIGITAL MULTIMETER FROM PARKING BRAKE SWITCH TERMINAL (SWITCH SIDE) TO GROUND.
   • MEASURE RESISTANCE WITH PARKING BRAKE ENGAGED.

LESS THAN 1.0 OHM | **MORE THAN 1.0 OHM** → **REPLACE PARKING BRAKE SWITCH.**

3. • DISCONNECT BRAKE FLUID LEVEL SWITCH CONNECTOR.
   • CONNECT A DIGITAL MULTIMETER ACROSS BRAKE FLUID SWITCH TERMINALS (SWITCH SIDE).
   • MEASURE RESISTANCE WHILE HOLDING FLOAT DOWN.

LESS THAN 1.0 OHM | **MORE THAN 1.0 OHM** → **REPLACE BRAKE FLUID LEVEL SWITCH.**

• CHECK FOR AN OPEN IN RED/BLK WIRE BETWEEN CCM AND JUNCTION BLOCK 3, PARKING BRAKE SWITCH AND JUNCTION BLOCK 3 OR BETWEEN BRAKE FLUID LEVEL SWITCH AND JUNCTION BLOCK 3.
• CHECK FOR AN OPEN IN WHT/BLK WIRE BETWEEN BRAKE FLUID LEVEL SWITCH AND G104.
IF OK, REPLACE JUNCTION BLOCK 3.

CCM lights CRUISE indicator light when CCM senses wheels turning and all cancel switches open. When one or more cancel switch is closed, CCM interrupts ground path to CRUISE indicator light, turning light off. When all cancel switches are open, CCM grounds CRUISE indicator light circuit.

NOTE: Test numbers refer to numbers on diagnostic chart.

1) Verifies CCM signal voltage.
2) Checks parking brake circuit.
3) Checks brake fluid level switch circuit.

DIAGNOSTIC AIDS

Verify vehicle BRAKE indicator light operation. An intermittent condition may be caused by rubbed-through insulation, or a wire broken inside insulation. Check harness connectors for backed-out or damaged terminals, improper mating or broken connector lock, before replacing component.

93A83667 93B83668

CHART 9B-5D
CRUISE INDICATOR LIGHT DOES NOT
GO OUT DURING CANCEL TEST
(PNP SWITCH CIRCUIT)

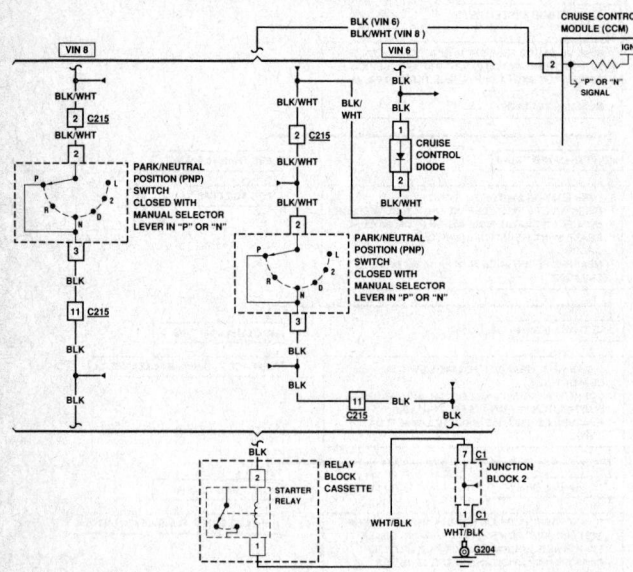

CCM lights CRUISE indicator light when CCM senses wheels turning and all cancel switches open. When one or more cancel switch is closed, CCM interrupts ground path to CRUISE indicator light, turning light off. When all cancel switches are open, CCM grounds CRUISE indicator light circuit.

NOTE: Test numbers refer to numbers on diagnostic chart.

1) Verifies CCM signal voltage.
2) Checks Black wire and cruise control diode for open (VIN 6).

DIAGNOSTIC AIDS

An intermittent condition may be caused by rubbed-through insulation, or a wire broken inside insulation. Check harness connectors for backed-out or damaged terminals, improper mating or broken connector lock, before replacing component.

IMPORTANT: BE SURE THAT CCM OBD SYSTEM CHECK HAS BEEN PERFORMED BEFORE CONTINUING DIAGNOSIS.

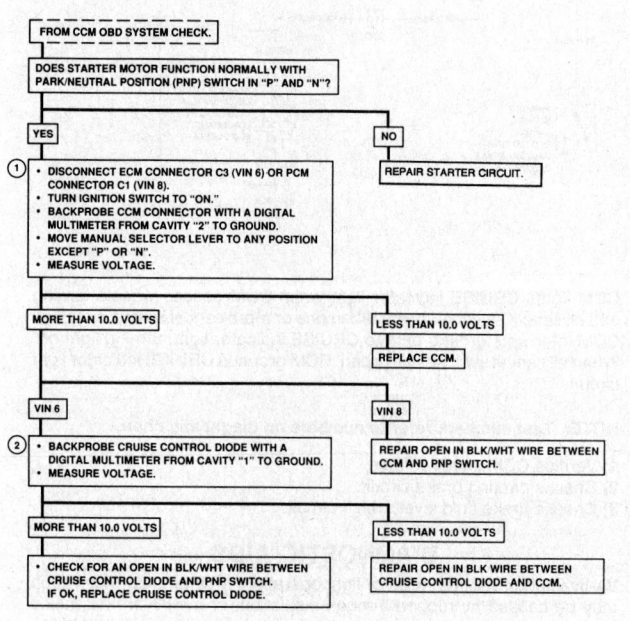

Courtesy of General Motors Corp.

CHART 9B-5E
CRUISE INDICATOR LIGHT DOES NOT GO OUT DURING CANCEL TEST
(CPP INTERRUPT SWITCH CIRCUIT)

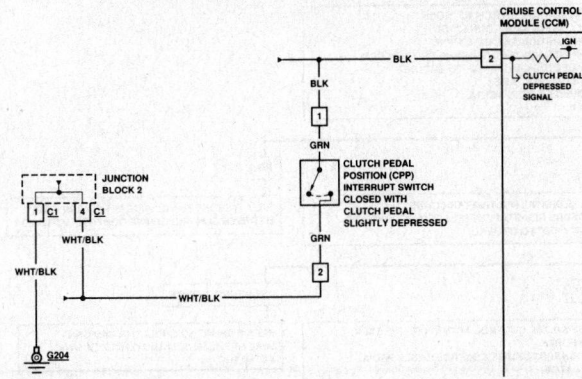

CCM lights CRUISE indicator light when CCM senses wheels turning and all cancel switches open. When one or more cancel switch is closed, CCM interrupts ground path to CRUISE indicator light, turning light off. When all cancel switches are open, CCM grounds CRUISE indicator light circuit.

NOTE: Test numbers refer to numbers on diagnostic chart.

1) Determines if CCM is faulty.
2) Checks for open in Black wire between CCM and CPP interrupt switch or for open ground circuit.

93G83671 93H83672

DIAGNOSTIC AIDS

An intermittent condition may be caused by rubbed-through insulation, or a wire broken inside insulation. Check harness connectors for backed-out or damaged terminals, improper mating or broken connector lock, before replacing component.

IMPORTANT: BE SURE THAT CCM OBD SYSTEM CHECK HAS BEEN PERFORMED BEFORE CONTINUING DIAGNOSIS.

FROM CCM OBD SYSTEM CHECK.

① • TURN IGNITION SWITCH TO "LOCK."
  • DISCONNECT CCM CONNECTOR.
  • CONNECT A DIGITAL MULTIMETER FROM CCM CONNECTOR CAVITY "2" TO GROUND.
  • MEASURE RESISTANCE WITH CLUTCH PEDAL DEPRESSED SLIGHTLY (DO NOT DEPRESS FULLY).

MORE THAN 1.0 OHM

LESS THAN 1.0 OHM

REPLACE CCM.

② • BACKPROBE CPP INTERRUPT SWITCH CONNECTOR WITH A DIGITAL MULTIMETER FROM CAVITY "2" TO GROUND.
  • MEASURE RESISTANCE.

MORE THAN 1.0 OHM

• CHECK FOR AN OPEN IN WHT/BLK WIRE BETWEEN CPP INTERRUPT SWITCH AND JUNCTION BLOCK 2. IF OK, REPLACE JUNCTION BLOCK 2.

LESS THAN 1.0 OHM

• CHECK FOR AN OPEN IN BLK WIRE BETWEEN CCM AND CPP INTERRUPT SWITCH AND CONDITION OF CRUISE CONTROL DIODE. IF OK, REPLACE CPP INTERRUPT SWITCH.

Courtesy of General Motors Corp.

DTC 11
OVERVOLTAGE ON MOTOR OPEN CIRCUIT

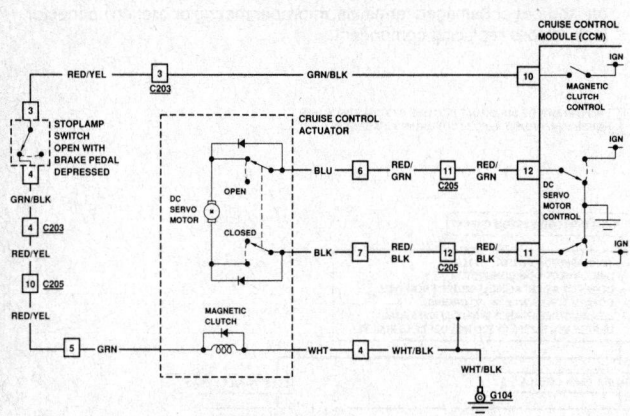

CCM applies voltage and ground to both the open side and close side of DC servo motor as driving conditions demand changing throttle angles.

NOTE: Test numbers refer to numbers on diagnostic chart.

1) Checks for short to voltage in Red/Green wire.
2) Checks for short to ground in Red/Green wire.
3) Checks for proper arm movement with magnetic clutch de-energized.
4) Checks for proper arm movement with magnetic clutch energized.
5) Checks for proper arm actuation with motor open circuit powered.
6) Checks for proper arm actuation with motor close circuit powered.

DIAGNOSTIC AIDS

Check cruise control cable for binding or damage. An intermittent condition may be caused by rubbed-through insulation, or a wire broken inside insulation. Check harness connectors for backed-out or damaged terminals, improper mating or broken connector lock, before replacing component.

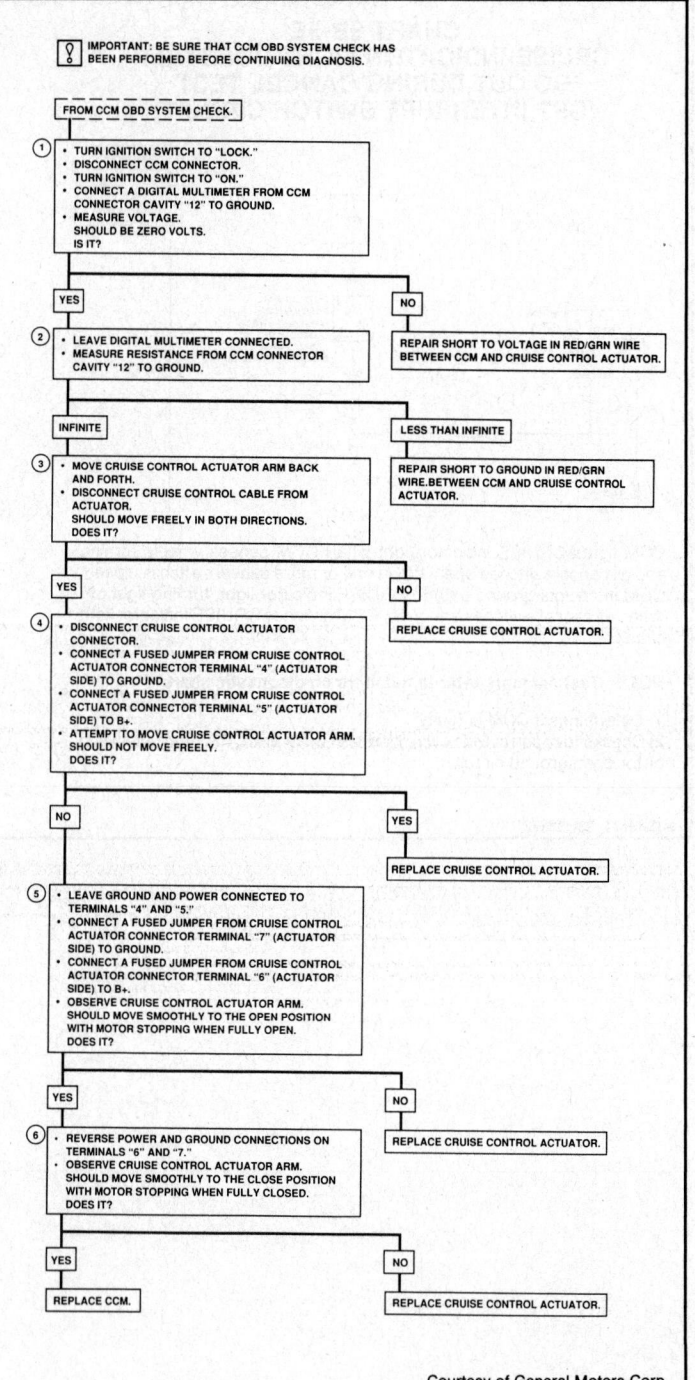

93I83673 93J83674 93A83675

DTC 12
OVERVOLTAGE ON MAGNETIC CLUTCH CIRCUIT

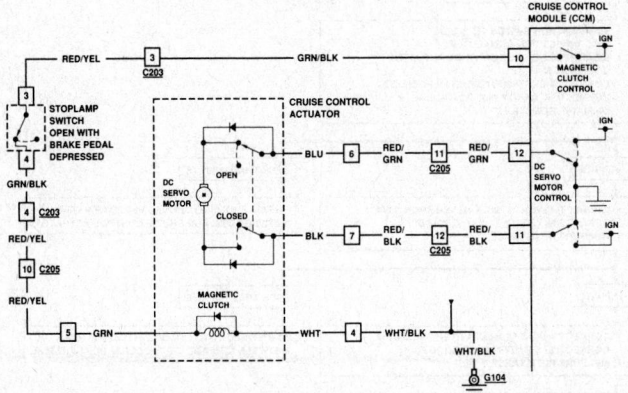

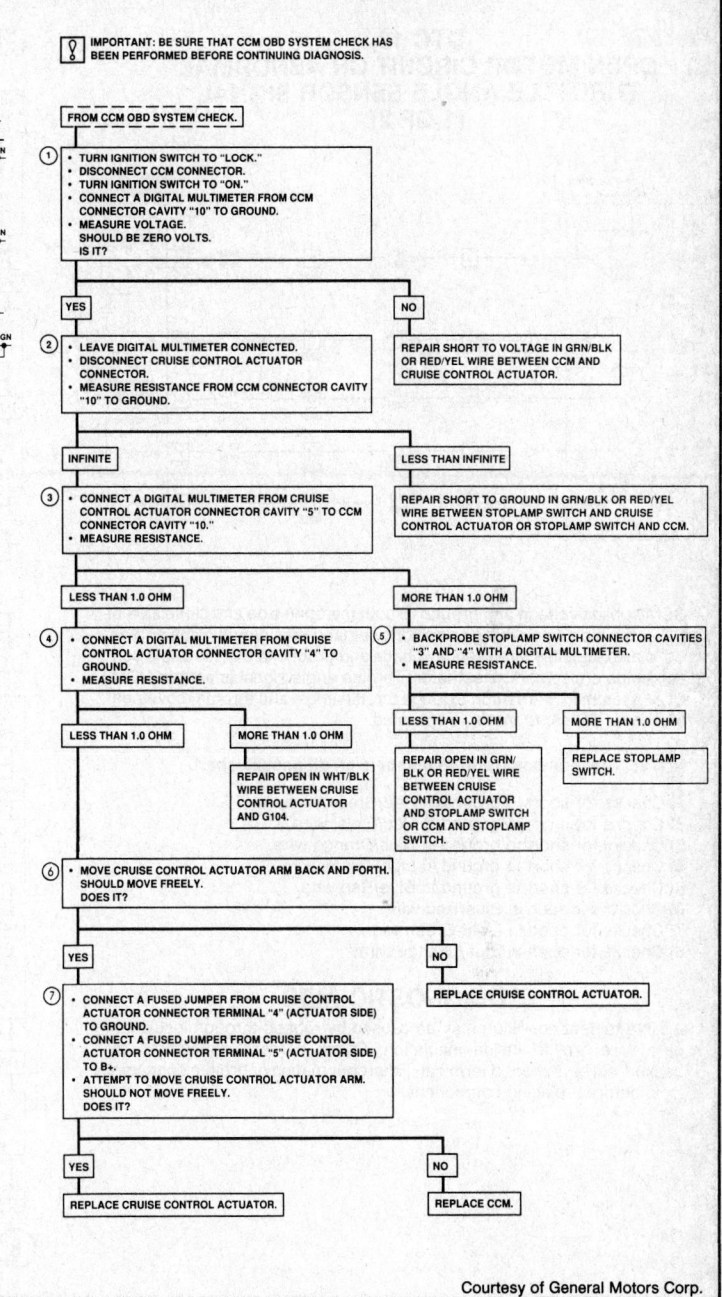

CCM applies voltage to magnetic clutch when cruise is engaged. Magnetic clutch mechanically connects DC servo motor to worm gear. Circuit is interrupted by stoplight switch whenever brake pedal is depressed.

NOTE: Test numbers refer to numbers on diagnostic chart.

1) Checks for short to voltage on Green/Black or Red/Yellow wire.
2) Checks for short to ground on Green/Black or Red/Yellow wire.
3) Checks for open in magnetic clutch circuit.
4) Checks for bad ground to magnetic clutch
5) Checks for an open in Green/Black or Red/Yellow wire or faulty stoplight circuit.
6) Checks cruise control actuator arm for free movement while magnetic clutch is not energized.
7) Checks cruise control actuator arm for malfunction while magnetic clutch is energized.

DIAGNOSTIC AIDS

Check stoplight switch adjustment. An intermittent condition may be caused by rubbed-through insulation, or a wire broken inside insulation. Check harness connectors for backed-out or damaged terminals, improper mating or broken connector lock, before replacing component.

93B83676 93C83677 93D83678

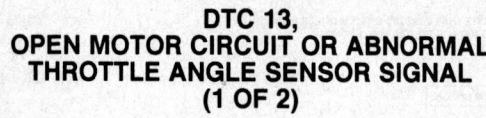

DTC 13,
OPEN MOTOR CIRCUIT OR ABNORMAL
THROTTLE ANGLE SENSOR SIGNAL
(1 OF 2)

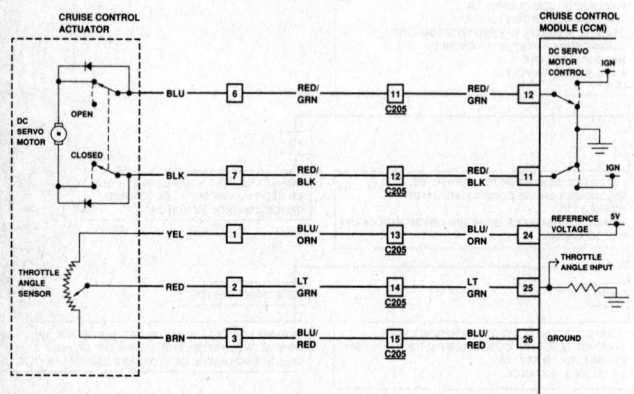

CCM applies voltage and ground to both the open side and close side of DC servo motor as driving conditions demand changing throttle angles. CCM also supplies a reference voltage and ground to throttle angle sensor inside cruise control actuator. Throttle angle signal is sent to CCM. CCM uses this information to judge throttle angle and throttle movement whenever DC servo motor is operated.

NOTE: Test numbers refer to numbers on diagnostic chart.

1) Checks for short to ground in Red/Green wire.
2) Checks for short to ground in Red/Black wire.
3) Checks for short to ground in Blue/Orange wire.
4) Checks for short to ground in Light Green wire.
5) Checks for short to ground in Blue/Red wire.
6) Checks for open in Blue/Red wire.
7) Checks for open in Light Green wire.
8) Checks for open in Blue/Orange wire.

DIAGNOSTIC AIDS

An intermittent condition may be caused by rubbed-through insulation, or a wire broken inside insulation. Check harness connectors for backed-out or damaged terminals, improper mating or broken connector lock, before replacing component.

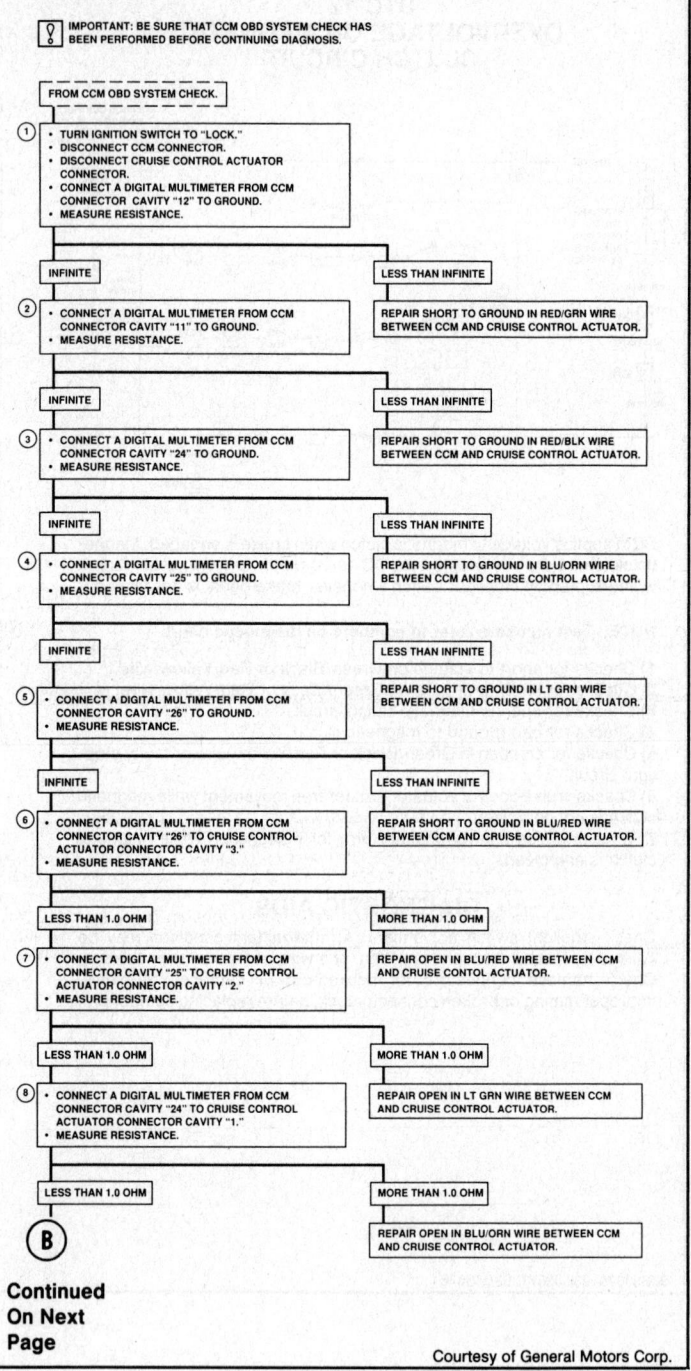

**Continued
On Next
Page**

93E83679 93H83680 93I83681

Courtesy of General Motors Corp.

DTC 13,
OPEN MOTOR CIRCUIT OR ABNORMAL
THROTTLE ANGLE SENSOR SIGNAL
(2 OF 2)

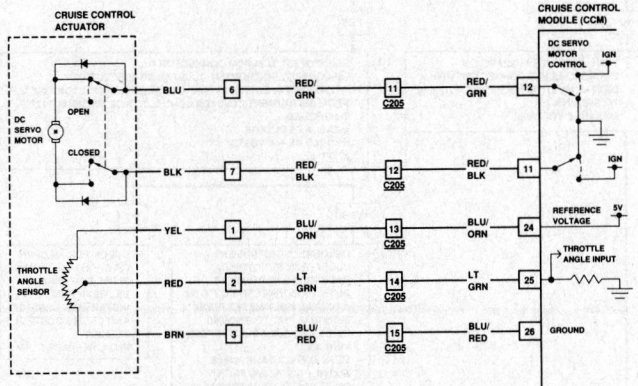

CCM applies voltage and ground to both the open side and close side of DC servo motor as driving conditions demand changing throttle angles. CCM also supplies a reference voltage and ground to throttle angle sensor inside cruise control actuator. Throttle angle signal is sent to CCM. CCM uses this information to judge throttle angle and throttle movement whenever DC servo motor is operated.

NOTE: Test numbers refer to numbers on diagnostic chart.

9) Checks for open in Red/Black wire.
10) Checks for open in Red/Green wire.
11) Checks resistance of throttle angle sensor.
12) Checks throttle angle sensor signal.
13) Checks for proper motor actuation in open direction.
14) Checks for proper motor actuation in close direction.

DIAGNOSTIC AIDS

An intermittent condition may be caused by rubbed-through insulation, or a wire broken inside insulation. Check harness connectors for backed-out or damaged terminals, improper mating or broken connector lock, before replacing component.

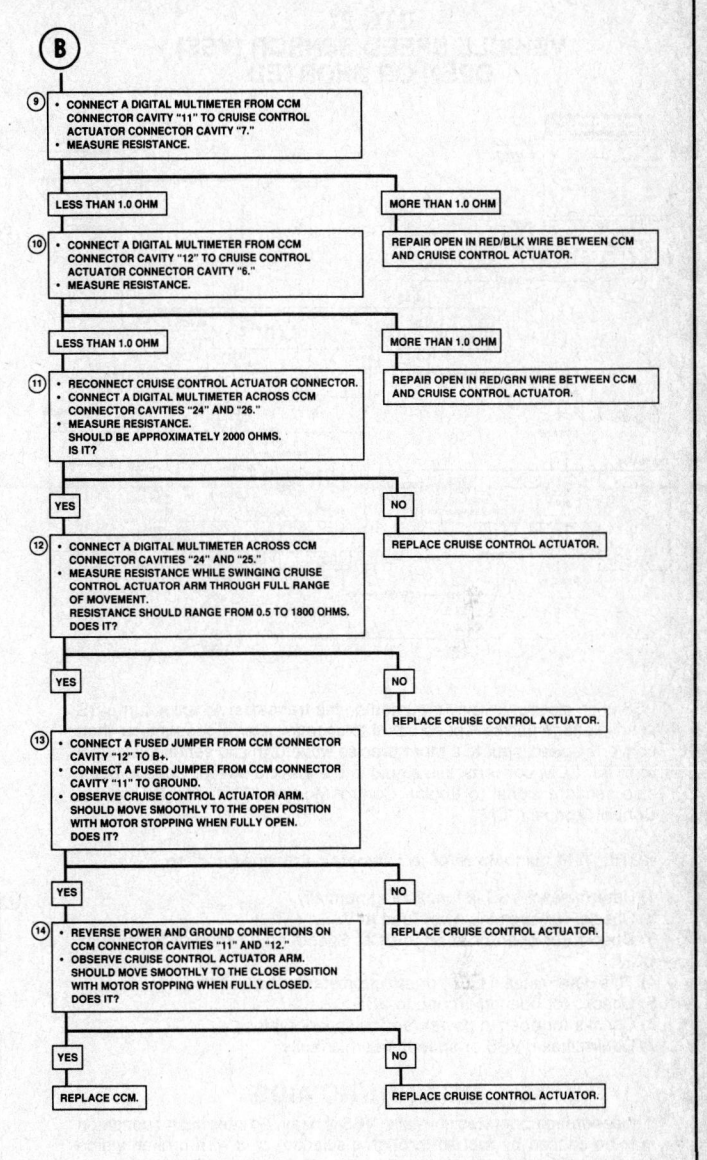

93E83679 93J83682 93A83683

Courtesy of General Motors Corp.

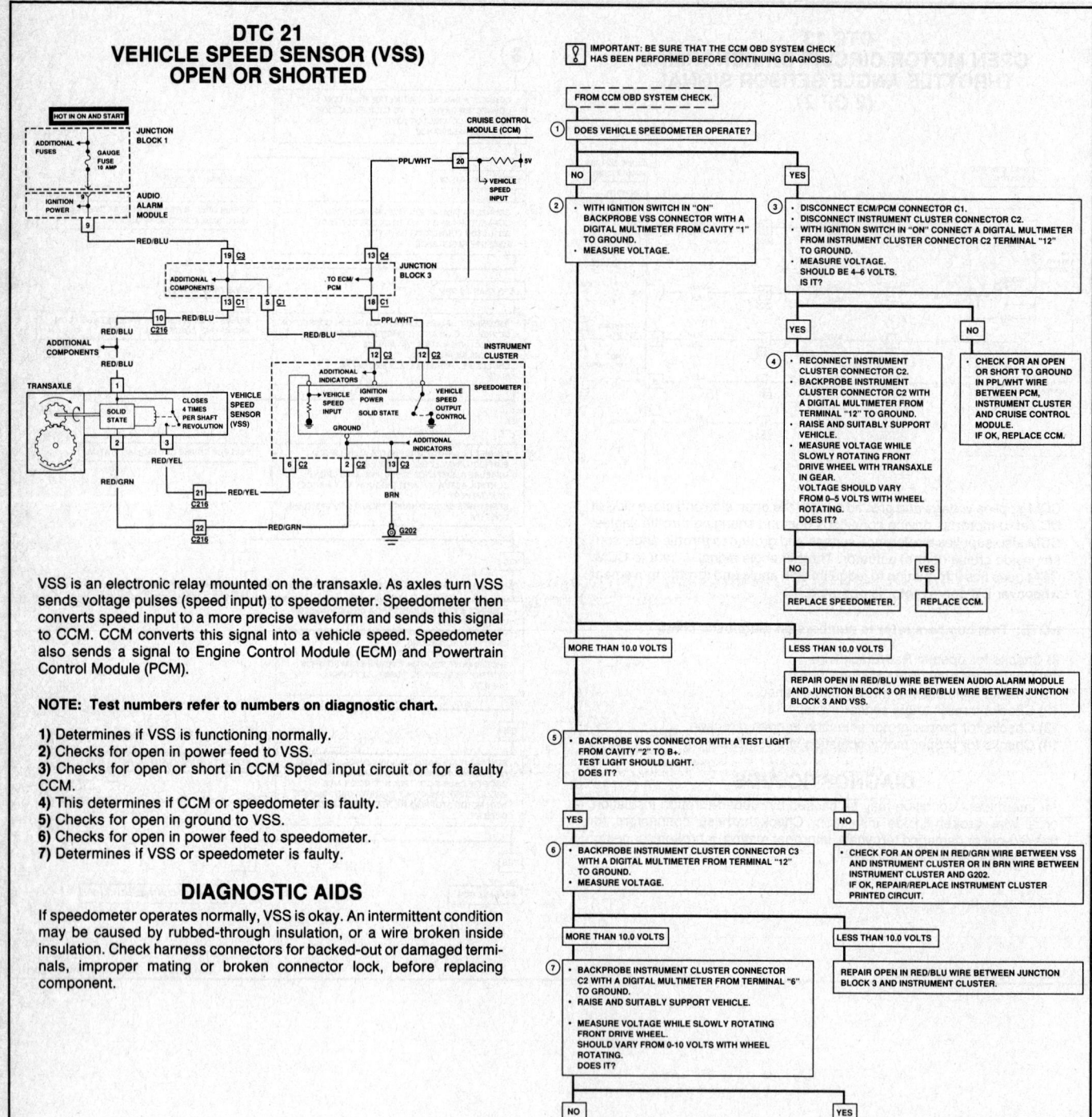

DTC 21
VEHICLE SPEED SENSOR (VSS)
OPEN OR SHORTED

VSS is an electronic relay mounted on the transaxle. As axles turn VSS sends voltage pulses (speed input) to speedometer. Speedometer then converts speed input to a more precise waveform and sends this signal to CCM. CCM converts this signal into a vehicle speed. Speedometer also sends a signal to Engine Control Module (ECM) and Powertrain Control Module (PCM).

NOTE: Test numbers refer to numbers on diagnostic chart.

1) Determines if VSS is functioning normally.
2) Checks for open in power feed to VSS.
3) Checks for open or short in CCM Speed input circuit or for a faulty CCM.
4) This determines if CCM or speedometer is faulty.
5) Checks for open in ground to VSS.
6) Checks for open in power feed to speedometer.
7) Determines if VSS or speedometer is faulty.

DIAGNOSTIC AIDS

If speedometer operates normally, VSS is okay. An intermittent condition may be caused by rubbed-through insulation, or a wire broken inside insulation. Check harness connectors for backed-out or damaged terminals, improper mating or broken connector lock, before replacing component.

93B83684 93C83685 93D83686

Courtesy of General Motors Corp.

DTC 23,
VEHICLE SPEED DROPS MORE THAN 10 MPH
UNDER SET SPEED (1 OF 2)

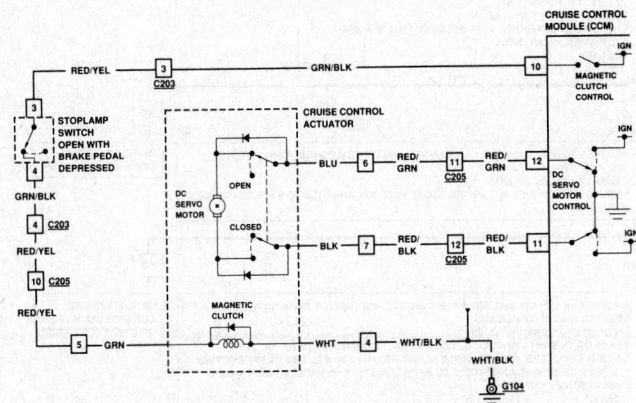

CCM programming will cancel cruise operation if vehicle speed drops more than 10 MPH from set speed. When CCM determines set speed cannot be maintained, cruise operation is cancelled as a safety feature.

NOTE: Test numbers refer to numbers on diagnostic chart.

1) Checks for voltage to magnetic clutch.
2) Checks for short to ground in Red/Black wire.
3) Checks for faulty stoplight circuit.
4) Checks for short to ground in Red/Green wire.
5) Checks for open in Red/Green wire.
6) Checks for open in Red/Black wire.
7) Checks for open in White/Black wire.
8) Checks cruise control actuator arm for free movement while magnetic clutch is not energized.
9) Checks cruise control actuator arm for free movement while magnetic clutch is energized.

DIAGNOSTIC AIDS

Check for loose cable at actuator or at accelerator pedal. An intermittent condition may be caused by rubbed-through insulation, or a wire broken inside insulation. Check harness connectors for backed-out or damaged terminals, improper mating or broken connector lock, before replacing component.

IMPORTANT: BE SURE THAT CCM OBD SYSTEM CHECK HAS BEEN PERFORMED BEFORE CONTINUING DIAGNOSIS.

FROM CCM OBD SYSTEM CHECK.

(1)
- START ENGINE AND PLACE MANUAL SELECTOR LEVER IN "D."
- RAISE AND SUITABLY SUPPORT VEHICLE.
- ACCELERATE ABOVE 40 KM/H (25 MPH) AND ENGAGE CRUISE CONTROL.
- BACKPROBE CRUISE CONTROL ACTUATOR CONNECTOR WITH A DIGITAL MULTIMETER FROM CAVITY "5" TO GROUND.
- MEASURE VOLTAGE.

MORE THAN 10.0 VOLTS / **LESS THAN 10.0 VOLTS**

(2)
- TURN IGNITION SWITCH TO "LOCK."
- DISCONNECT CCM CONNECTOR AND CRUISE CONTROL ACTUATOR CONNECTOR.
- CONNECT A DIGITAL MULTIMETER FROM CCM CONNECTOR CAVITY "11" TO GROUND.
- MEASURE RESISTANCE.

(3)
- BACKPROBE STOPLAMP SWITCH CONNECTOR WITH A DIGITAL MULTIMETER FROM CAVITY "3" TO GROUND.
- MEASURE VOLTAGE.

INFINITE / **LESS THAN INFINITE** / **LESS THAN 10.0 VOLTS** / **MORE THAN 10.0 VOLTS**

(4)
- CONNECT A DIGITAL MULTIMETER FROM CCM CONNECTOR CAVITY "12" TO GROUND.
- MEASURE RESISTANCE.

REPAIR SHORT TO GROUND IN RED/BLK WIRE BETWEEN CCM AND CRUISE CONTROL ACTUATOR.

CHECK FOR AN OPEN IN GRN/BLK OR RED/YEL WIRE BETWEEN CCM AND STOPLAMP SWITCH. IF OK, REPLACE CCM.

CHECK FOR AN OPEN IN GRN/BLK OR RED/YEL WIRE BETWEEN STOPLAMP SWITCH AND CRUISE CONTROL ACTUATOR. IF OK, REPLACE STOPLAMP SWITCH.

INFINITE / **LESS THAN INFINITE**

REPAIR SHORT TO GROUND IN RED/GRN WIRE BETWEEN CCM AND CRUISE CONTROL ACTUATOR.

(5)
- CONNECT A DIGITAL MULTIMETER FROM CCM CONNECTOR CAVITY "12" TO CRUISE CONTROL ACTUATOR CONNECTOR CAVITY "6".
- MEASURE RESISTANCE.

LESS THAN 1.0 OHM / **MORE THAN 1.0 OHM**

(6)
- CONNECT A DIGITAL MULTIMETER FROM CCM CONNECTOR CAVITY "11" TO CRUISE CONTROL ACTUATOR CONNECTOR CAVITY "7".
- MEASURE RESISTANCE.

REPAIR OPEN IN RED/GRN WIRE BETWEEN CCM AND CRUISE CONTROL ACTUATOR.

LESS THAN 1.0 OHM / **MORE THAN 1.0 OHM**

(7)
- CONNECT A DIGITAL MULTIMETER FROM CRUISE CONTROL ACTUATOR CONNECTOR CAVITY "4" TO GROUND.
- MEASURE RESISTANCE.

REPAIR OPEN IN RED/BLK WIRE BETWEEN CCM AND CRUISE CONTROL ACTUATOR.

LESS THAN 1.0 OHM / **MORE THAN 1.0 OHM**

(8)
- MOVE CRUISE CONTROL ACTUATOR ARM BACK AND FORTH.
SHOULD MOVE FREELY.
DOES IT?

REPAIR OPEN IN WHT/BLK WIRE BETWEEN CRUISE CONTROL ACTUATOR AND G104.

YES / **NO**

(9)
- RECONNECT CRUISE CONTROL ACTUATOR CONNECTOR.
- CONNECT A FUSED JUMPER FROM CCM CONNECTOR CAVITY "10" TO B+.
- ATTEMPT TO MOVE ACTUATOR ARM BACK AND FORTH. SHOULD NOT MOVE FREELY.
DOES IT?

REPLACE CRUISE CONTROL ACTUATOR.

NO / **YES**

(B)

REPLACE CRUISE CONTROL ACTUATOR.

**Continued
On Next
Page**

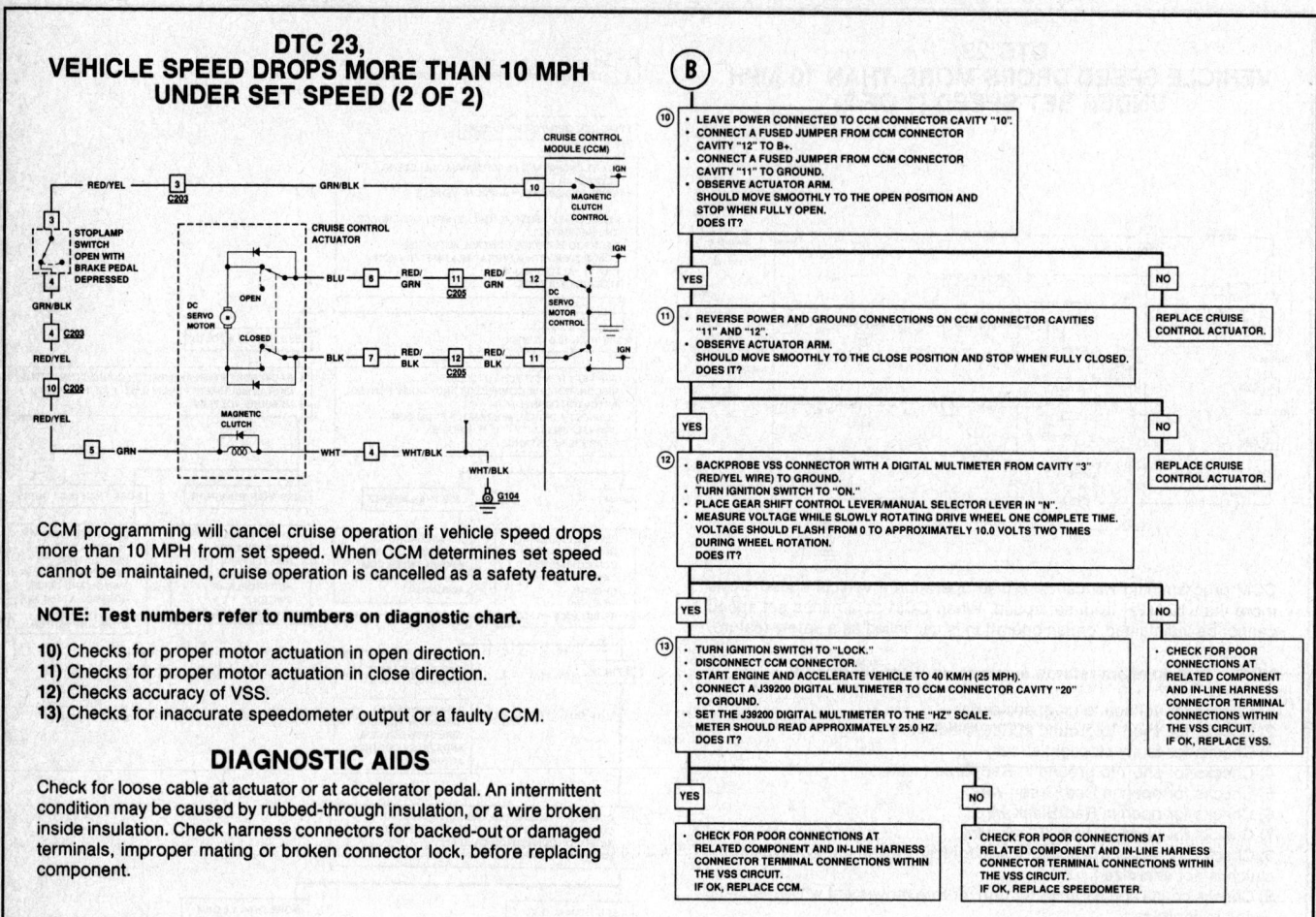

DTC 23,
VEHICLE SPEED DROPS MORE THAN 10 MPH
UNDER SET SPEED (2 OF 2)

CCM programming will cancel cruise operation if vehicle speed drops more than 10 MPH from set speed. When CCM determines set speed cannot be maintained, cruise operation is cancelled as a safety feature.

NOTE: Test numbers refer to numbers on diagnostic chart.

10) Checks for proper motor actuation in open direction.
11) Checks for proper motor actuation in close direction.
12) Checks accuracy of VSS.
13) Checks for inaccurate speedometer output or a faulty CCM.

DIAGNOSTIC AIDS

Check for loose cable at actuator or at accelerator pedal. An intermittent condition may be caused by rubbed-through insulation, or a wire broken inside insulation. Check harness connectors for backed-out or damaged terminals, improper mating or broken connector lock, before replacing component.

B

10) • LEAVE POWER CONNECTED TO CCM CONNECTOR CAVITY "10".
• CONNECT A FUSED JUMPER FROM CCM CONNECTOR CAVITY "12" TO B+.
• CONNECT A FUSED JUMPER FROM CCM CONNECTOR CAVITY "11" TO GROUND.
• OBSERVE ACTUATOR ARM.
SHOULD MOVE SMOOTHLY TO THE OPEN POSITION AND STOP WHEN FULLY OPEN.
DOES IT?

YES / NO → REPLACE CRUISE CONTROL ACTUATOR.

11) • REVERSE POWER AND GROUND CONNECTIONS ON CCM CONNECTOR CAVITIES "11" AND "12".
• OBSERVE ACTUATOR ARM.
SHOULD MOVE SMOOTHLY TO THE CLOSE POSITION AND STOP WHEN FULLY CLOSED.
DOES IT?

YES / NO → REPLACE CRUISE CONTROL ACTUATOR.

12) • BACKPROBE VSS CONNECTOR WITH A DIGITAL MULTIMETER FROM CAVITY "3" (RED/YEL WIRE) TO GROUND.
• TURN IGNITION SWITCH TO "ON."
• PLACE GEAR SHIFT CONTROL LEVER/MANUAL SELECTOR LEVER IN "N".
• MEASURE VOLTAGE WHILE SLOWLY ROTATING DRIVE WHEEL ONE COMPLETE TIME.
VOLTAGE SHOULD FLASH FROM 0 TO APPROXIMATELY 10.0 VOLTS TWO TIMES DURING WHEEL ROTATION.
DOES IT?

YES / NO → • CHECK FOR POOR CONNECTIONS AT RELATED COMPONENT AND IN-LINE HARNESS CONNECTOR TERMINAL CONNECTIONS WITHIN THE VSS CIRCUIT.
IF OK, REPLACE VSS.

13) • TURN IGNITION SWITCH TO "LOCK."
• DISCONNECT CCM CONNECTOR.
• START ENGINE AND ACCELERATE VEHICLE TO 40 KM/H (25 MPH).
• CONNECT A J39200 DIGITAL MULTIMETER TO CCM CONNECTOR CAVITY "20" TO GROUND.
• SET THE J39200 DIGITAL MULTIMETER TO THE "HZ" SCALE.
METER SHOULD READ APPROXIMATELY 25.0 HZ.
DOES IT?

YES → • CHECK FOR POOR CONNECTIONS AT RELATED COMPONENT AND IN-LINE HARNESS CONNECTOR TERMINAL CONNECTIONS WITHIN THE VSS CIRCUIT.
IF OK, REPLACE CCM.

NO → • CHECK FOR POOR CONNECTIONS AT RELATED COMPONENT AND IN-LINE HARNESS CONNECTOR TERMINAL CONNECTIONS WITHIN THE VSS CIRCUIT.
IF OK, REPLACE SPEEDOMETER.

93F83688 93A83691

DTC 32
CRUISE CONTROL SWITCH SHORTED

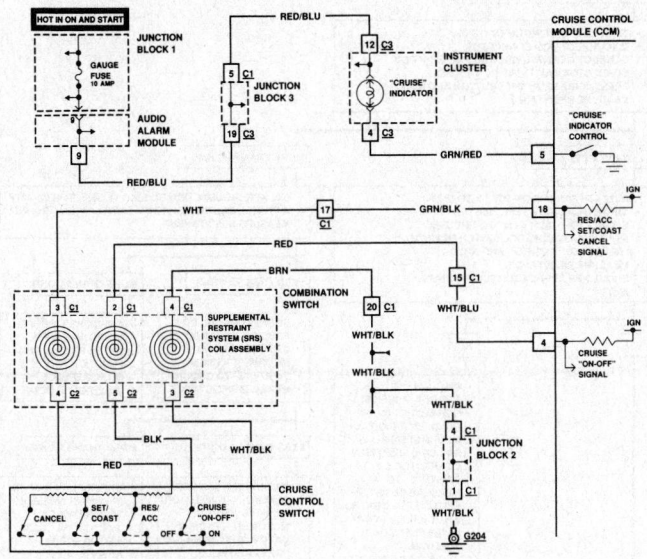

> **IMPORTANT:** BE SURE THAT CCM OBD SYSTEM CHECK HAS BEEN PERFORMED BEFORE CONTINUING DIAGNOSIS.

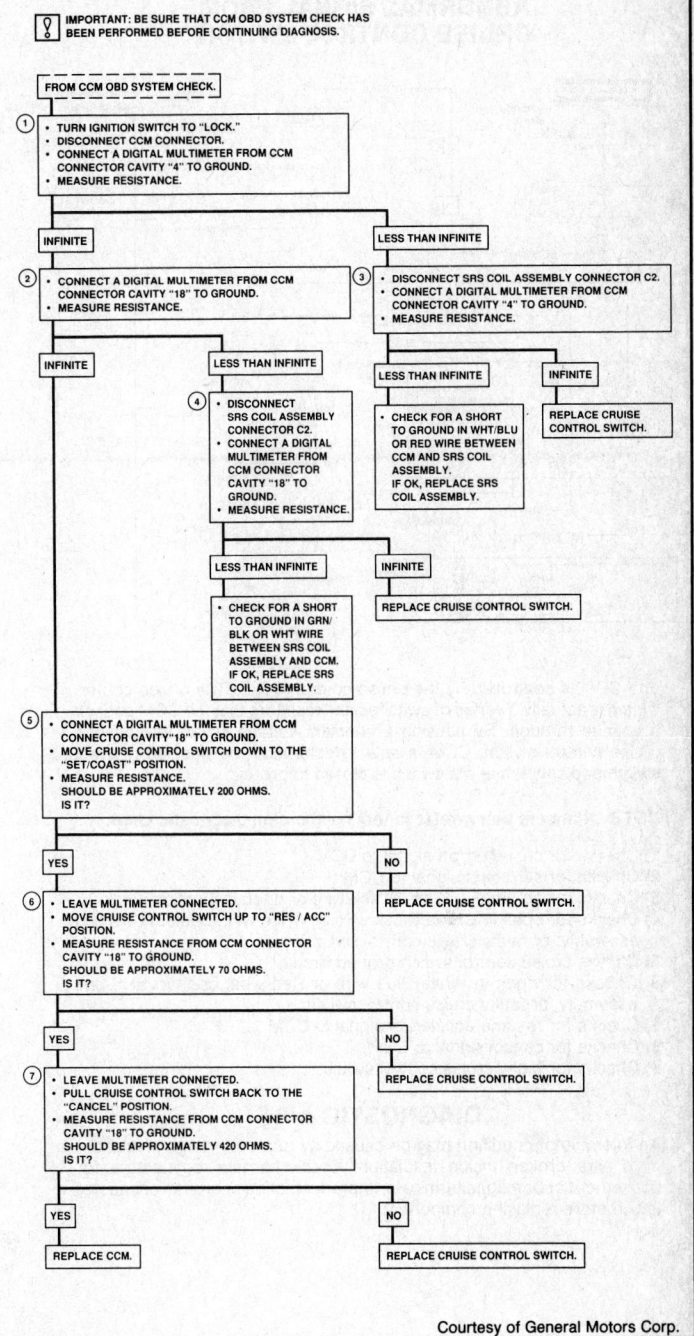

CCM is controlled by the cruise control switch. Cruise control switch is actually a series of switches and resistors that CCM passes a voltage through. By passing a constant voltage signal through cruise control switch, CCM is able to determine position of each switch and can sense if a switch is closed to ground.

NOTE: Test numbers refer to numbers on diagnostic chart.

1) Checks for short to ground in cruise on/off circuit.
2) Checks for short to ground in resume/accel, set/coast or cancel circuit.
3) Checks for short to ground in White/Blue wire or Red wire, or for a faulty SRS coil assembly.
4) Checks for short to ground in Green/Black wire or White wire, a shorted SRS coil assembly or a shorted cruise control switch.
5) Checks for correct resistance in set/coast circuit.
6) Checks for correct resistance in resume/accel circuit.
7) Checks for correct resistance in cancel circuit.

DIAGNOSTIC AIDS

An intermittent condition may be caused by rubbed-through insulation, or a wire broken inside insulation. Check harness connectors for backed-out or damaged terminals, improper mating or broken connector lock, before replacing component.

93D83694 93E83695 93F83696

Courtesy of General Motors Corp.

DTC 34
ABNORMAL SIGNAL FROM CRUISE CONTROL SWITCH

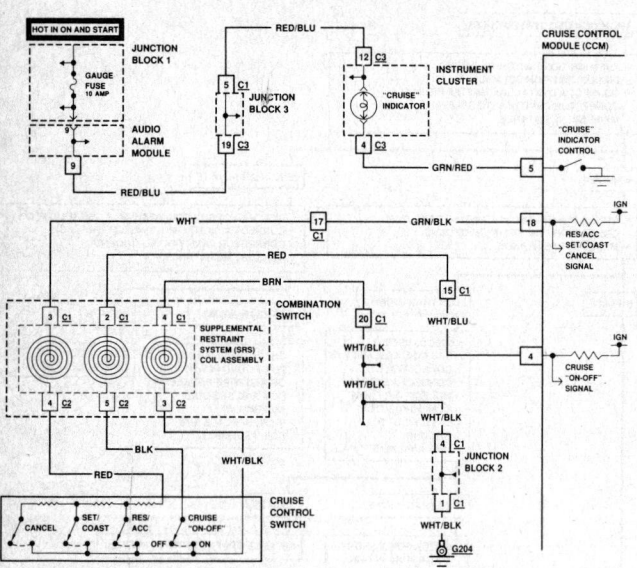

IMPORTANT: BE SURE THAT CCM OBD SYSTEM CHECK HAS BEEN PERFORMED BEFORE CONTINUING DIAGNOSIS.

FROM CCM OBD SYSTEM CHECK.

① • TURN IGNITION SWITCH TO "LOCK."
• DISCONNECT CCM CONNECTOR.
• CONNECT A DIGITAL MULTIMETER FROM CCM CONNECTOR CAVITY "4" TO GROUND.
• PRESS "CRUISE ON-OFF" BUTTON AND HOLD.
• MEASURE RESISTANCE.

LESS THAN 5.0 OHMS | **MORE THAN 5.0 OHMS**

② • RELEASE "CRUISE ON-OFF" BUTTON.
• CONNECT A DIGITAL MULTIMETER FROM CCM CONNECTOR CAVITY "18" TO GROUND.
• MOVE CRUISE CONTROL SWITCH DOWN TO "SET/COAST" POSITION AND HOLD.
• MEASURE RESISTANCE. SHOULD BE APPROXIMATELY 200 OHMS. IS IT?

③ • BACKPROBE JUNCTION BLOCK 2 CONNECTOR C1 WITH A DIGITAL MULTIMETER FROM CAVITY "4" TO GROUND.
• MEASURE RESISTANCE.

LESS THAN 5.0 OHMS | **MORE THAN 5.0 OHMS**

YES | **NO**

④ • DISCONNECT SRS COIL ASSEMBLY CONNECTOR C2.
• CONNECT A DIGITAL MULTIMETER FROM SRS COIL ASSEMBLY CONNECTOR C2 CAVITY "3" TO "4".
• MEASURE RESISTANCE WITH CRUISE CONTROL SWITCH HELD DOWN IN THE "SET/COAST" POSITION. SHOULD BE APPROXIMATELY 200 OHMS. IS IT?

⑤ • BACKPROBE SRS COIL ASSEMBLY CONNECTOR C2 WITH A DIGITAL MULTIMETER FROM CAVITY "3" TO GROUND.
• MEASURE RESISTANCE.

• CHECK FOR AN OPEN IN WHT/BLK WIRE BETWEEN G204 AND JUNCTION BLOCK 2. IF OK, REPLACE JUNCTION BLOCK 2.

LESS THAN 5.0 OHMS | **MORE THAN 5.0 OHMS**

⑥ • BACKPROBE SRS COIL ASSEMBLY CONNECTOR C2 WITH A DIGITAL MULTIMETER FROM CAVITY "5" TO GROUND.
• PRESS AND HOLD "CRUISE ON-OFF" BUTTON.
• MEASURE RESISTANCE.

• CHECK FOR AN OPEN IN BRN OR WHT/BLK WIRE BETWEEN JUNCTION BLOCK 2 AND SRS COIL ASSEMBLY. IF OK, REPLACE SRS COIL ASSEMBLY.

LESS THAN 5.0 OHMS | **MORE THAN 5.0 OHMS**

• CHECK FOR AN OPEN IN WHT/BLU OR RED WIRE BETWEEN CCM AND SRS COIL ASSEMBLY. IF OK, REPLACE SRS COIL ASSEMBLY.

REPLACE CRUISE CONTROL SWITCH.

YES | **NO**

• CHECK FOR AN OPEN IN GRN/BLK OR WHT WIRE BETWEEN CCM AND SRS COIL ASSEMBLY. IF OK, REPLACE SRS COIL ASSEMBLY.

REPLACE CRUISE CONTROL SWITCH.

⑦ • LEAVE MULTIMETER CONNECTED.
• MOVE CRUISE CONTROL SWITCH UP TO "RES / ACC" POSITION AND HOLD.
• MEASURE RESISTANCE FROM CCM CONNECTOR CAVITY "18" TO GROUND. SHOULD BE APPROXIMATELY 70 OHMS. IS IT?

YES | **NO**

⑧ • LEAVE MULTIMETER CONNECTED.
• PULL CRUISE CONTROL SWITCH BACK TO THE "CANCEL" POSITION AND HOLD.
• MEASURE RESISTANCE FROM CCM CONNECTOR CAVITY "18" TO GROUND. SHOULD BE APPROXIMATELY 420 OHMS. IS IT?

REPLACE CRUISE CONTROL SWITCH.

YES | **NO**

⑨ • CONNECT A DIGITAL MULTIMETER FROM SRS COIL ASSEMBLY CONNECTOR C2 CAVITY "3" TO "4."
• MOVE CRUISE CONTROL SWITCH UP TO "RES / ACC" AND DOWN TO "SET/COAST."
• RELEASE CRUISE CONTROL SWITCH (NEUTRAL POSITION).
• MEASURE RESISTANCE. SHOULD BE 1 OHM OR HIGHER. IS IT?

REPLACE CRUISE CONTROL SWITCH.

YES | **NO**

REPLACE CCM. | **REPLACE CRUISE CONTROL SWITCH.**

The CCM is controlled by the cruise control switch. The cruise control switch is actually a series of switches and resistors that the CCM passes a voltage through. By passing a constant voltage signal through the cruise control switch, CCM is able to determine the position of each switch and can sense if a switch is closed to ground.

NOTE: Numbers below refer to test numbers on diagnostic chart.

1) Checks for cruise on/off signal to CCM
2) Checks for set/coast signal to CCM.
3) Checks for an open in White/Black wire or open in junction block 2.
4) Checks for open in Green/Black wire or White wire, open in SRS coil assembly, or faulty cruise control switch.
5) Checks cruise control switch ground circuit.
6) Checks for open in White/Blue wire or Red wire, open in SRS coil assembly, or faulty cruise control switch.
7) Checks for resume/accelerate signal to CCM.
8) Checks for cancel signal to CCM.
9) Checks for faulty cruise control switch.

DIAGNOSTIC AIDS

An intermittent condition may be caused by rubbed-through insulation, or a wire broken inside insulation. Check harness connectors for backed-out or damaged terminals, improper mating or broken connector lock, before replacing component.

Metro, Prizm, Tracker

DESCRIPTION & OPERATION

Rear window defogger systems use a heating wire grid bonded to the inside of rear window. On Metro, with ignition switch and rear defogger switch on, voltage is applied through rear defogger fuse to rear defogger switch, defogger indicator light and rear defogger. Defogger will remain on until switch is turned off.

On Prizm, with ignition switch in the ACCY or RUN position, voltage is applied through GAUGE fuse and No. 3 junction block to rear defogger switch. Battery voltage is always present through rear defogger circuit breaker to rear defogger relay. When rear defogger switch is turned on, voltage is applied to rear defogger indicator light and coil of rear defogger relay. This causes rear defogger light to illuminate and the relay to energize. With rear defogger relay energized, battery voltage is applied to rear defogger. Defogger will automatically turn off after 12-18 minutes if switch is left on.

On Tracker, with ignition switch in the RUN position, voltage is applied through rear defogger fuse to rear defogger switch. When rear defogger switch is turned on, voltage is connected to defogger indicator light and to rear defogger. Defogger will remain on until switch is turned off.

TROUBLE SHOOTING

NOTE: Check possible faults in order listed. Repair or replace components and circuits as necessary.

Rear Defogger Inoperative – Blown DEF or GAUGE fuse. Poor defogger relay connections. Loose or corroded ground connections. Loose or corroded component connections. Faulty rear defogger switch. Visibly damaged rear defogger grid. On Prizm, ensure audio alarm module is mounted securely.
Indicator Light Inoperative – Faulty light bulb. Loose or corroded ground connections. Faulty rear defogger switch.

TESTING

SYSTEM TESTING (METRO)

Rear Defogger System Inoperative – 1) Turn ignition on. Using a test light, probe Yellow/White wire (Yellow/Green after splice) in rear defogger switch connector (located in instrument panel to left of steering wheel). If test light comes on, check for poor connection at rear defogger switch. If connection is okay, replace rear defogger switch. If test light does not come on, go to next step.
2) Check for poor connection at junction block (located behind left kick panel). If connection is okay, check Yellow/Green wire (Yellow/White after splice) for open between rear defogger switch and junction block. Repair wire as necessary. If wire is okay, replace junction block.
Indicator Light Comes On; Rear Defogger Grid Does Not Warm – 1)Turn ignition and rear defogger on. Using a test light, probe Black wire from rear defogger connector C1 (located at rear window) to ground. If test light comes on, go to next step. If test light does not come on, check for open in Black wire or Red/White wire rear defogger and rear defogger switch. Repair wire as necessary. If wire is okay, repair rear defogger grid.
2) Check Black wire for poor ground connection. Check for open in Black wire between rear defogger grid and ground. Repair connection or wire as necessary. If wire and ground connector are okay, repair rear defogger grid.
Indicator Light Inoperative; Rear Defogger Grid Warms – 1) Turn ignition and rear defogger on. Using a test light, probe Black wire in junction block 3-pin connector C6. If test light comes on, go to next step. If test light does not come on, check for poor connection at rear defogger switch. Check for open in Black wire between rear defogger switch and junction block. Repair connection or wire as necessary. If wire and ground connector are okay, replace rear defogger switch.
2) Check for poor ground at junction block. Check Black wire for poor connection at junction block. If connections are okay, replace junction block.

Indicator Remains On & Rear Defogger Does Not Cool; Rear Defogger Switch Off – Check for short to voltage in Red/White or Black wire(s) between rear defogger and rear defogger switch. repair wire(s) as necessary. If wire(s) are okay, replace rear defogger switch.

SYSTEM TESTING (PRIZM)

Rear Defogger System Inoperative – 1) Turn ignition on. Using a DVOM, check Red/Blue wire at rear defogger switch for voltage. If voltage is 10 volts or greater, go to step 3). If voltage is less than 10 volts, check terminal No. 19 (Red/Blue wire) at junction block No. 3 connector C3 for voltage. See Fig. 1. If voltage is less than 10 volts, go to next step. If voltage is 10 volts or greater, check for open in Red/Blue wire between rear defogger switch and junction block No. 3. Repair wire as necessary. If wire is okay, replace junction block No. 3.

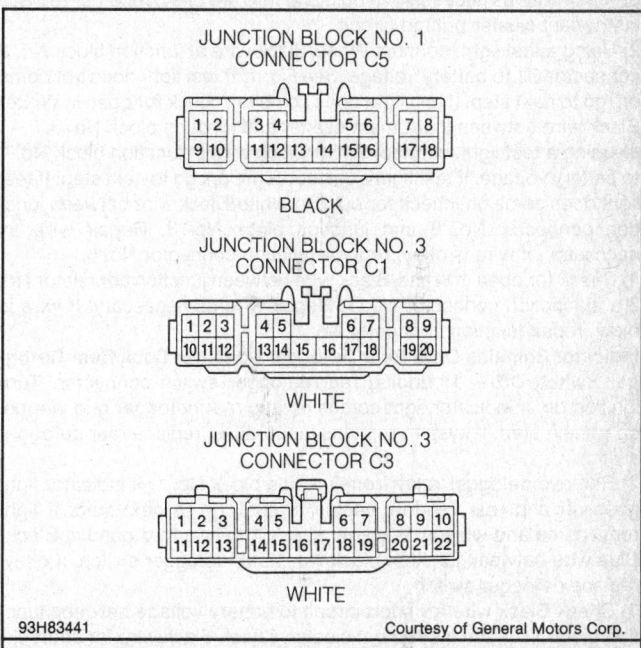

JUNCTION BLOCK NO. 1
CONNECTOR C5

BLACK

JUNCTION BLOCK NO. 3
CONNECTOR C1

WHITE

JUNCTION BLOCK NO. 3
CONNECTOR C3

WHITE

93H83441   Courtesy of General Motors Corp.

Fig. 1: Identifying Junction Block Connector Terminals (Prizm)

2) Check for open in Red/Blue wire between audio alarm module and junction block No. 3. Repair wire as necessary. If wire is okay, replace audio alarm module and retest system. If system is still inoperative, replace junction block No. 1.
3) Using a fused jumper wire, connect Black/Blue wire at rear defogger switch to ground. If indicator light comes on and rear defogger grid warms, go to next step. If rear defogger remains inoperative, check for open in Black/Blue between rear defogger switch and junction block No. 1. Repair wire as necessary. If wire is okay, replace rear defogger relay and retest system. If system remains inoperative, replace junction block No. 1.
4) Using a test light, connect White/Black wire at junction block connector C3 to battery voltage. See Fig. 1. If test light comes on, check for open in White/Black wire between rear defogger switch and junction block No. 3. Repair wire as necessary. If wire is okay, replace rear defogger switch. If test light does not come on, connect test light from White/Black wire at audio alarm module to battery voltage.
5) If test light does not come on, go to next step. If test light comes on, check for open in White/Black wire between junction block No. 3 and audio alarm module. Repair wire as necessary. If wire is okay, replace junction block No. 3.
6) Using a test light, connect White/Black wire at junction block No. 1 connector C5 to battery voltage. See Fig. 1. If test light does not come on, go to next step. If test light comes on, replace audio alarm module and retest system. If system remains inoperative, replace junction block No. 1.
7) Check for open in White/Black wire between junction connector No. 1 and junction block No. 1 or between junction connector 1 and ground. Repair wire(s) as necessary. If wire(s) is okay, replace junction connector No. 1.

Indicator Light Comes On; Rear Defogger Grid Does Not Warm –
1) Turn ignition and rear defogger on. Using a test light, probe Black wire at rear defogger grid connector. If test light comes on, repair Black wire between rear defogger grid and ground. If test light does not come on, go to next step.
2) Check for open in Black wire between junction block No. 1 and rear defogger grid. Repair wire as necessary. If wire is okay, replace junction block No. 1.

Indicator Light Inoperative; Rear Defogger Grid Warms – 1) Turn ignition and rear defogger on. Using a test light, connect White/Black wire at cluster connector C3 (16-terminal White connector) to battery voltage. If test light does not come on, go to next step. If test light comes on, check for open in Black wire between instrument cluster and junction block No. 1. Check for faulty indicator bulb. Replace bulb or repair wire as necessary. If bulb and wire are okay, repair or replace instrument cluster printed circuit.
2) Using a test light, connect White/Black wire at junction block No. 3 connector C1 to battery voltage. *See Fig. 1.* If test light does not come on, go to next step. If test light does come on, check for open in White/Black wire between instrument cluster and junction block No. 3.
3) Using a test light, connect White/Black wire at junction block No. 1 to battery voltage. If test light does not come on, go to next step. If test light does come on, check for open in White/Black wire between junction connector No. 3 and junction block No. 3. Repair wire as necessary. If wire is okay, replace junction connector No. 3.
4) Check for open in White/Black wire between junction connector No. 3 and junction connector No. 1. Repair wire as necessary. If wire is okay, repair junction connector No. 1.

Indicator Remains On & Rear Defogger Does Not Cool; Rear Defogger Switch Off – 1) Unplug rear defogger switch connector. Turn ignition on. If indicator light comes on and rear defogger grid warms, go to next step. If system remains inoperative, replace rear defogger switch.
2) Remove defogger relay from junction block No. 1. If indicator light goes off and rear window begins to cool, go to next step. If light remains on and window is warm, check for short to ground in Black/Blue wire between junction block No. 1 and defogger switch. If okay, replace defogger switch.
3) Check Black wire for short circuit to battery voltage between junction block No 1 and instrument cluster. Check Black wire for short circuit to battery voltage between junction block No. 1 and rear defogger grid. Repair wire as necessary. If wire is okay, replace junction block No. 1.

Rear Defogger Remains Operative For Less Than 10 Minutes Or More Than 20 Minutes – Replace rear defogger switch. Retest system.

Radio Static Heard When Radio & Rear Defogger Are On – Check Black wire for open between rear defogger switch and rear defogger noise filter. Repair as necessary. If wire is okay, replace rear defogger noise filter. If static continues, fault is in radio. Remove and repair radio.

SYSTEM TESTING (TRACKER)

Rear Defogger System Inoperative – Turn ignition on. Using a test light, probe Yellow/Green wire in rear defogger switch connector. If test light comes on, check for poor connection at rear defogger switch. If connection is okay, replace rear defogger switch. If test light does not come on, repair open in Yellow/Green wire between rear defogger switch and fuse block.

Indicator Light Comes On; Rear Defogger Grid Does Not Warm –
1) Turn ignition and rear defogger on. Using a test light, probe Red/White wire from rear defogger switch connector. If test light comes on, repair Black wire between rear defogger grid and ground. If test light does not come on, go to next step.
2) Probe Red/White wire at rear defogger switch. If test light comes on, repair open in Red/White wire between rear defogger and rear defogger switch. If test light does not come on, replace rear defogger switch.

Indicator Light Inoperative; Rear Defogger Grid Warms – Check for faulty light bulb in rear defogger switch. Check for open in Black wire

between rear defogger switch and ground. Repair wire as necessary. If wire is okay, replace rear defogger switch.

Indicator Remains On & Rear Defogger Does Not Cool; Rear Defogger Switch Off – Check for short to voltage in Red/White or Black wire(s) between rear defogger and rear defogger switch. repair wire(s) as necessary. If wire(s) are okay, replace rear defogger switch.

DEFOGGER GRID

1) Measure grid wire voltage using DVOM. Ground negative lead and lightly touch positive lead to each grid line. Voltage will decrease as lead is moved farther away from feed connection. *See Figs. 2 and 3.*
2) Test grid lines in at least 2 places to avoid bridging a break. Contact each grid line on either side of window centerline. If abnormal reading is apparent on any line, place lead on grid line and move until voltage drops significantly. This indicates a break.
3) If high voltage is shown at both ends of grid line, check for loose ground terminal to bus bar connections, or loose ground wire to body connection.

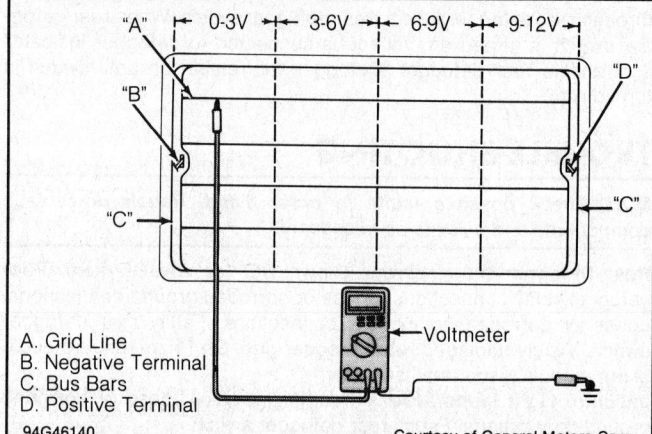

A. Grid Line
B. Negative Terminal
C. Bus Bars
D. Positive Terminal

94G46140   Courtesy of General Motors Corp.

Fig. 2: Testing Rear Defogger Grid Wire (Metro & Prizm)

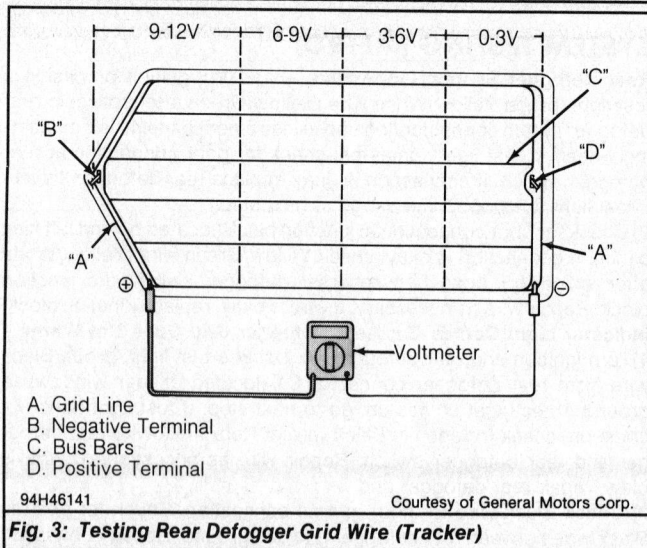

A. Grid Line
B. Negative Terminal
C. Bus Bars
D. Positive Terminal

94H46141   Courtesy of General Motors Corp.

Fig. 3: Testing Rear Defogger Grid Wire (Tracker)

ON-VEHICLE SERVICE

GRID FILAMENT REPAIR

1) Disconnect rear defogger electrical connector. Apply masking tape at upper and lower sides of grid wire to be repaired. *See Fig. 4.*
2) Using manufacturer's instructions, apply commercially available repair agent with a fine-tip brush. Allow 24-hour drying time before operating rear defogger.

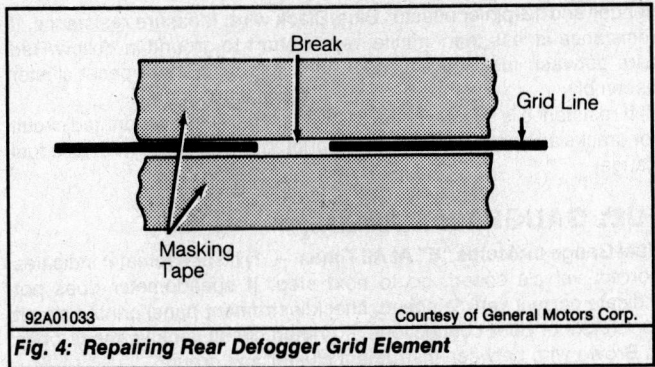

92A01033   Courtesy of General Motors Corp.

Fig. 4: Repairing Rear Defogger Grid Element

REMOVAL & INSTALLATION

REAR DEFOGGER SWITCH

Removal & Installation (Metro) – Disconnect negative battery cable. Remove steering column lower trim cover. Remove steering column mounting nuts. Lower and support steering column. Remove instrument panel bezel. Unplug rear defogger switch connector. Remove switch from instrument panel. To install, reverse removal procedure.

Removal & Installation (Prizm) – Disconnect negative battery cable. Remove ash tray. Pry trim bezel from center console. Unplug connectors from cigar lighter, defogger switch and hazard switch. Disengage lock tabs of rear defogger switch. Remove rear defogger switch from center console bezel. To install, reverse removal procedure.

Removal & Installation (Tracker) – Disconnect negative battery cable. Pry lower steering column panel cover from instrument panel. Pry switch from instrument panel. Unplug connector. To install, reverse removal procedure.

WIRING DIAGRAMS

NOTE: See ACCESSORIES & EQUIPMENT, Volume 5.

Metro, Prizm, Tracker

WARNING: Metro convertible and Prizm are equipped with Supplemental Inflatable Restraint (SIR) system, otherwise known as an air bag. Before proceeding, see SERVICE PRECAUTIONS in AIR BAG RESTRAINT SYSTEM article.

DESCRIPTION & OPERATION

Standard instrument cluster includes speedometer, coolant temperature and fuel gauges and warning lights. Warning lights are used for oil pressure, charging system, brake system, engine system, air bag system, low fuel, seat belts and upshift indicators. Tachometer, clock, oil pressure and voltmeter gauges are available as optional equipment.

TESTING

WARNING: Before testing ANY instrument panel component, Supplemental Restraint System (SRS) MUST be disabled. See DISABLING & ACTIVATING AIR BAG SYSTEM in AIR BAG RESTRAINT SYSTEM article. Accidental air bag deployment could cause serious bodily injury.

PRELIMINARY TESTING

Metro – Ensure all fuses and grounds are good. Unless gauge is known to be defective, check sending unit and wiring circuit first. If fuel gauge, coolant temperature gauge and tachometer are all inoperative, perform the following:
- Check for an open in Black/White wire between junction block and instrument panel cluster assembly.
- Check for an open in Black/Blue ground wire between instrument panel cluster assembly and ground.
- Check instrument panel cluster printed circuit for cracks and poor connections.

Prizm – Ensure gauge fuse, dome fuse and grounds are good. Ensure audio alarm module is securely mounted in junction block No. 1, located behind kick panel.

Tracker – **1)** Check IG-COIL METER fuse by starting vehicle. Ensure all grounds are clean and tight. If instrument panel cluster assembly is completely inoperative, check for an open circuit in Black/White wire between fuse block and instrument panel cluster assembly.

2) If instrument panel cluster assembly is partially inoperative, check for an open circuit in Black ground wire between instrument panel cluster assembly and ground, or an open circuit in Black/Yellow wire between instrument panel cluster assembly ground and instrument panel cluster printed circuit.

FUEL GAUGE TEST (METRO)

Fuel Gauge Indicates "E" At All Times – **1)** Unplug fuel gauge sending unit connector. Connect a fused jumper wire from connector cavity to chassis ground. If fuel gauge indicates "F", replace fuel gauge sending unit.

2) If fuel gauge still indicates "E", unplug 13-pin (White) instrument panel cluster assembly connector located behind upper left corner of instrument panel cluster assembly. Using a DVOM, check resistance between connector terminal No. 9 (Yellow/Red wire) and fuel gauge sending unit connector terminal.

3) If resistance is greater than 2 ohms, repair open in Yellow/Red wire between instrument panel cluster assembly and fuel gauge sending unit. If resistance is less than 2 ohms, check instrument panel cluster printed circuit for cracks and poor connections. If printed circuit is okay, replace fuel gauge.

Fuel Gauge Indicates "F" At All Times – **1)** Unplug fuel gauge sending unit connector located under rear seat. Turn ignition on. If fuel gauge does not indicates "E", replace fuel gauge sending unit.

2) If fuel gauge still indicates "F", Unplug 13-pin (White) instrument panel cluster assembly connector located behind upper left corner of instrument panel cluster assembly. Connect DVOM between fuel sender and 13-pin connector Blue/Black wire. Measure resistance. If resistance is less than infinite, repair short to ground in Yellow/Red wire between fuel gauge sending unit and instrument panel cluster assembly.

3) If resistance is infinite, check instrument panel cluster printed circuit for cracks and poor connections. If printed circuit is okay, replace fuel gauge.

FUEL GAUGE TEST (PRIZM)

Fuel Gauge Indicates "E" At All Times – **1)** If speedometer indicates correct vehicle speed, go to next step. If speedometer does not indicate correct vehicle speed, check instrument panel printed circuit for cracks or poor connections. If printed circuit is okay, repair open in Brown wire between instrument cluster and ground.

2) Unplug fuel gauge sending unit connector. Turn ignition on. If fuel gauge indicates "F", replace fuel gauge sending unit.

3) If fuel gauge still indicates "E", unplug 10-pin (Gray) instrument panel cluster assembly connector located behind instrument panel cluster assembly. Using a DVOM, check resistance between connector terminal No. 6 (Yellow/Red wire; Pink wire after splice) and fuel gauge sending unit connector terminal No. 2 (Pink wire).

4) If resistance is not infinite, repair short to ground in Yellow/Red wire (Pink wire after splice) between instrument panel cluster assembly and fuel gauge sending unit connector. If resistance is infinite, check instrument panel cluster printed circuit for cracks and poor connections. If printed circuit is okay, replace fuel gauge.

Fuel Gauge Indicates "F" At All Times – **1)** Unplug fuel gauge sending unit connector located under rear seat. Connect fused jumper wire between ground and Pink wire at connector. Turn ignition on. If fuel gauge indicates "E", replace fuel gauge sending unit.

2) If fuel gauge still indicates "F", disconnect fused jumper. Unplug 10-pin (Gray) instrument panel cluster assembly connector located behind instrument panel cluster assembly. Using a DVOM, check resistance between instrument cluster connector terminal No. 6 (Yellow/Red wire; Pink wire after splice) to fuel gauge sender unit connector terminal No. 2.

3) If resistance is greater than 2 ohms, repair open in Red/Yellow wire; Pink wire after splice) between instrument cluster connector and fuel gauge sender unit. If resistance is less than 2 ohms, check instrument panel cluster printed circuit for cracks and poor connections. If printed circuit is okay, replace fuel gauge.

FUEL GAUGE TEST (TRACKER)

Fuel Gauge Indicates "E" At All Times – **1)** Unplug fuel gauge sending unit connector. Using a DVOM, check resistance between sending unit connector terminal No. 1 (Black wire) and ground. If resistance is greater than 3 ohms, repair open in Black ground wire.

2) If resistance is less than 3 ohms, connect a fused jumper wire between fuel gauge sending unit connector terminal No. 2 (Yellow/Red wire) and ground. If fuel gauge indicates full, replace fuel gauge sending unit.

3) If fuel gauge continues to indicate empty, leave jumper connected and unplug 13-pin instrument panel cluster assembly connector. Using a DVOM, check resistance between connector terminal No. 4 and ground. If resistance is greater than 3 ohms, repair open circuit in Yellow/Red wire.

4) If resistance is less than 3 ohms, check instrument panel cluster printed circuit for cracks and poor connection. If printed circuit is okay, replace fuel gauge.

Fuel Gauge Indicates "F" At All Times – **1)** Unplug fuel gauge sending unit connector. If fuel gauge indicates "E", replace fuel gauge sending unit. If fuel gauge indicates "F", unplug 13-pin instrument panel cluster assembly connector. Using a DVOM, check resistance between terminal No. 4 (Yellow/Red wire) and ground.

2) If resistance is not infinite, repair short to ground in Yellow/Red wire. If resistance is infinite, check instrument panel cluster printed circuit for cracks and poor connection. If printed circuit is okay, replace fuel gauge.

TEMPERATURE GAUGE & SENDING UNIT TEST (METRO)

Gauge Indicates "C" At All Times – 1) Unplug sending unit connector. Connect a fused jumper wire from coolant temperature sending unit connector terminal to ground. Turn ignition on. If gauge indicates "H", replace coolant temperature sending unit.

2) Disconnect fused jumper. If gauge indicates "C", unplug 16-pin (White) instrument panel cluster assembly connector. Using a DVOM, check resistance between connector terminal No. 6 and coolant temperature sending unit terminal. If resistance is greater than 2 ohms, repair open circuit in Yellow/White wire between instrument panel cluster assembly and coolant temperature sending unit.

3) If resistance is less than 2 ohms, check instrument panel cluster printed circuit for cracks and poor connections. If printed circuit is okay, replace gauge.

Gauge Indicates "H" At All Times – 1) Unplug coolant temperature sending unit connector. If gauge indicates "C", replace coolant temperature sending unit.

2) If gauge indicates "H", unplug 16-pin (White) instrument panel cluster assembly connector. Connect DVOM between sender connector and Yellow/White wire terminal at connector. If resistance if infinite, check cluster printer circuit for cracks or bad connections. If okay, replace coolant gauge.

3) If resistance is less than infinite, repair short to ground in Yellow/White wire between cluster and coolant sender.

TEMPERATURE GAUGE & SENDING UNIT TEST (PRIZM)

Gauge Indicates "C" At All Times – 1) Unplug coolant temperature sender connector. Connect a fused jumper wire from connector terminal to ground. Turn ignition on. If gauge indicates "H", replace coolant temperature sender.

2) If gauge indicates "C", unplug 10-pin instrument panel cluster connector. Using a DVOM, check resistance between connector terminal No. 1 (Yellow/Green wire) and coolant temperature sender connector.

3) If resistance is greater than 2 ohms, repair open circuit in Yellow/Green wire between instrument cluster connector and coolant temperature sender. If resistance is less than 2 ohms, check instrument panel cluster printed circuit for cracks or poor connections. If printed circuit is okay, replace gauge.

Gauge Indicates "H" At All Times – 1) Unplug instrument panel cluster connector C1. Using a DVOM, check resistance between 10-pin connector terminal No. 1 (Yellow/Green wire) and ground. If resistance is not infinite, repair short to ground in Yellow/Green sending unit.

2) If resistance is infinite, check instrument panel cluster printed circuit for cracks or poor connections. If printed circuit is okay, replace gauge.

TEMPERATURE GAUGE & SENDING UNIT TEST (TRACKER)

Gauge Indicates "C" At All Times – 1) Unplug coolant temperature sending unit connector. Connect a fused jumper wire between connector terminal and ground. If gauge indicates "H", replace coolant temperature sending unit.

2) If gauge indicates "C", unplug 13-pin instrument panel cluster assembly connector. Using a DVOM, check resistance between connector terminal No. 13 and ground. If resistance is greater than 3 ohms, repair open circuit in Yellow/White wire. If resistance is less than 3 ohms, check printed circuit for cracks or poor connections. If printed circuit is okay, replace gauge.

Gauge Indicates "H" At All Times – 1) Unplug coolant temperature sending unit connector. If gauge indicates "C", replace coolant temperature sending unit. If gauge indicates "H", unplug 13-pin instrument panel cluster assembly connector. Using a DVOM, check resistance between connector terminal No. 13 and ground.

2) If resistance is infinite, check instrument panel cluster printed circuit for cracks or poor connections. If resistance is not infinite, repair short to ground in Yellow/White wire.

OIL PRESSURE SWITCH

Oil Pressure Indicator Does Not Light – 1) Disconnect oil pressure switch connector. Connect fused jumper jumper from switch cavity to ground. Turn ignition on. If indicator does not light, go to next step. If indicator lights, check for poor connection at switch connector. If connection is okay, replace switch.

2) Disconnect fused jumper wire. Disconnect 16-pin instrument cluster connector (13-pin connector on Prizm). Connect DVOM between cluster connector Yellow/Black wire terminal (Yellow wire terminal on Prizm) and oil pressure switch connector cavity. Measure resistance. If resistance is less than 0.5 ohm (one ohm on Prizm), check instrument cluster printed circuit for cracks or poor connections. If okay, replace indicator bulb. If resistance is more than 0.5 ohm (one ohm on Prizm), repair open in Yellow/Black wire (Yellow wire on Prizm) between cluster assembly and oil pressure switch.

Oil Pressure Indicator On With Engine Running (Metro) – 1) Disconnect oil pressure switch connector. Start engine. If indicator does not go out, go to next step. If indicator goes out, check engine oil pressure with gauge. If pressure is at least 4.5 psi, replace oil pressure switch. If pressure is less than 4.5 psi, problem exists in lubrication system.

2) Disconnect instrument panel 16-pin connector. Connect DVOM between cluster connector Yellow/Black wire and ground. Measure resistance. If resistance is less than infinite, repair short to ground in Yellow/Black wire. If resistance is infinite, repair or replace instrument cluster printed circuit.

Oil Pressure Indicator On With Engine Running (Prizm) – Disconnect oil pressure switch connector. Start engine. If indicator does not go out, repair short to ground in Yellow wire between instrument cluster and oil pressure switch. If indicator goes out, check oil pressure. If oil pressure is less than 3 psi, problem exists in lubrication system. If pressure is more than 3 psi, replace oil pressure switch.

Oil Pressure Indicator On With Engine Running (Tracker) – Disconnect oil pressure switch connector. If indicator goes off, replace oil pressure switch. If indicator remains on, repair short to ground in Yellow/Black wire between switch and instrument cluster printed circuit.

OIL PRESSURE SWITCH LOCATION

Model	Location
Metro	On Front Of Engine, Above Oil Filter
Prizm	On Right Front Of Engine, Behind Alternator
Tracker	On Left Front Of Engine, Above Oil Filter

BRAKE FLUID WARNING INDICATOR TEST

With engine stopped and ignition switch in ON position, warning light should glow regardless of brake fluid condition and/or parking brake operation. After engine is started, release parking brake. If light does not go off, brake fluid level is low or parking brake release switch is defective. Repair or replace as required.

HAZARD WARNING SWITCH TEST

NOTE: *Hazard switches for Metro, Storm and Tracker are incorporated in combination switch. See HAZARD WARNING SWITCH TEST under TESTING in STEERING COLUMN SWITCHES article.*

Prizm – 1) Ensure hazard fuse and turn signal flasher unit are okay. Disconnect battery negative cable. Unplug 10-pin hazard switch connector under left side of instrument panel.

2) With hazard switch off, check continuity between Green/White and Green/Red wires. If no continuity exists, replace hazard switch. If continuity exists, go to next step.

3) Turn hazard switch on. Check continuity between White and Green/Red wires. If no continuity exists, replace hazard switch. If continuity exists, check continuity between Green/White and Green/Black wires, and between Green/White and Green/Yellow wires.

HEADLIGHT SWITCH TEST

NOTE: *Headlight switches for Metro, Prizm and Tracker are incorporated in combination switch. See HEADLIGHT SWITCH TEST under TESTING in STEERING COLUMN SWITCHES article.*

PANEL LIGHT DIMMER SWITCH TEST

Metro & Tracker – Remove switch from dash. Using a jumper wire, connect battery negative terminal to terminal No. 1 (Black wire) of switch. Connect jumper lead from positive battery terminal to terminal No. 2 (Red/Yellow wire) of switch. Connect test light between terminal No. 3 (Red/Green wire) and switch terminal No. 2. Turning switch clockwise should brighten test light; counterclockwise should dim test light. Replace switch it does not operate as specified.

Prizm – Remove switch from dash. Using a jumper wire, connect battery positive terminal to terminal No. 1 (Green wire) of switch. Connect jumper lead from battery ground terminal to terminal No. 2 (White/Black wire) of switch. Connect test light between terminal No. 3 (White/Green wire) and battery positive terminal No. 1. Turning switch clockwise should brighten test light; counterclockwise should dim test light. Replace switch it does not operate as specified.

WIPER SWITCH TEST

For wiper testing information, see WIPER/WASHER SYSTEMS article.

TACHOMETER TEST

Metro – **1)** Start engine. Disconnect noise suppressor filter connector located on left hand strut tower, near bulkhead. Connect fused jumper between noise filter connector Brown and Brown/White wire terminals. If tachometer does not read correct engine RPM, go to next step. If correct RPM is indicated, check for poor connections at noise filter. If connections are okay, replace noise filter.

2) Turn engine off. Disconnect fused jumper. Disconnect ignition coil connector. Connect DVOM between coil connector Brown/White wire terminal and noise suppressor filter Brown/White wire terminal. Measure resistance. If resistance is less than one ohm, go to next step. If resistance is more than one ohm, repair open in Brown/White wire.

3) Disconnect instrument cluster 16-pin connector. Connect DVOM between cluster connector Brown wire terminal and noise filter Brown wire terminal. Measure resistance. If resistance is less than one ohm, check cluster printed circuit for cracks or poor connections. If okay, replace tachometer. If resistance is more than one ohm, check for poor connection at cluster assembly. If okay, repair open in Brown wire between cluster and noise filter.

Prizm – **1)** If tachometer does not register correct engine RPM, connect known good tachometer to Data Link Connector (DLC) terminal No. 19 (Black wire). Start engine. If correct RPM is not indicated, check for open in Black wire between DLC and igniter. If wire is okay, replace igniter.

2) If correct RPM is indicated, check for open in Black wire between instrument cluster connector and splice. Check cluster printed circuit for cracks or poor connections. If wiring and printed circuit are good, replace tachometer.

Tracker – **1)** Turn ignition off. Disconnect instrument cluster 16-pin connector. Connect DVOM between connector terminal No. 13 (Black wire) and ground. Measure resistance. If resistance is less than 0.3 ohm, go to next step. If resistance is more than 0.3 ohm, repair open in Black wire.

2) Disconnect engine control module connector. Connector is 24-pin on Federal models, or 22-pin on California models. Disconnect noise suppression filter connector. Connect DVOM between noise filter connector Brown wire terminal and 13-pin instrument cluster connector Brown wire terminal. Measure resistance. If resistance is less than 0.5 ohm, go to next step. If resistance is more than 0.5 ohm, repair open in Brown wire.

3) Disconnect ignition coil connector. Connect DVOM between coil connector Brown/White wire terminal and noise filter connector Brown/White wire terminal. Measure resistance. If resistance is less than 0.3 ohm, go to next step. If resistance is more than 0.3 ohm, repair open in Brown/White wire.

4) Reconnect all connectors and start engine. Connect fused jumper between noise suppression filter connector Brown and Brown/White wire terminals. If tachometer now displays engine RPM, go to next step. If tachometer still does not display correct RPM, check instrument cluster printed circuit for cracks or poor connections. If printed circuit is okay, replace tachometer.

5) Turn ignition off. Disconnect noise suppression filter. Using test light, backprobe noise filter connector terminal No. 1 (Black wire on Calif. models, Black/Green wire on Federal models) to battery power. If test light does not come on, repair open in Black or Black/Green wire between filter and ground connection. If test light comes on, repair open in Black or Black/Green wire between noise filter and splice. If wire is okay, replace noise suppression filter.

REMOVAL & INSTALLATION

WARNING: Before removing ANY instrument panel components, Supplemental Restraint System (SRS) MUST be disabled. See DISABLING & ACTIVATING AIR BAG SYSTEM in AIR BAG RESTRAINT SYSTEM article. Accidental air bag deployment could cause serious bodily injury.

INSTRUMENT CLUSTER

Removal & Installation (Metro) – **1)** Disable air bag system. See SERVICE PRECAUTIONS in AIR BAG RESTRAINT SYSTEM article. Disconnect negative battery cable. Remove 4 retaining screws from instrument cluster trim bezel. Unplug rear wiper/washer switch and rear defogger switch connectors. Remove both cluster hood and cluster switch panel as an assembly.

2) Unplug electrical connectors from cluster trim bezel-mounted switches. Remove retaining clip and speedometer cable at transaxle. Remove 4 screws and cluster assembly from instrument panel. Remove speedometer cable and all electrical connectors from back of cluster assembly. Remove cluster assembly from vehicle. To install instrument cluster, reverse removal procedure. See Fig. 1.

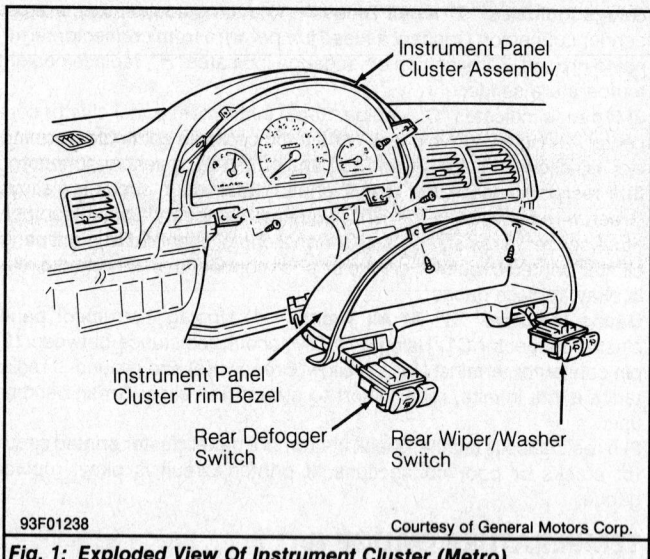

93F01238   Courtesy of General Motors Corp.

Fig. 1: Exploded View Of Instrument Cluster (Metro)

NOTE: No Prizm instrument cluster illustration is available from manufacturer.

Removal & Installation (Prizm) – Disable air bag system. See SERVICE PRECAUTIONS in AIR BAG RESTRAINT SYSTEM article. Disconnect negative battery cable. Remove 2 retaining screws of instrument panel lower trim panel. Disengage 2 lower clips and remove trim panel. Remove 4 instrument cluster bezel screws. Pull instrument cluster outward. Unplug 3 electrical connectors. Remove instrument cluster. To install, reverse removal procedure.

Removal & Installation (Tracker) – Disconnect negative battery cable. Remove 4 retaining screws from instrument cluster bezel/shroud and remove bezel/shroud. Remove 4 retaining screws from instrument cluster, and pull cluster outward. Unplug electrical connectors and speedometer cable from rear of cluster. Remove instrument cluster. To install, reverse removal procedure. See Fig. 2.

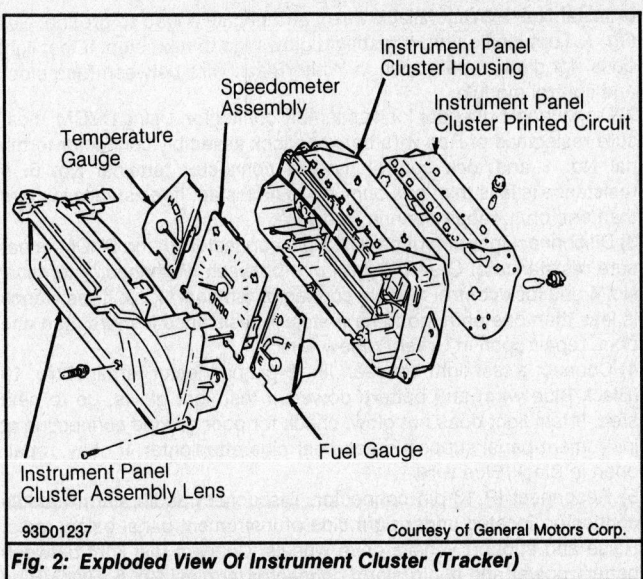

Temperature Gauge

Speedometer Assembly

Instrument Panel Cluster Housing

Instrument Panel Cluster Printed Circuit

Fuel Gauge

Instrument Panel Cluster Assembly Lens

93D01237

Courtesy of General Motors Corp.

Fig. 2: Exploded View Of Instrument Cluster (Tracker)

WIRING DIAGRAMS

NOTE: See ACCESSORIES & EQUIPMENT, Volume 5.

Metro

DESCRIPTION

Automatic power door lock system consists of an automatic door lock control module, vehicle speed sensor located in speedometer head, door lock switch and actuator assembly in each front door. A LOCK DOORS indicator is located in the instrument panel. Rear doors on 4-door models do not have automatic door locks.

OPERATION

Battery power is applied at all times to the lock control module through the 15-amp DOOR LOCK fuse. Battery power is applied to the lock control module through the 20-amp IG fuse when ignition switch is in ON or START positions. If left and/or right doors are unlocked, door lock switches are closed, providing a reference ground signal to lock control module. Module will use this signal to ground LOCK DOORS indicator. Indicator informs driver that one or more doors are unlocked.

Lock control module also receives an input from vehicle speed sensor (VSS), which is permanently grounded. If any door is unlocked, lock control module automatically locks door(s) when signal from VSS indicates vehicle speeds greater than 8 MPH. If doors are unlocked at speeds greater than 8 MPH, lock control module will not automatically lock doors again until vehicle is brought to a complete stop, and then once again accelerated to greater than 8 MPH.

TROUBLE SHOOTING

LOCK DOORS Indicator Lights, But Doors Will Not Lock – Go to TEST NO. 1.
LOCK DOORS Indicator Does Not Light, & Doors Will Not Lock – Go to TEST NO. 2.
Right Door Will Not Lock – Go to TEST NO. 3.
Left Door Will Not Lock – Go to TEST NO. 4.
LOCK DOORS Indicator Does Not Light, But Both Doors Lock – Go to TEST NO. 5.
LOCK DOORS Indicator Is Always On – Go to TEST NO. 6.
Doors Lock Automatically When Speed Is Less Than 6 MPH, Or More Than 10 MPH – Go to TEST NO. 7.
Lock Actuators Always Energized – Check for short to voltage in Red wire between lock control module and left and/or right door lock/ switch assembly. If wire is okay, replace lock control module.
Lock Actuators Frozen In Lock Position – Replace left and/or right lock actuator assemblies.
Doors Do Not Relock When Vehicle Is Stopped, Then Drive At Greater Than 8 MPH – Replace door lock control module.

TESTING

PRELIMINARY CHECKS

Ensure DOOR LOCK and IG fuses are good. Check that grounds are clean and tight. G200 is located above left side kick panel. G201 is located on right side kick panel. G202 is located on instrument panel support, to left of cigraette lighter. Check all wiring and connectors for proper connections. If more than one warning indicator is out, check instrument cluster printed circuit.

TEST NO. 1

1) Disconnect door lock control module connector located behind glove box inner panel. Connect positive lead of test light to connector

94F46123   Courtesy of General Motors Corp.

Fig. 1: Identifying Door Lock Control Module Connector Terminals

terminal No. 1 (White/Black wire), and negative lead to ground. *See Fig. 1.* Turn ignition on. If test light glows, go to next step. If test light does not glow, repair open in White/Black wire between fuse block and control module.
2) Disconnect right door lock assembly connector. Using DVOM, measure resistance of Red wire between lock assembly connector terminal No. 1 and lock control module connector terminal No. 6. If resistance is less than one ohm, go to next step. If resistance is more than one ohm, repair open in Red wire.
3) Disconnect instrument panel 13-pin connector. Using DVOM, measure resistance of Green/Yellow wire between IP connector terminal No. 4 and lock control module connector terminal No. 3. If resistance is less than one ohm, go to next step. If resistance is more than one ohm, repair open in Green/Yellow wire.
4) Connect a test light between IP 13-pin connector terminal No. 10 (Black/Blue wire) and battery power. If test light glows, go to next step. If test light does not glow, check for poor ground connection at instrument panel support brace near cigarette lighter. If okay, repair open in Black/Blue wire.
5) Reconnect IP 13-pin connector. Disconnect audio/alarm module connector, located under right side of instrument panel below radio. Raise and support vehicle drive wheels. Connect test light between battery power and audio/alarm connector terminal No. 6 (Black/Blue wire). Rotate left front wheel one revoluton. If test light goes on and off 2 times, replace lock control module. If test light does not go on and off 2 times, check instrument panel printed circuit for cracks or damage. If okay, replace speedometer.

TEST NO. 2

1) Turn ignition on. Using test light, backprobe lock control module connector terminal No. 4 (Black/White wire) to ground. If test light glows, go to next step. If test light does not glow, repair open in Black/ White wire between junction block and control module.
2) Using test light, backprobe lock control module connector terminal No. 5 (Black wire) to battery power. If test light glows, go to next step. If test light does not glow, repair open in Black wire between lock control module and main harness connector.
3) Unlock both doors. Disconnect lock control module connector. Connect test light between lock control module connector terminal No. 7 (Green/Black wire) and battery power. If test light glows, check for poor connections at module connector. If okay, replace lock control module. If test light does not glow, repair open in Green/Black wire.

TEST NO. 3

1) Using test light, backprobe right door lock assembly connector terminal No. 2 (Black wire) to battery power. If test light glows, go to next step. If test light does not glow, repair open in Black wire.
2) Check for poor connection at door lock assembly. If okay, check for open in Red wire between door lock assembly and harness connector. If okay, replace door lock assembly.

TEST NO. 4

1) Using test light, backprobe left door lock assembly connector terminal No. 2 (Black wire) to battery power. If test light glows, go to next step. If test light does not glow, repair open in Black wire.
2) Check for poor connection at door lock assembly. If okay, check for open in Red wire between door lock assembly and harness connector. If okay, replace door lock assembly.

TEST NO. 5

1) Disconnect door lock control module connector. Turn ignition on. Connect fused jumper wire between ground and lock control module connector terminal No. 2 (Green/White wire). If indicator does not light, go to next step. If indicator lights, check for poor connection at lock control module connector. If okay, replace lock control module.
2) Using fused jumper connected to ground, backprobe instrument panel cluster 16-pin connector terminal No. 10 (Green/White wire). If indicator lights, repair open in Green/White wire between cluster con-

nector and lock control module. If indicator does not light, check for poor connection at cluster connector. If okay, repair or replace IP cluster printed circuit.

TEST NO. 6

1) Disconnect door lock control module connector. Lock both front doors. Turn ignition on. If indicator does not turn off, go to next step. If indicator turns off, check for short to ground in Green/White wire between instrument cluster and lock control module. If okay, repair or replace instrument cluster printed circuit.

2) Reconnect lock control module. Disconnect right door lock assembly connector. If indicator stays on, go to next step. If indicator shuts off, replace right door lock assembly.

3) Disconnect left door lock assembly. If indicator stays on, go to next step. If indicator shuts off, replace left door lock assembly.

4) Check for short to ground in Green/Black wire between lock control module and right and left door lock assemblies. If wiring is okay, replace door lock control module.

TEST NO. 7

Disconnect door lock control module connector. Raise and support vehicle drive wheels. Connect test light between battery power and module connector terminal No. 3 (Yellow/Green wire). Rotate left front wheel one revolution. If test light goes on and off 2 times, replace lock control module. If test light does not go on and off 2 times, check instrument panel printed circuit for cracks or damage. If okay, replace speedometer.

REMOVAL & INSTALLATION

DOOR LOCK CONTROL MODULE

Removal & Installation – Open glove box door and remove 4 screws holding glove box inner panel. Remove inner panel and slide lock control module from holder. Disconnect electrical connector and remove module. To install, reverse removal procedure.

DOOR LOCK ASSEMBLY

Removal & Installation – Disconnect negative battery cable. Remove door trim. Unclip outer sealing strip from door. Remove screws and door trim bracket. Remove water deflector. If necessary, remove window and window guide channel. Disconnect lock and switch electrical connectors. Remove lock assembly. To install, reverse removal procedure.

WIRING DIAGRAM

NOTE: See ACCESSORIES & EQUIPMENT, Volume 5.

Prizm

DESCRIPTION & OPERATION

The major components of the power door lock system include: power door lock control module, door lock switches, door key position switches and door lock actuators.

Battery voltage is supplied at all times through the ACCESSORY fusible link to the power door lock control module. The power door lock control module and door lock switches are grounded to the chassis behind left kick panel.

DIAGNOSIS & TESTING

SYMPTOM DIAGNOSIS

All Doors Do Not Unlock Or Lock Automatically With Key Turned In Left Or Right Front Door Lock Or With Left Power Door Lock Switch – Proceed to TEST No. 1.

All Doors Do Not Unlock Or Lock Automatically With Key Turned In Left Front Door Lock – Check for open White/Black wire between left power door lock actuator and chassis ground. If okay, replace left front door lock actuator.

All Doors Do Not Unlock Or Lock Automatically With Key Turned In Right Front Door Lock – Check for open White/Black wire between right power door lock actuator and chassis ground. If okay, replace right front door lock actuator.

All Doors Do Not Unlock Or Lock Automatically With The Left Front Door Lock Switch – Check for open White/Black wires between left front door lock switch and chassis ground. If okay, replace left front door lock switch.

All Doors Do Not Lock Automatically With Key Turned In Left Door Lock Or With Left Front Door Lock Switch – Proceed to TEST No. 2.

All Doors Do Not Lock Automatically With Key Turned In Left Or Right Door Lock – Proceed to TEST No. 3.

All Doors Do Not Lock Automatically With Left Front Door Lock Switch – Proceed to TEST No. 4.

All Doors Do Not Unlock Automatically With Key Turned In Right Door Lock Or With Right Front Door Lock Switch – Proceed to TEST No. 5.

All Doors Do Not Unlock Automatically With Key Turned In Right Door Lock – Check for open Blue/Yellow wire between right door lock actuator and power door lock control module.

All Doors Do Not Unlock Automatically With Left Front Door Lock Switch – Check for open Blue/Yellow wire between left front door lock switch and power door lock control module.

Doors Do Not Automatically Unlock With Key Turned Twice In 3 Seconds In The Left Front Door Lock – Proceed to TEST No. 6.

Left Front Door Does Not Unlock Or Lock Automatically – Check for open Red wire between power door lock control module and left front door lock actuator. If okay, check for open Blue wire between power door lock control module and left front door lock actuator. If no faults are found in wiring, replace left front door lock actuator.

Right Front Door Does Not Unlock Or Lock Automatically – Check for open Red wire between power door lock control module and right front door lock actuator. If okay, check for open Blue wire between power door lock control module and right front door lock actuator. If no faults are found in wiring, replace right front door lock actuator.

Left Rear Door Does Not Unlock Or Lock Automatically – Check for open Red wire between power door lock control module and left rear door lock actuator. If okay, check for open Blue wire between power door lock control module and left rear door lock actuator. If no faults are found in wiring, replace left rear door lock actuator.

Right Rear Door Does Not Unlock Or Lock Automatically – Check for open Red wire between power door lock control module and right rear door lock actuator. If okay, check for open Blue wire between power door lock control module and right rear door lock actuator. If no faults are found in wiring, replace right front door lock actuator.

All Doors Unlock When Key Is Turned In Left Front Door Lock Only Once – Replace power door lock control module.

TEST NO. 1

All Doors Do Not Unlock Or Lock Automatically With The Key Turned In Left Or Right Door Lock Or With Left Power Door Lock Switch –
1) Using a voltmeter, backprobe power door lock control module connector between terminal No. 8 (White/Red wire) and ground. If more than 10 volts are present, go to next step. If less than 10 volts are present, check for open White/Red wire between junction block 1 and power door lock control module. If okay, replace junction block 1.
2) Backprobe power door lock control module connector, between terminal No. 16 (White/Black wire) and positive battery terminal. If more than 10 volts are present, replace power door lock module. If less than 10 volts are present, check for open White/Black wire between power door lock module and junction connector 1 (Black 6-pin connector behind center of instrument panel), or in White/Black wire between junction connector 1 and chassis ground (behind left kick panel). If okay, replace junction connector 1.

TEST NO. 2

All Doors Do Not Lock Automatically With The Key In Left Or Right Front Door Lock Or With Left Front Power Door Lock Switch – 1) Disconnect power door lock control module connector. Connect a test light to positive battery terminal and backprobe control module connector terminal No. 12 (Blue/Black wire). If test light glows, go to next step. If test light does not glow, go to step 3).
2) Leave test light connected to control module connector. Disconnect left front door lock actuator connector. If test light goes out, replace left front power door lock actuator. If test light does not go out, check for short to ground in Blue/Black wire between power door lock module left or right front door lock actuator. If no short is found, replace right front door lock actuator. If test light goes out, replace left front lock actuator.
3) Connect a test light to positive battery terminal and backprobe power door lock control module connector terminal No. 10 (Blue/White wire). If test light does not glow, replace power door lock control module. If test light glows, check for short to ground in Blue/White wire between power door lock control module and left and right front door lock switches. If no shorts are found replace left front door lock switch.

TEST NO. 3

All Doors Do Not Lock Automatically With Key Turned In Left Or Right Front Door Lock – 1) If power door locks do not operate when the key is turned in left front door, check for open in Blue/Black wire between power door lock control module and left front door lock actuator. If okay, replace left front door lock actuator.
2) If power door locks do not operate when the key is turned in right front door, check for open Blue/Black wire between power door lock control module and right front door lock actuator. If okay, replace right front door lock actuator.
3) If power door locks do not operate when the key is turned in either front door, perform both steps 1) and 2) in this test. If no wiring faults are found replace door lock control module.

TEST NO. 4

All Doors Do Not Lock Automatically With Left Door Lock Switch –
1) Disconnect power door lock control module connector. Connect a test light to positive battery terminal and backprobe control module connector terminal No. 10 (Blue/White wire). Press left power door lock switch to lock position. If test light glows, replace power door lock control module. If test light does not glow, go to next step.
2) Check for open Blue/White wire between power door lock module and left front door lock switch. If Blue/White wire is okay, replace left power door lock switch.

TEST NO. 5

All Doors Do Not Unlock Automatically With Key Turned In Right Front Door Or With Left Door Lock Switch – 1) Disconnect power door lock control module connector. Connect a test light to positive battery terminal and backprobe control module connector No. 11 (Blue/Yellow wire). If test light glows, go to next step. If test light does not glow, check for an open Blue/Yellow wire between power door lock control module and left door lock switch. If Blue/Yellow wire is okay, replace power door lock control module.

2) Leave test light connected to control module connector and disconnect left front door lock switch connector. If test light continues to glow, go to next step. If test light goes out, replace left front door lock switch.

3) Check for short to ground in Blue/Yellow wire between power door lock control module and left door lock switch connector and right front door lock actuator. If Blue/Yellow wire is okay, replace right front door lock actuator.

TEST NO. 6

All Doors Do Not Unlock With Key Turned Twice Within 3 Seconds In Left Front Door Lock – 1) Disconnect power door lock control module connector. Connect a test light to positive battery terminal. Insert key in left front door lock and turn clockwise to unlock position. If test light glows when key is held in unlock position, replace power door lock control module. If test light glows all the time, go to next step. If test light does not glow at all, go to step **3)**.

2) Check for short to ground in Blue/Yellow wire between power door lock control module and left front door lock actuator. If Blue/Yellow wire is okay, replace left front door lock actuator.

3) Check for open in Blue/Yellow wire between power door lock control module and left front door lock actuator. If Blue/Yellow wire is okay, replace left front door lock actuator.

REMOVAL & INSTALLATION

FRONT DOOR LOCKS/ACTUATORS

NOTE: Front actuators are not serviced separately. Replace lock assembly to service actuator.

Removal & Installation – 1) Disconnect negative battery cable. Remove door trim and pull water deflector far enough away to gain access to window regulator bolts.

2) Remove window regulator bolts. Lift and remove window from door. Pull window run rubber from rear guide channel. Remove 2 bolts and window guide channel from door.

3) Remove 3 control rods from door lock. Disconnect actuator electrical connector. Remove 3 screws and door lock from door. To install, reverse removal procedure.

LEFT FRONT DOOR LOCK SWITCH

Removal & Installation – Disconnect negative battery cable. Remove door trim. Gently pry lock switch housing from door trim. Gently pry switch from housing. To install, reverse removal procedure.

POWER DOOR LOCK CONTROL MODULE

Removal & Installation – Power door lock control module is located behind instrument panel, on upper portion of right instrument panel brace. Removal and installation procedures not available from manufacturer.

WIRING DIAGRAM

NOTE: See ACCESSORIES & EQUIPMENT, Volume 5.

Prizm

DESCRIPTION & OPERATION

Power mirrors are controlled by power mirror switch assembly located on left side of instrument panel. *See Fig. 1.* The selector switch directs current to desired mirror. The horizontal/vertical switch directs current to one of 2 motors located in mirror assembly. Mirror and motors are removed and serviced as an assembly.

Ignition switch must be in ON or ACCY position for power mirror operation. Power is supplied to control switch assembly from CIG-RADIO fuse, through audio alarm module and junction block No. 3. Power mirror switch is permanently grounded through junction block No. 3, junction connector No. 3 and junction connector No. 1 to ground connection G200 (located behind left kick panel).

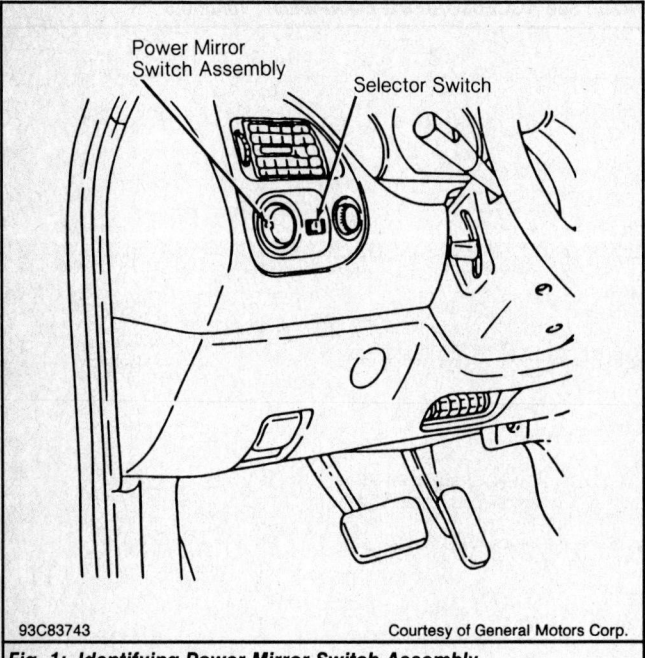

93C83743   Courtesy of General Motors Corp.

Fig. 1: Identifying Power Mirror Switch Assembly

TESTING

NOTE: *Illustrations are not available from manufacturer for all connectors. Connectors are illustrated, when possible. To identify connectors, terminals and circuits, see WIRING DIAGRAM.*

PRELIMINARY CHECKS

Ensure CIG-RADIO fuse is okay. Ensure ground connection G200 (located behind left kick panel) is clean and tight. Ensure audio alarm module is securely mounted in junction block No. 1 (located at lower shroud behind left kick panel). Before component replacement, check for poor connections at related component and in-line harness connector terminals.

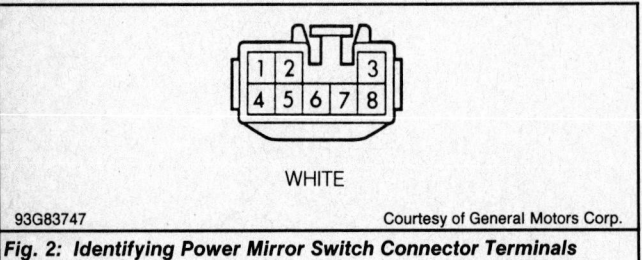

WHITE

93G83747   Courtesy of General Motors Corp.

Fig. 2: Identifying Power Mirror Switch Connector Terminals

POWER MIRROR SYSTEM INOPERATIVE

1) Turn ignition switch to ON or ACCY position. Using a test light, probe power mirror switch connector terminal No. 8. *See Fig. 2.* If test light comes on, got to step **4)**. If test light does not come on, go to next step.

2) Using a voltmeter, backprobe audio alarm module connector No. 1 (located behind left kick panel) with positive lead and ground remaining lead. If voltage is greater than 10 volts, go to next step. If voltage is less than 10 volts, replace audio alarm module and retest system. If system remains inoperative, replace junction block No. 1.

3) Check for open in Gray wire between audio alarm module and junction block No. 3. Also check for open in Gray wire between junction block No. 3 (located behind center of instrument panel) and power mirror switch. Repair wire as necessary. If wire is okay, replace junction block No. 3.

4) Connect a test light to battery voltage and probe power mirror switch connector terminal No. 3 (White/Black wire). *See Fig. 2.* If test light does not come on, go to step **6)**. If test light comes on, turn ignition to LOCK position. Unplug left power mirror assembly connector. Unplug power mirror switch connector. Using a DVOM, check resistance between left mirror assembly connector terminal No. 2 (Blue wire; Brown/Red wire after splice) and power mirror switch connector terminal No. 7 (Brown/Red wire).

5) If resistance is less than .5 ohm, replace power mirror switch. If resistance is greater than .5 ohm, check for open in Brown/Red wire between junction connector No. 3 and power mirror switch. Repair wire as necessary. If wire is okay, replace junction connector No. 3.

6) Connect a test light to battery voltage and probe power junction block No. 3 connector C1 terminal No, 20 (White/Black wire). If test light does not come on, go to next step. If test light comes on, check for open in White/Black wire between power mirror switch and junction block No. 3. Repair wire as necessary. If wire is okay, replace junction block No. 3.

7) Connect a test light to battery voltage and probe power junction connector No. 3 terminal No. 14 (White/Black wire). *See Fig. 3.* If test light comes on, go to next step. If test light does not come on, check for open in White/Black wire between junction connector No. 1 and junction connector No. 3. Also, check for open in White/Black wire between junction connector No. 1 and ground connection G200 (located behind left kick panel). *See Fig. 3.* Repair wire as necessary. If wire is okay, replace junction connector No. 1.

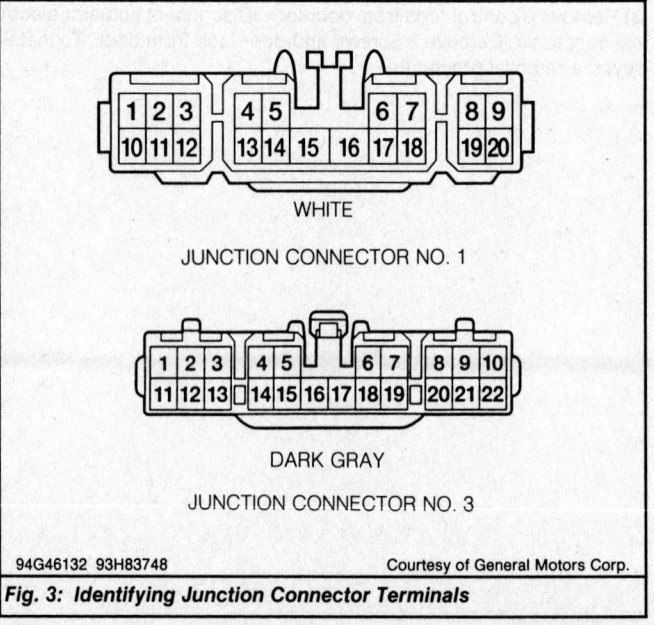

WHITE

JUNCTION CONNECTOR NO. 1

DARK GRAY

JUNCTION CONNECTOR NO. 3

94G46132 93H83748   Courtesy of General Motors Corp.

Fig. 3: Identifying Junction Connector Terminals

8) Check for open in White/Black wire between junction block No. 3 and junction connector No. 3. Repair wire as necessary. If wire is okay, replace junction connector No. 3.

LEFT MIRROR WILL NOT MOVE IN ANY DIRECTION

1) Turn ignition switch to ON or ACCY position. Set power mirror selector switch to "L". Hold power mirror switch in UP position. Using a test light, probe power mirror switch connector terminal No. 7 (Brown/Red wire). If test light comes on, go to next step. If test light does not come on, replace power mirror switch.

2) With power mirror switch held in UP position, probe left power mirror assembly connector terminal No. 2 (Blue wire; Brown/Red wire after splice). If test light comes on, go to next step. If test light does not come on, check for open in Blue wire (Brown/Red wire after splice) between junction connector No. 3 (located behind center of instrument panel) and left power mirror assembly. See Fig. 3. Repair wire as necessary. If wire is okay, replace junction connector No. 3.

3) With power mirror switch held in DOWN position, connect test light to battery voltage and probe power mirror switch connector terminal No. 7 (Brown/Red wire). See Fig. 2. If test light comes on, replace left power mirror assembly. If test light does not come on, replace power mirror switch.

LEFT MIRROR WILL NOT MOVE UP OR DOWN

1) Turn ignition switch to ON or ACCY position. Set power mirror selector switch to "L". Hold power mirror switch in DOWN position. Using a test light, probe power mirror switch connector terminal No. 4 (Light Green wire). See Fig. 2. If test light comes on, go to next step. If test light does not come on, replace power mirror switch.

2) With power mirror switch held in DOWN position, probe left power mirror assembly connector terminal No. 3 (Yellow wire; Light Green wire after splice). If test light comes on, go to next step. If test light does not come on, repair open in Light Green wire between power mirror switch and left power mirror assembly.

3) With power mirror switch held in UP position, connect test light to battery voltage and probe left power mirror switch connector terminal No. 4 (Light Green wire.) If test light comes on, replace left power mirror assembly. If test light does not come on, replace power mirror switch.

LEFT MIRROR WILL NOT MOVE LEFT OR RIGHT

1) Turn ignition switch to ON or ACCY position. Set power mirror selector switch to "L". Hold power mirror switch in LEFT position. Using a test light, probe power mirror switch connector terminal No. 1 (Blue wire). See Fig. 2. If test light comes on, go to next step. If test light does not come on, replace power mirror switch.

2) With power mirror switch held in LEFT position, probe left power mirror assembly connector terminal No. 1 (Blue wire.) If test light comes on, go to next step. If test light does not come on, repair open in Blue wire between power mirror switch and left power mirror assembly.

3) With power mirror switch held in RIGHT position, connect test light to battery voltage and probe left power mirror switch connector terminal No. 1 (Blue wire.) If test light comes on, replace left power mirror assembly. If test light does not come on, replace power mirror switch.

RIGHT MIRROR WILL NOT MOVE IN ANY DIRECTION

1) Turn ignition switch to ON or ACCY position. Set power mirror selector switch to "R". Hold power mirror switch in DOWN position. Using a test light, probe power mirror switch connector terminal No. 7 (Brown/Red wire). See Fig. 2. If test light comes on, go to next step. If test light does not come on, replace power mirror switch.

2) With power mirror switch held in DOWN position, probe right power mirror assembly connector terminal No. 2 (Blue wire; Brown/Red wire after splice). If test light comes on, go to next step. If test light does not come on, check for open in Brown/Red wire (Blue wire after splice) between junction connector No. 3 (located behind center of instrument panel) and right power mirror assembly. Repair wire as necessary. If wire is okay, replace junction connector No. 3.

3) With power mirror switch held in UP position, connect test light to battery voltage and probe power mirror switch connector terminal No. 7 (Brown/Red wire.) If test light comes on, replace right power mirror assembly. If test light does not come on, replace power mirror switch.

RIGHT MIRROR WILL NOT MOVE UP OR DOWN

1) Turn ignition switch to ON or ACCY position. Set power mirror selector switch to "R". Hold power mirror switch in UP position. Using a test light, probe power mirror switch connector terminal No. 6 (Red/Green wire). See Fig. 2. If test light comes on, go to next step. If test light does not come on, replace power mirror switch.

2) With power mirror switch held in UP position, probe right power mirror assembly connector terminal No. 3 (Yellow wire; Red/Green wire after splice). If test light comes on, go to next step. If test light does not come on, repair open in Yellow wire (Red/Green wire after splice) between power mirror switch and left power mirror assembly.

3) With power mirror switch held in DOWN position, connect test light to battery voltage and probe power mirror switch connector terminal No. 6 (Red/Green wire.) If test light comes on, replace right power mirror assembly. If test light does not come on, replace power mirror switch.

RIGHT MIRROR WILL NOT MOVE LEFT OR RIGHT

1) Turn ignition switch to ON or ACCY position. Set power mirror selector switch to "R". Hold power mirror switch in LEFT position. Using a test light, probe power mirror switch connector terminal No. 5 (Red wire). If test light comes on, go to next step. If test light does not come on, replace power mirror switch.

2) With power mirror switch held in LEFT position, probe right power mirror assembly connector terminal No. 1 (Light Green wire; Red wire after splice). If test light comes on, go to next step. If test light does not come on, repair open in Light Green wire (Red wire after splice) between power mirror switch and left power mirror assembly.

3) With power mirror switch held in RIGHT position, connect test light to battery voltage and probe left power mirror switch connector terminal No. 5 (Red wire.) If test light comes on, replace right power mirror assembly. If test light does not come on, replace power mirror switch.

REMOVAL & INSTALLATION

POWER MIRROR SWITCH

Removal & Installation – Disconnect negative battery cable. Remove 4 clips securing power mirror switch to left instrument panel outlet trim bezel. *See Fig. 1.* Carefully pull power mirror switch from trim bezel. Unplug switch connector and remove switch. To install, reverse removal procedure.

POWER MIRROR ASSEMBLY

Removal & Installation – Disconnect negative battery cable. Remove mirror mount garnish panel from door. *See Fig. 4.* Remove door trim panel. Unplug power mirror harness connector. Remove 3 mirror mounting bolts. Remove mirror. To Install, reverse removal procedure. Tighten mirror mounting bolts to 11 ft. lbs. (15 N.m).

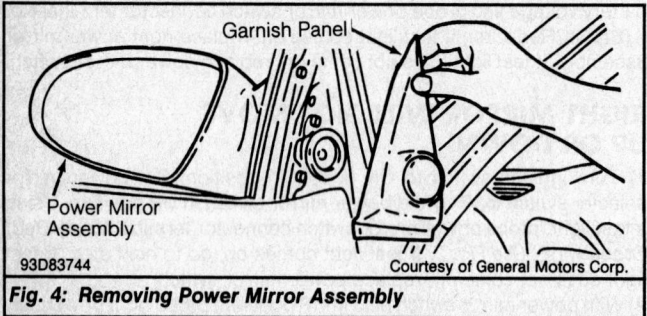

Garnish Panel

Power Mirror
Assembly

93D83744   Courtesy of General Motors Corp.

Fig. 4: Removing Power Mirror Assembly

WIRING DIAGRAM

NOTE: See ACCESSORIES & EQUIPMENT, Volume 5.

Prizm

DESCRIPTION & OPERATION

The ignition switch must be in ON or START position for sun roof to operate. Sun roof operation is controlled by sun roof switch, which sends signals to sun roof control module. Sun roof control module senses input from limit switches and processes information to decide if sun roof motor should operate.

Sun roof has a tilt mode and sliding mode. Sun roof must be returned to fully closed position to change from sliding mode to tilt mode, or vice versa. When closing sun roof in sliding mode, sun roof will stop halfway until sun roof switch is pressed a second time, sun roof will then close completely.

Power for the sun roof system is through ACCESSORY fusible link in junction block 1. Power to turn on sun roof system is supplied from ignition switch through GAUGE fuse and activates ACCESSORY power relay. Sun roof system chassis ground is located behind left kick panel.

ADJUSTMENTS

SUN ROOF PANEL
HORIZONTAL ADJUSTMENT

1) Remove headliner. Unclip sun roof interior trim from sun roof panel, slide rearward and remove from vehicle. Loosen 6 sun roof panel bolts.
2) To adjust sun roof panel, move panel side to side, or front to back. Gap between sun roof panel weatherstrip and roof should be 0-.039" (0.0-1.0 mm).
3) Tighten sun roof panel bolts to 70 INCH Lbs. (7.9 N.m) Slide sun roof interior trim into position. Ensure 2 guide pin slide into interior trim brackets. Clip sun roof trim onto sun roof panel. Install headliner.

SUN ROOF PANEL
VERTICAL ADJUSTMENT

1) Remove headliner. Unclip sun roof interior trim from sun roof panel, slide rearward and remove from vehicle. Loosen 6 sun roof panel bolts.
2) To adjust sun roof panel vertical height, remove or add shims between sun roof housing and sun roof panel. See Fig. 1. Sun roof panel should be flush with roof when properly adjusted.
3) Tighten sun roof panel bolts to 70 INCH Lbs. (7.9 N.m) Slide sun roof interior trim into position. Ensure 2 guide pin slide into interior trim brackets. Clip sun roof trim onto sun roof panel. Install headliner.

TROUBLE SHOOTING

PRELIMINARY CHECKS

Begin trouble shooting by checking GAUGE fuse and ACCESSORY fusible link in junction block 1, with fuse tester or test light. Ensure accessory power relay is mounted securely. Before replacing a component inspect connector terminals for backed out pins, corroded or dirty connections and loose terminals. Check that ground is clean and tight.

SUN ROOF IS INOPERATIVE
IN ANY OR ALL SWITCH POSITIONS

1) Turn ignition switch to ON position. Backprobe accessory power relay connector with a DVOM from terminal No. 3 (Red/Blue wire) to ground. If more than 10 volts exist, go to next step. If less than 10 volts exist, backprobe audio alarm module connector terminal No. 9 (Red/Blue wire). If less than 10 volts exist, replace audio alarm module. If more than 10 volts exist, check for open in Red/Blue wire between junction block 3 and audio alarm module and/or accessory power relay. If okay, replace junction block 3.

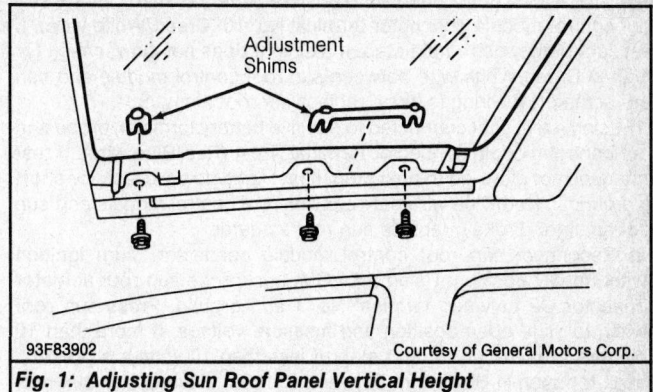

93F83902   Courtesy of General Motors Corp.

Fig. 1: Adjusting Sun Roof Panel Vertical Height

2) Connect a test light to positive battery terminal and backprobe accessory power relay connector terminal No. 2 (White/Black wire). If test light glows, go to next step. If test light does not glow, check for open in White/Black wire between accessory power relay and chassis ground (behind left kick panel).
3) Using a DVOM, backprobe accessory power relay connector between terminal No. 1 (White/Red wire) and ground. If less than 10 volts are present, check for open in White/Red wire between junction block 1 and accessory power relay. If okay, replace junction block 1. If more than 10 volts are present, backprobe junction block 1, connector C7, terminal No. 12 (Black wire) and measure voltage. If more than 10 volts are present, go to next step. If less than 10 volts are present, check for open in Black wire between junction block 1 and accessory power relay. If okay, replace accessory power relay.
4) Using a DVOM, backprobe sun roof control module connector between terminal No. 6 (Black wire) and ground. If more than 10 volts are present, go to next step. If less than 10 volts are present, check for open in Black wire between junction block 1 and sun roof control module. If okay, replace junction block 1.
5) Using a DVOM, backprobe sun roof control module connector, between terminal No. 12 (White/Black wire) and battery voltage. If less than 10 volts are present, go to next step. If more than 10 volts are present, backprobe sun roof switch connector, between terminal No. 4 (White/Black wire) and battery voltage. If more than 10 volts are present, go to step 7). If less than 10 volts are present, repair White/Black wire between splice junction S346 (in roof harness about 3 inches from dome light connector lead). See Fig. 2.
6) Using a DVOM, backprobe junction block 1 connector C5 between terminal No. 15 (White/Black wire) and battery voltage. If less than 10 volts are present, check for open in White/Black wire between junction block 1 and junction connector 1. If okay, replace junction connector 1. If more than 10 volts are present check for open in White/Black wire between sun roof control module and junction block 1. If okay, replace junction block 1.
7) Turn ignition switch to LOCK position. Disconnect sun roof control module connector. Using a DVOM, backprobe sun roof actuator connector C1 terminal No. 4 (Red/Blue wire) and battery voltage. If more than 10 volts are present, go to next step. If less than 10 volts are present, repair open in White/Black wire between sun roof actuator and splice junction S306 (in roof harness about 5 inches from dome light connector lead). See Fig. 2.
8) If sun roof is tilted open, go to step 14). If sun roof is slid open, go to step 20). If sun roof is closed, connect a test light to positive battery terminal. Probe sun roof control module connector terminal No. 2 (Red/Yellow wire). If test light glows, go to next step. If test light does not glow, check for open in Red/Yellow wire between sun roof control module and sun roof switch. If okay, replace sun roof switch.
9) Using a test light connected to battery voltage, probe sun roof control module connector terminal No. 8 (Pink wire) and press sun roof switch to slide open position. If test light glows, go to next step. If test light does not glow, check for open in Pink wire between sun roof control module and sun roof switch. If okay, replace sun roof switch.

10) Using a test light connected to positive battery terminal, probe sun roof control module connector terminal No. 10 (Green/White wire). If test light glows, go to next step. If test light does not glow, check for open in Green/White wire between sun roof control module and sun roof actuator. If wiring is okay, replace sunroof actuator.

11) Using a test light connected to positive battery terminal, probe sun roof control module connector terminal No. 4 (Red/Blue wire). If test light does not glow, go to next step. If test light glows, check for short to ground in Red/Blue wire between sun roof control module and sun roof actuator. If okay, replace sun roof actuator.

12) Reconnect sun roof control module connector. Turn ignition switch to ON position. Using a DVOM, backprobe sun roof actuator connector C2 between terminal No. 1 and ground. Press sun roof switch to slide open position and measure voltage. If more than 10 volts are present, go to next step. If less than 10 volts are present, check for open in Black wire between sun roof actuator and sun roof control module. If okay, replace sun roof control module.

13) Using a DVOM, backprobe sun roof actuator connector between terminals No. 1 (Green wire) and No. 3 (Red wire). Measure voltage while pressing sun roof switch to slide open position. If more than 10 volts are present, replace sun roof actuator. If less than 10 volts are present, check for open in Red wire between sun roof actuator and sun roof control module. If okay, replace sun roof control module.

14) If, in step **8)** sunroof was tilted up, use a test light connected to positive battery terminal and probe control module connector terminal No. 2 (Red/Yellow wire). If test light does not glow, go to next step. If test light glows, check for short to ground in Red/Yellow wire between sun roof control module and sun roof switch. If okay, replace sunroof switch.

15) Using a test light connected to positive battery terminal, probe sun roof control module connector terminal No. 9 (Red/White wire) and press sun roof switch to tilt down position. If test light glows, go to next step. If test light does not glow, check for short to ground in Red/Yellow wire between sun roof control module and sun roof switch. If okay, replace sun roof switch.

16) Using a test light connected to positive battery terminal, probe sun roof control module connector terminal No. 10 (Green/White wire). If test light does not glow, go to next step. If test light glows, check for short to ground in Green/White wire between sun roof control module and sun roof actuator. If okay, replace sun roof actuator.

17) Using a test light connected to positive battery terminal, probe sun roof control module connector terminal No. 4 (Red/Blue wire). If test light does not glow, go to next step. If test light glows, check for short to ground in Red/Blue wire between sun roof control module and sun roof actuator. If okay, replace sun roof actuator.

18) Reconnect sun roof control module connector. Turn ignition switch to ON position. Using a DVOM, backprobe sun roof actuator connector C2, between terminal No. 1 (Green wire) and ground. Press sun roof switch to tilt down position while measuring voltage. If more than 10 volts are present, go to next step. If less than 10 volts are present, check for open in Black wire between sun roof control module and sun roof actuator. If okay, replace sun roof control module.

19) Using a DVOM, backprobe sun roof actuator connector C2, between terminals No. 1 (Black wire) and No. 3 (Red wire). Measure voltage while pressing sun roof switch to tilt down position. If more than 10 volts are present, replace sun roof actuator. If less than 10 volts are present, check for open in Red wire between sun roof control module and sun roof actuator. if okay, replace sun roof control module.

20) If, in step **8)** sunroof was open, use a test light connected to positive battery terminal and backprobe sun roof control module connector terminal No. 8 (Pink wire). If test light does not glow, go to next step. If test light glows, check for short to ground in Pink wire between sun roof control module and sun roof switch. If okay, replace sun roof switch.

21) Using a test light connected to positive battery terminal, backprobe sun roof control module connector terminal No. 7 (Green/Yellow wire). Observe test light while pressing sun roof switch to slide close position. If test light glows, go to next step. If test light does not glow, Check for open in Green/Yellow wire between sun roof control module and sun roof switch. If okay, replace sun roof switch assembly.

22) Using a test light connected to positive battery terminal, backprobe sun roof control module connector terminal No. 10 (Green/White wire). If test light glows, go to next step. If test light does not glow, check for open in Green/White wire between sun roof control module and sun roof actuator. If okay, replace sun roof actuator.

23) Using a test light connected to positive battery terminal, backprobe sun roof control module connector terminal No. 4 (Red/Blue wire). If test light glows, go to next step. If test light does not glow, check for open in Blue/Red wire between sun roof control module and sun roof actuator. If okay, replace sun roof actuator.

24) Reconnect sun roof control module connector. Turn ignition switch to ON position. Using a DVOM, backprobe sun roof actuator connector C2, between terminal No. 3 (Red wire) and ground. Press sun roof switch to slide close position and measure voltage. If more than 10 volts are present, go to next step. If less than 10 volts are present, check for open in Red wire between sun roof control module and sun roof actuator. If okay, replace sun roof control module.

25) Using a DVOM, backprobe sun roof actuator connector C2, between terminals No. 1 (Black wire) and No. 3 (Red wire). Measure voltage while pressing sun roof switch to slide close position. If more than 10 volts are present, replace sun roof actuator. If less than 10 volts are present, check for open in Black wire between sun roof control module and sun roof actuator. If okay, replace sun roof control module.

SUN ROOF IS OPERATIONAL WITH IGNITION SWITCH IN LOCK POSITION

1) Disconnect connector C7 of junction block 1. Using a test light connected to ground, backprobe connector C7, terminal No. 12 (Black wire). If test light glows, go to next step. If test light does not glow, check for a short to voltage in Black wire between sun roof control module and junction block 1. If okay, replace junction block 1.

2) Check for short to voltage in Black wire between junction block 1 and accessory power relay, or right front power window switch (if equipped). If okay, replace accessory power relay.

REMOVAL & INSTALLATION

SUN ROOF MOTOR/ACTUATOR

Removal & Installation – Disconnect negative battery cable. Remove headliner from vehicle. Disconnect electrical connectors. *See Fig. 2*. Remove 3 mounting bolts and remove motor from vehicle. To install, reverse removal procedure.

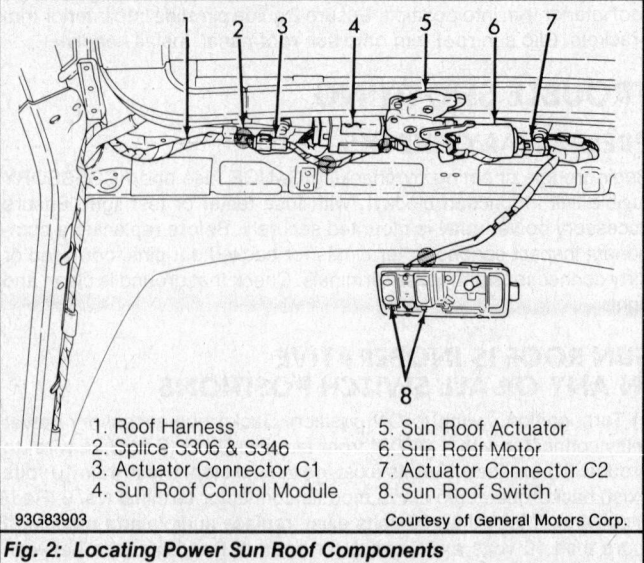

1. Roof Harness	5. Sun Roof Actuator
2. Splice S306 & S346	6. Sun Roof Motor
3. Actuator Connector C1	7. Actuator Connector C2
4. Sun Roof Control Module	8. Sun Roof Switch

93G83903   Courtesy of General Motors Corp.

Fig. 2: Locating Power Sun Roof Components

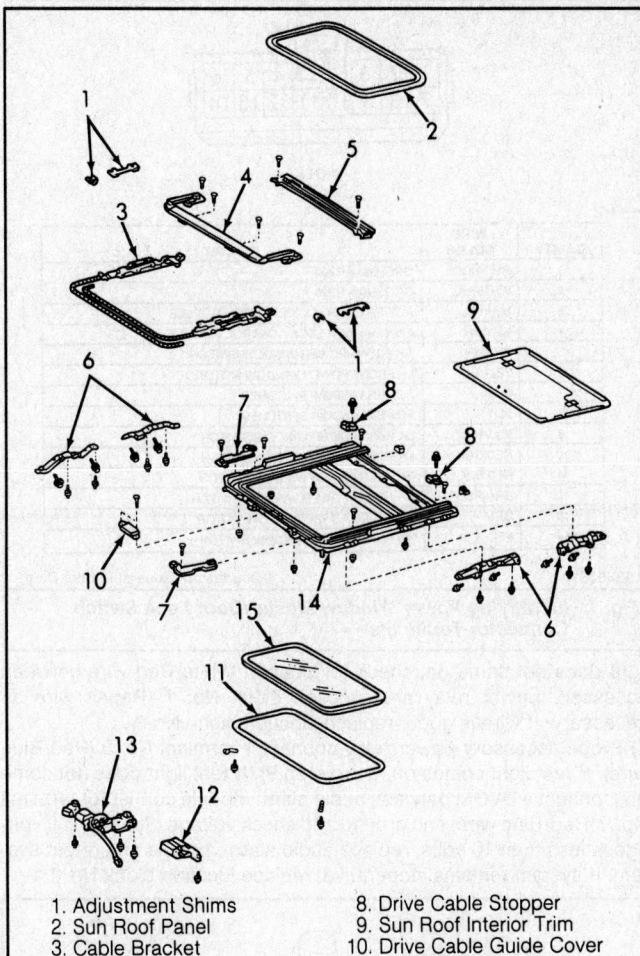

1. Adjustment Shims
2. Sun Roof Panel
3. Cable Bracket
4. Wind Deflector
5. Drip Channel
6. Sun Roof Housing
   Mounting Brackets
7. Drive Cable Guide Block
8. Drive Cable Stopper
9. Sun Roof Interior Trim
10. Drive Cable Guide Cover
11. Weatherstrip
12. Sun Roof Relay
13. Sun Roof Motor/Actuator
14. Sun Roof Housing
15. Weatherstrip

93H83904   Courtesy of General Motors Corp.

Fig. 3: Exploded View Of Sun Roof Assembly

SUN ROOF PANEL

Removal – Remove headliner from vehicle. unclip sun roof interior trim from sun roof panel. Slide interior trim rearward and remove from vehicle. Note number and location of shims on either side of sun roof panel. Remove 6 bolts and sun roof panel from vehicle.

Installation – Place sun roof panel onto sun roof housing. Install mounting bolts loosely. Insert shims to original location. Adjust sun roof panel. See SUN ROOF PANEL HORIZONTAL ADJUSTMENT and SUN ROOF PANEL VERTICAL ADJUSTMENT under ADJUST-MENTS. Tighten sun roof panel bolts. To complete installation, reverse removal procedure. Tighten sun roof panel mounting bolts to 70 INCH Lbs. (7.9 N.m).

SUN ROOF HOUSING

NOTE: For sun roof housing disassembly procedure, see exploded view. See Fig. 3.

Removal & Installation – 1) Disconnect negative battery cable. Remove headliner from vehicle. Remove sun roof relay. Remove sun roof motor mounting bolts and sun roof motor.

2) Loosen drain hose clamps and remove 4 drain hoses from sun roof housing assembly. Remove 18 bolts and 4 nuts. Remove sun roof housing assembly from vehicle. To install, reverse removal procedure.

WIRING DIAGRAM

NOTE: See ACCESSORIES & EQUIPMENT, Volume 5.

Prizm

DESCRIPTION & OPERATION

A permanent magnet motor operates each of the power windows. The driver's master switch assembly controls all of the power window motors. Each window switch controls only one of the power window motors. If the window lock switch is pressed, only driver's window may be operated. Passenger's windows cannot be controlled by individual window switches, but can still be controlled from driver's master switch. Press window lock switch again to unlock windows.

AUTO DOWN feature permits driver's window to be fully lowered without holding switch until window has reached the end of its travel. Moving switch all the way back will engage AUTO DOWN feature. Electronic Circuit Breaker (ECB) incorporated in window motor will stop motor at then end of window travel.

With ignition switch in ON position, voltage is applied through GAUGE fuse, audio alarm module, and junction block No. 3 to accessory power relay. Accessory power relay provides voltage to driver's power window switch. Driver's power window master switch (combined with power door lock switch, if equipped) distributes voltage to remaining power window switches and motors.

TESTING

NOTE: Illustrations are not available from manufacturer for all connectors. Connectors are illustrated, when possible. To identify connectors, terminals and circuits, see diagram under WIRING DIAGRAM.

PRELIMINARY CHECKS

Ensure GAUGE fuse and accessory fusible link are good. Ensure ground connection G200 (located behind left kick panel) is clean and tight. Ensure audio alarm module is securely mounted in junction block No. 1 (located at lower shroud behind left kick panel). Before component replacement, check for poor connections at related component and in-line harness connector terminals.

NOTE: Some components incorporate a short harness between component and connector. Wire color may be different from that used in main harness. Both wire colors are noted. Example: Red wire (Green wire after connector).

POWER WINDOW SYSTEM INOPERATIVE

1) Turn ignition on. Using a test light, probe power window master switch connector terminals No. 7 and 8 (Black wires at both terminals). *See Fig. 1.* If test light does not come on at both terminals or only comes on at one terminal, go to step **4)**. If test light comes on at both terminals, go to next step.
2) Connect test light to battery voltage and probe power window master switch connector terminals No. 1 and 2 (White/Black wire on both terminals). *See Fig. 1.* If test light comes on at both terminals, replace power window master switch.
3) If test light comes on at only one terminal, repair open in White/Black wire between terminal that did not come and splice S503 (located at left front door harness near power window master switch). If test light does not come on at either terminal, repair open in White/Black wire between splices S503 and S240 (located at instrument panel harness near accessory power relay).
4) If test light does not come on at either terminal, go to next step. If test light comes on at only one terminal, repair open in Black wire between terminal that did not come on and splice S502 (located at left front door harness near power door lock actuator).
5) Using a test light, probe power accessory relay connector terminal No. 4 (Black wire). If test light does not come on, go to next step. If test light comes on, repair open in Black wire between accessory power relay and splice S502.
6) Using a test light, probe power accessory relay connector terminal No. 1 (White/Red wire). If test light comes on, go to next step. If test

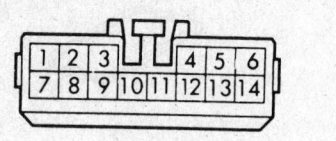

WHITE

CAVITY	WIRE COLOR	CIRCUIT
1	WHT/BLK	GROUND – G200
2	WHT/BLK	GROUND – G200
3	BLU/YEL	POWER DOOR LOCK CONTROL MODULE
4	BLU/WHT	POWER DOOR LOCK CONTROL MODULE
5	BLU/WHT	RH FRONT POWER WINDOW SWITCH
6	YEL	LH FRONT POWER WINDOW MOTOR
7	BLK	POWER WINDOW SWITCHES
8	BLK	POWER WINDOW SWITCHES
9	BLU/BLK	LH REAR POWER WINDOW SWITCH
10	RED/GRN	LH REAR POWER WINDOW SWITCH
11	RED/BLK	RH REAR POWER WINDOW SWITCH
12	GRN/RED	RH FRONT POWER WINDOW SWITCH
13	GRN	LH FRONT POWER WINDOW MOTOR
14	YEL	RH REAR POWER WINDOW SWITCH

93E83810   Courtesy of General Motors Corp.

Fig. 1: Identifying Power Window Master/Door Lock Switch Connector Terminals

light does not come on, check for open in White/Red wire between accessory power relay and junction block No. 1. Repair wire as necessary. If wire is good, replace junction block No. 1.
7) Probe accessory power relay connector terminal No. 3 (Red/Blue wire). If test light comes on, go to step **9)**. If test light does not come on, connect a DVOM between audio alarm module connector terminal No. 9 (Red/Blue wire) and ground and check voltage. *See Fig. 2.* If voltage is less than 10 volts, replace audio alarm module and retest system. If system remains inoperative, replace junction block No. 1.

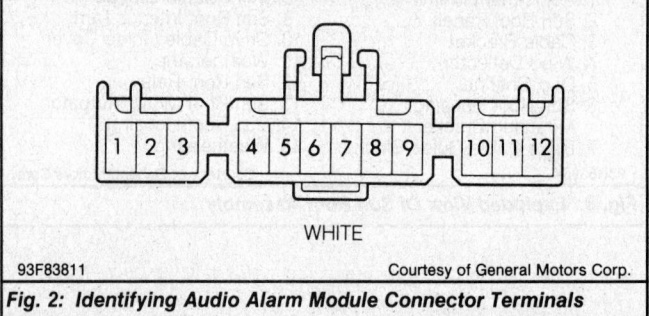

WHITE

93F83811   Courtesy of General Motors Corp.

Fig. 2: Identifying Audio Alarm Module Connector Terminals

8) If voltage is greater than 10 volts, check for open in Red/Blue wire between audio alarm module and junction block No. 3. Check for open in Red/Blue wire between junction block No. 3 and power accessory relay. Repair wire as necessary. If wire is good, replace junction block No. 3.
9) Connect test light from battery voltage to accessory power relay terminal No. 2 (White/Black wire). If test light comes on, replace accessory power relay. If test light comes on, check for open in White/Black wire between accessory power relay and junction connector No. 1. Check for open in White/Black wire between junction connector No. 1 and ground connector G200 (located behind left kick panel). Repair wire as necessary. If wire is good, replace junction connector No. 1.

LEFT FRONT WINDOW DOES NOT OPEN

1) Turn ignition on. Using test light, probe left front motor connector terminal No. 1 (Red wire; Green wire after connector). Depress and hold left front window control on power window master switch. If test light comes on, go to next step. If test light does not come on, check for open in Red wire (Green wire after connector) between power window master switch and left front window motor. If wire is okay, replace master window switch.

2) Ensure left front power window switch is released. Connect test light to battery voltage and probe left front power window motor connector terminal No. 2 (Green wire; Yellow wire after connector). If test light comes on, replace motor. If test light does not come on, check for open in Green wire (Yellow wire after connector) between power window master switch and motor. Repair wire as necessary. If wire is good, replace power window master switch.

LEFT FRONT WINDOW DOES NOT CLOSE

1) Turn ignition on. Pull up and hold left front power window switch. Using a test light, probe left front power window motor connector terminal No. 2 (Green wire; Yellow wire after connector). If test light comes on, go to next step. If test light does not come on, check for open in Green wire (Yellow wire after connector) between power window master switch and left front power window motor. If wire is okay, replace window switch.

2) Ensure power window switch is released. Connect test light to battery voltage and probe left front power window motor connector terminal No. 1 (Red wire). If test light comes on, replace motor. If test light does not come on, check for open in Yellow wire (Green wire after connector) between power window master switch and motor. Repair wire as necessary. If wire is good, replace power window master switch.

RIGHT FRONT WINDOW DOES NOT OPEN WITH MASTER OR RIGHT FRONT DOOR SWITCH

1) Turn ignition on. Using a test light, probe right front power window switch (located in right front door) terminal No. 2 (Blue/White wire). *See Fig. 3.* Depress right front power window switch in power window master switch (located in driver's door). If test light comes on, go to next step. If test light does not come on, Check for open in Blue/White wire between right front power window switch and master switch. Repair wire as necessary. If wire is good, replace power window master switch.

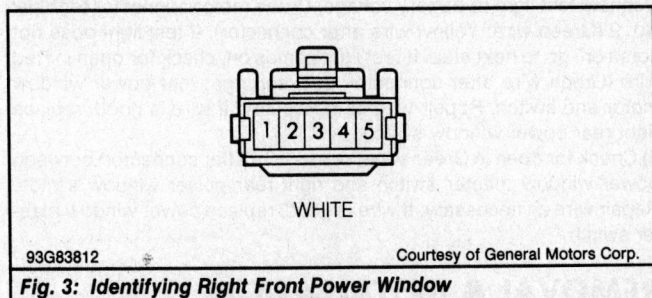

Fig. 3: Identifying Right Front Power Window Switch Connector Terminals

2) Probe right front power window motor connector terminal No. 1 (Red wire; Green wire after connector). *See Fig. 3.* Depress right front power window switch in master switch. If test light comes on, go to next step. If test light does not come on, check for open in Red wire (Green wire after connector) between right front power window switch and motor. Repair wire as necessary. If wire is good, replace right front power window switch.

3) Turn ignition to lock and unplug right front power window motor connector. Connect test light to battery voltage and probe motor connector terminal No. 2 (Green wire; Yellow wire after connector). *See Fig. 3.* If test light does not come on, go to next step. If test light comes on, replace right front power window motor.

4) Ensure right front and master power window switches are released. Connect test light to battery voltage and probe right front power window switch connector terminal No. 5 (Green/Red wire). If test light does not come on, go to next step. If test light comes on, check for open in Green wire (Yellow wire after connector) between right front power window switch and motor. Repair wire as necessary. If wire is good, right front power window switch.

5) Check for open in Green/Red wire between power window master switch and right front power window switch. Repair wire as necessary. If wire is good, replace power window master switch.

RIGHT FRONT WINDOW DOES NOT CLOSE WITH MASTER OR RIGHT FRONT DOOR SWITCH

1) Turn ignition on. Using a test light, probe right front power window switch (located in right front door) terminal No. 5 (Green/Red wire). *See Fig. 3.* Pull right front power window switch in power window master switch (located in driver's door) to UP position. If test light comes on, go to next step. If test light does not come on, Check for open in Green/Red wire between right front power window switch and master switch. Repair wire as necessary. If wire is good, replace power window master switch.

2) Probe right front power window motor connector terminal No. 2 (Green wire; Yellow wire after connector). Pull right front power window switch in power window master switch (located in driver's door) to UP position. If test light comes on, go to next step. If test light does not come on, check for open in Green wire (Yellow wire after connector) between right front power window switch and motor. Repair wire as necessary. If wire is good, replace right front power window switch.

3) Turn ignition off and unplug right front power window motor connector. Connect test light to battery voltage and probe motor connector terminal No. 1 (Red wire; Green wire after connector). If test light does not come on, go to next step. If test light comes on, replace right front power window motor.

4) Ensure right front and master power window switches are released. Connect test light to battery voltage and probe right front power window switch connector terminal No. 2 (Blue/White wire). *See Fig. 3.* If test light does not come on, go to next step. If test light comes on, check for open in Green wire (Yellow wire after connector) between right front power window switch and motor. Repair wire as necessary. If wire is good, right front power window switch.

5) Check for open in Blue/White wire between power window master switch and right front power window switch. Repair wire as necessary. If wire is good, replace power window master switch.

LEFT REAR WINDOW DOES NOT OPEN WITH MASTER OR LEFT REAR DOOR SWITCH

1) Turn ignition on. Using a test light, probe left rear power window switch (located in left rear door) terminal No. 2 (Blue/Black wire). *See Fig. 4.* Depress left rear power window switch in power window master switch (located in driver's door) to DOWN position. If test light comes on, go to next step. If test light does not come on, check for open in Blue/Black wire between left rear power window switch and master switch. Repair wire as necessary. If wire is good, replace power window master switch.

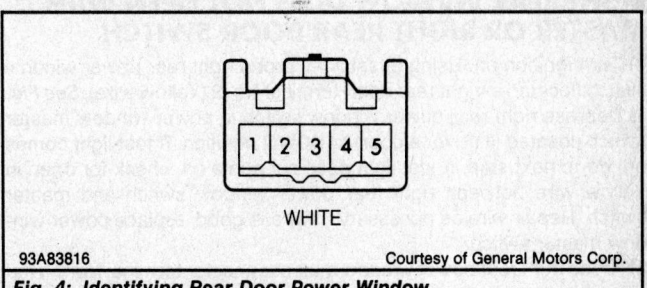

Fig. 4: Identifying Rear Door Power Window Switch Connector Terminals

2) Probe left rear power window motor connector terminal No. 1 (Red wire; Green wire after connector). Depress left rear power window switch in power window master switch (located in driver's door) to DOWN position. If test light comes on, go to next step. If test light does not come on, check for open in Red wire (Green wire after connector) between left rear power window switch and motor. Repair wire as necessary. If wire is good, replace left rear power window switch.

3) Turn ignition to lock and unplug left rear power window motor connector. Connect test light to battery voltage and probe motor connector terminal No. 2 (Green wire; Yellow wire after connector). If test light does not come on, go to next step. If test light comes on, replace left rear power window motor.

4) Ensure left rear and master power window switches are released. Connect test light to battery voltage and probe left rear power window switch connector terminal No. 4 (Red/Green wire). *See Fig. 4.* If test light does not come on, go to next step. If test light comes on, check for open in Green wire (Yellow wire after connector) between left rear power window switch and motor. Repair wire as necessary. If wire is good, replace left rear power window switch.

5) Check for open in Red/Green wire between power window master switch and left rear power window switch. Repair wire as necessary. If wire is good, replace power window master switch.

LEFT REAR WINDOW DOES NOT CLOSE WITH MASTER OR LEFT REAR DOOR SWITCH

1) Turn ignition on. Using a test light, probe left rear power window switch (located in left rear door) terminal No. 4 (Red/Green wire). *See Fig. 4.* Pull left rear power window switch in power window master switch (located in driver's door) to UP position. If test light comes on, go to next step. If test light does not come on, Check for open in Red/Green wire between left rear power window switch and master switch. Repair wire as necessary. If wire is good, replace power window master switch.

2) Probe left rear power window motor connector terminal No. 2 (Green wire; Yellow wire after connector). Pull left rear power window switch in power window master switch (located in driver's door) to UP position. If test light comes on, go to next step. If test light does not come on, check for open in Green wire (Yellow wire after connector) between left rear power window switch and motor. Repair wire as necessary. If wire is good, replace left rear power window switch.

3) Turn ignition to lock and unplug left rear power window motor connector. Connect test light to battery voltage and probe motor connector terminal No. 1 (Red wire; Green wire after connector). If test light does not come on, go to next step. If test light comes on, replace left rear power window motor.

4) Ensure left rear and master power window switches are released. Connect test light to battery voltage and probe left rear power window switch connector terminal No. 2 (Blue/Black wire). *See Fig. 4.* If test light does not come on, go to next step. If test light comes on, check for open in Green wire (Yellow wire after connector) between left rear power window switch and motor. Repair wire as necessary. If wire is good, left rear power window switch.

5) Check for open in Blue/Black wire between power window master switch and left rear power window switch. Repair wire as necessary. If wire is good, replace power window master switch.

RIGHT REAR WINDOW DOES NOT OPEN WITH MASTER OR RIGHT REAR DOOR SWITCH

1) Turn ignition on. Using a test light, probe right rear power window switch (located in right rear door) terminal No. 2 (Yellow wire). *See Fig. 4.* Depress right rear power window switch in power window master switch (located in driver's door) to DOWN position. If test light comes on, go to next step. If test light does not come on, check for open in Yellow wire between right rear power window switch and master switch. Repair wire as necessary. If wire is good, replace power window master switch.

2) Probe right rear power window motor connector terminal No. 1 (Red wire; Green wire after connector). Depress right rear power window switch in power window master switch (located in driver's door) to DOWN position. If test light comes on, go to next step. If test light does not come on, check for open in Green wire (Red wire after connector) between right rear power window switch and motor. Repair wire as necessary. If wire is good, replace right rear power window switch.

3) Turn ignition to lock and unplug right rear power window motor connector. Connect test light to battery voltage and probe motor connector terminal No. 2 (Green wire; Yellow after connector). If test light does not come on, go to next step. If test light comes on, replace right rear power window motor.

4) Ensure right rear and master power window switches are released. Connect test light to battery voltage and probe right rear power window switch connector terminal No. 4 (Red/Black wire). *See Fig. 4.* If test light does not come on, go to next step. If test light comes on, check for open in Green wire (Yellow wire after connector) between right rear power window switch and motor. Repair wire as necessary. If wire is good, right rear power window switch.

5) Check for open in Red/Black wire between power window master switch and right rear power window switch. Repair wire as necessary. If wire is good, replace power window master switch.

RIGHT REAR WINDOW DOES NOT CLOSE WITH MASTER OR RIGHT REAR DOOR SWITCH

1) Turn ignition on. Using a test light, probe right rear power window switch (located in right rear door) terminal No. 4 (Red/Black wire). *See Fig. 4.* Pull right rear power window switch in power window master switch (located in driver's door) to UP position. If test light comes on, go to next step. If test light does not come on, check for open in Red/Black wire between right rear power window switch and master switch. Repair wire as necessary. If wire is good, replace power window master switch.

2) Probe right rear power window motor connector terminal No. 2 (Green wire; Yellow wire after connector). Pull right rear power window switch in power window master switch (located in driver's door) to UP position. If test light comes on, go to next step. If test light does not come on, check for open in wiring between right rear power window switch and motor. Repair wire as necessary. If wire is good, replace right rear power window switch.

3) Turn ignition to lock and unplug right rear power window motor connector. Connect test light to battery voltage and probe motor connector terminal No. 1 (Red wire; Green wire after connector). If test light does not come on, go to next step. If test light comes on, replace right rear power window motor.

4) Ensure right rear and master power window switches are released. Connect test light to battery voltage. Probe motor connector terminal No. 2 (Green wire; Yellow wire after connector). If test light does not come on, go to next step. If test light comes on, check for open in Red wire (Green wire after connector) between right rear power window motor and switch. Repair wire as necessary. If wire is good, replace right rear power window switch.

5) Check for open in Green wire (Yellow wire after connector) between power window master switch and right rear power window switch. Repair wire as necessary. If wire is good, replace power window master switch.

REMOVAL & INSTALLATION

WINDOW MOTOR/REGULATOR ASSEMBLY

NOTE: On some applications, power window motor and regulator can only be serviced as an assembly.

Removal & Installation – 1) Disconnect negative battery cable. Remove armrest and door trim panel. Unplug power window switch connector. Pull water deflector away sufficiently to access window-to-regulator bolts. Remove window-to-regulator bolts and lift window from door.

2) Remove inner door brace. Remove 3 regulator mount bolts. Remove motor/regulator assembly. *See Fig. 5.* To install, reverse removal procedure.

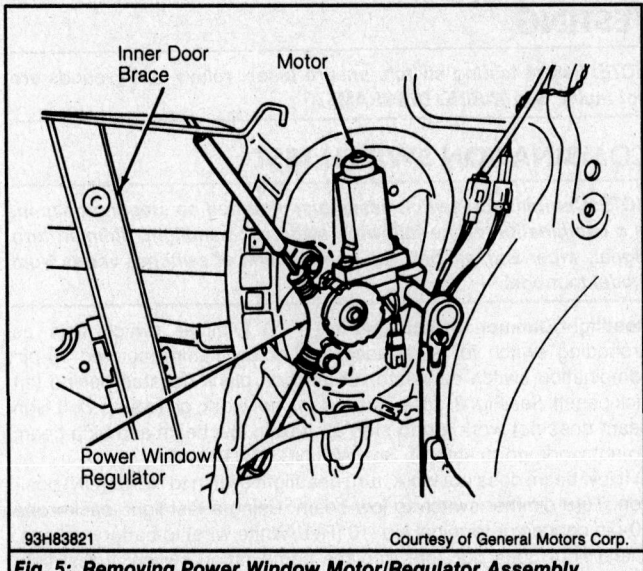

Inner Door Brace

Motor

Power Window Regulator

93H83821

Courtesy of General Motors Corp.

Fig. 5: Removing Power Window Motor/Regulator Assembly

WINDOW SWITCH

Removal & Installation (Master Switch) – Disconnect negative battery cable. Unclip armrest pad from armrest. Remove armrest mounting screws. Carefully pull armrest away from door trim panel. Unplug power window master/door lock switch connectors. Unclip and remove power window master/door lock switch assembly from armrest. To install, reverse removal procedure.

Removal & Installation (Passenger's Switch) – Disconnect negative battery cable. Remove armrest mounting screws and armrest. Remove door handle bezel. Release snap ring and remove window regulator handle. Unclip control rod from inside door handle. Unplug power window switch connector. Remove door trim panel. Remove power window switch from door trim panel. To install, reverse removal procedure.

WIRING DIAGRAM

NOTE: See ACCESSORIES & EQUIPMENT, Volume 5.

Metro, Prizm, Tracker

WARNING: Prizm is equipped with Supplemental Restraint System (SRS) with driver side and passenger side air bags. DO NOT apply electrical power to any component on steering column without disabling SRS. Before performing ANY tests or repairs on steering column switches, SRS MUST be disabled. See DISABLING & ACTIVATING SRS. Accidental air bag deployment could cause serious bodily injury.

DISABLING & ACTIVATING SRS

WARNING: Wait about 2 minutes after disabling SRS before servicing. System maintains SRS voltage for about 2 minutes. Servicing SRS before 2 minutes may cause accidental air bag deployment and possible personal injury.

Prizm – **1)** Ensure front wheels face straight ahead. Turn ignition switch to LOCK position. Remove CIG/RADIO fuse and IGN fuse from junction block. Locate driver side air bag Yellow 2-pin connector at base of steering column. *See Fig. 1.* Remove Connector Position Assurance (CPA) clip and disconnect Yellow 2-pin connector. Lower glove box and remove passenger side air bag connector cover located above glove box. *See Fig. 2.* Remove Connector Position Assurance (CPA) clip and disconnect Yellow 2-pin connector. Wait about 2 minutes before servicing.

2) To activate SRS, turn ignition switch to LOCK position. Connect Yellow 2-pin connectors and CPA clips at base of steering column and above glove box. Install IGN and CIG/RADIO fuses to junction block. Turn ignition switch to ACC or ON position and ensure air bag indicator illuminates for about 6 seconds, then turns off. See SYSTEM OPERATION CHECK in AIR BAG RESTRAINT SYSTEM article.

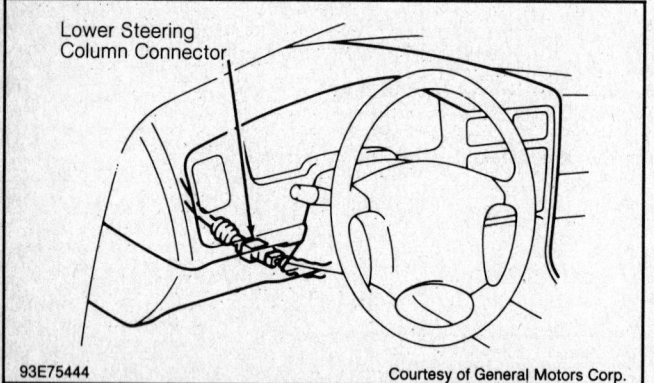

93E75444   Courtesy of General Motors Corp.
Fig. 1: Locating SRS 2-Pin Lower Steering Column Connector

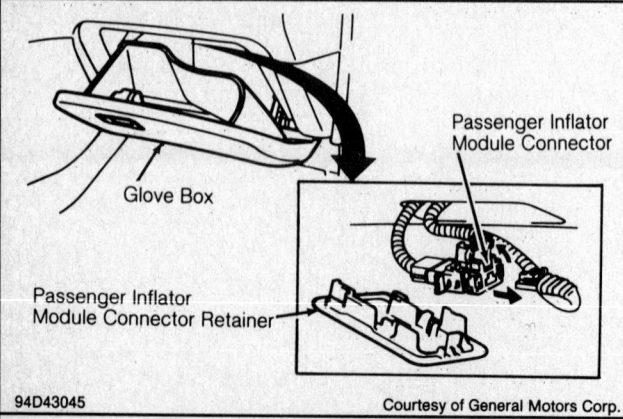

94D43045   Courtesy of General Motors Corp.
Fig. 2: Locating Passenger Side SRS 2-Pin Connector

TESTING

NOTE: Before testing switch, ensure fuses, relays and grounds are not faulty. See WIRING DIAGRAMS.

COMBINATION SWITCH TEST

NOTE: Combination switch assembly, mounted on steering column, is a combination of the following switches: headlight, dimmer, turn signal, wiper and washer. The combination of switches varies from model to model.

Headlight/Dimmer Switch (Metro) – **1)** Dimmer switch acts as grounding switch for all headlights. Locate Natural colored 10-pin combination switch connector at junction block (located behind left kick panel). *See Fig. 3.* If low beam does not work, go to step **2)**. If high beam does not work, go to step **3)**. If both low beam and high beam do not work, go to step **4)**. See WIRING DIAGRAMS.

2) If low beam does not work, turn headlight switch to HEAD (ON) position. Turn dimmer switch to low beam. Using a test light, backprobe 10-pin connector terminal No. 10 (Red/White wire) to battery voltage. If test light does not light, replace combination switch. If test light lights, check for an open in Red/White wire between junction block Natural colored 14-pin harness connector terminal No. 12 and headlights. If Red/White wire is okay, replace junction block.

3) If high beam does not work, turn headlight switch to HEAD (ON) position. Turn dimmer switch to high beam. Using a test light, backprobe 10-pin connector terminal No. 3 (Red wire) to battery voltage. If test light does not light, replace combination switch. If test light lights, check for an open in Red wire between junction block Natural colored 14-pin harness connector terminal No. 7 and headlights. If Red wire is okay, replace junction block.

4) If both low beam and high beam do not work, locate Natural colored 6-pin connector at bottom of junction block. Using a test light, backprobe 6-pin connector terminal No. 1 (Black wire) to battery voltage. If test light lights, replace combination switch. If test light does not light, replace junction block.

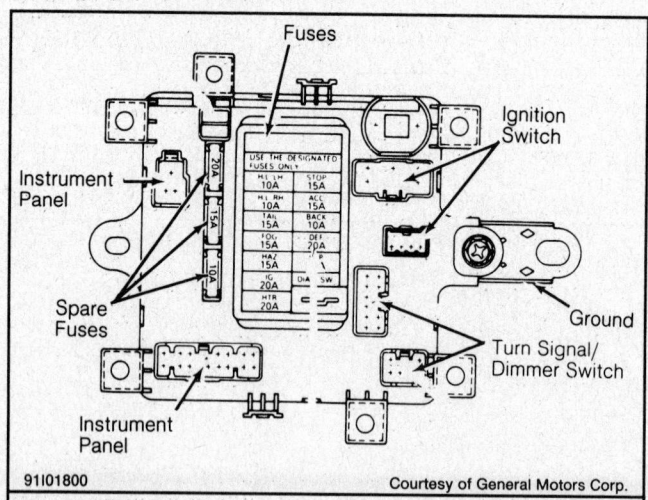

91I01800   Courtesy of General Motors Corp.
Fig. 3: Identifying Junction/Fuse Block Harness Connectors (Metro)

Headlight/Dimmer Switch (Prizm) – **1)** Headlight switch completes ground for headlight and taillight relays. High beam circuit ground is provided through dimmer switch.

2) Remove lower dash panel trim cover. Locate combination switch harness 14-pin connector near steering column. Turn headlight switch to HEAD (ON) position. Using a fused jumper wire, backprobe 14-pin connector terminal No. 12 (Red/Yellow wire) to ground. See COMBINATION SWITCH 14-PIN CONNECTOR TERMINALS (PRIZM) table. *See Fig. 4.* See WIRING DIAGRAMS. If high beams do not come on, go to next step. If high beams come on, go to step **4)**.

3) Locate Black 16-pin junction block No. 1 connector at lower left shroud behind kick panel. Using a fused jumper wire, backprobe 16-pin connector terminal No. 12 (Red/Yellow wire) to ground. If headlight high beams do not light, repair open in Red/Yellow wire between junction block No. 1 and headlight high beam Red/Yellow wire junction from headlights. If headlight high beams light, check for an open in Red/Yellow wire between junction block No. 1 and combination switch. If Red/Yellow wire is okay, replace junction block No. 1.

4) Using a test light, backprobe combination switch 14-pin connector terminal No. 9 (White/Black wire) and battery voltage. If test light lights, go to next step. If test light does not light, check for an open in White/Black wire between combination switch and White 6-pin junction connector No. 1 (attached to right instrument panel support brace) specification. If White/Black wire is okay, replace 6-pin junction connector No. 1.

5) Move dimmer switch forward to high beam position. Using a test light, backprobe combination 14-pin connector terminal No. 12 (Red/Yellow wire) to battery voltage. If test light does not light, replace combination switch. If test light lights, go to next step.

6) Move dimmer switch back to flash-to-pass position, and hold. Using a test light, backprobe combination switch 14-pin connector terminal No. 12 (Red/Yellow wire) to battery voltage and then from terminal No. 14 (Red/White wire) to battery voltage. If test light does not light, replace combination switch. If test light lights, check for an open in Red/White wire between 14-pin connector terminal No. 14 and Dark Gray 22-pin junction connector No. 2 (attached to junction block No. 3, behind center instrument panel) terminal No. 19. If Red/White wire is okay, replace Dark Gray 22-pin junction connector No. 2.

COMBINATION SWITCH 14-PIN CONNECTOR TERMINALS (PRIZM)

Terminal No.	Wire Color	Circuit
1	Green/White	Hazard
2	Lt. Green	Taillight Relay
3	Not Used	....
4	Not Used	....
5	Green/Black	Left Turn
6	Not Used	....
7	Not Used	....
8	Green/Yellow	Right Turn
9	White/Black	Ground
10	Green/Red	Horn Relay
11	White/Black	Ground
12	Red/Yellow	Headlight/High Beams
13	Red/White	Headlight Relay
14	Red/White	Headlight Relay

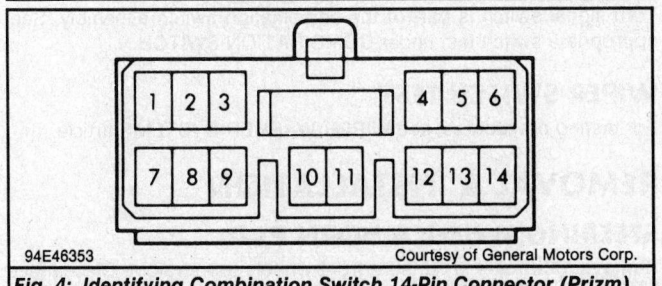

94E46353   Courtesy of General Motors Corp.

Fig. 4: Identifying Combination Switch 14-Pin Connector (Prizm)

Headlight/Dimmer Switch (Tracker) – 1) Headlight switch acts only as grounding switch for headlight circuits. Switch ground connection is behind left instrument panel, on support post above ECM. Ensure left and right headlight fuses, located in fuse block under left instrument panel, are good.

2) Turn headlights on (low-beam position). If headlights do not come on go to step **5)**. If headlights come on, push dimmer switch stalk forward to turn on high beams. If high beams do not come on, leave switch in this position and go to step **4)**. If high beams come on, go to next step.

3) Pull dimmer switch stalk backward to operate high-beam flash-to-pass position. If lights do not come on in this position, replace combination switch. If lights come on, combination switch is okay.

4) Remove left and right headlight fuses, located in fuse block under left instrument panel. Locate combination switch harness 20-pin connector behind instrument panel, near steering column. Using a DVOM, backprobe combination switch harness 20-pin connector from terminal No. 1 (Red wire) to ground and measure resistance. If resistance is more than .3 ohm, replace combination switch. If resistance is less than .3 ohm, switch is okay. Repair open in Red wire circuit to headlights. See appropriate wiring diagram under HEADLIGHT SYSTEMS in ACCESSORIES & EQUIPMENT. Install left and right headlight fuses.

5) If headlights did not come on, remove left and right headlight fuses. Locate combination switch harness 20-pin connector behind instrument panel, near steering column. Using a DVOM, backprobe combination switch harness 20-pin connector from terminal No. 20 (Black wire) to ground and measure resistance. If resistance is more than .3 ohm, repair Black wire between combination switch and ground. If resistance is less than .3 ohm, go to next step.

6) Using a DVOM, backprobe combination switch harness 20-pin connector from terminal No. 11 (Red/White wire) to ground and measure resistance. If resistance is more than .3 ohm, replace combination switch. If resistance is less than .3 ohm, repair open in Red/White wire between combination switch and junction of Red/White wire from headlights. See appropriate wiring diagram under HEADLIGHT SYSTEMS in ACCESSORIES & EQUIPMENT. Install left and right headlight fuses.

Turn Signal Switch (Metro) – 1) Disconnect switch harness connectors from junction/fuse block located under left lower dash panel. See Fig. 3. Move turn signal stalk to left-turn position.

2) Check for continuity between Green wire and Green/Red wire terminals of switch 5-pin connector. If no continuity exists, replace combination switch assembly. If continuity exists, go to next step.

3) Move turn signal stalk to right-turn position. Check for continuity between Green wire and Green/Yellow wire terminals of switch 5-pin connector. If no continuity exists, replace combination switch assembly.

Turn Signal Switch (Prizm) – 1) Ensure fuses, flasher and hazard switch are good before testing turn signal switch. Disconnect negative battery cable. Remove lower dash panel trim cover. Disconnect combination switch 14-pin harness connector near steering column.

2) Move turn signal stalk to left-turn position. Check for continuity between terminals No. 1 (Green/White wire) and No. 5 (Green/Black wire) of connector. See COMBINATION SWITCH 14-PIN CONNECTOR TERMINALS (PRIZM) table. See Fig. 4. If no continuity exists, replace combination switch assembly. If continuity exists, go to next step.

3) If continuity exists, move turn signal stalk to right-turn position. Check for continuity between terminals No. 1 (Green/White wire) and No. 8 (Green/Yellow wire). If no continuity exists, replace combination switch assembly.

Turn Signal Switch (Tracker) – 1) Before testing switch, ensure turn signal fuse and relay are good. Relay, used in place of flasher, is mounted on top of fuse block, under left side of instrument panel. Ensure hazard switch is off. Remove turn signal/back-up fuse from fuse block under left side of instrument panel.

2) Locate combination switch 20-pin harness connector under instrument panel, near steering column. Check for continuity between Yellow wire and Yellow/White wire terminals of switch connector. If no continuity exists, hazard switch is defective. Replace combination switch assembly. If continuity exists, go to next step.

3) Move turn signal stalk to left-turn position. Check for continuity between Green wire and Green/Red wire terminals of switch connector. If no continuity exists, replace combination switch assembly. If continuity exists, go to next step.

4) If continuity exists, move turn signal stalk to right-turn position. Check for continuity between Green wire and Green/Yellow wire terminals of switch connector. If no continuity exists, replace combination switch assembly.

HAZARD WARNING SWITCH TEST

NOTE: For Prizm, see HAZARD WARNING SWITCH TEST under TESTING in Instrument Panels article.

Metro – Ensure hazard fuse and turn signal flasher unit are okay. Using a test light, backprobe Green/Red and Green/Yellow wires at combination switch connector. If test light does not flash at each position, replace combination switch.

Tracker – **1)** Ensure hazard fuse and turn signal relay are okay. Relay, used in place of flasher, is mounted on top of fuse block, under left instrument panel. Remove hazard fuse from fuse block. Push hazard switch to ON position.

2) Locate combination switch 20-pin harness connector under instrument panel, near steering column. Check for continuity between White/Green wire and Yellow/White wire connector terminals. If no continuity exists, replace combination switch.

HEADLIGHT SWITCH TEST

Headlight switch is part of combination switch assembly. See appropriate switch test under COMBINATION SWITCH.

IGNITION SWITCH TEST

See IGNITION SWITCH TEST in STARTERS – REDUCTION GEAR article in ELECTRICAL.

HORN PAD SWITCH TEST

Metro – **1)** If horn does not sound, operate hazard flashers. If flashers operate, hazard fuse in fuse block under left dash panel is good. Using test light, backprobe horn relay connector terminals No. 1 (White/Red wire) and No. 2 (White/Red wire) to ground. If test light comes on, go to next step. If test light does not come on, check for an open in White/Red wire between horn relay and junction block or a poor connection at junction block. If wire and connection are okay, replace junction block. See WIRING DIAGRAMS.

2) Using a test light, backprobe between horn relay connector terminal No. 3 (Blue/Green wire) and battery voltage. Depress horn switch. If test light does not come on, go to step **4)**. If test light comes on, disconnect horn relay connector. Connect a fused jumper wire between horn relay connector terminals No. 2 (White/Red wire) and No. 4 (White wire). If horn sounds, replace horn relay. If horn does not sound, go to next step.

3) Remove fused jumper wire and using a test light, backprobe horn 2-pin connector Black wire to battery voltage. If test light comes on, check for an open in White wire between horn relay and horn. If White wire is okay, replace horn. If test light does not come on, check for an open in Black wire between horn and ground connection. See WIRING DIAGRAMS.

4) Locate junction block Natural colored 10-pin connector under instrument panel. Using a test light, backprobe from 10-pin connector terminal No. 7 (Blue/Green wire) to battery voltage. If test light comes on, check for an open in Blue/Green wire between junction block and horn relay. If Blue/Green wire is okay, replace junction block. If test light does not come on, go to next step.

5) Connect a test light from horn switch Black wire to battery voltage and depress horn switch. If test light does not light, replace horn switch. If test light comes on, check for an open in Blue/Green wire between horn brush/slip ring and junction block. If Blue/Green wire is okay, replace complete horn switch/center pad assembly. See STEERING WHEEL & HORN PAD under REMOVAL & INSTALLATION.

WARNING: Prizm is equipped with Supplemental Restraint System (SRS) with driver side and passenger side air bags. DO NOT apply electrical power to any component on steering column without disabling SRS. Before performing ANY tests or repairs on steering column switches, SRS MUST be disabled. See DISABLING & ACTIVATING SRS. Accidental air bag deployment could cause serious bodily injury.

Prizm – **1)** If horn does not sound, using a test light, backprobe fuse/relay box White 10-pin connector terminal No. 5 (White wire) to ground. If test comes on when horn switch is depressed, check for an open in White wire between fuse/relay box and horn. If White wire is okay, replace horn. If test light does not come on, go to next step. See WIRING DIAGRAMS.

2) Using a fused jumper wire, backprobe fuse/relay box White 10-pin connector terminal No. 9 (Green/Red wire) to ground. If horn does not sound, replace horn relay and retest system. If horn still does not sound, replace fuse/relay box. If horn sounds, go to next step.

3) Disable SRS. See DISABLING & ACTIVATING SRS. Disconnect SRS coil assembly White 6-pin connector. Using a test light, connect SRS coil assembly White 6-pin connector terminal No. 6 (Black wire) to battery voltage. See WIRING DIAGRAMS. Depress horn switch. If test light does not come on, replace horn switch. If test light comes on, check for an open in Green/Red wire between fuse/relay box and SRS coil assembly. If Green/Red wire is okay, replace SRS coil assembly. See STEERING WHEEL & HORN PAD under REMOVAL & INSTALLATION.

Tracker – **1)** Ensure stop/horn fuse is good by operating stop lights. Connect a fused jumper wire between horn relay connector terminals No. 2 (Green wire) and No. 4 (Green/Black wire). If horn sounds, remove fused jumper wire and go to next step. If horn does not sound, ensure horn operates and Green/Black wire between horn and horn relay is okay and Black ground wire from horn is okay.

2) Using a DVOM, backprobe horn relay connector terminal No. 3 (Blue/Green wire). See WIRING DIAGRAMS. Depress horn switch and measure resistance. If resistance is greater than one ohm, go to next step. If resistance is less than one ohm, connect a test light from horn relay connector terminal No. 1 (Green wire) to ground. If test light lights, replace horn relay. If test light does not light, repair open in Green wire between horn relay connector terminal No. 1 and terminal No. 2, and fuse block.

3) Locate combination switch harness 20-pin connector under instrument panel, near steering column. Using a DVOM, backprobe 20-pin connector terminal No. 4 (Blue/Green wire) to ground. See WIRING DIAGRAMS. Depress horn switch and measure resistance. If resistance is less than one ohm, repair open in Blue/Green wire between 20-pin connector and horn relay connector terminal No. 3. If resistance is greater than one ohm, check for an open between 20-pin connector terminal No. 4 (Blue/Green wire) and horn switch Black wire. If no open is found, replace horn switch. See WIRING DIAGRAMS.

TURN SIGNAL SWITCH TEST

Turn signal switch is part of the combination switch assembly. See appropriate switch test under COMBINATION SWITCH.

WIPER SWITCH TEST

For testing procedures, see WIPER/WASHER SYSTEMS article.

REMOVAL & INSTALLATION

STEERING WHEEL & HORN PAD

Removal (Metro) – **1)** Ensure front wheels are straight. Disconnect negative battery cable. Pull horn pad assembly from steering wheel. *See Fig. 5.* Remove steering wheel retaining nut.

2) Remove contact plate screws. Disconnect wires and remove contact plate. Mark steering wheel and shaft for reassembly reference. Using steering wheel puller, remove steering wheel. *See Fig 8.*

Installation – **1)** Align reference marks made during removal, and install steering wheel. Install retaining nut on shaft. Tighten retaining nut to specification. See TORQUE SPECIFICATIONS.

2) Connect horn wires and install contact plate. Ensure wires run through center of plate, not underneath it. Install horn switch/center pad assembly on contact plate. Connect negative battery cable.

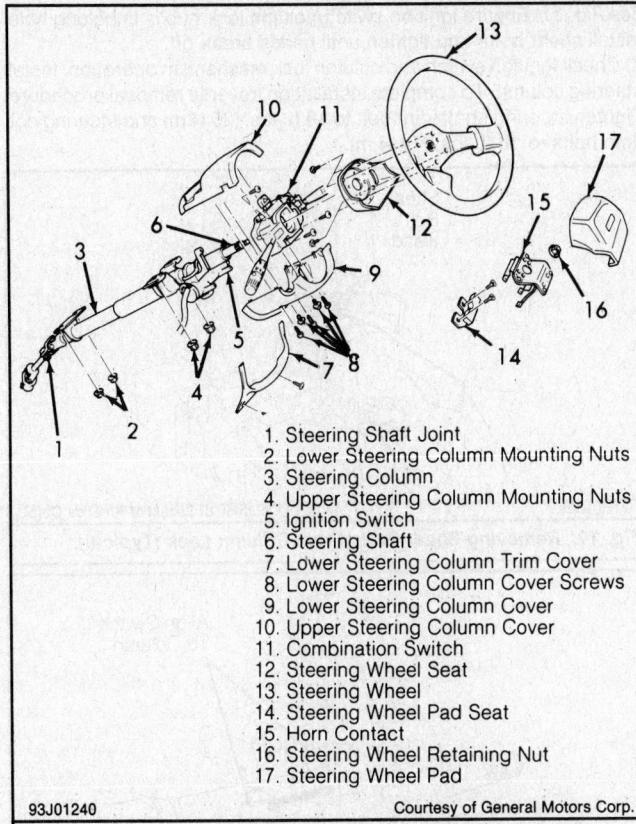

1. Steering Shaft Joint
2. Lower Steering Column Mounting Nuts
3. Steering Column
4. Upper Steering Column Mounting Nuts
5. Ignition Switch
6. Steering Shaft
7. Lower Steering Column Trim Cover
8. Lower Steering Column Cover Screws
9. Lower Steering Column Cover
10. Upper Steering Column Cover
11. Combination Switch
12. Steering Wheel Seat
13. Steering Wheel
14. Steering Wheel Pad Seat
15. Horn Contact
16. Steering Wheel Retaining Nut
17. Steering Wheel Pad

93J01240   Courtesy of General Motors Corp.

Fig. 5: Exploded View Of Steering Column Assembly (Metro)

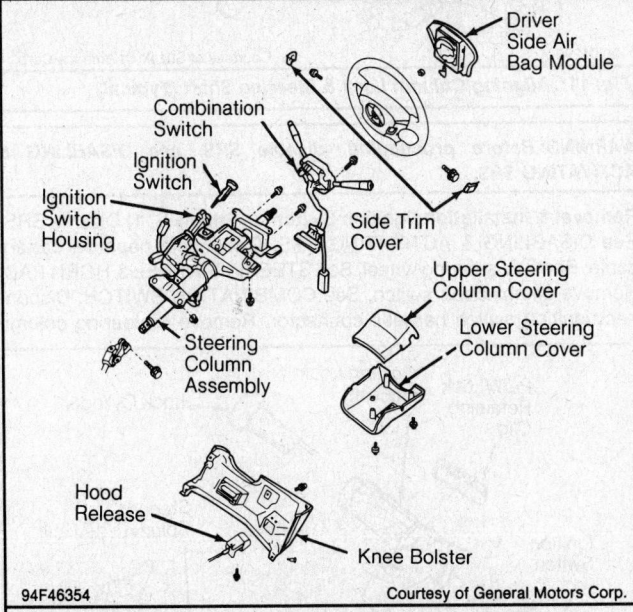

94F46354   Courtesy of General Motors Corp.

Fig. 6: Exploded View Of Steering Column Assembly (Prizm)

WARNING: On Prizm, before proceeding, see DISABLING & ACTIVATING SRS.

Removal (Prizm) – 1) Disable SRS, see DISABLING & ACTIVATING SRS. Ensure front wheels are straight. Remove 2 side trim covers, located behind steering wheel, from steering column. Remove 2 Torx head screws. Release Connector Position Assurance (CPA) and disconnect upper steering column connector. Remove driver side air bag module. See Fig. 6. Disconnect horn switch and cruise control (if equipped) connector.

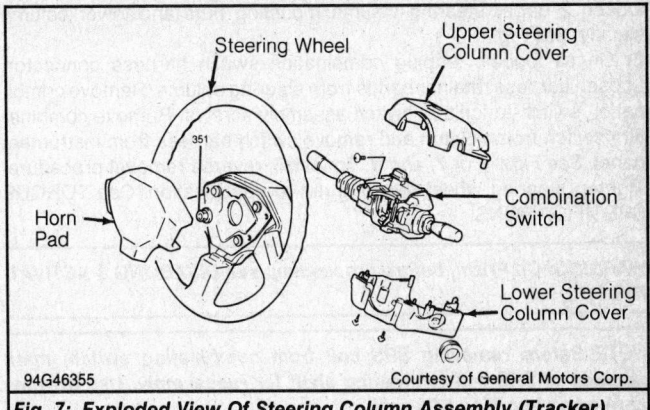

94G46355   Courtesy of General Motors Corp.

Fig. 7: Exploded View Of Steering Column Assembly (Tracker)

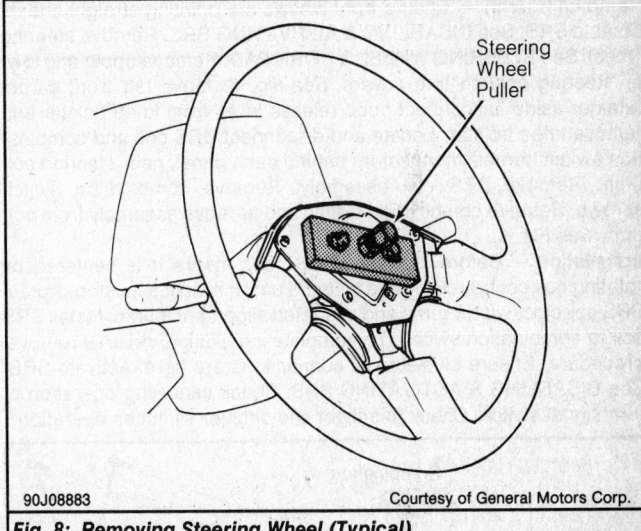

90J08883   Courtesy of General Motors Corp.

Fig. 8: Removing Steering Wheel (Typical)

2) Remove steering wheel retaining nut. Mark steering wheel and shaft for reassembly reference. Using steering wheel puller, remove steering wheel. See Fig. 8.

Installation – 1) Align steering wheel and shaft reference marks made during removal. Install steering wheel and retaining nut on shaft. 2) Tighten retaining nut to specification. See TORQUE SPECIFICATIONS. Connect horn switch and cruise control (if equipped) connectors. Connect upper steering column connector and secure CPA. Install driver side air bag module and tighten Torx head screws to specification. See TORQUE SPECIFICATIONS. Check steering wheel center point. Activate SRS. See DISABLING & ACTIVATING SRS.

Removal (Tracker) – Ensure front wheels are straight. Disconnect negative battery cable. Pull horn pad assembly from steering wheel. See Fig. 7. Remove steering wheel retaining nut. Scribe mark on shaft and steering wheel for reassembly reference. Using steering wheel puller, remove steering wheel. See Fig. 8.

Installation – Align reference marks made during removal. Install steering wheel and retaining nut on shaft. Tighten retaining nut to specification. See TORQUE SPECIFICATIONS. Install horn pad assembly to steering wheel contact plate.

COMBINATION SWITCH

NOTE: Combination switch assembly, mounted on steering column, is a combination of the following switches: headlight, dimmer, turn signal, wiper and washer. The combination of switches varies from model to model.

Removal & Installation (Metro & Tracker) – 1) Remove steering wheel. See STEERING WHEEL & HORN PAD. Remove upper and lower steering column covers and lower dash panel cover. On Metro, loosen 2 upper steering column mounting nuts and lower column slightly. *See Fig. 5.*

2) On all models, unplug combination switch harness connector. Loosen harness retainer bands from steering column. Remove combination switch-to-ignition switch assembly screws. Remove combination switch from column and remove switch harness from instrument panel. *See Figs. 5 or 7, and 9.* To install, reverse removal procedure. Tighten steering wheel retaining nut to specification. See TORQUE SPECIFICATIONS.

WARNING: On Prizm, before proceeding, see DISABLING & ACTIVATING SRS.

NOTE: Before removing SRS coil from combination switch, mark position of SRS coil to steering shaft for reassembly. Use extreme care when handling SRS coil.

Removal (Prizm) – Ensure front wheels are pointing straight ahead. Disable SRS. See DISABLING & ACTIVATING SRS. Remove steering wheel. See STEERING WHEEL & HORN PAD. Remove upper and lower steering column trim covers. *See Fig. 6.* Move left front carpet retainer aside, disconnect hood release lever from knee bolster and remove knee bolster. Locate and disconnect SRS coil and combination switch harness connectors behind dash panel, near steering column. Remove SRS coil assembly. Remove combination switch screws. Remove combination switch and harness assembly from column. *See Fig. 9.*

Installation – Before installing SRS coil, ensure it is centered by rotating coil counterclockwise by hand until it reaches its stop. Rotate SRS coil clockwise 3 turns and align Red alignment marks. Install SRS coil to combination switch. To complete installation, reverse removal procedure. Ensure all electrical connections are tight. Activate SRS. See DISABLING & ACTIVATING SRS. Check canceling operation of turn signal switch. Check headlight and dimmer switches operation.

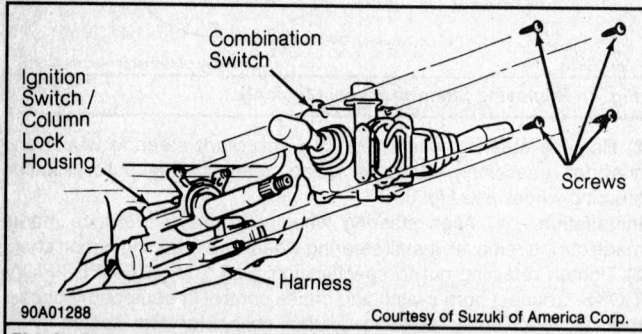

Fig. 9: Removing Combination Switch (Typical)

HEADLIGHT SWITCH

Removal & Installation (Metro, Prizm & Tracker) – Headlight switch is part of the combination switch assembly. See COMBINATION SWITCH.

IGNITION SWITCH & LOCK CYLINDER

Removal (Metro) – **1)** Remove steering wheel. See STEERING WHEEL & HORN PAD. Remove combination switch assembly. See COMBINATION SWITCH.

2) Disconnect ignition switch harness connectors from junction/fuse block. *See Fig. 3.* Remove 4 steering column mounting bolts. Remove retaining bolt from upper steering shaft joint. Remove steering column. *See Fig. 5.*

3) Using chisel, create slots on top of mounting bolts, and using a screwdriver, remove 2 mounting bracket shear bolt heads. DO NOT damage ignition switch housing. Remove ignition switch/column lock housing from column.

Installation – **1)** Ensure ignition switch is in LOCK position. Align ignition switch/column lock housing with oblong hole in steering shaft.

See Fig. 11. Ensure ignition switch/column lock hub is in oblong hole. Install shear bolts and tighten until heads break off.

2) Check ignition switch and column lock mechanism operation. Install steering column. To complete installation, reverse removal procedure. Tighten steering shaft joint bolt to 18 ft. lbs. (25 N.m) and steering column bolts to 10 ft. lbs. (14 N.m).

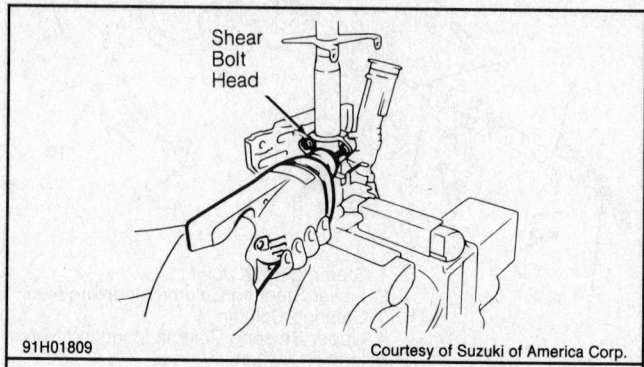

Fig. 10: Removing Shear Bolts From Column Lock (Typical)

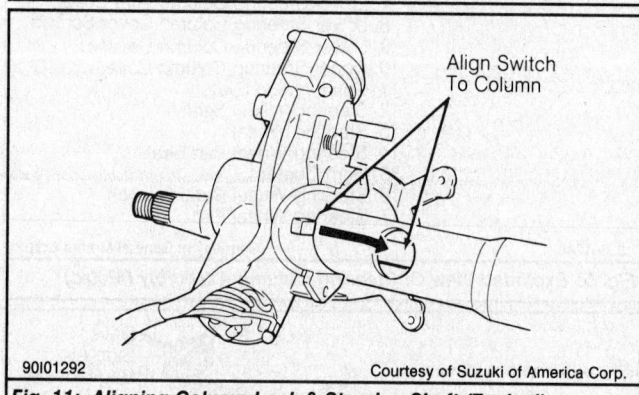

Fig. 11: Aligning Column Lock & Steering Shaft (Typical)

WARNING: Before proceeding, disable SRS. see DISABLING & ACTIVATING SRS.

Removal & Installation (Ignition Switch – Prizm) – **1)** Disable SRS. See DISABLING & ACTIVATING SRS. Disconnect negative battery cable. Remove steering wheel. See STEERING WHEEL & HORN PAD. Remove combination switch. See COMBINATION SWITCH. Disconnect ignition switch harness connector. Remove 4 steering column

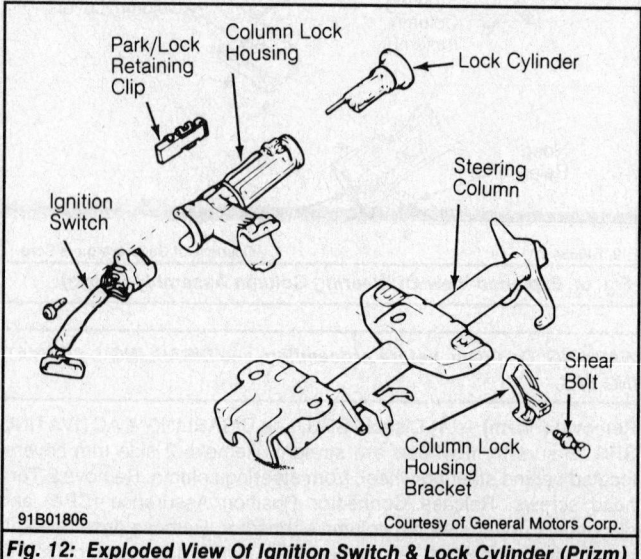

Fig. 12: Exploded View Of Ignition Switch & Lock Cylinder (Prizm)

mounting bolts and nuts. Remove retaining bolt from upper steering shaft joint. Remove steering column. Mount steering column in a soft-jawed vise. *See Figs. 6 and 9.*

2) Using center punch and power drill with 1/8-5/32" (3-4 mm) drill bit, drill out 2 mounting bracket shear bolt heads. *See Figs. 10 and 12.* Using a bolt extractor, remove shear bolt heads. Remove ignition switch/lock housing from column. To install, reverse removal procedure. Tighten ignition switch shear bolts until bolt heads break off.

Removal & Installation (Lock Cylinder – Prizm) – Remove ignition switch. See IGNITION SWITCH – PRIZM. Install key and turn ignition switch to ACC position. Using small punch, push down lock pin and pull lock set from ignition switch housing. *See Fig. 13.* To install, reverse removal procedure. Activate SRS. See DISABLING & ACTIVATING SRS.

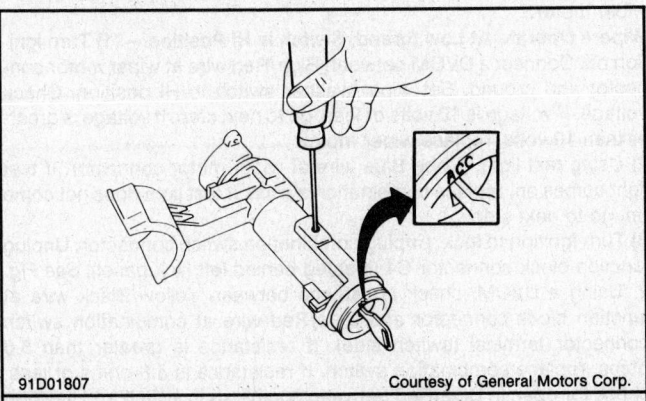

91D01807   Courtesy of General Motors Corp.

Fig. 13: Removing Ignition Lock Cylinder (Prizm)

Removal (Tracker) – 1) Disconnect negative battery cable. Remove steering wheel. See STEERING WHEEL & HORN PAD. Remove lower dash trim cover and both steering column covers. Disconnect ignition switch harness connector from behind instrument panel, near steering column.

2) Remove steering column upper bracket bolts. Remove lower steering shaft joint bolt. Remove steering column. Mount steering column in a soft-jawed vise.

3) Using chisel, create slots on top of mounting bolts, and using a screwdriver, remove 2 mounting bracket shear bolt heads. Use care not to damage aluminum ignition switch housing. Turn key to ON or ACC position. Remove ignition switch/lock housing from column.

Installation – 1) Ensure ignition switch is in LOCK position. Align ignition switch/column lock housing with oblong hole in steering shaft. *See Fig. 11.* Ensure ignition switch/column lock hub is in oblong hole. Tighten ignition switch shear bolts until bolt heads break off.

2) Check ignition switch and column lock mechanism operation. Install steering column. To complete installation, reverse removal procedure. Tighten steering shaft joint bolt to 18 ft. lbs. (25 N.m) and steering column bolts to 10 ft. lbs. (14 N.m).

TURN SIGNAL SWITCH

Removal & Installation – Turn signal switch is part of the combination switch. See COMBINATION SWITCH.

WIPER SWITCH

Removal & Installation (Metro, Prizm & Tracker) – Wiper switch is part of the combination switch. See COMBINATION SWITCH.

TORQUE SPECIFICATIONS

TORQUE SPECIFICATIONS

Application	Ft. Lbs. (N.m)
Steering Wheel Nut	
Metro & Tracker	24 (33)
Prizm	25 (34)
Steering Column Mounting Bolts & Nuts	
Metro & Tracker	10 (14)
Prizm	19 (26)
Steering Shaft Joint Pinch Bolts	
Metro & Tracker	18 (25)
Prizm	26 (35)
	INCH Lbs. (N.m)
Air Bag Module	
Prizm (Driver Side)	78 (9)

WIRING DIAGRAMS

NOTE: See ACCESSORIES & EQUIPMENT, Volume 5.

Metro, Prizm, Tracker

DESCRIPTION

Front windshield wipers are either 2-speed or 3-speed type. The optional 3-speed wiper system includes an intermittent wipe cycle. Windshield washer electric pump is a separate unit, mounted in bottom of windshield washer reservoir. An optional one-speed rear wiper/washer system is available on all models except Prizm.

TESTING

NOTE: Before testing, ensure fuses, circuit breakers, relays and grounds are good. Illustrations are not available from manufacturer for all connectors. Connectors are illustrated, when possible. To identify connectors, terminals and circuits, see WIRING DIAGRAMS.

FRONT WIPER SYSTEM TESTS (METRO)

Wipers & Washer Pump Inoperative – Turn ignition on. Using a test light, probe Yellow/Black wire at junction block connector (located behind left kick panel). If test light comes on, replace combination switch. If test light does not come on, replace junction block.

Washer Pump Inoperative – Turn ignition on. Using a test light, probe Blue/Black wire at washer pump connector (located at left front of engine compartment, under washer reservoir). Operate switch lever. If test light comes on, check for open in Black wire between washer pump and ground. Repair wire as necessary. If wire is okay, replace front washer pump. If test light does not come on, check for open in Blue/Black wire between combination switch and washer pump. Repair wire as necessary. If wire is okay, replace combination switch.

Washer Operates; Wipers Do Not Complete One Full Sweep – 1) Turn ignition on. Using a test light, probe Blue wire at wiper motor connector. Operate switch lever. If test light comes on, go to next step. If test light does not come on, check Blue wire for open between wiper motor and combination switch. Repair wire as necessary. If wire is okay, replace combination switch.

2) Using a test light, probe Yellow/Blue wire at wiper motor connector. If test light comes on, got to next step. If test light does not come on, Check for open in Yellow/Blue wire between wiper motor connector and junction block connector C8 (terminal No. 8). *See Fig. 1.* Repair wire as necessary. If wire is okay, replace junction block.

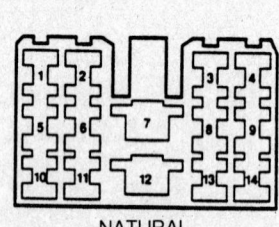

NATURAL

CAVITY	WIRE COLOR	CIRCUIT
1	WHT/RED	HAZ FUSE/HORN RELAY
2	—	NOT USED
3	BLU/GRN	HORN SWITCH/HORN RELAY
4	GRN/YEL	RH FRONT TURN LAMP
5	PPL/YEL	ECM DIAGNOSTIC REQUEST SIGNAL
6	YEL	BACK FUSE
7	RED	HEADLAMPS
8	YEL/BLU	WIP FUSE/FRONT WIPER MOTOR
9	GRN/RED	LH FRONT TURN LAMP
10	WHT	TAIL FUSE
11	—	NOT USED
12	RED/WHT	HEADLAMPS
13	RED/YEL	LIGHT SWITCH
14	—	NOT USED

93J83377 93A83378   Courtesy of General Motors Corp.

Fig. 1: Identifying Junction Block Connector C8 Terminals

3) Manually move wipers out of park position. Using a test light, probe Blue/White wire at motor connector. If test light comes on, check for open in Blue/White wire combination switch and wiper motor. Repair wire as necessary. If wire is okay, replace combination switch. If test light does not come on, replace wiper motor.

Wipers Operate; Wiper Switch Turned Off – Unplug junction block connector C8 (located behind left kick panel). *See Fig. 1.* Turn ignition on. If wipers stop, replace wiper motor. If wipers do not stop, check for short circuit to voltage in Blue/Red wire between combination switch and wiper motor. If wire is okay, replace combination switch.

Wipers Operate At High Speed; Switch In LO Position – Turn ignition on. Set wiper/washer switch to LO position. Using test light, probe Blue/Red wire at wiper motor connector. If test light comes on, replace combination switch. If test light does not come on, replace wiper motor.

Wipers Operate At Low Speed; Switch In HI Position – 1) Turn ignition on. Connect a DVOM between Blue/Red wire at wiper motor connector and ground. Set wiper/washer switch to HI position. Check voltage. If voltage is 10 volts or less, go to next step. If voltage is greater than 10 volts, replace wiper motor.

2) Using test light, probe Blue wire at wiper motor connector. If test light comes on, replace combination switch. If test light does not come on, go to next step.

3) Turn ignition to lock. Unplug combination switch connector. Unplug junction block connector C4 (located behind left kick panel). *See Fig. 2.* Using a DVOM, check resistance between Yellow/Black wire at junction block connector and Blue/Red wire at combination switch connector terminal (switch side). If resistance is greater than 5.0 ohms, replace combination switch. If resistance is 5.0 ohms or less, check for open in Blue/Red between combination switch and junction block connector C4. If wire is okay, replace wiper motor.

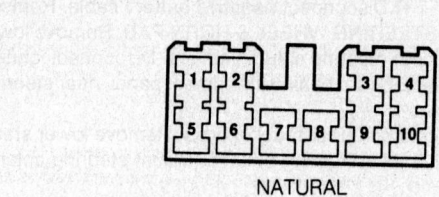

NATURAL

CAVITY	WIRE COLOR	CIRCUIT
1	YEL/BLU	HAZARD LAMPS POWER FEED
2	—	NOT USED
3	RED	HEADLAMPS/HIGH BEAMS
4	WHT	TAIL FUSE
5	BLU	PARKING LAMPS
6	—	NOT USED
7	BLU/GRN	HORN RELAY
8	YEL/BLK	WIP FUSE
9	PNK/YEL	BACK FUSE
10	RED/WHT	HEADLAMPS/LOW BEAMS

93B83379 93E83380   Courtesy of General Motors Corp.

Fig. 2: Identifying Junction Block Connector C4 Terminals

Wipers Do Not Operate; Switch In HI Position – Turn ignition on. Using test light, probe Blue/Red wire at wiper motor connector. Set wiper/washer switch to HI position. If test light comes on, replace wiper motor. If test light does not come on, check for open in Blue/Red wire between combination switch and wiper motor. If wire is okay, replace combination switch.

NOTE: The following procedure is used only on vehicles equipped with pulse (intermittent) wiper system.

Wipers Do Not Operate; Switch Set To INT – Using a test light, connect Black wire at junction block connector C3 (located behind left kick panel) to battery voltage. If test light comes on, replace combination switch. If test light does not come on, replace junction block.

REAR WIPER SYSTEM TESTS (METRO)

Wiper & Washer Pump Inoperative – Turn ignition on. Using a test light, probe Yellow/Blue wire at wiper/washer switch connector. If test light comes on, replace wiper/washer switch. If test light does not come on, check for open in Yellow/Blue wire between junction block (Located behind left kick panel) and wiper/washer switch (located in instrument panel to right of steering column). If wire is okay, replace junction block.

Washer Pump Inoperative – Turn ignition on. Using a test light, probe Black/Green wire at washer pump connector. Press and hold washer switch. If test light comes on, check for open in Black wire between washer pump and ground. If wire is okay, replace washer pump. If test light does not come on, check for open in Black/Green wire between rear wiper/washer switch and washer pump. Repair wire as necessary. If wire is okay, replace wiper/washer switch.

Wiper Motor Inoperative – Turn ignition and rear wiper on. Using a test light, probe Orange wire at wiper motor connector. If test light comes on, check for open in Black wire between wiper motor and ground. Repair wire as necessary. If wire is okay, replace wiper/washer switch. If test light does not come on, check for open in Orange wire between wiper/washer switch and wiper motor. Repair wire as necessary. If wire is okay, replace wiper/washer switch.

Wiper Does Not Return To Park Position – 1) Turn ignition on. Using a test light, probe Yellow wire at wiper motor connector. If test light comes on, go to next step. If test light does not come on, check for open in Yellow/Blue wire between junction block and wiper motor. Repair wire as necessary. If wire is okay, replace junction block.
2) Manually move wiper from park position. Using a test light, probe Light Green wire (Blue/Green, then Blue after splices) at wiper/washer switch connector. If test light comes on, replace wiper/washer switch. If test light does not come on, check for open in Blue/Green wire between wiper/washer switch and motor. Repair wire as necessary. If wire is okay, replace wiper motor.

Wiper Motor Runs Continuously; Ignition On – 1) Unplug junction block connector C10 (located behind left kick panel). Turn ignition on. If wiper operates, go to next step. If wiper does not operate, replace rear wiper motor.
2) Turn ignition to lock. Unplug wiper/washer switch connector. Turn ignition on. If wiper operates, repair short to battery voltage in Orange wire between wiper/washer switch and wiper motor. If wiper does not operate, check for short to voltage in Blue/Green wire between wiper/washer switch and wiper motor. If wire is okay, replace wiper/washer switch.

WIPER SYSTEM TESTS (PRIZM)

Washer Pump Does Not Operate – 1) Turn ignition on. Using a test light, probe Blue wire at washer pump connector. If test light comes on, go to next step. If test light does not come on, check for open in Blue wire between junction block No. 1 connector C2 (located behind left kick panel) and windshield washer pump motor (located at left front of engine compartment, under washer reservoir). See Fig. 3. Repair wire as necessary. If wire is okay, replace junction block No. 1.
2) Connect fused jumper wire from Blue/Yellow wire at combination switch to ground. If pump operates, go to next step. If pump does not operate, check for open in Blue/Yellow wire between washer pump and combination switch. If wire is okay, replace windshield washer pump.
3) Connect a test light between the White/Black wire at junction connector No. 1 (located under center of instrument panel) and battery voltage. If test light comes on, go to next step. If test light does not come on, check for open in White/Black wire between junction connector No. 1 and ground. Repair wire as necessary. If wire is okay, replace junction connector No. 1.
4) Check for open in White/Black wire between combination switch and junction connector No. 1. Repair wire as necessary. If wire is okay, replace combination switch.

Wipers Do Not Operate; Switch In Any Position – 1) Turn ignition on. Using a test light, probe Blue/White wire at combination switch. If test light comes on, go to next step. If test light does not come on, check for open in Blue wire between wiper motor and combination switch.

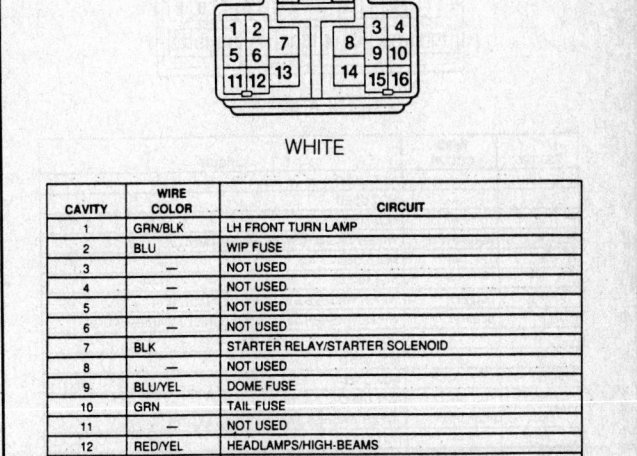

CAVITY	WIRE COLOR	CIRCUIT
1	GRN/BLK	LH FRONT TURN LAMP
2	BLU	WIP FUSE
3	—	NOT USED
4	—	NOT USED
5	—	NOT USED
6	—	NOT USED
7	BLK	STARTER RELAY/STARTER SOLENOID
8	—	NOT USED
9	BLU/YEL	DOME FUSE
10	GRN	TAIL FUSE
11	—	NOT USED
12	RED/YEL	HEADLAMPS/HIGH-BEAMS
13	BLK/ORN	IGNITION SWITCH
14	BLK/RED	FUSIBLE LINK AM2/IGNITION SWITCH
15	BLK/ORN	IGN FUSE
16	GRN/YEL	RH FRONT TURN LAMP

93A83386 93B83387   Courtesy of General Motors Corp.

Fig. 3: Identifying Junction Block No. 1 Connector C2 Terminals

Repair wire as necessary. If wire is okay, replace junction block No. 1. connector C2. See Fig. 3.
2) Using a test light, probe Blue/Black wire at combination switch. Set wiper/washer switch in LO position. If test light comes on, check for open in White/Black wire combination switch and ground. Repair wire as necessary. If wire is okay, replace windshield wiper motor. If test light does not come on, replace combination switch.

Wipers Sweep, But Do Not Return To Park Position – 1) Turn ignition on. Using test light, probe Blue wire at wiper motor connector. If test light comes on, go to next step. If test light does not come on, check for open in Blue wire between junction block No. 1 (located behind kick panel) and wiper motor. Repair wire as necessary. If wire is okay, replace junction block No. 1. connector C2.
2) Turn ignition to lock. Unplug combination switch connector C1. Connect DVOM between Red/Blue and Blue/Black wires at connector. See Fig. 4. Ensure wiper/washer switch is in OFF position. Check resistance. If resistance is 3.0 ohms or less, check for open in Blue/White wire between combination switch and wiper motor. If resistance is greater than 3.0 ohms, replace combination switch.

Wipers Continue Operation; Wiper Switch Turned Off – 1) Turn ignition on. Using test light, probe Blue/Orange wire at wiper motor connector. If test light does not come on, go to next step. If test light comes on, check for short circuit to battery voltage in Blue/Orange wire between combination switch and wiper motor. Repair wire as necessary. If wire is okay, replace combination switch.
2) Turn ignition to lock. Unplug wiper motor connector. Probe Blue/Black wire at wiper motor connector. If test light comes on, replace combination switch. If test light does not come on replace wiper motor.

Wipers Operate At High Speed; Switch In LO Position – Unplug wiper motor connector. Turn ignition on. Set wiper/washer switch to LO position. Using test light, probe Blue/Orange wire at wiper motor connector. If test light comes on, check for short to battery voltage in Blue/Orange wire between combination switch and wiper motor. Repair wire as necessary. If wire is okay, replace combination switch. If test light does not come on, replace wiper motor.

Wipers Do Not Operate; Switch In HI Position – Turn ignition on. Using test light, probe Blue/Orange wire at wiper motor connector. Set wiper/washer switch in HI position. If test light comes on, replace wiper motor. If test light does not come on, check for open in Blue/Orange wire between combination switch and wiper motor. Repair wire as necessary. If wire is okay, replace combination switch.

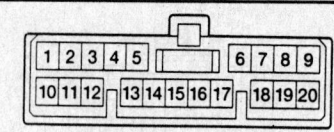

BLACK

CAVITY	WIRE COLOR	CIRCUIT
1	—	NOT USED
2	—	NOT USED
3	—	NOT USED
4	BLU/WHT	WIPER WASHER SWITCH/WIPER MOTOR
5	—	NOT USED
6	—	NOT USED
7	BLU/BLK	WIPER WASHER SWITCH/WIPER MOTOR
8	BLU/YEL	WIPER WASHER SWITCH/WINDSHIELD WASHER PUMP
9	—	NOT USED
10	—	NOT USED
11	—	NOT USED
12	—	NOT USED
13	BLU/ORN	WIPER WASHER SWITCH/WIPER MOTOR
14	—	NOT USED
15	WHT/BLU	CRUISE CONTROL SWITCH/CRUISE CONTROL MODULE
16	WHT/BLK	WIPER WASHER SWITCH – G200
17	GRN/BLK	CRUISE CONTROL SWITCH/CRUISE CONTROL MODULE
18	BLU	WIP FUSE
19	—	NOT USED
20	WHT/BLK	CRUISE CONTROL SWITCH – G204

93G83382 93H83383   Courtesy of General Motors Corp.

Fig. 4: Identifying Combination Switch Terminals

Wipers Operate At Lo Speed; Switch In HI Position – 1) Turn ignition on. Connect a DVOM between Blue/Orange wire at wiper motor connector and ground. Set wiper/washer switch to HI position. Measure voltage. If voltage is less than 10 volts, go to next step. If voltage is greater than 10 volts, replace wiper motor.
2) Turn ignition to lock. Unplug combination switch connector C1. *See Fig. 4.* Using a DVOM, check resistance between combination switch terminals No. 18 (Blue/White wire) and No. 13 (Blue/Orange wire). If

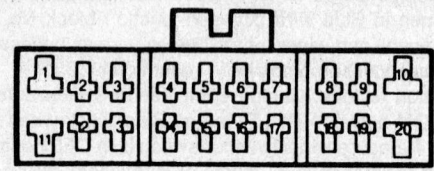

NATURAL

CAVITY	WIRE COLOR	CIRCUIT
1	RED	Dimmer Switch (High-Beam)
2	GRN/RED	Turn Signal Switch (LH)
3	YEL/WHT	Turn Signal and Hazard Switch
4	BLU/GRN	Horn/Brush Slip Ring
5	BLU	Wiper/Washer Switch (LO)
6	BLU/RED	Wiper/Washer Switch (HI)
7	BLU/WHT	Wiper/Washer Switch (PARK)
8	RED/YEL	Light Switch (PARK)
9	—	Not Used (USA)
	BRN/YEL	Daytime Running Lights (DRL) Controller (Canada)
10	WHT	Tail Dome Fuse
11	RED/WHT	Dimmer Switch (Low-Beam)
12	GRN/YEL	Turn Signal Switch (RH)
13	GRN	Turn Signal and Hazard Switch
14	—	Not Used
15	—	Not Used
16	BLU/BLK	Wiper/Washer Switch (WASH)
17	YEL/BLU	Wiper Washer Fuse
18	WHT/GRN	Hazard Fuse
19	YEL	Turn Back Fuse
20	BLK	Light Switch (Ground)

93G83374 94I46142   Courtesy of General Motors Corp.

Fig. 5: Identifying Combination Switch Terminals

resistance is greater than 5.0 ohms, replace combination switch. If resistance is less than 5.0 ohms, check for open in Blue/Orange wire between combination switch and wiper motor. Repair wire as necessary. If wire is okay, replace wiper motor. If resistance is more than 5.0 ohms, replace combination switch.

FRONT WIPER SYSTEM TESTS (TRACKER)

Washer Pump Inoperative – 1) Turn ignition on. Using test light, check Yellow/Blue wire at combination switch connector. If test light comes on, go to next step. If test light does not come on, repair open in Yellow/Blue wire between fuse block and combination switch.
2) Activate washer switch. Using test light, check Blue/Black wire at combination switch connector. If test light comes on, go to next step. If test light does not come on, replace combination switch.
3) Turn ignition to lock. Unplug washer pump connector (located under washer reservoir). Using test light, probe Blue/Black wire at pump connector. Turn ignition on. Activate washer switch. If test light comes on, go to next step. If test light does not come on, repair open in Blue/Black wire between combination switch and washer pump.
4) Using DVOM, measure resistance of Black wire between washer pump connector and ground. If resistance is less than one ohm, replace washer pump. If resistance is more than one ohm, repair Black wire between pump and ground.

Wipers Inoperative in Low Or High Speeds – 1) If wipers are inoperative in low speed, replace combination switch. If wipers are inoperative in high speed, turn ignition on and use test light to backprobe wiper motor connector Blue/Red wire terminal to ground. If test light does not come on, go to next step. If test light comes on, replace wiper motor.
2) Turn ignition on. Using test light, backprobe combination switch connector Blue/Red wire terminal to ground. *See Fig. 5.* If test light does not come on, replace combination switch. If test light comes on, repair open in Blue/Red wire between switch and wiper motor.

Wipers Do Not Operate In MIST Position – Using test light, backprobe Blue wire terminal at combination switch connector to ground. Operate switch in MIST position. If test light comes on, replace front wiper motor. If test light does not come on, repair open in Blue wire between combination switch and wiper motor.

Wipers Operate More Than Once In MIST Position – 1) Using test light, backprobe wiper motor connector Blue wire terminal to ground. Press combination switch to MIST position and release. If test light comes on steadily, go to next step. If test light comes on and goes off, replace wiper motor.
2) Disconnect combination switch connector. Connect test light between ground and connector Blue wire terminal at harness side. If test light does not come on, replace combination switch. If test light comes on, repair short to voltage in Blue wire between switch and wiper motor.

Wipers Sweep, But Do Not Return To Park – 1) Turn ignition on. Manually move wipers out of park position. Using test light, backprobe Blue/White wire at wiper motor connector to ground. If test light comes on, go to next step. If test light does not come on, repair open in Yellow/Blue wire between wiper motor and splice. If wiring is okay, replace wiper motor.
2) With wipers out of park position, probe Blue/White wire between combination switch and wiper motor. If test light comes on, check for open in Blue/White wire. If test light does not come on, replace combination switch.

Wipers Operate At High Speed; Switch in LO Position – 1) Turn ignition on. Backprobe wiper motor connector Blue/Red wire terminal to ground. If test light comes on, go to next step. If test light does not come on, replace wiper motor.
2) Disconnect combination switch connector. Using test light, check Blue/Red wire terminal on switch side to ground. If test light does not come on, replace combination switch. If test light comes on, repair short to voltge in Blue/Red wire between switch and motor.

Wipers Operate At LO Speed; Switch in HI Position – 1) Turn ignition on. Backprobe wiper motor connector Blue wire terminal to ground. If test light comes on, go to next step. If test light does not come on, use a DVOM and measure resistance of Blue/Red wire. If more than 3 ohms are present, repair Blue/Red wire. If less than 3 ohms are present, replace wiper motor.

2) Disconnect combination switch connector. Turn ignition on. Using test light, check Blue wire terminal at connector to ground. If test light does not come on, replace combination switch. If test light comes on, repair short to voltage in Blue wire between switch and wiper motor.

NOTE: *The following procedure is used only on vehicles equipped with pulse (intermittent) wiper system.*

Wipers Inoperative; Switch Set To INT – Using a test light, connect Black wire at combination switch to battery voltage. If test light comes on, replace combination switch. If test light does not come on, repair open in Black wire between wiper motor and ground.

REAR WIPER SYSTEM TESTS (TRACKER)

Washer Pump Inoperative – **1)** Turn ignition on. Using test light, check Black wire at washer pump connector while pressing washer switch. If test light comes on, go to next step. If test light does not come on, replace rear wiper/washer switch.
2) Using test light, check Black/Green wire at washer pump connector while pressing washer switch. If test light comes on, go to next step. If test light does not come on, repair open in Black/Green wire between switch and pump.
3) Using DVOM, measure resistance of Black wire between washer pump connector and ground. If resistance is less than one ohm, replace washer pump. If resistance is more than one ohm, repair Black wire between pump and ground.
Wiper Motor Inoperative – **1)** Turn ignition and rear wiper on. Using test light, backprobe wiper/washer switch connector Yellow/Blue wire to ground. If test light comes on, go to next step. If test light does not come on, repair open in Yellow/Blue wire between fuse block and switch.
2) Using DVOM, backprobe Orange wire at switch connector to ground. If test light comes on, go to next step. If test light does not come on, replace switch.
3) Backprobe wiper motor connector Orange wire terminal to ground. If test light comes on, replace wiper motor. If test light does not come on, repair open in Orange wire between switch and motor.
Wiper Does Not Return To Park Position – **1)** Turn ignition on. Using test light, backprobe rear motor connector Yellow/Blue wire terminal to ground. If test light comes on, go to next step. If test light does not come on, repair open in Yellow/Blue wire between motor and wiring splice.
2) Manually move wiper out of park position. Using test light, backprobe motor connector Blue/Green wire terminal to ground. If test light comes on, go to next step. If test light does not come on, replace wiper motor.
3) Using test light, backprobe rear switch connector Blue/Green wire terminal to ground. If test light comes on, replace rear switch. If test light does not come on, repair open in Blue/Green wire between switch and motor.
Wiper Does Not Turn Off – **1)** With wiper running, disconnect rear wiper switch connector. If wiper turns off, go to next step. If wiper does not turn off, repair short to voltage in Orange wire between rear switch and motor.
2) Using DVOM, connect leads across Yellow/Blue and Black/Green terminals of rear switch. Measure resistance. If resistance is infinite, replace rear motor. If resistance is less than infinity, replace rear switch.
Washer Pump Runs Continuously – Disconnect rear washer switch connector. If pump stops operating, replace rear washer switch. If pump still runs, repair short to voltage in Black/Green wire between rear switch and rear pump.

REMOVAL & INSTALLATION

FRONT WIPER SWITCH

Removal & Installation (All Models) – See COMBINATION SWITCH under REMOVAL & INSTALLATION in STEERING COLUMN SWITCHES article.

FRONT WIPER MOTOR

Removal & Installation (Metro & Tracker) – Unplug electrical connector from motor. Remove mounting bolts holding wiper motor support plate to firewall. Carefully pry front wiper linkage from wiper motor crank arm. To install, reverse removal procedure.

NOTE: *Front wiper motor crank arm is not serviced separately. DO NOT disconnect arm from front wiper motor. Crank arm is positioned on wiper motor to allow front wiper arms to return to their normal park position.*

Removal & Installation (Prizm) – Unplug electrical connector from wiper motor. Remove mounting bolts attaching motor to firewall. Remove wiper arm linkage retaining nut from motor. To install, reverse removal procedure.

REAR WIPER SWITCH

Removal & Installation (Metro) – **1)** Disconnect negative battery cable. Remove steering column lower trim panel. Loosen 2 upper steering column mounting nuts. Lower and support steering column. DO NOT allow column to hang by the lower support bracket.
2) Remove instrument panel cluster trim bezel. Disconnect rear wiper/washer switch connector. Disengage switch locking tabs and push switch outward through panel. To install, reverse removal procedure. Tighten upper steering column mouting nuts to 10 ft. lbs. (15 N.m).
Removal & Installation (Tracker) – Remove lower steering column cover panel. Disengage switch locking tabs and push switch outward through panel. Disconnect electrical connector from switch. To install, reverse removal procedure.

REAR WIPER MOTOR

Removal & Installation (Metro) – Remove rear speakers from door panel (if equipped). Remove rear door lower panel plastic retaining pins and remove rear panel. Unplug wiper motor electrical connector and unscrew ground wire connection. Remove crank arm retaining nut from motor. Remove motor mounting bolts. To install, reverse removal procedure.
Removal & Installation (Tracker) – Remove spare tire. Remove wiper blade/arm assembly and spacers. Remove rear door interior trim panel. Disconnect wiper motor harness connector. Remove motor mounting bolts. To install, reverse removal procedure.

WIRING DIAGRAMS

NOTE: *See ACCESSORIES & EQUIPMENT, Volume 5.*

NOTE: For repair procedures not covered in this article, see ENGINE OVERHAUL PROCEDURES article in GENERAL INFORMATION.

ENGINE IDENTIFICATION

Engine can be identified by eighth character of Vehicle Identification Number (VIN), located on top of dash panel, at lower left corner of windshield.

ENGINE IDENTIFICATION CODE

Application	VIN
1.0L 3-Cylinder	6

ADJUSTMENTS

VALVE CLEARANCE ADJUSTMENT

Hydraulic Valve Lash (HVL) Adjusters are used; no adjustment is required.

REMOVAL & INSTALLATION

NOTE: For reassembly reference, label all electrical connectors, vacuum hoses and fuel lines before removal. Also place mating marks on engine hood and other major assemblies before removal.

FUEL PRESSURE RELEASE

1) Set parking brake. Place transaxle in Neutral (M/T) or Park (A/T). Locate fuel pump relay in engine compartment fuse box. *See Fig. 1.*

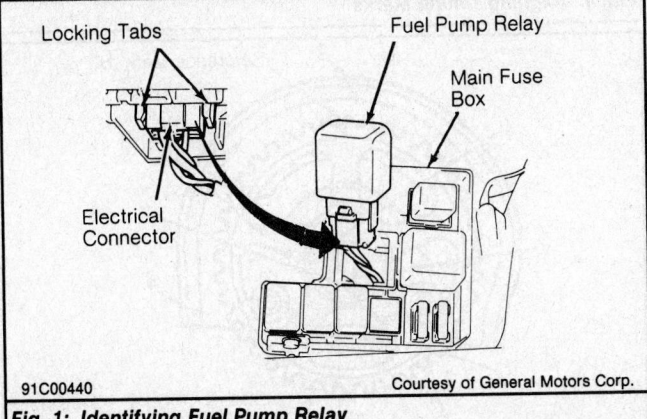

Locking Tabs
Fuel Pump Relay
Main Fuse Box
Electrical Connector

91C00440   Courtesy of General Motors Corp.

Fig. 1: Identifying Fuel Pump Relay

2) Release locking tabs and remove fuel pump relay. Disconnect electrical connector from fuel pump relay. Remove fuel tank filler cap to release pressure from fuel tank.
3) Start engine, and operate until engine stalls. Crank engine 3 additional seconds, to relieve residual fuel pressure. Pressure is now released.

ENGINE

NOTE: Engine and transaxle are removed as an assembly.

Removal – 1) Release fuel pressure. See FUEL PRESSURE RELEASE. Mark and remove hood. Disconnect battery cables.
2) Drain cooling system. Drain engine oil and transaxle oil. Remove cooling fan, radiator and air cleaner assembly. Disconnect necessary electrical connections, vacuum hoses, fuel lines and coolant hoses at engine and transaxle.
3) Disconnect accelerator cable at throttle body. Raise and support vehicle. On M/T models, disconnect clutch cable and shift control rod from transaxle.
4) On A/T models, disconnect oil cooler lines and control cables at transaxle. Disconnect torque rod bracket from transaxle.

5) On all models, disconnect speedometer cable from transaxle. Disconnect exhaust pipe at exhaust manifold. Remove front wheels. Remove staked area from axle shaft nut at hub assembly. Remove nut and washer from axle shafts.
6) Remove ball joint-to-steering knuckle bolt. Separate ball joint from steering knuckle. Using 2 screwdrivers, pry axle shafts from transaxle case. Separate axle shafts from steering knuckle assemblies, and remove axle shafts.
7) Support engine using hoist. Disconnect engine and transaxle mounts. Remove engine and transaxle assembly.
Installation – To install, reverse removal procedure. Tighten all fasteners to specification. See TORQUE SPECIFICATIONS. Adjust all control cables. Adjust fluid levels.

INTAKE MANIFOLD

Removal – 1) Release fuel pressure. See FUEL PRESSURE RELEASE. Disconnect negative battery cable. Drain cooling system. Remove air cleaner assembly.
2) Disconnect necessary electrical connections, coolant hoses, fuel lines and vacuum hoses from throttle body and intake manifold. Disconnect control cables from throttle body. Remove intake manifold bolts, intake manifold, throttle body unit and gasket.
Installation – To install, reverse removal procedure. Tighten fasteners to specification. See TORQUE SPECIFICATIONS.

EXHAUST MANIFOLD

Removal & Installation – Disconnect negative battery cable. Raise and support vehicle. Disconnect oxygen sensor connector. Disconnect exhaust pipe from exhaust manifold. Remove exhaust manifold fasteners, exhaust manifold, and gasket. To install, reverse removal procedure. Tighten fasteners to specification. See TORQUE SPECIFICATIONS.

CYLINDER HEAD

Removal – 1) Release fuel pressure. See FUEL PRESSURE RELEASE. Disconnect negative battery cable. Drain cooling system. Remove air cleaner assembly.
2) Disconnect necessary electrical connections, coolant hoses, fuel lines and vacuum hoses from throttle body and intake manifold. Disconnect control cables from throttle body. Remove intake manifold and throttle body unit. See INTAKE MANIFOLD. Remove exhaust manifold. See EXHAUST MANIFOLD.
3) Remove timing belt. See TIMING BELT. Disconnect oxygen sensor lead (if necessary). Disconnect exhaust pipe from exhaust manifold. Remove valve cover. Loosen 8 cylinder head bolts evenly. Remove cylinder head and gasket.
Inspection – 1) Clean cylinder head with solvent, air dry and remove carbon. Check cylinder head for cracks in intake and exhaust ports, combustion chambers, and head surface.
2) Inspect cylinder head for warpage at 6 points of sealing surface. Check manifold surfaces for warpage. Surface cylinder head if warpage exceeds specification. See CYLINDER HEAD table under ENGINE SPECIFICATIONS.
3) Inspect deck surface warpage of cylinder block. Resurface cylinder block if deck warpage exceeds specification. See CYLINDER BLOCK table under ENGINE SPECIFICATIONS.
Installation – 1) To install, reverse removal procedure. Install cylinder head gasket with TOP mark away from cylinder block, toward crankshaft pulley side of cylinder block.
2) Apply light coat of engine oil to shank and threads of cylinder head bolts before installation. Tighten cylinder head bolts in sequence a little at a time, repeating tightening sequence 3-4 times. *See Fig. 2.* See TORQUE SPECIFICATIONS. To complete installation, reverse removal procedure. Fill cooling system.

CRANKSHAFT FRONT SEAL

Removal & Installation – Crankshaft front seal is mounted in oil pump housing. Manufacturer lists replacement procedure with oil pump removed. See OIL PUMP under ENGINE OILING.

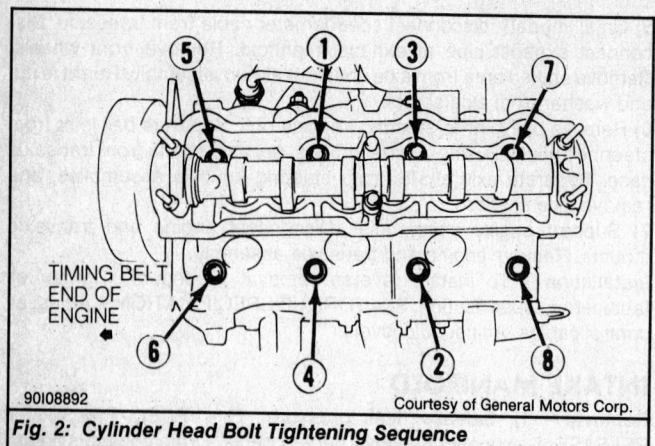

Fig. 2: Cylinder Head Bolt Tightening Sequence

TIMING BELT

Removal – 1) Disconnect negative battery cable. Remove lower right engine undercover. Remove all accessory drive belts. Remove water pump pulley.

2) Remove outer bolts retaining crankshaft pulley. Remove 5 crankshaft pulley bolts and crankshaft pulley. DO NOT remove crankshaft pulley center bolt.

3) Remove timing belt cover and seal. *See Fig. 3.* Rotate crankshaft and align 4 timing marks. *See Fig. 4.* Remove tensioner spring and tensioner stud. Loosen, but DO NOT remove, tensioner bolt.

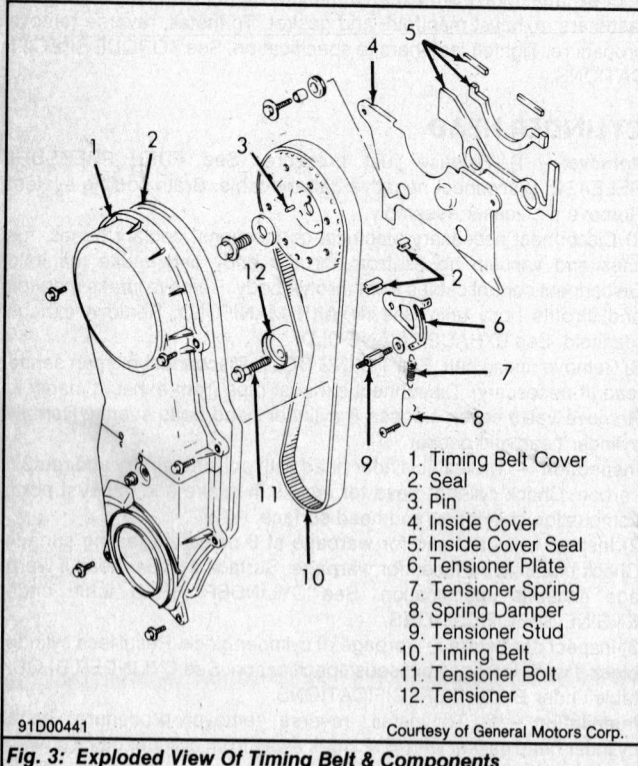

1. Timing Belt Cover
2. Seal
3. Pin
4. Inside Cover
5. Inside Cover Seal
6. Tensioner Plate
7. Tensioner Spring
8. Spring Damper
9. Tensioner Stud
10. Timing Belt
11. Tensioner Bolt
12. Tensioner

91D00441   Courtesy of General Motors Corp.

Fig. 3: Exploded View Of Timing Belt & Components

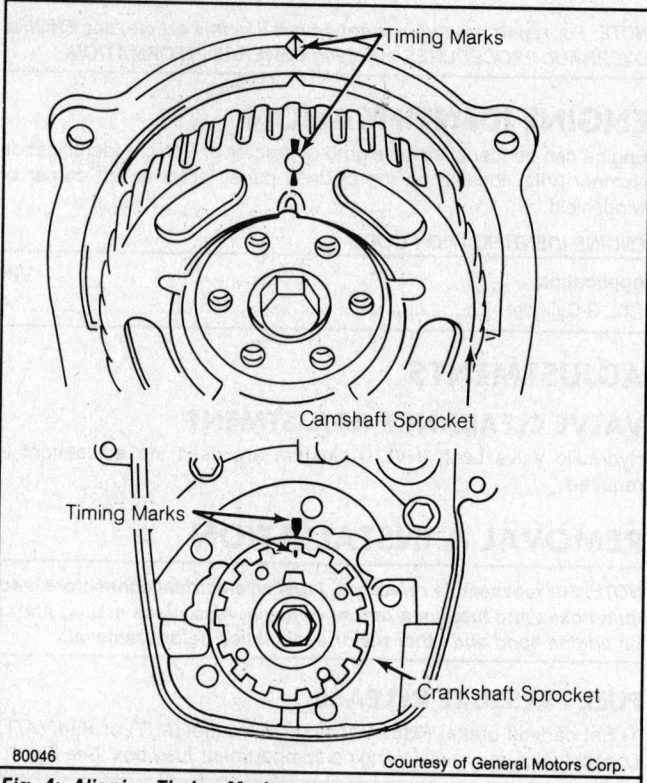

80046   Courtesy of General Motors Corp.

Fig. 4: Aligning Timing Marks

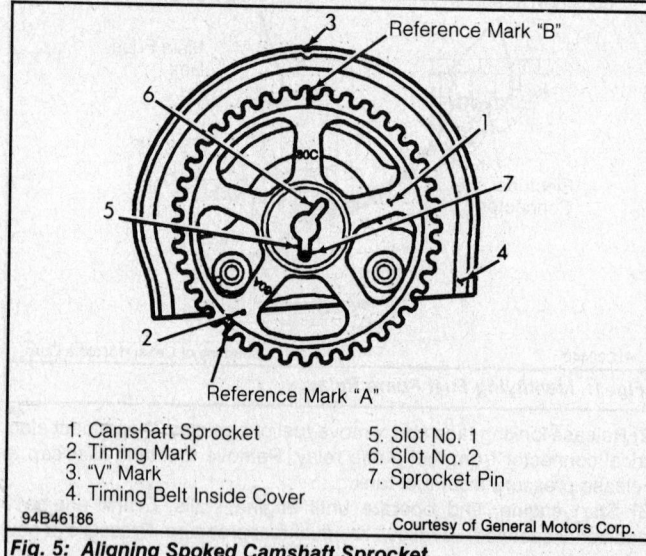

1. Camshaft Sprocket
2. Timing Mark
3. "V" Mark
4. Timing Belt Inside Cover
5. Slot No. 1
6. Slot No. 2
7. Sprocket Pin

94B46186   Courtesy of General Motors Corp.

Fig. 5: Aligning Spoked Camshaft Sprocket

4) If reusing timing belt, mark rotation direction. Remove belt tensioner, tensioner plate, tensioner spring, spring damper and timing belt.

5) If removing crankshaft sprocket, remove sprocket retaining center bolt, crankshaft sprocket and timing belt guide (located behind crankshaft sprocket) from crankshaft.

CAUTION: DO NOT rotate crankshaft or camshaft when timing belt is removed; piston damage may result. Note direction of timing belt guide for installation. Concave side of timing belt guide faces away from timing belt.

6) If camshaft sprocket is to be removed, remove valve cover. Insert a .39" (10 mm) diameter rod through hole in camshaft, to prevent camshaft from turning. Use a shop towel to protect cylinder head and valve cover mating surfaces. Remove camshaft sprocket bolt and camshaft sprocket.

Inspection – Inspect timing belt for damaged teeth, cracking and oil contamination. Ensure tensioner rotates freely. Replace damaged components.

CAUTION: A running production change was made to the camshaft sprocket which requires an additional installation procedure. If camshaft sprocket is installed incorrectly, severe damage to valvetrain and/or pistons may result. Camshaft sprocket may have either a solid or spoked interior. If camshaft sprocket was removed and has a solid interior, go to installation step 2). If camshaft sprocket was removed and has a spoked interior, go to installation step 3).

Installation – **1)** Install timing belt inside cover and seal (if removed). Install timing belt guide, key and crankshaft sprocket. Tighten crankshaft sprocket bolt to specification. See TORQUE SPECIFICATIONS.

CAUTION: Ensure concave side of timing belt guide faces oil pump. Flat side of timing belt guide goes against crankshaft sprocket.

2) When installing camshaft sprocket with solid interior (if removed), align dowel pin to camshaft pin hole. Tighten camshaft sprocket retaining bolt to specification. See TORQUE SPECIFICATIONS. Tighten camshaft sprocket retaining bolt to specification. See TORQUE SPECIFICATIONS.

3) Camshaft sprocket with spoked interior, has 2 reference marks, "A" and "B", and one timing mark. When installing camshaft sprocket (if removed), align dowel pin to camshaft pin slot No. 1. See Fig. 5. When correctly aligned, reference mark "A" will be close to the eight o'clock position. recommend mark "B" will be aligned with "V" mark on valve cover. Tighten camshaft sprocket retaining bolt to specification. See TORQUE SPECIFICATIONS.

CAUTION: Ensure tensioner plate moves when tensioner is moved toward timing belt. If tensioner plate does not move, ensure lug is engaged in hole on tensioner.

4) If tensioner was removed, install tensioner plate on tensioner. Ensure tensioner plate lug engages hole on rear of tensioner. Install tensioner assembly on cylinder block. Tighten tensioner bolt finger tight to allow movement of tensioner.

5) Ensure all timing marks align. See Figs. 4 and 5. If timing marks are not aligned, rotate camshaft or crankshaft to align timing marks. DO NOT rotate camshaft or crankshaft so timing mark moves more than 90 degrees; engine damage may occur. See Fig. 6.

CAUTION: Install timing belt so arrow on timing belt, or mark made during removal, points in direction of crankshaft rotation. Crankshaft rotates clockwise.

6) Install tensioner spring and spring damper, push tensioner plate upward and tighten tensioner bolt. Install timing belt so arrow on timing belt, or mark made during removal, points in direction of crankshaft rotation. Ensure no slack exists on drive side of timing belt. Loosen tensioner bolt and allow spring tension to remove slack in timing belt. Tighten tensioner bolt.

7) Rotate crankshaft 2 revolutions clockwise to ensure all slack is removed from timing belt. Ensure all timing marks are aligned.

8) Tighten tensioner stud and tensioner bolt. See TORQUE SPECIFICATIONS. To install remaining components, reverse removal procedure.

CAMSHAFT

Removal – **1)** Disconnect negative battery cable. Remove air cleaner assembly and valve cover. Mark distributor location for reassembly reference. Remove distributor.

2) Remove timing belt. See TIMING BELT. Insert a .39" (10 mm) diameter rod through hole in camshaft near sprocket to prevent camshaft from turning during camshaft sprocket removal. Use a shop towel to protect cylinder head and valve cover mating surfaces. Ensure camshaft sprocket timing mark is positioned 60 degrees left of 12 o'clock position. Remove retaining bolt and camshaft sprocket.

3) Note location and direction of camshaft bearing caps. Loosen camshaft bearing caps evenly. Remove camshaft bearing caps, camshaft and oil seal.

Inspection – **1)** Inspect components for damage. Measure camshaft lobe height and journal runout. Replace camshaft if lobe height and journal runout are not within specification. See CAMSHAFT table under ENGINE SPECIFICATIONS.

2) Measure cylinder head camshaft bore and camshaft journal diameter. Determine camshaft oil clearance. Replace camshaft/cylinder head if oil clearance is not within specification. See CAMSHAFT table under ENGINE SPECIFICATIONS.

CAUTION: Before installing camshaft, ensure pin hole on end of camshaft points straight down to prevent valve-to-piston contact.

Installation – **1)** Coat camshaft, camshaft journal and lobes with engine oil before installing. Install camshaft in cylinder head so camshaft sprocket pin is at 6 o'clock position.

NOTE: Ensure No. 1 camshaft bearing cap is at timing belt end of cylinder head. Ensure arrow on bearing cap points toward timing belt. No. 1 bearing cap is used for correct camshaft thrust position. Install No. 1 bearing cap first, but do not tighten fully at this time.

2) Apply sealant on cylinder head-to-camshaft bearing cap surfaces for No. 1 and 3 camshaft bearing caps. Install camshaft bearing caps so arrow points to timing belt end of engine.

3) Coat camshaft bearing cap bolts with engine oil, and install bolts. Tighten bearing cap bolts in sequence. See Fig. 7. Tighten camshaft bearing cap bolts evenly in several steps to specification. See TORQUE SPECIFICATIONS.

4) Coat camshaft oil seal with engine oil. Install oil seal until it is even with bearing cap surface. To install remaining components, reverse removal procedure.

CAUTION: DO NOT rotate or start engine for about 30 minutes after installing camshaft. HVL adjusters remain pumped up for about 30 minutes. Operating engine with HVL adjusters pumped up may result in engine damage.

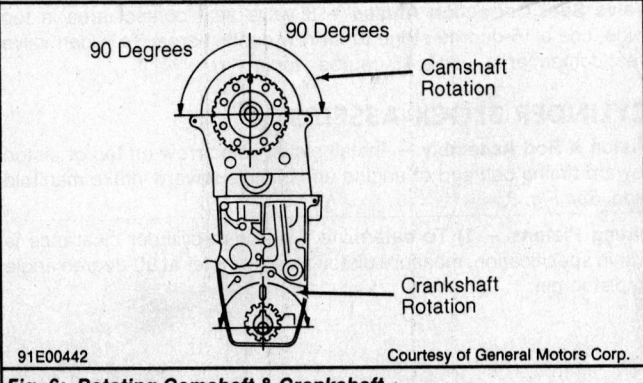

90 Degrees

90 Degrees

Camshaft Rotation

150 Degrees

Crankshaft Rotation

91E00442   Courtesy of General Motors Corp.

Fig. 6: Rotating Camshaft & Crankshaft

CAUTION: A running production change was made to the camshaft sprocket which requires an additional installation procedure. If camshaft sprocket is installed incorrectly, severe damage to valvetrain and/or pistons may result. Camshaft sprocket may have either a solid or spoked interior. If camshaft sprocket was removed and has a solid interior, go to TIMING BELT installation step 2). If camshaft sprocket was removed and has a spoked interior, go to TIMING BELT installation step 3).

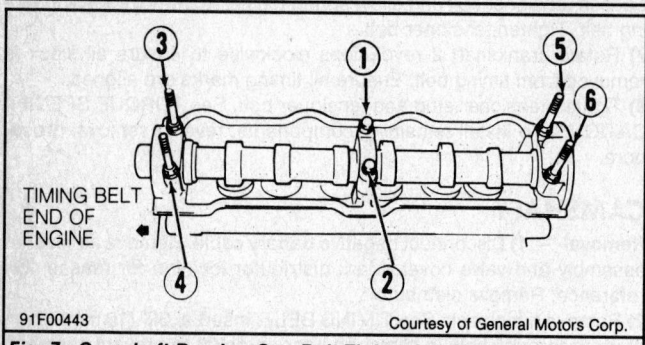

TIMING BELT END OF ENGINE

91F00443 — Courtesy of General Motors Corp.

Fig. 7: Camshaft Bearing Cap Bolt Tightening Sequence

HYDRAULIC VALVE LASH (HVL) ADJUSTER

CAUTION: Store HVL adjusters in engine oil after it has been removed from engine. If HVL adjuster is not stored in engine oil, DO NOT lay on its side or with body facing upward. Store HVL adjuster with body facing downward to prevent air from entering adjuster. DO NOT compress HVL adjuster.

Removal – Remove camshaft. See CAMSHAFT. Note HVL adjusters location for installation reference. Remove HVL adjusters from cylinder head.
Inspection – Inspect HVL adjuster and bore for damage. Measure O.D. of HVL adjuster and cylinder head bore. Determine HVL adjuster oil clearance. Replace HVL adjuster/cylinder head if oil clearance is not within specification. See HYDRAULIC VALVE LASH (HVL) ADJUSTER table under ENGINE SPECIFICATIONS at end of article.

CAUTION: Before installing HVL adjuster, pour engine oil through camshaft journal oil holes. Ensure oil flows from oil holes for HVL adjusters.

CAUTION: DO NOT rotate or start engine for about 30 minutes after installing HVL adjuster and camshaft. Ensure HVL adjusters have correct operating clearance, or damage to valves may result.

Installation – Reverse removal procedure. Ensure components are installed in original locations. Coat HVL adjuster with engine oil before installing. See TORQUE SPECIFICATIONS.

CRANKSHAFT REAR OIL SEAL

Removal & Installation – 1) Remove transmission. See TRANSMISSION REMOVAL & INSTALLATION article (A/T), or CLUTCHES article (M/T). Remove clutch assembly (M/T models). Mark flywheel/flexplate-to-engine position and remove flywheel/flexplate. Using universal seal puller, remove seal from seal housing.
2) Coat seal lip with engine oil, and install seal in seal housing. To complete installation, reverse removal procedure. Apply Loctite (262) to bolts and tighten to specification. See TORQUE SPECIFICATIONS.

WATER PUMP

Removal & Installation – Remove timing belt. See TIMING BELT. Remove water pump rubber seals, retaining bolts, water pump and gasket. To install, reverse removal procedure. See TORQUE SPECIFICATIONS. Fill cooling system.

OIL PAN

Removal – 1) Disconnect negative battery cable. Raise and support vehicle. Drain engine oil. Remove flywheel inspection cover. Disconnect exhaust pipe from exhaust manifold.
2) Remove 14 oil pan bolts and 2 oil pan nuts and oil pan. Remove oil pump pick-up tube for oil pan removal (if necessary).
Installation – Apply RTV Sealant (1052917) to oil pan seal surface before installing. Install NEW gasket on oil pump pick-up tube. Install oil pump pick-up tube and oil pan. See TORQUE SPECIFICATIONS.

OVERHAUL

CYLINDER HEAD

Cylinder Head – Clean head thoroughly. Inspect cylinder head for cracks in intake and exhaust ports, combustion chambers and head surface. Measure cylinder head surface in 6 places for warpage. Replace cylinder head if warpage cannot be corrected by resurfacing. See CYLINDER HEAD table under ENGINE SPECIFICATIONS.
Valve Springs – Ensure valve spring free length, pressure and out-of-square are within specification. See VALVES & VALVE SPRINGS table under ENGINE SPECIFICATIONS. Install springs with tight coils toward cylinder head.

NOTE: Replace valve stem oil seals and valve guides if cylinder head is disassembled.

Valve Stem Oil Seals – Lubricate new oil seal with engine oil before installing. Install oil seal using handle and Valve Guide/Seal Installer (J-37968). Ensure valve stem oil seal is fully seated in valve guide.

CAUTION: When installing valve guide seals using Valve Guide Seal Installer (J-37968), use hand pressure only. DO NOT tap with hammer.

Valve Guides – 1) To determine valve stem-to-guide clearance, subtract valve stem outside diameter from valve guide inside diameter. See CYLINDER HEAD table under ENGINE SPECIFICATIONS. Ensure valve stem diameter is within specification. Valve guide can be replaced if clearance exceeds specification.
2) Use hammer and Valve Guide Remover (J-37968) to replace valve guide. Drive valve guide from combustion side of cylinder head toward valve spring side.

CAUTION: Ensure valve guide installed height is .45" (11.4 mm) above cylinder head surface.

3) To install valve guide, ream guide hole using Reamer (J-37972) to remove any burrs or nicks. Heat cylinder head to 176-212°F (80-100°C). Using hammer and Valve Guide/Seal Installer (J-37968), drive valve guide into cylinder head until installer contacts cylinder head surface. Using Reamer (J-37971), ream valve guide.
Valve Seat – Replacement information is not available.
Valves – Ensure valve stem diameter and valve margin are within specification. See VALVES & VALVE SPRINGS table under ENGINE SPECIFICATIONS.
Valve Seat Correction Angles – If valve seat contact area is too wide, use a 15-degree stone to narrow contact area. To widen valve seat contact area, use a 45-degree stone.

CYLINDER BLOCK ASSEMBLY

Piston & Rod Assembly – Install piston with arrow on top of piston toward timing belt end of engine and oil hole toward intake manifold side. See Fig. 8.

Fitting Pistons – 1) To determine if piston-to-cylinder clearance is within specification, measure piston skirt diameter at 90-degree angle to piston pin.

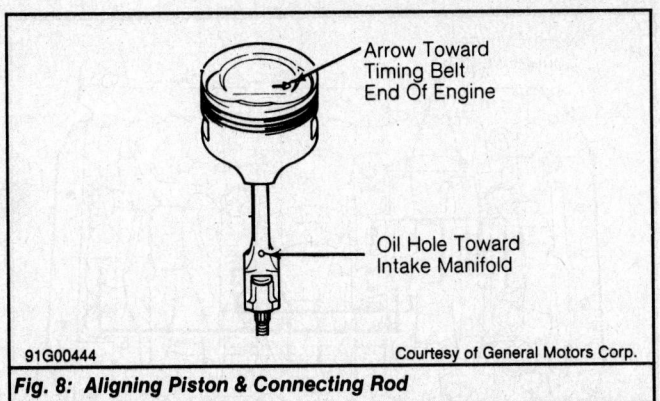

91G00444   Courtesy of General Motors Corp.

Fig. 8: Aligning Piston & Connecting Rod

NOTE: Two standard piston sizes and cylinder bore diameters are used. Piston and cylinder bores are marked "1" or "2". Mark is on top of piston or cylinder block deck surface. See Fig 9.

2) Piston diameter is measured at .59" (15 mm) from bottom of piston skirt for Metro base models or .45" (11.5 mm) from bottom of piston skirt for Metro XFi. Two different sized standard pistons are used. Piston size can be identified by "1" or "2" stamped on top of piston. *See Fig. 9.*

3) Ensure piston diameter is within specification. See PISTONS, PINS & RINGS table under ENGINE SPECIFICATIONS.

4) Cylinder bore diameter is measured at 1.96" (49.8 mm) and 3.74" (94.9 mm) from top of cylinder bore. Cylinder bore diameter can be identified by "1" or "2" stamped on deck surface in accordance with cylinder location. *See Fig. 9.*

5) Ensure cylinder bore diameter is within specification. Determine piston clearance. Replace piston or rebore cylinder block if clearance is not within specification. See CYLINDER BLOCK table under ENGINE SPECIFICATIONS.

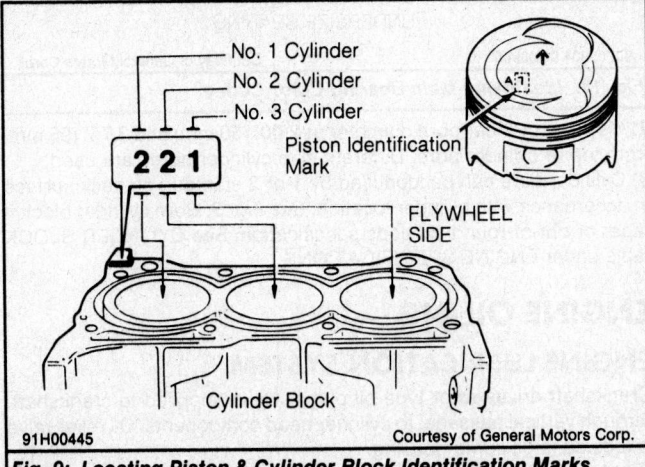

91H00445   Courtesy of General Motors Corp.

Fig. 9: Locating Piston & Cylinder Block Identification Marks

Piston Rings – On Metro base models, measure compression and oil ring end gap with ring at top of cylinder bore. On Metro XFi models, measure compression and oil ring end gap with ring 4.72" (120 mm) into cylinder bore. Ensure ring end gap and side clearance are within specification. See PISTONS, PINS & RINGS table under ENGINE SPECIFICATIONS. Ensure identification marks on piston rings (if equipped) face toward top of piston. Position piston rings at designated areas. *See Fig. 10.*

NOTE: Metro base models use 2 compression rings and one oil ring. Metro XFi models use one compression ring and one oil ring.

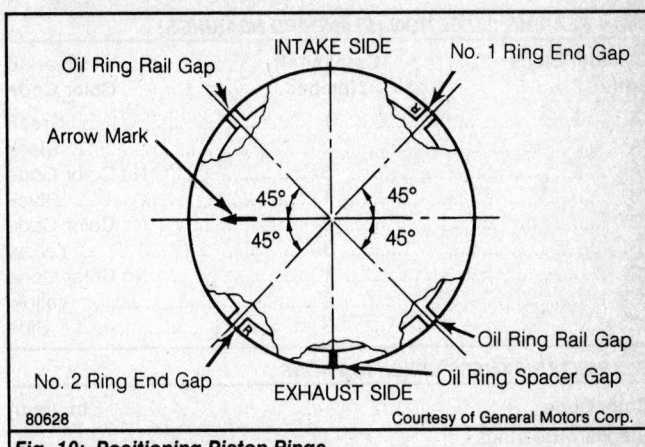

80628   Courtesy of General Motors Corp.

Fig. 10: Positioning Piston Rings

Rod Bearings – **1)** Note direction of connecting rod and cap installation before removing. Install connecting rod with oil hole toward intake manifold side of engine. *See Fig. 8.* Ensure arrow mark on connecting rod cap points toward timing belt end of engine.

2) Ensure bearing oil clearance and side play are within specification. See CRANKSHAFT, MAIN & CONNECTING ROD BEARINGS and CONNECTING RODS tables under ENGINE SPECIFICATIONS.

Crankshaft & Main Bearings – **1)** Before disassembly ensure main bearing caps are numbered for location. Ensure arrow on cap points toward timing belt end of engine.

2) Cylinder block main bearing bore size is indicated by a letter "A", "B" or "C" stamped on cylinder block. *See Fig. 11.* Ensure main bearing bore is within specification. See MAIN BEARING BORE SPECIFICATIONS table.

3) Crankshaft main bearing journal size is indicated by numerical size mark on No. 1 cylinder crankshaft counterweights. *See Fig. 12.* Ensure main bearing journal is within specification. See MAIN BEARING JOURNAL DIAMETER SPECIFICATIONS table.

NOTE: Main bearings are color code marked on side of main bearing. Standard main bearings contain only one color code mark and undersize main bearings contain 2 color code marks. See Fig. 13.

4) If color code on original bearing cannot be obtained, use letter size mark on cylinder block and number on crankshaft to determine proper main bearing size. See MAIN BEARING SELECTION (STANDARD BEARINGS) table. See BEARING THICKNESS SPECIFICATIONS table for standard bearing thickness.

5) Main bearings are available in undersizes. Undersize bearings are coded with 2 color code marks. *See Fig. 13.* Undersize bearings are available in 5 thickness variations. See BEARING THICKNESS SPECIFICATIONS table.

6) If necessary, regrind main bearing journals to .010" (.25 mm) undersize with a finished diameter of 1.7612-1.7618" (44.732-44.750 mm). Using finished journal diameter and letter marked on cylinder block, determine undersize bearing color code. See MAIN BEARING SELECTION (UNDERSIZE BEARINGS) table.

MAIN BEARING BORE SPECIFICATIONS

Letter Stamped On Cylinder Block	Diameter In. (mm)
"A"	1.9291-1.9294 (49.000-49.006)
"B"	1.9294-1.9296 (49.006-49.012)
"C"	1.9296-1.9298 (49.012-49.018)

MAIN BEARING JOURNAL DIAMETER SPECIFICATIONS

Number On Crankshaft Counterweight	Diameter In. (mm)
1	1.7714-1.7716 (44.994-45.000)
2	1.7712-1.7714 (44.988-44.994)
3	1.7710-1.7712 (44.982-44.988)

MAIN BEARING SELECTION (STANDARD BEARINGS)

Cylinder Block Letter	Crankshaft Number	Bearing Color Code
"A"	1	Green
"A"	2	Black
"A"	3	No Color Code
"B"	1	Black
"B"	2	No Color Code
"B"	3	Yellow
"C"	1	No Color Code
"C"	2	Yellow
"C"	3	Blue

BEARING THICKNESS SPECIFICATIONS

Color Code	In. (mm)
Standard Bearings	
Green	.0786-.0787 (1.996-1.999)
Black	.0787-.0788 (1.999-2.002)
No Color Code	.0788-.0789 (2.002-2.005)
Yellow	.0789-.0790 (2.005-2.008)
Blue	.0790-.0791 (2.008-2.011)
Undersize Bearings	
Green & Red	.0835-.0836 (2.121-2.124)
Black & Red	.0836-.0838 (2.124-2.128)
Red Only	.0837-.0839 (2.127-2.131)
Yellow & Red	.0839-.0840 (2.131-2.134)
Blue & Red	.0840-.0841 (2.134-2.137)

MAIN BEARING SELECTION (UNDERSIZE BEARINGS)

Finished Journal Diameter In. (mm)	Cylinder Block Letter	Bearing Color Code
1.7612-1.7614 (44.732-44.738)	"A"	Red Only
	"B"	Yellow & Red
	"C"	Blue & Red
1.7614-1.7616 (44.738-44.744)	"A"	Black & Red
	"B"	Red Only
	"C"	Yellow & Red
1.7616-1.7618 (44.744-44.750)	"A"	Green & Red
	"B"	Black & Red
	"C"	Red Only

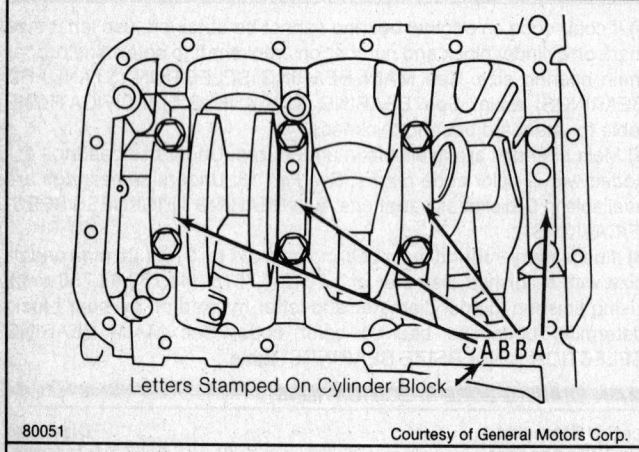

80051   Courtesy of General Motors Corp.

Fig. 11: Identifying Cylinder Block Main Bearing Bores

Thrust Bearing – Install thrust bearing on main bearing with grooves toward crankshaft, away from cylinder block. Replace thrust bearing if crankshaft end play is not within specification. See CRANKSHAFT, MAIN & CONNECTING ROD BEARINGS table under ENGINE SPECIFICATIONS.

Cylinder Block – **1)** Using feeler gauge and straightedge, check cylinder block head surface warpage. If warpage exceeds specification, repair as necessary. See CYLINDER BLOCK table under ENGINE SPECIFICATIONS.

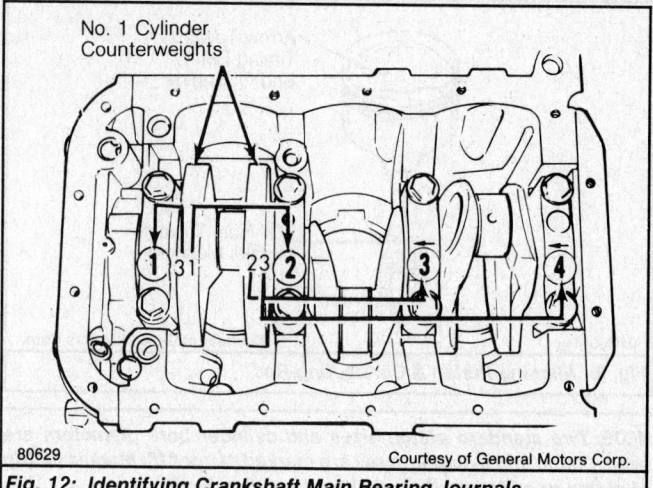

80629   Courtesy of General Motors Corp.

Fig. 12: Identifying Crankshaft Main Bearing Journals

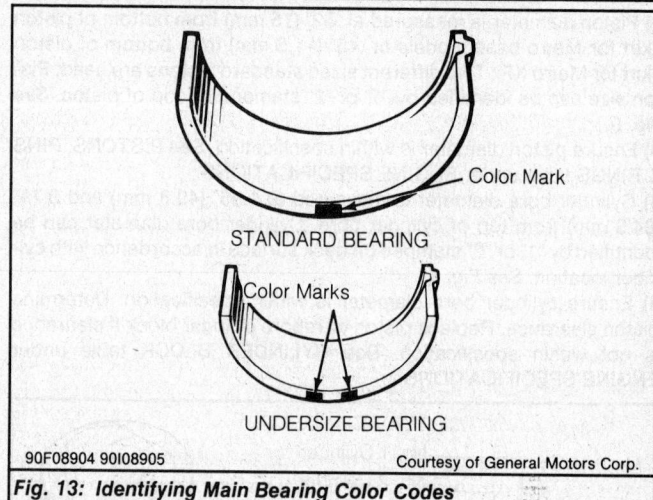

90F08904 90I08905   Courtesy of General Motors Corp.

Fig. 13: Identifying Main Bearing Color Codes

2) Measure cylinder bore diameter at 2.00" (50 mm) and 3.75" (95 mm) from top of cylinder bore. Different size cylinder bores are used.

3) Cylinder bore can be identified by 1 or 2 stamped on deck surface in accordance with cylinder location. See Fig. 9. Bore cylinder block if taper or out-of-round exceeds specification. See CYLINDER BLOCK table under ENGINE SPECIFICATIONS.

ENGINE OILING

ENGINE LUBRICATION SYSTEM

Crankshaft drives rotor-type oil pump. Oil is supplied to crankshaft, through vertical passage, to cylinder head components. Oil relief valve is located in oil pump housing.

Crankcase Capacity – Crankcase capacity with oil filter change is 3.7 qts. (3.5L).

Oil Pressure – With engine at normal operating temperature, oil pressure should be 46.9-61.1 psi (3.3-4.3 kg/cm²) at 4000 RPM.

OIL PUMP

Removal & Disassembly – **1)** Remove timing belt and crankshaft sprocket. See TIMING BELT under REMOVAL & INSTALLATION. Remove oil pan and oil pump pick-up tube. See OIL PAN under REMOVAL & INSTALLATION.

2) Remove dipstick tube from oil pump housing. Remove oil pump retaining bolts, oil pump and gasket.

CAUTION: Note bolt length and location for reassembly reference.

3) Remove oil pump cover from rear of oil pump. Remove oil seal from oil pump housing. Remove snap ring, spring and relief valve from oil pump housing.

Inspection – 1) Inspect components for damage. Ensure relief valve slides freely in bore. Using feeler gauge, measure radial clearance between outer rotor and oil pump housing.

2) With rotors installed in oil pump housing, place straightedge across oil pump housing. Measure rotor side clearance between both rotors and straightedge. Replace oil pump assembly if either clearance exceeds specification. See OIL PUMP SPECIFICATIONS table.

OIL PUMP SPECIFICATIONS

Application	In. (mm)
Radial Clearance (Max.)	.0122 (.310)
Side Clearance (Max.)	.0059 (.149)

Reassembly & Installation – 1) To reassemble, reverse disassembly procedure. Coat components with engine oil before installing. Tighten oil pump cover bolts to specification. See TORQUE SPECIFICATIONS. Ensure rotors rotate freely by hand after oil pump cover is reassembled.

2) To install, reverse removal procedure. Ensure oil pump pins are installed in cylinder block before installing oil pump. Install Oil Seal Guide (J-34853) on crankshaft to prevent damaging oil seal during oil pump installation. Coat oil seal guide with oil before installing oil pump.

3) Ensure bolts are installed in proper location and thread sealant is applied on appropriate bolt. See Fig. 14. Tighten bolts to specification. See TORQUE SPECIFICATIONS. Cut oil pump gasket even with cylinder block. Remove oil seal guide.

4) To install remaining components, reverse removal procedure. Use NEW "O" ring on dipstick tube and NEW seal on oil pump pick-up tube. Install NEW seal between oil pump and water pump.

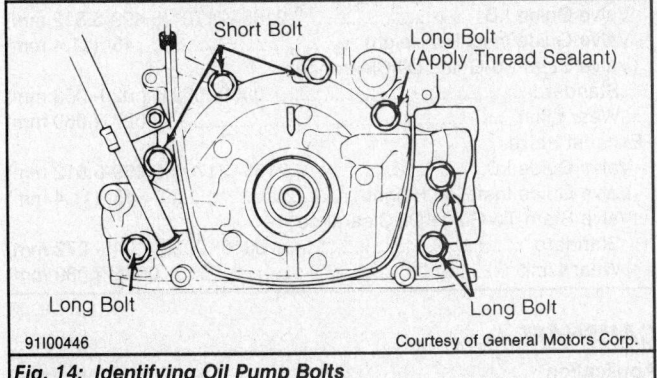

Short Bolt
Long Bolt
(Apply Thread Sealant)
Long Bolt
Long Bolt
91I00446
Courtesy of General Motors Corp.

Fig. 14: Identifying Oil Pump Bolts

TORQUE SPECIFICATIONS

TORQUE SPECIFICATIONS

Application	Ft. Lbs. (N.m)
A/C Compressor Mounting Bolt	
12-mm Bolt	21 (28)
14-mm Bolt	33 (45)
Axle Shaft Nut	129 (175)
Ball Joint-To-Steering Knuckle Nut	44 (60)
Camshaft Sprocket Bolt	44 (60)
Crankshaft Pulley Bolt	12 (16)
Connecting Rod Nut	26 (35)
Crankshaft Sprocket Bolt	81 (110)
Cylinder Head Bolt	[1] 54 (73)
Engine Oil Drain Plug	26 (35)
Exhaust Manifold-To-Head Bolt/Nut	17 (23)
Exhaust Manifold-To-Front Exhaust Pipe Bolts	33 (45)
Front Exhaust Pipe-To-TWC Catalytic Converter	29 (40)

[1] – Tighten bolts to specification in sequence. See Fig. 2.
[2] – Tighten bolts to specification in sequence. See Fig. 7.
[3] – Apply thread sealant to designated bolt. See Fig. 14.

TORQUE SPECIFICATIONS (Cont.)

Application	Ft. Lbs. (N.m)
Flywheel Bolt	52 (70)
Intake Manifold Bolt/Nut	17 (23)
Main Bearing Cap Bolt	40 (54)
Spark Plug	18 (24)
Tensioner Bolt	20 (27)
Water Pump Pulley Bolts	18 (24)
Wheel Lug Nut	44 (60)

	INCH Lbs. (N.m)
Camshaft Bearing Cap Bolt	[2] 97 (11)
Oil Pan Bolt/Nuts	97 (11)
Oil Pump Cover Bolt	97 (11)
Oil Pump Mounting Bolt	[3] 97 (11)
Oil Pump Pick-Up Tube Bolt	97 (11)
Tensioner Stud	97 (11)
Timing Belt Cover Bolt	97 (11)
Valve Cover Bolt	44 (5)
Water Pump Bolt	115 (13)

[1] – Tighten bolts to specification in sequence. See Fig. 2.
[2] – Tighten bolts to specification in sequence. See Fig. 7.
[3] – Apply thread sealant to designated bolt. See Fig. 14.

ENGINE SPECIFICATIONS

GENERAL SPECIFICATIONS

Application	Specification
Displacement	61 Cu. In. (1.0L)
Bore	2.91" (73.9 mm)
Stroke	3.03" (76.9 mm)
Compression Ratio	9.5:1
Fuel System	TBI
Horsepower @ RPM (Except XFi)	55 @ 5700
Horsepower @ RPM (XFi)	49 @ 4700
Torque Ft. Lbs. @ RPM	58 @ 3300

CRANKSHAFT, MAIN & CONNECTING ROD BEARINGS

Application	In. (mm)
Crankshaft	
End Play	
Standard	.0044-.0122 (.112-.310)
Wear Limit	.0149 (.378)
Runout	.0023 (.058)
Main Bearings	
Journal Diameter [1]	
No. 1	1.7614-1.7616 (44.994-45.000)
No. 2	1.7712-1.7714 (44.988-44.994)
No. 3	1.7710-1.7712 (44.982-44.988)
Journal Out-Of-Round	.0004 (.010)
Journal Taper	.0004 (.010)
Oil Clearance	
Standard	.0008-.0015 (.020-.038)
Wear Limit	.0023 (.058)
Crankpin Journal	
Journal Diameter	1.6529-1.6535 (41.982-41.999)
Journal Out-Of-Round	.0004 (.010)
Journal Taper	.0004 (.010)
Oil Clearance	
Standard	.0012-.0019 (.030-.048)
Wear Limit	.0031 (.079)

[1] – Use number stamped on crankshaft counterweight to determine journal diameter. See Fig. 12.

CONNECTING RODS

Application	In. (mm)
Maximum Bend	.0002 (.005)
Maximum Twist	.0039 (.099)
Side Play	
Standard	.0039-.0078 (.099-.199)
Wear Limit	.0137 (.349)

PISTONS, PINS & RINGS

Application	In. (mm)
Pistons	
Clearance	.0008-.0015 (.020-.038)
Diameter [1]	
No. 1	2.9126-2.9130 (73.980-73.990)
No. 2	2.9122-2.9126 (73.970-73.980)
Rings [2]	
No. 1 (Compression)	
End Gap	
Standard	.0079-.0118 (.200-.300)
Wear Limit	.0275 (.699)
Side Clearance	.0012-.0027 (.030-.069)
No. 2 (Compression)	
End Gap	
Standard	.0079-.0118 (.200-.300)
Wear Limit	.0275 (.699)
Side Clearance	.0008-.0023 (.020-.058)
No. 3 (Oil)	
End Gap	
Standard	.0079-.0236 (.200-.599)
Wear Limit	.071 (1.80)

[1] – Piston diameter is determined by piston identification mark on top of piston. *See Fig. 9.*

[2] – Metro XFi only uses No. 1 compression ring and oil control ring. XFi compression ring measurement is taken 4.72" (120 mm) from top of cylinder bore.

CYLINDER BLOCK

Application	In. (mm)
Cylinder Bore	
Standard Diameter [1]	
No. 1	2.9138-2.9142 (74.011-74.021)
No. 2	2.9134-2.9138 (74.000-74.011)
Maximum Diameter	2.9193" (74.15)
Maximum Taper	.0039 (.099)
Maximum Out-Of-Round	.0039 (.099)
Maximum Deck Warpage	.0024 (.061)

[1] – Cylinder bore diameter is determined by number on deck surface of cylinder block. *See Fig. 9.*

HYDRAULIC VALVE LASH (HVL) ADJUSTERS

Application	In. (mm)
Bore Diameter	1.2205-1.2214 (31.000-31.024)
Lifter Diameter	1.2188-1.2194 (30.958-30.973)
Oil Clearance	
Standard	.0010-.0025 (.025-.064)
Wear Limit	.0059 (.150)

VALVES & VALVE SPRINGS

Application	Specification
Intake Valves	
Face Angle	45°
Minimum Margin	.023" (.58 mm)
Stem Diameter	.2148-.2157" (5.457-5.479 mm)
Exhaust Valves	
Face Angle	45°
Minimum Margin	.027" (.68 mm)
Stem Diameter	.2142-.2144" (5.440-5.445 mm)
Valve Springs	
Free Length	
Standard	1.6649" (42.29 mm)
Wear Limit	1.6142" (41.00 mm)
Out-Of-Square	.079" (2.01 mm)

	Lbs. @ In. (kg @ mm)
Pressure	
Valve Closed	
Standard	41-47 @ 1.28 (18.5-21.3 @ 32.6)
Wear Limit	36 @ 1.28 (16.3 @ 32.6)

CYLINDER HEAD

Application	Specification
Maximum Warpage	
Cylinder Block Surface	.002" (.05 mm)
Manifold Surface	.004" (.10 mm)
Valve Seats	
Seat Angle	45°
Seat Width	.0512-.0590" (1.300-1.499 mm)
Valve Guides	
Intake Valve	
Valve Guide I.D.	.2165-.2170" (5.499-5.512 mm)
Valve Guide Installed Height	.45" (11.4 mm)
Valve Stem-To-Guide Oil Clearance	
Standard	.0008-.0021 (.020-.053 mm)
Wear Limit	.0027" (.069 mm)
Exhaust Valve	
Valve Guide I.D.	.2165-.2170" (5.499-5.512 mm)
Valve Guide Installed Height	.45" (11.4 mm)
Valve Stem-To-Guide Oil Clearance	
Standard	.0018-.0028" (.045-.072 mm)
Wear Limit	.0035" (.089 mm)

CAMSHAFT

Application	In. (mm)
Bore Diameter [1]	
Except No. 1	1.1811-1.1819 (29.999-30.020)
No. 1	1.0236-1.0244 (25.999-26.020)
Journal Diameter [1]	
Except No. 1	1.1795-1.1803 (29.959-29.980)
No. 1	1.0220-1.0228 (25.959-25.979)
Journal Runout	.0039 (.010)
Lobe Height	
Metro Except XFi	
Standard	1.5911-1.5974 (40.415-40.575)
Wear Limit	1.5872 (40.315)
Metro XFi	
Standard	1.5602-1.5665 (39.628-39.788)
Wear Limit	1.5562 (39.528)
Oil Clearance	
Standard	.0008-.0024 (.020-.061)
Wear Limit	.0047 (.119)

[1] – No. 1 is at timing belt end of camshaft.

NOTE: For repair procedures not covered in this article, see ENGINE OVERHAUL PROCEDURES article in GENERAL INFORMATION.

ENGINE IDENTIFICATION

Vehicle Identification Number (VIN) is located on top of dash panel, near lower left corner of windshield. Engine may be identified by the eighth character of VIN.

ENGINE IDENTIFICATION CODES

Application	Code
Prizm 1.6L	6
Prizm LSi 1.8L	8

ADJUSTMENTS

VALVE CLEARANCE ADJUSTMENT

NOTE: Adjust valve clearance with engine cold.

1) Disconnect negative battery cable. Disconnect all necessary control cables, hoses and electrical connections. Remove valve cover and gasket.

2) Rotate crankshaft so No. 1 cylinder is at TDC of compression stroke. Valve lifters on No. 1 cylinder should be loose and valve lifters on No. 4 cylinder should be tight. If they are not, rotate crankshaft one revolution. Ensure timing mark on crankshaft pulley aligns with "0" mark on timing belt cover.

3) Using feeler gauge, check clearance between camshaft lobe and adjusting shim for the following: all valves on No. 1 cylinder, intake valves on No. 2 cylinder and exhaust valves on No. 3 cylinder. Record all readings.

4) Rotate crankshaft 360 degrees. Check clearance between camshaft lobe and adjusting shim for the following: all valves on No. 4 cylinder, intake valves on No. 3 cylinder and exhaust valves on No. 2 cylinder. If clearance is not within specification, adjust by replacing adjusting shim. See VALVE CLEARANCE SPECIFICATIONS table.

VALVE CLEARANCE SPECIFICATIONS

Application	Clearance In. (mm)
Exhaust	[1] .010-.014 (.25-.35)
Intake	[1] .006-.010 (.15-.25)

[1] – Adjust valve clearance with engine cold.

5) Rotate engine until camshaft lobe faces away from valve to be adjusted. Insert Valve Spring Depressor (J-39871-1) between camshaft and adjusting shim. *See Fig. 1.*

6) Install Valve Lash Spring Spacer (J-39871-2) between camshaft and valve lifter. Ensure bottom edge of valve lash spring spacer contacts valve lifter, NOT adjusting shim. Remove valve spring depressor. Using small screwdriver and magnet, remove adjusting shim from valve lifter.

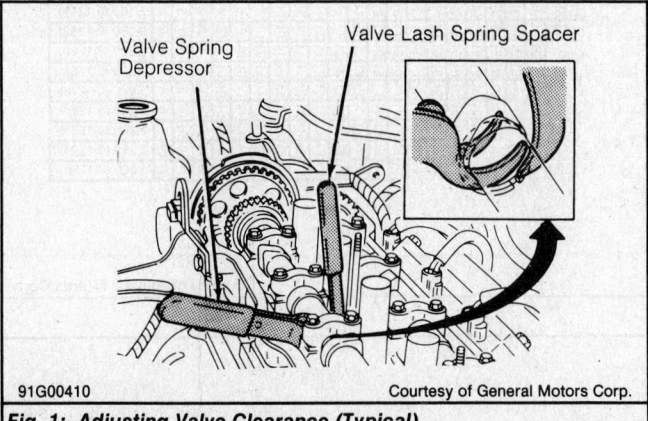

Valve Spring Depressor

Valve Lash Spring Spacer

91G00410   Courtesy of General Motors Corp.

Fig. 1: Adjusting Valve Clearance (Typical)

7) To determine correct adjusting shim thickness for shim replacement, measure and record thickness of removed shim. Locate measured values of removed shim and valve clearance on appropriate adjusting shim selection chart to determine correct shim thickness. *See Figs. 2 and 3.*

8) Install correct shim thickness to obtain proper clearance. See VALVE CLEARANCE SPECIFICATIONS table. Repeat procedure if necessary. Before installing valve cover, install NEW gasket to cylinder head and NEW seal washers to valve cover. Install valve cover in reverse order of removal.

REMOVAL & INSTALLATION

NOTE: For installation reference, label all electrical connectors, vacuum hoses and fuel lines before removing. Also place mating marks on engine hood and other major assemblies before removing.

FUEL PRESSURE RELEASE

1) Loosen fuel tank cap to release fuel tank pressure. Disconnect circuit opening relay, located behind radio. Start engine and allow engine to stall. Crank engine again for an addition 3 seconds, to ensure relief of any remaining pressure.

2) Disconnect negative battery cable. Connect circuit opening relay and tighten fuel filler cap. Wrap fuel component or fitting with shop towel during removal. Disconnect component.

ENGINE

NOTE: Engine and transaxle are removed as an assembly.

Removal – 1) Release fuel pressure. See FUEL PRESSURE RELEASE. Disconnect battery cables, and remove battery. Remove hood.

2) Drain engine oil and cooling system. Disconnect necessary coolant hoses and fuel lines. Remove air intake duct and control cables from throttle body. Remove air cleaner.

3) Disconnect necessary vacuum hoses. Disconnect electrical connections at A/C SV valve, MAP sensor, data link connector, A/C triple switch and engine ground wires. Remove cruise control actuator (if equipped). On A/T models, disconnect shift cable and oil cooler lines from transaxle. On M/T models, disconnect clutch and shift control cables.

4) On all models, disconnect speedometer cable at transaxle. Remove coolant recovery bottle and bracket. Remove radiator and cooling fan. Remove power steering pump and A/C compressor (if equipped) with hoses attached and set aside.

5) Remove knee bolster, glove box and center console from vehicle. Remove radio. Remove one bolt and set aside left-side carpet bracket. Remove cruise control module mounting bolts and set aside. Disconnect PCM. From engine compartment side, pull wiring harness and grommet through fire wall.

6) Raise and support vehicle. Remove lower engine covers. Drain transaxle fluid. Disconnect exhaust pipe at exhaust manifold. Disconnect oxygen sensor connector. Remove front tire and wheel assemblies.

7) Remove tie rod nuts from left and right steering knuckle. Separate tie rods from steering knuckles. Remove lower ball joints from steering knuckles. Separate lower control arms from steering knuckles.

8) Using a pry bar or large screwdriver, pry axle shafts from transaxle case. Support engine with hoist. Remove bolt from engine mount near timing belt cover. Remove transaxle mount bolts. If necessary, remove crossmember located below transaxle. Before removing engine, ensure all wires and hoses are disconnected. Remove engine and transaxle. Separate engine from transaxle.

Installation – 1) To install, reverse removal procedure. Tighten all fasteners to specification. See TORQUE SPECIFICATIONS.

2) Adjust all control cables. Adjust fluid levels. On A/T models, fill transaxle with Dexron-II. On M/T models, fill transaxle with SAE 75W-90 GL-5 gear lubricant.

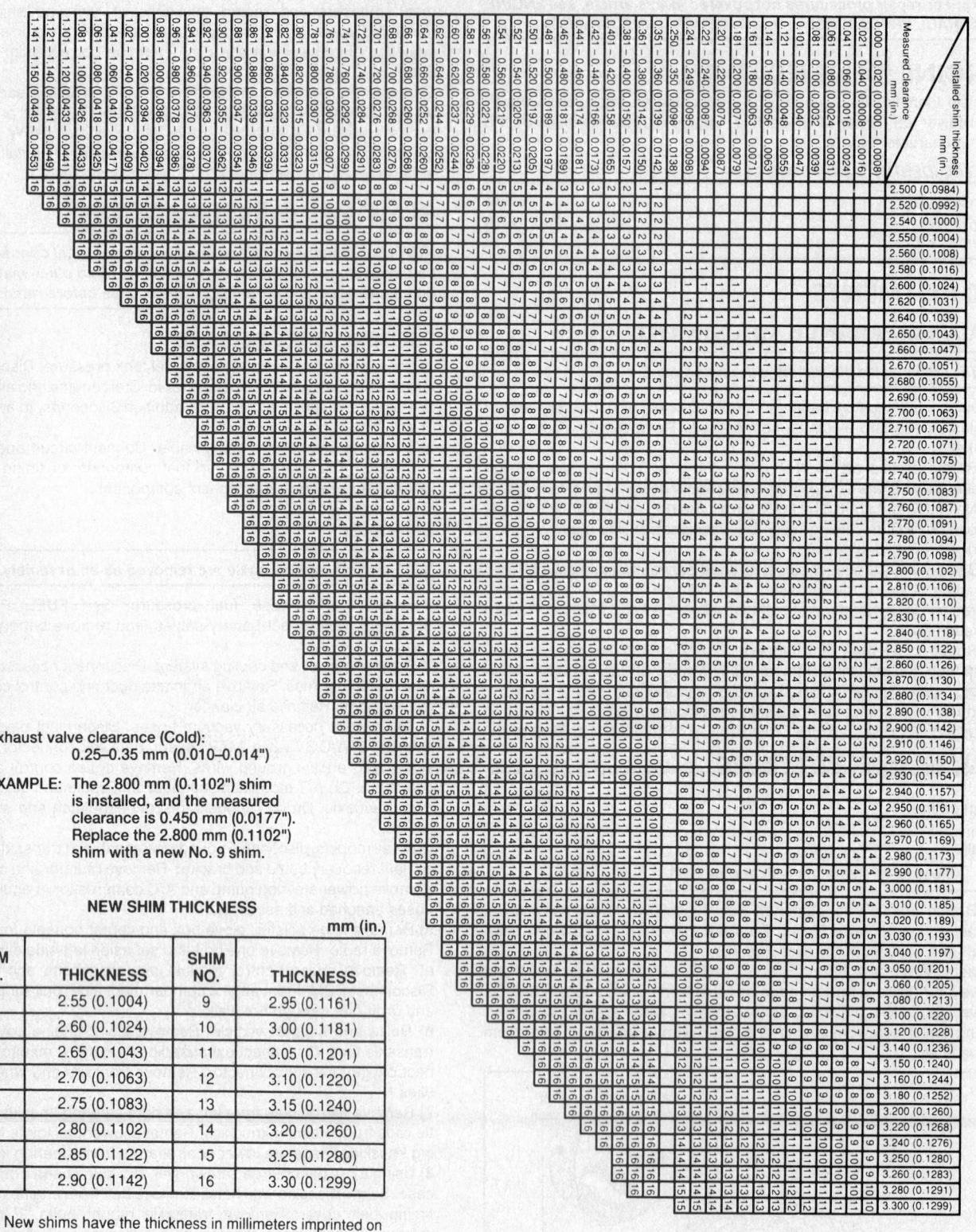

Exhaust valve clearance (Cold):
0.25–0.35 mm (0.010–0.014")

EXAMPLE: The 2.800 mm (0.1102") shim
is installed, and the measured
clearance is 0.450 mm (0.0177").
Replace the 2.800 mm (0.1102")
shim with a new No. 9 shim.

NEW SHIM THICKNESS

mm (in.)

SHIM NO.	THICKNESS	SHIM NO.	THICKNESS
1	2.55 (0.1004)	9	2.95 (0.1161)
2	2.60 (0.1024)	10	3.00 (0.1181)
3	2.65 (0.1043)	11	3.05 (0.1201)
4	2.70 (0.1063)	12	3.10 (0.1220)
5	2.75 (0.1083)	13	3.15 (0.1240)
6	2.80 (0.1102)	14	3.20 (0.1260)
7	2.85 (0.1122)	15	3.25 (0.1280)
8	2.90 (0.1142)	16	3.30 (0.1299)

HINT: New shims have the thickness in millimeters imprinted on
the face.

93F82151

Courtesy of General Motors Corp.

Fig. 2: Exhaust Valve Adjusting Shim Selection Chart

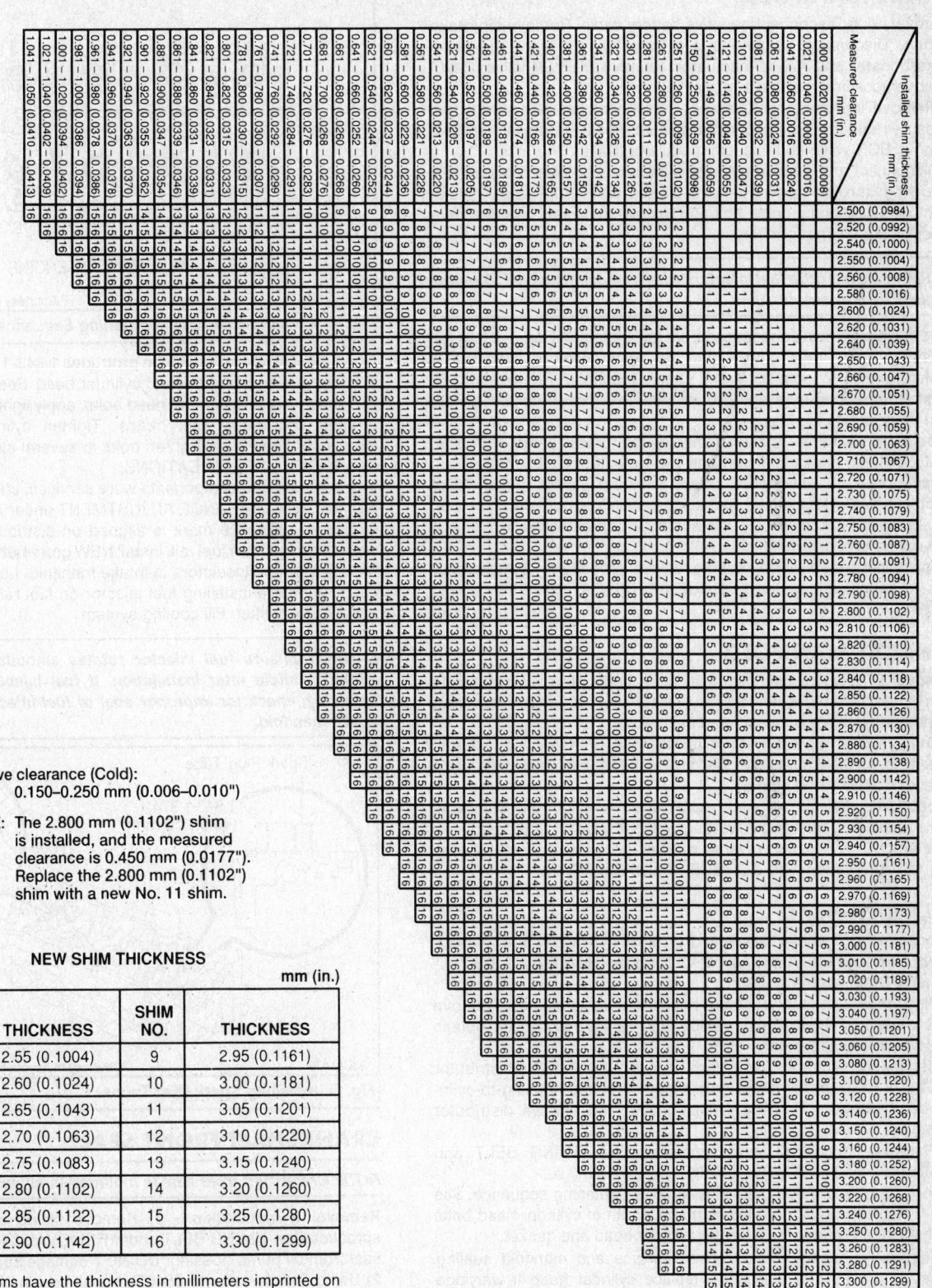

Intake valve clearance (Cold):
0.150–0.250 mm (0.006–0.010")

EXAMPLE: The 2.800 mm (0.1102") shim
is installed, and the measured
clearance is 0.450 mm (0.0177").
Replace the 2.800 mm (0.1102")
shim with a new No. 11 shim.

NEW SHIM THICKNESS
mm (in.)

SHIM NO.	THICKNESS	SHIM NO.	THICKNESS
1	2.55 (0.1004)	9	2.95 (0.1161)
2	2.60 (0.1024)	10	3.00 (0.1181)
3	2.65 (0.1043)	11	3.05 (0.1201)
4	2.70 (0.1063)	12	3.10 (0.1220)
5	2.75 (0.1083)	13	3.15 (0.1240)
6	2.80 (0.1102)	14	3.20 (0.1260)
7	2.85 (0.1122)	15	3.25 (0.1280)
8	2.90 (0.1142)	16	3.30 (0.1299)

HINT: New shims have the thickness in millimeters imprinted on the face.

93G82152

Courtesy of General Motors Corp.

Fig. 3: Intake Valve Adjusting Shim Selection Chart

INTAKE MANIFOLD

Removal – 1) Disconnect negative battery cable. Remove air intake ducting. Disconnect vacuum hoses from fuel pressure regulator, brake booster and A/C idle actuator. Remove EGR SV valve (Calif.) Remove accelerator cable and bracket.

2) Remove intake manifold brace. Disconnect fuel hose from fuel pressure regulator. Remove metal vacuum lines from intake manifold. Remove EGR valve and vacuum modulator (Calif.).

3) Disconnect and remove necessary vacuum and electrical connections from throttle body. Remove throttle body from upper intake chamber. Disconnect union bolt and remove fuel inlet hose. Remove upper intake chamber cover.

CAUTION: Do not drop fuel injectors when removing fuel rail. Damage to injectors may result.

---

4) Remove electrical connections from fuel injectors. Remove fuel rail mounting bolts and remove fuel rail with injectors. Remove 4 insulators and 2 spacers from intake manifold. Remove intake manifold mounting nuts and ground strap. Remove intake manifold from cylinder head.

Inspection – Check intake manifold for cracks and warpage. Replace intake manifold if warpage exceeds .0039" (.099 mm).

Installation – 1) Install NEW intake manifold gasket. Install NEW injector insulators in intake manifold. Install fuel rail with injectors. Ensure injectors rotate freely. If injectors do not rotate freely, "O" rings may not be properly installed.

2) To complete installation, reverse removal procedure. Tighten bolts/ nuts to specification. See TORQUE SPECIFICATIONS. Fill cooling system.

EXHAUST MANIFOLD

Removal – 1) Disconnect negative battery cable. Remove heat shield from exhaust manifold. If necessary, disconnect oxygen sensor wiring connector. Remove exhaust manifold brace.

2) Remove warm-up catalyst (California models). Disconnect exhaust pipe from exhaust manifold. Remove exhaust manifold bolts/nuts, exhaust manifold and gasket.

Inspection – Check exhaust manifold for cracks and warpage. Replace exhaust manifold if warpage exceeds .0039" (.099 mm).

Installation – To install, reverse removal procedure. Tighten bolts/ nuts to specification. See TORQUE SPECIFICATIONS.

CYLINDER HEAD

Removal – 1) Remove intake and exhaust manifolds. See INTAKE MANIFOLD and EXHAUST MANIFOLD under REMOVAL & INSTALLATION. Drain engine coolant.

2) Disconnect necessary coolant hoses and vacuum lines. Remove EGR valve and lines. Raise vehicle and remove right side splash shield. Remove alternator.

3) Disconnect electrical connections at distributor. Remove distributor cap. Mark rotor-to-distributor housing position and housing-to-cylinder head position. Remove retaining bolt, and remove distributor assembly.

4) Remove timing belt and camshafts. See TIMING BELT and CAMSHAFT under REMOVAL & INSTALLATION.

5) Loosen cylinder head bolts in reverse of tightening sequence. *See Fig. 4.* Remove bolts, note location and length of cylinder head bolts for installation reference. Remove cylinder head and gasket.

Inspection – Inspect cylinder head surface and manifold sealing areas for cracks and warpage. Replace cylinder head if warpage exceeds specification. Inspect cylinder block deck warpage along all 4 edges and diagonally across cylinder head. Replace cylinder block if warpage exceeds specification. See CYLINDER HEAD and CYLINDER BLOCK tables under ENGINE SPECIFICATIONS.

Installation – 1) If spark plug tubes were removed or new cylinder head is installed, install spark plug tubes before head is installed on engine block. Use RTV silicone sealer/adhesive or equivalent to coat bore of cylinder head for spark plug tube. Using Press, install spark

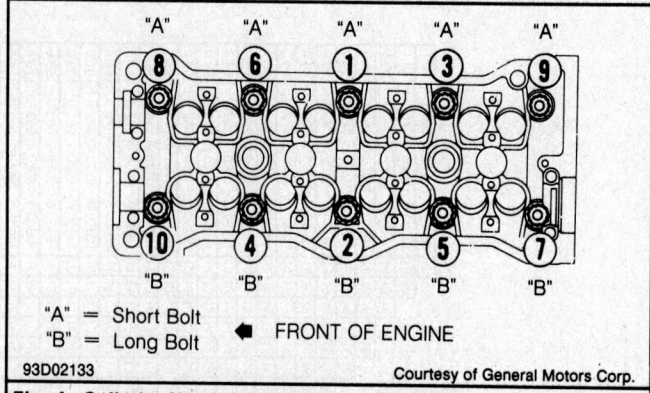

"A" = Short Bolt
"B" = Long Bolt   ◀ FRONT OF ENGINE
93D02133   Courtesy of General Motors Corp.

Fig. 4: Cylinder Head Bolt Tightening Sequence

plug tubes into bores until tube protrudes 1.843-1.874" (46.8-47.6 mm) from top horizontal surface of cylinder head. *See Fig. 5.*

2) Before installing cylinder head bolts, apply light coat of engine oil to threads and below bolt heads. Tighten cylinder head bolts in sequence. *See Fig. 4.* Tighten bolts in several steps to specification. See TORQUE SPECIFICATIONS.

3) If cylinder head components were serviced, check valve clearance. See VALVE CLEARANCE ADJUSTMENT under ADJUSTMENTS.

4) Ensure reference mark is aligned on distributor. If fuel injectors were removed from fuel rail, install NEW grommet and "O" ring on each fuel injector and insulators in intake manifold. Lubricate "O" ring with gasoline before installing fuel injector on fuel rail. Install valve cover using NEW gasket. Fill cooling system.

CAUTION: Ensure fuel injector rotates smoothly on fuel rail and intake manifold after installation. If fuel injector does not rotate smoothly, check for improper seal of fuel injector on fuel rail and intake manifold.

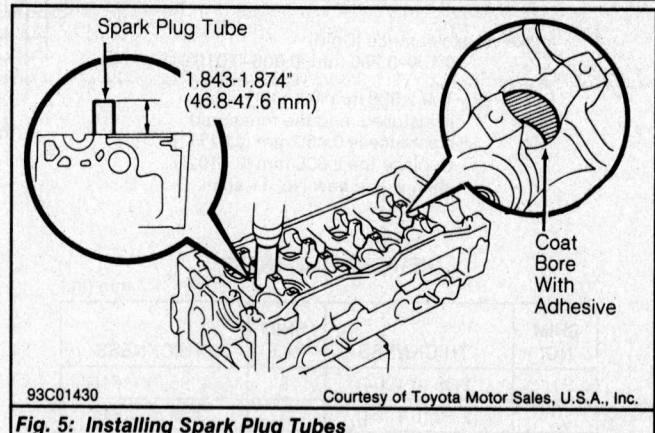

93C01430   Courtesy of Toyota Motor Sales, U.S.A., Inc.

Fig. 5: Installing Spark Plug Tubes

CRANKSHAFT FRONT SEAL

NOTE: Crankshaft front seal is mounted in oil pump housing.

Removal & Installation – 1) Remove timing belt and crankshaft sprocket. See TIMING BELT under REMOVAL & INSTALLATION. Pry seal from oil pump housing. DO NOT damage sealing surfaces.

2) Using Seal Installer (J-35403), install seal in oil pump housing. To install remaining components, reverse removal procedure.

TIMING BELT

CAUTION: Do not turn crankshaft or camshaft independently when timing belt is removed. Binding or damage to engine components could result.

Removal – 1) Disconnect negative battery cable. Remove cruise control actuator. Raise and support vehicle. Remove right front wheel and engine undercover. Loosen water pump pulley bolts. Remove accessory drive belts.

2) Remove windshield washer reservoir (with standard brakes). If necessary, remove A/C compressor with hoses attached. Remove valve cover. Remove spark plugs. Align crankshaft to cylinder No. 1 TDC. Ensure valve lifters on No. 1 cylinder are loose. If not, rotate crankshaft one complete revolution.

3) Disconnect engine ground wire from right fender apron. Support engine with floor jack. Remove through-bolt at engine mount, located near timing belt cover. Raise engine slightly. Remove water pump pulley. Using Crankshaft Pulley Puller (J-18592D-03) and Crankshaft Pulley Holder (J-86142D-01), remove crankshaft pulley. Lower engine. Remove timing belt covers.

4) Remove timing belt guide. *See Fig. 6.* Loosen belt tensioner bolt. Move belt tensioner pulley away from timing belt, and temporarily tighten belt tensioner pulley bolt. Remove timing belt.

CAUTION: If timing belt is to be reused, mark direction of timing belt rotation, and place reference marks on timing belt and sprockets for installation reference.

---

5) Remove camshaft sprocket (if necessary) by removing retaining bolt while holding camshaft at hexagonal section with wrench. If crankshaft sprocket is to be removed, gently pry off using 2 flat-bladed screwdrivers.

Inspection – 1) Inspect timing belt for cracks or damaged teeth. Ensure timing belt is not contaminated with oil. Check belt tensioner pulley for smooth rotation. Replace damaged components.

2) Check free length of belt tensioner spring. Free length is measured from inside end to inside end of spring (not coil area). Replace spring if free length is not 1.390" (35.3 mm) on 1.6L engine or 1.252 (31.8) on 1.8L engine. Stretch spring to 1.988" (50.5 mm), which is its installed length, and measure spring tension. Replace spring if tension is not 13.0 lbs. (5.9 kg) on 1.6L engine or 26.5 lbs. (12.0 kg) on 1.8L engine.

Installation – 1) Install crankshaft and camshaft sprockets (if removed). Tighten retaining bolt to specification. See TORQUE SPECIFICATIONS.

2) Ensure all timing marks are aligned. *See Fig. 7.* Install timing belt. If reusing old timing belt, ensure belt is installed in original rotating direction. Ensure marks made on old belt align with camshaft and crankshaft sprockets.

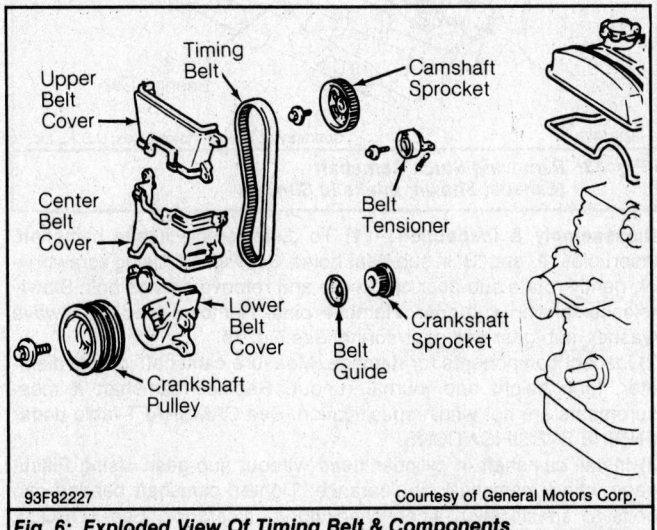

93F82227   Courtesy of General Motors Corp.

Fig. 6: Exploded View Of Timing Belt & Components

3) Loosen belt tensioner bolt to allow tension to be applied on timing belt. Rotate crankshaft clockwise 2 revolutions. Ensure all timing marks are aligned. Tighten timing belt idler pulley bolts to specification. See TORQUE SPECIFICATIONS.

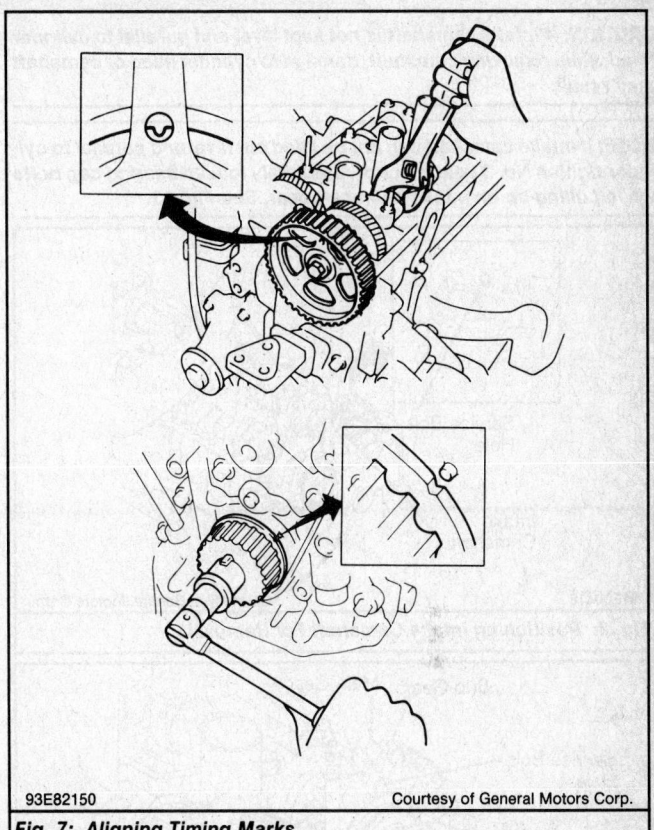

93E82150   Courtesy of General Motors Corp.

Fig. 7: Aligning Timing Marks

4) Measure timing belt deflection halfway between camshaft and crankshaft sprockets. With 4.4 lbs. (2.0 kg) applied to timing belt, deflection should be .20-.24" (5-6 mm). If belt deflection is not within specification, repeat steps **3)** and **4)**.

CAUTION: Ensure all timing marks are aligned once timing belt is adjusted.

---

5) To install remaining components, reverse removal procedure. Tighten bolts to specification. See TORQUE SPECIFICATIONS. Install valve cover with NEW valve cover gasket.

CAMSHAFT

Removal – 1) Remove timing belt, valve cover and camshaft sprocket. See TIMING BELT under REMOVAL & INSTALLATION. Using dial indicator, check camshaft end play before removing camshaft.

2) If end play is greater than specification, replace camshaft and check camshaft end play again. If end play is still greater than specification, replace camshaft bearing caps and cylinder head as a set. See CAMSHAFT table under ENGINE SPECIFICATIONS.

NOTE: Camshaft bearing caps are marked either with an "I" for intake camshaft or an "E" for exhaust camshaft. Camshaft bearing caps are numbered starting with No. 1 at timing belt end of cylinder head. Ensure arrow on bearing cap points toward timing belt end of engine.

---

3) To remove intake camshaft, rotate camshafts so knock pin on exhaust camshaft is at 10 o'clock position and service bolt hole on intake camshaft is at 12 o'clock position. *See Fig. 8.* Remove No. 1 camshaft bearing caps on exhaust and intake camshafts. Install a bolt with dimensions of 6mm x 1.0mm x approximately 18mm in length into service bolt hole in intake camshaft gear. *See Fig. 9.*

4) Loosen remaining intake camshaft bearing caps evenly in sequence. *See Fig. 10.* Remove camshaft bearing caps and remove intake camshaft. Ensure camshaft remains level and parallel to cylinder head during removal.

CAUTION: *If intake camshaft is not kept level and parallel to cylinder head while removing camshaft, damage to cylinder head or camshaft may result.*

NOTE: *If intake camshaft can not be lifted out level and parallel to cylinder tighten No. 3 bearing cap. Alternately loosen bearing cap bolts while pulling up on intake camshaft gear. See Fig. 13.*

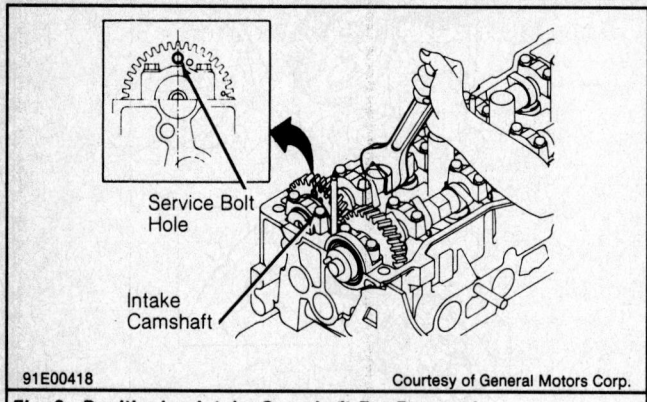

Fig. 8: **Positioning Intake Camshaft For Removal**

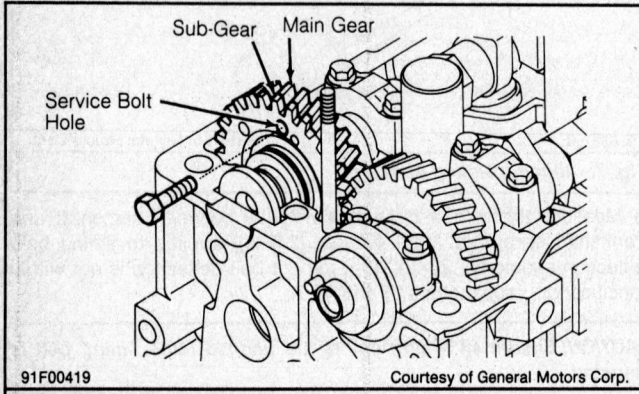

Fig. 9: **Installing Service Bolt**

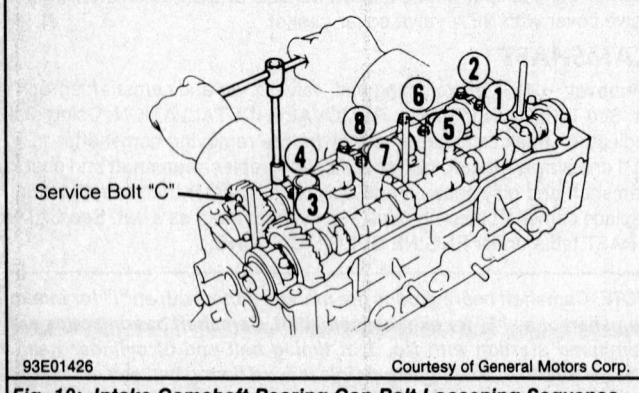

Fig. 10: **Intake Camshaft Bearing Cap Bolt Loosening Sequence**

5) To remove exhaust camshaft, rotate camshaft so knock pin is positioned in 5 o'clock position. *See Fig. 11.* Note location and direction of camshaft bearing caps.

6) Loosen remaining exhaust camshaft bearing caps evenly in sequence. *See Fig. 12.* Remove camshaft bearing caps, camshaft and oil seal. If camshaft binds during removal procedure DO NOT force camshaft from cylinder head, tighten No. 3 camshaft bearing cap. Loosen bolts evenly while lifting camshaft. *See Fig. 13.*

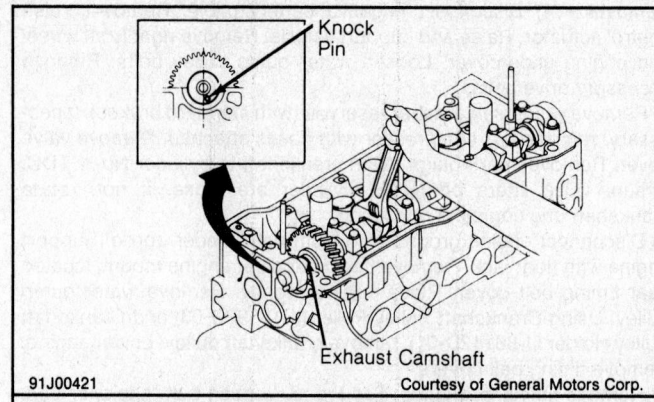

Fig. 11: **Positioning Exhaust Camshaft For Removal**

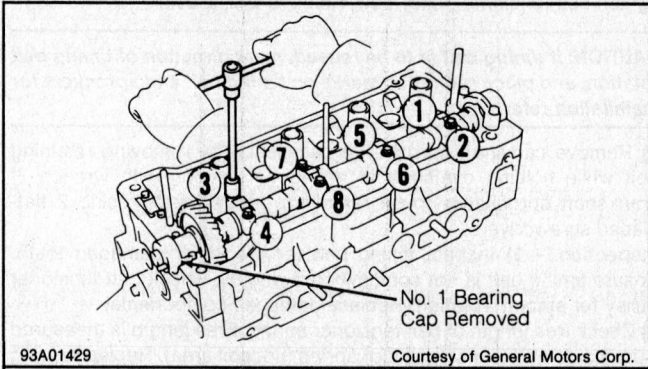

Fig. 12: **Exhaust Camshaft Bearing Cap Bolt Loosening Sequence**

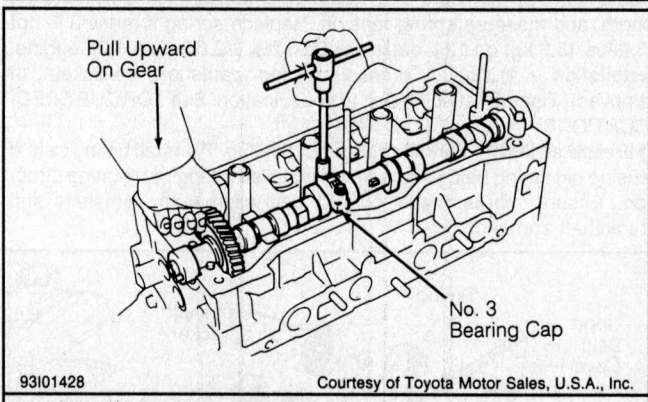

Fig. 13: **Removing Stuck Camshaft**
(Exhaust Shown; Intake Is Similar)

Disassembly & Inspection – 1) To disassemble intake camshaft, insert pins "A" and "B" in sub-gear holes. *See Fig. 14.* Using screwdriver, gently rotate sub-gear clockwise and remove service bolt. Slowly release tension sub-gear. Remove pins. Remove snap ring, wave washer, sub-gear and gear spring. *See Fig. 15.*

2) Inspect components for damage. Measure camshaft journal diameter, lobe height and journal runout. Replace camshaft if measurements are not within specification. See CAMSHAFT table under ENGINE SPECIFICATIONS.

3) Install camshaft in cylinder head without sub-gear. Using Plastigage, check camshaft oil clearance. Tighten camshaft bearing cap bolts to specification when checking oil clearance. See TORQUE SPECIFICATIONS. Replace camshaft and/or cylinder head if oil clearance is not within specification. See CAMSHAFT table under ENGINE SPECIFICATIONS.

4) Check camshaft end play with camshaft bearing cap bolts tightened to specification. Replace camshaft and/or cylinder head if end play is not within specification. See CAMSHAFT table under ENGINE SPECIFICATIONS.

5) Use a dial indicator to check gear backlash between camshaft gears. Replace both camshafts if backlash exceeds specification. See CAMSHAFT table under ENGINE SPECIFICATIONS.

6) Measure distance between ends of gear spring. Replace gear spring if distance is not .669-.693" (17.0-17.6 mm).

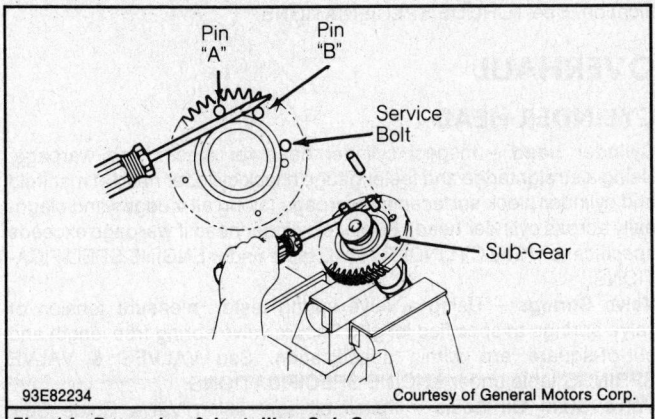

Fig. 14: Removing & Installing Sub-Gear

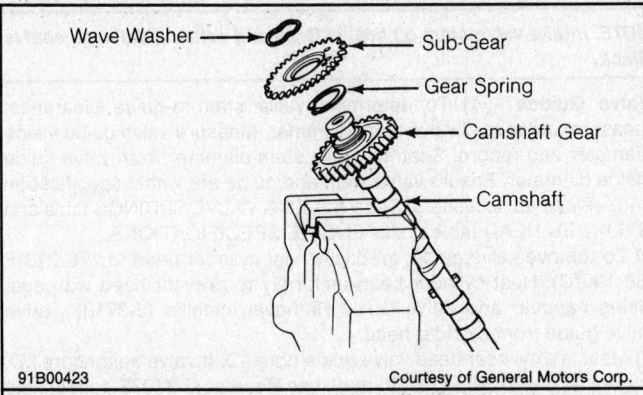

Fig. 15: Exploded View Of Intake Camshaft & Components

Reassembly & Installation – 1) Install gear spring, sub-gear and wave washer. *See Fig. 15.* Align pin on gear with gear spring ends. Install snap ring. Install pins "A" and "B" in sub-gear. *See Fig. 14.* Using screwdriver, gently rotate sub-gear clockwise. Install service bolt and remove pins.

CAUTION: Keep camshaft level during installation, or camshaft binding and breakage may occur.

2) To install exhaust camshaft, lubricate thrust area of camshaft with lithium grease. Install exhaust camshaft so knock pin is in 4 o'clock position. This angle allows No. 1 and No. 3 cylinder cam lobes to push on valve lifters evenly. Apply RTV sealer (1052917) to No. 1 bearing cap. Apply engine oil to bolt threads and underside of bolt heads. Install exhaust camshaft bearing caps and bolts on cylinder head.

CAUTION: Ensure arrow on camshaft bearing cap points toward timing belt end of engine. Install caps so numbers are in order.

3) Tighten bolts on exhaust camshaft bearing caps evenly in sequence. *See Fig. 16.* Tighten bolts to specification. See TORQUE SPECIFICATIONS.

4) Apply lithium grease on camshaft oil seal. Using Seal Installer (J-35403), install seal on exhaust camshaft.

CAUTION: DO NOT confuse TDC marks with camshaft aligning marks. During camshaft installation, ensure installing marks, not TDC marks, are aligned.

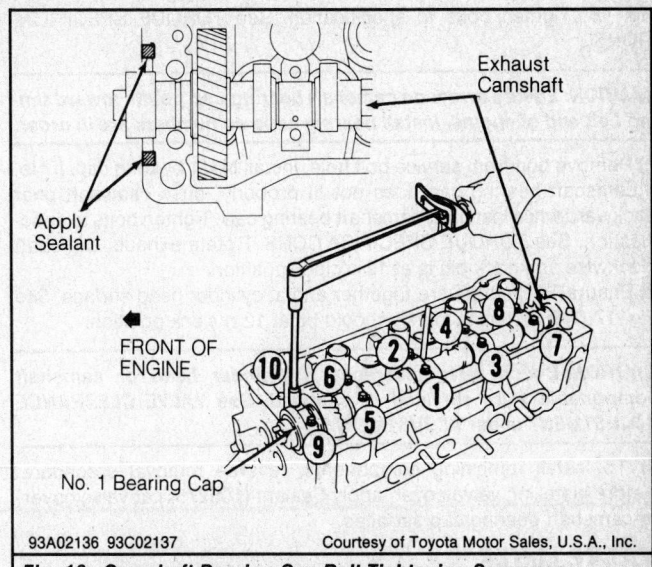

Fig. 16: Camshaft Bearing Cap Bolt Tightening Sequence (Exhaust Shown; Intake Is Similar)

5) To install intake camshaft, rotate exhaust camshaft so knock pin is at about 10 o'clock position. *See Fig. 17.* Lubricate thrust area of camshaft with multipurpose grease. Install intake camshaft so installing marks on camshaft gears are aligned.

6) Install all camshaft bearing caps, except No. 1, on cylinder head. Tighten both bolts on each camshaft bearing cap in sequence. *See*

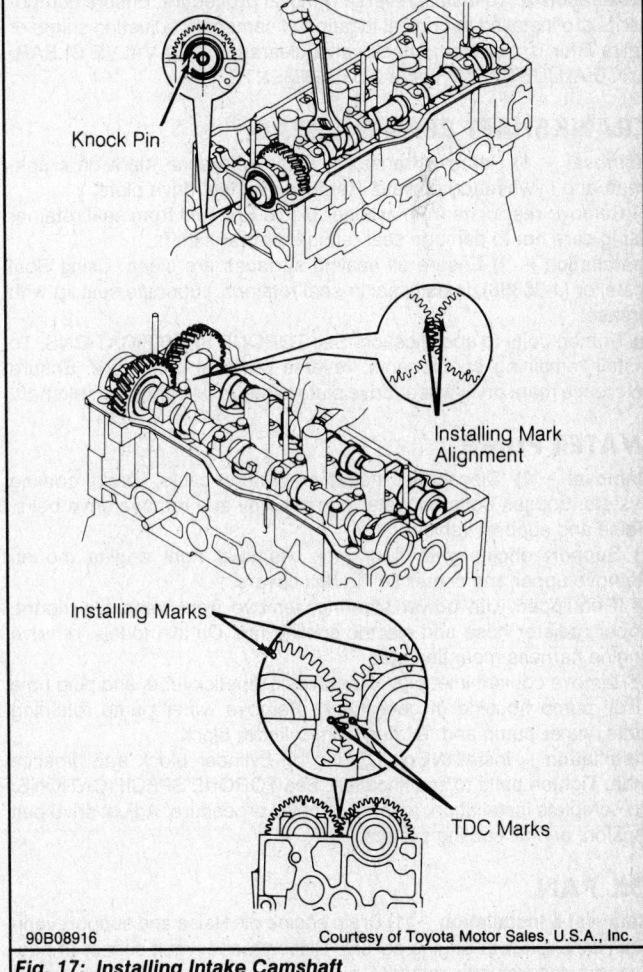

Fig. 17: Installing Intake Camshaft

Fig. 16. Tighten bolts to specification. See TORQUE SPECIFICATIONS.

CAUTION: Ensure arrow on camshaft bearing cap points toward timing belt end of engine. Install bearing caps so numbers are in order.

---

7) Remove bolt from service bolt hole. Install No. 1 bearing cap. If No. 1 camshaft bearing cap does not fit properly, push camshaft gear backward while installing camshaft bearing cap. Tighten bolts to specification. See TORQUE SPECIFICATIONS. Rotate exhaust camshaft clockwise so knock pin is at 12 o'clock position.
8) Ensure TDC marks are together and at cylinder head surface. *See Fig. 17.* The installing marks should be at 12 o'clock position.

CAUTION: Check valve clearance if cylinder head or camshaft components were serviced or changed. See VALVE CLEARANCE ADJUSTMENT under ADJUSTMENTS.

---

9) To install remaining components, reverse removal procedure. Before installing valve cover, apply Sealant (1052751) at valve cover-to-camshaft bearing cap surfaces.

VALVE LIFTER

Removal – Remove camshaft. See CAMSHAFT under REMOVAL & INSTALLATION. Note location of adjusting shims and valve lifter for installation reference. Remove adjusting shim and valve lifter from cylinder head.
Inspection – Inspect valve lifter and bore for damage. Measure O.D. of valve lifter. Replace valve lifter if damaged, or O.D. is not within specification. See VALVE LIFTERS table under ENGINE SPECIFICATIONS at end of article.
Installation – To install, reverse removal procedure. Ensure components are installed in original location. If camshaft, adjusting shims or valve lifter is replaced, check valve clearance. See VALVE CLEARANCE ADJUSTMENT under ADJUSTMENTS.

CRANKSHAFT REAR OIL SEAL

Removal – **1)** Remove transaxle. Place reference mark on crankshaft and flywheel/drive plate. Remove flywheel/drive plate.
2) Remove rear plate from cylinder block. Pry seal from seal retainer using care not to damage seal retainer or crankshaft.
Installation – **1)** Ensure all sealing surfaces are clean. Using Seal Installer (J-35388), install seal in seal retainer. Lubricate seal lip with grease.
2) Tighten bolts to specification. See TORQUE SPECIFICATIONS. To install remaining components, reverse removal procedure. Ensure reference mark on flywheel/drive plate aligns with mark on crankshaft.

WATER PUMP

Removal – **1)** Disconnect negative battery cable. Drain cooling system. Loosen bolts on water pump pulley and remove drive belts. Raise and support vehicle.
2) Support engine with floor jack. Remove right engine mount. Remove upper and center timing belt covers.
3) If equipped with power steering, remove front transaxle mount, upper radiator hose and electric cooling fan. On all models, remove engine harness mounting bolt.
4) Remove coolant inlet pipe. Remove oil dipstick tube, and plug hole in oil pump housing (if necessary). Remove water pump retaining bolts, water pump and "O" ring from cylinder block.
Installation – Install NEW "O" ring on cylinder block and dipstick tube. Tighten bolts to specification. See TORQUE SPECIFICATIONS. To complete installation, reverse removal procedure. Adjust drive belt tension, and fill cooling system.

OIL PAN

Removal & Installation – **1)** Drain engine oil. Raise and support vehicle. Remove lower engine covers. Disconnect oxygen sensor (if necessary) and remove exhaust pipe. Remove engine reinforcement bracket (if equipped). Remove oil pan bolts and oil pan.

2) On 1.8L, remove oil pan baffle plate. Remove upper oil pan by removing 3 upper oil pan-to-transaxle bolts. Remove remaining upper oil pan bolts.
3) On all models, to install, reverse removal procedure. Apply Sealant (1050026) to oil pan gasket(s) before installing. Tighten bolts to specification. See TORQUE SPECIFICATIONS.

OVERHAUL

CYLINDER HEAD

Cylinder Head – Inspect cylinder head for cracks and warpage. Using a straightedge and feeler gauge check cylinder head at manifold and cylinder block surfaces for warpage (along all 4 edges and diagonally across cylinder head). Replace cylinder head if warpage exceeds specification. See CYLINDER HEAD table under ENGINE SPECIFICATIONS.
Valve Springs – Using a valve spring tester, measure tension of valve springs at specified length. Ensure valve spring free length and out-of-square are within specification. See VALVES & VALVE SPRINGS table under ENGINE SPECIFICATIONS.
Valve Stem Oil Seals – Install oil seal using Valve Guide Seal Installer (J-38232).

NOTE: Intake valve stem oil seal is Gray and exhaust valve oil seal is Black.

Valve Guides – **1)** To determine valve stem-to-guide clearance, measure and record valve stem diameter. Measure valve guide inside diameter and record. Subtract valve stem diameter from valve guide inside diameter. Ensure valve stem and guide are within specification and replace as necessary. See VALVES & VALVE SPRINGS table and CYLINDER HEAD table under ENGINE SPECIFICATIONS.
2) To remove valve guide, gradually heat cylinder head to 176-212°F (80-100°C). Heat cylinder head uniformly to prevent head warpage. Using hammer and Valve Guide Remover/Installer (J-37133), drive valve guide from cylinder head.
3) Measure cylinder head valve guide bore I.D. If valve guide bore I.D. is greater than .4341" (11.026 mm), use Reamer (J-37972) to machine cylinder head bore to .4350-.4361" (11.049-11.077 mm) for oversized valve guide. If valve guide bore I.D. is greater than .4361" (11.077 mm), replace cylinder head.
4) To install valve guide, gradually heat cylinder head to 176-212°F (80-100°C). Heat cylinder head uniformly to prevent head warpage. Using hammer, Valve Guide Remover/Installer (J-37133) and Adapter (J-38277), drive valve guide into cylinder head.

CAUTION: Install valve guide so installed height above cylinder head surface is .500-.516" (12.70-13.11 mm).

---

5) Using Reamer (J-38342), ream valve guide to obtain correct valve stem oil clearance. See CYLINDER HEAD table under ENGINE SPECIFICATIONS.
Valve Seat – Replacement information is not available from manufacturer.
Valves – Ensure valve stem diameter and valve margin are within specification. Check valve contact pattern and overall length. See VALVES & VALVE SPRINGS table under ENGINE SPECIFICATIONS.
Seat Correction Angles – To lower valve seat surface on valve, cut seat at 30 degrees and 45 degrees. To raise valve seat surface on valve, cut seat at 60 degrees and 45 degrees.

CYLINDER BLOCK ASSEMBLY

Piston & Rod Assembly – **1)** Note direction of connecting rod installation on piston before removing. Check rods for bend and twist. Replace rods if bend or twist exceeds specification. See CONNECTING RODS table under ENGINE SPECIFICATIONS.
2) Measure connecting rod bolts for stretching. On 1.6L, measure rod bolt .59" (15 mm) from rod *See Fig. 18.* Minimum diameter is .3386" (8.60 mm). On 1.8L, measure rod bolt .787" (20 mm) from head of bolt.

See Fig. 18. Minimum diameter is .276" (7.0mm). On all engines, replace rod bolt and nut if less than minimum diameter.

3) Note mark at center of connecting rod. Ensure mark is aligned with front mark on top of piston. *See Fig. 19*. Install connecting rod in original direction. Install piston with front mark on piston top toward timing belt end of engine.

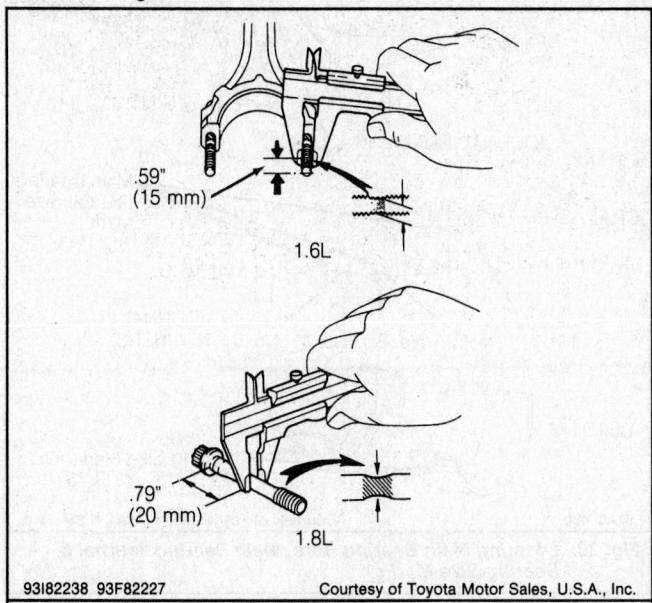

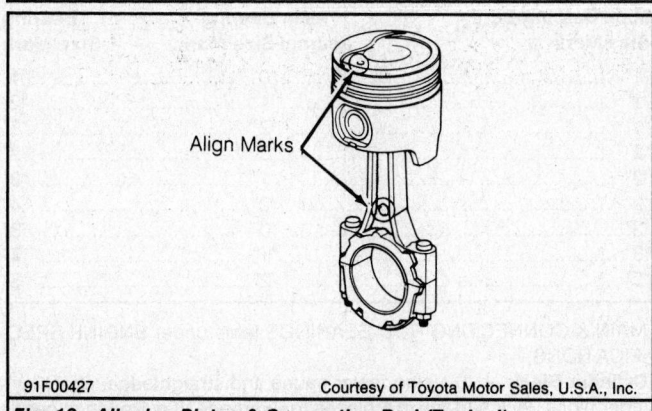

93I82238 93F82227

Courtesy of Toyota Motor Sales, U.S.A., Inc.

Fig. 18: Measuring Connecting Rod Bolts For Stretching

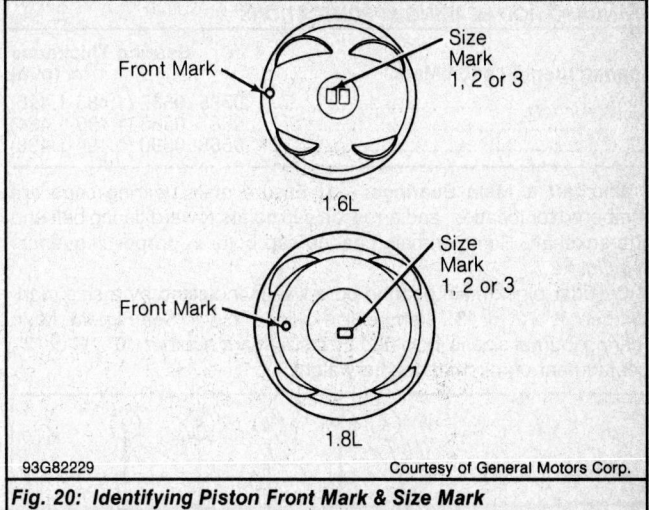

93G82229

Courtesy of General Motors Corp.

Fig. 20: Identifying Piston Front Mark & Size Mark

4) To determine piston clearance, subtract piston diameter from cylinder diameter. If clearance exceeds specification and cylinder taper and out-of-round are within specification, replace piston with standard piston. If any cylinder measurement exceeds specification, bore all cylinders to uniform diameter and replace all pistons with oversize pistons to maintain balance. See PISTONS, PINS & RINGS table under ENGINE SPECIFICATIONS.

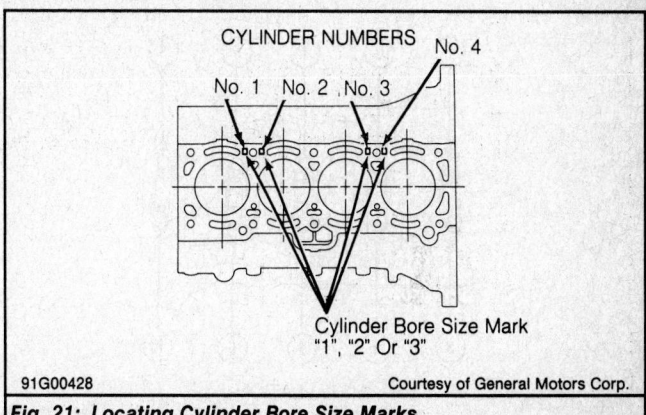

91G00428

Courtesy of General Motors Corp.

Fig. 21: Locating Cylinder Bore Size Marks

91F00427

Courtesy of Toyota Motor Sales, U.S.A., Inc.

Fig. 19: Aligning Piston & Connecting Rod (Typical)

NOTE: Three different standard sizes of piston and cylinder bore are used. Piston and cylinder bore sizes are identified by a numerical size mark, "1", "2" or "3". Piston size is stamped on piston top and cylinder bore size is stamped on cylinder block deck surface. See Figs. 20 and 21.

Fitting Pistons – 1) To determine if piston-to-cylinder clearance is within specification, measure piston skirt diameter at 90-degree angle to piston pin, .956" (24.5 mm) from top of piston.
2) Three standard piston sizes are used. Piston size is identified by a numerical size mark, "1", "2" or "3", stamped on top of piston. *See Fig. 20.* See PISTONS, PINS & RINGS table under ENGINE SPECIFICATIONS to obtain piston diameter specification for the specific size mark number. Ensure piston diameter is within specification.
3) Three standard cylinder bore sizes are used. Cylinder bore size is identified by a numerical size mark, "1", "2" or "3", stamped on deck surface. *See Fig. 21.* See CYLINDER BLOCK table under ENGINE SPECIFICATIONS to obtain diameter specification for specific size mark number. Cylinder bore diameter is measured .39" (10 mm) from top and bottom of bore, and at middle of bore. Make 2 measurements (front-to-rear and side-to-side) at top middle and bottom of each cylinder to find taper and out-of-round.

Piston Rings – Ensure ring end gap and side clearance are within specification. See PISTONS, PINS & RINGS table under ENGINE SPECIFICATIONS. Position piston ring gaps 90 degrees apart. Ensure ring end gaps are not aligned, and ensure ring gaps do not align with piston pin.
Rod Bearings – 1) Note direction of connecting rod and cap before removal for reassembly reference. If bearings are to be reused, measure bearing oil clearance using Plastigage before removing pistons. Check rod side play. See CONNECTING RODS and CRANKSHAFT, MAIN & CONNECTING ROD BEARINGS tables under ENGINE SPECIFICATIONS.
2) Rod bearings are available in 3 standard sizes. Rod bearing size is indicated by a numerical identification mark, "1", "2" or "3", stamped on back side bearing shell and on connecting rod cap . Identification mark is used to determine bearing thickness. See STANDARD ROD BEARING SPECIFICATIONS table.
3) Install piston and rod assembly. Check rod bearing clearance using Plastigage method. Tighten rod bolts in 2 steps to specification, then turn nut an additional 90 degrees. If rod bearing clearance is excessive, measure crankpin journal diameter. If crankpin journal diameter is within specification, replace bearing with a standard bearing. If crankpin journal is less than minimum specification, a .0098" (.25mm) undersize bearing is available. Regrind crankshaft to fit undersize bearing if necessary.

STANDARD ROD BEARING SPECIFICATIONS

Bearing Identification Mark	Bearing Thickness In. (mm)
"1"	.0585-.0587 (1.486-1.490)
"2"	.0587-.0588 (1.490-1.494)
"3"	.0588-.0590 (1.494-1.498)

Crankshaft & Main Bearings – 1) Ensure main bearing caps are numbered for location, and arrow on cap points toward timing belt end of crankshaft. Remove main bearing cap bolts in proper sequence. *See Fig. 22.*

2) Cylinder block main bearing bore size is indicated by a size mark number, "1", "2" or "3", stamped on cylinder block. *See Fig. 23.* Main bearing journal size is indicated by a size mark number, "0", "1" or "2", located near crankshaft counterweight.

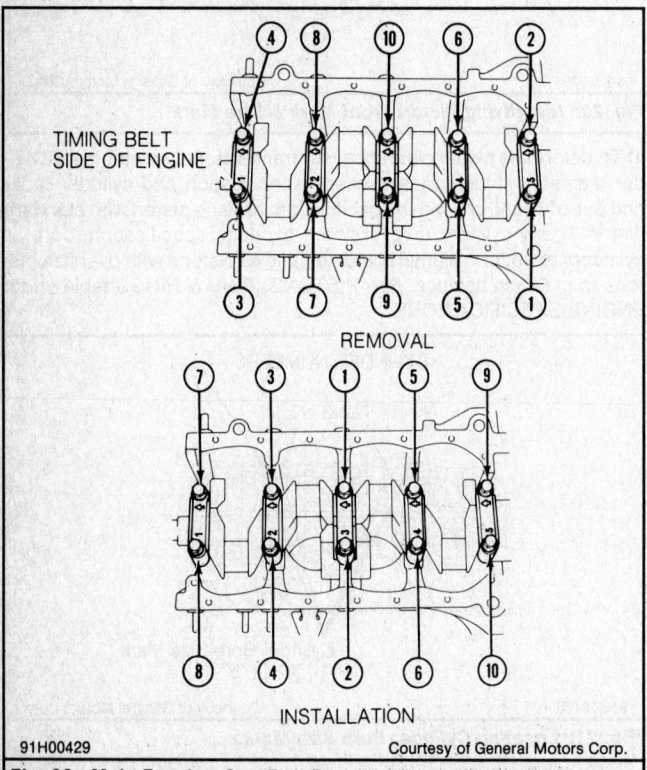

TIMING BELT SIDE OF ENGINE

REMOVAL

INSTALLATION

91H00429 Courtesy of General Motors Corp.

Fig. 22: Main Bearing Cap Bolt Removal & Installation Sequence

3) Measure main bearing clearance using Plastigage method. Main bearing clearance should be .0006-.0013" (.015-.033 mm). Maximum wear tolerance is .004 (.10 mm). If bearing clearance is excessive, measure crankshaft main bearing journals. Measure journals at each end of journal and 90 degrees from first readings. Grind crankshaft to .0098" (.25mm) undersize or replace crankshaft if journal minimum diameter, taper or out-of-round are not within specification.

4) When replacing worn bearings on a crankshaft that is within original specification, use size markings on bearings to identify replacement bearing. If bearing size mark on original bearing cannot be obtained, use number on cylinder block (main bearing bore size mark) and number on crankshaft (main bearing journal size mark) to determine bearing number. See MAIN BEARING SELECTION table.

5) When installing main bearing caps, ensure arrow on cap points toward timing belt end of crankshaft. Tighten bolts in sequence. *See Fig. 22.*

6) Tighten bolts to specification. See TORQUE SPECIFICATIONS. Ensure crankshaft end play is within specification. See CRANK-SHAFT, MAIN & CONNECTING ROD BEARINGS table under ENGINE SPECIFICATIONS.

Thrust Bearing – Install thrust bearing on main bearing, with grooves toward crankshaft, away from cylinder block. Replace thrust bearing if crankshaft end play is not within specification. See CRANKSHAFT,

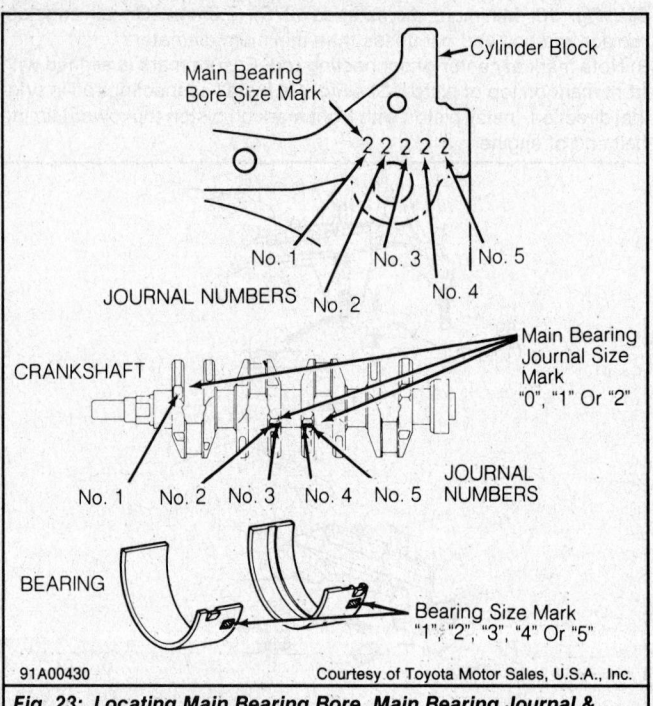

91A00430 Courtesy of Toyota Motor Sales, U.S.A., Inc.

Fig. 23: Locating Main Bearing Bore, Main Bearing Journal & Bearing Size Marks

MAIN BEARING SELECTION

Main Bearing Bore Size Mark	Main Bearing Journal Size Mark	Bearing Size Mark
"1"	"0"	"1"
"1"	"1"	"2"
"1"	"2"	"3"
"2"	"0"	"2"
"2"	"1"	"3"
"2"	"2"	"4"
"3"	"0"	"3"
"3"	"1"	"4"
"3"	"2"	"5"

MAIN & CONNECTING ROD BEARINGS table under ENGINE SPECIFICATIONS.

Cylinder Block – 1) Using feeler gauge and straightedge, check cylinder block deck surface in 6 places for warpage. If warpage exceeds specification, replace cylinder block. See CYLINDER BLOCK table under ENGINE SPECIFICATIONS.

2) Check cylinder bore wear and taper in 3 places. Cylinder block bore diameter is measured .39" (10 mm) from top and bottom of bore, and at middle of bore.

3) Various cylinder bore sizes are used. Cylinder bore size is identified by a numerical size mark, "1", "2" or "3", stamped on deck surface. *See Fig. 21.* Bore cylinder block if taper exceeds specification. See CYLINDER BLOCK table under ENGINE SPECIFICATIONS.

ENGINE OILING

ENGINE LUBRICATION SYSTEM

The crankshaft-driven oil pump provides lubrication to the main gallery. *See Fig. 24.*

Crankcase Capacity – Crankcase capacity with oil filter change is 3.5 qts. (3.3L) for 1.6L and 3.9 qts. (3.7L) for 1.8L.

Oil Pressure – With engine at normal operating temperature, oil pressure should be greater than 4.3 psi (.3 kg/cm²) at idle and 36-71 psi (2.5-5.0 kg/cm²) at 3000 RPM.

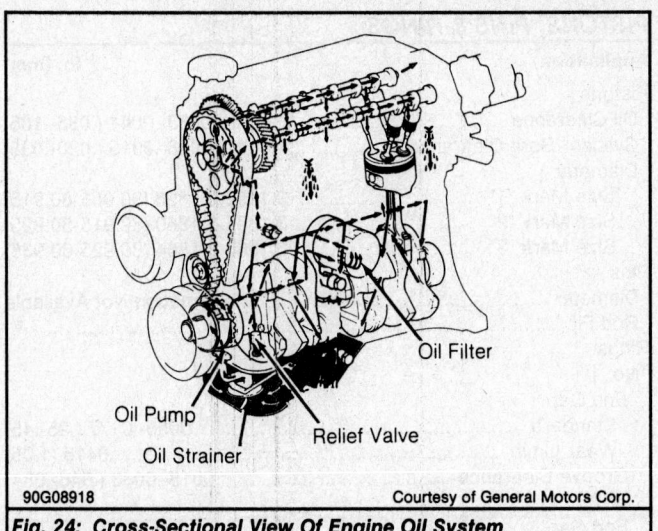

90G08918   Courtesy of General Motors Corp.

Fig. 24: Cross-Sectional View Of Engine Oil System

OIL PUMP

Removal & Disassembly – 1) Remove timing belt and crankshaft sprocket. See TIMING BELT under REMOVAL & INSTALLATION. Remove front exhaust pipe. Remove engine stiffener bracket (if equipped) and oil pan. See OIL PAN under REMOVAL & INSTALLATION.

2) Remove oil pump pickup. Remove dipstick from oil pump housing. Remove oil pump retaining bolts, and remove oil pump. Remove oil pump cover from rear of oil pump. Remove oil seal from oil pump housing. Remove snap ring, spring and relief valve from oil pump housing.

Inspection – 1) Inspect components for damage. Ensure relief valve slides freely in bore. Using feeler gauge, measure clearance between driven gear (outer gear) and oil pump housing. Replace pump assembly if clearance exceeds specification. See OIL PUMP SPECIFICATIONS table.

2) Measure tip clearance between driven gear (outer gear) and drive gear (inner gear). Replace gear set if clearance exceeds specification.

3) With all gears in oil pump housing, place straightedge across oil pump housing. Measure gear end clearance between both gears and straightedge. Replace oil pump assembly if clearance exceeds specification. See OIL PUMP SPECIFICATIONS table.

OIL PUMP SPECIFICATIONS

Application	In. (mm)
Rotor Side Clearance	.0010-.0033 (.025-.085)
Limit	.0039 (.099)
Rotor Tip Clearance	.0010-.0033 (.025-.085)
Limit	.0138 (.35)
Driven Gear-To-Pump Body Clearance	.0031-.0071 (.079-.180)
Limit	.0079 (.201)

Reassembly & Installation – 1) To reassemble, reverse disassembly procedure. Install oil seal using seal installer. Coat seal lip with grease. Tighten oil pump cover bolts to specification. See TORQUE SPECIFICATIONS.

2) To install, reverse removal procedure. Use new oil pump gaskets. Tighten all bolts to specification. See TORQUE SPECIFICATIONS.

TORQUE SPECIFICATIONS

TORQUE SPECIFICATIONS

Application	Ft. Lbs. (N.m)
A/C Compressor Bolts	18 (24)
A/C Compressor Mounting Bolts	35 (47)
Camshaft Sprocket Bolt	43 (58)
Center Transaxle Mount-To-Crossmember Nut	47 (64)
Connecting Rod Nut	
Step 1	21 (29)
Step 2 Turn Additional 90 Degrees	
Crankshaft Pulley Bolt	87 (118)
Cylinder Head Bolt	
Step 1	[1] 22 (30)
Step 2	[1] Turn Additional 90 Degrees
Step 3	[1] Turn Additional 90 Degrees
Drive Axle Nut	159 (216)
Exhaust Manifold Bolt/Nut	25 (34)
Flywheel/Drive Plate Bolt	
A/T	47 (64)
M/T	58 (79)
Fuel Rail Bolt	11 (15)
Fuel Inlet Union Bolt	22 (30)
Intake Manifold Support Bolts	
12 mm Bolts	14 (19)
14 mm Bolts	29 (39)
Intake Manifold Bolt/Nut	14 (19)
Lower Ball Joint-To-Steering	
Knuckle Nut	105 (142)
Main Bearing Cap Bolt	[2] 44 (60)
Oil Pump Bolt	16 (22)
Power Steering Pump Bolt	29 (39)
Power Steering Pump Bracket Bolt	32 (43)
Rear Transaxle Mount Through Bolt	64 (87)
Right Engine Mount (Timing Belt Side) Engine Mount	
Bracket-To-Body Mounting Bolt	18 (24)
Bracket-To-Engine Mount Bolts	47 (64)
Engine Mount Stud Nuts	38 (52)
Through Bolt Nut	
1.6L	134 (181)
1.8L	47 (64)
Spark Plugs	13 (18)
Starter Bolts	29 (39)
Transaxle-To-Engine Bolts	
A/T	47 (64)
M/T	34 (46)
Tie Rod End-To-Steering Knuckle Nut	40 (54)
Timing Belt Idler Pulley Bolt	27 (37)
Upper Oil Pan (1.8L)	
Torx Bolt	11 (15)
To-transaxle Bolt	17 (23)
Water Pump Bolt	11 (15)
Water Pump Pulley Bolt	17 (23)
Wheel Lug Nut	76 (103)
	INCH Lbs. (N.m)
Camshaft Bearing Cap Bolt	[3] 115 (13)
Oil Pan Bolt	44 (5)
Oil Pump Cover Bolt (Rotor Plate)	89 (10)
Oil Pump Pick-Up Tube Bolt	84 (9.5)
Upper Oil Pan-To-Engine Hex Bolts (1.8L)	69 (7.8)
Rear Seal Retainer Bolt	82 (9.3)
Timing Belt Cover Bolt	62 (7)
Valve Cover Bolt	53 (6)

[1] – Tighten bolts to specification in sequence. *See Fig. 4.*
[2] – Tighten bolts to specification in sequence. *See Fig. 22.*
[3] – Tighten bolt to specification in sequence. *See Fig. 16.*

ENGINE SPECIFICATIONS

GENERAL SPECIFICATIONS

Application	Specification
1.6L	
Displacement	97 Cu. In. (1.6L)
Bore	3.19" (81 mm)
Stroke	3.03" (77 mm)
Compression Ratio	9.5:1
Fuel System	MFI
Horsepower @ RPM	[1] 105 @ 5800
Torque Ft. Lbs. @ RPM	100 @ 4800
1.8L	
Displacement	108 Cu. In. (1.8L)
Bore	3.19" (81 mm)
Stroke	3.37" (85.5 mm)
Compression Ratio	9.5:1
Fuel System	MFI
Horsepower @ RPM	[2] 115 @ 5600
Torque Ft. Lbs. @ RPM	115 @ 2800

[1] – Horsepower For California Model Is 100 @ 5800
[2] – Horsepower For California Model Is 110 @ 5600

CRANKSHAFT, MAIN & CONNECTING ROD BEARINGS

Application	In. (mm)
Crankshaft	
End Play	
Standard	.0008-.0087 (.020-.221)
Wear Limit	.0118 (.300)
Maximum Runout	.0012 (.003)
Main Bearings	
Journal Diameter	
Size Mark "0"	1.8895-1.8898 (47.994-48.000)
Size Mark "1"	1.8893-1.8895 (47.988-47.994)
Size Mark "2"	1.8891-1.8893 (47.982-47.988)
Journal Out-Of-Round	.0008 (.020)
Journal Taper	.0008 (.020)
Oil Clearance	.0006-.0013 (.015-.033)
Connecting Rod Bearings	
Journal Diameter	
1.6L	1.5742-1.5748 (39.985-39.999)
1.8L	1.8892-1.8898 (47.985-48.000)
Journal Out-Of-Round	.0008 (.020)
Journal Taper	.0008 (.020)
Oil Clearance	
Standard	.0008-.0017 (.020-.044)
Wear Limit	.0031 (.079)

CONNECTING RODS

Application	In. (mm)
Maximum Bend	.002 Per 3.94 (.051 Per 100.1)
Maximum Twist	.002 Per 3.94 (.051 Per 100.1)
Connecting Rod Bolt Diameter	
1.6L	[1] .3386-.3543 (8.600-9.000)
1.8L	[1] .2760-.2870 (7.010-7.290)
Side Play	
Standard	.006-.01 (.015-.25)
Wear Limit	.0118 (.300)

[1] – Measure connecting rod bolt diameter at a point .60-.79" (15-20 mm) from head of bolt.

PISTONS, PINS & RINGS

Application	In. (mm)
Pistons	
Oil Clearance	.0033-.0041 (.085-.105)
Cylinder Bore Clearance	.0008-.0015 (.020-.038)
Diameter [1]	
Size Mark "1"	3.1852-3.1856 (80.905-80.915)
Size Mark "2"	3.1856-3.1860 (80.915-80.925)
Size Mark "3"	3.1860-3.1864 (80.925-80.935)
Pins	
Diameter	Information Not Available
Rod Fit	[2]
Rings	
No. 1	
End Gap	
Standard	.0098-.0177 (.25-.45)
Wear Limit	.0413 (1.05)
Groove Clearance	.0018-.0033 (.046-.084)
No. 2	
End Gap	
Standard	.0138-.0197 (.35-.50)
Wear Limit	.0472 (1.20)
Groove Clearance	.0012-.0028 (.030-.071)
No. 3 (Oil)	
End Gap	
Standard	.0059-.0177 (.15-.45)
Wear Limit	.0413 (1.05)

[1] – Piston diameter is determined by numerical size mark on top of piston. See Fig. 20.
[2] – Ensure piston moves freely back and forth on piston pin. Replace piston or piston pin if worn or damaged.

CYLINDER BLOCK

Application	In. (mm)
Cylinder Bore	
Standard Diameter [1]	
Size Mark "1"	3.1890-3.1894 (81.001-81.010)
Size Mark "2"	3.1894-3.1898 (81.010-81.020)
Size Mark "3"	3.1898-3.1902 (81.020-81.030)
Cylinder Bore Limit	3.2177 (81.73)
Maximum Deck Warpage	.002 (.05)

[1] – Cylinder bore diameter is determined by numerical size mark on deck surface. See Fig. 21.

VALVES & VALVE SPRINGS

Application	Specification
Valve Head Refinishing Angles	
Above Seat Contact Surface	30°
Below Seat Contact Surface	75°
Seat Contact Surface	45°
Valve Seat Contact Width	.047-.063" (1.19-1.60 mm)
Valve Head Thickness	.031-.047" (.79-1.19 mm)
Minimum Head Thickness	.020" (.50 mm)
Exhaust Valves	
Overall Length (Min)	3.4390 (87.35)
Stem Diameter	.2348-.2354" (5.96-5.98 mm)
Intake Valves	
Overall Length (Min)	3.4232 (86.95)
Stem Diameter	.2350-.2356" (5.969-5.984 mm)
Valve Springs	
Free Length	1.5185" (38.569 mm)
Out-Of-Square	.079" (2.0 mm)

	Lbs. @ In. (kg @ mm)
Pressure With Valve Closed	37.3 @ 1.25 (16.9 @ 31.7)

CYLINDER HEAD

Application	Specification
Maximum Warpage	
Cylinder Head Surface	.002" (.05 mm)
Manifold Surfaces	.004" (.10 mm)
Intake & Exhaust	
Cylinder Head Valve Guide Bore (Max)	[1] .4341" (11.026 mm)
Valve Seats	
Above Seat Contact Surface	30°
Below Seat Contact Surface	75°
Seat Contact Surface	45°
Valve Seat Contact Width	.047-.063" (1.19-1.60 mm)
Valve Guide I.D.	.2366-.2374" (6.010-6.029 mm)
Valve Guide Protrusion	.500-.516" (12.70-13.11 mm)
Intake	
Valve Stem-To-Guide Oil Clearance	
Standard	.0010-.0024" (.025-.061 mm)
Wear Limit	.0031" (.078 mm)
Exhaust	
Valve Stem-To-Guide Oil Clearance	
Standard	.0012-.0026" (.030-.066 mm)
Wear Limit	.0039" (.099 mm)

[1] – If diameter exceeds specification, cylinder head must be machined for oversized valve guide.

CAMSHAFT

Application	In. (mm)
Camshaft Gear Backlash Standard	.0008-.0079 (.020-.201)
Wear Limit	.0118 (.300)
Exhaust Camshaft	
End Play	
Standard	.0014-.0035 (.035-.090)
Wear Limit	.004 (.11)
Journal Diameter	.9035-.9041 (22.949-22.965)
Lobe Height	
Standard	1.6520-1.6560 (41.960-41.060)
Minimum	1.6358 (41.55)
Intake Camshaft	
End Play	
Standard	.0012-.0033 (.030-.084)
Wear Limit	.004 (.11)
Journal Diameter	.9035-.9041 (22.949-22.965)
Lobe Height	
Standard	1.6500-1.6539 (41.910-42.010)
Minimum	1.6338 (41.50)

VALVE LIFTERS

Application	In. (mm)
Bore Diameter	1.2205-1.2215 (31.000-31.025)
Lifter Diameter	1.2191-1.2195 (30.966-30.976)
Oil Clearance	
Standard	.0009-.0023 (.023-.058)
Maximum	.0028 (.071)

1994 ENGINES
1.6L 4-Cylinder – Tracker

NOTE: For repair procedures not covered in this article, see ENGINE OVERHAUL PROCEDURES article in GENERAL INFORMATION.

ENGINE IDENTIFICATION

Engine can be identified by eighth character of Vehicle Identification Number (VIN), located on top of dash panel, at lower left corner of windshield.

ENGINE IDENTIFICATION CODE

Application	VIN
1.6L 4-Cylinder	
8-Valve, Federal	U
16-Valve, California	6

ADJUSTMENTS

VALVE CLEARANCE ADJUSTMENT

NOTE: Valve clearance can be adjusted with engine cold or hot.

1) On California models, disconnect battery. On all models, remove air cleaner assembly and valve cover. Rotate crankshaft until No. 1 cylinder is at TDC of compression stroke. Ensure timing "V" mark on crankshaft pulley aligns with "0" mark on timing belt cover.
2) Remove distributor cap. Ensure rotor aligns with No. 1 distributor terminal. If rotor is not aligned with No. 1 distributor terminal, rotate crankshaft pulley clockwise 360 degrees.
3) Measure clearance between adjustment screw and valve stem using a feeler gauge. Check clearance of intake valve(s) of cylinders No. 1 and 2, and exhaust valve(s) of cylinders No. 1 and 3.
4) Rotate crankshaft clockwise 360 degrees. Check clearance of intake valve(s) of cylinders No. 3 and 4, and exhaust valve(s) of cylinders No. 2 and 4.
5) Adjust valve clearance if not within specification. See VALVE CLEARANCE SPECIFICATIONS table. Adjust clearance by loosening adjusting screw lock nut and rotating adjusting screw. Tighten adjusting screw lock nut to 13 ft. lbs. (18 N.m) while holding adjusting screw.

VALVE CLEARANCE SPECIFICATIONS

Valve	[1] Hot In. (mm)	[2] Cold In. (mm)
8-Valve		
Intake	.009-.011 (.23-.28)	.005-.007 (.13-.18)
Exhaust	.010-.011 (.25-.28)	.006-.008 (.15-.20)
16-Valve		
Intake	.007-.008 (.18-.20)	.005-.007 (.13-.18)
Exhaust	.007-.008 (.18-.20)	.005-.007 (.13-.18)

[1] – With engine coolant temperature greater than 154°F (68°C).
[2] – With engine coolant temperature less than 77°F (25°C).

REMOVAL & INSTALLATION

NOTE: For reassembly reference, label all electrical connectors, vacuum hoses and fuel lines before removal. Also place mating marks on engine hood and other major assemblies before removal.

CAUTION: ALWAYS relieve fuel pressure before disconnection any fuel injection-related component. DO NOT allow fuel to contact engine or electrical components.

FUEL PRESSURE RELEASE

1) Place transmission in Neutral (M/T) or Park (A/T). Set parking brake and block wheels. Loosen fuel tank cap to release fuel tank pressure. Disconnect fuel pump relay connector, located under left side of dash. Start engine and allow engine to stall. Crank engine again for an additional 3 seconds, to ensure relief of any remaining pressure.

2) Disconnect negative battery cable. Connect fuel pump relay connector and tighten fuel filler cap. Cover fuel line or component to be disconnected with shop rag during removal procedure.

ENGINE

NOTE: Leave transmission in vehicle when removing engine.

Removal – 1) Release fuel pressure. See FUEL PRESSURE RELEASE under REMOVAL & INSTALLATION. Mark and remove hood. Disconnect battery cables.
2) Drain cooling system and engine oil. On A/T models, disconnect transmission oil cooler lines. Remove cooling fan and clutch, fan shroud and radiator. Remove A/C condenser and compressor (if equipped), leaving hoses connected. Remove air cleaner and air intake tubing. Disconnect accelerator cable and kick down cable (if equipped).
3) Disconnect necessary electrical connections, vacuum hoses, fuel lines and coolant hoses. Raise and support vehicle. Remove skid plate. Remove starter motor. Disconnect exhaust pipe from exhaust manifold.
4) On M/T models, disconnect clutch cable from bracket near starter motor. On A/T models, remove torque converter housing lower plate and torque converter-to-flexplate bolts.
5) On all models, lower vehicle. Support transmission. Remove transmission-to-cylinder block bolts. Mark distributor housing position cylinder head and remove distributor. Make match marks on hood and remove hood. Install chain hoist to engine. Remove engine mount bolts and remove engine.
Installation – To install, reverse removal procedure. Install a NEW rear main seal. Apply a enough Loctite (414) to coat flywheel retaining bolt threads. Tighten all fasteners to specification. See TORQUE SPECIFICATIONS. Adjust all control cables. Adjust all fluid levels.

INTAKE MANIFOLD

Removal – 1) Release fuel pressure. See FUEL PRESSURE RELEASE under REMOVAL & INSTALLATION. Drain cooling system. Remove air cleaner assembly.
2) Label and disconnect necessary electrical connections, fuel lines, coolant hoses, vacuum hoses and control cables from throttle body and intake manifold. Remove intake manifold bolts and nuts, intake manifold and gasket.
Installation – To install, reverse removal procedure. Tighten bolts and nuts to specification. See TORQUE SPECIFICATIONS. Adjust all control cables. Refill cooling system.

EXHAUST MANIFOLD

Removal & Installation – 1) Disconnect negative battery cable and oxygen sensor connector. Remove air cleaner bracket. Remove covers from exhaust manifold. Disconnect exhaust pipe at exhaust manifold. Remove retaining bolts and nuts, exhaust manifold and gasket.
2) To install, reverse removal procedure. Tighten bolts and nuts to specification. See TORQUE SPECIFICATIONS.

CYLINDER HEAD

NOTE: On 8-valve engines, remove cylinder head with intake and exhaust manifolds connected.

Removal (8-Valve) – 1) Release fuel pressure. See FUEL PRESSURE RELEASE under REMOVAL & INSTALLATION. Disconnect negative battery terminal. Drain cooling system.
2) Remove air cleaner assembly. Label and disconnect all relevant electrical connections, fuel lines, coolant hoses, vacuum hoses and control cables from distributor, throttle body and intake manifold.
3) Raise vehicle and disconnect exhaust pipe from exhaust manifold. Lower vehicle and remove cooling fan, fan clutch and fan shroud. Remove timing belt. Before removing timing belt, ensure timing marks are aligned. See TIMING BELT under REMOVAL & INSTALLATION.

4) Raise and support vehicle. Disconnect oxygen sensor connector. Disconnect exhaust pipe at exhaust manifold. Lower vehicle. Loosen A/C system (if equipped) support brackets and clamps, and without discharging system, position out of the way. Remove valve cover. Loosen valve adjusting screw lock nuts and adjusting screws until rocker arms are loose, to ensure all valves are closed.

5) Loosen cylinder head bolts in reverse order of tightening sequence. See Fig. 1. Loosen head bolts evenly in 3 steps to prevent cylinder head warpage. Remove cylinder head bolts, cylinder head and gasket. Remove intake and exhaust manifolds (if necessary).

Removal (16-Valve) – 1) Release fuel pressure. See FUEL PRESSURE RELEASE under REMOVAL & INSTALLATION. Disconnect negative battery terminal. Drain cooling system.

2) Remove air cleaner assembly. Label and disconnect all relevant electrical connections, fuel lines, coolant hoses, vacuum hoses and control cables from distributor, throttle body and intake manifold.

3) Remove intake manifold with gasket, intake surge tank and throttle body. Remove exhaust manifold heat shield. Raise vehicle and disconnect exhaust pipe from exhaust manifold. Lower vehicle and remove exhaust manifold. Remove cooling fan, water pump pulley and cooling fan shroud.

4) Remove timing belt. Before removing timing belt, ensure timing marks are aligned. See TIMING BELT under REMOVAL & INSTALLATION. Using Camshaft Gear Spanner Wrench (J-41840), remove camshaft timing belt gear.

5) If equipped with A/C, loosen support brackets and clamps, and without discharging system, position out of the way. Remove valve cover. Remove distributor, valve cover and distributor case. Loosen all valve adjusting screw lock nuts and adjusting screws until rocker arms are loose, to ensure all valves are closed.

CAUTION: On 16-valve engines, camshaft can be damaged if camshaft carrier bolts are removed in a random order.

---

6) Remove camshaft, see CAMSHAFT (16-Valve) under REMOVAL & INSTALLATION. Loosen cylinder head bolts in reverse order of tightening sequence. See Fig. 2. Loosen head bolts evenly in 3 steps to prevent cylinder head warpage. Remove cylinder head bolts, cylinder head and gasket.

Inspection (All Models) – 1) Inspect cylinder head surface for warpage. Inspect cylinder head manifold seating surfaces for warpage. Replace cylinder head if warpage cannot be corrected by surfacing. See CYLINDER HEAD table under ENGINE SPECIFICATIONS.

2) Inspect cylinder block deck surface for warpage. Resurface cylinder block if warpage exceeds specification. See CYLINDER BLOCK table under ENGINE SPECIFICATIONS.

3) On 16-valve, inspect cylinder head oil jet for obstructions. Oil jet is located at timing belt end of head in head-to-block mating surface. See Fig. 3. Tighten oil jet to 44 INCH lbs. (5 N.m).

CAUTION: Install cylinder head gasket with TOP facing away from cylinder block and positioned at crankshaft pulley end of cylinder block.

Installation (8-Valve) – 1) Install intake and exhaust manifolds to head before installing head to block. Tighten intake and exhaust manifold bolts and nuts at the same time to specification. See TORQUE SPECIFICATIONS. To complete installation, reverse removal procedure. Lubricate cylinder head bolts with engine oil before installing. Tighten cylinder head bolts in sequence during 3-4 passes to specification. See Fig. 1. See TORQUE SPECIFICATIONS.

2) Ensure timing marks are in correct alignment. See Fig. 5. Adjust valve clearance. See VALVE CLEARANCE ADJUSTMENT under ADJUSTMENTS.

3) To install remaining components, reverse removal procedure. Tighten bolts and nuts to specification. See TORQUE SPECIFICATIONS.

4) Before installing fuel supply line on throttle body, apply a thin coat of engine oil on "O" ring. Adjust all control cables. Refill cooling system.

Installation (16-Valve) – 1) To install, reverse removal procedure. Lubricate cylinder head bolts with engine oil before installing. Tighten cylinder head bolts in 3 passes in sequence to specification. Tighten cylinder head bolts to specified torque during each pass. See Fig. 2. See TORQUE SPECIFICATIONS.

2) Apply RTV sealant to bottom of camshaft cap No. 6 (closest to distributor drive gear). Install camshaft and camshaft carrier caps. See CAMSHAFT under REMOVAL & INSTALLATION. Ensure timing marks are in correct alignment. See Fig. 5. Adjust valve clearance. See VALVE CLEARANCE ADJUSTMENT under ADJUSTMENTS.

3) Apply RTV sealant to surface of distributor case that mates with rear of rocker arm shaft. Install distributor case and tighten 3 bolts to specification. To install remaining components, reverse removal procedure. Tighten bolts and nuts to specification. See TORQUE SPECIFICATIONS.

4) Adjust all control cables. Refill cooling system and check engine oil level.

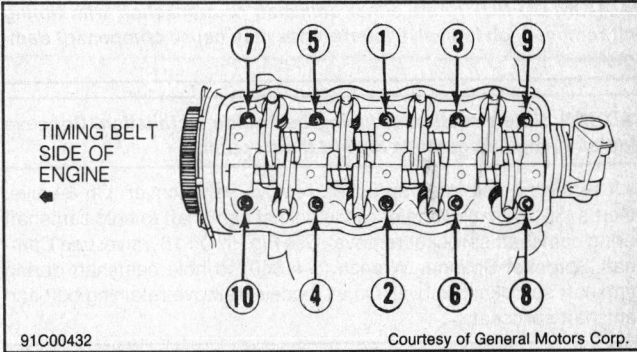

91C00432   Courtesy of General Motors Corp.
Fig. 1: Cylinder Head Bolt Tightening Sequence (8-Valve)

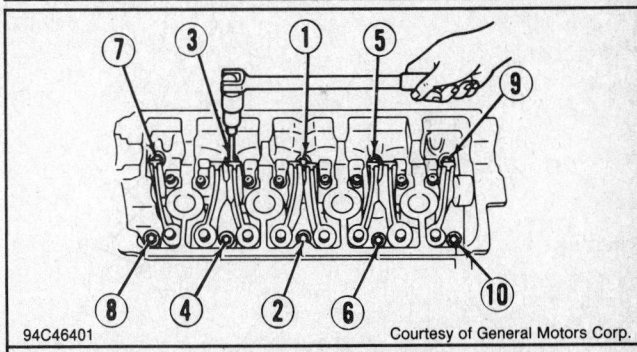

94C46401   Courtesy of General Motors Corp.
Fig. 2: Cylinder Head Bolt Tightening Sequence (16-Valve)

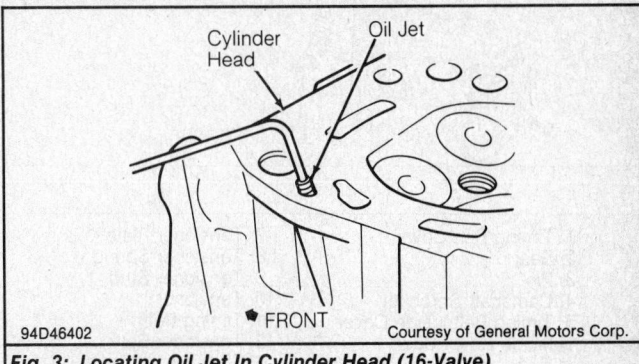

94D46402   Courtesy of General Motors Corp.
Fig. 3: Locating Oil Jet In Cylinder Head (16-Valve)

CRANKSHAFT FRONT SEAL

NOTE: Crankshaft front seal is mounted in oil pump housing. Manufacturer lists replacement procedure with oil pump removed. See OIL PUMP under ENGINE OILING.

TIMING BELT

Removal – **1)** Disconnect negative battery cable. Remove accessory drive belts. Remove cooling fan, fan shroud and water pump pulley.
2) Remove outer bolts retaining crankshaft pulley. Remove crankshaft pulley. It is not necessary to remove center bolt from crankshaft pulley. Raise vehicle and remove skid plate (if equipped).
3) Remove timing belt cover and seal. *See Fig. 4*. On 16-valve, ensure timing marks are aligned before removing timing belt (camshaft sprocket timing mark "E" is aligned with notch in valve cover and crankshaft timing gear punch mark is aligned with arrow on oil pump housing). On all models, remove tensioner spring and tensioner stud. Loosen tensioner bolt. DO NOT remove tensioner bolt.
4) Push tensioner plate upward, and remove timing belt. If removing crankshaft sprocket, remove retaining bolt, crankshaft sprocket, key and timing belt guide (located behind crankshaft sprocket) from crankshaft.

CAUTION: DO NOT rotate either camshaft or crankshaft with timing belt removed, piston/valve interference may cause component damage.

CAUTION: Note direction of timing belt guide installation. Concave side of timing belt guide is toward the oil pump.

5) If removing camshaft sprocket, remove valve cover. On 8-valve, insert a .35" (9 mm) diameter rod in hole of camshaft to hold camshaft during camshaft sprocket removal. *See Fig. 5*. On 16-valve, use Camshaft Sprocket Spanner Wrench (J-41840) to hold camshaft during camshaft sprocket removal. On all models, remove retaining bolt and camshaft sprocket.

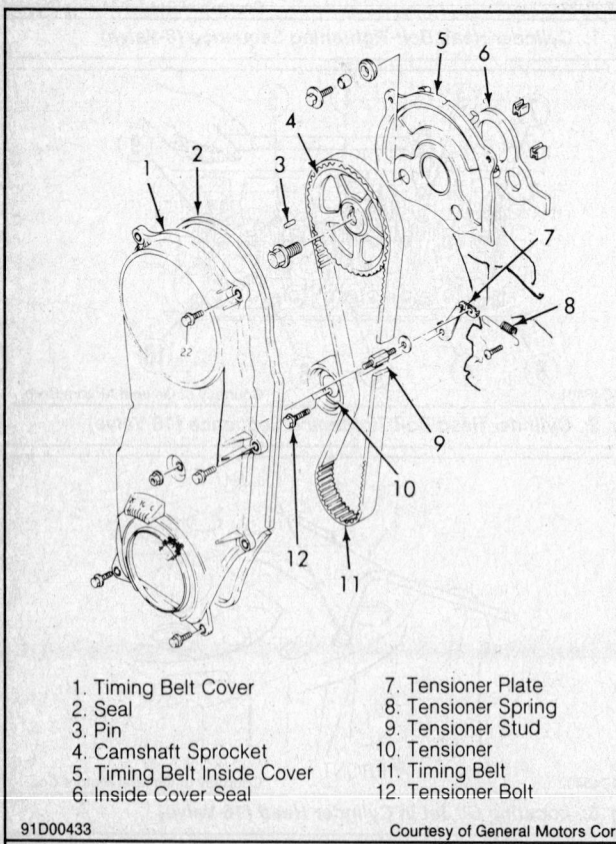

1. Timing Belt Cover
2. Seal
3. Pin
4. Camshaft Sprocket
5. Timing Belt Inside Cover
6. Inside Cover Seal
7. Tensioner Plate
8. Tensioner Spring
9. Tensioner Stud
10. Tensioner
11. Timing Belt
12. Tensioner Bolt

91D00433   Courtesy of General Motors Corp.

Fig. 4: Exploded View Of Timing Belt & Components (8-Valve Shown; 16-Valve Is Similar)

Inspection – Inspect timing belt for damaged teeth or cracking. Ensure timing belt is not contaminated with oil. Check tensioner for freedom of rotation. Replace components if damaged.

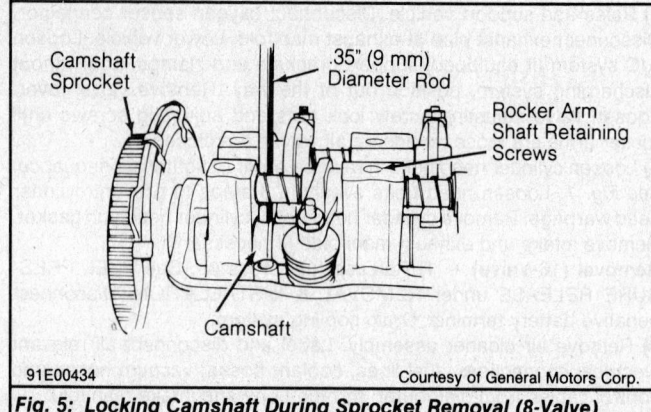

Camshaft Sprocket

.35" (9 mm) Diameter Rod

Rocker Arm Shaft Retaining Screws

Camshaft

91E00434   Courtesy of General Motors Corp.

Fig. 5: Locking Camshaft During Sprocket Removal (8-Valve)

Installation (8-Valve) – **1)** Install timing belt inside cover and seal (if removed). Install timing belt guide, key and crankshaft sprocket. Tighten crankshaft sprocket bolt to specification. See TORQUE SPECIFICATIONS.

CAUTION: Ensure concave side of timing belt guide is toward the oil pump. Flat side of belt guide goes against crankshaft sprocket.

2) Install camshaft sprocket (if removed). Ensure sprocket aligns with pin in camshaft. Tighten camshaft sprocket retaining bolt to specification. See TORQUE SPECIFICATIONS.
3) If tensioner was removed, install tensioner plate on tensioner. Ensure lug of tensioner plate engages in hole on rear of tensioner. Install tensioner, tensioner plate and tensioner spring on cylinder block. Tighten tensioner bolt finger tight to allow movement of tensioner.

CAUTION: Ensure tensioner plate moves when tensioner is moved toward timing belt. If tensioner plate does not move, ensure lug engages in tensioner hole.

4) Remove valve cover. Loosen all valve adjusting screws to fully close valves, before installing timing belt. Ensure camshaft rotates freely during belt tension adjustment. Rotate camshaft clockwise, and align timing mark on camshaft sprocket with timing mark on timing belt inside cover. *See Fig. 6*.
5) Rotate crankshaft clockwise, and align timing mark on crankshaft sprocket with timing mark on oil pump housing. *See Fig. 6*. Install timing belt so arrow on timing belt aligns with direction of crankshaft rotation. Ensure there is no slack on right side of timing belt.

CAUTION: Install timing belt so that direction arrow on timing belt is aligned with direction of crankshaft rotation. See Fig. 6.

6) Install tensioner spring. Finger tighten tensioner stud. Rotate crankshaft 2 revolutions clockwise to ensure all slack is removed from timing belt.
7) Tighten tensioner stud to specification. Tighten tensioner bolt to specification. See TORQUE SPECIFICATIONS. Ensure all timing marks align. If timing marks are not aligned, remove timing belt and repeat procedure.
8) Adjust valve clearance. See VALVE CLEARANCE ADJUSTMENT under ADJUSTMENTS. To install remaining components, reverse removal procedure. See TORQUE SPECIFICATIONS.
Installation (16-Valve) – **1)** Install timing belt inside cover and seal (if removed). Install timing belt tensioner plate and tensioner. Finger tighten tensioner stud and bolt.
2) Install camshaft sprocket (if removed). Ensure sprocket aligns with pin in camshaft. Tighten camshaft sprocket retaining bolt to specification. See TORQUE SPECIFICATIONS.

3) Push timing belt tensioner plate up and install timing belt onto camshaft sprocket and crankshaft timing gear. Install timing belt so arrow on timing belt aligns with direction of crankshaft rotation. Ensure there is no slack on right side of timing belt. Ensure timing marks are aligned. *See Fig. 6.* Install tensioner spring to timing belt tensioner plate.

CAUTION: Ensure tensioner plate moves when tensioner is moved toward timing belt. If tensioner plate does not move, ensure lug engages in tensioner hole.

4) Rotate crankshaft clockwise 2 complete revolutions to remove timing belt slack and to seat timing belt. Ensure timing marks are in alignment (camshaft sprocket timing mark "E" is aligned with notch in valve cover and crankshaft timing gear punch mark is aligned with arrow on oil pump housing). *See Fig. 6.*

5) Tighten tensioner stud and bolt to specification. See TORQUE SPECIFICATIONS. Ensure all timing marks align. To install remaining components, reverse removal procedure.

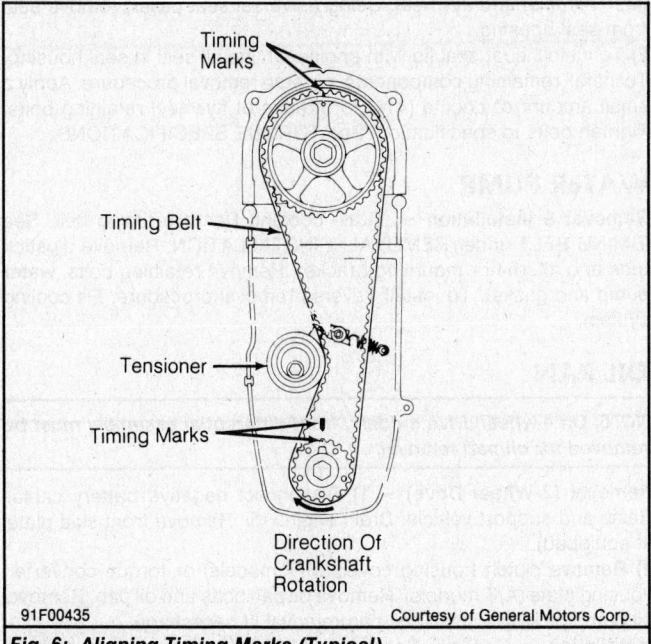

Fig. 6: Aligning Timing Marks (Typical)

ROCKER ARM SHAFTS

Removal (8-Valve) – **1)** Disconnect negative battery cable. Remove grill and upper radiator support. Drain cooling system. Remove cooling fan and shroud. Remove radiator.

2) Remove timing belt. See TIMING BELT under REMOVAL & INSTALLATION. Remove timing belt inside cover. Remove air cleaner assembly and valve cover.

3) Insert a .35" (9 mm) diameter rod in hole of camshaft to hold camshaft during camshaft sprocket removal. *See Fig. 5.* Remove retaining bolt and camshaft sprocket.

4) Fully loosen all valve adjusting screws. Remove rocker arm shaft retaining screws. *See Fig. 5.* Note location of rocker arm components for reassembly reference. Remove rocker arm shafts, rocker arms and springs. Keep components in order removed to ensure installation in original position.

Inspection – See VALVE TRAIN under OVERHAUL.

Installation – **1)** To install, reverse removal procedure. Lubricate components with engine oil before installing.

CAUTION: Intake and exhaust rocker shafts are different and must be installed in original location. To identify rocker shafts measure stepped ends of rocker shafts. See fig. 6. Intake rocker shaft stepped end dimension is .55" (14 mm). Exhaust rocker shaft stepped end dimension is .59" (15 mm).

2) Install intake rocker arm shaft with stepped side toward camshaft sprocket. Install exhaust rocker arm shaft with stepped side toward distributor. *See Fig. 7.*

3) Tighten rocker arm shaft retaining screws to specification. See TORQUE SPECIFICATIONS. To install remaining components, reverse removal procedure.

4) Adjust valve clearance. See VALVE CLEARANCE ADJUSTMENT under ADJUSTMENTS. To complete installation, reverse removal procedure.

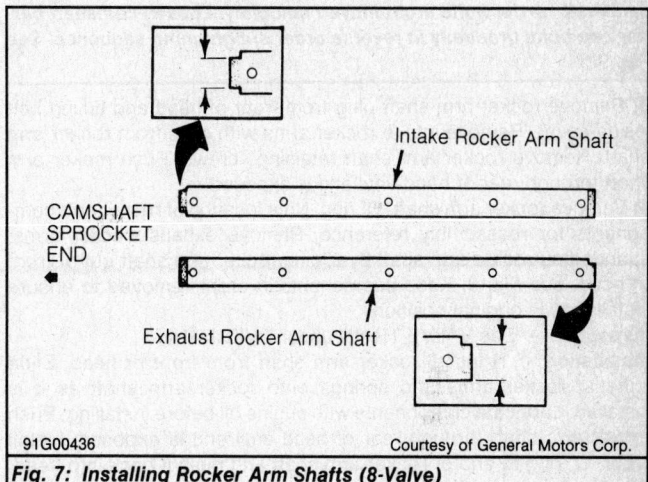

Fig. 7: Installing Rocker Arm Shafts (8-Valve)

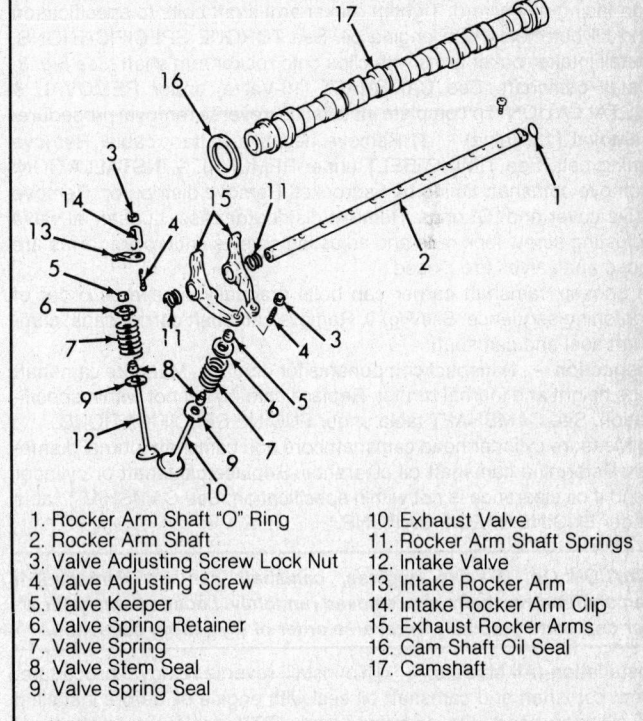

1. Rocker Arm Shaft "O" Ring	10. Exhaust Valve
2. Rocker Arm Shaft	11. Rocker Arm Shaft Springs
3. Valve Adjusting Screw Lock Nut	12. Intake Valve
4. Valve Adjusting Screw	13. Intake Rocker Arm
5. Valve Keeper	14. Rocker Arm Shaft Clip
6. Valve Spring Retainer	15. Exhaust Rocker Arms
7. Valve Spring	16. Cam Shaft Oil Seal
8. Valve Stem Seal	17. Camshaft
9. Valve Spring Seal	

Fig. 8: Exploded View Of Camshaft, Rocker Arms & Rocker Arm Shaft (16-Valve)

Removal (16-Valve) – **1)** Disconnect negative battery cable. Remove front grille and header panel. Remove timing belt. See TIMING BELT under REMOVAL & INSTALLATION. Remove camshaft sprocket. Remove valve cover, distributor and distributor housing.

2) Loosen all valve adjusting screw lock nuts and adjusting screws until valves are fully closed. *See Fig. 8.* Remove camshaft. See CAMSHAFT (16-Valve) under REMOVAL & INSTALLATION.

CAMSHAFT

Removal (8-Valve) – **1)** Remove cylinder head. See CYLINDER HEAD under REMOVAL & INSTALLATION. Remove distributor case from rear of cylinder head.

2) Remove rocker arms. See ROCKER ARM SHAFTS (8-Valve) under REMOVAL & INSTALLATION. Remove camshaft from rear of cylinder head.

CAUTION: On 16-valve engines, camshaft can be damaged if camshaft carrier bolts are removed randomly. Loosen camshaft carrier cap bolts gradually in reverse order of tightening sequence. See Fig. 9.

3) Remove rocker arm shaft plug from front of head and timing belt inside cover. Remove intake rocker arms with clips from rocker arm shaft. Remove rocker arm shaft retaining screws. Push rocker arm shaft through rear of head until end is exposed.

4) Remove rocker arm shaft "O" ring. Note location of rocker arm components for reassembly reference. Remove exhaust rocker arms, springs and rocker arm shaft by sliding rocker arm shaft out of front of head. *See Fig. 8.* Keep components in order removed to ensure installation in original position.

Inspection – See VALVE TRAIN under OVERHAUL.

Installation – **1)** Install rocker arm shaft from front of head. Slide exhaust rocker arms and springs onto rocker arm shaft as it is installed. Lubricate components with engine oil before installing. Push rocker arm shaft through rear of head until end is exposed. Install NEW "O" ring to end of rocker arm shaft and push it back into head. *See Fig. 8.*

2) Rotate rocker arm shaft so that flat machined surface is horizontal and facing downward. Tighten rocker arm shaft bolts to specification and fill bolt holes with engine oil. See TORQUE SPECIFICATIONS. Install intake rocker arms with clips onto rocker arm shaft. *See Fig. 8.* Install camshaft. See CAMSHAFT (16-Valve) under REMOVAL & INSTALLATION. To complete installation, reverse removal procedure.

Removal (16-Valve) – **1)** Remove negative battery cable. Remove timing belt. See TIMING BELT under REMOVAL & INSTALLATION. Remove camshaft timing belt sprocket. Remove distributor. Remove valve cover and "O" rings. Remove distributor case. Loosen all valve adjusting screw lock nuts and adjusting screws until rocker arms are loose and valves are closed.

2) Loosen camshaft carrier cap bolts gradually in reverse order of tightening sequence. *See Fig. 9.* Remove camshaft carrier caps, camshaft seal and camshaft.

Inspection – **1)** Inspect components for damage. Measure camshaft lobe height and journal runout. Replace camshaft if not within specification. See CAMSHAFT table under ENGINE SPECIFICATIONS.

2) Measure cylinder head camshaft bore and camshaft journal diameter. Determine camshaft oil clearance. Replace camshaft or cylinder head if oil clearance is not within specification. See CAMSHAFT table under ENGINE SPECIFICATIONS.

CAUTION: On 16-valve engines, camshaft can be damaged if camshaft carrier bolts are removed randomly. Loosen camshaft carrier cap bolts gradually in reverse order of tightening sequence.

Installation (All Models) – **1)** To install, reverse removal procedure. Coat camshaft and camshaft oil seal with engine oil before installing in cylinder head. On 16-valve, apply RTV sealant to bottom of camshaft carrier cap No. 6. Tighten camshaft carrier cap bolts gradually in sequence and tighten bolts to specification. *See Fig. 9.* See TORQUE SPECIFICATIONS.

2) Adjust valve clearance. See VALVE CLEARANCE ADJUSTMENT under ADJUSTMENTS. To install remaining components, reverse removal procedure.

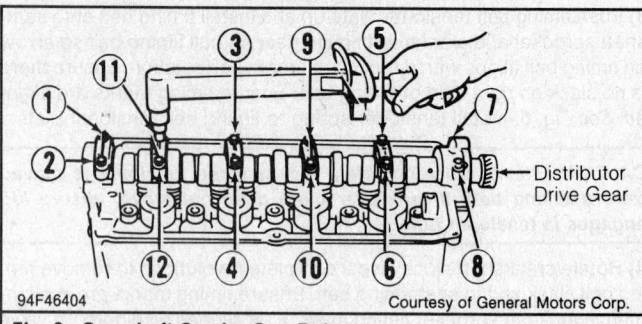

Fig. 9: Camshaft Carrier Cap Bolts
Tightening Sequence (16-Valve)

REAR CRANKSHAFT OIL SEAL

Removal & Installation – **1)** Remove transmission, clutch assembly (M/T models) and flywheel. Using universal seal puller, remove seal from seal housing.

2) To install, coat seal lip with engine oil. Install seal in seal housing. To install remaining components, reverse removal procedure. Apply a small amount of Loctite (414) to threads of flywheel retaining bolts. Tighten bolts to specification. See TORQUE SPECIFICATIONS.

WATER PUMP

Removal & Installation – Drain coolant. Remove timing belt. See TIMING BELT under REMOVAL & INSTALLATION. Remove dipstick tube and alternator mounting bracket. Remove retaining bolts, water pump and gasket. To install, reverse removal procedure. Fill cooling system.

OIL PAN

NOTE: On 4-wheel drive models, front differential assembly must be removed for oil pan removal.

Removal (2-Wheel Drive) – **1)** Disconnect negative battery cable. Raise and support vehicle. Drain engine oil. Remove front skid plate (if equipped).

2) Remove clutch housing cover (M/T models) or torque converter housing plate (A/T models). Remove oil pan bolts and oil pan. Remove oil pump pick-up tube for oil pan removal (if necessary).

Installation – **1)** Apply Sealant (1050026) to oil pan seal surface before installation. Install NEW gasket on oil pump pick-up tube. Install oil pump pick-up tube and oil pan.

2) Tighten oil pan bolts to specification, starting at center and moving outward. See TORQUE SPECIFICATIONS.

Removal (4-Wheel Drive) – **1)** Disconnect negative battery cable. Raise and support vehicle. Remove front skid plate (if equipped). Drain front differential. Remove front wheels. Disconnect drive shaft from differential. Remove locking hub cap by unscrewing counterclockwise. Remove locking hub retaining bolts, locking hubs and "O" ring. Remove snap ring and washer from end of axle shafts.

2) Separate tie rod from right from right lower control arm. Support right suspension with floor jack. Separate steering knuckle and lower ball joint from control arm. Slowly lower floor jack. Swing steering knuckle outward and pull axle shaft from knuckle assembly.

3) Install Shaft Removal Fork (J-37780) between right axle shaft and differential housing. Tap on shaft removal fork and remove right axle shaft. Make a match mark on left axle shaft flange to be used for installation. Disconnect and separate left axle shaft from inner axle shaft flange at front differential housing.

4) Support differential assembly. To ensure drive shaft balance, make a match mark on drive shaft pinion flange and pinion flange yoke before drive shaft is removed. Remove drive shaft. Remove front differential-to-bracket mounting bolts. Remove front differential assembly. Drain engine oil.

5) Remove clutch housing cover (M/T models) or torque converter housing plate (A/T models). Remove oil pan bolts and oil pan. Remove oil pump pick-up tube for oil pan removal (if necessary).

Installation – 1) Apply Sealant (1050026) to oil pan seal surface before installation. Install NEW gasket on oil pump pick-up tube. Install oil pump pick-up tube and oil pan.

2) Tighten oil pan bolts to specification, starting at center and moving outward. See TORQUE SPECIFICATIONS. When installing front differential, install all differential-to-bracket bolts before tightening bolts to specification.

3) To install remaining components, reverse removal procedure. Tighten bolts to specification. See TORQUE SPECIFICATIONS. When installing locking hub, use NEW "O" ring. Fill front differential and engine with lubricant.

OVERHAUL

CYLINDER HEAD

Cylinder Head – Inspect cylinder head for cracks in intake and exhaust ports, combustion chamber and head surface. Inspect cylinder head gasket surface and manifold seating surfaces for warpage. Replace cylinder head if warpage cannot be corrected by resurfacing. See CYLINDER HEAD table under ENGINE SPECIFICATIONS.

Valve Springs – Ensure valve spring free length, pressure and out-of-square is within specification. See VALVES & VALVE SPRINGS table under ENGINE SPECIFICATIONS.

CAUTION: Install valve springs with tightest coil area on spring seat and larger coil area at spring retainer.

NOTE: DO NOT reuse valve stem oil seals if they have been removed.

Valve Stem Oil Seals – Remove valve stem oil seal from valve guide. Lubricate oil seal with engine oil before installing. Install oil seal using Seal Installer (J-34834 for 8-valve; J-37968 for 16-valve). Ensure valve stem oil seal is fully seated in valve guide.

Valve Guides – 1) Check valve stem-to-valve guide oil clearance. See CYLINDER HEAD table under ENGINE SPECIFICATIONS. Ensure valve stem diameter is within specification. Valve guide can be replaced if clearance exceeds specification.

NOTE: DO NOT reuse valve guides if they have been removed.

2) To replace valve guide, use hammer and Valve Guide Remover (J-34833 for 8-valve; J-37968 for 16-valve). Drive valve guide from combustion side of cylinder head toward the valve spring side. Using a reamer (J-34832 for 8-valve; J-37972 for 16-valve), ream guide hole to remove burrs.

3) Install valve guide using a hammer and Valve Guide Installer (J-34834 for 8-valve; J-37968 for 16-valve), drive valve guide into cylinder head from valve spring side of cylinder head until valve guide installer contacts cylinder head. Using Reamer (J-34831 for 8-valve; J-37971 for 16-valve), ream valve guide and clean hole.

NOTE: Ensure valve guide installed height above cylinder head surface is .55" (14.0 mm) on 8-valve and is .45" (11.4 mm) on 16-valve.

Valve Seat – Replacement information is not available from manufacturer.

Valves – Ensure valve stem diameter, valve margin and contact width are within specification. See VALVES & VALVE SPRINGS table under ENGINE SPECIFICATIONS at end of article.

Valve Seat Correction Angles – Valve seat contact area can be made wider using a 45-degree seat cutter. Seat contact area can be narrowed using a 15-degree cutter on outer seat area. On 8-valve, seat contact area also can be narrowed using a 60-degree cutter on the inner area furthest from the combustion chamber.

VALVE TRAIN

CAUTION: Note rocker arm component locations for reassembly reference.

Rocker Arm Assembly – 1) Disassemble rocker arm shaft assembly. Inspect components for excessive wear or damage.

2) Measure O.D. of rocker arm shaft in rocker arm operating areas. Measure I.D. of rocker arm. Determine oil clearance. Replace components if not within specification. See ROCKER ARM ASSEMBLY SPECIFICATIONS table.

3) Using dial indicator and "V" blocks, check rocker arm shaft runout. Replace shaft if runout exceeds specification. See ROCKER ARM ASSEMBLY SPECIFICATIONS table. To reassemble, coat components with engine oil and reverse disassembly procedure.

ROCKER ARM ASSEMBLY SPECIFICATIONS

Application	In. (mm)
Rocker Arm I.D.	.630-.631 (16.00-16.02)
Rocker Arm Shaft O.D.	.628-.629 (15.97-15.99)
Rocker Arm Shaft Oil Clearance	
8-Valve	.0005-.0017 (.013-.043)
16-Valve	.0001-.0014 (.003-.036)
Rocker Arm Shaft Runout	
8-Valve	.004 (.10)
16-Valve	.008 (.20)

CYLINDER BLOCK ASSEMBLY

Piston & Rod Assembly – Install piston with arrow on top of piston toward timing belt end of engine and oil hole toward intake manifold side. *See Fig. 10.*

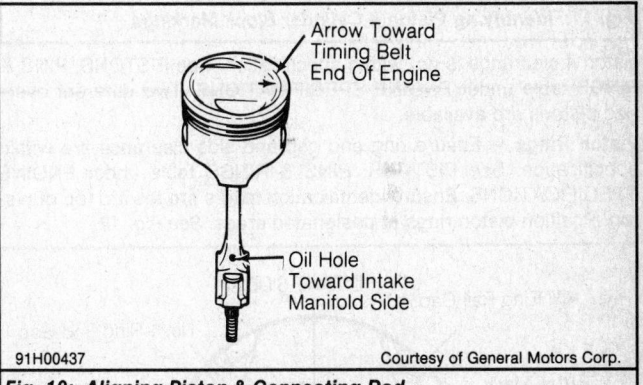

91H00437   Courtesy of General Motors Corp.

Fig. 10: Aligning Piston & Connecting Rod

NOTE: Two different standard piston sizes and cylinder bore diameters are used. Piston and cylinder bores are marked "1" or "2". Mark is placed on top of piston or on cylinder block deck surface. See Fig. 11.

Fitting Pistons – 1) To determine if piston-to-cylinder clearance is within specification, measure piston skirt diameter at 90-degree angle to piston pin.

2) Piston diameter is measured .63" (16 mm) from bottom of piston skirt. Different sized standard pistons are used. Piston size can be identified by "1" or "2" stamped in piston identification mark area on top of piston. *See Fig. 11.*

3) Ensure piston diameter is within specification. See PISTONS, PINS & RINGS table under ENGINE SPECIFICATIONS.

4) Cylinder bore diameter is measured 2" (50 mm) from top of cylinder bore, and on 8-valve, 4.13" (105 mm) or on 16-valve, 3.74" (95 mm) from top of cylinder bore. Original cylinder bore size can be identified by "1" or "2" stamped on deck surface in accordance with cylinder location. *See Fig. 11.*

5) Ensure cylinder bore diameter is within specification. See CYLINDER BLOCK table under ENGINE SPECIFICATIONS. Determine piston clearance. Replace piston or bore cylinder block for oversize

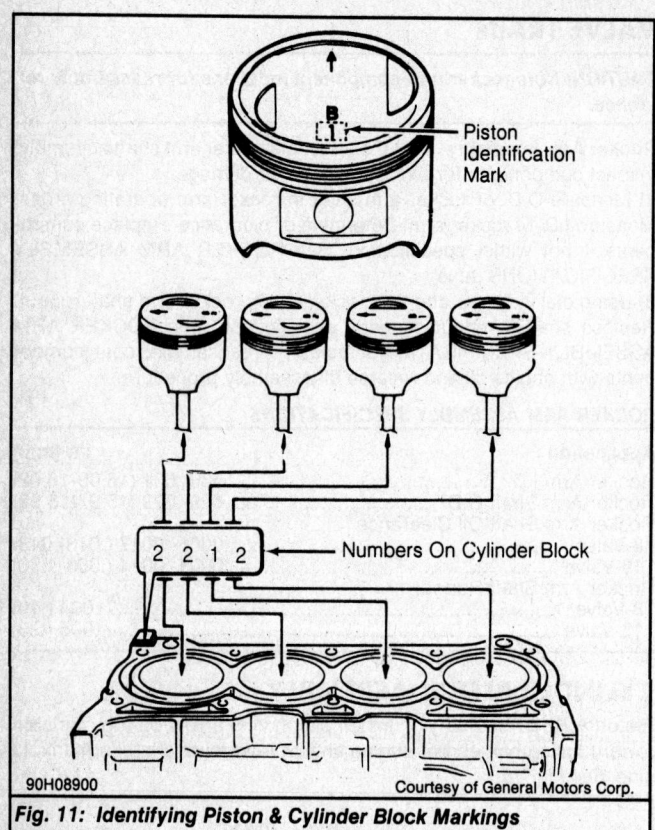

Fig. 11: Identifying Piston & Cylinder Block Markings

piston if clearance is not within specification. See PISTONS, PINS & RINGS table under ENGINE SPECIFICATIONS. Two different oversize pistons are available.

Piston Rings – Ensure ring end gap and side clearance are within specification. See PISTONS, PINS & RINGS table under ENGINE SPECIFICATIONS. Ensure identification marks are toward top of piston. Position piston rings at designated areas. *See Fig. 12.*

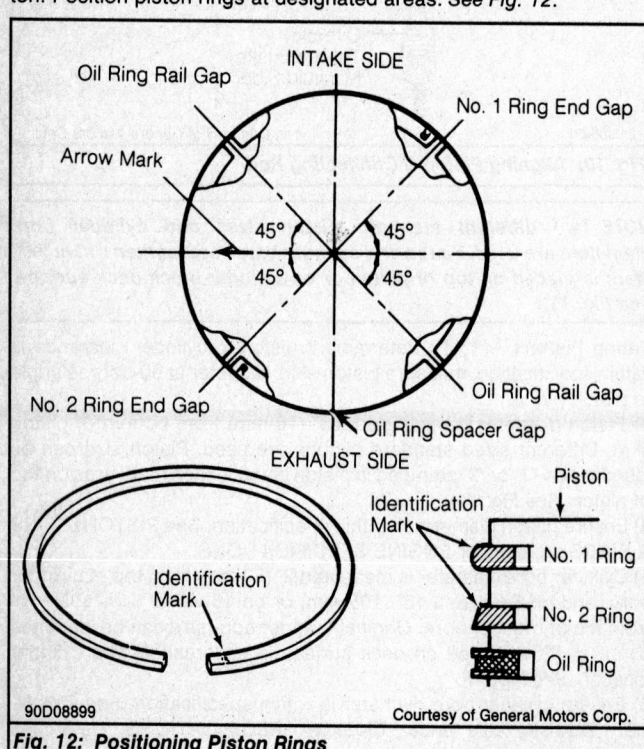

Fig. 12: Positioning Piston Rings

Rod Bearings – **1)** Note direction of connecting rod and cap before disassembly. Install connecting rod with oil hole toward intake manifold side of engine. *See Fig. 10.* Ensure arrow mark on connecting rod cap points toward timing belt end of engine.

2) Ensure bearing oil clearance and side play are within specification. See CRANKSHAFT, MAIN & CONNECTING ROD BEARINGS and CONNECTING RODS tables under ENGINE SPECIFICATIONS.

Crankshaft & Main Bearings – **1)** Ensure main bearing caps are numbered for location and arrow on cap points toward timing belt end of crankshaft.

2) Cylinder block main bearing bore size is indicated by a letter "A", "B" or "C" stamped on cylinder block *See Fig. 13.* Ensure main bearing bore is within specification. See MAIN BEARING BORE SPECIFICATIONS table.

3) Crankshaft main bearing journal size is indicated by numerical size mark, located near crankshaft counterweight. *See Fig. 14.* Ensure main bearing journal is within specification. See MAIN BEARING JOURNAL DIAMETER SPECIFICATIONS table.

4) If main bearing journal and main bearing bore are within specification replace main bearings with original size grade (color code). If color code on original bearing cannot be obtained, use size mark letter on cylinder block and number on crankshaft to determine proper size main bearing to be used. See MAIN BEARING SELECTION (STANDARD BEARINGS) table. Standard bearing thickness is as listed. See BEARING THICKNESS SPECIFICATIONS table.

5) Main bearings are available in .010" (.25 mm) undersize. Undersize bearings are coded with 2 color code marks. *See Fig. 15.* Undersize bearings are available in 5 thickness variations. See BEARING THICKNESS SPECIFICATIONS table.

6) If necessary, regrind main bearing journals to .010" (.25 mm) undersize with a finished diameter of 2.0367-2.0374" (51.732-51.750 mm). Using finished journal diameter and letter marked on cylinder block, determine color code undersize bearing to be used. See MAIN BEARING SELECTION (UNDERSIZE BEARINGS) table.

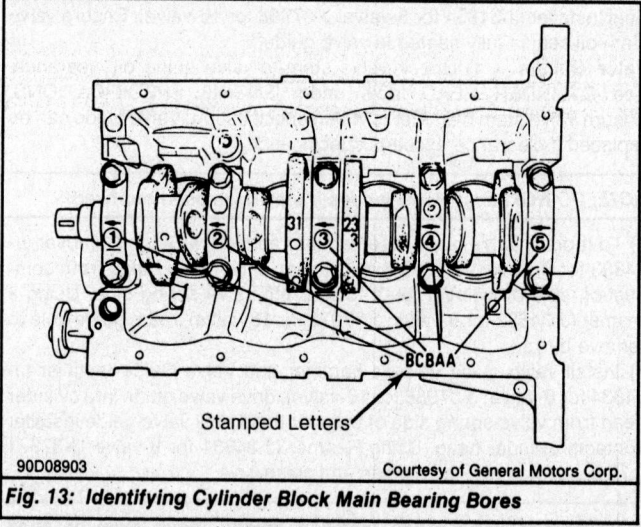

Fig. 13: Identifying Cylinder Block Main Bearing Bores

MAIN BEARING BORE SPECIFICATIONS

Letter Stamped On Cylinder Block	Diameter In. (mm)
A	2.2047-2.2050 (56.000-56.006)
B	2.2050-2.2052 (56.006-56.012)
C	2.2052-2.2054 (56.012-56.018)

MAIN BEARING JOURNAL DIAMETER SPECIFICATIONS

Number On Crankshaft Counterweight	Diameter In. (mm)
1	2.0470-2.0472 (51.994-52.000)
2	2.0468-2.0470 (51.988-51.994)
3	2.0465-2.0468 (51.982-51.988)

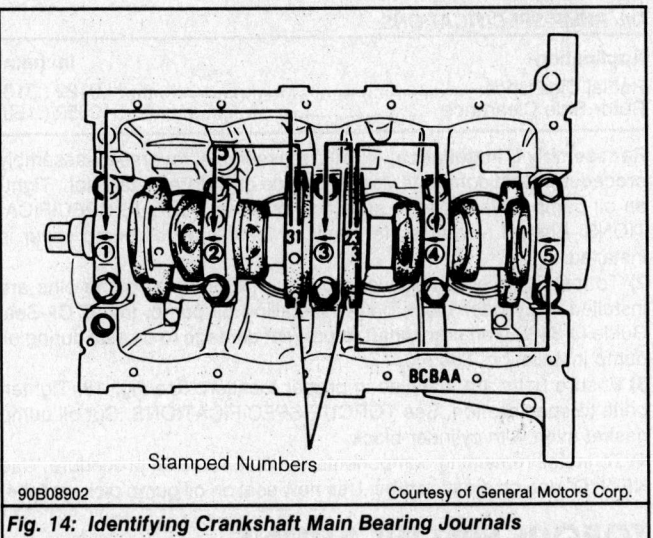

Stamped Numbers

BCBAA

90B08902   Courtesy of General Motors Corp.

Fig. 14: Identifying Crankshaft Main Bearing Journals

NOTE: *Main bearings contain a color code marked on the side of main bearing. Standard main bearings contain only one color code, and undersize main bearings contain 2 color codes. See Fig. 15.*

MAIN BEARING SELECTION (STANDARD BEARINGS)

Cylinder Block Letter	Crankshaft Number	Bearing Color Code
A	1	Green
A	2	Black
A	3	No Color Code
B	1	Black
B	2	No Color Code
B	3	Yellow
C	1	No Color Code
C	2	Yellow
C	3	Blue

BEARING THICKNESS SPECIFICATIONS

Color Code	In. (mm)
Standard Bearings	
Green	.0786-.0787 (1.996-1.999)
Black	.0787-.0788 (1.999-2.003)
No Color Code	.0788-.0789 (2.002-2.006)
Yellow	.0789-.0790 (2.005-2.009)
Blue	.0790-.0791 (2.008-2.012)
Undersize Bearings	
Green & Red	.0835-.0836 (2.121-2.124)
Black & Red	.0836-.0837 (2.124-2.127)
Red Only	.0837-.0838 (2.127-2.131)
Yellow & Red	.0838-.0839 (2.130-2.133)
Blue & Red	.0839-.0841 (2.133-2.137)

MAIN BEARING SELECTION (UNDERSIZE BEARINGS)

Finished Journal Diameter In. (mm)	Cylinder Block Letter	Bearing Color Code
2.0371-2.0374 (51.744-51.750)	A	Green & Red
	B	Black & Red
	C	Red Only
2.0369-2.0371 (51.738-51.744)	A	Black & Red
	B	Red Only
	C	Yellow & Red
2.0367-2.0369 (51.732-51.738)	A	Red Only
	B	Yellow & Red
	C	Blue & Red

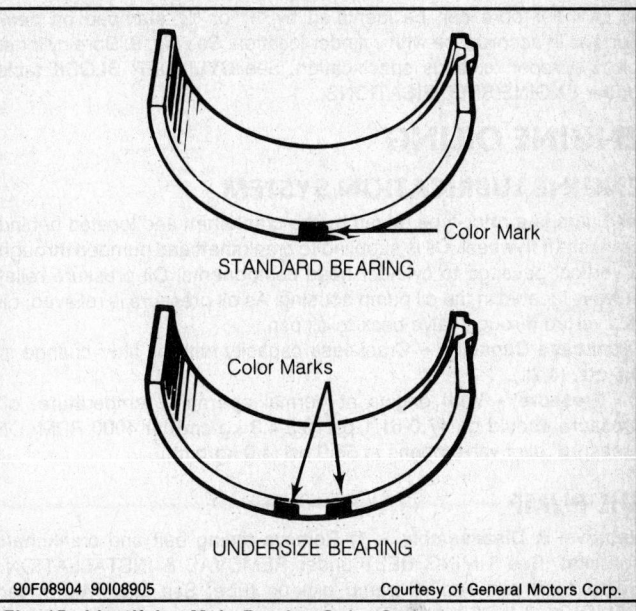

Color Mark

STANDARD BEARING

Color Marks

UNDERSIZE BEARING

90F08904 90I08905   Courtesy of General Motors Corp.

Fig. 15: Identifying Main Bearing Color Codes

Thrust Bearing – Install thrust bearing on main bearing with grooves toward crankshaft, away from cylinder block. Replace thrust bearing if crankshaft end play is not within specification. See CRANKSHAFT, MAIN & CONNECTING ROD BEARINGS table under ENGINE SPECIFICATIONS. *See Fig. 16 .*

Cylinder Block – **1)** Using feeler gauge and straightedge, check cylinder block head surface warpage. If warpage exceeds specification, correct as necessary. See CYLINDER BLOCK table under ENGINE SPECIFICATIONS.

2) Check cylinder bore wear and taper. Cylinder bore diameter is measured 2" (50 mm) and 4.13" (105 mm) from top of cylinder bore. Different sized cylinder bores are used.

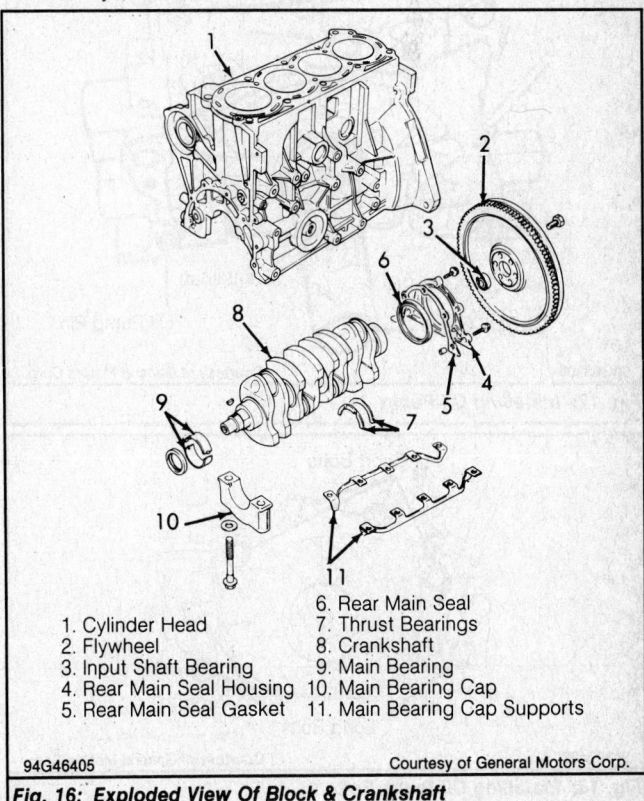

1. Cylinder Head
2. Flywheel
3. Input Shaft Bearing
4. Rear Main Seal Housing
5. Rear Main Seal Gasket
6. Rear Main Seal
7. Thrust Bearings
8. Crankshaft
9. Main Bearing
10. Main Bearing Cap
11. Main Bearing Cap Supports

94G46405   Courtesy of General Motors Corp.

Fig. 16: Exploded View Of Block & Crankshaft

3) Cylinder bore can be identified by "1" or "2" stamped on deck surface in accordance with cylinder location. *See Fig. 8.* Bore cylinder block if taper exceeds specification. See CYLINDER BLOCK table under ENGINE SPECIFICATIONS.

ENGINE OILING

ENGINE LUBRICATION SYSTEM

Oil pump is a rotor-type driven by the crankshaft and located behind crankshaft flywheel. Oil is supplied to crankshaft and pumped through a vertical passage to cylinder head components. Oil pressure relief valve is located in the oil pump housing. As oil pressure is relieved, oil is diverted through valve back to oil pan.

Crankcase Capacity – Crankcase capacity with oil filter change is 4.5 qts. (4.2L).

Oil Pressure – With engine at normal operating temperature, oil pressure should be 47.0-61.1 psi (3.3-4.3 kg/cm²) at 4000 RPM. Oil pressure relief valve opens at 56.9 psi (4.0 kg/cm²).

OIL PUMP

Removal & Disassembly – 1) Remove timing belt and crankshaft sprocket. See TIMING BELT under REMOVAL & INSTALLATION. Remove oil pan and oil pump pick-up tube. See OIL PAN under REMOVAL & INSTALLATION.

2) Remove dipstick tube from oil pump housing. Remove oil pump retaining bolts, oil pump and gasket. Remove oil pump cover from rear of oil pump. Remove oil seal from oil pump housing. Remove snap ring, spring and relief valve from oil pump housing.

Inspection – 1) Inspect components for damage. Ensure relief valve slides freely in bore. Using feeler gauge, measure radial clearance between outer rotor and oil pump housing.

2) With all rotors installed in oil pump housing, place straightedge across oil pump housing. Measure rotor side clearance between both rotors and straightedge. Replace oil pump assembly if clearance exceeds specification. See OIL PUMP SPECIFICATIONS table.

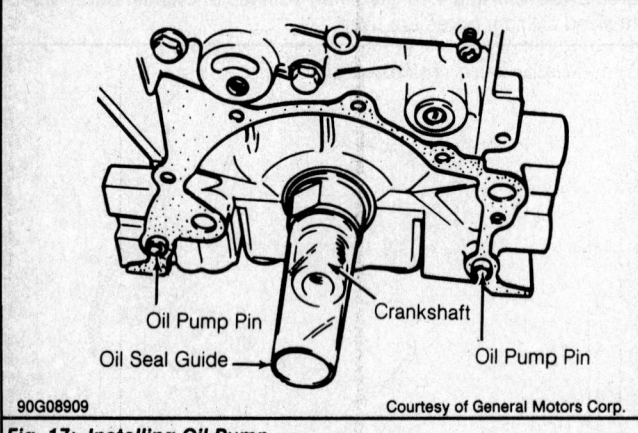

90G08909   Courtesy of General Motors Corp.
Fig. 17: Installing Oil Pump

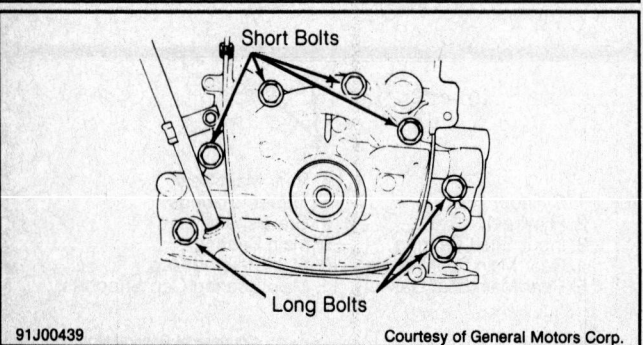

91J00439   Courtesy of General Motors Corp.
Fig. 18: Installing Oil Pump Bolts

OIL PUMP SPECIFICATIONS

Application	In. (mm)
Radial Clearance	.0122 (.310)
Rotor Side Clearance	.0059 (.150)

Reassembly & Installation – 1) To reassemble, reverse disassembly procedure. Coat components with engine oil before installation. Tighten oil pump cover bolts to specification. See TORQUE SPECIFICATIONS. Ensure rotors rotate freely by hand after oil pump cover is installed.

2) To install, reverse removal procedure. Ensure oil pump pins are installed in cylinder block before installing oil pump. Install Oil Seal Guide (J-34853) on crankshaft to prevent damage to oil seal during oil pump installation. *See Fig. 17.*

3) Ensure bolts are installed in proper location. *See Fig. 18.* Tighten bolts to specification. See TORQUE SPECIFICATIONS. Cut oil pump gasket even with cylinder block.

4) To install remaining components, reverse removal procedure. Use NEW "O" ring on dipstick tube. Use new seal on oil pump pick-up tube.

TORQUE SPECIFICATIONS

TORQUE SPECIFICATIONS (8-Valve Federal)

Application	Ft. Lbs. (N.m)
A/C Compressor Bolt	
8-mm Bolt	21 (29)
10-mm Bolt	33 (45)
Camshaft Sprocket Retaining Bolt	44 (60)
Connecting Rod Nut	26 (35)
Crankshaft Pulley Bolt	12 (16)
Crankshaft Sprocket Bolt	81 (110)
Cylinder Head Bolt	[1] 54 (73)
Engine Mounting Bolts	40 (54)
Engine Skid Plate Bolts	40 (54)
Exhaust Manifold Bolt	17 (23)
Flywheel Bolt	58 (79)
Intake Manifold Bolt	17 (23)
Main Bearing Cap Bolt	40 (54)
Oil Pressure Switch	10 (14)
Power Steering Pump Mounting Bolt	22 (30)
Power Steering Pump Pressure Hose	43 (60)
Spark Plug	21 (29)
Timing Belt Tensioner Bolt	20 (27)
Torque Converter Bolt	40 (54)
Transaxle-To-Cylinder Block Bolt	62 (84)
Valve Adjusting Screw Lock Nut	13 (18)
Wheel Lug Nut	70 (95)

Application	INCH Lbs. (N.m)
Distributor Case Bolts	89 (10)
Fan Clutch Nuts	97 (11)
Locking Hub Cover Bolts	106 (12)
Oil Pan Bolt	97 (11)
Oil Pump Cover Bolt	97 (11)
Oil Pump Mounting Bolt	97 (11)
Oil Pump Pick-Up Tube Bolt	97 (11)
Rear Seal Housing Bolt	97 (11)
Rocker Arm Shaft Retaining Screw	97 (11)
Tensioner Stud	97 (11)
Timing Belt Cover Nut & Bolts	89 (10)
Valve Cover Bolt	44 (5)
Water Pump Bolt	106 (12)

[1] – Tighten bolts to specification in sequence. *See Fig. 1.*

TORQUE SPECIFICATIONS – 16-Valve California

Application	Ft. Lbs. (N.m)
A/C Compressor Bolt	
8-mm Bolt	21 (29)
10-mm Bolt	33 (45)
Camshaft Sprocket Retaining Bolt	44 (61)
Connecting Rod Nut	26 (35)
Crankshaft Pulley Bolt	12 (16)
Crankshaft Sprocket Bolt	81 (110)
Cylinder Head Bolt [1]	
First Pass	26 (35)
Second Pass	41 (56)
Third Pass	52 (71)
Engine Mounting Bolts	40 (54)
Engine Skid Plate Bolts	40 (54)
Exhaust Manifold Bolt	17 (23)
Flywheel Bolt	58 (79)
HO2S Sensor	32 (43)
Intake Manifold Bolt	17 (23)
Left Axle Shaft Flange Bolt	43 (60)
Main Bearing Cap Bolt	40 (54)
Oil Pressure Switch	10 (14)
Power Steering Pump Mounting Bolt	22 (30)
Power Steering Pump Pressure Hose	43 (60)
Spark Plug	21 (28)
Timing Belt Tensioner Bolt	20 (27)
Throttle Body Bolt	17 (23)
Torque Converter Bolt	40 (54)
Transaxle-To-Cylinder Block Bolt	62 (84)
Valve Adjusting Screw Lock Nut	13 (18)
Wheel Lug Nut	70 (95)

	INCH Lbs. (N.m)
Camshaft Carrier Cap Bolts	89 (10)
Distributor Case Bolts	89 (10)
Fan Clutch Nuts	97 (11)
Oil Pan Bolt	97 (11)
Oil Pump Cover Bolt	97 (11)
Oil Pump Mounting Bolt	97 (11)
Oil Pump Pick-Up Tube Bolt	97 (11)
Rear Seal Housing Bolt	97 (11)
Rocker Arm Shaft Bolts	89 (10)
Tensioner Stud	97 (11)
Timing Belt Cover Bolt	97 (11)
Valve Cover Bolt	89 (10)
Water Pump Bolt	106 (12)

[1] – Head bolts must be tightened in 3 separate passes. Tighten bolts to specification in sequence. See Fig. 2.

ENGINE SPECIFICATIONS

GENERAL SPECIFICATIONS

Application	Specification
Displacement	97 Cu. In. (1.6L)
Bore	2.95" (75 mm)
Stroke	3.54" (90 mm)
Compression Ratio	
8-Valve	8.9:1
16-Valve	9.5:1
	Fuel System
8-Valve	TBI
16-Valve	MFI
Horsepower @ RPM	
8-Valve	80 @ 5400
16-Valve	95 @ 5600
Torque Ft. Lbs. @ RPM	
8-Valve	94 @ 3000
16-Valve	98 @ 4000

CRANKSHAFT, MAIN & CONNECTING ROD BEARINGS

Application	In. (mm)
Crankshaft	
End Play	
Standard	.004-.012 (.01-.11)
Wear Limit	.015 (.38)
Maximum Runout	.0023 (.058)
Main Bearings	
Journal Diameter [1]	
No. 1	2.0470-2.0472 (51.994-52.000)
No. 2	2.0468-2.0470 (51.988-51.994)
No. 3	2.0465-2.0468 (51.982-51.988)
Undersized	2.0367-2.0373 (51.732-51.750)
Journal Out-Of-Round	.0004 (.010)
Journal Taper	.0004 (.010)
Oil Clearance	
Standard	.0008-.0016 (.020-.040)
Wear Limit	.0023 (.058)
Connecting Rod Bearings	
Journal Diameter	
Standard	1.7316-1.7323 (43.982-44.000)
.0098" (.25 mm) Undersized	1.7218-1.7224 (43.732-43.750)
Journal Out-Of-Round	.0004 (.010)
Oil Clearance	
Standard	.0008-.0019 (.020-.048)
Wear Limit	.0031 (.080)

[1] – Use number stamped on crankshaft counterweight to determine journal diameter. See Fig. 14.

PISTONS, PINS & RINGS

Application	In. (mm)
Pistons	
Clearance	.0008-.0015 (.020-.038)
Diameter [1]	
No. 1	2.9520-2.9524 (74.981-74.991)
No. 2	2.9516-2.9520 (74.971-74.981)
Pins	
Diameter	.7478-.7480 (18.995-19.000)
Rod Bore	.7481-.7485 (19.003-19.011)
Rings	
No. 1	
End Gap	.0079-.0137 (.201-.348)
Side Clearance	.0012-.0027 (.030-.069)
No. 2	
End Gap	.0079-.0137 (.201-.348)
Side Clearance	.0008-.0023 (.020-.058)
No. 3 (Oil)	
End Gap	.0079-.0275 (.201-.699)

[1] – Piston diameter is determined by piston identification mark on top of piston. See Fig. 11.

CYLINDER BLOCK

Application	In. (mm)
Cylinder Bore	
Standard Diameter [1]	
No. 1	2.9531-2.9535 (75.009-75.019)
No. 2	2.9528-2.9531 (75.001-75.009)
Bore Limit	2.9586 (75.15)
Maximum Taper	.0039 (.099)
Maximum Out-Of-Round	.0039 (.099)
Maximum Deck Warpage	.0024 (.060)

[1] – Original cylinder bore diameter is determined by number on deck surface of cylinder block. See Fig. 11.

CONNECTING RODS

Application	In. (mm)
Maximum Bend	.002 (.05)
Maximum Twist	.0039 (.099)
Side Play	
Standard	.0039-.0078 (.10-.20)
Wear Limit	.0137 (.35)

VALVES & VALVE SPRINGS (8-Valve)

Application	Specification
Valve Head Refinishing Angles	
Above Seat Contact Surface	15°
Below Seat Contact Surface	60°
Seat Contact Surface	45°
Intake Valves	
Valve Head Thickness	
Standard	.039" (.99 mm)
Service Limit	.023" (.58 mm)
Stem Diameter	.2742-.2748" (6.965-6.980 mm)
Maximum Head Radial Runout	.003" (.08 mm)
Exhaust Valves	
Valve Head Thickness	
Standard	.039" (.99 mm)
Service Limit	.027" (.69 mm)
Minimum Margin	.027" (.69 mm)
Stem Diameter	.2737-.2742" (6.951-6.965 mm)
Maximum Head Radial Runout	.003" (.08 mm)
Valve Guide Inside Diameter	.2756-.2761" (7.000-7.015 mm)
Valve Springs	
Free Length	1.9094-1.9866" (48.498-50.460 mm)
Out-Of-Square	.079" (2.01 mm)

	Lbs. @ In. (kg @ mm)
Pressure	
Valve Closed	50.2-64.3 @ 1.63 (22.8-29.2 @ 41.4)

VALVES & VALVE SPRINGS (16-Valve)

Application	Specification
Valve Head Refinishing Angles	
Above Seat Contact Surface	15°
Seat Contact Surface	45°
Intake Valves	
Valve Head Thickness	
Standard	.030-.047" (.80-1.19 mm)
Service Limit	.023" (.58 mm)
Stem Diameter	.2742-.2748" (6.965-6.980 mm)
Maximum Head Radial Runout	.003" (.08 mm)
Exhaust Valves	
Valve Head Thickness	
Standard	.030-.047" (.80-1.19 mm)
Service Limit	.027" (.69 mm)
Stem Diameter	.2737-.2742" (6.951-6.965 mm)
Maximum Head Radial Runout	.003" (.08 mm)
Valve Guide Inside Diameter	.2166-.2170" (5.500-5.512 mm)
Valve Springs	
Free Length	1.4043-1.4500" (35.67-36.83 mm)
Out-Of-Square	.079" (2.01 mm)

	Lbs. @ In. (kg @ mm)
Pressure	
Valve Closed	23.6-27.5 @ 1.24 (10.7-12.5 @ 31.5)

CYLINDER HEAD (8-VALVE)

Application	Specification
Maximum Warpage	
Cylinder Block Surface	.002" (.05 mm)
Manifold Surface	.004" (.10 mm)
Valve Seats	
Intake & Exhaust Valve	
Seat Angle	45°
Seat Width	.0512-.0590" (1.300-1.499 mm)
Valve Guides	
Valve Guide I.D.	.2756-.2761" (7.000-7.013 mm)
Valve Guide Installed Height	.55" (14.0 mm)
Intake Valve	
Valve Stem-To-Guide Oil Clearance	
Standard	.0008-.0019" (.020-.048 mm)
Wear Limit	.0027" (.069 mm)
Exhaust Valve	
Valve Stem-To-Guide Oil Clearance	
Standard	.0014-.0025" (.036-.064 mm)
Wear Limit	.0035" (.089 mm)

CYLINDER HEAD (16-VALVE)

Application	Specification
Maximum Warpage	
Cylinder Block Surface	.0012-.0024" (.03-.06 mm)
Manifold Surface	.004" (.10 mm)
Valve Seats	
Intake & Exhaust Valve	
Seat Angle	45°
Seat Width	.0433-.0512" (1.100-1.300 mm)
Valve Guides	
Valve Guide I.D.	.2166-.2170" (5.500-5.512 mm)
Valve Guide Installed Height	.45" (11.4 mm)
Intake Valve	
Valve Stem-To-Guide Oil Clearance	
Standard	.0008-.0018" (.020-.048 mm)
Wear Limit	.0027" (.069 mm)
Exhaust Valve	
Valve Stem-To-Guide Oil Clearance	
Standard	.0018-.0028" (.046-.071 mm)
Wear Limit	.0035" (.089 mm)

CAMSHAFT (8-VALVE)

Application	In. (mm)
Bore Diameter [1]	
No. 1	1.7402-1.7408 (44.201-44.216)
No. 2	1.7480-1.7487 (44.400-44.416)
No. 3	1.7559-1.7565 (44.600-44.616)
No. 4	1.7638-1.7644 (44.800-44.816)
No. 5	1.7716-1.7723 (45.000-45.016)
Journal Diameter [1]	
No. 1	1.7372-1.7382 (44.125-44.150)
No. 2	1.7451-1.7460 (44.325-44.350)
No. 3	1.7529-1.7539 (44.525-44.550)
No. 4	1.7608-1.7618 (44.725-44.750)
No. 5	1.7687-1.7697 (44.925-44.950)
Journal Oil Clearance	.0020-.0036 (.051-.091)
Journal Runout	.0039 (.099)
Lobe Height	
Intake	1.4724-1.4763 (37.399-37.498)
Exhaust	1.4724-1.4749 (37.399-37.462)

[1] – No. 1 is at timing belt end of camshaft.

CAMSHAFT (16-VALVE)

Application	In. (mm)
Bore Diameter [1]	
....	1.1024-1.1031 (28.001-28.019)
Journal Diameter	1.1000-1.1008 (27.940-27.960)
Journal Oil Clearance [2]	.0016-.0032 (.041-.081)
Maximum Journal Oil Clearance	.0047 (.119)
Journal Runout	.0039 (.099)
Lobe Height	
Intake	
Standard	1.4241-1.4303 (36.172-36.330)
Service Limit	1.4202 (36.073)
Exhaust	
Standard	1.4314-1.4376 (36.358-36.515)
Service Limit	1.4275 (36.259)

[1] – Measurement is with camshaft carrier cap bolts installed and tightened to 89 INCH lbs. (10 N.m).
[2] – Measure using plastic-type gauging material with camshaft and camshaft carrier caps installed and bolts tightened to 89 INCH lbs. (10 N.m).

ROCKER ARM ASSEMBLY SPECIFICATIONS

Application	In. (mm)
Rocker Arm I.D.	.630-.631 (16.00-16.02)
Rocker Arm Shaft O.D.	.628-.629 (15.97-15.99)
Rocker Arm Shaft Oil Clearance	
8-Valve	.0005-.0017 (.013-.043)
16-Valve	.0001-.0014 (.003-.036)
Rocker Arm Shaft Runout	
8-Valve	.004 (.10)
16-Valve	.008 (.20)

Metro, Prizm, Tracker

SPECIFICATIONS

BELT ADJUSTMENT

BELT ADJUSTMENT

Application	Specification [1] Belt Deflection
Metro	
A/C Belt	.20-.25" (5.1-6.4 mm)
Alternator/Water Pump Belt	
New Belt	.20-.27" (5.1-6.9 mm)
Used Belt [3]	.25-.32" (6.4-8.1 mm)
Prizm	
A/C Belt	
New Belt	.20-.32" (5.1-8.1 mm)
Used Belt [3]	.33-.37" (8.4-9.4 mm)
P/S Belt	.20-.32" (5.1-8.1 mm)
Alternator/Water Pump Belt	
New Belt	.20-.31" (5.1-7.9 mm)
Used Belt [3]	.24-.35" (6.1-8.9 mm)
Tracker	
A/C Belt	.20-.25" (5.1-6.4 mm)
P/S Belt	.24-.35" (6.1-8.9 mm)
Alternator/Water Pump Belt	
New Belt	.20-.27" (5.1-6.9 mm)
Used Belt [3]	.24-.31" (6.1-7.9 mm)
	[2] Belt Tension
Prizm	
P/S Belt	
New Belt	100-150 lbs. (45-68 kg)
Used Belt [3]	60-121 lbs. (27-55 kg)
Alternator/Water Pump Belt	
New Belt	141-182 lbs. (64-83 kg)
Used Belt [3]	111-152 lbs. (50-69 kg)

[1] – Belt deflection is checked with 22 lbs. (10 kg) pressure applied midway on longest belt run.
[2] – Belt tension is checked using a J23600-B "V" Belt tension gauge.
[3] – A drive belt is considered used after 5 minutes of engine operation.

COOLING SYSTEM SPECIFICATIONS

COOLING SYSTEM SPECIFICATIONS

Application	Specification
Cooling System Capacity [1]	
Metro	
Automatic Transaxle	4.2 Qts. (4.0L)
Manual Transaxle	4.1 Qts. (3.9L)
Prizm	6.7 Qts. (6.3L)
Tracker	
A/T	5.5 Qts. (5.2L)
M/T	5.6 Qts. (5.3L)
Pressure Cap	
Metro	12.8 psi (88 kPa)
Prizm	10.7-14.9 psi (74-103 kPa)
Tracker	13 psi (90 kPa)
Thermostat Opening	
Metro	
"A" Thermostat	[2] 187.3-192.7°F (86.3-89.3°C)
"B" Thermostat [3]	[2] 194.3-199.7°F (90.2-93.2°C)
Prizm	[4] 176-183°F (80-84°C)
Tracker	[4] 176-203°F (80-95°C)

[1] – Includes heater core.
[2] – "A" thermostat will be fully open at 212°F (100°C). "B" thermostat will be fully open at 221°F (105°C).
[3] – "B" thermostat is used in Metro XFi. Ensure replacement thermostat has same temperature specification as original.
[4] – If thermostat valve lift is not greater than .31" (8 mm) at 203°F (95°C), replace thermostat.

NOTE: For thermoswitch, relay and motor testing, see COMPONENT TESTING. For cooling fan system testing, see appropriate SYSTEM TESTING procedure.

ELECTRIC COOLING FAN

NOTE: For diagnosis of A/C condenser cooling fans see appropriate article in MITCHELL® AIR CONDITIONING & HEATING SERVICE & REPAIR manual.

SYSTEM TESTING

Radiator Fan (Metro) – 1) Check cooling system fluid level. Ensure thermostat operates properly. Start and run engine. Ensure coolant temperature is less than 190°F (88°C). If cooling fan operates, go to next step. If cooling fan does not operate, go to step 3).
2) Disconnect cooling fan thermoswitch, located near distributor. *See Fig. 1.* If cooling fan stops running, replace cooling fan thermoswitch. If cooling fan continues to operate after cooling fan thermoswitch is disconnected, disconnect cooling fan relay. If cooling fan continues to run, check for short to voltage in Blue/Red wire between cooling fan relay and cooling fan motor. If cooling fan stops when relay is disconnected, check for a short to voltage in Blue wire between fan thermoswitch and cooling fan relay.

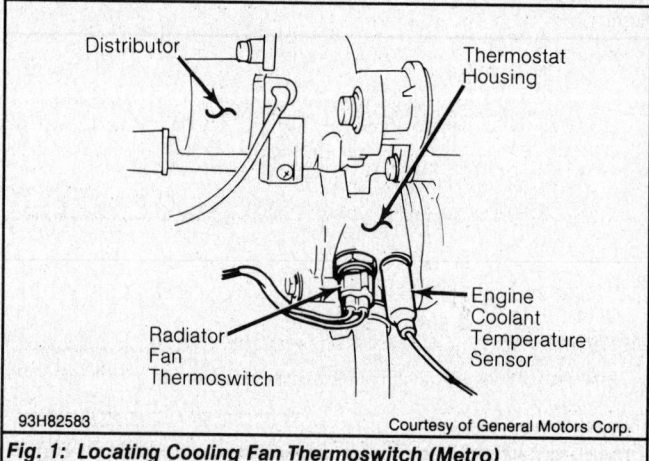

Fig. 1: Locating Cooling Fan Thermoswitch (Metro)

3) If cooling fan does not operate with coolant temperature less than 190°F (88°C), run engine until engine coolant temperature is more than 208°F (98°C). Feel radiator hoses for proper thermostat operation. If cooling fan operates, system is okay. If cooling fan does not operate, check fusible link "B", radiator fan fuse and IGN fuse in fuse block. If fuses are okay and cooling fan does not operate, go to next step.
4) With cooling fan thermoswitch connector disconnected, connect a fused jumper wire between thermoswitch harness connector terminals (Black/White and Blue wires). If cooling fan operates with ignition on, replace cooling fan thermoswitch. If cooling fan does not operate, go to next step.
5) Remove cooling fan relay. Connect a fused jumper wire between cooling fan relay connector terminals No. 2 (White/Blue wire) and No. 4 (Blue/Red wire). If cooling fan does not operate with ignition on, check White/Blue wire between fuse block and cooling fan relay. If okay, check Blue/Red wire between cooling fan relay and fan motor harness 2-pin connector. Repair wires as necessary. If cooling fan still does not operate, go to next step.

NOTE: Radiator fan and cooling fan relay chassis ground point is located at left front inner fender near radiator on hardtop models and at left side instrument panel above kick panel on convertible models.

6) Check ground circuit of cooling fan and cooling fan relay (Black wires) and repair wires/connections as necessary. If cooling fan still does not operate, check Blue wire between fan thermoswitch and cooling fan relay. If Blue wire is okay, replace radiator cooling fan.

Radiator Fan Does Not Operate (Prizm) – **1)** Check IGN fuse, ECU-IGN fuse and A/C fuse. If radiator fan does not run, remove fuse and relay box from inner fender. Remove lower inspection cover from fuse and relay box. Disconnect connector C6 from fuse and relay box. *See Fig. 2*. Turn ignition switch to ON position. If fan does not run, go to next step. If fan runs, check Light Green/Black and Light Green wires between fan No. 1 relay and fan thermoswitch for short to ground.

2) If fan does not run in step **1)**, backprobe fuse and relay box connector C1, terminal No. 4 (Blue/Black wire), with test light connected to battery voltage. *See Fig. 2*. If test light does not glow, go to next step. If test light glows, repair short to ground in Blue/Black wire between A/C fan No. 2 relay connector and fuse and relay box.

3) Backprobe fuse and relay box connector C3, terminal No. 6 (Black/Yellow wire), with a test light connected to ground. *See Fig. 2*. If test light glows, go to next step. If test light does not glow, backprobe junction block No. 3 (behind center of instrument panel) connector C3 (White Connector) terminal No. 17 (Black/Yellow wire). If test light glows, check for an open in Black/Yellow wire between fuse and relay box and junction block No. 3. If test light does not glow, check for an open in Black/Yellow wire between junction block No. 1 and junction block No. 3. If okay, replace junction block No. 1.

4) Backprobe fuse and relay box connector C1, terminal No. 3 (White/Black wire), with a test light connected to battery voltage. *See Fig. 2*. If test light glows, go to next step. If test light does not glow, repair open or poor connection in White/Black wire between fuse and relay box and chassis ground point G102 (behind left headlight).

5) Turn ignition off. Remove engine main relay from fuse and relay box. Connect a fused jumper from engine main relay connector terminal No. 4 to terminal No. 5. *See Fig. 2*. Turn ignition on. If fan motor still does not run, go to next step. If fan motor starts to run, inspect fuse and relay box connections. If okay, replace engine main relay.

6) Turn ignition off. Remove fused jumper from engine main relay connector and reinstall relay. Remove fan No. 1 relay. Connect a fused jumper from fan No. 1 relay connector terminal No. 3 to terminal No. 4. *See Fig. 2*. Turn ignition on. If fan motor still does not run, go to next step. If fan motor starts to run, inspect fuse and relay box connections. If okay, replace engine main relay.

7) Turn ignition off. Remove fused jumper from fan relay connector. Reinstall fan No. 1 relay. Backprobe radiator fan motor connector terminal No. 1 (White/Black wire), with a test light connected to battery voltage. If test light glows, go to next step. If test light does not glow, check for open in White/Black wire between radiator fan motor and fuse and relay box. If White/Black wire is okay, replace fuse and relay box.

8) With a fused jumper connected to battery positive, backprobe radiator fan motor connector terminal No. 2 (Blue wire). If radiator fan motor does not run, replace fan motor. If radiator fan motor runs, check for open in Black/Red wire between radiator fan motor and fuse and relay box. If Black/Red wire is okay, replace fuse and relay box.

Radiator Fan Operates Continuously With Key On (Prizm) – **1)** Ensure engine coolant is less than 194°F (90°C). Remove fan No. 1 relay from fuse and relay box. Turn ignition on. If fan motor does not run, check for short to voltage in Black/Red wire between fuse and relay box, radiator fan motor and A/C fan No. 2 relay. If Black/Red wire is okay, replace fuse and relay box.

2) Check fan No. 1 relay connector terminal No. 1, with test light connected to battery voltage. If test light does not glow, go to next step. If test light glows, replace fan No. 1 relay and check system operation. If fan motor continues to run, replace fuse and relay box.

NOTE: Models not equipped with A/C have a shorting clip in place of A/C triple pressure switch.

---

3) Backprobe A/C triple pressure switch connector terminal No. 2 (Light Green wire) with a test light connected to battery voltage. If test light glows, go to next step. If test light does not glow, check for open in Light Green wire between A/C triple pressure switch connector and fan thermoswitch. If Light green wire is okay, replace fan thermoswitch.

4) Check for open in Light Green/Black wire between fuse and relay box and A/C triple pressure switch connector. If Light Green/Black wire is okay, replace A/C triple pressure switch (A/C equipped models) or shorting clip (non-A/C models).

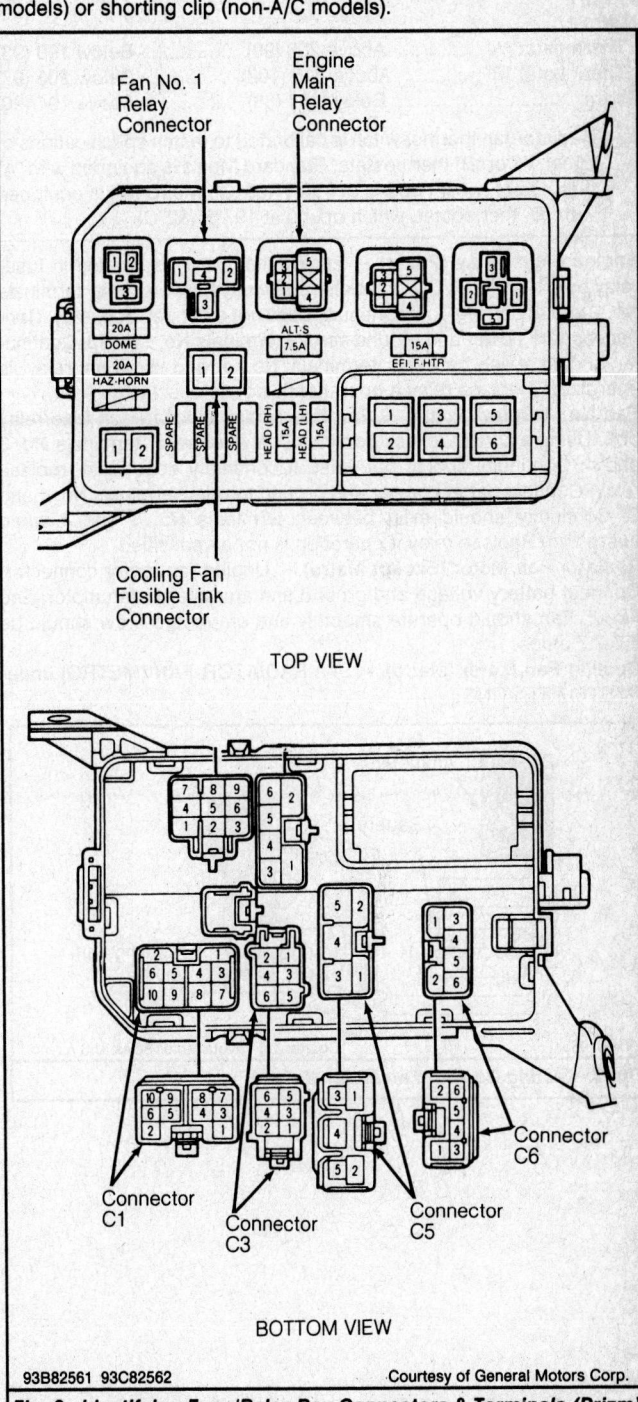

TOP VIEW

BOTTOM VIEW

93B82561 93C82562   Courtesy of General Motors Corp.

Fig. 2: Identifying Fuse/Relay Box Connectors & Terminals (Prizm)

COMPONENT TESTING

Radiator Fan Thermoswitch (Metro & Prizm) – To test radiator fan thermoswitch, remove thermoswitch from vehicle. Using ohmmeter, ensure continuity exists between wire connector and thermoswitch body (or both thermoswitch terminals on Metro) at indicated temperatures. Thermoswitch may be gradually heated in water for testing. See RADIATOR FAN THERMOSWITCH table.

RADIATOR FAN THERMOSWITCH

Model	Continuity °F (°C)	No Continuity °F (°C)
Metro [1]		
Thermostat "A"	Above 208 (98)	Below 199 (93)
Thermostat "B"	Above 215 (102)	Below 206 (97)
Prizm	Below 181 (83)	Above 194 (90)

[1] – Radiator fan thermoswitch is calibrated to match specifications of either "A" or "B" thermostats. Standard Metro is equipped with "A" thermostat, which opens at 190°F (88°C). Metro XFi is equipped with "B" thermostat, which opens at 197°F (92°C).

Engine Main Relay (Prizm) – Engine main relay is located in fuse/relay box. Using a DVOM, check for continuity between relay terminals No. 2 and 4. See Fig. 2. If continuity does not exist, replace relay. Connect battery power and ground across terminals No. 1 and 3. Continuity should exist between terminals No. 4 and 5 when relay is energized. Replace relay if operation is not as specified.

Fan No. 1 Relay (Prizm) – Fan No. 1 relay is located in fuse/relay box. Using a DVOM, check continuity between relay terminals No. 3 and 4. Continuity should not exist. If continuity does exist, replace relay. Connect battery power and ground to relay terminals No. 1 and 2. Continuity should exist between terminals No. 3 and 4 when energized. Replace relay if operation is not as specified.

Radiator Fan Motor (Except Metro) – Unplug fan motor connector. Connect battery voltage and ground and ammeter to fan motor. See Fig. 3. Fan should operate smoothly and amperage draw should be 5.7-7.7 amps.

Cooling Fan Motor (Metro) – See RADIATOR FAN (METRO) under SYSTEM TESTING.

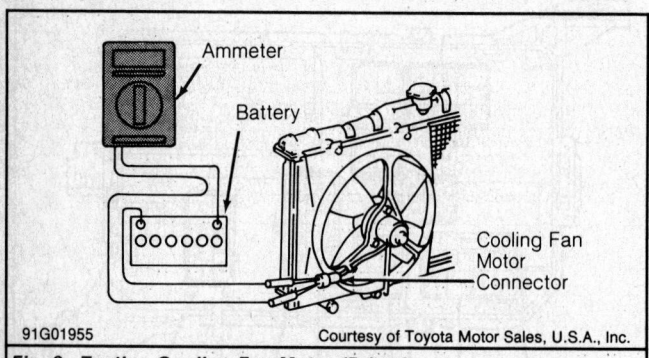

91G01955   Courtesy of Toyota Motor Sales, U.S.A., Inc.

Fig. 3: Testing Cooling Fan Motor (Prizm)

WIRING DIAGRAMS

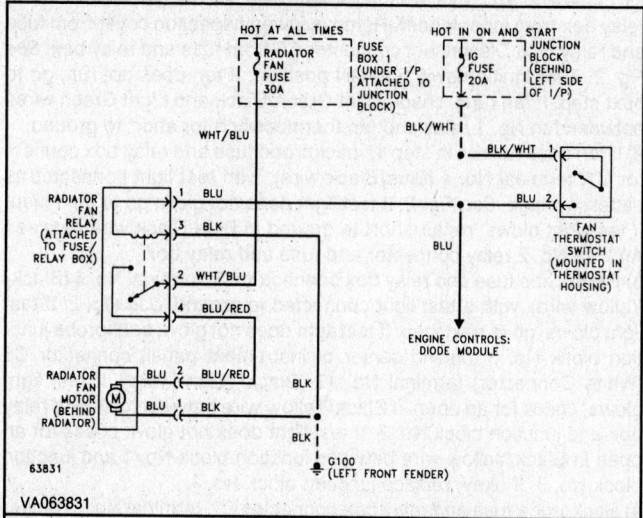

63831

VA063831

Fig. 4: Electric Cooling Fan Wiring Diagram (Metro)

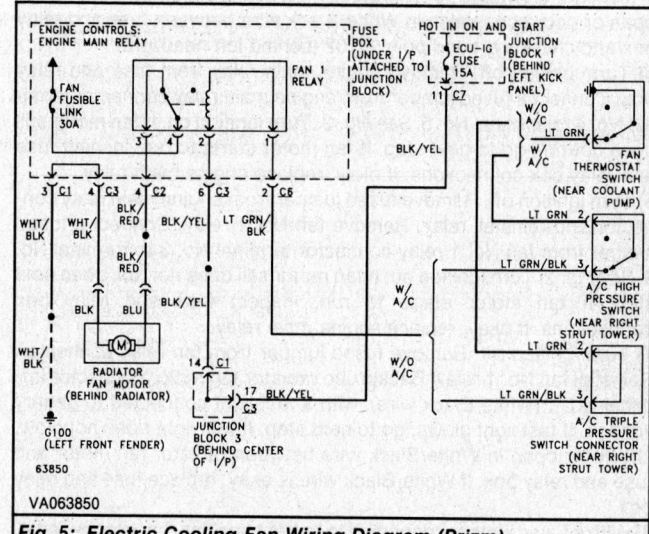

63850

VA063850

Fig. 5: Electric Cooling Fan Wiring Diagram (Prizm)

Metro, Prizm

DESCRIPTION

Clutches are single disc type. A diaphragm spring is used to engage pressure plate. On Metro, clutch is mechanically controlled by the clutch pedal, clutch cable, return spring, release fork and release bearing. On Prizm, clutch is hydraulically operated by clutch master cylinder and housing-mounted slave cylinder. On all models, a Clutch Pedal Position (CPP) switch is used to disable starter if clutch pedal is not fully depressed.

ADJUSTMENTS

CLUTCH PEDAL HEIGHT

NOTE: Clutch pedal free play must be adjusted after adjusting clutch pedal height. See CLUTCH PEDAL FREE PLAY.

Metro – Loosen clutch pedal stop bolt and adjust until clutch pedal is within .3" (8 mm) of being level with brake pedal. Turning clutch pedal stop bolt clockwise will lower clutch pedal height. Tighten lock nut after adjusting.

Prizm – Remove lower instrument cluster trim panel and air duct. Rotate clutch pedal stop bolt at top of pedal assembly to adjust pedal height. Measure clutch pedal height from floor board to top of clutch pedal. See CLUTCH PEDAL SPECIFICATIONS table. *See Fig. 1.*

CLUTCH PEDAL FREE PLAY

NOTE: Ensure clutch pedal height is correct before adjusting free play. See CLUTCH PEDAL HEIGHT under ADJUSTMENTS.

Metro – Move clutch pedal by hand, and stop when resistance is felt. Measure distance of clutch pedal free play. Ensure clutch pedal free play is within specification. See CLUTCH PEDAL SPECIFICATIONS table. If clutch pedal free play is NOT within specification, loosen or tighten clutch cable adjustment nut at lever end of cable to adjust free play. If clutch pedal free play is adjusted to specification, measure clutch release lever free travel. If clutch release lever free travel is not .08-.15" (2.0-3.8 mm), check clutch release shaft return spring and release lever-to-shaft alignment.

Prizm – Move clutch pedal by hand, and stop when resistance is felt. Measure distance of clutch pedal free play. Ensure clutch pedal free play is within specification. See CLUTCH PEDAL SPECIFICATIONS table. If clutch pedal free play is NOT within specification, adjust clutch master cylinder by loosening lock nut on clutch master cylinder push rod. Turn push rod in or out to adjust free play. *See Fig. 1.*

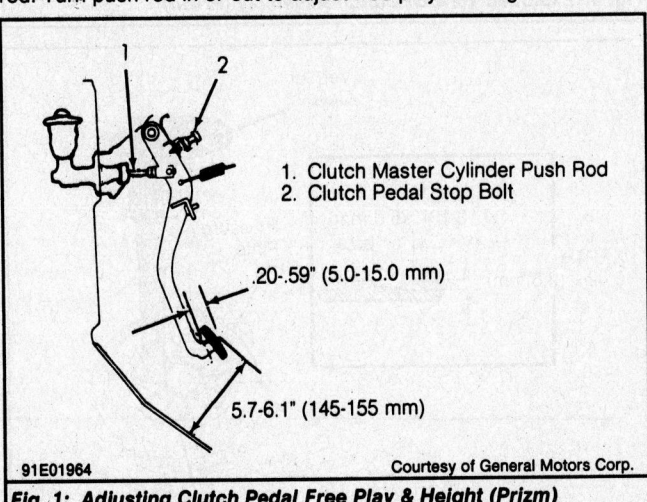

1. Clutch Master Cylinder Push Rod
2. Clutch Pedal Stop Bolt

.20-.59" (5.0-15.0 mm)

5.7-6.1" (145-155 mm)

91E01964   Courtesy of General Motors Corp.

Fig. 1: Adjusting Clutch Pedal Free Play & Height (Prizm)

CLUTCH PEDAL SPECIFICATIONS

Application	Free Play In. (mm)	Pedal Height In. (mm)
Metro	0.6-0.8 (15-20)	[1]
Prizm	.20-.59 (5-15)	5.7-6.1 (145-155)

[1] – Clutch pedal height is within .3" (8 mm) of being level with brake pedal.

CLUTCH PEDAL POSITION (CPP) SWITCH

Metro – 1) Apply parking brake. Place gearshift lever in Neutral. Disconnect clutch pedal position switch electrical connector. Connect ohmmeter between switch terminals. Loosen lock nut and turn switch outward. Depress clutch pedal to floor.

2) Return clutch pedal along its travel from floor and stop at specified height. See CLUTCH PEDAL POSITION SWITCH ADJUSTMENT table. Slowly screw CPP switch in until ohmmeter indicates continuity exists. Hold switch at this position and tighten lock nut. Connect clutch pedal position switch electrical connector.

CLUTCH PEDAL POSITION SWITCH ADJUSTMENT

Application	Height From Floor In. (mm)
Metro	0.6-1.2 (15-30)
Prizm	[1] .079-.240 (2.0-6.1)

[1] – Clearance is measured between clutch pedal position switch and clutch pedal arm.

NOTE: Ensure clutch pedal height is correct before adjusting clutch pedal position switch. See CLUTCH PEDAL HEIGHT under ADJUSTMENTS.

Prizm – Depress clutch pedal to floor. Measure clearance between end of threaded portion (not switch button) of clutch pedal position switch and clutch pedal arm contact area. *See Fig. 2.* Clearance should be .079" (2.0 mm).

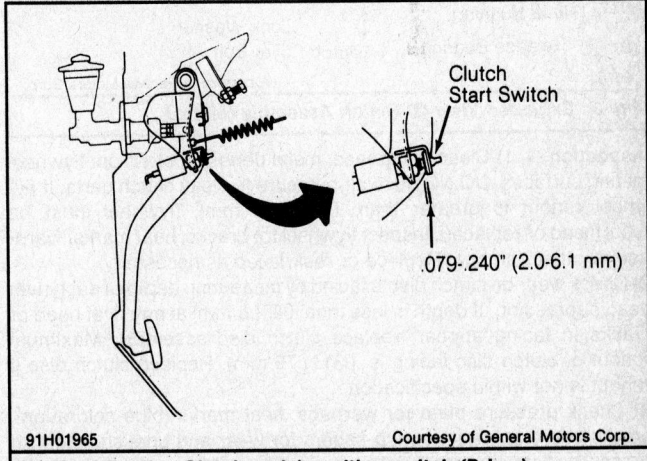

Clutch Start Switch

.079-.240" (2.0-6.1 mm)

91H01965   Courtesy of General Motors Corp.

Fig. 2: Adjusting Clutch pedal position switch (Prizm)

REMOVAL & INSTALLATION

CLUTCH ASSEMBLY

Removal (Metro) – 1) Disconnect negative battery cable at battery and transaxle. Disconnect clutch cable from release lever. Disconnect wiring harness clamps and connectors.

2) Disconnect speedometer cable. Remove upper transaxle-to-engine bolts. Remove starter motor and starter motor retaining plate. Disconnect vacuum hoses.

3) Install engine support. Raise and support vehicle. Drain transaxle fluid. Disconnect gearshift control shaft bolt and nut. Disconnect control shaft from gearshift shaft.

4) Remove extension rod bolts, nuts and washers. Remove clutch housing lower plate. Remove left front wheel. Disconnect left tie rod.

5) Disconnect left ball joint by removing ball joint stud bolt. Disconnect drive axles from transaxle. See FWD AXLE SHAFTS article in DRIVE AXLES. Remove transaxle-to-engine nuts and bolts.

6) Support transaxle with jack. Remove rear transaxle mounting nuts. Remove nuts and bolts securing left transaxle mounting bracket. Remove left transaxle mounting bracket.

7) Lower engine and transaxle enough to remove rear engine mounting through bolt. Pull transaxle straight out toward left side and disconnect input shaft from clutch cover. Lower transaxle assembly.

8) Mark pressure plate and flywheel for reassembly reference. Install clutch centering tool to support clutch assembly. Loosen pressure plate-to-flywheel bolts evenly (one turn at a time) until spring pressure is released. Remove pressure plate-to-flywheel bolts. Remove pressure plate and clutch disc. See Fig. 3.

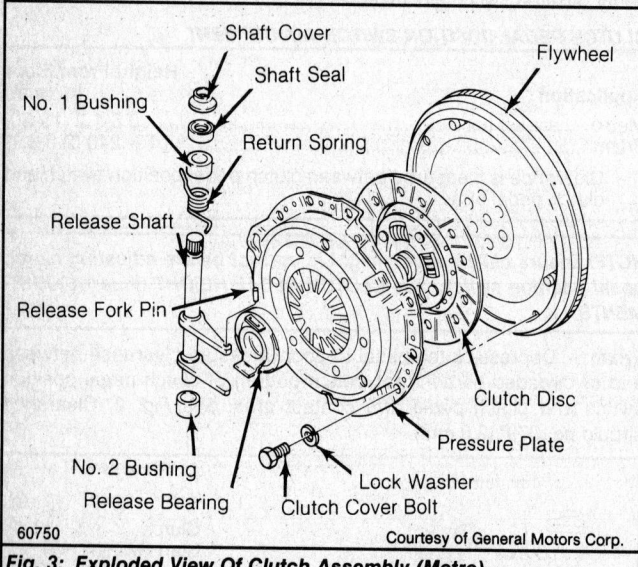

Fig. 3: Exploded View Of Clutch Assembly (Metro)

Inspection – 1) Clean oil, grease, metal deposits, etc. from flywheel mating surfaces. DO NOT use air pressure to clean clutch parts. If flywheel runout is greater than .004" (.10 mm), flywheel must be resurfaced or replaced. Inspect flywheel for cracks, heat marks, warpage or other damage. Replace or resurfaced as necessary.

2) Check wear on clutch disc's facing by measuring depth of each rivet head depression. If depth is less than .02" (.5 mm) at any rivet head or cracks in facing appear, replace clutch disc assembly. Maximum runout of clutch disc facing is .031" (.79 mm). Replace clutch disc if runout is not within specification.

3) Check pressure plate for warpage, heat marks (blue coloration), cracks and diaphragm spring fingers for wear and uneven height. If pressure plate is excessively worn or damaged, replace pressure plate assembly. Check pilot bearing for smooth operation. If bearing does not spin freely, replace it.

Installation – 1) Position clutch disc and pressure plate on flywheel using Clutch Centering Tool (J-34860). Clutch disc is installed with damper springs facing toward transaxle.

2) Install pressure plate bolts, and tighten evenly to avoid clutch distortion. Lightly lubricate release bearing sliding surfaces and input shaft with grease.

3) To complete installation, reverse removal procedure. Tighten all nuts and bolts to specification. See TORQUE SPECIFICATIONS. Fill transaxle with 75W GL-5 Fluid (12345349).

Removal (Prizm) – 1) Install Engine Support Fixture (J-28467-A). Remove battery, battery tray and air cleaner assembly. Disconnect back-up light switch electrical connector. Disconnect ground strap. Remove clutch slave cylinder. Disconnect shift control cables.

2) Remove left transaxle mount cover, brace and mount through bolt. Remove upper transaxle-to-engine bolts. Remove upper starter bolt. Disconnect vehicle speed sensor (3-wire connector on back of transaxle). Raise and support vehicle.

3) Remove splash shields. Drain transaxle fluid. Disconnect starter electrical connections. Remove bottom starter bolt and remove starter. Disconnect drive axles from transaxle. See FWD AXLE SHAFTS article in DRIVE AXLES.

4) Remove front and center transaxle mount through bolt shields. Remove center crossmember-to-radiator support bolts. Disconnect exhaust hanger from transaxle.

WARNING: Hold onto center crossmember when lowering main crossmember to prevent center crossmember from falling and causing injury.

---

5) Support main crossmember. Remove main crossmember-to-body bolts. Slowly lower main crossmember while holding center crossmember. Remove center crossmember. Remove lower A-frame bracket-to-body bolts.

6) Remove front mount and bracket from transaxle. Remove center mount from transaxle. Remove flywheel inspection cover. Remove lower transaxle bracket-to-mount bolts. Lower vehicle.

7) Remove remaining transaxle bracket-to-mount bolts. Lower Engine Support Fixture (J-28467-A) to gain clearance for transaxle removal. Remove transaxle mount. Raise and support vehicle. Support transaxle. Remove front and rear lower transaxle-to-engine bolts. Remove transaxle.

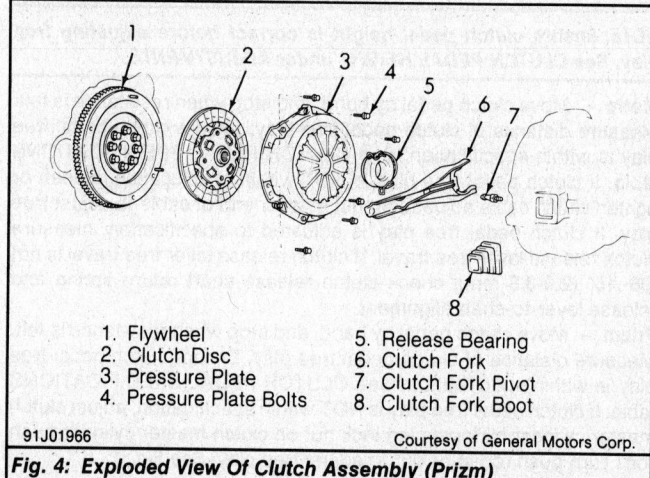

1. Flywheel
2. Clutch Disc
3. Pressure Plate
4. Pressure Plate Bolts
5. Release Bearing
6. Clutch Fork
7. Clutch Fork Pivot
8. Clutch Fork Boot

Fig. 4: Exploded View Of Clutch Assembly (Prizm)

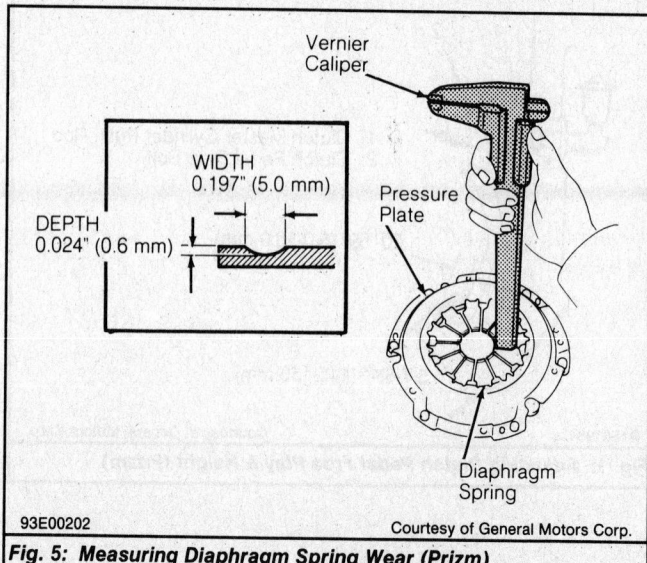

Fig. 5: Measuring Diaphragm Spring Wear (Prizm)

8) Mark pressure plate and flywheel for reassembly reference. Loosen pressure plate attaching bolts alternately until pressure plate is released. Remove clutch disc and pressure plate. *See Fig. 4.*

Inspection – 1) Check wear on disc's facing by measuring depth of each rivet head. Minimum depth at any rivet is .012" (.30 mm). Maximum runout of clutch disc facing is .031" (0.8 mm). Replace clutch disc if not within specification.

2) Check pressure plate for warpage, heat marks (blue coloration) and cracks. Check diaphragm spring fingers for uneven height and wear at throw out bearing contact area. *See Fig. 5.* Replace pressure plate if worn. Check pilot bearing rotation. If roughness is felt, replace bearing.

3) Inspect flywheel runout. Maximum flywheel runout is .004" (.10 mm). If runout is excessive, replace flywheel. Clean oil, grease and metal deposits from flywheel and pressure plate. Inspect for damage, cracks or warpage. Slight surface scoring can be removed with sandpaper. Replace or repair as necessary.

Installation – 1) Use clutch centering tool to center clutch disc on flywheel. If replacing pressure plate, transfer match mark from old pressure plate to new pressure plate so balance is maintained. Tighten pressure plate bolts alternately and evenly in a diagonal pattern to specification. See TORQUE SPECIFICATIONS.

2) Apply a small amount of grease to release fork contact surfaces, release bearing and hub. Lightly lubricate clutch disc splines using Lubricant (1051344). To complete installation, reverse removal procedure.

RELEASE BEARING

Removal & Installation – 1) Remove transaxle. See CLUTCH ASSEMBLY under REMOVAL & INSTALLATION. On Metro, disconnect return spring from shaft fork. Remove clutch release bearing pin and clutch release bearing from transaxle. On Prizm, spread lock clip and remove clutch fork from bearing release groove and remove fork boot. Remove clutch release bearing from transaxle.

2) On all models, inspect release bearing for rough rotation, wear or damage. Clean clutch release bearing with a clean, dry, solvent free cloth. If necessary, replace bearing.

3) Lightly lubricate release bearing with grease. Install clutch release bearing on transaxle retainer. Ensure bearing pads are located on fork ends (pads must be indexed) and both spring ends are in fork holes, with spring completely seated in bearing groove.

4) To complete installation, reverse removal procedure. Tighten all nuts and bolts to specification. See TORQUE SPECIFICATIONS.

PILOT BEARING

Removal & Installation – 1) Remove transaxle, pressure plate and clutch disc. See CLUTCH ASSEMBLY under REMOVAL & INSTALLATION. Using Puller (J-34839), remove pilot bearing from flywheel. Inspect pilot bearing for rough rotation, wear or damage.

2) Replace bearing if necessary. Use Installer (J-34848) and Adapter (J-36190). To complete installation, reverse removal procedure. Tighten all nuts and bolts to specification. See TORQUE SPECIFICATIONS.

CLUTCH CABLE

Removal (Metro) – Remove clutch cable adjustment nut. Disconnect cable from release arm. Remove clutch cable bracket retaining bolts. Remove bracket from cable. Remove clutch cable grommet from bulkhead. Remove clutch cable clevis from clutch pedal lever. Remove clutch cable from vehicle from engine compartment side.

Installation – Apply grease to clutch cable clevis before installing. To complete installation, reverse removal procedure. Tighten retaining bolts to specification. See TORQUE SPECIFICATIONS. Adjust clutch pedal free play. See CLUTCH PEDAL FREE PLAY under ADJUSTMENTS.

CLUTCH MASTER CYLINDER

Removal & Installation (Prizm) – 1) Disconnect clutch master cylinder push rod at clutch pedal. Disconnect hydraulic line at clutch master cylinder. Remove clutch master cylinder mounting nuts. Remove clutch master cylinder from firewall.

2) To install, reverse removal procedure. Tighten all nuts and bolts to specification. See TORQUE SPECIFICATIONS. Adjust clutch pedal height and free play. See CLUTCH PEDAL HEIGHT and CLUTCH PEDAL FREE PLAY under ADJUSTMENTS. Bleed hydraulic system.

OVERHAUL

CLUTCH MASTER CYLINDER

Disassembly (Prizm) – Remove master cylinder. See CLUTCH MASTER CYLINDER under REMOVAL & INSTALLATION. Remove retaining bolt and reservoir. Pull back boot and remove snap ring on push rod. Remove piston, push rod, cup and remaining internal components. *See Fig. 6.*

Reassembly – Clean all parts that are to be reused. Inspect for wear or damage. Coat piston and new cylinder cups with fresh DOT 3 brake fluid. To complete assembly, reverse disassembly procedure.

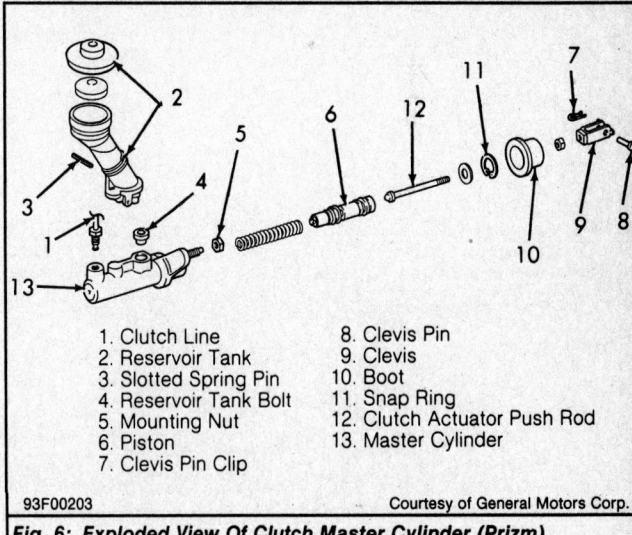

1. Clutch Line	8. Clevis Pin
2. Reservoir Tank	9. Clevis
3. Slotted Spring Pin	10. Boot
4. Reservoir Tank Bolt	11. Snap Ring
5. Mounting Nut	12. Clutch Actuator Push Rod
6. Piston	13. Master Cylinder
7. Clevis Pin Clip	

93F00203   Courtesy of General Motors Corp.

Fig. 6: Exploded View Of Clutch Master Cylinder (Prizm)

CLUTCH SLAVE CYLINDER

Disassembly & Reassembly (Prizm) – 1) Remove slave cylinder. Remove rubber boot and push rod. Remove piston assembly and spring. Remove bleeder screw. *See Fig. 7.*

2) Clean all parts that are to be reused. Inspect for wear or damage. Coat piston and cylinder cup with fresh DOT 3 brake fluid. Reassemble components in reverse order of disassembly.

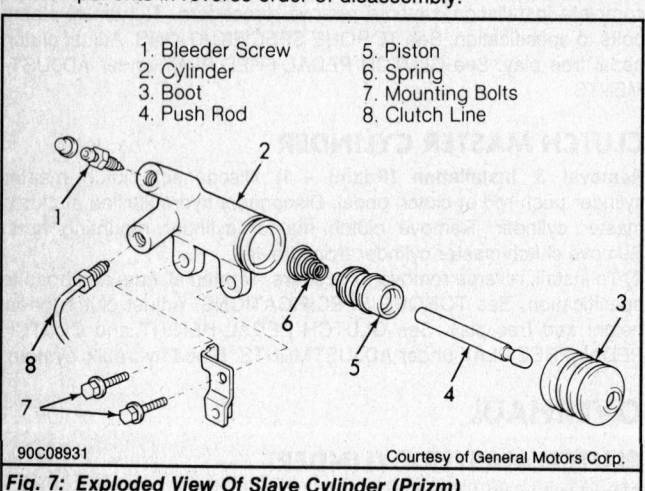

1. Bleeder Screw	5. Piston
2. Cylinder	6. Spring
3. Boot	7. Mounting Bolts
4. Push Rod	8. Clutch Line

90C08931   Courtesy of General Motors Corp.

Fig. 7: Exploded View Of Slave Cylinder (Prizm)

TORQUE SPECIFICATIONS

TORQUE SPECIFICATIONS

Application	Ft. Lbs. (N.m)
Metro	
Ball Joint Stud Bolt	44 (60)
Clutch Cable Bracket Bolts	17 (23)
Clutch Cable Grommet Bolts	[1]
Clutch Pedal Shaft Bolt & Nut	15 (20)
Clutch Start Switch Lock Nut	[2]
Clutch Release Lever Bolt & Nut	12 (16)
Engine Rear Mount Nuts	37 (50)
Extension Rod Nuts	24 (33)
Flywheel Bolts	45 (61)
Gearshift Shaft Bolts	15 (20)
Pressure Plate Bolts	17 (23)
Release Arm Bolts	10 (14)
Transaxle Left Mount Bracket Nuts & Bolts	37 (50)
Transaxle-To-Engine Nuts & Bolts	37 (50)
Prizm	
Bleeder Screw	[3]
Center Crossmember-To-Radiator Support Bolts	45 (61)
Center & Rear Mount Bolts	45 (61)
Clutch Line Tube	11 (15)
Clutch Master Cylinder Mount Nuts	11 (15)
Flywheel Bolts	58 (78)
Front Mount Through Bolt	69 (93)
Lower Control Arm Bracket-To-Body Bolts	94 (127)
Lower Mount Bolts	45 (61)
Main Crossmember-To-Body Bolts	152 (206)
Mount Cover Bolts	45 (61)
Pedal Assembly Bracket-To-Instrument Panel Bolt	11 (15)
Pressure Plate Bolts	14 (19)
Slave Cylinder Mounting Bolts	[4]
Starter Bolts	29 (39)
Transaxle-To-Engine Bolts	34 (46)
Upper Transaxle Mount Bolts	45 (61)

[1] – 53 INCH lbs. (6 N.m)
[2] – 115 INCH lbs. (13 N.m)
[3] – 97 INCH lbs. (11 N.m)
[4] – 106 INCH lbs. (12 N.m)

Tracker

DESCRIPTION

Clutch is a single disc type. A diaphragm spring is used to engage pressure plate. Clutch is mechanically controlled by the clutch pedal, clutch cable, return spring, release fork and sealed release bearing. *See Fig. 1.* A Clutch Pedal Position (CPP) switch is used to disable starter if clutch pedal is not fully depressed.

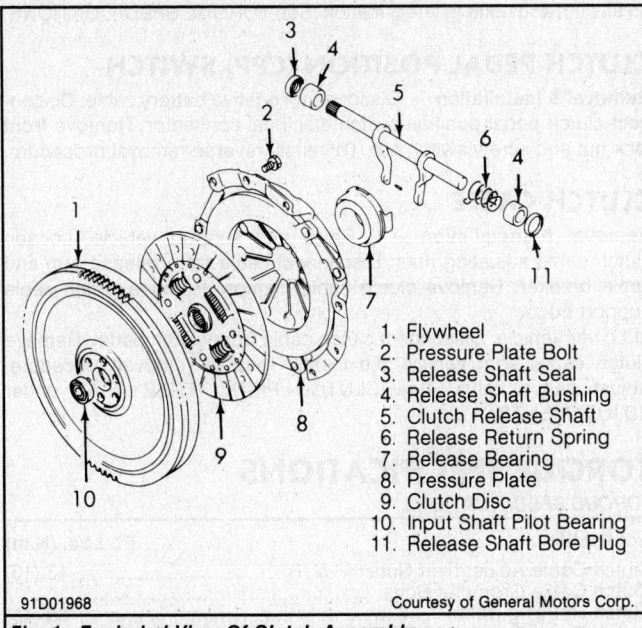

1. Flywheel
2. Pressure Plate Bolt
3. Release Shaft Seal
4. Release Shaft Bushing
5. Clutch Release Shaft
6. Release Return Spring
7. Release Bearing
8. Pressure Plate
9. Clutch Disc
10. Input Shaft Pilot Bearing
11. Release Shaft Bore Plug

91D01968   Courtesy of General Motors Corp.

Fig. 1: Exploded View Of Clutch Assembly

ADJUSTMENTS

CLUTCH PEDAL HEIGHT

NOTE: Adjust clutch pedal free play after adjusting clutch pedal height. See CLUTCH PEDAL FREE PLAY under ADJUSTMENTS.

Loosen clutch pedal stop bolt, and adjust until clutch pedal is .2" (5 mm) higher than brake pedal. Tighten lock nut after adjustment.

CLUTCH PEDAL FREE PLAY

NOTE: Ensure clutch pedal height is correct before adjusting free play. See CLUTCH PEDAL HEIGHT under ADJUSTMENTS.

1) Depress clutch pedal lightly until tension on clutch cable can be felt. Measured clutch pedal free play should be 0.6-1.1" (15-28 mm).
2) Raise and support vehicle. If clutch pedal free play is less than specification, loosen adjustment nut "B" at clutch cable bracket until clutch pedal free play is within specification. Then tighten adjustment nut "A". *See Fig. 2.*
3) If pedal free play is greater than specification, loosen both adjustment nuts "A" and "B" at clutch cable bracket. Tighten clutch cable adjustment nut "A" until clutch pedal free play is within specification. Then tighten adjustment nut "B". *See Fig. 2.* See TORQUE SPECIFICATIONS table.

CLUTCH RELEASE LEVER FREE PLAY

1) Raise and support vehicle. Measure clutch release lever free play. Free play should be 0.02-0.06" (0.5-1.5 mm). *See Fig. 2.* If clutch release lever free play is less than specification, loosen clutch release lever adjustment nut until release lever is within specification. If clutch release lever free play is greater than specification, tighten release lever adjustment nut until free play is within specification.

2) Ensure index marks on clutch release lever and clutch release shaft are aligned with each other. *See Fig. 2.* If marks are not aligned, remove clutch release lever from clutch release shaft, align marks and repeat free play adjustment procedure.

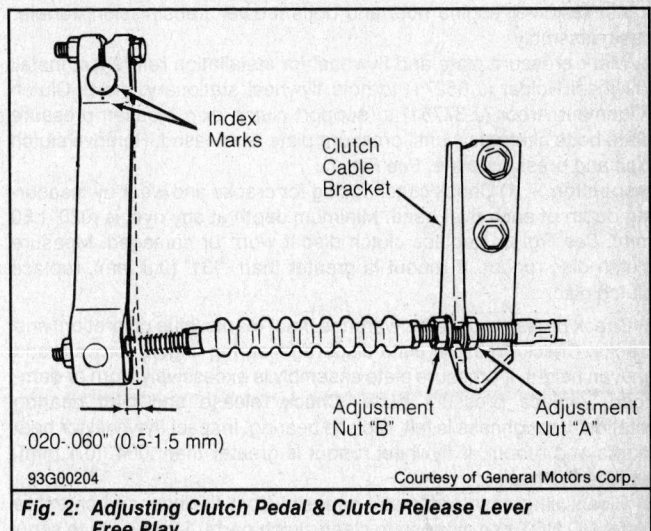

.020-.060" (0.5-1.5 mm)

93G00204   Courtesy of General Motors Corp.

Fig. 2: Adjusting Clutch Pedal & Clutch Release Lever Free Play

CLUTCH PEDAL POSITION (CPP) SWITCH

1) Apply parking brake. Place gearshift lever in Neutral. Disconnect clutch start switch electrical connector. Connect ohmmeter between switch terminals. Loosen lock nut and turn switch outward. Depress clutch pedal to floor.
2) Allow clutch pedal to return from floor and stop 2.0-2.7" (50-69 mm) from floor. Slowly screw switch in until ohmmeter indicates continuity exists. Hold switch at this position and tighten lock nut. Connect switch electrical connector.

REMOVAL & INSTALLATION

CLUTCH ASSEMBLY

Removal – 1) Disconnect negative battery cable. Disconnect gearshift and transfer case levers. Remove bolt directly behind gearshift lever case. Remove fan shroud bolts. Remove upper transmission-to-engine bolts.
2) Raise and support vehicle. Drain transfer case and transmission fluid. Remove starter. Remove front and rear drive shafts. On 4-wheel drive models, remove transfer case skid plate. On all models, disconnect speedometer cable. Disconnect catalytic converter mounting bolts. Remove catalytic converter.

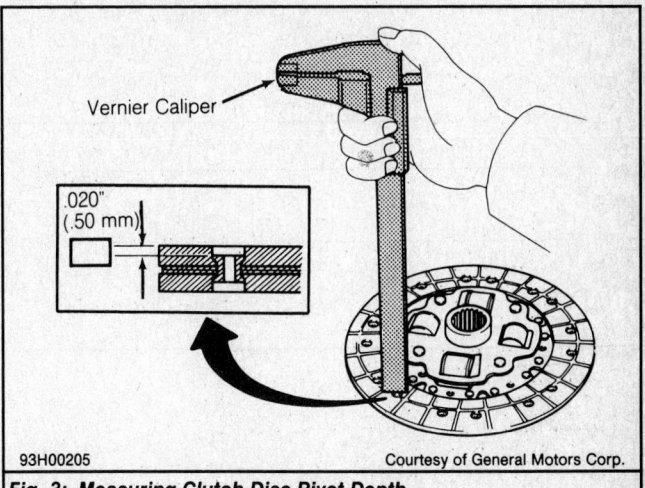

Vernier Caliper

.020"
(.50 mm)

93H00205   Courtesy of General Motors Corp.

Fig. 3: Measuring Clutch Disc Rivet Depth

3) Support transmission with transmission jack. Remove rear transmission mount and crossmember. Disconnect breather hose and all electrical connectors. Disconnect clutch cable and remove clutch release lever. Remove flywheel inspection cover. Remove remaining transmission-to-engine nuts and bolts. Lower transmission/transfer case assembly.

4) Mark pressure plate and flywheel for installation reference. Install Flywheel Holder (J-35271) to hold flywheel stationary. Install Clutch Alignment Arbor (J-37761) to support clutch disc. Loosen pressure plate bolts alternately until pressure plate is released. Remove clutch disc and pressure plate. *See Fig. 1.*

Inspection – **1)** Check clutch facing for cracks and wear by measuring depth of each rivet head. Minimum depth at any rivet is .020" (.50 mm). *See Fig. 3.* Replace clutch disc if worn or damaged. Measure clutch disc runout. If runout is greater than .031" (0.8 mm), replace clutch disc.

2) Check pressure plate for warpage, heat marks (blue coloration) and cracks. Check pressure plate diaphragm spring fingers for wear and uneven height. If pressure plate assembly is excessively worn or damaged, replace pressure plate. Check release and pilot bearing rotation. If roughness is felt, replace bearing. Inspect flywheel for heat marks and runout. If flywheel runout is greater than .004" (0.1 mm), replace flywheel.

3) Clean oil, grease and metal deposits from flywheel and pressure plate. DO NOT use air hose to clean clutch parts. Slight surface scoring can be removed with sandpaper. Replace or repair as necessary.

Installation – To install, reverse removal procedure. Tighten all nuts and bolts to specification. See TORQUE SPECIFICATIONS. Fill transmission and transfer case with 75W-90 GL-4 transmission fluid.

RELEASE BEARING

Removal & Installation – **1)** Remove transaxle. See CLUTCH ASSEMBLY under REMOVAL & INSTALLATION. Remove pin and release bearing from clutch release shaft. Release spring by sliding release shaft forward. Remove release bearing.

2) Check bearing for rough rotation, replace if necessary. Lubricate input shaft, release bearing sliding surface and release lever with grease (1051344). To install, reverse removal procedure. Tighten all nuts and bolts to specification. See TORQUE SPECIFICATIONS.

PILOT BEARING

Removal & Installation – **1)** Remove transaxle, pressure plate and clutch disc. See CLUTCH ASSEMBLY under REMOVAL & INSTALLATION. Using slide hammer and Pilot Bearing Adapter (J-34839), remove pilot bearing from flywheel. Inspect pilot bearing for rough rotation, wear or damage.

2) Replace bearing if necessary. Use Installer (J-34848) and Adapter (J-36190). To complete installation, reverse removal procedure. Tighten all nuts and bolts to specification. See TORQUE SPECIFICATIONS.

CLUTCH PEDAL POSITION (CPP) SWITCH

Removal & Installation – Disconnect negative battery cable. Disconnect clutch pedal position switch electrical connector. Remove front lock nut and screw switch out. To install, reverse removal procedure.

CLUTCH CABLE

Removal & Installation – **1)** Raise and support vehicle. Loosen clutch cable adjusting nuts. Disconnect cable from release arm and cable bracket. Remove clutch cable clamps. Remove clutch cable support bolts.

2) Lower vehicle. Disconnect clutch cable from clutch pedal. Remove clutch cable from vehicle. To install, reverse removal procedure. Adjust clutch cable. See CLUTCH PEDAL FREE PLAY under ADJUSTMENTS.

TORQUE SPECIFICATIONS
TORQUE SPECIFICATIONS

Application	Ft. Lbs. (N.m)
Clutch Cable Adjustment Nuts "A" & "B"	13 (18)
Clutch Cable Grommet Bolts	[1]
Clutch Housing Bolts	33 (45)
Clutch Pedal Position (CPP) Switch Lock Nut	[2]
Clutch Pedal Shaft Nut & Bolt	18 (24)
Clutch Pedal Stop Lock Nut	[2]
Flywheel Bolts	48 (65)
Pressure Plate	17 (23)
Transmission Rear Mounting Bolts	44 (60)
Transmission-To-Engine Bolts	72 (98)

[1] – Tighten bolts to 70 INCH lbs. (8 N.m).
[2] – Tighten lock nut to 115 INCH lbs. (13 N.m).

Metro, Prizm, Tracker

DESCRIPTION & OPERATION

Axle shaft consists of inner and outer constant velocity joint assembly joined by an axle shaft. The inner joint (differential side) is flexible and has in-and-out movement capability. Outer joint (wheel side) is flexible but does not have in-and-out movement capability. Various types of joints are used in accordance with application. See JOINT APPLICATION table.

JOINT APPLICATION

Application	Inner Joint	Outer Joint
Metro	Tripod	Ball Type
Prizm	Tripod	Ball Type
Tracker	[1] DOJ	Ball Type

[1] – DOJ is double-offset joint.

TROUBLE SHOOTING

NOTE: See TROUBLE SHOOTING article in GENERAL INFORMATION.

REMOVAL, DISASSEMBLY, REASSEMBLY & INSTALLATION

FWD AXLE SHAFT

Removal (Metro) – 1) Raise and support vehicle. Remove front wheels. Drain transaxle fluid. Remove center cap from hub. Unstake axle shaft nut, and remove nut and washer from axle shaft.

2) Remove ball joint-to-steering knuckle bolt. Separate ball joint from steering knuckle. Using 2 screwdrivers, pry axle shaft from transaxle case. Separate axle shaft from steering knuckle assembly, and remove axle shaft.

NOTE: On Metro, if vehicle is to be lowered and moved, front wheel bearings must be supported. Install a 9/16" (14 mm) bolt and nut through shaft opening in hub with a 1 3/4" (44.5 mm) washer on outside and a 2" (50.8 mm) washer on inside. Tighten bolt and nut to 40 ft. lbs. (54 N.m).

CAUTION: DO NOT attempt to disassemble outer CV joint or spider assembly on inner joint. If components are worn or damaged, replace spider assembly or entire tripod joint assembly. DO NOT use solvents or degreasers to clean boots or spider assembly.

Disassembly – Remove boot bands from boot on tripod housing. See Fig. 1. Remove snap ring and tripod spider from axle shaft. Remove boot bands, drive shaft dust cover, and boot from outer joint assembly.

Inspection – Inspect boots for cracks and deterioration. Clean all components. DO NOT clean spider assembly using solvent; grease will be removed from needle bearings. Inspect components for damage, and replace components as necessary.

Reassembly – 1) Coat outer joint assembly with grease supplied with boot kit. Install boot on outer joint. Fill boot with about 2.5 ounces (70 grams) of grease, and install boot and boot bands. Press dust cover onto drive axle using Drive Axle Dust Cover Installer (J-41130). Install dust cover, dust cover installer (J-41130) and axle nut. Tighten axle nut until dust cover installer makes contact with outer joint. Drive Axle Dust Cover Installer (J-41130) may be damaged if axle nut is over tightened.

2) Coat tripod joint assembly with grease supplied with boot kit. Install spider on axle shaft, with chamfered side toward outer joint assembly. Install snap ring.

3) Install boot, and fill boot with about 3.2 ounces (90 grams) of grease. Install tripod housing and boot bands.

Installation – To install, reverse removal procedure. Apply thread sealant to transaxle drain plug. When installing axle shaft in differential, ensure snap ring seats fully in differential assembly. Tighten all fasteners to specification. See TORQUE SPECIFICATIONS. Fill transaxle.

Removal (Prizm) – 1) Disconnect negative battery cable. Raise and support vehicle. Remove lower engine covers. Drain transaxle fluid. Remove front wheels. Remove wheel speed sensor from steering knuckle.

2) Remove axle shaft cotter pin, hub nut cap, hub nut and washer. Remove tie rod nut from steering knuckle. Separate tie rod from steering knuckle.

3) Remove lower ball joint-to-control arm bolts. Separate lower control arm from ball joint. Separate outer joint from hub assembly.

4) Remove inner joint from transaxle by gently prying joint away from transaxle case with pry bar or large screwdriver. Pull axle shafts from transaxle.

NOTE: On Prizm, if vehicle is to be lowered and moved, front wheel bearings must be supported. Install a 9/16" (14 mm) bolt and nut through shaft opening in hub with a 1 3/4" (44.5 mm) washer on outside and a 2" (50.8 mm) washer on inside. Tighten bolt and nut to 40 ft. lbs. (54 N.m).

CAUTION: DO NOT attempt to disassemble outer CV joint or spider assembly on inner joint. If components are worn or damaged, replace spider assembly or entire tripod joint assembly. DO NOT use solvents or degreasers to clean boots or spider assembly.

Disassembly – 1) To disassemble outer ball-type Constant Velocity (CV) joint, remove both boot clamps. Place mating marks on axle shaft and joint for reassembly reference. Expand outer joint snap ring. See Fig. 2. Pull outer joint from axle shaft.

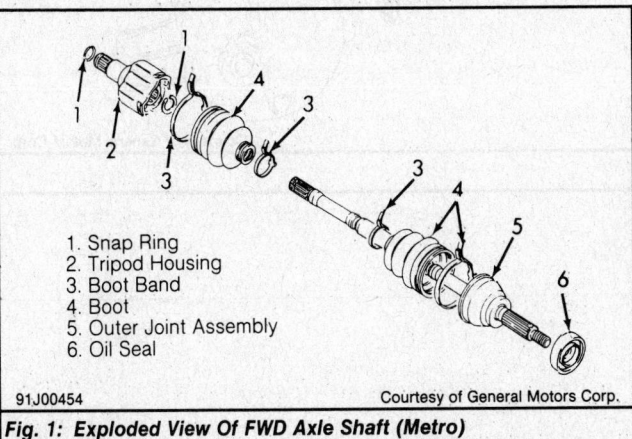

1. Snap Ring
2. Tripod Housing
3. Boot Band
4. Boot
5. Outer Joint Assembly
6. Oil Seal

91J00454   Courtesy of General Motors Corp.

Fig. 1: Exploded View Of FWD Axle Shaft (Metro)

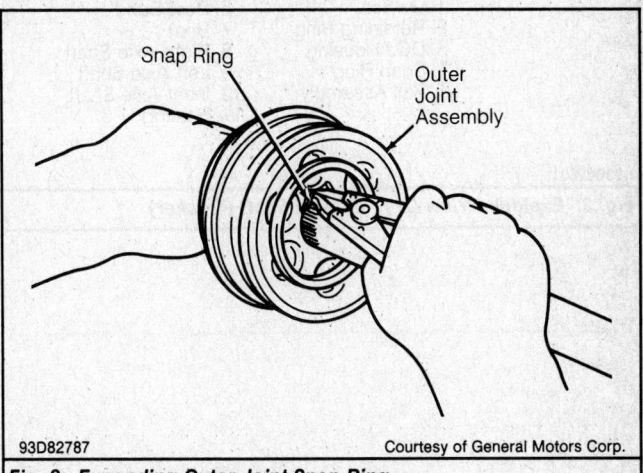

93D82787   Courtesy of General Motors Corp.

Fig. 2: Expanding Outer Joint Snap Ring

2) To disassemble inner tripod joint assembly, remove boot clamps and pull boot back away from joint. Mark axle shaft, tripod joint housing and spider for reassembly reference.

3) Remove tripod joint housing from axle shaft. Remove inner joint snap ring. Pull tripod spider assembly from axle shaft. Remove boot.

Inspection – Inspect boots for cracks and deterioration. Inspect components for damage. Replace damaged components.

Reassembly – **1)** To reassemble tripod joint, reverse disassembly procedure. Ensure all reference marks are aligned. Apply about 8.5 ounces (241 grams) CV joint grease in tripod housing and on spider assembly before assembling. Install tripod boot clamps using Boot Clamp Pliers (J-35566).

2) Pack outer joint assembly with about 5 ounces (142 grams) CV joint grease. Install outer joint assembly to axle shaft. Ensure all snap rings are fully seated. Install boot clamps using Boot Clamp Pliers (J-22610).

Installation – To install, reverse removal procedure. Tighten all fasteners to specification. See TORQUE SPECIFICATIONS. Fill transaxle.

Removal (Tracker 4-Wheel Drive) – **1)** Raise and support vehicle. Remove skid plate (if equipped). Remove front wheels. Remove locking hub retaining bolts, locking hubs and "O" rings. Remove snap ring and washer from end of axle shafts.

2) Disconnect stabilizer bar from control arms. Remove stabilizer bar mount bolts, and remove stabilizer bar.

3) Support lower control arm using floor jack. Remove 3 ball joint-to-control arm bolts. Slowly lower floor jack until coil spring tension is relieved. Swing steering knuckle outward. Pull outer CV joint from steering knuckle.

4) To remove right axle shaft from differential housing, Use Shaft Removal Fork (J-37780). Tap on shaft removal fork and remove right axle shaft.

5) To remove left axle shaft from differential housing, make index marks on flanges, remove left axle shaft flange bolts and remove axle shaft.

NOTE: Manufacturer's recommends disassembly of Double-Offset Joint (DOJ) for boot replacement only. Do not disassemble outer CV joint. Remove boot for inspection of joint only.

Disassembly – **1)** To disassemble DOJ, remove boot clamps. Pull DOJ outer housing from axle assembly. Remove snap ring from end of axle shaft. *See Fig. 3.*

2) Remove joint assembly from axle shaft. Remove inner and outer boots from axle shaft.

Inspection – Inspect boots for cracks or deterioration. Inspect components for damage, and replace components as necessary. Ensure outer CV joint turns smoothly.

CAUTION: DO NOT pull outward on inner joint assembly housing. If inner joint housing is pulled outward, joint may overextend and separate from axle shaft.

Reassembly – Install outer CV boot then inner CV boot on axle shaft. Add about 2.5 ounces (71 grams) CV joint grease to outer joint. To reassemble DOJ joint, reverse disassembly procedure. Pack inner joint assembly with about 3.2 ounces (90 grams) CV joint Grease before securing boot clamps.

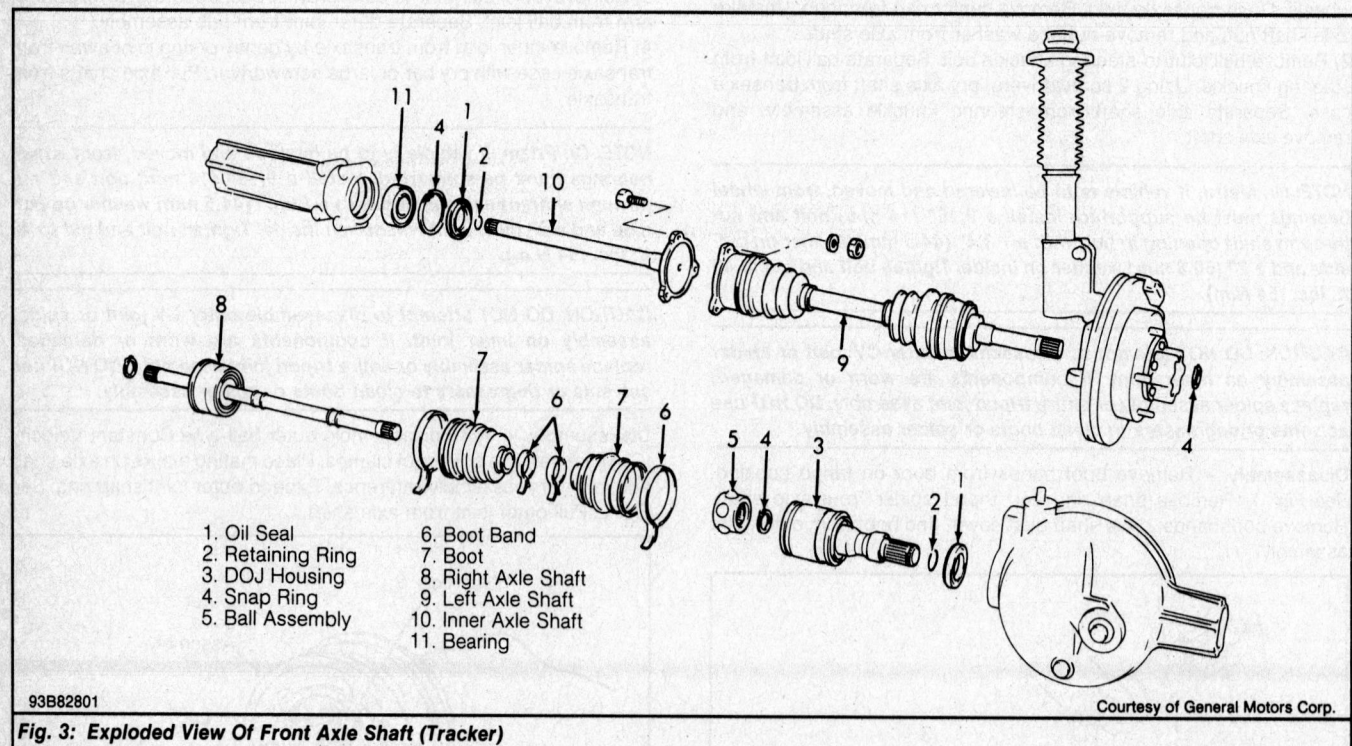

1. Oil Seal
2. Retaining Ring
3. DOJ Housing
4. Snap Ring
5. Ball Assembly
6. Boot Band
7. Boot
8. Right Axle Shaft
9. Left Axle Shaft
10. Inner Axle Shaft
11. Bearing

93B82801

Courtesy of General Motors Corp.

Fig. 3: Exploded View Of Front Axle Shaft (Tracker)

Installation – **1)** Install left axle shaft. Align index marks and tighten axle shaft-to-inner axle shaft flange bolts to specification. See TORQUE SPECIFICATIONS.

2) Install right axle shaft. Ensure snap ring on axle shaft seats in differential carrier.

3) To install remaining components, reverse removal procedure. Tighten bolts to specification. See TORQUE SPECIFICATIONS. When installing locking hub, use NEW "O" ring.

INNER AXLE SHAFT BEARING

Tracker – **1)** Raise and support vehicle. Remove left axle shaft. See FWD AXLE SHAFTS under REMOVAL & INSTALLATION.

2) Remove left inner axle shaft from differential housing using Shaft Removal Fork (J-37780) and soft faced mallet. Place shaft removal fork on inner axle shaft flange and tap axle shaft out of differential housing.

3) Using a slide hammer and Seal Hook Adapter (J-26941), pull seal from differential housing. Remove axle bearing snap ring. See Fig. 3.

4) Using a slide hammer and Bearing Removal Adapter (J-29369), pull bearing from differential housing.

Inspection – Check axle shaft bearing for roughness or wear, and replace as necessary. Inspect differential housing at sealing surface for scratches.

Installation – **1)** Install bearing into axle housing using Bearing Installer (J-8092). Install axle bearing snap ring. Install inner axle shaft seal using Seal Installer (J-37770).

2) To complete installation, reverse removal procedure. Tighten bolts to specification. See TORQUE SPECIFICATIONS. Fill differential with 75W-90 GL-4 synthetic gear lubricant.

TORQUE SPECIFICATIONS

TORQUE SPECIFICATIONS

Application	Ft. Lbs. (N.m)
Axle Shaft Nut	
Metro	129 (175)
Prizm	159 (216)
Ball Joint Nut	
Metro	44 (60)
Ball Joint-To-Lower Control Arm Bolt	
Prizm	105 (142)
Tracker	63 (85)
Left Axle Shaft-To-Inner Flange Bolt (Tracker)	44 (60)
Locking Hub Cover Bolt (Tracker)	18 (24)
Skid Plate (Tracker If Equipped)	40 (54)
Stabilizer Bar Mount Bolt (Tracker)	38 (51)
Stabilizer Bar-To-Control Arm Bolt (Tracker)	21 (28)
Tie Rod-To-Steering Knuckle Bolt	
Prizm	40 (54)
Tracker	30 (41)
Transaxle Drain Plug	21 (28)
Wheel Lug Nut	
Metro	44 (60)
Prizm	76 (103)
Tracker	70 (95)

	INCH Lbs. (N.m)
ABS Speed Sensor Bolt (Prizm)	71 (8)
Splash Shield Bolt (Prizm)	71 (8)

1994 DRIVE AXLES
Differentials & Axle Shafts

Tracker
DESCRIPTION & OPERATION

Front differential assembly uses a hypoid beveled ring and pinion gear set mounted in an aluminum housing to reduce weight. Rear differential assembly uses a hypoid beveled ring and pinion gear set mounted in a steel housing. Beveled ring and pinion gear sets for front and rear differential assemblies are not interchangeable. Reduction ratio for manual transmission vehicles is different from automatic transmission vehicles.

AXLE RATIO IDENTIFICATION
AXLE RATIO SPECIFICATIONS

Application	Ratio
A/T	
California	4.30:1
Federal	4.62:1
M/T	5.12:1

LUBRICATION
CAPACITY
DIFFERENTIAL CAPACITIES

Application	Qts. (L)
Front	1.06 (1.0)
Rear	2.32 (2.2)

FLUID TYPE

Use 75W-90 GL-5 Synthetic Gear Lubricant (12345871).

TROUBLE SHOOTING

NOTE: See TROUBLE SHOOTING article in GENERAL INFORMATION.

REMOVAL & INSTALLATION
DRIVE SHAFT

Before removing drive shaft, index pinion flange yoke to differential pinion flange. When installing, ensure index marks are mated.

PINION FLANGE

Removal & Installation – 1) Using pinion Flange Holder (J-8614-01), hold pinion flange stationary. Unstake and remove flange nut. Remove pinion flange. Using Oil Seal Remover (J-26941) and Slide Hammer (J-2619-01), remove pinion oil seal.

CAUTION: Do not overtighten pinion flange nut when adjusting pinion bearing preload. Tighten pinion flange nut gradually and measure bearing preload frequently. If pinion flange nut is overtightened collapsible spacer will crush and will require replacement.

2) Install pinion oil seal using Seal Installer (J-25273). Install pinion flange and nut. Using pinion Flange Holder (J-8614-01), hold pinion flange stationary. Tighten pinion flange nut in increments of 44 INCH lbs. (5 N.m). Between each increment, remove flange holder and rotate pinion flange 5 turns. Continue this procedure until bearing preload starting torque is 11 INCH lbs. (1.2 N.m). Measure pinion bearing preload again after rotating pinion 5 turns to ensure bearings are seated. Tighten pinion nut gradually until starting torque specification is obtained and restake flange nut.

FRONT CARRIER ASSEMBLY

Removal & Installation – 1) Raise and support vehicle. Remove skid plate (if equipped). Drain differential fluid. Make match marks on front drive shaft position for installation reference. Remove front drive shaft.

2) Remove right and left front axle shafts. See FRONT AXLE SHAFTS. Remove 4 bolts from left differential mounting bracket. Remove 2 bolts from rear differential mounting bracket.
3) Remove 3 bolts from right differential mounting bracket. Support differential carrier. Remove front differential carrier-to-axle housing mounting nuts. Lower differential carrier.
4) To install, reverse removal procedure. Apply sealant to differential carrier and axle housing mating surfaces. Align match marks made on drive shaft during removal procedure. Tighten all nuts and bolts to specification. See TORQUE SPECIFICATIONS. Fill differential.

REAR CARRIER ASSEMBLY

Removal & Installation – 1) Raise and support vehicle. Drain differential fluid. Mark rear drive shaft position for installation reference. Remove rear drive shaft.
2) Remove right and left rear axle shafts. See REAR AXLE SHAFTS. Remove rear wheel speed sensor cover from differential carrier. Disconnect wheel speed sensor electrical harness.
3) Remove 4 bolts from upper rear suspension arm. Support differential carrier. Remove rear differential carrier-to-axle housing mounting nuts. Lower differential carrier.
4) To install, reverse removal procedure. Apply sealant to differential carrier and axle housing mating surfaces. Align marks made on drive shaft during removal procedure. Tighten all nuts and bolts to specification. See TORQUE SPECIFICATIONS. Fill differential.

FRONT AXLE SHAFTS

Removal & Installation – See FWD AXLE SHAFTS article for removal and overhaul procedures.

REAR AXLE SHAFTS

CAUTION: DO NOT remove brake backing plate with axle shaft, as this may cause axle shaft inner seal damage.

Removal & Installation – 1) Raise and support vehicle. Remove wheels. Remove rear brake drums. Drain differential fluid. Remove rear wheel bearing retaining nuts from axle housing. Using axle shaft Puller (J-37781) with slide hammer, remove axle shaft.
2) To install, reverse removal procedure. Install NEW inner oil seal. See REAR AXLE INNER OIL SEAL. Apply wheel bearing grease to inner oil seal lip. Apply sealant to mating surface of wheel bearing retainer and brake backing plate. Tighten wheel bearing retaining nuts to specification. See TORQUE SPECIFICATIONS. Fill differential.

NOTE: Rear axle shafts are different lengths. Measure length from outside edge of axle shaft flange to splined end. Right side axle is 28.4" (722.5 mm). Left side axle is 26.8" (679.5 mm).

REAR AXLE BEARING & SEALS

Removal & Installation – 1) Raise and support vehicle. Remove rear axle shafts. See REAR AXLE SHAFTS. Remove bearing retainer ring from axle shaft using a grinder to flatten 2 opposite sides of bearing retainer ring.
2) Remove bearing retainer with a cold chisel and hammer. Using a press, remove wheel bearing from axle shaft. Remove axle shaft bearing retainer and pry outer axle shaft seal from retainer. To install, reverse removal procedure.

REAR AXLE INNER OIL SEAL

Removal & Installation – Raise and support vehicle. Remove rear axle shafts. See REAR AXLE SHAFTS. Using a slide hammer and Seal Remover Hook (J-26941), remove axle shaft inner oil seal from differential axle housing. Install new inner axle seal using Seal Installer (J-29039). To complete installation, reverse removal procedure.

REAR AXLE HOUSING

Removal & Installation – 1) Raise and support vehicle. Drain differential fluid. Remove wheels and brake drums. Disconnect brake lines from wheel cylinders. Remove rear axle shafts. See REAR AXLE SHAFTS.

2) Disconnect metal brake line from flexible hose and "E" clip. Remove brake lines from axle housing. Remove breather hose from axle housing. Make match marks on rear drive shaft and differential flange and remove rear drive shaft.

3) Support center of rear axle housing. Remove ball joint bracket from differential carrier. Remove rear wheel speed sensor cover from differential carrier. Disconnect wheel speed sensor electrical harness. Remove differential carrier assembly. See REAR CARRIER ASSEMBLY. Remove rear mount nuts from trailing rods. DO NOT remove bolts.

4) Remove shock absorber lower mount bolts. Lower differential housing until suspension coil spring tension becomes loose. Remove trailing rod mount bolts. Remove coil springs. Lower rear axle housing. To install, reverse removal procedure.

OVERHAUL

FRONT & REAR DIFFERENTIAL ASSEMBLIES

Disassembly – 1) Mount differential carrier in Holding Fixture (J-3289-21) and Adapter (J-37769). Match mark differential side bearing caps for installation reference. *See Fig. 8 or 9.*

2) Remove side bearing lock plates and caps. Remove side bearing adjusters and outer bearing races. On rear differentials, remove rear wheel speed sensor. On front or rear differentials, remove ring gear assembly.

3) On rear differentials, separate differential case halves. Using a copper hammer, remove exciter ring. Tap evenly along outer edge of exciter ring.

4) On front or rear differentials, turn differential carrier in fixture 90 degrees. Using pinion Flange Holder (J-8614-01), remove pinion flange nut. Remove pinion flange. Remove pinion shaft. Using Oil Seal Remover (J-26941) and Slide Hammer (J-2619-01), remove pinion oil seal.

5) Remove outer pinion bearing from differential carrier. Remove outer and inner pinion bearing races. Using side bearing Puller (J-22888-D) and Side Bearing Pilot (J-8107-4), remove differential side bearings.

6) Mount differential case in vise. Using arbor punch and hammer, remove roll pins. *See Fig. 1.* Remove differential side gears, selective shims, pinion gears, thrust washers, and shafts.

7) Using Inner Pinion Bearing separator (J-22912-01), remove collapsible spacer and inner pinion bearing. Discard collapsible spacer.

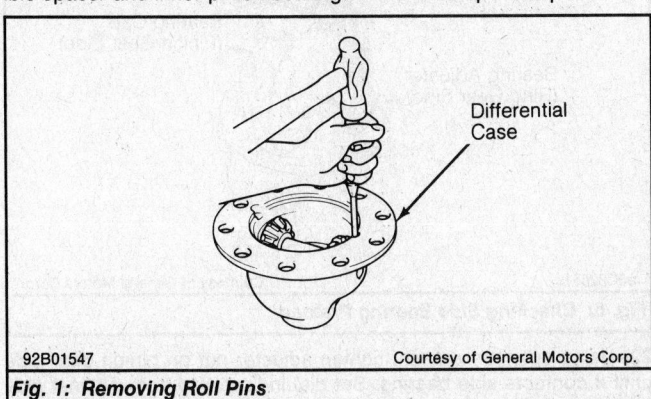

92B01547   Courtesy of General Motors Corp.

Fig. 1: Removing Roll Pins

NOTE: Ring gear, pinion and taper roller bearings and races must be replaced as a set.

Inspection – Check differential case halves for cracks or stripped threads. Inspect ring and pinion gear for excessive or unusual wear, overheating or other damage. Inspect bearings for roughness, brinelling or overheating. Replace parts as necessary.

Reassembly & Adjustments – 1) On rear differentials, install rear wheel anti-lock brake exciter ring to differential case using Exciter Ring Installer (J-38891), Differential Side Bearing Pilot (J-8107-04) and press. Pressure exerted on exciter ring should not exceed 1103 lbs. (500 kg).

2) Ensure press fit is applied evenly around perimeter of exciter ring. Install wheel speed sensor. On front or rear differentials, install differential pinion gears, thrust washers and side gear with selective shim in differential case. *See Fig. 2.*

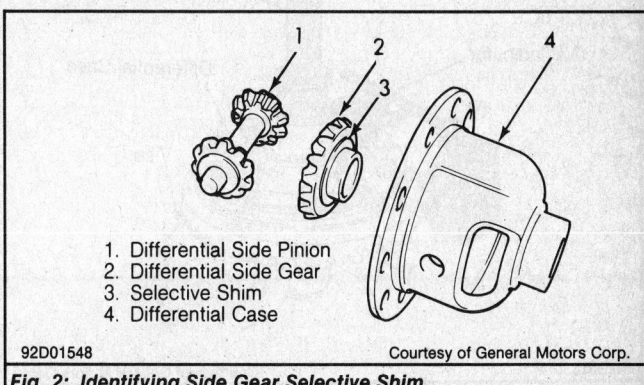

1. Differential Side Pinion
2. Differential Side Gear
3. Selective Shim
4. Differential Case

92D01548   Courtesy of General Motors Corp.

Fig. 2: Identifying Side Gear Selective Shim

3) Using dial indicator, measure differential side gear end play. *See Fig. 3.* If end play is not .005-.014" (.12-.37 mm), select another shim to obtain correct end play.

4) Install roll pins into differential case until flush with differential case surface. Install differential side gear, selective shim and ring gear to differential case.

5) Tighten ring gear bolts to specification. See TORQUE SPECIFICATIONS. Using dial indicator with plunger extension and Universal End Play Measuring Tool (J-35138), measure differential side gear end play. *See Fig. 4.* If end play is not .005-.014" (.12-.37 mm), select another shim to obtain correct end play.

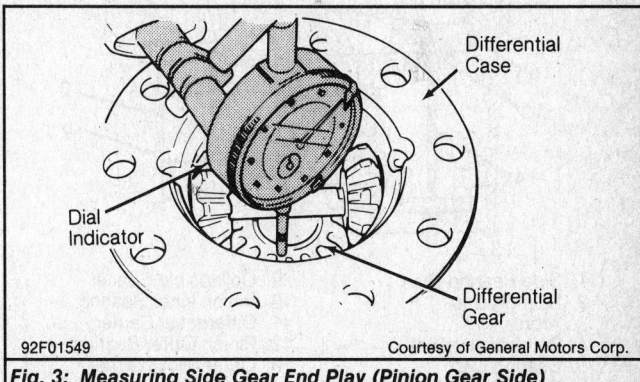

Differential Case

Dial Indicator

Differential Gear

92F01549   Courtesy of General Motors Corp.

Fig. 3: Measuring Side Gear End Play (Pinion Gear Side)

NOTE: After proper end play is obtained, remove ring gear bolts and install Loctite 414 to threads of ring gear bolts. Install ring gear bolts and tighten to specification. See TORQUE SPECIFICATIONS.

6) Using Bearing Installer (J-24433) with Driver Handle (J-8092), press differential side bearings on to case. Using Inner Bearing Race Installer (J-37759) with Driver Handle (J-8092), press pinion gear inner and outer bearing races into differential carrier.

7) Lubricate inner and outer pinion bearings with GM Axle Lubricant (1051344). While holding pinion bearings in position, install Gauge Plate (J-21777-102), Inner Pilot Washer (J-23597-12), Stud and Nut (J-21777-43), and Outer Pilot Washer (J-21777-42). *See Fig. 5.*

8) Hold stud stationary, and tighten lock nut to 18 INCH lbs. (2 N.m). Rotate gauge plate 25 revolutions to seat pinion bearings. To ensure bearings are seated, tighten lock nut again to 18 INCH lbs. (2 N.m).

9) Install 2 Side Bearing Discs (J-21777-101) on side bearing bores with Arbor (J-23597-1) installed through side bearing discs. Rotate gauge plate until gauging areas are paralleled with both side discs.

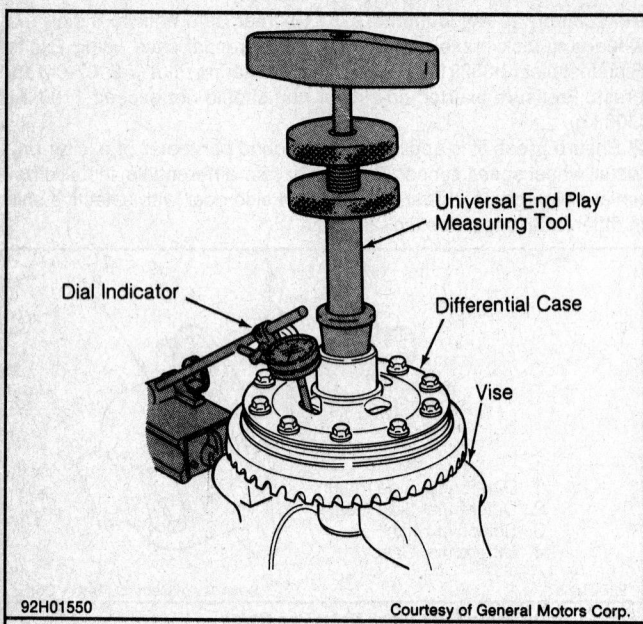

92H01550　　　　Courtesy of General Motors Corp.

Fig. 4: Measuring Side Gear End Play (Ring Gear Side)

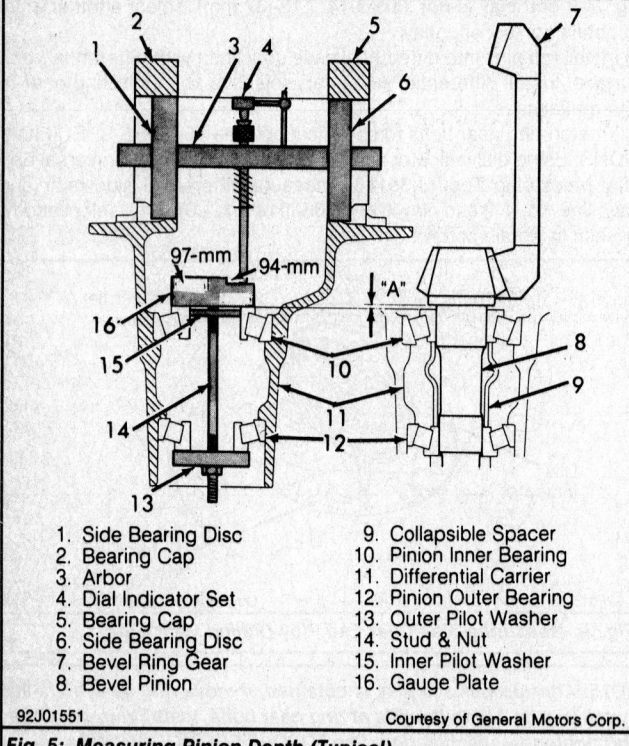

1. Side Bearing Disc
2. Bearing Cap
3. Arbor
4. Dial Indicator Set
5. Bearing Cap
6. Side Bearing Disc
7. Bevel Ring Gear
8. Bevel Pinion
9. Collapsible Spacer
10. Pinion Inner Bearing
11. Differential Carrier
12. Pinion Outer Bearing
13. Outer Pilot Washer
14. Stud & Nut
15. Inner Pilot Washer
16. Gauge Plate

92J01551　　　　Courtesy of General Motors Corp.

Fig. 5: Measuring Pinion Depth (Typical)

10) On front differentials, position dial indicator rod over 97-mm portion of gauge plate. On rear differentials, position dial indicator on 97-mm portion of gauge plate.

11) On front or rear differentials, connect dial indicator to arbor. Position gauge shaft over dial indicator rod. Install side bearing caps and tighten to specification. See TORQUE SPECIFICATIONS.

12) Set dial indicator to zero. On front differentials, slowly rotate arbor on 97-mm step of gauge plate to determine point of greatest deflection, and reset dial indicator to zero. See Fig. 5.

13) On rear differentials, slowly rotate arbor on 97-mm step of gauge plate to determine point of greatest deflection, and reset dial indicator to zero. On front or rear differentials, slowly rotate arbor until dial indicator is no longer on gauge plate. See Fig. 5.

14) Record dial indicator reading. This reading indicates selective shim required for correct pinion depth. Select appropriate shim thickness. Shims are available from .012 (.30 mm) to .050" (1.27 mm).

15) Install pinion pre-selected shim on pinion gear shaft. Using Bearing Installer (J-6133-01) and press, install inner bearing on pinion gear shaft. Install new collapsible spacer on pinion gear shaft with short shank toward pinion.

16) Install outer pinion bearing in differential carrier. Using Oil Seal Installer (J-25273), install pinion oil seal. Apply lubricant to oil seal lip. Install pinion flange, washer and flange nut using Pinion Flange Holder (J-8614-01).

CAUTION: Tightening pinion flange nut will preload pinion bearings. Exceeding preload specification will compress collapsible spacer too far, and will require replacement of collapsible spacer.

---

17) Tighten pinion flange nut in increments of 44 INCH lbs. (5 N.m). Between each increment, remove flange holder and rotate pinion flange 5 turns. Continue this procedure until bearing preload starting torque is 11 INCH lbs. (1.2 N.m). Measure pinion bearing preload again after rotating pinion 5 turns to ensure bearings are seated.

18) Tighten pinion nut gradually until starting torque specification is obtained and restake flange nut. Install side bearing races on differential side bearings. Install differential case on differential carrier.

19) Install side bearing adjusters and bearing caps. Align caps with differential carrier match marks made during disassembly procedure. Tighten differential side bearing cap bolts to 30 ft. lbs. (40 N.m). Do not tighten differential side bearing cap bolts to final specification until side bearing preload and differential backlash have been correctly adjusted.

NOTE: Side bearing adjuster nut are identified as ring gear side or pinion gear side.

---

20) Using spanner wrench, loosen adjuster nut on pinion gear (left) side of differential until it does not contact side bearing race. Tighten adjuster nut on ring gear (right) side of differential until ring gear is fully engaged into pinion gear with zero backlash.

21) Check adjuster nut on pinion gear side to ensure it still does not contact side bearing race. Rotate pinion gear to ensure no binding is evident. To adjust bearing preload, install dial indicator to differential case. See Fig. 6.

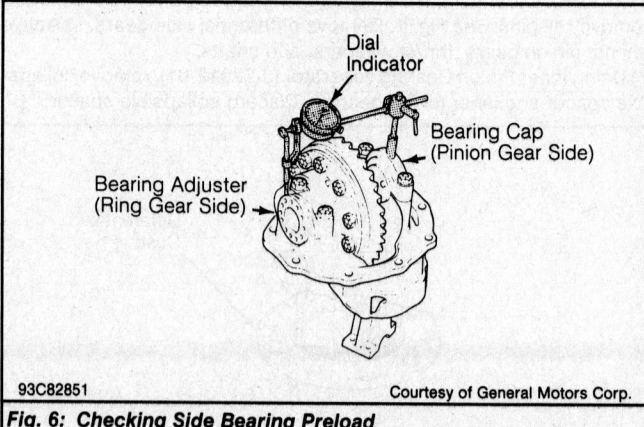

93C82851　　　　Courtesy of General Motors Corp.

Fig. 6: Checking Side Bearing Preload

22) Using spanner wrench, tighten adjuster nut on pinion gear side until it contacts side bearing. Set dial indicator to zero against side bearing cap. Adjust side bearing preload by tightening adjuster nut on pinion side with spanner wrench until dial indicator reads .002-.006" (.05-.15 mm).

23) To check gear backlash, install dial indicator to differential case. See Fig. 7. Hold pinion gear from turning and rock ring gear back and forth. If backlash is not .008-.015" (.20-.38 mm), use spanner wrench to loosen the appropriate adjuster nut and tighten opposite nut an equal amount. This will maintain side bearing preload.

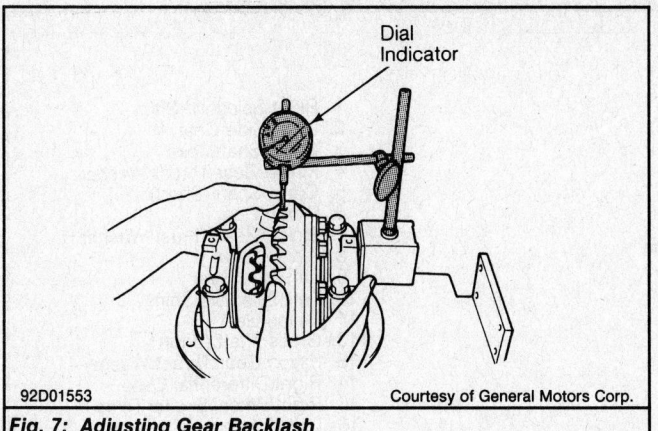

92D01553   Courtesy of General Motors Corp.

Fig. 7: Adjusting Gear Backlash

24) Tighten side bearing cap bolts to specification. See TORQUE SPECIFICATIONS. Install bearing lock plates and tighten bolts to specification. See TORQUE SPECIFICATIONS. Using gear marking compound, check gear tooth contact pattern. See GEAR TOOTH CONTACT PATTERNS article in GENERAL INFORMATION. Stake pinion flange nut.

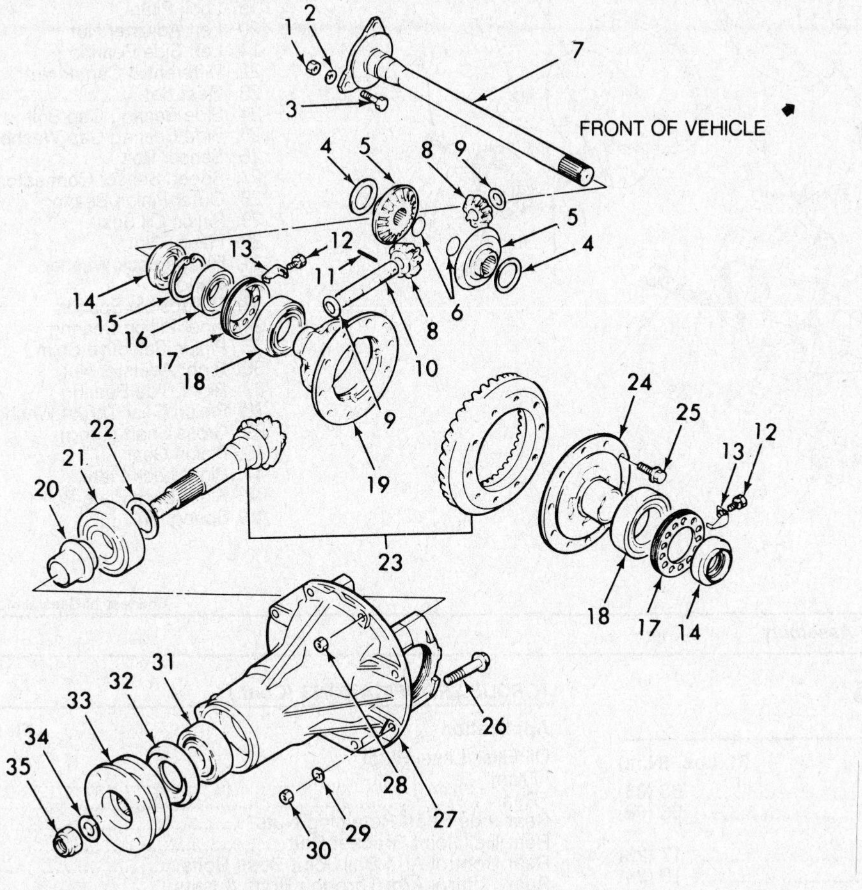

FRONT OF VEHICLE

1. Shaft Nut
2. Lock Washer
3. Shaft Bolt
4. Selective Shim
5. Differential Gear
6. Axle Shaft Snap Ring
7. Front Axle Shaft
8. Differential Pinion Gear
9. Pinion Thrust Washer
10. Differential Pinion Shaft
11. Shaft Pin
12. Bearing Lock Plate Bolt
13. Bearing Lock Plate
14. Axle Shaft Oil Seal
15. Bearing Snap Ring
16. Axle Shaft Bearing
17. Bearing Adjuster Nut
18. Differential Side Bearing
19. Left Differential Case
20. Collapsible Spacer
21. Pinion Inner Bearing
22. Pinion Selective Shim
23. Bevel Pinion Gear Set
24. Right Differential Case
25. Bevel Gear Bolt
26. Side Bearing Cap Bolt
27. Front Differential Carrier Case
28. Carrier Nut
29. Lock Washer
30. Carrier Unit
31. Pinion Outer Bearing
32. Pinion Oil Seal
33. Universal Joint Flange
34. Flange Washer
35. Flange Nut

92F01554   Courtesy of General Motors Corp.

Fig. 8: Exploded View Of Front Differential Assembly

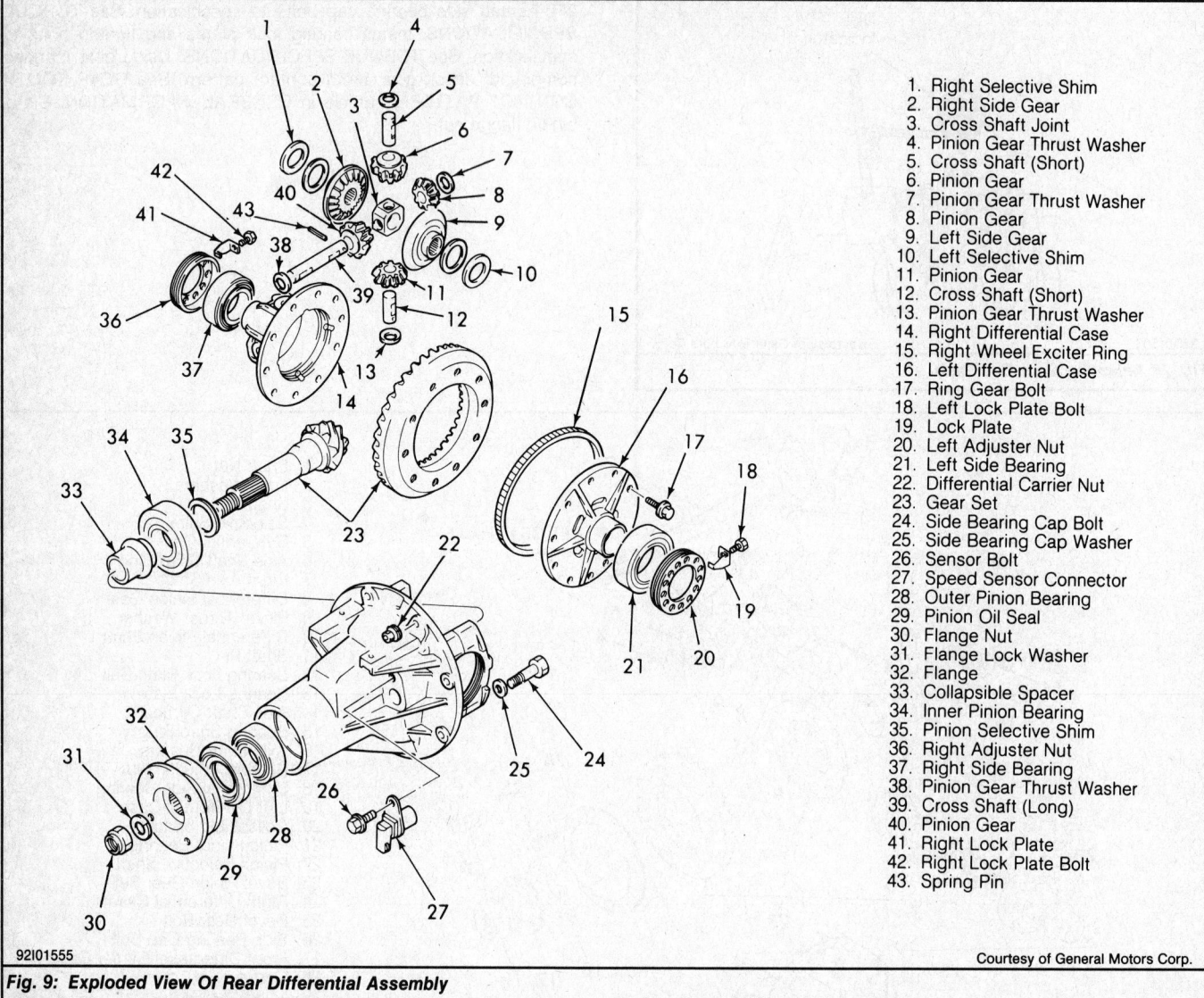

1. Right Selective Shim
2. Right Side Gear
3. Cross Shaft Joint
4. Pinion Gear Thrust Washer
5. Cross Shaft (Short)
6. Pinion Gear
7. Pinion Gear Thrust Washer
8. Pinion Gear
9. Left Side Gear
10. Left Selective Shim
11. Pinion Gear
12. Cross Shaft (Short)
13. Pinion Gear Thrust Washer
14. Right Differential Case
15. Right Wheel Exciter Ring
16. Left Differential Case
17. Ring Gear Bolt
18. Left Lock Plate Bolt
19. Lock Plate
20. Left Adjuster Nut
21. Left Side Bearing
22. Differential Carrier Nut
23. Gear Set
24. Side Bearing Cap Bolt
25. Side Bearing Cap Washer
26. Sensor Bolt
27. Speed Sensor Connector
28. Outer Pinion Bearing
29. Pinion Oil Seal
30. Flange Nut
31. Flange Lock Washer
32. Flange
33. Collapsible Spacer
34. Inner Pinion Bearing
35. Pinion Selective Shim
36. Right Adjuster Nut
37. Right Side Bearing
38. Pinion Gear Thrust Washer
39. Cross Shaft (Long)
40. Pinion Gear
41. Right Lock Plate
42. Right Lock Plate Bolt
43. Spring Pin

92I01555

Courtesy of General Motors Corp.

Fig. 9: Exploded View Of Rear Differential Assembly

TORQUE SPECIFICATIONS

TORQUE SPECIFICATIONS

Application	Ft. Lbs. (N.m)
Ball Joint Nut	63 (85)
Brake Caliper Bolt	65 (88)
Differential Drain Plug	
Front	17 (23)
Rear	18 (24)
Drive Shaft Bolt & Nut	
Front	43 (58)
Rear	37 (50)
Front Axle Housing Mount Bracket Bolts	
Left, Right & Center	44 (60)
Front Brake Caliper Bolt	65 (88)
Front Differential	
Carrier Nut	17 (23)
Ring Gear Bolt	74 (100)
Side Bearing Cap Bolt	52 (70)
Side Bearing Lock Plate Bolt	11 (15)
Front Locking Hub Bolt	18 (24)
Front Skid Plate Bolts	40 (54)
Front Stabilizer Bar Mount Bolt	37 (50)
Front Stabilizer Bar-To-Control Arm Bolt	21 (28)
Left Front Axle Shaft-To-Inner Axle Shaft	
Flange Bolt	44 (60)
Locking Hub Cover Bolts	18 (24)

TORQUE SPECIFICATIONS (Cont.)

Application	Ft. Lbs. (N.m)
Oil Filler/Level Plug	
Front	33 (45)
Rear	37 (50)
Rear Axle Shaft Retaining Nuts	17 (23)
Rear Ball Joint Bracket Bolt	37 (50)
Rear Control Arm Ball Joint Boss Bolts	37 (50)
Rear Control Arm Through Bolts & Nuts	44 (60)
Rear Differential	
Carrier Nut	41 (55)
Ring Gear Bolt	74 (100)
Side Bearing Cap Bolt	74 (100)
Side Bearing Lock Plate Bolt	24 (33)
Rear Shock Absorber Nut	66 (90)
Rear Trailing Rod Nut	66 (90)
RWAL Brake Speed Sensor Cover Bolts	11 (15)
RWAL Speed Sensor Bolt	17 (23)
Stabilizer Bar Mount Bolt	38 (51)
Stabilizer Bar-To-Control Arm Bolt	21 (29)
Tie Rod-To-Steering Knuckle Nut	30 (41)
Transfer Case Drain & Level/Filler Plugs	21 (28)
Wheel Lug Nut	70 (95)

Metro, Prizm, Tracker

DESCRIPTION & OPERATION

All models are equipped with front disc brakes and rear drum brakes. On Prizm and Tracker, hydraulic system is split front and rear. On Metro, hydraulic pressure is distributed diagonally through 2 circuits. The left front and right rear brakes are activated by the master cylinder front service port.

The right front and left rear brakes are activated by the master cylinder rear service port. On all models, parking brake lever assembly sets rear brakes using a cable and mechanical linkage system.

BLEEDING BRAKE SYSTEM

NOTE: On Prizm equipped with 4-Wheel Anti-Lock Braking System (ABS) see 4-WHEEL ANTI-LOCK-PRIZM article in BRAKES for ABS bleeding procedures. On Tracker equipped with Rear Anti-Lock Braking System (RWAL ABS) see REAR ANTI-LOCK article in BRAKES for ABS bleeding procedures.

Manual Bleeding – 1) Clean master cylinder cap and surrounding area, then remove cap. Fill master cylinder and install cap. Have an assistant slowly depress brake pedal and hold. Loosen master cylinder brake line fitting to purge air from master cylinder bore.
2) Tighten brake line fitting and then release brake pedal slowly. Wait 15 seconds and repeat procedure, including 15 second wait, until air is removed. Repeat this operation with each brake line at master cylinder. If brake pedal is firm and not spongy, bleeding is complete. If brake pedal is spongy go to next step and bleed each wheel in sequence.
3) Install clear vinyl bleeder hose onto first wheel bleeder screw to be serviced. See BRAKE LINE BLEEDING SEQUENCE table. Place other end of hose in clean, transparent container. Partially fill container with clean brake fluid so end of hose is submerged in fluid. Open bleeder screw and slowly depress brake pedal and hold.
4) Close bleeder screw, and release pedal. Gently pump pedal several times to push air toward wheel calipers/cylinders. Repeat procedure until flow of brake fluid is clear and bubble free. Proceed to next bleeder screw. See BRAKE LINE BLEEDING SEQUENCE table. Add brake fluid to master cylinder after bleeding all wheels.
Pressure Tank Bleeding – 1) Clean master cylinder cap and surrounding area, and remove cap. With pressure tank at least 1/2 full, charge tank to 20-25 psi (1.4-1.8 Kg/cm²). Install appropriate pressure bleeder adapter to master cylinder and connect pressure tank.
2) Attach vinyl bleeder hose to first bleeder screw to be serviced. See BRAKE LINE BLEEDING SEQUENCE table. Place other end of hose in clean, transparent container. Partially fill container with clean brake fluid until end of hose is submerged in fluid.
3) Open release valve on pressure tank. Open bleeder screw, noting fluid flow. When fluid flowing into container is clear and bubble free, close bleeder screw securely. Finish bleeding system, in the same manner, using appropriate sequence. See BRAKE LINE BLEEDING SEQUENCE table. Close release valve, and remove pressure tank from master cylinder. Check master cylinder reservoir fluid level. Ensure brake pedal is firm. If brake pedal is spongy or soft, bleed system again.

BLEEDING SEQUENCE

BRAKE LINE BLEEDING SEQUENCE

Application	Sequence
Metro	RR, LF, LR, RF
Prizm	RR, LR, RF, LF
Tracker	¹ LR, RF, LF

¹ – There is no bleeder valve on right rear brake. Rear brakes can only be bled through left rear brake. Start with longest line first.

ADJUSTMENTS

BRAKE PEDAL HEIGHT

Metro & Tracker – On Metro, brake pedal height should be .3" (8 mm) lower than clutch pedal. On all models, remove power brake unit. Measure distance between power brake unit mounting surface (with gasket removed on Metro and gasket installed on Tracker) and center of brake push rod clevis pin. Correct distance is 4.51-4.54" (114.5-115.3 mm) on Metro and 4.94" (125.5 mm) on Tracker.
Prizm – Brake pedal height should be 5.7-6.1" (144-154 mm), measured from face of brake pedal pad to floor under carpet. See Fig. 1. To adjust pedal height, loosen stoplight switch and lock nut on brake pedal push rod. Turn brake pedal push rod until specified pedal height is obtained. Tighten lock nut on brake pedal push rod after adjusting pedal height. Adjust stoplight switch. See STOPLIGHT SWITCH under ADJUSTMENTS.

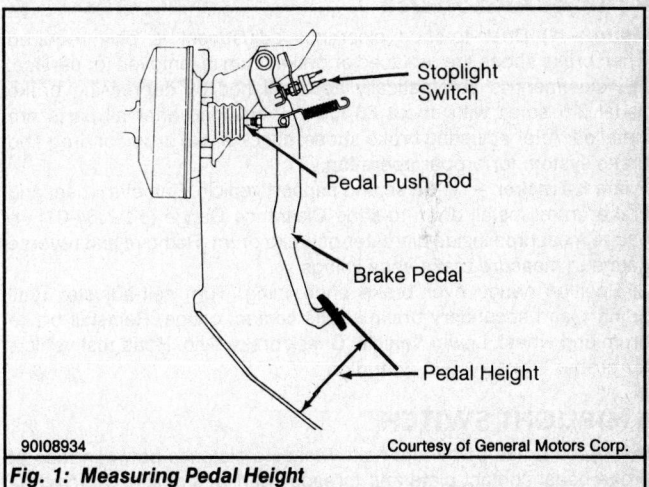

90I08934   Courtesy of General Motors Corp.

Fig. 1: Measuring Pedal Height

BRAKE PEDAL FREE PLAY

NOTE: Brake pedal free play adjustment procedure for Metro and Tracker is not available from manufacturer.

Prizm – 1) Start and run engine at 1000 RPM for about one minute. Turn engine off and depress brake pedal several times to exhaust vacuum from power brake unit. Depress brake pedal by hand and measure brake pedal travel until initial resistance is felt.
2) Brake pedal free play should be .04-.24" (1.0-6.0 mm). If brake pedal free play is not within specification, ensure stoplight switch adjustment and brake height are correct. See STOPLIGHT SWITCH and BRAKE PEDAL HEIGHT under ADJUSTMENTS. If stoplight switch and brake pedal height are correct, ensure there are no leaks or air in hydraulic system. See BLEEDING BRAKE SYSTEM. See Fig. 1.

BRAKE PEDAL TRAVEL

Metro, Prizm, & Tracker – 1) With engine off, pump brake pedal until all vacuum is exhausted from power brake unit. Push brake pedal with a force of about 66 lbs. (30 kg). Measure distance between brake pedal face and floor.
2) Distance must not be less than 2.36" (60 mm) on Metro, 2.76" (70 mm) on Prizm, and 5.1" (130 mm) on Tracker. If measured distance is less than specified, check for air in hydraulic system, worn rear brake shoes, defective rear brake self-adjusters and improper brake pedal push rod adjustment.

PARKING/EMERGENCY BRAKE

NOTE: Ensure rear brakes are correctly adjusted before adjusting parking brake. See REAR BRAKE SHOES under ADJUSTMENTS.

Metro & Tracker – 1) Using 44-55 lbs. (20-25 kg), apply parking brake lever and count number of notches lever travels. Adjustment is okay if lever clicks 4-9 notches on Metro and 7-9 notches on Tracker. **2)** If parking brake cable adjustment is required, remove parking brake lever assembly trim cover. Loosen parking brake cable lock nut. Turn cable adjusting nut as required to obtain correct number of clicks at parking brake lever. After adjustment, check for brake drag with parking brake off.

Prizm – 1) Pull parking brake lever up fully and count number of notches lever travels. Adjustment is okay if 4-7 clicks are heard. Adjust if necessary.

2) If parking brake cable adjustment is required, remove console box. Loosen jam nut, and adjust parking brake cable. Tighten jam nut, and repeat step 1). After adjustment, check for brake drag with parking brake off.

REAR BRAKE SHOES

Metro – 1) Drum-to-shoe clearance adjustment is only required when brake shoes are replaced or brake drum is removed for service. **2)** Adjustment is automatically accomplished by depressing brake pedal 3-5 times with about 66 lbs. (30 kg) load after all parts are installed. After adjusting brake shoes, check brake drum for drag and brake system for proper operation.

Prizm & Tracker – 1) Raise and support vehicle. Remove wheel and brake drum. Install drum-to-shoe Clearance Gauge (J-22364-01) so gauge measures inside diameter of brake drum. Remove and reverse gauge to measure brake shoe linings.

2) Position gauge over brake shoe lining. Turn self-adjuster until primary and secondary brake shoes contact gauge. Reinstall brake drum and wheel. Lower vehicle. Check brake fluid. Road test vehicle for proper brake system operation.

STOPLIGHT SWITCH

Pull up on brake pedal and hold. Measure distance between face of brake pedal contact plate and threaded part of stoplight switch. *See Fig. 2.* On Metro and Tracker, distance should be .02-.04" (.5-1.0 mm). On Prizm distance should be .02-.09" (.5-2.5 mm). Adjust stoplight switch if distance is not within specification. Tighten stoplight switch lock nut to specification. See TORQUE SPECIFICATIONS.

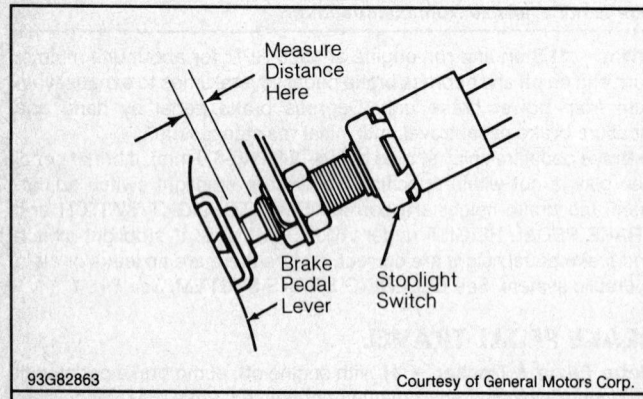

93G82863   Courtesy of General Motors Corp.
Fig. 2: Adjusting Stoplight Switch

PUSH ROD

1) Place Booster Piston Rod Gauge (J-39567 for Metro and Tracker; J-34873-A for Prizm) on master cylinder with master cylinder gasket in place. Lower booster piston rod gauge pin until its tip just touches end of master cylinder primary piston. *See Fig. 3.*

2) Remove booster piston rod gauge, turn it upside down, and place it on front of brake booster assembly. *See Fig. 4.* No clearance should be present between master cylinder primary piston and booster piston rod.

3) If clearance is present, adjust booster piston rod length by turning adjustment nut at end of piston rod until rod just touches master cylinder primary piston.

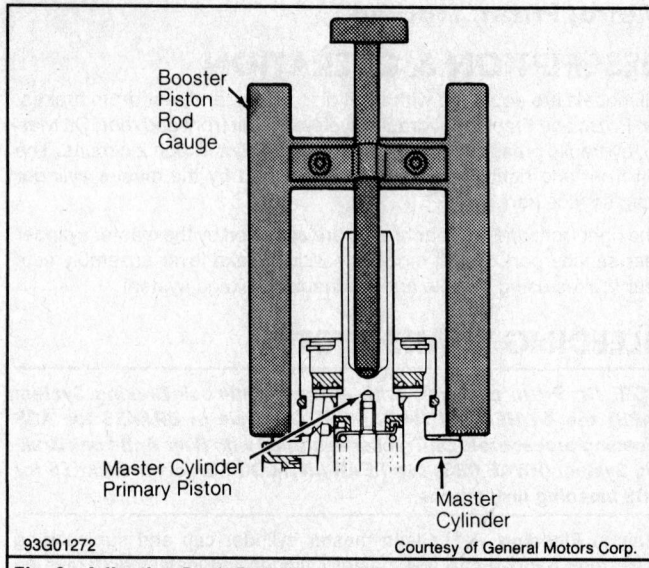

93G01272   Courtesy of General Motors Corp.
Fig. 3: Adjusting Push Rod (Gauge Shown On Master Cylinder)

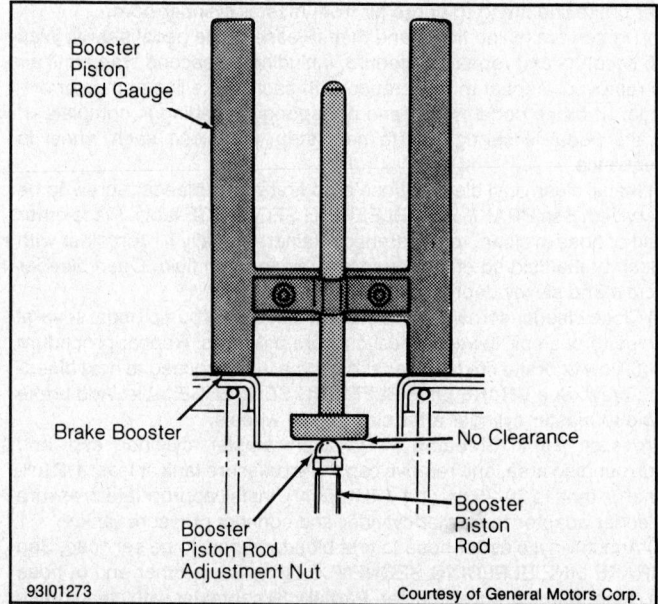

93I01273   Courtesy of General Motors Corp.
Fig. 4: Adjusting Push Rod (Gauge Shown On Brake Booster)

REMOVAL & INSTALLATION

FRONT DISC BRAKE PADS

Removal & Installation – 1) Raise and support vehicle. Remove wheel. Compress caliper piston with large "C" clamp. Remove caliper guide pin bolts. Hold inner disc pad while removing caliper from knuckle. Support caliper using wire. Remove inner and outer disc pad, pad clips and springs. See Fig. 9, 10 or 11.

2) To install, reverse removal procedure. Coat slide bushings with silicone grease. Tighten caliper guide pin bolts to specification. See TORQUE SPECIFICATIONS.

FRONT DISC BRAKE ROTOR

Removal (Metro) – 1) Raise and support vehicle, allowing suspension to hang freely. Remove wheel.

2) Unstake drive axle nut. Depress brake pedal to lock brake disc. Remove and discard drive axle nut. Remove hub/rotor retaining bolts.

3) Remove caliper bolts. Remove caliper and wire aside. Remove hub and outer spacer with slide hammer and Adapter (J-34866). Remove brake rotor.

Installation – Install brake rotor disc onto wheel hub. Apply a light coat of wheel bearing grease to outside of hub shaft. Using a press, install hub and spacer. Tighten hub/rotor bolts to specification. See TORQUE SPECIFICATIONS. Install NEW drive axle nut during assembly and stake in place. Tighten bolts to specification. See TORQUE SPECIFICATIONS. *See Fig. 5.*

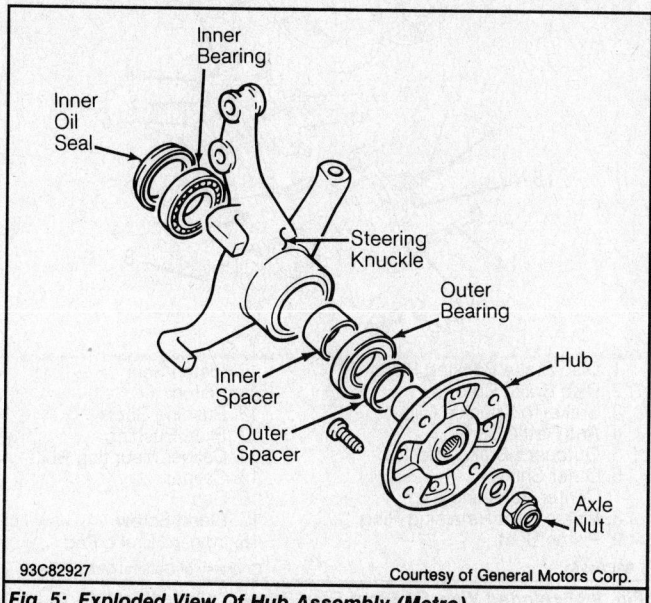

Fig. 5: *Exploded View Of Hub Assembly (Metro)*

Remove & Installation (Prizm & Tracker) – Remove about two-thirds of brake fluid from master cylinder. Compress caliper piston with large "C" clamp. Remove caliper union bolt. Remove caliper guide pin bolts. Hold inner disc pad while removing caliper from knuckle. Support caliper using wire. Remove inner and outer disc pad, pad clips and springs. Remove caliper support bracket and remove rotor. To install, reverse removal procedure. Tighten bolts to specification. See TORQUE SPECIFICATIONS.

MASTER CYLINDER

Removal – Disconnect negative battery cable. Remove electrical connector from reservoir cap (if equipped). On Prizm, disconnect intake air temperature sensor and remove air intake hose and cover from throttle body. On all models, disconnect brake lines from master cylinder. Cap brake lines and plug master cylinder ports to prevent fluid spillage and contamination. Remove nuts and washers attaching master cylinder to power brake unit. Remove master cylinder.

Installation – To install, reverse removal procedure. Tighten nuts to specification. See TORQUE SPECIFICATIONS. Fill master cylinder reservoir. Bleed brake system. See BLEEDING BRAKE SYSTEM. Check and adjust brake pedal height if necessary. See BRAKE PEDAL HEIGHT under ADJUSTMENTS.

VACUUM BOOSTER

Removal & Installation – 1) Disconnect negative battery cable. Disconnect brake fluid level sensor connector. Remove master cylinder from vacuum booster. See MASTER CYLINDER. Disconnect vacuum booster push rod clevis from brake pedal arm. Disconnect vacuum hose from vacuum booster.

2) Remove vacuum booster attaching nuts. Remove vacuum booster unit. To install, reverse removal procedure. Tighten nuts to specification. See TORQUE SPECIFICATIONS.

REAR BRAKE SHOES

Removal (Metro) – 1) Raise and support vehicle. Remove wheel. Remove spindle cap. Straighten staked portion of spindle nut. Remove and discard spindle nut. Remove washer.

2) Using Adapter (J-34866) and a Slide Hammer (J-2619-01), remove drum/hub assembly from spindle. Remove return and hold-down springs and anti-rattle spring. Remove brake self-adjusting strut. Disconnect parking brake cable. Remove brake shoes. *See Fig. 6.*

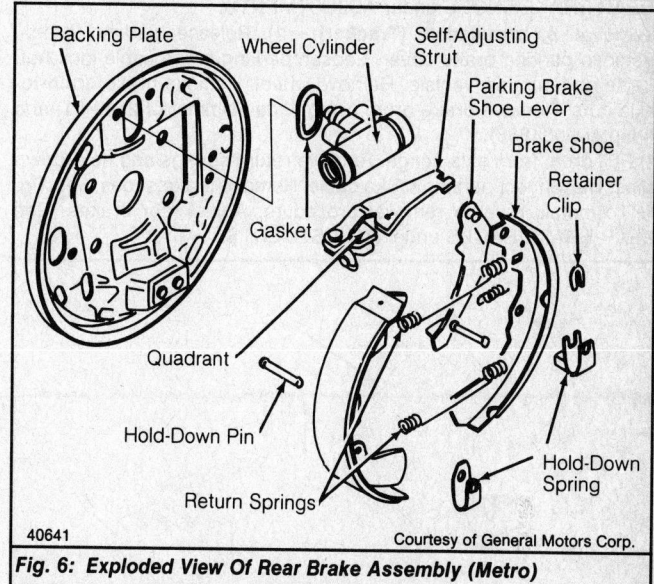

Fig. 6: *Exploded View Of Rear Brake Assembly (Metro)*

Installation – 1) Install parking brake shoe lever and self-adjusting strut. Install parking brake cable in lever. Install hold-down springs. Install brake shoes and return springs.

2) Install brake drum, washer and new spindle nut. Tighten spindle nut to 129 ft. lbs. (175 N.m). Stake spindle nut in place. Install spindle cap. Adjust rear brakes. See REAR BRAKE SHOES under ADJUSTMENTS.

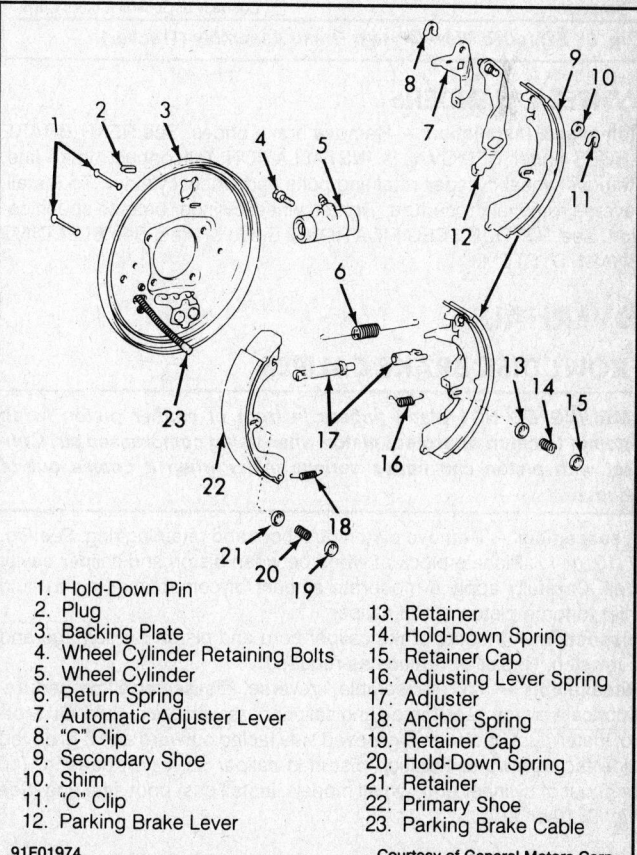

1. Hold-Down Pin
2. Plug
3. Backing Plate
4. Wheel Cylinder Retaining Bolts
5. Wheel Cylinder
6. Return Spring
7. Automatic Adjuster Lever
8. "C" Clip
9. Secondary Shoe
10. Shim
11. "C" Clip
12. Parking Brake Lever
13. Retainer
14. Hold-Down Spring
15. Retainer Cap
16. Adjusting Lever Spring
17. Adjuster
18. Anchor Spring
19. Retainer Cap
20. Hold-Down Spring
21. Retainer
22. Primary Shoe
23. Parking Brake Cable

Courtesy of General Motors Corp.

Fig. 7: *Exploded View Of Rear Brake Assembly (Prizm)*

Removal & Installation (Prizm) – Raise and support vehicle. Remove wheel and brake drum. Remove return and hold-down springs. Disconnect parking brake cable. Remove brake shoes. See Fig. 7. To install, reverse removal procedure. Adjust rear brakes. See REAR BRAKE SHOES under ADJUSTMENTS.

Removal & Installation (Tracker) – 1) Release parking brake. Remove parking brake cover. Loosen parking brake cable lock nut. Raise and support vehicle. Remove wheel. Remove brake drum-to-axle nuts. Remove brake drum using Slide Hammer (J-2619-01) and Adapter (J-34866).

2) Pull drum from axle flange. Remove return springs and hold-down clips. Disconnect parking brake cable. Remove brake shoes. See Fig. 8. To install, reverse removal procedure. Adjust rear brakes. See REAR BRAKE SHOES under ADJUSTMENTS.

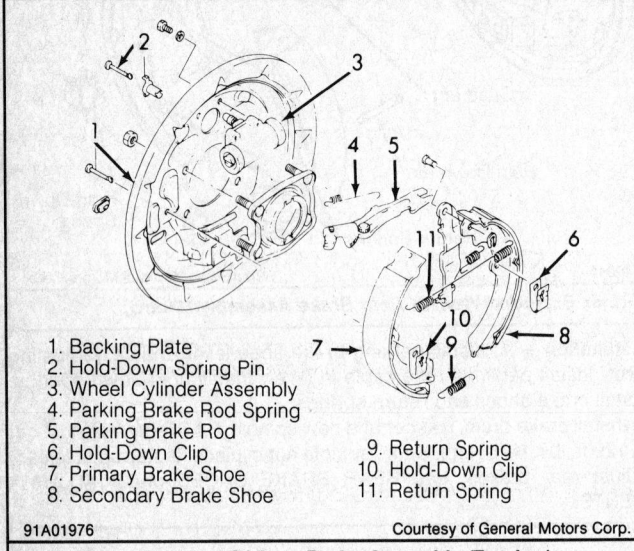

1. Backing Plate
2. Hold-Down Spring Pin
3. Wheel Cylinder Assembly
4. Parking Brake Rod Spring
5. Parking Brake Rod
6. Hold-Down Clip
7. Primary Brake Shoe
8. Secondary Brake Shoe
9. Return Spring
10. Hold-Down Clip
11. Return Spring

91A01976　　　　Courtesy of General Motors Corp.

Fig. 8: Exploded View Of Rear Brake Assembly (Tracker)

WHEEL CYLINDERS

Removal & Installation – Remove brake shoes. See REAR BRAKE SHOES under REMOVAL & INSTALLATION. Disconnect brake line. Remove wheel cylinder retaining bolts and wheel cylinder. To install, reverse removal procedure. Tighten wheel cylinder bolts to specification. See TORQUE SPECIFICATIONS. Bleed brakes. See BLEEDING BRAKE SYSTEM.

OVERHAUL

FRONT DISC BRAKE CALIPER

WARNING: DO NOT place fingers in front of caliper piston in an attempt to catch or protect piston when using compressed air. Contact with piston can cause serious injury when it comes out of caliper.

Disassembly – Remove piston dust boot and retaining ring. See Fig. 9, 10, or 11. Place a block of wood between piston and caliper cavity wall. Carefully apply a moderate amount of compressed air to fluid inlet to force piston out of caliper.

Inspection – Inspect brake caliper bore and piston for damage and corrosion. Repair or replace as required.

Reassembly – To reassemble, reverse disassembly procedure. Lubricate piston seal, piston and caliper bore with brake fluid. On Metro, install dust boot with 3-grooved side facing outward and 2-grooved side facing inward. Position piston in caliper so it protrudes .4" (10 mm) out of cylinder end. On all models, install dust boot seal ring. See Fig. 9, 10 or 11.

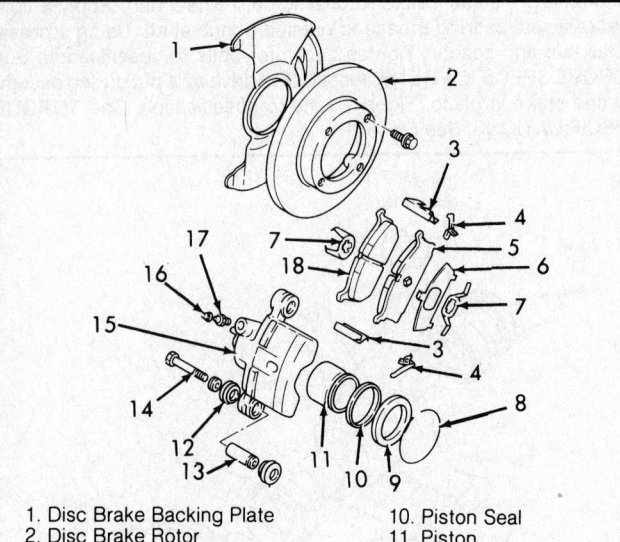

1. Disc Brake Backing Plate
2. Disc Brake Rotor
3. Brake-To-Knuckle Clip
4. Anti-Rattle Spring
5. Outboard Brake Pad
6. Outer Shim
7. Center Retaining Clip
8. Piston Boot Retaining Ring
9. Piston Boot
10. Piston Seal
11. Piston
12. Bushing Boot
13. Slide Bushing
14. Caliper Mounting Bolt
15. Caliper
16. Cap
17. Bleed Screw
18. Inboard Brake Pad

93C01251　　　　Courtesy of General Motors Corp.

Fig. 9: Exploded View Of Front Disc Brake Caliper (Metro)

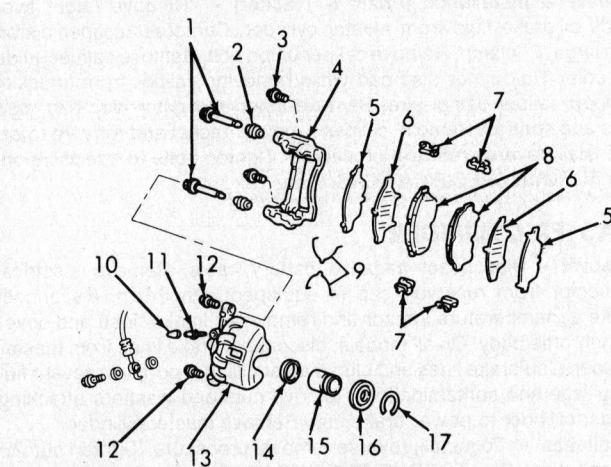

1. Slide Pins
2. Dust Boots
3. Caliper Carrier Mounting Bolts
4. Caliper Carrier
5. Anti-Squeal Shim (Outer)
6. Anti-Squeal Shim (Inner)
7. Anti-Rattle Spring
8. Brake Pads
9. Anti-Squeal Springs
10. Cap
11. Bleeder Screw
12. Caliper Mounting Bolt
13. Caliper Housing
14. Piston Seal
15. Piston
16. Piston Boot
17. Boot Ring

93H82906　　　　Courtesy of General Motors Corp.

Fig. 10: Exploded View Of Front Disc Brake Caliper (Prizm)

MASTER CYLINDER

Disassembly (Metro & Tracker) – Using a drift, remove brake fluid reservoir roll pin and remove reservoir. Remove piston stopper circlip and primary piston from end of master cylinder. See Fig. 12. Remove secondary piston by removing secondary stopper bolt from bottom of master cylinder and applying low air pressure in stopper bolt hole.

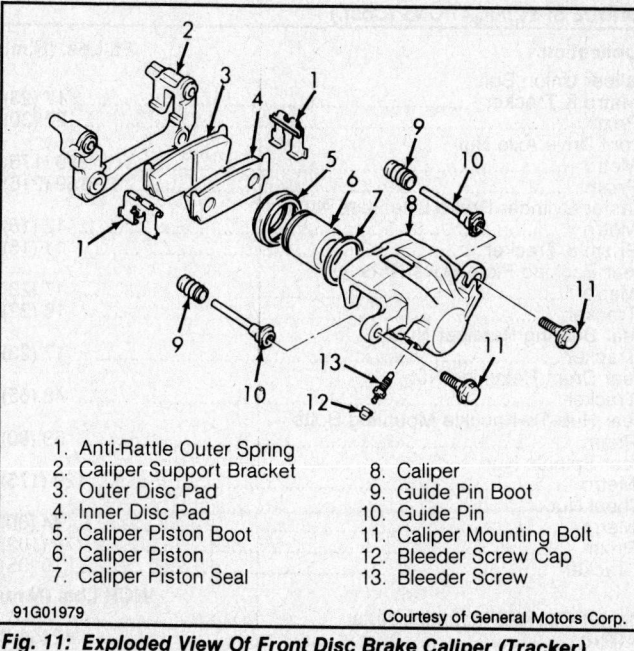

1. Anti-Rattle Outer Spring
2. Caliper Support Bracket
3. Outer Disc Pad
4. Inner Disc Pad
5. Caliper Piston Boot
6. Caliper Piston
7. Caliper Piston Seal
8. Caliper
9. Guide Pin Boot
10. Guide Pin
11. Caliper Mounting Bolt
12. Bleeder Screw Cap
13. Bleeder Screw

91G01979   Courtesy of General Motors Corp.

Fig. 11: Exploded View Of Front Disc Brake Caliper (Tracker)

Cleaning & Inspection – Note position of piston cups before removing. DO NOT reuse piston cups. Clean parts in clean brake fluid or denatured alcohol, and blow dry. Inspect master cylinder bore for scoring and corrosion. DO NOT recondition cylinder bore. Replace as required.

Reassembly – 1) Coat all parts with clean brake fluid or brake assembly lube. Install NEW piston cups on pistons. Install secondary piston return spring, return spring seat and secondary piston in cylinder bore. Install primary piston in cylinder bore. See Fig. 12.

2) Install sealing rings on piston stopper, and install stopper in cylinder bore. Depress primary piston and install piston stopper circlip in cylinder. Press primary piston into bore until seated.

3) Install and tighten secondary stopper bolt in bottom of cylinder. Install reservoir on master cylinder using NEW grommets coated with clean brake fluid. Bench-bleed master cylinder before installing in vehicle. Bleed entire brake system after installation. See BLEEDING BRAKE SYSTEM.

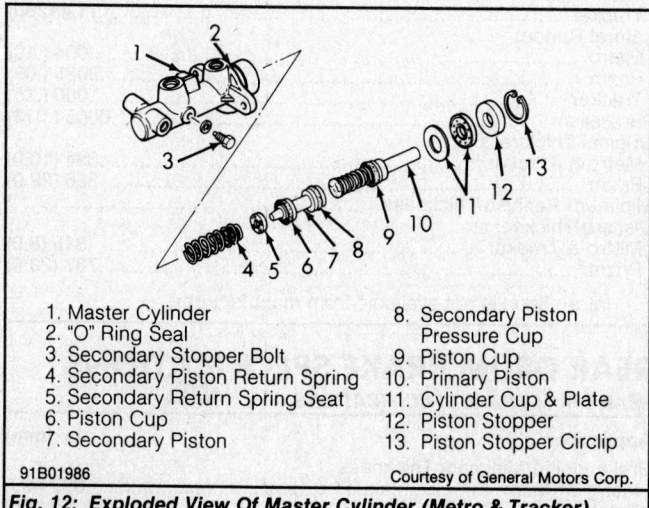

1. Master Cylinder
2. "O" Ring Seal
3. Secondary Stopper Bolt
4. Secondary Piston Return Spring
5. Secondary Return Spring Seat
6. Piston Cup
7. Secondary Piston
8. Secondary Piston Pressure Cup
9. Piston Cup
10. Primary Piston
11. Cylinder Cup & Plate
12. Piston Stopper
13. Piston Stopper Circlip

91B01986   Courtesy of General Motors Corp.

Fig. 12: Exploded View Of Master Cylinder (Metro & Tracker)

Disassembly (Prizm) – Remove reservoir retaining screw. Remove reservoir. Mount cylinder in soft-jawed vise. Push pistons into cylinder bore, and remove piston stopper bolt. Remove snap ring, and pull out piston assemblies. See Fig. 13. Disassemble piston assemblies by removing springs, retainers and cups.

Cleaning & Inspection – Wash all parts in clean brake fluid or denatured alcohol. Inspect for wear, damage and corrosion. Replace defective parts as necessary.

Reassembly – To reassemble, reverse disassembly procedure using NEW rubber parts. See Fig. 13. Lubricate all components with clean brake fluid. Bench-bleed master cylinder before installing in vehicle. Bleed entire brake system after installation. See BLEEDING BRAKE SYSTEM.

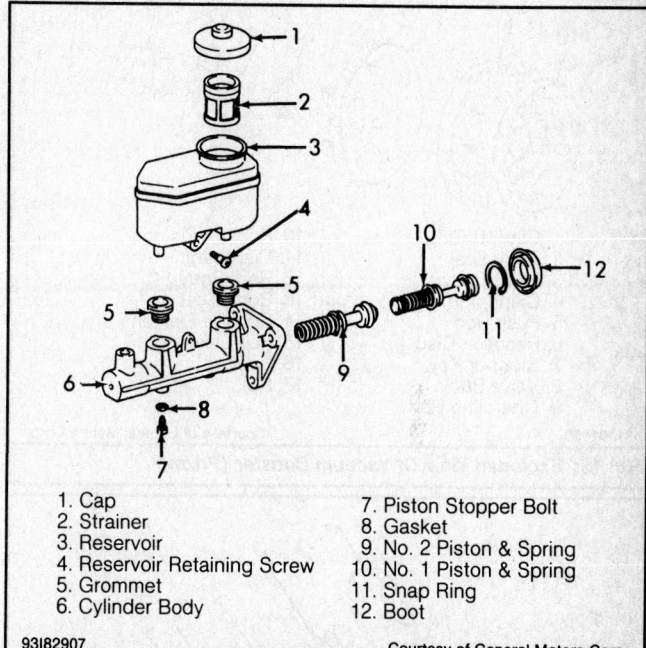

1. Cap
2. Strainer
3. Reservoir
4. Reservoir Retaining Screw
5. Grommet
6. Cylinder Body
7. Piston Stopper Bolt
8. Gasket
9. No. 2 Piston & Spring
10. No. 1 Piston & Spring
11. Snap Ring
12. Boot

93I82907   Courtesy of General Motors Corp.

Fig. 13: Exploded View Of Master Cylinder (Prizm)

VACUUM BOOSTER UNIT

NOTE: Use illustration for exploded view of vacuum booster unit. See Fig. 14, 15 or 16.

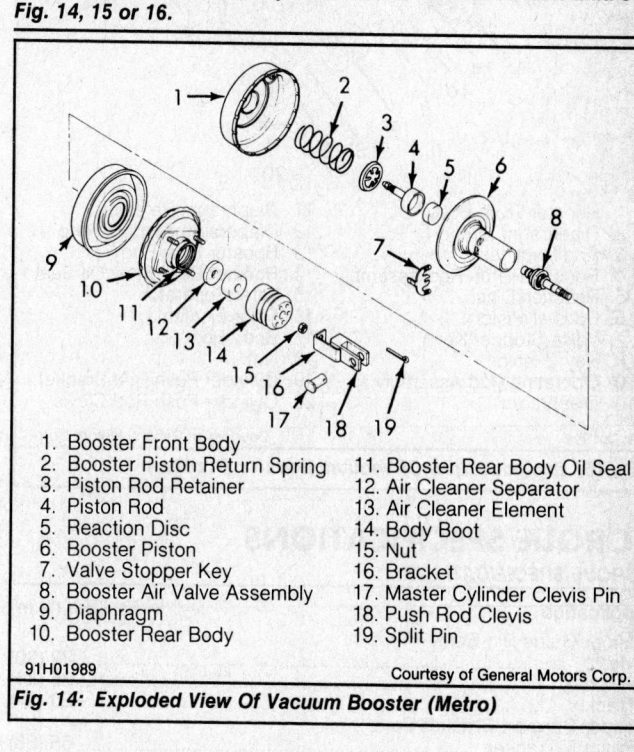

1. Booster Front Body
2. Booster Piston Return Spring
3. Piston Rod Retainer
4. Piston Rod
5. Reaction Disc
6. Booster Piston
7. Valve Stopper Key
8. Booster Air Valve Assembly
9. Diaphragm
10. Booster Rear Body
11. Booster Rear Body Oil Seal
12. Air Cleaner Separator
13. Air Cleaner Element
14. Body Boot
15. Nut
16. Bracket
17. Master Cylinder Clevis Pin
18. Push Rod Clevis
19. Split Pin

91H01989   Courtesy of General Motors Corp.

Fig. 14: Exploded View Of Vacuum Booster (Metro)

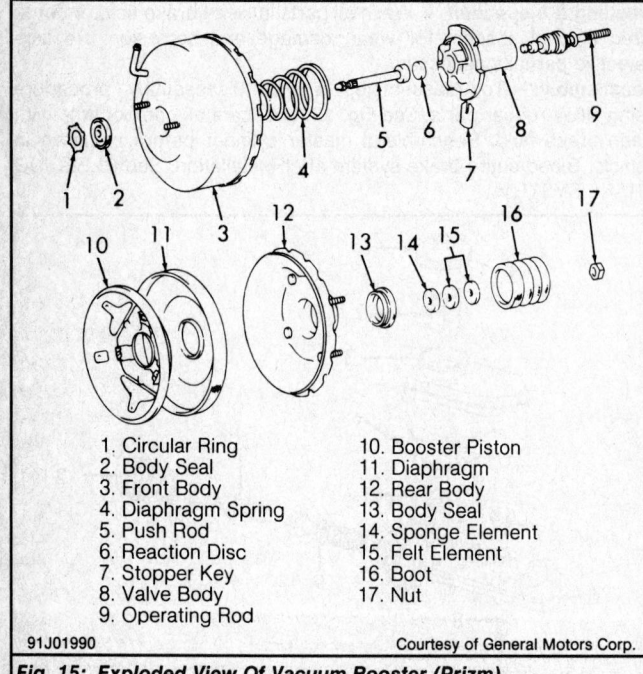

1. Circular Ring
2. Body Seal
3. Front Body
4. Diaphragm Spring
5. Push Rod
6. Reaction Disc
7. Stopper Key
8. Valve Body
9. Operating Rod
10. Booster Piston
11. Diaphragm
12. Rear Body
13. Body Seal
14. Sponge Element
15. Felt Element
16. Boot
17. Nut

91J01990   Courtesy of General Motors Corp.

Fig. 15: Exploded View Of Vacuum Booster (Prizm)

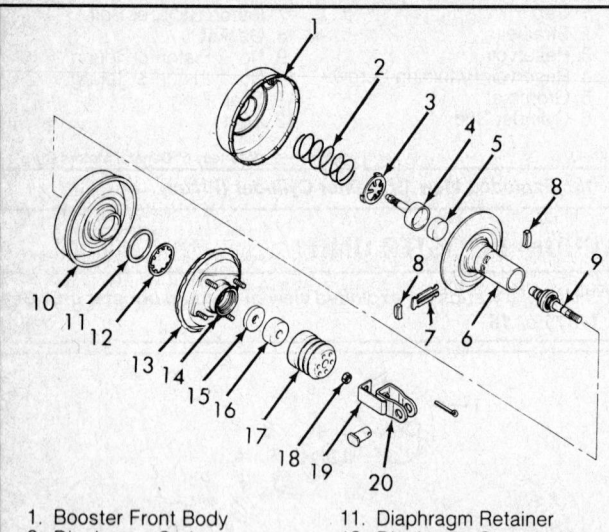

1. Booster Front Body
2. Diaphragm Spring
3. Rod Retainer
4. Booster Piston Rod Assembly
5. Reaction Disc
6. Booster Piston
7. Valve Stopper Key
8. Key Cushion
9. Operating Rod Assembly
10. Diaphragm
11. Diaphragm Retainer
12. Diaphragm Stopper Ring
13. Booster Rear Body
14. Booster Rear Body Oil Seal
15. Filter Separator
16. Filter Element
17. Body Boot
18. Nut
19. Cylinder Push Rod Bracket
20. Cylinder Push Rod Clevis

91D01992   Courtesy of General Motors Corp.

Fig. 16: Exploded View Of Vacuum Booster (Tracker)

TORQUE SPECIFICATIONS
TORQUE SPECIFICATIONS

Application	Ft. Lbs. (N.m)
Caliper Guide Pin Bolts	
Metro	22 (30)
Prizm	25 (34)
Tracker	20 (27)
Caliper Support Bracket Bolts	
Prizm & Tracker	65 (88)

TORQUE SPECIFICATIONS (Cont.)

Application	Ft. Lbs. (N.m)
Caliper Union Bolt	
Metro & Tracker	17 (23)
Prizm	22 (30)
Front Drive Axle Nut	
Metro	129 (175)
Prizm	159 (216)
Master Cylinder Brake Line Flare Nuts	
Metro	12 (16)
Prizm & Tracker	11 (15)
Rear Backing Plate Bolts/Nuts	
Metro	17 (23)
Tracker	16 (22)
Rear Bearing Retainer Nuts	
Tracker	17 (23)
Rear Drum Retaining Nut	
Tracker	48 (65)
Rear Hub-To-Knuckle Mounting Bolts	
Prizm	59 (80)
Rear Spindle Nut	
Metro	129 (175)
Wheel Nut	
Metro	44 (60)
Prizm	76 (103)
Tracker	70 (95)
	INCH Lbs. (N.m)
Master Cylinder Mounting Nuts	
Metro	124 (14)
Prizm	115 (13)
Tracker	142 (16)
Master Cylinder Piston Stopper Bolts	89 (10)
Proportioning Valve Bolt (Metro)	7 (0.8)
Reservoir Retaining Screw	
Prizm	15 (1.7)
Stoplight Switch Lock Nut	
Metro	115 (13)
Prizm & Tracker	89 (10)
Vacuum Booster Mounting Nuts	115 (13)
Wheel Cylinder Retaining Bolts	89 (10)

FRONT DISC BRAKE SPECIFICATIONS
FRONT DISC BRAKE SPECIFICATIONS

Application	In. (mm)
Disc Diameter	
Metro	8.4 (213)
Prizm	10.03 (255)
Tracker	11.4 (290)
Lateral Runout	
Metro	.004 (.10)
Prizm	.0035 (.09)
Tracker	.006 (.15)
Parallelism	.0005 (.013)
Original Thickness	
Metro & Tracker	.394 (10.0)
Prizm	.866 (22.0)
Minimum Refinish Thickness	[1]
Discard Thickness	
Metro & Tracker	.315 (8.0)
Prizm	.787 (20.0)

[1] – Information is not available from manufacturer.

REAR DRUM BRAKE SPECIFICATIONS
REAR DRUM BRAKE SPECIFICATIONS

Application	In. (mm)
Brake Lining Minimum Thickness	
Metro & Prizm	.039 (.99)
Tracker	.12 (3.0)
Drum Inside Diameter	
Metro	7.09 (180.0)
Prizm	7.87 (200.0)
Tracker	8.66 (220.0)
Discard Thickness	
Metro	7.17 (182.0)
Prizm	7.91 (201.0)
Tracker	8.74 (222.0)

Tracker

DESCRIPTION

The Rear Wheel Anti-Lock (RWAL) brake system is designed to control braking force of rear wheels. This serves to eliminate wheel lock and maintain directional stability during hard brake application. System consists of a wheel speed sensor (mounted in rear differential), pressure limit valve, RWAL Electronic Brake Control Module (EBCM) and connecting wiring harness.

Power is supplied to the RWAL EBCM through the RWAL power relay. System also utilizes a self-diagnostic function, which enables technician to quickly trouble shoot system by monitoring stored RWAL trouble codes through flashes of the BRAKE warning light.

NOTE: *For information on brake system not covered, see DISC & DRUM article in BRAKES.*

OPERATION

The RWAL EBCM continuously monitors various input signals to determine control of the pressure limit valve and BRAKE warning light. Available input signals include rear wheel speed sensor, stoplight switch, pressure differential switch (located on proportioning/differential valve), monitor coupler signal (diagnostic test), parking brake switch and 4WD switch (if equipped).

RWAL EBCM

Based upon wheel speed input signals, RWAL EBCM controls hydraulic brake pressure to both rear wheels. Under normal conditions, RWAL system functions like a conventional brake system.

Normal wheel speed-to-acceleration/deceleration braking is programmed into RWAL EBCM memory. If the difference between optimum rear wheel braking speed and actual rear wheel braking speed exceeds programmed limits, RWAL system will enter anti-lock mode.

PRESSURE LIMIT VALVE

During anti-lock operation, pressure in rear wheel hydraulic circuit is modulated by EBCM through pressure limit valve. This prevents rear wheel lock, while providing maximum stopping and directional stability. Pressure limit valve is located under the master cylinder and actually consists of 2 valves: a dump valve which releases pressure into an accumulator and an isolation valve which maintains rear wheel hydraulic pressure.

During anti-lock operation, a series of rapid pulsations (caused by the fluctuating position of the pressure limit valve) will be felt at the brake pedal. These pulsations, in conjunction with possible tire "chirping" (on dry pavement), are considered normal during anti-lock operation and will cease when normal braking is resumed or vehicle comes to a complete stop.

WHEEL SPEED SENSOR

The 2-wire rear wheel speed sensor is mounted in the rear differential carrier. Sensor transmits wheel speed information to the RWAL EBCM. This low AC voltage signal is generated through magnetic induction when a toothed exciter ring inside the differential passes the stationary magnetic coil of the sensor. This voltage signal increases in both frequency and amplitude as rear wheel speed increases.

BRAKE WARNING LIGHT

As a bulb check, the BRAKE warning light will turn on when the ignition switch is turned to the BULB CHECK position. Light should go out when ignition switch is turned to the ON position. BRAKE light will also illuminate if parking brake lever is not fully released or if brake fluid level is low.

Should the RWAL system malfunction, RWAL EBCM will turn on the BRAKE warning light and disable the anti-lock function. BRAKE warning light is used to retrieve stored malfunction codes from RWAL sys-

tem by jumpering appropriate terminals of diagnostic connector. See RETRIEVING CODES under DIAGNOSIS & TESTING.

CAUTION: *See ANTI-LOCK BRAKE SAFETY PRECAUTIONS article in GENERAL INFORMATION.*

BLEEDING BRAKE SYSTEM

When bleeding hydraulic system, follow normal manual or pressure bleeding procedures. Rear brakes can only be bled from left rear wheel cylinder. Bleed brakes starting at left rear, then right front and then left front.

ADJUSTMENTS

NOTE: *For adjustment information on push rod, see DISC & DRUM article in BRAKES.*

PEDAL HEIGHT

Remove power brake unit. Measure distance between power brake unit mounting surface with gasket installed and center of brake push rod clevis pin. Correct distance is 4.94" (125.5 mm).

PEDAL TRAVEL

1) With engine off, pump brake pedal until all vacuum is exhausted from power brake unit. Push brake pedal with a force of approximately 66 lbs. (30 kg). Measure distance between brake pedal face and floor.
2) Distance must not be less than 5.1" (130 mm). If measured distance is less than specified, check for air in hydraulic system, worn front brake pads or rear brake shoes, defective rear brake self-adjusters and/or improper brake pedal push rod adjustment.

PEDAL FREE PLAY

1) With engine off, depress brake pedal several times to exhaust vacuum from power brake unit. Depress brake pedal and measure brake pedal travel until initial resistance is felt.
2) Brake pedal free play should be .04-.32" (1.0-8.0 mm). If brake pedal free play is not within specification, check stoplight switch for proper adjustment. See STOPLIGHT SWITCH under ADJUSTMENTS.
3) If stoplight adjustment is okay, check brake pedal push rod and master cylinder pin for looseness. If brake pedal push rod and master cylinder pin are okay, check brake pedal height. See PEDAL HEIGHT under ADJUSTMENTS.

STOPLIGHT SWITCH

Pull up and hold brake pedal. Measure distance between face of brake pedal arm and stoplight switch. Adjust stoplight switch if distance is not .02-.04" (.5-1.0 mm). Tighten stoplight switch lock nut to 10 ft. lbs. (14 N.m).

PARKING BRAKE

NOTE: *Ensure rear brakes are correctly adjusted before adjusting parking brake.*

1) Using 44 lbs. (20 kg), apply parking brake lever, and count number of notches lever travels. Adjustment is okay if lever clicks 7-9 notches.
2) If parking brake cable adjustment is required, remove parking brake lever assembly trim cover. Loosen parking brake cable lock nut. Turn cable adjusting nut as required to obtain correct number of clicks at parking brake lever. After adjustment, check for brake shoe drag with parking brake off.

TROUBLE SHOOTING

To trouble shoot electronic portion of RWAL system, perform RWAL SYSTEM CHECK. *See Fig. 1.*

DIAGNOSIS & TESTING

NOTE: To identify RWAL EBCM connector terminals, see Fig. 3.

RETRIEVING CODES

NOTE: To retrieve trouble codes, BRAKE warning light must function correctly. If BRAKE warning light does not function correctly, perform RWAL system check. See Fig. 1.

CAUTION: Before beginning diagnosis and testing, park vehicle on a level area and place blocks around vehicle wheels to prevent vehicle from moving. If vehicle moves during diagnosis and testing, injury or damage could result.

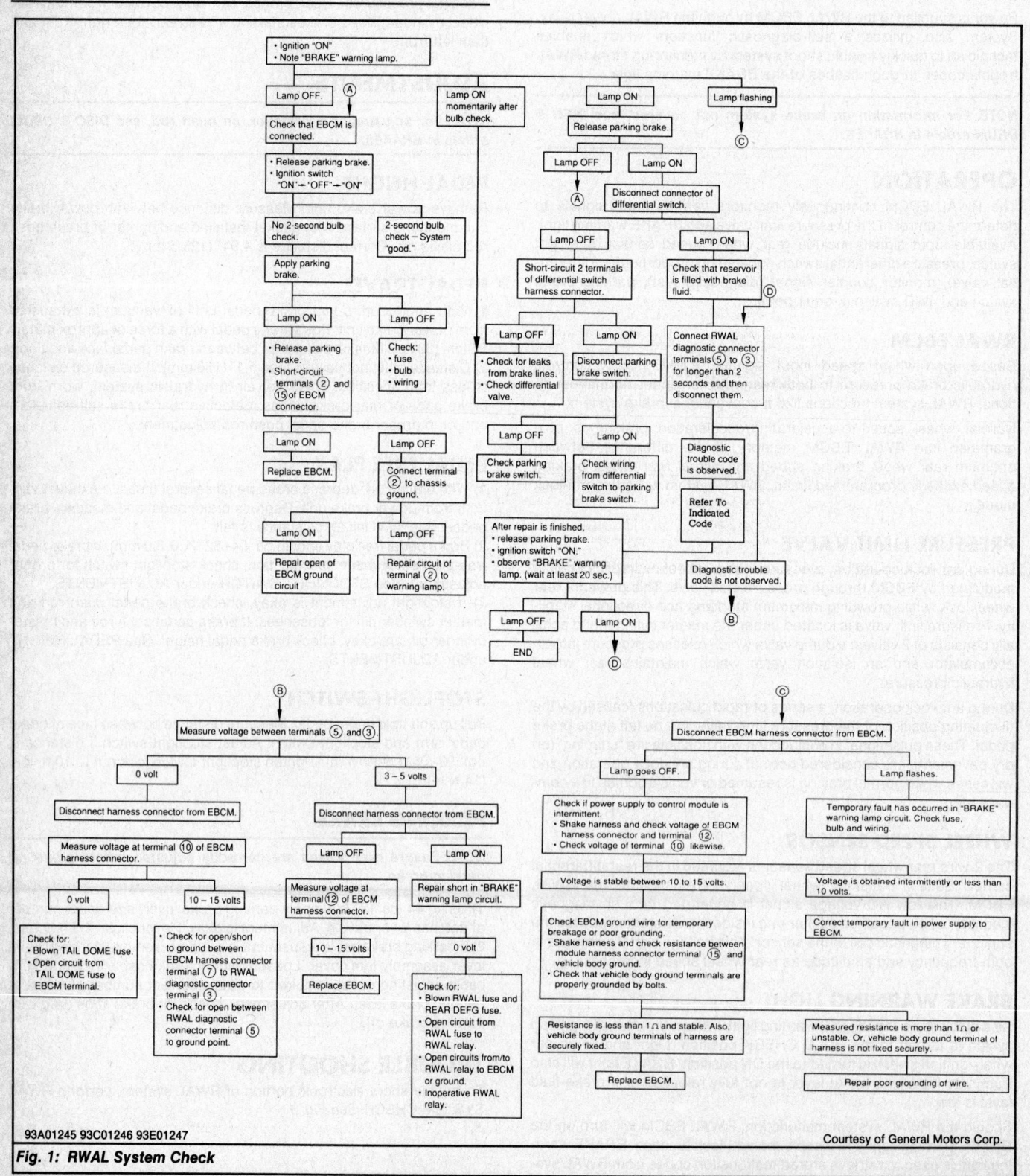

93A01245 93C01246 93E01247

Courtesy of General Motors Corp.

Fig. 1: RWAL System Check

To retrieve stored RWAL trouble codes, release parking brake and ensure brake fluid level is okay. Turn ignition switch to ON position. Connect a jumper wire between terminals No. 3 and No. 5 of 10-pin RWAL diagnostic connector for longer than 2 seconds, then remove jumper wire. *See Fig 2*. The 10-pin diagnostic connector is located under dash, behind RWAL EBCM.

Stored trouble codes are flashed by BRAKE warning light. Trouble codes consist of short flashes followed by one long flash signifying last flash of that code. Count both short flashes and long flash. Trouble codes will flash until ignition switch is turned to OFF position. Trouble code may be lost if ignition is turned to OFF position before trouble code is identified.

See RWAL TROUBLE CODES for identification and testing procedures. If more than one fault is present, only lowest number code will flash repeatedly until it is repaired and cleared from memory. If BRAKE warning light does not operate or self-diagnosis does not pinpoint fault, proceed to RWAL SYSTEM CHECK. *See Fig. 1*.

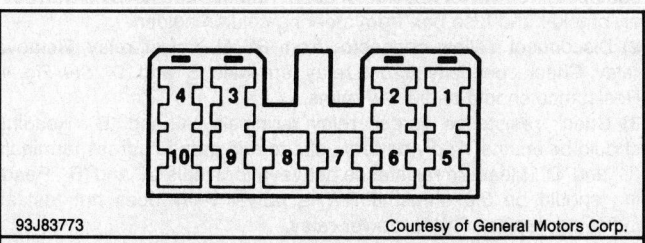

93J83773   Courtesy of General Motors Corp.

Fig. 2: Identifying RWAL Data Link Connector Terminals

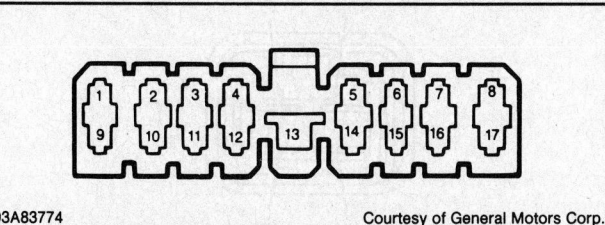

93A83774   Courtesy of General Motors Corp.

Fig. 3: Identifying RWAL Electronic Brake Control Module Connector Terminals

CLEARING TROUBLE CODES

To clear all trouble codes, turn ignition switch to OFF after trouble code diagnostics has been entered. Only Codes 4 and 5 will store as "hard" codes. To clear Code 4 or 5, disconnect negative battery cable for at least 5 seconds.

RWAL TROUBLE CODES

RWAL TROUBLE CODE IDENTIFICATION

Code	Condition/Circuit
2	Open Isolation Solenoid Circuit
3	Open Dump Solenoid Circuit
4	Limit Valve Reset Switch Closed
5	Excessive Dump Valve Action
6	[1] Wheel Speed Sensor Signal Changed Rapidly
7	Shorted Isolation Solenoid Circuit
8	Shorted Dump Solenoid Circuit
9	Open Rear Wheel Speed Sensor Circuit
10	[2] Stoplight Switch On Constantly
11	Shorted Rear Wheel Speed Sensor
13	RWAL EBCM Malfunction

[1] – This condition is only detected at speeds greater than 35 MPH.
[2] – This condition is only detected at speeds greater than 38 MPH.

Code 2, Open Isolation Solenoid Circuit – 1) Turn ignition off. Disconnect RWAL EBCM connector. Measure resistance between EBCM harness connector terminal No. 1 (Green wire) and ground. *See Fig. 3*.
2) If resistance reading is 3-6 ohms, check RWAL EBCM connections. If connections are okay, replace RWAL EBCM.

3) If resistance reading is greater than 6 ohms, disconnect pressure limit valve connector. Measure resistance between limit valve isolation solenoid terminal No. 1 (Green wire) and ground terminal No. 4 (Black wire).
4) If resistance is now 3-6 ohms, repair open in harness Green or Black wire. If resistance is greater than 6 ohms, isolation solenoid winding is open. Replace pressure limit valve.
Code 3, Open Dump Solenoid Circuit – 1) Turn ignition off. Disconnect RWAL EBCM connector. Measure resistance between RWAL EBCM terminal No. 9 (White/Green wire) and ground.
2) If resistance reading is 1-3 ohms, check RWAL EBCM connections. If connections are okay, replace RWAL EBCM.
3) If resistance reading is greater than 3 ohms, disconnect pressure limit valve connector. Measure resistance between limit valve connector terminal No. 3 (White/Green wire) and connector ground terminal No. 4 (Black wire).
4) If resistance is now 1-3 ohms, repair open in harness White/Green or Black wire. If resistance is greater than 3 ohms, dump solenoid winding is open. Replace pressure limit valve.
Code 4, Limit Valve Reset Switch Closed – 1) Turn ignition off. Disconnect RWAL EBCM connector. Measure resistance between EBCM harness connector terminal No. 4 (Blue wire) and ground.
2) If resistance reading is greater than 10,000 ohms, check RWAL EBCM connections. If connections are okay, replace RWAL EBCM. If resistance reading is less than 10,000 ohms, disconnect pressure limit valve connector.
3) Measure resistance between pressure limit valve reset switch connector (switch side) terminal No. 2 (Blue wire) and No. 4 (Black wire). If resistance is less than 10,000 ohms, replace pressure limit valve.
4) If resistance is greater than 10,000 ohms, measure resistance between pressure limit valve connector (harness side) terminal No. 2 (Blue wire) and ground. If resistance is less than 100,000 ohms, repair short to ground in Blue wire of harness.
5) If resistance is greater than 100,000 ohms, firmly depress brake pedal. Measure resistance between limit valve connector (valve side) terminals No. 2 (Blue wire) and No. 4 (Black wire). If resistance is less than 10,000 ohms, replace pressure limit valve. If resistance is greater than 10,000 ohms, replace RWAL EBCM.
Code 5, Excessive Dump Valve Action – 1) Ensure rear brakes are not dragging. If rear brakes are dragging, repair mechanical problem before proceeding with electronic testing. If rear brakes are not dragging on 2WD models, go to step **4)**. If rear brakes are not dragging on 4WD models, go to next step.
2) If rear brakes are not dragging on 4WD models, turn ignition off and disconnect RWAL EBCM connector. Shift into 4WD. Turn ignition on.
3) Measure voltage at RWAL EBCM harness connector terminal No. 3 (Orange/Black wire). If reading is less than one volt, go to next step. If reading is greater than one volt, repair 4WD switch or open in Orange/Black wire between RWAL EBCM, 4WD switch and 4WD indicator light.
4) On 2WD and 4WD vehicles, replace pressure limit valve. Clear Code 5. See CLEARING TROUBLE CODES. Drive vehicle in 2WD setting. In a safe area, firmly apply brakes and ensure rear wheels do not lock.
Code 6, Wheel Speed Sensor Signal Changed Rapidly – 1) Turn ignition off. Disconnect RWAL EBCM connector. Check resistance between EBCM terminals No. 16 (Orange wire) and No. 17 (White wire) while wiggling wire harness between sensor and RWAL EBCM. If reading is not 1000-2000 ohms and steady, go to step **4)**.
2) If reading is 1000-2000 ohms and steady, remove speed sensor from rear differential case. Inspect tip of sensor for metal particles. If metal particles are present, replace sensor and go to next step.
3) Inspect exciter ring through sensor hole in differential case. Rotate exciter ring and check for damaged teeth and lateral runout. If exciter ring is damaged or lateral runout is present, replace exciter ring. If exciter ring is okay, go to step **6)**.
4) If resistance between terminals No. 16 (Orange wire) and No. 17 (White wire) of RWAL EBCM connector is not 1000-2000 ohms and steady, disconnect speed sensor connector. Measure resistance across sensor connector terminals. If resistance is 1000-2000 ohms, repair open or short in White wire and/or Orange wire between RWAL EBCM and speed sensor. Ensure connector is clean and tight.

5) If resistance is greater than 2000 ohms or less than 1000 ohms, replace wheel speed sensor. After replacing speed sensor, ensure sensor output voltage is greater than 650 millivolts using procedure described in step **6)**.

6) On all models, install speed sensor and connect connector. Reconnect RWAL EBCM connector. Raise vehicle, and support with rear wheels off of floor. Ensure vehicle is in 2H mode (2WD). Start engine, and turn wheels a least 20 MPH. Backprobe between RWAL EBCM terminals No. 16 (Orange wire) and No. 17 (White wire) using a 1-megohm DVOM on AC-volts scale.

7) If voltage reading is greater than 650 millivolts and steady, replace RWAL EBCM. If voltage reading is less than 650 millivolts or is erratic, replace wheel speed sensor.

Code 7, Shorted Isolation Solenoid Circuit – **1)** Turn ignition off. Disconnect pressure limit valve connector. Measure resistance between pressure limit valve connector terminals No. 1 (Green wire) and No. 4 (Black wire).

2) If resistance is less than 3 ohms, replace pressure limit valve. If resistance is 3-6 ohms, disconnect RWAL EBCM connector. Measure resistance between RWAL EBCM harness connector terminal No. 1 (Green wire) and ground.

3) If resistance is greater than 20,000 ohms, replace RWAL EBCM. If resistance is less than 20,000 ohms, repair short to ground in RWAL EBCM harness Green wire.

Code 8, Shorted Dump Solenoid Circuit – **1)** Turn ignition off. Disconnect pressure limit valve connector. Measure resistance between pressure limit valve connector terminals No. 3 (White/Green wire) and No. 4 (Black wire).

2) If resistance is less than one ohm, replace pressure limit valve. If resistance is 1-3 ohms, disconnect RWAL EBCM connector. Measure resistance between RWAL EBCM harness connector terminal No. 9 (White/Green wire) and ground.

3) If resistance is greater than 20,000 ohms, replace RWAL EBCM. If resistance is less than 20,000 ohms, repair short to ground in RWAL EBCM harness White/Green wire.

Code 9, Open Rear Wheel Speed Sensor Circuit – **1)** Turn ignition off. Disconnect speed sensor connector. Measure resistance across speed sensor terminals. If resistance is greater than 2000 ohms, replace speed sensor.

2) If resistance is 1000-2000 ohms, disconnect RWAL EBCM connector. Reconnect speed sensor connector. Measure resistance between RWAL EBCM terminals No. 16 (Orange wire) and No. 17 (White wire). If resistance is greater than 2000 ohms, repair open in speed sensor wiring. If resistance is 1000-2000 ohms, replace RWAL EBCM.

Code 10, Stoplight Switch On Constantly – **1)** Turn ignition off. Disconnect RWAL EBCM harness connector from RWAL EBCM. Turn ignition on. Measure voltage between RWAL EBCM harness connector terminal No. 8 (Green/White wire) and ground.

2) If reading is less than 10 volts, replace RWAL EBCM. If reading is 10-15 volts, replace or adjust stoplight switch or repair short to voltage in Green/White wire between RWAL EBCM, stoplight switch and stoplights.

Code 11, Shorted Rear Wheel Speed Sensor – **1)** Turn ignition off. Disconnect speed sensor connector, and measure resistance across sensor terminals. If resistance is less than 1000 ohms, replace speed sensor.

2) If resistance is 1000-2000 ohms, disconnect RWAL EBCM connector. Measure resistance between RWAL EBCM terminal No. 16 (Orange wire) and chassis ground. If resistance is less than 20,000 ohms, repair short to ground in Orange wire.

3) If resistance is greater than 20,000 ohms, measure resistance between RWAL EBCM terminals No. 16 (Orange wire) and No. 17 (White wire). If resistance is greater than 20,000 ohms, replace RWAL EBCM. If resistance is less than 20,000 ohms, repair short between Orange and White wires in speed sensor harness.

Code 13, RWAL EBCM Malfunction – Replace RWAL EBCM.

WHEEL SPEED SENSOR

Remove wheel speed sensor from differential. Using a DVOM, measure resistance across sensor terminals and between terminals and sensor body. Resistance between terminals at 77°F (25°C) should be 1282.5-1567.5 ohms. Replace wheel speed sensor if resistance between sensor terminals and sensor body is less than 100,000 ohms. Ensure tip of sensor is free of metal particles.

STOPLIGHT SWITCH

Disconnect stoplight switch connector. Connect ohmmeter across switch terminals. With brake pedal depressed, continuity should exist between switch terminals. With brake pedal released, continuity should not exist.

RWAL POWER RELAY

1) Disconnect negative battery cable. Remove radio speaker (if equipped) from lower left side of dash. Remove engine ECM with cover, bracket and fuse box from steering column holder.

2) Disconnect Yellow connector from RWAL power relay. Remove relay. Check continuity across relay terminals "B" and "D". See Fig. 4. Resistance should be 90-110 ohms.

3) Check resistance across relay terminals "A" and "B". Reading should be infinite. Apply battery voltage and ground across terminals "C" and "D". Measure resistance between terminals "A" and "B". Reading should be 3.0 ohms. If RWAL power relay does not test as indicated, replace RWAL power relay.

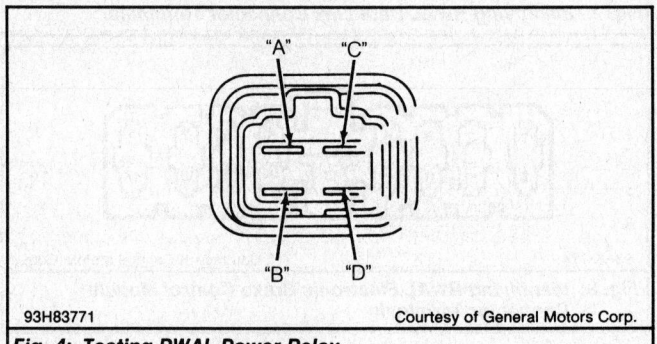

93H83771　　　　　　　　　　Courtesy of General Motors Corp.

Fig. 4: Testing RWAL Power Relay

PRESSURE LIMIT VALVE

1) Disconnect pressure limit valve connector. Check resistance of isolation valve solenoid winding between ISO and GND terminals. *See Fig. 5.* If resistance is not 3-6 ohms at approximately 68°F (20°C), replace pressure limit valve.

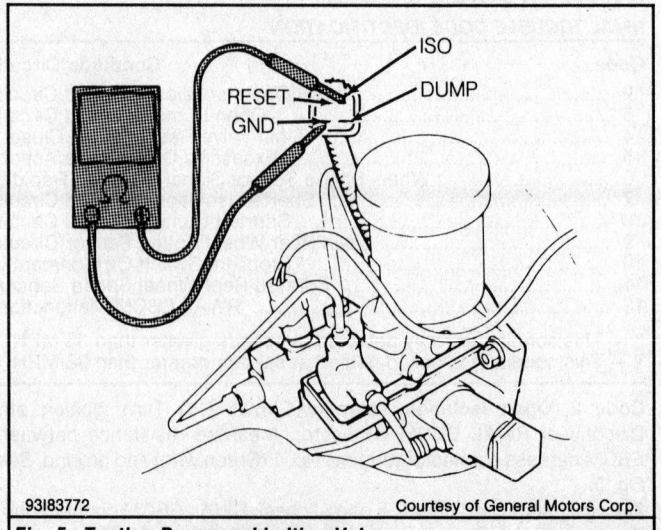

93I83772　　　　　　　　　　Courtesy of General Motors Corp.

Fig. 5: Testing Pressure Limiting Valve

RWAL EBCM PIN VOLTAGES

Terminal No.	Circuit	Normal Voltage	Condition
1	Isolation Solenoid	0	During Normal Driving
		10-15	During Hard Braking
2	BRAKE Warning Light	10-15	When BRAKE Light Is Off
		0-3	When BRAKE Light Is On
3	4WD Signal	10-15	In 2WD
		0-0.5	In 4WD
4	Valve Reset Switch	4-5	During Normal Driving
		0-0.5	During Hard Braking
5	Not Used	....	.....
6	Not Used	....	.....
7	Diagnostic Test	3-5	When Terminal Is Open
		0-0.5	When Terminal Is Grounded
8	Stoplight Switch	0-0.5	With Pedal Released
		10-15	With Pedal Depressed
9	Dump Valve Solenoid	0	Normal Driving
10	Power Supply (Battery)	10-15	Normal Condition
12	Power Supply (Ignition)	10-15	With Ignition On
15	EBCM Ground	0	Normal Condition
16 & 17	Wheel Speed Sensor	[1] 3.5	At About 20 MPH

[1] – Approximate AC voltage.

2) Check resistance of dump valve solenoid winding between pressure limit valve DUMP and GND terminals. If resistance is not 1-3 ohms at approximately 68°F (20°C), replace pressure limit valve.
3) Check resistance of reset switch across RESET terminal and pressure limit valve body. Resistance reading should be infinite. If any resistance value is not within specification, replace pressure limit valve as an assembly.

RWAL SYSTEM ELECTRICAL CIRCUIT CHECK

1) Remove RWAL EBCM from under dash so rear of harness connector can be accessed with a DVOM. See RWAL ELECTRONIC BRAKE CONTROL MODULE under REMOVAL & INSTALLATION.
2) Check voltage at each terminal of connector under conditions described in RWAL EBCM PIN VOLTAGES table. See Fig. 3.

REMOVAL & INSTALLATION

RWAL ELECTRONIC BRAKE CONTROL MODULE

Removal – Disconnect negative battery cable. Remove engine ECM with cover, bracket and fuse box from steering column holder. Disconnect RWAL EBCM connector. Remove RWAL EBCM from dash panel.
Installation – Install RWAL EBCM to dash panel. Tighten nuts to 35 INCH lbs. (4 N.m). If specified torque cannot be obtained, replace nuts with new ones. DO NOT overtighten nuts.

WHEEL SPEED SENSOR

Removal – Turn ignition off. Raise and support vehicle. Remove sensor cover on rear differential. Unplug sensor connector. Remove sensor retaining bolt. Remove sensor.

Installation – To install, reverse removal procedure. Replace "O" ring if damaged. Ensure tip of sensor is free of metal particles. Coat "O" ring with differential lubricant. Tighten sensor retaining bolt to specification. See TORQUE SPECIFICATIONS.

PRESSURE LIMIT & PRESSURE/DIFFERENTIAL VALVES

Removal – 1) Disconnect negative battery cable. Remove air cleaner. Disconnect master cylinder fluid level sensor connector. Clean outside of brake fluid reservoir. Using a syringe, remove as much fluid from reservoir as possible. Remove heat shield. Unplug pressure/differential valve electrical connector. Unplug pressure limit valve electrical connector.
2) Disconnect brake hydraulic lines which lead from master cylinder to wheels. Remove heat protector bolt from master cylinder bracket. Remove 2 master cylinder attaching bolts. Remove master cylinder, pressure/differential valve and pressure limit valve assembly from vehicle. Remove pressure limit valve. Remove pressure/differential valve.
Installation – To install valves, reverse removal procedure. Tighten nuts and hydraulic flare fittings to specification. See TORQUE SPECIFICATIONS.

TORQUE SPECIFICATIONS

TORQUE SPECIFICATIONS

Application	Ft. Lbs. (N.m)
Tubing Flare Nuts	12 (16)
Wheel Speed Sensor Bolt	17 (23)
4WD Switch	15 (20)

	INCH Lbs. (N.m)
Master Cylinder Nuts	89-142 (10-16)
RWAL EBCM Nuts	35 (4)

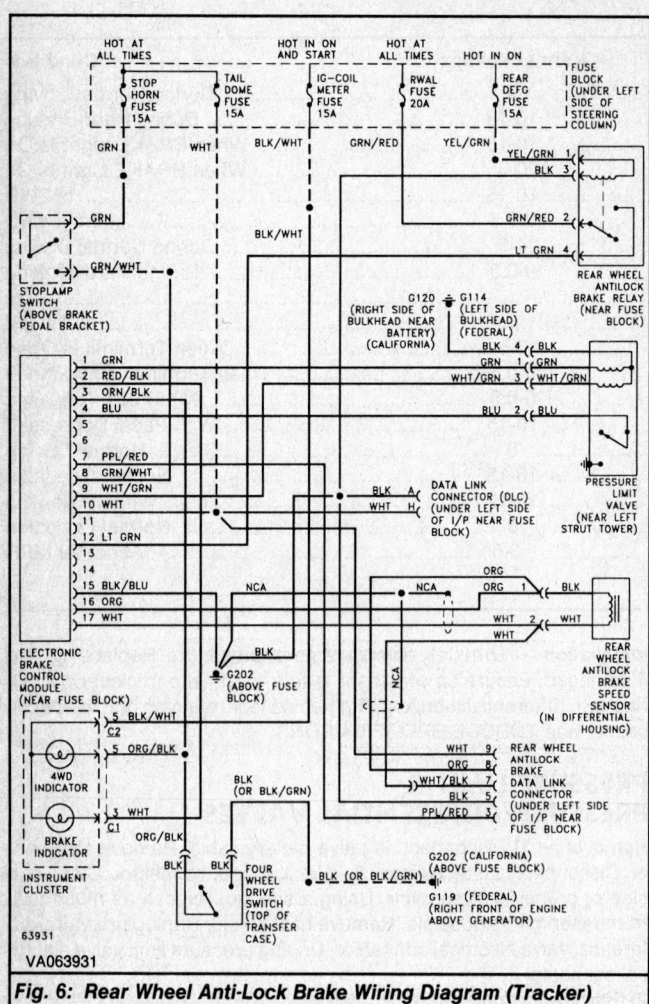

Fig. 6: Rear Wheel Anti-Lock Brake Wiring Diagram (Tracker)

DESCRIPTION

Prizm is equipped with ABS VI anti-lock brake system. ABS-VI system uses electric motors to modulate displacement pistons. Anti-Lock Brake System (ABS) operates on each front wheel and both rear wheels. ABS-VI system consists of Electronic Brake Control Module (EBCM), system enable relay, 4 wheel speed sensors, hydraulic unit, 3 warning light and brake switch.

EBCM uses signals from wheel speed sensor to determine when a wheel is about to lockup and adjust hydraulic pressure to maintain optimum braking. ABS-VI cannot increase brake pressure greater than master cylinder pressure generated by driver. ABS-VI cannot apply brakes by itself.

NOTE: For more information on brake system, see appropriate DISC & DRUM article.

OPERATION

ELECTRONIC BRAKE CONTROL MODULE (EBCM)

EBCM, located under carpet on right side floorboard, monitors speed of each wheel to determine if a wheel is beginning to lock when brakes are applied. If a locking condition is detected, brake pressure is adjusted to that particular wheel to provide for maximum braking without wheel lock.

HYDRAULIC UNIT

Hydraulic unit is mounted in right front section of engine compartment. Hydraulic unit components consist of 3 motors, 2 solenoid valves (front calipers), pressure control pistons and check valves.

Check Valve – Check valve controls brake fluid flow into piston chamber. System brake pressure is limited to pressure generated by master cylinder when ABS is activated. If brake pressure at wheels becomes greater than master cylinder pressure, check valve unseats and brake fluid returns to master cylinder until pressure is equalized. If ABS was activated during low brake pressure, such as on ice, pressure control piston on front brakes will be driven to top of chamber. Check valve will be unseated and system returned to base braking pressure until wheel lockup occurs again.

Motor – Motor operates pressure control piston based on EBCM signal.

Pressure Control Piston – Pressure control piston is used to increase or decrease brake pressure to each front caliper or both rear wheel cylinders.

Solenoid Valve – Solenoid valve is used on front caliper brake to isolate pressure path. When solenoid valve is closed it holds caliper fluid pressure to front disc brake as determined by EBCM signal.

ABS ENABLE RELAY

ABS enable relay is a normally-open contact type mounted on right front section of engine compartment next to hydraulic unit. ABS enable relay provides battery voltage to EBCM from 50-amp ABS fusible link, which provides power to motors and solenoids during braking. ABS enable relay is energized when brake switch is closed.

ABS, ABS ACTIVE & BRAKE WARNING LIGHTS

Amber ABS, Blue ABS ACTIVE and Red BRAKE warning lights are located on instrument panel. ABS and ABS ACTIVE lights will illuminate during engine start for about 3 seconds. The Red BRAKE warning light will quickly flash on also.

Red BRAKE light will stay on if parking brake is on, brake fluid is low, and when ignition is on and engine is off. EBCM will also turn Red BRAKE light on when it does not control engine or when an ABS malfunction could interfere with normal brake operation. Blue ABS ACTIVE light will come on when vehicle in involved in an ABS stop. If Amber ABS light stays on, a malfunction is present in ABS system. If Amber ABS light flashes, ABS malfunction is affecting normal brake operation and EBCM can not turn Red BRAKE light on. Anti-lock braking function will be disabled until system is repaired.

WHEEL SPEED SENSOR

Wheel speed sensor is attached to steering knuckle on front wheels and on rear suspension knuckles on rear wheels, and consists of a sensor and a toothed sensor ring. *See Fig. 1 or 3.* Air gap is not adjustable and sensor is not repairable. Front outside drive axle or rear hub and bearing assembly must be replaced if sensor ring is damaged.

CAUTION: See ANTI-LOCK BRAKE SAFETY PRECAUTIONS article in GENERAL INFORMATION.

BLEEDING BRAKE SYSTEM

NOTE: Use DOT 3 brake fluid. DO NOT use DOT 5 (silicone) brake fluid.

NOTE: For all diagnostic and component function testing, manufacturer recommends using a TK-0-A TECH 1 Modular Diagnostic System (Tech 1).

BLEEDING PRECAUTIONS

Before bleeding system, the front and rear displacement cylinder pistons must be returned to the top-most (home) position. A Tech 1 Scan Tester (Tech 1) is required to re-home displacement cylinder pistons. Any stored Diagnostic Trouble Code (DTC) must be cleared and system malfunctions repaired before performing motor re-home function.

ABS Motor Re-Homing Procedure – 1) Raise and support vehicle so drive wheels are off the ground. Start engine and engage drive wheels. Operate to about 3 MPH for at least 10 seconds.

2) Observe ABS indicator. Ensure indicator goes off in about 3 seconds. If ABS indicator stays on, diagnose malfunction before proceeding. If ABS indicator turns off, stop engine and repeat steps **1)** and **2)** before proceeding to next step.

3) Using Tech 1, enter manual control function and apply front and rear motors. The entire brake system should now be ready for bleeding. See BLEEDING PROCEDURES. After bleeding system, go to next step.

4) Turn ignition on. Depress brake pedal with moderate force and hold in position. Note pedal travel and feel. If pedal travel feels firm and constant, go to next step. If pedal feels soft or has excessive travel either initially or after starting engine, go to step **6)**.

5) Start engine. Recheck pedal travel. If pedal is still firm and constant and travel is not excessive, road test vehicle. Make several normal (non-ABS) stops from moderate speed to ensure proper brake function.

6) Using Tech 1, release then apply motors 3 times and cycle solenoid 10 times. Apply motors to ensure pistons are in the home position. Repeat bleeding procedure.

BLEEDING PROCEDURES

NOTE: Frequently check brake fluid level in master cylinder during bleeding sequence.

CAUTION: DO NOT release brake pedal until bleeder screw has been tightened.

Manual Bleeding – 1) Using Tech 1, re-home ABS motors. See ABS MOTOR RE-HOMING PROCEDURE under BLEEDING PRECAUTIONS. Clean master cylinder cap and surrounding area, then remove cap. Fill master cylinder and install cap.

2) Bleed hydraulic modulator. Attach clear vinyl bleeder hose to rear bleeder valve on hydraulic modulator. Place other end of hose in clean, transparent container. Partially fill container with clean brake fluid until end of hose is submerged in fluid.

3) Open bleeder valve about one half turn. Depress brake pedal and hold. Close bleeder valve and release brake pedal. Wait 5 seconds before repeating procedure. Repeat step **2)** to bleed hydraulic modulator front bleeder valve. When fluid flows from both hydraulic modulator bleeder valves, bleed wheels.

4) Ensure master cylinder is full. Install clear vinyl bleeder hose onto first wheel bleeder screw to be serviced. See BRAKE LINE BLEEDING SEQUENCE table. Place other end of hose in clean, transparent container. Partially fill container with clean brake fluid so end of hose is submerged in fluid. Open bleeder screw and slowly depress brake pedal and hold.

5) Close bleeder screw, and release pedal. Gently pump pedal several times to push air toward wheel cylinders. Repeat procedure until flow of brake fluid is clear and bubble free. Proceed to next bleeder screw. See BRAKE LINE BLEEDING SEQUENCE table. Add brake fluid to master cylinder after bleeding all wheels. Because air may still be trapped in hydraulic modulator, repeat steps **1) to 3)** without bleeding wheels.

Pressure Tank Bleeding – 1) Clean master cylinder cap and surrounding area, and remove cap. With pressure tank at least 1/2 full, charge tank to 20-25 psi (1.4-1.8 Kg/cm²). Connect pressure tank to master cylinder using proper adapter(s). Start engine and allow it to idle.

2) Bleed hydraulic modulator. Attach clear vinyl bleeder hose to rear bleeder valve on hydraulic modulator. Place other end of hose in clean, transparent container. Partially fill container with clean brake fluid until end of hose is submerged in fluid.

3) Open release valve on pressure tank. Open bleeder screw about one half turn, noting fluid flow. When fluid flowing into container is clear and bubble free, close bleeder screw securely. Repeat step **2)** to bleed hydraulic modulator front bleeder valve. When fluid flows from both hydraulic modulator bleeder valves without air bubbles, bleed wheels.

4) Attach vinyl bleeder hose to first bleeder screw to be serviced. See BRAKE LINE BLEEDING SEQUENCE table. Place other end of hose in clean, transparent container. Partially fill container with clean brake fluid until end of hose is submerged in fluid.

5) Open release valve on pressure tank. Open bleeder screw, noting fluid flow. When fluid flowing into container is clear and bubble free, close bleeder screw securely. Finish bleeding system, in the same manner, using appropriate sequence. Close release valve, and remove pressure tank from master cylinder. Check master cylinder reservoir fluid level.

BRAKE LINE BLEEDING SEQUENCE

Application	Sequence
Prizm	RR, LR, RF, LF

DIAGNOSIS & TESTING

ABS FUNCTION TEST

1) Turn ignition to LOCK position. Raise and support vehicle. Install Tech 1. Turn ignition on. Pump brake pedal to deplete vacuum from power booster. Select a channel to test left front, right front or rear brakes.

2) Firmly depress brake pedal. Pedal should remain high and firm. Have an assistant attempt to rotate wheel being tested. If wheel does not rotate, base brake apply is functioning properly.

3) With brake pedal still depressed, press UP arrow button on scan tester to begin test. Tech 1 will display RELEASE and assistant should be able to rotate wheel for about 2 seconds. Brake pedal should remain high and firm. If brake pedal height drops, ensure solenoid harness connectors are connected to correct solenoid.

4) Tech 1 will switch to hold mode and display HOLD. With brake pedal still depressed, have an assistant attempt to rotate wheel. Wheel should rotate with little or no resistance for the full 18 seconds of the test. After 18 seconds, brake pressure will be applied, and a slight bump may be felt in brake pedal. Wheel should not be able to be turned at this point.

RETRIEVING CODES

NOTE: DTCs can only be retrieved through the use of Tech 1. There is no provision for "flash code" diagnostics.

ABS SYMPTOM TABLE

Chart [1]	Symptom
A	ABS Amber Indicator On Constantly, No DTC's Stored
B	ABS Amber Indicator On Intermittently, No DTC's Stored
C	ABS Amber Indicator Off Constantly, No DTC's Stored
D	TECH-1 Displays Undefined DTC's
E	ABS Active Indicator Malfunctioning

[1] – See DIAGNOSTIC CIRCUIT CHECK.

ABS DIAGNOSTIC TROUBLE CODE IDENTIFICATION

Code	System Affected
A014	ABS Enable Relay Circuit Open
A015	ABS Enable Relay Circuit Shorted To Battery Or Always Closed
A016	ABS Enable Relay Coil Circuit Open
A017	ABS Enable Relay Coil Circuit Shorted To Ground
A018	ABS Enable Relay Coil Circuit Shorted To Battery Voltage
A021	Left Front Wheel Speed=0 Or Unreasonable
A022	Right Front Wheel Speed=0 Or Unreasonable
A023	Left Rear Wheel Speed=0 Or Unreasonable
A024	Right Rear Wheel Speed=0 Or Unreasonable
A025	Left Front Excessive Wheel Speed Variation
A026	Right Front Excessive Wheel Speed Variation
A027	Left Rear Excessive Wheel Speed Variation
A028	Right Rear Excessive Wheel Speed Variation
A036	Low System Voltage
A037	High System Voltage
A038	Left Front ESB Will Not Hold Motor
A041	Right Front ESB Will Not Hold Motor
A042	Rear ESB Will Not Hold Motor
A044	Left Front Channel Will Not Move
A045	Right Front Channel Will Not Move
A046	Rear Channel Will Not Move
A047	Left Front Motor Free Spins
A048	Right Front Motor Free Spins
A051	Rear Axle Motor Free Spins
A052	Left Front Channel In Release Too Long
A053	Left Front Channel In Release Too Long
A054	Rear Axle Channel In Release Too Long
A055	EBCM Malfunction
A056	Left Front Motor Circuit Open
A057	Left Front Motor Circuit Shorted To Ground
A058	Left Front Motor Circuit Shorted To Battery
A061	Right Front Motor Circuit Open
A062	Right Front Motor Circuit Shorted To Ground
A063	Right Front Motor Circuit Shorted To Battery
A064	Rear Motor Circuit Open
A065	Rear Motor Circuit Shorted To Ground
A066	Rear Motor Circuit Shorted To Battery
A076	Left Front Solenoid Circuit Open Or Shorted To Battery
A077	Left Front Solenoid Circuit Shorted To Ground
A078	Right Front Solenoid Circuit Open Or Shorted To Battery
A081	Right Front Solenoid Circuit Shorted To Ground
A082	Calibration Malfunction
A086	EBCM Turned On The Red Brake Warning Light
A087	Red Brake Warning Indicator Light Circuit Open
A088	Red Brake Warning Indicator Light Circuit Shorted To Battery
A091	Open Brake Switch During Deceleration
A092	Open Brake Switch When ABS Was Required
A093	Code A091 Or A092 Set In Current Or Previous Ignition Cycle
A094	Brake Switch Contacts Always Closed
A095	Brake Switch Circuit Open
A096	Rear Brakelight Circuit Open

CLEARING CODES

NOTE: EBCM will not permit clearing of codes until all DTCs have been displayed. DTCs cannot be cleared by disconnecting ECBM, battery terminals or turning ignition switch to LOCK position.

Tech 1 must be used to clear DTCs by selecting "F2" for trouble codes. After viewing all DTCs, scan tester will prompt "Clear Codes?". Hit "Yes" and scan tester will then read "History Data Will Be Lost. Clear Codes?". Hit "Yes" again and DTCs will be cleared.

Although not an acceptable method for clearing trouble codes, DTCs will also clear after 100 DTC free drive cycles. A drive cycle occurs when ignition is turned on and vehicle is driven at greater than 10 MPH.

MOTOR TESTING

NOTE: Test described is for operation of front motors. Rear motor can be tested in similar manner, except for a slight pedal drop and rise (bump) during test.

1) Turn ignition to LOCK position. Install Tech 1 with Mass Storage Cartridge (MSC). Turn on ignition, engine off. Pump brake pedal several times to deplete vacuum reserve. Depress and hold brake pedal.
2) Using scan tester, release one of the motors. Brake pedal should drop smoothly. As pedal drops, feedback current should momentarily drop to only a few amps (indicated motor movement) and then equalize to command current (6 amps). This indicates motor is no longer moving since piston has bottomed out.
3) A rough or jumpy pedal movement indicates an intermittent motor connection. With brake pedal still depressed, apply the same motor. Brake pedal should smoothly rise back to the top of its travel. Feedback current should momentarily drop to a few amps, then quickly increase to command current (10 amps). This indicates motor is no longer moving since piston reached the top of its travel.
4) If brake pedal does not move both up and down as indicated and no DTCs are present, monitor the feedback current closely while performing the test again. If feedback current is only a few amps, motor is free spinning. Separate motor pack from hydraulic unit to diagnose problem. See MOTOR PACK FUNCTION TEST.

MOTOR PACK FUNCTION TEST

Remove hydraulic modulator/motor pack assembly and separate motor pack from hydraulic modulator. Using Tech 1, rotate each motor in both directions. If any motor does rotate in either direction, replace motor pack. If all 3 motors operate, rotate each gear on hydraulic modulator. If gear does not move, see NO GEAR MOVEMENT TEST.

NO GEAR MOVEMENT TEST

1) Remove hydraulic modulator/motor pack assembly and separate motor pack from hydraulic modulator. Rotate each gear by hand on hydraulic modulator. Front gears (non center gear) should rotate about 5 full turns lock-to-lock. If gear does not turn freely or at least 5 turns are not possible, replace hydraulic modulator.
2) The rear gear should rotate about 4 turns. If gear does not turn freely or at least 4 turns are not possible, replace hydraulic modulator.

SOLENOID TEST

NOTE: Solenoid test should only be used when no DTC's are stored and a leaky solenoid or check valve is suspected.

1) Turn ignition to LOCK position. Install Tech 1 with Mass Storage Cartridge (MSC). Turn ignition on, engine off. Pump brake pedal several times to deplete vacuum reserve. Select left front or right front. Release motor on channel being tested. Select solenoid for the same channel.
2) With no brake pressure applied, turn solenoid on. Depress brake pedal. If brake pedal is high and firm, go to next step. If brake pedal sinks to the floor, go to step **4)**. solenoid is leaking and not closing or check ball is leaking.
3) With brake pressure still applied, turn solenoid off. If brake pedal sinks to floor, solenoid operation is normal. If brake pedal does not sink to floor, go to step **4)**.
4) Ensure solenoid connectors are connected to correct solenoids (right front solenoid is on the rear of modulator, closest to brake power booster). If connections are incorrect, switch solenoid connectors, go to step **1)** and repeat testing to channel in question. If connections are correct, switch solenoids, go to step **1)** and repeat testing to channel in question. When second testing is complete, go to next step.

5) If channel works properly, test the other channel. If this channel fail testing, replace solenoid currently installed in this channel. If test fails for the same channel, the check valve is leaking. Replace hydraulic modulator. When testing is complete, bleed hydraulic brake system. See BLEEDING BRAKE SYSTEM.

REMOVAL & INSTALLATION

ELECTRONIC BRAKE CONTROL MODULE (EBCM)

Removal & Installation – EBCM is located under carpet on right floorboard. Disconnect negative battery terminal. Loosen passenger compartment floor carpet from under dashboard. Pull carpet to expose ECBM cover panel. Disconnect EBCM connector. Remove EBCM. To install, reverse removal procedure. Tighten all fasteners to specification. See TORQUE SPECIFICATIONS table.

FRONT WHEEL SPEED SENSOR

Removal & Installation – **1)** Disconnect battery negative terminal. Raise and support vehicle. Remove wheelhousing from wheelwell. Disconnect wheel speed sensor connector. Remove 3 speed sensor cable bolts.
2) Remove wheel speed sensor bolt on steering knuckle. Remove wheel speed sensor. See Fig. 1. To install, reverse removal procedure. Tighten all fasteners to specification. See TORQUE SPECIFICATIONS table.

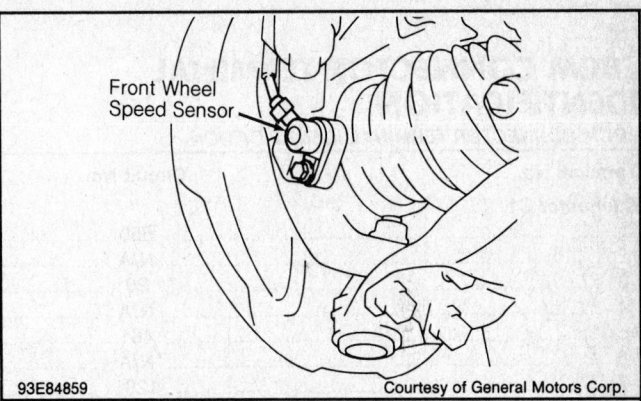

Front Wheel Speed Sensor

93E84859   Courtesy of General Motors Corp.

Fig. 1: Removing Front Wheel Speed Sensor

HYDRAULIC MODULATOR

CAUTION: When displacement cylinder pistons are in HOME position, each motor has a prevailing torque or gear tension. To avoid injury or component damage, relieve hydraulic modulator gear tension before removing unit from vehicle. Using Tech 1, perform GEAR TENSION RELIEF FUNCTION according to TECH-1 manufacturer instructions.

Removal & Installation – **1)** Using Tech 1, perform GEAR TENSION RELIEF FUNCTION. Refer to tester manufacturer instructions.
2) Disconnect negative battery terminal. Disconnect harness connectors from hydraulic modulator. Protect motor pack and connectors using shop towels placed under assembly to catch brake fluid. Disconnect and plug all brake lines hydraulic modulator and proportioning block. Remove assembly from vehicle. See Fig. 2.
3) To install, reverse removal procedure and bleed brake system. See BLEEDING BRAKE SYSTEM. Tighten all fasteners to specification. See TORQUE SPECIFICATIONS table.

REAR WHEEL SPEED SENSOR

Removal & Installation – Disconnect negative battery terminal. Remove rear seat and side panel. Disconnect speed sensor connector located behind side panel. Raise and support vehicle. Remove grommet and pull speed sensor harness out through body. Remove clips, sensor cable bolt, sensor retaining bolt and speed sensor. See Fig. 3. To install, reverse removal procedure. Tighten all fasteners to specification. See TORQUE SPECIFICATIONS table.

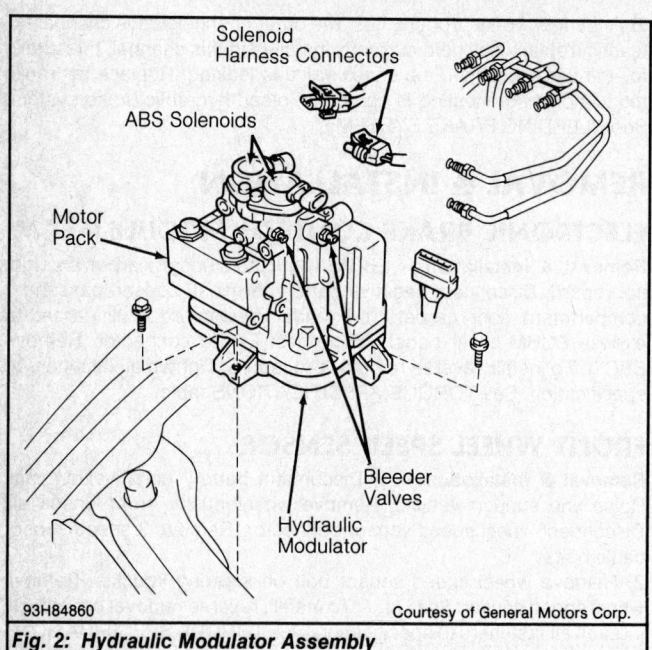

Fig. 2: Hydraulic Modulator Assembly

93H84860

Courtesy of General Motors Corp.

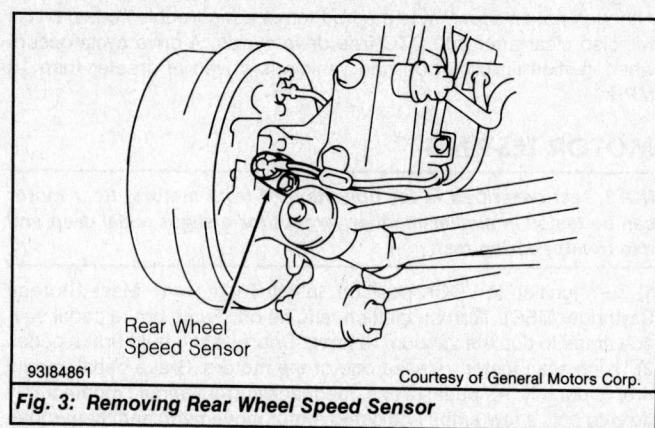

Fig. 3: Removing Rear Wheel Speed Sensor

93I84861

Courtesy of General Motors Corp.

TORQUE SPECIFICATIONS
TORQUE SPECIFICATIONS

Application	Ft. Lbs. (N.m)
Brake Line Fittings	11 (15)
Wheel Lug Nut	87 (118)

	INCH Lbs. (N.m)
EBCM Mounting Nut	53 (6.0)
Front & Rear Wheel Speed Sensor	
Mounting Bolt	70 (8.0)
Cable Retaining Bolt	48 (5.4)
Hydraulic Modulator Assembly Bolt	48 (5.4)

EBCM CONNECTOR TERMINAL IDENTIFICATION
EBCM CONNECTOR TERMINAL IDENTIFICATION

Terminal No.	Circuit No.	Wire Color	Circuit
Connector C1			
1	850	RED/WHT	Right Front Motor High
2	N/A	N/A	Not Used
3	20	GRN/WHT	Stoplight Switch Input
4	N/A	N/A	Not Used
5	461	PPL	Serial Data Line Information
6	N/A	N/A	Not Used
7	1281	BLU/WHT	Left Front Motor Low
8	N/A	N/A	Not Used
9	1280	BLU/RED	Left Front Motor High
10	873	RED	Left Front Wheel Signal Input
11	833	BLK	Right Front Wheel Signal Input
12	872	WHT	Right Front Wheel Signal Input
13	882	YEL	Right Rear Wheel Signal Input
14	883	BRN	Right Rear Wheel Signal Input
15	N/A	N/A	Not Used
16	1285	GRN/YEL	Rear Motor Low
17	1283	RED/GRN	Right Front Motor Low
18	N/A	N/A	Not Used
19	N/A	N/A	Not Used
20	34	GRN/RED	"ABS ACTIVE" Indicator Control
21	852	RED/YEL	"ABS" Indicator Control
22	879	BLU/BLK	ABS Enable Relay Control
23	33	RED/BLK	"BRAKE" Indicator Control
24	140	BLU/YEL	B+ Feed
25	350	GRY	Switched Ignition
26	830	GRN	Left Front Wheel Signal Input
27	884	BLU	Left Rear Wheel Signal Input
28	885	PPL	Left Rear Wheel Signal Input
29	1289	BRN/WHT	Right Front ABS Solenoid
30	1288	BRN/RED	Left Front ABS Solenoid
31	N/A	N/A	Not Used
32	1284	GRN/BLK	Rear Motor High
Connector C2			
1	850	BLU/ORG	Switched Battery Input
2	150A	WHT/BLK	Ground – G103

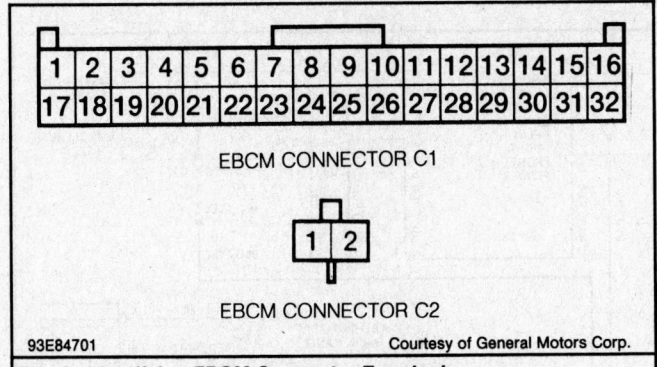

EBCM CONNECTOR C1

EBCM CONNECTOR C2

93E84701

Courtesy of General Motors Corp.

Fig. 4: Identifying EBCM Connector Terminals

ABS Connector Location

Connector	Pins (Color)/Location
C201	12 (BLU)/Behind Left Kick Panel At Junction Block No. 1
C203	4 (WHT)/Behind Left Instrument Panel Above Brake Pedal
C206	18 (BLU)/Behind Right Kick Panel
C212	18 (WHT)/Behind Left Kick Panel
C217	3 (NA)/Behind Instrument Panel Left Of Steering Column

WIRING DIAGRAM

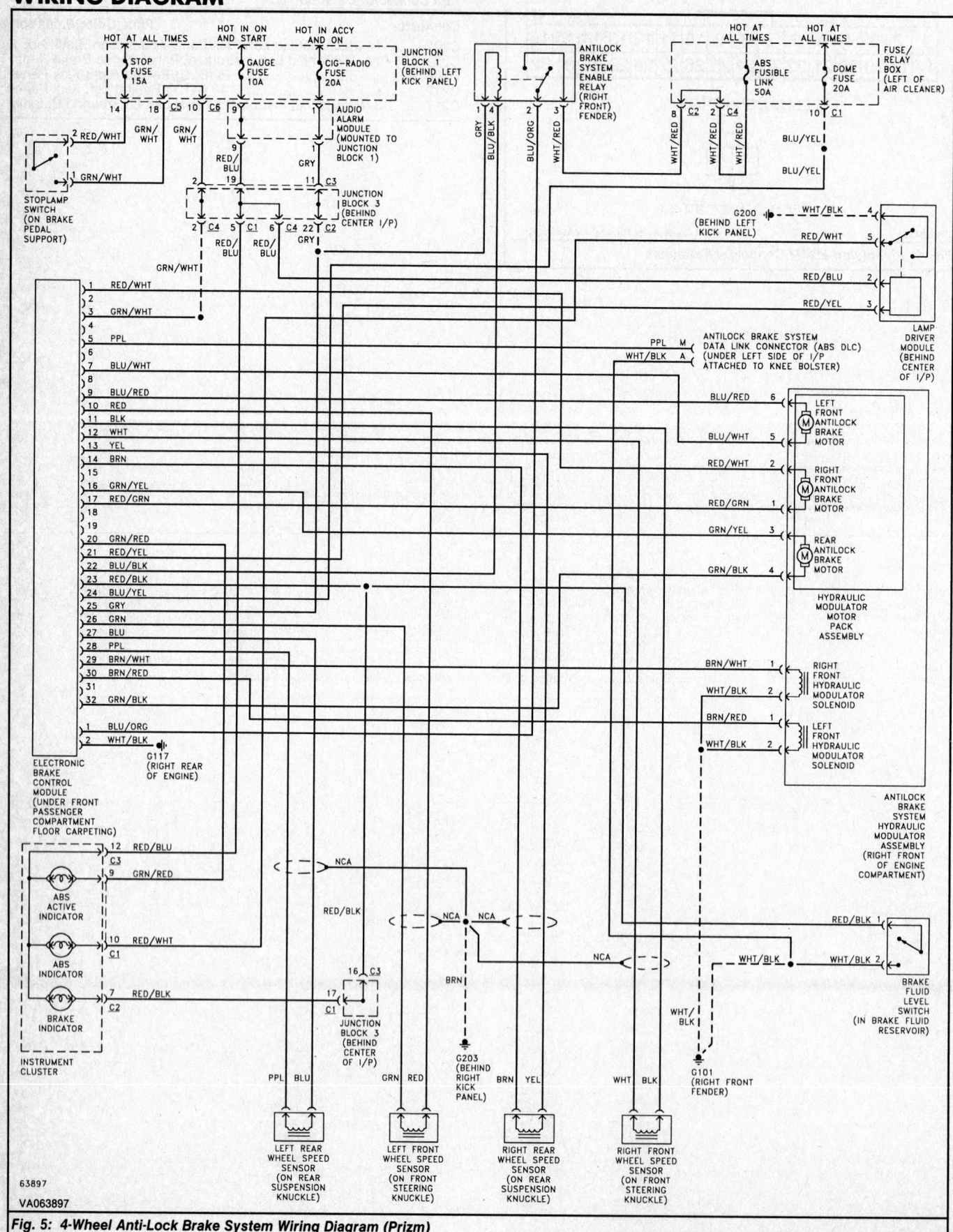

Fig. 5: 4-Wheel Anti-Lock Brake System Wiring Diagram (Prizm)

63897
VA063897

DIAGNOSTIC TROUBLE CODES (DTC)

DIAGNOSTIC CIRCUIT CHECK

Diagnostic circuit check is an organized approach in identifying a problem created by an anti-lock brake system malfunction. It must be the starting point for any ABS complaint diagnosis, because it directs the service technician to the next logical step in diagnosing a complaint. Understanding the chart and using it correctly will reduce diagnostic time and prevent unnecessary replacement of good parts.

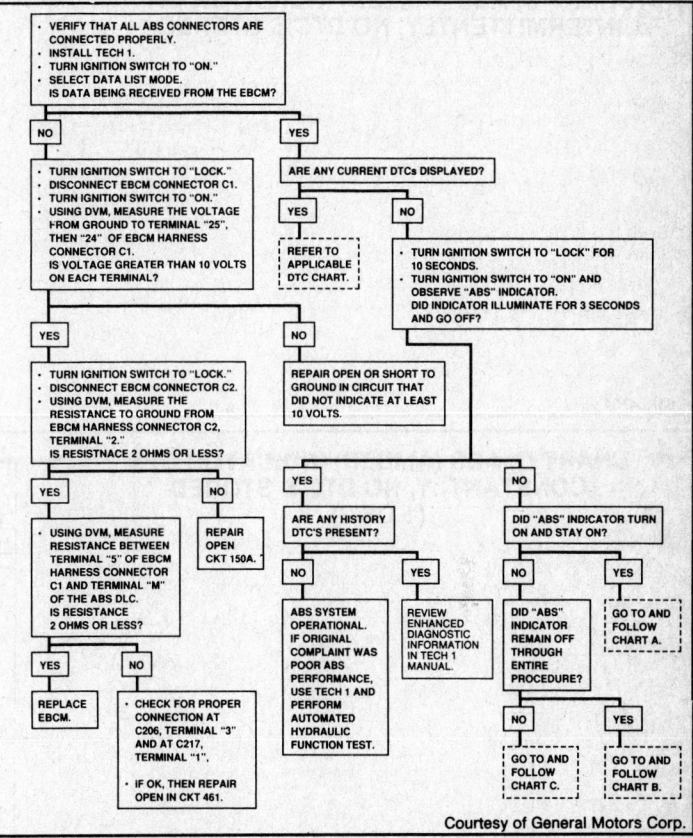

93F84702

Courtesy of General Motors Corp.

CHART A, ABS (AMBER) INDICATOR ON CONSTANTLY, NO DTC'S STORED

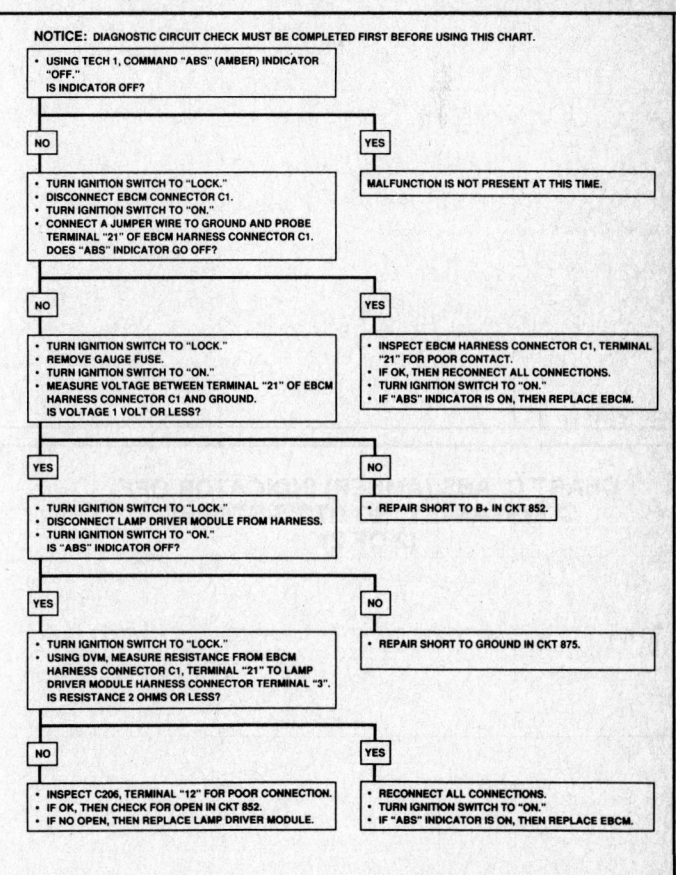

93G84703

Courtesy of General Motors Corp.

1994 BRAKES
4-Wheel Anti-Lock – Prizm (Cont.)

CHART B, ABS (AMBER) INDICATOR ON INTERMITTENTLY, NO DTC'S STORED

NOTICE: DIAGNOSTIC CIRCUIT CHECK MUST BE COMPLETED BEFORE USING THIS CHART.
• TURN IGNITION SWITCH TO "LOCK". • DISCONNECT EBCM CONNECTOR C1. CONNECT A TEST LIGHT TO GROUND AND PROBE TERMINAL "24" OF EBCM HARNESS CONNECTOR C1. OBSERVE TEST LIGHT WHEN MOVING WIRE HARNESS AND CONNECTORS. DOES TEST LIGHT REMAIN ON STEADY?
YES
NO
• CONNECT TEST LIGHT BETWEEN GROUND AND EBCM HARNESS CONNECTOR C1 TERMINAL "25". TURN IGNITION SWITCH TO "ON" AND OBSERVE TEST LIGHT WHEN MOVING WIRE HARNESS AND CONNECTORS. DOES TEST LIGHT REMAIN ON STEADY?
REPAIR INTERMITTENT CONNECTION IN CKT 140.
YES
NO
PROBLEM IS NOT PRESENT AT THIS TIME. INTERMITTENTS COULD BE CAUSED BY INCORRECT WIRING HARNESS ROUTING OR LOOSE GROUND CONNECTIONS.
REPAIR INTERMITTENT CONNECTION IN CKT 350A.

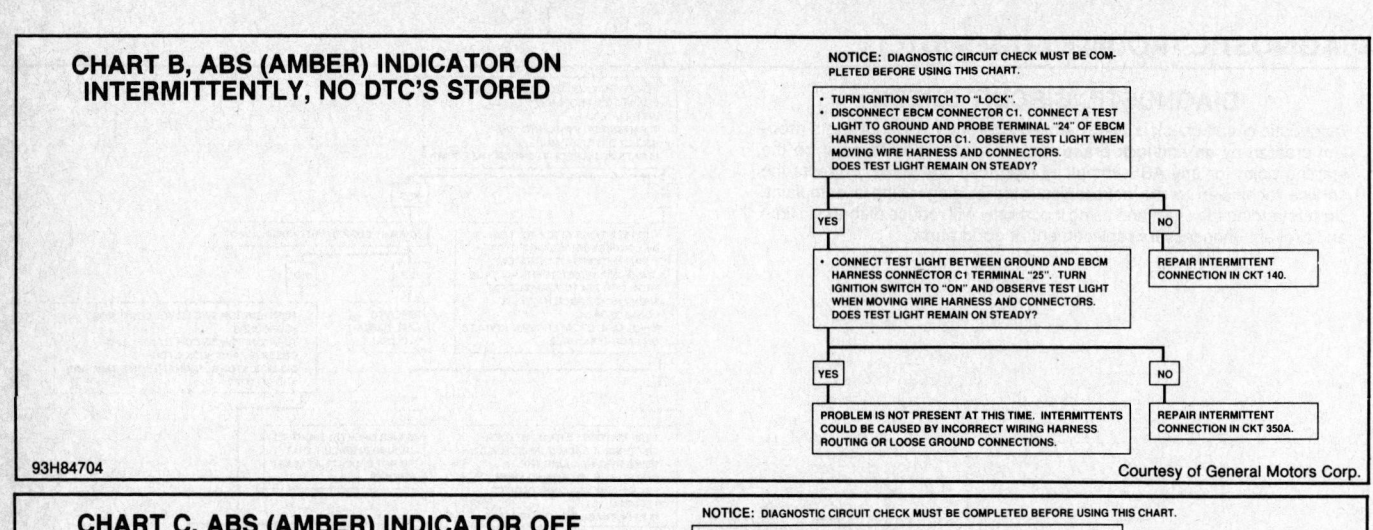

93H84704

Courtesy of General Motors Corp.

CHART C, ABS (AMBER) INDICATOR OFF CONSTANTLY, NO DTC'S STORED (1 OF 2)

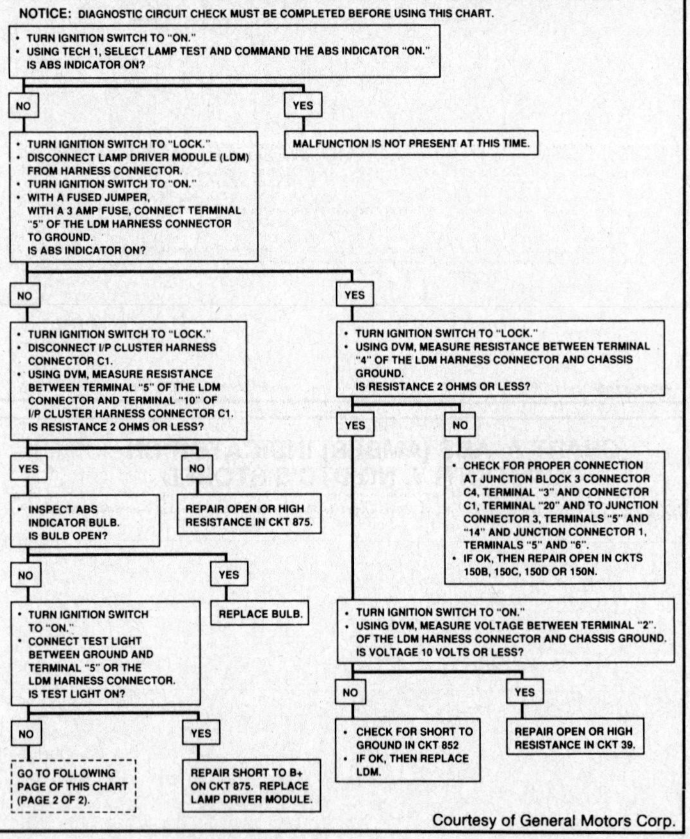

NOTICE: DIAGNOSTIC CIRCUIT CHECK MUST BE COMPLETED BEFORE USING THIS CHART.
• TURN IGNITION SWITCH TO "ON." • USING TECH 1, SELECT LAMP TEST AND COMMAND THE ABS INDICATOR "ON." IS ABS INDICATOR ON?
NO
YES
MALFUNCTION IS NOT PRESENT AT THIS TIME.
• TURN IGNITION SWITCH TO "LOCK." • DISCONNECT LAMP DRIVER MODULE (LDM) FROM HARNESS CONNECTOR. • TURN IGNITION SWITCH TO "ON." • WITH A FUSED JUMPER, WITH A 3 AMP FUSE, CONNECT TERMINAL "5" OF THE LDM HARNESS CONNECTOR TO GROUND. IS ABS INDICATOR ON?
NO
YES
• TURN IGNITION SWITCH TO "LOCK." • DISCONNECT I/P CLUSTER HARNESS CONNECTOR C1. • USING DVM, MEASURE RESISTANCE BETWEEN TERMINAL "5" OF THE LDM CONNECTOR AND TERMINAL "10" OF I/P CLUSTER HARNESS CONNECTOR C1. IS RESISTANCE 2 OHMS OR LESS?
• TURN IGNITION SWITCH TO "LOCK." • USING DVM, MEASURE RESISTANCE BETWEEN TERMINAL "4" OF THE LDM HARNESS CONNECTOR AND CHASSIS GROUND. IS RESISTANCE 2 OHMS OR LESS?
YES
NO
YES
NO
• INSPECT ABS INDICATOR BULB. IS BULB OPEN?
REPAIR OPEN OR HIGH RESISTANCE IN CKT 875.
• CHECK FOR PROPER CONNECTION AT JUNCTION BLOCK 3 CONNECTOR C4, TERMINAL "3" AND CONNECTOR C1, TERMINAL "20" AND TO JUNCTION CONNECTOR 3, TERMINALS "5" AND "14" AND JUNCTION CONNECTOR 1, TERMINALS "5" AND "6". • IF OK, THEN REPAIR OPEN IN CKTS 150B, 150C, 150D OR 150N.
NO
YES
• TURN IGNITION SWITCH TO "ON." • CONNECT TEST LIGHT BETWEEN GROUND AND TERMINAL "5" OR THE LDM HARNESS CONNECTOR. IS TEST LIGHT ON?
REPLACE BULB.
• TURN IGNITION SWITCH TO "ON." • USING DVM, MEASURE VOLTAGE BETWEEN TERMINAL "2". OF THE LDM HARNESS CONNECTOR AND CHASSIS GROUND. IS VOLTAGE 10 VOLTS OR LESS?
NO
YES
NO
YES
GO TO FOLLOWING PAGE OF THIS CHART (PAGE 2 OF 2).
REPAIR SHORT TO B+ ON CKT 875. REPLACE LAMP DRIVER MODULE.
• CHECK FOR SHORT TO GROUND IN CKT 852 • IF OK, THEN REPLACE LDM.
REPAIR OPEN OR HIGH RESISTANCE IN CKT 39.

93I84705

Courtesy of General Motors Corp.

CHART C, ABS (AMBER) INDICATOR OFF CONSTANTLY, NO DTC'S STORED (2 OF 2)

CONTINUED FROM CHART C (PAGE 1 OF 2).
• TURN IGNITION SWITCH TO "LOCK." • RECONNECT LDM CONNECTOR AND I/P CLUSTER CONNECTOR C1. • DISCONNECT EBCM CONNECTOR C1. • TURN IGNITION SWITCH TO "ON." DOES ABS INDICATOR ILLUMINATE FOR 3 SECONDS THEN GO OFF?
NO
YES
REPLACE EBCM.
PROBLEM IS INTERMITTENT.

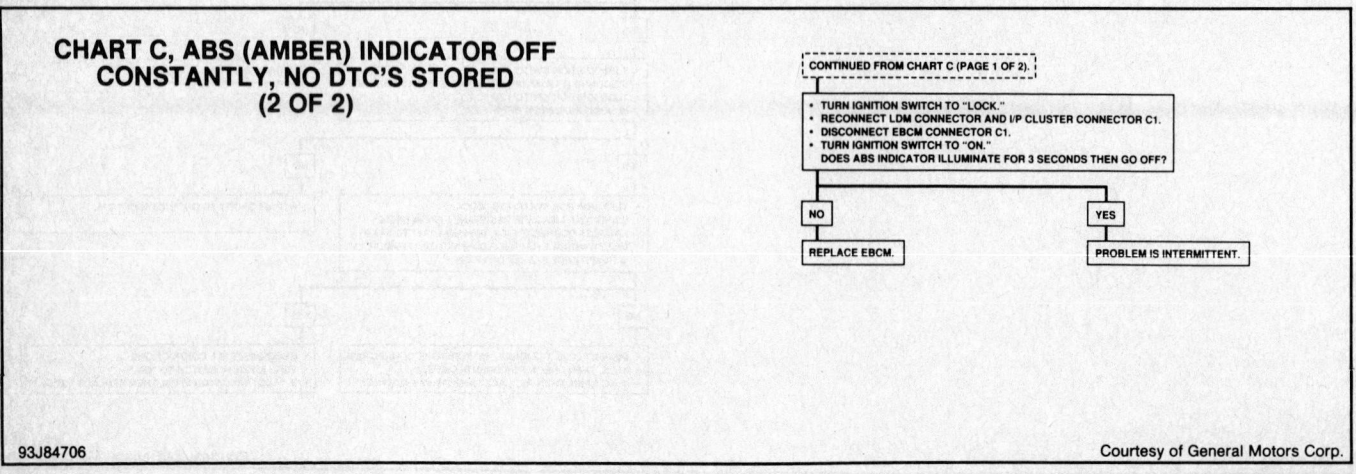

93J84706

Courtesy of General Motors Corp.

CHART D, TECH-1 DISPLAYS UNDEFINED DTC'S

💡 **Important**
- USE THIS CHART IF ANY OF THE FOLLOWING UNDEFINED DTCs ARE SET - A011, A012, A013, A031, A043, A067, A068, A071, A072, A073, A074, A075, A083, A084, A085, A097, OR A098

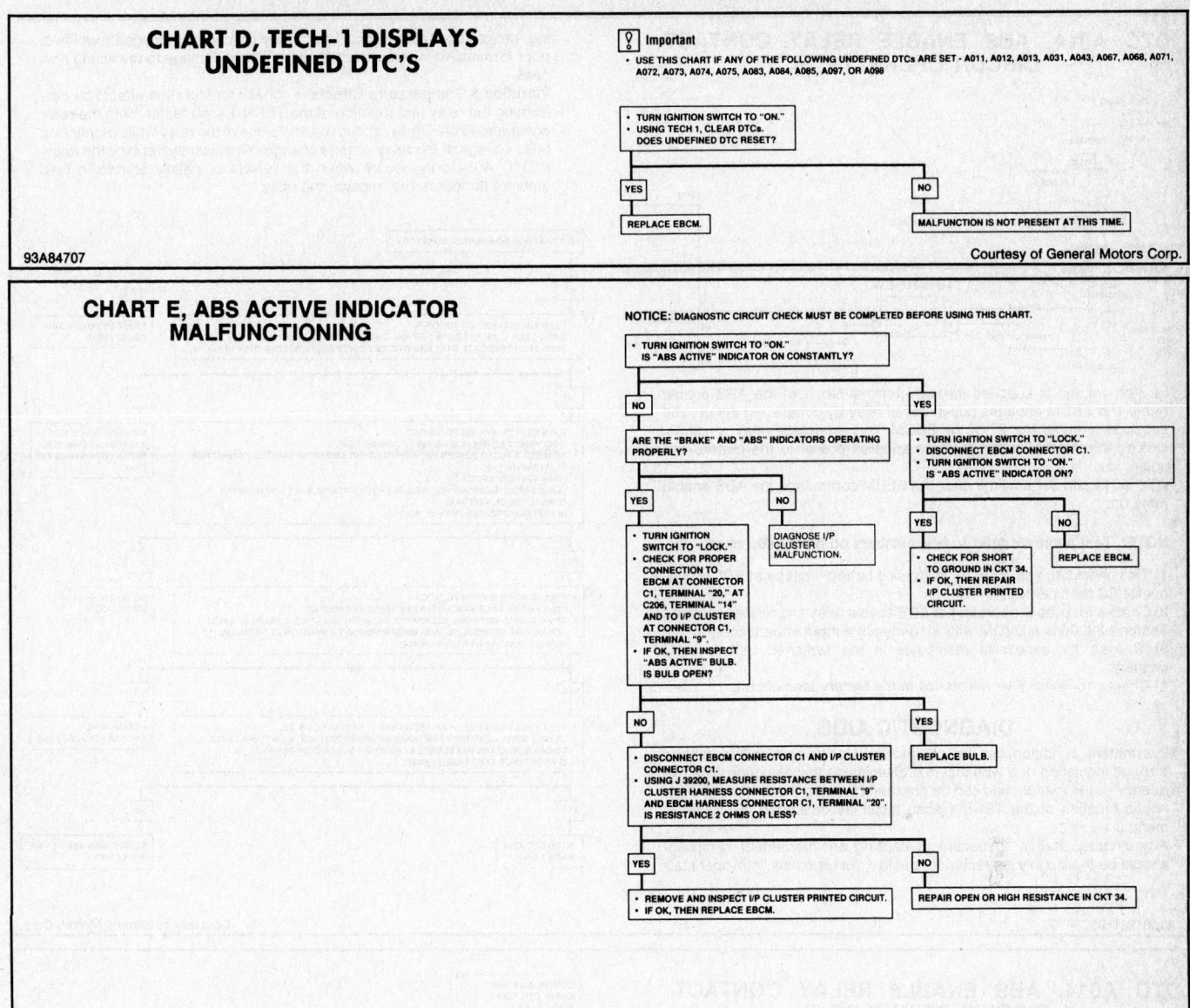

- TURN IGNITION SWITCH TO "ON."
- USING TECH 1, CLEAR DTCs.
DOES UNDEFINED DTC RESET?

YES → REPLACE EBCM.

NO → MALFUNCTION IS NOT PRESENT AT THIS TIME.

93A84707

Courtesy of General Motors Corp.

CHART E, ABS ACTIVE INDICATOR MALFUNCTIONING

NOTICE: DIAGNOSTIC CIRCUIT CHECK MUST BE COMPLETED BEFORE USING THIS CHART.

- TURN IGNITION SWITCH TO "ON."
IS "ABS ACTIVE" INDICATOR ON CONSTANTLY?

NO

ARE THE "BRAKE" AND "ABS" INDICATORS OPERATING PROPERLY?

YES
- TURN IGNITION SWITCH TO "LOCK."
- CHECK FOR PROPER CONNECTION TO EBCM AT CONNECTOR C1, TERMINAL "20," AT C206, TERMINAL "14" AND TO I/P CLUSTER AT CONNECTOR C1, TERMINAL "9."
- IF OK, THEN INSPECT "ABS ACTIVE" BULB. IS BULB OPEN?

NO
- DIAGNOSE I/P CLUSTER MALFUNCTION.

NO
- DISCONNECT EBCM CONNECTOR C1 AND I/P CLUSTER CONNECTOR C1.
- USING J 39200, MEASURE RESISTANCE BETWEEN I/P CLUSTER HARNESS CONNECTOR C1, TERMINAL "9" AND EBCM HARNESS CONNECTOR C1, TERMINAL "20". IS RESISTANCE 2 OHMS OR LESS?

YES → REPLACE BULB.

YES
- REMOVE AND INSPECT I/P CLUSTER PRINTED CIRCUIT.
- IF OK, THEN REPLACE EBCM.

NO → REPAIR OPEN OR HIGH RESISTANCE IN CKT 34.

YES
- TURN IGNITION SWITCH TO "LOCK."
- DISCONNECT EBCM CONNECTOR C1.
- TURN IGNITION SWITCH TO "ON."
IS "ABS ACTIVE" INDICATOR ON?

YES
- CHECK FOR SHORT TO GROUND IN CKT 34.
- IF OK, THEN REPAIR I/P CLUSTER PRINTED CIRCUIT.

NO → REPLACE EBCM.

93B84708

Courtesy of General Motors Corp.

DTC A014, ABS ENABLE RELAY CONTACT CIRCUIT OPEN (1 OF 5)

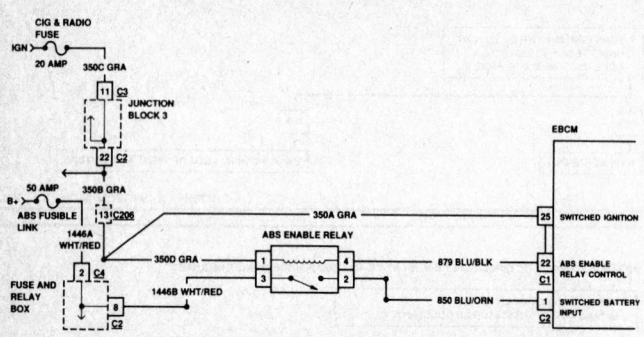

Ignition voltage is supplied through terminal No. 1 of the ABS enable relay. The EBCM engages pull-in coil of relay by completing the ground circuit at terminal No. 22 of the EBCM. This energizes relay windings, closing the internal contacts which supplies power to the motors and solenoids.
DTC A014 can set anytime after the EBCM commands the ABS enable relay on.

NOTE: Test numbers refer to test numbers on diagnostic chart.

1) This checks to see if EBCM is sensing battery voltage at EBCM connector C2 terminal No. 1.
2) Checks for proper operation of ABS enable relay and related circuitry. Tester J 39200 is a DVOM with a 10-megohm input impedance.
3) Checks for excessive resistance in the switched battery input circuitry.
4) Checks for excessive resistance in the battery feed circuit.

DIAGNOSTIC AIDS

Intermittent condition can be caused by a poor connection, rubbed through insulation or a wire that is broken inside the insulation. The frequency of the malfunction can be checked by using the enhanced diagnostic function of the TECH-1 scan tester as described in the tester manual.
Any circuitry that is suspected of causing an intermittent complaint should be thoroughly inspected for backed out terminals, improper mat-

ing, broken connector locks, improperly formed or damaged terminals, poor terminal-to-wire connections or physical damage to the wiring harness.
Vibration & Temperature Effects – Check for vibration effects by performing the relay test function of the TECH-1 scan tester. With the relay commanded on, lightly tap the top and sides of the relay while monitoring relay voltage. If the relay voltage changes significantly, replace the relay. If DTC A014 only occurs when the vehicle is initially started in cold ambient temperatures, replace the relay.

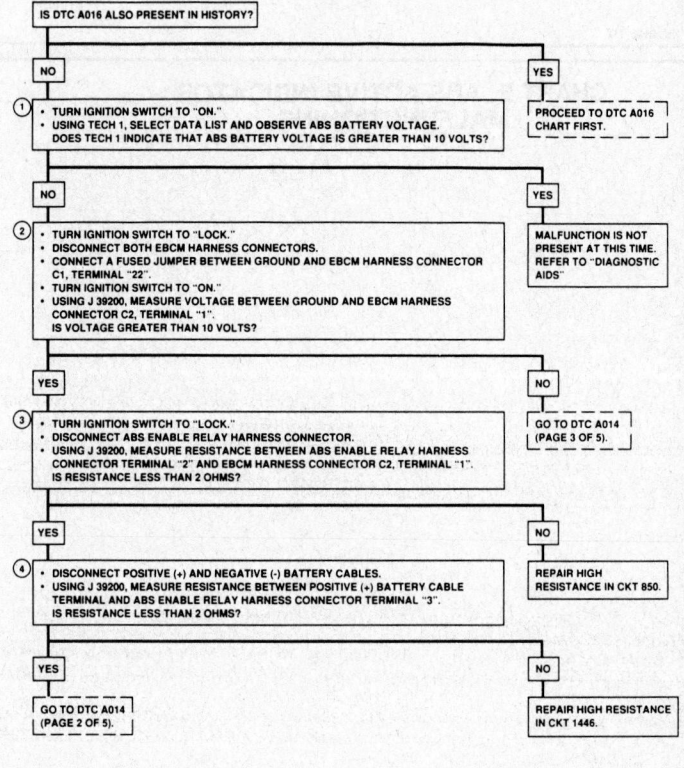

93A84681 93C84709

DTC A014, ABS ENABLE RELAY CONTACT CIRCUIT OPEN (2 OF 5)

NOTE: Test numbers refer to test numbers on diagnostic chart.

5) Determines if the malfunction is due to a poor connection.
6) Determines if the malfunction is due to the EBCM.

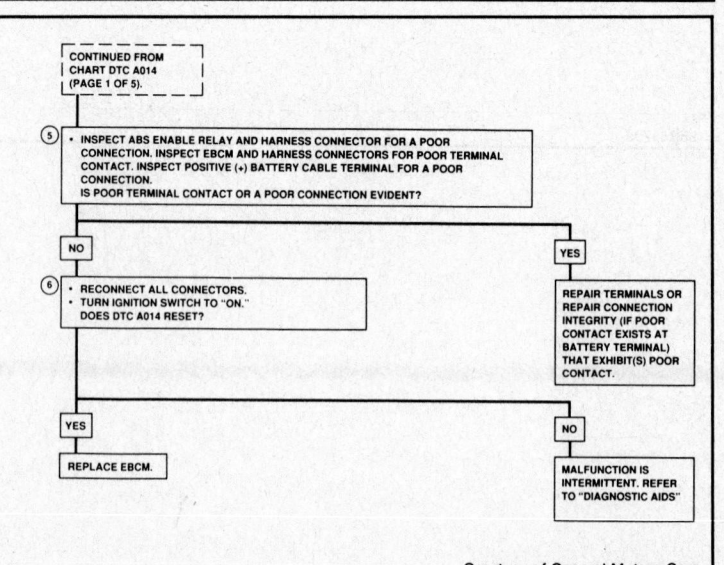

93F84710

DTC A014, ABS ENABLE RELAY CONTACT CIRCUIT OPEN (3 OF 5)

NOTE: Test numbers refer to test numbers on diagnostic chart.

7) Checks for excessive resistance in the ABS relay control circuitry.
8) Checks for proper battery voltage.
9) Checks for an open in the battery feed circuit.
10) Checks for an open in the switched battery feed circuit.
11) Checks for proper operation of the ABS enable relay.

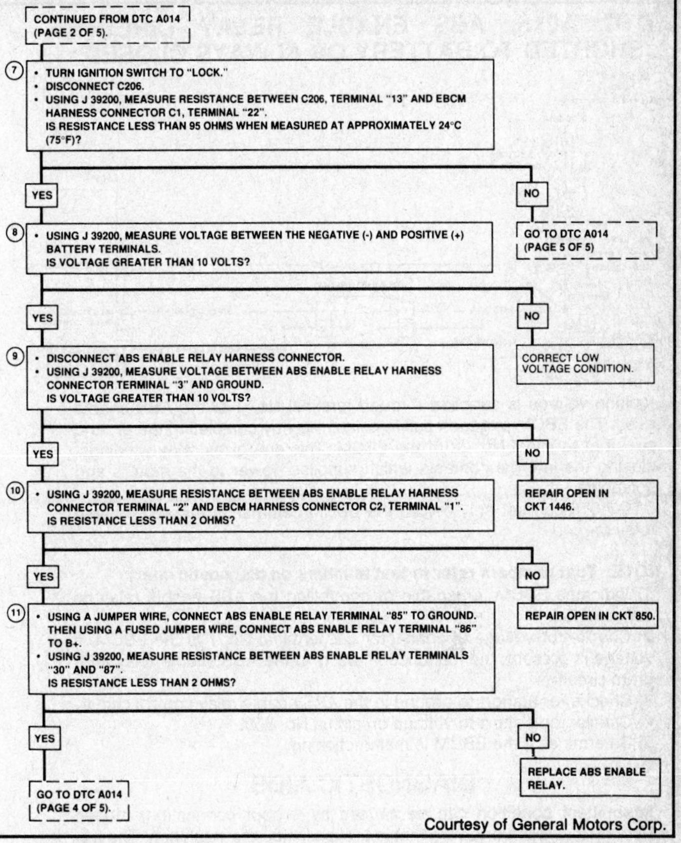

93G84711

Courtesy of General Motors Corp.

DTC A014, ABS ENABLE RELAY CONTACT CIRCUIT OPEN (4 OF 5)

NOTE: Test numbers refer to test numbers on diagnostic chart.

12) Checks for excessive resistance in the ignition switch feed when ignition switch is in the ON position (CIG and RADIO fuse).

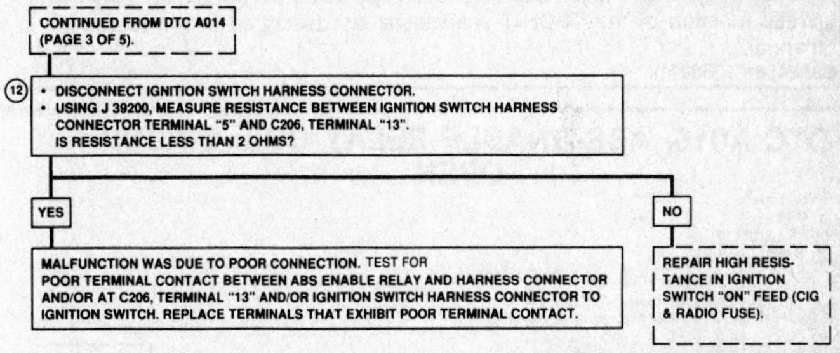

93H84712

Courtesy of General Motors Corp.

DTC A014, ABS ENABLE RELAY CONTACT CIRCUIT OPEN (5 OF 5)

NOTE: Test numbers refer to test numbers on diagnostic chart.

13) Checks for excessive resistance in the ABS enable relay coil.
14) Checks for excessive resistance in the ABS enable relay circuit between the relay and connector C206.
15) Checks for excessive resistance in the ABS enable relay control circuit between the relay and connector C206.

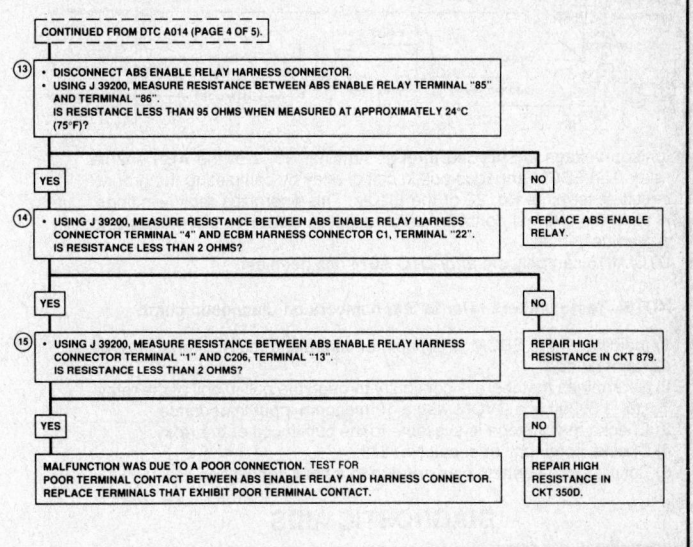

93I84713

Courtesy of General Motors Corp.

DTC A015, ABS ENABLE RELAY CIRCUIT SHORTED TO BATTERY OR ALWAYS CLOSED

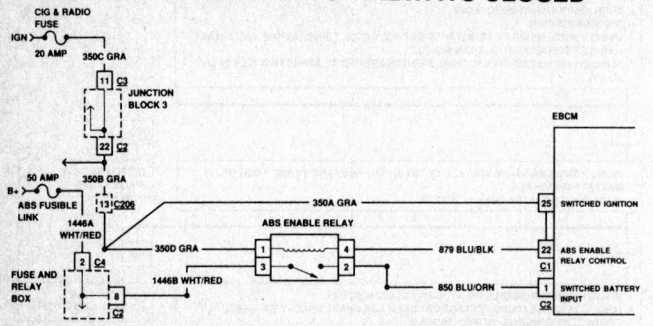

Ignition voltage is supplied through terminal No. 1 of the ABS enable relay. The EBCM engages pull-in coil of relay by completing the ground circuit at terminal No. 22 of the EBCM. This energizes relay windings, closing the internal contacts which supplies power to the motors and solenoids.

DTC A015 can set only before the EBCM commands the ABS enable relay on.

NOTE: Test numbers refer to test numbers on diagnostic chart.

1) Indicates EBCM is capable of controlling the ABS enable relay as commanded.

2) Checks for voltage at connector C2, terminal No. 1 of the EBCM. If voltage is present, the malfunction exists in the ABS enable relay and/or its circuitry.

3) Checks for a short to ground in the ABS enable relay control circuit.

4) Checks for a short to voltage on circuit No. 850.

5) Determines if the EBCM is malfunctioning.

DIAGNOSTIC AIDS

Intermittent condition can be caused by a poor connection, rubbed through insulation or a wire that is broken inside the insulation. The frequency of the malfunction can be checked by using the enhanced diagnostic function of the TECH-1 scan tester as described in the tester manual.

93A84681 93J84714

Any circuitry that is suspected of causing an intermittent complaint should be thoroughly inspected for backed out terminals, improper mating, broken connector locks, improperly formed or damaged terminals, poor terminal-to-wire connections or physical damage to the wiring harness.

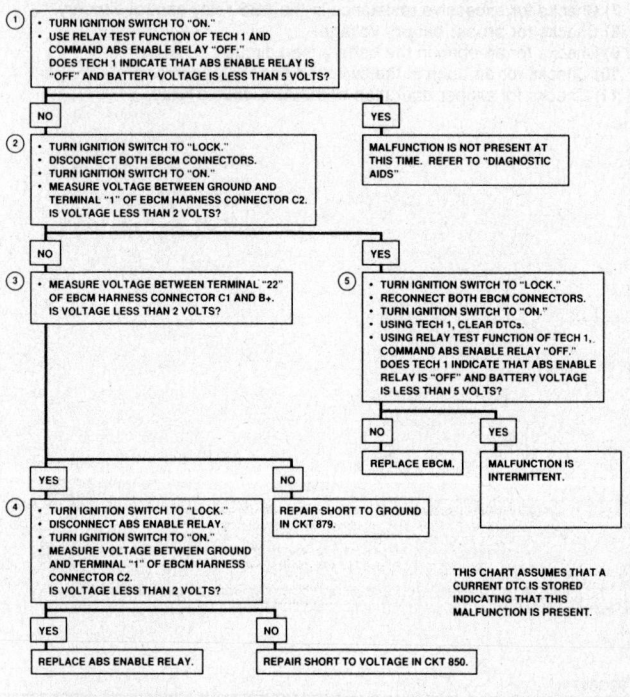

THIS CHART ASSUMES THAT A CURRENT DTC IS STORED INDICATING THAT THIS MALFUNCTION IS PRESENT.

AFTER DIAGNOSIS IS COMPLETE, CLEAR DTCs AND TEST DRIVE VEHICLE FOR THREE (3) DRIVE CYCLES TO VERIFY DTC DOES NOT RESET. A DRIVE CYCLE CONSISTS OF STARTING THE VEHICLE, DRIVING ABOVE 16 km/h (10 MPH) AND THEN KEYING DOWN.

Courtesy of General Motors Corp.

DTC A016, ABS ENABLE RELAY COIL CIRCUIT OPEN

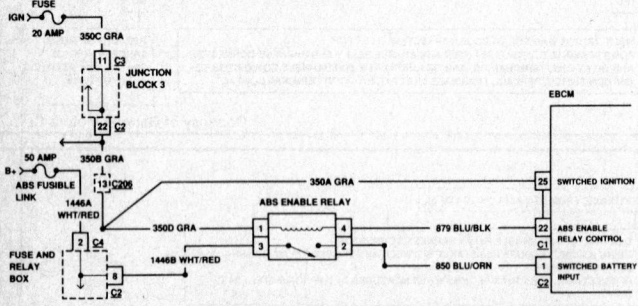

Ignition voltage is supplied through terminal No. 1 of the ABS enable relay. The EBCM engages pull-in coil of relay by completing the ground circuit at terminal No. 22 of the EBCM. This energizes relay windings, closing the internal contacts which supplies power to the motors and solenoids.

DTC A016 can only set after DTC A014 has been set.

NOTE: Test numbers refer to test numbers on diagnostic chart.

1) Indicates if the EBCM is capable of controlling the ABS enable relay as commanded.

2) Determines that there is continuity through the pull-in coil of the relay. Tester J 39200 is a DVOM with a 10-megohm input impedance.

3) Checks that voltage is available to the pull-in coil of the relay.

4) Checks continuity of circuit No. 879.

5) Ensures code setting was not due to a poor connection.

DIAGNOSTIC AIDS

Intermittent condition can be caused by a poor connection, rubbed through insulation or a wire that is broken inside the insulation. The fre-

quency of the malfunction can be checked by using the enhanced diagnostic function of the TECH-1 scan tester as described in the tester manual.

Any circuitry that is suspected of causing an intermittent complaint should be thoroughly inspected for backed out terminals, improper mating, broken connector locks, improperly formed or damaged terminals, poor terminal-to-wire connections or physical damage to the wiring harness.

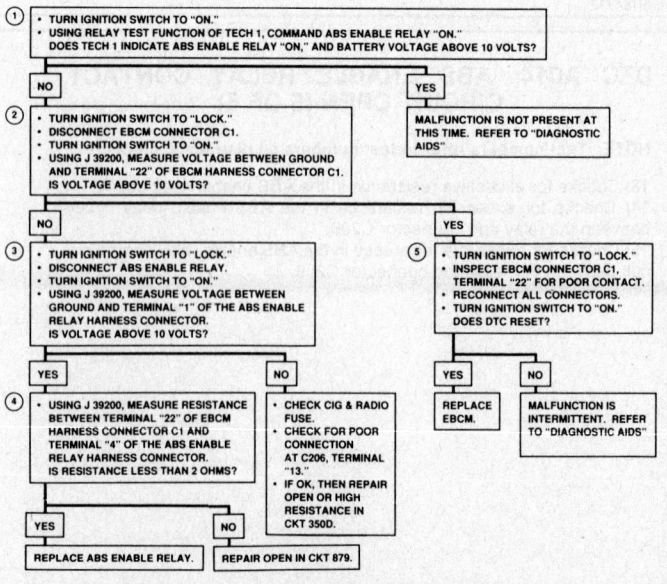

AFTER DIAGNOSIS IS COMPLETE, CLEAR DTCs AND TEST DRIVE VEHICLE FOR THREE (3) DRIVE CYCLES TO VERIFY DTC DOES NOT RESET. A DRIVE CYCLE CONSISTS OF STARTING THE VEHICLE, DRIVING OVER 16 km/h (10 MPH) AND THEN KEYING DOWN.

93A84681 93A84715

Courtesy of General Motors Corp.

DTC A017, ABS ENABLE RELAY COIL CIRCUIT SHORTED TO GROUND

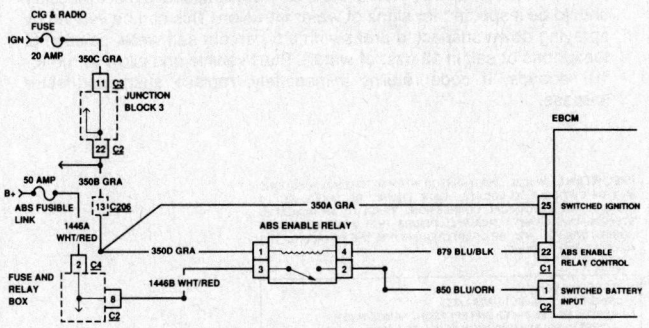

Ignition voltage is supplied through terminal No. 1 of the ABS enable relay. The EBCM engages pull-in coil of relay by completing the ground circuit at terminal No. 22 of the EBCM. This energizes relay windings, closing the internal contacts which supplies power to the motors and solenoids.

DTC A017 can set before the EBCM commands the ABS enable relay on.

NOTE: Test numbers refer to test numbers on diagnostic chart.

1) Indicates if EBCM is capable of controlling the ABS enable relay as commanded.
2) Checks to ensure ABS enable relay or control circuit No. 879 is not shorted to ground.
3) Ensures code was not set due to a poor connection.

DIAGNOSTIC AIDS

Intermittent condition can be caused by a poor connection, rubbed through insulation or a wire that is broken inside the insulation. The fre-quency of the malfunction can be checked by using the enhanced diagnostic function of the TECH-1 scan tester as described in the tester manual.

Any circuitry that is suspected of causing an intermittent complaint should be thoroughly inspected for backed out terminals, improper mating, broken connector locks, improperly formed or damaged terminals, poor terminal-to-wire connections or physical damage to the wiring harness.

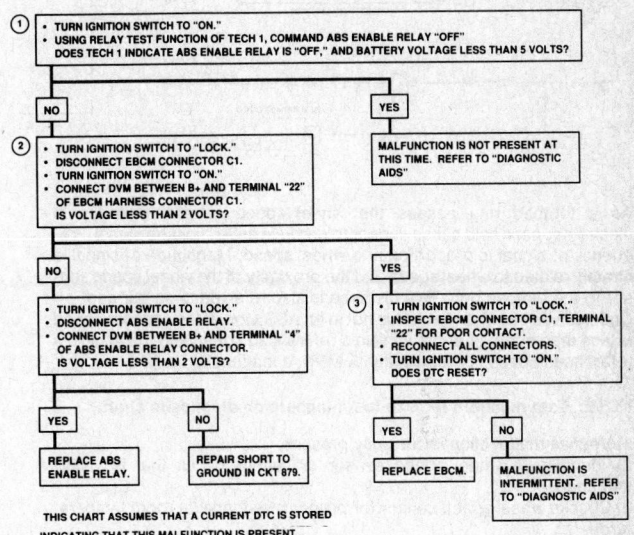

93A84681 93B84716

DTC A018, ABS ENABLE RELAY COIL CIRCUIT SHORTED TO BATTERY VOLTAGE

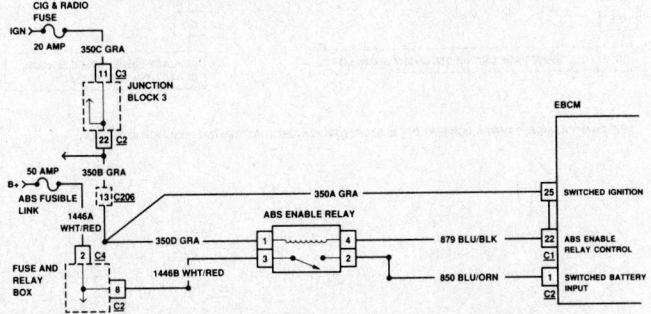

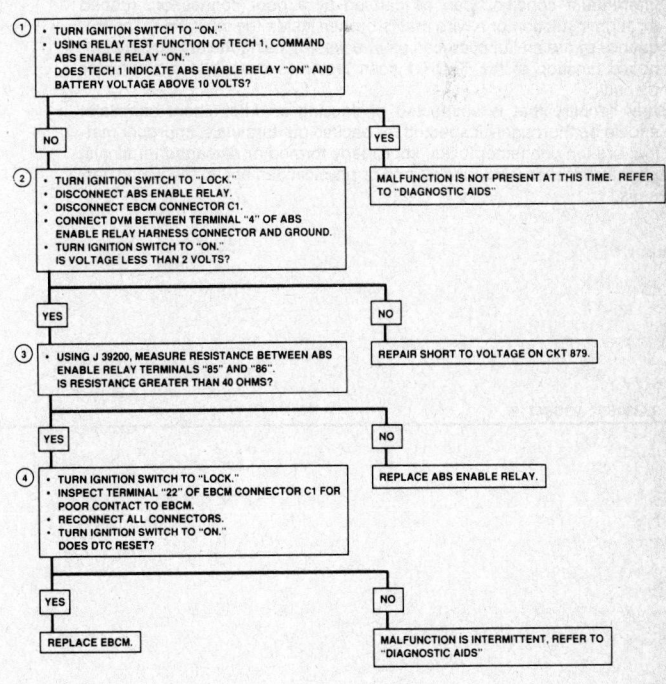

Ignition voltage is supplied through terminal No. 1 of the ABS enable relay. The EBCM engages pull-in coil of relay by completing the ground circuit at terminal No. 22 of the EBCM. This energizes relay windings, closing the internal contacts which supplies power to the motors and solenoids.

DTC A018 can be set after the EBCM commands the ABS enable relay on.

NOTE: Test numbers refer to test numbers on diagnostic chart.

1) Indicates if the EBCM is capable of controlling the ABS enable relay as commanded.
2) With the ABS enable relay removed, voltage should not be available at terminal No. 4. Voltage at this point would indicate that circuit No. 879 is shorted to a battery voltage source.
3) Checks for a shorted coil. Tester J 39200 is a DVOM with a 10-megohm input impedance.
4) Ensures malfunction is not due to a poor connection.

93A84681 93C84717

DTC A021, LEFT FRONT WHEEL SPEED=0 OR UNREASONABLE (1 OF 3)

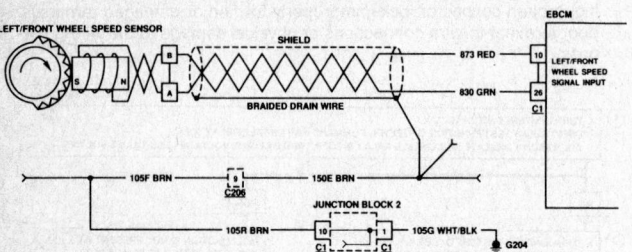

As a toothed ring passes the wheel speed sensor, changes in electromagnetic field cause sensor to produce an AC voltage signal. Frequency of signal is proportional to wheel speed. Magnitude of signal is directly related to wheel speed and the proximity of the wheel speed sensor to the toothed ring. This distance is also referred to as "air gap" Code can be set when vehicle is not in an ABS stop. If the sensors speed is less than one-half of the vehicle's referenced speed and the vehicle's referenced speed is greater than 5 MPH, a malfunction exists.

NOTE: Test numbers refer to test numbers on diagnostic chart.

1) Verifies malfunction is currently present.
2) Identifies a wheel speed sensor or sensor circuit that is visibly damaged.
3) Checks wheel speed sensor for proper resistance (at room temperature).
4) Ensures wheel speed sensor and sensor ring generate the proper voltage.
5) Ensures wheel speed sensor is not shorted to ground. Tester J 39200 is a DVOM with a 10-megohm input impedance.

DIAGNOSTIC AIDS

Intermittent condition can be caused by a poor connection, rubbed through insulation or a wire that is broken inside the insulation. The frequency of the malfunction can be checked by using the enhanced diagnostic function of the TECH-1 scan tester as described in the tester manual.

Any circuitry that is suspected of causing an intermittent complaint should be thoroughly inspected for backed out terminals, improper mating, broken connector locks, improperly formed or damaged terminals, poor terminal-to-wire connections or physical damage to the wiring harness.

If driver's complaint reflects that ABS indicator is only on during moist conditions (rain, snow, wash, etc.), all wheel speed sensor circuitry should be inspected for signs of water intrusion. This can be verified by spraying down suspected areas with a 5 percent salt water solution (2 teaspoons of salt in 12 ozs. of water). Start vehicle and allow to run for 10 seconds. If code returns immediately, replace suspected/tester harness.

IMPORTANT: WHEEL SPEED SENSOR INTERMITTENT MALFUNCTIONS MAY BE DIFFICULT TO LOCATE. CARE SHOULD BE TAKEN NOT TO DISTURB ANY ELECTRICAL CONNECTIONS PRIOR TO AN INDICATED STEP OF THIS CHART. THIS WILL INSURE THAT AN INTERMITTENT CONNECTION WILL NOT BE CORRECTED BEFORE THE SOURCE OF THE MALFUNCTION IS FOUND.

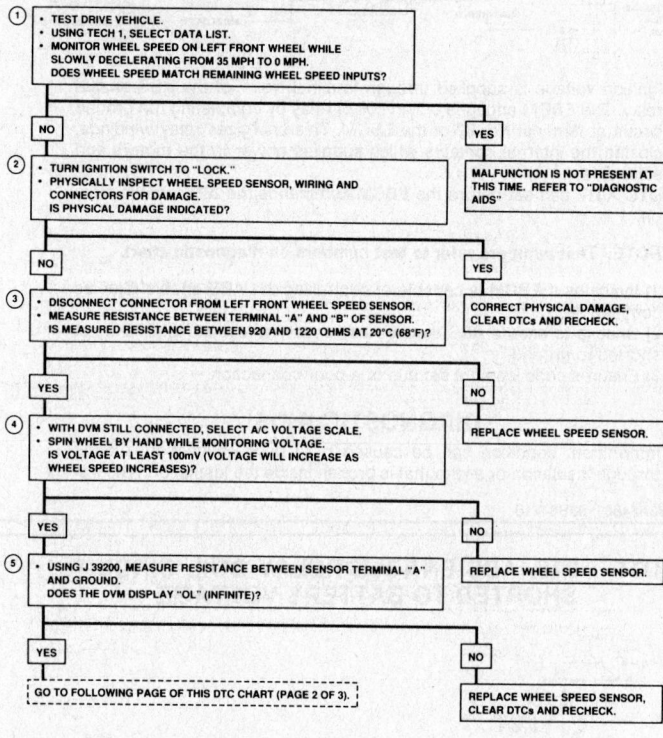

THIS CHART ASSUMES THAT A CURRENT DTC IS STORED INDICATING THAT THIS MALFUNCTION IS PRESENT.

93B84682 93D84718

Courtesy of General Motors Corp.

DTC A021, LEFT FRONT WHEEL SPEED=0 OR UNREASONABLE (2 OF 3)

NOTE: Test numbers refer to test numbers on diagnostic chart.

6) Checks for proper voltages at speed sensor harness connector.
7) Ensures wheel speed sensor circuitry is not internally shorted.
8) Checks for open in circuit NO. 873.
9) Checks for open in circuit No. 830.

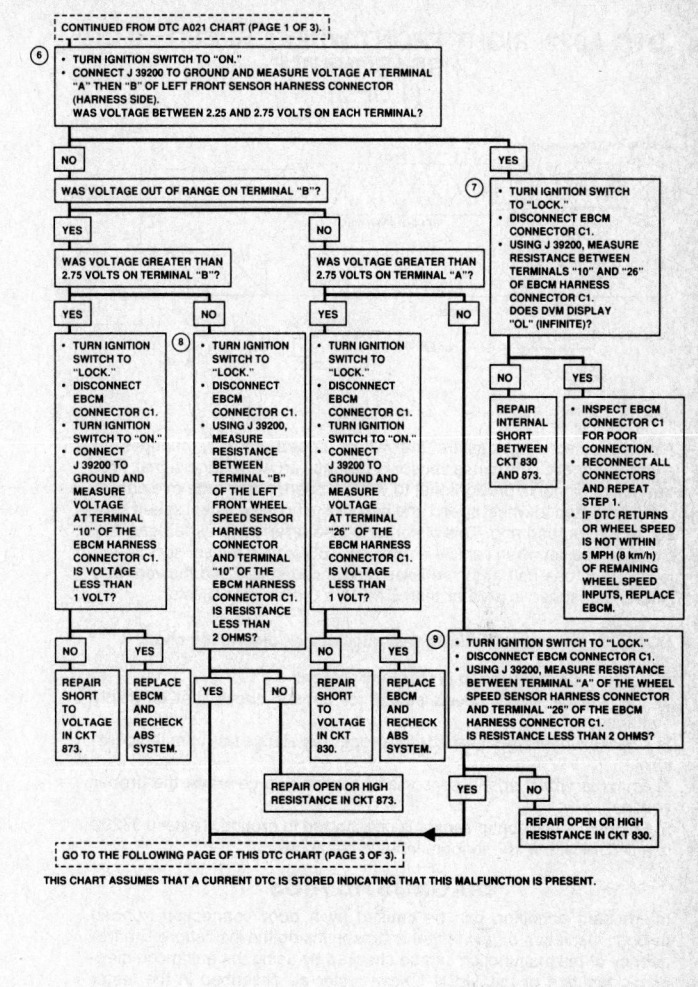

THIS CHART ASSUMES THAT A CURRENT DTC IS STORED INDICATING THAT THIS MALFUNCTION IS PRESENT.

93E84719

Courtesy of General Motors Corp.

DTC A021, LEFT FRONT WHEEL SPEED=0 OR UNREASONABLE (3 OF 3)

NOTE: Test numbers refer to test numbers on diagnostic chart.

10) Checks for short to ground in both wheel speed signal circuits.
11) Ensures code was not set due to a poor connection.

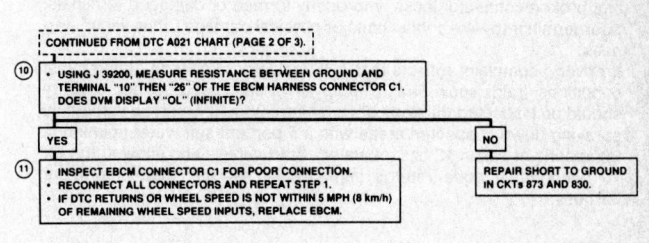

THIS CHART ASSUMES THAT A CURRENT DTC IS STORED INDICATING THAT THIS MALFUNCTION IS PRESENT.

93H84720

Courtesy of General Motors Corp.

DTC A022, RIGHT FRONT WHEEL SPEED = 0 OR UNREASONABLE
(1 OF 3)

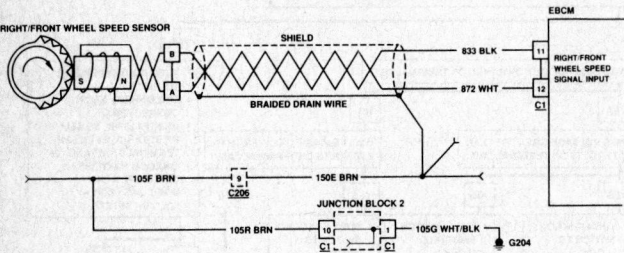

As a toothed ring passes the wheel speed sensor, changes in electromagnetic field cause sensor to produce an AC voltage signal. Frequency of signal is proportional to wheel speed. Magnitude of signal is directly related to wheel speed and the proximity of the wheel speed sensor to the toothed ring. This distance is also referred to as "air gap" Code can be set when vehicle is not in an ABS stop. If the sensors speed is less than one-half of the vehicles referenced speed and the vehicle's referenced speed is greater than 5 MPH, a malfunction exists.

NOTE: Test numbers refer to test numbers on diagnostic chart.

1) Verifies the malfunction is currently present.
2) Identifies a wheel speed sensor or sensor circuit that is visibly damaged.
3) Checks wheel speed sensor for proper resistance (at room temperature).
4) Ensures wheel speed sensor and sensor ring generate the proper voltage.
5) Ensures wheel speed sensor is not shorted to ground. Tester J 39200 is a DVOM with a 10-megohm input impedance.

DIAGNOSTIC AIDS

Intermittent condition can be caused by a poor connection, rubbed through insulation or a wire that is broken inside the insulation. The frequency of the malfunction can be checked by using the enhanced diagnostic function of the TECH-1 scan tester as described in the tester manual.

Any circuitry that is suspected of causing an intermittent complaint should be thoroughly inspected for backed out terminals, improper mating, broken connector locks, improperly formed or damaged terminals, poor terminal-to-wire connections or physical damage to the wiring harness.

If driver's complaint reflects that ABS indicator is only on during moist conditions (rain, snow, wash, etc.), all wheel speed sensor circuitry should be inspected for signs of water intrusion. This can be verified by spraying down suspected areas with a 5 percent salt water solution (2 teaspoons of salt in 12 ozs. of water). Start vehicle and allow to run for 10 seconds. If code returns immediately, replace suspected/tester harness.

IMPORTANT: WHEEL SPEED SENSOR INTERMITTENT MALFUNCTIONS MAY BE DIFFICULT TO LOCATE. CARE SHOULD BE TAKEN NOT TO DISTURB ANY ELECTRICAL CONNECTIONS PRIOR TO AN INDICATED STEP OF THIS CHART. THIS WILL INSURE THAT AN INTERMITTENT CONNECTION WILL NOT BE CORRECTED BEFORE THE SOURCE OF THE MALFUNCTION IS FOUND.

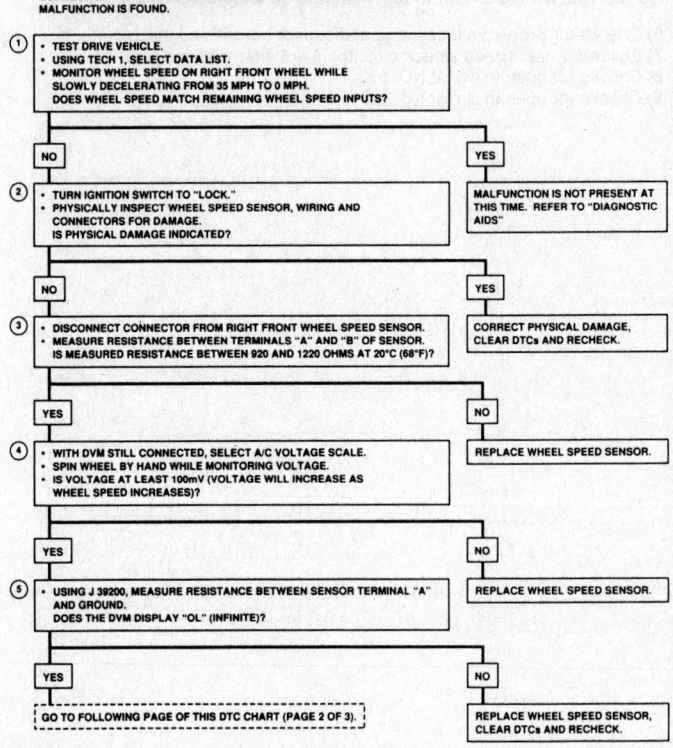

THIS CHART ASSUMES THAT A CURRENT DTC IS STORED INDICATING THAT THIS MALFUNCTION IS PRESENT.

93C84683 93I84721

DTC A022, RIGHT FRONT WHEEL SPEED = 0 OR UNREASONABLE (2 OF 3)

NOTE: Test numbers refer to test numbers on diagnostic chart.

6) Checks for proper voltages at speed sensor harness connector.
7) Ensures wheel speed sensor circuitry is not internally shorted.
8) Checks for open in circuit NO. 833.
9) Checks for open in circuit No. 872.

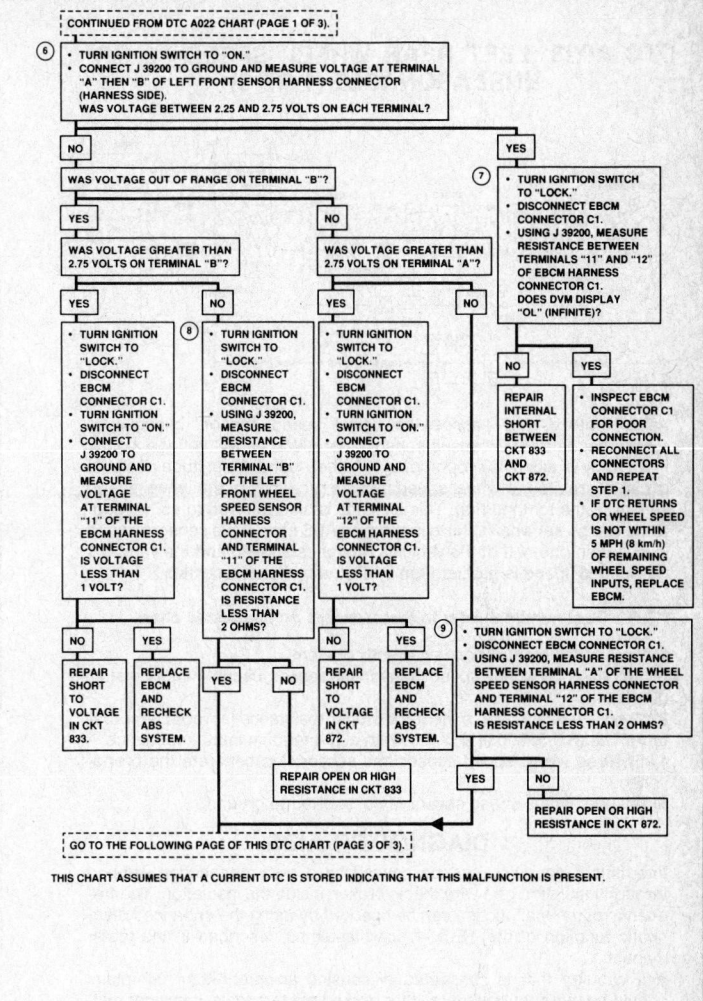

THIS CHART ASSUMES THAT A CURRENT DTC IS STORED INDICATING THAT THIS MALFUNCTION IS PRESENT.

93J84722

Courtesy of General Motors Corp.

DTC A022, RIGHT FRONT WHEEL SPEED = 0 OR UNREASONABLE (3 OF 3)

NOTE: Test numbers refer to test numbers on diagnostic chart.

10) Checks for short to ground in both wheel speed signal circuits.
11) Ensures code was not set due to a poor connection.

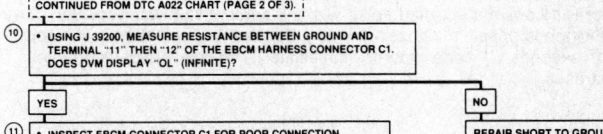

CONTINUED FROM DTC A022 CHART (PAGE 2 OF 3).

10) • USING J 39200, MEASURE RESISTANCE BETWEEN GROUND AND TERMINAL "11" THEN "12" OF THE EBCM HARNESS CONNECTOR C1. DOES DVM DISPLAY "OL" (INFINITE)?

YES → 11) • INSPECT EBCM CONNECTOR C1 FOR POOR CONNECTION. • RECONNECT ALL CONNECTORS AND REPEAT STEP 1. • IF DTC RETURNS OR WHEEL SPEED IS NOT WITHIN 5 MPH (8 km/h) OF REMAINING WHEEL SPEED INPUTS, REPLACE EBCM.

NO → REPAIR SHORT TO GROUND IN CKTs 833 AND 872.

THIS CHART ASSUMES THAT A CURRENT DTC IS STORED INDICATING THAT THIS MALFUNCTION IS PRESENT.

93A84723

Courtesy of General Motors Corp.

DTC A023, LEFT REAR WHEEL SPEED=0 OR UNREASONABLE (1 OF 3)

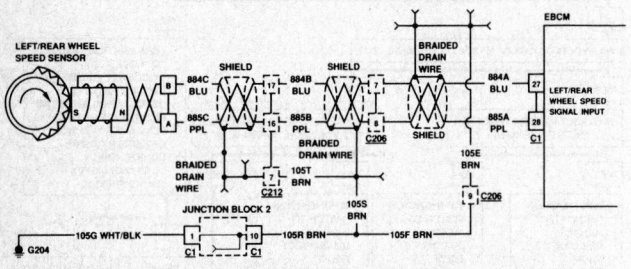

As a toothed ring passes the wheel speed sensor, changes in electromagnetic field causes sensor to produce an AC voltage signal. Frequency of signal is proportional to wheel speed. Magnitude of signal is directly related to wheel speed and the proximity of the wheel speed sensor to the toothed ring. This distance is also referred to as "air gap" Code can be set when vehicle is not in an ABS stop. If the sensors speed is less than one-half of the vehicles referenced speed and the vehicle's referenced speed is greater than 5 MPH, a malfunction exists.

NOTE: Test numbers refer to test numbers on diagnostic chart.

1) Verifies the malfunction is currently present.
2) Identifies a wheel speed sensor or sensor circuit that is visibly damaged.
3) Checks wheel speed sensor for proper resistance (at room temperature). Tester J 39200 is a DVOM with a 10-megohm input impedance.
4) Ensures wheel speed sensor and sensor ring generate the proper voltage.
5) Ensures wheel speed sensor is not shorted to ground.

DIAGNOSTIC AIDS

Intermittent condition can be caused by a poor connection, rubbed through insulation or a wire that is broken inside the insulation. The frequency of the malfunction can be checked by using the enhanced diagnostic function of the TECH-1 scan tester as described in the tester manual.

Any circuitry that is suspected of causing an intermittent complaint should be thoroughly inspected for backed out terminals, improper mating, broken connector locks, improperly formed or damaged terminals, poor terminal-to-wire connections or physical damage to the wiring harness.

If driver's complaint reflects that ABS indicator is only on during moist conditions (rain, snow, wash, etc.), all wheel speed sensor circuitry should be inspected for signs of water intrusion. This can be verified by spraying down suspected areas with a 5 percent salt water solution (2 teaspoons of salt in 12 ozs. of water). Start vehicle and allow to run for 10 seconds. If code returns immediately, replace suspected/tester harness.

IMPORTANT: WHEEL SPEED SENSOR INTERMITTENT MALFUNCTIONS MAY BE DIFFICULT TO LOCATE. CARE SHOULD BE TAKEN NOT TO DISTURB ANY ELECTRICAL CONNECTIONS PRIOR TO AN INDICATED STEP OF THIS CHART. THIS WILL INSURE THAT AN INTERMITTENT CONNECTION WILL NOT BE CORRECTED BEFORE THE SOURCE OF THE MALFUNCTION IS FOUND.

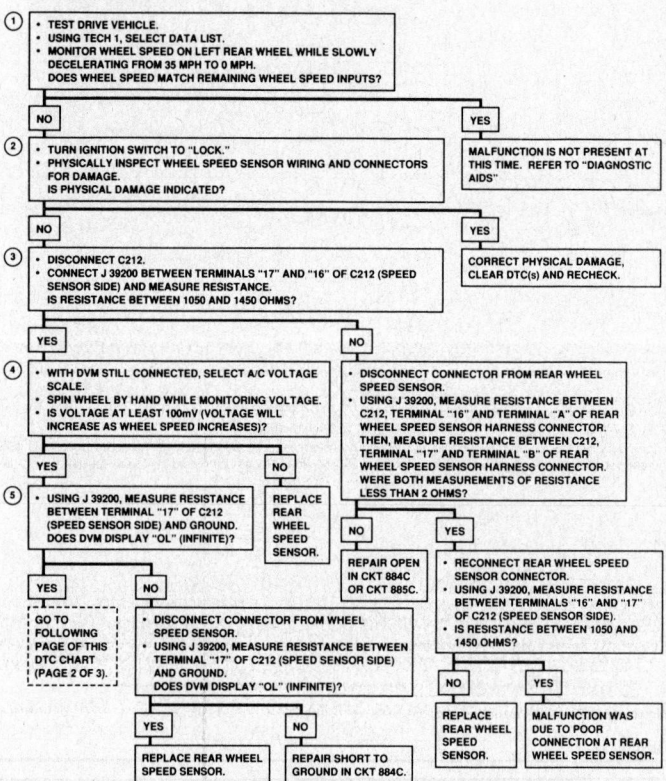

THIS CHART ASSUMES THAT A CURRENT DTC IS STORED INDICATING THAT THIS MALFUNCTION IS PRESENT

93D84684 93B84724

Courtesy of General Motors Corp.

DTC A023, LEFT REAR WHEEL SPEED=0 OR UNREASONABLE (2 OF 3)

NOTE: Test numbers refer to test numbers on diagnostic chart.

6) Checks for proper voltages at speed sensor harness connector.
7) Ensures that wheel speed sensor circuitry is not internally shorted.
8) Checks for open in circuit NO. 884.
9) Checks for open in circuit No. 885.

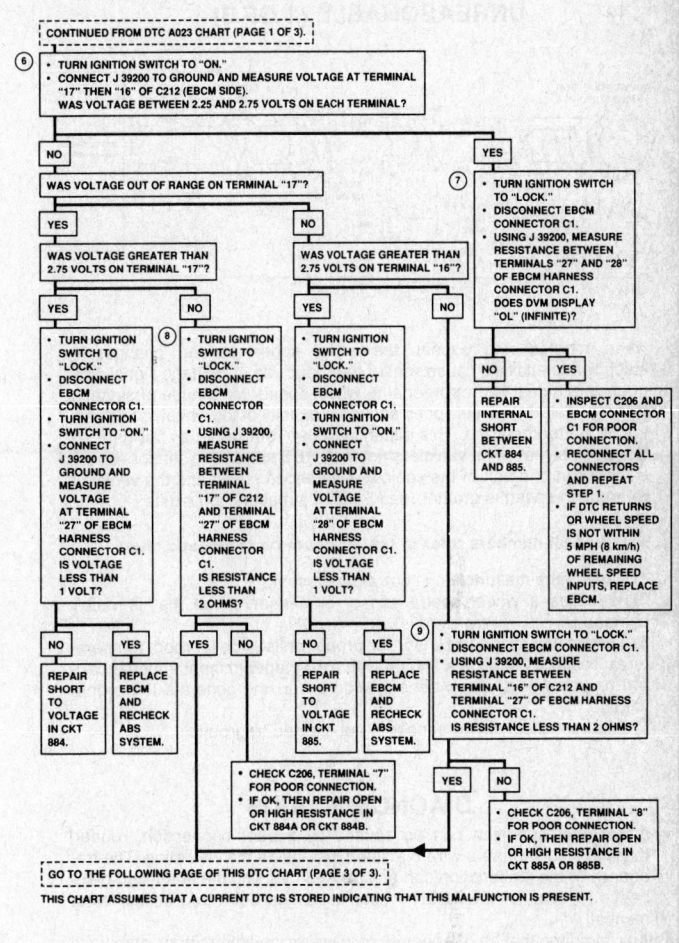

93C84725

Courtesy of General Motors Corp.

DTC A023, LEFT REAR WHEEL SPEED=0 OR UNREASONABLE (3 OF 3)

NOTE: Test numbers refer to test numbers on diagnostic chart.

10) Checks for short to ground in both wheel speed signal circuits.
11) Ensures code was not set due to a poor connection.

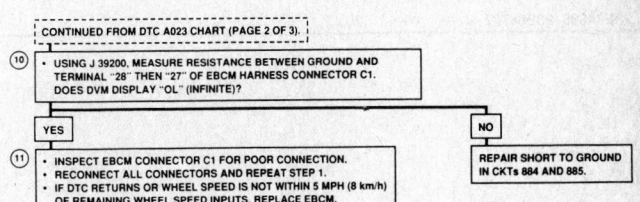

THIS CHART ASSUMES THAT A CURRENT DTC IS STORED INDICATING THAT THIS MALFUNCTION IS PRESENT.

93D84726

Courtesy of General Motors Corp.

DTC A024, RIGHT REAR WHEEL SPEED=0 OR UNREASONABLE (1 OF 3)

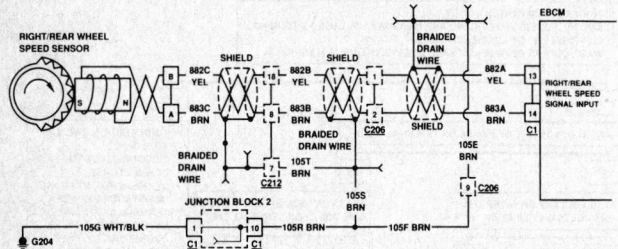

As a toothed ring passes the wheel speed sensor, changes in electromagnetic field cause sensor to produce an AC voltage signal. Frequency of signal is proportional to wheel speed. Magnitude of signal is directly related to wheel speed and the proximity of the wheel speed sensor to the toothed ring. This distance is also referred to as "air gap" Code can be set when vehicle is not in an ABS stop. If the sensors speed is less than one-half of the vehicles referenced speed and the vehicle's referenced speed is greater than 5 MPH, a malfunction exists.

NOTE: Test numbers refer to test numbers on diagnostic chart.

1) Verifies the malfunction is currently present.
2) Identifies a wheel speed sensor or sensor circuit that is visibly damaged.
3) Checks wheel speed sensor for proper resistance (at room temperature). Tester J 39200 is a DVOM with a 10-megohm input impedance.
4) Ensures wheel speed sensor and sensor ring generate the proper voltage.
5) Ensures wheel speed sensor is not shorted to ground.

DIAGNOSTIC AIDS

Intermittent condition can be caused by a poor connection, rubbed through insulation or a wire that is broken inside the insulation. The frequency of the malfunction can be checked by using the enhanced diagnostic function of the TECH-1 scan tester as described in the tester manual.
Any circuitry that is suspected of causing an intermittent complaint should be thoroughly inspected for backed out terminals, improper mating, broken connector locks, improperly formed or damaged terminals, poor terminal-to-wire connections or physical damage to the wiring harness.

93E84685 93E84727

If driver's complaint reflects that ABS indicator is only on during moist conditions (rain, snow, wash, etc.), all wheel speed sensor circuitry should be inspected for signs of water intrusion. This can be verified by spraying down suspected areas with a 5 percent salt water solution (2 teaspoons of salt in 12 ozs. of water). Start vehicle and allow to run for 10 seconds. If code returns immediately, replace suspected/tester harness.

IMPORTANT: WHEEL SPEED SENSOR INTERMITTENT MALFUNCTIONS MAY BE DIFFICULT TO LOCATE. CARE SHOULD BE TAKEN NOT TO DISTURB ANY ELECTRICAL CONNECTIONS PRIOR TO AN INDICATED STEP OF THIS CHART. THIS WILL INSURE THAT AN INTERMITTENT CONNECTION WILL NOT BE CORRECTED BEFORE THE SOURCE OF THE MALFUNCTION IS FOUND.

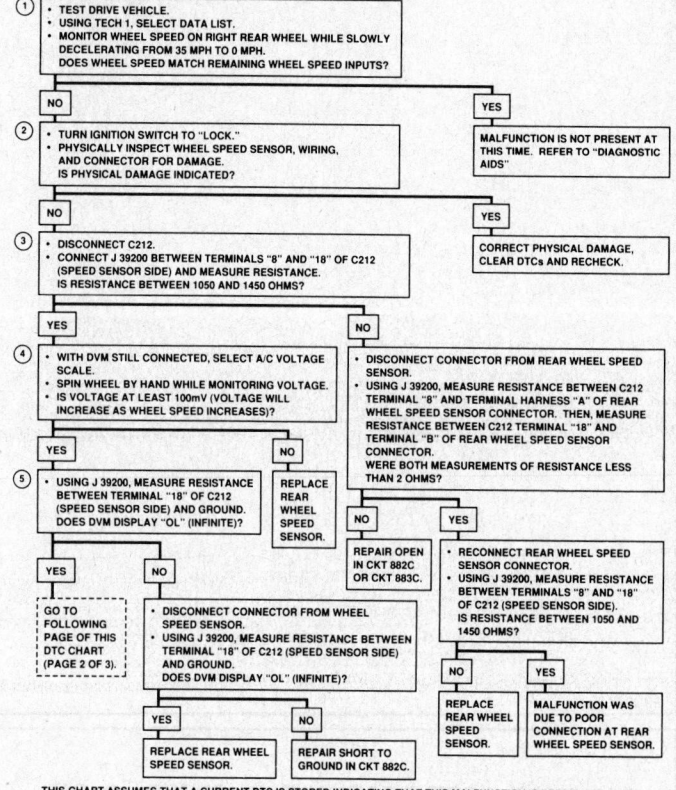

THIS CHART ASSUMES THAT A CURRENT DTC IS STORED INDICATING THAT THIS MALFUNCTION IS PRESENT.

Courtesy of General Motors Corp.

DTC A024, RIGHT REAR WHEEL SPEED=0 OR UNREASONABLE (2 OF 3)

NOTE: Test numbers refer to test numbers on diagnostic chart.

6) Checks for proper voltages at speed sensor harness connector.
7) Ensures wheel speed sensor circuitry is not internally shorted.
8) Checks for open in circuit NO. 882.
9) Checks for open in circuit No. 883.

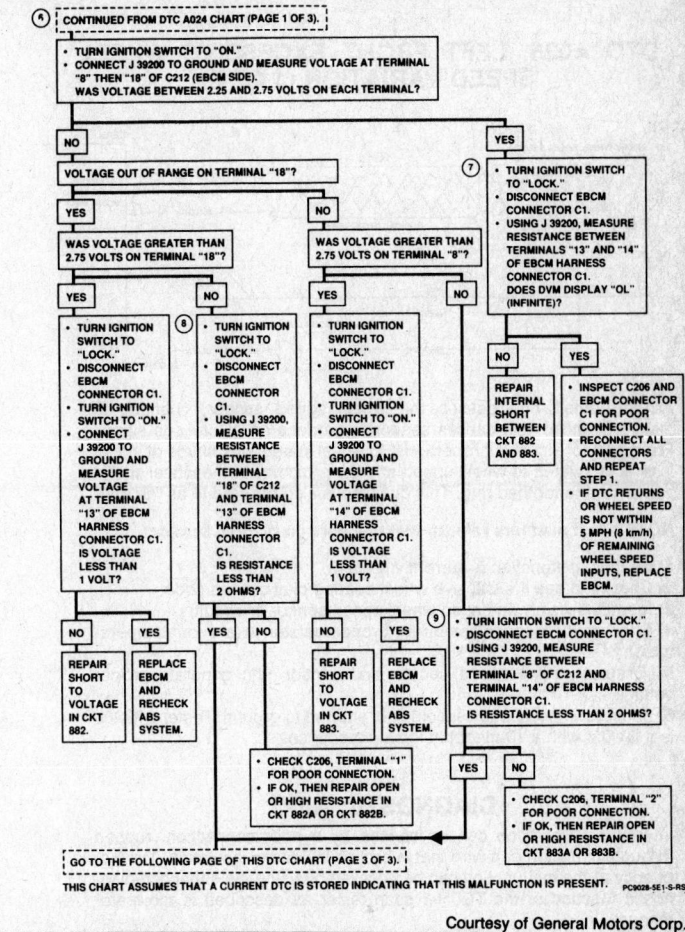

THIS CHART ASSUMES THAT A CURRENT DTC IS STORED INDICATING THAT THIS MALFUNCTION IS PRESENT.

PC9028-5E1-S-RS

93F84728

Courtesy of General Motors Corp.

DTC A024, RIGHT REAR WHEEL SPEED=0 OR UNREASONABLE (3 OF 3)

NOTE: Test numbers refer to test numbers on diagnostic chart.

10) Checks for short to ground in both wheel speed signal circuits.
11) Ensures code was not set due to a poor connection.

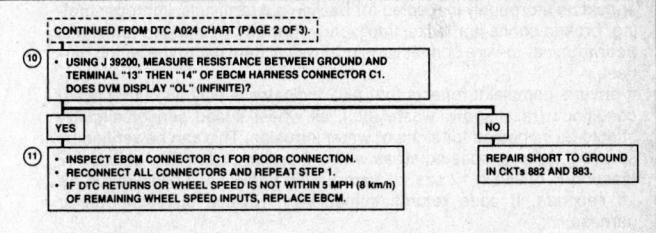

THIS CHART ASSUMES THAT A CURRENT DTC IS STORED INDICATING THAT THIS MALFUNCTION IS PRESENT.

93G84729

Courtesy of General Motors Corp.

DTC A025, LEFT FRONT EXCESSIVE WHEEL SPEED VARIATION (1 OF 3)

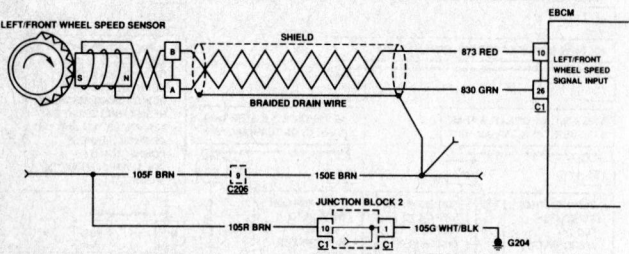

As a toothed ring passes the wheel speed sensor, changes in electromagnetic field causes sensor to produce an AC voltage signal. Frequency of signal is proportional to wheel speed. Magnitude of signal is directly related to wheel speed and the proximity of the wheel speed sensor to the toothed ring. This distance is also referred to as "air gap"

NOTE: Test numbers refer to test numbers on diagnostic chart.

1) Verifies malfunction is currently present.
2) Checks to see if excessive wheel bearing play caused code.
3) Identifies visibly damaged wheel speed sensor or circuitry.
4) Checks wheel speed sensor for proper resistance (at room temperature).
5) Ensures wheel speed sensor and sensor ring generate proper voltage.
6) Ensures wheel speed sensor is not shorted to ground. Tester J 39200 is a DVOM with a 10-megohm input impedance.

DIAGNOSTIC AIDS

Intermittent condition can be caused by a poor connection, rubbed through insulation or a wire that is broken inside the insulation. The frequency of the malfunction can be checked by using the enhanced diagnostic function of the TECH-1 scan tester as described in the tester manual.

Any circuitry that is suspected of causing an intermittent complaint should be thoroughly inspected for backed out terminals, improper mating, broken connector locks, improperly formed or damaged terminals, poor terminal-to-wire connections or physical damage to the wiring harness.

If driver's complaint reflects that ABS indicator is only on during moist conditions (rain, snow, wash, etc.), all wheel speed sensor circuitry should be inspected for signs of water intrusion. This can be verified by spraying down suspected areas with a 5 percent salt water solution (2 teaspoons of salt in 12 ozs. of water). Start vehicle and allow to run for 10 seconds. If code returns immediately, replace suspected/tester harness.

IMPORTANT: WHEEL SPEED SENSOR INTERMITTENT MALFUNCTIONS MAY BE DIFFICULT TO LOCATE. CARE SHOULD BE TAKEN NOT TO DISTURB ANY ELECTRICAL CONNECTIONS PRIOR TO AN INDICATED STEP OF THIS CHART. THIS WILL INSURE THAT AN INTERMITTENT CONNECTION WILL NOT BE CORRECTED BEFORE THE SOURCE OF THE MALFUNCTION IS FOUND.

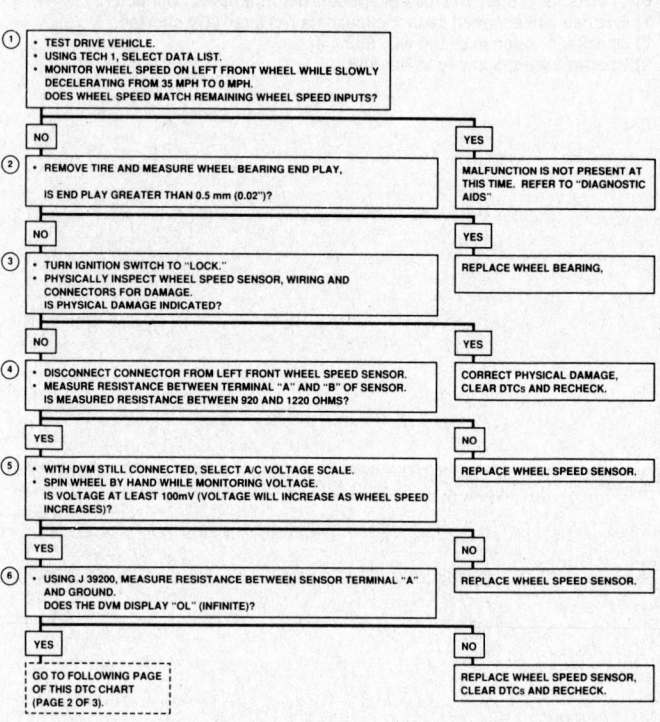

THIS CHART ASSUMES THAT A CURRENT DTC IS STORED INDICATING THAT THIS MALFUNCTION IS PRESENT.

DTC A025, LEFT FRONT EXCESSIVE WHEEL SPEED VARIATION (2 OF 3)

NOTE: Test numbers refer to test numbers on diagnostic chart.

6) Checks for proper voltages at speed sensor harness connector.
7) Checks for proper voltages at speed sensor harness connector.
8) Ensures wheel speed sensor circuitry is not internally shorted.
9) Checks for open in circuit No. 873.
10) Checks for open in circuit No. 830.

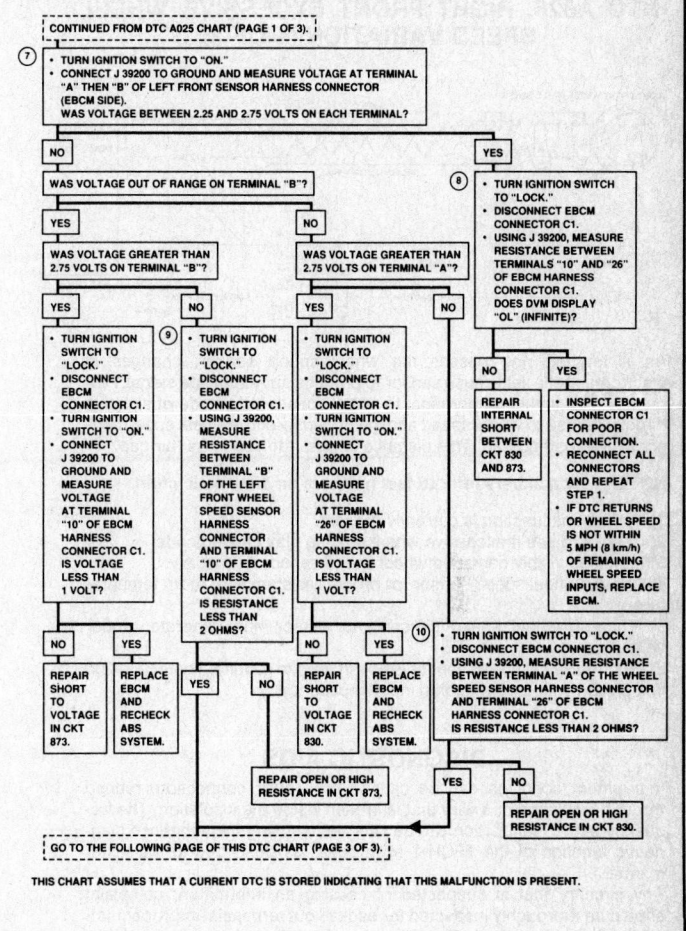

THIS CHART ASSUMES THAT A CURRENT DTC IS STORED INDICATING THAT THIS MALFUNCTION IS PRESENT.

93A84731

Courtesy of General Motors Corp.

DTC A025, LEFT FRONT EXCESSIVE WHEEL SPEED VARIATION (3 OF 3)

NOTE: Test numbers refer to test numbers on diagnostic chart.

11) Checks for short to ground in both wheel speed signal circuits.
12) Ensures code was not set due to a poor connection between EBCM connector and EBCM.

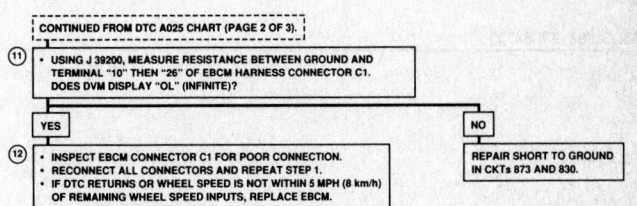

93B84732

Courtesy of General Motors Corp.

DTC A026, RIGHT FRONT EXCESSIVE WHEEL SPEED VARIATION (1 OF 3)

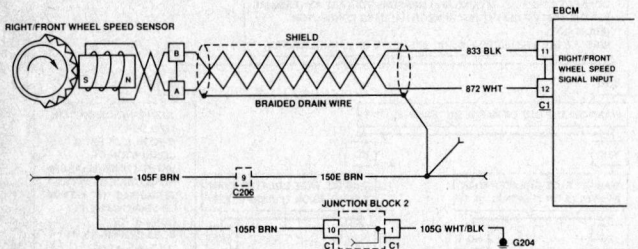

As a toothed ring passes the wheel speed sensor, changes in electromagnetic field cause sensor to produce an AC voltage signal. Frequency of signal is proportional to wheel speed. Magnitude of signal is directly related to wheel speed and the proximity of the wheel speed sensor to the toothed ring. This distance is also referred to as "air gap"

NOTE: Test numbers refer to test numbers on diagnostic chart.

1) Verifies malfunction is currently present.
2) Checks to see if excessive wheel bearing play caused code.
3) Identifies visibly damaged wheel speed sensor or circuitry.
4) Checks wheel speed sensor for proper resistance (at room temperature).
5) Ensures wheel speed sensor and sensor ring generate proper voltage.
6) Ensures wheel speed sensor is not shorted to ground. Tester J 39200 is a DVOM with a 10-megohm input impedance.

DIAGNOSTIC AIDS

Intermittent condition can be caused by a poor connection, rubbed through insulation or a wire that is broken inside the insulation. The frequency of the malfunction can be checked by using the enhanced diagnostic function of the TECH-1 scan tester as described in the tester manual.

Any circuitry that is suspected of causing an intermittent complaint should be thoroughly inspected for backed out terminals, improper mating, broken connector locks, improperly formed or damaged terminals, poor terminal-to-wire connections or physical damage to the wiring harness.

If driver's complaint reflects that ABS indicator is only on during moist conditions (rain, snow, wash, etc.), all wheel speed sensor circuitry should be inspected for signs of water intrusion. This can be verified by spraying down suspected areas with a 5 percent salt water solution (2 teaspoons of salt in 12 ozs. of water). Start vehicle and allow to run for 10 seconds. If code returns immediately, replace suspected/tester harness.

IMPORTANT: WHEEL SPEED SENSOR INTERMITTENT MALFUNCTIONS MAY BE DIFFICULT TO LOCATE. CARE SHOULD BE TAKEN NOT TO DISTURB ANY ELECTRICAL CONNECTIONS PRIOR TO AN INDICATED STEP OF THIS CHART. THIS WILL INSURE THAT AN INTERMITTENT CONNECTION WILL NOT BE CORRECTED BEFORE THE SOURCE OF THE MALFUNCTION IS FOUND.

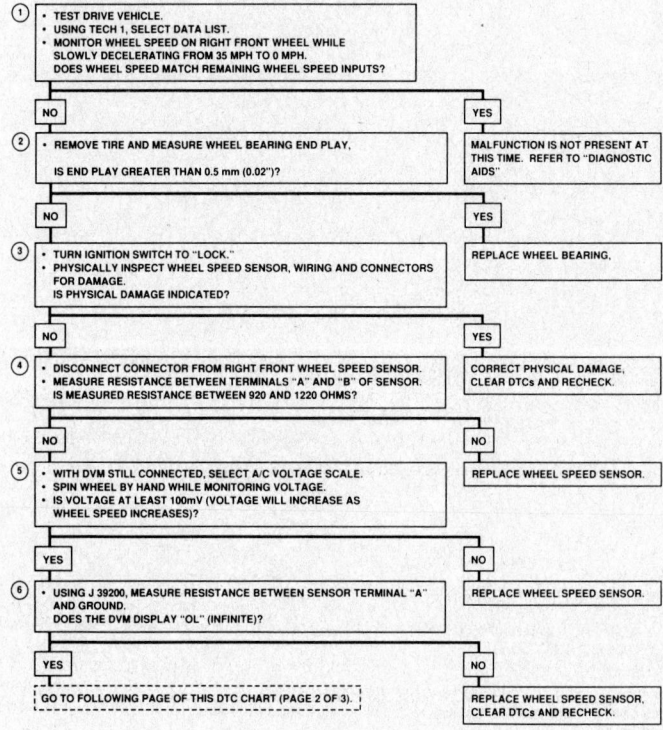

THIS CHART ASSUMES THAT A CURRENT DTC IS STORED INDICATING THAT THIS MALFUNCTION IS PRESENT.

DTC A026, RIGHT FRONT EXCESSIVE WHEEL SPEED VARIATION (2 OF 3)

NOTE: Test numbers refer to test numbers on diagnostic chart.

7) Checks for proper voltages at speed sensor harness connector.
8) Ensures wheel speed sensor circuitry is not internally shorted.
9) Checks for open in circuit No. 833.
10) Checks for open in circuit No. 873.

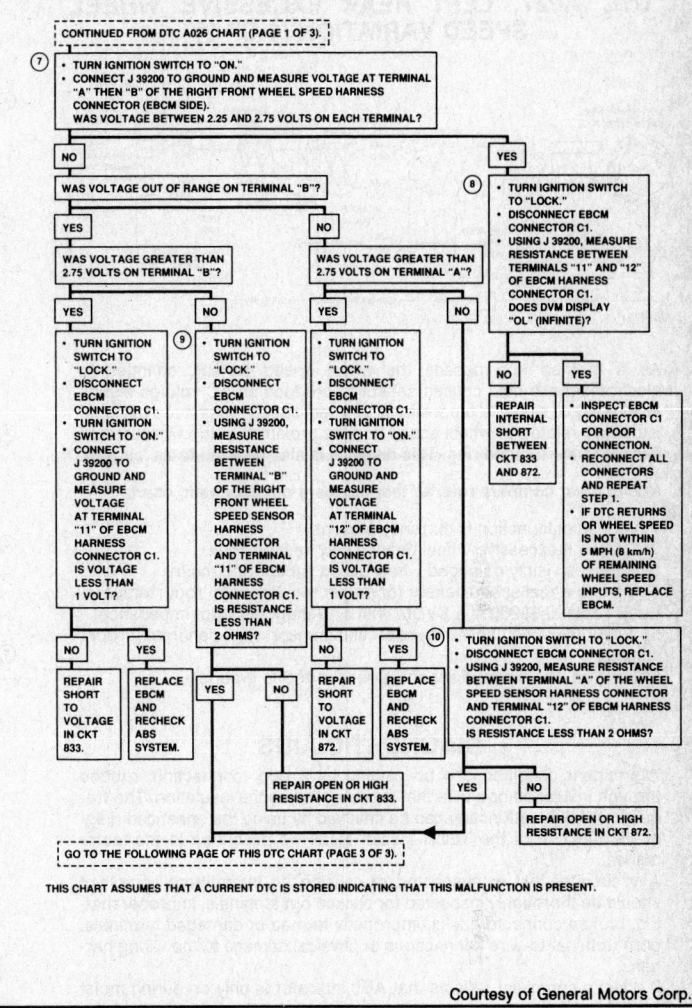

THIS CHART ASSUMES THAT A CURRENT DTC IS STORED INDICATING THAT THIS MALFUNCTION IS PRESENT.

93D84734

Courtesy of General Motors Corp.

DTC A026, RIGHT FRONT EXCESSIVE WHEEL SPEED VARIATION (3 OF 3)

NOTE: Test numbers refer to test numbers on diagnostic chart.

11) Checks for short to ground in both wheel speed signal circuits.
12) Ensures code was not set due to a poor connection between EBCM connector and EBCM.

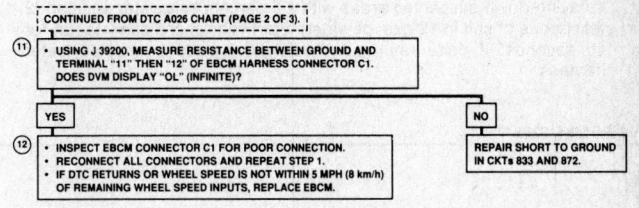

THIS CHART ASSUMES THAT A CURRENT DTC IS STORED INDICATING THAT THIS MALFUNCTION IS PRESENT.

93E84735

Courtesy of General Motors Corp.

DTC A027, LEFT REAR EXCESSIVE WHEEL SPEED VARIATION (1 OF 3)

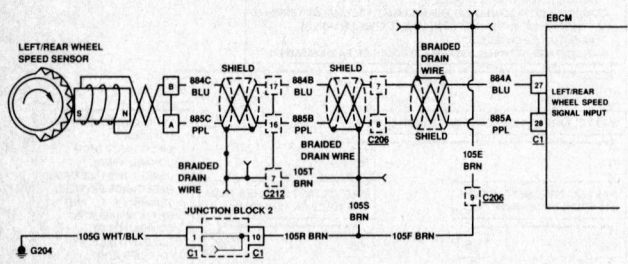

As a toothed ring passes the wheel speed sensor, changes in electromagnetic field causes sensor to produce an AC voltage signal. Frequency of signal is proportional to wheel speed. Magnitude of signal is directly related to wheel speed and the proximity of the wheel speed sensor to the toothed ring. This distance is also referred to as "air gap"

NOTE: Test numbers refer to test numbers on diagnostic chart.

1) Verifies malfunction is currently present.
2) Checks if excessive wheel bearing play caused code.
3) Identifies visibly damaged wheel speed sensor or circuitry.
4) Checks wheel speed sensor for proper resistance (at room temperature). Tester J 39200 is a DVOM with a 10-megohm input impedance.
5) Ensures wheel speed sensor and sensor ring generate proper voltage.
6) Ensures wheel speed sensor is not shorted to ground.

DIAGNOSTIC AIDS

Intermittent condition can be caused by a poor connection, rubbed through insulation or a wire that is broken inside the insulation. The frequency of the malfunction can be checked by using the enhanced diagnostic function of the TECH-1 scan tester as described in the tester manual.

Any circuitry that is suspected of causing an intermittent complaint should be thoroughly inspected for backed out terminals, improper mating, broken connector locks, improperly formed or damaged terminals, poor terminal-to-wire connections or physical damage to the wiring harness.

If driver's complaint reflects that ABS indicator is only on during moist conditions (rain, snow, wash, etc.), all wheel speed sensor circuitry should be inspected for signs of water intrusion. This can be verified by spraying down suspected areas with a 5 percent salt water solution (2 teaspoons of salt in 12 ozs. of water). Start vehicle and allow to run for 10 seconds. If code returns immediately, replace suspected/tester harness.

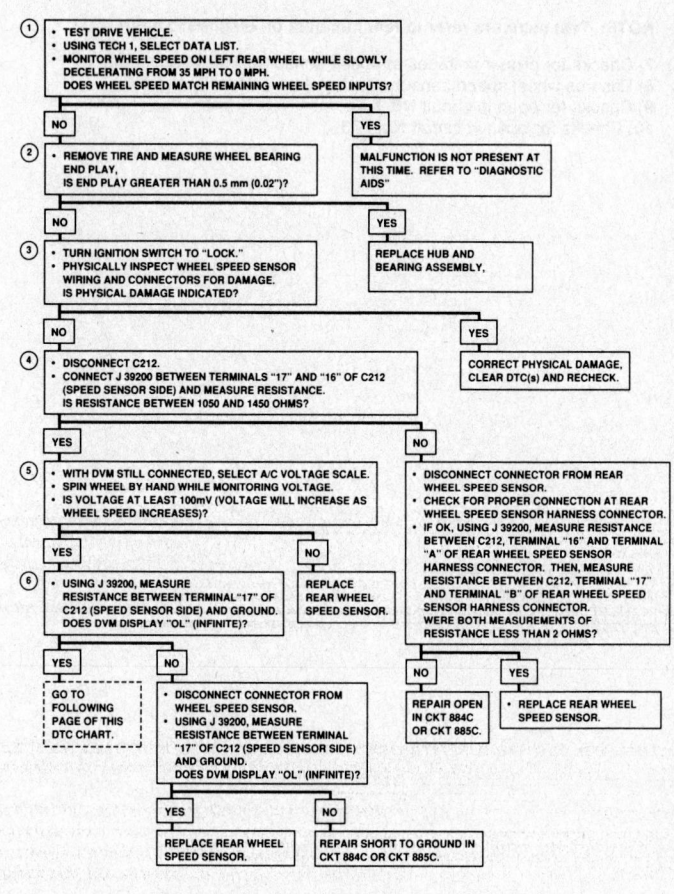

THIS CHART ASSUMES THAT A CURRENT DTC IS STORED INDICATING THAT THIS MALFUNCTION IS PRESENT.

93D84684 93F84736

DTC A027, LEFT REAR EXCESSIVE WHEEL SPEED VARIATION (2 OF 3)

NOTE: Test numbers refer to test numbers on diagnostic chart.

7) Checks for proper voltages at speed sensor harness connector.
8) Ensures wheel speed sensor circuitry is not internally shorted.
9) Checks for open in circuit No. 884A or 884B.
10) Checks for open in circuit No. 885A or 885B.

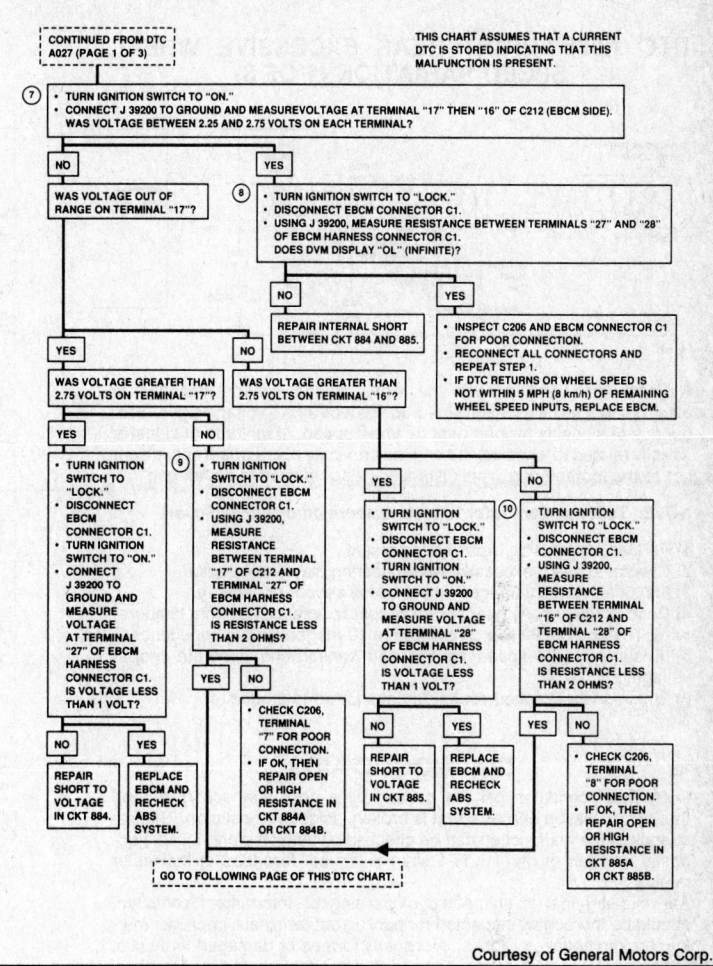

93G84737

Courtesy of General Motors Corp.

DTC A027, LEFT REAR EXCESSIVE WHEEL SPEED VARIATION (3 OF 3)

NOTE: Test numbers refer to test numbers on diagnostic chart.

11) Checks for short to ground in both wheel speed signal circuits.
12) Ensures code was not set due to a poor connection between EBCM connector and EBCM.

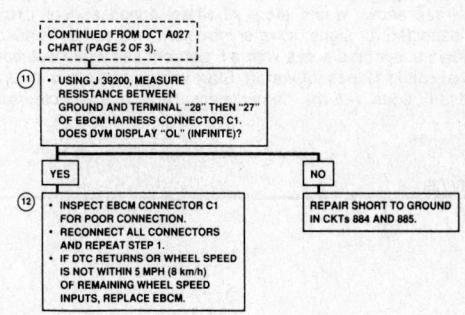

THIS CHART ASSUMES THAT A CURRENT DTC IS STORED INDICATING THAT THIS MALFUNCTION IS PRESENT.

93H84738

Courtesy of General Motors Corp.

DTC A028, RIGHT REAR EXCESSIVE WHEEL SPEED VARIATION (1 OF 3)

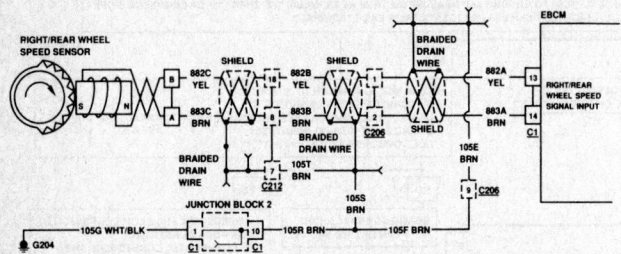

As a toothed ring passes the wheel speed sensor, changes in electromagnetic field cause sensor to produce an AC voltage signal. Frequency of signal is proportional to wheel speed. Magnitude of signal is directly related to wheel speed and the proximity of the wheel speed sensor to the toothed ring. This distance is also referred to as "air gap"

NOTE: Test numbers refer to test numbers on diagnostic chart.

1) Verifies malfunction is currently present.
2) Checks to see if excessive wheel bearing play caused code.
3) Identifies visibly damaged wheel speed sensor or circuitry.
4) Checks wheel speed sensor for proper resistance (at room temperature). Tester J 39200 is a DVOM with a 10-megohm input impedance.
5) Ensures wheel speed sensor and sensor ring generate proper voltage.
6) Ensures wheel speed sensor is not shorted to ground.

DIAGNOSTIC AIDS

Intermittent condition can be caused by a poor connection, rubbed through insulation or a wire that is broken inside the insulation. The frequency of the malfunction can be checked by using the enhanced diagnostic function of the TECH-1 scan tester as described in the tester manual.

Any circuitry that is suspected of causing an intermittent complaint should be thoroughly inspected for backed out terminals, improper mating, broken connector locks, improperly formed or damaged terminals, poor terminal-to-wire connections or physical damage to the wiring harness.

If driver's complaint reflects that ABS indicator is only on during moist conditions (rain, snow, wash, etc.), all wheel speed sensor circuitry should be inspected for signs of water intrusion. This can be verified by spraying down suspected areas with a 5 percent salt water solution (2 teaspoons of salt in 12 ozs. of water). Start vehicle and allow to run for 10 seconds. If code returns immediately, replace suspected/tester harness.

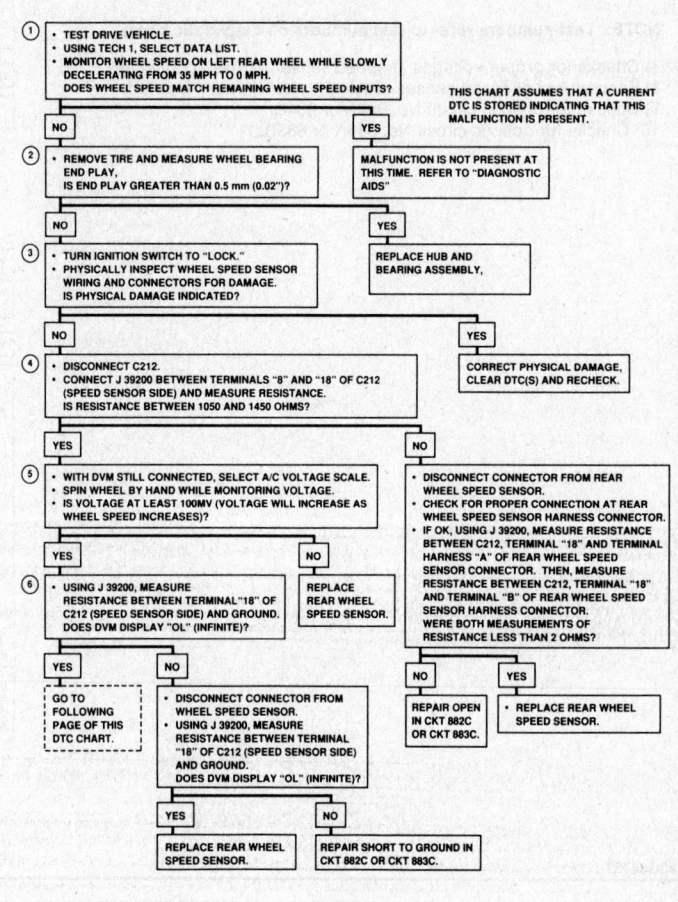

DTC A028, RIGHT REAR EXCESSIVE WHEEL SPEED VARIATION (2 OF 3)

NOTE: Test numbers refer to test numbers on diagnostic chart.

7) Checks for proper voltages at speed sensor harness connector.
8) Ensures wheel speed sensor circuitry is not internally shorted.
9) Checks for open in circuit No. 882A or 882B.
10) Checks for open in circuit No. 883A or 883B.

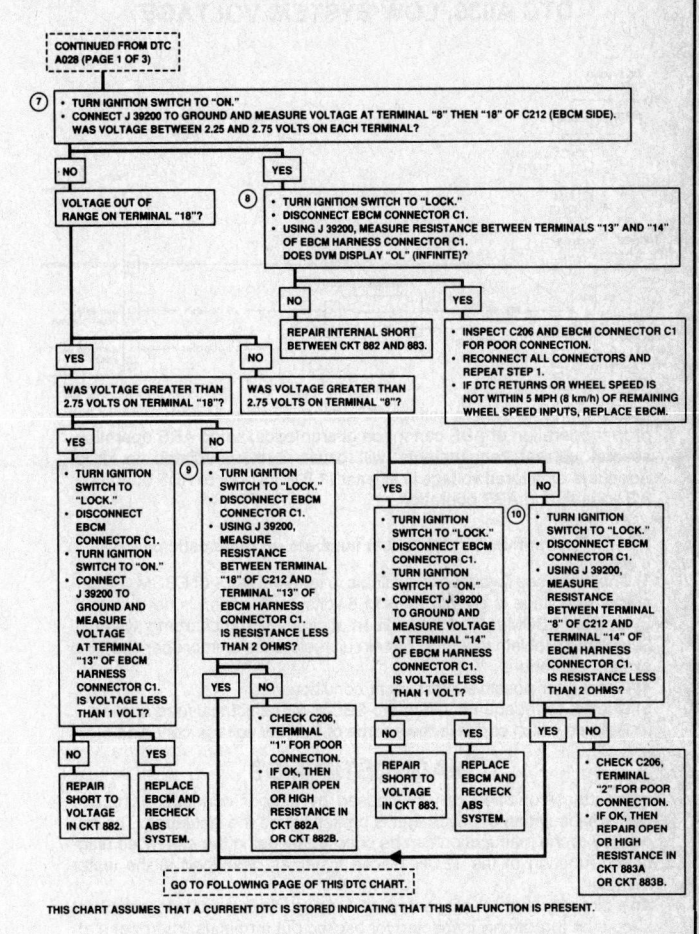

93B84740

Courtesy of General Motors Corp.

DTC A028, RIGHT REAR EXCESSIVE WHEEL SPEED VARIATION (3 OF 3)

NOTE: Test numbers refer to test numbers on diagnostic chart.

11) Checks for short to ground in both wheel speed signal circuits.
12) Ensures code was not set due to a poor connection between EBCM connector and EBCM.

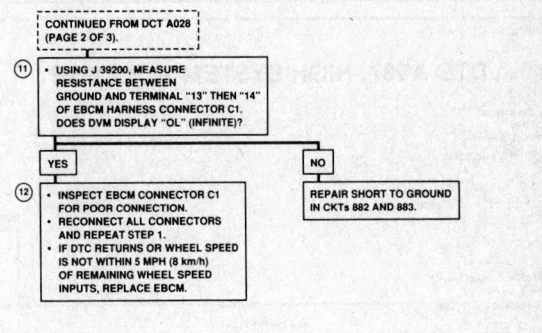

93C84741

Courtesy of General Motors Corp.

DTC A036, LOW SYSTEM VOLTAGE

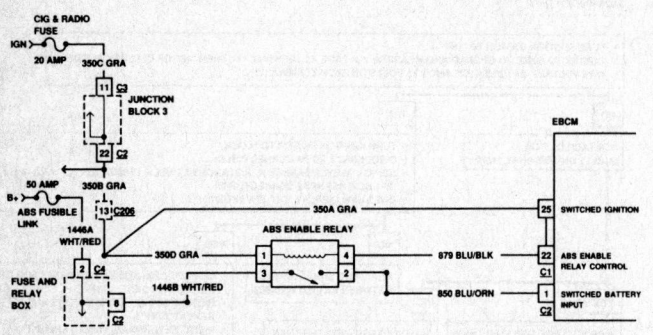

EBCM monitors system voltage. If voltage drops to less than 11 volts, proper operation of ABS cannot be guaranteed. During ABS operation, several current requirements will cause system voltage to drop. Adequate monitored voltage is at least 11.8 volts prior to ABS operation, 9.3 volts during ABS operation.

NOTE: Test numbers refer to test numbers on diagnostic chart.

1) Checks to see if voltage is available to terminal No. 1 of EBCM C1 connector. If voltage is greater than 11.8 volts, malfunction is not present.
2) Isolates EBCM to check condition of circuitry and charging system.
3) Isolates problem to either high circuit resistance or improper charging system operation.
4) Checks for possible intermittent condition.
5) Checks for adequate voltage to EBCM with electrical load applied.
6) Isolates which circuit is the source of the low voltage condition.

DIAGNOSTIC AIDS

Intermittent condition can be caused by a poor connection, rubbed through insulation or a wire that is broken inside the insulation. The frequency of the malfunction can be checked by using the enhanced diagnostic function of the TECH-1 scan tester as described in the tester manual.

Any circuitry that is suspected of causing an intermittent complaint should be thoroughly inspected for backed out terminals, improper mating, broken connector locks, improperly formed or damaged terminals, poor terminal-to-wire connections or physical damage to the wiring harness.

While performing a voltage load test, if it is noted that only ignition voltage drops below acceptable voltage levels, circuit No. 350D should be checked for high resistance or an open condition.

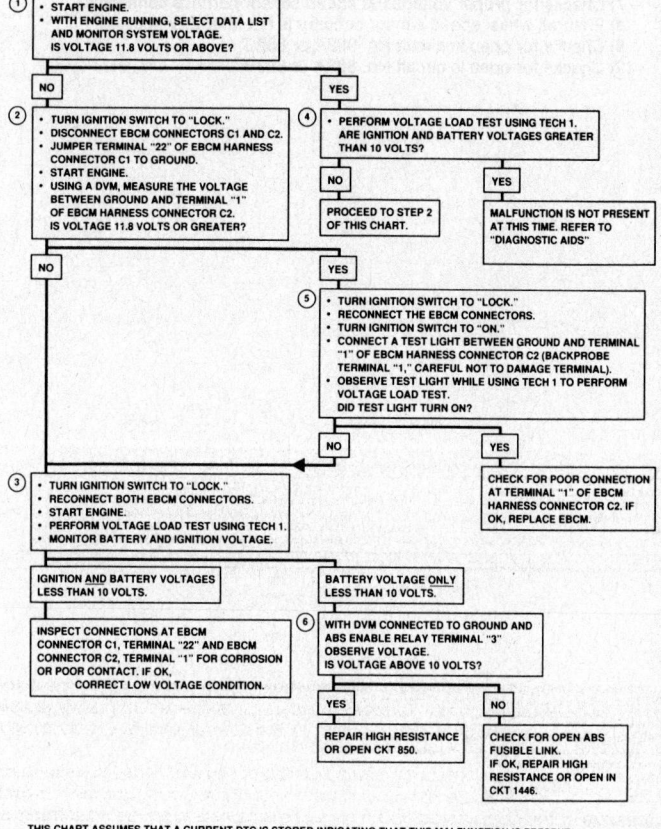

THIS CHART ASSUMES THAT A CURRENT DTC IS STORED INDICATING THAT THIS MALFUNCTION IS PRESENT.

93A84681 93D84742

Courtesy of General Motors Corp.

DTC A037, HIGH SYSTEM VOLTAGE

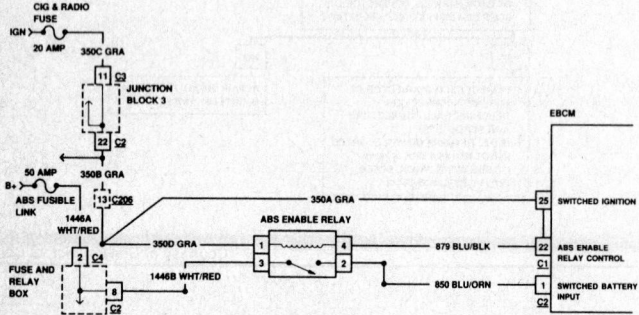

If EBCM detects high system voltage prior to any required motor movement (initialization or ABS operation). If excessive voltage exists, demagnetization of motor magnets may occur, which would eventually affect or eliminate ABS performance.

NOTE: Test numbers refer to test numbers on diagnostic chart.

1) Checks voltage being received by EBCM.
2) Indicates whether high voltage condition is caused by malfunctioning charging system or by EBCM.

DIAGNOSTIC AIDS

Intermittent condition can be caused by a poor connection, rubbed through insulation or a wire that is broken inside the insulation. The frequency of the malfunction can be checked by using the enhanced diagnostic function of the TECH-1 scan tester as described in the tester manual.

Any circuitry that is suspected of causing an intermittent complaint should be thoroughly inspected for backed out terminals, improper mating, broken connector locks, improperly formed or damaged terminals, poor terminal-to-wire connections or physical damage to the wiring harness.

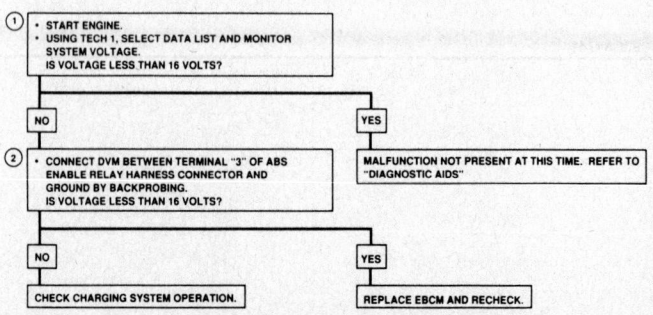

THIS CHART ASSUMES THAT A CURRENT DTC IS STORED INDICATING THAT THIS MALFUNCTION IS PRESENT.

93A84681 93E84743

Courtesy of General Motors Corp.

DTC A038, LEFT FRONT ESB WILL NOT HOLD MOTOR

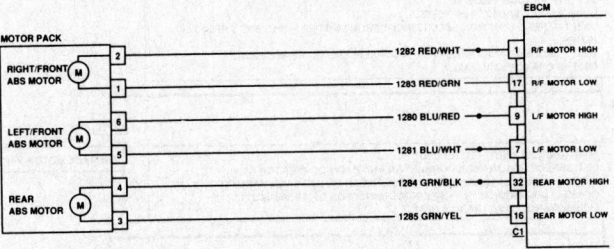

EBCM monitors ESB for slippage. During initialization and braking, motor is rehomed. If ESB slips, motor/piston will move. During the next ignition initialization, a rehome of the motor verifies motor/piston remained at home position. If motor movement is detected, ESB must be slipping.

NOTE: Test numbers refer to test numbers on diagnostic chart.

1) Checks ESB. A broken or defective ESB would result in the left front piston being backdriven by hydraulic pressure and pedal movement would result.
2) Checks for high resistance in motor high circuit.
3) Checks for high resistance in motor low circuit. Tester J 39200 is a DVOM with a 10-megohm input impedance.
4) Checks for high resistance in motor.
5) Determines if fault is due to poor terminal contact or corrosion.
6) Determines if fault is due to faulty EBCM.

DIAGNOSTIC AIDS

An intermittent malfunction may result from a mechanical part sticking, binding or slipping.

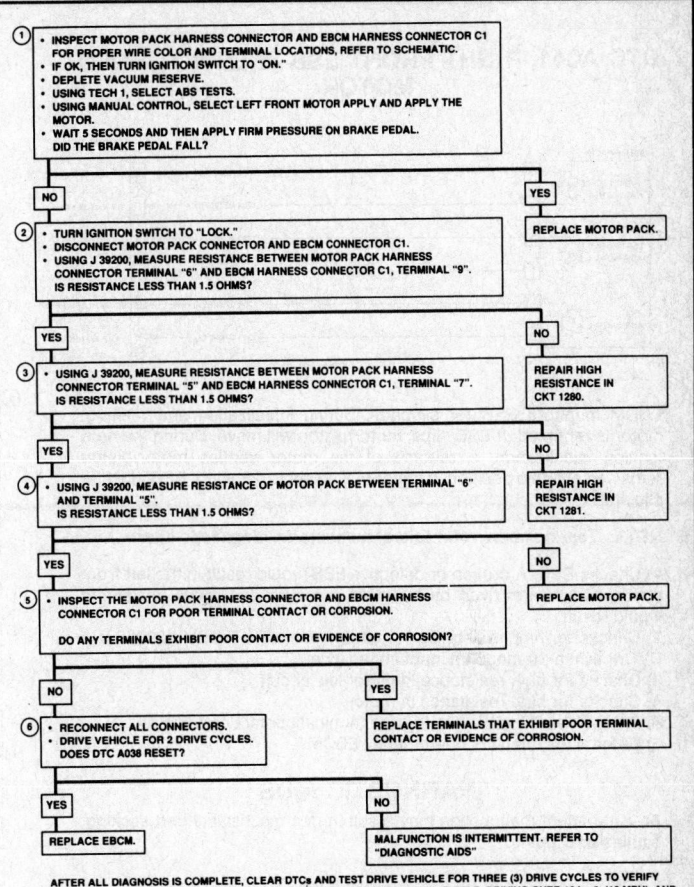

1)
- INSPECT MOTOR PACK HARNESS CONNECTOR AND EBCM HARNESS CONNECTOR C1 FOR PROPER WIRE COLOR AND TERMINAL LOCATIONS, REFER TO SCHEMATIC.
- IF OK, THEN TURN IGNITION SWITCH TO "ON."
- DEPLETE VACUUM RESERVE.
- USING TECH 1, SELECT ABS TESTS.
- USING MANUAL CONTROL, SELECT LEFT FRONT MOTOR APPLY AND APPLY THE MOTOR.
- WAIT 5 SECONDS AND THEN APPLY FIRM PRESSURE ON BRAKE PEDAL.
  DID THE BRAKE PEDAL FALL?

NO → YES → REPLACE MOTOR PACK.

2)
- TURN IGNITION SWITCH TO "LOCK."
- DISCONNECT MOTOR PACK CONNECTOR AND EBCM CONNECTOR C1.
- USING J 39200, MEASURE RESISTANCE BETWEEN MOTOR PACK HARNESS CONNECTOR TERMINAL "6" AND EBCM HARNESS CONNECTOR C1, TERMINAL "9".
  IS RESISTANCE LESS THAN 1.5 OHMS?

YES → NO → REPAIR HIGH RESISTANCE IN CKT 1280.

3)
- USING J 39200, MEASURE RESISTANCE BETWEEN MOTOR PACK HARNESS CONNECTOR TERMINAL "5" AND EBCM HARNESS CONNECTOR C1, TERMINAL "7".
  IS RESISTANCE LESS THAN 1.5 OHMS?

YES → NO → REPAIR HIGH RESISTANCE IN CKT 1281.

4)
- USING J 39200, MEASURE RESISTANCE OF MOTOR PACK BETWEEN TERMINAL "6" AND TERMINAL "5".
  IS RESISTANCE LESS THAN 1.5 OHMS?

YES → NO → REPLACE MOTOR PACK.

5)
- INSPECT THE MOTOR PACK HARNESS CONNECTOR AND EBCM HARNESS CONNECTOR C1 FOR POOR TERMINAL CONTACT OR CORROSION.

  DO ANY TERMINALS EXHIBIT POOR CONTACT OR EVIDENCE OF CORROSION?

NO → YES → REPLACE TERMINALS THAT EXHIBIT POOR TERMINAL CONTACT OR EVIDENCE OF CORROSION.

6)
- RECONNECT ALL CONNECTORS.
- DRIVE VEHICLE FOR 2 DRIVE CYCLES.
  DOES DTC A038 RESET?

YES → REPLACE EBCM.

NO → MALFUNCTION IS INTERMITTENT. REFER TO "DIAGNOSTIC AIDS"

AFTER ALL DIAGNOSIS IS COMPLETE, CLEAR DTCs AND TEST DRIVE VEHICLE FOR THREE (3) DRIVE CYCLES TO VERIFY THAT DTC DOES NOT RESET. A DRIVE CYCLE CONSISTS OF STARTING THE VEHICLE, DRIVING OVER 16 km/h (10 MPH), AND THEN KEYING DOWN.

93F84686 93F84744

DTC A041, RIGHT FRONT ESB WILL NOT HOLD MOTOR

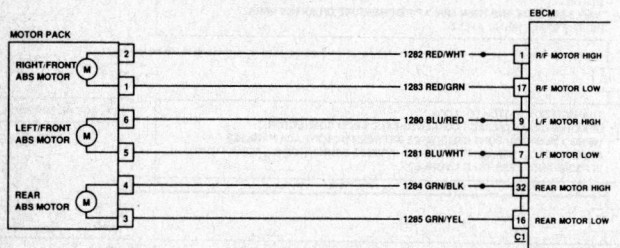

EBCM monitors ESB for slippage. During initialization and braking, motor is rehomed. If ESB slips, motor/piston will move. During the next ignition initialization, a rehome of the motor verifies motor/piston remained at home position. If motor movement is detected, ESB must be slipping.

NOTE: Test numbers refer to test numbers on diagnostic chart.

1) Checks ESB. A broken or defective ESB would result in the left front piston being backdriven by hydraulic pressure and pedal movement would result.
2) Checks for high resistance in motor high circuit. Tester J 39200 is a DVOM with a 10-megohm input impedance.
3) Checks for high resistance in motor low circuit.
4) Checks for high resistance in motor.
5) Determines if fault is due to poor terminal contact or corrosion.
6) Determines if fault is due to faulty EBCM.

DIAGNOSTIC AIDS

An intermittent malfunction may result from a mechanical part sticking, binding or slipping.

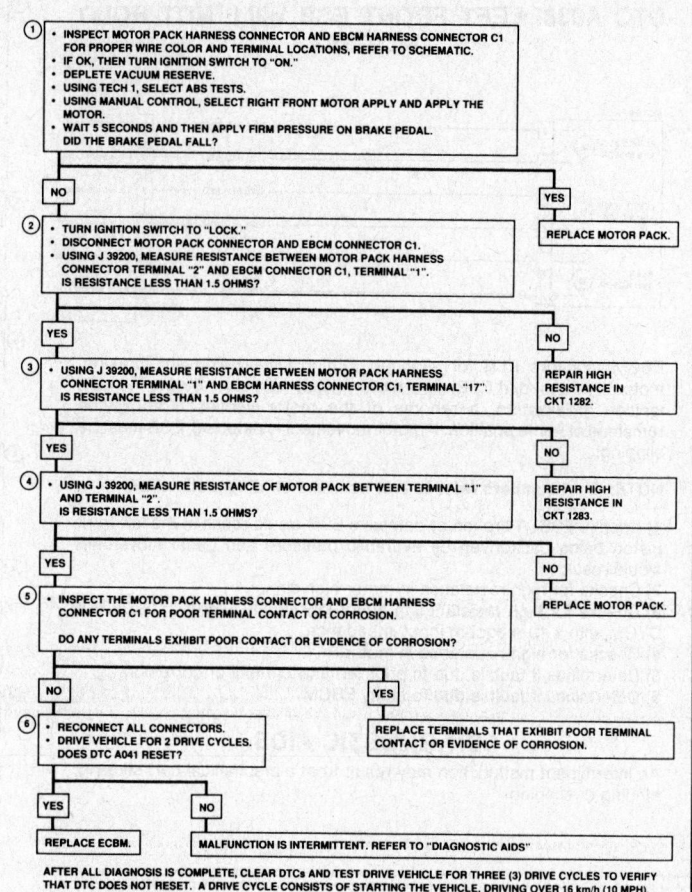

1
- INSPECT MOTOR PACK HARNESS CONNECTOR AND EBCM HARNESS CONNECTOR C1 FOR PROPER WIRE COLOR AND TERMINAL LOCATIONS, REFER TO SCHEMATIC.
- IF OK, THEN TURN IGNITION SWITCH TO "ON."
- DEPLETE VACUUM RESERVE.
- USING TECH 1, SELECT ABS TESTS.
- USING MANUAL CONTROL, SELECT RIGHT FRONT MOTOR APPLY AND APPLY THE MOTOR.
- WAIT 5 SECONDS AND THEN APPLY FIRM PRESSURE ON BRAKE PEDAL. DID THE BRAKE PEDAL FALL?

NO → YES → REPLACE MOTOR PACK.

2
- TURN IGNITION SWITCH TO "LOCK."
- DISCONNECT MOTOR PACK CONNECTOR AND EBCM CONNECTOR C1.
- USING J 39200, MEASURE RESISTANCE BETWEEN MOTOR PACK HARNESS CONNECTOR TERMINAL "2" AND EBCM CONNECTOR C1, TERMINAL "1". IS RESISTANCE LESS THAN 1.5 OHMS?

YES → NO → REPAIR HIGH RESISTANCE IN CKT 1282.

3
- USING J 39200, MEASURE RESISTANCE BETWEEN MOTOR PACK HARNESS CONNECTOR TERMINAL "1" AND EBCM HARNESS CONNECTOR C1, TERMINAL "17". IS RESISTANCE LESS THAN 1.5 OHMS?

YES → NO → REPAIR HIGH RESISTANCE IN CKT 1283.

4
- USING J 39200, MEASURE RESISTANCE OF MOTOR PACK BETWEEN TERMINAL "1" AND TERMINAL "2". IS RESISTANCE LESS THAN 1.5 OHMS?

YES → NO → REPLACE MOTOR PACK.

5
- INSPECT THE MOTOR PACK HARNESS CONNECTOR AND EBCM HARNESS CONNECTOR C1 FOR POOR TERMINAL CONTACT OR CORROSION.
  DO ANY TERMINALS EXHIBIT POOR CONTACT OR EVIDENCE OF CORROSION?

NO → YES → REPLACE TERMINALS THAT EXHIBIT POOR TERMINAL CONTACT OR EVIDENCE OF CORROSION.

6
- RECONNECT ALL CONNECTORS.
- DRIVE VEHICLE FOR 2 DRIVE CYCLES. DOES DTC A041 RESET?

YES → REPLACE ECBM.   NO → MALFUNCTION IS INTERMITTENT. REFER TO "DIAGNOSTIC AIDS"

AFTER ALL DIAGNOSIS IS COMPLETE, CLEAR DTCs AND TEST DRIVE VEHICLE FOR THREE (3) DRIVE CYCLES TO VERIFY THAT DTC DOES NOT RESET. A DRIVE CYCLE CONSISTS OF STARTING THE VEHICLE, DRIVING OVER 16 km/h (10 MPH), AND THEN KEYING DOWN.

93F84686 93G84745

Courtesy of General Motors Corp.

DTC A042, REAR ESB WILL NOT HOLD MOTOR

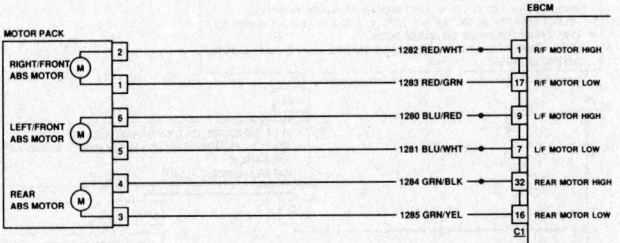

EBCM monitors ESB for slippage. During initialization and braking, motor is rehomed. If ESB slips, motor/piston will move. During the next ignition initialization, a rehome of the motor verifies motor/piston remained at home position. If motor movement is detected, ESB must be slipping.

NOTE: Test numbers refer to test numbers on diagnostic chart.

1) Checks ESB. A broken or defective ESB would result in the left front piston being backdriven by hydraulic pressure and pedal movement would result.
2) Checks for high resistance in motor high circuit. Tester J 39200 is a DVOM with a 10-megohm input impedance.
3) Checks for high resistance in motor low circuit.
4) Checks for high resistance in motor.
5) Determines if fault is due to poor terminal contact or corrosion.
6) Determines if fault is due to faulty EBCM.

DIAGNOSTIC AIDS

An intermittent malfunction may result from a mechanical part sticking, binding or slipping.

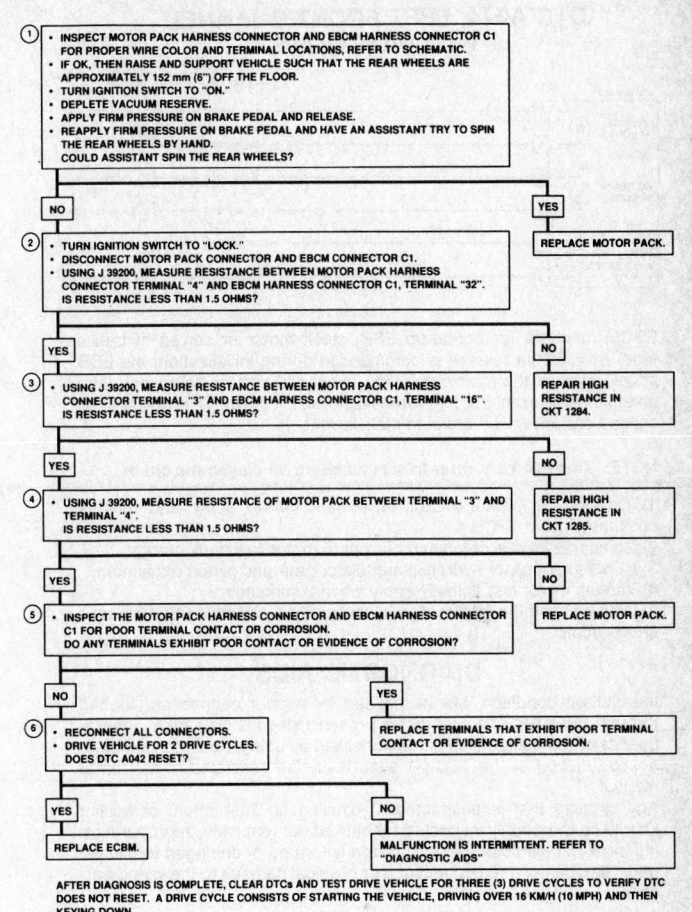

AFTER DIAGNOSIS IS COMPLETE, CLEAR DTCs AND TEST DRIVE VEHICLE FOR THREE (3) DRIVE CYCLES TO VERIFY DTC DOES NOT RESET. A DRIVE CYCLE CONSISTS OF STARTING THE VEHICLE, DRIVING OVER 16 KM/H (10 MPH) AND THEN KEYING DOWN.

93F84686 93H84746

Courtesy of General Motors Corp.

DTC A044, LEFT FRONT CHANNEL WILL NOT MOVE

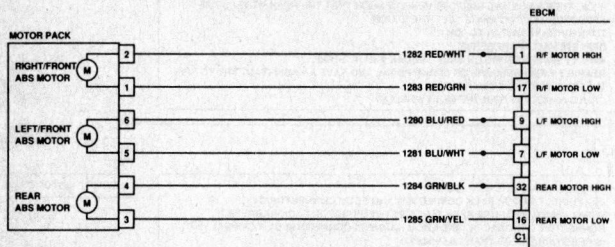

EBCM monitors for bound-up ESB, stuck motor or seized hydraulic modulator. When release is commanded during initialization, the ESB should release the motor, resulting in sensed current being less than commanded current (motor is spinning freely). If the motor is not moving, sensed current will be equal to stall current.

NOTE: Test numbers refer to test numbers on diagnostic chart.

1) Checks for proper motor movement during apply and release commands from TECH-1.
2) Compares EBCM command current to motor feedback current.
3) Checks for proper hydraulic modulator gear and piston movement.
4) Verifies motor can actually apply when commanded.
5) Determines if the malfunction is caused by a defective EBCM or by a short circuit.

DIAGNOSTIC AIDS

Intermittent condition can be caused by a poor connection, rubbed through insulation or a wire that is broken inside the insulation. The frequency of the malfunction can be checked by using the enhanced diagnostic function of the TECH-1 scan tester as described in the tester manual.

Any circuitry that is suspected of causing an intermittent complaint should be thoroughly inspected for backed out terminals, improper mating, broken connector locks, improperly formed or damaged terminals, poor terminal-to-wire connections or physical damage to the wiring harness.

93F84686 94D46766

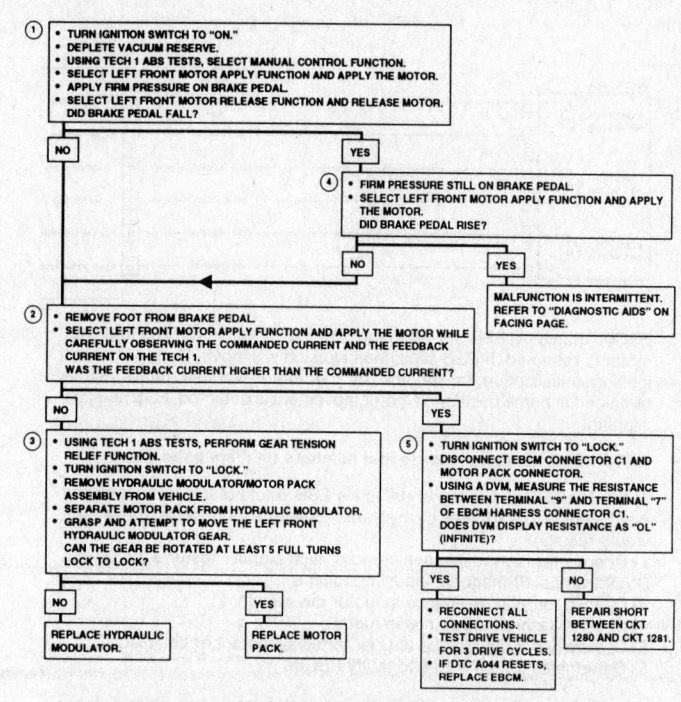

* AFTER ALL DIAGNOSIS IS COMPLETE, CLEAR DTCs AND TEST DRIVE VEHICLE FOR THREE (3) DRIVE CYCLES TO VERIFY THAT DTC DOES NOT RESET. A DRIVE CYCLE CONSISTS OF STARTING THE VEHICLE, DRIVING OVER 16 KM/H (10 MPH), AND THEN KEYING DOWN.

THIS CHART ASSUMES THAT A CURRENT DTC IS STORED INDICATING THAT THIS MALFUNCTION IS PRESENT.

DTC A045, RIGHT FRONT CHANNEL WILL NOT MOVE

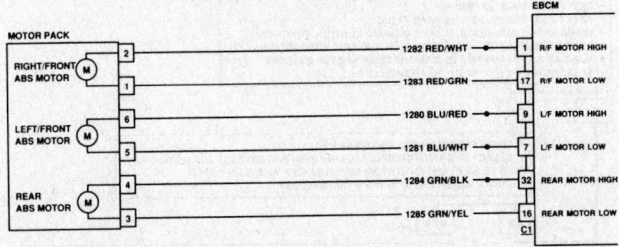

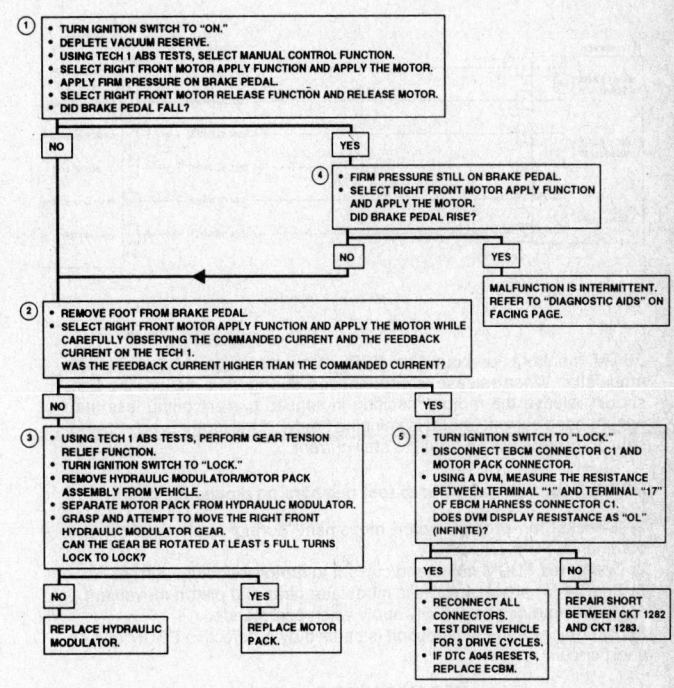

EBCM monitors for bound-up ESB, stuck motor or seized hydraulic modulator. When release is commanded during initialization, the ESB should release the motor, resulting in sensed current being less than commanded current (motor is spinning freely). If the motor is not moving, sensed current will be equal to stall current.

NOTE: Test numbers refer to test numbers on diagnostic chart.

1) Checks for proper motor movement during apply and release commands from TECH-1.
2) Compares EBCM command current to motor feedback current.
3) Checks for proper hydraulic modulator gear and piston movement.
4) Verifies motor can actually apply when commanded.
5) Determines if the malfunction is caused by a defective EBCM or by a short circuit.

DIAGNOSTIC AIDS

Intermittent condition can be caused by a poor connection, rubbed through insulation or a wire that is broken inside the insulation. The frequency of the malfunction can be checked by using the enhanced diagnostic function of the TECH-1 scan tester as described in the tester manual.

Any circuitry that is suspected of causing an intermittent complaint should be thoroughly inspected for backed out terminals, improper mating, broken connector locks, improperly formed or damaged terminals, poor terminal-to-wire connections or physical damage to the wiring harness.

* AFTER ALL DIAGNOSIS IS COMPLETE, CLEAR DTCs AND TEST DRIVE VEHICLE FOR THREE (3) DRIVE CYCLES TO VERIFY THAT DTC DOES NOT RESET. A DRIVE CYCLE CONSISTS OF STARTING THE VEHICLE, DRIVING OVER 16 KM/H (10 MPH), AND THEN KEYING DOWN.

THIS CHART ASSUMES THAT A CURRENT DTC IS STORED INDICATING THAT THIS MALFUNCTION IS PRESENT.

93F84686 94E46767

DTC A046, REAR CHANNEL WILL NOT MOVE

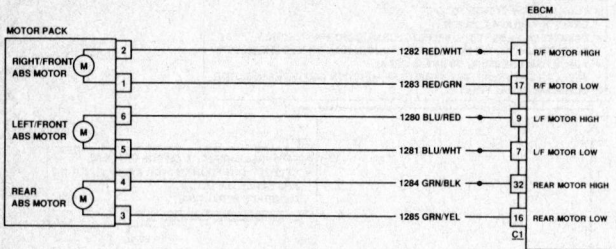

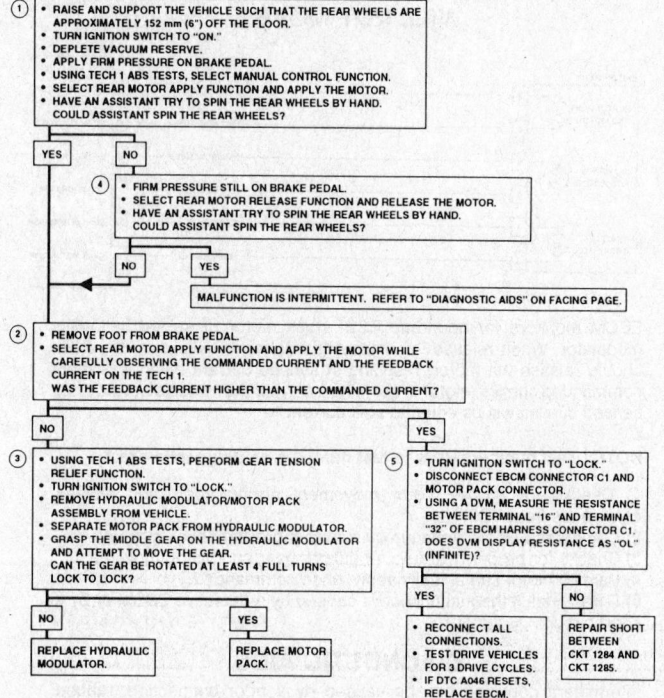

EBCM monitors for bound-up ESB, stuck motor or seized hydraulic modulator. When release is commanded during initialization, the ESB should release the motor, resulting in sensed current being less than commanded current (motor is spinning freely). If the motor is not moving, sensed current will be equal to stall current.

NOTE: Test numbers refer to test numbers on diagnostic chart.

1) Checks for proper motor movement during apply and release commands from TECH-1.
2) Compares EBCM command current to motor feedback current.
3) Checks for proper hydraulic modulator gear and piston movement.
4) Verifies motor can actually apply when commanded.
5) Determines if the malfunction is caused by a defective EBCM or by a short circuit.

DIAGNOSTIC AIDS

Intermittent condition can be caused by a poor connection, rubbed through insulation or a wire that is broken inside the insulation. The frequency of the malfunction can be checked by using the enhanced diagnostic function of the TECH-1 scan tester as described in the tester manual.
Any circuitry that is suspected of causing an intermittent complaint should be thoroughly inspected for backed out terminals, improper mating, broken connector locks, improperly formed or damaged terminals, poor terminal-to-wire connections or physical damage to the wiring harness.

* AFTER ALL DIAGNOSIS IS COMPLETE, CLEAR DTCs AND TEST DRIVE VEHICLE FOR THREE (3) DRIVE CYCLES TO VERIFY THAT DTC DOES NOT RESET. A DRIVE CYCLE CONSISTS OF STARTING THE VEHICLE, DRIVING OVER 16 km/h (10 MPH), AND THEN KEYING DOWN.

THIS CHART ASSUMES THAT A CURRENT DTC IS STORED INDICATING THAT THIS MALFUNCTION IS PRESENT.

DTC A047, LEFT FRONT MOTOR FREE SPINS (1 OF 2)

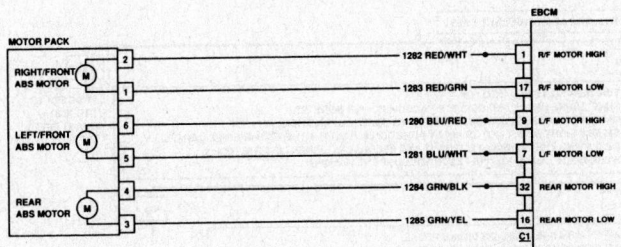

EBCM can detect a stripped nut or gear assembly during initialization. During the homing sequence, the piston should reach the top of the bore, resulting in a stalled motor. If this does not occur, the motor must be spinning with little or no resistance. This indicates a nut/screw or gear malfunction.

NOTE: Test numbers refer to test numbers on diagnostic chart.

1) Checks to see if the corresponding code is also set.
2) Verifies motor was actually applied as commanded by observing feedback current.
3) Verifies motor can release.
4) Verifies that motor can be applied by observing pedal movement.
5) Checks for a stripped gear on the motor pack.
6) Checks for stripped gear on the hydraulic modulator.
7) Checks for a malfunctioning EBCM.

DIAGNOSTIC AIDS

An intermittent malfunction may result from a mechanical part sticking, binding or slipping.

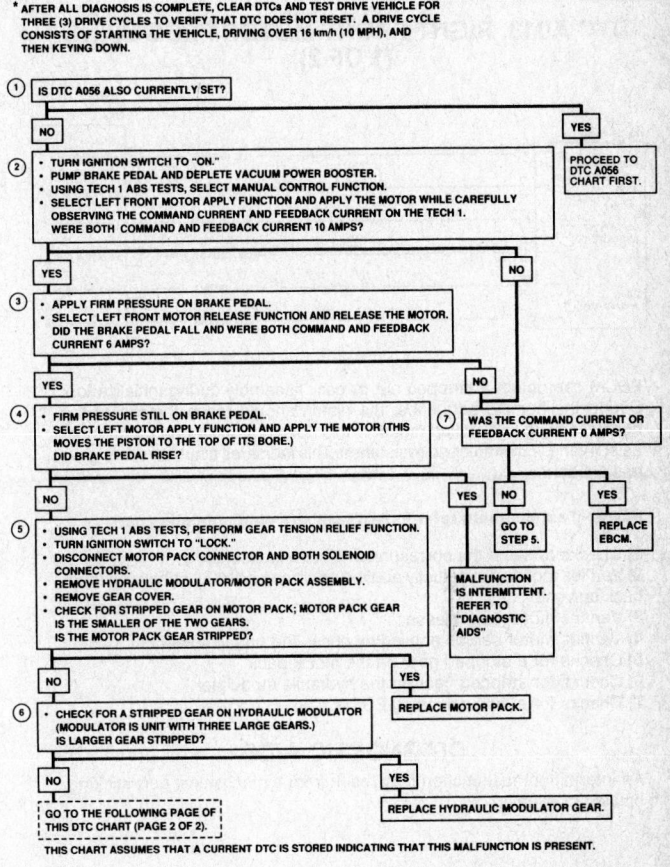

* AFTER ALL DIAGNOSIS IS COMPLETE, CLEAR DTCs AND TEST DRIVE VEHICLE FOR THREE (3) DRIVE CYCLES TO VERIFY THAT DTC DOES NOT RESET. A DRIVE CYCLE CONSISTS OF STARTING THE VEHICLE, DRIVING OVER 16 km/h (10 MPH), AND THEN KEYING DOWN.

THIS CHART ASSUMES THAT A CURRENT DTC IS STORED INDICATING THAT THIS MALFUNCTION IS PRESENT.

93F84686 93E84750

Courtesy of General Motors Corp.

DTC A047, LEFT FRONT MOTOR FREE SPINS (2 OF 2)

NOTE: Test numbers refer to test numbers on diagnostic chart.

8) Determines whether motor pack has an internal malfunctioning.
9) Checks for high resistance in motor high circuit. Tester J 39200 is a DVOM with a 10-megohm input impedance.
10) Checks for high resistance in motor low circuit.
11) Determines whether fault is due to a faulty hydraulic modulator or a faulty motor pack.

DIAGNOSTIC AIDS

An intermittent malfunction may result from a mechanical part sticking, binding or slipping.

- CONTINUED FROM DTC A047 (PAGE 1 OF 2)

8)
- RECONNECT ELECTRICAL CONNECTORS.
- SECURELY POSITION HYDRAULIC MODULATOR ASSEMBLY WITH COVER REMOVED SUCH THAT THE GEAR SET CAN BE OBSERVED. BE CAREFUL NOT TO DAMAGE GEAR SET OR ALLOW THE HYDRAULIC MODULATOR TO MOVE WHILE TESTING.
- TURN IGNITION SWITCH TO "ON."
- USING TECH 1 ABS TESTS, SELECT MANUAL CONTROL FUNCTION.
- SELECT LEFT FRONT MOTOR APPLY AND APPLY THE MOTOR WHILE OBSERVING THE GEAR SET.
- SELECT LEFT FRONT MOTOR RELEASE FUNCTION AND RELEASE THE MOTOR WHILE STILL OBSERVING THE GEAR SET.
- SELECT LEFT FRONT MOTOR APPLY FUNCTION AND APPLY THE MOTOR.
- DID GEAR SET MOVE IN BOTH DIRECTIONS FOR AT LEAST ONE REVOLUTION?

YES | NO → REPLACE MOTOR PACK

9)
- TURN IGNITION SWITCH TO "LOCK."
- DISCONNECT MOTOR PACK CONNECTOR AND EBCM CONNECTOR C1.
- USING J 39200, MEASURE RESISTANCE BETWEEN MOTOR PACK HARNESS CONNECTOR TERMINAL "6" AND EBCM HARNESS CONNECTOR C1, TERMINAL "9". IS RESISTANCE LESS THAN 1.5 OHMS?

YES | NO → REPAIR HIGH RESISTANCE IN CKT 1280.

10)
- MEASURE RESISTANCE BETWEEN MOTOR PACK HARNESS CONNECTOR TERMINAL "5" AND EBCM HARNESS CONNECTOR C1, TERMINAL "7". IS RESISTANCE LESS THAN 1.5 OHMS?

YES | NO → REPAIR HIGH RESISTANCE IN CKT 1281.

11)
- MEASURE RESISTANCE OF MOTOR PACK BETWEEN TERMINAL "5" AND TERMINAL "6". IS RESISTANCE LESS THAN 1.5 OHMS?

YES → REPLACE HYDRAULIC MODULATOR. | NO → REPLACE MOTOR PACK.

93F84751

Courtesy of General Motors Corp.

DTC A048, RIGHT FRONT MOTOR FREE SPINS (1 OF 2)

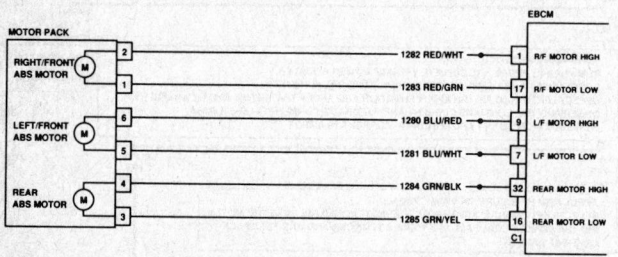

EBCM can detect a stripped nut or gear assembly during initialization. During the homing sequence, the piston should reach the top of the bore, resulting in a stalled motor. If this does not occur, the motor must be spinning with little or no resistance. This indicates a nut/screw or gear malfunction.

NOTE: Test numbers refer to test numbers on diagnostic chart.

1) Checks to see if the corresponding code is also set.
2) Verifies motor was actually applied as commanded by observing feedback current.
3) Verifies motor can release.
4) Verifies motor can be applied by observing pedal movement.
5) Checks for a stripped gear on the motor pack.
6) Checks for stripped gear on the hydraulic modulator.
7) Checks for a malfunctioning EBCM.

DIAGNOSTIC AIDS

An intermittent malfunction may result from a mechanical part sticking, binding or slipping.

* AFTER ALL DIAGNOSIS IS COMPLETE, CLEAR DTCs AND TEST DRIVE VEHICLE FOR THREE (3) DRIVE CYCLES TO VERIFY THAT DTC DOES NOT RESET. A DRIVE CYCLE CONSISTS OF STARTING THE VEHICLE, DRIVING OVER 16 km/h (10 MPH), AND THEN KEYING DOWN.

1 | IS DTC A061 ALSO CURRENTLY SET?

NO → 2 | • TURN IGNITION SWITCH TO "ON."
• PUMP BRAKE PEDAL AND DEPLETE VACUUM POWER BOOSTER.
• USING TECH 1 ABS TESTS, SELECT MANUAL CONTROL FUNCTION.
• SELECT RIGHT FRONT MOTOR APPLY FUNCTION AND APPLY THE MOTOR WHILE CAREFULLY OBSERVING THE COMMAND CURRENT AND FEEDBACK CURRENT ON THE TECH 1. WERE BOTH COMMAND AND FEEDBACK CURRENT 10 AMPS?

YES → PROCEED TO DTC A061 CHART FIRST.

YES → 3 | • APPLY FIRM PRESSURE ON BRAKE PEDAL.
• SELECT RIGHT FRONT MOTOR RELEASE FUNCTION AND RELEASE THE MOTOR. DID THE BRAKE PEDAL FALL AND WERE BOTH COMMAND AND FEEDBACK CURRENT 6 AMPS?

YES → 4 | • FIRM PRESSURE STILL ON BRAKE PEDAL.
• SELECT RIGHT MOTOR APPLY FUNCTION AND APPLY THE MOTOR (THIS MOVES THE PISTON TO THE TOP OF ITS BORE.) DID BRAKE PEDAL RISE?

7 | WAS THE COMMAND CURRENT OR FEEDBACK CURRENT 0 AMPS?

YES → GO TO STEP 5.
NO → REPLACE EBCM.
YES → REPLACE EBCM.

MALFUNCTION IS INTERMITTENT. REFER TO "DIAGNOSTIC AIDS"

NO → 5 | • USING TECH 1 ABS TESTS, PERFORM GEAR TENSION RELIEF FUNCTION.
• TURN IGNITION SWITCH TO "LOCK."
• DISCONNECT MOTOR PACK CONNECTOR AND BOTH SOLENOID CONNECTORS.
• REMOVE HYDRAULIC MODULATOR/MOTOR PACK ASSEMBLY.
• REMOVE GEAR COVER.
• CHECK FOR STRIPPED GEAR ON MOTOR PACK; MOTOR PACK GEAR IS THE SMALLER OF THE TWO GEARS. IS THE MOTOR PACK GEAR STRIPPED?

YES → REPLACE MOTOR PACK.

NO → 6 | • CHECK FOR A STRIPPED GEAR ON HYDRAULIC MODULATOR (MODULATOR IS UNIT WITH THREE LARGE GEARS.) IS LARGER GEAR STRIPPED?

YES → REPLACE HYDRAULIC MODULATOR GEAR.

NO → GO TO THE FOLLOWING PAGE OF THIS DTC CHART (PAGE 2 OF 2).

THIS CHART ASSUMES THAT A CURRENT DTC IS STORED INDICATING THAT THIS MALFUNCTION IS PRESENT.

93F84686 93G84752

Courtesy of General Motors Corp.

DTC A048, RIGHT FRONT MOTOR FREE SPINS (2 OF 2)

NOTE: Test numbers refer to test numbers on diagnostic chart.

8) Determines whether motor pack has an internal malfunctioning.
9) Checks for high resistance in motor high circuit. Tester J 39200 is a DVOM with a 10-megohm input impedance.
10) Checks for high resistance in motor low circuit.
11) Determines whether fault is due to a faulty hydraulic modulator or a faulty motor pack.

DIAGNOSTIC AIDS

An intermittent malfunction may result from a mechanical part sticking, binding or slipping.

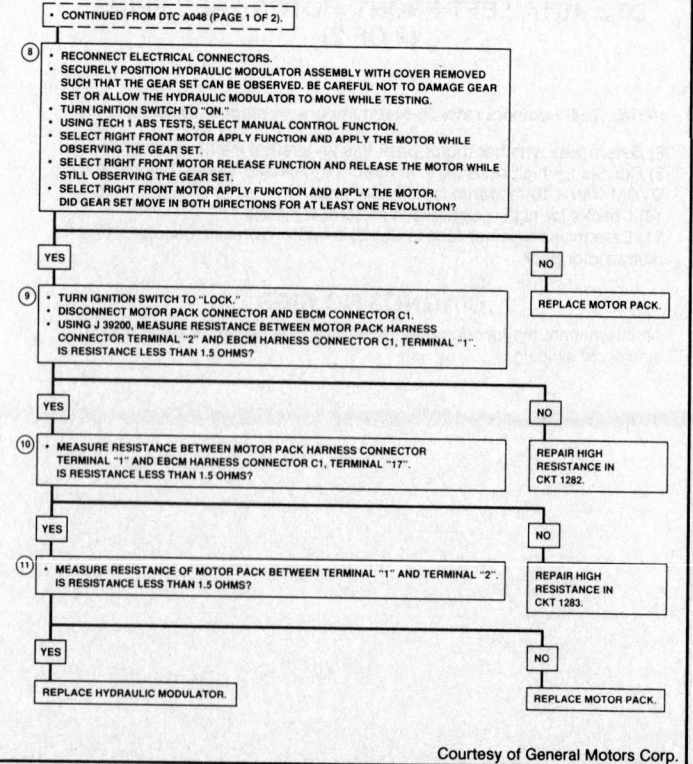

CONTINUED FROM DTC A048 (PAGE 1 OF 2).

8 | • RECONNECT ELECTRICAL CONNECTORS.
• SECURELY POSITION HYDRAULIC MODULATOR ASSEMBLY WITH COVER REMOVED SUCH THAT THE GEAR SET CAN BE OBSERVED. BE CAREFUL NOT TO DAMAGE GEAR SET OR ALLOW THE HYDRAULIC MODULATOR TO MOVE WHILE TESTING.
• TURN IGNITION SWITCH TO "ON."
• USING TECH 1 ABS TESTS, SELECT MANUAL CONTROL FUNCTION.
• SELECT RIGHT FRONT MOTOR APPLY FUNCTION AND APPLY THE MOTOR WHILE OBSERVING THE GEAR SET.
• SELECT RIGHT FRONT MOTOR RELEASE FUNCTION AND RELEASE THE MOTOR WHILE STILL OBSERVING THE GEAR SET.
• SELECT RIGHT FRONT MOTOR APPLY FUNCTION AND APPLY THE MOTOR. DID GEAR SET MOVE IN BOTH DIRECTIONS FOR AT LEAST ONE REVOLUTION?

NO → REPLACE MOTOR PACK.

YES → 9 | • TURN IGNITION SWITCH TO "LOCK."
• DISCONNECT MOTOR PACK CONNECTOR AND EBCM CONNECTOR C1.
• USING J 39200, MEASURE RESISTANCE BETWEEN MOTOR PACK HARNESS CONNECTOR TERMINAL "2" AND EBCM HARNESS CONNECTOR C1, TERMINAL "1". IS RESISTANCE LESS THAN 1.5 OHMS?

NO → REPAIR HIGH RESISTANCE IN CKT 1282.

YES → 10 | • MEASURE RESISTANCE BETWEEN MOTOR PACK HARNESS CONNECTOR TERMINAL "1" AND EBCM HARNESS CONNECTOR C1, TERMINAL "17". IS RESISTANCE LESS THAN 1.5 OHMS?

NO → REPAIR HIGH RESISTANCE IN CKT 1283.

YES → 11 | • MEASURE RESISTANCE OF MOTOR PACK BETWEEN TERMINAL "1" AND TERMINAL "2". IS RESISTANCE LESS THAN 1.5 OHMS?

NO → REPLACE MOTOR PACK.

YES → REPLACE HYDRAULIC MODULATOR.

93H84753

Courtesy of General Motors Corp.

DTC A051, REAR MOTOR FREE SPINS (1 OF 2)

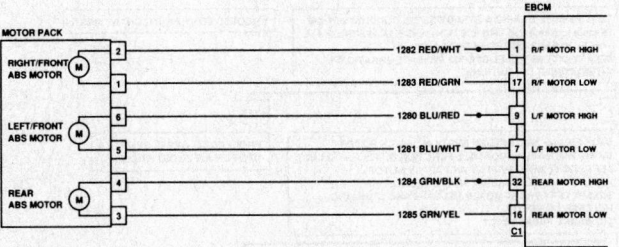

EBCM can detect a stripped nut or gear assembly during initialization. During the homing sequence, the piston should reach the top of the bore, resulting in a stalled motor. If this does not occur, the motor must be spinning with little or no resistance. This indicates a nut/screw or gear malfunction.

NOTE: Test numbers refer to test numbers on diagnostic chart.

1) Checks to see if the corresponding code is also set.
2) Verifies motor was actually applied as commanded by observing feedback current.
3) Verifies motor can release.
4) Verifies motor can be applied by observing pedal movement.
5) Checks for a stripped gear on the motor pack.
6) Checks for stripped gear on the hydraulic modulator.
7) Checks for a malfunctioning EBCM.

DIAGNOSTIC AIDS

An intermittent malfunction may result from a mechanical part sticking, binding or slipping.

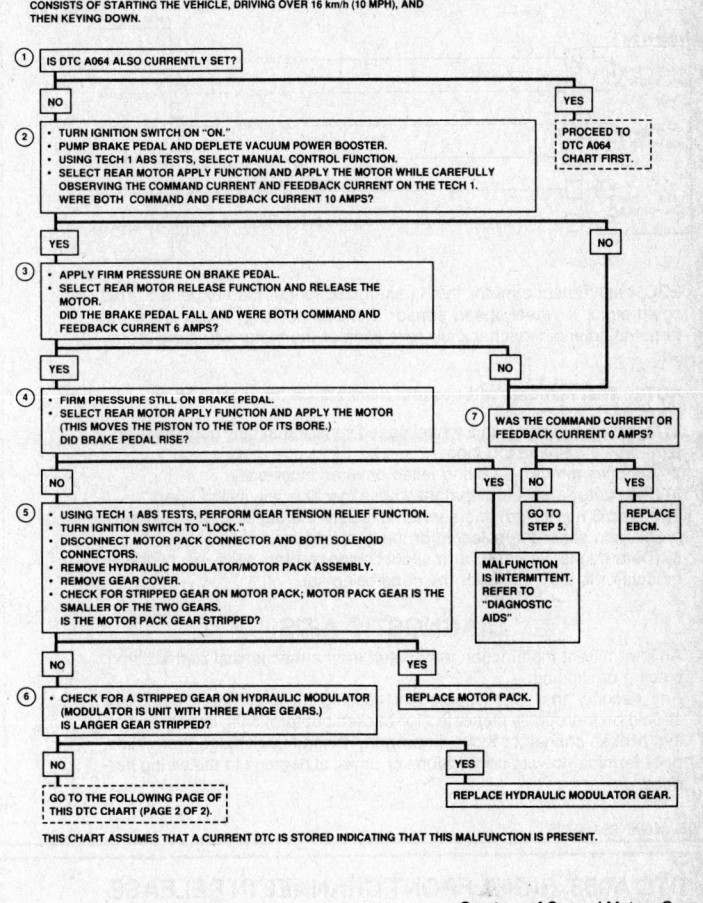

93F84686 93I84754

Courtesy of General Motors Corp.

DTC A051, REAR MOTOR FREE SPINS (2 OF 2)

NOTE: Test numbers refer to test numbers on diagnostic chart.

8) Determines whether motor pack has an internal malfunctioning.
9) Checks for high resistance in motor high circuit. Tester J 39200 is a DVOM with a 10-megohm input impedance.
10) Checks for high resistance in motor low circuit.
11) Determines whether fault is due to a faulty hydraulic modulator or a faulty motor pack.

DIAGNOSTIC AIDS

An intermittent malfunction may result from a mechanical part sticking, binding or slipping.

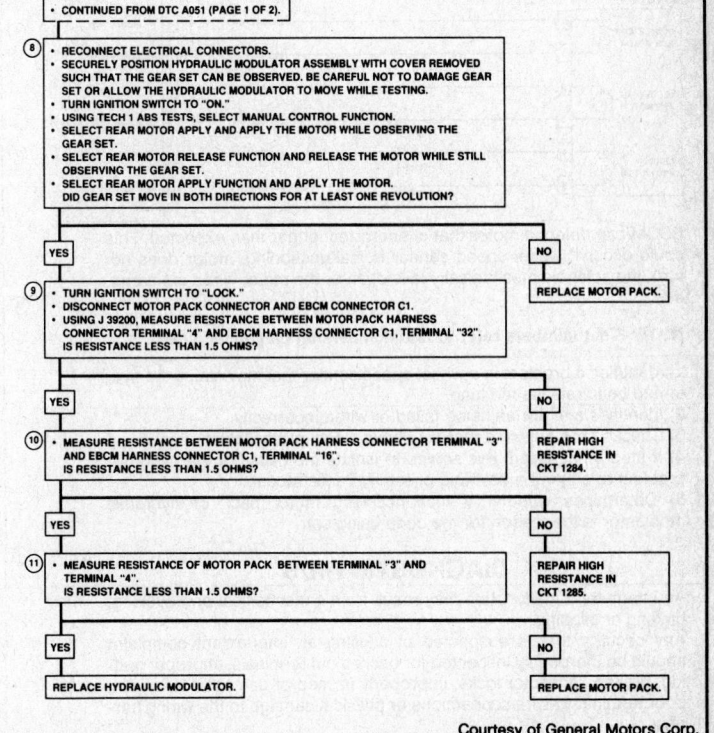

93J84755

Courtesy of General Motors Corp.

DTC A052, LEFT FRONT CHANNEL IN RELEASE TOO LONG

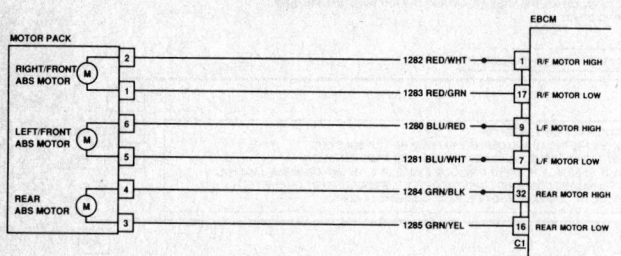

MOTOR PACK

		EBCM
RIGHT/FRONT ABS MOTOR	2 — 1282 RED/WHT — 1	R/F MOTOR HIGH
	1 — 1283 RED/GRN — 17	R/F MOTOR LOW
LEFT/FRONT ABS MOTOR	6 — 1280 BLU/RED — 9	L/F MOTOR HIGH
	5 — 1281 BLU/WHT — 7	L/F MOTOR LOW
REAR ABS MOTOR	4 — 1284 GRN/BLK — 32	REAR MOTOR HIGH
	3 — 1285 GRN/YEL — 16	REAR MOTOR LOW
		C1

EBCM can detect a motor that is energized longer than expected. This could occur if wheel speed sensor is malfunctioning, motor does not turn, the solenoid mechanically fails open or the motor wires are crossed.

NOTE: Test numbers refer to test numbers on diagnostic chart.

1) Identifies a problem in a wheel speed sensor that may cause the system to be in release too long.
2) Identifies a motor as being failed or wired incorrectly.
3) Checks for a solenoid that may have mechanically failed open.
4) If step 3 has failed, this serves to isolate the cause of the hydraulic problem to either the solenoid or the hydraulic modulator.
5) Determines whether a malfunctioning motor pack or hydraulic modulator is the reason for the code being set.

DIAGNOSTIC AIDS

An intermittent malfunction may result from a mechanical part sticking, binding or slipping.
Any circuitry that is suspected of causing an intermittent complaint should be thoroughly inspected for backed out terminals, improper mating, broken connector locks, improperly formed or damaged terminals, poor terminal-to-wire connections or physical damage to the wiring harness.

93F84686 93A84756

IMPORTANT: EXCESSIVE DRAG OR HIGH RESISTANCE IN THE BASE BRAKE OR SUSPENSION SYSTEM MUST BE INSPECTED AND CORRECTED BEFORE PROCEEDING WITH DTC DIAGNOSIS.

ARE ANY WHEEL SPEED DTCs OR DTC A056 CURRENTLY SET?
- NO
- YES → PROCEED TO THAT DTC CHART FIRST.

(1) • TEST VEHICLE DURING A STEADY DECEL CONDITION FROM 56 km/h to 0 km/h (35 MPH to 0 MPH) WHILE MONITORING ALL WHEEL SPEEDS ON TECH 1 DATA LIST. DO ANY OF THE WHEEL SPEEDS INDICATE ERRATIC OR INTERMITTENT OPERATION?
- NO
- YES → PROCEED TO WHEEL SPEED = 0 DTC FOR AFFECTED WHEEL.

(2) • STOP ENGINE AND RETURN IGNITION SWITCH TO "ON." • USING THE MANUAL CONTROL FUNCTION OF TECH 1, SELECT LEFT FRONT MOTOR APPLY AND APPLY MOTOR. • APPLY FIRM PRESSURE ON BRAKE PEDAL. • SELECT LEFT FRONT MOTOR RELEASE AND COMMAND RELEASE OF MOTOR. DID BRAKE PEDAL FALL?
- YES
- NO → BRAKE PEDAL DID NOT MOVE. / BRAKE PEDAL ROSE. → REPAIR CROSSED WIRES TO LEFT FRONT ABS MOTOR CIRCUIT.

(3) • REMOVE FOOT FROM BRAKE PEDAL. • SELECT LEFT FRONT SOLENOID APPLY FUNCTION OF TECH 1 AND ENERGIZE SOLENOID. • APPLY FIRM PRESSURE TO BRAKE PEDAL. DID BRAKE PEDAL FALL?
- NO
- YES → PROCEED TO STEP 4 OF THIS CHART.

(5) • USING TECH 1, PERFORM GEAR TENSION RELIEF FUNCTION. • SEPARATE MOTOR PACK FROM HYDRAULIC MODULATOR. • GRASP THE LEFT FRONT GEAR ON THE HYDRAULIC MODULATOR AND ATTEMPT TO MOVE THE GEAR IN EITHER DIRECTION. CAN GEAR BE MOVED BY HAND?
- YES → REPLACE MOTOR PACK.
- NO → REPLACE HYDRAULIC MODULATOR.

• FIRM PRESSURE STILL APPLIED TO BRAKE PEDAL. • USING TECH 1, COMMAND LEFT FRONT SOLENOID "OFF." DID BRAKE PEDAL FALL?
- NO
- YES

(4) • SWITCH LEFT FRONT SOLENOID WITH RIGHT FRONT SOLENOID AND REPEAT PREVIOUS TEST. DID BRAKE PEDAL FALL?
- MALFUNCTION IS NOT PRESENT AT THIS TIME. REFER TO "DIAGNOSTIC AIDS"
- YES
- NO

• USING TECH 1, PERFORM GEAR TENSION RELIEF FUNCTION. • REPLACE HYDRAULIC MODULATOR.

REPLACE SOLENOID THAT FAILED STEP 3 OF THIS CHART.

* AFTER DIAGNOSIS IS COMPLETE, CLEAR DTCs AND TEST DRIVE VEHICLE FOR THREE (3) DRIVE CYCLES TO VERIFY DTC DOES NOT RESET. A DRIVE CYCLE CONSISTS OF STARTING THE VEHICLE, DRIVING OVER 16 km/h (10 MPH) AND THEN KEYING DOWN.

THIS CHART ASSUMES THAT A CURRENT DTC IS STORED INDICATING THAT THIS MALFUNCTION IS PRESENT.

Courtesy of General Motors Corp.

DTC A053, RIGHT FRONT CHANNEL IN RELEASE TOO LONG

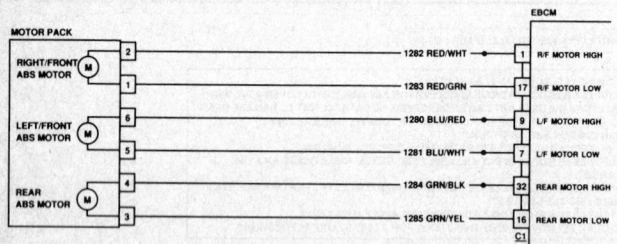

MOTOR PACK

		EBCM
RIGHT/FRONT ABS MOTOR	2 — 1282 RED/WHT — 1	R/F MOTOR HIGH
	1 — 1283 RED/GRN — 17	R/F MOTOR LOW
LEFT/FRONT ABS MOTOR	6 — 1280 BLU/RED — 9	L/F MOTOR HIGH
	5 — 1281 BLU/WHT — 7	L/F MOTOR LOW
REAR ABS MOTOR	4 — 1284 GRN/BLK — 32	REAR MOTOR HIGH
	3 — 1285 GRN/YEL — 16	REAR MOTOR LOW
		C1

EBCM can detect a motor that is energized longer than expected. This could occur if wheel speed sensor is malfunctioning, motor does not turn, the solenoid mechanically fails open or the motor wires are crossed.

NOTE: Test numbers refer to test numbers on diagnostic chart.

1) Identifies a problem in a wheel speed sensor that may cause the system to be in release too long.
2) Identifies a motor as being failed or wired incorrectly.
3) Checks for a solenoid that may have mechanically failed open.
4) If step 3 has failed, this serves to isolate the cause of the hydraulic problem to either the solenoid or the hydraulic modulator.
5) Determines whether a malfunctioning motor pack or hydraulic modulator is the reason for the code being set.

DIAGNOSTIC AIDS

An intermittent malfunction may result from a mechanical part sticking, binding or slipping.
Any circuitry that is suspected of causing an intermittent complaint should be thoroughly inspected for backed out terminals, improper mating, broken connector locks, improperly formed or damaged terminals, poor terminal-to-wire connections or physical damage to the wiring harness.

93F84686 93B84757

IMPORTANT: EXCESSIVE DRAG OR HIGH RESISTANCE IN THE BASE BRAKE OR SUSPENSION SYSTEM MUST BE INSPECTED AND CORRECTED BEFORE PROCEEDING WITH DTC DIAGNOSIS.

ARE ANY WHEEL SPEED DTCs OR DTC A061 CURRENTLY SET?
- NO
- YES → PROCEED TO THAT DTC CHART FIRST.

(1) • TEST VEHICLE DURING A STEADY DECEL CONDITION FROM 56 km/h to 0 km/h (35 MPH to 0 MPH) WHILE MONITORING ALL WHEEL SPEEDS ON TECH 1 DATA LIST. DO ANY OF THE WHEEL SPEEDS INDICATE ERRATIC OR INTERMITTENT OPERATION?
- NO
- YES → PROCEED TO WHEEL SPEED = 0 DTC FOR AFFECTED WHEEL.

(2) • STOP ENGINE AND RETURN IGNITION SWITCH TO "ON." • USING THE MANUAL CONTROL FUNCTION OF TECH 1, SELECT RIGHT FRONT MOTOR APPLY AND APPLY MOTOR. • APPLY FIRM PRESSURE ON BRAKE PEDAL. • SELECT RIGHT FRONT MOTOR RELEASE AND COMMAND RELEASE OF MOTOR. DID BRAKE PEDAL FALL?
- YES
- NO → BRAKE PEDAL DID NOT MOVE. / BRAKE PEDAL ROSE. → REPAIR CROSSED WIRES TO RIGHT FRONT ABS MOTOR CIRCUIT.

(3) • REMOVE FOOT FROM BRAKE PEDAL. • SELECT RIGHT FRONT SOLENOID APPLY FUNCTION OF TECH 1 AND ENERGIZE SOLENOID. • APPLY FIRM PRESSURE TO BRAKE PEDAL. DID BRAKE PEDAL FALL?
- NO
- YES → PROCEED TO STEP 4 OF THIS CHART.

(5) • USING TECH 1, PERFORM GEAR TENSION RELIEF FUNCTION. • SEPARATE MOTOR PACK FROM HYDRAULIC MODULATOR. • GRASP THE RIGHT FRONT GEAR ON THE HYDRAULIC MODULATOR AND ATTEMPT TO MOVE THE GEAR IN EITHER DIRECTION. CAN GEAR BE MOVED BY HAND?
- YES → REPLACE MOTOR PACK.
- NO → REPLACE HYDRAULIC MODULATOR.

• FIRM PRESSURE STILL APPLIED TO BRAKE PEDAL. • USING TECH 1, COMMAND RIGHT FRONT SOLENOID "OFF." DID BRAKE PEDAL FALL?
- NO
- YES

(4) • SWITCH RIGHT FRONT SOLENOID WITH LEFT FRONT SOLENOID AND REPEAT PREVIOUS TEST. DID BRAKE PEDAL FALL?
- MALFUNCTION IS NOT PRESENT AT THIS TIME. REFER TO "DIAGNOSTIC AIDS"
- YES
- NO

USING TECH 1, PERFORM GEAR TENSION RELIEF FUNCTION.

REPLACE SOLENOID THAT FAILED STEP 3 OF THIS CHART.

REPLACE ABS HYDRAULIC MODULATOR.

* AFTER DIAGNOSIS IS COMPLETE, CLEAR DTCs AND TEST DRIVE VEHICLE FOR THREE (3) DRIVE CYCLES TO VERIFY DTC DOES NOT RESET. A DRIVE CYCLE CONSISTS OF STARTING THE VEHICLE, DRIVING OVER 16 km/h (10 MPH) AND THEN KEYING DOWN.

THIS CHART ASSUMES THAT A CURRENT DTC IS STORED INDICATING THAT THIS MALFUNCTION IS PRESENT.

Courtesy of General Motors Corp.

DTC A054, REAR CHANNEL IN RELEASE TOO LONG (1 OF 2)

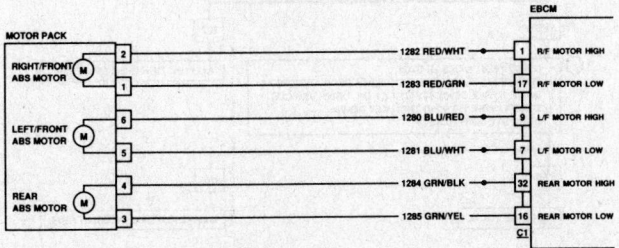

EBCM can detect a motor that is energized longer than expected. This could occur if wheel speed sensor is malfunctioning, motor does not turn, the solenoid mechanically fails open or the motor wires are crossed.

NOTE: Test numbers refer to test numbers on diagnostic chart.

1) Identifies a problem in a wheel speed sensor that may cause the system to be in release too long.

2) Checks for a wheel that may stick or bind because of a mechanical fault.

3) Checks to see if the motor is capable of moving and applying the hydraulic piston for the rear wheels.

DIAGNOSTIC AIDS

An intermittent malfunction may result from a mechanical part sticking, binding or slipping.

Any circuitry that is suspected of causing an intermittent complaint should be thoroughly inspected for backed out terminals, improper mating, broken connector locks, improperly formed or damaged terminals, poor terminal-to-wire connections or physical damage to the wiring harness.

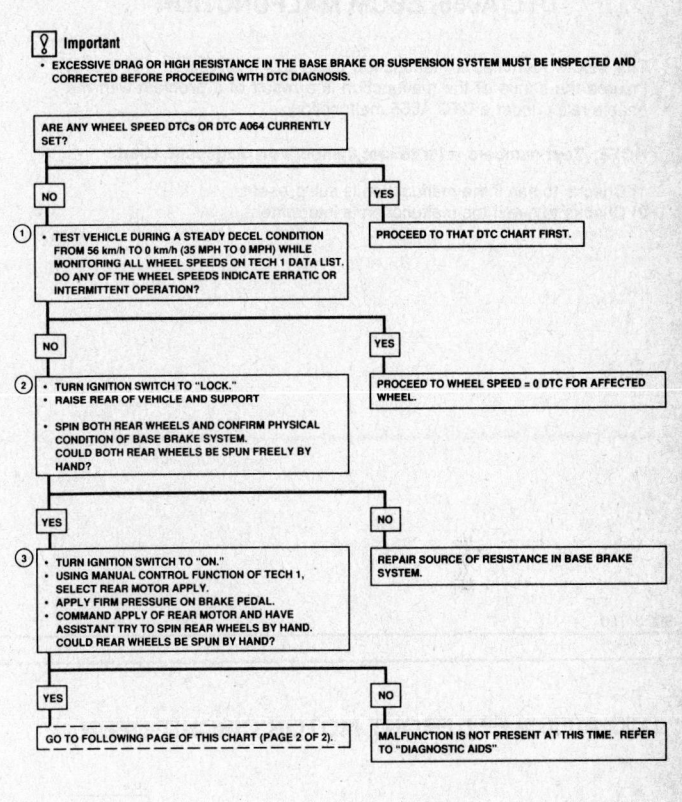

93F84686 93C84758

Courtesy of General Motors Corp.

DTC A054, REAR CHANNEL IN RELEASE TOO LONG (2 OF 2)

NOTE: Test numbers refer to test numbers on diagnostic chart.

4) Ensures that motor wiring is not crossed.

5) Isolates the fault of a no-apply situation to either the motor pack or the hydraulic modulator.

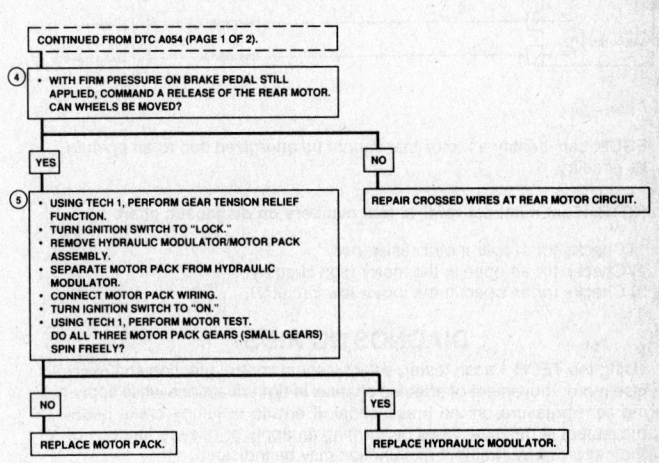

93D84759

Courtesy of General Motors Corp.

DTC A055, EBCM MALFUNCTION

The EBCM identifies a malfunction using the MDI custom IC. It also insures the cause of the malfunction is a result of a problem with the enable relay under a DTC A055 malfunction.

NOTE: Test numbers refer to test numbers on diagnostic chart.

1) Checks to see if the malfunction is still present.
2) Checks to see if the malfunction is intermittent.

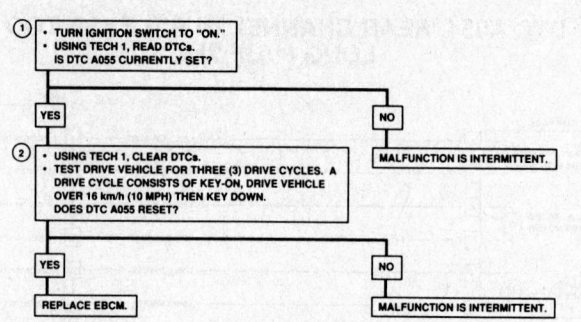

THIS CHART ASSUMES THAT A CURRENT DTC IS STORED INDICATING THAT THIS MALFUNCTION IS PRESENT.

93G84760

Courtesy of General Motors Corp.

DTC A056, LEFT FRONT MOTOR CIRCUIT OPEN

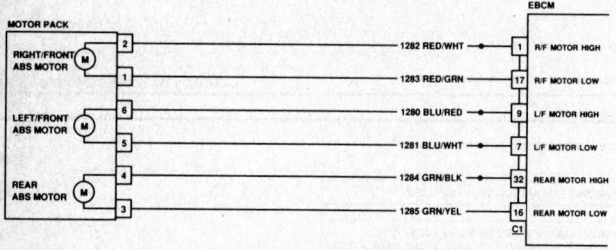

EBCM can identify a motor that cannot be energized due to an open in its circuitry.

NOTE: Test numbers refer to test numbers on diagnostic chart.

1) Checks for proper motor resistance.
2) Checks for an open in the motor high circuitry.
3) Checks for an open in the motor low circuitry.

DIAGNOSTIC AIDS

Using the TECH-1 scan tester, select manual control function and exercise motor movement of affected channel in both directions while applying light pressure on the brake pedal. If erratic or jumpy brake pedal movement is detected while performing an apply or release function of the motor, an intermittent malfunction may be indicated.
Intermittent condition can be caused by a poor connection, rubbed through insulation or a wire that is broken inside the insulation. The frequency of the malfunction can be checked by using the enhanced diagnostic function of the TECH-1 scan tester as described in the tester manual.
Any circuitry that is suspected of causing an intermittent complaint should be thoroughly inspected for backed out terminals, improper mating, broken connector locks, improperly formed or damaged terminals, poor terminal-to-wire connections or physical damage to the wiring harness.

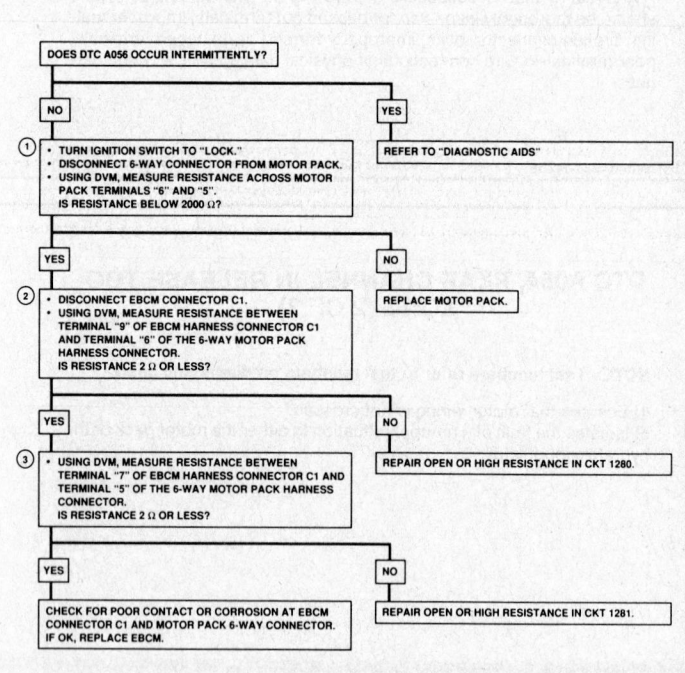

* AFTER ALL DIAGNOSIS IS COMPLETE, CLEAR DTCs AND TEST DRIVE VEHICLE FOR THREE (3) DRIVE CYCLES TO VERIFY THAT DTC DOES NOT RESET. A DRIVE CYCLE CONSISTS OF STARTING THE VEHICLE, DRIVING OVER 16 km/h (10 MPH), AND THEN KEYING DOWN.

THIS CHART ASSUMES THAT A CURRENT DTC IS STORED INDICATING THAT THIS MALFUNCTION IS PRESENT.

93F84686 93H84761

Courtesy of General Motors Corp.

DTC A057, LEFT FRONT MOTOR CIRCUIT SHORTED TO GROUND

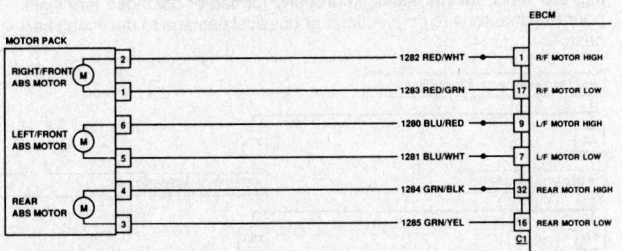

EBCM can identify a motor circuit that is shorted to ground. This malfunction will not allow the motor to be controlled at the commanded current rate or will cause the driver circuit to allow current directly to ground.

NOTE: Test numbers refer to test numbers on diagnostic chart.

1) Checks for a short to ground in the motor high circuit.
2) Checks for a short to ground in the motor low circuit.
3) Checks for a motor that is internally shorted to ground.

DIAGNOSTIC AIDS

Using the TECH-1 scan tester, select manual control function and exercise motor movement of affected channel in both directions while applying light pressure on the brake pedal. If erratic or jumpy brake pedal movement is detected while performing an apply or release function of the motor, an intermittent malfunction may be indicated.

Intermittent condition can be caused by a poor connection, rubbed through insulation or a wire that is broken inside the insulation. The frequency of the malfunction can be checked by using the enhanced diagnostic function of the TECH-1 scan tester as described in the tester manual.

Any circuitry that is suspected of causing an intermittent complaint should be thoroughly inspected for backed out terminals, improper mating, broken connector locks, improperly formed or damaged terminals, poor terminal-to-wire connections or physical damage to the wiring harness.

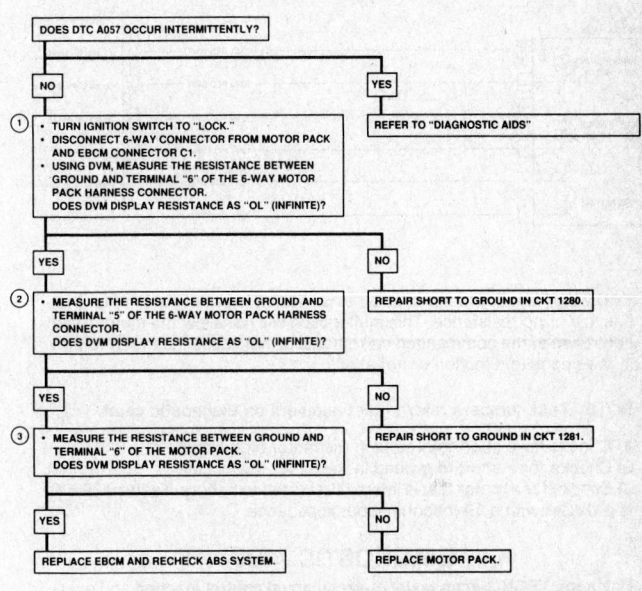

* AFTER ALL DIAGNOSIS IS COMPLETE, CLEAR DTCs AND TEST DRIVE VEHICLE FOR THREE (3) DRIVE CYCLES TO VERIFY THAT DTC DOES NOT RESET. A DRIVE CYCLE CONSISTS OF STARTING THE VEHICLE, DRIVING OVER 16 km/h (10 MPH), AND THEN KEYING DOWN.

THIS CHART ASSUMES THAT A CURRENT DTC IS STORED INDICATING THAT THIS MALFUNCTION IS PRESENT.

93F84686 93I84762

DTC A058, LEFT FRONT MOTOR CIRCUIT SHORTED TO BATTERY

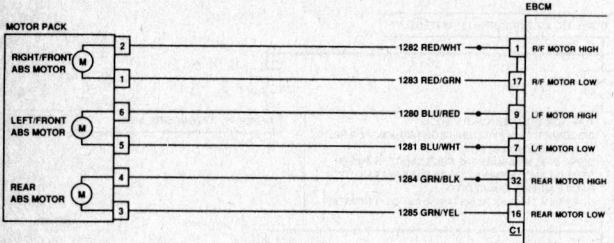

EBCM can detect a motor circuit that is shorted to battery or a motor that has low or no resistance. This malfunction will not allow the motor to be controlled at the commanded current rate or will cause the motor to turn in the opposite direction or not at all.

NOTE: Test numbers refer to test numbers on diagnostic chart.

1) Checks for a short to ground in the motor high circuit.
2) Checks for a short to ground in the motor low circuit.
3) Checks for a motor that is internally shorted to battery. Tester J 39200 is a DVOM with a 10-megohm input impedance.

DIAGNOSTIC AIDS

Using the TECH-1 scan tester, select manual control function and exercise motor movement of affected channel in both directions while applying light pressure on the brake pedal. If erratic or jumpy brake pedal movement is detected while performing an apply or release function of the motor, an intermittent malfunction may be indicated.

Intermittent condition can be caused by a poor connection, rubbed through insulation or a wire that is broken inside the insulation. The frequency of the malfunction can be checked by using the enhanced diagnostic function of the TECH-1 scan tester as described in the tester manual.

Any circuitry that is suspected of causing an intermittent complaint should be thoroughly inspected for backed out terminals, improper mating, broken connector locks, improperly formed or damaged terminals, poor terminal-to-wire connections or physical damage to the wiring harness.

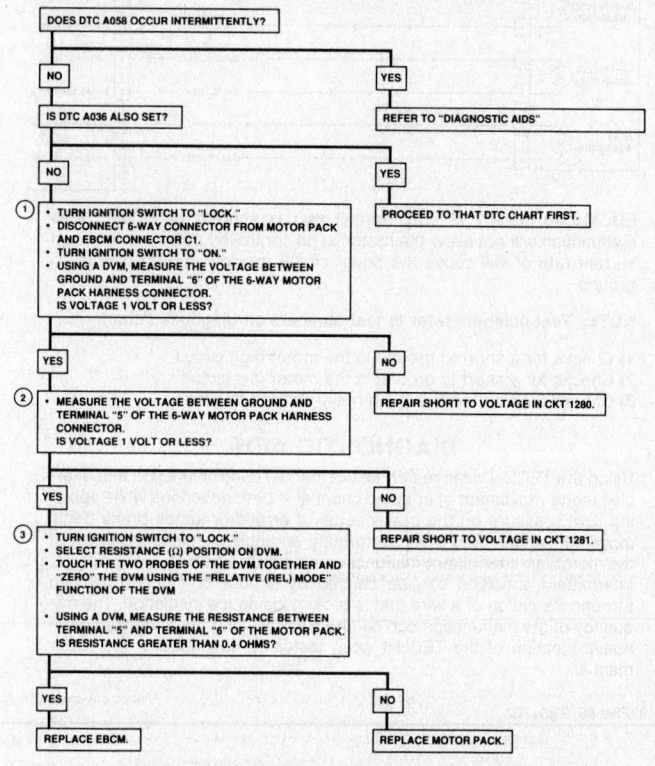

* AFTER ALL DIAGNOSIS IS COMPLETE, CLEAR DTCs AND TEST DRIVE VEHICLE FOR THREE (3) DRIVE CYCLES TO VERIFY THAT DTC DOES NOT RESET. A DRIVE CYCLE CONSISTS OF STARTING THE VEHICLE, DRIVING OVER 16 km/h (10 MPH), AND THEN KEYING DOWN.

THIS CHART ASSUMES THAT A CURRENT DTC IS STORED INDICATING THAT THIS MALFUNCTION IS PRESENT.

DTC A061, RIGHT FRONT MOTOR CIRCUIT OPEN

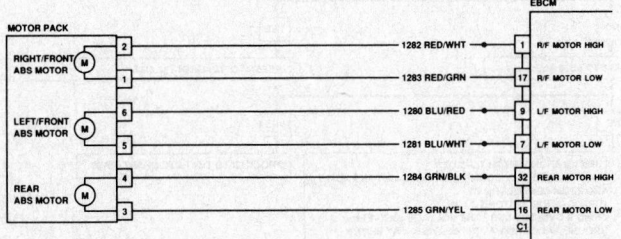

EBCM can identify a motor that cannot be energized due to an open in its circuitry.

NOTE: Test numbers refer to test numbers on diagnostic chart.

1) Checks for proper motor resistance.
2) Checks for an open in the motor high circuitry.
3) Checks for an open in the motor low circuitry.

DIAGNOSTIC AIDS

Using the TECH-1 scan tester, select manual control function and exercise motor movement of affected channel in both directions while applying light pressure on the brake pedal. If erratic or jumpy brake pedal movement is detected while performing an apply or release function of the motor, an intermittent malfunction may be indicated.

Intermittent condition can be caused by a poor connection, rubbed through insulation or a wire that is broken inside the insulation. The frequency of the malfunction can be checked by using the enhanced diagnostic function of the TECH-1 scan tester as described in the tester manual.

93F84686 93A84764

Any circuitry that is suspected of causing an intermittent complaint should be thoroughly inspected for backed out terminals, improper mating, broken connector locks, improperly formed or damaged terminals, poor terminal-to-wire connections or physical damage to the wiring harness.

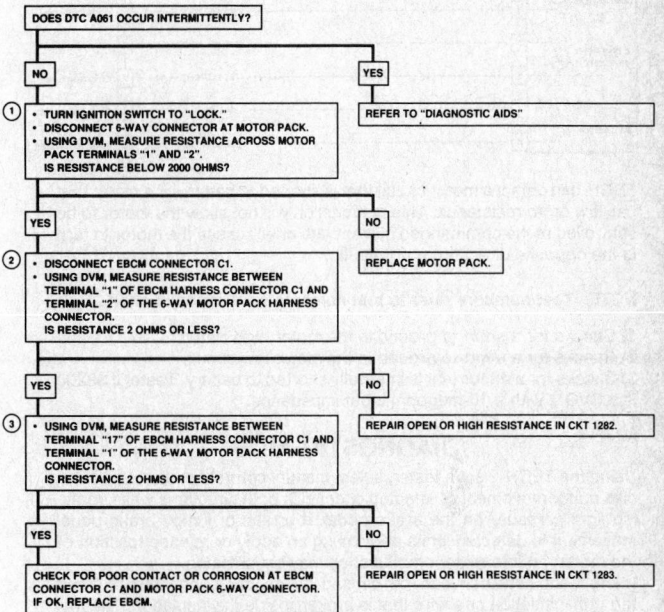

AFTER ALL DIAGNOSIS IS COMPLETE, CLEAR DTCs AND TEST DRIVE VEHICLE FOR THREE (3) DRIVE CYCLES TO VERIFY THAT DTC DOES NOT RESET. A DRIVE CYCLE CONSISTS OF STARTING THE VEHICLE, DRIVING OVER 16 km/h (10 MPH), AND THEN KEYING DOWN.

THIS CHART ASSUMES THAT A CURRENT DTC IS STORED INDICATING THAT THIS MALFUNCTION IS PRESENT.

Courtesy of General Motors Corp.

DTC A062, RIGHT FRONT MOTOR CIRCUIT SHORTED TO GROUND

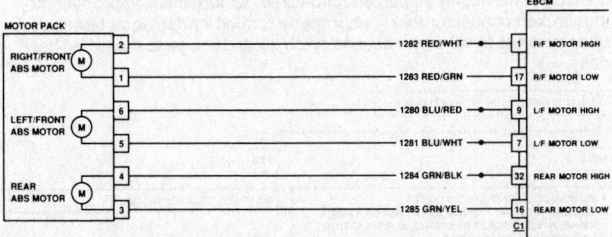

EBCM can identify a motor circuit that is shorted to ground. This malfunction will not allow the motor to be controlled at the commanded current rate or will cause the driver circuit to allow current directly to ground.

NOTE: Test numbers refer to test numbers on diagnostic chart.

1) Checks for a short to ground in the motor high circuit.
2) Checks for a short to ground in the motor low circuit.
3) Checks for a motor that is internally shorted to ground.

DIAGNOSTIC AIDS

Using the TECH-1 scan tester, select manual control function and exercise motor movement of affected channel in both directions while applying light pressure on the brake pedal. If erratic or jumpy brake pedal movement is detected while performing an apply or release function of the motor, an intermittent malfunction may be indicated.

Intermittent condition can be caused by a poor connection, rubbed through insulation or a wire that is broken inside the insulation. The frequency of the malfunction can be checked by using the enhanced diagnostic function of the TECH-1 scan tester as described in the tester manual.

93F84686 93B84765

Any circuitry that is suspected of causing an intermittent complaint should be thoroughly inspected for backed out terminals, improper mating, broken connector locks, improperly formed or damaged terminals, poor terminal-to-wire connections or physical damage to the wiring harness.

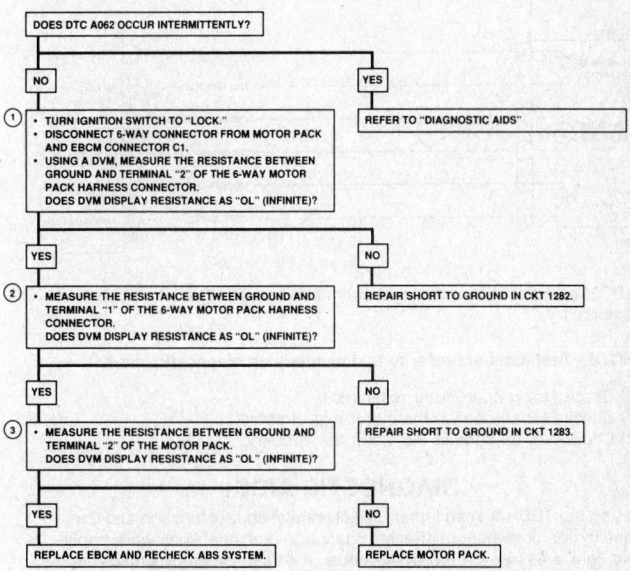

AFTER ALL DIAGNOSIS IS COMPLETE, CLEAR DTCs AND TEST DRIVE VEHICLE FOR THREE (3) DRIVE CYCLES TO VERIFY THAT DTC DOES NOT RESET. A DRIVE CYCLE CONSISTS OF STARTING THE VEHICLE, DRIVING OVER 16 km/h (10 MPH), AND THEN KEYING DOWN.

THIS CHART ASSUMES THAT A CURRENT DTC IS STORED INDICATING THAT THIS MALFUNCTION IS PRESENT.

Courtesy of General Motors Corp.

DTC A063, RIGHT FRONT MOTOR CIRCUIT SHORTED TO BATTERY

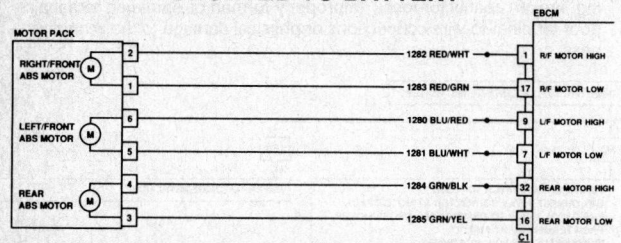

EBCM can detect a motor circuit that is shorted to battery or a motor that has low or no resistance. This malfunction will not allow the motor to be controlled at the commanded current rate or will cause the motor to turn in the opposite direction or not at all.

NOTE: Test numbers refer to test numbers on diagnostic chart.

1) Checks for a short to ground in the motor high circuit.
2) Checks for a short to ground in the motor low circuit.
3) Checks for a motor that is internally shorted to battery. Tester J 39200 is a DVOM with a 10-megohm input impedance.

DIAGNOSTIC AIDS

Using the TECH-1 scan tester, select manual control function and exercise motor movement of affected channel in both directions while applying light pressure on the brake pedal. If erratic or jumpy brake pedal movement is detected while performing an apply or release function of the motor, an intermittent malfunction may be indicated.

Intermittent condition can be caused by a poor connection, rubbed through insulation or a wire that is broken inside the insulation. The frequency of the malfunction can be checked by using the enhanced diagnostic function of the TECH-1 scan tester as described in the tester manual.

Any circuitry that is suspected of causing an intermittent complaint should be thoroughly inspected for backed out terminals, improper mating, broken connector locks, improperly formed or damaged terminals, poor terminal-to-wire connections or physical damage to the wiring harness.

93F84686 93C84766

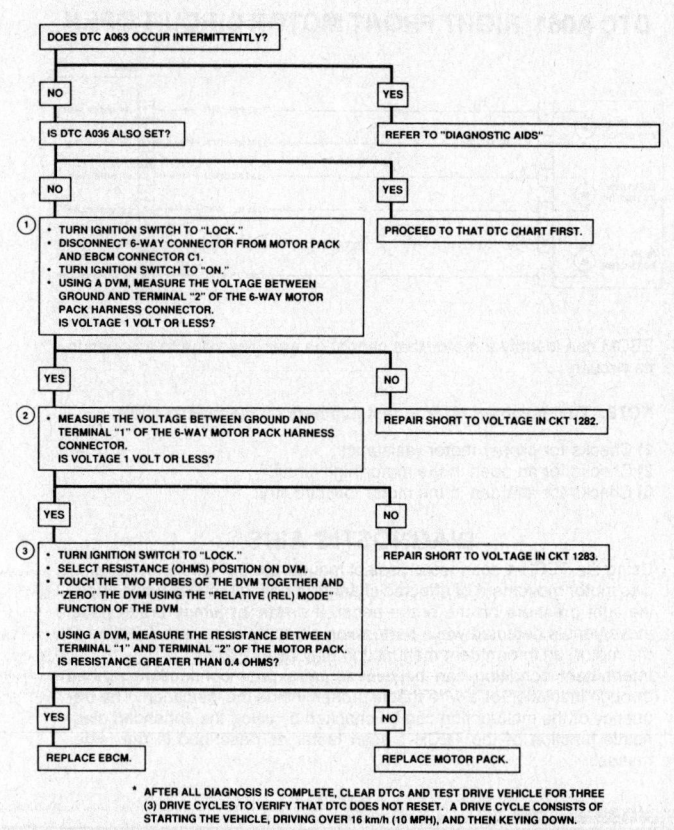

* AFTER ALL DIAGNOSIS IS COMPLETE, CLEAR DTCs AND TEST DRIVE VEHICLE FOR THREE (3) DRIVE CYCLES TO VERIFY THAT DTC DOES NOT RESET. A DRIVE CYCLE CONSISTS OF STARTING THE VEHICLE, DRIVING OVER 16 km/h (10 MPH), AND THEN KEYING DOWN.

THIS CHART ASSUMES THAT A CURRENT DTC IS STORED INDICATING THAT THIS MALFUNCTION IS PRESENT.

Courtesy of General Motors Corp.

DTC A064, REAR MOTOR CIRCUIT OPEN

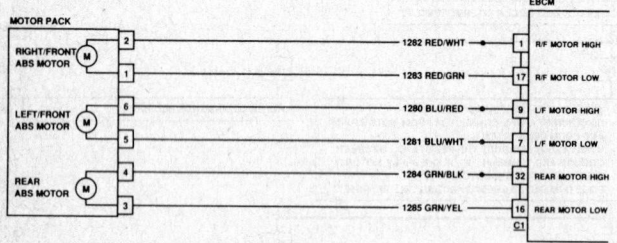

EBCM can identify a motor that cannot be energized due to an open in its circuitry.

NOTE: Test numbers refer to test numbers on diagnostic chart.

1) Checks for proper motor resistance.
2) Checks for an open in the motor high circuitry.
3) Checks for an open in the motor low circuitry.

DIAGNOSTIC AIDS

Using the TECH-1 scan tester, select manual control function and exercise motor movement of affected channel in both directions while applying light pressure on the brake pedal. If erratic or jumpy brake pedal movement is detected while performing an apply or release function of the motor, an intermittent malfunction may be indicated.

Intermittent condition can be caused by a poor connection, rubbed through insulation or a wire that is broken inside the insulation. The frequency of the malfunction can be checked by using the enhanced diagnostic function of the TECH-1 scan tester as described in the tester manual.

93F84686 93D84767

Any circuitry that is suspected of causing an intermittent complaint should be thoroughly inspected for backed out terminals, improper mating, broken connector locks, improperly formed or damaged terminals, poor terminal-to-wire connections or physical damage to the wiring harness.

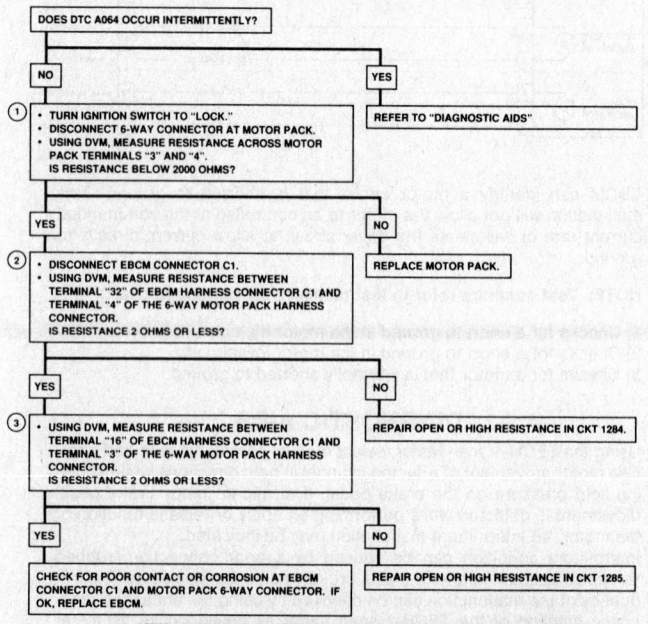

* AFTER ALL DIAGNOSIS IS COMPLETE, CLEAR DTCs AND TEST DRIVE VEHICLE FOR THREE (3) DRIVE CYCLES TO VERIFY THAT DTC DOES NOT RESET. A DRIVE CYCLE CONSISTS OF STARTING THE VEHICLE, DRIVING OVER 16 km/h (10 MPH), AND THEN KEYING DOWN.

THIS CHART ASSUMES THAT A CURRENT DTC IS STORED INDICATING THAT THIS MALFUNCTION IS PRESENT.

Courtesy of General Motors Corp.

DTC A065, REAR MOTOR CIRCUIT SHORTED TO GROUND

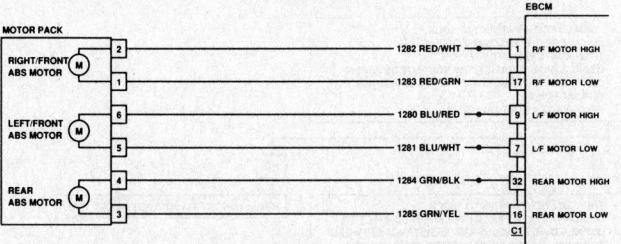

EBCM can identify a motor circuit that is shorted to ground. This malfunction will not allow the motor to be controlled at the commanded current rate or will cause the driver circuit to allow current directly to ground.

NOTE: Test numbers refer to test numbers on diagnostic chart.

1) Checks for a short to ground in the motor high circuit.
2) Checks for a short to ground in the motor low circuit.
3) Checks for a motor that is internally shorted to ground.

DIAGNOSTIC AIDS

Using the TECH-1 scan tester, select manual control function and exercise motor movement of affected channel in both directions while applying light pressure on the brake pedal. If erratic or jumpy brake pedal movement is detected while performing an apply or release function of the motor, an intermittent malfunction may be indicated.

Intermittent condition can be caused by a poor connection, rubbed through insulation or a wire that is broken inside the insulation. The frequency of the malfunction can be checked by using the enhanced diagnostic function of the TECH-1 scan tester as described in the tester manual.

93F84686 93E84768

Any circuitry that is suspected of causing an intermittent complaint should be thoroughly inspected for backed out terminals, improper mating, broken connector locks, improperly formed or damaged terminals, poor terminal-to-wire connections or physical damage to the wiring harness.

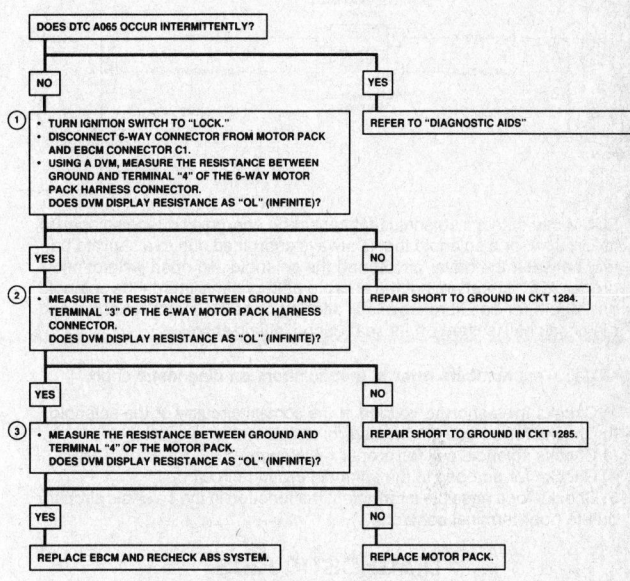

* AFTER ALL DIAGNOSIS IS COMPLETE, CLEAR DTCs AND TEST DRIVE VEHICLE FOR THREE (3) DRIVE CYCLES TO VERIFY THAT DTC DOES NOT RESET. A DRIVE CYCLE CONSISTS OF STARTING THE VEHICLE, DRIVING OVER 16 km/h (10 MPH), AND THEN KEYING DOWN.

THIS CHART ASSUMES THAT A CURRENT DTC IS STORED INDICATING THAT THIS MALFUNCTION IS PRESENT.

Courtesy of General Motors Corp.

DTC A066, REAR MOTOR CIRCUIT SHORTED TO BATTERY

EBCM can detect a motor circuit that is shorted to battery or a motor that has low or no resistance. This malfunction will not allow the motor to be controlled at the commanded current rate or will cause the motor to turn in the opposite direction or not at all.

NOTE: Test numbers refer to test numbers on diagnostic chart.

1) Checks for a short to ground in the motor high circuit.
2) Checks for a short to ground in the motor low circuit.
3) Checks for a motor that is internally shorted to battery. Tester J 39200 is a DVOM with a 10-megohm input impedance.

DIAGNOSTIC AIDS

Using the TECH-1 scan tester, select manual control function and exercise motor movement of affected channel in both directions while applying light pressure on the brake pedal. If erratic or jumpy brake pedal movement is detected while performing an apply or release function of the motor, an intermittent malfunction may be indicated.

Intermittent condition can be caused by a poor connection, rubbed through insulation or a wire that is broken inside the insulation. The frequency of the malfunction can be checked by using the enhanced diagnostic function of the TECH-1 scan tester as described in the tester manual.

Any circuitry that is suspected of causing an intermittent complaint should be thoroughly inspected for backed out terminals, improper mating, broken connector locks, improperly formed or damaged terminals, poor terminal-to-wire connections or physical damage to the wiring harness.

93F84686 93F84769

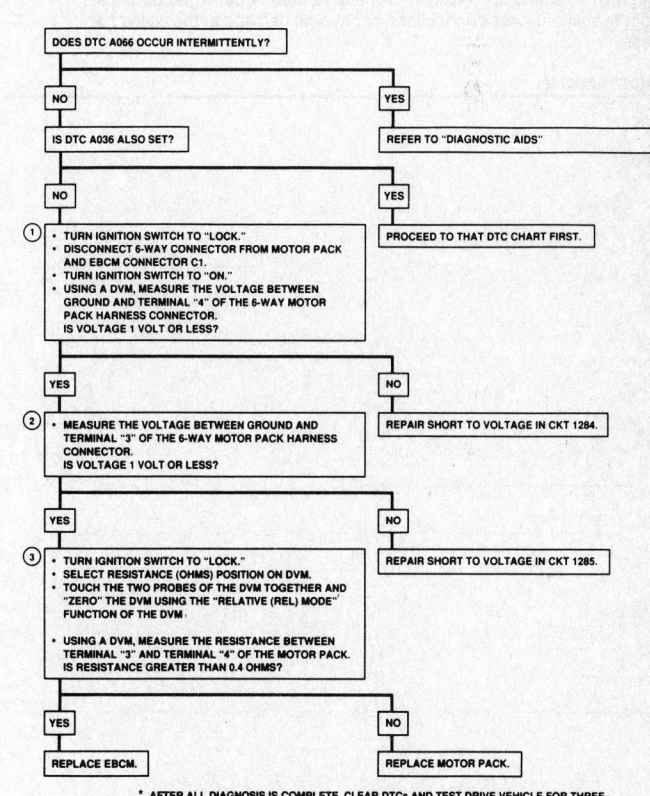

* AFTER ALL DIAGNOSIS IS COMPLETE, CLEAR DTCs AND TEST DRIVE VEHICLE FOR THREE (3) DRIVE CYCLES TO VERIFY THAT DTC DOES NOT RESET. A DRIVE CYCLE CONSISTS OF STARTING THE VEHICLE, DRIVING OVER 16 km/h (10 MPH), AND THEN KEYING DOWN.

THIS CHART ASSUMES THAT A CURRENT DTC IS STORED INDICATING THAT THIS MALFUNCTION IS PRESENT.

Courtesy of General Motors Corp.

DTC A076, LEFT FRONT SOLENOID CIRCUIT OPEN OR SHORTED TO BATTERY

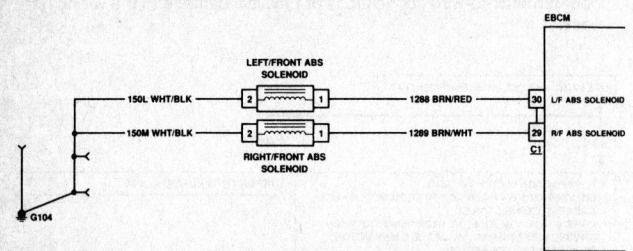

EBCM can detect a solenoid that cannot be energized due to an open in its circuitry, or a solenoid that is always energized due to a short to battery between the driver circuit and the solenoid. An open will not allow proper ABS operation, but the short to battery simply turns the solenoid on. A path for base brakes is still allowed once the motor rehomes and the check ball is lifted off its seat during initialization.

NOTE: Test numbers refer to test numbers on diagnostic chart.

1) Checks for a short to voltage in the control circuitry of the solenoid.
2) Checks for an open in the control circuit of the solenoid.
3) Checks solenoid coil for proper resistance.
4) Checks for an open in the solenoid ground circuit.
5) Checks for a possible intermittent malfunction in the solenoid circuitry due to poor terminal contact.

DIAGNOSTIC AIDS

Intermittent condition can be caused by a poor connection, rubbed through insulation or a wire that is broken inside the insulation. The frequency of the malfunction can be checked by using the enhanced diagnostic function of the TECH-1 scan tester as described in the tester manual.

Any circuitry that is suspected of causing an intermittent complaint should be thoroughly inspected for backed out terminals, improper mating, broken connector locks, improperly formed or damaged terminals, poor terminal-to-wire connections or physical damage to the wiring harness.

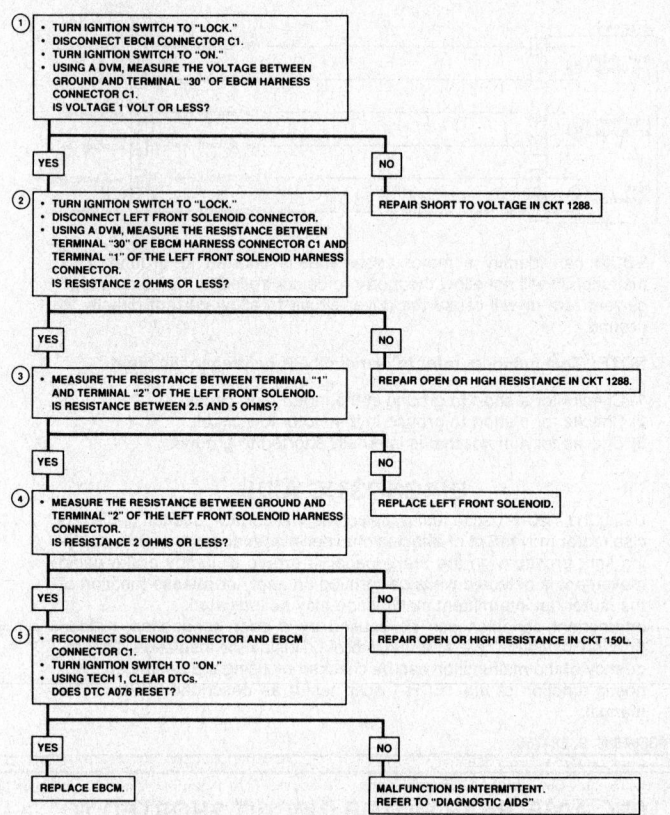

THIS CHART ASSUMES THAT A CURRENT DTC IS STORED INDICATING THAT THIS MALFUNCTION IS PRESENT.

93G84687 93I84770

Courtesy of General Motors Corp.

DTC A077, LEFT FRONT SOLENOID CIRCUIT SHORTED TO GROUND

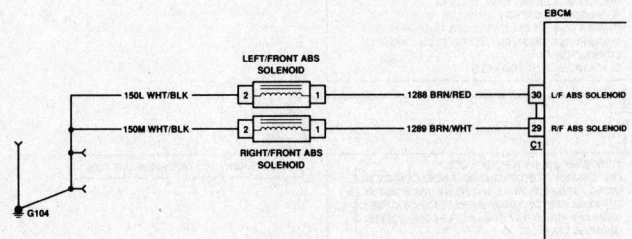

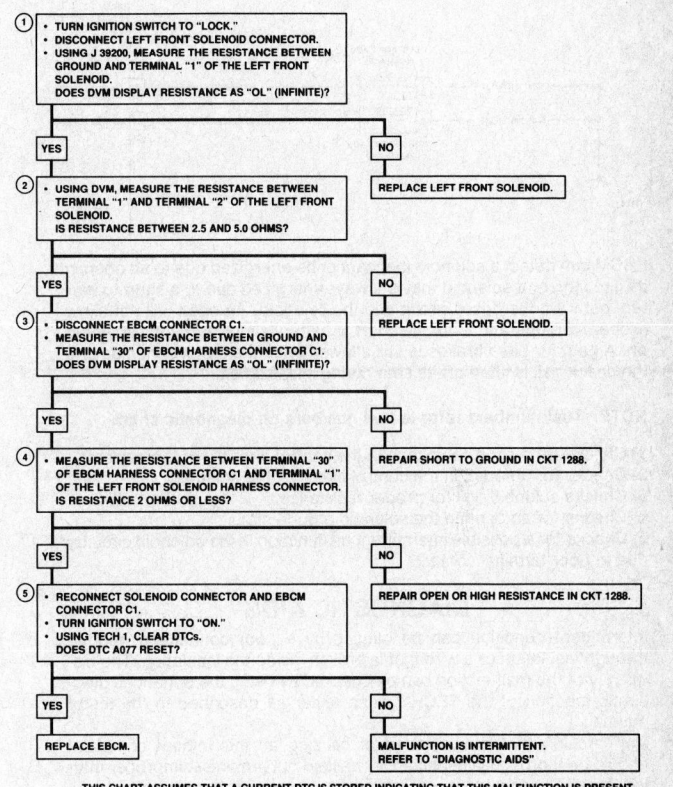

The EBCM identifies a solenoid that cannot be energized due to an open in its driver circuitry or a short to ground between the solenoid driver and the solenoid. These malfunctions can affect ABS operation since the flow of brake fluid to the caliper cannot be stopped, making ABS operation for that channel impossible.

NOTE: Test numbers refer to test numbers on diagnostic chart.

1) Checks for a solenoid that is internally shorted to ground. Tester J 39200 is a DVOM with a 10-megohm input impedance.
2) Checks for a solenoid that is not within proper resistance values.
3) Indicates if a short to ground exists in the solenoid circuitry.
4) Checks for an open control circuit to the EBCM.
5) Checks for a possible intermittent malfunction in the solenoid circuitry due to poor terminal contact.

DIAGNOSTIC AIDS

Intermittent condition can be caused by a poor connection, rubbed through insulation or a wire that is broken inside the insulation. The frequency of the malfunction can be checked by using the enhanced diagnostic function of the TECH-1 scan tester as described in the tester manual.

Any circuitry that is suspected of causing an intermittent complaint should be thoroughly inspected for backed out terminals, improper mating, broken connector locks, improperly formed or damaged terminals, poor terminal-to-wire connections or physical damage to the wiring harness.

THIS CHART ASSUMES THAT A CURRENT DTC IS STORED INDICATING THAT THIS MALFUNCTION IS PRESENT.

Courtesy of General Motors Corp.

DTC A078, RIGHT FRONT SOLENOID CIRCUIT OPEN OR SHORTED TO BATTERY

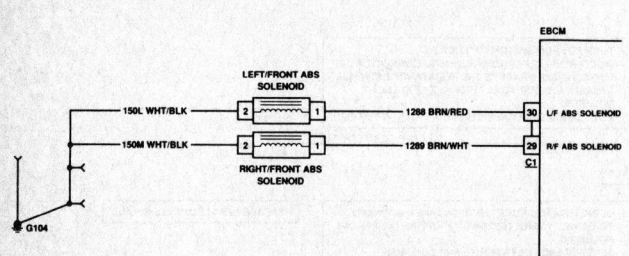

EBCM can detect a solenoid that cannot be energized due to an open in its circuitry, or a solenoid that is always energized due to a short to battery between the driver circuit and the solenoid. An open will not allow proper ABS operation, but the short to battery simply turns the solenoid on. A path for base brakes is still allowed once the motor rehomes and the check ball is lifted off its seat during initialization.

NOTE: Test numbers refer to test numbers on diagnostic chart.

1) Checks for a short to voltage in the control circuitry of the solenoid.
2) Checks for an open in the control circuit of the solenoid.
3) Checks solenoid coil for proper resistance.
4) Checks for an open in the solenoid ground circuit.
5) Checks for a possible intermittent malfunction in the solenoid circuitry due to poor terminal contact.

DIAGNOSTIC AIDS

Intermittent condition can be caused by a poor connection, rubbed through insulation or a wire that is broken inside the insulation. The frequency of the malfunction can be checked by using the enhanced diagnostic function of the TECH-1 scan tester as described in the tester manual.

Any circuitry that is suspected of causing an intermittent complaint should be thoroughly inspected for backed out terminals, improper mating, broken connector locks, improperly formed or damaged terminals, poor terminal-to-wire connections or physical damage to the wiring harness.

93G84687 93A84772

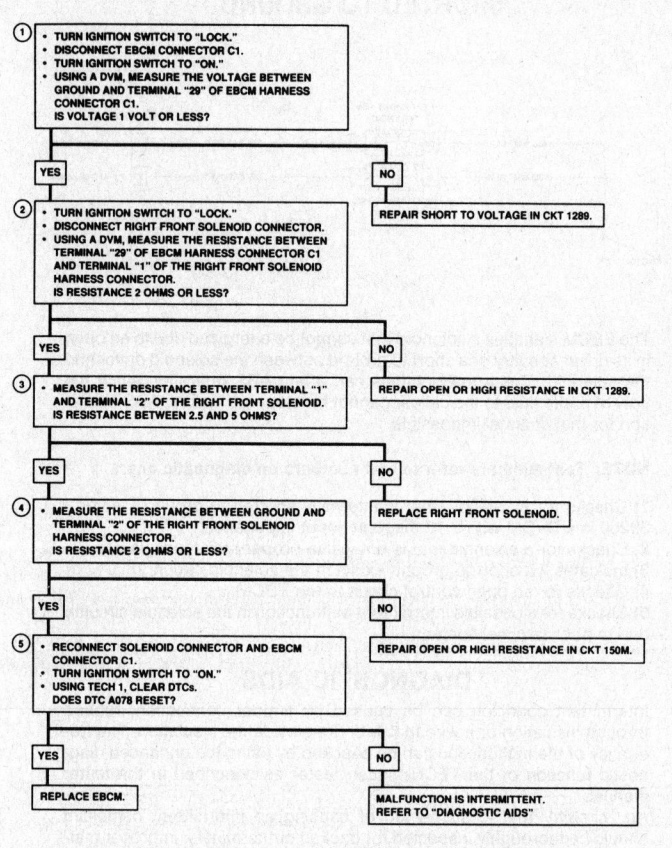

THIS CHART ASSUMES THAT A CURRENT DTC IS STORED INDICATING THAT THIS MALFUNCTION IS PRESENT.

Courtesy of General Motors Corp.

DTC A081, RIGHT FRONT SOLENOID CIRCUIT SHORTED TO GROUND

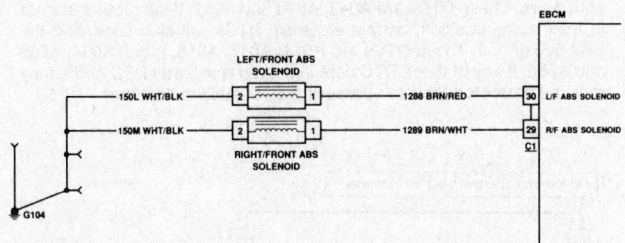

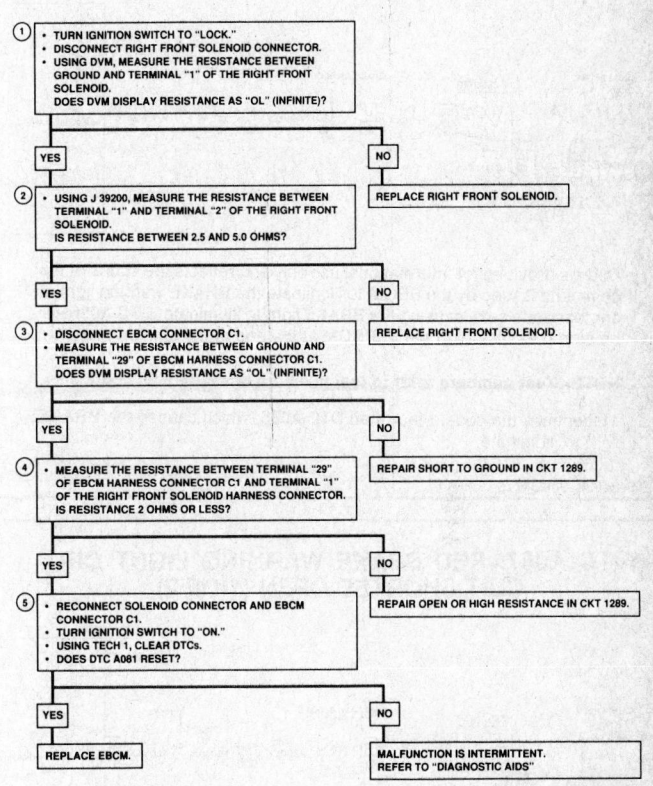

The EBCM identifies a solenoid that cannot be energized due to an open in its driver circuitry or a short to ground between the solenoid driver and the solenoid. These malfunctions can affect ABS operation since the flow of brake fluid to the caliper cannot be stopped, making ABS operation for that channel impossible.

NOTE: Test numbers refer to test numbers on diagnostic chart.

1) Checks for a solenoid that is internally shorted to ground.
2) Checks for a solenoid that is not within proper resistance values. Tester J 39200 is a DVOM with a 10-megohm input impedance.
3) Indicates if a short to ground exists in the solenoid circuitry.
4) Checks for an open control circuit to the EBCM.
5) Checks for a possible intermittent malfunction in the solenoid circuitry due to poor terminal contact.

DIAGNOSTIC AIDS

Intermittent condition can be caused by a poor connection, rubbed through insulation or a wire that is broken inside the insulation. The frequency of the malfunction can be checked by using the enhanced diagnostic function of the TECH-1 scan tester as described in the tester manual.

Any circuitry that is suspected of causing an intermittent complaint should be thoroughly inspected for backed out terminals, improper mating, broken connector locks, improperly formed or damaged terminals, poor terminal-to-wire connections or physical damage to the wiring harness.

THIS CHART ASSUMES THAT A CURRENT DTC IS STORED INDICATING THAT THIS MALFUNCTION IS PRESENT.

93G84687 93B84773

DTC A082, CALIBRATION MALFUNCTION

EBCM checks for a malfunction by comparing the calibration value to a known value stored in the EEPROM. Code is also used as a security measure to prevent improper use of calibrations or changes of these calibrations that may alter the designed function of ABS.

NOTE: Test numbers refer to test numbers on diagnostic chart.

1) Checks to see if the malfunction is present during diagnosis. If present, the EBCM is not functioning correctly and must be replaced.

DIAGNOSTIC AIDS

An intermittent code may be caused by a bad cell in the EEPROM that is sensitive to temperature changes. If code has set more than once, but is still intermittent, replace EBCM.

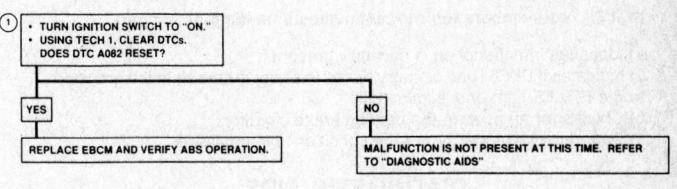

THIS CHART ASSUMES THAT A CURRENT DTC IS STORED INDICATING THAT THIS MALFUNCTION IS PRESENT.

93C84774

DTC A086, EBCM TURNED ON THE RED BRAKE WARNING LIGHT

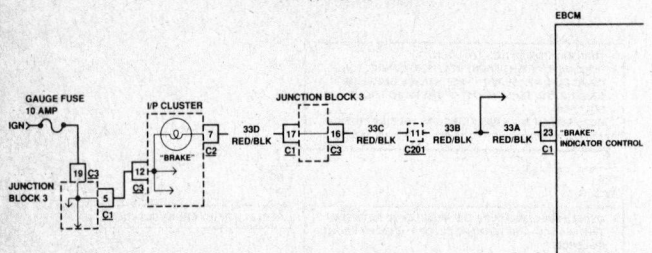

Code is provided for informational use only and reflects the status of the command issued by the EBCM to illuminate the BRAKE warning light. If another code sets, causing the BRAKE light to illuminate, DTC A086 will be stored as history in the EEPROM at the end of the ignition cycle.

NOTE: Test numbers refer to test numbers on diagnostic chart.

1) Identifies the code, other than DTC A086, which caused the BRAKE light to illuminate.

DIAGNOSTIC AIDS

Any ABS mechanical code that issues a command to illuminate the BRAKE light will also result in DTC A086 being stored in EEPROM during shut down. These DTCs are A042, A046 and A051. If the motors are not in their home position, certain electrical DTCs will also command the BRAKE light on. These DTCs are A014, A016, A018, A055, A064, A065 and A066. If any of these DTCs are indicated along with DTC A086, they must be corrected prior to addressing DTC A086 malfunction.

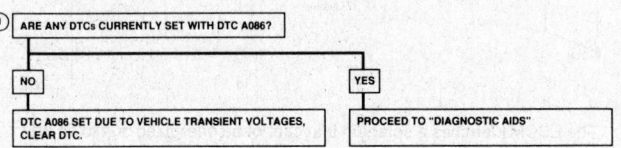

THIS CHART ASSUMES THAT A CURRENT DTC IS STORED INDICATING THAT THIS MALFUNCTION IS PRESENT.

93H84688 93D84775 · Courtesy of General Motors Corp.

DTC A087, RED BRAKE WARNING LIGHT CIRCUIT SHORTED OPEN (1 OF 2)

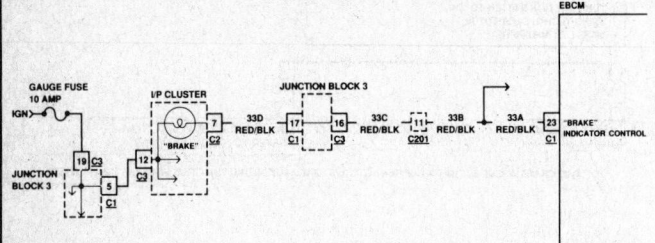

Code is used to verify the EBCM has continuity to the BRAKE light in case the EBCM must turn it on. This will only occur if an ABS malfunction is detected that may degrade base brake operation. Because ABS is not the only device controlling the BRAKE indicator (parking brake switch and brake fluid level switch may also turn on light), a short to ground in this circuit cannot be detected.

NOTE: Test numbers refer to test numbers on diagnostic chart.

1) Identifies if malfunction is currently present.
2) Indicates if EBCM and circuitry have the ability to complete the ground to the BRAKE light and illuminate it.
3) Checks for an open in the parking brake circuitry.
4) Determines whether or not the condition is intermittent.

DIAGNOSTIC AIDS

Intermittent condition can be caused by a poor connection, rubbed through insulation or a wire that is broken inside the insulation. The frequency of the malfunction can be checked by using the enhanced diagnostic function of the TECH-1 scan tester as described in the tester manual.

Any circuitry that is suspected of causing an intermittent complaint should be thoroughly inspected for backed out terminals, improper mating, broken connector locks, improperly formed or damaged terminals, poor terminal-to-wire connections or physical damage to the wiring harness.

THIS CHART ASSUMES THAT A CURRENT DTC IS STORED INDICATING THAT THIS MALFUNCTION IS PRESENT.

93H84688 93E84776 · Courtesy of General Motors Corp.

DTC A087, RED BRAKE WARNING LIGHT CIRCUIT SHORTED OPEN (2 OF 2)

NOTE: Test numbers refer to test numbers on diagnostic chart.

5) Because the BRAKE light has current supplied to it through the GAUGE fuse, this step would indicate if the ignition circuit is complete to the instrument panel cluster.

6) Determines whether the open circuit is due to an EBCM failure or an open wire to the BRAKE light.

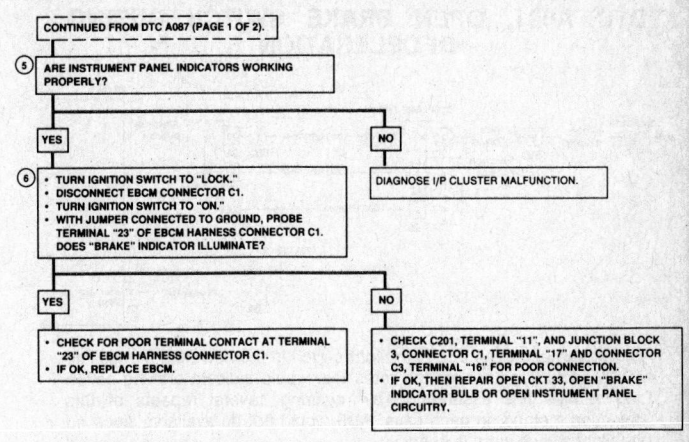

THIS CHART ASSUMES THAT A CURRENT DTC IS STORED INDICATING THAT THIS MALFUNCTION IS PRESENT.

93F84777

Courtesy of General Motors Corp.

DTC A088, RED BRAKE WARNING LIGHT CIRCUIT SHORTED TO BATTERY

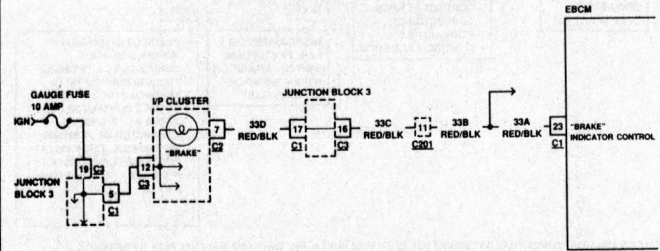

EBCM identifies a short to battery between the EBCM and the BRAKE light or an open driver that does not allow the BRAKE light to be illuminated by the EBCM. This will only occur if an ABS fault is detected that may degrade base brake performance.

NOTE: Test numbers refer to test numbers on diagnostic chart.

1) Identifies if the ground circuit to the BRAKE light is being completed by a source other than the EBCM.

2) Identifies if the malfunction is currently present.

3) By removing the GAUGE fuse, the voltage source is eliminated. This test indicates if voltage is being supplied from a source other than the GAUGE fuse.

4) Checks for DTC A086 also being set.

DIAGNOSTIC AIDS

Intermittent condition can be caused by a poor connection, rubbed through insulation or a wire that is broken inside the insulation. The frequency of the malfunction can be checked by using the enhanced diagnostic function of the TECH-1 scan tester as described in the tester manual.

Any circuitry that is suspected of causing an intermittent complaint should be thoroughly inspected for backed out terminals, improper mating, broken connector locks, improperly formed or damaged terminals, poor terminal-to-wire connections or physical damage to the wiring harness.

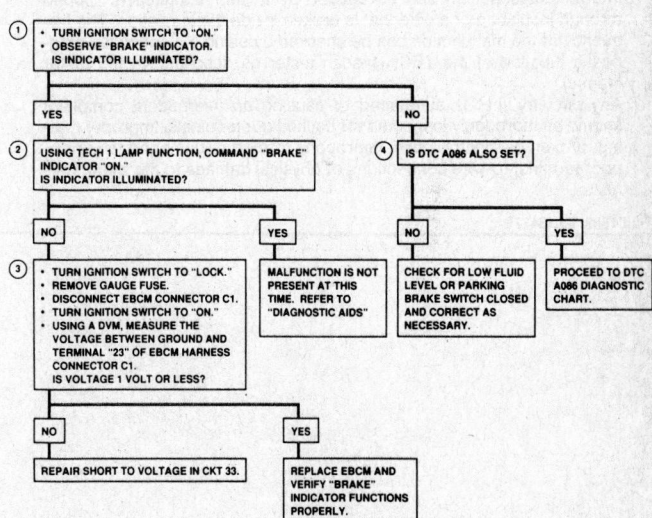

THIS CHART ASSUMES THAT A CURRENT DTC IS STORED INDICATING THAT THIS MALFUNCTION IS PRESENT.

93H84688 93G84778

Courtesy of General Motors Corp.

DTC A091, OPEN BRAKE SWITCH DURING DECELERATION

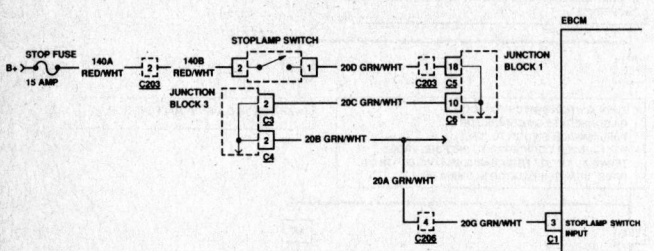

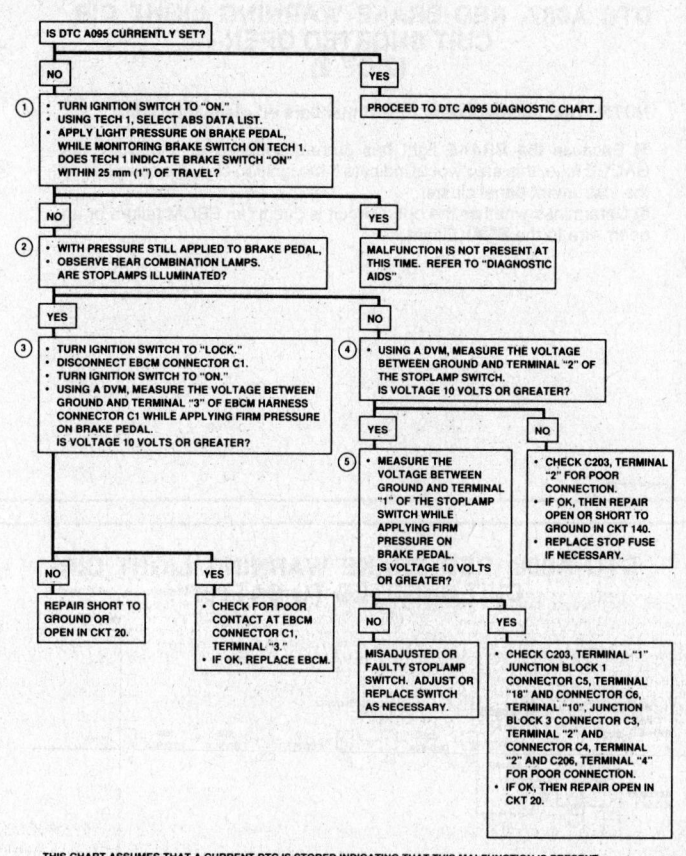

EBCM can detect an open stoplight switch in the non-ABS mode. The EBCM looks for deceleration rates that would indicate braking action and verifies this assumption by requiring several repeats of this detection method. In each case, ABS would not be available since no stoplight switch input is seen.

NOTE: Test numbers refer to test numbers on diagnostic chart.

1) Indicates stoplight switch signal is being received by the EBCM.
2) Indicates if an open circuit exists in the stoplight switch or the rear combination light circuitry.
3) Isolates the open circuit to either the stoplight switch input circuitry or the EBCM.
4) Verifies that voltage is available to the stoplight switch.
5) Verifies that the stoplight switch is functioning properly.

DIAGNOSTIC AIDS

Intermittent condition can be caused by a poor connection, rubbed through insulation or a wire that is broken inside the insulation. The frequency of the malfunction can be checked by using the enhanced diagnostic function of the TECH-1 scan tester as described in the tester manual.

Any circuitry that is suspected of causing an intermittent complaint should be thoroughly inspected for backed out terminals, improper mating, broken connector locks, improperly formed or damaged terminals, poor terminal-to-wire connections or physical damage to the wiring harness.

THIS CHART ASSUMES THAT A CURRENT DTC IS STORED INDICATING THAT THIS MALFUNCTION IS PRESENT.

93I84689 93H84779

DTC A092, OPEN BRAKE SWITCH WHEN ABS WAS REQUIRED

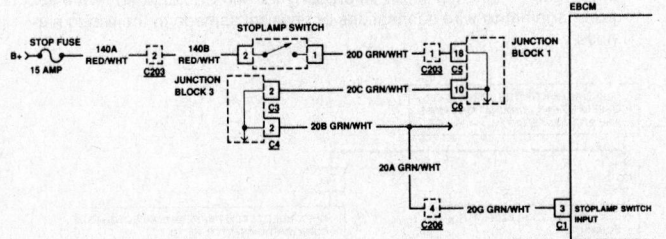

EBCM can determine proper operation of stoplight switch. This is important because ABS is activated when the stoplight switch is closed. If stoplight switch is open, ABS will never be activated. Since this malfunction is difficult to detect under normal braking conditions, this malfunction is only detected when ABS is required.

NOTE: Test numbers refer to test numbers on diagnostic chart.

1) Indicates if stoplight switch signal is being received by the EBCM.
2) Indicates if an open circuit exists in the stoplight switch or the rear combination light circuitry.
3) Isolates open circuit to either the stoplight switch input circuitry or the EBCM.
4) Verifies voltage is available at the stoplight switch.
5) Verifies the stoplight switch is functioning properly.

DIAGNOSTIC AIDS

Intermittent condition can be caused by a poor connection, rubbed through insulation or a wire that is broken inside the insulation. The frequency of the malfunction can be checked by using the enhanced diagnostic function of the TECH-1 scan tester as described in the tester manual.
Any circuitry that is suspected of causing an intermittent complaint should be thoroughly inspected for backed out terminals, improper mating, broken connector locks, improperly formed or damaged terminals, poor terminal-to-wire connections or physical damage to the wiring harness.

93I84689 93A84780

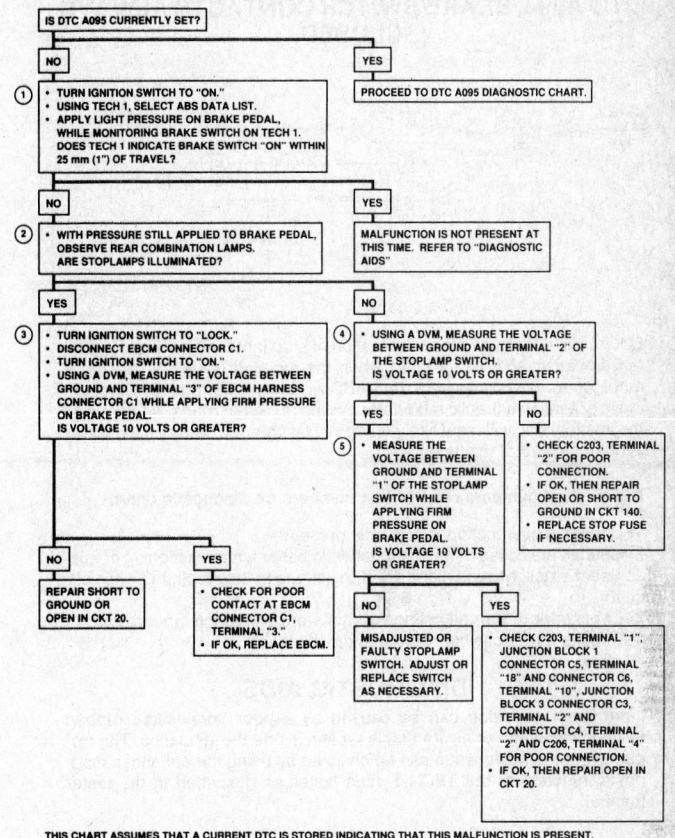

THIS CHART ASSUMES THAT A CURRENT DTC IS STORED INDICATING THAT THIS MALFUNCTION IS PRESENT.

Courtesy of General Motors Corp.

DTC A093, CODE A091 OR A092 SET IN CURRENT OR PREVIOUS IGNITION CYCLE

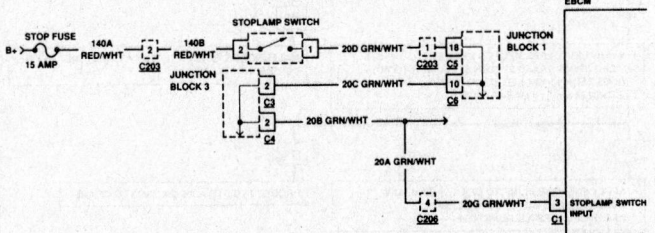

This code is the second portion of DTCs A091 and A092. If these DTCs set during the last ignition cycle, DTC A093 becomes a current failure during the next ignition cycle, keeping ABS disabled until stoplight switch input is seen. When a change is seen during an ignition cycle in which DTC A093 is a current malfunction, DTC A091 or A092 will clear itself at the end of the current ignition cycle and ABS will enable itself at the start of the next ignition cycle. DTC A093 alone indicates DTC A091 or A092 failed previously, but is intermittent or has been corrected.

NOTE: Test numbers refer to test numbers on diagnostic chart.

1) Indicates which DTC caused DTC A093 to set.
2) Insures that DTC that set is repaired so that DTC A093 can be cleared.

DIAGNOSTIC AIDS

Intermittent condition can be caused by a poor connection, rubbed through insulation or a wire that is broken inside the insulation. The frequency of the malfunction can be checked by using the enhanced diagnostic function of the TECH-1 scan tester as described in the tester manual.
Any circuitry that is suspected of causing an intermittent complaint should be thoroughly inspected for backed out terminals, improper mating, broken connector locks, improperly formed or damaged terminals, poor terminal-to-wire connections or physical damage to the wiring harness.
Also, verify proper stoplight switch operation using scan tester display. As the brake is applied the tester should display on status within one inch of travel.

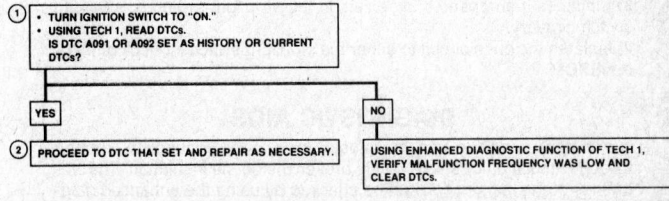

93I84689 93B84781

Courtesy of General Motors Corp.

DTC A094, BRAKE SWITCH CONTACTS ALWAYS CLOSED

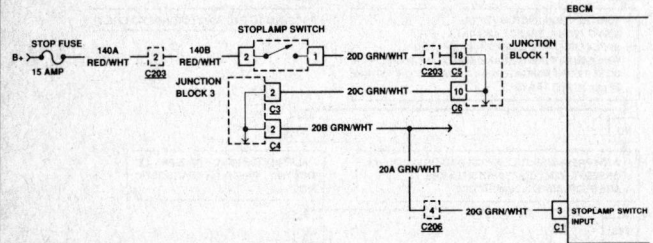

EBCM can determine proper operation of stoplight switch. This is important because ABS is activated when the stoplight switch is closed. If stoplight switch is always closed, ABS will always be requested, resulting in potential hydraulic modulator cycling on rough roads. Additionally, this malfunction will most likely result in a discharged battery if the driver is not informed of malfunction.

NOTE: Test numbers refer to test numbers on diagnostic chart.

1) Checks if malfunction is currently present.
2) Isolates the cause of the malfunction to either a malfunctioning or misadjusted stoplight switch or a short to voltage in the stoplight switch circuitry.
3) Checks for unwanted voltage on the stoplight switch input circuit.
4) Checks for a possible intermittent malfunction.

DIAGNOSTIC AIDS

Intermittent condition can be caused by a poor connection, rubbed through insulation or a wire that is broken inside the insulation. The frequency of the malfunction can be checked by using the enhanced diagnostic function of the TECH-1 scan tester as described in the tester manual.

Any circuitry that is suspected of causing an intermittent complaint should be thoroughly inspected for backed out terminals, improper mating, broken connector locks, improperly formed or damaged terminals, poor terminal-to-wire connections or physical damage to the wiring harness.

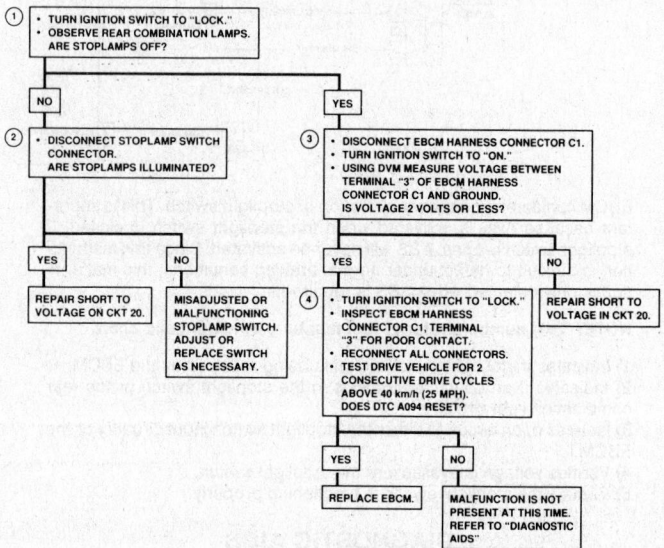

THIS CHART ASSUMES THAT A CURRENT DTC IS STORED INDICATING THAT THIS MALFUNCTION IS PRESENT.

93I84689 93C84782   Courtesy of General Motors Corp.

DTC A095, BRAKE SWITCH CIRCUIT OPEN

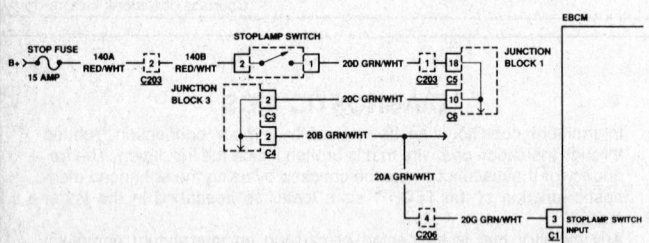

EBCM is able to recognize an open brake stoplight switch circuit which would prevent input to the EBCM from changing status when the brake is applied. DTC A095 is used in conjunction with DTCs A091 and A092 to determine the cause of the open circuit.

NOTE: Test numbers refer to test numbers on diagnostic chart.

1) Confirms an open in the stoplight circuit currently exists.
2) Indicates if the stoplight switch signal is being received by the EBCM.
3) Indicates if an open circuit exists in the stoplight switch or stoplight switch circuitry.
4) Isolates the open circuit to either the stoplight switch input circuitry or the EBCM.

DIAGNOSTIC AIDS

Intermittent condition can be caused by a poor connection, rubbed through insulation or a wire that is broken inside the insulation. The frequency of the malfunction can be checked by using the enhanced diagnostic function of the TECH-1 scan tester as described in the tester manual.

Any circuitry that is suspected of causing an intermittent complaint should be thoroughly inspected for backed out terminals, improper mating, broken connector locks, improperly formed or damaged terminals, poor terminal-to-wire connections or physical damage to the wiring harness.

THIS CHART ASSUMES THAT A CURRENT DTC IS STORED INDICATING THAT THIS MALFUNCTION IS PRESENT.

93I84689 93D84783   Courtesy of General Motors Corp.

DTC A096, REAR BRAKE LIGHT CIRCUIT OPEN

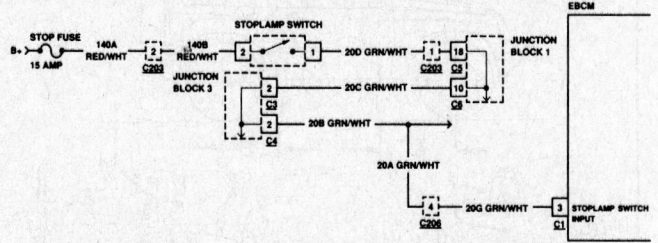

DTC A096 isolates the cause of a DTC A095 malfunction and indicates to the circuit driver that ABS is available. If DTC A095 fails with DTC A096, the stoplights circuits are open. The presence of battery voltage at the stoplight switch input indicates that a valid stoplight switch input is still available.

NOTE: Test numbers refer to test numbers on diagnostic chart.

1) As a result of a malfunction of an additional stoplight switch circuit DTC, DTC A096 may be set. To insure proper diagnosis, any additional stoplight switch DTC must be repaired first.
2) Identifies if the malfunction is currently present.

93184689 93E84784

DIAGNOSTIC AIDS

Intermittent condition can be caused by a poor connection, rubbed through insulation or a wire that is broken inside the insulation. The frequency of the malfunction can be checked by using the enhanced diagnostic function of the TECH-1 scan tester as described in the tester manual.

Any circuitry that is suspected of causing an intermittent complaint should be thoroughly inspected for backed out terminals, improper mating, broken connector locks, improperly formed or damaged terminals, poor terminal-to-wire connections or physical damage to the wiring harness.

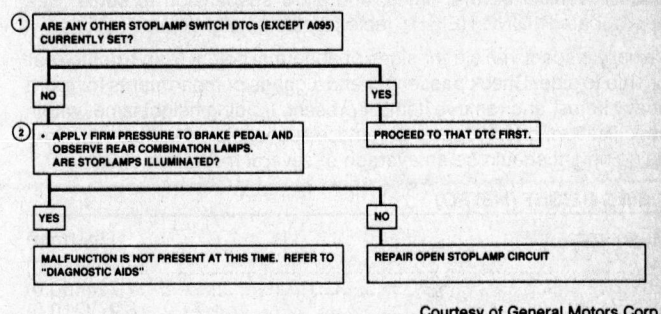

1994 WHEEL ALIGNMENT
Specifications & Procedures

Metro, Prizm, Tracker

NOTE: Prior to performing wheel alignment, perform preliminary visual and mechanical inspection of wheels, tires and suspension components. See PRE-ALIGNMENT INSTRUCTIONS in WHEEL ALIGNMENT THEORY & OPERATION article in GENERAL INFORMATION.

RIDING HEIGHT ADJUSTMENT

Before adjusting alignment, check riding height. *See Fig. 1, 2 or 3.* Riding height must be checked with vehicle on level floor, tires properly inflated, no extraneous weight in vehicle and at least 1/2 tank of fuel. Bounce vehicle several times, and allow suspension to settle. See appropriate RIDING HEIGHT table for riding height specifications.

Visually inspect vehicle for signs of abnormal height from front to rear or side to side. Check passenger and luggage compartments for extra heavy items, and remove items if present. If riding height is not within specification, check, repair or replace suspension components. True riding height should be an average of several measurements.

RIDING HEIGHT (METRO)

Measurement [1]	In. (mm)
"A"	17.72 (450.0)
"B"	17.72 (450.0)
"J"	8.27 (210.0)
"K"	8.86 (225.0)
"Z"	1.77 (45.0)

[1] – See Fig. 1.

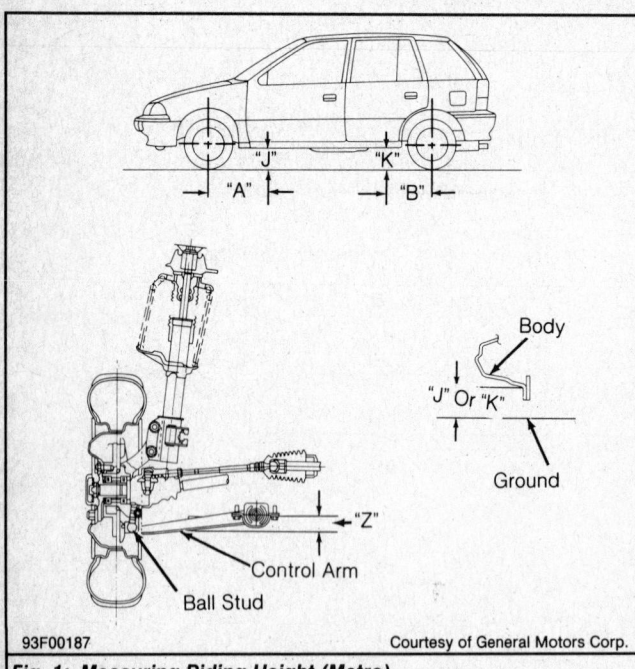

93F00187   Courtesy of General Motors Corp.

Fig. 1: Measuring Riding Height (Metro)

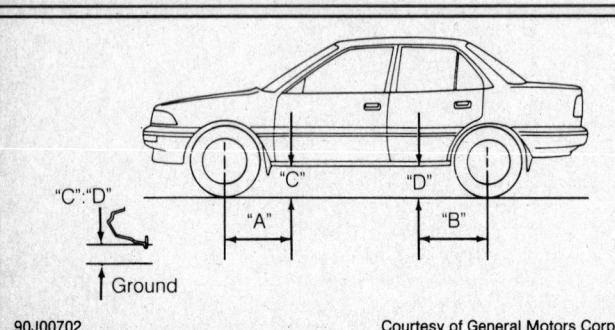

90J00702   Courtesy of General Motors Corp.

Fig. 2: Measuring Riding Height (Prizm)

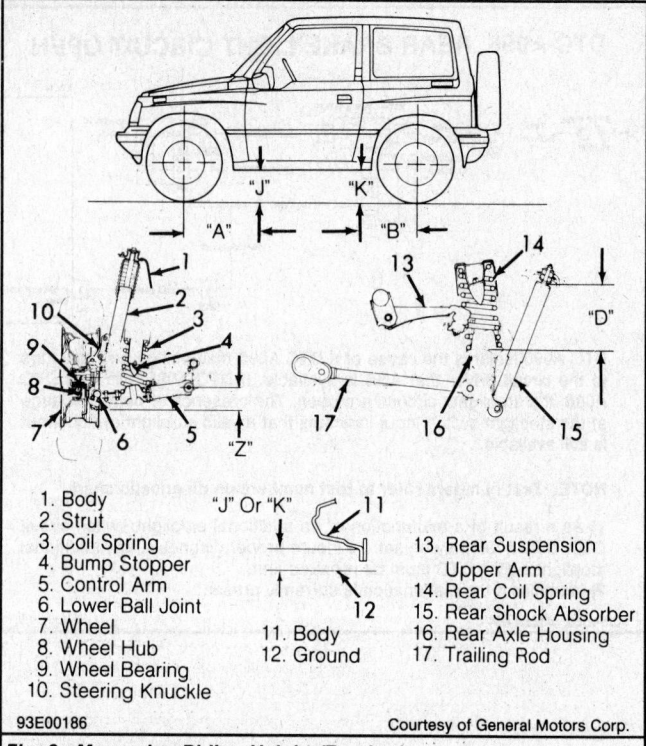

1. Body
2. Strut
3. Coil Spring
4. Bump Stopper
5. Control Arm
6. Lower Ball Joint
7. Wheel
8. Wheel Hub
9. Wheel Bearing
10. Steering Knuckle
11. Body
12. Ground
13. Rear Suspension Upper Arm
14. Rear Coil Spring
15. Rear Shock Absorber
16. Rear Axle Housing
17. Trailing Rod

93E00186   Courtesy of General Motors Corp.

Fig. 3: Measuring Riding Height (Tracker)

RIDING HEIGHT (PRIZM)

Measurement [1]	In. (mm)
"A"	19.76 (502.0)
"B"	20.51 (521.0)
"C"	7.10 (180.0)
"D"	7.30 (185.0)

[1] – See Fig. 2.

RIDING HEIGHT (TRACKER 2WD)

Measurement [1]	In. (mm)
"A"	19.70 (500.0)
"B"	19.70 (500.0)
"D"	8.35 (212.0)
"J"	11.10 (282.0)
"K"	11.93 (303.0)
"Z"	3.60 (91.0)

[1] – See Fig. 3.

RIDING HEIGHT (TRACKER 4WD)

Measurement [1]	In. (mm)
"A"	19.70 (500.0)
"B"	19.70 (500.0)
"D"	8.35 (212.0)
"J"	11.85 (301.0)
"K"	12.68 (322.0)
"Z"	3.60 (91.0)

[1] – See Fig. 3.

JACKING & HOISTING

CAUTION: When jacking or lifting vehicle at side rails or any other prescribed lifting point, ensure lift pads do not contact catalytic converter or brake or fuel lines. Since center of gravity is farther forward on front wheel drive vehicles, support vehicle to prevent it from tipping forward when removing major components.

FLOOR JACK

Metro – Use floor jack only under center of front or rear crossmember. *See Fig. 4.*

Prizm – Use floor jack only under engine lower crossmember or rear subframe. *See Fig. 6.*

Tracker – Use floor jack only under front crossmember or rear axle housing. *See Fig. 7.*

HOIST

Position hoist lift pads under prescribed areas. *See Fig. 5, 6 or 7.*

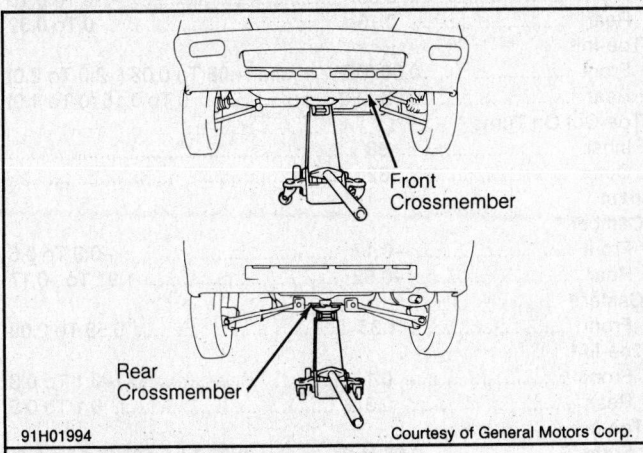

Fig. 4: Locating Jacking Points (Metro)

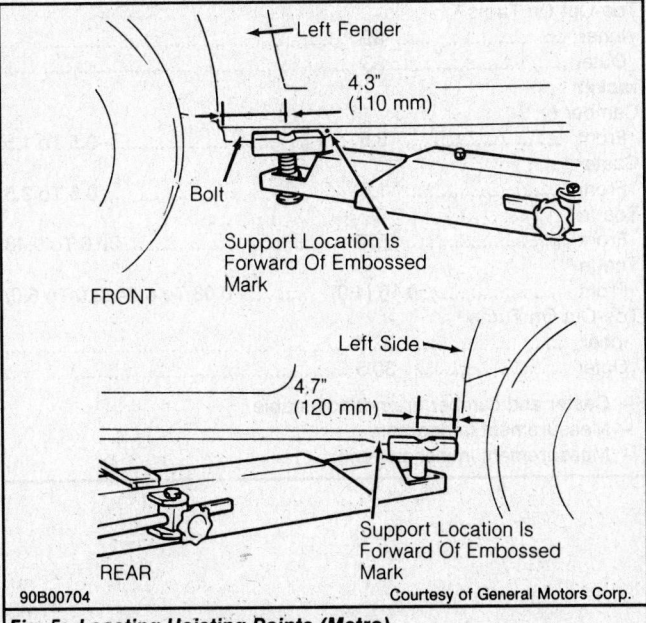

Fig. 5: Locating Hoisting Points (Metro)

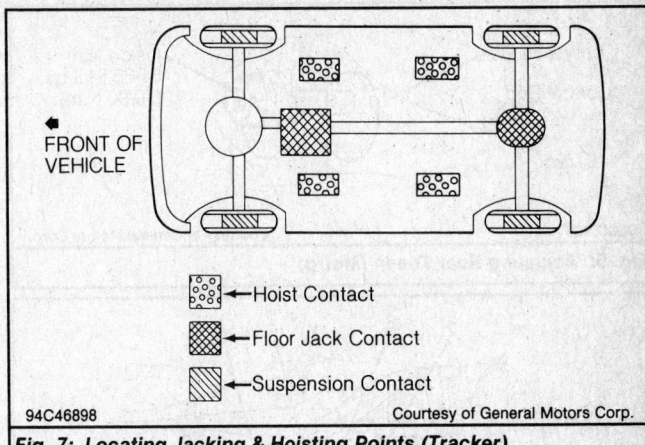

Fig. 7: Locating Jacking & Hoisting Points (Tracker)

WHEEL ALIGNMENT PROCEDURES

NOTE: To prevent incorrect alignment reading, bounce vehicle several times before inspecting.

CAMBER ADJUSTMENT

NOTE: Strut-to-knuckle mounting bolt holes may be slightly enlarged to attain some camber adjustment.

Front and rear camber cannot be adjusted. If camber is not within specification, check for damaged, loose, bent, dented or worn suspension parts. See WHEEL ALIGNMENT SPECIFICATIONS.

CASTER ADJUSTMENT

Front and rear caster cannot be adjusted. If caster is not within specification, check for damaged, loose, bent, dented or worn suspension parts. See WHEEL ALIGNMENT SPECIFICATIONS.

TOE-IN ADJUSTMENT (FRONT)

Adjust front wheel toe-in by changing tie rod length. Loosen rack boot clamps (small end), and slide clamps from boot (except Tracker). Loosen right and left tie rod end lock nuts.

2) Turn right and left tie rods same amount to adjust toe-in to specification. See WHEEL ALIGNMENT SPECIFICATIONS. Tighten tie rod end nuts to specification. See TORQUE SPECIFICATIONS. Dimension "A" should be the same on left and right tie rods. *See Fig. 8.*

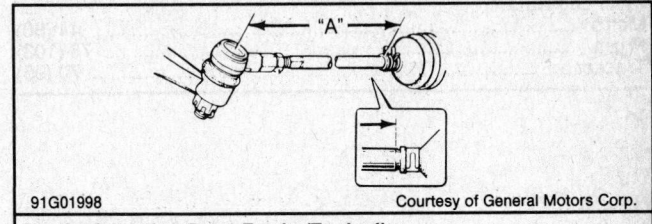

Fig. 8: Adjusting Front Toe-In (Typical)

TOE-IN ADJUSTMENT (REAR)

Metro – 1) Adjust rear wheel toe-in by rotating control rod inside bolt (cam bolt). *See Fig. 9.* Loosen right and left control rod inside nuts. Turn right and left control rod inside bolts same amount to set toe-in to specification. See WHEEL ALIGNMENT SPECIFICATIONS.

2) After adjustment, tighten right and left control rod inside nuts to specification while holding control rod inside bolts. See TORQUE SPECIFICATIONS.

Prizm – Adjust toe-in by changing lateral link length. Loosen right and left lateral link lock nuts. *See Fig. 10.* Turn right and left lateral links evenly to set toe-in to specification. See WHEEL ALIGNMENT SPECIFICATIONS. Tighten lateral link lock nuts to specification. See TORQUE SPECIFICATIONS.

Fig. 6: Locating Jacking & Hoisting Points (Prizm)

1994 WHEEL ALIGNMENT
Specifications & Procedures (Cont.)

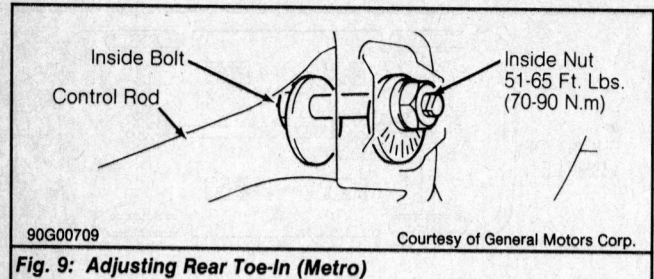

Fig. 9: Adjusting Rear Toe-In (Metro)

90G00709   Courtesy of General Motors Corp.

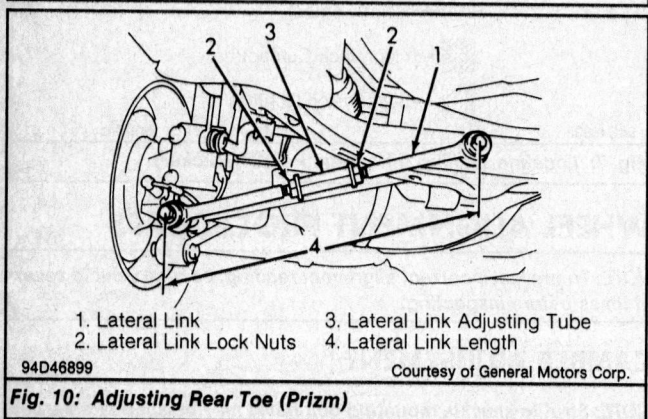

1. Lateral Link
2. Lateral Link Lock Nuts
3. Lateral Link Adjusting Tube
4. Lateral Link Length

94D46899   Courtesy of General Motors Corp.

Fig. 10: Adjusting Rear Toe (Prizm)

TORQUE SPECIFICATIONS
TORQUE SPECIFICATIONS

Application	Ft. Lbs. (N.m)
Control Rod Inside Nuts (Metro)	59 (80)
Front Wheel Bearing Lock Nut Tracker	155 (210)
Lateral Link Lock Nuts	
Prizm	41 (56)
Spindle Nut	
Prizm (Front)	159 (216)
Metro (Front & Rear)	129 (175)
Strut-To-Knuckle Nuts & Bolts	
Metro	59 (80)
Prizm	
Front	203 (275)
Rear	105 (142)
Tracker	66 (90)
Tie Rod End Lock Nuts	
Metro	33 (45)
Prizm	41 (56)
Tracker	48 (65)
Wheel Lug Nuts	
Metro	44 (60)
Prizm	76 (103)
Tracker	70 (95)

WHEEL ALIGNMENT SPECIFICATIONS
WHEEL ALIGNMENT SPECIFICATIONS

Application	Preferred	Range
Metro [1]		
Camber [2]		
Front & Rear	0	−0.5 To 0.5
Caster [2]		
Front	3	2 To 4
Toe-In [2]		
Front	0.00	−.16 To 0.16
Rear	0.16	0 To 0.32
Toe-In [3]		
Front	0.00 (0.0)	−.08 To 0.08 (−2.0 To 2.0)
Rear	0.08 (2.0)	0 To 0.16 (0 To 4.0)
Toe-Out On Turns [2]		
Inner	38	.....
Outer	32	.....
Prizm [1]		
Camber [2]		
Front	−0.17	−0.9 To 0.6
Rear	−0.92	−1.97 To −0.17
Caster [2]		
Front	1.33	0.58 To 2.08
Toe-In [2]		
Front	0.1	−0.1 To 0.3
Rear	0.3	0.1 To 0.5
Toe-In [3]		
Front	0.05 (1.5)	−0.05 To 0.15 (−1.5 To 4.0)
Rear	0.15 (4)	0.05 To 0.25 (1.5 To 6.5)
Toe-Out On Turns [2]		
Inner	39	.....
Outer	33	.....
Tracker [1]		
Camber [2]		
Front	0.5	−0.5 To 1.5
Caster [2]		
Front	1.5	0.5 To 2.5
Toe-In [2]		
Front	0.32	0.16 To 0.48
Toe-In [3]		
Front	0.16 (4.0)	0.08 To 0.24 (2.0 To 6.0)
Toe-Out On Turns [2]		
Inner	32.5	.....
Outer	30.5	.....

[1] – Caster and camber are not adjustable.
[2] – Measurement in degrees.
[3] – Measurement in inches (mm).

1994 SUSPENSION
Rear – Metro

DESCRIPTION

Strut-type rear suspension with separate coil spring and lower control arm is used. Control rods between rear knuckle and body are used to control lateral movement. See Fig. 1.

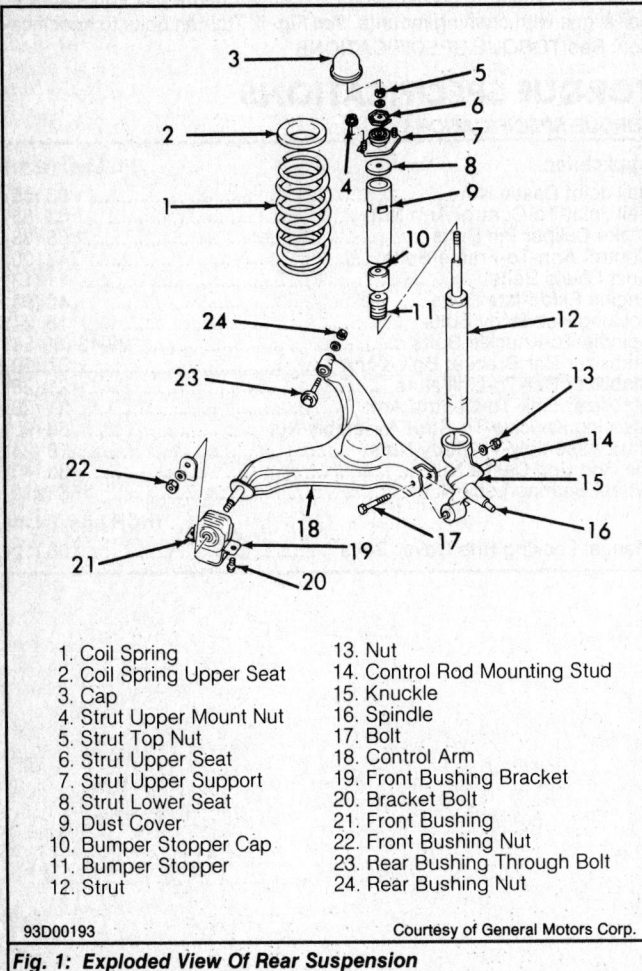

1. Coil Spring	13. Nut
2. Coil Spring Upper Seat	14. Control Rod Mounting Stud
3. Cap	15. Knuckle
4. Strut Upper Mount Nut	16. Spindle
5. Strut Top Nut	17. Bolt
6. Strut Upper Seat	18. Control Arm
7. Strut Upper Support	19. Front Bushing Bracket
8. Strut Lower Seat	20. Bracket Bolt
9. Dust Cover	21. Front Bushing
10. Bumper Stopper Cap	22. Front Bushing Nut
11. Bumper Stopper	23. Rear Bushing Through Bolt
12. Strut	24. Rear Bushing Nut

93D00193   Courtesy of General Motors Corp.

Fig. 1: Exploded View Of Rear Suspension

ADJUSTMENTS & INSPECTION

WHEEL ALIGNMENT
SPECIFICATIONS & PROCEDURES

NOTE: See SPECIFICATIONS & PROCEDURES article in WHEEL ALIGNMENT.

WHEEL BEARING

Wheel bearings are not adjustable. To check wheel bearing for excessive wear, raise and support vehicle. Remove wheel. Mount dial indicator to drum/hub assembly. See Fig. 2. Grasp drum/hub assembly and apply force in and out. If measurement exceeds .002" (.05 mm), replace bearings.

REMOVAL & INSTALLATION

CONTROL RODS

Removal – 1) Raise and support vehicle, allowing suspension to hang freely. Disconnect brake flexhose from control rod. Scribe location marks on mounting bracket and toe adjustment cam for installation reference.
2) Remove outer control rod nut at knuckle. Remove adjustment cam nut and bolt. Remove control rod. Check control rod bushings for wear.

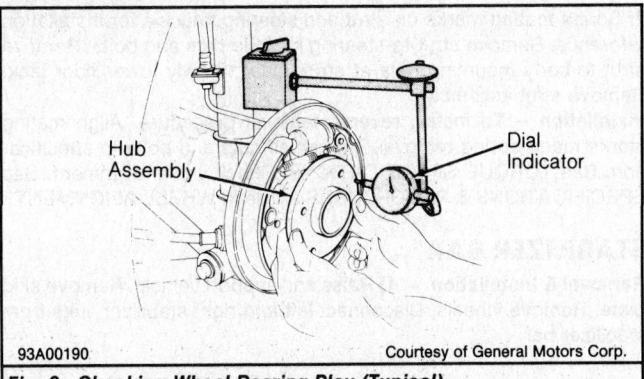

93A00190   Courtesy of General Motors Corp.

Fig. 2: Checking Wheel Bearing Play (Typical)

Installation – Install control rod with adjustment cam facing down, and brake flexhose bracket facing toward front of vehicle. Align cam with mating marks made during removal by turning bolt head. Hold bolt head to keep toe adjustment cam stationary and tighten nut to specification. See TORQUE SPECIFICATIONS. Connect brake flexhose to control rod. Ensure rear alignment is correct. See SPECIFICATIONS & PROCEDURES article in WHEEL ALIGNMENT.

COIL SPRING & LOWER CONTROL ARM

Removal – 1) Raise and support vehicle on safety stands, allowing rear suspension to hang freely. Remove rear wheel. Disconnect control rod from knuckle mounting stud. See Fig. 1.
2) Support suspension control arm with floor jack. Remove control arm-to-knuckle bolt and nut. Pull knuckle assembly away from control arm.
3) Slowly lower floor jack and remove coil spring. See Fig. 3. Remove control arm front mounting bracket bolts. Remove control arm rear bushing through bolt and nut. Remove control arm from body.

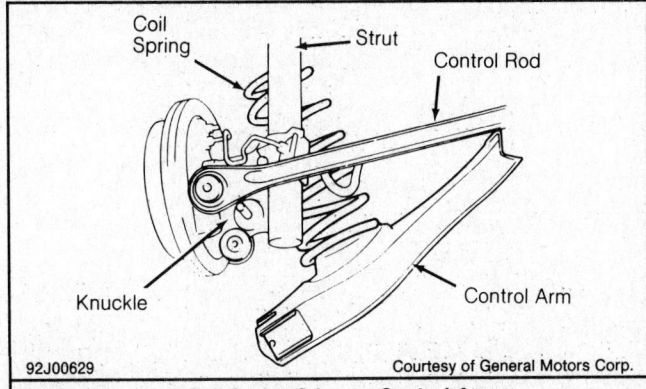

92J00629   Courtesy of General Motors Corp.

Fig. 3: Removing Coil Spring & Lower Control Arm

Installation – 1) Connect control arm to body. Tighten control arm rear through bolt and nut and bushing bracket bolts to specification. Tighten front bushing bolt and nut, ensure washer (behind nut) has flat section facing down and round section facing up. See Fig. 1. See TORQUE SPECIFICATIONS. Match bottom of spring with stepped part of control arm. Bottom of spring is larger. Install coil spring in control arm.
2) Raise control arm with jack. Install control arm-to-knuckle bolt and tighten to specification. See TORQUE SPECIFICATIONS. Remove jack. Install control rod to knuckle mounting stud and tighten nut to specification. See TORQUE SPECIFICATIONS. Install wheel. Check rear toe-in adjustment. See SPECIFICATIONS & PROCEDURES article in WHEEL ALIGNMENT.

STRUT

Removal – 1) Open rear hatchback door. Raise and support vehicle so that top and bottom of strut are accessible. Remove wheel. Support lower control arm with floor jack. Remove lower strut-to-knuckle pinch bolt. Remove upper strut mounting nuts.

2) Scribe mating marks on strut and steering knuckle for installation reference. Remove strut-to-steering knuckle nuts and bolts. Remove strut-to-body mounting nuts at strut tower. Slowly lower floor jack. Remove strut assembly.

Installation – To install, reverse removal procedure. Align mating marks made during removal. Tighten all nuts and bolts to specification. See TORQUE SPECIFICATIONS. Check wheel alignment. See SPECIFICATIONS & PROCEDURES article in WHEEL ALIGNMENT.

STABILIZER BAR

Removal & Installation – **1)** Raise and support vehicle. Remove skid plate. Remove wheels. Disconnect left and right stabilizer links from stabilizer bar.

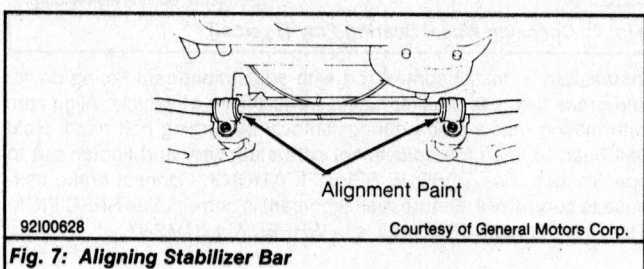

Alignment Paint

92l00628   Courtesy of General Motors Corp.

Fig. 7: Aligning Stabilizer Bar

2) Disconnect right and left stabilizer brackets from body. Remove stabilizer bar from vehicle. To install, reverse removal procedure. Do not fully tighten bolts and nuts until all stabilizer bolts and nuts have been installed. Tighten stabilizer bar-to-link nuts first then tighten stabilizer bar mounting bracket bolts and nuts. Ensure paint on stabilizer bar aligns with bushing mounts. See Fig. 7. Tighten bolts to specification. See TORQUE SPECIFICATIONS.

TORQUE SPECIFICATIONS

TORQUE SPECIFICATIONS

Application	Ft. Lbs. (N.m)
Ball Joint Castle Nut	63 (85)
Ball Joint-To-Control Arm Nut	63 (85)
Brake Caliper Pin Bolts	65 (88)
Control Arm-To-Frame Bolts	74 (100)
Dust Shield Bolts	11 (15)
Engine Skid Plate Bolts	40 (54)
Locking Hub Body Bolts	18 (24)
Spindle-To-Knuckle Bolts	29-43 (39-58)
Stabilizer Bar Bracket Bolt & Nut	37 (50)
Stabilizer Bar-To-Link Nuts	21 (28)
Stabilizer Link-To-Control Arm	21 (28)
Steering Knuckle-To-Strut Assembly Nut	66 (90)
Strut Assembly-To-Body Nuts	18 (24)
Tie Rod End Castle Nut	30 (40)
Wheel Bearing Lock Nut	155 (210)
	INCH Lbs. (N.m)
Manual Locking Hub Cover Bolts	106 (12)

CAUTION: To prevent brake flexhose from stretching or coil spring from coming out of control arm, DO NOT lower floor jack more than necessary during strut removal.

2) Compress and remove strut. If strut will not come out of knuckle, open slit of knuckle (as little as possible) by wedging a chisel or screwdriver into slit. Check strut for leaks or damage. Replace if necessary.

Installation – 1) Compress strut. Install strut in knuckle. Align strut projection with slit in knuckle. *See Fig. 4.*

2) Attach upper end of strut to body and tighten mounting nuts to specification. Install strut lower pinch bolt and tighten to specification. See TORQUE SPECIFICATIONS. To complete installation, reverse removal procedure.

STEERING KNUCKLE

Removal – 1) Raise and support vehicle, allowing suspension to hang freely. Remove wheel. Remove brake drum/hub assembly. See WHEEL BEARING.

2) Remove brake line from knuckle bracket. Disconnect brake line from wheel cylinder. Remove backing plate bolts and backing plate.

3) Remove nut on outboard side of control rod, and separate control rod from knuckle. Place jack under lower control arm for support.

4) Remove knuckle pinch bolt. Remove control arm-to-knuckle bolt and nut. Slide knuckle off strut. If strut will not come out of knuckle, open slit of knuckle (as little as possible) by wedging a chisel or screwdriver into slit. Remove knuckle.

Installation – 1) Install knuckle on strut. Align strut projection with knuckle slit. *See Fig. 4.* Install strut pinch bolt and nut, and tighten to specification. See TORQUE SPECIFICATIONS. Align knuckle with control arm and install control arm-to-knuckle bolt and nut.

2) Tighten control arm-to-knuckle bolt and nut. See TORQUE SPECIFICATIONS. Install control rod to knuckle mounting stud and tighten nut to specification. Remove jack from under lower control arm.

3) Apply sealant to mating surface of brake backing plate and rear knuckle. Install and tighten brake backing plate bolts to specification. See TORQUE SPECIFICATIONS. Install brake line. Install brake drum/hub assembly. Install NEW spindle nut and tighten to 129 ft. lbs. (175 N.m). Stake spindle nut.

4) Install wheel. Lower vehicle. Bleed and adjust brakes. Check rear toe-in. See SPECIFICATIONS & PROCEDURES article in WHEEL ALIGNMENT.

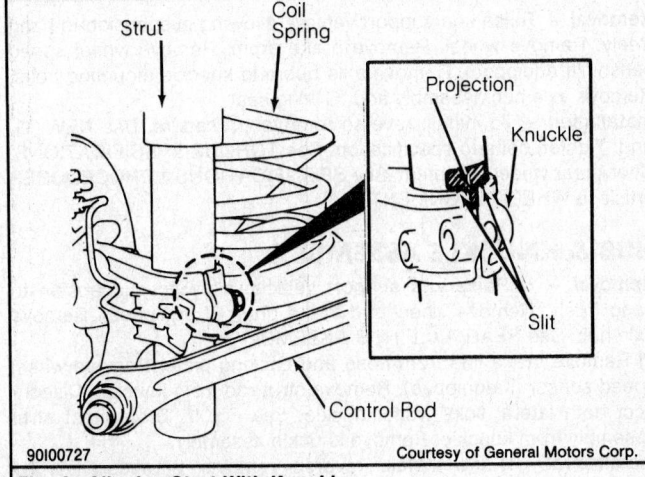

Fig. 4: Aligning Strut With Knuckle

WHEEL BEARING

Removal – 1) Raise and support vehicle, allowing suspension to hang freely. Remove wheel. Remove spindle cap. Unstake spindle nut. Remove and discard spindle nut. Remove washer.

NOTE: Always use NEW spindle nut when old nut is removed.

2) Tap on brake drum/hub assembly with a hammer to ease removal. Using a punch and hammer, remove inner wheel bearing, then outer wheel bearing out of brake drum/hub assembly.

Installation – 1) Using a hammer and Bearing Installer (J-34842), install outer (smaller) bearing into brake drum/hub. Install spacer in hub with inner lip of spacer toward outer bearing. Install inner (larger) bearing. *See Fig. 5.*

2) Install brake drum/hub assembly on spindle. Install NEW spindle nut and tighten to 129 ft. lbs. (175 N.m). Stake spindle nut. To complete installation, reverse removal procedure.

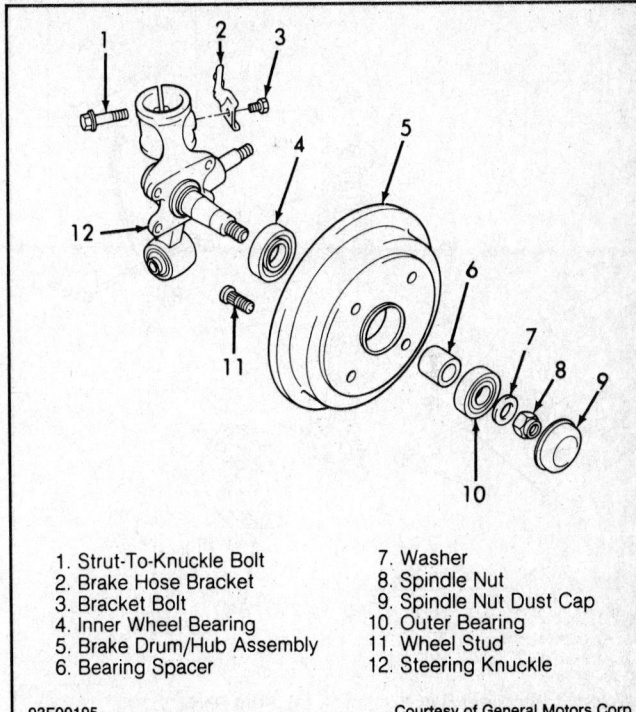

1. Strut-To-Knuckle Bolt
2. Brake Hose Bracket
3. Bracket Bolt
4. Inner Wheel Bearing
5. Brake Drum/Hub Assembly
6. Bearing Spacer
7. Washer
8. Spindle Nut
9. Spindle Nut Dust Cap
10. Outer Bearing
11. Wheel Stud
12. Steering Knuckle

93F00195   Courtesy of General Motors Corp.

Fig. 5: Exploded View Of Knuckle, Brake Drum/Hub & Bearing Assemblies

TORQUE SPECIFICATIONS
TORQUE SPECIFICATIONS

Application	Ft. Lbs. (N.m)
Brake Backing Plate Bolts	17 (23)
Brake Flexhose Bracket Bolt	17 (23)
Brake Fluid Pipe Flair Nut	12 (16)
Control Arm-To-Knuckle Nut	37 (50)
Control Arm	
Front Bushing Bracket Bolts	33 (45)
Front Bushing Nut	44 (60)
Rear Bushing Through Bolt & Nut	37 (50)
Knuckle-To-Strut Pinch Bolt	44 (60)
Control Rod	
Inside Cam Nut	59 (80)
Outboard Nut	59 (80)
Spindle Nut	129 (175)
Strut Upper Mounting Nuts	22 (30)
Wheel Lug Nut	44 (60)

DESCRIPTION

Rear suspension is MacPherson strut-type, independent suspension. Upper end of strut is anchored to body by a strut support. Stabilizer bar and link are anchored by strut assembly. Lower end of rear suspension knuckle attaches to strut rod and 2 lateral links. *See Fig. 1.*

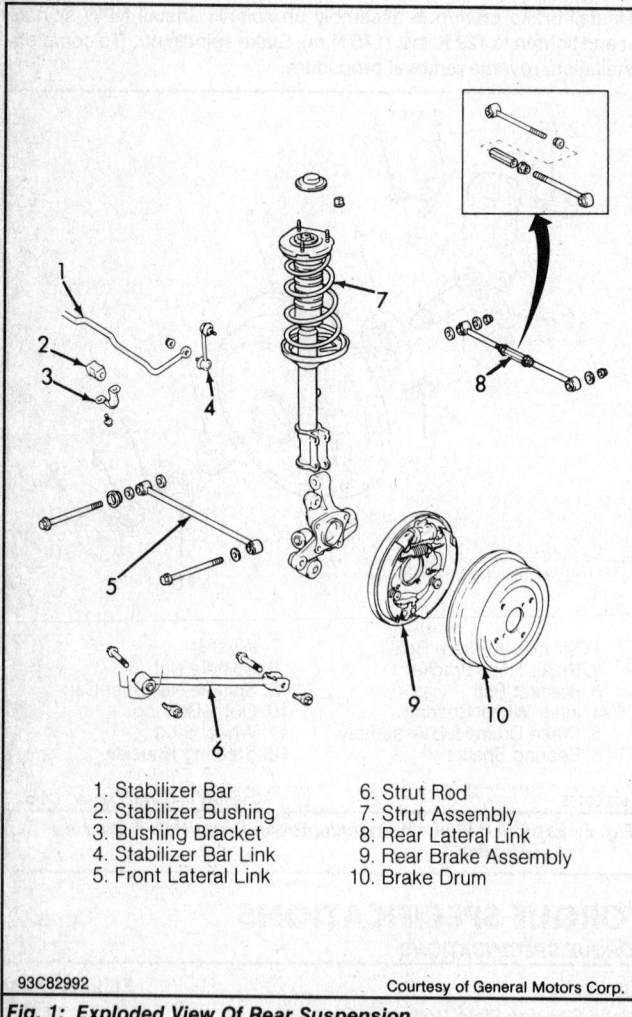

1. Stabilizer Bar
2. Stabilizer Bushing
3. Bushing Bracket
4. Stabilizer Bar Link
5. Front Lateral Link
6. Strut Rod
7. Strut Assembly
8. Rear Lateral Link
9. Rear Brake Assembly
10. Brake Drum

93C82992   Courtesy of General Motors Corp.

Fig. 1: Exploded View Of Rear Suspension

ADJUSTMENTS & INSPECTION

SUSPENSION COMPONENTS

1) With help, raise vehicle by lifting up on rear bumper as high as possible. Release slowly and allow vehicle to settle to normal height. Measure distance from floor to center of bumper.

2) Push down on rear bumper. Release slowly and allow vehicle to settle to normal height. Measure distance from floor to center of bumper.

3) Distance between 2 measurements should be less than .5" (12.7 mm). If difference is greater than .5" (12.7 mm), inspect rear suspension components for damage or wear.

WHEEL ALIGNMENT
SPECIFICATIONS & PROCEDURES

NOTE: *See SPECIFICATIONS & PROCEDURES article in WHEEL ALIGNMENT.*

WHEEL BEARING

Wheel bearings are not adjustable. To check wheel bearing for excessive wear, raise and support vehicle. Remove wheel. Remove brake drum. With dial indicator stem mounted against center (outboard side) of axle hub, measure end play. *See Fig. 2*. If end play is more than .002" (.05 mm), replace rear axle hub assembly.

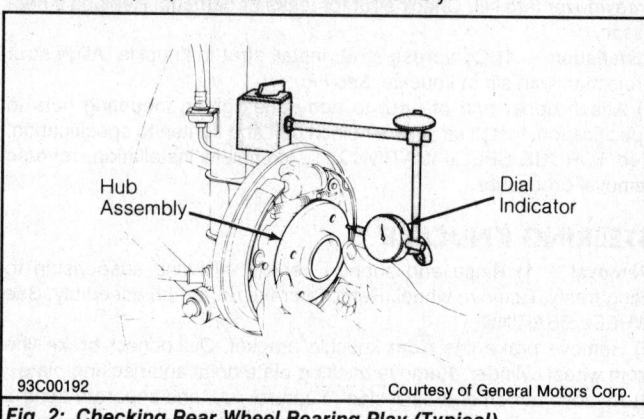

Hub Assembly   Dial Indicator

93C00192   Courtesy of General Motors Corp.

Fig. 2: Checking Rear Wheel Bearing Play (Typical)

REMOVAL & INSTALLATION

STABILIZER BAR

Removal – Raise and support vehicle, allowing suspension to hang freely. Remove stabilizer bar links from strut assemblies. *See Fig. 1.* Make match marks between stabilizer bar bushings, stabilizer bar and body. Remove stabilizer bar bushings. Support fuel tank and remove both fuel tank bands. Support rear suspension crossmember with a jack. Remove 6 crossmember bolts and lower rear suspension crossmember. Disconnect exhaust hangers from tailpipe. Remove stabilizer bar from vehicle.

Installation – To install, reverse removal procedure. Tighten all nuts and bolts to specification. See TORQUE SPECIFICATIONS.

REAR AXLE HUB ASSEMBLY

NOTE: *Rear wheel bearing is serviced by replacing rear axle hub assembly.*

Removal – Raise and support vehicle, allowing suspension to hang freely. Remove wheel. Remove brake drum. Remove wheel speed sensor (if equipped). Remove axle hub and knuckle mounting bolts. Remove axle hub assembly and "O" ring seal.

Installation – To install, reverse removal procedure. Use NEW "O" ring. Tighten bolts to specification. See TORQUE SPECIFICATIONS. Check rear wheel alignment. See SPECIFICATIONS & PROCEDURES article in WHEEL ALIGNMENT.

HUB & KNUCKLE ASSEMBLY

Removal – 1) Raise and support vehicle, allowing suspension to hang freely. Remove wheel and brake drum (if equipped). Remove axle hub. See REAR AXLE HUB ASSEMBLY.

2) Remove brake line from hose and backing plate. Remove wheel speed sensor (if equipped). Remove strut rod from knuckle. Disconnect both lateral links from knuckle. *See Fig. 1.* Disconnect strut assembly from knuckle. Remove knuckle assembly.

Installation – 1) To install, reverse removal procedure. When connecting lateral links and strut rod to knuckle, partially tighten bolts and nuts. Lower vehicle.

2) Bounce vehicle to settle suspension. Tighten lateral link mounting bolts and strut rod nuts to specification. See TORQUE SPECIFICATIONS. Bleed brakes and check rear wheel alignment. See SPECIFICATIONS & PROCEDURES article in WHEEL ALIGNMENT.

STRUT ASSEMBLY

Removal – 1) Remove rear lower seat cushion and seat back cushion. Raise and support vehicle, allowing suspension to hang freely. Remove wheels. Disconnect brake line from backing plate and plug hose to prevent fluid loss. Remove brake line from bracket on strut.

2) Remove wheel speed sensor wire harness (if equipped). Remove stabilizer bar link from strut assembly. *See Fig. 1.* Remove strut assembly mounting bolts and nuts from knuckle. Remove upper strut mounting nuts. Remove strut assembly from vehicle.

Coil Spring Replacement – 1) Using spring compressor, compress spring far enough to remove strut assembly piston nut. Release spring compressor tension. Remove suspension support, dust seal, spring seat, upper insulator and coil spring.

2) Install components in reverse order of removal. Tighten strut assembly piston nut to specification. See TORQUE SPECIFICATIONS.

Installation – To install, reverse removal procedure. Tighten all nuts and bolts to specification. See TORQUE SPECIFICATIONS. Check rear wheel alignment. See SPECIFICATIONS & PROCEDURES article in WHEEL ALIGNMENT.

STRUT ROD & LATERAL LINKS

Removal – Raise and support vehicle, allowing suspension to hang freely. Remove strut rod. Remove 2 nuts and washers and remove rear lateral link. *See Fig. 1.* Remove resonator/intermediate pipe assembly, muffler/tail pipe assembly and intermediate pipe heat shield. Support rear suspension crossmember with a jack and remove 4 mounting bolts. Lower suspension crossmember. Remove 2 bolts and 4 washers and remove front lateral link. *See Fig. 1.*

NOTE: DO NOT install front lateral link nuts until rear lateral link is installed.

Installation – 1) To install, reverse removal procedure. Tighten intermediate pipe heat shield bolts to 48 INCH lbs. (5.4 N.m). Tighten muffler/tail pipe-to-body bolts to 115 INCH lbs. (13 N.m).

2) Tighten all nuts and bolts to specification. See TORQUE SPECIFICATIONS. Check rear wheel alignment. See SPECIFICATIONS & PROCEDURES article in WHEEL ALIGNMENT.

TORQUE SPECIFICATIONS

TORQUE SPECIFICATIONS

Application	Ft. Lbs. (N.m)
Brake Line-To-Backing Plate Nut	11 (15)
Fuel Tank Band Bolt	29 (39)
Rear Axle Hub Mounting Bolts	59 (80)
Resonator-To-Catalytic Converter Bolts	32 (43)
Resonator-To-Muffler Bolts	14 (19)
Stabilizer Bar Link-To-Strut Assembly Nut	32 (43)
Stabilizer Bar-To-Stabilizer Link Nuts	26 (35)
Stabilizer Bushing Bracket Mounting Bolts	14 (19)
Strut Piston Nut	36 (49)
Strut Upper Mounting Nuts	29 (39)
Strut-To-Knuckle Bolts & Nuts	105 (142)
Strut Rod Bolts & Nuts	67 (91)
Suspension Crossmember-To-Body Bolts	43 (58)
Lateral Link Mounting Bolts	87 (118)
Wheel Lug Nuts	76 (103)

1994 SUSPENSION
Rear – Tracker

DESCRIPTION

Suspension is a solid axle coil spring type, using upper control arms and trailing rods. Coil springs and shock absorbers are mounted between axle and chassis member.

The trailing rods allow for vertical movement of rear axle assembly. The upper control arms prevent lateral or rotational movement of rear axle assembly. *See Fig. 1.*

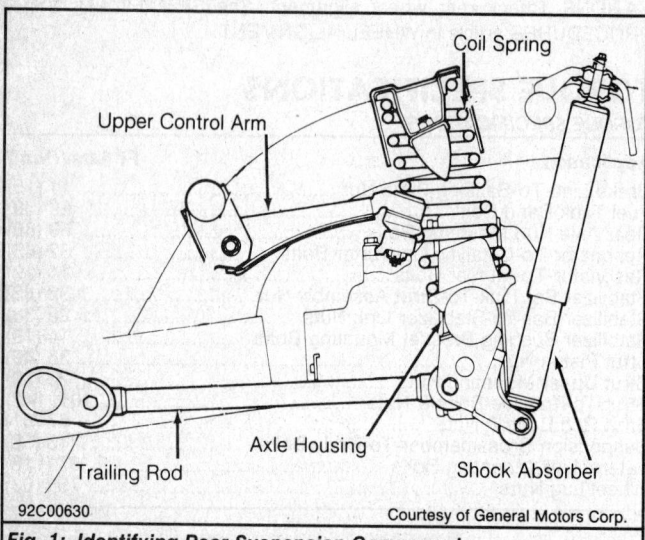

Fig. 1: Identifying Rear Suspension Components

Coil Spring

Upper Control Arm

Trailing Rod

Axle Housing

Shock Absorber

92C00630   Courtesy of General Motors Corp.

ADJUSTMENTS & INSPECTION

RIDE HEIGHT

For ride height adjustment information, see WHEEL ALIGNMENT SPECIFICATIONS & PROCEDURES article.

WHEEL ALIGNMENT SPECIFICATIONS & PROCEDURES

Rear wheel alignment is not adjustable.

REMOVAL & INSTALLATION

AXLE BEARING

For rear axle bearing removal and installation procedures, see DIFFERENTIALS & AXLE SHAFTS article.

COIL SPRING

Removal & Installation – 1) Raise and support vehicle. Use floor jack to support axle housing. Remove nut and bolt holding shock absorber to rear axle housing. *See Fig. 1.*
2) Slowly lower axle housing, using care not to stretch brake line or parking brake cable. Remove coil spring. To install, reverse removal procedure. Tighten all bolts and nuts to specification. See TORQUE SPECIFICATIONS.

SHOCK ABSORBER

Removal & Installation – Raise and support vehicle. Support rear axle housing with floor jack. Remove upper shock absorber mounting nut. Remove through bolt retaining shock absorber to rear axle housing. Remove shock absorber. To install, reverse removal procedure. Tighten all bolts to specification. See TORQUE SPECIFICATIONS.

TRAILING ROD & BUSHING

Removal & Installation – 1) Raise and support vehicle. Remove wheels. Disconnect parking brake cable from trailing rod. Use floor jack to support axle housing. Remove nuts and bolts attaching trailing rod to body and axle housing. *See Fig. 1.* Remove trailing rod.
2) To replace trailing rod bushing, mount trailing rod in press with Bushing Adapters (J-29792-3 and J-28685-2). Press bushing from trailing rod. To install new bushing, reverse removal procedure using same press adapters.
3) To install trailing rod, reverse removal procedure. Ensure parking brake cable hanger is leaning toward middle of vehicle. Tighten trailing rod bolts and nuts to specification. See TORQUE SPECIFICATIONS. Remove jack. Install parking brake cable to trailing rod. Install wheels and lower vehicle.

UPPER CONTROL ARM

Removal – 1) Raise and support vehicle. Remove wheels. Use floor jack to support axle assembly. Disconnect ball joint mount from axle assembly. Remove bolts and nuts holding upper control arm to body. Remove upper control arm. *See Fig. 1.*
2) Remove cotter pin and castle nut from upper control arm ball joint. Using a 2 jaw gear puller, separate ball joint from mounting bracket. Remove ball joint dust seal retainer and dust seal.
Installation – 1) Install a NEW ball joint dust seal and dust seal retainer, if removed. Tighten ball joint castle nut to specification. See TORQUE SPECIFICATIONS. Install upper control arm to body without tightening through bolts and nuts. Install ball joint mount to axle assembly and tighten bolts to specification.
2) Tighten control arm through bolts and nuts to specification. Install wheels and lower vehicle to ground. Tighten all remaining bolts and nuts to specification.

TORQUE SPECIFICATIONS
TORQUE SPECIFICATIONS

Application	Ft. Lbs. (N.m)
Control Arm Ball Joint	
Castle Nut	43 (58)
Mount Nut	37 (50)
Control Arms-To-Body Bolts	66 (90)
Shock Absorber Lock Nut	21 (28)
Shock Absorber Nut	
Lower (Bolt & Nut)	63 (85)
Upper	21 (28)
Trailing Rod Nuts & Bolts (Front & Rear)	66 (90)
Wheel Lug Nut	70 (95)
	INCH Lbs. (N.m)
Parking Brake Cable Nut & Bolt	89 (10)

Metro, Prizm, Tracker

DESCRIPTION & OPERATION

Steering columns are an energy-absorbing, collapsible design. Components include upper and lower column sections, steering shaft and universal joints which connect column and steering gear. Some models may have a tilt steering column.

WARNING: Prizm is equipped with Supplemental Restraint System (SRS) with driver side and passenger side air bags. DO NOT apply electrical power to any component on steering column without disabling SRS. Before performing ANY tests or repairs on steering column, SRS MUST be disabled. See DISABLING & ACTIVATING SRS. Accidental air bag deployment could cause serious bodily injury.

DISABLING & ACTIVATING SRS

WARNING: Wait about 2 minutes after disabling SRS before servicing. System maintains SRS voltage for about 2 minutes. Servicing SRS before 2 minutes may cause accidental air bag deployment and possible personal injury.

Prizm – 1) Ensure front wheels face straight ahead. Turn ignition switch to LOCK position. Remove CIG & RADIO fuse and IGN fuse from junction block. *See Fig. 1.* Locate driver side air bag Yellow 2-pin connector at base of steering column. *See Fig. 2.* Remove Connector Position Assurance (CPA) clip and disconnect Yellow 2-pin connector.
2) Lower glove box and remove passenger side air bag connector cover located above glove box. *See Fig. 3.* Remove Connector Position Assurance (CPA) clip and disconnect Yellow 2-pin connector.
3) Wait about 2 minutes before servicing. To activate SRS, turn ignition switch to LOCK position. Connect Yellow 2-pin connectors and CPA clips at base of steering column and above glove box. Install

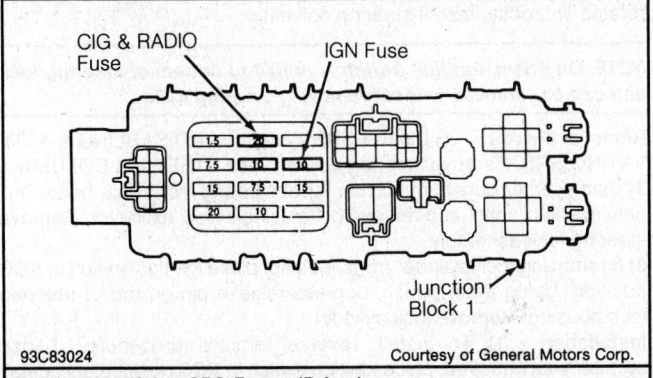

CIG & RADIO Fuse

IGN Fuse

Junction Block 1

93C83024   Courtesy of General Motors Corp.

Fig. 1: Identifying SRS Fuses (Prizm)

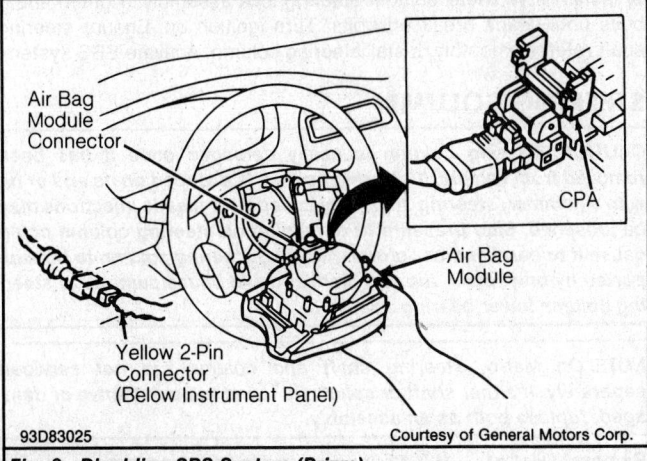

Air Bag Module Connector

CPA

Air Bag Module

Yellow 2-Pin Connector (Below Instrument Panel)

93D83025   Courtesy of General Motors Corp.

Fig. 2: Disabling SRS System (Prizm)

IGN and CIG & RADIO fuses to junction block. Turn ignition switch to ACC or ON position and ensure air bag indicator illuminates steadily for about 6 seconds, then turns off. See SYSTEM OPERATION CHECK in AIR BAG RESTRAINT SYSTEM article.

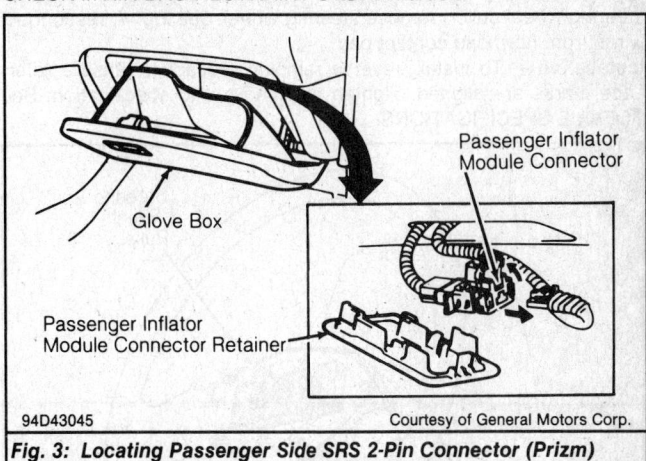

Passenger Inflator Module Connector

Glove Box

Passenger Inflator Module Connector Retainer

94D43045   Courtesy of General Motors Corp.

Fig. 3: Locating Passenger Side SRS 2-Pin Connector (Prizm)

REMOVAL & INSTALLATION

STEERING WHEEL & AIR BAG MODULE

WARNING: On Prizm with Supplemental Restraint System (SRS), disable system before attempting steering column service. See DISABLING & ACTIVATING SRS. DO NOT apply electrical power to any component on steering column without disabling SRS. Use caution when working around steering column (air bag could deploy).

WARNING: When moving or carrying air bag module, ensure outward side (pad surface area) is away from you. DO NOT store air bag module pad side down. Accidental deployment could cause serious injury. Store air bag module with pad surface upward and away from work area. DO NOT disassemble or tamper with air bag module.

Removal (Prizm) – 1) Disable SRS system. See DISABLING & ACTIVATING SRS. Ensure front wheels face straight ahead. Remove side trim covers from steering column. *See Fig. 7.* Remove 2 Torx screws and pull air bag module from steering wheel. Release CPA clip and disconnect air bag module connector. Remove air bag module. *See Fig. 2.*
2) Disconnect horn and cruise control harness connectors from steering wheel. Remove steering wheel retaining nut. Mark steering wheel and shaft for reassembly reference. Using steering wheel puller, remove steering wheel. *See Fig. 4.*
Installation – To install, reverse removal procedure. Ensure reference marks are aligned. Tighten retaining nut to specification. See TORQUE SPECIFICATIONS. Activate SRS system. See DISABLING & ACTIVATING SRS.

STEERING WHEEL & HORN PAD

Removal (Metro) – 1) Ensure front wheels are facing straight ahead. Disconnect negative battery cable. Pull horn pad assembly from steering wheel.
2) Remove horn contact plate screws. Disconnect wires, and remove contact plate. Remove steering wheel retaining nut. Mark steering wheel and shaft for reassembly reference. Using steering wheel puller, remove steering wheel. *See Fig. 4.*
Installation – 1) Align reference marks made during removal and install steering wheel. Install retaining nut on shaft. Tighten retaining nut to specification. See TORQUE SPECIFICATIONS.
2) Connect horn wires, and install contact plate. Ensure wires run through center of plate, not underneath it. Install horn switch/center pad assembly.

Removal (Tracker) – **1)** Ensure front wheels face straight ahead. Disconnect negative battery cable. Pull horn pad from steering wheel by hand. Remove steering wheel retaining nut.

2) Mark steering wheel and shaft for reassembly reference. Using steering wheel puller, remove steering wheel. *See Fig. 4*. Disconnect wires from horn pad contact pad.

Installation – To install, reverse removal procedure. Ensure reference marks are aligned. Tighten retaining nut to specification. See TORQUE SPECIFICATIONS.

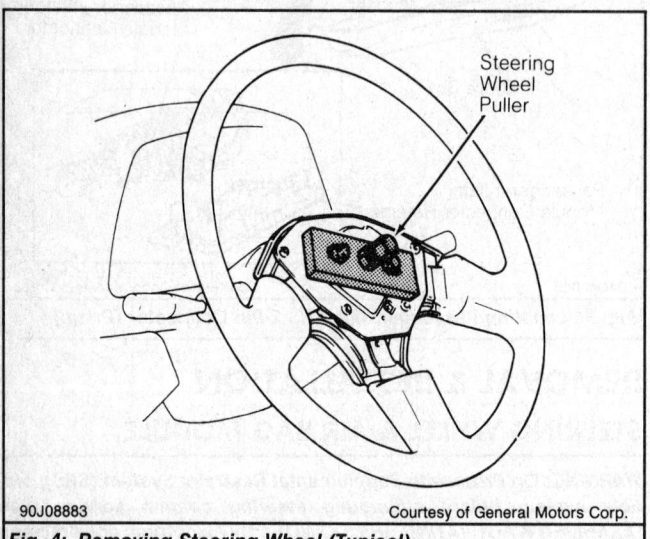

Fig. 4: *Removing Steering Wheel (Typical)*

90J08883   Courtesy of General Motors Corp.

SRS COIL

Removal (Prizm) – **1)** Ensure front wheels are facing straight ahead. Disconnect negative battery cable. Disable SRS system. See DISABLING & ACTIVATING SRS.

2) Remove steering wheel. See STEERING WHEEL & AIR BAG MODULE under REMOVAL & INSTALLATION. Remove upper and lower steering column covers. Disconnect hood release from knee bolster. Remove knee bolster from instrument panel.

3) Remove tape and separate SRS coil harness from combination switch harness. Unplug SRS coil harness connector. Remove 4 screws retaining SRS coil and remove SRS coil from combination switch.

Installation – **1)** Ensure front wheels are facing straight ahead. Center SRS coil by gently turning coil by hand counterclockwise until it reaches its stop. Turn coil 3 turns clockwise and align Red alignment marks. *See Fig. 5*. SRS coil is now centered and ready to be installed.

2) To complete installation, reverse removal procedure. Tighten bolts to specification. See TORQUE SPECIFICATIONS. Activate SRS system. See DISABLING & ACTIVATING SRS.

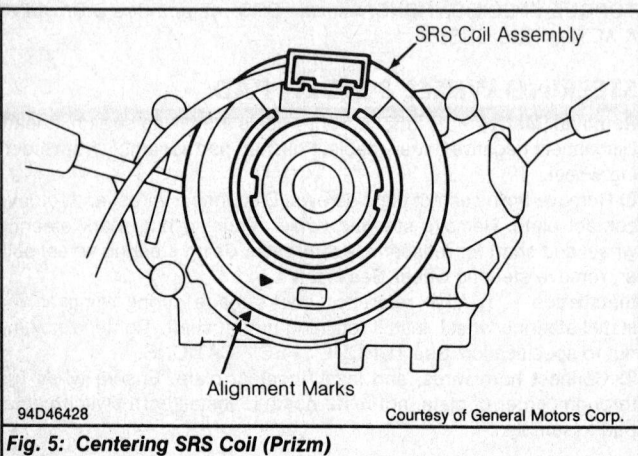

Fig. 5: *Centering SRS Coil (Prizm)*

94D46428   Courtesy of General Motors Corp.

COMBINATION SWITCH

Removal (Metro & Tracker) – **1)** Remove steering wheel. See STEERING WHEEL & HORN PAD. Remove covers from steering column.

2) Disconnect electrical connection from combination switch. Remove electrical wiring retaining straps. Remove combination switch retaining screws and combination switch.

Installation – To install, reverse removal procedure. Tighten bolts to specification. See TORQUE SPECIFICATIONS.

Removal (Prizm) – Disable SRS system. See DISABLING & ACTIVATING SRS. Remove SRS coil. See SRS COIL under REMOVAL & INSTALLATION. Disconnect electrical connection from combination switch. Remove combination switch retaining screws and combination switch.

Installation – To install, reverse removal procedure. Ensure SRS coil is centered and wheels face straight ahead. See SRS COIL under REMOVAL & INSTALLATION. Activate SRS system. See DISABLING & ACTIVATING SRS.

IGNITION SWITCH/STEERING LOCK

Removal (Metro & Tracker) – Ignition switch is incorporated in steering lock. Remove steering column. See STEERING COLUMN. Center punch and drill shear bolts on steering lock assembly. Remove bolts using an extractor. Insert key in ignition switch and turn ignition switch to ON or ACC position. Remove steering lock assembly from steering column.

Installation – **1)** Rotate steering shaft so slot in steering shaft aligns with steering lock hole in steering column. Ensure ignition switch is in ON position. Install steering lock assembly on steering column.

2) Turn ignition switch to LOCK position and remove ignition key. Align hub on ignition switch with steering shaft hole. Rotate steering shaft to ensure steering shaft is locked.

3) Install NEW shear bolts in steering lock assembly. Tighten bolts until head breaks off bolt. Turn ignition on. Ensure steering shaft rotates smoothly. Install steering column.

NOTE: On Prizm, ignition switch is bolted to bottom of steering lock and can be removed without removing steering lock.

Removal (Prizm) – **1)** Disable SRS system. See DISABLING & ACTIVATING SRS. Remove steering column. See STEERING COLUMN.

2) Using center punch, punch center of steering lock shear bolts. Drill hole in shear bolts, and remove bolts using screw extractor. Remove steering lock assembly.

3) If removing lock cylinder from housing, place ignition switch in ACC position. Using a pin punch, depress release pin on top of steering lock housing. Remove lock cylinder.

Installation – **1)** To install, reverse removal procedure. If lock cylinder was removed, place ignition switch in ACC position and install switch in steering lock housing. Ensure lock cylinder is fully seated.

2) Install NEW shear bolts in steering lock assembly. Tighten shear bolts until heads break off bolts. Turn ignition on. Ensure steering shaft rotates smoothly. Install steering column. Activate SRS system.

STEERING COLUMN

CAUTION: Steering column is easily damaged once it has been removed from vehicle. If steering column is dropped on its end or hit with a hammer, steering shaft may collapse or plastic injections may be loosened. Side pressure to or leaning on steering column could cause it to bend and/or deform. Allowing steering column to be supported by only lower support bracket could cause damage to steering column lower bearing adapter.

NOTE: On Metro, steering shaft and column are not serviced separately. If either shaft or column is found to be defective or damaged, replace both as an assembly.

Removal (Metro) – **1)** If steering column is being removed to service a steering column component, remove steering wheel. See STEER-

ING WHEEL & HORN PAD and COMBINATION SWITCH. If steering column is being removed to gain access to instrument panel components, do not remove steering wheel.

2) Disconnect negative battery cable. Remove lower steering column trim cover screws. *See Fig. 6*. Remove knee bolster. Disconnect steering column electrical connectors. Loosen 2 upper steering column mounting nuts, and lower column slightly.

3) If steering wheel was removed, remove upper and lower steering column covers. Disconnect combination switch electrical connector. Loosen combination switch electrical harness wire bands. Remove combination switch from steering column.

4) Remove steering shaft joint cover by hand. Remove steering shaft joint upper pinch bolt. Separate steering shaft from joint. Remove lower steering column mounting nuts. Remove upper steering column mounting nuts and lower steering column onto seat. On A/T models, remove shift interlock cable from ignition switch by removing one screw. Remove steering column from vehicle.

Inspection – Ensure upper steering column mounting bracket capsules are contacting bottom of mounting slots. Ensure steering column length between center of steering shaft joint and end of steering column tube is 20.79" (528.0 mm). Replace steering column assembly if length is less than specification.

Installation – To install, reverse removal procedure. Ensure flat area on steering column shaft aligns with bolt hole on steering shaft lower joint. Tighten fasteners to specification. See TORQUE SPECIFICATIONS.

WARNING: On Prizm, disable SRS before attempting steering column service. See DISABLING & ACTIVATING SRS.

Removal (Prizm) – 1) If steering column is being removed to service a steering column component, remove steering wheel and SRS coil before removing steering column. See STEERING WHEEL & AIR BAG MODULE and SRS COIL under REMOVAL & INSTALLATION. If steering column is being removed to gain access to instrument panel components, disable SRS system and do not remove steering wheel. See DISABLING & ACTIVATING SRS.

2) Remove knee bolster and steering column covers. *See Fig. 7*. Disconnect steering column electrical connectors. Disconnect steering column joint pinch bolt. Remove steering column mounting nuts and bolts and disconnect steering column from instrument panel. Remove steering column from vehicle.

Inspection – If any injected plastic has sheared, replace steering shaft. Remove intermediate steering shaft from steering column tube. Ensure intermediate steering shaft runout is less than .063" (1.6 mm). Replace intermediate steering shaft if runout is greater than specification.

Installation – To install, reverse removal procedure. Ensure SRS coil is centered. See SRS COIL under REMOVAL & INSTALLATION. Tighten fasteners to specification. See TORQUE SPECIFICATIONS.

Removal (Tracker) – 1) If steering column is being removed to service a steering column component, remove steering wheel. See STEERING WHEEL & HORN PAD and COMBINATION SWITCH. If steering column is being removed to gain access to instrument panel components, do not remove steering wheel.

2) Remove steering column covers. Disconnect ignition switch wiring connector. On A/T models, disconnect backdrive cable. On all models, remove 4 bolts securing steering column to bulkhead. Remove bolt at lower joint-to-steering column shaft. Remove steering column mount bolts. Remove steering column assembly.

NOTE: On Tracker, upper steering shaft and column are not serviced separately. If either shaft or column is found to be defective or damaged, replace both as an assembly.

Inspection – Ensure upper steering column mounting bracket capsules are not loose. If capsules are loose, replace steering column assembly. Measure upper steering shaft length and lower steering shaft length to determine if either assembly should be replaced. See Fig. 8. Replace steering column if upper steering shaft length is less

than 30.63" (778.0 mm). Replace steering column if distance between upper shaft steering wheel end and top of steering column tube is less than 3.90" (99.0 mm). Replace lower shaft if length is less than 11.30" (287.0 mm) for models with power steering or 13.07" (332.0 mm) for models with manual steering. If lower shaft runout is greater than .079" (2.0 mm), replace lower shaft.

Installation – To install, reverse removal procedure. Tighten fasteners to specification. See TORQUE SPECIFICATIONS.

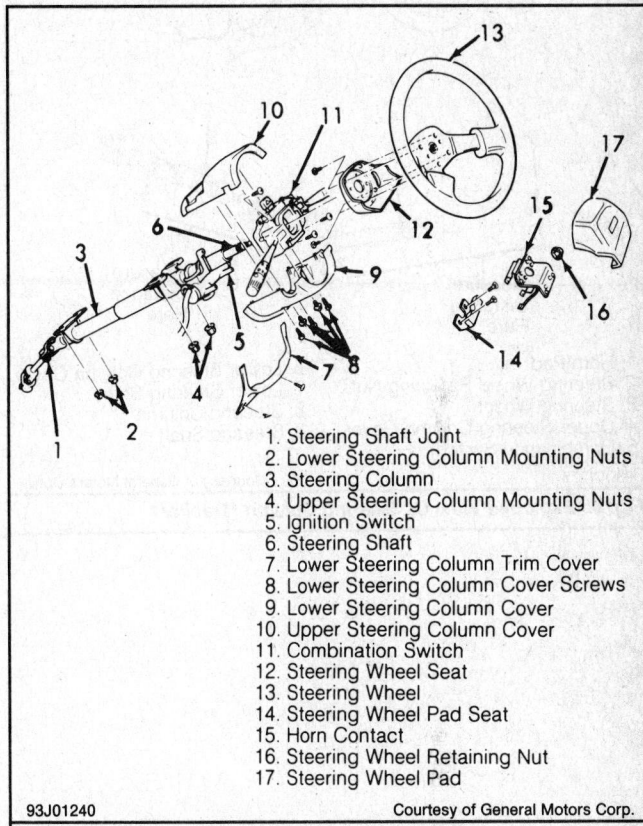

1. Steering Shaft Joint
2. Lower Steering Column Mounting Nuts
3. Steering Column
4. Upper Steering Column Mounting Nuts
5. Ignition Switch
6. Steering Shaft
7. Lower Steering Column Trim Cover
8. Lower Steering Column Cover Screws
9. Lower Steering Column Cover
10. Upper Steering Column Cover
11. Combination Switch
12. Steering Wheel Seat
13. Steering Wheel
14. Steering Wheel Pad Seat
15. Horn Contact
16. Steering Wheel Retaining Nut
17. Steering Wheel Pad

93J01240   Courtesy of General Motors Corp.

Fig. 6: Exploded View Of Steering Column (Metro)

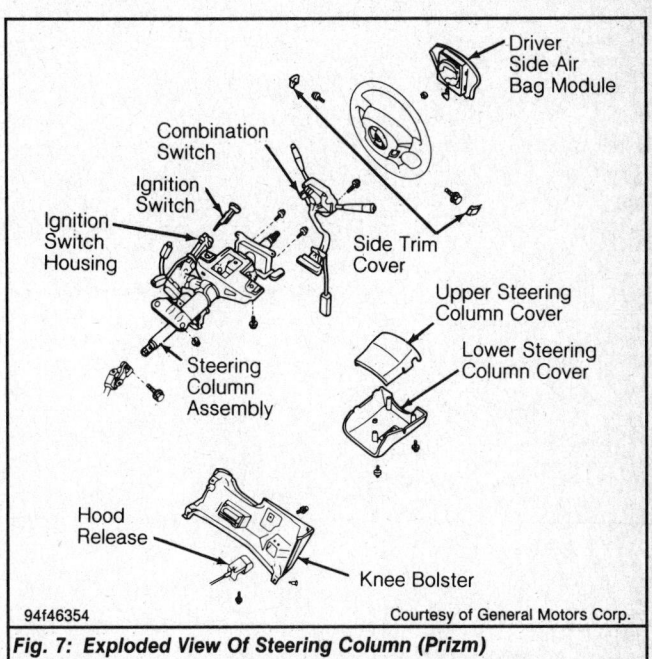

94f46354   Courtesy of General Motors Corp.

Fig. 7: Exploded View Of Steering Column (Prizm)

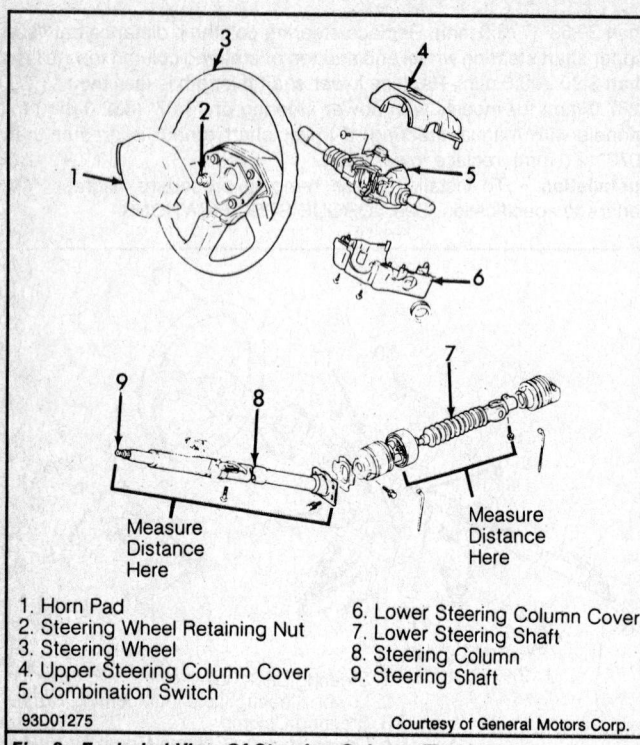

1. Horn Pad
2. Steering Wheel Retaining Nut
3. Steering Wheel
4. Upper Steering Column Cover
5. Combination Switch
6. Lower Steering Column Cover
7. Lower Steering Shaft
8. Steering Column
9. Steering Shaft

93D01275   Courtesy of General Motors Corp.

Fig. 8: Exploded View Of Steering Column (Tracker)

OVERHAUL

NOTE: *Use illustrations for exploded views of steering columns. See Figs. 6-8.*

NOTE: *On Metro and Tracker, steering column and shaft components are not serviceable. If column unit requires repair, replace column/shaft assembly.*

TORQUE SPECIFICATIONS
TORQUE SPECIFICATIONS

Application	Ft. Lbs. (N.m)
Steering Column Mounting Bolts & Nuts	
Metro & Tracker	10 (14)
Prizm	19 (26)
Steering Shaft Joint Pinch Bolts	
Metro & Tracker	18 (25)
Prizm	26 (35)
Steering Wheel Nut	
Metro & Tracker	24 (33)
Prizm	25 (34)
	INCH Lbs. (N.m)
Air Bag Module	
Prizm (Driver Side)	78 (9)

Metro, Prizm

DESCRIPTION

Steering gear is a rack and pinion type. Rotating steering wheel turns the pinion against the rack, causing movement of the rack. Rack movement is transferred to the steering knuckles by the tie rods.

LUBRICATION

FLUID TYPE

Use General Motors Manual Steering Gear Lube (1052182).

ADJUSTMENTS

PINION PRELOAD

Metro – 1) Back off rack adjusting screw. *See Fig. 1.* Tighten rack adjusting screw until it is snug. Using an INCH-lb. torque wrench and Socket (J-34871), measure rotational torque of pinion gear.
2) Torque reading is 10.6 INCH lbs. (1.2 N.m). If torque reading is greater than specification, back off adjusting screw (up to 90 degrees or a quarter turn). If torque reading is less than specification, tighten adjusting screw until specified torque is achieved. Ensure rack moves smoothly. Install cap on adjusting screw.
Prizm (Pinion Bearing Adjusting Screw Preload) – 1) Pinion bearing adjusting screw preload is checked without rack guide seat, rack guide, spring and "O" ring NOT installed. *See Fig. 2.* Line up cutout portion of rack with pinion gear. Ensure pinion gear is firmly seated in pinion lower bearing.
2) Using an INCH-lb. torque wrench and Pinion Preload Socket (J-35422), measure turning torque of pinion gear. Using a Steering Screw Wrench (J-35416), tighten or loosen pinion bearing adjuster until pinion gear turning torque is 3.5 INCH lbs. (0.4 N.m).
3) Tighten adjuster lock nut to 83 ft. lbs. (113 N.m). If pinion bearing adjusting screw preload adjustment is okay, ensure total pinion preload is okay.
Prizm (Total Pinion Preload) – 1) Back off lock nut and rack guide set bolt. *See Fig. 2.* Using a 4 mm hex wrench, tighten rack guide set bolt until it is snug. Using an INCH-lb. torque wrench and Pinion Preload Socket (J-35422), measure turning torque of pinion gear.
2) Torque reading should be 6.1-13 INCH lbs. (.7-1.5 N.m). Back off rack guide set bolt until specified torque is achieved. Ensure rack moves smoothly. Tighten lock nut to specification. See TORQUE SPECIFICATIONS.

REMOVAL & INSTALLATION

STEERING GEAR

Removal (Metro) – 1) Pull back joint cover on lower steering shaft from inside vehicle. Loosen, but DO NOT remove, pinch bolt at steering shaft joint assembly located at bottom of steering column (not steering gear).
2) Remove pinch bolt from (lower) steering shaft joint assembly at steering gear. Slide shaft assembly upward, away from steering gear. Raise and support vehicle. Remove front wheels.
3) Remove tie rod-to-steering knuckle retaining nuts. Separate tie rods from steering knuckles. Remove steering gear mounting bolts and brackets. Remove steering gear assembly through a front wheel opening.

Installation – To install, reverse removal procedure. Tighten bolts and nuts to specification. See TORQUE SPECIFICATIONS.
Removal (Prizm) – 1) Remove cover on steering shaft at steering gear. Remove pinch bolt from steering column yoke at steering gear. Raise and support vehicle. Remove front wheels.

NOTE: On Prizm, crossmembers below engine and transaxle must be removed for steering gear removal. Center crossmember is connected at radiator support and main crossmember. Main crossmember is attached to body.

---

2) Using Engine Support Fixture (J-28467-A), support engine and transaxle. Remove necessary mount bolts for crossmember removal. Support main crossmember. Remove main crossmember-to-center crossmember bolts.
3) Remove center crossmember-to-radiator support bolts. Remove main crossmember-to-body bolts. Remove lower "A" frame bracket-to-body bolts. Lower main crossmember while holding center crossmember. Remove both crossmembers.
4) Remove tie rod-to-steering knuckle retaining nuts. Separate tie rods from steering knuckles. Remove steering gear mounting bolts and brackets. Remove steering gear from right side wheelwell opening.
Installation – To install, reverse removal procedure. Tighten all bolts and nuts to specification. See TORQUE SPECIFICATIONS.

OVERHAUL

STEERING GEAR

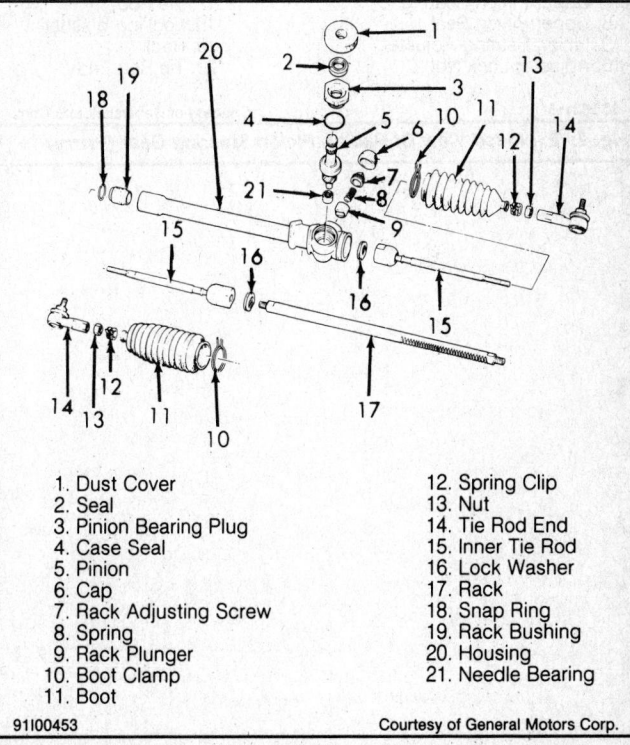

1. Dust Cover	12. Spring Clip
2. Seal	13. Nut
3. Pinion Bearing Plug	14. Tie Rod End
4. Case Seal	15. Inner Tie Rod
5. Pinion	16. Lock Washer
6. Cap	17. Rack
7. Rack Adjusting Screw	18. Snap Ring
8. Spring	19. Rack Bushing
9. Rack Plunger	20. Housing
10. Boot Clamp	21. Needle Bearing
11. Boot	

91I00453   Courtesy of General Motors Corp.

Fig. 1: Exploded View Of Rack & Pinion Steering Gear (Metro)

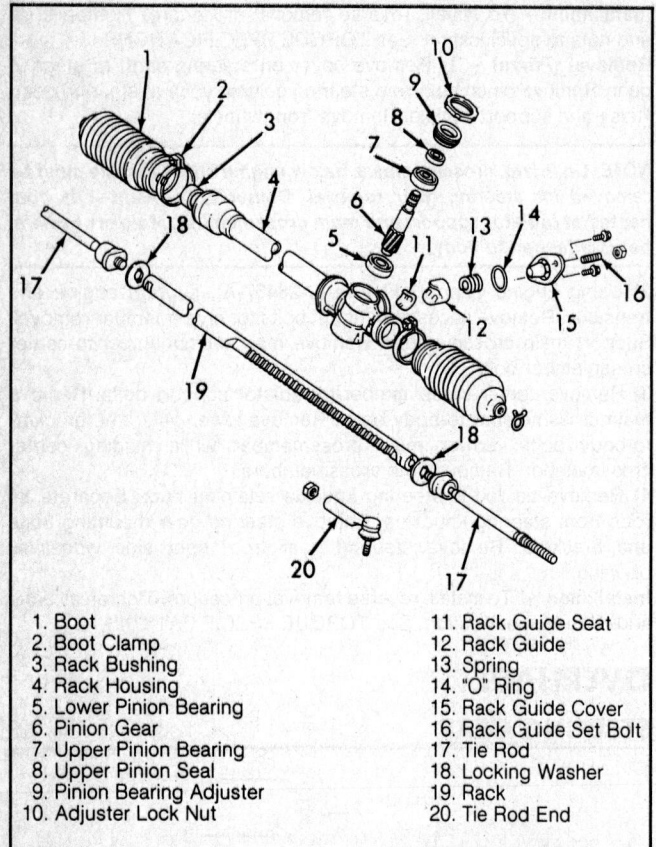

1. Boot
2. Boot Clamp
3. Rack Bushing
4. Rack Housing
5. Lower Pinion Bearing
6. Pinion Gear
7. Upper Pinion Bearing
8. Upper Pinion Seal
9. Pinion Bearing Adjuster
10. Adjuster Lock Nut
11. Rack Guide Seat
12. Rack Guide
13. Spring
14. "O" Ring
15. Rack Guide Cover
16. Rack Guide Set Bolt
17. Tie Rod
18. Locking Washer
19. Rack
20. Tie Rod End

93D83165   Courtesy of General Motors Corp.

Fig. 2: Exploded View Of Rack & Pinion Steering Gear (Prizm)

MANUAL RACK & PINION SPECIFICATIONS

Application	Specification
Metro	
Pinion Gear Preload	10.6 INCH Lbs. (1.2 N.m)
Steering Rack Runout	.016" (.41 mm)
Prizm	
Total Pinion Gear Preload	6.1-13.0 INCH Lbs. (.7-1.5 N.m)
Pinion Bearing Adjusting Screw Preload	3.5 INCH Lbs. (.4 N.m)
Steering Rack Runout	.006" (.15 mm)

TORQUE SPECIFICATIONS
TORQUE SPECIFICATIONS

Application	Ft. Lbs. (N.m)
Metro	
Inner Tie Rod-To-Rack	63 (85)
Pinion Bearing Plug	70 (95)
Steering Gear Mounting Bolt	18 (24)
Steering Shaft Joint Pinch Bolt	18 (24)
Tie Rod End Castle Nut	32 (43)
Tie Rod End Lock Nut	32 (43)
Wheel Lug Nut	44 (60)
Prizm	
Center Crossmember-To-Main Crossmember Bolt	45 (61)
Center Crossmember-To-Radiator Support Bolt	45 (61)
Inner Tie Rod-To-Rack	53 (72)
Lower "A" Frame-To-Body Bolt	94 (127)
Main Crossmember-To-Body Bolt	152 (206)
Pinion Bearing Adjustment Screw Lock Nut	83 (113)
Rack Guide Set Bolt Lock Nut	16 (21)
Steering Column Yoke Pinch Bolt	20 (27)
Steering Rack Mounting Bolt	45 (61)
Tie Rod End Lock Nut	41 (56)
Wheel Lug Nut	76 (103)
	INCH Lbs. (N.m)
Rack Guide Cover Bolts	106 (12)

Prizm

DESCRIPTION & OPERATION

Power-assisted rack and pinion steering system consists of a vane pump, rotary valve assembly and an oil reservoir. The vane pump draws fluid from the reservoir and supplies it to the rotary valve assembly. Rotary valve assembly supplies fluid to the rack piston when the steering wheel is turned.

LUBRICATION

CAPACITY

Information is not available from manufacturer.

FLUID TYPE

Use General Motors Power Steering Fluid (1050017), or equivalent.

FLUID LEVEL CHECK

1) With engine speed at 1000 RPM or less, turn steering wheel from stop to stop several times until fluid temperature increases to about 176° F (80° C).
2) Check fluid level using reservoir dipstick. Fluid level should be at MAX or FULL mark. Add fluid if necessary.
3) If fluid level is correct and foaming exists, air is present in system. Bleed air from system. See HYDRAULIC SYSTEM BLEEDING.

HYDRAULIC SYSTEM BLEEDING

1) Raise and support front of vehicle. Turn wheels fully left. With engine stopped, fill fluid reservoir to MIN or COLD mark on reservoir dipstick. Start engine, and operate it at fast idle for about 15 seconds.
2) Stop engine, and recheck fluid level. Fill fluid reservoir to MIN or COLD mark on reservoir dipstick. Start engine, and turn steering wheel from side to side 3-4 times. Stop engine, and recheck fluid level.
3) If fluid has a light Tan color, air exists in system. Repeat steps 1) and 2) until no air exists. Once system reaches normal operating temperature, stop engine and ensure fluid level is at MAX or FULL mark on reservoir dipstick.
4) Return wheels to center position. Lower vehicle to ground and continue to idle engine for 2-3 minutes. Road test vehicle to ensure steering functions normally and is free of noise. Check for fluid leaks. Ensure fluid level is still at MAX or FULL level.

ADJUSTMENTS

DRIVE BELTS

Using Belt Tension Gauge (J-23600-B), check belt tension at center point on longest run of power steering belt. Adjust belt if it is not within specification. See BELT TENSION SPECIFICATIONS table.

BELT TENSION SPECIFICATIONS [1]

Application	[2] New Belt Lbs. (kg)	[3] Used Belt Lbs. (kg)
P/S	100-150 (45-68)	60-120 (27-54)
Alternator	141-182 (64-83)	111-152 (50-69)

[1] – Using Belt Tension Gauge (J-23600-B).
[2] – New belt is a belt in operation less than 5 minutes.
[3] – Used belt is a belt in operation more than 5 minutes.

TESTING

STEERING PUMP PRESSURE

Information not available from manufacturer.

REMOVAL & INSTALLATION

POWER STEERING PUMP

Removal – 1) Remove alternator drive belt. Remove power steering pump drive belt. Loosen hose retaining clamp and disconnect return hose from power steering pump. Remove pressure hose from pump.
2) Remove upper mounting bolt from pump. Remove vacuum hoses from power steering pressure switch. Remove 3 pump mounting bracket bolts. Remove mounting bracket and power steering pump from vehicle.
Installation – To install, reverse removal procedure. Tighten all fasteners to specification. See TORQUE SPECIFICATIONS. Adjust tension of drive belts. See ADJUSTMENTS. Fill and bleed system. See HYDRAULIC SYSTEM BLEEDING under LUBRICATION.

POWER RACK & PINION

CAUTION: Failure to lock steering with front wheels in straight-ahead position could cause damage to SIR coil.

Removal – 1) Lock steering wheel in straight-ahead position. Remove air cleaner. Raise and support vehicle. Place a drain pan under vehicle. Remove both front wheels. Remove left and right stone shields.
2) Disconnect steering column yoke from rack. Remove cotter pins and tie rod end nuts. Using Tie Rod End Remover (J-21687-02), remove tie rod ends from steering knuckles. Remove center crossmember and main crossmember. Make match marks on universal joint and control valve shaft. Remove steering column-to-control valve shaft universal joint. Remove pressure hose from steering rack.
3) Loosen hose retaining clamp, and disconnect return hose from steering rack. Remove 2 nuts and 2 bolts retaining steering rack. Remove steering rack from vehicle through right wheel opening.
Installation – To install, reverse removal procedure. Tighten all fasteners to specification. See TORQUE SPECIFICATIONS. Fill and bleed system. See HYDRAULIC SYSTEM BLEEDING under LUBRICATION.

OVERHAUL

POWER STEERING PUMP

Disassembly – 1) Mount pump in a soft-jawed vise. Remove power steering pump pulley. Remove pump reservoir and reservoir "O" ring from power steering pump. Remove air control valve and union seat from pressure tube. Remove pressure port union, "O" ring and flow control valve and spring from front housing. Remove rear pump cover, 2 "O" rings and wave washer from pump.
2) Place match mark on cam ring at notched part of rear plate for installation. Remove rear plate from cam ring. Place match mark on cam ring in relation to power steering pump for installation. Remove cam ring from rotor. Remove rotor vane plates from rotors. Remove snap ring, rotor and 2 straight pins. Remove power steering pump shaft and pump shaft seal from power steering pump front housing. *See Fig. 1.*
Inspection – 1) Check power steering pump housing, shaft and pulley for cracks, distortion, excessive wear or scoring. Check rotor and vanes for excessive wear. If cracks or excessive wear are present, replace pump.
2) Ensure flow control valve moves smoothly within its bore. Replace flow control valve if it binds or sticks. Flow control valve spring free length should be 1.28"-1.34" (32.5-34.0 mm). If flow control valve spring length is not within specification, replace spring.
3) Check power steering flow control valve for leakage. Cover one fluid passage and apply 57-71 psi (4-5 Kg/cm²) air pressure to opposite passage. If there is air leakage at either end of flow control valve, replace flow control valve. If it is necessary to replace flow control valve, replacement control valve must have same letter marking as power steering pump front housing. An "A", "B", "C", "D", "E" or "F" will be stamped into power steering pump front housing.
4) Clearance between power steering shaft and shaft bushing should be .0012"-.0020" (.03-.05 mm). If power steering shaft and shaft bushing clearance is greater than .0020" (.05 mm), replace power steering pump assembly.
5) Rotor vane plate height is .339" (8.61 mm), length is .590" (14.99 mm) and thickness is .055" (1.40 mm). If any rotor vane plate is less than specified, replace ALL rotor vane plates. Clearance between

rotor and rotor vane plate should be .0014" (.036 mm). If rotor vane plate clearance is greater than specified, replace rotor and rotor vane plates according to numbers stamped on cam ring and rotor. See ROTOR VANE PLATE LENGTH REPLACEMENT table.

ROTOR VANE PLATE LENGTH REPLACEMENT

Number On Rotor & Cam Ring	Rotor Vane Plate Length
Blank	.59051"-.59059" (14.999-15.001 mm)
1	.59043"-.59051" (14.997-14.999 mm)
2	.59035"-.59043" (14.995-14.997 mm)
3	.59027"-.59035" (14.993-14.995 mm)
4	.59020"-.59027" (14.991-14.993 mm)

Reassembly – To assemble, reverse disassembly procedure. Install rotor, cam ring and vanes in respective order using match marks made during disassembly. Lubricate internal components, including "O" rings, with power steering fluid. Tighten rear housing bolts to 12 ft. lbs. (16 N.m). Ensure power steering pump shaft rotates smoothly. Check if power steering shaft preload is less than 2.2 INCH lbs. (.2 N.m). If preload is not as specified, replace power steering pump assembly.

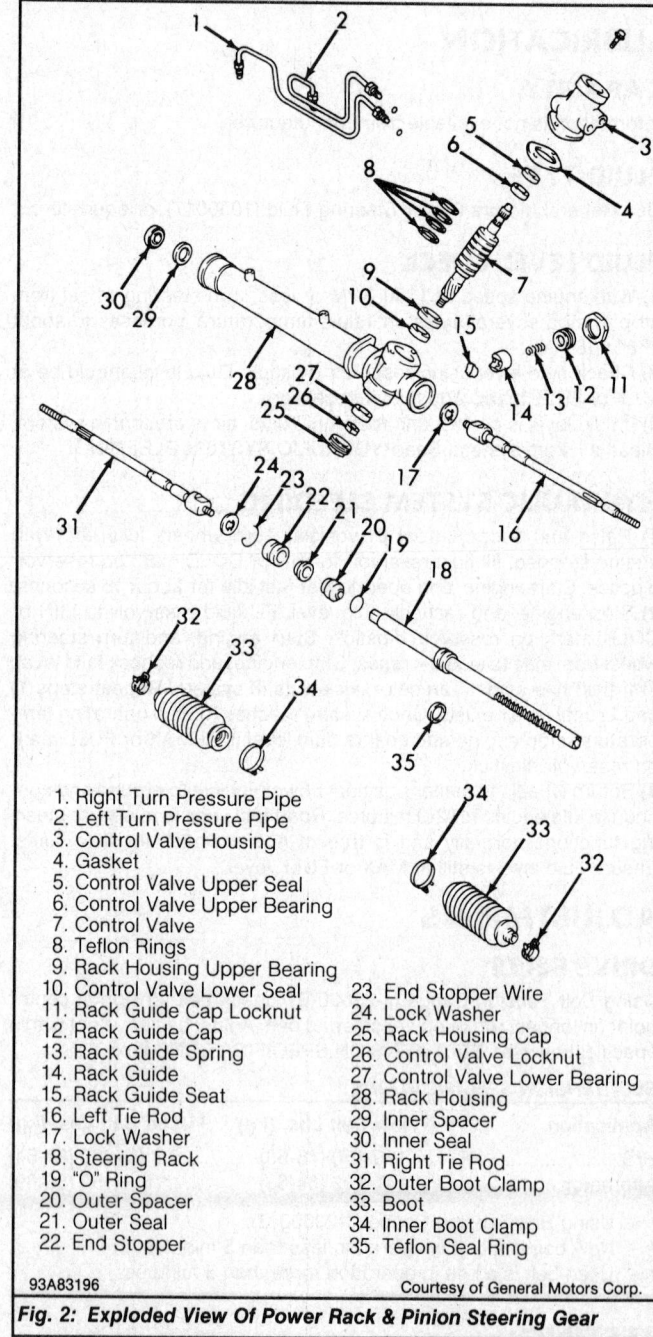

1. Right Turn Pressure Pipe
2. Left Turn Pressure Pipe
3. Control Valve Housing
4. Gasket
5. Control Valve Upper Seal
6. Control Valve Upper Bearing
7. Control Valve
8. Teflon Rings
9. Rack Housing Upper Bearing
10. Control Valve Lower Seal
11. Rack Guide Cap Locknut
12. Rack Guide Cap
13. Rack Guide Spring
14. Rack Guide
15. Rack Guide Seat
16. Left Tie Rod
17. Lock Washer
18. Steering Rack
19. "O" Ring
20. Outer Spacer
21. Outer Seal
22. End Stopper
23. End Stopper Wire
24. Lock Washer
25. Rack Housing Cap
26. Control Valve Locknut
27. Control Valve Lower Bearing
28. Rack Housing
29. Inner Spacer
30. Inner Seal
31. Right Tie Rod
32. Outer Boot Clamp
33. Boot
34. Inner Boot Clamp
35. Teflon Seal Ring

93A83196   Courtesy of General Motors Corp.

Fig. 2: Exploded View Of Power Rack & Pinion Steering Gear

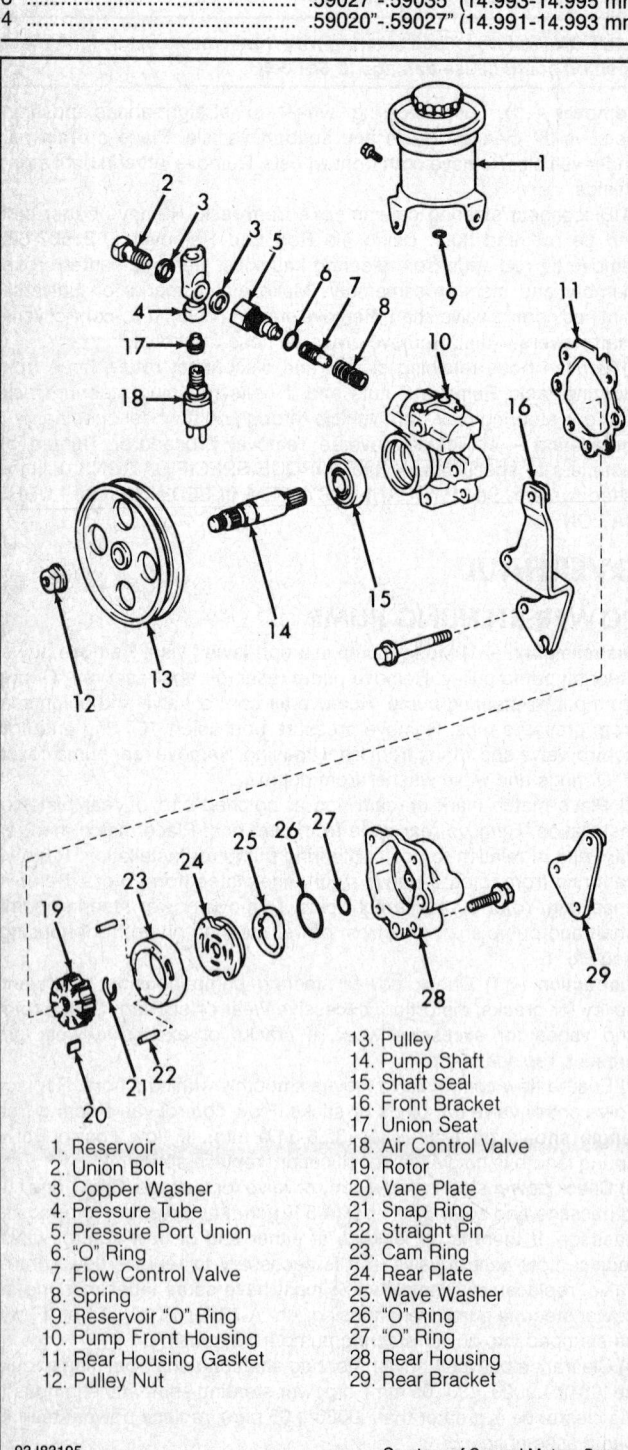

13. Pulley
14. Pump Shaft
15. Shaft Seal
16. Front Bracket
17. Union Seat
18. Air Control Valve
19. Rotor
20. Vane Plate
21. Snap Ring
22. Straight Pin
23. Cam Ring
24. Rear Plate
25. Wave Washer
26. "O" Ring
27. "O" Ring
28. Rear Housing
29. Rear Bracket

1. Reservoir
2. Union Bolt
3. Copper Washer
4. Pressure Tube
5. Pressure Port Union
6. "O" Ring
7. Flow Control Valve
8. Spring
9. Reservoir "O" Ring
10. Pump Front Housing
11. Rear Housing Gasket
12. Pulley Nut

93J83195   Courtesy of General Motors Corp.

Fig. 1: Exploded View Of Power Steering Pump

STEERING GEAR

CAUTION: When power steering gear is mounted in a vise, DO NOT overtighten vise. Power steering gear housing can distort if excessive pressure is exerted on its exterior.

Disassembly – 1) Mount rack and pinion in a soft-jawed vise. Remove right and left turn pressure pipes. Remove inner and outer boot clamps and slide boots toward tie rod ends. Unstake tie rod lock washers. Using Tie Rod Housing Wrench (J-35414) and Steering Rack End Wrench (J-35418), remove tie rods from steering rack.

2) Using Lock Nut Wrench (J-35309-1), remove rack guide cap lock nut. Using Adjusting Plug (J-35309-2), remove rack guide cap, rack guide spring, rack guide and rack guide seat. Remove rack housing cap. Using Pinion Preload Socket (J-35428), remove control valve lock nut. Remove control valve housing. See Fig. 2.

3) Using Cylinder End Stopper Wrench (J-39901), turn cylinder end stopper until both ends of cylinder end stopper wire appear in slot on top of rack housing. Continue turning cylinder end stopper until the loose end of cylinder end stopper wire is fed out slot on top of rack housing. Remove cylinder end stopper wire and cylinder end stopper. See Fig. 2.

4) Install Rack Seal Protector (J-36595) over teeth on steering rack to protect inner rack seal. Remove steering rack, steering rack outer spacer and outer seal. Using Driver Handle (J-35434-2) and Rack Cylinder Seal Remover (J-35434-1), remove inner seal and spacer. Using a brass drift punch, remove control valve lower bearing. Using Control Valve Bearing Remover (J-39902), remove rack housing upper bearing. See Fig. 2.

Inspection – Check rack mounting bushings. Check rack housing for cracks, distortion or porosity. Check tie rod boots for splits and cracks. Check tie rods for wear and damage. Measure runout at center of rack. Maximum runout is .006" (.15 mm).

Reassembly & Adjustments – 1) Ensure rack and pinion assembly components are cleaned in mineral spirits using a lint-free rag. DO NOT use a wire brush.

2) Using Control Valve Bearing Installer (J-39903), install rack housing upper bearing and control valve lower seal. Place Rack Seal Protector (J-36595) over toothed part of steering rack. Slide inner seal and then inner spacer over Rack Seal Protector and onto steering rack.

3) Install steering rack into rack housing. Using a plastic hammer, tap steering rack until inner spacer and seal are seated in rack housing. Remove Rack Seal Protector. Install NEW "O" ring and outer seal into outer spacer. Install outer spacer into rack housing. See Fig. 2.

4) Install end stopper into rack housing. Using Cylinder End Stopper Wrench (J-39901), turn end stopper until wire end hole appears in slot on top of rack housing. Place hooked end of end stopper wire into hole of end stopper and turn end stopper. Feed end stopper wire into slot on top of rack housing until both ends of end stopper wire are hidden.

5) Connect a vacuum pump to rack housing and apply a vacuum. If rack housing does not hold 15" Hg vacuum. inspect inner and outer seals. Using a NEW gasket, install control valve housing to rack housing. Tighten control valve housing bolts to specification. See TORQUE SPECIFICATIONS.

6) Install control valve lower bearing and control valve lock nut. Using Pinion Preload Socket (J-35428) to hold control valve, tighten control valve lock nut to 106 INCH lbs. (12 N.m). Apply Loctite pipe sealant to rack housing cap threads and tighten to 51 ft. lbs. (69 N.m).

7) Install rack guide seat, rack guide and rack guide spring into rack housing. Apply Loctite pipe sealant to rack guide cap threads and using Adjusting Plug (J-35309-2), tighten rack guide cap to 18 ft. lbs. (24 N.m). Loosen rack guide cap 15 degrees and turn control valve pinion shaft right and left one rotation each. Further loosen rack guide cap until all tension on rack guide spring is released.

8) Using an INCH-lbs torque wrench, check control valve pinion shaft preload (starting torque). See Fig. 3. Tighten or loosen rack guide cap until pinion shaft preload is 6.9-11.3 INCH lbs. (0.8-1.3 N.m). When specified preload is obtained, install rack guide cap lock nut. Using Adjusting Plug (J-35309-2) to hold rack guide cap, use Lock Nut Wrench (J-35309-1) to tighten rack guide cap lock nut to 33 ft. lbs. (45 N.m). Ensure pinion shaft preload has not changed.

9) Install NEW lock washers to rack. Install left and right tie rods to rack and tighten to specification. See TORQUE SPECIFICATIONS. Stake lock washers to flat surfaces of tie rods. Install left and right tie rod boots to tie rods. Install inner and outer tie rod boot clamps. Install tie rod end lock nuts to tie rods. DO NOT tighten lock nuts.

10) Install left and right turn pressure pipes with NEW "O" rings if needed. Tighten flare nuts to 18 ft. lbs. (25 N.m). To complete installation reverse removal procedures. DO NOT tighten tie rod end lock nuts

until wheel alignment is performed. See SPECIFICATIONS & PROCEDURES article in WHEEL ALIGNMENT.

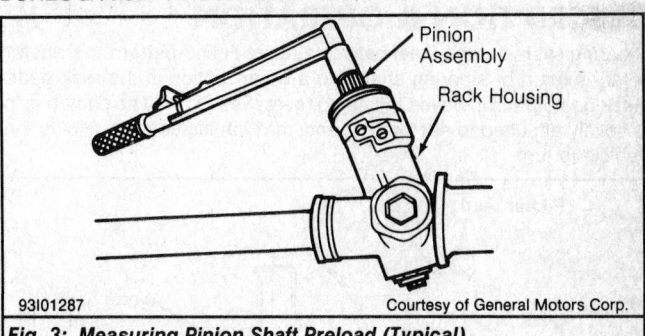

93I01287　　　　　　　　　　　Courtesy of General Motors Corp.

Fig. 3: Measuring Pinion Shaft Preload (Typical)

CONTROL VALVE

Disassembly – Mark position of return line elbow on control valve housing and remove elbow. Using a plastic hammer, remove control valve and lower control valve seal from control valve housing. Remove Teflon seal rings from control valve. Remove control valve upper bearing and seal.

Inspection – Check valve Teflon seal ring grooves for burrs or excessive wear. Check control valve bearings. Replace components as necessary.

NOTE: *During installation of Teflon seal rings, do not expand rings any more than necessary.*

Reassembly & Adjustments – Apply liberal amounts of power steering fluid to Teflon seal rings and Spool Valve Seal Sizer (J-38250). Install rings onto Spool Valve Seal Sizer and then onto control valve. Install control valve upper bearing and seal. Using Spool Valve Installer (J-38251), install control valve into control valve housing. Install control valve lower seal. Install return elbow to position marked previously. Tighten return line elbow flare nut to 32 ft. lbs. (43 N.m).

TORQUE SPECIFICATIONS

TORQUE SPECIFICATIONS (PRIZM)

Application	Ft. Lbs. (N.m)
Air Control Valve	27 (37)
Alternator Mounting Bolts	
Lower	26 (35)
Upper	17 (23)
Center Crossmember-To-Main Crossmember Bolt	45 (61)
Center Crossmember-To-Radiator Support Bolt	45 (61)
Center Engine Mounting Bracket	29 (39)
Control Valve Housing Bolts	13 (18)
Control Valve Lock Nut	[1]
Left & Right Turn Pressure Pipes Flare Nut	18 (25)
Main Crossmember-To-Body Bolt	152 (206)
Pinion Shaft Lock Nut	44 (59)
Power Steering Pump Mounting Bolts	29 (39)
Pressure Hose-To-Rack Fitting	32 (45)
Pressure Port Union	61 (83)
Pressure Tube Union Bolt	51 (69)
Pulley Nut	32 (43)
Pump Mounting Bracket Bolt & Nut	29 (39)
Pump Rear Housing Bolts	12 (16)
Pump Reservoir Tank Bolts	
Front	[2]
Rear	12 (16)
Rack Guide Spring Cap Lock Nut	33 (45)
Rack Housing Cap	51 (69)
Return Line Elbow Flare Nut	32 (43)
Right Engine Mount Bolt	69 (94)
Steering Column Yoke Pinch Bolt	26 (35)
Steering Gear Mounting Bolts & Nuts	43 (58)
Tie Rod-To-Rack	61 (83)
Tie Rod End Castle Nut	36 (49)
Wheel Lug Nut	76 (103)

[1] – Tighten to 106 INCH lbs. (12 N.m).
[2] – Tighten to 115 INCH lbs. (13 N.m).

Tracker

DESCRIPTION & OPERATION

Steering system uses steel balls in a recirculating pattern to transfer rotary motion of steering shaft into a linear motion in the rack gear. Rack gear, in turn, moves the sector gear. *See Fig. 1.* The pitman arm is solidly attached to sector gear and, through the tie rods, allows the vehicle to turn.

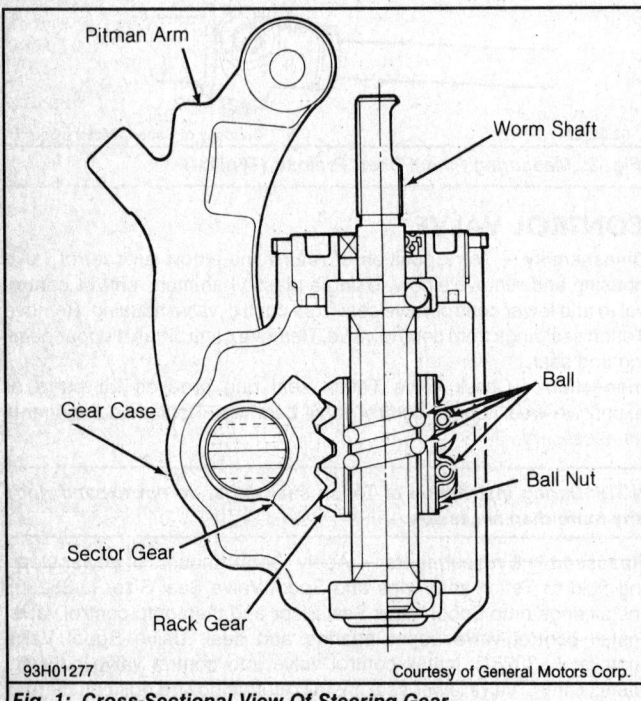

Fig. 1: Cross-Sectional View Of Steering Gear

LUBRICATION

FLUID TYPE

Steering gear uses SAE 90W gear oil. Gear oil should be visible 1.38" (35 mm) below steering gear fill/breather plug, located on top of gear box.

ADJUSTMENTS

WORM SHAFT OPERATING TORQUE

NOTE: Perform worm shaft operating torque adjustment with steering gear removed from vehicle.

1) Check worm shaft to ensure it is free of thrust play. Position pitman arm 11 degrees inward from parallel with worm shaft. *See Fig. 2.* This position is the sector gear high point.
2) Connect Socket (J-34871-A) and INCH-pound torque wrench to worm shaft. Check operating torque in this position. Operating torque should be 9 INCH lbs. (1.0 N.m).
3) If operating torque is not to specification, loosen or tighten adjusting nut as necessary. Recheck operating torque. If operating torque cannot be adjusted to specification, replace steering gear assembly.

REMOVAL & INSTALLATION

IDLER ARM & BUSHING

Removal & Installation – 1) Raise and support vehicle. Remove idler arm cotter pin and castle nut from center link. Remove idler arm from center link with Puller (J-21687-02). Remove idler arm bushing nut. Remove idler arm and washers.
2) Remove bushing from idler arm with press. Press new bushing into idler. To install, reverse removal procedure. Use new idler arm cotter

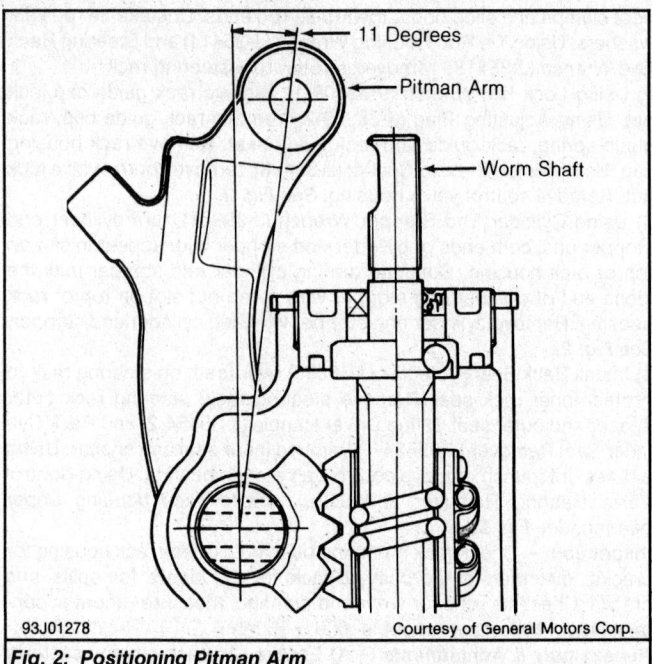

Fig. 2: Positioning Pitman Arm

pin. Tighten bolts and nuts to specification. See TORQUE SPECIFICATIONS.

PITMAN ARM

Removal – Raise and support vehicle. Remove engine skid plate (if equipped). Remove splash shield from wheelwell. Remove cotter pin and castle nut from center link. Separate pitman arm from center link using Puller (J-29107). Remove sector shaft nut and remove pitman arm from steering gear.
Installation – Install pitman arm on sector shaft. Ensure reference marks align. Install sector shaft nut and tighten to specification. See TORQUE SPECIFICATIONS. To complete installation, reverse removal procedure.

STEERING GEAR

Removal – 1) Raise and support vehicle. Remove engine skid plate (if equipped). Remove splash shield from left inner wheelwell. Remove cotter pin and castle nut from center link. Separate pitman arm from center link using Puller (J-29107).
2) Remove sector shaft nut and remove pitman arm from steering gear. Remove lower steering shaft from steering gear box by removing yoke joint pinch bolt. Remove steering gear mounting bolts and remove steering gear from vehicle.
Installation – To install, reverse removal procedure. Install steering gear attaching bolts from inside engine compartment. Tighten bolts to specification.

OVERHAUL

Steering gear is non-serviceable.

TORQUE SPECIFICATIONS
TORQUE SPECIFICATIONS

Application	Ft. Lbs. (N.m)
Center Link-To-Pitman Arm Castle Nut	40 (54)
Idler Arm Bushing Nut	55 (75)
Idler Arm Castle Nut	33 (45)
Pitman Arm-To-Sector Shaft Nut	95 (129)
Skid Plate Bolt	20 (27)
Steering Gear Attaching Bolt	74 (100)
Tie Rod Castle Nut	33 (45)
Tie Rod End Lock Nut	48 (65)

Tracker

DESCRIPTION & OPERATION

The power steering gear is an integral-type, consisting of conventional ball/screw-type steering gear. The gear combines with a rotary and torsion bar-type control valve and power cylinder. The belt-driven oil pump is a constant delivery vane-type.

LUBRICATION

FLUID CAPACITY

Information is not available from manufacturer.

FLUID TYPE

Use GM Power Steering Fluid (1050017), or equivalent.

HYDRAULIC SYSTEM BLEEDING

1) Start engine and turn wheels all the way left. Turn engine off. Add power steering fluid to reservoir until it reaches COLD mark fluid level indicator. Leave cap off reservoir.

2) Start engine and run at fast idle for approximately 15 seconds. Stop engine and check fluid level. If necessary, add fluid to bring level to COLD mark again.

3) Start engine and bleed system by turning wheels from side to side 3-4 times. Stop engine and check fluid color and level in reservoir. Fluid with a light Tan color indicates air is in system. Repeat steps until fluid is purged of air and fluid is Red in appearance.

ADJUSTMENTS

POWER STEERING PUMP BELT

Belt deflection is .24-.35" (6-9 mm) with 22 lbs. (10 kg) of force applied to side of belt. Measure between pump and crankshaft pulley (without air conditioning), or between air conditioning compressor and crankshaft pulley (with air conditioning).

REMOVAL & INSTALLATION

POWER STEERING PUMP

Removal – 1) Disconnect negative battery cable. Remove drive belt by loosening air conditioning compressor or power steering pump mounting bolts (as necessary). Raise and support vehicle. Remove engine skid plate (if equipped). Remove union bolt and pressure hose from power steering pump.

2) Loosen hose clamp and remove suction hose. Disconnect electrical connector from power steering pump pressure switch. Remove engine oil filter. Remove all mounting bolts from power steering pump and bracket. Remove pump from vehicle.

Installation – To install, reverse removal procedure. Install engine oil filter and ensure oil level is correct. Adjust belt. See ADJUSTMENTS. Refill with fluid, bleed system and check for leaks.

POWER STEERING GEAR

Removal – 1) Remove pressure and return hoses from steering gear. Plug hoses to contain fluid. Raise and support vehicle. Remove engine skid plate (if equipped). Remove splash shield from left inner wheel well.

2) Remove cotter pin and castle nut from center link ball joint. Use a pitman arm puller and separate pitman arm from center link. Lower steering shaft from power steering gear by removing pinch bolt. Remove 2 power steering gear mounting and one pilot bolt, and remove steering gear from vehicle.

Installation – To install, reverse removal procedure. If pitman arm was removed, ensure match marks on sector shaft and pitman arm are aligned. Tighten nuts and bolts to specification. See TORQUE SPECIFICATIONS. Refill system with fluid. Bleed system. Check for leaks.

OVERHAUL

POWER STEERING PUMP

Disassembly – Mount pump in vise. Remove power steering pump pulley. Disconnect pressure switch. Remove 2 bolts and suction hose connector. Remove pressure connector and flow control valve. Remove rear pump cover, cam ring and "O" ring seal from pump. See Fig. 1.

Inspection – Check pump housing for cracks. Check rotor and vanes for excessive wear. If cracks or excessive wear are present, replace pump.

Reassembly – To assemble, reverse disassembly procedure. Install rotor, cam ring and vanes in respective order. Lubricate internal components with power steering fluid.

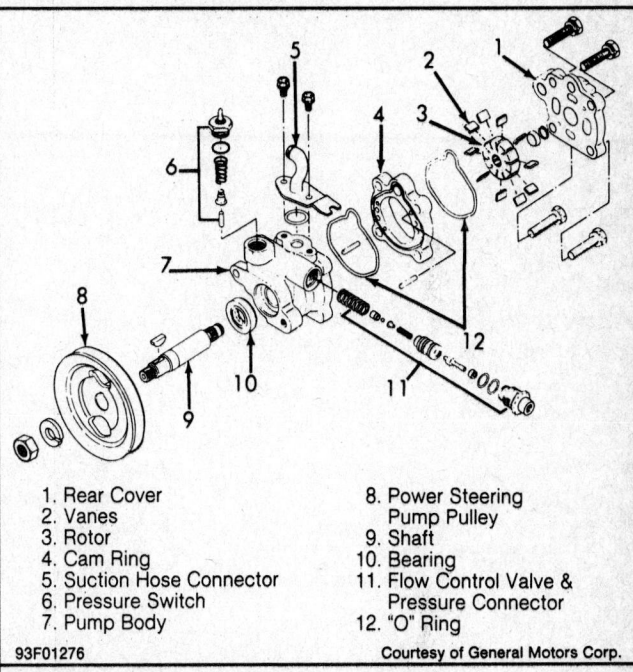

1. Rear Cover	8. Power Steering
2. Vanes	Pump Pulley
3. Rotor	9. Shaft
4. Cam Ring	10. Bearing
5. Suction Hose Connector	11. Flow Control Valve &
6. Pressure Switch	Pressure Connector
7. Pump Body	12. "O" Ring

93F01276   Courtesy of General Motors Corp.

Fig. 1: Exploded View Of Power Steering Pump

POWER STEERING GEAR

NOTE: No overhaul procedures are available from the manufacturer.

TORQUE SPECIFICATIONS

TORQUE SPECIFICATIONS

Application	Ft. Lbs. (N.m)
A/C Compressor Mounting Bolts	
8 mm Bolts	21 (28)
10 mm Bolts	33 (45)
Pitman Arm-To-Center Link Attaching Nut	41 (56)
Pitman Arm-To-Steering Gear Attaching Nut	96 (130)
Pressure Hose Union Bolt	29 (39)
Pressure Switch	22 (30)
Pulley Retaining Nut	32 (43)
Pump Body Bolts	17 (23)
Pump Mounting Bolts	22 (30)
Pump Pressure Connector	43 (58)
Skid Plate	20 (27)
Steering Shaft Coupler Pinch Bolt	29 (39)
Steering Gear Mounting & Pilot Bolts	74 (100)
Suction Hose Connector Bolts	[1]

[1] – Tighten bolts to 89 INCH lbs. (10 N.m).

Metro, Prizm, Tracker

IDENTIFICATION

AUTOMATIC TRANSMISSION APPLICATIONS

Model	Transmission
Metro	Suzuki 3-Speed Transaxle
Prizm	A131L 3-Speed Transaxle
Prizm LSi	A245E Electronic 4-Speed Transaxle
Tracker	[1] General Motors 3L30

[1] – Also known as Turbo Hydra-Matic 180C.

LUBRICATION

SERVICE INTERVALS

Metro – Manufacturer recommends replacing transaxle oil cooler hoses at 45,000-mile intervals. Replace transaxle fluid, and clean filter and pan magnet every 100,000 miles under normal driving conditions. Change fluid, and clean filter and pan magnet every 15,000 miles under severe driving conditions.

Prizm & Prizm LSi – Replace transaxle fluid, and clean filter and pan magnet, on all models and differential fluid on 3-speed transaxle, every 100,000 miles under normal driving conditions. Replace transaxle fluid, and clean filter and pan magnet every 15,000 miles or 15 months under severe driving conditions.

Tracker – 1) Manufacturer recommends replacing transmission oil cooler hoses at 45,000-mile intervals. Under normal driving conditions, replace transmission fluid, and clean filter and pan magnet every 100,000 miles. Replace transfer case fluid initially at 7500 miles and then at 30,000 miles or 30 month intervals.

2) Under severe driving conditions or towing a trailer, replace transmission fluid, and clean filter and pan magnet every 15,000 miles or 15 months. Replace transfer case fluid initially at 7500 miles and then at 15,000 miles or 15 months intervals.

Severe Conditions (All Vehicles) – Severe driving conditions are when vehicle is operated under one or more of the following conditions:

- Most driving is in stop-and-go traffic when outside temperatures are greater than 90° F (32° C).
- Delivery service, Taxi or Police vehicles.
- Trailer towing.
- In hilly or mountainous terrain.
- Most trips are less than 4 miles.
- Most trips are less than 10 miles, and outside temperatures remain below freezing.
- Driving in dusty areas.

CHECKING FLUID LEVEL

CAUTION: Check differential fluid level on Prizm (3-speed) and transfer case level on Tracker.

Transaxle & Transmission – 1) Engine must be at normal operating temperature. Park vehicle on level surface, and apply parking brake. Place selector lever in Park.
2) Start engine, and allow it to idle. Apply brakes, shift through all gears and return selector lever to Park.
3) Remove dipstick, wipe dipstick off and reinsert fully. Remove dipstick and read level. Fluid level should be in HOT or FULL HOT range. Add fluid (if necessary), and recheck level. DO NOT overfill.
Differential (Prizm 3-Speed) – Differential ATF reservoir is separate from transaxle fluid reservoir. Remove differential fill plug from transaxle case. Ensure fluid level is at bottom of fill plug hole. *See Fig. 1.*
Transfer Case (Tracker) – Remove transfer case fill plug (upper plug) from rear of transfer case. Fill plug is located near speedometer gear housing. Fluid level must be at bottom of fill plug hole. Install fill plug, and tighten it to 21 ft. lbs. (28 N.m).

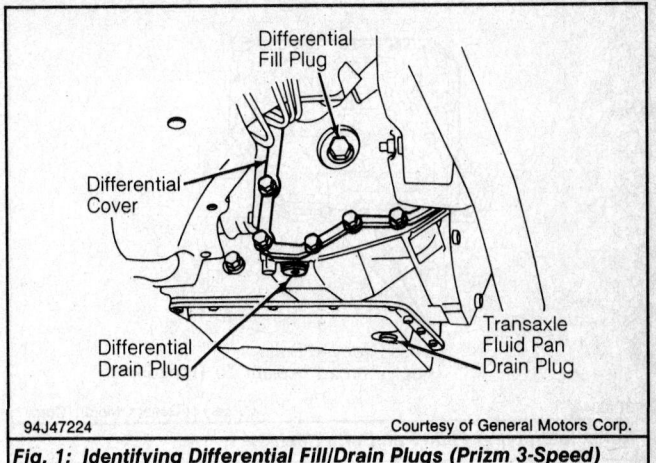

Fig. 1: Identifying Differential Fill/Drain Plugs (Prizm 3-Speed)

RECOMMENDED FLUID

Transaxle & Transmission (All Models) – Use Dexron-IIE ATF (12345881).
Differential (Prizm) – Uses Dexron-IIE ATF (12345881).
Transfer Case (Tracker) – Use SAE 75W-90 or 80W-90 gear oil with GL-4 rating.

FLUID CAPACITIES

TRANSMISSION REFILL CAPACITIES

Application	Pan Removal Qts. (L)	[1] Overhaul Qts. (L)
Metro	1.6 (1.5)	[2] 3.7 (3.5)
Prizm (3-Speed)	2.6 (2.5)	5.8 (5.5)
Prizm LSi (4-Speed)	3.5 (3.3)	8.0 (7.6)
Tracker	1.6 (1.5)	[3] 3.7 (3.5)

[1] – Overhaul refill without torque converter.
[2] – Overhaul refill with new torque converter is 5.2 qts. (4.9L).
[3] – Overhaul refill with new torque converter is 5.1 qts. (4.8L).

DIFFERENTIAL REFILL CAPACITIES

Application	Qts. (L)
Prizm (3-Speed)	1.5 (1.4)

TRANSFER CASE REFILL CAPACITIES

Application	Qts. (L)
Tracker	1.8 (1.7)

DRAINING & REFILLING

CAUTION: Manufacturer recommends flushing oil cooler whenever transmission or transaxle is removed.

Metro – 1) Remove drain plug from bottom of transaxle fluid pan, and drain fluid. Remove 15 fluid pan bolts, fluid pan, fluid pan guard, gasket and filter screen. Note position of 2 cross-grooved fluid pan bolts. *See Fig. 2.* If fluid pan is frozen to transaxle case, use a rubber mallet and a wood block to remove it. DO NOT pry fluid pan away from transfer case.
2) Install cleaned filter screen and a new gasket. Tighten retaining bolts to 53 INCH lbs. (6 N.m). Install fluid pan and NEW gasket. Apply thread sealant to threads of 2 cross-grooved bolts. DO NOT apply thread sealant to other 13 bolts. Tighten fluid pan bolts to 53 INCH lbs. (6 N.m). Tighten drain plug to 17 ft. lbs. (23 N.m).
3) Add 1.6 qts. (1.5L) of Dexron-IIE through dipstick tube. Check fluid level. See CHECKING FLUID LEVEL.

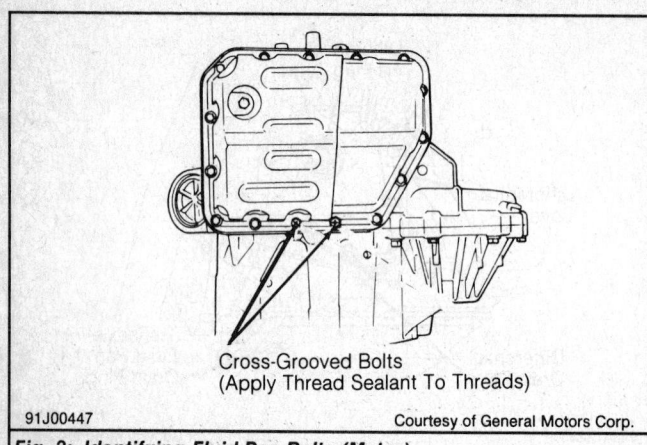

Cross-Grooved Bolts
(Apply Thread Sealant To Threads)

91J00447   Courtesy of General Motors Corp.

Fig. 2: Identifying Fluid Pan Bolts (Metro)

Prizm (Transaxle) – 1) Raise and support vehicle. Remove left splash shield. Remove drain plug and drain fluid. Remove fluid pan bolts, fluid pan and gasket. If fluid pan is frozen to transaxle case, use a rubber mallet and a wood block to remove it. DO NOT pry fluid pan away from transfer case. Remove filter screen bolts and filter screen, noting bolt length and position for reassembly reference.
2) Install cleaned filter screen and NEW gasket. Ensure bolts are installed in original locations. See Fig. 1. Tighten filter screen bolts to 89 INCH lbs. (10 N.m). Install fluid pan using NEW gasket. Tighten bolts to 44 INCH lbs. (5 N.m). Install drain plug, and tighten it to 29 ft. lbs. (39 N.m). Install left splash shield and tighten bolts to 44 INCH lbs. (5 N.m).
3) Add correct amount of Dexron-IIE through dipstick tube. See TRANSMISSION REFILL CAPACITIES table. Check fluid level.
Prizm (Differential) – Remove drain plug in bottom of differential cover, and drain fluid. See Fig. 1. Install drain plug, and tighten it to 29 ft. lbs. (39 N.m). Remove fill plug on side of differential cover. Fill with Dexron-IIE until fluid runs from fill hole. Install fill plug.
Prizm LSi – 1) Raise and support vehicle. Remove left splash shield. Remove drain plug from fluid pan. Drain fluid. Remove 18 fluid pan bolts, fluid pan protector, fluid pan and gasket. If fluid pan is frozen to transaxle case, use a rubber mallet and a wood block to remove it. DO NOT pry fluid pan away from transfer case. Remove filter screen and gasket.
2) Install cleaned filter screen and NEW gasket. Tighten filter screen bolts to 89 INCH lbs. (10 N.m). Install fluid pan, NEW gasket and fluid pan protector. Tighten fluid pan bolts to 44 INCH lbs. (5 N.m). Tighten drain plug to 13 ft. lbs. (17 N.m). Install left splash shield and tighten bolts to 44 INCH lbs. (5 N.m).
3) Add correct amount of Dexron-IIE through dipstick tube. See TRANSMISSION REFILL CAPACITIES table. Check fluid level.
Tracker (Transmission) – 1) Raise and support vehicle. Place a match marks on drive shaft and flange and disconnect front drive shaft from front differential flange. Remove all transmission fluid pan bolts except 3 bolts on rear of fluid pan. Loosen remaining 3 bolts, allowing pan to tip downward so fluid will drain. Once fluid is drained, remove remaining fluid pan bolts, fluid pan and gasket. Remove filter screen and gasket.
2) Install cleaned filter screen and NEW gasket. Tighten filter screen bolts to 14 ft. lbs. (19 N.m). Install fluid pan using NEW gasket. Tighten fluid pan bolts to 10 ft. lbs. (14 N.m). Install drive shaft, and tighten drive shaft flange bolts to 37 ft. lbs. (51 N.m). Fill transmission with 1.6 qts. (1.5L) of Dexron-IIE, and check fluid level.
Tracker (Transfer Case) – 1) Raise and support vehicle. Remove drain plug from back of transfer case, below speedometer gear housing, and drain fluid. Install drain plug. Tighten it to 21 ft. lbs. (28 N.m).
2) Remove transfer case fill plug (upper plug) from rear of transfer case. Fill plug is located near speedometer gear housing.
3) Fill transfer case with SAE 75W-90 or 80W-90 gear oil with GL-4 rating until fluid level is at bottom of fill plug hole. Install fill plug, and tighten it to 21 ft. lbs. (28 N.m).

ADJUSTMENTS
BAND

Low Band Servo (Tracker) – 1) Raise and support vehicle. Remove transmission fluid pan. Remove filter screen. Remove Torque Converter Clutch (TCC) pipes from valve body. Disconnect wires from TCC solenoid and fluid pressure switch.
2) Remove 6 bolts securing reinforcement plate and remove reinforcement plate. Remove 4 bolts and low band piston servo cover.
3) Hold servo piston with open-end wrench. See Fig. 3. Loosen lock nut on adjusting sleeve. Using a torque wrench with a 5 mm Allen head socket, tighten servo piston adjusting screw to 18 ft. lbs. (24 N.m.).
4) Back off servo piston adjusting screw exactly 5 turns. Tighten lock nut to 14 ft. lbs. (19 N.m.). Ensure adjusting screw does not turn while tightening lock nut.
5) Replace servo piston cover gasket. Install servo piston cover and tighten to 18 ft. lbs. (25 N.m.). Install reinforcement plate and tighten to 14 ft. lbs. (19 N.m.). To complete installation reverse removal procedure. Tighten bolts to specification see TORQUE SPECIFICATIONS.

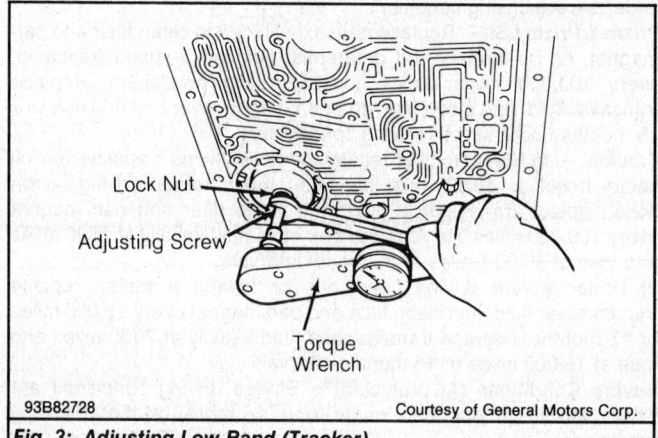

Lock Nut

Adjusting Screw

Torque Wrench

93B82728   Courtesy of General Motors Corp.

Fig. 3: Adjusting Low Band (Tracker)

INTERLOCK CABLE

NOTE: Interlock system will not allow gearshift to move from Park unless ignition is turned on. It also prevents ignition key removal unless gearshift is in Park.

Metro & Tracker – 1) Remove center console cover and manual selector cover. Place gearshift in Park. Loosen interlock cable bolt. Rotate key release plate and insert a small screwdriver into hole in lower key release plate. Retaining spring will move interlock cable bracket into position. Tighten interlock cable bolt to 115 INCH lbs. (13 N.m). See Fig. 4.

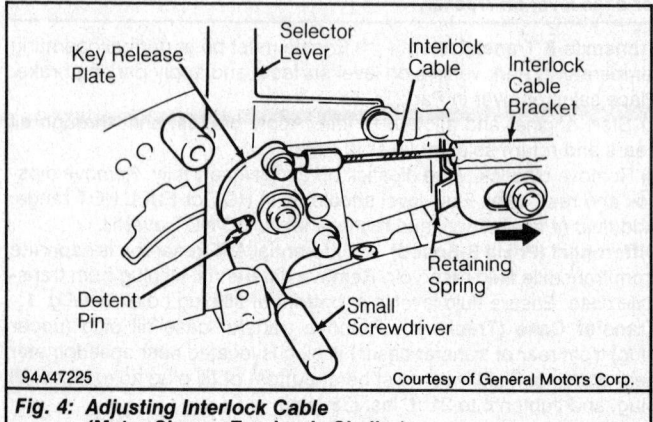

Key Release Plate

Selector Lever

Interlock Cable

Interlock Cable Bracket

Detent Pin

Small Screwdriver

Retaining Spring

94A47225   Courtesy of General Motors Corp.

**Fig. 4: Adjusting Interlock Cable
(Metro Shown; Tracker Is Similar)**

2) Ensure ignition switch operates from ACC to LOCK position and ignition key can be removed when gearshift is in Park. Move transaxle gearshift lever to any other position. Ensure ignition switch cannot be turned from ACC to LOCK position. If ignition switch will turn, readjust interlock cable.

SHIFT LOCK SOLENOID

NOTE: Shift lock solenoid prevents gear selector lever from being moved from Park unless brake pedal is applied.

Metro – 1) Remove center console. Solenoid should be adjusted so that when ignition switch is in OFF position, solenoid is NOT operating (lock position). With ignition is in ON position and brake pedal depressed, solenoid is operating (unlock position). Ensure lock plate detent pin is in correct position. *See Fig. 5.*
2) If operation is not as specified loosen solenoid mounting screws and reposition solenoid. With ignition off, gearshift should not shift from Park. If manual override is enabled with ignition off, gearshift should move from Park to other gear positions.
Prizm & Tracker – Shift lock solenoid requires no adjustment. For diagnostic procedures, see appropriate MITCHELL® TRANSMISSION SERVICE & REPAIR manual.

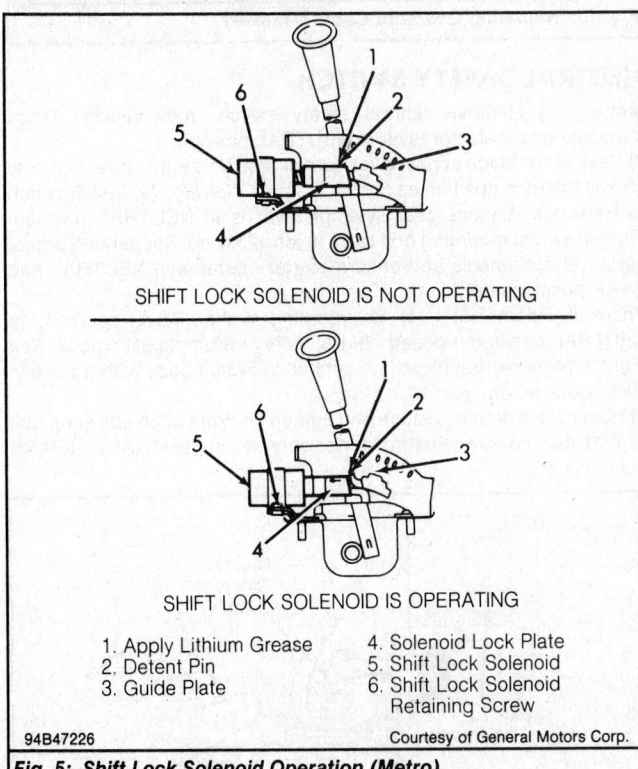

SHIFT LOCK SOLENOID IS NOT OPERATING

SHIFT LOCK SOLENOID IS OPERATING

1. Apply Lithium Grease
2. Detent Pin
3. Guide Plate
4. Solenoid Lock Plate
5. Shift Lock Solenoid
6. Shift Lock Solenoid Retaining Screw

94B47226   Courtesy of General Motors Corp.

Fig. 5: Shift Lock Solenoid Operation (Metro)

THROTTLE VALVE CABLE

Metro – 1) Ensure accelerator cable is adjusted. Accelerator cable should have .39-.59" (10-15 mm) end play at throttle body with accelerator at idle position and engine off.
2) Warm engine to normal operating temperature. Ensure base idle speed (hot) is to specification. Turn engine off. Remove Throttle Valve (TV) cable cover. Check boot-to-inner cable stopper clearance. *See Fig. 6.*
3) If clearance is greater than .02" (.5 mm), loosen lower adjustment lock nuts and adjust cable length. If lower adjustment lock nuts do not provide enough adjustment, use upper adjustment lock nuts to change cable length. *See Fig. 6.* Tighten all lock nuts.

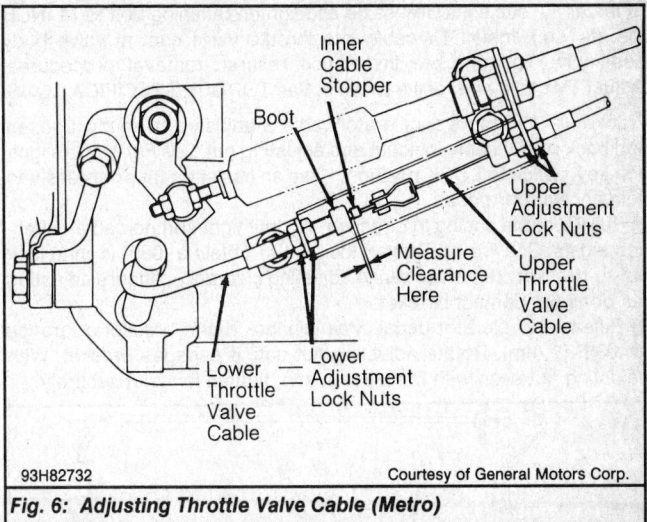

93H82732   Courtesy of General Motors Corp.

Fig. 6: Adjusting Throttle Valve Cable (Metro)

Prizm & Prizm LSi – Ensure throttle valve is fully closed on 4-speed transaxle and wide open throttle on 3-speed transaxle. Adjust Throttle Valve (TV) cable housing so distance between end of outer cable boot and cable stopper is 0-0.04" (0-1.0 mm). *See Fig. 7.* Tighten TV cable adjusting and lock nuts to 71 INCH lbs. (8 N.m).

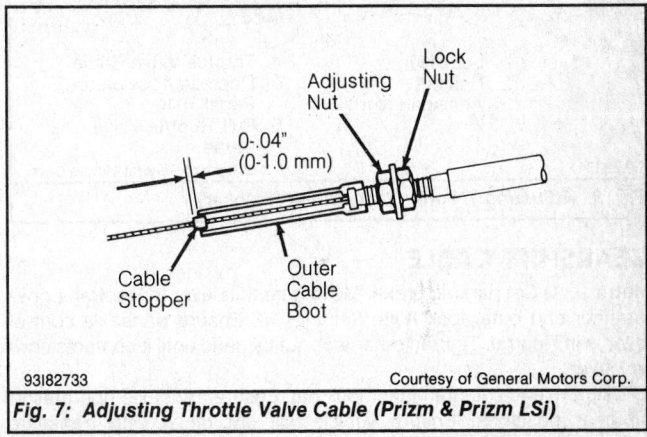

93I82733   Courtesy of General Motors Corp.

Fig. 7: Adjusting Throttle Valve Cable (Prizm & Prizm LSi)

NOTE: On Prizm & Prizm LSi, use following procedure if installing new throttle valve cable.

Prizm & Prizm LSi (Cable Replacement) – 1) Disconnect negative battery cable. Loosen Throttle Valve (TV) cable adjusting and lock nuts. Remove TV cable from throttle valve linkage and TV cable bracket. Remove left splash shield. Remove neutral safety switch. Drain transaxle fluid and remove fluid pan. Remove TV cable from throttle valve cam at valve body assembly. Remove TV cable from transaxle. If installing a new TV cable, go to next step. If installing old TV cable, go to step **3)**.
2) If installing a new TV cable, stake a NEW stopper in position. Bend cable so it has about a 7.870 (200.00 mm) radius. *See Fig. 8.* Pull on inner cable until a slight resistance is felt. Stake TV cable stopper .031-.059" (0.78-1.50 mm) from end of TV cable. To complete TV cable installation, go to next step.

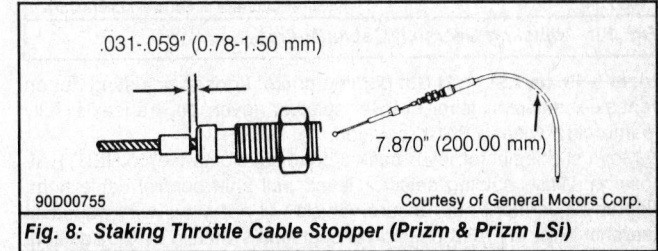

.031-.059" (0.78-1.50 mm)

7.870" (200.00 mm)

90D00755   Courtesy of General Motors Corp.

Fig. 8: Staking Throttle Cable Stopper (Prizm & Prizm LSi)

3) Install TV cable into transaxle and tighten retaining bolt to 71 INCH lbs. (8 N.m). Install TV cable into throttle valve cam at valve body assembly. To complete installation reverse removal procedures. Adjust TV cable and refill transaxle. See TORQUE SPECIFICATIONS.

Tracker – 1) Ensure accelerator cable is adjusted correctly. Loosen and back off TV cable lock nut and adjusting nut. See Fig. 9. Turn ignition key switch to LOCK position. Have an assistant fully depress and hold accelerator pedal.

2) Pull TV cable casing in direction "A" until tight and no cable deflection exists. See Fig. 9. Tighten lock nut to obtain a .039" (1 mm) lock nut-to-bracket clearance. When adjusting clearance, ensure adjusting nut does not contact bracket.

3) Release accelerator pedal. Maintain lock nut-to-bracket clearance at .039" (1 mm). Rotate adjusting nut until it engages bracket. With adjusting nut even with bracket surface, tighten lock nut securely.

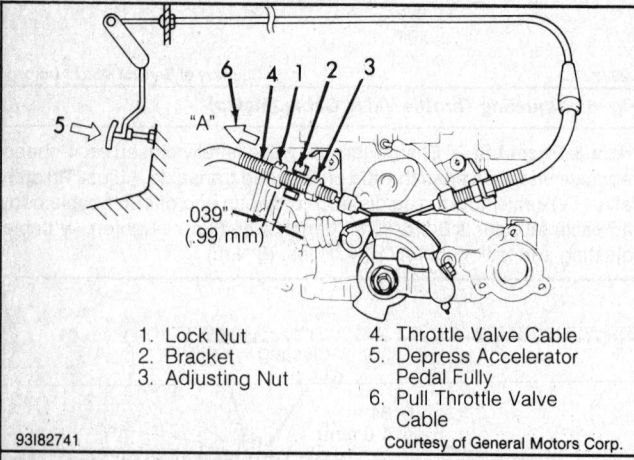

1. Lock Nut
2. Bracket
3. Adjusting Nut
4. Throttle Valve Cable
5. Depress Accelerator Pedal Fully
6. Pull Throttle Valve Cable

93182741   Courtesy of General Motors Corp.

Fig. 9: Adjusting Throttle Valve Cable (Tracker)

GEARSHIFT CABLE

Metro – 1) Set parking brake. Move gearshift lever to Neutral. Loosen inner and outer lock nuts. See Fig. 10. Ensure transaxle control lever is in Neutral. Tighten outer lock nut by hand until it contacts control lever.

2) Using wrench, tighten inner lock nut. Ensure transaxle operates in all gear positions. Ensure vehicle will not move with transaxle gearshift lever in PARK position and ignition switch in LOCK position.

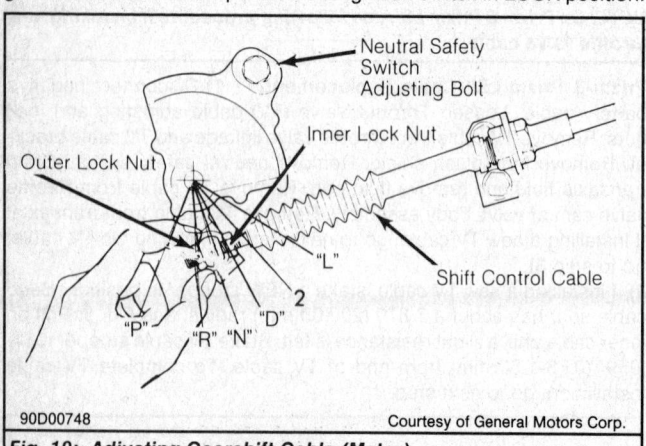

90D00748   Courtesy of General Motors Corp.

Fig. 10: Adjusting Gearshift Cable (Metro)

Prizm & Prizm LSi – 1) Set parking brake. Loosen adjusting nut on transaxle selector lever. Move selector lever on transaxle fully counterclockwise to PARK position.

2) Move shift selector lever back 2 notches (clockwise) to NEUTRAL position. While holding selector lever, pull shift control cable tight. Tighten adjustment nut. Ensure vehicle will not move with transaxle gearshift lever in PARK position and ignition switch in LOCK position. Ensure correct operation in other gearshift positions.

Tracker – 1) Remove center console covers. Place gearshift in Neutral. Loosen adjusting nut and lock nut. See Fig. 11.

2) Ensure shift lever on transmission is in Neutral position. Pull shift control cable tight.

3) Tighten adjusting nut and then lock nut. Ensure gearshift operates properly in all gear ranges. Install console covers.

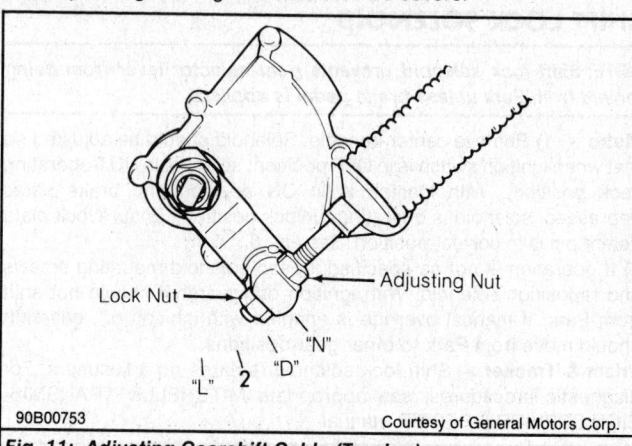

90B00753   Courtesy of General Motors Corp.

Fig. 11: Adjusting Gearshift Cable (Tracker)

NEUTRAL SAFETY SWITCH

Metro – 1) Remove neutral safety switch from vehicle. Place transaxle gear selector lever in NEUTRAL position.

2) Using a flat blade screwdriver, turn slotted hole either direction until click is heard in position as shown in figure. See Fig. 12. Install switch to transaxle. Ensure gear selector lever is in NEUTRAL position. Tighten switch mounting bolt to 17 ft. lbs. (23 N.m). Set parking brake, block vehicle wheels and ensure starter operates in NEUTRAL and PARK positions only.

Prizm & Prizm LSi – 1) Set parking brake. Place gearshift in NEUTRAL position. Loosen neutral safety switch adjusting bolt. See Fig. 13. Align neutral basic line scribed in switch body with groove in switch sleeve. See Fig. 13.

2) Hold switch at this position and tighten neutral safety switch adjusting bolt to 17 ft. lbs. (23 N.m). Ensure starter operates in NEUTRAL and PARK positions only.

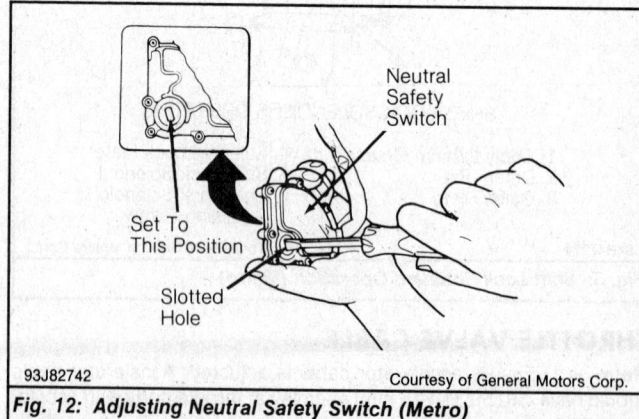

93J82742   Courtesy of General Motors Corp.

Fig. 12: Adjusting Neutral Safety Switch (Metro)

Tracker – 1) Disconnect negative battery cable. Ensure gearshift lever and transmission shift selector lever are in NEUTRAL position. Loosen neutral safety switch retaining bolt. Disconnect neutral safety switch 2 wire connector. See Fig. 14.

2) Connect a DVOM to neutral safety switch connector terminals. Rotate neutral safety switch as far clockwise (downward) as possible.

3) Slowly rotate neutral safety switch counterclockwise (upward) until a click is heard and continuity is obtained on DVOM. Tighten switch retaining bolt to 15 ft. lbs. (20 N.m). Connect neutral safety switch connector and negative battery cable.

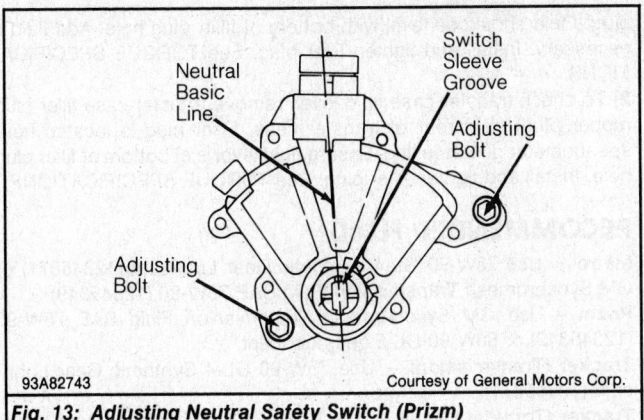

93A82743   Courtesy of General Motors Corp.

Fig. 13: Adjusting Neutral Safety Switch (Prizm)

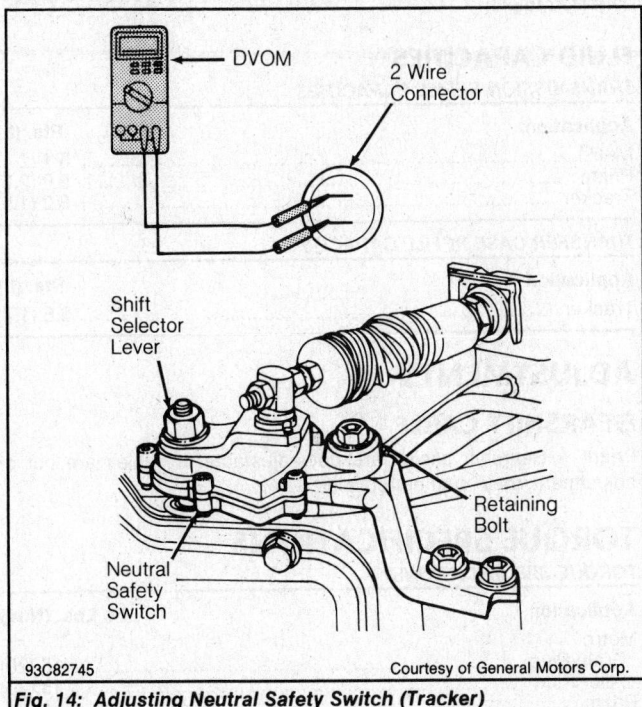

93C82745   Courtesy of General Motors Corp.

Fig. 14: Adjusting Neutral Safety Switch (Tracker)

VACUUM MODULATOR INSPECTION

Tracker – 1) Raise and support vehicle. Remove vacuum hose from modulator. Remove modulator from transmission using Modulator Wrench (J-23100).

2) Inspect modulator for fluid leakage. Replace vacuum modulator if any transmission fluid drains from modulator. With diaphragm rod in place, test for vacuum leakage by attaching vacuum pump to fitting on vacuum modulator. Apply 20 in. Hg of vacuum to modulator. If vacuum gauge on pump indicates a vacuum loss, replace vacuum modulator. Inspect vacuum modulator "O" ring for cuts and other damage. To install components, reverse removal procedure.

TORQUE SPECIFICATIONS

TORQUE SPECIFICATIONS

Application	Ft. Lbs. (N.m)
Metro	
Drain Plug	17 (23)
Fluid Pan	17 (23)
Neutral Switch	17 (23)
Prizm	
Differential Drain/Fill Plugs	29 (39)
Filter Screen	[1]
Fluid Pan	[2]
Neutral Switch	[3]
Transaxle Drain Plug	29 (39)
Prizm LSi	
Drain Plug	13 (17)
Fluid Pan	[2]
Neutral Switch	[2]
Tracker	
Filter Screen Bolt	14 (19)
Fluid Pan	10 (13)
Reinforcement Plate	14 (19)
Servo Piston Cover	18 (25)
Transfer Case Drain/Fill Plugs	21 (28)

[1] – Tighten to 89 INCH Lbs. (10 N.m)
[2] – Tighten to 44 INCH Lbs. (5 N.m).
[3] – Tighten to 70 INCH Lbs. (8 N.m).

1994 TRANSMISSION SERVICING
Manual Transmission

Metro, Prizm, Tracker

IDENTIFICATION
MANUAL TRANSMISSION APPLICATIONS

Model	Transaxle/Transmission
Metro	5-Speed Suzuki Transaxle
Prizm	5-Speed Toyota Transaxle
Tracker	5-Speed Suzuki Transmission

LUBRICATION

SERVICE INTERVALS

Metro – Replace transmission fluid every 30,000 miles under normal conditions. Under severe conditions, replace transmission fluid every 12,000 miles.

Prizm – Check fluid and add as required during normal periodic maintenance. Under severe conditions, replace transmission fluid every 15,000 miles.

Tracker – Replace transmission and transfer case fluid initially at 7500 miles and then every 30,000 miles or 30 months under normal driving conditions. Under severe driving conditions, replace transfer case and transmission fluid initially at 7500 miles and then every 15,000 miles or 15 months.

Severe Conditions (All Vehicles) – Severe driving conditions are when vehicle is operated under one or more of the following conditions:

- Most driving is in stop-and-go traffic when outside temperatures are greater than 89° F (32° C)
- Delivery service, Taxi or Police vehicles
- Trailer towing
- In hilly or mountainous terrain
- Most trips are less than 4 miles
- Most trips are less than 10 miles, and outside temperatures remain below freezing
- Driving in dusty areas.

CHECKING FLUID LEVEL

Metro & Prizm – Park vehicle on level surface. Remove filler plug on side of transaxle case. Fluid level should be level with bottom of filler plug hole. Add fluid if necessary. Install and tighten filler plug. See TORQUE SPECIFICATIONS.

NOTE: On Metro, if transaxle fluid is changed, clean drain plug and apply Sealant (1052080) to plug threads. Tighten drain plug to 15 ft. lbs. (20 N.m).

Tracker (Transmission & Transfer Case) – **1)** Transmission and transfer case have separate drain and filler plugs. Park vehicle on level surface. To check transmission fluid level, remove transmission filler plug. Fluid should be level with bottom of filler plug hole. Add fluid if necessary. Install and tighten filler plug. See TORQUE SPECIFICATIONS.

2) To check transfer case fluid level, remove transfer case filler plug (upper plug) from rear of transfer case. Filler plug is located near speedometer gear housing. Ensure fluid level is at bottom of filler plug hole. Install and tighten filler plug. See TORQUE SPECIFICATIONS.

RECOMMENDED FLUID

Metro – Use 75W-90 GL-4 Synthetic Gear Lubricant (12345871) or GM Synchromesh Transmission Fluid SAE 75W-90 (12345349).
Prizm – Use GM Synchromesh Transmission Fluid SAE 75W-90 (12345349) or 80W-90 GL-5 gear lubricant.
Tracker (Transmission) – Use 75W-90 GL-4 Synthetic Gear Lubricant (12345871).
Tracker (Transfer Case) – Use 75W-90 GL-4 Synthetic Gear Lubricant (12345871).

FLUID CAPACITIES
TRANSMISSION REFILL CAPACITIES

Application	Pts. (L)
Metro	5.1 (2.4)
Prizm	5.6 (2.7)
Tracker	3.2 (1.5)

TRANSFER CASE REFILL CAPACITY

Application	Pts. (L)
Tracker	3.6 (1.7)

ADJUSTMENTS

GEARSHIFT CABLE

Prizm – Gearshift cables are not adjustable. If cables are out of adjustment, they must be replaced.

TORQUE SPECIFICATIONS
TORQUE SPECIFICATIONS

Application	Ft. Lbs. (N.m)
Metro	
Drain Plug	15 (20)
Filler Plug	15 (20)
Prizm	
Drain Plug	1
Filler Plug	1
Tracker	
Drain Plug	21 (28)
Filler Plug	21 (28)

1 – Tighten to 97 INCH Lbs. (11 N.m).

Metro, Prizm, Tracker

MANUAL

NOTE: For manual transmission/transaxle removal and installation procedures, see appropriate CLUTCHES article.

AUTOMATIC

METRO

Removal – 1) Disconnect negative battery cable. Remove Throttle Valve (TV) cable located on top of transaxle. Remove shift select cable from bracket on top of transaxle. Remove accelerator cable from bracket on top of transaxle. Remove engine harness bracket from rear of transaxle case. Disconnect Vehicle Speed Sensor (VSS), Shift solenoid and Park/Neutral Position (PNP) switch connectors. Disconnect speedometer cable.

2) Disconnect and plug oil cooler lines from transaxle. Disconnect ground cable at transaxle. Remove starter motor. Disconnect rear transaxle mount. Remove 2 upper transaxle-to-engine bolts. Using Universal Support Fixture (J-28467-A) and Support adapters (J-28467-89), support engine. Raise and support vehicle. Drain transaxle fluid. Remove 10 splash shield retaining clips and splash shields.

CAUTION: Overextending inner CV joint may result in separation of internal components and possible joint failure.

3) Separate ball joints from steering knuckles. Install Drive Axle Boot Protectors (J-28712) to drive axles. Remove front wheels. Unstake axle shaft nuts and remove nuts and washers. Using 2 large screwdrivers, pry axle shafts from transaxle case and remove differential side gear snap ring. Remove inner CV joint from transaxle case and then outer CV joint from steering knuckle.

4) Remove 3 bolts and rear engine torque rod from transaxle case. Remove lower cover from torque converter housing. Hold flexplate by engaging a screwdriver into ring gear through notch provided at underside of transaxle case. Remove 6 flexplate-to-torque converter bolts.

5) Remove muffler mounting from rear engine mount bracket exhaust hanger. Remove rear engine mount. Lower vehicle and using engine support, lower engine slightly. Raise vehicle and support transaxle. Support transaxle with a jack. Disconnect transaxle mounts. Remove one lower transaxle-to-engine bolt. Remove transaxle assembly.

Installation – 1) To install transaxle, apply grease around pilot cup at center of torque converter and reverse removal procedure.

2) Ensure torque converter is correctly installed. Distance from top of torque converter flange nuts to engine mating surface of transaxle housing should be at least .85" (21.4 mm).

3) Tighten all fasteners to specification. See TORQUE SPECIFICATIONS. Adjust all control cables. Fill and check fluid levels.

PRIZM

Removal – 1) Disconnect battery cables. Remove battery and tray. Disconnect Intake Air Temperature (IAT) sensor connector. Remove air cleaner assembly. Disconnect Park/Neutral Position (PNP) switch and solenoid wire harness connectors. Disconnect ground cable at transaxle.

2) Disconnect Throttle Valve (TV) cable at throttle body. Disconnect shift select cable from shift lever and transaxle. Disconnect TV cable guide bracket from transaxle case. Disconnect Vehicle Speed Sensor (VSS) connector from transaxle.

3) Remove 2 upper transaxle-to-engine bolts. Remove upper starter motor retaining bolt. Install Universal Support Fixture (J-28467-A). Remove left side brace connecting upper part of transaxle to transaxle mount.

4) Raise and support vehicle. Drain transaxle fluid. On 3-speed transaxle, remove drain plug from under differential cover and drain differential fluid. On all models, remove lower starter retaining bolt and

remove starter motor. Disconnect and plug oil cooler lines from transaxle. Remove 12 splash shields bolts and remove splash shields. Remove wheels.

CAUTION: Overextending inner CV joint may result in separation of internal components and possible joint failure. On models equipped with ABS brakes use care not to damage ABS speed sensor ring on outer CV joint.

5) Remove ABS sensor from steering knuckle (if equipped). Remove axle shaft nuts from both axle shafts. Remove tie rod nuts from steering knuckles. Separate tie rods from steering knuckles. Remove one bolt and 2 nuts from lower ball joint at lower control arm. Separate both lower control arms from ball joint and steering knuckles. Remove outer CV joint from steering knuckle. Gently pry inner CV joint from differential housing and remove axle shaft.

6) Remove exhaust pipe hanger-to-center crossmember bolts and remove exhaust pipe hanger. Disconnect exhaust pipe from 3-way catalyst and exhaust manifold flange. Remove front exhaust pipe.

7) Remove plastic access cover from center crossmember. Remove 2 bolts from front transaxle mount and 3 nuts from rear transaxle mount. Supporting center crossmember with jack, remove 2 bolts from center crossmember and 10 bolts front crossmember and remove crossmembers. On 3-speed transaxle, remove 4 bolts and remove lower engine-to-transaxle brace.

8) Support transaxle with jack. Remove flexplate access cover from engine rear end plate. Remove 6 flexplate-to-torque converter bolts. Remove remaining transaxle-to-engine bolts. It may be necessary to lower engine slightly so transaxle can clear body.

Installation – 1) To install, reverse removal procedure. Before installing, apply grease around pilot at center of torque converter.

2) Ensure torque converter is correctly installed. Distance from torque converter drive lugs to engine mating surface of transaxle housing should be greater than .91" (23 mm).

3) Tighten all fasteners to specification. See TORQUE SPECIFICATIONS. Adjust all control cables. Fill and check fluid levels.

CAUTION: Differential portion of 3-speed transaxle is separated from the rest of the transaxle and must be drained and refilled through separate drain and refill holes. Refill differential with approximately 3 pts (1.4 L) of Dexron-IIE automatic transmission fluid. Ensure fluid level is even with bottom of differential filler plug hold.

TRACKER

Removal – 1) On 4-wheel drive models, remove transfer case shift lever knob. Remove console box. Remove shift lever boot and bracket. Remove transfer case shift lever retaining plate. Remove shift lever.

2) On all models, disconnect negative battery cable. Remove transmission dip stick. Remove vacuum modulator hose at intake manifold. Disconnect Park/Neutral Position (PNP) switch under intake manifold. Remove starter.

3) Remove 2 upper engine-to-transmission retaining bolts. Remove 4 fan shroud bolts at radiator. Raise and support vehicle. On 4-wheel drive models, remove transfer case skid plate. Put match marks on front drive shaft and flange yoke. Remove front drive shaft. On 4-wheel drive models, drain transfer case.

4) On all models, loosen transmission fluid pan bolts and drain transmission. Clean fluid pan and fluid pan magnet. Clean or replace filter screen and needed. Install filter screen and tighten retaining bolts to 14 ft. lbs. (19 N.m). Using a NEW fluid pan gasket, install fluid pan and tighten bolts to 115 INCH lbs. (13 N.m). Put match marks on rear drive shaft and flange yoke. Remove rear drive shaft. Support transmission with a jack.

5) On 4WD models, remove speedometer cable from transfer case. Remove speedometer cable clip and ground wire from torque stopper housing. Remove transfer adapter case and catalytic converter. Support transfer case with a jack.

6) Remove 2 bolts from torque stopper bracket and transfer case crossmember. Put a wood block 1.8" x 5" x 8" between distributor gear housing and bulkhead. Wood block is to protect distributor and other components when transfer case is lowered. Slowly lower transfer case until engine support point contacts wood block. Remove breather hose from gearshift lever case and remove transfer case.

7) On 2WD models, remove 2 rear transmission mount bolts and rear transmission crossmember. Disconnect speedometer cable. On all models, remove select cable and filler tube from transmission. Disconnect Throttle Valve (TV) cable from transmission. Disconnect and plug oil cooler lines from transmission.

8) Remove flywheel inspection cover from converter housing. Remove 3 torque converter-to-flywheel bolts. On 2WD models, 2 bolts, 2 nuts and exhaust pipe bracket from extension housing. Put a wood block 1.8" x 5" x 8" between distributor gear housing and bulkhead. Wood block is to protect distributor and other components when transfer case is lowered. Slowly lower transmission until engine support point contacts wood block.

9) On all models, remove vent tube at top of transmission. Remove remaining transmission-to-engine bolts and slowly lower transmission from vehicle.

Installation – To install, reverse removal procedure. Tighten all fasteners to specification. See TORQUE SPECIFICATIONS. Ensure reference marks are aligned on drive shaft flanges and yokes. Adjust all control cables. Fill and check fluid levels.

TORQUE SPECIFICATIONS
TORQUE SPECIFICATION (METRO)

Application	Ft. Lbs. (N.m)
Axle Shaft Nut	129 (175)
Ball Joint Pinch Bolt & Nut	44 (60)
Flywheel-To-Torque Converter Bolts	14 (19)
Rear Engine Torque Rod	40 (54)
Starter Mounting Bolts	17 (23)
Tie Rod End Lock Nuts	33 (45)
Torque Converter Bolt	14 (19)
Transaxle Drain Plug	17 (23)
Transaxle Mounting Bolts & Nuts	40 (54)
Wheel Lug Nuts	44 (60)

TORQUE SPECIFICATIONS (PRIZM)

Application	Ft. Lbs. (N.m)
Axle Shaft Nut	159 (216)
Ball Joint-To-Lower Control Arm Bolt & Nuts	105 (142)
Center Crossmember Bolts	45 (61)
Differential Drain Plug (3-Speed)	29 (39)
Differential Filler Plug (3-Speed)	29 (39)
Exhaust Pipe Support Bolts & Nut	14 (19)
Exhaust Pipe-To-Manifold Nuts	46 (62)
Exhaust Pipe-To-Catalytic Converter	
California	46 (62)
Federal	32 (43)
Flywheel-To-Torque Converter Bolt	14 (19)
Front Crossmember-To-Body Bolts	152 (206)
Front Mount-To-Transaxle Bolt	13 (18)
Left Transaxle Mounting Bracket Bolts	35 (47)
Left Transaxle Bracket Reinforcement Bolts	15 (20)
Lower Engine Reinforcement Brace Bolt (3-Speed)	47 (64)
Lower Transaxle-To-Engine Bolts	47 (64)
Rear Transaxle Mount Bolts	42 (57)
Starter Mounting Bolts	29 (39)
Tie Rod End Nuts	40 (54)
Transaxle-To-Engine Bolt	47 (64)
Transaxle Drain Plug (3-Speed)	36 (49)
Transaxle Drain Plug (4-Speed)	13 (18)
Upper Transaxle Mount Bracket Bolt	45 (61)
Upper Transaxle Mount Through Bolt	64 (87)
Wheel Lug Nuts	76 (103)

Application	INCH Lbs. (N.m)
Air Cleaner Bolts	44 (5)
ABS Speed Sensor Bolt	71 (8)
Ground Cable-To-Transaxle Case	115 (13)
Shift Select Cable Nut	115 (13)
Splash Shield Bolts	44 (5)
TV Cable Guide Bracket Bolt	71 (8)

TORQUE SPECIFICATION (TRACKER)

Application	Ft. Lbs. (N.m)
Crossmember Bolt	63 (85)
Drive Shaft Flange Bolts	37 (50)
Exhaust Pipe Bracket (2WD)	17 (23)
Exhaust Pipe Bracket (4WD)	44 (60)
Exhaust-To-Catalytic Converter	37 (50)
Filler Tube Bracket Bolt	17 (23)
Flywheel-To-Torque Converter Bolts	40 (54)
Front Locking Hub Bolt	18 (24)
Front Wheel Bearing Nut	155 (210)
Locking Hub Cover Bolts	18 (24)
Rear Transmission Crossmember-To-Body (2WD)	45 (61)
Rear Transmission Mounting Bolts (2WD)	43 (58)
Reinforcement Plate Bolts	14 (19)
Skid Plate Bolts	40 (54)
Starter Mounting Bolts	22 (30)
Torque Mount Bracket Bolts (4WD)	37 (50)
Transfer Adapter Case Bolts	23 (31)
Transfer Case Filler/Drain Plugs (4WD)	21 (28)
Transfer Case Mounting Bolts	37 (50)
Transfer Case-To-Transmission Bolts	21 (28)
Transmission-To-Engine Bolts	62 (84)
Wheel Lug Nuts	70 (95)

Application	INCH Lbs. (N.m)
Fan Shroud Bolts	89 (10)
Flywheel Inspection Cover	89 (10)
Speedometer Guide Bracket Bolt (2WD)	80 (9)
Speedometer Case Retaining Bolt (4WD)	89 (10)
Speedometer Cable Clip Bolt (4WD)	89 (10)
Transmission Fluid Pan	115 (13)

ENGINE PERFORMANCE

NOTE: For Passport information, see Rodeo in ISUZU section.

ELECTRICAL

NOTE: For Passport information, see Rodeo in ISUZU section.

WIRING DIAGRAMS

ACCESSORIES & EQUIPMENT

CRUISE CONTROL SYSTEMS

NOTE: For Passport information, see Rodeo in ISUZU section.

1994 MODEL COVERAGE

MODEL	BODY/ENGINE [1]	ENGINE [2]	FUEL SYSTEM	IGNITION SYSTEM [3]
Accord	CD5, CD7, CE1	2.2L 4-Cyl. (F22B1) [4]	MFI	Magnetic
	CD5, CD7, CE1	2.2L 4-Cyl. (F22B2)	MFI	Magnetic
Civic	EG8, EH2, EJ2	1.5L 4-Cyl. (D15B7)	MFI	Magnetic
	EH2	1.5L 4-Cyl. (D15B8)	MFI	Magnetic
	EH2	1.5L 4-Cyl. (D15Z1) [4]	MFI	Magnetic
	EG9, EH2, EJ1	1.6L 4-Cyl. (D16Z6) [4]	MFI	Magnetic
Civic Del Sol	EG1	1.5L 4-Cyl. (D15B7)	MFI	Magnetic
	EG2	1.6L 4-Cyl. (D16A3) [4]	MFI	Magnetic
	EH6	1.6L 4-Cyl. (D16Z6) [4]	MFI	Magnetic
Passport	G (2WD)/E	2.6L 4-Cyl. (4ZE1)	MFI	Optical
	G (2WD)/V	3.2L V6 (6VD1)	MFI	DIS
	Y (4WD)/V	3.2L V6 (6VD1)	MFI	DIS
Prelude	BA8	2.2L 4-Cyl. (F22A1) [5]	MFI	Magnetic
	BB1	2.2L 4-Cyl. (H22A1) [4] [6] [7]	MFI	Magnetic
	BB2	2.3L 4-Cyl. (H23A1) [6] [7]	MFI	Magnetic

[1] – On all models except Passport, Body/Engine ID is the fourth, fifth and sixth digits of VIN. On Passport, Body/Engine ID is the fifth, sixth, seventh and eighth digits of VIN.
[2] – Engine code is the first 5 characters of the 12 characters stamped or tagged on engine block.
[3] – Ignition timing is controlled by Engine Control Module (ECM).
[4] – Variable Valve Timing with Electronic Control (VTEC).
[5] – With single intake and exhaust manifolds.
[6] – With dual intake and exhaust manifolds.
[7] – Dual Overhead Camshafts (DOHC).

VIN DEFINITION

JHMCB766*RC000001

① ② ③ ④ ⑤ ⑥ ⑦ ⑧ ⑨ ⑩ ⑪ ⑫ ⑬ ⑭ ⑮ ⑯ ⑰

① Indicates Nation of Origin.
② Indicates Manufacturer.
③ Indicates Vehicle Type.
④⑤⑥ **Indicates Body/Engine Type.**
⑦ Indicates Body and Transmission Type.
⑧ Indicates Vehicle Grade.
⑨ Indicates Check Digit (0-9 or X).
⑩ **Indicates Model Year.**
⑪ Indicates Assembly Plant.
⑫⑬⑭⑮⑯⑰ Indicates Plant Sequential Number.

MODEL YEAR VIN CODE APPLICATION

VIN Code	Model Year
N	1992
P	1993
R	1994

ENGINE CODE LOCATION

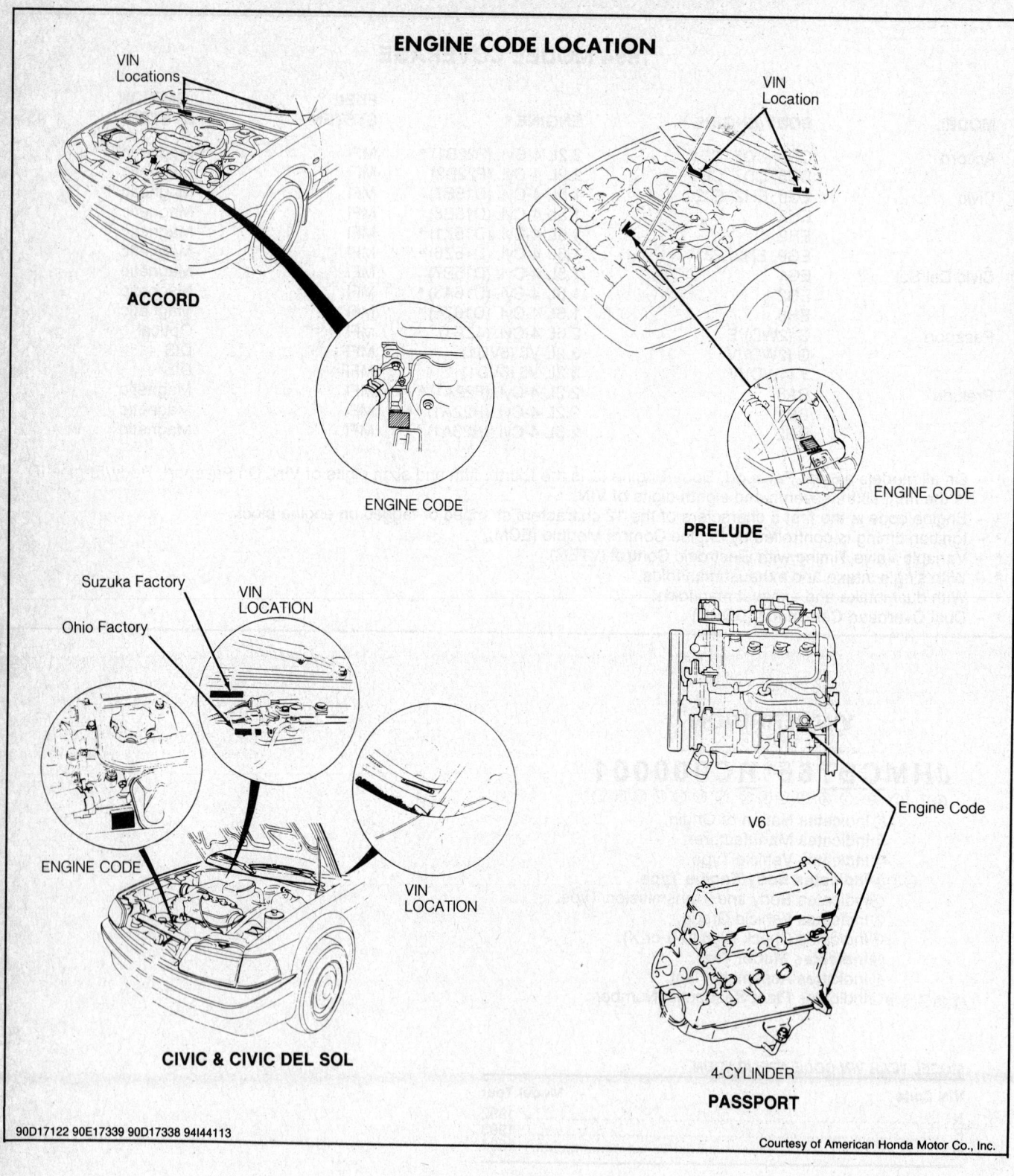

VIN
Locations

ACCORD

ENGINE CODE

VIN
Location

ENGINE CODE

PRELUDE

Suzuka Factory

Ohio Factory

VIN
LOCATION

ENGINE CODE

CIVIC & CIVIC DEL SOL

VIN
LOCATION

V6

Engine Code

4-CYLINDER
PASSPORT

1994 HONDA

Model, Engine & Fuel System	Emission Control Systems & Devices
Accord	
2.2L 4-Cyl. MFI	**PCV, EVAP, TWC, EGR, SPK, HO2S, CEC, MIL,** EVAP-CPCS, EVAP-CPCV, EVAP-VC, EGR-CVCV, EGR-PS, EGR-SOL, SPK-CC
Civic	
1.5L 4-Cyl. MFI	**PCV, EVAP, TWC, [1] EGR, SPK, HO2S, [2] O2S, CEC, MIL,** EVAP-CPCS, EVAP-CPCV, EVAP-VC, [1] EGR-CVCV, [1] EGR-SOL, SPK-CC
1.6L 4-Cyl. MFI	**PCV, EVAP, TWC, SPK, HO2S, CEC, MIL,** EVAP-CPCS, EVAP-CPCV, EVAP-VC, SPK-CC
Civic Del Sol	
1.5L & 1.6L 4-Cyl. MFI	**PCV, EVAP, TWC, SPK, HO2S, CEC, MIL,** EVAP-CPCS, EVAP-CPCV, EVAP-VC, SPK-CC
Passport	
2.6L 4-Cyl. MFI	**PCV, EVAP, TWC, FR, [3] EGR, [4] BP/EGR, SPK, AP, HO2S, CEC, MIL,** EVAP-CKV, EVAP-CPCV, EVAP-VC, EVAP-VSV, [3] EGR-DSOL, [3] EGR-VRV, [3] EGR-CSOL, BP/EGR-TVV, [4] BP/EGR-BPT, [3] BP/EGR-VSV, SPK-CC, AP-AMV
3.2L V6 MFI	**PCV, EVAP, TWC, FR, BP/EGR, SPK, HO2S, CEC, MIL,** EVAP-CPCS, EVAP-VC, EVAC-VSV, BP/EGR-BPT, BP/EGR-VSV, SPK-CC
Prelude	
2.2L & 2.3L 4-Cyl. MFI	**PCV, EVAP, TWC, EGR, SPK, HO2S, CEC, MIL,** EVAP-CPCS, EVAP-CPCV, EVAP-VC, EGR-CVCV, EGR-PS, EGR-SOL, SPK-CC

[1] – Engine model D15Z1 only.
[2] – Non-heated O2S sensor on Federal engine model D15B8.
[3] – Calif. only.
[4] – Federal only.

NOTE: For quick reference, major emission control systems and devices are listed in bold type; components and other related devices are listed in light type.

AP – Air Pump
AP-AMV – AP Air Management Valve
BP/EGR – Backpressure EGR System
BP/EGR-BPT – BP/EGR Backpressure Transducer
BP/EGR-TVV – BP/EGR Thermal Vacuum Valve
BP/EGR-VSV – BP/EGR Vacuum Switching Valve
CEC – Computerized Engine Controls
EGR – Exhaust Gas Recirculation
EGR-CSOL – EGR Cut-Off Solenoid
EGR-CVCV – EGR Constant Vacuum Control Valve
EGR-DSOL – EGR Duty Solenoid
EGR-PS – EGR Position Sensor
EGR-SOL – EGR Solenoid
EGR-VRV – EGR Vacuum Regulator Valve

EVAP – Fuel Evaporative System
EVAP-CKV – EVAP Check Valve
EVAP-CPCS – EVAP Canister Purge Control Solenoid
EVAP-CPCV – EVAP Canister Purge Control Valve
EVAP-VC – EVAP Vapor Canister
EVAP-VSV – EVAP Vacuum Switching Valve
FR – Fillpipe Restrictor
HO2S – Heated Oxygen Sensor
MFI – Multipoint Electronic Fuel Injection
MIL – Malfunction Indicator Light
O2S – Oxygen Sensor
PCV – Positive Crankcase Ventilation
SPK – Spark Controls
SPK-CC – SPK Computer Controlled
TWC – Three-Way Catalyst

1994 ENGINE PERFORMANCE
Service & Adjustment Specifications

Accord, Civic, Civic Del Sol, Passport, Prelude

INTRODUCTION

Use this article to quickly find specifications related to servicing and on-vehicle adjustments. This is a quick-reference article to use when you are familiar with an adjustment procedure and only need a specification.

CAPACITIES

BATTERY SPECIFICATIONS

Application	Amp Hr. Rating
Accord & Civic	52
Civic Del Sol	36
Passport	60
Prelude	55

FLUID CAPACITIES

Application	Quantity
Crankcase (Includes Filter)	
Accord	4.0 Qts. (3.8L)
Civic & Civic Del Sol	
Except B16A3 Engine	3.5 Qts. (3.3L)
B16A3 Engine	4.2 Qts. (4.0L)
Passport	
2.6L	4.4 Qts. (4.2L)
3.2L	5.7 Qts. (5.4L)
Prelude	
2.2L Engine (F22A1)	4.0 Qts. (3.8L)
2.2L Engine (H22A1)	5.1 Qts. (4.8L)
2.3L Engine (H23A1)	4.5 Qts. (4.3L)
Cooling System (Includes Heater)	
Accord	
Automatic Transaxle	7.2 Qts. (6.8L)
Manual Transaxle	7.3 Qts. (6.9L)
Civic & Civic Del Sol	
Automatic Transaxle	
1.5L Engine	4.6 Qts. (4.4L)
1.6L Engine	5.0 Qts. (4.7L)
Manual Transaxle	
1.5L Engine (D15B7 & D15B8)	4.8 Qts. (4.5L)
1.5L Engine (D15Z1)	4.6 Qts. (4.4L)
1.6L Engine (B16A3)	5.1 Qts. (4.8L)
1.6L Engine (D16Z6)	4.6 Qts. (4.4L)
Passport	
2.6L	9.5 Qts. (9.0L)
3.2L	
Automatic Transmission	9.3 Qts. (8.8L)
Manual Transmission	9.7 Qts. (9.2L)
Prelude	
Automatic Transaxle	
2.2L Engine (F22A1)	7.4 Qts. (7.0L)
2.3L Engine (H23A1)	7.7 Qts. (7.3L)
Manual Transaxle	
2.2L Engine (F22A1)	7.5 Qts. (7.1L)
2.2L Engine (H22A1)	8.5 Qts. (8.0L)
2.3L Engine (H23A1)	7.8 Qts. (7.4L)
Automatic Transaxle (Dexron-II)	
Accord	
Oil Change	3.4 Qts. (3.2L)
Overhaul	6.3 Qts. (6.0L)
Civic	
Oil Change	3.0 Qts. (2.8L)
Overhaul	6.2 Qts. (5.9L)
Civic Del Sol	
Oil Change	2.9 Qts. (2.7L)
Overhaul	6.2 Qts. (5.9L)
Prelude	
Oil Change	2.5 Qts. (2.4L)
Overhaul	6.3 Qts. (6.0L)

FLUID CAPACITIES (Cont.)

Application	Quantity
Manual Transaxle (SAE 30W, 10W-40 & 20W-40)	
Accord	
Oil Change	2.0 Qts. (1.9L)
Overhaul	2.1 Qts. (2.0L)
Civic & Civic Del Sol	
Except B16A3 Engine	
Oil Change	1.9 Qts. (1.8L)
Overhaul	2.0 Qts. (1.9L)
B16A3 Engine	
Oil Change	2.3 Qts. (2.2L)
Overhaul	2.4 Qts. (2.3L)
Prelude	
Oil Change	2.0 Qts. (1.9L)
Overhaul	2.1 Qts. (2.0L)
Automatic Transmission (Dexron-II)	
Passport	
Dry Refill	9.1 Qts. (8.6L)
Manual Transmission	
Passport	
2.6L	2.4 Qts. (2.2L)
3.2L	3.1 Qts. (2.9L)
Differential [1]	
Passport	
Front Axle	1.6 Qts. (1.5L)
Rear Axle	1.9 Qts. (1.8L)
Transfer Case [2]	
Passport	1.5 Qts. (1.4L)

[1] – On standard differentials, use SAE 80W-90/API GL-5 gear oil. On limited slip models, use SAE 80W-90/API GL-5 gear oil rated for limited slip axles.

[2] – Use SAE 5W-30 SF engine oil with ambient temperatures less than 90°F (32°C) or SAE 40W with temperatures greater than 90°F (32°C).

QUICK-SERVICE

SERVICE INTERVALS & SPECIFICATIONS
REPLACEMENT INTERVALS

Component	Interval (Miles)
Air Filter	30,000
Brake Fluid	30,000
Coolant	45,000
Fuel Filter	60,000
Oil & Filter	7500
Spark Plugs	30,000
Transaxle Fluid	30,000

BELT ADJUSTMENT

Application	Deflection – In. (mm)
Alternator	
Accord & Prelude [1]	13/32-15/32 (10-12)
Civic & Civic Del Sol [1]	17/64-13/32 (7-10.5)
Passport	
2.6L	13/32 (10)
3.2L	[2]
A/C Compressor	
Accord & Prelude [1]	13/32-15/32 (10-12)
Civic & Civic Del Sol [1]	3/16-9/32 (5-7)
Passport	
2.6L	13/32 (10)
3.2L	5/16 (8)
Power Steering	
Accord & Prelude [1]	33/64-5/8 (13-16)
Civic & Civic Del Sol [1]	5/16-15/32 (8-12)
Passport	
2.6L	13/32 (10)
3.2L	[2]

[1] – With 22 lbs. (10 kg) pressure applied midway on longest belt run.
[2] – Specification is not available from manufacturer.

MECHANICAL CHECKS

ENGINE COMPRESSION

Check engine compression at specified cranking speed, with engine at normal operating temperature, all spark plugs removed and throttle wide open.

ENGINE COMPRESSION

Model	Standard psi (kg/cm²)	Minimum psi (kg/cm²)	Minimum RPM
Accord & Prelude [1]	178 (12.5)	135 (9.5)	250
Civic & Civic Del Sol [1]			
Except B16A3	185 (13.0)	135 (9.5)	250
B16A3	220 (15.5)	135 (9.5)	250
Passport	170 (12.0)	128 (9.0)	250

[1] – Maximum variation between cylinders is 28 psi (2.0 kg/cm²).

VALVE CLEARANCE

VALVE CLEARANCE ADJUSTMENT SPECIFICATIONS

Model	Intake In. (mm)	Exhaust In. (mm)
Accord	.009-.011 (.23-.28)	.011-.013 (.28-.32)
Civic & Civic Del Sol		
1.5L	.007-.009 (.17-.23)	.009-.011 (.23-.28)
1.6L		
B16A3 Engine	.007-.009 (.18-.22)	.007-.010 (.23-.27)
D16Z6 Engine	.007-.009 (.17-.23)	.009-.011 (.23-.28)
Passport		
2.6L	.006 (.15)	.010 (.25)
3.2L	[1]	[1]
Prelude		
2.2L	.009-.011 (.23-.28)	.011-.013 (.28-.32)
2.3L	.003-.004 (.07-.11)	.006-.007 (.15-.19)

[1] – 3.2L engine is equipped with hydraulic lash adjusters. No adjustment is required.

IGNITION SYSTEM

IGNITION COIL

IGNITION COIL RESISTANCE – Ohms @ 68°F (20°C)

Application	Primary	Secondary
Accord & Prelude	.6-.8	14,000-22,000
Civic & Civic Del Sol	.6-.8	12,800-19,200
Passport	.8-1.0	7,500-11,300

DISTRIBUTOR SENSORS

Triggering of fuel injectors is dependent upon pulsed voltage signals generated by TDC/CKP/CYP sensors. For testing of these signals, see BASIC DIAGNOSTIC PROCEDURES article.

TDC/CKP/CYP SENSOR RESISTANCE

Application	Ohms
Accord	260-500
Civic, Civic Del Sol & Prelude	350-700
Passport	[1]

[1] – Specification is not available from manufacturer.

HIGH TENSION WIRE RESISTANCE

HIGH TENSION WIRE RESISTANCE

Application	Ohms
Except Passport	25,000 Maximum
Passport	
2.6L	22,400 Maximum
3.2L	16,000 Maximum

SPARK PLUGS

SPARK PLUG TYPE

Application	NGK
Accord	ZFR5F-11
Civic	
1.5L Engine (D15B7)	ZFR5F-11
1.5L Engine (D15B8 & D15Z1)	ZFR4F-11
1.6L Engine (D16Z6)	ZFR5J-11
Civic Del Sol	
1.5L Engine (D15B7)	ZFR5F-11
1.6L Engine (B16A3)	PFR6L-13
1.6L Engine (D16Z6)	ZFR6J-11
Passport	
2.6L Engine	BPR6ES-11
3.2L Engine	BKR5E-11
Prelude	
2.2L Engine	
F22A1	ZFR5F-11
H22A1	PZFR6F-11
2.3L Engine	ZFR6F-11

SPARK PLUG SPECIFICATIONS

Application	Gap In. (mm)	Torque Ft. Lbs. (N.m)
Except Passport	.039-.043 (1.0-1.1)	13 (18)
Passport		
2.6L	.043 (1.1)	14 (19)
3.2L	.040-.043 (1.0-1.1)	14 (19)

FIRING ORDER & TIMING MARKS

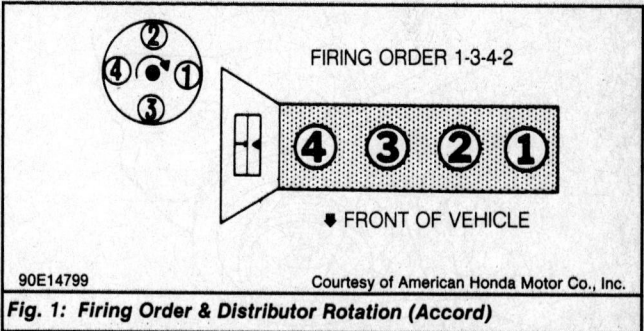

90E14799   Courtesy of American Honda Motor Co., Inc.

Fig. 1: Firing Order & Distributor Rotation (Accord)

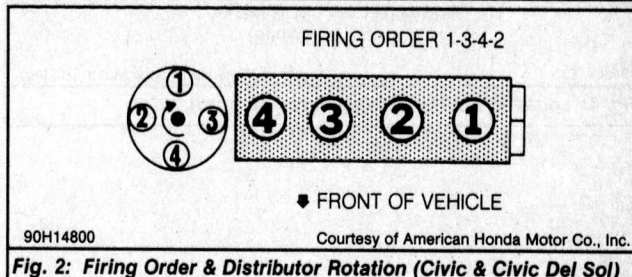

90H14800   Courtesy of American Honda Motor Co., Inc.

Fig. 2: Firing Order & Distributor Rotation (Civic & Civic Del Sol)

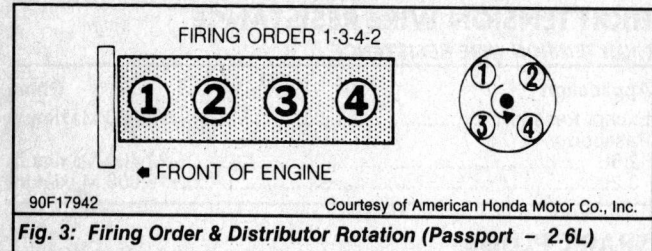

Fig. 3: Firing Order & Distributor Rotation (Passport – 2.6L)

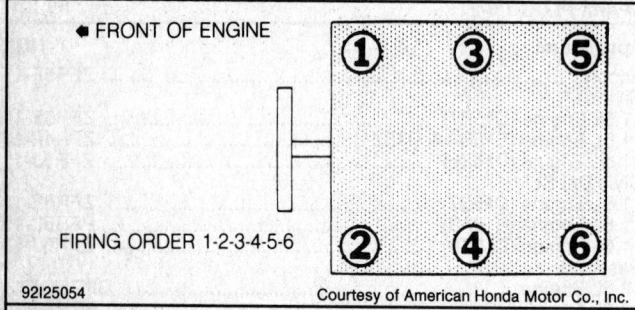

Fig. 4: Firing Order & Distributor Rotation (Passport – 3.2L)

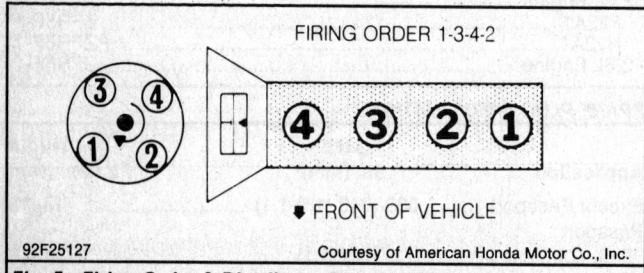

Fig. 5: Firing Order & Distributor Rotation (Prelude)

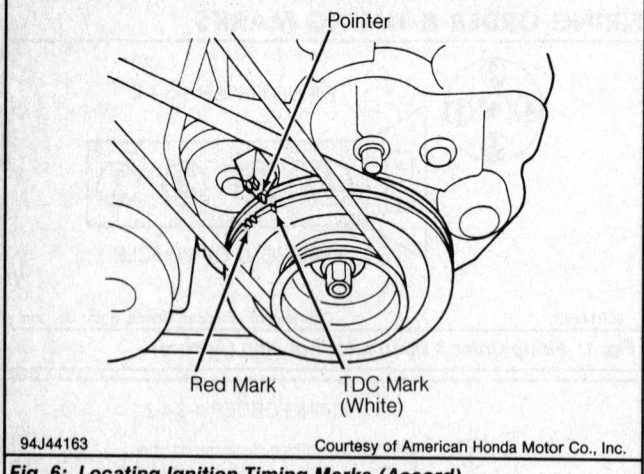

Fig. 6: Locating Ignition Timing Marks (Accord)

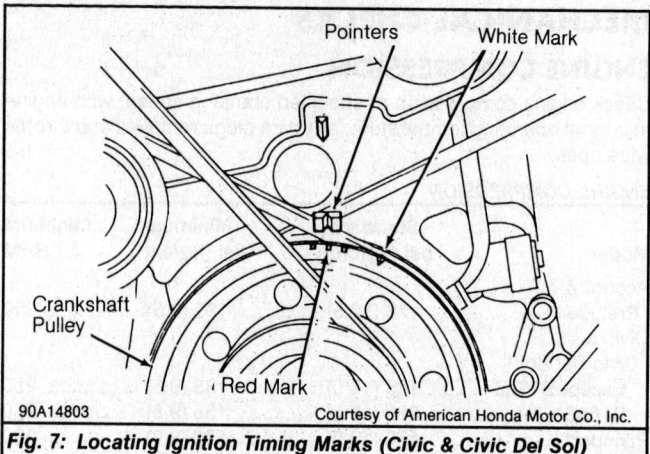

Fig. 7: Locating Ignition Timing Marks (Civic & Civic Del Sol)

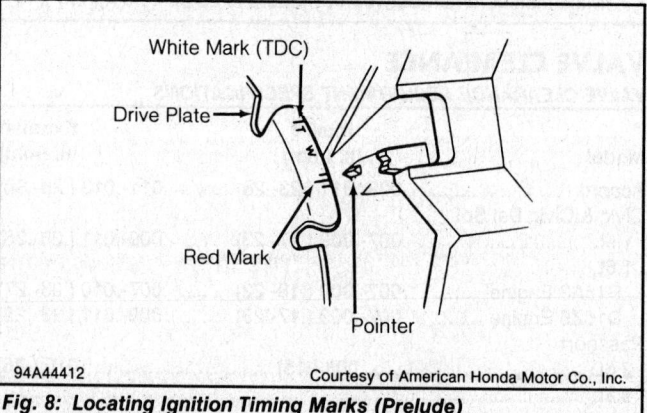

Fig. 8: Locating Ignition Timing Marks (Prelude)

IGNITION TIMING

IGNITION TIMING (Degrees BTDC @ RPM)

Application	Specification
Accord & Prelude	13-17 @ 650-750
Civic & Civic Del Sol	
1.5L Engine (D15B7)	
A/T	16 @ 650-750
M/T	16 @ 620-720
1.5L Engine (D15B8)	12 @ 620-720
1.5L Engine (D15Z1)	16 @ 550-650
1.6L Engine (B16A3)	16 @ 650-750
1.6L Engine (D16Z6)	
A/T	16 @ 650-750
M/T	16 @ 620-720
Passport	
2.6L Engine	12 @ 900
3.2L Engine [1]	10-13 @ 900-1000

[1] – Ignition timing is controlled by the Engine Control Module (ECM) and cannot be adjusted.

FUEL SYSTEM

FUEL PUMP
REGULATED FUEL PRESSURE

Application	At Idle psi (kg/cm²)
Accord, Civic & Civic Del Sol [1]	
Vacuum Hose Disconnected	40-47 (2.8-3.3)
Vacuum Hose Connected	30-38 (2.1-2.7)
Passport	
2.6L Engine [2]	35 (2.4)
3.2L Engine [3]	25-30 (1.8-2.1)
Prelude [1]	
2.2L Engine (F22A1)	
Vacuum Hose Disconnected	36-43 (2.5-3.0)
Vacuum Hose Connected	28-35 (2.0-2.5)
2.2L Engine (H22A1)	
Vacuum Hose Disconnected	33-40 (2.3-2.8)
Vacuum Hose Connected	25-32 (1.8-2.3)
2.3L Engine (H23A1)	
Vacuum Hose Disconnected	36-43 (2.5-3.0)
Vacuum Hose Connected	28-35 (2.0-2.5)

[1] – Measure regulated fuel pressure with vacuum hose connected and disconnected from pressure regulator.

[2] – With pressure regulator vacuum hose connected and Vacuum Switching Valve (VSV) disconnected.

[3] – With engine at idle or with 12-14 in. Hg vacuum manually applied to pressure regulator.

INJECTOR RESISTANCE
FUEL INJECTOR RESISTANCE

Application	Ohms
Accord & Prelude	
Injector	1.5-2.5
Injector Resistor	5-7
Civic & Civic Del Sol	
Injector	10-13
Passport	
Injector	
2.6L	13.8
3.2L	11.8-12.6

IDLE SPEED & CO MIXTURE

For further information on idle speed adjustments and specifications, see ON-VEHICLE ADJUSTMENTS article.

IDLE SPEED SPECIFICATIONS

Application	RPM
Accord & Prelude [1]	500-600
Civic & Civic Del Sol [1]	
A/T	650-750
M/T	
Except B16A3 Engine	620-720
B16A3 Engine	650-760
Passport	
2.6L	900
3.2L [2]	750

[1] – With Electronic Air Control Valve (EACV) disconnected, headlights and cooling fan off, and transmission in Neutral or Park.

[2] – Idle speed is controlled by ECM and is not adjustable.

IDLE CO LEVEL

Application	CO Level
Except Passport	0.1%
Passport	[1]

[1] – Specification is not available from manufacturer.

THROTTLE POSITION (TP) SENSOR

NOTE: For testing procedures, refer to SELF-DIAGNOSTICS or SYSTEM & COMPONENT TESTING article.

THROTTLE POSITION (TP) SENSOR VOLTAGE

Condition	Volts
Except Passport	
Throttle Valve	
Fully Closed	.5
Wide Open	4.5
Passport	
Throttle Valve	
Fully Closed	Less Than .085
Wide Open	[1]

[1] – Specification is not available from manufacturer.

Accord, Civic, Civic Del Sol, Passport, Prelude

NOTE: For on-vehicle adjustments on Passport, refer to Rodeo in Isuzu ON-VEHICLE ADJUSTMENTS article.

ENGINE MECHANICAL

Before performing any on-vehicle adjustments to fuel or ignition system, ensure engine mechanical condition is okay.

VALVE CLEARANCE

VALVE CLEARANCE ADJUSTMENT SPECIFICATIONS

Model	Intake In. (mm)	Exhaust In. (mm)
Accord	.009-.011 (.23-.28)	.011-.013 (.28-.32)
Civic & Civic Del Sol		
1.5L Engine	.007-.009 (.17-.23)	.009-.011 (.23-.28)
1.6L Engine		
B16A3 Engine	.006-.007 (.18-.22)	.007-.008 (.23-.27)
D16Z6 Engine	.007-.009 (.17-.23)	.009-.011 (.23-.28)
Prelude		
2.2L Engine	.009-.011 (.23-.28)	.011-.013 (.28-.32)
2.3L Engine	.003-.004 (.07-.11)	.006-.007 (.15-.19)

DUAL OVERHEAD CAMSHAFTS (DOHC)

1) With engine cold, remove upper timing belt cover, valve cover, spark plugs and distributor cap. Adjustment of exhaust and intake valves are done at same time.

NOTE: On some applications, the word UP will be cast into the camshaft pulley. On other applications the UP mark will be represented by an arrow pointing to the outer edge of the camshaft pulley.

2) Rotate crankshaft to bring piston No. 1 to TDC on compression stroke. UP marks on camshaft pulleys should be at top, and TDC grooves on camshaft pulleys should align with cylinder head surface. *See Fig. 1.* Distributor rotor should point to spark plug wire No. 1 on cap.

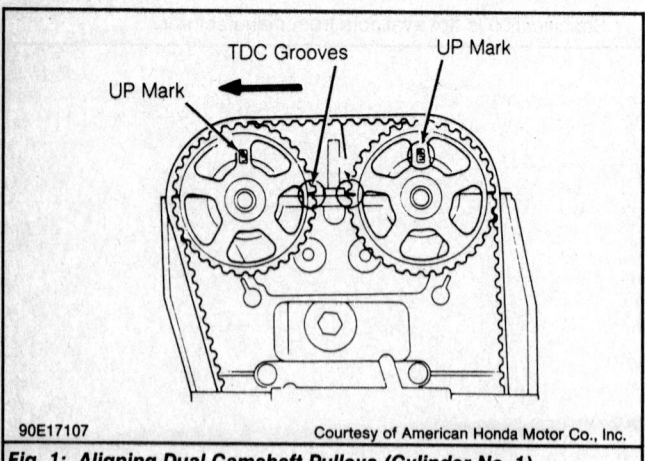
90E17107   Courtesy of American Honda Motor Co., Inc.
Fig. 1: Aligning Dual Camshaft Pulleys (Cylinder No. 1)

3) Loosen lock nuts on valves for cylinder No. 1, and adjust valve clearances to specification. *See Fig. 2.* See VALVE CLEARANCE ADJUSTMENT SPECIFICATIONS table.
4) Tighten valve adjuster lock nuts to 15 ft. lbs. (20 N.m). Recheck valve clearance. Readjust valve clearance, if necessary.
5) Rotate crankshaft counterclockwise 180 degrees. Ensure cylinder No. 3 is at TDC. Adjust valves on cylinder No. 3. For remaining cylinders, repeat steps 3) - 5).
6) Replace valve cover and distributor cap. Tighten timing cover bolts and valve cover crown nuts to 7 INCH lbs. (10 N.m).

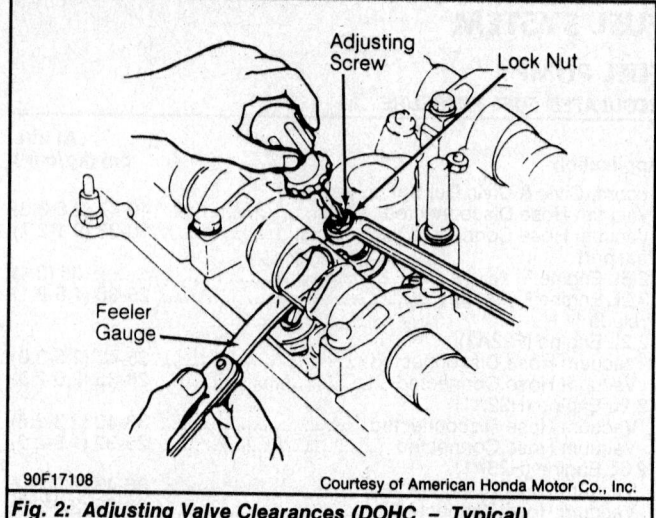
90F17108   Courtesy of American Honda Motor Co., Inc.
Fig. 2: Adjusting Valve Clearances (DOHC – Typical)

SINGLE OVERHEAD CAMSHAFT (SOHC)

1) With engine cold, remove timing belt upper cover, valve cover, spark plugs and distributor cap. Adjust exhaust and intake valves at the same time.
2) Rotate crankshaft to bring piston No. 1 to TDC on compression stroke. UP mark on camshaft pulley should be at top, and TDC grooves on camshaft pulley should align with cylinder head surface. *See Fig. 3.* Distributor rotor should point to spark plug wire No. 1 on distributor cap.

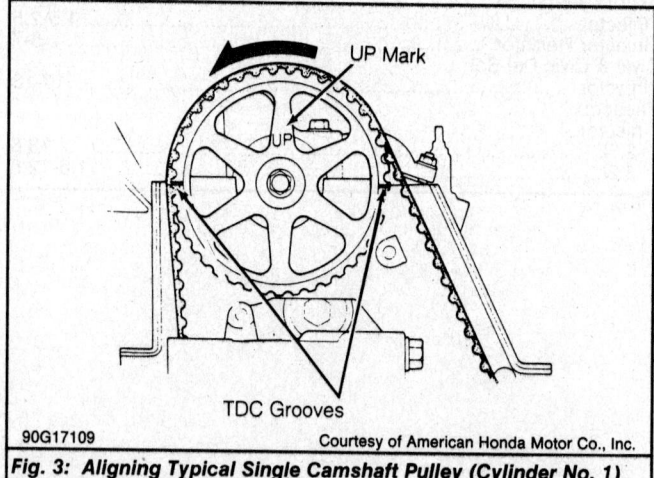
90G17109   Courtesy of American Honda Motor Co., Inc.
Fig. 3: Aligning Typical Single Camshaft Pulley (Cylinder No. 1)

3) Loosen lock nuts on valves for cylinder No. 1, and adjust valve clearances to specification. See VALVE CLEARANCE ADJUSTMENT SPECIFICATIONS table. *See Fig. 4.*
4) Tighten valve adjuster lock nuts on Accord and Prelude to 14 ft. lbs. (20 N.m). Tighten valve adjuster lock nuts on Civic and Civic Del Sol with D15Z1 or D16Z6 engines to 14 ft. lbs. (20 N.m). On all other Civic and Civic Del Sol applications, tighten valve adjuster lock nuts to 10 ft. lbs. (14 N.m). Recheck valve clearance and repeat adjustment, if necessary.
5) Rotate crankshaft counterclockwise 180 degrees. Ensure cylinder No. 3 is at TDC. Adjust valves on cylinder No. 3. For remaining cylinders, repeat steps 3) through 5).
6) Replace valve cover and distributor cap. Tighten timing cover bolts and valve cover crown nuts to 7 INCH lbs. (10 N.m).

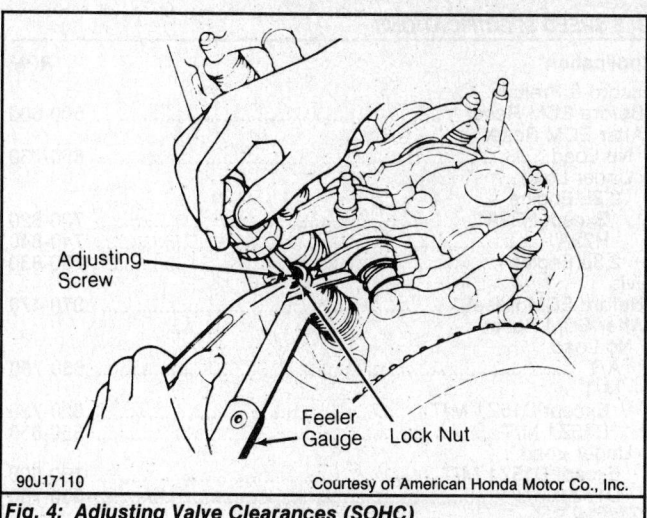

Fig. 4: Adjusting Valve Clearances (SOHC)

Adjusting Screw

Feeler Gauge   Lock Nut

90J17110   Courtesy of American Honda Motor Co., Inc.

IGNITION TIMING

Accord – 1) Start engine and run under no-load condition at about 3000 RPM until cooling fan comes on. Let engine slow to idle. Pull out service check connector (2-pin), located behind the glove box. *See Fig. 5.* Plug SCS Service Connector (07PAZ-0010100) into service check connector.

CAUTION: DO NOT attempt any connection to 3-pin Data Link Connector (DLC) located near service check connector.

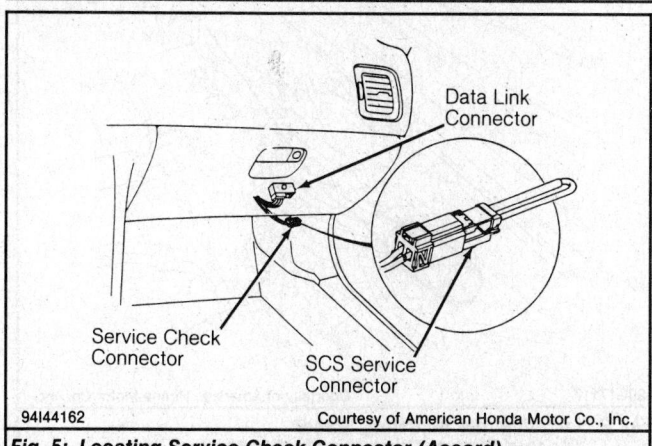

Fig. 5: Locating Service Check Connector (Accord)

Data Link Connector

Service Check Connector

SCS Service Connector

94I44162   Courtesy of American Honda Motor Co., Inc.

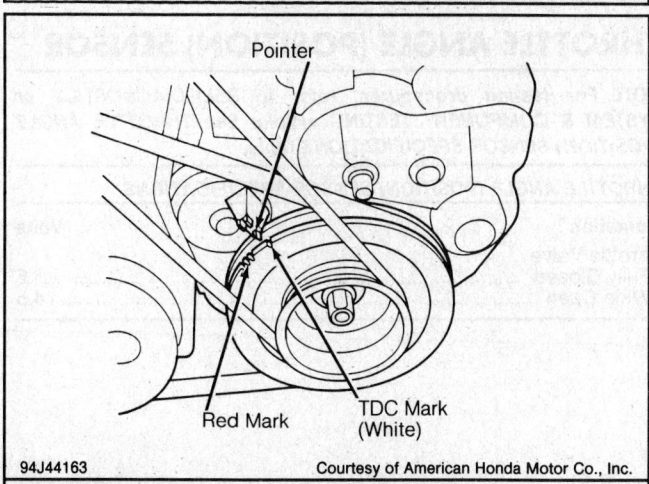

Fig. 6: Locating Ignition Timing Marks (Accord)

Pointer

Red Mark   TDC Mark (White)

94J44163   Courtesy of American Honda Motor Co., Inc.

2) Check idle speed and adjust as necessary. See IDLE SPEED SPECIFICATIONS table. Connect a timing light to spark plug wire No. 1. Check base ignition timing with timing light. Timing marks are located on timing belt cover and accessory drive belt pulley. Red mark indicates 15 degrees BTDC. White mark indicates TDC. *See Fig. 6.* See IGNITION TIMING table.

3) Loosen hold-down bolts and rotate distributor to adjust timing. Tighten distributor hold-down bolts to 13 ft. lbs. (18 N.m). Recheck timing to ensure it hasn't changed.

4) Remove timing light. Remove SCS service connector from ignition timing service check connector.

IGNITION TIMING (Degrees BTDC @ RPM)

Application	Specification
Accord & Prelude	13-17 @ 650-750
Civic & Civic Del Sol	
1.5L Engine (D15B7)	
A/T	16 @ 650-750
M/T	16 @ 620-720
1.5L Engine (D15B8)	12 @ 620-720
1.5L Engine (D15Z1)	16 @ 550-650
1.6L Engine (B16A3)	16 @ 650-750
1.6L Engine (D16Z6)	
A/T	16 @ 650-750
M/T	16 @ 620-720

Civic, Civic Del Sol & Prelude – 1) To view timing marks on Prelude, remove rubber cap from inspection window on cylinder block by bellhousing. On Civic and Civic Del Sol, timing marks are on timing belt cover and crankshaft pulley. On all models, start and warm engine to normal operating temperature (cooling fan comes on). Connect timing light.

2) Ignition timing check connector is located behind passenger-side kick panel (Civic and Civic Del Sol) or under center of dash (Prelude). *See Fig. 7 or 8.* Connect jumper wire between Brown and Black wire terminals (Civic and Civic Del Sol) or Blue/White and Brown/White wire terminals (Prelude).

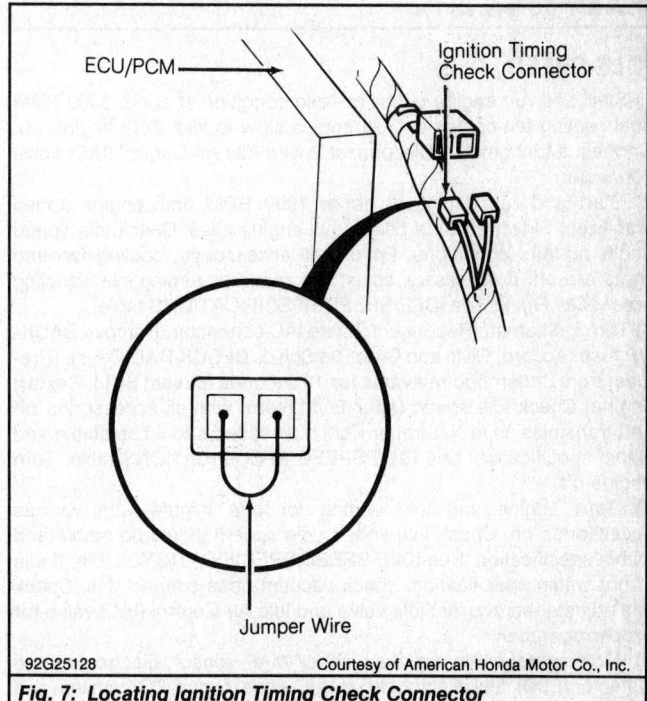

Fig. 7: Locating Ignition Timing Check Connector (Civic & Civic Del Sol)

ECU/PCM

Ignition Timing Check Connector

Jumper Wire

92G25128   Courtesy of American Honda Motor Co., Inc.

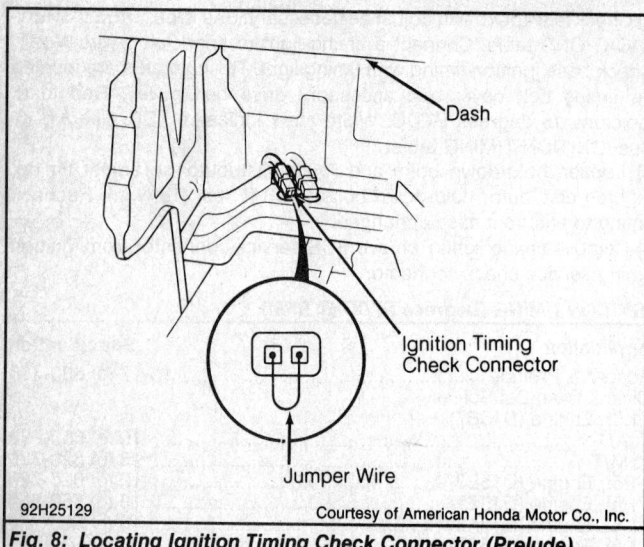

Fig. 8: Locating Ignition Timing Check Connector (Prelude)

3) Check ignition timing and adjust to specification, if necessary. See IGNITION TIMING table. To adjust, loosen distributor hold-down bolts and turn distributor housing counterclockwise to advance or clockwise to retard timing. Align pointer with Red timing mark.

4) Tighten distributor hold-down bolts to 16 ft. lbs. (22 N.m). Recheck timing. Remove jumper wire from ignition timing check connector. Reinstall cap into inspection window on Prelude.

IDLE SPEED & MIXTURE

IDLE MIXTURE

NOTE: Idle mixture is computer controlled and is not adjustable. Maximum CO level is .1%.

IDLE SPEED

1) Start and run engine under no-load condition at about 3000 RPM until cooling fan comes on. Let engine slow to idle. Turn engine off. Connect a tachometer. Disconnect 2-wire Idle Air Control (IAC) valve connector.

2) Start and run engine at about 1000 RPM until engine speed stabilizes. Slowly release pedal until engine idles. Check idle speed under no-load conditions. Ensure all accessories, cooling fan and lights are off. If necessary, adjust idle speed by turning idle adjusting screw. *See Fig. 9.* See IDLE SPEED SPECIFICATIONS table.

3) Turn ignition off. Reconnect 2-wire IAC connector. Remove BACK-UP fuse (Accord, Civic and Civic Del Sol) or CLOCK RADIO fuse (Prelude) from underhood relay box for 10 seconds to reset ECM. Restart engine. Check idle speed (after ECM reset) with all accessories off and transmission in Neutral or Park. Idle speed should be stable and within specification. See IDLE SPEED SPECIFICATIONS table. Turn engine off.

4) Start engine and idle engine for one minute with various accessories on. Check idle speed. Idle speed should be stable and within specification. See IDLE SPEED SPECIFICATIONS table. If idle is not within specification, check vacuum hose connections. Check idle adjuster screw, fast idle valve and Idle Air Control (IAC) valve for proper operation.

5) If idle components are okay, check MAP sensor, Electronic Load Detector (ELD), fuel injector circuit, A/C signal circuit, EGR system and lock-up control solenoid (if equipped) for proper operation. For component testing procedures, see SELF-DIAGNOSTICS and SYSTEM & COMPONENT TESTING articles.

IDLE SPEED SPECIFICATIONS

Application	RPM
Accord & Prelude	
Before ECM Reset [1]	500-600
After ECM Reset	
No Load	650-750
Under Load	
2.2L Engine	
Except H22A1	720-820
H22A1	740-840
2.3L Engine	730-830
Civic	
Before ECM Reset [1]	370-470
After ECM Reset	
No Load	
A/T	650-750
M/T	
Except D15Z1 M/T	620-720
D15Z1 M/T	550-650
Under Load	
Except D15Z1 M/T	700-800
D15Z1 M/T	650-750
Civic Del Sol	
Before ECM Reset [1]	370-470
After ECM Reset	
No Load	
A/T	650-750
M/T	
Except B16A3 M/T	620-720
B16A3 M/T	650-750
Under Load	700-800

[1] – With Idle Air Control (IAC) valve disconnected, headlights and cooling fan off and transmission in Neutral or Park.

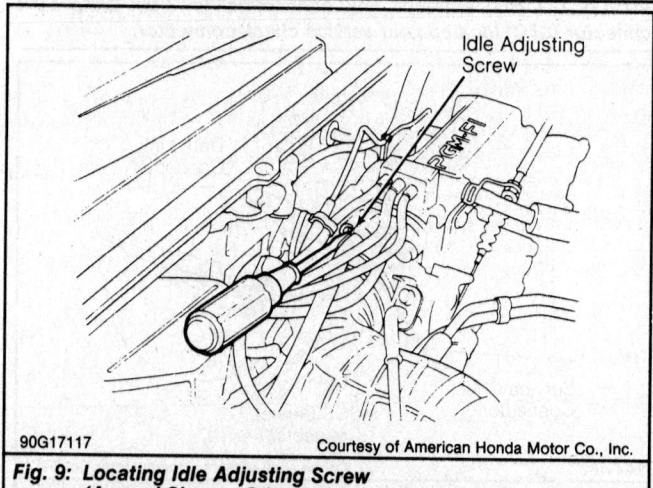

Fig. 9: Locating Idle Adjusting Screw (Accord Shown; Other Models Are Similar)

THROTTLE ANGLE (POSITION) SENSOR

NOTE: For testing procedures, refer to SELF-DIAGNOSTICS or SYSTEM & COMPONENT TESTING article. See THROTTLE ANGLE (POSITION) SENSOR SPECIFICATIONS table.

THROTTLE ANGLE (POSITION) SENSOR SPECIFICATIONS

Condition	Volts
Throttle Valve	
Fully Closed	.5
Wide Open	4.5

Accord, Civic, Civic Del Sol, Passport, Prelude

NOTE: For theory and operation information on Passport, refer to Rodeo in Isuzu THEORY & OPERATION article.

INTRODUCTION

This article covers basic description and operation of engine performance-related systems and components. Read this article before diagnosing vehicles or systems with which you are not completely familiar.

AIR INDUCTION SYSTEM

Air Intake System – System consists of an air cleaner, air intake pipe, throttle body, Idle Air Control (IAC) valve, fast idle mechanism and intake manifold. On Prelude, except 2.2L (F22A1) engine, a by-pass control system is used. On all models, a resonator chamber in the air intake pipe reduces noise as air is drawn into system.

By-Pass Control System (Prelude – Except F22A1) – By-pass control system consists of 2 separate intake paths in intake manifold, a by-pass valve, a by-pass control diaphragm and a normally open by-pass control solenoid valve. ECM selects air intake path(s) most favorable for engine performance by operating by-pass valves to direct airflow through one or both intake paths. The longer, smaller intake path is used for operation when engine speed is less than 4600 RPM on 2.2L (H22A1) engine and 4800 RPM on 2.3L engine. The shorter, larger intake path is opened in addition to the smaller path for better performance at high RPM.

Intake Control System – The intake control system consists of an intake control diaphragm and an intake control solenoid valve. When engine speed drops to less than 3500-4000 RPM and engine air requirements drop, the ECM activates the intake control solenoid valve. This supplies intake manifold vacuum to intake control diaphragm. Intake control diaphragm closes off one of the 2 air intakes, along with resonator chamber, and reduces intake air noise.

Throttle Body – Throttle body is a single-barrel sidedraft type. Lower portion of throttle valve is heated by engine coolant from cylinder head. Idle adjusting screw (to increase and decrease by-pass air) and canister/purge port are both located on top of throttle body.

VARIABLE VALVE TIMING

VARIABLE VALVE TIMING & LIFT ELECTRONIC CONTROL SYSTEM (VTEC)

Accord 2.2L (F22B1) – VTEC system is used on the 2.2L engine. The system utilizes 3 different intake cam lobes and rocker arms. At low speed, the primary and secondary intake valves are operated by their own separate cam lobes. The connecting (middle) rocker is operated by the high speed cam lobe at all times. At low speed, the connecting rocker arm is not connected to primary or secondary rocker arms or valves and has no effect on engine operation.

When engine speed exceeds 4800 RPM and other conditions are met (as determined by ECM), oil pressure is applied (through spool valve) to synchronizing pistons located in primary and connecting rocker arms. This locks primary, connecting (middle) and secondary rocker arms together so they are driven as a single unit by the higher lift and duration cam that operates the connecting (middle) rocker arm.

Civic 1.5L (D15Z1) – Engine is equipped with 4 valves per cylinder. At low engine speeds, the primary intake valve operates with normal lift characteristics and secondary intake valve lifts slightly to prevent fuel accumulation in intake port.

When engine speed exceeds 2500 RPM and other conditions are met (determined by ECM), oil pressure is applied through a spool valve to timing and synchronizing pistons located in valve rocker arms. Synchronizing piston locks primary and secondary rocker arms together, causing both valves to operate at the higher lift and duration of the primary cam and valve. This system of locking rocker arms together is designated VTEC-E.

Civic & Civic Del Sol 1.6L (B16A3 DOHC & D16Z6 SOHC) – VTEC system used on the 1.6L engines differs from the VTEC-E system used on the 1.5L engine. VTEC system used on the 1.6L engines functions in the same manner as the system on 2.2L engine on Accord. Valve function changeover is accomplished when certain conditions are met (as determined by ECM).

Prelude 2.2L (H22A1) – VTEC system used on the 2.2L (DOHC) engine functions in the same manner as the system on 2.2L engine on Accord. Valve function changeover is accomplished when engine speed exceeds 4900 RPM and other conditions are met (as determined by ECM).

COMPUTERIZED ENGINE CONTROLS

ENGINE CONTROL MODULE (ECM)

Computerized engine controls are used to control fuel, ignition and emission control systems. Engine Control Module (ECM) receives input signals from various sensors and components. ECM then compares each signal with a preprogrammed parameter in its memory. Based on this comparison, output signals are then adjusted to allow vehicle to perform optimally under all operating conditions. ECM is located under passenger-side carpet on Accord and Prelude. On Civic and Civic Del Sol, ECM is located behind passenger-side kick panel.

NOTE: Components are grouped into 2 categories. First category covers INPUT DEVICES, which control or produce voltage signals monitored by ECM. Second category is OUTPUT SIGNALS, which are components controlled by ECM.

INPUT DEVICES

Vehicles are equipped with different combinations of input devices. Not all devices are used on all models. To determine component usage of a specific model, see appropriate wiring diagram in WIRING DIAGRAMS article. Available input signals include the following:

A/C Switch Signal – This switch signals ECM of demand for air conditioning. ECM then increases engine RPM to compensate for additional engine load.

Alternator (FR) Signal – This signals ECM when alternator field circuit is energized. ECM compensates for changes in idle speed and low battery voltage which can cause erratic injector pulse width.

Automatic Transmission Shift Position Signal – This signals ECM when transmission selector lever is in Park, Neutral or D4 position.

Barometric Pressure (BARO) Sensor – BARO sensor converts barometric (atmospheric) pressure into electrical signals and relays information to ECM.

Battery Voltage (IGN.1) – This provides ECM with battery voltage signal from ignition circuit when ignition is on.

Brake Switch Signal – This signals ECM when brake pedal is depressed.

Electric Load Detector (ELD) – This signals ECM when an electrical load (headlights, radio, etc.) exists so ECM can compensate for additional engine load.

Engine Coolant Temperature (ECT) Sensor – Coolant temperature sensor is a temperature-dependent variable resistor (thermistor). Resistance of thermistor decreases as coolant temperature increases.

Exhaust Gas Recirculation Valve Lift Sensor – EGR valve lift sensor detects amount of EGR valve lift and sends information to ECM. ECM uses this information, along with other sensor inputs, to determine regulation of EGR control solenoid valve.

Intake Air Temperature (IAT) Sensor – Intake air temperature sensor is a temperature-dependent variable resistor (thermistor). Thermistor resistance decreases as intake air temperature increases.

Knock Sensor (Prelude) – Sensor is located on engine block, near oil filter. Sensor signals ECM when a knock condition exists. ECM adjusts timing to compensate condition.

Manifold Absolute Pressure (MAP) Sensor – MAP sensor converts manifold absolute pressure into electrical signals and sends signals to ECM. MAP sensor signals are a measurement of engine load.

Manual Transmission Clutch Switch (Civic) – Switch is mounted above clutch pedal. Switch signals ECM when clutch is engaged to provide for idle speed adjustment.

Oxygen Sensor (O2S) – Oxygen sensor detects oxygen content of exhaust gases and sends signal to ECM, which varies air/fuel ratio to maintain a 14.7:1 ratio under most conditions. This ratio is most efficient for combustion and catalytic converter operation.

All models except Civic with D15Z1 engine use heated oxygen sensors. Civic with D15Z1 engine uses a heated linear air/fuel ratio type oxygen sensor which performs the same function as standard oxygen sensor, but over a wider range.

Power Steering Pressure Switch – This switch signals ECM when power steering load is high. ECM then compensates for load by increasing engine RPM.

Starter Signal – Signals ECM when engine is cranking.

TDC/CKP/CYP Sensor – TDC/CKP/CYP sensor is a combination sensor located inside distributor. Each sensor generates a separate signal. CKP sensor detects engine RPM to determine fuel injection timing and ignition of each cylinder. TDC sensor determines ignition timing at start-up (cranking) and detects when crank angle signal is abnormal. CYP sensor detects position of cylinder No. 1 for sequential fuel injection to each cylinder.

Throttle Position (TP) Sensor – TP sensor is a 3-wire potentiometer connected to throttle shaft. As throttle position changes, TP sensor varies voltage signal monitored by ECM. Sensor voltage ranges from about one volt at closed throttle to about 5 volts at wide open throttle.

Valve Timing Oil Pressure Switch – Located on Variable Valve Timing Electronic Control (VTEC) spool valve, switch signals ECM when VTEC system is operating. Switch will set a code in case of failure in circuit.

Vehicle Speed Sensor/Pulser (VSS) – Vehicle speed signal is generated by speed sensor (sometimes called a speed pulser), which produces 4 pulses (switch grounded) per speedometer cable revolution.

OUTPUT SIGNALS

NOTE: Vehicles are equipped with different combinations of computer-controlled components. Not all components listed below are used on every vehicle. For theory and operation on each output component, refer to system indicated after component.

A/C Clutch Engagement Delay – See IDLE SPEED under FUEL SYSTEM.

Alternator – See CHARGING SYSTEM under MISCELLANEOUS CONTROLS.

By-Pass Control Solenoid Valve – See AIR INDUCTION SYSTEM.

EGR Control Solenoid Valve – See EXHAUST GAS RECIRCULATION (EGR) SYSTEM under EMISSION SYSTEMS.

Fuel Injector – See FUEL CONTROL under FUEL SYSTEM.

Ignition Control Module (ICM) – See IGNITION SYSTEM.

Intake Air Control Valve – See IDLE SPEED under FUEL SYSTEM.

Intake Control Solenoid Valve – See AIR INDUCTION SYSTEM.

Main Relay – See FUEL DELIVERY under FUEL SYSTEM.

Malfunction Indicator Light (MIL) – See SELF-DIAGNOSTIC SYSTEM.

Oxygen Sensor Heater – See FUEL CONTROL under FUEL SYSTEM.

Purge Control Cut-Off Solenoid Valve – See EVAPORATIVE EMISSION SYSTEM (EVAP) under EMISSION SYSTEMS.

Radiator Fan Control Module – See COOLING SYSTEM under MISCELLANEOUS CONTROLS

Spool Solenoid Valve – See VARIABLE VALVE TIMING.

FUEL SYSTEM

FUEL DELIVERY

Fuel Injection – Fuel system consists of an in-tank high pressure electric fuel pump, main relay, fuel filter, pressure regulator, injectors and injector resistor(s). This system delivers pressure-regulated fuel to injectors and cuts fuel delivery when engine is not running.

Fuel Pump – Fuel pump consists of a DC motor, a circumference flow pump assembly, an internal relief valve for protecting fuel line system, an internal check valve for retaining residual pressure, an inlet port and discharge port. Pump assembly consists of impeller (driven by motor), pump casing (which forms pumping chamber) and pump cover.

Fuel Pressure Regulator – Fuel pressure regulator maintains proper fuel pressure to injectors. Regulator uses manifold vacuum to sense engine load and modifies fuel pressure to maintain driveability.

When manifold vacuum is high, vacuum diaphragm is drawn back, overcoming spring pressure. Excess fuel passes through pressure regulator and is returned to tank via fuel return line. When manifold vacuum decreases (engine load increases), spring pressure closes off return passage, thereby maintaining fuel pressure and volume.

Injector Resistor(s) – Injector resistor(s) lowers current supplied to injectors to prevent damage to injector coils, allowing injectors a faster response time.

Main Relay – Main relay contains 2 individual relays. One relay is energized whenever ignition is on. It supplies battery voltage to ECM, power to injectors and power for second relay. Second relay supplies power to fuel pump. Second relay is energized for 2 seconds when ignition switch is initially turned on and when engine is running.

FUEL CONTROL

Programmed Fuel Injection – Programmed fuel injection system is controlled by Powertrain Control Module (PCM). See POWERTRAIN CONTROL MODULE (PCM) in COMPUTERIZED ENGINE CONTROLS. The basic fuel injector duration is built into PCM memory. The PCM modifies basic injector duration according to input signals from various sensors to obtain final injector duration for fuel delivery.

Fuel Injector – Fuel injector consists of a solenoid, plunger needle valve and housing. When current is applied to solenoid coil, valve lifts and pressurized fuel is injected close to intake valve. Since needle valve lift and fuel pressure are constant, air/fuel ratio is determined by time valve is open (duration of current supplied to solenoid coil).

Injector is sealed by an "O" ring and seal ring at top and bottom. All seals, "O" rings and rubber mounts reduce injector operating noise and heat transfer.

Oxygen Sensor Heater – The oxygen sensor detects the oxygen content in exhaust gas and signals the PCM. PCM bases fuel injection duration on these signals. An internal heater, activated by the PCM, stabilizes sensor output for more accurate readings.

IDLE SPEED

A/C Clutch Engagement Delay – When ECM receives a demand for cooling from air conditioning system (A/C switch), it delays A/C clutch relay activation for a short time. This prevents compressor clutch from being energized until ECM enriches the fuel injection mixture, ensuring smooth transition into A/C mode without overloading engine.

Idle Air Control (IAC) Valve – Engine idle speed is controlled by IAC and fast idle valve. IAC varies amount of air by-passing throttle plate (into intake manifold) in response to signals from ECM. After engine starts, IAC opens for a short time to increase idle speed. Activation time is dependent upon engine coolant temperature. When coolant temperature is low, IAC is held open to obtain proper fast idle speed. After engine reaches normal operating temperature, IAC is activated only to maintain minimum idle speed.

Idle Air Control (IAC) Thermal Valve – Formerly called fast idle valve, IAC thermal valve allows additional air to by-pass throttle plate into intake manifold. Increased idle speed prevents engine from running erratically during warm-up. Valve is controlled by a thermowax plunger, which contracts when cold and expands when hot.

IGNITION SYSTEM

IGNITION TIMING CONTROL

ECM has complete control of ignition timing. Timing is controlled in response to signals from various sensors. Input signals from TDC, CRANK and CYL, throttle angle, coolant temperature, and MAP sensors are all used by ECM to determine optimum ignition timing control.

Battery voltage is supplied through ignition switch to ignition coil and Ignition Control Module (ICM). ECM triggers ICM based upon signals from TDC, CRANK and/or CYL and other sensors. High voltage from ignition coil is distributed to each spark plug by distributor.

EMISSION SYSTEMS

EXHAUST GAS RECIRCULATION (EGR) SYSTEM

EGR System – EGR system reduces oxides of nitrogen (NOx) emissions by recirculating exhaust gases through EGR valve into intake manifold and back to combustion chambers.

System is composed of EGR valve, Constant Vacuum Control (CVC) valve and EGR control solenoid valve. EGR control solenoid valve is controlled by ECM, which analyzes input signals from EGR valve lift sensor and various sensors to provide optimum EGR flow.

EGR flow is cut when combustion gas temperatures are low (when the engine emits a relatively low NOx emission) to ensure good cold driveability.

EGR Valve – When opened, EGR valve circulates exhaust gas through intake manifold and back into combustion chamber to be reburned, resulting in reduced combustion chamber temperature. Lower temperature reduces oxides of nitrogen (NOx) and helps to control spark knock.

EGR Control Solenoid Valve – When ECM determines it is necessary to recirculate exhaust gases, it grounds EGR control solenoid valve, regulating vacuum controlling EGR valve. By regulating vacuum to EGR valve, EGR flow is adjusted for optimum control of NOx emission.

Exhaust Gas Recirculation Valve Lift Sensor – The EGR valve lift sensor detects EGR valve lift and sends information to ECM. The ECM uses this information, along with other sensor inputs, to determine regulation of EGR control solenoid valve.

EVAPORATIVE EMISSION SYSTEM (EVAP)

Evaporative emission system minimizes fuel vapor escaping into atmosphere. For emission control applications and components used for each model and engine, see EMISSION APPLICATIONS and VACUUM DIAGRAMS articles.

Charcoal Canister – Charcoal canister temporarily stores fuel vapor until it can be purged, drawn into engine and burned in combustion chamber.

Fuel Tank Vapor Control System – Fuel tank vapor control system consists of a fuel cut-off valve, liquid/vapor separator, a 2-way valve and fuel filler cap. All fuel vapor inside fuel tank is directed to charcoal canister through fuel cut-off valve and liquid/vapor separator.

Fuel cut-off valve and liquid/vapor separator prohibit liquid fuel from entering 2-way valve. When fuel vapor pressure in fuel tank is greater than set value of 2-way valve, valve opens and regulates flow of fuel vapor into canister. The 2-way valve regulates both pressure and vacuum in tank. The filler cap contains a relief valve to prevent excessive pressure or vacuum build-up.

Vapor Purge Control System – The vapor purge control system controls when charcoal canister is to be purged. Canister purging is accomplished when ECM activates purge control cut-off solenoid valve, allowing fresh air to be drawn through bottom of charcoal canister and into a port on throttle body.

POSITIVE CRANKCASE VENTILATION (PCV) SYSTEM

The Positive Crankcase Ventilation (PCV) system is designed to prevent blow-by gases (in engine crankcase) from escaping into atmosphere. The PCV valve contains a spring-loaded plunger. When engine starts, plunger in PCV valve is lifted in proportion to intake manifold vacuum, and blow-by gas is drawn directly into intake manifold.

SELF-DIAGNOSTIC SYSTEM

MALFUNCTION INDICATOR LIGHT (MIL)

When ignition is initially turned on, ECM provides ground to illuminate Malfunction Indicator Light (MIL). The light remains on until engine starts. When an abnormal sensor signal occurs, ECM lights MIL and stores Diagnostic Trouble Codes (DTCs) in erasable memory. On Accord, DTCs are indicated by MIL when SCS service connector is plugged into diagnostic check connector. On all other models, DTCs are indicated by MIL when diagnostic test connector is jumpered. For additional information, see SELF-DIAGNOSTICS article.

MISCELLANEOUS CONTROLS

NOTE: Although not considered true engine performance-related systems, some controlled devices may affect driveability if they malfunction.

A/C CLUTCH

When a demand for air conditioning exists in A/C switch circuit, ECM supplies ground to A/C clutch relay to operate the A/C compressor. ECM can also change engine idle RPM to compensate for additional engine load.

CHARGING SYSTEM

Alternator – The internal ECM alternator control system monitors and adjusts voltage generated at alternator. To improve fuel economy, the ECM reduces alternator output through the voltage regulator when engine is at normal operating temperatures and the ECM detects low amperage demand conditions.

COOLING SYSTEM

Radiator Fan Control Module – Located next to ECM (Prelude) or in left side kick panel (Accord), radiator fan control module works with ECM to determine when to activate the cooling fans. On Accord, module applies voltage through fuse No. 21 (A/C) and fuse No. 34 (radiator) to fan relays when ECM indicates A/C switch is in ON position. On Prelude, module applies voltage through fuse No. 45 (A/C) and fuse No. 47 (radiator) to fan relays when ECM indicates A/C switch is in ON position.

Accord, Civic, Civic Del Sol, Passport, Prelude

INTRODUCTION

The following diagnostic steps will help prevent overlooking a simple problem. This is also where to begin diagnosis for a no-start condition.

The first step in diagnosing any driveability problem is verifying the customer's complaint with a test drive under the conditions the problem reportedly occurred.

Before entering self-diagnostics, perform a careful and complete visual inspection. Most engine control problems result from mechanical breakdowns, poor electrical connections or damaged/misrouted vacuum hoses. Before condemning computerized system, perform each test listed in this article.

NOTE: Perform all voltage tests with a Digital Volt-Ohmmeter (DVOM) with a minimum 10-megohm input impedance, unless stated otherwise in test procedure.

PRELIMINARY INSPECTION & ADJUSTMENTS

VISUAL INSPECTION

Visually inspect all electrical wiring for chafed, stretched, cut or pinched wiring. Ensure electrical connectors fit tightly and are not corroded. Ensure vacuum hoses are properly routed and not pinched or cut. See VACUUM DIAGRAMS article to verify routing and connections. Inspect air induction system for possible vacuum leaks.

MECHANICAL INSPECTION

Compression – Check engine mechanical condition with a compression gauge, vacuum gauge, or an engine analyzer. See engine analyzer manual for specific instructions.

WARNING: DO NOT use ignition switch during compression tests on fuel injected vehicles. Use a remote starter to crank engine. Fuel injectors on many models are triggered by ignition switch during cranking mode, which can create a fire hazard or contaminate the engine's oiling system.

Check compression pressure with engine at normal operating temperature, all spark plugs removed, throttle valves wide open and at specified cranking speed. Crank engine at least 6 revolutions to determine engine compression. See ENGINE COMPRESSION table.

ENGINE COMPRESSION

Model	Standard psi (kg/cm²)	Minimum psi (kg/cm²)	Minimum RPM
Accord & Prelude [1]	178 (12.5)	135 (9.5)	250
Civic & Civic Del Sol [1] Except B16A3 Engine	185 (13.0)	135 (9.5)	250
B16A3 Engine	220 (13.0)	135 (9.5)	250
Passport	170 (12.0)	128 (9.0)	250

[1] – Maximum variation between cylinders is 28 psi (2.0 kg/cm²).

Exhaust System Backpressure – Exhaust system can be checked using a vacuum or pressure gauge. Remove oxygen sensor (O2S) or heated oxygen sensor (HO2S). Connect a 0-5 psi pressure gauge, and run engine at 2500 RPM. If exhaust system backpressure exceeds 1 3/4 - 2 psi (.12-.14 kg/cm²), exhaust system or catalytic converter is plugged.

If using a vacuum gauge, connect vacuum gauge hose to intake manifold vacuum port and start engine. Observe vacuum gauge. Open throttle part way and hold steady. If vacuum slowly drops after stabilizing, check exhaust system for restrictions.

FUEL SYSTEM

WARNING: Always relieve fuel pressure before disconnecting any fuel injection-related component. DO NOT allow fuel to contact engine or electrical components.

FUEL SYSTEM PRESSURE RELEASE

Except Passport – Remove negative battery cable. Loosen fuel tank filler cap. Locate 6-mm service bolt on fuel rail (on fuel filter on Civic and Civic Del Sol). Place clean shop rag around service bolt. To relieve system pressure, slowly loosen service bolt one complete turn. Always replace washer under 6-mm service bolt after loosening.

Passport – 1) Loosen fuel tank filler cap to relieve tank pressure. Remove fuel pump relay from underhood fuse/relay box. Start and operate engine until it stalls. Crank engine an additional 30 seconds. **2)** Loosen fuel line hose clamp on side of pressure regulator coming from fuel line inlet distributor pipe. Cover fuel hose with a shop towel, and slowly pull hose from pressure regulator to relieve any remaining fuel pressure. When fuel stops leaking, reinstall hose and clamp.

FUEL PRESSURE

NOTE: If vehicle starts and runs, fuel pump main relay is okay.

Basic Diagnosis – Begin basic diagnosis of fuel system by determining fuel system pressure. If fuel pump fails to run, inspect power supply to main relay. If all power supplies are present (i.e., battery, ignition and starter switch during cranking), perform functional test of main relay. See WIRING DIAGRAMS and SYSTEM & COMPONENT TESTING articles.

Pressure Testing (Except Passport) – 1) Disconnect negative battery cable. Release fuel pressure. See FUEL SYSTEM PRESSURE RELEASE. Connect Fuel Pressure Gauge (07406-0040001) at 6-mm bolt. Reconnect negative battery cable. Start engine, and note fuel pressure. If vehicle will not start, check for spark. If spark is present and no fuel pressure is evident, inspect fuel pump main relay.
2) Remove connector from fuel pump main relay. *See Fig. 1.* Using a test light, check power on Black/Yellow wire at fuel pump relay connector. If power is present, go to next step. If power does not exist, repair open wire between fuel pump main relay connector and fuse No. 2 on fuse box. Go to step **4)**.

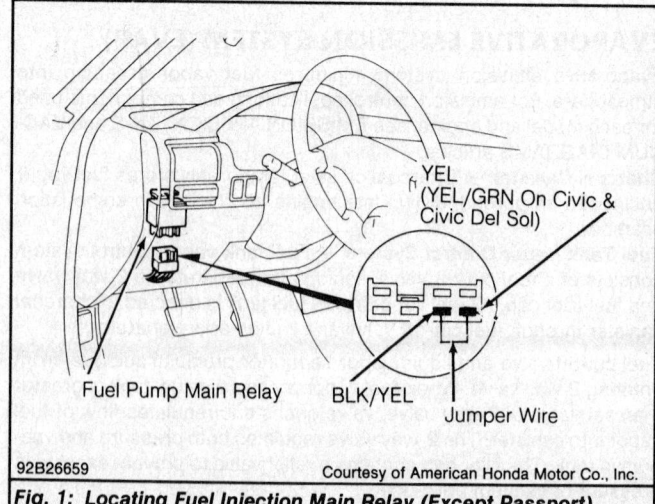

YEL (YEL/GRN On Civic & Civic Del Sol)

Fuel Pump Main Relay

BLK/YEL

Jumper Wire

92B26659   Courtesy of American Honda Motor Co., Inc.

Fig. 1: Locating Fuel Injection Main Relay (Except Passport)

3) Connect jumper wire between Black/Yellow wire (B+) and Yellow wire (Yellow/Green wire on Civic & Civic Del Sol). If fuel pump runs, go to next step. If fuel pump fails to run, see SYSTEM & COMPONENT TESTING article.
4) Start engine. Disconnect vacuum hose from pressure regulator, and check for manifold vacuum. If vacuum is not present, check for restriction in vacuum port or hose. Plug vacuum hose and inspect fuel pressure gauge reading. Gauge reading should be within specifica-

tion. See REGULATED FUEL PRESSURE table. Pressure should drop slightly when vacuum hose is reconnected.

Pressure Testing (Passport 2.6L) – **1)** Release fuel pressure. See FUEL SYSTEM PRESSURE RELEASE. Install a fuel pressure gauge between fuel pressure regulator and fuel distributor pipe. *See Fig. 2.* Bleed air from fuel line going to pressure gauge.

2) Unplug fuel pressure regulator Vacuum Switching Valve (VSV) connector on right side fender skirt. This is a 4-wire connector with Black and Blue wires in harness. ECM controls VSV to cut vacuum to fuel pressure regulator during hot engine starts.

3) Start engine and measure fuel pressure at idle. Disconnect fuel pressure regulator vacuum hose. Note fuel pressure at idle with vacuum hose disconnected (no vacuum). Fuel pressure should be 42 psi (3.0 kg/cm²).

4) If fuel pump pressure is low, check for fuel leaks, restrictions in intake side of fuel pump, leaking injectors, faulty pressure regulator or faulty fuel pump. If fuel pressure is high, check for restrictions in return line to tank or faulty pressure regulator. If pressure does not change when pressure regulator is disconnected, replace pressure regulator.

5) Reconnect pressure regulator vacuum hose and check fuel pressure (with vacuum). Fuel pressure should be 35 psi (2.5 kg/cm²). Apply battery voltage to VSV connector Blue wire terminal, and ground Black wire terminal (with vacuum). *See Fig. 3.* Fuel pressure gauge should read approximately 42 psi (3.0 kg/cm²). If fuel pressure is not within specification, check for defective VSV.

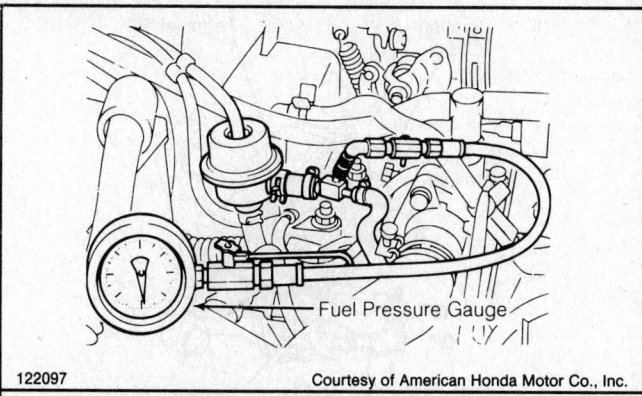

Fig. 2: Installing Fuel Pressure Gauge (Passport 2.6L)

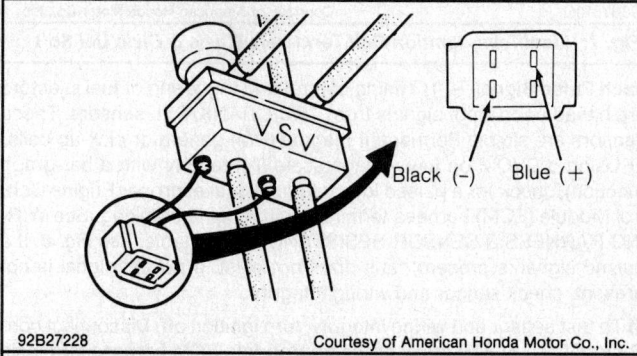

Fig. 3: Identifying Pressure Regulator VSV Terminals (Passport 2.6L)

6) Disconnect and plug vacuum hose from fuel pressure regulator. Stop engine. Ensure fuel pressure remains greater than 35 psi (2.5 kg/cm²) for 4 minutes after engine stops.

7) If pressure drops, check for leaking injectors, faulty pressure regulator or bad check valve in fuel pump. If engine does not start, by-pass fuel pump relay to check for fuel pressure.

NOTE: If vehicle starts and runs, fuel pump main relay is okay.

8) Remove fuel pump relay from underhood fuse/relay box. Connect a jumper wire between terminals No. 1 and 3 of fuel pump relay connector in fuse block. *See Figs. 4 and 5.*

9) If fuel pump does not operate, check for battery voltage to terminal No. 3. If battery voltage is present, check for open in fuel pump circuit. If fuel pump operates with jumper wire installed, check fuel pump relay and relay energizing circuit. Repair as necessary.

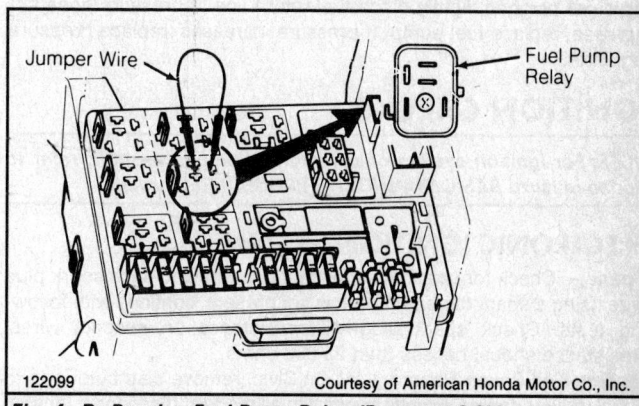

Fig. 4: By-Passing Fuel Pump Relay (Passport 2.6L)

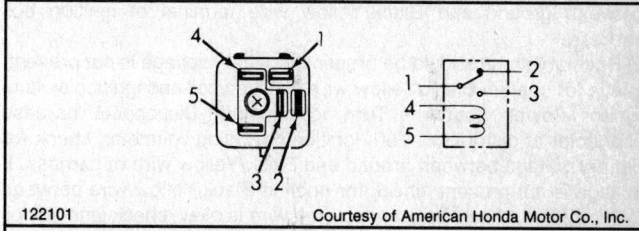

Fig. 5: Identifying Fuel Pump Relay Terminals (Passport 2.6L)

Pressure Testing (Passport 3.2L) – **1)** Relieve fuel system pressure. See FUEL SYSTEM PRESSURE RELEASE. Attach Fuel Pressure Gauge Set (J-34730-1) and Adapter (J-35957-1) to outlet side of fuel filter. Disconnect pressure regulator vacuum hose. Turn ignition on. Allow fuel pump to run for about 2 seconds. Fuel system pressure should be about 40-46 psi (2.8-3.2 kg/cm²).

2) Start engine and check for leaks. With engine idling, fuel pressure should be 25-30 psi (1.8-2.1 kg/cm²). Connect pressure regulator vacuum hose.

3) If engine will not start, remove fuel pump relay. Connect jumper wire between fuel pump relay connector terminal No. 2 (Red/Black wire; Red/White wire before fuse) and terminal No. 4 (Black/Red wire). Turn ignition on. If fuel pump operates for about 10 seconds, replace fuel pump relay. If fuel pump does not operate at all, repair open in Red/Black wire (Red/White wire before fuse).

REGULATED FUEL PRESSURE

Application	At Idle psi (kg/cm²)
Accord, Civic & Civic Del Sol [1]	
Vacuum Hose Disconnected	40-47 (2.8-3.3)
Vacuum Hose Connected	30-38 (2.1-2.7)
Passport	
2.6L Engine [2]	35 (2.4)
3.2L Engine [3]	25-30 (1.8-2.1)
Prelude [1]	
2.2L Engine (F22A1)	
Vacuum Hose Disconnected	36-43 (2.5-3.0)
Vacuum Hose Connected	28-35 (2.0-2.5)
2.2L Engine (H22A1)	
Vacuum Hose Disconnected	33-40 (2.3-2.8)
Vacuum Hose Connected	25-32 (1.8-2.3)
2.3L Engine (H23A1)	
Vacuum Hose Disconnected	36-43 (2.5-3.0)
Vacuum Hose Connected	28-35 (2.0-2.5)

[1] – Measure regulated fuel pressure with vacuum hose connected and disconnected from pressure regulator.

[2] – With pressure regulator vacuum hose connected and Vacuum Switching Valve (VSV) disconnected.

[3] – With engine at idle or with 12-14 in. Hg vacuum manually applied to pressure regulator.

4) If pressure is higher than specified, inspect for pinched or clogged fuel return line between fuel rail and fuel tank. If no problem is found in fuel line, replace pressure regulator.

5) If pressure is less than specified, inspect for plugged fuel filter. If filter is not plugged, lightly pinch fuel return line. If pressure does not increase, replace fuel pump. If pressure increases, replace pressure regulator.

IGNITION CHECKS

NOTE: For Ignition system check information on Passport, refer to Rodeo in Isuzu BASIC DIAGNOSTIC PROCEDURES article.

ELECTRONIC IGNITION SYSTEM

Spark – Check for spark at secondary coil wire and each spark plug wire using a spark tester. If spark is not present, continue with following tests. Check spark plug wire resistance on suspect wires. Resistance should be less than 25,000 ohms.

Ignition Coil Power Source – **1)** On Civic, remove distributor cap to check power source directly at coil. On all models, disconnect ignition coil primary leads. Turn ignition on. Using voltmeter, check voltage between ground and Black/Yellow wire terminal of ignition coil harness.

2) Battery voltage should be present. If battery voltage is not present, check for open in Black/Yellow wire between coil and ignition switch.

Ignitor Power Source – Turn ignition off. Disconnect harness connector at distributor. Turn ignition on. Using voltmeter, check for battery voltage between ground and Black/Yellow wire of harness. If voltage is not present, check for open in Black/Yellow wire between ignition coil and harness connector. If wire is okay, check ignition coil resistance (for internal short to ground).

Ignitor Check – Check TDC/CRANK/CYL sensor resistance values. See TACH PULSE SIGNAL. Check power sources. If no problems are found and spark is not present, replace ignitor.

Ignition Coil Resistance (Accord & Prelude) – **1)** Remove primary and secondary leads from ignition coil. Using an ohmmeter, check resistance between primary terminals "A" and "C" (Accord) or terminals "A" and "B" (Prelude) of ignition coil. *See Fig. 6.* Resistance should be .6-.8 ohm at room temperature.

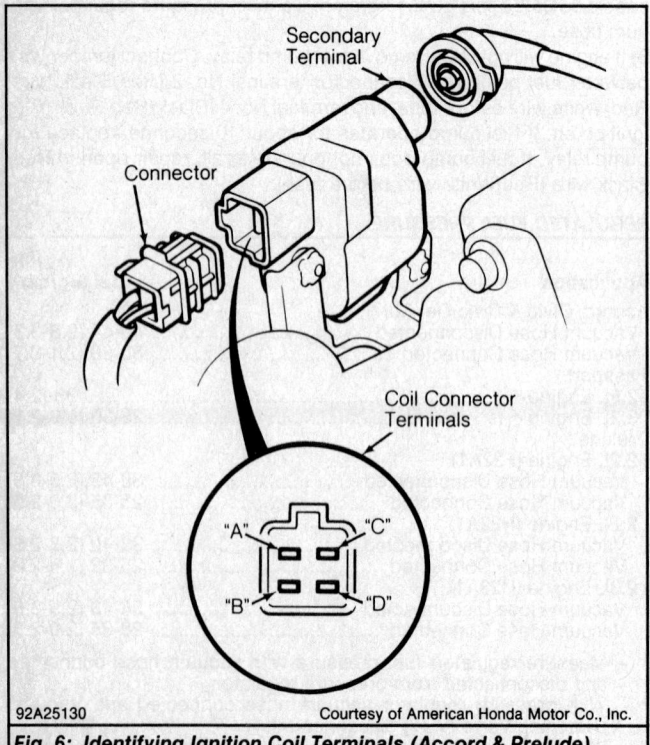

92A25130   Courtesy of American Honda Motor Co., Inc.

Fig. 6: Identifying Ignition Coil Terminals (Accord & Prelude)

2) On Accord, check resistance between terminals "B" and "D" of ignition coil (tachometer circuit). Resistance should be about 2090-2310 ohms at room temperature.

3) On all models, check secondary resistance between terminal "A" and secondary output terminal (coil tower). See IGNITION COIL RESISTANCE table. Check for continuity between terminals "A" and "B" (Accord) or terminals "A" and "C" (Prelude). Continuity should exist. If readings are not within specification, replace coil.

IGNITION COIL RESISTANCE – Ohms @ 68°F (20°C)

Application	Primary	Secondary
Accord & Prelude	.6-.8	14,000-22,000
Passport	.8-1.0	7,500-11,300
Civic & Civic Del Sol	.6-.8	12,800-19,200

Ignition Coil Resistance (Civic & Civic Del Sol) – **1)** Turn ignition off. Remove distributor cap. Remove 2 Phillips screws retaining primary ignition leads to ignition coil. Remove primary leads from ignition coil. Using an ohmmeter, check resistance between primary terminals "A" and "B" on ignition coil. *See Fig. 7.* Resistance should be .6-.8 ohm at room temperature.

2) Check secondary resistance between terminal "A" and secondary output terminal (coil tower) at room temperature. See IGNITION COIL RESISTANCE table. If readings are not within specification, replace coil.

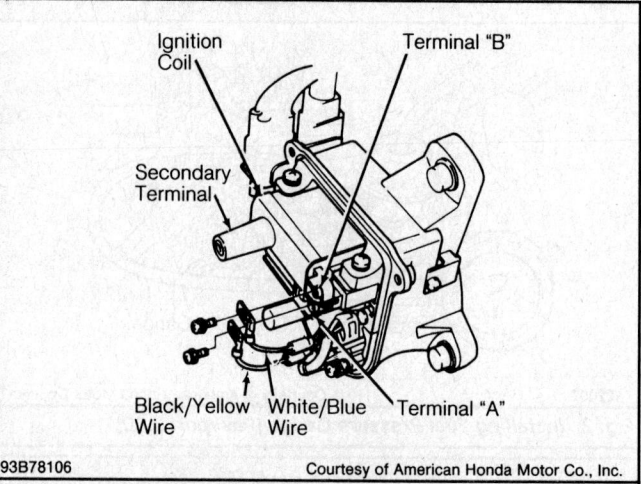

93B78106   Courtesy of American Honda Motor Co., Inc.

Fig. 7: Identifying Ignition Coil Terminals (Civic & Civic Del Sol)

Tach Pulse Signal – **1)** Timing control and triggering of fuel injectors are based upon input signals from TDC/CRANK/CYL sensors. These sensors are simple Permanent Magnet (PM) generator pick-up coils.

2) Using a DVOM on low voltage scale (preferably with a bar-graph function), check for a pulsed low-voltage signal at proper Engine Control Module (ECM) harness terminals with engine cranking. See WIRING HARNESS & SENSOR RESISTANCE TEST table. *See Fig. 8.* If a pulsed signal is present, fault does not exist. If pulsed signal is not present, check sensor and wiring integrity.

3) To test sensor and wiring integrity, turn ignition off. Disconnect connectors from ECM. Lightly probe appropriate ECM harness terminals to check for proper winding resistance of each sensor. See WIRING HARNESS & SENSOR RESISTANCE TEST table. If resistance is within specification, go to step **5)**. If resistance is not within specification, go to next step.

4) Check resistance of TDC/CRANK/CYL sensor directly at sensor connector. *See Fig. 9.* See TDC/CRANK/CYL SENSOR RESISTANCE TEST table. If sensor resistance is within specification, repair open, short or corrosion in wire harness between sensor(s) and ECM. If resistance is not within specification, replace sensor.

5) Check continuity to ground at each ECM sensor terminal. If continuity is not present, replace distributor housing. If continuity is present, go to next step.

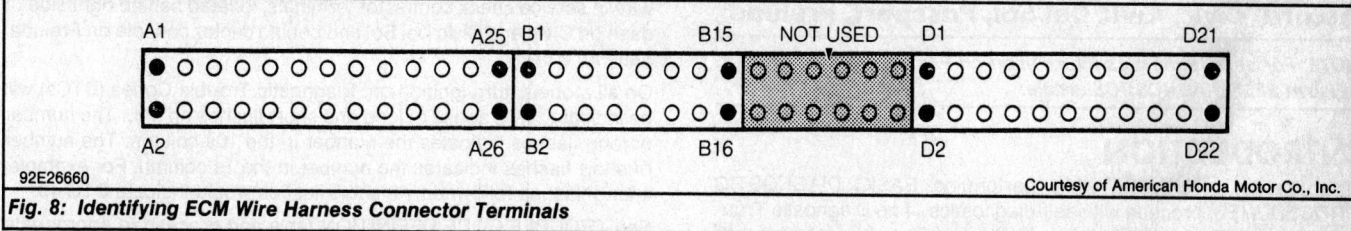

92E26660   Courtesy of American Honda Motor Co., Inc.

Fig. 8: Identifying ECM Wire Harness Connector Terminals

6) Disconnect sensor(s) and recheck for continuity to ground at ECM harness sensor terminals. If continuity no longer exists, go to next step. If continuity to ground is still present, repair short to ground in ECM harness between ECM and sensor(s).

7) Check continuity to ground on each sensor connector terminal. See TDC/CRANK/CYL SENSOR RESISTANCE TEST table. See Fig. 9. Continuity should not exist. If continuity to ground exists, replace sensor.

WIRING HARNESS & SENSOR RESISTANCE TEST

Application	Terminals	Ohms
Accord		
CRANK	B15 & B16	260-500
CYL	B11 & B12	260-500
TDC	B13 & B14	260-500
Civic, Civic Del Sol & Prelude		
CRANK	B15 & B16	350-700
CYL	B11 & B12	350-700
TDC	B13 & B14	350-700

TDC/CRANK/CYL SENSOR RESISTANCE TEST

Application	Terminals	Wire Color
CRANK Sensor Wire		
1 Of 2	"B"	Blue/Green
2 Of 2	"F"	Blue/Yellow
CYL Sensor Wire		
1 Of 2	"D"	Orange
2 Of 2	"H"	White
TDC Sensor Wire		
1 Of 2	"C"	Orange/Blue
2 Of 2	"G"	White/Blue

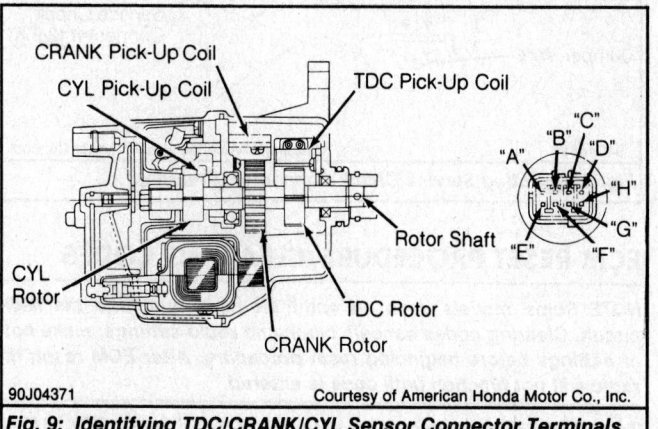

90J04371   Courtesy of American Honda Motor Co., Inc.

Fig. 9: Identifying TDC/CRANK/CYL Sensor Connector Terminals

IDLE SPEED & IGNITION TIMING

Ensure idle speed and ignition timing are set to specification. See IDLE SPEED SPECIFICATIONS and IGNITION TIMING tables. For adjustment procedures, see ON-VEHICLE ADJUSTMENTS article.

IDLE SPEED SPECIFICATIONS

Application	RPM
Accord & Prelude [1]	500-600
Civic & Civic Del Sol [1]	
A/T	650-750
M/T	
Except B16A3 Engine	620-720
B16A3 Engine	650-760
Passport	
2.6L	900
3.2L [2]	750

[1] – With Electronic Air Control Valve (EACV) disconnected, headlights and cooling fan off and transmission in Neutral or Park.

[2] – Idle speed is controlled by ECM and is not adjustable.

IGNITION TIMING (Degrees BTDC @ RPM)

Application	Specification
Accord & Prelude	13-17 @ 650-750
Civic & Civic Del Sol	
1.5L Engine (D15B7)	
A/T	16 @ 650-750
M/T	16 @ 620-720
1.5L Engine (D15B8)	12 @ 620-720
1.5L Engine (D15Z1)	16 @ 550-650
1.6L Engine (B16A3)	16 @ 650-750
1.6L Engine (D16Z6)	
A/T	16 @ 650-750
M/T	16 @ 620-720
Passport	
2.6L Engine	12 @ 900
3.2L Engine [1]	10-13 @ 900-1000

[1] – Ignition timing is controlled by the Engine Control Module (ECM) and cannot be adjusted.

SUMMARY

If no faults were found while performing BASIC DIAGNOSTIC PROCEDURES, proceed to SELF-DIAGNOSTICS article. If no hard codes are found in self-diagnostics, proceed to TROUBLE SHOOTING – NO CODES article for diagnosis by symptom (i.e., ROUGH IDLE, NO-START, etc.), or intermittent diagnostic procedures.

1994 ENGINE PERFORMANCE
Self-Diagnostics

Accord, Civic, Civic Del Sol, Passport, Prelude

NOTE: For self-diagnostics information on Passport, refer to Rodeo in Isuzu SELF-DIAGNOSTICS article.

INTRODUCTION

If no faults were found while performing BASIC DIAGNOSTIC PROCEDURES, proceed with self-diagnostics. If no Diagnostic Trouble Codes (DTCs) or only pass codes are present after entering self-diagnostics, proceed to TROUBLE SHOOTING – NO CODES article for diagnosis by symptom (i.e., ROUGH IDLE, NO START, etc.).

SELF-DIAGNOSTIC SYSTEM

SELF-DIAGNOSTICS DIRECTORY (DTC CHARTS)

Application	Page
Accord	1-20
Civic & Civic Del Sol	1-64
Prelude	1-125

Hard Failures – Hard failures cause Malfunction Indicator Light (MIL) to illuminate and remain on until problem is repaired. If light comes on and remains on (light may flash) during vehicle operation, cause of malfunction must be determined by retrieving DTCs and using TROUBLE CODE CHARTS. See RETRIEVING CODES. If a sensor fails, control unit will use a substitute value in its calculations to continue engine operation. In this condition, commonly known as limp-in mode, the vehicle runs but driveability will not be optimum.

Intermittent Failures – Intermittent failures may cause Malfunction Indicator light (MIL) to flicker or illuminate and go out after the intermittent fault goes away. The corresponding DTC will be retained in ECM memory. If related fault does not reoccur within 50 starter operations, related DTC will be erased from control unit memory. Intermittent failures may be caused by sensor, connector or wiring related problems. See INTERMITTENTS in TROUBLE SHOOTING – NO CODES article.

MALFUNCTION INDICATOR LIGHT (MIL)

All models are equipped with an MIL. As a bulb check, light illuminates when ignition is on and engine is not running. MIL also illuminates when a system failure has been detected and a corresponding DTC has been set in ECM memory. Not all trouble codes will activate MIL. If MIL is on and no DTCs are in memory, problem may be intermittent. See INTERMITTENTS in TROUBLE SHOOTING – NO CODES article.

RETRIEVING CODES

Turn ignition off. On Accord, connect SCS Service Connector (07PAZ-0010100) to service check connector, located behind right side of dash. *See Fig. 1.* On Civic, Civic Del Sol and Prelude, insert jumper wire in service check connector terminals, located behind right side of dash on Civic and Civic Del Sol and behind center console on Prelude. *See Fig. 2 or 3.*

On all models, turn ignition on. Diagnostic Trouble Codes (DTCs) will be indicated by a series of long and short flashes on MIL. The number of long flashes indicates the number in the 10s column. The number of short flashes indicates the number in the 1s column. For example, 4 long flashes followed by 3 short flashes would indicate DTC 43.

See TROUBLE CODE DEFINITION table and proceed to appropriate TROUBLE CODE CHART for testing. All voltage tests should be performed with a Digital Volt-Ohmmeter (DVOM) with a minimum 10-megohm input impedance, unless specifically stated differently in testing procedure.

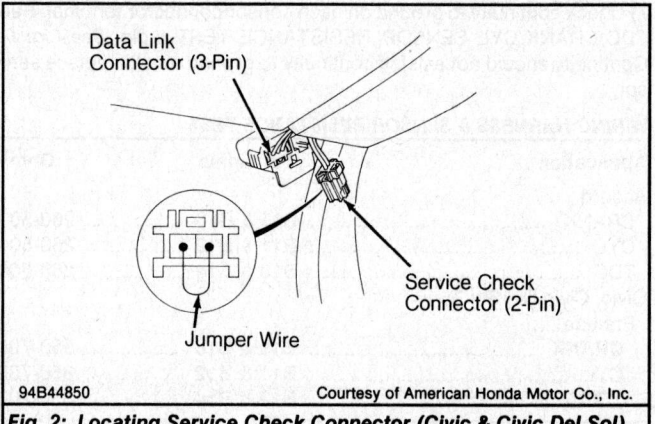

94B44850   Courtesy of American Honda Motor Co., Inc.

Fig. 2: Locating Service Check Connector (Civic & Civic Del Sol)

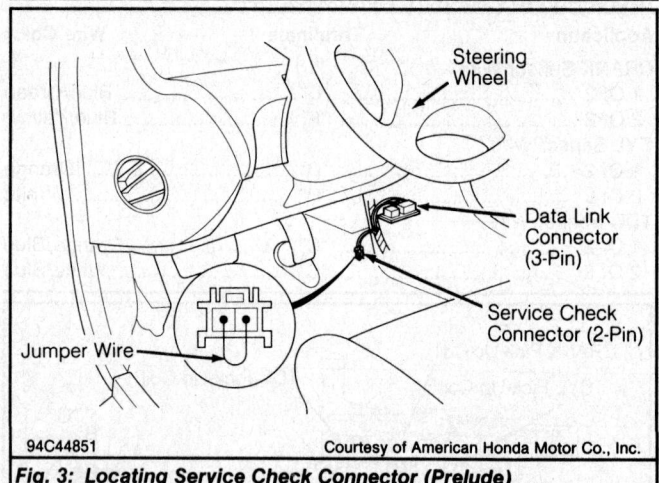

94C44851   Courtesy of American Honda Motor Co., Inc.

Fig. 3: Locating Service Check Connector (Prelude)

ECM RESET PROCEDURE/CLEARING CODES

NOTE: Some models have an anti-theft code built into the radio circuit. Clearing codes cancels clock and radio settings; make note of settings before beginning reset procedure. After ECM reset, the radio will not function until code is entered.

To reset ECM (clear codes), remove BACK UP fuse (CLOCK/RADIO fuse on Prelude) from underhood fuse/relay block. Leave fuse out for 10 seconds to reset ECM.

ECM LOCATION

On Prelude, ECM is located under carpet in passenger-side footwell. On Accord, Civic and Civic Del Sol, ECM is located in passenger side kick panel.

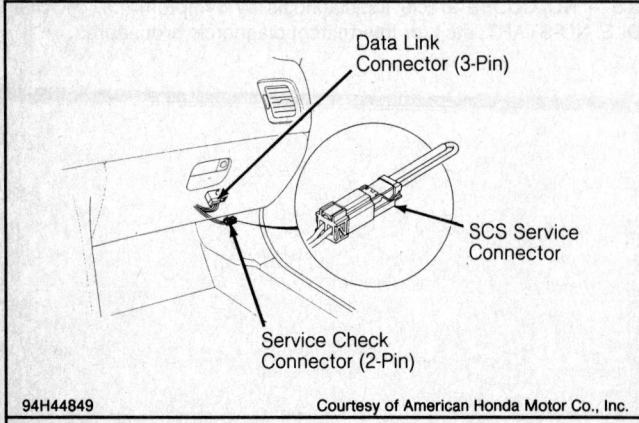

94H44849   Courtesy of American Honda Motor Co., Inc.

Fig. 1: Locating Service Check Connector (Accord)

DIAGNOSTIC TROUBLE CODE DEFINITION
DIAGNOSTIC TROUBLE CODE IDENTIFICATION CHART

Code [1]	System Affected	Probable Cause
MIL Never On (Accord)	MIL	MIL Circuit Fault
MIL Always On (Accord)	ECM	No Signal To ECM
0 (Civic, Civic Del Sol & Prelude)	ECM	No Signal To ECM
1	Heated Oxygen Sensor (HO2S)	HO2S Circuit Fault
3	MAP Sensor	Electrical Problem In MAP Sensor
4	Crankshaft Position (CKP) Sensor	Open Or Shorted Signal Circuit
5 (Civic, Civic Del Sol & Prelude)	MAP Sensor	Mechanical Problem In MAP Sensor
6	Engine Coolant Temperature (ECT) Sensor	Open Or Shorted Signal Circuit
7	Throttle Position (TP) Sensor	Open Or Shorted Signal Circuit
8	Top Dead Center Position (TDC) Sensor	Open Or Shorted Signal Circuit
9	No. 1 Cylinder Position (CYP) Sensor	Open Or Shorted Signal Circuit
10	Intake Air Temperature (IAT)	Sensor Fault
12 (Accord, Civic & Prelude)	EGR System	EGR System Fault
13	Barometric Pressure (BARO) Sensor	BARO Sensor Fault
14	Idle Air Control (IAC) Valve	Open Or Shorted Signal Circuit
15	Ignition Output Signal	Electrical Problem In Signal Circuit
16	Fuel Injector	Fuel Injector Circuit Fault
17	Vehicle Speed Sensor (VSS)	Open Or Shorted Signal Circuit
19 (Civic & Civic Del Sol)	A/T Lock-Up Control Solenoid Valve	Lock-Up Solenoid Circuit Fault
20 [2]	Electrical Load Detector (ELD)	ELD Circuit Fault
21	VTEC Solenoid Valve	VTEC Solenoid Valve Circuit Fault
22	VTEC Oil Pressure Switch	VTEC Oil Pressure Switch Circuit Fault
23 (Civic Del Sol & Prelude)	Knock Sensor	Knock Sensor Circuit Fault
30 (Accord & Prelude)	A/T FI Signal A	A/T FI Signal A Circuit Fault
31 (Accord & Prelude)	A/T FI Signal B	Problem In A/T Control Unit & ECM Circuit
41	Heated Oxygen Sensor (HO2S) Heater	HO2S Heater Circuit Fault
43	Fuel Supply System	Problem With HO2S Circuit Or Fuel System
48 (Civic – Federal D15Z1 Engine)	Heated Oxygen Sensor (HO2S)	HO2S Circuit Fault

[1] – If codes other than these are indicated, repeat self-diagnosis. If code(s) reappear, substitute a known good ECM, and recheck codes. If code(s) clear, replace ECM.

[2] – MIL does not come on when there is a malfunction in ELD circuit, but code is stored in ECM memory.

SUMMARY

If no hard trouble codes (or only pass codes) are present, driveability symptoms exist or intermittent codes exist, proceed to TROUBLE SHOOTING – NO CODES article for diagnosis by symptom (i.e., ROUGH IDLE, NO START, etc.) or intermittent diagnostic procedure.

DIAGNOSTIC TROUBLE CODE CHARTS

NOTE: In the following diagnostic trouble code charts, illustrations and schematics are courtesy of American Honda Motor Co., Inc.

Using Diagnostic Trouble Code Charts – To use DIAGNOSTIC TROUBLE CODE CHARTS, see RETRIEVING CODES under SELF-DIAGNOSTIC SYSTEM. After codes have been recorded, proceed to appropriate DIAGNOSTIC TROUBLE CODE CHART.

When directed by chart to install ECM test harness, turn ignition off. Connect ECM Test Harness (07LAJ-PT3010A) between ECM and connector. *See Fig. 4.* Follow code chart directions.

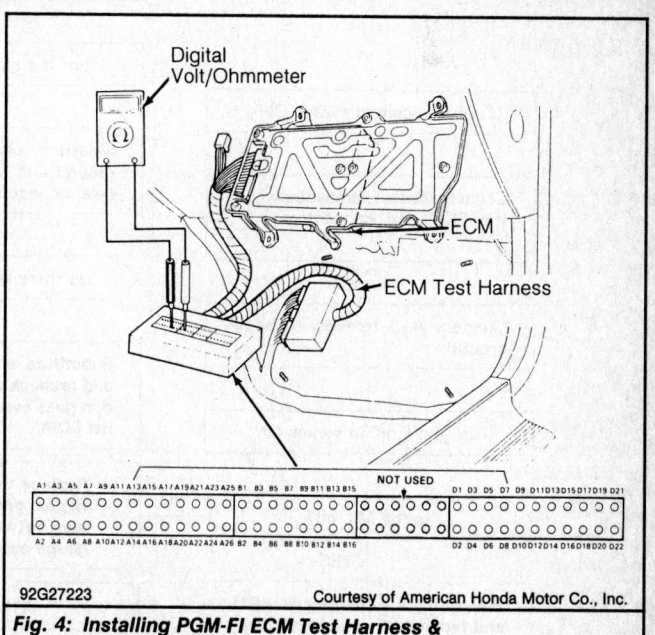

92G27223   Courtesy of American Honda Motor Co., Inc.

Fig. 4: Installing PGM-FI ECM Test Harness & Identifying Terminals

**MALFUNCTION INDICATOR LIGHT
(MIL) INOPERATIVE
ACCORD**

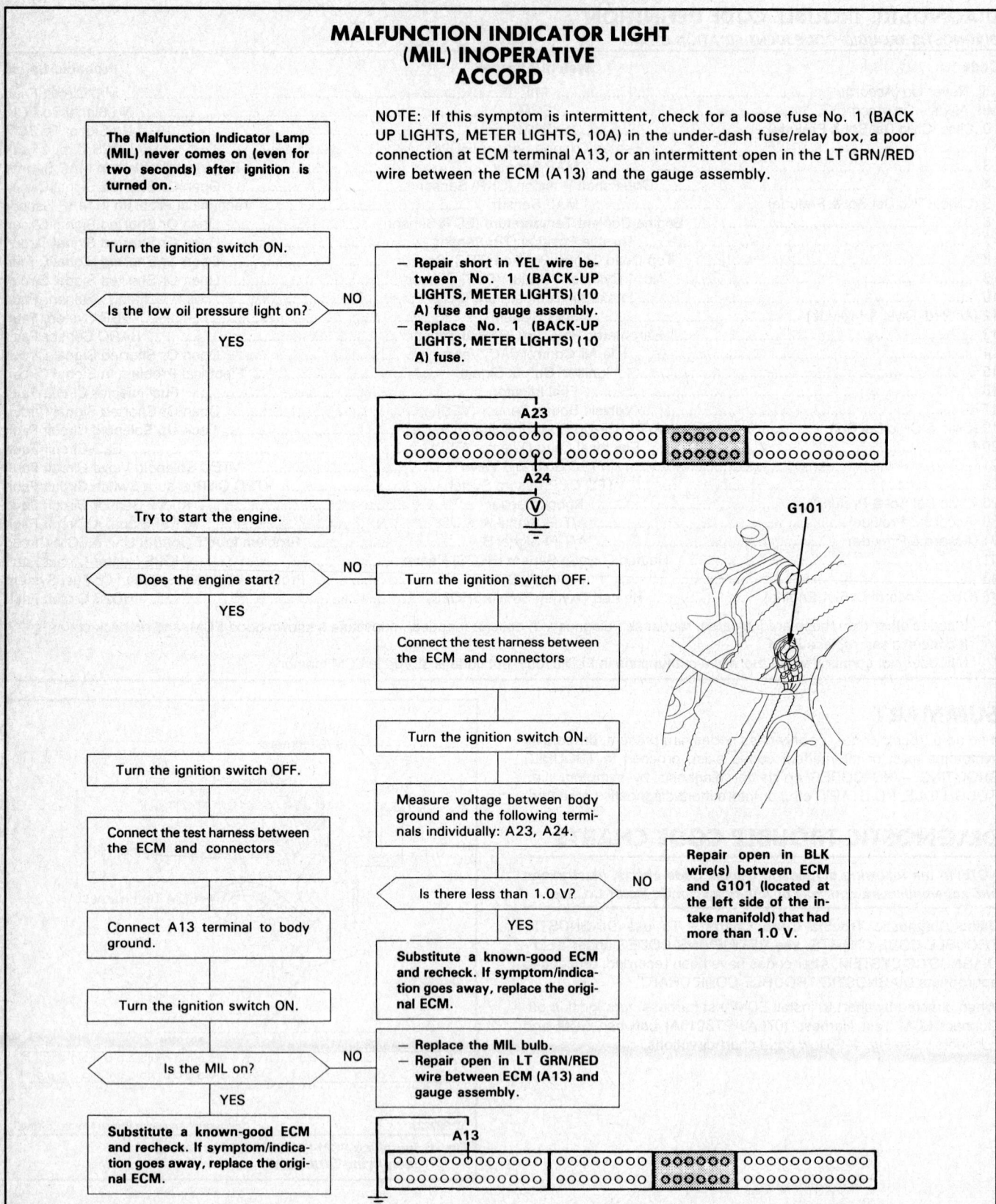

NOTE: If this symptom is intermittent, check for a loose fuse No. 1 (BACK UP LIGHTS, METER LIGHTS, 10A) in the under-dash fuse/relay box, a poor connection at ECM terminal A13, or an intermittent open in the LT GRN/RED wire between the ECM (A13) and the gauge assembly.

The Malfunction Indicator Lamp (MIL) never comes on (even for two seconds) after ignition is turned on.

Turn the ignition switch ON.

Is the low oil pressure light on? — NO

- Repair short in YEL wire between No. 1 (BACK-UP LIGHTS, METER LIGHTS) (10 A) fuse and gauge assembly.
- Replace No. 1 (BACK-UP LIGHTS, METER LIGHTS) (10 A) fuse.

YES

A23

A24

G101

Try to start the engine.

Does the engine start? — NO

Turn the ignition switch OFF.

YES

Connect the test harness between the ECM and connectors

Turn the ignition switch OFF.

Turn the ignition switch ON.

Connect the test harness between the ECM and connectors

Measure voltage between body ground and the following terminals individually: A23, A24.

Repair open in BLK wire(s) between ECM and G101 (located at the left side of the intake manifold) that had more than 1.0 V.

Is there less than 1.0 V? — NO

Connect A13 terminal to body ground.

YES

Substitute a known-good ECM and recheck. If symptom/indication goes away, replace the original ECM.

Turn the ignition switch ON.

Is the MIL on? — NO

- Replace the MIL bulb.
- Repair open in LT GRN/RED wire between ECM (A13) and gauge assembly.

YES

Substitute a known-good ECM and recheck. If symptom/indication goes away, replace the original ECM.

A13

94E44713

MALFUNCTION INDICATOR LIGHT (MIL)
STAYS ON AFTER 2 SECONDS (1 OF 3)
ACCORD

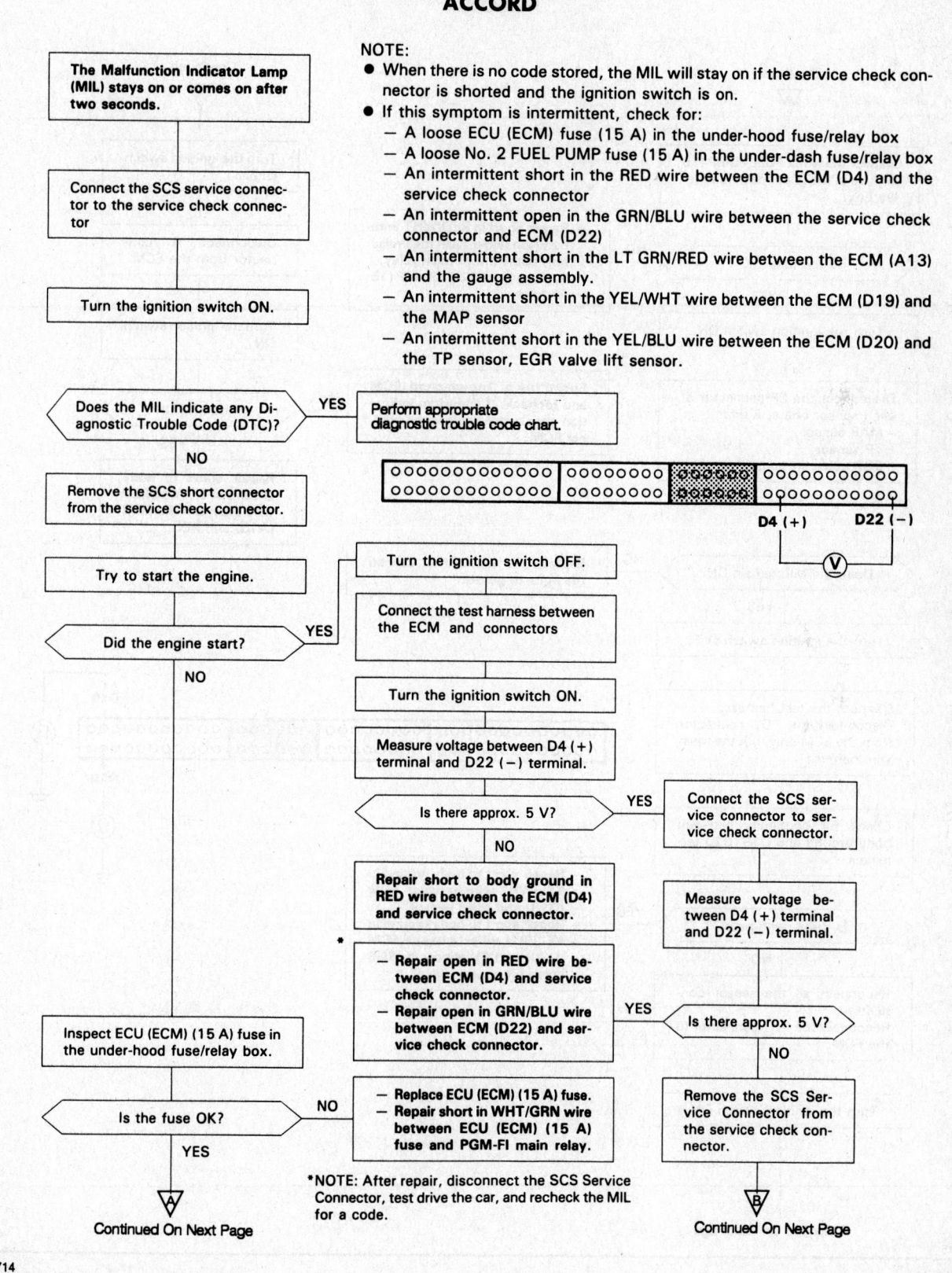

NOTE:
- When there is no code stored, the MIL will stay on if the service check connector is shorted and the ignition switch is on.
- If this symptom is intermittent, check for:
  - A loose ECU (ECM) fuse (15 A) in the under-hood fuse/relay box
  - A loose No. 2 FUEL PUMP fuse (15 A) in the under-dash fuse/relay box
  - An intermittent short in the RED wire between the ECM (D4) and the service check connector
  - An intermittent open in the GRN/BLU wire between the service check connector and ECM (D22)
  - An intermittent short in the LT GRN/RED wire between the ECM (A13) and the gauge assembly.
  - An intermittent short in the YEL/WHT wire between the ECM (D19) and the MAP sensor
  - An intermittent short in the YEL/BLU wire between the ECM (D20) and the TP sensor, EGR valve lift sensor.

The Malfunction Indicator Lamp (MIL) stays on or comes on after two seconds.

Connect the SCS service connector to the service check connector

Turn the ignition switch ON.

Does the MIL indicate any Diagnostic Trouble Code (DTC)? — YES → Perform appropriate diagnostic trouble code chart.

NO

Remove the SCS short connector from the service check connector.

D4 (+)   D22 (−)

Try to start the engine.

Did the engine start? — YES → Turn the ignition switch OFF.

NO

Connect the test harness between the ECM and connectors

Turn the ignition switch ON.

Measure voltage between D4 (+) terminal and D22 (−) terminal.

Is there approx. 5 V? — YES → Connect the SCS service connector to service check connector.

NO

Repair short to body ground in RED wire between the ECM (D4) and service check connector.

Measure voltage between D4 (+) terminal and D22 (−) terminal.

*
- Repair open in RED wire between ECM (D4) and service check connector.
- Repair open in GRN/BLU wire between ECM (D22) and service check connector.

YES ← Is there approx. 5 V?

NO

Inspect ECU (ECM) (15 A) fuse in the under-hood fuse/relay box.

Remove the SCS Service Connector from the service check connector.

Is the fuse OK? — NO →
- Replace ECU (ECM) (15 A) fuse.
- Repair short in WHT/GRN wire between ECU (ECM) (15 A) fuse and PGM-FI main relay.

YES

*NOTE: After repair, disconnect the SCS Service Connector, test drive the car, and recheck the MIL for a code.

A
Continued On Next Page

B
Continued On Next Page

94F44714

MALFUNCTION INDICATOR LIGHT (MIL)
STAYS ON AFTER 2 SECONDS (2 OF 3)
ACCORD

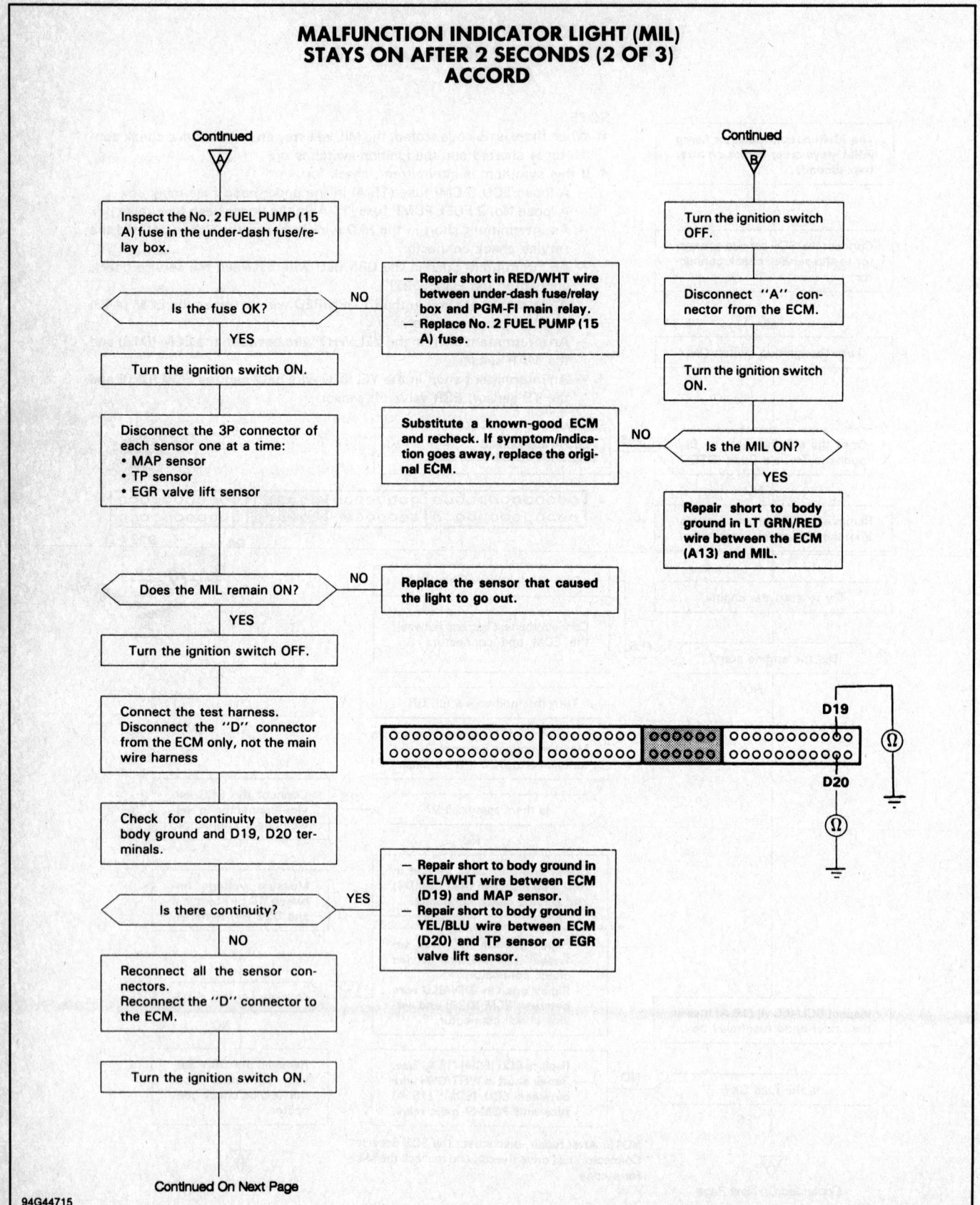

Continued **(A)**

Inspect the No. 2 FUEL PUMP (15 A) fuse in the under-dash fuse/relay box.

Is the fuse OK? — NO →
— Repair short in RED/WHT wire between under-dash fuse/relay box and PGM-FI main relay.
— Replace No. 2 FUEL PUMP (15 A) fuse.

YES

Turn the ignition switch ON.

Disconnect the 3P connector of each sensor one at a time:
• MAP sensor
• TP sensor
• EGR valve lift sensor

Does the MIL remain ON? — NO →
Replace the sensor that caused the light to go out.

YES

Turn the ignition switch OFF.

Connect the test harness. Disconnect the "D" connector from the ECM only, not the main wire harness

Check for continuity between body ground and D19, D20 terminals.

Is there continuity? — YES →
— Repair short to body ground in YEL/WHT wire between ECM (D19) and MAP sensor.
— Repair short to body ground in YEL/BLU wire between ECM (D20) and TP sensor or EGR valve lift sensor.

NO

Reconnect all the sensor connectors.
Reconnect the "D" connector to the ECM.

Turn the ignition switch ON.

Continued **(B)**

Turn the ignition switch OFF.

Disconnect "A" connector from the ECM.

Turn the ignition switch ON.

Substitute a known-good ECM and recheck. If symptom/indication goes away, replace the original ECM. ← NO — Is the MIL ON?

YES

Repair short to body ground in LT GRN/RED wire between the ECM (A13) and MIL.

D19
D20

Continued On Next Page

94G44715

MALFUNCTION INDICATOR LIGHT (MIL)
STAYS ON AFTER 2 SECONDS (3 OF 3)
ACCORD

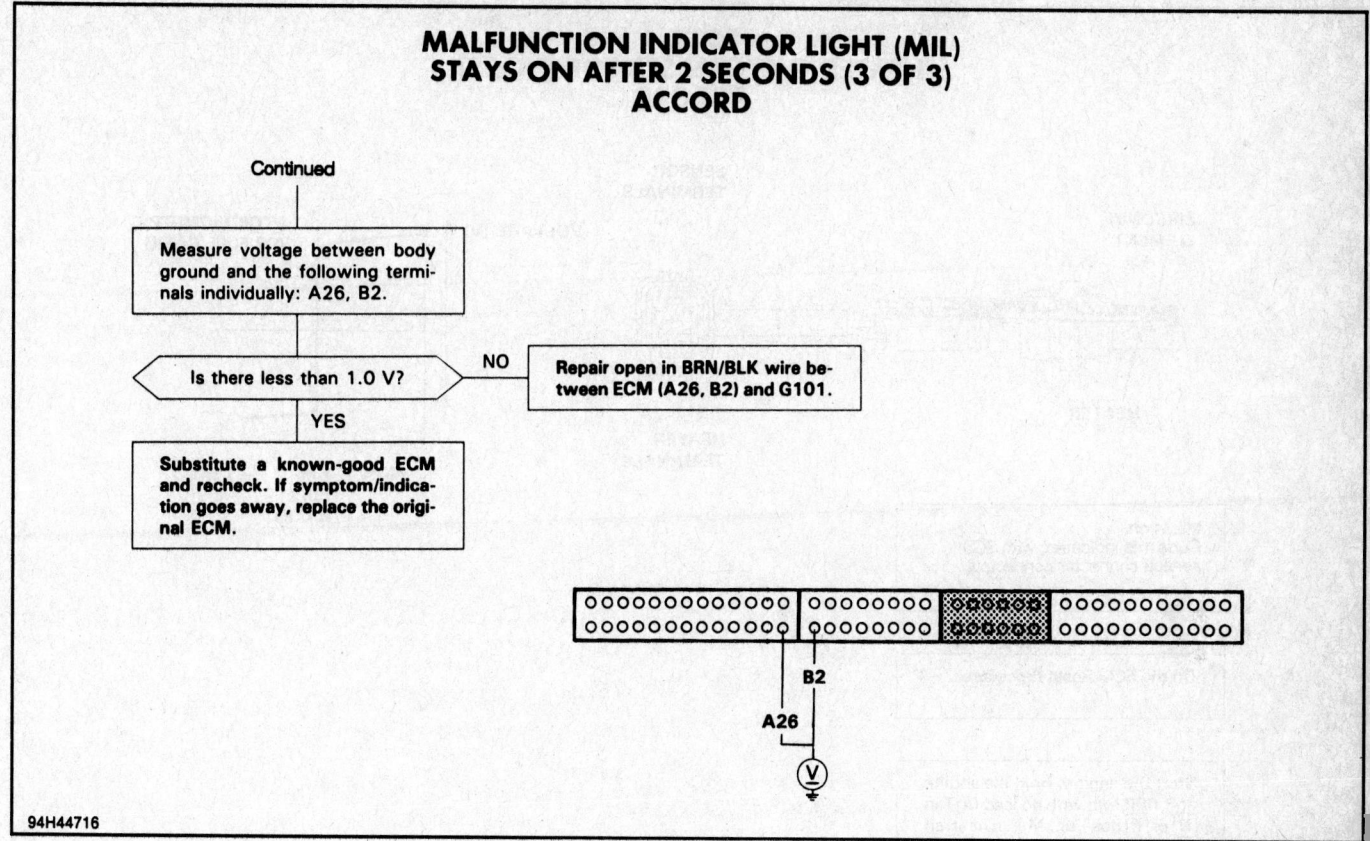

94H44716

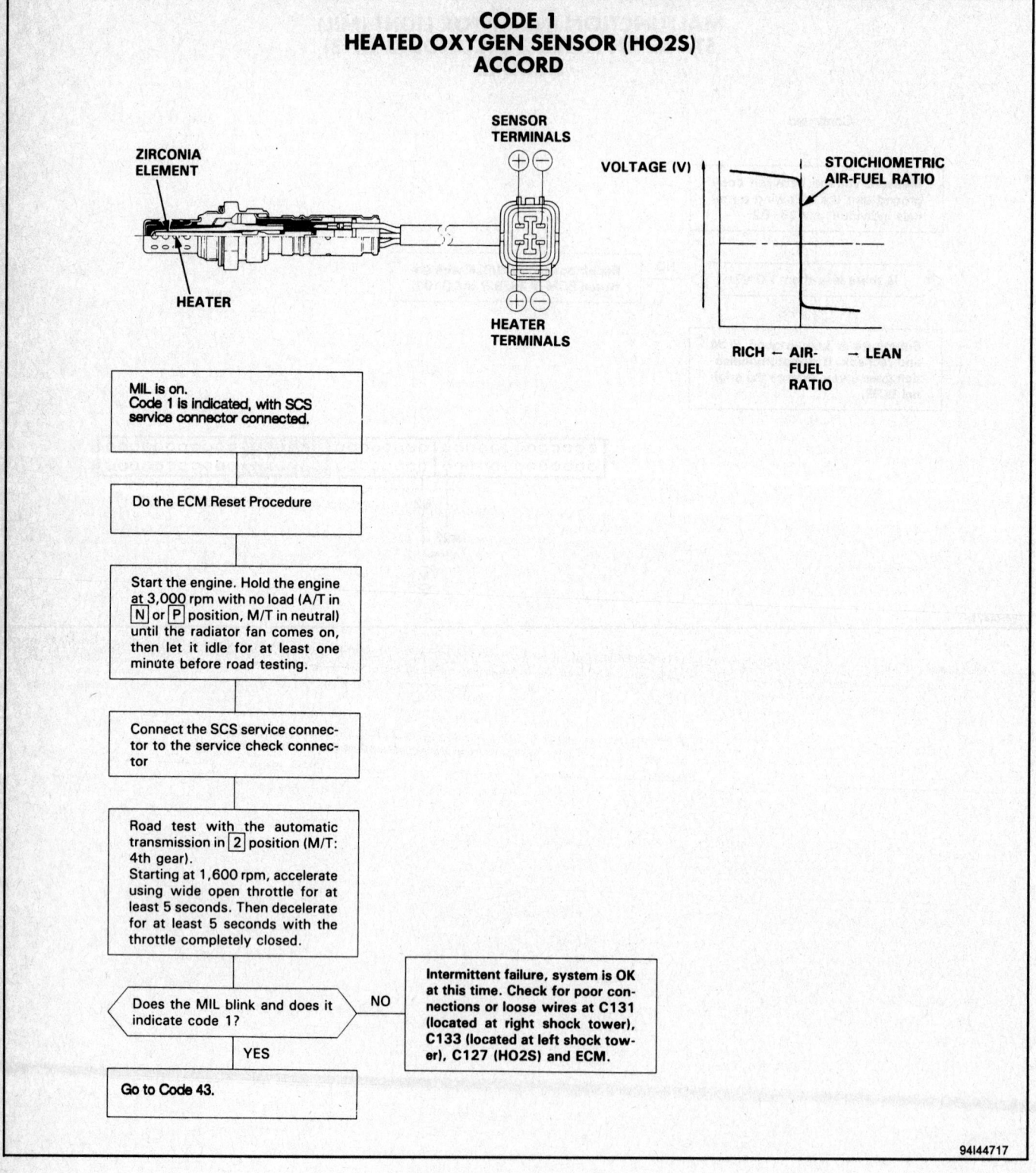

CODE 1
HEATED OXYGEN SENSOR (HO2S)
ACCORD

ZIRCONIA ELEMENT

HEATER

SENSOR TERMINALS

HEATER TERMINALS

VOLTAGE (V)

STOICHIOMETRIC AIR-FUEL RATIO

RICH ← AIR-FUEL RATIO → LEAN

MIL is on.
Code 1 is indicated, with SCS service connector connected.

Do the ECM Reset Procedure

Start the engine. Hold the engine at 3,000 rpm with no load (A/T in N or P position, M/T in neutral) until the radiator fan comes on, then let it idle for at least one minute before road testing.

Connect the SCS service connector to the service check connector

Road test with the automatic transmission in 2 position (M/T: 4th gear).
Starting at 1,600 rpm, accelerate using wide open throttle for at least 5 seconds. Then decelerate for at least 5 seconds with the throttle completely closed.

Does the MIL blink and does it indicate code 1?

NO → Intermittent failure, system is OK at this time. Check for poor connections or loose wires at C131 (located at right shock tower), C133 (located at left shock tower), C127 (HO2S) and ECM.

YES

Go to Code 43.

94I44717

CODE 3 (1 OF 3)
MAP SENSOR CIRCUIT
ACCORD

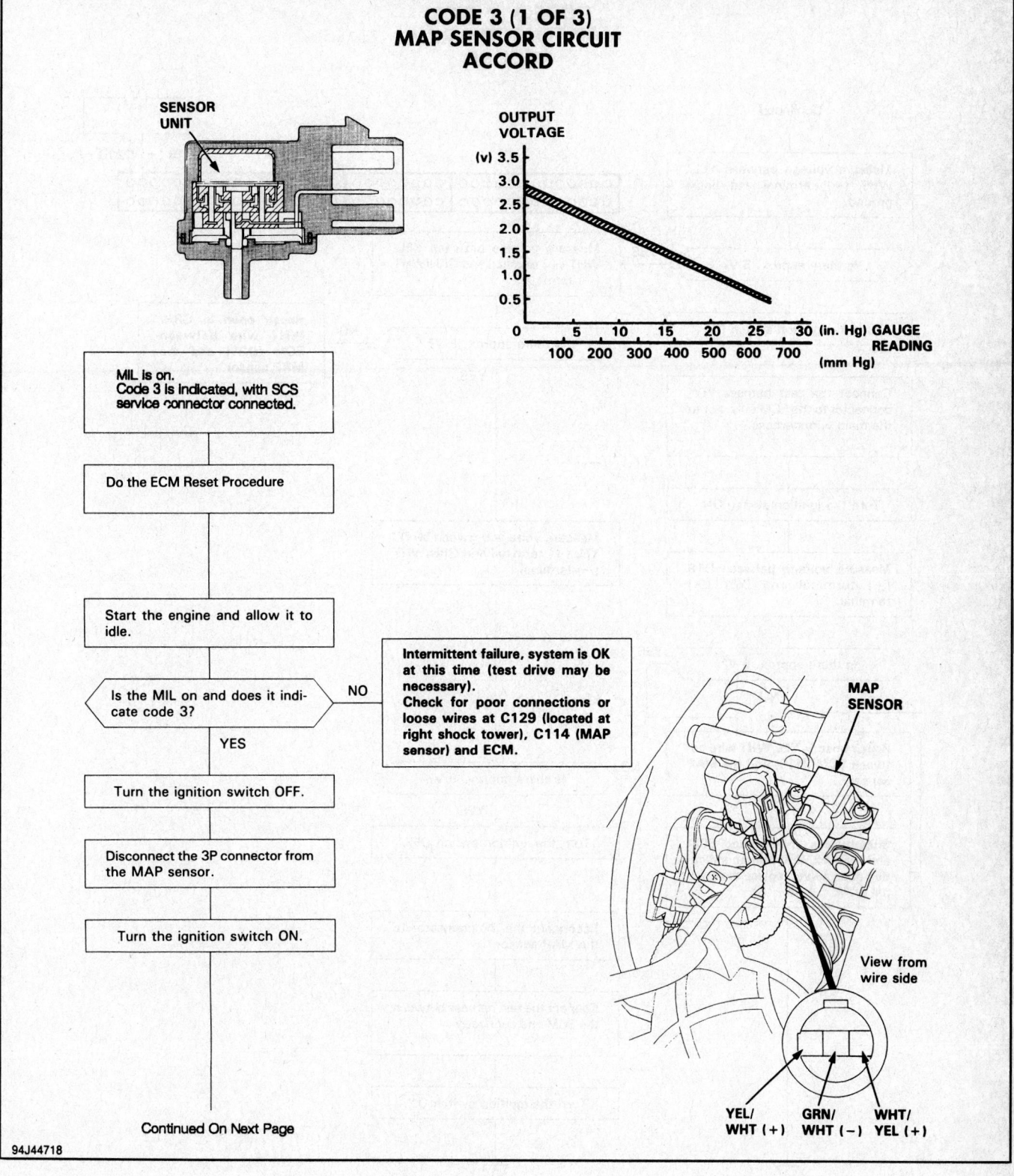

SENSOR UNIT

OUTPUT VOLTAGE

MIL is on.
Code 3 is indicated, with SCS service connector connected.

Do the ECM Reset Procedure

Start the engine and allow it to idle.

Is the MIL on and does it indicate code 3?

NO → Intermittent failure, system is OK at this time (test drive may be necessary).
Check for poor connections or loose wires at C129 (located at right shock tower), C114 (MAP sensor) and ECM.

YES

Turn the ignition switch OFF.

Disconnect the 3P connector from the MAP sensor.

Turn the ignition switch ON.

MAP SENSOR

View from wire side

YEL/WHT (+)   GRN/WHT (−)   WHT/YEL (+)

Continued On Next Page

94J44718

CODE 3 (2 OF 3)
MAP SENSOR CIRCUIT
ACCORD

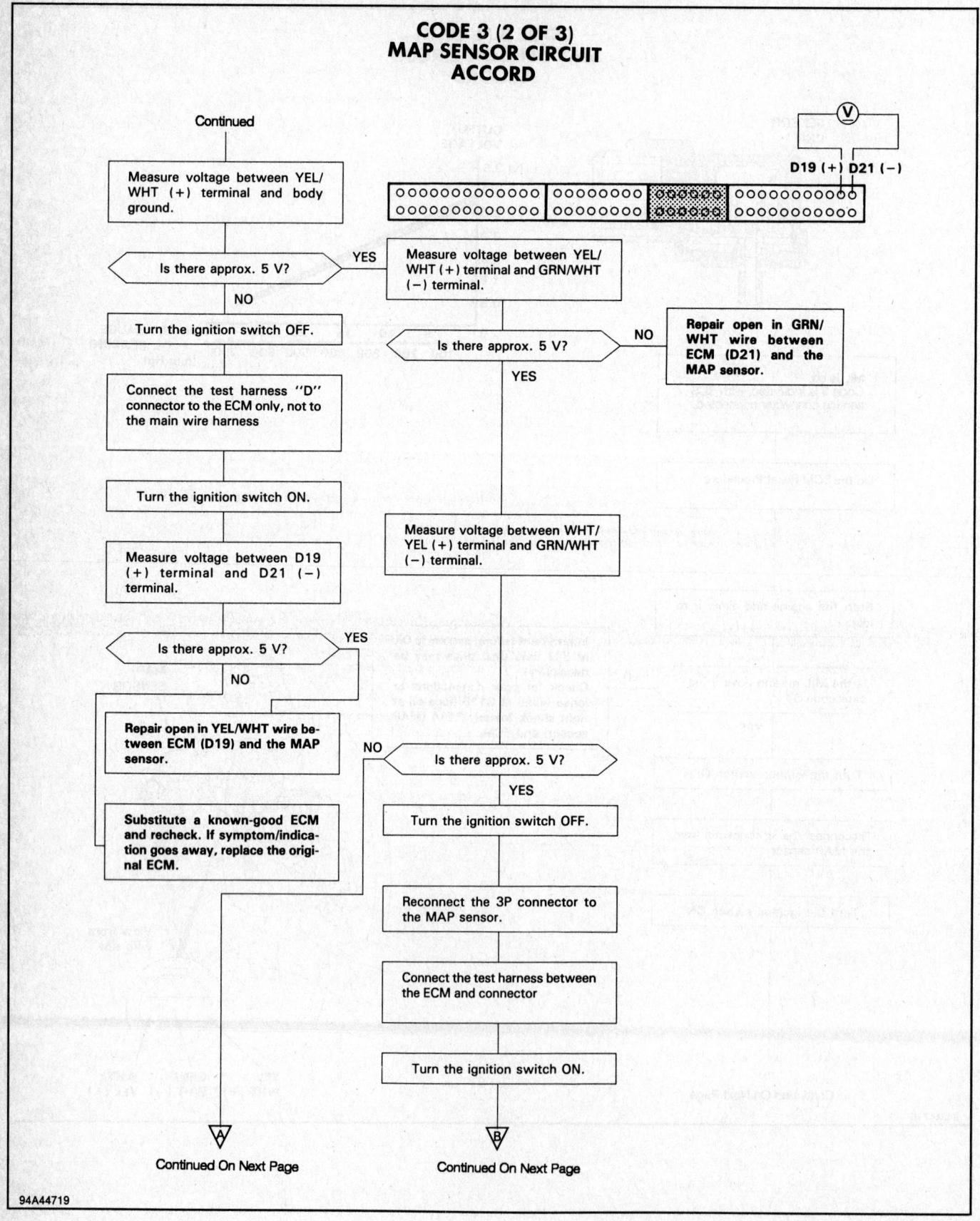

94A44719

CODE 3 (3 OF 3)
MAP SENSOR CIRCUIT
ACCORD

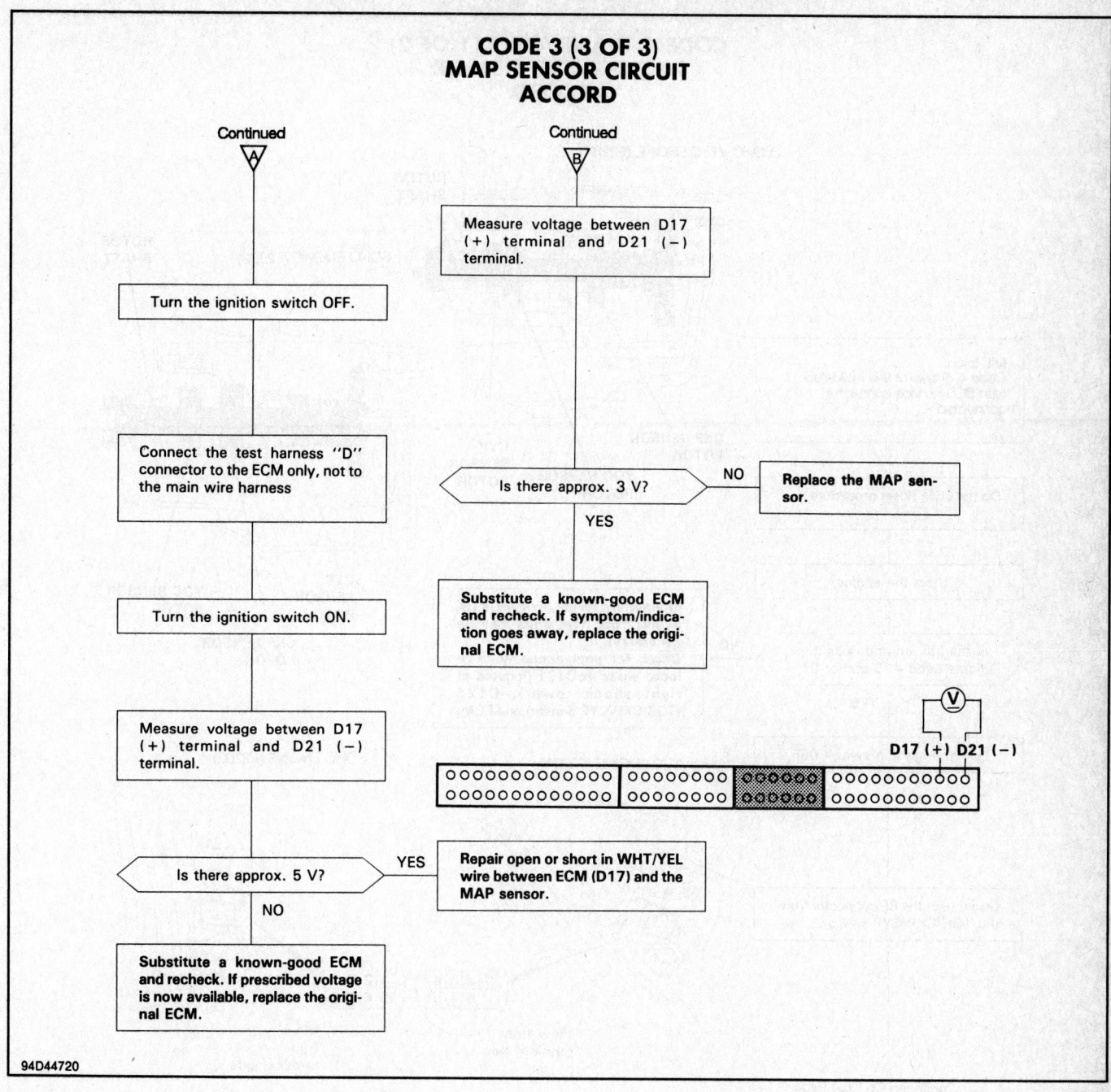

94D44720

CODE 4, 8 AND/OR 9 (1 OF 2)
TDC/CKP/CYP SENSOR
ACCORD

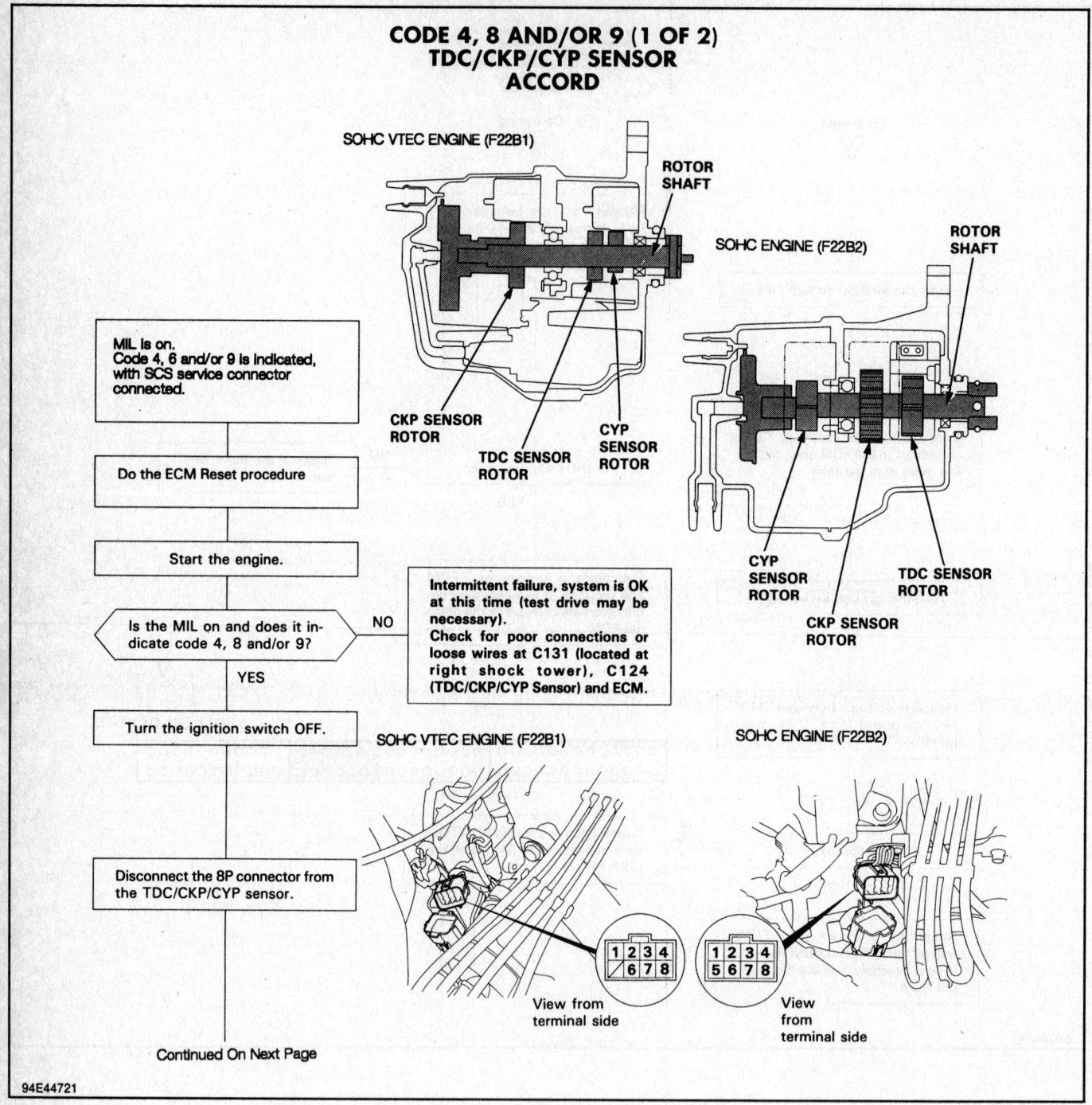

MIL is on.
Code 4, 6 and/or 9 is indicated, with SCS service connector connected.

Do the ECM Reset procedure

Start the engine.

Is the MIL on and does it indicate code 4, 8 and/or 9? — NO → Intermittent failure, system is OK at this time (test drive may be necessary).
Check for poor connections or loose wires at C131 (located at right shock tower), C124 (TDC/CKP/CYP Sensor) and ECM.

YES

Turn the ignition switch OFF.

Disconnect the 8P connector from the TDC/CKP/CYP sensor.

SOHC VTEC ENGINE (F22B1)

SOHC ENGINE (F22B2)

ROTOR SHAFT

CKP SENSOR ROTOR

TDC SENSOR ROTOR

CYP SENSOR ROTOR

CYP SENSOR ROTOR

TDC SENSOR ROTOR

CKP SENSOR ROTOR

View from terminal side

View from terminal side

Continued On Next Page

94E44721

CODE 4, 8 AND/OR 9 (2 OF 2)
TDC/CKP/CYP SENSOR
ACCORD

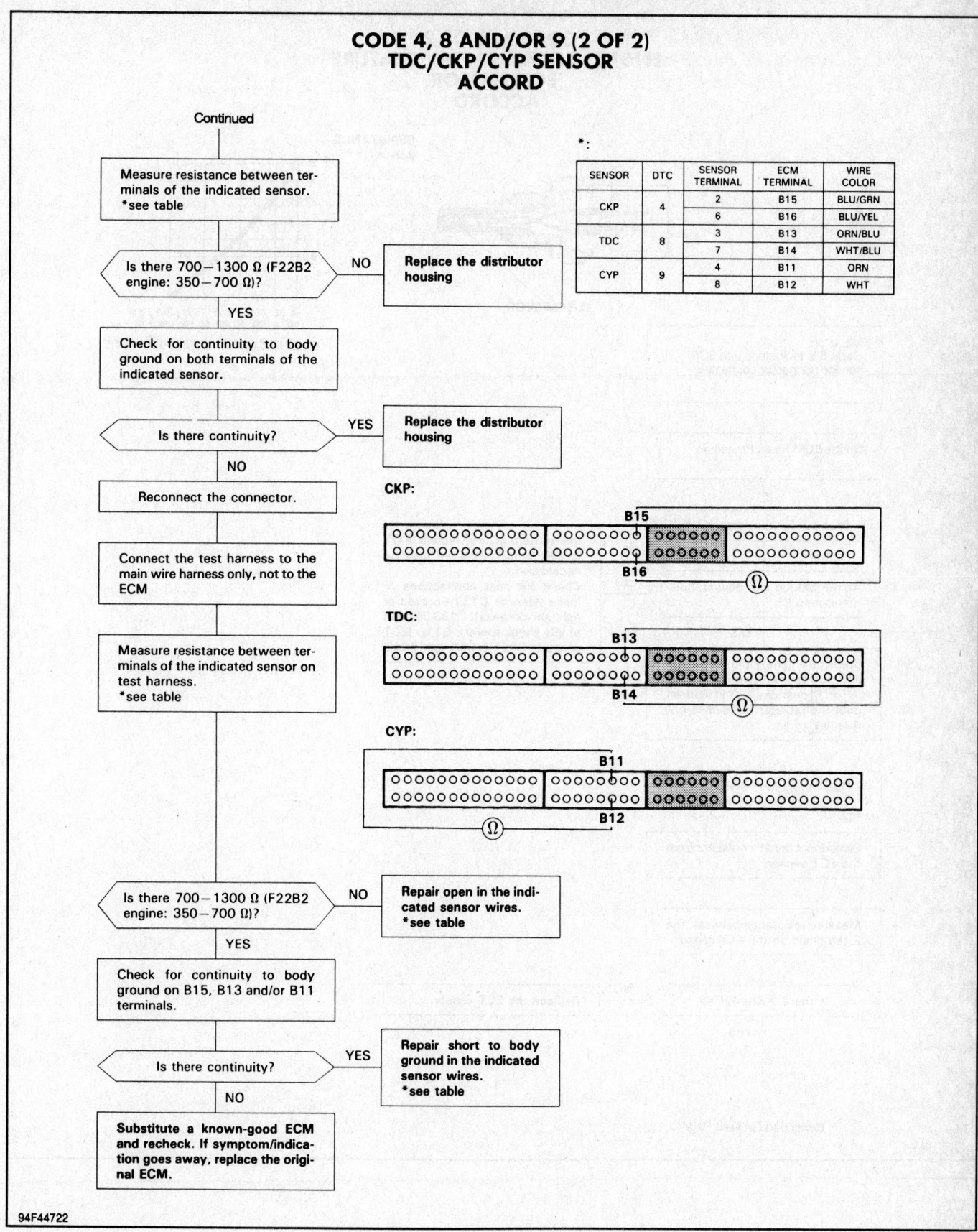

Continued

Measure resistance between terminals of the indicated sensor. *see table

Is there 700—1300 Ω (F22B2 engine: 350—700 Ω)? — NO → **Replace the distributor housing**

YES

Check for continuity to body ground on both terminals of the indicated sensor.

Is there continuity? — YES → **Replace the distributor housing**

NO

Reconnect the connector.

Connect the test harness to the main wire harness only, not to the ECM

Measure resistance between terminals of the indicated sensor on test harness. *see table

Is there 700—1300 Ω (F22B2 engine: 350—700 Ω)? — NO → **Repair open in the indicated sensor wires. *see table**

YES

Check for continuity to body ground on B15, B13 and/or B11 terminals.

Is there continuity? — YES → **Repair short to body ground in the indicated sensor wires. *see table**

NO

Substitute a known-good ECM and recheck. If symptom/indication goes away, replace the original ECM.

*:

SENSOR	DTC	SENSOR TERMINAL	ECM TERMINAL	WIRE COLOR
CKP	4	2	B15	BLU/GRN
		6	B16	BLU/YEL
TDC	8	3	B13	ORN/BLU
		7	B14	WHT/BLU
CYP	9	4	B11	ORN
		8	B12	WHT

CKP:

B15
B16
Ω

TDC:

B13
B14
Ω

CYP:

B11
B12
Ω

94F44722

CODE 6 (1 OF 2)
ENGINE COOLANT TEMPERATURE
(ECT) SENSOR
ACCORD

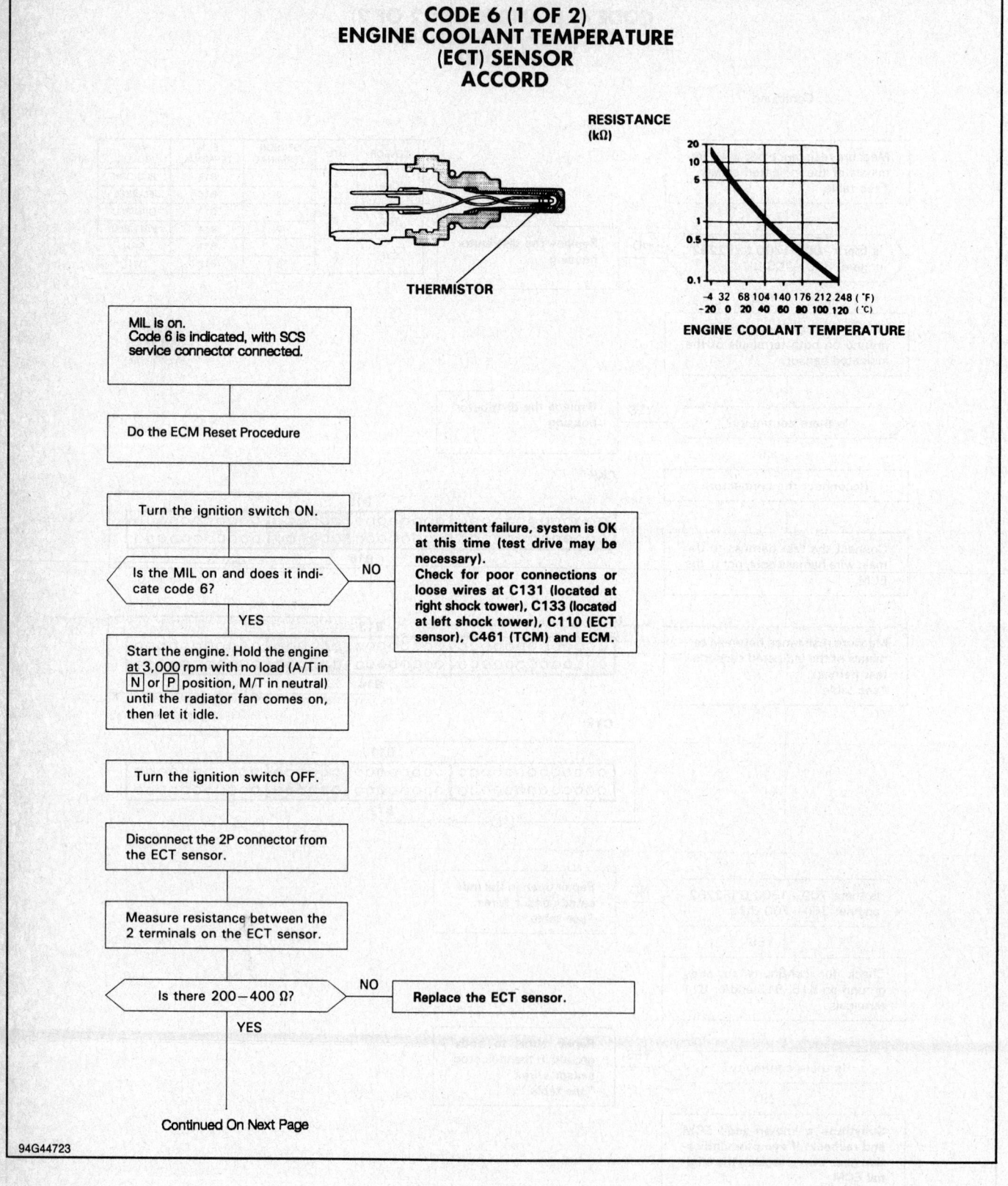

RESISTANCE (kΩ)

THERMISTOR

ENGINE COOLANT TEMPERATURE

MIL is on.
Code 6 is indicated, with SCS service connector connected.

Do the ECM Reset Procedure

Turn the ignition switch ON.

Is the MIL on and does it indicate code 6? — NO → Intermittent failure, system is OK at this time (test drive may be necessary).
Check for poor connections or loose wires at C131 (located at right shock tower), C133 (located at left shock tower), C110 (ECT sensor), C461 (TCM) and ECM.

YES

Start the engine. Hold the engine at 3,000 rpm with no load (A/T in N or P position, M/T in neutral) until the radiator fan comes on, then let it idle.

Turn the ignition switch OFF.

Disconnect the 2P connector from the ECT sensor.

Measure resistance between the 2 terminals on the ECT sensor.

Is there 200—400 Ω? — NO → Replace the ECT sensor.

YES

Continued On Next Page

94G44723

CODE 6 (2 OF 2)
ENGINE COOLANT TEMPERATURE
(ECT) SENSOR
ACCORD

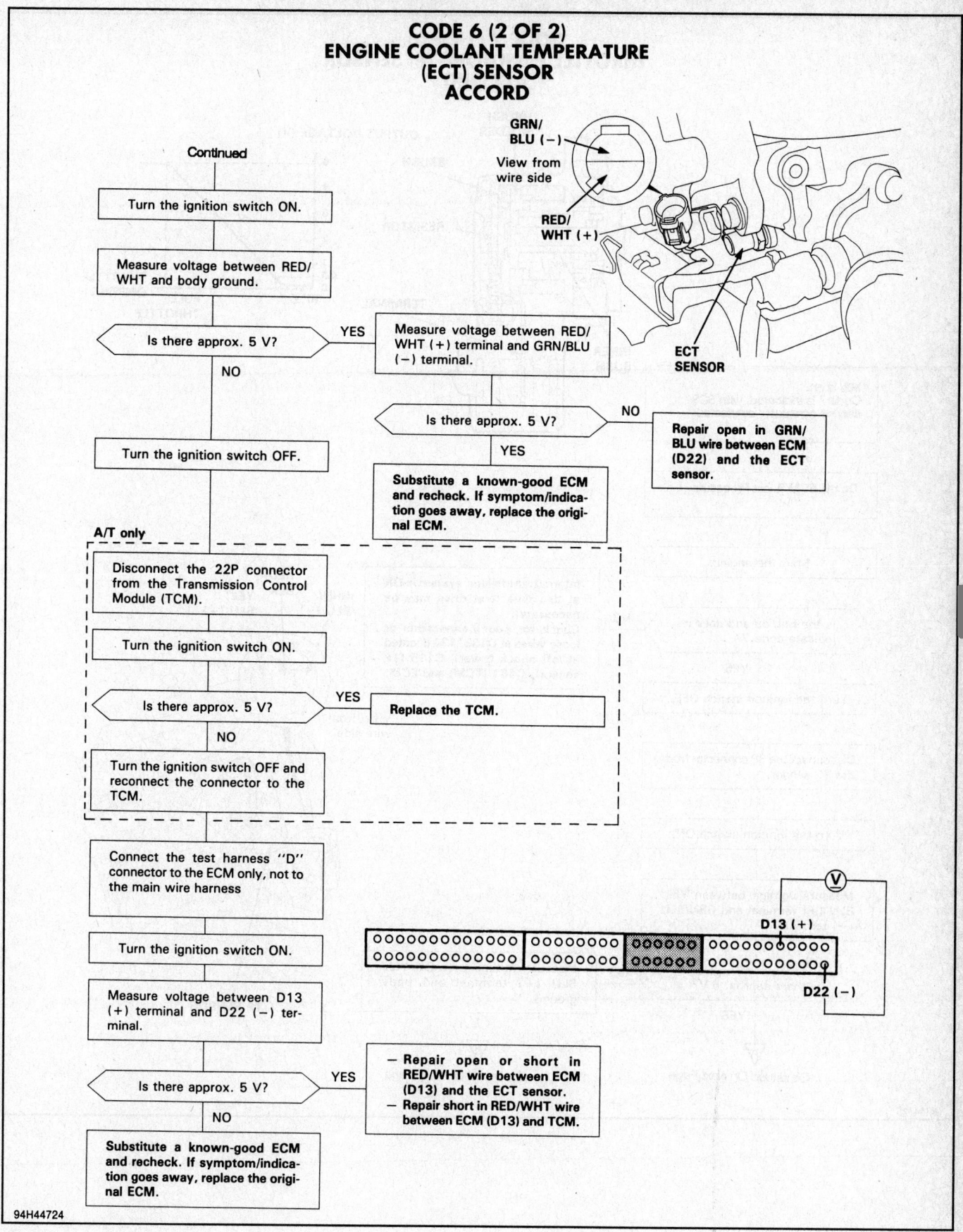

Continued

Turn the ignition switch ON.

Measure voltage between RED/WHT and body ground.

Is there approx. 5 V? — YES → Measure voltage between RED/WHT (+) terminal and GRN/BLU (−) terminal.

NO

Is there approx. 5 V? — NO → Repair open in GRN/BLU wire between ECM (D22) and the ECT sensor.

YES

Turn the ignition switch OFF.

Substitute a known-good ECM and recheck. If symptom/indication goes away, replace the original ECM.

GRN/BLU (−)
View from wire side
RED/WHT (+)
ECT SENSOR

A/T only

Disconnect the 22P connector from the Transmission Control Module (TCM).

Turn the ignition switch ON.

Is there approx. 5 V? — YES → Replace the TCM.

NO

Turn the ignition switch OFF and reconnect the connector to the TCM.

Connect the test harness "D" connector to the ECM only, not to the main wire harness

Turn the ignition switch ON.

Measure voltage between D13 (+) terminal and D22 (−) terminal.

Is there approx. 5 V? — YES →
- Repair open or short in RED/WHT wire between ECM (D13) and the ECT sensor.
- Repair short in RED/WHT wire between ECM (D13) and TCM.

NO

Substitute a known-good ECM and recheck. If symptom/indication goes away, replace the original ECM.

D13 (+)
D22 (−)

94H44724

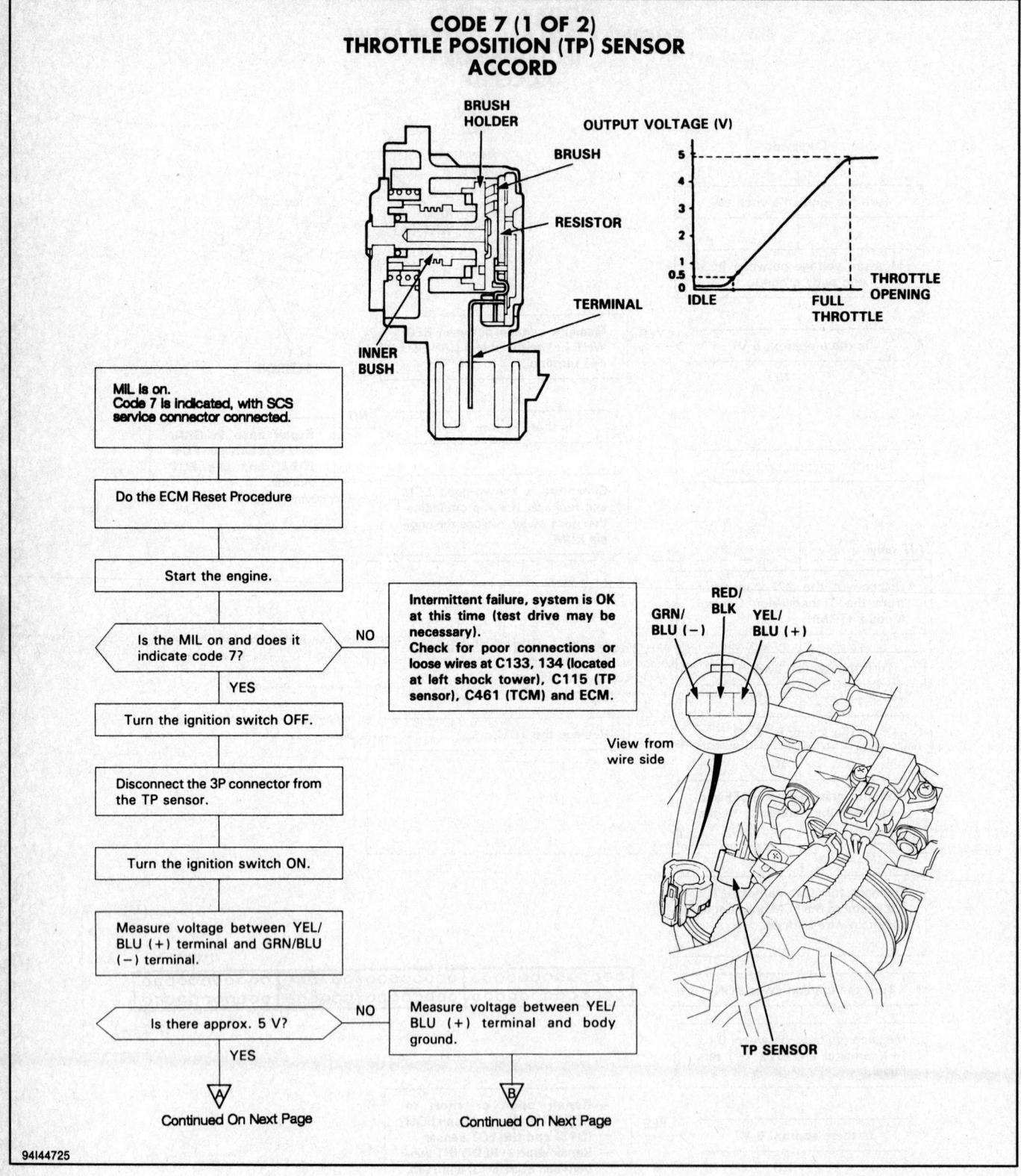

CODE 7 (1 OF 2)
THROTTLE POSITION (TP) SENSOR
ACCORD

BRUSH HOLDER

BRUSH

RESISTOR

TERMINAL

INNER BUSH

OUTPUT VOLTAGE (V)

IDLE

FULL THROTTLE

THROTTLE OPENING

MIL is on.
Code 7 is indicated, with SCS service connector connected.

Do the ECM Reset Procedure

Start the engine.

Is the MIL on and does it indicate code 7? — NO → Intermittent failure, system is OK at this time (test drive may be necessary).
Check for poor connections or loose wires at C133, 134 (located at left shock tower), C115 (TP sensor), C461 (TCM) and ECM.

YES

Turn the ignition switch OFF.

Disconnect the 3P connector from the TP sensor.

Turn the ignition switch ON.

Measure voltage between YEL/BLU (+) terminal and GRN/BLU (−) terminal.

Is there approx. 5 V? — NO → Measure voltage between YEL/BLU (+) terminal and body ground.

YES

GRN/BLU (−)   RED/BLK   YEL/BLU (+)

View from wire side

TP SENSOR

Ⓐ Continued On Next Page

Ⓑ Continued On Next Page

94144725

CODE 7 (2 OF 2)
THROTTLE POSITION (TP) SENSOR
ACCORD

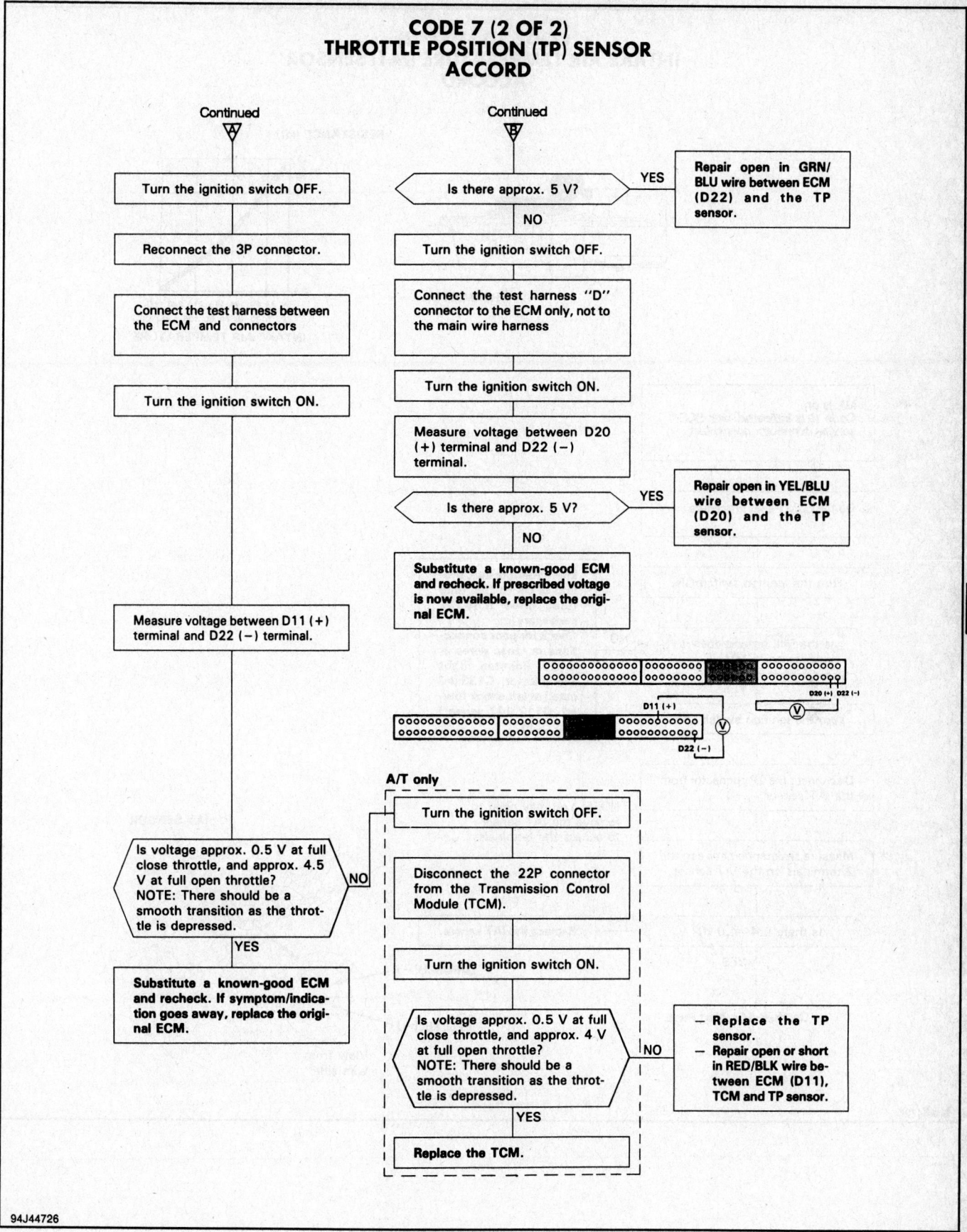

CODE 10 (1 OF 2)
INTAKE AIR TEMPERATURE (IAT) SENSOR
ACCORD

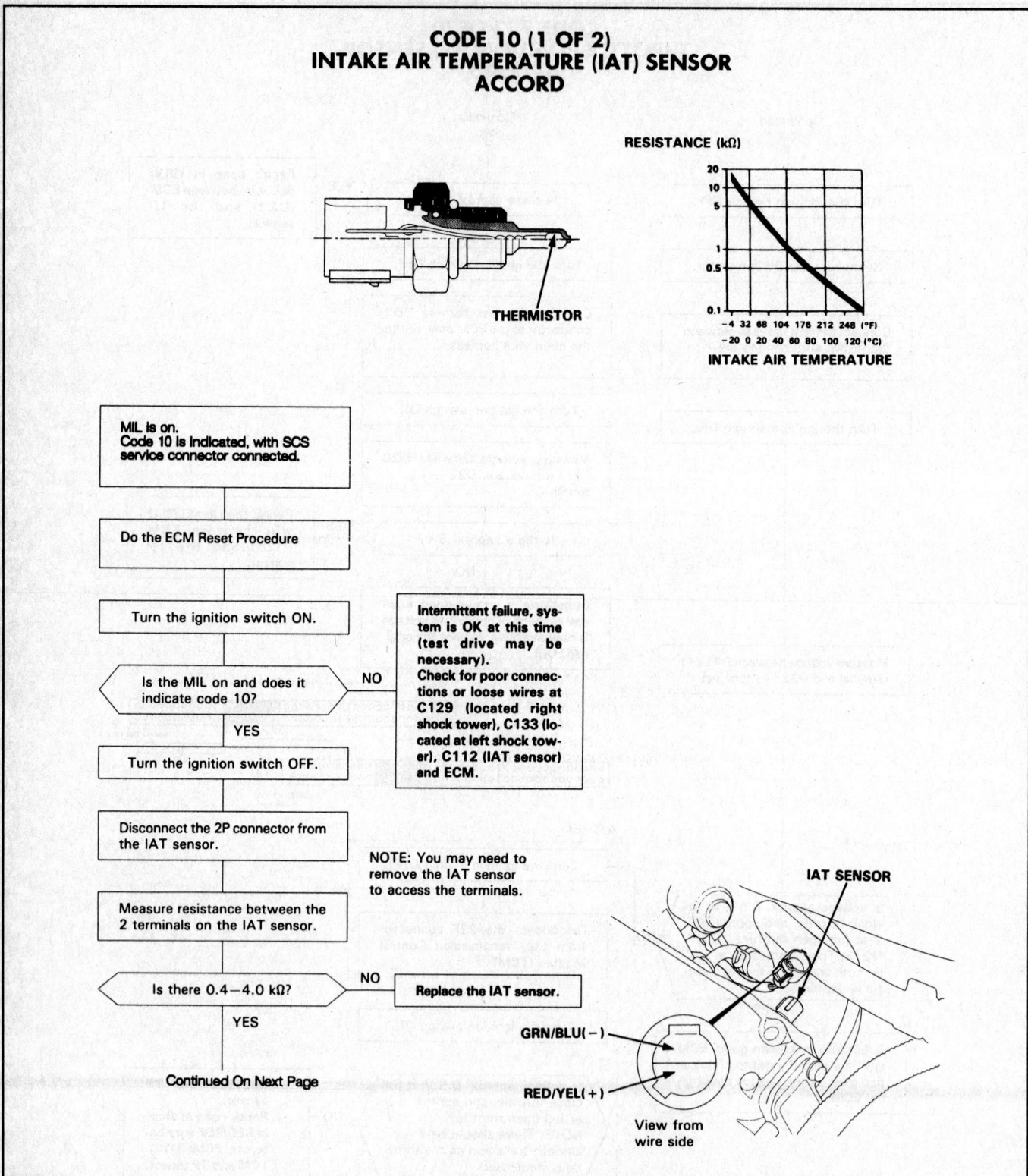

RESISTANCE (kΩ)

INTAKE AIR TEMPERATURE

THERMISTOR

MIL is on.
Code 10 is indicated, with SCS service connector connected.

↓

Do the ECM Reset Procedure

↓

Turn the ignition switch ON.

↓

Is the MIL on and does it indicate code 10? — **NO** → Intermittent failure, system is OK at this time (test drive may be necessary).
Check for poor connections or loose wires at C129 (located right shock tower), C133 (located at left shock tower), C112 (IAT sensor) and ECM.

YES

↓

Turn the ignition switch OFF.

↓

Disconnect the 2P connector from the IAT sensor.

NOTE: You may need to remove the IAT sensor to access the terminals.

↓

Measure resistance between the 2 terminals on the IAT sensor.

↓

Is there 0.4—4.0 kΩ? — **NO** → Replace the IAT sensor.

YES

↓

Continued On Next Page

IAT SENSOR

GRN/BLU(−)

RED/YEL(+)

View from wire side

94A44727

CODE 10 (2 OF 2)
INTAKE AIR TEMPERATURE (IAT) SENSOR
ACCORD

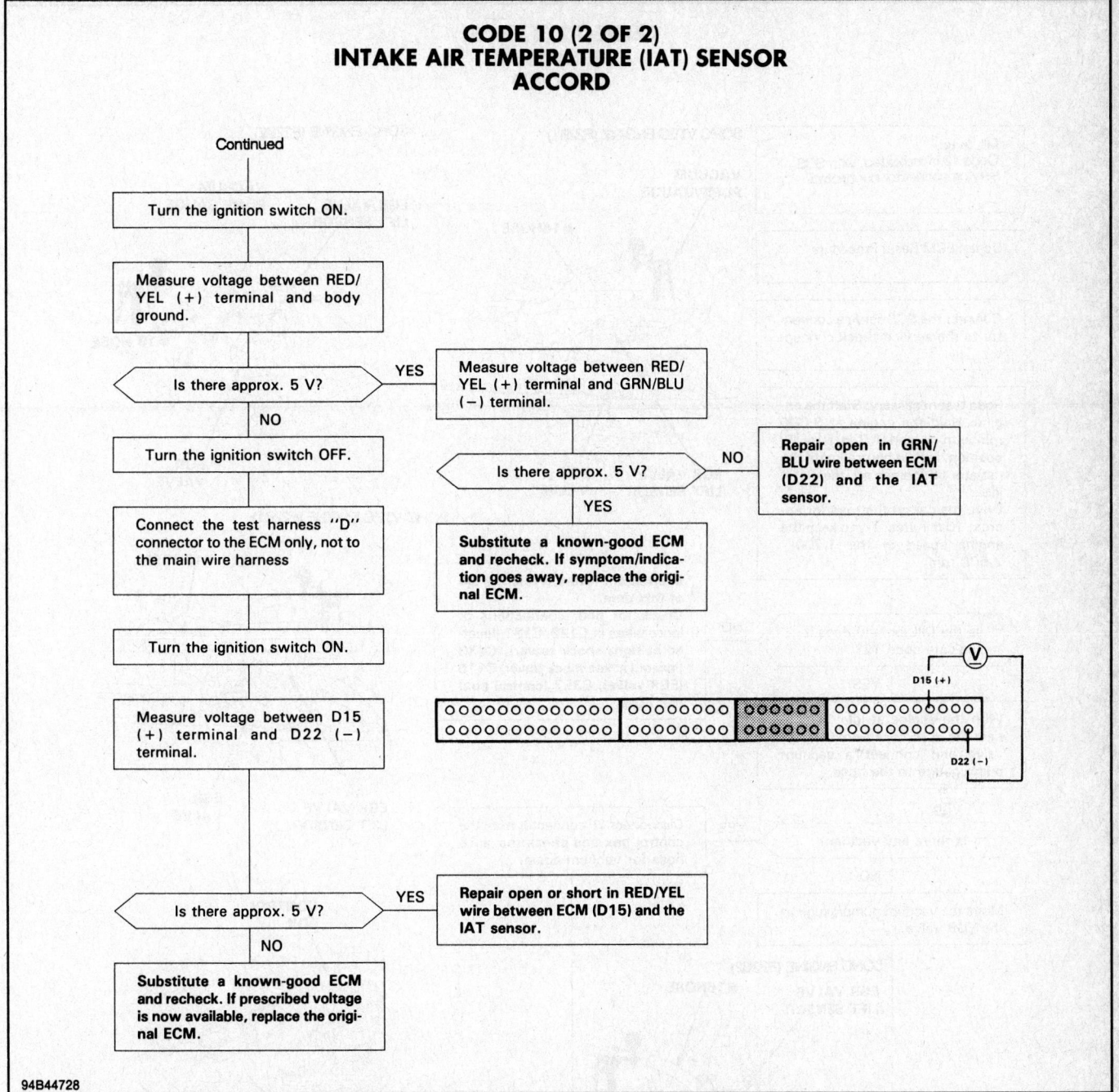

CODE 12 (1 OF 5)
EGR SYSTEM
ACCORD

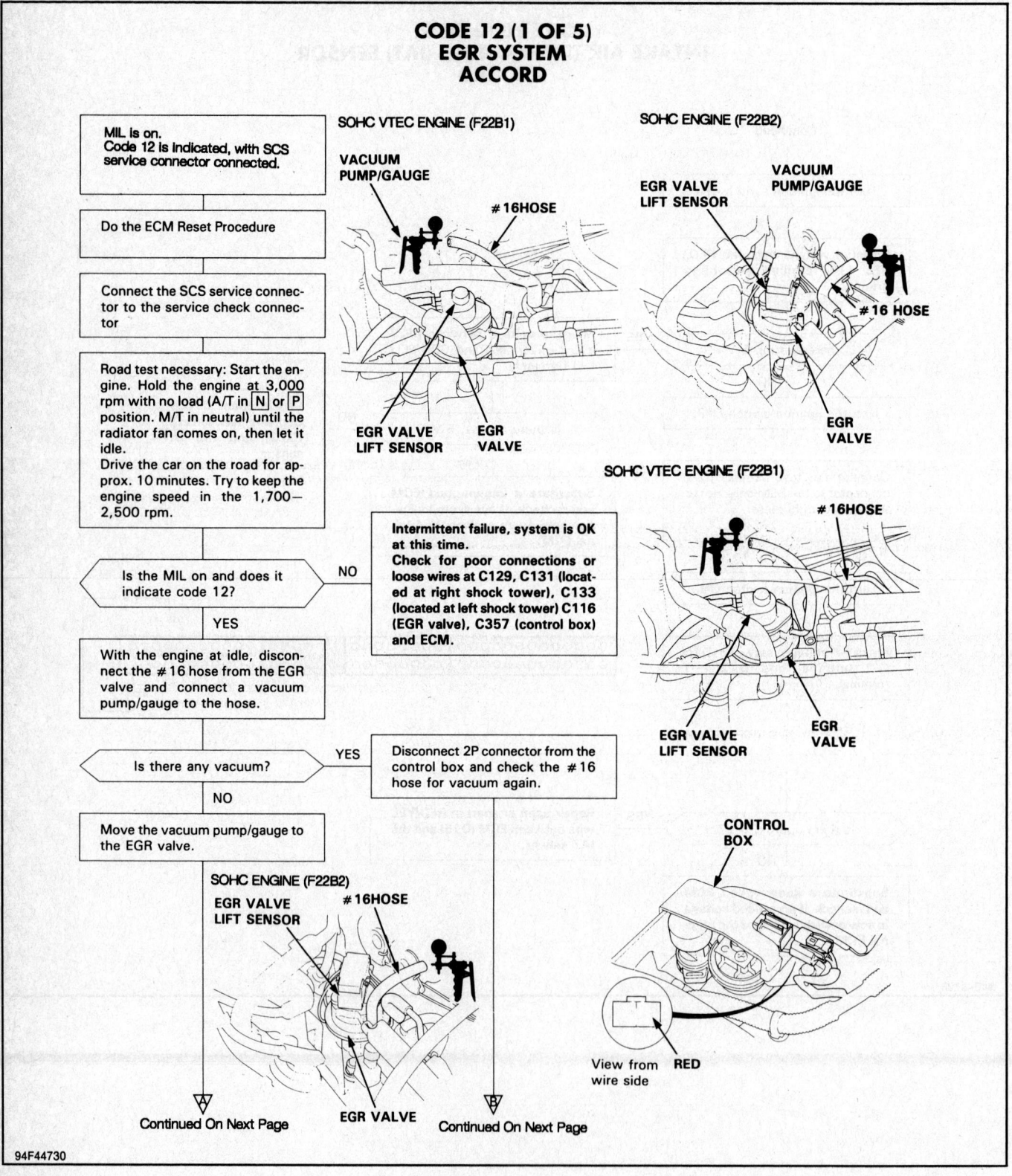

MIL is on.
Code 12 is indicated, with SCS service connector connected.

Do the ECM Reset Procedure

Connect the SCS service connector to the service check connector

Road test necessary: Start the engine. Hold the engine at 3,000 rpm with no load (A/T in [N] or [P] position. M/T in neutral) until the radiator fan comes on, then let it idle.
Drive the car on the road for approx. 10 minutes. Try to keep the engine speed in the 1,700—2,500 rpm.

Is the MIL on and does it indicate code 12? — NO

YES

With the engine at idle, disconnect the #16 hose from the EGR valve and connect a vacuum pump/gauge to the hose.

Is there any vacuum? — YES

NO

Move the vacuum pump/gauge to the EGR valve.

Intermittent failure, system is OK at this time.
Check for poor connections or loose wires at C129, C131 (located at right shock tower), C133 (located at left shock tower) C116 (EGR valve), C357 (control box) and ECM.

Disconnect 2P connector from the control box and check the #16 hose for vacuum again.

SOHC VTEC ENGINE (F22B1)

VACUUM PUMP/GAUGE

#16HOSE

EGR VALVE LIFT SENSOR

EGR VALVE

SOHC ENGINE (F22B2)

EGR VALVE LIFT SENSOR

VACUUM PUMP/GAUGE

#16 HOSE

EGR VALVE

SOHC VTEC ENGINE (F22B1)

#16HOSE

EGR VALVE LIFT SENSOR

EGR VALVE

SOHC ENGINE (F22B2)

EGR VALVE LIFT SENSOR

#16HOSE

EGR VALVE

CONTROL BOX

View from wire side   RED

Continued On Next Page

Continued On Next Page

94F44730

**CODE 12 (2 OF 5)
EGR SYSTEM
ACCORD**

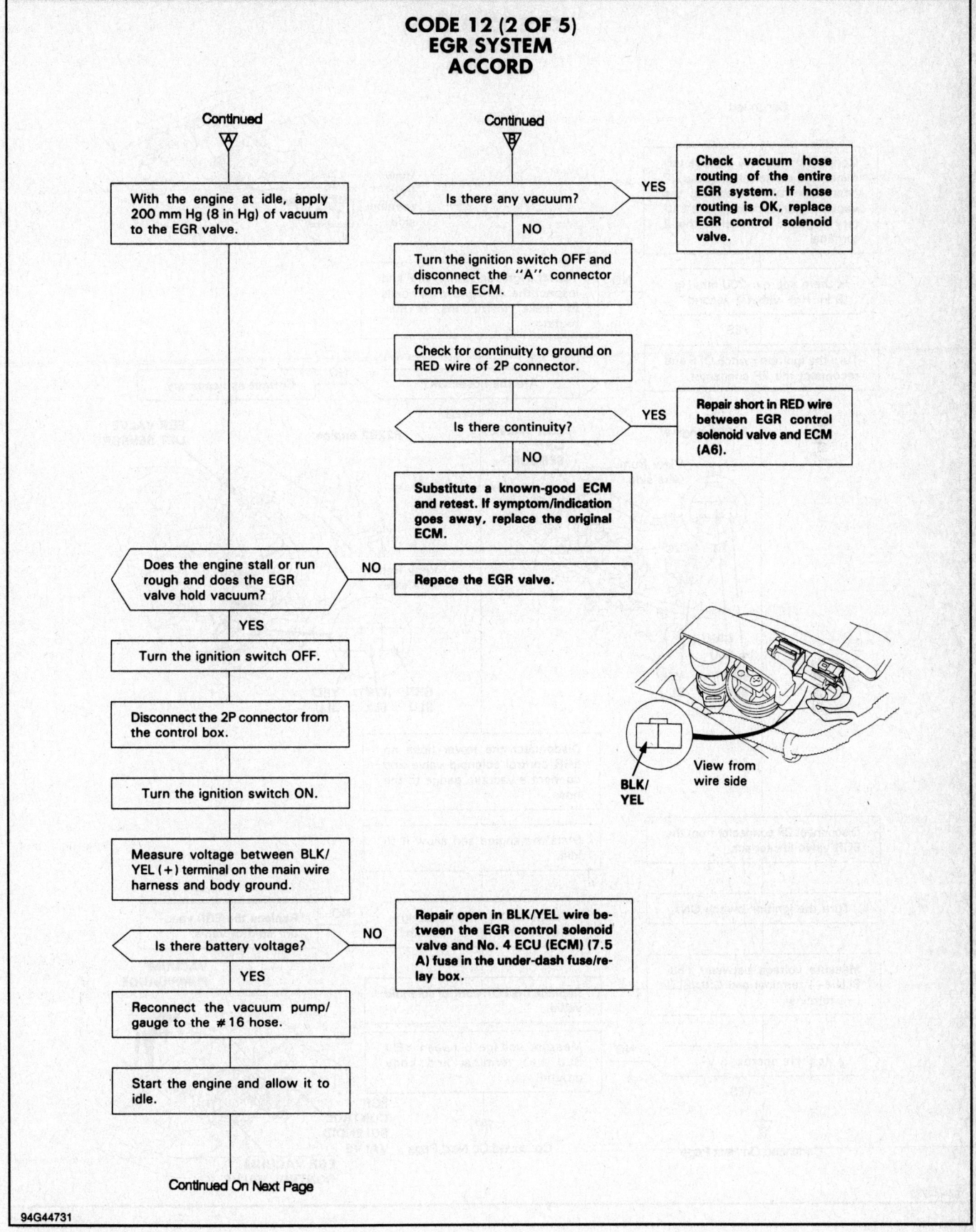

Continued

With the engine at idle, apply 200 mm Hg (8 in Hg) of vacuum to the EGR valve.

Continued

Is there any vacuum? — YES → Check vacuum hose routing of the entire EGR system. If hose routing is OK, replace EGR control solenoid valve.

NO

Turn the ignition switch OFF and disconnect the ''A'' connector from the ECM.

Check for continuity to ground on RED wire of 2P connector.

Is there continuity? — YES → Repair short in RED wire between EGR control solenoid valve and ECM (A6).

NO

Substitute a known-good ECM and retest. If symptom/indication goes away, replace the original ECM.

Does the engine stall or run rough and does the EGR valve hold vacuum? — NO → Repace the EGR valve.

YES

Turn the ignition switch OFF.

Disconnect the 2P connector from the control box.

Turn the ignition switch ON.

Measure voltage between BLK/YEL (+) terminal on the main wire harness and body ground.

Is there battery voltage? — NO → Repair open in BLK/YEL wire between the EGR control solenoid valve and No. 4 ECU (ECM) (7.5 A) fuse in the under-dash fuse/relay box.

YES

Reconnect the vacuum pump/gauge to the #16 hose.

Start the engine and allow it to idle.

BLK/YEL

View from wire side

**CODE 12 (3 OF 5)
EGR SYSTEM
ACCORD**

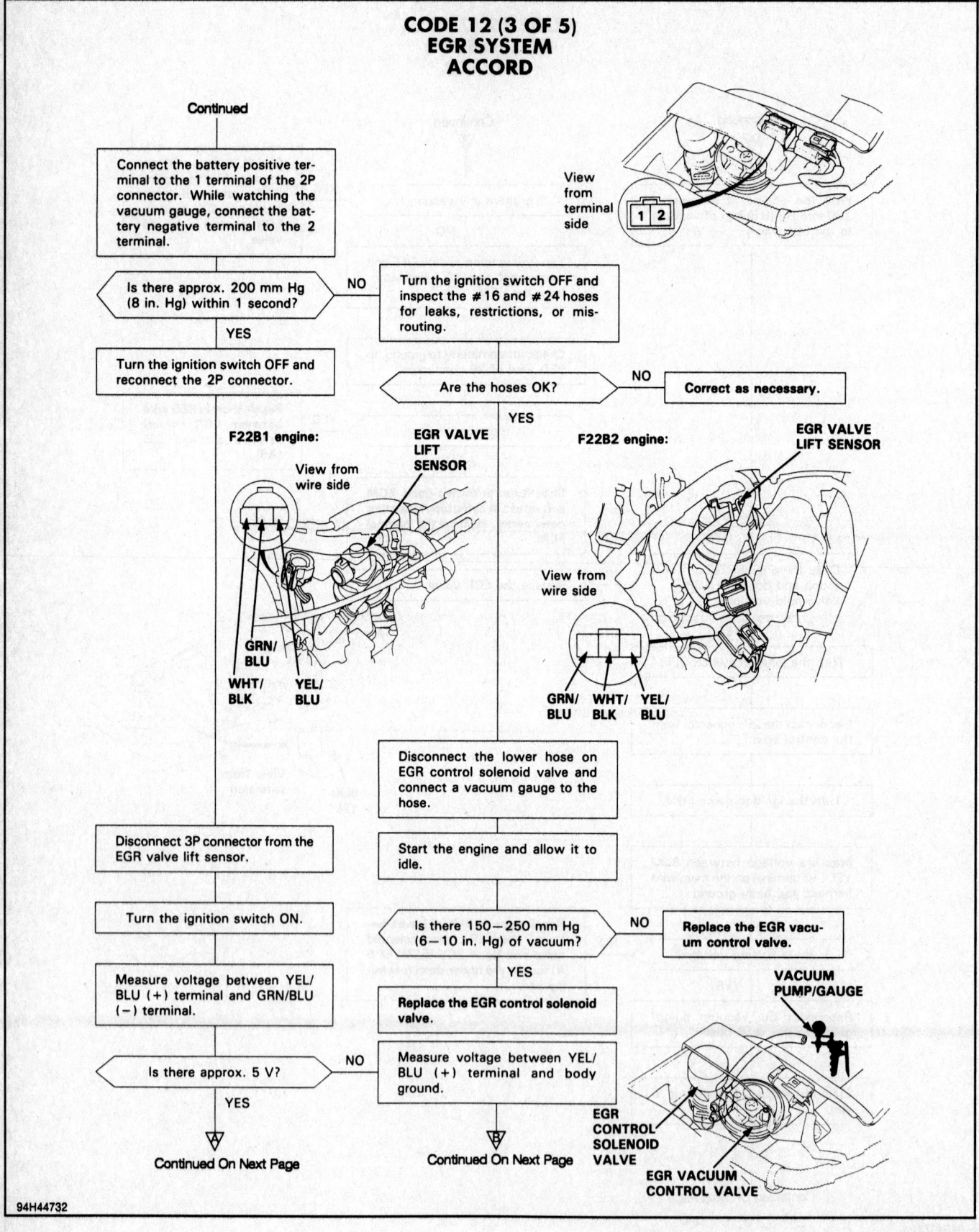

Continued

Connect the battery positive terminal to the 1 terminal of the 2P connector. While watching the vacuum gauge, connect the battery negative terminal to the 2 terminal.

Is there approx. 200 mm Hg (8 in. Hg) within 1 second?

NO → Turn the ignition switch OFF and inspect the #16 and #24 hoses for leaks, restrictions, or misrouting.

YES

Turn the ignition switch OFF and reconnect the 2P connector.

View from terminal side

1 2

Are the hoses OK? — NO → Correct as necessary.

YES

F22B1 engine:

EGR VALVE LIFT SENSOR

View from wire side

GRN/BLU
WHT/BLK   YEL/BLU

F22B2 engine:

EGR VALVE LIFT SENSOR

View from wire side

GRN/BLU   WHT/BLK   YEL/BLU

Disconnect the lower hose on EGR control solenoid valve and connect a vacuum gauge to the hose.

Disconnect 3P connector from the EGR valve lift sensor.

Start the engine and allow it to idle.

Turn the ignition switch ON.

Is there 150—250 mm Hg (6—10 in. Hg) of vacuum? — NO → Replace the EGR vacuum control valve.

YES

Measure voltage between YEL/BLU (+) terminal and GRN/BLU (−) terminal.

Replace the EGR control solenoid valve.

VACUUM PUMP/GAUGE

Is there approx. 5 V? — NO → Measure voltage between YEL/BLU (+) terminal and body ground.

YES

Continued On Next Page

Continued On Next Page

EGR CONTROL SOLENOID VALVE

EGR VACUUM CONTROL VALVE

94H44732

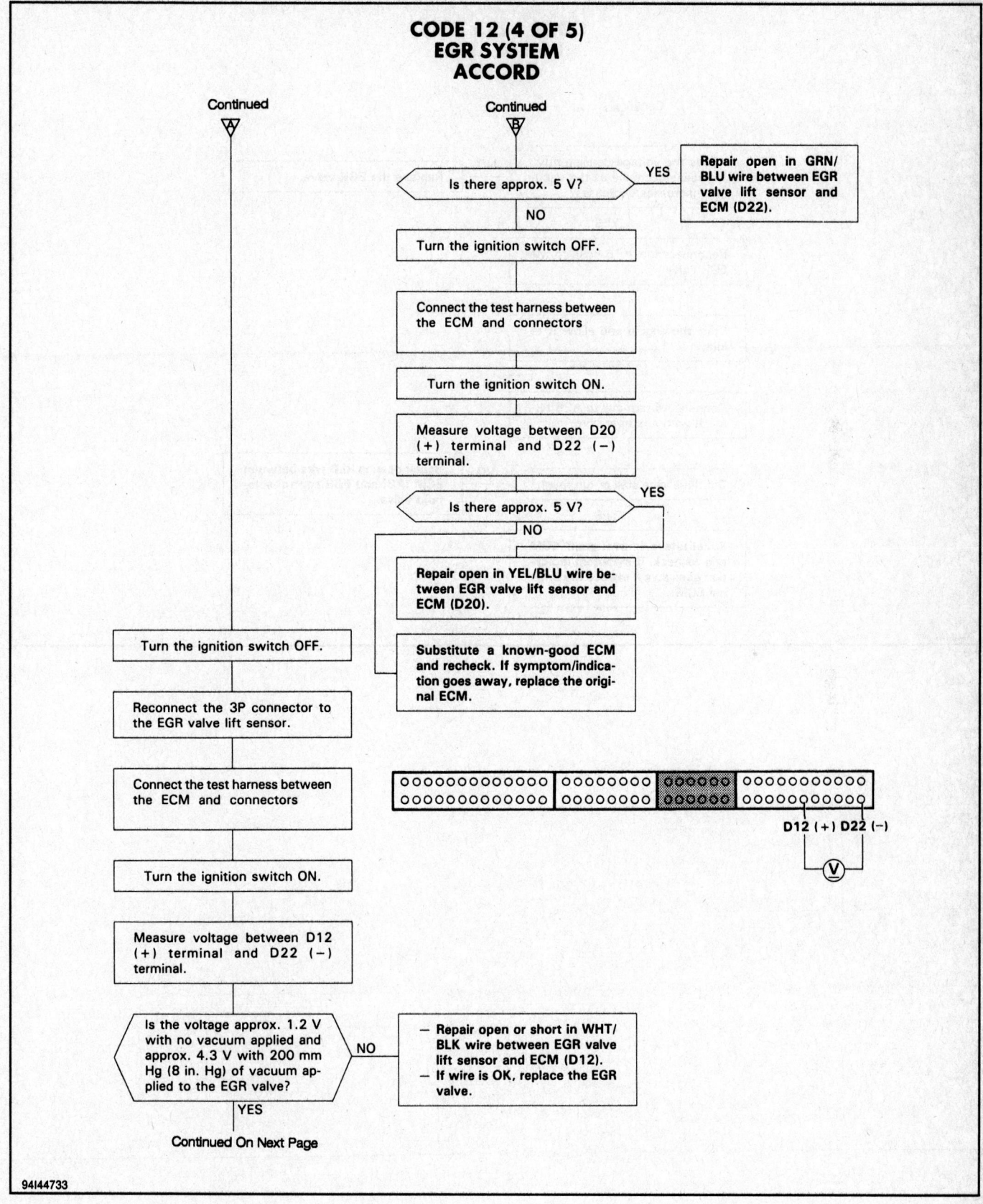

**CODE 12 (4 OF 5)
EGR SYSTEM
ACCORD**

Continued

Continued

Is there approx. 5 V? — YES → Repair open in GRN/BLU wire between EGR valve lift sensor and ECM (D22).

NO

Turn the ignition switch OFF.

Connect the test harness between the ECM and connectors

Turn the ignition switch ON.

Measure voltage between D20 (+) terminal and D22 (−) terminal.

Is there approx. 5 V? — YES

NO

Repair open in YEL/BLU wire between EGR valve lift sensor and ECM (D20).

Substitute a known-good ECM and recheck. If symptom/indication goes away, replace the original ECM.

Turn the ignition switch OFF.

Reconnect the 3P connector to the EGR valve lift sensor.

Connect the test harness between the ECM and connectors

Turn the ignition switch ON.

Measure voltage between D12 (+) terminal and D22 (−) terminal.

D12 (+) D22 (−)

Is the voltage approx. 1.2 V with no vacuum applied and approx. 4.3 V with 200 mm Hg (8 in. Hg) of vacuum applied to the EGR valve? — NO → — Repair open or short in WHT/BLK wire between EGR valve lift sensor and ECM (D12).
— If wire is OK, replace the EGR valve.

YES

Continued On Next Page

94144733

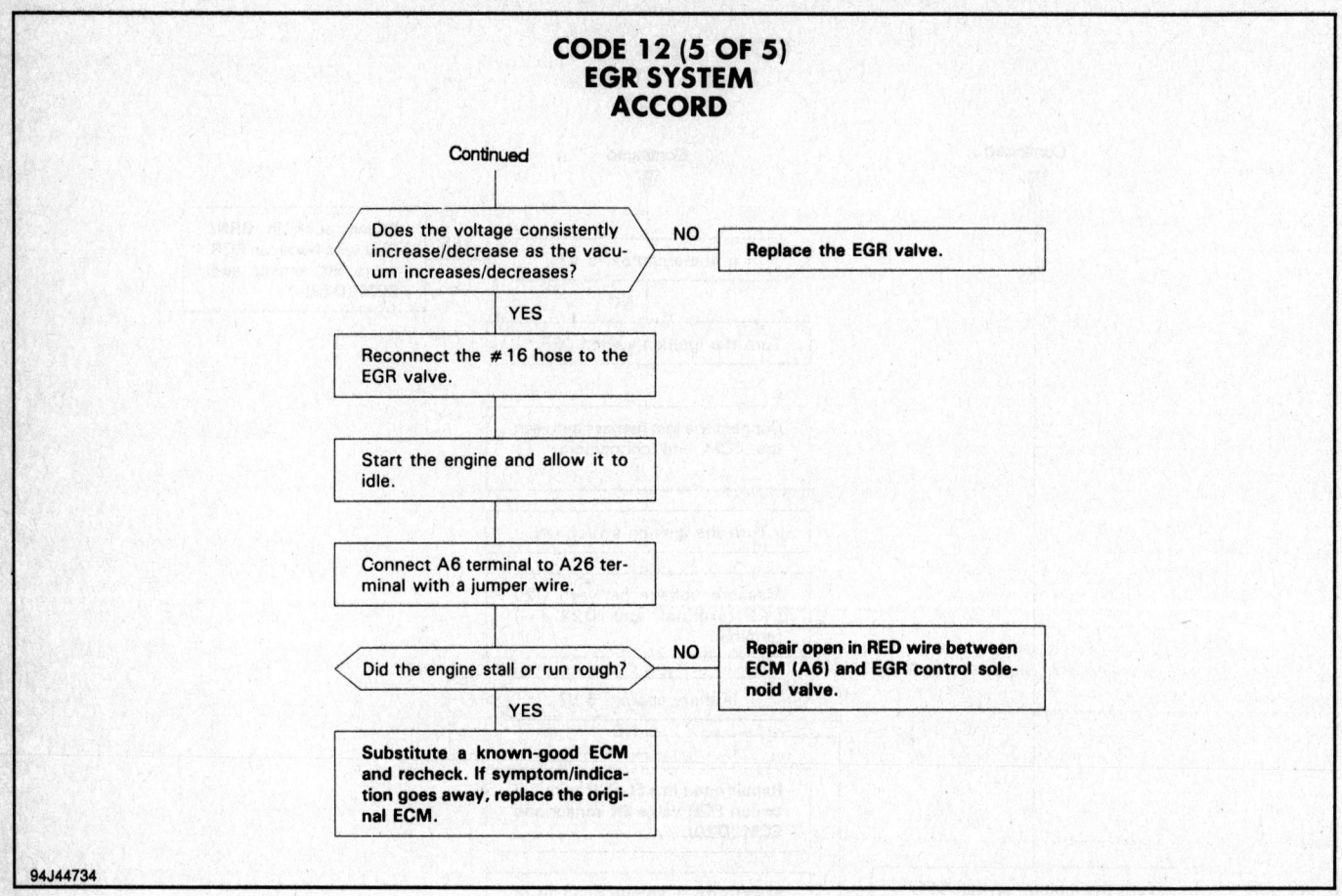

CODE 12 (5 OF 5)
EGR SYSTEM
ACCORD

Continued

Does the voltage consistently increase/decrease as the vacuum increases/decreases? — NO → Replace the EGR valve.

YES

Reconnect the #16 hose to the EGR valve.

Start the engine and allow it to idle.

Connect A6 terminal to A26 terminal with a jumper wire.

Did the engine stall or run rough? — NO → Repair open in RED wire between ECM (A6) and EGR control solenoid valve.

YES

Substitute a known-good ECM and recheck. If symptom/indication goes away, replace the original ECM.

94J44734

CODE 13
BAROMETRIC PRESSURE (BARO) SENSOR
ACCORD

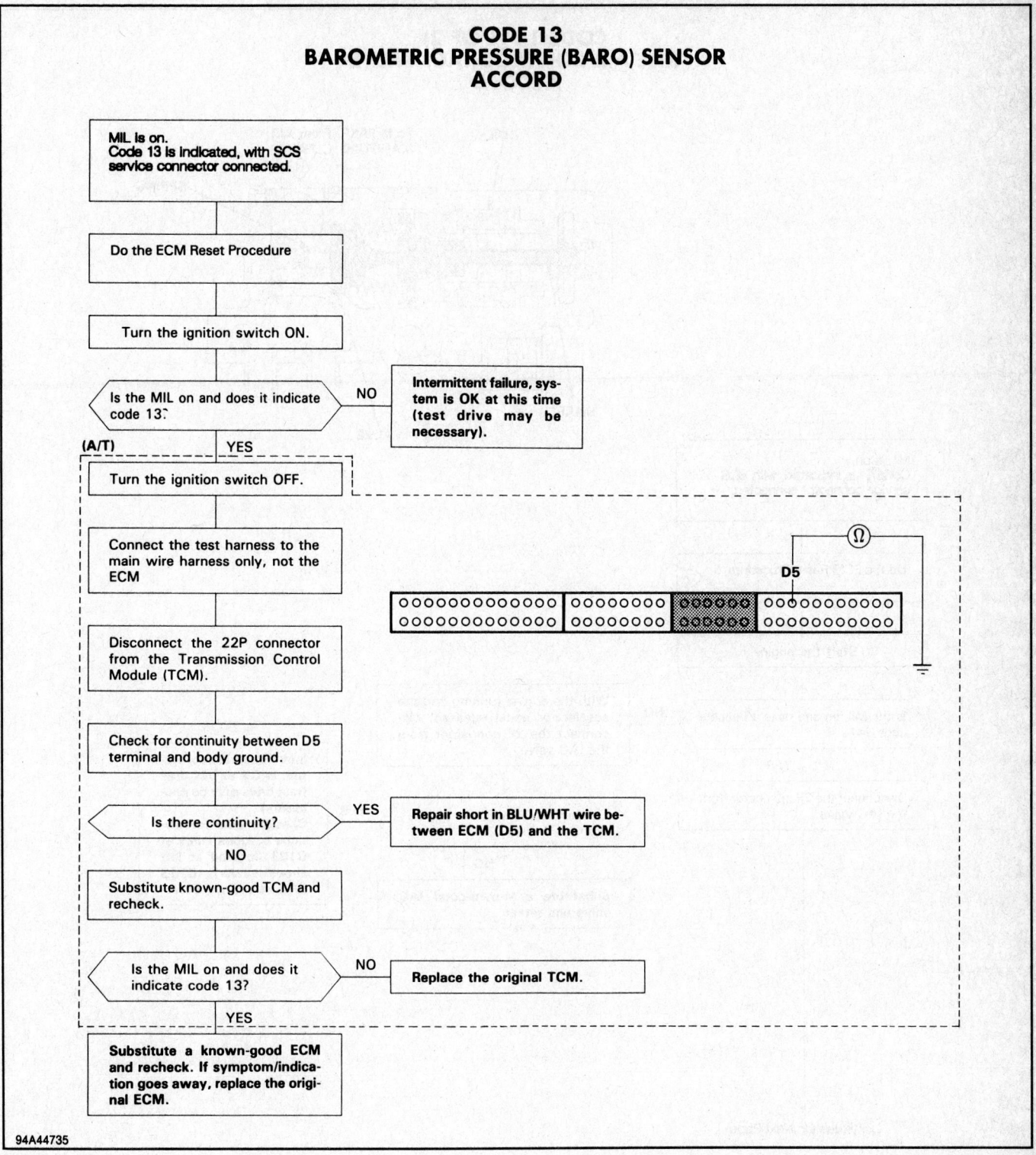

MIL is on.
Code 13 is indicated, with SCS service connector connected.

Do the ECM Reset Procedure

Turn the ignition switch ON.

Is the MIL on and does it indicate code 13? — **NO** → Intermittent failure, system is OK at this time (test drive may be necessary).

(A/T)   **YES**

Turn the ignition switch OFF.

Connect the test harness to the main wire harness only, not the ECM

Disconnect the 22P connector from the Transmission Control Module (TCM).

Check for continuity between D5 terminal and body ground.

Is there continuity? — **YES** → Repair short in BLU/WHT wire between ECM (D5) and the TCM.

NO

Substitute known-good TCM and recheck.

Is the MIL on and does it indicate code 13? — **NO** → Replace the original TCM.

YES

Substitute a known-good ECM and recheck. If symptom/indication goes away, replace the original ECM.

94A44735

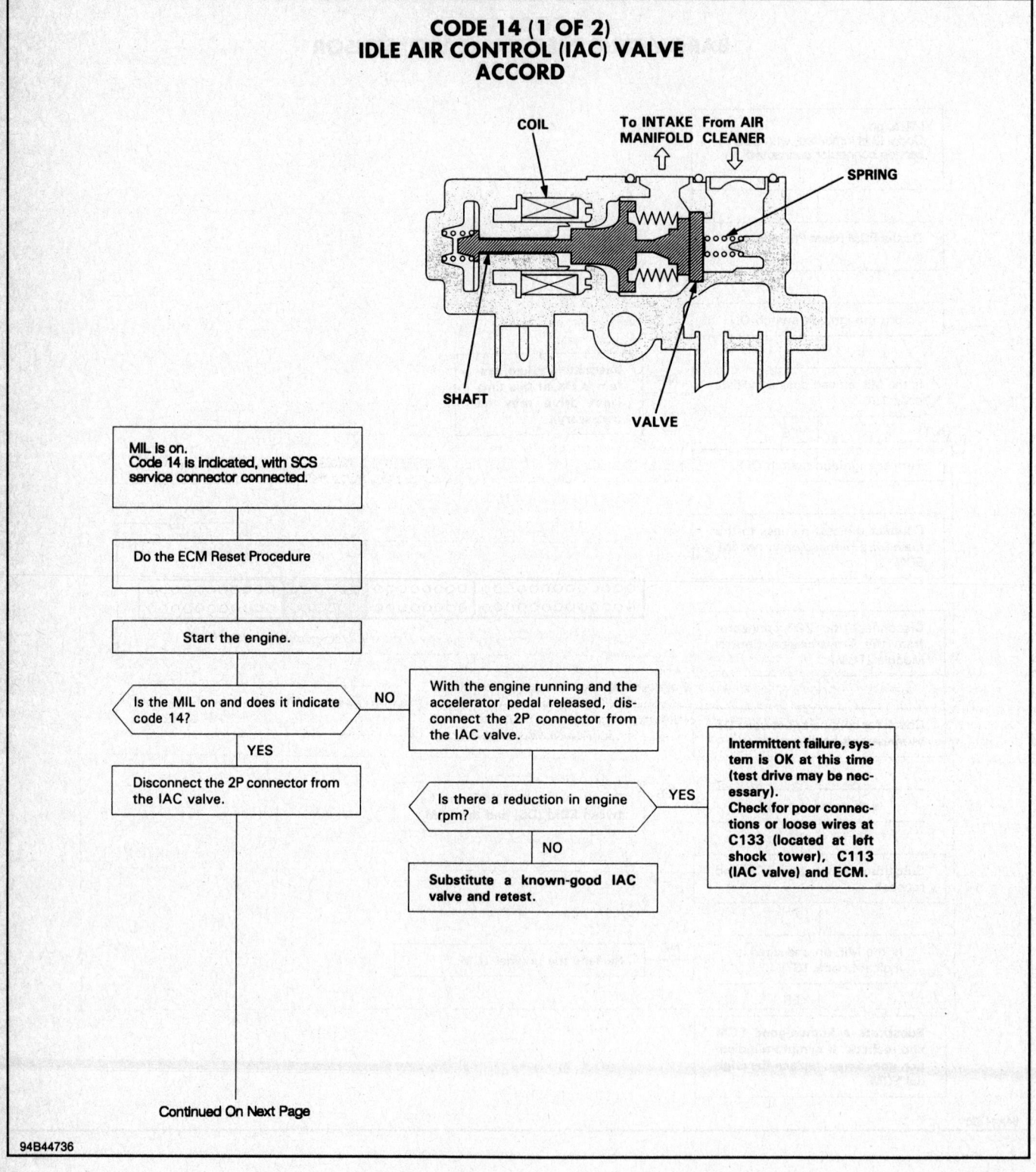

CODE 14 (1 OF 2)
IDLE AIR CONTROL (IAC) VALVE
ACCORD

COIL

To INTAKE MANIFOLD

From AIR CLEANER

SPRING

SHAFT

VALVE

MIL is on.
Code 14 is indicated, with SCS service connector connected.

Do the ECM Reset Procedure

Start the engine.

Is the MIL on and does it indicate code 14?

NO → With the engine running and the accelerator pedal released, disconnect the 2P connector from the IAC valve.

YES

Disconnect the 2P connector from the IAC valve.

Is there a reduction in engine rpm?

YES → Intermittent failure, system is OK at this time (test drive may be necessary).
Check for poor connections or loose wires at C133 (located at left shock tower), C113 (IAC valve) and ECM.

NO

Substitute a known-good IAC valve and retest.

Continued On Next Page

94B44736

CODE 14 (2 OF 2)
IDLE AIR CONTROL (IAC) VALVE
ACCORD

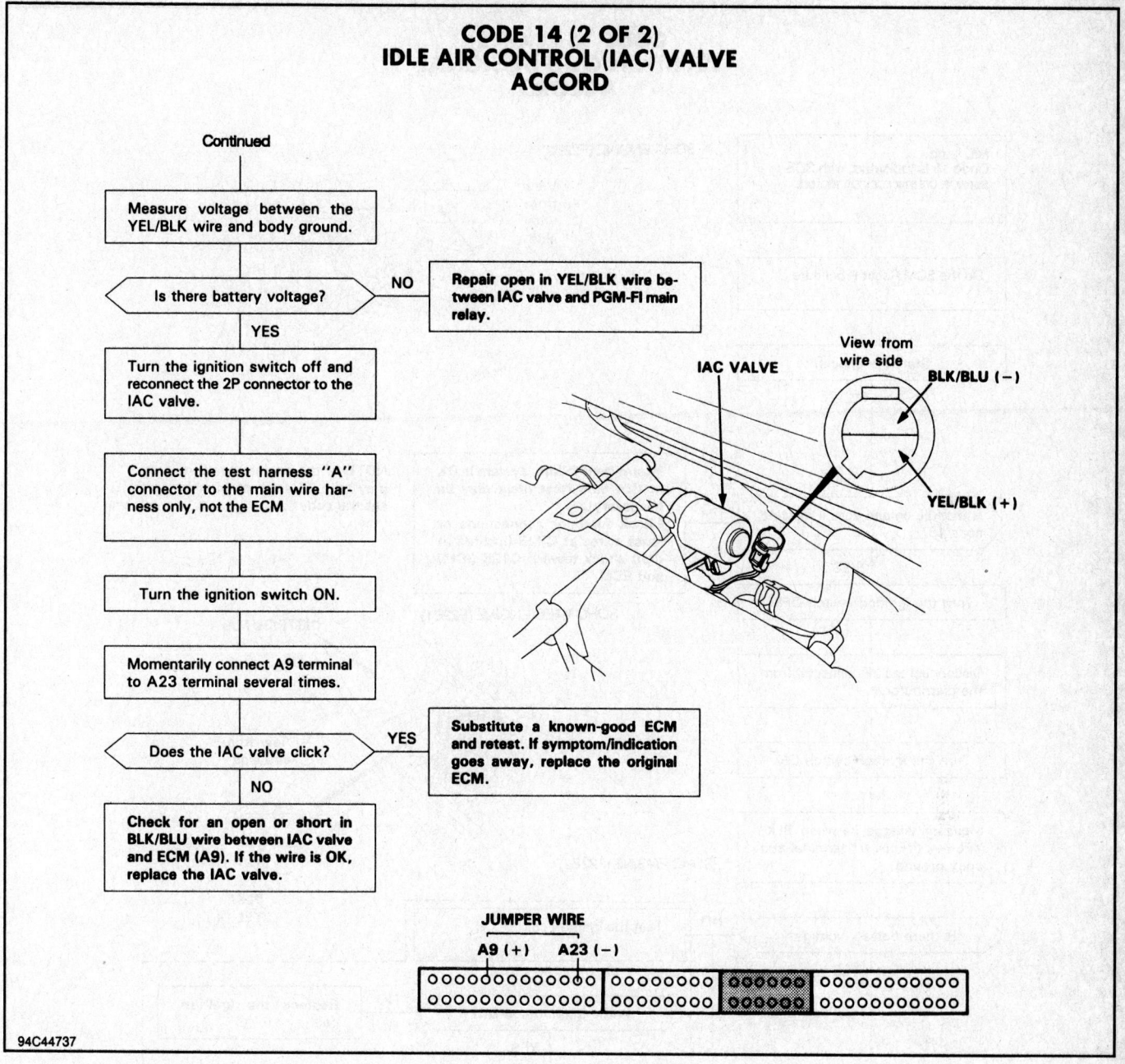

Continued

Measure voltage between the YEL/BLK wire and body ground.

Is there battery voltage? — **NO** → Repair open in YEL/BLK wire between IAC valve and PGM-FI main relay.

YES

Turn the ignition switch off and reconnect the 2P connector to the IAC valve.

Connect the test harness "A" connector to the main wire harness only, not the ECM

Turn the ignition switch ON.

Momentarily connect A9 terminal to A23 terminal several times.

Does the IAC valve click? — **YES** → Substitute a known-good ECM and retest. If symptom/indication goes away, replace the original ECM.

NO

Check for an open or short in BLK/BLU wire between IAC valve and ECM (A9). If the wire is OK, replace the IAC valve.

IAC VALVE

View from wire side

BLK/BLU (−)

YEL/BLK (+)

JUMPER WIRE
A9 (+)   A23 (−)

94C44737

CODE 15 (1 OF 2)
IGNITION OUTPUT SIGNAL
ACCORD

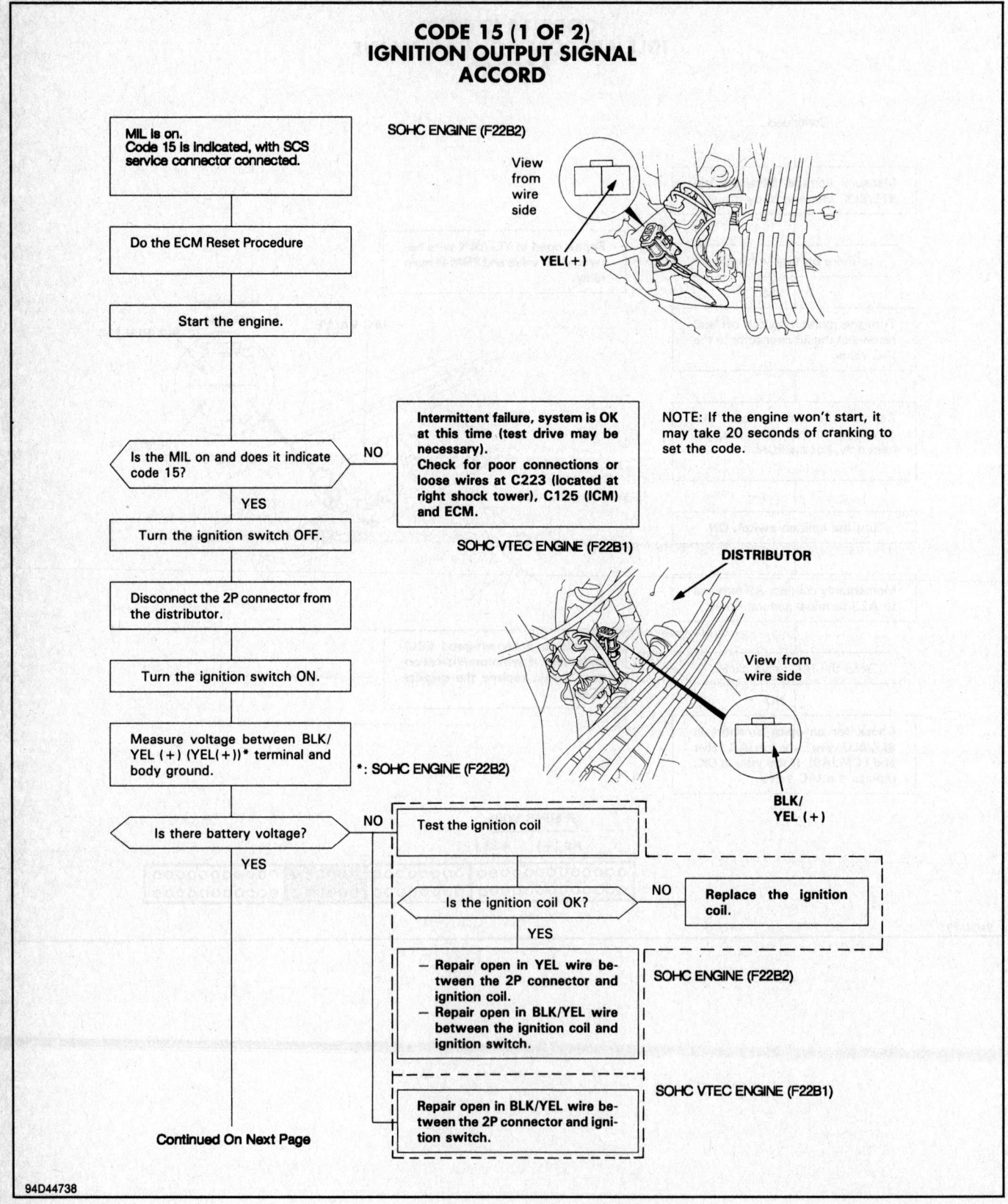

MIL is on.
Code 15 is indicated, with SCS
service connector connected.

Do the ECM Reset Procedure

Start the engine.

Is the MIL on and does it indicate
code 15? — NO → Intermittent failure, system is OK
at this time (test drive may be
necessary).
Check for poor connections or
loose wires at C223 (located at
right shock tower), C125 (ICM)
and ECM.

YES

Turn the ignition switch OFF.

Disconnect the 2P connector from
the distributor.

Turn the ignition switch ON.

Measure voltage between BLK/
YEL (+) (YEL(+))* terminal and
body ground.   *: SOHC ENGINE (F22B2)

Is there battery voltage? — NO → Test the ignition coil

YES

Is the ignition coil OK? — NO → Replace the ignition
coil.

YES

— Repair open in YEL wire between the 2P connector and
ignition coil.
— Repair open in BLK/YEL wire
between the ignition coil and
ignition switch.   SOHC ENGINE (F22B2)

Repair open in BLK/YEL wire between the 2P connector and ignition switch.   SOHC VTEC ENGINE (F22B1)

SOHC ENGINE (F22B2)

View
from
wire
side

YEL(+)

NOTE: If the engine won't start, it
may take 20 seconds of cranking to
set the code.

SOHC VTEC ENGINE (F22B1)

DISTRIBUTOR

View from
wire side

BLK/
YEL (+)

Continued On Next Page

94D44738

CODE 15 (2 OF 2)
IGNITION OUTPUT SIGNAL
ACCORD

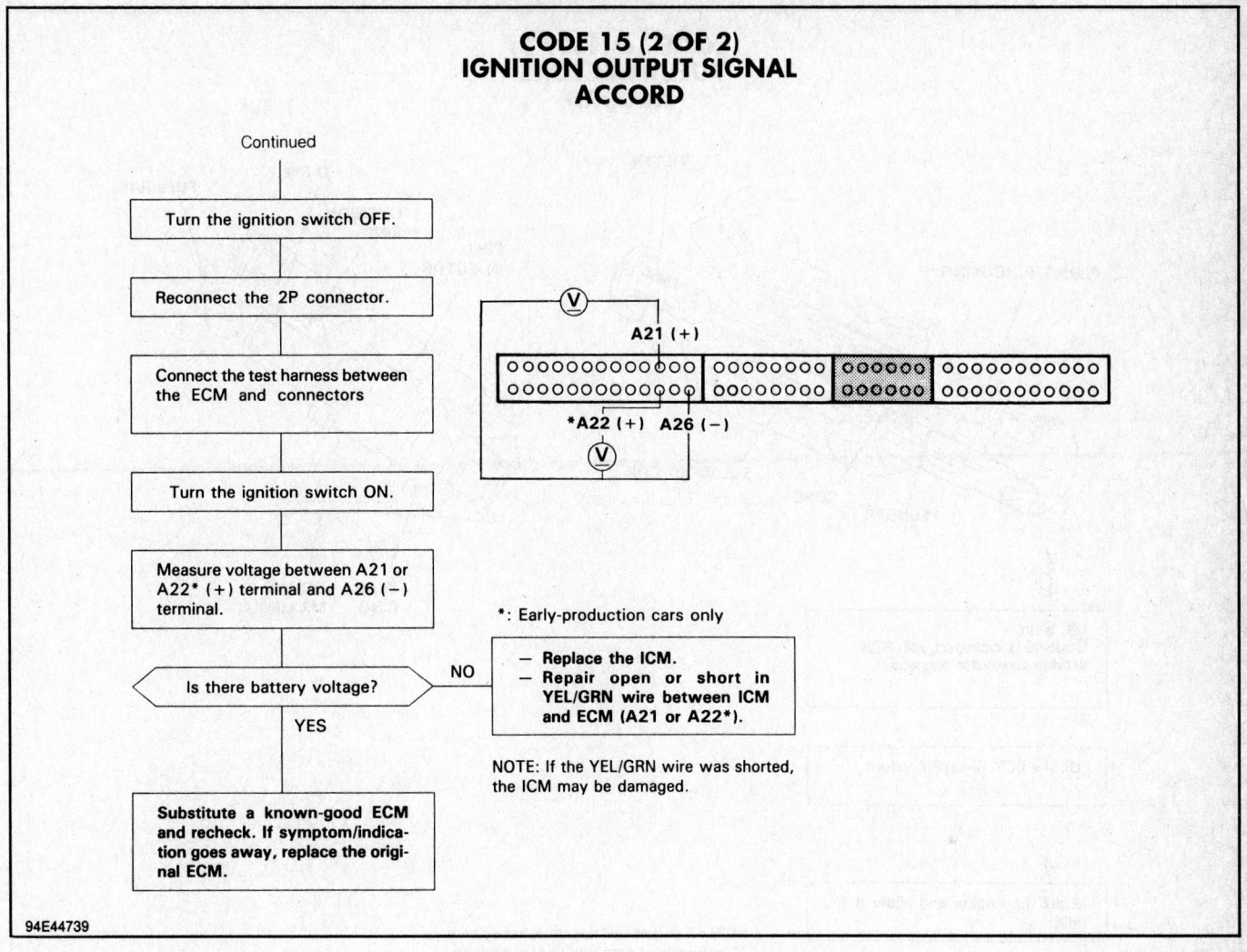

Continued

Turn the ignition switch OFF.

Reconnect the 2P connector.

Connect the test harness between the ECM and connectors

Turn the ignition switch ON.

Measure voltage between A21 or A22* (+) terminal and A26 (−) terminal.

A21 (+)

*A22 (+)   A26 (−)

*: Early-production cars only

Is there battery voltage? — NO →
— Replace the ICM.
— Repair open or short in YEL/GRN wire between ICM and ECM (A21 or A22*).

NOTE: If the YEL/GRN wire was shorted, the ICM may be damaged.

YES

Substitute a known-good ECM and recheck. If symptom/indication goes away, replace the original ECM.

94E44739

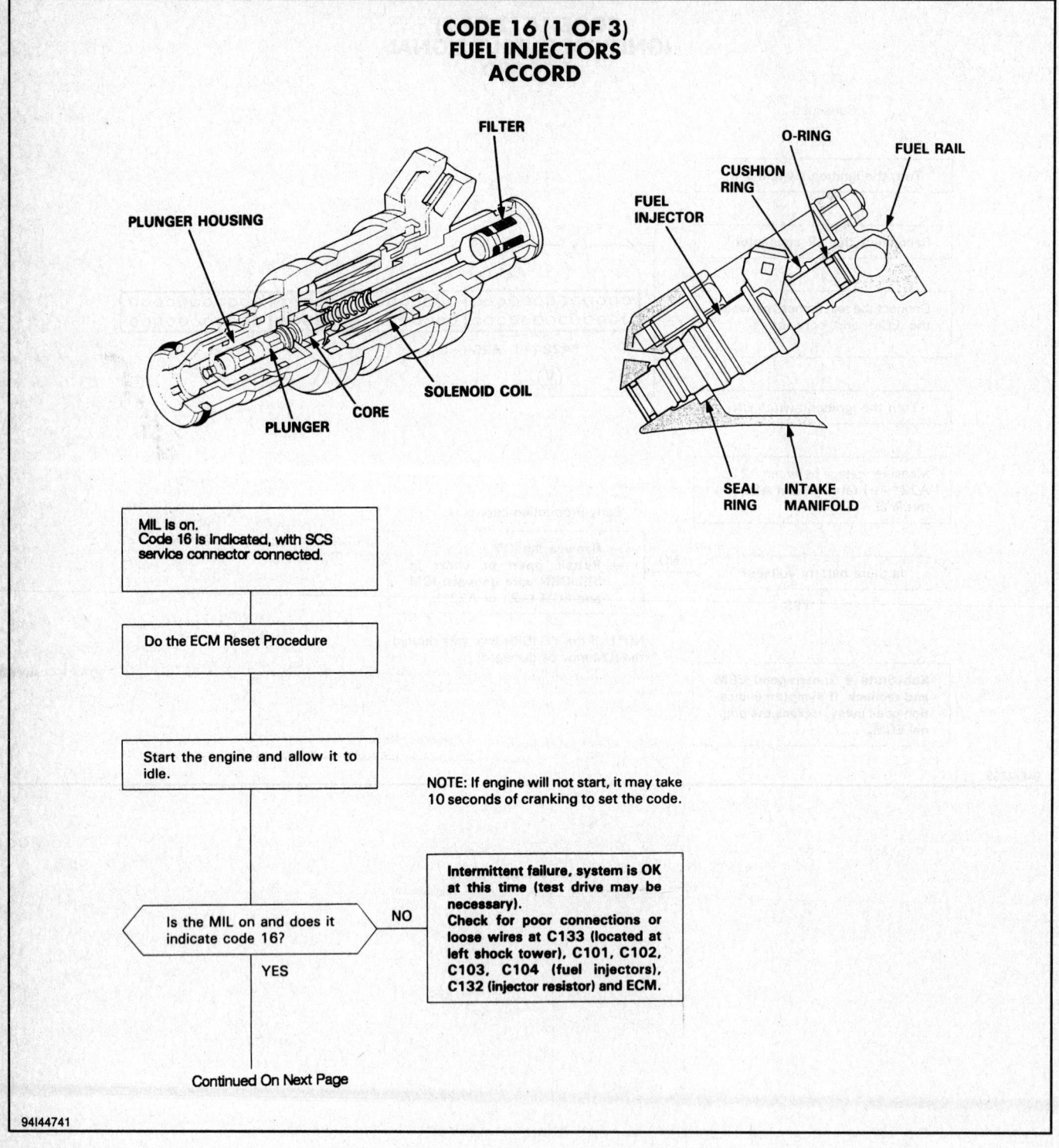

CODE 16 (1 OF 3)
FUEL INJECTORS
ACCORD

FILTER

PLUNGER HOUSING

SOLENOID COIL

CORE

PLUNGER

O-RING

FUEL RAIL

CUSHION RING

FUEL INJECTOR

SEAL RING

INTAKE MANIFOLD

MIL is on.
Code 16 is indicated, with SCS service connector connected.

Do the ECM Reset Procedure

Start the engine and allow it to idle.

NOTE: If engine will not start, it may take 10 seconds of cranking to set the code.

Is the MIL on and does it indicate code 16?

NO

YES

Intermittent failure, system is OK at this time (test drive may be necessary).
Check for poor connections or loose wires at C133 (located at left shock tower), C101, C102, C103, C104 (fuel injectors), C132 (injector resistor) and ECM.

Continued On Next Page

94I44741

CODE 16 (2 OF 3)
FUEL INJECTORS
ACCORD

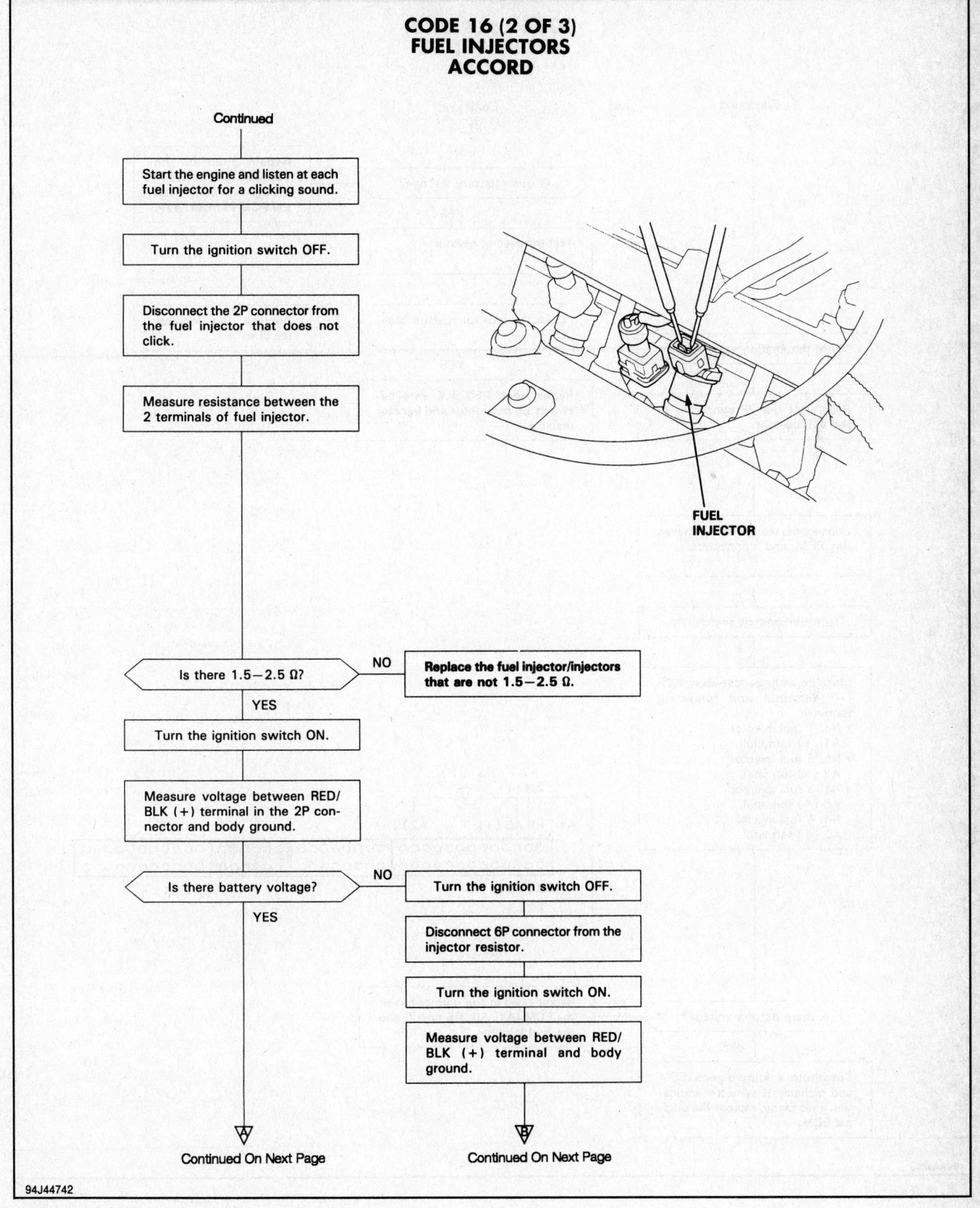

Continued

Start the engine and listen at each fuel injector for a clicking sound.

Turn the ignition switch OFF.

Disconnect the 2P connector from the fuel injector that does not click.

Measure resistance between the 2 terminals of fuel injector.

FUEL INJECTOR

Is there 1.5 – 2.5 Ω? — NO → Replace the fuel injector/injectors that are not 1.5 – 2.5 Ω.

YES

Turn the ignition switch ON.

Measure voltage between RED/ BLK (+) terminal in the 2P connector and body ground.

Is there battery voltage? — NO → Turn the ignition switch OFF.

YES

Disconnect 6P connector from the injector resistor.

Turn the ignition switch ON.

Measure voltage between RED/ BLK (+) terminal and body ground.

Continued On Next Page

Continued On Next Page

94J44742

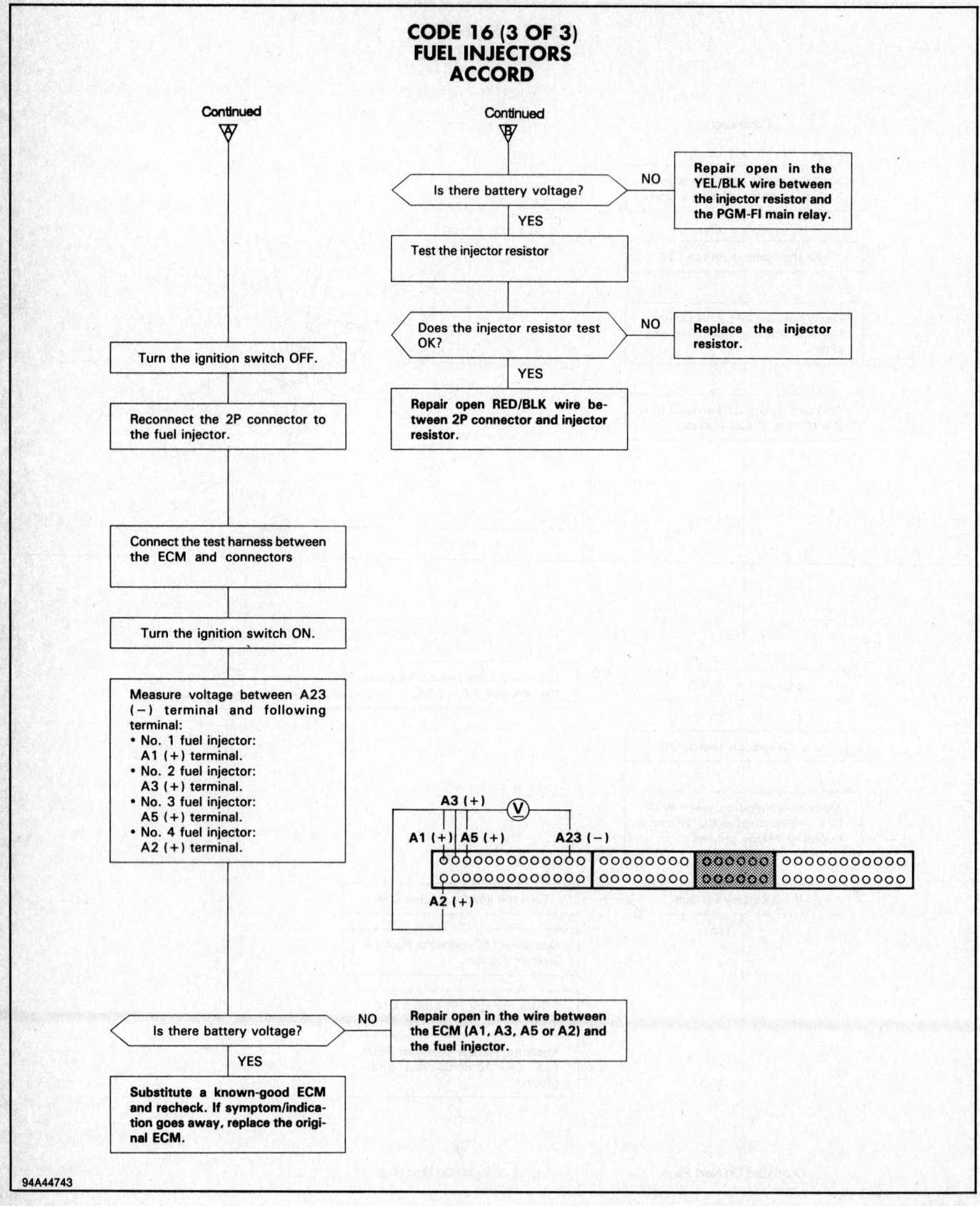

CODE 16 (3 OF 3)
FUEL INJECTORS
ACCORD

Continued
A

Continued
B

Is there battery voltage? — NO → Repair open in the YEL/BLK wire between the injector resistor and the PGM-FI main relay.

YES

Test the injector resistor

Does the injector resistor test OK? — NO → Replace the injector resistor.

YES

Repair open RED/BLK wire between 2P connector and injector resistor.

Turn the ignition switch OFF.

Reconnect the 2P connector to the fuel injector.

Connect the test harness between the ECM and connectors

Turn the ignition switch ON.

Measure voltage between A23 (−) terminal and following terminal:
• No. 1 fuel injector: A1 (+) terminal.
• No. 2 fuel injector: A3 (+) terminal.
• No. 3 fuel injector: A5 (+) terminal.
• No. 4 fuel injector: A2 (+) terminal.

A3 (+) V
A1 (+) A5 (+)   A23 (−)
A2 (+)

Is there battery voltage? — NO → Repair open in the wire between the ECM (A1, A3, A5 or A2) and the fuel injector.

YES

Substitute a known-good ECM and recheck. If symptom/indication goes away, replace the original ECM.

94A44743

CODE 17 (1 OF 2)
VEHICLE SPEED SENSOR (VSS)
ACCORD

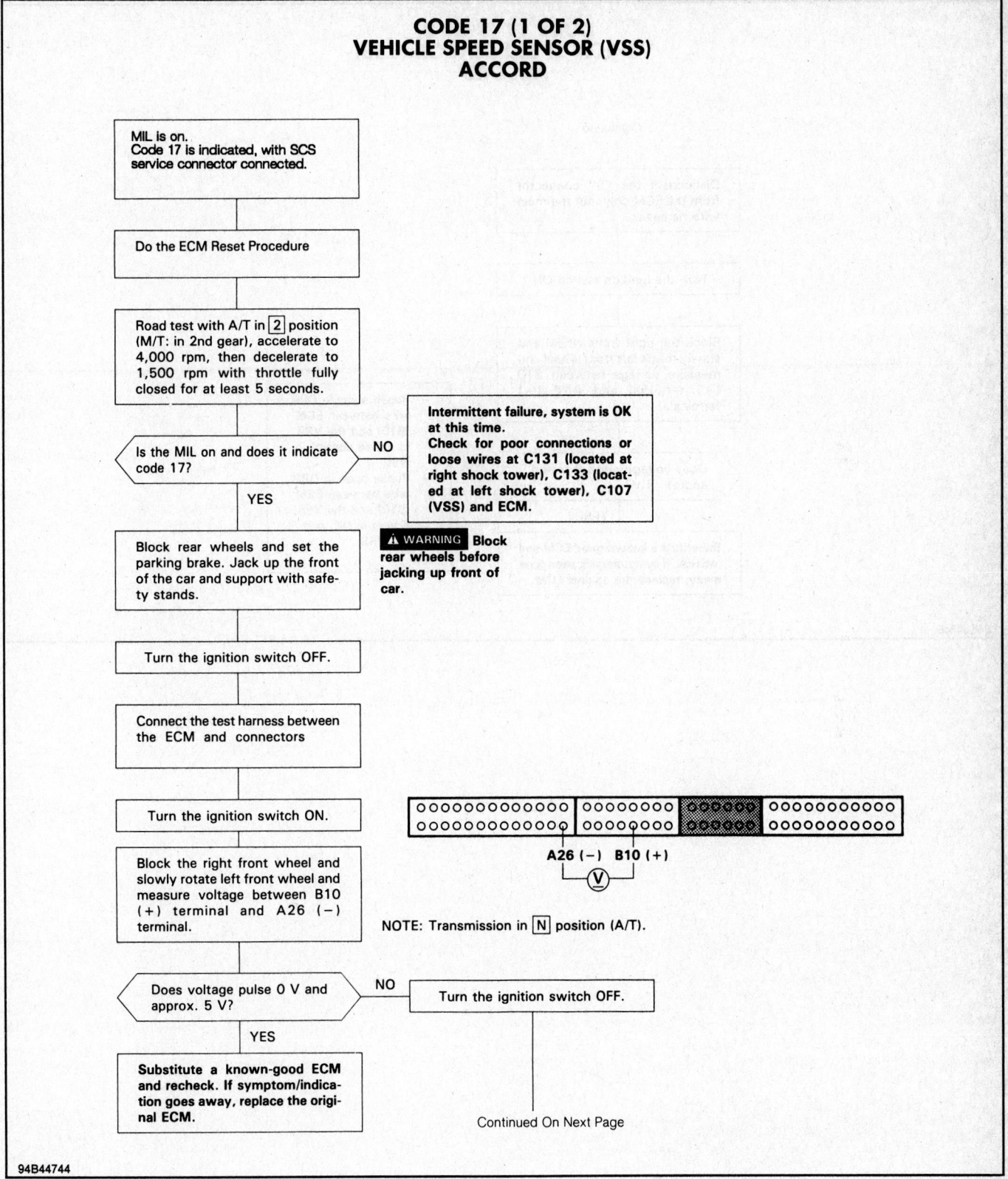

MIL is on.
Code 17 is indicated, with SCS service connector connected.

Do the ECM Reset Procedure

Road test with A/T in 2 position (M/T: in 2nd gear), accelerate to 4,000 rpm, then decelerate to 1,500 rpm with throttle fully closed for at least 5 seconds.

Is the MIL on and does it indicate code 17?

NO → Intermittent failure, system is OK at this time.
Check for poor connections or loose wires at C131 (located at right shock tower), C133 (located at left shock tower), C107 (VSS) and ECM.

YES

⚠ WARNING Block rear wheels before jacking up front of car.

Block rear wheels and set the parking brake. Jack up the front of the car and support with safety stands.

Turn the ignition switch OFF.

Connect the test harness between the ECM and connectors

Turn the ignition switch ON.

A26 (−)   B10 (+)
Ⓥ

Block the right front wheel and slowly rotate left front wheel and measure voltage between B10 (+) terminal and A26 (−) terminal.

NOTE: Transmission in N position (A/T).

Does voltage pulse 0 V and approx. 5 V?

NO → Turn the ignition switch OFF.

YES

Substitute a known-good ECM and recheck. If symptom/indication goes away, replace the original ECM.

Continued On Next Page

94B44744

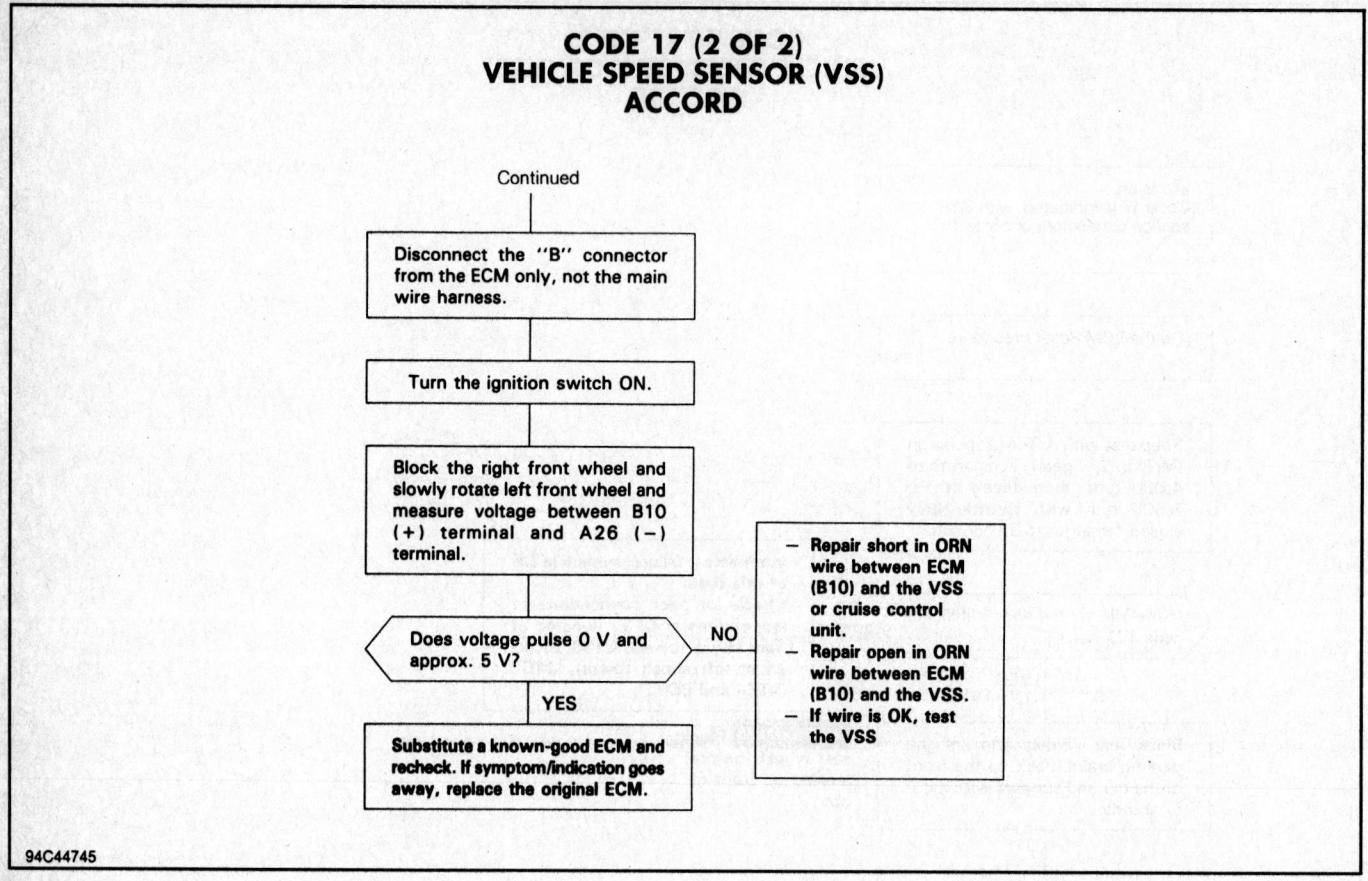

CODE 17 (2 OF 2)
VEHICLE SPEED SENSOR (VSS)
ACCORD

Continued

Disconnect the "B" connector from the ECM only, not the main wire harness.

Turn the ignition switch ON.

Block the right front wheel and slowly rotate left front wheel and measure voltage between B10 (+) terminal and A26 (−) terminal.

Does voltage pulse 0 V and approx. 5 V?

NO

– Repair short in ORN wire between ECM (B10) and the VSS or cruise control unit.
– Repair open in ORN wire between ECM (B10) and the VSS.
– If wire is OK, test the VSS

YES

Substitute a known-good ECM and recheck. If symptom/indication goes away, replace the original ECM.

94C44745

CODE 20 (1 OF 2)
ELECTRICAL LOAD DETECTOR (ELD)
ACCORD

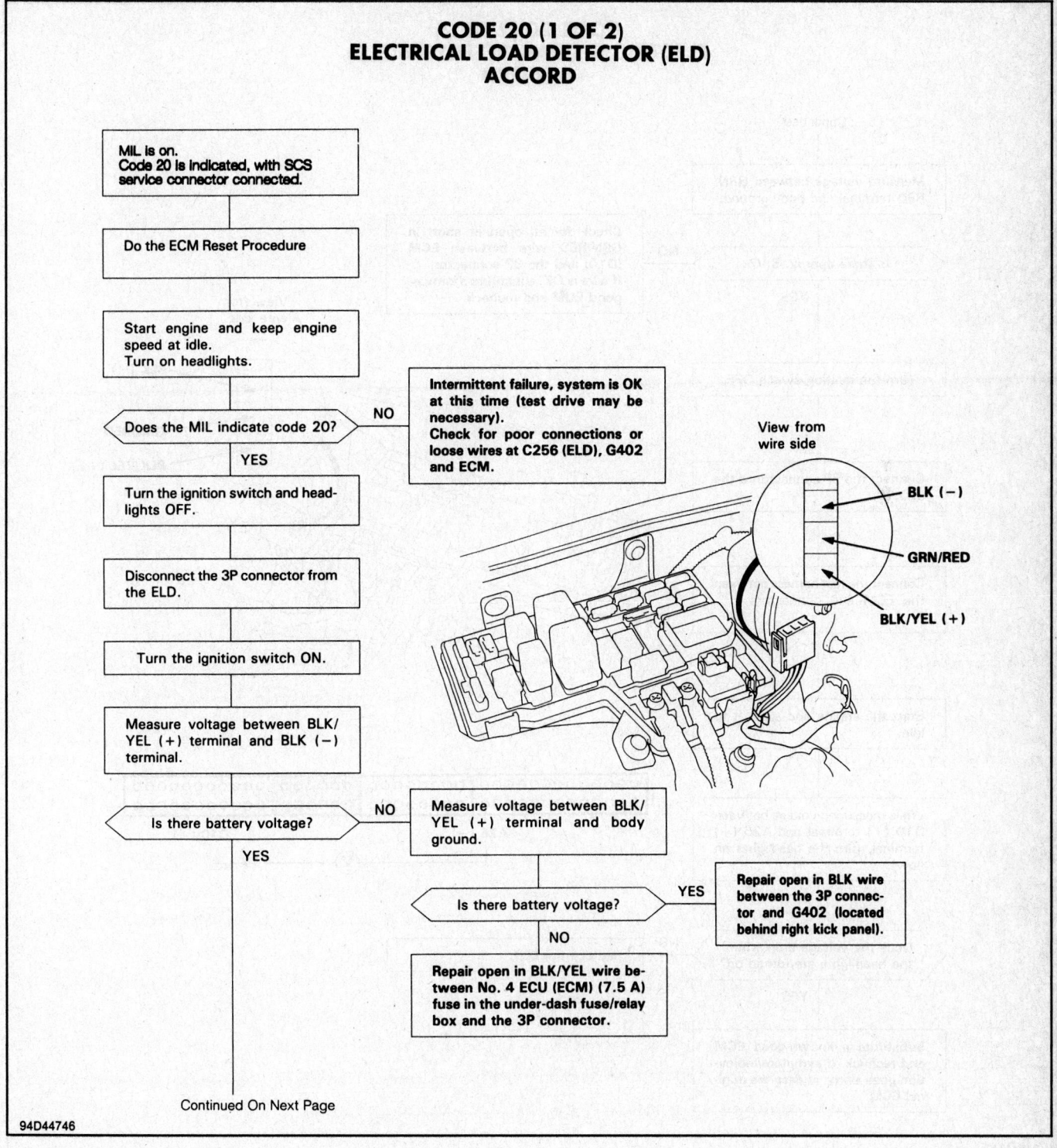

MIL is on.
Code 20 is indicated, with SCS service connector connected.

Do the ECM Reset Procedure

Start engine and keep engine speed at idle.
Turn on headlights.

Does the MIL indicate code 20? — NO → Intermittent failure, system is OK at this time (test drive may be necessary).
Check for poor connections or loose wires at C256 (ELD), G402 and ECM.

YES

Turn the ignition switch and head-lights OFF.

Disconnect the 3P connector from the ELD.

Turn the ignition switch ON.

Measure voltage between BLK/YEL (+) terminal and BLK (−) terminal.

Is there battery voltage? — NO → Measure voltage between BLK/YEL (+) terminal and body ground.

YES

Is there battery voltage? — YES → Repair open in BLK wire between the 3P connec-tor and G402 (located behind right kick panel).

NO

Repair open in BLK/YEL wire be-tween No. 4 ECU (ECM) (7.5 A) fuse in the under-dash fuse/relay box and the 3P connector.

View from wire side

BLK (−)

GRN/RED

BLK/YEL (+)

Continued On Next Page

94D44746

1994 ENGINE PERFORMANCE
Self-Diagnostics (Cont.)

CODE 20 (2 OF 2)
ELECTRICAL LOAD DETECTOR (ELD)
ACCORD

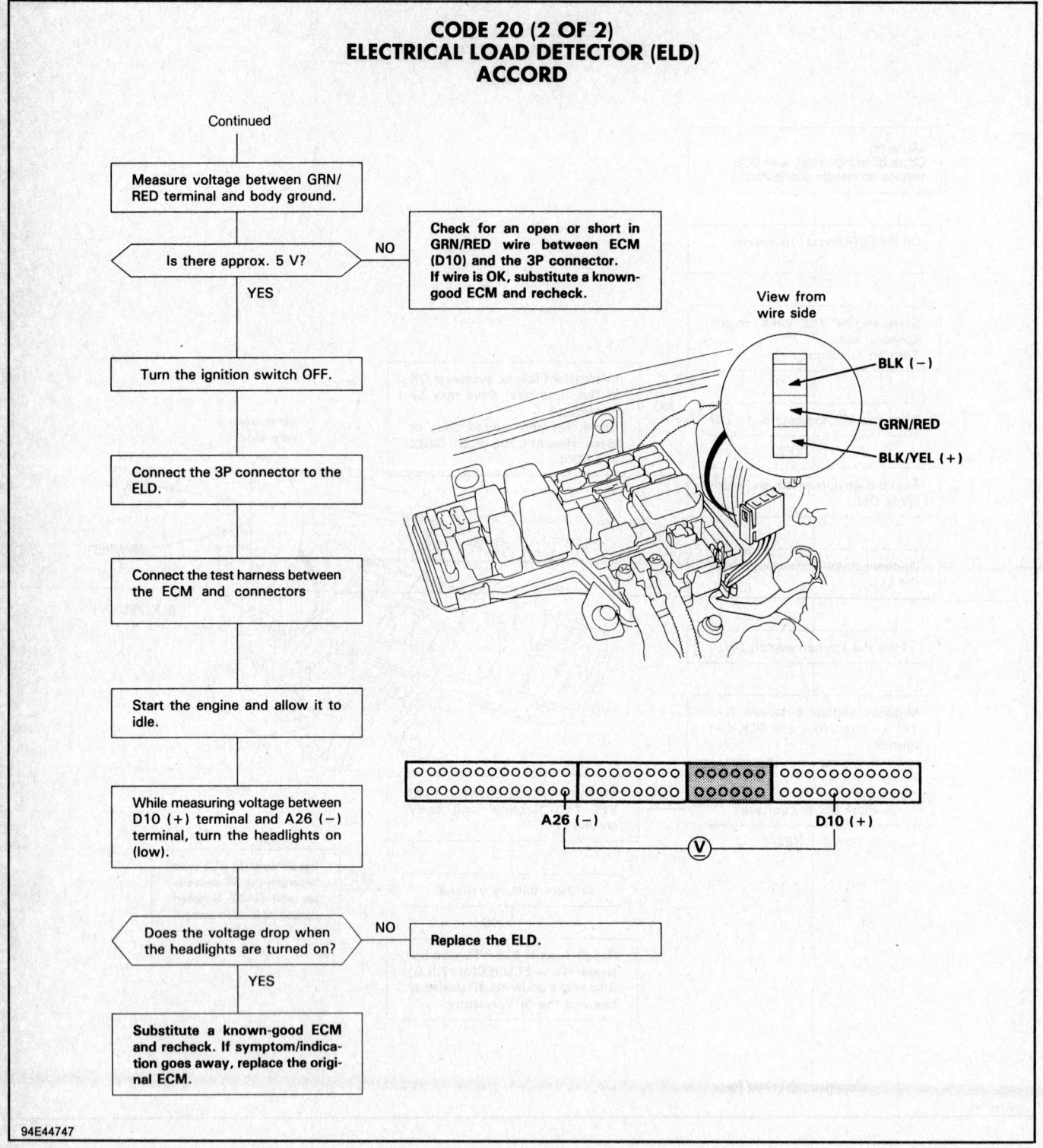

Continued

Measure voltage between GRN/RED terminal and body ground.

Is there approx. 5 V? — NO → Check for an open or short in GRN/RED wire between ECM (D10) and the 3P connector. If wire is OK, substitute a known-good ECM and recheck.

YES

Turn the ignition switch OFF.

Connect the 3P connector to the ELD.

Connect the test harness between the ECM and connectors

Start the engine and allow it to idle.

While measuring voltage between D10 (+) terminal and A26 (−) terminal, turn the headlights on (low).

Does the voltage drop when the headlights are turned on? — NO → Replace the ELD.

YES

Substitute a known-good ECM and recheck. If symptom/indication goes away, replace the original ECM.

View from wire side

BLK (−)
GRN/RED
BLK/YEL (+)

A26 (−)   D10 (+)

94E44747

CODE 21 (1 OF 2)
VTEC SOLENOID VALVE
ACCORD

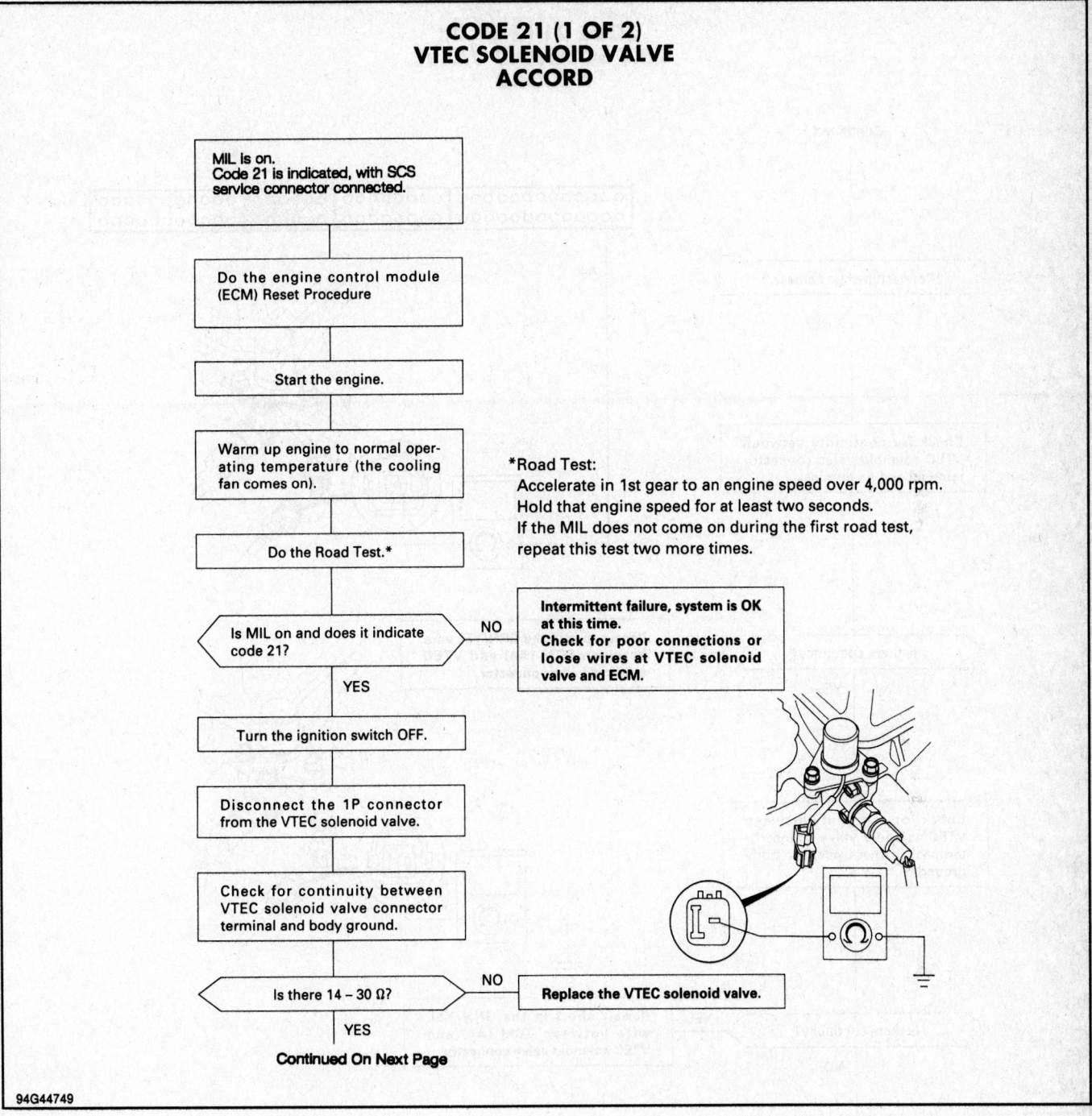

MIL is on.
Code 21 is indicated, with SCS service connector connected.

Do the engine control module (ECM) Reset Procedure

Start the engine.

Warm up engine to normal operating temperature (the cooling fan comes on).

Do the Road Test.*

*Road Test:
Accelerate in 1st gear to an engine speed over 4,000 rpm.
Hold that engine speed for at least two seconds.
If the MIL does not come on during the first road test, repeat this test two more times.

Is MIL on and does it indicate code 21?

NO — Intermittent failure, system is OK at this time.
Check for poor connections or loose wires at VTEC solenoid valve and ECM.

YES

Turn the ignition switch OFF.

Disconnect the 1P connector from the VTEC solenoid valve.

Check for continuity between VTEC solenoid valve connector terminal and body ground.

Is there 14 – 30 Ω?

NO — **Replace the VTEC solenoid valve.**

YES

Continued On Next Page

94G44749

CODE 21 (2 OF 2)
VTEC SOLENOID VALVE
ACCORD

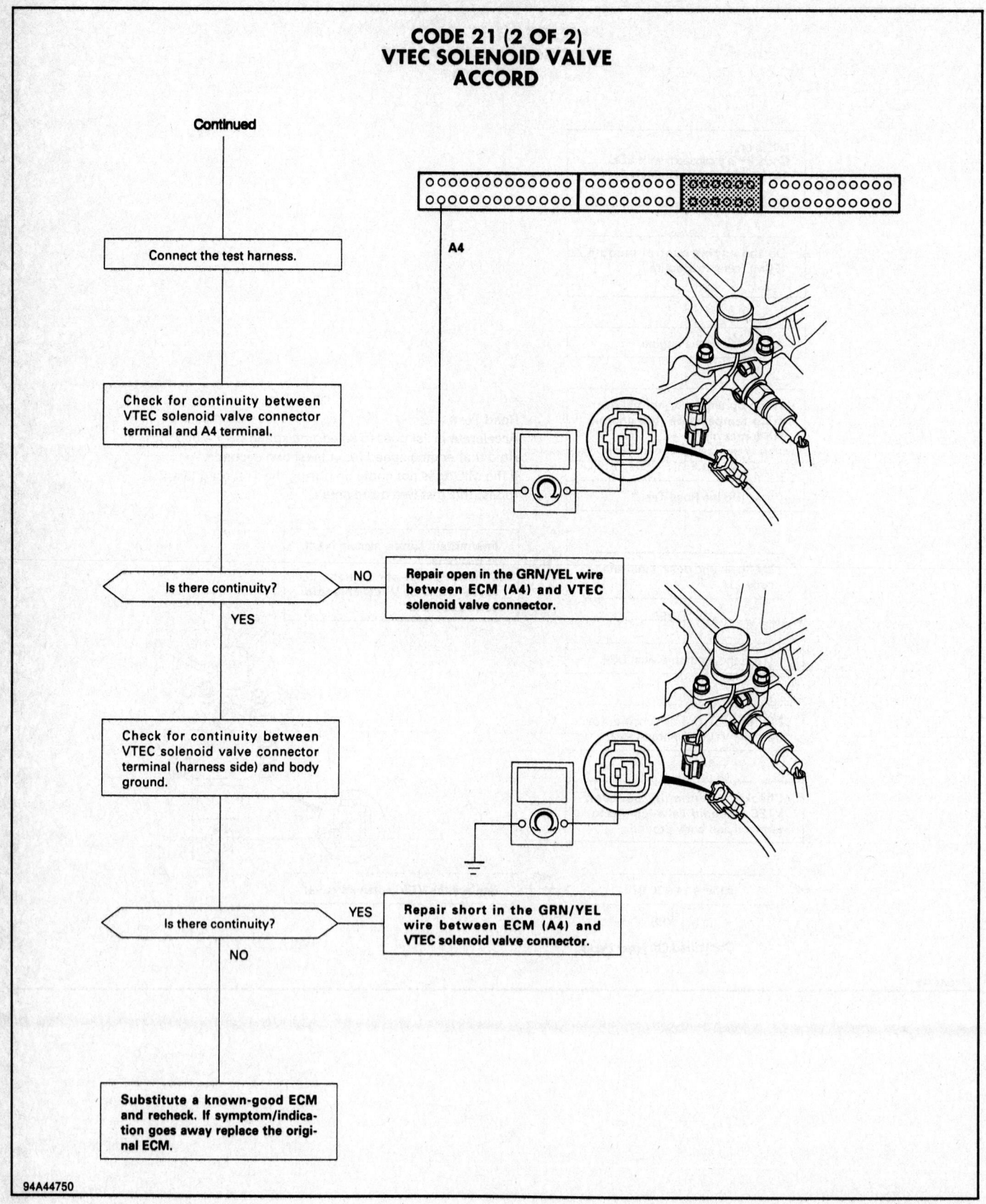

Continued

Connect the test harness.

A4

Check for continuity between
VTEC solenoid valve connector
terminal and A4 terminal.

Is there continuity? — NO → Repair open in the GRN/YEL wire
between ECM (A4) and VTEC
solenoid valve connector.

YES

Check for continuity between
VTEC solenoid valve connector
terminal (harness side) and body
ground.

Is there continuity? — YES → Repair short in the GRN/YEL
wire between ECM (A4) and
VTEC solenoid valve connector.

NO

Substitute a known-good ECM
and recheck. If symptom/indica-
tion goes away replace the original ECM.

94A44750

CODE 22 (1 OF 3)
VTEC PRESSURE SWITCH
ACCORD

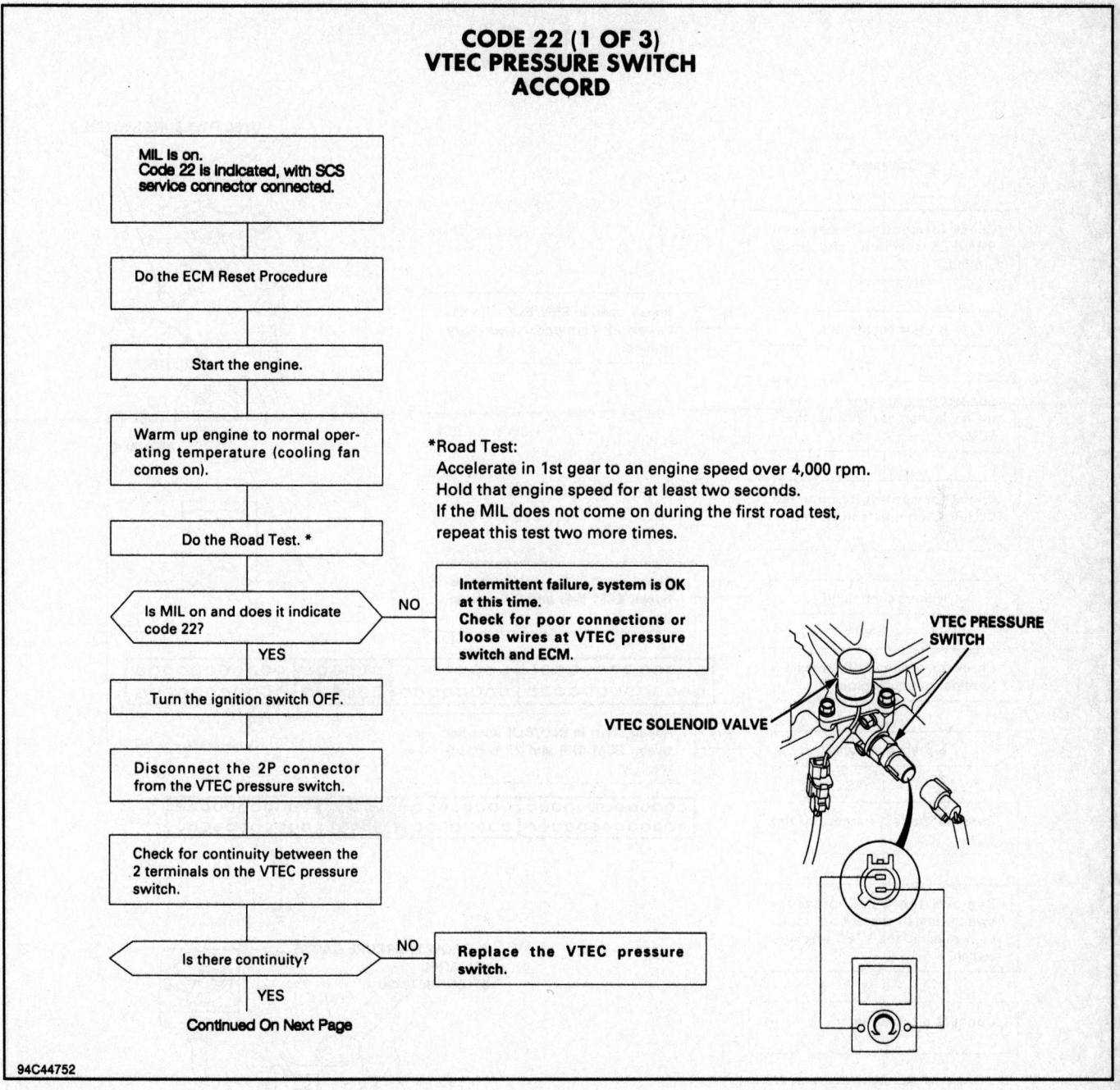

MIL is on.
Code 22 is indicated, with SCS service connector connected.

Do the ECM Reset Procedure

Start the engine.

Warm up engine to normal operating temperature (cooling fan comes on).

Do the Road Test. *

Is MIL on and does it indicate code 22? — NO → Intermittent failure, system is OK at this time.
Check for poor connections or loose wires at VTEC pressure switch and ECM.

YES

Turn the ignition switch OFF.

Disconnect the 2P connector from the VTEC pressure switch.

Check for continuity between the 2 terminals on the VTEC pressure switch.

Is there continuity? — NO → Replace the VTEC pressure switch.

YES

Continued On Next Page

*Road Test:
Accelerate in 1st gear to an engine speed over 4,000 rpm.
Hold that engine speed for at least two seconds.
If the MIL does not come on during the first road test, repeat this test two more times.

VTEC PRESSURE SWITCH

VTEC SOLENOID VALVE

94C44752

CODE 22 (2 OF 3)
VTEC PRESSURE SWITCH
ACCORD

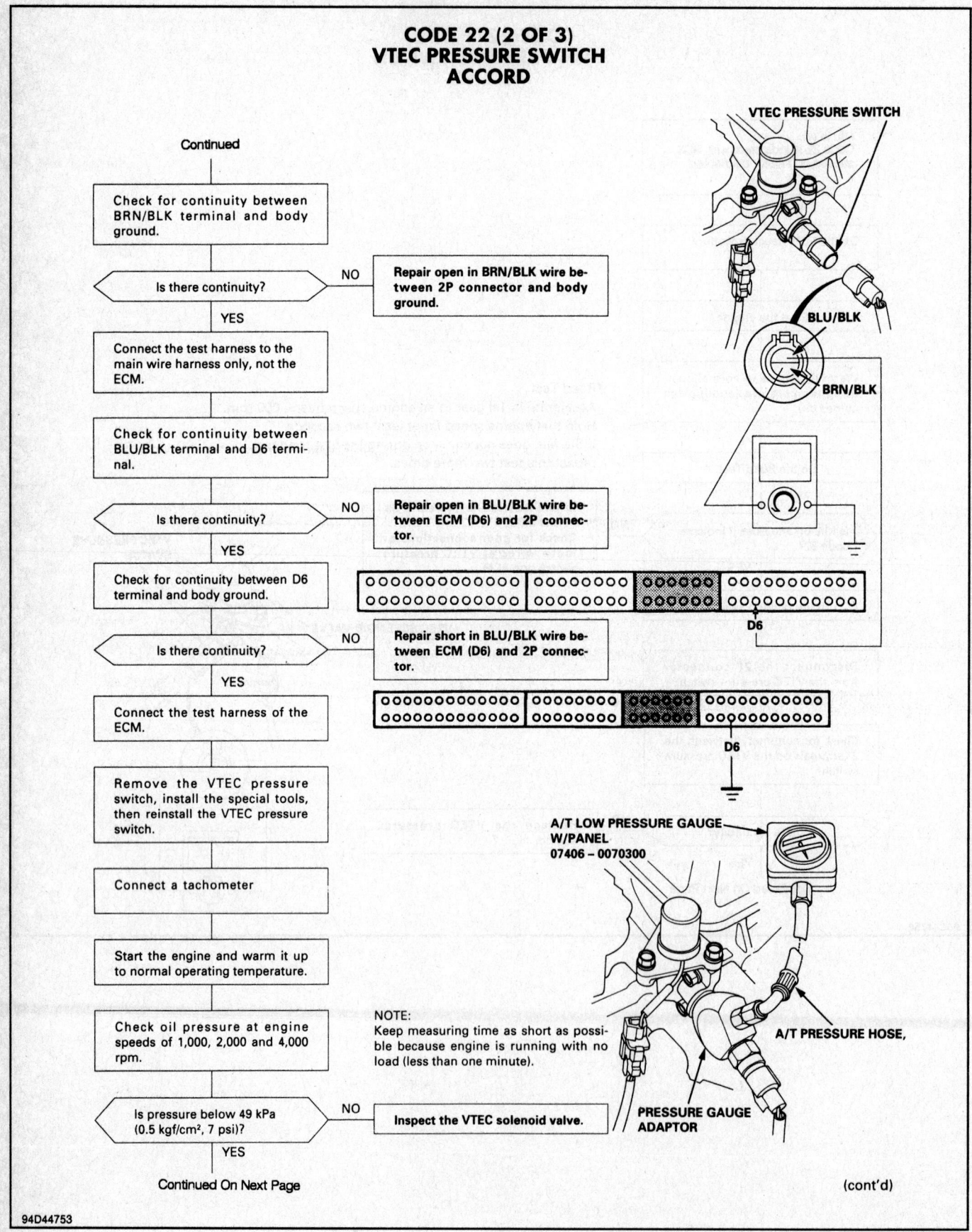

Continued

Check for continuity between BRN/BLK terminal and body ground.

Is there continuity? — NO → Repair open in BRN/BLK wire between 2P connector and body ground.

YES

Connect the test harness to the main wire harness only, not the ECM.

Check for continuity between BLU/BLK terminal and D6 terminal.

Is there continuity? — NO → Repair open in BLU/BLK wire between ECM (D6) and 2P connector.

YES

Check for continuity between D6 terminal and body ground.

Is there continuity? — NO → Repair short in BLU/BLK wire between ECM (D6) and 2P connector.

YES

Connect the test harness of the ECM.

Remove the VTEC pressure switch, install the special tools, then reinstall the VTEC pressure switch.

Connect a tachometer

Start the engine and warm it up to normal operating temperature.

Check oil pressure at engine speeds of 1,000, 2,000 and 4,000 rpm.

NOTE:
Keep measuring time as short as possible because engine is running with no load (less than one minute).

Is pressure below 49 kPa (0.5 kgf/cm², 7 psi)? — NO → Inspect the VTEC solenoid valve.

YES

Continued On Next Page

VTEC PRESSURE SWITCH

BLU/BLK

BRN/BLK

D6

D6

A/T LOW PRESSURE GAUGE W/PANEL
07406 – 0070300

A/T PRESSURE HOSE,

PRESSURE GAUGE ADAPTOR

(cont'd)

94D44753

CODE 22 (3 OF 3)
VTEC PRESSURE SWITCH
ACCORD

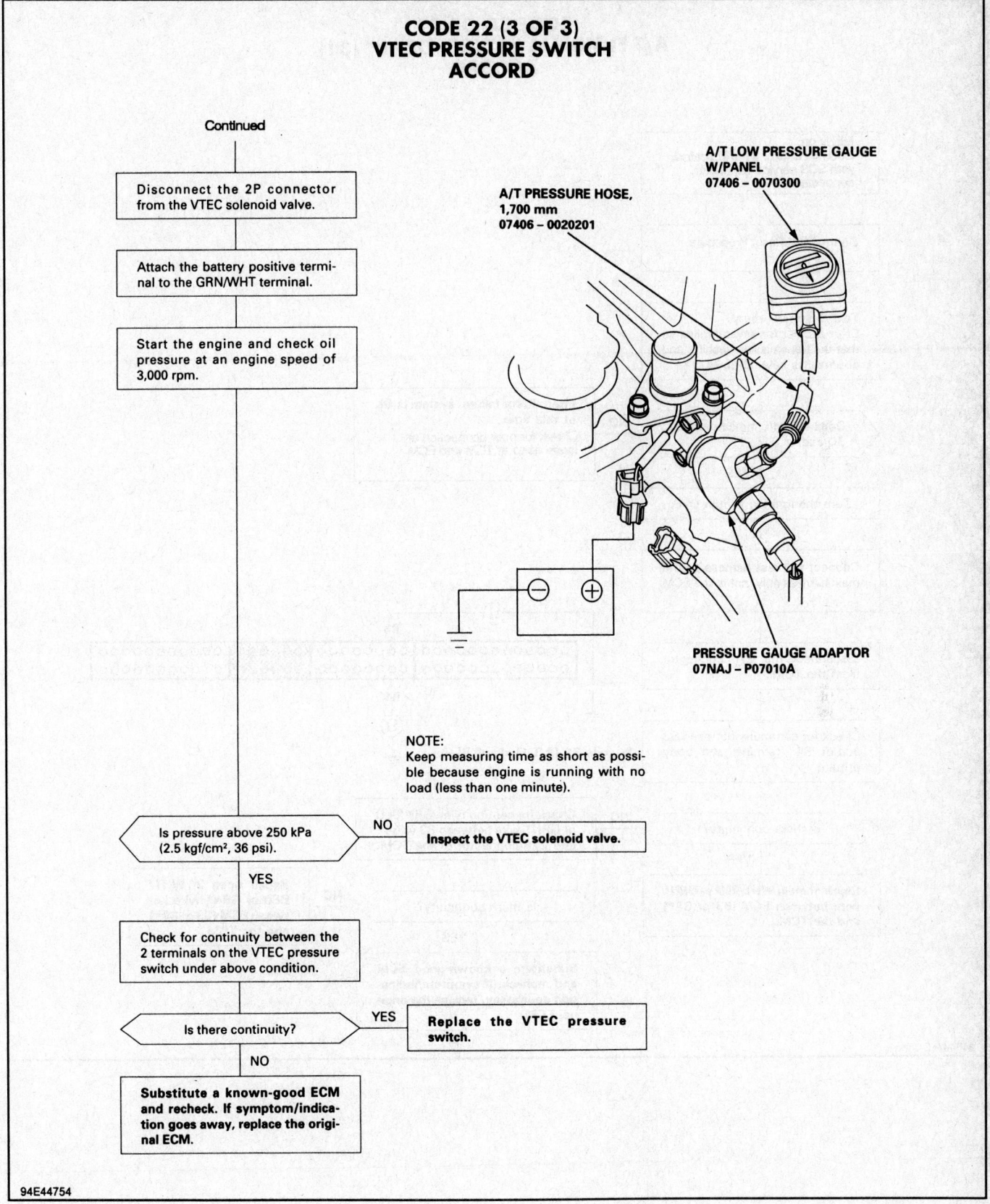

Continued

Disconnect the 2P connector from the VTEC solenoid valve.

Attach the battery positive terminal to the GRN/WHT terminal.

Start the engine and check oil pressure at an engine speed of 3,000 rpm.

A/T LOW PRESSURE GAUGE W/PANEL
07406 – 0070300

A/T PRESSURE HOSE,
1,700 mm
07406 – 0020201

PRESSURE GAUGE ADAPTOR
07NAJ – P07010A

NOTE:
Keep measuring time as short as possible because engine is running with no load (less than one minute).

Is pressure above 250 kPa (2.5 kgf/cm², 36 psi). — NO → **Inspect the VTEC solenoid valve.**

YES

Check for continuity between the 2 terminals on the VTEC pressure switch under above condition.

Is there continuity? — YES → **Replace the VTEC pressure switch.**

NO

Substitute a known-good ECM and recheck. If symptom/indication goes away, replace the original ECM.

94E44754

1994 ENGINE PERFORMANCE
Self-Diagnostics (Cont.)

CODE 30 OR 31
A/T FI SIGNAL "A" (30) OR "B" (31)
ACCORD

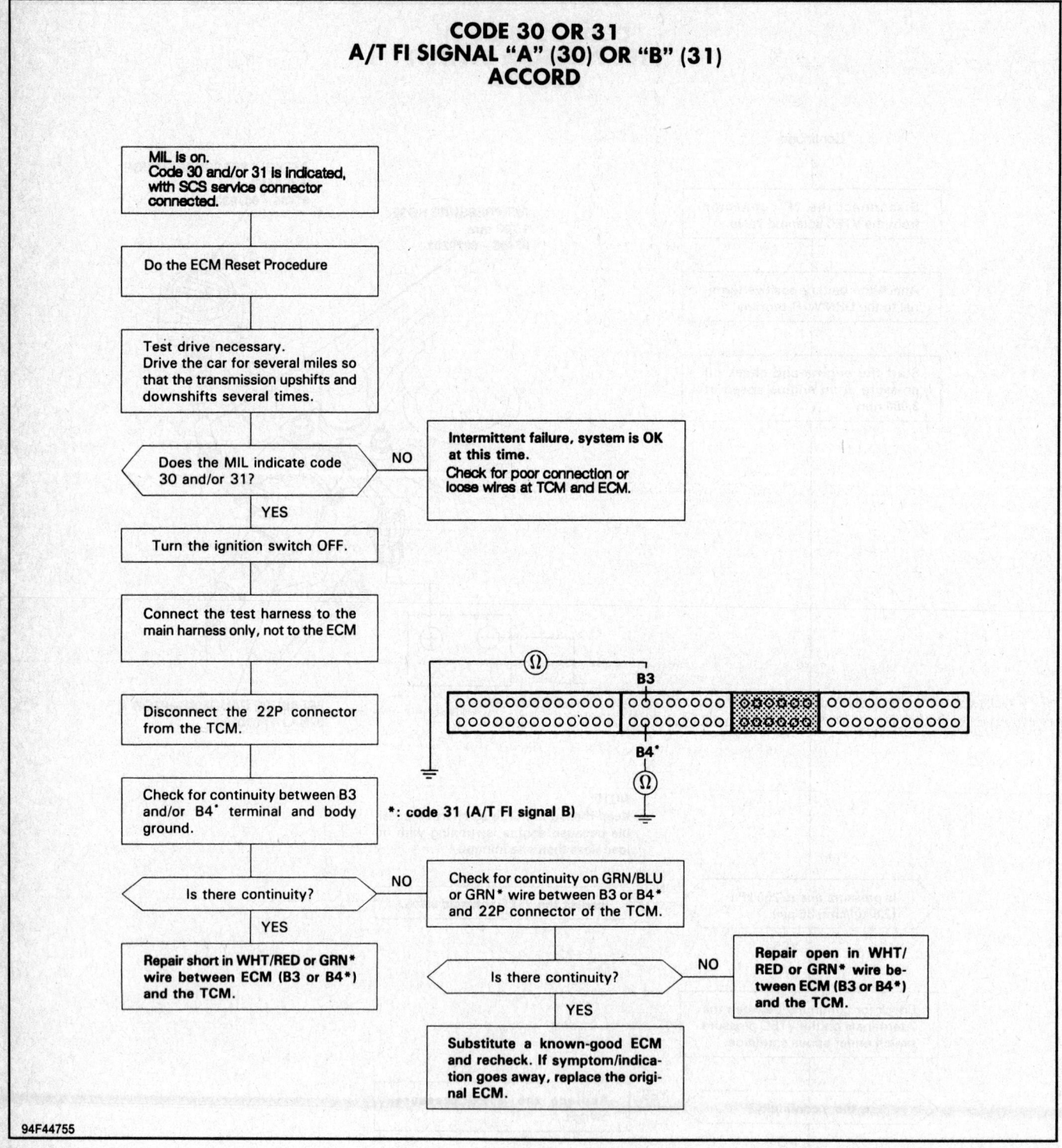

MIL is on.
Code 30 and/or 31 is indicated, with SCS service connector connected.

Do the ECM Reset Procedure

Test drive necessary.
Drive the car for several miles so that the transmission upshifts and downshifts several times.

Does the MIL indicate code 30 and/or 31?

NO → Intermittent failure, system is OK at this time.
Check for poor connection or loose wires at TCM and ECM.

YES

Turn the ignition switch OFF.

Connect the test harness to the main harness only, not to the ECM

Disconnect the 22P connector from the TCM.

Check for continuity between B3 and/or B4* terminal and body ground.

*: code 31 (A/T FI signal B)

Is there continuity?

NO → Check for continuity on GRN/BLU or GRN* wire between B3 or B4* and 22P connector of the TCM.

YES

Repair short in WHT/RED or GRN* wire between ECM (B3 or B4*) and the TCM.

Is there continuity?

NO → Repair open in WHT/RED or GRN* wire between ECM (B3 or B4*) and the TCM.

YES

Substitute a known-good ECM and recheck. If symptom/indication goes away, replace the original ECM.

94F44755

CODE 41 (1 OF 3)
HEATED OXYGEN SENSOR (HO2S) HEATER
ACCORD

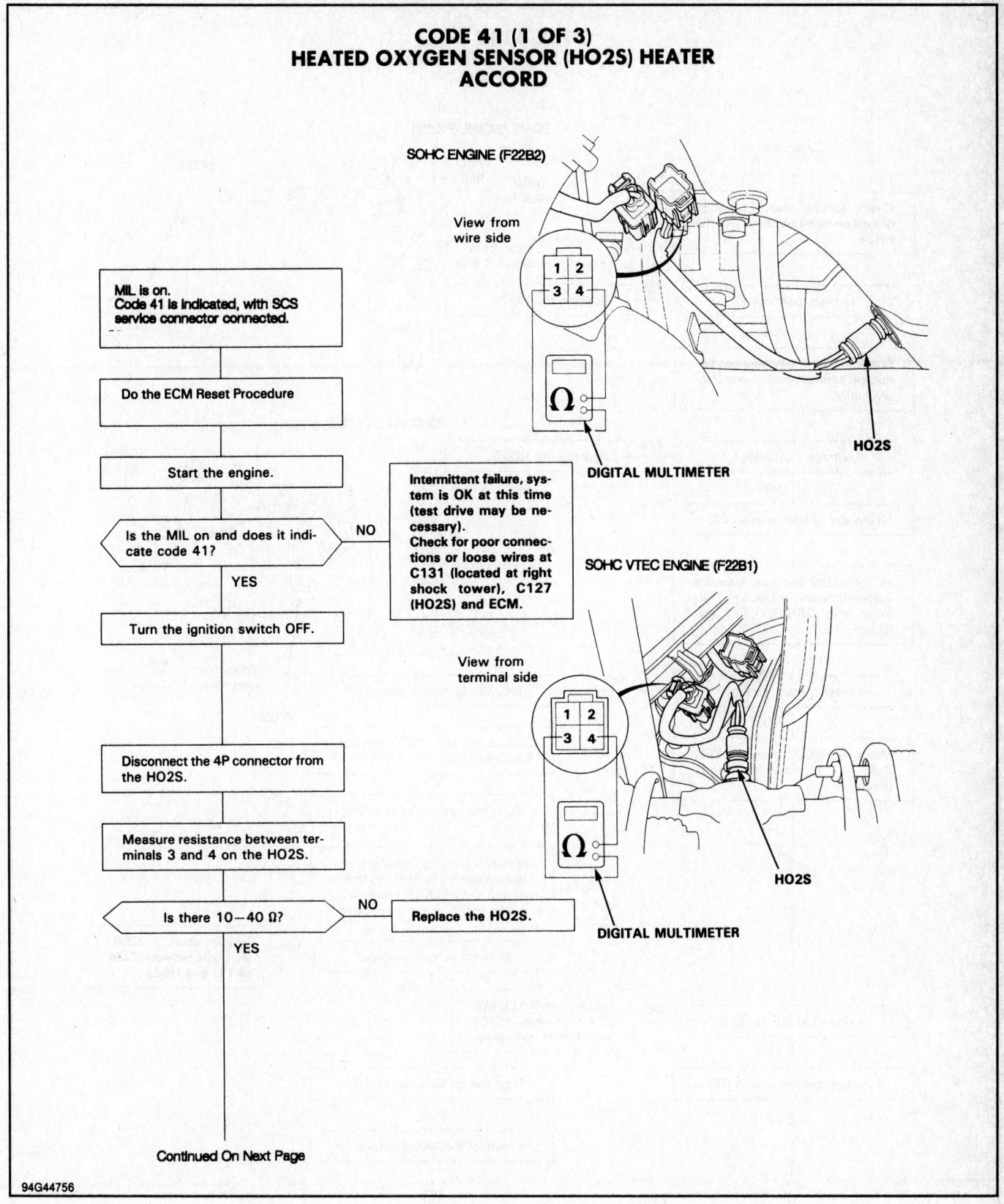

SOHC ENGINE (F22B2)

View from wire side

| 1 | 2 |
| 3 | 4 |

DIGITAL MULTIMETER

HO2S

SOHC VTEC ENGINE (F22B1)

View from terminal side

| 1 | 2 |
| 3 | 4 |

DIGITAL MULTIMETER

HO2S

MIL is on.
Code 41 is indicated, with SCS service connector connected.

Do the ECM Reset Procedure

Start the engine.

Is the MIL on and does it indicate code 41?

NO → Intermittent failure, system is OK at this time (test drive may be necessary).
Check for poor connections or loose wires at C131 (located at right shock tower), C127 (HO2S) and ECM.

YES

Turn the ignition switch OFF.

Disconnect the 4P connector from the HO2S.

Measure resistance between terminals 3 and 4 on the HO2S.

Is there 10—40 Ω?

NO → Replace the HO2S.

YES

Continued On Next Page

94G44756

CODE 41 (2 OF 3)
HEATED OXYGEN SENSOR (HO2S) HEATER
ACCORD

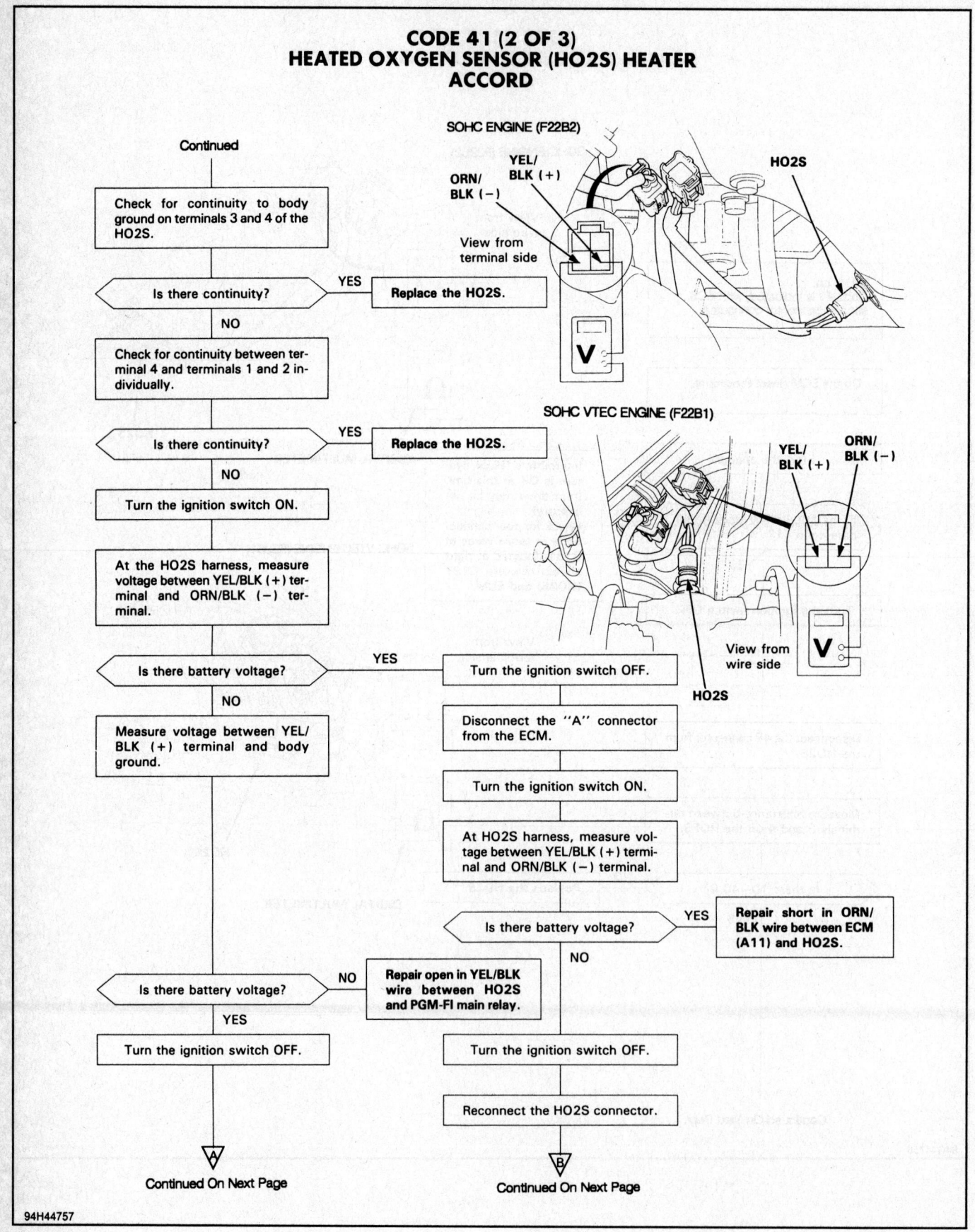

SOHC ENGINE (F22B2)

YEL/BLK (+)

ORN/BLK (−)

HO2S

View from terminal side

SOHC VTEC ENGINE (F22B1)

YEL/BLK (+)

ORN/BLK (−)

HO2S

View from wire side

Continued

Check for continuity to body ground on terminals 3 and 4 of the HO2S.

Is there continuity? → YES → Replace the HO2S.

NO

Check for continuity between terminal 4 and terminals 1 and 2 individually.

Is there continuity? → YES → Replace the HO2S.

NO

Turn the ignition switch ON.

At the HO2S harness, measure voltage between YEL/BLK (+) terminal and ORN/BLK (−) terminal.

Is there battery voltage? → YES → Turn the ignition switch OFF.

NO

Measure voltage between YEL/BLK (+) terminal and body ground.

Disconnect the "A" connector from the ECM.

Turn the ignition switch ON.

At HO2S harness, measure voltage between YEL/BLK (+) terminal and ORN/BLK (−) terminal.

Is there battery voltage? → YES → Repair short in ORN/BLK wire between ECM (A11) and HO2S.

NO

Is there battery voltage? → NO → Repair open in YEL/BLK wire between HO2S and PGM-FI main relay.

YES

Turn the ignition switch OFF.

Turn the ignition switch OFF.

Reconnect the HO2S connector.

A
Continued On Next Page

B
Continued On Next Page

94H44757

CODE 41 (3 OF 3)
HEATED OXYGEN SENSOR (HO2S) HEATER
ACCORD

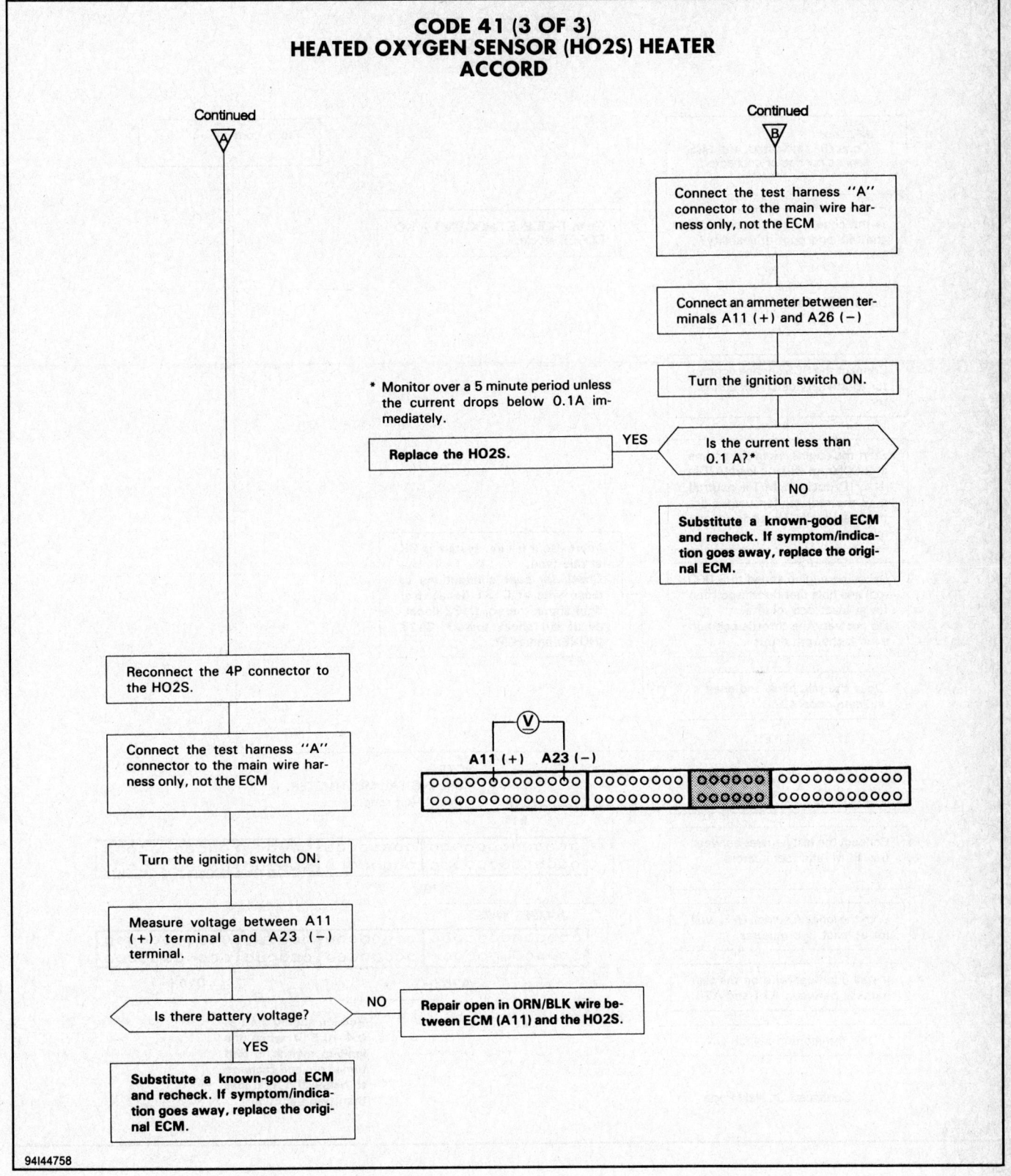

Continued (A)

Continued (B)

Connect the test harness "A" connector to the main wire harness only, not the ECM

Connect an ammeter between terminals A11 (+) and A26 (−)

Turn the ignition switch ON.

* Monitor over a 5 minute period unless the current drops below 0.1A immediately.

Replace the HO2S. ← YES ← Is the current less than 0.1 A?*

NO

Substitute a known-good ECM and recheck. If symptom/indication goes away, replace the original ECM.

A11 (+) A23 (−)

Reconnect the 4P connector to the HO2S.

Connect the test harness "A" connector to the main wire harness only, not the ECM

Turn the ignition switch ON.

Measure voltage between A11 (+) terminal and A23 (−) terminal.

Is there battery voltage? → NO → Repair open in ORN/BLK wire between ECM (A11) and the HO2S.

YES

Substitute a known-good ECM and recheck. If symptom/indication goes away, replace the original ECM.

94I44758

CODE 43 (1 OF 2)
FUEL SUPPLY SYSTEM
ACCORD

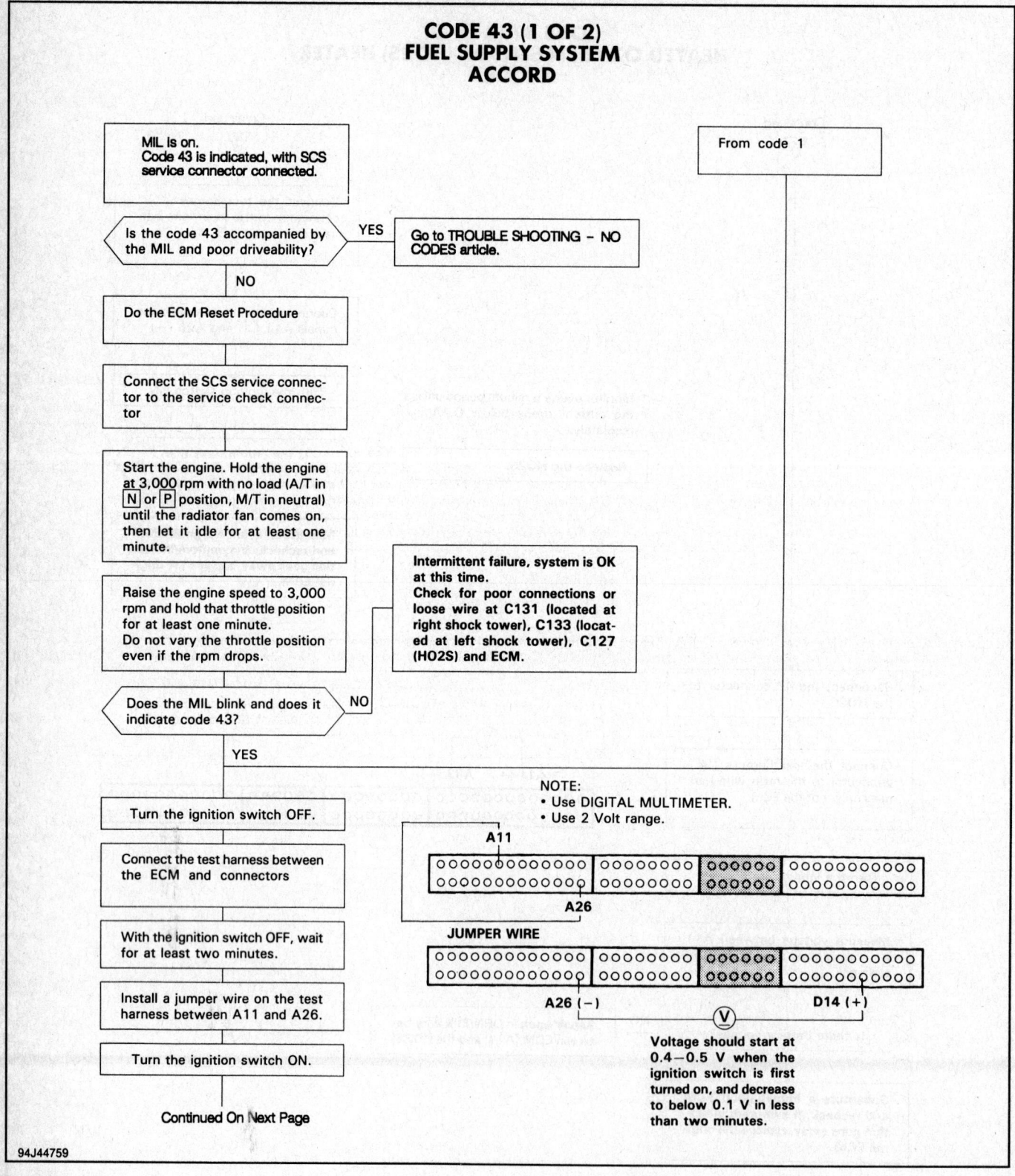

MIL is on.
Code 43 is indicated, with SCS service connector connected.

Is the code 43 accompanied by the MIL and poor driveability?

YES → Go to TROUBLE SHOOTING – NO CODES article.

NO

Do the ECM Reset Procedure

Connect the SCS service connector to the service check connector

Start the engine. Hold the engine at 3,000 rpm with no load (A/T in N or P position, M/T in neutral) until the radiator fan comes on, then let it idle for at least one minute.

Raise the engine speed to 3,000 rpm and hold that throttle position for at least one minute.
Do not vary the throttle position even if the rpm drops.

Does the MIL blink and does it indicate code 43?

NO → Intermittent failure, system is OK at this time.
Check for poor connections or loose wire at C131 (located at right shock tower), C133 (located at left shock tower), C127 (HO2S) and ECM.

YES

Turn the ignition switch OFF.

Connect the test harness between the ECM and connectors

With the ignition switch OFF, wait for at least two minutes.

Install a jumper wire on the test harness between A11 and A26.

Turn the ignition switch ON.

Continued On Next Page

From code 1

NOTE:
• Use DIGITAL MULTIMETER.
• Use 2 Volt range.

A11

A26

JUMPER WIRE

A26 (−)   D14 (+)

Voltage should start at 0.4–0.5 V when the ignition switch is first turned on, and decrease to below 0.1 V in less than two minutes.

CODE 43 (2 OF 2)
FUEL SUPPLY SYSTEM
ACCORD

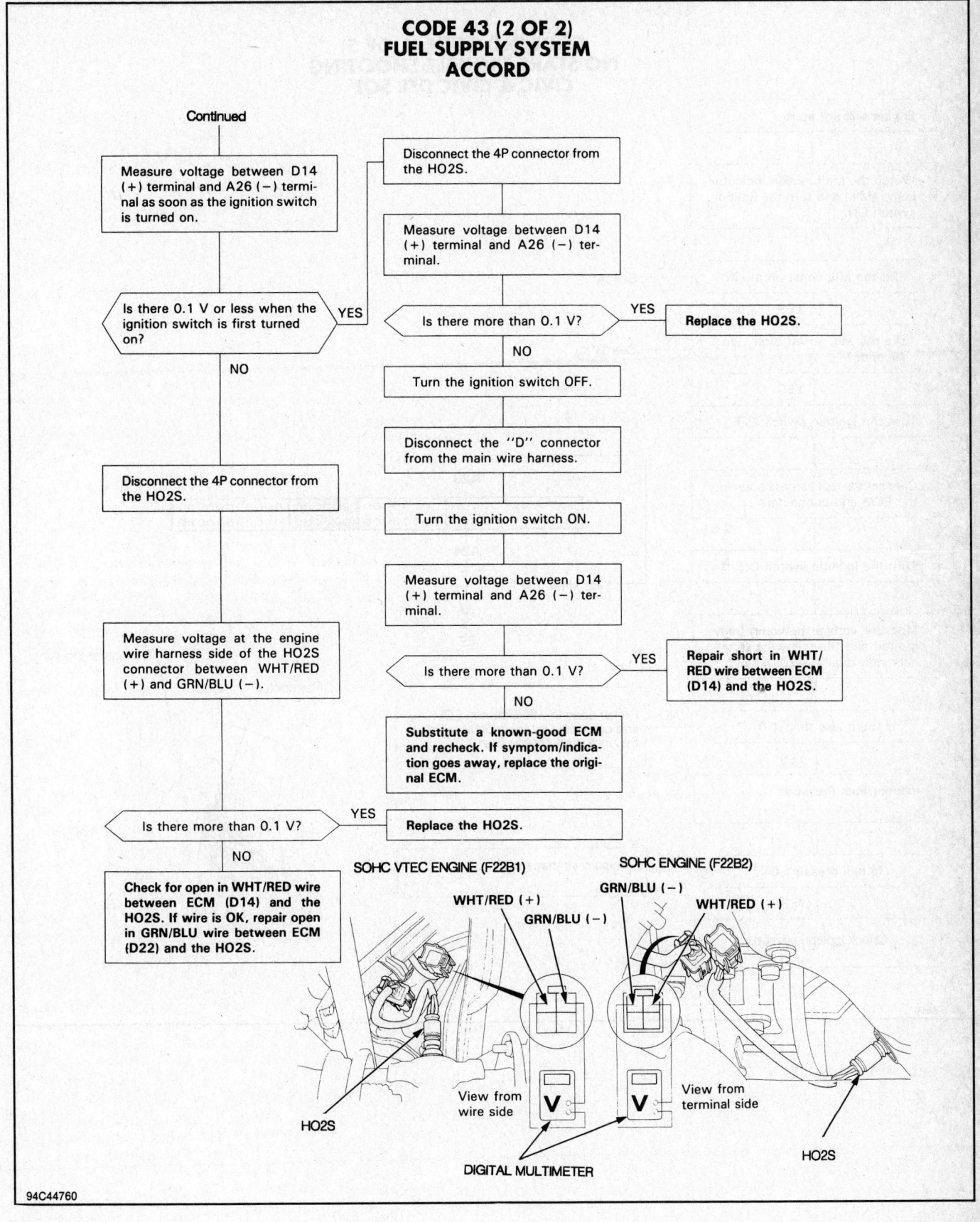

Continued

Measure voltage between D14 (+) terminal and A26 (−) terminal as soon as the ignition switch is turned on.

Is there 0.1 V or less when the ignition switch is first turned on? — NO

Disconnect the 4P connector from the HO2S.

Measure voltage at the engine wire harness side of the HO2S connector between WHT/RED (+) and GRN/BLU (−).

Is there more than 0.1 V? — YES → Replace the HO2S.

NO

Check for open in WHT/RED wire between ECM (D14) and the HO2S. If wire is OK, repair open in GRN/BLU wire between ECM (D22) and the HO2S.

Disconnect the 4P connector from the HO2S.

Measure voltage between D14 (+) terminal and A26 (−) terminal.

Is there more than 0.1 V? — YES → Replace the HO2S.

NO

Turn the ignition switch OFF.

Disconnect the "D" connector from the main wire harness.

Turn the ignition switch ON.

Measure voltage between D14 (+) terminal and A26 (−) terminal.

Is there more than 0.1 V? — YES → Repair short in WHT/RED wire between ECM (D14) and the HO2S.

NO

Substitute a known-good ECM and recheck. If symptom/indication goes away, replace the original ECM.

SOHC VTEC ENGINE (F22B1)
WHT/RED (+)
GRN/BLU (−)

SOHC ENGINE (F22B2)
GRN/BLU (−)
WHT/RED (+)

HO2S

View from wire side

View from terminal side

HO2S

DIGITAL MULTIMETER

94C44760

CODE/NO CODE (1 OF 5)
NO START TROUBLE SHOOTING
CIVIC & CIVIC DEL SOL

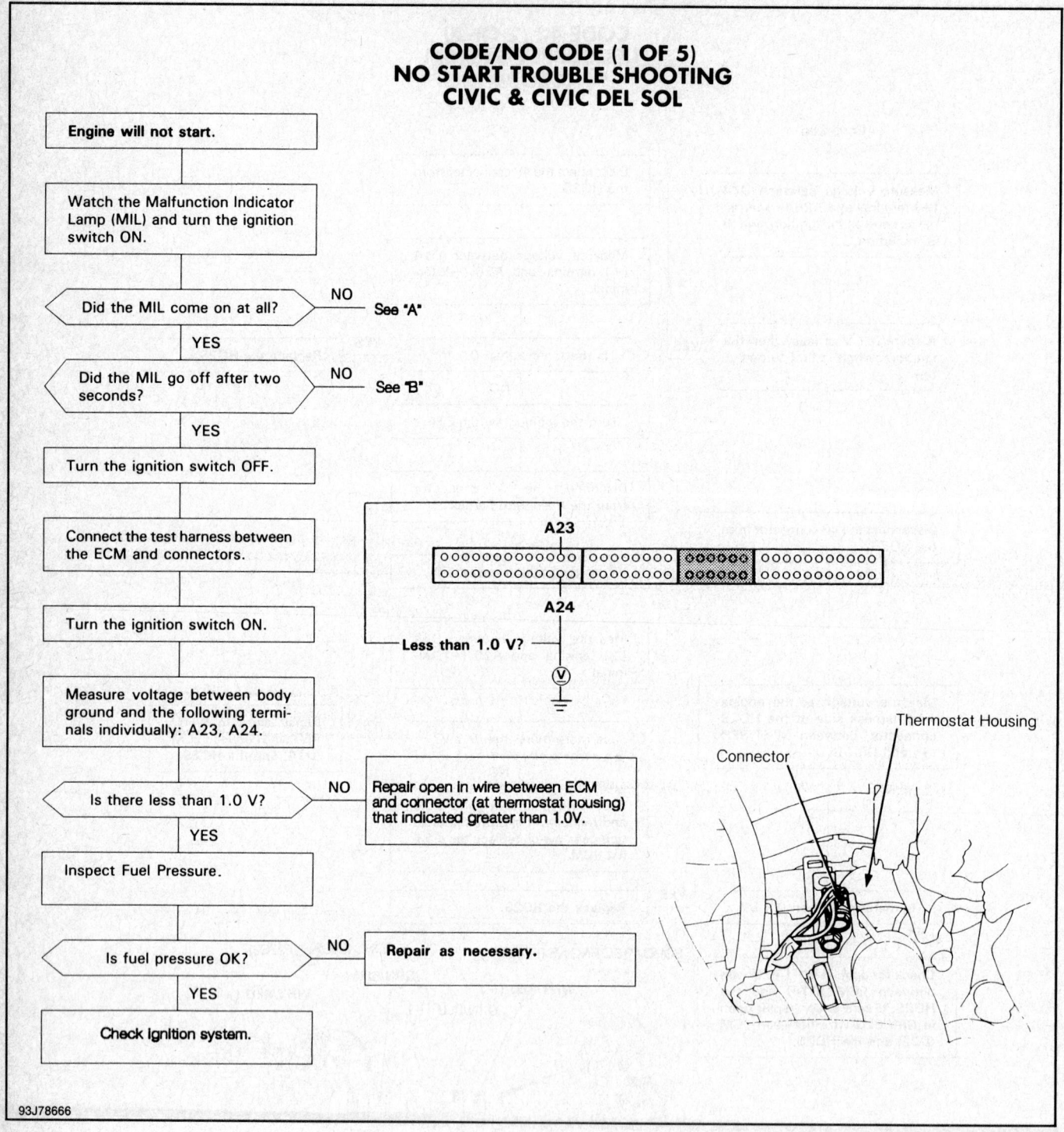

Engine will not start.

Watch the Malfunction Indicator Lamp (MIL) and turn the ignition switch ON.

Did the MIL come on at all? — NO → See "A"

YES

Did the MIL go off after two seconds? — NO → See "B"

YES

Turn the ignition switch OFF.

Connect the test harness between the ECM and connectors.

Turn the ignition switch ON.

Measure voltage between body ground and the following terminals individually: A23, A24.

Is there less than 1.0 V? — NO → Repair open in wire between ECM and connector (at thermostat housing) that indicated greater than 1.0V.

YES

Inspect Fuel Pressure.

Is fuel pressure OK? — NO → Repair as necessary.

YES

Check ignition system.

A23

A24

Less than 1.0 V?

Thermostat Housing

Connector

93J78666

CODE/NO CODE (2 OF 5)
NO START TROUBLE SHOOTING
CIVIC & CIVIC DEL SOL

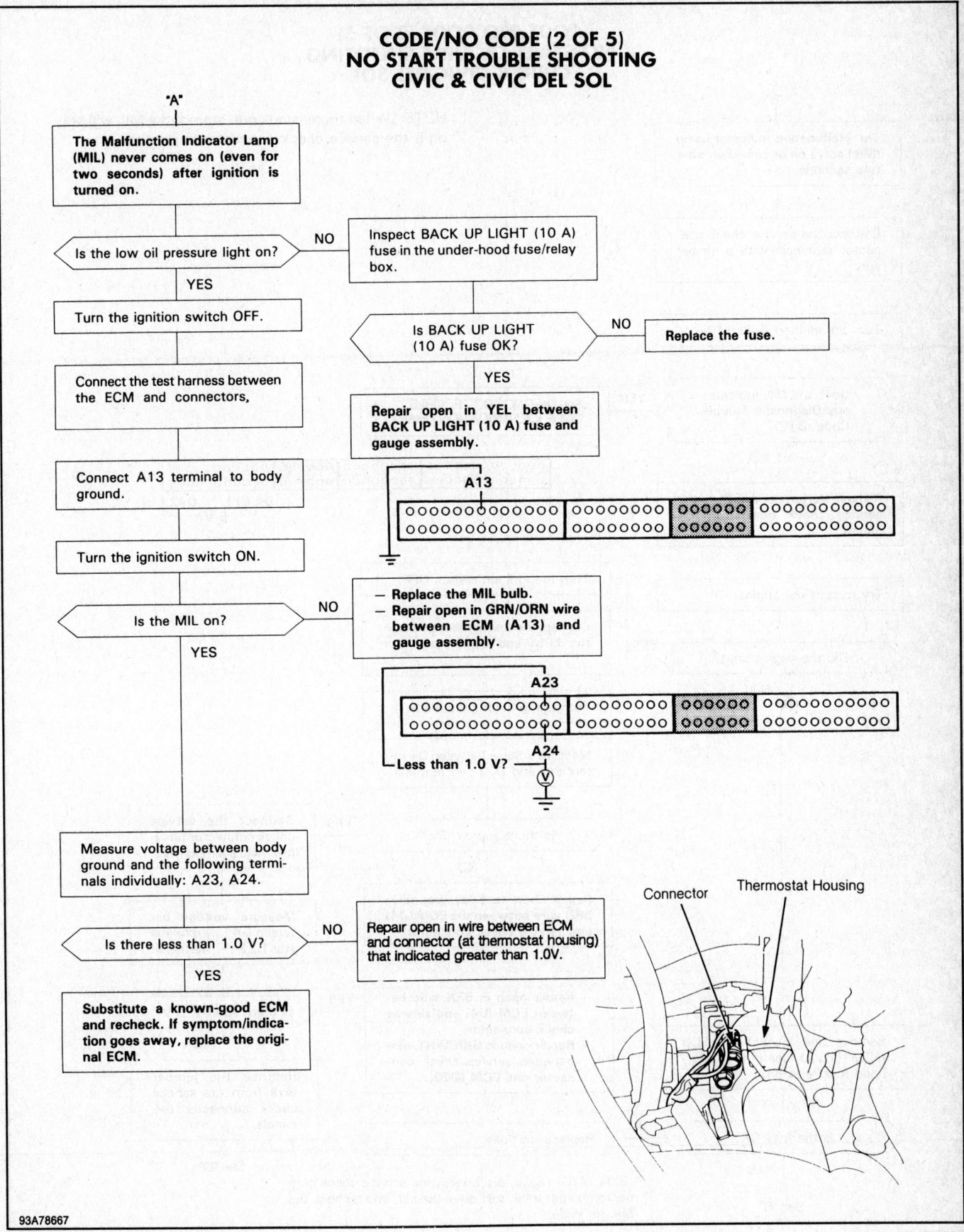

"A"

The **Malfunction Indicator Lamp** (MIL) never comes on (even for two seconds) after ignition is turned on.

Is the low oil pressure light on? — NO → Inspect BACK UP LIGHT (10 A) fuse in the under-hood fuse/relay box.

YES

Turn the ignition switch OFF.

Is BACK UP LIGHT (10 A) fuse OK? — NO → **Replace the fuse.**

Connect the test harness between the ECM and connectors,

YES

Repair open in YEL between BACK UP LIGHT (10 A) fuse and gauge assembly.

Connect A13 terminal to body ground.

A13

Turn the ignition switch ON.

Is the MIL on? — NO →
— Replace the MIL bulb.
— Repair open in GRN/ORN wire between ECM (A13) and gauge assembly.

YES

A23

A24

Less than 1.0 V?

Measure voltage between body ground and the following terminals individually: A23, A24.

Is there less than 1.0 V? — NO → Repair open in wire between ECM and connector (at thermostat housing) that indicated greater than 1.0V.

YES

Substitute a known-good ECM and recheck. If symptom/indication goes away, replace the original ECM.

Connector   Thermostat Housing

CODE/NO CODE (3 OF 5)
NO START TROUBLE SHOOTING
CIVIC & CIVIC DEL SOL

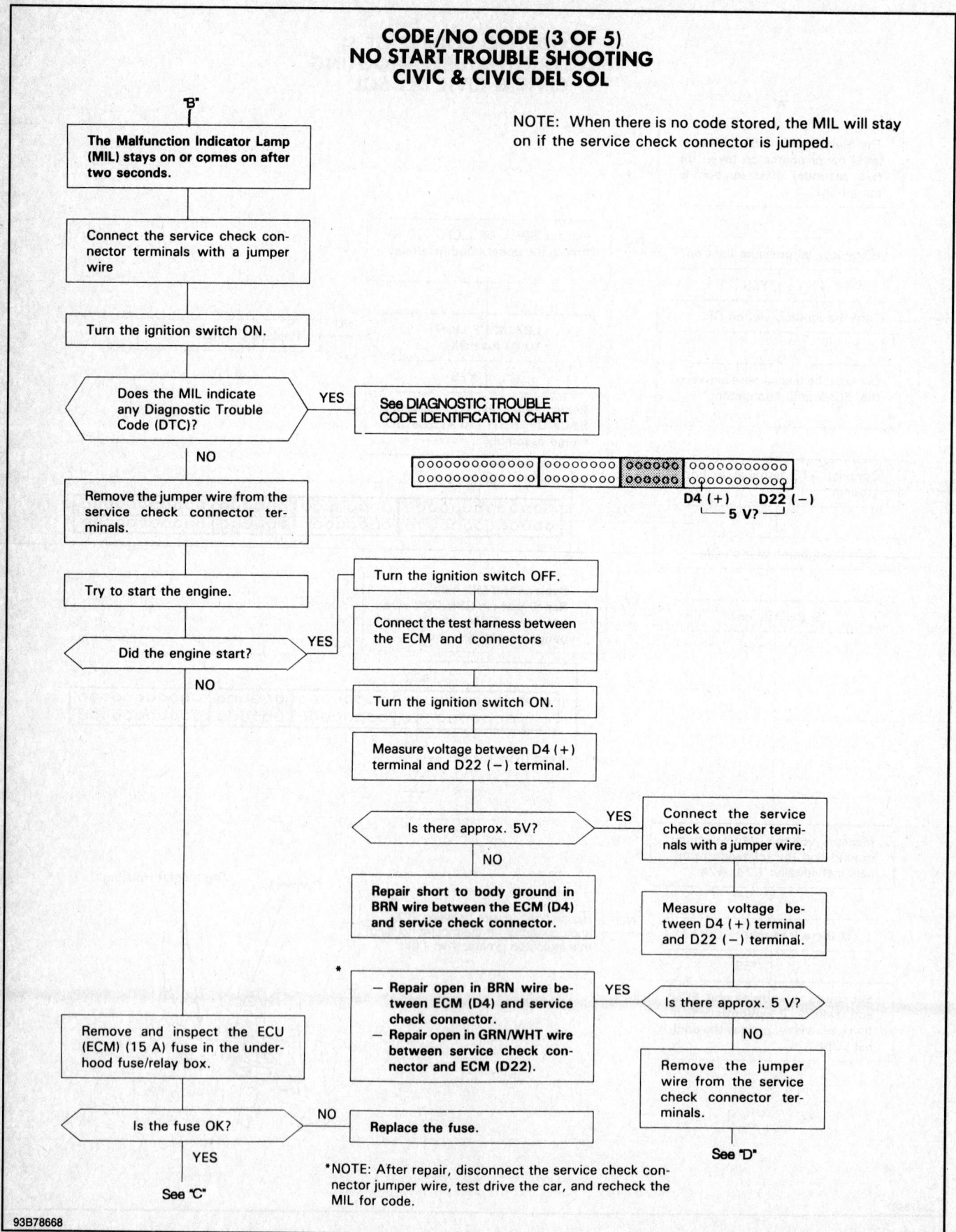

"B"

The Malfunction Indicator Lamp (MIL) stays on or comes on after two seconds.

Connect the service check connector terminals with a jumper wire

Turn the ignition switch ON.

Does the MIL indicate any Diagnostic Trouble Code (DTC)? — **YES** → See DIAGNOSTIC TROUBLE CODE IDENTIFICATION CHART

NO

Remove the jumper wire from the service check connector terminals.

Try to start the engine.

Did the engine start? — **YES** →

NO

Remove and inspect the ECU (ECM) (15 A) fuse in the underhood fuse/relay box.

Is the fuse OK? — **NO** → Replace the fuse.

YES

See "C"

NOTE: When there is no code stored, the MIL will stay on if the service check connector is jumped.

D4 (+)   D22 (−)
⌞ 5 V? ⌟

Turn the ignition switch OFF.

Connect the test harness between the ECM and connectors

Turn the ignition switch ON.

Measure voltage between D4 (+) terminal and D22 (−) terminal.

Is there approx. 5V? — **YES** → Connect the service check connector terminals with a jumper wire.

NO

Repair short to body ground in BRN wire between the ECM (D4) and service check connector.

Measure voltage between D4 (+) terminal and D22 (−) terminal.

Is there approx. 5 V? — **YES** →
— Repair open in BRN wire between ECM (D4) and service check connector.
— Repair open in GRN/WHT wire between service check connector and ECM (D22).

NO

Remove the jumper wire from the service check connector terminals.

See "D"

*NOTE: After repair, disconnect the service check connector jumper wire, test drive the car, and recheck the MIL for code.

93B78668

CODE/NO CODE (4 OF 5)
NO START TROUBLE SHOOTING
CIVIC & CIVIC DEL SOL

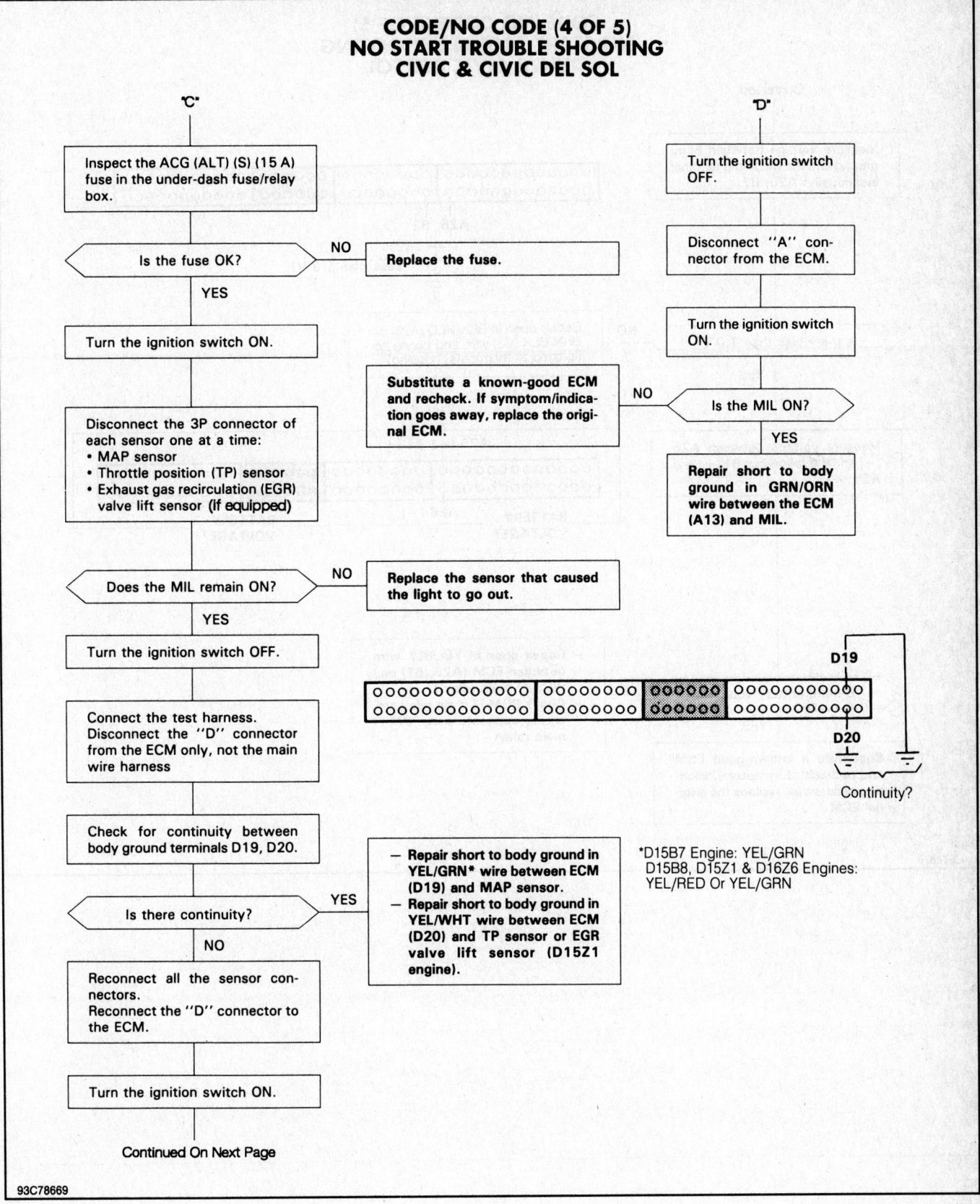

"C"

Inspect the ACG (ALT) (S) (15 A) fuse in the under-dash fuse/relay box.

Is the fuse OK? — NO → Replace the fuse.

YES

Turn the ignition switch ON.

Disconnect the 3P connector of each sensor one at a time:
• MAP sensor
• Throttle position (TP) sensor
• Exhaust gas recirculation (EGR) valve lift sensor (if equipped)

Does the MIL remain ON? — NO → Replace the sensor that caused the light to go out.

YES

Turn the ignition switch OFF.

Connect the test harness. Disconnect the "D" connector from the ECM only, not the main wire harness

Check for continuity between body ground terminals D19, D20.

Is there continuity? — YES →
— Repair short to body ground in YEL/GRN* wire between ECM (D19) and MAP sensor.
— Repair short to body ground in YEL/WHT wire between ECM (D20) and TP sensor or EGR valve lift sensor (D15Z1 engine).

NO

Reconnect all the sensor connectors.
Reconnect the "D" connector to the ECM.

Turn the ignition switch ON.

Continued On Next Page

"D"

Turn the ignition switch OFF.

Disconnect "A" connector from the ECM.

Turn the ignition switch ON.

Substitute a known-good ECM and recheck. If symptom/indication goes away, replace the original ECM. ← NO — Is the MIL ON?

YES

Repair short to body ground in GRN/ORN wire between the ECM (A13) and MIL.

D19

D20

Continuity?

*D15B7 Engine: YEL/GRN
D15B8, D15Z1 & D16Z6 Engines: YEL/RED Or YEL/GRN

93C78669

CODE/NO CODE (5 OF 5)
NO START TROUBLE SHOOTING
CIVIC & CIVIC DEL SOL

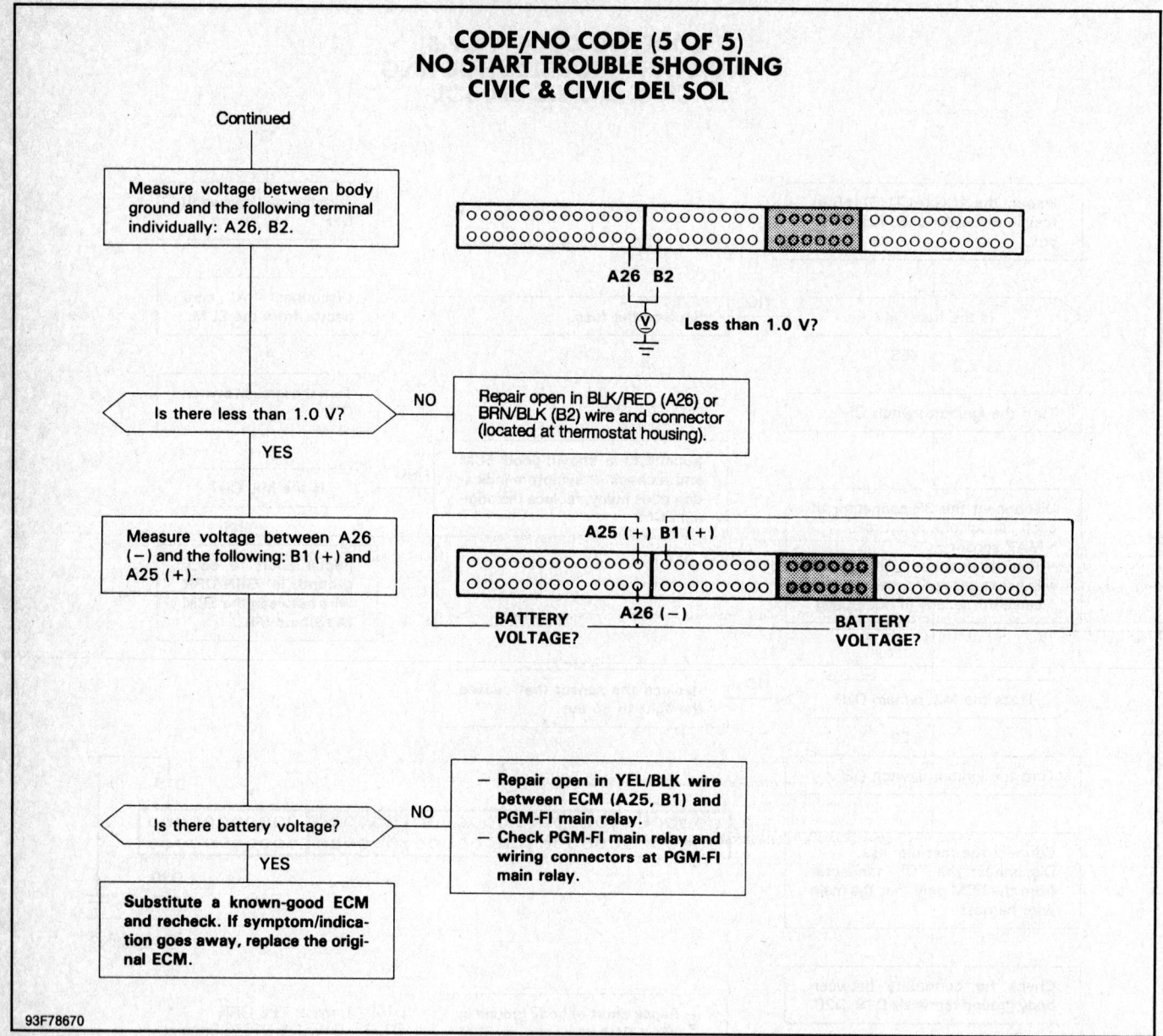

Continued

Measure voltage between body ground and the following terminal individually: A26, B2.

A26 B2

Less than 1.0 V?

Is there less than 1.0 V? — NO → Repair open in BLK/RED (A26) or BRN/BLK (B2) wire and connector (located at thermostat housing).

YES

Measure voltage between A26 (−) and the following: B1 (+) and A25 (+).

A25 (+) B1 (+)

BATTERY VOLTAGE?   A26 (−)   BATTERY VOLTAGE?

Is there battery voltage? — NO → — Repair open in YEL/BLK wire between ECM (A25, B1) and PGM-FI main relay.
— Check PGM-FI main relay and wiring connectors at PGM-FI main relay.

YES

Substitute a known-good ECM and recheck. If symptom/indication goes away, replace the original ECM.

93F78670

1994 ENGINE PERFORMANCE
Self-Diagnostics (Cont.)

CODE 1 (1 OF 2)
OXYGEN SENSOR (O2S) CIRCUIT
CIVIC & CIVIC DEL SOL

D15B8 FEDERAL MODEL

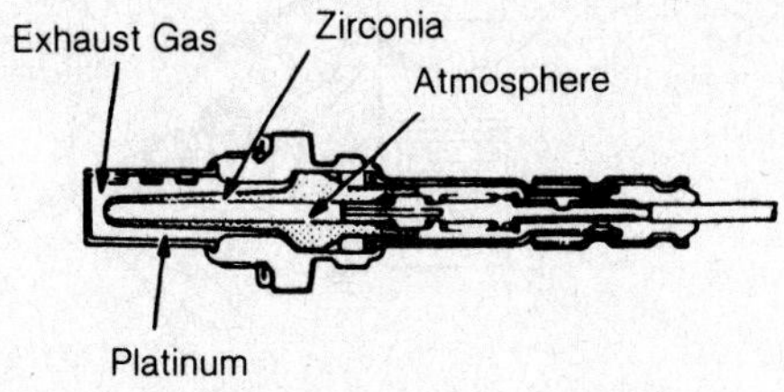

Exhaust Gas
Zirconia
Atmosphere
Platinum

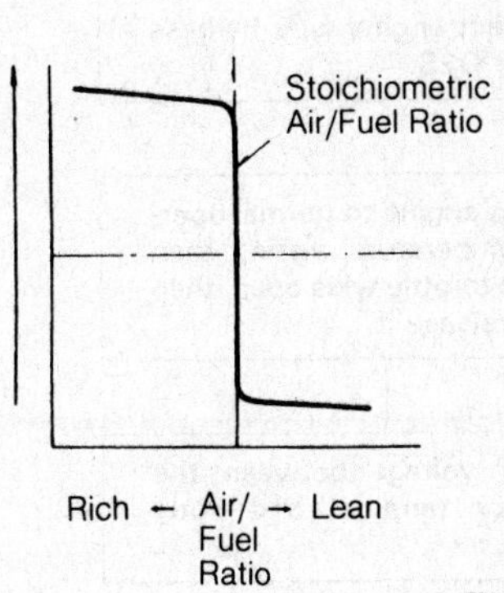

Voltage (V)
Stoichiometric
Air/Fuel Ratio
Rich ← Air/Fuel Ratio → Lean

- **The MIL has been reported on.**
- **With service check connector jumped, code 1 is indicated.**

↓

Perform ECM Reset Procedure.

↓

Inspect fuel pressure regulator.

↓

Is it normal?

- NO → **Replace the fuel pressure regulator**
- YES ↓

Warm up engine to normal operating temperature (the radiator fan comes on).

↓

Road test with the automatic transmission in [2] position (M/T: 4th gear).
Starting at 1600 rpm, accelerate using wide open throttle for at least 5 seconds. Then decelerate for at least 5 seconds with the throttle completely closed.

↓

Is the MIL on and does it indicate code 1.

- NO → Intermittent failure system is okay at this time. Check for loose wires or poor connections at O2S and ECM.
- YES ↓

Continued On Next Page.

93G78671

1994 ENGINE PERFORMANCE
Self-Diagnostics (Cont.)

CODE 1 (2 OF 2)
OXYGEN SENSOR (O2S) CIRCUIT
CIVIC & CIVIC DEL SOL

D15B8 FEDERAL MODEL

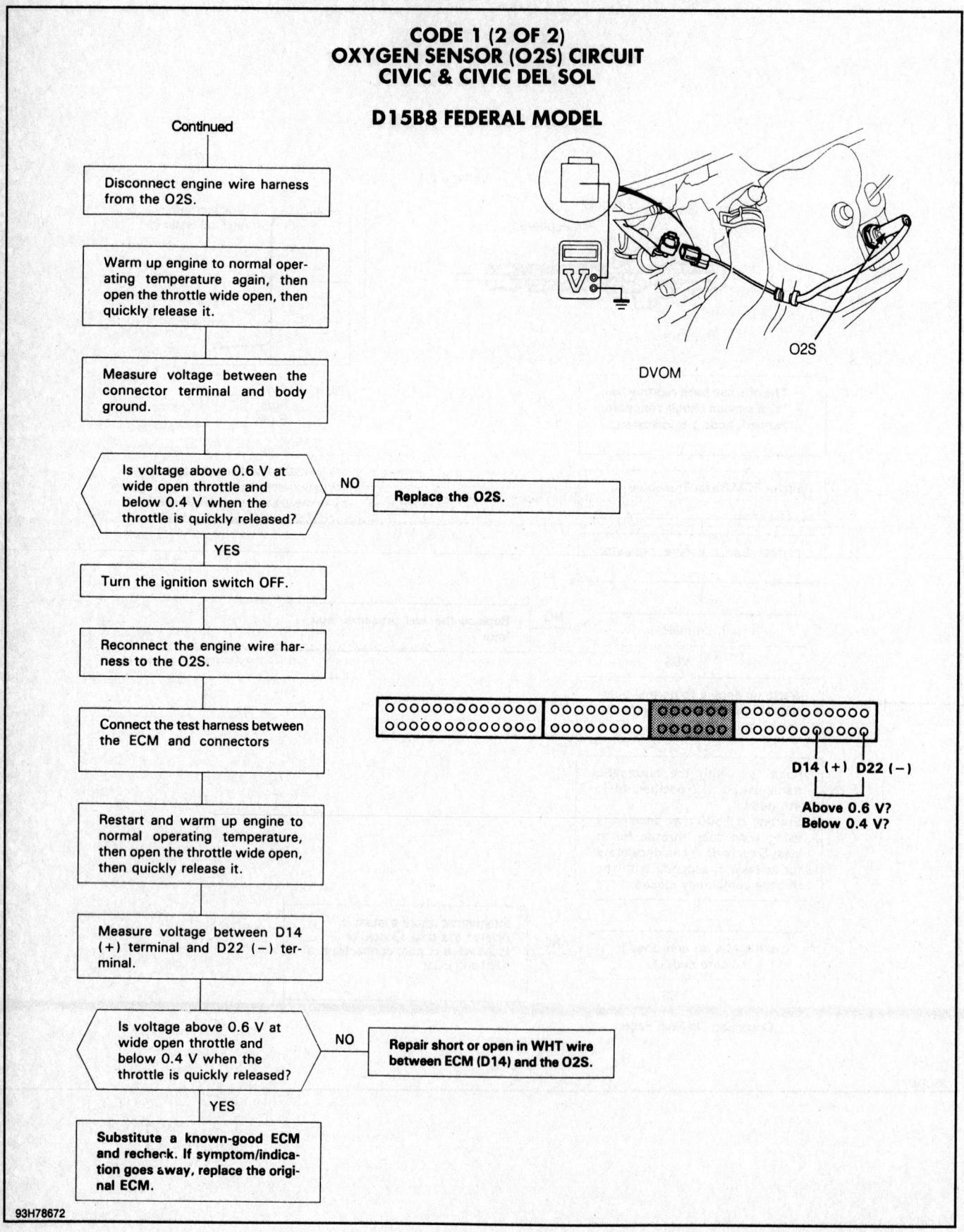

Continued

Disconnect engine wire harness from the O2S.

Warm up engine to normal operating temperature again, then open the throttle wide open, then quickly release it.

Measure voltage between the connector terminal and body ground.

Is voltage above 0.6 V at wide open throttle and below 0.4 V when the throttle is quickly released? — NO → Replace the O2S.

YES

Turn the ignition switch OFF.

Reconnect the engine wire harness to the O2S.

Connect the test harness between the ECM and connectors

Restart and warm up engine to normal operating temperature, then open the throttle wide open, then quickly release it.

Measure voltage between D14 (+) terminal and D22 (−) terminal.

Is voltage above 0.6 V at wide open throttle and below 0.4 V when the throttle is quickly released? — NO → Repair short or open in WHT wire between ECM (D14) and the O2S.

YES

Substitute a known-good ECM and recheck. If symptom/indication goes away, replace the original ECM.

O2S

DVOM

D14 (+) D22 (−)

Above 0.6 V?
Below 0.4 V?

93H78672

CODE 1
HEATED OXYGEN SENSOR (HO2S) CIRCUIT
CIVIC & CIVIC DEL SOL

ALL ENGINES EXCEPT
D15B8 FEDERAL MODEL

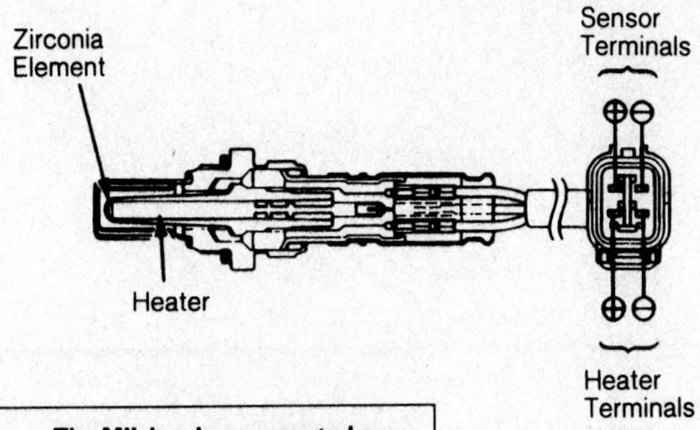

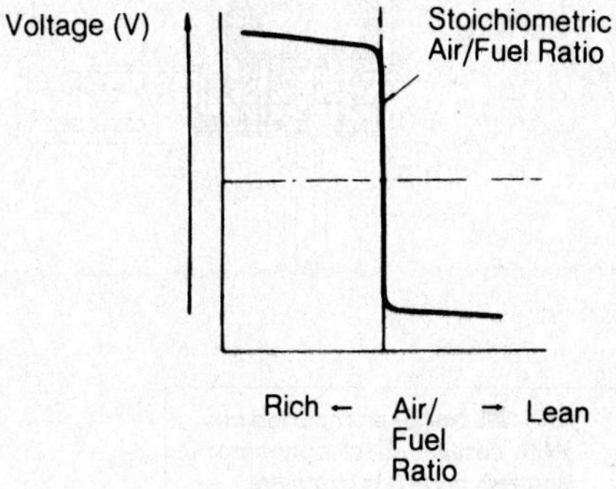

Zirconia Element

Heater

Sensor Terminals

Heater Terminals

Voltage (V)

Stoichiometric Air/Fuel Ratio

Rich ←   Air/ Fuel Ratio   → Lean

- The MIL has been reported on.
- With service check connector jumped, code 1 is indicated.

↓

Perform ECM Reset Procedure.

↓

Warm up engine to normal operating temperature (the radiator fan comes on).

↓

Run engine for 60 seconds.

↓

Road test with the automatic transmission in [2] position (M/T: 4th gear).
Starting at 1600 rpm, accelerate using wide open throttle for at least 5 seconds. Then decelerate for at least 5 seconds with the throttle completely closed.

↓

Is the MIL on and does it indicate code 1? — NO → Intermittent failure system is okay at this time. Check for loose wires or poor connections at HO2S and ECM.

↓ YES

Proceed to CODE 43 chart and perform procedures.

93178673

CODE 3 (1 OF 3)
MAP SENSOR CIRCUIT
CIVIC & CIVIC DEL SOL

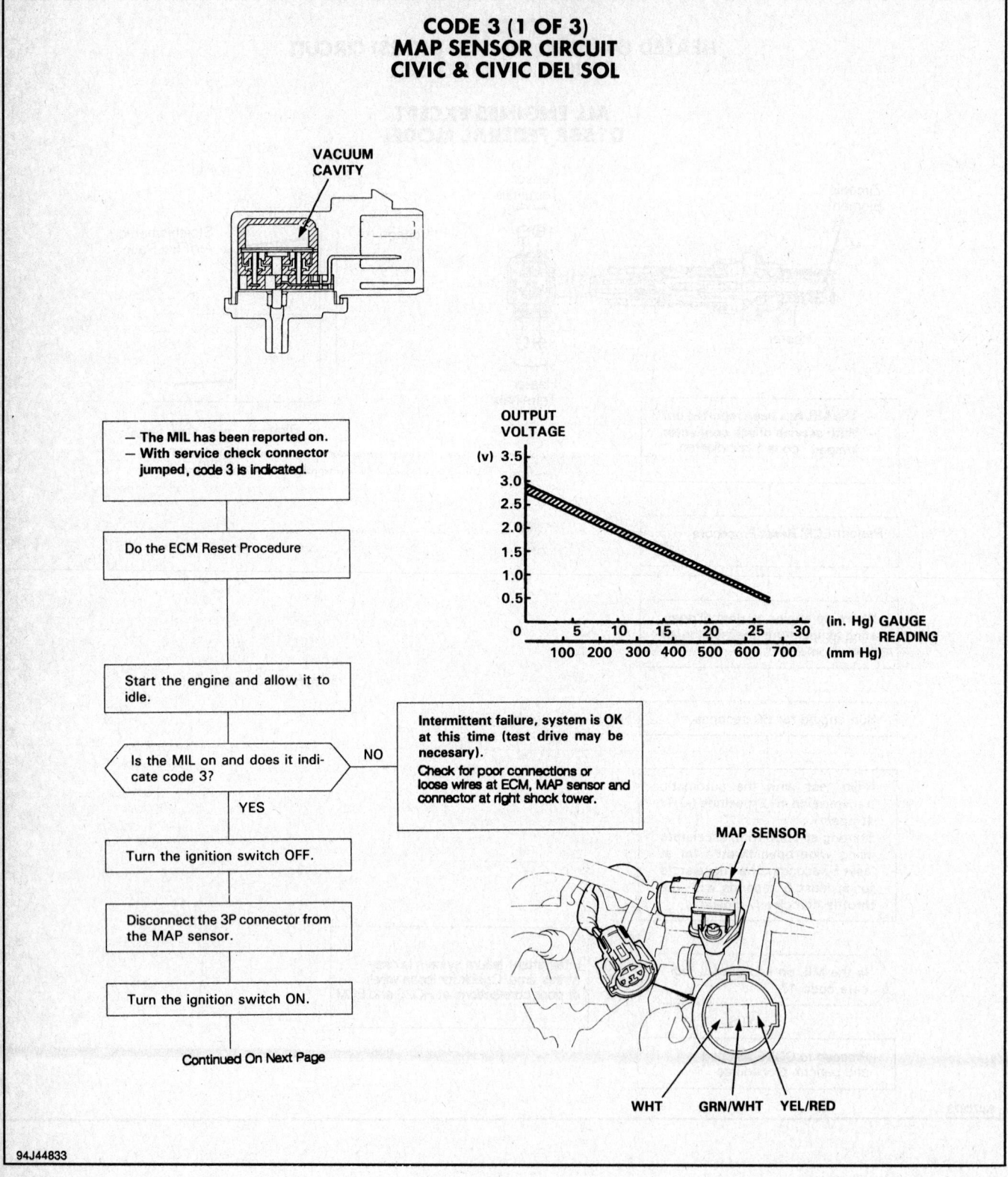

VACUUM CAVITY

- The MIL has been reported on.
- With service check connector jumped, code 3 is indicated.

Do the ECM Reset Procedure

Start the engine and allow it to idle.

Is the MIL on and does it indicate code 3?

NO → Intermittent failure, system is OK at this time (test drive may be necesary).
Check for poor connections or loose wires at ECM, MAP sensor and connector at right shock tower.

YES

Turn the ignition switch OFF.

Disconnect the 3P connector from the MAP sensor.

Turn the ignition switch ON.

Continued On Next Page

OUTPUT VOLTAGE

(v) 3.5
3.0
2.5
2.0
1.5
1.0
0.5

0 5 10 15 20 25 30 (in. Hg) GAUGE READING
100 200 300 400 500 600 700 (mm Hg)

MAP SENSOR

WHT   GRN/WHT   YEL/RED

94J44833

CODE 3 (2 OF 3)
MAP SENSOR CIRCUIT
CIVIC & CIVIC DEL SOL

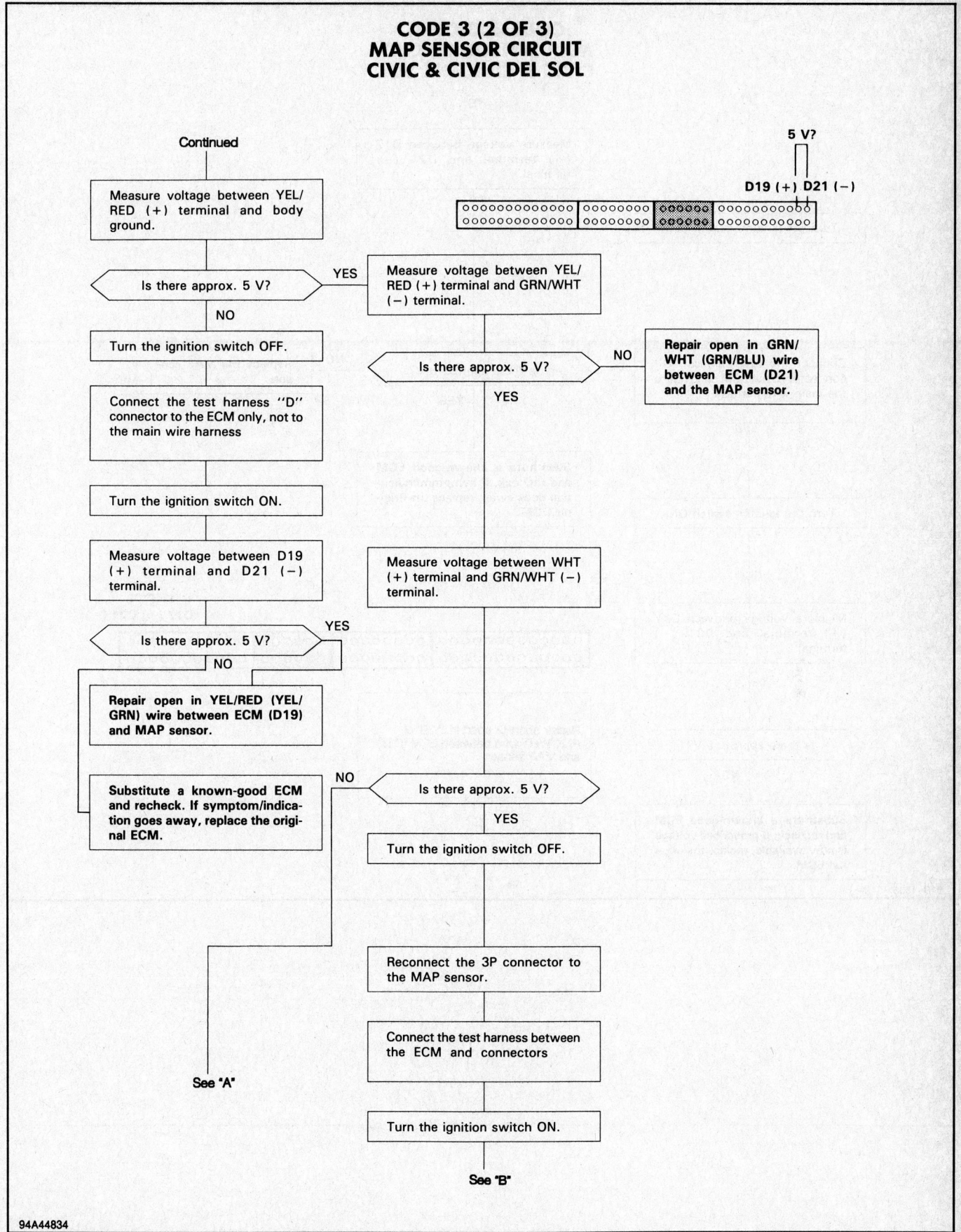

CODE 3 (3 OF 3)
MAP SENSOR CIRCUIT
CIVIC & CIVIC DEL SOL

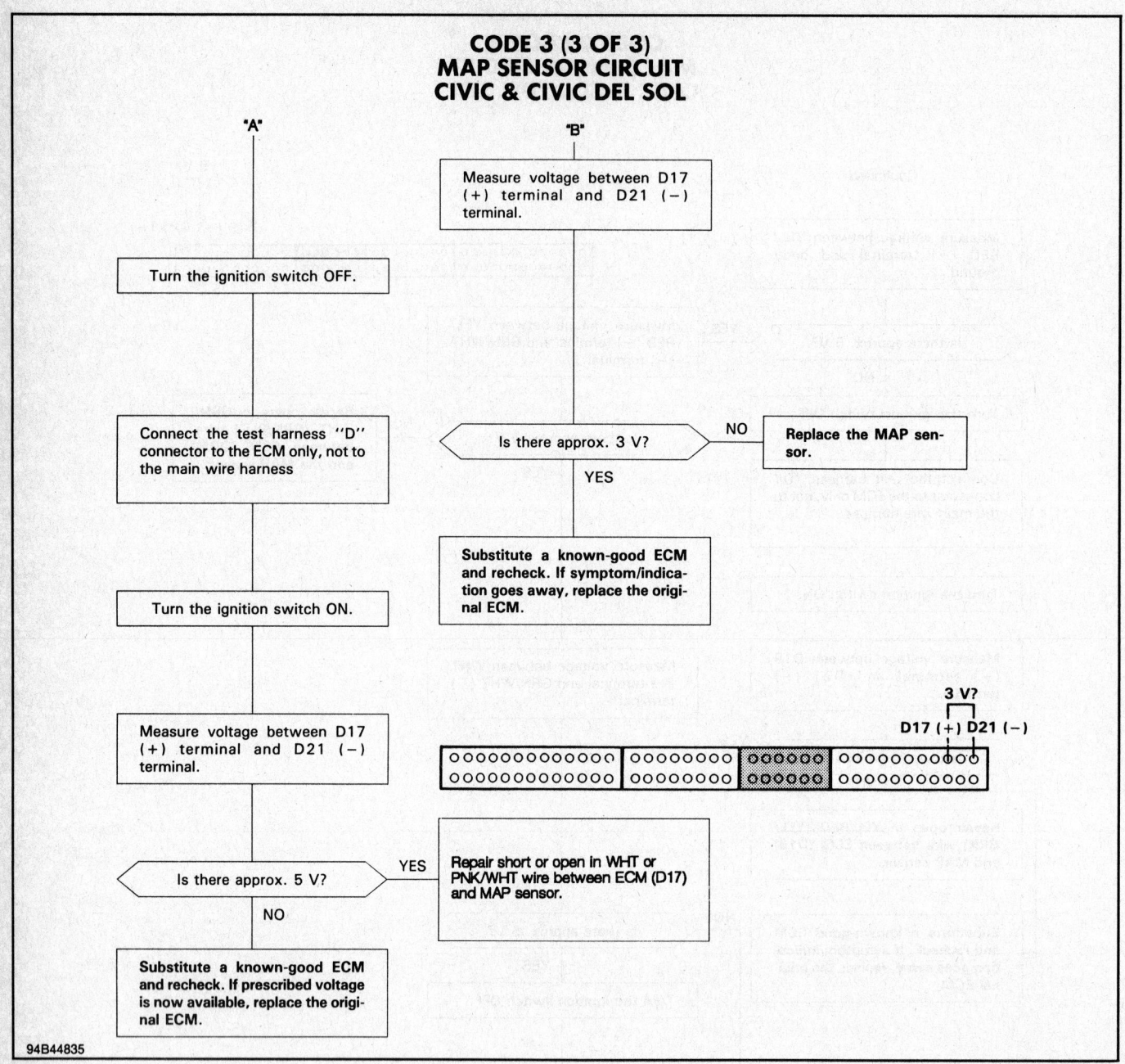

"A"

"B"

Measure voltage between D17 (+) terminal and D21 (−) terminal.

Turn the ignition switch OFF.

Connect the test harness "D" connector to the ECM only, not to the main wire harness

Is there approx. 3 V?   NO → Replace the MAP sensor.

YES

Substitute a known-good ECM and recheck. If symptom/indication goes away, replace the original ECM.

Turn the ignition switch ON.

3 V?

D17 (+) D21 (−)

Measure voltage between D17 (+) terminal and D21 (−) terminal.

Is there approx. 5 V?   YES → Repair short or open in WHT or PNK/WHT wire between ECM (D17) and MAP sensor.

NO

Substitute a known-good ECM and recheck. If prescribed voltage is now available, replace the original ECM.

94B44835

CODE 4, 8 AND/OR 9 (1 OF 2)
TDC/CKP/CYP SENSOR
CIVIC & CIVIC DEL SOL

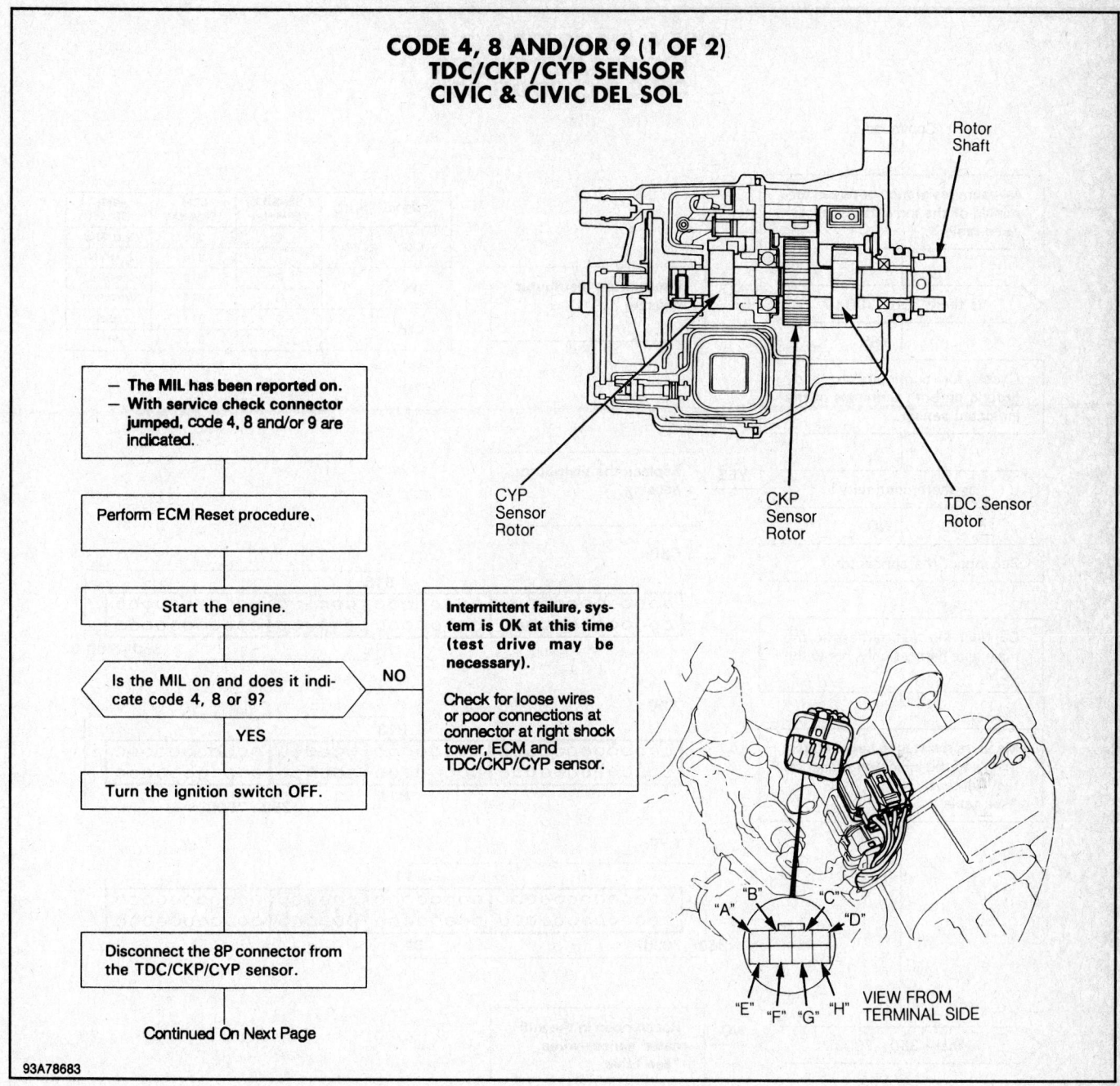

Rotor
Shaft

CYP
Sensor
Rotor

CKP
Sensor
Rotor

TDC Sensor
Rotor

— The MIL has been reported on.
— With service check connector jumped, code 4, 8 and/or 9 are indicated.

Perform ECM Reset procedure.

Start the engine.

Is the MIL on and does it indicate code 4, 8 or 9?

NO → Intermittent failure, system is OK at this time (test drive may be necessary).

Check for loose wires or poor connections at connector at right shock tower, ECM and TDC/CKP/CYP sensor.

YES

Turn the ignition switch OFF.

Disconnect the 8P connector from the TDC/CKP/CYP sensor.

Continued On Next Page

"A"   "B"   "C"   "D"

"E"   "F"   "G"   "H"   VIEW FROM TERMINAL SIDE

93A78683

CODE 4, 8 AND/OR 9 (2 OF 2)
TDC/CKP/CYP SENSOR
CIVIC & CIVIC DEL SOL

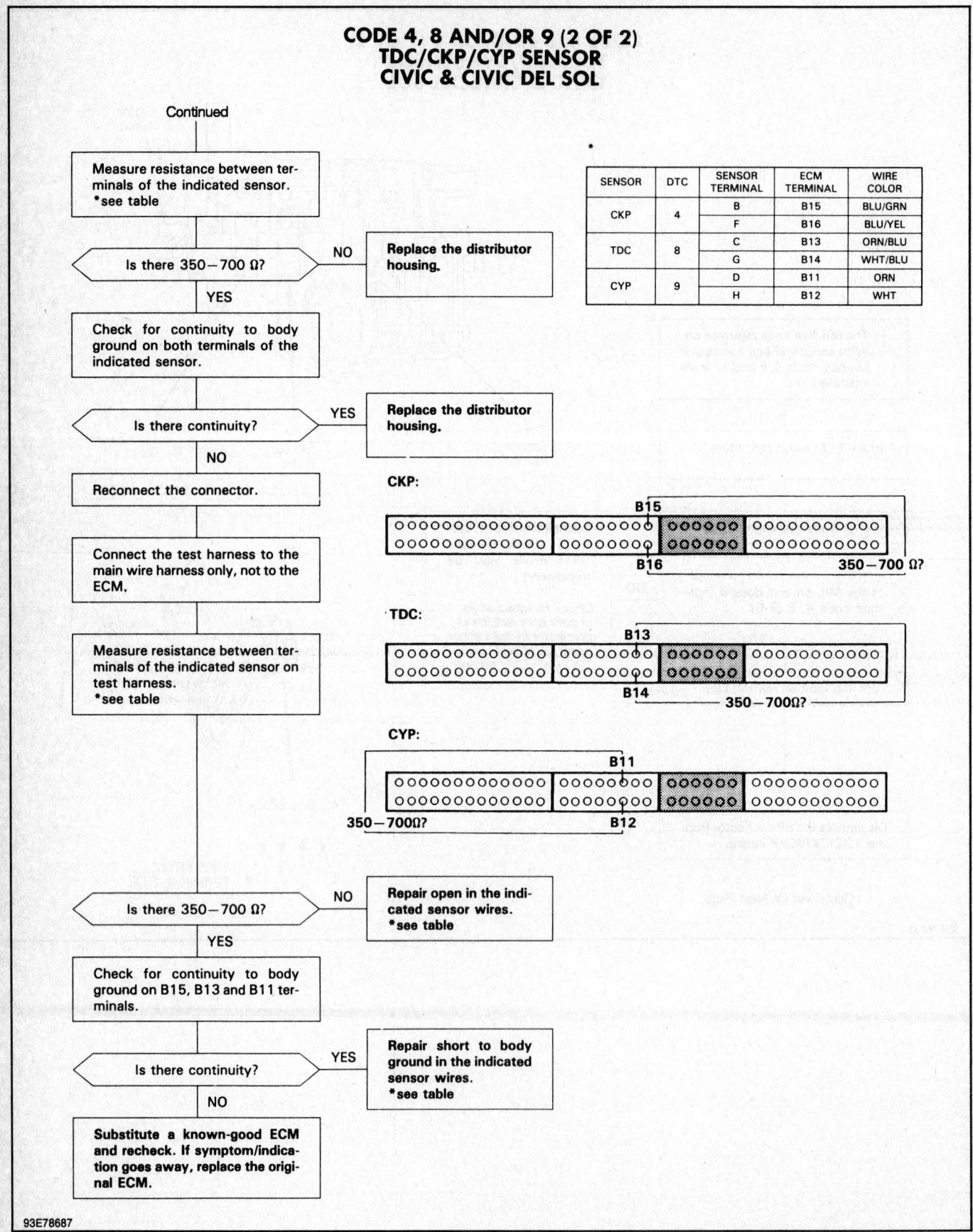

Continued

Measure resistance between terminals of the indicated sensor. *see table

Is there 350—700 Ω? — NO → Replace the distributor housing.

YES

Check for continuity to body ground on both terminals of the indicated sensor.

Is there continuity? — YES → Replace the distributor housing.

NO

Reconnect the connector.

Connect the test harness to the main wire harness only, not to the ECM.

Measure resistance between terminals of the indicated sensor on test harness. *see table

Is there 350—700 Ω? — NO → Repair open in the indicated sensor wires. *see table

YES

Check for continuity to body ground on B15, B13 and B11 terminals.

Is there continuity? — YES → Repair short to body ground in the indicated sensor wires. *see table

NO

Substitute a known-good ECM and recheck. If symptom/indication goes away, replace the original ECM.

*

SENSOR	DTC	SENSOR TERMINAL	ECM TERMINAL	WIRE COLOR
CKP	4	B	B15	BLU/GRN
		F	B16	BLU/YEL
TDC	8	C	B13	ORN/BLU
		G	B14	WHT/BLU
CYP	9	D	B11	ORN
		H	B12	WHT

CKP:
B15
B16
350—700 Ω?

TDC:
B13
B14
350—700Ω?

CYP:
B11
350—700Ω?
B12

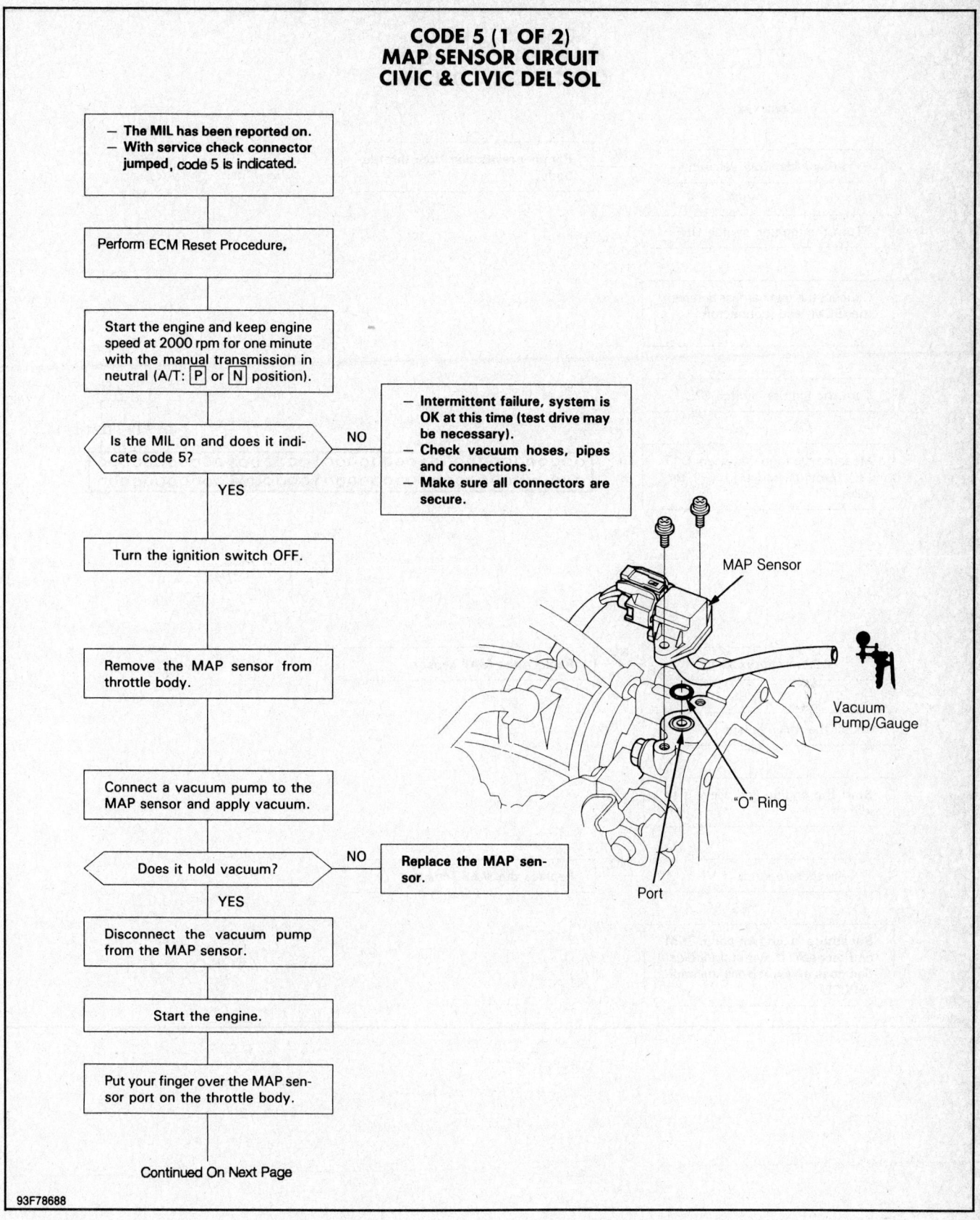

CODE 5 (1 OF 2)
MAP SENSOR CIRCUIT
CIVIC & CIVIC DEL SOL

- The MIL has been reported on.
- With service check connector jumped, code 5 is indicated.

Perform ECM Reset Procedure.

Start the engine and keep engine speed at 2000 rpm for one minute with the manual transmission in neutral (A/T: P or N position).

Is the MIL on and does it indicate code 5?

NO →
- Intermittent failure, system is OK at this time (test drive may be necessary).
- Check vacuum hoses, pipes and connections.
- Make sure all connectors are secure.

YES

Turn the ignition switch OFF.

Remove the MAP sensor from throttle body.

Connect a vacuum pump to the MAP sensor and apply vacuum.

Does it hold vacuum? NO → Replace the MAP sensor.

YES

Disconnect the vacuum pump from the MAP sensor.

Start the engine.

Put your finger over the MAP sensor port on the throttle body.

MAP Sensor

Vacuum Pump/Gauge

"O" Ring

Port

Continued On Next Page

93F78688

CODE 5 (2 OF 2)
MAP SENSOR CIRCUIT
CIVIC & CIVIC DEL SOL

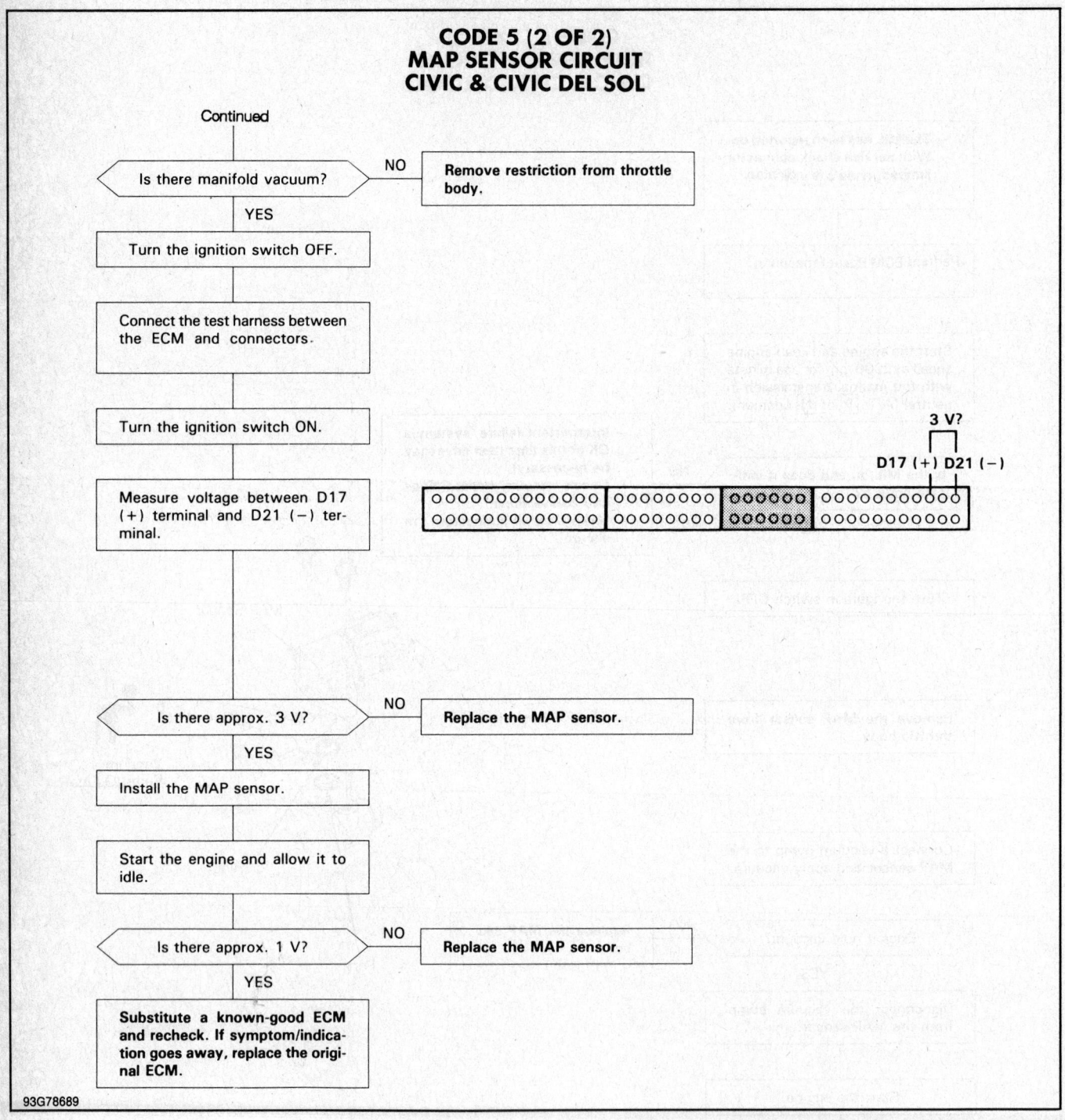

Continued

Is there manifold vacuum? → NO → Remove restriction from throttle body.

YES

Turn the ignition switch OFF.

Connect the test harness between the ECM and connectors.

Turn the ignition switch ON.

Measure voltage between D17 (+) terminal and D21 (−) terminal.

3 V?
D17 (+) D21 (−)

Is there approx. 3 V? → NO → Replace the MAP sensor.

YES

Install the MAP sensor.

Start the engine and allow it to idle.

Is there approx. 1 V? → NO → Replace the MAP sensor.

YES

Substitute a known-good ECM and recheck. If symptom/indication goes away, replace the original ECM.

93G78689

CODE 6 (1 OF 2)
ENGINE COOLANT TEMPERATURE
(ECT) SENSOR
CIVIC & CIVIC DEL SOL

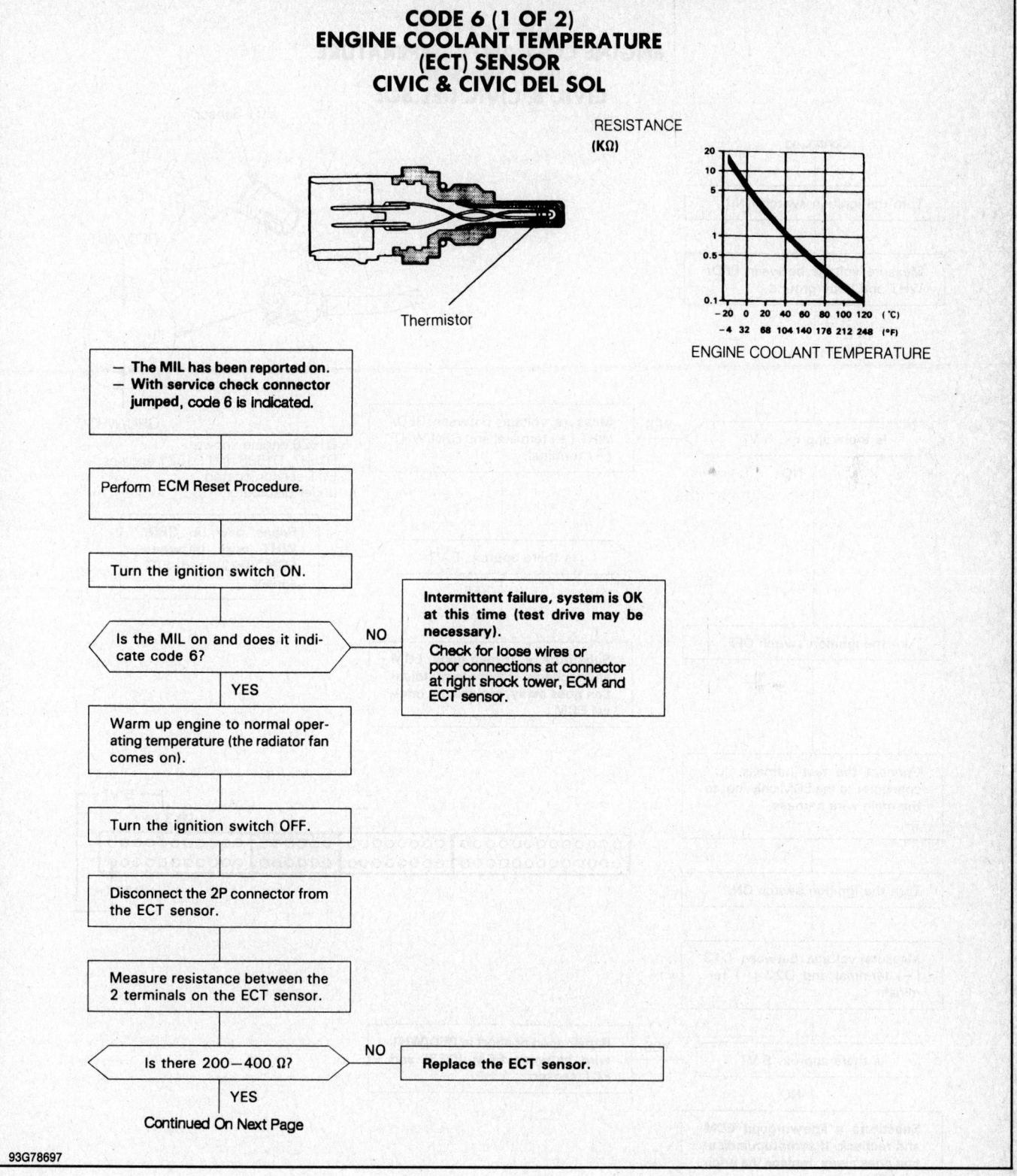

RESISTANCE
(KΩ)

Thermistor

ENGINE COOLANT TEMPERATURE

— The MIL has been reported on.
— With service check connector jumped, code 6 is indicated.

Perform ECM Reset Procedure.

Turn the ignition switch ON.

Is the MIL on and does it indicate code 6? — **NO** → **Intermittent failure, system is OK at this time (test drive may be necessary).** Check for loose wires or poor connections at connector at right shock tower, ECM and ECT sensor.

YES

Warm up engine to normal operating temperature (the radiator fan comes on).

Turn the ignition switch OFF.

Disconnect the 2P connector from the ECT sensor.

Measure resistance between the 2 terminals on the ECT sensor.

Is there 200—400 Ω? — **NO** → **Replace the ECT sensor.**

YES

Continued On Next Page

93G78697

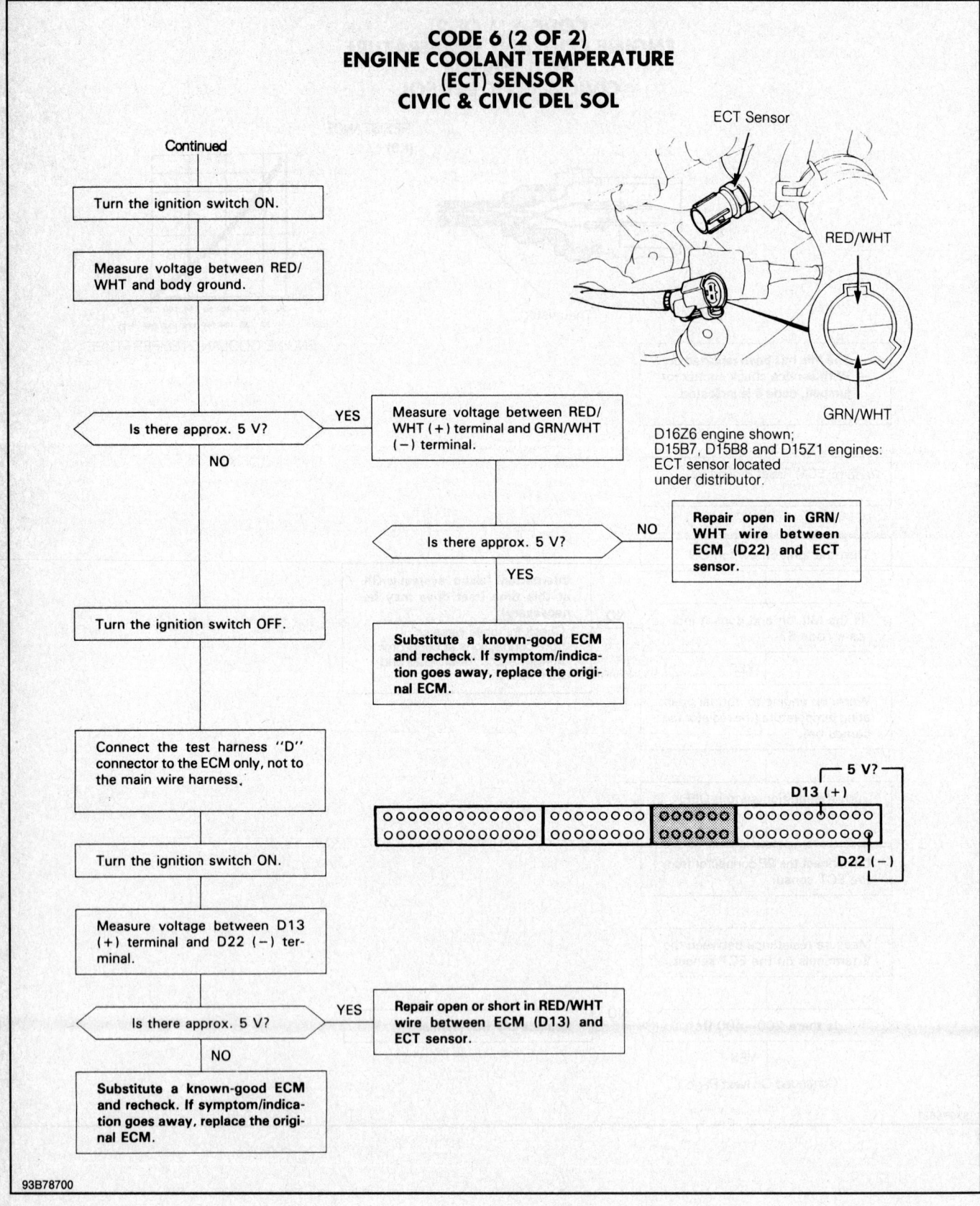

CODE 6 (2 OF 2)
ENGINE COOLANT TEMPERATURE
(ECT) SENSOR
CIVIC & CIVIC DEL SOL

Continued

Turn the ignition switch ON.

Measure voltage between RED/WHT and body ground.

Is there approx. 5 V? — YES → Measure voltage between RED/WHT (+) terminal and GRN/WHT (−) terminal.

NO

Is there approx. 5 V? — NO → Repair open in GRN/WHT wire between ECM (D22) and ECT sensor.

YES

Substitute a known-good ECM and recheck. If symptom/indication goes away, replace the original ECM.

Turn the ignition switch OFF.

Connect the test harness "D" connector to the ECM only, not to the main wire harness.

Turn the ignition switch ON.

Measure voltage between D13 (+) terminal and D22 (−) terminal.

Is there approx. 5 V? — YES → Repair open or short in RED/WHT wire between ECM (D13) and ECT sensor.

NO

Substitute a known-good ECM and recheck. If symptom/indication goes away, replace the original ECM.

ECT Sensor

RED/WHT

GRN/WHT

D16Z6 engine shown; D15B7, D15B8 and D15Z1 engines: ECT sensor located under distributor.

5 V?
D13 (+)
D22 (−)

93B78700

CODE 7 (1 OF 2)
THROTTLE POSITION (TP) SENSOR
CIVIC & CIVIC DEL SOL

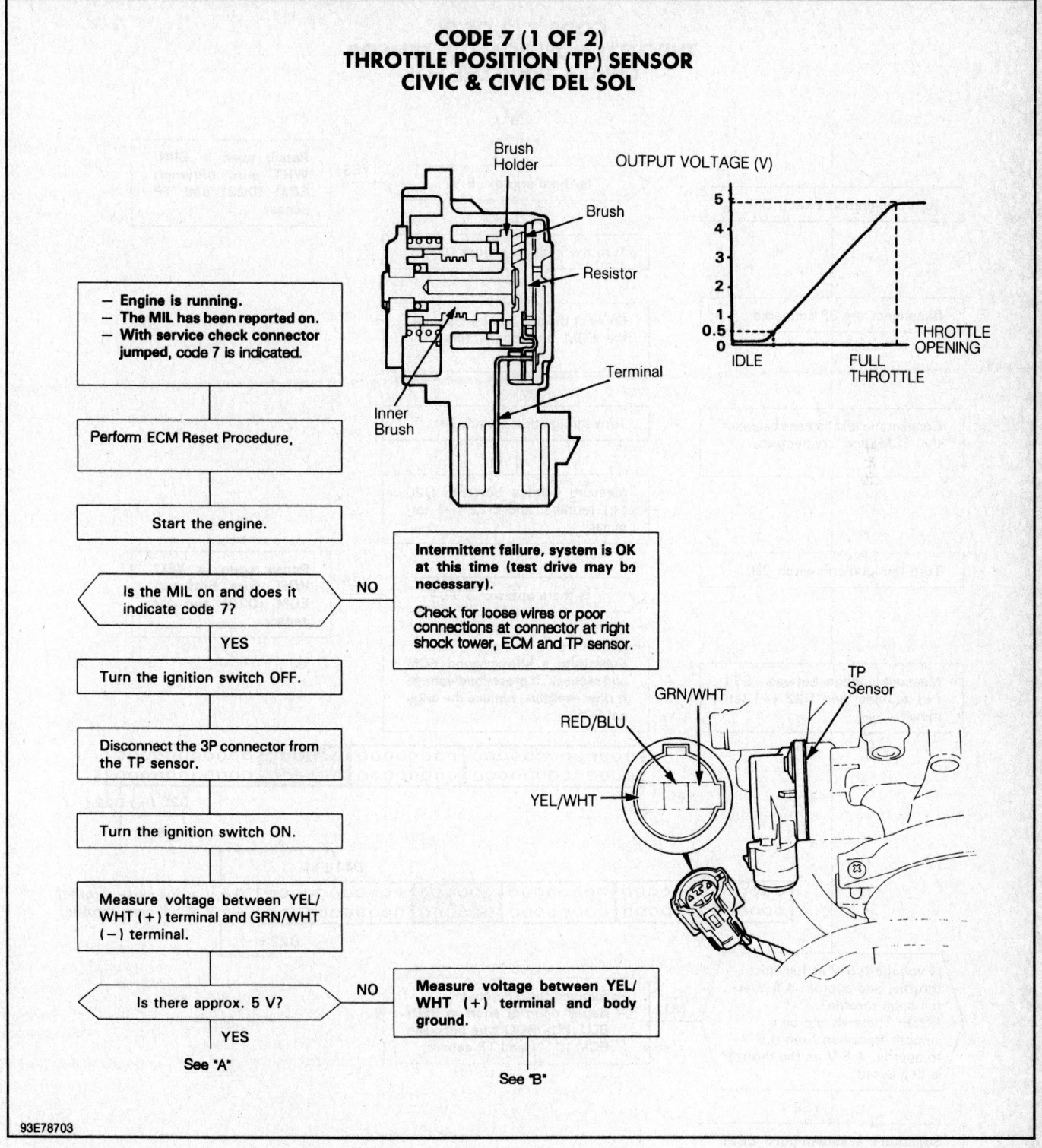

- Engine is running.
- The MIL has been reported on.
- With service check connector jumped, code 7 is indicated.

Perform ECM Reset Procedure.

Start the engine.

Is the MIL on and does it indicate code 7? — NO →

Intermittent failure, system is OK at this time (test drive may be necessary).

Check for loose wires or poor connections at connector at right shock tower, ECM and TP sensor.

YES

Turn the ignition switch OFF.

Disconnect the 3P connector from the TP sensor.

Turn the ignition switch ON.

Measure voltage between YEL/WHT (+) terminal and GRN/WHT (−) terminal.

Is there approx. 5 V? — NO →

Measure voltage between YEL/WHT (+) terminal and body ground.

YES

See "A"

See "B"

OUTPUT VOLTAGE (V)

THROTTLE OPENING

IDLE   FULL THROTTLE

Brush Holder
Brush
Resistor
Terminal
Inner Brush

GRN/WHT
RED/BLU
YEL/WHT
TP Sensor

93E78703

CODE 7 (2 OF 2)
THROTTLE POSITION (TP) SENSOR
CIVIC & CIVIC DEL SOL

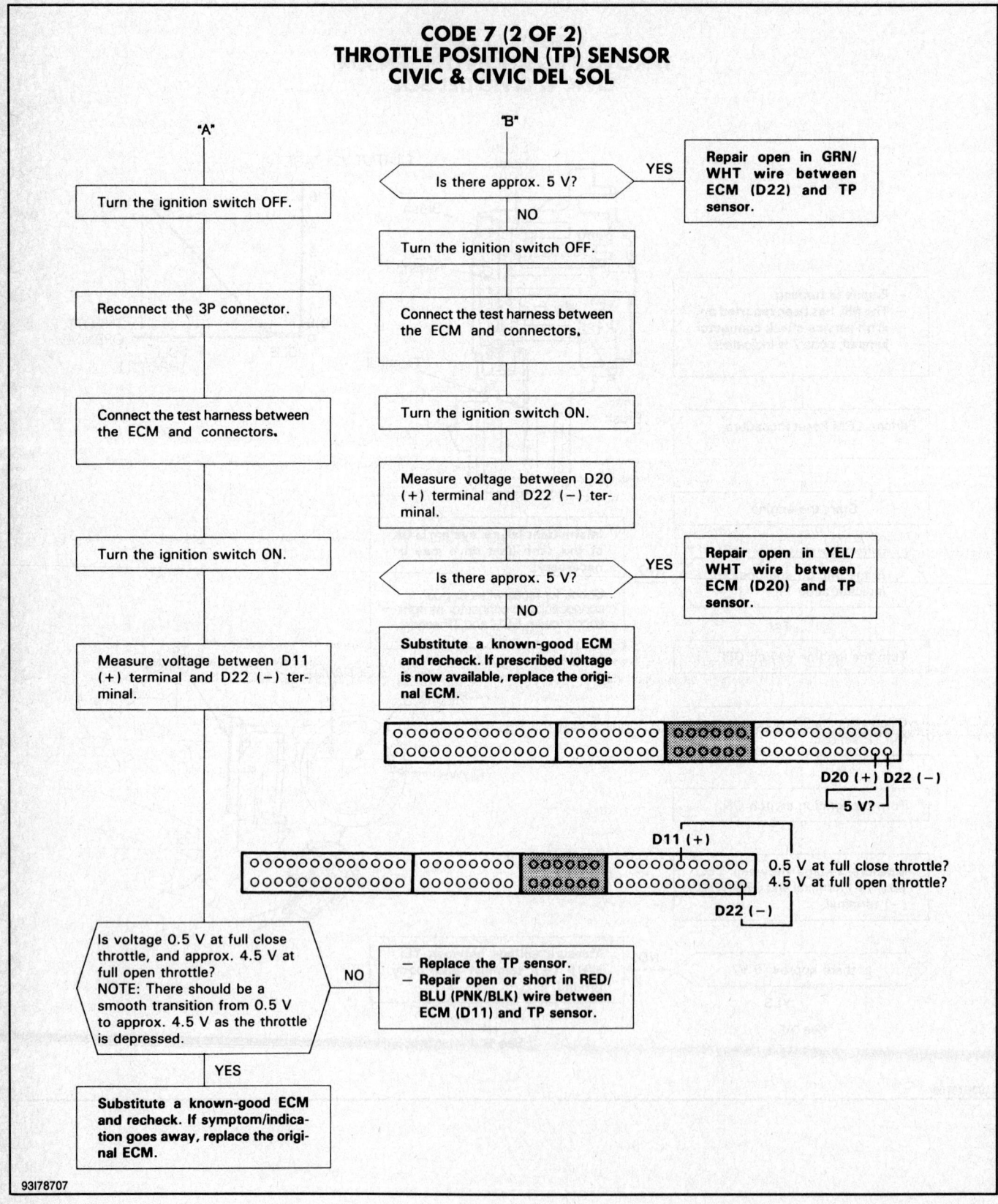

"A"

Turn the ignition switch OFF.

Reconnect the 3P connector.

Connect the test harness between the ECM and connectors.

Turn the ignition switch ON.

Measure voltage between D11 (+) terminal and D22 (−) terminal.

"B"

Is there approx. 5 V? — YES → Repair open in GRN/WHT wire between ECM (D22) and TP sensor.

NO

Turn the ignition switch OFF.

Connect the test harness between the ECM and connectors.

Turn the ignition switch ON.

Measure voltage between D20 (+) terminal and D22 (−) terminal.

Is there approx. 5 V? — YES → Repair open in YEL/WHT wire between ECM (D20) and TP sensor.

NO

Substitute a known-good ECM and recheck. If prescribed voltage is now available, replace the original ECM.

D20 (+) D22 (−)
5 V?

D11 (+)

0.5 V at full close throttle?
4.5 V at full open throttle?

D22 (−)

Is voltage 0.5 V at full close throttle, and approx. 4.5 V at full open throttle?
NOTE: There should be a smooth transition from 0.5 V to approx. 4.5 V as the throttle is depressed.

— NO →
— Replace the TP sensor.
— Repair open or short in RED/BLU (PNK/BLK) wire between ECM (D11) and TP sensor.

YES

Substitute a known-good ECM and recheck. If symptom/indication goes away, replace the original ECM.

93I78707

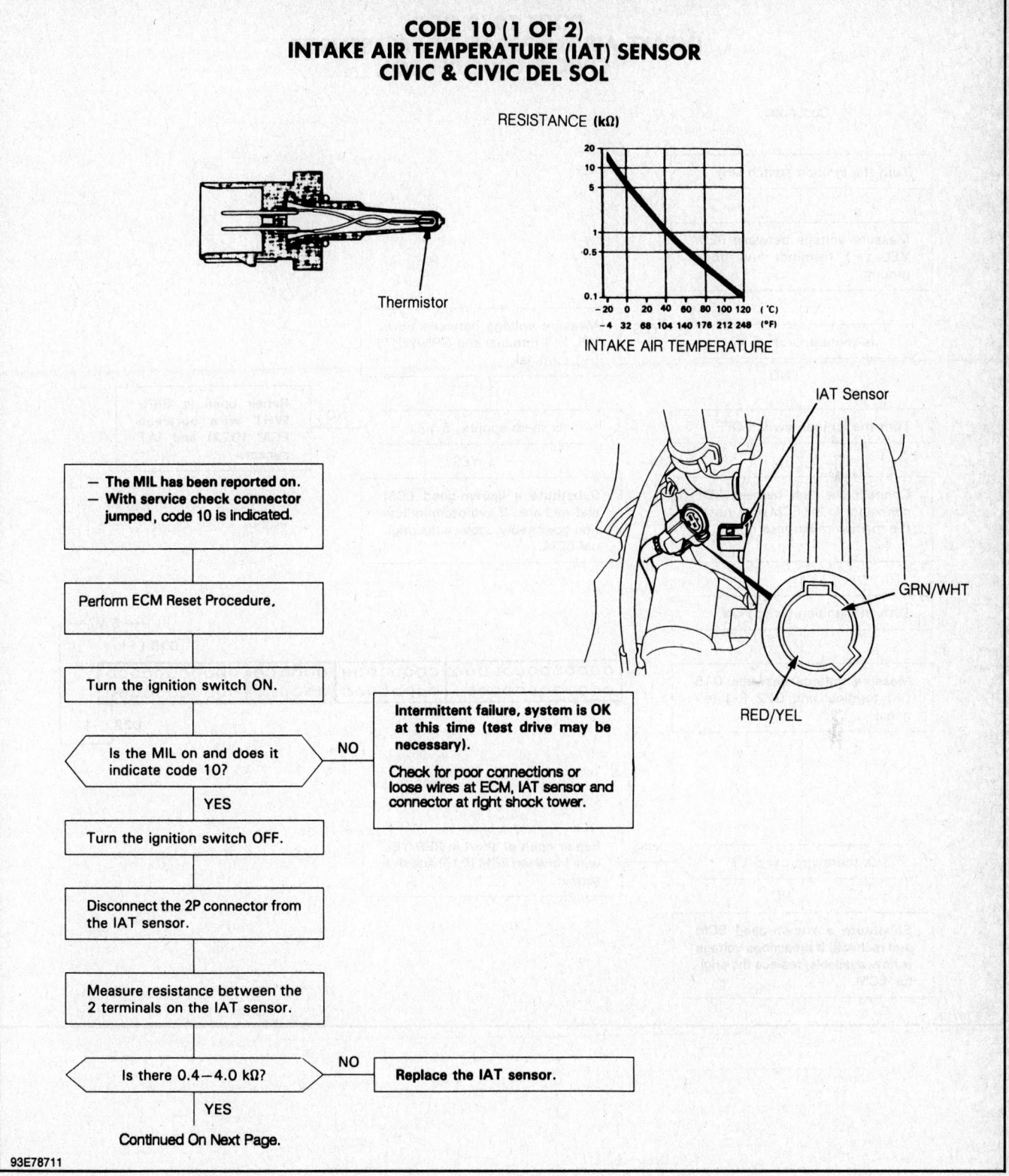

CODE 10 (1 OF 2)
INTAKE AIR TEMPERATURE (IAT) SENSOR
CIVIC & CIVIC DEL SOL

RESISTANCE (kΩ)

INTAKE AIR TEMPERATURE

Thermistor

IAT Sensor

GRN/WHT

RED/YEL

- The MIL has been reported on.
- With service check connector jumped, code 10 is indicated.

Perform ECM Reset Procedure.

Turn the ignition switch ON.

Is the MIL on and does it indicate code 10? — **NO** →

Intermittent failure, system is OK at this time (test drive may be necessary).

Check for poor connections or loose wires at ECM, IAT sensor and connector at right shock tower.

YES

Turn the ignition switch OFF.

Disconnect the 2P connector from the IAT sensor.

Measure resistance between the 2 terminals on the IAT sensor.

Is there 0.4—4.0 kΩ? — **NO** → **Replace the IAT sensor.**

YES

Continued On Next Page.

93E78711

CODE 10 (2 OF 2)
INTAKE AIR TEMPERATURE (IAT) SENSOR
CIVIC & CIVIC DEL SOL

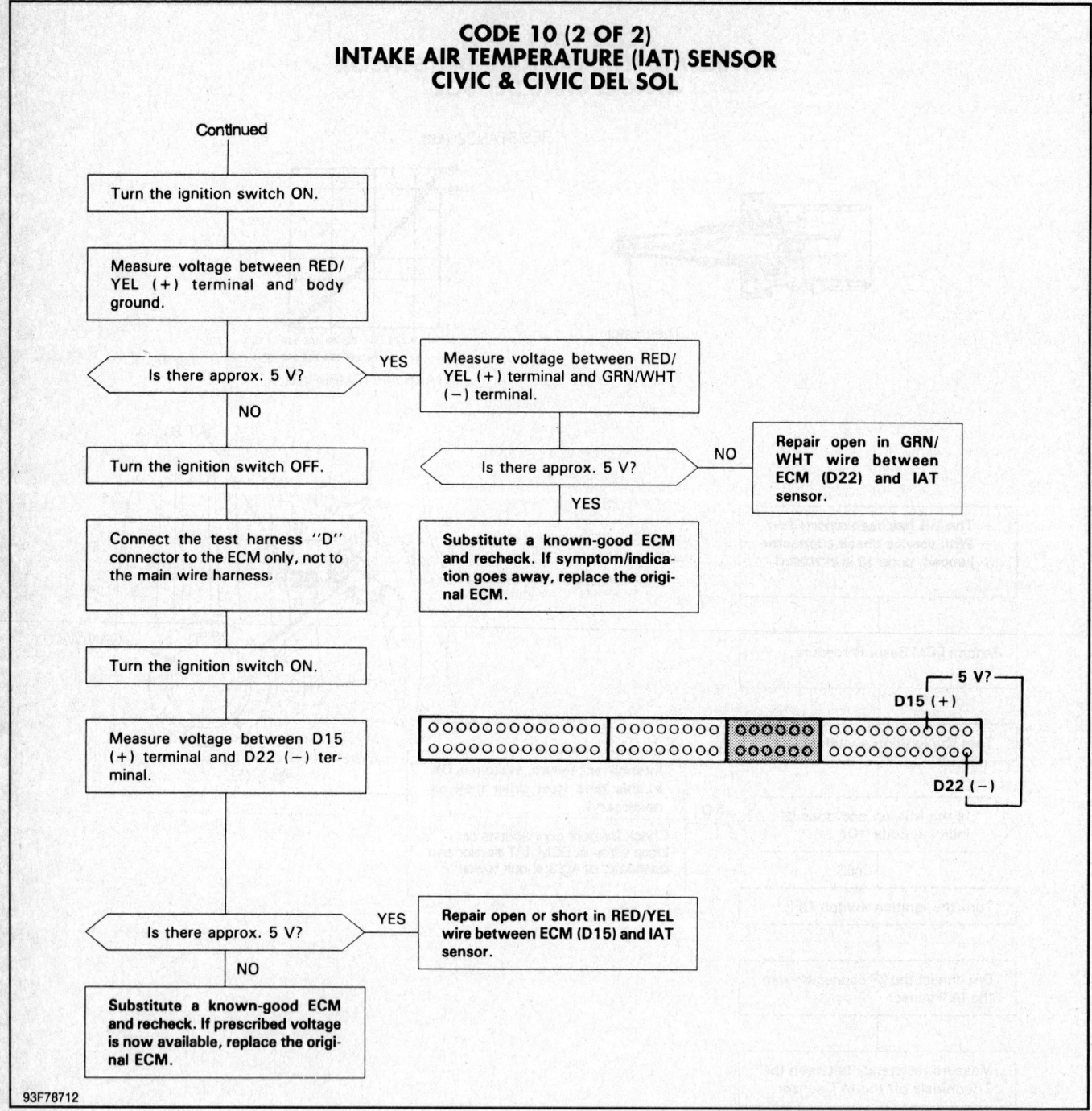

93F78712

CODE 12 (1 OF 5)
EGR SYSTEM
CIVIC

D15Z1 ENGINE ONLY

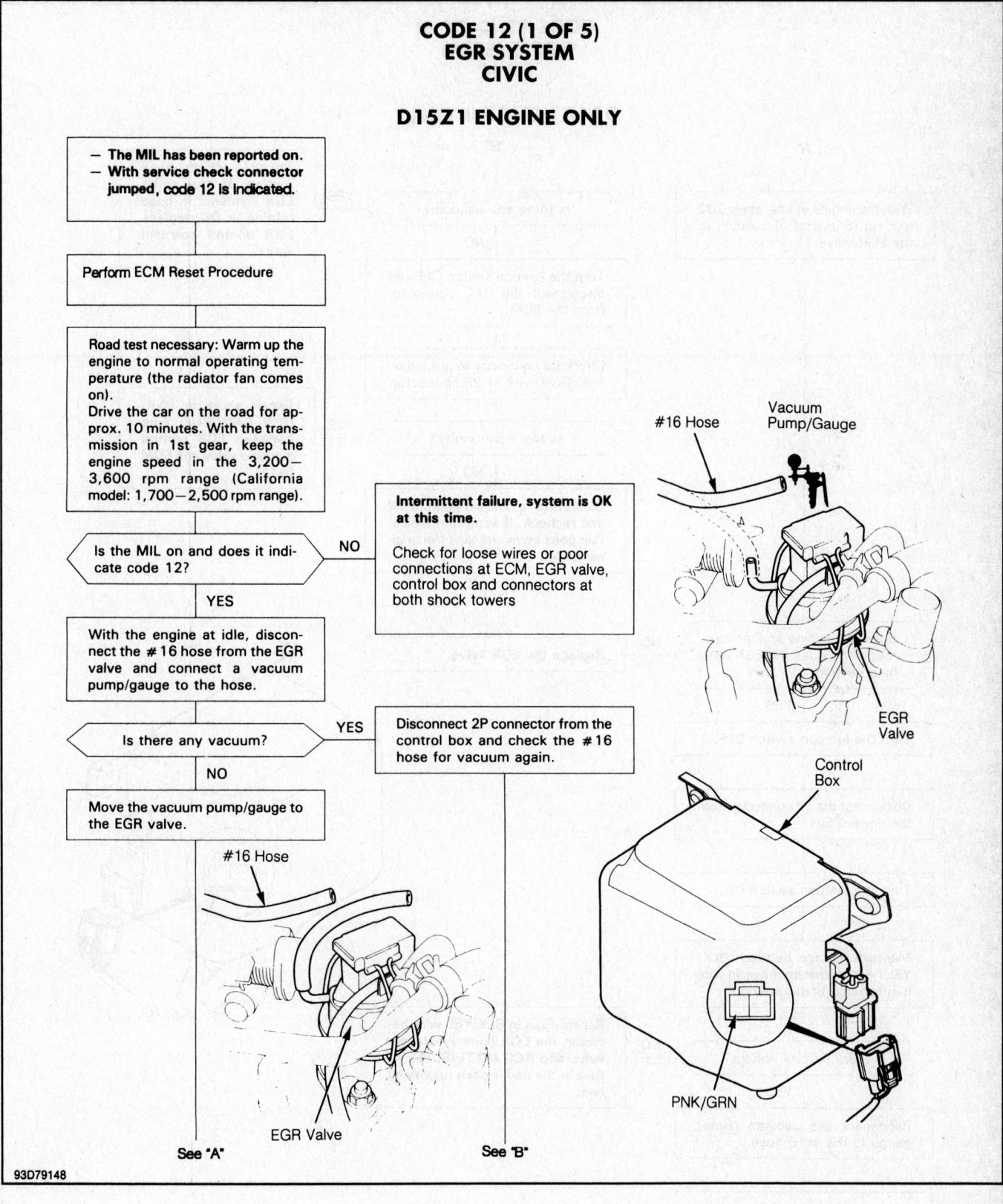

- The MIL has been reported on.
- With service check connector jumped, code 12 is indicated.

↓

Perform ECM Reset Procedure

↓

Road test necessary: Warm up the engine to normal operating temperature (the radiator fan comes on).
Drive the car on the road for approx. 10 minutes. With the transmission in 1st gear, keep the engine speed in the 3,200—3,600 rpm range (California model: 1,700—2,500 rpm range).

↓

Is the MIL on and does it indicate code 12? — NO → **Intermittent failure, system is OK at this time.**

Check for loose wires or poor connections at ECM, EGR valve, control box and connectors at both shock towers

↓ YES

With the engine at idle, disconnect the #16 hose from the EGR valve and connect a vacuum pump/gauge to the hose.

↓

Is there any vacuum? — YES → Disconnect 2P connector from the control box and check the #16 hose for vacuum again.

↓ NO

Move the vacuum pump/gauge to the EGR valve.

#16 Hose

Vacuum Pump/Gauge

EGR Valve

Control Box

PNK/GRN

#16 Hose

EGR Valve

See "A"

See "B"

93D79148

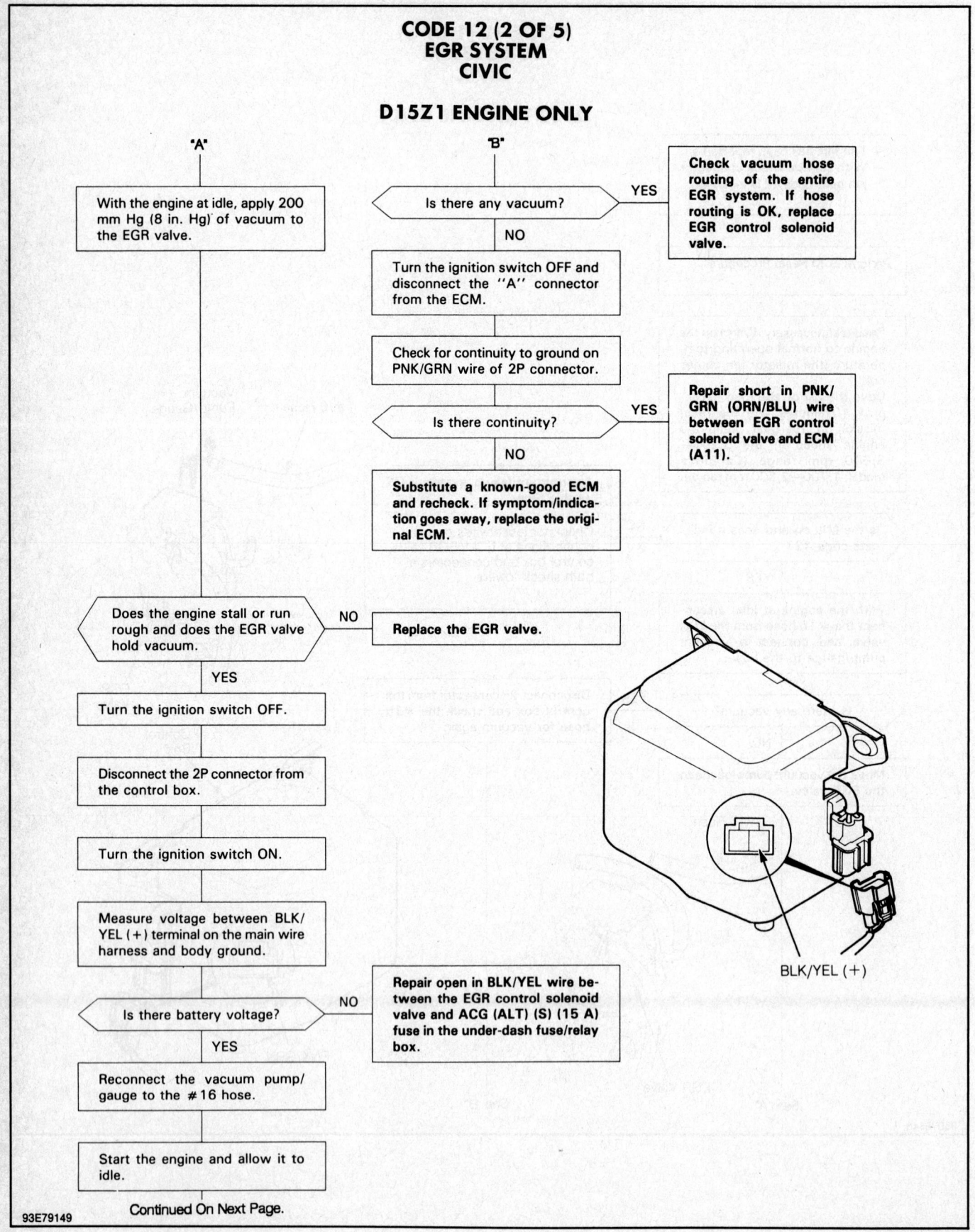

CODE 12 (2 OF 5)
EGR SYSTEM
CIVIC

D15Z1 ENGINE ONLY

"A"

With the engine at idle, apply 200 mm Hg (8 in. Hg) of vacuum to the EGR valve.

"B"

Is there any vacuum? — YES → Check vacuum hose routing of the entire EGR system. If hose routing is OK, replace EGR control solenoid valve.

NO

Turn the ignition switch OFF and disconnect the "A" connector from the ECM.

Check for continuity to ground on PNK/GRN wire of 2P connector.

Is there continuity? — YES → Repair short in PNK/GRN (ORN/BLU) wire between EGR control solenoid valve and ECM (A11).

NO

Substitute a known-good ECM and recheck. If symptom/indication goes away, replace the original ECM.

Does the engine stall or run rough and does the EGR valve hold vacuum. — NO → Replace the EGR valve.

YES

Turn the ignition switch OFF.

Disconnect the 2P connector from the control box.

Turn the ignition switch ON.

Measure voltage between BLK/YEL (+) terminal on the main wire harness and body ground.

Is there battery voltage? — NO → Repair open in BLK/YEL wire between the EGR control solenoid valve and ACG (ALT) (S) (15 A) fuse in the under-dash fuse/relay box.

YES

Reconnect the vacuum pump/gauge to the #16 hose.

Start the engine and allow it to idle.

BLK/YEL (+)

Continued On Next Page.

93E79149

CODE 12 (3 OF 5)
EGR SYSTEM
CIVIC & CIVIC DEL SOL

D15Z1 ENGINE ONLY

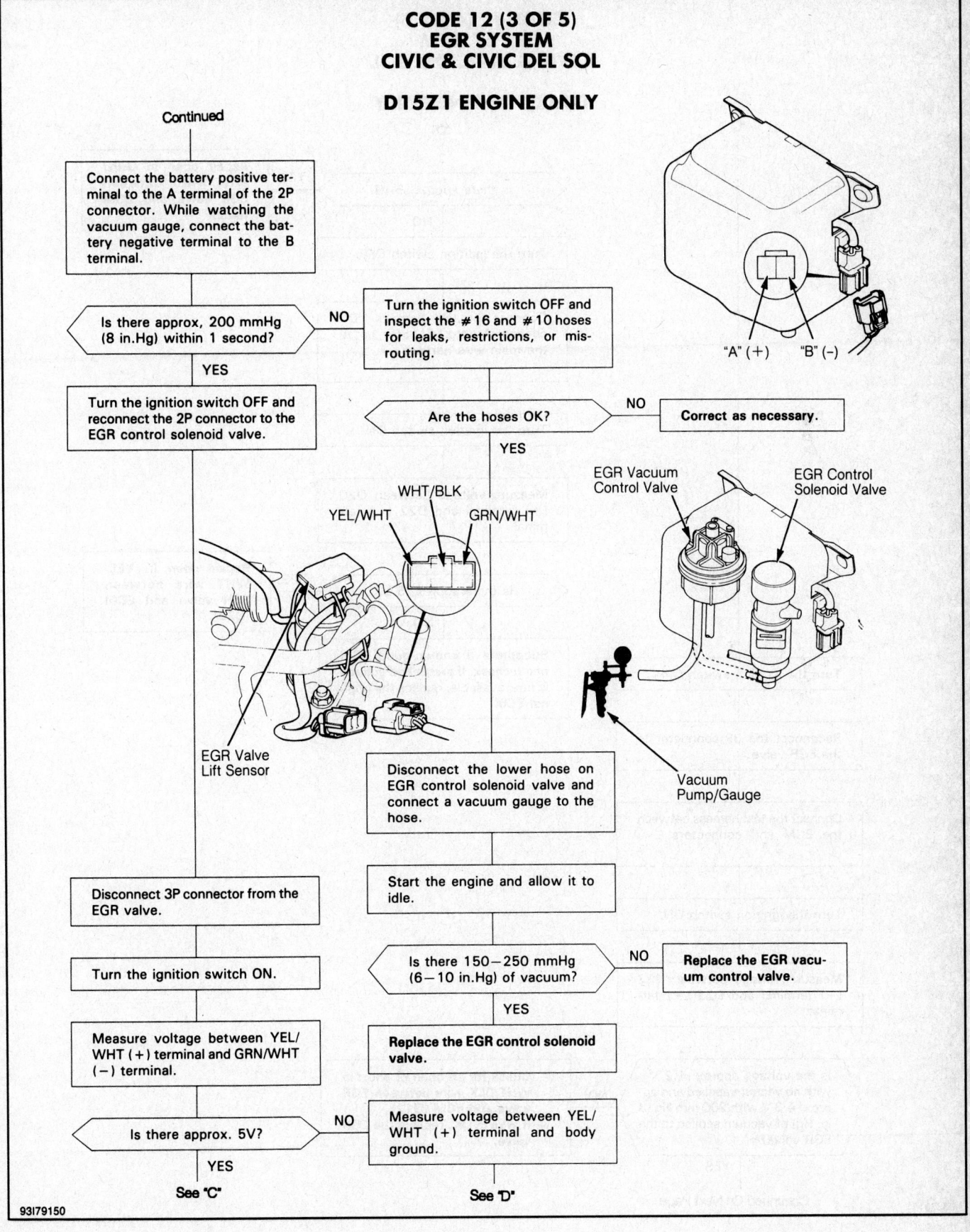

Continued

Connect the battery positive terminal to the A terminal of the 2P connector. While watching the vacuum gauge, connect the battery negative terminal to the B terminal.

Is there approx, 200 mmHg (8 in.Hg) within 1 second? —NO→ Turn the ignition switch OFF and inspect the #16 and #10 hoses for leaks, restrictions, or misrouting.

YES↓

Turn the ignition switch OFF and reconnect the 2P connector to the EGR control solenoid valve.

Are the hoses OK? —NO→ Correct as necessary.

YES↓

"A" (+)   "B" (−)

WHT/BLK
YEL/WHT   GRN/WHT

EGR Vacuum Control Valve   EGR Control Solenoid Valve

EGR Valve Lift Sensor

Vacuum Pump/Gauge

Disconnect the lower hose on EGR control solenoid valve and connect a vacuum gauge to the hose.

Disconnect 3P connector from the EGR valve.

Start the engine and allow it to idle.

Turn the ignition switch ON.

Is there 150−250 mmHg (6−10 in.Hg) of vacuum? —NO→ Replace the EGR vacuum control valve.

YES↓

Measure voltage between YEL/WHT (+) terminal and GRN/WHT (−) terminal.

Replace the EGR control solenoid valve.

Is there approx. 5V? —NO→ Measure voltage between YEL/WHT (+) terminal and body ground.

YES↓

See "C"

See "D"

93I79150

CODE 12 (4 OF 5)
EGR SYSTEM
CIVIC & CIVIC DEL SOL

D15Z1 ENGINE ONLY

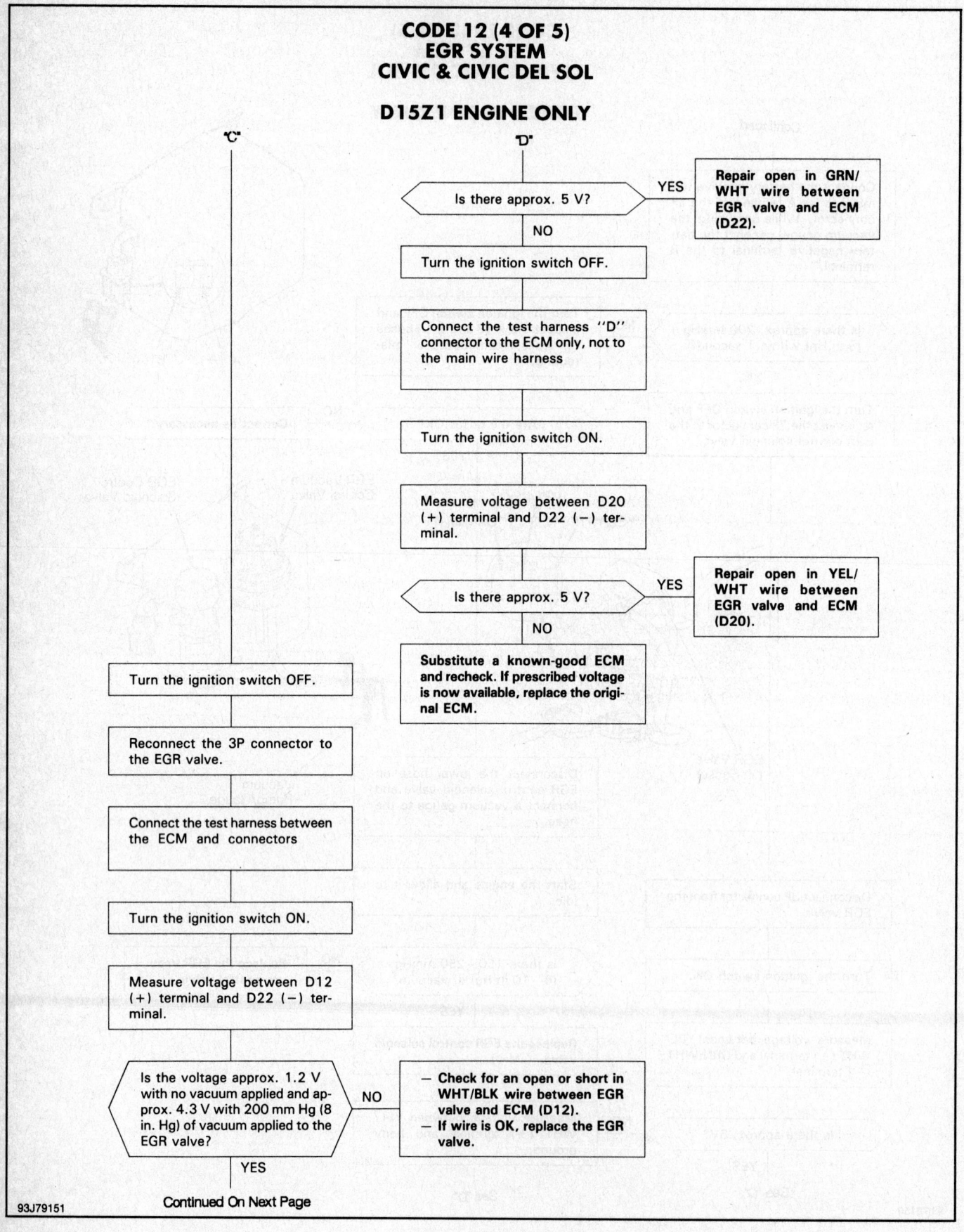

"C"

"D"

Is there approx. 5 V? —— YES —→ Repair open in GRN/WHT wire between EGR valve and ECM (D22).

NO

Turn the ignition switch OFF.

Connect the test harness "D" connector to the ECM only, not to the main wire harness

Turn the ignition switch ON.

Measure voltage between D20 (+) terminal and D22 (−) terminal.

Is there approx. 5 V? —— YES —→ Repair open in YEL/WHT wire between EGR valve and ECM (D20).

NO

Substitute a known-good ECM and recheck. If prescribed voltage is now available, replace the original ECM.

Turn the ignition switch OFF.

Reconnect the 3P connector to the EGR valve.

Connect the test harness between the ECM and connectors

Turn the ignition switch ON.

Measure voltage between D12 (+) terminal and D22 (−) terminal.

Is the voltage approx. 1.2 V with no vacuum applied and approx. 4.3 V with 200 mm Hg (8 in. Hg) of vacuum applied to the EGR valve? —— NO —→ — Check for an open or short in WHT/BLK wire between EGR valve and ECM (D12). — If wire is OK, replace the EGR valve.

YES

Continued On Next Page

93J79151

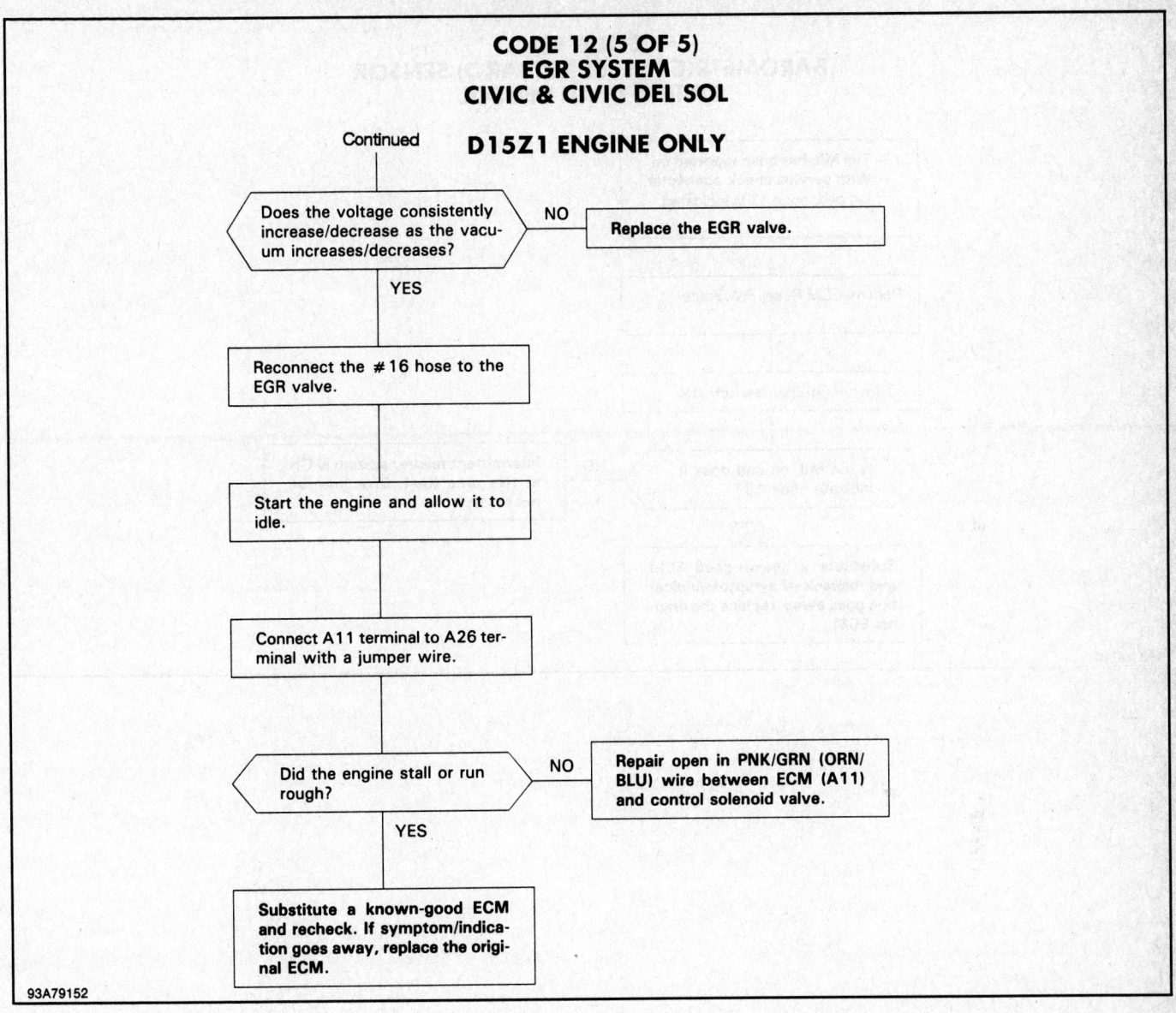

**CODE 12 (5 OF 5)
EGR SYSTEM
CIVIC & CIVIC DEL SOL**

D15Z1 ENGINE ONLY

Continued

Does the voltage consistently increase/decrease as the vacuum increases/decreases? — NO → Replace the EGR valve.

YES

Reconnect the #16 hose to the EGR valve.

Start the engine and allow it to idle.

Connect A11 terminal to A26 terminal with a jumper wire.

Did the engine stall or run rough? — NO → Repair open in PNK/GRN (ORN/BLU) wire between ECM (A11) and control solenoid valve.

YES

Substitute a known-good ECM and recheck. If symptom/indication goes away, replace the original ECM.

93A79152

1994 ENGINE PERFORMANCE
Self-Diagnostics (Cont.)

CODE 13
BAROMETRIC PRESSURE (BARO) SENSOR
CIVIC & CIVIC DEL SOL

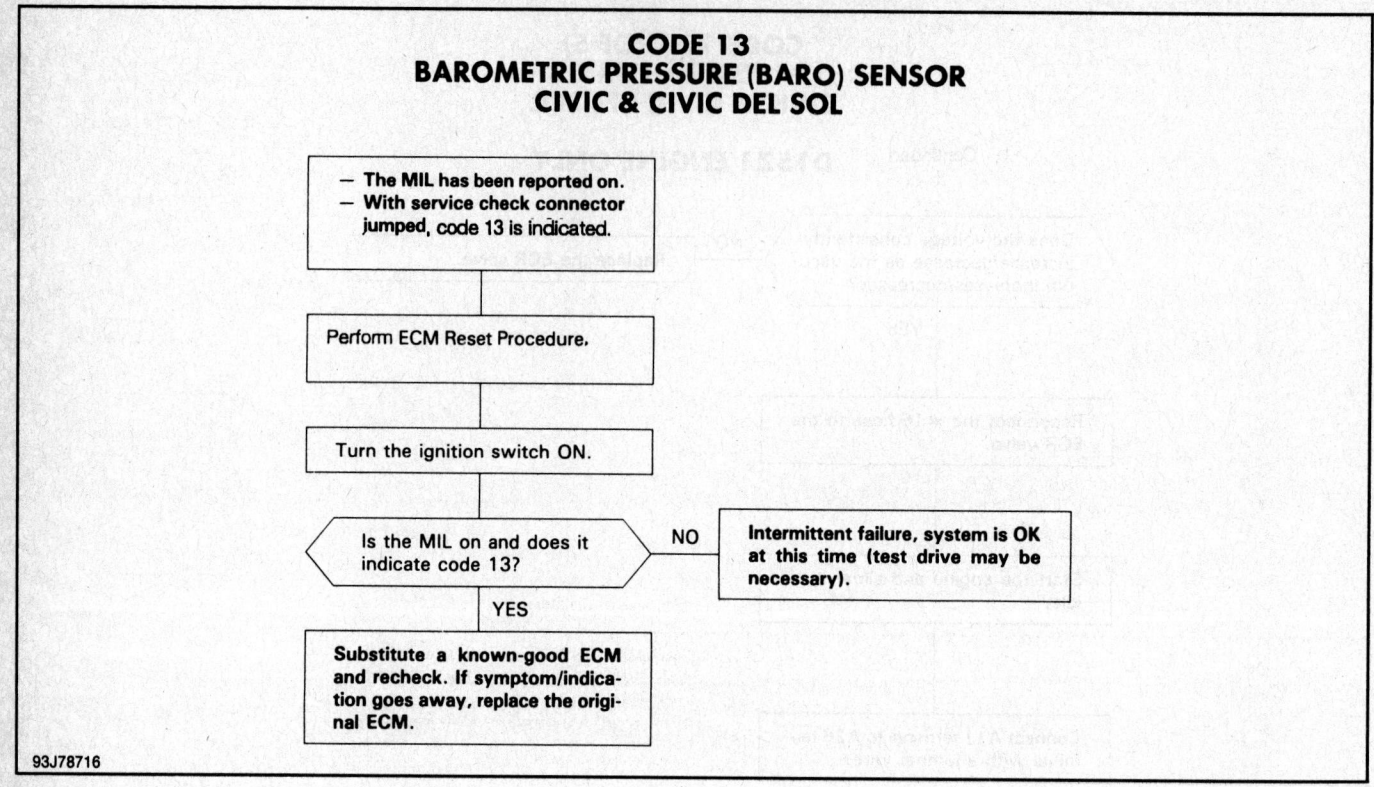

93J78716

CODE 14 (1 OF 2)
IDLE AIR CONTROL (IAC) VALVE
CIVIC & CIVIC DEL SOL

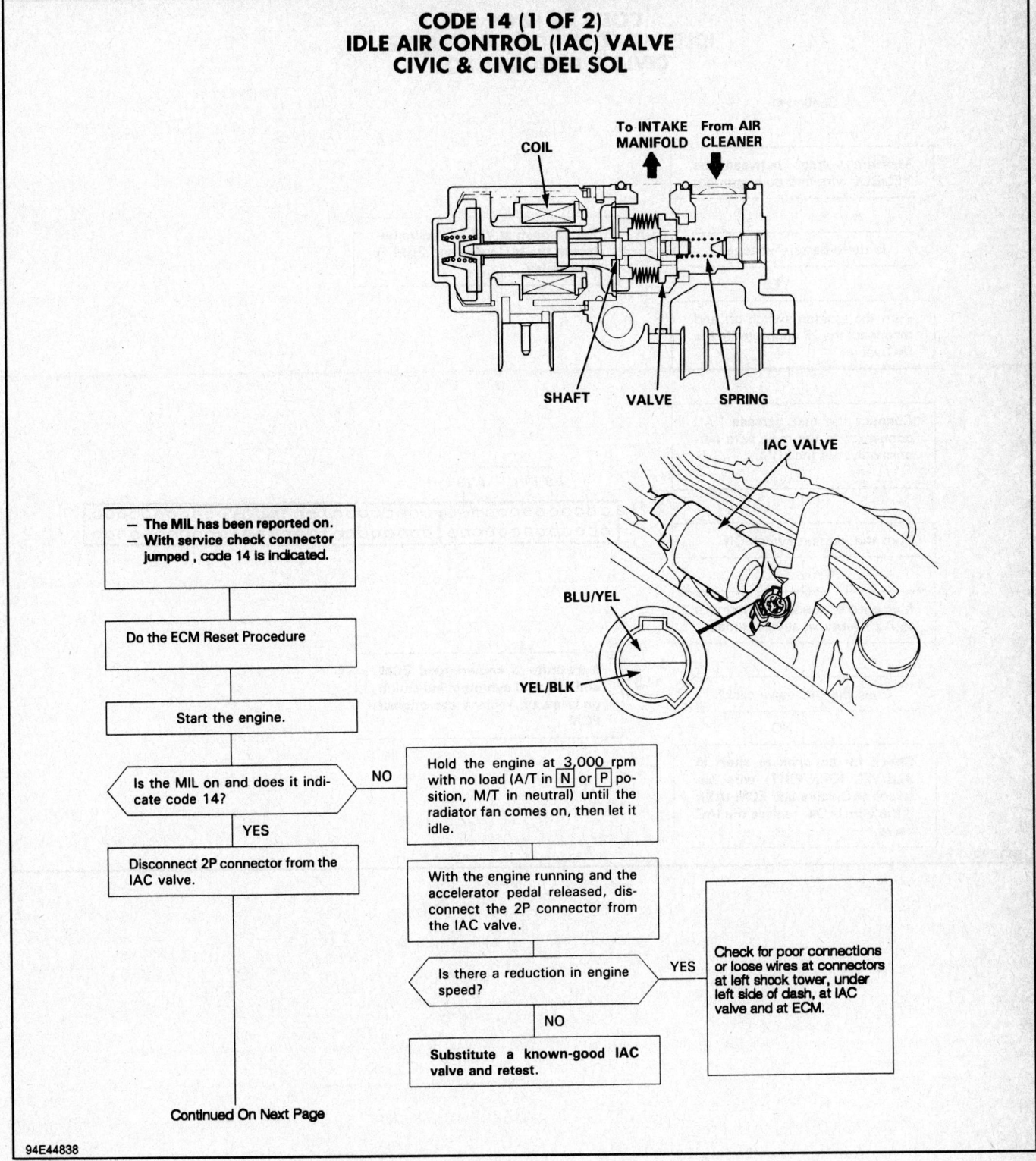

To INTAKE MANIFOLD   From AIR CLEANER

COIL

SHAFT   VALVE   SPRING

IAC VALVE

BLU/YEL

YEL/BLK

— The MIL has been reported on.
— With service check connector jumped, code 14 is indicated.

↓

Do the ECM Reset Procedure

↓

Start the engine.

↓

Is the MIL on and does it indicate code 14? — NO → Hold the engine at 3,000 rpm with no load (A/T in N or P position, M/T in neutral) until the radiator fan comes on, then let it idle.

YES

Disconnect 2P connector from the IAC valve.

With the engine running and the accelerator pedal released, disconnect the 2P connector from the IAC valve.

↓

Is there a reduction in engine speed? — YES → Check for poor connections or loose wires at connectors at left shock tower, under left side of dash, at IAC valve and at ECM.

NO

Substitute a known-good IAC valve and retest.

Continued On Next Page

94E44838

CODE 14 (2 OF 2)
IDLE AIR CONTROL (IAC) VALVE
CIVIC & CIVIC DEL SOL

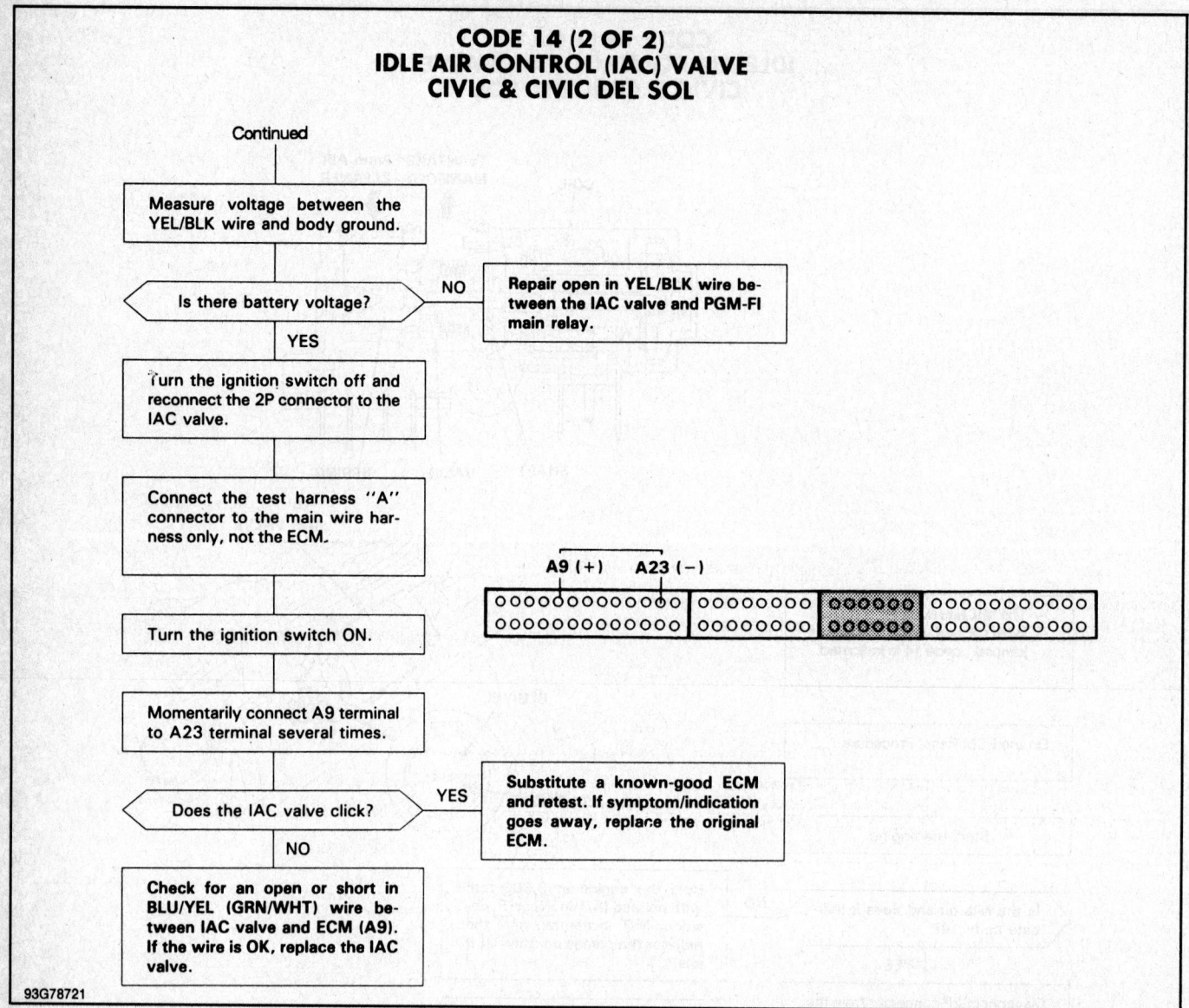

Continued

Measure voltage between the YEL/BLK wire and body ground.

Is there battery voltage? — NO → Repair open in YEL/BLK wire between the IAC valve and PGM-FI main relay.

YES

Turn the ignition switch off and reconnect the 2P connector to the IAC valve.

Connect the test harness "A" connector to the main wire harness only, not the ECM.

A9 (+)   A23 (−)

Turn the ignition switch ON.

Momentarily connect A9 terminal to A23 terminal several times.

Does the IAC valve click? — YES → Substitute a known-good ECM and retest. If symptom/indication goes away, replace the original ECM.

NO

Check for an open or short in BLU/YEL (GRN/WHT) wire between IAC valve and ECM (A9). If the wire is OK, replace the IAC valve.

93G78721

CODE 15 (1 OF 2)
IGNITION OUTPUT SIGNAL
CIVIC & CIVIC DEL SOL

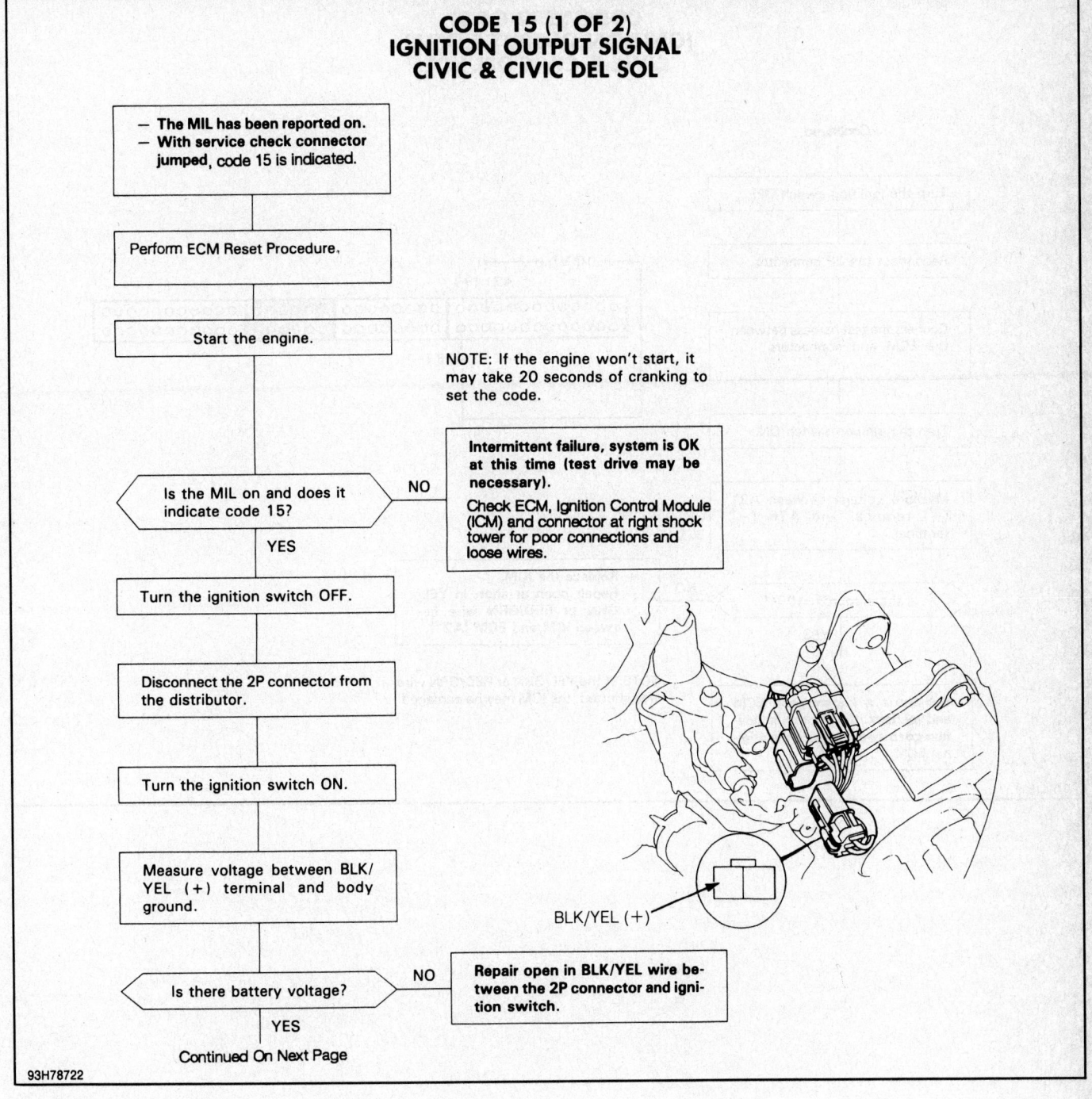

- The MIL has been reported on.
- With service check connector jumped, code 15 is indicated.

Perform ECM Reset Procedure.

Start the engine.

NOTE: If the engine won't start, it may take 20 seconds of cranking to set the code.

Is the MIL on and does it indicate code 15?

NO → Intermittent failure, system is OK at this time (test drive may be necessary).

Check ECM, Ignition Control Module (ICM) and connector at right shock tower for poor connections and loose wires.

YES

Turn the ignition switch OFF.

Disconnect the 2P connector from the distributor.

Turn the ignition switch ON.

Measure voltage between BLK/YEL (+) terminal and body ground.

BLK/YEL (+)

Is there battery voltage?

NO → Repair open in BLK/YEL wire between the 2P connector and ignition switch.

YES

Continued On Next Page

93H78722

1994 ENGINE PERFORMANCE
Self-Diagnostics (Cont.)

CODE 15 (2 OF 2)
IGNITION OUTPUT SIGNAL
CIVIC & CIVIC DEL SOL

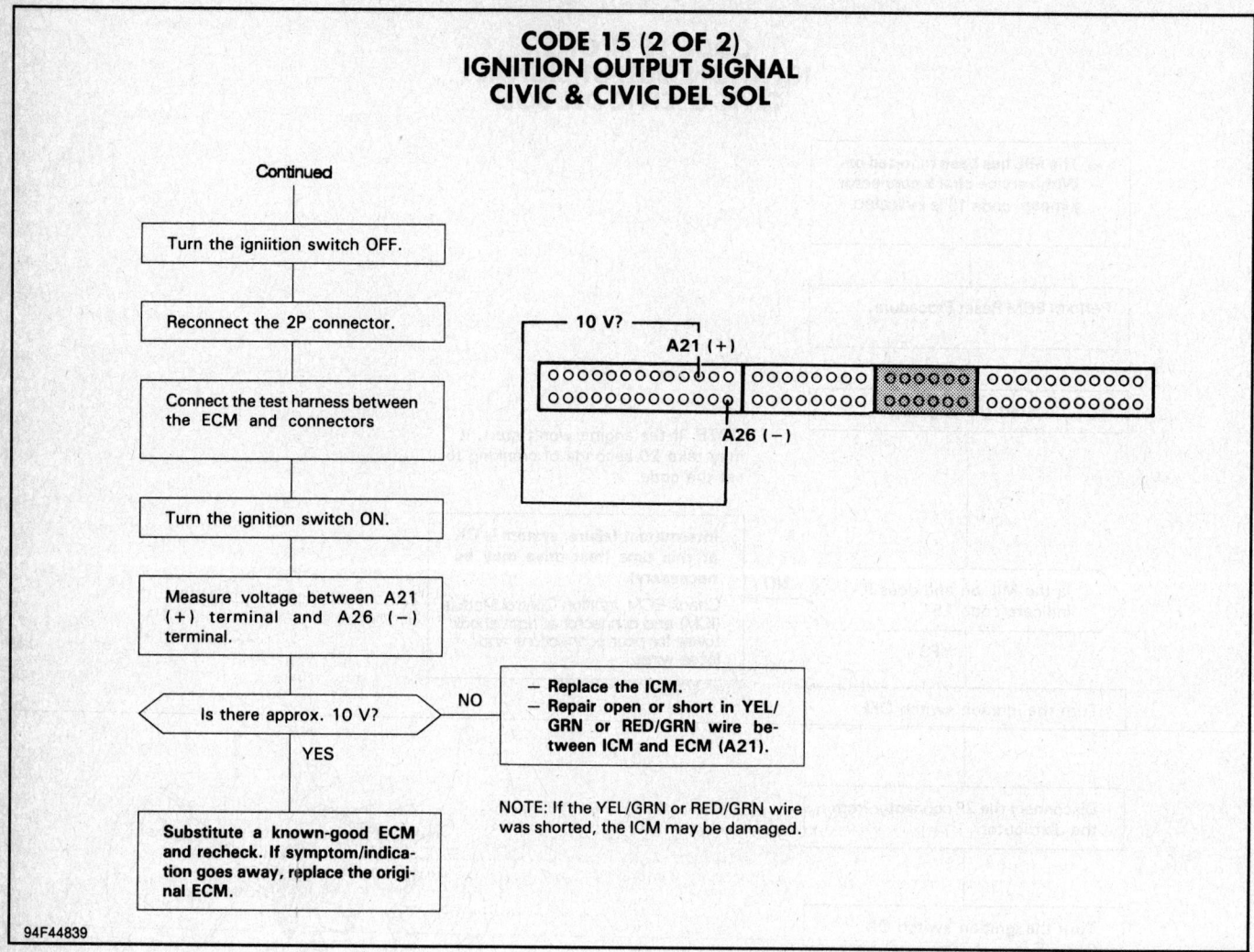

Continued

Turn the igniition switch OFF.

Reconnect the 2P connector.

Connect the test harness between the ECM and connectors

Turn the ignition switch ON.

Measure voltage between A21 (+) terminal and A26 (−) terminal.

Is there approx. 10 V? — NO →
— **Replace the ICM.**
— **Repair open or short in YEL/ GRN or RED/GRN wire between ICM and ECM (A21).**

YES

Substitute a known-good ECM and recheck. If symptom/indication goes away, replace the original ECM.

10 V?
A21 (+)
A26 (−)

NOTE: If the YEL/GRN or RED/GRN wire was shorted, the ICM may be damaged.

94F44839

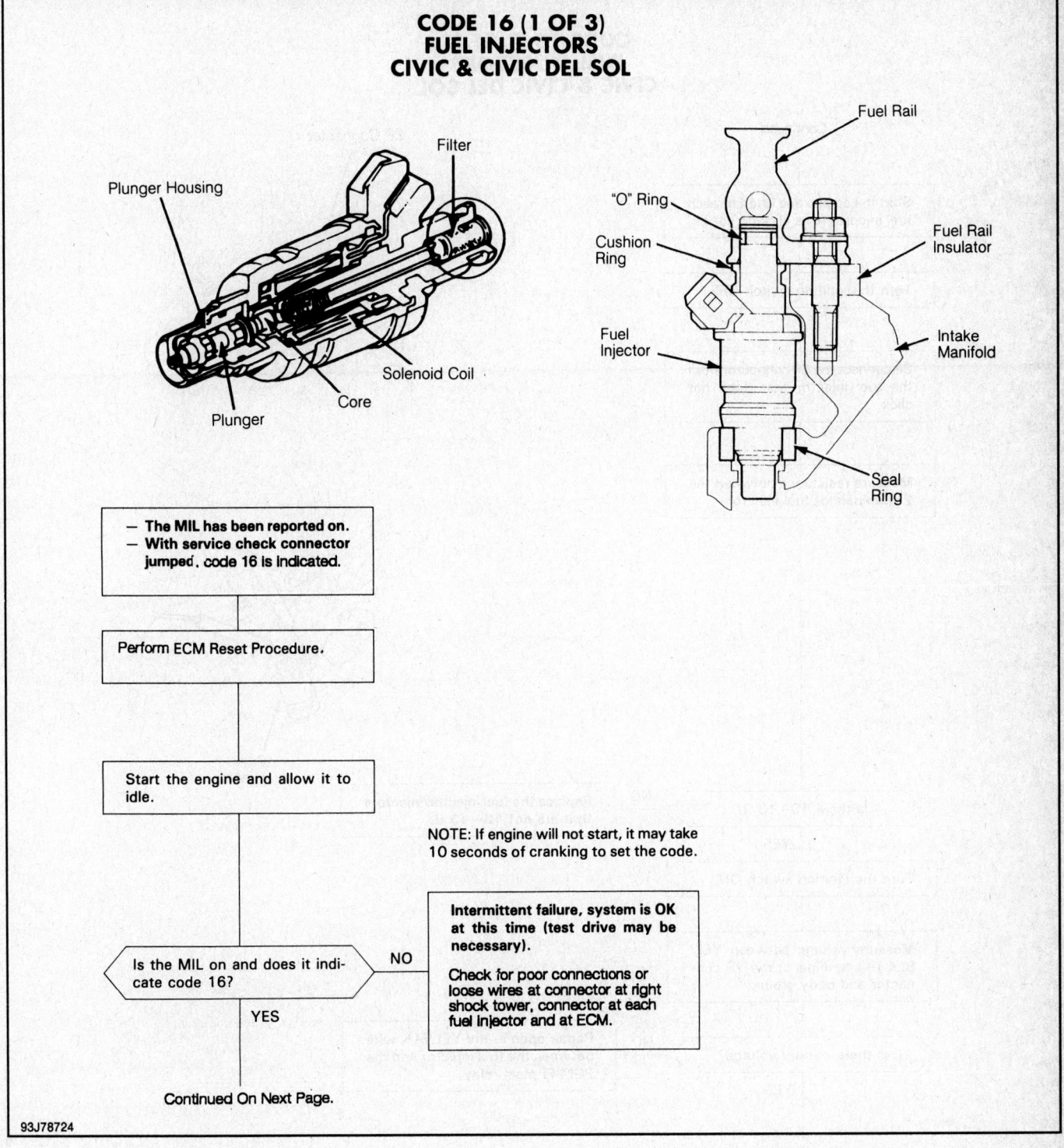

CODE 16 (1 OF 3)
FUEL INJECTORS
CIVIC & CIVIC DEL SOL

Plunger Housing

Filter

"O" Ring

Cushion Ring

Fuel Rail

Fuel Rail Insulator

Fuel Injector

Solenoid Coil

Core

Plunger

Intake Manifold

Seal Ring

— The MIL has been reported on.
— With service check connector jumped, code 16 is indicated.

Perform ECM Reset Procedure.

Start the engine and allow it to idle.

NOTE: If engine will not start, it may take 10 seconds of cranking to set the code.

Is the MIL on and does it indicate code 16?

NO → Intermittent failure, system is OK at this time (test drive may be necessary).

Check for poor connections or loose wires at connector at right shock tower, connector at each fuel injector and at ECM.

YES

Continued On Next Page.

93J78724

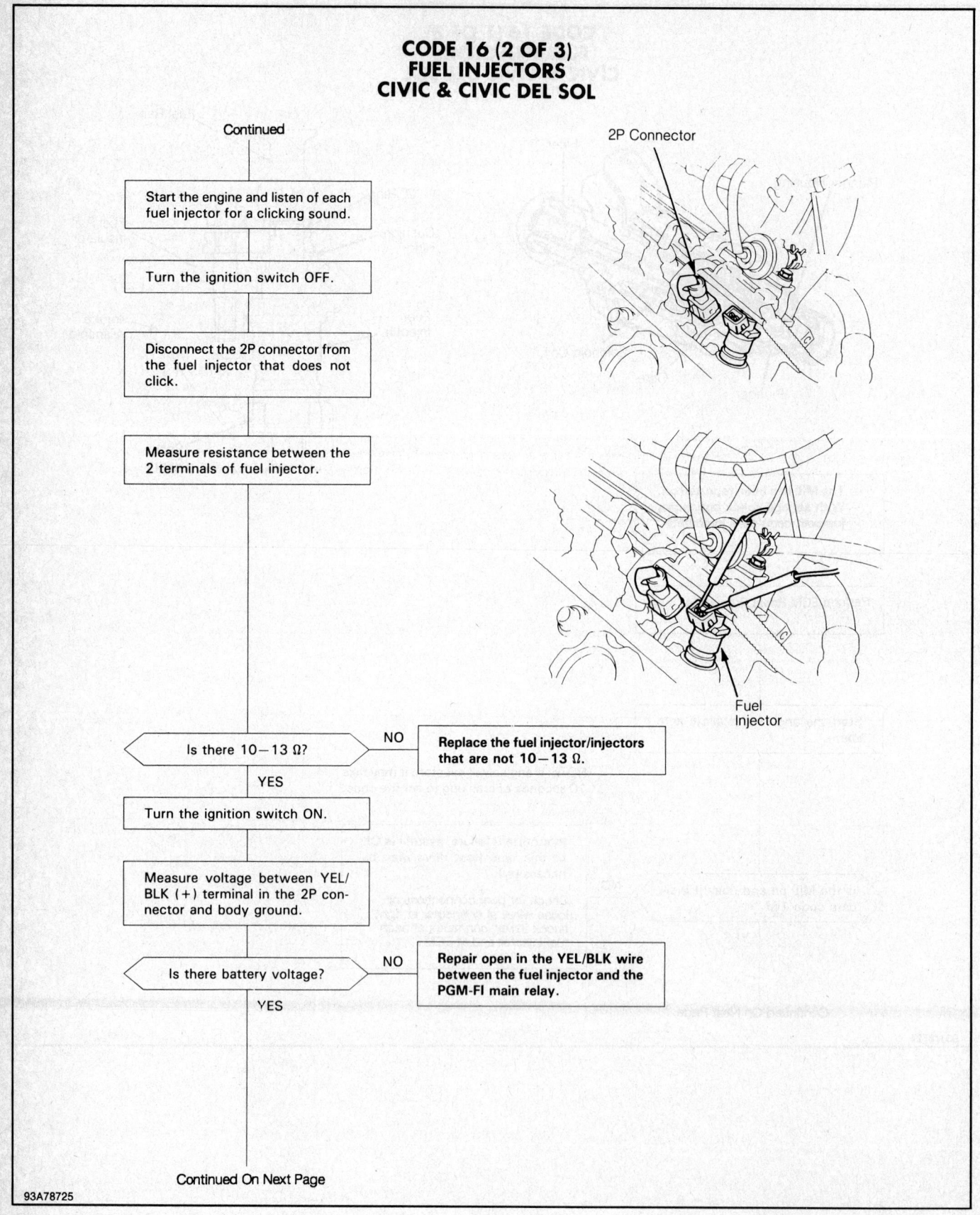

CODE 16 (2 OF 3)
FUEL INJECTORS
CIVIC & CIVIC DEL SOL

2P Connector

Continued

Start the engine and listen of each fuel injector for a clicking sound.

Turn the ignition switch OFF.

Disconnect the 2P connector from the fuel injector that does not click.

Measure resistance between the 2 terminals of fuel injector.

Fuel Injector

Is there 10–13 Ω? — NO → Replace the fuel injector/injectors that are not 10–13 Ω.

YES

Turn the ignition switch ON.

Measure voltage between YEL/BLK (+) terminal in the 2P connector and body ground.

Is there battery voltage? — NO → Repair open in the YEL/BLK wire between the fuel injector and the PGM-FI main relay.

YES

Continued On Next Page

93A78725

CODE 16 (3 OF 3)
FUEL INJECTORS
CIVIC & CIVIC DEL SOL

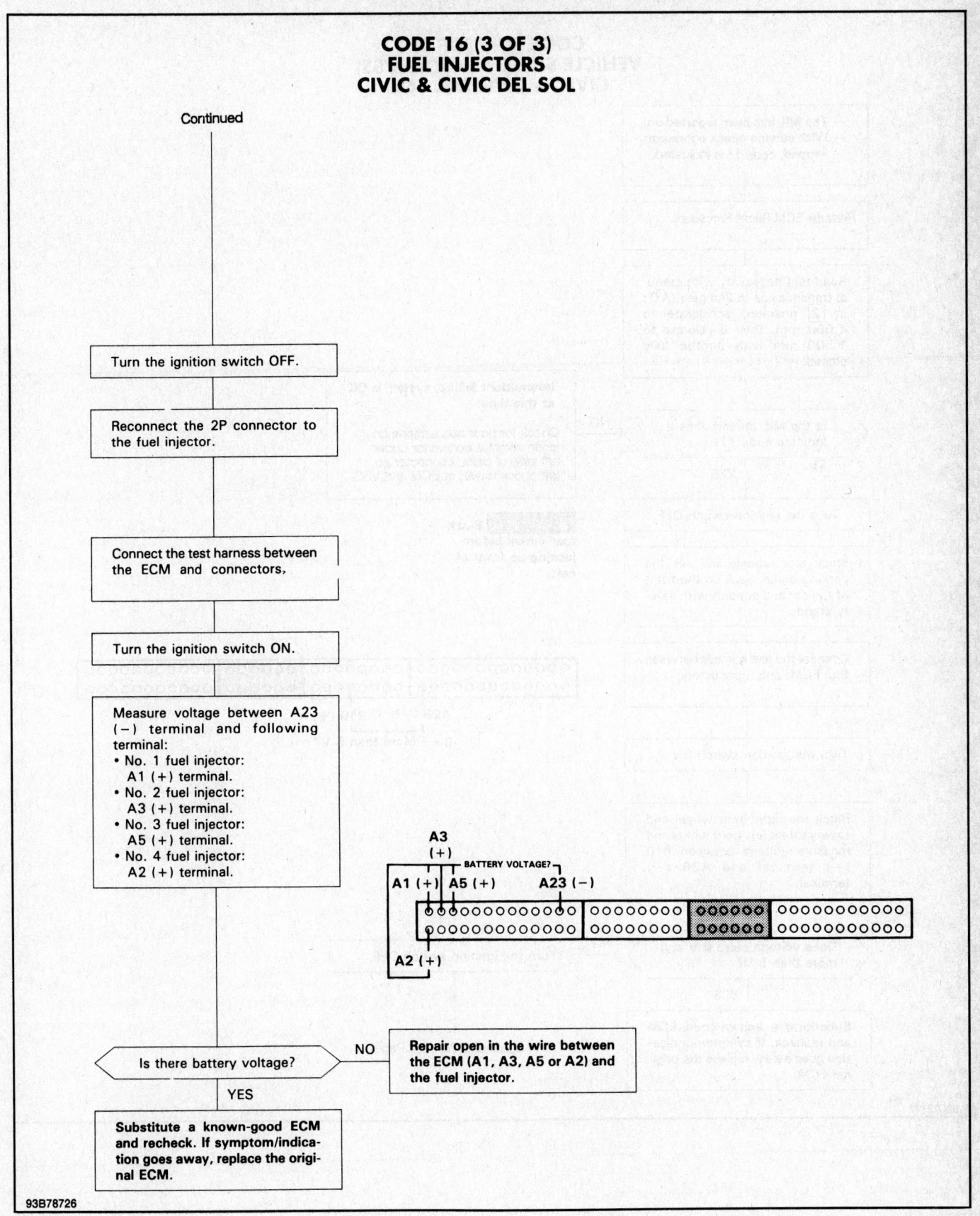

Continued

Turn the ignition switch OFF.

Reconnect the 2P connector to the fuel injector.

Connect the test harness between the ECM and connectors.

Turn the ignition switch ON.

Measure voltage between A23 (−) terminal and following terminal:
- No. 1 fuel injector: A1 (+) terminal.
- No. 2 fuel injector: A3 (+) terminal.
- No. 3 fuel injector: A5 (+) terminal.
- No. 4 fuel injector: A2 (+) terminal.

A3 (+)

BATTERY VOLTAGE?

A1 (+)   A5 (+)   A23 (−)

A2 (+)

Is there battery voltage? — NO → Repair open in the wire between the ECM (A1, A3, A5 or A2) and the fuel injector.

YES

Substitute a known-good ECM and recheck. If symptom/indication goes away, replace the original ECM.

93B78726

CODE 17 (1 OF 2)
VEHICLE SPEED SENSOR (VSS)
CIVIC & CIVIC DEL SOL

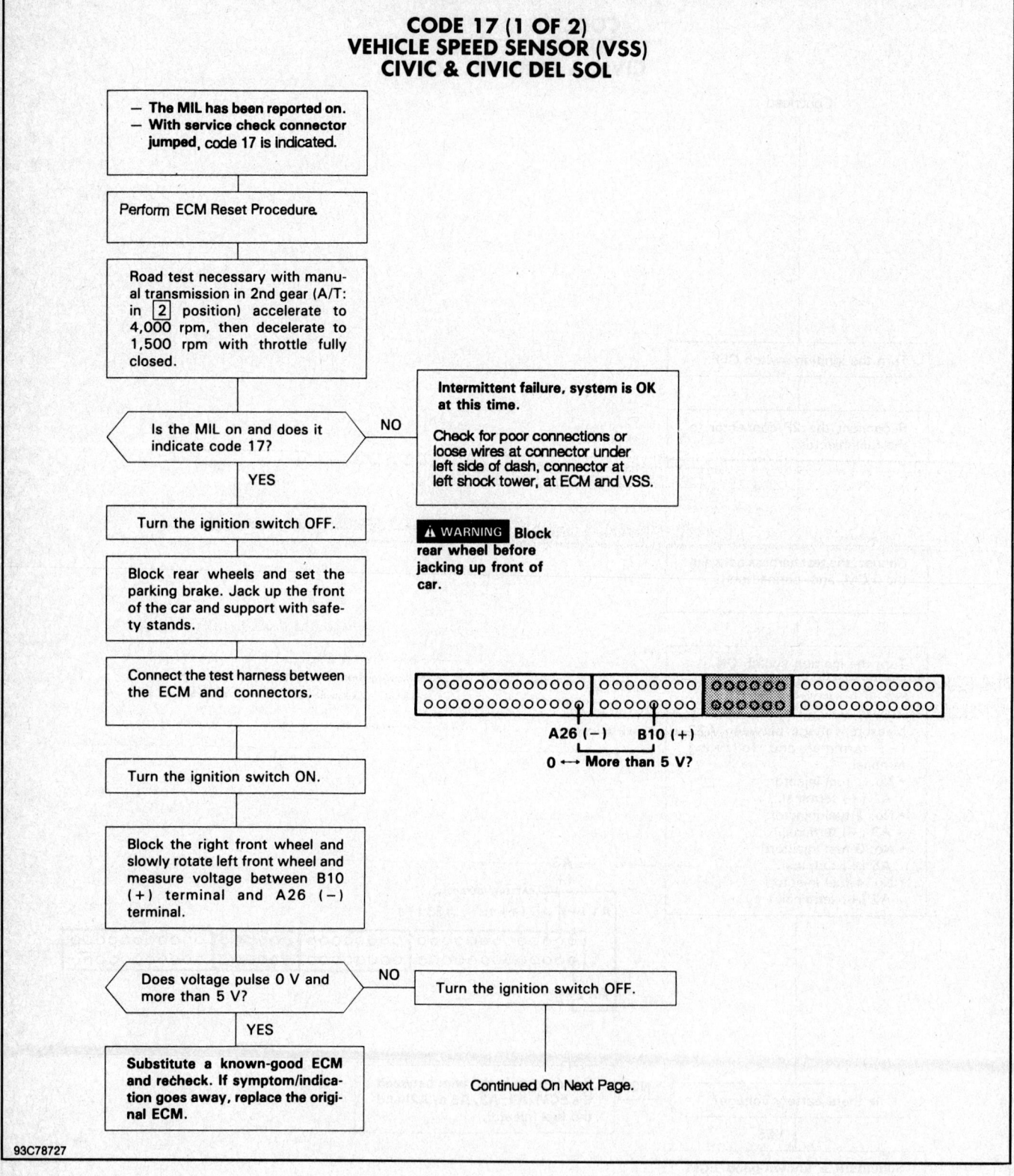

— The MIL has been reported on.
— With service check connector jumped, code 17 is indicated.

Perform ECM Reset Procedure.

Road test necessary with manual transmission in 2nd gear (A/T: in 2 position) accelerate to 4,000 rpm, then decelerate to 1,500 rpm with throttle fully closed.

Is the MIL on and does it indicate code 17?

NO → Intermittent failure, system is OK at this time.

Check for poor connections or loose wires at connector under left side of dash, connector at left shock tower, at ECM and VSS.

⚠ WARNING Block rear wheel before jacking up front of car.

YES

Turn the ignition switch OFF.

Block rear wheels and set the parking brake. Jack up the front of the car and support with safety stands.

Connect the test harness between the ECM and connectors.

A26 (−)   B10 (+)

0 ⟷ More than 5 V?

Turn the ignition switch ON.

Block the right front wheel and slowly rotate left front wheel and measure voltage between B10 (+) terminal and A26 (−) terminal.

Does voltage pulse 0 V and more than 5 V?

NO → Turn the ignition switch OFF.

YES

Substitute a known-good ECM and recheck. If symptom/indication goes away, replace the original ECM.

Continued On Next Page.

93C78727

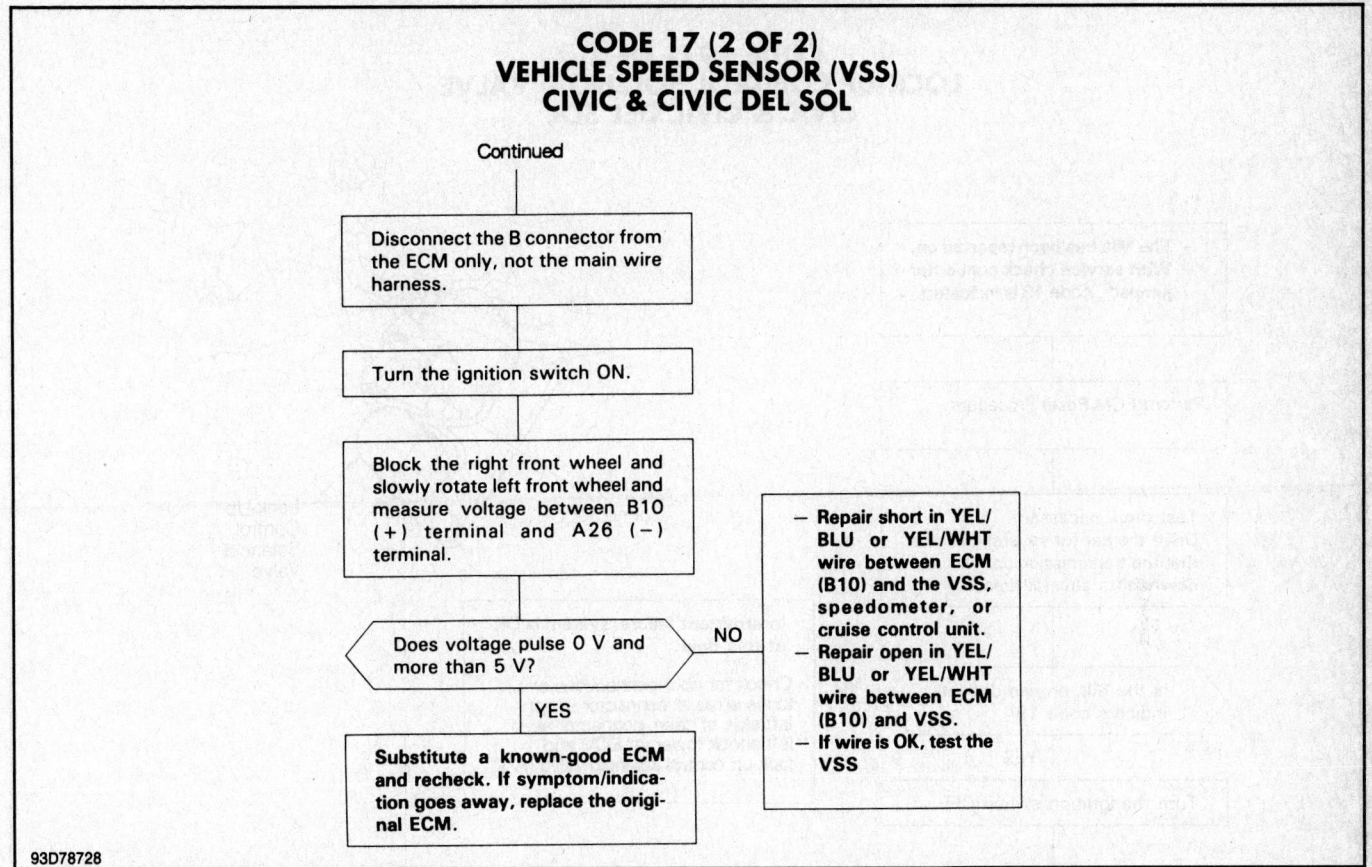

CODE 17 (2 OF 2)
VEHICLE SPEED SENSOR (VSS)
CIVIC & CIVIC DEL SOL

Continued

Disconnect the B connector from the ECM only, not the main wire harness.

Turn the ignition switch ON.

Block the right front wheel and slowly rotate left front wheel and measure voltage between B10 (+) terminal and A26 (−) terminal.

Does voltage pulse 0 V and more than 5 V?

NO →
- Repair short in YEL/BLU or YEL/WHT wire between ECM (B10) and the VSS, speedometer, or cruise control unit.
- Repair open in YEL/BLU or YEL/WHT wire between ECM (B10) and VSS.
- If wire is OK, test the VSS

YES

Substitute a known-good ECM and recheck. If symptom/indication goes away, replace the original ECM.

93D78728

CODE 19 (1 OF 2)
LOCK-UP CONTROL SOLENOID VALVE
CIVIC & CIVIC DEL SOL

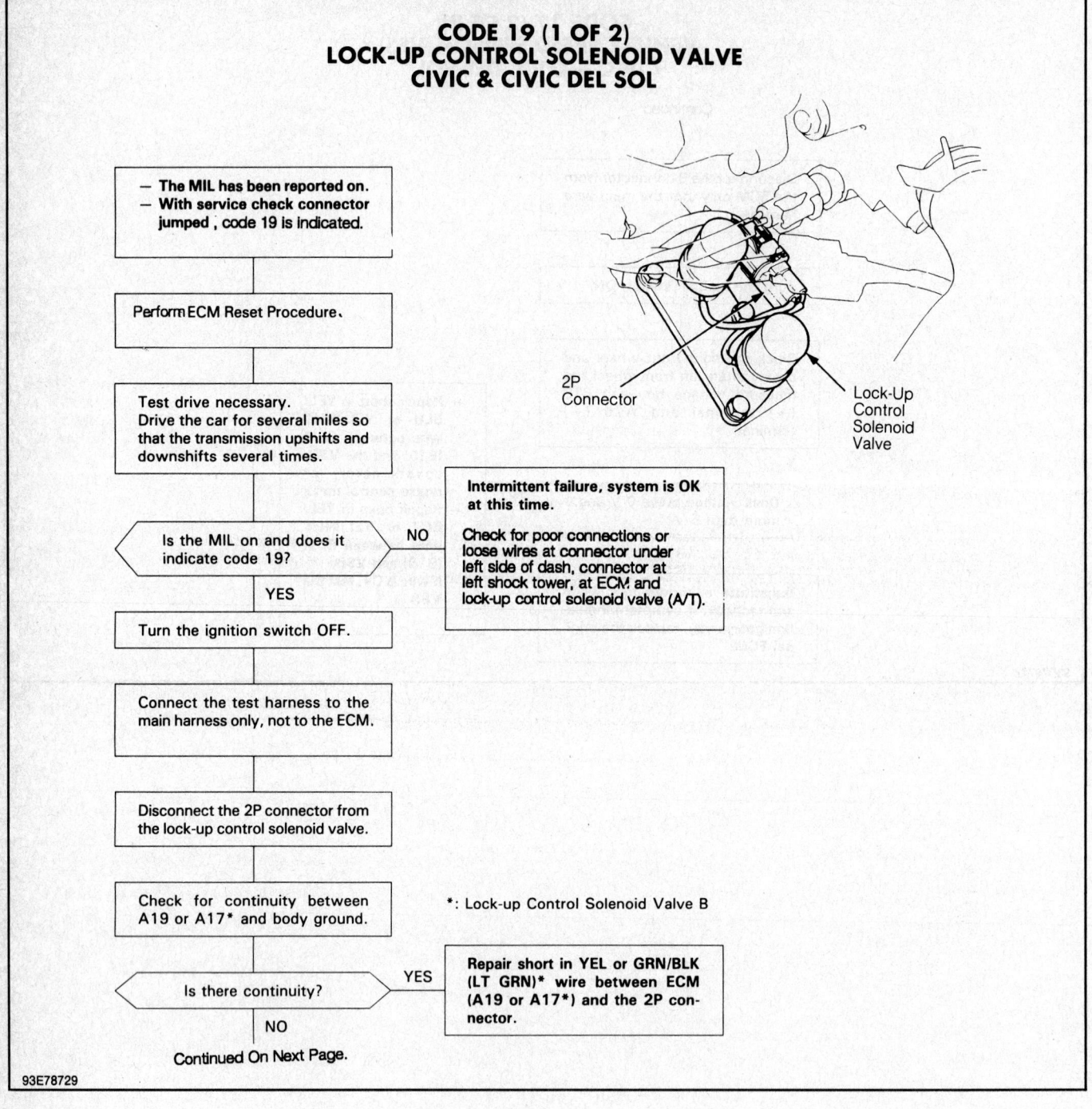

- The MIL has been reported on.
- With service check connector jumped , code 19 is indicated.

Perform ECM Reset Procedure.

Test drive necessary.
Drive the car for several miles so that the transmission upshifts and downshifts several times.

Is the MIL on and does it indicate code 19?

NO → Intermittent failure, system is OK at this time.

Check for poor connections or loose wires at connector under left side of dash, connector at left shock tower, at ECM and lock-up control solenoid valve (A/T).

YES

Turn the ignition switch OFF.

Connect the test harness to the main harness only, not to the ECM.

Disconnect the 2P connector from the lock-up control solenoid valve.

Check for continuity between A19 or A17* and body ground.

*: Lock-up Control Solenoid Valve B

Is there continuity?

YES → Repair short in YEL or GRN/BLK (LT GRN)* wire between ECM (A19 or A17*) and the 2P connector.

NO

Continued On Next Page.

2P Connector

Lock-Up Control Solenoid Valve

93E78729

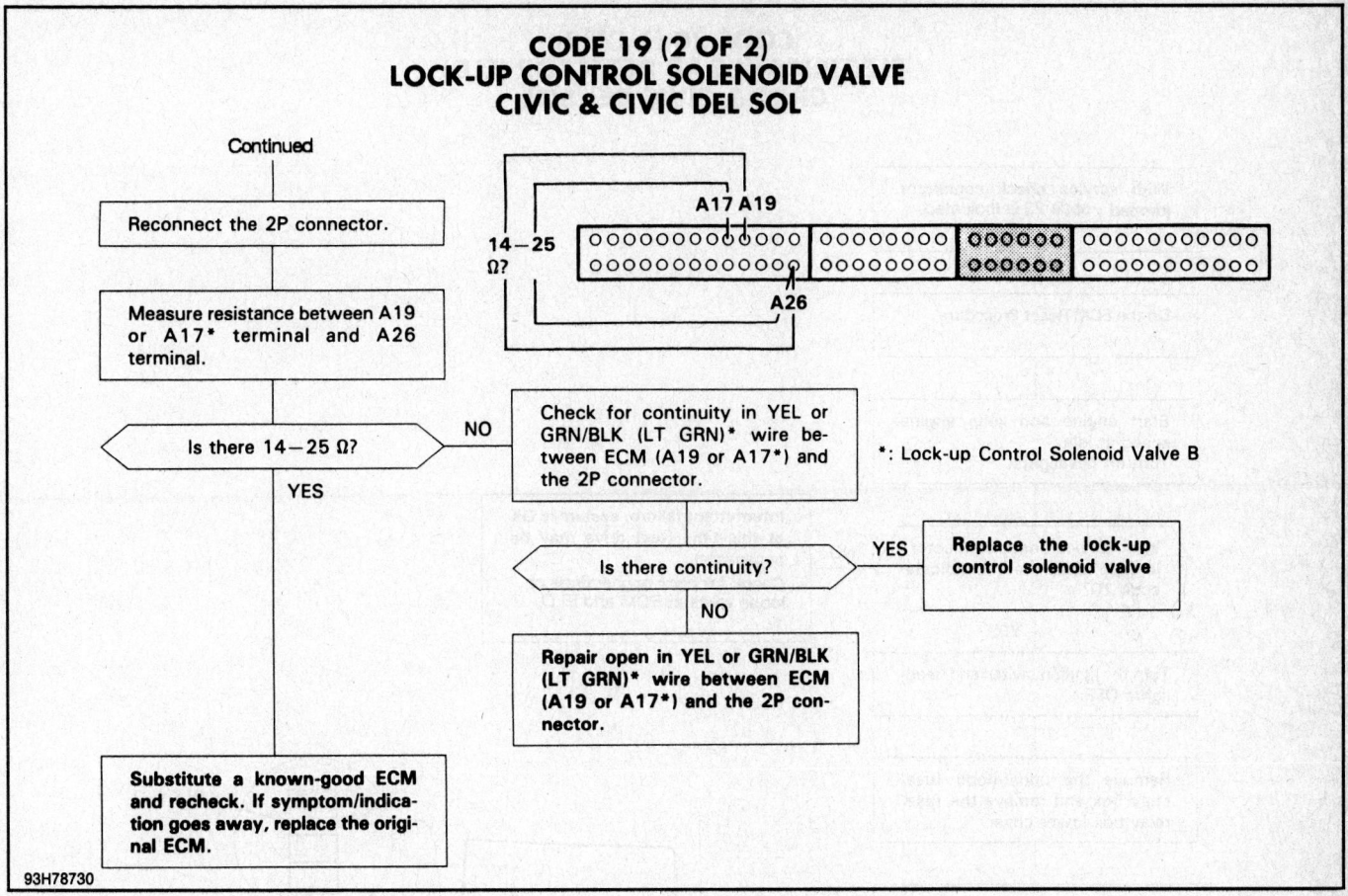

CODE 19 (2 OF 2)
LOCK-UP CONTROL SOLENOID VALVE
CIVIC & CIVIC DEL SOL

Continued

Reconnect the 2P connector.

Measure resistance between A19 or A17* terminal and A26 terminal.

14 — 25 Ω?

A17 A19

A26

Is there 14 — 25 Ω? — NO → Check for continuity in YEL or GRN/BLK (LT GRN)* wire between ECM (A19 or A17*) and the 2P connector.

YES

*: Lock-up Control Solenoid Valve B

Is there continuity? — YES → Replace the lock-up control solenoid valve

NO

Repair open in YEL or GRN/BLK (LT GRN)* wire between ECM (A19 or A17*) and the 2P connector.

Substitute a known-good ECM and recheck. If symptom/indication goes away, replace the original ECM.

93H78730

CODE 20 (1 OF 2)
ELECTRICAL LOAD DETECTOR (ELD)
CIVIC & CIVIC DEL SOL

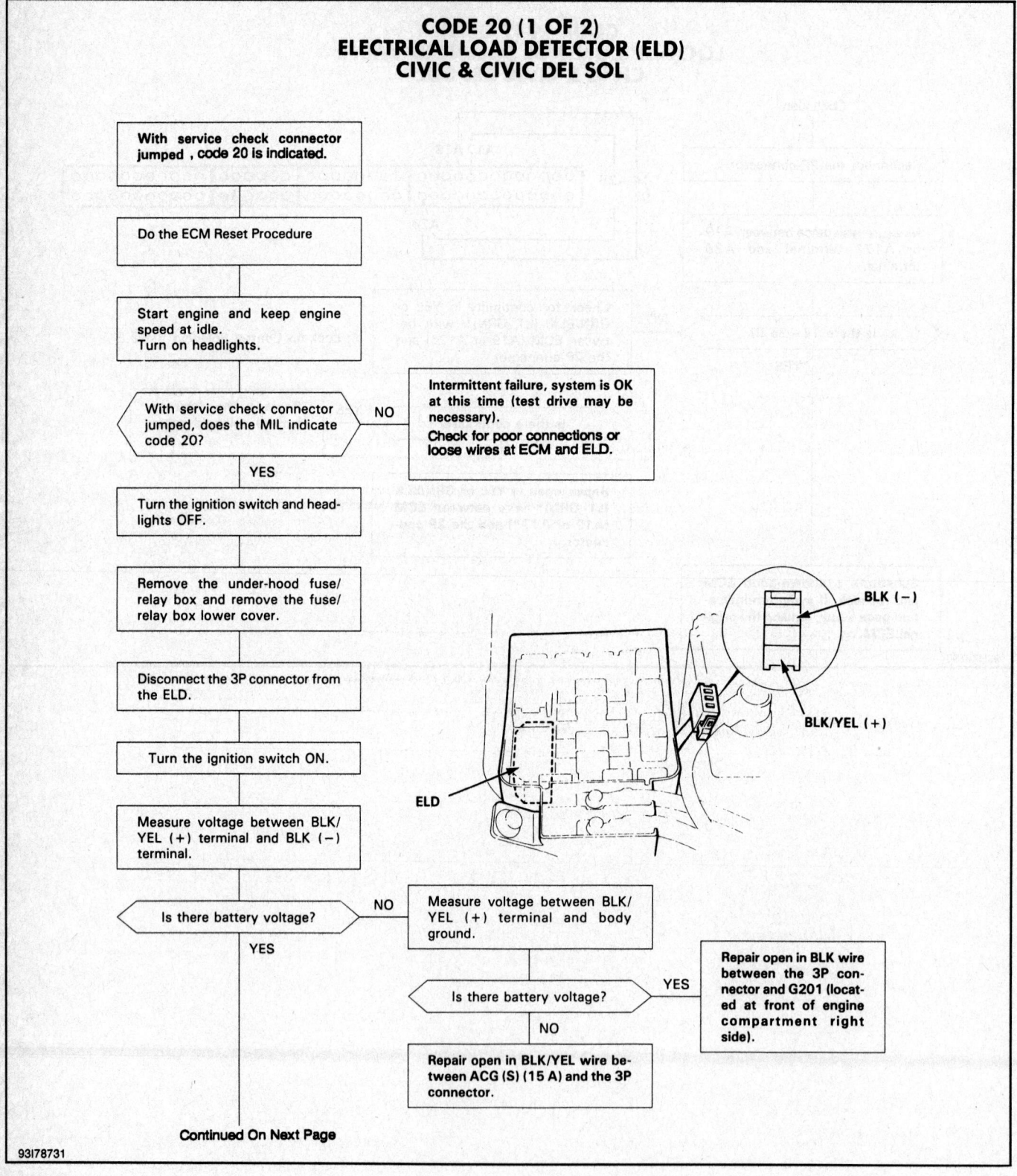

With service check connector jumped , code 20 is indicated.

Do the ECM Reset Procedure

Start engine and keep engine speed at idle.
Turn on headlights.

With service check connector jumped, does the MIL indicate code 20?

NO → Intermittent failure, system is OK at this time (test drive may be necessary).
Check for poor connections or loose wires at ECM and ELD.

YES

Turn the ignition switch and headlights OFF.

Remove the under-hood fuse/relay box and remove the fuse/relay box lower cover.

Disconnect the 3P connector from the ELD.

Turn the ignition switch ON.

Measure voltage between BLK/YEL (+) terminal and BLK (−) terminal.

ELD

BLK (−)

BLK/YEL (+)

Is there battery voltage?

NO → Measure voltage between BLK/YEL (+) terminal and body ground.

YES

Is there battery voltage?

YES → Repair open in BLK wire between the 3P connector and G201 (located at front of engine compartment right side).

NO

Repair open in BLK/YEL wire between ACG (S) (15 A) and the 3P connector.

Continued On Next Page

93I78731

CODE 20 (2 OF 2)
ELECTRICAL LOAD DETECTOR (ELD)
CIVIC & CIVIC DEL SOL

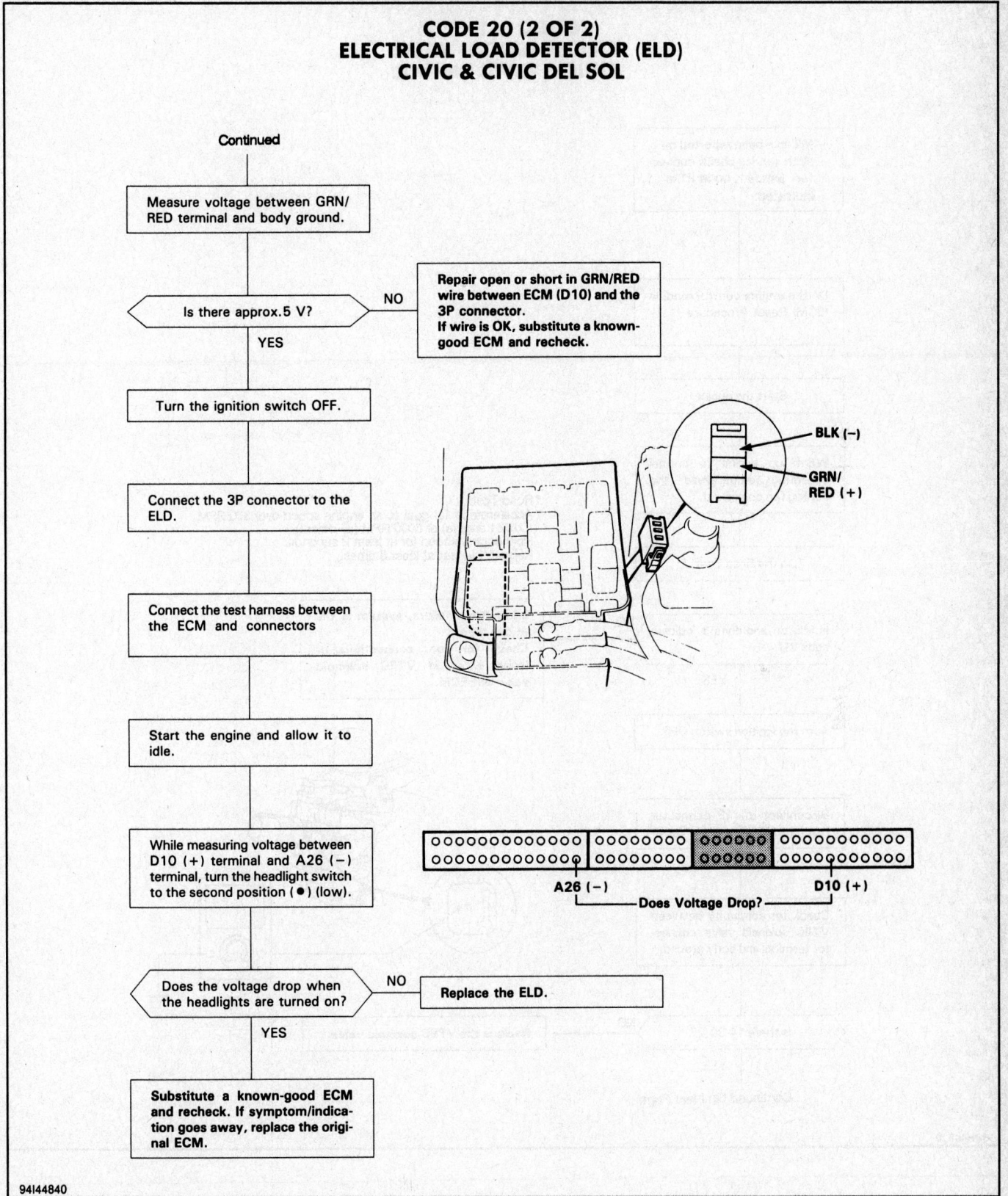

Continued

Measure voltage between GRN/RED terminal and body ground.

Is there approx. 5 V? — NO → Repair open or short in GRN/RED wire between ECM (D10) and the 3P connector.
If wire is OK, substitute a known-good ECM and recheck.

YES

Turn the ignition switch OFF.

BLK (−)

GRN/RED (+)

Connect the 3P connector to the ELD.

Connect the test harness between the ECM and connectors

Start the engine and allow it to idle.

While measuring voltage between D10 (+) terminal and A26 (−) terminal, turn the headlight switch to the second position (●) (low).

A26 (−) — Does Voltage Drop? — D10 (+)

Does the voltage drop when the headlights are turned on? — NO → Replace the ELD.

YES

Substitute a known-good ECM and recheck. If symptom/indication goes away, replace the original ECM.

94I44840

CODE 21 (1 OF 2)
VTEC SOLENOID VALVE
CIVIC & CIVIC DEL SOL

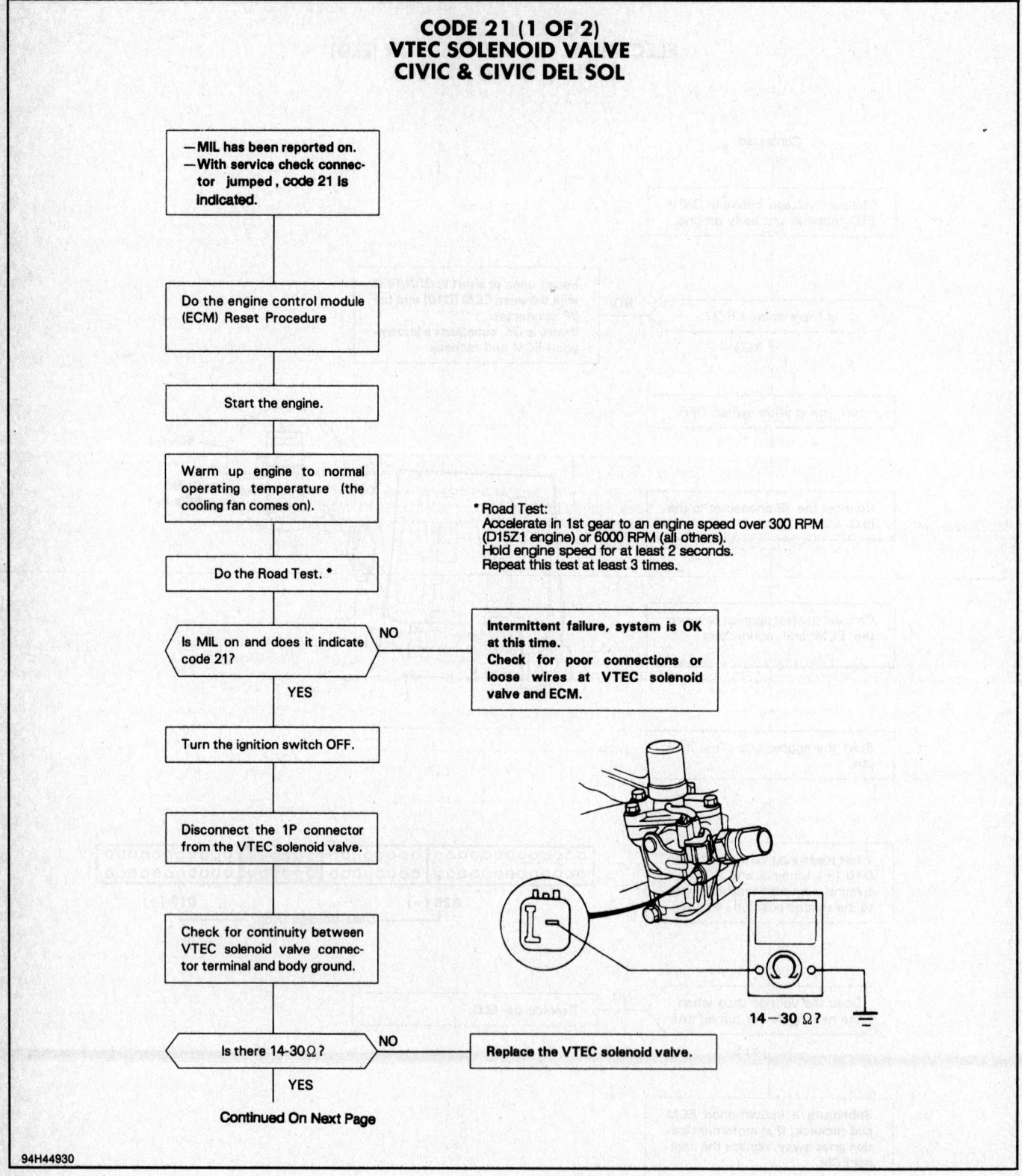

—MIL has been reported on.
—With service check connector jumped, code 21 is indicated.

Do the engine control module (ECM) Reset Procedure

Start the engine.

Warm up engine to normal operating temperature (the cooling fan comes on).

Do the Road Test. *

Is MIL on and does it indicate code 21?

NO → Intermittent failure, system is OK at this time.
Check for poor connections or loose wires at VTEC solenoid valve and ECM.

YES

Turn the ignition switch OFF.

Disconnect the 1P connector from the VTEC solenoid valve.

Check for continuity between VTEC solenoid valve connector terminal and body ground.

Is there 14-30 Ω?

NO → Replace the VTEC solenoid valve.

YES

Continued On Next Page

* Road Test:
Accelerate in 1st gear to an engine speed over 300 RPM (D15Z1 engine) or 6000 RPM (all others).
Hold engine speed for at least 2 seconds.
Repeat this test at least 3 times.

14—30 Ω?

94H44930

CODE 21 (2 OF 2)
VTEC SOLENOID VALVE
CIVIC & CIVIC DEL SOL

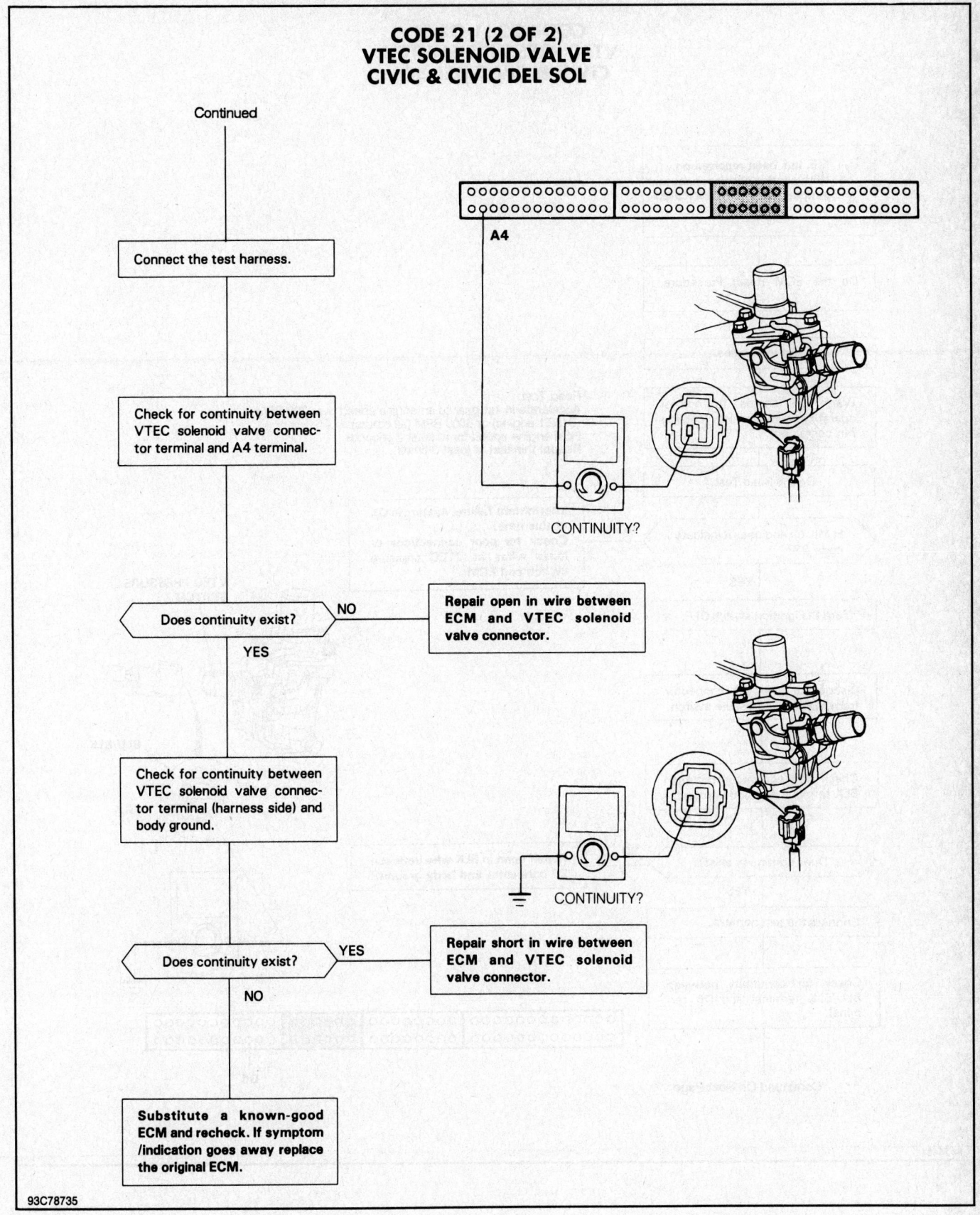

Continued

Connect the test harness.

A4

Check for continuity between VTEC solenoid valve connector terminal and A4 terminal.

CONTINUITY?

Does continuity exist? — NO → Repair open in wire between ECM and VTEC solenoid valve connector.

YES

Check for continuity between VTEC solenoid valve connector terminal (harness side) and body ground.

CONTINUITY?

Does continuity exist? — YES → Repair short in wire between ECM and VTEC solenoid valve connector.

NO

Substitute a known-good ECM and recheck. If symptom /indication goes away replace the original ECM.

93C78735

CODE 22 (1 OF 3)
VTEC PRESSURE SWITCH
CIVIC & CIVIC DEL SOL

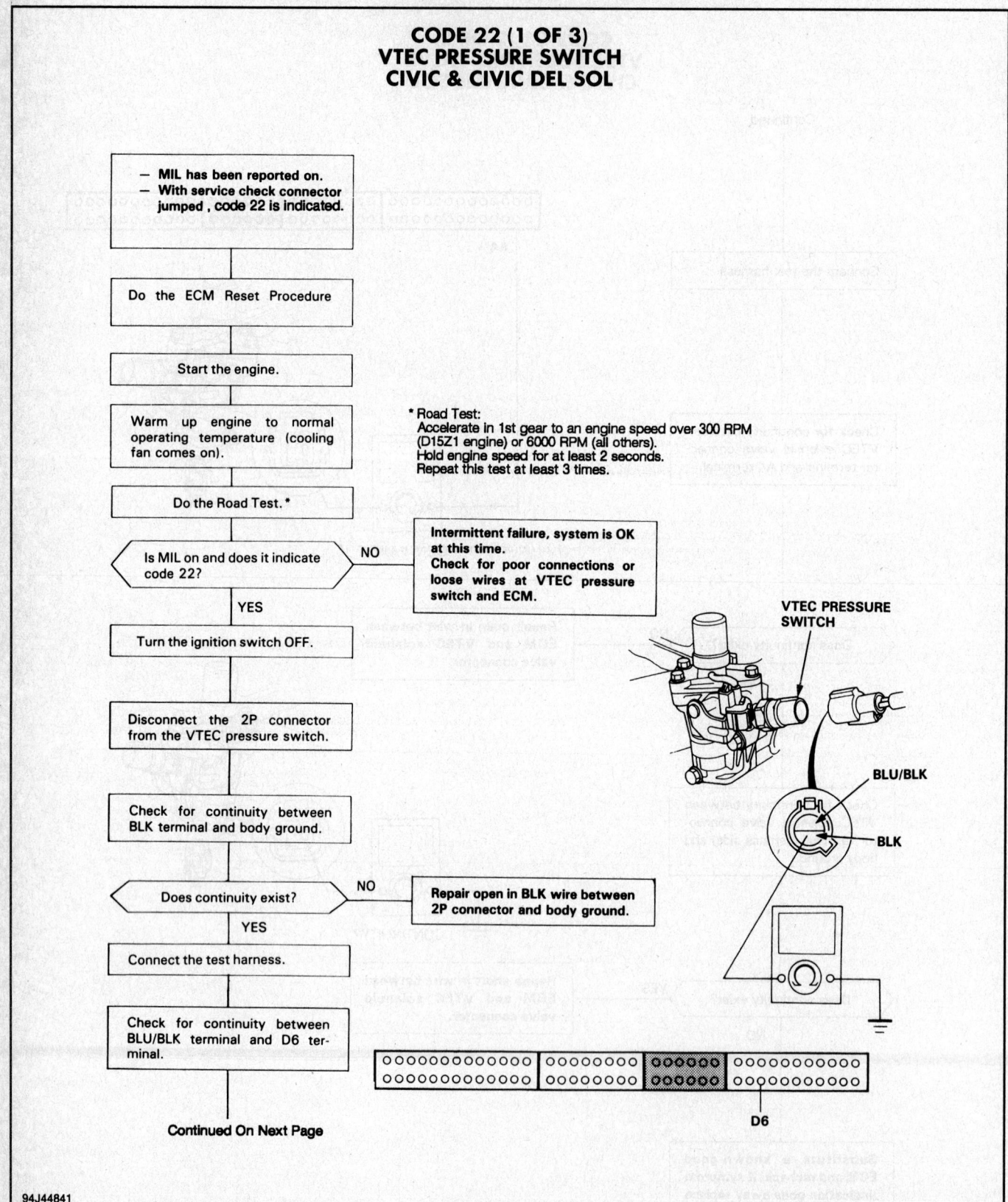

- MIL has been reported on.
- With service check connector jumped, code 22 is indicated.

Do the ECM Reset Procedure

Start the engine.

Warm up engine to normal operating temperature (cooling fan comes on).

Do the Road Test. *

Is MIL on and does it indicate code 22? — NO → Intermittent failure, system is OK at this time.
Check for poor connections or loose wires at VTEC pressure switch and ECM.

YES

Turn the ignition switch OFF.

Disconnect the 2P connector from the VTEC pressure switch.

Check for continuity between BLK terminal and body ground.

Does continuity exist? — NO → Repair open in BLK wire between 2P connector and body ground.

YES

Connect the test harness.

Check for continuity between BLU/BLK terminal and D6 terminal.

Continued On Next Page

* Road Test:
Accelerate in 1st gear to an engine speed over 300 RPM (D15Z1 engine) or 6000 RPM (all others).
Hold engine speed for at least 2 seconds.
Repeat this test at least 3 times.

VTEC PRESSURE SWITCH

BLU/BLK

BLK

D6

94J44841

CODE 22 (2 OF 3)
VTEC PRESSURE SWITCH
CIVIC & CIVIC DEL SOL

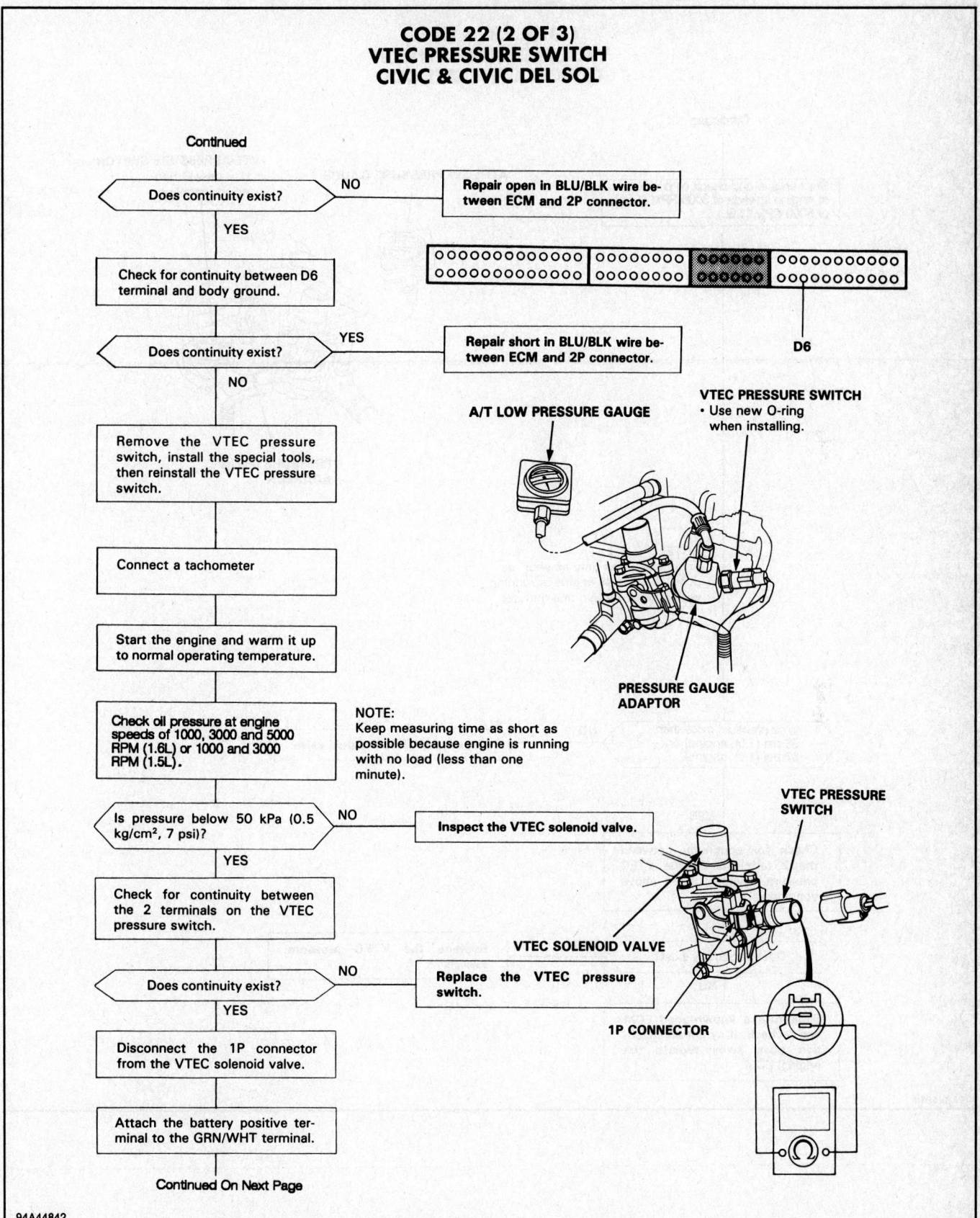

Continued

Does continuity exist? — **NO** → Repair open in BLU/BLK wire between ECM and 2P connector.

YES

Check for continuity between D6 terminal and body ground.

Does continuity exist? — **YES** → Repair short in BLU/BLK wire between ECM and 2P connector.

NO

Remove the VTEC pressure switch, install the special tools, then reinstall the VTEC pressure switch.

Connect a tachometer

Start the engine and warm it up to normal operating temperature.

Check oil pressure at engine speeds of 1000, 3000 and 5000 RPM (1.6L) or 1000 and 3000 RPM (1.5L).

NOTE:
Keep measuring time as short as possible because engine is running with no load (less than one minute).

Is pressure below 50 kPa (0.5 kg/cm², 7 psi)? — **NO** → Inspect the VTEC solenoid valve.

YES

Check for continuity between the 2 terminals on the VTEC pressure switch.

Does continuity exist? — **NO** → Replace the VTEC pressure switch.

YES

Disconnect the 1P connector from the VTEC solenoid valve.

Attach the battery positive terminal to the GRN/WHT terminal.

D6

A/T LOW PRESSURE GAUGE

VTEC PRESSURE SWITCH
• Use new O-ring when installing.

PRESSURE GAUGE ADAPTOR

VTEC PRESSURE SWITCH

VTEC SOLENOID VALVE

1P CONNECTOR

Continued On Next Page

94A44842

CODE 22 (3 OF 3)
VTEC PRESSURE SWITCH
CIVIC & CIVIC DEL SOL

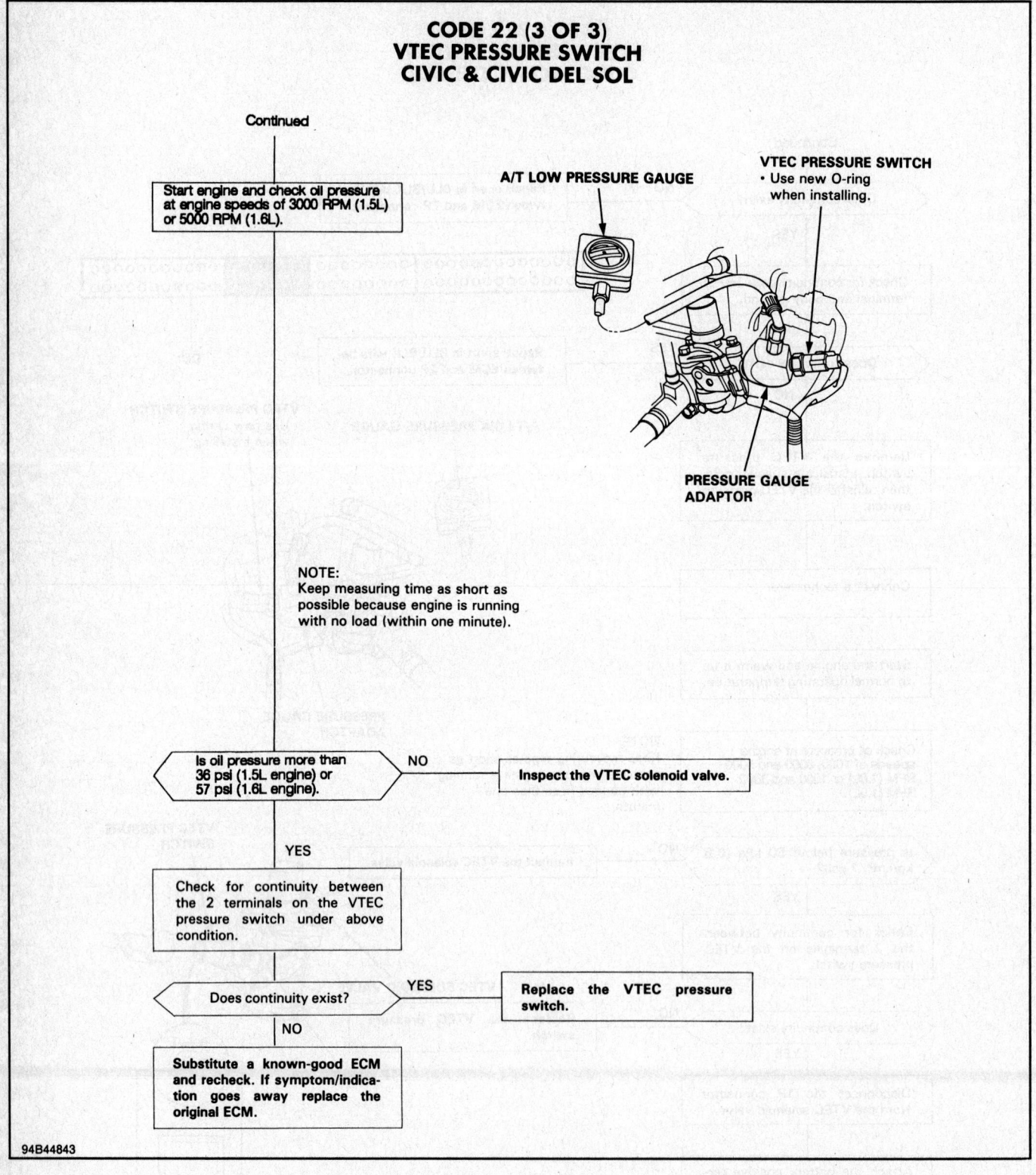

Continued

Start engine and check oil pressure at engine speeds of 3000 RPM (1.5L) or 5000 RPM (1.6L).

A/T LOW PRESSURE GAUGE

VTEC PRESSURE SWITCH
• Use new O-ring when installing.

PRESSURE GAUGE ADAPTOR

NOTE:
Keep measuring time as short as possible because engine is running with no load (within one minute).

Is oil pressure more than 36 psi (1.5L engine) or 57 psi (1.6L engine).   NO ──▶   Inspect the VTEC solenoid valve.

YES

Check for continuity between the 2 terminals on the VTEC pressure switch under above condition.

Does continuity exist?   YES ──▶   Replace the VTEC pressure switch.

NO

Substitute a known-good ECM and recheck. If symptom/indication goes away replace the original ECM.

94B44843

CODE 41 (1 OF 3)
HEATED OXYGEN SENSOR (HO2S) HEATER
CIVIC & CIVIC DEL SOL

ALL MODELS EXCEPT
D15Z1 FEDERAL MODEL

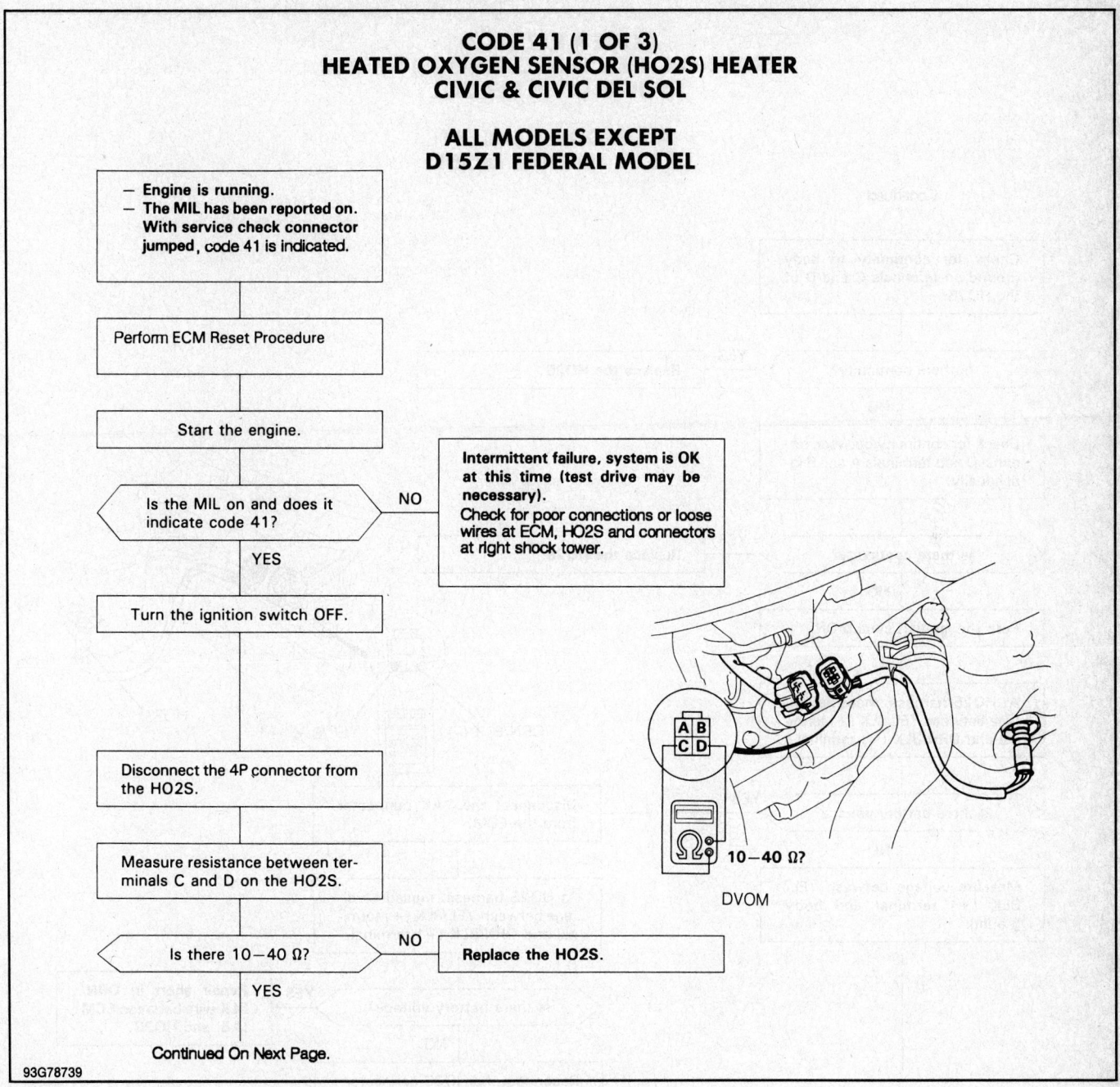

- Engine is running.
- The MIL has been reported on. With service check connector jumped, code 41 is indicated.

Perform ECM Reset Procedure

Start the engine.

Is the MIL on and does it indicate code 41? — NO → Intermittent failure, system is OK at this time (test drive may be necessary). Check for poor connections or loose wires at ECM, HO2S and connectors at right shock tower.

YES

Turn the ignition switch OFF.

Disconnect the 4P connector from the HO2S.

Measure resistance between terminals C and D on the HO2S.

Is there 10—40 Ω? — NO → Replace the HO2S.

YES

10—40 Ω?

DVOM

Continued On Next Page.

93G78739

CODE 41 (2 OF 3)
HEATED OXYGEN SENSOR (HO2S) HEATER
CIVIC & CIVIC DEL SOL

ALL MODELS EXCEPT
D15Z1 FEDERAL MODEL

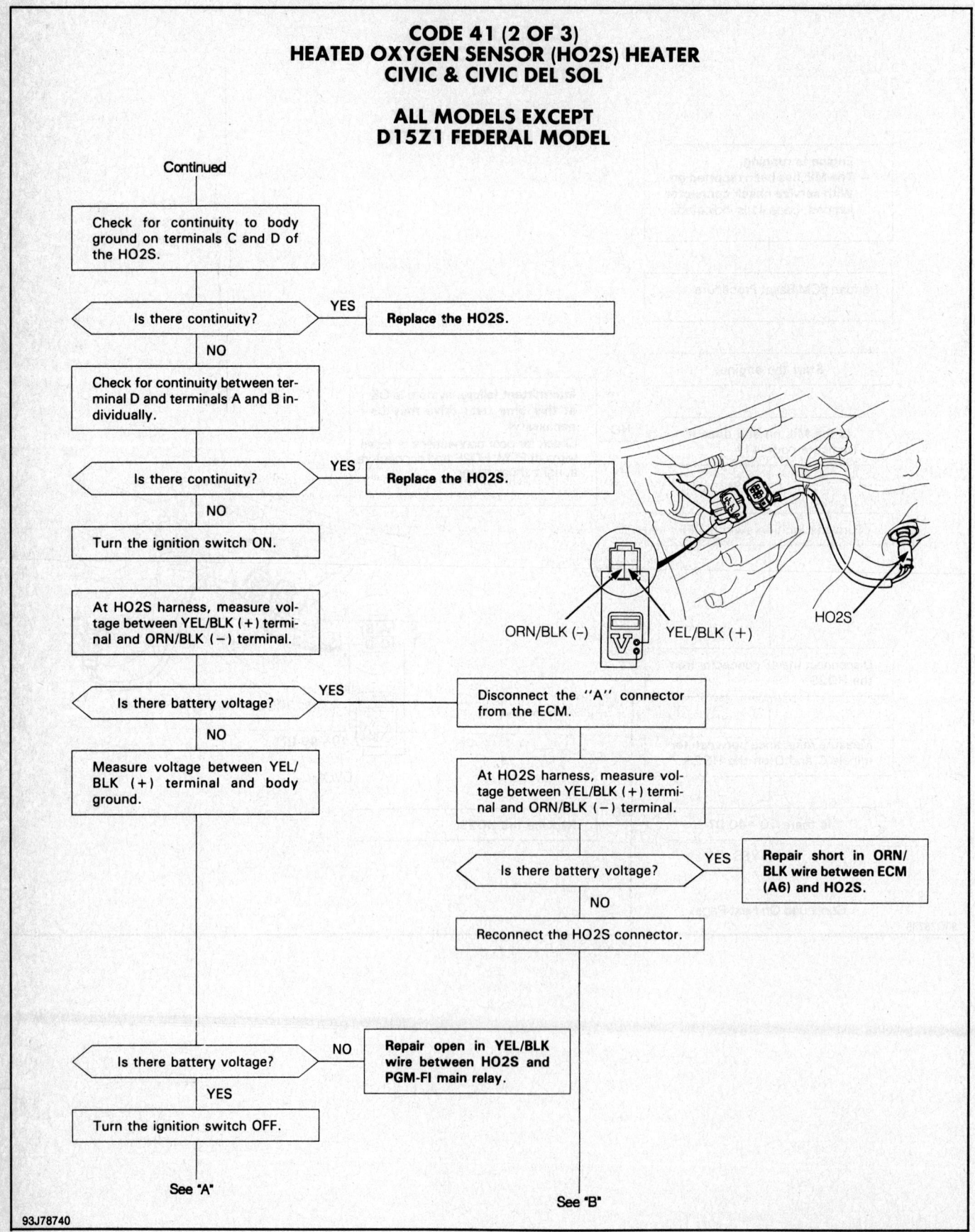

Continued

Check for continuity to body ground on terminals C and D of the HO2S.

Is there continuity? — YES → Replace the HO2S.

NO

Check for continuity between terminal D and terminals A and B individually.

Is there continuity? — YES → Replace the HO2S.

NO

Turn the ignition switch ON.

At HO2S harness, measure voltage between YEL/BLK (+) terminal and ORN/BLK (−) terminal.

Is there battery voltage? — YES → Disconnect the "A" connector from the ECM.

NO

Measure voltage between YEL/BLK (+) terminal and body ground.

At HO2S harness, measure voltage between YEL/BLK (+) terminal and ORN/BLK (−) terminal.

Is there battery voltage? — YES → Repair short in ORN/BLK wire between ECM (A6) and HO2S.

NO

Reconnect the HO2S connector.

Is there battery voltage? — NO → Repair open in YEL/BLK wire between HO2S and PGM-FI main relay.

YES

Turn the ignition switch OFF.

ORN/BLK (−)   YEL/BLK (+)   HO2S

See "A"   See "B"

93J78740

CODE 41 (3 OF 3)
HEATED OXYGEN SENSOR (HO2S) HEATER
CIVIC & CIVIC DEL SOL

ALL MODELS EXCEPT
D15Z1 FEDERAL MODEL

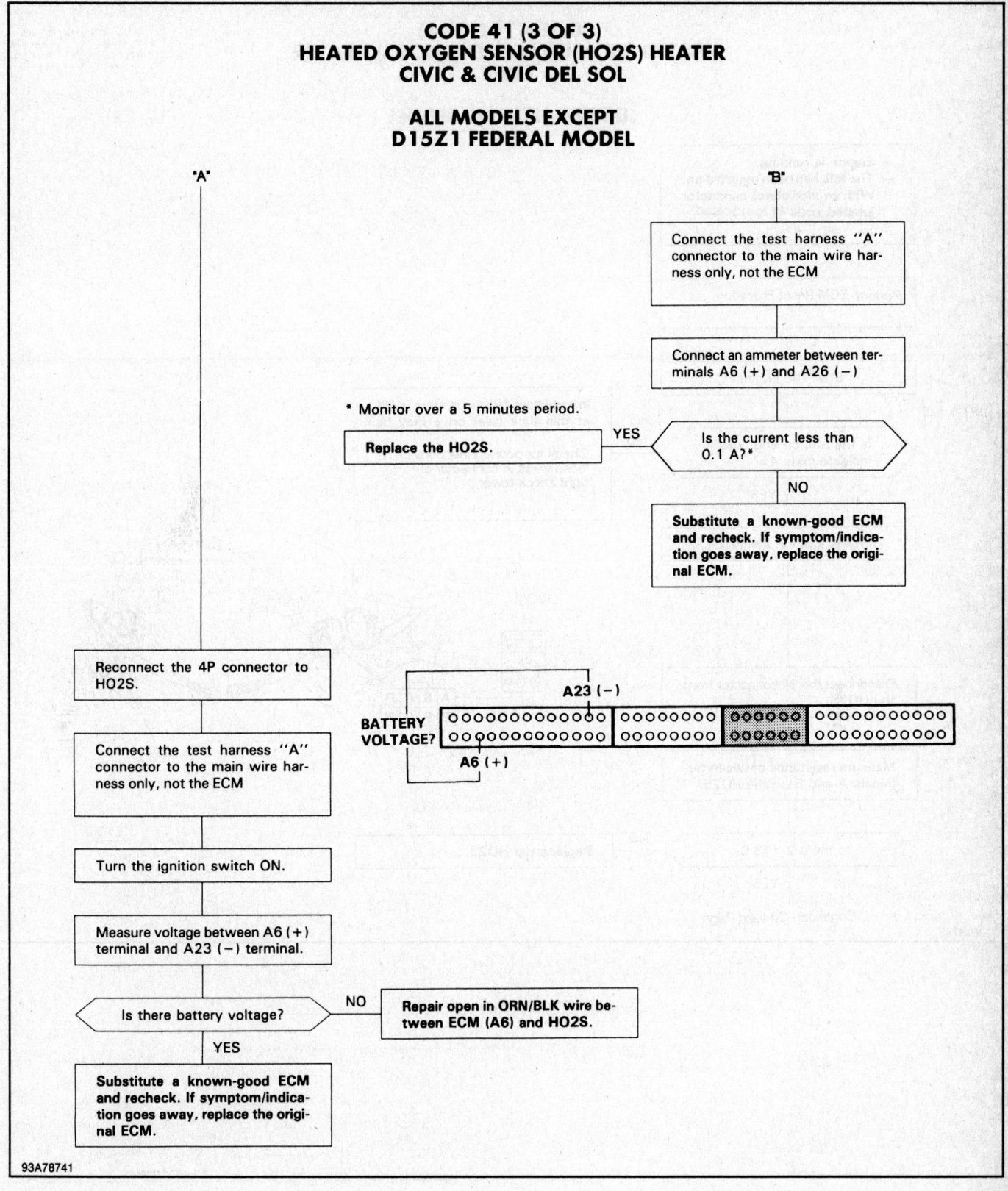

"A"

"B"

Connect the test harness "A" connector to the main wire harness only, not the ECM

Connect an ammeter between terminals A6 (+) and A26 (−)

* Monitor over a 5 minutes period.

Replace the HO2S.

YES

Is the current less than 0.1 A?*

NO

Substitute a known-good ECM and recheck. If symptom/indication goes away, replace the original ECM.

Reconnect the 4P connector to HO2S.

A23 (−)

BATTERY VOLTAGE?

A6 (+)

Connect the test harness "A" connector to the main wire harness only, not the ECM

Turn the ignition switch ON.

Measure voltage between A6 (+) terminal and A23 (−) terminal.

Is there battery voltage?

NO

Repair open in ORN/BLK wire between ECM (A6) and HO2S.

YES

Substitute a known-good ECM and recheck. If symptom/indication goes away, replace the original ECM.

93A78741

CODE 41 (1 OF 3)
HEATED OXYGEN SENSOR (HO2S) HEATER
CIVIC

D15Z1 FEDERAL MODEL

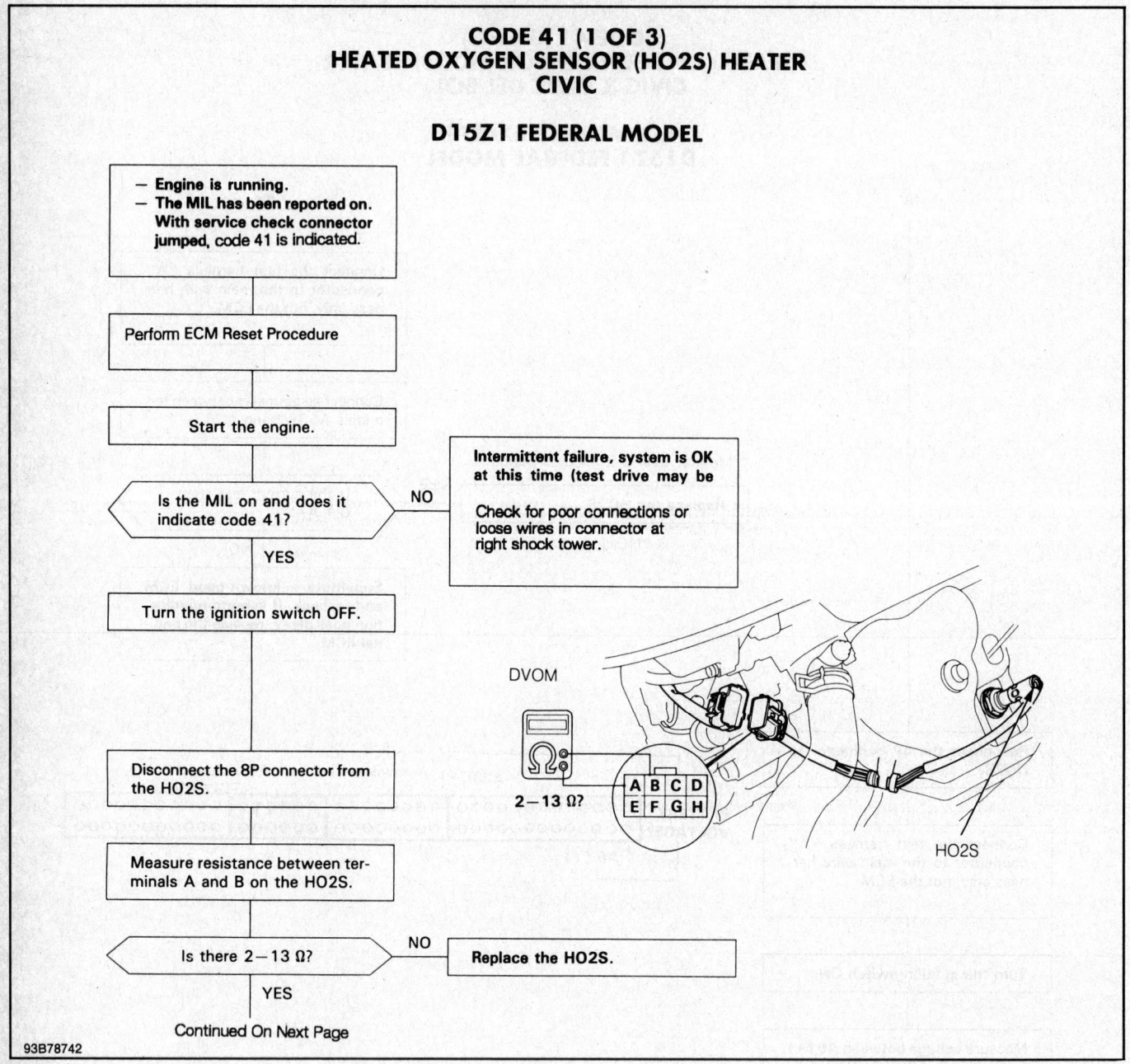

— Engine is running.
— The MIL has been reported on. With service check connector jumped, code 41 is indicated.

Perform ECM Reset Procedure

Start the engine.

Is the MIL on and does it indicate code 41?

NO → Intermittent failure, system is OK at this time (test drive may be

Check for poor connections or loose wires in connector at right shock tower.

YES

Turn the ignition switch OFF.

DVOM

2—13 Ω?

A	B	C	D
E	F	G	H

HO2S

Disconnect the 8P connector from the HO2S.

Measure resistance between terminals A and B on the HO2S.

Is there 2—13 Ω?

NO → Replace the HO2S.

YES

Continued On Next Page

93B78742

CODE 41 (2 OF 3)
HEATED OXYGEN SENSOR (HO2S) HEATER
CIVIC

D15Z1 FEDERAL MODEL

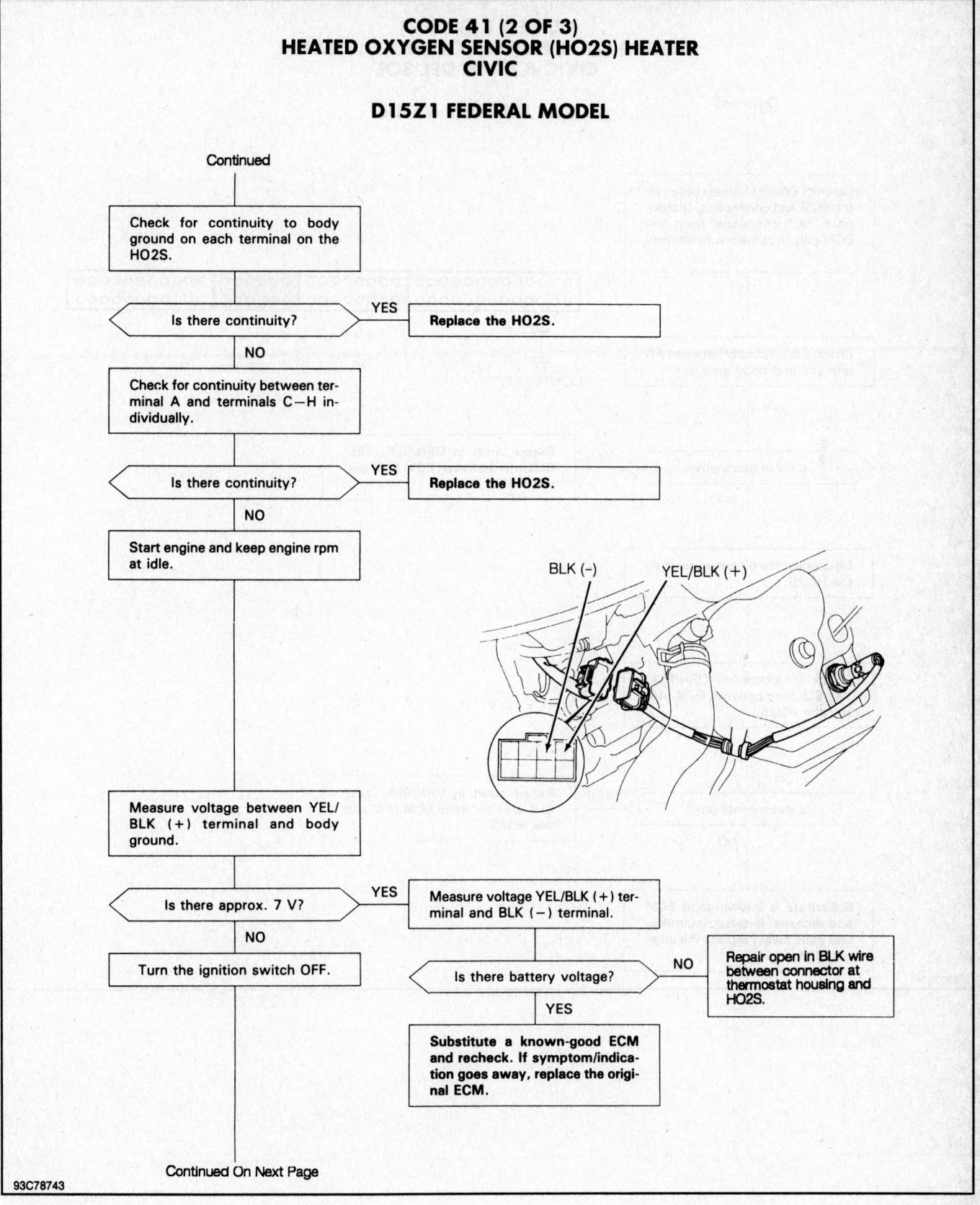

Continued

Check for continuity to body ground on each terminal on the HO2S.

Is there continuity? — YES → **Replace the HO2S.**

NO

Check for continuity between terminal A and terminals C—H individually.

Is there continuity? — YES → **Replace the HO2S.**

NO

Start engine and keep engine rpm at idle.

BLK (−)   YEL/BLK (+)

Measure voltage between YEL/BLK (+) terminal and body ground.

Is there approx. 7 V? — YES → Measure voltage YEL/BLK (+) terminal and BLK (−) terminal.

NO

Turn the ignition switch OFF.

Is there battery voltage? — NO → **Repair open in BLK wire between connector at thermostat housing and HO2S.**

YES

Substitute a known-good ECM and recheck. If symptom/indication goes away, replace the original ECM.

Continued On Next Page

93C78743

CODE 41 (3 OF 3)
HEATED OXYGEN SENSOR (HO2S) HEATER
CIVIC & CIVIC DEL SOL

D15Z1 FEDERAL MODEL

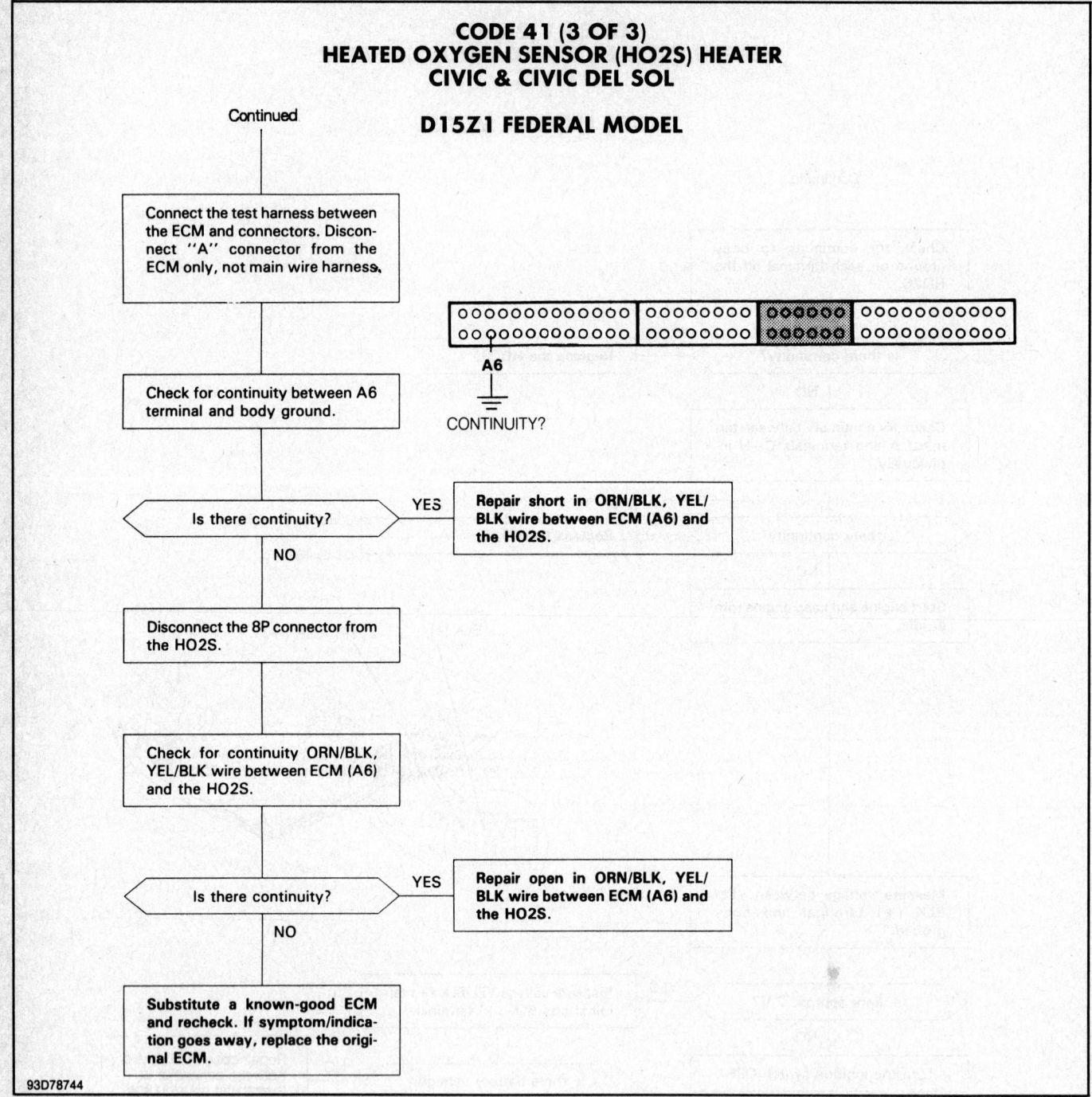

Continued

Connect the test harness between the ECM and connectors. Disconnect "A" connector from the ECM only, not main wire harness.

A6

CONTINUITY?

Check for continuity between A6 terminal and body ground.

Is there continuity? — YES — Repair short in ORN/BLK, YEL/BLK wire between ECM (A6) and the HO2S.

NO

Disconnect the 8P connector from the HO2S.

Check for continuity ORN/BLK, YEL/BLK wire between ECM (A6) and the HO2S.

Is there continuity? — YES — Repair open in ORN/BLK, YEL/BLK wire between ECM (A6) and the HO2S.

NO

Substitute a known-good ECM and recheck. If symptom/indication goes away, replace the original ECM.

93D78744

CODE 43 (1 OF 2)
HEATED OXYGEN SENSOR (HO2S) CIRCUIT
OR FUEL SUPPLY SYSTEM
CIVIC & CIVIC DEL SOL

ALL MODELS EXCEPT
D15B8 CALIF. MODEL

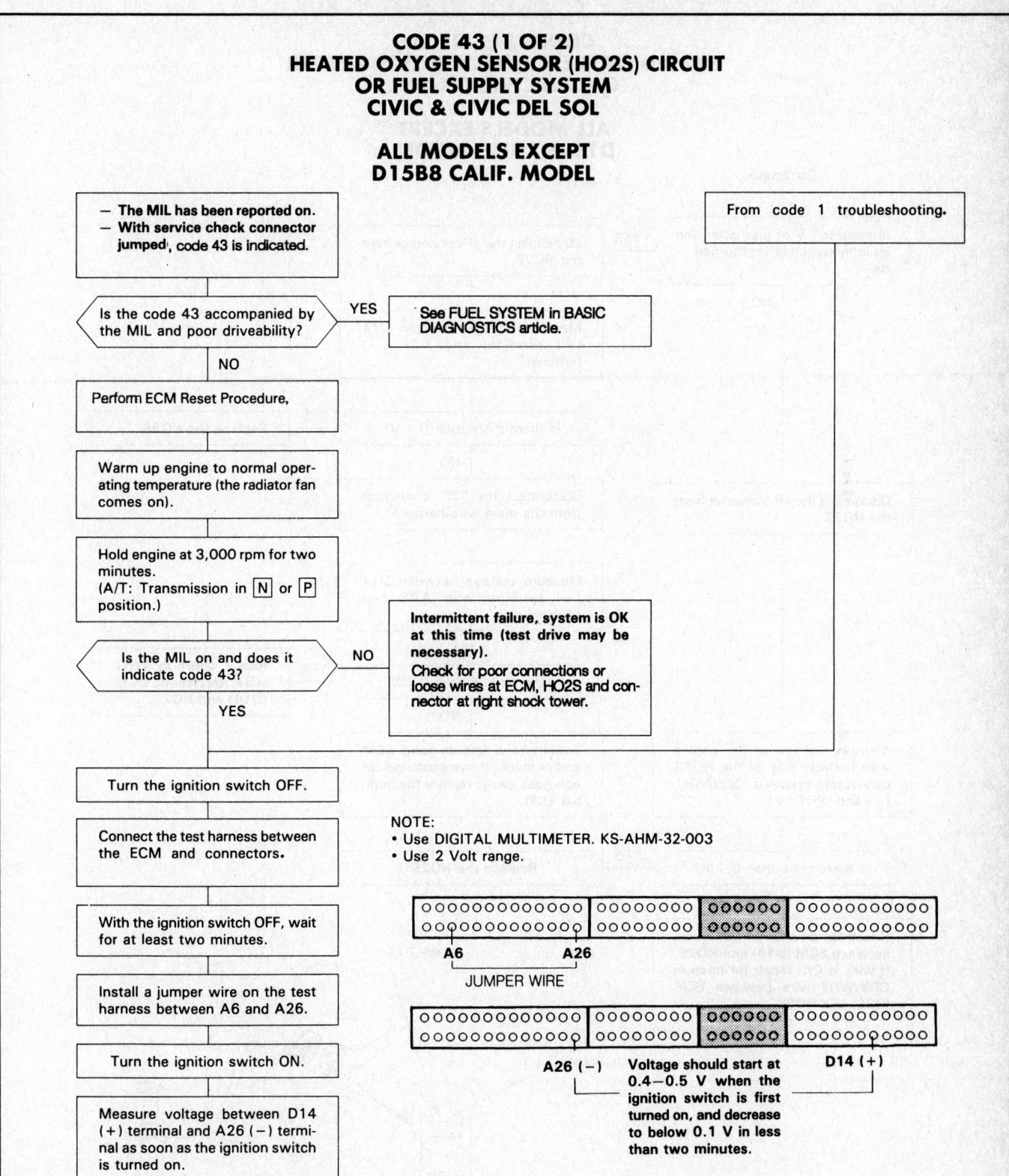

— The MIL has been reported on.
— With service check connector jumped, code 43 is indicated.

Is the code 43 accompanied by the MIL and poor driveability? — **YES** → See FUEL SYSTEM in BASIC DIAGNOSTICS article.

NO

Perform ECM Reset Procedure,

Warm up engine to normal operating temperature (the radiator fan comes on).

Hold engine at 3,000 rpm for two minutes.
(A/T: Transmission in N or P position.)

Is the MIL on and does it indicate code 43? — **NO** → Intermittent failure, system is OK at this time (test drive may be necessary).
Check for poor connections or loose wires at ECM, HO2S and connector at right shock tower.

YES

Turn the ignition switch OFF.

Connect the test harness between the ECM and connectors.

With the ignition switch OFF, wait for at least two minutes.

Install a jumper wire on the test harness between A6 and A26.

Turn the ignition switch ON.

Measure voltage between D14 (+) terminal and A26 (−) terminal as soon as the ignition switch is turned on.

From code 1 troubleshooting.

NOTE:
• Use DIGITAL MULTIMETER. KS-AHM-32-003
• Use 2 Volt range.

A6   A26
JUMPER WIRE

A26 (−)   Voltage should start at 0.4—0.5 V when the ignition switch is first turned on, and decrease to below 0.1 V in less than two minutes.   D14 (+)

Continued On Next Page

93E78745

CODE 43 (2 OF 2)
HEATED OXYGEN SENSOR (HO2S) HEATER
CIVIC & CIVIC DEL SOL

ALL MODELS EXCEPT
D15B8 CALIF. MODEL

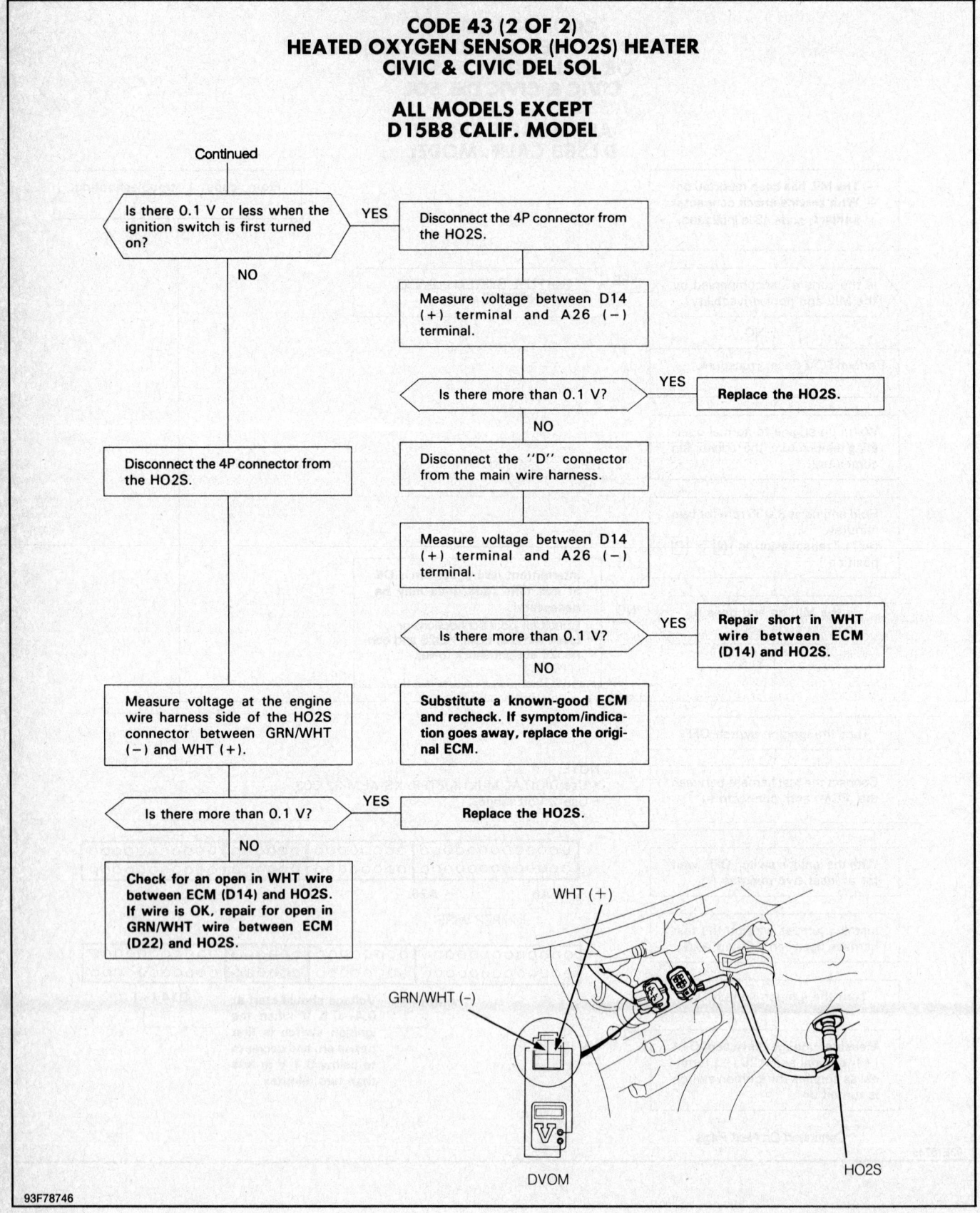

Continued

Is there 0.1 V or less when the ignition switch is first turned on?

YES → Disconnect the 4P connector from the HO2S.

NO

Measure voltage between D14 (+) terminal and A26 (−) terminal.

Is there more than 0.1 V? — YES → Replace the HO2S.

NO

Disconnect the 4P connector from the HO2S.

Disconnect the "D" connector from the main wire harness.

Measure voltage between D14 (+) terminal and A26 (−) terminal.

Is there more than 0.1 V? — YES → Repair short in WHT wire between ECM (D14) and HO2S.

NO

Measure voltage at the engine wire harness side of the HO2S connector between GRN/WHT (−) and WHT (+).

Substitute a known-good ECM and recheck. If symptom/indication goes away, replace the original ECM.

Is there more than 0.1 V? — YES → Replace the HO2S.

NO

Check for an open in WHT wire between ECM (D14) and HO2S. If wire is OK, repair for open in GRN/WHT wire between ECM (D22) and HO2S.

WHT (+)

GRN/WHT (−)

DVOM

HO2S

93F78746

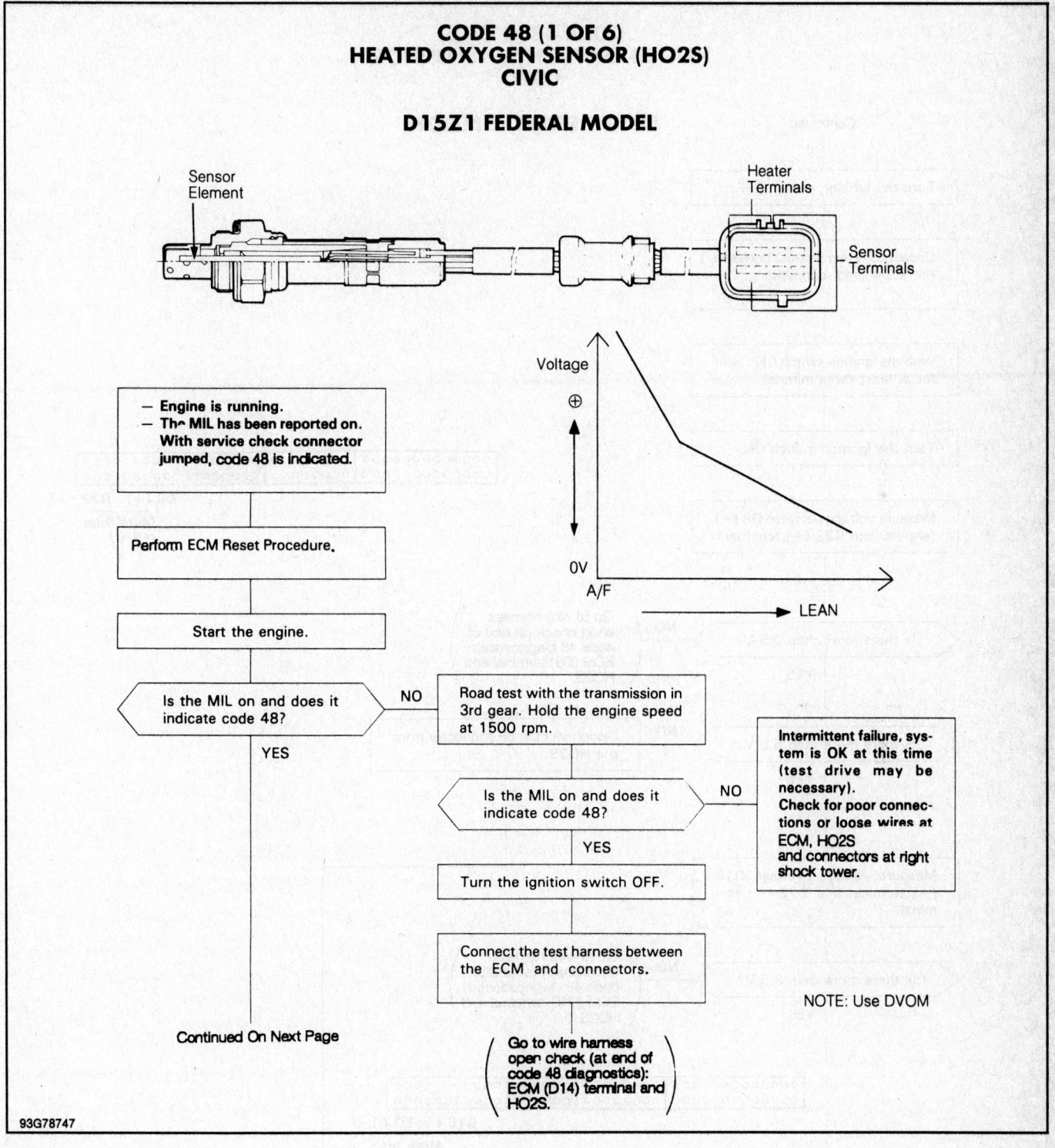

CODE 48 (1 OF 6)
HEATED OXYGEN SENSOR (HO2S)
CIVIC

D15Z1 FEDERAL MODEL

Sensor Element

Heater Terminals

Sensor Terminals

Voltage

$\oplus$

0V

A/F

LEAN

— Engine is running.
— The MIL has been reported on. With service check connector jumped, code 48 is indicated.

Perform ECM Reset Procedure.

Start the engine.

Is the MIL on and does it indicate code 48?

NO → Road test with the transmission in 3rd gear. Hold the engine speed at 1500 rpm.

YES

Is the MIL on and does it indicate code 48?

NO → Intermittent failure, system is OK at this time (test drive may be necessary). Check for poor connections or loose wires at ECM, HO2S and connectors at right shock tower.

YES

Turn the ignition switch OFF.

Connect the test harness between the ECM and connectors.

NOTE: Use DVOM

Continued On Next Page

Go to wire harness open check (at end of code 48 diagnostics): ECM (D14) terminal and HO2S.

93G78747

1994 ENGINE PERFORMANCE
Self-Diagnostics (Cont.)

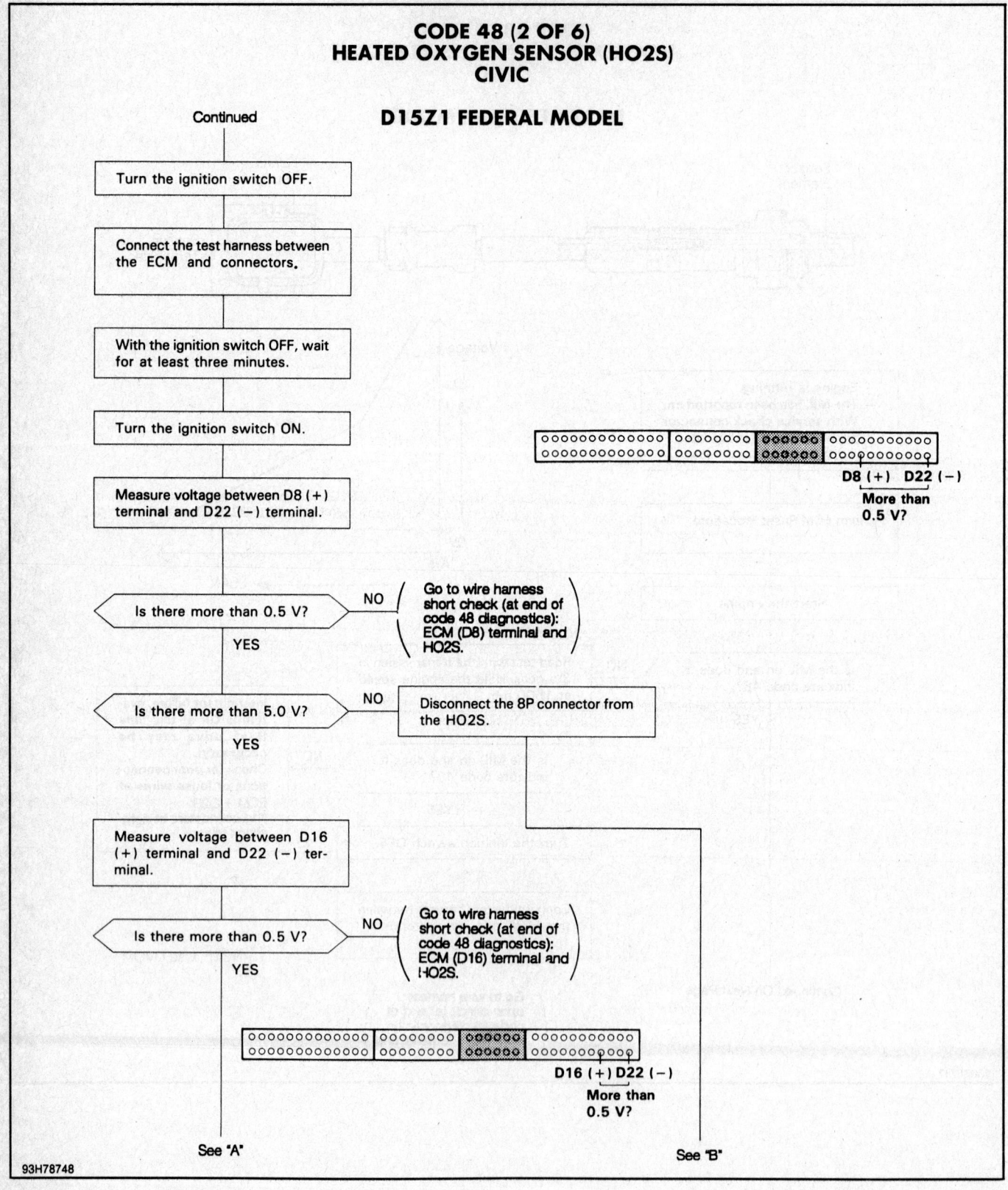

CODE 48 (2 OF 6)
HEATED OXYGEN SENSOR (HO2S)
CIVIC

D15Z1 FEDERAL MODEL

Continued

Turn the ignition switch OFF.

Connect the test harness between the ECM and connectors.

With the ignition switch OFF, wait for at least three minutes.

Turn the ignition switch ON.

Measure voltage between D8 (+) terminal and D22 (−) terminal.

D8 (+)   D22 (−)
More than
0.5 V?

Is there more than 0.5 V? — NO → Go to wire harness short check (at end of code 48 diagnostics): ECM (D8) terminal and HO2S.

YES

Is there more than 5.0 V? — NO → Disconnect the 8P connector from the HO2S.

YES

Measure voltage between D16 (+) terminal and D22 (−) terminal.

Is there more than 0.5 V? — NO → Go to wire harness short check (at end of code 48 diagnostics): ECM (D16) terminal and HO2S.

YES

D16 (+) D22 (−)
More than
0.5 V?

See "A"

See "B"

93H78748

CODE 48 (3 OF 6)
HEATED OXYGEN SENSOR (HO2S)
CIVIC

D15Z1 FEDERAL MODEL

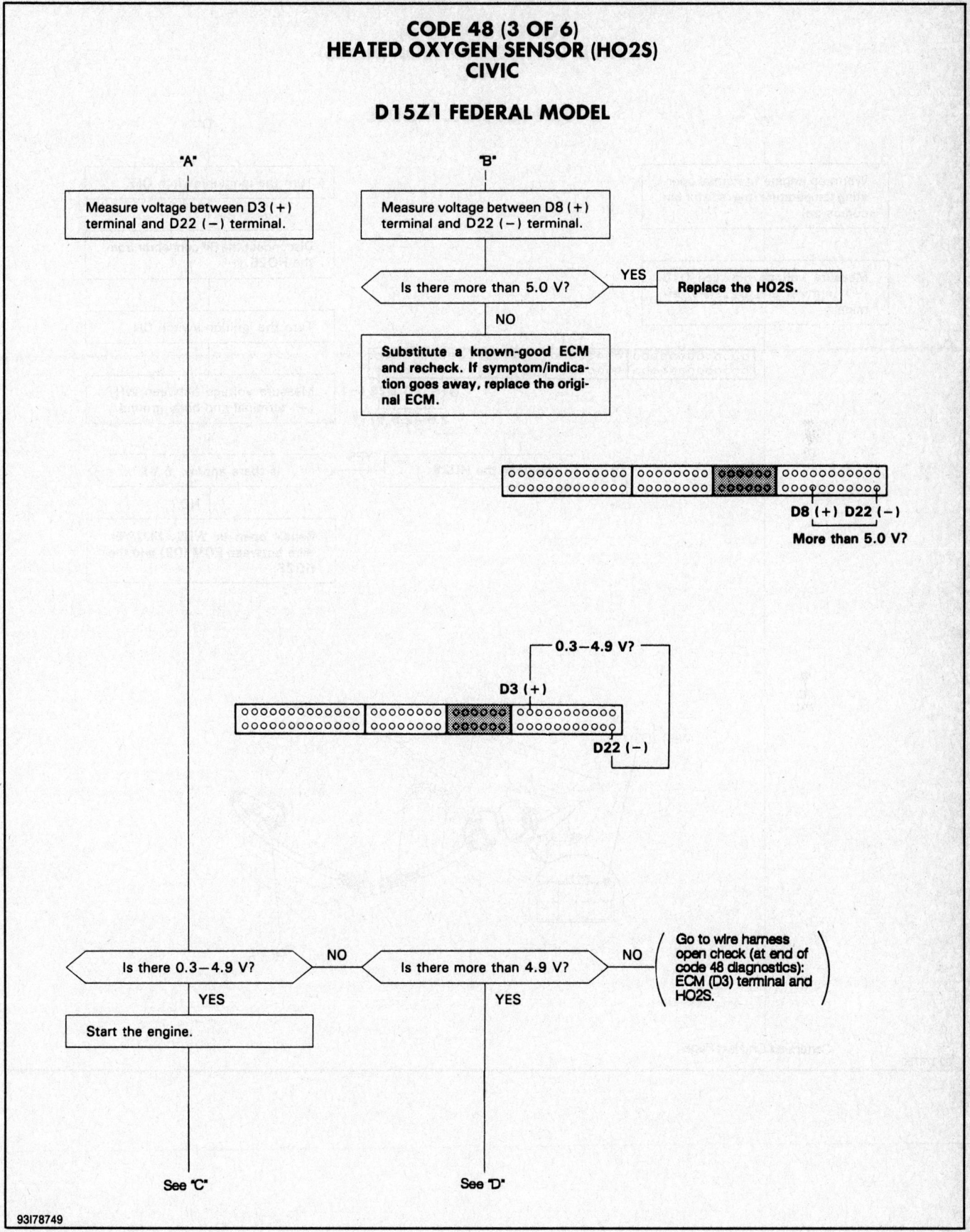

"A"

Measure voltage between D3 (+) terminal and D22 (−) terminal.

"B"

Measure voltage between D8 (+) terminal and D22 (−) terminal.

Is there more than 5.0 V? — YES → Replace the HO2S.

NO

Substitute a known-good ECM and recheck. If symptom/indication goes away, replace the original ECM.

D8 (+) D22 (−)

More than 5.0 V?

0.3−4.9 V?

D3 (+)

D22 (−)

Is there 0.3−4.9 V? — NO → Is there more than 4.9 V? — NO → Go to wire harness open check (at end of code 48 diagnostics): ECM (D3) terminal and HO2S.

YES

Start the engine.

YES

See "C"

See "D"

93I78749

CODE 48 (4 OF 6)
HEATED OXYGEN SENSOR (HO2S)
CIVIC

D15Z1 FEDERAL MODEL

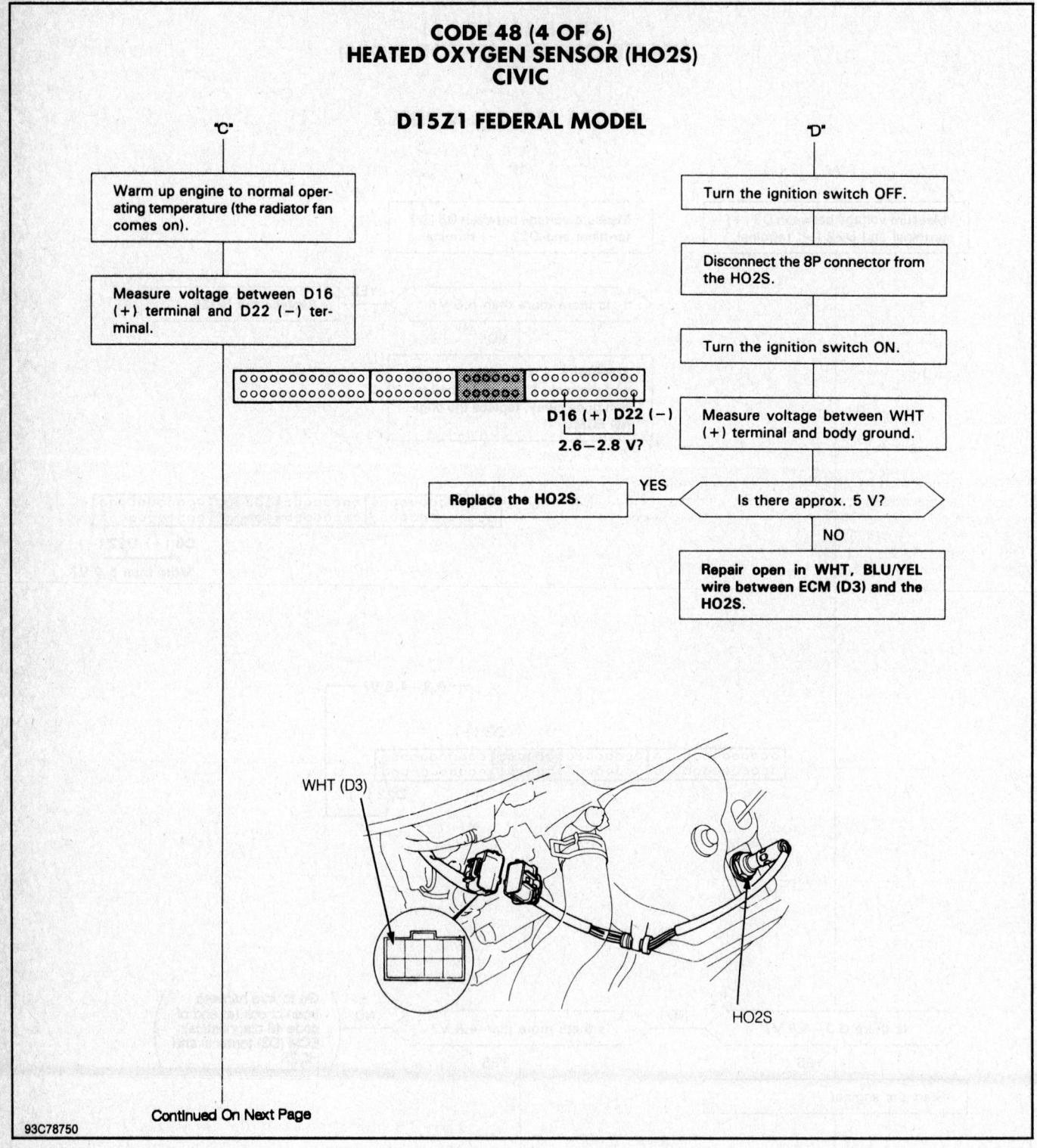

"C"

Warm up engine to normal operating temperature (the radiator fan comes on).

Measure voltage between D16 (+) terminal and D22 (−) terminal.

D16 (+) D22 (−)

2.6 − 2.8 V?

Replace the HO2S. ⟵ YES

"D"

Turn the ignition switch OFF.

Disconnect the 8P connector from the HO2S.

Turn the ignition switch ON.

Measure voltage between WHT (+) terminal and body ground.

Is there approx. 5 V?

NO

Repair open in WHT, BLU/YEL wire between ECM (D3) and the HO2S.

WHT (D3)

HO2S

Continued On Next Page

93C78750

CODE 48 (5 OF 6)
HEATED OXYGEN SENSOR (HO2S)
CIVIC

D15Z1 FEDERAL MODEL

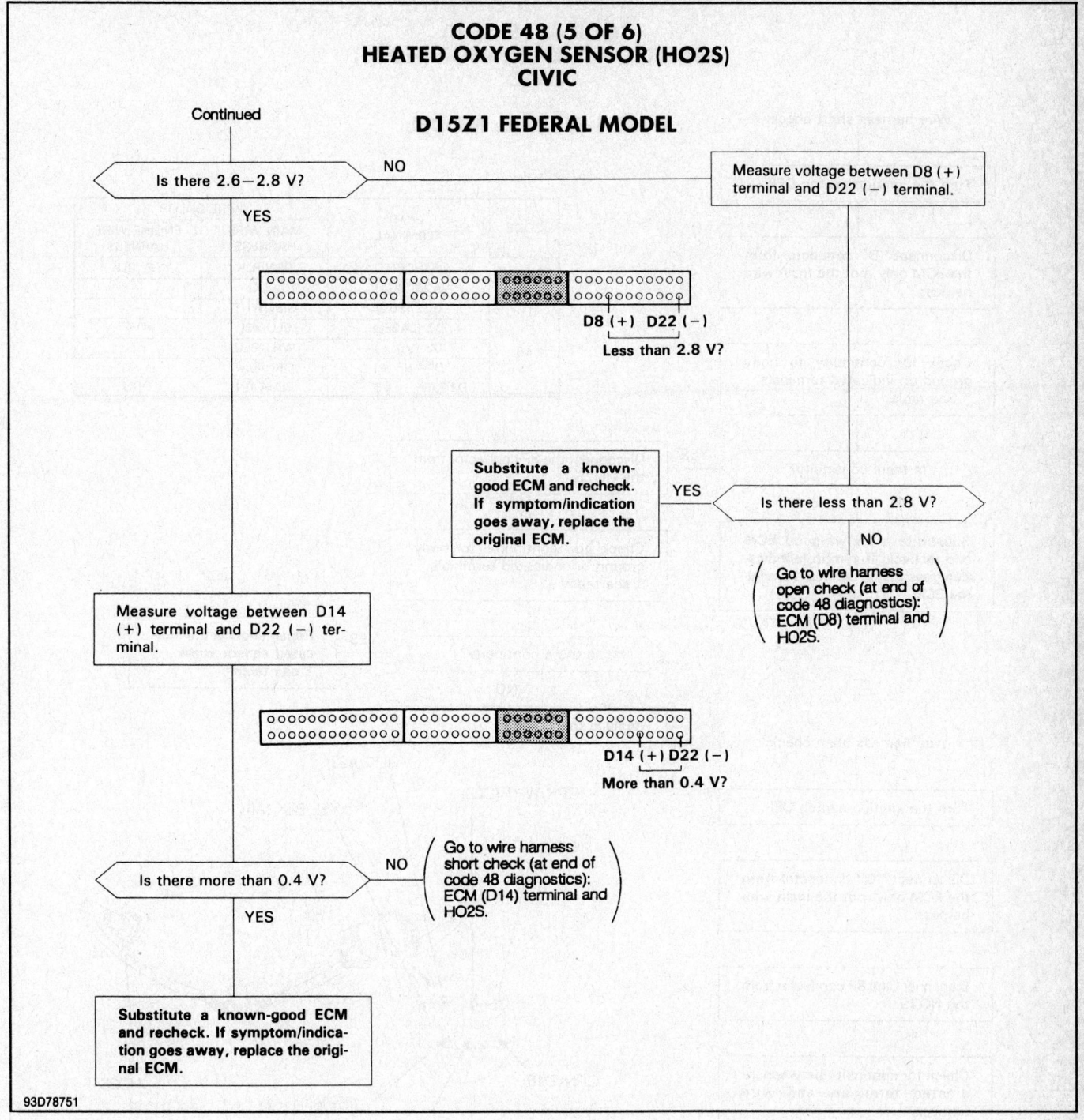

Continued

Is there 2.6—2.8 V? — NO → Measure voltage between D8 (+) terminal and D22 (−) terminal.

YES

D8 (+) D22 (−)
Less than 2.8 V?

Substitute a known-good ECM and recheck. If symptom/indication goes away, replace the original ECM. ← YES — Is there less than 2.8 V?

NO

Go to wire harness open check (at end of code 48 diagnostics): ECM (D8) terminal and HO2S.

Measure voltage between D14 (+) terminal and D22 (−) terminal.

D14 (+) D22 (−)
More than 0.4 V?

Is there more than 0.4 V? — NO → Go to wire harness short check (at end of code 48 diagnostics): ECM (D14) terminal and HO2S.

YES

Substitute a known-good ECM and recheck. If symptom/indication goes away, replace the original ECM.

93D78751

CODE 48 (6 OF 6)
HEATED OXYGEN SENSOR (HO2S)
CIVIC

D15Z1 FEDERAL MODEL

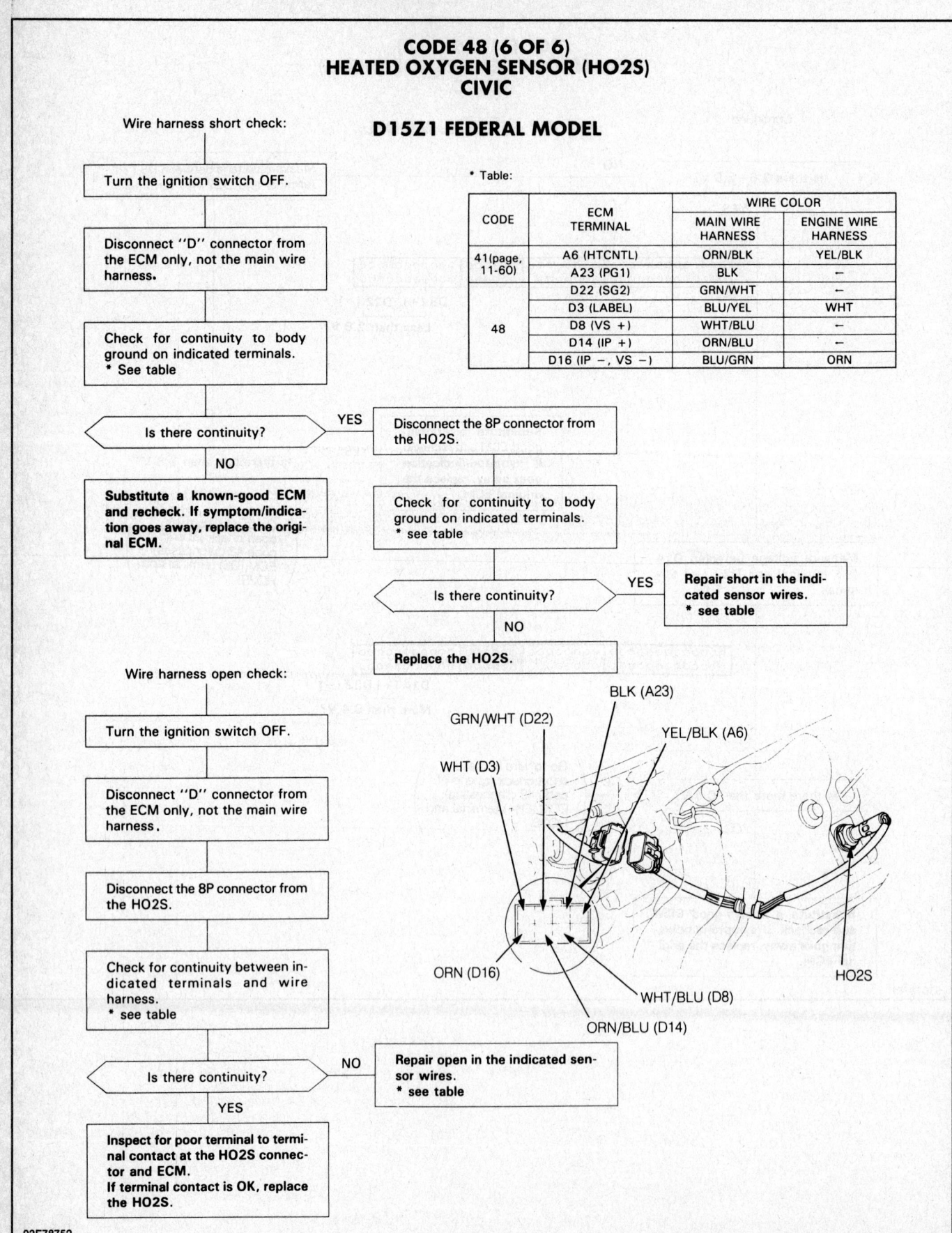

Wire harness short check:

Turn the ignition switch OFF.

Disconnect "D" connector from the ECM only, not the main wire harness.

Check for continuity to body ground on indicated terminals. * See table

Is there continuity? — NO

Substitute a known-good ECM and recheck. If symptom/indication goes away, replace the original ECM.

Is there continuity? — YES → Disconnect the 8P connector from the HO2S.

Check for continuity to body ground on indicated terminals. * see table

Is there continuity? — YES → **Repair short in the indicated sensor wires. * see table**

Is there continuity? — NO

Replace the HO2S.

* Table:

CODE	ECM TERMINAL	WIRE COLOR	
		MAIN WIRE HARNESS	ENGINE WIRE HARNESS
41(page, 11-60)	A6 (HTCNTL)	ORN/BLK	YEL/BLK
	A23 (PG1)	BLK	←
48	D22 (SG2)	GRN/WHT	←
	D3 (LABEL)	BLU/YEL	WHT
	D8 (VS +)	WHT/BLU	←
	D14 (IP +)	ORN/BLU	←
	D16 (IP −, VS −)	BLU/GRN	ORN

Wire harness open check:

Turn the ignition switch OFF.

Disconnect "D" connector from the ECM only, not the main wire harness.

Disconnect the 8P connector from the HO2S.

Check for continuity between indicated terminals and wire harness. * see table

Is there continuity? — NO → **Repair open in the indicated sensor wires. * see table**

Is there continuity? — YES

Inspect for poor terminal to terminal contact at the HO2S connector and ECM. If terminal contact is OK, replace the HO2S.

BLK (A23)
GRN/WHT (D22)
YEL/BLK (A6)
WHT (D3)
ORN (D16)
WHT/BLU (D8)
ORN/BLU (D14)
HO2S

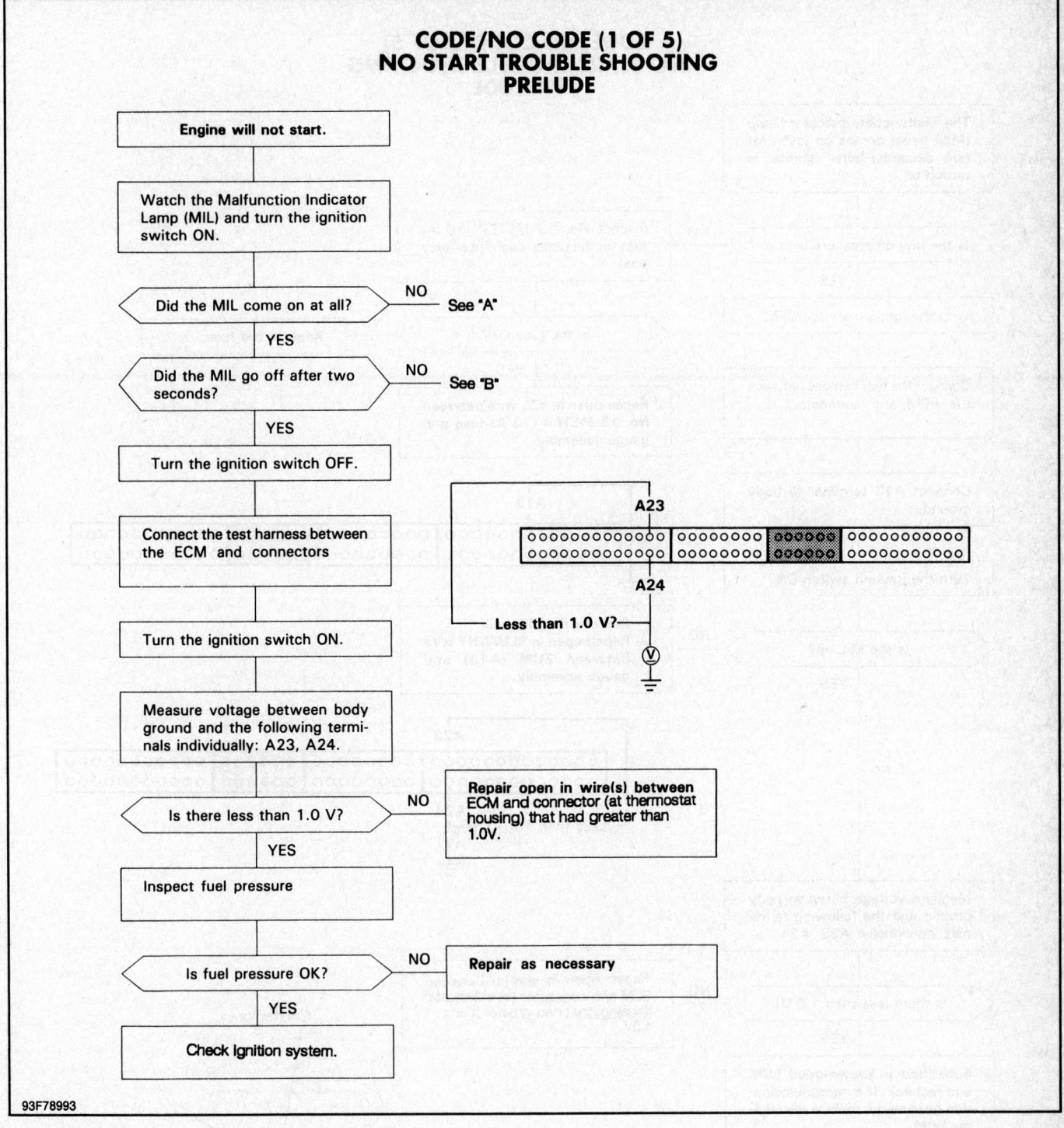

CODE/NO CODE (1 OF 5)
NO START TROUBLE SHOOTING
PRELUDE

Engine will not start.

Watch the Malfunction Indicator Lamp (MIL) and turn the ignition switch ON.

Did the MIL come on at all? — NO → See "A"

YES

Did the MIL go off after two seconds? — NO → See "B"

YES

Turn the ignition switch OFF.

Connect the test harness between the ECM and connectors

Turn the ignition switch ON.

Measure voltage between body ground and the following terminals individually: A23, A24.

Is there less than 1.0 V? — NO → Repair open in wire(s) between ECM and connector (at thermostat housing) that had greater than 1.0V.

YES

Inspect fuel pressure

Is fuel pressure OK? — NO → Repair as necessary

YES

Check ignition system.

A23

A24

Less than 1.0 V?

93F78993

CODE/NO CODE (2 OF 5)
NO START TROUBLE SHOOTING
PRELUDE

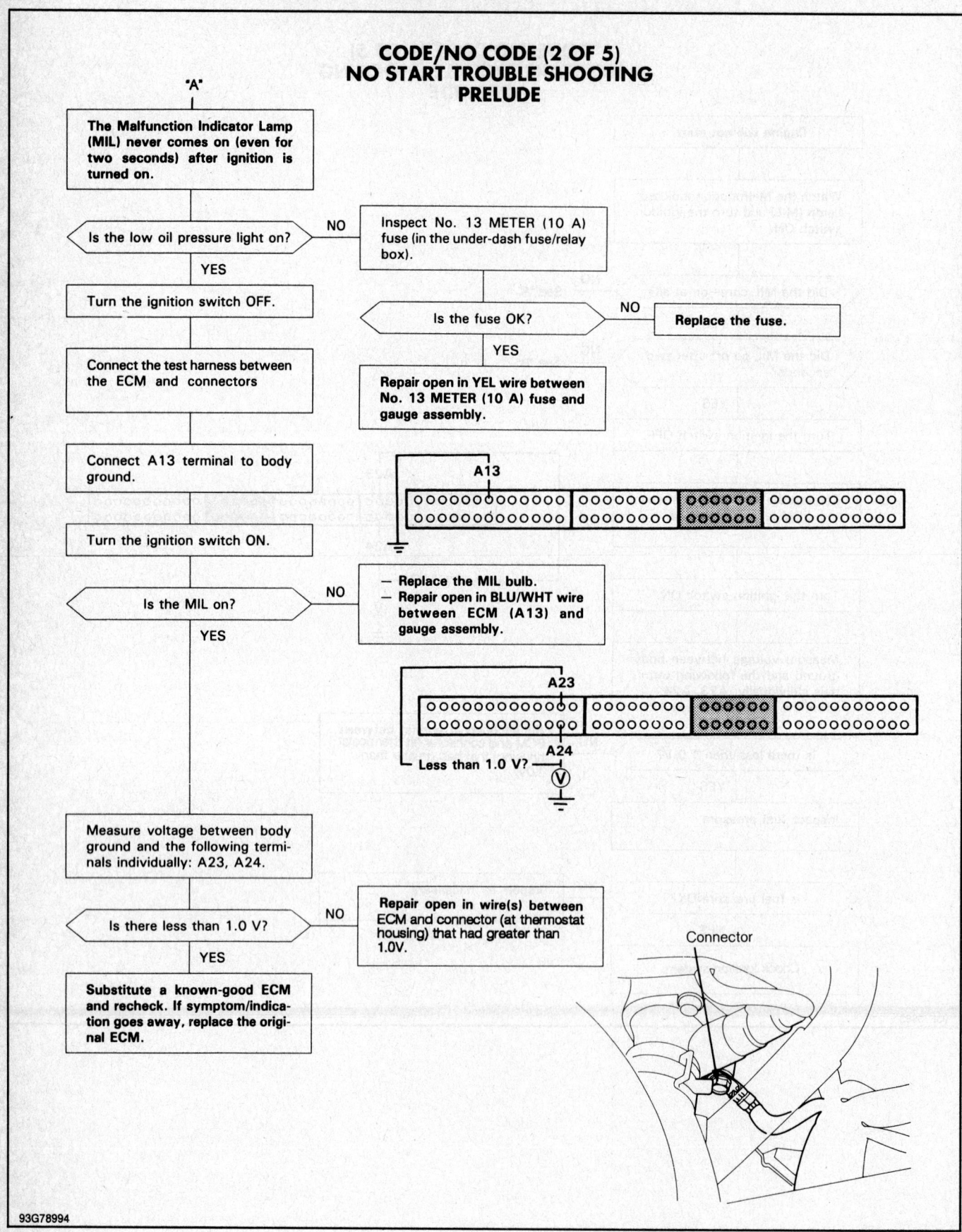

"A"

The Malfunction Indicator Lamp (MIL) never comes on (even for two seconds) after ignition is turned on.

Is the low oil pressure light on? — NO → Inspect No. 13 METER (10 A) fuse (in the under-dash fuse/relay box).

YES

Turn the ignition switch OFF.

Is the fuse OK? — NO → Replace the fuse.

YES

Connect the test harness between the ECM and connectors

Repair open in YEL wire between No. 13 METER (10 A) fuse and gauge assembly.

Connect A13 terminal to body ground.

A13

Turn the ignition switch ON.

Is the MIL on? — NO →
— Replace the MIL bulb.
— Repair open in BLU/WHT wire between ECM (A13) and gauge assembly.

YES

A23

A24

└ Less than 1.0 V? ┐

Measure voltage between body ground and the following terminals individually: A23, A24.

Is there less than 1.0 V? — NO → Repair open in wire(s) between ECM and connector (at thermostat housing) that had greater than 1.0V.

YES

Connector

Substitute a known-good ECM and recheck. If symptom/indication goes away, replace the original ECM.

93G78994

CODE/NO CODE (3 OF 5)
NO START TROUBLE SHOOTING
PRELUDE

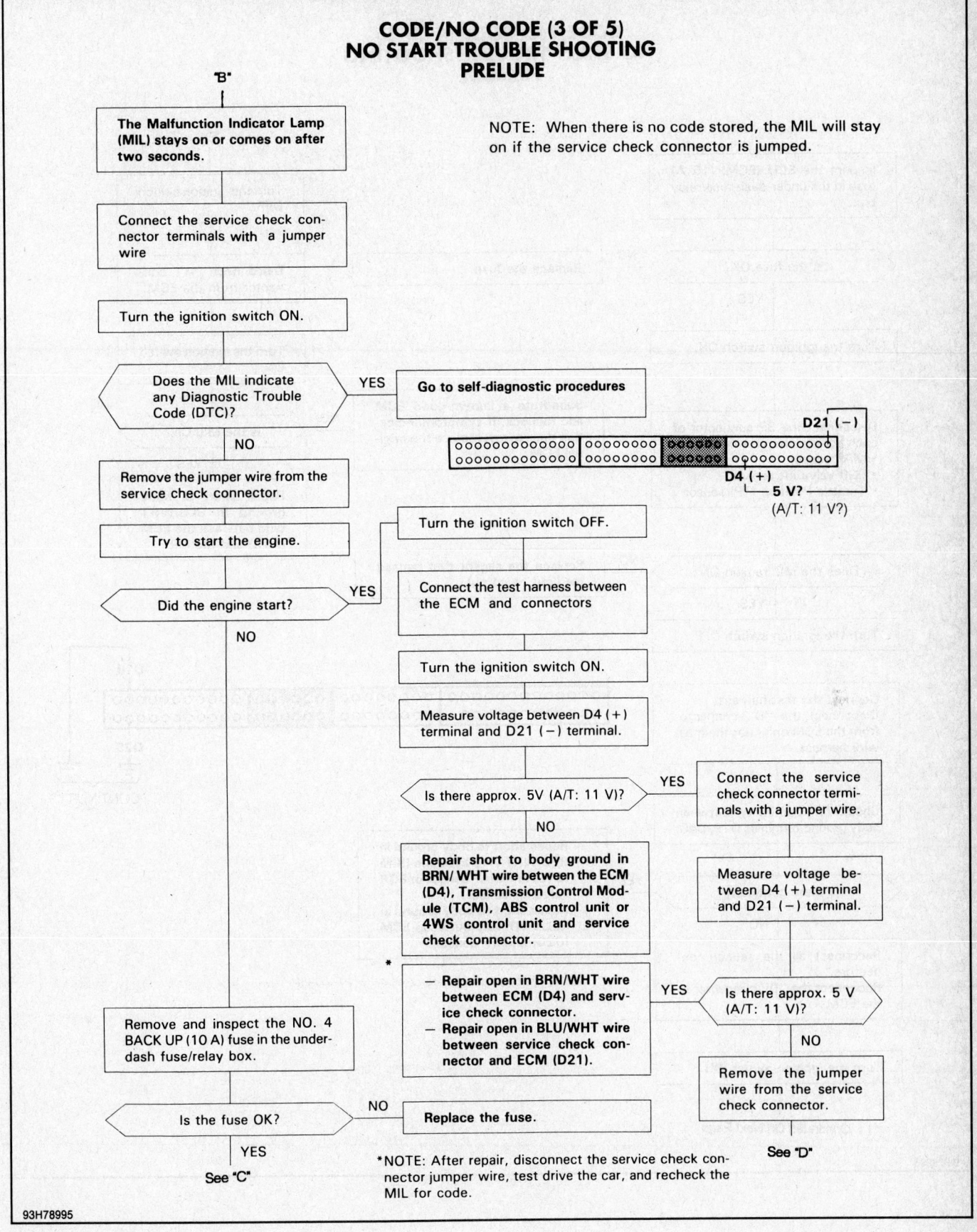

"B"

The Malfunction Indicator Lamp (MIL) stays on or comes on after two seconds.

Connect the service check connector terminals with a jumper wire

Turn the ignition switch ON.

Does the MIL indicate any Diagnostic Trouble Code (DTC)? — YES → Go to self-diagnostic procedures

NO

Remove the jumper wire from the service check connector.

Try to start the engine.

Did the engine start? — YES

NO

Remove and inspect the NO. 4 BACK UP (10 A) fuse in the under-dash fuse/relay box.

Is the fuse OK? — NO → Replace the fuse.

YES

See "C"

NOTE: When there is no code stored, the MIL will stay on if the service check connector is jumped.

D21 (−)

D4 (+)

5 V?
(A/T: 11 V?)

Turn the ignition switch OFF.

Connect the test harness between the ECM and connectors

Turn the ignition switch ON.

Measure voltage between D4 (+) terminal and D21 (−) terminal.

Is there approx. 5V (A/T: 11 V)? — YES → Connect the service check connector terminals with a jumper wire.

NO

Repair short to body ground in BRN/WHT wire between the ECM (D4), Transmission Control Module (TCM), ABS control unit or 4WS control unit and service check connector.

Measure voltage between D4 (+) terminal and D21 (−) terminal.

*

— Repair open in BRN/WHT wire between ECM (D4) and service check connector.
— Repair open in BLU/WHT wire between service check connector and ECM (D21).

Is there approx. 5 V (A/T: 11 V)? — YES

NO

Remove the jumper wire from the service check connector.

See "D"

*NOTE: After repair, disconnect the service check connector jumper wire, test drive the car, and recheck the MIL for code.

93H78995

CODE/NO CODE (4 OF 5)
NO START TROUBLE SHOOTING
PRELUDE

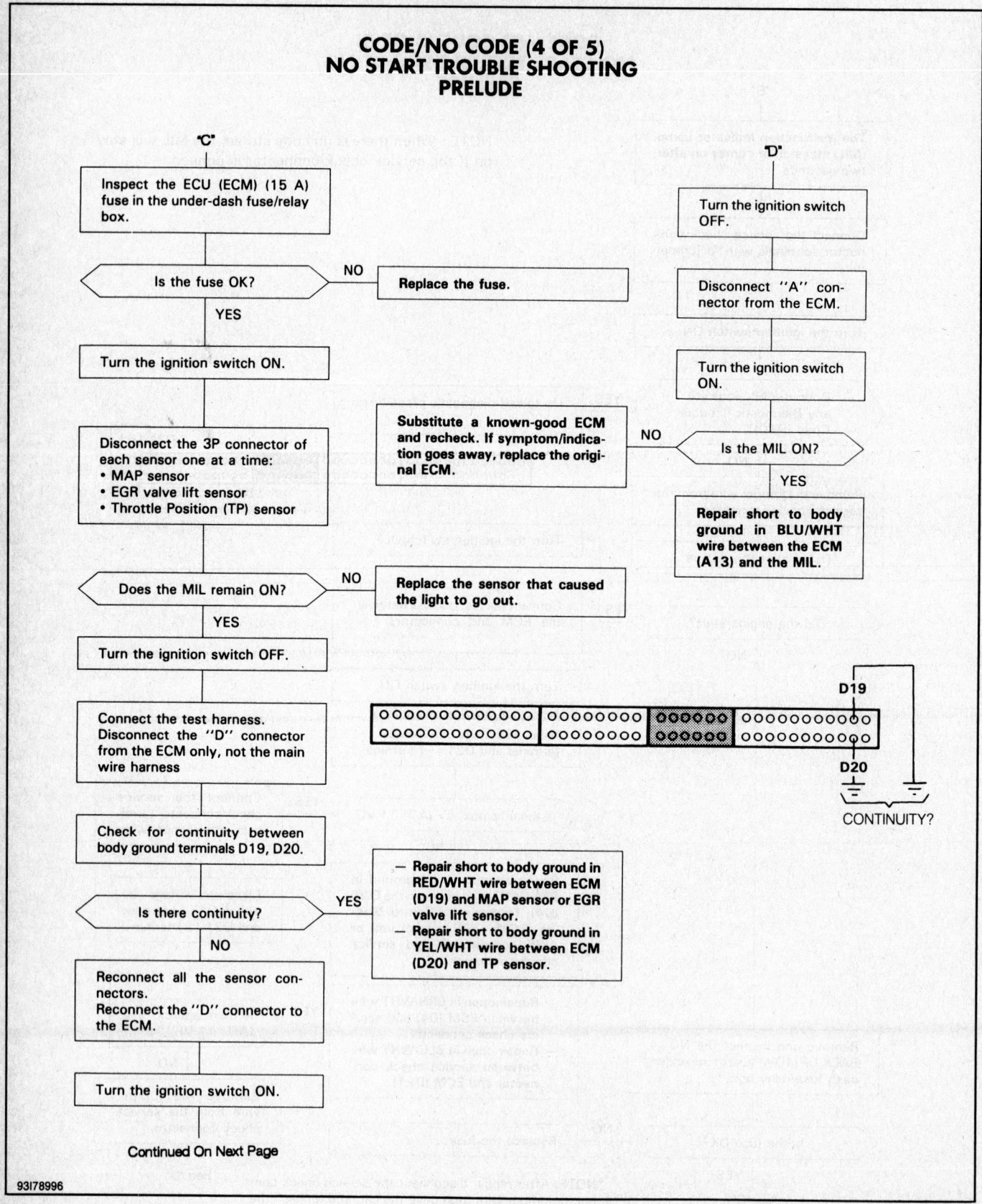

"C"

Inspect the ECU (ECM) (15 A) fuse in the under-dash fuse/relay box.

Is the fuse OK? — **NO** → Replace the fuse.

YES

Turn the ignition switch ON.

Disconnect the 3P connector of each sensor one at a time:
• MAP sensor
• EGR valve lift sensor
• Throttle Position (TP) sensor

Does the MIL remain ON? — **NO** → Replace the sensor that caused the light to go out.

YES

Turn the ignition switch OFF.

Connect the test harness. Disconnect the "D" connector from the ECM only, not the main wire harness

Check for continuity between body ground terminals D19, D20.

Is there continuity? — **YES** →
— Repair short to body ground in RED/WHT wire between ECM (D19) and MAP sensor or EGR valve lift sensor.
— Repair short to body ground in YEL/WHT wire between ECM (D20) and TP sensor.

NO

Reconnect all the sensor connectors.
Reconnect the "D" connector to the ECM.

Turn the ignition switch ON.

Continued On Next Page

"D"

Turn the ignition switch OFF.

Disconnect "A" connector from the ECM.

Turn the ignition switch ON.

Is the MIL ON? — **NO** → Substitute a known-good ECM and recheck. If symptom/indication goes away, replace the original ECM.

YES

Repair short to body ground in BLU/WHT wire between the ECM (A13) and the MIL.

D19

D20

CONTINUITY?

93I78996

CODE/NO CODE (5 OF 5)
NO START TROUBLE SHOOTING
PRELUDE

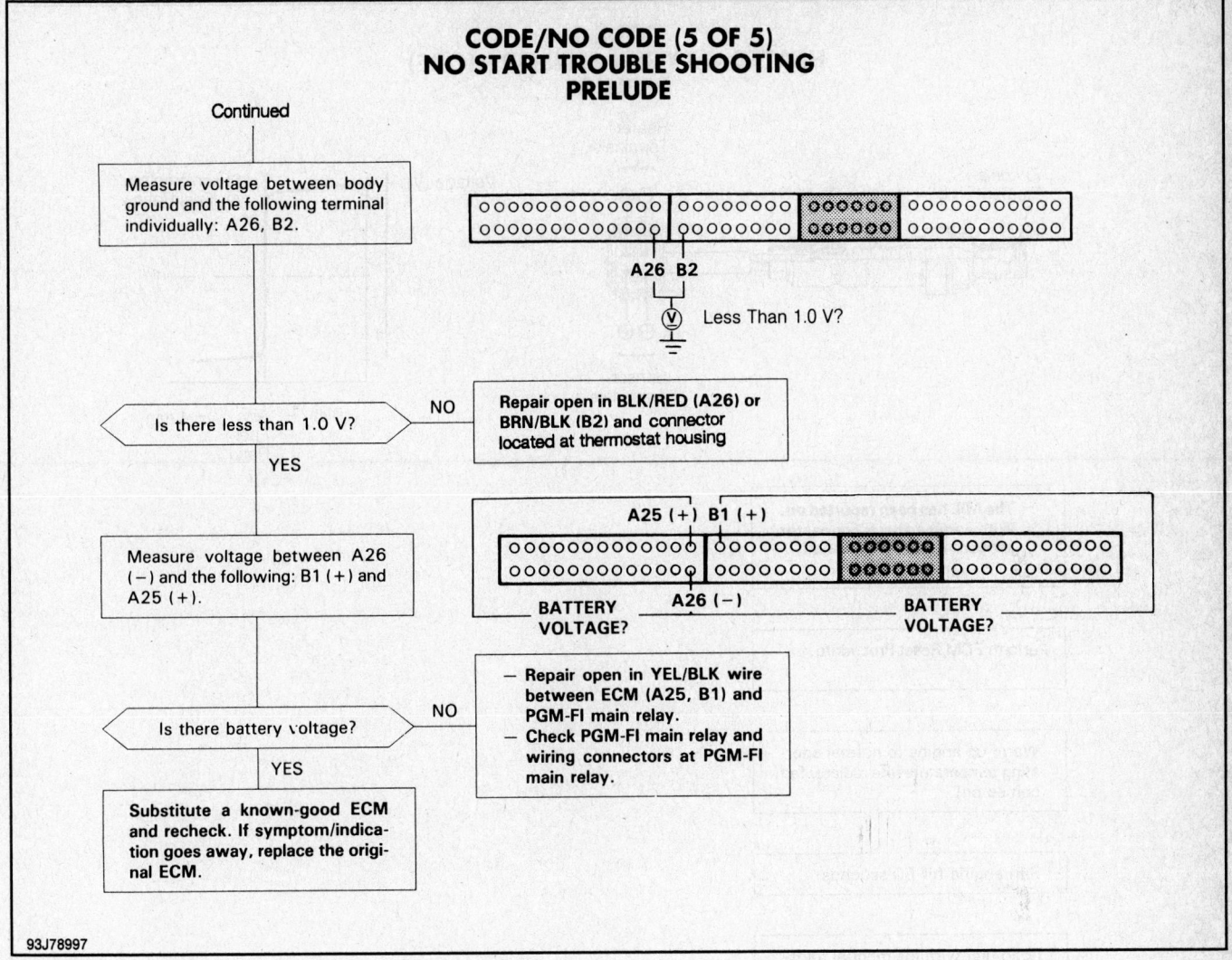

Continued

Measure voltage between body ground and the following terminal individually: A26, B2.

A26 B2

Less Than 1.0 V?

Is there less than 1.0 V? — NO → Repair open in BLK/RED (A26) or BRN/BLK (B2) and connector located at thermostat housing

YES

A25 (+) B1 (+)

Measure voltage between A26 (−) and the following: B1 (+) and A25 (+).

BATTERY VOLTAGE?   A26 (−)   BATTERY VOLTAGE?

Is there battery voltage? — NO →
— Repair open in YEL/BLK wire between ECM (A25, B1) and PGM-FI main relay.
— Check PGM-FI main relay and wiring connectors at PGM-FI main relay.

YES

Substitute a known-good ECM and recheck. If symptom/indication goes away, replace the original ECM.

93J78997

CODE 1
HEATED OXYGEN SENSOR (HO2S)
PRELUDE

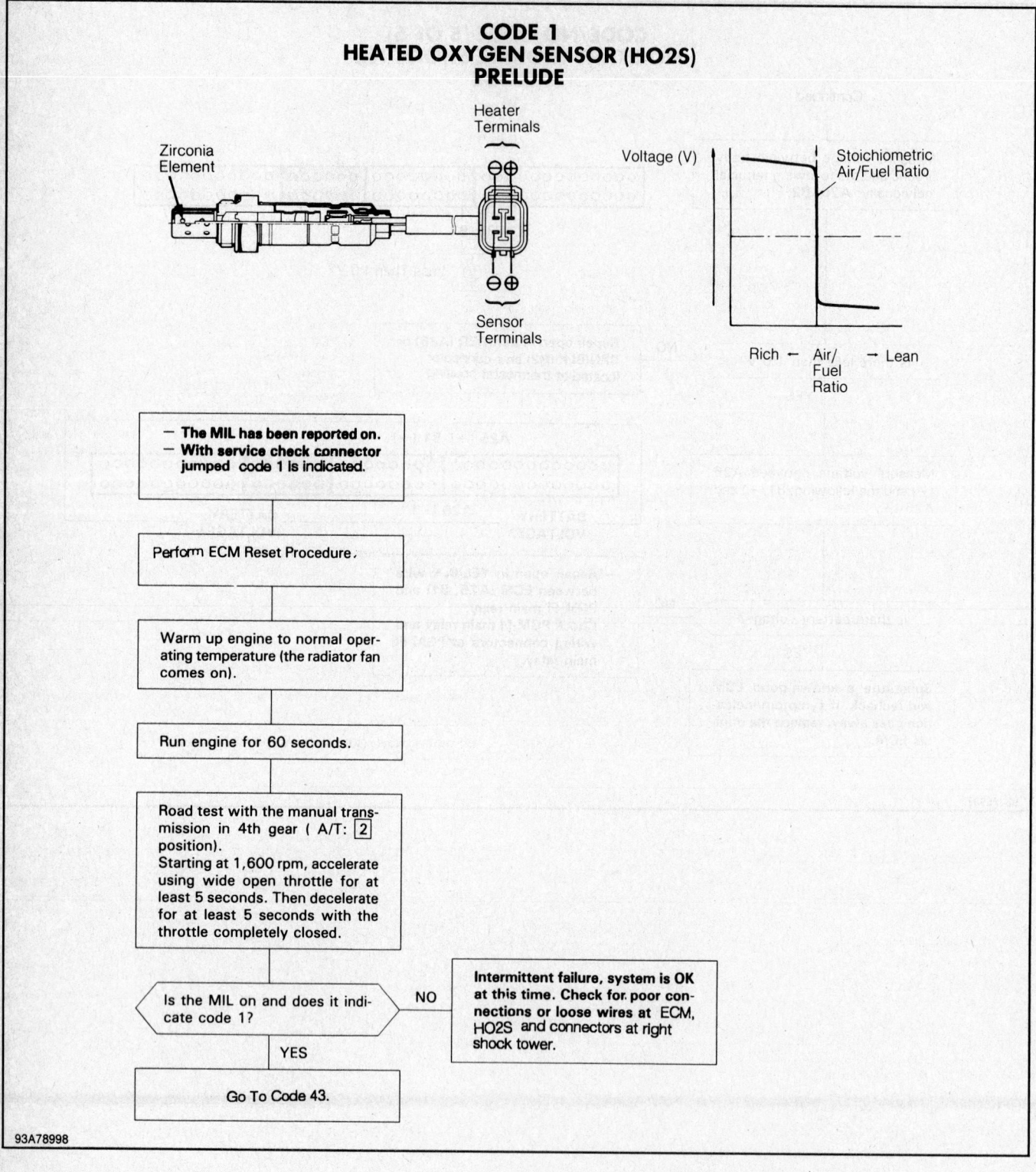

Zirconia Element

Heater Terminals

Sensor Terminals

Voltage (V)

Stoichiometric Air/Fuel Ratio

Rich ← Air/Fuel Ratio → Lean

- The MIL has been reported on.
- With service check connector jumped code 1 is indicated.

↓

Perform ECM Reset Procedure.

↓

Warm up engine to normal operating temperature (the radiator fan comes on).

↓

Run engine for 60 seconds.

↓

Road test with the manual transmission in 4th gear (A/T: 2 position).
Starting at 1,600 rpm, accelerate using wide open throttle for at least 5 seconds. Then decelerate for at least 5 seconds with the throttle completely closed.

↓

Is the MIL on and does it indicate code 1? —NO→ Intermittent failure, system is OK at this time. Check for poor connections or loose wires at ECM, HO2S and connectors at right shock tower.

YES

Go To Code 43.

93A78998

CODE 3 (1 OF 3)
MAP SENSOR CIRCUIT
PRELUDE

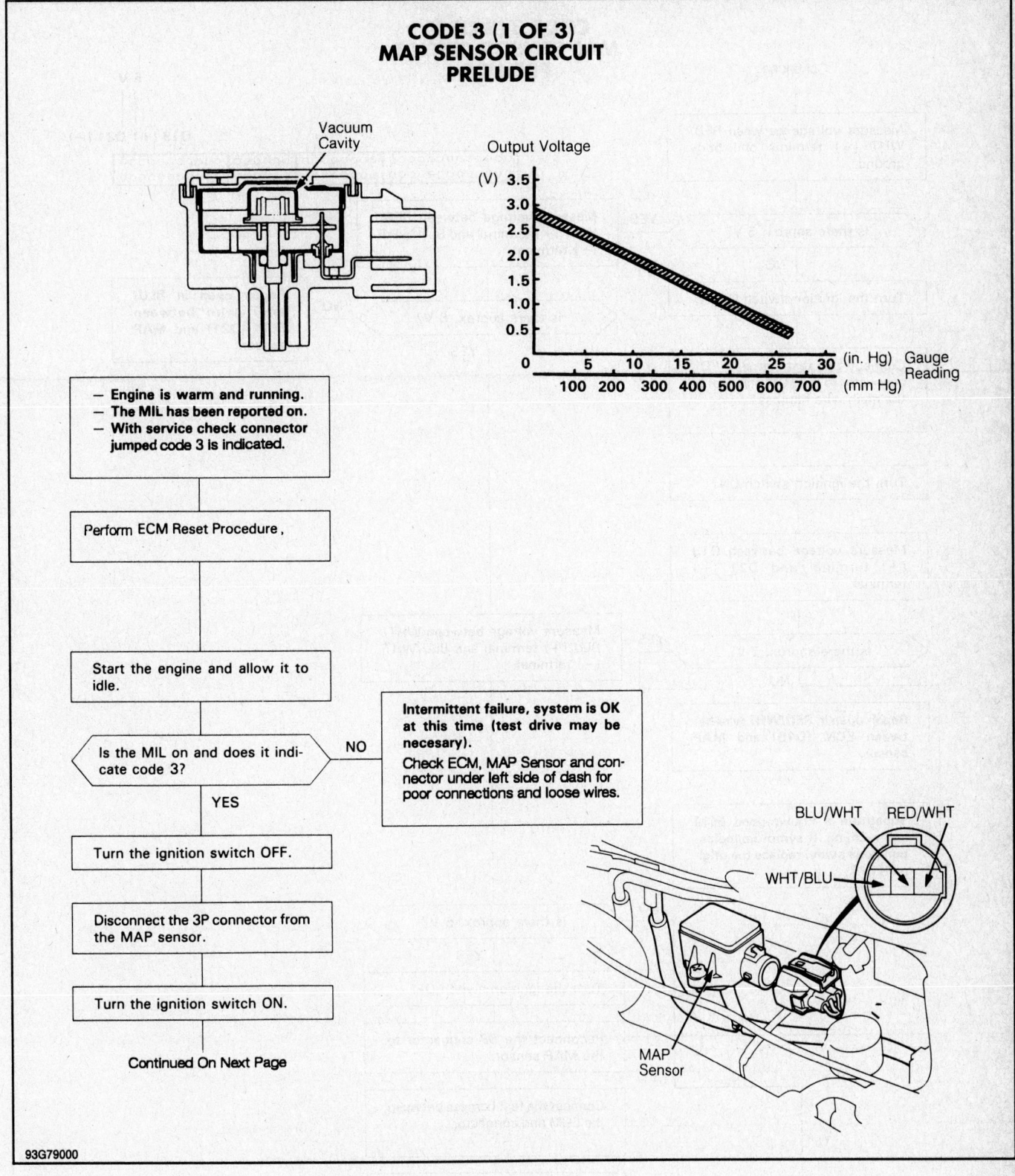

Vacuum Cavity

Output Voltage

- Engine is warm and running.
- The MIL has been reported on.
- With service check connector jumped code 3 is indicated.

Perform ECM Reset Procedure .

Start the engine and allow it to idle.

Is the MIL on and does it indicate code 3?

NO → Intermittent failure, system is OK at this time (test drive may be necesary).
Check ECM, MAP Sensor and connector under left side of dash for poor connections and loose wires.

YES

Turn the ignition switch OFF.

Disconnect the 3P connector from the MAP sensor.

Turn the ignition switch ON.

Continued On Next Page

BLU/WHT   RED/WHT
WHT/BLU
MAP Sensor

93G79000

CODE 3 (2 OF 3)
MAP SENSOR CIRCUIT
PRELUDE

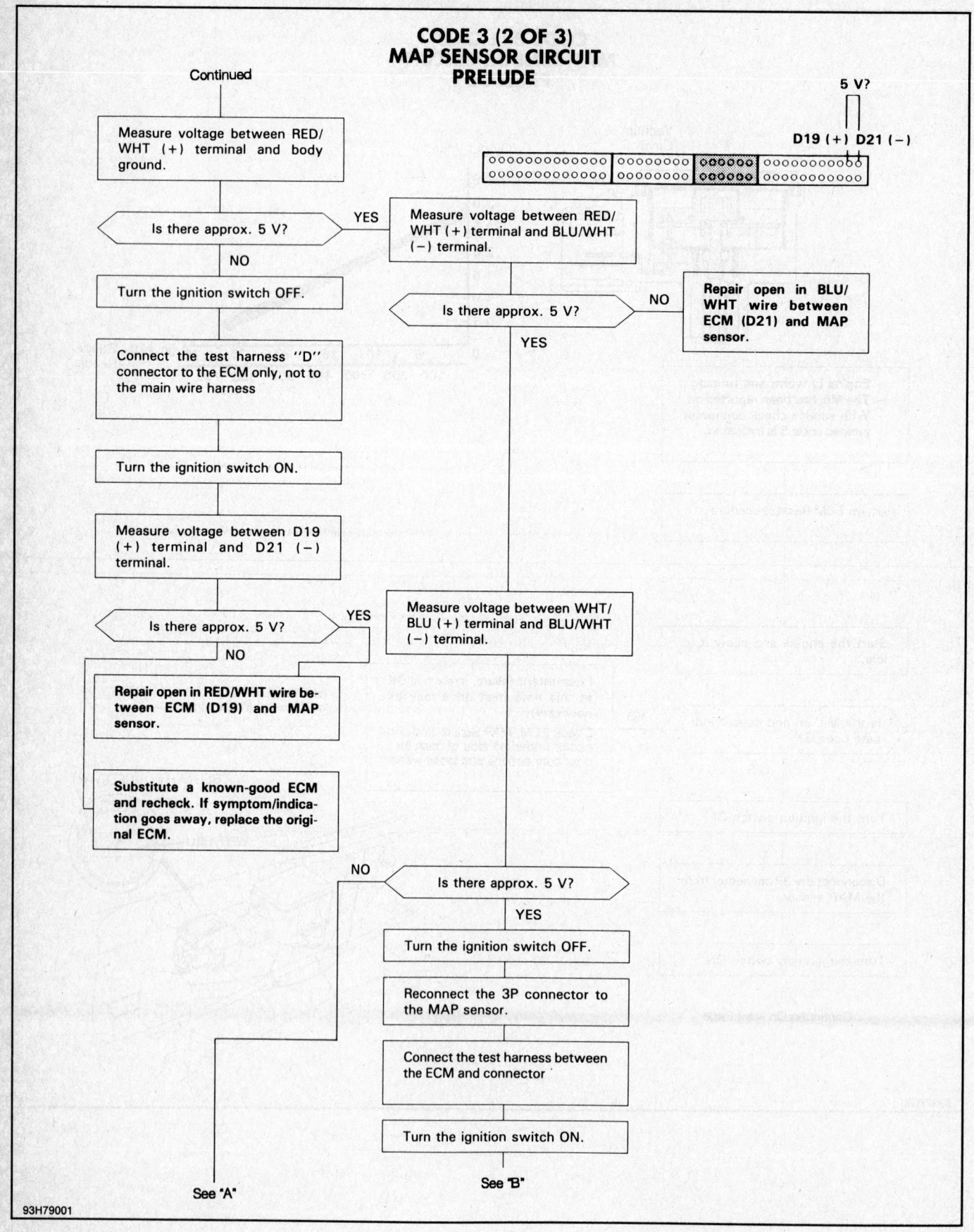

Continued

Measure voltage between RED/WHT (+) terminal and body ground.

Is there approx. 5 V? — YES → Measure voltage between RED/WHT (+) terminal and BLU/WHT (−) terminal.

NO

Turn the ignition switch OFF.

Is there approx. 5 V? — NO → Repair open in BLU/WHT wire between ECM (D21) and MAP sensor.

YES

Connect the test harness "D" connector to the ECM only, not to the main wire harness

Turn the ignition switch ON.

Measure voltage between D19 (+) terminal and D21 (−) terminal.

Is there approx. 5 V? — YES → Measure voltage between WHT/BLU (+) terminal and BLU/WHT (−) terminal.

NO

Repair open in RED/WHT wire between ECM (D19) and MAP sensor.

Substitute a known-good ECM and recheck. If symptom/indication goes away, replace the original ECM.

5 V?

D19 (+) D21 (−)

NO — Is there approx. 5 V?

YES

Turn the ignition switch OFF.

Reconnect the 3P connector to the MAP sensor.

Connect the test harness between the ECM and connector

Turn the ignition switch ON.

See "A"   See "B"

**CODE 3 (3 OF 3)
MAP SENSOR CIRCUIT
PRELUDE**

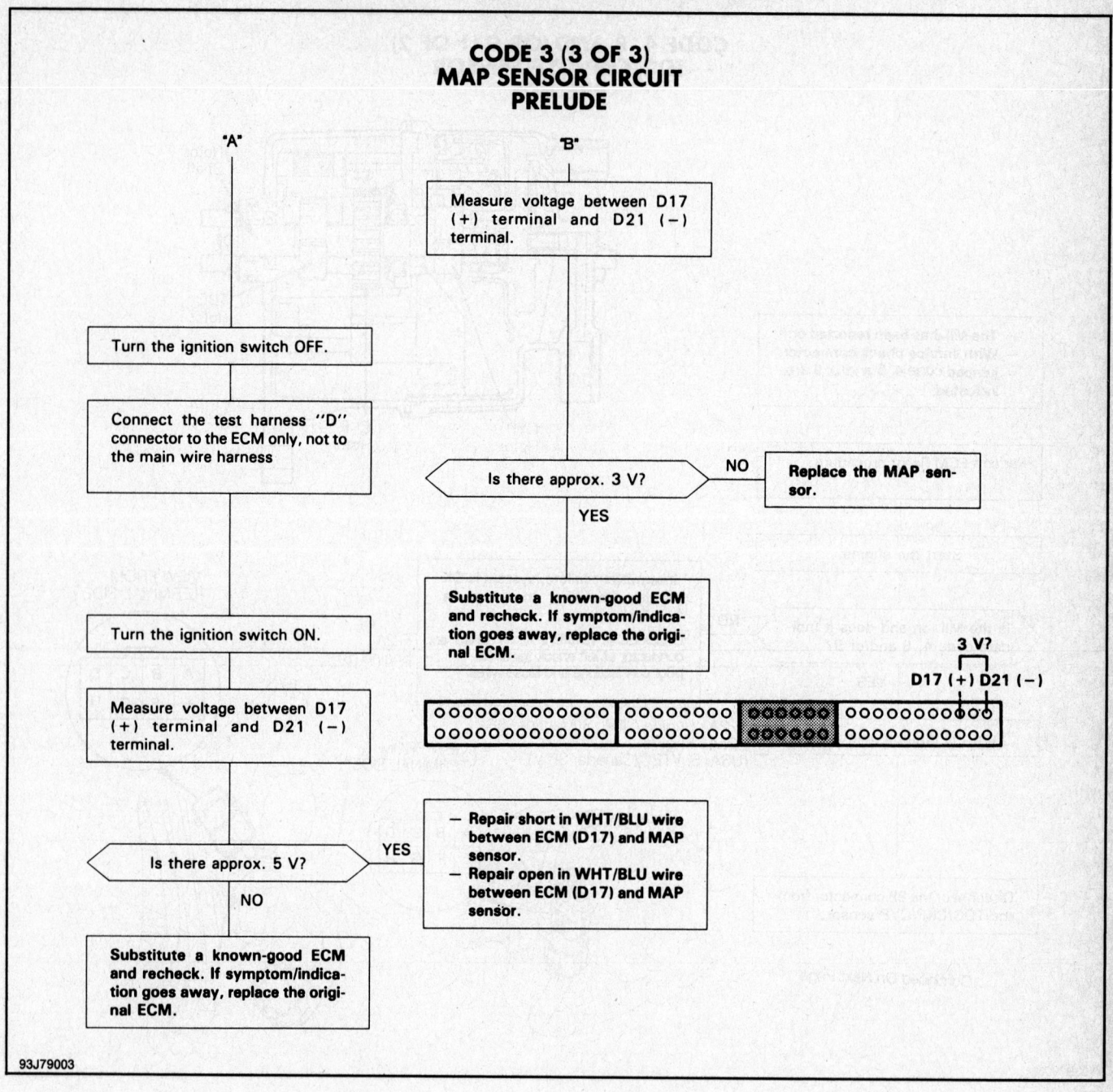

"A"

"B"

Measure voltage between D17 (+) terminal and D21 (−) terminal.

Turn the ignition switch OFF.

Connect the test harness "D" connector to the ECM only, not to the main wire harness

Is there approx. 3 V? — NO → Replace the MAP sensor.

YES

Substitute a known-good ECM and recheck. If symptom/indication goes away, replace the original ECM.

Turn the ignition switch ON.

Measure voltage between D17 (+) terminal and D21 (−) terminal.

3 V?

D17 (+) D21 (−)

Is there approx. 5 V? — YES →
— Repair short in WHT/BLU wire between ECM (D17) and MAP sensor.
— Repair open in WHT/BLU wire between ECM (D17) and MAP sensor.

NO

Substitute a known-good ECM and recheck. If symptom/indication goes away, replace the original ECM.

93J79003

1994 ENGINE PERFORMANCE
Self-Diagnostics (Cont.)

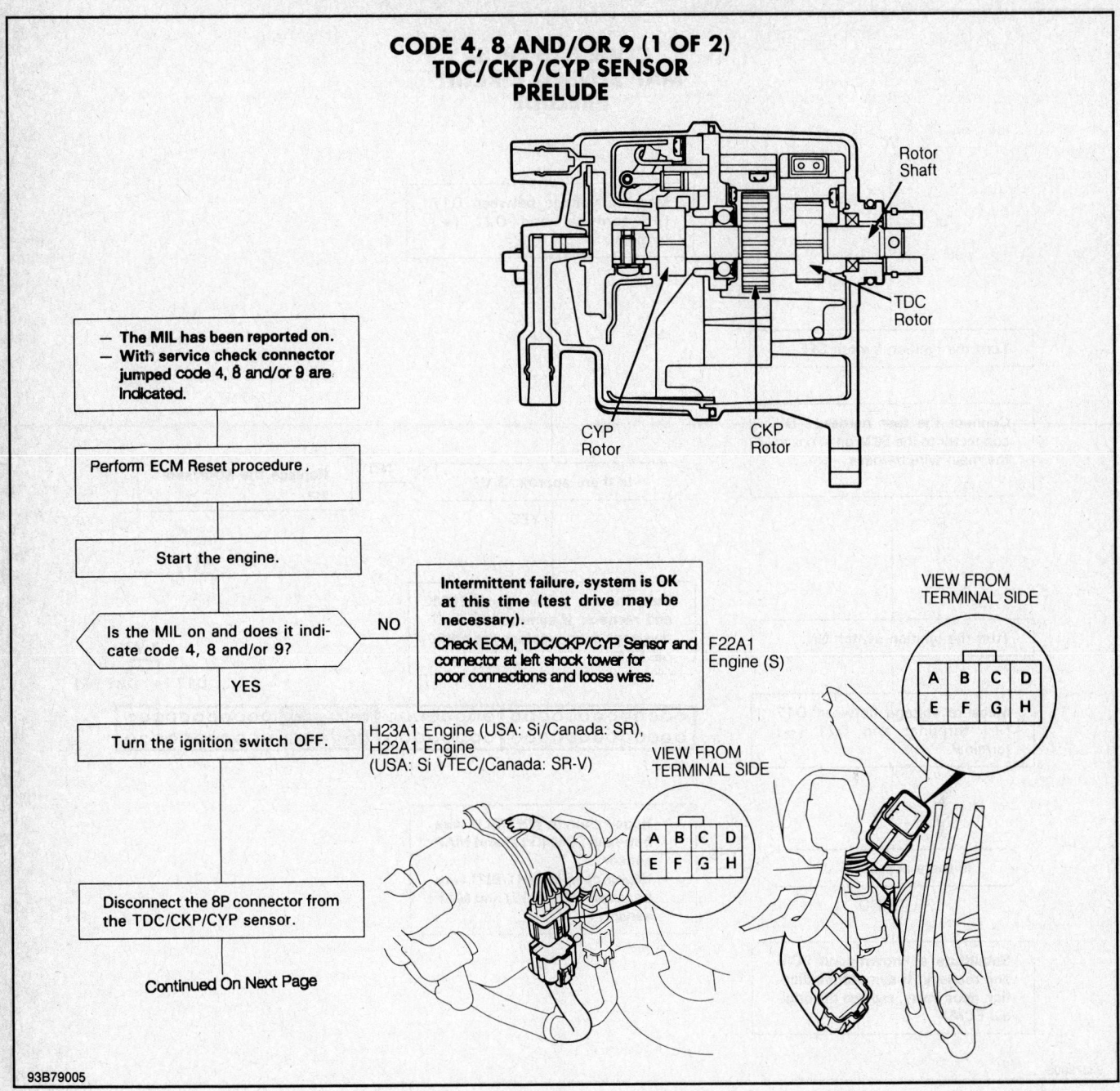

CODE 4, 8 AND/OR 9 (1 OF 2)
TDC/CKP/CYP SENSOR
PRELUDE

- The MIL has been reported on.
- With service check connector jumped code 4, 8 and/or 9 are indicated.

↓

Perform ECM Reset procedure.

↓

Start the engine.

↓

Is the MIL on and does it indicate code 4, 8 and/or 9? —NO→ Intermittent failure, system is OK at this time (test drive may be necessary).

Check ECM, TDC/CKP/CYP Sensor and connector at left shock tower for poor connections and loose wires.

↓ YES

Turn the ignition switch OFF.

↓

Disconnect the 8P connector from the TDC/CKP/CYP sensor.

Rotor Shaft

TDC Rotor

CYP Rotor

CKP Rotor

F22A1 Engine (S)

H23A1 Engine (USA: Si/Canada: SR),
H22A1 Engine
(USA: Si VTEC/Canada: SR-V)

VIEW FROM TERMINAL SIDE

A	B	C	D
E	F	G	H

VIEW FROM TERMINAL SIDE

A	B	C	D
E	F	G	H

Continued On Next Page

93B79005

CODE 4, 8 AND/OR 9 (2 OF 2)
TDC/CKP/CYP SENSOR
PRELUDE

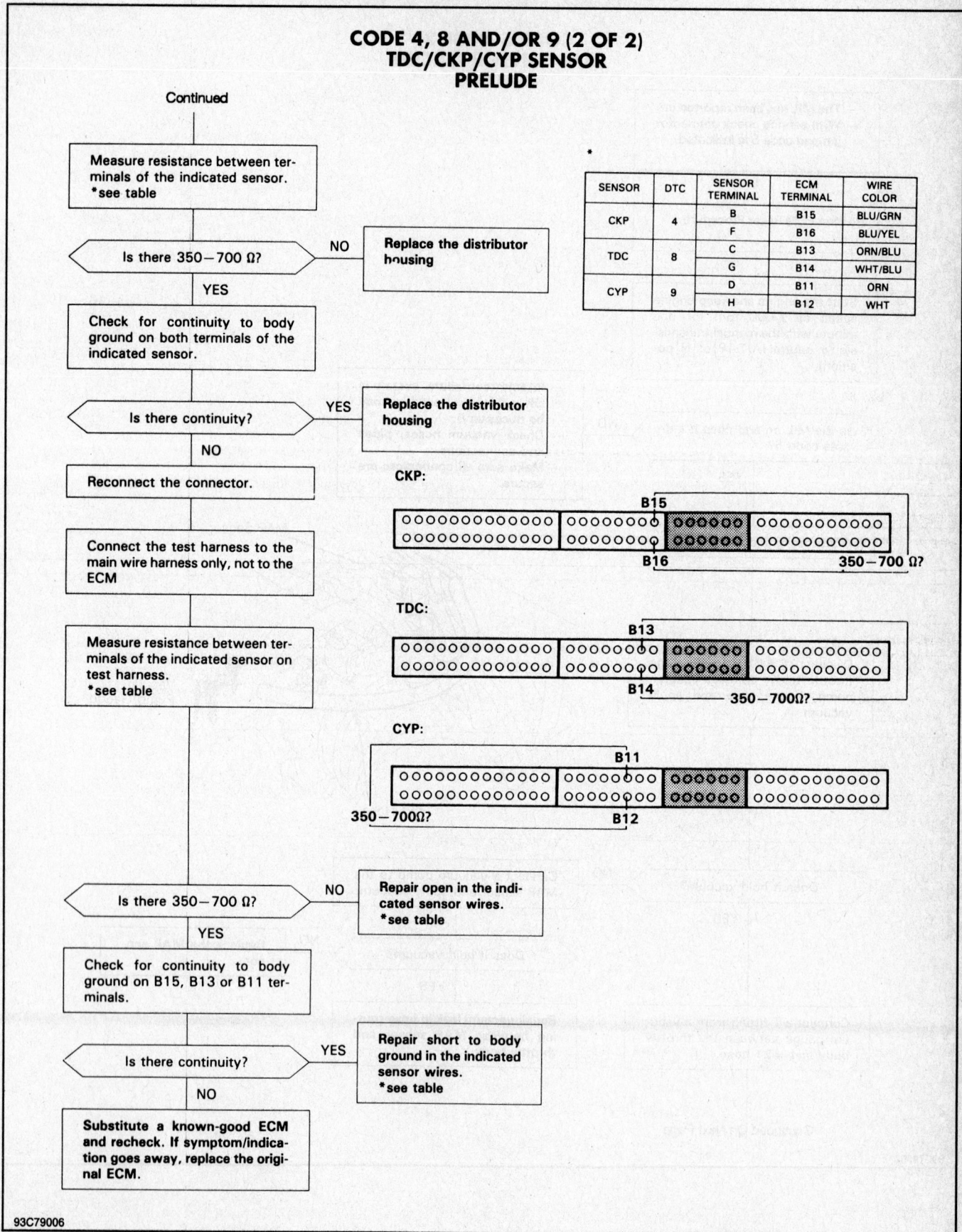

Continued

Measure resistance between terminals of the indicated sensor.
*see table

Is there 350—700 Ω? — NO → Replace the distributor housing

YES

Check for continuity to body ground on both terminals of the indicated sensor.

Is there continuity? — YES → Replace the distributor housing

NO

Reconnect the connector.

Connect the test harness to the main wire harness only, not to the ECM

Measure resistance between terminals of the indicated sensor on test harness.
*see table

SENSOR	DTC	SENSOR TERMINAL	ECM TERMINAL	WIRE COLOR
CKP	4	B	B15	BLU/GRN
		F	B16	BLU/YEL
TDC	8	C	B13	ORN/BLU
		G	B14	WHT/BLU
CYP	9	D	B11	ORN
		H	B12	WHT

CKP:

B15
B16
350—700 Ω?

TDC:

B13
B14
350—700Ω?

CYP:

B11
350—700Ω?
B12

Is there 350—700 Ω? — NO → Repair open in the indicated sensor wires.
*see table

YES

Check for continuity to body ground on B15, B13 or B11 terminals.

Is there continuity? — YES → Repair short to body ground in the indicated sensor wires.
*see table

NO

Substitute a known-good ECM and recheck. If symptom/indication goes away, replace the original ECM.

93C79006

CODE 5 (1 OF 2)
MAP SENSOR CIRCUIT
PRELUDE

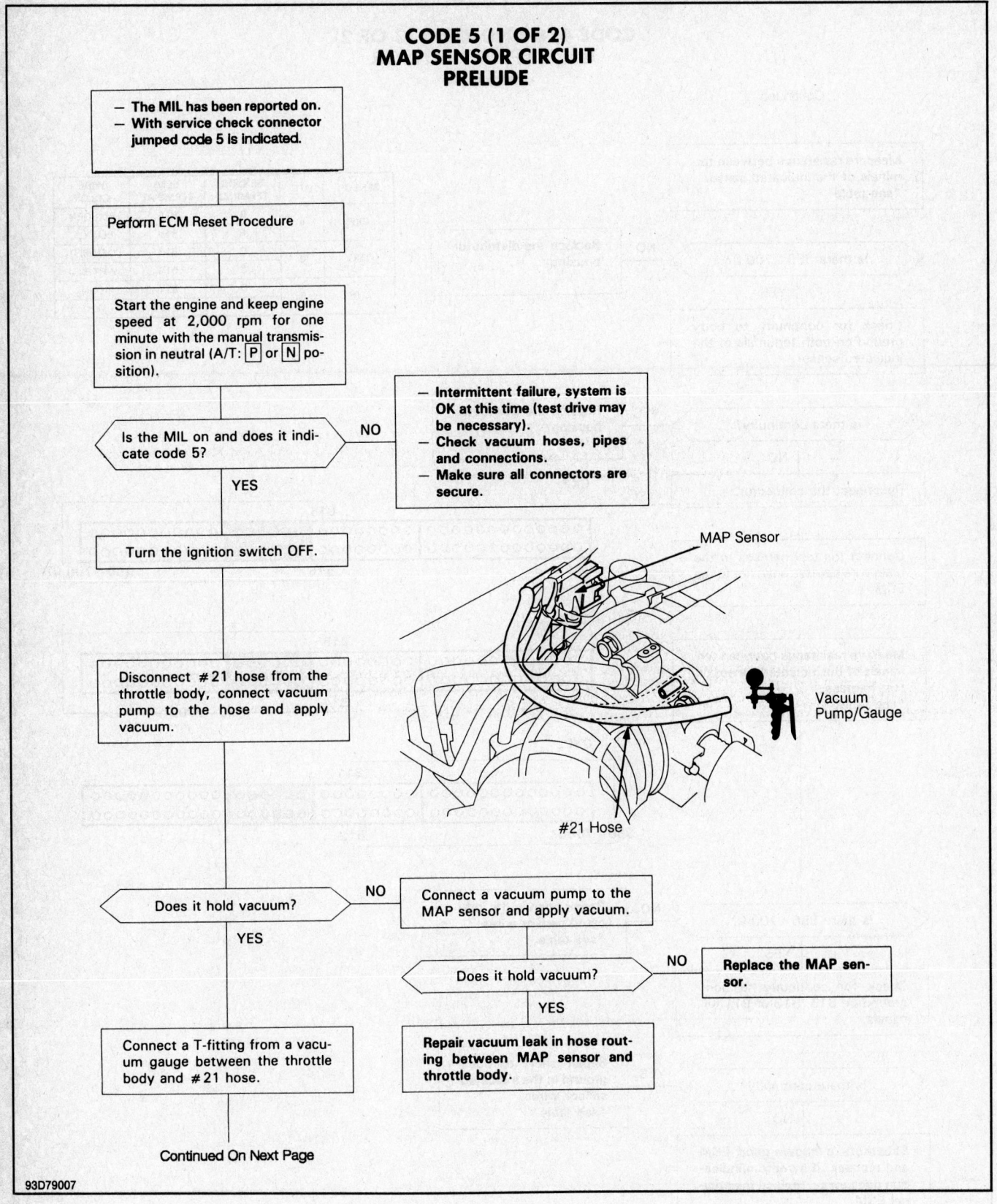

- The MIL has been reported on.
- With service check connector jumped code 5 is indicated.

Perform ECM Reset Procedure

Start the engine and keep engine speed at 2,000 rpm for one minute with the manual transmission in neutral (A/T: P or N position).

Is the MIL on and does it indicate code 5? → NO →
- Intermittent failure, system is OK at this time (test drive may be necessary).
- Check vacuum hoses, pipes and connections.
- Make sure all connectors are secure.

YES

Turn the ignition switch OFF.

Disconnect #21 hose from the throttle body, connect vacuum pump to the hose and apply vacuum.

MAP Sensor

Vacuum Pump/Gauge

#21 Hose

Does it hold vacuum? → NO → Connect a vacuum pump to the MAP sensor and apply vacuum.

YES

Does it hold vacuum? → NO → Replace the MAP sensor.

YES

Connect a T-fitting from a vacuum gauge between the throttle body and #21 hose.

Repair vacuum leak in hose routing between MAP sensor and throttle body.

Continued On Next Page

93D79007

**CODE 5 (2 OF 2)
MAP SENSOR CIRCUIT
PRELUDE**

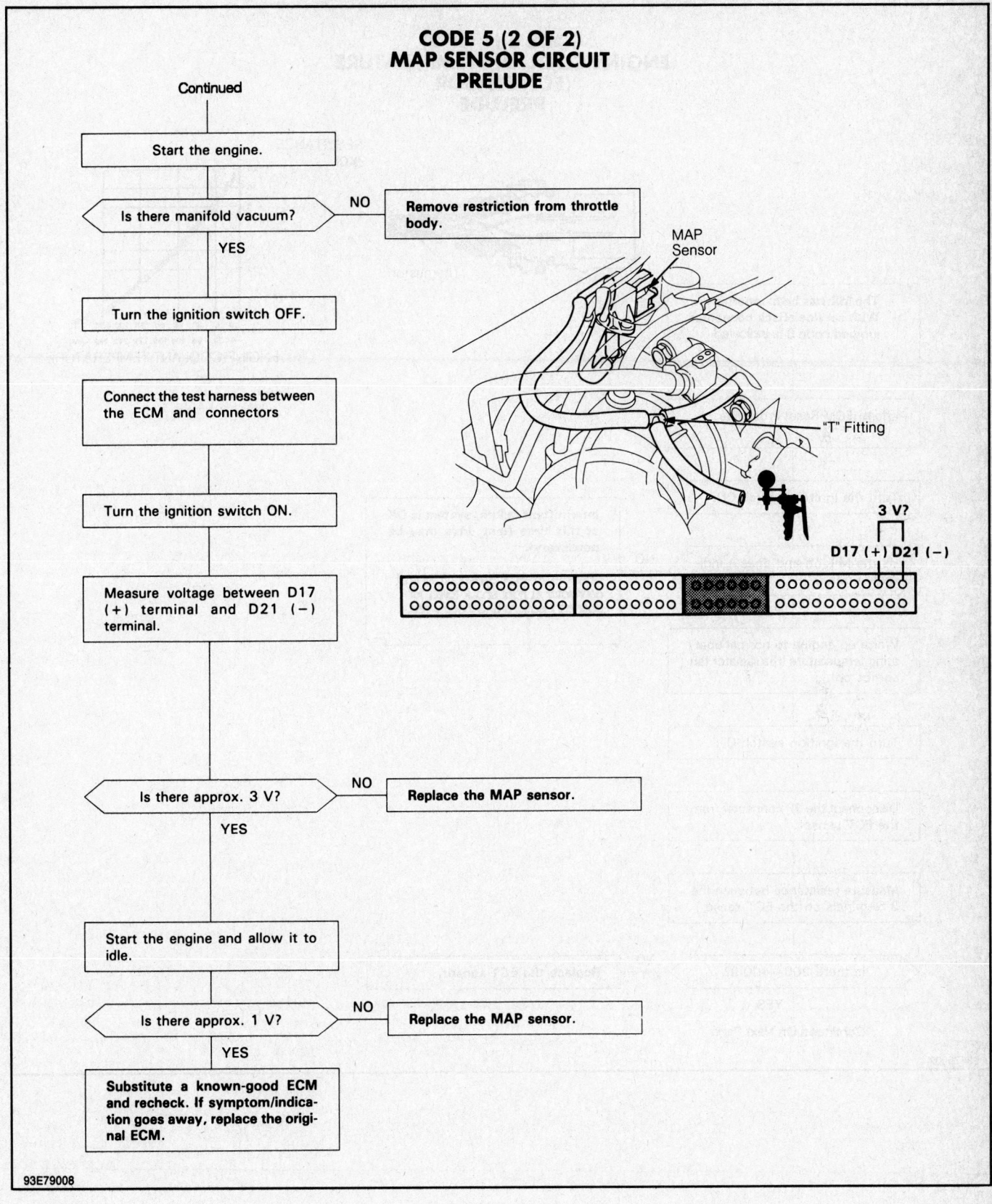

Continued

Start the engine.

Is there manifold vacuum? — NO → Remove restriction from throttle body.

YES

Turn the ignition switch OFF.

Connect the test harness between the ECM and connectors

Turn the ignition switch ON.

Measure voltage between D17 (+) terminal and D21 (−) terminal.

MAP Sensor

"T" Fitting

3 V?

D17 (+) D21 (−)

Is there approx. 3 V? — NO → Replace the MAP sensor.

YES

Start the engine and allow it to idle.

Is there approx. 1 V? — NO → Replace the MAP sensor.

YES

Substitute a known-good ECM and recheck. If symptom/indication goes away, replace the original ECM.

93E79008

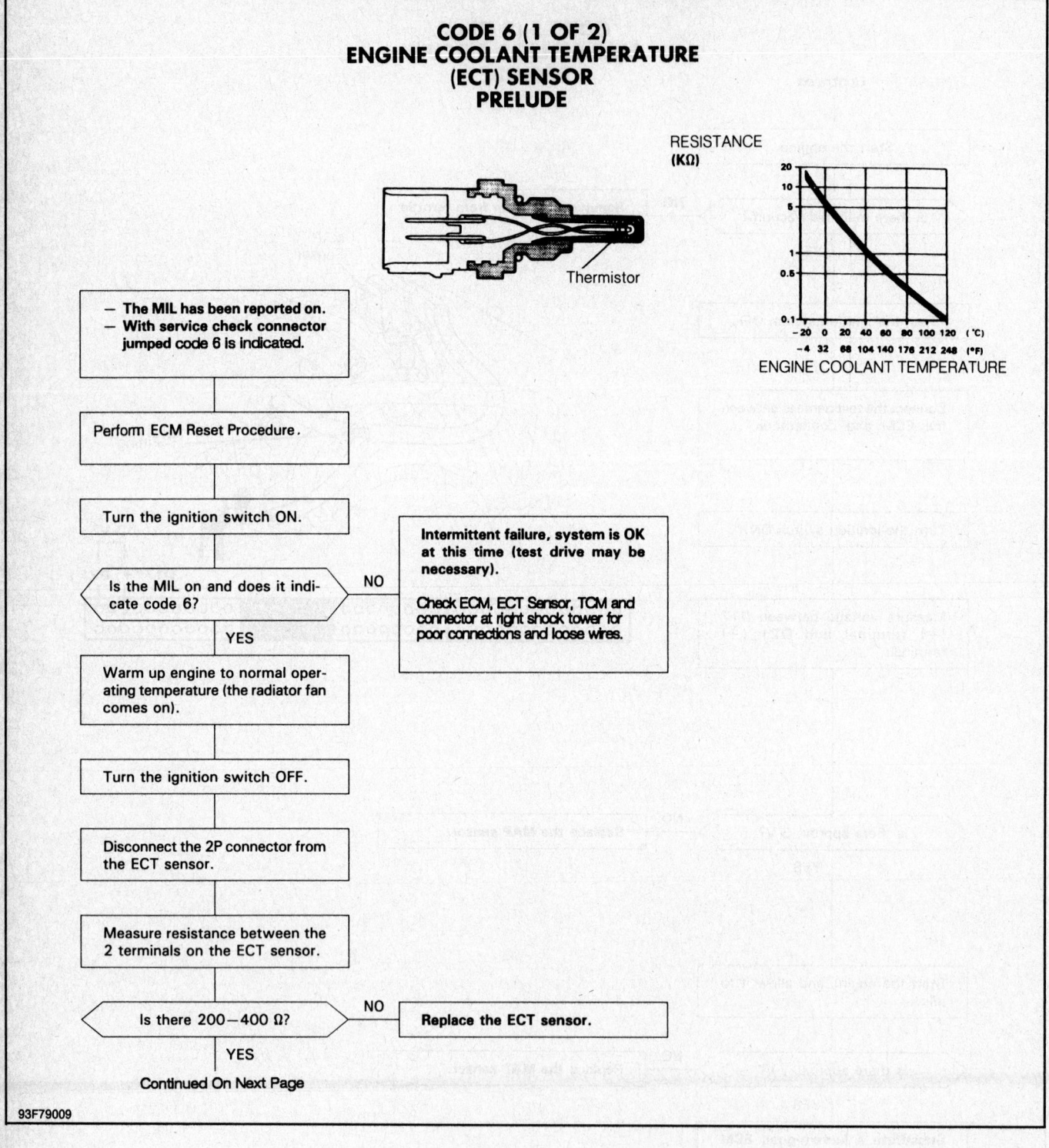

CODE 6 (1 OF 2)
ENGINE COOLANT TEMPERATURE
(ECT) SENSOR
PRELUDE

Thermistor

RESISTANCE (KΩ)

ENGINE COOLANT TEMPERATURE

- The MIL has been reported on.
- With service check connector jumped code 6 is indicated.

Perform ECM Reset Procedure.

Turn the ignition switch ON.

Is the MIL on and does it indicate code 6?

NO →

Intermittent failure, system is OK at this time (test drive may be necessary).

Check ECM, ECT Sensor, TCM and connector at right shock tower for poor connections and loose wires.

YES

Warm up engine to normal operating temperature (the radiator fan comes on).

Turn the ignition switch OFF.

Disconnect the 2P connector from the ECT sensor.

Measure resistance between the 2 terminals on the ECT sensor.

Is there 200—400 Ω?   **NO** →   Replace the ECT sensor.

YES

Continued On Next Page

93F79009

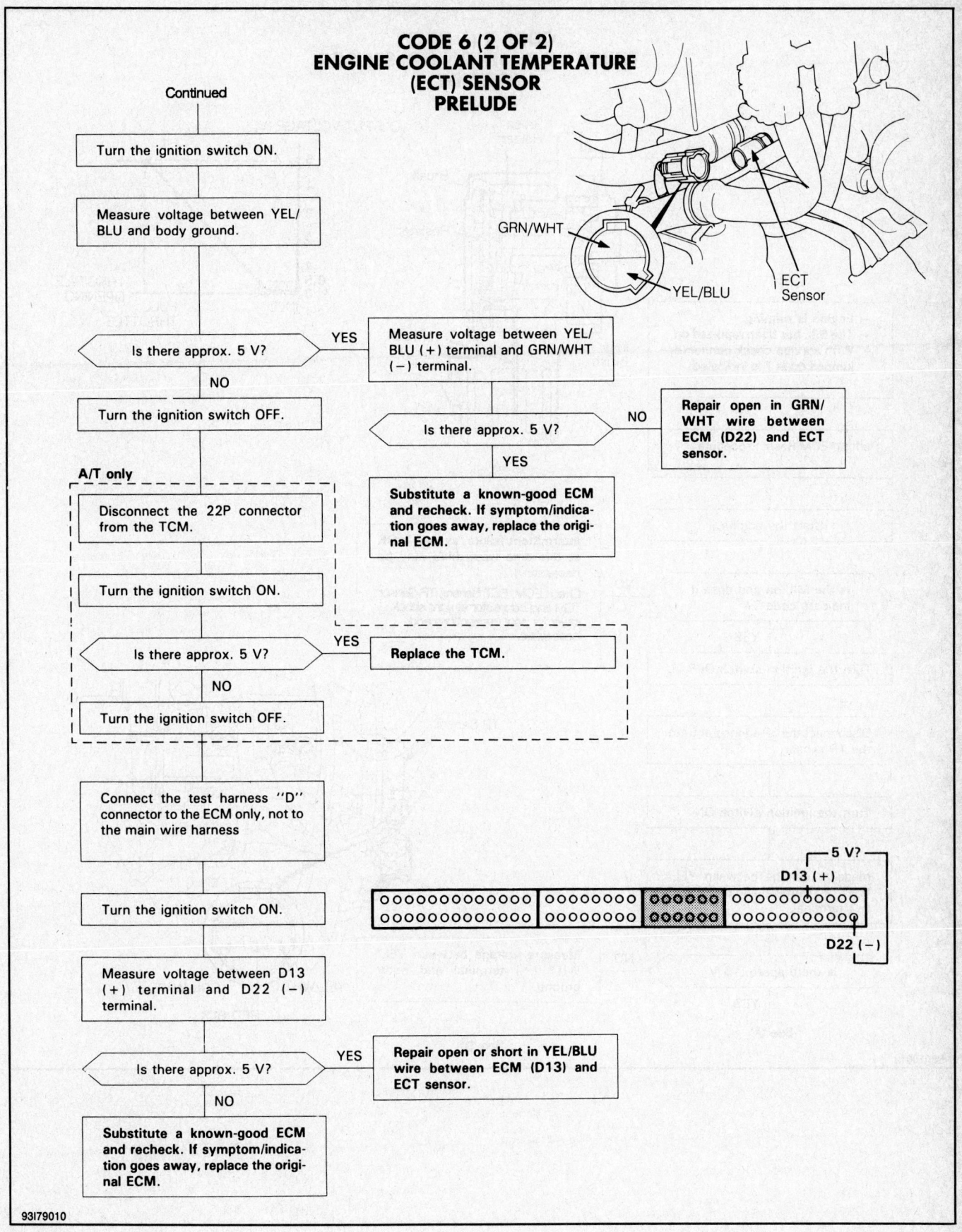

CODE 6 (2 OF 2)
ENGINE COOLANT TEMPERATURE
(ECT) SENSOR
PRELUDE

Continued

Turn the ignition switch ON.

Measure voltage between YEL/BLU and body ground.

Is there approx. 5 V? — YES → Measure voltage between YEL/BLU (+) terminal and GRN/WHT (−) terminal.

NO

Turn the ignition switch OFF.

Is there approx. 5 V? — NO → Repair open in GRN/WHT wire between ECM (D22) and ECT sensor.

YES

Substitute a known-good ECM and recheck. If symptom/indication goes away, replace the original ECM.

A/T only

Disconnect the 22P connector from the TCM.

Turn the ignition switch ON.

Is there approx. 5 V? — YES → Replace the TCM.

NO

Turn the ignition switch OFF.

Connect the test harness "D" connector to the ECM only, not to the main wire harness

Turn the ignition switch ON.

Measure voltage between D13 (+) terminal and D22 (−) terminal.

Is there approx. 5 V? — YES → Repair open or short in YEL/BLU wire between ECM (D13) and ECT sensor.

NO

Substitute a known-good ECM and recheck. If symptom/indication goes away, replace the original ECM.

GRN/WHT
YEL/BLU
ECT Sensor

5 V?
D13 (+)
D22 (−)

93I79010

CODE 7 (1 OF 2)
THROTTLE POSITION (TP) SENSOR
PRELUDE

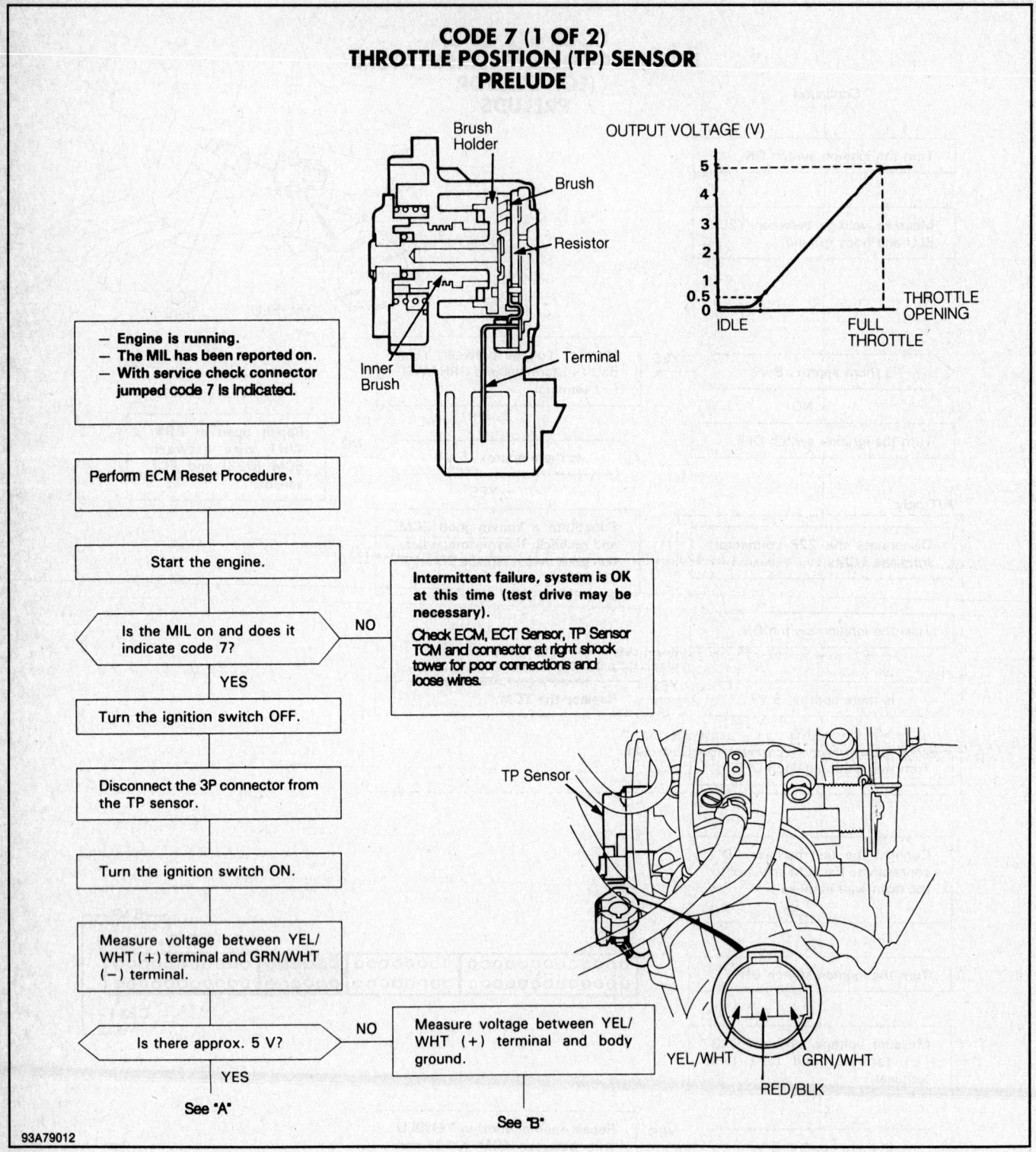

OUTPUT VOLTAGE (V)

- Engine is running.
- The MIL has been reported on.
- With service check connector jumped code 7 is indicated.

Perform ECM Reset Procedure.

Start the engine.

Is the MIL on and does it indicate code 7? — NO → Intermittent failure, system is OK at this time (test drive may be necessary).

Check ECM, ECT Sensor, TP Sensor TCM and connector at right shock tower for poor connections and loose wires.

YES

Turn the ignition switch OFF.

Disconnect the 3P connector from the TP sensor.

Turn the ignition switch ON.

Measure voltage between YEL/WHT (+) terminal and GRN/WHT (–) terminal.

Is there approx. 5 V? — NO → Measure voltage between YEL/WHT (+) terminal and body ground.

YES

See "A"

See "B"

YEL/WHT   GRN/WHT

RED/BLK

93A79012

CODE 7 (2 OF 2)
THROTTLE POSITION (TP) SENSOR
PRELUDE

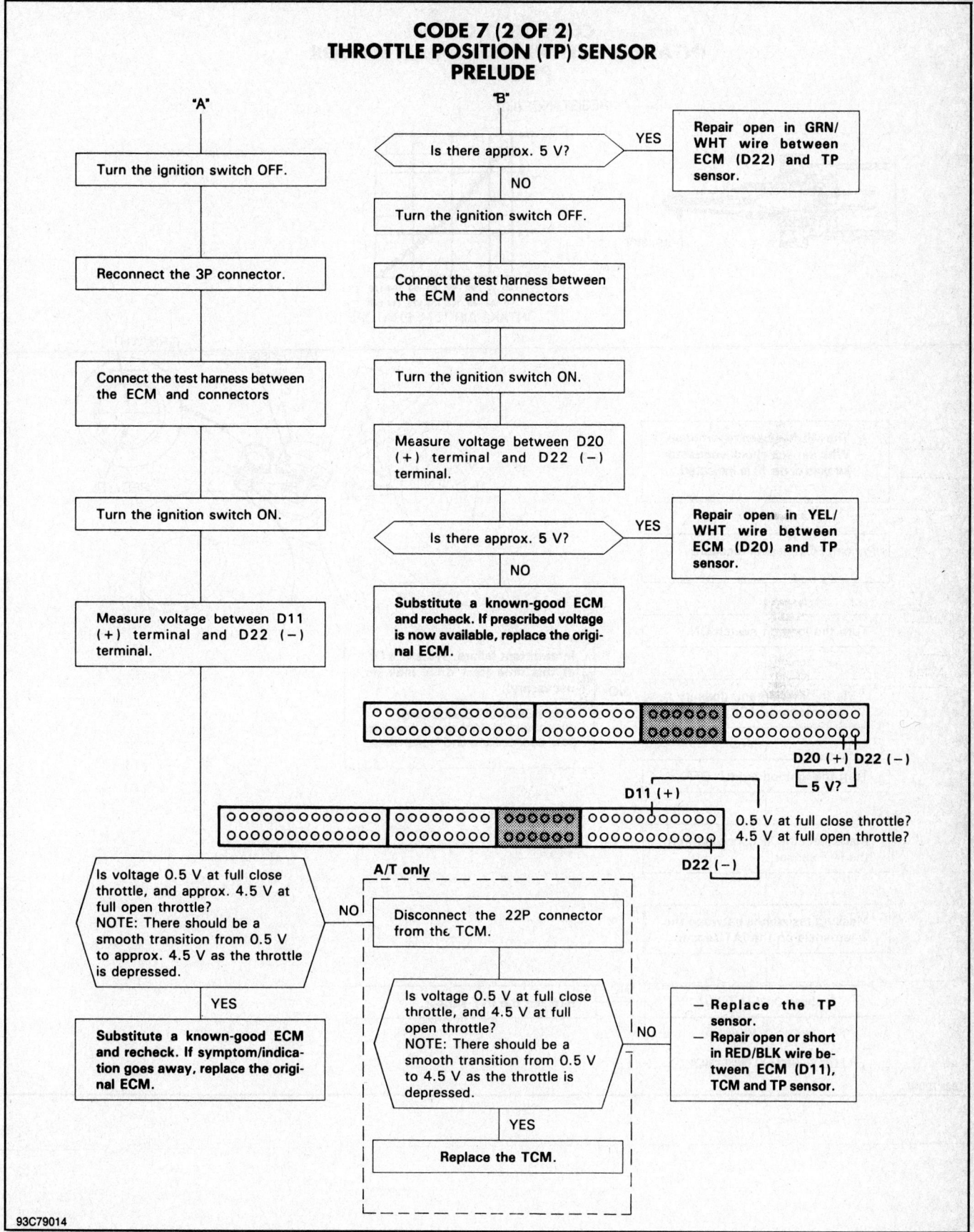

"A"

Turn the ignition switch OFF.

Reconnect the 3P connector.

Connect the test harness between the ECM and connectors

Turn the ignition switch ON.

Measure voltage between D11 (+) terminal and D22 (−) terminal.

Is voltage 0.5 V at full close throttle, and approx. 4.5 V at full open throttle?
NOTE: There should be a smooth transition from 0.5 V to approx. 4.5 V as the throttle is depressed.

YES

Substitute a known-good ECM and recheck. If symptom/indication goes away, replace the original ECM.

"B"

Is there approx. 5 V? — YES → Repair open in GRN/WHT wire between ECM (D22) and TP sensor.

NO

Turn the ignition switch OFF.

Connect the test harness between the ECM and connectors

Turn the ignition switch ON.

Measure voltage between D20 (+) terminal and D22 (−) terminal.

Is there approx. 5 V? — YES → Repair open in YEL/WHT wire between ECM (D20) and TP sensor.

NO

Substitute a known-good ECM and recheck. If prescribed voltage is now available, replace the original ECM.

D20 (+) D22 (−)
5 V?

D11 (+)
D22 (−)

0.5 V at full close throttle?
4.5 V at full open throttle?

A/T only

NO →

Disconnect the 22P connector from the TCM.

Is voltage 0.5 V at full close throttle, and 4.5 V at full open throttle?
NOTE: There should be a smooth transition from 0.5 V to 4.5 V as the throttle is depressed.

NO →
− Replace the TP sensor.
− Repair open or short in RED/BLK wire between ECM (D11), TCM and TP sensor.

YES

Replace the TCM.

CODE 10 (1 OF 2)
INTAKE AIR TEMPERATURE (IAT) SENSOR
PRELUDE

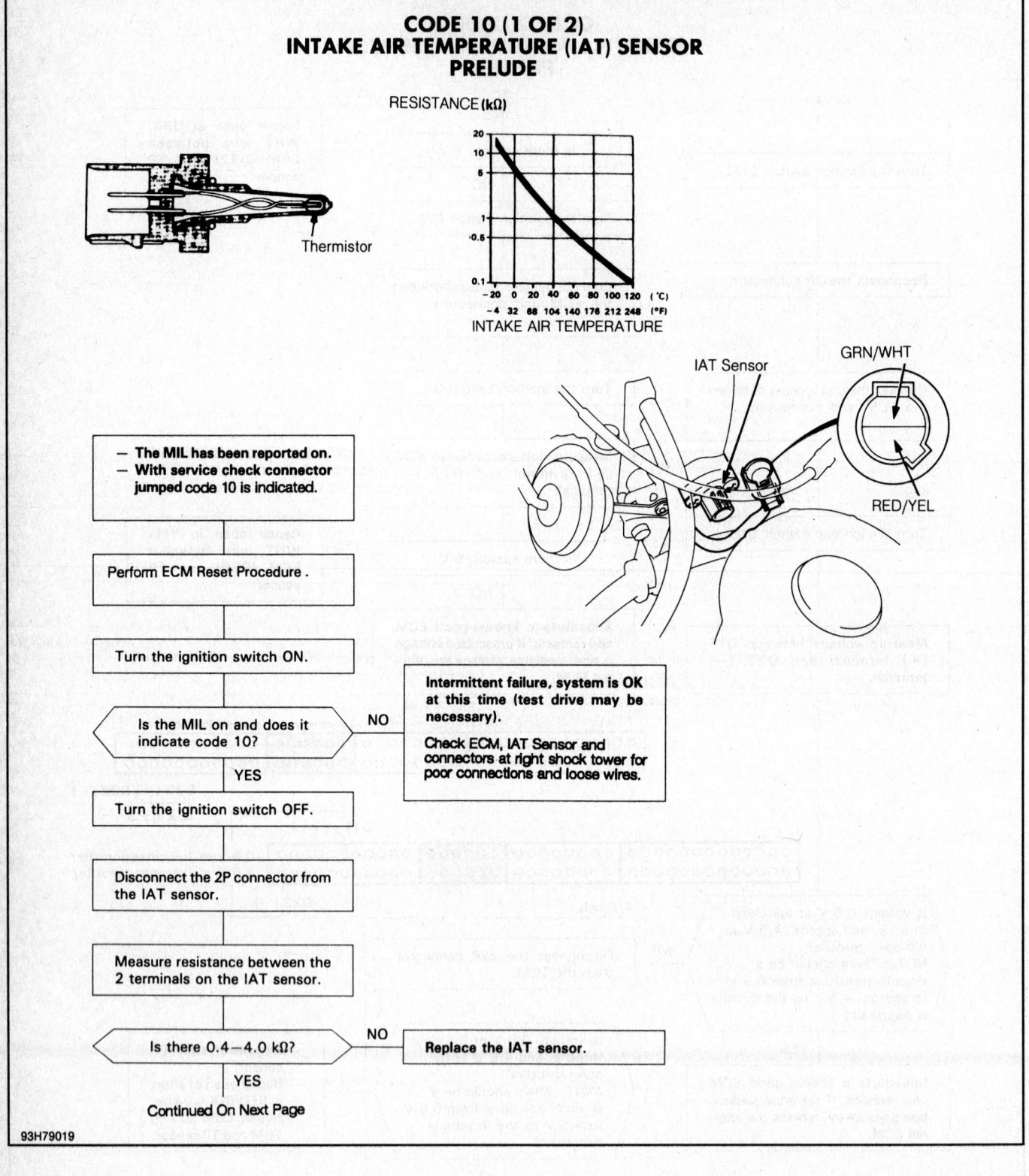

RESISTANCE (kΩ)

INTAKE AIR TEMPERATURE

Thermistor

IAT Sensor

GRN/WHT

RED/YEL

- The MIL has been reported on.
- With service check connector jumped code 10 is indicated.

Perform ECM Reset Procedure .

Turn the ignition switch ON.

Is the MIL on and does it indicate code 10? — NO → Intermittent failure, system is OK at this time (test drive may be necessary).

Check ECM, IAT Sensor and connectors at right shock tower for poor connections and loose wires.

YES

Turn the ignition switch OFF.

Disconnect the 2P connector from the IAT sensor.

Measure resistance between the 2 terminals on the IAT sensor.

Is there 0.4—4.0 kΩ? — NO → Replace the IAT sensor.

YES

Continued On Next Page

93H79019

**CODE 10 (2 OF 2)
INTAKE AIR TEMPERATURE (IAT) SENSOR
PRELUDE**

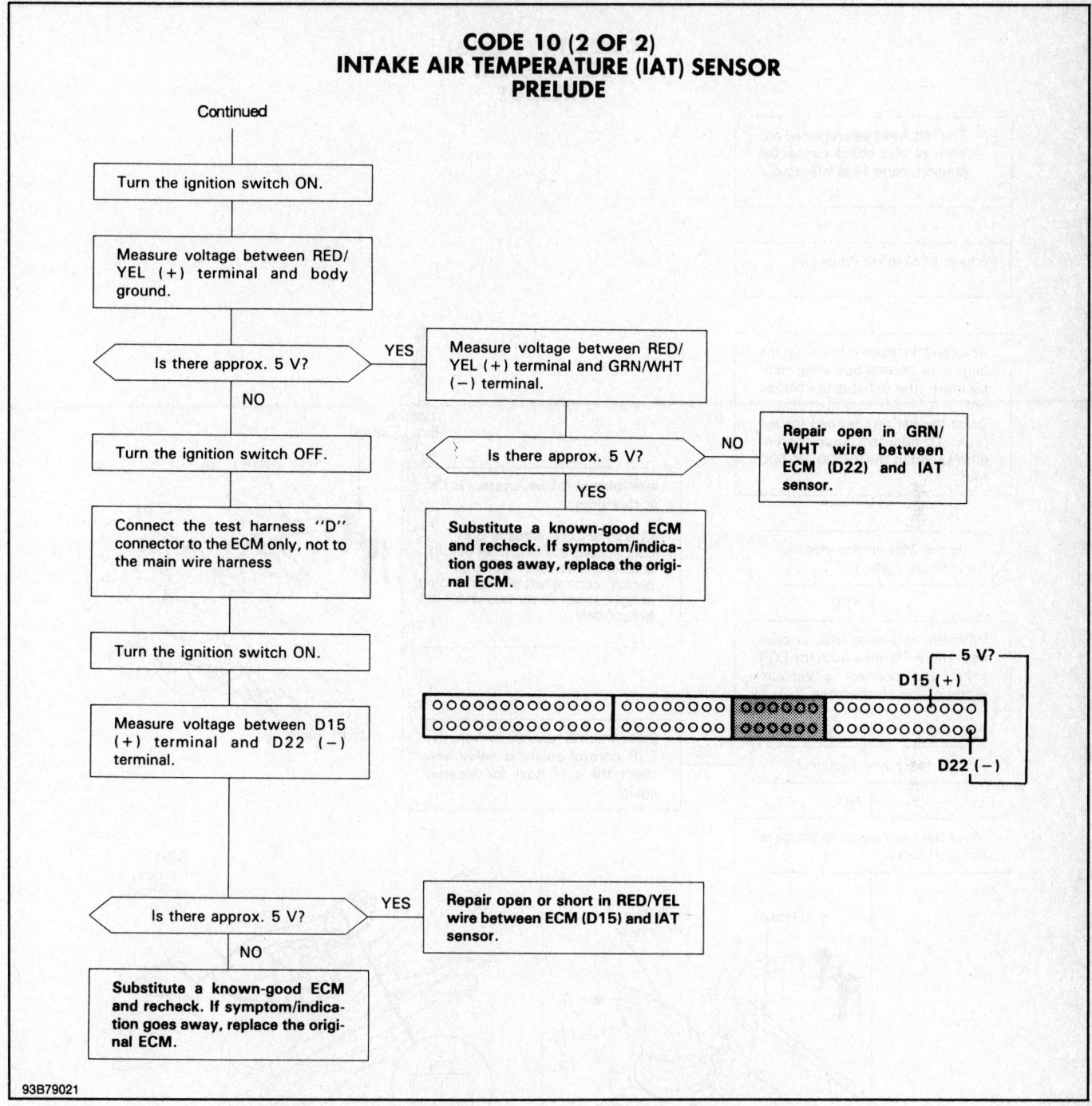

Continued

Turn the ignition switch ON.

Measure voltage between RED/YEL (+) terminal and body ground.

Is there approx. 5 V? — YES → Measure voltage between RED/YEL (+) terminal and GRN/WHT (−) terminal.

NO

Turn the ignition switch OFF.

Is there approx. 5 V? — NO → Repair open in GRN/WHT wire between ECM (D22) and IAT sensor.

YES

Connect the test harness ''D'' connector to the ECM only, not to the main wire harness

Substitute a known-good ECM and recheck. If symptom/indication goes away, replace the original ECM.

Turn the ignition switch ON.

5 V?
D15 (+)
D22 (−)

Measure voltage between D15 (+) terminal and D22 (−) terminal.

Is there approx. 5 V? — YES → Repair open or short in RED/YEL wire between ECM (D15) and IAT sensor.

NO

Substitute a known-good ECM and recheck. If symptom/indication goes away, replace the original ECM.

93B79021

CODE 12 (1 OF 5)
EGR SYSTEM
PRELUDE

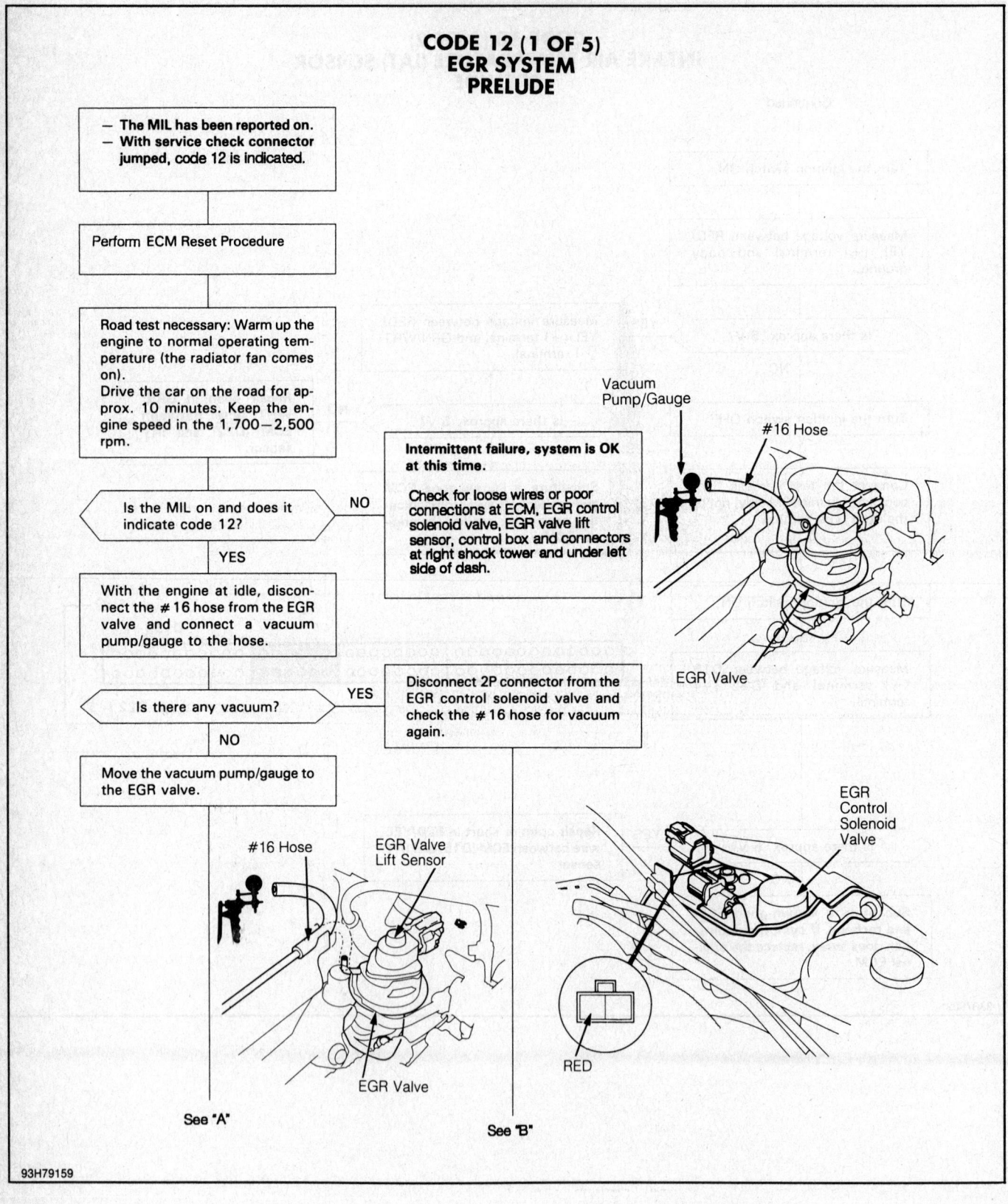

— The MIL has been reported on.
— With service check connector jumped, code 12 is indicated.

Perform ECM Reset Procedure

Road test necessary: Warm up the engine to normal operating temperature (the radiator fan comes on).
Drive the car on the road for approx. 10 minutes. Keep the engine speed in the 1,700—2,500 rpm.

Is the MIL on and does it indicate code 12? — **NO** →

Intermittent failure, system is OK at this time.

Check for loose wires or poor connections at ECM, EGR control solenoid valve, EGR valve lift sensor, control box and connectors at right shock tower and under left side of dash.

YES

With the engine at idle, disconnect the #16 hose from the EGR valve and connect a vacuum pump/gauge to the hose.

Is there any vacuum? — **YES** →

Disconnect 2P connector from the EGR control solenoid valve and check the #16 hose for vacuum again.

NO

Move the vacuum pump/gauge to the EGR valve.

Vacuum Pump/Gauge

#16 Hose

EGR Valve

#16 Hose

EGR Valve Lift Sensor

EGR Valve

EGR Control Solenoid Valve

RED

See "A"

See "B"

93H79159

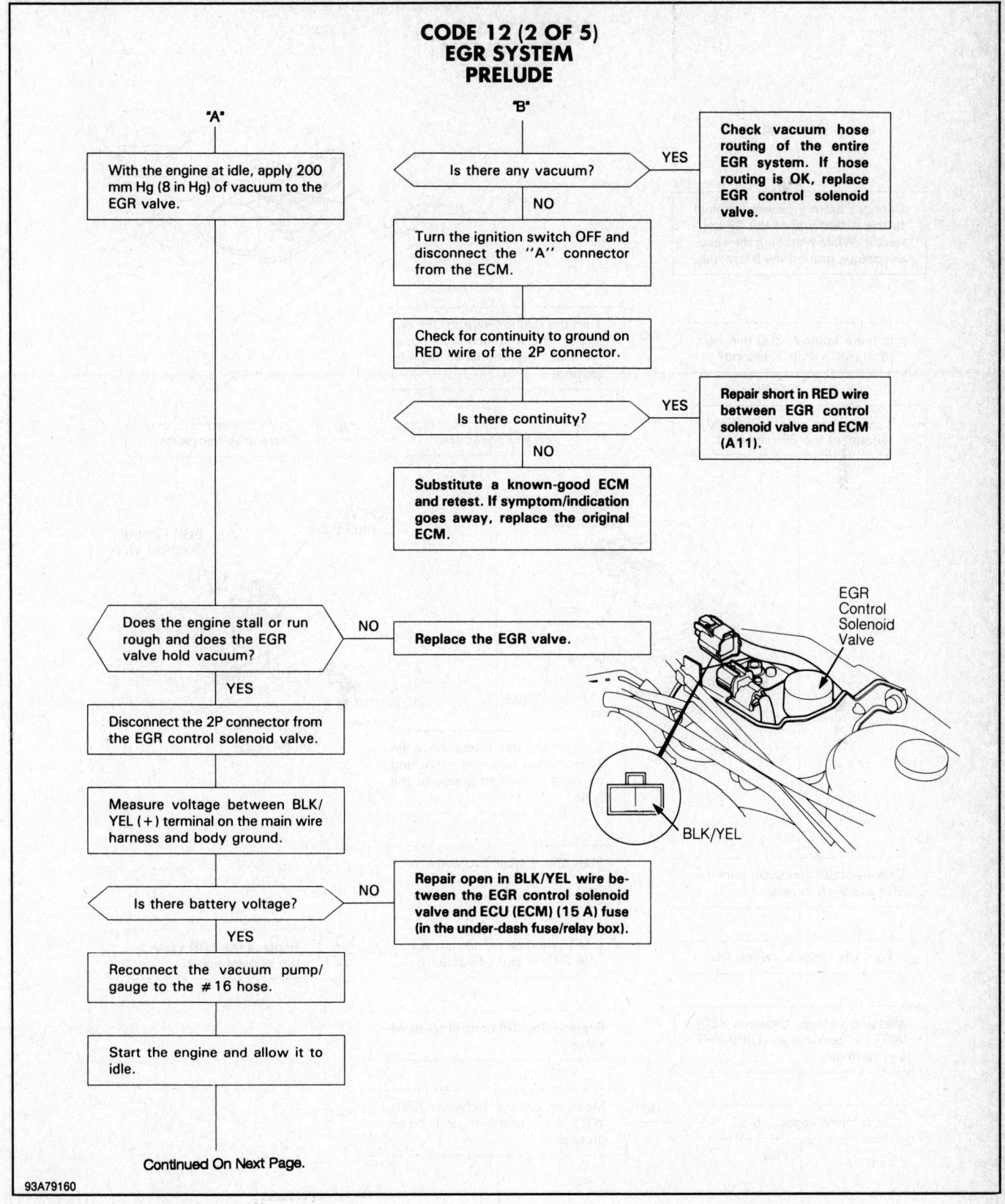

CODE 12 (2 OF 5)
EGR SYSTEM
PRELUDE

"A"

With the engine at idle, apply 200 mm Hg (8 in Hg) of vacuum to the EGR valve.

"B"

Is there any vacuum? — **YES** → Check vacuum hose routing of the entire EGR system. If hose routing is OK, replace EGR control solenoid valve.

NO

Turn the ignition switch OFF and disconnect the "A" connector from the ECM.

Check for continuity to ground on RED wire of the 2P connector.

Is there continuity? — **YES** → Repair short in RED wire between EGR control solenoid valve and ECM (A11).

NO

Substitute a known-good ECM and retest. If symptom/indication goes away, replace the original ECM.

Does the engine stall or run rough and does the EGR valve hold vacuum? — **NO** → Replace the EGR valve.

YES

Disconnect the 2P connector from the EGR control solenoid valve.

Measure voltage between BLK/YEL (+) terminal on the main wire harness and body ground.

Is there battery voltage? — **NO** → Repair open in BLK/YEL wire between the EGR control solenoid valve and ECU (ECM) (15 A) fuse (in the under-dash fuse/relay box).

YES

Reconnect the vacuum pump/gauge to the #16 hose.

Start the engine and allow it to idle.

EGR Control Solenoid Valve

BLK/YEL

Continued On Next Page.

93A79160

CODE 12 (3 OF 5)
EGR SYSTEM
PRELUDE

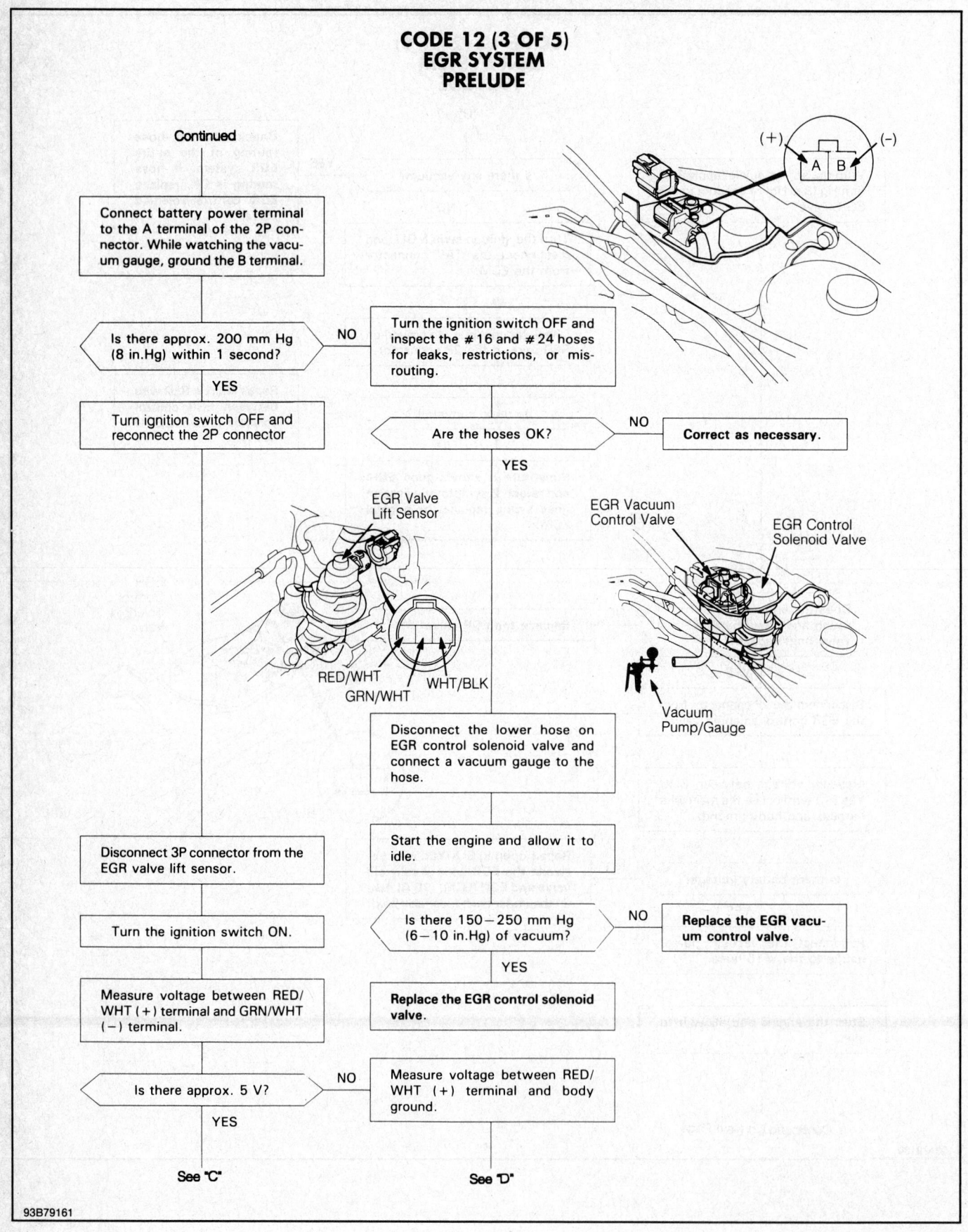

Continued

Connect battery power terminal to the A terminal of the 2P connector. While watching the vacuum gauge, ground the B terminal.

Is there approx. 200 mm Hg (8 in.Hg) within 1 second? — **NO** → Turn the ignition switch OFF and inspect the #16 and #24 hoses for leaks, restrictions, or misrouting.

YES

Turn ignition switch OFF and reconnect the 2P connector

Are the hoses OK? — **NO** → Correct as necessary.

YES

(+) A B (−)

EGR Valve Lift Sensor

EGR Vacuum Control Valve

EGR Control Solenoid Valve

RED/WHT GRN/WHT WHT/BLK

Vacuum Pump/Gauge

Disconnect the lower hose on EGR control solenoid valve and connect a vacuum gauge to the hose.

Disconnect 3P connector from the EGR valve lift sensor.

Start the engine and allow it to idle.

Turn the ignition switch ON.

Is there 150—250 mm Hg (6—10 in.Hg) of vacuum? — **NO** → **Replace the EGR vacuum control valve.**

YES

Measure voltage between RED/WHT (+) terminal and GRN/WHT (−) terminal.

Replace the EGR control solenoid valve.

Is there approx. 5 V? — **NO** → Measure voltage between RED/WHT (+) terminal and body ground.

YES

See "C"

See "D"

CODE 12 (4 OF 5)
EGR SYSTEM
PRELUDE

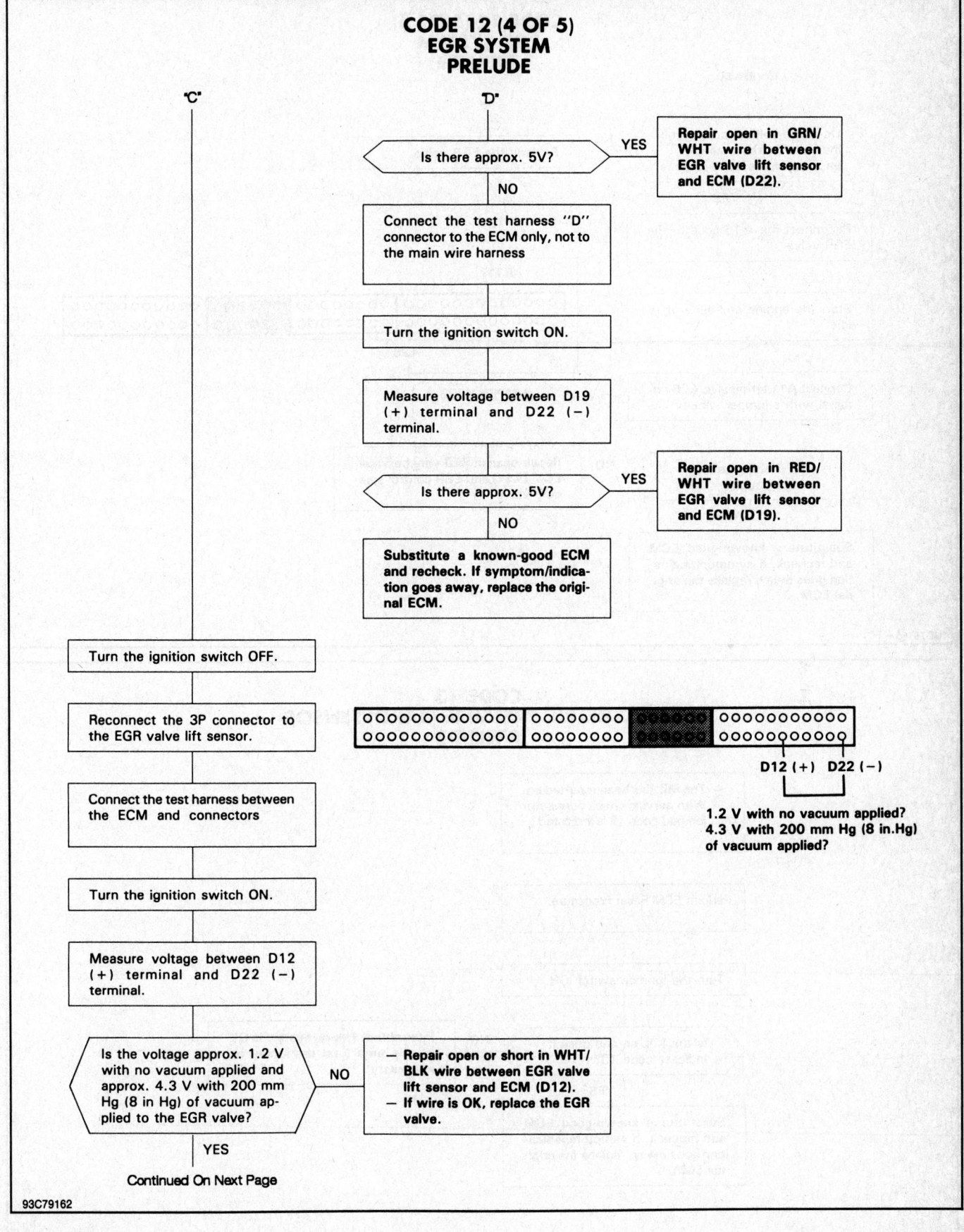

"C"

"D"

Is there approx. 5V? — **YES** → Repair open in GRN/WHT wire between EGR valve lift sensor and ECM (D22).

NO

Connect the test harness "D" connector to the ECM only, not to the main wire harness

Turn the ignition switch ON.

Measure voltage between D19 (+) terminal and D22 (−) terminal.

Is there approx. 5V? — **YES** → Repair open in RED/WHT wire between EGR valve lift sensor and ECM (D19).

NO

Substitute a known-good ECM and recheck. If symptom/indication goes away, replace the original ECM.

Turn the ignition switch OFF.

Reconnect the 3P connector to the EGR valve lift sensor.

Connect the test harness between the ECM and connectors

Turn the ignition switch ON.

Measure voltage between D12 (+) terminal and D22 (−) terminal.

D12 (+)   D22 (−)

1.2 V with no vacuum applied?
4.3 V with 200 mm Hg (8 in.Hg) of vacuum applied?

Is the voltage approx. 1.2 V with no vacuum applied and approx. 4.3 V with 200 mm Hg (8 in Hg) of vacuum applied to the EGR valve? — **NO** →
— Repair open or short in WHT/BLK wire between EGR valve lift sensor and ECM (D12).
— If wire is OK, replace the EGR valve.

YES

Continued On Next Page

93C79162

CODE 12 (5 OF 5)
EGR SYSTEM
PRELUDE

Continued

Does the voltage consistenly increase/decrease as the vacuum increases/decreases?

NO → Replace the EGR valve.

YES

Reconnect the #16 hose to the EGR valve.

Start the engine and allow it to idle.

Connect A11 terminal to A26 terminal with a jumper wire.

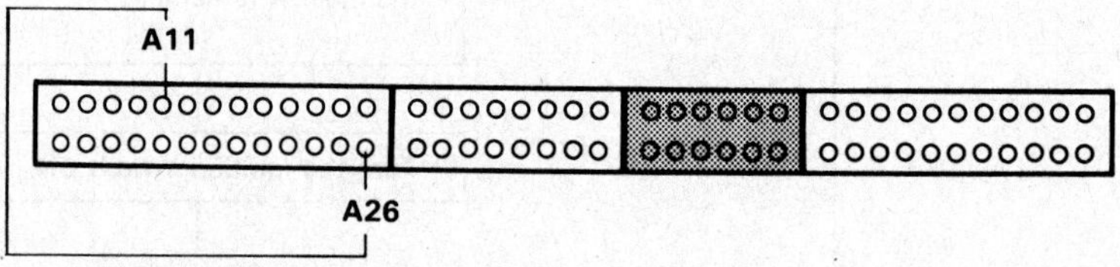

A11

A26

JUMPER WIRE

Did the engine stall or run rough?

NO → Repair open in RED wire between ECM (A11) and EGR control solenoid valve.

YES

Substitute a known-good ECM and recheck. If symptom/indication goes away, replace the original ECM.

93D79163

CODE 13
BAROMETRIC PRESSURE (BARO) SENSOR
PRELUDE

— The MIL has been reported on.
— With service check connector jumped code 13 is indicated ,

Perform ECM Reset Procedure.

Turn the ignition switch ON.

Is the MIL on and does it indicate code 13?

NO → Intermittent failure, system is OK at this time (test drive may be necessary).

YES

Substitute a known-good ECM and recheck. If symptom/indication goes away, replace the original ECM.

93C79022

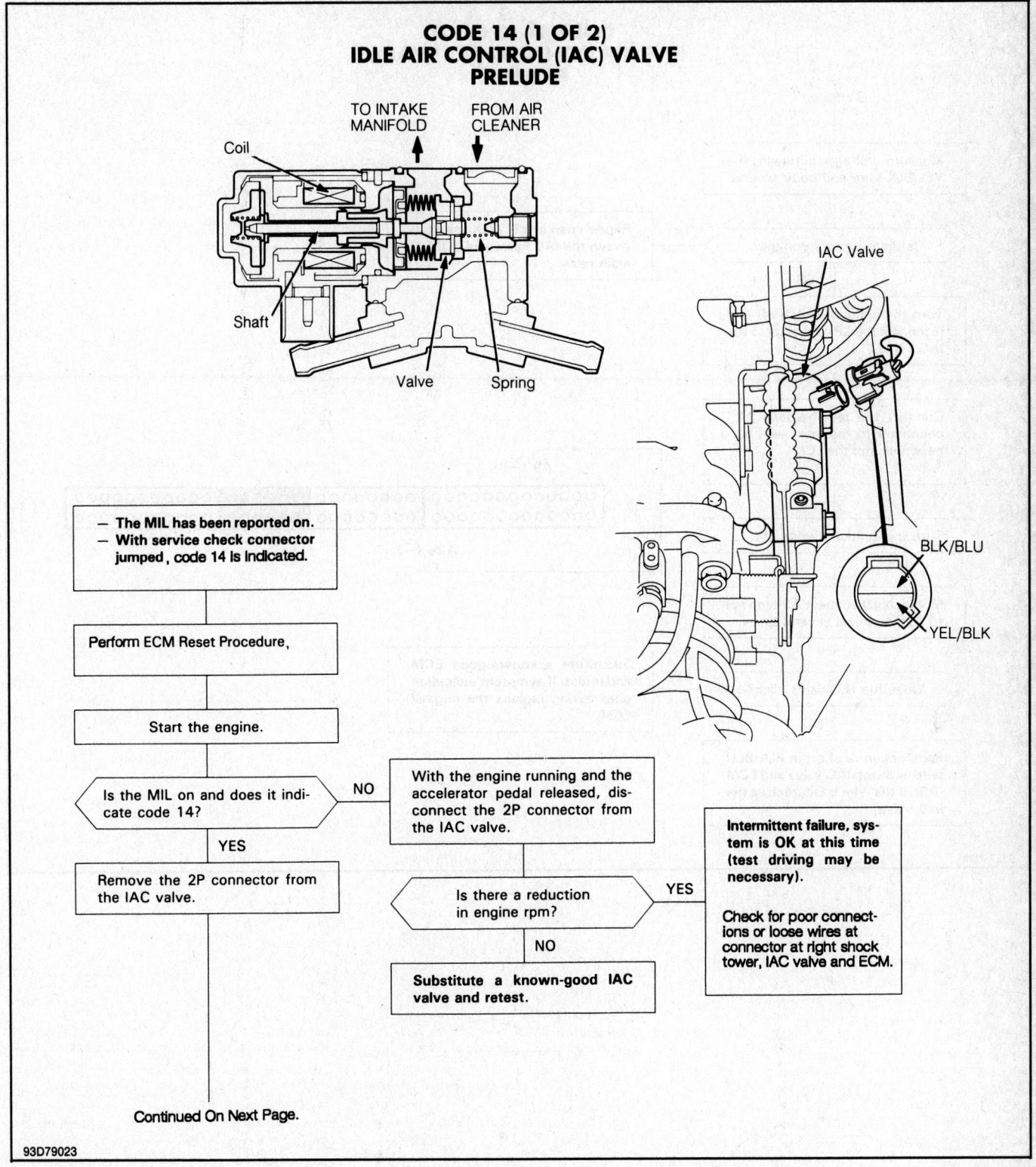

**CODE 14 (1 OF 2)
IDLE AIR CONTROL (IAC) VALVE
PRELUDE**

TO INTAKE MANIFOLD

FROM AIR CLEANER

Coil

Shaft

Valve

Spring

IAC Valve

BLK/BLU

YEL/BLK

- The MIL has been reported on.
- With service check connector jumped, code 14 is indicated.

↓

Perform ECM Reset Procedure,

↓

Start the engine.

↓

Is the MIL on and does it indicate code 14? — **NO** →

YES

↓

Remove the 2P connector from the IAC valve.

→ With the engine running and the accelerator pedal released, disconnect the 2P connector from the IAC valve.

↓

Is there a reduction in engine rpm? — **YES** →

NO

↓

Substitute a known-good IAC valve and retest.

Intermittent failure, system is OK at this time (test driving may be necessary).

Check for poor connections or loose wires at connector at right shock tower, IAC valve and ECM.

Continued On Next Page.

93D79023

CODE 14 (2 OF 2)
IDLE AIR CONTROL (IAC) VALVE
PRELUDE

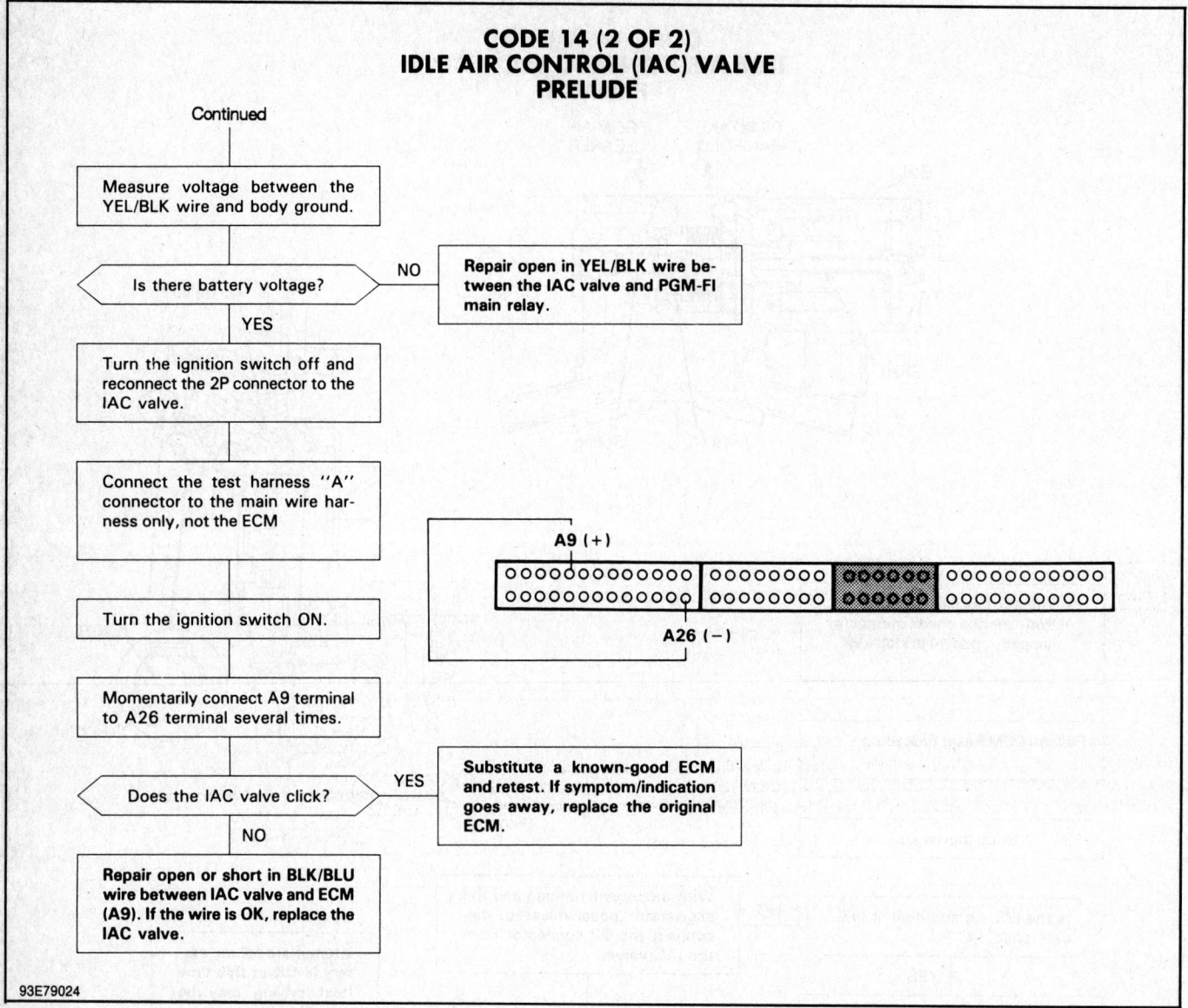

Continued

Measure voltage between the YEL/BLK wire and body ground.

Is there battery voltage? — NO → Repair open in YEL/BLK wire between the IAC valve and PGM-FI main relay.

YES

Turn the ignition switch off and reconnect the 2P connector to the IAC valve.

Connect the test harness "A" connector to the main wire harness only, not the ECM

A9 (+)

A26 (−)

Turn the ignition switch ON.

Momentarily connect A9 terminal to A26 terminal several times.

Does the IAC valve click? — YES → Substitute a known-good ECM and retest. If symptom/indication goes away, replace the original ECM.

NO

Repair open or short in BLK/BLU wire between IAC valve and ECM (A9). If the wire is OK, replace the IAC valve.

93E79024

CODE 15 (1 OF 2)
IGNITION OUTPUT SIGNAL
PRELUDE

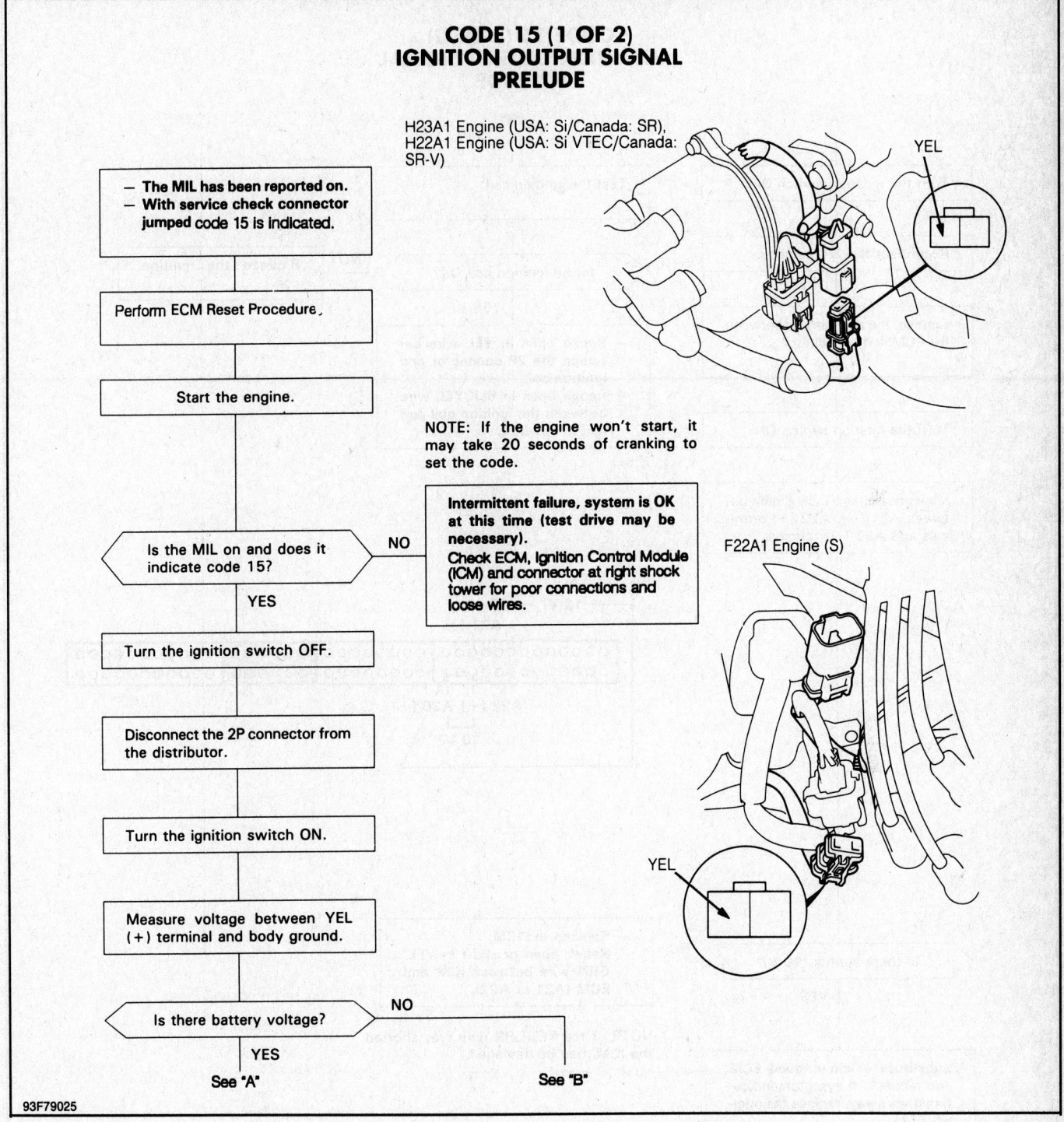

H23A1 Engine (USA: Si/Canada: SR),
H22A1 Engine (USA: Si VTEC/Canada: SR-V)

YEL

- The MIL has been reported on.
- With service check connector jumped code 15 is indicated.

↓

Perform ECM Reset Procedure.

↓

Start the engine.

NOTE: If the engine won't start, it may take 20 seconds of cranking to set the code.

Is the MIL on and does it indicate code 15? —NO→ Intermittent failure, system is OK at this time (test drive may be necessary).
Check ECM, Ignition Control Module (ICM) and connector at right shock tower for poor connections and loose wires.

YES
↓

Turn the ignition switch OFF.

↓

Disconnect the 2P connector from the distributor.

↓

Turn the ignition switch ON.

↓

Measure voltage between YEL (+) terminal and body ground.

↓

Is there battery voltage? —NO→

F22A1 Engine (S)

YEL

YES
↓

See "A"   See "B"

93F79025

1994 ENGINE PERFORMANCE
Self-Diagnostics (Cont.)

CODE 15 (2 OF 2)
IGNITION OUTPUT SIGNAL
PRELUDE

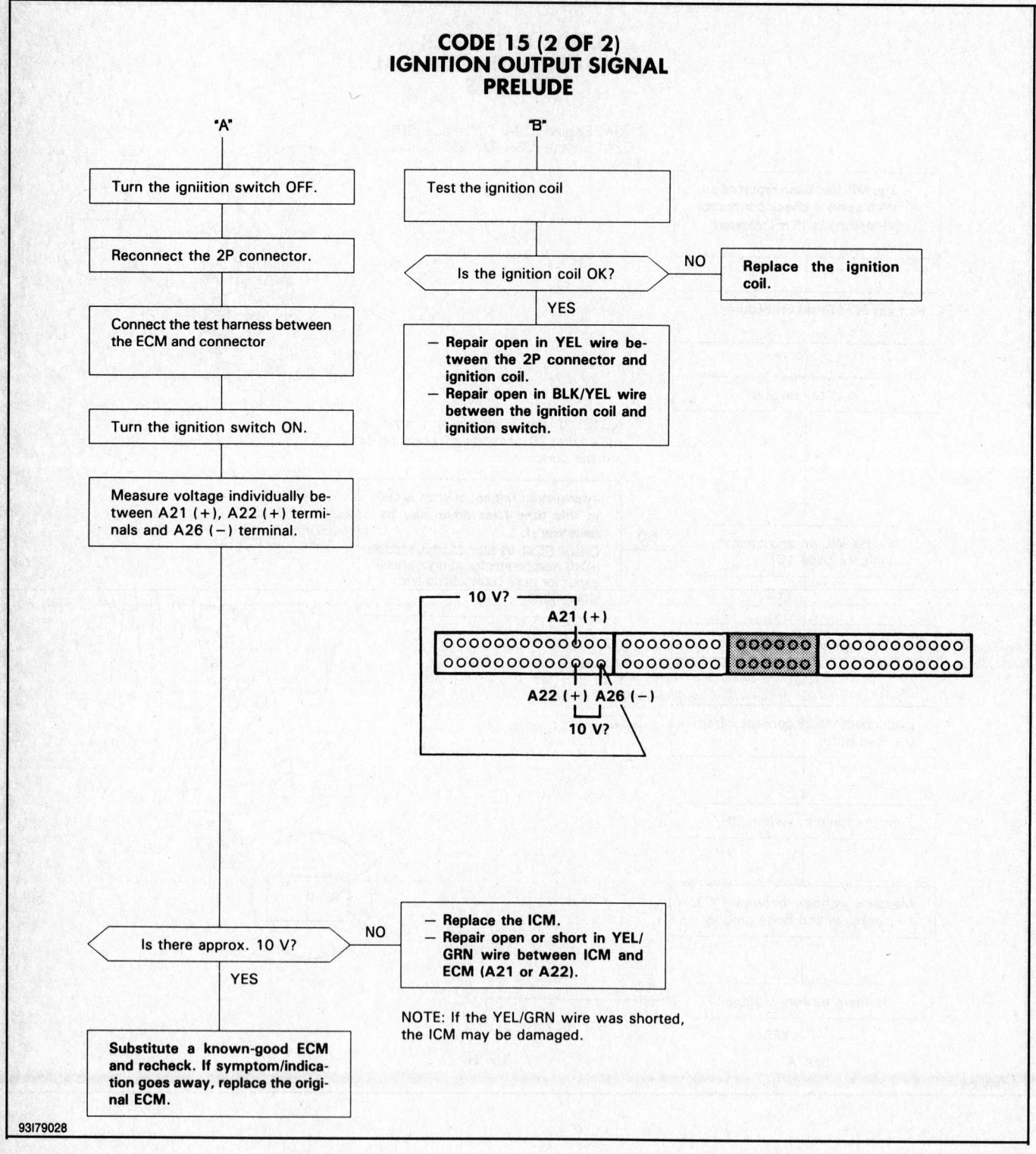

93I79028

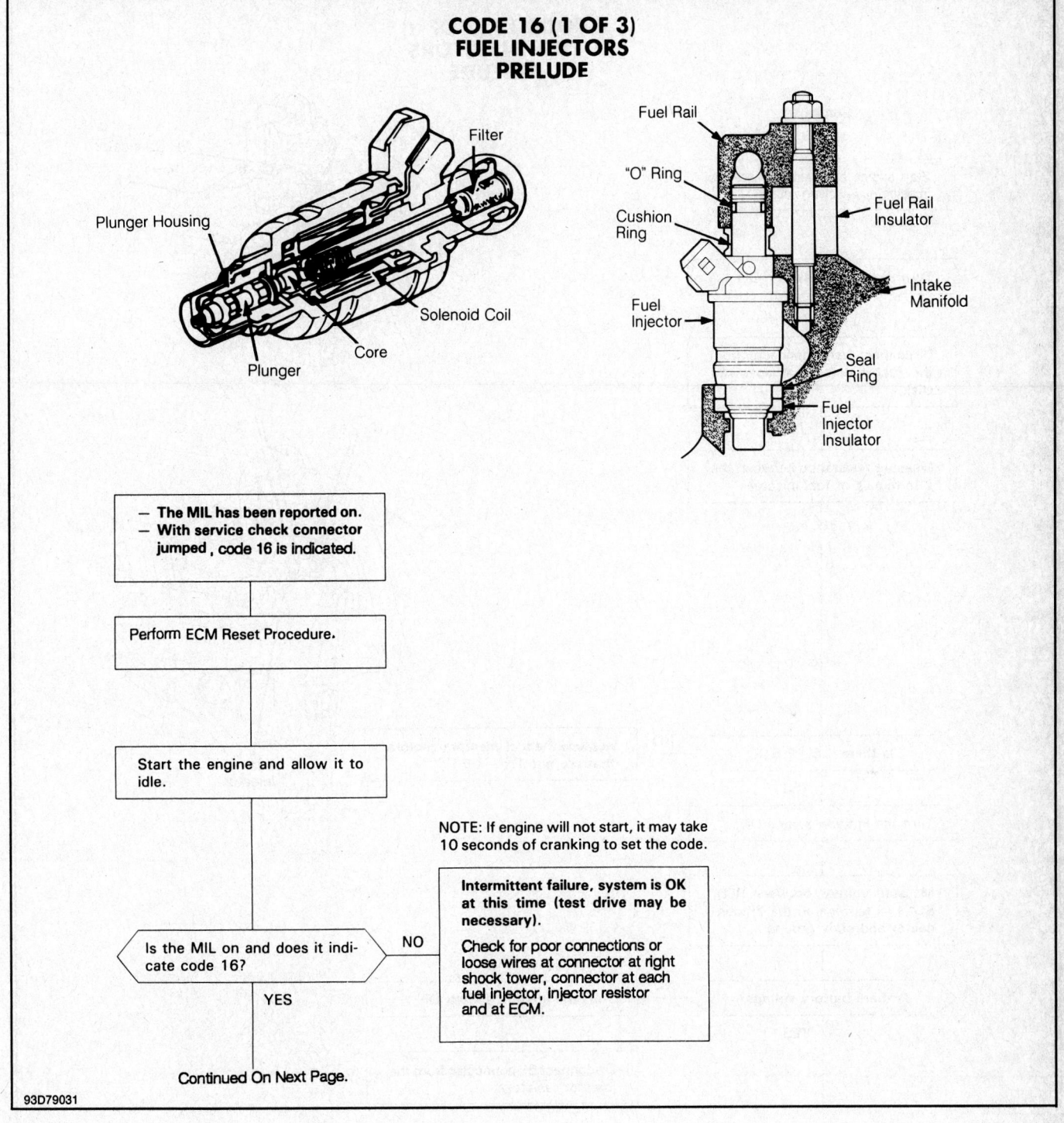

**CODE 16 (1 OF 3)
FUEL INJECTORS
PRELUDE**

Filter

Plunger Housing

Solenoid Coil

Core

Plunger

Fuel Rail

"O" Ring

Cushion Ring

Fuel Rail Insulator

Fuel Injector

Intake Manifold

Seal Ring

Fuel Injector Insulator

— The MIL has been reported on.
— With service check connector jumped , code 16 is indicated.

Perform ECM Reset Procedure.

Start the engine and allow it to idle.

NOTE: If engine will not start, it may take 10 seconds of cranking to set the code.

Is the MIL on and does it indicate code 16? — NO →

Intermittent failure, system is OK at this time (test drive may be necessary).

Check for poor connections or loose wires at connector at right shock tower, connector at each fuel injector, injector resistor and at ECM.

YES

Continued On Next Page.

93D79031

CODE 16 (2 OF 3)
FUEL INJECTORS
PRELUDE

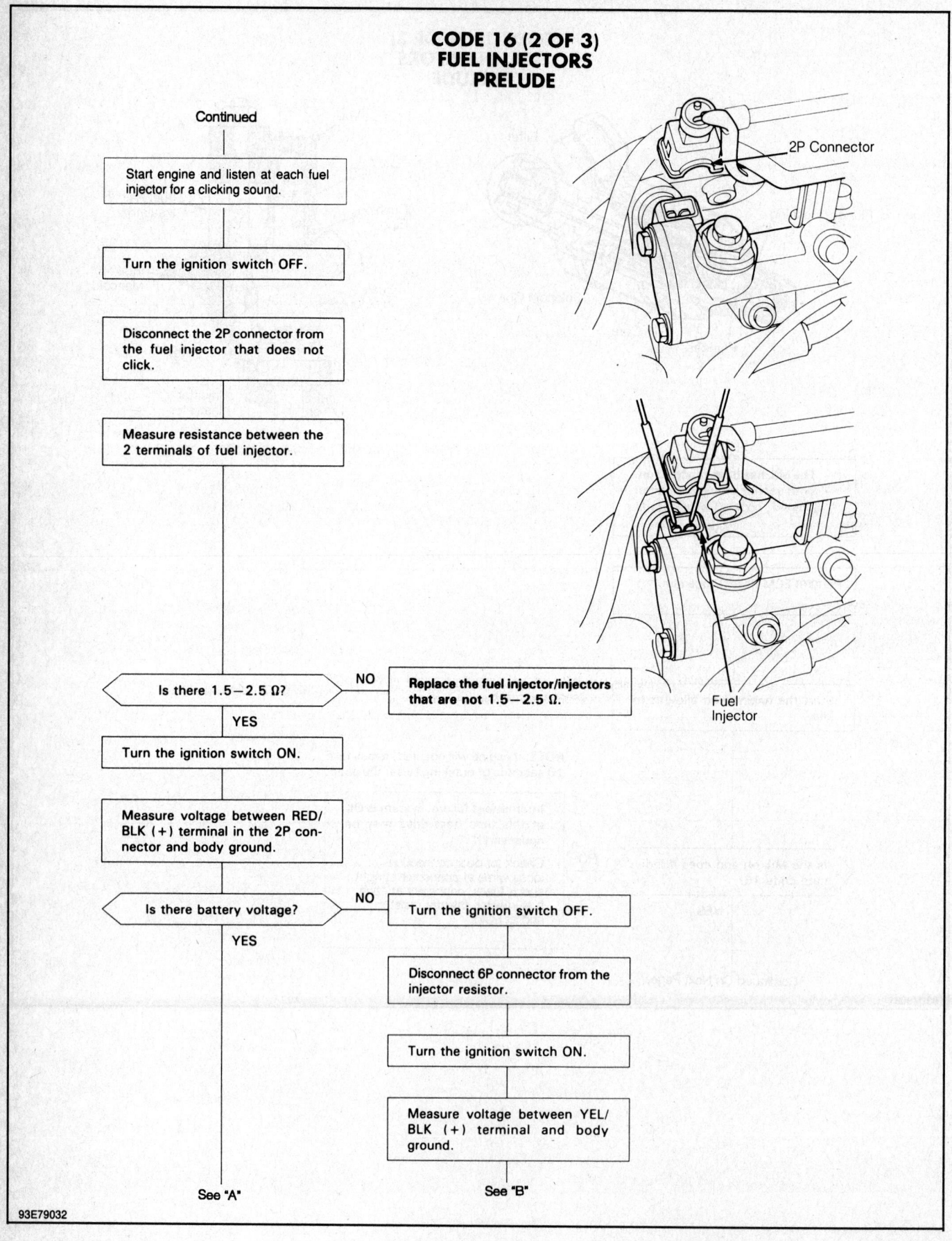

Continued

Start engine and listen at each fuel injector for a clicking sound.

Turn the ignition switch OFF.

Disconnect the 2P connector from the fuel injector that does not click.

Measure resistance between the 2 terminals of fuel injector.

Is there 1.5—2.5 Ω? — NO → Replace the fuel injector/injectors that are not 1.5—2.5 Ω.

YES

Turn the ignition switch ON.

Measure voltage between RED/BLK (+) terminal in the 2P connector and body ground.

Is there battery voltage? — NO → Turn the ignition switch OFF.

YES

Disconnect 6P connector from the injector resistor.

Turn the ignition switch ON.

Measure voltage between YEL/BLK (+) terminal and body ground.

See "A"

See "B"

2P Connector

Fuel Injector

93E79032

CODE 16 (3 OF 3)
FUEL INJECTORS
PRELUDE

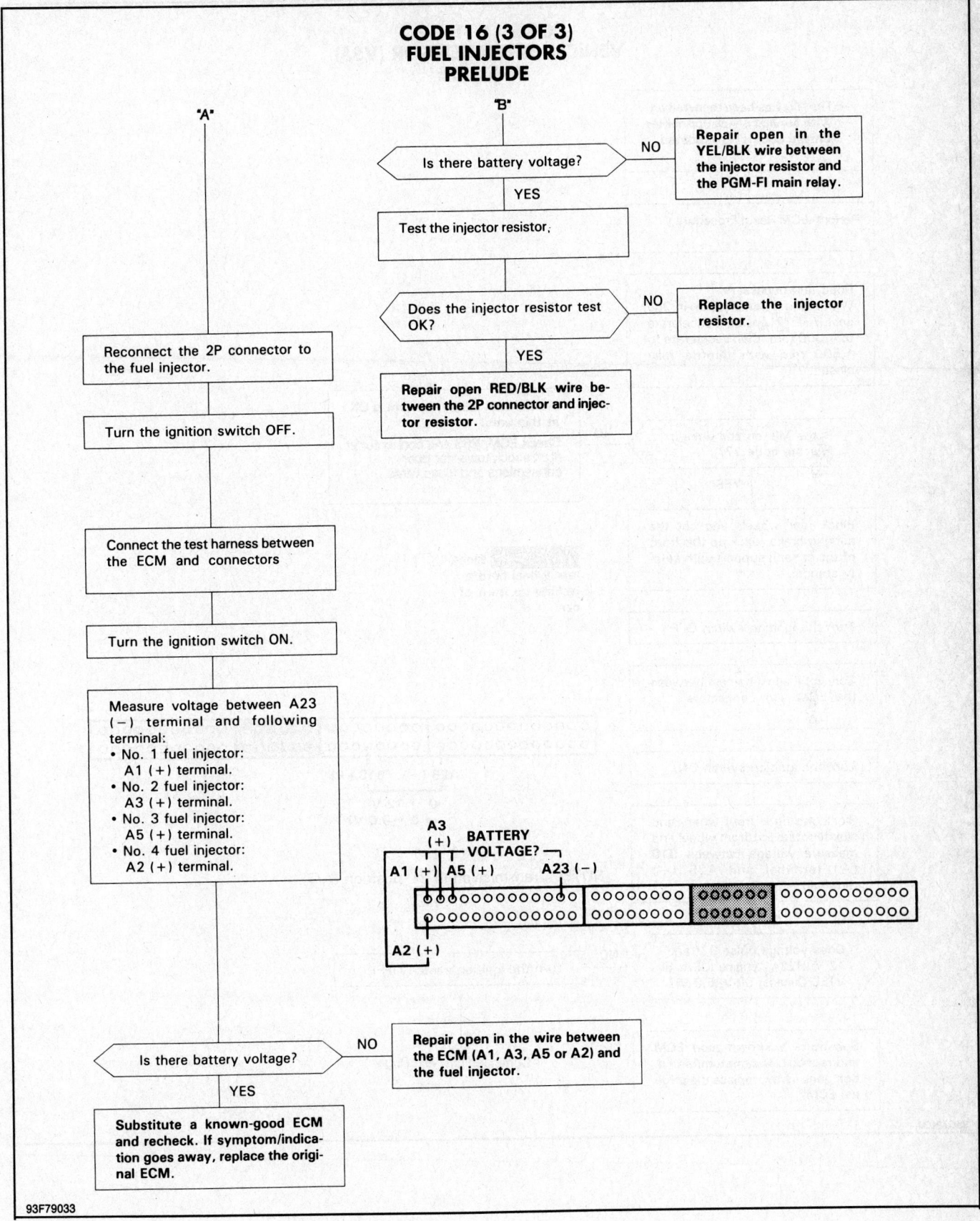

"A"

"B"

Is there battery voltage? — NO → Repair open in the YEL/BLK wire between the injector resistor and the PGM-FI main relay.

YES

Test the injector resistor.

Does the injector resistor test OK? — NO → Replace the injector resistor.

YES

Repair open RED/BLK wire between the 2P connector and injector resistor.

Reconnect the 2P connector to the fuel injector.

Turn the ignition switch OFF.

Connect the test harness between the ECM and connectors

Turn the ignition switch ON.

Measure voltage between A23 (−) terminal and following terminal:
- No. 1 fuel injector: A1 (+) terminal.
- No. 2 fuel injector: A3 (+) terminal.
- No. 3 fuel injector: A5 (+) terminal.
- No. 4 fuel injector: A2 (+) terminal.

A3 (+)
BATTERY VOLTAGE?
A1 (+) A5 (+) A23 (−)
A2 (+)

Is there battery voltage? — NO → Repair open in the wire between the ECM (A1, A3, A5 or A2) and the fuel injector.

YES

Substitute a known-good ECM and recheck. If symptom/indication goes away, replace the original ECM.

93F79033

CODE 17 (1 OF 2)
VEHICLE SPEED SENSOR (VSS)
PRELUDE

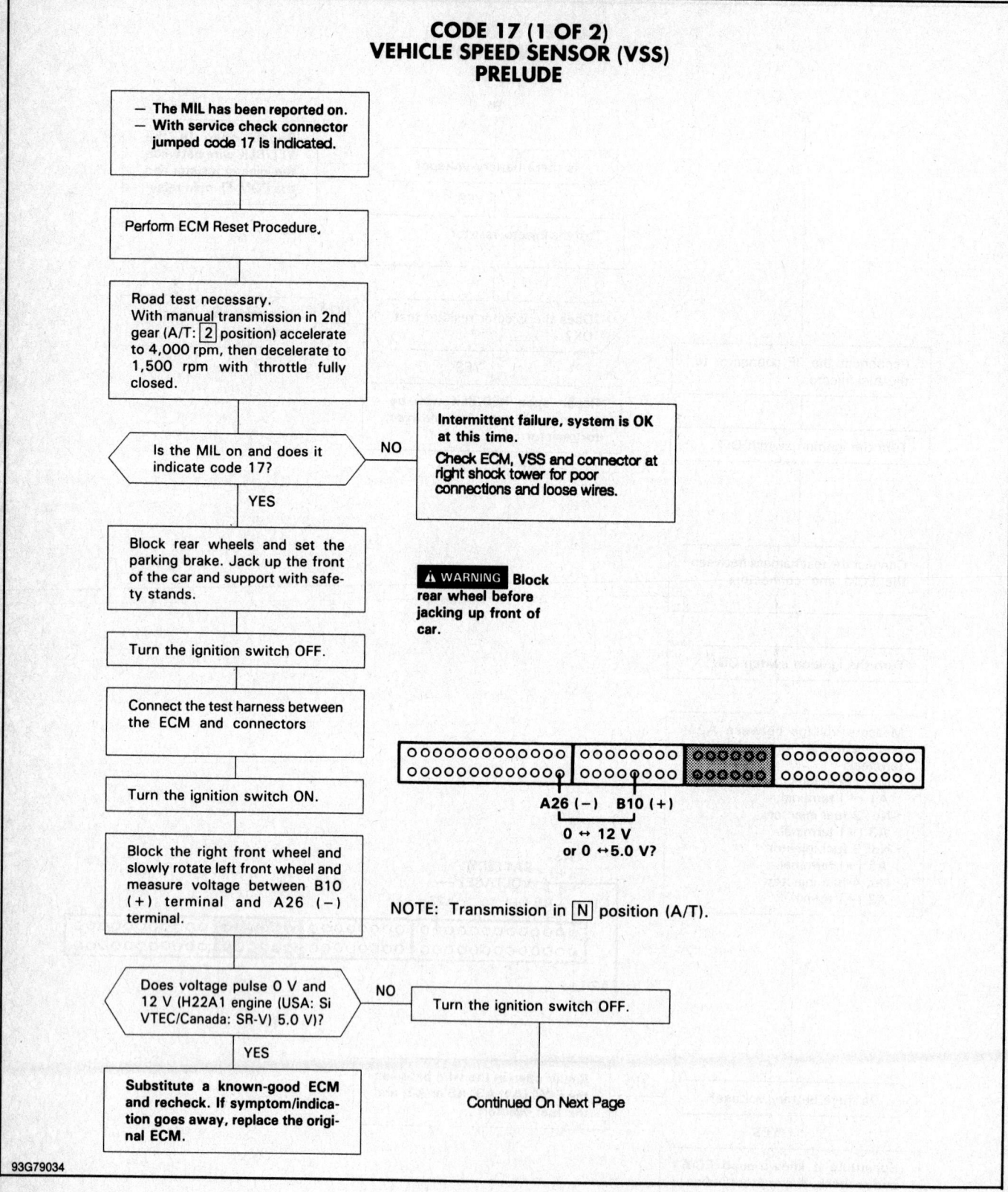

— The MIL has been reported on.
— With service check connector jumped code 17 is indicated.

Perform ECM Reset Procedure.

Road test necessary.
With manual transmission in 2nd gear (A/T: 2 position) accelerate to 4,000 rpm, then decelerate to 1,500 rpm with throttle fully closed.

Is the MIL on and does it indicate code 17?

NO → Intermittent failure, system is OK at this time.
Check ECM, VSS and connector at right shock tower for poor connections and loose wires.

YES

Block rear wheels and set the parking brake. Jack up the front of the car and support with safety stands.

⚠ WARNING Block rear wheel before jacking up front of car.

Turn the ignition switch OFF.

Connect the test harness between the ECM and connectors

Turn the ignition switch ON.

Block the right front wheel and slowly rotate left front wheel and measure voltage between B10 (+) terminal and A26 (−) terminal.

A26 (−)   B10 (+)
0 ↔ 12 V
or 0 ↔ 5.0 V?

NOTE: Transmission in N position (A/T).

Does voltage pulse 0 V and 12 V (H22A1 engine (USA: Si VTEC/Canada: SR-V) 5.0 V)?

NO → Turn the ignition switch OFF.

YES

Substitute a known-good ECM and recheck. If symptom/indication goes away, replace the original ECM.

Continued On Next Page

93G79034

CODE 17 (2 OF 2)
VEHICLE SPEED SENSOR (VSS)
PRELUDE

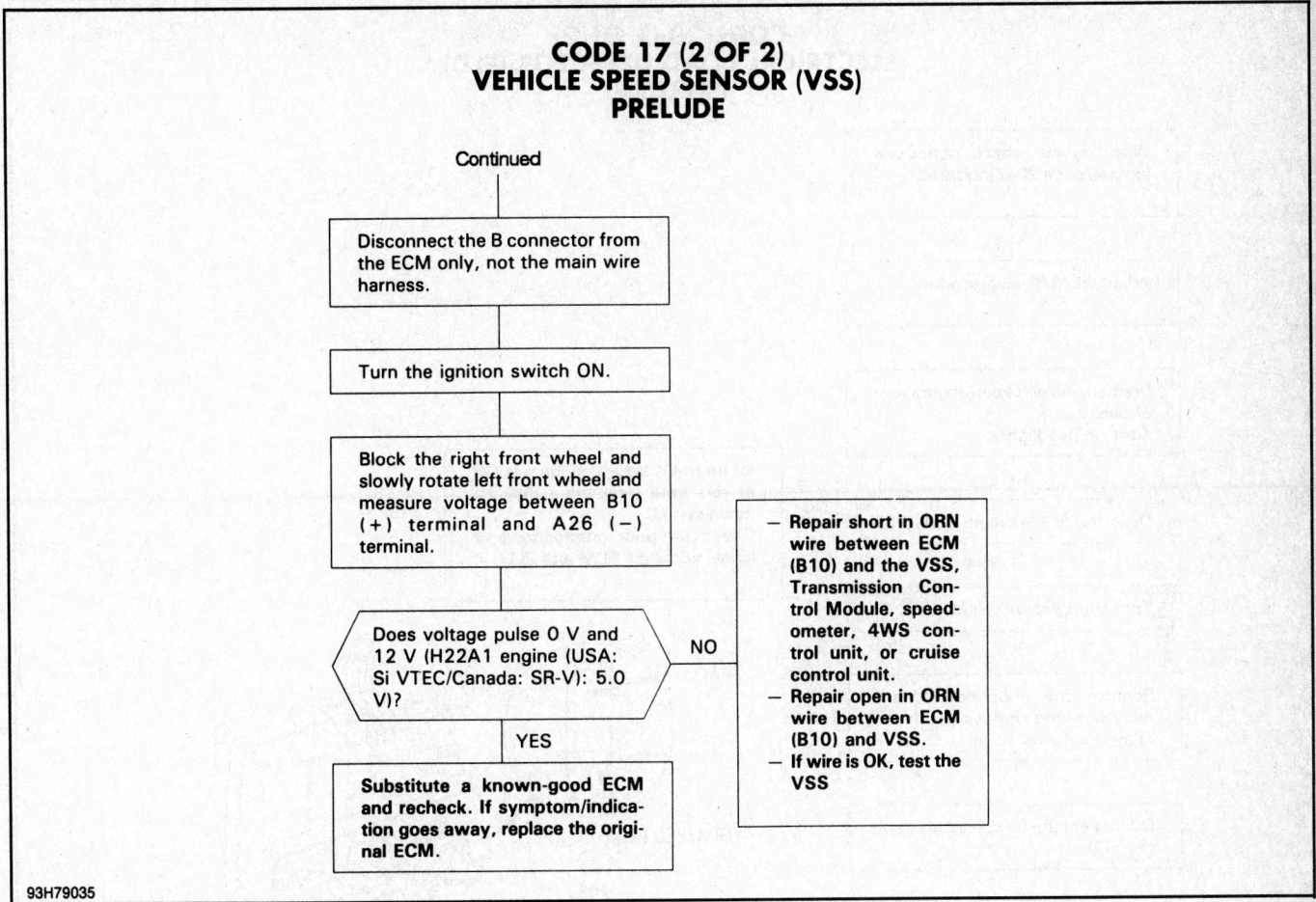

Continued

Disconnect the B connector from the ECM only, not the main wire harness.

Turn the ignition switch ON.

Block the right front wheel and slowly rotate left front wheel and measure voltage between B10 (+) terminal and A26 (−) terminal.

Does voltage pulse 0 V and 12 V (H22A1 engine (USA: Si VTEC/Canada: SR-V): 5.0 V)?

NO

— Repair short in ORN wire between ECM (B10) and the VSS, Transmission Control Module, speedometer, 4WS control unit, or cruise control unit.
— Repair open in ORN wire between ECM (B10) and VSS.
— If wire is OK, test the VSS

YES

Substitute a known-good ECM and recheck. If symptom/indication goes away, replace the original ECM.

93H79035

CODE 20 (1 OF 2)
ELECTRICAL LOAD DETECTOR (ELD)
PRELUDE

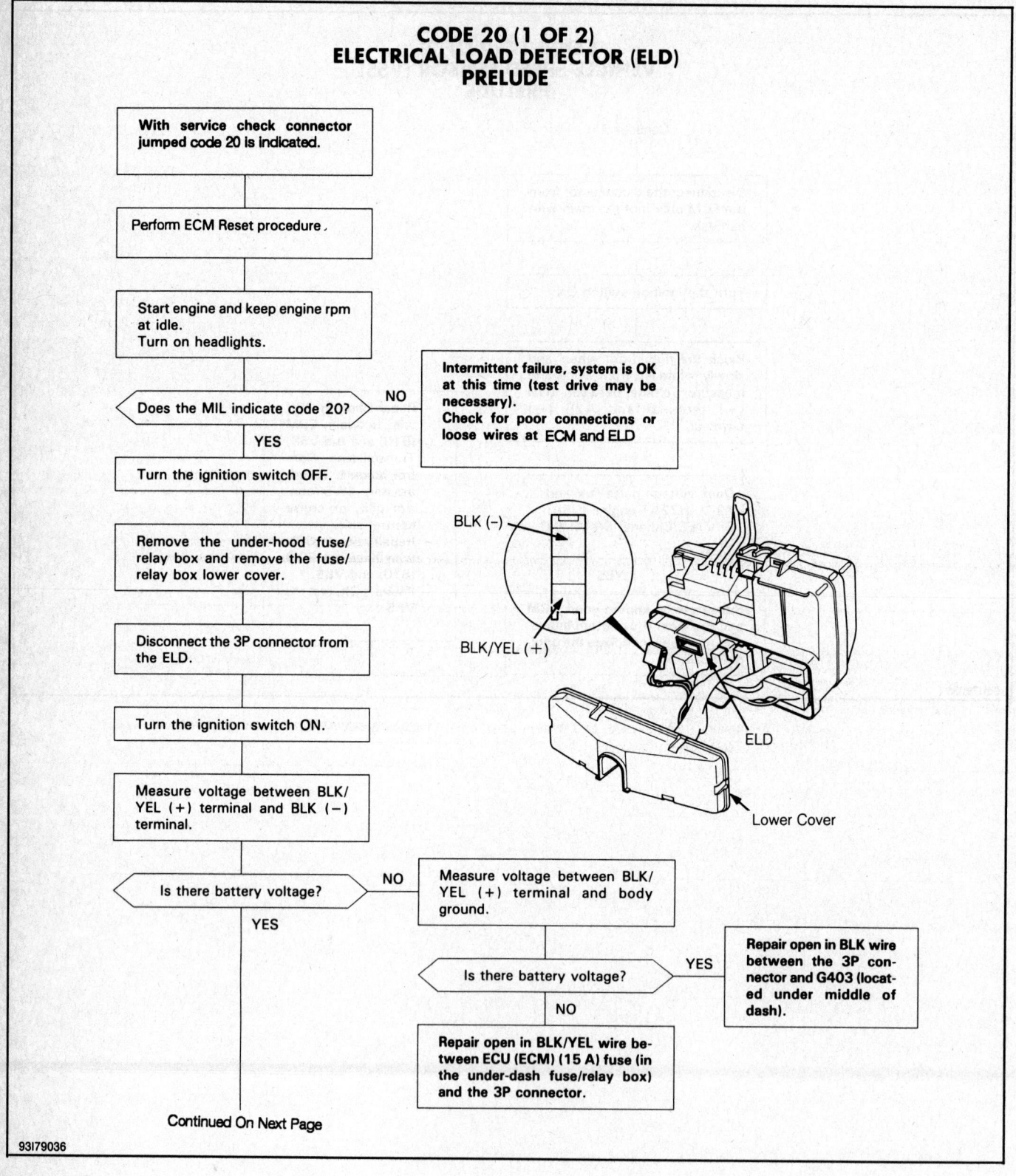

With service check connector jumped code 20 is indicated.

Perform ECM Reset procedure.

Start engine and keep engine rpm at idle.
Turn on headlights.

Does the MIL indicate code 20? — **NO** → Intermittent failure, system is OK at this time (test drive may be necessary).
Check for poor connections or loose wires at ECM and ELD

YES

Turn the ignition switch OFF.

Remove the under-hood fuse/relay box and remove the fuse/relay box lower cover.

Disconnect the 3P connector from the ELD.

Turn the ignition switch ON.

Measure voltage between BLK/YEL (+) terminal and BLK (−) terminal.

Is there battery voltage? — **NO** → Measure voltage between BLK/YEL (+) terminal and body ground.

YES

Is there battery voltage? — **YES** → Repair open in BLK wire between the 3P connector and G403 (located under middle of dash).

NO

Repair open in BLK/YEL wire between ECU (ECM) (15 A) fuse (in the under-dash fuse/relay box) and the 3P connector.

BLK (−)

BLK/YEL (+)

ELD

Lower Cover

Continued On Next Page

93I79036

CODE 20 (2 OF 2)
ELECTRICAL LOAD DETECTOR (ELD)
PRELUDE

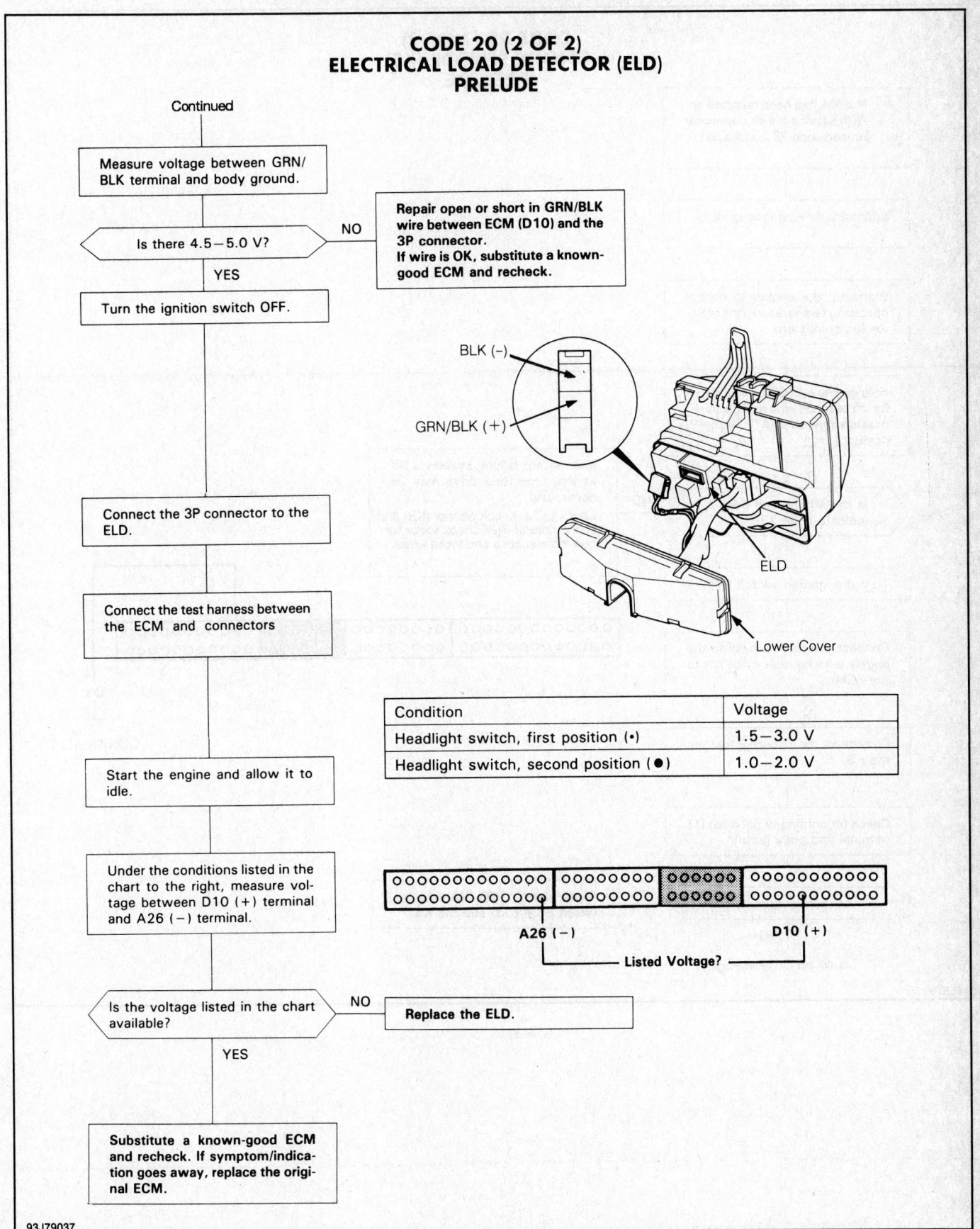

Continued

Measure voltage between GRN/BLK terminal and body ground.

Is there 4.5—5.0 V? — NO → Repair open or short in GRN/BLK wire between ECM (D10) and the 3P connector. If wire is OK, substitute a known-good ECM and recheck.

YES

Turn the ignition switch OFF.

BLK (−)

GRN/BLK (+)

Connect the 3P connector to the ELD.

Connect the test harness between the ECM and connectors

ELD

Lower Cover

Condition	Voltage
Headlight switch, first position (•)	1.5—3.0 V
Headlight switch, second position (●)	1.0—2.0 V

Start the engine and allow it to idle.

Under the conditions listed in the chart to the right, measure voltage between D10 (+) terminal and A26 (−) terminal.

A26 (−) D10 (+)

Listed Voltage?

Is the voltage listed in the chart available? — NO → Replace the ELD.

YES

Substitute a known-good ECM and recheck. If symptom/indication goes away, replace the original ECM.

93J79037

CODE 23 (1 OF 2)
KNOCK SENSOR (KS)
PRELUDE

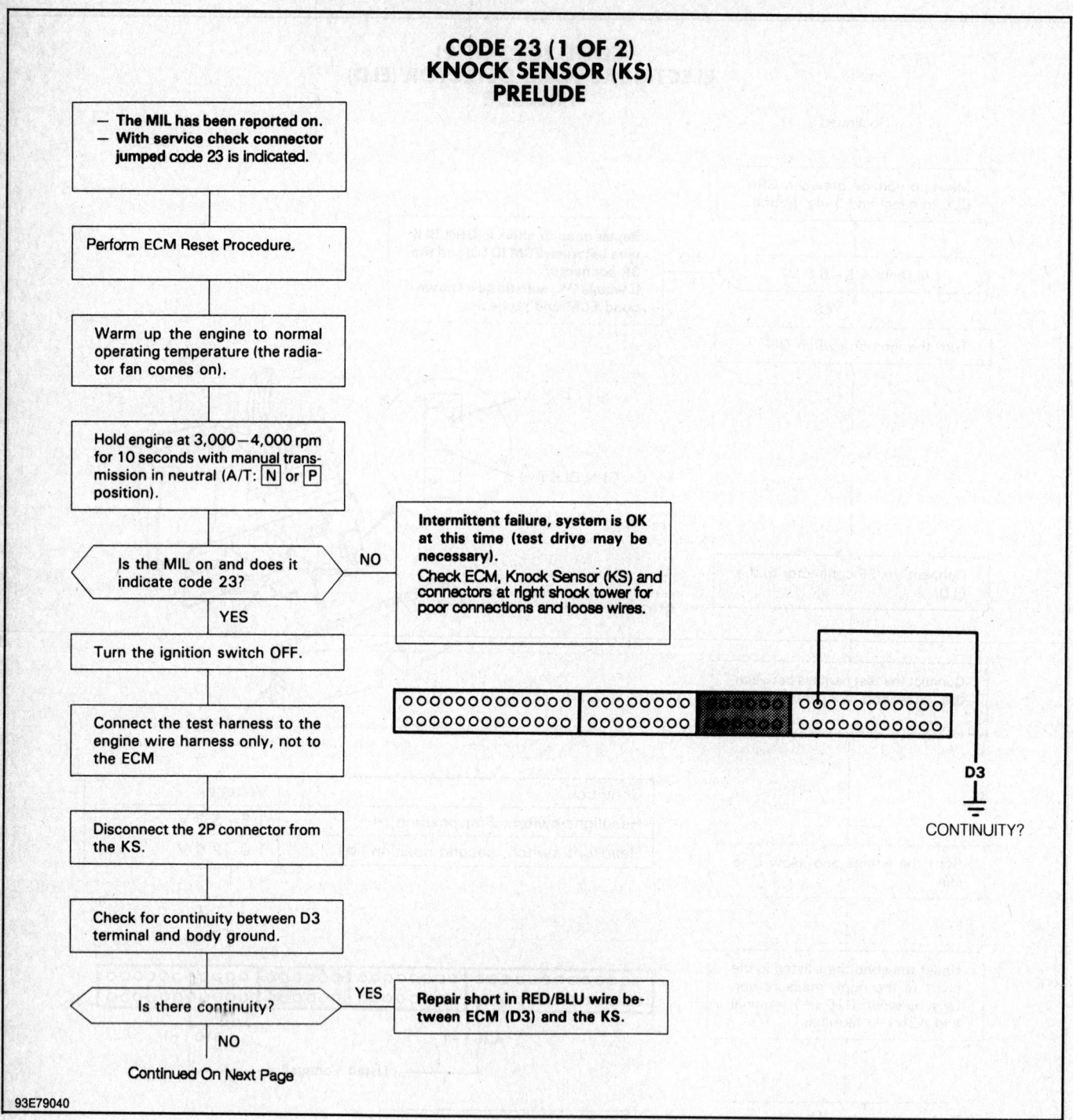

- The MIL has been reported on.
- With service check connector jumped code 23 is indicated.

Perform ECM Reset Procedure.

Warm up the engine to normal operating temperature (the radiator fan comes on).

Hold engine at 3,000—4,000 rpm for 10 seconds with manual transmission in neutral (A/T: N or P position).

Is the MIL on and does it indicate code 23?

NO → Intermittent failure, system is OK at this time (test drive may be necessary).
Check ECM, Knock Sensor (KS) and connectors at right shock tower for poor connections and loose wires.

YES

Turn the ignition switch OFF.

Connect the test harness to the engine wire harness only, not to the ECM

Disconnect the 2P connector from the KS.

Check for continuity between D3 terminal and body ground.

Is there continuity?

YES → Repair short in RED/BLU wire between ECM (D3) and the KS.

NO

D3
CONTINUITY?

Continued On Next Page

93E79040

**CODE 23 (2 OF 2)
KNOCK SENSOR (KS)
PRELUDE**

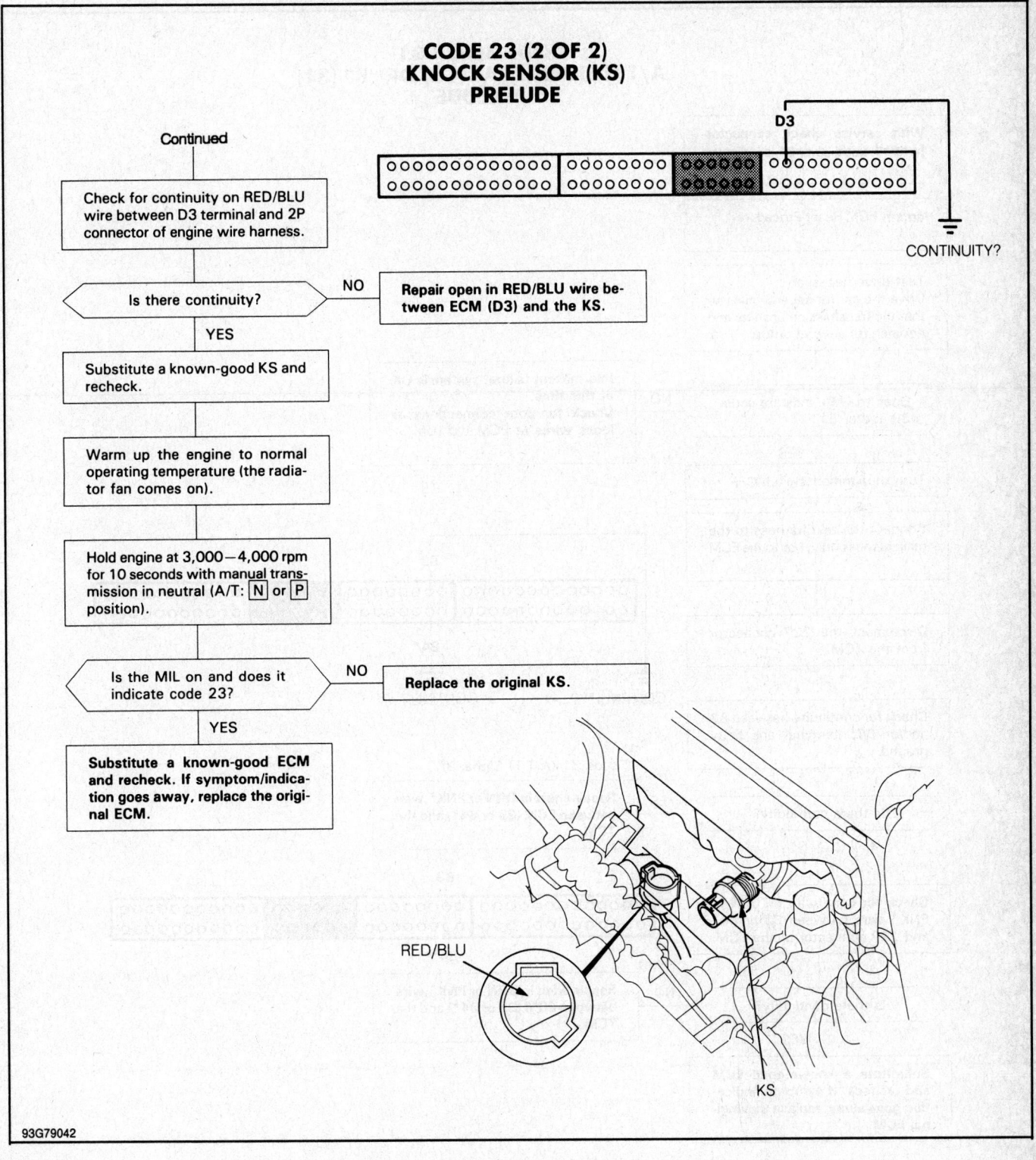

Continued

Check for continuity on RED/BLU wire between D3 terminal and 2P connector of engine wire harness.

CONTINUITY?

Is there continuity? — NO → Repair open in RED/BLU wire between ECM (D3) and the KS.

YES

Substitute a known-good KS and recheck.

Warm up the engine to normal operating temperature (the radiator fan comes on).

Hold engine at 3,000—4,000 rpm for 10 seconds with manual transmission in neutral (A/T: N or P position).

Is the MIL on and does it indicate code 23? — NO → Replace the original KS.

YES

Substitute a known-good ECM and recheck. If symptom/indication goes away, replace the original ECM.

RED/BLU

KS

93G79042

CODE 30 OR 31
A/T FI SIGNAL "A" (30) OR "B" (31)
PRELUDE

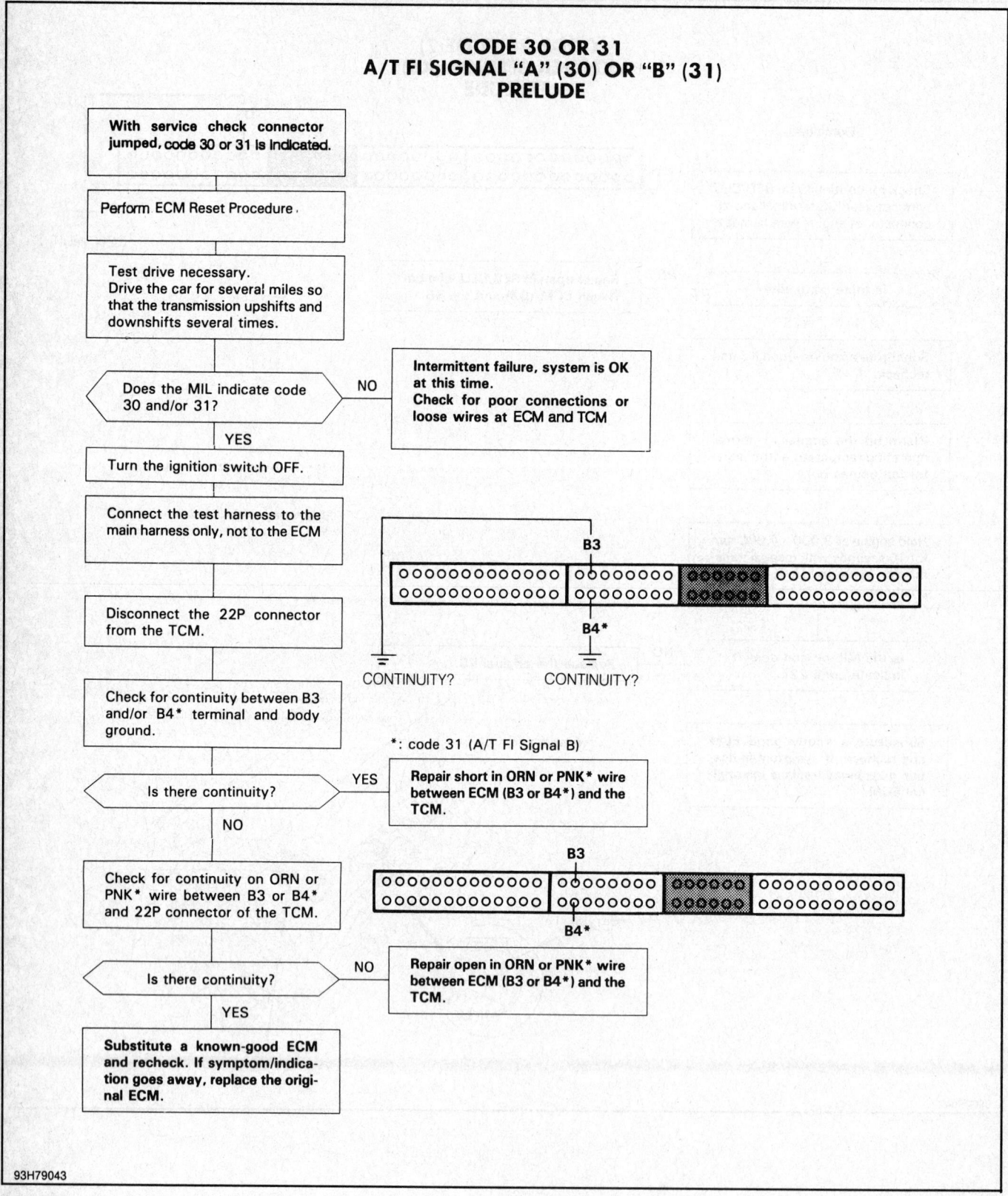

With service check connector jumped, code 30 or 31 is indicated.

Perform ECM Reset Procedure.

Test drive necessary.
Drive the car for several miles so that the transmission upshifts and downshifts several times.

Does the MIL indicate code 30 and/or 31? — NO → Intermittent failure, system is OK at this time.
Check for poor connections or loose wires at ECM and TCM

YES

Turn the ignition switch OFF.

Connect the test harness to the main harness only, not to the ECM

Disconnect the 22P connector from the TCM.

B3
B4*
CONTINUITY?   CONTINUITY?

Check for continuity between B3 and/or B4* terminal and body ground.

*: code 31 (A/T FI Signal B)

Is there continuity? — YES → Repair short in ORN or PNK* wire between ECM (B3 or B4*) and the TCM.

NO

Check for continuity on ORN or PNK* wire between B3 or B4* and 22P connector of the TCM.

B3
B4*

Is there continuity? — NO → Repair open in ORN or PNK* wire between ECM (B3 or B4*) and the TCM.

YES

Substitute a known-good ECM and recheck. If symptom/indication goes away, replace the original ECM.

93H79043

CODE 41 (1 OF 3)
HEATED OXYGEN SENSOR (HO2S) HEATER
PRELUDE

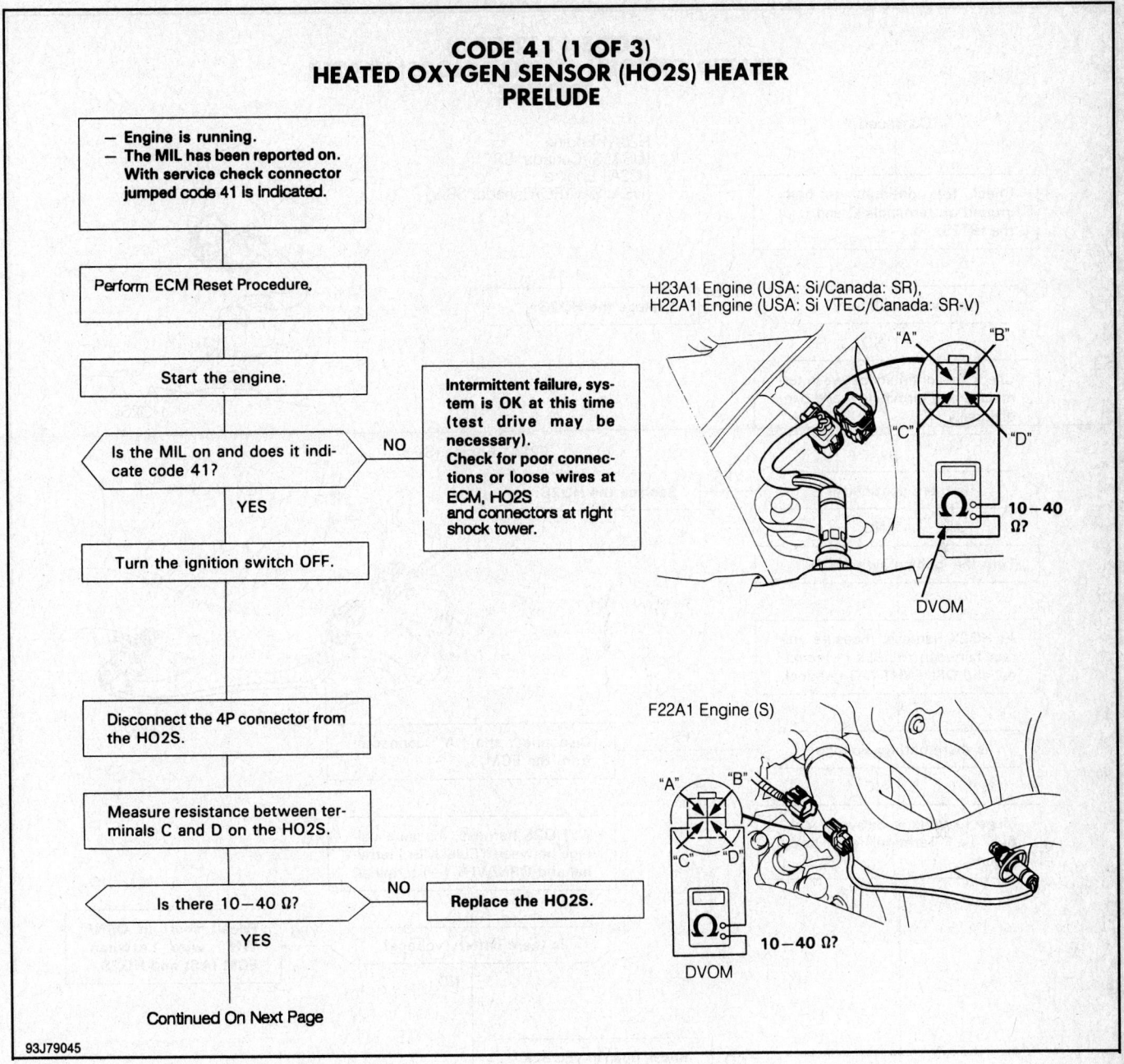

- Engine is running.
- The MIL has been reported on. With service check connector jumped code 41 is indicated.

Perform ECM Reset Procedure.

Start the engine.

Is the MIL on and does it indicate code 41? — **NO** → Intermittent failure, system is OK at this time (test drive may be necessary). Check for poor connections or loose wires at ECM, HO2S and connectors at right shock tower.

YES

Turn the ignition switch OFF.

Disconnect the 4P connector from the HO2S.

Measure resistance between terminals C and D on the HO2S.

Is there 10–40 Ω? — **NO** → Replace the HO2S.

YES

H23A1 Engine (USA: Si/Canada: SR), H22A1 Engine (USA: Si VTEC/Canada: SR-V)

"A" "B" "C" "D"

Ω 10–40 Ω?

DVOM

F22A1 Engine (S)

"A" "B" "C" "D"

Ω 10–40 Ω?

DVOM

Continued On Next Page

93J79045

CODE 41 (2 OF 3)
HEATED OXYGEN SENSOR (HO2S) HEATER
PRELUDE

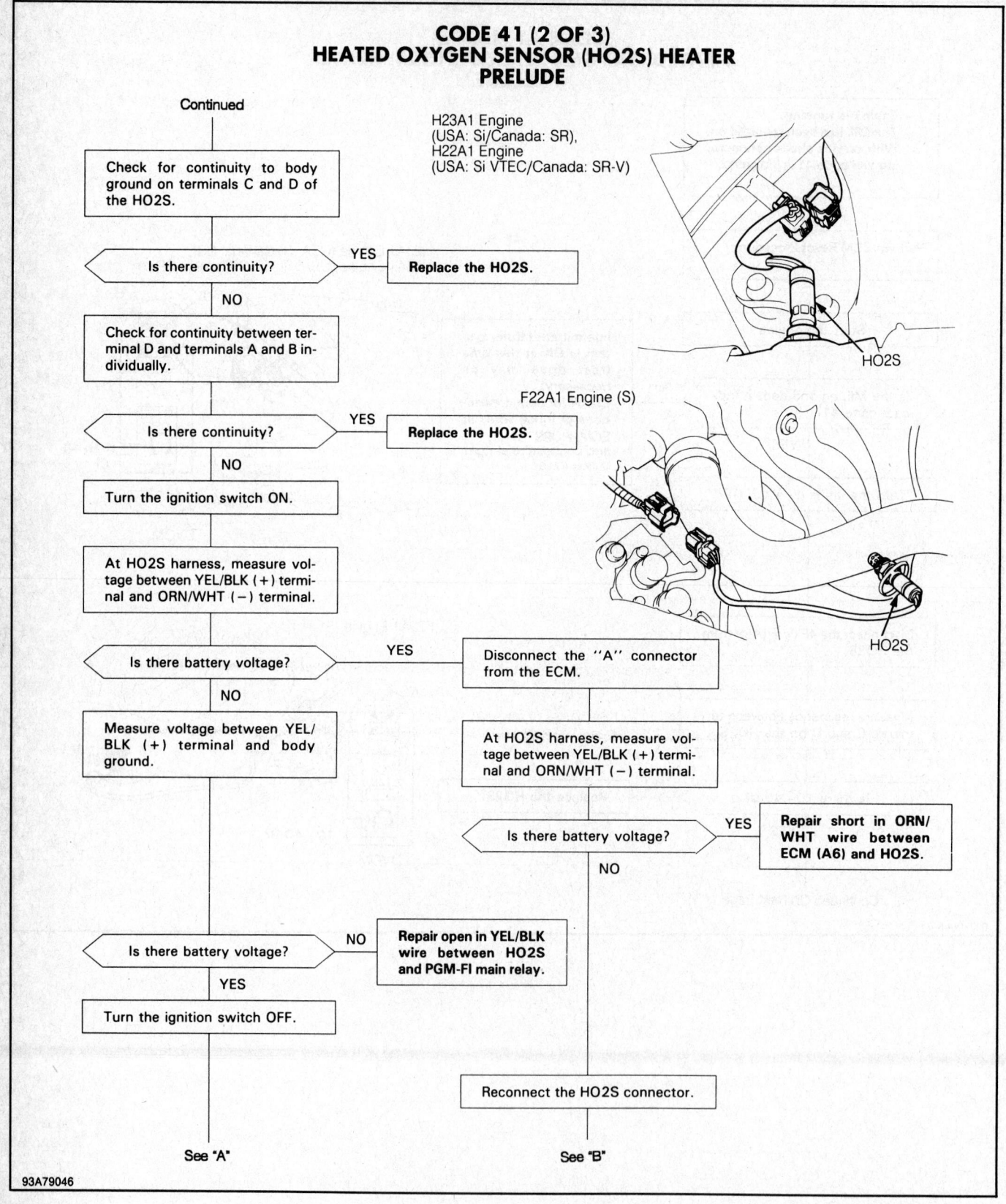

Continued

H23A1 Engine
(USA: Si/Canada: SR),
H22A1 Engine
(USA: Si VTEC/Canada: SR-V)

Check for continuity to body ground on terminals C and D of the HO2S.

Is there continuity? — YES → Replace the HO2S.

NO

Check for continuity between terminal D and terminals A and B individually.

F22A1 Engine (S)

Is there continuity? — YES → Replace the HO2S.

NO

Turn the ignition switch ON.

At HO2S harness, measure voltage between YEL/BLK (+) terminal and ORN/WHT (−) terminal.

HO2S

Is there battery voltage? — YES → Disconnect the "A" connector from the ECM.

NO

Measure voltage between YEL/BLK (+) terminal and body ground.

At HO2S harness, measure voltage between YEL/BLK (+) terminal and ORN/WHT (−) terminal.

Is there battery voltage? — YES → Repair short in ORN/WHT wire between ECM (A6) and HO2S.

NO

Is there battery voltage? — NO → Repair open in YEL/BLK wire between HO2S and PGM-FI main relay.

YES

Turn the ignition switch OFF.

Reconnect the HO2S connector.

See "A"

See "B"

93A79046

CODE 41 (3 OF 3)
HEATED OXYGEN SENSOR (HO2S) HEATER
PRELUDE

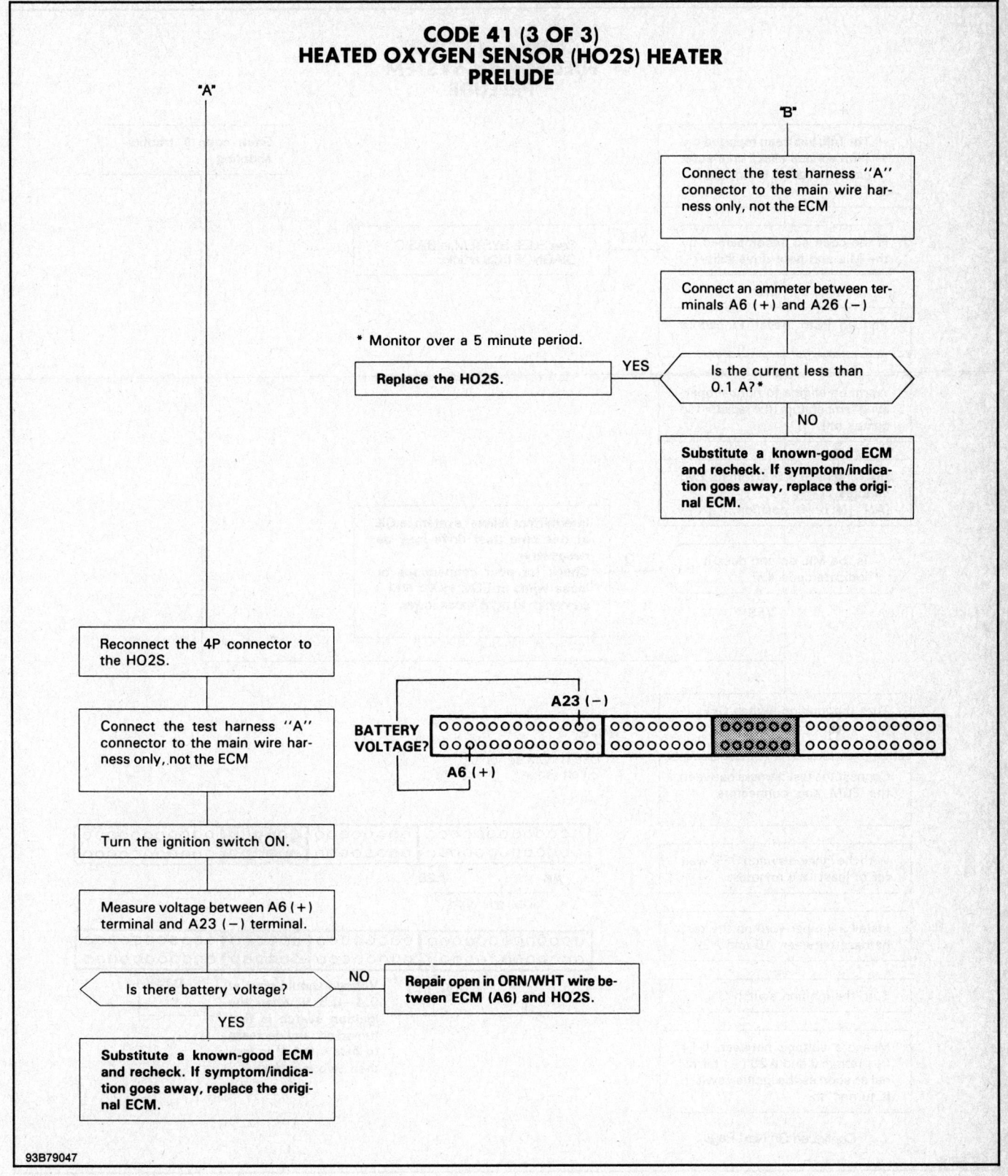

"A"

"B"

Connect the test harness "A" connector to the main wire harness only, not the ECM

Connect an ammeter between terminals A6 (+) and A26 (−)

* Monitor over a 5 minute period.

Replace the HO2S. ◄ **YES** ─ Is the current less than 0.1 A? *

NO

Substitute a known-good ECM and recheck. If symptom/indication goes away, replace the original ECM.

Reconnect the 4P connector to the HO2S.

Connect the test harness "A" connector to the main wire harness only, not the ECM

BATTERY VOLTAGE?

A23 (−)

A6 (+)

Turn the ignition switch ON.

Measure voltage between A6 (+) terminal and A23 (−) terminal.

Is there battery voltage? ─ **NO** ─ Repair open in ORN/WHT wire between ECM (A6) and HO2S.

YES

Substitute a known-good ECM and recheck. If symptom/indication goes away, replace the original ECM.

93B79047

CODE 43 (1 OF 2)
FUEL SUPPLY SYSTEM
PRELUDE

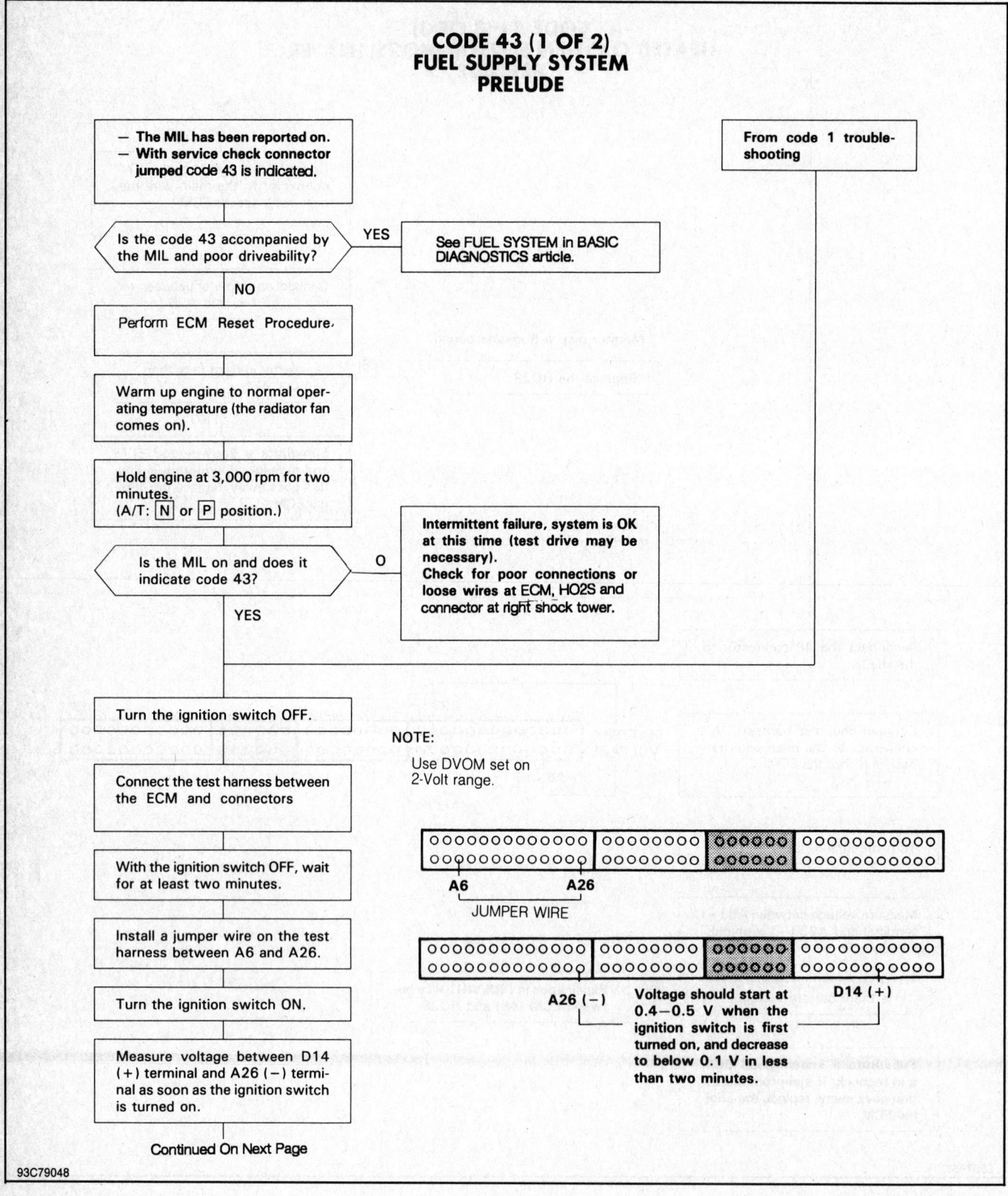

- The MIL has been reported on.
- With service check connector jumped code 43 is indicated.

From code 1 trouble-shooting

Is the code 43 accompanied by the MIL and poor driveability? — **YES** → See FUEL SYSTEM in BASIC DIAGNOSTICS article.

NO

Perform ECM Reset Procedure.

Warm up engine to normal operating temperature (the radiator fan comes on).

Hold engine at 3,000 rpm for two minutes. (A/T: N or P position.)

Is the MIL on and does it indicate code 43? — **O** → Intermittent failure, system is OK at this time (test drive may be necessary). Check for poor connections or loose wires at ECM, HO2S and connector at right shock tower.

YES

Turn the ignition switch OFF.

Connect the test harness between the ECM and connectors

With the ignition switch OFF, wait for at least two minutes.

Install a jumper wire on the test harness between A6 and A26.

Turn the ignition switch ON.

Measure voltage between D14 (+) terminal and A26 (−) terminal as soon as the ignition switch is turned on.

NOTE:

Use DVOM set on 2-Volt range.

A6   A26
JUMPER WIRE

A26 (−)   D14 (+)

Voltage should start at 0.4−0.5 V when the ignition switch is first turned on, and decrease to below 0.1 V in less than two minutes.

Continued On Next Page

93C79048

CODE 43 (2 OF 2)
FUEL SUPPLY SYSTEM
PRELUDE

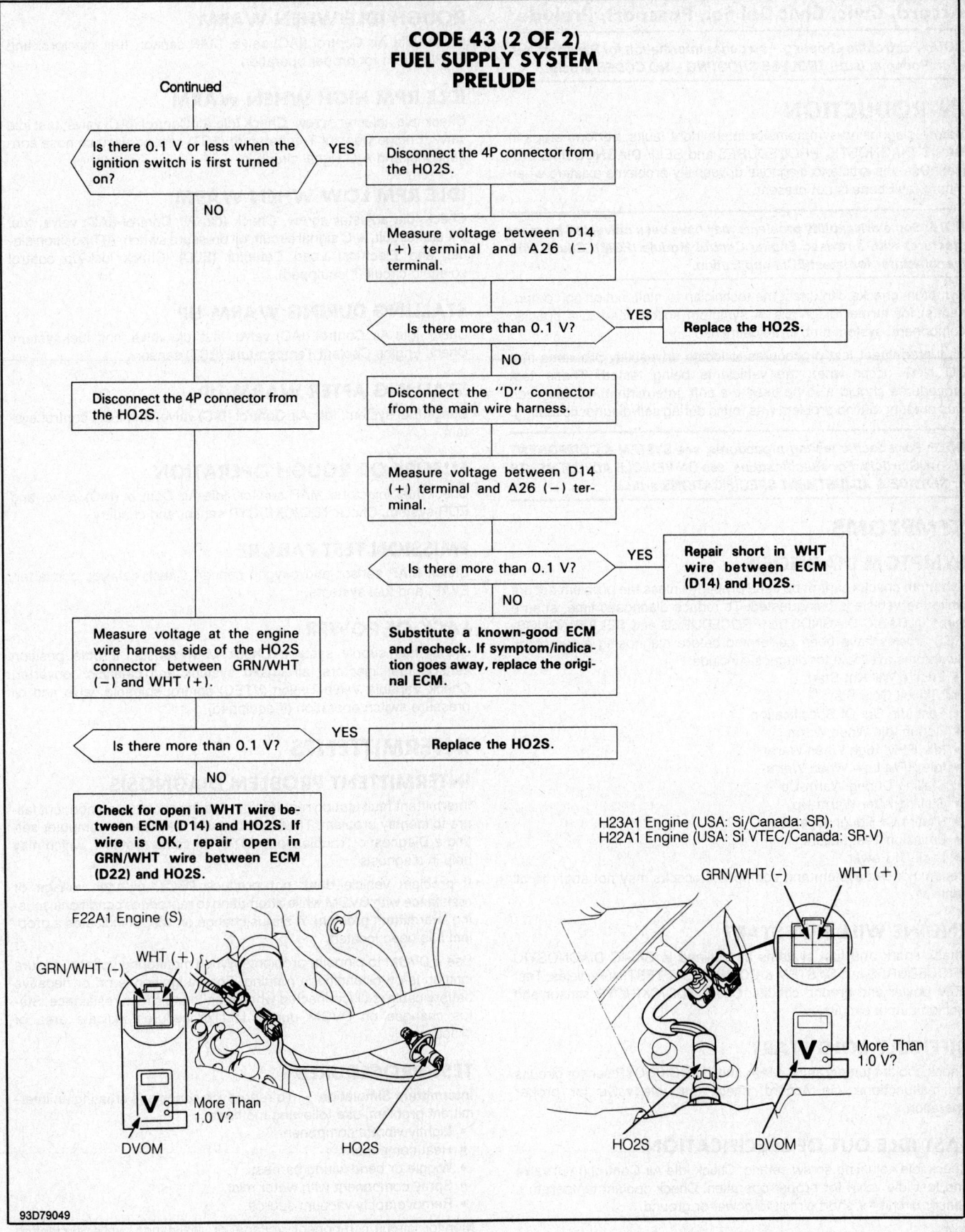

Continued

Is there 0.1 V or less when the ignition switch is first turned on? — **YES** → Disconnect the 4P connector from the HO2S.

NO

Measure voltage between D14 (+) terminal and A26 (–) terminal.

Is there more than 0.1 V? — **YES** → **Replace the HO2S.**

NO

Disconnect the 4P connector from the HO2S.

Disconnect the "D" connector from the main wire harness.

Measure voltage between D14 (+) terminal and A26 (–) terminal.

Is there more than 0.1 V? — **YES** → **Repair short in WHT wire between ECM (D14) and HO2S.**

NO

Measure voltage at the engine wire harness side of the HO2S connector between GRN/WHT (–) and WHT (+).

Substitute a known-good ECM and recheck. If symptom/indication goes away, replace the original ECM.

Is there more than 0.1 V? — **YES** → **Replace the HO2S.**

NO

Check for open in WHT wire between ECM (D14) and HO2S. If wire is OK, repair open in GRN/WHT wire between ECM (D22) and HO2S.

F22A1 Engine (S)

GRN/WHT (–)   WHT (+)

More Than 1.0 V?

DVOM   HO2S

H23A1 Engine (USA: Si/Canada: SR),
H22A1 Engine (USA: Si VTEC/Canada: SR-V)

GRN/WHT (–)   WHT (+)

More Than 1.0 V?

HO2S   DVOM

93D79049

1994 ENGINE PERFORMANCE
Trouble Shooting – No Codes

Accord, Civic, Civic Del Sol, Passport, Prelude

NOTE: For trouble shooting – no codes information for Passport, refer to Rodeo in Isuzu TROUBLE SHOOTING – NO CODES article.

INTRODUCTION

Before diagnosing symptoms or intermittent faults, perform steps in BASIC DIAGNOSTIC PROCEDURES and SELF-DIAGNOSTICS articles. Use this article to diagnose driveability problems existing when a hard fault code is not present.

NOTE: Some driveability problems may have been corrected by manufacturer with a revised Engine Control Module (ECM). Check with manufacturer for latest ECM application.

Symptom checks can direct the technician to malfunctioning component(s) for further diagnosis. A symptom should lead to a specific component, system test, or adjustment.

Use intermittent test procedures to locate driveability problems that DO NOT occur when the vehicle is being tested. These test procedures should also be used if a soft (intermittent) trouble code was present, but no problem was found during self-diagnostic testing.

NOTE: For specific testing procedures, see SYSTEM & COMPONENT TESTING article. For specifications, see ON-VEHICLE ADJUSTMENTS or SERVICE & ADJUSTMENT SPECIFICATIONS article.

SYMPTOMS

SYMPTOM DIAGNOSIS

Symptom checks cannot be used properly unless the problem occurs while the vehicle is being tested. To reduce diagnostic time, ensure steps in BASIC DIAGNOSTIC PROCEDURES and SELF-DIAGNOSTICS articles have been performed before diagnosing a symptom. Symptoms available for diagnosis include:

- Engine Will Not Start
- Difficult Cold Start
- Fast Idle Out Of Specification
- Rough Idle When Warm
- Idle RPM High When Warm
- Idle RPM Low When Warm
- Stalling During Warm-Up
- Stalling After Warm-Up
- Misfire Or Rough Operation
- Emission Test Failure
- Lack Of Power

Recommended system and component checks may not apply to all vehicles.

ENGINE WILL NOT START

Check spark and fuel systems as outlined in BASIC DIAGNOSTIC PROCEDURES and SYSTEM & COMPONENT TESTING articles. Test ECM power and ground circuits. Check TDC/CKP/CYP sensor and ignition output circuits.

DIFFICULT COLD START

Check coolant temperature, MAP, and TDC/CKP/CYP sensor circuits for malfunctions. On Accord, check fast idle valve for proper operation.

FAST IDLE OUT OF SPECIFICATION

Check idle adjusting screw setting. Check Idle Air Control (IAC) valve and fast idle valve for proper operation. Check coolant temperature sensor circuit for short circuit to power or ground.

ROUGH IDLE WHEN WARM

Check Idle Air Control (IAC) valve, MAP sensor, fuel injectors, and EGR system for proper operation.

IDLE RPM HIGH WHEN WARM

Check idle adjuster screw. Check Idle Air Control (IAC) valve, fast idle valve, Engine Coolant Temperature (ECT) sensor, vacuum hose connections, and A/C signal circuit.

IDLE RPM LOW WHEN WARM

Check idle adjuster screw. Check Idle Air Control (IAC) valve, fuel injector circuit, A/C signal circuit, oil pressure switch, A/T position signal, and Electrical Load Detector (ELD). Check lock-up control solenoid circuit (if equipped).

STALLING DURING WARM-UP

Check Idle Air Control (IAC) valve, fast idle valve, and fuel system. Check Engine Coolant Temperature (ECT) sensor.

STALLING AFTER WARM-UP

Check fuel system, Idle Air Control (IAC) valve, and EGR control system.

MISFIRE OR ROUGH OPERATION

Check fuel injectors, MAP sensor, Idle Air Control (IAC) valve, and EGR system. Check TDC/CKP/CYP sensor and circuitry.

EMISSION TEST FAILURE

Check MAP sensor and oxygen sensor. Check catalytic converter, EVAP, and fuel systems.

LACK OF POWER

Check fuel supply system. Check MAP sensor, throttle position sensor, fuel injectors, air intake system, and catalytic converter. Check Variable Valve Timing (VTEC) control solenoid valve and oil pressure switch operation (if equipped).

INTERMITTENTS

INTERMITTENT PROBLEM DIAGNOSIS

Intermittent fault testing requires duplicating circuit or component failure to identify problem. These procedures may lead to computer setting a Diagnostic Trouble Code (DTC) on some systems, which may help in diagnosis.

If problem vehicle does not produce DTCs, monitor voltage or resistance with DVOM while attempting to reproduce conditions causing intermittent problem. A status change on DVOM indicates a problem has been located.

Use a DVOM to pinpoint problems. When monitoring voltage, ensure ignition is on or engine is running. Ensure ignition is off or negative battery cable is disconnected when monitoring circuit resistance. Status changes on DVOM during test procedures indicate area of problem.

TEST PROCEDURES

Intermittent Simulation – To reproduce conditions creating an intermittent problem, use following methods:

- Lightly vibrate component.
- Heat component.
- Wiggle or bend wiring harness.
- Spray component with water mist.
- Remove/apply vacuum source.

Monitor circuit/component voltage or resistance while simulating intermittent. If engine is running, monitor for self-diagnostic codes. Use test results to identify a defective component or circuit.

Accord, Civic, Civic Del Sol, Passport, Prelude

NOTE: For system and component testing procedures on Passport, see RODEO in Isuzu SYSTEM & COMPONENT TESTING article.

INTRODUCTION

NOTE: For testing and diagnosis of Variable Valve Timing (VTEC) system, see CODE 21 and CODE 22 charts in SELF-DIAGNOSTICS article.

Before testing separate components or systems, perform procedures in BASIC DIAGNOSTIC PROCEDURES article. Since many computer-controlled and monitored components set trouble codes if they malfunction, also perform procedures in SELF-DIAGNOSTICS article.

NOTE: Perform all voltage tests using a Digital Volt-Ohmmeter (DVOM) with a minimum 10-megohm input impedance, unless stated otherwise in test procedure. Testing individual components does not isolate shorts or opens. Use ohmmeter to isolate wiring harness shorts or opens.

AIR INDUCTION SYSTEMS

AIR INTAKE SYSTEM

NOTE: DO NOT adjust by-pass valve full-close screw. Adjustment is preset at factory.

Intake Air By-Pass (IAB) Valve (Prelude – H22A1 & H23A1 Engines) – **1)** Check valve shaft for binding and sticking. Check valve for smooth movement. Ensure tab on valve contacts stopper when valve is fully open. *See Fig. 1.*
2) Ensure tab of by-pass valve contacts full-close screw when valve is fully closed. If any fault is found, clean linkage and shafts using carburetor cleaner. If problem still exists after cleaning, disassemble intake manifold and inspect by-pass valve.

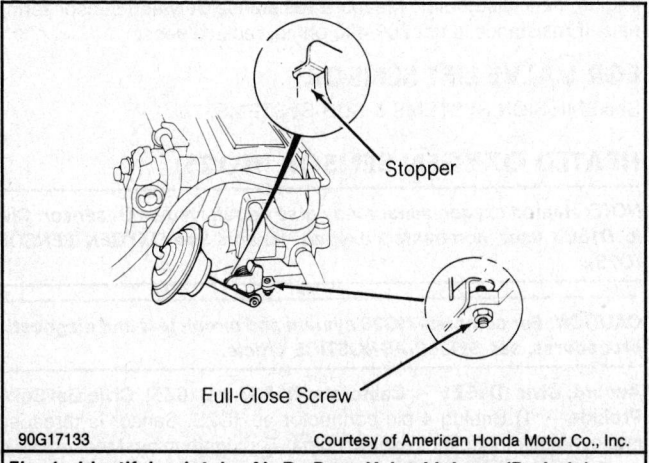

90G17133   Courtesy of American Honda Motor Co., Inc.

Fig. 1: Identifying Intake Air By-Pass Valve Linkage (Prelude)

IAB Control Solenoid Valve (Prelude – H22A1 & H23A1 Engines) –
1) Start and idle engine. Remove vacuum hose No. 13 from by-pass control diaphragm. *See Fig. 2.* Connect vacuum gauge to hose. If vacuum exists, go to next step. If vacuum does not exist, remove vacuum hose No. 12 from vacuum tank. Check for vacuum. If vacuum exists, go to step **3)**. If vacuum does not exist, repair blockage or leak between vacuum tank and intake manifold. Retest system.
2) Increase engine speed to 5000 RPM. Check for vacuum at hose No. 13. If vacuum does not exist, solenoid is okay. If vacuum exists, unplug connector at solenoid. Check for vacuum again. If vacuum still exists, replace solenoid valve. If vacuum no longer exists, solenoid valve is okay.

3) Unplug connector at solenoid. Measure voltage between Black/Yellow (positive) wire terminal and Pink (negative) wire terminal. If battery voltage exists, replace by-pass control solenoid valve. If battery voltage does not exist, check continuity of harness wiring to solenoid valve.

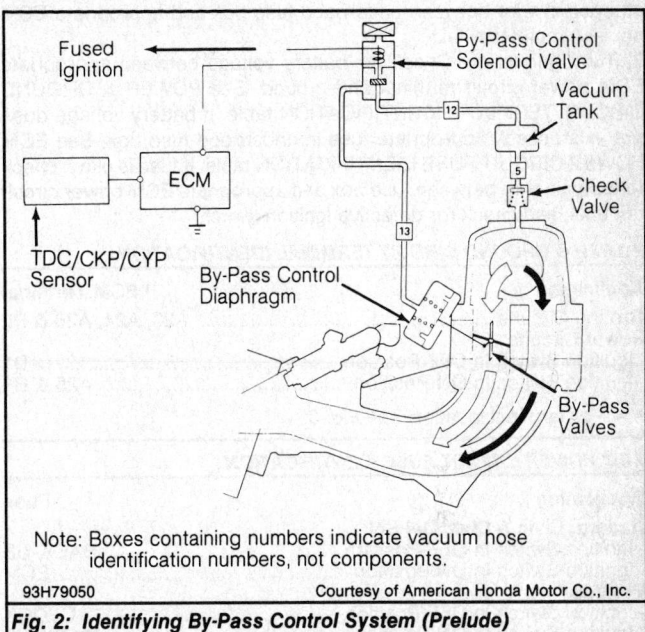

Note: Boxes containing numbers indicate vacuum hose identification numbers, not components.

93H79050   Courtesy of American Honda Motor Co., Inc.

Fig. 2: Identifying By-Pass Control System (Prelude)

Intake Control Diaphragm (Prelude – H22A1 & H23A1 Engines) – Connect vacuum pump to vacuum hose on intake control diaphragm. Apply vacuum. If diaphragm holds vacuum, intake diaphragm is okay. If vacuum does not hold, inspect vacuum line for improper connection and disconnected hose. If hose is okay, replace intake control diaphragm.

Intake Control Solenoid Valve (Prelude – H22A1 & H23A1 Engines) – **1)** Start and idle engine. Remove upper vacuum hose from intake control solenoid valve, located at top of engine, on left side. Connect vacuum gauge to solenoid valve. If vacuum does not exist, go to next step. If vacuum exists, increase engine speed to 4600 RPM (H22A1 engine) or 4800 RPM (H23A1 engine). If vacuum still exists, go to step **4)**. If vacuum no longer exists, solenoid valve is okay.
2) Disconnect lower vacuum hose of solenoid valve from air chamber. Connect vacuum gauge. If vacuum exists, go to next step. If vacuum does not exist, inspect vacuum line for improper connection, cracks and blockage in hose. If vacuum line is okay, clean manifold port.
3) Unplug connector from intake control solenoid valve. Measure voltage between Black/Yellow and Pink wire terminals. If battery voltage does not exist, solenoid valve is okay. If battery voltage exists, replace intake control solenoid valve.
4) Unplug connector from solenoid valve. If vacuum no longer exists, solenoid valve is okay. If vacuum still exists, replace solenoid valve.

COMPUTERIZED ENGINE CONTROLS

ENGINE CONTROL MODULE (ECM)

Ground Circuits – **1)** Measure resistance to ground at appropriate ECM ground terminals. See POWER & GROUND CIRCUITS TERMINAL IDENTIFICATION table. *See Fig. 3.* Resistance should be zero ohms for each circuit. If resistance is not zero ohms, repair open to ground.
2) Connect negative lead of DVOM to a good ground. Connect positive lead to each ground terminal. With engine running, voltmeter should indicate less than 0.1 volt. If voltage is greater than 0.1 volt, check for open, corrosion, or loose connection on ground lead.

Power Circuits – **1)** Check for battery voltage between ECM power terminal and ground. See POWER & GROUND CIRCUIT TERMINAL IDENTIFICATION table. *See Fig. 3.* If battery voltage does not exist, check appropriate ECM fuse in underhood fuse box. See ECM POWER CIRCUIT FUSE IDENTIFICATION table. If fuse is okay, check for an open in wire between underhood fuse box and appropriate ECM power circuit terminal.

2) Turn ignition on. Check for battery voltage between appropriate ECM power circuit terminal and ground. See POWER & GROUND CIRCUIT TERMINAL IDENTIFICATION table. If battery voltage does not exist, check appropriate fuse in underhood fuse box. See ECM POWER CIRCUIT FUSE IDENTIFICATION table. If fuse is okay, check for open in wire between fuse box and appropriate ECM power circuit terminal, and check for defective ignition switch.

POWER & GROUND CIRCUIT TERMINAL IDENTIFICATION

Application	[1] ECM Terminal
Ground Circuits	A23, A24, A26 & B2
Power Circuits	
Ignition Switch In OFF Position	D1
Ignition Switch In ON Position	A25 & B1

[1] – For terminal location, *see Fig. 3.*

ECM POWER CIRCUIT FUSE IDENTIFICATION

Application	Fuse
Accord, Civic & Civic Del Sol	
Ignition Switch In OFF Position	BACK-UP
Ignition Switch In ON Position	ECM
Prelude	
Ignition Switch In OFF Position	CLOCK
Ignition Switch In ON Position	BACK-UP

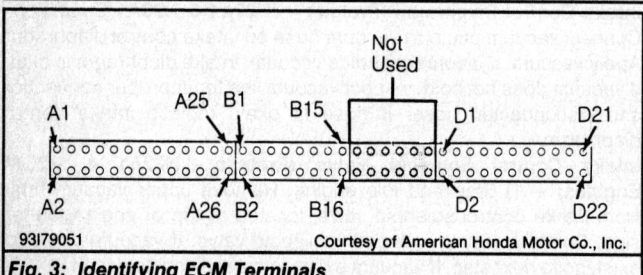

93I79051   Courtesy of American Honda Motor Co., Inc.

Fig. 3: Identifying ECM Terminals

ENGINE SENSORS & SWITCHES

NOTE: Test Harness (07LAJ-PT3010A) is required for testing certain components or systems. See Fig. 4. Connect test harness between control unit and main wiring harness connectors.

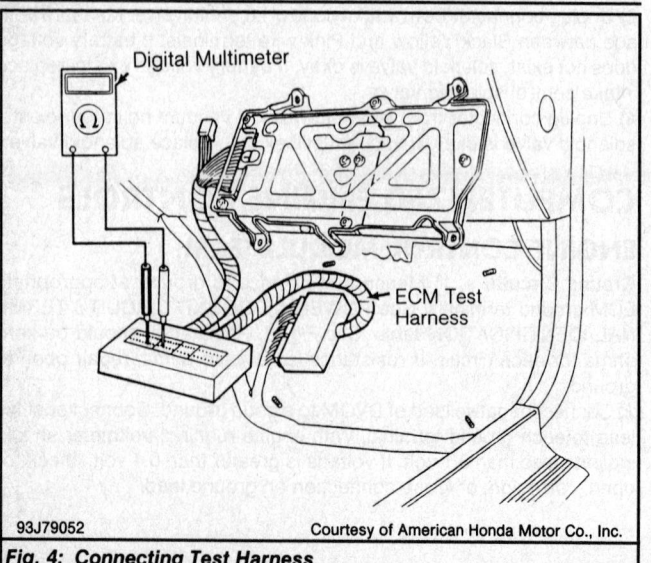

93J79052   Courtesy of American Honda Motor Co., Inc.

Fig. 4: Connecting Test Harness

AIR CONDITIONING (A/C) SIGNAL SWITCH

Voltage Test – **1)** Connect test harness between ECM and main wiring harness. *See Fig. 4.* Unplug connector "B" from main harness, but not from ECM. Turn ignition on. Measure voltage between terminals A26 and B5. *See Fig. 3.*

2) If voltage is about 5 volts, go to next step. If voltage is not about 5 volts, substitute known-good ECM and retest system. If voltage is now about 5 volts, replace ECM. If voltage is still not about 5 ohms, check and repair wiring between A/C switch and ECM. See WIRING DIAGRAMS article.

3) Turn ignition off. Reconnect main harness. Turn ignition on. Momentarily connect ECM terminals A15 and A26 together. If A/C clutch does not click, go to next step. If clutch clicks, start engine and turn A/C on. If A/C operates, A/C signal exists. If A/C does not operate, go to step **5)**.

4) Using jumper, connect Red/Blue wire from A/C compressor control unit to chassis ground. See WIRING DIAGRAMS article. If A/C clutch clicks, repair open circuit between ECM and A/C compressor control unit. If clutch does not click, repair A/C system. See appropriate MITCHELL® AIR CONDITIONING & HEATING SERVICE & REPAIR manual.

5) With engine running and A/C on, measure voltage between terminals A26 and B5. If voltage is less than one volt, substitute a known-good ECM. If A/C now functions, replace ECM. If voltage is greater than one volt, repair open circuit between ECM and A/C switch. See WIRING DIAGRAMS article.

BAROMETRIC PRESSURE (BARO) SENSOR

Barometric pressure (BARO) sensor is built into ECM. See SELF-DIAGNOSTICS article for testing.

ENGINE COOLANT TEMPERATURE (ECT) SENSOR

Resistance Test – Start engine and warm it to normal operating temperature. Unplug sensor connector. Sensor is located on front of engine, near distributor. Measure resistance between sensor terminals. If resistance is not 200-400 ohms, replace sensor.

EGR VALVE LIFT SENSOR

See EMISSION SYSTEMS & SUB-SYSTEMS.

HEATED OXYGEN SENSOR (HO2S)

NOTE: Heated oxygen sensor may also be referred as O₂ sensor. Civic D15B8 uses non-heated oxygen sensor. See OXYGEN SENSOR (O2S).

CAUTION: For complete HO2S system and circuit test and diagnostic procedures, see SELF-DIAGNOSTICS article.

Accord, Civic (D15Z1 – California, D15B7 & D16Z6), Civic Del Sol & Prelude – **1)** Unplug 4-pin connector at HO2S. Sensor is threaded into exhaust manifold or exhaust pipe. Turn ignition on. Measure voltage between White and Green/White wires at HO2S connector. If voltage is less than .1 volt, go to next step. If voltage is greater than .1 volt, replace HO2S.

2) Check for open in White wire between ECM connector terminal D14 and HO2S. Check Green/White wire of ECM connector terminal D22. Repair wire(s) as necessary. Recheck system.

Civic (D15Z1 – Federal) – **1)** Turn ignition off. Connect test harness between ECM and main harness. *See Fig. 4.* Wait at least 3 minutes. Turn ignition on. Measure voltage between terminals D8 and D22. *See Fig. 3.* If voltage is greater than 0.5 volt, go to next step. If voltage is not greater than 0.5 volt, check White/Blue wire between sensor and ECM for shorts. If wiring is okay, go to next step.

2) Recheck voltage between terminals D8 and D22. If voltage is greater than 5.0 volts, go to next step. If voltage is not greater than 5.0 volts, go to step **7)**.

3) Measure voltage between terminals D16 and D22. If voltage is greater than 0.5 volt, go to next step. If voltage is not greater than 0.5 volt, check Blue/Green wire between sensor and ECM for shorts.

4) Measure voltage between terminals D3 and D22. If voltage is 0.3-4.9 volts, go to next step. If voltage is not 0.3-4.9 volts, go to step **8)**.

5) Start engine, and warm it until radiator fan comes on. Measure voltage between terminals D16 and D22. If voltage is 2.6-2.8 volts, go to next step. If voltage is not 2.6-2.8 volts, go to step **9)**.

6) Measure voltage between terminals D14 and D22. If voltage is greater than 0.4 volt, replace ECM and retest system. If voltage is not greater than 0.4 volt, repair short in Orange/Blue wire between sensor and ECM.

7) Unplug connector from sensor. Sensor is threaded into exhaust manifold. Measure voltage between terminals D8 and D22. If voltage is greater than 5 volts, replace sensor. If voltage is not greater than 5 volts, replace ECM and retest system.

8) Turn ignition off. Unplug connector from sensor. Sensor is threaded into exhaust manifold. Turn ignition on. Measure voltage between White wire on harness connector and ground. If voltage is about 5 volts, replace sensor. If voltage is not about 5 ohms, repair open in White wire or Blue/Yellow wire between sensor and ECM.

9) Measure voltage between terminals D8 and D22. If voltage is less than 2.8 volts, replace ECM and retest system. If voltage is not less than 2.8 volts, repair open in White/Blue wire or Green/White wire between sensor and ECM.

INTAKE AIR TEMPERATURE (IAT) SENSOR

Resistance Test – Unplug sensor connector. On Accord and Prelude, sensor is located at top of engine, on left side. On Civic and Civic Del Sol, sensor is located on rear side of engine, near center. Measure resistance between sensor terminals. Resistance should be as specified. See INTAKE AIR TEMPERATURE (IAT) SENSOR RESISTANCE table. If resistance is not within specification, replace sensor.

INTAKE AIR TEMPERATURE (IAT) SENSOR RESISTANCE

Temperature °F (°C)	Ohms
-4 (-20)	15,000-18,000
68 (20)	1000-4000
176 (80)	200-400

MANIFOLD ABSOLUTE PRESSURE (MAP) SENSOR

Voltage Test (Except Accord) – 1) Connect test harness between ECM and main harness. See Fig. 4. Turn ignition on. Measure voltage between terminals D17 and D21. See Fig. 3.

2) If voltage is about 3 volts, go to Vacuum Test. If voltage is not about 3 volts, check wiring between sensor and ECM for continuity or shorts. If wiring is okay, replace MAP sensor.

Voltage Test (Accord) – 1) Connect test harness between ECM and main harness. See Fig. 4. Turn ignition on. Measure voltage between terminals D19 and D21. See Fig. 3.

2) If voltage is about 5 volts, go to VACUUM TEST. If voltage is not about 5 volts, check wiring between sensor and ECM for open or short. If wiring is okay, replace MAP sensor.

Vacuum Test – Connect vacuum pump to MAP sensor. On Accord and Prelude, MAP sensor is located at top center of firewall. On Civic and Civic Del Sol, MAP sensor is located near throttle body. Apply vacuum. If MAP sensor does not hold vacuum, replace sensor.

OXYGEN SENSOR (O2S)

NOTE: All models except Civic D15B8 use heated oxygen sensor. See HEATED OXYGEN SENSOR (HO2S). Oxygen sensor may be referred to as O2 sensor.

Civic (D15B8) – 1) Turn ignition off. Connect test harness between ECM and vehicle wiring harness. See Fig. 4. Wait at least 2 minutes. Connect jumper wire between test harness terminals A6 and A26.

Connect DVOM between terminals A26 and D14. Turn ignition on. Immediately observe DVOM. Voltage should be 0.4-0.5 volt and then decrease to 0.1 volt or less within 2 minutes. If voltage is not as specified, go to next step. If voltage is as specified, go to step **3)**.

2) Unplug connector from O2S, threaded into exhaust manifold. Measure voltage at harness connector White and Green/White wires. If voltage is greater than 0.1 volt, replace O2S. If voltage is not greater than 0.1 volt, repair open in White or Green/White wire between ECM and O2S.

3) Unplug connector from O2S, threaded into exhaust manifold. Measure voltage at harness connector White and Green/White wires. If voltage is not greater than 0.1 volt, go to next step. If voltage is greater than 0.1 volt, replace O2S.

4) Unplug connector "D" from main wiring harness. Measure voltage between terminals A26 and D14. If voltage is greater than 0.1 volt, repair short to voltage in White wire between ECM and O2S. If voltage is not greater than 0.1 volt, replace ECM and retest system.

POWER STEERING PRESSURE (PSP) SWITCH

1) Connect test harness between ECM and wiring harness. See Fig. 4. Turn ignition on. Measure voltage between test harness terminals B8 and A26. See Fig. 3. If voltage is greater than one volt, go to next step. If voltage is not greater than one volt, go to step **4)**.

2) Unplug connector on PSP switch. Switch is located on steering gear. On Accord, connect jumper wire between Green and Black wire terminals. On Civic and Civic Del Sol, connect jumper wire between Brown/Red and Black wire terminals. On Prelude, connect jumper wire between Red/Green and Black wire terminals.

3) On all models, check for voltage at test harness terminals A26 and B8. If voltage does not exist, replace PSP switch. If voltage exists, repair open in Green wire (Accord), Brown/Red wire (Civic and Civic Del Sol) or Red/Green wire (Prelude) between ECM terminal B8 and PSP switch, or Black wire between PSP switch and ground.

4) Start engine. Turn steering wheel slowly. Measure voltage between test harness terminals A26 and B8. If battery voltage exists, PSP signal is okay. If battery voltage does not exist, go to next step.

5) Turn ignition off. Unplug test harness connector "B" from main wiring harness only, not ECM. Turn ignition on. If battery voltage exists, go to next step. If battery voltage does not exist, replace ECM and retest system.

6) Reconnect harness connector "B" to main wiring harness. Unplug connector from PSP switch. If battery voltage exists, replace PSP switch. If battery voltage does not exist, repair short in Green, Brown/Red or Red/Green wire between ECM terminal B8 and PSP switch.

TDC/CKP/CYP SENSOR

1) Unplug TDC/CKP/CYP sensor connector, located at distributor. Measure resistance between terminals "B" and "F". Measure resistance between terminals "C" and "G". See Fig. 5. Measure resistance

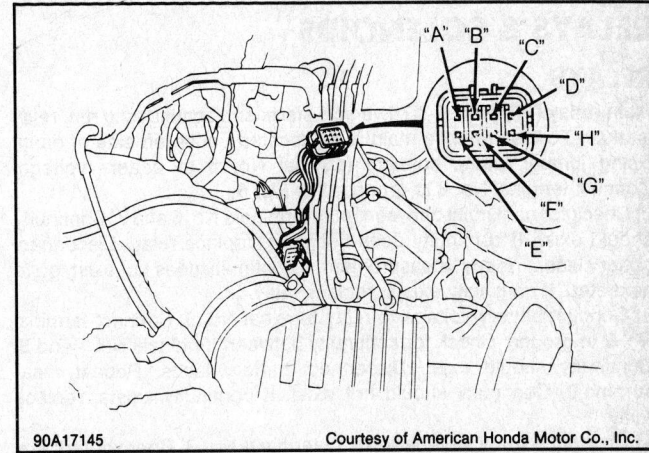

90A17145   Courtesy of American Honda Motor Co., Inc.

Fig. 5: Identifying TDC/CKP/CYP Sensor Connector Terminals (Accord Shown; Other Models Are Similar)

between terminals "D" and "H". If resistance is 350-700 ohms (700-1300 ohms for Accord F22B2 Engine) for each pair, go to next step. If any measurement is not as specified, replace distributor.

2) Check for continuity between each terminal and chassis ground. If continuity exists at any terminal, replace distributor.

THROTTLE POSITION (TP) SENSOR

1) Turn ignition off. Connect test harness between ECM and vehicle harness connector. *See Fig. 4.*

2) Turn ignition on. Measure voltage between test harness terminals D11 and D22. Open and close throttle while observing voltmeter. Voltage should be about 0.5 volt with throttle fully closed and 4.5 volts with throttle wide open. Voltage should change smoothly as throttle opens and closes.

3) If voltage is not as specified on Accord M/T, Civic, Civic Del Sol and Prelude M/T, replace TP sensor. If voltage is as specified, replace ECM and retest system. If voltage is not as specified on Accord A/T and Prelude A/T, go to next step.

4) Unplug 22-pin connector from Transmission Control Module (TCM). TCM is located below center of dashboard. Measure voltage again as throttle is opened and closed. If voltage does not change as specified in step **2)**, go to next step. If voltage now changes as specified, replace TCM.

5) If voltage is not as specified, check for short or open in Red/Black wire between ECM terminal D11 and TP sensor. If wire is okay, replace TP sensor. If problem still exists, see SELF-DIAGNOSTICS article.

VEHICLE SPEED SENSOR (VSS)

1) Turn ignition off. Connect test harness between ECM and main harness connector. *See Fig. 4.* Raise and support front of vehicle so front wheels are free to rotate. Connect voltmeter between ECM terminals B10 and A26. *See Fig. 3.*

2) Turn ignition on. Slowly rotate left front wheel. Voltage should pulse between zero and specified voltage. See VEHICLE SPEED SENSOR (VSS) TEST table. If voltage pulses as specified, replace ECM and retest system. If voltage does not pulse as specified, check for open or short in wiring between ECM terminal B10 and speed sensor. See WIRING DIAGRAMS article. If wiring is okay, replace defective VSS or ECM.

VEHICLE SPEED SENSOR (VSS) TEST

Application	[1] Volts
Accord	5
Civic & Civic Del Sol	More Than 5
Prelude	
Except H22A1 Engine	5
H22A1 Engine	12

[1] – Voltage will fluctuate between zero and specified value.

RELAYS & SOLENOIDS

RELAYS

Main Relay (PGM-FI) – 1) If vehicle starts and continues to run, relay is okay. To test, remove main relay, located under left side of dash. Using jumper wires, connect terminal No. 6 to battery voltage. Connect terminal No. 8 to ground. *See Fig. 6.*

2) Check for continuity between relay terminals No. 5 and 7. Continuity should exist. If continuity does not exist, replace relay. Disconnect battery leads. Repeat measurement. If continuity does not exist, go to next step. If continuity exists, replace relay.

3) Connect battery voltage to relay terminal No. 5. Connect terminal No. 2 to ground. Check for continuity between terminals No. 1 and 3. Continuity should exist. Disconnect battery leads. Repeat measurement. Continuity should not exist. If continuity exists, replace relay.

4) Connect battery voltage to relay terminal No. 3. Connect terminal No. 8 to ground. Check for continuity between terminals No. 5 and 7.

Disconnect battery leads. Repeat measurement. If continuity does not exist, relay is okay. If continuity exists, replace relay. If fuel pump still fails to operate, test main relay harness. See MAIN RELAY HARNESS under FUEL CONTROL under FUEL SYSTEM.

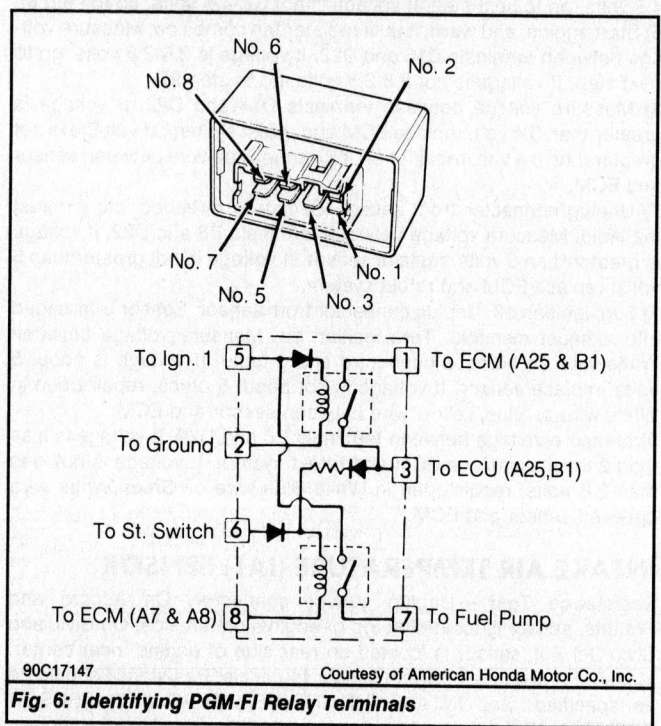

No. 6
No. 8
No. 2
No. 7
No. 5
No. 1
No. 3

To Ign. 1 [5] — [1] To ECM (A25 & B1)
To Ground [2]
[3] To ECU (A25,B1)
To St. Switch [6]
To ECM (A7 & A8) [8] — [7] To Fuel Pump

90C17147
Courtesy of American Honda Motor Co., Inc.

Fig. 6: Identifying PGM-FI Relay Terminals

SOLENOIDS

IAB Control Solenoid (Accord F22A6 & Prelude 2.3L) – See AIR INDUCTION SYSTEMS.

Idle Air Control (IAC) Valve – See IDLE CONTROL SYSTEM.

EGR Control Solenoid Valve – See EXHAUST GAS RECIRCULATION (EGR) SYSTEM under EMISSION SYSTEMS & SUB-SYSTEMS.

Intake Air Control Solenoid Valve (Accord & Prelude) – See AIR INDUCTION SYSTEMS.

EVAP Purge Control Solenoid Valve – See FUEL EVAPORATION under EMISSION SYSTEMS & SUB-SYSTEMS.

FUEL SYSTEM

FUEL DELIVERY

NOTE: For fuel system pressure testing, see BASIC DIAGNOSTIC PROCEDURES article.

FUEL CONTROL

Fuel Injectors – Unplug connector at injector. Measure resistance between injector terminals. Resistance should be as specified. See FUEL INJECTOR RESISTANCE table. If resistance is not as specified, replace injector.

INJECTOR RESISTANCE

FUEL INJECTOR RESISTANCE

Application	Ohms
Accord & Prelude	
Injector	1.5-2.5
Injector Resistor	5.0-7.0
Civic & Civic Del Sol	
Injector [1]	10.0-13.0

[1] – Injectors have internal resistor.

Fuel Injector Resistor (Accord & Prelude) – Unplug injector resistor harness connector. Injector resistor is located over left front fenderwell on Accord and at upper left firewall on Prelude. Measure resistance between each injector resistor terminal ("B", "C", "D" and "E") and power terminal ("A"). *See Fig. 7.* Resistance should be 5-7 ohms for each pair of terminals. If any measurement is not as specified, replace injector resistor.

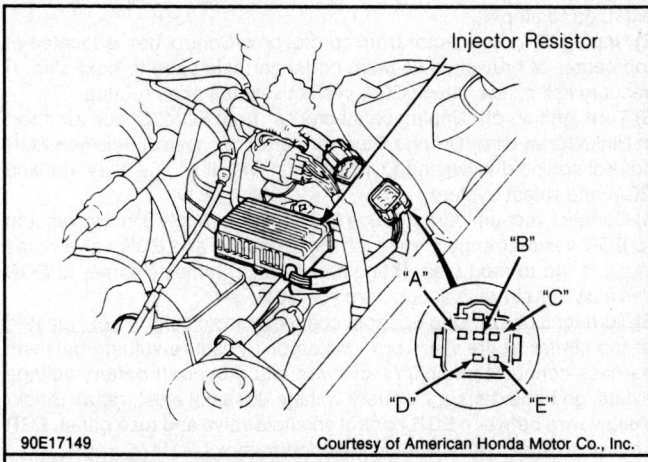

90E17149   Courtesy of American Honda Motor Co., Inc.

Fig. 7: Identifying Injector Resistor Connector Terminals (Accord Shown; Prelude Is Similar)

Main Relay Harness – **1)** Turn ignition off. Unplug main relay harness connector. Check for continuity between connector terminal No. 2 and chassis ground. *See Fig. 8.* If continuity exists, go to next step. If continuity does not exist, repair open in Black wire from terminal No. 2 to ground. See WIRING DIAGRAMS article.

2) Measure voltage between connector terminal No. 1 and body ground. If battery voltage exists, go to next step. If battery voltage does not exist, check wiring between battery and main relay, and check ECM fuse in underhood relay box. Repair as necessary.

3) Turn ignition on. Measure voltage between relay connector terminal No. 5 and body ground. If battery voltage exists, go to next step. If battery voltage does not exist, check wiring from ignition switch and main relay. Check fuse No. 23 on Prelude, No. 2 on Accord, or No. 18 on Civic and Civic Del Sol. Check wiring from fuse box to main relay. Repair or replace as necessary.

4) Connect voltmeter to connector terminal No. 6 and body ground. Turn ignition switch to START position. If battery voltage exists, go to next step. If battery voltage does not exist, check wiring between ignition switch and main relay. Check wiring from fuse box to main relay. Repair or replace fuse or wiring as necessary.

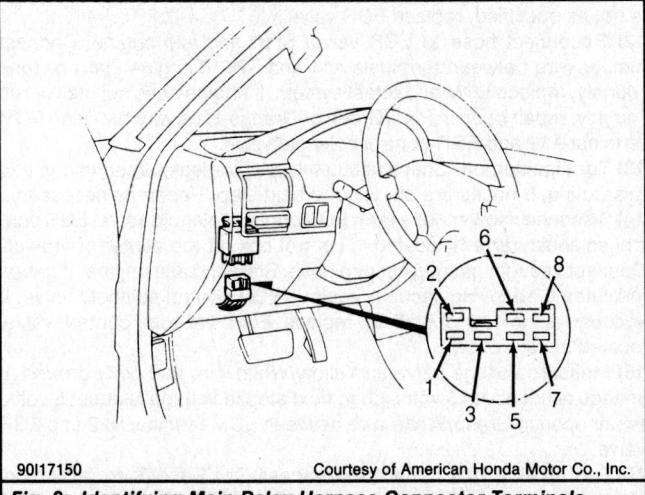

90I17150   Courtesy of American Honda Motor Co., Inc.

Fig. 8: Identifying Main Relay Harness Connector Terminals (Accord Shown; Other Models Are Similar)

5) Connect jumper between connector terminals No. 5 and 7. Turn ignition on. Fuel pump should operate. If fuel pump fails to operate, check fuel pump wiring.

IDLE CONTROL SYSTEM

Electric Load Detector – **1)** Unplug 3-pin ELD connector (located on right fender apron near underhood fuse panel). Turn ignition on. Measure voltage between Black/Yellow wire (+) and Black wire (–) at ELD connector. If battery voltage exists, go to step 3). If battery voltage does not exist, go to next step.

2) Measure voltage between Black/Yellow wire and chassis ground. If battery voltage exists, repair open in Black wire between ELD connector and ground connection behind right kick panel. If battery voltage does not exist, repair open in Black/Yellow wire between ELD connector and No. 4 fuse (Accord), AGC fuse (Civic and Civic Del Sol) or ECM fuse (Prelude) in underhood fuse panel.

3) Measure voltage in Green/Red wire between ELD connector and ground. If voltage is about 5 volts, go to next step. If voltage is not as specified, check for open or short in Green/Red wire between ECM and ELD connector. Repair wire as necessary.

4) Turn ignition off. Reconnect ELD connector. Connect test harness between ECM and connectors. *See Fig. 4.* Start engine and allow it to idle. While measuring voltage between terminals A26 and D10 of ECM connector, turn headlights on low beam. If voltage does not drop when headlights are turned on, replace ELD. If voltage drops, replace ECM with known-good unit. If voltage drop symptom disappears, replace original ECM.

Idle Air Control (IAC) Valve – **1)** Turn ignition off. Unplug IAC valve connector. IAC is located near throttle body. Turn ignition on. Measure voltage between Yellow/Black wire on harness connector and ground. If battery voltage exists, go to next step. If battery voltage does not exist, repair Yellow/Black wire between IAC valve and PGM-FI main relay.

2) Turn ignition off. Connect test harness to vehicle wiring harness, not to ECM. *See Fig. 4.* Turn ignition on. Momentarily connect terminal A9 to terminal A23 (A26 on Prelude). If IAC valve clicks, substitute known-good ECM and retest system. If IAC valve does not click, repair Black/Blue wire between IAC and ECM terminal A9.

Fast Idle Thermo Valve (Accord & Prelude) – **1)** Start engine. Remove fast idle valve cover. Fast idle valve is located near throttle body. Place finger on valve seat area. Check for airflow with engine cold and idling. If airflow does not exist, replace fast idle valve.

2) Warm engine to full operating temperature (cooling fan comes on). Verify valve is completely closed. Valve is leaking if engine speed decreases when lower port is covered and suction can be felt in valve seat area. Replace valve if valve operation is not as specified.

Fast Idle Thermo Valve (Civic & Civic Del Sol) – **1)** Disconnect air intake duct from throttle body. Start engine. Place finger over lower port on throttle body. Check for airflow with engine cold and idling. If airflow does not exist, replace fast idle valve. Fast idle valve is located near throttle body.

2) Warm engine to full operating temperature (cooling fan comes on). Verify valve is completely closed. Valve is leaking if suction can be felt in lower port on throttle body. Replace fast idle valve if operation is not as specified.

IGNITION SYSTEM

NOTE: For basic ignition checks, see BASIC DIAGNOSTIC PROCEDURES article.

EMISSION SYSTEMS & SUB-SYSTEMS

EXHAUST GAS RECIRCULATION (EGR) SYSTEM

EGR Valve – Ensure all connectors between EGR valve lift sensor and ECM are securely connected. Warm engine to full operating temperature. Disconnect vacuum hose from EGR valve. Connect vacuum pump to EGR valve. Apply vacuum. EGR valve should hold vacuum and engine should die once vacuum is applied. If results are not as specified, replace EGR valve.

Accord & Prelude – 1) Start and idle engine. Disconnect hose No. 16 from EGR valve, located at top of engine. Connect vacuum pump/gauge to hose. If vacuum exists, go to next step. If vacuum does not exist, go to step **4)**.

2) On Accord, unplug 2-pin connector from control box, located at top of firewall, toward passenger side. On Prelude, unplug 2-pin connector from EGR control solenoid valve, located over left front fenderwell. On all models, check for vacuum on hose No. 16. If vacuum does not exist, go to next step. If vacuum exists, check EGR system vacuum hose routing. If hoses are okay, replace EGR control solenoid valve.

3) Turn ignition off. Unplug connector "A" from ECM. Check for continuity between ground and Pink wire (Accord) or Red wire (Prelude) at 2-pin connector. If continuity exists, repair short in appropriate wire. If continuity does not exist, replace ECM and retest system.

4) Connect vacuum pump/gauge to EGR valve. With engine idling, apply 8 in. Hg vacuum to EGR valve. If engine stalls or runs roughly, and EGR valve holds vacuum, go to next step. If engine operation remains same or EGR valve does not hold vacuum, replace EGR valve.

5) Turn ignition off. On Accord, unplug 2-pin connector from control box, located at top of firewall, toward passenger side. On Prelude, unplug 2-pin connector from EGR control solenoid valve, located over left front fenderwell. On all models, turn ignition on. Measure voltage between harness connector Black/Yellow wire and ground. If battery voltage exists, go to next step. If battery voltage does not exist, repair Black/Yellow wire between harness connector and fuse panel.

6) Connect vacuum pump/gauge to hose disconnected in step **1)**. Connect fused jumper wire between positive battery terminal and Red wire on EGR solenoid valve connector. Observe voltmeter while connecting jumper wire between Black/Yellow wire on EGR solenoid valve connector and negative battery terminal.

7) On all models, gauge should indicate about 8 in. Hg within one second. If gauge indicates as specified, go to next step. If gauge does not indicate as specified, go to step **13)**.

8) Turn ignition off. Reconnect vehicle harness. Unplug 3-pin connector from EGR valve lift sensor, located on EGR valve. Turn ignition on. On Accord, measure voltage between Yellow/Blue and Green/Blue wires on harness connector. On Prelude, measure voltage between Red/White and Green/White wires on harness connector. If voltage is about 5 volts, go to step **9)**. If voltage is not about 5 volts, go to step **15)**.

9) Turn ignition off. Reconnect wiring to valve lift sensor. Connect test harness. *See Fig. 4.* Turn ignition on. Measure voltage between terminals D12 and D22 with no vacuum applied to EGR valve. Apply 8 in. Hg vacuum to EGR valve. Voltage should be about 1.2 volts with no vacuum applied and 4.3 volts with vacuum applied. If voltage is not as specified, go to next step. If voltage is as specified, go to step **11)**.

10) Check for open or short circuit in White/Black wire between EGR valve and ECM terminal D12. *See Fig. 3.* If wire is okay, replace EGR valve.

11) Observe voltmeter as vacuum is applied and released. If voltage increases and decreases smoothly, go to next step. If voltage does not change smoothly, replace EGR valve.

12) Reconnect hose to EGR valve. Start and idle engine. Connect jumper wire between terminals A6 (A11 on Prelude) and A26. If engine stalls or runs roughly, replace ECM and retest system. If engine does not stall or run rough, repair open in Red wire between ECM terminal A6 (A11 on Prelude) and EGR control solenoid valve.

13) Turn ignition off. Inspect hoses No. 16 and 24 for leaks, restrictions and misrouting. If hoses are okay, go to next step. Make any repairs as necessary.

14) Disconnect lower hose from EGR control solenoid. Connect vacuum pump/gauge to hose. Start and idle engine. If 6-10 in. Hg vacuum exists, replace EGR solenoid valve. If vacuum is not 6-10 in. Hg, replace EGR valve.

15) Measure voltage at Yellow/Blue (Accord) or Red/White (Prelude) wire. If voltage is not about 5 volts, go to next step. If voltage is about 5 volts, repair open in wire between EGR valve and ECM terminal D22.

16) Turn ignition off. Connect test harness connector "D" to ECM only, not to vehicle harness. Turn ignition on. Measure voltage between ter-

minals D20 and D22. If voltage is about 5 volts, repair open in Yellow/Blue (Accord) or Red/White (Prelude) wire between EGR lift sensor and ECM terminal D20. If voltage is not about 5 volts, replace ECM and retest system.

Civic (D15Z1) – 1) Start and idle engine. Disconnect vacuum hose from EGR valve, located to rear of distributor. Connect vacuum pump/gauge to hose. If vacuum exists, go to next step. If vacuum does not exist, go to step **4)**.

2) Unplug 2-pin connector from control box. Control box is located at top center of firewall. If vacuum no longer exists, go to next step. If vacuum still exists, check EGR system vacuum hose routing.

3) Turn ignition off. Unplug connector "A" from ECM. Check for short in Pink/Green wire (Orange/Blue wire after connector) between EGR control solenoid valve and ECM terminal A11. If wire is okay, replace ECM and retest system.

4) Connect vacuum pump/gauge to EGR valve. Apply 8 in. Hg vacuum to EGR valve. If engine stalls or runs roughly, and EGR valve holds vacuum, go to next step. If engine operation remains same, or EGR valve does not hold vacuum, replace EGR valve.

5) Turn ignition off. Unplug 2-pin connector from control box, located at top center of firewall. Turn ignition on. Measure voltage between harness connector Black/Yellow wire and ground. If battery voltage exists, go to next step. If battery voltage does not exist, repair Black/Yellow wire between EGR control solenoid valve and fuse panel. EGR control solenoid valve is located in control box.

6) Reconnect vacuum pump/gauge to hose. Start and idle engine. Connect fused jumper wire between terminal "A" (Black/Yellow wire on mating harness connector) of control box connector and positive battery terminal.

7) Observe vacuum gauge while connecting remaining control box terminal to ground. If gauge indicates about 8 in. Hg within one second, go to next step. If gauge indication is not as specified, go to step **13)**.

8) Turn ignition off. Reconnect vehicle harness to control box. Unplug 3-pin connector from EGR valve. EGR valve is located behind distributor. Turn ignition on. Measure voltage between Yellow/White and Green/White wires at harness connector. If voltage is about 5 volts, go to next step. If voltage is not about 5 volts, go to step **15)**.

9) Turn ignition off. Reconnect vehicle harness to EGR valve. Connect test harness. *See Fig. 4.* Turn ignition on. Measure voltage between terminals D12 and D22 with no vacuum applied to EGR valve. Apply 8 in. Hg vacuum to EGR valve. Voltage should be about 1.2 volts with no vacuum applied and 4.3 volts with vacuum applied. If voltage is as specified, go to step **11)**.

10) If voltage is not as specified, check for open or short circuit in White/Black wire between EGR valve and ECM terminal D12. If wire is okay, replace EGR valve.

11) Observe voltmeter as vacuum is applied and released. If voltage increases and decreases smoothly, go to next step. If voltage change is not as specified, replace EGR valve.

12) Reconnect hose to EGR valve. Start and idle engine. Connect jumper wire between terminals A11 and A26. If engine stalls or runs roughly, replace ECM and retest system. If engine does not stall or run roughly, repair open in Pink/Green or Orange/Blue wire between ECM terminal A11 and EGR control solenoid valve.

13) Turn ignition off. Check vacuum hoses for leaks, restrictions and misrouting. If hoses are okay, go to next step. Repair as necessary.

14) Disconnect lower hose from EGR control solenoid valve. EGR control solenoid valve is located in control box, at top center of firewall. Connect vacuum gauge/pump to hose. Start and idle engine. If gauge indicates 6-10 in. Hg vacuum, replace EGR control solenoid valve. If vacuum is not as specified, replace EGR vacuum control valve, located in control box.

15) Measure voltage between Yellow/White wire and body ground. If voltage is not about 5 volts, go to next step. If voltage is about 5 volts, repair open in Green/White wire between ECM terminal D22 and EGR valve.

16) Turn ignition off. Connect test harness. *See Fig. 4.* Turn ignition on. Measure voltage between terminals D20 and D22. If voltage is about 5 volts, repair open in Yellow/White wire between EGR valve and ECM terminal D20. If voltage is not about 5 volts, replace ECM and retest system.

FUEL EVAPORATION

EVAP Purge Control Solenoid Valve – 1) Disconnect vacuum hose from EVAP purge control diaphragm valve, located on charcoal canister. Connect vacuum gauge to hose. Start and idle engine. Engine coolant temperature must be less than 167°F (75°C).

2) If vacuum does not exist, go to step **4)**. If vacuum exists, unplug connector at EVAP purge control solenoid valve. See EVAP PURGE CONTROL SOLENOID LOCATION table. Measure voltage between specified wires. See EVAP PURGE CONTROL SOLENOID CONNECTOR IDENTIFICATION table.

EVAP PURGE CONTROL SOLENOID LOCATION

Application	Location
Accord	In Control Box On Firewall
Civic & Civic Del Sol	Left Of IAC Valve
Prelude	Near Throttle Position Sensor

EVAP PURGE CONTROL SOLENOID CONNECTOR IDENTIFICATION

Application	Positive Terminal Wire Color	Negative Terminal Wire Color
Accord	Yellow/Black	Red/Yellow
Civic & Civic Del Sol	Yellow/Black	Red
Prelude	Black/Yellow	Red/Green

3) If battery voltage exists, inspect vacuum hose for leaks, blockage and incorrect routing. If hose is okay, replace EVAP purge control solenoid valve. If voltage does not exist, measure voltage between positive terminal and chassis ground. If battery voltage does not exist, repair open circuit in appropriate positive wire. If voltage exists, check for open circuit between negative terminal and ECM. If wire is okay, replace ECM.

4) Warm engine to full operating temperature (cooling fan comes on). Turn off and restart engine. If vacuum now exists, go to EVAP CANISTER. If vacuum does not exist, unplug connector at EVAP purge control solenoid valve.

5) If vacuum now exists, check for short circuit in negative wire between harness connector and ECM. If wire is okay, substitute known good ECM. Retest system. If system now operates properly, replace ECM. If vacuum still does not exist, check vacuum hose for leaks, blockage and improper routing. If hose is okay, replace EVAP purge control solenoid valve.

NOTE: EVAP canister may also be referred to as charcoal canister or EVAP charcoal canister.

EVAP Canister – Connect vacuum gauge to canister purge air hose, located at bottom of canister. See Fig. 9. Start engine. Increase engine speed to 3500 RPM. Vacuum should register on gauge within one minute. If results are not as specified, inspect purge hose for blockage. If hose is okay, replace charcoal canister.

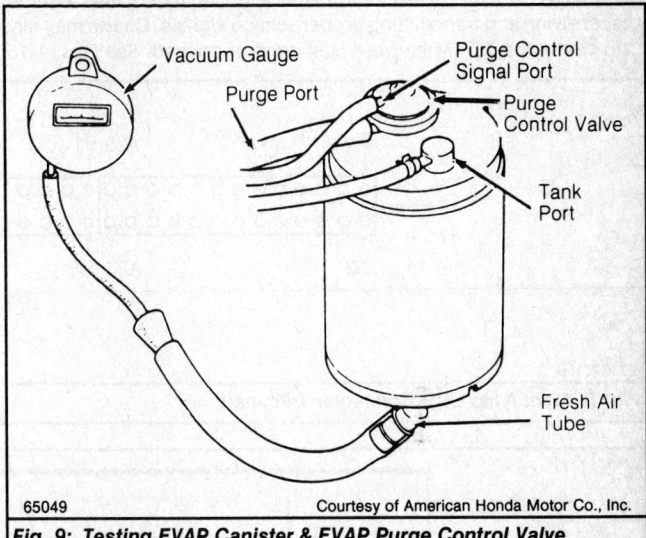

65049   Courtesy of American Honda Motor Co., Inc.

Fig. 9: Testing EVAP Canister & EVAP Purge Control Valve

EVAP 2-Way Valve – 1) Remove fuel filler cap. Disconnect vapor hose from fuel tank side of 2-way valve, located in fuel tank area. Install "T" fitting into hose. Connect vacuum gauge and vacuum pump to "T" fitting.

2) Slowly apply vacuum while observing vacuum gauge. Vacuum should stabilize momentarily at 0.2-0.6 in. Hg. If vacuum is as specified, go to next step. If vacuum is not as specified, replace 2-way valve. Retest system.

3) Move vacuum hose from vacuum to pressure fitting side of vacuum pump. Slowly pressurize vapor line while observing gauge. If pressure stabilizes at 0.4-1.4 in. Hg, valve is okay. If pressure stabilizes at less than 0.4 in. Hg or greater than 1.4 in. Hg, replace valve and retest.

POSITIVE CRANKCASE VENTILATION (PCV)

Inspect crankcase ventilation hoses and connections for leaks and clogging. Start engine. With engine at idle, pinch and release PCV hose. Valve should click. If valve does not click, check for vacuum at PCV valve end of hose. If manifold vacuum exists, replace PCV valve and recheck. If vacuum does not exist, clear blockage in hose.

1994 ENGINE PERFORMANCE
Pin Voltage Charts

Accord, Civic, Civic Del Sol, Passport, Prelude

NOTE: For pin voltage information on Passport, refer to Rodeo in Isuzu PIN VOLTAGE CHARTS article.

NOTE: Unless stated otherwise in testing procedures, perform all voltage tests using a Digital Volt-Ohmmeter (DVOM) with a minimum 10-megohm input impedance. Voltage readings may vary slightly due to battery condition or charging rate.

INTRODUCTION

Pin voltage charts are supplied to reduce diagnostic time. Checking pin voltages at the Engine Control Module (ECM) determines whether it is receiving and transmitting proper voltage signals. Charts may also help determine if ECM harness is shorted or opened. *See Figs. 1-15.*

NOTE: For terminal identification on all models, see Fig. 1.

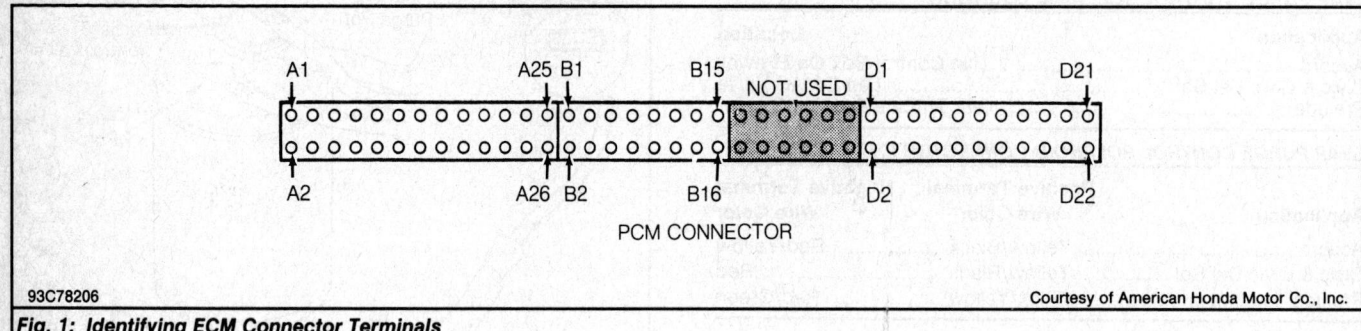

93C78206

Courtesy of American Honda Motor Co., Inc.

Fig. 1: Identifying ECM Connector Terminals

	Terminal ID.	Function/Description	Voltage Value (DC Volts Unless Otherwise Specified)
Brown	A1	Injector No. 1	Battery Voltage With KOEO [1]
Yellow	A2	Injector No. 4	Battery Voltage With KOEO [1]
Red	A3	Injector No. 2	Battery Voltage With KOEO [1]
	A4	BLANK	N/A
Blue	A5	Injector No. 3	Battery Voltage With KOEO [1]
Red	A6	EGR Control Solenoid Valve	N/A
Green/Black	A7 & A8	Fuel Pump Control Circuit	Battery Voltage With KOEO [1]
Black/Blue	A9	Intake Air Control (IAC) Valve	Battery Voltage KOEO [1] On Warm Engine
Green/White	A10	Engine Mount Control Solenoid Valve	N/A
Green/Black	A11	Heated Oxygen Sensor (HO2S) Circuit	Battery Voltage With KOEO [1]
Green	A12	Radiator Fan & Compressor Fan Control Relay	N/A
Green/Red	A13	Malfunction Indicator Light (MIL) Circuit	N/A
Red/Blue	A14 & A17	BLANK	N/A
White/Green	A15	A/C Compressor Control Unit Signal	N/A
Brown/White	A16	Alternator Control Circuit	N/A
Orange/Green	A18	A/T Control Unit Link (A/T Only)	N/A
Red/Yellow	A19	Intake Air Control (IAC) Solenoid Valve	Battery Voltage With KOEO [1]
Yellow/Green	A20	Purge Cut-Off Solenoid Valve Circuit	N/A
Black	A21 & A22	Ignition Control Module Circuit	Battery Voltage With KOEO [1]
Yellow/Black	A23 & A24	Power Ground	Less Than 1V
Brown/Black	A25	B + From Main Relay	Battery Voltage With KOEO [1]
	A26	Ground	Less Than 1V

[1] – KOEO – Key on, engine off.

94B44546

Courtesy of American Honda Motor Co., Inc.

Fig. 2: ECM Pin Voltage Chart For Connector Section "A" (Accord)

	Terminal ID.	Function/Description	Voltage Value (DC Volts Unless Otherwise Specified)
Yellow/Black	B1	B + From Main Relay	Battery Voltage With KOEO [1]
Brown/Black	B2	Ground	Less Than 1V
White/Red	B3	A/T Control Unit Link (A/T Only)	N/A
Green	B4	A/T Control Unit Link (A/T Only)	N/A
Red/White	B5	A/C Switch Input	About 5V KOER [2] (A/C Off); Below 1V (A/C On)
	B6	BLANK	N/A
Light Green	B7	Park/Neutral Switch (A/T)	Below 1V In P/N KOEO [1]; 11V In Other Positions
Green	B8	Power Steering Oil Pressure Switch	0V KOER [2]; B + While Turning Wheel
Red/Blue (A/T)	B9	Start Signal Input	Battery Voltage In START Position
Black/Green (M/T)	B9	Start Signal Input	Battery Voltage In START Position
Orange	B10	Vehicle Speed Sensor	Pulses 0-5V While Turning Left Front Wheel
Orange	B11	CYP Sensor Input	N/A
White	B12	CYP Sensor Signal	N/A
Orange/Blue	B13	TDC Sensor Input	N/A
White/Blue	B14	TDC Sensor Signal	N/A
Blue/Green	B15	CKP Sensor Input	N/A
Blue/Yellow	B16	CKP Sensor Signal	N/A
White/Yellow	D1	B + From Battery Through Fuse Box	Battery Voltage At All Times
Green/White	D2	Brake Switch Input Signal	0V KOEO [1] w/Brake Pedal Released; Battery Voltage w/Brake Pedal Depressed
	D3, D8 & D16	BLANK	N/A
Orange/Red	D4	Service Check Connector	5V KOEO [1]
Blue/White	D5	Transmission Control Module	N/A
Blue/Black	D6	VTEC Pressure Switch	N/A
Light Green/Red	D7	Data Link Connector (DLC)	N/A
White/Red	D9	Alternator Charging Signal	About 5V KOEO [1]; Decreases Under Electrical Load (Headlights & Rear Defogger On) At Warm Idle
Green/Red	D10	Electrical Load Detector (ELD) Input	N/A
Red/Black	D11	Throttle Position (TP) Sensor Signal	About 0.5V KOEO [1] With Throttle Fully Closed; About 4.5V KOEO [1] With Throttle Fully Open
White/Black	D12	EGR Valve Lift Sensor	About 1.2V KOER [2] at Idle
Red/White	D13	Coolant Temperature Sensor Signal	About 5V KOEO [1] (Varies With Temperature)
White/Red	D14	Heated Oxygen Sensor (HO2S) Signal	0.4-0.5V When Ignition First Turned On; Decreases To Below 0.1V In Less Than 2 Minutes
Red/Yellow	D15	Intake Air Temperature (IAT) Signal	0.5-4.5V KOEO [1] (Varies With Temperature)
White/Yellow	D17	MAP Sensor Signal	About 3V KOEO [1] (Varies w/Manifold Vacuum)
Lt. Green/Black	D18	A/T Control Unit Link (A/T Only)	N/A
Yellow/White	D19	Sensor Power	About 5V KOEO [1]
Yellow/Blue	D20	Sensor Power	About 5V KOEO [1]
Green/White	D21	Sensor Ground	Less Than 1V
Blue/White	D22	Sensor Ground	Less Than 1V

[1] – KOEO – Key on, engine off.
[2] – KOER – Key on, engine running.

94C44547

Courtesy of American Honda Motor Co., Inc.

Fig. 3: ECM Pin Voltage Chart For Connector Sections "B" & "D" (Accord)

	Terminal ID.	Function/Description	Voltage Value (DC Volts Unless Otherwise Specified)
Brown →	A1	Injector No. 1	Battery Voltage With KOEO [1]
Yellow →	A2	Injector No. 4	Battery Voltage With KOEO [1]
Red →	A3	Injector No. 2	Battery Voltage With KOEO [1]
Orange/White →	A4	VTEC Spool Solenoid Valve Control	N/A
Light Blue →	A5	Injector No. 3	Battery Voltage With KOEO [1]
Orange/Black →	A6	Heated Oxygen Sensor (HO2S) Control	Battery Voltage With KOEO [1]
Green/Yellow →	A7	Fuel Pump Control	Battery Voltage With KOEO [1]
	A8	BLANK	N/A
Green/White →	A9	IAC Control	Battery Voltage With KOEO [1]
	A10 & A11	BLANK	N/A
Yellow/Green →	A12	Cooling Fan	N/A
Green/Orange →	A13	Malfunction Indicator Light (MIL) Control	Battery Voltage With KOEO [1]
	A14	BLANK	N/A
Black/Red →	A15	Compressor Clutch Relay	Battery Voltage With A/C On
White/Yellow →	A16	Alternator Output Signal	N/A
Light Green →	A17	A/T Lock-Up Control	Battery Voltage With KOEO [1]
	A18	BLANK	N/A
Yellow →	A19	A/T Lock-Up Control	Battery Voltage With KOEO [1]
Red →	A20	Purge Control Solenoid	N/A
Red/Green →	A21	Ignition Control Module (ICM) Output Signal	About 10V With KOEO [1]
	A22	BLANK	N/A
Black →	A23 & A24	Ground	Less Than 1V
Yellow/Black →	A25	B + From Battery Through Fuse Box	Battery Voltage At All Times
Black/Red →	A26	Ground	Less Than 1V

[1] – KOEO – Key on, engine off.

94D44548

Courtesy of American Honda Motor Co., Inc.

Fig. 4: ECM Pin Voltage Chart For Connector Section "A" (Civic Except VX 1.5L)

Terminal ID.	Function/Description	Voltage Value (DC Volts Unless Otherwise Specified)
Yellow/Black → B1	B + From Battery Through Fuse Box	Battery Voltage At All Times
Brown/Black → B2	Ground	Less Than 1V
Green/Blue → B3	A/T Shift Selector Input	Battery Voltage With KOEO [1]
Green/Black → B4	A/T Shift Selector Input	Battery Voltage With KOEO [1]
Blue/Red → B5	A/C Request Input	About 5V KOER [2] (A/C Off); Below 1V (A/C On)
B6	BLANK	N/A
Green → B7	Park/Neutral Input	About 5V With KOEO [1]
Brown/Red → B8	Power Steering Switch Input	Battery Voltage (Steering Wheel Turning)
Blue/White → B9	START Signal Input	Battery Voltage In START Position
Yellow/Blue → B10	Vehicle Speed Sensor Input	Pulses Zero To More Than 5V With Wheels Turning
Orange → B11	CYP Sensor Input	N/A
White → B12	CYP Sensor Signal	N/A
Orange/Blue → B13	TDC Sensor Input	N/A
White/Blue → B14	TDC Sensor Signal	N/A
Blue/Green → B15	CKP Sensor Input	N/A
Blue/Yellow → B16	CKP Sensor Signal	N/A

[1] – KOEO – Key on, engine off.
[2] – KOER – Key on, engine running.

94E44549

Courtesy of American Honda Motor Co., Inc.

Fig. 5: ECM Pin Voltage Chart For Connector Section "B" (Civic Except VX 1.5L)

1994 ENGINE PERFORMANCE
Pin Voltage Charts (Cont.)

	Terminal ID.	Function/Description	Voltage Value (DC Volts Unless Otherwise Specified)
White/Blue →	D1	B + From Battery (Input)	Battery Voltage At All Times
Green/White →	D2	Brakelight Switch Input	Battery Voltage At All Times
	D3	BLANK	N/A
Brown →	D4	Service Check Connector	About 5V With KOEO [1]
	D5	BLANK	N/A
Orange/Blue →	D6	VTEC Oil Pressure Switch Input	0.5-4.5V KOEO [1] (Varies With Pressure)
Light Blue →	D7	Serial Data Link	N/A
	D8	BLANK	N/A
Pink →	D9	Alternator FR Signal	About 4.5V With KOEO [1]
Green/Red →	D10	Electrical Load Detector (ELD) Input	N/A
Pink/Black →	D11	Throttle Position (TP) Sensor Input	.5V With Closed Throttle 4.5V With Wide Open Throttle
	D12	BLANK	N/A
Red/White →	D13	Coolant Temperature Sensor Input	About 5V
Orange/Blue →	D14	HO2S Sensor Input	Less Than .4V With Closed Throttle Greater Than .6V With Wide Open Throttle
Red/Yellow →	D15	Intake Air Temperature Sensor Input	About 5V With KOEO [1]
	D16	BLANK	N/A
Pink/White →	D17	Sensor Ground	Less Than 1V
White/Red →	D18	Shift Lock Control	N/A
Yellow/Green →	D19	Reference Voltage	About 5V With KOEO [1]
Yellow/White →	D20	Reference Voltage	About 5V With KOEO [1]
Green/Blue [2] →	D21	MAP Sensor Input	About 3V
Green/White →	D22	Sensor Ground	Less Than 1V

[1] – KOEO – Key on, engine off.
[2] – Green/Blue on CX, EX & Si Models; Green/White on DX & LX Models.

94I44550

Courtesy of American Honda Motor Co., Inc.

Fig. 6: ECM Pin Voltage Chart For Connector Section "D" (Civic Except VX 1.5L)

1994 ENGINE PERFORMANCE
Pin Voltage Charts (Cont.)

	Terminal ID.	Function/Description	Voltage Value (DC Volts Unless Otherwise Specified)
Brown	A1	Injector No. 1	Battery Voltage With KOEO [1]
Yellow	A2	Injector No. 4	Battery Voltage With KOEO [1]
Red	A3	Injector No. 2	Battery Voltage With KOEO [1]
Orange/White	A4	VTEC Spool Solenoid Valve Control	N/A
Light Blue	A5	Injector No. 3	Battery Voltage With KOEO [1]
Orange/Black	A6	Heated Oxygen Sensor Heater (HO2S)	Battery Voltage With KOEO [1]
Green/Yellow	A7	Fuel Pump Control No. 1	Battery Voltage With KOEO [1]
Green/Yellow	A8	Fuel Pump Control No. 2	Battery Voltage With KOEO [1]
Green/White	A9	IAC Valve Control	Battery Voltage With KOEO [1]
	A10	BLANK	N/A
Pink/Green	A11	EGR Control Solenoid Valve	Battery Voltage With KOEO [1]
Yellow/Orange	A12	Cooling Fan	N/A
Green/Orange	A13	Malfunction Indicator Light (MIL) Control	Battery Voltage With KOEO [1]
	A14	BLANK	N/A
Black/Red	A15	Compressor Clutch Relay	Battery Voltage With A/C On
White/Yellow	A16	Alternator Output Signal	N/A
	A17 & A18	BLANK	N/A
	A19	BLANK	N/A
Red	A20	Purge Control Solenoid	N/A
Red/Green	A21	Ignition Control Module (ICM) Output Signal	About 10V With KOEO [1]
	A22	BLANK	N/A
Black	A23 & A24	Ground	Less Than 1V
Yellow/Black	A25	B + From Battery Through Fuse Box	Battery Voltage At All Times
Black/Red	A26	Ground	Less Than 1V

[1] - KOEO - Key on, engine off.

94J44551

Courtesy of American Honda Motor Co., Inc.

Fig. 7: ECM Pin Voltage Chart For Connector Section "A" (Civic VX 1.5L)

	Terminal ID.	Function/Description	Voltage Value (DC Volts Unless Otherwise Specified)
Yellow/Black ➡	B1	B + From Battery Through Fuse Box	Battery Voltage At All Times
Brown/Black ➡	B2	Ground	Less Than 1V
	B3 & B4	BLANK	N/A
Blue/Red ➡	B5	A/C Request Input	About 5V With KOEO [1]
	B6	BLANK	N/A
Green ➡	B7	M/T Clutch Switch	About 5V With KOEO [1]
Brown/Red ➡	B8	Power Steering Switch Input	Battery Voltage (Steering Wheel Turning)
Blue/White ➡	B9	Start Signal Input	Battery Voltage In START Position
Yellow/Blue ➡	B10	Vehicle Speed Sensor Input	Pulses Zero To More Than 5V With Wheels Turning
Orange ➡	B11	CYP Sensor Input	N/A
White ➡	B12	CYP Sensor Signal	N/A
Orange/Blue ➡	B13	TDC Sensor Input	N/A
White/Blue ➡	B14	TDC Sensor Signal	N/A
Blue/Green ➡	B15	CKP Sensor Input	N/A
Blue/Yellow ➡	B16	CKP Sensor Signal	N/A

[1] – KOEO – Key on, engine off.

94A44552

Fig. 8: ECM Pin Voltage Chart For Connector Section "B" (Civic VX 1.5L)

	Terminal ID.	Function/Description	Voltage Value (DC Volts Unless Otherwise Specified)
White/Blue	D1	B + From Battery (Input)	Battery Voltage At All Times
Green/White	D2	Brakelight Switch Input	Battery Voltage At All Times
Blue/Yellow	D3	Heated Oxygen Sensor (HO2S) Control	N/A
Brown	D4	Service Check Connector	About 5V With KOEO [1]
	D5	BLANK	N/A
Orange/Blue	D6	VTEC Oil Pressure Switch Input	0.5-4.5V KOEO [1] (Varies With Pressure)
Light Blue	D7	Data Link Connector (DLC)	N/A
White/Blue	D8	Sensor Input	Less Than 5V
Pink	D9	Alternator FR Signal	About 4.5V With KOEO [1]
Green/Red	D10	Electrical Load Detector (ELD) Input	N/A
Pink/Black	D11	Throttle Position (TP) Sensor Input	.5V With Closed Throttle 4.5V With Wide Open Throttle
White/Black	D12	EGR Valve Lift Sensor Input	1.2V Without Vacuum Applied 4.3V With 8 In. Hg Vacuum Applied
Red/White	D13	Coolant Temperature Sensor Input	About 5V
Orange/Blue	D14	HO2S Sensor Input	Less Than .4V With Closed Throttle Greater Than .6V With Wide Open Throttle
Red/Yellow	D15	Intake Air Temperature (IAT) Sensor Input	About 5V With KOEO [1]
Blue/Green	D16	Sensor Ground	Less Than 1V
Pink/White	D17	Sensor Ground	Less Than 1V
Pink/Green	D18	Economy Driving Indicator Control	N/A
Yellow/Green	D19	Reference Voltage	About 5V With KOEO [1]
Yellow/White	D20	Reference Voltage	About 5V
Green/Blue	D21	MAP Sensor Input	About 3V
Green/White	D22	Sensor Ground	Less Than 1V

[1] – KOEO – Key on, engine off.

94B44553

Fig. 9: ECM Pin Voltage Chart For Connector Section "D" (Civic VX 1.5L)

1994 ENGINE PERFORMANCE
Pin Voltage Charts (Cont.)

	Terminal ID.	Function/Description	Voltage Value (DC Volts Unless Otherwise Specified)
Brown	A1	Injector No. 1	Battery Voltage With KOEO [1]
Yellow	A2	Injector No. 4	Battery Voltage With KOEO [1]
Red	A3	Injector No. 2	Battery Voltage With KOEO [1]
Orange/White	A4	VTEC Spool Solenoid Valve Control	N/A
Light Blue	A5	Injector No. 3	Battery Voltage With KOEO [1]
Orange/Black	A6	Heated Oxygen Sensor (HO2S) Control	Battery Voltage With KOEO [1]
Green/Yellow	A7	Fuel Pump Control	Battery Voltage With KOEO [1]
	A8	BLANK	N/A
Green/White	A9	IAC Valve Control	Battery Voltage With KOEO [1]
	A10 & A11	BLANK	N/A
Yellow/Green	A12	Cooling Fan	N/A
Green/Orange	A13	Malfunction Indicator Light (MIL) Control	Battery Voltage With KOEO [1]
	A14	BLANK	N/A
Black/Red	A15	Compressor Clutch Relay	Battery Voltage With A/C On
White/Yellow	A16	Alternator Output Signal	N/A
Green/Black	A17	A/T Lock-Up Control	Battery Voltage With KOEO [1]
	A18	BLANK	N/A
Yellow	A19	A/T Lock-Up Control	Battery Voltage With KOEO [1]
Red	A20	Purge Control Solenoid	N/A
Red/Green	A21	Ignition Control Module (ICM) Output Signal	About 10V With KOEO [1]
	A22	BLANK	N/A
Black	A23 & A24	Ground	Less Than 1V
Yellow/Black	A25	B + From Battery Through Fuse Box	Battery Voltage At All Times
Black/Red	A26	Ground	Less Than 1V

[1] – KOEO – Key on, engine off.

94C44554

Courtesy of American Honda Motor Co., Inc.

Fig. 10: ECM Pin Voltage Chart For Connector Section "A" (Civic Del Sol)

	Terminal ID.	Function/Description	Voltage Value (DC Volts Unless Otherwise Specified)
Yellow/Black →	B1	B + From Battery Through Fuse Box	Battery Voltage At All Times
Brown/Black →	B2	Ground	Less Than 1V
Green/Blue →	B3	A/T Shift Selector Input	Battery Voltage With KOEO [1]
Green/Black →	B4	A/T Shift Selector Input	Battery Voltage With KOEO [1]
Blue/Red →	B5	A/C Request Input	About 5V With KOEO [1]
	B6	BLANK	N/A
Green →	B7	Park/Neutral Input	About 5V With KOEO [1]
Brown/Red →	B8	Power Steering Switch Input	Battery Voltage (Steering Wheel Turning)
Blue/White →	B9	START Signal Input	Battery Voltage In START Position
Yellow/Blue →	B10	Vehicle Speed Sensor Input	Pulses 0-12V (Wheels Turning)
Orange →	B11	CYP Sensor Input	N/A
White →	B12	CYP Sensor Signal	N/A
Orange/Blue →	B13	TDC Sensor Input	N/A
White/Blue →	B14	TDC Sensor Signal	N/A
Blue/Green →	B15	CKP Sensor Input	N/A
Blue/Yellow →	B16	CKP Sensor Signal	N/A

[1] – KOEO – Key on, engine off.

94D44555

Courtesy of American Honda Motor Co., Inc.

Fig. 11: ECM Pin Voltage Chart For Connector Section "B" (Civic Del Sol)

1994 ENGINE PERFORMANCE
Pin Voltage Charts (Cont.)

	Terminal ID.	Function/Description	Voltage Value (DC Volts Unless Otherwise Specified)
White/Blue →	D1	B + From Battery (Input)	Battery Voltage At All Times
Green/White →	D2	Brakelight Switch Input	Battery Voltage At All Times
Red/Blue →	D3	Knock Sensor (B16A3 Engine)	N/A
Brown →	D4	Service Check Connector	About 5V With KOEO [1]
	D5	BLANK	N/A
Orange/Blue →	D6	VTEC Oil Pressure Switch Input	0.5-4.5V KOEO [1] (Varies With Pressure)
Light Blue →	D7	Data Link Connector (DLC)	N/A
	D8	BLANK	N/A
Pink →	D9	Alternator FR Signal	About 4.5V With KOEO [1]
Green/Red →	D10	Electrical Load Detector (ELD) Input	N/A
Red/Blue →	D11	Throttle Position (TP) Sensor Input	.5V With Closed Throttle 4.5V With Wide Open Throttle
	D12	BLANK	N/A
Red/White →	D13	Coolant Temperature Sensor Input	About 5V
White →	D14	Heated Oxygen Sensor (HO2S) Input	0.4-0.5V When Ignition Is Turned On; Drops To Less Than 0.1V Within 1 Minute
Red/Yellow →	D15	Intake Air Temperature (IAT) Sensor Input	About 5V With KOEO [1]
	D16	BLANK	N/A
White →	D17	MAP Sensor Input	About 3V
White/Red →	D18	Shift Lock Control	N/A
Yellow/Green →	D19	Reference Voltage	About 5V With KOEO [1]
Yellow/White →	D20	Reference Voltage	About 5V With KOEO [1]
Green/Blue →	D21	Sensor Ground	Less Than 1V
Green/White →	D22	Sensor Ground	Less Than 1V

[1] – KOEO – Key on, engine off.

94E44556

Courtesy of American Honda Motor Co., Inc.

Fig. 12: ECM Pin Voltage Chart For Connector Section "D" (Civic Del Sol)

1994 ENGINE PERFORMANCE
Pin Voltage Charts (Cont.)

	Terminal ID.	Function/Description	Voltage Value (DC Volts Unless Otherwise Specified)
Brown	A1	Injector No. 1	Battery Voltage With KOEO [1]
Yellow	A2	Injector No. 4	Battery Voltage With KOEO [1]
Red	A3	Injector No. 2	Battery Voltage With KOEO [1]
Green/Yellow	A4	VTEC Solenoid Valve Control	N/A
Blue	A5	Injector No. 3	Battery Voltage With KOEO [1]
Orange/White	A6	Heated Oxygen Sensor (HO2S) Circuit	Battery Voltage With KOEO [1]
Green/Black	A7 & A8	Fuel Pump Control Circuit	Battery Voltage With KOEO [1]
Black/Blue	A9	Intake Air Control (IAC) Valve	About 10V KOEO [1] On Warm Engine
	A10 & A14	BLANK	N/A
Red	A11	EGR Control Solenoid Valve	N/A
Blue/Red	A12	Fan Relay Control	N/A
Blue/White	A13	Malfunction Indicator Light (MIL) Circuit	N/A
Red/Blue	A15	A/C Compressor Control Unit Signal	N/A
White/Green	A16	Alternator Output Signal	N/A
Pink	A17	By-Pass Control Solenoid Valve Control	N/A
Orange/Red	A18	Transmission Control Module (A/T)	N/A
White	A19	Intake Control Solenoid	Battery Voltage With KOEO [1]
Red/Green	A20	Purge Cut-Off Solenoid Valve Circuit	N/A
Yellow/Green	A21 & A22	Ignition Control Module (ICM) Output Signal	About 10V KOEO [1]
Black	A23 & A24	Power Ground	Less Than 1V
Yellow/Black	A25	B + From Main Relay	Battery Voltage With KOEO [1]
Black/Red	A26	Ground	Less Than 1V

[1] - Key on, engine off.

94F44557

Courtesy of American Honda Motor Co., Inc.

Fig. 13: ECM Pin Voltage Chart For Connector Section "A" (Prelude)

1994 ENGINE PERFORMANCE
Pin Voltage Charts (Cont.)

Yellow/Black
Brown/Black
Orange
Pink
Blue/Black

Light Green

Red/Green

Blue/Red

Orange
Orange
White
Orange/Blue
White/Blue
Blue/Green
Blue/Yellow

Terminal ID.	Function/Description	Voltage Value (DC Volts Unless Otherwise Specified)
B1	B + From Main Relay	Battery Voltage With KOEO [1]
B2	Ground	Less Than 1V
B3	Upshift/Downshift Comparative Input	N/A
B4	Upshift/Downshift Comparative Input	N/A
B5	A/C Switch Input	About 5V With KOEO [1] & A/C Off; Less Than 1V KOER [2] With A/C & Blower On
B6	BLANK	N/A
B7	Park/Neutral Switch (A/T)	Less Than 1V In Park Or Neutral With KOEO [1]; 5V In Park Or Neutral With KOER [2]; Battery Voltage In All Other Positions
B8	Power Steering Oil Pressure Switch	0V KOEO [1]; Battery Voltage KOER [2] While Slowly Turning Steering Wheel
B9	Start Signal Input	Battery Voltage In START Position (Clutch Depressed On M/T Models)
B10	Vehicle Speed Sensor	Pulses 0-12V While Turning Left Front Wheel
B11	CYP Sensor Input	N/A
B12	CYP Sensor Signal	N/A
B13	TDC Sensor Input	N/A
B14	TDC Sensor Signal	N/A
B15	CKP Sensor Input	N/A
B16	CKP Sensor Signal	N/A

[1] – KOEO – Key on, engine off.
[2] – KOER – Key on, engine running.

94G44848

Fig. 14: ECM Pin Voltage Chart For Connector Section "B" (Prelude)

1994 ENGINE PERFORMANCE
Pin Voltage Charts (Cont.)

	Terminal ID.	Function/Description	Voltage Value (DC Volts Unless Otherwise Specified)
White/Yellow	D1	B + From Battery Through Fuse Box	Battery Voltage at All Times
Green/White	D2	Stoplight Switch	Battery Voltage at All Times
Red/Blue	D3	Knock Sensor	N/A
Brown/White	D4	Service Check Connector	About 5V (M/T); About 11V (A/T)
	D5	BLANK	N/A
Lt. Blue	D6	VTEC Pressure Switch Input	N/A
Lt. Green/Red	D7	Data Link Connector (DLC)	N/A
	D8	BLANK	N/A
White/Red	D9	Alternator Charging Signal	About 4.5V KOEO [1]; Decreases Under Electrical Load (Headlights & Rear Defogger On) At Warm Idle
Green/Black	D10	Electrical Load Detector (ELD) Input	N/A
Red/Black	D11	Throttle Position (TP) Sensor Signal	About 0.5V KOEO [1] With Throttle Fully Closed; About 4.5V KOEO [1] With Throttle Fully Open
White/Black	D12	EGR Valve Lift Sensor	About 1.2V KOEO
Yellow/Blue	D13	Coolant Temperature Sensor Signal	About 5V KOEO [1] (Varies With Temperature)
White	D14	Heated Oxygen Sensor (HO2S) Signal	0.4-0.5V When Ignition Is Turned On; Drops To Less Than 0.1V Within 2 Minutes
Red/Yellow	D15	Intake Air Temperature (IAT) Signal	0.5-4.5V KOEO [1] (Varies With Temperature)
	D16	BLANK	N/A
White/Blue	D17	MAP Sensor Signal	About 3V KOEO [1] (Varies With Manifold Vacuum)
Lt. Green/Black	D18	Transmission Control Module (A/T Only)	N/A
Red/White	D19	Reference Voltage	About 5V KOEO [1]
Yellow/White	D20	Reference Voltage	About 5V KOEO [1]
Blue/White	D21	Sensor Ground	Less Than 1V
Green/White	D22	Sensor Ground	Less Than 1V

[1] - KOEO - Key on, engine off.

94G44558

Courtesy of American Honda Motor Co., Inc.

Fig. 15: ECM Pin Voltage Chart For Connector Section "D" (Prelude)

1993 ENGINE PERFORMANCE
Sensor Operating Range Charts

Accord, Civic, Civic Del Sol, Passport, Prelude

NOTE: For sensor operating range charts for Passport, refer to Rodeo in Isuzu SENSOR OPERATING RANGE CHARTS article.

INTRODUCTION

Sensor operating range information can help determine if a sensor is out of calibration. Although an out-of-calibration sensor may not set a trouble code, it may cause driveability problems.

NOTE: Unless stated otherwise in test procedure, perform all voltage tests using a Digital Volt-Ohmmeter (DVOM) with a minimum 10-megohm input impedance.

COOLANT TEMPERATURE (ECT) SENSOR RESISTANCE TEST [1]

Temperature – °F (°C)	Ohms
−4 (−20)	15,000-18,000
68 (20)	1000-4000
176 (80)	200-400

[1] – Measure resistance across sensor terminals.

INTAKE AIR TEMPERATURE (IAT) SENSOR RESISTANCE TEST [1]

Temperature – °F (°C)	Ohms
−4 (−20)	15,000-18,000
68 (20)	1000-4000
176 (80)	200-400

[1] – Measure resistance across sensor terminals.

MAP SENSOR VOLTAGE TEST [1]

Vacuum Applied – In. Hg	Volts
0	2.8-3.0
5	2.3-2.5
10	1.8-2.0
15	1.3-1.5
20	.8-1.0
25	.3-.5

[1] – Measure voltage at appropriate ECM terminals. See WIRING DIAGRAMS article in ENGINE PERFORMANCE.

EGR LIFT SENSOR VOLTAGE TEST [1]

Position	Volts (Approximate)
Fully Closed	1.2
Fully Open	4.3

[1] – Measure voltage at appropriate ECM terminals. See WIRING DIAGRAMS article in ENGINE PERFORMANCE. Voltage should increase smoothly as vacuum is applied.

OXYGEN SENSOR VOLTAGE TEST [1]

Condition	Volts
Lean	Less Than 0.4
Rich	Greater Than 0.6

[1] – Measure voltage between ground and oxygen sensor terminal using a high-impedance DVOM.

THROTTLE ANGLE (POSITION) SENSOR SPECIFICATIONS

Condition	[1] Volts
Throttle Valve	
Fully Closed	.5
Wide Open	4.5

[1] – Voltage change from fully closed to wide open should be smooth.

VEHICLE SPEED SENSOR (VSS) TEST [1]

Application	[2] Voltage
Accord	5
Civic & Civic Del Sol	More Than 5
Prelude	
Except H22A1 Engine	5
H22A1 Engine	12

[1] – Backprobe terminals at sensor.
[2] – Voltage will fluctuate between zero and specified value.

Accord, Civic, Civic Del Sol, Prelude

NOTE: For Vacuum Diagrams on Passport, refer to Rodeo in Isuzu Vacuum Diagrams article.

INTRODUCTION

This article contains underhood views or schematics of vacuum hose routing. Use these vacuum diagrams during the visual inspection in BASIC DIAGNOSTIC PROCEDURES article. This will assist in identifying improperly routed vacuum hoses, which cause driveability and/or computer-indicated malfunctions.

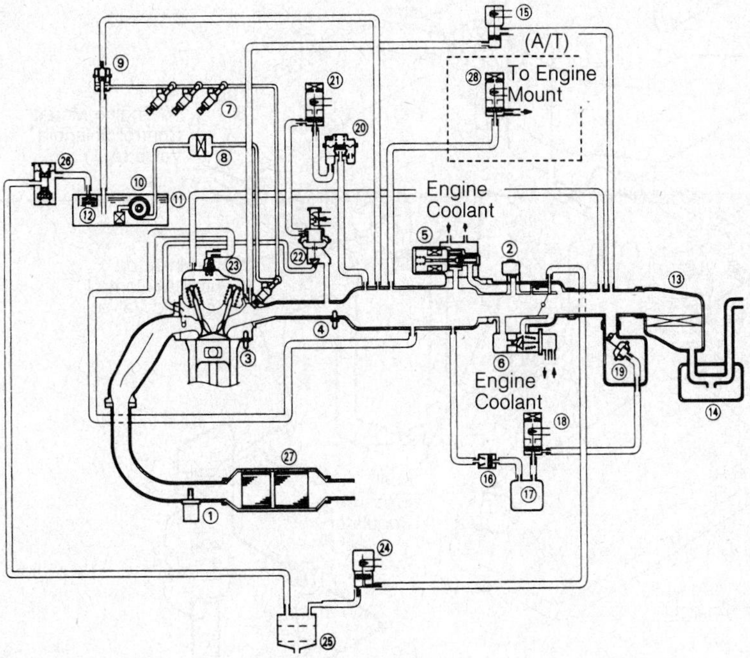

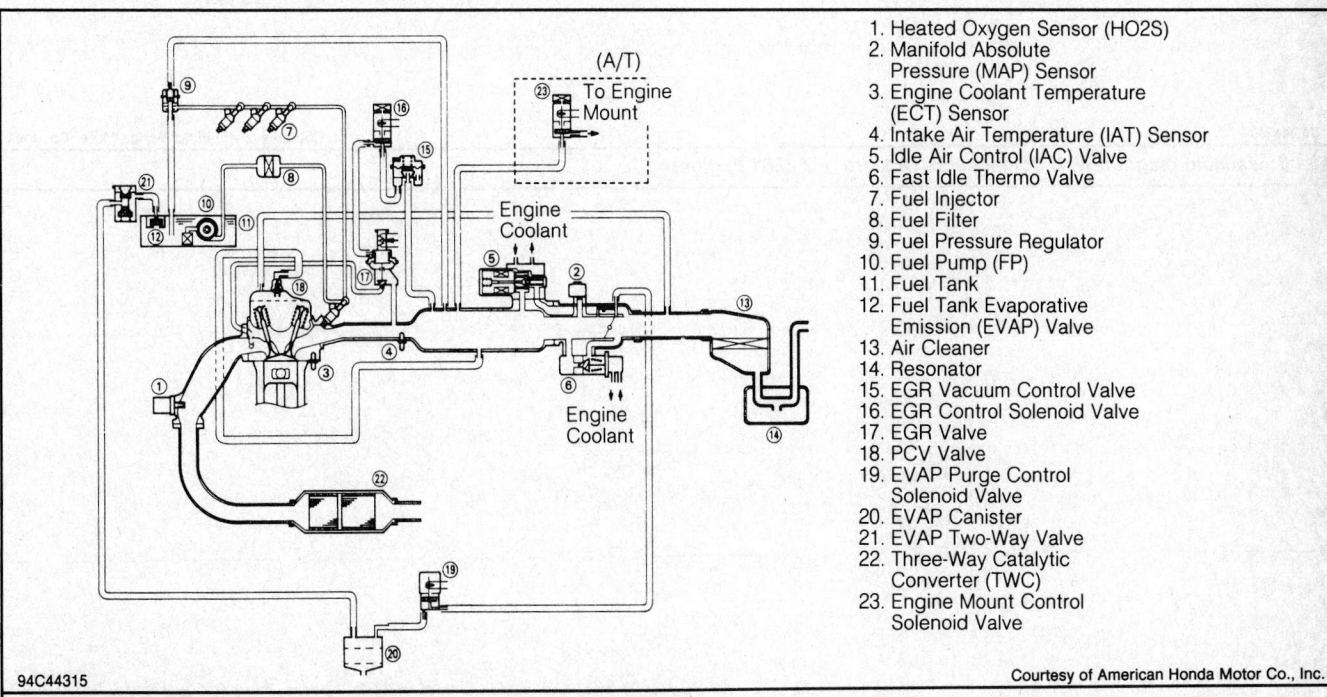

1. Heated Oxygen Sensor (HO2S)
2. Manifold Absolute Pressure (MAP) Sensor
3. Engine Coolant Temperature (ECT) Sensor
4. Intake Air Temperature (IAT) Sensor
5. Idle Air Control (IAC) Valve
6. Fast Idle Thermo Valve
7. Fuel Injector
8. Fuel Filter
9. Fuel Pressure Regulator
10. Fuel Pump (FP)
11. Fuel Tank
12. Fuel Tank Evaporative Emission (EVAP) Valve
13. Air Cleaner
14. Resonator
15. Fuel Injector Air (FIA) Control Solenoid Valve
16. Intake Air Resonator (IAR) Check Valve
17. Intake Air Resonator (IAR) Vacuum Tank
18. Intake Air Resonator (IAR) Control Solenoid Valve
19. Intake Air Resonator (IAR) Control Diaphragm
20. EGR Vacuum Control Valve
21. EGR Control Solenoid Valve
22. EGR Valve
23. PCV Valve
24. EVAP Purge Control Solenoid Valve
25. EVAP Canister
26. EVAP Two-Way Valve
27. Three-Way Catalytic Converter (TWC)
28. Engine Mount Control Solenoid Valve

Courtesy of American Honda Motor Co., Inc.

94B44314

Fig. 1: Vacuum Diagram Without Components (Accord – F22B1 Engine)

1. Heated Oxygen Sensor (HO2S)
2. Manifold Absolute Pressure (MAP) Sensor
3. Engine Coolant Temperature (ECT) Sensor
4. Intake Air Temperature (IAT) Sensor
5. Idle Air Control (IAC) Valve
6. Fast Idle Thermo Valve
7. Fuel Injector
8. Fuel Filter
9. Fuel Pressure Regulator
10. Fuel Pump (FP)
11. Fuel Tank
12. Fuel Tank Evaporative Emission (EVAP) Valve
13. Air Cleaner
14. Resonator
15. EGR Vacuum Control Valve
16. EGR Control Solenoid Valve
17. EGR Valve
18. PCV Valve
19. EVAP Purge Control Solenoid Valve
20. EVAP Canister
21. EVAP Two-Way Valve
22. Three-Way Catalytic Converter (TWC)
23. Engine Mount Control Solenoid Valve

Courtesy of American Honda Motor Co., Inc.

94C44315

Fig. 2: Vacuum Diagram Without Components (Accord – F22B2 Engine)

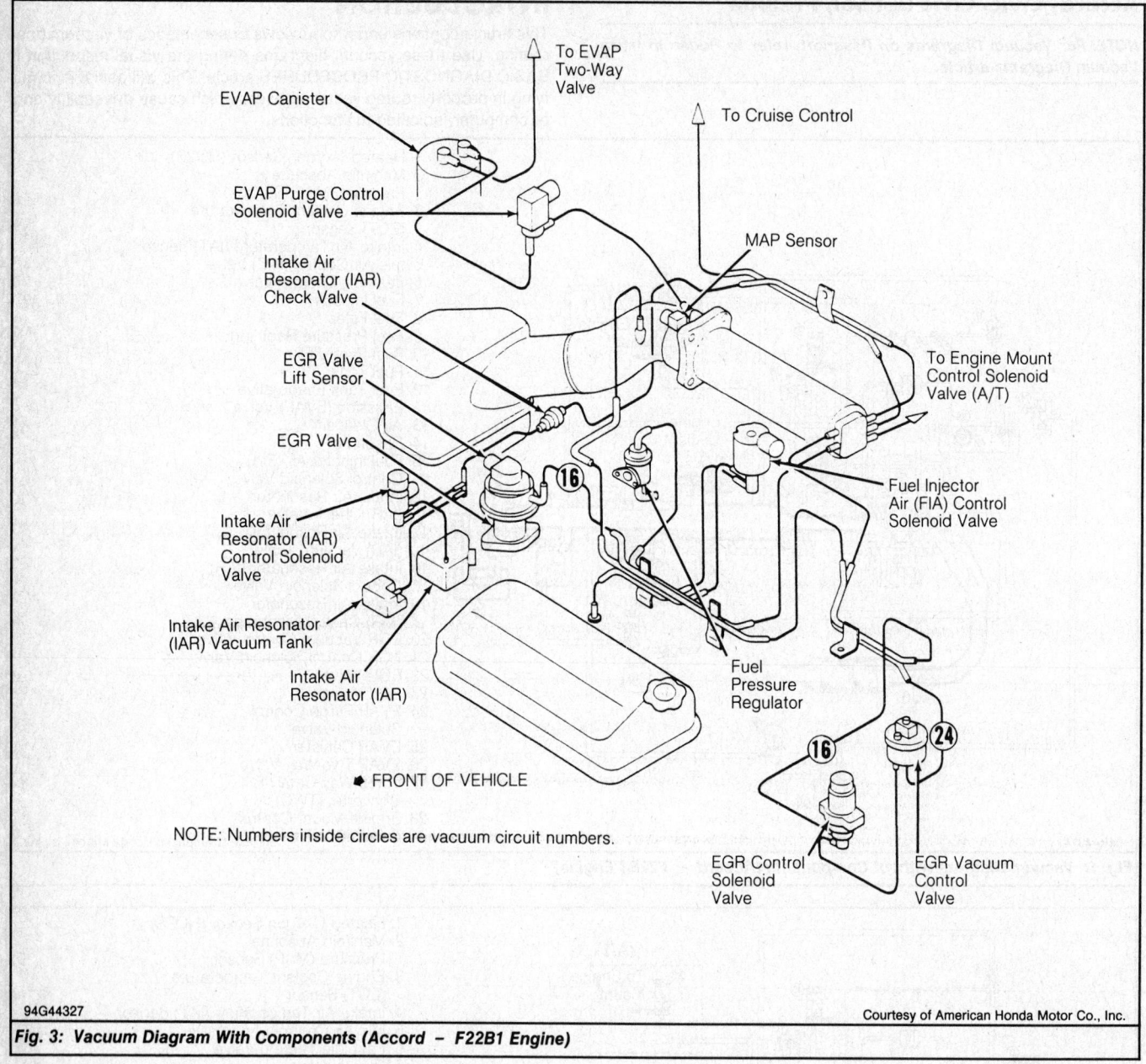

94G44327

Courtesy of American Honda Motor Co., Inc.

Fig. 3: Vacuum Diagram With Components (Accord – F22B1 Engine)

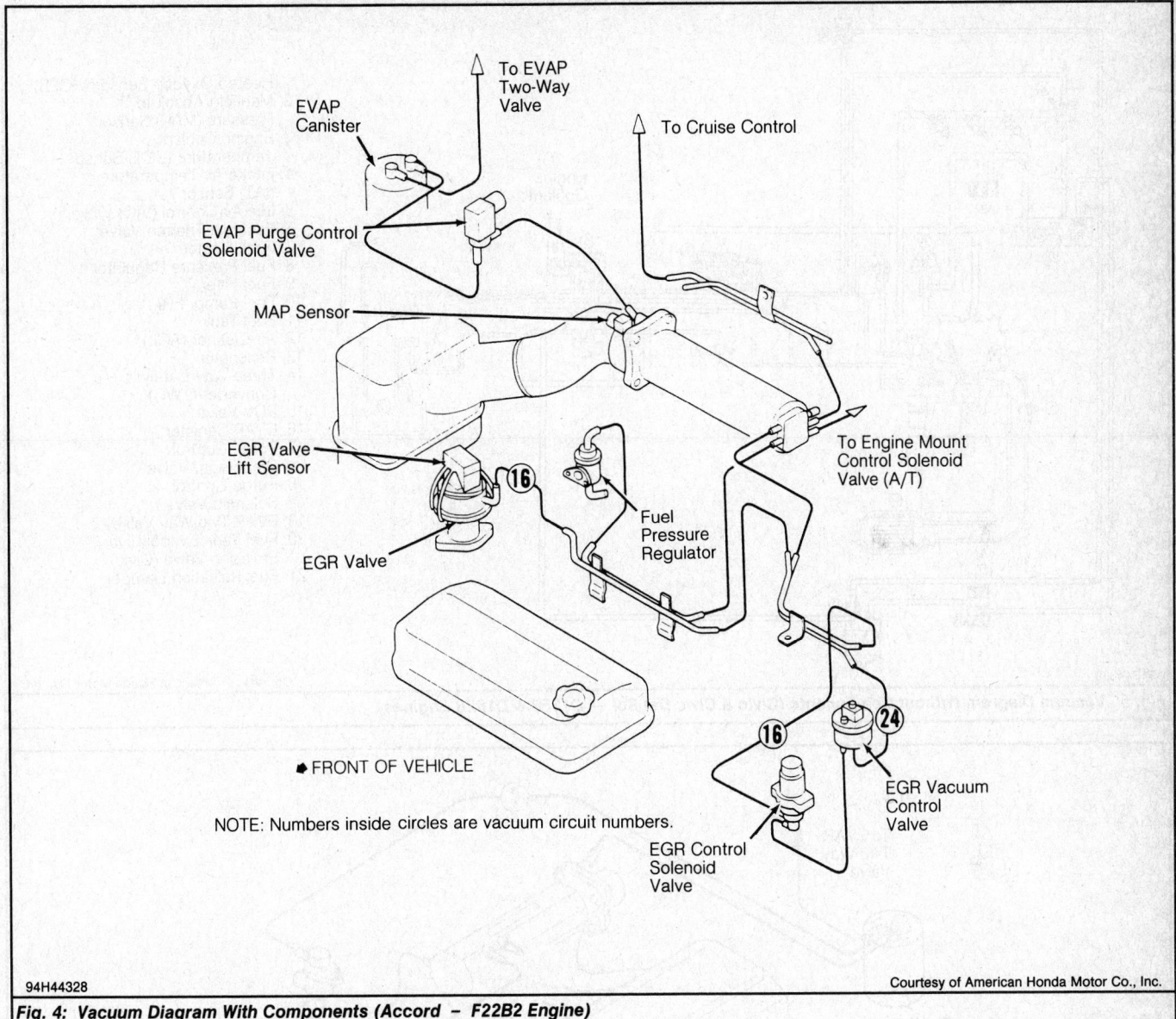

Fig. 4: Vacuum Diagram With Components (Accord – F22B2 Engine)

94H44328

Courtesy of American Honda Motor Co., Inc.

1994 ENGINE PERFORMANCE
Vacuum Diagrams (Cont.)

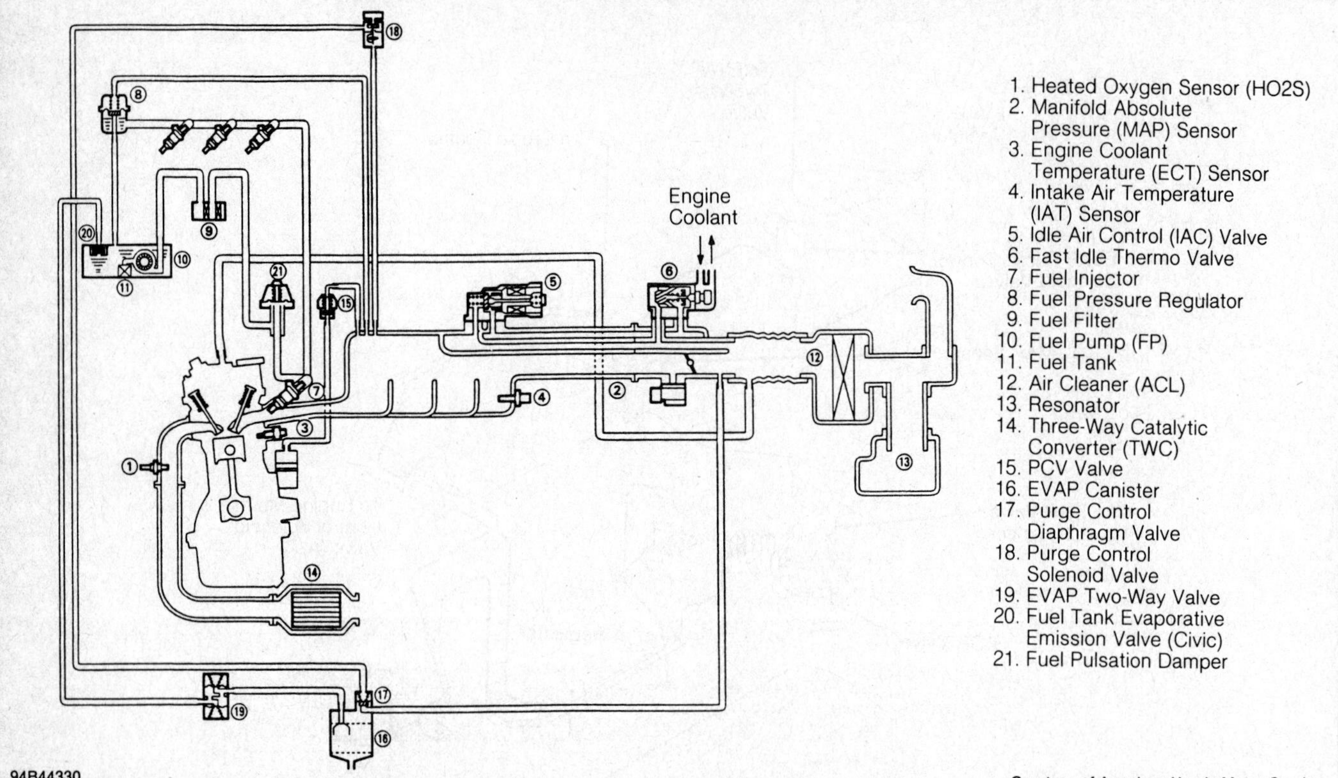

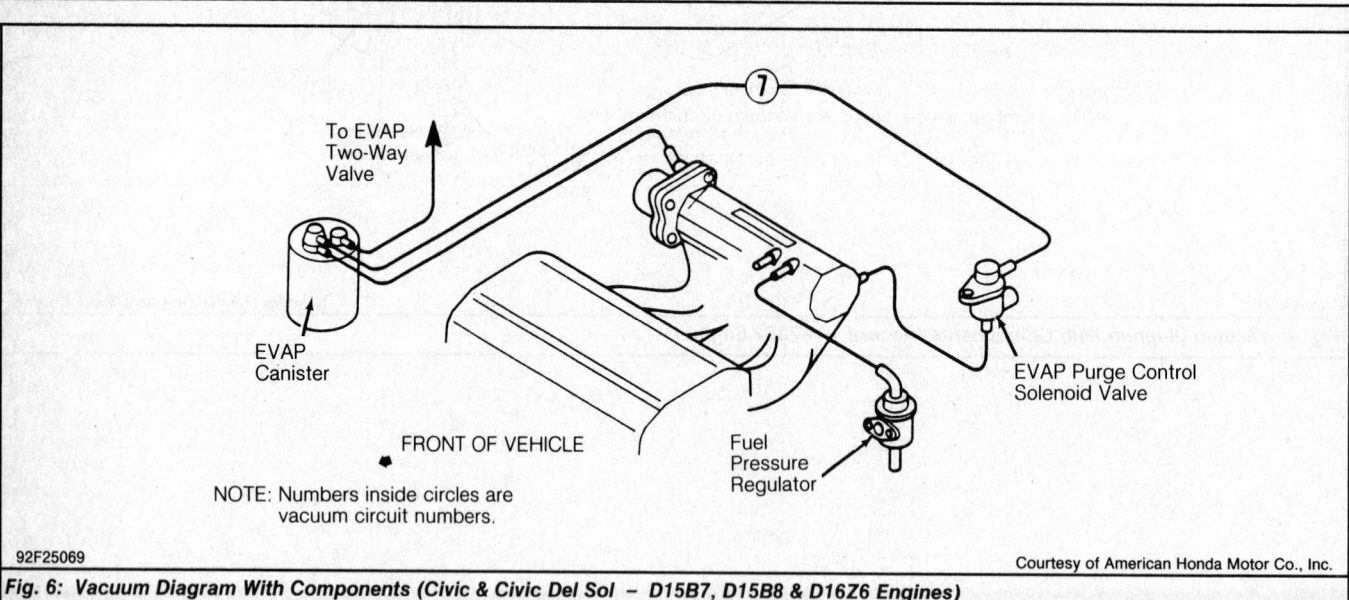

1. Heated Oxygen Sensor (HO2S)
2. Manifold Absolute Pressure (MAP) Sensor
3. Engine Coolant Temperature (ECT) Sensor
4. Intake Air Temperature (IAT) Sensor
5. Idle Air Control (IAC) Valve
6. Fast Idle Thermo Valve
7. Fuel Injector
8. Fuel Pressure Regulator
9. Fuel Filter
10. Fuel Pump (FP)
11. Fuel Tank
12. Air Cleaner (ACL)
13. Resonator
14. Three-Way Catalytic Converter (TWC)
15. PCV Valve
16. EVAP Canister
17. Purge Control Diaphragm Valve
18. Purge Control Solenoid Valve
19. EVAP Two-Way Valve
20. Fuel Tank Evaporative Emission Valve (Civic)
21. Fuel Pulsation Damper

Engine Coolant

94B44330

Courtesy of American Honda Motor Co., Inc.

Fig. 5: Vacuum Diagram Without Components (Civic & Civic Del Sol – D15B7 & D16Z6 Engines)

To EVAP Two-Way Valve

EVAP Canister

FRONT OF VEHICLE

NOTE: Numbers inside circles are vacuum circuit numbers.

Fuel Pressure Regulator

EVAP Purge Control Solenoid Valve

92F25069

Courtesy of American Honda Motor Co., Inc.

Fig. 6: Vacuum Diagram With Components (Civic & Civic Del Sol – D15B7, D15B8 & D16Z6 Engines)

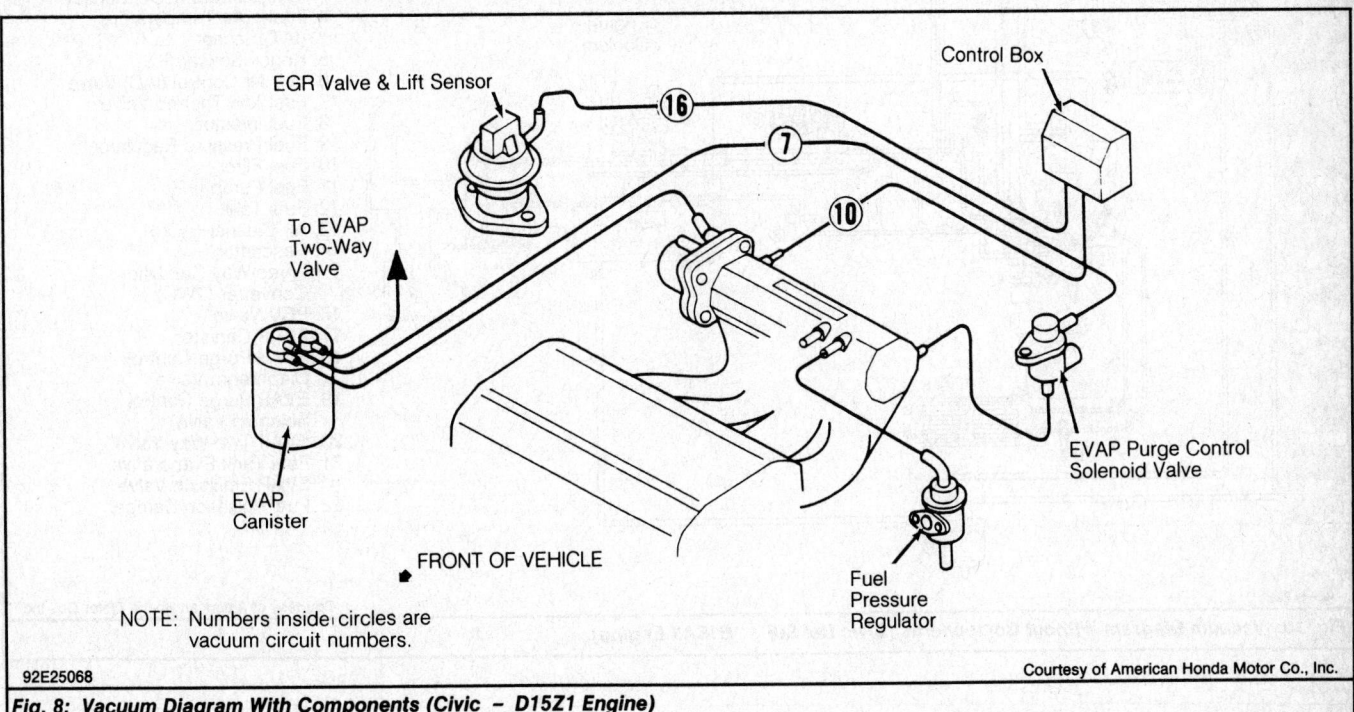

(D15Z1 Engine only)

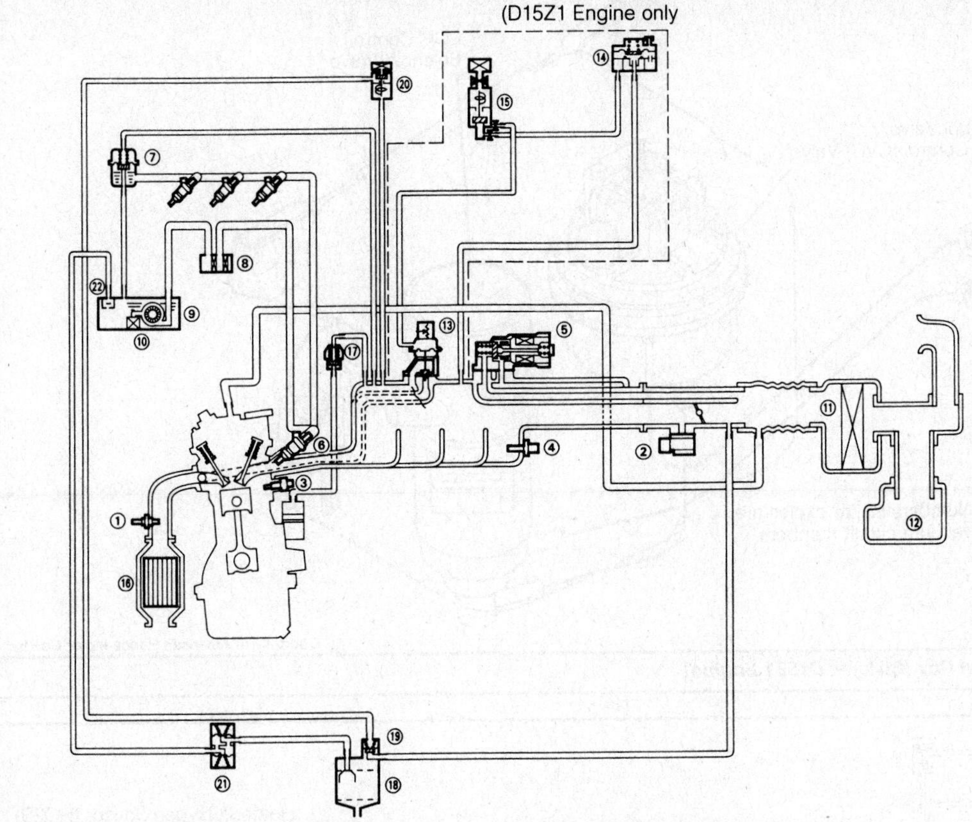

1. Heated Oxygen Sensor (HO2S)
2. Manifold Absolute Pressure (MAP) Sensor
3. Engine Coolant Temperature (ECT) Sensor
4. Intake Air Temperature (IAT) Sensor
5. Idle Air Control (IAC) Valve
6. Fuel Injector
7. Fuel Pressure Regulator
8. Fuel Filter
9. Fuel Pump (FP)
10. Fuel Tank
11. Air Cleaner (ACL)
12. Resonator
13. EGR Valve
14. EGR Vacuum Control Valve
15. EGR Control Solenoid Valve
16. Three-Way Catalytic Converter (TWC)
17. PCV Valve
18. EVAP Canister
19. Purge Control Diaphragm Valve
20. Purge Control Solenoid Valve
21. EVAP Two-Way Valve
22. Fuel Tank Evaporative Emission (EVAP) Valve

93D78132

Courtesy of American Honda Motor Co., Inc.

Fig. 7: Vacuum Diagram Without Components (Civic – D15B8 & D15Z1 Engines)

EGR Valve & Lift Sensor

Control Box

To EVAP Two-Way Valve

EVAP Canister

FRONT OF VEHICLE

EVAP Purge Control Solenoid Valve

Fuel Pressure Regulator

NOTE: Numbers inside circles are vacuum circuit numbers.

92E25068

Courtesy of American Honda Motor Co., Inc.

Fig. 8: Vacuum Diagram With Components (Civic – D15Z1 Engine)

1994 ENGINE PERFORMANCE
Vacuum Diagrams (Cont.)

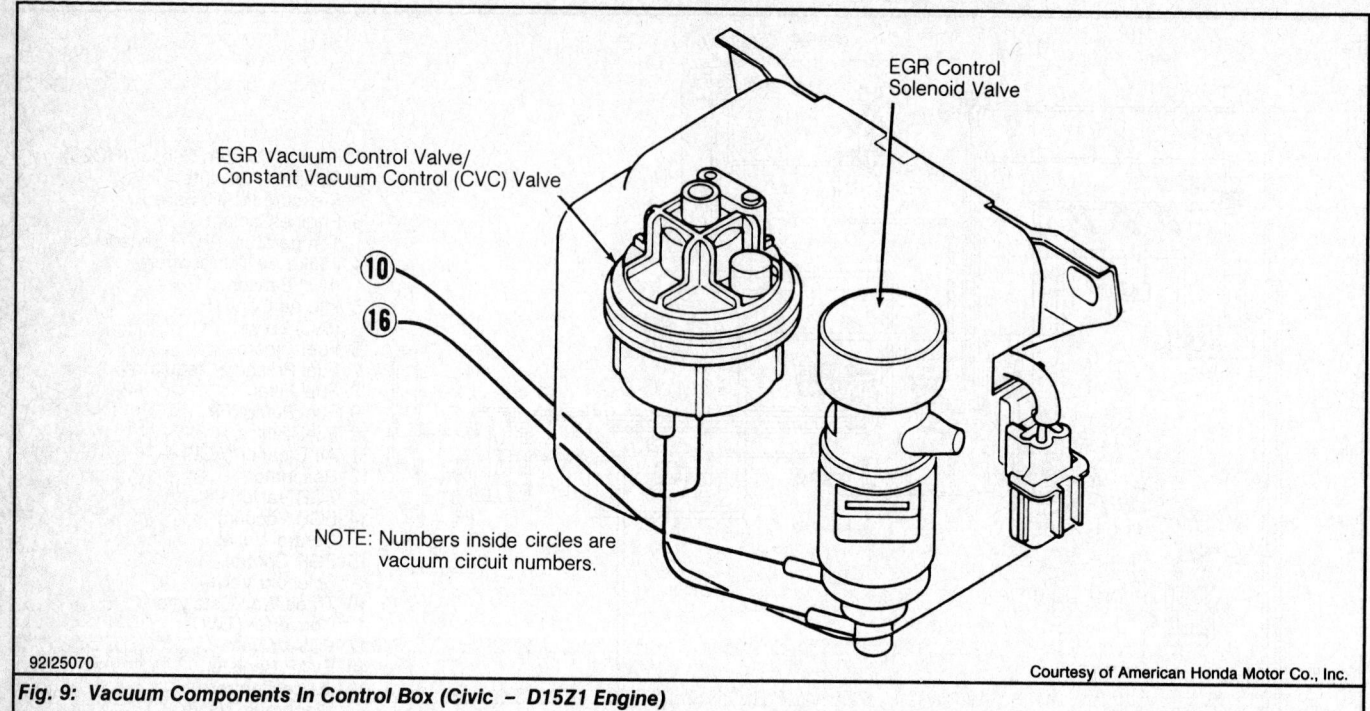

EGR Control
Solenoid Valve

EGR Vacuum Control Valve/
Constant Vacuum Control (CVC) Valve

⑩

⑯

NOTE: Numbers inside circles are
vacuum circuit numbers.

92I25070

Courtesy of American Honda Motor Co., Inc.

Fig. 9: Vacuum Components In Control Box (Civic – D15Z1 Engine)

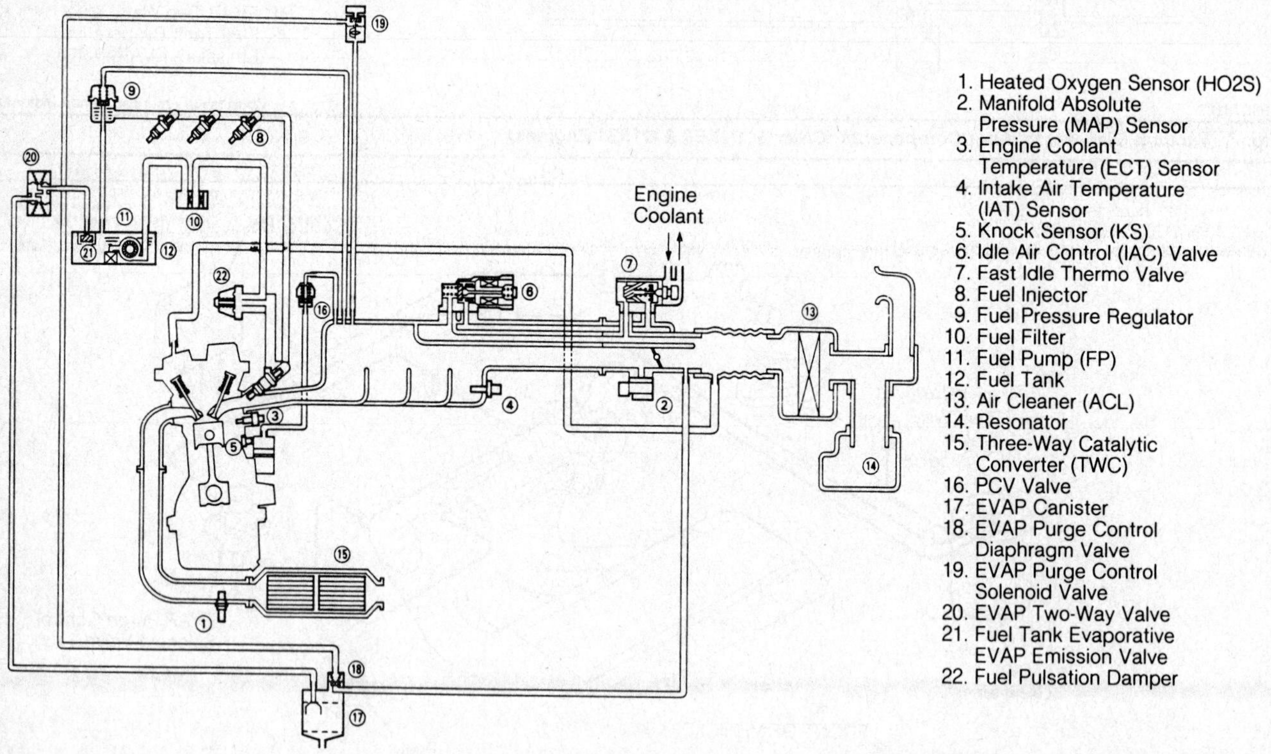

Engine
Coolant

1. Heated Oxygen Sensor (HO2S)
2. Manifold Absolute
   Pressure (MAP) Sensor
3. Engine Coolant
   Temperature (ECT) Sensor
4. Intake Air Temperature
   (IAT) Sensor
5. Knock Sensor (KS)
6. Idle Air Control (IAC) Valve
7. Fast Idle Thermo Valve
8. Fuel Injector
9. Fuel Pressure Regulator
10. Fuel Filter
11. Fuel Pump (FP)
12. Fuel Tank
13. Air Cleaner (ACL)
14. Resonator
15. Three-Way Catalytic
    Converter (TWC)
16. PCV Valve
17. EVAP Canister
18. EVAP Purge Control
    Diaphragm Valve
19. EVAP Purge Control
    Solenoid Valve
20. EVAP Two-Way Valve
21. Fuel Tank Evaporative
    EVAP Emission Valve
22. Fuel Pulsation Damper

94F44342

Courtesy of American Honda Motor Co., Inc.

Fig. 10: Vacuum Diagram Without Components (Civic Del Sol – B16A3 Engine)

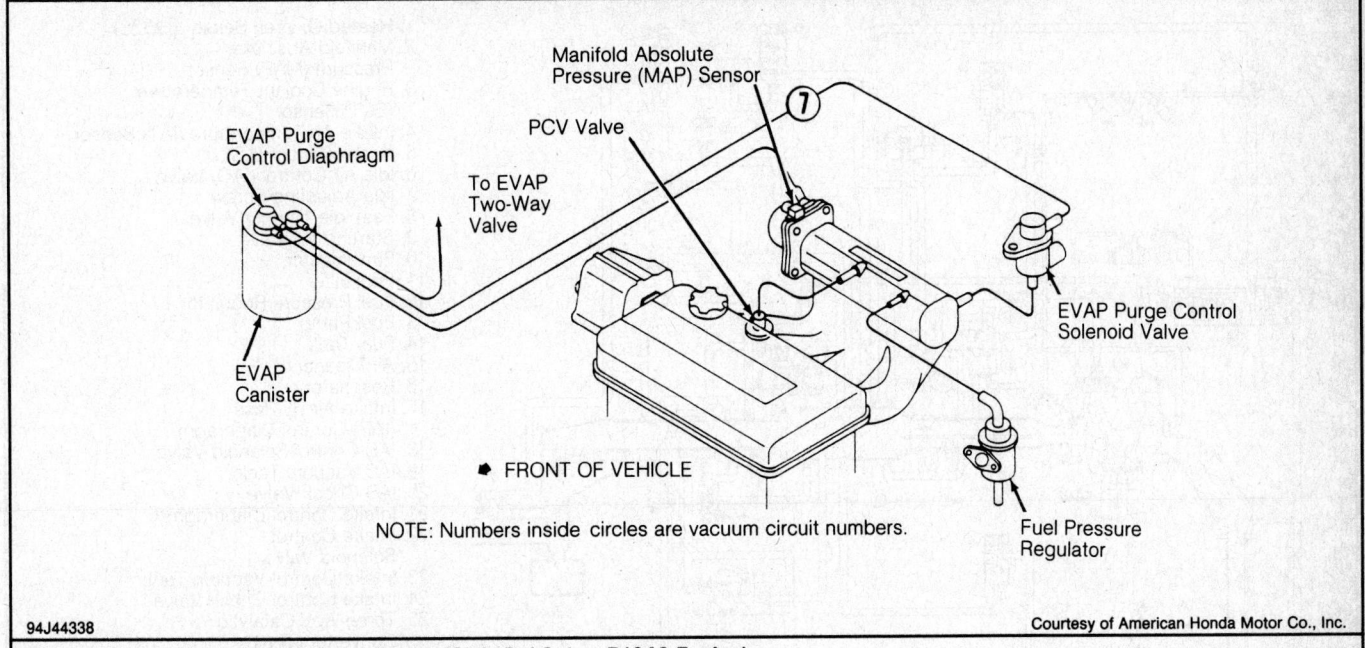

Manifold Absolute
Pressure (MAP) Sensor

PCV Valve

EVAP Purge
Control Diaphragm

To EVAP
Two-Way
Valve

EVAP Purge Control
Solenoid Valve

EVAP
Canister

FRONT OF VEHICLE

Fuel Pressure
Regulator

NOTE: Numbers inside circles are vacuum circuit numbers.

94J44338

Courtesy of American Honda Motor Co., Inc.

Fig. 11: Vacuum Diagram With Components (Civic Del Sol – B16A3 Engine)

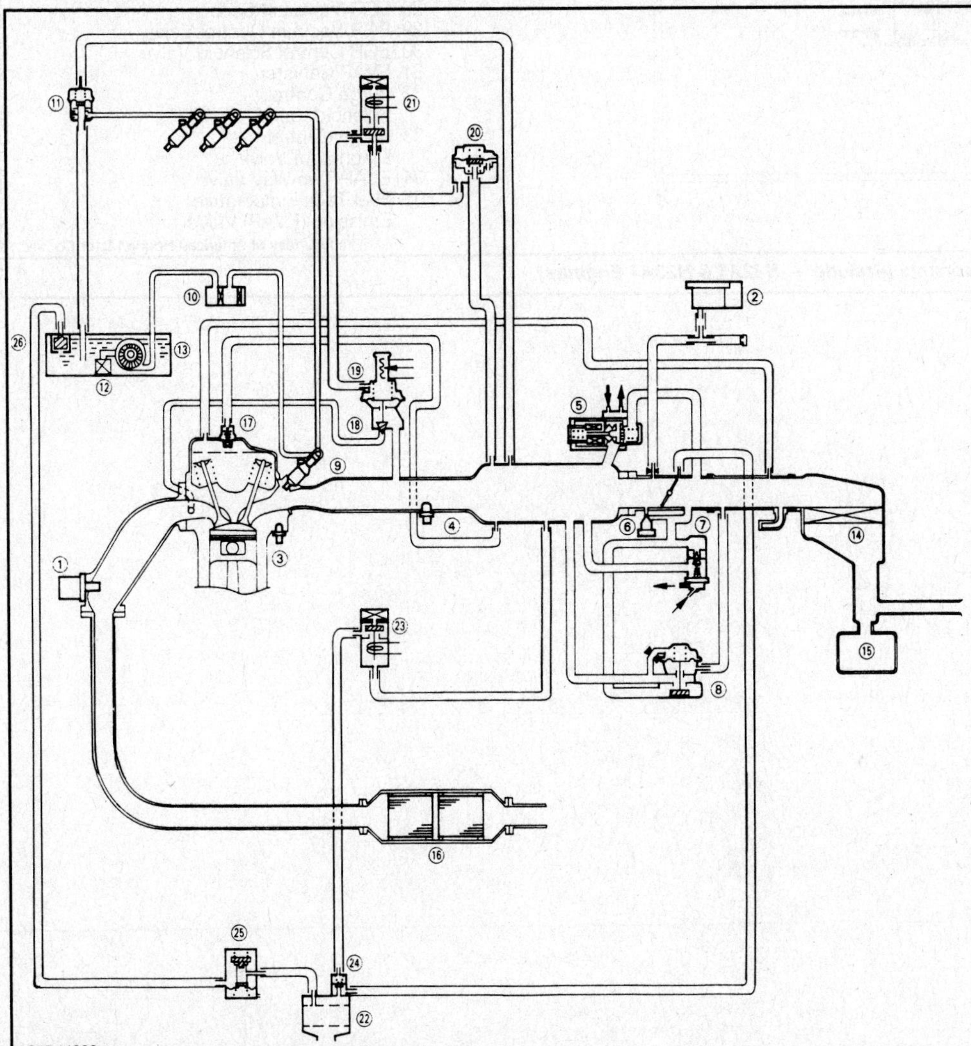

1. Heated Oxygen Sensor (HO2S)
2. Manifold Absolute
   Pressure (MAP) Sensor
3. Engine Coolant Temperature
   (ECT) Sensor
4. Intake Air Temperature (IAT) Sensor
5. Idle Air Control (IAC) Valve
6. Idle Adjusting Screw
7. Fast Idle Thermo Valve
8. Starting Air Valve
9. Fuel Injector
10. Fuel Filter
11. Fuel Pressure Regulator
12. Fuel Pump
13. Fuel Tank
14. Air Cleaner
15. Resonator
16. Three-Way Catalytic Converter
17. PCV Valve
18. EGR Valve
19. EGR Valve Lift Sensor
20. Constant Vacuum
    Control (CVC) Valve
21. EGR Control Solenoid Valve
22. EVAP Canister
23. Purge Control
    Solenoid Valve
24. Purge Control
    Diaphragm Valve
25. Two-Way Valve
26. Fuel Tank Evaporative
    Emission (EVAP) Valve

94D44308

Courtesy of American Honda Motor Co., Inc.

Fig. 12: Vacuum Diagram Without Components (Prelude – F22A1 Engine)

1994 ENGINE PERFORMANCE
Vacuum Diagrams (Cont.)

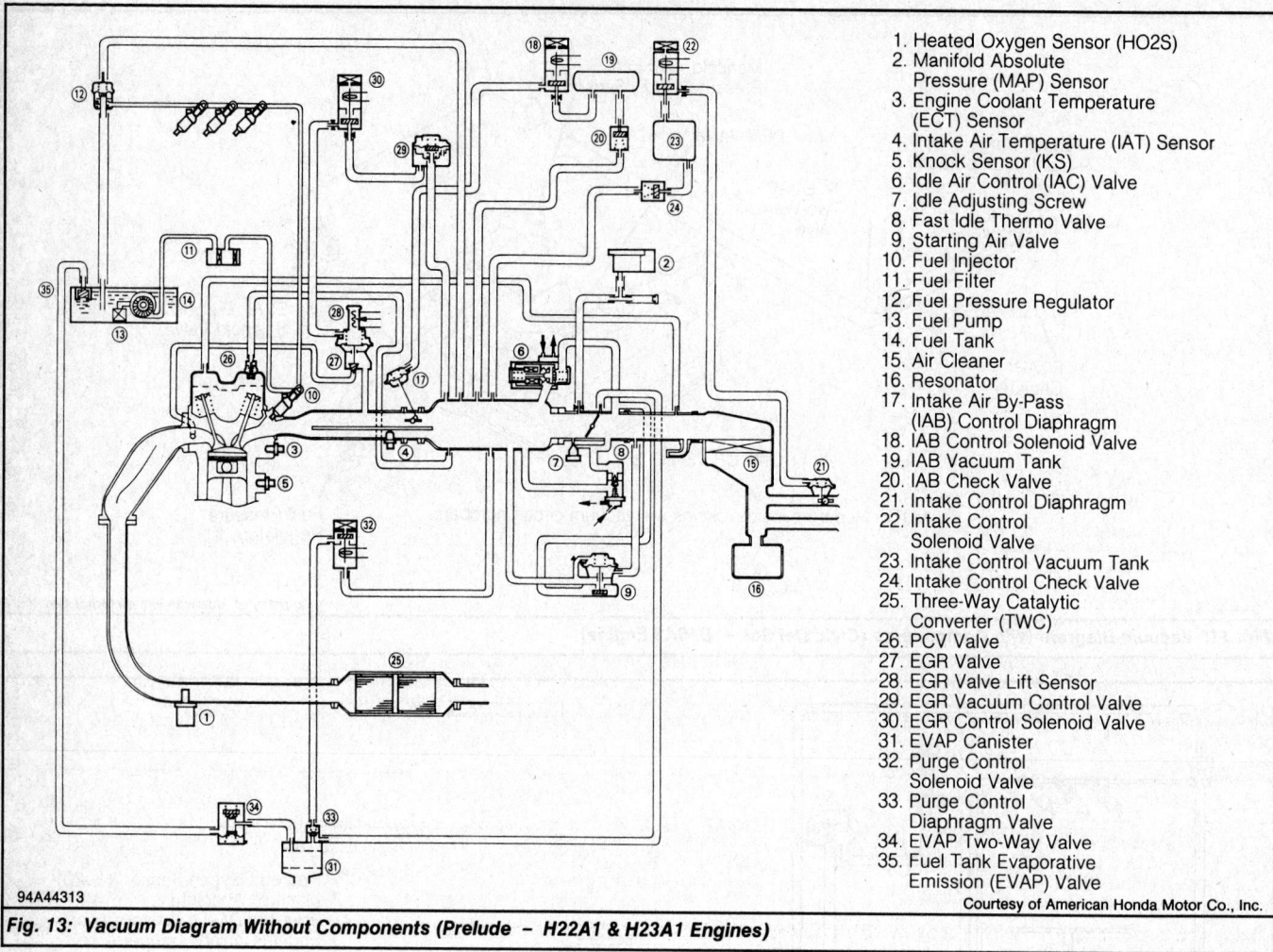

1. Heated Oxygen Sensor (HO2S)
2. Manifold Absolute Pressure (MAP) Sensor
3. Engine Coolant Temperature (ECT) Sensor
4. Intake Air Temperature (IAT) Sensor
5. Knock Sensor (KS)
6. Idle Air Control (IAC) Valve
7. Idle Adjusting Screw
8. Fast Idle Thermo Valve
9. Starting Air Valve
10. Fuel Injector
11. Fuel Filter
12. Fuel Pressure Regulator
13. Fuel Pump
14. Fuel Tank
15. Air Cleaner
16. Resonator
17. Intake Air By-Pass (IAB) Control Diaphragm
18. IAB Control Solenoid Valve
19. IAB Vacuum Tank
20. IAB Check Valve
21. Intake Control Diaphragm
22. Intake Control Solenoid Valve
23. Intake Control Vacuum Tank
24. Intake Control Check Valve
25. Three-Way Catalytic Converter (TWC)
26. PCV Valve
27. EGR Valve
28. EGR Valve Lift Sensor
29. EGR Vacuum Control Valve
30. EGR Control Solenoid Valve
31. EVAP Canister
32. Purge Control Solenoid Valve
33. Purge Control Diaphragm Valve
34. EVAP Two-Way Valve
35. Fuel Tank Evaporative Emission (EVAP) Valve

Courtesy of American Honda Motor Co., Inc.

94A44313

Fig. 13: Vacuum Diagram Without Components (Prelude – H22A1 & H23A1 Engines)

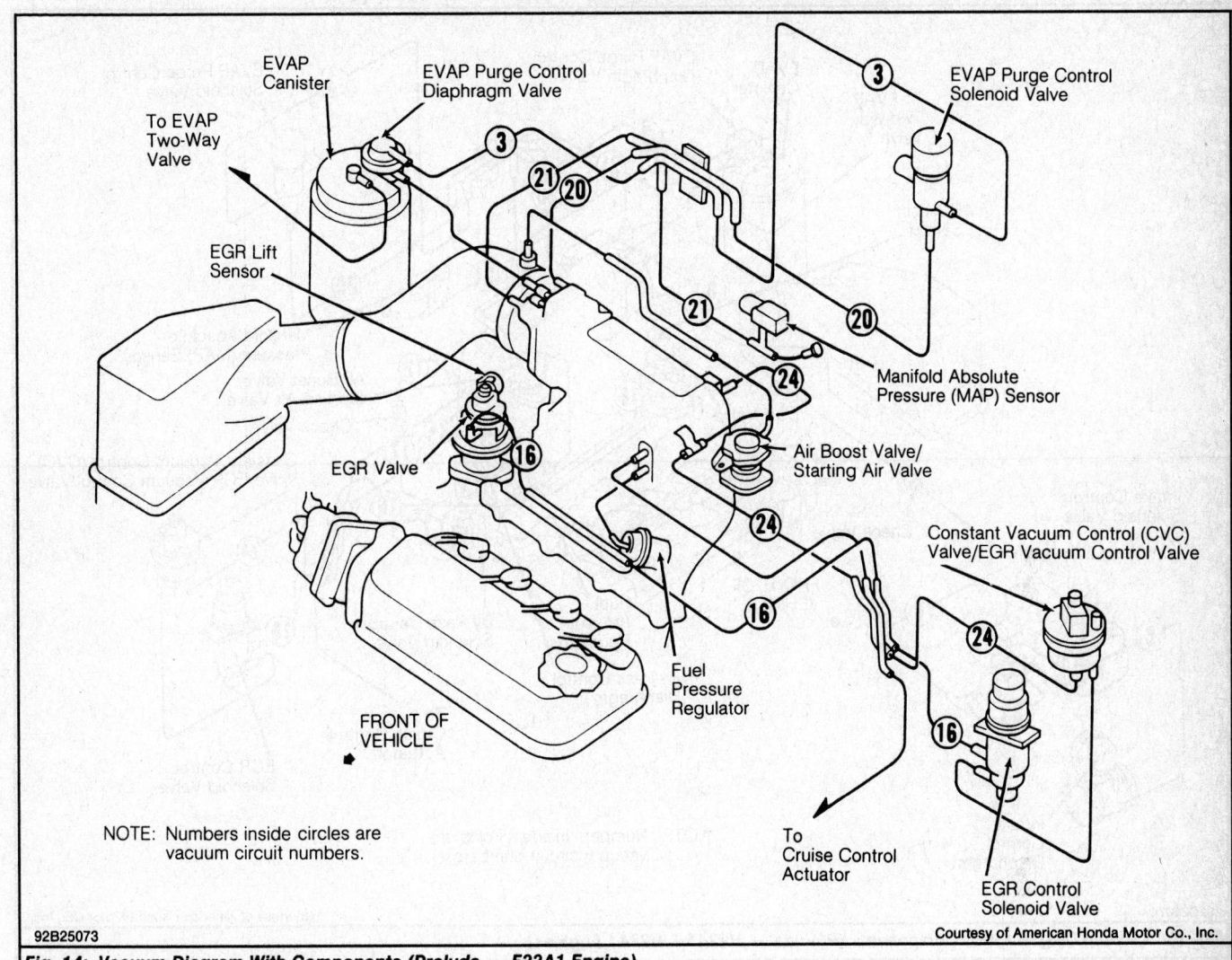

NOTE: Numbers inside circles are vacuum circuit numbers.

92B25073

Courtesy of American Honda Motor Co., Inc.

Fig. 14: Vacuum Diagram With Components (Prelude – F22A1 Engine)

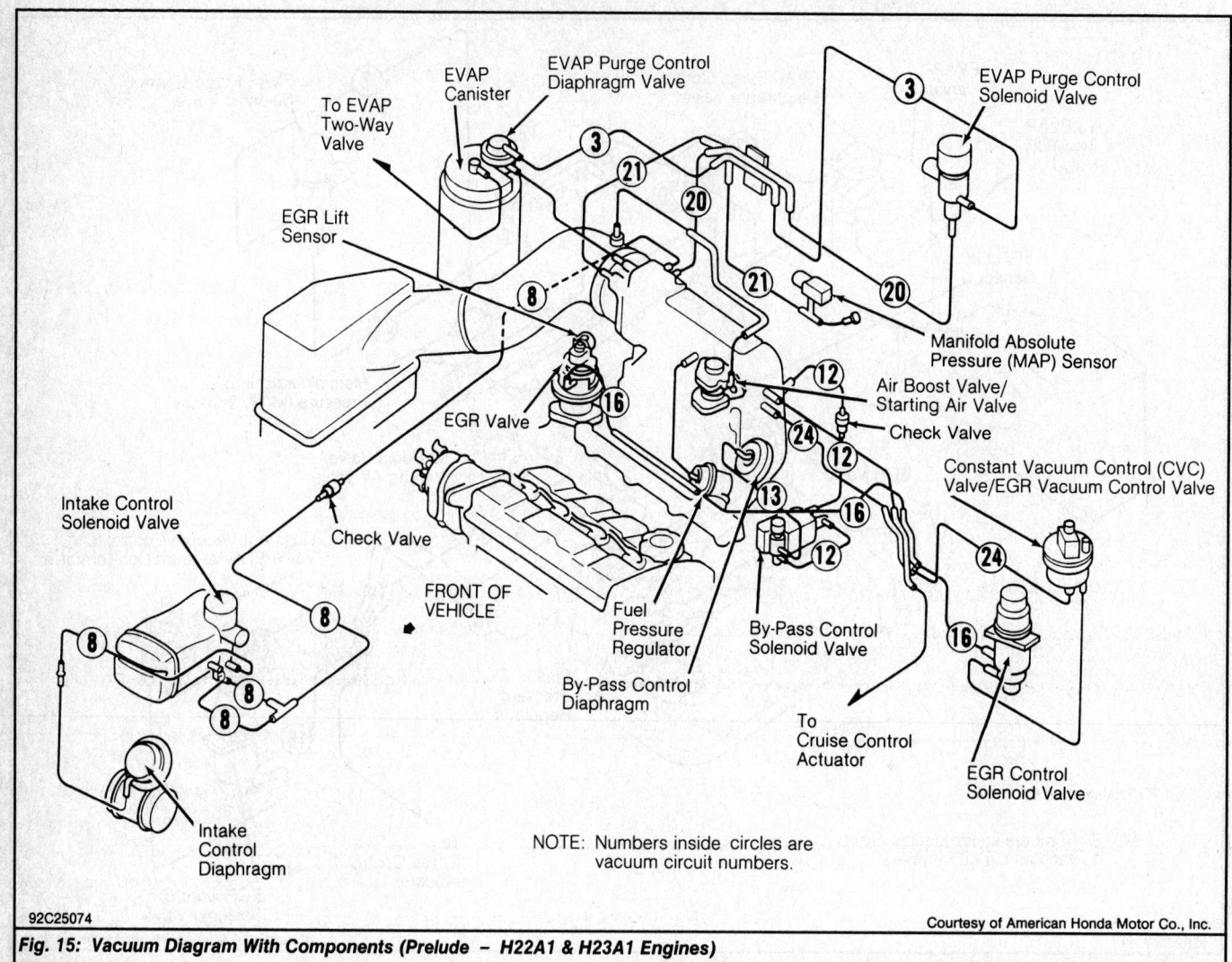

EVAP Purge Control
Diaphragm Valve

EVAP
Canister

To EVAP
Two-Way
Valve

EVAP Purge Control
Solenoid Valve

EGR Lift
Sensor

Manifold Absolute
Pressure (MAP) Sensor

Air Boost Valve/
Starting Air Valve

EGR Valve

Check Valve

Constant Vacuum Control (CVC)
Valve/EGR Vacuum Control Valve

Intake Control
Solenoid Valve

Check Valve

FRONT OF
VEHICLE

Fuel
Pressure
Regulator

By-Pass Control
Solenoid Valve

To
Cruise Control
Actuator

EGR Control
Solenoid Valve

By-Pass Control
Diaphragm

Intake
Control
Diaphragm

NOTE: Numbers inside circles are
vacuum circuit numbers.

92C25074

Courtesy of American Honda Motor Co., Inc.

Fig. 15: Vacuum Diagram With Components (Prelude – H22A1 & H23A1 Engines)

Accord, Civic, Civic Del Sol, Passport, Prelude

NOTE: For Removal, Overhaul and installation information for Passport, refer to Rodeo in Isuzu REMOVAL, OVERHAUL & INSTALLATION article.

INTRODUCTION

Removal, overhaul and installation procedures (when given by manufacturer) are covered in this article. If component removal and installation is primarily an unbolt and bolt-on procedure, only a torque specification may be furnished.

COMPUTERIZED ENGINE CONTROLS

ENGINE CONTROL MODULE (ECM)

Removal & Installation (Accord & Prelude) – Disconnect negative battery cable. Remove right door sill molding. Pull carpet back to access ECM. Remove ECM cover screws. Unplug ECM connectors. Remove mounting screws. Remove ECM. To install, reverse removal procedure.

Removal & Installation (Civic & Civic Del Sol) – Disconnect negative battery cable. Remove right front kick panel. Unplug ECM connectors. Remove mounting screws. Remove ECM. To install, reverse removal procedure.

IGNITION SYSTEM

DISTRIBUTOR

Removal & Installation – Disconnect 2-pin and 8-pin connectors from distributor. Disconnect spark plug wires and coil wire from distributor cap. Remove distributor hold-down bolts. Remove distributor from cylinder head. To install, coat NEW "O" ring with engine oil and put into place. To complete installation, reverse removal procedure. Set timing to specification. See ON-VEHICLE ADJUSTMENTS article.

NOTE: Lugs on distributor shaft and mating grooves in camshaft end are offset to eliminate possibility of installing distributor 180 degrees out of time.

NOTE: Manufacturer's overhaul instructions are not available. See Figs. 1 and 2.

IGNITION COIL

NOTE: Accord (F22B2 Engine) and Prelude ignition coils are externally mounted in engine compartment.

Removal & Installation (Accord – F22B1 Engine, Civic & Civic Del Sol) – Ensure ignition switch is in OFF position. Remove distributor cap, cap seal and leak cover. Remove 2 screws to disconnect Black/Yellow and White/Blue wires from coil primary terminals. Remove 2 mounting screws. Slide ignition coil out of distributor housing.

FUEL SYSTEM

WARNING: ALWAYS relieve fuel pressure before disconnecting any fuel injection related component. DO NOT allow fuel to contact engine or electrical components.

FUEL SYSTEM PRESSURE RELEASE

Remove negative battery cable. Loosen fuel tank filler cap. Locate 6-mm service bolt on fuel rail (on fuel filter of Civic and Civic Del Sol). Place clean shop rag around service bolt. To relieve system pressure, slowly loosen service bolt one complete turn. Always replace washer under 6-mm service bolt after loosening.

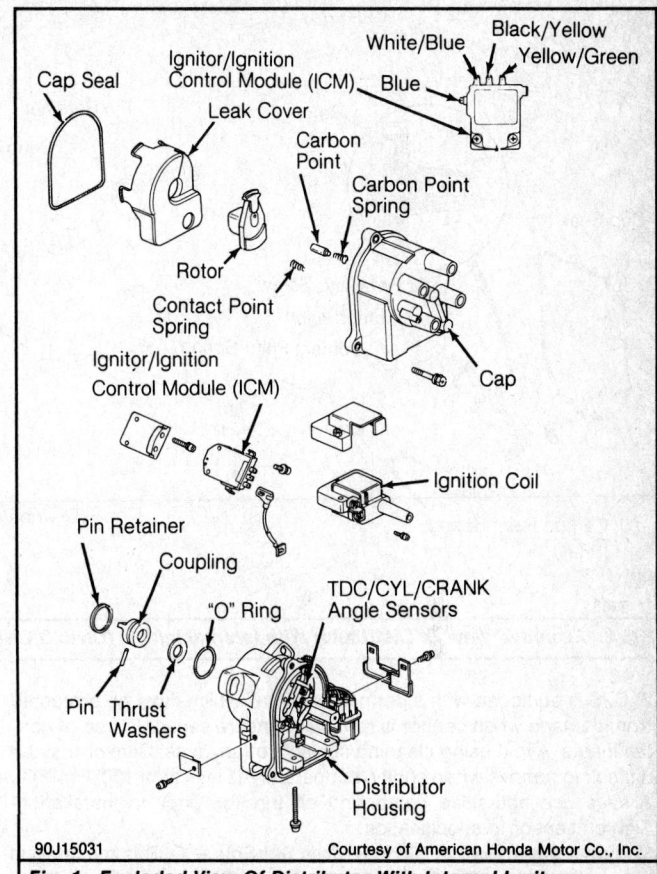

90J15031   Courtesy of American Honda Motor Co., Inc.

Fig. 1: Exploded View Of Distributor With Internal Ignitor (Accord & Prelude)

FUEL PUMP

WARNING: Keep open flames away from work area.

Removal & Installation – On Accord, remove fuel tank. On Civic, remove rear seat, remove access cover. On Prelude and Civic Del Sol, remove left maintenance access cover in luggage compartment. On all models, disconnect fuel lines and harness connector. Remove fuel pump mounting bolts. Remove fuel pump from fuel tank. To install, reverse removal procedure.

FUEL RAIL & INJECTORS

Removal – Relieve fuel pressure. See FUEL SYSTEM PRESSURE RELEASE. Disconnect electrical connectors from injectors. Disconnect vacuum and fuel return hoses from fuel pressure regulator. Place a shop towel over hoses before disconnecting them. Loosen retaining nuts on fuel rail and harness holder. Disconnect fuel rail. Remove injectors from intake manifold.

Installation – Place NEW "O" rings on injectors, and coat with engine oil. Assemble injectors on fuel rail. Install fuel rail assembly into intake manifold. To complete installation, reverse removal procedure.

OXYGEN SENSOR (O2S) OR HEATED OXYGEN SENSOR (HO2S)

NOTE: For removal and installation procedures, Heated Oxygen Sensor (HO2S) will be referred to as O2S.

Removal & Installation (Accord & Prelude) – **1)** On models with double exhaust manifold outlets, O2S is mounted in exhaust pipe just below exhaust header. On models with single outlet exhaust manifold, O2S is mounted in exhaust manifold above exhaust pipe flange.

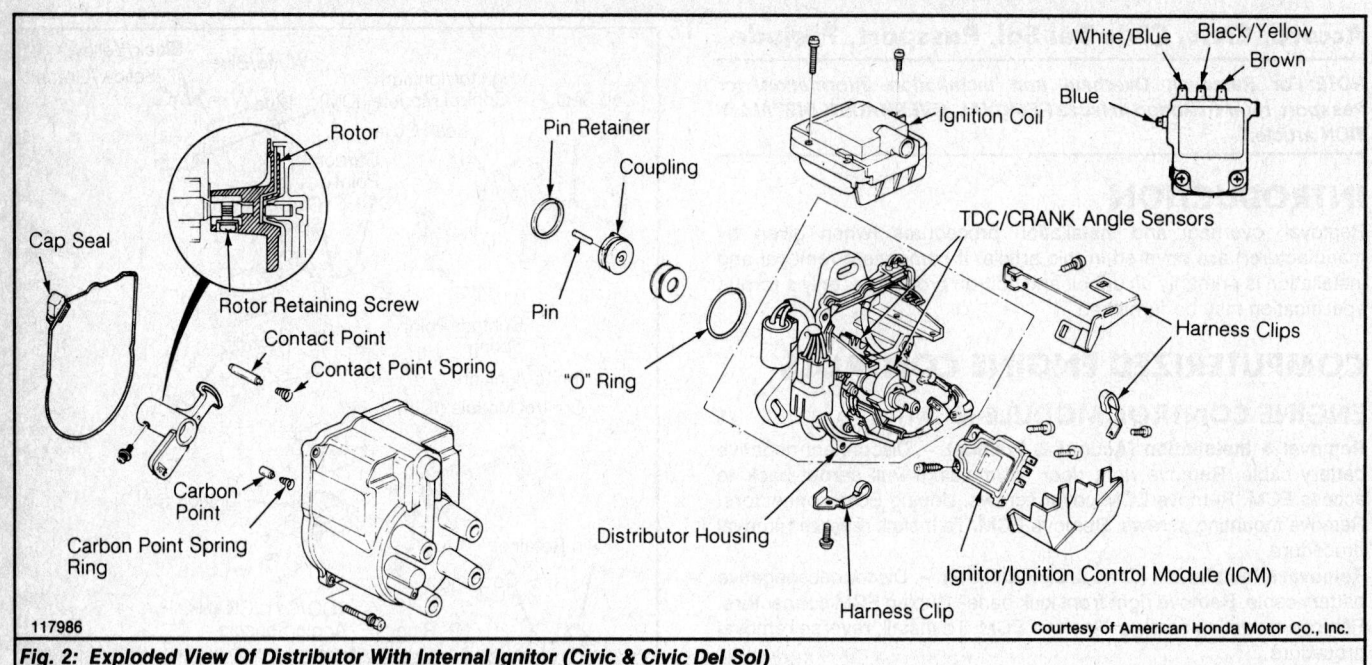

Fig. 2: Exploded View Of Distributor With Internal Ignitor (Civic & Civic Del Sol)

Courtesy of American Honda Motor Co., Inc.

2) O2S is equipped with a permanent pigtail which must be protected from damage when sensor is removed. Ensure sensor is free of contaminants. Avoid using cleaning solvents of any type. Sensor may be difficult to remove when engine temperature is less than 120°F (49°C). Always use anti-seize compound on threads prior to installation. Tighten sensor to specification.

Removal & Installation (Civic & Civic Del Sol) – O2S is mounted in exhaust manifold above exhaust pipe flange. Sensor is equipped with a permanent pigtail which must be protected from damage when sensor is removed. Ensure sensor is free of contaminants. Avoid using cleaning solvents of any type. Sensor may be difficult to remove when engine temperature is less than 120°F (49°C). Always use anti-seize compound on threads prior to installation. Tighten sensor to specification.

THROTTLE BODY

NOTE: Torque throttle body mount nuts to 16 ft. lbs. (22 N.m).

TORQUE SPECIFICATIONS
TORQUE SPECIFICATIONS

Application	Ft. Lbs. (N.m)
Banjo Bolt	16 (22)
Distributor Retaining Nuts	18 (24)
Fuel Tank	
Drain Bolt	36 (50)
Mounting Nuts	16 (22)
Oxygen Sensor (O2S)	33 (45)
Service Bolt	16 (22)
Throttle Body Mounting Nuts	16 (22)
	INCH Lbs. (N.m)
Fuel Pump Retaining Nuts	48 (6)

Accord, Civic, Civic Del Sol, Passport, Prelude

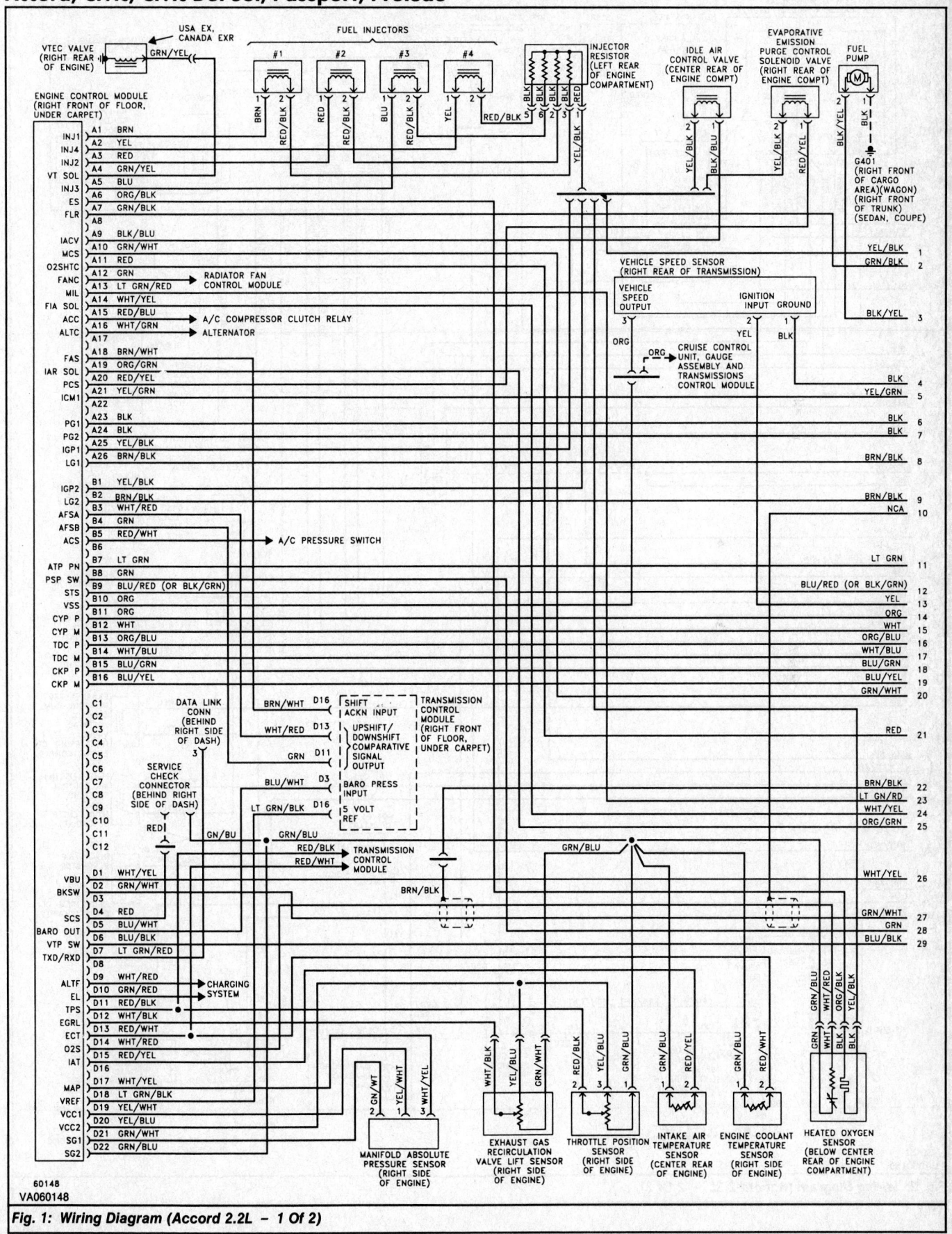

Fig. 1: Wiring Diagram (Accord 2.2L – 1 Of 2)

60148
VA060148

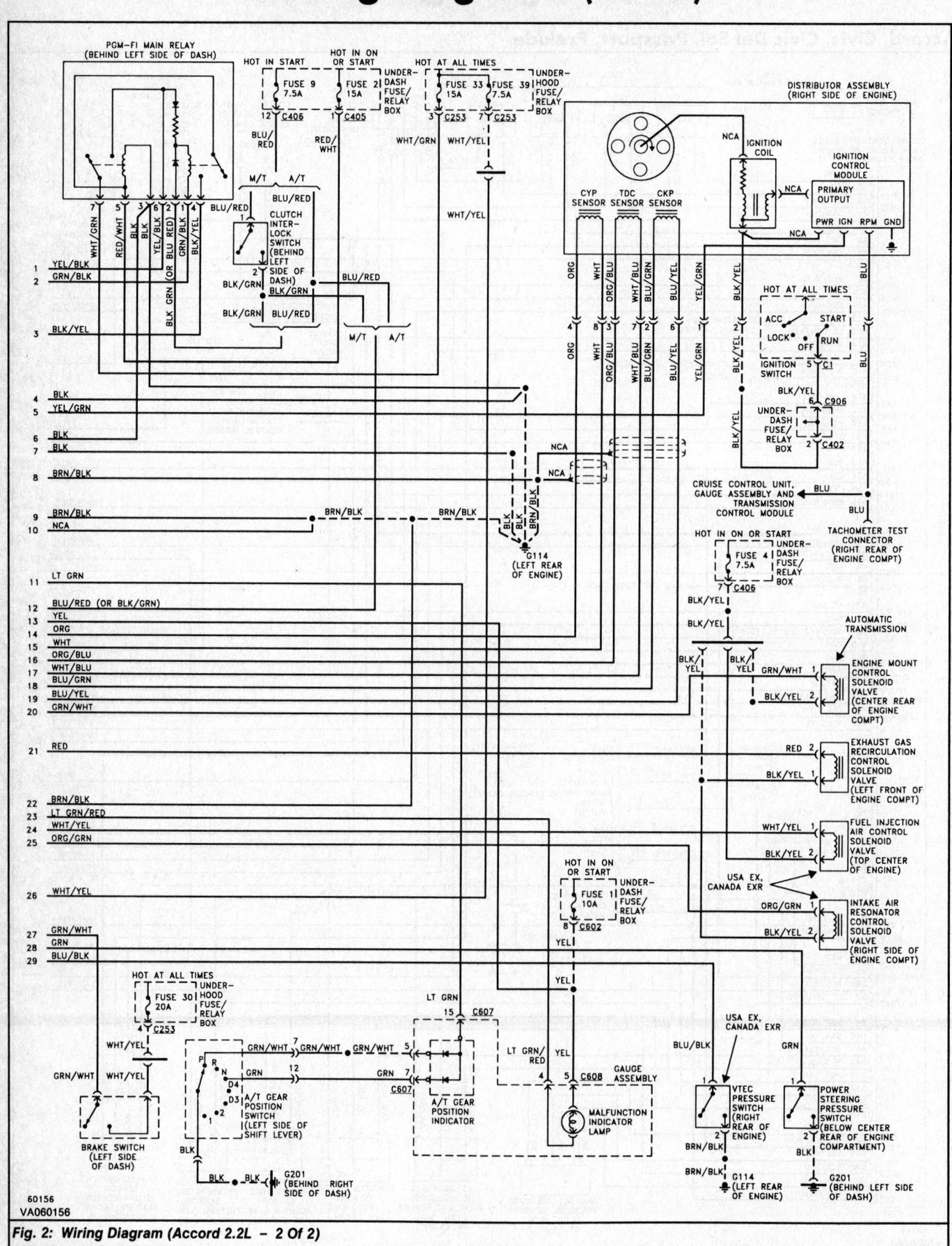

Fig. 2: Wiring Diagram (Accord 2.2L – 2 Of 2)

60156
VA060156

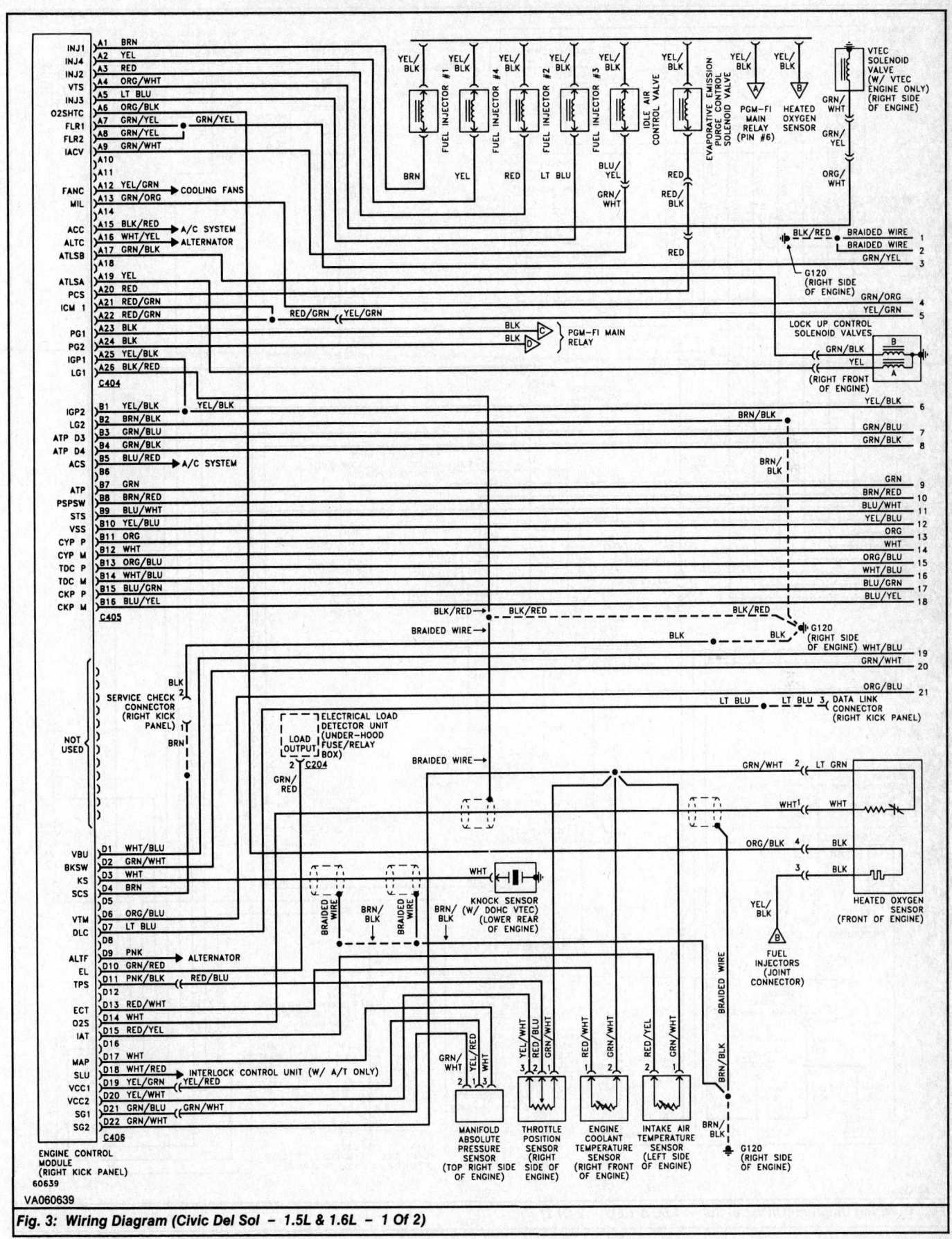

Fig. 3: Wiring Diagram (Civic Del Sol - 1.5L & 1.6L - 1 Of 2)

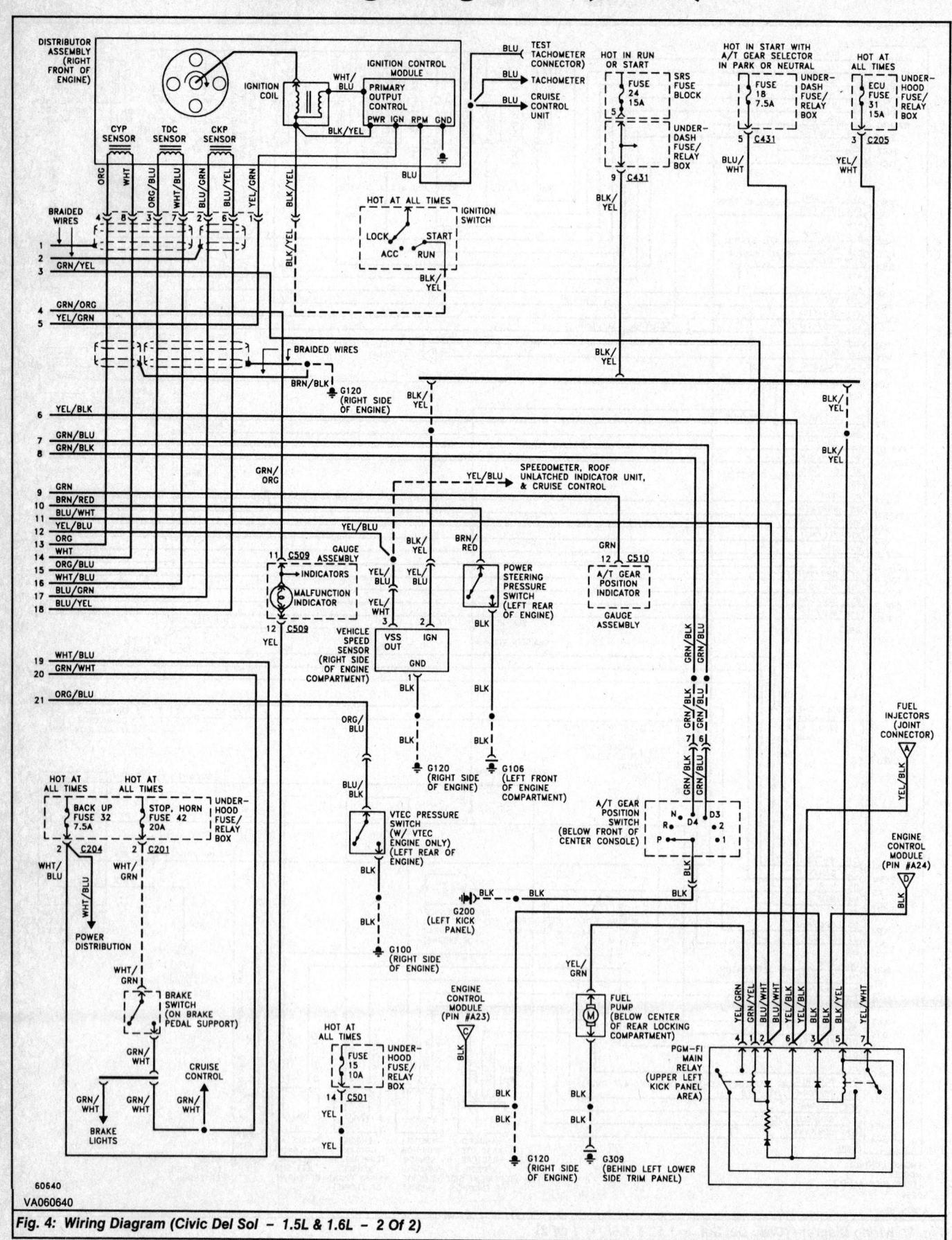

Fig. 4: Wiring Diagram (Civic Del Sol - 1.5L & 1.6L - 2 Of 2)

60640

VA060640

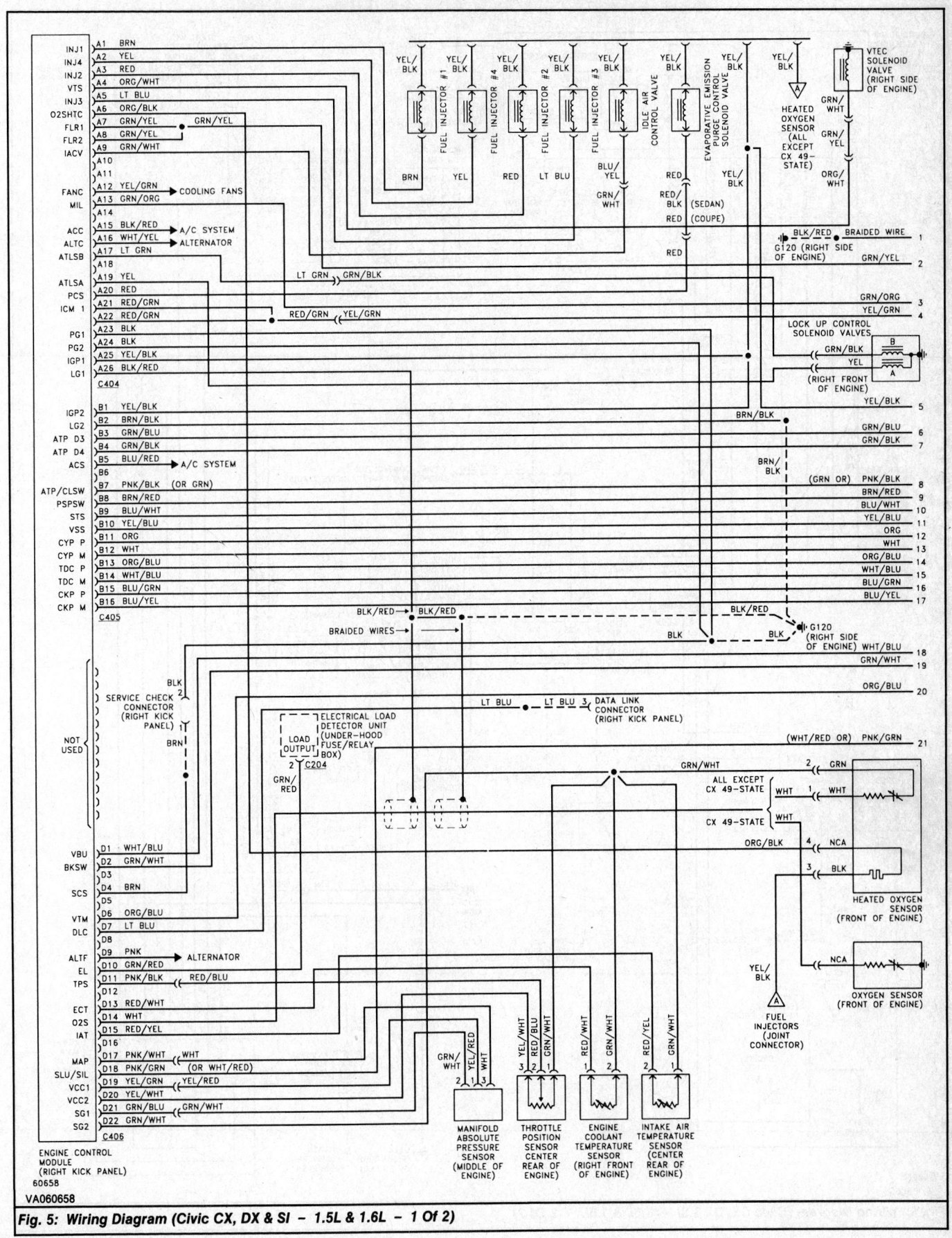

Fig. 5: Wiring Diagram (Civic CX, DX & SI - 1.5L & 1.6L - 1 Of 2)

1994 ENGINE PERFORMANCE
Wiring Diagrams (Cont.)

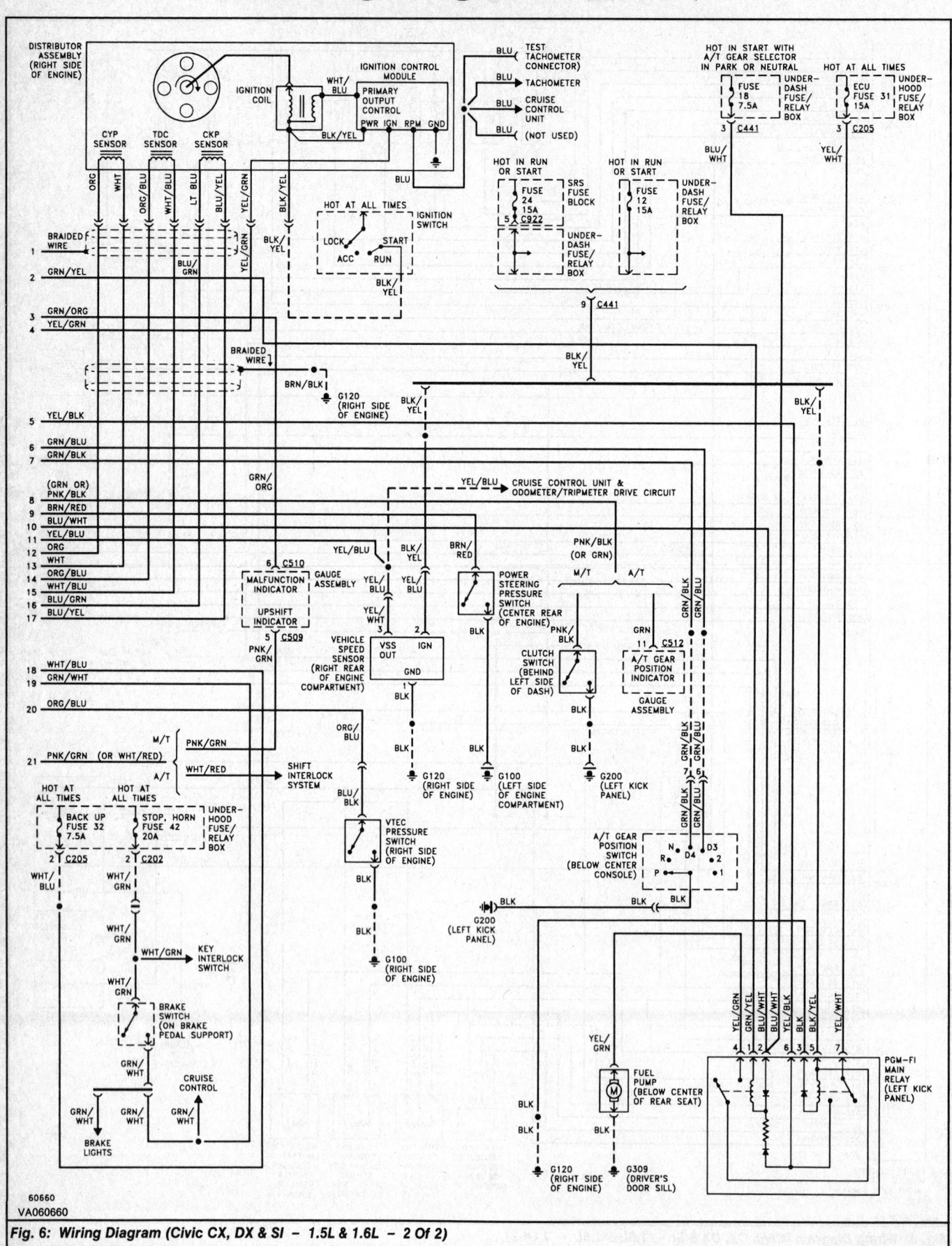

Fig. 6: Wiring Diagram (Civic CX, DX & SI - 1.5L & 1.6L - 2 Of 2)

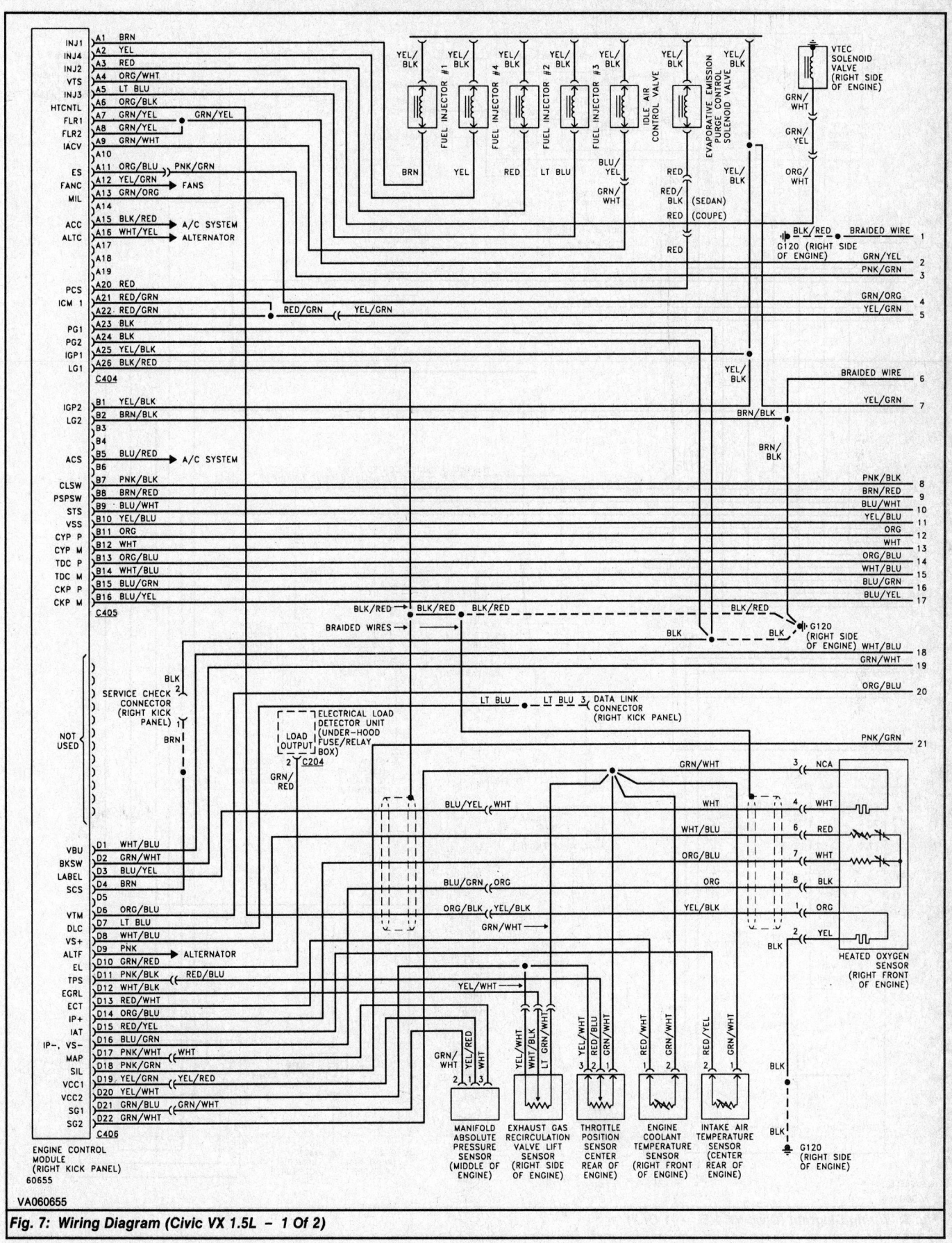

Fig. 7: Wiring Diagram (Civic VX 1.5L - 1 Of 2)

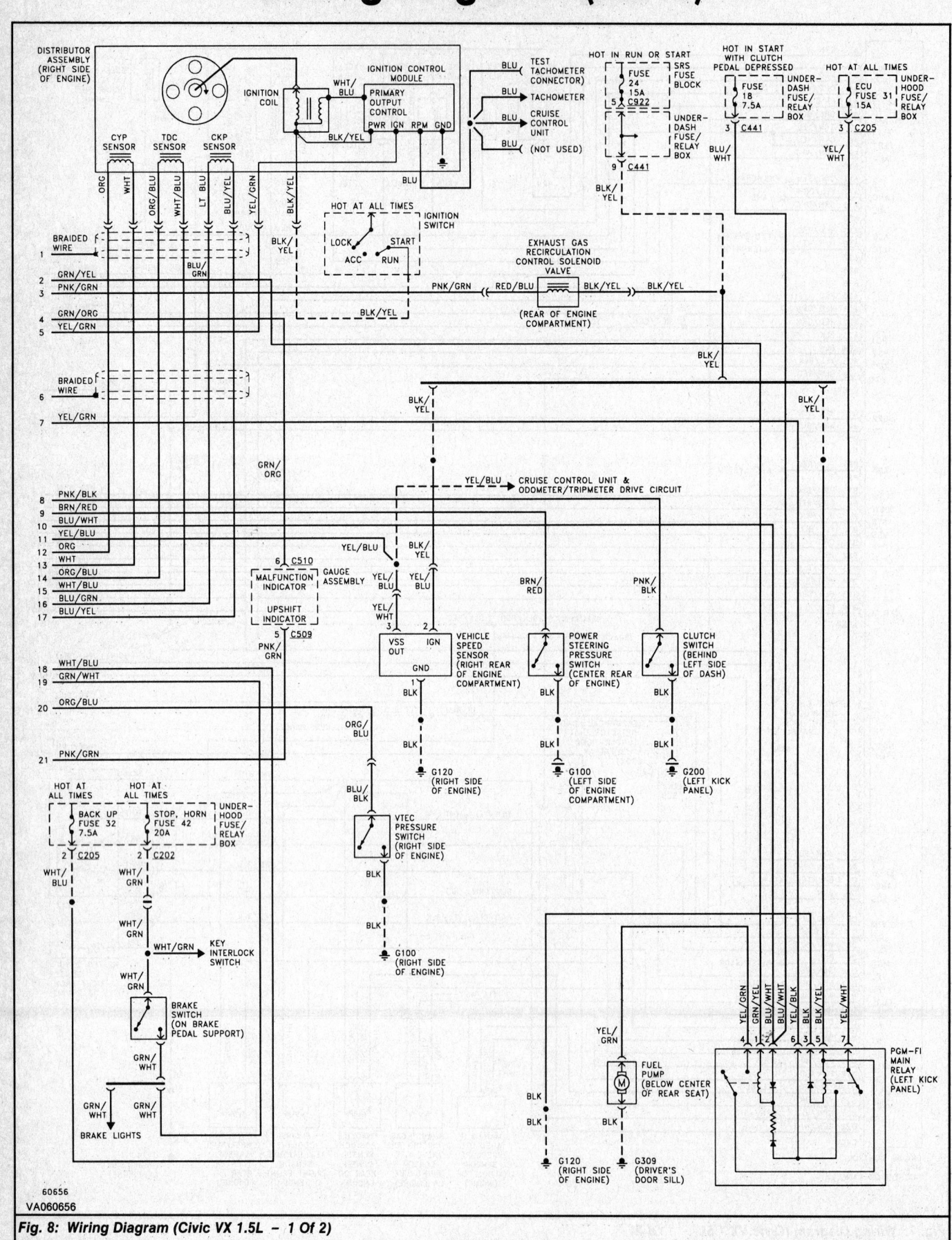

Fig. 8: *Wiring Diagram (Civic VX 1.5L – 1 Of 2)*

60656

VA060656

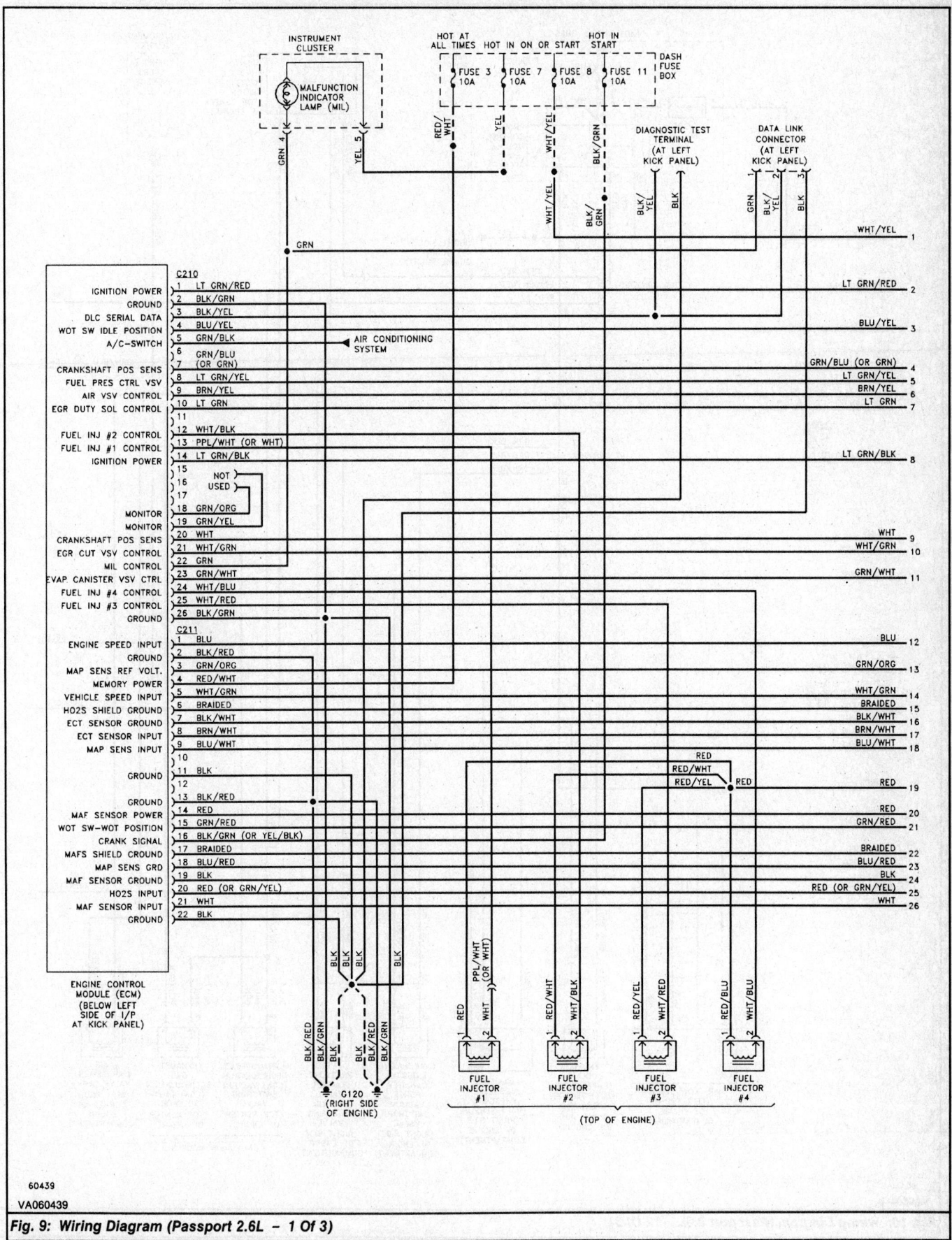

Fig. 9: Wiring Diagram (Passport 2.6L - 1 Of 3)

60439
VA060439

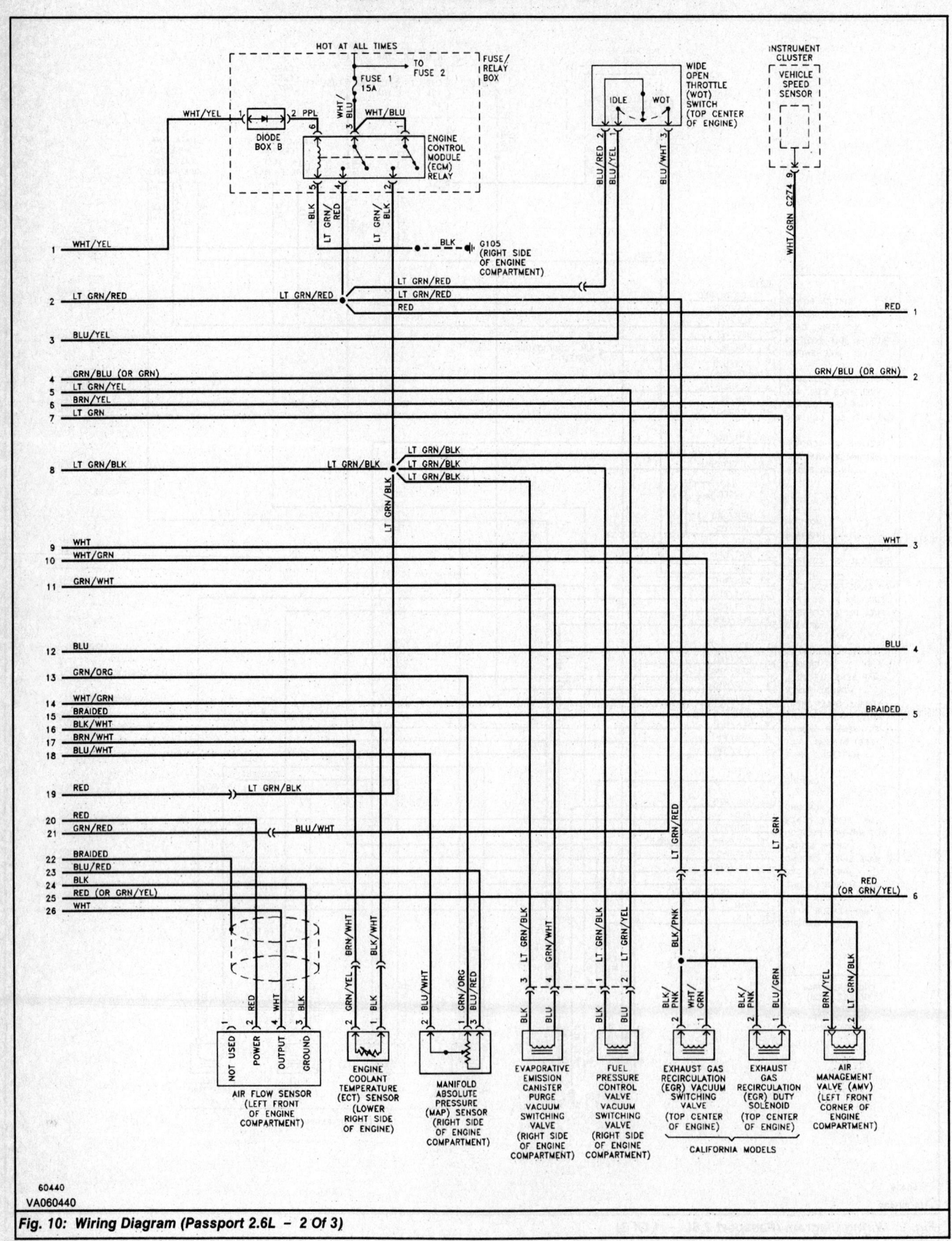

Fig. 10: Wiring Diagram (Passport 2.6L – 2 Of 3)

60440
VA060440

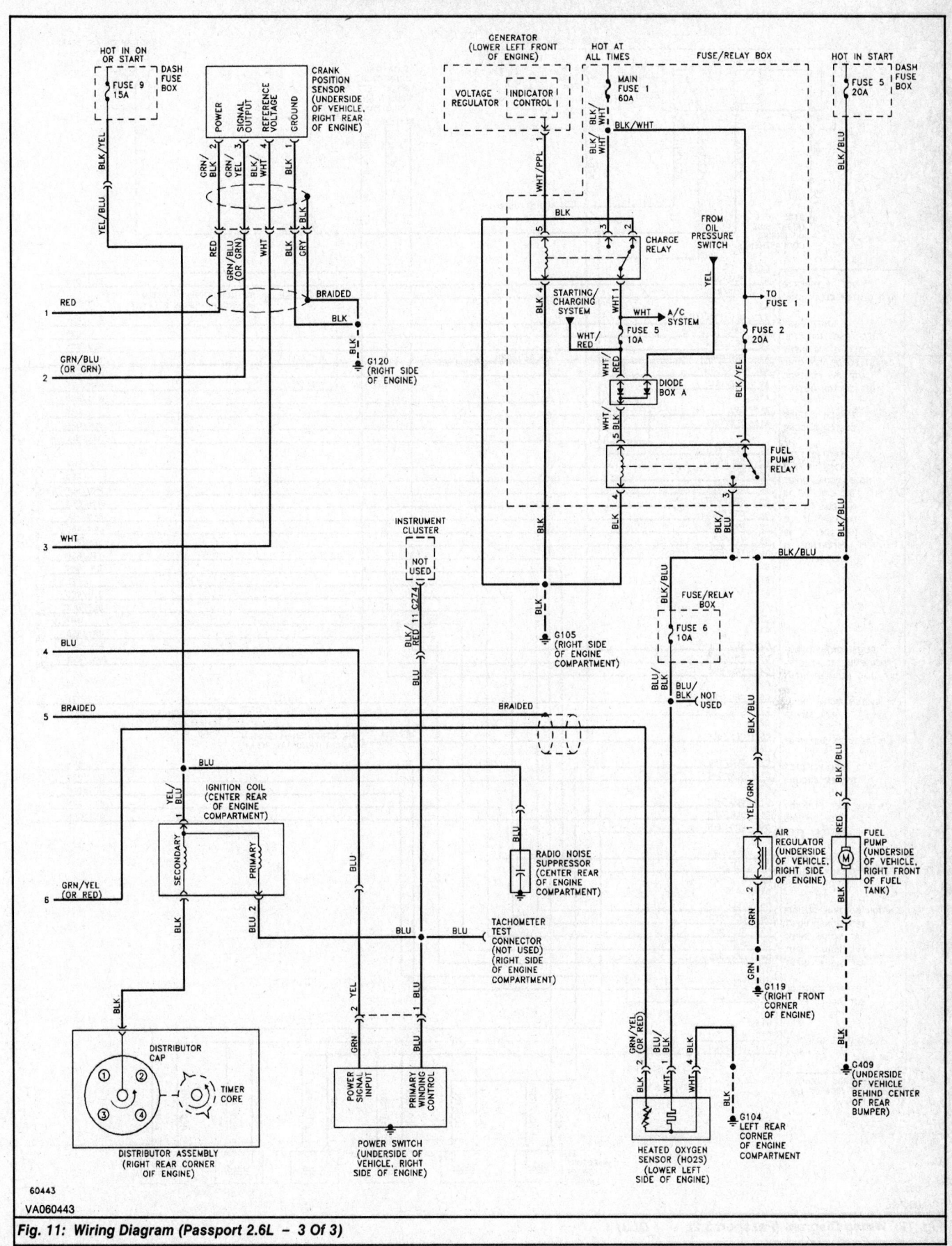

Fig. 11: Wiring Diagram (Passport 2.6L – 3 Of 3)

60443

VA060443

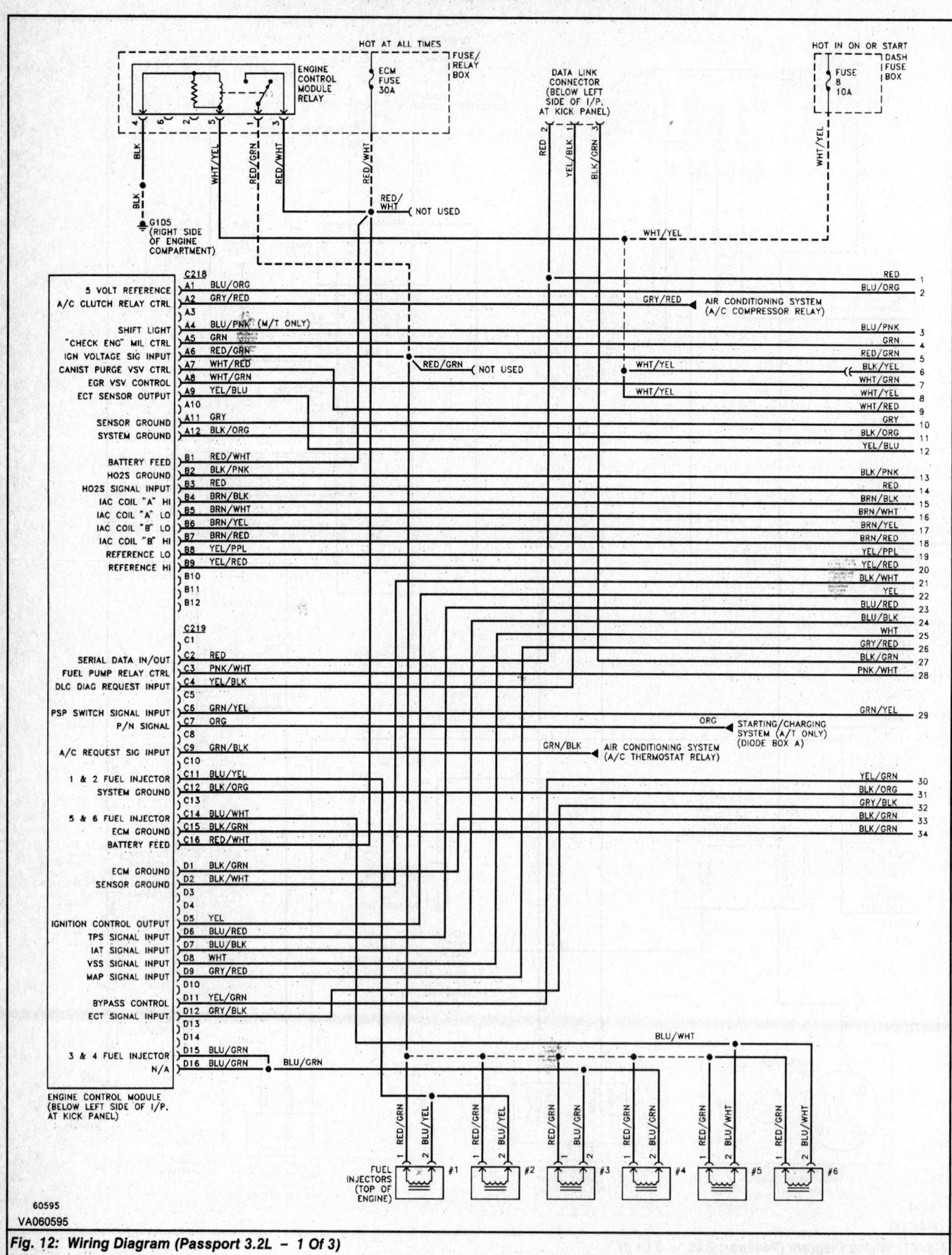

Fig. 12: Wiring Diagram (Passport 3.2L – 1 Of 3)

60595

VA060595

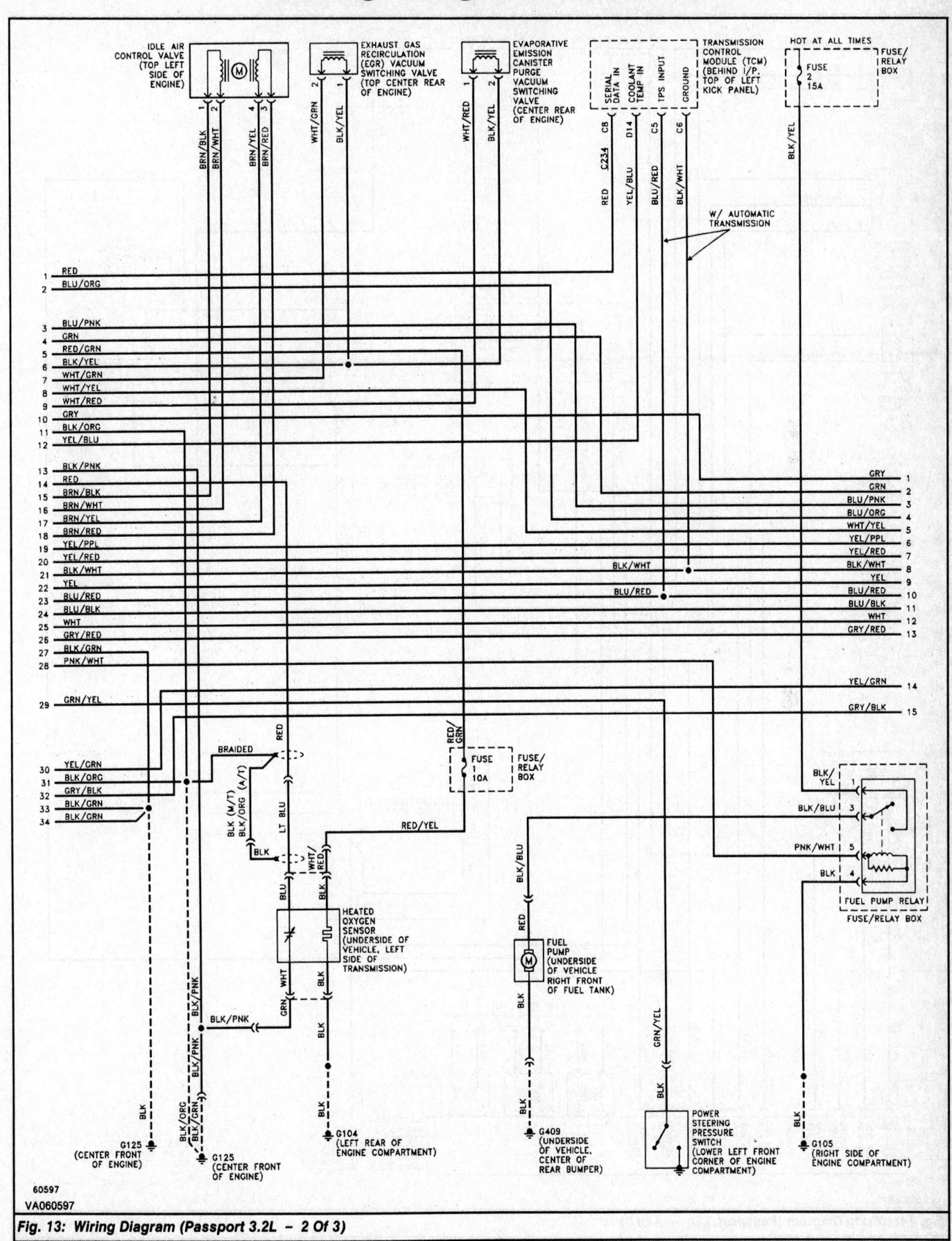

Fig. 13: Wiring Diagram (Passport 3.2L - 2 Of 3)

60597

VA060597

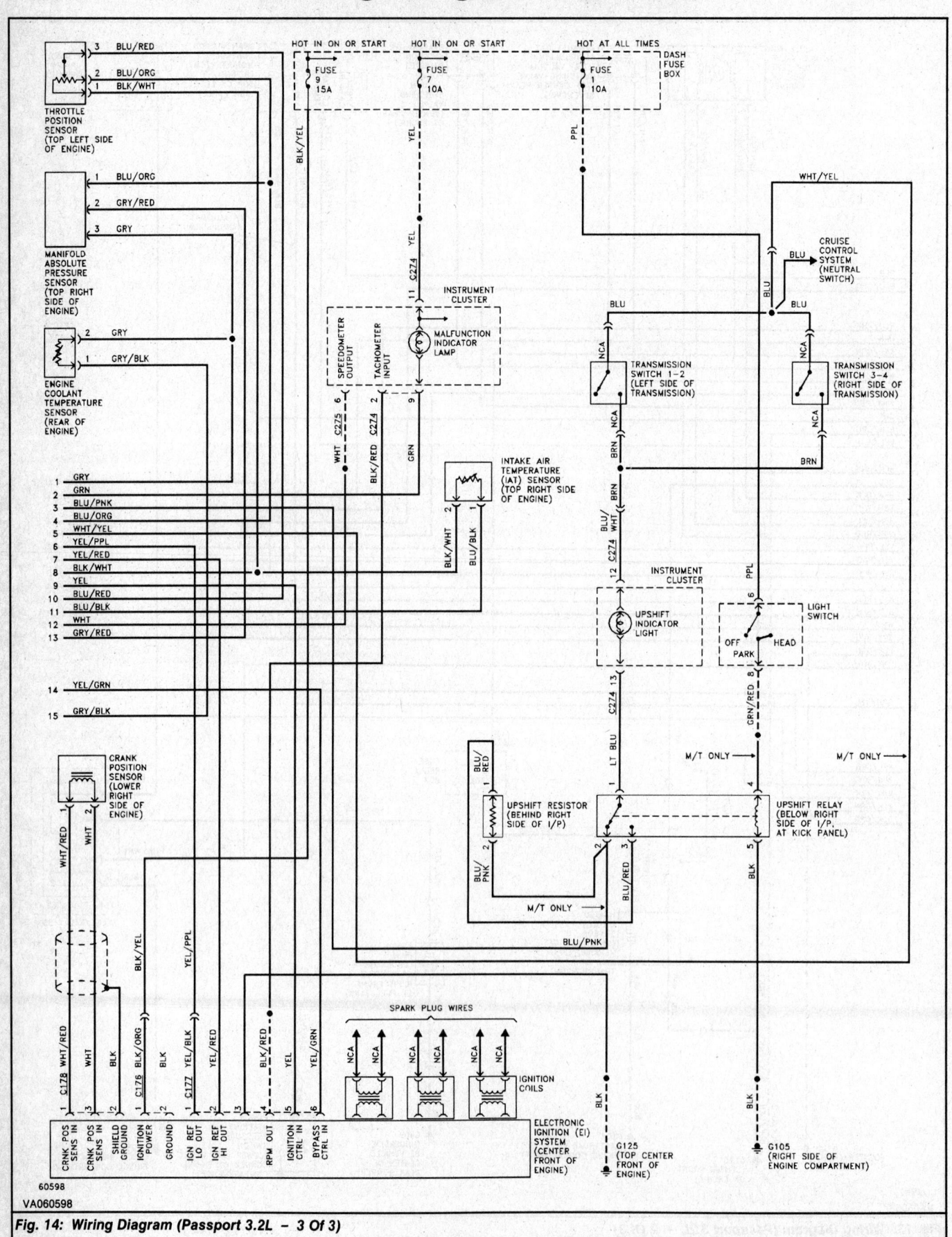

60598

VA060598

Fig. 14: Wiring Diagram (Passport 3.2L – 3 Of 3)

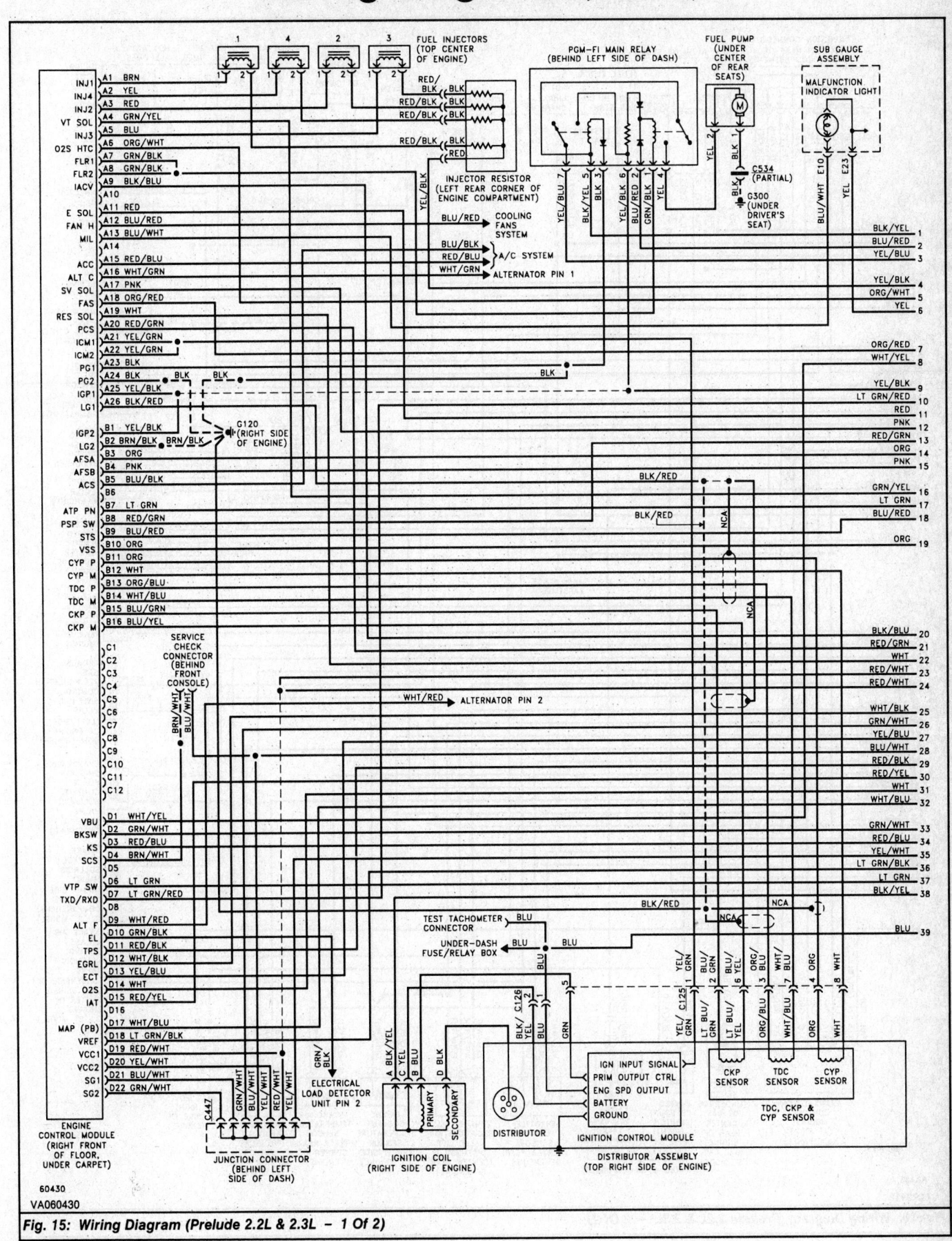

Fig. 15: Wiring Diagram (Prelude 2.2L & 2.3L - 1 Of 2)

VA060430
60430

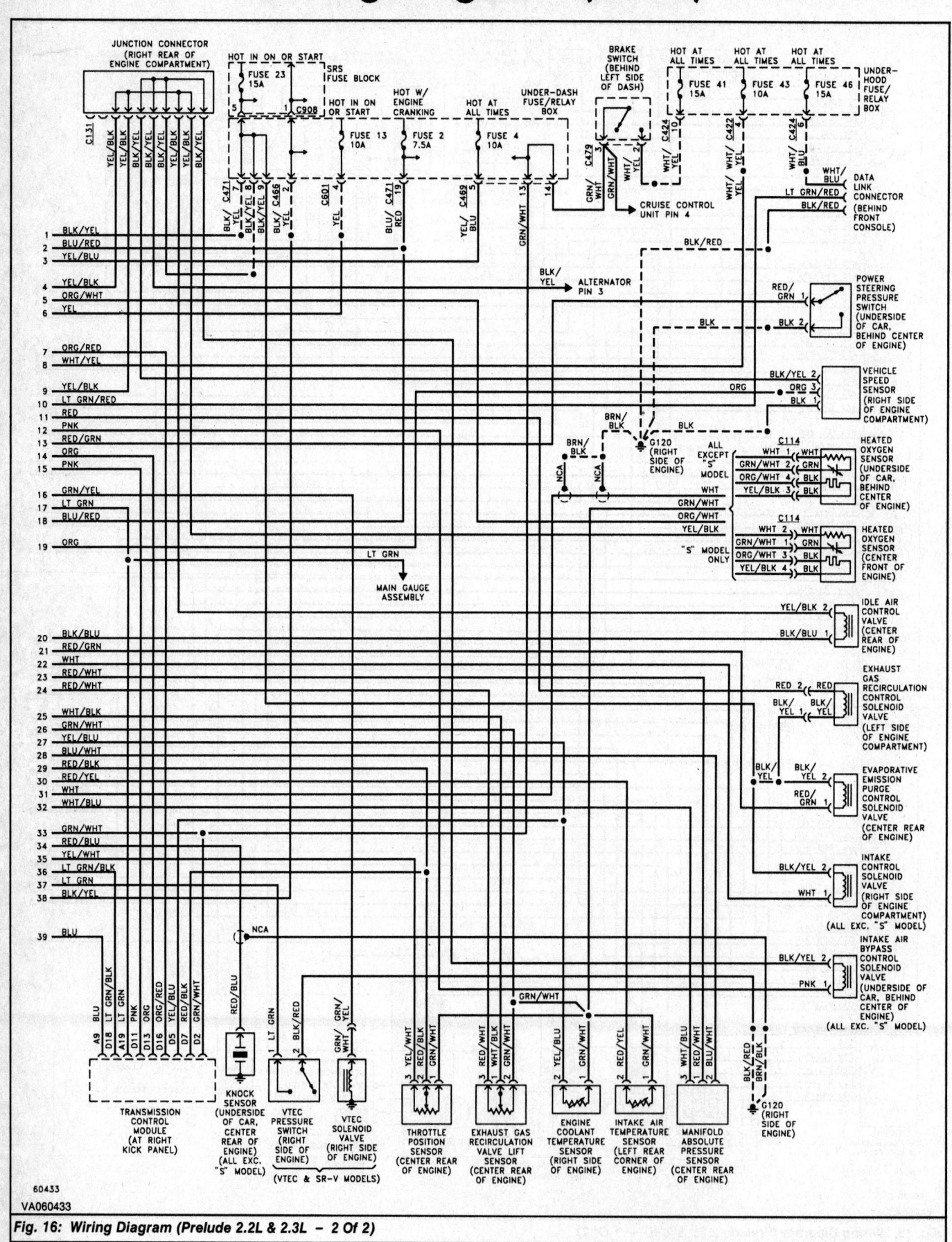

Fig. 16: Wiring Diagram (Prelude 2.2L & 2.3L – 2 Of 2)

60433

VA060433

Civic, Civic Del Sol

NOTE: Some Civic and Civic Del Sol models are equipped with Nippondenso alternators and regulators. See ALTERNATORS & REGULATORS – NIPPONDENSO article.

DESCRIPTION

The Mitsubishi alternator uses 8 diodes to rectify current and 3 diodes to supply current to voltage regulator. Charging system voltage is controlled by a voltage regulator which is part of alternator.

Charging system incorporates an Electric Load Detector (ELD) which measures load on the charging system. ELD sends signal to PGM-FI (engine) ECM which controls voltage regulator. Adjusting voltage needs allows engine ECM to reduce mechanical load on engine for greatest fuel economy.

NOTE: For wiring circuit information, see appropriate wiring diagram in WIRING DIAGRAMS.

ADJUSTMENTS
ALTERNATOR BELT ADJUSTMENT

Application	^{1} Deflection – In. (mm)
Civic & Civic Del Sol	5/16-13/32 (8-10)

^{1} – Deflection is with 22 lbs. (10 kg) pressure applied midway on the longest belt run.

TROUBLE SHOOTING

NOTE: See TROUBLE SHOOTING article in GENERAL INFORMATION.

ON-VEHICLE TESTING

PRELIMINARY INSPECTION

Check alternator wiring harness connections and drive belt tension. Ensure battery is fully charged and has good cable connections. If equipped with air bag system, check fuse No. 24 (15-amp) in dash fuse box. If not equipped with air bag system, check fuse No. 12 (15-amp) in dash fuse box. Repair or replace as necessary.

ALTERNATOR OUTPUT TEST

1) With engine at normal operating temperature, remove alternator harness connector. See Fig. 1. Turn ignition switch to ON position. Ensure battery voltage exists between Black/Yellow wire terminal of harness connector and ground.

2) If battery voltage is not present, check fuse No. 12 (15-amp) or fuse No. 24 (15-amp) in dash fuse box. Check for open circuit in Black/Yellow wire between dash fuse box and alternator. Check for open circuit in White/Yellow wire between engine ECM and alternator.

3) Turn ignition off. Reconnect alternator harness connector. Connect Alternator Tester (Sun VAT 40) with integral carbon pile to system. Set tester switch to position No. 1. Ensure all accessories are off. Start engine. Operate engine at 2000 RPM and check output voltage. If voltage is greater than 15.1 volts, replace voltage regulator.

4) Let engine idle. Set tester switch to position No. 2. Remove tester inductive pick-up and zero ammeter. Reconnect inductive pick-up. Operate engine at 2000 RPM and check voltage. If voltage is less than 13.9 volts, test battery.

5) Using carbon pile function of tester, apply load to charging system until voltage drops to 12-13.5 volts. Amperage should be 40 amps or greater. If amperage reading is as specified, charging system is okay. If amperage is not as specified, perform full field test. See FULL FIELD TEST. At full field, amperage should be 40 amps or greater.

6) If amperage is not within specification, replace alternator. If amperage is as specified, check Black/Yellow wire for battery voltage. Ensure battery voltage exists. If battery voltage is not present, repair or replace wire.

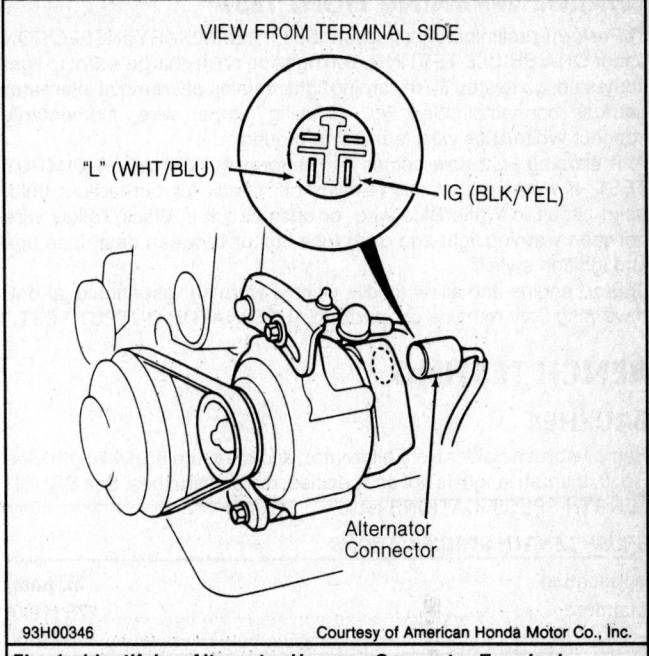

VIEW FROM TERMINAL SIDE

"L" (WHT/BLU)   IG (BLK/YEL)

Alternator Connector

93H00346   Courtesy of American Honda Motor Co., Inc.

Fig. 1: Identifying Alternator Harness Connector Terminals

7) Also check White/Yellow wire for a short circuit to ground. If Black/Yellow and White/Yellow wires are okay, internal voltage regulator is faulty and must be replaced.

NOTE: Charging system will not charge if White/Yellow wire is shorted to ground or engine ECM is defective.

FULL FIELD TEST

CAUTION: When performing full field test on alternator, charging voltage will rise quickly. DO NOT allow voltage to rise above 18 volts, or electrical system will be damaged.

Remove protector from full field access hole located at rear of alternator end cover. See Fig. 2. Insert screwdriver into hole of alternator to by-pass voltage regulator. Increase engine speed to 2000 RPM, and monitor voltage and amperage increase. Voltage should be greater than 15.1 volts. Amperage should be greater than 40 amps. If amperage or both voltage and amperage are less than specification, replace or repair alternator.

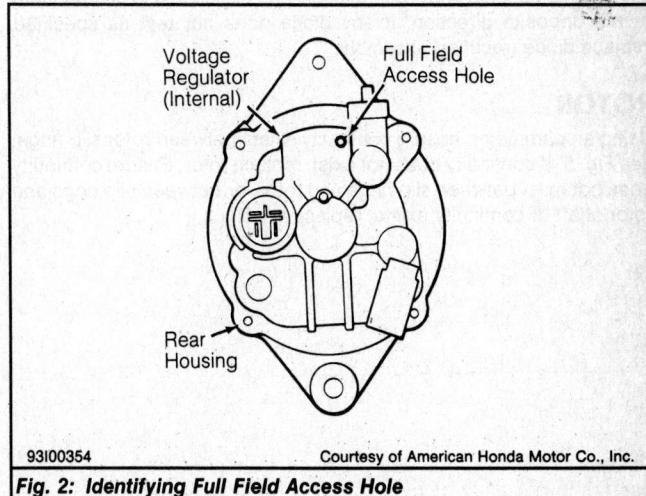

Voltage Regulator (Internal)   Full Field Access Hole

Rear Housing

93I00354   Courtesy of American Honda Motor Co., Inc.

Fig. 2: Identifying Full Field Access Hole

CHARGE WARNING LIGHT TEST

1) Perform preliminary inspection. See PRELIMINARY INSPECTION under ON-VEHICLE TESTING. Turn ignition on. If charge warning light comes on, go to step **3)**. If warning light remains off, remove alternator harness connector. *See Fig. 1.* Using jumper wire, momentarily connect White/Blue wire terminal to ground.

2) If warning light now comes on, perform ALTERNATOR OUTPUT TEST. If warning light still remains off, check for burned-out bulb, open circuit in White/Blue wire, or open circuit in Black/Yellow wire between warning light and dash fuse box or between dash fuse box and ignition switch.

3) Start engine and allow to idle. Charge warning light should go out. If warning light remains on, perform ALTERNATOR OUTPUT TEST.

BENCH TESTING

BRUSHES

Remove brush holder from alternator, and measure brush length. *See Fig. 3.* If brush length is not as specified, replace brushes. See BRUSH LENGTH SPECIFICATIONS table.

BRUSH LENGTH SPECIFICATIONS

Application	In. (mm)
Standard	.75 (19.0)
Limit	.20 (5.0)

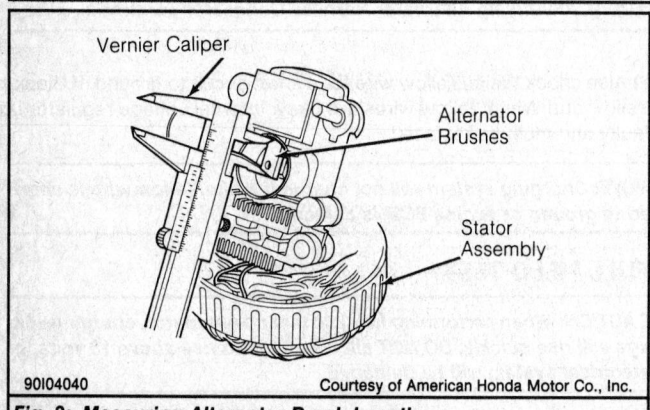

Fig. 3: Measuring Alternator Brush Length

DIODE ASSEMBLY

1) Remove diode (rectifier) assembly from alternator. Check continuity on each diode in both directions by reversing test probes between diode terminals. *See Fig. 4.*

2) All diodes should show continuity in one direction and no continuity in the opposite direction. If any diode does not test as specified, replace diode (rectifier) assembly.

ROTOR

Using an ohmmeter, ensure continuity exists between rotor slip rings. *See Fig. 5.* If continuity does not exist, replace rotor. Ensure continuity does not exist between slip rings and rotor, or between slip rings and rotor shaft. If continuity exists, replace rotor.

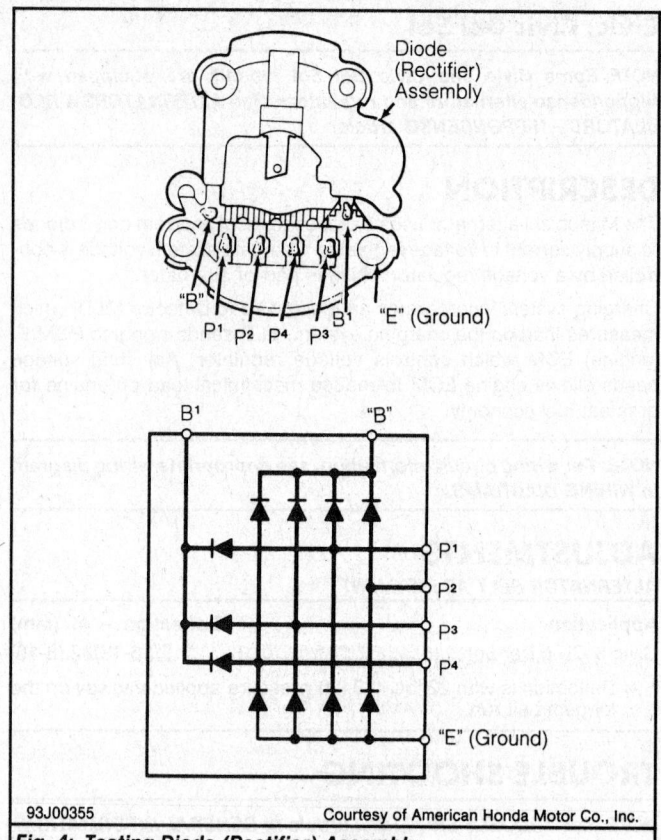

Fig. 4: Testing Diode (Rectifier) Assembly

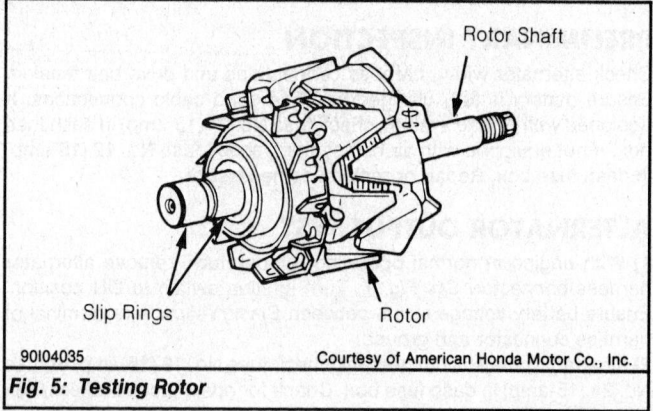

Fig. 5: Testing Rotor

STATOR

Ensure continuity exists between each pair of leads on stator winding. If continuity does not exist, replace stator. Ensure continuity does not exist between each stator winding lead and coil core. If continuity exists, replace stator.

OVERHAUL

NOTE: Use illustration for exploded view of alternator. See Fig. 6.

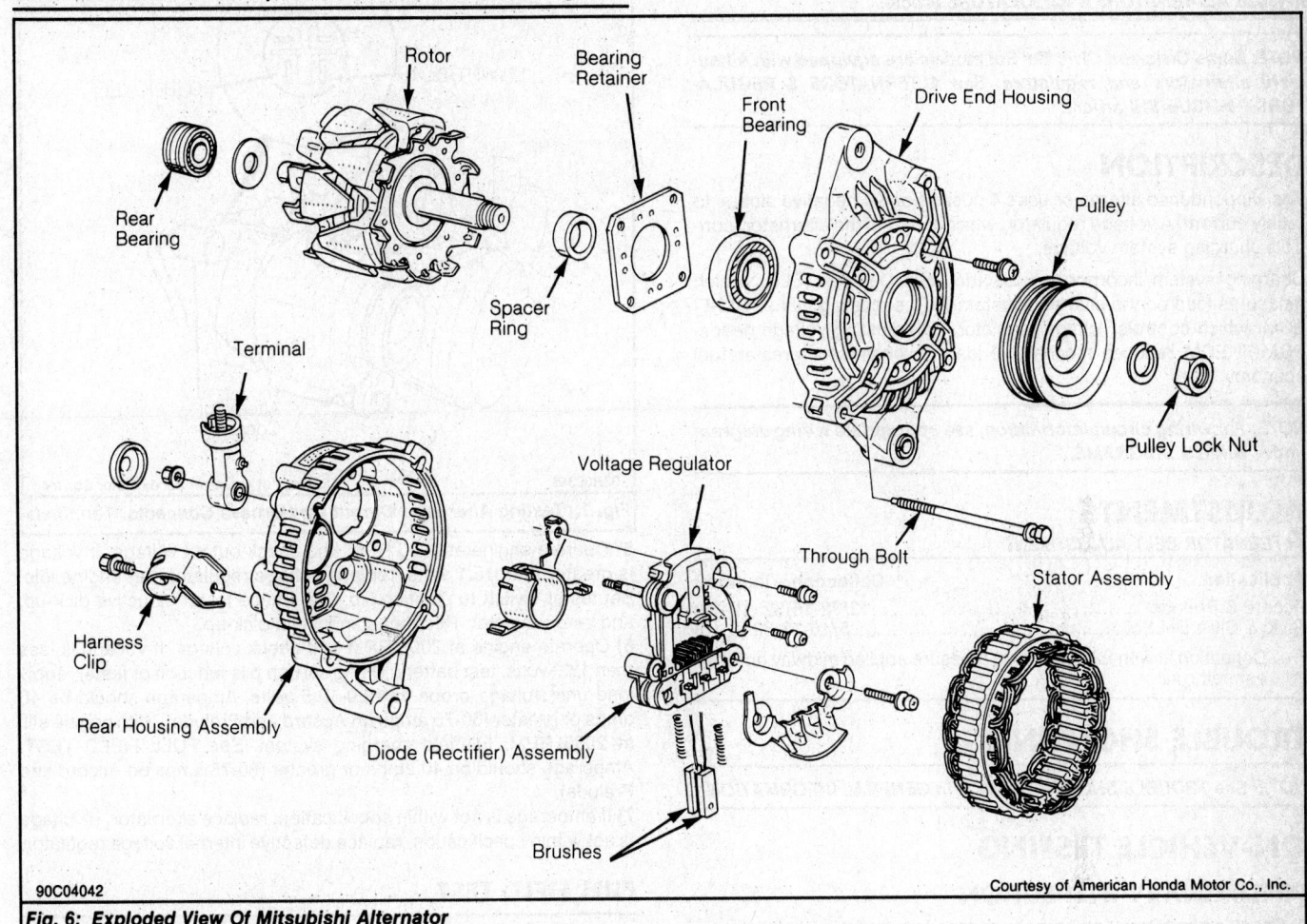

90C04042

Courtesy of American Honda Motor Co., Inc.

Fig. 6: Exploded View Of Mitsubishi Alternator

WIRING DIAGRAM

*NOTE: See appropriate Wiring Diagram in ALTERNATOR & REGULA-
TORS – Nippondenso article.*

1994 ELECTRICAL
Alternators & Regulators – Nippondenso

Accord, Civic, Civic Del Sol, Passport, Prelude

NOTE: For charging system information on Passport, refer to Rodeo in Isuzu ALTERNATORS & REGULATORS article.

NOTE: Some Civic and Civic Del Sol models are equipped with Mitsubishi alternators and regulators. See ALTERNATORS & REGULATORS – MITSUBISHI article.

DESCRIPTION

The Nippondenso alternator uses 4 positive and 4 negative diodes to rectify current. A voltage regulator, which is part of the alternator, controls charging system voltage.

Charging system incorporates Electric Load Detector (ELD), which measures load on the charging system. ELD sends signal to PGM-FI ECM, which controls voltage regulator. By adjusting voltage needs, PGM-FI ECM reduces mechanical load on engine for greater fuel economy.

NOTE: For wiring circuit information, see appropriate wiring diagram under WIRING DIAGRAMS.

ADJUSTMENTS

ALTERNATOR BELT ADJUSTMENT

Application	¹ Deflection – In. (mm)
Accord & Prelude	13/32-15/32 (10-12)
Civic & Civic Del Sol	5/16-13/32 (8-10)

¹ – Deflection is with 22 lbs. (10 kg) pressure applied midway on longest belt run.

TROUBLE SHOOTING

NOTE: See TROUBLE SHOOTING article in GENERAL INFORMATION.

ON-VEHICLE TESTING

PRELIMINARY INSPECTION

1) Check alternator wiring harness connections and drive belt tension. Ensure battery is fully charged and connections at battery cables, alternator and main fuses are good.

2) On Accord, check fuse No. 4 (7.5-amp) in dash fuse box. On Civic and Civic Del Sol, check fuse No. 24 (15-amp) in dash fuse box if equipped with air bag system or fuse No. 12 (15-amp) if not equipped with air bag system. On Prelude, check fuse No. 23 (15-amp). On all models, replace fuse as necessary.

NOTE: If any fuse is blown, charge warning light will come on even if charging system is working properly.

ALTERNATOR OUTPUT TEST

1) With engine at normal operating temperature, remove alternator harness connector. *See Fig. 1.* Turn ignition switch to ON position.

2) Check for battery voltage between Black/Yellow wire terminal of harness connector and ground. Ensure battery voltage is also present between White/Green (White/Yellow on Civic and Civic Del Sol) wire terminal and ground. If battery voltage is present, go to step **4)**.

3) If battery voltage is not present, check dash fuse No. 4 (7.5-amp) on Accord, fuse No. 12 (15-amp) or fuse No. 24 (15-amp) on Civic and Civic Del Sol or fuse No. 19 (15-amp) or fuse No. 23 (15-amp) on Prelude. Check for open circuit in Black/Yellow wire between dash fuse box and alternator. Check for open circuit in White/Green (White/Yellow on Civic and Civic Del Sol) wire between PGM-FI ECM and alternator.

4) Turn ignition off. Reconnect alternator harness connector. Connect alternator tester with integral carbon pile (Sun VAT-40) to system. Set tester switch to position No. 1. Ensure all accessories are off. Start engine.

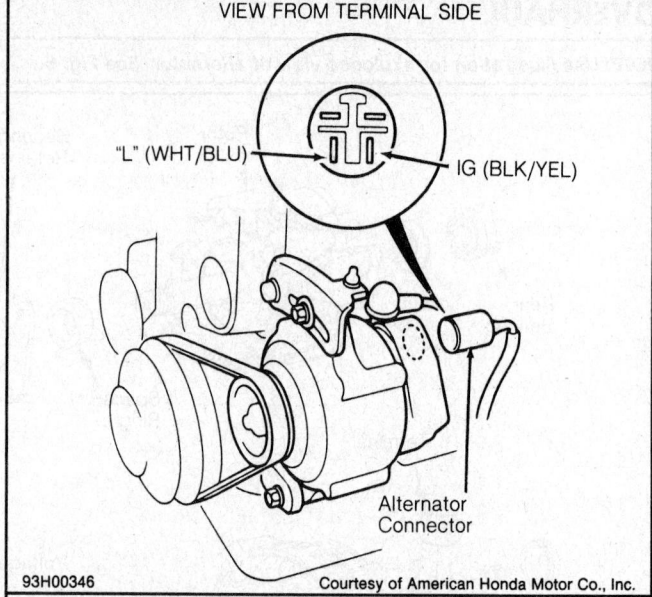

93H00346   Courtesy of American Honda Motor Co., Inc.

Fig. 1: Testing Alternator Output On Harness Connector Terminals

5) Operate engine at 2000 RPM and check output voltage. If voltage is greater than 15.1 volts, replace voltage regulator. Let engine idle. Set tester switch to position No. 2. Remove tester inductive pick-up, and zero ammeter. Reconnect inductive pick-up.

6) Operate engine at 2000 RPM and check voltage. If voltage is less than 13.9 volts, test battery. Using carbon pile function of tester, apply load until voltage drops to 12.0-13.5 volts. Amperage should be 40 amps or greater (60-75 amps on Accord and Prelude). With engine still at 2000 RPM, full-field charging system. See FULL FIELD TEST. Amperage should be 40 amps or greater (60-75 amps on Accord and Prelude).

7) If amperage is not within specification, replace alternator. If voltage is not within specification, replace defective internal voltage regulator.

FULL FIELD TEST

CAUTION: When performing full field test on alternator, charging voltage will increase quickly. DO NOT allow voltage to increase above 18 volts; electrical system will be damaged.

Remove protector from full field access hole, located at rear of alternator end cover. *See Fig. 2.* Insert screwdriver into hole of alternator, by-passing voltage regulator. Increase engine speed to 2000 RPM and monitor voltage and amperage increase. Voltage should be more than 15.1 volts. Amperage should be more than 40 amps. If amperage or voltage is less than specification, replace or repair alternator.

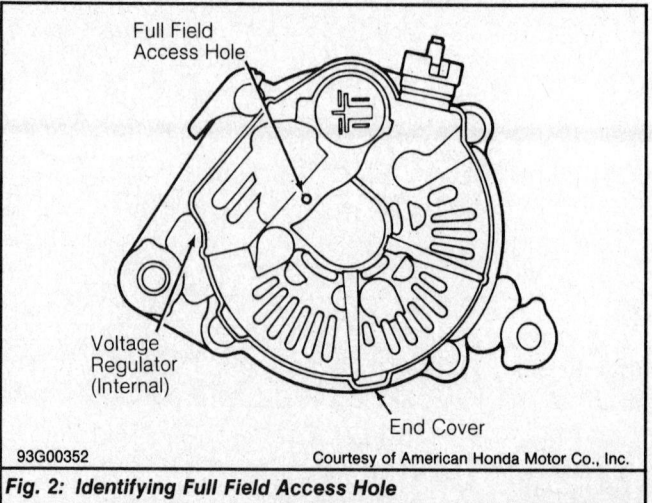

93G00352   Courtesy of American Honda Motor Co., Inc.

Fig. 2: Identifying Full Field Access Hole

CHARGE WARNING LIGHT TEST

Accord & Prelude – **1)** Perform preliminary inspection. See PRELIMINARY INSPECTION. Turn ignition on. If charge warning light comes on, go to step **3)**. If warning light remains off, remove alternator harness connector. *See Fig. 1*. Using jumper wire, momentarily connect White/Blue wire terminal to ground.

2) If warning light comes on, perform ALTERNATOR OUTPUT TEST. If warning light remains off, check for burned bulb, open circuit in White/Blue wire or open circuit in Black/Yellow wire between warning light and dash fuse box or between dash fuse box and ignition switch.

3) Start engine, and allow it to idle. If charge warning light goes out, turn off engine and go to next step. If warning light remains on, perform ALTERNATOR OUTPUT TEST.

4) Turn ignition on. Disconnect alternator harness connector. On Accord, disconnect integrated control unit and ABS control unit. On Prelude, disconnect ABS control unit, integrated control unit and 4WS control unit. Check charge warning light after disconnecting each unit. Charge warning light should go out.

5) If warning light goes out, control unit disconnected before light went out is shorted. Replace faulty control unit. If warning light remains on, repair short circuit to ground in White/Blue wire between warning light and dash fuse box or between dash fuse box and voltage regulator.

Civic & Civic Del Sol – **1)** Perform preliminary inspection. See PRELIMINARY INSPECTION. Turn ignition on. If charge warning light comes on, go to step **3)**. If warning light remains off, remove alternator harness connector. *See Fig. 1*. Using jumper wire, momentarily connect White/Blue wire terminal to ground.

2) If warning light now comes on, perform ALTERNATOR OUTPUT TEST. If warning light remains off, check for burned bulb, open circuit in White/Blue wire or open circuit in Black/Yellow wire between warning light and dash fuse box or between dash fuse box and ignition switch.

3) Start engine, and allow it to idle. Charge warning light should go out. If warning light remains on, perform ALTERNATOR OUTPUT TEST.

BENCH TESTING

BRUSHES

Remove brush holder from alternator. Using vernier caliper, measure brush length. *See Fig. 3*. If brush length is not as specified, replace brushes. See BRUSH LENGTH SPECIFICATIONS table.

BRUSH LENGTH SPECIFICATIONS

Application	In. (mm)
Standard	.41 (10.5)
Limit	.22 (5.6)

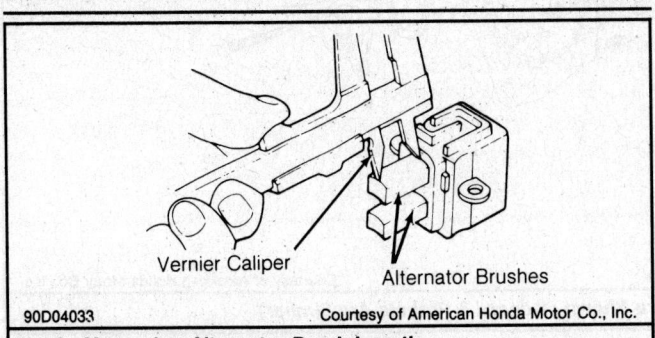

90D04033   Courtesy of American Honda Motor Co., Inc.

Fig. 3: Measuring Alternator Brush Length

DIODE ASSEMBLY

1) Remove diode (rectifier) assembly from alternator. Check for continuity in both directions by reversing test probes between terminal "B"

and terminals P^1, P^2, P^3 and P^4. Check for continuity in both directions between terminal "E" (ground) and terminals P^1, P^2, P^3 and P^4. *See Fig. 4*.

2) All diodes should show continuity in one direction and no continuity in opposite direction. If any diode does not test as specified, replace entire diode (rectifier) assembly.

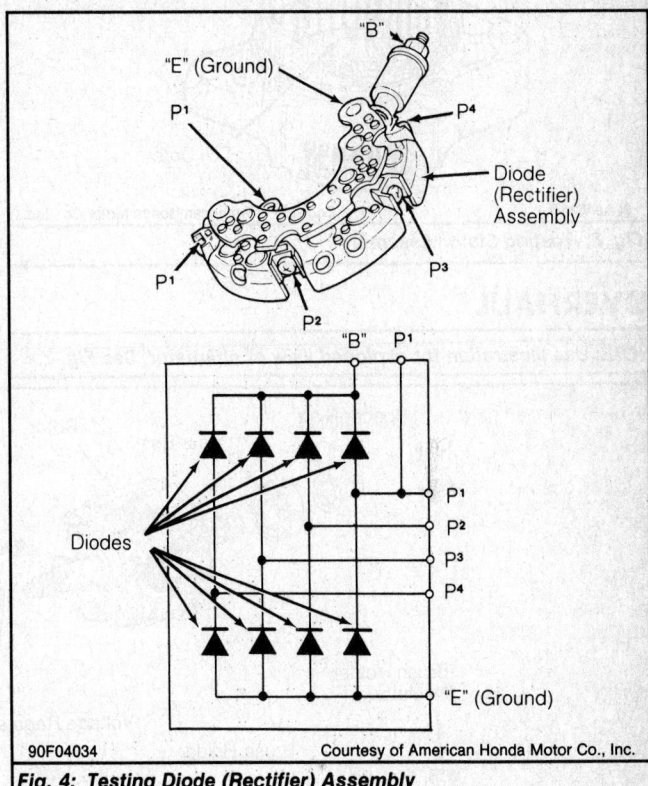

90F04034   Courtesy of American Honda Motor Co., Inc.

Fig. 4: Testing Diode (Rectifier) Assembly

ROTOR

Using an ohmmeter, ensure continuity exists between rotor slip rings. *See Fig. 5*. If continuity does not exist, replace rotor assembly. Ensure continuity does not exist between slip rings and rotor or between slip rings and rotor shaft. If continuity exists, replace rotor.

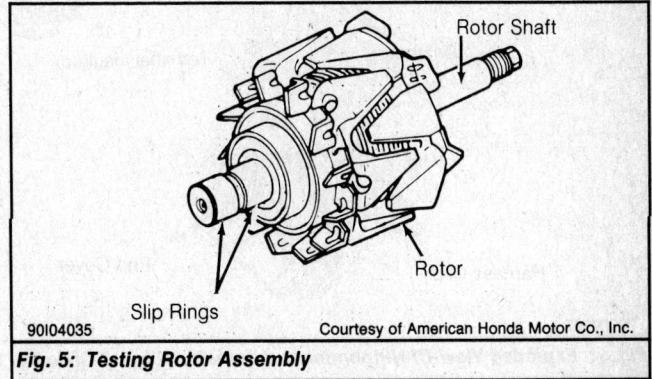

90I04035   Courtesy of American Honda Motor Co., Inc.

Fig. 5: Testing Rotor Assembly

STATOR

Ensure continuity exists between each pair of leads on stator winding. *See Fig. 6*. If continuity does not exist, replace stator assembly. Ensure continuity does not exist between any stator winding lead and coil core. If continuity exists, replace stator assembly.

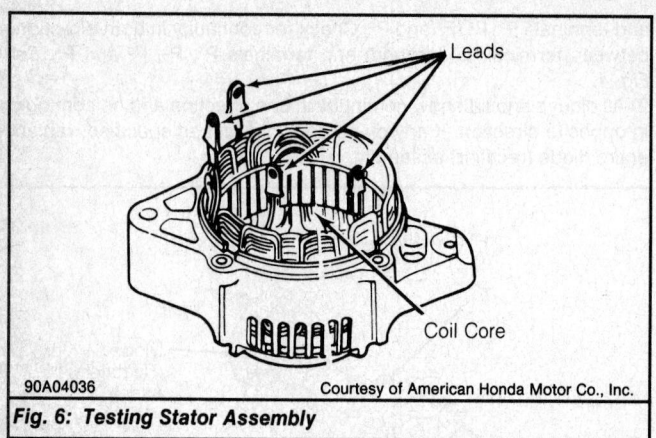

90A04036   Courtesy of American Honda Motor Co., Inc.

Fig. 6: Testing Stator Assembly

OVERHAUL

NOTE: Use illustration for exploded view of alternator. See Fig. 7.

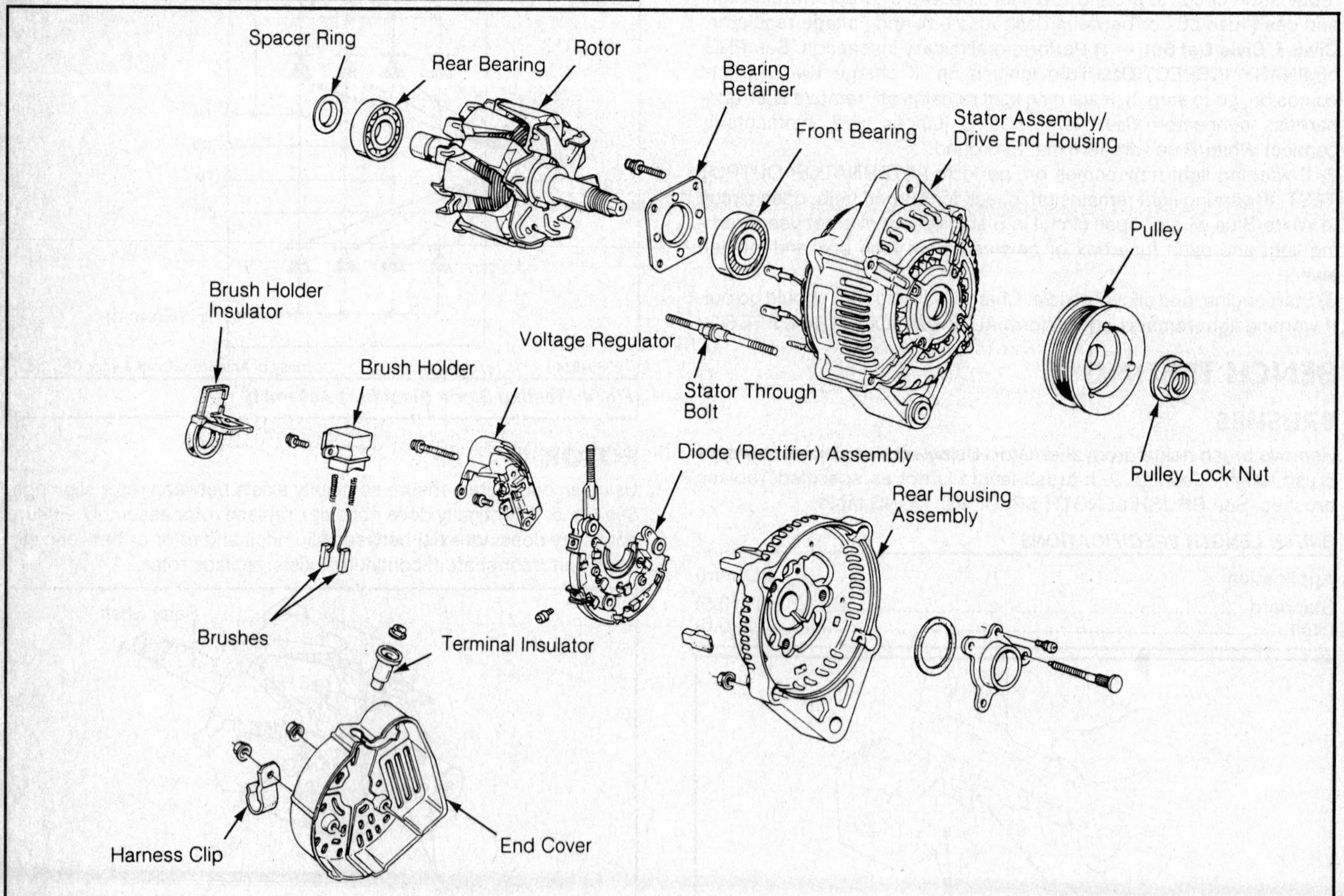

90C04037   Courtesy of American Honda Motor Co., Inc.

Fig. 7: Exploded View Of Nippondenso Alternator (Civic & Civic Del Sol Are Shown ; Accord & Prelude Are Similar)

WIRING DIAGRAMS

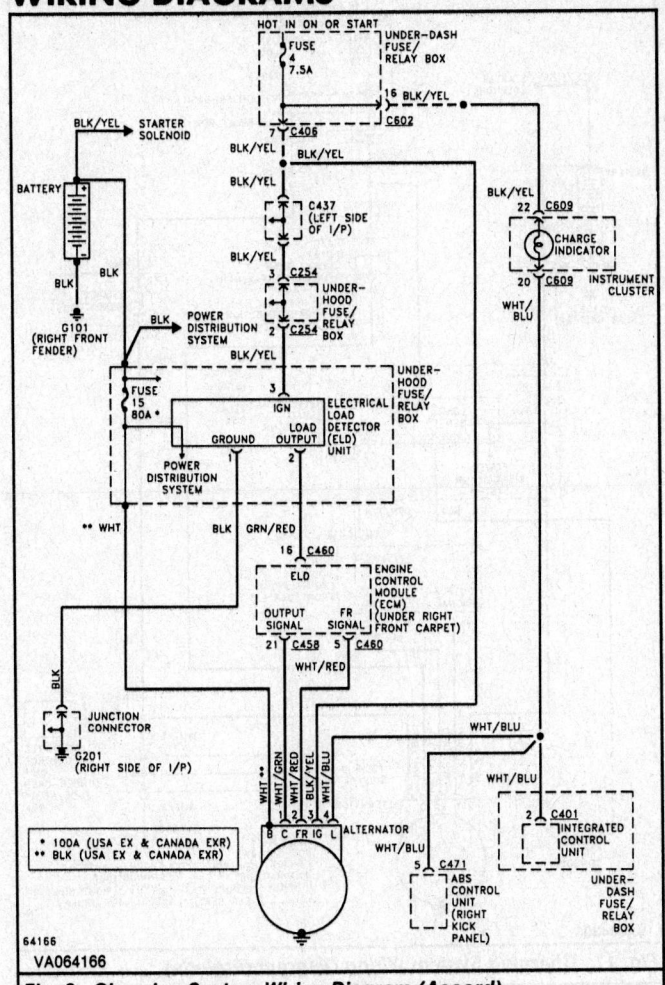

Fig. 8: Charging System Wiring Diagram (Accord)

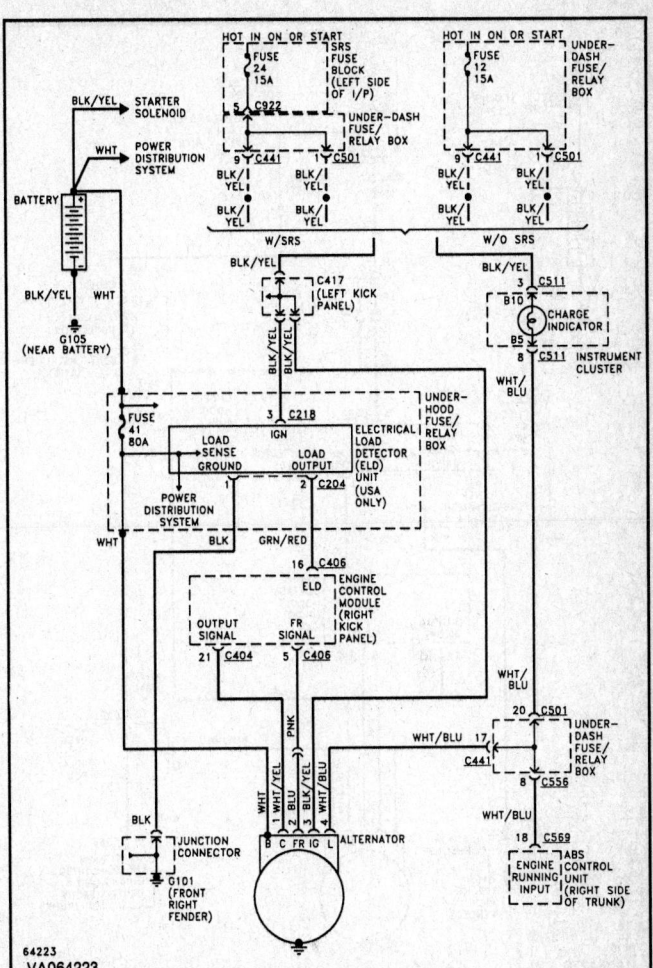

Fig. 9: Charging System Wiring Diagram (Civic)

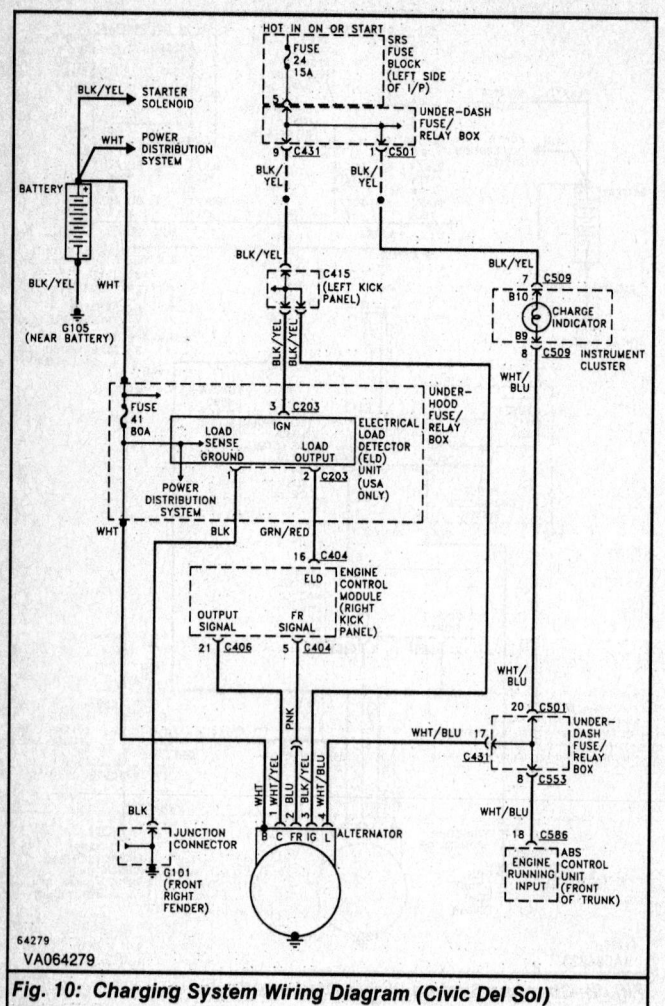

Fig. 10: Charging System Wiring Diagram (Civic Del Sol)

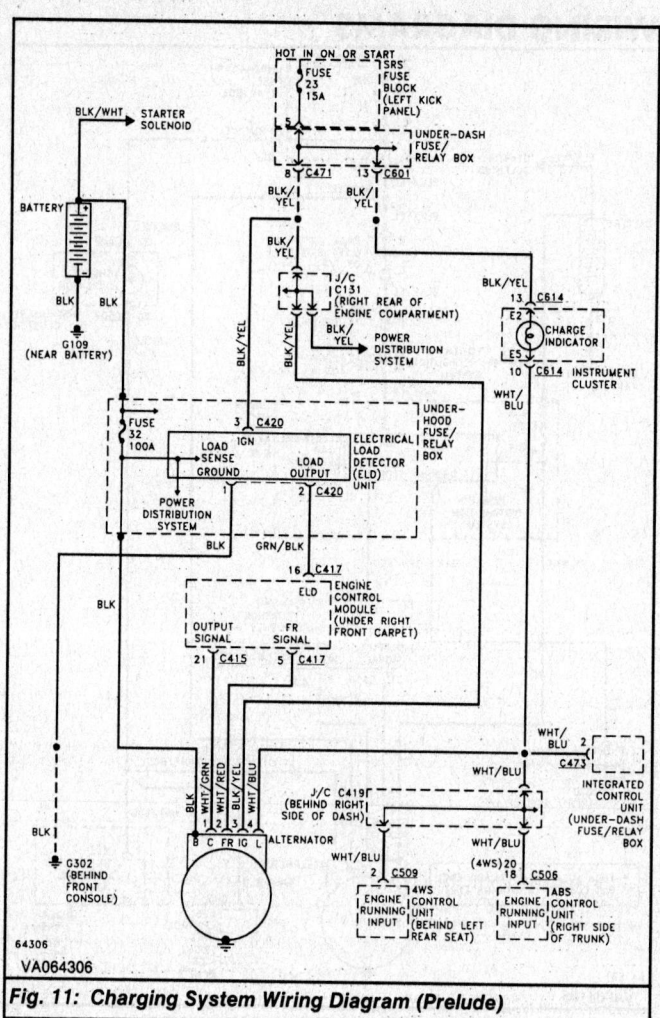

Fig. 11: Charging System Wiring Diagram (Prelude)

Civic

NOTE: Some Civic models are equipped with Mitsuba and Nippon-denso reduction gear starters. See STARTERS – MITSUBA & NIPPON-DENSO REDUCTION GEAR article.

DESCRIPTION

Starter is a conventional 12-volt, permanent field magnet, 4-pole brush-type motor with direct gear drive. When starter is energized, starter-mounted solenoid shifts overrunning clutch and drive gear into flywheel.

TROUBLE SHOOTING

NOTE: See TROUBLE SHOOTING article in GENERAL INFORMATION.

ON-VEHICLE TESTING

NOTE: On M/T vehicles, engine will not crank unless clutch pedal is fully depressed.

CRANKING TEST

1) Disconnect 2-pin connector (ignition coil primary lead) from distributor to disable ignition system. *See Fig. 1.* Connect voltmeter and ammeter to battery. *See Fig. 2.*

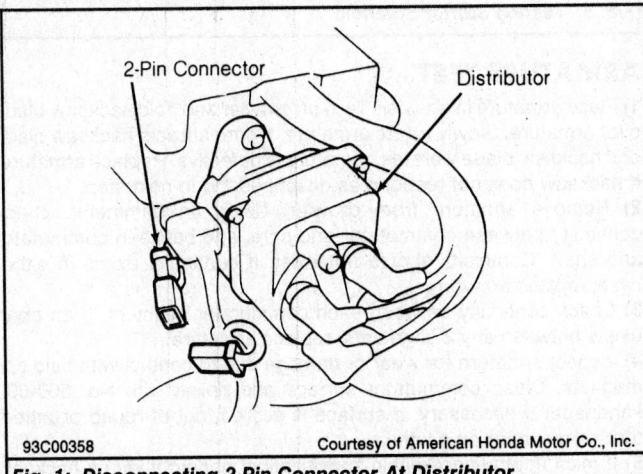

93C00358   Courtesy of American Honda Motor Co., Inc.

Fig. 1: Disconnecting 2-Pin Connector At Distributor

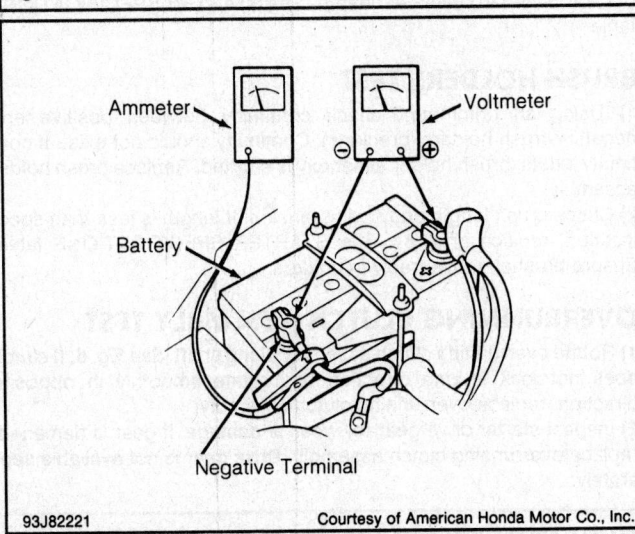

93J82221   Courtesy of American Honda Motor Co., Inc.

Fig. 2: Starter Cranking Test

NOTE: Use commercially available starter tester to perform cranking test. Follow manufacturer's instructions. If starter tester is unavailable, perform test as described in steps 2) through 6).

2) Connect tachometer to engine. Turn ignition switch to START position, and crank engine. Check starter cranking voltage and current draw on appropriate meter. See CRANKING TEST SPECIFICATIONS table.

CRANKING TEST SPECIFICATIONS

Starter Type	Cranking Voltage (Volts)	Current Draw (Amps)
Hitachi	8.0	[1] 400

[1] – Cranking speed should be greater than 100 RPM.

3) If engine does not crank, check battery, battery cables and connections for looseness or corrosion. If engine still does not crank, go to next step.
4) Disconnect Black/White wire from starter. Connect jumper wire from positive battery terminal to starter solenoid "S" terminal. Engine should crank. If engine still does not crank, repair or replace starter.
5) If engine cranks, check for open circuit in Black/White wire between starter and ignition switch. Check connections for looseness or corrosion. Check ignition switch.
6) Check neutral/safety switch and connector on A/T vehicles. Check starter relay, clutch interlock switch and connectors on M/T vehicles. See CLUTCH INTERLOCK SWITCH TEST.

CLUTCH INTERLOCK SWITCH TEST

M/T Vehicles – 1) Remove lower instrument panel cover and driver's side knee bolster to gain access to clutch interlock switch connector. Disconnect 2-pin connector from switch.
2) Check continuity between switch terminals. Ensure continuity exists when clutch pedal is depressed. Continuity should not exist when clutch pedal is not depressed.

STARTER RELAY TEST

NOTE: Relay connector appearance may between individual vehicles. Test procedure remains the same.

A/T Vehicles – Remove starter relay under left side of dash. Connect battery voltage and ground between terminals "C" and "D". *See Fig. 3.* Ensure continuity exists between terminals "A" and "B". Disconnect battery source from terminals "C" and "D". Continuity should no longer exist between terminals "A" and "B".

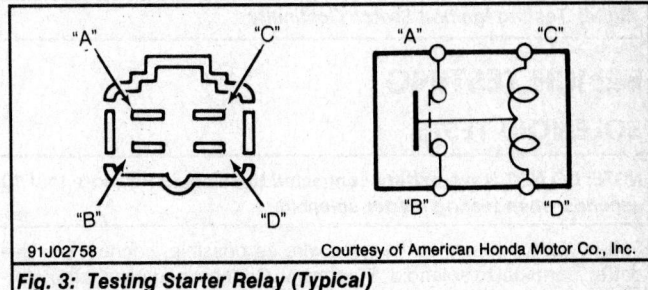

91J02758   Courtesy of American Honda Motor Co., Inc.

Fig. 3: Testing Starter Relay (Typical)

IGNITION SWITCH TEST

Remove lower instrument panel cover and driver-side knee bolster. Disconnect 5-pin and 7-pin connectors from dash fuse box. Use an ohmmeter to check continuity at connector terminals with switch in indicated position. *See Fig. 4.* If continuity is not as specified, replace ignition switch.

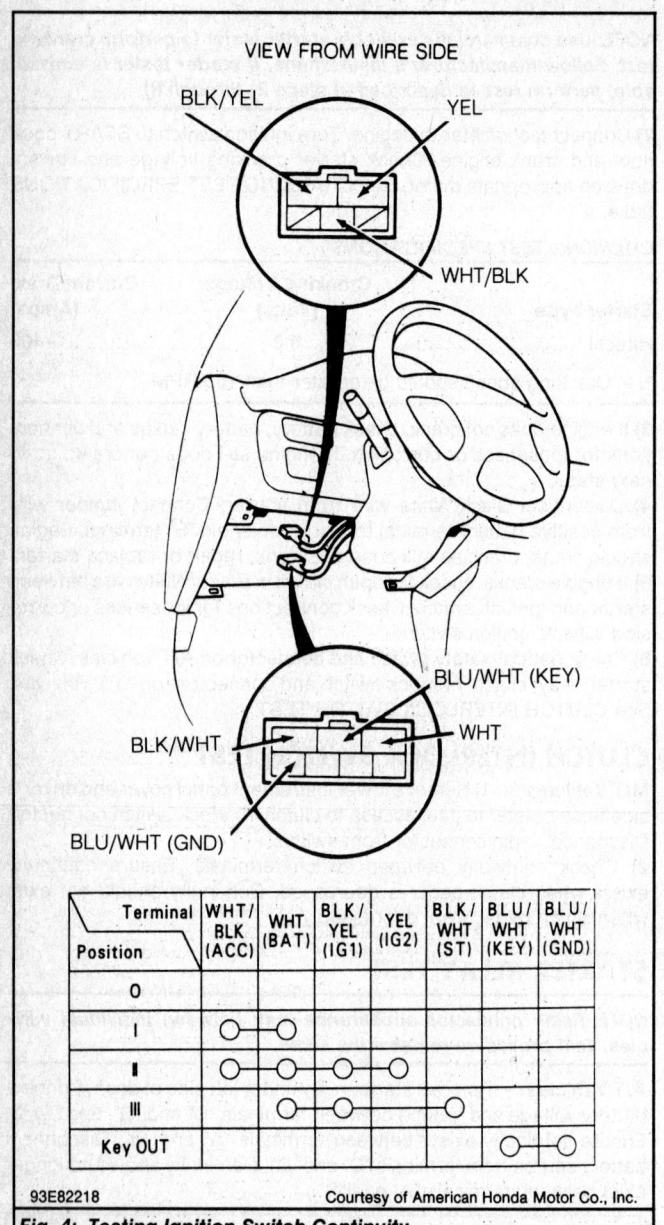

VIEW FROM WIRE SIDE

Terminal Position	WHT/ BLK (ACC)	WHT (BAT)	BLK/ YEL (IG1)	YEL (IG2)	BLK/ WHT (ST)	BLU/ WHT (KEY)	BLU/ WHT (GND)
O							
I	○—○						
II	○—○	○—○	○				
III		○—○	○—○	○			
Key OUT						○—○	

93E82218   Courtesy of American Honda Motor Co., Inc.

Fig. 4: Testing Ignition Switch Continuity

BENCH TESTING
SOLENOID TESTS

NOTE: DO NOT leave battery connected to solenoid for more that 10 seconds when testing starter solenoid.

Pull-In Test – Using as heavy a wire as possible, connect positive battery terminal to solenoid "S" terminal. Connect negative battery terminal to solenoid "M" terminal. *See Fig. 5.* Solenoid should actuate and pinion should protrude to drive position. If actuation does not occur, replace starter solenoid.

Hold-In Test – Using as heavy wire a as possible, connect positive battery terminal to solenoid "S" terminal. Connect negative battery terminal to armature housing (ground). Manually pull out drive pinion until it reaches its stop. If pinion does not snap back when released, hold-in coil is okay. If pinion snaps back, replace starter solenoid.

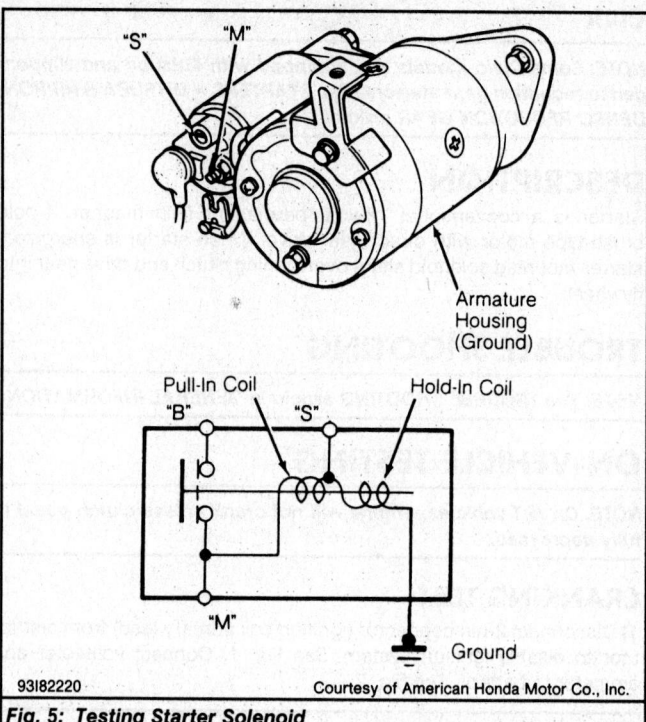

93182220   Courtesy of American Honda Motor Co., Inc.

Fig. 5: Testing Starter Solenoid

ARMATURE TEST

1) Place armature in growler. Turn on growler and hold hacksaw blade over armature. Slowly rotate armature. If core attracts hacksaw blade or if hacksaw blade vibrates, armature is defective. Replace armature. If hacksaw does not respond as described, go to next step.
2) Remove armature from growler. Using an ohmmeter, check continuity between commutator and core, and between commutator and shaft. Continuity should not exist. If continuity exists in either case, replace armature.
3) Check continuity between each commutator segment. If an open exists between any 2 segments, replace armature.
4) Inspect armature for wear or damage due to contact with field coil magnets. Clean commutator surface and polish with No. 500-600 sandpaper if necessary. If surface is scored, out-of-round or pitted, turn commutator on a lathe.
5) If mica depth is not within specification, undercut with a hacksaw blade to standard minimum depth. See STARTER SPECIFICATIONS table.

BRUSH HOLDERS TEST

1) Using an ohmmeter, check continuity between positive and negative brush holders (brackets). Continuity should not exist. If continuity exists, brush holder assembly is shorted. Replace brush holder assembly.
2) Check brush length and spring tension. If length is less than specification, replace brushes. See STARTER SPECIFICATIONS table. Ensure brushes move freely in holders.

OVERRUNNING CLUTCH ASSEMBLY TEST

1) Rotate overrunning clutch assembly along shaft. *See Fig. 6.* If clutch does not lock in one direction and rotate smoothly in opposite direction, replace overrunning clutch assembly.
2) Inspect starter drive gear for wear or damage. If gear is damaged, replace overrunning clutch assembly. Drive gear is not available separately.

NOTE: If starter drive gear teeth are damaged, check condition of flywheel or torque converter ring gear.

OVERHAUL

NOTE: Use illustration for exploded view of starter. See Fig. 7.

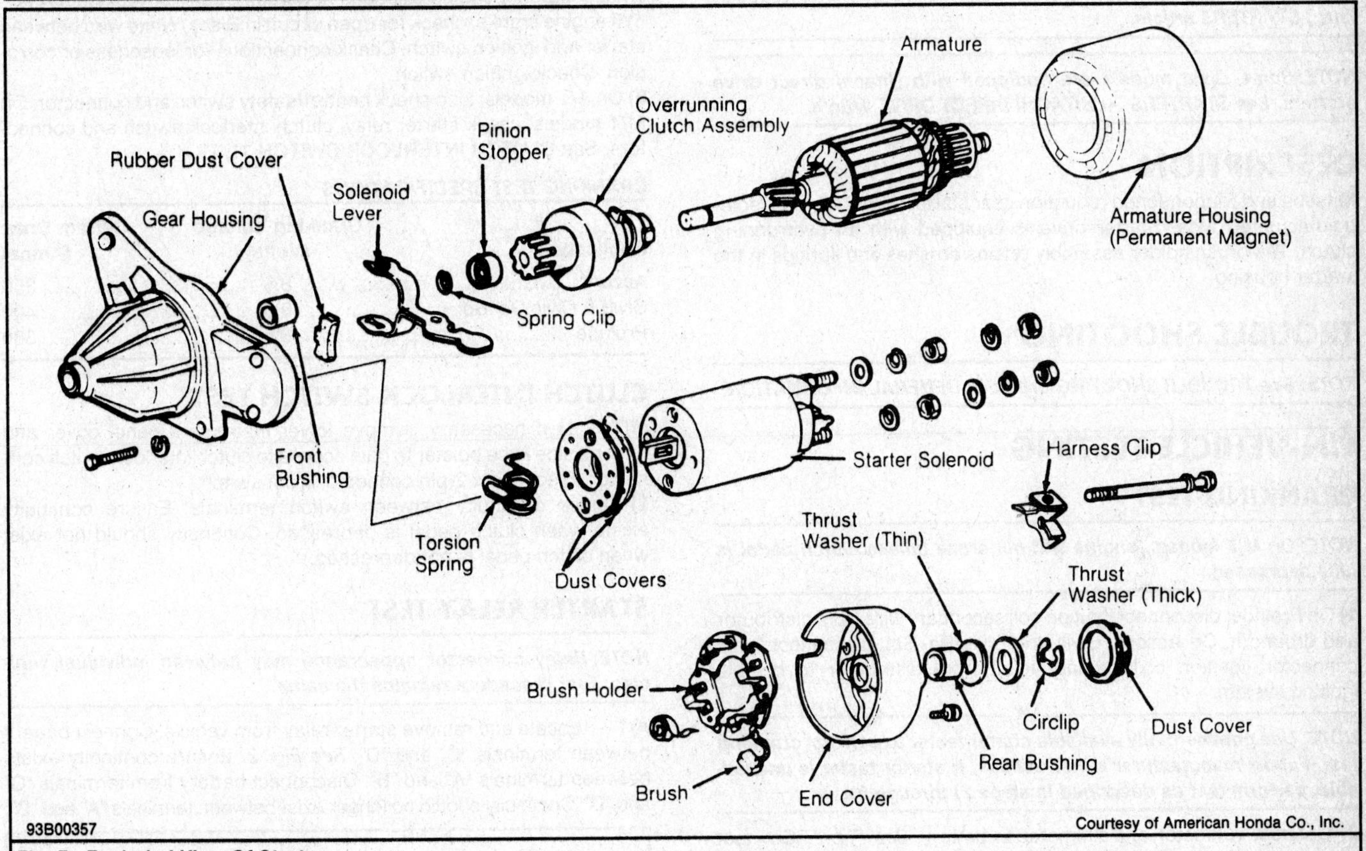

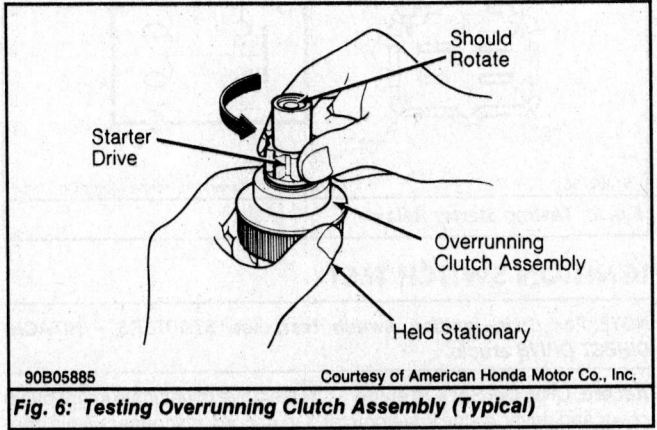

93B00357

Courtesy of American Honda Co., Inc.

Fig. 7: Exploded View Of Starter

90B05885   Courtesy of American Honda Motor Co., Inc.

Fig. 6: Testing Overrunning Clutch Assembly (Typical)

STARTER SPECIFICATIONS

STARTER SPECIFICATIONS

Application	Specification
Brush Length (Minimum)	.43" (10.9 mm)
Brush Spring Tension	2.9 Lbs. (1.3 kg)
Commutator Diameter (Minimum)	1.54" (39.1 mm)
Commutator Mica Depth (Minimum)	.008" (.20 mm)
Commutator Runout (Maximum)	.002" (.05 mm)

TORQUE SPECIFICATIONS

TORQUE SPECIFICATIONS

Application	Ft. Lbs. (N.m)
Starter Mounting Bolts	33 (45)

WIRING DIAGRAM

NOTE: See appropriate Wiring Diagram in STARTERS – Mitsuba & Nippondenso Reduction Gear article.

Accord, Civic, Civic Del Sol, Passport, Prelude

NOTE: *For starting system information on Passport, refer to Rodeo in Isuzu STARTERS article.*

NOTE: *Some Civic models are equipped with Hitachi direct drive starters. See STARTERS – HITACHI DIRECT DRIVE article.*

DESCRIPTION

Mitsuba and Nippondenso reduction gear starters are a 4-brush, solenoid-actuated type. Starter drive is equipped with an overrunning clutch. The brush holder assembly retains brushes and springs in the starter housing.

TROUBLE SHOOTING

NOTE: *See TROUBLE SHOOTING article in GENERAL INFORMATION.*

ON-VEHICLE TESTING

CRANKING TEST

NOTE: *On M/T models, engine will not crank unless clutch pedal is fully depressed.*

1) On Prelude, disconnect ignition coil secondary wire from distributor and ground it. On Accord, Civic and Civic Del Sol, disconnect 2-pin connector (ignition coil primary lead) from distributor to disable ignition system.

NOTE: *Use commercially available starter tester to perform cranking test. Follow manufacturer's instructions. If starter tester is unavailable, perform test as described in steps 2) through 6).*

2) Connect voltmeter and ammeter to battery. *See Fig. 1.* Connect tachometer to engine. Turn ignition switch to START position and crank engine. Check starter cranking voltage and current draw on appropriate meter. See CRANKING TEST SPECIFICATIONS table.

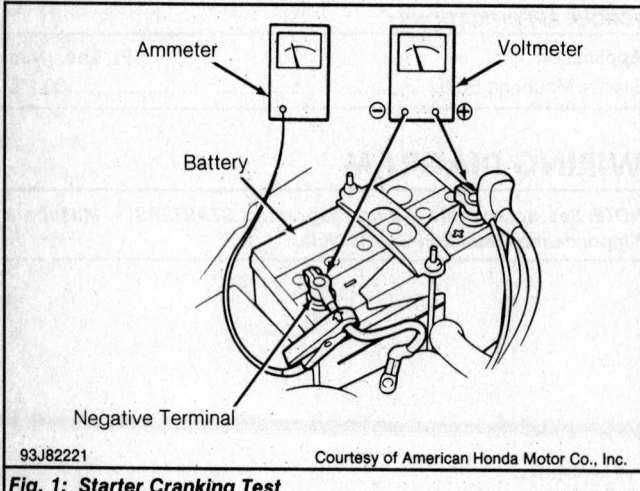

Fig. 1: *Starter Cranking Test*

3) If engine does not crank, check battery and battery cables. Check connections for looseness or corrosion. If engine still does not crank, by-pass ignition switch circuit as follows.

4) Disconnect Black/White wire from starter. Connect jumper wire from battery positive terminal to starter solenoid terminal. Engine should crank. If engine still does not crank, repair or replace starter.
5) If engine cranks, check for open circuit in Black/White wire between starter and ignition switch. Check connections for looseness or corrosion. Check ignition switch.
6) On A/T models, also check neutral/safety switch and connector. On M/T models, check starter relay, clutch interlock switch and connectors. See CLUTCH INTERLOCK SWITCH TEST.

CRANKING TEST SPECIFICATIONS

Application	Cranking Voltage (Volts)	Current Draw (Amps)
Accord	8.5	350
Civic & Civic Del Sol	8.0	400
Prelude	8.5	380

CLUTCH INTERLOCK SWITCH TEST

M/T – 1) If necessary, remove lower instrument panel cover and driver's side knee bolster to gain access to clutch interlock switch connector. Disconnect 2-pin connector from switch.
2) Check continuity between switch terminals. Ensure continuity exists when clutch pedal is depressed. Continuity should not exist when clutch pedal is not depressed.

STARTER RELAY TEST

NOTE: *Relay connector appearance may between individual vehicles. Test procedure remains the same.*

A/T – Locate and remove starter relay from vehicle. Connect battery between terminals "C" and "D". *See Fig. 2.* Ensure continuity exists between terminals "A" and "B". Disconnect battery from terminals "C" and "D". Continuity should no longer exist between terminals "A" and "B".

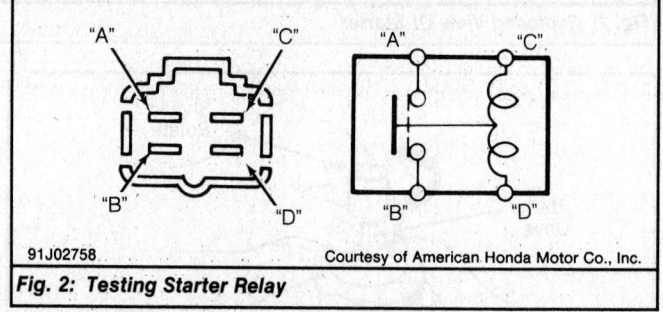

Fig. 2: *Testing Starter Relay*

IGNITION SWITCH TEST

NOTE: *For Civic ignition switch test, see STARTERS – HITACHI DIRECT DRIVE article.*

Accord, Civic Del Sol & Prelude – 1) Remove lower instrument panel cover and driver's side knee bolster. On Accord, disconnect 7-pin connector from dash fuse box. On Civic Del Sol, disconnect 5-pin connector from dash fuse box and 7-pin connector from main harness.
2) On Prelude, disconnect 6-pin connector from dash fuse box and 3-pin connector from main wire harness. *See Fig. 3 or 4.* Use an ohmmeter to check continuity at connector terminals with switch in indicated position. If continuity is not as specified, replace ignition switch.

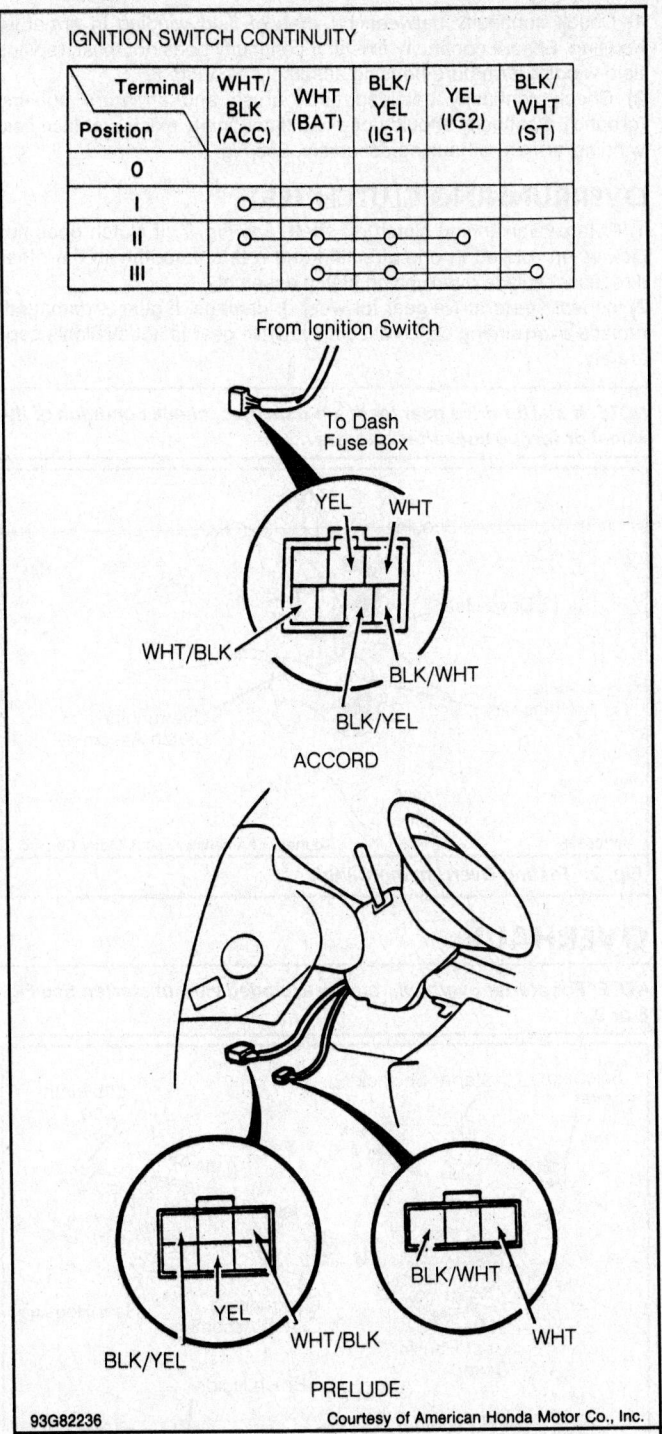

IGNITION SWITCH CONTINUITY

Terminal / Position	WHT/BLK (ACC)	WHT (BAT)	BLK/YEL (IG1)	YEL (IG2)	BLK/WHT (ST)
0					
I	○——○				
II	○——○		○——○		
III		○——○	○		○

From Ignition Switch

To Dash Fuse Box

YEL / WHT

WHT/BLK / BLK/WHT

BLK/YEL

ACCORD

BLK/YEL / YEL / WHT/BLK

BLK/WHT / WHT

PRELUDE

93G82236   Courtesy of American Honda Motor Co., Inc.

Fig. 3: Testing Ignition Switch Continuity (Accord & Prelude)

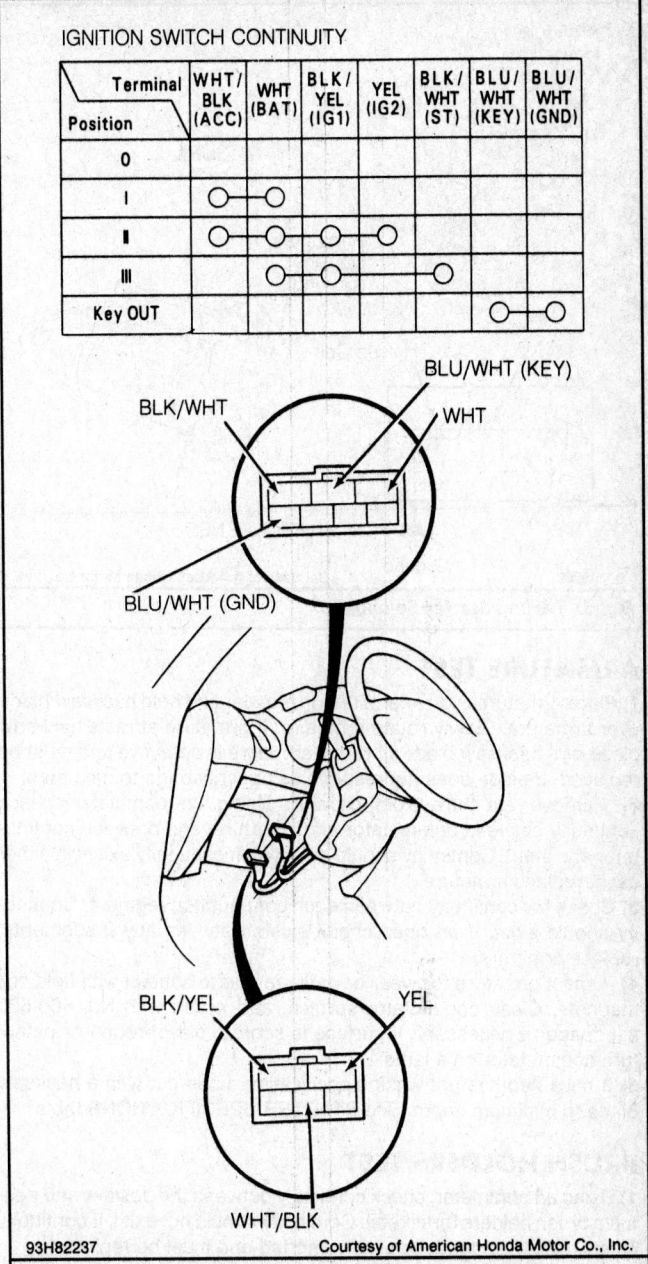

IGNITION SWITCH CONTINUITY

Terminal / Position	WHT/BLK (ACC)	WHT (BAT)	BLK/YEL (IG1)	YEL (IG2)	BLK/WHT (ST)	BLU/WHT (KEY)	BLU/WHT (GND)
0							
I	○——○						
II	○——○		○——○				
III		○——○	○		○		
Key OUT						○——○	

BLU/WHT (KEY)

BLK/WHT / WHT

BLU/WHT (GND)

BLK/YEL / YEL

WHT/BLK

93H82237   Courtesy of American Honda Motor Co., Inc.

Fig. 4: Testing Ignition Switch Continuity (Civic Del Sol)

BENCH TESTING

SOLENOID TESTS

Pull-In Test – Check continuity between starter solenoid terminals "S" and "M". See Fig. 5. If continuity exists, pull-in coil is okay. If continuity does not exist, replace starter solenoid.

Hold-In Test – Check continuity between terminal "S" and armature housing (ground). See Fig. 5. If continuity exists, hold-in coil is okay. If continuity does not exist, replace starter solenoid.

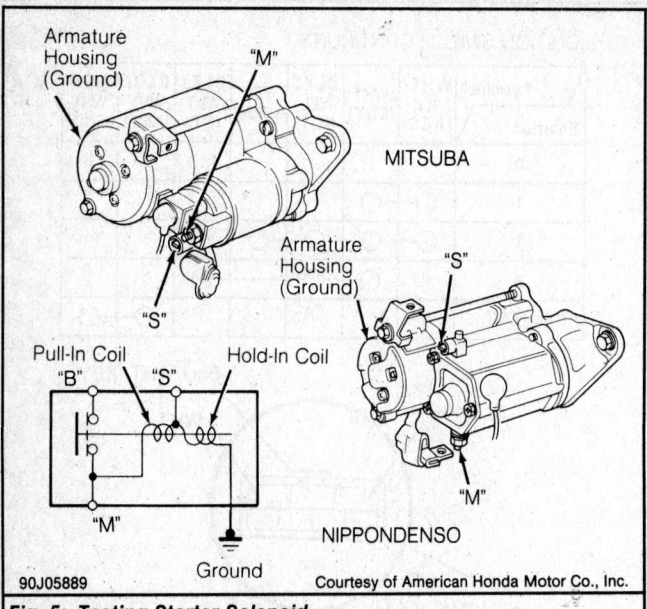

Fig. 5: Testing Starter Solenoid

ARMATURE TEST

1) Place armature in growler. Turn on growler and hold hacksaw blade over armature. Slowly rotate armature. If armature attracts hacksaw blade or if hacksaw blade vibrates, armature is defective and must be replaced. If blade does not respond as described, go to next step.

2) Remove armature from growler. Using an ohmmeter, check continuity between commutator and armature, and between commutator and shaft. Continuity should not exist. If continuity exists in either case, replace armature.

3) Check for continuity between each commutator segment. Continuity should exist. If an open circuit exists between any 2 segments, replace armature.

4) Inspect armature for wear or damage due to contact with field coil magnets. Clean commutator surface, and polish with No. 500-600 sandpaper if necessary. If surface is scored, out-of-round or pitted, turn commutator on a lathe.

5) If mica depth is not within specification, undercut with a hacksaw blade to minimum depth. See STARTER SPECIFICATIONS table.

BRUSH HOLDERS TEST

1) Using an ohmmeter, check continuity between the positive and negative brush holders (brackets). Continuity should not exist. If continuity exists, brush holder assembly is shorted and must be replaced.

2) Check brush length and spring tension. If brush length or spring tension is less than specification, replace brushes. See STARTER SPECIFICATIONS table. Ensure brushes move freely in holders.

FIELD WINDINGS TEST

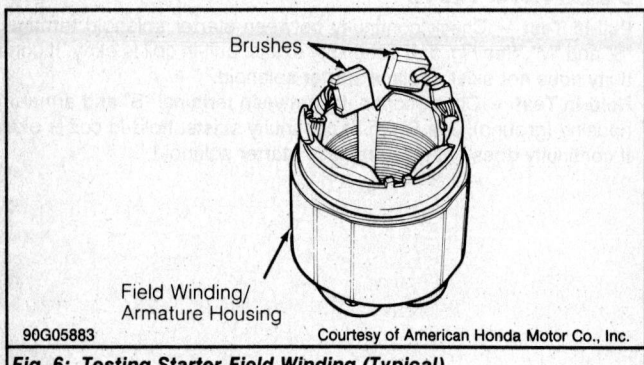

Fig. 6: Testing Starter Field Winding (Typical)

1) Check continuity between brushes of field winding in armature housing. Ensure continuity exists. If continuity does not exist, replace field winding/armature housing assembly. See Fig. 6.

2) Check continuity between each brush and armature housing (ground). Continuity should not exist. If continuity exists, replace field winding/armature housing assembly. See Fig. 6.

OVERRUNNING CLUTCH TEST

1) Rotate overrunning clutch on shaft. See Fig. 7. If clutch does not lock when rotated in one direction and rotate smoothly in the other direction, replace overrunning clutch assembly.

2) Inspect starter drive gear for wear or damage. If gear is damaged, replace overrunning clutch assembly. Drive gear is not available separately.

NOTE: If starter drive gear teeth are damaged, check condition of flywheel or torque converter ring gear.

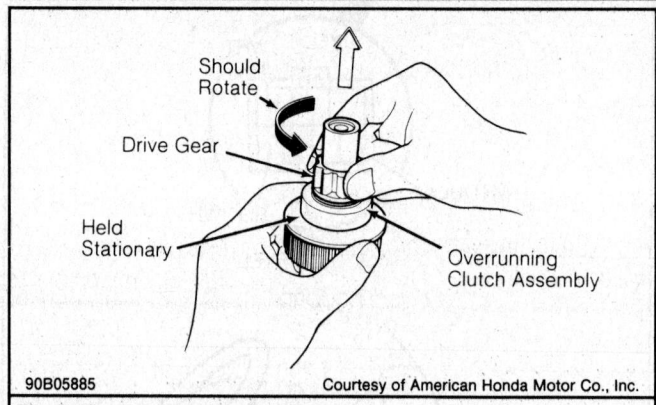

Fig. 7: Testing Overrunning Clutch

OVERHAUL

NOTE: For starter overhaul, refer to exploded view of starter. See Fig. 8 or 9.

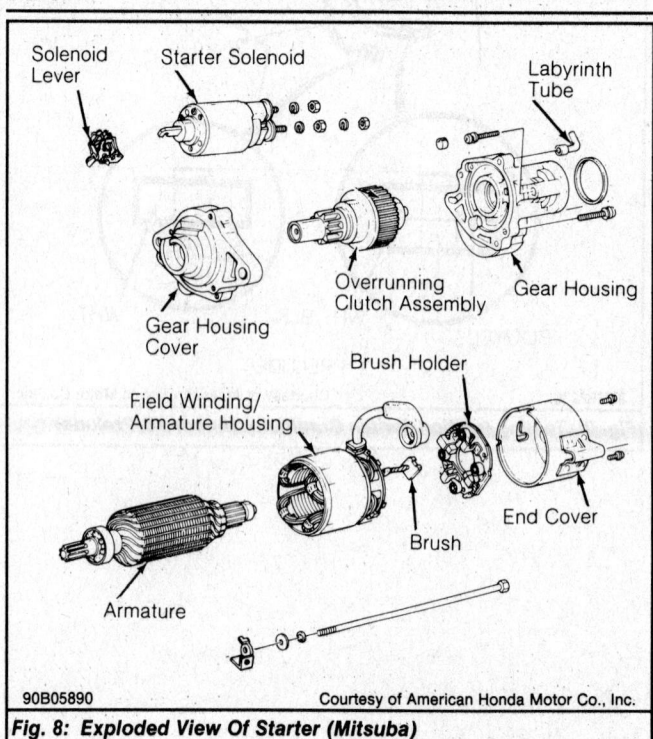

Fig. 8: Exploded View Of Starter (Mitsuba)

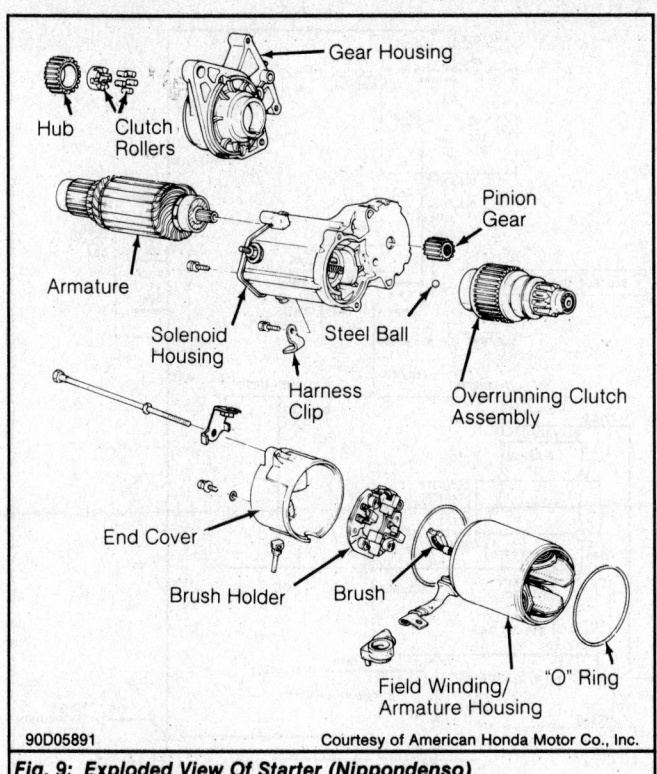

Fig. 9: Exploded View Of Starter (Nippondenso)

90D05891 — Courtesy of American Honda Motor Co., Inc.

STARTER SPECIFICATIONS

STARTER SPECIFICATIONS

Application	Specification
Brush Length (Minimum)	
Accord & Prelude	
Mitsuba	.43" (11.0 mm)
Nippondenso	.39" (10.0 mm)
Civic	
Mitsuba	
1.0 & 1.2 KW	.37" (9.3 mm)
1.4 KW	.43" (11.0 mm)
Nippondenso	.33" (8.5 mm)
Civic Del Sol	
Mitsuba	.37" (9.3 mm)
Nippondenso	.33" (8.5 mm)
Brush Spring Tension	
Mitsuba	
Accord & Prelude	3.5-4.0 Lbs. (1.6-1.8 kg)
Civic & Civic Del Sol	
1.0 & 1.2 KW	4.1-5.2 Lbs. (1.9-2.4 kg)
1.4 KW	3.5-4.0 Lbs. (1.6-1.8 kg)
Nippondenso	
Accord	3.7-5.3 Lbs. (1.7-2.4 kg)
Civic & Civic Del Sol	
1.0 KW	3.7-5.3 Lbs. (1.7-2.4 kg)
1.2 KW	2.3-4.6 Lbs. (1.3-2.1 kg)
Commutator Diameter (Minimum)	
Mitsuba	1.08" (27.5 mm)
Nippondenso	1.14" (29.0 mm)
Commutator Mica Depth (Minimum)	
Mitsuba	.006" (.15 mm)
Nippondenso	.008" (.20 mm)
Commutator Runout (Maximum)	.002" (.05 mm)

TORQUE SPECIFICATIONS

TORQUE SPECIFICATIONS

Application	Ft. Lbs. (N.m)
Starter Mounting Bolts	33 (45)

WIRING DIAGRAMS

NOTE: For circuit information on Civic models equipped with Hitachi direct drive starters, see STARTERS – HITACHI DIRECT DRIVE article.

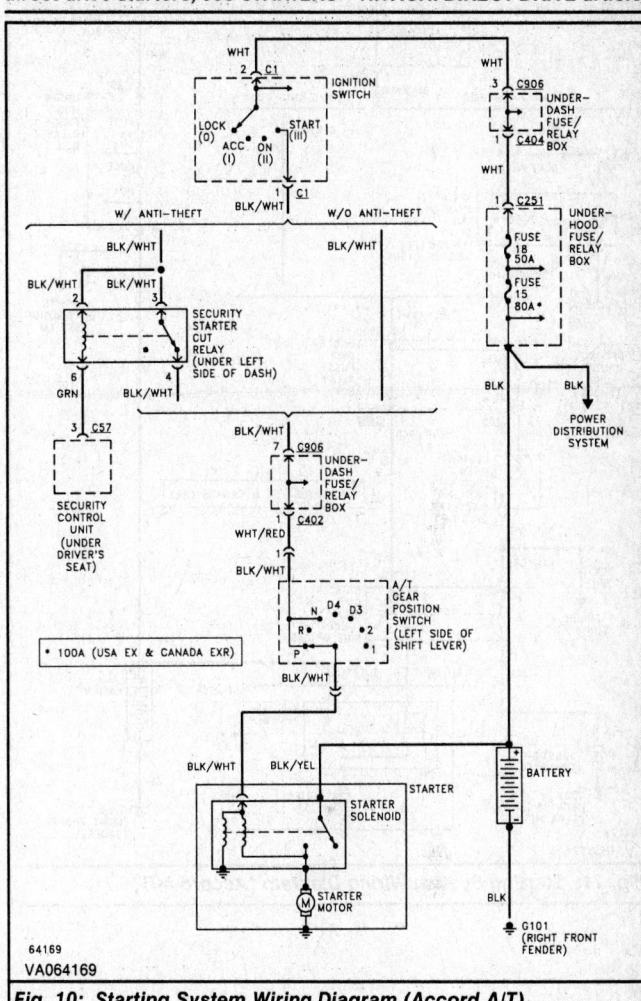

Fig. 10: Starting System Wiring Diagram (Accord A/T)

64169
VA064169

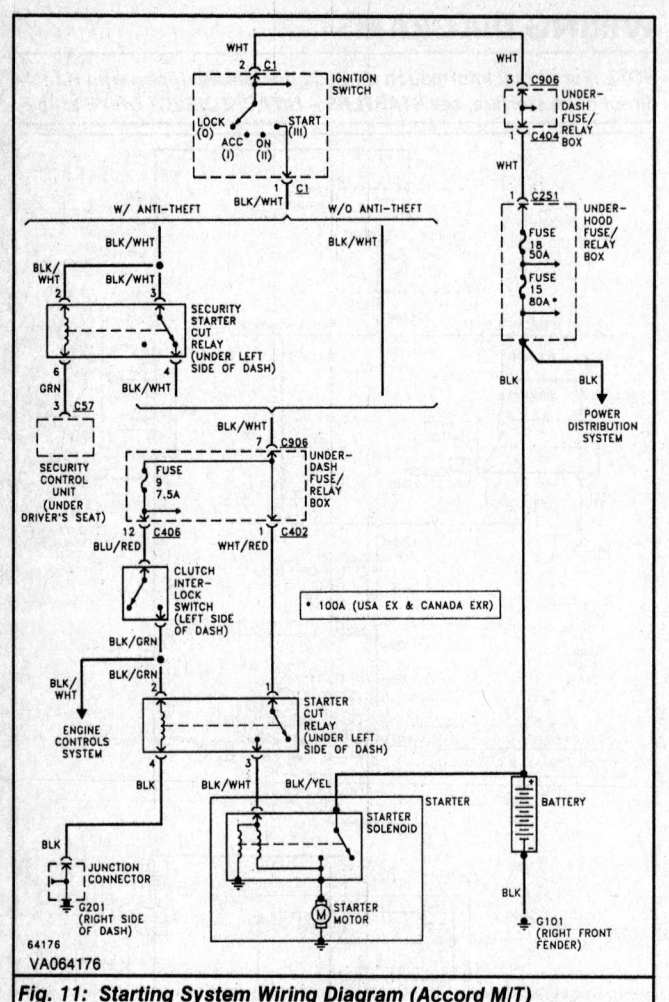

Fig. 11: *Starting System Wiring Diagram (Accord M/T)*

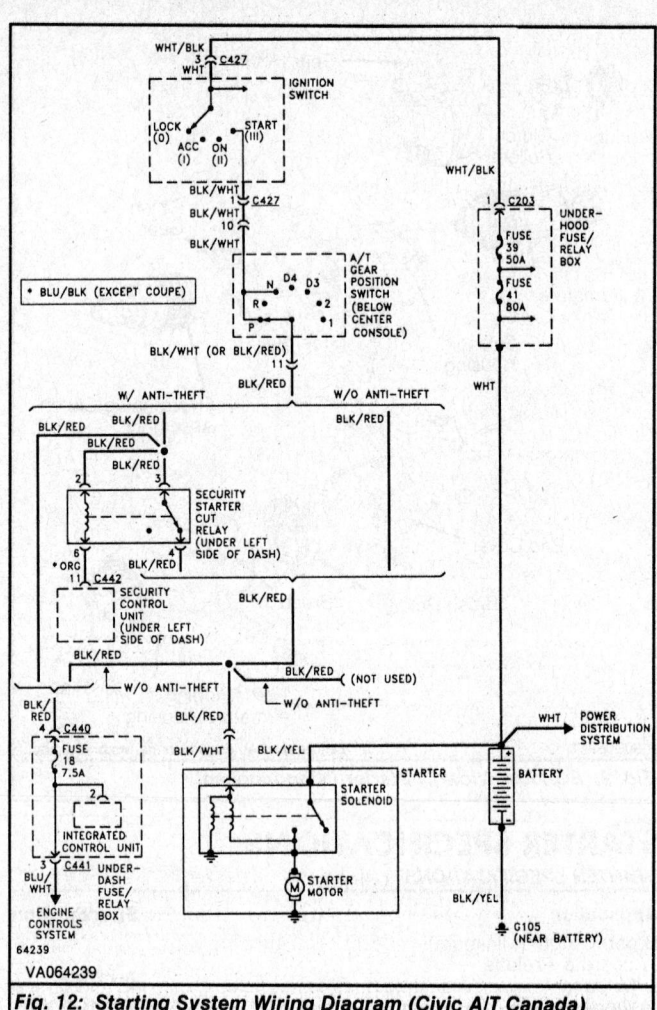

Fig. 12: *Starting System Wiring Diagram (Civic A/T Canada)*

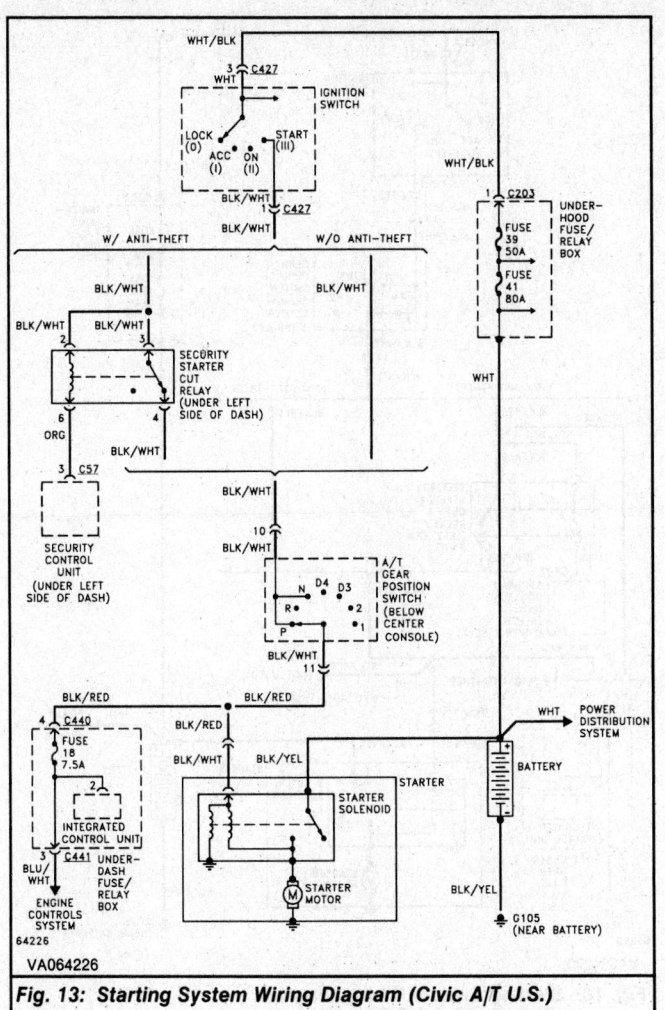

Fig. 13: Starting System Wiring Diagram (Civic A/T U.S.)

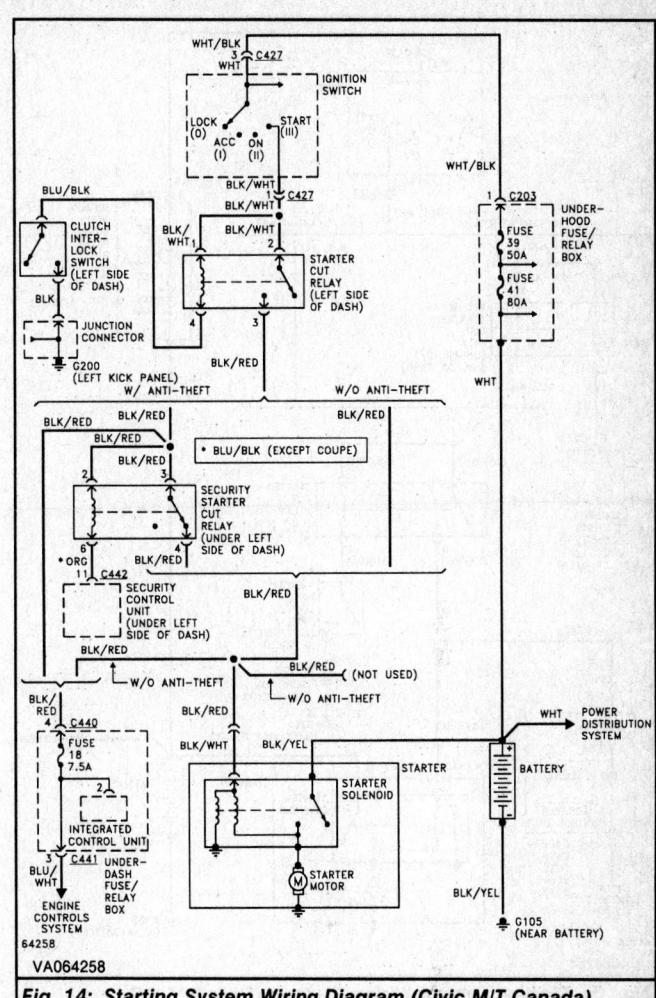

Fig. 14: Starting System Wiring Diagram (Civic M/T Canada)

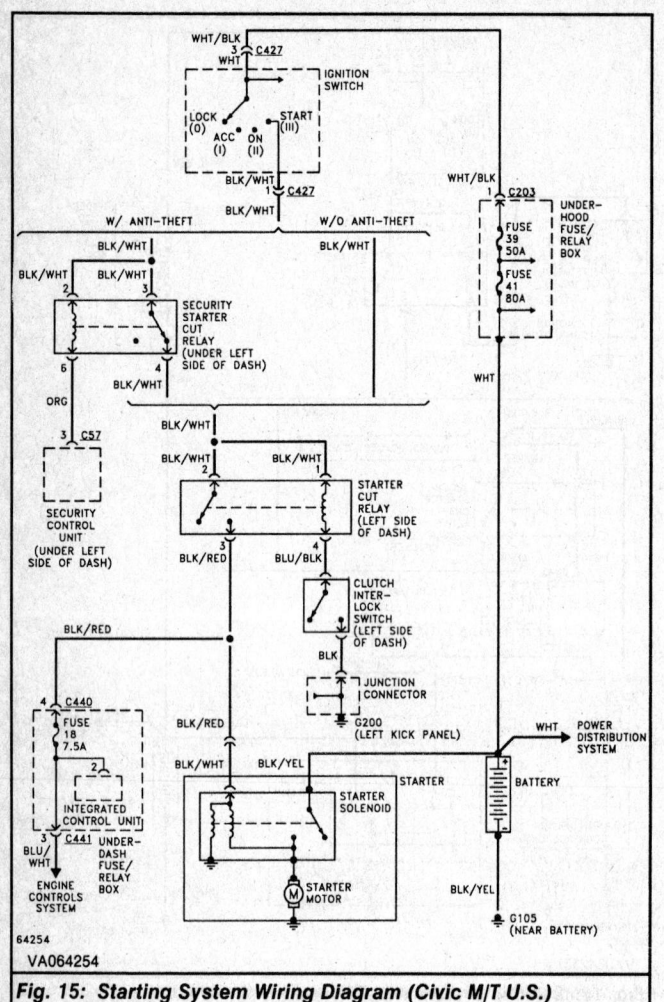

Fig. 15: Starting System Wiring Diagram (Civic M/T U.S.)

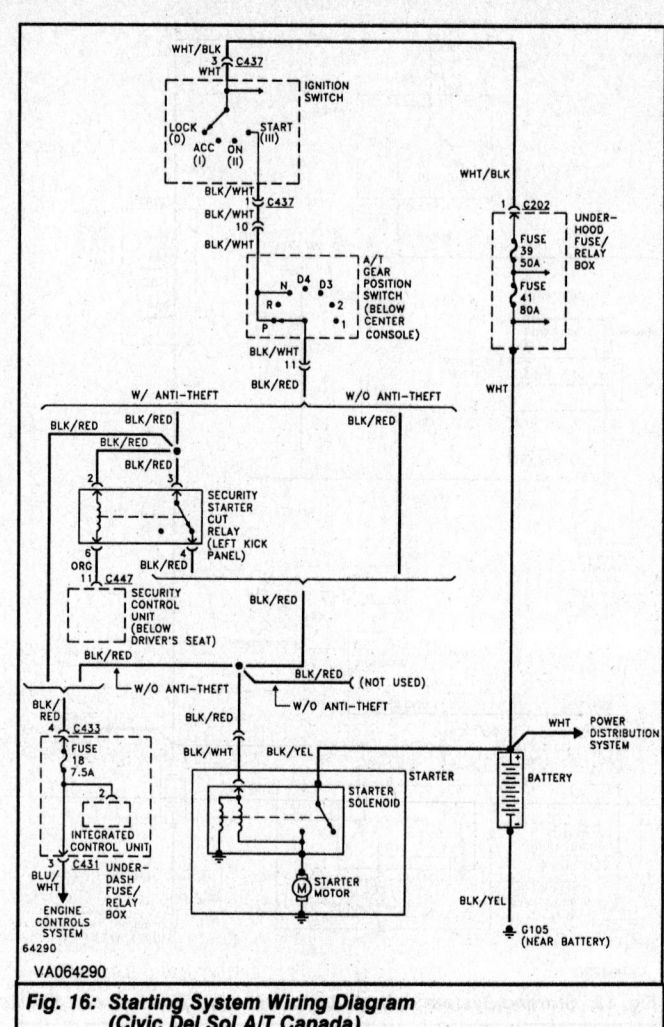

Fig. 16: Starting System Wiring Diagram (Civic Del Sol A/T Canada)

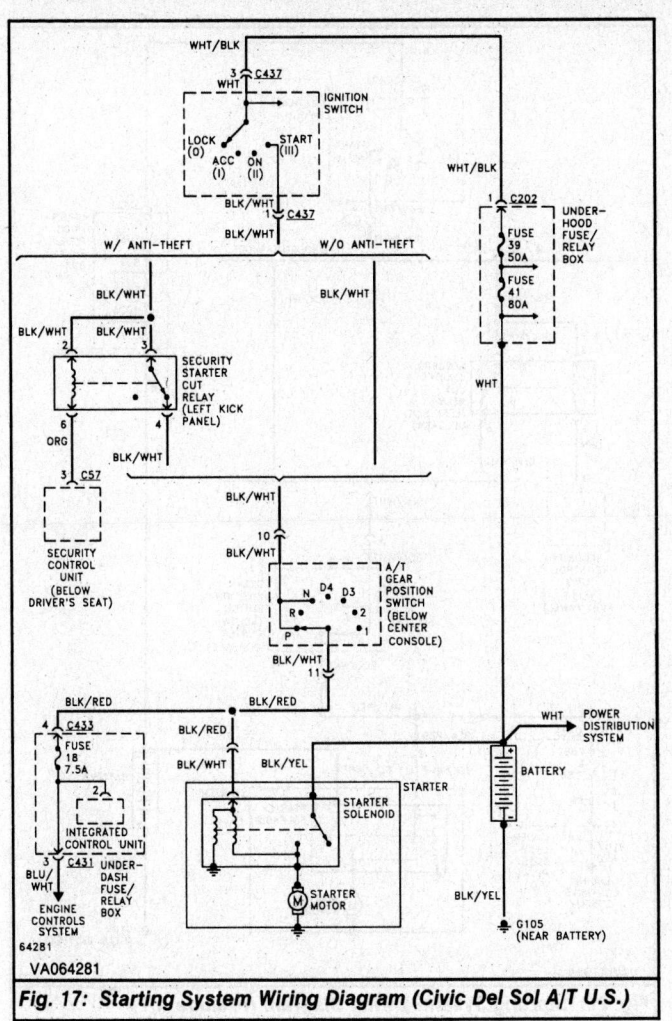

Fig. 17: Starting System Wiring Diagram (Civic Del Sol A/T U.S.)

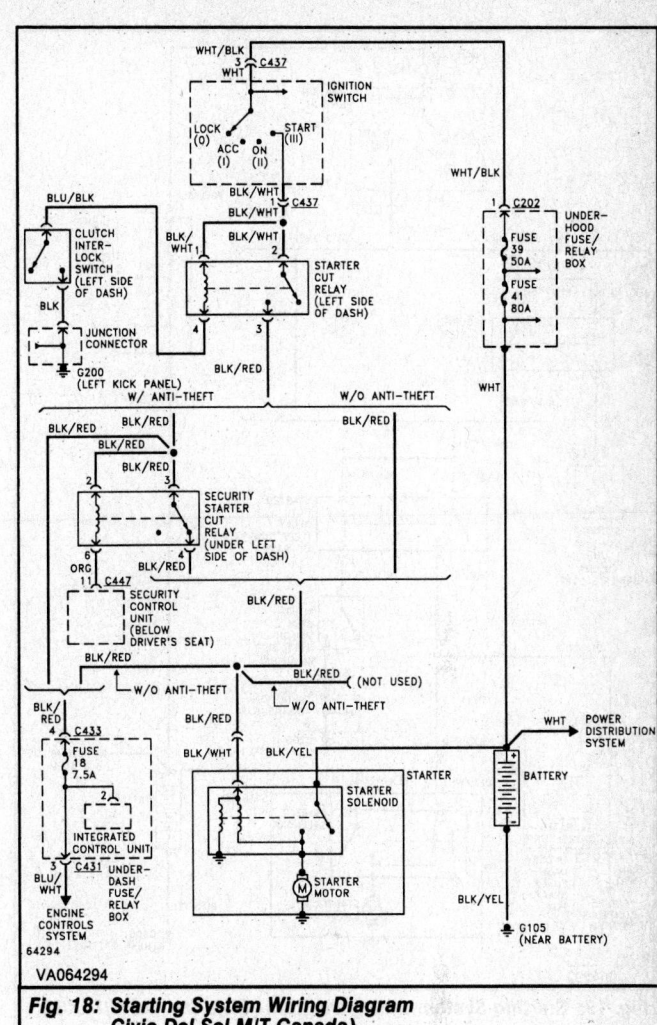

Fig. 18: Starting System Wiring Diagram Civic Del Sol M/T Canada)

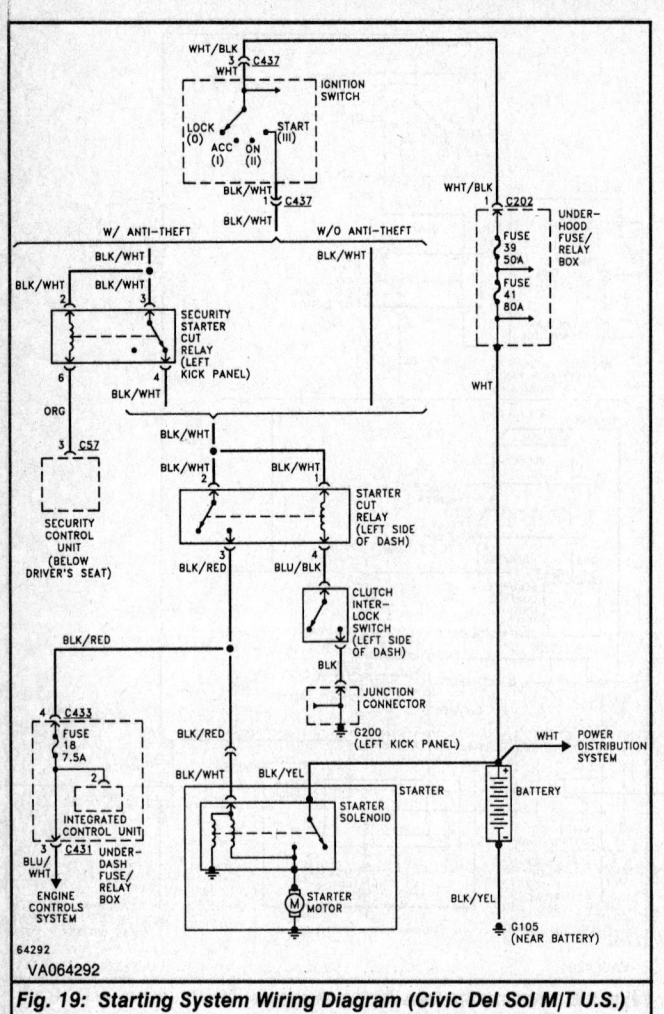

Fig. 19: Starting System Wiring Diagram (Civic Del Sol M/T U.S.)

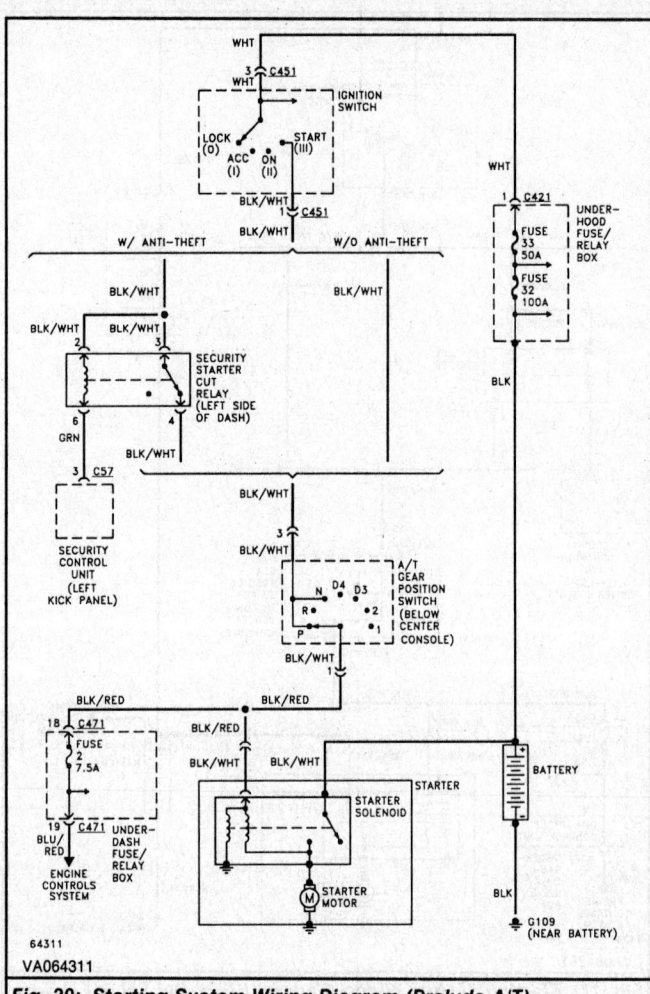

Fig. 20: Starting System Wiring Diagram (Prelude A/T)

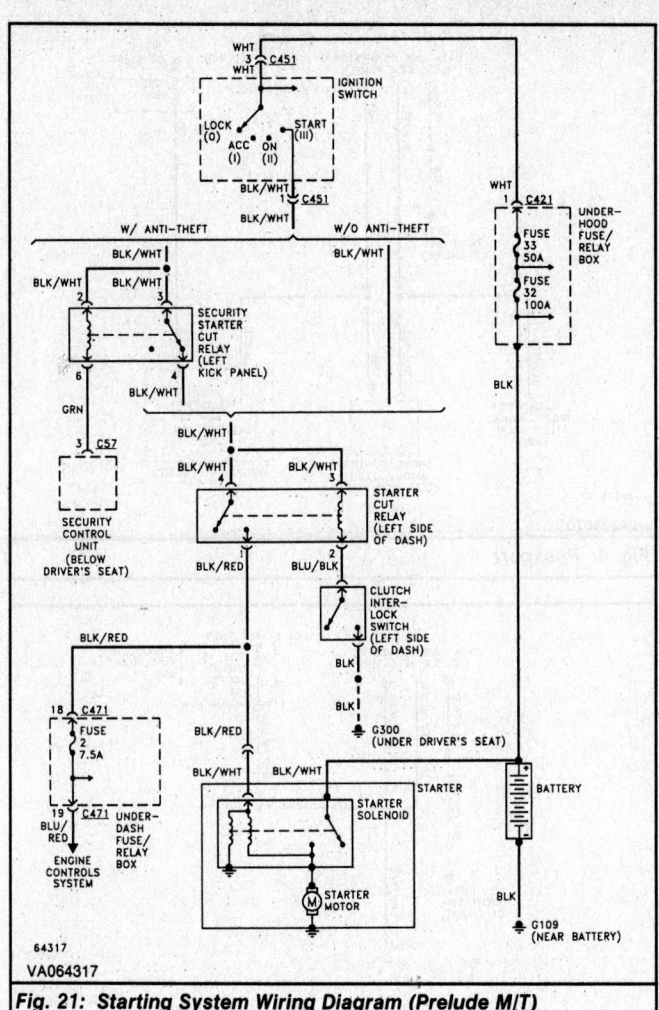

Fig. 21: Starting System Wiring Diagram (Prelude M/T)

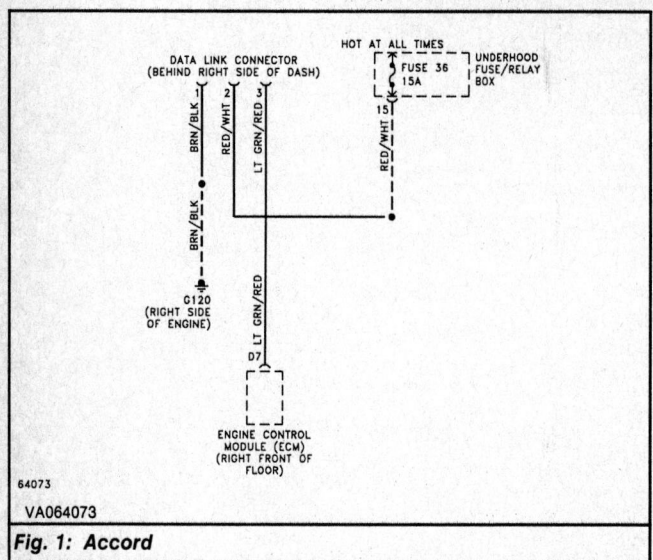

Fig. 1: Accord

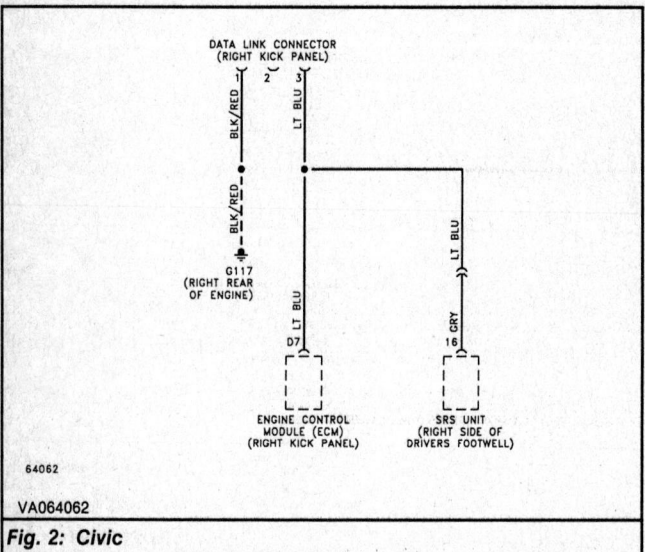

Fig. 2: Civic

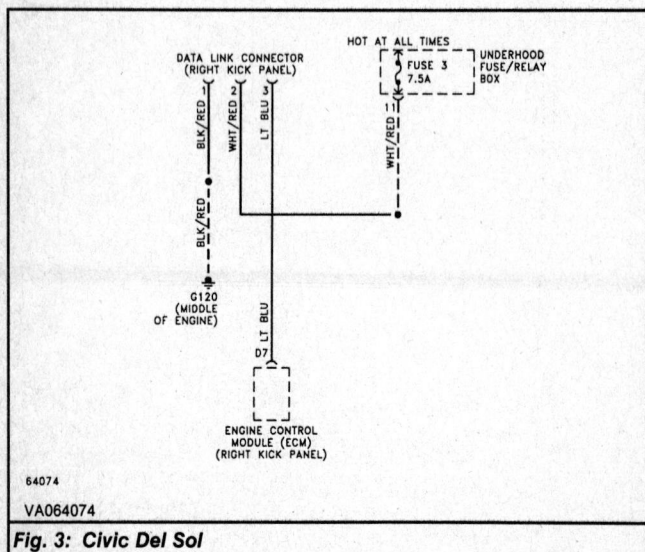

Fig. 3: Civic Del Sol

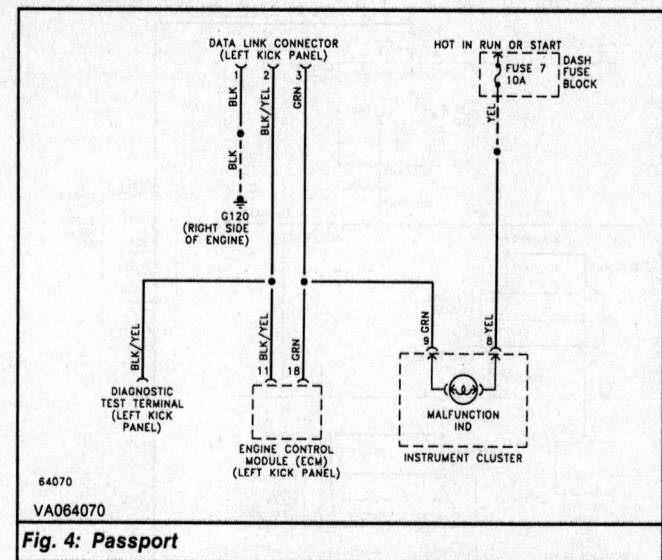

Fig. 4: Passport

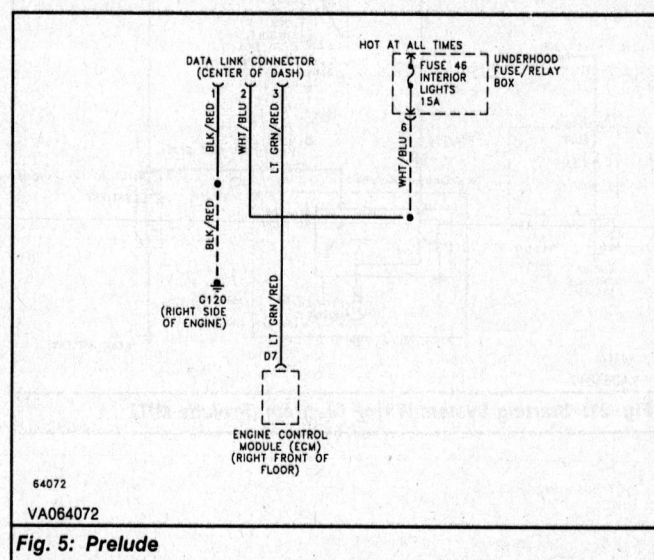

Fig. 5: Prelude

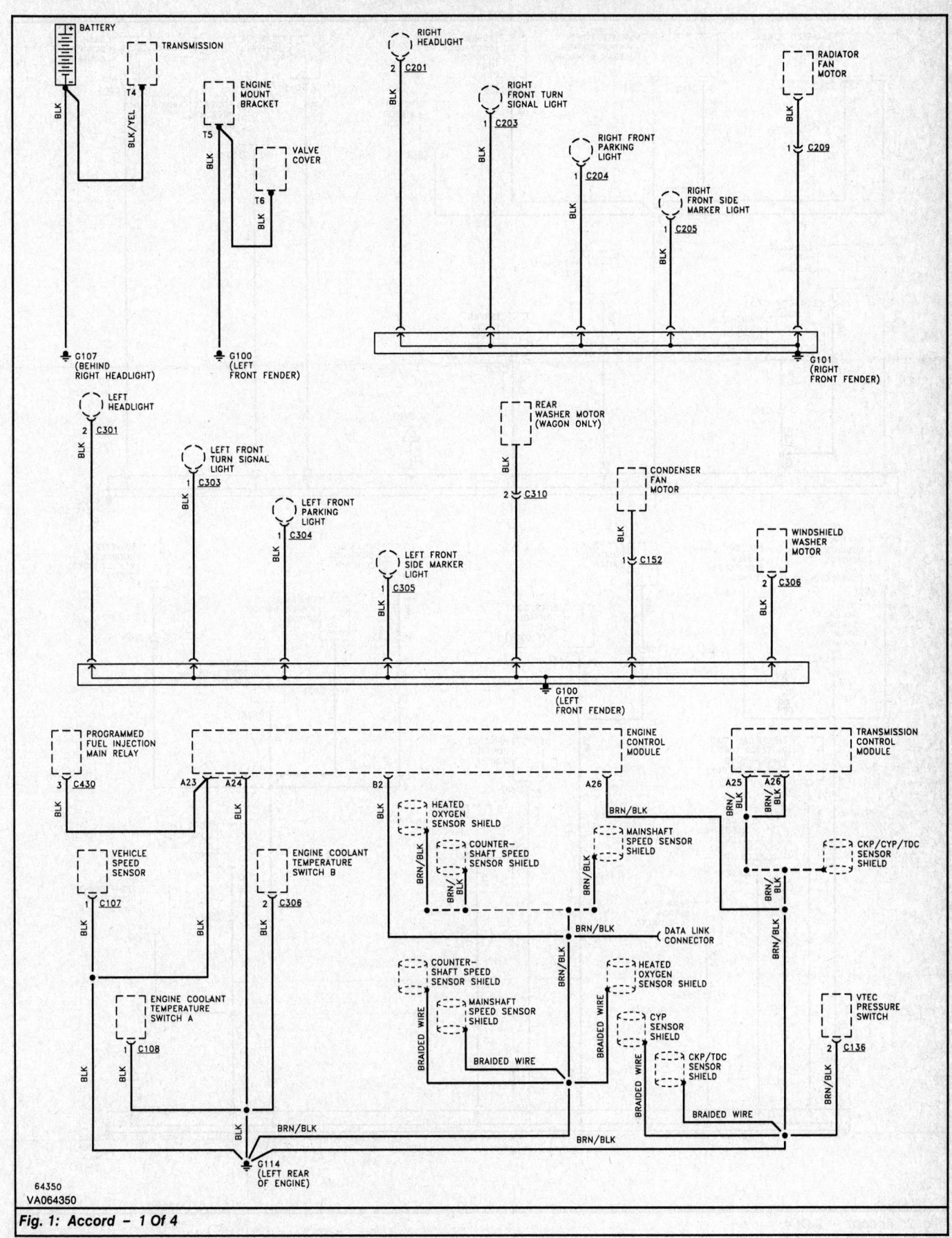

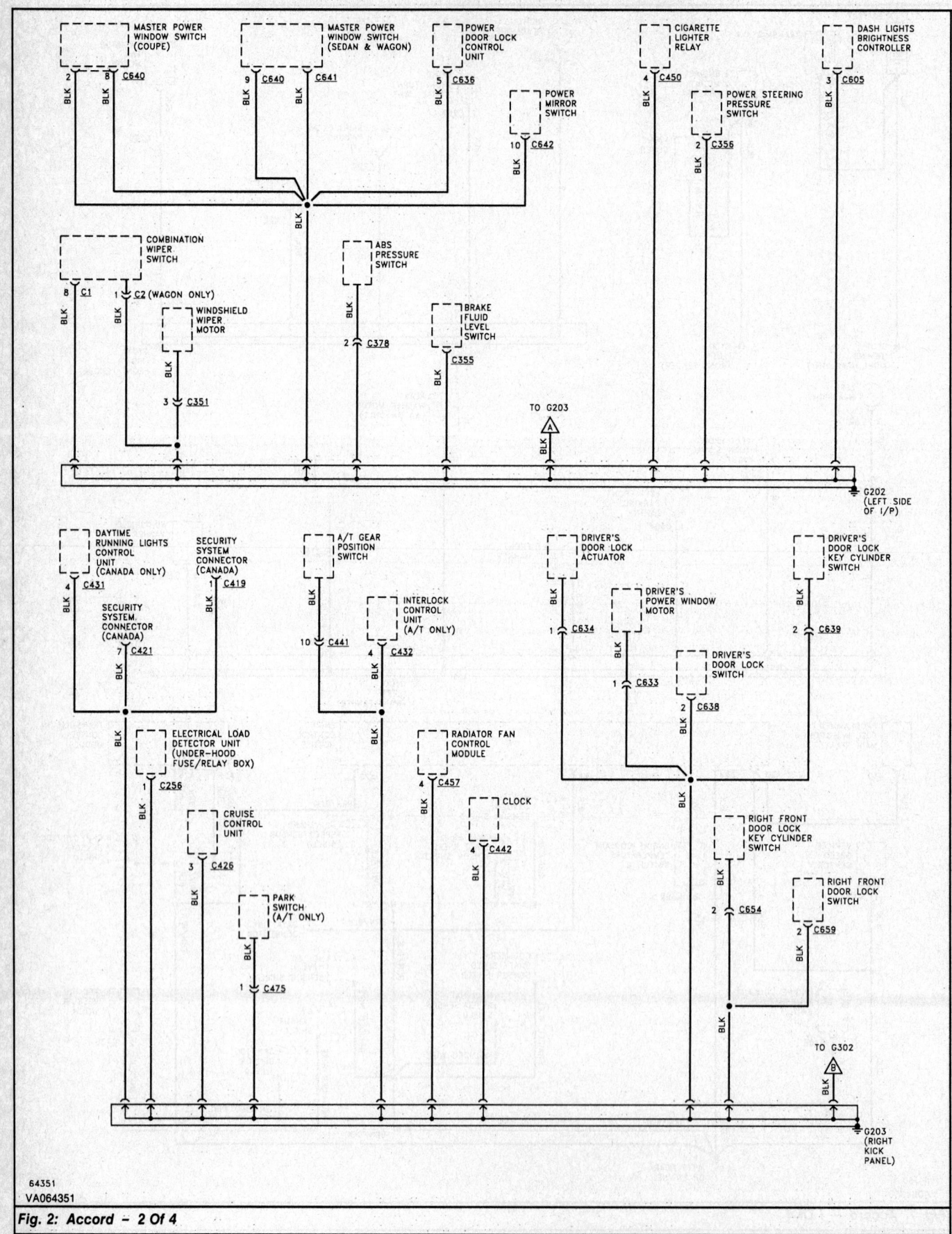

64351
VA064351

Fig. 2: Accord – 2 Of 4

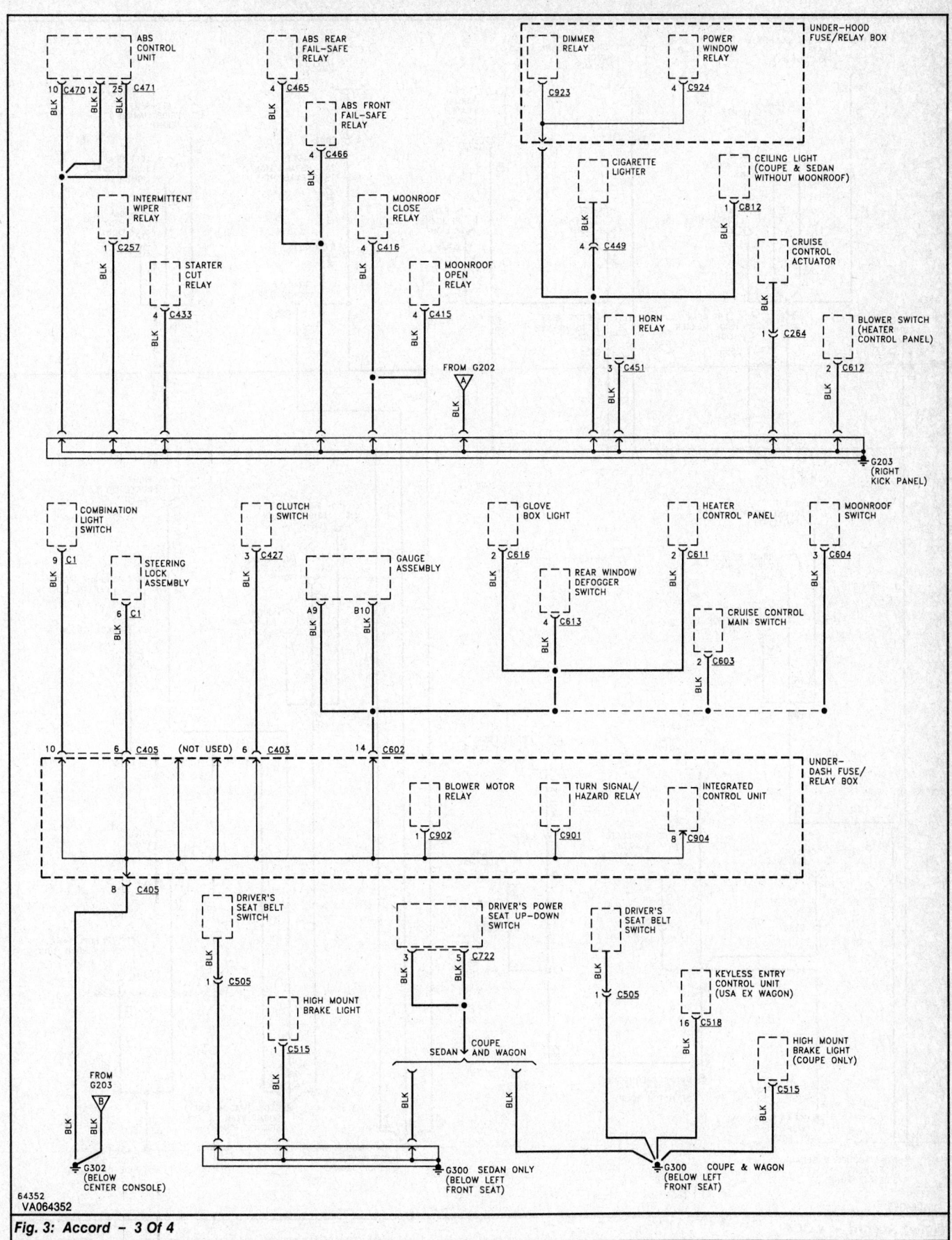

64352
VA064352

Fig. 3: Accord – 3 Of 4

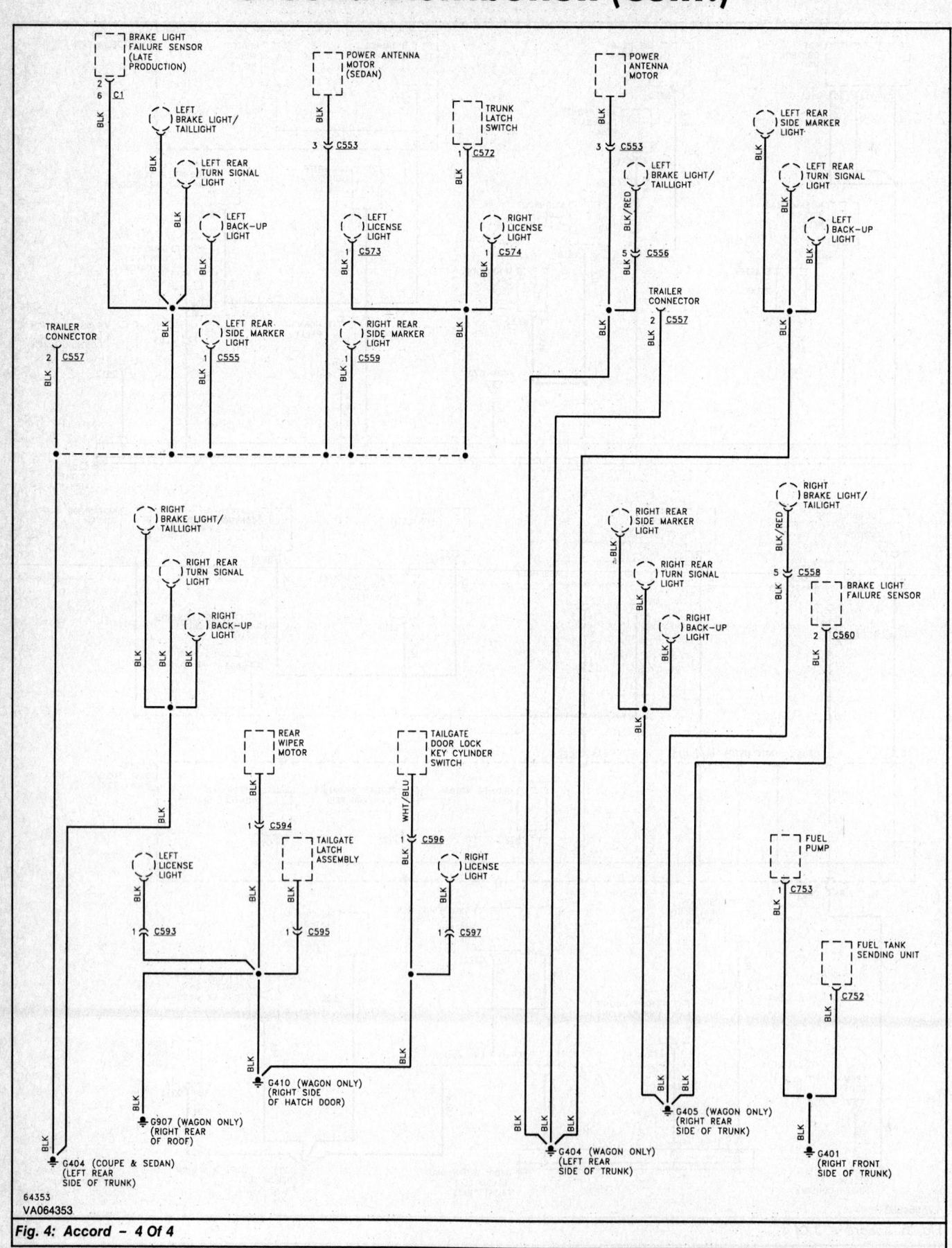

Fig. 4: Accord – 4 Of 4

64353
VA064353

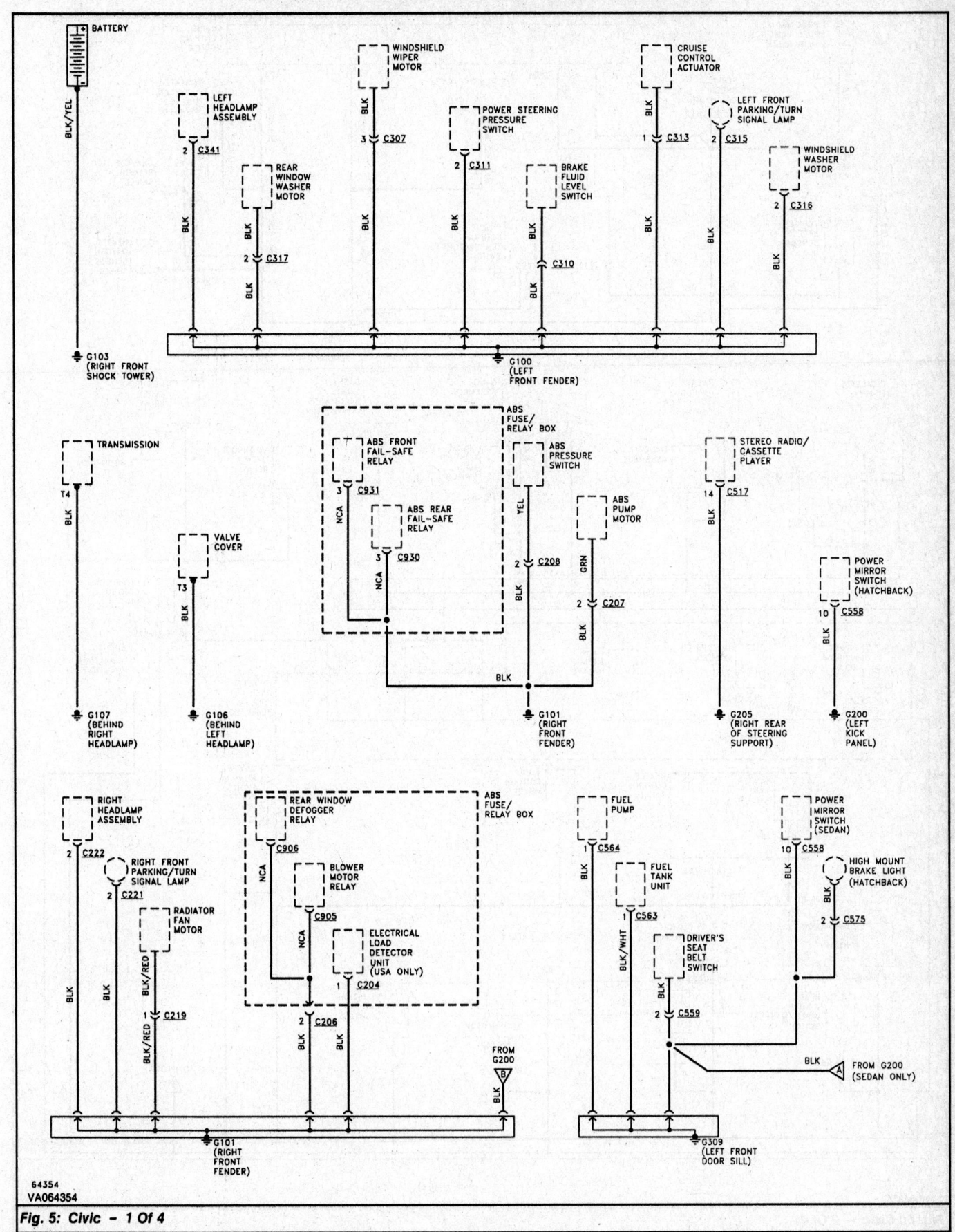

Fig. 5: Civic - 1 Of 4

64354
VA064354

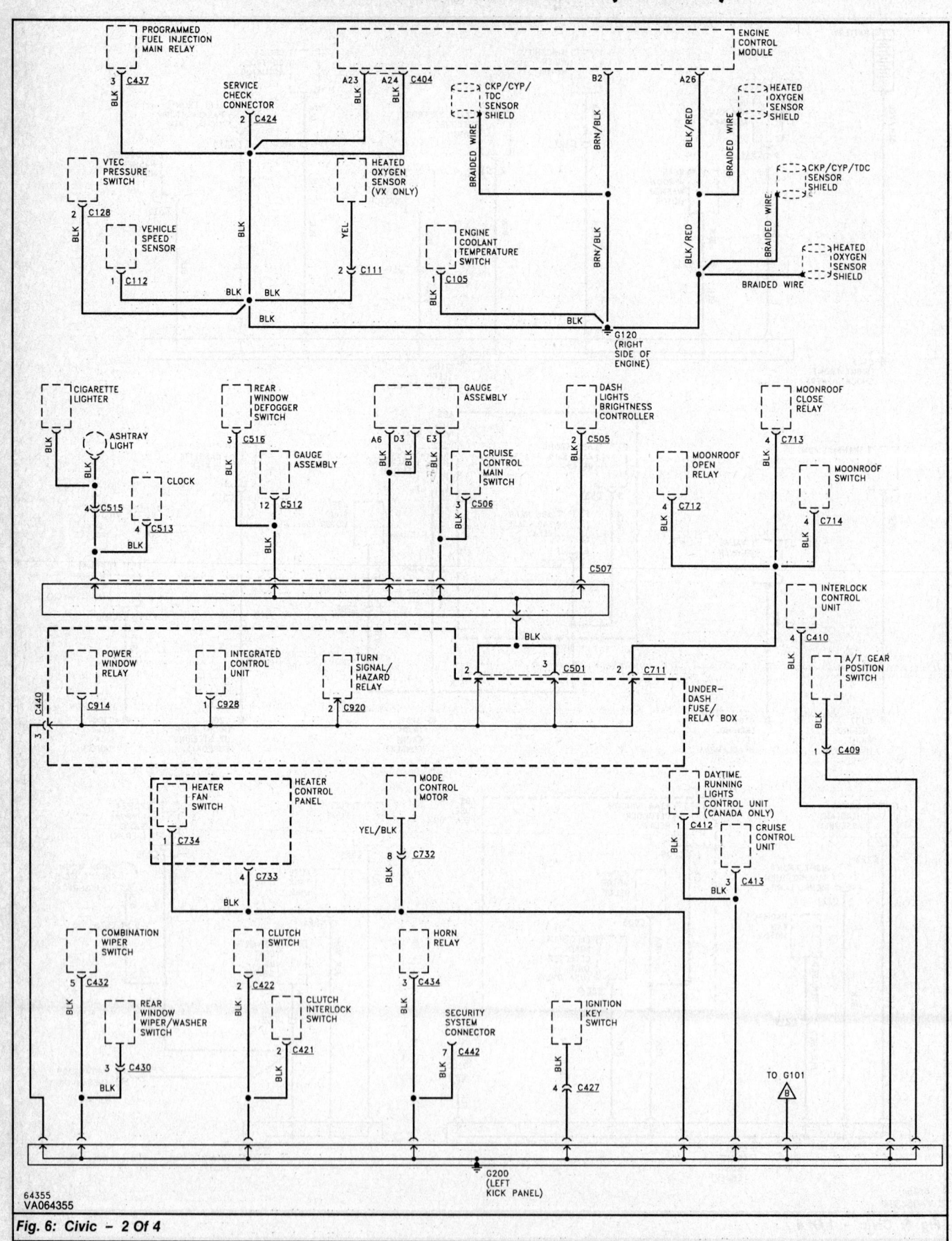

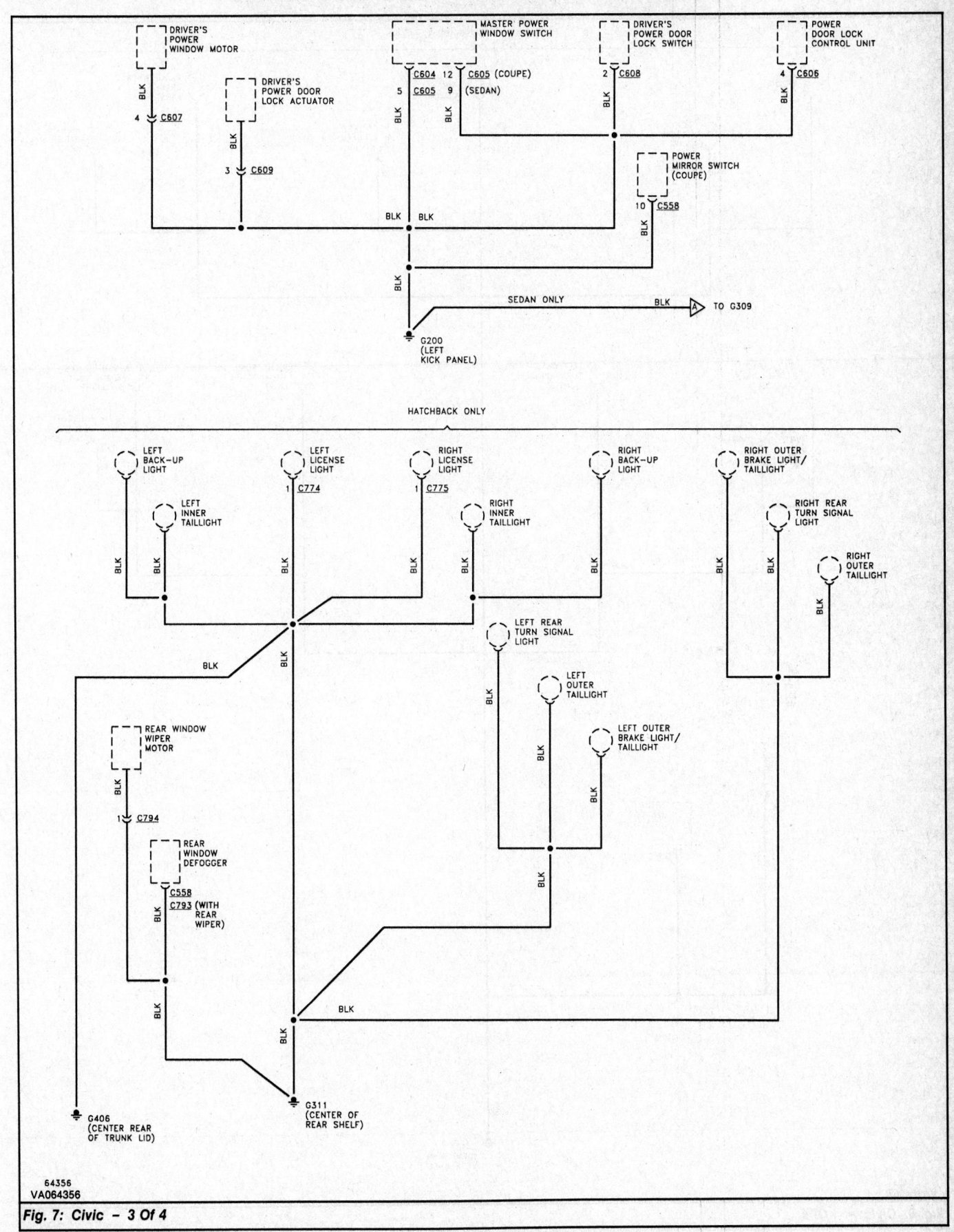

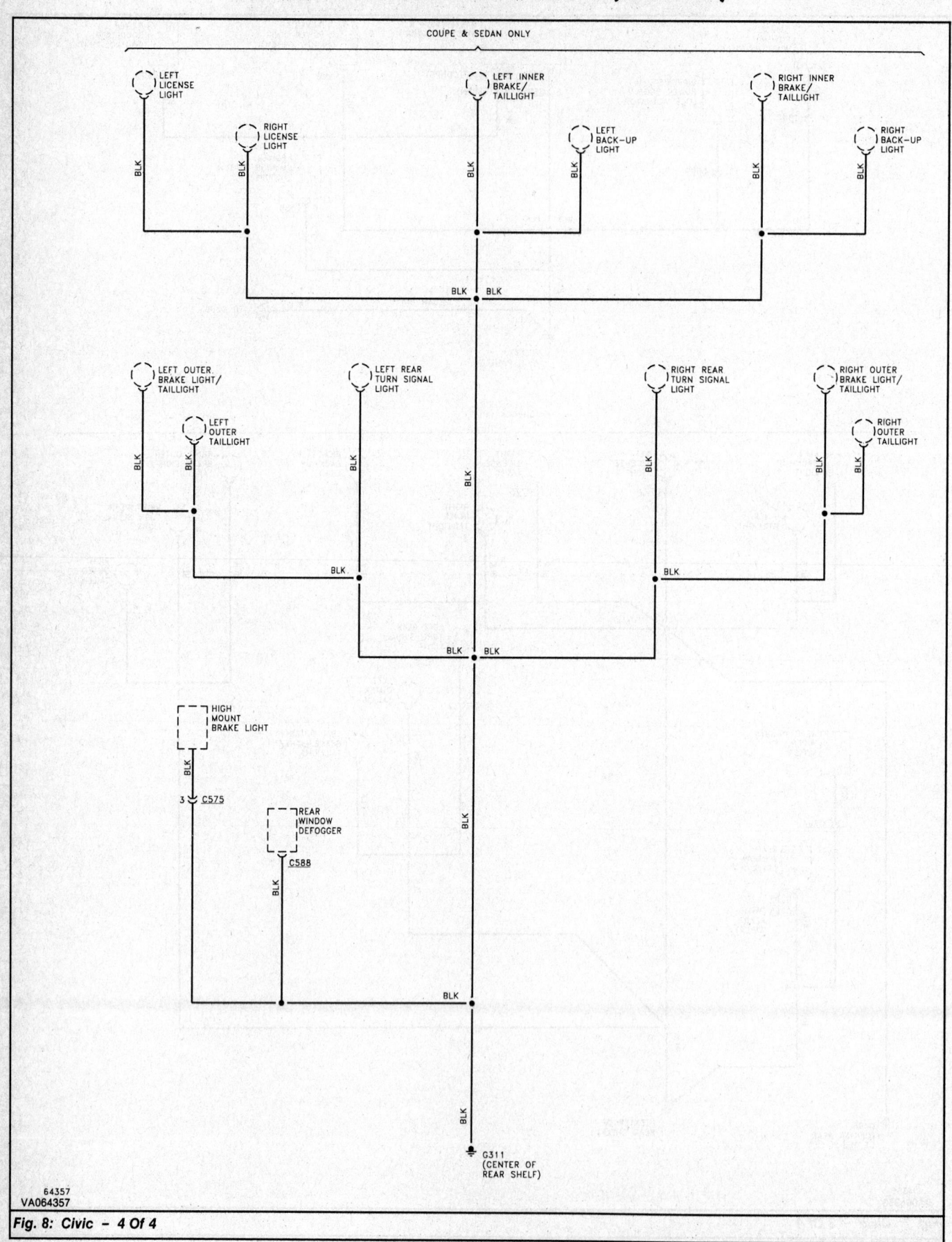

64357
VA064357

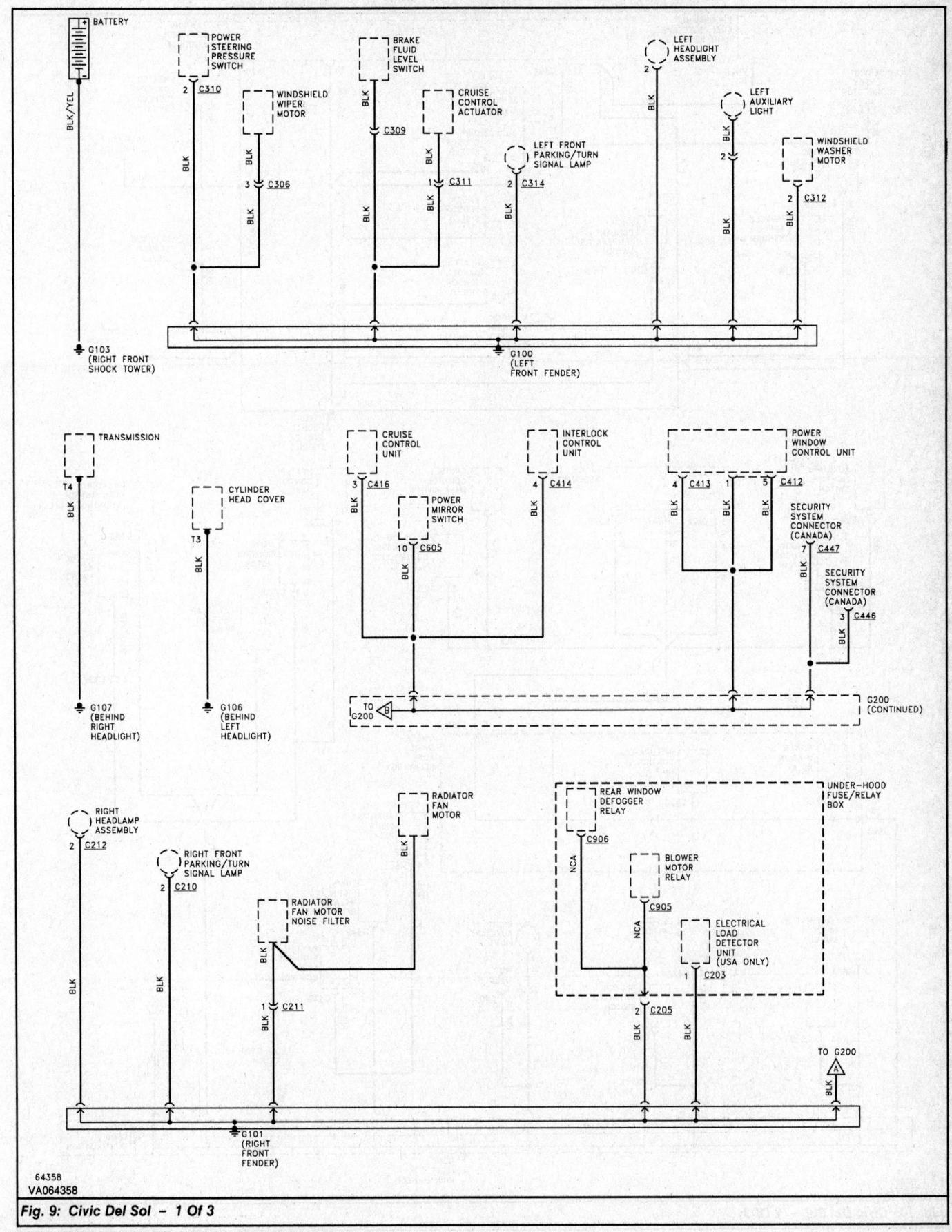

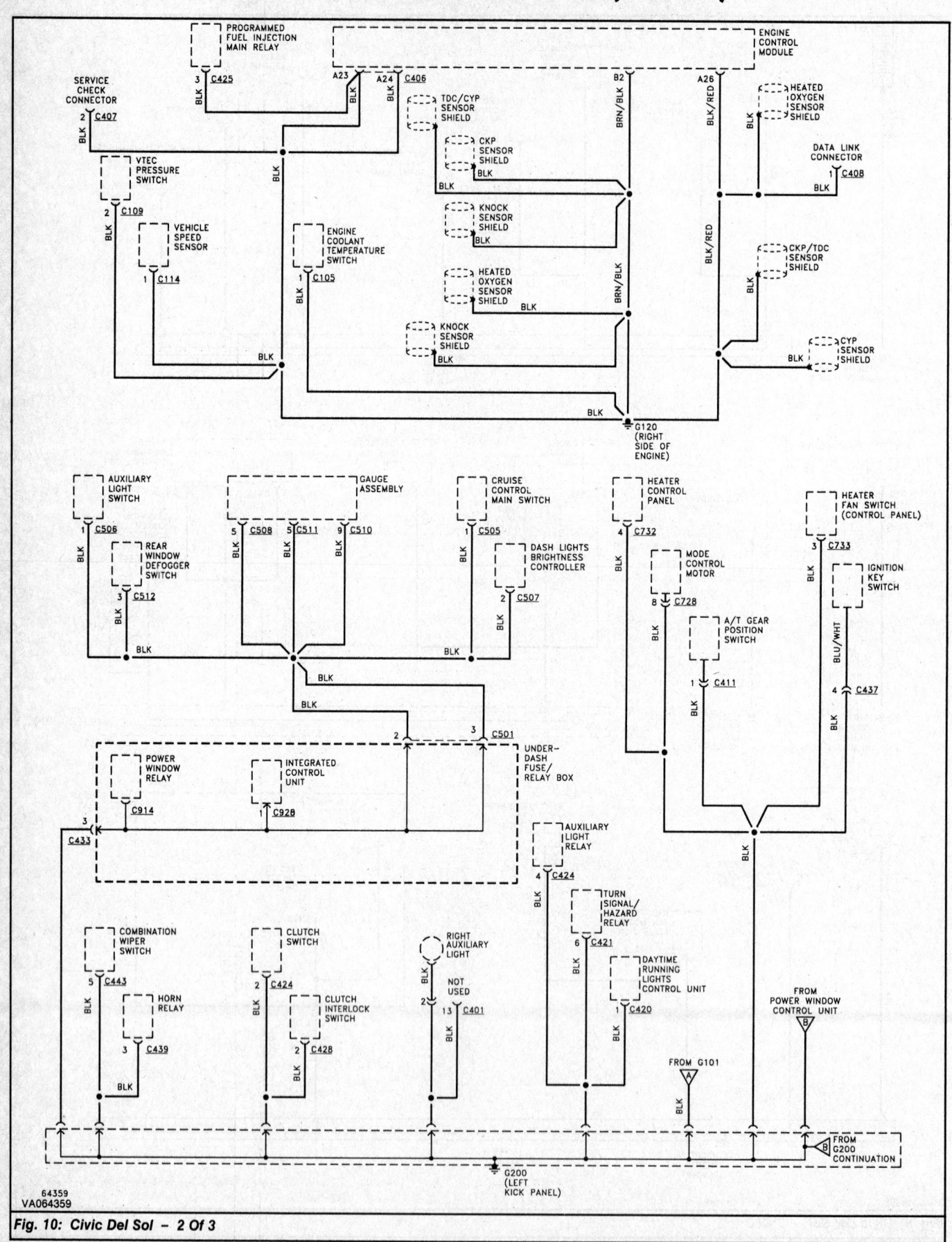

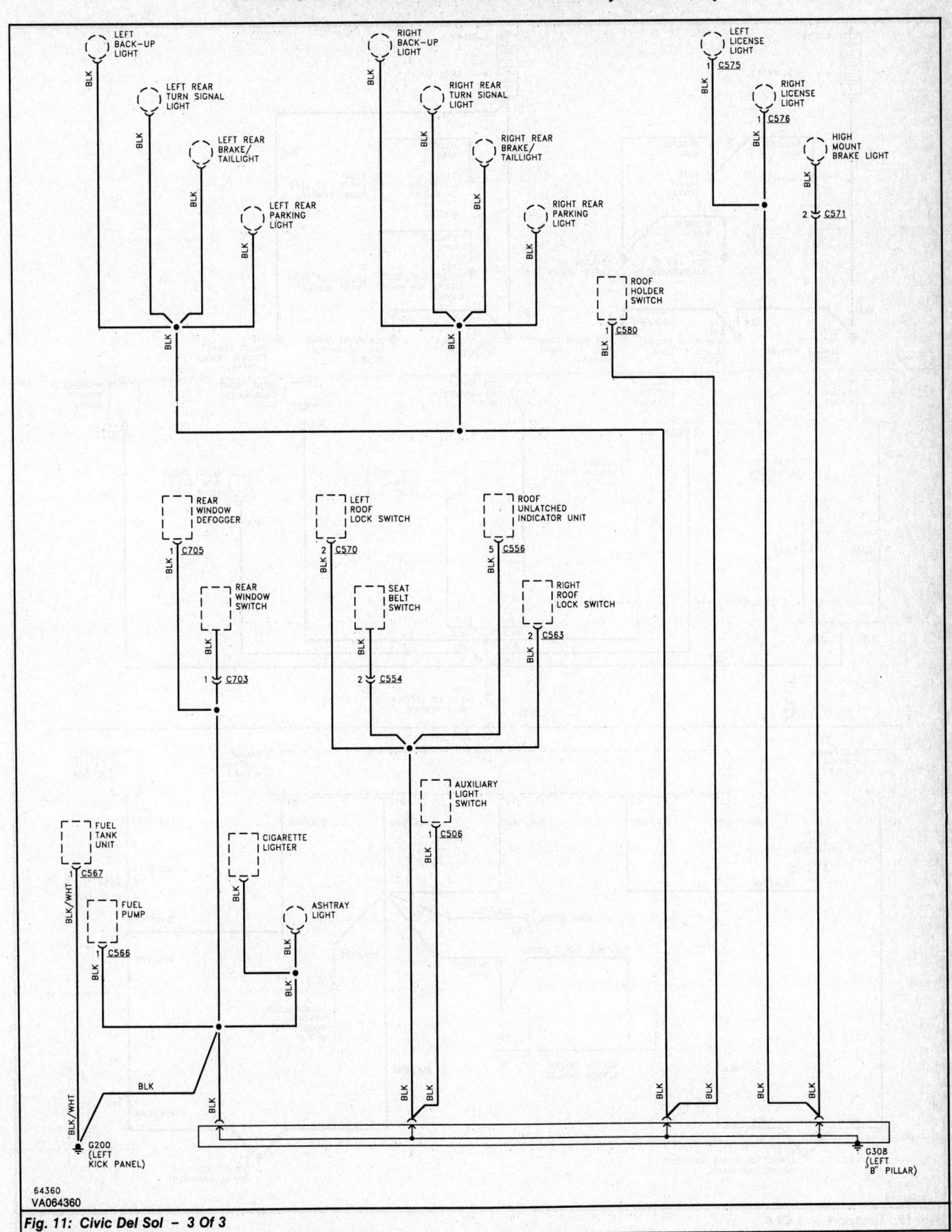

64360
VA064360

Fig. 11: Civic Del Sol – 3 Of 3

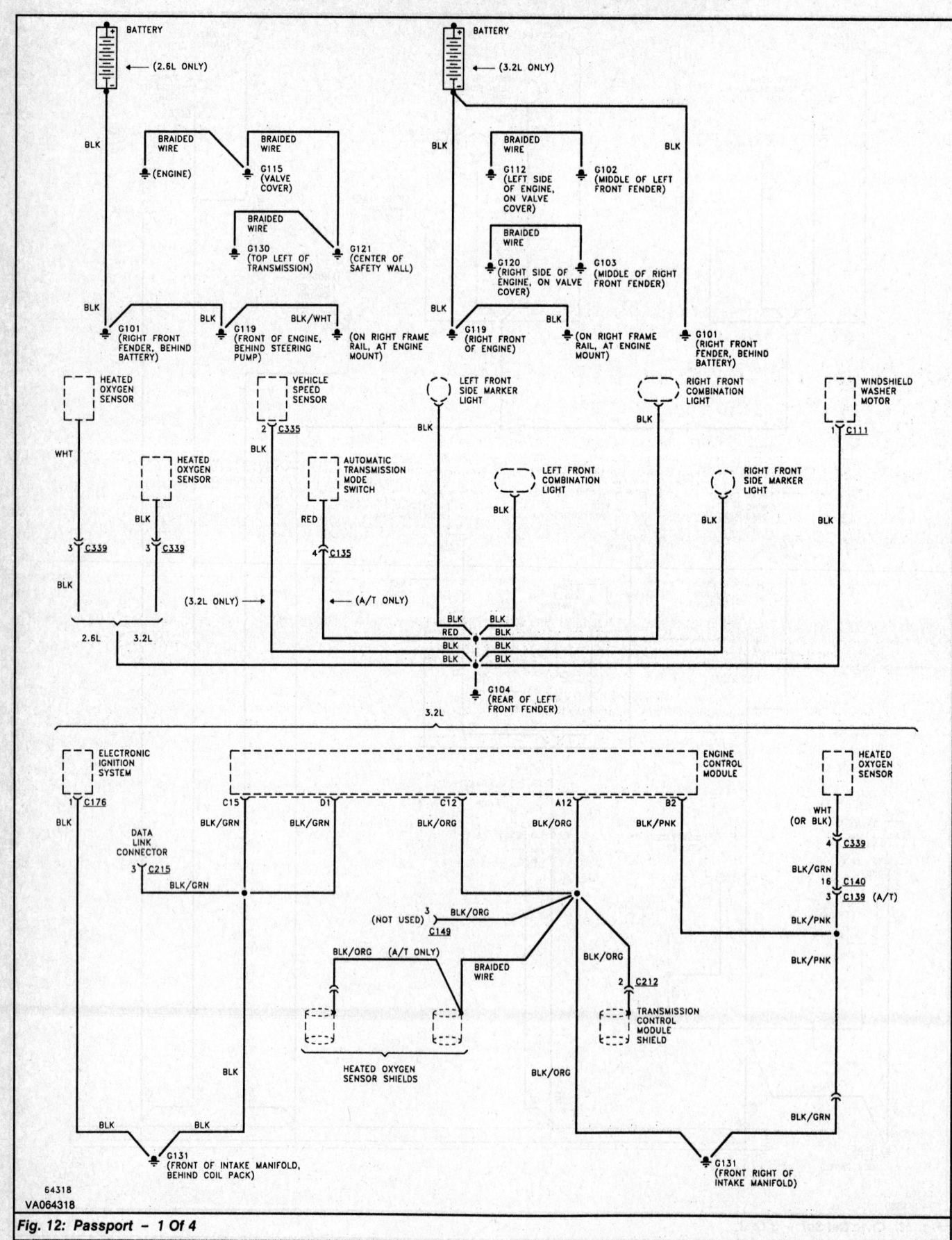

64318
VA064318

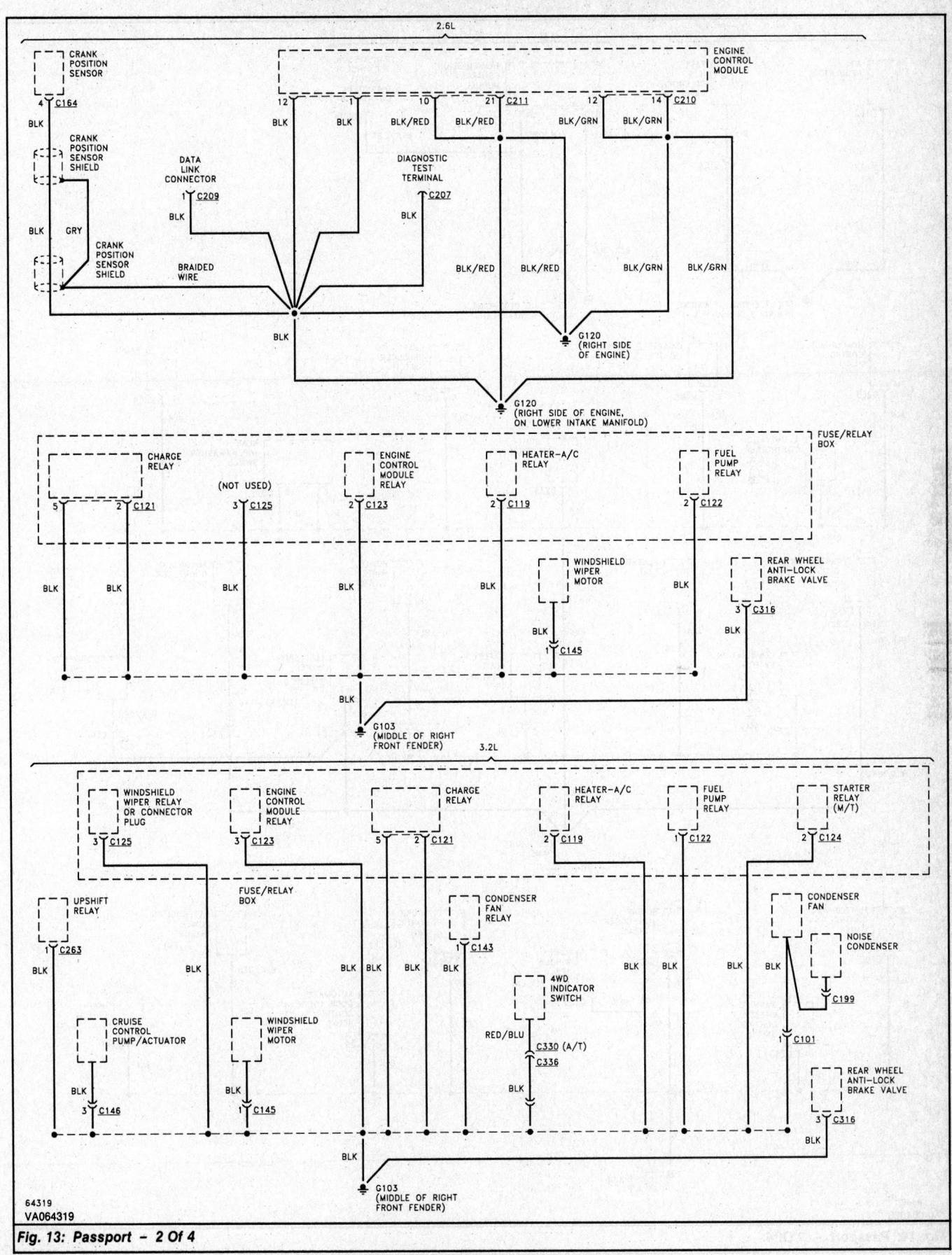

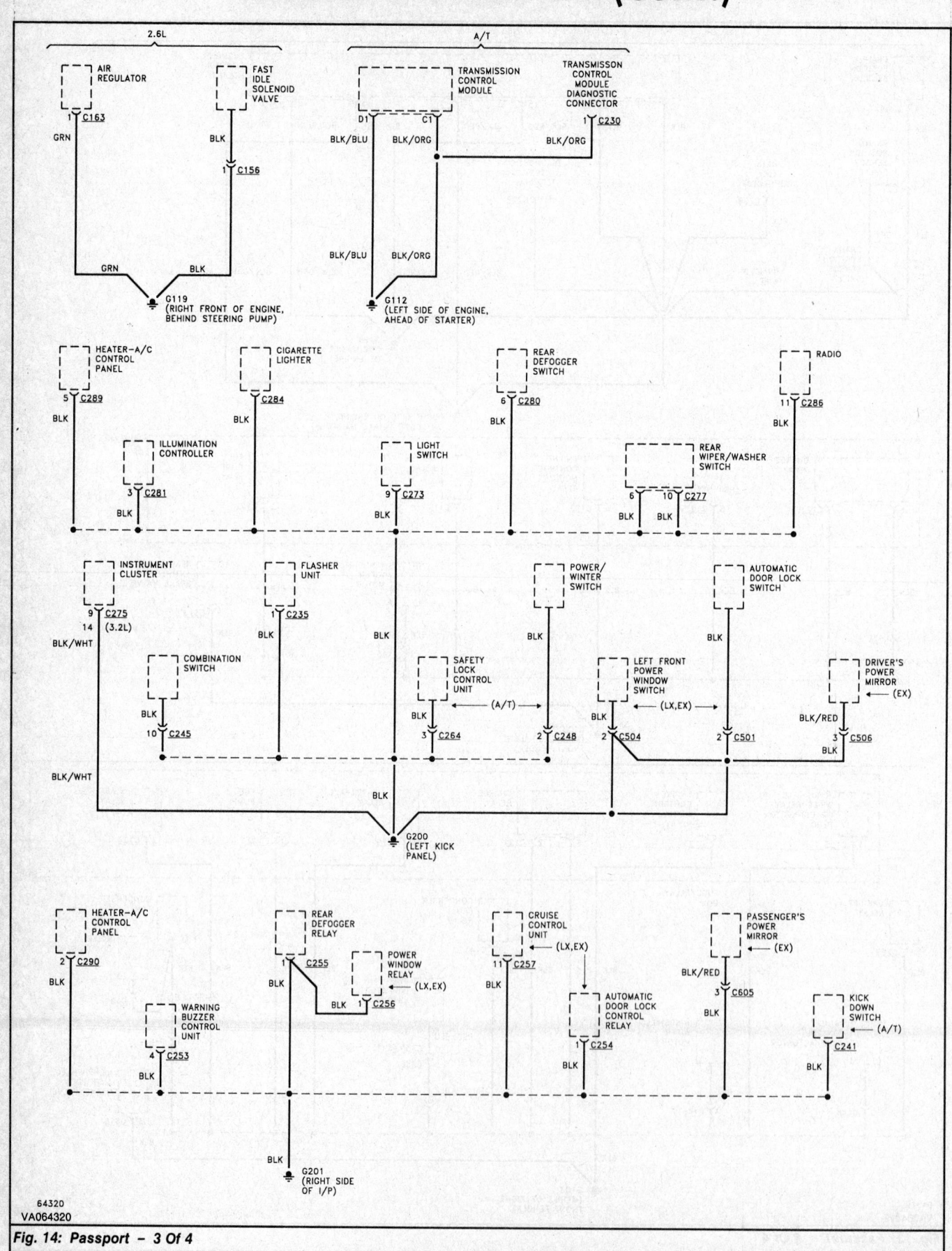

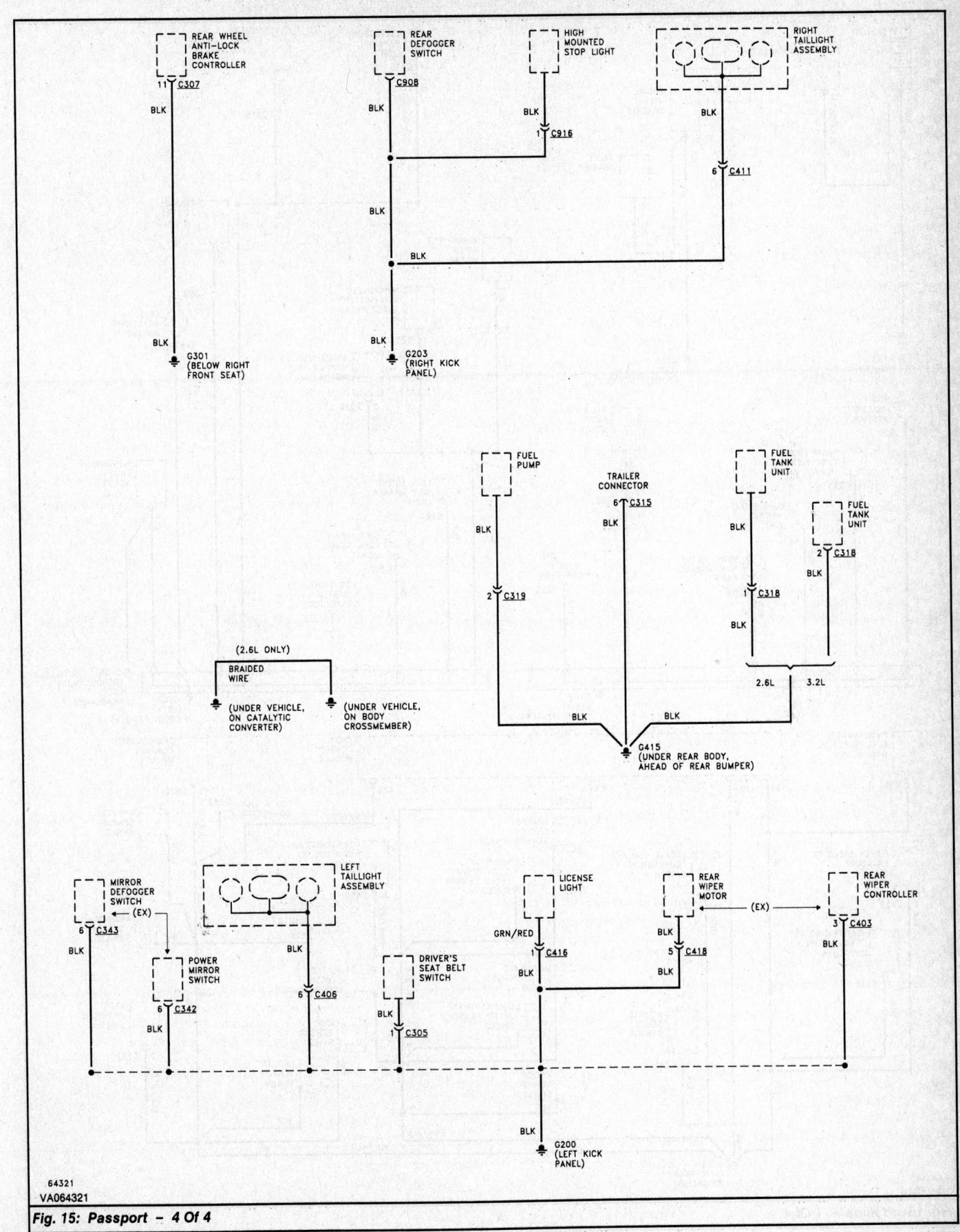

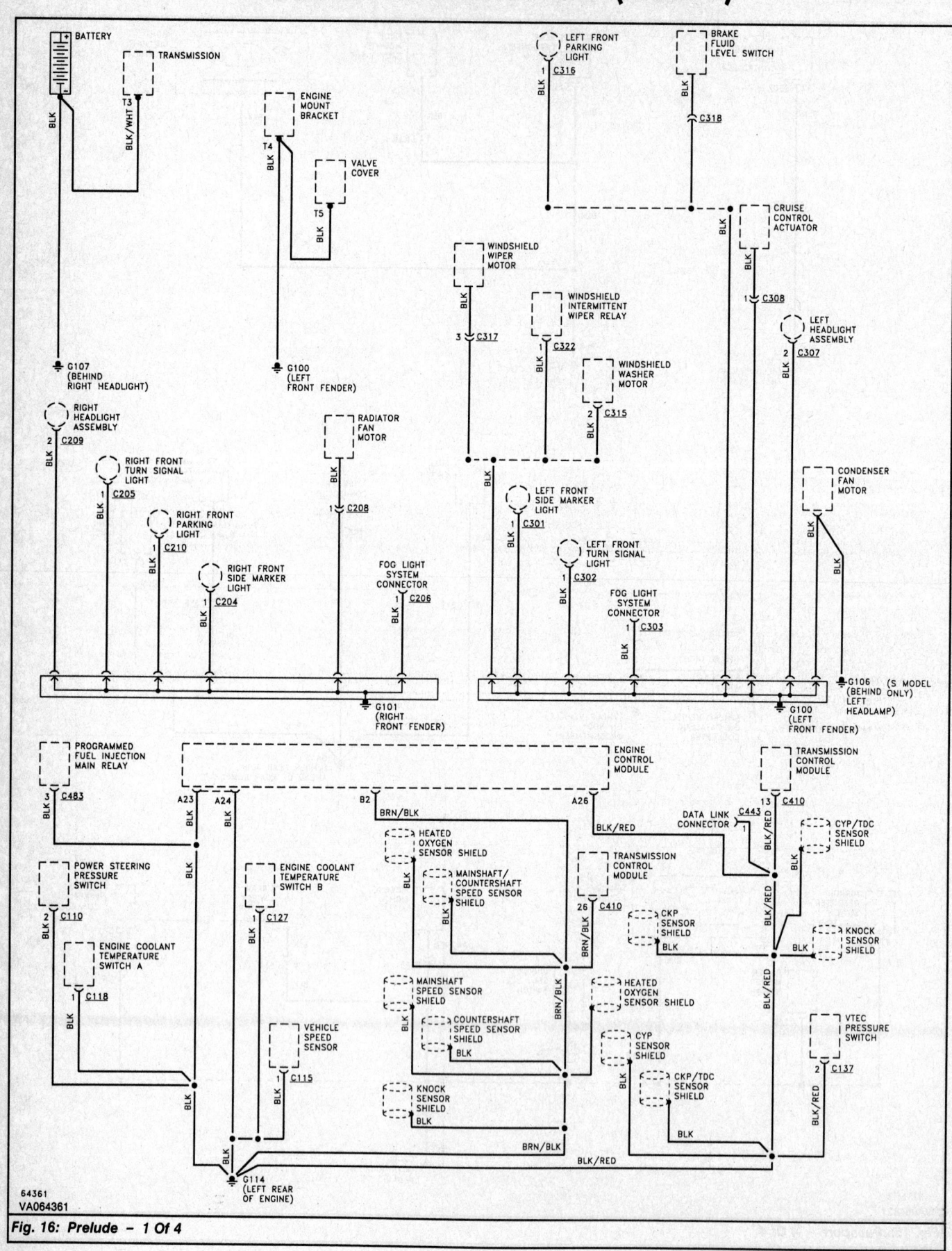

Fig. 16: Prelude – 1 Of 4

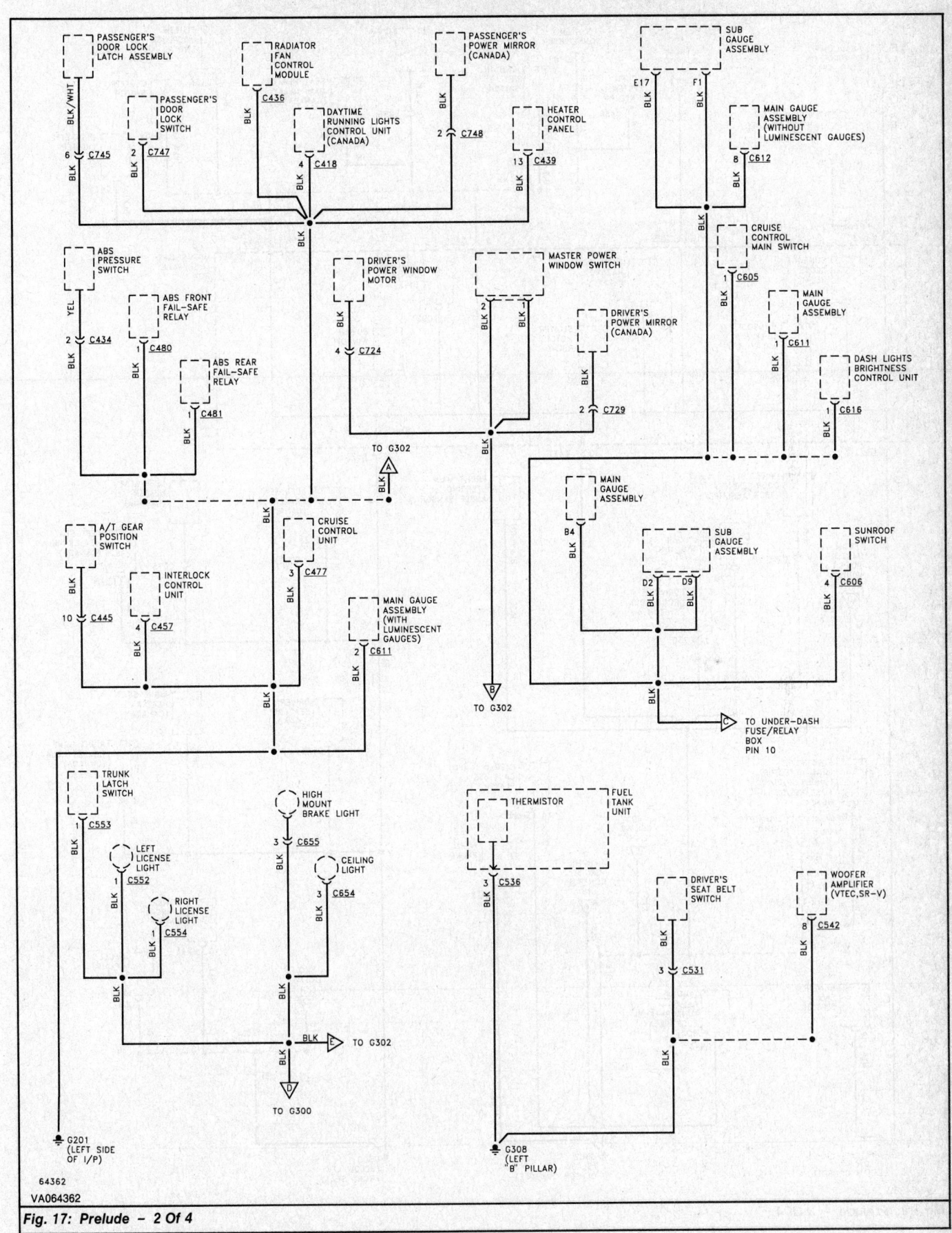

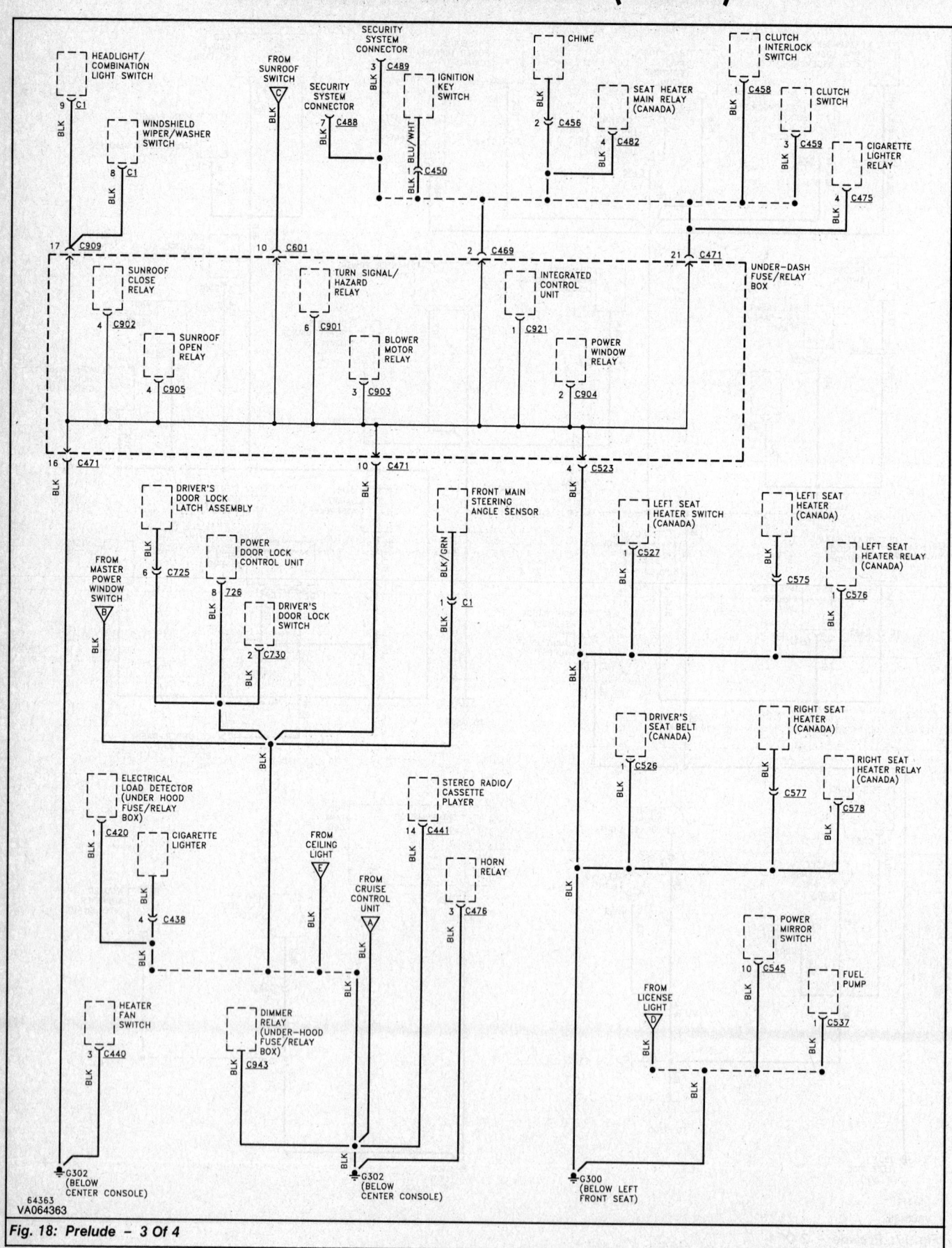

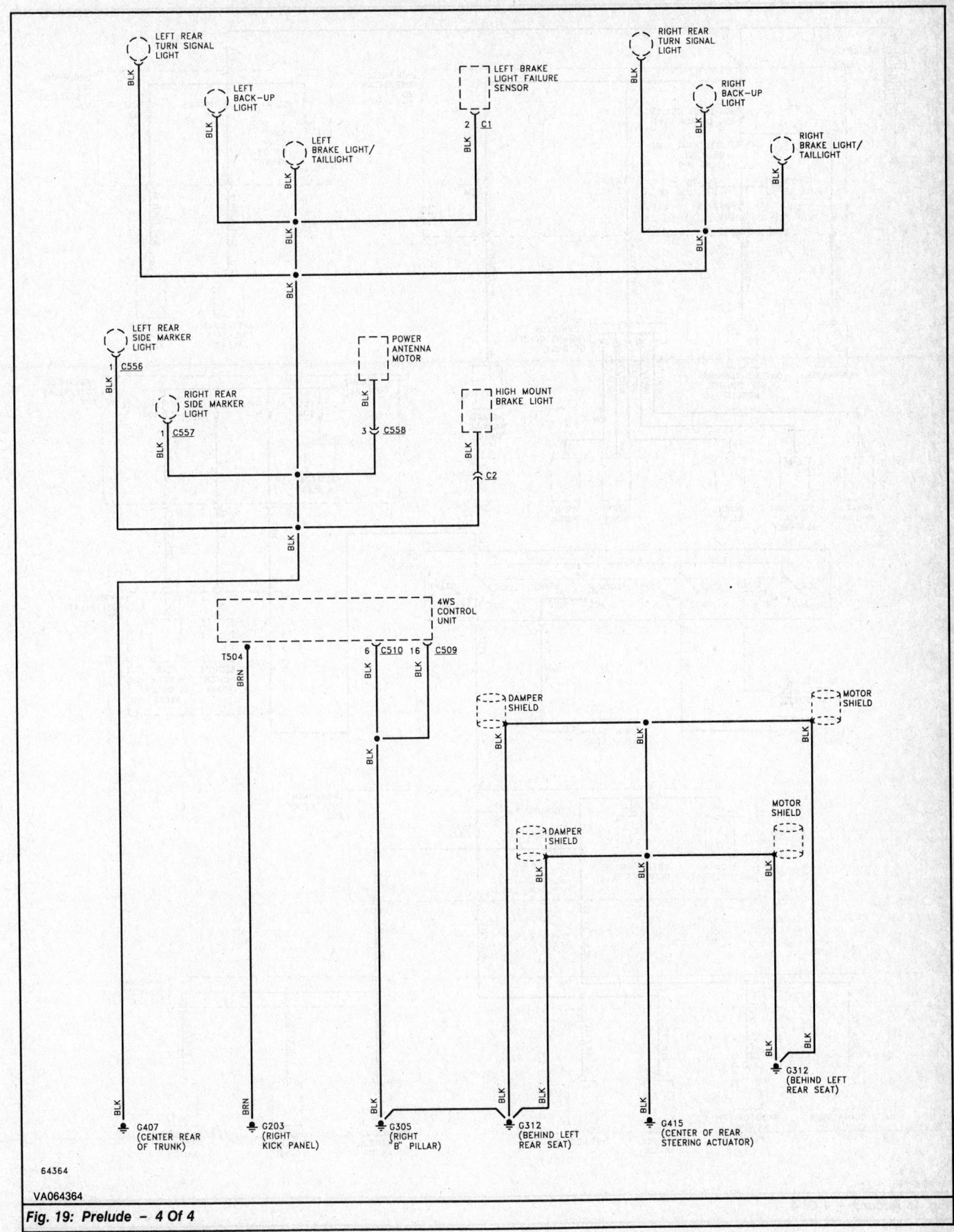

64364

VA064364

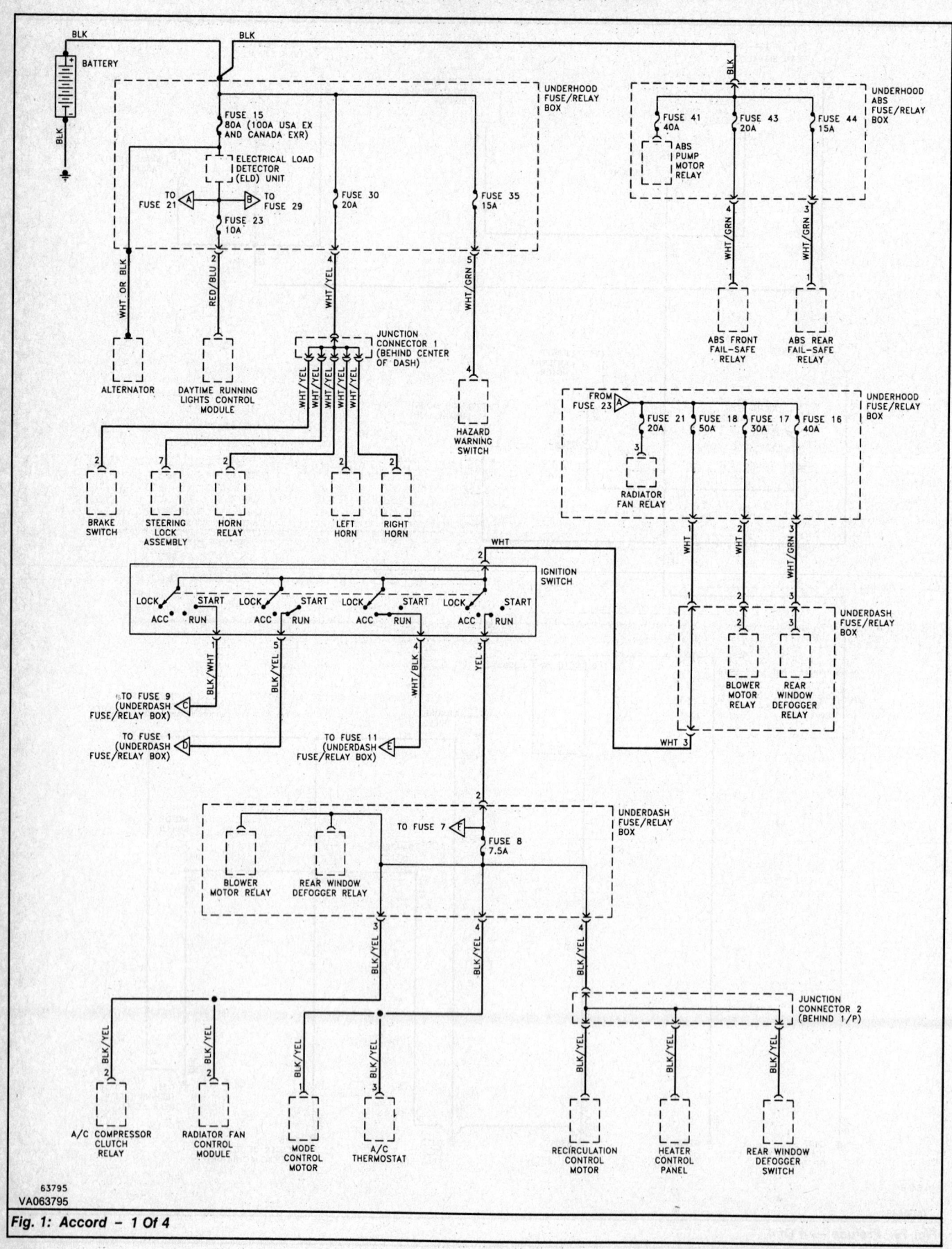

Fig. 1: Accord – 1 Of 4

63795
VA063795

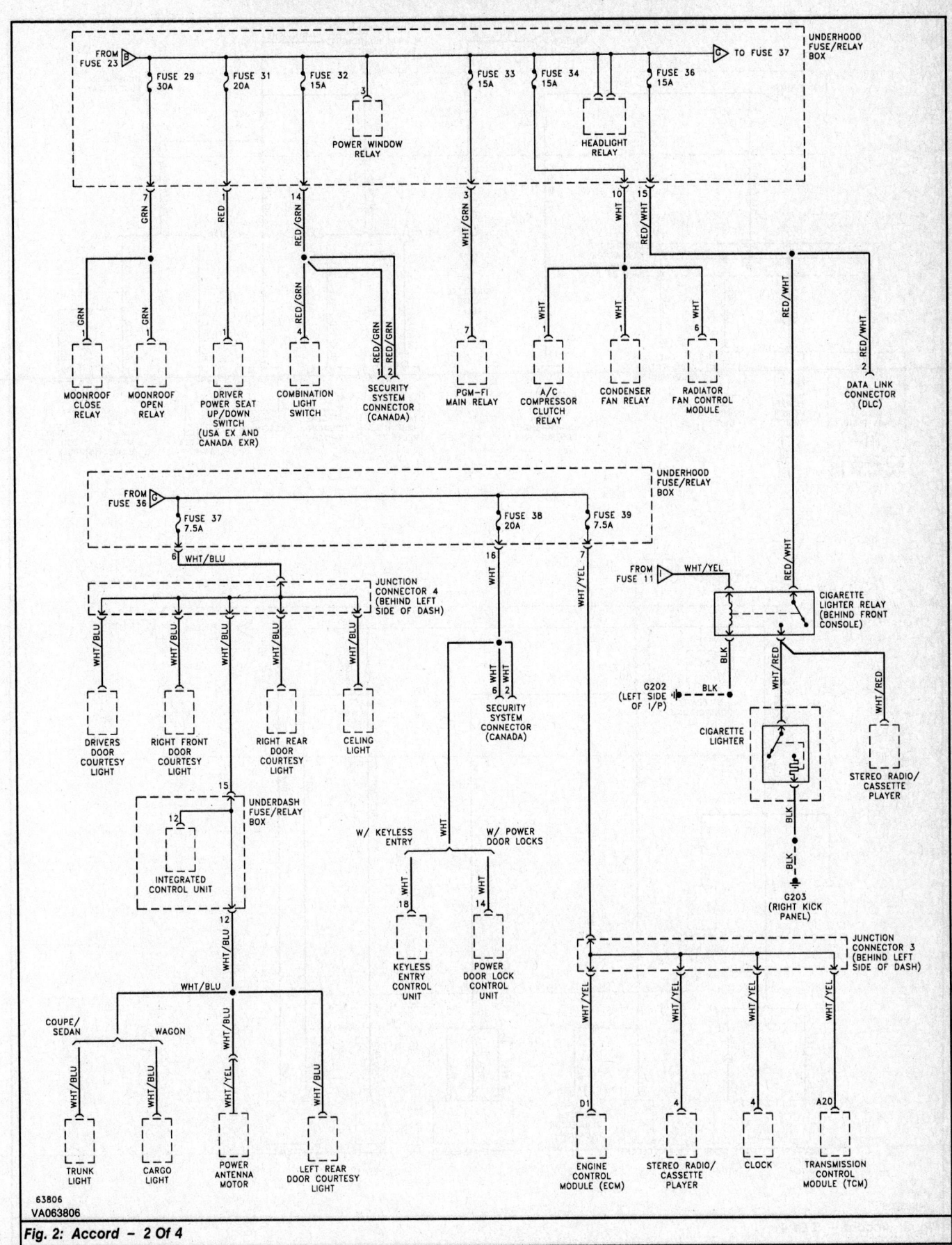

63806
VA063806

Fig. 2: Accord – 2 Of 4

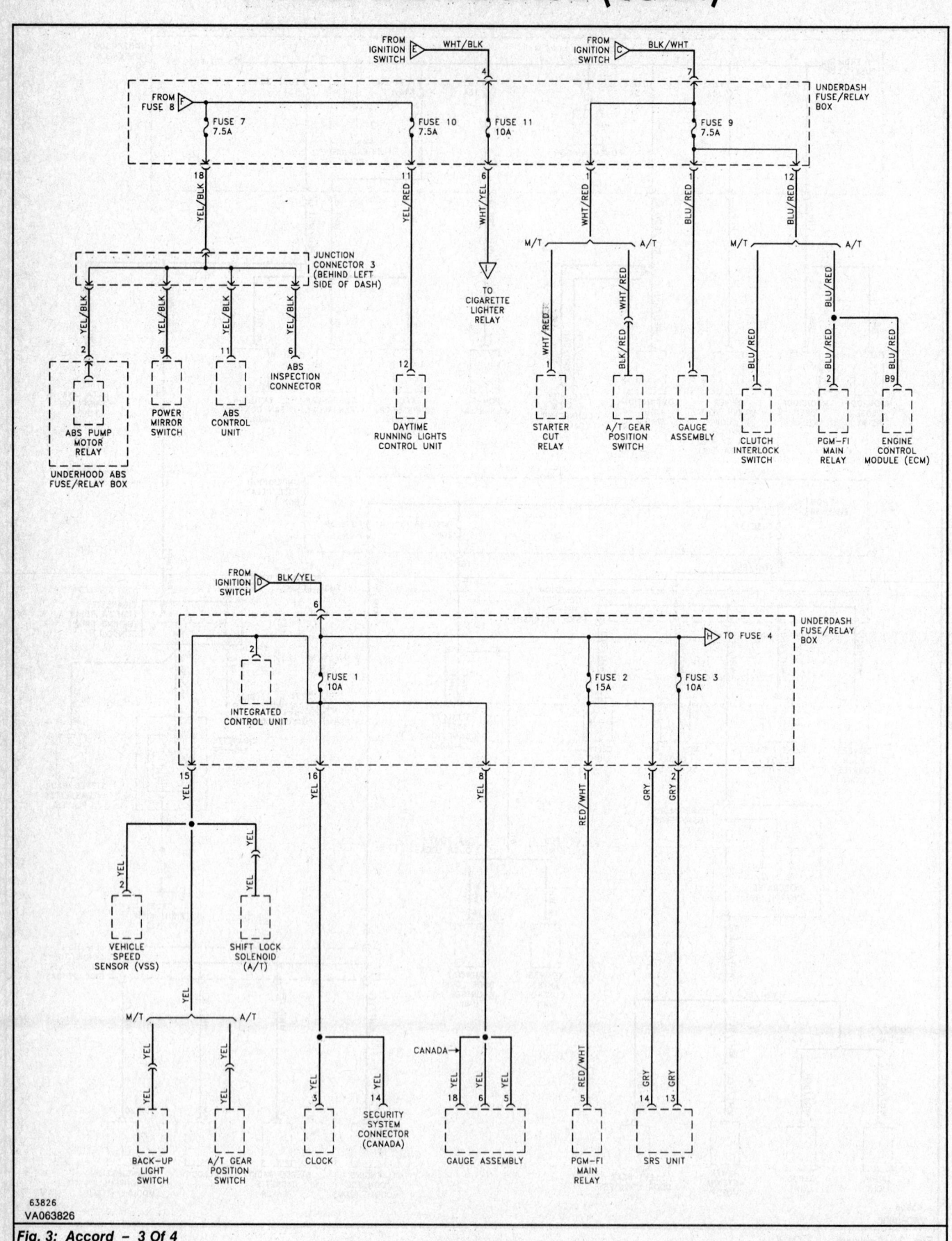

63826
VA063826

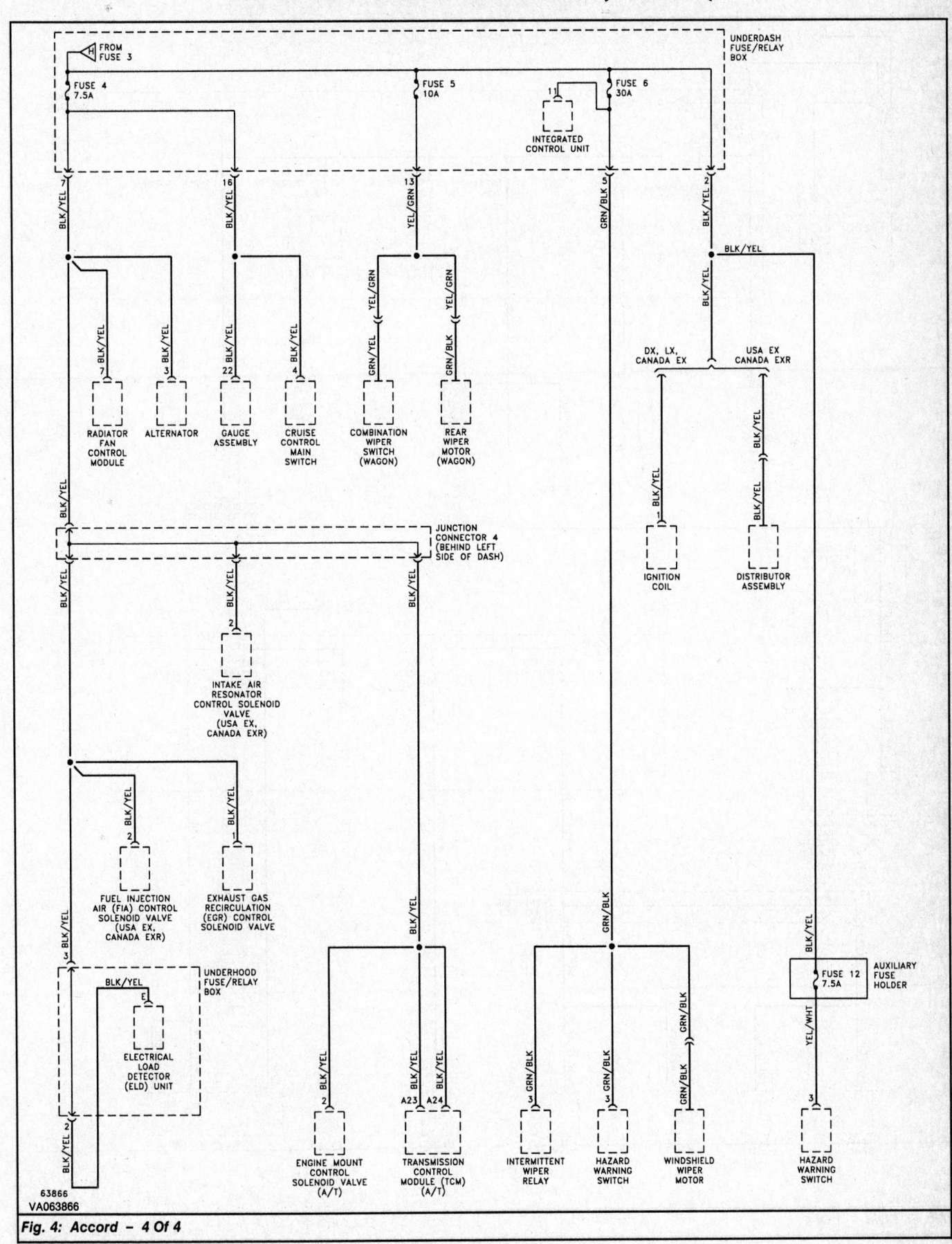

Fig. 4: Accord – 4 Of 4

63866
VA063866

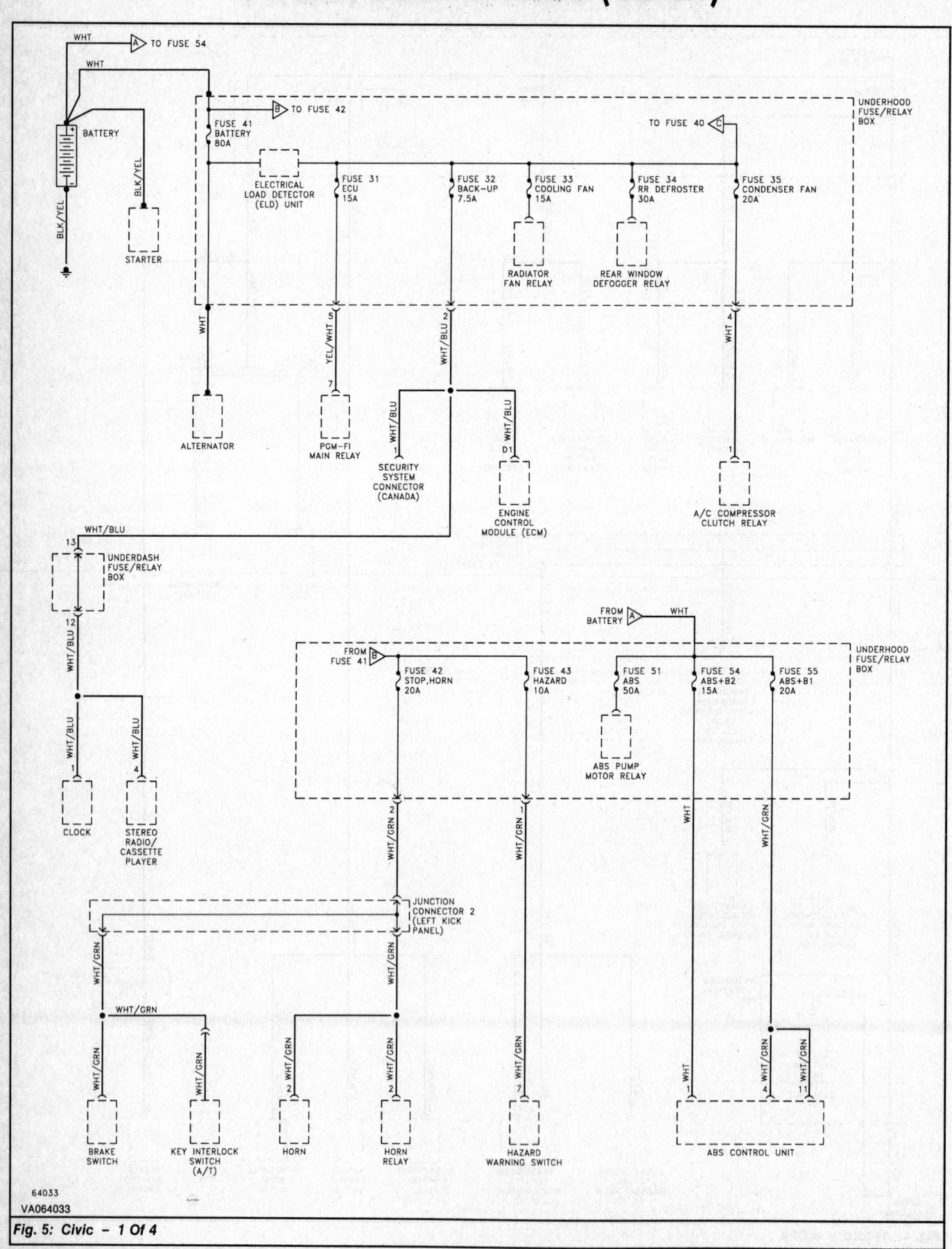

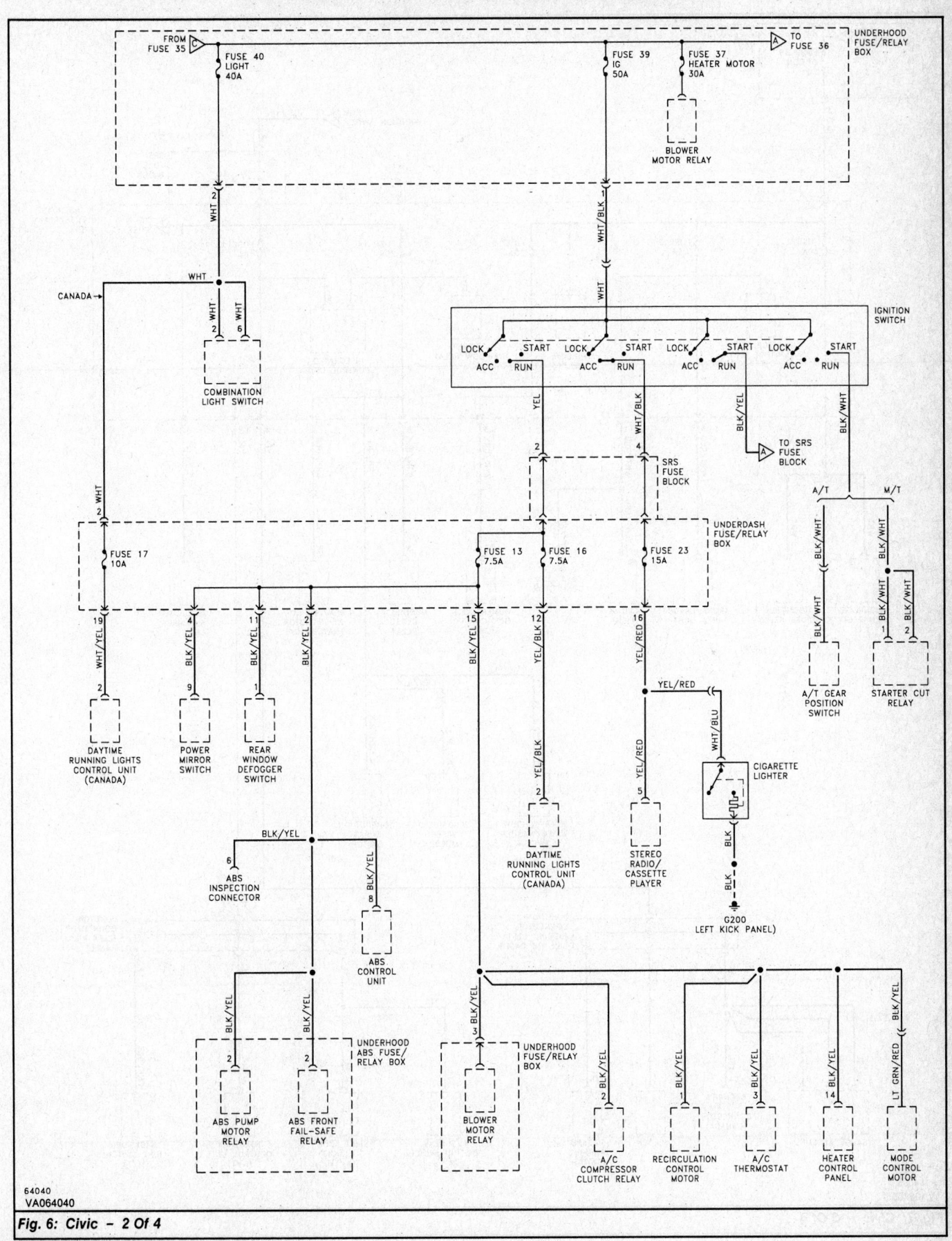

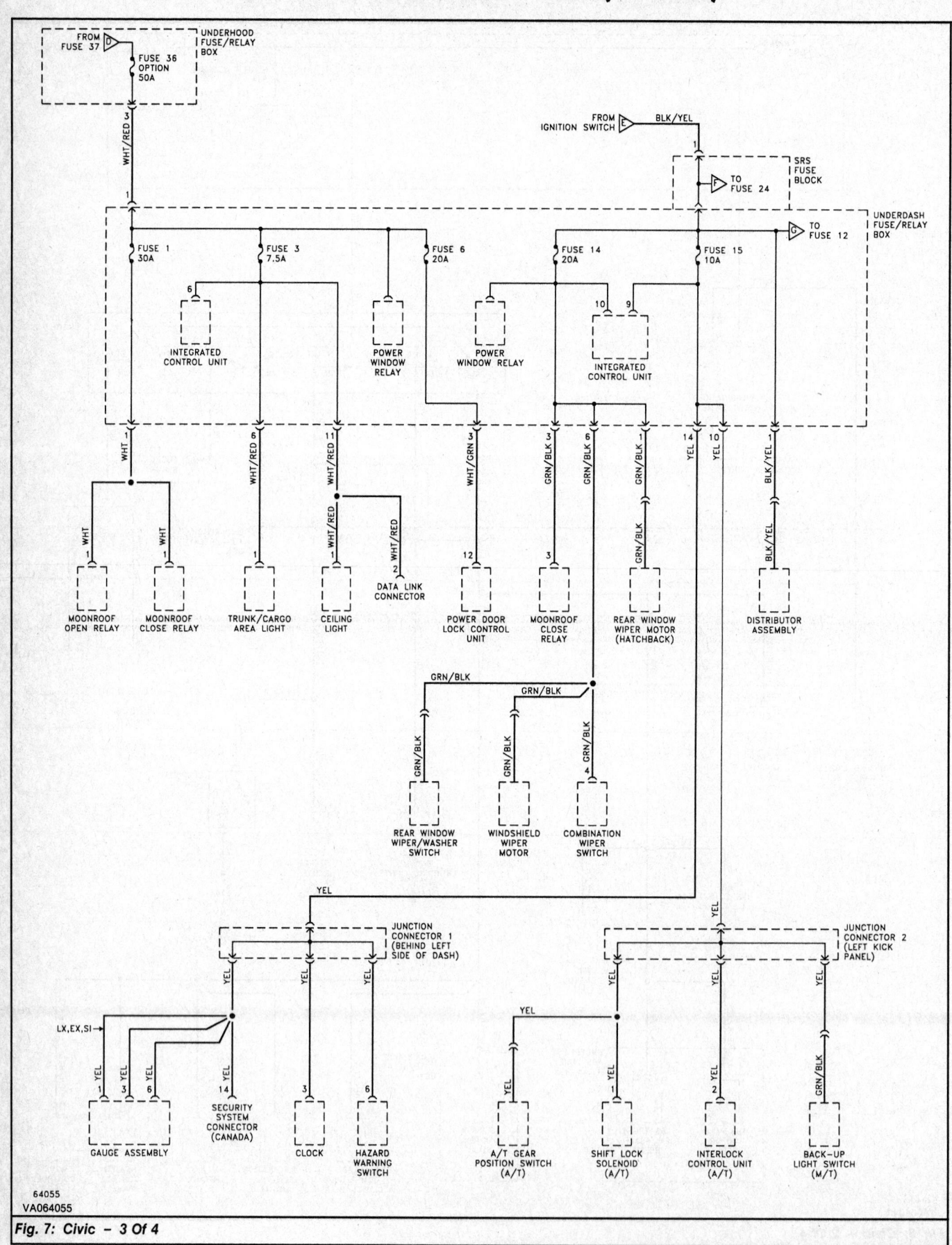

64055
VA064055

Fig. 7: Civic – 3 Of 4

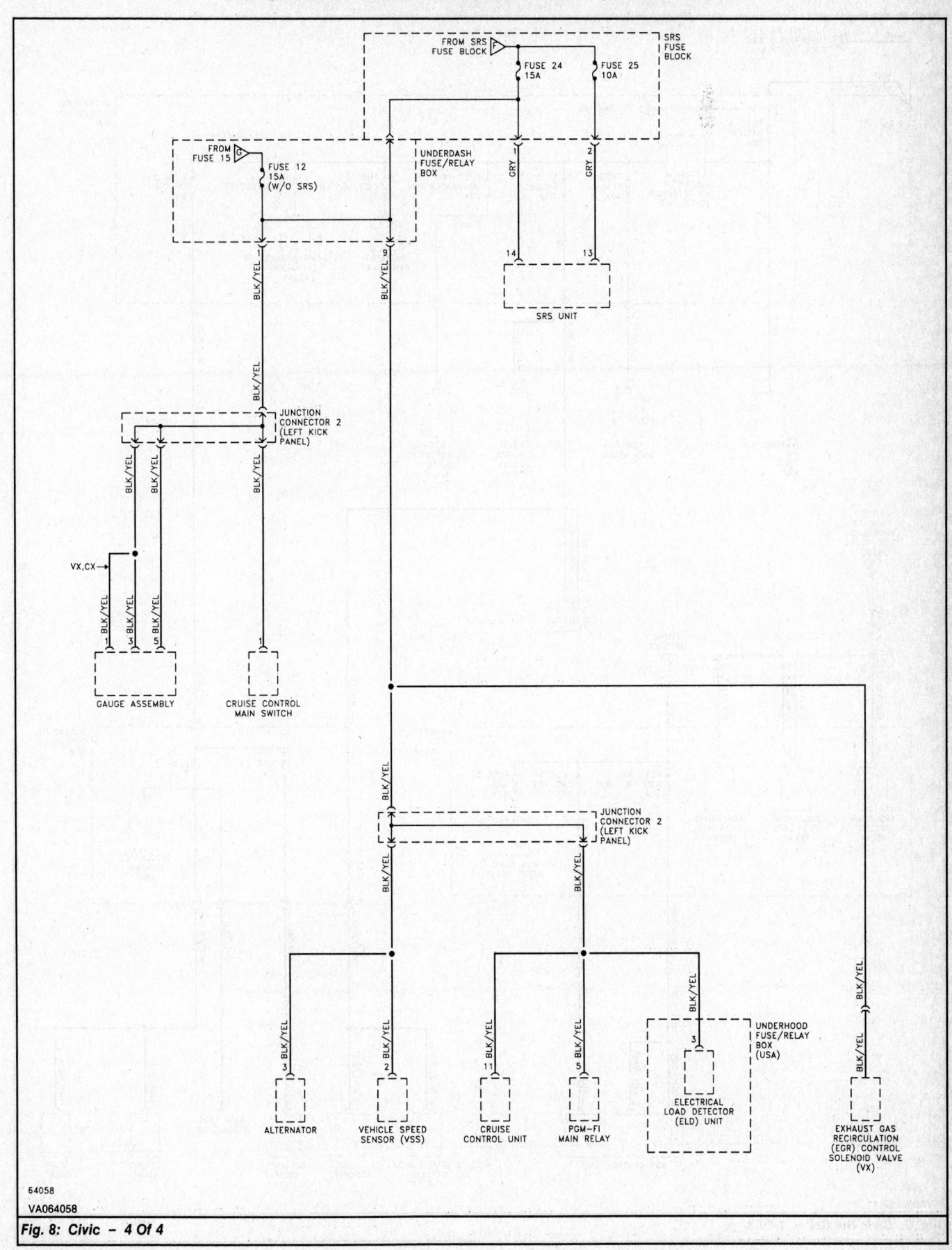

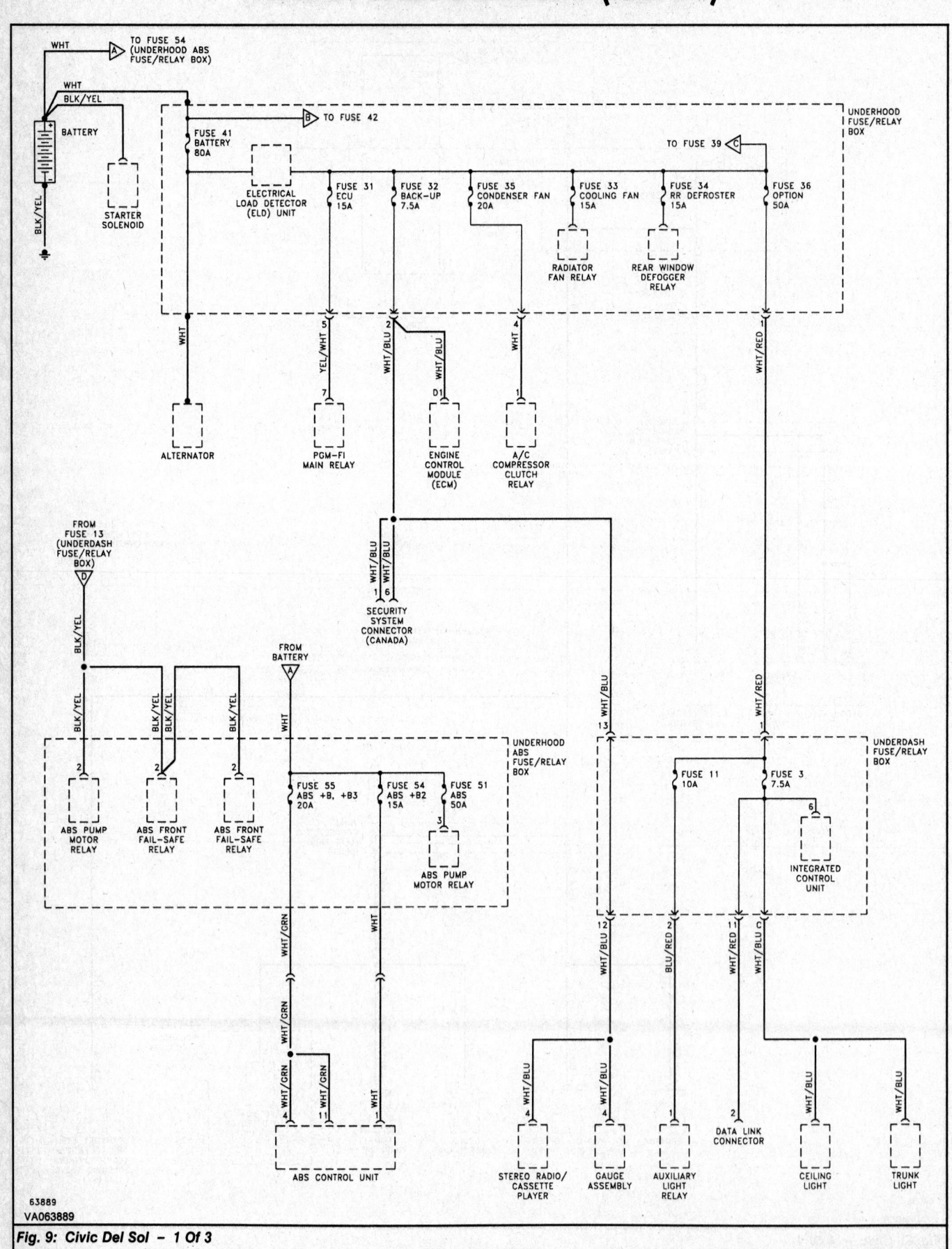

63889
VA063889

Fig. 9: Civic Del Sol — 1 Of 3

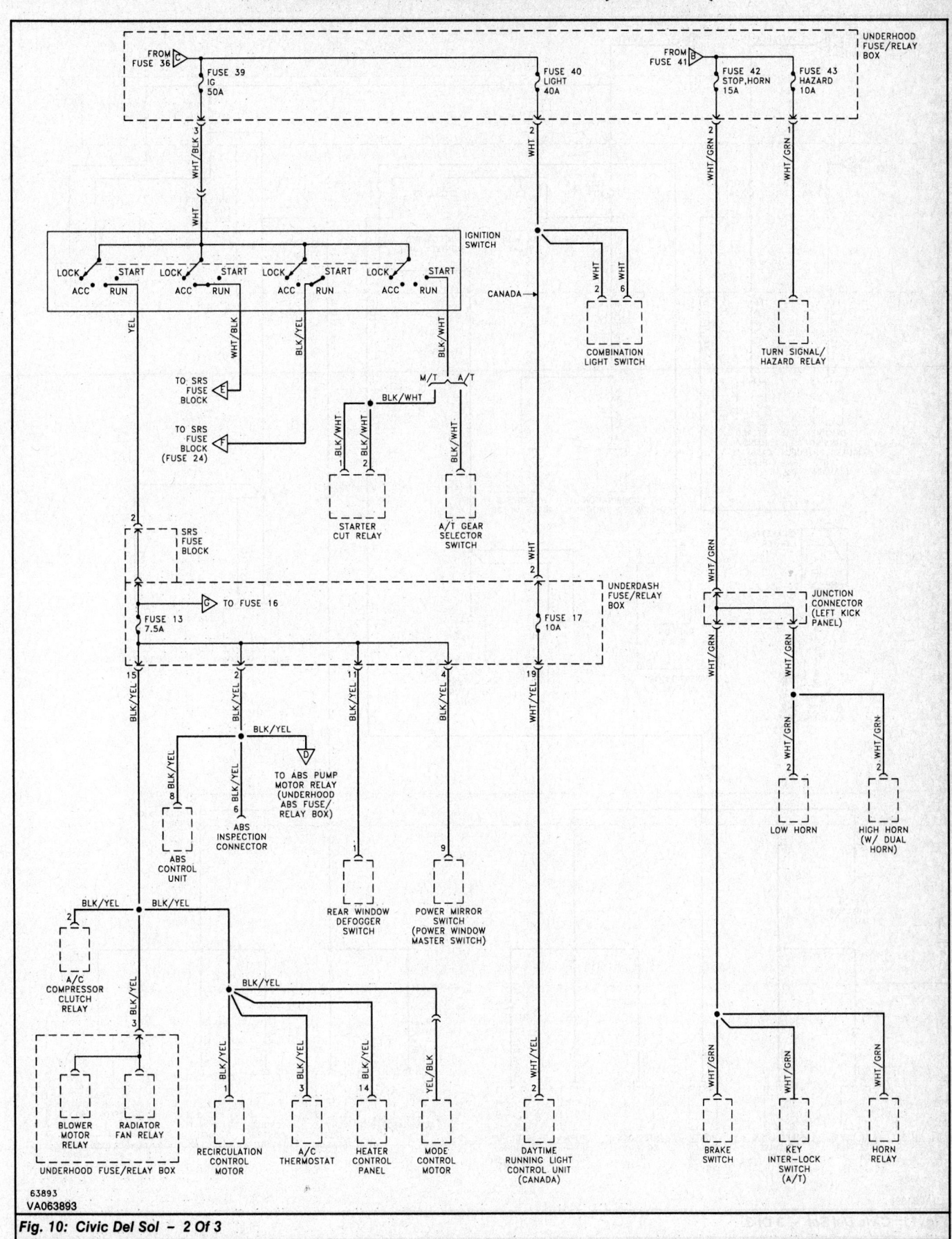

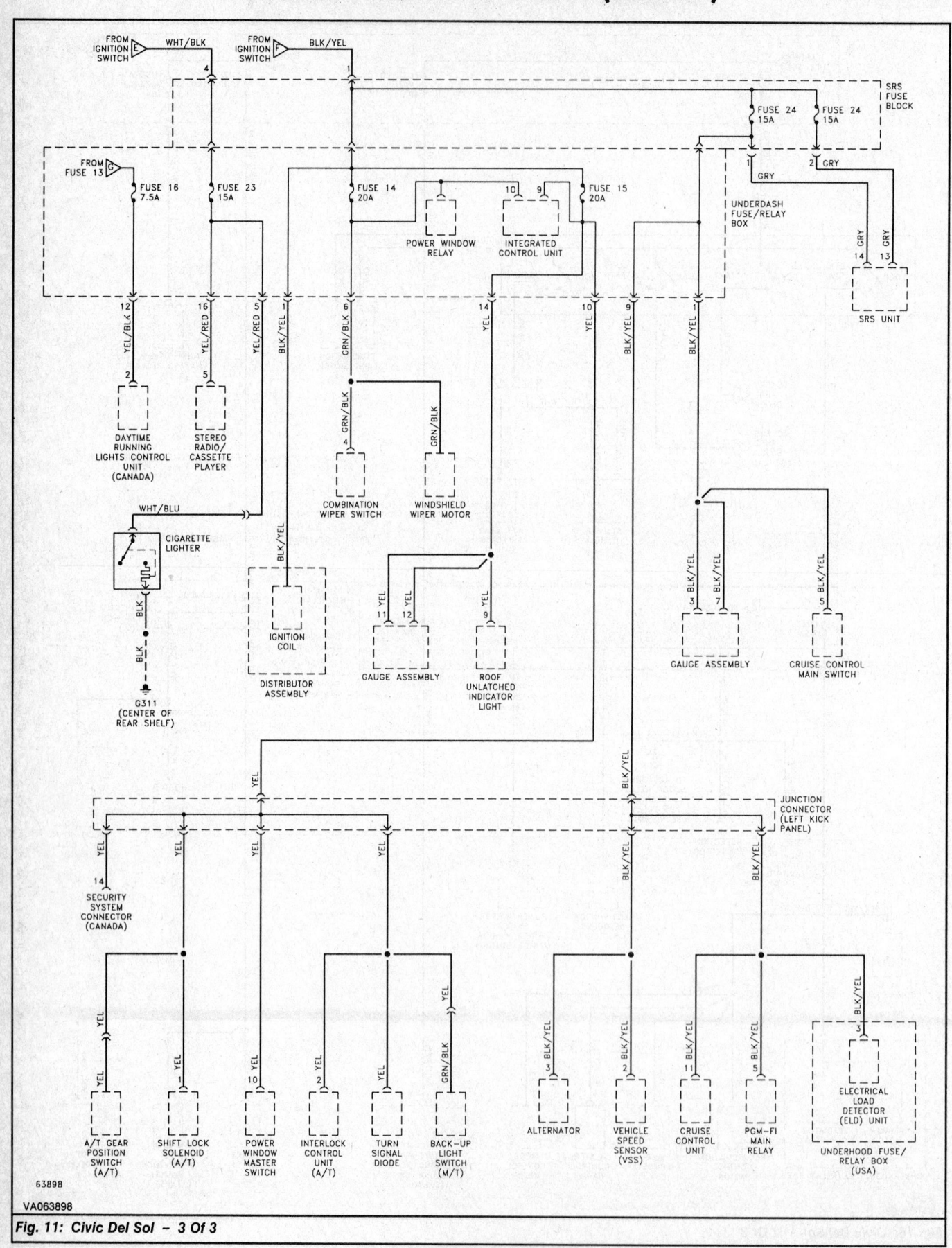

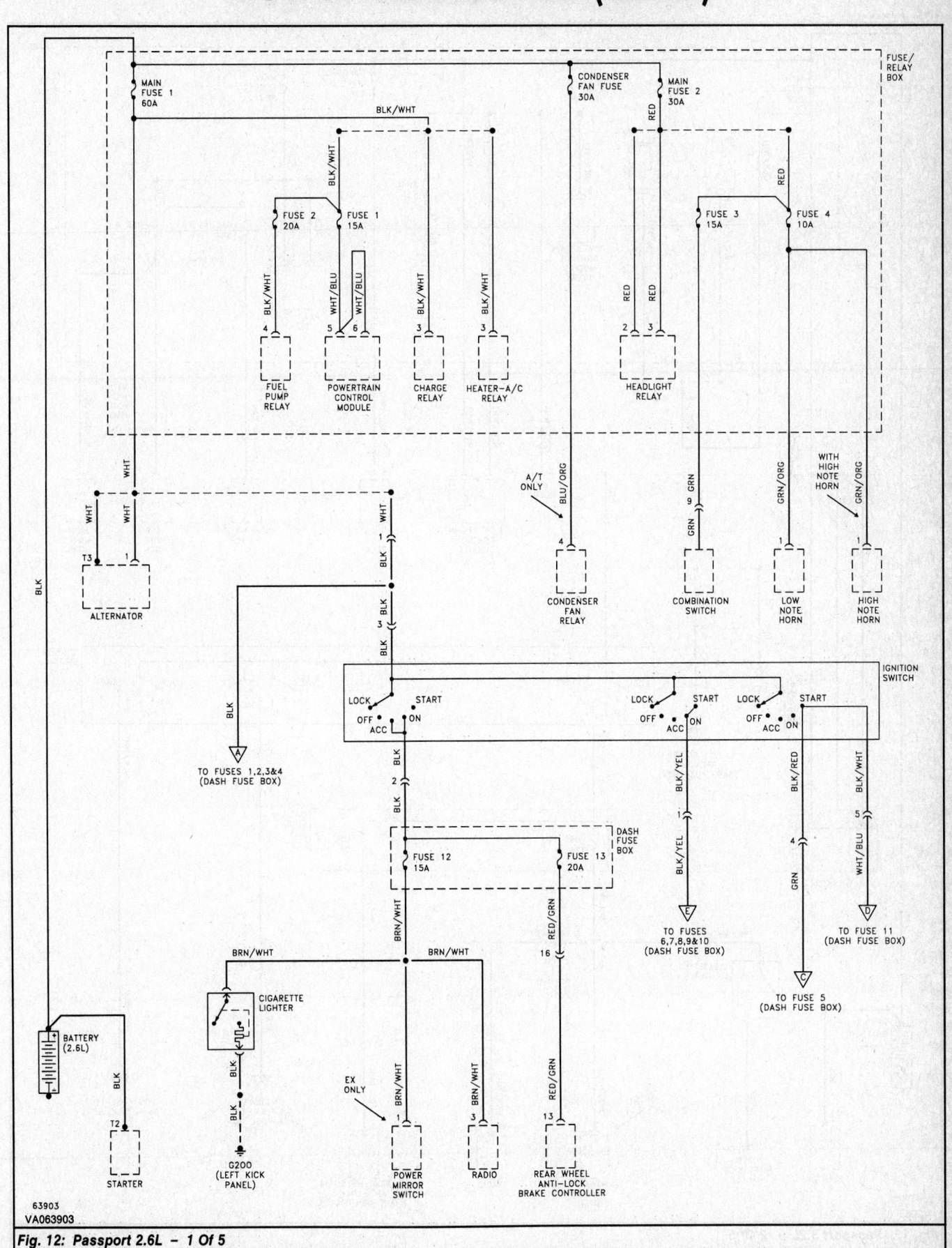

63903
VA063903

Fig. 12: Passport 2.6L – 1 Of 5

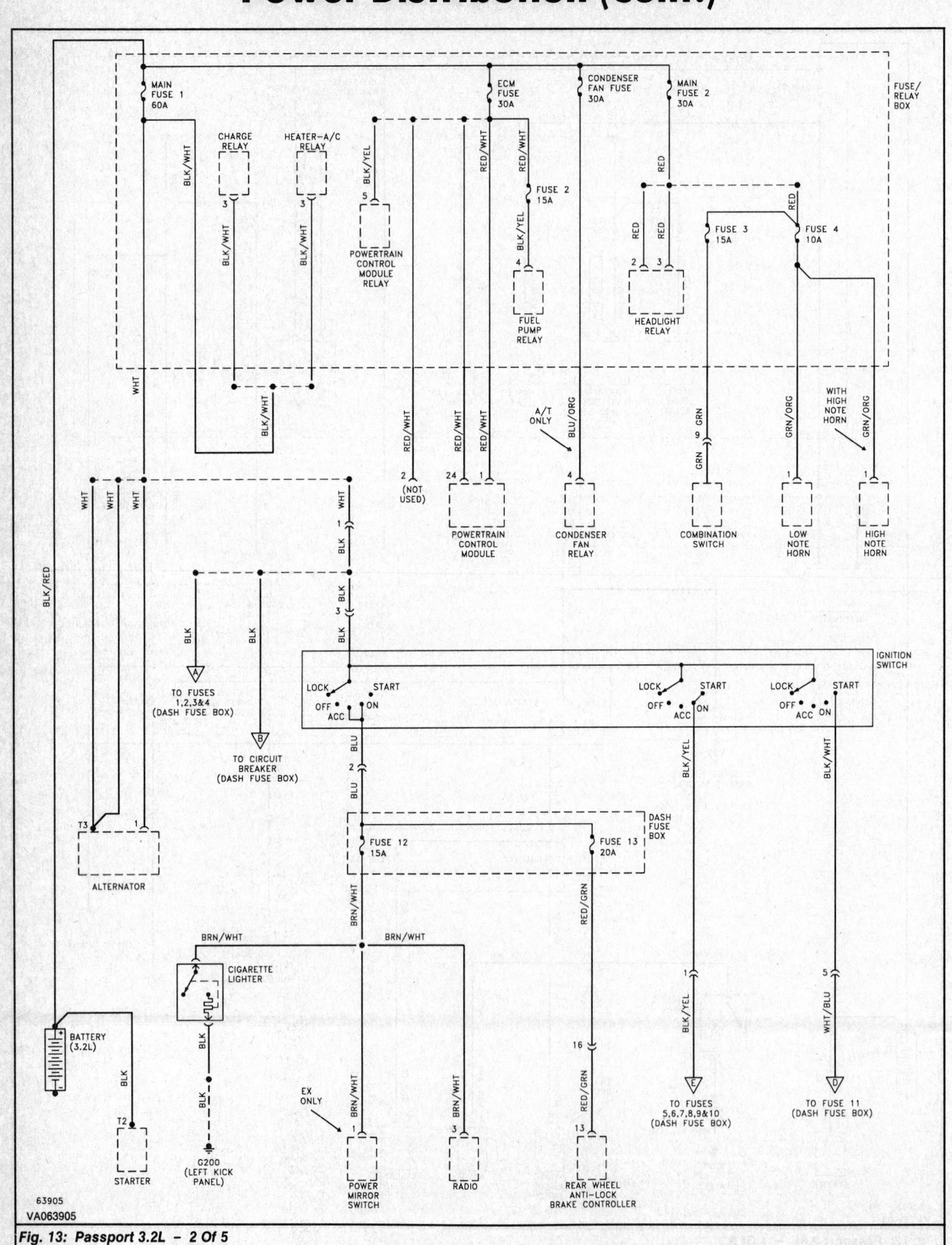

63905
VA063905

Fig. 13: Passport 3.2L – 2 Of 5

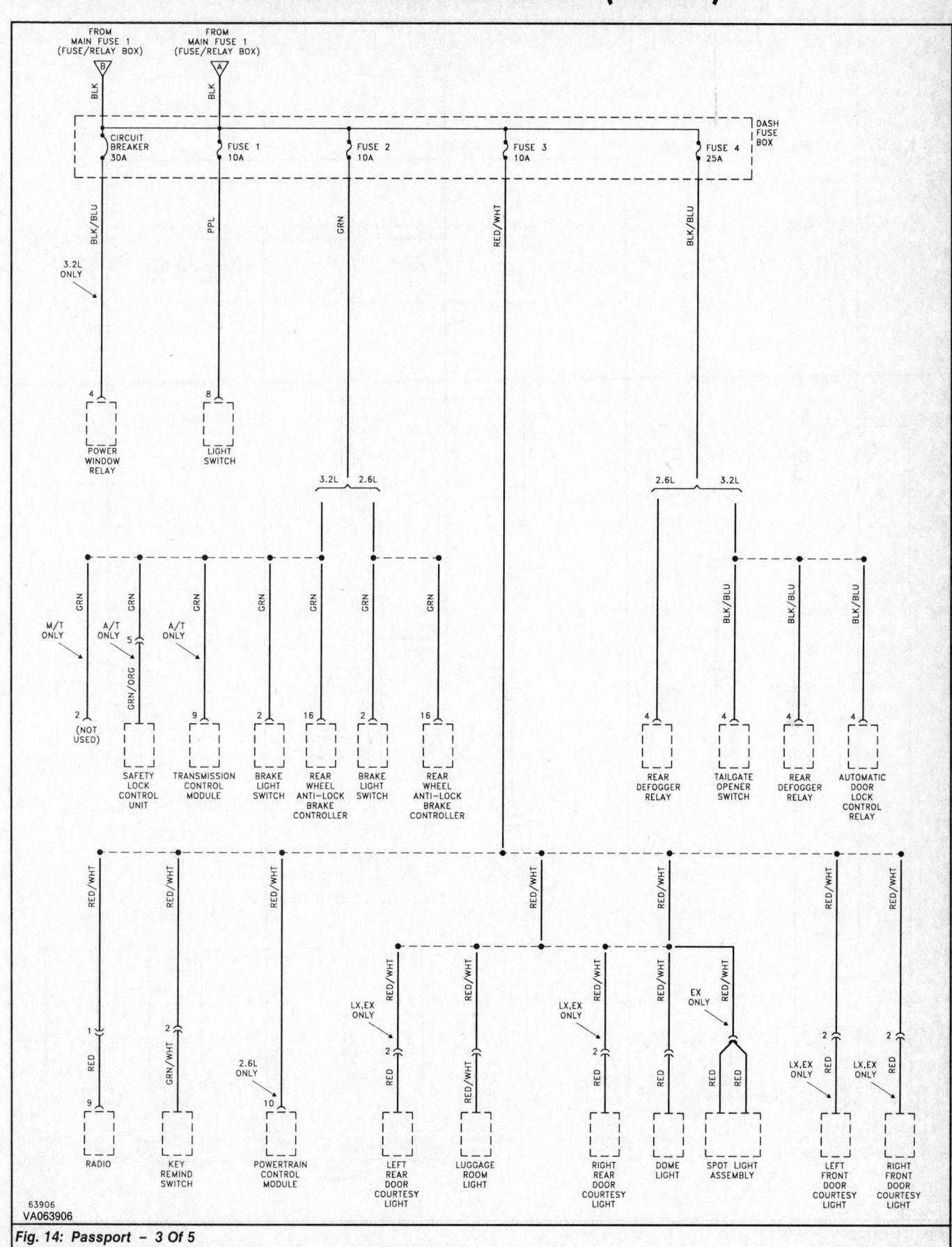

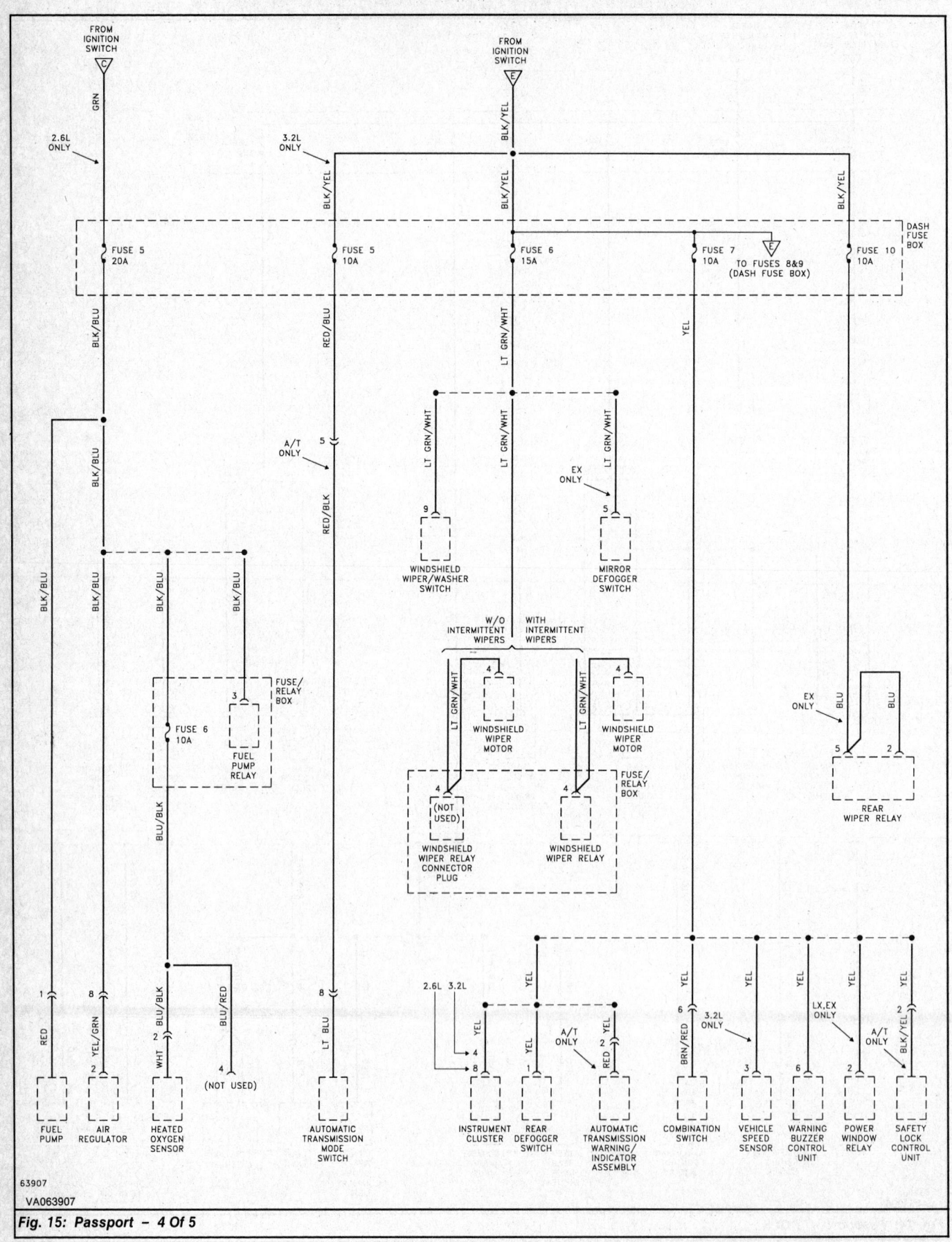

63907

VA063907

Fig. 15: Passport – 4 Of 5

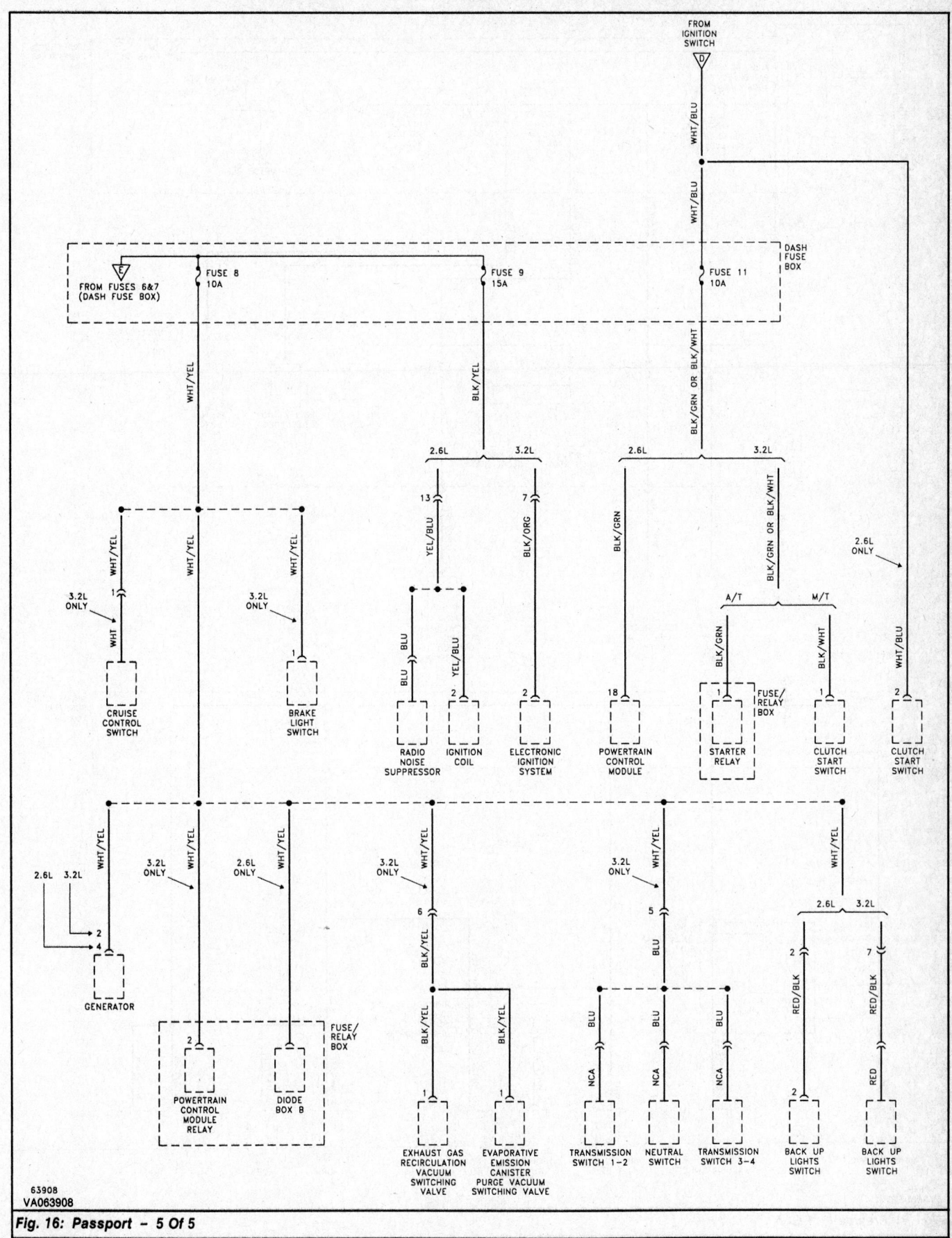

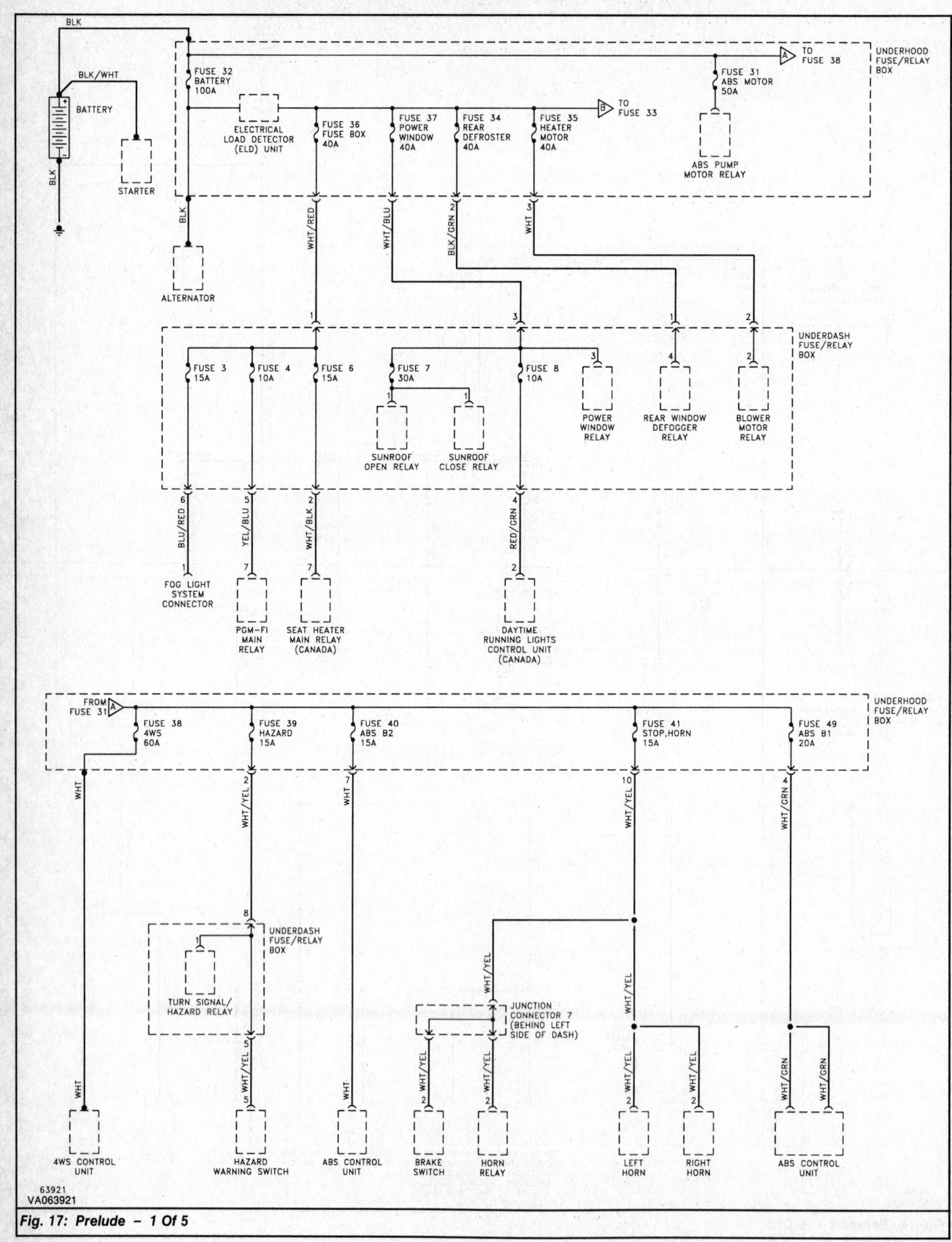

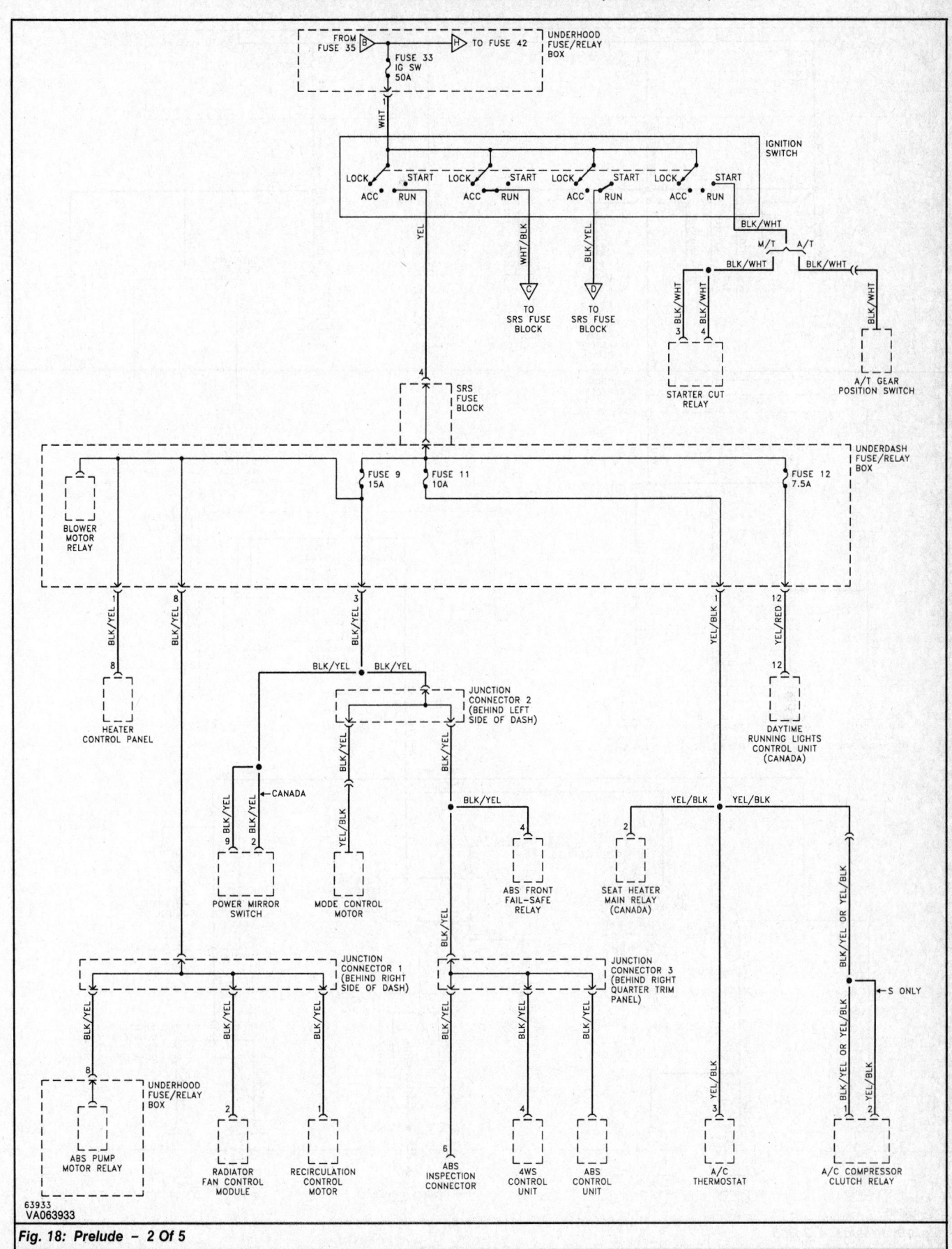

Fig. 18: Prelude - 2 Of 5

63933
VA063933

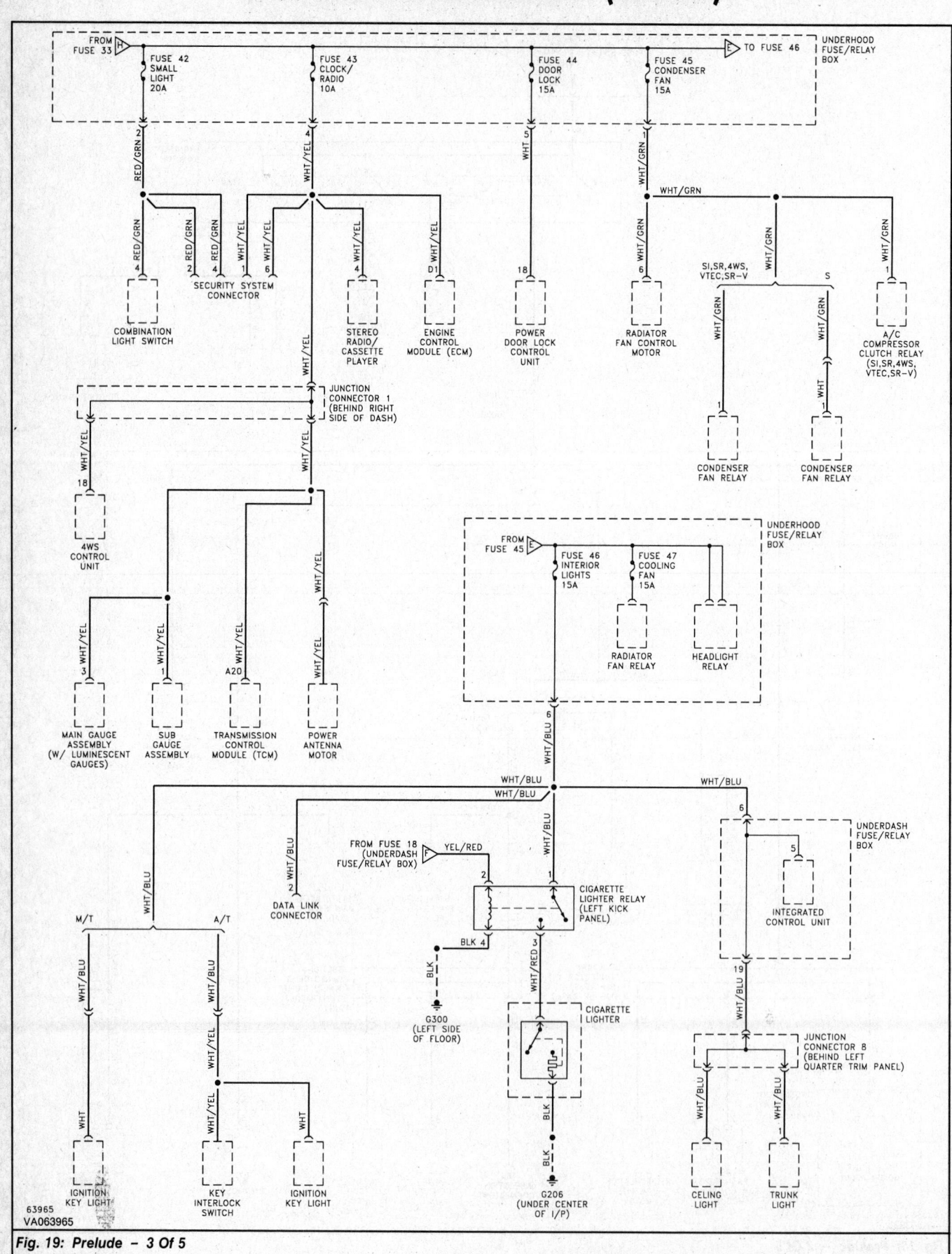

63965
VA063965

Fig. 19: Prelude – 3 Of 5

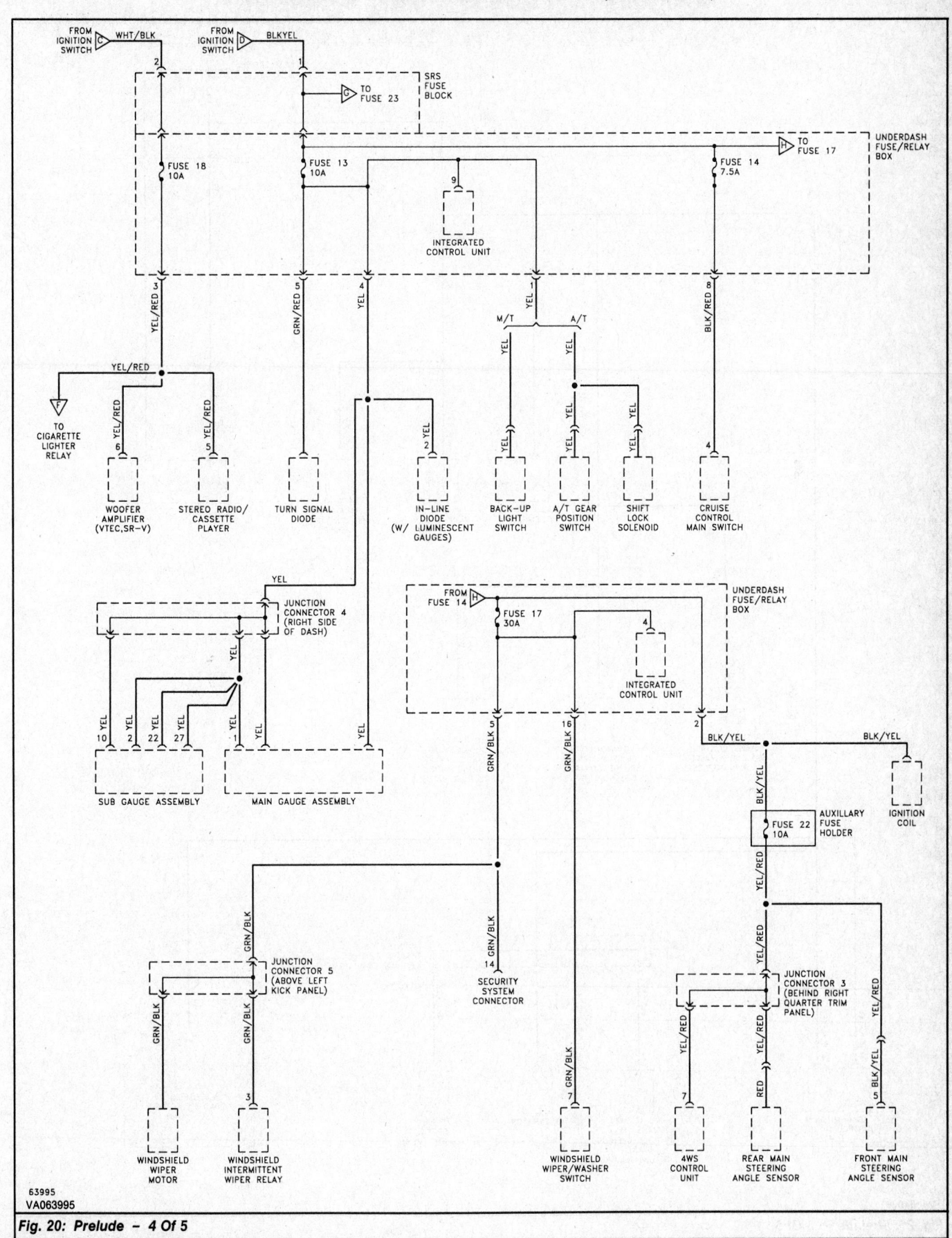

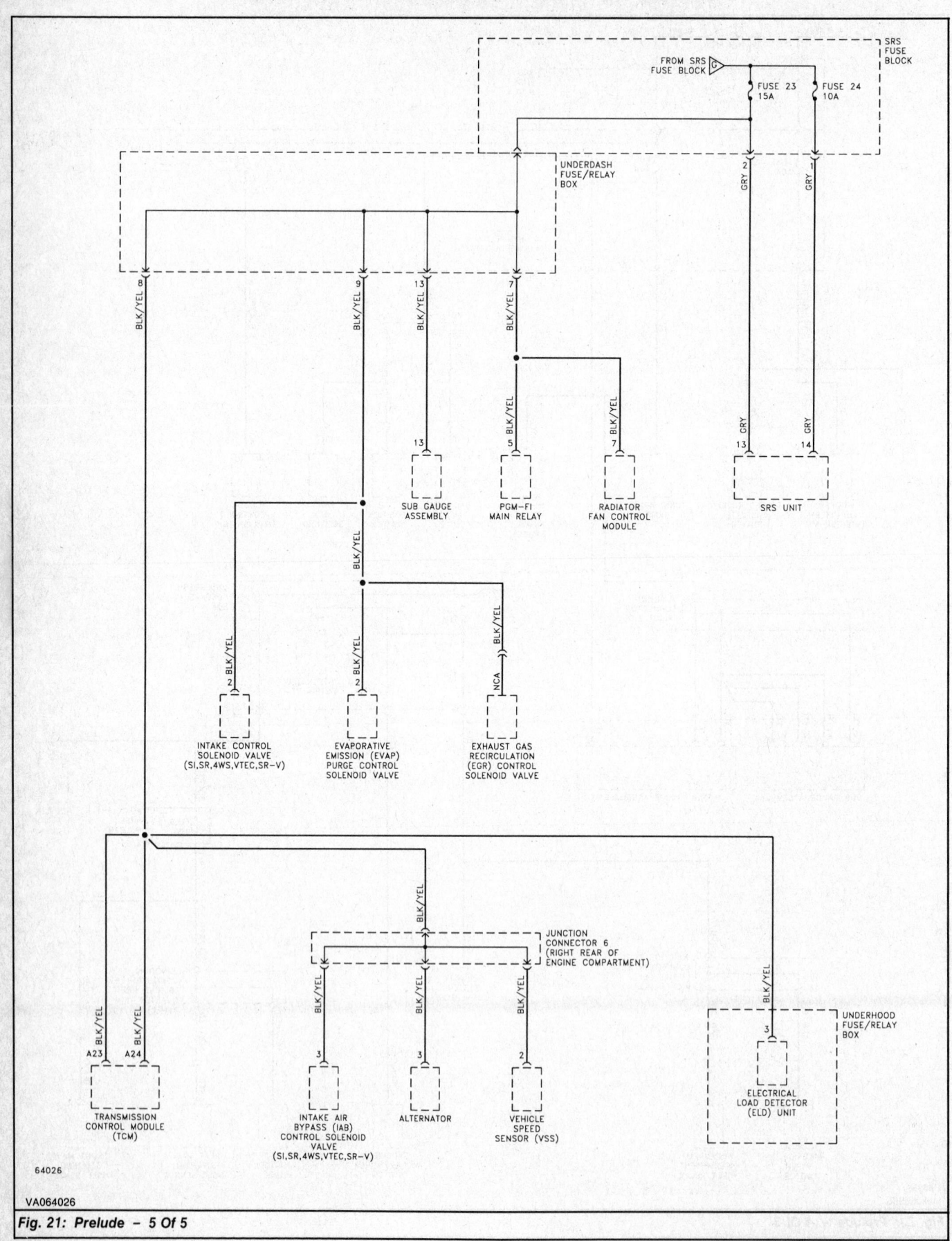

64026

VA064026

Accord, Civic, Civic Del Sol, Prelude

WARNING: To avoid injury from accidental air bag deployment, read and carefully follow all WARNINGS and SERVICE PRECAUTIONS.

NOTE: For information on air bag DIAGNOSIS & TESTING or DISPOSAL PROCEDURES, see the MITCHELL® AIR BAG SERVICE & REPAIR MANUAL, DOMESTIC & IMPORTED MODELS.

DESCRIPTION & OPERATION

NOTE: Outer insulation on SRS wiring harness is Yellow.

The Supplemental Restraint System (SRS) activates when the vehicle receives a sufficient front-end impact. System is composed of SRS control unit, driver-side air bag assembly, passenger-side air bag assembly (if equipped), left and right dash sensors, cowl sensor(s) inside SRS control unit, and cable reel. See Figs. 1-4. If vehicle battery

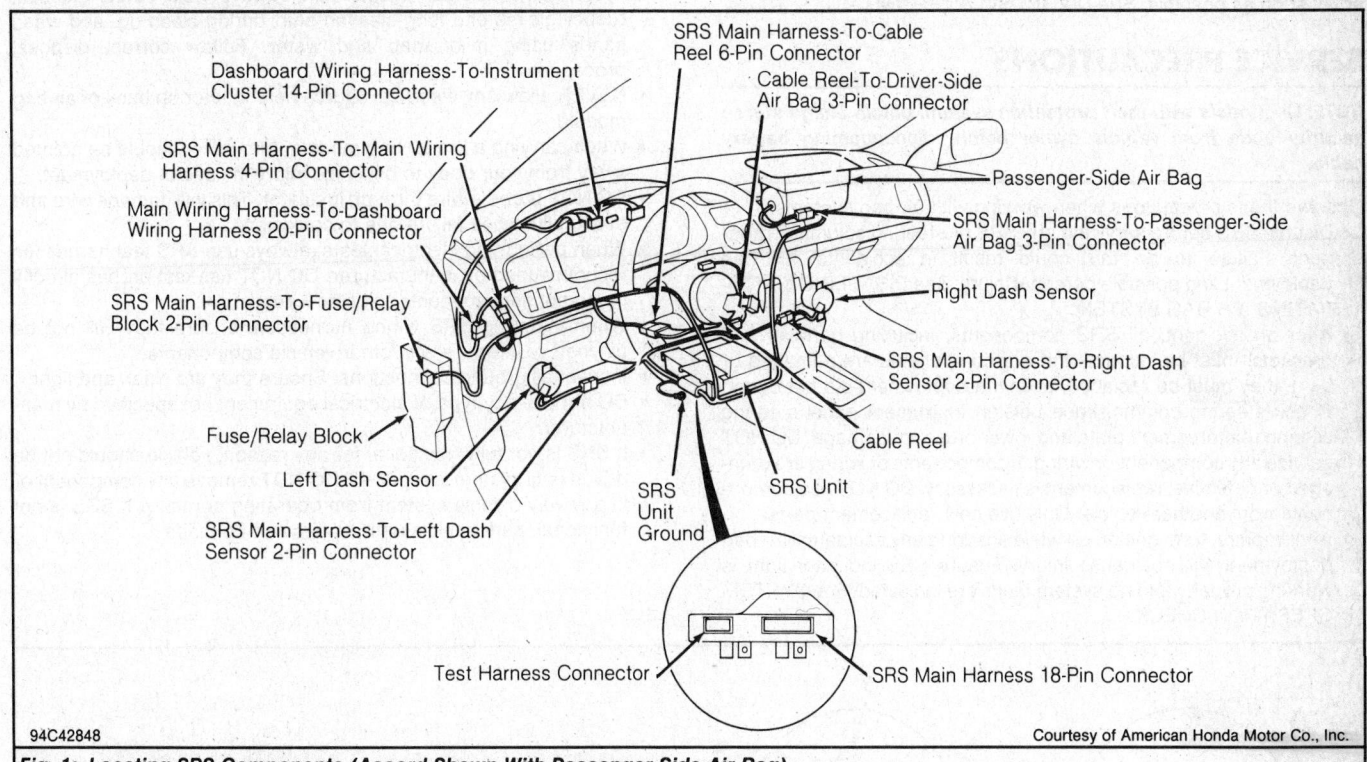

94C42848

Courtesy of American Honda Motor Co., Inc.

Fig. 1: Locating SRS Components (Accord Shown With Passenger-Side Air Bag)

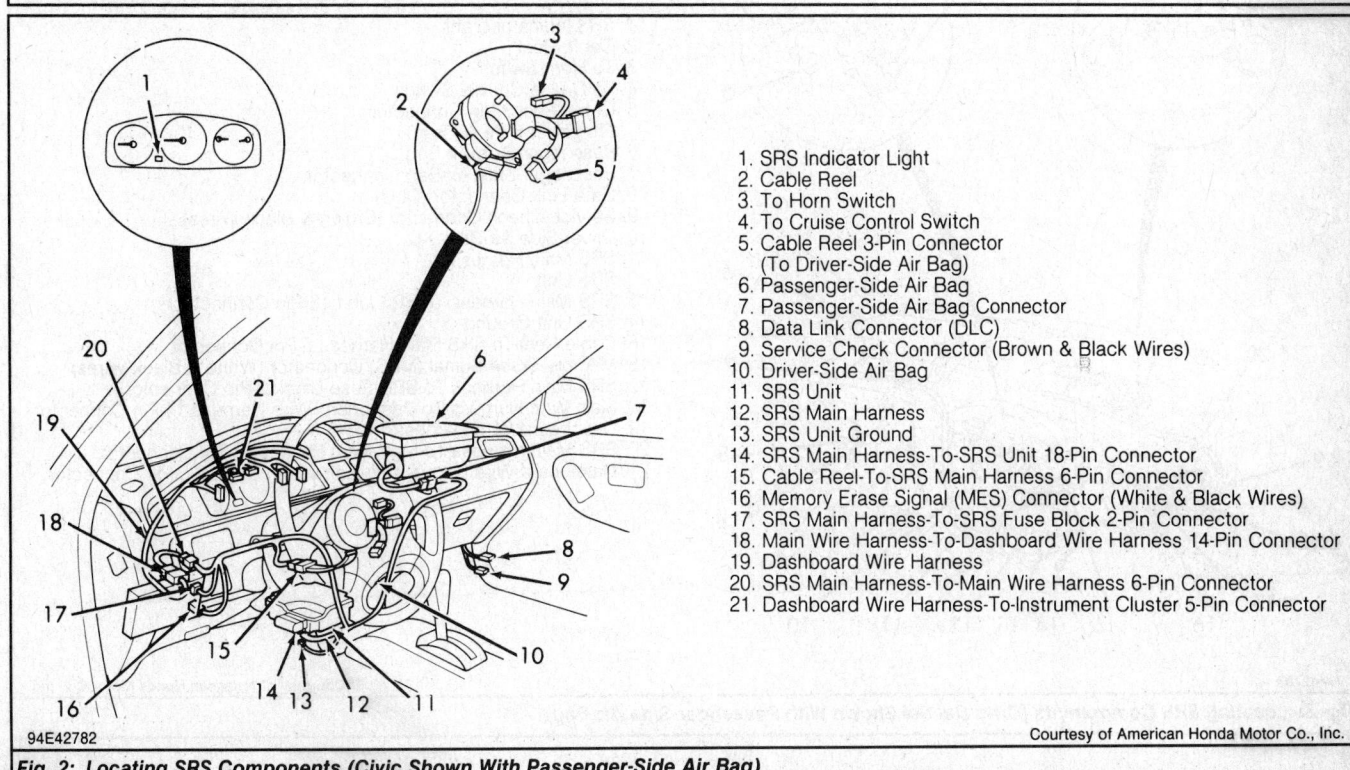

1. SRS Indicator Light
2. Cable Reel
3. To Horn Switch
4. To Cruise Control Switch
5. Cable Reel 3-Pin Connector (To Driver-Side Air Bag)
6. Passenger-Side Air Bag
7. Passenger-Side Air Bag Connector
8. Data Link Connector (DLC)
9. Service Check Connector (Brown & Black Wires)
10. Driver-Side Air Bag
11. SRS Unit
12. SRS Main Harness
13. SRS Unit Ground
14. SRS Main Harness-To-SRS Unit 18-Pin Connector
15. Cable Reel-To-SRS Main Harness 6-Pin Connector
16. Memory Erase Signal (MES) Connector (White & Black Wires)
17. SRS Main Harness-To-SRS Fuse Block 2-Pin Connector
18. Main Wire Harness-To-Dashboard Wire Harness 14-Pin Connector
19. Dashboard Wire Harness
20. SRS Main Harness-To-Main Wire Harness 6-Pin Connector
21. Dashboard Wire Harness-To-Instrument Cluster 5-Pin Connector

94E42782

Courtesy of American Honda Motor Co., Inc.

Fig. 2: Locating SRS Components (Civic Shown With Passenger-Side Air Bag)

voltage is low or lost, back-up power unit inside SRS control unit will activate SRS. For air bags to deploy, cowl sensor and at least one front sensor must input a signal to the SRS control unit.

SYSTEM OPERATION CHECK

When ignition is turned on, SRS indicator light will glow for about 6 seconds and then go off. If indicator does not glow, does not go off after about 6 seconds or glows while driving, system must be inspected as soon as possible. See DIAGNOSIS & TESTING.

SERVICE PRECAUTIONS

NOTE: On models with theft protection system, obtain 5-digit stereo security code from vehicle owner before disconnecting battery cable.

Observe these precautions when working with air bag systems:

- Disable SRS before servicing any SRS or steering column component. Failure to do this could result in accidental air bag deployment and possible personal injury. See DISABLING & ACTIVATING AIR BAG SYSTEM.
- After an accident, all SRS components, including harness and brackets, must be inspected. If any components are damaged or bent, they must be replaced, even if a deployment did not occur. Check steering column, knee bolster, instrument panel steering column reinforcement plate and lower brace for damage. DO NOT service any component or wiring. If components or wiring are damaged or defective, replacement is necessary. DO NOT use components from another vehicle. Only use new replacement parts.
- After repairs, turn ignition on while ensuring any accidental air bag deployment will not cause injury. Ensure SRS indicator light is working properly and no system faults are indicated. See SYSTEM OPERATION CHECK.

- Always wear safety glasses when servicing or handling an air bag.
- Air bag module must be stored in its original special container until used for service. It must be stored in a clean, dry place, away from sources of extreme heat, sparks and high electrical energy.
- When placing a live air bag module on a bench or other surface, always face air bag and trim cover up, away from surface. This will reduce motion of module if it is accidentally deployed.
- After deployment, air bag surface may contain deposits of sodium hydroxide, which can irritate skin. Always wear safety glasses, rubber gloves and long-sleeved shirt during clean-up, and wash hands using mild soap and water. Follow correct disposal procedures.
- NEVER allow any electrical source near inflator on back of air bag module.
- When carrying a live air bag module, trim cover should be pointed away from your body to minimize injury in case of deployment.
- DO NOT probe a wire through insulator. This will damage wire and eventually cause failure due to corrosion.
- When performing electrical tests, always use SRS test harnesses recommended by manufacturer. DO NOT use test probes directly on component connector pins or wires.
- When installing SRS wiring harnesses, ensure they will not be pinched or interfere with other vehicle components.
- Inspect all ground connections. Ensure they are clean and tight.
- DO not use any type of electrical equipment not specified by manufacturer.
- If SRS is not fully functional for any reason, vehicle should not be driven until system is repaired. DO NOT remove any component or in any way disable system from operating normally. If SRS is not functional, park vehicle until repairs can be made.

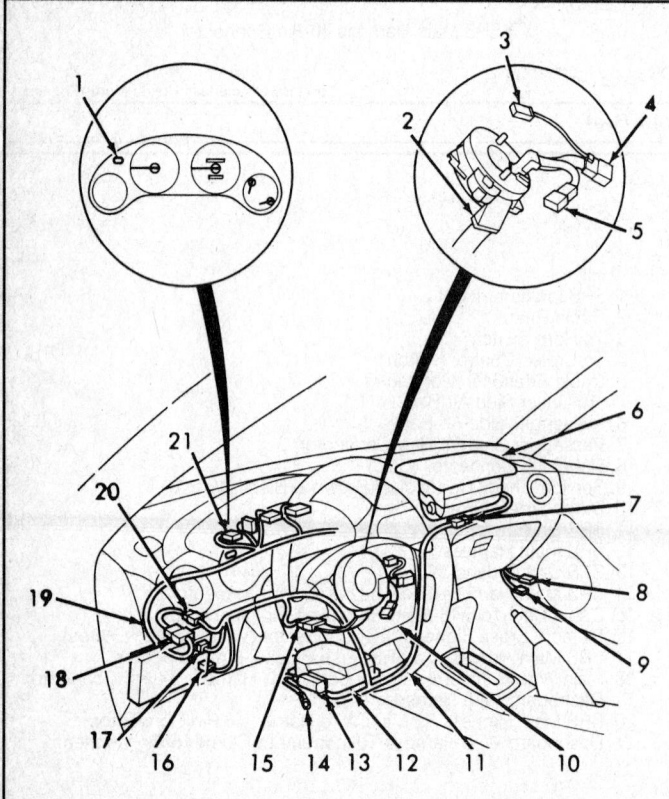

1. SRS Indicator Light
2. Cable Reel
3. To Horn Switch
4. To Cruise Control Switch
5. Cable Reel 3-Pin Connector (To Driver-Side Air Bag)
6. Passenger-Side Air Bag
7. Passenger-Side Air Bag Connector
8. Data Link Connector (DLC)
9. Service Check Connector (Brown & Black Wires)
10. Driver-Side Air Bag
11. SRS Main Harness
12. SRS Unit
13. SRS Main Harness-To-SRS Unit 18-Pin Connector
14. SRS Unit Ground
15. Cable Reel-To-SRS Main Harness 6-Pin Connector
16. Memory Erase Signal (MES) Connector (White & Black Wires)
17. SRS Main Harness-To-SRS Fuse Block 2-Pin Connector
18. Main Wire Harness-To-Dashboard Wire Harness 14-Pin Connector
19. Dashboard Wire Harness
20. SRS Main Harness-To-Main Wire Harness 6-Pin Connector
21. Dashboard Wire Harness-To-Instrument Cluster 5-Pin Connector

94F42783

Courtesy of American Honda Motor Co., Inc.

Fig. 3: Locating SRS Components (Civic Del Sol Shown With Passenger-Side Air Bag)

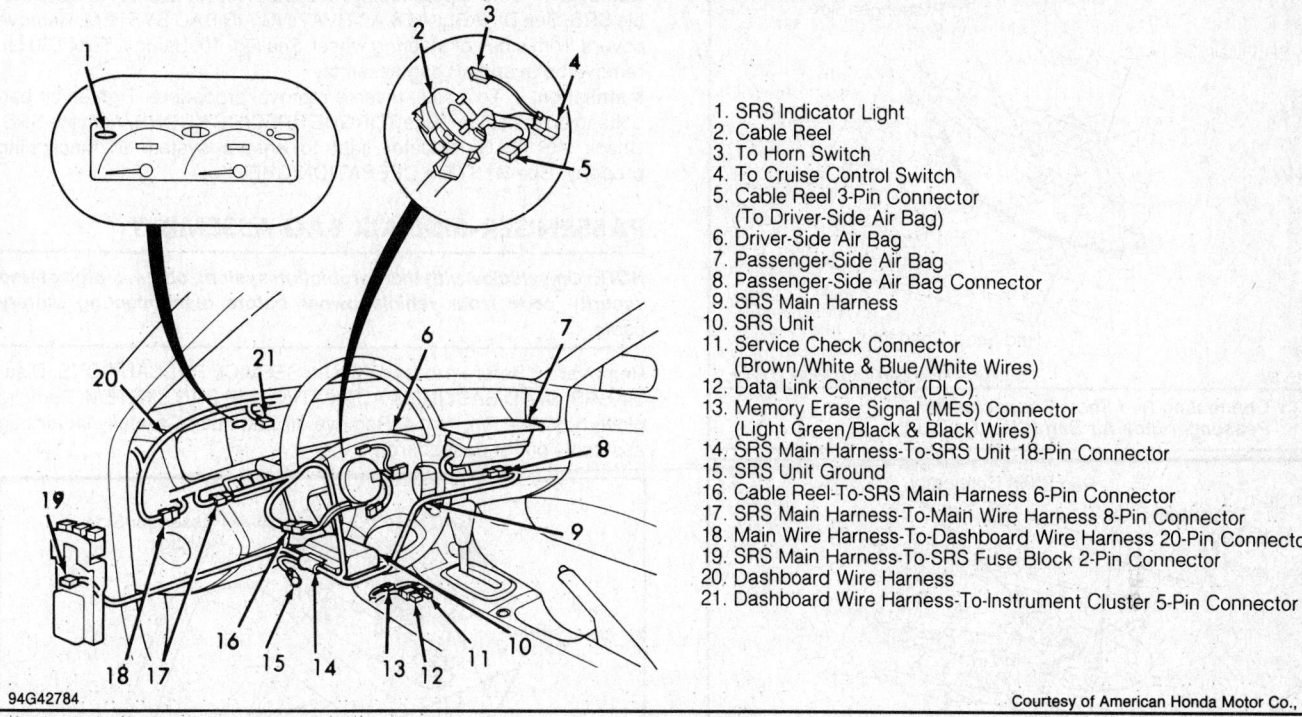

1. SRS Indicator Light
2. Cable Reel
3. To Horn Switch
4. To Cruise Control Switch
5. Cable Reel 3-Pin Connector
   (To Driver-Side Air Bag)
6. Driver-Side Air Bag
7. Passenger-Side Air Bag
8. Passenger-Side Air Bag Connector
9. SRS Main Harness
10. SRS Unit
11. Service Check Connector
    (Brown/White & Blue/White Wires)
12. Data Link Connector (DLC)
13. Memory Erase Signal (MES) Connector
    (Light Green/Black & Black Wires)
14. SRS Main Harness-To-SRS Unit 18-Pin Connector
15. SRS Unit Ground
16. Cable Reel-To-SRS Main Harness 6-Pin Connector
17. SRS Main Harness-To-Main Wire Harness 8-Pin Connector
18. Main Wire Harness-To-Dashboard Wire Harness 20-Pin Connector
19. SRS Main Harness-To-SRS Fuse Block 2-Pin Connector
20. Dashboard Wire Harness
21. Dashboard Wire Harness-To-Instrument Cluster 5-Pin Connector

94G42784

Courtesy of American Honda Motor Co., Inc.

Fig. 4: Locating SRS Components (Prelude Shown With Passenger-Side Air Bag)

DISABLING & ACTIVATING AIR BAG SYSTEM

NOTE: On models with theft protection system, obtain 5-digit stereo security code from vehicle owner before disconnecting battery cable.

DISABLING AIR BAG SYSTEM

Driver-Side Air Bag – Disconnect battery cables, negative cable first. Remove access panel from steering wheel. *See Fig. 5.* Remove Red short connector, located on inside of access panel. Disconnect air bag connector from cable reel connector. Connect Red short connector to air bag connector.

Passenger-Side Air Bag – Disable driver-side air bag. Open glove box (remove it on Accord and Civic). Disconnect air bag connector from main harness connector. *See Figs. 6-9.* Connect Red short connector to air bag connector.

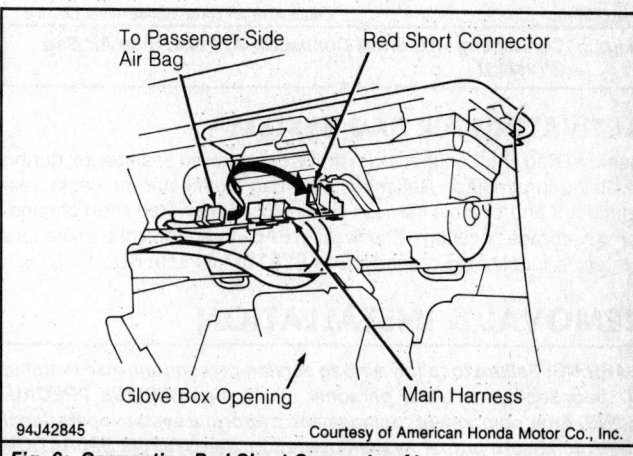

94J42845

Courtesy of American Honda Motor Co., Inc.

Fig. 6: Connecting Red Short Connector At Passenger-Side Air Bag (Accord)

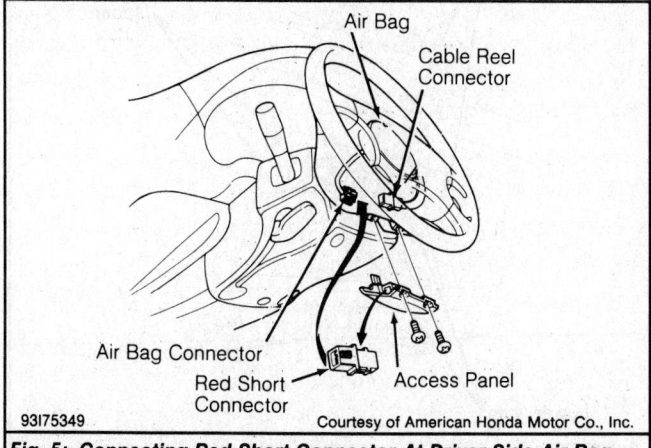

93I75349

Courtesy of American Honda Motor Co., Inc.

Fig. 5: Connecting Red Short Connector At Driver-Side Air Bag

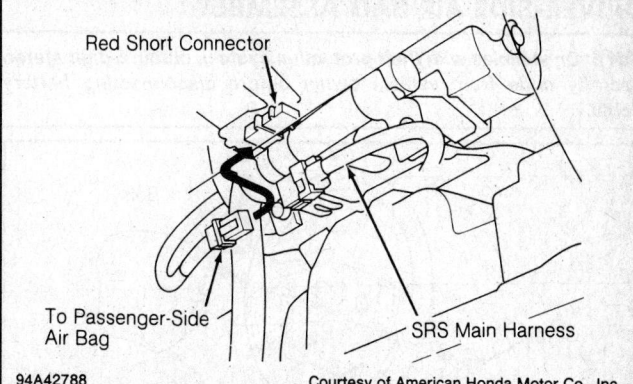

94A42788

Courtesy of American Honda Motor Co., Inc.

Fig. 7: Connecting Red Short Connector At Passenger-Side Air Bag (Civic)

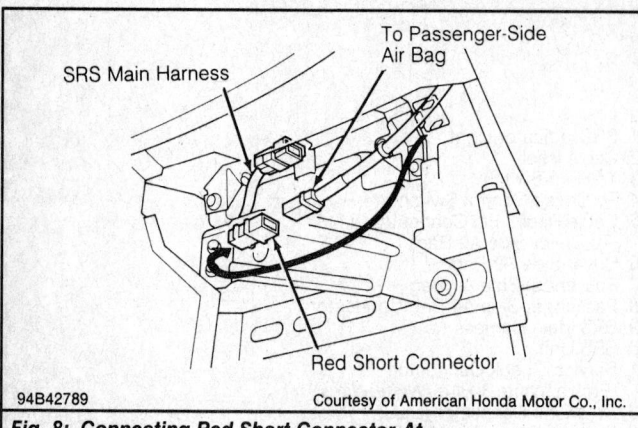

94B42789   Courtesy of American Honda Motor Co., Inc.

Fig. 8: Connecting Red Short Connector At Passenger-Side Air Bag (Civic Del Sol)

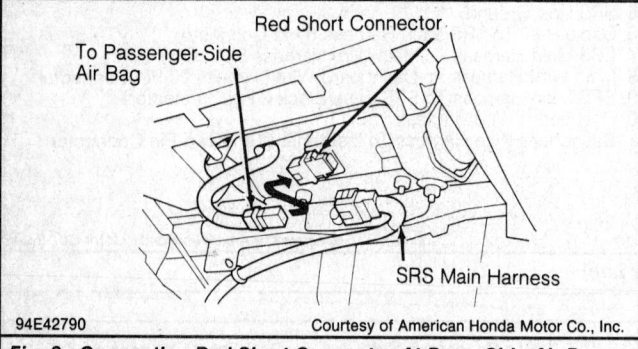

94E42790   Courtesy of American Honda Motor Co., Inc.

Fig. 9: Connecting Red Short Connector At Pass. Side Air Bag (Prelude)

ACTIVATING AIR BAG SYSTEM

Remove Red short connector(s) that were installed at air bag(s) during disabling procedure. Reconnect air bag connector to cable reel connector and/or main harness connector. Return Red short connector to storage location. Check AIR BAG indicator light to ensure system is functioning properly. See SYSTEM OPERATION CHECK.

REMOVAL & INSTALLATION

WARNING: Failure to follow air bag service precautions may result in air bag deployment and personal injury. See SERVICE PRECAUTIONS. After component replacement, perform a system operational check to ensure proper system operation. See SYSTEM OPERATION CHECK.

DRIVER-SIDE AIR BAG ASSEMBLY

NOTE: On vehicles with theft protection system, obtain 5-digit stereo security code from vehicle owner before disconnecting battery cable.

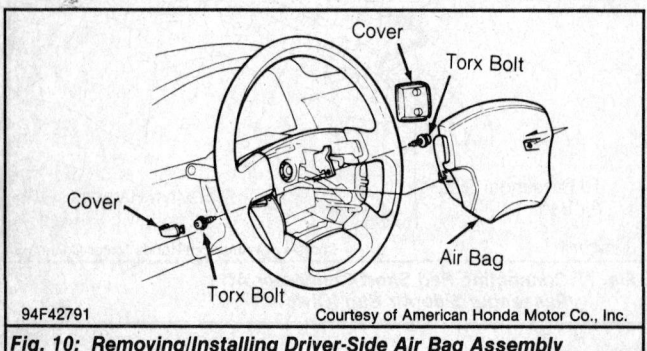

94F42791   Courtesy of American Honda Motor Co., Inc.

Fig. 10: Removing/Installing Driver-Side Air Bag Assembly

Removal – Before proceeding, see SERVICE PRECAUTIONS. Disable SRS. See DISABLING & ACTIVATING AIR BAG SYSTEM. Remove covers from sides of steering wheel. See Fig. 10. Using a Torx T30 bit, remove bolts and air bag assembly.

Installation – To install, reverse removal procedure. Tighten air bag bolts to specification. See TORQUE SPECIFICATIONS. Activate SRS. Check AIR BAG indicator light to ensure system is functioning properly. See SYSTEM OPERATION CHECK.

PASSENGER-SIDE AIR BAG ASSEMBLY

NOTE: On vehicles with theft protection system, obtain 5-digit stereo security code from vehicle owner before disconnecting battery cable.

Removal – Before proceeding, see SERVICE PRECAUTIONS. Disable SRS. See DISABLING & ACTIVATING AIR BAG SYSTEM. Remove glove box. See Fig. 11-14. Remove air bag nuts. Carefully lift air bag assembly out of dashboard.

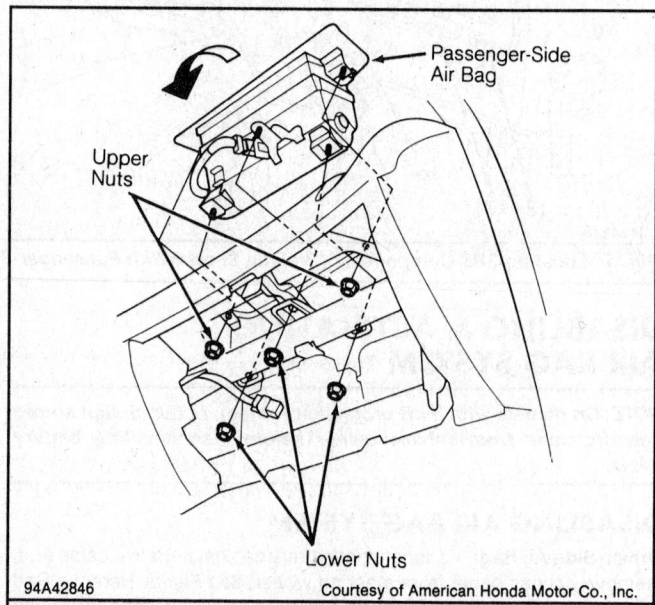

94A42846   Courtesy of American Honda Motor Co., Inc.

Fig. 11: Removing/Installing Passenger-Side Air Bag (Accord)

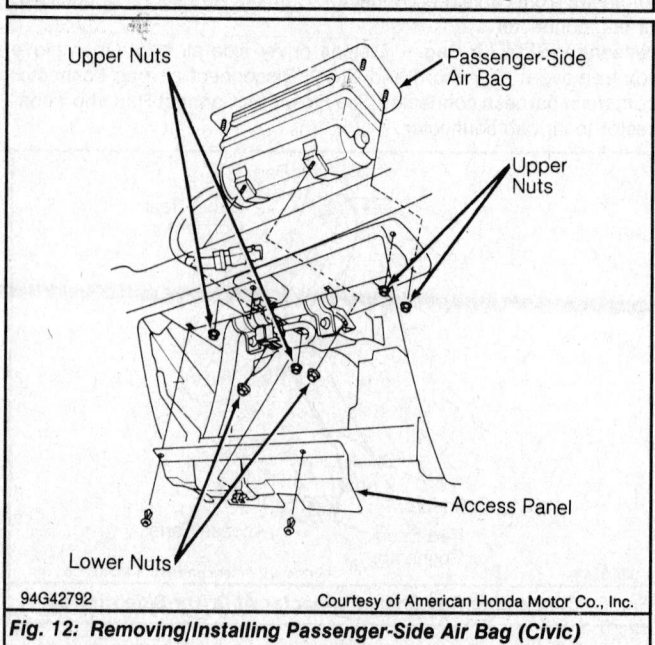

94G42792   Courtesy of American Honda Motor Co., Inc.

Fig. 12: Removing/Installing Passenger-Side Air Bag (Civic)

Installation – To install, reverse removal procedure. Tighten air bag bolts to specification. See TORQUE SPECIFICATIONS. Activate SRS. See DISABLING & ACTIVATING AIR BAG SYSTEM. Check AIR BAG indicator light to ensure system is functioning properly. See SYSTEM OPERATION CHECK.

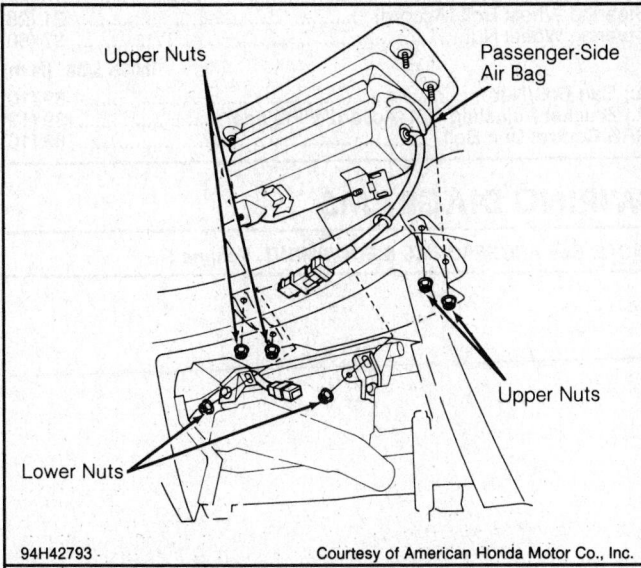

Fig. 13: *Removing/Installing Passenger-Side Air Bag (Civic Del Sol)*

94H42793 · Courtesy of American Honda Motor Co., Inc.

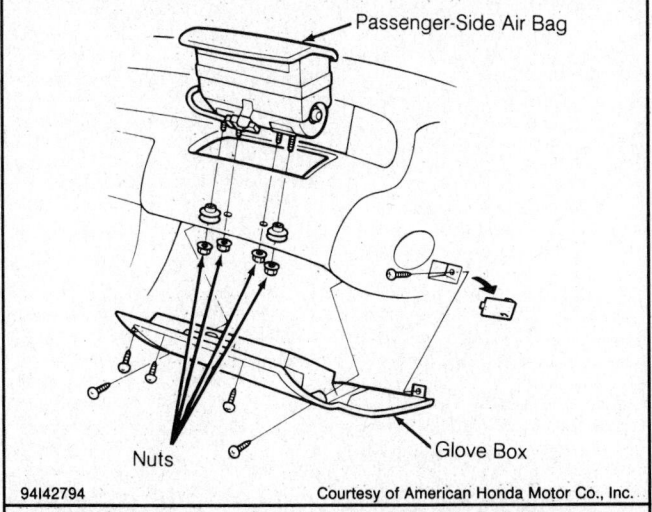

Fig. 14: *Removing/Installing Passenger-Side Air Bag (Prelude)*

94I42794 Courtesy of American Honda Motor Co., Inc.

CABLE REEL

NOTE: On vehicles with theft protection system, obtain 5-digit stereo security code from vehicle owner before disconnecting battery cable.

Removal – **1)** Before proceeding, see SERVICE PRECAUTIONS. Disable SRS. See DISABLING & ACTIVATING AIR BAG SYSTEM. Ensure front wheels are facing straight ahead.
2) Remove dashboard lower cover and knee bolster under steering column. Remove air bag assembly from steering wheel. See DRIVER-SIDE AIR BAG ASSEMBLY. Disconnect connectors from horn and cruise control switches at steering wheel hub. Remove steering wheel nut.
3) Mark steering wheel in relation to steering shaft. Remove steering wheel. Remove upper and lower column covers. Disconnect cable reel 6-pin connector from SRS main harness under steering column. Remove connector holder. Remove cable reel.

Installation – **1)** Align grooves in cancel sleeve with projections on cable reel. *See Fig. 15.* Install cable reel. Center cable reel. See CABLE REEL CENTERING under ADJUSTMENTS. Install column covers.
2) Install steering wheel. Reconnect electrical connectors. Install steering wheel nut. Tighten nut to specification. See TORQUE SPECIFICATIONS. Install air bag assembly. Tighten bolts to specification.
3) To complete installation, reverse removal procedure. Activate SRS. Check AIR BAG indicator light to ensure system is functioning properly. See SYSTEM OPERATION CHECK.

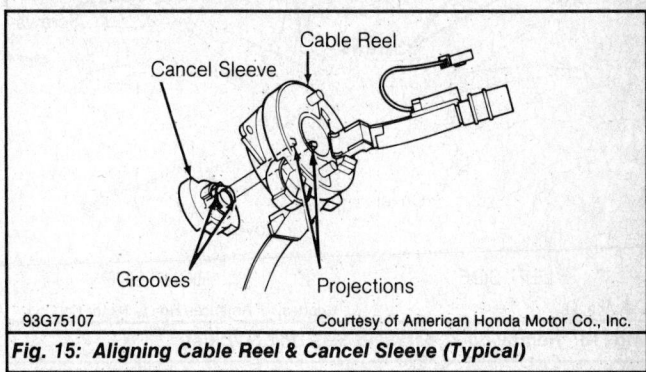

Fig. 15: *Aligning Cable Reel & Cancel Sleeve (Typical)*

93G75107 Courtesy of American Honda Motor Co., Inc.

DASH SENSORS

NOTE: On models with theft protection system, obtain 5-digit stereo security code from vehicle owner before disconnecting battery cable.

Removal & Installation (Left) – **1)** Before proceeding, see SERVICE PRECAUTIONS. Disable SRS. See DISABLING & ACTIVATING AIR BAG SYSTEM. Dash sensor is located in left footwell. *See Figs. 1-4.*
2) On Accord, pull back carpeting. Remove steering joint cover at base of steering column. Pull back rubber floor pad. On Civic, Civic Del Sol and Prelude, remove footrest and door sill molding. Pull back carpeting. On all models, remove dash sensor protector and dash sensor.
3) To install, reverse removal procedure. Tighten dash sensor bolts to specification. See TORQUE SPECIFICATIONS. Activate SRS. Ensure system is functioning properly. See SYSTEM OPERATION CHECK.
Removal & Installation (Right) – **1)** Before proceeding, see SERVICE PRECAUTIONS. Disable SRS. See DISABLING & ACTIVATING AIR BAG SYSTEM. Dash sensor is in right footwell. *See Figs. 1-4.*
2) Remove right side door sill molding. Pull back carpeting. On Prelude, remove or reposition engine control unit (and automatic transmission control unit, if equipped) as necessary. On all models, disconnect dash sensor connector. Remove dash sensor protector. Remove dash sensor.
3) To install, reverse removal procedure. Tighten dash sensor bolts to specification. See TORQUE SPECIFICATIONS. Activate SRS. Ensure system is functioning properly. See SYSTEM OPERATION CHECK.

SRS UNIT

NOTE: On vehicles with theft protection system, obtain 5-digit stereo security code from vehicle owner before disconnecting battery cable.

Removal – Before proceeding, see SERVICE PRECAUTIONS. Disable SRS. See DISABLING & ACTIVATING AIR BAG SYSTEM. SRS unit is located under instrument panel, forward of center console. *See Figs. 1-4.* Remove cover from each side of SRS unit. *See Fig. 16.* Disconnect SRS unit connector. Remove SRS unit bolts. Remove SRS unit through left opening.
Installation – To install, reverse removal procedure. Tighten SRS unit bolts to specification. See TORQUE SPECIFICATIONS. Activate SRS. Check AIR BAG indicator light to ensure system is functioning properly. See SYSTEM OPERATION CHECK.

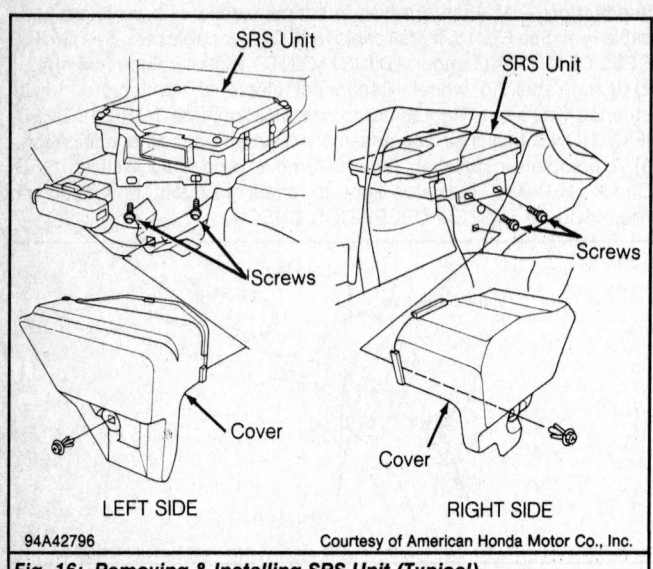

94A42796   Courtesy of American Honda Motor Co., Inc.

Fig. 16: Removing & Installing SRS Unit (Typical)

ADJUSTMENTS

CABLE REEL CENTERING

After installing cable reel onto steering column shaft, rotate cable reel clockwise until it stops. Rotate cable reel counterclockwise about 2 turns until Yellow gear tooth lines up with mark on cover and arrow on cable reel label points straight up. *See Fig. 9.*

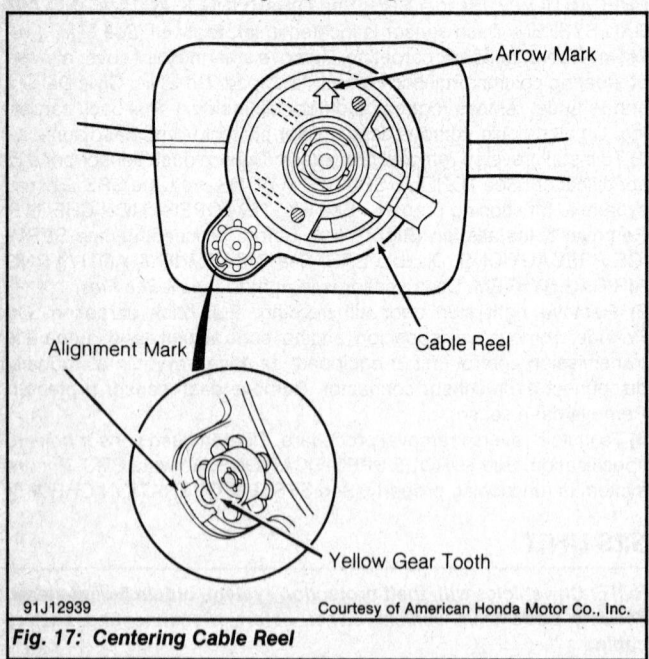

91J12939   Courtesy of American Honda Motor Co., Inc.

Fig. 17: Centering Cable Reel

WIRE REPAIR

DO NOT attempt to repair SRS wiring or harness connectors. If SRS wiring or harness connectors are faulty, replace faulty wiring harness.

TORQUE SPECIFICATIONS

TORQUE SPECIFICATIONS

Application	Ft. Lbs. (N.m)
Dash Sensor Bolts	16 (22)
Steering Wheel Bolt (Accord)	21 (28)
Steering Wheel Nut	37 (50)

	INCH Lbs. (N.m)
Air Bag Bolt/Nut	89 (10)
"L" Bracket Adjusting Nut (Accord & Prelude)	89 (10)
SRS Control Unit Bolt	89 (10)

WIRING DIAGRAMS

NOTE: See ACCESSORIES & EQUIPMENT, Volume 5.

Accord, Civic, Civic Del Sol, Passport, Prelude

NOTE: For cruise control system information for Passport, refer to Rodeo in Isuzu CRUISE CONTROL SYSTEMS article.

DESCRIPTION

The cruise control system uses mechanical, electrical and vacuum operated devices to maintain selected vehicle speeds greater than 25 MPH. The cruise control unit receives command signals from cruise control main switch and cruise control SET/RESUME switch. It also receives operating signals from brakelight switch, ignition coil, speed sensor, clutch switch (M/T) or shift position switch (A/T).

The cruise control unit compares actual vehicle speed to selected speed. The brakelight switch releases system control of throttle when brake pedal is pressed. The clutch switch and shift position switch send a disengage signal to the cruise control unit.

OPERATION

The cruise control system will set and automatically maintain any set speed greater than 25 MPH. To set, ensure main switch is on. Press SET switch after reaching desired speed. Pressing SET switch with main switch on will cause CRUISE CONTROL light display to come on. Pushing main switch to off, will cancel cruise control system operation and erase vehicle speed from memory.

If system is disengaged temporarily by brakelight switch, clutch switch or shift position switch, pressing RESUME switch will cause vehicle to automatically return to previous set speed. Holding RESUME switch will gradually increase vehicle speed without having to depress accelerator pedal. This sends an acceleration signal input to cruise control unit. When RESUME switch is released, system is reprogrammed for new speed.

For gradual deceleration without pressing brake pedal, push SET switch and hold switch until desired speed is reached. This sends a deceleration signal input to cruise control unit. When desired speed is reached, release SET switch. This reprograms system for new speed.

TROUBLE SHOOTING

WARNING: All models are equipped with Supplemental Restraint System (SRS). SRS wiring harness is routed close to instrument cluster, steering wheel, and related components. All SRS wiring harnesses are covered by Yellow outer insulation. DO NOT use electrical test equipment on these circuits. Before working on steering column components, disable air bag system and follow all service procedures. See AIR BAG RESTRAINT SYSTEM article in ACCESSORIES & EQUIPMENT.

ACCORD

Preliminary Checks – 1) Before trouble shooting by symptom, check underhood fuses No. 15 (80-amp;100-amp on F22B1 engine), No. 19 (50-amp) and No. 25 (20-amp). Replace fuses as necessary.
2) Check underdash fuses No. 1 (10-amp) and No. 4 (7.5-amp). Replace fuses as necessary. Ensure horn and tachometer operate properly. Ensure all connections are clean and tight. For circuit identification, see WIRING DIAGRAMS.

NOTE: Check possible faults in order listed. Repair or replace components and circuits as necessary.

Cruise Control Will Not Set – 1) Faulty main switch. Faulty SET/RESUME switch. Faulty brakelight switch. Faulty clutch switch (M/T) or shift lever position switch (A/T). Faulty cruise control unit inputs.
3) Open in one or more of the following wires:
- Light Green/Red wire between cable reel and cruise control unit.
- Light Green wire between main switch and cruise control unit.
- Gray wire between brakelight switch and cruise control unit.
- Orange wire between Vehicle Speed Sensor (VSS) and cruise control unit.

- Brown/White wire between cruise control unit and cruise control actuator.
- Brown/Black wire between cruise control unit and cruise control actuator.
- Brown wire between cruise control unit and cruise control actuator.
- Blue wire (on early production cars) between Ignition Control Module (ICM) and cruise control unit.
- Pink wire between clutch switch (M/T) or shift lever position switch (A/T) and cruise control unit.

4) Faulty ground connection G402 (located behind right kick panel). Faulty ground connection G404 (located under center of dash).
Cruise Control Will Set, But Indicator Light Will Not Come On – Defective bulb for cruise control indicator. Faulty dimming circuit for gauges. Open Yellow wire between underdash fuse No. 1 (10-amp) and instrument light dimming circuit. Open Blue/Black wire between cruise indicator light and cruise control unit.
Cruise Speed Noticeably Higher Or Lower Than Setting – Faulty Vehicle Speed Sensor (VSS). Incorrect actuator cable free play. Faulty cruise control unit inputs.
Excessive Hunting When Trying To Achieve Set Speed – Incorrect actuator cable free play. Faulty actuator assembly. Faulty cruise control unit inputs.
Set Speed Will Not Hold, Even On Flat Road – Faulty Vehicle Speed Sensor (VSS). Incorrect actuator cable free play. Faulty cruise control unit inputs.
Vehicle Will Not Decelerate Or Accelerate When Set Or Resume Button Is Pushed – Faulty SET/RESUME switch. Faulty cruise control unit inputs. Open Light Green/Black wire and/or Light Green/Red wire between cable reel and cruise control unit.
Set Speed Will Not Cancel When Clutch Pedal Is Pushed (M/T) – Faulty clutch switch. Faulty cruise control unit inputs. Open in Pink wire between cruise control unit and clutch switch.
Set Speed Will Not Cancel When Shift Lever Is Moved To Neutral (A/T) – Faulty shift lever position switch. Faulty cruise control unit inputs. Open in Pink wire between cruise control unit and gear position switch.
Set Speed Will Not Cancel When Brake Pedal Is Pushed – Faulty brakelight switch. Faulty cruise control unit inputs. Open in Green/White wire between brakelight switch and cruise control unit.
Set Speed Will Not Cancel When Main Switch Is Turned Off – Faulty main switch. Faulty cruise control unit inputs. Open in Light Green wire between main switch and cruise control unit.
Set Speed Will Not Resume When Resume Button Is Pressed With Main Switch On, But Set Speed Will Temporarily Cancel – Faulty SET/RESUME switch. Faulty cruise control unit inputs. Open Light Green/Black wire and/or Light Green/Red wire between cable reel and cruise control unit.

CIVIC

Preliminary Checks – 1) Before trouble shooting by symptom, check underdash fuses No. 15 (10-amp) and No. 24 (15-amp). Replace fuses as necessary.
2) Check underhood fuses No. 39 (50-amp), No. 41 (80-amp) and No. 42 (20-amp). Replace fuses as necessary. Ensure horn and tachometer operate properly. Ensure all connections are clean and tight. For circuit identification, see WIRING DIAGRAMS.

NOTE: Check possible faults in order listed. Repair or replace components and circuits as necessary.

Cruise Control Will Not Set – 1) Faulty cruise control unit inputs. Faulty main switch. Faulty SET/RESUME switch. Faulty brakelight switch. Faulty clutch switch (M/T) or shift lever position switch (A/T).
2) Faulty ground connection G201 (located in right front corner of engine compartment). Faulty ground connection G301 (located in left front corner of engine compartment). Faulty ground connection G401 (located behind left kick panel).

3) Open one or more of the following wires:
- Blue/Red wire between horns and SET/RESUME switch.
- Light Green/Red wire between SET/RESUME switch and cruise control unit.
- Blue wire between ignition switch and cruise control unit.
- Black/Yellow wire between underdash fuse No. 24 (15-amp) and main switch. Wire also splices to cruise control unit.
- Light Green wire between main switch, brakelight switch and cruise control unit.
- Gray wire between brakelight switch and cruise control unit.
- Yellow/Red wire between speed sensor and cruise control unit.
- Brown wire between actuator assembly and cruise control unit.
- Brown/Black wire between actuator assembly and cruise control unit.
- Brown/White wire between actuator assembly and cruise control unit.
- Pink wire between clutch switch (M/T) or shift lever position switch (A/T) and cruise control unit.

Cruise Control Will Set, But Indicator Light Will Not Come On –
1) Faulty cruise control unit inputs. Faulty dimming circuit for gauges. Open Yellow wire between underdash fuse No. 14 (10-amp) and dimming circuit for gauges. Open Red/Blue wire between dimming circuit for gauges and cruise control unit.
2) Faulty ground connection G201 (located in right front corner of engine compartment). Faulty ground connection G401 (located behind left kick panel).

Cruise Speed Noticeably Higher Or Lower Than Setting – Faulty speed sensor. Incorrect actuator free play. Faulty actuator assembly. Faulty cruise control unit inputs.

Excessive Hunting When Trying To Achieve Set Speed – Incorrect actuator cable free play. Faulty actuator assembly. Faulty speed sensor signal. Faulty cruise control unit inputs.

Set Speed Will Not Hold, Even On Flat Road – Faulty speed sensor signal. Incorrect actuator cable free play. Faulty actuator assembly. Faulty cruise control unit inputs.

Vehicle Will Not Decelerate Or Accelerate When Set Or Resume Button Is Pushed – Faulty SET/RESUME switch. Faulty cruise control unit inputs. Open Light Green/Black wire and/or Light Green/Red wire between SET/RESUME switch and cruise control unit.

Set Speed Will Not Cancel When Clutch Pedal Is Pushed (M/T) – Faulty clutch switch. Faulty control unit inputs.

Set Speed Will Not Cancel When Shift Lever Is Moved To Neutral (A/T) – Faulty shift lever position switch. Faulty cruise control unit inputs.

Set Speed Will Not Cancel When Brake Pedal Is Pushed – Faulty brakelight switch. Faulty cruise control unit inputs.

Set Speed Will Not Cancel When Main Switch Is Turned Off – Faulty main switch. Faulty cruise control unit inputs.

Set Speed Will Not Resume When Resume Button Is Pressed With Main Switch On, But Set Speed Will Temporarily Cancel – Faulty SET/RESUME switch. Faulty cruise control unit inputs. Open Light Green/Black wire between SET/RESUME switch and cruise control unit. Open Light Green/Red wire between SET/RESUME switch and cruise control unit.

CIVIC DEL SOL

Preliminary Checks – 1) Before trouble shooting by symptom, check underdash fuses No. 15 (10-amp) and No. 24 (15-amp). Replace fuses as necessary.
2) Check underhood fuses No. 39 (50-amp), No. 41 (80-amp) and No. 42 (20-amp). Replace fuses as necessary. Ensure horn and tachometer operate properly. Ensure all connections are clean and tight. For circuit identification, see WIRING DIAGRAMS.

NOTE: Check possible faults in order listed. Repair or replace components and circuits as necessary.

Cruise Control Will Not Set – 1) Faulty main switch. Faulty cruise control unit inputs. Faulty SET/RESUME switch.
2) Faulty brakelight switch. Faulty clutch switch (M/T) or shift lever position switch (A/T).

3) Faulty ground connection G201 (located in right front corner of engine compartment). Faulty ground connection G301 (located in left front corner of engine compartment). Faulty ground connection G401 (located behind left kick panel).
4) Open Black/Yellow wire between underdash fuse box and cruise control unit. Open Light Green wire between main switch and cruise control unit.

Cruise Control Will Set, But Indicator Light Will Not Come On –
1) Faulty dimming circuit for gauges. Faulty cruise control unit inputs.
2) Open Yellow wire between underdash fuse No. 15 (10-amp) and gauge light dimming circuit. Open Red/Blue wire between gauge light dimming circuit and cruise control unit.

Cruise Speed Noticeably Higher Or Lower Than Setting – Faulty speed sensor signal. Incorrect actuator cable free play. Faulty actuator assembly. Faulty cruise control unit inputs.

Excessive Hunting When Trying To Achieve Set Speed – Incorrect actuator cable free play. Faulty actuator assembly. No speed sensor signal. Faulty cruise control unit inputs. Open or shorted Yellow/Blue wire between cruise control unit and vehicle speed sensor.

Set Speed Will Not Hold, Even On Flat Road – Faulty speed sensor signal. Incorrect actuator cable free play. Faulty actuator assembly. Faulty cruise control unit inputs.

Vehicle Will Not Decelerate Or Accelerate When Set Or Resume Button Is Pushed – Faulty brakelight switch or switch adjustment. Faulty cruise control unit inputs.

Set Speed Will Not Cancel When Clutch Pedal Is Pushed (M/T) – Faulty clutch switch or switch adjustment. Faulty cruise control unit inputs.

Set Speed Will Not Cancel When Shift Lever Is Moved To Neutral (A/T) – Faulty shift lever position switch. Faulty cruise control unit inputs.

Set Speed Will Not Cancel When Brake Pedal Is Pushed – Faulty brakelight switch or switch adjustment. Faulty cruise control unit inputs.

Set Speed Will Not Cancel When Main Switch Is Turned Off – Faulty main switch. Faulty cruise control unit inputs.

Set Speed Will Not Resume When Resume Button Is Pressed With Main Switch On, But Set Speed Will Temporarily Cancel – Faulty main switch. Faulty cruise control unit inputs.

PRELUDE

Preliminary Checks – 1) Before trouble shooting by symptom, check underdash fuses No. 13 (10-amp) and No. 14 (7.5-amp).
2) Check underhood fuses No. 32 (100-amp), No. 33 (50-amp) and No. 41 (15-amp). Replace fuses as necessary. Ensure horn and tachometer operate properly. Ensure all connections are clean and tight. For circuit identification, see WIRING DIAGRAMS.

NOTE: Check possible faults in order listed. Repair or replace components and circuits as necessary.

Cruise Control Will Not Set – 1) Faulty main switch. Faulty SET/RESUME switch. Faulty cruise control unit inputs.
2) Faulty ground connection G401 (located under right side of dashboard, near base of windshield). Faulty ground connection G402 (located on left side of left side rail, on center console). Faulty ground connection G404 (located on top of left side rail, on center console). Faulty ground connection G521 (located on floor on left side near driver's seat).
3) Open one or more of the following wires:
- Light Green/Black wire between SET/RESUME switch and cruise control unit.
- Light Green/Red wire between SET/RESUME switch and cruise control unit.
- Brown/White wire between cruise control actuator and cruise control unit.
- Brown/Black wire between cruise control actuator and cruise control unit.
- Brown/Red wire between cruise control actuator and cruise control unit.
- Orange wire between vehicle speed sensor and cruise control unit.

- Light Green wire between main switch and cruise control unit. Wire splices to brakelight switch.
- Light Green/Red wire between SET/RESUME switch and cruise control unit.

Cruise Control Will Set, But Indicator Light Will Not Come On – 1) Faulty dimming circuit for gauges. Open Yellow wire between underdash fuse No. 13 (10-amp) and dashlight dimming circuit. Open Red wire between dashlight dimming circuit and cruise control unit. Open Red/Black wire between combination switch and main switch.
2) Faulty ground connection G401 (located under right side of dashboard, near base of windshield). Faulty ground connection G402 (located on left side of left side rail, on center console). Faulty ground connection G404 (located on top of left side rail, on center console) Faulty ground connection G521 (located on floor on left side near driver's seat).

Cruise Speed Noticeably Higher Or Lower Than Setting – Incorrect actuator cable free play. Faulty actuator assembly. Faulty cruise control unit inputs. Faulty speed sensor signal.

Excessive Hunting When Trying To Achieve Set Speed – Incorrect actuator cable free play. Faulty actuator assembly. Faulty cruise control unit inputs. Faulty speed sensor signal.

Set Speed Will Not Hold, Even On Flat Road – Incorrect actuator cable free play. Faulty actuator assembly. Leaking or plugged actuator vacuum connections. Leaking vacuum reservoir. Faulty cruise control unit inputs. Faulty speed sensor signal.

Vehicle Will Not Decelerate Or Accelerate When Set Or Resume Button Is Pushed – **1)** Faulty SET/RESUME switch. Faulty cruise control unit inputs.

Set Speed Will Not Cancel When Clutch Pedal Is Pushed (M/T) – Faulty clutch switch. Faulty cruise control unit inputs. Open Pink wire between cruise control unit and clutch switch.

Set Speed Will Not Cancel When Shift Lever Is Moved To Neutral (A/T) – Faulty shift lever position switch. Faulty cruise control unit inputs. Open Pink wire between cruise control unit and shift lever position switch.

Set Speed Will Not Cancel When Brake Pedal Is Pushed – Faulty brakelight switch. Faulty cruise control unit inputs. Open Gray and/or Green/White wires between brakelight switch and cruise control unit.

Set Speed Will Not Cancel When Main Switch Is Turned Off – Faulty main switch. Faulty cruise control unit inputs. Open Light Green wire between main switch and cruise control unit. Check wire splice to brakelight switch for poor connection.

Set Speed Will Not Resume When Resume Button Is Pressed With Main Switch On, But Set Speed Will Temporarily Cancel – Faulty SET/RESUME switch. Faulty cruise control unit inputs.

ADJUSTMENTS

ACTUATOR CABLE

1) Ensure actuator cable operates smoothly without binding or sticking. Start engine. Measure actuator rod movement before cable

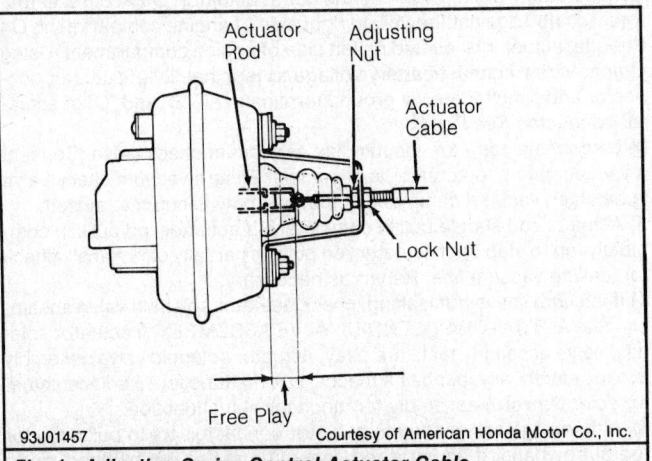

93J01457   Courtesy of American Honda Motor Co., Inc.

Fig. 1: Adjusting Cruise Control Actuator Cable (Civic & Civic Del Sol Is Shown; Accord Is Similar)

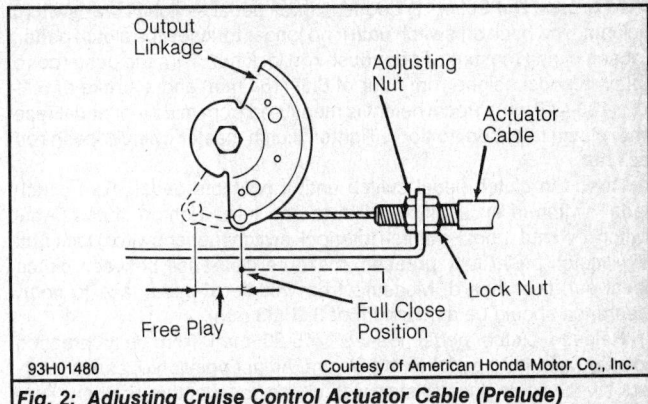

93H01480   Courtesy of American Honda Motor Co., Inc.

Fig. 2: Adjusting Cruise Control Actuator Cable (Prelude)

pulls on accelerator lever (engine speed starts to increase). This is amount of cable free play. *See Fig. 1 or 2.* See ACTUATOR CABLE FREE PLAY SPECIFICATIONS table.

ACTUATOR CABLE FREE PLAY SPECIFICATIONS

Application	In. (mm)
Except Accord	.37-.49 (9.5-12.5)
Accord	.18-.22 (4.5-5.5)

2) If free play is not as specified, loosen lock nut and turn adjusting nut as necessary. *See Fig. 1 or 2.* Tighten lock nut and recheck free play. Test drive vehicle and ensure actual speed is within 2 MPH of set speed. If necessary, check throttle cable free play.

BRAKE PEDAL HEIGHT

1) Loosen brakelight switch lock nut, and back off switch until it no longer touches brake pedal. Loosen brake pedal push rod lock nut, and screw push rod in or out until correct pedal height is obtained. See BRAKE PEDAL HEIGHT SPECIFICATIONS table. Tighten lock nut to specification. See TORQUE SPECIFICATIONS.
2) Screw in brakelight switch until plunger is fully pressed (threaded end touching pad on pedal arm). Back off switch until clearance between threaded end and pad is .012" (.30 mm) and tighten lock nut firmly. Ensure brakelights work when brake pedal is pressed.

BRAKE PEDAL HEIGHT SPECIFICATIONS

Application	Auto. Trans. In. (mm)	Man. Trans. In. (mm)
Accord	7.5 (193)	7.6 (192)
Civic & Civic Del Sol	6.5 (165)	6.3 (160)
Prelude	7.3 (186)	6.5 (165)

CABLE REEL CENTERING

For cable reel centering procedure, see AIR BAG RESTRAINT SYSTEM article in ACCESSORIES & EQUIPMENT.

CLUTCH PEDAL HEIGHT

Accord – 1) Loosen clutch pedal switch (lower switch) lock nut, and back off switch until it no longer touches clutch pedal. Loosen clutch master cylinder push rod lock nut. Turn push rod to obtain a pedal height from floor of 7.2" (184 mm) and a stroke of 5.6-6.0" (142-152 mm). Pedal height is measured from middle of pedal face (with clutch released) to floor. Tighten clutch master cylinder push rod lock nut.
2) Thread in clutch pedal switch until it contacts pedal. Turn clutch pedal switch in an additional 1/4 to 1/2 turn. Tighten clutch pedal switch lock nut. Loosen clutch interlock switch (upper switch) lock nut. With clutch pedal fully pressed, measure clearance between clutch pedal and floor board. Measure from middle of pedal face to floor. Clearance should be a minimum of 3.5" (89 mm).
3) Release clutch pedal .59-.79" (15-20 mm) from fully pressed position, and hold pedal at this height. Adjust position of clutch interlock switch so engine will start with clutch pedal at this position. Turn clutch interlock switch in an additional 1/4 to 1/2 turn. Tighten clutch interlock switch lock nut.

Civic & Civic Del Sol – **1)** Loosen clutch pedal switch (lower switch) lock nut, and back off switch until it no longer touches the clutch pedal. Loosen clutch master cylinder push rod lock nut. Turn the push rod to obtain a pedal height from floor of 6.5" (164 mm) and a stroke of 5.1-5.5" (130-140 mm). Pedal height is measured from middle of pedal face (with clutch released) to floor. Tighten clutch master cylinder push rod lock nut.

2) Thread in clutch pedal switch until it contacts pedal. Turn clutch pedal switch in an additional 3/4 to one turn. Tighten clutch pedal switch lock nut. Loosen clutch interlock switch (upper switch) lock nut. With clutch pedal fully pressed, measure clearance between clutch pedal and floor board. Measure from middle of pedal face to floor. Clearance should be a minimum of 3.3" (83 mm).

3) Release clutch pedal .59-.79" (15-20 mm) from fully pressed position, and hold pedal at this height. Adjust position of clutch interlock switch so engine will start with clutch pedal at this position. Turn clutch interlock switch in an additional 3/4 to one turn. Tighten clutch interlock switch lock nut.

Prelude – **1)** Loosen clutch pedal switch (lower switch) lock nut, and back off switch until it no longer touches clutch pedal. Loosen clutch master cylinder push rod lock nut. Turn push rod to obtain a pedal height from floor of 7.5" (190 mm) and a stroke of 5.3-5.7" (135-145 mm). Pedal height is measured from middle of pedal face (with clutch released) to floor. Tighten clutch master cylinder push rod lock nut.

2) Thread in clutch pedal switch until it contacts pedal. Turn clutch pedal switch in an additional 1/4 to 1/2 turn. Tighten clutch pedal switch lock nut. Loosen clutch interlock switch (upper switch) lock nut. With clutch pedal fully pressed, measure clearance between clutch pedal and floor board. Measure from middle of pedal face to floor. Clearance should be a minimum of 3.7" (94 mm).

3) Release clutch pedal .59-.79" (15-20 mm) from fully pressed position, and hold pedal at this height. Adjust position of clutch interlock switch so engine will start with clutch pedal at this position. Turn clutch interlock switch in an additional 1/4 to 1/2 turn. Tighten clutch interlock switch lock nut.

SHIFT LEVER POSITION SWITCH

1) Turn ignition off. Set parking brake. Remove front console to access shift lever position switch located on side of shift lever mechanism. Disconnect shift lever position switch 12 or 14-pin connector. Ensure shift lever is in Park.

2) Loosen 2 shift lever position switch mounting bolts. Slowly slide switch toward front or rear of vehicle while checking for continuity between shift lever position switch 12 or 14-pin connector terminals. See SHIFT LEVER POSITION SWITCH TERMINAL IDENTIFICATION table. See Fig. 3, 4 or 5. Continuity should be present.

3) If adjustment is possible to get continuity, shift lever position switch is functioning properly. Tighten 2 shift lever position switch mounting bolts. Ensure vehicle starts with shift lever in Park and Neutral.

4) If adjustment is not possible to get continuity, check shift lever detent and bracket for damage. If no damage is evident, replace faulty shift lever position switch.

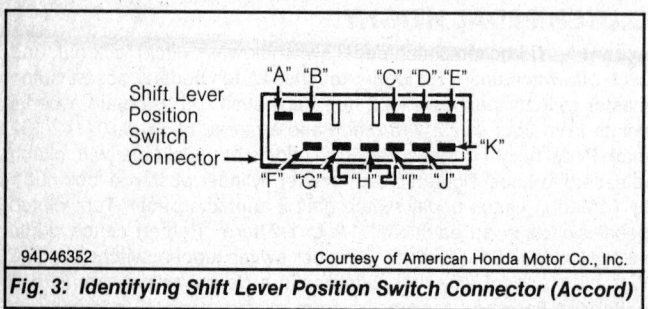

94D46352   Courtesy of American Honda Motor Co., Inc.

Fig. 3: Identifying Shift Lever Position Switch Connector (Accord)

SHIFT LEVER POSITION SWITCH TERMINAL IDENTIFICATION

Application	Terminals
Accord [1]	"I" & "F"
Civic & Civic Del Sol [2]	7 & 10
Prelude [1]	8 & 11

[1] – Shift lever position switch has a 12-pin connector.
[2] – Shift lever position switch has a 14-pin connector.

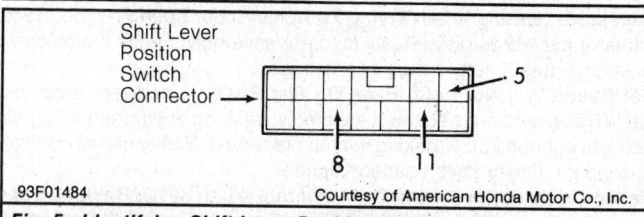

93D01483   Courtesy of American Honda Motor Co., Inc.

Fig. 4: Identifying Shift Lever Position Switch Connector (Civic & Civic Del Sol)

93F01484   Courtesy of American Honda Motor Co., Inc.

Fig. 5: Identifying Shift Lever Position Switch Connector (Prelude)

DIAGNOSIS & TESTING

WARNING: All models are equipped with Supplemental Restraint System (SRS). SRS wiring harness is routed close to instrument cluster, steering wheel, and related components. All SRS wiring harnesses are covered by Yellow outer insulation. DO NOT use electrical test equipment on these circuits. Before working on steering column components, disable air bag system and follow all service procedures. See AIR BAG RESTRAINT SYSTEM article in ACCESSORIES & EQUIPMENT.

NOTE: Some Accord and Prelude models are equipped with stereo theft protection system. Obtain 5-digit security code before disconnecting battery cable.

ACTUATOR ASSEMBLY

NOTE: If testing results in replacement of actuator solenoid valve assembly, ensure NEW "O" rings are installed.

Accord & Prelude – **1)** Turn ignition off. Disconnect actuator cable from actuator. Unplug 4-pin connector at actuator. On Accord, actuator is located against firewall on right side of engine compartment. On Prelude, actuator is located on left side of engine compartment. Using jumper wires, connect battery voltage to terminal "D" of actuator connector and simultaneously ground terminals "A", "B" and "C" of actuator connector. See Fig. 6.

2) Disconnect actuator vacuum line at vacuum check valve. Connect a vacuum pump to actuator vacuum line. Ensure vacuum check valve is between vacuum pump and actuator. Apply vacuum to system.

3) Actuator rod should pull in completely. If actuator rod pulls in completely, go to step 5). If actuator rod pulls in partially or not at all, check for leaking vacuum line. Repair as necessary.

4) If vacuum line is not leaking, check actuator solenoid valve assembly. See ACTUATOR SOLENOID VALVE ASSEMBLY. If actuator solenoid valve assembly tests are okay, actuator solenoid valve assembly is okay electrically, but has a mechanical malfunction. Replace actuator solenoid valve assembly for mechanical malfunction.

5) With voltage still applied to actuator connector, try to pull actuator rod out by hand. If actuator rod cannot be pulled out by hand, go to next step. If actuator rod can be pulled out by hand, replace malfunctioning actuator assembly.

6) Disconnect ground wire from actuator connector terminal "C". *See Fig. 6.* Actuator rod should return to "rest" position. If actuator rod does not return to "rest" position, replace malfunctioning actuator solenoid valve assembly. If actuator rod returns to "rest" position, repeat steps 1) through 6), but when step 6) is reached, disconnect ground from actuator connector terminal "A" instead of "C". *See Fig. 6.*

7) If actuator rod returns to "rest" position after disconnecting ground from actuator terminal "A", actuator assembly is functioning properly. If actuator rod does not return to "rest" position after disconnecting ground from actuator terminal "A", replace malfunctioning actuator solenoid valve assembly.

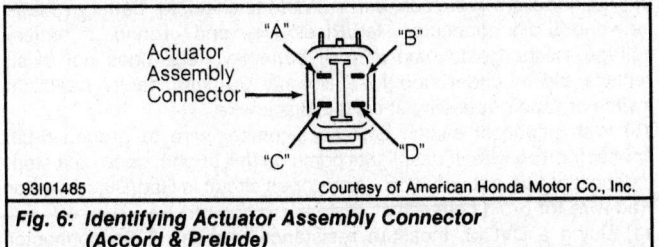

93I01485   Courtesy of American Honda Motor Co., Inc.

Fig. 6: Identifying Actuator Assembly Connector (Accord & Prelude)

Civic & Civic Del Sol – 1) Unplug 4-pin connector at actuator. Actuator is located on left side of engine compartment. Using jumper wires, connect battery voltage to terminal "D" of actuator connector and terminal "A" of actuator connector to ground. *See Fig. 7.*

2) Check for clicking sound from magnetic clutch, and ensure output linkage is locked. If actuator output linkage is not locked, replace actuator. Check actuator motor operation in each output linkage position. *See Fig. 7.* If actuator motor operates as specified, actuator assembly is operating properly. If actuator motor does not operate as specified, replace actuator assembly.

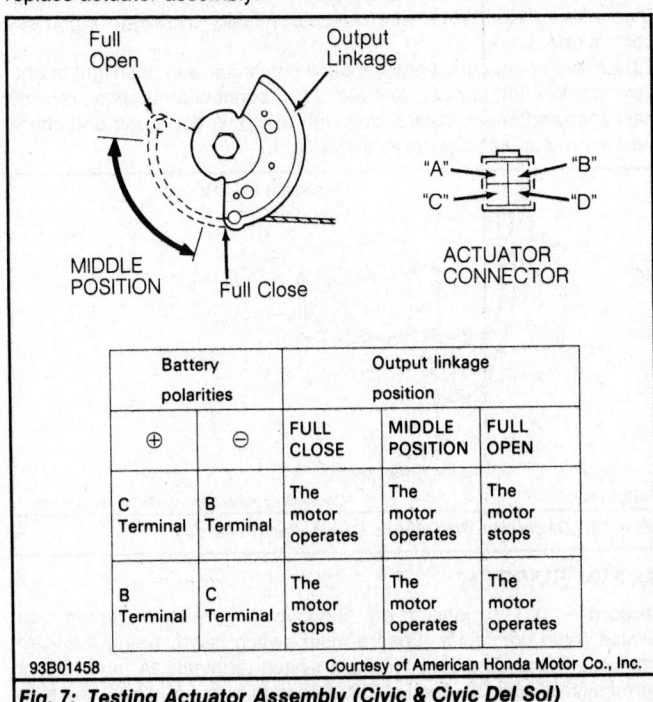

Battery polarities		Output linkage position		
$\oplus$	$\ominus$	FULL CLOSE	MIDDLE POSITION	FULL OPEN
C Terminal	B Terminal	The motor operates	The motor operates	The motor stops
B Terminal	C Terminal	The motor stops	The motor operates	The motor operates

93B01458   Courtesy of American Honda Motor Co., Inc.

Fig. 7: Testing Actuator Assembly (Civic & Civic Del Sol)

ACTUATOR SOLENOID VALVE ASSEMBLY

NOTE: *Actuator solenoid valve assembly is used only on Accord and Prelude.*

Accord & Prelude – 1) Turn ignition off. Unplug actuator assembly 4-pin connector. Using a DVOM, measure resistance between actuator assembly 4-pin connector terminals. *See Fig. 6.*

2) See ACTUATOR SOLENOID VALVE ASSEMBLY RESISTANCE table. If resistance is as not as specified, replace actuator solenoid valve assembly. Ensure NEW "O" rings are installed.

ACTUATOR SOLENOID VALVE ASSEMBLY RESISTANCE

Solenoid	Terminals	Ohms
Accord		
Safety	"A" & "D"	40-60
Vacuum	"B" & "D"	30-50
Vent	"C" & "D"	40-60
Prelude		
Safety	"A" & "D"	40-60
Vacuum	"B" & "D"	70-110
Vent	"C" & "D"	80-120

BRAKELIGHT SWITCH

1) Unplug 4-pin connector from brakelight switch. Using a DVOM, check for continuity between brakelight switch terminals "A" and "D". *See Fig. 8.* Continuity should exist. Check for continuity between brakelight switch terminals "B" and "C". Continuity should not exist.

2) Depress brake pedal and hold. Check for continuity between brakelight switch terminals "A" and "D". Continuity should not exist. Check for continuity between brakelight switch terminals "B" and "C". Continuity should exist. If continuity is not as specified, check brake pedal height. See BRAKE PEDAL HEIGHT under ADJUSTMENTS. If brake pedal height is okay, replace brakelight switch.

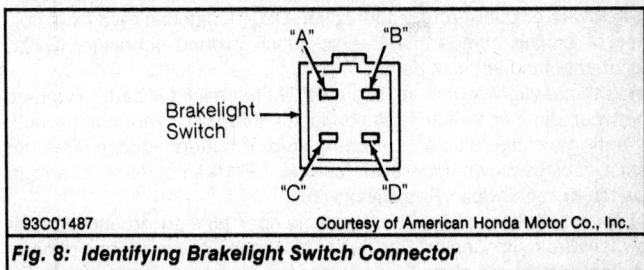

93C01487   Courtesy of American Honda Motor Co., Inc.

Fig. 8: Identifying Brakelight Switch Connector

CABLE REEL

Cable reel testing procedures are incorporated into SET/RESUME switch testing. See SET/RESUME SWITCH.

CLUTCH SWITCH

Accord & Prelude – 1) Unplug 3-pin connector from clutch switch. Using a DVOM, check for continuity between clutch switch terminals "B" and "C". *See Fig. 9.* Continuity should exist. Depress clutch pedal and hold. Check for continuity between terminals "B" and "C".

2) Continuity should not exist. If continuity exists, check clutch pedal height. See CLUTCH PEDAL HEIGHT under ADJUSTMENTS. If clutch pedal height is okay, replace clutch pedal switch.

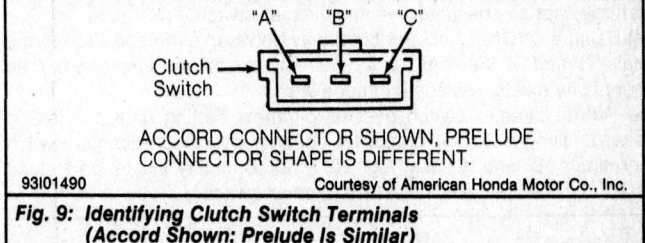

ACCORD CONNECTOR SHOWN, PRELUDE CONNECTOR SHAPE IS DIFFERENT.

93I01490   Courtesy of American Honda Motor Co., Inc.

Fig. 9: Identifying Clutch Switch Terminals (Accord Shown; Prelude Is Similar)

Civic & Civic Del Sol – 1) Unplug 2-pin connector from clutch switch. Using a DVOM, check for continuity between clutch switch terminals. Continuity should exist. Depress clutch pedal and hold. Check for continuity between clutch switch terminals.

2) Continuity should not exist. If continuity is not as specified, check clutch pedal height. See CLUTCH PEDAL HEIGHT under ADJUSTMENTS. If clutch pedal height is okay, replace clutch pedal switch.

DIMMER SWITCH CIRCUIT

Accord – 1) Turn ignition off. Carefully pry dimmer switch from dashboard. Dashlight brightness controller is built into dimmer switch assembly. Unplug dimmer switch 3-pin connector.

2) With headlight switch on or off, use a DVOM to check for continuity between dimmer switch 3-pin connector Black wire and ground. If continuity exists, go to next step. If no continuity exists, repair open Black wire. Check ground connection G401 (located behind left kick panel). Check ground connection G403 (located behind right kick panel).

3) With headlight switch on, use a DVOM to check for battery voltage between dimmer switch 3-pin connector Red/Black wire and ground. If battery voltage exists, go to next step. If battery voltage does not exist, replace blown underhood fuse No. 32 (15-amp), faulty headlight switch or repair open Red/Black wire.

4) With headlight switch on, use a jumper wire to ground dimmer switch 3-pin connector Red wire. If dashlights come on, dimmer switch circuits are okay. Replace dimmer switch. If dashlights do not come on, repair open Red/Black wire or Red wire for dimmer switch 3-pin connector.

Civic & Civic Del Sol – 1) Turn ignition off. Carefully pry dimmer switch from dashboard. Dashlight brightness controller is built into dimmer switch assembly. Unplug dimmer switch 3-pin connector and inspect connector and switch terminals for damage or corrosion. Repair or replace as necessary.

2) With headlight switch on or off, use a DVOM to check for continuity between dimmer switch 3-pin connector Black wire and ground. If continuity exists, go to next step. If no continuity exists, repair open Black wire or poor ground connection G201 located in right front corner of engine compartment. Also check ground connector G401, located behind left kick panel.

3) With headlight switch on, use a DVOM to check for battery voltage between dimmer switch 3-pin connector Red/Black wire and ground. If battery voltage exists, go to next step. If battery voltage does not exist, replace blown underdash fuse No. 19 (10-amp), faulty headlight switch or repair open Red/Black wire.

4) With headlight switch on, use a jumper wire to ground dimmer switch 3-pin connector Red wire. If dashlights come on, dimmer switch circuits are okay. Replace dimmer switch. If dashlights do not come on, repair open Red/Black wire or Red wire for dimmer switch 3-pin connector.

Prelude – 1) Turn ignition off. Carefully pry dimmer switch from dashboard. Dimmer switch is removed with 2 other switches in a pod. Unplug dimmer switch 6-pin connector.

2) Using a DVOM, measure resistance of dimmer switch terminals "C" and "E". *See Fig. 10*. Resistance should be 8000-10,000 ohms. Resistance will vary slightly with temperature. If resistance is as specified, go to next step. If resistance is not as specified, replace dimmer switch.

3) Using a DVOM, measure resistance of dimmer switch terminals "D" and "E". *See Fig. 10*. Resistance should vary between zero and 10,000 ohms when dimmer switch dial is rotated. Resistance will vary slightly with temperature. If resistance is as specified, go to next step. If resistance is not as specified, replace dimmer switch.

4) Using a DVOM, check for continuity between dimmer switch terminals "B" and "F". *See Fig. 10*. If continuity exists, go to next step. If no continuity exists, replace dimmer switch.

5) Rotate dimmer switch past its dimmest setting until a "click" is heard. Using a DVOM, check for continuity between dimmer switch terminals "B" and "F". *See Fig. 10*. If no continuity exists, go to next step. If continuity exists, replace dimmer switch.

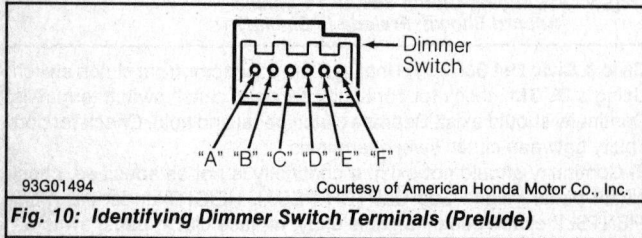

93G01494   Courtesy of American Honda Motor Co., Inc.

Fig. 10: *Identifying Dimmer Switch Terminals (Prelude)*

6) Remove 4 screws from sub-gauge assembly located in center of dashboard. Pull out sub-gauge assembly far enough to unplug electrical connectors. Remove sub-gauge assembly.

7) Access dashlight brightness control unit located behind sub-gauge assembly. Unplug dashlight brightness control unit 6-pin connector. *See Fig. 10*. With headlight switch on or off, use a DVOM to check for continuity between 6-pin connector Black wire and ground. If continuity exists, go to next step 9). If no continuity exists, go to next step.

8) Repair open Black wire or poor ground connection G401, located under right side of dashboard near base of windshield. Check ground connection G402, located on left side of left side rail on center console. Checck ground connection G404 (located on top of left side rail, on center console).Check ground connection G521 (located on floor on left side near driver's seat).

9) With headlight switch on, use a DVOM to check for battery voltage between 6-pin connector Red/Black wire and ground. If battery voltage exists, go to next step. If battery voltage does not exist, replace blown underhood fuse No. 42 (20-amp), faulty headlight switch or repair open circuit in Red/Black wire.

10) With headlight switch on, use a jumper wire to ground 6-pin connector Red wire. If dashlights come on (full bright), go to next step. If dashlights do not come on, repair open circuit in Red/Black wire or Red wire for 6-pin connector.

11) Using a DVOM, measure resistance between 6-pin connector Red/Green wire and Red/White wire. Resistance should be 8000-12,000 ohms at all times when dimmer switch dial is rotated. Resistance will vary slightly with temperature. If resistance is as specified, go to next step. If resistance is not as specified, repair open circuit in Red/Green wire or Red/White wire or replace faulty dashlight brightness control unit.

12) Using a DVOM, measure resistance between 6-pin connector Red/Blue wire and Red/White wire. Resistance should vary between zero and 10,000 ohms when dimmer switch dial is rotated. Resistance will vary slightly with temperature. If resistance is as specified, go to next step. If resistance is not as specified, repair open circuit in Red/Blue wire or Red/White wire or replace faulty dashlight brightness control unit.

13) Ensure connection between 6-pin connector and dashlight brightness control unit is okay. *See Fig. 11*. If connection is okay, replace dashlight brightness control unit with a known good unit and check operation of cruise control indicator light.

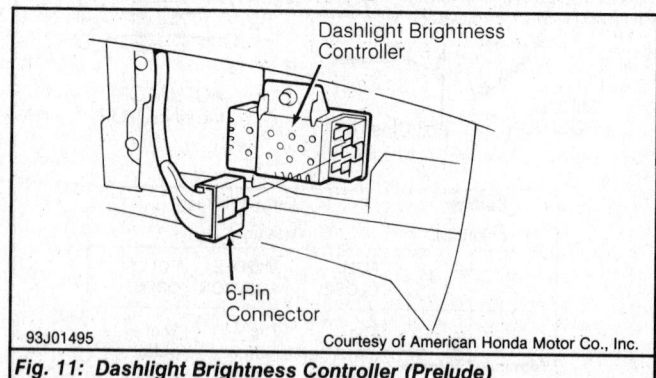

93J01495   Courtesy of American Honda Motor Co., Inc.

Fig. 11: *Dashlight Brightness Controller (Prelude)*

MAIN SWITCH

Accord – 1) Turn ignition off. Remove main switch. Unplug main switch 5-pin connector. Ensure main switch is off. Using a DVOM, check for continuity between main switch terminals "A" and "B" and terminals "D" and "E". *See Fig. 12*. If continuity exists, go to next step. If no continuity exists, replace main switch.

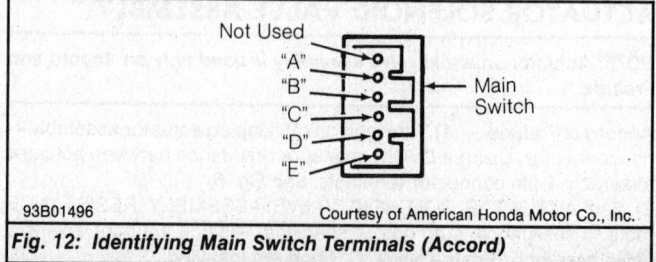

93B01496   Courtesy of American Honda Motor Co., Inc.

Fig. 12: *Identifying Main Switch Terminals (Accord)*

2) Turn main switch on. Using a DVOM, check for continuity between main switch terminals "A" and "B", "B" and "C", and "D" and "E". *See Fig. 12.* If continuity exists, main switch is okay. If no continuity exists, replace main switch.

Civic (Except Civic Del Sol) – 1) Turn ignition and main switch off. Remove main switch. Using a DVOM, check for continuity between main switch terminals "B" and "C" and terminals "D" and "E". *See Fig. 13.* If continuity exists, go to next step. If no continuity exists, replace defective bulb inside main switch. Recheck switch continuity. If main switch continuity is still not as specified, replace main switch.

2) Turn main switch on. Using a DVOM, check for continuity between main switch terminals "A" and "B", "B" and "C", and "D" and "E". *See Fig. 13.* If continuity exists, main switch is okay. If no continuity exists between main switch terminals "A" and "B", replace main switch. If no continuity exists between main switch terminals "B" and "C" and terminals "D" and "E", go to next step.

3) Replace defective bulb inside main switch. Recheck switch continuity. If main switch continuity is still not as specified, replace main switch.

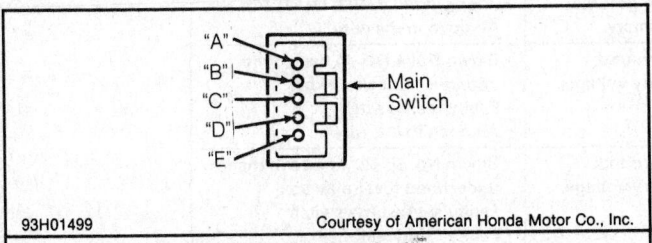

93H01499   Courtesy of American Honda Motor Co., Inc.

**Fig. 13: Identifying Main Switch Terminals
(Prelude Shown; Civic & Civic Del Sol Are Similar)**

Civic Del Sol – 1) Turn main switch off. Using DVOM, check for continuity between main switch terminals "A" and "B", and terminals "C" and "D". *See Fig. 13.* If continuity exists, go to next step. If continuity does not exist, replace defective bulb inside main switch. Recheck main switch continuity. If continuity is still not as specified, replace main switch.

2) Turn main switch on. Using DVOM, check for continuity between main switch terminals "A" and "B", terminals "B" and "E", and terminals "C" and "D". *See Fig. 13.* If continuity exists, switch is okay. If no continuity exists between terminals "B" and "E", replace main switch. If no continuity exists between terminals "A" and "B", and terminals "C" and "D", go to next step.

3) Replace defective bulb inside main switch. Recheck main switch continuity. If continuity is still not as specified, replace main switch.

Prelude – 1) Turn ignition and main switch off. Remove main switch. Using DVOM, check for continuity between main switch terminals "A" and "B", and terminals "C" and "E". *See Fig. 13.* If continuity exists, go to next step. If no continuity exists, replace defective bulb inside main switch. Recheck main switch continuity. If continuity is still not as specified, replace main switch.

2) Turn main switch on. Using a DVOM, check for continuity between main switch terminals "A" and "B", "C" and "E", and "B" and "D". *See Fig. 13.* If continuity exists, main switch is okay. If no continuity exists between terminals "B" and "D", replace main switch. If no continuity exists between main switch terminals "A" and "B" and terminals "C" and "E", go to next step.

3) Replace defective bulb inside main switch. Recheck main switch continuity. If continuity is still not as specified, replace main switch.

SET/RESUME SWITCH

1) Disable air bag system. See AIR BAG RESTRAINT SYSTEM article in ACCESSORIES & EQUIPMENT. Connect SRS Test Harness "C" (07LAZ-SL40300) to cable reel 6-pin connector. Using a DVOM, check for continuity between SRS Test Harness "C" connector terminal No. 2 (Light Green/Red wire on cable reel harness) and terminal No. 3 (Blue/Red wire on cable reel harness) with SET pressed. *See Fig. 14.* If continuity exists, go to next step. If no continuity exists, go to step 3).

2) Using a DVOM, check for continuity between SRS Test Harness "C" connector terminal No. 1 (Light Green/Black wire on cable reel harness) and terminal No. 3 (Blue/Red wire on cable reel harness) with RESUME pressed. *See Fig. 14.* If continuity exists, SET/RESUME switch and cable reel are okay. If no continuity exists, go to next step.

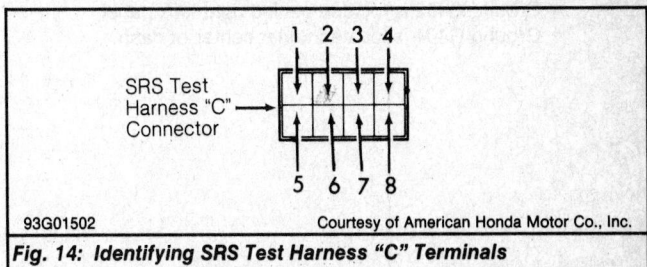

93G01502   Courtesy of American Honda Motor Co., Inc.

Fig. 14: Identifying SRS Test Harness "C" Terminals

3) Remove SET/RESUME switch from steering wheel. See SET/RESUME SWITCH under REMOVAL & INSTALLATION. Using a DVOM, check for continuity between SET/RESUME switch terminals "A" or "A' " and "C" with SET pressed. *See Fig. 15.* If continuity exists, go to next step. If no continuity exists, replace SET/RESUME switch.

4) Using a DVOM, check for continuity between SET/RESUME switch terminals "A" or "A' " and "B" with RESUME pressed. *See Fig. 15.* If continuity exists, replace cable reel. See CABLE REEL under REMOVAL & INSTALLATION. If no continuity exists, replace SET/RESUME switch.

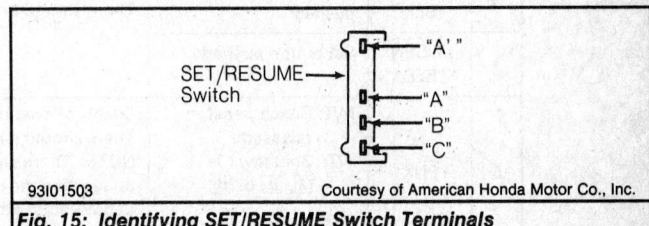

93I01503   Courtesy of American Honda Motor Co., Inc.

Fig. 15: Identifying SET/RESUME Switch Terminals

SHIFT LEVER POSITION SWITCH

NOTE: Only A/T vehicles are equipped with shift lever position switch.

1) Remove front console to access shift lever position switch located on side of shift lever mechanism. Unplug shift lever position switch 12 or 14-pin connector.

2) Using a DVOM, check for continuity between shift lever position switch 12 or 14-pin connector terminals with shift lever in "2", "D$_3$" and "D$_4$" positions. See SHIFT LEVER POSITION SWITCH TERMINAL IDENTIFICATION table. *See Fig. 3, 4 or 5.*

3) If continuity exists in each position, shift lever position switch is okay. If no continuity exists, go to next step.

4) Check shift lever position switch adjustment. See SHIFT LEVER POSITION SWITCH under ADJUSTMENTS. If shift lever position switch adjustment is okay, replace shift lever position switch.

SHIFT LEVER POSITION SWITCH TERMINAL IDENTIFICATION

Application	Terminals
Accord [1]	"A" & "I"
Civic & Civic Del Sol [2]	7 & 10
Prelude [1]	8 & 11

[1] – Shift lever position switch has a 12-pin connector.
[2] – Shift lever position switch has a 14-pin connector.

CRUISE CONTROL UNIT INPUT

Accord – 1) Turn ignition off. Remove dashboard lower left cover. Cruise control unit is located under left side of dashboard, near kick panel. Unplug cruise control unit 14-pin connector.

2) Using a DVOM, perform cruise control unit input tests. *See Fig. 16.* If all input test results are okay, check cruise control unit connector for damage and proper fit to cruise control unit. If connector is okay and cruise control is still malfunctioning, replace cruise control unit.

- Numbers 1 through 13 refer to test numbers, not terminal numbers.
- Ground G402 is located behind right kick panel.
- Ground G404 is located under center of dash.

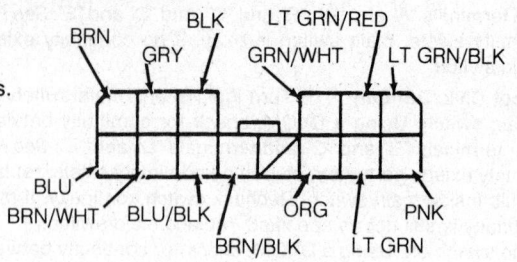

VIEW FROM WIRE SIDE

No.	Wire	Test condition	Test: Desired result	Possible cause if result is not obtained
1	BLK	Under all conditions	Check for continuity to ground: There should be continuity.	• Poor ground (G402, G404) • An open in the wire
2	LT GRN	Ignition switch ON (II) and main switch ON	Check for voltage to ground: There should be battery voltage.	• Blown No. 4 (7.5 A) fuse in the underdash fuse/relay box • Faulty main switch • An open in the wire
3	LT GRN/ BLK	Resume button pushed	Check for voltage to ground: There should be battery voltage.	• Blown No. 30 (20 A) fuse in the underhood fuse/relay box • Faulty set/resume switch • Faulty cable reel • An open in the wire
4	LT GRN/ RED	Set button pushed		
5	PNK	M/T: Clutch pedal released A/T: Shift lever in ②, D₃ or D₄	Check for continuity to ground: There should be continuity. NOTE: There should be no continuity when the clutch pedal is depressed or when the shift lever is in other positions.	• Faulty or misadjusted clutch switch (M/T) • Faulty A/T gear position switch • Poor ground (G402, G404) • An open in the wire
6	ORG	Ignition switch ON (II) and main switch ON; raise the front of the car, and rotate one wheel slowly.	Check for voltage between the ORN ⊕ and BLK ⊖ terminals: There should be 0 – 5 V or more –0 – 5 V or more repeatedly.	• Faulty vehicle speed sensor (VSS) • An open in the wire
7	GRY	Ignition switch ON (II), main switch ON and brake pedal pushed, then released	Check for voltage to ground: There should be 0 V with the pedal pushed and battery voltage with the pedal released.	• Faulty brake switch • An open in the wire
8	GRN/WHT	Brake pedal pushed, then released	Check for voltage to ground: There should be battery voltage with the pedal pushed, and 0 V with the pedal released.	• Blown No. 30 (20 A) fuse in the underhood fuse/relay box • Faulty brake switch • An open in the wire
9	BLU/BLK	Ignition switch ON (II)	Attach to ground: Cruise indicator light in the gauge assembly comes on.	• Blown bulb • Blown No. 1 (10 A) fuse in the underdash fuse/relay box • Faulty dimming circuit in the gauge assembly • An open in the wire
10	BRN/WHT	Under all conditions	Check for resistance to ground: There should be 80 – 120 Ω.	• Faulty actuator solenoid • An open in the wire
11	BRN/BLK	Under all conditions	Check for resistance to ground: There should be 70 – 110 Ω.	
12	BRN	Under all conditions	Check for resistance to ground: There should be 40 – 60 Ω.	
13	BLU*	Engine running	Check for voltage to ground: There should be battery voltage.	• Faulty ignition system • An open in the wire

*Early production cars only.

94A46359

Fig. 16: Cruise Control Unit Input Test (Accord)

- Numbers 1 through 14 refer to test numbers, not terminal numbers.
- Ground G201 is located in right front corner of engine compartment. G201 is a multi-wire connector sharing one common ground.
- Ground G301 is located in left front corner of engine compartment. G301 is a multi-wire connector sharing one common ground.
- Ground G401 is located behind left kick panel. G401 is a multi-wire connector sharing one common ground.

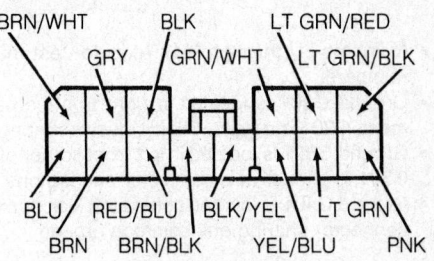

VIEW FROM WIRE SIDE

No.	Wire	Test condition	Test: Desired result	Possible cause if result is not obtained
1	BLK	Under all conditions.	Check for continuity to ground: There should be continuity:	• Poor ground (G201). • An open in the wire.
2	LT GRN	Ignition switch ON and main switch ON.	Check for voltage to ground: There should be battery voltage.	• Blown No. 24 (15 A) fuse in the under-dash fuse/relay box. • Faulty main switch. • An open in the wire.
3	LT GRN/ BLK	RESUME button pushed.	Check for voltage to ground: There should be battery voltage.	• Blown No. 42 (20 A) fuse in the under-hood fuse/relay box. • Faulty SET/RESUME switch. • Faulty cable reel. • An open in the wire.
4	LT GRN/ RED	SET button pushed.		
5	PNK	M/T: Clutch pedal released. A/T: Shift lever in ②, D₃, or D₄.	Check for continuity to ground: There should be continuity. NOTE: There should be no continuity when the clutch pedal is depressed or when the shift lever is in other positions.	• Faulty or misadjusted clutch switch (M/T). • Faulty A/T gear position switch (A/T). • Poor ground (G201, G401). • An open in the wire.
6	BLU	Start the engine.	Check for voltage to ground: There should be battery voltage.	• Faulty ignition system or ECM. • An open in the wire.
7	YEL/BLU	Ignition switch ON and main switch ON. Raise the front of the car, rotate one wheel slowly.	Check for voltage between the YEL/BLU ⊕ and BLK ⊖ terminals: There should be 0—12—0—12 V repeatedly.	• Faulty vehicle speed sensor (VSS). • An open in the wire.
8	GRY	Ignition switch ON, main switch ON and brake pedal pushed, then released.	Check for voltage to ground: There should be 0 V with the pedal pushed and battery voltage with the pedal released.	• Faulty brake switch. • An open in the wire.
9	GRN/WHT	Brake pedal pushed, then released.	Check for voltage to ground: There should be battery voltage with the pedal pushed, and 0 V with the pedal released.	• Faulty brake switch. • An open in the wire.
10	RED/BLU	Ignition switch ON.	Attach to ground: Indicator light in the gauge assembly comes on.	• Blown bulb. • Blown No. 15 (10 A) fuse in the under-dash fuse/relay box. • Faulty dimming circuit in the gauge assembly. • An open in the wire.
11	BRN	Connect the battery power to the BRN terminal and ground to the BRN/BLK terminal.	Check the operation of the actuator motor: You should be able to hear the motor.	• Faulty actuator. • An open in the wire.
12	BRN/BLK			
13	BRN/WHT	Connect the battery power to the BRN/WHT terminal.	Check the operation of the magnetic clutch: Clutch should click and output link should be locked.	• Faulty actuator. • An open in the wire. • Poor ground (G301).
14	BLK/YEL	Ignition switch ON.	Check for voltage to ground: There should be battery voltage.	• Blown No. 24 (15 A) fuse in the under-dash fuse/relay box. • An open in the wire.

93A83063

Courtesy of American Honda Motor Co., Inc.

Fig. 17: Cruise Control Unit Input Test (Civic)

- Numbers 1 through 14 refer to test numbers, not terminal numbers.
- Ground G201 is located in right front corner of engine compartment. G201 is a multi-wire connector sharing one common ground.
- Ground G301 is located in left front corner of engine compartment. G301 is a multi-wire connector sharing one common ground.
- Ground G401 is located behind left kick panel. G401 is a multi-wire connector sharing one common ground.

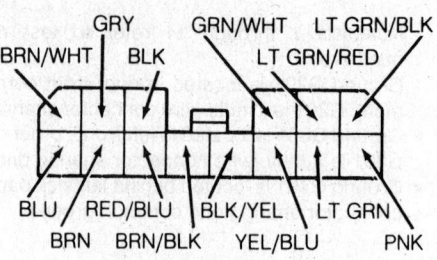

VIEW FROM WIRE SIDE

No.	Wire	Test condition	Test: Desired result	Possible cause if result is not obtained
1	BLK	Under all conditions.	Check for continuity to ground: There should be continuity.	• Poor ground (G201, G401). • An open circuit in the wire.
2	BLK/YEL	Ignition switch ON.	Check for voltage to ground: There should be battery voltage.	• Blown No. 24 (15 A) fuse. • An open circuit in the BLK/YEL wire.
3	LT GRN	Ignition switch ON and main switch ON.	Check for voltage to ground: There should be battery voltage.	• Blown No. 24 (15 A) fuse. • Faulty main switch. • An open circuit in the LT GRN or BLK/YEL wire.
4	LT GRN/ BLK	RESUME button pushed.	Ground each terminal: Horn should sound as the switch is pushed.	• Blown No. 42 (15 A) fuse. • Faulty SET/RESUME switch. • Faulty cable reel. • An open circuit in the WHT/GRN, BLU/GRN, BLU/RED, LT GRN/BLK or LT GRN/RED wire.
5	LT GRN/ RED	SET button pushed.		
6	PNK	M/T: Clutch pedal released. A/T: Shift lever in [2], [D3], or [D4].	Check for continuity to ground: There should be continuity. NOTE: There should be no continuity when the clutch pedal is pushed or when the A/T shift lever is in other positions.	• Faulty or misadjusted clutch switch (M/T). • Faulty A/T gear position switch (A/T). • Poor ground (G201, G401). • An open circuit in the wire.
7	BLU	Start the engine.	Check for voltage to ground: There should be battery voltage.	• Faulty ignition system. • An open circuit in the wire.
8	YEL/BLU	Ignition switch ON and main switch ON. Raise the front of the car, rotate one wheel slowly.	Check for voltage between the YEL/BLU ⊕ and BLK ⊖ terminals: There should be 0−12−0−12 V repeatedly.	• Faulty vehicle speed sensor (VSS). • An open circuit in the wire. • Short to ground.
9	GRY	Ignition switch ON, main switch ON and brake pedal pushed, then released.	Check for voltage to ground: There should be 0 V with the pedal pushed, and battery voltage with the pedal released.	• Faulty brake switch. • An open circuit in the GRY or LT GRN wire.
10	GRN/WHT	Brake pedal pushed, then released.	Check for voltage to ground: There should be battery voltage with the pedal pushed, and 0 V with the pedal released.	• Faulty brake switch. • An open circuit in the wire.
11	RED/BLU	Ignition switch ON.	Connect to ground: Cruise light in the gauge assembly should come on.	• Blown bulb. • Blown No. 15 (10 A) fuse. • Faulty dimming circuit in the gauge assembly. • An open circuit in the wire.
12	BRN	Connect battery power to the BRN terminal and ground to the BRN/BLK terminal.	Check the operation of the actuator motor: You should be able to hear the motor.	• Faulty actuator. • An open circuit in the wire.
13	BRN/BLK			
14	BRN/WHT	Connect battery power to the BRN/WHT terminal.	Check the operation of the magnetic clutch: Clutch should click and output link should be locked.	• Faulty actuator. • An open circuit in the wire. • Poor ground (G301).

94I46365

Courtesy of American Honda Motor Co., Inc.

Fig. 18: *Cruise Control Unit Input Test (Civic Del Sol)*

- Numbers 1 through 13 refer to test numbers, not terminal numbers.
- Ground G101 is located at thermostat housing on engine. G101 is a 2-wire ground connection sharing one common ground.
- Ground G401 is located under right side of dashboard near base of windshield. G401 is a 2-wire ground connection sharing one common ground.
- Ground G402 is located under middle of dashboard on left side rail on center console. G402 is a 2-wire ground connection sharing one common ground.
- Ground G404 is located under middle of dashboard. G404 is a 2-wire ground connection sharing one common ground.
- Ground G521 is a 1-wire ground connection located on floor on left side near driver's seat.

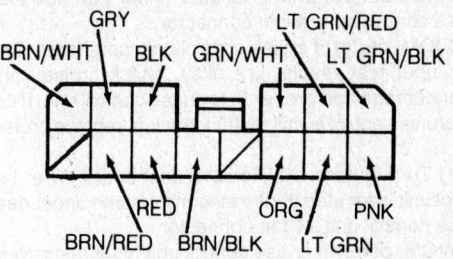

VIEW FROM WIRE SIDE

No.	Wire	Test condition	Test: Desired result	Possible cause if result is not obtained
1	BLK	Under all conditions	Check for continuity to ground: There should be continuity.	• Poor ground (G401, G402, G404, G521) • An open in the wire
2	LT GRN	Ignition switch ON, and main switch ON	Check for voltage to ground: There should be battery voltage.	• Blown No. 14 (7.5 A) fuse (In the underdash fuse/relay box) • Faulty main switch • An open in the wire
3	LT GRN/ BLK	RESUME button pushed	Check for voltage to ground: There should be battery voltage.	• Blown No. 41 (15 A) fuse (In the underhood fuse/relay box) • Faulty SET/RESUME switch • Faulty cable reel • An open in the wire
4	LT GRN/ RED	SET button pushed		
5	PNK	M/T: Clutch pedal pushed A/T: Shift lever in 2 , D3 , or D4	Check for continuity to ground: There should be continuity. NOTE: There should be no continuity when the clutch pedal is released or when the A/T shift lever is in other positions.	• Faulty or misadjusted clutch switch (M/T) • Faulty or misadjusted A/T gear position switch • Poor ground (G401, G402, G404, G521) • An open in the wire
6	ORN	Ignition switch ON, and main switch ON; raise the front of the car, rotate one wheel slowly.	Check for voltage between the ORN ⊕ and BLK ⊖ terminals: It should be 0—12—0—12 V repeatedly.	• Faulty vehicle speed sensor (VSS) • Poor ground (G101) • An open in the wire
7	GRY	Ignition switch ON, main switch ON; brake pedal is pushed, then released.	Check for voltage to ground: There should be 0 V with the pedal pushed, and battery voltage with the pedal released.	• Faulty brake switch • An open in the wire
8	GRN/WHT	Brake pedal is pushed, then released.	Check for voltage to ground: There should be battery voltage with the pedal pushed, and 0 V with the pedal released.	• Faulty brake switch • An open in the wire
9	RED	Ignition switch ON	Connect to ground: Cruise indicator in the gauge assembly comes on.	• Blown bulb • Blown No. 13 (10 A) fuse (In the underdash fuse/relay box) • Faulty dimming circuit in the gauge assembly • An open in the wire
10	BRN/RED	Under all conditions	Check for resistance to ground: There should be 80—120 Ω.	• Faulty actuator solenoid • An open in the wire
11	BRN/BLK	Under all conditions	Check for resistance to ground: There should be 70—110 Ω.	
12	BRN/WHT	Under all conditions	Check for resistance to ground: There should be 40—60 Ω.	

94B46368

Fig. 19: Cruise Control Unit Input Test (Prelude)

Civic & Civic Del Sol – 1) Turn ignition off. Remove dashboard lower left cover. Cruise control unit is located under left side kick panel. Unplug cruise control unit 14-pin connector.

2) Using a DVOM, perform cruise control unit input tests. *See Fig. 17 or 18*. If all input test results are okay, check cruise control unit connector for damage and proper fit to cruise control unit. If connector is okay and cruise control is still malfunctioning, replace cruise control unit.

Prelude – 1) Turn ignition off. Remove dashboard lower left cover. Cruise control unit is located above steering column under dashboard. Unplug cruise control unit 14-pin connector.

2) Using a DVOM, perform cruise control unit input tests. *See Fig. 19*. If all input test results are okay, check cruise control unit connector for damage and proper fit to cruise control unit. If connector is okay and cruise control is still malfunctioning, replace cruise control unit.

REMOVAL & INSTALLATION

WARNING: All models are equipped with Supplemental Restraint System (SRS). SRS wiring harness is routed close to instrument cluster, steering wheel and related components. All SRS wiring harnesses are covered by Yellow outer insulation. DO NOT use electrical test equipment on these circuits. Before working on steering column components, disable air bag system and follow all service procedures. See AIR BAG RESTRAINT SYSTEM article in ACCESSORIES & EQUIPMENT.

NOTE: Some Accord and Prelude models are equipped with stereo theft protection system. Obtain 5-digit security code before disconnecting battery cable.

CABLE REEL

For removal and installation procedure, see AIR BAG RESTRAINT SYSTEM article in ACCESSORIES & EQUIPMENT.

CRUISE CONTROL UNIT

Removal & Installation – Turn ignition off. Disconnect negative battery cable. Remove dashboard lower left cover. Unplug cruise control unit connector. Remove control unit mounting screws. Remove control unit. To install, reverse removal procedure.

MAIN SWITCH

Removal & Installation (Except Civic Del Sol) – Carefully pry 2-switch assembly (3-switch assembly on Prelude) from dash. Unplug harness connector. Remove 2 screws attaching main switch to switch assembly. Remove main switch. To install, reverse removal procedure.

Removal & Installation (Civic Del Sol) – Carefully pry 2-switch housing from instrument panel. Unplug harness connector. Remove main switch from switch housing. To install, reverse removal procedure.

SET/RESUME SWITCH

Removal & Installation – Carefully pry cover from side of SET/RESUME/CANCEL switch. Remove 2 screws attaching SET/RESUME/CANCEL switch to steering wheel. Remove SET/RESUME/CANCEL switch from steering wheel. To install, reverse removal procedure.

WIRING DIAGRAMS

NOTE: See ACCESSORIES & EQUIPMENT, Volume 5.

Accord, Civic, Civic Del Sol, Passport, Prelude

NOTE: For rear window defogger information on Passport, refer to Rodeo in Isuzu REAR WINDOW DEFOGGER article.

DESCRIPTION & OPERATION

Rear window defogger system uses a heating grid wire bonded to inside of window. Heat is regulated by a dash-mounted control switch with indicator light, relay and Integrated Control Unit (ICU). Power is supplied to control switch through a fuse in fuse/relay box. On Accord and Prelude, ICU will supply power to grid for 25 minutes, or until ignition is turned off. On Civic and Civic Del Sol, timer is located in rear window defogger switch.

TROUBLE SHOOTING

NOTE: When diagnosing vehicle by symptom, check for possible failures in the following order. When component tests are indicated, see appropriate procedure under TESTING.

DEFOGGER INOPERATIVE

Accord – Check the following fuses: No. 1 (10-amp) and No. 8 (7.5-amp) in dash fuse/relay box (located at left kick panel). Check defogger timer circuit input (in ICU). Check for poor ground connections. Check for short or open in Black/Green, Yellow/Black or Yellow/Green wires.

Civic & Civic Del Sol – Check for blown fuse No. 13 (7.5-amp) in underdash fuse/relay box (located under left side of dash). Check defogger timer circuit input (located in defogger switch). Check for poor ground connections. Perform defogger grid filament test. Check for short or open in Yellow, Blue/Yellow or Black/Yellow wire.

Prelude – Check for blown fuse No. 13 (10-amp) in dash fuse/relay box (located at left side kick panel). Check defogger timer circuit input (in ICU). Check for poor ground connections. Check for short or open in Black/Yellow wire.

INDICATOR LIGHT INOPERATIVE (DEFOGGER OPERATES)

On all models, check for burned-out bulb. On Accord and Prelude, check for short or open in Yellow/Black or Yellow/Green wires. On Civic and Civic Del Sol, check for short or open in Black/Yellow wire.

INDICATOR LIGHT OPERATES (DEFOGGER INOPERATIVE)

Accord – Check for blown fuse No. 16 (40-amp) in underhood fuse/relay box. Check for poor ground connections. Perform defogger grid and defogger relay tests. Check for short or open in Yellow/Green or Black/Yellow wires.

Civic & Civic Del Sol – Check for blown fuse No. 34 (20-amp) in underhood fuse/relay box. Check for poor ground connections. Perform defogger grid and defogger relay tests. Check for short or open in Blue/Yellow, Black/Green or Black/Yellow wires.

Prelude – Check for blown fuse No. 34 (40-amp) in underhood fuse/relay box. Check for blown fuse No. 11 (10-amp) in dash fuse/relay box. Perform defogger grid and defogger relay tests. Check for poor ground connections. Check for short or open in Yellow/Black, Yellow/White or Black/Green wires.

OPERATION TIME TOO LONG OR TOO SHORT

1) On Accord and Prelude, check defogger timer circuit input (in ICU). On Civic and Civic Del Sol, check defogger timer circuit, located in defogger switch.

2) On Accord, check for open or disconnected terminal in Yellow/White or Black wires. On Civic and Civic Del Sol, check for open or disconnected terminal in Blue/Yellow, Black/Yellow or Black/Green wires. On Prelude, check for open or disconnected terminal in Yellow/White wire.

TESTING

DEFOGGER SWITCH TEST

Accord – Carefully pry switch from instrument panel. Using an ohmmeter, ensure continuity exists between wire terminals "D" and "F" when control switch is pushed. If continuity does not exist, replace

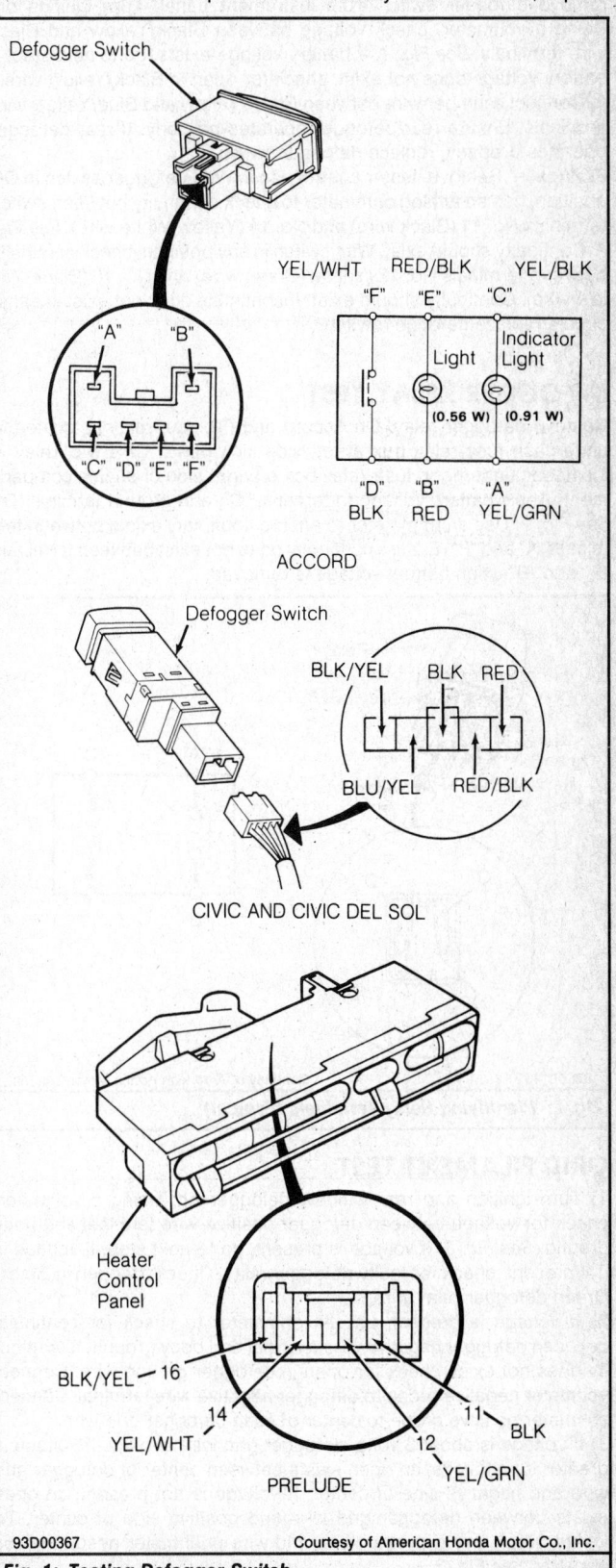

Fig. 1: Testing Defogger Switch

93D00367   Courtesy of American Honda Motor Co., Inc.

switch. Continuity should exist between wire terminals "A" and "C" (indicator light), and wire terminals "B" and "E" (light) at all times. *See Fig. 1.*

Civic & Civic Del Sol – 1) Check fuse No. 13 (7.5-amp). Replace fuse if necessary. On Civic, remove 4 retaining screws and remove instrument panel. Remove defogger switch. On Civic Del Sol, carefully remove defogger switch from instrument panel. Turn ignition on. Using a voltmeter, check voltage between Black/Yellow and Black wire terminals. *See Fig. 1.* If battery voltage exists, go to next step. If battery voltage does not exist, check for open in Black/Yellow wire.

2) Connect a jumper wire between Black/Yellow and Blue/Yellow wire terminals. Ensure rear defogger operates properly. If rear defogger operates properly, replace defogger switch.

Prelude – Remove heater control panel. With defogger switch in ON position, use an analog ohmmeter to check continuity between switch terminals No. 11 (Black wire) and No. 14 (Yellow/White wire). *See Fig. 1.* Continuity should exist. With switch in any position, check continuity between terminals No. 12 (Yellow/Green wire) and No. 16 (Black/Yellow wire). Continuity should exist. If continuity does not exist in either circuit, replace defogger switch.

DEFOGGER RELAY TEST

Remove defogger relay. On Accord and Prelude, relay is located in underdash fuse/relay box at left side kick panel. On Civic, relay is located in underhood fuse/relay box on right side of engine compartment. Apply battery voltage to terminal "C", and ground terminal "D". *See Fig. 2.* Use an ohmmeter to ensure continuity exists between terminals "A" and "B". Ensure continuity does not exist between terminals "A" and "B" when battery voltage is removed.

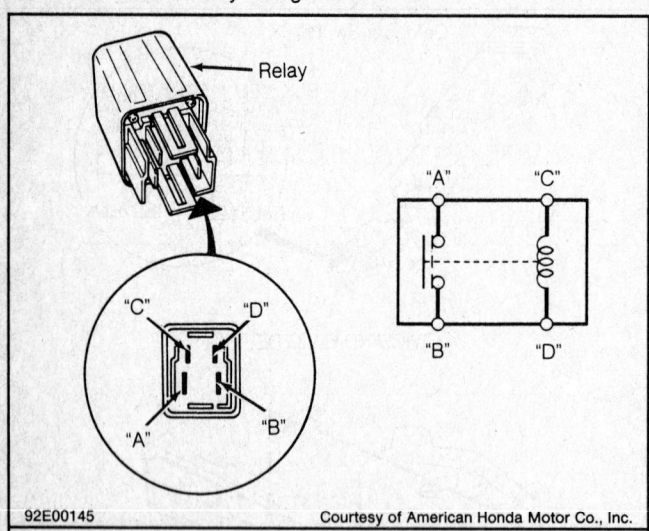

92E00145   Courtesy of American Honda Motor Co., Inc.

Fig. 2: Identifying Relay Terminals (Typical)

GRID FILAMENT TEST

1) Turn ignition and rear window defogger on. Using a voltmeter, check for voltage between defogger positive wire terminal and body ground. *See Fig. 3.* If voltage is present, go to next step. If voltage is not present, check for faulty defogger relay. Check for open in Black/Green defogger relay wire.

2) If voltage is present, use an ohmmeter to check for continuity between defogger negative wire terminal and body ground. If continuity does not exist, check for open in defogger ground wire. Connect voltmeter negative probe to defogger negative wire terminal. Connect voltmeter positive probe to center of each defogger grid wire.

3) If voltage is about 6 volts, defogger grid wire is okay. If voltage is greater than 6 volts, an open exists between center of defogger grid wire and negative side of center. If voltage is not present, an open exists between defogger grid wire and positive side of center. To locate break, move probe along grid wire until meter needle moves abruptly. *See Fig. 3.*

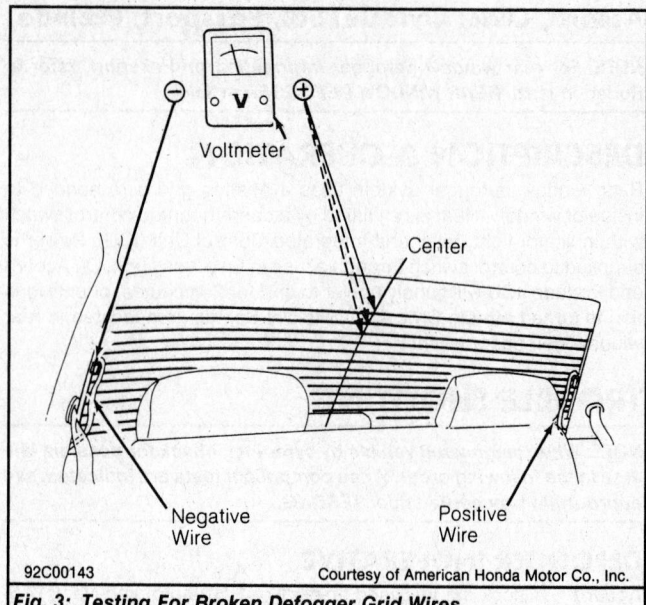

92C00143   Courtesy of American Honda Motor Co., Inc.

Fig. 3: Testing For Broken Defogger Grid Wires

ON-VEHICLE SERVICE
GRID FILAMENT REPAIR

Clean broken wire tips thoroughly. Place masking tape along both sides of broken wire. *See Fig. 4.* Apply Repair Paste (Dupont 4817) to broken section of grid. Remove masking tape after paste has dried. Wait 24 hours before using defogger.

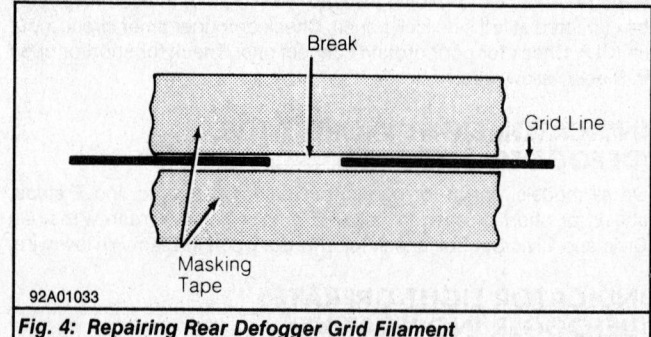

92A01033

Fig. 4: Repairing Rear Defogger Grid Filament

WIRING DIAGRAMS

NOTE: See ACCESSORIES & EQUIPMENT, Volume 5.

Accord, Civic, Civic Del Sol, Passport, Prelude

NOTE: For instrument panel information on Passport, refer to Rodeo in Isuzu INSTRUMENT PANELS article.

DESCRIPTION & OPERATION

The instrument panel contains a speedometer, tachometer (if equipped), fuel gauge, coolant temperature gauge, and warning light displays. Cross-coil type gauges, in which 2 intersecting coils are wound around a permanent magnet, are used. An electronic speedometer is used.

TESTING

FUEL GAUGE TEST

CAUTION: In Step 3), turn ignition off before fuel gauge pointer reaches "F" mark. Failure to turn ignition off before pointer reaches "F" mark may damage fuel gauge.

Accord & Civic – 1) Turn ignition switch to OFF position. On Accord, check fuse No. 1 (10-amp) in dash fuse box. On Civic and Civic Del Sol, check fuse No. 15 (10-amp) in dash fuse box. On all models, remove fuel gauge sending unit access cover in luggage compartment. Disconnect 3-pin connector from sending unit.
2) Connect voltmeter positive lead to Yellow/White wire and negative lead to Black wire (Black/White wire on Civic and Civic Del Sol). Turn ignition on. Voltage should be 5-8 volts. If voltage is incorrect, check for open circuit in Yellow, Yellow/White, Black and Black/White wires. Check for poor ground connection.
3) Turn ignition off. Install jumper wire between Yellow/White wire and Black wire (Black/White wire on Civic and Civic Del Sol). Turn ignition on. Ensure fuel gauge pointer starts to move toward "F" mark on gauge. If fuel gauge pointer does not move, replace fuel gauge. If fuel gauge is okay, check fuel gauge sending unit.
Prelude – 1) Ensure ignition switch is in OFF position. Check fuse No.13 (10-amp) in dash fuse box. If fuse is okay, remove luggage compartment carpet. Remove access panel. Disconnect 5-pin connector from fuel gauge sending unit.
2) Connect voltmeter positive lead to Yellow/Green wire and negative lead to body ground. Turn ignition switch to ON position. Indicated voltage should be 5-8 volts. If voltage is not as specified, check for open circuit in Yellow and/or Yellow/Green wire. Check for poor ground connection.
3) Turn ignition switch to OFF position. Connect Yellow/Green and Yellow/White wires with a jumper wire. Turn ignition switch to ON position. Ensure fuel gauge pointer starts to move toward "F" mark on gauge. If fuel gauge pointer does not move, replace gauge. If fuel gauge is okay, check sending unit.

FUEL GAUGE SENDING UNIT TEST

1) Ensure ignition switch is in OFF position. Remove fuel gauge sending unit access cover in luggage compartment. Disconnect connector from fuel gauge sending unit.
2) Remove fuel gauge sending unit. Use an ohmmeter to measure resistance between fuel gauge sending unit terminals with sending unit float held at empty (down), half-full (middle) and full (up) positions. Compare readings with FUEL GAUGE SENDING UNIT RESISTANCE table. If resistance values are incorrect, replace fuel gauge sending unit.

FUEL GAUGE SENDING UNIT RESISTANCE

Float Position	Ohms
Accord	
Empty	105-110
Half-Full	25.5-39.5
Full	3-5

FUEL GAUGE SENDING UNIT RESISTANCE (Cont.)

Float Position	Ohms
Civic & Civic Del Sol	
Empty	105-110
Half-Full	25.5-39.5
Full	2-5
Prelude	
Empty	16-32
Half-Full	116-188
Full	239-314

TEMPERATURE GAUGE TEST

CAUTION: In Step 1), turn ignition off before gauge pointer reaches "H" mark. Failure to turn ignition off before pointer reaches "H" mark may damage gauge.

Accord – 1) Ensure ignition switch is in OFF position. Disconnect and ground Red wire on coolant temperature gauge sender. Turn ignition switch on. Ensure gauge pointer starts to move toward "H" mark.
2) If gauge pointer does not move, check fuse No. 1 (10-amp) in dash fuse box. Check Red wire for an open circuit. If fuse and wiring are okay, replace temperature gauge. If gauge is okay, test temperature gauge sending unit.
Civic & Civic Del Sol – 1) Ensure ignition switch is in OFF position. Disconnect and ground Yellow/Green wire on coolant temperature gauge sender. Turn ignition switch to ON position. Ensure gauge pointer starts to move toward "H" mark.
2) If gauge pointer does not move, check fuse No. 15 (10-amp) in dash fuse box. Check Yellow or Yellow/Green wire for an open circuit. If fuse and wiring are okay, replace temperature gauge. If gauge is okay, test temperature gauge sending unit.

CAUTION: On Prelude, turn ignition off immediately after all gauge segments illuminate. Failure to turn ignition off immediately may damage gauge.

Prelude – 1) Ensure ignition switch is in OFF position. Disconnect and ground Red wire on coolant temperature gauge sender. Turn ignition on. Ensure all light segments of gauge illuminate properly.
2) If gauge light segments do not illuminate, check fuse No. 13 (10-amp). Check Red or Yellow wire for an open circuit. If fuse and wiring are okay, replace temperature gauge. If gauge is okay, test temperature gauge sending unit.

TEMPERATURE GAUGE SENDING UNIT TEST

Accord & Prelude – 1) Disconnect Yellow/Red wire (Red wire on Prelude) from temperature gauge sending unit. Use an ohmmeter to measure resistance of temperature gauge sending unit with engine cold. Start engine and allow coolant temperature to rise.
2) Measure temperature gauge sending unit resistance as coolant temperature rises. If resistance values differ from specifications, replace temperature gauge sending unit. See TEMPERATURE GAUGE SENDING UNIT RESISTANCE table.
Civic & Civic Del Sol – 1) Disconnect Yellow/Green wire from temperature gauge sending unit. Use an ohmmeter to measure resistance of temperature gauge sending unit with engine cold. Start engine and allow coolant temperature to rise.
2) Measure temperature gauge sending unit resistance as coolant temperature rises. If resistance values differ from specifications, replace temperature gauge sending unit. See TEMPERATURE GAUGE SENDING UNIT RESISTANCE table.

TEMPERATURE GAUGE SENDING UNIT RESISTANCE

Temperature	Ohms
Accord, Civic & Prelude	
133°F (56°C)	142
185-212°F (85-100°C)	49-32
Civic Del Sol	
133°F (56°C)	137
185-212°F (85-100°C)	46-30.4

1994 ACCESSORIES & EQUIPMENT
Instrument Panels (Cont.)

OIL PRESSURE SWITCH TEST

Disconnect Yellow/Red wire from oil pressure switch. Use an ohmmeter to check continuity of oil pressure switch. With engine off, continuity should exist between oil pressure switch terminal and ground. With engine running, continuity should not exist. If switch fails to operate as described, check engine oil level and oil pump pressure. If oil level and oil pump pressure are okay, replace pressure switch.

HAZARD WARNING SWITCH TEST

Accord – Carefully pry hazard warning switch from front console panel. Disconnect hazard warning switch 10-pin connector. With hazard switch in specified position, use an ohmmeter to check continuity between switch terminals. *See Fig. 1.* If continuity is not as specified, replace hazard warning switch.

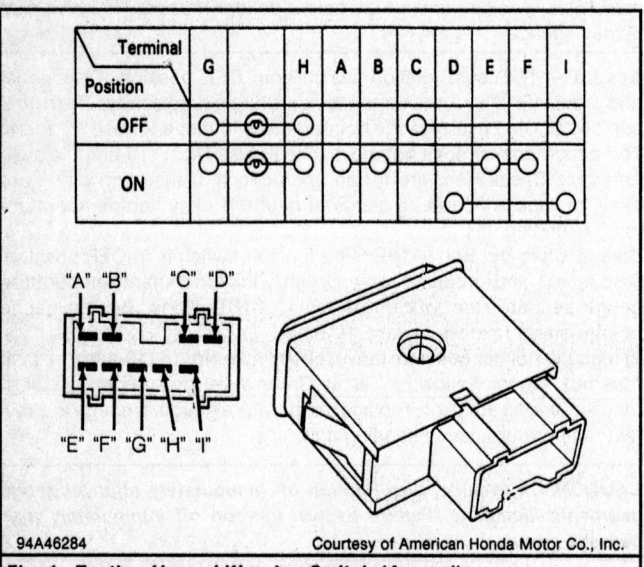

Terminal Position	G	H	A	B	C	D	E	F	I
OFF									
ON									

Fig. 1: Testing Hazard Warning Switch (Accord)

94A46284   Courtesy of American Honda Motor Co., Inc.

Civic – Carefully pry hazard warning switch from dash. Disconnect hazard warning switch 10-pin connector. With hazard switch in specified position, use an ohmmeter to check continuity between switch terminals. *See Fig. 2.* If continuity is not as specified, replace hazard warning switch.

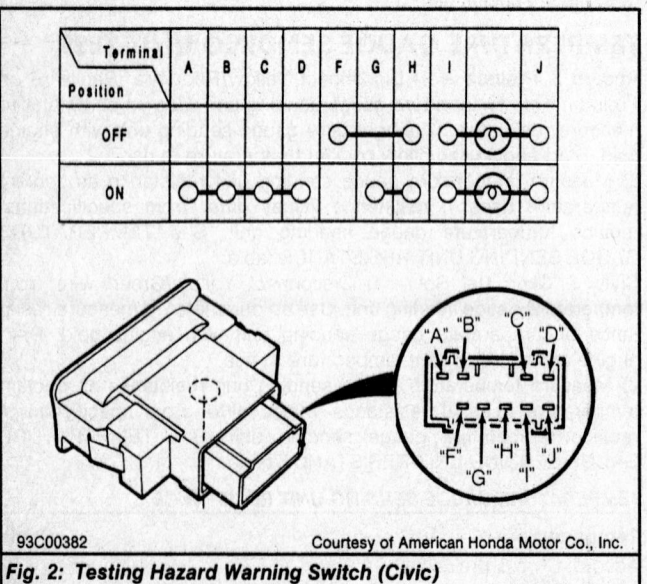

Terminal Position	A	B	C	D	F	G	H	I	J
OFF									
ON									

Fig. 2: Testing Hazard Warning Switch (Civic)

93C00382   Courtesy of American Honda Motor Co., Inc.

Civic Del Sol – Carefully pry hazard warning switch and rear window defogger switch from dash together. Disconnect switch connectors. With hazard switch in specified position, use an ohmmeter to check continuity between switch terminals. *See Fig. 3.* If continuity is not as specified, replace hazard warning switch.

Terminal Position	B	C	D	E	F
OFF					
ON					

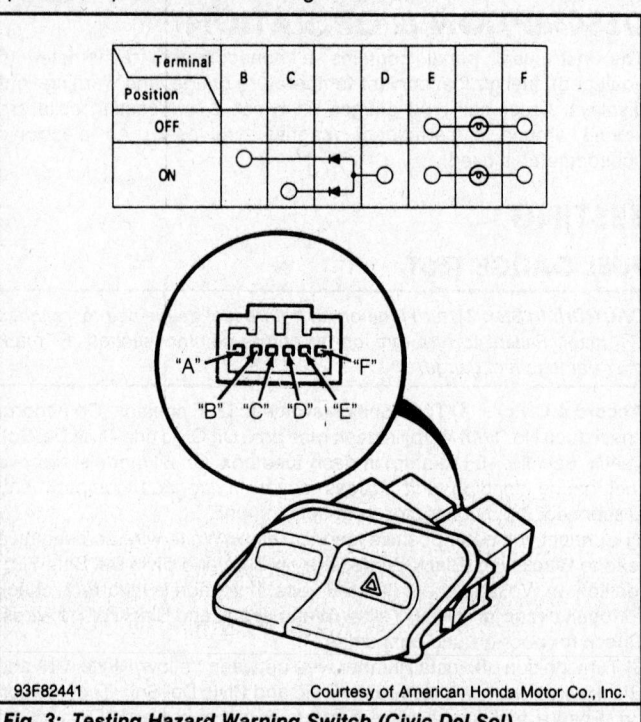

Fig. 3: Testing Hazard Warning Switch (Civic Del Sol)

93F82441   Courtesy of American Honda Motor Co., Inc.

Prelude – Remove center console trim panel. Remove retaining screw from switch. Slowly rotate switch clockwise and remove from console. Disconnect 6-pin connector. With hazard switch in specified position, use an ohmmeter to check continuity between switch terminals. *See Fig. 4.* If continuity is not as specified, replace hazard warning switch.

Terminal Position	B	C	D	E	F
ON					
OFF					

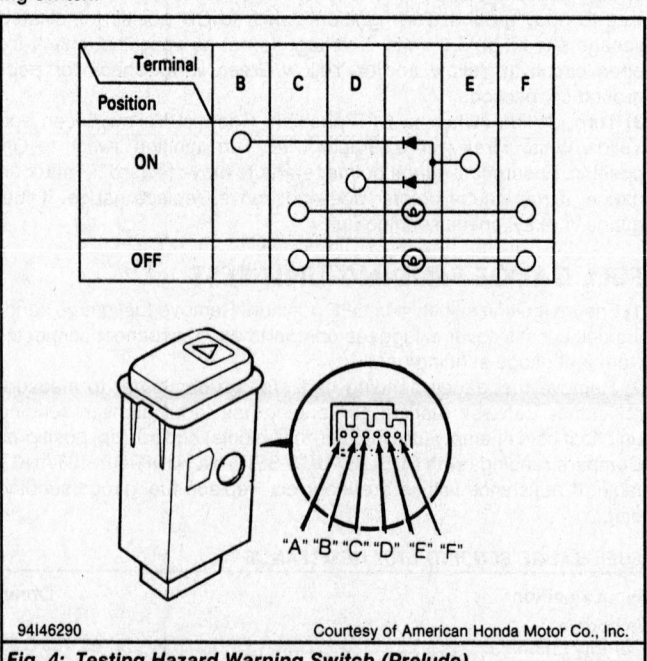

Fig. 4: Testing Hazard Warning Switch (Prelude)

94I46290   Courtesy of American Honda Motor Co., Inc.

SPEED SENSOR INPUT TEST

1) Check 10-amp fuse No. 1 on Accord, No. 24 on Civic and Civic Del Sol or No. 23 on Prelude in dash fuse box. Disconnect 3-pin connector from speed sensor, located on right side of engine.

2) Use an ohmmeter to check continuity between Black wire and ground. If continuity exists, go to next step. If continuity does not exist, check Black wire for an open circuit. Also check for poor ground.

3) Turn ignition switch to ON position. Use a voltmeter to check voltage between Yellow wire (Yellow/Blue wire on Civic and Civic Del Sol, Black/Yellow wire on Prelude) and ground. If battery voltage is present, go to next step. If battery voltage is not present, check Yellow wire (Yellow/Blue wire on Civic and Civic Del Sol, Black/Yellow wire on Prelude) for an open circuit.

4) With ignition on, check voltage between Orange wire (Yellow/White wire on Civic and Civic Del Sol) and ground. If voltage is about 5 volts, go to next step. If voltage is not as specified, check Orange wire (Yellow/White wire on Civic and Civic Del Sol) for an open circuit.

5) If continuity and voltage checks are okay, but speedometer/odometer/trip meter does not operate properly, replace speed sensor.

REMOVAL & INSTALLATION

INSTRUMENT CLUSTER

Removal & Installation (Accord) – **1)** Remove rear console. Remove front console panel. remove stereo radio/cassette player. Remove switches from instrument panel. Remove instrument panel. If necessary, disconnect air mix control cable from the heater unit.

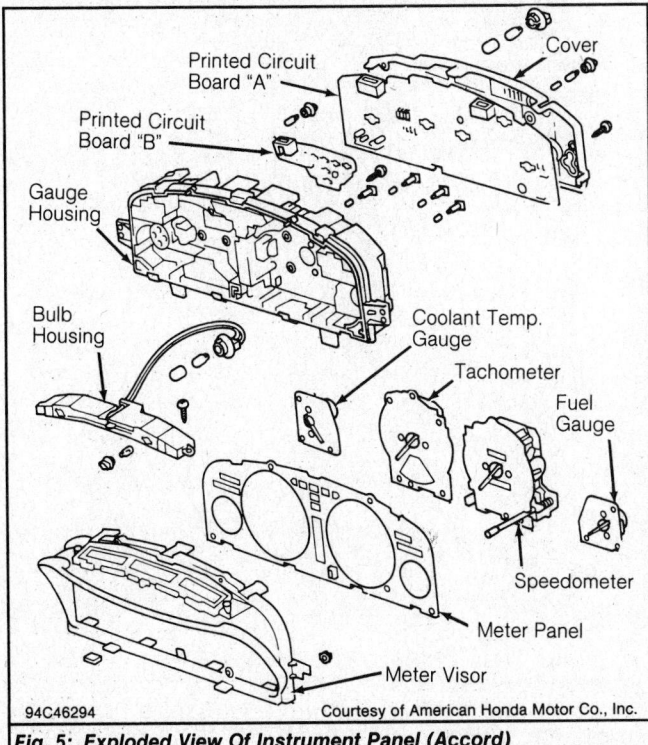

94C46294 Courtesy of American Honda Motor Co., Inc.

Fig. 5: Exploded View Of Instrument Panel (Accord)

2) Tilt steering column fully down. Cover steering column with protective cloth. Remove 4 gauge assembly mounting screws. Gently pry gauge assembly from dash. Unplug harness connectors. Remove gauge assembly. *See Fig. 5.* To install, reverse removal procedure.

Removal & Installation (Civic) – **1)** Carefully pry hazard warning switch from instrument panel. Remove 3 trim panel mounting screws. Carefully pull trim panel from dashboard. Disconnect 4-pin connector and remove trim panel.

2) Remove screws and partially pull out instrument panel. Disconnect wiring harness connectors from instrument panel. *See Fig. 6.* To install, reverse removal procedure.

Removal & Installation (Civic Del Sol) – **1)** Carefully pry hazard warning and rear window defogger switches from instrument panel.

Remove 2 panel visor mounting screws. Carefully pull panel visor from dashboard.

2) Remove screws and partially pull out instrument panel. Disconnect wiring harness connectors from instrument panel. *See Fig. 7.* To install, reverse removal procedure.

Removal & Installation (Prelude) – **1)** Remove speaker covers. Remove instrument visor from above instrument cluster. Remove black face panel from dash. Disconnect 6-pin connector from clock reset switch.

2) Remove main gauge assembly retaining screws. Place cloth over dash to protect main instrument panel. Remove main instrument panel, and disconnect its connectors. Remove sub instrument panel in similar manner. *See Fig. 8* To install main and sub instrument panels, reverse removal procedure.

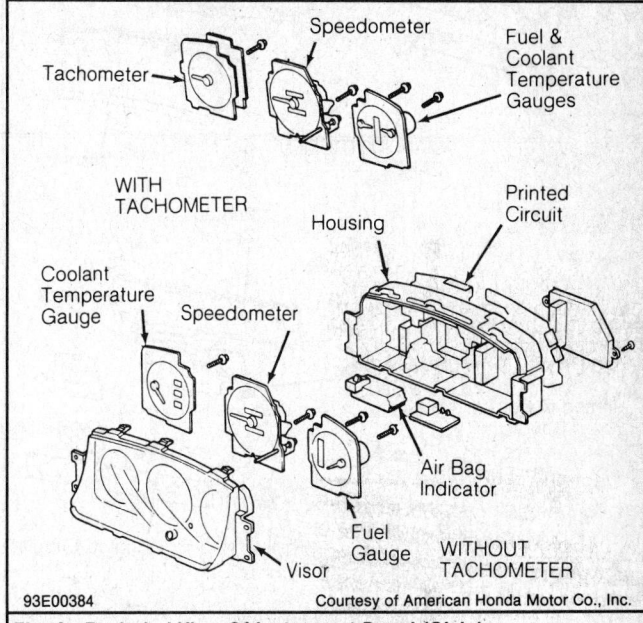

93E00384 Courtesy of American Honda Motor Co., Inc.

Fig. 6: Exploded View Of Instrument Panel (Civic)

93G82442 Courtesy of American Honda Motor Co., Inc.

Fig. 7: Exploded View Of Instrument Panel (Civic Del Sol)

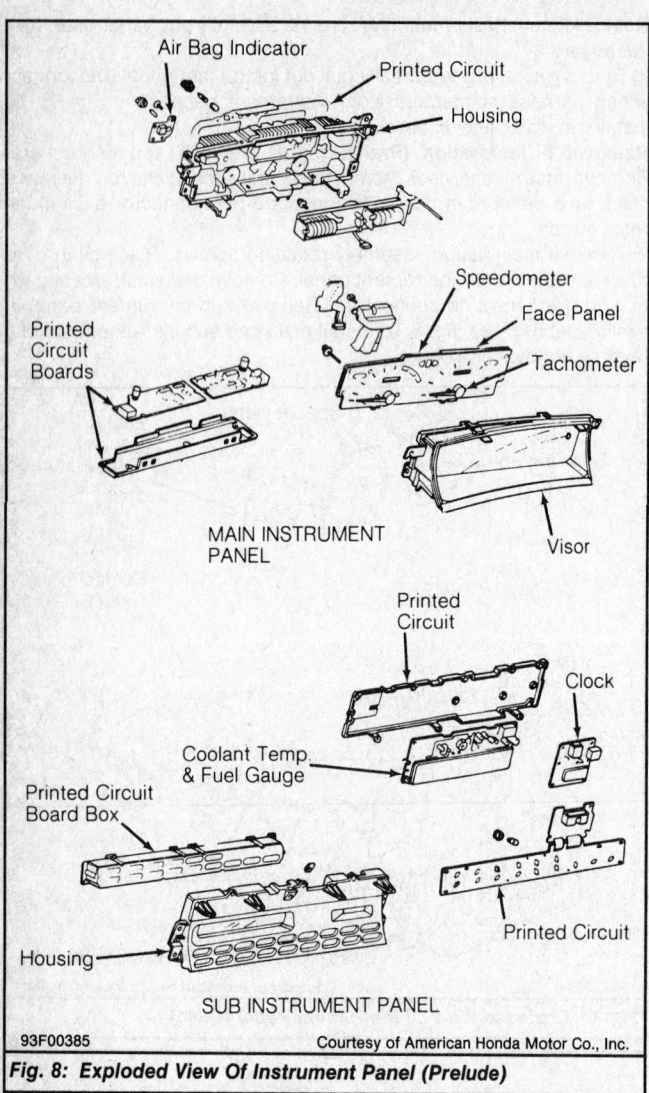

Air Bag Indicator — Printed Circuit — Housing

Speedometer — Face Panel — Tachometer

Printed Circuit Boards

MAIN INSTRUMENT PANEL — Visor

Printed Circuit — Clock

Coolant Temp & Fuel Gauge

Printed Circuit Board Box

Housing — Printed Circuit

SUB INSTRUMENT PANEL

93F00385   Courtesy of American Honda Motor Co., Inc.

Fig. 8: Exploded View Of Instrument Panel (Prelude)

WIRING DIAGRAMS

NOTE: See ACCESSORIES & EQUIPMENT, Volume 5.

Accord, Civic, Passport, Prelude

NOTE: For power door locks information on Passport, refer to Rodeo in Isuzu POWER DOOR LOCKS article.

DESCRIPTION & OPERATION

Power door locks are controlled by driver or front passenger switches which send signals to a control unit. The control unit sends lock or unlock signal to individual door lock actuators.

Accord wagon may be equipped with an optional keyless entry system. A programmable remote transmitter sends signal to keyless entry control unit (located under driver's seat). Control unit sends lock or unlock signal to all door lock actuators except tailgate.

On Accord wagon, a switch in the driver's door sends a signal to actuator which releases the tailgate.

CAUTION: All models are equipped with Supplemental Restraint System (SRS). SRS wiring harness is routed close to instrument cluster, steering wheel, and related components. All SRS wiring harnesses are covered by Yellow outer insulation. DO NOT use electrical test equipment on these circuits. Before working on steering column components, disable air bag system. See AIR BAG RESTRAINT SYSTEM article in ACCESSORIES & EQUIPMENT.

TRANSMITTER PROGRAMMING

1) Open driver's door. Press and hold driver's master power door lock switch in the UNLOCK position.
2) Within 10 seconds, insert and remove key from ignition switch 5 times. On the sixth key insertion, leave key in ignition switch. All doors should unlock, indicating system is now in programming mode.
3) Release driver's master door lock switch. Press either button on the transmitter. All doors except driver's door will lock and unlock indicating system has accepted transmitter into its memory. If either transmitter button is pressed again, all doors will lock and unlock.
4) To program a second transmitter, press either button on that transmitter. The door will lock and unlock indicating that the second transmitter has been accepted into accepted into the system memory.
5) To exit the programming mode, close driver's door and remove key from ignition switch. Check door lock operation at both front door locks. If door locks door not function properly, repeat programming procedure.

TROUBLE SHOOTING

NOTE: Ensure all component terminals and ground connections are clean and tight. Check possible faults in order listed. Repair or replace components and circuits as necessary.

NOTE: Some wires have been assigned a superscript to distinguish them from other wires of the same color. For example, the Yellow/Green[1] wire is not the same as the Yellow/Green[2] wire.

ACCORD (COUPE, SEDAN & WAGON WITHOUT KEYLESS ENTRY SYSTEM)

System Does Not Work At All – Blown fuse No. 38 (20-amp) in underhood fuse/relay box. Faulty control unit inputs. Open in White wire.

No Doors Lock Using Driver's Door Lock Switch (All Doors) – Faulty driver's door lock switch. Faulty control unit inputs. Open in Black/White (Blue/White on wagon) or Orange wire.

No Doors Lock Using Driver's Door Lock Switch (One Or More Doors) – Faulty passenger's door lock switch. Faulty driver's door lock switch. Obstructed or disconnected door lock linkage. Open in Yellow/Red or White/Red wire.

No Doors Lock Using Front Passenger's Door Lock Switch (All Doors) – Blown fuse No. 38 (20-amp) in underhood fuse/relay box. Faulty passenger's door lock switch. Faulty control unit inputs. Open in Orange or Blue/White wire.

No Doors Lock Using Passenger's Front Door Lock Switch (One Or More Doors) – Faulty passenger's door lock actuator. Faulty driver's door lock actuator. Obstructed or disconnected door lock linkage. Open in Yellow/Red or White/Red wire.

No Doors Lock Using Driver's Door Lock Knob Switch (All Doors) – Blown fuse No. 38 (20-amp) in underhood fuse/relay box. Faulty driver's door lock knob switch (located in actuator). Faulty control unit inputs. Open in Black/Red or Pink wire.

No Doors Lock Using Driver's Door Lock Knob Switch (One Or More Doors) – Faulty driver's door lock actuator. Faulty passenger's door lock actuator. Obstructed or disconnected door lock linkage. Open in Yellow/Red or White/Red wire.

No Doors Lock Using Passenger's Door Key (All Doors) – Blown fuse No. 38 (20-amp) in underhood fuse/relay box. Faulty front passenger's key cylinder switch. Faulty control unit inputs. Open in Orange or Blue/White wire.

No Doors Lock Using Passenger's Door Key (One Or More Doors) – Faulty driver's door lock actuator. Faulty passenger's door lock actuator. Obstructed or disconnected door lock linkage. Open in Yellow/Red or White/Red wire.

No Doors Lock Using Driver's Door Key (Driver's Door) – Faulty driver's door lock actuator. Faulty driver's key cylinder switch. Obstructed or disconnected door lock linkage. Open in Yellow/Red or White/Red wire.

No Doors Lock Using Driver's Door Key (All Doors) – Blown fuse No. 38 (20-amp) in underhood fuse/relay box. Faulty driver's door key cylinder switch. Faulty control unit inputs. Open in Blue, White/Red or Yellow/Red wire.

ACCORD (WAGON WITH KEYLESS ENTRY SYSTEM)

System Does Not Work At All – Blown fuse No. 38 (20-amp) in underhood fuse/relay box. Faulty control unit inputs. Open in White wire.

No Doors Lock Using Driver's Door Lock Switch (All Doors) – Faulty driver's door lock switch. Faulty control unit inputs. Open in Green/White or Yellow/White wire.

No Doors Lock Using Driver's Door Lock Switch (One Or More Doors) – Faulty passenger's door lock actuator. Faulty driver's door lock knob switch.

No Doors Lock Using Front Passenger's Door Lock Switch (All Doors) – Blown fuse No. 38 (20-amp) in underhood fuse/relay box. Faulty passenger's door lock switch. Faulty control unit inputs. Open in Green/White or Yellow/White wire.

No Doors Lock Using Passenger's Front Door Lock Switch (One Or More Doors) – Faulty passenger's door lock actuator. Faulty driver's door lock knob switch.

Power Door Lock Systems Operates; Keyless Entry System Inoperative – Dead battery in remote transmitter. Faulty control unit inputs. Open in Green/White[1], Green/Black[2] or White/Blue wire.

No Doors Lock Using Driver's Door Lock Knob Switch (All Passenger's Doors) – Blown fuse No. 38 (20-amp) in underhood fuse/relay box. Faulty driver's door lock knob switch (located in actuator). Faulty control unit inputs. Open in Yellow/Red or White/Red wire.

No Doors Lock Using Driver's Door Lock Knob Switch (One Or More Passenger's Doors) – Faulty passenger's door lock actuator. Open in Yellow/Red or White/Red wire.

No Doors Lock Using Passenger's Door Key (All Doors) – Blown fuse No. 38 (20-amp) in underhood fuse/relay box. Faulty front passenger's key cylinder switch. Faulty control unit inputs. Obstructed or disconnected door lock linkage. Open in Green/White or Yellow/White wire.

No Doors Lock Using Passenger's Door Key (One Or More Doors) – Faulty passenger's door lock actuator. Open in Yellow/Red or White/Red wire.

No Doors Lock Using Tailgate Key Switch (All Doors) – Faulty tailgate lock knob switch (key cylinder switch). Obstructed or disconnected door lock linkage.Faulty control unit inputs. Open in Green/Yellow or Yellow wire.

No Doors Lock Using Tailgate Key Switch (One Or More Doors) – Faulty passenger,s door lock actuator. Open in Yellow/Red or Yellow/White wire.

CIVIC

System Does Not Work At All – Blown fuse No. 6 (20-amp) in underdash fuse/relay box. Faulty control unit inputs. Open in White/Green wire.

No Doors Lock Using Driver's Door Lock Knob Switch (All Doors) – Blown fuse No. 6 (20-amp) in underdash fuse panel. Faulty door lock knob switch. Faulty control unit inputs. Open in Blue/White wire.

No Doors Lock Using Driver's Door Lock Knob Switch (One Or More Doors) – Faulty passenger's door lock actuator. Disconnected or obstructed door lock linkage. Open in Yellow/Red or White/Red wire.

No Doors Lock Using Driver's Door Lock Switch (All Doors) – Blown fuse No. 6 (20-amp) in underdash fuse panel. Faulty driver's door lock switch. Faulty control unit inputs. Disconnected or obstructed door lock linkage. Open in Green/Red, Green/White, Yellow/Red or White/Red wire.

No Doors Lock Using Driver's Door Lock Switch (One Or More Doors) – Faulty passenger's door lock actuator. Disconnected or obstructed door lock linkage. Open in Yellow/Red or White/Red wire.

PRELUDE

System Does Not Work At All – Blown fuse No. 44 (15-amp) in underhood fuse/relay box. Faulty control unit inputs. Open in White wire.

No Doors Lock Using Driver's Door Lock Switch (Both Doors) – Faulty driver's door lock switch. Faulty control unit inputs. Open in Green/Red[1] or Green/White wire.

No Doors Lock Using Driver's Door Lock Switch (One Door) – Disconnected or obstructed door lock linkage. Faulty driver's or passenger's door lock actuator. Open in Yellow/Red or White/Red wire.

No Doors Lock Using Passenger's Door Lock Switch (Both Doors) – Faulty passenger's door lock switch. Faulty control unit inputs. Open in Black/White or Black/Red wire.

No Doors Lock Using Passenger's Door Lock Switch (One Door) – Disconnected or obstructed door lock linkage. Faulty driver's or passenger's door lock actuator. Faulty control unit inputs. Open in Yellow/Red or White/Red wire.

No Doors Lock Using Driver's Door Lock Knob; Ignition Key Out; Doors Closed (Both Doors) – Faulty driver's lock knob switch. Faulty control unit inputs. Open in Blue/Red or Blue/White[1] wire.

No Doors Lock Using Driver's Door Lock Knob; Ignition Key Out; Doors Closed (One Door) – Disconnected or obstructed door lock linkage. Faulty driver's or passenger's door lock actuator. Faulty control unit inputs. Open in Yellow/Red or White/Red wire.

No Doors Lock Using Passenger's Door Key Cylinder Switch (Both Doors) – Faulty passenger's door key cylinder. Faulty control unit inputs. Open in Black/White or Black/Red wire.

No Doors Lock Using Passenger's Door Key Cylinder Switch (One Door) – Disconnected or obstructed door lock linkage. Faulty driver's or passenger's door lock actuator. Faulty control unit inputs. Open in Yellow/Red or White/Red wire.

Doors Lock With Key In Ignition; Driver's Door Open – Faulty ignition key switch. Faulty driver's door switch. Faulty passenger's door switch. Faulty control unit inputs. Open in Blue/White[2], Green/Red[2] or Green/Blue wire.

TESTING

CAUTION: All models are equipped with Supplemental Restraint System (SRS). SRS wiring harness is routed close to instrument cluster, steering wheel, and related components. All SRS wiring harnesses are covered by Yellow outer insulation. DO NOT use electrical test equipment on these circuits. Before working on steering column components, disable air bag system. See AIR BAG RESTRAINT SYSTEM article in ACCESSORIES & EQUIPMENT.

ACTUATOR TEST

CAUTION: To prevent damage to the actuator motor, apply power and ground only momentarily.

Accord (Driver's Door) – 1) Remove door panel. Unplug connector. Using fused jumper wire, connect battery voltage to actuator connector terminal No. 5. Momentarily connect terminal No. 4 to ground. Actuator should move to lock position. *See Fig. 1.* Check continuity between connector terminals No. 1 and 3. Continuity should exist.
2) Connect battery voltage to actuator connector terminal No. 4. Momentarily connect terminal No. 5 to ground. Actuator should move to unlock position. Check continuity between connector terminals No. 1 and 6. Continuity should exist. Replace actuator if operation or continuity is not as specified.

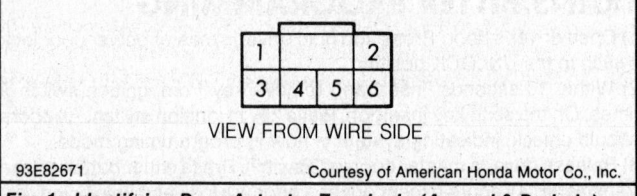

93E82671   Courtesy of American Honda Motor Co., Inc.

Fig. 1: Identifying Door Actuator Terminals (Accord & Prelude)

Accord (Passenger's Door) – 1) Remove door panel. Unplug connector. Using fused jumper wire, connect battery voltage to actuator connector terminal No. 1. Momentarily connect terminal No. 2 to ground. Actuator should move to lock position. *See Fig. 2.*
2) Connect battery voltage to actuator connector terminal No. 2. Momentarily connect terminal No. 1 to ground. Actuator should move to unlock position. Replace actuator if operation is not as specified.

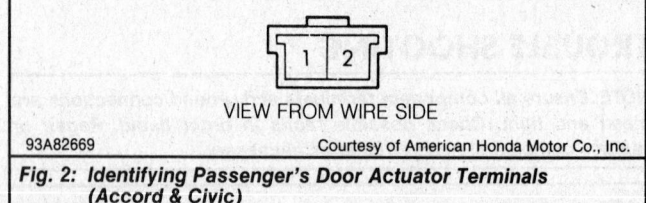

93A82669   Courtesy of American Honda Motor Co., Inc.

Fig. 2: Identifying Passenger's Door Actuator Terminals (Accord & Civic)

Civic (Driver's Door) – 1) Remove door panel. Unplug connector. Using fused jumper wire, connect battery voltage to actuator connector terminal No. 4. Momentarily connect terminal No. 3 to ground. Actuator should move to lock position. *See Fig. 3.* Check continuity between connector terminals No. 1 and 2. Continuity should not exist.
2) Connect battery voltage to actuator connector terminal No. 3. Momentarily connect terminal No. 4 to ground. Actuator should move to unlock position. Check continuity between connector terminals No. 1 and 2. Continuity should not exist. Replace actuator if operation or continuity is not as specified.

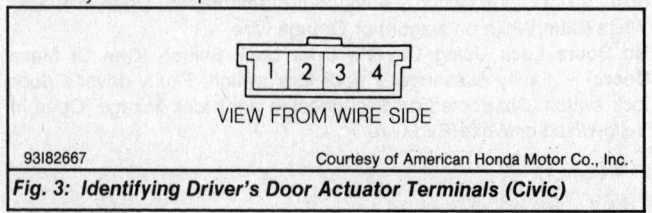

93I82667   Courtesy of American Honda Motor Co., Inc.

Fig. 3: Identifying Driver's Door Actuator Terminals (Civic)

Civic (Passenger's Door) – 1) Remove door panel. Unplug connector. Using fused jumper wire, connect battery voltage to actuator connector terminal No. 1. Momentarily connect terminal No. 2 to ground. Actuator should move to lock position. *See Fig. 2.*

2) Connect battery voltage to actuator connector terminal No. 2. Momentarily connect terminal No. 1 to ground. Actuator should move to unlock position. Replace actuator if operation is not as specified.

Prelude – 1) Remove door panel. Unplug connector. Using fused jumper wire, connect battery voltage to actuator connector terminal No. 4. Momentarily connect terminal No. 5 to ground. Actuator should move to lock position. *See Fig. 1.* Check continuity between connector terminals No. 3 and 6. Continuity should exist.

2) Connect battery voltage to actuator connector terminal No. 5. Momentarily connect terminal No. 4 to ground. Actuator should move to unlock position. Check continuity between connector terminals No. 1 and 3. Continuity should exist. Replace actuator if operation or continuity is not as specified.

CONTROL UNIT INPUTS

Accord (Coupe, Sedan & Wagon Without Keyless Entry System) – Remove left door panel. Using a DVOM, perform power door lock unit input tests. *See Fig. 4.* If all input test results are okay, inspect connector and terminals for damage and proper fit. If connector is okay and power door lock still malfunctions, replace power door lock control unit.

Accord (Accord Wagon With Keyless Entry System) – Slide driver's seat forward. Using a DVOM, perform power door lock unit input tests. *See Figs. 5 and 6.* If all input test results are okay, inspect connector and terminals for damage and proper fit. If connector is okay and power door lock still malfunctions, replace power door lock control unit.

Civic & Prelude – Remove left door panel. Using a DVOM, perform power door lock unit input tests. *See Fig. 7 or 8.* If all input test results are okay, inspect connector and terminals for damage and proper fit. If connector is okay and power door lock still malfunctions, replace power door lock control unit.

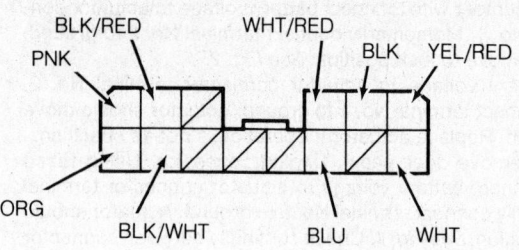

BLK/RED   WHT/RED

PNK   BLK   YEL/RED

ORG

BLK/WHT   BLU   WHT

VIEW FROM WIRE SIDE

NOTE: Numbers 1 through 6 refer to test numbers,
not terminal numbers.

Disconnect 14-pin connector from power door lock control unit.

No.	Wire	Test condition	Test: Desired result	Possible cause if result is not obtained
1	BLK	Under all conditions	Check for continuity to ground: There should be continuity.	• Poor ground (G401, G403) • An open in the wire
2	WHT/RED and YEL/RED	Connect the YEL/RED terminal to the WHT terminal, and the WHT/RED terminal to the BLK terminal momentarily.	Check door lock operation: All doors should unlock.	• Faulty actuator • An open in the wire • Blown No. 38 (20 A) fuse in the under hood fuse/relay box
		Connect the WHT/RED terminal to the WHT terminal, and the YEL/RED terminal to the BLK terminal momentarily.	Check door lock operation: All doors should lock.	

Reconnect 14-pin connector to power door lock control unit.

No.	Wire	Test condition	Test: Desired result	Possible cause if result is not obtained
3	WHT	Under all conditions	Check for voltage to ground: There should be battery voltage.	• Blown No. 38 (20 A) fuse in the underhood fuse/relay box • An open in the wire
4	BLK/WHT	Driver's door lock switch in LOCK	Check for voltage to ground: There should be 1 V or less.	• Faulty driver's door lock switch • Poor ground (G402, G404) • An open in the wire
	ORG	Driver's door lock switch in UNLOCK		
	BLK/WHT	Front passenger's door lock switch in LOCK	Check for voltage to ground: There should be 1 V or less.	• Faulty front passenger's door lock switch • Poor ground (G402, G404) • An open in the wire
	ORG	Front passenger's door lock switch in UNLOCK		
	BLK/WHT	Front passenger's door key cylinder in LOCK	Check for voltage to ground: There should be 1 V or less as the switch is turned.	• Faulty front passenger's door key cylinder switch • Poor ground (G402, G404) • An open in the wire
	ORG	Front passenger's door key cylinder in UNLOCK		
5	PNK	Driver's door lock knob in LOCK	Check for voltage to ground: There should be 1 V or less.	• Faulty driver's door lock actuator • Poor ground (G402, G404) • An open in the wire
	BLK/RED	Driver's door lock knob in UNLOCK		
6	BLU	Driver's door key cylinder in UNLOCK	Check for voltage to ground: There should be 1 V or less as the switch is turned.	• Faulty driver's door key cylinder switch • Poor ground (G402, G404) • An open in the wire

CAUTION: To prevent motor damage, connect power and ground only
momentarily.

Courtesy of American Honda Motor Co., Inc.

Fig. 4: Power Door Locks Control Unit Input Test (Accord Coupe, Sedan & Wagon Without Keyless Entry System)

NOTE: Numbers 1 through 10 refer to test numbers, not terminal numbers.

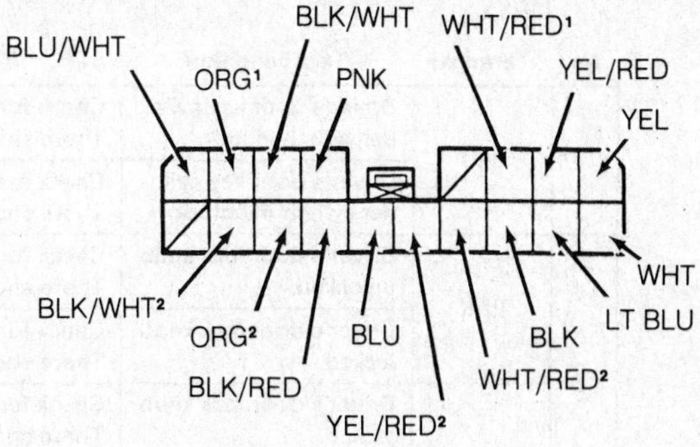

BLU/WHT ORG[1] PNK BLK/WHT WHT/RED[1] YEL/RED YEL

BLK/WHT[2] ORG[2] BLK/RED BLU YEL/RED[2] WHT/RED[2] BLK LT BLU WHT

VIEW FROM WIRE SIDE

No.	Terminal	Test condition	Test: Desired result	Possible cause if result is not obtained
1	BLK	Under all conditions	Check for continuity to ground: There should be continuity.	• Poor ground (G502) • An open in the wire
2	WHT	Under all conditions	Check for voltage to ground: There should be battery voltage.	• Blown No. 27 (20 A) fuse • An open in the wire
3	BLK/WHT[1] (or ORG[2])	Driver's door lock switch in neutral	Check for voltage to ground: There should be 5 V or more.	• Faulty driver's door lock switch • Poor ground (G502) • An open in the wire
		Driver's door lock switch in lock (or unlock)	Check for voltage to ground: There should be less than 1 V.	
		Front passenger's door lock switch in neutral	Check for voltage to ground: There should be 5 V or more.	• Faulty front passenger's door lock switch • Poor ground (G502) • An open in the wire
		Front passenger's door lock switch in lock (or unlock)	Check for voltage to ground: There should be less than 1 V.	
		Front passenger's door key cylinder switch in neutral	Check for voltage to ground: There should be 5 V or more.	• Faulty front passenger's key cylinder switch • Poor ground (G502) • An open in the wire
		Front passenger's door key cylinder switch in lock (or unlock)	Check for voltage to ground: There should be less than 1 V.	
		Tailgate key cylinder switch in neutral	Check for voltage to ground: There should be 5 V or more.	• Faulty tailgate key cylinder switch • Poor ground (G554) • Open in the wire
		Tailgate key cylinder switch in lock (or unlock)	Check for voltage to ground: There should be less than 1 V.	

94C46203

Courtesy of American Honda Motor Co., Inc.

Fig. 5: Power Door Locks Control Unit Input Test (Accord Wagon With Keyless Entry System – 1 Of 2)

1994 ACCESSORIES & EQUIPMENT
Power Door Locks & Tailgate Release (Cont.)

No.	Terminal	Test condition	Test: Desired result	Possible cause if result is not obtained
4	BLU	Driver's door key cylinder switch in lock.	Check for voltage to ground: There should be 5 V or more.	• Faulty driver's door key cylinder switch. • Poor ground (G402). • An open in the wire.
		Driver's door key cylinder switch in unlock.	Check for voltage to ground: There should be less than 1 V.	
5	PNK	Driver's door lock knob unlocked.	Check for voltage to ground: There should be 5 V or more.	• Faulty driver's door lock actuator. • Poor ground (G402). • An open in the wire.
		Driver's door lock knob locked.	Check for voltage to ground: There should be less than 1 V.	
	BLK/RED	Driver's door lock knob locked.	Check for voltage to ground: There should be 5 V or more.	• Faulty driver's door lock actuator. • Poor ground (G502). • An open in the wire.
		Driver's door lock knob unlocked.	Check for voltage to ground: There should be less than 1 V.	
6	ORN[1]	Tailgate open.	Check for voltage to ground: There should be less than 1 V.	• Faulty tailgate latch switch. • Poor ground (G554). • An open in the wire.
7	BLK/WHT[2]	Driver's door open.	Check for voltage to ground: There should be 1 V or less.	• Faulty driver's door switch. • An open in the wire.
8	BLU/WHT	Ignition key is in the ignition switch.	Check for voltage to ground: There should be battery voltage.	• Faulty ignition key switch. • An open in the wire.
9	Disconnect the connector and make these tests at the wire terminals.	Connect the WHT terminal to the WHT/RED terminal, and the YEL/RED (or YEL) terminal to the BLK terminal momentarily.	Check door lock operation: All passenger's doors (or driver's door) should lock as the wires are connected momentarily.	• Faulty passenger's door lock actuator. • Faulty driver's door lock actuator. • An open in the wire.
		Connect the WHT terminal to the YEL/RED (or YEL) terminal, and the WHT/RED terminal to the BLK terminal momentarily.	Check door unlock operation: All passenger's doors (or driver's door) should unlock as the wires are connected momentarily.	
10	LT BLU	Connect the BLK/WHT[2] terminal to the BLK terminal.	The ceiling light should come on.	• An open in the wire.

CAUTION: To prevent motor damage, connect power and ground only momentarily.

94D46204

Courtesy of American Honda Motor Co., Inc.

Fig. 6: Power Door Locks Control Unit Input Test (Accord Wagon With Keyless Entry System – 2 Of 2)

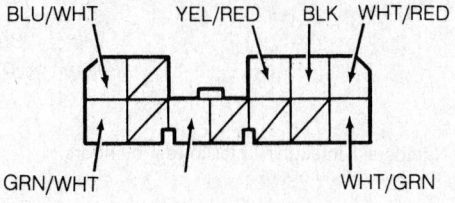

VIEW FROM WIRE SIDE

NOTE: Numbers 1 through 6 refer to test numbers, not terminal numbers.

Disconnect 12-pin connector from control unit.

No.	Wire	Test Condition	Test: Desired result	Possible cause if result is not obtained
1	BLK	Under all conditions.	Check for continuity to ground: There should be continuity.	• Poor ground (G552). • An open in the wire.
2	WHT/RED and YEL/RED	Connect the YEL/RED terminal to the WHT/GRN terminal, and the WHT/RED terminal to the BLK terminal momentarily.	Check door lock operation: All doors should unlock.	• Fauly actuator. • An open in the wire.
		Connect the WHT/RED terminal to the WHT/GRN terminal, and the YEL/RED terminal to the BLK terminal momentarily.	Check door lock operation: All doors should lock.	

Reconnect 12-pin connector to control unit.

No.	Wire	Test Condition	Test: Desired result	Possible cause if result is not obtained
3	WHT/GRN	Under all conditions.	Check for voltage to ground: There should be battery voltage.	• Blown No. 6 (20 A) fuse in the under-dash fuse/relay box. • An open in the wire.
4	GRN/WHT	Move the driver's power door lock switch from the neutral position to LOCK.	Check for voltage to ground: There should be 1 V or less.	• Faulty driver's door lock switch. • Poor ground (G552). • An open in the wire.
5	GRN/RED	Move the driver's power door lock switch from the neutral position to UNLOCK.		
6	BLU/WHT	Driver's door lock knob in LOCK.	Check for voltage to ground: There should be 1 V or less.	• Faulty driver's door actuator. • Poor ground (G552). • An open in the wire.

CAUTION: To prevent motor damage, connect power and ground only momentarily.

93H82625

Courtesy of American Honda Motor Co., Inc.

Fig. 7: Power Door Locks Control Unit Input Test (Civic)

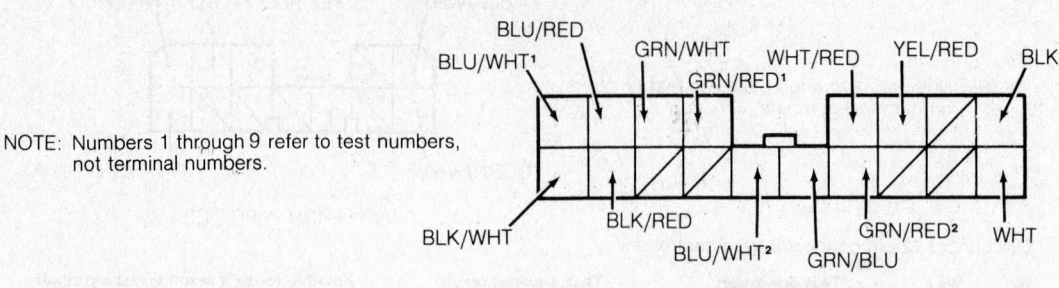

NOTE: Numbers 1 through 9 refer to test numbers, not terminal numbers.

VIEW FROM WIRE SIDE

Disconnect 18-pin connector from control unit.

No.	Wire	Test condition	Test: Desired result	Possible cause if result is not obtained
1	BLK	Under all conditions.	Check for continuity to ground: There should be continuity.	• Poor ground (G401, G402, G404). • An open in the wire.
2	WHT/RED and YEL/RED	Connect the YEL/RED terminal to the WHT terminal, and the WHT/RED terminal to the BLK terminal momentarily.	Check door lock operation: All doors should unlock.	• Fauly actuator. • An open in the wire.
		Connect the WHT/ RED terminal to the WHT terminal, and the YEL/RED terminal to the BLK terminal momentarily.	Check door lock operation: All doors should lock.	

Reconnect 18-pin connector to control unit.

No.	Wire	Test condition	Test: Desired result	Possible cause if result is not obtained
3	WHT	Under all conditions.	Check for voltage to ground: There should be battery voltage.	• Blown No. 44 (15 A) fuse. (In the underhood fuse/relay box) • An open in the wire.
4	GRN/WHT	Driver's door lock switch in LOCK.	Check for voltage to ground: There should be 1 V or less.	• Faulty driver's door lock switch. • Poor ground (G401, G402, G404). • An open in the wire.
	GRN/RED[1]	Driver's door lock switch in UNLOCK.		
5	BLK/RED	Passenger's door lock switch in LOCK.	Check for voltage to ground: There should be 1 V or less.	• Faulty passenger's door lock switch. • Poor ground (G401, G402, G404). • An open in the wire.
	BLK/WHT	Passenger's door lock switch in UNLOCK.		
6	BLU/WHT[1]	Driver's door lock knob in LOCK.	Check for voltage to ground: There should be 1 V or less.	• Faulty driver's door lock actuator. • Poor ground (G401, G402, G404). • An open in the wire.
	BLU/RED	Driver's door lock knob in UNLOCK.		
7	GRN/BLU	Driver's door open.	Check for voltage to ground: There should be 1 V or less. NOTE: Before testing, remove No. 46 (15 A) fuse in the under-hood fuse/relay box.	• Faulty door switch. • Poor ground. • An open in the wire.
	GRN/RED[2]	Passenger's door open.		
8	BLU/WHT[2]	Ignition key is in the ignition switch.	Check for voltage to ground: There should be 1 V or less.	• Faulty ignition key switch. • Poor ground (G401, G402, G404). • An open in the wire.
9	BLK/RED	Passenger's door key cylinder in LOCK.	Check for voltage to ground: There should be 1 V or less as the switch is turned.	• Faulty passenger's door cylinder. • Poor ground (G401, G402, G404). • An open in the wire.
	BLK/WHT	Passenger's door key cylinder in UNLOCK.		

CAUTION: To prevent motor damage, connect power and ground only momentarily.

93I82626

Fig. 8: Power Door Locks Control Unit Input Test (Prelude)

DOOR KEY SWITCH

NOTE: On Accord, driver's door key switch utilizes only connector terminals No. 1 and 2.

Accord (Driver's Door) – 1) Remove door panel. Unplug 3-pin connector from actuator. Set switch to off position. Check continuity between terminals No. 1 and 2. Continuity should not exist. *See Fig. 9.*
2) Set switch to unlock position. Check continuity between terminals No. 1 and 2. Continuity should exist. If continuity is not as specified, replace door key switch.

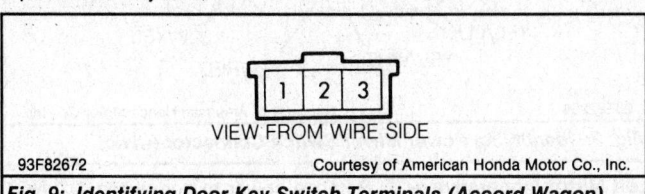

VIEW FROM WIRE SIDE

93F82672   Courtesy of American Honda Motor Co., Inc.

Fig. 9: Identifying Door Key Switch Terminals (Accord Wagon)

Accord (Passenger's Door) – 1) Remove door panel. Unplug 3-pin connector from actuator. Set switch to lock position. Check continuity between terminals No. 1 and 2. Continuity should not exist. Check continuity between terminals No. 2 and 3. Continuity should exist. *See Fig. 9.*
2) Set switch to unlock position. Check continuity between terminals No. 1 and 2. Continuity should exist. Check continuity between terminals No. 2 and 3. Continuity should not exist.
Prelude – 1) Remove door panel. Unplug 6-pin connector from actuator. Set switch to lock position. Check continuity between terminals No. 1 and 3. Continuity should not exist. Check continuity between terminals No. 3 and 6. Continuity should exist. *See Fig. 1.*
2) Set switch to unlock position. Check continuity between terminals No. 1 and 3. Continuity should exist. Check continuity between terminals No. 3 and 6. Continuity should not exist.

DOOR LOCK SWITCHES

Accord & Prelude – 1) On Accord wagon, remove trim plate. On Prelude, remove door handle panel. Unplug 3-pin connector. Set switch to unlock position. Check continuity between terminals "A" and "B". Continuity should not exist. Check continuity between terminals "B" and "C". Continuity should exist. *See Fig. 10.*
2) Set switch to off position. Check continuity between terminals "A" and "B". Continuity should not exist. Check continuity between terminals "B" and "C". Continuity should not exist.
3) Set switch to lock position. Check continuity between terminals "A" and "B". Continuity should exist. Check continuity between terminals "B" and "C". Continuity should not exist. Replace switch if continuity is not as specified.

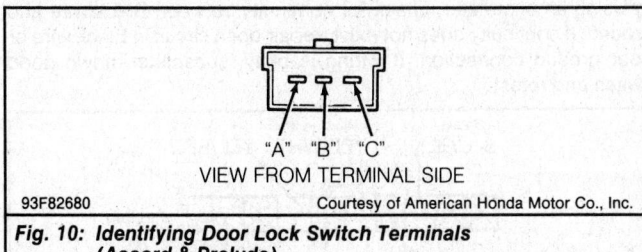

"A" "B" "C"
VIEW FROM TERMINAL SIDE

93F82680   Courtesy of American Honda Motor Co., Inc.

Fig. 10: Identifying Door Lock Switch Terminals (Accord & Prelude)

Civic – 1) Remove trim plate. Unplug connector. Set switch to unlock position. Check continuity between terminals No. 1 and 2. Continuity should exist. Check continuity between terminals No. 2 and 3. Continuity should not exist. *See Fig. 11.*

2) Set switch to off position. Check continuity between terminals No. 1 and 2. Continuity should not exist. Check continuity between terminals No. 2 and 3. Continuity should not exist.
3) Set switch to lock position. Check continuity between terminals No. 1 and 2. Continuity should not exist. Check continuity between terminals No. 2 and 3. Continuity should exist. Replace switch if continuity is not as specified.

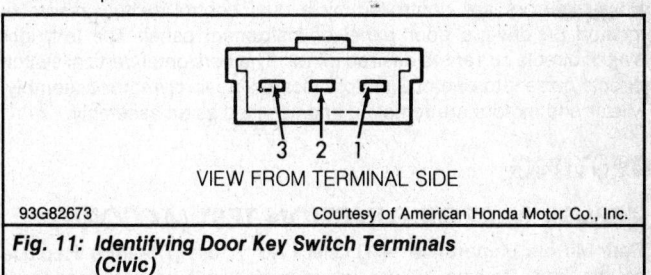

VIEW FROM TERMINAL SIDE

93G82673   Courtesy of American Honda Motor Co., Inc.

Fig. 11: Identifying Door Key Switch Terminals (Civic)

TAILGATE LOCK ACTUATOR TEST

Accord – Remove tailgate inner trim panel. Unplug 2-pin and 4-pin connectors. Using fused jumper wire, connect battery voltage to actuator connector terminal No. 3. *See Fig. 12.* Connect terminal No. 4 to ground. Reverse jumper wires. Replace solenoid if it does not operate in both directions.

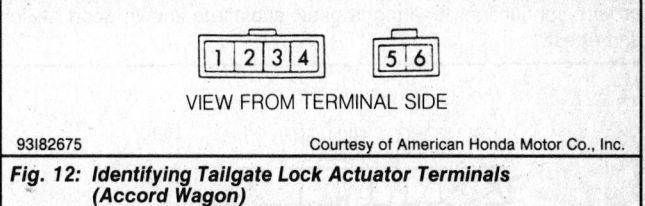

VIEW FROM TERMINAL SIDE

93I82675   Courtesy of American Honda Motor Co., Inc.

Fig. 12: Identifying Tailgate Lock Actuator Terminals (Accord Wagon)

REMOVAL & INSTALLATION

CAUTION: When battery is disconnected, vehicle computer and memory systems may lose memory data. Driveability problems may exist until computer systems have completed a relearn cycle. See COMPUTER RELEARN PROCEDURES article in GENERAL INFORMATION before disconnecting battery.

ACTUATORS

Removal & Installation – Remove door panel from door or tailgate. Remove plastic cover. Remove rear channel if necessary. Disconnect linkage. Unplug connector. Remove mounting screws and actuator. To install, reverse removal procedure.

CONTROL UNIT

Removal & Installation (With Keyless Entry System) – Power door lock unit is located under driver's seat. Turn ignition off. Slide seat all the way forward. Unplug connector. Remove mounting screws and control unit. To install, reverse removal procedure.
Removal & Installation (Without Keyless Entry System) – Power door lock control unit is located behind left front door panel. Turn ignition off. Remove door panel. Unplug connector. Remove mounting screws and control unit. To install, reverse removal procedure.

DOOR LOCK SWITCHES

Removal & Installation – Remove trim plate. Unplug connector. Remove switch from trim plate. To install, reverse removal procedure.

WIRING DIAGRAMS

NOTE: See ACCESSORIES & EQUIPMENT, Volume 5.

1994 ACCESSORIES & EQUIPMENT
Power Mirrors

Accord, Civic, Civic Del Sol, Passport, Prelude

NOTE: For power mirrors window information on Passport, refer to Rodeo in Isuzu POWER MIRRORS article.

DESCRIPTION & OPERATION

Power mirrors are controlled by a dual control switch assembly located on driver's door panel or instrument panel. The left/right switch directs current to desired mirror. The horizontal/vertical switch directs current to one of 2 motors located in mirror/motor assembly. Mirror and motors are removed and serviced as an assembly.

TESTING

POWER MIRROR FUNCTION TEST (ACCORD)

Both Mirrors Inoperative – 1) Check No. 7 fuse (7.5-amp). Replace as required. Remove power mirror switch, but do not disconnect switch from harness. See POWER MIRROR SWITCH under REMOVAL & INSTALLATION.

2) Turn ignition on. Using a voltmeter, check for voltage between Yellow/Black wire and ground. *See Fig. 1.* If battery voltage exists, go to next step. If battery voltage does not exist, repair open in Yellow/Black wire between mirror switch and fuse box.

3) Using an ohmmeter, check for continuity between Black wire and ground. If continuity does not exist, repair open in Black wire or poor ground connection. If wiring is okay, substitute known good switch and retest.

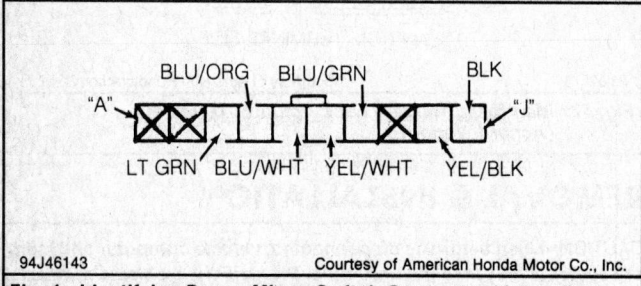

94J46143　　　Courtesy of American Honda Motor Co., Inc.

Fig. 1: Identifying Power Mirror Switch Connector (Accord)

Left Mirror Inoperative – 1) Remove power mirror switch. DO NOT disconnect switch from harness. See POWER MIRROR SWITCH under REMOVAL & INSTALLATION. Turn ignition on. Using jumper wires, connect Blue/Green wire to Yellow/Black wire, and either Blue/White or Blue/Orange wire to ground.

2) If mirror does not tilt down (or swing left), check for open in Blue/White or Blue/Orange wire between mirror switch and mirror. If wiring is okay, check mirror motor. See POWER MIRROR MOTOR TEST (ACCORD). If mirror operates correctly, check mirror switch. See POWER MIRROR SWITCH TEST.

Right Mirror Inoperative – 1) Remove power mirror switch. DO NOT disconnect switch from harness. See POWER MIRROR SWITCH under REMOVAL & INSTALLATION. Turn ignition on. Using jumper wires, connect Yellow/Black wire to Yellow/White wire, and either Blue/White or Light Green wire to ground.

2) If mirror does not tilt down (or swing left), check for open in Blue/White or Light Green wire between mirror switch and mirror. If wiring is okay, check mirror motor. See POWER MIRROR MOTOR TEST (ACCORD). If mirror operates correctly, check mirror switch. See POWER MIRROR SWITCH TEST.

POWER MIRROR FUNCTION TEST (CIVIC)

Both Mirrors Inoperative – 1) Check No. 13 fuse (7.5-amp). Replace as required. Remove power mirror switch. DO NOT disconnect switch from harness. See POWER MIRROR SWITCH under REMOVAL & INSTALLATION.

2) Turn ignition on. Using a voltmeter, check for voltage between Black/Yellow wire and ground. *See Fig. 2.* If battery voltage exists, go to next step. If battery voltage does not exist, repair open circuit between mirror switch and fuse box.

3) Using an ohmmeter, check for continuity between Black wire and ground. If continuity does not exist, repair open circuit in Black wire or poor ground connection. If wiring is okay, substitute known good switch and retest.

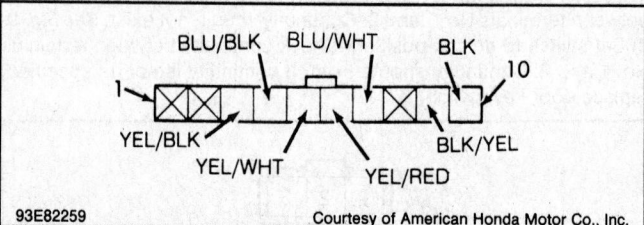

93E82259　　　Courtesy of American Honda Motor Co., Inc.

Fig. 2: Identifying Power Mirror Switch Connector (Civic)

Left Mirror Inoperative – 1) Remove power mirror switch. DO NOT disconnect switch from harness. See POWER MIRROR SWITCH under REMOVAL & INSTALLATION. Turn ignition on. Using jumper wires, connect Black/Yellow wire to Yellow/Red wire (Blue/White wire on Coupe), and either Yellow/White or Blue/Black wire to ground.

2) If mirror does not tilt down (or swing left), check for open in Yellow/White or Blue/Black wire between mirror switch and mirror. If wiring is okay, check mirror motor. See POWER MIRROR MOTOR TEST (CIVIC). If mirror operates correctly, check mirror switch. See POWER MIRROR SWITCH TEST.

Right Mirror Inoperative – 1) Remove power mirror switch. DO NOT disconnect switch from harness. See POWER MIRROR SWITCH under REMOVAL & INSTALLATION. Turn ignition on. Using jumper wires, connect Black/Yellow wire to Blue/White wire (Yellow/Red wire on coupe), and either Yellow/White or Yellow/Black wire to ground.

2) If mirror does not tilt down (or swing left), check for open in Yellow/White or Yellow/Black wire between mirror switch and mirror. If wiring is okay, check mirror motor. See POWER MIRROR MOTOR TEST (CIVIC). If mirror operates correctly, check mirror switch. See POWER MIRROR SWITCH TEST.

POWER MIRROR FUNCTION TEST (CIVIC DEL SOL)

Both Mirrors Inoperative – 1) Check No. 13 fuse (7.5-amp). Replace as required. Remove power mirror switch. DO NOT disconnect switch from harness. See POWER MIRROR SWITCH under REMOVAL & INSTALLATION.

2) Turn ignition on. Using a voltmeter, check for voltage between Black/Yellow wire and ground. *See Fig. 3.* If battery voltage exists, go to next step. If battery voltage does not exist, repair open circuit between mirror switch and fuse box.

3) Using an ohmmeter, check for continuity between Black wire and ground. If continuity does not exist, repair open circuit in Black wire or poor ground connection. If wiring is okay, substitute known good switch and retest.

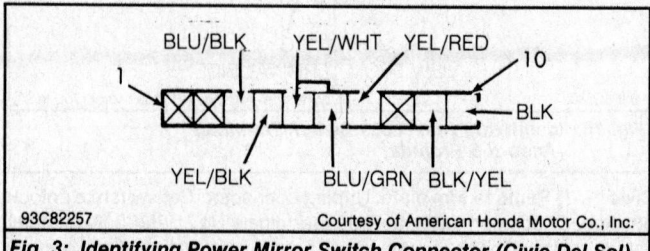

93C82257　　　Courtesy of American Honda Motor Co., Inc.

Fig. 3: Identifying Power Mirror Switch Connector (Civic Del Sol)

Left Mirror Inoperative – 1) Remove power mirror switch. DO NOT disconnect switch from harness. See POWER MIRROR SWITCH under REMOVAL & INSTALLATION. Turn ignition on. Using jumper wires, connect Black/Yellow wire to Blue/Green (Yellow/Red after splice) wire, and either Yellow/White or Yellow/Black wire to ground.

2) If mirror does not tilt down (or swing left), check for open in Blue/Green, Yellow/Red, Yellow/White or Yellow/Black wire(s) between mirror switch and mirror. If wiring is okay, check mirror motor. See POWER MIRROR MOTOR TEST (CIVIC DEL SOL). If mirror operates correctly, check mirror switch. See POWER MIRROR SWITCH TEST.

Right Mirror Inoperative – 1) Remove power mirror switch. DO NOT disconnect switch from harness. See POWER MIRROR SWITCH under REMOVAL & INSTALLATION. Turn ignition on. Using jumper wires, connect Black/Yellow wire to Yellow/Red wire, and either Yellow/White or Blue/Black wire to ground.

2) If mirror does not tilt down (or swing left), check for open in Yellow/Red or Blue/Green wire between mirror switch and mirror. If wiring is okay, check mirror motor. See POWER MIRROR MOTOR TEST (CIVIC DEL SOL). If mirror operates correctly, check mirror switch. See POWER MIRROR SWITCH TEST.

POWER MIRROR FUNCTION TEST (PRELUDE)

Both Mirrors Inoperative – 1) Check No. 9 fuse (15-amp). Replace as required. Remove power mirror switch. DO NOT disconnect switch from harness. See POWER MIRROR SWITCH under REMOVAL & INSTALLATION.

2) Turn ignition on. Using a voltmeter, check for voltage between Black/Yellow wire and ground. *See Fig. 4.* If battery voltage exists, go to next step. If battery voltage does not exist, repair open circuit between mirror switch and fuse box.

3) Using an ohmmeter, check for continuity between Black wire and ground. If continuity does not exist, repair open circuit in Black wire or poor ground connection. If wiring is okay, substitute known good switch and retest.

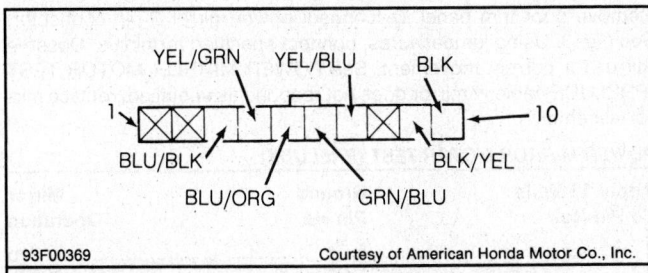

93F00369   Courtesy of American Honda Motor Co., Inc.

Fig. 4: Identifying Power Mirror Switch Connector (Prelude)

Left Mirror Inoperative – 1) Remove power mirror switch. DO NOT disconnect switch from harness. See POWER MIRROR SWITCH under REMOVAL & INSTALLATION. Turn ignition on. Using jumper wires, connect Black/Yellow wire to Yellow/Blue wire, and either Blue/Orange or Yellow/Green wire to ground.

2) If mirror does not tilt down (or swing left), check for open in Blue/Orange or Yellow/Green wire between mirror switch and mirror. If wiring is okay, check mirror motor. See POWER MIRROR MOTOR TEST (PRELUDE). If mirror operates correctly, check mirror switch. See POWER MIRROR SWITCH TEST.

Right Mirror Inoperative – 1) Remove power mirror switch. DO NOT disconnect switch from harness. See POWER MIRROR SWITCH under REMOVAL & INSTALLATION. Turn ignition on. Using jumper wires, connect Black/Yellow wire to Green/Blue wire, and either Blue/Orange or Blue/Black wire to ground.

2) If mirror does not tilt down (or swing left), check for open in Blue/Orange or Blue/Black wire between mirror switch and mirror. If wiring is okay, check mirror motor. See POWER MIRROR MOTOR TEST (PRELUDE). If mirror operates correctly, check mirror switch. See POWER MIRROR SWITCH TEST.

POWER MIRROR SWITCH TEST

Remove power mirror switch. See POWER MIRROR SWITCH under REMOVAL & INSTALLATION. Using an ohmmeter, check for continuity between appropriate mirror switch terminals. See POWER MIRROR SWITCH CONTINUITY TEST table. *See Fig. 1, 2, 3 or 4.* If switch fails any test, replace switch.

POWER MIRROR SWITCH CONTINUITY TEST

Application	Terminals No.
Accord	
Left Mirror	
Off	C, E, F & J
Up	E & I; D, G & J
Down	E & J; D, G & I
Left	D & J; E, G & I
Right	D & I; E, G & J
Right Mirror	
Off	C, E, F & J
Up	E & I; C, F & J
Down	E & J; C, F & I
Left	C & J; E, F & I
Right	C & I; E, F & J
Civic & Prelude	
Left Mirror	
Off	4, 5, 7 & 10
Up	4, 7 & 10; 5 & 9
Down	4, 7 & 9; 5 & 10
Left	5, 7 & 9; 4 & 10
Right	5, 7 & 10; 4 & 9
Right Mirror	
Off	3, 5, 6 & 10
Up	3, 6 & 10; 5 & 9
Down	3, 6 & 9; 5 & 10
Left	5, 6 & 9; 3 & 10
Right	5, 6 & 10; 3 & 9
Civic Del Sol	
Left Mirror	
Off	4, 5, 7 & 10
Up	5 & 9
Down	4 & 9; 7 & 9
Left	5 & 9; 7 & 9
Right	4 & 9
Right Mirror	
Off	3, 4, 6 & 10
Up	5 & 9
Down	3 & 9; 6 & 9
Left	5 & 9; 6 & 9
Right	3 & 9

POWER MIRROR MOTOR TEST (ACCORD)

Pry out cover at base of mirror inside door. Disconnect power mirror 8-pin connector. *See Fig. 5.* Using jumper wires, connect specified terminals. Observe mirror for correct movement. See POWER MIRROR MOTOR TEST (ACCORD) table. If mirror does not respond as specified, replace mirror assembly.

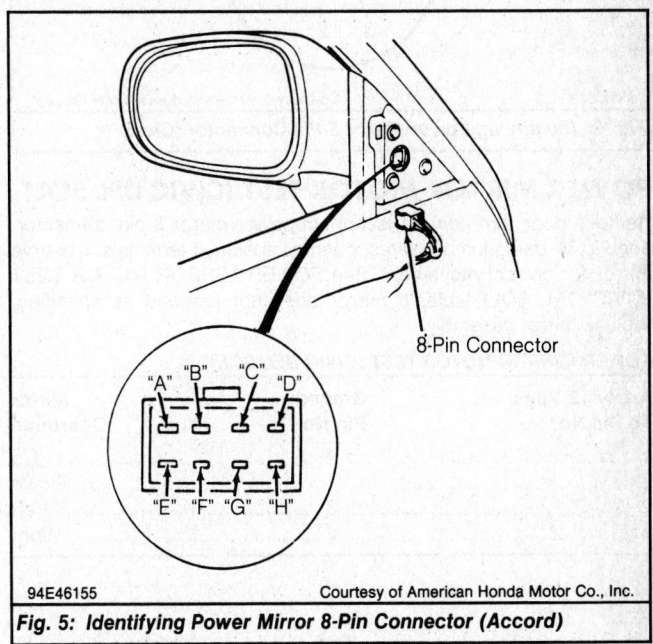

94E46155   Courtesy of American Honda Motor Co., Inc.

Fig. 5: Identifying Power Mirror 8-Pin Connector (Accord)

POWER MIRROR MOTOR TEST (ACCORD)

Apply 12 Volts To Pin No.	Ground Pin No.	Mirror Operation
H	G	Up
G	H	Down
G	7	Left
7	G	Right

POWER MIRROR MOTOR TEST (CIVIC)

Remove door trim panel. Disconnect power mirror 8-pin connector. *See Fig. 6.* Using jumper wires, connect specified terminals. Observe mirror for correct movement. See POWER MIRROR MOTOR TEST (CIVIC) table. If mirror does not respond as specified, replace mirror assembly.

POWER MIRROR MOTOR TEST (CIVIC)

Apply 12 Volts To Pin No.	Ground Pin No.	Mirror Operation
1	2	Up
2	1	Down
2	3	Left
3	2	Right

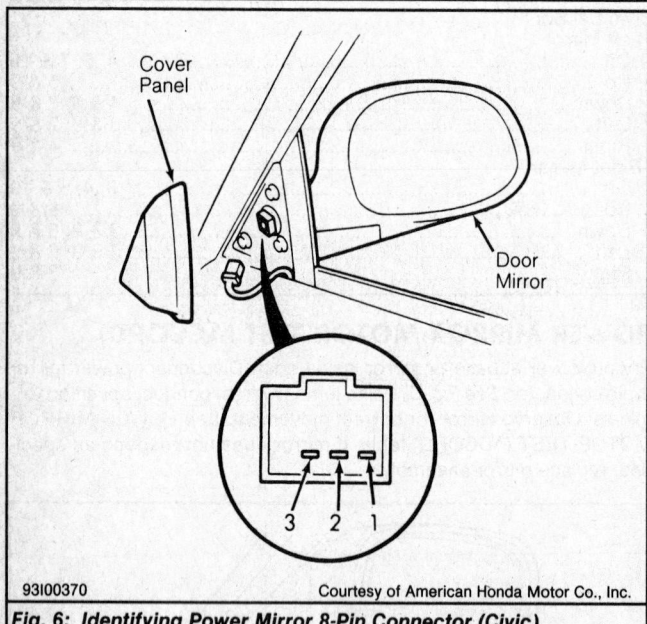

Fig. 6: Identifying Power Mirror 8-Pin Connector (Civic)

POWER MIRROR MOTOR TEST (CIVIC DEL SOL)

Remove door trim panel. Disconnect power mirror 8-pin connector. *See Fig. 7.* Using jumper wires, connect specified terminals. Observe mirror for correct movement. See POWER MIRROR MOTOR TEST (CIVIC DEL SOL) table. If mirror does not respond as specified, replace mirror assembly.

POWER MIRROR MOTOR TEST (CIVIC DEL SOL)

Apply 12 Volts To Pin No.	Ground Pin No.	Mirror Operation
1	2	Up
2	1	Down
2	3	Left
3	2	Right

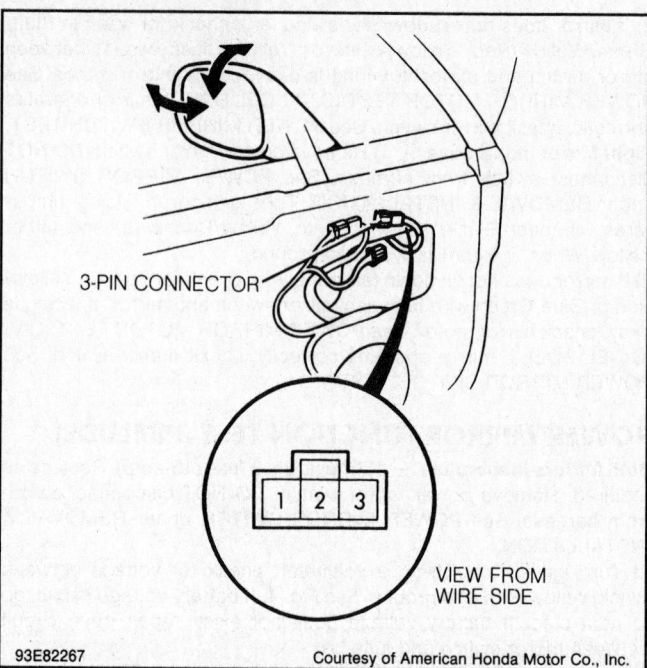

Fig. 7: Identifying Power Mirror 3-Pin Connector (Civic Del Sol)

POWER MIRROR MOTOR TEST (PRELUDE)

Remove door trim panel. Disconnect power mirror 3-pin connector. *See Fig. 8.* Using jumper wires, connect specified terminals. Observe mirror for correct movement. See POWER MIRROR MOTOR TEST (PRELUDE) table. If mirror does not respond as specified, replace mirror assembly.

POWER MIRROR MOTOR TEST (PRELUDE)

Apply 12 Volts To Pin No.	Ground Pin No.	Mirror Operation
3	4	Up
4	3	Down
4	5	Left
5	4	Right

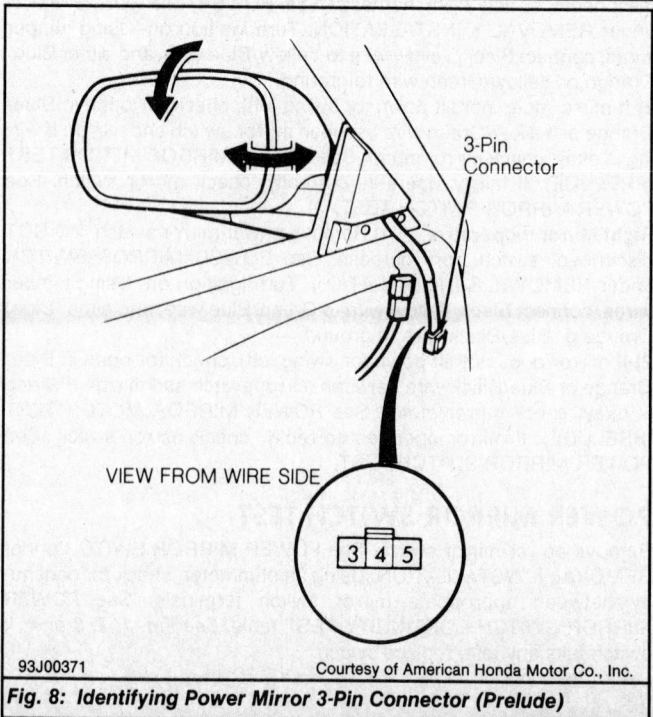

Fig. 8: Identifying Power Mirror 3-Pin Connector (Prelude)

REMOVAL & INSTALLATION

POWER MIRROR SWITCH

Removal & Installation (Accord) – 1) Remove door trim panel. Disconnect all electrical connectors. Remove arm rest retaining screws and arm rest.

2) Remove power window master switch retaining screws and power window master switch. Push power mirror switch from reverse side of power window master switch. To install, reverse removal procedure.

Removal & Installation (Civic) – Carefully pry switch from lower left instrument panel. Push switch out of instrument panel. Disconnect 10-pin connector and remove switch. To install, reverse removal procedure.

Removal & Installation (Civic Del Sol) – Remove door trim panel. Disconnect electrical connectors. Remove 3 screws and bracket from switch. Remove switch from door panel. To install, reverse removal procedure.

Removal & Installation (Prelude) – Taking care to avoid damaging door panel or switch, pry switch from door panel. Disconnect 10-pin connector from switch. To install, reverse removal procedure. Ensure switch snaps firmly into door panel.

POWER MIRROR ASSEMBLY

Removal & Installation (Accord & Civic) – Pry out cover at base of mirror inside door. Disconnect power mirror 8-pin connector. *See Fig. 5 or 6.* Remove 3 mirror mounting screws, and remove mirror. To install, reverse removal procedure.

Removal & Installation (Civic Del Sol) – Remove door trim panel. Reaching through access hole, remove 3-pin connector. *See Fig. 7.* Remove 3 mounting nuts. Remove mirror. To install, reverse removal procedure.

Removal & Installation (Prelude) – Lower window. Pry out cover at base of mirror inside door. Remove door trim panel. Disconnect power mirror 3-pin or 6-pin connector. *See Fig. 8.* Remove 3 mirror mounting screws, and remove mirror. To install, reverse removal procedure.

WIRING DIAGRAMS

NOTE: See ACCESSORIES & EQUIPMENT, Volume 5.

Accord, Civic, Prelude

DESCRIPTION & OPERATION

Power sun roof is operated with ignition switch in ON position. Accord and Civic are equipped with a glass sun roof. This unit may also be referred to as a moon roof. Prelude is equipped with a steel sun roof. Sun roof slides rearward on all models. Civic has added tilt feature allowing sun roof to tilt upward at rear for limited ventilation. All models use a permanent magnet type motor to operative a cable drive to open and close sun roof. If sun roof power drive fails, sun roof can be operated manually by using a socket inserted through access hole near drive motor.

ADJUSTMENTS

CABLE DRIVE CLUTCH

Information not available from manufacturer.

SUN ROOF HEIGHT

Accord – Roof panel should be even with glass weatherstrip within 0.02-0.06" (0.5-1.5 mm). *See Fig. 1.* If adjustment is required in front, pry out rail holder cover and loosen nut. Install or remove shims between frame and sunshade rail holder. If adjustment is required in rear, install or remove shims between guide rail and sunshade rail.

Civic – Roof panel should be even with glass weatherstrip within 0.05-0.09" (1.3-2.3 mm). *See Fig. 1.* If adjustment is required, open glass fully and pry plug out of bracket cover. Loosen screw and slide bracket cover off to rear. Loosen mounting nuts. Install or remove shims between glass and glass bracket. Repeat procedure on other side.

Prelude – Roof panel should be even with sun roof panel seal within 0.06-0.09" (1.4-2.4 mm). *See Fig. 1.* If adjustment is required, remove sun roof inner liner. Remove sun roof panel mounting nuts. Install or remove shims between sun roof panel and panel bracket.

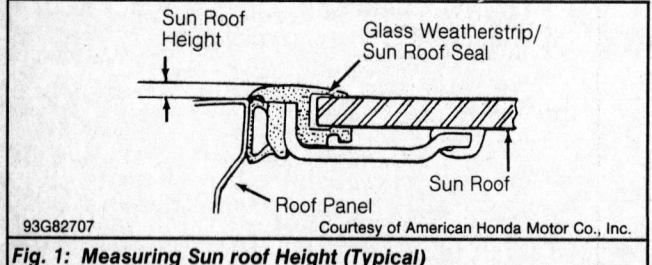

93G82707   Courtesy of American Honda Motor Co., Inc.

Fig. 1: Measuring Sun roof Height (Typical)

WIND DEFLECTOR

Open sun roof. Pry rail covers off both sides. Loosen mounting nuts. Adjust wind deflector forward or backward so deflector seal touches roof panel evenly across entire front edge. Measure wind deflector height from top edge of deflector to roof panel at center of deflector. Wind deflector height should be 0.7" (17 mm) on Accord and 0.61" (15.5 mm) on Civic. Deflector arm cannot be adjusted. If arm or deflector is damaged, replace wind deflector assembly.

MAINTENANCE

DRAIN TUBES

Periodically, pour a small amount of water into drain rails at edges of sun roof to ensure drain tubes remain clear. On Accord and Prelude, water should drop from drain tubes at rear of right front and left rear wheel wells. On Civic, water should drop from drain tubes at rear of each left side wheel well.

LUBRICATION

Periodic lubrication is not required. When components are removed for repair or replacement, apply multipurpose grease lightly to all moving parts, except cables. Use molybdenum grease on cable assemblies.

TROUBLE SHOOTING

CAUTION: All models are equipped with Supplemental Restraint System (SRS). SRS wiring harness is routed close to instrument cluster, steering wheel, and related components. All SRS wiring harnesses are covered by Yellow outer insulation. DO NOT use electrical test equipment on these circuits. Before working on steering column components, disable air bag system. See AIR BAG RESTRAINT SYSTEM article in ACCESSORIES & EQUIPMENT.

NOTE: Ensure all component terminals and ground connections are clean and tight. Check possible faults in order listed. Repair or replace components and circuits as necessary.

ACCORD

Sun Roof Does Not Move, Motor Runs – Clutch out of adjustment. Foreign matter jammed in guide. Outer cable not properly attached.

Sun Roof Does Not Move, Motor Does Not Run (Any Switch) – Blown fuse No. 37 (7.5-amp) in underhood fuse/relay box. Blown No. 29 (30-amp) fuse in underhood fuse/relay box. Blown No. 28 (20-amp) fuse in underhood fuse/relay box. Faulty sun roof relay. Faulty sun roof motor. Faulty sun roof switch. Open in Green, Green/White, White/Red, Gray/Yellow or Gray/Red wire(s).

Sun Roof Does Not Move, Motor Does Not Run (OPEN Switch) – Faulty opening relay. Faulty closing relay. Faulty sun roof switch. Open in Green/Yellow or Green/Red wire.

Sun Roof Does Not Move, Motor Does Not Run (CLOSE Switch) – Faulty closing relay. Faulty opening relay. Open in Green/Red or Green/Yellow wire.

Sun Roof Does Not Move Within 10 Minutes Of Ignition Being Turned Off – Blown fuse No. 37 (7.5-amp) in underhood fuse/relay box. Faulty door switch. Faulty key-on timer circuit in Integrated Control Unit (ICU).

CIVIC

Sun Roof Does Not Move, Motor Runs – Clutch out of adjustment. Foreign matter jammed in guide. Outer cable not properly attached.

Sun Roof Does Not Move, Motor Does Not Run (Any Switch) – Blown fuse No. 1 (30-amp) in underhood fuse/relay box. Blown fuse No. 14 (20-amp) in dash fuse box. Faulty sun roof switch. Faulty sun roof motor. Open in White, Green/Black, Green/Yellow or Green/Red wire.

Sun Roof Does Not Move, Motor Does Not Run (OPEN Switch) – Faulty opening relay. Faulty closing relay. Faulty sun roof switch. Open in Green/Yellow or Green/Red wire.

Sun Roof Does Not Move, Motor Does Not Run (CLOSE Switch) – Faulty closing relay. Faulty opening relay. Faulty sun roof switch. Open in Green/Red or Green/Yellow wire.

Sun Roof Does Not Move, Motor Does Not Run (TILT Switch) – Faulty opening relay. Faulty closing relay. Faulty TILT switch. Faulty sun roof switch. Open in Green/Red or Green/Yellow wire.

PRELUDE

Sun Roof Does Not Move, Motor Runs – Clutch out of adjustment. Foreign matter jammed in guide. Outer cable not properly attached.

Sun Roof Does Not Move, Motor Does Not Run (Any Switch) – Blown fuse No. 37 (40-amp) in underhood fuse/relay box. Blown fuse No. 7 (30-amp) or fuse No. 17 (30-amp) fuse in dash fuse box. Power window relay. Faulty sun roof motor. Open in White/Blue, Black/Yellow, Green/Yellow or Green/Red wire.

Sun Roof Does Not Move, Motor Does Not Run (OPEN Switch) – Faulty opening relay. Faulty closing relay. Faulty sun roof switch. Open in Green/Yellow or Green/Red wire.

Sun Roof Does Not Move, Motor Does Not Run (CLOSE Switch) – Faulty closing relay. Faulty opening relay. Faulty sun roof switch. Open in Green/Red or Green/Yellow wire.

TESTING
FUNCTION TEST

NOTE: Function test for Prelude is not available from manufacturer.

Accord – 1) Carefully pry sun roof switch/cruise control switch out of instrument panel. Unplug connectors from switches. Connect jumper wire between Gray/Yellow wire and body ground. Turn ignition on. If sun roof opens, check switch. If sun roof does not open, check for open in Gray/Yellow wire. Repair or replace as necessary.
2) Connect jumper wire between Gray/Red wire and body ground. Turn ignition on. If sun roof closes, check switch. If sun roof does not open, check for open in Gray/Red wire.
3) Using an ohmmeter, check for continuity between Black wire and body ground. If no continuity exists, check for open in Black wire. Repair as necessary.

Civic – 1) Carefully pry sun roof switch/cruise control switch out of instrument panel. Unplug connectors from switches. Using an ohmmeter, check for continuity between Black wire and body ground. If no continuity exists, check for open in Black wire. Repair as necessary.
2) Connect jumper wire between Yellow wire and body ground. Turn ignition on. If sun roof opens, check switch. If sun roof does not open, check for open in Yellow wire. Repair or replace as necessary.
3) Connect jumper wire between Yellow/Red wire and body ground. Turn ignition switch to "II" position. If sun roof closes, check switch. If sun roof does not open, check for open in Yellow/Red wire.
4) Connect jumper wire between Blue wire and body ground. Turn ignition on. If sun roof tilts upward at rear, check switch. If sun roof does not tilt, check for open in Blue wire.

MOTOR TEST

On Prelude, remove high mount brake light cover. On all models, remove headliner. Unplug 2-pin connector from the motor. Using jumper wires, connect connector terminals to battery voltage and ground. Check for motor operation. Reverse jumper wires and retest. Replace motor if it does not operation in both directions.

RELAY TEST

NOTE: Sun roof system is equipped with separate relays for opening and closing functions.

Remove sun roof relay from dash fuse/relay box. Test continuity with an ohmmeter. Continuity should exist between terminals "B" and "C". *See Fig. 2.* Using jumper wires, connect terminals "D" and "E" to battery voltage and ground. If continuity does not exist between terminals "A" and "C", replace relay.

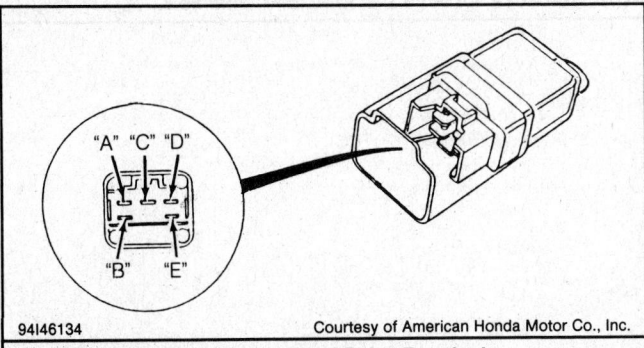

94I46134   Courtesy of American Honda Motor Co., Inc.

Fig. 2: Identifying Power Sun Roof Relay Terminals

SWITCH TEST

Carefully remove sun roof switch from instrument panel. See SWITCH under REMOVAL & INSTALLATION. Using an ohmmeter, check resistance of switch terminals with switch in indicated positions. If continuity is not as specified, replace switch. *See Fig. 3, 4 or 5.*

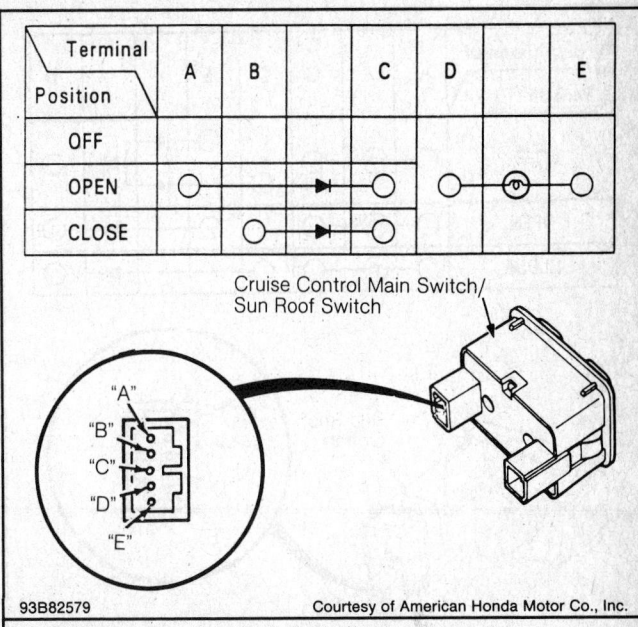

Terminal Position	A	B	C	D	E
OFF					
OPEN	○———	——▶|———	○	○———◎———	○
CLOSE	○———	——▶|———	○		

Cruise Control Main Switch/ Sun Roof Switch

93B82579   Courtesy of American Honda Motor Co., Inc.

Fig 3: Testing Sun Roof Switch Continuity (Accord)

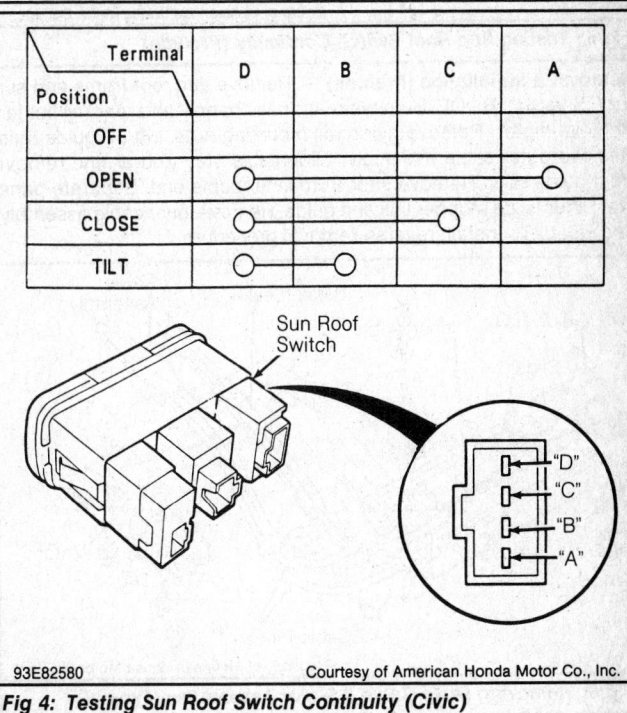

Terminal Position	D	B	C	A
OFF				
OPEN	○———	———	———	———○
CLOSE	○———	———	———○	
TILT	○———	———○		

Sun Roof Switch

93E82580   Courtesy of American Honda Motor Co., Inc.

Fig 4: Testing Sun Roof Switch Continuity (Civic)

REMOVAL & INSTALLATION
DRIVE CABLES

Removal & Installation (Accord) – Remove sun roof. See SUN ROOF. Remove motor from sun roof frame. Remove guide rail mounting nuts. Lift off guide rails. If necessary, remove sun shade rail and drain seal from frame. Remove inner cables with sliders attached. *See Fig. 6.* To install, reverse removal procedure.

Removal & Installation (Civic) – Remove sun roof frame. Remove sun roof. See SUN ROOF. Remove motor from sun roof frame. Remove guide rail mounting nuts. Lift off guide rails. Remove cable assembly with sliders attached. *See Fig. 6.* To install, reverse removal procedure.

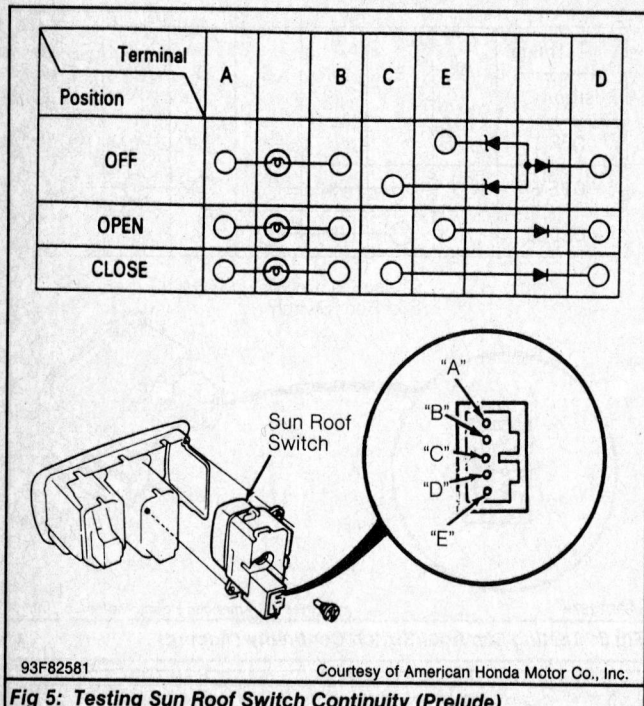

Terminal / Position	A		B	C	E			D
OFF	○	⊙	○		○	▷	◁	○
				○	○			
OPEN	○	⊙	○		○	▷		○
CLOSE	○	⊙	○	○		◁		○

Sun Roof Switch

"A"
"B"
"C"
"D"
"E"

93F82581   Courtesy of American Honda Motor Co., Inc.

Fig 5: Testing Sun Roof Switch Continuity (Prelude)

Removal & Installation (Prelude) – Remove sun roof frame and sun roof. See SUN ROOF. Remove rear drain channel and rear rail holder. Remove motor. Remove guide rail mounting nuts. Lift off guide rails. Remove outer cable assembly. Slide cable stay to rear and remove from guide rails. Remove lifter from inner cable end. Separate panel stay, lifter, slide stopper link and guide. Remove inner cable assembly. See Fig. 6. To install, reverse removal procedure.

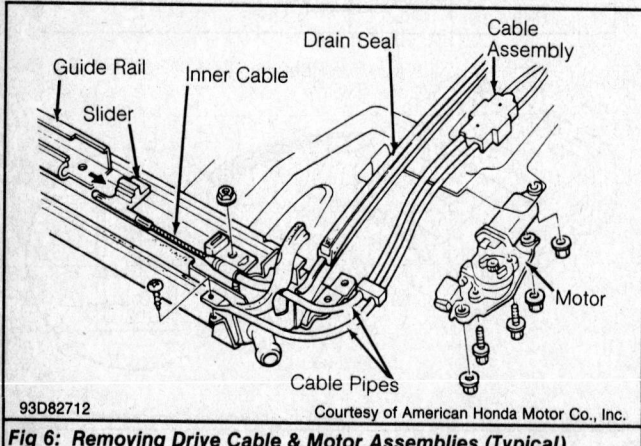

Cable Assembly
Drain Seal
Guide Rail
Inner Cable
Slider
Motor
Cable Pipes

93D82712   Courtesy of American Honda Motor Co., Inc.

Fig 6: Removing Drive Cable & Motor Assemblies (Typical)

DRIVE MOTOR

Removal & Installation – Remove headliner. See HEADLINER. Unplug motor harness connector. Remove mounting bolts and nuts. Remove motor. To install, reverse removal procedure.

HEADLINER

NOTE: Headliner removal and installation for all models is similar. It is not necessary to remove all listed components on all models. Remove only components necessary to provide needed clearance.

Removal & Installation – Remove sun visors, dome light, rear view mirror, pillar trim and grab handles. Remove rear seat and front passenger's seat. Recline driver's seat fully. Remove retaining clips. DO NOT bend headliner, remove headliner starting at right rear corner. To install, reverse removal procedure.

SUN ROOF

Removal & Installation (Accord) – Open sun shade fully. Partially open glass. Pry plug out of each bracket cover. Remove screws and slide bracket cover off to the rear. Remove glass bracket bolts. Remove glass by carefully lifting up and pulling forward at the same time. Remove sun shade in a similar manner. To install, reverse removal procedure.

Removal & Installation (Civic) – Close sun roof fully. Slide sun shade all the way back. Pry plugs out of bracket covers and remove screws. Slide bracket cover off to rear. Remove glass bracket mounting nuts from both sides. Remove glass lifting up and pulling forward. To install, reverse removal procedure.

Removal & Installation (Prelude) – Remove front roof trim. Align position "A" of frame to mounting screw. See Fig. 7. Remove mounting screws and clips. Slide sun roof slightly forward. Taking care not scratch sun roof liner, slide from under sun roof and remove it. Remove mounting screws from panel brackets on both sides. Lift up and remove sun roof panel. To install, reverse removal procedure.

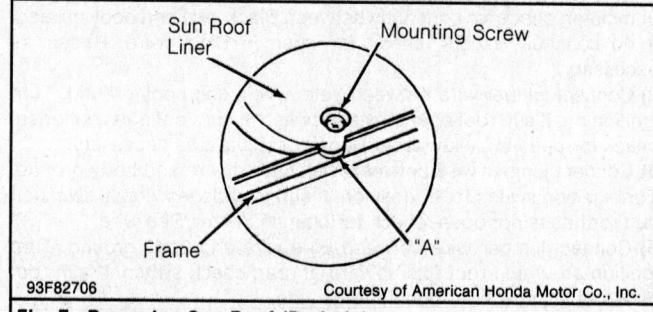

Sun Roof Liner
Mounting Screw
Frame
"A"

93F82706   Courtesy of American Honda Motor Co., Inc.

Fig. 7: Removing Sun Roof (Prelude)

SWITCH

Removal & Installation – Carefully pry switch panel from instrument panel. Unplug connectors from switches. Remove retaining screws (if equipped) and separate switch from panel. To install, reverse removal procedure.

WIND DEFLECTOR

Removal & Installation – Open sun roof fully. Pry up rail cover and rail holder cover. Remove sun shade rail stopper and link stopper. Remove wind deflector retaining nuts and remove wind deflector. To install, reverse removal procedure. Adjust wind deflector. See WIND DEFLECTOR under ADJUSTMENTS.

WIRING DIAGRAMS

NOTE: See ACCESSORIES & EQUIPMENT, Volume 5.

Accord, Civic, Civic Del Sol, Passport, Prelude

NOTE: For power window information on Passport, refer to Rodeo in Isuzu POWER WINDOWS article.

DESCRIPTION & OPERATION

A permanent magnet motor operates each of the power windows. The driver's master switch assembly controls all of the power window motors. Each window switch controls only one of the power window motors. If the main switch is in OFF position, only driver's window may be operated. Passenger's windows and rear window (Civic Del Sol) cannot be controlled by rear window switches, but can still be controlled from driver's master switch.

Accord and Prelude power windows may be operated for about 10 minutes after ignition switch is turned from the ON position to the ACCESSORY or OFF position. Time delay function is operative as long as neither front door has been opened.

AUTO mode permits driver's window to be fully lowered or raised without holding switch until window has reached the end of its travel. Moving switch past its first stop will engage AUTO mode. AUTO mode is controlled by a pulser integrated in driver's window motor assembly. Pulser cannot be serviced separately.

Power window control unit is integrated in power window master control switch. Control unit is not serviced separately.

TROUBLE SHOOTING

CAUTION: All models are equipped with Supplemental Restraint System (SRS). SRS wiring harness is routed close to instrument cluster, steering wheel, and related components. All SRS wiring harnesses are covered by Yellow outer insulation. DO NOT use electrical test equipment on these circuits. Before working on steering column components, disable air bag system. See AIR BAG RESTRAINT SYSTEM article in ACCESSORIES & EQUIPMENT.

NOTE: Ensure all component terminals and ground connections are clean and tight. Check possible faults in order listed. Repair or replace components and circuits as necessary.

ACCORD

All Windows Inoperative – Blown fuse No. 15 (80-amp) in underhood fuse box. Blown fuse No. 37 (7.5-amp) in underhood fuse box. Faulty power window relay. Faulty key-off timer circuit in integrated control unit. Open in White/Red wire.

Driver's Window inoperative – Blown fuse No. 28 (20-amp) in underhood fuse box. Faulty driver's window motor. Faulty window regulator. Driver's switch input. Open in Green/White wire.

Driver's Window Inoperative In AUTO – Master switch faulty. Faulty pulser (in driver's motor). Faulty driver's switch input. Open in Red wire.

Passenger's Window Inoperative – Blown 20-amp fuse(s) No. 26 (right front), No. 24. (right rear) and/or No. 25 (left rear) in underhood fuse box. Faulty master switch. Faulty passenger's switch. Faulty passenger's window motor. Faulty window regulator. Open in Blue/Black wire (right front), White/Black wire (left rear) and/or White/Yellow (right rear) wire.

All Windows Inoperative Within 10 Minutes Of Ignition Switch Turned Off – Blown fuse No. 37 (7.5-amp) in underhood fuse box. Faulty door switches. Faulty key-off timer circuit in integrated control unit.

CIVIC

All Windows Inoperative – Blown fuse No. 14 (20-amp) in underhood fuse box. Power window relay. Open in Black/Yellow or White/Red wires.

Driver's Window inoperative – Blown fuse No. 5 (20-amp) in underhood fuse box. Faulty driver's window motor. Faulty window regulator. Faulty master switch. Faulty master switch input. Open in White/Yellow wire.

Driver's Window Inoperative In AUTO – Faulty pulser (in driver's window motor). Faulty power window master switch. Master switch input. Open in Blue wire.

Passenger's Window Inoperative – Blown 20-amp fuse(s) No. 8 (right front), No. 4. (right rear) and/or No. 7 (left rear) in underhood fuse box. Faulty power window master switch. Faulty passenger's switch. Faulty passenger's window motor. Faulty window regulator. Open in Blue/Black wire (right front), Green/Black wire (left rear) and/or Yellow/Black (right rear) wire.

CIVIC DEL SOL

All Windows Inoperative – Blown fuse No. 36 (50-amp) in underhood fuse box. Blown fuse No. 14 (20-amp) or No. 15 (20-amp) in dash fuse box. Power window relay. Open in Yellow, Black/Yellow or White/Red wires.

Driver's Window inoperative – Blown fuse No. 8 (20-amp) in dash fuse box. Faulty driver's window motor. Faulty master switch. Faulty master switch input. Faulty window regulator. Open in White/Yellow wire.

Driver's Window Inoperative In AUTO – Faulty master switch. Faulty pulser (in driver's window motor). Master switch input. Open in Blue or Blue/Yellow wires.

Passenger's Window Inoperative – Blown fuse No. 5 (20-amp) in dash fuse box. Faulty passenger's switch. Faulty passenger's window motor. Faulty window regulator. Open in Blue/Black wire.

Rear Window Inoperative – Blown fuse No. 7 (20-amp) in dash fuse box. Faulty rear window motor. Faulty master switch. Power window control input. Faulty window regulator. Open in Green/Black wire.

PRELUDE

All Windows Inoperative – Blown fuse No. 37 (40-amp) in dash fuse box. Power window relay. Key-off timer circuit in integrated control unit. Open in Green/Black wire.

Driver's Window inoperative – Blown fuse No. 15 (20-amp) in dash fuse box. Faulty driver's window motor. Faulty window regulator. Master switch input. Open in White/Black wire.

Driver' Window Inoperative In AUTO – Faulty master switch. Faulty pulser (in driver's window motor). Master switch input. Open in Blue wire.

Passenger's Window Inoperative – Blown fuse No. 16 (20-amp) in dash fuse box. Faulty power window master switch. Faulty passenger's switch. Faulty passenger's window motor. Faulty window regulator. Open in Blue/Black wire.

All Windows Inoperative Within 10 Minutes Of Ignition Switch Turned Off – Blown fuse No. 37 (40-amp) in dash fuse box. Faulty door switches. Faulty key-off timer circuit in integrated control unit.

TESTING

MOTOR TEST

Driver's Window Motor Test (Except Accord) – Remove door panel. Unplug 4-pin connector from motor. Using jumper wires, connect terminals No. 3 and 4 to battery voltage and ground. See Fig. 1. Check for motor operation. Reverse jumper wires and retest. Replace motor if it does not operation in both directions.

Driver's Window Motor Test (Accord) – Remove door panel. Unplug 4-pin connector from motor. Using jumper wires, connect terminals No. 1 and 2 to battery voltage and ground. See Fig. 1. Check for motor operation. Reverse jumper wires and retest. Replace motor if it does not operation in both directions.

Passenger's Window Motor Test – Remove door panel. Unplug 2-pin connector from motor. Using jumper wires, connect connector terminals to battery voltage and ground. See Fig. 1. Check for motor operation. Reverse jumper wires and retest. Replace motor if it does not operate in both directions.

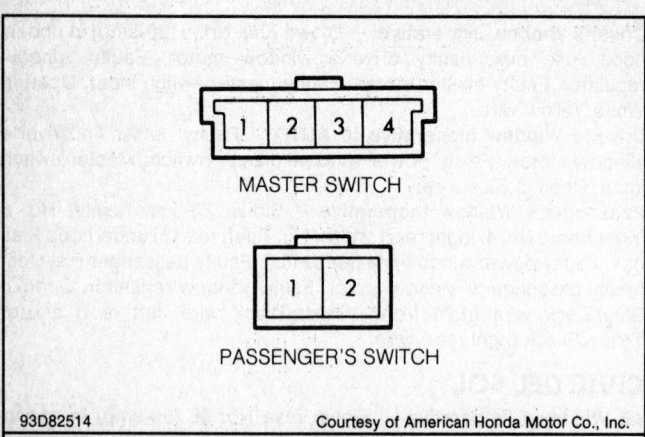

93D82514   Courtesy of American Honda Motor Co., Inc.

Fig 1: Identifying Power Window Motor Connector Terminals

Rear Window Motor Test (Civic Del Sol) – Remove rear window panel assembly. Unplug 2-pin connector from motor. Using jumper wires, connect connector terminals to battery voltage and ground. *See Fig. 1.* Check for motor operation. Reverse jumper wires. Replace motor if it does not operation in both directions.

PULSER TEST (DRIVER'S WINDOW MOTOR)

NOTE: Pulser is integral part of driver's window motor assembly. If pulser is defective, motor assembly must be replaced.

Connect test leads of analog ohmmeter to motor connector terminals No. 1 and 2 (terminals No. 3 and 4 on Accord). Using jumper wires, connect terminals No. 3 and 4 (terminals No. 1 and 2 on Accord) to battery voltage and ground. *See Fig. 1.* If ohmmeter needle does not alternately move back and forth while motor is operating, replace motor.

SWITCH INPUTS TEST

NOTE: Some wires have been assigned a superscript to distinguish them from other wires of the same color. For example, the Yellow/Green[1] wire is not the same as the Yellow/Green[2] wire.

Turn ignition off. Remove driver's door panel. Unplug connectors from master switch. Using a DVOM, perform appropriate switch input tests. *See Figs. 2-8.* If all input test results are okay, inspect connector and terminals for damage and proper fit. If connector is okay and power windows still malfunction, replace master switch.

NOTE: Numbers 1 through 5 refer to test number, not terminal numbers.

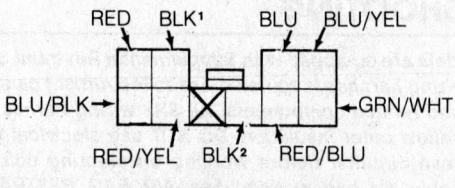

VIEW FROM WIRE SIDE

No.	Wire	Test condition	Test: Desired result	Possible cause if result is not obtained
1	BLK[1] / BLK[2]	Under all conditions	Check for continuity to ground: There should be continuity.	• Poor ground (G401, G403) • An open in the wire
2	GRN/WHT / BLU/BLK	Ignition switch ON(II)	Check for voltage to ground: There should be battery voltage.	• Blown No. 26 or 28 (20 A) fuse in the underhood fuse/relay box. • Faulty power window relay • An open in the wire
3	RED/BLU and RED/YEL	Connect the GRN/WHT terminal to the RED/BLU terminal, and the RED/YEL terminal to the BLK[2] terminal, then turn the ignition switch ON (II).	Check the driver's window motor: It should run (the window moves down).	• Faulty driver's window motor • An open in the wire
4	BLU/YEL and BLU	Connect the BLU/BLK terminal to the BLU/YEL terminal, and the BLU terminal to the BLK[1] terminal, then turn the ignition switch ON (II).	Check the front passenger's window motor: It should run (the window moves down).	• Faulty passenger's window motor • Faulty passenger's window switch • An open in the wire
5	RED and BLK[2]	Connect the GRN/WHT terminal to the RED/YEL terminal, and the BLK[1] terminal to the RED/BLU terminal, then turn the ignition switch ON (II).	Check for resistance between the RED and BLK[2] terminals: Between 20 – 50 ohms should be indicated as the driver's motor runs.	• Faulty pulser • Faulty driver's window motor • An open in the wire

Fig 2: Switch Input Test (Accord Coupe)

NOTE: Numbers 1 through 7 refer to test number, not terminal numbers.

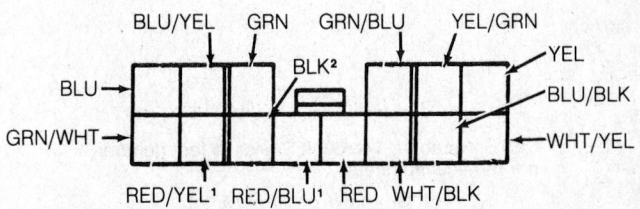

VIEW FROM WIRE SIDE

No.	Wire	Test condition	Test: Desired result	Possible cause if result is not obtained
1	BLK² BLK²	Under all conditions	Check for continuity to ground: There should be continuity.	• Poor ground (G401, G403) • An open in the wire
2	GRN/WHT BLU/BLK WHT/YEL WHT/BLK	Ignition switch ON (II)	Check for voltage to ground: There should be battery voltage.	• Blown No. 24, 25, 26 or 28 (20 A) fuse in the under-hood fuse/relay box • Faulty power window relay • An open in the wire
3	RED/BLU¹ and RED/YEL¹	Connect the GRN/WHT terminal to the RED/BLU¹ terminal, and the RED/YEL¹ terminal to the BLK² terminal, then turn the ignition switch ON (II).	Check the driver's window motor: It should run (the window moves down).	• Faulty driver's window motor • An open in the wire
4	BLU/YEL and BLU	Connect the BLU/BLK terminal to the BLU/YEL terminal, and the BLU terminal to the BLK¹ terminal, then turn the ignition switch ON (II).	Check the front passenger's window motor: It should run (the window moves down).	• Faulty front passenger's window motor • Faulty front passenger's window switch • An open in the wire
5	YEL and YEL/GRN	Connect the YEL/BLK terminal to the YEL/GRN terminal, and the YEL terminal to the BLK¹ terminal, then turn the ignition switch ON (II).	Check the right rear motor: It should run (the window moves down).	• Faulty right window rear motor • Faulty right window switch • An open in the wire
6	GRN/BLU and GRN	Connect the GRN/BLU terminal to the GRN terminal, and the GRN/YEL terminal to the BLK¹ terminal, then turn the ignition switch ON (II).	Check the left rear motor: It should run (the window moves down).	• Faulty left rear window motor • Faulty left rear window switch • An open in the wire
7	RED and BLK²	Connect the GRN/WHT terminal to the RED/YEL¹ terminal, and the BLK¹ terminal to the RED/BLU¹ terminal, then turn the ignition switch ON.	Check for resistance between the RED and BLK² terminals: Between 20-50 ohms should be indicated as the driver's motor runs.	• Faulty pulser • Faulty driver's window motor • An open in the wire

94F46164

Fig 3: Switch Input Test (Accord Sedan/Wagon)

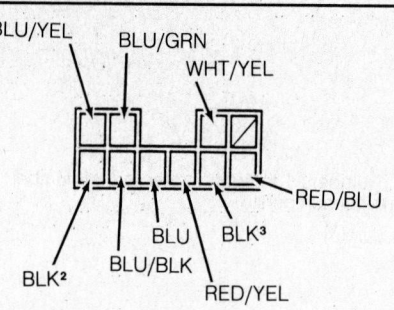

BLU/YEL BLU/GRN WHT/YEL

RED/BLU

BLK² BLU BLK³
BLU/BLK RED/YEL

NOTE: Numbers 1 through 5 refer to test number,
not terminal numbers.

VIEW FROM WIRE SIDE

No.	Terminal	Test condition	Test: Desired result	Possible cause if result is not obtained
1	BLK²	Under all conditions.	Check for continuity to ground: There should be continuity.	• Poor ground • An open in the wire.
2	WHT/YEL BLU/BLK	Ignition switch is ON.	Check for voltage to ground: There should be battery voltage.	• Blown No. 5 or 8 (20 A) fuse in the under-dash fuse/relay box. • Faulty power window relay. • An open in the wire.
3	RED/BLU and RED/YEL	Connect the WHT/YEL terminal to the RED/BLU terminal, and the RED/YEL terminal to the BLK² terminal, then turn ignition switch ON.	Check the driver's motor operation: It should run (the window moves down).	• Faulty driver's motor. • An open in the wire.
4	BLU/YEL and BLU/GRN	Connect the BLU/BLK terminal to the BLU/GRN terminal, and the BLU/YEL terminal to the BLK² terminal, then turn ignition switch ON.	Check the passenger's motor operation: It should run (the window moves down).	• Faulty passenger's motor. • Faulty passenger's switch. • An open in the wire.
5	BLU and BLK³	Connect the WHT/YEL terminal to the RED/YEL terminal, and the BLK² terminal to the RED/BLU¹ terminal, then turn ignition switch ON.	Check for resistance between the BLU and BLK³ terminals: Between 20 — 50 ohms should be indicated as the driver's motor runs (the window moves up).	• Faulty pulser. • Faulty driver's motor. • An open in the wire.

93J82536

Fig 4: Switch Input Test (Civic Coupe)

YEL/GRN   GRN/YEL
RED/YEL   YEL   RED/BLU   GRN

YEL/BLK   BLU
BLU/BLK   BLK³   GRN/BLK
WHT/YEL   BLU/GRN
BLU/YEL

VIEW FROM WIRE SIDE

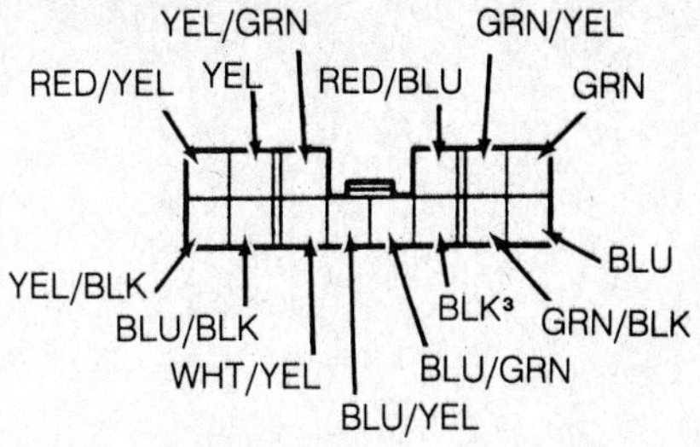

NOTE: Numbers 1 through 7 refer to test number, not terminal numbers.

No.	Terminal	Test condition	Test: Desired result	Possible cause if result is not obtained
1	BLK²	Under all conditions.	Check for continuity to ground: There should be continuity.	• Poor ground • An open in the wire.
2	WHT/YEL BLU/BLK YEL/BLK GRN/BLK	Ignition switch is ON.	Check for voltage to ground: There should be battery voltage.	• Blown No. 4, 5, 7 or 8 (20 A) fuse in the under-dash fuse/relay box. • Faulty power window relay. • An open in the wire.
3	RED/BLU¹ and RED/YEL¹	Connect the WHT/YEL terminal to the RED/BLU¹ terminal, and the RED/YEL¹ terminal to the BLK² terminal, then turn ignition switch ON.	Check the driver's motor operation: It should run (the window moves down).	• Faulty driver's motor. • An open in the wire.
4	BLU/YEL and BLU/GRN	Connect the BLU/BLK terminal to the BLU/GRN terminal, and the BLU/YEL terminal to the BLK² terminal, then turn ignition switch ON.	Check the right front motor operation: It should run (the window moves down).	• Faulty right front motor. • Faulty right front switch. • An open in the wire.
5	YEL and YEL/GRN	Connect the YEL/BLK terminal to the YEL/GRN terminal, and the YEL terminal to the BLK² terminal, then turn ignition switch ON.	Check the right rear motor operation: It should run (the window moves down).	• Faulty right rear motor. • Faulty right rear switch. • An open in the wire.
6	GRN/YEL and GRN	Connect the GRN/BLK terminal to the GRN terminal, and the GRN/YEL terminal to the BLK² terminal, then turn ignition switch ON.	Check the left rear motor operation: It should run (the window moves down).	• Faulty left rear motor. • Faulty left rear switch. • An open in the wire.
7	BLU and BLK³	Connect the WHT/YEL terminal to the RED/YEL¹ terminal, and the BLK² terminal to the RED/BLU¹ terminal, then turn ignition switch ON.	Check for resistance between the BLU and BLK² terminals: Between 20 — 50 ohms should be indicated as the driver's motor runs.	• Faulty pulser. • Faulty driver's motor. • An open in the wire.

93A82537

Courtesy of American Honda Motor Co., Inc.

Fig 5: Switch Input Test (Civic Sedan)

1994 ACCESSORIES & EQUIPMENT
Power Windows (Cont.)

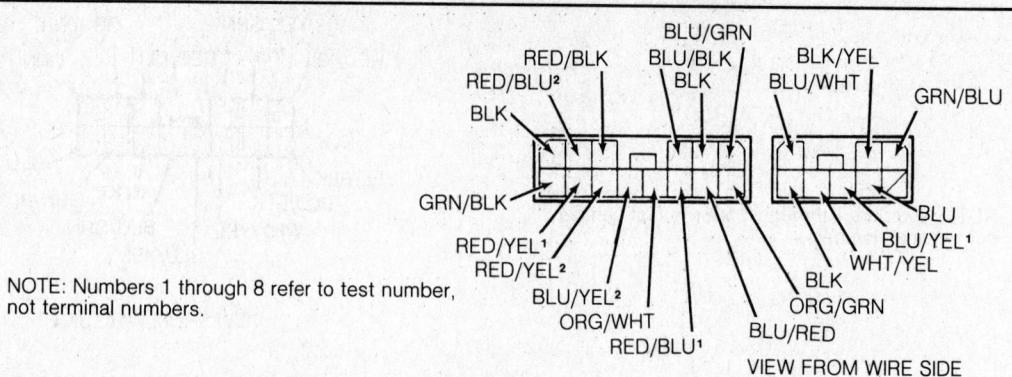

NOTE: Numbers 1 through 8 refer to test number, not terminal numbers.

VIEW FROM WIRE SIDE

No.	Terminal	Test condition	Test: Desired result	Possible cause if result is not obtained
1	BLK	Under all conditions.	Check for continuity to ground: There should be continuity.	• Poor ground • A break in the wire.
2	WHT/YEL GRN/BLK BLU/BLK	Ignition switch is ON.	Check for voltage to ground: There should be battery voltage.	• Blown No. 5, 7 or 8 (20 A) fuse. • Faulty power window relay. • A break in the wire.
3	BLU/RED and BLU/WHT	Connect the WHT/YEL terminal to the BLU/WHT terminal, and the BLU/RED terminal to the BLK terminal, then turn ignition switch ON.	Check the driver's window motor operation: It should run (the window moves down).	• Faulty driver's window motor. • A break in the wire.
4	BLU/YEL² and BLU/GRN	Connect the BLU/BLK terminal to the BLU/GRN terminal, and the BLU/YEL² terminal to the BLK terminal, then turn ignition switch ON.	Check the passenger's window motor operation: It should run (the window moves down).	• Faulty passenger's window motor. • A break in the wire.
5	RED/YEL² and RED/BLU²	Connect the GRN/BLK terminal to the RED/BLU² terminal, and the RED/YEL² terminal to the BLK terminal, then turn ignition switch ON.	Check the rear window motor operation: It should run (the window moves down).	• Faulty rear window motor. • A break in the wire.
6	BLU and BLU/YEL¹	Connect the WHT/YEL terminal to the BLU/WHT terminal, and the BLU/RED terminal to the BLK terminal, then turn ignition switch ON.	Check for resistance between the BLU and BLU/YEL¹ terminals: Between 20 — 50 ohms should be indicated as the driver's window motor runs.	• Faulty pulser. • Faulty driver's window motor. • A break in the wire.
7	GRN/BLU	Driver's window switch is in "AUTO" position.	Check for voltage to ground: There should be battery voltage.	• Blown No. 15 (10 A) fuse. • Faulty master switch. • A break in the wire.
	BLK/YEL	Driver's window switch is in "DOWN" position.		
	RED/BLU¹	Driver's window switch is in "UP" position.		

NOTE: Turn the main switch (in the master switch) ON, then go to No. 8 test.

Fig 6: Switch Input Test (Civic Del Sol - 1 Of 2)

8	ORN/GRN	Passenger's window switch is in "DOWN" position.	Check for voltage to ground: There should be battery voltage.	• Blown No. 15 (10 A) fuse. • Faulty master switch. • Faulty passenger's switch. • A break in the wire.
	ORN/WHT	Passenger's window switch is in "UP" position.		
	RED/BLK	Rear window switch is in "DOWN" position.		
	RED/YEL[1]	Rear window switch is in "UP" position.		

93C82539

Courtesy of American Honda Motor Co., Inc.

Fig 7: Switch Input Test (Civic Del Sol – 2 Of 2)

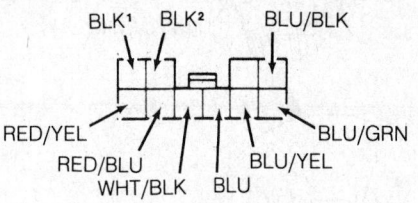

VIEW FROM WIRE SIDE

NOTE: Numbers 1 through 5 refer to test number, not terminal numbers.

No.	Terminal	Test condition	Test: Desired result	Possible cause if result is not obtained
1	BLK[1]	Under all conditions.	Check for continuity to ground: There should be continuity.	• Poor ground • An open in the wire.
2	WHT/BLK BLU/BLK	Ignition switch ON.	Check for voltage to ground: There should be battery voltage.	• Blown No. 15 or 16 (20 A) fuse. (In the under-dash fuse/relay box) • Faulty power window relay. • An open in the wire.
3	RED/BLU and RED/YEL	Connect the WHT/BLK terminal to the RED/BLU terminal, and the RED/YEL terminal to the BLK[1] terminal, then turn the ignition switch ON.	Check the driver's window motor: It should run.	• Faulty driver's window motor. • An open in the wire.
4	BLU/YEL and BLU/GRN	Connect the BLU/BLK terminal to the BLU/GRN terminal, and the BLU/YEL terminal to the BLK terminal, then turn the ignition switch ON.	Check the passenger's window motor: It should run.	• Faulty passenger's window motor. • Faulty passenger's window switch. • An open in the wire.
5	BLU and BLK[2]	Connect the WHT/BLK terminal to the RED/YEL terminal, and the BLK[2] terminal to the RED/BLU terminal, then turn the ignition switch ON.	Connect an analog ohmmeter to the BLU and BLK[2] terminals: The meter needle should move back and forth as the driver's window motor runs.	• Faulty pulser. • Faulty driver's window motor. • An open in the wire.

93F82540

Courtesy of American Honda Motor Co., Inc.

Fig 8: Switch Input Test (Prelude)

SWITCH TEST

Master Switch Test – Remove power window master switch. See MASTER POWER WINDOW SWITCH under REMOVAL & INSTALLATION. Using an ohmmeter, check resistance of switch terminals with switch in indicated positions. If continuity is not as specified, replace switch. *See Figs. 9-16.* See appropriate POWER WINDOW SWITCH CONTINUITY TEST table.

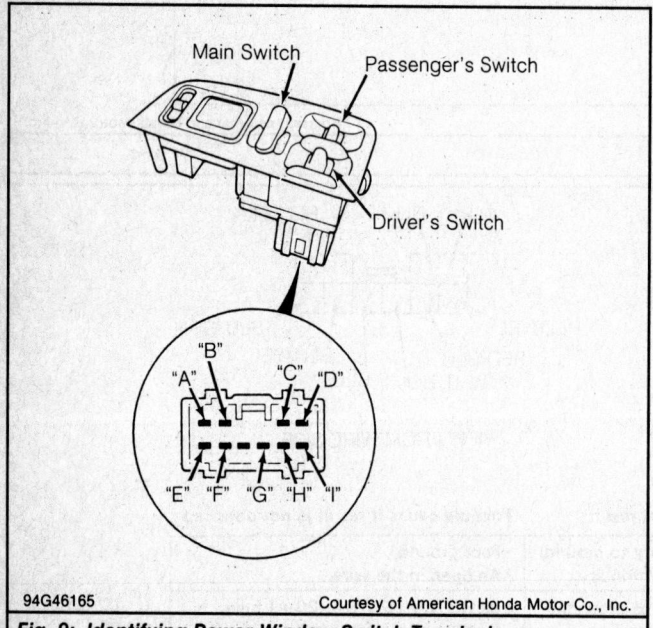

94G46165   Courtesy of American Honda Motor Co., Inc.

Fig. 9: Identifying Power Window Switch Terminals (Accord Coupe)

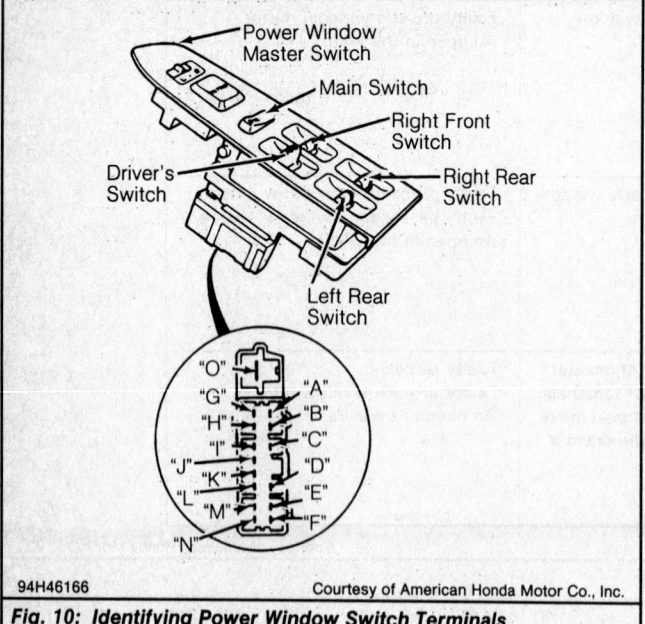

94H46166   Courtesy of American Honda Motor Co., Inc.

Fig. 10: Identifying Power Window Switch Terminals (Accord Sedan/Wagon)

NOTE: *Driver's power window switch on Accord is combined with the power window control unit. Switch cannot be isolated for testing. Perform appropriate switch inputs test. See SWITCH INPUTS TEST.*

POWER WINDOW MASTER SWITCH TEST (ACCORD COUPE)

Position	Main Switch	Pin Continuity
Passenger's Switch		
Off	On	"B", "C" & "D"
	Off	"C" & "D"
Up	On	"B" & "C"; "D" & "E"
	Off	"D" & "E"
Down	On	"B" & "D"; "C" & "E"
	Off	"C" & "E"

[1] – Main switch position does not affect driver's switch operation.

POWER WINDOW MASTER SWITCH TEST (ACCORD SEDAN/WAGON)

Position	Main Switch	Pin Continuity
Right Front Switch		
Off	On	"A", "B" & "O"
	Off	"A" & "B"
Up	On	"A" & "O"; "M" & "B"
	Off	"M" & "B"
Down	On	"B" & "O"; "M" & "A"
	Off	"M" & "A"
Right Rear Switch		
Off	On	"F", "E" & "O"
	Off	"F" & "E"
Up	On	"E" & "O"; "N" & "F"
	Off	"N" & "F"
Down	On	"F" & "O"; "N" & "E"
	Off	"N" & "E"
Left Rear Switch		
Off	On	"C", "D" & "O"
	Off	"C" & "D"
Up	On	"C" & "O"; "L" & "D"
	Off	"L" & "D"
Down	On	"D" & "O"; "L" & "C"
	Off	"L" & "C"

[1] – Main switch position does not affect driver's switch operation.

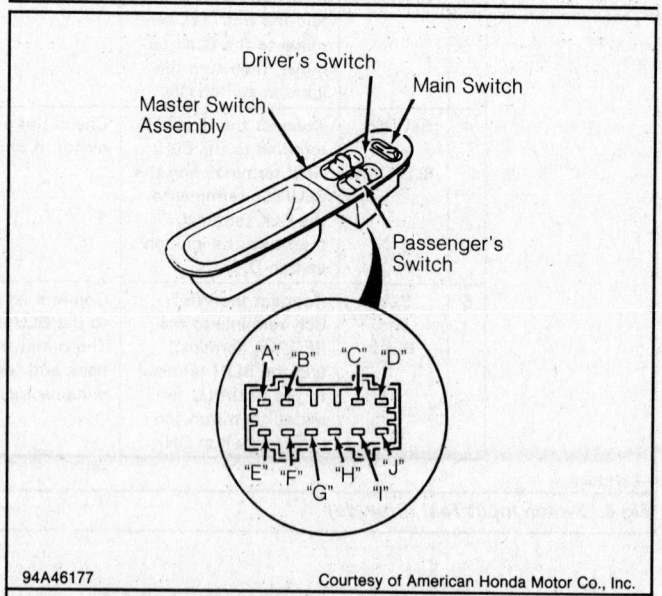

94A46177   Courtesy of American Honda Motor Co., Inc.

Fig 11: Identifying Power Window Switch Terminals (Civic Coupe)

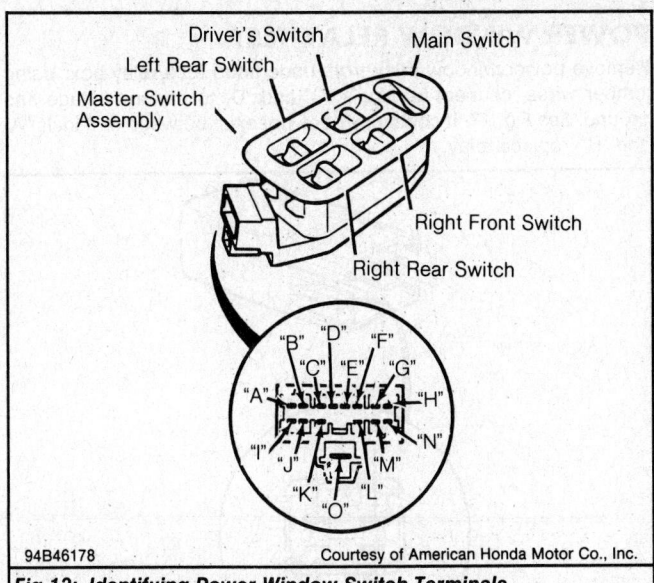

94B46178   Courtesy of American Honda Motor Co., Inc.

Fig 12: Identifying Power Window Switch Terminals (Civic Sedan)

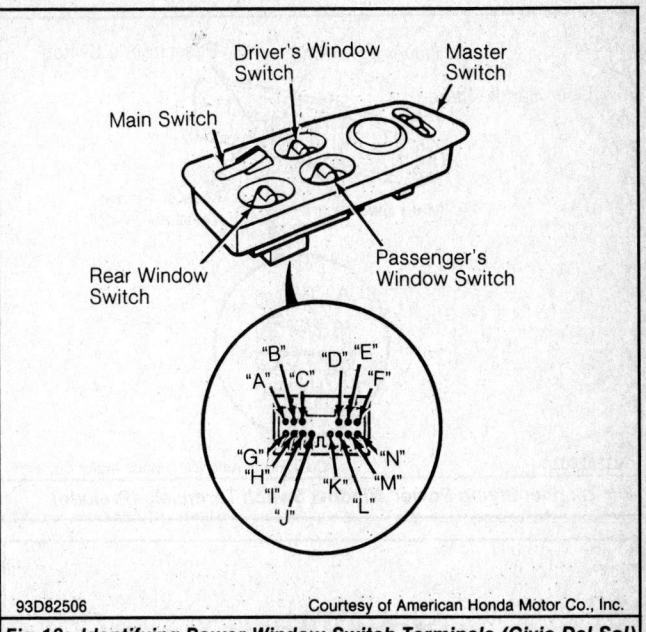

93D82506   Courtesy of American Honda Motor Co., Inc.

Fig 13: Identifying Power Window Switch Terminals (Civic Del Sol)

POWER WINDOW MASTER SWITCH TEST (CIVIC COUPE)

Position	Main Switch	Pin Continuity
Driver's Switch		
Off	[1]	"H", "I" & "J"
Up	[1]	"C" & "J"; "H" & "I"
Down	[1]	"C" & "H"; "I" & "J"
Down (AUTO)	[1]	"C" & "H"; "I" & "J"
Passenger's Switch		
Off	On	"A", "B" & "E"
	Off	"A" & "B"
Up	On	"A" & "F"; "B" & "E"
	Off	"A" & "F"
Down	On	"A" & "E"; "B" & "F"
	Off	"B" & "F"

[1] – Main switch position does not affect driver's switch operation.

POWER WINDOW MASTER SWITCH TEST (CIVIC SEDAN)

Position	Main Switch	Pin Continuity
left Front Switch		
Off	[1]	"N", "C" & "K"
Up	[1]	"N" & "C"; "F" & "K"
Down	[1]	"F" & "N"; "C" & "K"
Down (AUTO)	[1]	"F" & "N"; "C" & "K"
Right Front Switch		
Off	On	"D", "E" & "O"
	Off	"D" & "E"
Up	On	"D" & "O"; "E" & "G"
	Off	"E" & "G"
Down	On	"E" & "O"; "D" & "G"
	Off	"D" & "G"
Right Rear Switch		
Off	On	"L", "M" & "O"
	Off	"L" & "M"
Up	On	"L" & "O"; "M" & "H"
	Off	"M" & "H"
Down	On	"M" & "O"; "L" & "H"
	Off	"L" & "H"
Left Rear Switch		
Off	On	"I", "J" & "O"
	Off	"I" & "J"
Up	On	"I" & "O"; "J" & "B"
	Off	"J" & "B"
Down	On	"J" & "O"; "I" & "B"
	Off	"I" & "B"

[1] – Main switch position does not affect driver's switch operation.

POWER WINDOW MASTER SWITCH TEST (CIVIC DEL SOL)

Position	Continuity
Main Switch	
On	"F" & "J"
OFF	[1]
Driver's Switch	
Off	[1]
Up	"I" & "J"
Down	"C" & "J"
Down (AUTO)	"C", "B" & "J"
Passenger's Switch	
Up	"L" & "F"
Down	"K" & "F"
Rear Window Switch	
Up	"N" & "F"
Down	"M" & "F"

[1] – No continuity exists.

POWER WINDOW MASTER SWITCH TEST (PRELUDE)

Position	Main Switch	Pin Continuity
Driver's Switch		
Off	[1]	"B", "E" & "F"
Up	[1]	"F" & "G"
Down	[1]	"E" & "G"
Down (AUTO)	[1]	"E" & "G"
Passenger's Switch		
Off	On	"A", "I" & "J"
	Off	"I" & "J"
Up	On	"D" & "I"; "A" & "J"
	Off	"D" & "I"
Down	On	"A" & "I"; "D" & "J"
	Off	"D" & "J"

[1] – Main switch position does not affect driver's switch operation.

Passenger's Window Switch Test – Remove power window master switch. See MASTER POWER WINDOW SWITCH under REMOVAL & INSTALLATION. Using an ohmmeter, check resistance of switch terminals with switch in indicated positions. If continuity is not as specified, replace switch. See Fig. 15 or 16. See appropriate POWER WINDOW PASSENGER SWITCH CONTINUITY TEST table.

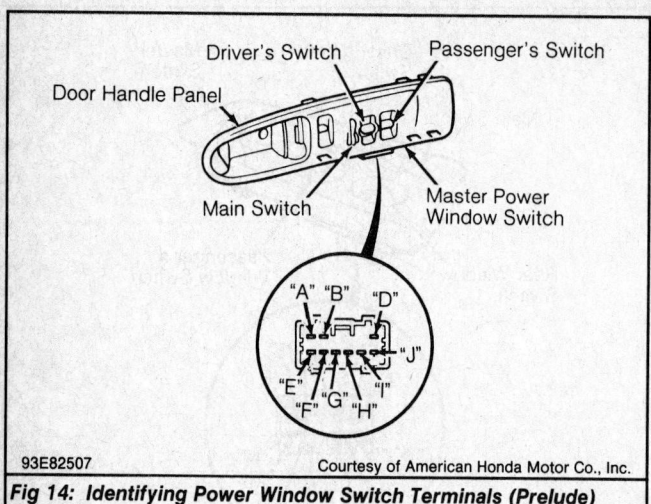

93E82507   Courtesy of American Honda Motor Co., Inc.

Fig 14: Identifying Power Window Switch Terminals (Prelude)

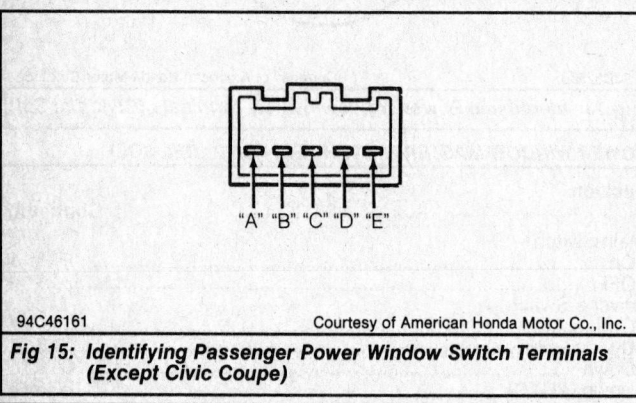

94C46161   Courtesy of American Honda Motor Co., Inc.

Fig 15: Identifying Passenger Power Window Switch Terminals (Except Civic Coupe)

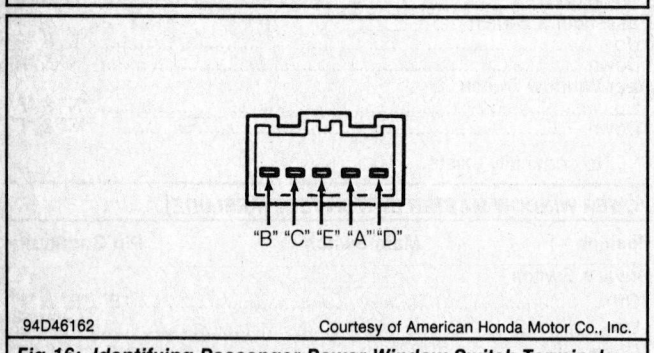

94D46162   Courtesy of American Honda Motor Co., Inc.

Fig 16: Identifying Passenger Power Window Switch Terminals (Civic Coupe)

PASSENGER'S POWER WINDOW SWITCH TEST

Position   **Pin Continuity**

Position	Pin Continuity
Accord	
Off	"D" & "E"; "B" & "C"
Up	"A" & "D"; "B" & "C"
Down	"A" & "C"; "D" & "E"
Civic	
Off	"A" & "D"; "B" & "C"
Up	"B" & "C"; "D" & "E"
Down	"A" & "C"; "D" & "E"
Civic Del Sol	
Up	"A" & "C"
Down	"A" & "E"
Prelude	
Off	"B" & "C"; "D" & "E"
Up	"A" & "D"
Down	"A" & "C"

POWER WINDOW RELAY TEST

Remove power window relay from underhood fuse/relay box. Using jumper wires, connect terminals "C" and "D" to battery voltage and ground. *See Fig. 17.* If continuity does not exist between terminals "A" and "B", replace relay.

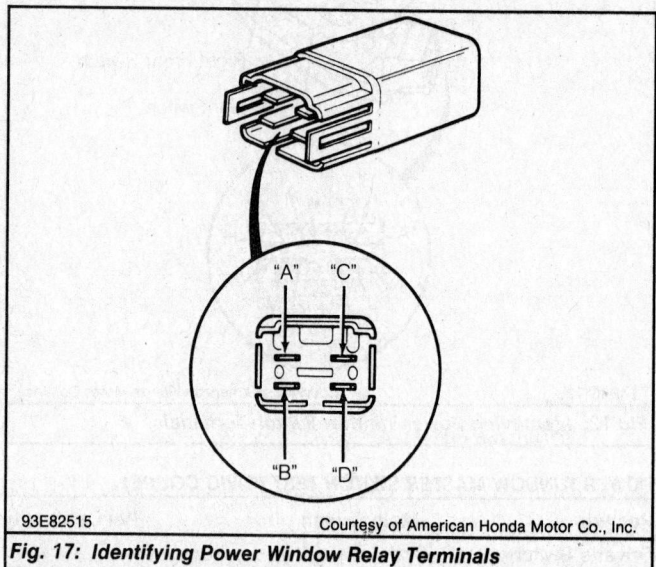

93E82515   Courtesy of American Honda Motor Co., Inc.

Fig. 17: Identifying Power Window Relay Terminals

REMOVAL & INSTALLATION

WINDOW MOTOR

Removal and installation procedures are not available from manufacturer.

MASTER POWER WINDOW SWITCH

Removal & Installation (Except Accord) – Remove left front door panel. Unplug electrical connectors. Remove master switch mounting screws. Remove master switch. To install, reverse removal procedure.

Removal & Installation (Accord) – Remove left front door panel. Unplug all electrical connectors from door panel. Remove armrest retainer and retainer screws. Remove armrest. Remove master switch mounting screws. Remove master switch. To install, reverse removal procedure.

WIRING DIAGRAMS

NOTE: See ACCESSORIES & EQUIPMENT, Volume 5.

Accord, Civic, Civic Del Sol, Passport, Prelude

NOTE: For information on steering column switches for Passport, refer to Rodeo in Isuzu STEERING COLUMN SWITCHES article.

WARNING: Before performing ANY tests or repairs on steering column switches, Supplemental Restraint System (SRS) MUST be disabled. See DISABLING & ACTIVATING AIR BAG SYSTEM. Accidental air bag deployment could cause serious bodily injury.

DISABLING & ACTIVATING AIR BAG SYSTEM

NOTE: Some Accord and Prelude models are equipped with stereo theft protection system. Technician should obtain 5-digit security code before disconnecting battery cable.

DISABLING AIR BAG

Disconnect both battery cables. Remove maintenance lid from bottom rear of steering wheel. Remove Red short connector, located on inside of maintenance lid. Disconnect connector between air bag and cable reel. Connect Red short connector to air bag side of connector. See Fig. 2.

ACTIVATING AIR BAG

1) To activate SRS, remove Red short connector from air bag side of connector and reconnect the connector between air bag and cable reel.
2) Return Red short connector to storage location on inside of maintenance lid. Install maintenance lid on back of steering wheel.
3) Reconnect battery cables. Check AIR BAG indicator light to ensure system is functioning properly.

TESTING

COMBINATION SWITCH

Accord – Disable air bag system. See DISABLING & ACTIVATING AIR BAG SYSTEM. Remove instrument cluster lower trim panel and left knee bolster. Disconnect combination switch 20-pin connector. With combination switch in indicated positions, check continuity between specified switch connector terminals. See Fig. 1.

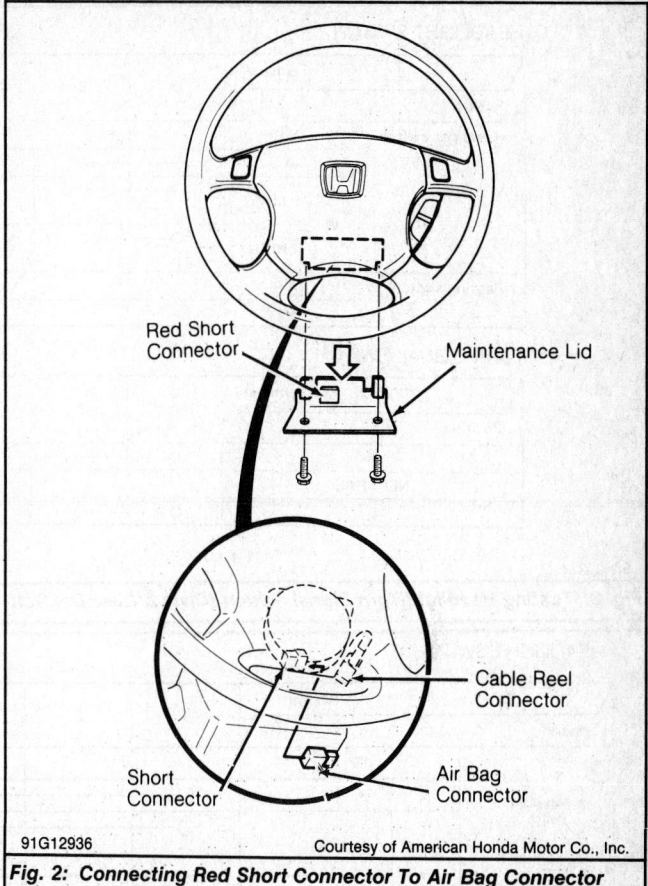

Civic & Civic Del Sol – Disable air bag system. See DISABLING & ACTIVATING AIR BAG SYSTEM. Remove steering column covers. Disconnect combination switch 4-pin and 7-pin connectors. With combination switch in indicated positions, check continuity between specified switch connector terminals. See Fig. 3.

91G12936 — Courtesy of American Honda Motor Co., Inc.

Fig. 2: Connecting Red Short Connector To Air Bag Connector

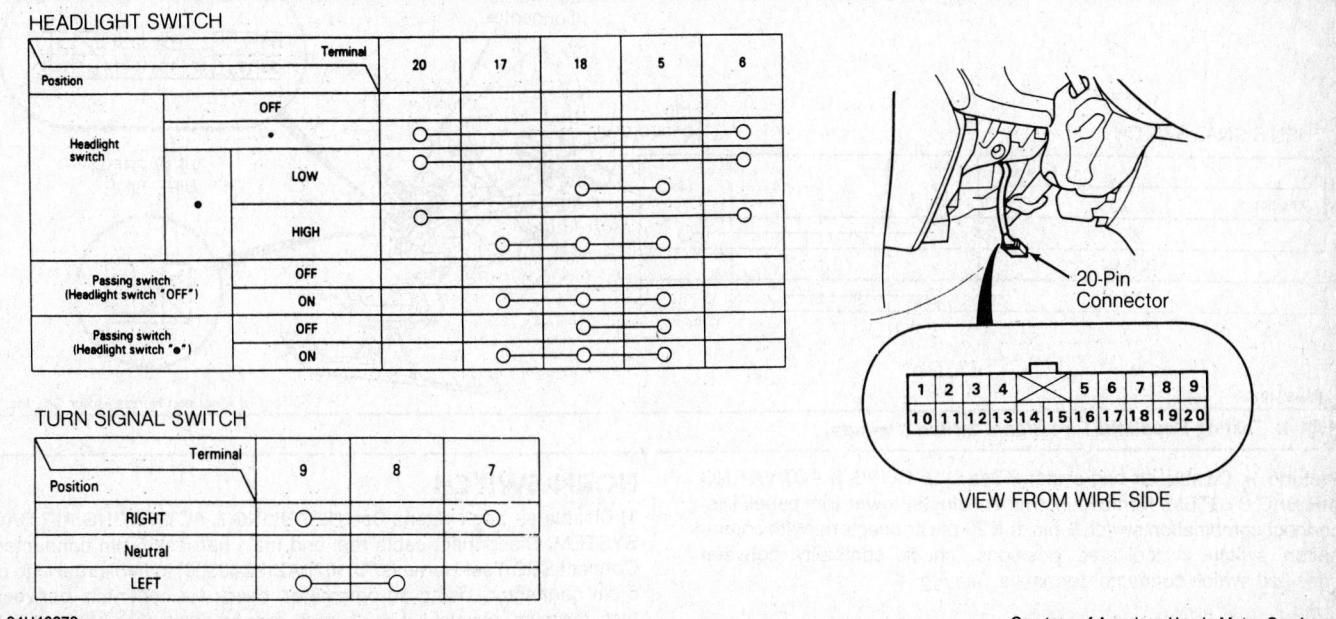

HEADLIGHT SWITCH

Position		Terminal	20	17	18	5	6
Headlight switch		OFF					
		•		O			O
				O			O
		LOW		O	O	O	
		HIGH	O	O	O		
Passing switch (Headlight switch "OFF")		OFF					
		ON		O	O	O	
Passing switch (Headlight switch "•")		OFF				O	
		ON	O	O	O		

TURN SIGNAL SWITCH

Position	Terminal	9	8	7
RIGHT		O		O
Neutral				
LEFT		O	O	

94H46273

Courtesy of American Honda Motor Co., Inc.

Fig. 1: Testing Headlight/Turn Signal Switch (Accord)

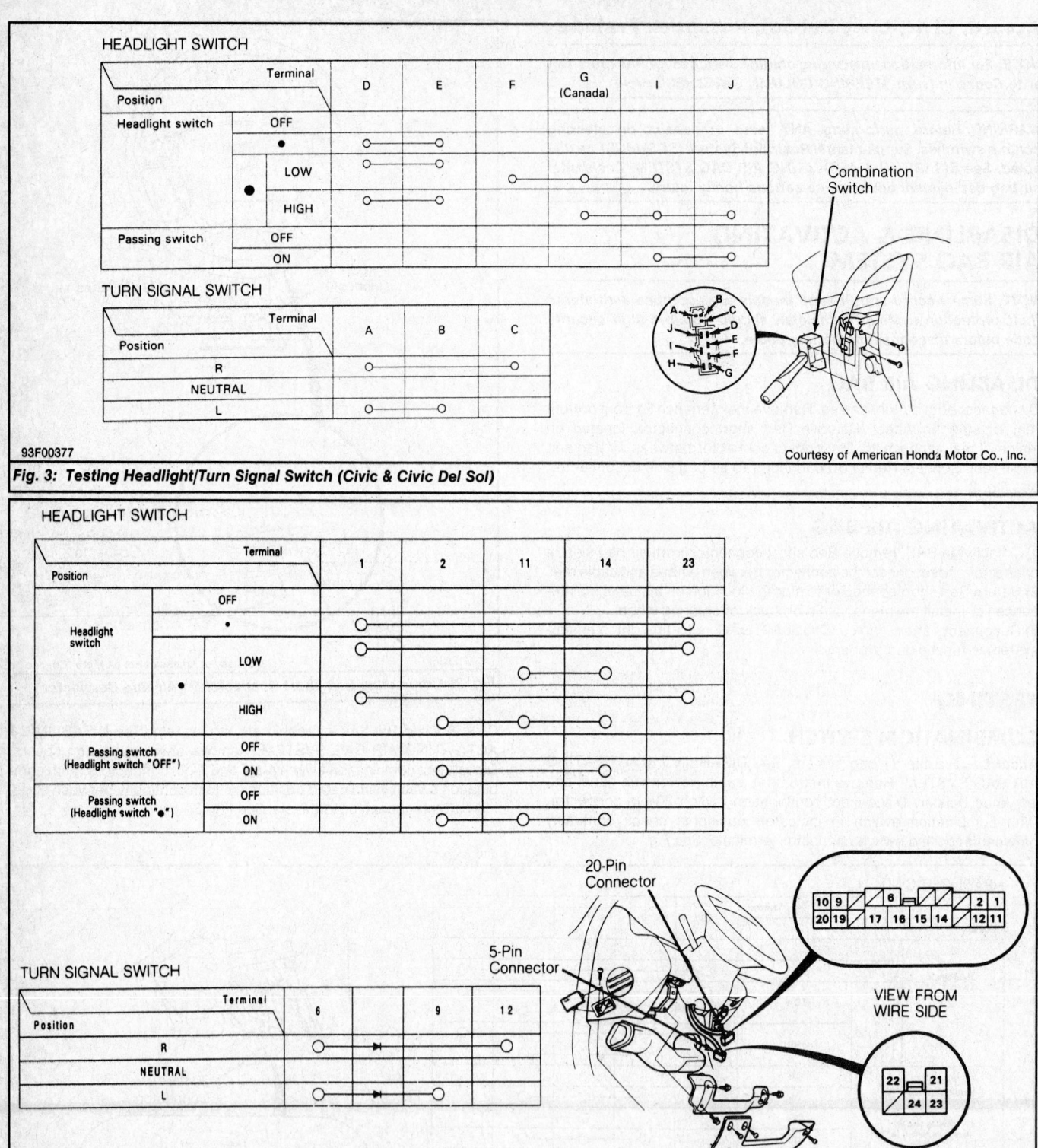

HEADLIGHT SWITCH

Position		Terminal	D	E	F	G (Canada)	I	J
Headlight switch	OFF							
	•		O—————O					
		LOW	O—————O		O————O————O		
	•	HIGH	O—————O			O————O————O	
Passing switch	OFF							
	ON					O————O		

TURN SIGNAL SWITCH

Position	Terminal	A	B	C
	R	O——————————————————O	
	NEUTRAL			
	L	O————O		

93F00377

Courtesy of American Honda Motor Co., Inc.

Fig. 3: Testing Headlight/Turn Signal Switch (Civic & Civic Del Sol)

HEADLIGHT SWITCH

Position		Terminal	1	2	11	14	23
Headlight switch		OFF					
	•		O———————————————————O			
			O				O
	•	LOW	O		O————O		
		HIGH		O————O————O		
Passing switch (Headlight switch "OFF")	OFF					
	ON		O————————————O		
Passing switch (Headlight switch "•")	OFF					
	ON		O————O————O		

TURN SIGNAL SWITCH

Position	Terminal	6	9	12
	R	O——————▶——————————O	
	NEUTRAL			
	L	O——————◀——————————O	

93H82427

Courtesy of American Honda Motor Co., Inc.

20-Pin Connector

5-Pin Connector

VIEW FROM WIRE SIDE

| 10 | 9 | | | 6 | | | | 2 | 1 |
| 20 | 19 | | 17 | 16 | 15 | 14 | | 12 | 11 |

| 22 | | | 21 |
| | 24 | 23 | |

Fig. 4: Testing Headlight/Turn Signal Switch (Prelude)

Prelude – Disable air bag system. See DISABLING & ACTIVATING AIR BAG SYSTEM. Remove instrument cluster lower trim panel. Disconnect combination switch 5-pin and 20-pin connectors. With combination switch in indicated positions, check continuity between specified switch connector terminals. *See Fig. 4.*

HAZARD WARNING SWITCH

For hazard warning switch testing, see INSTRUMENT PANELS article.

HORN SWITCH

1) Disable air bag system. See DISABLING & ACTIVATING AIR BAG SYSTEM. Disconnect cable reel and main harness 6-pin connector. Connect SRS Test Harness "C" (07LAZ-SL40300) to cable reel side of 6-pin connector. Using an ohmmeter, check for continuity between test harness terminal No. 3 and ground with the horn switch depressed. Continuity should exist.

2) If continuity exists, switch is okay. If continuity does not exist, remove air bag assembly using T30 TORX screwdriver to remove retaining screws. Remove air bag assembly and place on workbench with pad surface facing up.

WARNING: Pad surface MUST face up. If air bag is stored face down, accidental deployment could propel assembly sufficiently to cause serious bodily injury.

3) With horn switch depressed, check for continuity between horn positive cable and steering column shaft. *See Fig. 5.* Continuity should exist. If no continuity exists, replace horn switch. See HORN SWITCH under REMOVAL & INSTALLATION.

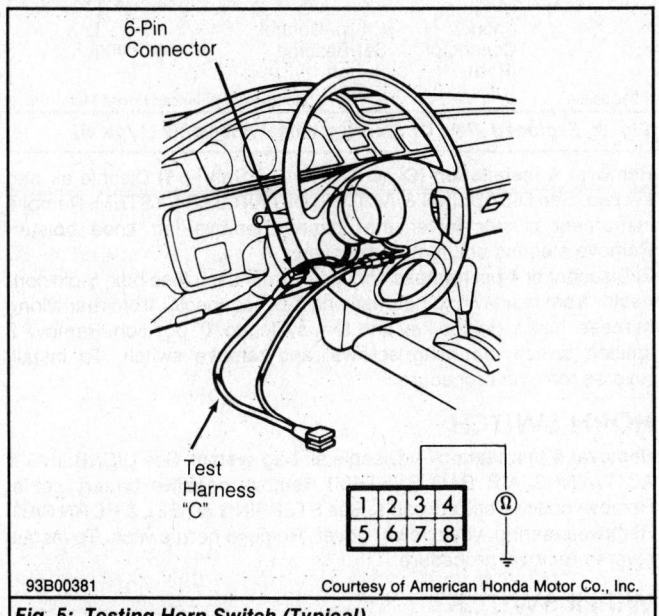

93B00381   Courtesy of American Honda Motor Co., Inc.

Fig. 5: Testing Horn Switch (Typical)

IGNITION SWITCH

Accord – Disable air bag system. See DISABLING & ACTIVATING AIR BAG SYSTEM. Remove instrument cluster lower trim panel. Remove left knee bolster and kick panel. Disconnect 7-pin connector from dash fuse block. With ignition switch in indicated positions, check continuity between specified switch terminals. *See Fig. 6.*

Civic & Civic Del Sol – Disable air bag system. See DISABLING & ACTIVATING AIR BAG SYSTEM. Remove instrument cluster lower trim panel. Remove left knee bolster and kick panel. Disconnect 5-pin and 7-pin connectors from dash fuse block. With ignition switch in indicated positions, check continuity between specified switch terminals. *See Fig. 7.*

Prelude – Disable air bag system. See DISABLING & ACTIVATING AIR BAG SYSTEM. Disconnect 5-pin connector from dash fuse block. Disconnect 3-pin connector from main wiring harness. With ignition switch in indicated positions, check continuity between specified switch terminals. *See Fig. 6.*

WIPER SWITCH

For wiper switch testing, see WIPER/WASHER SYSTEMS article.

REMOVAL & INSTALLATION

STEERING WHEEL & HORN PAD

Removal & Installation – 1) Disconnect negative battery cable. Disconnect positive battery cable. Disable air bag system. See DISABLING & ACTIVATING AIR BAG SYSTEM. To remove air bag assembly, remove 2 Torx bolts using a T30 bit.

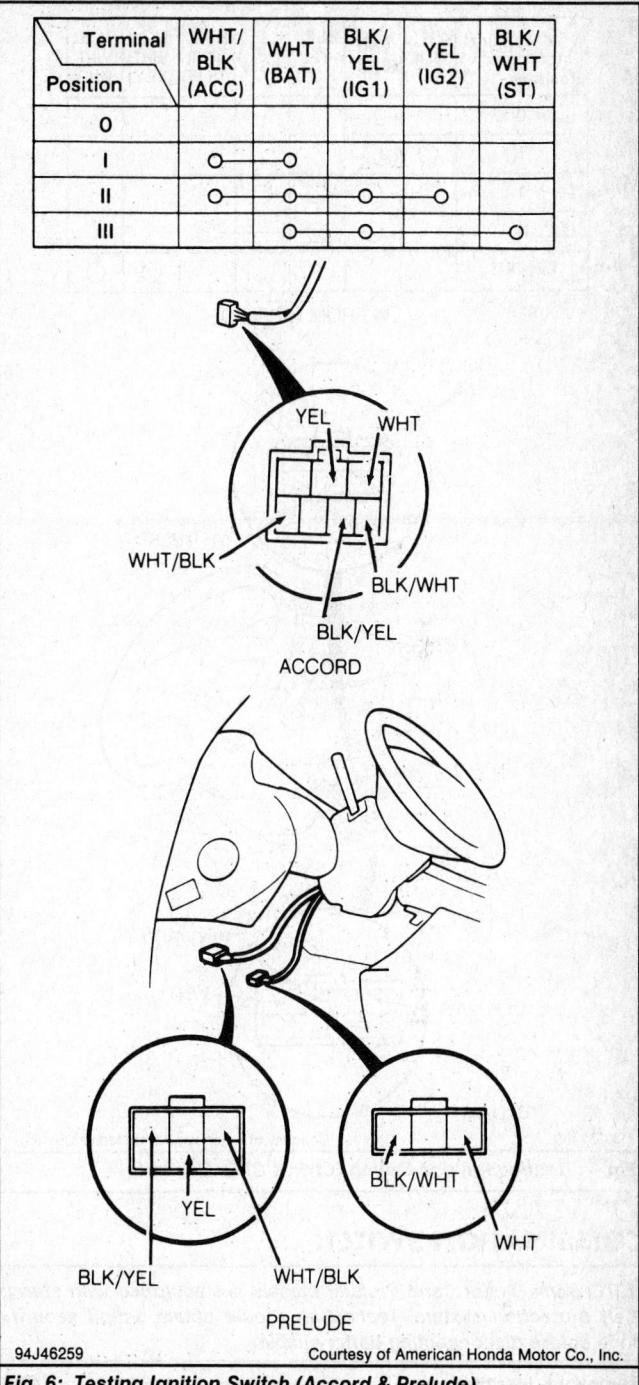

Terminal Position	WHT/ BLK (ACC)	WHT (BAT)	BLK/ YEL (IG1)	YEL (IG2)	BLK/ WHT (ST)
O					
I	○——	——○			
II	○——	——○	○——	——○	
III	○——	——○	——○		○

94J46259   Courtesy of American Honda Motor Co., Inc.

Fig. 6: Testing Ignition Switch (Accord & Prelude)

WARNING: Place air bag assembly on workbench. Pad surface MUST face up. If air bag is stored face down, accidental deployment could propel assembly sufficiently to cause serious bodily injury.

2) Remove steering wheel nut. *See Fig. 8.* Using a slight side-to-side motion, remove steering wheel assembly by pulling outward by hand. To install, reverse removal procedure.

CAUTION: DO NOT install an air bag assembly that is dented, cracked or shows signs of having been dropped.

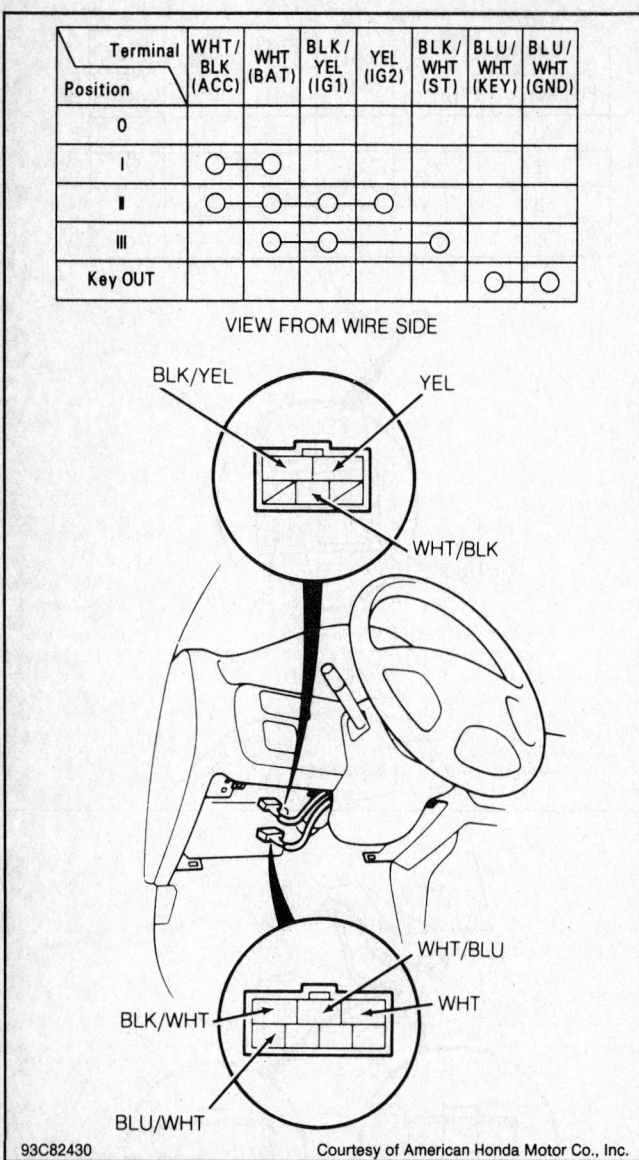

Terminal / Position	WHT/BLK (ACC)	WHT (BAT)	BLK/YEL (IG1)	YEL (IG2)	BLK/WHT (ST)	BLU/WHT (KEY)	BLU/WHT (GND)
0							
I	O——O						
II	O——O	O——O	O——O				
III		O——O	O——O		O		
Key OUT						O——O	

VIEW FROM WIRE SIDE

93C82430   Courtesy of American Honda Motor Co., Inc.

Fig. 7: Testing Ignition Switch (Civic & Civic Del Sol)

COMBINATION SWITCH

NOTE: Some Accord and Prelude models are equipped with stereo theft protection system. Technician should obtain 5-digit security code before disconnecting battery cable.

Removal & Installation – Before proceeding, disable SRS. See DISABLING & ACTIVATING AIR BAG SYSTEM. Remove dashboard lower cover and knee bolster. On Prelude, remove air duct. Remove upper and lower column covers. Disconnect combination switch connectors. Remove mounting screws. Remove combination switch. To install, reverse removal procedure.

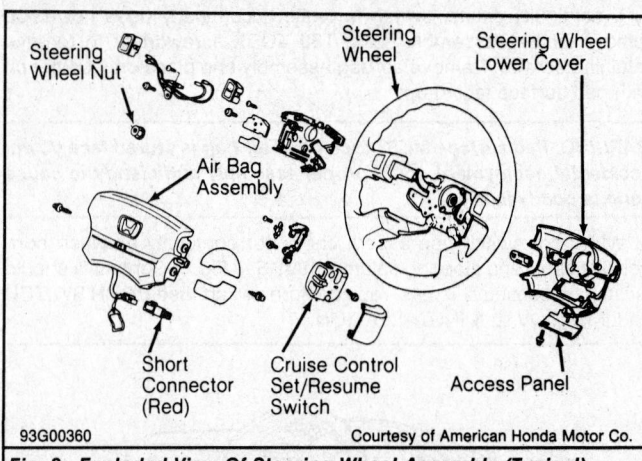

93G00360   Courtesy of American Honda Motor Co.

Fig. 8: Exploded View Of Steering Wheel Assembly (Typical)

Removal & Installation (Civic & Civic Del Sol) – 1) Disable air bag system. See DISABLING & ACTIVATING AIR BAG SYSTEM. Remove instrument cluster lower trim panel. Remove left knee bolster. Remove steering column lower cover.
2) Disconnect 4-pin harness connector from dash fuse box, 5-pin connector from main wiring harness and 7-pin connector from rear wiring harness. Insert ignition key and turn switch to "0" position. Remove 2 ignition switch mounting screws, and remove switch. To install, reverse removal procedure.

HORN SWITCH

Removal & Installation – Disable air bag system. See DISABLING & ACTIVATING AIR BAG SYSTEM. Remove negative battery cable. Remove positive battery cable. See STEERING WHEEL & HORN PAD. Remove steering wheel lower cover. Remove horn switch. To install, reverse removal procedure.

WIPER SWITCH

Removal & Installation (Accord & Prelude) – Disable air bag system. See DISABLING & ACTIVATING AIR BAG SYSTEM. Remove dash lower trim cover and knee bolster. Remove steering column covers. Disconnect wiper/washer switch 10-pin connector (8-pin connector on Prelude). Remove 2 screws and wiper/washer switch. To install, reverse removal procedure.
Removal & Installation (Civic & Civic Del Sol) – Disable air bag system. See DISABLING & ACTIVATING AIR BAG SYSTEM. Remove dash lower trim cover. Remove steering column covers. Disconnect wiper/washer switch 6-pin (Civic only) and 8-pin connectors. Remove 2 screws and slide wiper/washer switch out of housing. To install, reverse removal procedure.

TORQUE SPECIFICATIONS
TORQUE SPECIFICATIONS

Application	Ft. Lbs. (N.m)
Steering Wheel Nut	37 (50)

	INCH Lbs. (N.m)
Air Bag Assembly Torx Bolts	89 (10)

WIRING DIAGRAMS

NOTE: See ACCESSORIES & EQUIPMENT, Volume 5.

Accord, Civic, Civic Del Sol, Passport, Prelude

NOTE: For wiper/washer system information on Passport, refer to Rodeo in Isuzu WIPER/WASHER SYSTEM article.

DESCRIPTION & OPERATION

A 2-speed front wiper motor with intermittent feature is used on all models. Wiper switch is part of the combination switch on the steering column. Some models are also equipped with a rear wiper/washer system.

TROUBLE SHOOTING

ACCORD

Wipers Do Not Operate In Any Position – Blown fuse No. 6 (30-amp) in dash fuse block. Faulty wiper motor assembly. Disconnected wiper linkage. Faulty wiper switch. Poor ground. Check for open circuit in Green/Black wire. Check for loose or disconnected terminals.

Wipers Do Not Operate In INT (Intermittent) Position – Faulty wiper switch. Faulty wiper motor assembly. Faulty intermittent wiper relay. Check for open circuit in Green or Blue/White wire. Check for loose or disconnected terminals.

Wipers Do Not Operate In LO Or HI Position – Faulty wiper switch. Faulty wiper motor assembly. Check for open circuit in Blue/Yellow or Blue wire. Check for loose or disconnected terminals.

Wipers Do Not Operate In MIST Position – Faulty mist switch.

Wipers Do Not Return To Park Position With Switch Turned Off – Faulty wiper motor assembly. Faulty wiper switch. Check for open circuit in Blue/White wire. Check for loose or disconnected terminals.

Erratic Or No Intermittent Cycle – Check for faulty intermittent wiper relay. Check for open circuit in Green, Green/Black, Blue/White or Green/Red wire. Check for loose or disconnected terminals. Check for open in Green, Green/Black, Green/Red and/or Blue/White wires.

Little Or No Washer Fluid Is Pumped – Insufficient washer fluid in reservoir. Disconnected or blocked washer fluid hose. Clogged washer fluid nozzle. Faulty washer motor. Faulty washer switch. Poor ground. Check Black/Yellow wire (Green/Black wire for rear washer) for open circuit. Check for loose or disconnected terminals.

Wipers Do Not Operate Simultaneously With Washer – Faulty wiper/washer control unit. Check Black/Yellow wire for open circuit. Check for loose or disconnected terminals.

Rear Wiper Does Not Operate – Blown fuse No. 5 (10-Amp) in dash fuse block. Faulty wiper motor assembly. Faulty wiper switch. Check for open circuit in Yellow/Green and Green wires. Check for loose or disconnected terminals or poor ground connections.

CIVIC & CIVIC DEL SOL

Wipers Do Not Operate In Any Position – Blown fuse No. 14 (20-amp) in dash fuse block. Faulty wiper motor assembly. Disconnected wiper linkage. Faulty wiper switch. Poor ground. Inspect Green/Black wire for open circuit. Check for loose or disconnected terminals.

Wipers Do Not Operate In INT (Intermittent) Position – Faulty wiper switch. Faulty wiper motor assembly. Faulty intermittent wiper relay circuit (in integrated control unit). Inspect Blue/Green, Blue/White and/or Yellow/Blue wires for open circuit. Check for loose or disconnected terminals.

Wipers Do Not Operate In LO Or HI Position – Faulty wiper switch.

Wipers Do Not Operate In MIST Position – Faulty mist switch.

Rear Window Wiper Does Not Operate (Civic) – Blown fuse No. 14 (20-amp) in dash fuse block. Faulty wiper motor assembly. Faulty wiper switch. Poor ground. Inspect Green/Black and/or Green wires for open circuit. Check for loose or disconnected terminals.

Wipers Do Not Return To Park Position With Switch Turned Off – Faulty wiper motor assembly. Faulty wiper switch. Check for open circuit in Blue/White and/or Light Green/Black wire. Poor ground. Check for loose or disconnected terminals.

Erratic Or No Intermittent Cycle – Faulty wiper switch. Faulty intermittent wiper relay circuit (in integrated control unit). Inspect Blue/Green, Blue/White, Green/Black (Civic Del Sol) or Yellow/Blue wire(s) for open circuit. Check for loose or disconnected terminals.

Little Or No Washer Fluid Is Pumped – Insufficient washer fluid in reservoir. Disconnected or blocked washer fluid hose. Clogged washer fluid nozzle. Faulty washer motor. Faulty washer switch. Poor ground. Inspect Black/Green and/or Green/Yellow wire for open circuit. Check for loose or disconnected terminals.

PRELUDE

Wipers Do Not Operate In Any Position – Blown fuse No. 17 (30-amp) in dash fuse block. Disconnected wiper linkage. Faulty wiper motor assembly. Faulty wiper switch. Poor ground. Inspect Green/Black wire for open circuit. Check for loose or disconnected terminals.

Wipers Do Not Operate In INT (Intermittent) Position – Faulty wiper switch. Faulty wiper motor assembly. Faulty intermittent wiper relay circuit. Inspect Green and Blue/White wires for open circuit. Check for loose or disconnected terminals.

Wipers Do Not Operate In LO Or HI Position – Faulty wiper switch. Faulty wiper motor assembly. Inspect Blue and Blue/Yellow wires for open circuit. Check for loose or disconnected terminals

Wipers Do Not Operate In MIST Position – Faulty mist switch.

Wipers Do Not Return To Park Position With Switch Turned Off – Faulty wiper motor assembly. Faulty wiper switch. Inspect Blue/White wire for open circuit. Check for loose or disconnected terminals.

Erratic Or No Intermittent Cycle – Faulty wiper switch. Faulty intermittent wiper relay circuit.

Little Or No Washer Fluid Is Pumped – Insufficient washer fluid in reservoir. Disconnected or blocked washer fluid hose. Clogged washer fluid nozzle. Faulty washer motor. Faulty washer switch. Poor ground. Inspect Black/Yellow wire for open circuit. Check for loose or disconnected terminals.

Wipers And Washer Do Not Work At Same Time – Faulty integrated control unit. Inspect Black/Yellow wire for open circuit. Check for loose or disconnected terminals.

TESTING

FRONT WIPER MOTOR TEST

1) Disconnect front wiper motor 5-pin connector. Using jumper wires, connect positive battery terminal to Green/Black wire terminal and negative battery terminal to Blue wire terminal at wiper motor connector. Ensure wiper motor operates on low speed.

2) Using jumper wires, connect positive battery terminal to Green/Black wire terminal and negative battery terminal to Blue/Yellow wire terminal at wiper motor connector. Wiper motor should operate on high speed. Replace front wiper motor if it fails to operate.

REAR WIPER MOTOR TEST

1) Remove tailgate lower trim panel. Disconnect rear wiper motor 4-pin connector. Connect positive battery terminal to terminal No. 1 (Yellow/Green wire) and negative battery terminal to terminal No. 2 (Green wire). *See Fig. 1 or 2.* Wiper motor should operate smoothly. Replace rear wiper motor if it fails to operate.

2) Reconnect 4-pin connector. Turn rear wiper switch on. While motor is running, check voltage between terminal No. 3 (Light Green/Black wire) and terminal No. 4 (Black wire). Voltage should alternate from zero volts to more than 4 volts. If voltage is not as specified, replace rear wiper motor.

WASHER MOTOR TEST

Remove front bumper. Disconnect washer motor 2-pin connector. Connect battery voltage across washer motor terminals. Washer motor should operate smoothly. If motor runs smoothly but little or no washer fluid is pumped, check for disconnected or blocked washer fluid hose or a clogged pump outlet in motor.

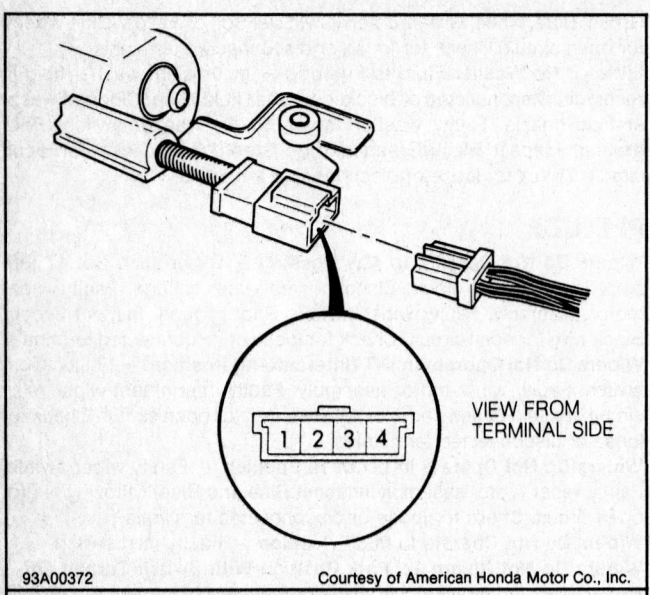

93A00372   Courtesy of American Honda Motor Co., Inc.

Fig. 1: Testing Rear Wiper (Accord)

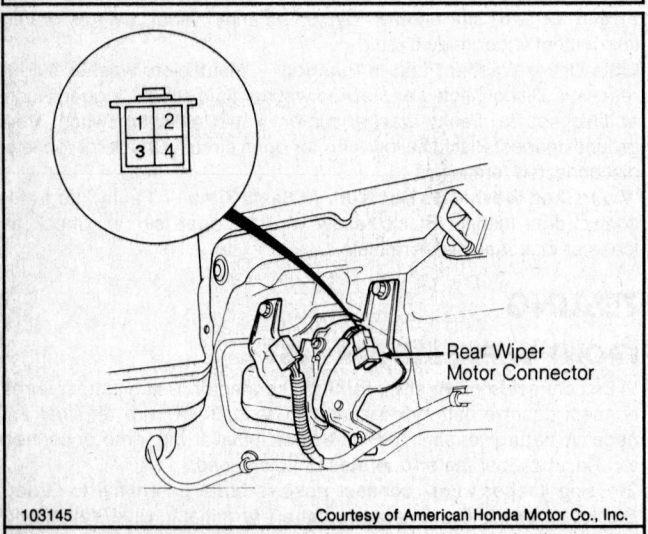

103145   Courtesy of American Honda Motor Co., Inc.

Fig. 2: Testing Rear Wiper (Civic)

WIPER/WASHER SWITCH TEST

Accord – Remove instrument cluster lower trim panel and knee bolster. Disconnect wiper/washer switch 7-pin connector. Check continuity between specified switch connector terminals with wiper/washer switch in indicated positions. *See Fig. 3.* If continuity is not as specified, replace wiper/washer switch.

Civic – Remove steering column covers. Disconnect 6-pin and 8-pin connectors from wiper/washer switch. Check continuity between specified terminals with switch in indicated positions. *See Fig. 4.* If continuity is not as specified, replace wiper/washer switch.

Civic Del Sol – Remove steering column cover. Disconnect 8-pin connector from wiper/washer switch. Check continuity between specified terminals with switch in indicated positions. *See Fig. 5.* If continuity is not as specified, replace wiper/washer switch.

Prelude – Remove instrument cluster lower trim panel. Disconnect steering column 10-pin connector. Check continuity between specified switch connector terminals with wiper/washer switch in indicated positions. *See Fig. 6.* If continuity is not as specified, replace wiper/washer switch.

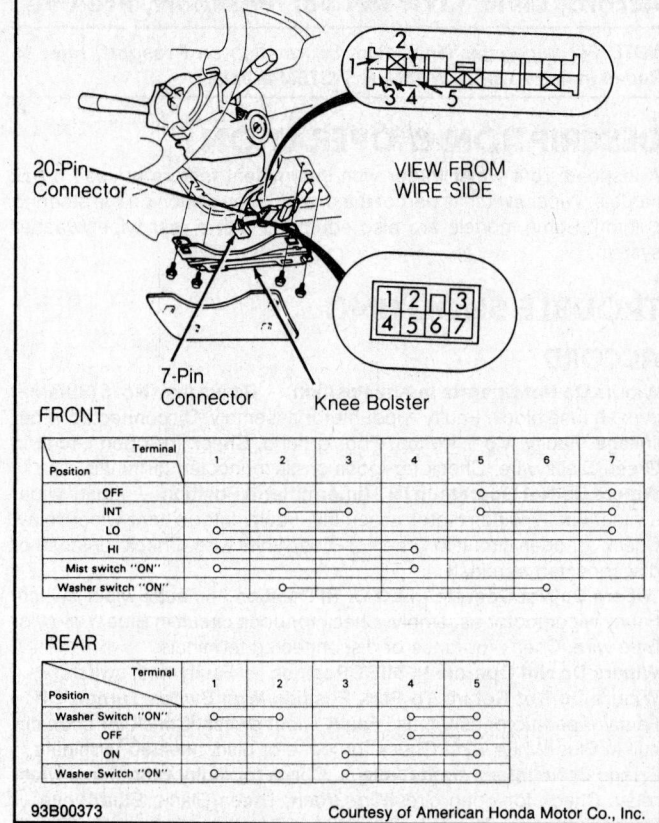

FRONT

Position \ Terminal	1	2	3	4	5	6	7
OFF					O		O
INT		O	O				O
LO	O						O
HI	O			O			
Mist switch "ON"	O			O			
Washer switch "ON"		O				O	

REAR

Position \ Terminal	1	2	3	4	5
Washer Switch "ON"		O		O	
OFF				O	O
ON			O	O	
Washer Switch "ON"	O		O		

93B00373   Courtesy of American Honda Motor Co., Inc.

Fig. 3: Testing Wiper/Washer Switch (Accord)

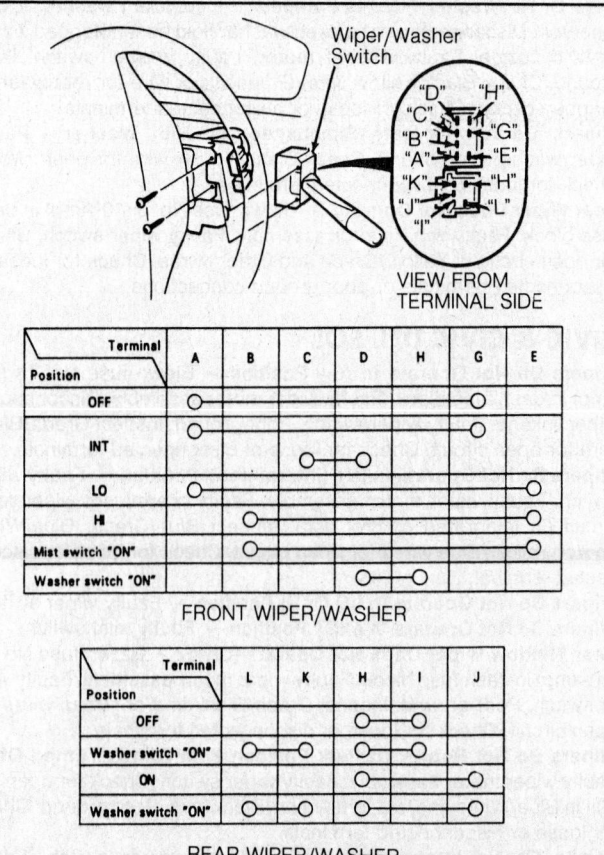

Position \ Terminal	A	B	C	D	H	G	E
OFF	O					O	
INT	O		O	O		O	
LO	O						O
HI		O					O
Mist switch "ON"		O					O
Washer switch "ON"				O		O	

FRONT WIPER/WASHER

Position \ Terminal	L	K	H	I	J
OFF			O	O	
Washer switch "ON"	O	O	O	O	
ON			O		O
Washer switch "ON"	O	O	O		O

REAR WIPER/WASHER

93G82244   Courtesy of American Honda Motor Co., Inc.

Fig. 4: Testing Wiper/Washer Switch (Civic)

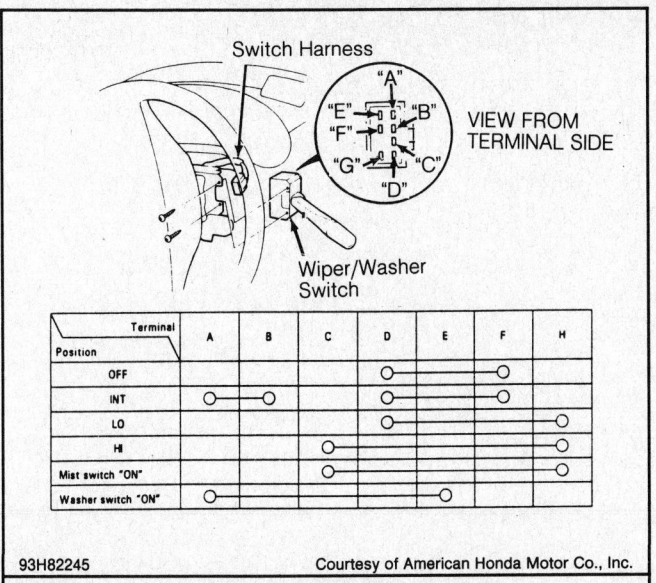

Terminal / Position	A	B	C	D	E	F	H
OFF				O		O	
INT	O	O	O	O		O	
LO				O		O	
HI			O			O	
Mist switch "ON"			O			O	
Washer switch "ON"	O	O			O		

93H82245   Courtesy of American Honda Motor Co., Inc.

Fig. 5: Testing Wiper/Washer Switch (Civic Del Sol)

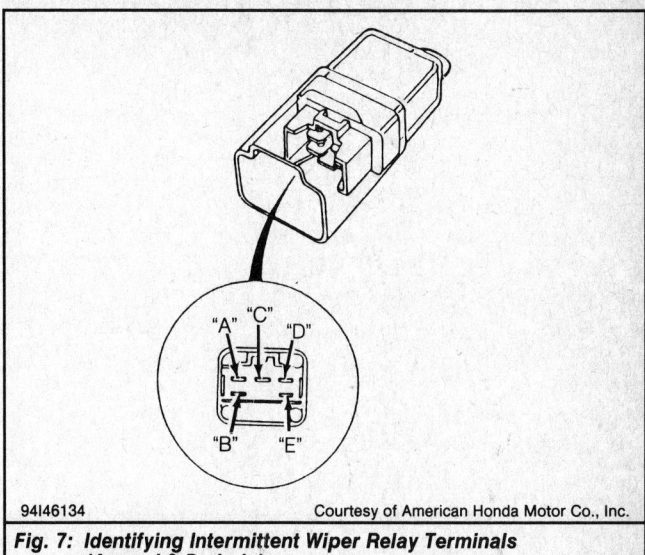

94I46134   Courtesy of American Honda Motor Co., Inc.

Fig. 7: Identifying Intermittent Wiper Relay Terminals (Accord & Prelude)

Terminal / Position	14	15	16	17	21	22	24
OFF					O		O
INT			O	O	O		
LO	O			O			
HI	O					O	
Mist switch 'ON'	O					O	
Washer switch 'ON'			O	O			

93D00375   Courtesy of American Honda Motor Co., Inc.

Fig. 6: Testing Wiper/Washer Switch (Prelude)

INTERMITTENT WIPER RELAY TEST

Accord & Prelude – Remove intermittent wiper relay. Relay is located on right rear corner of engine compartment, next to fuse/relay block. With battery voltage applied across terminals "D" and "E", continuity should exist between terminals "A" and "C". See Fig. 7. With battery disconnected, continuity should exist between terminals "B" and "C". If continuity does not exist as indicated, replace relay.

REMOVAL & INSTALLATION

FRONT WIPER MOTOR

Removal & Installation – **1)** Open hood. Remove cap nuts from wiper arms. Carefully remove wiper arms. Remove hood seal and air scoop by prying off trim clips and removing screws.
2) Disconnect wiper motor 5-pin connector. Remove 3 bolts, nut and wiper linkage assembly. Remove wiper motor assembly. To install, reverse removal procedure.

REAR WIPER MOTOR

Removal & Installation – Outside vehicle, remove wiper arm cover, nut, wiper arm, seal retainer nut and washer, and outer seal rubber from wiper motor shaft. Inside vehicle, remove hatch or tailgate trim panel. Disconnect rear wiper motor 4-pin connector. Remove 3 bolts and rear wiper motor. To install, reverse removal procedure.

WIPER/WASHER SWITCH

CAUTION: Air bag system MUST be disabled BEFORE removing any steering column component. See DISABLING & ACTIVATING AIR BAG SYSTEM in STEERING COLUMN SWITCHES article.

Removal & Installation (Accord & Prelude) – Disable air bag system. Disconnect negative battery cable. Remove dash lower trim cover and knee bolster. Remove steering column covers. Disconnect wiper/washer switch 8-pin connector. Remove 2 screws and wiper/washer switch. To install, reverse removal procedure.
Removal & Installation (Civic & Civic Del Sol) – Disable air bag system. Remove dash lower trim cover. Remove steering column covers. On Civic, disconnect wiper/washer switch 6-pin and 8-pin connectors. On Civic Del Sol, disconnect wiper/washer switch 8-pin connector. Remove 2 screws and slide wiper/washer switch out of housing. To install, reverse removal procedure.

WASHER FLUID RESERVOIR & NOZZLE

Removal & Installation – On Accord, remove inner fender. On Civic and Civic Del Sol, remove front bumper. On Prelude, remove reservoir filler neck and inner fender. On all models, remove 3 bolts and washer fluid reservoir. Disconnect hose and 2-pin connector from washer motor. Remove deflector, washer nozzles and washer fluid hoses as necessary. To install, reverse removal procedure.

WIRING DIAGRAMS

NOTE: See ACCESSORIES & EQUIPMENT, Volume 5.

NOTE: For engine information on Passport, refer to Rodeo in appropriate Isuzu ENGINES article.

NOTE: For repair procedures not covered in this article, see ENGINE OVERHAUL PROCEDURES article in GENERAL INFORMATION.

ENGINE IDENTIFICATION

Engine serial number is located on exhaust side of engine block, below cylinder head near bellhousing. The first 5 characters of engine serial number identify engine type.

ENGINE IDENTIFICATION CODES

Application	Code
1.5L 16-Valve	D15B7
1.5L (8-Valve)	D15B8
1.5L (16-Valve VTEC-E)	D15Z1
1.6L	
DOHC (16-Valve VTEC)	B16A3
SOHC (16-Valve VTEC)	D16Z6

ADJUSTMENTS

VALVE CLEARANCE ADJUSTMENT

CAUTION: Always rotate engine in direction of normal rotation (counterclockwise as viewed from front of engine). Reverse rotation may cause timing belt to jump time.

1.5L & 1.6L SOHC – 1) Adjust valves with engine temperature at 100°F (38°C) or less. Remove valve cover. Rotate crankshaft counterclockwise until No. 1 piston is at TDC of compression stroke.

UP mark on camshaft sprocket should face up. See Fig. 1. Ensure crankshaft pulley timing mark aligns with pointer on lower timing belt cover.

2) Adjust valve clearance to specification on both valves for No. 1 cylinder. See VALVE CLEARANCE SPECIFICATIONS table. Rotate crankshaft counterclockwise 180 degrees (camshaft sprocket rotates 90 degrees). UP mark on camshaft sprocket should be on exhaust side. Adjust valve clearance on both valves for No. 3 cylinder.

3) Rotate crankshaft counterclockwise 180 degrees (camshaft sprocket rotates 90 degrees). UP mark on camshaft sprocket should be down. Adjust valve clearance on both valves for No. 4 cylinder.

4) Rotate crankshaft counterclockwise 180 degrees (camshaft sprocket rotates 90 degrees). UP mark on camshaft sprocket should be on intake side. Adjust valve clearance on both valves for No. 2 cylinder.

5) Tighten crankshaft pulley bolt if it loosened during valve adjustment procedure. See TORQUE SPECIFICATIONS. Apply nonhardening sealant to rounded surfaces of front and rear camshaft caps before installing valve cover gasket. Install valve cover. Tighten nuts to specification.

1.6L DOHC – 1) Adjust valves with engine temperature at 100°F (38°C) or less. Remove valve cover. Rotate crankshaft counterclockwise until No. 1 piston is at TDC of compression stroke.

2) Ensure UP marks on camshaft sprockets are at top, and TDC grooves on sprockets are aligned with cylinder head surface. See Fig. 2. Adjust clearance on valves for No. 1 cylinder. Loosen lock nut. Turn adjuster screw until clearance is as specified. See VALVE CLEARANCE SPECIFICATIONS table.

3) Rotate crankshaft 180 degrees counterclockwise (camshaft sprockets turn 90 degrees) until No. 3 piston is at TDC of compression stroke. The UP marks will be on exhaust side. Adjust clearance on valves for No. 3 cylinder.

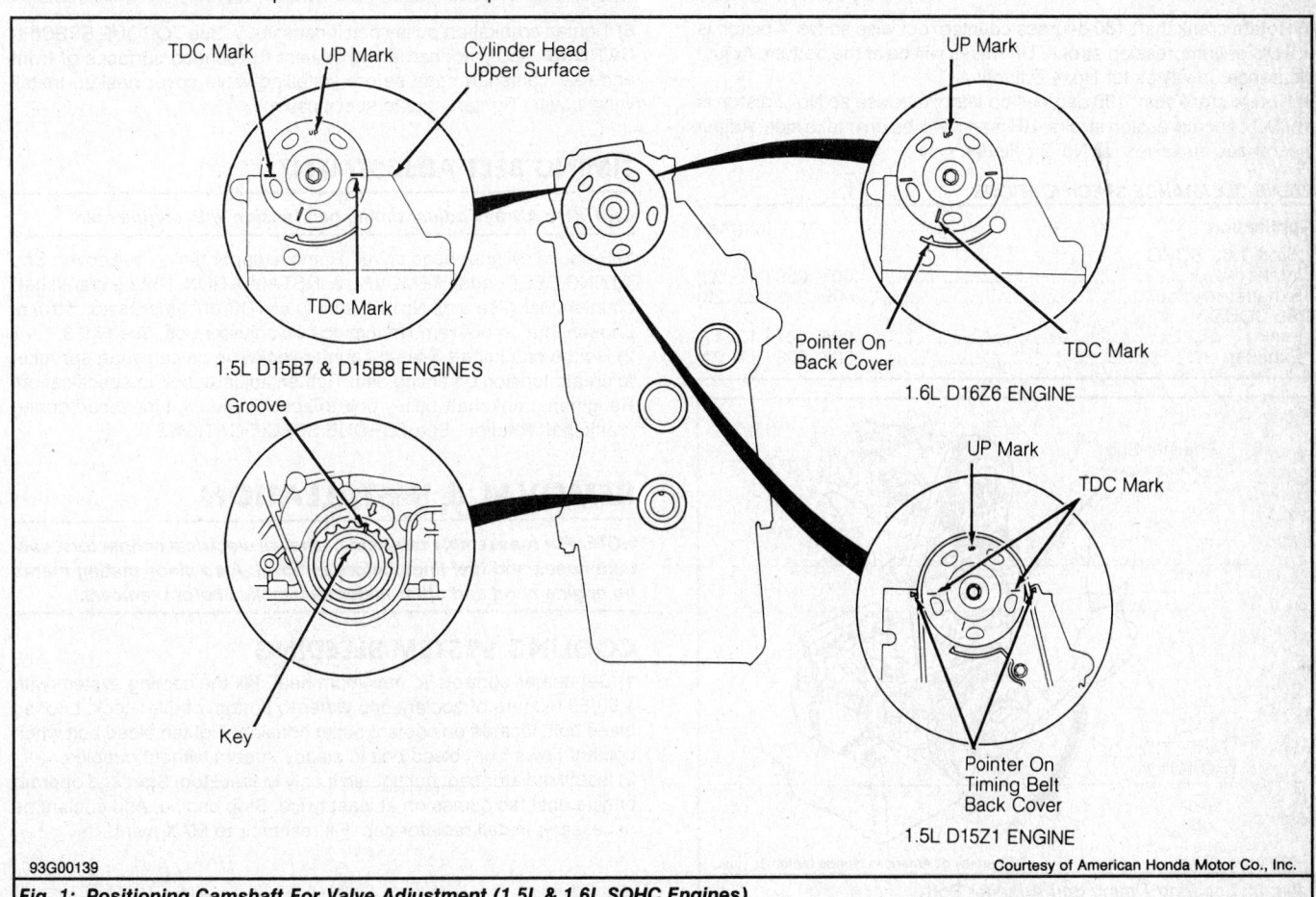

93G00139

Courtesy of American Honda Motor Co., Inc.

Fig. 1: Positioning Camshaft For Valve Adjustment (1.5L & 1.6L SOHC Engines)

HONDA
5-2

1994 ENGINES
1.5L & 1.6L 4-Cylinder – Civic & Civic Del Sol (Cont.)

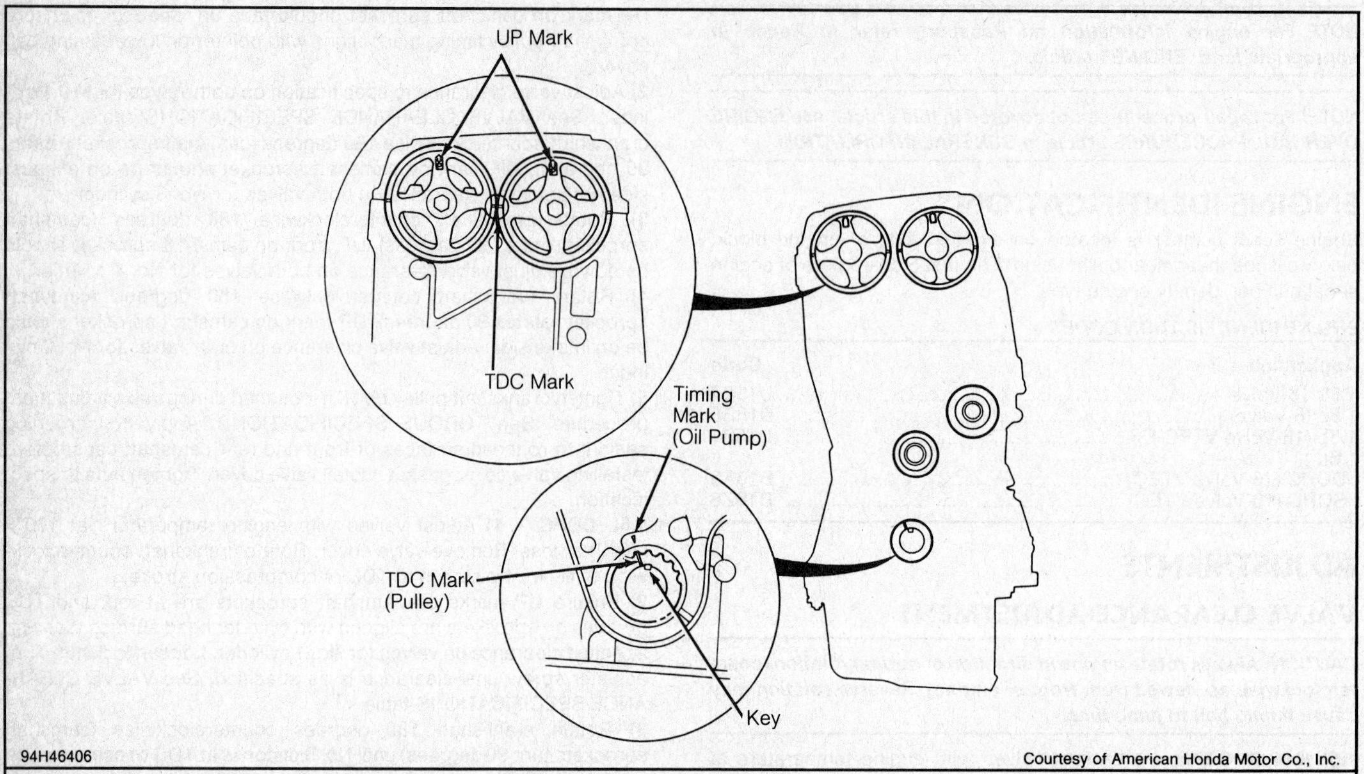

UP Mark

TDC Mark

Timing Mark (Oil Pump)

TDC Mark (Pulley)

Key

94H46406   Courtesy of American Honda Motor Co., Inc.

Fig. 2: Positioning Camshaft Sprockets For Valve Clearance Adjustment (1.6L DOHC)

4) Rotate crankshaft 180 degrees counterclockwise so No. 4 piston is at TDC of compression stroke. UP marks will be at the bottom. Adjust clearance on valves for No. 4 cylinder.
5) Rotate crankshaft 180 degrees counterclockwise so No. 2 piston is at TDC of compression stroke. UP marks will be on intake side. Adjust clearances on valves for No. 2 cylinder.

VALVE CLEARANCE SPECIFICATIONS

Application	In. (mm)
1.5L & 1.6L SOHC	
Intake	.007-.009 (.17-.22)
Exhaust	.009-.011 (.23-.28)
1.6L DOHC	
Intake	.006-.007 (.13-.17)
Exhaust	.007-.008 (.17-.21)

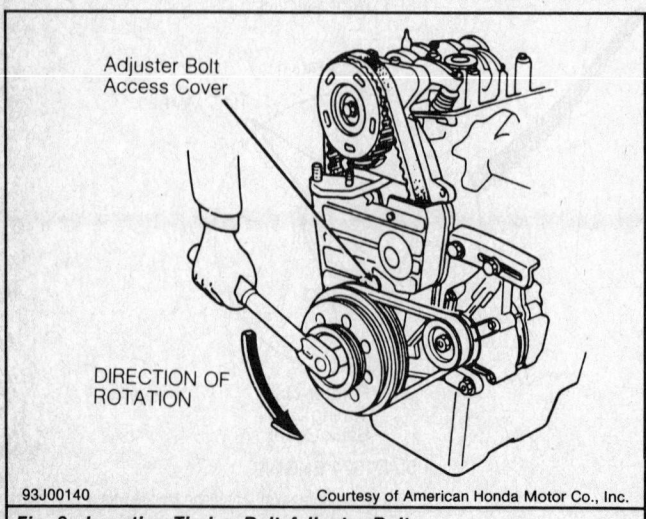

Adjuster Bolt Access Cover

DIRECTION OF ROTATION

93J00140   Courtesy of American Honda Motor Co., Inc.

**Fig. 3: Locating Timing Belt Adjuster Bolt
SOHC Is shown; DOHC Is Similar**

6) Tighten crankshaft pulley bolt if necessary. See TORQUE SPECIFICATIONS. Apply nonhardening sealant to rounded surfaces of front and rear camshaft caps before installing valve cover gasket. Install valve cover. Tighten nuts to specification.

TIMING BELT ADJUSTMENT

CAUTION: Always adjust timing belt tension with engine cold.

1) Remove cylinder head cover. Remove upper timing belt cover. See TIMING BELT under REMOVAL & INSTALLATION. Rotate crankshaft counterclockwise until No. 1 piston is at TDC of compression stroke. Loosen, but do not remove, timing belt adjuster bolt. *See Fig. 3.*
2) Rotate crankshaft 3 teeth counterclockwise on camshaft sprocket to create tension on timing belt. Tighten adjuster bolt to specification. Retighten crankshaft pulley bolt to specification if it loosened during crankshaft rotation. See TORQUE SPECIFICATIONS.

REMOVAL & INSTALLATION

NOTE: For reassembly reference, label all electrical connectors, vacuum hoses and fuel lines before removal. Also place mating marks on engine hood and other major assemblies before removal.

COOLING SYSTEM BLEEDING

1) Set heater controls to maximum heat. Fill the cooling system with a 50/50 mixture of coolant and water to bottom of filler neck. Loosen bleed bolt, located on coolant outlet housing. Tighten bleed bolt when coolant flows from bleed bolt in steady stream without bubbles.
2) Install radiator cap, but tighten it only to first stop. Start and operate engine until fan comes on at least twice. Stop engine. Add coolant as necessary. Install radiator cap. Fill reservoir to MAX mark.

1994 ENGINES
1.5L & 1.6L 4-Cylinder – Civic & Civic Del Sol (Cont.)

HONDA
5-3

FUEL PRESSURE RELEASE

CAUTION: Fuel system is under pressure. Release pressure before servicing fuel system components.

Remove fuel tank filler cap. Place a shop towel on top of fuel filter. Release fuel injection system pressure by slowly loosening fuel injection service bolt. *See Fig. 4.*

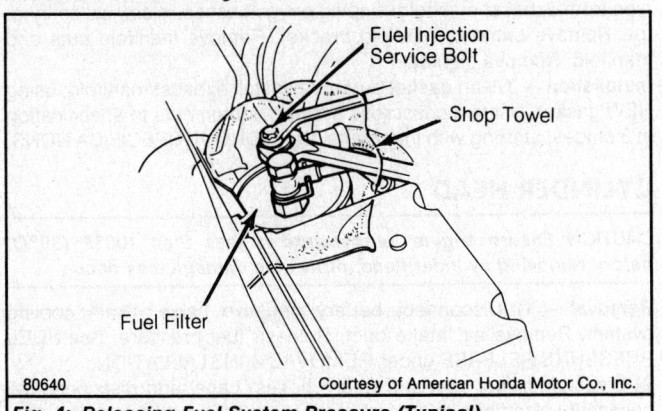

Fuel Injection Service Bolt

Shop Towel

Fuel Filter

80640   Courtesy of American Honda Motor Co., Inc.

Fig. 4: Releasing Fuel System Pressure (Typical)

ENGINE

Removal – 1) Disconnect battery cables. Remove radiator cap. Raise and support vehicle. Drain engine oil, transaxle fluid, and coolant. Remove front wheels and engine splash shield. Lower vehicle. Remove air cleaner housing, resonator, and air intake duct.

2) Secure hood as far open as possible. On models with B16A3 engine, remove the strut brace. On all models, remove ABS fuse/relay box. Release fuel pressure. See FUEL PRESSURE RELEASE. Disconnect fuel inlet hose. Disconnect throttle cable and clutch cable (if equipped). Label and disconnect all necessary electrical wires, vacuum lines, and control cables.

3) Unplug wiring harness at left side of engine compartment. Disconnect fuel return and brake booster hoses. Disconnect wire harnesses and clamps on right side of engine compartment. Disconnect battery/starter cable from fuse/relay box. Disconnect ABS cable from battery terminal.

4) Disconnect ground cable from cylinder head. Remove power steering pump, leaving hoses attached. Set power steering pump aside. Disconnect transmission fluid cooler lines (if equipped). Disconnect transmission ground cable. Remove radiator and heater hoses.

5) Remove A/C compressor (if equipped), leaving hoses connected. Set compressor aside. Disconnect exhaust pipe and brace. On A/T models, disconnect shift cable. On M/T models, remove clutch slave cylinder, leaving hose connected. On M/T models, disconnect shift rod and extension rod.

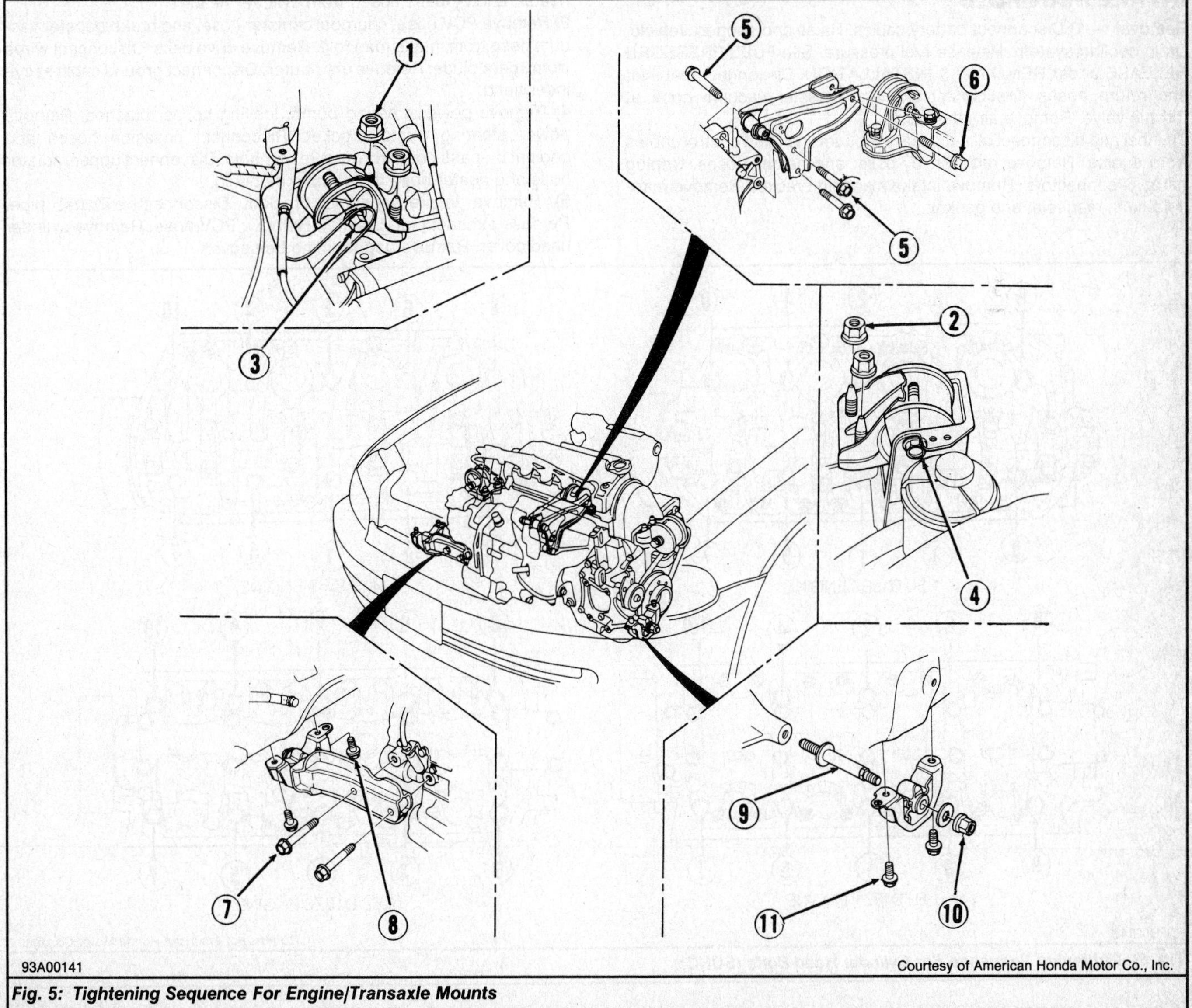

93A00141   Courtesy of American Honda Motor Co., Inc.

Fig. 5: Tightening Sequence For Engine/Transaxle Mounts

HONDA
5-4

1994 ENGINES
1.5L & 1.6L 4-Cylinder – Civic & Civic Del Sol (Cont.)

6) On all models, remove drive axles. See FWD AXLE SHAFTS article in DRIVE AXLES. Attach engine hoist to engine lift hooks. Remove left and right front stopper cushions and brackets. Remove rear engine mount bracket.

7) Remove engine support nuts. Loosen side engine mount bolt, and pivot side engine mount aside. Remove transaxle mount nuts. Loosen transaxle side mount bolt, and pivot side mount aside.

8) Remove all slack from hoist chain. Ensure engine/transaxle assembly is free of all attachments. Lift engine and transaxle from vehicle.

Installation – 1) To install, reverse removal procedure. Tighten engine/transaxle mounts to specification in proper sequence. *See Fig. 5.* Improper tightening of engine mounts will result in engine vibration and premature mount wear.

2) Use NEW spring clips when installing drive axles. Install drive axles until spring clip clicks into groove of differential side gear. Ensure all wires and hoses are connected properly. Ensure cables are mounted properly.

3) Adjust throttle cable tension. On M/T models, adjust clutch pedal free play. See CLUTCH PEDAL under ADJUSTMENTS in FWD article in CLUTCHES. Verify transaxle shifts smoothly. On A/T models, ensure range indicator agrees with actual transaxle range.

4) Adjust drive belt tension. Fill fluids to proper level. Start engine. Open heater valve. Bleed cooling system. See COOLING SYSTEM BLEEDING.

INTAKE MANIFOLD

Removal – 1) Disconnect battery cables. Raise and support vehicle. Drain cooling system. Release fuel pressure. See FUEL PRESSURE RELEASE under REMOVAL & INSTALLATION. Disconnect fuel inlet and return hoses. Disconnect charcoal canister vacuum hose at throttle valve. Remove air intake duct.

2) Label and disconnect all necessary vacuum lines and control cables from engine. Remove radiator, by-pass, and heater hoses. Unplug harness connectors. Remove intake manifold bracket. Remove manifold nuts, manifold, and gasket.

Installation – Clean gasket surfaces. Install intake manifold, using NEW gasket. Using a crisscross pattern, tighten nuts to specification in 3 stages, starting with inner nuts. See TORQUE SPECIFICATIONS. To complete installation, reverse removal procedure.

EXHAUST MANIFOLD

Removal – Remove exhaust manifold shroud. Disconnect exhaust pipe from exhaust manifold. Unplug oxygen sensor electrical connector. Remove exhaust manifold bracket. Remove manifold nuts and manifold. Remove gasket.

Installation – Clean gasket surfaces. Install exhaust manifold, using NEW gasket. Using a crisscross pattern, tighten nuts to specification in 3 stages, starting with inner nuts. See TORQUE SPECIFICATIONS.

CYLINDER HEAD

CAUTION: Ensure engine temperature is less than 100°F (38°C) before removing cylinder head, otherwise damage may occur.

Removal – 1) Disconnect battery negative cable. Drain cooling system. Remove air intake duct. Release fuel pressure. See FUEL PRESSURE RELEASE under REMOVAL & INSTALLATION.

2) Disconnect fuel inlet and return hoses. Label and disconnect all necessary electrical wiring and vacuum lines from cylinder head. Disconnect throttle cable from throttle body. Disconnect upper radiator, heater, and by-pass hoses from cylinder head.

3) Remove PCV hose, charcoal canister hose, and brake booster vacuum hose from intake manifold. Remove drive belts. Disconnect wires from spark plugs. Remove distributor. Disconnect ground cable at cylinder head.

4) Remove power steering pump, leaving hoses attached. Remove power steering pump bracket. Disconnect emission hoses and coolant by-pass hose from intake manifold. Disconnect upper radiator hose and heater hose from intake manifold.

5) Remove intake manifold bracket. Disconnect exhaust pipe. Remove exhaust pipe bracket. Remove PCV hose. Remove cylinder head cover. Remove upper timing belt cover.

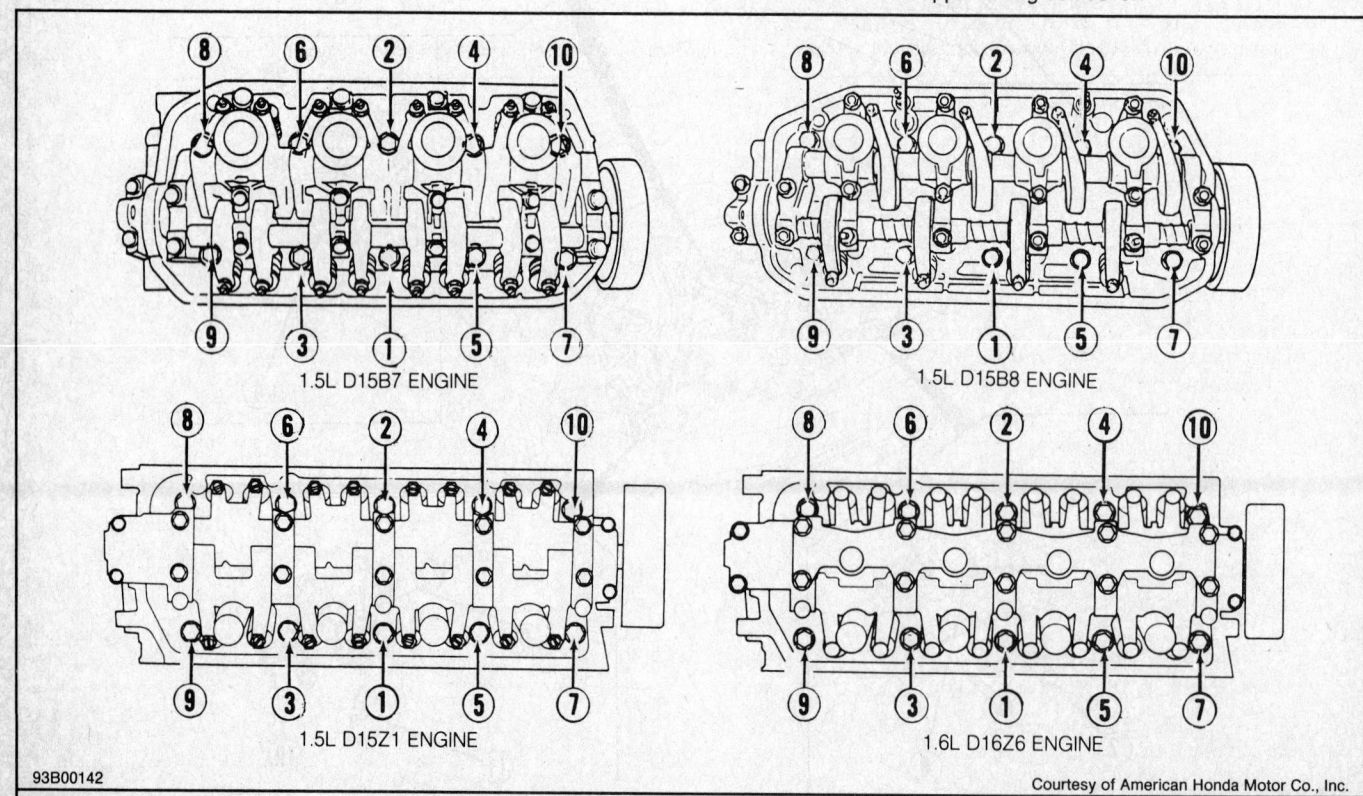

1.5L D15B7 ENGINE

1.5L D15B8 ENGINE

1.5L D15Z1 ENGINE

1.6L D16Z6 ENGINE

93B00142

Courtesy of American Honda Motor Co., Inc.

Fig. 6: Tightening Sequence For Cylinder Head Bolts (SOHC)

1.5L & 1.6L 4-Cylinder — Civic & Civic Del Sol (Cont.)

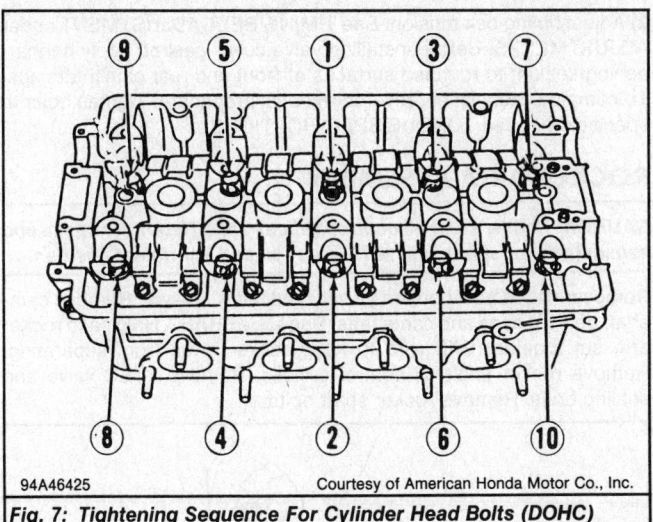

94A46425   Courtesy of American Honda Motor Co., Inc.

Fig. 7: Tightening Sequence For Cylinder Head Bolts (DOHC)

6) Loosen timing belt tension adjuster bolt. Push tensioner to release belt tension. Tighten adjuster bolt, and disengage timing belt from camshaft sprocket. Remove cylinder head bolts, 1/3 turn at a time, in reverse order of tightening sequence. See Fig. 6 or 7. Remove cylinder head and gasket. Separate intake and exhaust manifolds from cylinder head.

Inspection – Ensure all mating surfaces are clean. Measure cylinder head for warpage. Resurfacing is not required if warpage is less than .002" (.05 mm). Resurface cylinder head if warpage is .002-.008" (.05-.20 mm). Maximum resurface limit is .008" (.20 mm).

Installation – **1)** Ensure mating surfaces are clean. Install intake and exhaust manifolds, using NEW gaskets. Using a crisscross pattern, tighten nuts to specification in 3 stages, starting with inner nuts.

2) Ensure cylinder head dowel pins are installed in cylinder block. Ensure No. 1 piston is at TDC of compression stroke. Position camshaft sprocket with UP mark facing up. See Fig. 1 or 2.

3) Install NEW cylinder head gasket and cylinder head. Install and tighten cylinder head bolts to specification, in 2 stages. See Fig. 6 or 7. See TORQUE SPECIFICATIONS. Ensure cylinder head dowel pins are installed in block. See Fig. 8.

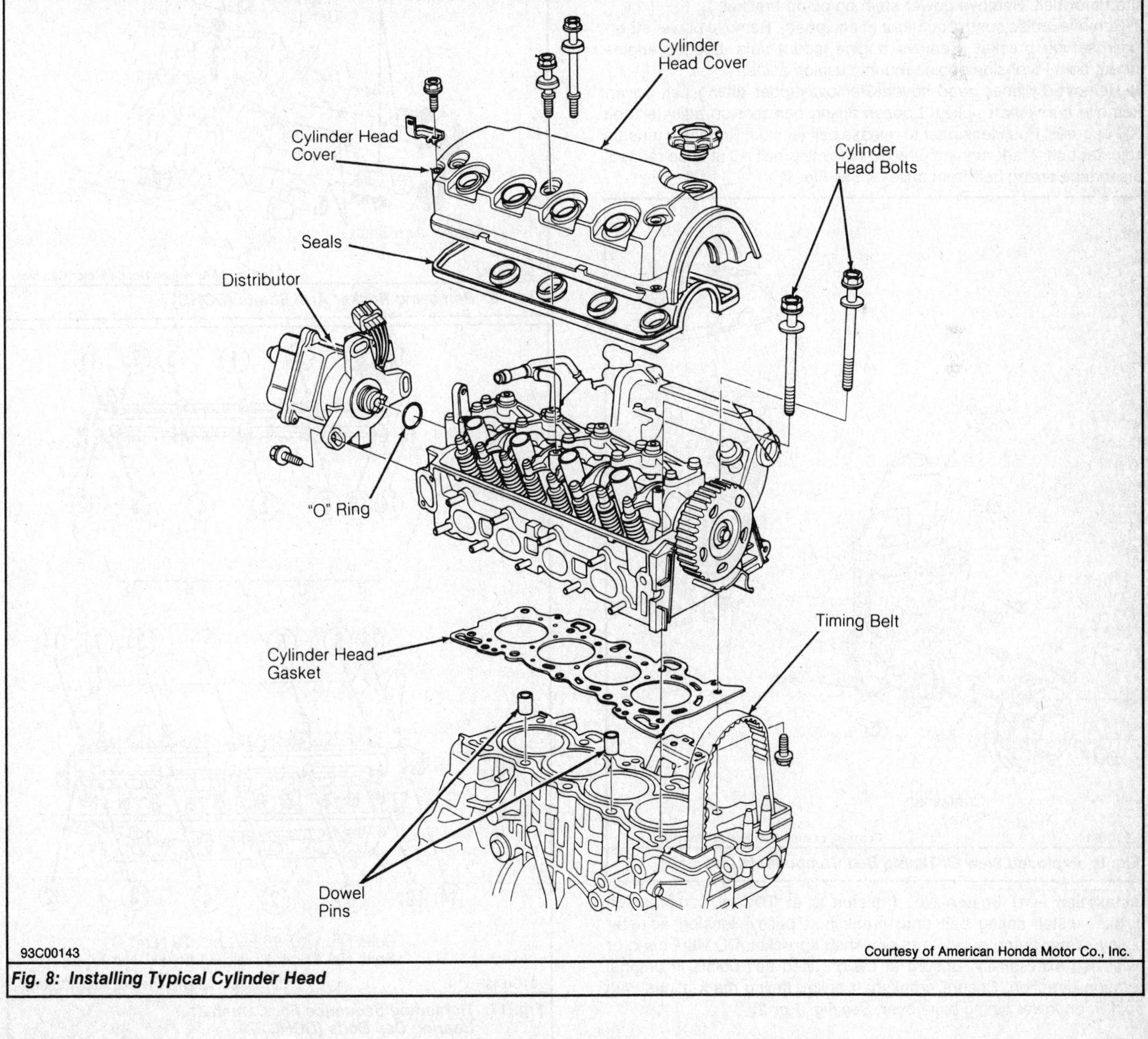

Cylinder
Head Cover

Cylinder Head
Cover

Cylinder
Head Bolts

Seals

Distributor

"O" Ring

Timing Belt

Cylinder Head
Gasket

Dowel
Pins

93C00143   Courtesy of American Honda Motor Co., Inc.

Fig. 8: Installing Typical Cylinder Head

HONDA
5-6

1994 ENGINES
1.5L & 1.6L 4-Cylinder – Civic & Civic Del Sol (Cont.)

4) Install and adjust timing belt. See TIMING BELT ADJUSTMENT under ADJUSTMENTS. To complete installation, reverse removal procedure. Check valve clearance, and adjust if necessary. See VALVE CLEARANCE ADJUSTMENT under ADJUSTMENTS.

FRONT CRANKSHAFT SEAL

Removal – Disconnect battery negative cable. Raise and support vehicle. Remove left front wheel. Remove wheelwell splash shield. Remove all drive belts. Remove power steering pump with hoses attached, and set aside. Remove timing belt. See TIMING BELT. Remove crankshaft pulley. Remove front crankshaft oil seal.

Installation – Apply light coating of grease to crankshaft and lip of new seal. Tap new seal into place, seal using Seal Driver (07947-SB00200). Ensure seal is fully seated. To complete installation, reverse removal procedure.

TIMING BELT

Removal – **1)** Disconnect battery negative cable. Rotate crankshaft counterclockwise until No. 1 piston is at TDC of compression stroke. Remove splash shield. Remove power steering pump, leaving hoses attached. Remove A/C belt idler pulley, bracket, and belt. Remove alternator belt. Remove power steering pump bracket.

2) Remove cruise control actuator (if equipped). Remove power steering reservoir bracket. Remove engine mount nuts. Loosen engine mount bolt. Pivot side engine mount cushion aside.

3) Remove cylinder head cover. Remove upper timing belt cover. Remove crankshaft pulley. Loosen timing belt tension adjuster bolt 180 degrees. Push tensioner to release belt tension. Retighten tension adjuster bolt. Mark running direction of timing belt if it is to be reused. Disengage timing belt from pulleys. *See Fig. 9.*

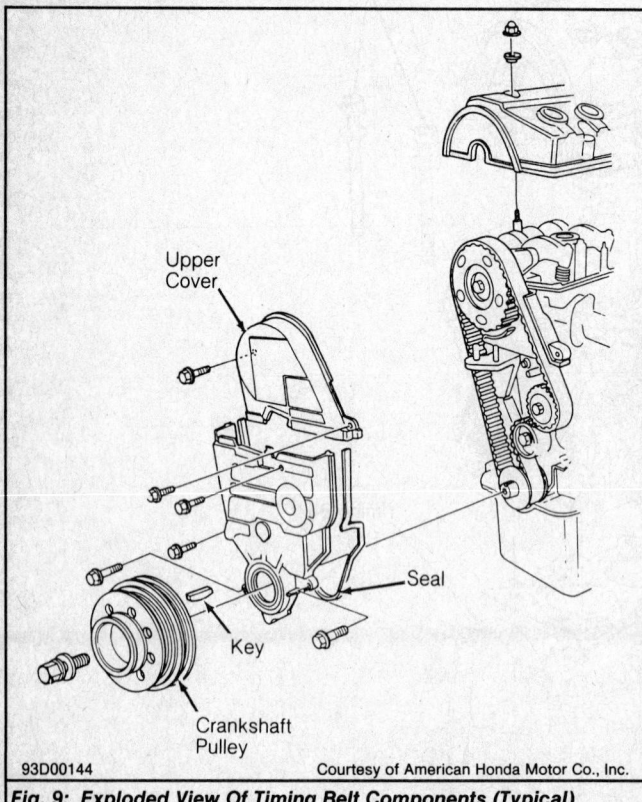

93D00144   Courtesy of American Honda Motor Co., Inc.
Fig. 9: Exploded View Of Timing Belt Components (Typical)

Installation – 1) Ensure No. 1 piston is at TDC of compression stroke. Install timing belt onto crankshaft pulley, tension adjuster pulley, water pump pulley, and camshaft sprocket. DO NOT bend or twist belt excessively. Ensure arrow on used belt points in original rotation direction. Ensure crankshaft pulley timing mark aligns with pointer on lower timing belt cover. *See Fig. 1 or 2.*

2) Adjust timing belt tension. See TIMING BELT ADJUSTMENT under ADJUSTMENTS. Before installing valve cover gasket, apply nonhardening sealant to rounded surfaces of front and rear camshaft caps. To complete installation, reverse removal procedure. Tighten bolts to specification. See TORQUE SPECIFICATIONS.

ROCKER ARM ASSEMBLY

CAUTION: Rocker shaft oil control orifices are different for intake and exhaust rocker shafts and MUST be replaced in original position.

Removal (DOHC) – Loosen all valve adjuster screws. Remove camshaft bearing caps and camshafts. See CAMSHAFT. Hold each rocker arm set together with wire to keep rocker arms from separating. Remove rocker shaft oil control orifices. Remove VTEC valve and sealing bolts. Remove rocker shaft bolts.

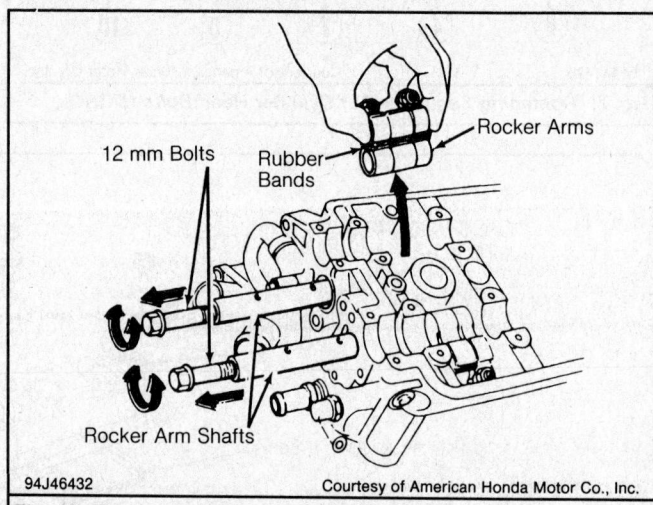

94J46432   Courtesy of American Honda Motor Co., Inc.
Fig. 10: Removing Rocker Arm Shafts (DOHC)

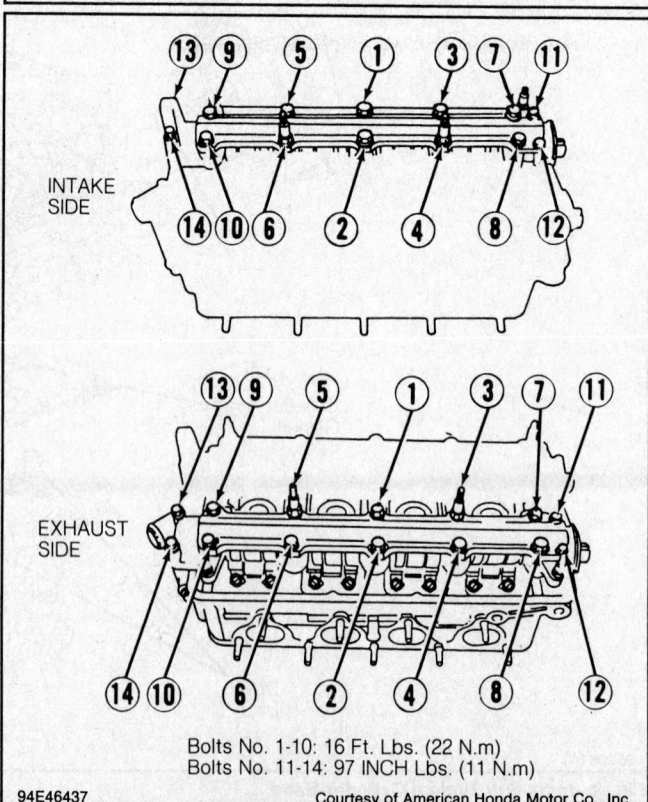

Bolts No. 1-10: 16 Ft. Lbs. (22 N.m)
Bolts No. 11-14: 97 INCH Lbs. (11 N.m)
94E46437   Courtesy of American Honda Motor Co., Inc.
Fig. 11: Tightening Sequence For Camshaft Bearing Cap Bolts (DOHC)

1994 ENGINES
1.5L & 1.6L 4-Cylinder – Civic & Civic Del Sol (Cont.)

HONDA
5-7

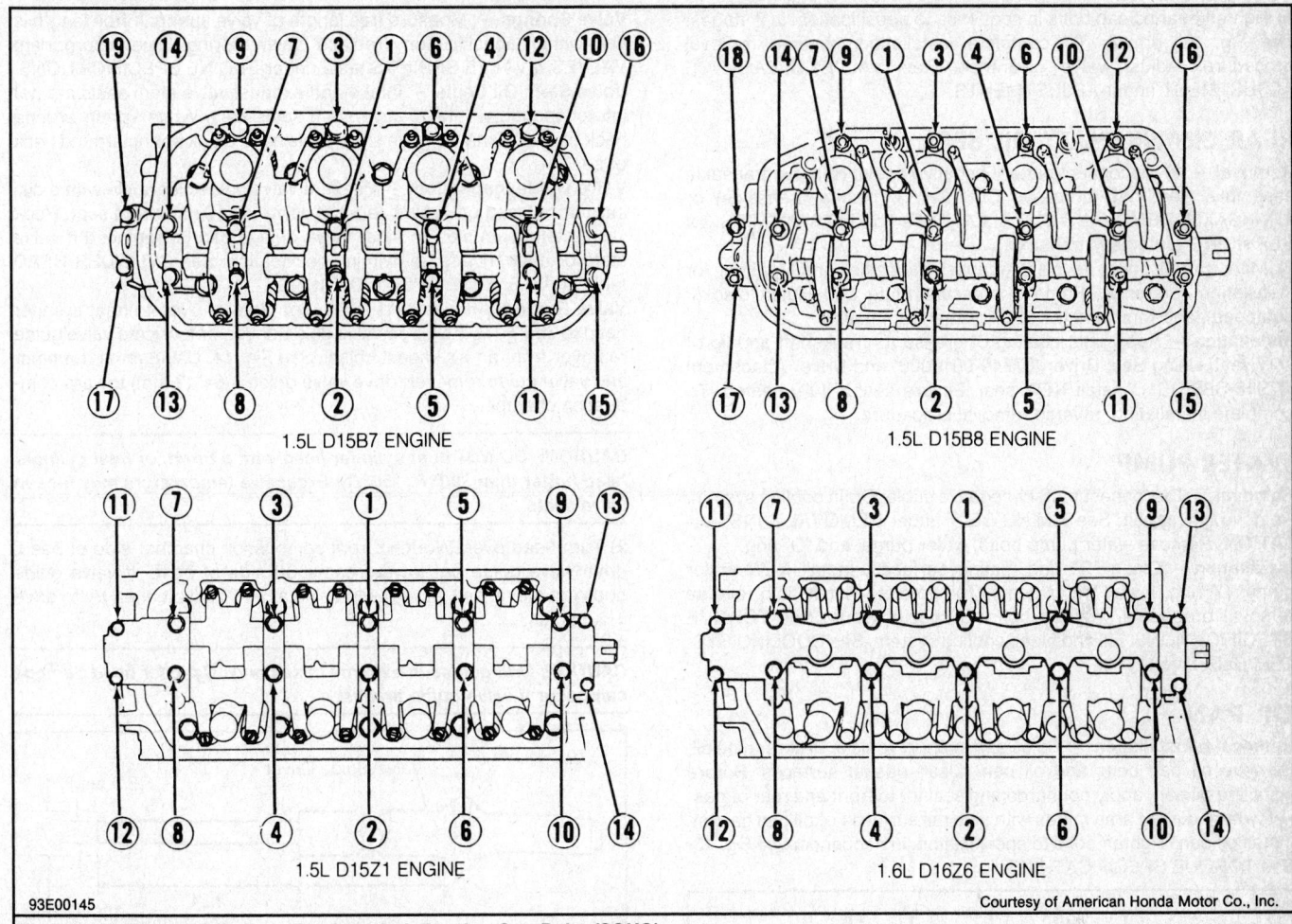

93E00145

Courtesy of American Honda Motor Co., Inc.

Fig. 12: Tightening Sequence For Camshaft Bearing Cap Bolts (SOHC)

2) Screw 12 mm bolts into rocker shaft. *See Fig. 10.* Remove each rocker arm set while pulling out on shaft.

Installation – To install, reverse removal procedure. Clean all parts in solvent. Lubricate all moving parts. Ensure all parts are installed into their original positions. Tighten camshaft bearing caps in sequence. *See Fig. 11.* Adjust valve clearance. See VALVE CLEARANCE ADJUSTMENT under ADJUSTMENTS.

NOTE: DO NOT remove camshaft bearing cap (cam holder) bolts from rocker arm assembly unless it is to be disassembled. The bolts keep cam holders, springs, and rocker arms on shaft.

Removal (SOHC) – Loosen all valve adjuster screws. Loosen, but DO NOT remove, camshaft bearing cap bolts 2 turns at a time in reverse order of tightening sequence. *See Fig. 12.* Remove bolts, rocker arms, and rocker shaft as an assembly. If rocker shafts and arms are to be disassembled, tag all parts for reassembly reference, and carefully unscrew cam holder bolts one at a time.

Installation – To install, reverse removal procedure. Clean all parts in solvent. Lubricate all moving parts. Ensure all parts are installed into their original positions. Tighten bolts in sequence, 2 turns at a time, to specification. *See Fig. 12.* See TORQUE SPECIFICATIONS. Adjust valve clearance. See VALVE CLEARANCE ADJUSTMENT under ADJUSTMENTS.

CAMSHAFT

NOTE: Camshaft removal and installation procedures for DOHC applications are similar to SOHC applications.

CAUTION: On SOHC applications, DO NOT remove camshaft bearing cap (cam holder) bolts from rocker arm assembly unless it is to be disassembled. The bolts keep cam holders, springs, and rocker arms on shaft.

Removal – 1) Ensure No. 1 piston is at TDC of compression stroke. Position UP mark on camshaft sprocket at top. Remove timing belt. See TIMING BELT under REMOVAL & INSTALLATION. Remove rocker arms and rocker shafts. See ROCKER ARM ASSEMBLY. Reinstall camshaft bearing caps.

2) Remove camshaft sprocket. Mark distributor for installation reference. Remove distributor. Measure camshaft end play by prying camshaft toward front of cylinder head. Attach dial indicator, and zero it against sprocket end of camshaft.

3) Pry camshaft away from dial indicator, and measure end play. Desired end play is .002-.006" (.05-.15 mm). Maximum allowable end play is .020" (.50 mm). If end play exceeds limit, replace camshaft.

4) Remove camshaft bearing cap bolts by turning bolts 2 turns at a time in reverse order of tightening sequence. *See Fig. 11 or 12.* Remove camshaft.

Inspection – 1) Inspect camshaft lobes and bearing journals for excessive wear or damage. Place camshaft on "V" blocks, and measure runout. Total runout must not exceed .001" (.03 mm).

2) Measure camshaft oil clearance, using Plastigage. If camshaft oil clearance exceeds service limit, replace camshaft or cylinder head. See CAMSHAFT table under ENGINE SPECIFICATIONS.

Installation – 1) Lubricate camshaft journals and journal surfaces in bearing caps and cylinder head. Install camshaft(s) with keyway(s) pointing upward (No. 1 piston at TDC). Loosely install camshaft bearing caps in original positions. Install NEW camshaft seals (if removed). Install rocker arms and shafts. See ROCKER ARM ASSEMBLY.

HONDA
5-8

1994 ENGINES
1.5L & 1.6L 4-Cylinder – Civic & Civic Del Sol (Cont.)

2) Tighten bearing cap bolts in sequence to specification, in 2 stages. *See Fig. 11 or 12.* To complete installation, reverse removal procedure. Adjust valve clearance. See VALVE CLEARANCE ADJUSTMENT under ADJUSTMENTS.

REAR CRANKSHAFT OIL SEAL

Removal – 1) Disconnect battery negative cable. Remove transaxle assembly. See FWD article in CLUTCHES (manual transaxle) or TRANSAXLE REMOVAL & INSTALLATION article in TRANSMISSION SERVICING (automatic transaxle).
2) Mark clutch pressure plate (manual transaxle) and flywheel for installation reference. Remove pressure plate and clutch disc (if equipped), and remove flywheel. Pry seal from cover.
Installation – Apply light coating of grease to crankshaft and lip of new seal. Using Seal Driver (07749-0010000) and Driver Attachment (07948-SB00101), install NEW seal. Ensure seal is fully seated. To complete installation, reverse removal procedure.

WATER PUMP

Removal – Disconnect battery negative cable. Drain cooling system. Remove timing belt. See TIMING BELT under REMOVAL & INSTALLATION. Remove water pump bolts, water pump, and "O" ring.
Installation – Clean "O" ring mating surfaces. Install NEW water pump "O" ring. Install water pump. To complete installation, reverse removal procedure. Tighten bolts to specifications. See TORQUE SPECIFICATIONS. Fill and bleed cooling system. See COOLING SYSTEM BLEEDING.

OIL PAN

Removal & Installation – Raise and support vehicle. Drain engine oil. Remove oil pan bolts and oil pan. Clean gasket surfaces. Before installing oil pan, apply nonhardening sealant to front and rear of gasket, where curved area mates with side rail surfaces of oil pan gasket. Install oil pan. Tighten bolts to specification, in sequence. *See Fig. 13.* See TORQUE SPECIFICATIONS.

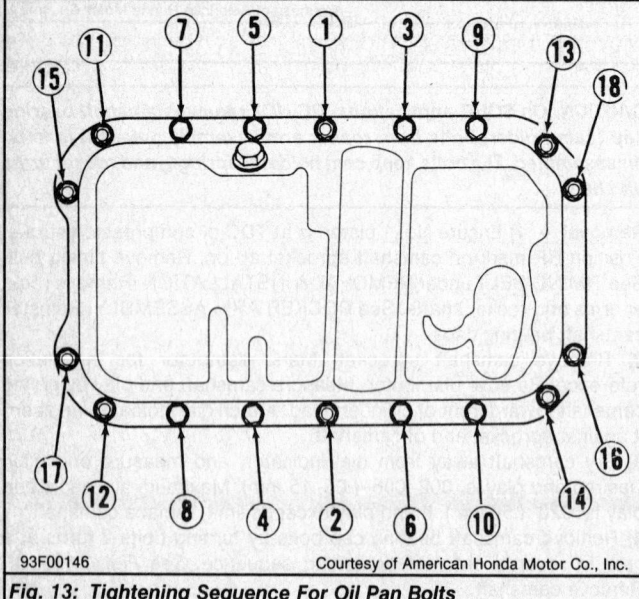

93F00146   Courtesy of American Honda Motor Co., Inc.

Fig. 13: Tightening Sequence For Oil Pan Bolts

OVERHAUL

CYLINDER HEAD

Cylinder Head – Ensure all mating surfaces are clean. Measure cylinder head warpage. If warpage is less than .002" (.05 mm), resurfacing is not required. If warpage is .002-.008" (.05-.20 mm), resurface cylinder head. Maximum resurface limit is .008" (.20 mm).

Valve Springs – Measure free length of valve spring. If free length is not within specification, replace valve spring. See appropriate VALVES & VALVE SPRINGS table under ENGINE SPECIFICATIONS.
Valve Stem Oil Seals – Intake and exhaust valve stem seals are not interchangeable. Intake valve stem seals have White spring around neck of seal. Exhaust valve stem seals have Black spring around neck of seal.
Valve Guide Inspection – Measure valve guide clearance with a dial indicator placed on valve head. Lift valve .4" (10 mm) from seat. Rock valve stem from side to side. Valve guides can be replaced if valve stem oil clearance is not within specification. See CYLINDER HEAD table under ENGINE SPECIFICATIONS.
Valve Guide Removal – 1) Use a hot plate or oven to heat cylinder head to 300°F (150°C). Use valve guide driver, or fabricate valve guide remover from an air impact chisel. *See Fig. 14.* Using an air hammer and valve guide remover, drive valve guide 5/64" (2 mm) toward combustion chamber.

CAUTION: DO NOT heat cylinder head with a torch, or heat cylinder head hotter than 300°F (150°C). Excessive temperature may loosen valve seats.

2) Turn head over. Working from combustion chamber side of head, drive valve guide out toward camshaft side of head. If valve guide does not move, drill valve guide using a 5/16" drill bit, then try to drive it out again.

CAUTION: Drill guides in extreme cases only. Cylinder head damage can occur if valve guide breaks.

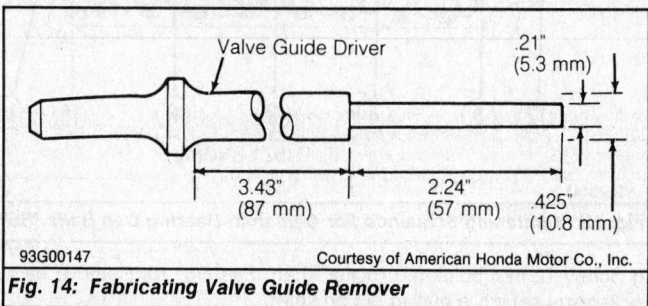

93G00147   Courtesy of American Honda Motor Co., Inc.

Fig. 14: Fabricating Valve Guide Remover

Valve Guide Installation – 1) Chill new valve guides in freezer for about one hour. Remove new valve guides from freezer as needed. Slip a 15/64" (6 mm) steel washer over valve guide driver.
2) Install new valve guides from camshaft side of cylinder head. Drive each guide into heated head until washer bottoms against head. If replacing all valve guides, reheat cylinder head as necessary.
3) Valve guide installed height must be as specified. See VALVE GUIDE INSTALLED HEIGHT in CYLINDER HEAD table under ENGINE SPECIFICATIONS. Using cutting oil, ream new valve guides by rotating Valve Guide Reamer (07742-0010100) clockwise the full length of valve guide bore. Measure valve stem oil clearance. See CYLINDER HEAD table under ENGINE SPECIFICATIONS.

NOTE: Always reface valve seat after replacing valve guide.

Valve Seat – Valve seat replacement procedure is not available from manufacturer.
Valve Seat Correction Angles – If valve guides are to be replaced, perform replacement before refacing valve seats. After refacing, if seat width is too wide, use 60-degree stone to raise seat, or 30-degree stone to lower seat. Ensure valve seat width is within specification. See CYLINDER HEAD table under ENGINE SPECIFICATIONS.
Valve Stem Installed Height – After servicing valves, measure valve stem installed height. *See Fig. 15.* If valve stem installed height exceeds specification for any valve, replace valve. See appropriate VALVES & VALVE SPRINGS table. If valve stem installed height still exceeds limit, replace cylinder head.

1994 ENGINES
1.5L & 1.6L 4-Cylinder – Civic & Civic Del Sol (Cont.)

HONDA
5-9

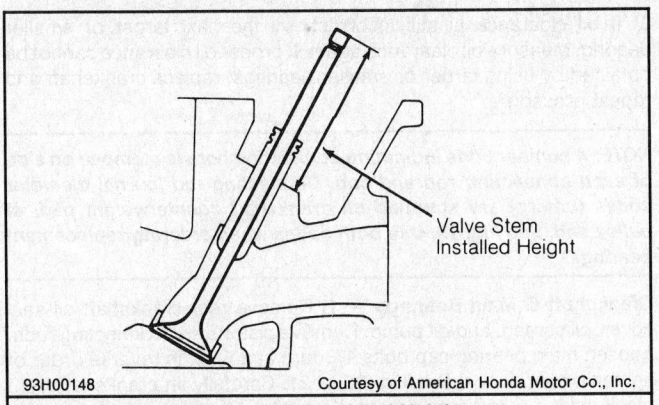

93H00148   Courtesy of American Honda Motor Co., Inc.

Fig. 15: Measuring Valve Stem Installed Height

VALVE TRAIN

Rocker Arm Shaft Assembly – 1) Label and remove all rocker arm components from shafts. Inspect shafts for signs of scoring or damage. Ensure all oil passages are clear. Inspect rocker arms for wear in cam and valve contact areas. Replace if damaged. Measure oil clearance between rocker arms and rocker shafts. Replace rocker arm and/or shaft if clearance exceeds .003" (.08 mm).

2) Lubricate rocker arms, and install all components onto shaft in original locations. Lubricate camshaft lobes. Apply sealing compound to mating surfaces of end cam bearing caps. Loosen rocker arm lock nuts before installing rocker arm assembly. Tighten bolts to specification, in sequence. *See Fig. 11 or 12.*

CYLINDER BLOCK ASSEMBLY

Piston & Rod Assembly – 1) Each rod is sorted into one of 4 tolerance ranges. Size depends on crank journal bore. A number between 1 and 4 is stamped on side of rod big end. Any combination of numbers between 1 and 4 may be found in any engine.

NOTE: Reference numbers are for big end bore code, and do not indicate rod position in engine.

2) Nominal connecting rod big end bore size is 1.89" (48 mm), except D15B8 engine, which is 1.77" (45 mm). Install piston and connecting rod so arrow on top of piston points toward timing belt, and connecting rod oil hole is toward rear of engine. *See Fig. 16.*

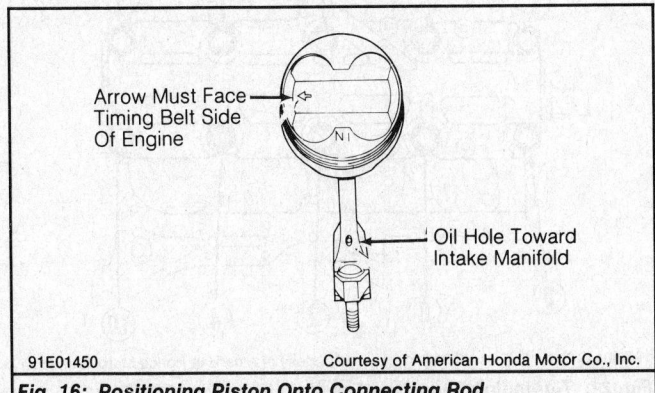

91E01450   Courtesy of American Honda Motor Co., Inc.

Fig. 16: Positioning Piston Onto Connecting Rod

Piston Pin Removal – 1) Install Piston Base Head (07HAF-PL20102 on DOHC; 07973-SB00100 on SOHC) and Piston Pin Base Insert (07GAF-PH60300 on DOHC; 07973-PE00400 on SOHC) into Base (07973-6570500). Turn handle on Piston Pin Driver (07973-PE00320) to adjust piston pin driver length. On DOHC applications, piston driver length is 2.04" (51.7 mm). On SOHC applications, piston driver length is 2.09" (53.0 mm).

2) Insert Piston Pin Driver Shaft (07973-PE00310) into Pilot Collar (07LAF-PR30100 on DOHC; 07973-PE00200 on SOHC). Place piston

onto base with embossed side facing up. Press out piston pin. Ensure recessed part of piston aligns with lugs on collar.

NOTE: All replacement piston pins are oversize.

Piston Pin Inspection – 1) Measure diameter of piston pin. Measure diameter of piston pin bore in piston. Piston pin clearance is difference between the two measurements.

2) Piston pin clearance must be .0004-.0009" (.010-.022 mm). If piston pin clearance is greater than .0009" (.022 mm), install an oversize piston pin and recheck clearance.

3) Determine difference between piston pin diameter and connecting rod small end bore. On DOHC applications, interference fit between piston pin and connecting rod must be .0005-.0013" (.013-.032 mm). On SOHC applications, interference fit between piston pin and connecting rod must be .0006-.0016" (.014-.040 mm).

Piston Pin Installation – 1) Ensure piston and connecting rod are positioned as shown. *See Fig. 17.* Turn handle on Piston Pin Driver (07973-PE00320) to adjust piston pin driver length. On DOHC applications, piston driver length is 2.04" (51.7 mm). On SOHC applications, piston driver length is 2.09" (53.0 mm).

2) Install Pilot Collar (07LAF-PR30100 on DOHC; 07973-PE00200 on SOHC) into piston and connecting rod. Lubricate new piston pin lightly. Place piston onto base with embossed side facing up. Press in piston pin.

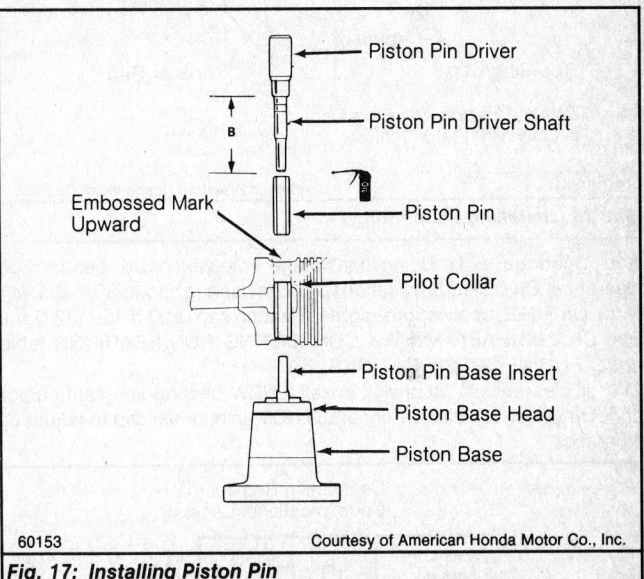

60153   Courtesy of American Honda Motor Co., Inc.

Fig. 17: Installing Piston Pin

Fitting Pistons – 1) Using a feeler gauge, measure clearance between piston and cylinder bore. If clearance is near or exceeds .002" (.05 mm), measure each piston and cylinder. Piston clearance is difference between cylinder bore and piston diameter. If piston clearance exceeds service limit, rebore cylinder and install oversize piston. Pistons are available in .010" (.25 mm) and .020" (.50 mm) oversize.

2) Remove all rings from piston. Clean piston thoroughly. Inspect piston for distortion and cracks. Measure piston diameter at .59-.63" (15-16 mm) from bottom of piston skirt. See PISTONS, PINS & RINGS table under ENGINE SPECIFICATIONS. If diameter is not within specification, replace piston.

Piston Rings – 1) Using inverted piston, push new piston ring into cylinder bore .6-.8" (15-20 mm) from bottom. Measure piston ring end gap, using a feeler gauge. Repeat for each ring. See PISTONS, PINS & RINGS table under ENGINE SPECIFICATIONS.

2) Clean piston ring grooves thoroughly. Install piston rings with identification mark toward top of piston. Using a feeler gauge, measure piston ring side clearance between ring and ring land.

3) If ring lands are excessively worn, replace piston. See PISTONS, PINS & RINGS table. Align piston ring end gaps properly on piston. *See Fig. 18.*

HONDA
5-10

1994 ENGINES
1.5L & 1.6L 4-Cylinder – Civic & Civic Del Sol (Cont.)

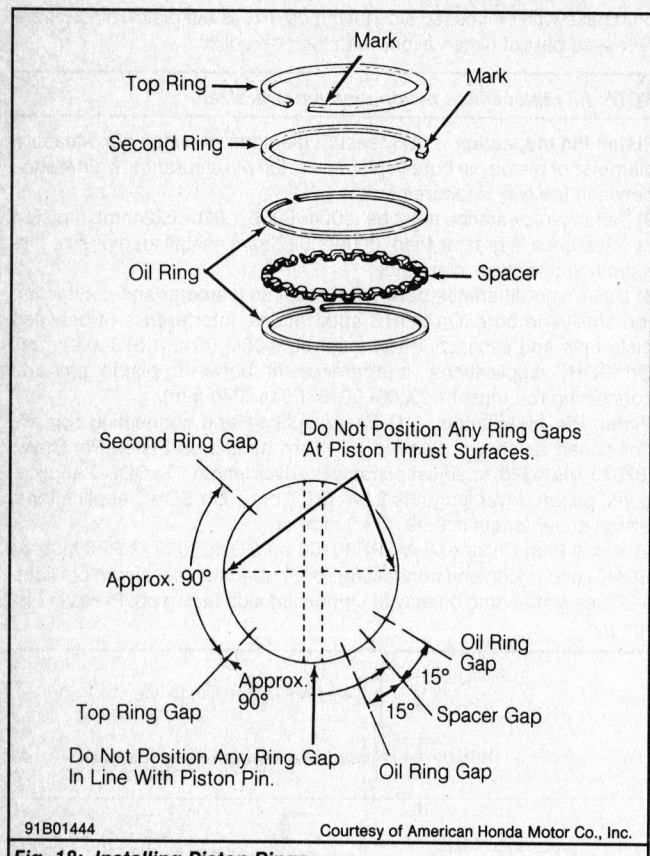

Fig. 18: Installing Piston Rings

91B01444   Courtesy of American Honda Motor Co., Inc.

Rod Bearings – 1) Using Plastigage, measure rod bearing oil clearance. On DOHC applications, tighten bearing cap to 30 ft. lbs. (41 N.m). On SOHC applications, tighten bearing cap to 23 ft. lbs. (32 N.m). See CRANKSHAFT, MAIN & CONNECTING ROD BEARINGS table under ENGINE SPECIFICATIONS.

2) If oil clearance is incorrect, install a NEW bearing set (same color code) and recheck oil clearance. DO NOT shim or file cap to adjust oil clearance.

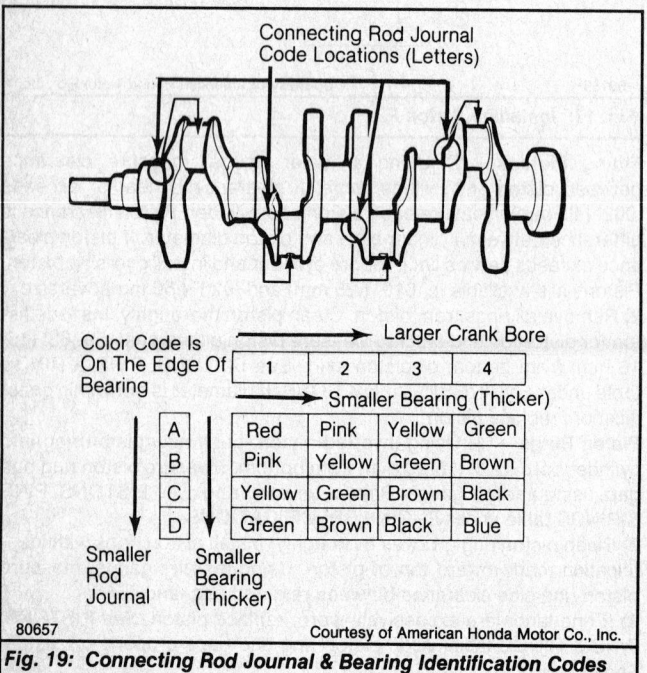

Fig. 19: Connecting Rod Journal & Bearing Identification Codes

80657   Courtesy of American Honda Motor Co., Inc.

Color Code Is On The Edge Of Bearing

Larger Crank Bore → Smaller Bearing (Thicker)

	1	2	3	4
A	Red	Pink	Yellow	Green
B	Pink	Yellow	Green	Brown
C	Yellow	Green	Brown	Black
D	Green	Brown	Black	Blue

Smaller Rod Journal   Smaller Bearing (Thicker)

3) If oil clearance is still incorrect, try the next larger or smaller bearing. Measure oil clearance again. If proper oil clearance cannot be obtained by using larger or smaller bearings, replace crankshaft and repeat procedure.

NOTE: A number code indicating connecting bore is stamped on side of each connecting rod and cap. Connecting rod journal diameter codes (letters) are stamped on crankshaft counterweight pad, at pulley end. See Fig. 19. Use both codes when ordering replacement bearings.

Crankshaft & Main Bearings – 1) Remove rear crankshaft oil seal cover, oil screen, and oil pump. Remove pistons and connecting rods. Loosen main bearing cap bolts 1/3 turn at a time, in reverse order of tightening sequence. See Fig. 20 or 21. Carefully lift crankshaft from block, taking care not to damage journals.

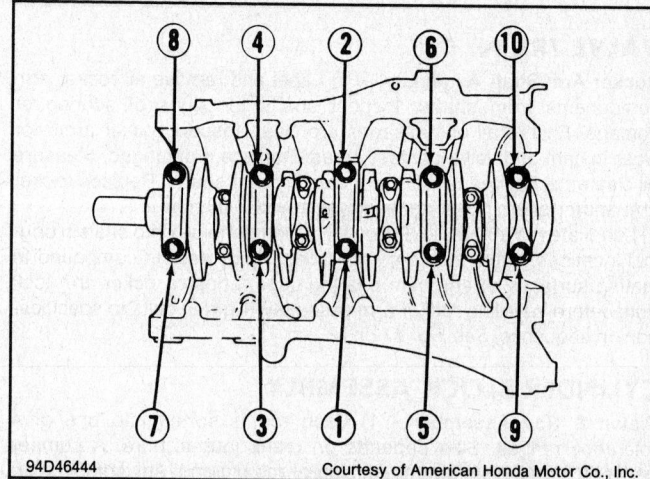

Fig. 20: Tightening Sequence For Main Bearings (DOHC)

94D46444   Courtesy of American Honda Motor Co., Inc.

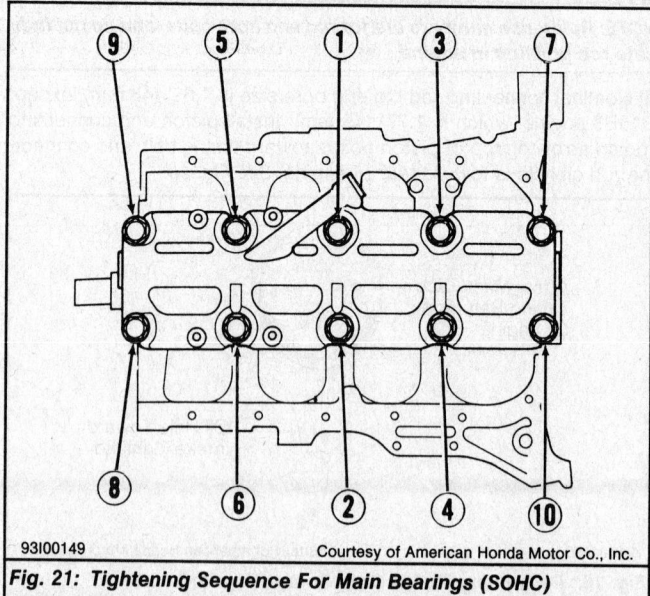

Fig. 21: Tightening Sequence For Main Bearings (SOHC)

93I00149   Courtesy of American Honda Motor Co., Inc.

2) Using a lathe or "V" blocks to support crankshaft, measure crankshaft runout, out-of-round, and taper. If any measurement exceeds service limit, replace crankshaft. See CRANKSHAFT, MAIN & CONNECTING ROD BEARINGS table under ENGINE SPECIFICATIONS.

3) Install crankshaft into block. Measure bearing oil clearance, using Plastigage. If engine is in vehicle, support counterweights, and measure only one bearing at a time. Tighten main bearing cap bolts to specification in 2 stages, in sequence. See Fig. 20 or 21. See TORQUE SPECIFICATIONS.

1994 ENGINES
1.5L & 1.6L 4-Cylinder – Civic & Civic Del Sol (Cont.)

HONDA
5-11

4) If oil clearance is incorrect, remove crankshaft upper bearing half. Install a NEW bearing (same color code), and remeasure oil clearance. If oil clearance is still incorrect, try next larger or smaller bearing, and measure oil clearance once more. If proper oil clearance cannot be achieved by using larger or smaller bearings, replace crankshaft and repeat procedure.

NOTE: *Letter codes indicating main journal bore diameters are stamped on cylinder block. See Fig. 22 or 23. Main journal diameter codes (numbers) are stamped on crankshaft counterweight pad. Use both codes to order correct replacement bearings.*

Thrust Bearing – **1)** Measure crankshaft end play, using a dial indicator. If end play exceeds specification, inspect thrust washers and thrust surface of crankshaft.
2) Replace worn parts as necessary. Thrust washer thickness is fixed. DO NOT change thrust washer thickness by grinding or shimming. Install thrust washers with grooved side facing out.
Cylinder Block – **1)** Measure cylinder bore out-of-round and taper. If either out-of-round or taper exceeds specification, rebore cylinder for oversize pistons. See CYLINDER BLOCK table under ENGINE SPEC-

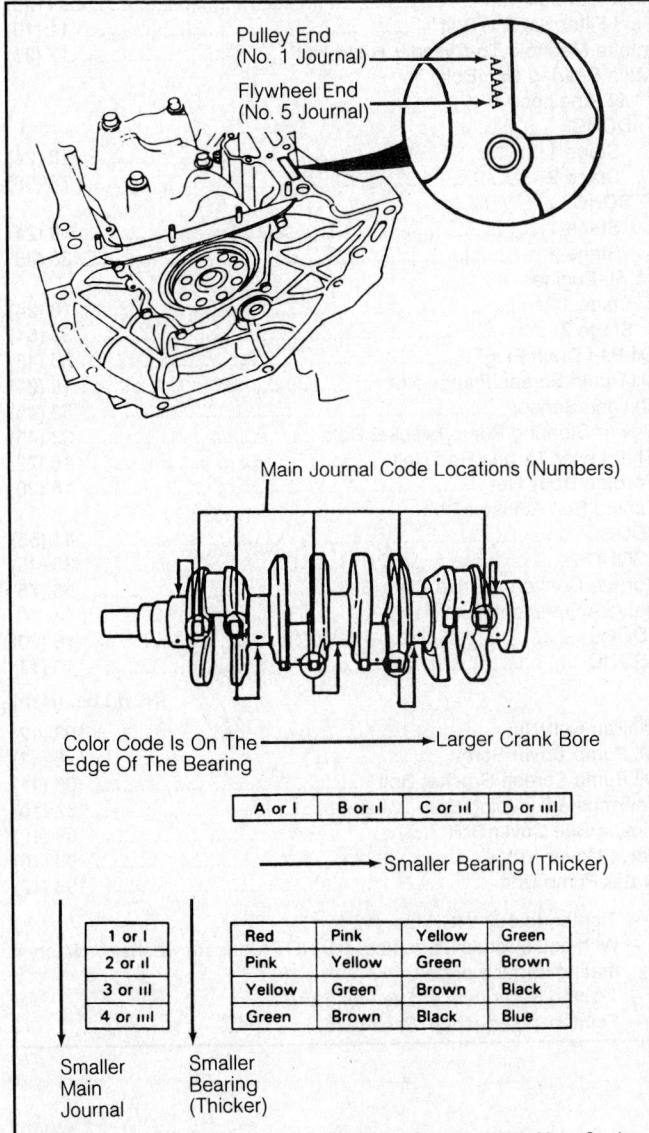

Color Code Is On The Edge Of The Bearing → Larger Crank Bore

A or I	B or II	C or III	D or IIII

→ Smaller Bearing (Thicker)

	A	B	C	D
1 or I	Red	Pink	Yellow	Green
2 or II	Pink	Yellow	Green	Brown
3 or III	Yellow	Green	Brown	Black
4 or IIII	Green	Brown	Black	Blue

Smaller Main Journal   Smaller Bearing (Thicker)

94E46445   Courtesy of American Honda Motor Co., Inc.

Fig. 22: Locating Crankshaft Main Journal & Bearing Identification Codes (DOHC)

Pulley End (No. 1 Journal)

Flywheel End (No. 5 Journal)

Main Journal Code Locations (Numbers)

Color Code Is on Edge of Bearing → Larger Crank Bore

	A	B	C	D
1	Red	Pink	Yellow	Green
2	Pink	Yellow	Green	Brown
3	Yellow	Green	Brown	Black
4	Green	Brown	Black	Blue

→ Smaller Bearing (Thicker)

Smaller Main Journal   Smaller Bearing (Thicker)

91I01452   Courtesy of American Honda Motor Co., Inc.

Fig. 23: Locating Crankshaft Main Journal & Bearing Identification Codes (SOHC)

IFICATIONS. If measurements in any cylinder exceed oversize bore service limit, replace cylinder block.
2) Using a feeler gauge and straightedge, inspect cylinder block deck surface for warpage. On DOHC applications, service limit is .003" (.08 mm). On SOHC applications, service limit is .004" (.10 mm). If cylinder bore is okay, hone cylinder to obtain a 60-degree crosshatch pattern. After honing, wash cylinder bore with hot, soapy water. Air-dry cylinder bore, and coat with engine oil to prevent rusting.

ENGINE OILING

ENGINE LUBRICATION SYSTEM

A rotor-type oil pump draws oil from oil pan, and delivers it under pressure to main and connecting rod bearings. An oil hole in each connecting rod lubricates thrust side of piston and cylinder wall. An oil passage carries oil to camshaft and rocker arms. Oil spray lubricates valve stems.
Crankcase Capacity – On DOHC applications, crankcase capacity is 4.2 qts. (4.0L) including oil filter. On SOHC applications, crankcase capacity is 3.5 qts. (3.3L) including oil filter.
Oil Pressure – Oil pressure at idle should be 10 psi (0.7 kg/cm²) minimum. Oil pressure at 3000 RPM should be 50 psi (3.5 kg/cm²) minimum.

HONDA
5-12

1994 ENGINES
1.5L & 1.6L 4-Cylinder – Civic & Civic Del Sol (Cont.)

OIL PUMP

Removal – Raise and support vehicle. Drain engine oil. Turn crankshaft counterclockwise until White mark on crankshaft pulley aligns with pointer on timing belt cover. Remove timing belt. See TIMING BELT under REMOVAL & INSTALLATION. Remove drive sprocket, oil pan, oil screen, and oil pump assembly.

Disassembly & Inspection – Remove pump housing screws. Separate housing and cover. Measure radial clearance between inner and outer rotors. Measure axial and radial clearance between housing and outer rotor. Inspect both rotors and pump housing for scoring or other damage. Replace components if clearance is not within specification. See OIL PUMP SPECIFICATIONS table.

OIL PUMP SPECIFICATIONS

Application	In. (mm)
Inner Rotor-To-Outer Rotor	
Radial Clearance	
Standard (New)	
DOHC	.002-.006 (.04-.15)
SOHC	.001-.006 (.02-.15)
Service Limit	.008 (.20)
Housing-To-Outer Rotor	
Axial Clearance	
Standard (New)	
DOHC	.001-.003 (.02-.08)
SOHC	.001-.003 (.02-.08)
Service Limit	.006 (.15)
Housing-To-Outer Rotor	
Radial Clearance	
Standard (New)	
DOHC	.004-.007 (.10-.19)
SOHC	.004-.007 (.10-.19)
Service Limit	.008 (.20)

Reassembly & Installation – **1)** Reassemble oil pump, using sealant on pump housing screws. Ensure pump turns freely. Install dowel pins and NEW "O" ring in cylinder block. Clean oil pump mating surfaces. Apply Liquid Sealant (08718-0001) to cylinder block and oil pump mating surface.

2) Apply sealant to threads of inner bolt holes. Install oil pump before sealant dries. Install oil screen and oil pump. Wait at least 30 minutes before filling crankcase with oil. To complete installation, reverse removal procedure.

TORQUE SPECIFICATIONS

TORQUE SPECIFICATIONS

Application	Ft. Lbs. (N.m)
A/C Compressor Bracket Bolt	33 (45)
Alternator Bracket Bolt	33 (45)
Camshaft Bearing Cap	
6-mm Bolt	[1]
8-mm Bolt	16 (22)
Camshaft Sprocket Bolt	
DOHC	38 (51)
SOHC	28 (38)
Connecting Rod Nut	
DOHC	30 (41)
SOHC	24 (32)
Crankshaft Pulley Bolt [2]	
SOHC	130 (180)
SOHC	134 (185)

[1] – Tighten to 108 INCH lbs. (12 N.m).
[2] – With bolt threads lubricated. DO NOT lubricate washer or washer mating surface of bolt.
[3] – Tighten in sequence. *See Fig. 6 or 7.*
[4] – Tighten in sequence. *See Fig. 5.*

TORQUE SPECIFICATIONS (Cont.)

Application	Ft. Lbs. (N.m)
Cylinder Head Bolt [3]	
DOHC (B16A3) Engine	
Stage 1	22 (30)
Stage 2	63 (85)
SOHC Engines	
D15B7 & D15B8	
Stage 1	22 (30)
Stage 2	48 (65)
D15Z1 & D16Z6	
Stage 1	22 (30)
Stage 2	53 (73)
Distributor Mount Bolt	18 (24)
Drive Shaft Flange Bolt	24 (32)
Engine Mount Bolts	[4] 48-63 (65-85)
Exhaust Manifold Bracket Bolt	33 (45)
Exhaust Manifold Nut	24 (32)
Exhaust Manifold Shroud Bolt	16 (22)
Exhaust Pipe Nut	41 (55)
Flywheel Bolt	89 (120)
Fuel Filter Service Bolt	11 (15)
Intake Manifold-To-Cylinder Head Nut	17 (23)
Main Bearing Cap Bolt	
1.6L Engines	
DOHC	
Stage 1	18 (24)
Stage 2	78 (58)
SOHC	
Stage 1	18 (24)
Stage 2	33 (45)
1.5L Engines	
Stage 1	18 (24)
Stage 2	38 (51)
Oil Pan Drain Plug	33 (45)
Oil Pump Screen Flange Nut	18 (24)
Oxygen Sensor	33 (45)
Power Steering Pump Bracket Bolt	33 (45)
Shift Lever Torque Rod Bolt	16 (22)
Throttle Body Nut	15 (20)
Timing Belt Adjuster Bolt	
DOHC	41 (55)
SOHC	33 (45)
Torque Converter Drive Plate Bolt	55 (75)
Valve Adjustment Nuts	
DOHC	15 (20)
SOHC	10 (14)

	INCH Lbs. (N.m)
Oil Pan Bolt/Nut	108 (12)
Oil Pump Cover Screw	62 (7)
Oil Pump Screen Bracket Bolt	96 (11)
Thermostat Housing Bolt	89 (10)
Timing Belt Cover Bolt	89 (10)
Valve Cover Nut	89 (10)
Water Pump Bolt	108 (12)

[1] – Tighten to 108 INCH lbs. (12 N.m).
[2] – With bolt threads lubricated. DO NOT lubricate washer or washer mating surface of bolt.
[3] – Tighten in sequence. *See Fig. 6 or 7.*
[4] – Tighten in sequence. *See Fig. 5.*

1994 ENGINES
1.5L & 1.6L 4-Cylinder – Civic & Civic Del Sol (Cont.)

HONDA
5-13

ENGINE SPECIFICATIONS
GENERAL SPECIFICATIONS

Application	Specification
Displacement	
1.5L	91 Cu. In.
1.6L	97 Cu. In.
Bore	
1.5L	2.95" (74.9 mm)
1.6L	
DOHC	3.18" (81.0 mm)
SOHC	2.95" (74.9 mm)
Stroke	
1.5L	3.33" (84.5 mm)
1.6L	
DOHC	3.04" (77.4 mm)
SOHC	3.54" (90.0 mm)
Compression Ratio	
1.5L	
D15B7	9.2:1
D15B8	9.1:1
D15Z1	9.3:1
1.6L	
B16A3	10.2:1
D16Z6	9.2:1
Horsepower @ RPM	
1.5L	
D15B7	70 @ 5000
D15B8	102 @ 5900
D15Z1	92 @ 5500
1.6L	125 @ 6500
B16A3	160 @ 6500
D16Z6	125 @ 6500
Torque Ft. Lbs. @ RPM	
1.5L	
D15B7	91 @ 5000
D15B8	98 @ 5000
D15Z1	97 @ 4500
1.6L	106 @ 5200

CRANKSHAFT, MAIN & CONNECTING ROD BEARINGS

Application	In. (mm)
Crankshaft	
End Play	
Standard	.004-.014 (.10-.35)
Service Limit	.018 (.45)
Runout	
Standard	.001 (.03)
Service Limit	.002 (.05)
Main Bearings	
Journal Diameter	
1.5L	1.7707-1.7717 (44.976-45.000)
1.6L	
DOHC	
Journals No. 1, 2, 4 & 5	2.1644-2.1654 (54.976-55.000)
Journal No. 3	2.1642-2.1651 (54.970-54.994)
SOHC	2.1644-2.1654 (54.976-55.000)
Journal Out-Of-Round	
1.5L	
Standard	.0001 (.003)
Service Limit	.0002 (.005)
1.6L	
DOHC	
Standard	.0001 (.003)
Service Limit	.0002 (.005)
SOHC	
Standard	.0001 (.003)
Service Limit	.0002 (.005)

CRANKSHAFT, MAIN & CONNECTING ROD BEARINGS (Cont.)

Application	In. (mm)
Journal Taper	
1.5L	
Standard	.0001 (.003)
Service Limit	.0002 (.005)
1.6L	
DOHC	
Standard	.0002 (.005)
Service Limit	.0004 (.010)
SOHC	
Standard	.0001 (.003)
Service Limit	.0002 (.005)
Oil Clearance	
1.5L	
Journals No. 1 & No. 5	
Standard	.0007-.0014 (.018-.036)
Service Limit	.002 (.05)
Journals No. 2, No. 3 & No. 4	
Standard	.0010-.0017 (.024-.042)
Service Limit	.002 (.05)
1.6L	
DOHC	
Journals No. 1, 2, 4 & 5	
Standard	.0010-.0017 (.024-.042)
Service Limit	.002 (.05)
Journal No. 3	
Standard	.0012-.0019 (.032-.050)
Service Limit	.002 (.05)
SOHC	
Journals No. 1 & 5	
Standard	.0007-.0014 (.018-.036)
Service Limit	.002 (.05)
Journals No. 2, No. 3 & No. 4	
Standard	.0010-.0017 (.024-.042)
Service Limit	.002 (.05)
Connecting Rod Bearings	
Journal Diameter	
1.5L	1.6525-1.6535 (41.976-42.000)
1.6L	1.7707-1.7717 (44.976-45.000)
Journal Out-Of-Round Taper	
1.5L	
Standard	.0001 (.003)
Service Limit	.0002 (.005)
1.6L	
DOHC	
Standard	.0001 (.003)
Service Limit	.0002 (.005)
SOHC	
Standard	.0001 (.003)
Service Limit	.0002 (.005)
Journal Taper	
1.5L	
Standard	.0001 (.003)
Service Limit	.0002 (.005)
1.6L	
DOHC	
Standard	.0002 (.005)
Service Limit	.0004 (.010)
SOHC	
Standard	.0001 (.003)
Service Limit	.0002 (.005)

HONDA
5-14

1994 ENGINES
1.5L & 1.6L 4-Cylinder – Civic & Civic Del Sol (Cont.)

CRANKSHAFT, MAIN & CONNECTING ROD BEARINGS (Cont.)

Application	In. (mm)
1.5L	
Standard	.0008-.0015 (.020-.038)
Service Limit	.002 (.05)
1.6L	
DOHC	
Standard	.0013-.0019 (.032-.050)
Service Limit	.002 (.05)
SOHC	
Standard	.0008-.0015 (.020-.038)
Service Limit	.002 (.05)

CONNECTING RODS

Application	In. (mm)
Bore Diameter	
Crankpin Bore	
1.5L	1.77 (45.0)
1.6L	1.89 (48.0)
Side Play	
Standard	.006-.012 (.15-.30)
Service Limit	.016 (.40)

PISTONS, PINS & RINGS

Application	In. (mm)
Pistons	
Clearance	
Standard	.0004-.0016 (.01-.04)
Service Limit	.002 (.05)
Diameter [1]	
1.5L	2.9520-2.9524 (74.98-74.99)
1.6L	
DOHC	3.1881-3.1885 (80.98-80.99)
SOHC	2.9520-2.9524 (74.98-74.99)
Piston Pins	
Diameter	
1.5L	.7478-.7480 (18.994-19.000)
1.6L	
DOHC	.8265-.8267 (20.994-21.000)
SOHC	.7478-.7480 (18.994-19.000)
Piston Fit	.0004-.0009 (.010-.022)
Rod Interference Fit	
1.5L	.0006-.0016 (.015-.040)
1.5L	
DOHC	.0005-.0012 (.013-.030)
SOHC	.0006-.0016 (.015-.040)
Rings	
No. 1	
1.5L	
End Gap	
Standard	.006-.012 (.15-.30)
Service Limit	.024 (.60)
Side Clearance	
Except D15Z1 Engine	.0012-.0024 (.030-.060)
D15Z1 Engine	.0014-.0024 (.035-.060)

[1] – Measure diameter at .63" (16 mm) from bottom of piston on D15B7 and D15B8 engines. Measure diameter at .59" (15 mm) from bottom of piston on B16A3, D15Z1 and D16Z6 engines.

PISTONS, PINS & RINGS (Cont.)

Application	In. (mm)
1.6L	
DOHC	
End Gap	
Riken Manufactured	
Standard	.008-.014 (.20-.35)
Service Limit	.024 (.60)
Teikoku Manufactured	
Standard	.008-.012 (.20-.30)
Service Limit	.024 (.60)
Side Clearance	.0017-.0028 (.045-.070)
SOHC	
End Gap	
Standard	.006-.012 (.15-.30)
Service Limit	.024 (.60)
Side Clearance	.0012-.0022 (.030-.055)
No. 2	
1.5L	
End Gap	
Standard	.0126-.017 (.30-.45)
Service Limit	.028 (.70)
Side Clearance	
Except D15Z1 Engine	.0012-.0024 (.030-.055)
D15Z1 Engine	
Riken Manufactured	.005-.009 (.14-.24)
Teikoku Manufactured	.005-.009 (.12-.22)
1.6L	
DOHC	
End Gap	.016-.022 (.40-.55)
Side Clearance	
Riken Manufactured	.015-.025 (.40-.65)
Teikoku Manufactured	.017-.028 (.45-.70)
SOHC	
End Gap	
Standard	.012-.017 (.30-.45)
Service Limit	.028 (.70)
Side Clearance	.0012-.0021 (.030-.055)
No. 3 (Oil)	
End Gap	
1.5L	
D15B7 & D15B8	
Standard	.008-.031 (.20-.80)
Service Limit	.031 (.80)
D15Z1	
Riken Manufactured	
Standard	.008-.019 (.20-.50)
Service Limit	.031 (.80)
Teikoku Manufactured	
Standard	.008-.028 (.20-.70)
Service Limit	.031 (.80)
1.6L	
DOHC	
Riken Manufactured	
Standard	.008-.019 (.20-.50)
Service Limit	.031 (.80)
Teikoku Manufactured	
Standard	.008-.018 (.20-.45)
Service Limit	.031 (.80)
SOHC	
Standard	.008-.028 (.20-.70)
Service Limit	.031 (.80)

[1] – Measure diameter at .63" (16 mm) from bottom of piston on D15B7 and D15B8 engines. Measure diameter at .59" (15 mm) from bottom of piston on B16A3, D15Z1 and D16Z6 engines.

1994 ENGINES
1.5L & 1.6L 4-Cylinder – Civic & Civic Del Sol (Cont.)

HONDA
5-15

VALVES & VALVE SPRINGS (B16A3 ENGINE)

Application	Specification
Intake Valves	
Face Angle	45°
Head Diameter	1.29-1.30" (32.9-33.1 mm)
Margin	
Standard	.041-.053" (1.05-1.35 mm)
Service Limit	.033" (.85 mm)
Stem Diameter	
Standard	.2157-.2161" (5.48-5.49 mm)
Service Limit	.215" (5.45 mm)
Valve Stem Installed Height [1]	
Standard	1.475-1.493" (37.47-37.94 mm)
Service Limit	1.503" (38.19 mm)
Exhaust Valves	
Face Angle	45°
Head Diameter	1.09-1.10" (27.9-28.1 mm)
Margin	
Standard	.064-.077" (1.65-1.95 mm)
Service Limit	.057" (1.45 mm)
Stem Diameter	
Standard	.2146-.2150" (5.45-5.46 mm)
Service Limit	.213" (5.42 mm)
Valve Stem Installed Height [1]	
Standard	1.463-1.482" (37.17-37.64 mm)
Service Limit	1.491" (37.89 mm)
Valve Springs	
Free Length	
Intake	
Inner	1.445" (36.71)
Outer	
Chuo Hatsujo Manufactured	1.610" (40.91 mm)
Nihon Hatsujo Manufactured	1.611" (40.92 mm)
Exhaust	
Chuo Hatsujo Manufactured	1.651" (41.94 mm)
Nihon Hatsujo Manufactured	1.652" (41.96 mm)

[1] – Measure from base of valve guide to tip of valve stem.

CYLINDER BLOCK

Application	In. (mm)
1.5L	
Cylinder Bore	
Standard Diameter	2.9526-2.9535 (75.000-75.020)
Service Limit	2.9555 (75.070)
Maximum Taper	.002 (.05)
Maximum Deck Warpage	.003 (.07)
Rebore Limit	.020 (.50)
1.6L	
DOHC	
Cylinder Bore	
Standard Diameter	3.1889-3.1897 (81.000-81.020)
Service Limit	3.1917 (81.070)
Maximum Taper	.002 (.05)
Maximum Deck Warpage	.002 (.05)
Rebore Limit	.010 (.25)
SOHC	
Cylinder Bore	
Standard Diameter	2.9526-2.9535 (75.000-75.020)
Service Limit	2.9555 (75.070)
Maximum Taper	.002 (.05)
Maximum Deck Warpage	.003 (.07)
Rebore Limit	.020 (.50)

CYLINDER HEAD

Application	Specification
Cylinder Head	
Height	
B16A3 Engine	5.589-5.593" (141.95-142.05 mm)
D15B7 & D15B8 Engines	3.738-3.742" (94.95-95.05 mm)
D15Z1 & D16Z6 Engines	3.659-3.663" (92.95-93.05 mm)
Maximum Warpage	.002 (.05 mm)
Maximum Resurface Limit	.008" (.20 mm)
Valve Seats	
Except B16A3 Engine	
Intake Valve	
Seat Angle	45°
Seat Width	
Standard	.033-.045" (.85-1.15 mm)
Service Limit	.06" (1.6 mm)
Exhaust Valve	
Seat Angle	45°
Seat Width	
Standard	.049-.061" (1.25-1.55 mm)
Service Limit	.078" (2.0 mm)
B16A3 Engine	
Intake Valve	
Seat Angle	45°
Seat Width	
Standard	.049-.061" (1.25-1.55 mm)
Service Limit	.078" (2.0 mm)
Exhaust Valve	
Seat Angle	45°
Seat Width	
Standard	.049-.061" (1.25-1.55 mm)
Service Limit	.078" (2.0 mm)
Valve Guides	
Intake	
Valve Guide I.D.	
Standard	.217-.218" (5.51-5.53 mm)
Service Limit	.218" (5.53 mm)
Valve Guide Installed Height	
B16A3 Engine	.494-.513" (12.55-13.05 mm)
D15B7 & D15B8 Engines	.628-.648" (15.95-16.45 mm)
D15Z1 & D16Z6 Engines	.703-.722" (17.85-18.35 mm)
Exhaust	
Valve Guide I.D.	
Standard	.217-.218" (5.51-5.53 mm)
Service Limit	.218" (5.53 mm)
Valve Guide Installed Height	
B16A3 Engine	.494-.513" (12.55-13.05 mm)
D15B7 & D15B8 Engines	.628-.648" (15.95-16.45 mm)
D15Z1 & D16Z6 Engines	.734-.754" (18.65-19.15 mm)
Valve Stem-to-Guide Oil Clearance	
Intake Valve	
Standard	.001-.002" (.02-.05 mm)
Service Limit	.003" (.08 mm)
Exhaust Valve	
Standard	.002-.003" (.05-.08 mm)
Service Limit	.005" (.12 mm)

HONDA
5-16

1994 ENGINES
1.5L & 1.6L 4-Cylinder – Civic & Civic Del Sol (Cont.)

VALVES & VALVE SPRINGS (D15B7 & D15B8 ENGINES)

Application	Specification
Intake Valves	
Face Angle	45°
Head Diameter	1.14-1.15" (28.9-29.1 mm)
Margin	
Standard	.033-.045" (.85-1.15 mm)
Service Limit	.026" (.65 mm)
Stem Diameter	
Standard	.2157-.2161" (5.48-5.49 mm)
Service Limit	.215" (5.45 mm)
Valve Stem Installed Height [1]	
Standard	1.850-1.868" (46.99-47.45 mm)
Service Limit	1.878" (47.70 mm)
Exhaust Valves	
Face Angle	45°
Head Diameter	.98-.99" (24.9-25.1 mm)
Margin	
Standard	.041-.053" (1.05-1.35 mm)
Service Limit	.037" (.95 mm)
Stem Diameter	
Standard	.2146-.2150" (5.45-5.46 mm)
Service Limit	.213" (5.42 mm)
Valve Stem Installed Height [1]	
Standard	1.928-1.946" (48.97-49.44 mm)
Service Limit	1.956" (49.68 mm)
Valve Springs	
Free Length	
Intake	
D15B7 Engine	
Chuo Hatsujo Manufactured	2.042" (51.880 mm)
Nihon Hatsujo Manufactured	2.043" (51.90 mm)
D15B8 Engine	1.913" (48.58 mm)
Exhaust	
D15B7 Engine	
Chuo Hatsujo Manufactured	2.178" (55.31 mm)
Nihon Hatsujo Manufactured	2.176" (55.28 mm)
D15B8 Engine	1.937" (49.19 mm)

[1] – Measure from base of valve guide to tip of valve stem.

CAMSHAFT

Application	In. (mm)
End Play	
Standard	.002-.006 (.05-.15)
Service Limit	.020 (.50)
Journal Runout	
Standard	.001 (.03)
Service Limit	.001 (.03)
Oil Clearance	
Standard	.002-.004 (.05-.09)
Service Limit	.006 (.15)

VALVES & VALVE SPRINGS (D15Z1 ENGINE)

Application	Specification
Intake Valves	
Face Angle	45°
Head Diameter	1.08-1.09" (27.4-27.6 mm)
Margin	
Standard	.033-.045" (.85-1.15 mm)
Service Limit	.026" (.65 mm)
Stem Diameter	
Standard	.2157-.2161" (5.48-5.49 mm)
Service Limit	.215" (5.45 mm)
Valve Stem Installed Height [1]	
Standard	2.093-2.112" (53.17-53.64 mm)
Service Limit	2.122" (53.89 mm)
Exhaust Valves	
Face Angle	45°
Head Diameter	.92-.93" (23.4-23.6 mm)
Margin	
Standard	.041-.053" (1.05-1.35 mm)
Service Limit	.037" (.95 mm)
Stem Diameter	
Standard	.2146-.2150" (5.45-5.46 mm)
Service Limit	.213" (5.41 mm)
Valve Stem Installed Height [1]	
Standard	2.093-2.112" (53.17-53.64 mm)
Service Limit	2.122" (53.89 mm)
Valve Springs	
Free Length	
Intake	2.157" (54.78 mm)
Exhaust	
Chuo Hatsujo Manufactured	2.294" (58.26 mm)
Nihon Hatsujo Manufactured	2.293" (58.23 mm)

[1] – Measure from base of valve guide to tip of valve stem.

VALVES & VALVE SPRINGS (D16Z6 ENGINE)

Application	Specification
Intake Valves	
Face Angle	45°
Head Diameter	1.18-1.19" (29.9-30.1 mm)
Margin	
Standard	.033-.045" (.85-1.15 mm)
Service Limit	.026" (.65 mm)
Stem Diameter	
Standard	.2157-.2161" (5.48-5.49 mm)
Service Limit	.215" (5.45 mm)
Valve Stem Installed Height [1]	
Standard	2.093-2.112" (53.17-53.64 mm)
Service Limit	2.122" (53.89 mm)
Exhaust Valves	
Face Angle	45°
Head Diameter	1.02-1.03" (25.9-26.1 mm)
Margin	
Standard	.041-.053" (1.05-1.35 mm)
Service Limit	.037" (.95 mm)
Stem Diameter	
Standard	.2146-.2150" (5.45-5.46 mm)
Service Limit	.213" (5.42 mm)
Valve Stem Installed Height [1]	
Standard	2.093-2.112" (53.17-53.64 mm)
Service Limit	2.122" (53.89 mm)
Valve Springs	
Free Length	
Intake	2.282" (57.97 mm)
Exhaust	2.300" (58.41 mm)

[1] – Measure from base of valve guide to tip of valve stem.

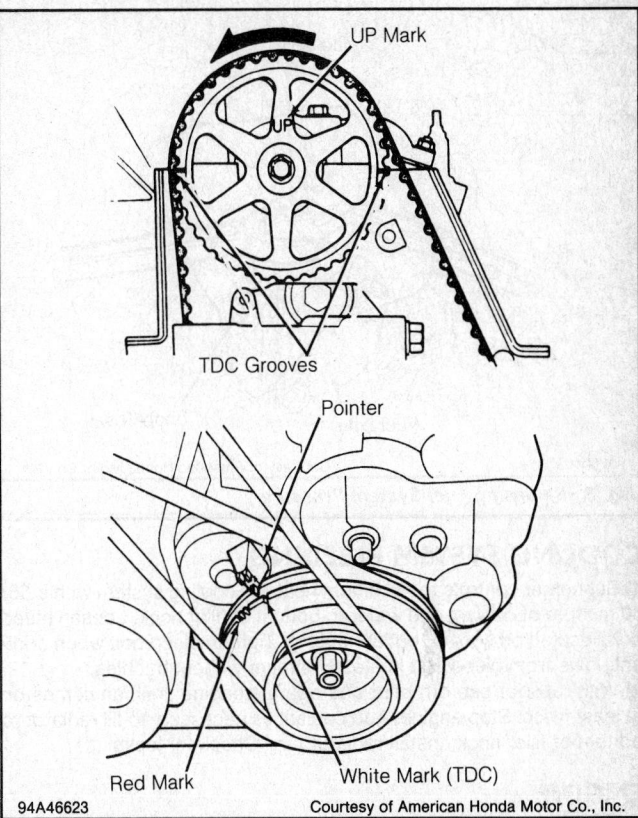

Fig. 1: Positioning Camshaft Sprocket For Valve Adjustment

NOTE: For engine information on Passport, refer to Rodeo in appropriate Isuzu ENGINES article.

NOTE: For repair procedures not covered in this article, see ENGINE OVERHAUL PROCEDURES article in GENERAL INFORMATION.

ENGINE IDENTIFICATION

Engine serial number is located on exhaust side of engine block, below cylinder head water outlet. First 5 characters of engine serial number identify engine type.

ENGINE CODE

Application	Code
2.2L SOHC VTEC	[1] F22B1
2.2L SOHC	F22B2

[1] – Equipped with dual exhaust manifold.

ADJUSTMENTS

VALVE CLEARANCE ADJUSTMENT

CAUTION: Always rotate engine in direction of normal rotation (counterclockwise as viewed from front of engine). Clockwise rotation may cause timing belt slip.

1) Adjust valves when engine temperature is 100°F (38°C) or less. Remove valve cover. Rotate crankshaft counterclockwise until No. 1 piston is at TDC of compression stroke. UP mark on camshaft pulley will be at top. *See Fig. 1.* Align grooves on camshaft pulley with top surface of cylinder head. Distributor rotor should point toward No. 1 spark plug wire.

2) Adjust valve clearance for both valves on No. 1 cylinder to specification. Loosen lock nut. Turn adjustment screw until clearance is correct. See VALVE CLEARANCE SPECIFICATIONS table. Tighten lock nut to specification. See TORQUE SPECIFICATIONS.

3) Rotate crankshaft 180 degrees counterclockwise (camshaft pulley will turn 90 degrees). UP mark on camshaft pulley will be on exhaust side of engine. Adjust valve clearance on both valves for No. 3 cylinder.

4) Rotate crankshaft 180 degrees counterclockwise. Grooves on camshaft pulley will align with cylinder head surface, and UP mark will face downward. Adjust valve clearance on both valves for No. 4 cylinder.

5) Rotate crankshaft 180 degrees counterclockwise. UP mark on camshaft pulley will be on intake side. Adjust valve clearance on both valves for No. 2 cylinder. Tighten crankshaft pulley bolt to specification if it loosened during adjustment procedure.

6) Apply nonhardening sealant to rounded surfaces of front and rear camshaft caps before installing valve cover gasket. Install valve cover. Tighten nuts to specification. See TORQUE SPECIFICATIONS.

VALVE CLEARANCE SPECIFICATIONS

Application	In. (mm)
Intake Valves	.009-.011 (.24-.28)
Exhaust Valves	.011-.013 (.28-.32)

TIMING & BALANCE SHAFT BELT ADJUSTMENT

Ensure engine is cold. With valve cover removed, rotate crankshaft until No. 1 piston is at TDC. Loosen tension adjuster nut approximately 2/3 turn. Tighten adjuster nut temporarily. *See Fig. 2.* Rotate crankshaft 3 teeth counterclockwise on camshaft pulley to apply tension to timing belt. Again loosen adjuster nut, then tighten to specification. See TORQUE SPECIFICATIONS.

REMOVAL & INSTALLATION

NOTE: For installation reference, label all electrical connectors, vacuum hoses, and fuel lines before removal. Also place mating marks on major assemblies before removal.

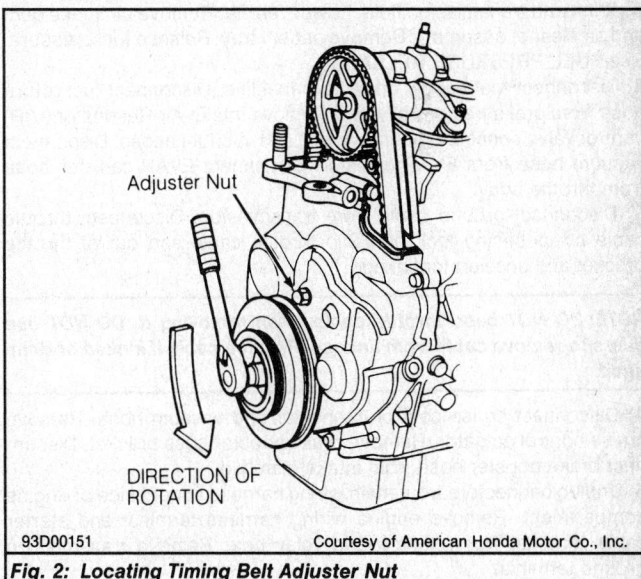

Fig. 2: Locating Timing Belt Adjuster Nut

FUEL PRESSURE RELEASE

CAUTION: Fuel system is under pressure. Release pressure before servicing fuel system components.

Remove fuel tank filler cap. Place shop towel on top of fuel filter. Release fuel injection system pressure by slowly loosening fuel injection service bolt. *See Fig. 3.*

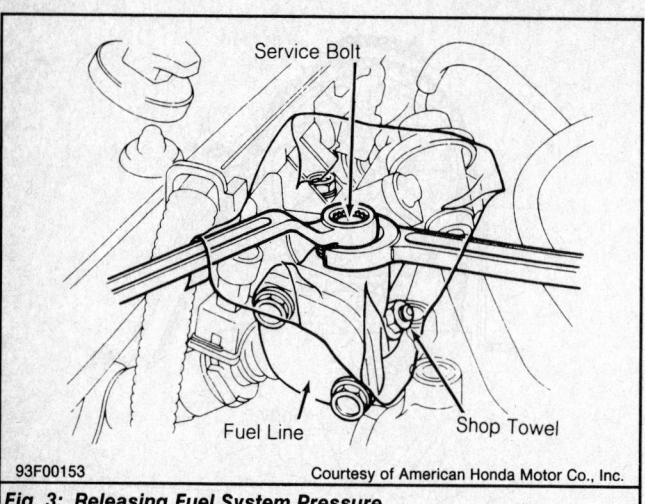

93F00153   Courtesy of American Honda Motor Co., Inc.

Fig. 3: Releasing Fuel System Pressure

COOLING SYSTEM BLEEDING

1) Set heater controls to maximum heat. Fill cooling system with a 50/50 mixture of coolant and water to bottom of filler neck. Loosen bleed bolt, located on coolant outlet housing. Tighten bleed bolt when coolant flows from bleed bolt in steady stream without bubbles.

2) With radiator cap off, start and operate engine until fan comes on at least twice. Stop engine. Add coolant as necessary to fill radiator to bottom of filler neck. Install radiator cap. Check for leaks.

ENGINE

Removal – 1) Disconnect battery cables. Remove battery. Secure hood in vertical position. Raise and support vehicle. Drain engine oil, coolant, and transmission fluid. Lower vehicle. Remove air intake duct and air cleaner assembly. Remove battery tray. Release fuel pressure. See FUEL PRESSURE RELEASE.

2) Disconnect fuel supply hose from fuel line. Disconnect fuel return hose from pressure control valve. Remove Intake Air Resonator (IAR) control valve connector. Remove IAR and vacuum hoses. Disconnect vacuum hose from EVAP canister. Disconnect EVAP canister hose from throttle body.

3) Disconnect ground cable from transmission. Disconnect throttle cable by loosening lock nut. Slip throttle cable end out of throttle bracket and accelerator linkage.

NOTE: DO NOT bend throttle cable when removing it. DO NOT use pliers to remove cable from linkage. Replace cable if kinked or damaged.

4) Disconnect cruise control connector and vacuum hose. Remove cruise control actuator. Remove brake booster hose bracket. Disconnect brake booster hose from intake manifold.

5) Unplug connectors from main wiring harness at right side of engine compartment. Remove engine wiring harness terminal and starter cable terminal from clamps and relay box. Remove transmission ground terminal.

6) Unplug connectors from main wiring harness and resistor at left side of engine compartment. Disconnect engine ground wire from valve cover. Remove power steering pump bracket.

7) Remove power steering and air conditioning drive belts. Remove mounting bolts from power steering pump. Without disconnecting hoses, pull pump away from mounting bracket. Remove mounting bolts from A/C compressor. Without disconnecting hoses, pull A/C compressor away from mounting bracket.

8) Disconnect heater inlet hose from cylinder head. Disconnect heater outlet hose from connector fitting. Disconnect radiator hoses, A/T cooler lines (if equipped), and fan connectors. Remove radiator assembly.

9) Remove speed sensor, leaving hoses and wiring attached. Remove center support beam. Disconnect Heated Oxygen Sensor (HO2S) connector. Remove exhaust pipe and bracket. Remove drive axles. See FWD AXLE SHAFTS article in DRIVE AXLES.

10) On M/T models, disconnect clutch release hose from clutch damper on transmission housing. Disconnect shift cable and select cable with bracket from transmission. DO NOT bend cables when removing it. DO NOT use pliers to remove cables. Always replace kinked or damaged cable.

11) On A/T models, remove engine stiffener brace, torque converter cover, cable holder, shift control lever bolt, and shift control cable. DO NOT bend shift control cable when removing. DO NOT use pliers to remove cable. Always replace kinked or damaged cable.

12) Attach engine hoist to engine. Remove all slack from chain. Remove rear engine mounting bolt. Remove front engine mounting bolt. Remove side transmission mount and mounting bolt. Ensure engine/transaxle assembly is free of all attachments. Lift engine and transaxle from vehicle.

Installation – 1) To install, reverse removal procedure. Tighten engine/transaxle mounts to specification in proper sequence. *See Fig. 4.* Improper tightening of engine mounts will result in engine vibration and premature mount wear.

2) Use NEW spring clips when installing drive axles. Install drive axles until spring clip clicks into groove of differential side gear. Ensure all wires and hoses are connected properly. Ensure cables are mounted properly.

3) Adjust throttle cable tension. On M/T equipped models, adjust clutch pedal free play. See CLUTCH PEDAL under ADJUSTMENTS in FWD article in CLUTCHES. Verify transaxle shifts smoothly. On A/T models, ensure range indicator agrees with actual transaxle range.

4) Adjust drive belt tension. Fill fluids to proper level. After installation is complete, turn ignition on. Inspect for fuel leakage. Repeat procedure 2 or 3 times. Ensure no fuel leaks exist. Bleed cooling system. See COOLING SYSTEM BLEEDING.

INTAKE MANIFOLD

Removal & Installation – 1) Disconnect battery negative cable. Drain cooling system. Release fuel pressure. See FUEL PRESSURE RELEASE. Disconnect fuel supply line. Disconnect vacuum, breather, and air inlet hoses. Remove water by-pass hose from cylinder head.

2) Disconnect EVAP canister hose from throttle body. On A/T models, remove brake booster vacuum hose and bracket from intake manifold. On all models, disconnect fuel return line and cruise control vacuum hose. Disconnect throttle cable from throttle body.

3) Disconnect or remove wiring and sensor connectors from intake manifold as required. Disconnect upper radiator hose and heater inlet hose from cylinder head. Remove heater outlet pipe bracket bolt from intake manifold. Remove cruise control servo, leaving cable attached.

4) Raise and support vehicle. Remove splash shield. Remove intake manifold bracket and intake manifold. Remove throttle body and air control components from manifold as required.

5) To install, reverse removal procedure. Using a crisscross pattern, tighten intake manifold nuts in 2 or 3 stages to specification. See TORQUE SPECIFICATIONS.

EXHAUST MANIFOLD

Removal – Disconnect oxygen sensor connector. Remove exhaust manifold heat shield. Raise and support vehicle. Remove splash shield. Disconnect exhaust pipe from exhaust manifold. Remove exhaust manifold bracket. Remove exhaust manifold nuts and manifold. Remove gasket.

Installation – To install, reverse removal procedure. Clean gasket surfaces. Install exhaust manifold with new gasket. Using a crisscross pattern, tighten exhaust manifold nuts in 2 or 3 stages to specification. See TORQUE SPECIFICATIONS.

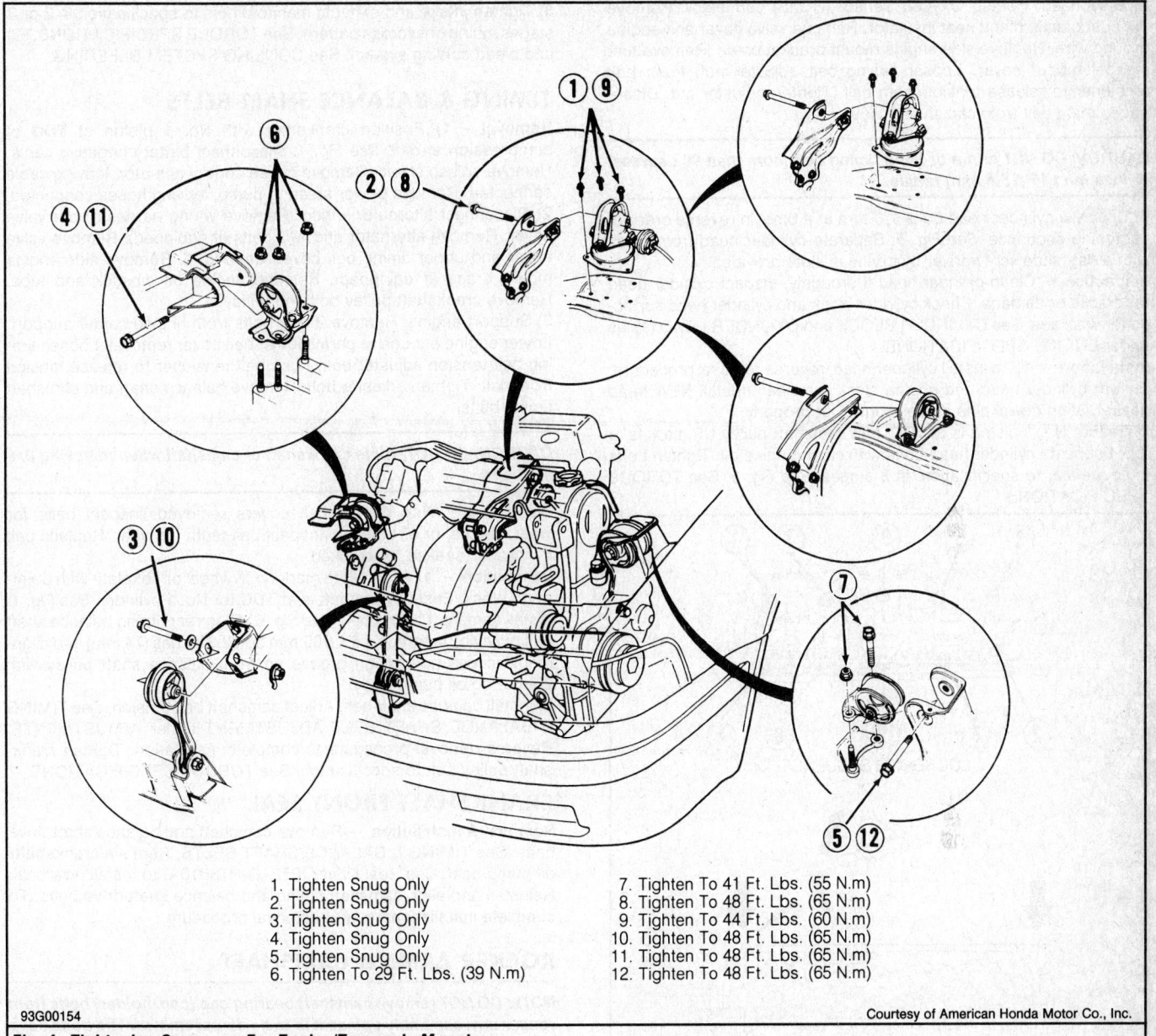

1. Tighten Snug Only
2. Tighten Snug Only
3. Tighten Snug Only
4. Tighten Snug Only
5. Tighten Snug Only
6. Tighten To 29 Ft. Lbs. (39 N.m)
7. Tighten To 41 Ft. Lbs. (55 N.m)
8. Tighten To 48 Ft. Lbs. (65 N.m)
9. Tighten To 44 Ft. Lbs. (60 N.m)
10. Tighten To 48 Ft. Lbs. (65 N.m)
11. Tighten To 48 Ft. Lbs. (65 N.m)
12. Tighten To 48 Ft. Lbs. (65 N.m)

93G00154

Courtesy of American Honda Motor Co., Inc.

Fig. 4: Tightening Sequence For Engine/Transaxle Mounts

CYLINDER HEAD

CAUTION: To avoid damage to cylinder head, DO NOT remove cylinder head until coolant temperature is less than 100°F (38°C).

Removal – 1) Inspect timing belt before removing cylinder head. Rotate crankshaft until No. 1 piston is at TDC of compression stroke. *See Fig. 1.* Mark all emission hoses before disconnecting or removing. Disconnect battery negative cable. Drain cooling system.
2) Release fuel pressure. See FUEL PRESSURE RELEASE. Disconnect fuel supply hose at fuel rail. Disconnect vacuum hoses, breather hose, and air intake duct. Remove water by-pass hose from cylinder head. Disconnect EVAP canister hose from throttle body.
3) On A/T models, disconnect brake booster vacuum hose. Remove vacuum hose bracket from intake manifold. On all models, disconnect fuel return hose. Disconnect cruise control vacuum hose. Disconnect throttle cable from throttle body.

NOTE: DO NOT bend cables when removing. DO NOT use pliers to remove cable from linkage. Always replace kinked or damaged cables.

4) Disconnect spark plug wires. Place reference mark on distributor for installation reference. Remove distributor. Remove Intake Air Resonator (IAR) control valve connector. Remove IAR and vacuum hoses.
5) Unplug alternator connector. Remove engine wiring harness from valve cover. Unplug engine wiring harness connectors. Remove harness clamps from cylinder head and intake manifold. Unplug all necessary electrical connectors from intake manifold and cylinder head.
6) Disconnect upper radiator hose and heater inlet hose from cylinder head. Remove heater outlet pipe bracket bolt. Remove thermostat. Remove cruise control actuator. Remove power steering pump, leaving hoses connected.
7) Raise and support vehicle. Remove front wheels and splash shield. Remove intake manifold bracket bolts and intake manifold. See INTAKE MANIFOLD under REMOVAL & INSTALLATION.

8) Disconnect Heated Oxygen Sensor (HO2S) connector. Remove exhaust manifold and heat insulator. Remove valve cover and engine ground wire. Remove side engine mount bracket brace. Remove timing belt upper cover. Loosen timing belt adjuster nut. Push belt tensioner to release tension from belt. Tighten adjuster nut. Disengage timing belt from camshaft pulley.

CAUTION: DO NOT crimp or bend timing belt more than 90 degrees, or less than 1" (25.4 mm) radius.

9) Unscrew cylinder head bolts 1/3 turn at a time, in reverse order of tightening sequence. *See Fig. 5.* Separate cylinder head from block with a flat-blade screwdriver by prying in slots provided.
Inspection – Clean cylinder head thoroughly. Inspect cylinder head for cracks or damage. Check cylinder block and cylinder head surfaces for warpage. See CYLINDER BLOCK and CYLINDER HEAD tables under ENGINE SPECIFICATIONS.
Installation – **1)** To install cylinder head, reverse removal procedure. Ensure cylinder head and engine block are clean. Install NEW head gasket. Align dowel pins and oil control jet properly.
2) Ensure No. 1 piston is at TDC, and camshaft pulley UP mark is at top. Lubricate cylinder head bolts with clean engine oil. Tighten bolts in sequence, to specification, in 3 stages. *See Fig. 5.* See TORQUE SPECIFICATIONS.

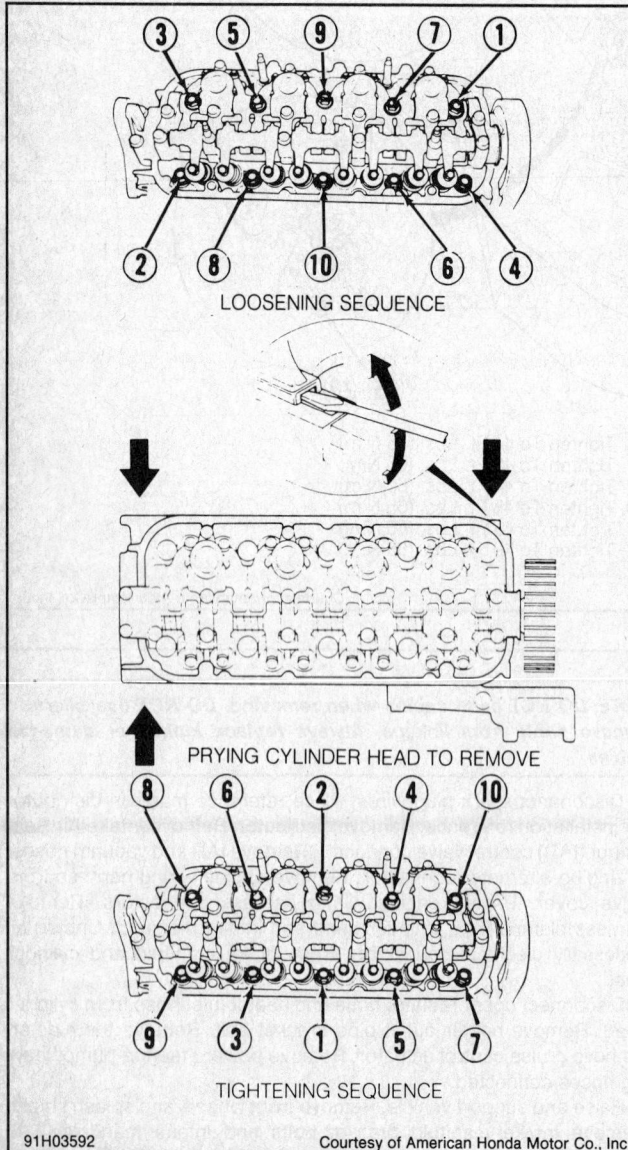

LOOSENING SEQUENCE

PRYING CYLINDER HEAD TO REMOVE

TIGHTENING SEQUENCE

91H03592   Courtesy of American Honda Motor Co., Inc.

Fig. 5: Removing & Installing Cylinder Head

3) Tighten intake and exhaust manifold nuts to specification in 2 or 3 stages, using crisscross pattern. See TORQUE SPECIFICATIONS. Fill and bleed cooling system. See COOLING SYSTEM BLEEDING.

TIMING & BALANCE SHAFT BELTS

Removal – **1)** Position crankshaft with No. 1 piston at TDC of compression stroke. *See Fig. 1.* Disconnect battery negative cable. Remove splash shield. Remove cruise control actuator, leaving cable connected. Remove power steering pump, leaving hoses connected.
2) Disconnect alternator wiring. Remove wiring harness from valve cover. Remove alternator and A/C belts (if equipped). Remove valve cover and upper timing belt cover. *See Fig. 6.* Remove side engine mount brace (if equipped). Remove engine oil dipstick and tube. Remove crankshaft pulley bolt and pulley.
3) Support engine. Remove 2 rear bolts from engine center support. Lower engine enough to permit lower belt cover removal. Loosen timing belt tension adjuster bolt. Push belt tensioner to release tension from belt. Tighten adjuster bolt. Remove balance shaft and camshaft timing belts.

CAUTION: DO NOT rotate crankshaft or camshaft when removing timing belts.

Inspection – With belt or belt covers removed, inspect belts for wear, cracks, or oil soaking. Inspect belt teeth for wear. Replace belt if worn, oil soaked, or cracked.
Installation – **1)** Align White mark on flywheel or flexplate with pointer on block. Ensure camshaft is at TDC for No. 1 cylinder. *See Fig. 1.* Install camshaft timing belt. *See Fig. 6.* Align rear timing balance shaft belt pulley by inserting a 6 x 100 mm bolt 2.9 inches (74 mm) into alignment access hole. Align groove on front balance shaft pulley with pointer on oil pump body.
2) Install balance shaft belt. Adjust camshaft belt tension. See TIMING & BALANCE SHAFT BELT ADJUSTMENT under ADJUSTMENTS. Reverse removal procedure to complete installation. Tighten crankshaft pulley bolt to specification. See TORQUE SPECIFICATIONS.

CRANKSHAFT FRONT SEAL

Removal & Installation – Remove camshaft and balance shaft drive belts. See TIMING & BALANCE SHAFT BELTS. Remove crankshaft/oil pump seal. Use Seal Driver (07LAD-PT3010A) to install new seal. Reinstall and align camshaft timing and balance shaft drive belts. To complete installation, reverse removal procedure.

ROCKER ARMS & CAMSHAFT

NOTE: DO NOT remove camshaft bearing cap (cam holder) bolts from rocker arm assembly unless it is to be disassembled. The bolts keep cam holders, springs, and rocker arms on shaft.

Removal – **1)** Ensure No. 1 piston is at TDC of compression stroke. UP mark on camshaft pulley should be at top, and grooves on camshaft pulley should align with cylinder head surface. *See Fig. 1.* Remove timing and balance shaft belts. See TIMING & BALANCE SHAFT BELTS.
2) Remove camshaft pulley bolt, special washer, camshaft pulley, and key. Remove back cover. Place reference mark on distributor for installation reference. Remove distributor. Loosen all rocker arm adjuster screws.
3) Pry camshaft toward front of cylinder head. Attach dial indicator and zero it against pulley end of camshaft. Pry camshaft away from dial indicator to measure end play. See CAMSHAFT table under ENGINE SPECIFICATIONS. If end play exceeds limit, replace camshaft.
4) On F22B1 engine, secure intake rocker arm sets with rubber bands to prevent disassembly during removal. *See Fig. 7.* On all applications, unscrew camshaft bearing cap bolts by turning bolts 2 turns at a time in a crisscross pattern. DO NOT remove cam holder bolts when removing rocker arm assembly. Bolts keep cam holders, springs, and rocker arms on shafts. *See Fig. 7 or 8.* Remove rocker arm assembly.

1994 ENGINES
2.2L 4-Cylinder – Accord (Cont.)

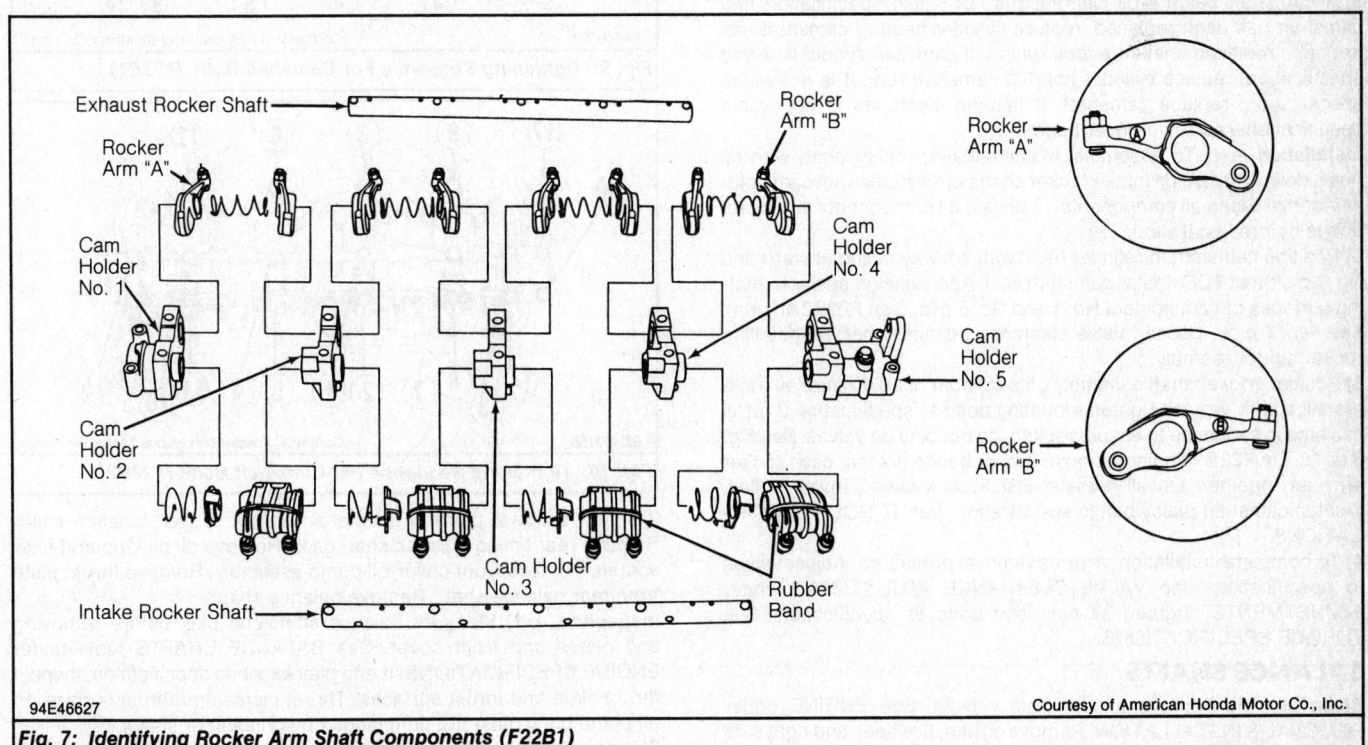

2.913" (74.0 mm)
6 x 100 mm Bolt
Mark
Maintenance Hole
Rear Balancer Shaft
Rear Balancer Shaft
Maintenance Hole
Washer
Maintenance Hole Plug
Alignment Drift
Valve Cover
Rubber Seals
Align Groove On Driven Pulley And Pointer On Oil Pump Body
Adjusting Nut
Upper Cover
Rubber Seals
Timing Belt
Key
Rubber Seals
Adjusting Nut 8 x 1.25 mm
Front Timing Balancer Driven Pulley
Special Bolt 14 x 1.25 mm
Crankshaft Pulley
Lower Cover
6 x 1.0 mm Bolts
Timing Balancer Belt
Timing Balancer Belt Drive Pulley
Rear Timing Balancer Belt Driven Pulley
91J03593
Courtesy of American Honda Motor Co., Inc.

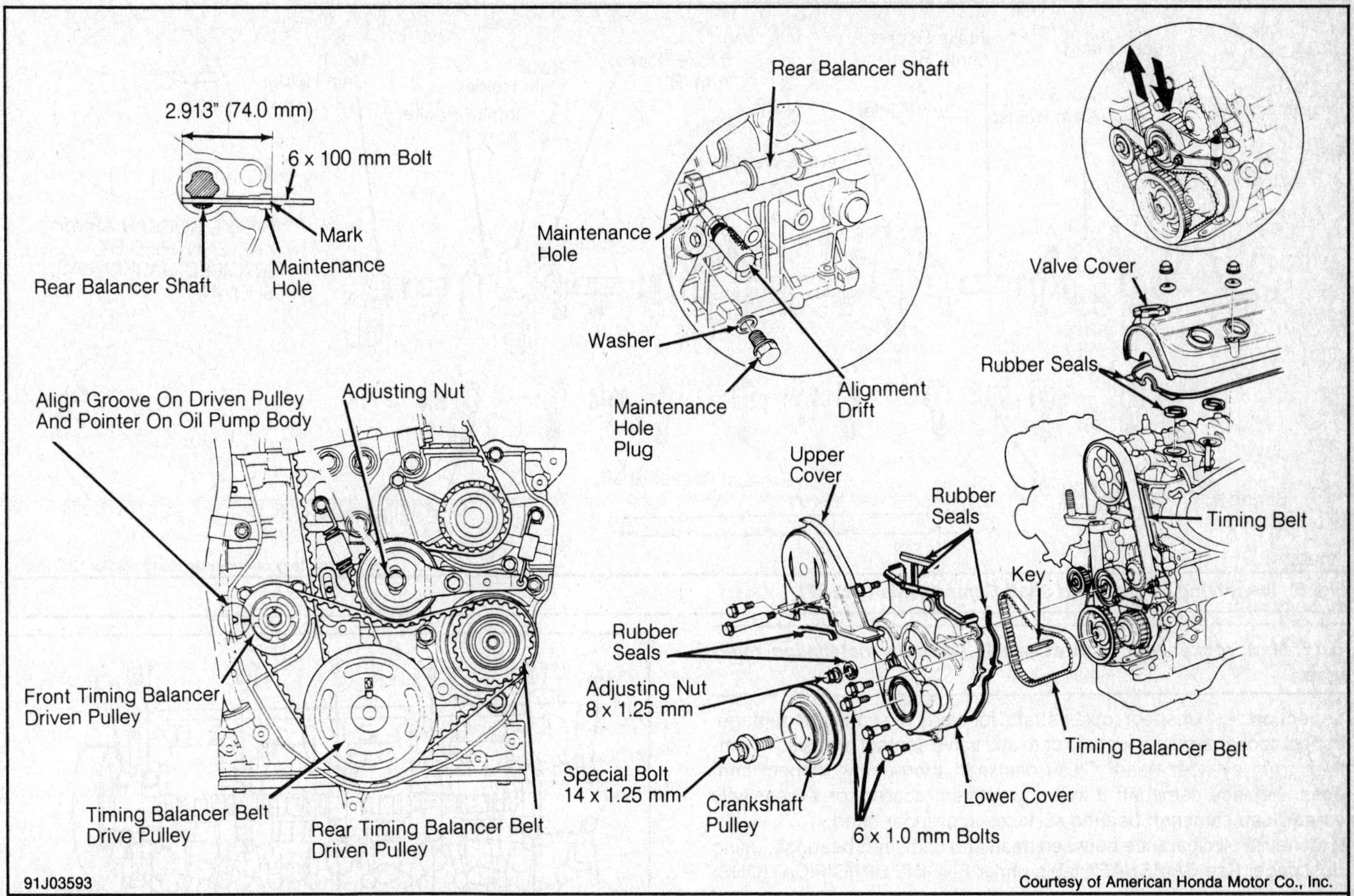

Fig. 6: Removing/Installing Timing & Balance Shaft Belts

Exhaust Rocker Shaft
Rocker Arm "B"
Rocker Arm "A"
Rocker Arm "A"
Cam Holder No. 1
Cam Holder No. 4
Cam Holder No. 5
Cam Holder No. 2
Rocker Arm "B"
Cam Holder No. 3
Rubber Band
Intake Rocker Shaft
94E46627
Courtesy of American Honda Motor Co., Inc.

Fig. 7: Identifying Rocker Arm Shaft Components (F22B1)

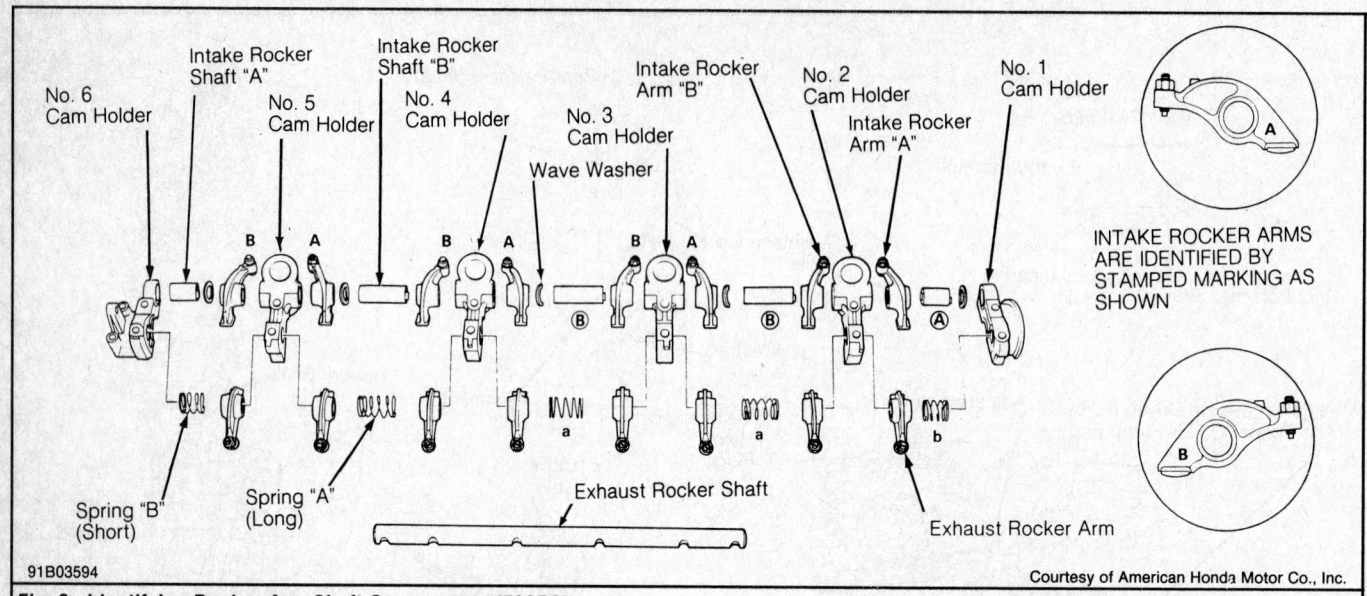

Fig. 8: Identifying Rocker Arm Shaft Components (F22B2)

NOTE: Mark rocker arm shaft assembly parts for installation reference.

Inspection – 1) Inspect rocker shafts for signs of scoring or damage. Inspect rocker arms for wear in cam and valve contact areas. Lift camshaft from cylinder head. Clean camshaft thoroughly. Inspect cam lobes. Replace camshaft if lobes are pitted, scored, or excessively worn. Clean camshaft bearing surfaces in cylinder head.

2) Measure oil clearance between head and camshaft bearings, using Plastigage. See CAMSHAFT table under ENGINE SPECIFICATIONS. Inspect rocker shafts for correct outside diameter, out-of-round, and straightness. Measure rocker arm bore diameter.

3) If camshaft bearing oil clearance is not within specification and camshaft has been replaced, replace cylinder head. If camshaft has not been replaced, measure total runout. If camshaft runout is within specification, replace cylinder head. If camshaft runout is not within specification, replace camshaft. If bearing clearance is not within specification, replace cylinder head.

Installation – 1) To assemble, install exhaust rocker shaft with oil holes downward. Align intake rocker shafts projections with cam holder indents. Clean all components. Lubricate all components at contact points before installation.

2) Position camshaft in cylinder head with keyway facing upward and No. 1 piston at TDC. Install camshaft seal. Apply gasket sealer to mating surfaces of cam holders No. 1 and No. 5 (No. 6 on F22B2 engine). *See Fig. 7 or 8.* Loosen valve clearance adjusters before installing rocker shaft assembly.

3) Position rocker shaft assembly onto cylinder head. Ensure all rockers align with valves. Tighten mounting bolts to specification 2 turns at a time in sequence to ensure rockers do not bind on valves. *See Fig. 8 or 10.* On F22B1 engine, remove rubber bands holding each rocker arm set together. On all models, install back cover. Install pulley. Tighten camshaft pulley bolt to specification. See TORQUE SPECIFICATIONS.

4) To complete installation, reverse removal procedure. Adjust valves to specification. See VALVE CLEARANCE ADJUSTMENT under ADJUSTMENTS. Tighten all nuts and bolts to specification. See TORQUE SPECIFICATIONS.

BALANCE SHAFTS

Removal – 1) Remove engine from vehicle. See ENGINE under REMOVAL & INSTALLATION. Remove oil pan, flywheel, and right side crankshaft oil seal cover. Remove timing belts. See TIMING & BALANCE SHAFT BELTS . Remove balance shaft drive gear case. *See Fig. 11.* Insert a screwdriver into front balance shaft to prevent rotation. Remove pulley.

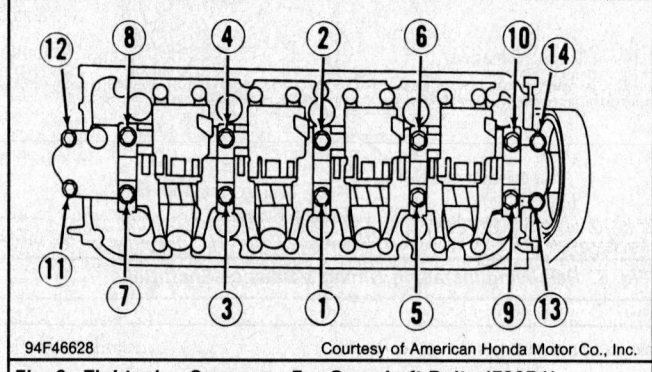

Fig. 9: Tightening Sequence For Camshaft Bolts (F22B1)

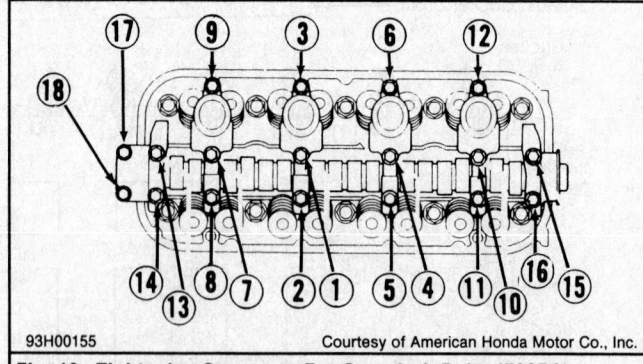

Fig. 10: Tightening Sequence For Camshaft Bolts (F22B2)

2) Insert a dowel pin into maintenance hole of rear balance shaft. Remove rear timing balance shaft gear. Remove oil pick-up and filter screen. Remove front cover/oil pump assembly. Remove thrust plate from rear balance shaft. Remove balance shafts.

Inspection – 1) Measure balance shaft end play before removing end plates and front cover. See BALANCE SHAFTS table under ENGINE SPECIFICATIONS. If end play exceeds specification, inspect thrust plate and thrust surfaces. Thrust plates and thrust surface on oil pump body must not be changed by grinding or shimming.

2) Inspect surface of balance shaft journal and balance shaft bearing. Replace if worn, damaged, or discolored. When replacing front bearing on rear balance shaft, replace oil pump body. Measure diameter of front and rear ends of bearing journals. Taper should not exceed .002" (.05 mm). Using "V" blocks, support shaft on front and rear bearings. Measure journal runout and diameter. See BALANCE SHAFTS table under ENGINE SPECIFICATIONS.

Installation – **1)** Insert balance shafts into engine block. Install thrust plate onto front balance shaft. Install right side cover, using liquid gasket. Install parts within 20 minutes of gasket application. Allow 30 minutes after installation before filling engine with oil.

2) Lubricate balance shaft and inner oil pump seal. Install oil pump cover. Install oil pick-up and filter screen. Lubricate all thrust surfaces of balance drive gears. Hold rear balance shaft with dowel, and install driven gear. Hold front balance shaft with a screwdriver, and install driven pulley.

3) Use dowel to align rear balance shaft. *See Fig. 11.* Align groove on balance shaft pulley with pointer on balance gear case. Install balance gear case. There is an additional mark on one pulley tooth for belt alignment.

4) To complete installation, reverse removal procedure. Tighten all nuts and bolts to specifications. See TORQUE SPECIFICATIONS.

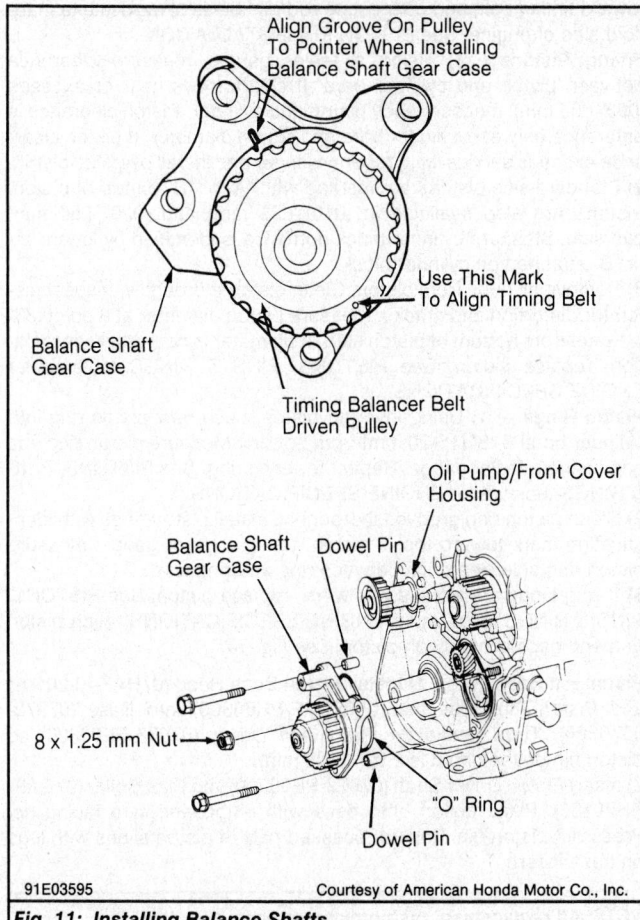

Align Groove On Pulley To Pointer When Installing Balance Shaft Gear Case

Use This Mark To Align Timing Belt

Balance Shaft Gear Case

Timing Balancer Belt Driven Pulley

Oil Pump/Front Cover Housing

Balance Shaft Gear Case

Dowel Pin

8 x 1.25 mm Nut

"O" Ring

Dowel Pin

91E03595   Courtesy of American Honda Motor Co., Inc.

Fig. 11: Installing Balance Shafts

REAR CRANKSHAFT SEAL

Removal & Installation – **1)** Remove transaxle assembly. Remove flywheel or drive plate. See appropriate article in CLUTCHES (manual transaxle) or TRANSMISSION SERVICING (automatic transaxle). Pry seal from rear seal plate. Clean crankshaft seal surface and seal plate. Lubricate seal lips and crankshaft with a light coating of grease.

2) Install seal with part number facing outward. Use Seal Driver (07749-0010000) to install drive seal into seal plate. Align hole in seal driver with pin on crankshaft. Drive seal in until driver bottoms against block. To complete installation, reverse removal procedure. Tighten all nuts and bolts to specifications. See TORQUE SPECIFICATIONS.

WATER PUMP

Removal & Installation – **1)** Disconnect battery negative cable. Drain cooling system. Remove camshaft and balance shaft drive belts. See TIMING & BALANCE SHAFT BELTS. Remove water pump bolts, water pump, and "O" ring.

2) Clean and inspect cylinder block mating surface. Install NEW "O" ring. Install water pump. Tighten bolts to specification. See TORQUE SPECIFICATIONS. To complete installation, reverse removal procedure. Fill and bleed cooling system. See COOLING SYSTEM BLEEDING.

OIL PAN

Removal & Installation – **1)** Raise and support vehicle. Remove exhaust pipe and center support beam. Drain engine oil. Remove oil pan bolts and oil pan. Clean all gasket surfaces.

2) To install, position new gasket on pan. Apply liquid gasket to oil pan gasket at corners of rear seal radius. Tighten oil pan bolts to specification in 2 stages, in sequence. *See Fig. 12.* See TORQUE SPECIFICATIONS. Tighten oil pan drain plug to specification.

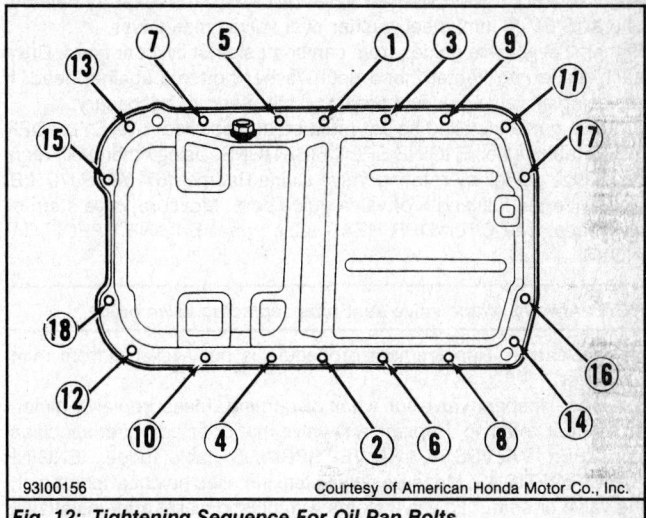

93I00156   Courtesy of American Honda Motor Co., Inc.

Fig. 12: Tightening Sequence For Oil Pan Bolts

OVERHAUL

CYLINDER HEAD

Cylinder Head – Ensure all mating surfaces are clean. Measure cylinder head warpage. If warpage is less than .002" (.05 mm), resurfacing is not required. If warpage is .002-.008" (.05-.20 mm), resurface cylinder head. Maximum resurface limit is .008" (.20 mm).

Valve Springs – Measure valve spring free length. Replace any spring shorter than minimum free length specification. See VALVES & VALVE SPRINGS table under ENGINE SPECIFICATIONS. Install springs with closer coils toward cylinder head. Check valve stem installed height.

Valve Stem Oil Seal Replacement – Mark valves and valve springs for reassembly reference. Tap each valve stem with a plastic mallet to loosen valve keepers. Remove valve keepers, collar, and spring. Use a valve seal puller to remove valve seals from valve guides.

NOTE: Intake and exhaust valve stem seals are NOT interchangeable. Intake seals have a White spring and exhaust seals have a Black spring around neck of seal.

Valve Guide Inspection – Measure valve guide clearance with a dial indicator placed on valve head. Lift valve .4" (10 mm) from seat. Rock valve stem from side to side. Valve guides can be replaced if valve stem oil clearance is not within specification. See CYLINDER HEAD table under ENGINE SPECIFICATIONS.

Valve Guide Removal – 1) Use a hot plate or oven to heat cylinder head to 300°F (150°C). Use valve guide driver, or fabricate valve guide remover from an air impact chisel. Using an air hammer and valve guide remover, drive valve guide 5/64" (2 mm) toward combustion chamber. This will remove carbon and make valve guide removal easier.

CAUTION: DO NOT heat cylinder head with a torch, or heat cylinder head hotter than 300°F (150°C). Excessive temperature may loosen valve seats.

2) Turn head over. Working from combustion chamber side of head, drive valve guide out toward camshaft side of head. If valve guide does not move, drill valve guide using a 5/16" drill bit, then try to drive it out again.

CAUTION: Drill guides in extreme cases only. Cylinder head damage can occur if valve guide breaks.

Valve Guide Installation – 1) Chill new valve guides in freezer for about one hour. Remove new valve guides from freezer as needed. Slip a 15/64" (6 mm) steel washer over valve guide driver.
2) Install new valve guides from camshaft side of cylinder head. Drive each guide into heated head until washer bottoms against head. If replacing all valve guides, reheat cylinder head as necessary.
3) Valve guide installed height must be as specified. See CYLINDER HEAD table under ENGINE SPECIFICATIONS. Using cutting oil, ream new valve guides by rotating Valve Guide Reamer (07HAH-PJ7010B) clockwise the full length of valve guide bore. Measure valve stem oil clearance. See CYLINDER HEAD table under ENGINE SPECIFICATIONS.

NOTE: Always reface valve seat after replacing valve guide.

Valve Seats – Replacement procedure is not available from manufacturer.
Valves – Inspect valve for wear or burning. Measure valve dimensions after refacing. Replace any valve that does not meet specification. See VALVES & VALVE SPRINGS table under ENGINE SPECIFICATIONS. Measure valve stem installed height after refinishing valve or seat. Tap valve stems with plastic mallet after installation to seat spring retainers and keepers.
Valve Seat Correction Angles – Replace valve guides, if necessary, before refacing valve seats. After refacing, if seat width is too wide, use 60-degree stone to raise seat, or 30-degree stone to lower seat. Ensure valve seat margin is within specification. See CYLINDER HEAD table under ENGINE SPECIFICATIONS.
Valve Stem Installed Height – After servicing valves, measure valve stem installed height. *See Fig. 13.* See VALVES & VALVE SPRINGS table under ENGINE SPECIFICATIONS. If valve stem installed height exceeds specification for any valve, replace valve. If valve stem installed height still exceeds limit, replace cylinder head.

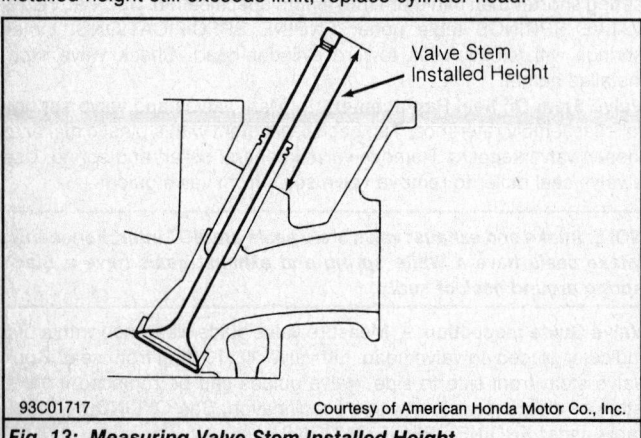

93C01717   Courtesy of American Honda Motor Co., Inc.

Fig. 13: Measuring Valve Stem Installed Height

VALVE TRAIN

Rocker Arm Shaft Assembly – Mark parts during disassembly for reassembly reference. Inspect rocker shafts and rocker arms for excessive wear or scoring. *See Fig. 7 or 8.* Service limit for clearance between rocker arm and rocker shaft is .003" (.08 mm). Replace shaft or rockers if worn beyond specification. Inspect rocker arm contact points for wear or scoring. Replace defective parts as necessary. Lubricate contact areas with engine oil before assembly.

CYLINDER BLOCK ASSEMBLY

NOTE: Reference numbers on connecting rods are for big end bore code, and do not indicate rod position in engine.

Piston & Rod Assembly – 1) Each rod is sorted into one of 4 tolerance ranges. Size depends on crank journal bore. A number between 1 and 4 is stamped on side of rod big end. Any combination of numbers between 1 and 4 may be found in any engine.
2) Install piston and connecting rod so arrow on top of piston points toward timing belt, and connecting rod oil hole is toward intake manifold side of engine. See PISTON PIN INSTALLATION.
Fitting Pistons – 1) Using a feeler gauge, measure clearance between piston and cylinder bore. If clearance is near or exceeds .002" (.05 mm), measure each piston and cylinder. Piston clearance is difference between cylinder bore and piston diameter. If piston clearance exceeds service limit, rebore cylinder and install oversize piston.
2) Standard size pistons are marked with "A" or "B" on top of piston. Pistons are also available in .010" (.25 mm) and .020" (.50 mm) oversize. Standard cylinder block bore size is identified by letters "A" or "B" stamped on cylinder block.
3) Remove all rings from piston. Clean piston thoroughly. Inspect piston for distortion and cracks. Measure piston diameter at a point .83" (21 mm) from bottom of piston skirt. If diameter is not within specification, replace piston. See PISTONS, PINS & RINGS table under ENGINE SPECIFICATIONS.
Piston Rings – 1) Using inverted piston, push new piston ring into cylinder bore .6-.8" (15-20 mm) from bottom. Measure piston ring end gap, using a feeler gauge. Repeat for each ring. See PISTONS, PINS & RINGS table under ENGINE SPECIFICATIONS.
2) Clean piston ring grooves thoroughly. Install piston rings with identification mark toward top of piston. Using a feeler gauge, measure piston ring side clearance between ring and ring land.
3) If ring lands are excessively worn, replace piston. See PISTONS, PINS & RINGS table under ENGINE SPECIFICATIONS. Align piston ring end gaps properly on piston. *See Fig. 14.*

Piston Pin Removal – 1) Install Piston Base Head (07HAF-PL20102) and Piston Pin Base Insert (07GAF-PH60300) into Base (07973-6570500). Turn handle on Piston Pin Driver (07973-PE00320) so piston pin driver length is 2.03" (51.5 mm).
2) Insert Piston Driver Shaft (07973-PE00310) into Pilot Collar (07GAF-PH70100). Place piston onto base with embossed side facing up. Press out piston pin. Ensure recessed part of piston aligns with lugs on base insert.

NOTE: All replacement piston pins are oversize.

Piston Pin Inspection – 1) Measure piston pin diameter. Measure piston pin bore in piston. Piston pin clearance is difference between the two measurements.
2) Piston pin clearance must be .0005-.0009" (.013-.024 mm). If piston pin clearance is greater than .0009" (.024 mm), install an oversize piston pin and recheck clearance.
3) Determine difference between piston pin diameter and connecting rod small end bore. Interference fit between piston pin and connecting rod must be .0005-.0013" (.013-.032 mm).
Piston Pin Installation – 1) Ensure piston and connecting rod are positioned as shown. *See Fig. 15.* Turn handle on Piston Pin Driver (07973-PE00320) so piston pin driver length is 2.03" (51.5 mm).

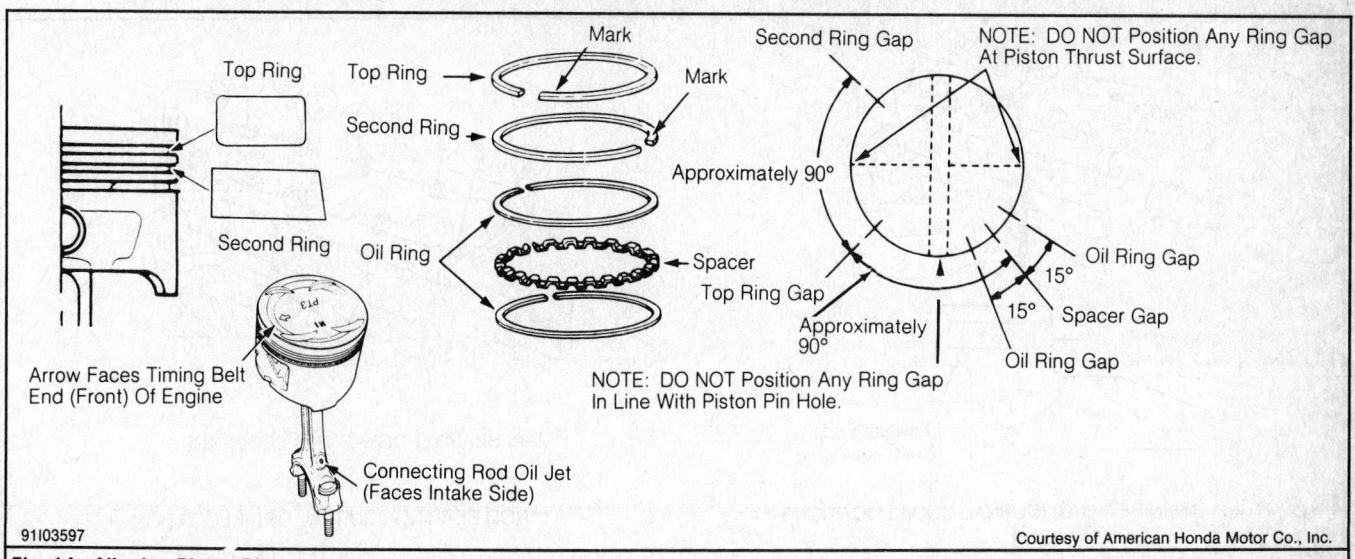

Fig. 14: Aligning Piston Rings

91I03597   Courtesy of American Honda Motor Co., Inc.

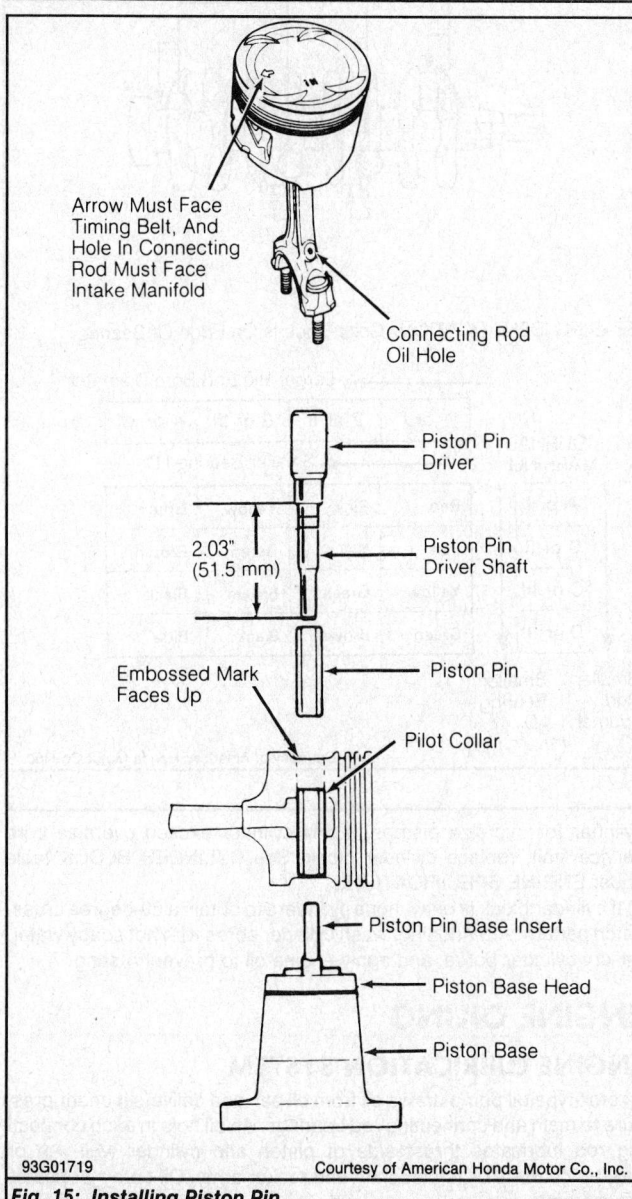

Fig. 15: Installing Piston Pin

93G01719   Courtesy of American Honda Motor Co., Inc.

2) Install Pilot Collar (07GAF-PH70100) into piston and connecting rod. Lubricate new piston pin lightly. Place piston onto base with embossed side facing up. Press in piston pin. See PISTONS, PINS & RINGS table under ENGINE SPECIFICATIONS.

Rod Bearings – 1) Using Plastigage, measure rod bearing oil clearance. Tighten bearing cap to 34 ft. lbs. (46 N.m). See CRANK-SHAFT, MAIN & CONNECTING ROD BEARINGS table under ENGINE SPECIFICATIONS.

2) If oil clearance is incorrect, install a new bearing set (same color code) and recheck oil clearance. DO NOT shim or file cap to adjust oil clearance.

3) If oil clearance is still incorrect, try the next larger or smaller bearing. Measure oil clearance again. If proper oil clearance cannot be obtained by using larger or smaller bearings, replace crankshaft and repeat procedure.

NOTE: A number code indicating connecting bore is stamped on side of each connecting rod and cap. Connecting rod journal diameter codes (letters) are stamped on crankshaft counterweights. See Fig. 16. Use both codes when ordering replacement bearings.

Crankshaft & Main Bearings – 1) Remove main bearing cap bridge and bearing caps in reverse order of sequence shown. *See Fig. 16.* Mark all bearing caps for reassembly reference. Lift crankshaft from block, being careful not to damage journals.

2) Using a lathe or "V" blocks to support crankshaft, measure crankshaft runout, out-of-round, and taper. If any measurement exceeds service limit, replace crankshaft. See CRANKSHAFT, MAIN & CONNECTING ROD BEARINGS table under ENGINE SPECIFICATIONS.

3) Install crankshaft into block. Measure main bearing oil clearance, using Plastigage. If engine is in vehicle, support counterweights, and measure only one bearing at a time. Before installing main bearing cap bolts, lubricate thrust washers and bolt threads. Tighten main bearing caps, in sequence, in 2 stages, first to 22 ft. lbs. (30 N.m), then to 54 ft. lbs. (73 N.m). *See Fig. 16.*

4) If oil clearance is incorrect, install a NEW bearing set (same color code) and recheck oil clearance. If oil clearance is still incorrect, try next larger or smaller bearing and measure oil clearance once more. If proper oil clearance cannot be obtained by using larger or smaller bearings, replace crankshaft and repeat procedure.

NOTE: A letter code indicating main journal bore diameters is stamped on cylinder block, on oil pan mating surface. See Fig. 14. Use these codes, together with crankshaft main journal diameter numbers, when ordering replacement bearings.

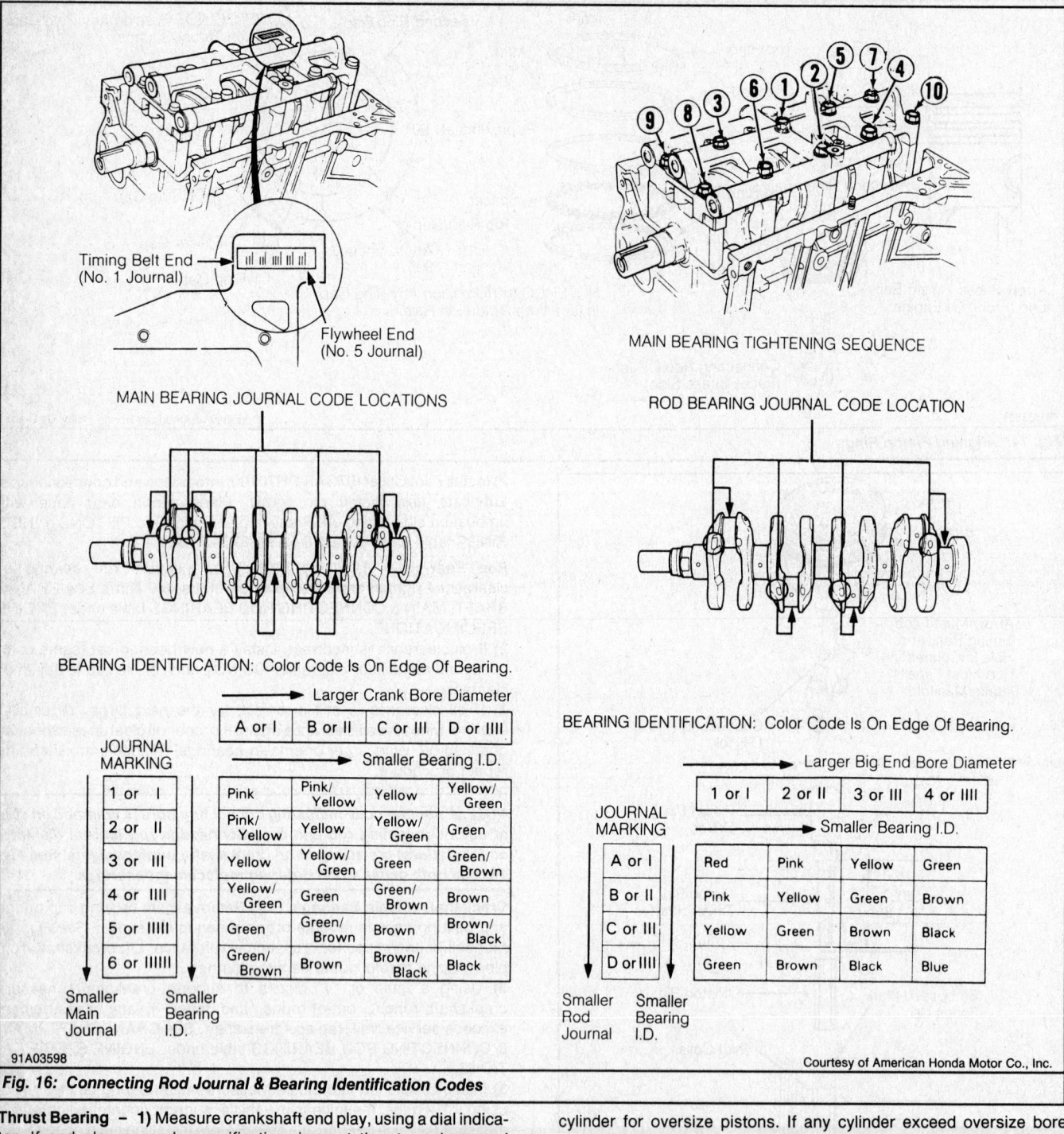

MAIN BEARING JOURNAL CODE LOCATIONS

MAIN BEARING TIGHTENING SEQUENCE

ROD BEARING JOURNAL CODE LOCATION

BEARING IDENTIFICATION: Color Code Is On Edge Of Bearing.

JOURNAL MARKING	Larger Crank Bore Diameter			
	A or I	B or II	C or III	D or IIII
	Smaller Bearing I.D.			
1 or I	Pink	Pink/Yellow	Yellow	Yellow/Green
2 or II	Pink/Yellow	Yellow	Yellow/Green	Green
3 or III	Yellow	Yellow/Green	Green	Green/Brown
4 or IIII	Yellow/Green	Green	Green/Brown	Brown
5 or IIIII	Green	Green/Brown	Brown	Brown/Black
6 or IIIIII	Green/Brown	Brown	Brown/Black	Black

Smaller Main Journal / Smaller Bearing I.D.

BEARING IDENTIFICATION: Color Code Is On Edge Of Bearing.

JOURNAL MARKING	Larger Big End Bore Diameter			
	1 or I	2 or II	3 or III	4 or IIII
	Smaller Bearing I.D.			
A or I	Red	Pink	Yellow	Green
B or II	Pink	Yellow	Green	Brown
C or III	Yellow	Green	Brown	Black
D or IIII	Green	Brown	Black	Blue

Smaller Rod Journal / Smaller Bearing I.D.

91A03598

Courtesy of American Honda Motor Co., Inc.

Fig. 16: Connecting Rod Journal & Bearing Identification Codes

Thrust Bearing – 1) Measure crankshaft end play, using a dial indicator. If end play exceeds specification, inspect thrust washers and thrust surface of crankshaft. See CRANKSHAFT, MAIN & CONNECTING ROD BEARINGS table under ENGINE SPECIFICATIONS.
2) Replace worn parts as necessary. Thrust washer thickness is fixed. DO NOT change thrust washer thickness by grinding or shimming. Install thrust washers with grooved side out.

CAUTION: After replacing any rod or main bearing, idle engine until it reaches normal operating temperature, then an additional 15 minutes.

Cylinder Block – 1) Measure cylinder block deck surface warpage. Service limit is .004" (.10 mm). Measure cylinder bore out-of-round and taper. If either out-of-round or taper exceeds .002" (.05 mm), rebore

cylinder for oversize pistons. If any cylinder exceed oversize bore service limit, replace cylinder block. See CYLINDER BLOCK table under ENGINE SPECIFICATIONS.
2) If cylinder block is okay, hone cylinders to obtain a 60-degree cross-hatch pattern. After honing, wash cylinder bores with hot soapy water. Air-dry cylinder bores, and apply engine oil to prevent rusting.

ENGINE OILING

ENGINE LUBRICATION SYSTEM

A rotor-type oil pump draws oil from oil pan and delivers it under pressure to main and connecting rod bearings. An oil hole in each connecting rod lubricates thrust side of piston and cylinder wall. An oil passage carries oil to camshaft and rocker arms. Oil spray lubricates valve stems.

Crankcase Capacity – Crankcase capacity, including oil filter, is 4.0 qts. (3.8L). Capacity is 5.2 qts. (4.9L) after engine overhaul.

Oil Pressure – Measure oil pressure relief valve with engine temperature at 176°F (80°C). At idle, minimum oil pressure should be 10 psi (0.7 kg/cm²). At 3000 RPM, minimum oil pressure should be 50 psi (3.5 kg/cm²).

OIL PUMP

Removal & Disassembly – Raise and support vehicle. Drain engine oil. Align No. 1 piston at TDC and remove timing belts. See TIMING & BALANCE SHAFT BELTS under REMOVAL & INSTALLATION. Remove oil pan and pick-up screen. Remove pump housing/front cover assembly. *See Fig. 17.* Remove pump cover from pump rotors. Remove oil seals.

Inspection – Check pump clearances. See OIL PUMP SPECIFICATIONS table. Remove rotors and examine for wear or damage.

Reassembly & Installation – Replace oil seals and "O" rings. Position rotors into pump housing. Install rotor cover on pump housing. Apply Loctite to cover screws, and tighten to 62 INCH lbs. (7 N.m). Fit dowel pins and NEW "O" rings to housing. To complete installation, reverse removal procedure.

OIL PUMP SPECIFICATIONS

Application	Specification
Capacity [1]	46.4 qts. (43.9L)
Standard	
Radial Clearance	
Inner Rotor-To-Outer Rotor	.0008-.0063" (.020-.160 mm)
Pump Body-To-Rotor	.0040-.0075" (.100-.190 mm)
Axial Clearance	
Pump Body-To-Rotor	.001-.003" (.02-.07 mm)
Service Limit	
Radial Clearance	
Inner Rotor-To-Outer Rotor	.008" (.20 mm)
Pump Body-To-Rotor	.0083" (.21 mm)
Axial Clearance	
Pump Body-To-Rotor	.005" (.12 mm)

[1] – Volume per minute at 6000 RPM.

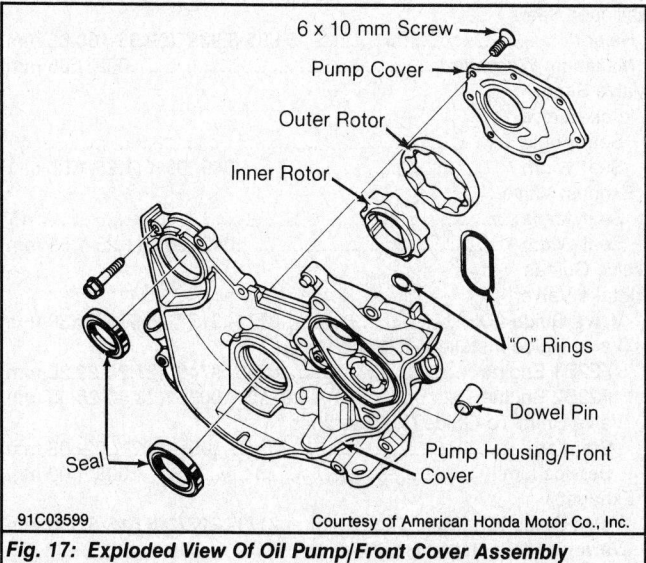

91C03599   Courtesy of American Honda Motor Co., Inc.

Fig. 17: Exploded View Of Oil Pump/Front Cover Assembly

Labels in figure: 6 x 10 mm Screw, Pump Cover, Outer Rotor, Inner Rotor, "O" Rings, Dowel Pin, Pump Housing/Front Cover, Seal

TORQUE SPECIFICATIONS

TORQUE SPECIFICATIONS

Application	Ft. Lbs. (N.m)
Balance Shaft Pulley Bolt	22 (30)
Belt Tensioner Adjuster Nut	32 (44)
Camshaft Pulley Bolt	27 (37)
Connecting Rod Nut	34 (46)
Crankshaft Pulley Bolt	162 (220)
Cylinder Head Bolt	
Stage 1	29 (39)
Stage 2	51 (69)
Stage 3	78 (98)
Drive Plate (Automatic Transaxle)	55 (74)
Exhaust Manifold Nut	23 (31)
Flywheel Bolt (Manual Transaxle)	76 (103)
Intake Manifold Nut	16 (22)
Main Bearing Cap Bolts/Bridge	
Stage 1	22 (30)
Stage 2	55 (74)
Oil Pan Bolts	10 (14)
Oil Pan Drain Plug	32 (44)
Rocker Arm Adjuster Lock Nut	15 (20)
Rocker Arm Mounting Bolts	
6-mm Bolt	[1]
8-mm Bolt	16 (22)
	INCH Lbs. (N.m)
Oil Pump Cover Screw	62 (7)
Oil Pump Housing Bolts	80 (9)
Valve Cover Cap Nut	90 (10)
VTEC Solenoid Bolt	106 (12)
Water Pump Bolt	106 (12)

[1] – Tighten to 108 INCH lbs. (12 N.m).

ENGINE SPECIFICATIONS

GENERAL SPECIFICATIONS

Application	Specification
Displacement	132 Cu. In. (2.2L)
Bore	
"A" Engine	3.3468-3.3472" (85.01-85.02 mm)
"B" Engine	3.3464-3.3468" (85.00-85.01 mm)
Stroke	3.74" (95 mm)
Compression Ratio	8.8:1
Fuel System	MFI
Horsepower @ RPM	
F22B1 Engine	145 @ 5600
F22B2 Engine	130 @ 5200
Torque Ft. Lbs. @ RPM	
F22B1 Engine	142 @ 4000
F22B2 Engine	139 @ 4500

CONNECTING RODS

Application	In. (mm)
Bore Diameter	
Pin Bore	.8649-.8654 (21.968-21.981)
Pin-To-Rod Interference Fit	.0005-.0013 (.013-.032)
Crankpin Bore	2.001 (51.00)
Side Play	
Standard	.006-.012 (.15-.30)
Service Limit	.016 (.40)

1994 ENGINES
2.2L 4-Cylinder – Accord (Cont.)

CRANKSHAFT, MAIN & CONNECTING ROD BEARINGS

Application	In. (mm)
Crankshaft	
End Play	
Standard	.004-.014 (.10-.35)
Service Limit	.018 (.45)
Runout	
Standard	.0012 (.03)
Service Limit	.0016 (.04)
Main Bearings	
Journal Diameter	
No. 1 & 4	1.9679-1.9688 (49.984-50.008)
No. 2	1.9676-1.9685 (49.976-50.000)
No. 3	1.9673-1.9683 (49.972-49.996)
No. 5	1.9680-1.9690 (49.988-50.012)
Journal Out-Of-Round	
Standard	.0002 (.005)
Service Limit	.0002 (.006)
Journal Taper	
Standard	.0002 (.005)
Service Limit	.0002 (.006)
Oil Clearance	
No. 1 & No. 4 Journal	
Standard	.0005-.0015 (.013-.037)
Service Limit	.002 (.05)
No. 2	
Standard	.0008-.0018 (.021-.045)
Service Limit	.002 (.05)
No. 3 Journal	
Standard	.0010-.0019 (.025-.049)
Service Limit	.002 (.05)
No. 5 Journal	
Standard	.0004-.0012 (.009-.033)
Service Limit	.002 (.05)
Connecting Rod Bearings	
Journal Diameter	1.8888-1.8898 (47.976-48.000)
Journal Out-Of-Round	
Standard	.0002 (.005)
Service Limit	.0002 (.006)
Journal Taper	
Standard	.0002 (.005)
Service Limit	.0002 (.006)
Oil Clearance	
Standard	.0008-.0019 (.021-.049)
Service Limit	.002 (.05)

CYLINDER BLOCK

Application	In. (mm)
Cylinder Bore	
"A" or "I" Block	
Standard Diameter	3.3468-3.3472 (85.010-85.020)
Service Limit	3.3492 (85.070)
Reboring Limit	.02 (.5)
"B" or "II" Block	
Standard Diameter	3.3465-3.3468 (85.000-85.010)
Service Limit	3.3492 (85.07)
Maximum Taper	.002 (.05)
Maximum Out-of-Round	.002 (.05)
Maximum Deck Warpage	
Standard	.003 (.07)
Service Limit	.004 (.10)

PISTONS, PINS & RINGS

Application	In. (mm)
Pistons	
Clearance	
Standard	.0008-.0016 (.020-.040)
Service Limit	.002 (.05)
Diameter [1]	
Except "B" Piston	
Standard	3.3456-3.3460 (84.980-84.990)
Service Limit	3.3452 (84.970)
"B" Piston	
Standard	3.3452-3.3456 (84.970-84.980)
Service Limit	3.3448 (84.960)
Pins	
Diameter	.8659-.8661 (21.994-22.000)
Piston Fit	.0004-.0009 (.010-.022)
Rod Fit	.0005-.0013 (.013-.032)
Rings	
Top Ring	
End Gap	.008-.014 (.20-.35)
Service Limit	.024 (.60)
Side Clearance	.0014-.0024 (.036-.060)
Service Limit	.005 (.13)
2nd Ring	
End Gap	.016-.022 (.40-.55)
Service Limit	.028 (.70)
Side Clearance	.0012-.0022 (.030-.055)
Service Limit	.005 (.13)
Oil Ring	
End Gap	.008-.028 (.20-.70)
Service Limit	.031 (.80)

[1] – Measure piston skirt diameter .83" (21.0 mm) from bottom of skirt.

CYLINDER HEAD

Application	Specification
Cylinder Head	
Height	3.935-3.939" (99.95-100.05 mm)
Maximum Warpage [1]	.002" (.05 mm)
Valve Seats	
Intake Valve	
Seat Angle	45°
Seat Width [2]	.049-.061" (1.25-1.55 mm)
Exhaust Valve	
Seat Angle	45°
Seat Width [2]	.049-.061" (1.25-1.55 mm)
Valve Guides	
Intake Valve	
Valve Guide I.D.	.2171-.2177" (5.515-5.530 mm)
Valve Guide Installed Height	
F22B1 Engine	.8346-.8740" (21.20-22.20 mm)
F22B2 Engine	.9252-1.0039" (23.50-25.50 mm)
Valve Stem-To-Guide Oil Clearance	
Standard	.001-.002" (.02-.05 mm)
Service Limit	.003" (.08 mm)
Exhaust	
Valve Guide I.D.	.2171-.2177" (5.515-5.530 mm)
Valve Guide Installed Height	
F22B1 Engine	.8122-.8516" (20.63-21.63 mm)
F22B2 Engine	.5826-.6220" (14.80-15.80 mm)
Valve Stem-To-Guide	
Oil Clearance	
Standard	.002-.003" (.05-.08 mm)
Service Limit	.005" (.12 mm)

[1] – Maximum warpage before resurfacing is required.
[2] – Maximum service limit is .079" (2.00 mm).

VALVES & VALVE SPRINGS

Application	Specification
Intake Valves	
Face Angle	45°
Head Diameter	
F22B1 Engine	1.335-1.343" (33.90-34.10 mm)
F22B2 Engine	1.256-1.264" (31.90-32.10 mm)
Overall Length	
F22B1 Engine	4.343-4.362" (110.30-110.80 mm)
F22B2 Engine	4.245-4.265" (107.82-108.32 mm)
Stem Diameter	
Standard	.2159-.2163" (5.485-5.495 mm)
Service Limit	.2148" (5.455 mm)
Seat Margin	
Standard	.033-.045" (.85-1.15 mm)
Service Limit	.026" (.65 mm)
Valve Stem Installed Height [1]	
F22B1 Engine	
Standard	1.8405-1.8720 (46.75-47.55)
Service Limit	1.9212 (48.80)
F22B2 Engine	
Standard	1.8929-1.9244 (48.08-48.88)
Service Limit	1.9342 (49.13)
Exhaust Valves	
Face Angle	45°
Head Diameter	1.138-1.146" (28.9-29.1 mm)
Overall Length	
F22B1 Engine	4.264-4.272" (108.30-108.50 mm)
F22B2 Engine	4.604-4.624" (116.95-117.45 mm)
Stem Diameter	
Standard	.2146-.2150" (5.450-5.460 mm)
Service Limit	.2134" (5.420 mm)
Seat Margin	
Standard	.041-.053" (1.05-1.35 mm)
Service Limit	.037" (.95 mm)
Valve Stem Installed Height [1]	
Standard	1.9732-2.0227 (50.15-50.95)
Service Limit	2.0197 (51.20)
Valve Spring Free Length	
Intake	
F22B1 Engine	2.0110" (51.08 mm)
F22B2 Engine	
Except Associated Manufactured	2.1031" (53.42 mm)
Associated Manufactured	2.1582" (54.82 mm)
Exhaust	
F22B1 Engine	2.1881" (55.58 mm)
F22B2 Engine	
Except Associated Manufactured	2.1519" (54.66 mm)
Associated Manufactured	2.2157" (56.28 mm)

[1] – Measure from stem tip of installed valve to spring seat surface.

CAMSHAFT

Application	In. (mm)
End Play	
Standard	.002-.006 (.05-.15)
Service Limit	.020 (.50)
Journal Diameter	[1]
Journal Runout	
Standard	.001 (.03)
Service Limit	.002 (.04)
Lobe Height	
F22B1 Engine	
Intake	
Primary	1.4872 (37.775)
Mid	1.5639 (39.725)
Secondary	1.3575 (34.481)
Exhaust	1.5266 (38.366)
F22B2 Engine	
Intake	1.5167 (38.526)
Exhaust	1.5266 (38.778)
Oil Clearance	
Standard	.002-.004 (.050-.089)
Service Limit	.006 (.15)

[1] – Information not available from manufacturer.

BALANCE SHAFTS

Application	In. (mm)
Journal Diameter	
No. 1	
Front Shaft	1.6820-1.6824 (42.722-42.734)
Rear Shaft	.8243-.8248 (20.938-20.950)
No. 2	1.5241-1.5246 (38.712-38.724)
No. 3	1.3670-1.3675 (34.722-34.734)
End Play	
Front Balance Shaft	.004-.016 (.10-.40)
Rear Balance Shaft	.004-.006 (.04-.15)
Runout (Maximum)	.0008 (.020)

NOTE: For engine information on Passport, refer to Rodeo in appropriate Isuzu ENGINES article.

NOTE: For repair procedures not covered in this article, see ENGINE OVERHAUL PROCEDURES article in GENERAL INFORMATION.

ENGINE IDENTIFICATION

Engine serial number is located on exhaust side of engine block, near bellhousing. The first 5 characters of engine serial number are for engine identification. See ENGINE IDENTIFICATION CODE table.

ENGINE IDENTIFICATION CODE

Application	Code
2.2L SOHC	F22A1
2.2L DOHC (VTEC)	H22A1
2.3L DOHC	H23A1

ADJUSTMENTS

VALVE CLEARANCE ADJUSTMENT

CAUTION: Always rotate engine in direction of normal rotation (counterclockwise as viewed from front of engine). Clockwise rotation may cause timing belt to slip.

2.2L (SOHC) – 1) Adjust valves when engine temperature is 100°F (38°C) or less. Remove valve cover. Rotate crankshaft counterclockwise until No. 1 piston is at TDC of compression stroke. UP mark on camshaft pulley will be at top. *See Fig. 1.* Align grooves on camshaft pulley with top surface of cylinder head. Distributor rotor should point toward No. 1 spark plug wire.

2) Adjust clearance for valves on No. 1 cylinder to specification. Loosen lock nut. Turn adjuster screw until clearance is as specified. See VALVE CLEARANCE SPECIFICATIONS table. Tighten lock nut.

3) Rotate crankshaft 180 degrees counterclockwise (camshaft pulley will turn 90 degrees). UP mark on camshaft pulley will be on exhaust side of engine. Adjust clearance on valves for No. 3 cylinder.

4) Rotate crankshaft 180 degrees counterclockwise. Grooves on camshaft pulley will align with cylinder head surface, and UP mark will face downward. Adjust clearance on valves for No. 4 cylinder.

5) Rotate crankshaft 180 degrees counterclockwise. UP mark on camshaft pulley will be on intake side. Adjust clearance on valves for No. 2 cylinder. Tighten crankshaft pulley bolt to specification if it loosened during adjustment procedure.

6) Apply nonhardening sealant to rounded surfaces of front and rear camshaft caps before installing valve cover gasket. Install valve cover. Tighten nuts to specification. See TORQUE SPECIFICATIONS.

VALVE CLEARANCE SPECIFICATIONS

Application	In. (mm)
2.2L	
DOHC	
Intake Valves	.006-.007 (.15-.19)
Exhaust Valves	.007-.008 (.17-.21)
SOHC	
Intake Valves	.009-.011 (.23-.28)
Exhaust Valves	.011-.013 (.27-.32)
2.3L	
Intake Valves	.003-.004 (.07-.11)
Exhaust Valves	.006-.007 (.15-.19)

2.2L (DOHC) & 2.3L – 1) Adjust valves when engine temperature is 100°F (38°C) or less. Remove valve cover. Rotate crankshaft counterclockwise until No. 1 piston is at TDC of compression stroke.

2) Ensure UP marks on camshaft sprockets are at top, and TDC grooves on sprockets are aligned with cylinder head surface. *See Fig. 2.* Adjust clearance on valves for No. 1 cylinder. Loosen lock nut. Turn adjuster screw until clearance is as specified. See VALVE CLEARANCE SPECIFICATIONS table.

3) Rotate crankshaft 180 degrees counterclockwise (camshaft sprockets turn 90 degrees) until No. 3 piston is at TDC of compression stroke. The UP marks will be on exhaust side. Adjust clearance on valves for No. 3 cylinder.

4) Rotate crankshaft 180 degrees counterclockwise so No. 4 piston is at TDC of compression stroke. UP marks will be at the bottom. Adjust clearance on valves for No. 4 cylinder.

5) Rotate crankshaft 180 degrees counterclockwise so No. 2 piston is at TDC of compression stroke. UP marks will be on intake side. Adjust clearances on valves for No. 2 cylinder.

6) Tighten crankshaft pulley bolt if necessary. See TORQUE SPECIFICATIONS. Apply nonhardening sealant to rounded surfaces of front and rear camshaft caps before installing valve cover gasket. Install valve cover. Tighten nuts to specification.

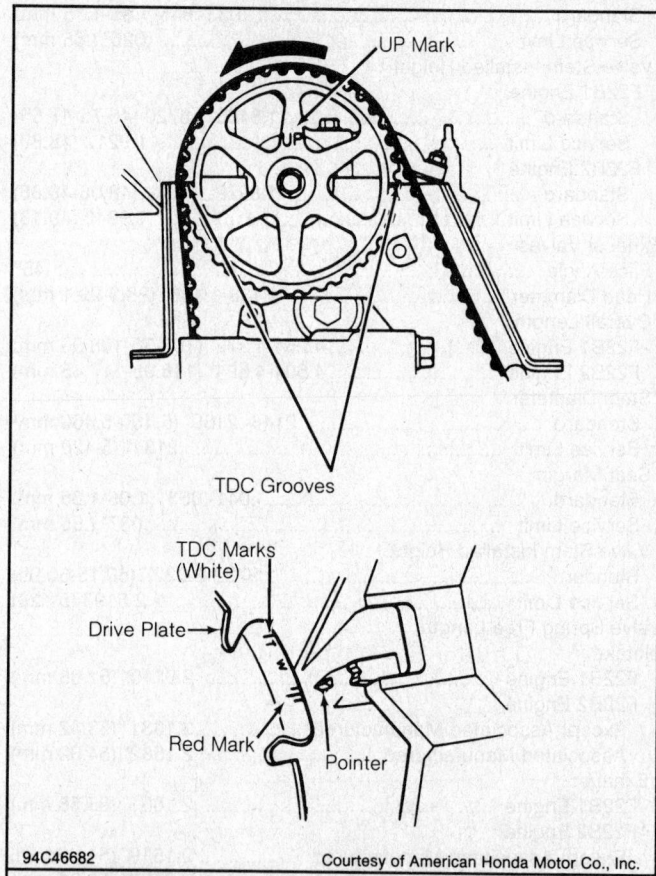

94C46682   Courtesy of American Honda Motor Co., Inc.

Fig. 1: Positioning Camshaft Sprocket For Valve Adjustment (2.2L SOHC)

TIMING BELT ADJUSTMENT

CAUTION: Always adjust timing belt tension with engine cold.

1) Rotate crankshaft counterclockwise until No. 1 piston is at TDC of compression stroke. *See Fig. 1.* Loosen, but do not remove, timing belt adjuster nut. *See Fig. 3.* Rotate crankshaft counterclockwise 3 teeth on camshaft pulley to create tension on timing belt.

2) Tighten adjuster bolt. Retighten crankshaft pulley bolt if it loosened while turning crankshaft. See TORQUE SPECIFICATIONS.

No. 1 Piston At TDC

UP Mark

TDC Grooves

UP Mark

No. 3 Piston At TDC

UP Mark

Exhaust Cam Sprocket

Intake Cam Sprocket

No. 4 Piston At TDC

No. 2 Piston At TDC

UP Mark

UP Mark

91D01435

Courtesy of American Honda Motor Co., Inc.

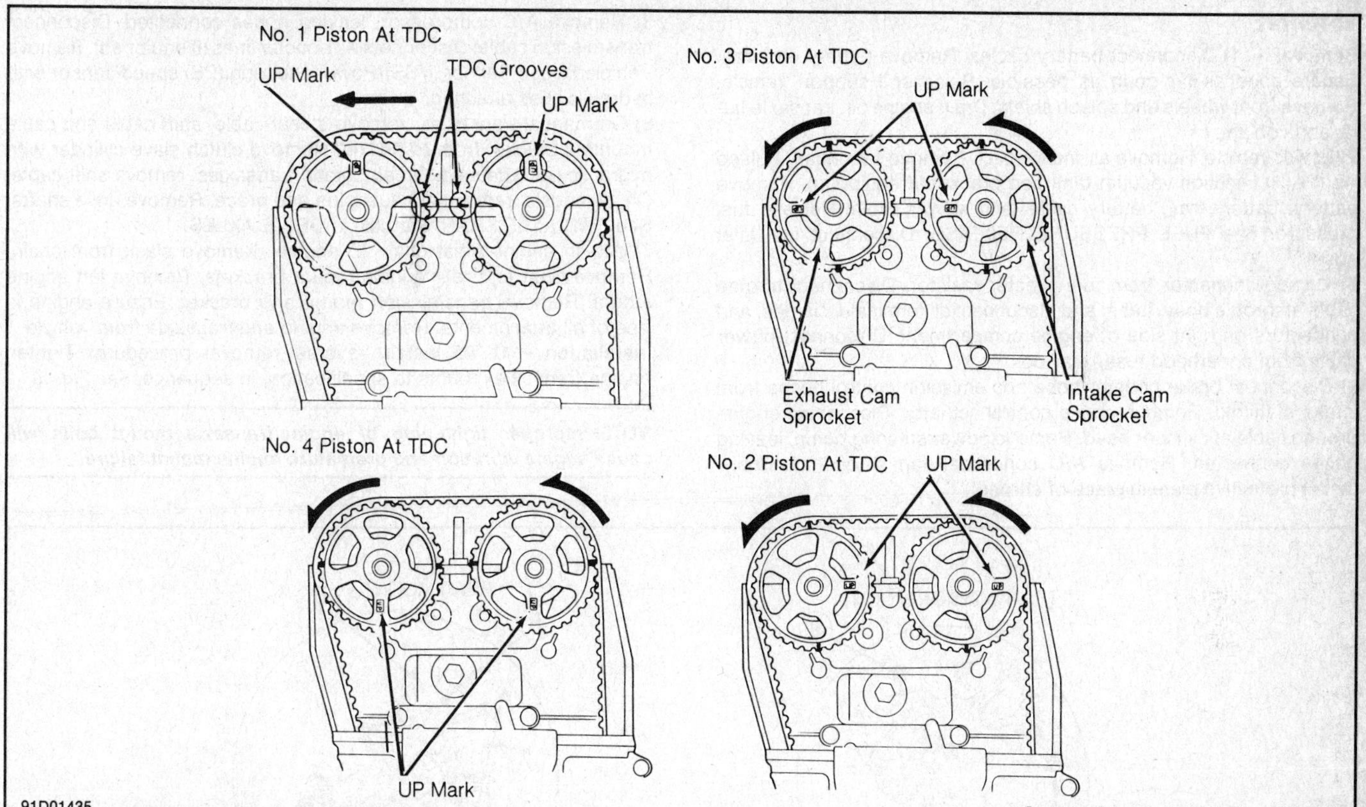

Fig. 2: Positioning Camshaft Sprockets For Valve Clearance (2.2L DOHC & 2.3L)

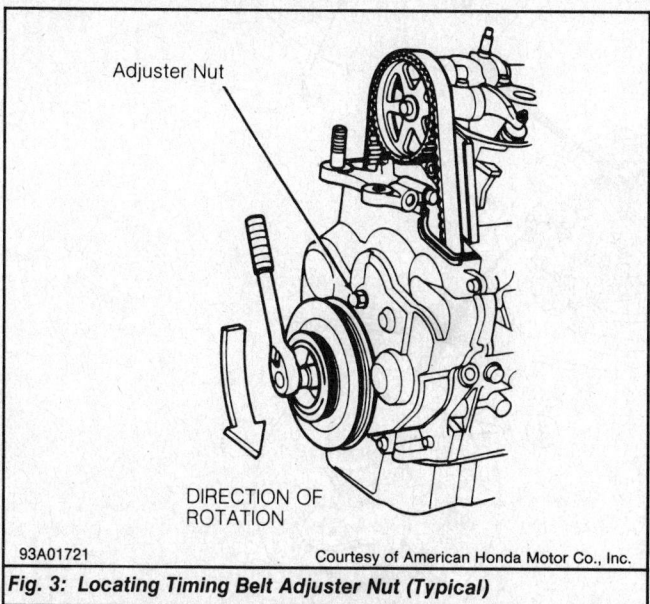

Adjuster Nut

DIRECTION OF ROTATION

93A01721

Courtesy of American Honda Motor Co., Inc.

Fig. 3: Locating Timing Belt Adjuster Nut (Typical)

REMOVAL & INSTALLATION

NOTE: For reassembly reference, label all electrical connectors, vacuum hoses, and fuel lines before removal. Also place mating marks on other major assemblies before removal.

NOTE: Radio/cassette or radio/CD player may be equipped with an anti-theft protection circuit. Whenever battery is disconnected, radio will go into anti-theft mode. When battery is reconnected, radio will display CODE, and will be inoperative until proper code number is entered. Obtain code number before disconnecting battery.

FUEL PRESSURE RELEASE

CAUTION: Fuel system is under pressure. Release pressure before servicing fuel system components.

Remove fuel tank filler cap. Place a shop towel on top of fuel filter. Slowly loosen fuel injection service bolt to release fuel injection system pressure. *See Fig. 4.*

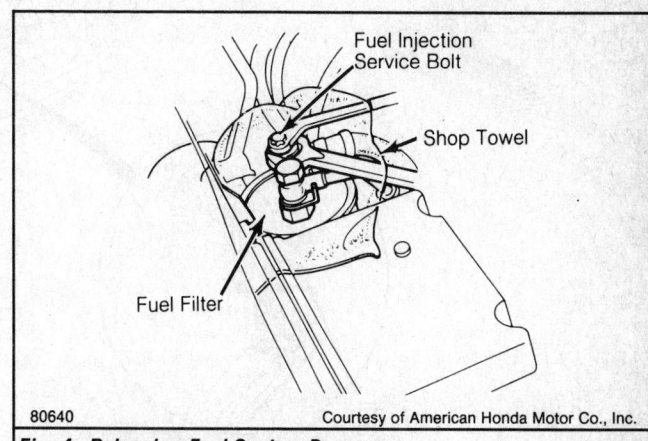

Fuel Injection Service Bolt

Shop Towel

Fuel Filter

80640

Courtesy of American Honda Motor Co., Inc.

Fig. 4: Releasing Fuel System Pressure

COOLING SYSTEM BLEEDING

1) Set heater controls to maximum heat. Fill cooling system with a 50/50 mixture of coolant and water to bottom of filler neck. Loosen bleed bolt, located on thermostat housing.

2) Tighten bleed bolt when coolant flows from bleed bolt in steady stream without bubbles. With radiator cap off, start and operate engine to normal operating temperature (fan comes on at least twice). Add coolant as necessary. Install radiator cap.

ENGINE

Removal – 1) Disconnect battery cables. Remove battery and tray. Secure hood as far open as possible. Raise and support vehicle. Remove front wheels and splash shield. Drain engine oil, transaxle fluid, and coolant.

2) Lower vehicle. Remove air intake duct. Remove secondary Pulsed Air (PAIR) injection vacuum tank and bracket (if equipped). Remove battery, battery tray, battery cable, and starter cable. Release fuel pressure. See FUEL PRESSURE RELEASE. Disconnect fuel inlet hose.

3) Unplug connector from fuel injector resistor. Disconnect throttle cable at throttle body. Label and disconnect all terminals, clamps, and connectors on right side of engine compartment. Disconnect power cable from underhood fuse/relay box.

4) Disconnect brake booster hose and emission control hoses from intake manifold. Remove cruise control actuator. Disconnect engine ground cable at cylinder head. Remove power steering pump, leaving hoses connected. Remove A/C condenser fan shroud assembly. Install protective plate in place of shroud.

5) Remove A/C compressor, leaving hoses connected. Disconnect transmission cable. Disconnect A/T cooler lines (if equipped). Remove Vehicle Speed Sensor (VSS)/Power Steering (PS) speed sensor with hydraulic lines attached.

6) On manual transaxles, remove select cable, shift cable and cable mounting bracket from transaxle. Remove clutch slave cylinder with hydraulic line attached. On automatic transaxles, remove shift cable. On all models, remove exhaust pipe and brace. Remove drive shafts. See FWD AXLE SHAFTS article in DRIVE AXLES.

7) Attach engine hoist chain to engine. Remove slack from chain. Remove front and rear engine mount brackets. Remove left engine mount. Remove transmission mount and bracket. Ensure engine is free of all attachments. Remove engine and transaxle from vehicle.

Installation – 1) To install, reverse removal procedure. Tighten engine/transaxle mounts to specification, in sequence. *See Fig. 5.*

NOTE: Improper tightening of engine/transaxle mount bolts will cause engine vibration and premature engine mount failure.

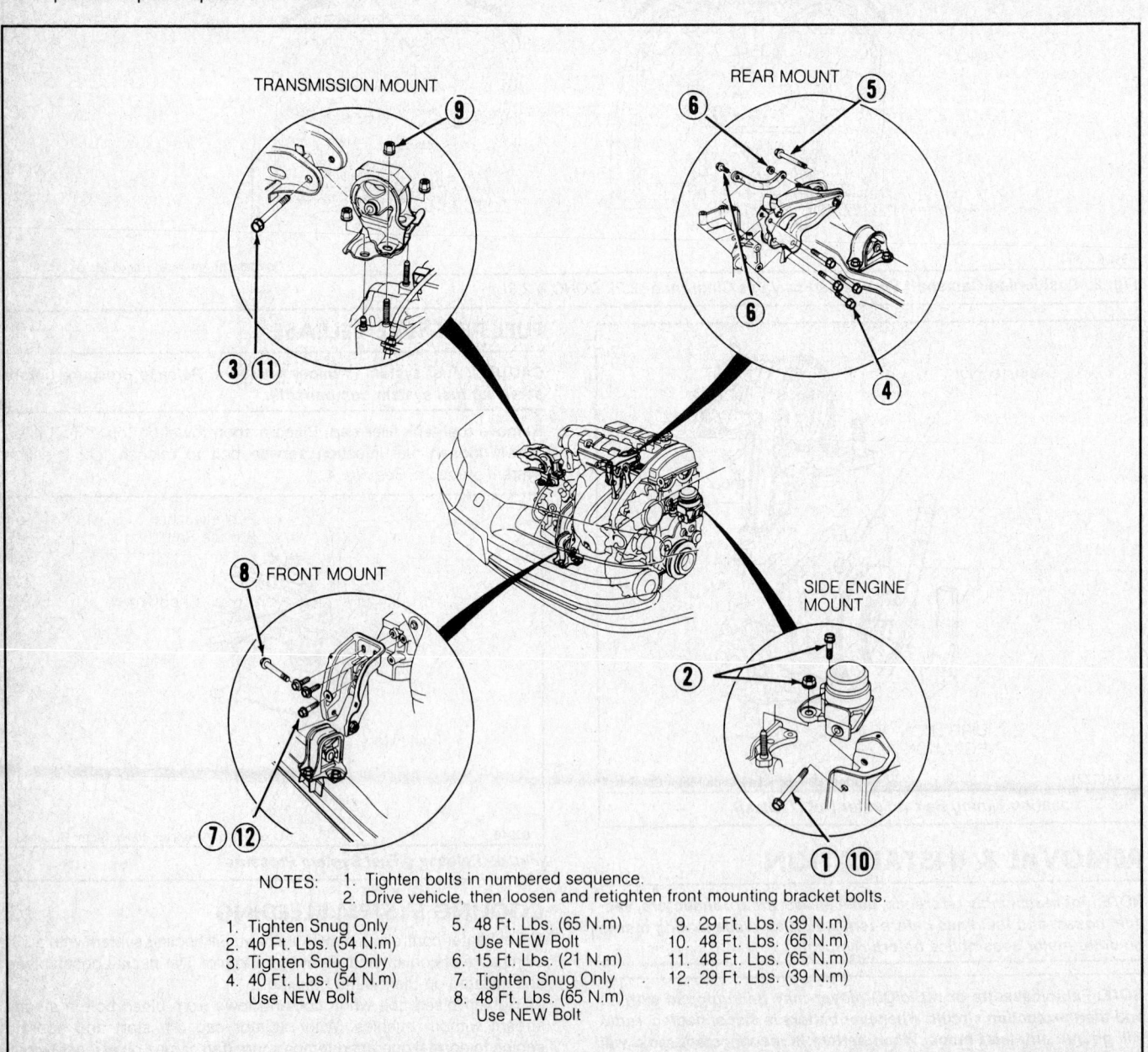

NOTES: 1. Tighten bolts in numbered sequence.
2. Drive vehicle, then loosen and retighten front mounting bracket bolts.

1. Tighten Snug Only	5. 48 Ft. Lbs. (65 N.m) Use NEW Bolt	9. 29 Ft. Lbs. (39 N.m)
2. 40 Ft. Lbs. (54 N.m)	6. 15 Ft. Lbs. (21 N.m)	10. 48 Ft. Lbs. (65 N.m)
3. Tighten Snug Only	7. Tighten Snug Only	11. 48 Ft. Lbs. (65 N.m)
4. 40 Ft. Lbs. (54 N.m) Use NEW Bolt	8. 48 Ft. Lbs. (65 N.m) Use NEW Bolt	12. 29 Ft. Lbs. (39 N.m)

93C01722

Courtesy of American Honda Motor Co., Inc.

Fig. 5: Tightening Sequence For Engine/Transaxle Mounts

2) Use NEW spring clips when installing drive axles. Install drive axles until spring clip clicks in groove of differential side gear. Ensure all wires and hoses are connected properly. Adjust throttle cable tension.
3) On M/T models, adjust clutch pedal free play. See CLUTCH PEDAL under ADJUSTMENTS in FWD article in CLUTCHES. On A/T models, ensure gear position agrees with shift indicator. On all models, adjust drive belt tension. Restore all fluids to proper level. Fill and bleed cooling system. See COOLING SYSTEM BLEEDING.

INTAKE MANIFOLD

Removal (2.2L DOHC & 2.3L) – **1)** Disconnect battery negative cable. Drain cooling system. Release fuel pressure. See FUEL PRESSURE RELEASE. Remove air intake duct. Disconnect fuel hoses and EVAP canister hose. Disconnect brake booster and cruise control vacuum hoses.
2) Disconnect throttle cable at throttle body. On A/T models, disconnect throttle control cable. Unplug wiring at alternator. Disconnect all wiring from cylinder head. Remove power steering pump, leaving hoses attached. Remove ignition coil. Disconnect upper radiator hose. Disconnect heater hose at intake manifold.
3) Disconnect coolant by-pass hose and emission hoses from intake manifold. Remove thermostat housing. Remove Intake Air By-pass (IAB) valve body assembly. Remove intake manifold bracket and manifold.
Removal (2.2L SOHC) – **1)** Disconnect battery negative cable. Drain cooling system. Release fuel pressure. See FUEL PRESSURE RELEASE. Disconnect breather hose and vacuum tube. Remove air intake duct. Disconnect fuel hoses and EVAP canister hose. Disconnect brake booster and cruise control vacuum hoses.
2) Disconnect throttle cable at throttle body. On A/T models, disconnect throttle control cable. On all models, remove ignition coil, spark plug caps, and distributor. Unplug wiring at alternator. Disconnect all wiring at intake manifold. Disconnect radiator and heater hoses. Disconnect coolant by-pass hose and emission hoses from intake manifold. Remove thermostat housing.
3) Disconnect engine ground cable at cylinder head. Remove power steering pump, leaving hoses attached. Remove intake manifold bracket and manifold.
Installation – Clean gasket surfaces. Install intake manifold, using NEW gasket. Tighten nuts to specification in 3 stages. Tighten in a crisscross pattern, starting with inner nuts. See TORQUE SPECIFICATIONS. To complete installation, reverse removal procedure.

EXHAUST MANIFOLD

Removal – Remove exhaust manifold heat shield. Disconnect exhaust pipe from exhaust manifold. Unplug oxygen sensor electrical connector. Remove exhaust manifold bracket. Remove exhaust manifold retaining nuts and manifold. Remove gasket.
Installation – Clean gasket surfaces. Install exhaust manifold using NEW gasket. Using a crisscross pattern, tighten nuts to specification in 3 stages. See TORQUE SPECIFICATIONS.

CYLINDER HEAD

CAUTION: DO NOT remove cylinder head until coolant temperature is less than 100°F (38°C), or cylinder head damage may occur.

Removal (2.2L DOHC & 2.3L) – **1)** Disconnect battery negative cable. Drain cooling system. Release fuel pressure. See FUEL PRESSURE RELEASE. Remove air intake duct. Disconnect fuel hoses and EVAP canister hose. Disconnect brake booster and cruise control vacuum hoses.
2) Disconnect throttle cable at throttle body. On A/T models, disconnect throttle control cable. Unplug wiring at alternator. Disconnect all wiring from cylinder head. Remove power steering pump, leaving hoses attached. Remove ignition coil. Disconnect upper radiator hose. Disconnect heater hose at intake manifold.
3) Disconnect coolant by-pass hose and emission hoses from intake manifold. Remove thermostat housing. Remove Intake Air By-pass (IAB) valve body assembly. Remove intake manifold bracket and man-

ifold. Disconnect exhaust pipe. Remove heat insulator (A/C models). Remove exhaust manifold bracket and exhaust manifold.
4) Remove valve cover. Remove cylinder head belt cover. Loosen timing belt tension adjuster bolt. Push tensioner to release belt tension. Tighten adjuster bolt. Disengage timing belt from camshaft sprockets. Remove camshaft pulleys.
5) Loosen all valve clearance adjuster screws. On 2.2L DOHC models, remove VTEC solenoid valve. On all models, remove camshaft bearing caps and camshafts. Remove engine mount bracket brace. Remove timing belt back cover. Remove cylinder head bolts, 1/3 turn at a time, in reverse order of tightening sequence. See Fig. 6. Remove cylinder head and gasket.

CAUTION: DO NOT crimp or bend timing belt more than 90 degrees or less than 1" (25 mm) radius.

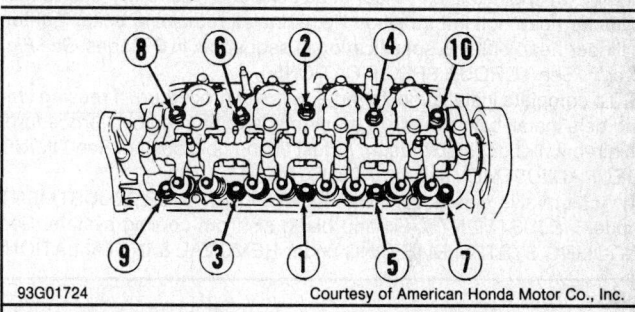

93G01724   Courtesy of American Honda Motor Co., Inc.

Fig. 6: Tightening Sequence For Cylinder Head Bolts (2.2L DOHC & 2.3L)

Removal (2.2L SOHC) – **1)** Disconnect battery negative cable. Drain cooling system. Release fuel pressure. See FUEL PRESSURE RELEASE. Disconnect breather hose and vacuum tube. Remove air intake duct. Disconnect fuel hoses and EVAP canister hose. Disconnect brake booster and cruise control vacuum hoses.
2) Disconnect throttle cable at throttle body. On A/T models, disconnect throttle control cable. On all models, remove ignition coil, spark plug caps, and distributor. Unplug wiring at alternator. Disconnect all wiring from cylinder head. Disconnect radiator and heater hoses. Disconnect coolant by-pass hose and emission hoses from intake manifold. Remove thermostat housing.
3) Disconnect engine ground cable at cylinder head. Remove power steering pump, leaving hoses attached. Remove intake manifold bracket and manifold.
4) Raise and support vehicle. Remove splash shield and front wheels. Remove heat insulator (A/C models). Disconnect exhaust pipe. Remove exhaust manifold bracket and exhaust manifold. Remove PCV hose. Remove upper timing belt cover.
5) Loosen timing belt tension adjuster bolt. Push tensioner to release belt tension. Tighten adjuster bolt. Disengage timing belt from camshaft sprocket. Remove cylinder head bolts, 1/3 turn at a time, in reverse order of tightening sequence. See Fig. 7. Remove cylinder head and gasket.

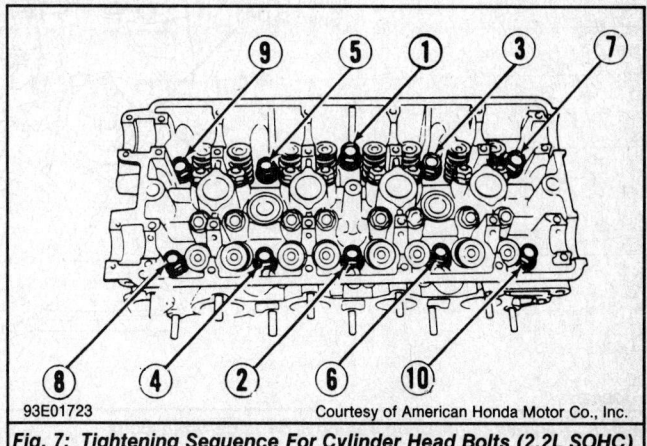

93E01723   Courtesy of American Honda Motor Co., Inc.

Fig. 7: Tightening Sequence For Cylinder Head Bolts (2.2L SOHC)

1994 ENGINES
2.2L & 2.3L 4-Cylinder – Prelude (Cont.)

CAUTION: *DO NOT crimp or bend timing belt more than 90 degrees or less than 1" (25 mm) radius.*

Inspection (All Models) – Ensure all mating surfaces are clean. Measure cylinder head for warpage. Resurfacing is not required if warpage is less than .002" (.05 mm). Resurface cylinder head if warpage is .002-.008" (.05-.20 mm). Maximum resurface limit is .008" (.20 mm). Ensure cylinder head dowel pins, oil control jet, and "O" ring are installed in block.

Installation (All Models) – **1)** Install NEW intake manifold gasket. Install intake manifold onto cylinder head. Tighten nuts to specification in a crisscross pattern, beginning with inner nuts. See TORQUE SPECIFICATIONS.

2) Ensure No. 1 piston and camshaft pulley are at TDC. Apply a light coating of engine oil to cylinder head bolts and washers. Install longer cylinder head bolt into position No. 3. Install remaining bolts. Tighten cylinder head bolts to specification in sequence, in 3 stages. *See Fig. 6 or 7.* See TORQUE SPECIFICATIONS.

3) To complete installation, reverse removal procedure. If reusing timing belt, install belt with arrow mark (made during removal procedure) in direction of original rotation. Adjust timing belt tension. See TIMING BELT ADJUSTMENT under ADJUSTMENTS.

4) Adjust valve clearance. See VALVE CLEARANCE ADJUSTMENT under ADJUSTMENTS. Fill and bleed air from cooling system. See COOLING SYSTEM BLEEDING under REMOVAL & INSTALLATION.

CRANKSHAFT FRONT SEAL

Removal & Installation – Remove camshaft and balance shaft drive belts. See TIMING & BALANCE SHAFT BELTS. Remove crankshaft/oil pump seal. Apply a light coat of engine oil to crankshaft and lip of new seal. Install seal using Seal Driver (07749-0010000). Ensure seal is fully seated. To complete installation, reverse removal procedure. See TORQUE SPECIFICATIONS.

TIMING & BALANCE SHAFT BELTS

Removal – **1)** Position crankshaft with No. 1 piston at TDC of compression stroke. *See Fig. 1 or 2.* Disconnect battery negative cable. Remove splash shield. Remove cruise control actuator, leaving cable connected. Remove power steering pump, leaving hoses connected.

2) Disconnect alternator wiring. Remove wiring harness from valve cover. Remove alternator and A/C belts (if equipped). Remove valve cover and middle timing belt cover. Remove side engine mount. Remove engine oil dipstick and tube. Remove crankshaft pulley bolt. Remove side engine mount. Remove engine oil dipstick and tube. Remove crankshaft pulley.

3) Support engine. Remove 2 rear bolts from engine center support beam. Lower engine enough to permit removal of lower timing belt cover. Remove rubber seal from belt tension adjuster nut. Remove lower timing belt cover.

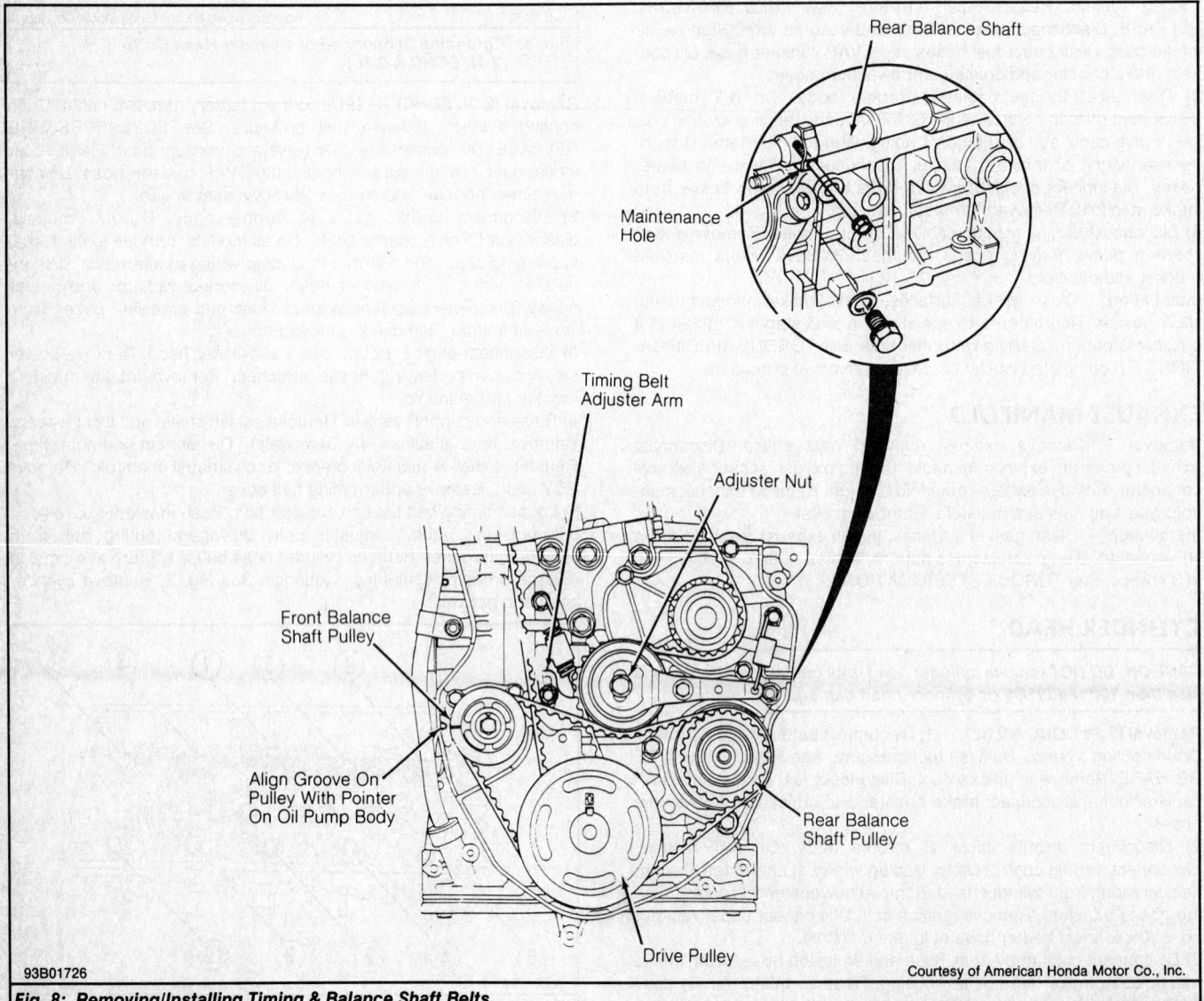

Courtesy of American Honda Motor Co., Inc.

93B01726

Fig. 8: *Removing/Installing Timing & Balance Shaft Belts*

4) Lock timing belt adjuster arm into position by installing one lower cover retaining bolt. Loosen belt tension adjuster bolt. Push belt tensioner to release tension from belt. Tighten adjuster bolt. Remove balance shaft and camshaft timing belts.

CAUTION: DO NOT rotate crankshaft or camshaft when removing and installing timing belts.

Inspection – With belt or belt covers removed, inspect belts for wear, cracks, or oil soaking. Inspect belt teeth for wear. Replace belt if worn, oil soaked, or cracked.

Installation – **1)** Align White mark on flywheel or drive plate (flexplate) with pointer on block. Ensure camshaft(s) is at TDC for No. 1 cylinder. *See Fig. 1 or 2.* Install camshaft timing belt. *See Fig. 8.* Align rear timing balance shaft belt pulley by inserting a 6 x 100 mm bolt 2.9 inches (74 mm) into alignment access hole. Align groove on front balance shaft pulley with pointer on oil pump body.

2) Install balance shaft and cam belts. Adjust belt tension. See TIMING BELT ADJUSTMENT under ADJUSTMENTS. Reverse removal procedure to complete installation. Tighten crankshaft pulley bolt to specification. See TORQUE SPECIFICATIONS.

ROCKER ARM

NOTE: DO NOT remove camshaft bearing cap (cam holder) bolts from rocker arm assembly unless it is to be disassembled. The bolts keep cam holders, springs, and rocker arms on shaft.

Removal & Installation (2.2L DOHC & 2.3L) – For removal and installation of rocker arms, see CAMSHAFT.

Removal (2.2L SOHC) – **1)** Ensure No. 1 piston is at TDC of compression stroke. UP mark on camshaft pulley should be at top, and grooves on camshaft pulley should align with cylinder head surface. *See Fig. 1.* Remove timing and balance shaft belts. See TIMING & BALANCE SHAFT BELTS.

2) Remove camshaft pulley retaining bolt, special washer, camshaft pulley, and key. Remove back cover. Place reference mark on distributor for installation reference. Remove distributor. Loosen all rocker arm adjuster screws.

3) Pry camshaft toward front of cylinder head. Attach dial indicator and zero it against pulley end of camshaft. Pry camshaft away from dial indicator to measure end play. See CAMSHAFT table under ENGINE SPECIFICATIONS. If end play exceeds limit, replace camshaft.

4) Unscrew camshaft bearing cap bolts by turning bolts 2 turns at a time in a crisscross pattern. DO NOT remove bearing cap (cam holder) bolts from rocker arm assembly. Bolts keep cam holders, springs, and rocker arms on shafts. *See Fig. 9.* Remove rocker arm assembly.

NOTE: Mark rocker arm shaft assembly parts for installation reference.

Installation – **1)** Clean all components. Lubricate all components at contact points before installation. Align intake rocker shafts projections with cam holder indents.

2) Position camshaft (if removed) onto cylinder head with keyway facing upward and No. 1 piston at TDC. Install camshaft seal. Apply gasket sealer to mating surfaces of cam holders No. 1 and 6. Loosen valve clearance adjusters before installing rocker shaft assembly.

3) Position rocker shaft assembly onto cylinder head. Ensure all rockers align with valves. Tighten mounting bolts 2 turns at a time in sequence. *See Fig. 10.* Install back cover. Install pulley. Tighten camshaft pulley bolt to specification. See TORQUE SPECIFICATIONS.

4) To complete installation, reverse removal procedure. Adjust valves to specification. See VALVE CLEARANCE ADJUSTMENT under ADJUSTMENTS. Tighten all nuts and bolts to specification. See TORQUE SPECIFICATIONS.

CAMSHAFT

Removal (2.2L DOHC & 2.3L) – **1)** Ensure No. 1 piston is at TDC of compression stroke. Ensure UP marks on camshaft sprockets are at the top, and TDC grooves on camshaft sprockets align with cylinder head surface. *See Fig. 2.* Disengage timing belt from camshaft sprockets. See TIMING & BALANCE SHAFT BELTS.

2) Remove camshaft sprockets. Place reference mark on distributor for installation reference. Remove distributor. Loosen rocker arm adjuster screws. Measure camshaft end play. If end play exceeds limit, replace camshaft. See CAMSHAFT table under ENGINE SPECIFICATIONS.

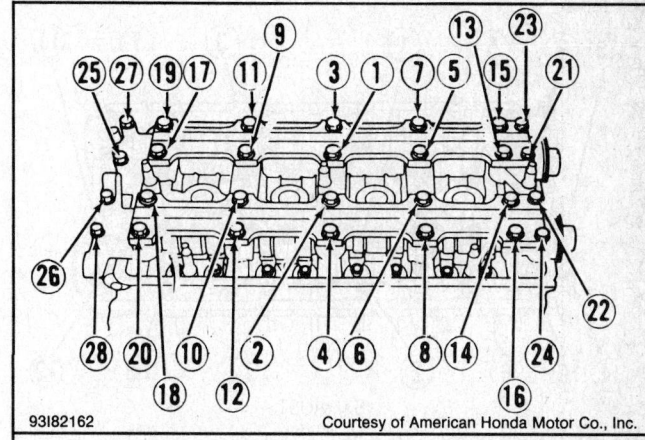

93I82162   Courtesy of American Honda Motor Co., Inc.

Fig. 10: Tightening Sequence For Camshaft Bolts (2.2L DOHC)

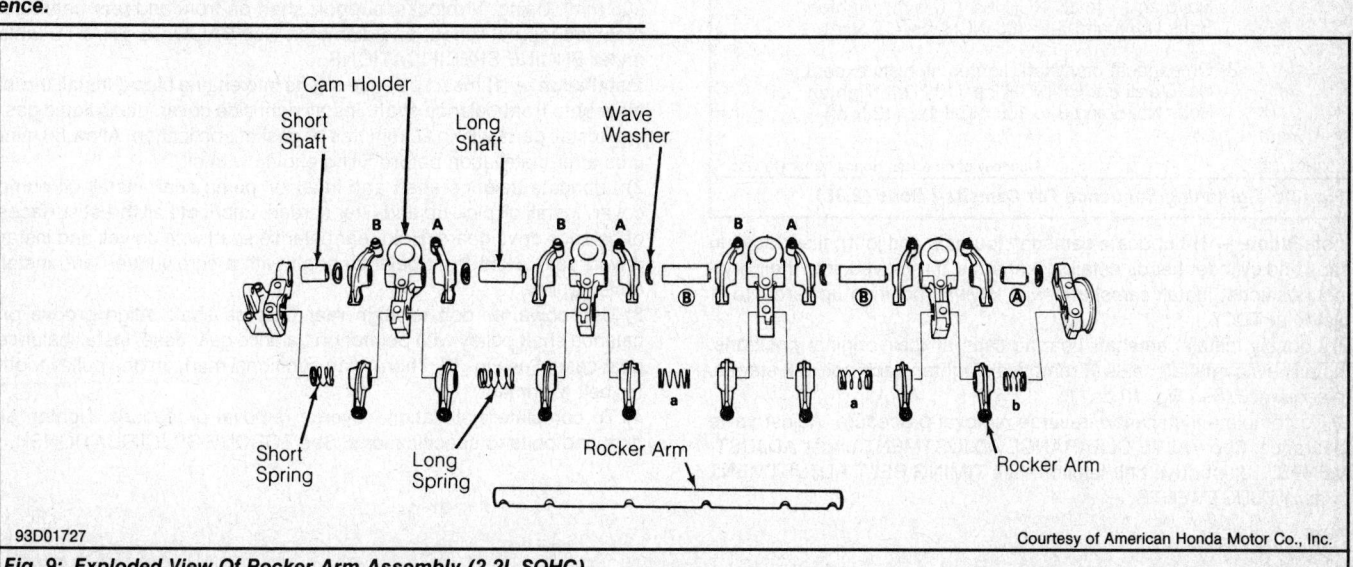

93D01727   Courtesy of American Honda Motor Co., Inc.

Fig. 9: Exploded View Of Rocker Arm Assembly (2.2L SOHC)

3) Remove camshaft bearing cap bolts by turning bolts 2 turns at a time in reverse order of tightening sequence. Remove camshafts. Label rocker arms for installation reference. Remove rocker arms (if necessary). *See Fig. 10 or 11.*

NOTE: If rocker arms are removed from 2.2L DOHC, secure each set of rocker arms and control pistons together with a rubber band and mark to ensure rockers remain properly assembled and are installed in original position.

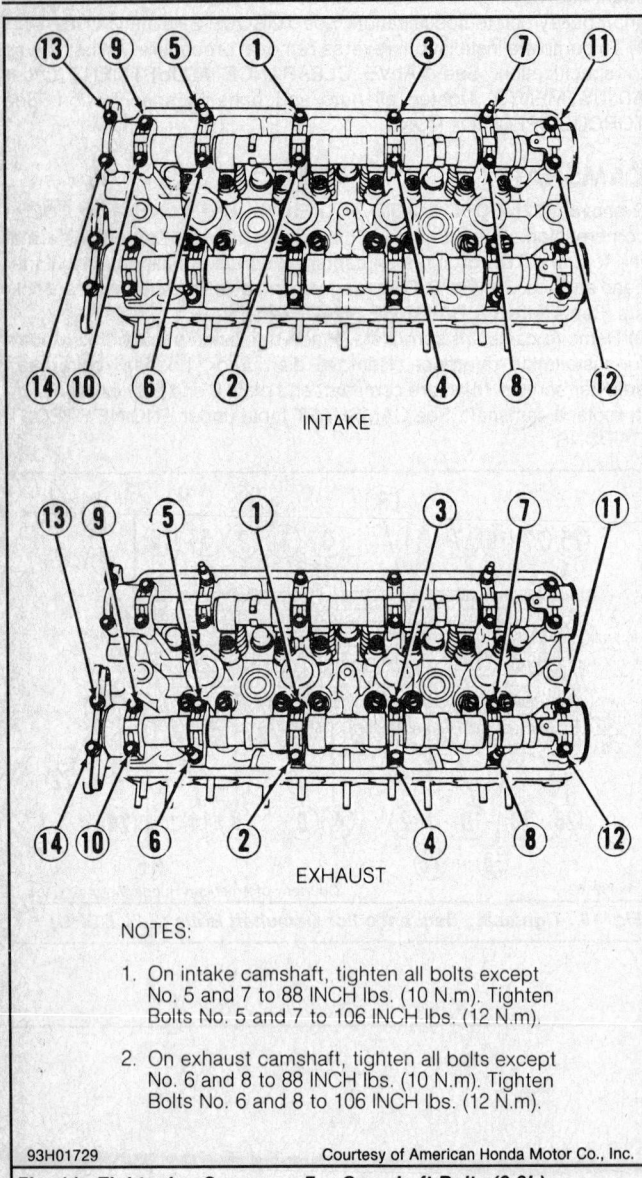

INTAKE

EXHAUST

NOTES:

1. On intake camshaft, tighten all bolts except No. 5 and 7 to 88 INCH lbs. (10 N.m). Tighten Bolts No. 5 and 7 to 106 INCH lbs. (12 N.m).

2. On exhaust camshaft, tighten all bolts except No. 6 and 8 to 88 INCH lbs. (10 N.m). Tighten Bolts No. 6 and 8 to 106 INCH lbs. (12 N.m).

93H01729   Courtesy of American Honda Motor Co., Inc.

Fig. 11: Tightening Sequence For Camshaft Bolts (2.3L)

Installation – 1) Lubricate camshaft journals and journal surfaces in caps and cylinder head. Install rocker arms, if removed, into their original positions. Install camshafts with keyway pointing upward (No. 1 piston at TDC).

2) Loosely install camshaft bearing caps at their original positions. Install new camshaft seals (if removed). Tighten each bolt in 2 stages, in sequence. *See Fig. 10 or 11.*

3) To complete installation, reverse removal procedure. Adjust valve clearance. See VALVE CLEARANCE ADJUSTMENT under ADJUSTMENTS. Adjust drive belt tension. See TIMING BELT ADJUSTMENT under ADJUSTMENTS.

NOTE: On 2.2L SOHC, DO NOT remove camshaft bearing cap (cam holder) bolts from rocker arm assembly unless it is to be disassembled. The bolts keep cam holders, springs, and rocker arms on shaft.

Removal & Installation (2.2L SOHC) – Remove rocker arm assembly. See ROCKER ARM. Carefully lift camshaft from cylinder head. To install camshaft, reverse removal procedure. Tighten mounting bolts 2 turns at a time in sequence. *See Fig. 12.* See TORQUE SPECIFICATIONS.

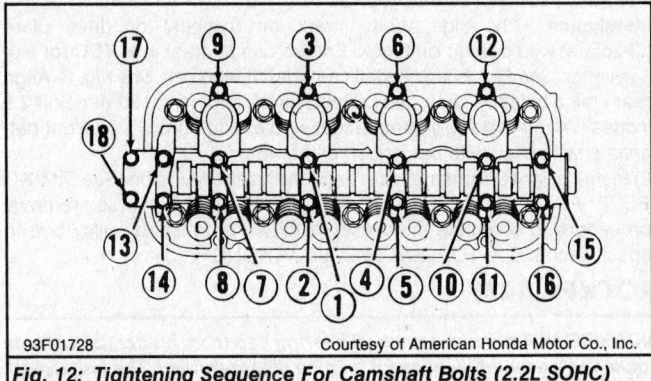

93F01728   Courtesy of American Honda Motor Co., Inc.

Fig. 12: Tightening Sequence For Camshaft Bolts (2.2L SOHC)

BALANCE SHAFTS

Removal – 1) Remove engine from vehicle. See ENGINE under REMOVAL & INSTALLATION. Remove oil pan, flywheel, and right side crankshaft oil seal cover. Remove timing belts. See TIMING & BALANCE SHAFT BELTS. Remove balance shaft drive gear case. Insert a screwdriver into front balance shaft to prevent rotation. Remove pulley.

2) Insert a bolt or dowel pin into maintenance hole of rear balance shaft. Remove baffle plate. Remove rear timing balance shaft gear. Remove oil pick-up and filter screen. Remove front cover/oil pump assembly. Remove thrust plate from rear balance shaft. Remove balance shafts.

Inspection – 1) Measure balance shaft end play before removing end plates and front cover. See BALANCE SHAFTS table under ENGINE SPECIFICATIONS. If end play exceeds specification, inspect thrust plate and thrust surfaces. Thrust plates and thrust surface on oil pump body must not be changed by grinding or shimming.

2) Inspect surface of balance shaft journal and balance shaft bearing. Replace if worn, damaged, or discolored. When replacing front bearing on rear balance shaft, replace oil pump body. Measure diameter of front and rear ends of bearing journals. Taper should not exceed .002" (.05 mm). Using "V" blocks, support shaft on front and rear bearings. Measure journal runout and diameter. See BALANCE SHAFTS table under ENGINE SPECIFICATIONS.

Installation – 1) Insert balance shafts into engine block. Install thrust plate onto front balance shaft. Install right side cover, using liquid gasket. Install parts within 20 minutes of gasket application. Allow 30 minutes after installation before filling engine with oil.

2) Lubricate balance shaft and inner oil pump seal. Install oil pump cover. Install oil pick-up and filter screen. Lubricate all thrust surfaces of balance drive gears. Hold rear balance shaft with dowel, and install driven gear. Hold front balance shaft with a screwdriver, and install driven pulley.

3) Use dowel or bolt to align rear balance shaft. Align groove on balance shaft pulley with pointer on balance gear case. Install balance gear case. *See Fig. 13.* There is an additional mark on one pulley tooth for belt alignment.

4) To complete installation, reverse removal procedure. Tighten all nuts and bolts to specifications. See TORQUE SPECIFICATIONS.

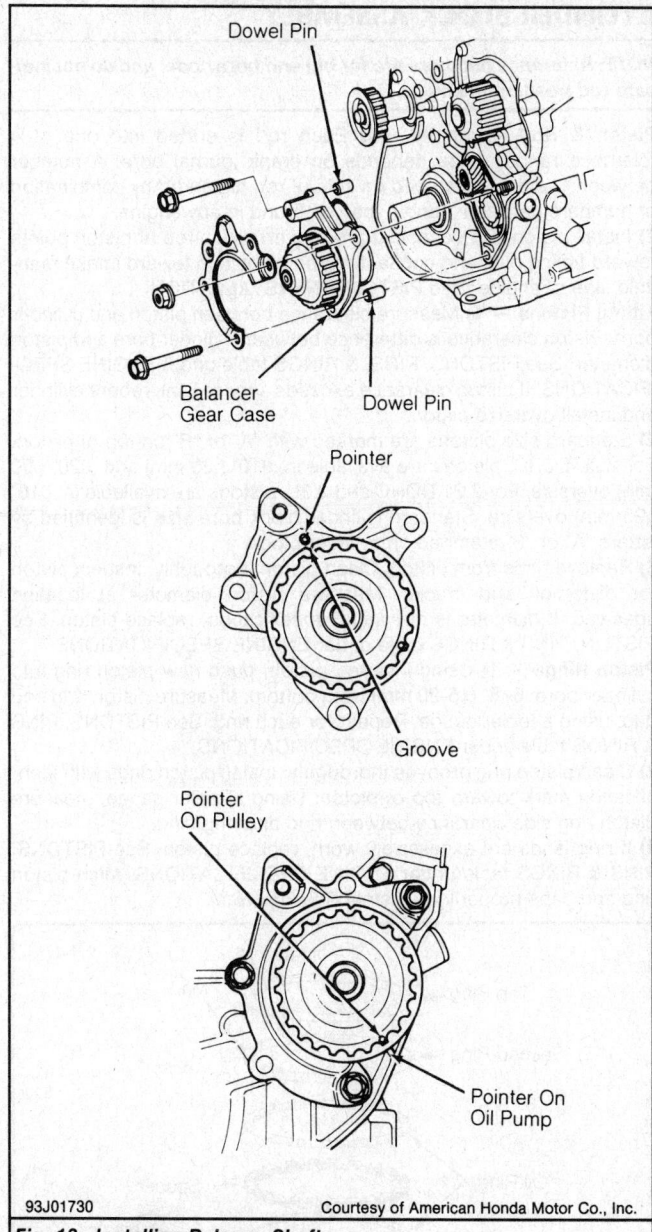

Fig. 13: Installing Balance Shafts

93J01730   Courtesy of American Honda Motor Co., Inc.

REAR CRANKSHAFT OIL SEAL

Removal & Installation – 1) Remove transaxle assembly. Remove flywheel or drive plate. See appropriate article in CLUTCHES (manual transaxle) or TRANSMISSION SERVICING (automatic transaxle). Pry seal from rear seal plate. Clean crankshaft seal surface and seal plate. Lubricate seal lips and crankshaft with a light coating of oil.

2) Install seal with part number facing outward. Use Seal Driver (07749-0010000) to install seal into seal plate. Align hole in seal driver with pin on crankshaft. Drive seal in until driver bottoms against block. To complete installation, reverse removal procedure. Tighten all nuts and bolts to specifications. See TORQUE SPECIFICATIONS.

WATER PUMP

Removal – Disconnect battery negative cable. Drain cooling system. Remove timing and balance shaft belts. See TIMING & BALANCE SHAFT BELTS. Remove water pump bolts, water pump, and "O" ring.
Installation – Clean gasket surfaces. Install NEW "O" ring and water pump. To complete installation, reverse removal procedure. Tighten bolts to specifications. See TORQUE SPECIFICATIONS. Fill and bleed cooling system. See COOLING SYSTEM BLEEDING.

OIL PAN

Removal & Installation – Raise and support vehicle. Drain oil. Remove oil pan retaining bolts. Remove oil pan. Clean gasket surfaces. Before installing oil pan, apply nonhardening sealant to front and rear of gasket where curved area mates with side rail surfaces of oil pan gasket. Install oil pan. Tighten bolts to specification, in sequence. See Fig. 14. See TORQUE SPECIFICATIONS.

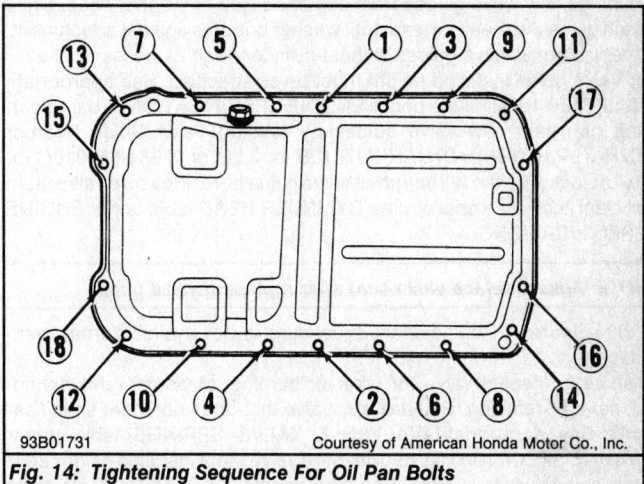

93B01731   Courtesy of American Honda Motor Co., Inc.

Fig. 14: Tightening Sequence For Oil Pan Bolts

OVERHAUL

CYLINDER HEAD

Cylinder Head – Ensure all mating surfaces are clean. Measure cylinder head warpage. If warpage is less than .002" (.05 mm), resurfacing is not required. If warpage is .002-.008" (.05-.20 mm), resurface cylinder head. Maximum resurface limit is .008" (.20 mm).
Valve Springs – Measure valve spring free length. Replace any spring shorter than minimum free length specification. See VALVE SPRING FREE LENGTH in appropriate VALVES & VALVE SPRINGS table under ENGINE SPECIFICATIONS. Install springs with closer coils toward cylinder head. See appropriate VALVES & VALVE SPRINGS table under ENGINE SPECIFICATIONS.
Valve Stem Oil Seal Replacement – Mark valves and valve springs for reassembly reference. Tap each valve stem with a plastic mallet to loosen valve keepers. Remove valve keepers, collar, and spring. Use a valve seal puller to remove valve seals from valve guides.

NOTE: Intake and exhaust valve stem seals are NOT interchangeable. Intake seals have a White spring, and exhaust seals have a Black spring around neck of seal.

Valve Guide Inspection – Measure valve guide clearance with a dial indicator placed on valve head. Lift valve .4" (10 mm) from seat. Rock valve stem from side to side. Valve guides can be replaced if valve stem oil clearance is not within specification. See appropriate CYLINDER HEAD table under ENGINE SPECIFICATIONS.
Valve Guide Removal – 1) Use a hot plate or oven to heat cylinder head to 300°F (150°C). Use valve guide driver, or fabricate valve guide remover from an air impact chisel. Using an air hammer and valve guide remover, drive valve guide 5/64" (2 mm) toward combustion chamber.

CAUTION: DO NOT heat cylinder head with a torch, or heat cylinder head hotter than 300°F (150°C). Excessive temperature may loosen valve seats.

2) Turn head over. Working from combustion chamber side of head, drive valve guide out toward camshaft side of head. If valve guide does not move, drill valve guide, using a 5/16" drill bit, then try to drive it out again.

CAUTION: *Drill guides in extreme cases only. Cylinder head damage can occur if valve guide breaks.*

Valve Guide Installation – 1) Chill new valve guides in freezer for about one hour. Remove new valve guides from freezer as needed. Slip a 15/64" (6 mm) steel washer between valve guide driver and driver attachment.

2) Install new valve guides from camshaft side of cylinder head. Drive each guide into heated head until washer bottoms against attachment. If replacing all valve guides, reheat cylinder head as necessary.

3) Valve guide installed height must be as specified. See appropriate CYLINDER HEAD table under ENGINE SPECIFICATIONS. Using cutting oil, ream new valve guides by rotating Valve Guide Reamer (07HAH-PJ7010A or 07HAH-PJ7010B for 2.2L, or 07984-657010C for 2.3L) clockwise the full length of valve guide bore. Measure valve stem oil clearance. See appropriate CYLINDER HEAD table under ENGINE SPECIFICATIONS.

NOTE: *Always reface valve seat after replacing valve guide.*

Valve Seats – Replacement procedure is not available from manufacturer.

Valves – Inspect valve for wear or burning. Measure valve dimensions after refacing. Replace any valve that does not meet specification. See appropriate VALVES & VALVE SPRINGS table under ENGINE SPECIFICATIONS. Measure valve stem installed height after refinishing valve or seat. See appropriate CYLINDER HEAD table under ENGINE SPECIFICATIONS. Tap valve stems with plastic mallet after installation to seat spring retainers and keepers.

Valve Seat Correction Angles – Replace valve guides, if necessary, before refacing valve seats. After refacing, if seat width is too wide, use 60-degree stone to raise seat, or 30-degree stone to lower seat. Ensure valve seat margin is within specification. See appropriate CYLINDER HEAD table under ENGINE SPECIFICATIONS.

Valve Stem Installed Height – After servicing valves, measure valve stem installed height. *See Fig. 15.* If valve stem installed height exceeds specification for any valve, replace valve. See appropriate CYLINDER HEAD table under ENGINE SPECIFICATIONS. If valve stem installed height still exceeds limit, replace cylinder head.

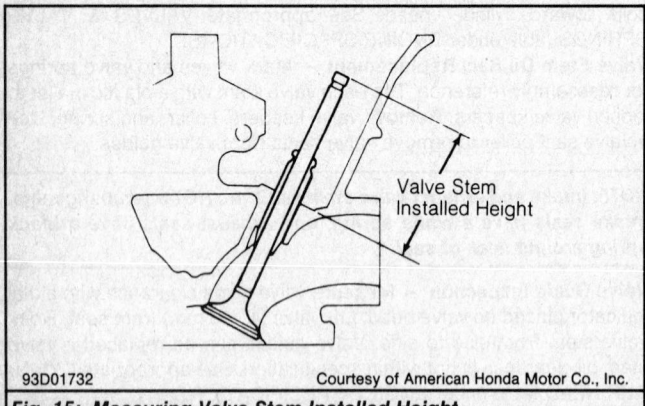

93D01732   Courtesy of American Honda Motor Co., Inc.

Fig. 15: Measuring Valve Stem Installed Height

VALVE TRAIN

Rocker Arm Shaft Assembly – Mark parts during disassembly for installation reference. Inspect rocker shafts (if equipped) and rocker arms for excessive wear or scoring. *See Fig. 9.* Service limit for clearance between rocker arm and rocker shaft is .003" (.08 mm). Replace shaft or rocker arms if worn beyond specification. Inspect rocker arm contact points for wear or scoring. Replace defective parts as necessary. Lubricate contact areas with engine oil before assembly.

CYLINDER BLOCK ASSEMBLY

NOTE: *Reference numbers are for big end bore code, and do not indicate rod position in engine.*

Piston & Rod Assembly – 1) Each rod is sorted into one of 4 tolerance ranges. Size depends on crank journal bore. A number between 1 and 4 is stamped on side of rod big end. Any combination of numbers between 1 and 4 may be found in any engine.

2) Install piston and connecting rod so arrow on top of piston points toward timing belt, and connecting rod oil hole is toward intake manifold side of engine. See PISTON PIN INSTALLATION.

Fitting Pistons – 1) Measure clearance between piston and cylinder bore. Piston clearance is difference between cylinder bore and piston diameter. See PISTONS, PINS, & RINGS table under ENGINE SPECIFICATIONS. If piston clearance exceeds service limit, rebore cylinder and install oversize piston.

2) Standard size pistons are marked with "A" or "B" on top of piston. For 2.2L SOHC, pistons are available in .010" (.25 mm) and .020" (.50 mm) oversize. For 2.2L DOHC and 2.3L, pistons are available in .010" (.25 mm) oversize. Standard cylinder block bore size is identified by letters "A" or "B" stamped on cylinder block.

3) Remove rings from piston. Clean piston thoroughly. Inspect piston for distortion and cracks. Measure piston diameter at location specified. If diameter is not within specification, replace piston. See PISTON, PINS & RINGS table under ENGINE SPECIFICATIONS.

Piston Rings – 1) Using inverted piston, push new piston ring into cylinder bore .6-.8" (15-20 mm) from bottom. Measure piston ring end gap, using a feeler gauge. Repeat for each ring. See PISTONS, PINS & RINGS table under ENGINE SPECIFICATIONS.

2) Clean piston ring grooves thoroughly. Install piston rings with identification mark toward top of piston. Using a feeler gauge, measure piston ring side clearance between ring and ring land.

3) If ring lands are excessively worn, replace piston. See PISTONS, PINS & RINGS table under ENGINE SPECIFICATIONS. Align piston ring end gaps properly on piston. *See Fig. 16.*

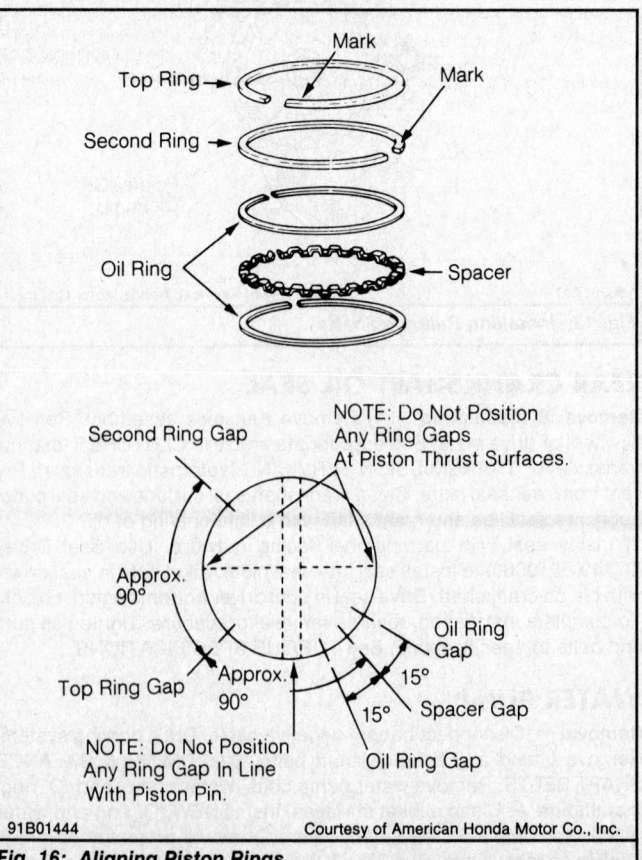

91B01444   Courtesy of American Honda Motor Co., Inc.

Fig. 16: Aligning Piston Rings

Piston Pin Removal – 1) Install Piston Base Head (07HAF-PL20102) and Piston Pin Base Insert (07GAF-PH60300) into Base (07973-6570500). Turn handle on Piston Pin Driver Head (07973-PE00320) so piston driver length is 2.03" (51.5 mm).
2) Insert Piston Driver Shaft (07973-PE00310) into Pilot Collar (07GAF-PH70100). Place piston onto base. Press out piston pin. When removing or installing piston pin, place piston into press with embossed side facing up. Ensure recessed part of piston aligns with lugs on base insert.

NOTE: All replacement piston pins are oversize.

Piston Pin Inspection – 1) Measure piston pin diameter. Measure piston pin bore in piston. Piston pin clearance is difference between the 2 measurements.
2) Piston pin clearance must be as specified in CONNECTING RODS table under ENGINE SPECIFICATIONS. If piston pin clearance is greater than specified, install an oversize piston pin and again measure clearance.
3) Determine difference between piston pin diameter and connecting rod small end bore. Interference fit between piston pin and connecting rod must be as specified in CONNECTING RODS table under ENGINE SPECIFICATIONS.
Piston Pin Installation – 1) Ensure piston and connecting rod are positioned as shown. *See Fig. 18.* Turn handle on Piston Pin Driver (07973-PE00320) so piston driver length is 2.03" (51.5 mm).
2) Install Pilot Collar (07GAF-PR30100) into piston and connecting rod. Lubricate new piston pin lightly. Place piston onto base. Press in piston pin. See CONNECTING RODS table under ENGINE SPECIFICATIONS.

NOTE: A number code indicating connecting rod bore diameter is stamped on side of each connecting rod and cap. Connecting rod journal diameter codes (letters) are stamped on crankshaft counterweights. See Fig. 17. Use both codes when ordering replacement bearings.

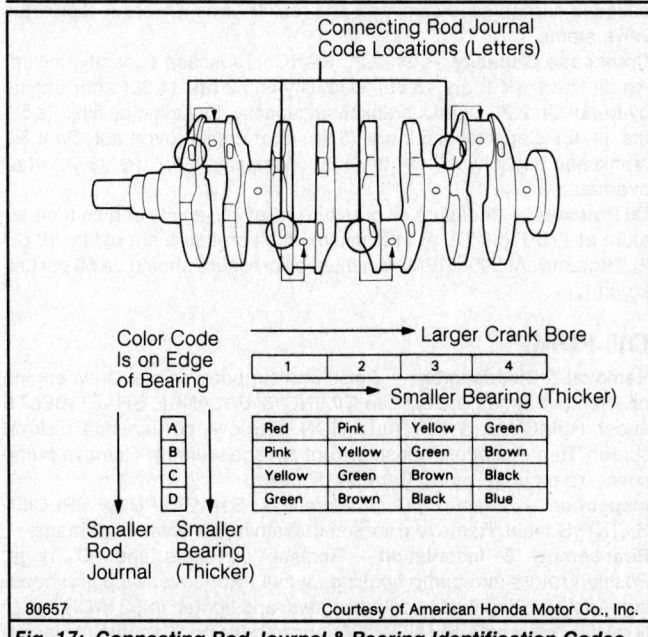

Color Code Is on Edge of Bearing

	1	2	3	4
A	Red	Pink	Yellow	Green
B	Pink	Yellow	Green	Brown
C	Yellow	Green	Brown	Black
D	Green	Brown	Black	Blue

80657   Courtesy of American Honda Motor Co., Inc.

Fig. 17: Connecting Rod Journal & Bearing Identification Codes

Rod Bearings – 1) Using Plastigage, measure rod bearing oil clearance. Tighten bearing cap to 35 ft. lbs. (47 N.m). See CRANKSHAFT, MAIN & CONNECTING ROD BEARINGS table under ENGINE SPECIFICATIONS.
2) If oil clearance is incorrect, install a new bearing set (same color code) and again measure oil clearance. DO NOT shim or file cap to adjust oil clearance.
3) If oil clearance is still incorrect, try the next larger or smaller bearing. Measure oil clearance again. If proper oil clearance cannot be

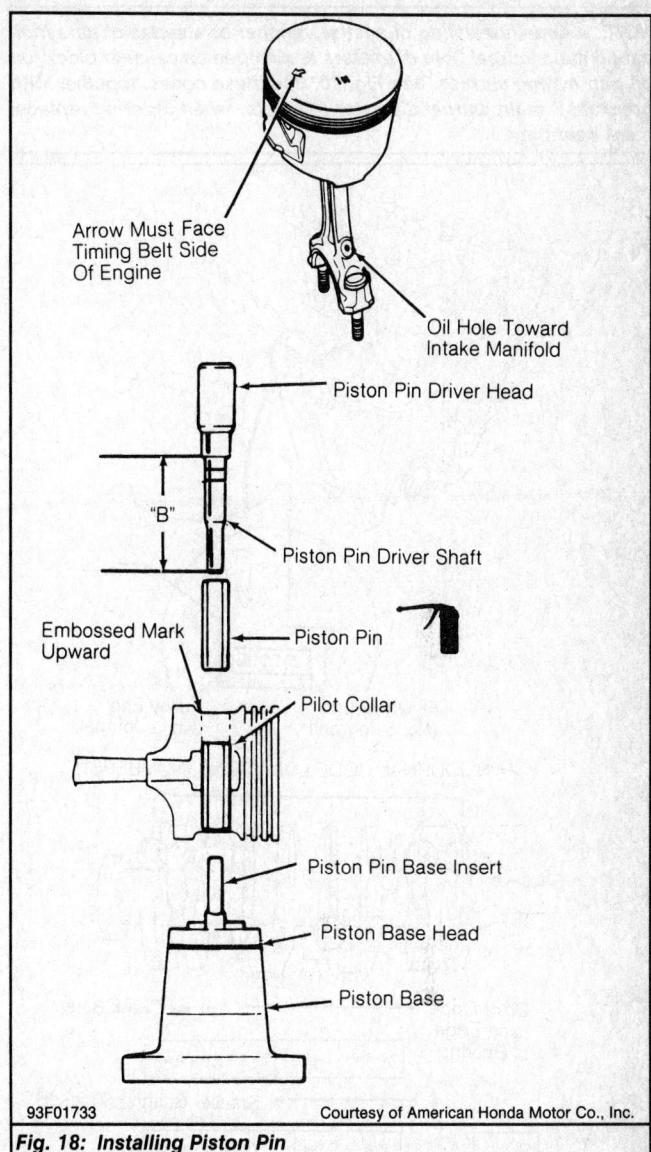

93F01733   Courtesy of American Honda Motor Co., Inc.

Fig. 18: Installing Piston Pin

obtained by using larger or smaller bearings, replace crankshaft and repeat procedure.
Crankshaft & Main Bearings – 1) Remove main bearing cap bridge and main bearing caps in reverse order of sequence shown in illustration. *See Fig 19.* Mark all bearing caps for reassembly reference. Lift crankshaft from block, being careful not to damage journals.

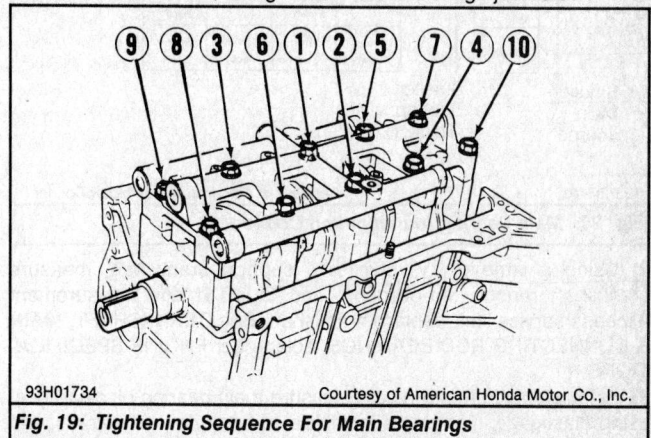

93H01734   Courtesy of American Honda Motor Co., Inc.

Fig. 19: Tightening Sequence For Main Bearings

NOTE: A code consisting of a letter, number or a series of bars indicating main journal bore diameters is stamped on cylinder block, on oil pan mating surface. See Fig. 20. Use these codes, together with crankshaft main journal diameter numbers, when ordering replacement bearings.

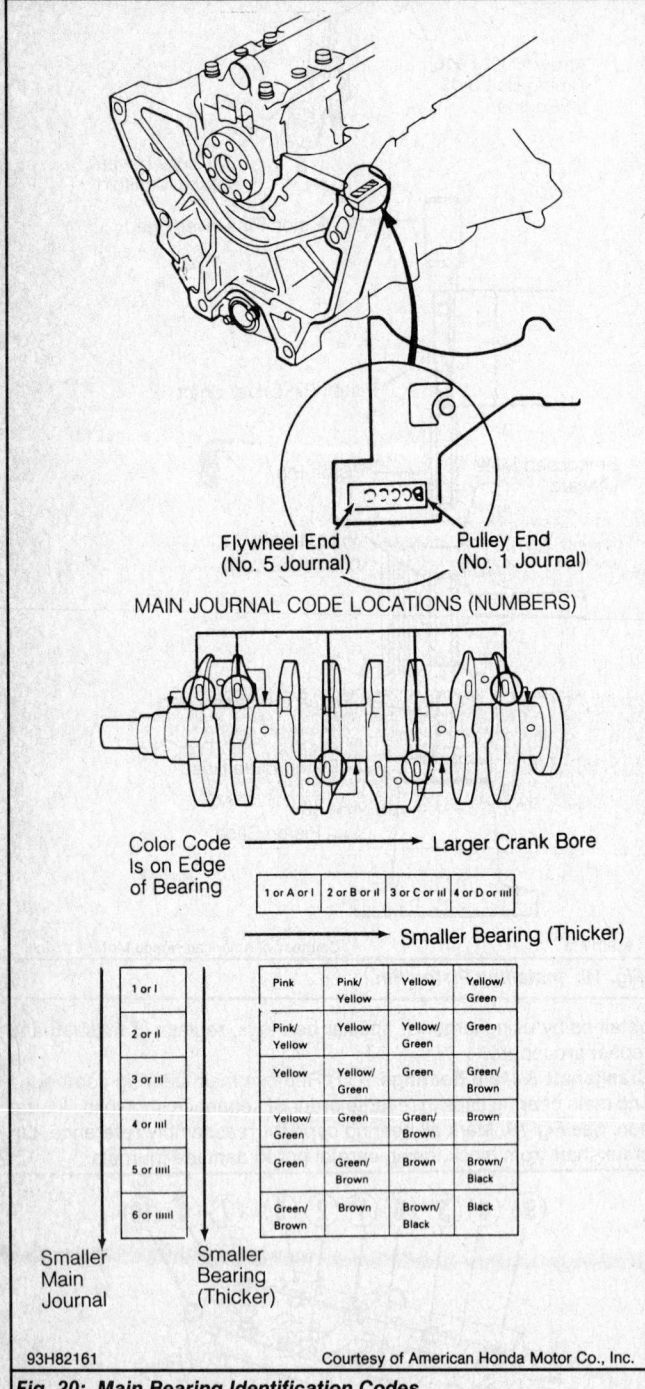

Flywheel End (No. 5 Journal)   Pulley End (No. 1 Journal)

MAIN JOURNAL CODE LOCATIONS (NUMBERS)

Color Code Is on Edge of Bearing ———→ Larger Crank Bore

| 1 or A or I | 2 or B or II | 3 or C or III | 4 or D or IIII |

———→ Smaller Bearing (Thicker)

	Pink	Pink/Yellow	Yellow	Yellow/Green
1 or I				
2 or II	Pink/Yellow	Yellow	Yellow/Green	Green
3 or III	Yellow	Yellow/Green	Green	Green/Brown
4 or IIII	Yellow/Green	Green	Green/Brown	Brown
5 or IIIII	Green	Green/Brown	Brown	Brown/Black
6 or IIIIII	Green/Brown	Brown	Brown/Black	Black

Smaller Main Journal   Smaller Bearing (Thicker)

93H82161   Courtesy of American Honda Motor Co., Inc.

Fig. 20: Main Bearing Identification Codes

2) Using a lathe or "V" blocks to support crankshaft, measure crankshaft runout, out-of-round, and taper. If any measurement exceeds service limit, replace crankshaft. See CRANKSHAFT, MAIN & CONNECTING ROD BEARINGS table under ENGINE SPECIFICATIONS.

3) Install crankshaft into block. Measure main bearing oil clearance, using Plastigage. If engine is in vehicle, support counterweights, and measure only one bearing at a time. Before installing main bearing cap

bolts, lubricate thrust washers and bolt threads. Tighten main bearing caps, in sequence, in 2 stages, first to 22 ft. lbs. (30 N.m), then to 55 ft. lbs. (75 N.m). *See Fig. 19.*

4) If oil clearance is incorrect, install a new bearing set (same color code) and recheck oil clearance. If oil clearance is still incorrect, try next larger or smaller bearing and measure oil clearance once more. If proper oil clearance cannot be obtained by using larger or smaller bearings, replace crankshaft and repeat procedure.

Thrust Bearing – 1) Measure crankshaft end play. If end play exceeds specification, inspect thrust washers and thrust surface of crankshaft. See CRANKSHAFT, MAIN & CONNECTING ROD BEARINGS table under ENGINE SPECIFICATIONS.

2) Replace worn parts as necessary. Thrust washer thickness is fixed. DO NOT change thrust washer thickness by grinding or shimming. Install thrust washers with grooved side out.

CAUTION: After replacing any rod or main bearing, idle engine until it reaches normal operating temperature, then an additional 15 minutes.

Cylinder Block – 1) Measure cylinder block deck surface warpage. Service limit is .004" (.10 mm). Measure cylinder bore out-of-round and taper. If out-of-round or taper exceeds .002" (.05 mm), rebore cylinder for oversize pistons. If any cylinder exceed oversize bore service limit, replace cylinder block. See CYLINDER BLOCK table under ENGINE SPECIFICATIONS.

2) If cylinder block is okay, hone cylinders to obtain a 60-degree cross-hatch pattern. After honing, wash cylinder bores with hot soapy water. Air-dry cylinder bores, and apply engine oil to prevent rusting.

ENGINE OILING

ENGINE LUBRICATION SYSTEM

A rotor-type oil pump draws oil from oil pan and delivers it under pressure to main and connecting rod bearings. An oil hole in each connecting rod lubricates thrust side of piston and cylinder wall. An oil passage carries oil to camshaft and rocker arms. Oil spray lubricates valve stems.

Crankcase Capacity – On 2.2L SOHC, crankcase capacity, including oil filter, is 4.0 qts. (3.8L). Capacity is 5.2 qts. (4.9L) after engine overhaul.On 2.2L DOHC, crankcase capacity, including oil filter, is 5.1 qts. (4.8L). Capacity is 6.2 qts. (5.9L) after engine overhaul. On 2.3L, crankcase capacity is 4.5 qts. (4.3L). Capacity is 5.7 qts. (5.4L) after overhaul.

Oil Pressure – Measure oil pressure relief valve with engine temperature at 176°F (80°C). At idle, minimum oil pressure should be 10 psi (0.7 kg/cm²). At 3000 RPM, minimum oil pressure should be 50 psi (3.5 kg/cm²).

OIL PUMP

Removal & Disassembly – Raise and support vehicle. Drain engine oil. Remove timing belts. See TIMING & BALANCE SHAFT BELTS under REMOVAL & INSTALLATION. Remove oil pan and pick-up screen. Remove pump housing/front cover assembly. Remove pump cover from pump rotors. Remove oil seals.

Inspection – Measure pump clearances. See OIL PUMP SPECIFICATIONS table. Remove rotors and examine for wear or damage.

Reassembly & Installation – Replace oil seals and "O" rings. Position rotors into pump housing. Install rotor cover on pump housing. Apply locking fluid to cover screws, and tighten to 62 INCH lbs. (7 N.m). Fit dowel pins and NEW "O" rings to housing. To complete installation, reverse removal procedure.

OIL PUMP SPECIFICATIONS

Application	Specification
Standard	
Radial Clearance	
Inner Rotor-To-Outer Rotor	.001-.006" (.02-.16 mm)
Pump Body-To-Rotor	.004-.007" (.10-.19 mm)
Side Clearance	
Pump Body-To-Rotor	.001-.003" (.02-.07 mm)
Service Limit	
Radial Clearance	
Inner Rotor-To-Outer Rotor	.008" (.20 mm)
Pump Body-To-Rotor	.0083" (.21 mm)
Side Clearance	
Pump Body-To-Rotor	.005" (.12 mm)

TORQUE SPECIFICATIONS

TORQUE SPECIFICATIONS

Application	Ft. Lbs. (N.m)
A/C Compressor Bracket Bolt	37 (50)
Alternator Bracket Adjuster Bolt	16 (22)
Alternator Bracket Bolt	33 (45)
Camshaft Pulley Bolt	
2.2L DOHC	37 (51)
2.2L SOHC & 2.3L	27 (37)
Connecting Rod Nut	35 (47)
Crankshaft Pulley Bolt	184 (250)
Cylinder Head Bolt [1]	
Stage 1	29 (40)
Stage 2	52 (70)
Stage 3	74 (100)
Distributor Mount Bolts	13 (18)
EGR Pipe-To-Exhaust Manifold	44 (60)
Engine Mount Bolts	[2]
Exhaust Manifold Bracket Bolt	33 (45)
Exhaust Manifold Nut [3]	24 (32)
Exhaust Manifold-To-Exhaust Pipe Nut	41 (55)
Exhaust Manifold-To-Heat Shield Bolt	16 (22)
Flywheel Bolt [3]	77 (105)
Intake Manifold Chamber Bolt/Nut	16 (22)
Intake Manifold-To-Cylinder Head Nut [3]	16 (22)
Main Bearing Cap Bolt	
Stage 1	22 (30)
Stage 2	55 (75)
Oil Pan Drain Plug	33 (45)
Oxygen Sensor	33 (45)
Power Steering Belt Adjuster Nut	11 (15)
Power Steering Pump Bracket Bolt	33 (45)
Power Steering Pump Mounting Bolt	16 (22)
Shift Cable Bracket Bolt	16 (22)
Throttle Body Nut	16 (22)
Timing Belt Tension Adjuster Nut	33 (45)
Torque Converter Drive Plate Bolt [3]	55 (75)
Valve Adjuster Lock Nut	
2.2L DOHC & 2.3L	20 (27)
2.2L SOHC	14 (20)

[1] – Tighten in sequence. *See Fig. 6 or 7.*
[2] – Tighten in sequence. *See Fig. 5.*
[3] – Tighten in a crisscross pattern.
[4] – Tighten 8-mm bolts to 16-19 ft. lbs. (22-26 N.m).
[5] – *See Fig. 12.*

TORQUE SPECIFICATIONS (Cont.)

Application	INCH Lbs. (N.m)
Camshaft Bearing Cap Bolt	
2.2L	
6 mm Bolts	108 (12)
8 mm Bolts	[4]
2.3L	[5]
EGR Pipe-To-Intake Manifold Nut	108 (12)
Fuel Filter Bracket Bolt	108 (12)
Oil Pan Bolt	108 (12)
Oil Pump Cover Screw	62 (7)
Oil Pump Housing Bolt	108 (12)
Oil Pump Screen Bolt	108 (12)
Thermostat Housing Bolt	108 (12)
Timing Belt Cover Bolt	108 (12)
Valve Cover Nut	90 (10)
Water Pump Bolt	108 (12)

[1] – Tighten in sequence. *See Fig. 6 or 7.*
[2] – Tighten in sequence. *See Fig. 5.*
[3] – Tighten in a crisscross pattern.
[4] – Tighten 8-mm bolts to 16-19 ft. lbs. (22-26 N.m).
[5] – *See Fig. 12.*

ENGINE SPECIFICATIONS

GENERAL SPECIFICATIONS

Application	Specification
Displacement	
2.2L	132 Cu. In. (2.2L)
2.3L	138 Cu. In. (2.3L)
Bore	
2.2L	
DOHC	3.43" (87 mm)
SOHC	3.35" (85 mm)
2.3L	3.43" (87 mm)
Stroke	
2.2L	
DOHC	3.57" (90.7 mm)
SOHC	3.74" (95 mm)
2.3L	3.74" (95 mm)
Compression Ratio	
2.2L	
DOHC	10.0:1
SOHC	8.8:1
2.3L	9.8:1
Fuel System	MFI
Horsepower @ RPM	
2.2L	
DOHC	190 @ 6800
SOHC	135 @ 5200
2.3L	160 @ 5800
Torque Ft. Lbs. @ RPM	
2.2L	
DOHC	158 @ 5300
SOHC	142 @ 4000
2.3L	156 @ 4500

CONNECTING RODS

Application	In. (mm)
Piston Pin Diameter	
Standard	.8659-.8661 (21.994-22.000)
Oversize	.8660-.8663 (21.997-22.003)
Piston Pin-To-Rod Interference	.0005-.0013 (.013-.032)
Piston Pin-To-Piston Clearance	
2.2L SOHC	.0005-.0009 (.012-.024)
2.2L DOHC & 2.3L	.0005-.0010 (.012-.026)

CRANKSHAFT, MAIN & CONNECTING ROD BEARINGS

Application	In. (mm)
Crankshaft	
End Play	
Standard	.004-.014 (.10-.35)
Service Limit	.018 (.45)
Runout	
Standard	.0012 (.030)
Service Limit	.0016 (.040)
Main Bearings	
Journal Diameter	
No. 1	
F22A1 & H23A1	1.9678-1.9688 (49.984-50.008)
H22A1	1.9676-1.9685 (49.976-50.000)
No. 2	1.9676-1.9685 (49.976-50.000)
No. 3	1.9674-1.9683 (49.972-49.996)
No. 4	1.9679-1.9688 (49.984-50.008)
No. 5	1.9680-1.9690 (49.988-50.012)
Journal Out-Of-Round	
Standard	
Except H22A1	.0002 (.005)
H22A1	.0002 (.004)
Service Limit	.0002 (.006)
Journal Taper	
Standard	.0002 (.005)
Service Limit	.0002 (.006)
Oil Clearance	
No. 1 Journals	
F22A1 & H23A1	
Standard	.0005-.0015 (.013-.037)
Service Limit	.002 (.050)
H22A1	
Standard	.0008-.0018 (.021-.045)
Service Limit	.002 (.050)
No. 2 Journals	
Standard	.0008-.0018 (.021-.045)
Service Limit	.002 (.050)
No. 3 Journal	
Standard	.0010-.0020 (.025-.049)
Service Limit	.0022 (.055)
No. 4 Journal	
Standard	.0005-.0015 (.013-.037)
Service Limit	.0020 (.050)
No. 5 Journal	
Standard	.0004-.0013 (.009-.033)
Service Limit	.0016 (.040)
Connecting Rod Bearings	
Journal Diameter	1.7707-1.7717 (44.976-45.000)
Journal Out-Of-Round	
F22A1 & H23A1	
Standard	.0002 (.005)
Service Limit	.0002 (.006)
H22A1	
Standard	.0002 (.004)
Service Limit	.0002 (.006)
Journal Taper	
Standard	.0002 (.005)
Service Limit	.0002 (.006)
Oil Clearance	
2.2L SOHC & 2.3L	
Standard	.0008-.0020 (.021-.049)
Service Limit	.0022 (.055)
2.2L DOHC	
Standard	.0011-.0022 (.027-.055)
Service Limit	.0024 (.060)

PISTONS, PINS & RINGS

Application	In. (mm)
2.2L SOHC	
Piston Clearance	
Standard	.0008-.0016 (.020-.040)
Service Limit	.002 (.05)
Piston Diameter [1]	
Standard	
Size "A" (Or No Letter)	3.3457-3.3461 (84.98-84.99)
Size "B"	3.3453-3.3457 (84.97-84.98)
Service Limit	
Size "A" (Or No Letter)	3.3453 (84.97)
Size "B"	3.3449 (84.96)
Piston Pin Clearance	
Standard	.0005-.0009 (.012-.024)
Service Limit	.0009 (.024)
Rings	
No. 1	
End Gap	
Standard	.008-.014 (.20-.35)
Service Limit	.024 (.60)
Side Clearance	
Standard	.0014-.0024 (.035-.060)
Service Limit	.005 (.13)
No. 2	
End Gap	
Standard	.016-.022 (.40-.55)
Service Limit	.028 (.70)
Side Clearance	
Standard	.0012-.0022 (.030-.055)
Service Limit	.005 (.13)
No. 3 (Oil)	
End Gap	.008-.028 (.20-.70)
2.2L DOHC & 2.3L	
Piston Clearance	
Standard	.0003-.0012 (.007-.030)
Service Limit	.0016 (.04)
Piston Diameter [2]	
Standard	
Size "A" (Or No Letter)	3.4248-3.4253 (86.990-87.003)
Size "B"	3.4244-3.4249 (86.980-86.993)
Service Limit	
Size "A" (Or No Letter)	3.4244 (86.980)
Size "B"	3.4240 (86.970)
Piston Pin Clearance	
Standard	.0005-.0010 (.012-.026)
Service Limit	.0010 (.026)
Rings	
No. 1	
End Gap	
Standard	.010-.014 (.25-.35)
Service Limit	.024 (.60)
Side Clearance	
Standard	.0018-.0027 (.045-.070)
Service Limit	.005 (.13)
No. 2	
End Gap	
Standard	.024-.030 (.60-.75)
Service Limit	.028 (.90)
Side Clearance	
Standard	.0016-.0027 (.040-.070)
Service Limit	.005 (.13)
No. 3 (Oil)	
End Gap [3]	
Standard	.008-.020 (.20-.50)
Service Limit [3]	.024 (.60)

[1] – Measured .83" (21 mm) from bottom of piston skirt.
[2] – Measured .59" (15 mm) from bottom of piston skirt.
[3] – Teikoku manufacturer.
[4] – Riken manufacturer.

CYLINDER BLOCK

Application	In. (mm)
2.2L SOHC	
Cylinder Bore	
F22A1	
Standard Diameter	
Size "A" (Or No Letter)	3.3468-3.3472 (85.010-85.020)
Size "B" (Or No Letter)	3.3464-3.3468 (85.000-85.010)
Service Limit	3.3492 (85.070)
H22A1 & H23A1	
Standard Diameter	
Size "A" (Or No Letter)	3.4255-3.4259 (87.010-87.020)
Size "B" (Or No Letter)	3.4251-3.4255 (87.000-87.010)
Service Limit	3.4279 (87.070)
Maximum Taper	.002 (.05)
Maximum Deck Warpage	.004 (.10)
Maximum Rebore Limit	.02 (.5)
2.2L DOHC & 2.3L	
Cylinder Bore	
Standard Diameter	3.425-3.426 (87.00-87.02)
Service Limit	3.428 (87.07)
Maximum Taper	.002 (.05)
Maximum Deck Warpage	.004 (.10)
Maximum Rebore Limit	.010 (.25)

VALVES & VALVE SPRINGS (2.2L DOHC)

Application	Specification
Intake Valves	
Face Angle	45°
Head Diameter	1.374-1.382" (34.90-35.10)
Margin	
Standard	.041-.053" (1.05-1.35 mm)
Service Limit	.033" (.85 mm)
Stem Diameter	
Standard	.2156-.2159" (5.475-5.485 mm)
Service Limit	.2144" (5.445 mm)
Exhaust Valves	
Face Angle	45°
Head Diameter	1.177-1.185" (29.90-30.10)
Margin	
Standard	.065-.078" (1.65-1.95 mm)
Service Limit	.057" (1.45 mm)
Stem Diameter	
Standard	.21556-.2159" (5.475-5.485 mm)
Service Limit	.2144" (5.445 mm)
Valve Spring	
Free Length	
Intake	
Inner	
Chuo Hatsujo	1.645" (41.78 mm)
Nihon Hatsujo	1.644" (41.75 mm)
Outer	
Chuo Hatsujo	1.778" (45.16 mm)
Nihon Hatsujo	1.802" (45.76 mm)
Exhaust	
Inner	
Chuo Hatsujo	1.548" (39.32 mm)
Nihon Hatsujo	1.546" (39.28 mm)
Outer	
Chuo Hatsujo	1.839" (46.72 mm)
Nihon Hatsujo	1.840" (46.74 mm)

VALVES & VALVE SPRINGS (2.2L SOHC)

Application	Specification
Intake Valves	
Face Angle	45°
Head Diameter	1.335-1.343" (33.9-34.10)
Margin	
Standard	.033-.045" (.85-1.15 mm)
Service Limit	.026" (.65 mm)
Stem Diameter	
Standard	.2159-.2163" (5.485-5.495 mm)
Service Limit	.2148" (5.455 mm)
Exhaust Valves	
Face Angle	45°
Head Diameter	1.138-1.146" (28.90-29.10 mm)
Margin	
Standard	.041-.053" (1.05-1.35 mm)
Service Limit	.037" (.95 mm)
Stem Diameter	
Standard	.2146-.2150" (5.450-5.460 mm)
Service Limit	.2134" (5.420 mm)
Valve Spring	
Free Length	
Intake	
Chuo Hatsujo	2.1578" (54.810 mm)
Nihon Hatsujo	2.1582" (54.820 mm)
Exhaust	
Chuo Hatsujo	2.2149" (56.260 mm)
Nihon Hatsujo	2.2157" (56.280 mm)

VALVES & VALVE SPRINGS (2.3L)

Application	Specification
Intake Valves	
Face Angle	45°
Head Diameter	1.335-1.343" (33.90-34.10)
Margin	
Standard	.033-.045" (.85-1.15 mm)
Service Limit	.026" (.65 mm)
Stem Diameter	
Standard	.2591-.2594" (6.580-6.590 mm)
Service Limit	.2579" (6.550 mm)
Exhaust Valves	
Face Angle	45°
Head Diameter	1.138-1.146" (28.90-29.10 mm)
Margin	
Standard	.041-.053" (1.05-1.35 mm)
Service Limit	.033" (.85 mm)
Stem Diameter	
Standard	.2579-.2583" (6.55-6.56 mm)
Service Limit	.2567" (6.520 mm)
Valve Spring	
Free Length	1.856" (47.14 mm)

CYLINDER HEAD (2.2L DOHC)

Application	Specification
Cylinder Head	
Height	5.785-5.789" (146.95-147.05 mm)
Maximum Warpage	[1] .002-.008" (.05-.20 mm)
Valve Seats	
Intake & Exhaust Valve	
Seat Angle	45°
Seat Width	
Standard	
Intake	.051-.059" (1.30-1.50 mm)
Exhaust	.049-.061" (1.25-1.55 mm)
Service Limit	.079" (2.00 mm)
Valve Guide Installed Height	
Intake	.573-.593 (14.55-15.05)
Exhaust	.589-.608 (14.95-15.45)
Valve Guide Oil Clearance	
Measured At Valve Head (Dial Indicator)	
Intake Valve	
Standard	.002-.004 (.05-.11)
Service Limit	.006 (.16)
Exhaust Valve	
Standard	.004-.006 (.10-.16)
Service Limit	.009 (.22)
Measured At Stem (Micrometer & Ball Gauge)	
Intake Valve	
Standard	.001-.002 (.025-.055)
Service Limit	.003 (.08)
Exhaust Valve	
Standard	.002-.003 (.05-.08)
Service Limit	.004 (.11)
Valve Stem Installed Height [2]	
Intake Valve	
Standard	1.475-1.494 (37.465-37.935)
Service Limit	1.503 (38.185)
Exhaust Valve	
Standard	1.463-1.482 (37.165-37.635)
Service Limit	1.492 (37.885)

[1] – Maximum resurface limit is .008" (.20 mm).
[2] – Measured from stem tip of installed valve to spring seat surface.

CYLINDER HEAD (2.2L SOHC)

Application	Specification
Cylinder Head	
Height	3.935-3.939" (99.95-100.05 mm)
Maximum Warpage	[1] .002-.008" (.05-.20 mm)
Valve Seats	
Intake & Exhaust Valve	
Seat Angle	45°
Seat Width	
Standard	.049-.061" (1.25-1.55 mm)
Service Limit	.079" (2.00 mm)
Valve Guide Installed Height	
Intake	.935-.955 (23.75-24.25)
Exhaust	.593-.612 (15.05-15.55)
Valve Guide Oil Clearance	
Measured At Valve Head (Dial Indicator)	
Intake Valve	
Standard	.0016-.0034 (.04-.09)
Service Limit	.006 (.16)
Exhaust Valve	
Standard	.004-.006 (.11-.16)
Service Limit	.009 (.24)

[1] – Maximum resurface limit is .008" (.20 mm).

CYLINDER HEAD (2.2L SOHC – Cont.)

Application	Specification
Measured At Stem (Micrometer & Ball Gauge)	
Intake Valve	
Standard	.0008-.0018 (.020-.045)
Service Limit	.003 (.08)
Exhaust Valve	
Standard	.002-.003 (.055-.080)
Service Limit	.005 (.12)
Valve Stem Installed Height [2]	
Intake Valve	
Standard	1.8994-1.9179 (48.245-48.715)
Service Limit	1.9278 (48.965)
Exhaust Valve	
Standard	1.9809-1.9994 (50.315-50.785)
Service Limit	2.0092 (51.035)

[2] – Measured from stem tip of installed valve to spring seat surface.

CYLINDER HEAD (2.3L)

Application	Specification
Cylinder Head	
Height	5.195-5.199" (131.95-132.05 mm)
Maximum Warpage	[1] .002-.008" (.05-.20 mm)
Valve Seats	
Intake & Exhaust Valve	
Seat Angle	45°
Seat Width	
Standard	.049-.061" (1.25-1.55 mm)
Service Limit	.079" (2.00 mm)
Valve Guide Installed Height	
Intake	.521-.541 (13.25-13.75)
Exhaust	.541-.561 (13.75-14.25)
Valve Guide Oil Clearance	
Measured At Valve Head (Dial Indicator)	
Intake Valve	
Standard	.002-.004 (.04-.10)
Service Limit	.006 (.16)
Exhaust Valve	
Standard	.004-.006 (.10-.16)
Service Limit	.009 (.22)
Measured At Stem (Micrometer & Ball Gauge)	
Intake Valve	
Standard	.001-.002 (.02-.05)
Service Limit	.003 (.08)
Exhaust Valve	
Standard	.002-.003 (.05-.08)
Service Limit	.004 (.11)
Valve Stem Installed Height [2]	
Intake Valve	
Standard	1.549-1.568 (39.365-39.835)
Service Limit	1.578 (40.085)
Exhaust Valve	
Standard	1.543-1.568 (39.195-39.635)
Service Limit	1.570 (39.885)

[1] – Maximum resurface limit is .008" (.20 mm).
[2] – Measured from stem tip of installed valve to spring seat surface.

CAMSHAFT

Application	In. (mm)
2.2L DOHC	
End Play	
Standard	.002-.006 (.05-.15)
Service Limit	.020 (.50)
Journal Runout	
Standard	.0012 (.03)
Service Limit	.002 (.050)
Oil Clearance	
Standard	.002-.004 (.050-.089)
Service Limit	.006 (.15)
Lobe Height	
Intake	
Primary	1.3402 (34.041)
Mid	1.4510 (36.856)
Secondary	1.3768 (34.971)
Exhaust	
Primary	1.3285 (33.745)
Mid	1.4300 (36.323)
Secondary	1.3655 (34.683)
2.2L SOHC	
End Play	
Standard	.002-.006 (.05-.15)
Service Limit	.020 (.50)
Journal Runout	
Standard	.001 (.03)
Service Limit	.002 (.04)
Oil Clearance	
Standard	.002-.004 (.050-.089)
Service Limit	.006 (.15)
Lobe Height	
Intake	1.5167 (38.526)
Exhaust	1.5266 (38.778)
2.3L	
End Play	
Standard	.002-.006 (.05-.15)
Service Limit	.020 (.50)
Journal Runout	
Standard	.001 (.03)
Service Limit	.002 (.04)
Oil Clearance	
Except Exhaust Journal No. 5	
Standard	.002-.004 (.050-.089)
Service Limit	.006 (.15)
Exhaust Journal No. 5	
Standard	.004-.005 (.100-.139)
Service Limit	.008 (.200)
Lobe Height	
Intake	1.3252 (33.661)
Exhaust	1.3278 (33.725)

BALANCE SHAFTS

Application	In. (mm)
End Play	
Front	.0040-.0138 (.100-.350)
Rear	.0024-.0070 (.060-.180)
Runout	.0008 (.020)
Oil Clearance	
No. 1 Journal (Rear)	
Standard	.0020-.0030 (.050-.075)
Service Limit	.0035 (.090)
No. 1 Journal (Front)	
Standard	.0026-.0038 (.066-.098)
Service Limit	.0047 (.120)
No. 2 Journal	
Standard	.0030-.0043 (.076-.108)
Service Limit	.0051 (.130)
No. 3 Journal	
Standard	.0026-.0038 (.066-.098)
Service Limit	.0047 (.120)

1994 ENGINE COOLING
Specifications & Electric Cooling Fans

Accord, Civic, Civic Del Sol, Passport, Prelude

NOTE: For water pump removal procedure, see appropriate article in ENGINES.

SPECIFICATIONS

BELT ADJUSTMENT

BELT ADJUSTMENT (EXCEPT PASSPORT)

Application	[1] Deflection In. (mm)
A/C Compressor	
Accord	
New	13/64-9/32 (5.0-7.0)
Used	5/16-25/64 (8.0-10.5)
Civic & Civic Del Sol	
New	13/64-9/32 (5.0-7.0)
Used	1/4-25/64 (6.5-10.5)
Prelude	
New	13/32-31/64 (10.0-12.0)
Used	3/16-9/32 (4.5-7.0)
Alternator	
Accord	
New	
With A/C	5/16-25/64 (8.0-10.5)
Without A/C	25/64-1/2 (10.5-12.5)
Used	5/16-31/64 (8.0-10.0)
Civic & Civic Del Sol	
New	7/32-5/16 (5.5-8.0)
Used	9/32-25/64 (7.0-10.5)
Prelude	
New	
With A/C	21/64-7/16 (8.5-11.0)
Without A/C	5/16-31/64 (8.0-10.0)
Used	
With A/C	13/32-31/64 (10.0-12.0)
Without A/C	25/64-1/2 (10.5-12.5)
Power Steering	
Accord	
New	7/16-1/2 (11.0-12.5)
Used	33/64-5/84 (13.0-16.0)
Civic & Civic Del Sol	
New	15/64-3/8 (6.0-9.5)
Used	5/16-31/64 (8.0-12.0)
Prelude	
New	3/8-29/64 (9.5-11.5)
Used	17/32-21/32 (13.5-16.5)

[1] – Deflection is with 22 lbs. (10 kg) pressure applied midway on longest belt run.

BELT ADJUSTMENT (PASSPORT)

Application	[1] Belt Tension Lbs. (kg)
A/C Compressor	80-120 (36-54)
Alternator	100-120 (45-54)
Power Steering Pump	70-110 (32-50)

[1] – Belt tension as measured with Burroughs tension gauge midway on longest belt run.

COOLING SYSTEM SPECIFICATIONS

COOLING SYSTEM SPECIFICATIONS

Application	Specification
Coolant Replacement Interval	[1]
Coolant Capacity [2]	
Accord	
Automatic Transaxle	7.2 Qts. (6.8L)
Manual Transaxle	7.3 Qts. (6.9L)
Civic & Civic Del Sol	
Automatic Transaxle	
1.5L Engine	4.6 Qts. (4.4L)
1.6L Engine	5.0 Qts. (4.7L)
Manual Transaxle	
1.5L Engine (D15B7 & D15B8)	4.8 Qts. (4.5L)
1.5L Engine (D15Z1)	4.6 Qts. (4.4L)
1.6L Engine (B16A3)	5.1 Qts. (4.8L)
1.6L Engine (D16Z6)	4.6 Qts. (4.4L)

[1] – 45,000 miles initially; 30,000 miles thereafter.
[2] – Including heater core and reservoir.

COOLING SYSTEM SPECIFICATIONS (Cont.)

Application	Specification
Passport	
2.6L	9.5 Qts. (9.0L)
3.2L	
Automatic Transmission	9.3 Qts. (8.8L)
Manual Transmission	9.7 Qts. (9.2L)
Prelude	
Automatic Transaxle	
2.2L Engine (F22A1)	7.4 Qts. (7.0L)
2.3L Engine (H23A1)	7.7 Qts. (7.3L)
Manual Transaxle	
2.2L Engine (F22A1)	7.5 Qts. (7.1L)
2.2L Engine (H22A1)	8.5 Qts. (8.0L)
2.3L Engine (H23A1)	7.8 Qts. (7.4L)
Pressure Cap	14-18 psi
Thermostat Opens	
Starts	
Accord, Civic Del Sol & Prelude	169-176°F (76-80°C)
Civic	
1.5L	179-183°F (80-84°C)
1.6L	169-179°F (76-80°C)
Passport	
2.6L	180°F (82°C)
3.2L	166-173°F (75-79°C)
Fully Open	
Accord, Civic Del Sol & Prelude	194°F (90°C)
Civic	
1.5L	203°F (95°C)
1.6L	194°F (90°C)
Passport	
2.6L	203°F (95°C)
1.5L	194°F (90°C)

[1] – 45,000 miles initially; 30,000 miles thereafter.
[2] – Including heater core and reservoir.

COOLING SYSTEM BLEEDING

Except Passport – 1) Set heater controls to maximum heat. Fill cooling system with a 50/50 mixture of coolant and water to bottom of filler neck. Loosen bleed bolt, located on thermostat housing.
2) Tighten bleed bolt when coolant flows from bleed bolt in steady stream without bubbles. With radiator cap off, start and operate engine to normal operating temperature (fan comes on at least twice). Add coolant as necessary. Install radiator cap.
Passport – Fill cooling system with a 50/50 mixture of coolant and water to bottom of filler neck. With radiator cap off, start and operate engine to normal operating temperature. Operate engine at 2500 RPM for about 30 minutes. Check coolant level periodically. Add coolant as necessary. When coolant level no longer drops, install radiator cap.

ELECTRIC COOLING FAN

NOTE: For wiring circuit information, see WIRING DIAGRAMS. Some wires have been assigned a superscript to distinguish them from other wires of the same color. For example, the Yellow/Green[1] wire is not the same as the Yellow/Green[2] wire.

NOTE: Trouble shooting procedures for Civic and Civic Del Sol are not available from the manufacturer.

TROUBLE SHOOTING – ACCORD

Cooling & Condenser Fans Do Not Operate – If both fans are not operating, check:
- No. 8 (7.5-amp) fuse blown. Located in underdash fuse box.
- Coolant temperature switch "A" or "B".
- Radiator fan control module.
- Ground circuit at coolant temperature switch "A" or "B".
- Open or loose terminal in Black/Yellow[2] wire circuit between underdash fuse box and radiator fan control module.
- Open or loose terminal in Green wire circuit between radiator fan relay and coolant temperature switch "A".

- Open or loose terminal in White/Green wire circuit between radiator fan control module and coolant temperature switch "B".

Only One Fan Operates – If only one fan is operating, check:
- No. 21 (20-amp) or No. 34 (15-amp) fuse blown. Located in underhood fuse box.
- Radiator or condenser fan relay.
- Radiator or condenser fan motor.
- Ground circuits at radiator fan control module.
- Open or loose terminal in Green wire circuit between radiator fan relay and coolant temperature switch "A".
- Open or loose terminal in White[1] wire circuit between underhood fuse box. radiator fan control module and condenser fan relay.
- Open or loose terminal in Blue/Black wire circuit between radiator fan relay and radiator fan.
- Open or loose terminal in Blue/Yellow wire circuit between condenser fan relay and condenser fan motor.
- Open or loose terminal in Yellow/White wire circuit between radiator fan control module and condenser fan relay.

Radiator Fan Control Module Malfunction – If radiator fan control module is not operating properly, check:
- No. 34 (15-amp) fuse blown. Located in underhood fuse box.
- No. 4 (7.5-amp) fuse blown. Located in underdash fuse box.
- Coolant temperature switch "B".
- Cooling fan control module.
- Ground circuits at radiator fan control module.
- Open or loose terminal in White[1] wire circuit between underhood relay box, radiator fan control module and condenser fan relay.
- Open or loose terminal in White/Green wire circuit between radiator fan control module and coolant temperature switch "B".
- Open or loose terminal in Yellow[1] wire circuit between radiator fan control module and radiator fan relay.
- Open or loose terminal in Black/Yellow[1] wire circuit between underdash fuse box and radiator fan control module.

TROUBLE SHOOTING – PRELUDE

Cooling & Condenser Fans Do Not Operate – If both fans are not operating, check:
- Fuss No. 9 (15-amp) in underdash fuse box.
- Coolant temperature switches "A" and "B".
- Radiator fan control module.
- Ground circuit at condenser fan motor.
- Open or loose terminal in both Black/Yellow[2] wire circuit between underdash fuse box and radiator fan control module.
- Open or loose terminal in both Blue/Red wire circuit between radiator fan relay and engine coolant temperature switch "A".
- Open or loose terminal in both White/Yellow wire circuit between radiator fan control module and engine coolant temperature switch "B".

Only One Fan Operates – If only one fan is operating, check:
- Fuses No. 47 (15-amp) and No. 45 (15-amp) in underhood relay box.
- Radiator or condenser fan relay.
- Radiator or condenser fan motor.
- Ground circuits at radiator fan motor, coolant temperature switch "B" and coolant fan motor.
- Open or loose terminal in Blue/Black wire circuit between radiator fan relay and radiator fan motor.
- Open or loose terminal in Blue/Yellow wire circuit between condenser fan relay and condenser fan motor.
- Open or loose terminal in Blue/Red wire circuit between radiator fan relay, condenser fan relay and coolant temperature switch "A".
- Open or loose terminal in White/Green wire circuit between underhood fuse box and radiator fan control module. Check for open in White/Green (or White wire) wire between splice and condenser fan relay.
- Open or loose terminal in Yellow[1] wire circuit between radiator fan relay and radiator fan control module.
- Open or loose terminal in Yellow/White wire circuit between condenser fan relay and radiator fan control module.

Radiator Fan Control Module Malfunction – If radiator fan control module is not operating properly, check:
- Fuses No. 33 (50-amp), No. 45 (15-amp) and No. 47 (15-amp) in underhood relay box.
- Radiator fan control module.
- A/C system.
- Ground circuits at coolant temperature switch "B" and radiator fan control module.
- Open or loose terminal in White/Yellow wire circuit between radiator fan control module and coolant temperature switch "B".
- Open or loose terminal in White/Green wire circuit between underhood fuse box and radiator fan control module.
- Open or loose terminal in Black/Yellow wire circuit between underdash relay box and radiator fan control module.
- Open or loose terminal in Yellow[1] wire circuit between radiator fan relay and radiator fan control module.

COMPONENT TESTING

Radiator Fan Control Module (Accord) – 1) Perform following checks with radiator fan control module connected and ignition on. Before performing tests, check fuses No. 4 and 8 in dash fuse box and

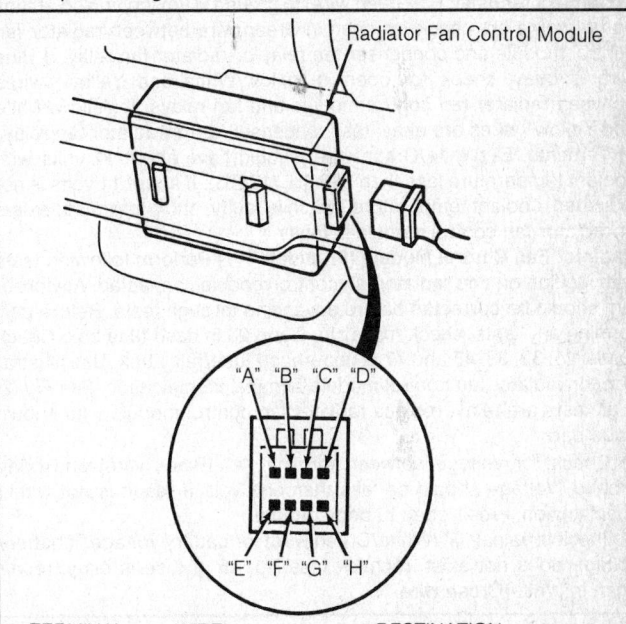

TERMINAL	WIRE	DESTINATION
A	YEL[1]	Radiator fan relay (Coil ⊕)
B	BLK/YEL[2]	Power supply (For radiator fan and condenser fan relays via radiator fan control module with ignition switch ON)
C	YEL/WHT	Condenser fan relay (Coil ⊕)
D	BLK	Ground (G402, G404)
E	WHT/GRN	Engine coolant temperature (ECT) switch B
F	WHT	Power supply (For radiator fan control module with ignition switch OFF)
G	BLK/YEL[1]	IG1 (Control module reset signal)
H	GRN	Radiator fan and condenser fan relays (Coil ⊖)

94D46675   Courtesy of American Honda Motor Co., Inc.

Fig. 1: Identifying Fan Control Module Terminals (Accord)

fuses No. 15, 18, 21 and 34 in underhood fuse/relay box. Use illustration for radiator fan control module terminal identification. *See Fig. 1.* Correct any problem before continuing. Terminal "D" (Black wire) should have continuity to body ground. If continuity to ground does not exist, repair open between terminal "D" and ground.

2) Terminal "F" (White wire) should have battery voltage present. If battery voltage is not present, check fuse No. 34 or repair open in White wire.

3) Terminal "G" (Black/Yellow[1] wire) should have battery voltage present. If battery voltage is not present, check fuse No. 4 or repair open in Black/Yellow[1] wire.

4) Terminal "B" (Black/Yellow[2] wire) should have battery voltage present. If battery voltage is not present, check fuse No. 8 or repair Black/Yellow[2] wire. Terminal "A" (Yellow/White wire) should have battery voltage present. If battery voltage is not present, replace radiator fan control module.

5) Terminal "A" (Yellow[1] wire), with ignition on, should indicate battery voltage. If battery voltage is not indicated, replace radiator fan control module. Before connecting replacement module, check for continuity between terminal "C" (Yellow/White wire) and ground. If continuity exists, repair short to ground in Yellow/White wire.

6) Connect terminal "H" (Green wire) to ground. Turn ignition on. If fans do not come on, check for open in Green wire between radiator fan control module and condenser fan relay or radiator fan relay. If Blue wire is okay, check for open in Yellow/White and Yellow[1] wires between radiator fan control module and fan relays. If Yellow/White and Yellow[1] wires are okay, test condenser fan or radiator fan relay.

7) Terminal "E" (White/Green wire) should have about 11 volts with coolant temperature less than 226.4°F (108°C). If about 11 volts is not indicated, coolant temperature switch is faulty, short to ground exists or radiator fan control module is faulty.

Radiator Fan Control Module (Prelude) – 1) Perform following tests with ignition on and radiator fan control module connected. Any problem should be corrected before advancing through tests. Before performing any tests, check fuses No. 9 and 23 in dash fuse box. Check fuses No. 32, 33, 45 and 47 in underhood fuse/relay box. Use illustration for radiator fan control module terminal identification. *See Fig. 2.* If all tests are okay, replace radiator fan control module with known good part.

2) Check for voltage between terminal "A" (Black wire) and body ground. Voltage should be less than one volt. If result is not within specification, repair open to body ground.

3) Check terminal "G" (White/Green wire) for battery voltage. If battery voltage does not exist, recheck fuse No. 45. If fuse is okay, repair open in White/Green wire.

NOTE: On Prelude, radiator fan control module has 2 Black/Yellow wires.

4) Check for battery voltage at terminal "F" (Black/Yellow[4] wire). If battery voltage does not exist, recheck fuse No. 23. If fuse is okay, repair open in Black/Yellow[4] wire.

5) Check for battery voltage at terminal "C" (Black/Yellow[3] wire). If battery voltage does not exist, recheck fuse No. 9. If fuse is okay, repair open in Black/Yellow[3] wire.

6) Check for battery voltage at terminal "B" (Yellow/White wire). Turn ignition on. Check for battery voltage at terminal "D" (Yellow wire). If battery voltage does not exist on both terminals, replace radiator fan control module. Before connecting replacement radiator fan control module, check for continuity between Yellow/White wire and ground using an ohmmeter. Check for continuity between Yellow wire and ground. Continuity should not exist. If continuity exists, DO NOT connect control module.

7) Check for voltage between terminal "E" (Blue/Red wire) and body ground. Turn ignition on. Condenser fan and radiator fan should come on. If fans do not turn on, check for open in Blue/Red wire between radiator fan control module and condenser fan relay and radiator fan relay. If circuits are okay, check for open in Yellow/White wire between radiator fan control module and condenser fan relay. Also check for open in Yellow wire between radiator fan control module and radiator fan relay. If circuits are okay, test both fan relays.

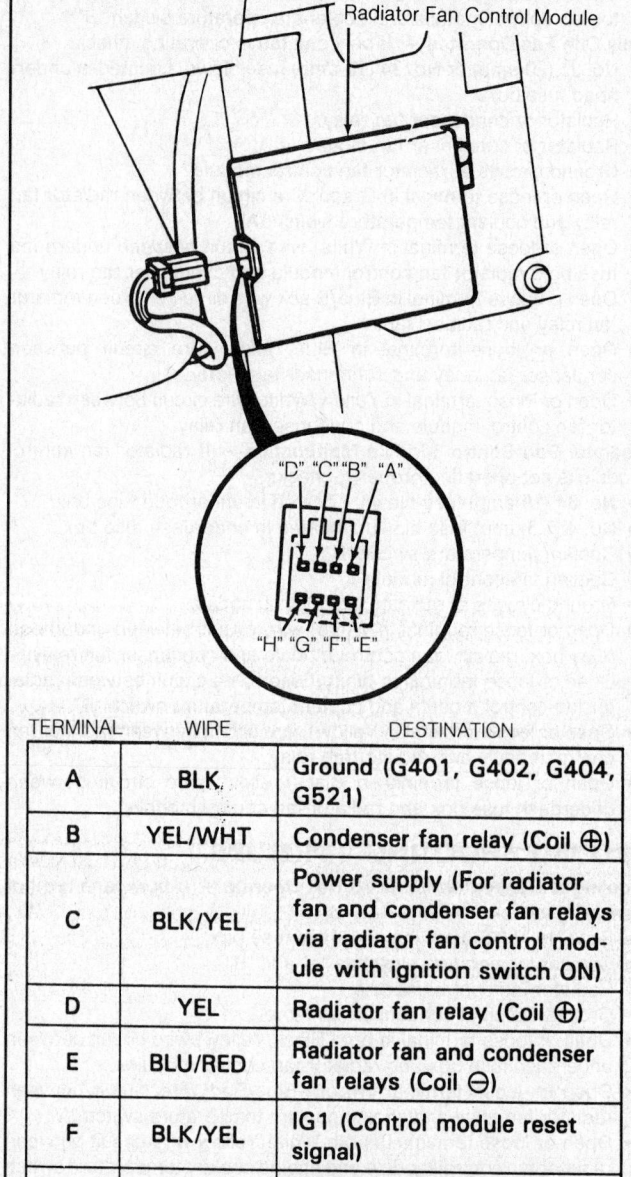

TERMINAL	WIRE	DESTINATION
A	BLK	Ground (G401, G402, G404, G521)
B	YEL/WHT	Condenser fan relay (Coil ⊕)
C	BLK/YEL	Power supply (For radiator fan and condenser fan relays via radiator fan control module with ignition switch ON)
D	YEL	Radiator fan relay (Coil ⊕)
E	BLU/RED	Radiator fan and condenser fan relays (Coil ⊖)
F	BLK/YEL	IG1 (Control module reset signal)
G	WHT/GRN	Power supply (For radiator fan control module with ignition switch OFF)
H	WHT/YEL	Engine coolant temperature (ECT) switch B

94E46676   Courtesy of American Honda Motor Co., Inc.

Fig. 2: Identifying Fan Control Module Terminals (Prelude)

8) Check for voltage at terminal "H" (White/Yellow wire). With coolant temperature less than 223°F (106°C), voltage should be about 11 volts. If voltage is not as specified, check coolant temperature switch "B". Check for short to body ground. If ground is okay, replace radiator fan control module.

Coolant Temperature Switch (Civic & Civic Del Sol) – 1) Remove coolant temperature switch (located on rear of engine block). Suspend temperature switch and thermometer in a container with a 50/50 mixture of coolant and water. DO NOT allow thermometer or temperature switch to touch bottom of container. Heat coolant mixture.

2) Check continuity between temperature switch terminals. With coolant temperature 181-191°F (83-91°C), continuity should not exist. With coolant temperature 191-203°F (91-95°C), continuity should be present.

Coolant Temperature Switch "A" (Accord) – 1) Remove coolant temperature switch "A" from radiator. Suspend temperature switch and thermometer in a container with a 50/50 mixture of coolant and water. DO NOT allow thermometer or temperature switch to touch bottom of container. Heat coolant mixture.

2) Check continuity between temperature switch terminals. With coolant temperature greater than 194-205°F (90-96°C) for switch "A", continuity should exist. With coolant temperature 181-193°F (83-89°C), continuity should not exist. If readings are not correct, replace switch.

Coolant Temperature Switch "A" (Prelude) – 1) Remove coolant temperature switch "A" from thermostat housing. Suspend temperature switch and thermometer in a container with a 50/50 mixture of coolant and water. DO NOT allow thermometer or temperature switch to touch bottom of container. Heat coolant mixture.

2) Check continuity between temperature switch terminals. On 2.2L SOHC and 2.3L engines, with coolant temperature greater than 194-205°F (90-96°C), continuity should exist. With coolant temperature 181-193°F (83-89°C), continuity should not exist.

3) On 2.2L DOHC engine, with coolant temperature greater than 198-208°F (92-98°C), continuity should exist. With coolant temperature 187-197°F (86-91°C), continuity should not exist. If readings are not correct, replace switch.

Coolant Temperature Switch "B" (Accord & Prelude) – 1) On Accord, remove coolant temperature switch "B" from water outlet cover. On Prelude, remove coolant temperature switch "B" from thermostat housing.

2) With coolant temperature greater than 217-228°F (103-109°C) for switch "B", continuity should exist. With temperature 204-216°F (96-102°C), continuity should not exist. If readings are not correct, replace switch.

Fan Motor – Unplug 2-pin connector from fan motor. Connect battery power to either fan motor terminal. Connect ground to other fan motor terminal. Replace motor if it fails to run.

Relays – 1) Remove radiator and condenser fan relays. On Accord and Prelude, both condenser and radiator fan relays are located inside underhood relay box. On Civic & Civic Del Sol, radiator fan relay is located on right front inner fender and condenser fan relay is located on left front inner fender (if equipped).

2) On all models, connect positive battery power to relay terminal "C" and connect terminal "D" to ground. For terminal identification, see WIRING DIAGRAMS. Continuity should be present between relay terminals "A" and "B". No continuity should be present when battery power is disconnected.

WIRING DIAGRAMS

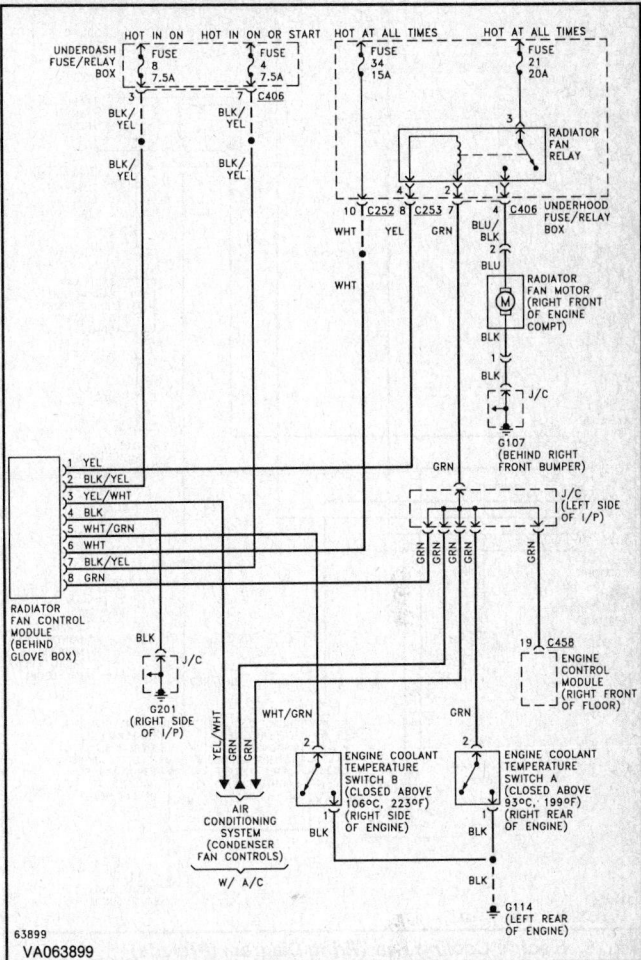

Fig. 3: Electric Cooling Fan Wiring Diagram (Accord)

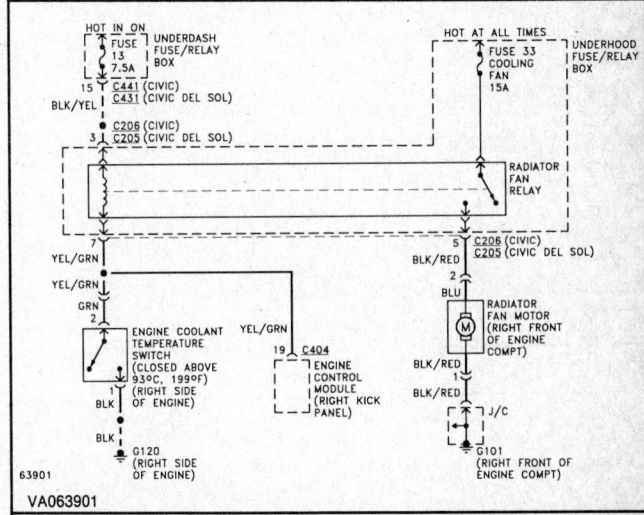

Fig. 4: Electric Cooling Fan Wiring Diagram (Civic & Civic Del Sol)

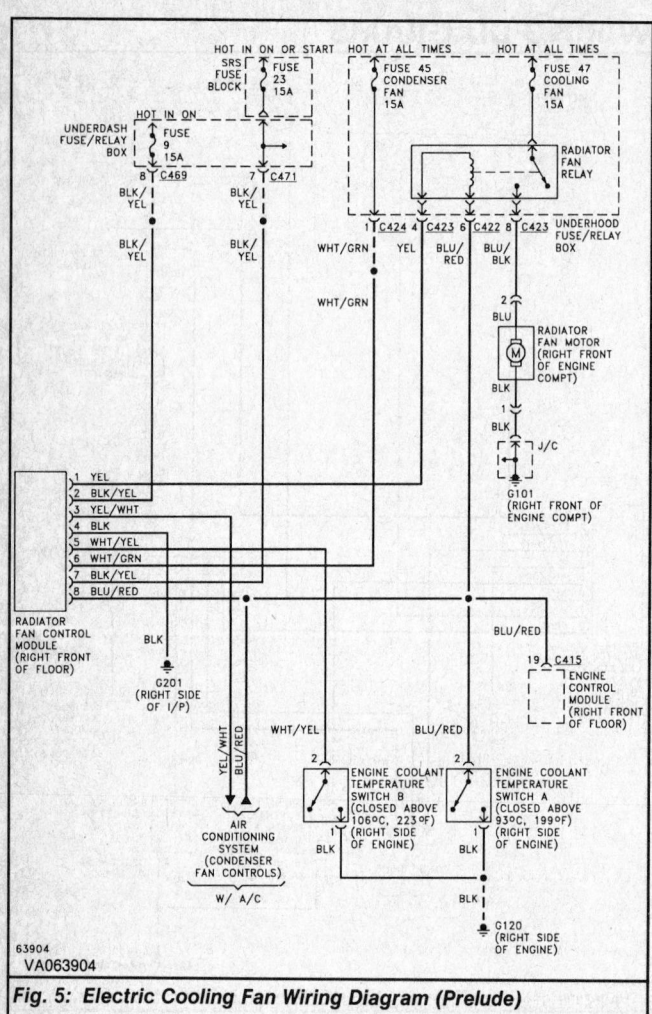

Fig. 5: Electric Cooling Fan Wiring Diagram (Prelude)

Accord, Civic, Civic Del Sol, Prelude

NOTE: For clutch information on Passport, refer to Rodeo in Isuzu CLUTCHES article.

DESCRIPTION

The clutch assembly is a single disc type with a diaphragm spring pressure plate. All models use a hydraulically-controlled clutch system consisting of a master cylinder, release cylinder, release lever and release bearing.

ADJUSTMENTS

CLUTCH PEDAL

1) Loosen lock nut "A", and back off clutch pedal switch "A" until it breaks contact with clutch pedal. See Fig. 1. Loosen lock nut "C", and turn clutch pedal push rod until correct pedal height is obtained. See CLUTCH PEDAL SPECIFICATIONS table. Tighten lock nut "C" to specification. See TORQUE SPECIFICATIONS.

2) Turn clutch pedal switch "A" in until it contacts clutch pedal. Turn switch in another 1/4-1/2 turn. Tighten lock nut "A" to specification. Loosen lock nut "B" and clutch pedal switch "B". Measure clearance between floor board and clutch pedal with clutch pedal fully depressed. See DISENGAGEMENT HEIGHT (FROM FLOOR) table.

3) Release clutch pedal .6-.8" (15-20 mm) from fully depressed position, and hold it there. Adjust position of clutch pedal switch "B" so engine will start with clutch pedal in this position. Turn clutch pedal switch in another 1/4-1/2 turn (3/4-1 turn on Civic and Civic Del Sol). Tighten lock nut "B" to specification.

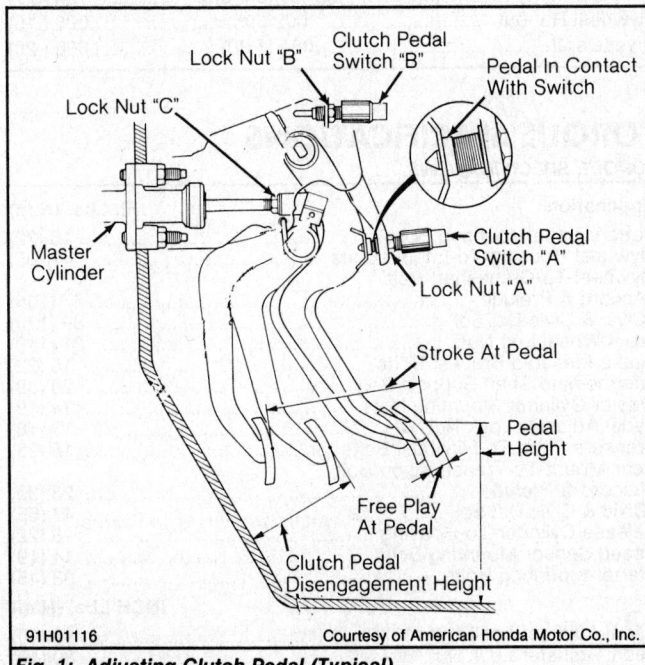

91H01116   Courtesy of American Honda Motor Co., Inc.

Fig. 1: Adjusting Clutch Pedal (Typical)

CLUTCH PEDAL SPECIFICATIONS

Application	Free Play In. (mm)	Pedal Height In. (mm)
Accord	.04-.28 (1.0-7.0)	7.2 (184)
Civic & Civic Del Sol	.04-.39 (1.0-10.0)	6.5 (164)
Prelude	.04-.28 (1.0-7.0)	7.5 (190)

DISENGAGEMENT HEIGHT (FROM FLOOR)

Application	In. (mm)
Accord	3.5 (90)
Civic & Civic Del Sol	3.3 (83)
Prelude	3.7 (93)

REMOVAL & INSTALLATION

CLUTCH ASSEMBLY

Removal (Accord & Prelude) – 1) Remove negative and positive battery cables, and remove battery. Remove air intake hoses and battery base. On Accord models with F22B1 engine, remove Intake Air Resonator. On all models, disconnect starter wiring, and remove starter. Disconnect transaxle ground cable. Disconnect back-up light switch. Shift transaxle into reverse. Remove shift cable stay and cables as an assembly. See Fig. 2.

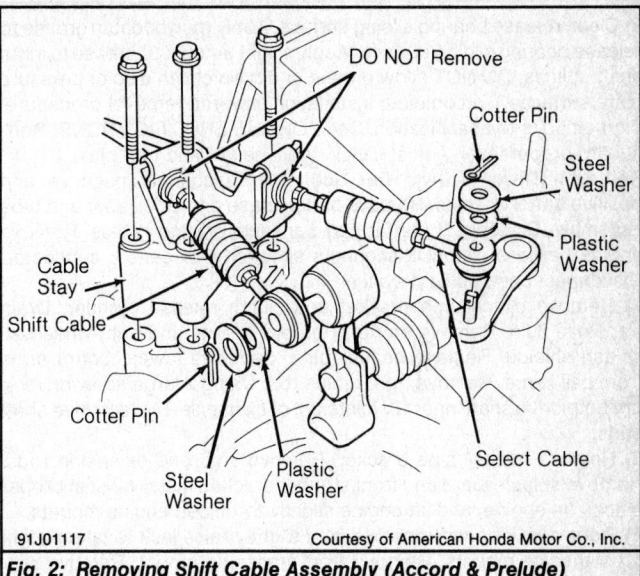

91J01117   Courtesy of American Honda Motor Co., Inc.

Fig. 2: Removing Shift Cable Assembly (Accord & Prelude)

2) Disconnect electrical connector, and remove speed sensor, leaving hoses attached. Remove both front wheels. Remove undercarriage splash shield. Drain transaxle fluid. Remove clutch release cylinder, tubing and push rod. Remove clutch hose joint.

3) Remove clutch damper and support with wire. Remove center beam and header pipe. Separate left and right lower control arms from ball joints. Remove strut fork bolt. Pry drive shafts out of differential and intermediate shaft, and remove drive shafts. Lower bearing support, and remove intermediate shaft.

4) Remove right strut pinch bolt, and separate strut fork and strut damper. Remove right radius rod. Remove engine stiffener and clutch cover. Remove intake manifold bracket. Remove rear engine mount bracket stay and bracket. Remove transaxle housing mount bolt from engine side.

5) Place a transaxle jack under transaxle, and slightly raise transaxle to take weight off mounts. Remove transaxle mount, and loosen mount bracket bolts. Remove remaining transaxle housing mount bolts. Lower transaxle from engine.

Inspection – 1) Check pressure plate diaphragm spring fingers for wear and unevenness on release bearing contact area. Check spring finger height using feeler gauge and Clutch Disc Aligner Assembly (07JAF-PM7011A, 07LAF-PT00110 and 07936-3710100).

2) Verify clearance between tool flange and finger is at least .02" (0.6 mm) for new pressure plate and at most .03" (0.8 mm) for existing pressure plate.

3) If necessary, install Ring Gear Holder Assembly (07924-PD20003) to hold flywheel stationary while pressure plate and clutch disc are being removed.

4) With pressure plate and clutch removed, inspect pressure plate surface for wear, cracks, burning and warpage. Maximum face warpage is .006" (.15 mm). Using straightedge and feeler gauge, measure clearance at several points.

5) Inspect clutch disc lining for slipping, excessive wear, burning and oil contamination. Measure disc thickness and rivet depth. See CLUTCH SPECIFICATIONS table. Check for loose rubber torsion dampers. Replace disc if any dampers are loose. Check disc runout.

6) Inspect flywheel ring gear teeth for excessive wear and damage. Inspect flywheel surface for wear, burning and cracks. Check flywheel runout and flywheel pilot bearing. Resurface or replace as necessary.

Installation – 1) Align flywheel dowels with dowel holes in clutch cover. Using clutch alignment tool and ring gear holder, install disc and pressure plate. Tighten bolts evenly in a crisscross pattern. Ensure 2 dowel pins are installed in clutch housing.

NOTE: New spring clips must be used on both axle shafts. Slide axles in until spring clips engage differential.

---

2) Clean release bearing sliding surface. Apply molybdenum grease to release bearing sliding surface. Apply a light amount of grease to input shaft splines. DO NOT allow grease or dirt on clutch disc or pressure plate surfaces. To complete installation, reverse removal procedure. Tighten bolts to specification. See TORQUE SPECIFICATIONS. Refill fluid to proper level. Adjust clutch pedal height and free play.

Removal (Civic & Civic Del Sol) – 1) Disconnect negative and positive battery cables. Remove battery base and air cleaner and tube assembly. Disconnect starter and transaxle ground cables. Remove engine harness clamp. Disconnect speedometer sensor connector. Disconnect back-up light switch.

2) Remove clutch pipe bracket and clutch release cylinder. Drain transaxle fluid. Remove starter. Remove engine and right wheelwell splash shields. Remove header pipe. Separate lower control arms from ball joints. Remove right radius rod. Using 2 large screwdrivers, pry both drive shaft inner CV joints out of transaxle. Protect drive shaft ends.

3) Remove header pipe bracket. Remove shift and extension rods. Remove splash guard and front stopper bracket. Install hoist at proper places on engine, and lift engine slightly to unload engine mounts.

4) Place a jack under transaxle, and slightly raise jack to take weight off transaxle mounts. Remove front transaxle mount. Remove rear transaxle mount bracket. Remove side transaxle mount. Remove transaxle housing mount bolts. Pull transaxle away from engine, and remove transaxle.

Inspection – 1) Check pressure plate diaphragm spring fingers for wear and unevenness on release bearing contact area. Check spring finger height using feeler gauge and Clutch Disc Aligner Assembly (07JAF-PM7012A and 07936-3710100).

2) Verify clearance between tool flange and finger is at least .03" (0.8 mm) for new pressure plate and at most .04" (1.0 mm) for existing pressure plate. If necessary, install Ring Gear Holder Assembly (07924-PD20003 or 07LAB-PV00100) to hold flywheel stationary while removing pressure plate and clutch disc.

3) With pressure plate and clutch removed, inspect pressure plate surface for wear, cracks, burning and warpage. Maximum face warpage is .006" (.15 mm). Measure using straightedge and feeler gauge at several points.

4) Inspect clutch disc lining for slipping, excessive wear, burning and oil contamination. Measure disc thickness and rivet depth. Check for loose rubber torsion dampers. Replace disc if any dampers are loose. Check disc runout. See CLUTCH SPECIFICATIONS table.

5) Inspect flywheel ring gear teeth for excessive wear and damage. Inspect flywheel surface for wear, burning and cracks. Check flywheel runout and flywheel pilot bearing. Resurface or replace as necessary.

Installation – Before installation, use NEW circlips on inboard side of drive axle shafts. Use NEW self-locking nuts on front end of radius rod

and header pipe bracket. Use NEW through bolt on firewall side transaxle mount. To install transaxle, reverse removal procedure. Tighten bolts to specification. See TORQUE SPECIFICATIONS.

CLUTCH MASTER CYLINDER

Removal & Installation – Pry out cotter pin, and pull pedal pin out of yoke. Disconnect and plug hydraulic line. Remove nuts and bolts attaching master cylinder to firewall. To install, reverse removal procedure. Refill master cylinder, and bleed air from system.

CLUTCH RELEASE CYLINDER

Removal & Installation – Disconnect clutch pipe from release cylinder. Remove release cylinder from transaxle clutch housing. To install, reverse removal procedure. Refill release cylinder, and bleed air from system.

OVERHAUL

NOTE: Manufacturer recommends replacement of faulty clutch master and release cylinders and does not provide overhaul procedures.

CLUTCH SPECIFICATIONS
CLUTCH SPECIFICATIONS

Application	Range In. (mm)	Service Limit In. (mm)
Disc Thickness		
Except Accord	.33-.36 (8.4-9.1)	.24 (6.1)
Accord	.33-.35 (8.4-9.0)	.24 (6.1)
Flywheel Runout	.002 (.05)	.006 (.15)
Rivet Depth	.051 (1.30)	.008 (.20)

TORQUE SPECIFICATIONS
TORQUE SPECIFICATIONS

Application	Ft. Lbs. (N.m)
Battery Base Mounting Bolts	16 (22)
Flywheel Housing-To-Engine Bolts	47 (65)
Flywheel-To-Crankshaft Bolt	
Accord & Prelude	77 (105)
Civic & Civic Del Sol	89 (120)
Front Wheel Lug Nuts	81 (110)
Intake Manifold Bracket Bolts	16 (22)
Intermediate Shaft Support Bolt	28 (39)
Master Cylinder Mounting Nuts	14 (19)
Pedal Adjuster Lock Nut "C"	13 (18)
Pressure Plate-To-Flywheel Bolts	18 (25)
Rear Mount-To-Transmission Bolt	
Accord & Prelude	28 (39)
Civic & Civic Del Sol	47 (65)
Release Cylinder-To-Housing	16 (22)
Speed Sensor Mounting Bolts	14 (19)
Starter Mounting Bolts	33 (45)

	INCH Lbs. (N.m)
Pedal Adjuster Lock Nut "A"	89 (10)
Pedal Adjuster Lock Nut "B"	89 (10)

Accord, Civic, Civic Del Sol, Prelude

NOTE: For axle shaft, differential, drive shaft and locking hub information on Passport, refer to Rodeo in appropriate Isuzu 4WD DIFFERENTIALS and AXLE SHAFTS article.

DESCRIPTION & OPERATION

Axle shafts transfer power from the transaxle to the driving wheels. Axle shafts consist of a shaft with a flexible Constant Velocity (CV) joint at each end. Inner CV joint is splined to transaxle. Outer CV joint is splined to hub assembly and secured by spindle shaft nut.

CV joint boots protect CV joints by maintaining proper lubrication and preventing contaminants from entering joint. Boots must be replaced when leakage or cracks are present. Inner CV joint can be repaired without replacing the assembly. Outer CV joint must be replaced as an assembly.

Inner CV joint is a plunging Tripod Joint (TJ), sometimes referred to as a tripod. The plunging action allows axle shaft length to change as suspension moves up and down. Outer CV joint, which is either a Double-Offset Joint (DOJ) or Birfield Joint (BJ), cannot be rebuilt.

TROUBLE SHOOTING

NOTE: See TROUBLE SHOOTING article in GENERAL INFORMATION.

REMOVAL, DISASSEMBLY, REASSEMBLY & INSTALLATION

FWD AXLE SHAFT

Removal – 1) Raise and support vehicle. Remove front wheels. Drain transaxle if removing right or both axle shafts. Draining transaxle is unnecessary if removing left axle shaft only. Spread locking tab on spindle nut and remove nut. Remove damper fork bolt and damper pinch bolt. Remove damper fork. *See Fig. 1.*

2) Remove lower ball joint cotter pin, and loosen castle nut half length of ball joint threads. Using a ball joint puller, separate ball joint from front hub. Remove ball joint castle nut. Lower control arm and steering knuckle. Pull steering knuckle outward and remove axle shaft from hub assembly. If necessary, use a plastic hammer to drive axle shaft out of hub.

NOTE: DO NOT pull on inner CV joint or disassembly may occur. Be careful not to damage seals.

3) Using a large screwdriver, carefully pry inner CV joint and shaft assembly about .5" (12.7 mm) out of transaxle, dislodging retaining ring from its groove at end of drive axle. Grip both sides of inner CV joint and remove axle shaft and CV joint from vehicle.

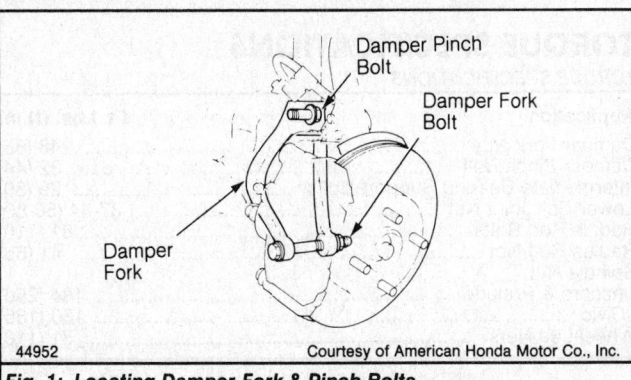

Fig. 1: Locating Damper Fork & Pinch Bolts

NOTE: DO NOT attempt to disassemble outer CV joint; it must be replaced as an assembly. On inner CV joint, mark rollers and roller grooves for reassembly reference.

Disassembly – 1) Remove axle shaft from vehicle, and place it on work bench. Remove and discard inner CV joint boot clamps. Slide boot toward outer CV joint to access inner CV joint. *See Fig. 2.*
2) Index axle shaft, inner CV joint housing and spider roller to ensure reassembly in original positions. Remove housing from spider assembly. Index rollers and spider to ensure reassembly to original locations. Remove rollers from spider.
3) Remove snap ring securing spider to axle shaft, and remove spider. Remove snap ring, and slide boot off axle shaft. Remove outer CV joint boot clamps. Slide boot off axle shaft inner CV joint end. DO NOT attempt to disassemble outer CV joint. Replace outer CV joint as an assembly only.

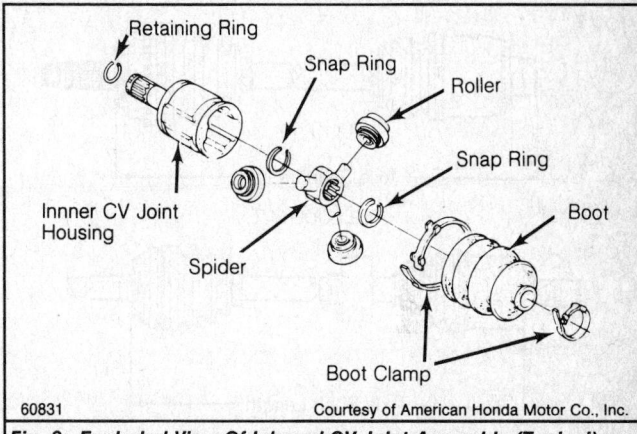

Fig. 2: Exploded View Of Inboard CV Joint Assembly (Typical)

Reassembly – 1) Thoroughly clean and inspect axle shaft for wear. Replace all defective parts. Wrap axle shaft splines using vinyl tape to prevent damage to dynamic damper and CV joint boots.
2) Install outer CV joint boot, dynamic damper and inner CV joint boot. Remove vinyl tape from axle shaft. DO NOT install CV joint boot clamps yet.
3) Install snap ring in groove on axle shaft. Install spider on axle shaft by aligning marks made at disassembly. Install snap ring into groove. Pack outer CV joint boot with molybdenum disulfide grease. Lube spider and inside bores of rollers.
4) Ensure rollers are aligned with marks made at disassembly and high side of rollers face outward. Install rollers. Pack inner CV joint and boot with molybdenum disulfide grease. Align housing marks made at disassembly and install housing on spider assembly.
5) Adjust standard length of axle shaft. *See Fig. 3.* Refer to AXLE SHAFT LENGTH SPECIFICATIONS table. Position boots halfway between full compression and full extension and install NEW boot clamps.

AXLE SHAFT LENGTH SPECIFICATIONS

Application	In. (mm)
Accord	
A/T	
Left	33.27-33.46 (845-850)
Right	19.13-19.33 (486-491)
M/T	19.13-19.33 (486-491)
Civic	
With Damper & Civic Del Sol	
Left	30.40-30.60 (773-778)
Right	19.70-19.90 (501-506)
Without Damper	19.70-19.90 (501-506)
Prelude	
Left	
M/T	20.50-20.70 (520.9-525.9)
A/T	33.97-34.17 (862.9-867.9)
Right	20.00-20.20 (507.9-512.9)

CAUTION: Always use a NEW retaining ring when installing axle shaft.

6) Position dynamic damper to correct distance from edge of boot. *See Fig. 4.* See DYNAMIC DAMPER DISTANCE SPECIFICATIONS table.

Bend down lock tab of each boot clamp and lightly tap doubled-over portion of boot clamp to reduce clamp height. Install a NEW retaining ring on end of inner CV joint, and install axle shaft.

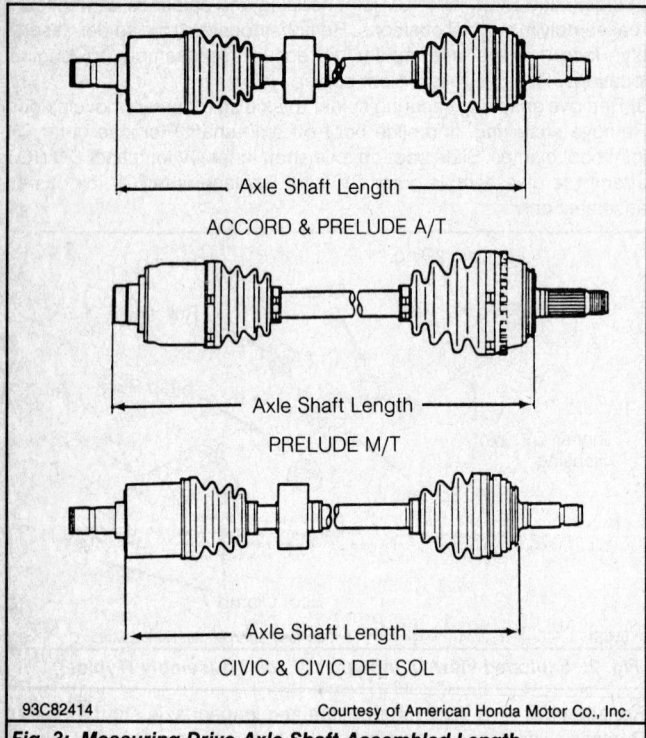

ACCORD & PRELUDE A/T

PRELUDE M/T

CIVIC & CIVIC DEL SOL

93C82414 — Courtesy of American Honda Motor Co., Inc.

Fig. 3: Measuring Drive Axle Shaft Assembled Length

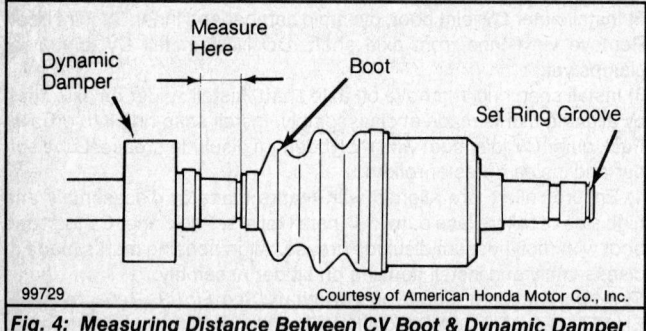

99729 — Courtesy of American Honda Motor Co., Inc.

Fig. 4: Measuring Distance Between CV Boot & Dynamic Damper

DYNAMIC DAMPER DISTANCE SPECIFICATIONS

Application	In. (mm)
Accord	
Left (A/T)	6.60-6.80 (169.0-173.0)
Civic & Civic Del Sol	
Left	2.87-3.03 (73.0-77.0)
Right	2.09-2.25 (53.0-57.0)
Prelude	6.10-7.70 (173.0-177.0)

Installation – 1) Slide axle into transaxle or intermediate shaft. Ensure inner joint housing locks into differential side gear groove and joint sub-axle bottoms in differential or intermediate shaft.

2) Install damper fork over drive shaft and onto lower control arm. Install damper in damper fork so aligning tab aligns with slot in damper fork. Loosely install damper pinch bolt using NEW damper fork nut.

3) Pull hub assembly away from axle shaft, and slide axle into hub assembly. Install and lightly tighten spindle shaft nut. Position ball joint in hub. Raise lower control arm using floor jack, and install ball joint nut. Tighten ball joint nut to specification. See TORQUE SPECIFICATIONS.

4) Install and secure cotter pin. Remove floor jack. Tighten spindle nut to specification. Install wheels. Lower vehicle. With vehicle weight on damper, tighten damper pinch bolt to specification. Refill transaxle.

INTERMEDIATE SHAFT

Removal – 1) Drain fluid from transaxle. Remove outer axle shaft assembly from intermediate shaft assembly. See FWD AXLE SHAFT. Remove bolts attaching intermediate shaft bearing support.

2) Remove intermediate shaft from transaxle assembly. Use care not to damage seal in transaxle by holding shaft in a horizontal position when removing.

Disassembly – 1) Remove heat shield (if equipped). Remove intermediate shaft outer seal. Remove 38-mm external circlip. Press intermediate shaft out of shaft bearing and support.

2) Remove intermediate shaft inner seal, and remove 58-mm internal circlip. Press intermediate shaft bearing out of bearing support. Inspect all components for wear and damage, and replace components if necessary. *See Fig. 5.*

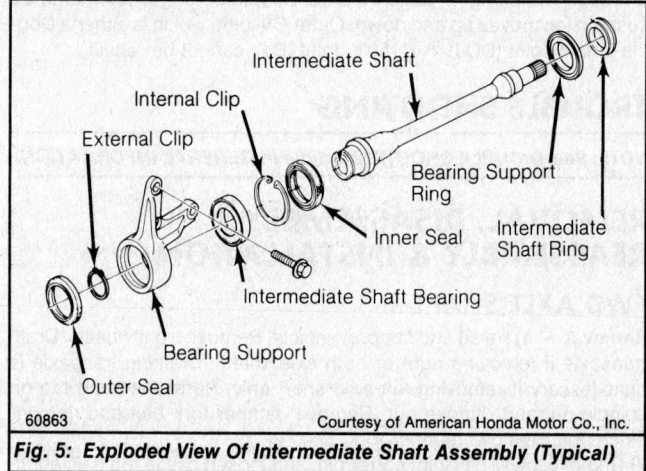

60863 — Courtesy of American Honda Motor Co., Inc.

Fig. 5: Exploded View Of Intermediate Shaft Assembly (Typical)

CAUTION: Ensure internal circlip is installed with tapered end facing out.

Reassembly – 1) Press intermediate shaft bearing into bearing support. Seat 58-mm circlip in groove of bearing support with tapered end facing out.

2) Press intermediate shaft inner seal into bearing support. Press intermediate shaft into shaft bearing. Seat 38-mm external circlip in groove of intermediate shaft with tapered end facing out. Press outer seal into bearing support.

Installation – To install intermediate shaft assembly, reverse removal procedure. Add fluid to transaxle.

TORQUE SPECIFICATIONS
TORQUE SPECIFICATIONS

Application	Ft. Lbs. (N.m)
Damper Fork Nut	48 (65)
Damper Pinch Bolt	32 (44)
Intermediate Bearing Support Bolts	29 (39)
Lower Ball Joint Nut	37-44 (50-60)
Radius Rod Bolts	81 (110)
Radius Rod Nut	41 (55)
Spindle Nut	
Accord & Prelude	184 (250)
Civic	136 (185)
Wheel Lug Nuts	81 (110)

Accord, Civic, Civic Del Sol, Prelude

NOTE: For information on Passport brakes, refer to Rodeo in Isuzu BRAKES – DISC & DRUM article.

DESCRIPTION

All models use front disc brakes. Rear brakes may be either disc type or self-adjusting drum type. Parking brake cable mechanism applies rear brakes.

BLEEDING BRAKE SYSTEM

BLEEDING PROCEDURES

Raise and support vehicle. Fill master cylinder to maximum. Check fluid level after bleeding each wheel position. Bleed brakes in following sequence: RR, LF, LR and RF.

ADJUSTMENTS

BRAKE PEDAL HEIGHT

Loosen brakelight switch lock nut, and back off switch until it no longer touches brake pedal. Loosen brake pedal push rod lock nut, and screw push rod in or out until correct pedal height is obtained. See BRAKE PEDAL HEIGHT SPECIFICATIONS table. Tighten lock nut to specification. See TORQUE SPECIFICATIONS.

BRAKE PEDAL HEIGHT SPECIFICATIONS

Application	Auto. Trans. In. (mm)	Man. Trans. In. (mm)
Accord	7.59 (193)	7.55 (192)
Civic & Civic Del Sol	6.5 (165)	6.3 (160)
Prelude	7.3 (186)	6.5 (165)

BRAKE WARNING LIGHT

Brake warning light indicates parking brake is engaged and/or brake fluid level is low. To adjust parking brake light operation, turn ignition on. Bend switch plate down until light comes on when parking brake lever is pulled one notch and goes out when lever is released.

MASTER CYLINDER PUSH ROD

NOTE: Check and adjust master cylinder push rod-to-piston clearance before installing master cylinder.

1) Install Push Rod Adjustment Gauge (07JAG-SD40100) so gauge rod makes light contact with secondary piston of master cylinder. *See Fig. 1.* Ensure gasket is in position when adjusting rod clearance.
2) Remove push rod adjustment gauge from master cylinder, and install gauge onto brake booster. *See Fig. 2.* Tighten mounting nuts to specification. Using engine or outside vacuum source, apply at least 10 in. Hg vacuum to brake booster. Check clearance using feeler gauge. See MASTER CYLINDER PUSH ROD CLEARANCE table. Adjust push rod clearance by turning nut at end of push rod.

MASTER CYLINDER PUSH ROD CLEARANCE

Application	Clearance
Accord, Civic & Civic Del Sol	0-.016" (0-.40 mm)
Prelude	
With ABS	0-.016" (0-.40 mm)
Without ABS	0-.008" (0-.20 mm)

PARKING BRAKE

NOTE: Before adjusting parking brake, loosen equalizer adjusting nut. Start engine, and depress brake pedal several times to set self-adjusting brakes before adjusting parking brake.

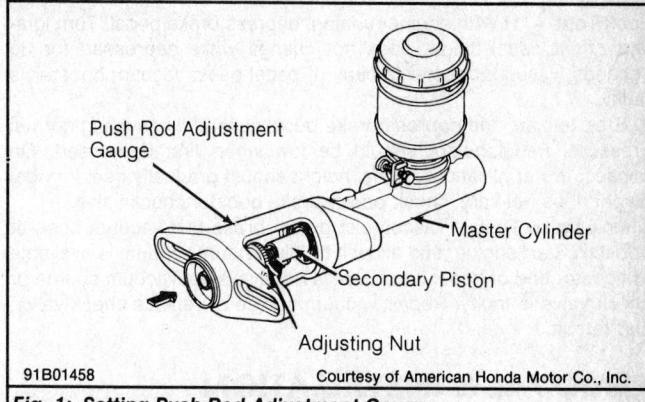

91B01458   Courtesy of American Honda Motor Co., Inc.

Fig. 1: Setting Push Rod Adjustment Gauge

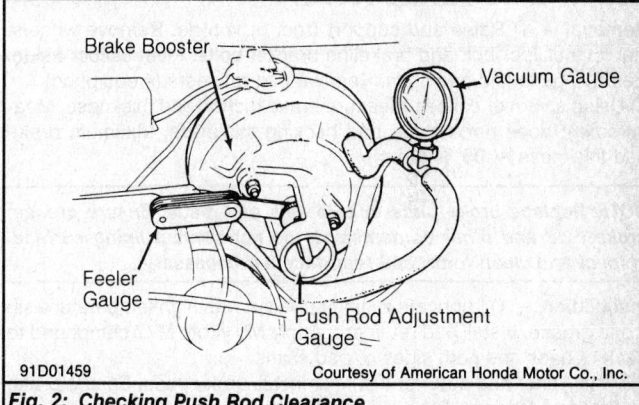

91D01459   Courtesy of American Honda Motor Co., Inc.

Fig. 2: Checking Push Rod Clearance

1) With rear brakes adjusted, raise and support rear of vehicle. Loosen equalizer nut, and pull parking brake lever up one notch. Tighten equalizer adjusting nut until rear wheels drag slightly.
2) Release parking brake lever. Rear wheels should rotate freely. Rear wheels should lock when parking brake lever is pulled up 4-8 clicks on Accord with rear drum brakes or 7-11 clicks with rear disc brakes. On all other models, rear wheels should lock when parking brake lever is pulled up 6-10 clicks.

REAR DRUM BRAKE SHOES

Rear brake shoes will self-adjust through brake pedal action. No in-service adjustment is required.

STOPLIGHT SWITCH

1) Stoplight switch is located under dash, above brake pedal. To adjust, loosen lock nuts and turn switch until plunger is fully depressed (threaded end touching pedal arm pad).
2) Back off switch 1/4 turn, and tighten lock nuts. Clearance between threaded end of switch body and brake pedal switch contact pad should be about .012" (.30 mm). Ensure brakelights go off when pedal is released.

TESTING

POWER BRAKE BOOSTER

Functional Test – 1) Start engine. Turn ignition off. Depress brake pedal several times. Depress pedal firmly and hold pressure for 15 seconds. If pedal sinks, master cylinder, brake line or wheel cylinder is faulty.
2) With pedal depressed, start engine. If pedal sinks slightly, vacuum unit is working properly. If pedal height does not vary, booster or check valve is faulty.

Leak Test – **1)** With engine running, depress brake pedal. Turn ignition off. If pedal height does not change while depressed for 30 seconds, vacuum booster is okay. If pedal rises, vacuum booster is faulty.

2) Stop engine, and depress brake pedal several times using normal pressure. Pedal height should be low when first depressed. On consecutive applications, pedal height should gradually rise. If pedal height does not vary, check power brake booster check valve.

Check Valve Test – Disconnect power brake unit vacuum hose at booster. Start engine, and allow it to idle. Ensure vacuum is available at booster end of hose. If vacuum is not available, vacuum source or check valve is faulty. Repair vacuum source or replace check valve, and retest.

REMOVAL & INSTALLATION

FRONT DISC BRAKE PADS

Removal – **1)** Raise and support front of vehicle. Remove wheels. Remove caliper bolt and brakeline bracket bolts. Pivot caliper aside. Remove pads and pad shim. Remove pad retainers (if equipped).

2) Using a vernier caliper, measure brake friction pad thickness. Measurement does not include pad backing thickness. Minimum brake pad thickness is .06" (1.6 mm).

NOTE: Replace brake pads in axle sets of 4 pads. Ensure grease, brake fluid and other contaminants do not contact lining surface. Inspect and clean rotor, and resurface it if necessary.

Installation – **1)** Lubricate sliding surfaces with high temperature silicone grease. Install pad retainers. Apply Molykote M77 compound to back of pads and both sides of pad shims.

2) Install inner and outer pad shims. Install brake pads. Ensure brake pad with pad wear indicator is installed inside. Loosen bleeder screw, and slowly push piston into caliper bore.

3) Tighten bleeder screw. Ensure brake fluid does not contaminate pads. Position caliper, and install lower guide pin or caliper bolts. Depress brake pedal several times to seat pads. Bleed brakes as necessary. See BLEEDING BRAKE SYSTEM.

FRONT BRAKE CALIPER

NOTE: Front disc brake calipers are of same basic design. Only caliper-to-bracket attachments and anti-rattle springs or clips differ among models.

Removal – **1)** Raise and support front of vehicle. Remove wheels. Remove banjo bolt and copper washers connecting brake line to caliper. Plug hydraulic line and caliper.

2) Detach caliper guide pins or bolts, and remove caliper. DO NOT damage splash guard on upper caliper bolt side (if equipped) during removal. Remove disc pads, pad retainers, upper and lower anti-rattle springs and shim.

Installation – To install, reverse removal procedure. Install NEW copper banjo bolt washers when installing brake flexhose. Bleed brake system. See BLEEDING BRAKE SYSTEM.

FRONT BRAKE ROTOR

NOTE: On Accord, hub and bearing assembly must be removed to remove rotor. See WHEEL BEARING under REMOVAL & INSTALLATION in FRONT article in SUSPENSION.

Removal & Installation (Civic, Civic Del Sol & Prelude) – **1)** Raise and support vehicle. Remove wheels. Remove caliper assembly, and suspend it using wire. See FRONT BRAKE CALIPER. Attach dial indicator to caliper mount. Check rotor runout before removal. See DISC BRAKE SPECIFICATIONS table.

2) Detach and remove two 6-mm rotor retaining screws. Install two 8 x 1.25 x 12-mm bolts in existing holes. To prevent warpage, alternately turn bolts 2 turns at a time until disc can be removed from hub.

3) Clean rotor of all rust, and inspect rotor surfaces for cracks and grooves. Resurface or replace rotor as necessary. To install, reverse removal procedure. Tighten retaining screws. Bleed hydraulic system (if necessary). See BLEEDING BRAKE SYSTEM.

REAR DISC BRAKE PADS

Removal – Raise and support rear of vehicle. Remove wheels. Remove caliper shield (if equipped). Detach parking brake cable from caliper. Remove caliper mounting bolts. Remove caliper from bracket. Suspend caliper using wire. Remove brake pads.

Inspection – Using a vernier caliper, measure friction pad thickness. Service limit is .06" (1.5 mm).

Installation – **1)** Apply Molykote M77 compound to both sides of inner and outer pad shims. Install brake pads and shims. Rotate caliper piston clockwise in caliper (if necessary). Ensure cutout in piston aligns with tab on inner pad.

2) Avoid twisting piston boot. If boot is twisted, back out piston and reposition boot. Install brake caliper and parking brake cable. Install caliper shield. Tighten shield mounting bolts to specification. See TORQUE SPECIFICATIONS.

3) Pump brake pedal several times to seat pads. Bleed brakes as necessary. See BLEEDING BRAKE SYSTEM.

REAR BRAKE CALIPER

Removal – **1)** Raise and support rear of vehicle. Remove wheels. Detach caliper shield mounting bolts. Remove shield. Remove parking brake cable from caliper.

2) Remove banjo bolt and copper washers connecting brakeline to caliper. Plug hydraulic line and caliper. Detach caliper mounting bolts, and remove caliper.

Installation – To install, reverse removal procedure. Replace copper banjo bolt washers when installing brake flexhose. Bleed brake system. See BLEEDING BRAKE SYSTEM.

REAR BRAKE ROTOR

Removal & Installation – **1)** Raise and support vehicle. Remove wheels. Remove caliper assembly. See REAR BRAKE CALIPER. Suspend caliper using wire. Attach dial indicator to control arm assembly. Check rotor runout before removal. See DISC BRAKE SPECIFICATIONS table.

2) Detach and remove two 6-mm rotor retaining screws. Install two 8 x 1.25 x 12-mm bolts in existing holes. To prevent warpage, alternately turn bolts 2 turns at a time until disc can be removed from hub.

3) Clean rotor of all rust, and inspect rotor surfaces for excessive wear, cracks and grooves. Resurface or replace rotor as necessary. To install, reverse removal procedure. Tighten retaining screws. Bleed hydraulic system (if necessary). See BLEEDING BRAKE SYSTEM.

BRAKE DRUM

Removal & Installation – **1)** Raise and support vehicle. Remove rear wheels. Loosen parking brake. Pull brake drum off hub.

2) Inspect lining friction surface of drum for grooves, excessive wear and damage. Using an inside micrometer, measure I.D. of brake drum. If I.D. is not within specification, replace brake drum. See DRUM BRAKE SPECIFICATIONS table.

3) Resurface drum when new linings are installed. Replace drum if specification is exceeded. To install, reverse removal procedure.

REAR BRAKE SHOES

Removal – **1)** Raise and support rear of vehicle. Remove rear wheels and brake drums. On Accord, remove upper return spring. On all models, detach shoe tension pins by pushing in on retaining spring and turning tension pin 90 degrees to align with spring slot.

2) Lower brake shoe assembly to clear wheel cylinder, and remove lower return spring. Note original position of all springs. *See Fig. 3.*

CAUTION: Ensure wheel cylinder rubber dust covers are not damaged during brake shoe removal.

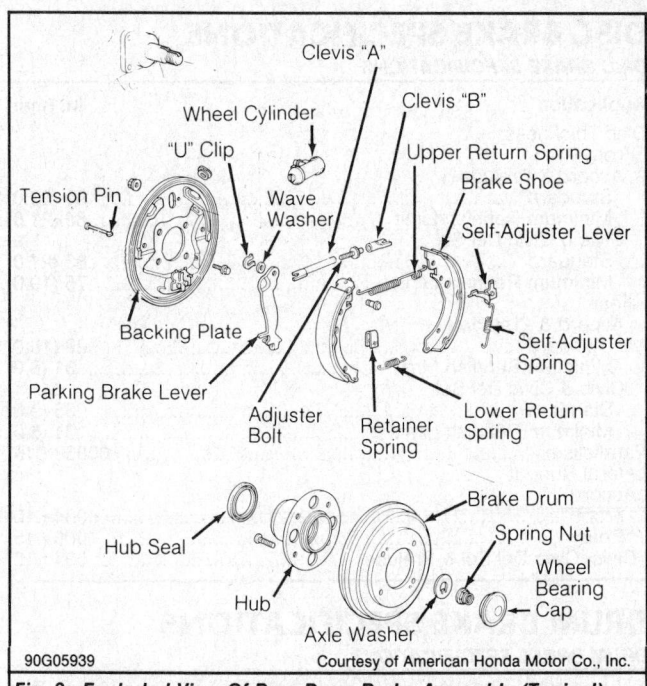

90G05939   Courtesy of American Honda Motor Co., Inc.

Fig. 3: Exploded View Of Rear Drum Brake Assembly (Typical)

3) Remove brake shoe assembly. Disconnect parking brake cable from parking brake lever assembly. On Civic and Civic Del Sol, remove upper return spring. On all models, separate brake shoes. Remove self-adjuster bolt, lever and spring.

4) Pry off circlip, and remove washer, pivot pin and parking brake lever (if necessary). Mark parking brake lever for left or right position.

Inspection – 1) Check self-adjuster lever for worn or damaged ratchet teeth. Inspect brake shoes for distortion, nicks or burrs, and loose, glazed, cracked or oil-soaked linings. Check all springs for weakness and damage. Inspect brake linings for excessive wear and damage. Lining service limit is .080" (2.00 mm).

2) Replace linings (and springs) in axle sets only. Resurface brake drums when new linings are installed.

Installation – 1) Apply light coat of high-temperature grease to threads of adjuster assembly, sliding surfaces of brake shoes and metal contact areas of backing plate. Install parking brake lever to brake shoe.

2) Screw in self-adjuster bolt until it stops. Install parking brake cable on lever. To complete installation, reverse removal procedure. Bleed system as necessary. See BLEEDING BRAKE SYSTEM.

3) Depress brake pedal several times to set self-adjusting brake. Adjust parking brake. See PARKING BRAKE under ADJUSTMENTS.

MASTER CYLINDER

Removal & Installation – Drain master cylinder reservoir. Disconnect fluid level switch connector. Disconnect brake fluid lines. Plug openings to prevent fluid loss and contamination. Remove master cylinder mounting nuts. Remove master cylinder. Bleed master cylinder before installation. To install, reverse removal procedure. Bleed system as necessary. See BLEEDING BRAKE SYSTEM.

POWER BRAKE BOOSTER

Removal – Power brake booster may be removed with master cylinder attached, if desired. Disconnect vacuum hose from power brake booster. From inside vehicle, remove retaining clip from booster rod pin on brake pedal. Remove pin from brake pedal. Remove brake booster mounting nuts. Remove power brake booster assembly from engine compartment.

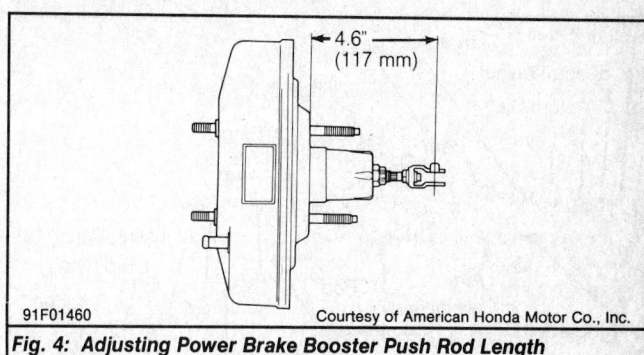

91F01460   Courtesy of American Honda Motor Co., Inc.

Fig. 4: Adjusting Power Brake Booster Push Rod Length

Installation – Check length of brake booster rod. *See Fig. 4.* Install power brake booster. Tighten mounting nuts to specification. See TORQUE SPECIFICATIONS. To complete installation, reverse removal procedure. Bleed system as necessary. See BLEEDING BRAKE SYSTEM.

REAR AXLE BEARINGS & OIL SEAL

NOTE: All models use a permanently sealed bearing assembly that requires removal of hub assembly from vehicle. See REAR article in SUSPENSION.

OVERHAUL

DISC BRAKE CALIPER

CAUTION: DO NOT spill brake fluid on painted surfaces or damage to finish will result. DO NOT place fingers in front of piston when air pressure is used for removal.

NOTE: For exploded views of disc brake calipers, see Figs. 5 and 6.

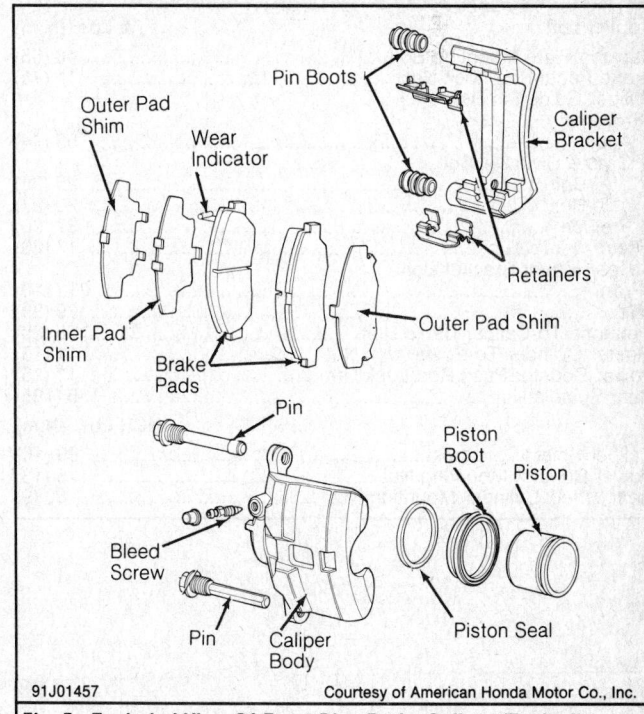

91J01457   Courtesy of American Honda Motor Co., Inc.

Fig. 5: Exploded View Of Front Disc Brake Caliper (Typical)

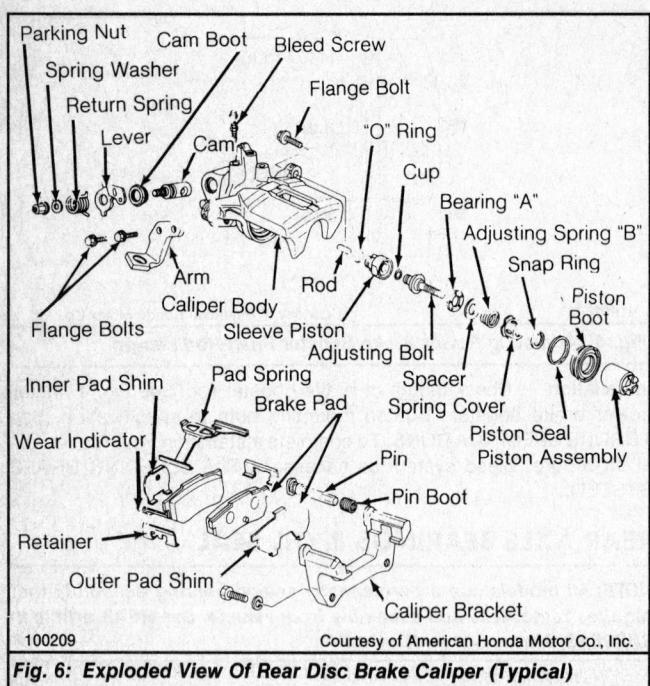

Courtesy of American Honda Motor Co., Inc.

Fig. 6: Exploded View Of Rear Disc Brake Caliper (Typical)

MASTER CYLINDER & POWER BRAKE BOOSTER

NOTE: Faulty master cylinder or power brake booster must be replaced as complete assembly. Overhaul procedure is not available from manufacturer.

TORQUE SPECIFICATIONS
TORQUE SPECIFICATIONS

Application	Ft. Lbs. (N.m)
Backing Plate Mounting Bolt	48 (65)
Brake Pedal Rod Lock Nut	11 (15)
Caliper Guide Pin Bolt	
Front	
Accord	55 (74)
Civic & Civic Del Sol	
"A" Bolt	26 (35)
"B" Bolt	20 (27)
Prelude	37 (50)
Rear	17 (23)
Caliper Mount Bracket Bolt	
Front	81 (110)
Rear	29 (39)
Flexhose-To-Caliper Banjo Bolt	26 (35)
Master Cylinder-To-Power Unit Nut	11 (15)
Power Booster Push Rod Lock Nut	11 (15)
Rear Spindle Nut	136 (185)

	INCH Lbs. (N.m)
Caliper Shield	89 (10)
Power Booster Mounting Nut	115 (13)
Rear Wheel Cylinder Mounting Nut	80 (9)

DISC BRAKE SPECIFICATIONS
DISC BRAKE SPECIFICATIONS

Application	In. (mm)
Disc Thickness	
Front	
Accord & Prelude	
Standard	.90 (23.0)
Minimum Refinish Limit	.83 (21.0)
Civic & Civic Del Sol	
Standard	.83 (21.0)
Minimum Refinish Limit	.75 (19.0)
Rear	
Accord & Prelude	
Standard	.39 (10.0)
Minimum Refinish Limit	.31 (8.0)
Civic & Civic Del Sol	
Standard	.35 (9.0)
Minimum Refinish Limit	.31 (8.0)
Parallelism	.0006 (.015)
Lateral Runout	
Accord	
Front	.004 (.10)
Rear	.006 (.15)
Civic, Civic Del Sol & Prelude	.004 (.10)

DRUM BRAKE SPECIFICATIONS
DRUM BRAKE SPECIFICATIONS

Application	In. (mm)
Drum Diameter	
Accord	
Standard	8.66 (220.0)
Service Limit	8.70 (221.0)
Civic	
1.5L A/T & 1.6L	
Standard	7.87 (200.0)
Service Limit	7.91 (201.0)
1.5L M/T	
Standard	7.09 (180.0)
Service Limit	7.13 (181.0)
Civic Del Sol	
Standard	7.09 (180.0)
Service Limit	7.13 (181.0)

NOTE: For information on Passport anti-lock brakes, refer to Rodeo in Isuzu BRAKES – REAR ANTI-LOCK article.

DESCRIPTION

The Anti-Lock Brake System (ABS) is designed to prevent wheel lock-up during hard braking, allowing driver to maintain vehicle control. System consists of control unit, accumulator, ABS pump (power unit), 4 speed sensors, modulator, warning light, master cylinder, power booster assembly and connecting wiring. See Fig. 1.

NOTE: For more information on brake system, see DISC & DRUM article in BRAKES.

OPERATION

ABS PUMP (POWER UNIT)

The power unit consists of an electric motor, filter, guide, piston rod and cylinder body. Guide is positioned off-set to the center of the motor shaft. Rotation of motor and cylinder body provides the reciprocating motion to the piston rod. This pressurizes brake fluid which is fed to relief valve, accumulator and modulator.

As the motor rotates and pressure in the accumulator exceeds a predetermined level, the pressure switch is turned on. Upon receiving this switching signal, the control unit stops motor relay operation. If accumulator pressure does not reach predetermined level after motor has run continuously for at least 2 minutes, the control unit stops motor operation and turns on ABS warning light in instrument panel.

ACCUMULATOR

The accumulator is a pneumatic, nitrogen-gas filled reservoir which accumulates high-pressure brake fluid. Accumulator feeds high-pressure brake fluid to modulator valve through inlet side of solenoid valve. Accumulator charging pressure is 3625 psi (250 kg/cm²). Maximum operating pressure is 5075 psi (350 kg/cm²).

CONTROL UNIT

The control unit has a main function, sub-function, self-diagnostic function and fail-safe function.

Main Function – Controls overall ABS system operation by interpreting speed sensor signals and activating solenoid valve in modulator unit.

Sub-Function – Controls pump motor and self-diagnostic function.

Self-Diagnostic Function – Monitors the main ABS system. When an abnormality is detected, ABS warning light comes on.

Fail-Safe Function – When an abnormality is detected in the main system, solenoid valve operation is turned off by fail-safe relay. Under these conditions, the ABS system operates as a conventional brake system. The fail-safe function comes on with ABS warning light.

MODULATOR

The modulator consists of 4 modulator pistons and 3 sets of solenoid valves. Each solenoid valve set consists of an inlet and outlet valve. Individual pistons and solenoid valve sets are used for the front wheels. Individual modulator pistons are used for each rear wheel, but are connected to a single solenoid valve set used for both rear wheels. The modulator pistons for the rear brakes have proportioning control valves to prevent rear wheel lock-up if ABS system malfunctions.

PRESSURE SWITCH

The pressure switch monitors accumulator pump pressure. When pressure switch is turned off, the control unit activates pump motor relay to operate ABS pump motor. If accumulator pressure does not reach predetermined level, ABS warning light comes on.

SPEED SENSOR

The speed sensor detects wheel rotation speed. Speed sensor consists of a permanent magnet, coil and trigger wheel (pulser). As trigger wheel rotates, the magnetic flux around the coil in each speed sensor alternates, generating a voltage frequency proportional to wheel rotation speed. These pulses are sent to the control unit to determine wheel speed.

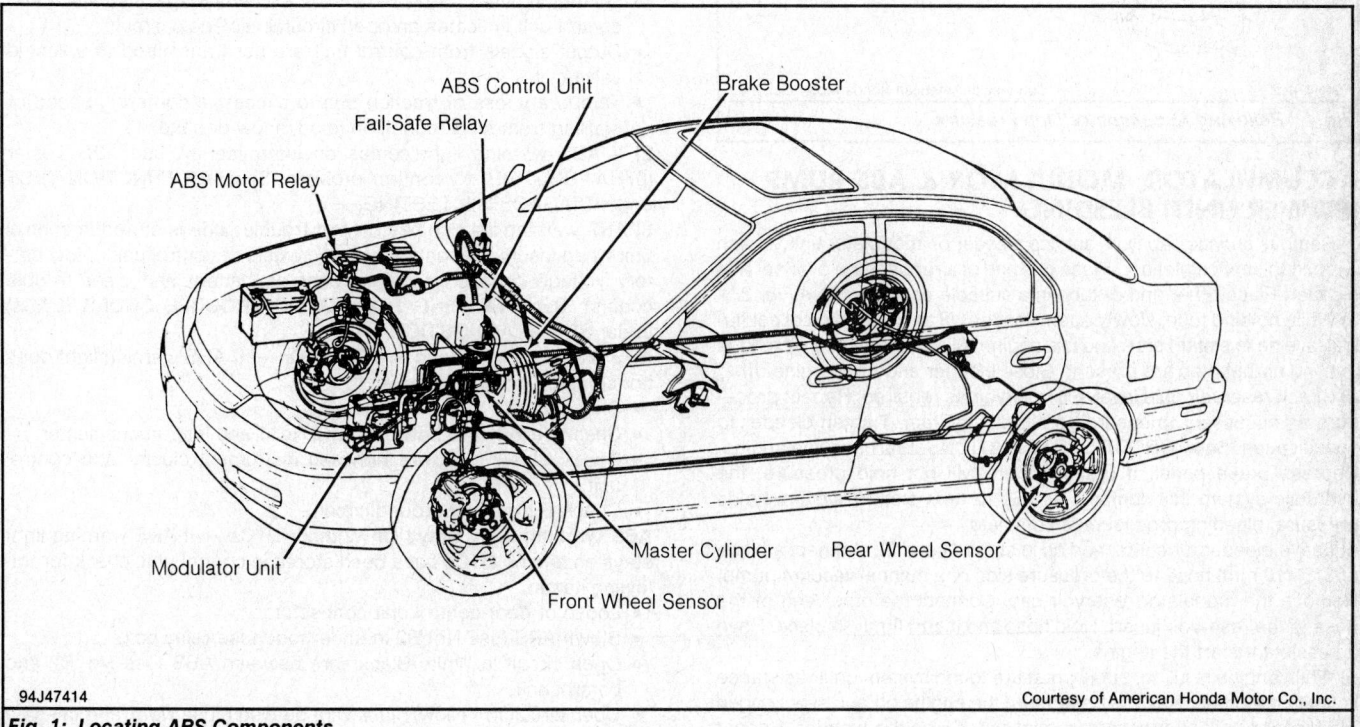

94J47414

Courtesy of American Honda Motor Co., Inc.

Fig. 1: Locating ABS Components

BLEEDING BRAKE SYSTEM
HYDRAULIC SYSTEM BLEEDING

CAUTION: DO NOT spill brake fluid on painted surfaces. To avoid paint damage, clean any spilled brake fluid with a clean cloth and clear water, immediately.

Fill master cylinder with clean brake fluid. Fluid should meet DOT 3 or DOT 4 specifications. Bleed master cylinder with bleeder valves (if equipped). Bleed wheel positions in following sequence: RR, LF, LR, RF.

RELIEVING ACCUMULATOR/LINE PRESSURE

1) Remove service cap from service bleeder on modulator unit. Attach wrench to service bleeder. Place one end of a rubber tube over service bleeder. Place other end of tube in a suitable container. *See Fig. 2.*
2) While holding tube, slowly open bleeder 1/8 to 1/4 turn to collect fluid. Tighten bleeder to specification. See TORQUE SPECIFICATIONS.

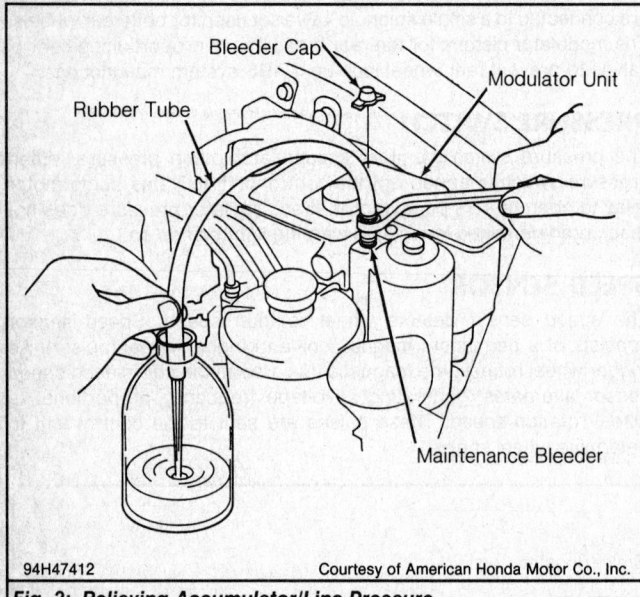

Bleeder Cap

Modulator Unit

Rubber Tube

Maintenance Bleeder

94H47412   Courtesy of American Honda Motor Co., Inc.

Fig. 2: Relieving Accumulator/Line Pressure

ACCUMULATOR, MODULATOR & ABS PUMP (POWER UNIT) BLEEDING

1) Remove service cap from service bleeder on modulator unit. Attach wrench to service bleeder. Place one end of a rubber tube over service bleeder. Place other end of tube in a suitable container. *See Fig. 2.*
2) While holding tube, slowly open bleeder 1/8 to 1/4 turn to collect fluid. Have an assistant start and idle engine. Allow fluid to flow from tube until no air bubbles are present. Close bleeder and turn engine off.
3) Check reservoir fluid level. Fill reservoir as required. Repeat procedure as necessary to ensure no air is in system. Tighten bleeder to specification. See TORQUE SPECIFICATIONS. Start and idle engine. Depress brake pedal. If brake system will not hold pressure, the hydraulic system still contains air. Go to next step. If system holds pressure, bleeding procedure is complete.
4) Leave bleeder tube attached as in steps 1) and 2). Connect a piece of 3/8" (10 mm) hose to the pressure side of a manual vacuum pump. Remove the modulator reservoir cap. Connect the other end of the hose to the reservoir insert. Hold hose and insert firmly in place. Have an assistant start the engine.
5) While engine is idling, apply pressure to the system until resistance is felt in the pump. Have assistant turn the engine off and slowly open the bleeder until all pressure is released. Close the bleeder. Repeat procedure 5 times to ensure air pocket is purged from modulator. If ABS control unit has a stored Diagnostic Trouble Code (DTC), clear DTC from control unit memory. See CLEARING DTCs under SELF-DIAGNOSTICS.

ADJUSTMENTS
PARKING BRAKE

NOTE: Before adjusting parking brake, loosen park brake equalizer adjusting nut. Start engine, and depress brake pedal several times to set self-adjusting brakes before adjusting parking brake.

1) With rear brakes adjusted, raise and support rear of vehicle. Loosen equalizer nut, and pull parking brake lever up one notch. Tighten equalizer adjusting nut until rear wheels drag slightly.
2) Release parking brake lever. Rear wheels should rotate freely. Rear wheels should lock when parking brake lever is pulled up 6-10 clicks.

BRAKE WARNING LIGHT

To adjust parking brake light operation, turn ignition on. Bend switch plate down until light comes on when parking brake lever is pulled one notch, and goes out when lever is released.

TROUBLE SHOOTING
ANTI-LOCK (ABS) WARNING LIGHT

NOTE: ABS system is okay if ABS warning light goes out after engine is started.

NOTE: Diagnostic Trouble Codes (DTCs) may also be referred to as problem codes.

Diagnostic Trouble Code (DTC) Recognition – 1) ABS control unit recognizes system related problems and causes ABS warning light to come on and stay on under any of following conditions:
- ABS pump runs longer than 2 minutes.
- Vehicle is driven with parking brake on longer than 30 seconds.
- One rear wheel is locked.
- Wheel speed sensor does not transmit a signal.
- Vehicle is driven on extremely rough road.
- Low battery voltage.
- Operation time of solenoid valves exceeds a specified value and control unit indicates an open circuit in solenoid circuit.
- Output signals from control unit are not transmitted to solenoid valves.
- Temporary loss of traction due to excessive cornering speed or starting from stuck condition (mud, snow or sand).

2) If ABS warning light comes on intermittently, use ABS Tester (07HAJ-SG0010B) to confirm problem. See ABS FUNCTION TEST under DIAGNOSIS & TESTING.
3) ABS warning light comes on and trouble code is stored in control unit when insufficient battery voltage exists at control unit. If low battery voltage caused problem, recharge battery and clear trouble code(s). See CLEARING DIAGNOSTIC TROUBLE CODES (DTCs) under SELF-DIAGNOSTICS.

ABS Warning Light Does Not Come On – If ABS warning light does not come on when ignition is on:
- Check bulb.
- Check Yellow wire between fuse No. 1 and instrument cluster.
- Check Blue/White wire between instrument cluster and control unit.
- Check control unit ground circuit.

ABS Warning Light Stays On Without DTCs – If ABS warning light stays on and no DTCs have been stored in control unit, check for following items:
- Loose or poor control unit connector.
- Blown ABS fuse No. B2 in underhood fuse/relay box.
- Open circuit in White/Black wire between ABS fuse No. B2 and control unit.
- Open circuit in Yellow/Black wire between fuse No. 7 and fail-safe relays.
- Short circuit in Blue/White wire between instrument cluster and control unit.
- Open circuit in White/Blue wire between alternator and control unit.

If problem cannot be found, substitute a known good control unit, and retest.

ABS Warning Light Stays On With DTCs – Turn ignition on. Ensure ABS warning light comes on. Start engine and observe ABS warning light. If ABS warning light stays on, retrieve and record trouble codes. See RETRIEVING DIAGNOSTIC TROUBLE CODES (DTCs) under SELF-DIAGNOSTICS. If ABS warning light goes out after engine starts, ABS system is okay.

DIAGNOSIS & TESTING

ABS FUNCTION TEST

WARNING: DO NOT drive vehicle with ABS tester connected to vehicle, or brake system failure may occur.

Preliminary Procedure – Confirm ABS warning light indicates system malfunction. See ANTI-LOCK (ABS) WARNING LIGHT under TROUBLE SHOOTING. Park vehicle on level surface. Block wheels, and put automatic transmission in Park or manual transmission in Neutral.

CAUTION: DO NOT move mode selector switch while TEST IN PROGRESS light is on.

Testing – **1)** With ignition off, connect ABS Tester (07HAJ-SG0010B) to Orange 6-pin test connector, located under passenger's seat. Start engine. Release parking brake. Place mode selector to "1" position. Push START TEST button. *See Fig. 3.* TEST IN PROGRESS light should come on. Within 1-2 seconds, all 4 monitor lights should come on. If tester lights do not illuminate, ABS tester is faulty.

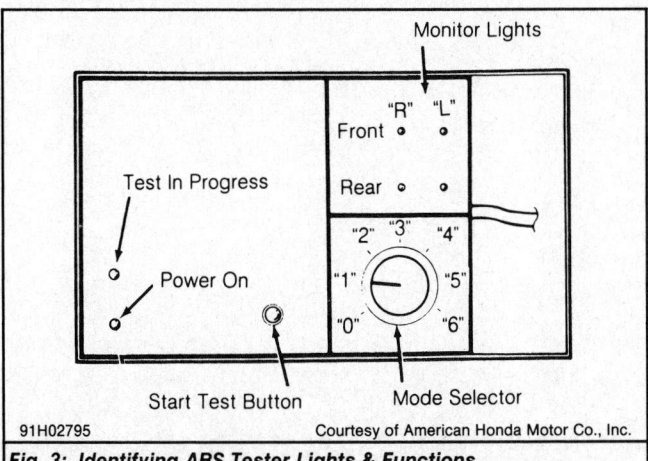

91H02795   Courtesy of American Honda Motor Co., Inc.

Fig. 3: Identifying ABS Tester Lights & Functions

2) If ABS warning light comes on, 6-pin connector or ABS tester harness is faulty. Turn mode selector to "2" position. Press brake pedal. Push START TEST button. ABS warning light should not come on and kickback should be felt on brake pedal.
3) If ABS warning light comes on or kickback is not felt, see ANTI-LOCK (ABS) WARNING LIGHT under TROUBLE SHOOTING. Place mode selector in "3", "4" and then "5" positions. Repeat step **2)** for each test mode. Results should be same as in test mode "2". If results are not same as in test mode "2", see ANTI-LOCK (ABS) WARNING LIGHT under TROUBLE SHOOTING.
4) Breakdown of each test mode is as follows:
Mode 1 – Sends simulated driving signal of each wheel to control unit to check self-diagnostic circuit. No kickback should be felt in brake pedal.
Mode 2 – Sends driving signal of each wheel, and then sends lock signal of left rear wheel to control unit. A kickback should be felt in brake pedal.
Mode 3 – Sends driving signal of each wheel, and then sends lock signal of right rear wheel to control unit. A kickback should be felt in brake pedal.

Mode 4 – Sends driving signal of each wheel, and then sends lock signal of left front wheel to control unit. A kickback should be felt in brake pedal.
Mode 5 – Sends driving signal of each wheel, and then sends lock signal of right front wheel to control unit. A kickback should be felt in brake pedal.
Mode 6 – Not used on this model.
5) If brake pedal does not kickback in Modes 2-5 as indicated and ABS indicator light does not come on, repeat function test several times. If test results remain the same. check for air in high pressure line, restriction in high pressure line or faulty modulator unit.

SPEED SENSOR TEST

1) Turn ignition off, and connect ABS Tester (07HAJ-SG0010B) to Orange 6-pin test connector, located under passenger's seat. Turn ignition on. Place ABS tester mode selector to "0" position.
2) Raise and support vehicle so wheels can be turned. Place transmission in Neutral. Turn wheels by hand at one revolution per second. Appropriate monitor light should blink each time wheel is rotated.
3) In some instances, front wheels may not rotate fast enough to make tester light blink. If this happens, start engine. Slowly accelerate and decelerate front wheels. If light does not blink, check appropriate speed sensor, sensor air gap and wiring.

RELAY TEST

Check continuity between relay terminals "A" and "B". *See Fig. 4.* Continuity should not exist. Apply battery voltage across terminals "C" and "D". Continuity should exist between terminals "A" and "B". If continuity is not as indicated, replace relay.

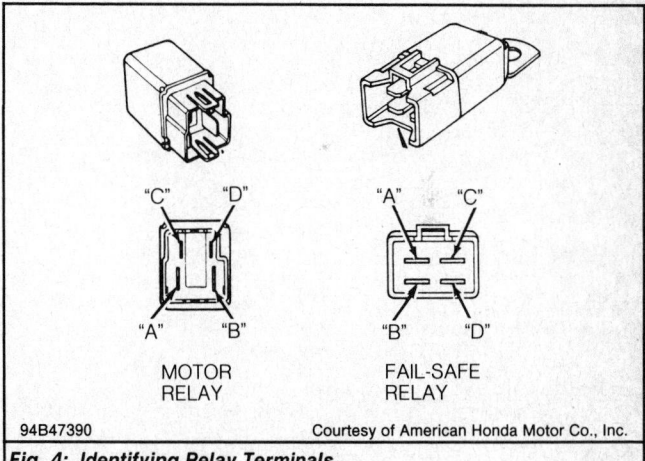

94B47390   Courtesy of American Honda Motor Co., Inc.

Fig. 4: Identifying Relay Terminals

REMOVAL & INSTALLATION

ABS CONTROL UNIT

Removal & Installation – Remove right side kick panel. Disconnect electrical connectors. Remove ABS control unit bolts, and remove control unit. *See Fig. 1.* To install, reverse removal procedure. Turn ignition on and observe ABS warning light. ABS system is okay if ABS warning light goes out after engine is started.

ACCUMULATOR

WARNING: Accumulator contains high-pressure nitrogen gas. DO NOT puncture, expose to flame or attempt to disassemble accumulator. Explosion and serious injury could result.

Removal & Installation – **1)** Remove modulator/pump assembly. See MODULATOR/PUMP ASSEMBLY. Secure pump assembly in vise. Open relief plug 3 1/2 turns and wait 3 minutes to allow high pressure nitrogen gas to escape. Remove accumulator from modulator/pump assembly.

2) To install, reverse removal procedure. If necessary, bleed air from system. See ACCUMULATOR, MODULATOR and ABS PUMP (POWER UNIT) BLEEDING under BLEEDING BRAKE SYSTEM.

SPEED SENSOR

Removal & Installation – Unplug speed sensor connector. Remove mounting bolts. Remove speed sensor from vehicle. To install, reverse removal procedure. Ensure air gap between speed sensor and trigger wheel (pulser) is .016-.039" (.40-1.0 mm). If air gap exceeds specification at any point, probable cause is a distorted knuckle. Replace knuckle. See HUB & KNUCKLE under REMOVAL & INSTALLATION in appropriate SUSPENSION article.

PULSER (TRIGGER WHEEL)

Removal and installation procedures not available from manufacturer.

MODULATOR/PUMP ASSEMBLY

Removal & Installation – 1) Relieve accumulator/line pressure. See RELIEVING ACCUMULATOR/LINE PRESSURE. Drain fluid from modulator assembly. Remove intake air duct and emission control box. Disconnect solenoid, pump motor and pressure switch connectors.

2) Disconnect brake pipes from modulator. Disconnect brake hose from modulator reservoir. Remove clamp from modulator bracket. Remove mounting bolts. Remove modulator assembly. To install, reverse removal procedure. Bleed hydraulic system. See BLEEDING BRAKE SYSTEM.

PRESSURE SWITCH

Removal & Installation – Secure modulator/pump assembly in vise. Remove banjo bolt and sealing washers. Remove pressure switch. To install, reverse removal procedure, using NEW sealing washers.

TORQUE SPECIFICATIONS
TORQUE SPECIFICATIONS

Application	Ft. Lbs. (N.m)
Banjo Bolt Fittings	26 (35)
Brake Line Flare Nuts	14 (19)
Modulator Mounting Bolts	16 (22)

	INCH Lbs. (N.m)
ABS Control Unit Mounting Bolts	84 (9.5)
ABS Pump Mounting Bolts	89 (10)
Accumulator Mounting Bolts	89 (10)
Maintenance Bleeder Screw	97 (11)
Pump Motor Flange Bolts	97 (11)

WIRING DIAGRAM

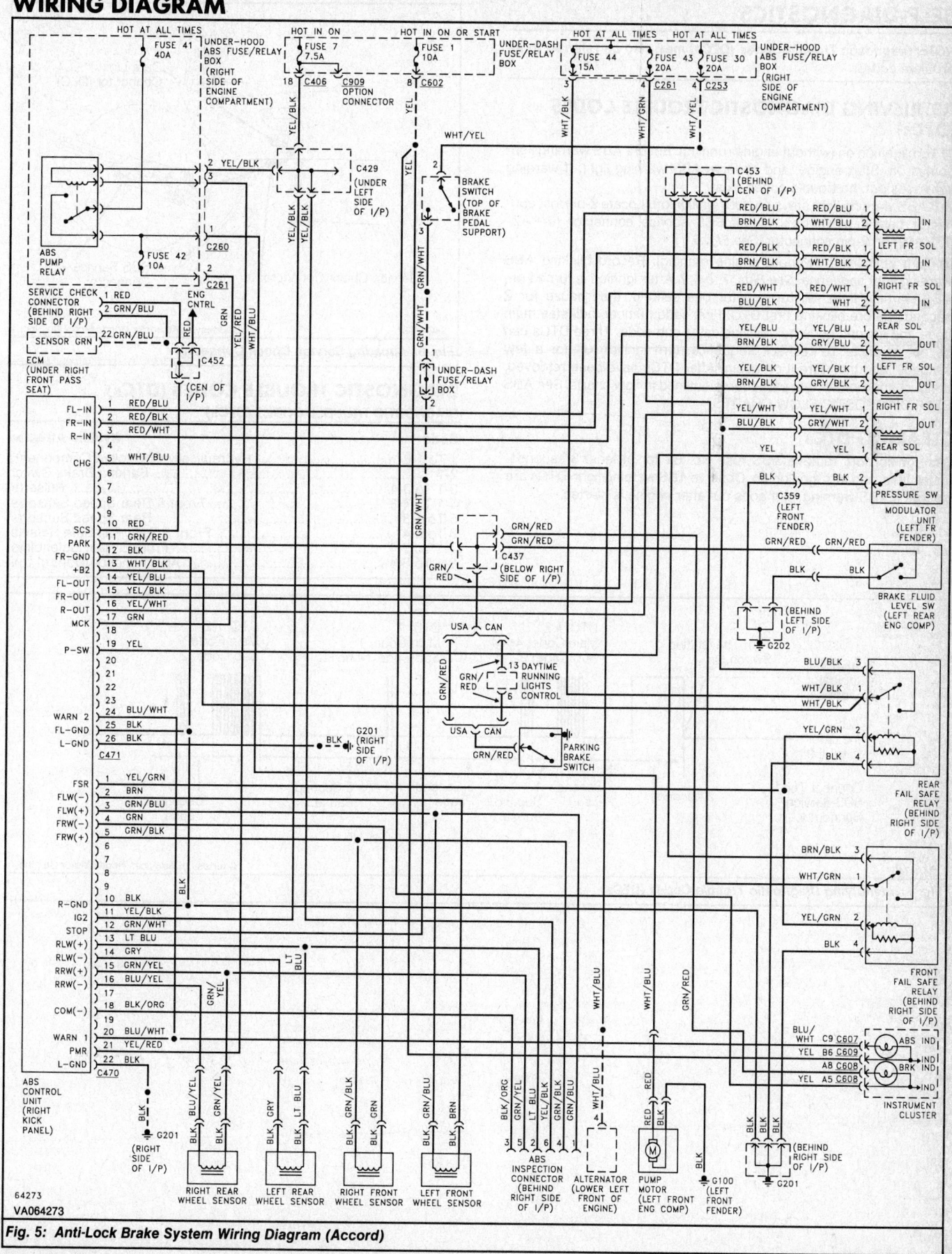

64273
VA064273

Fig. 5: Anti-Lock Brake System Wiring Diagram (Accord)

SELF-DIAGNOSTICS

NOTE: Diagnostic Trouble Codes (DTCs) may also be referred to as problem codes.

RETRIEVING DIAGNOSTIC TROUBLE CODES (DTCs)

1) Turn ignition on (without engine running). Ensure ABS warning light comes on. Start engine, and observe ABS warning light. If warning light goes out, no trouble codes exist.

2) If ABS warning light stays on, turn ignition off. Locate 2-pin test connector behind glove box. Install SCS service connector (07PAZ-0010100) on 2-pin connector. *See Fig. 6.*

3) Turn ignition on (without engine running). Record blinking ABS warning light sequence. *See Figs. 7, 8 & 9.* After ignition is turned on, ABS warning light will turn on for one second, then pause for 2 seconds before blinking first DTC. First code number indicates main code and second code number indicates sub code. Three DTCs can be set at once. To recheck sequence, turn ignition off for a few seconds, and then turn it on again. After DTCs have been retrieved, conduct appropriate test procedures outlined in flow charts. See ABS SELF-DIAGNOSTIC FLOW CHARTS.

CLEARING DTCs

With ignition off, remove ABS fuse No. B2 for at least 3 seconds. Install fuse, and turn ignition on. Observe ABS warning light. DTCs are cleared if ABS warning light goes out after engine is started.

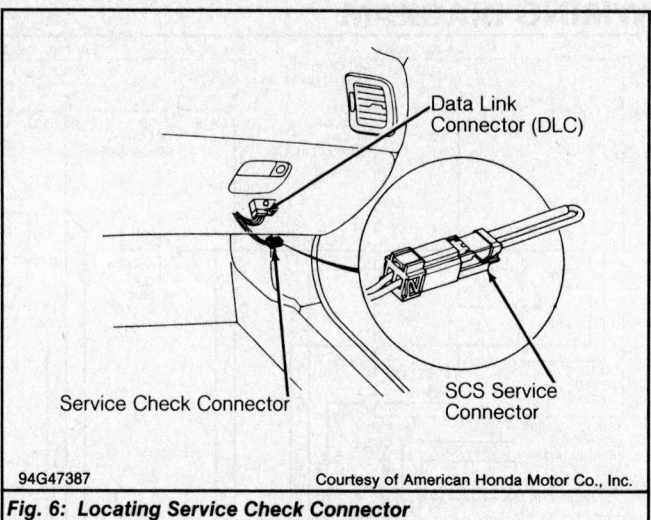

94G47387   Courtesy of American Honda Motor Co., Inc.

Fig. 6: Locating Service Check Connector

DIAGNOSTIC TROUBLE CODES (DTCs)
DIAGNOSTIC TROUBLE CODES (DTCs)

Code	System Affected
1 To 1-8	Hydraulically Controlled Components
2-1	Parking Brake Switch
3-1 To 3-4	Pulser(s)
4-1 To 4-8	Front & Rear Speed Sensor(s)
5 To 5-8	Rear Speed Sensor(s)
6 To 6-4	Front & Rear Fail-Safe Relay(s)
7-1 To 7-4	Front & Rear Solenoid(s)
8-1 To 8-4	ABS Function/Control Unit

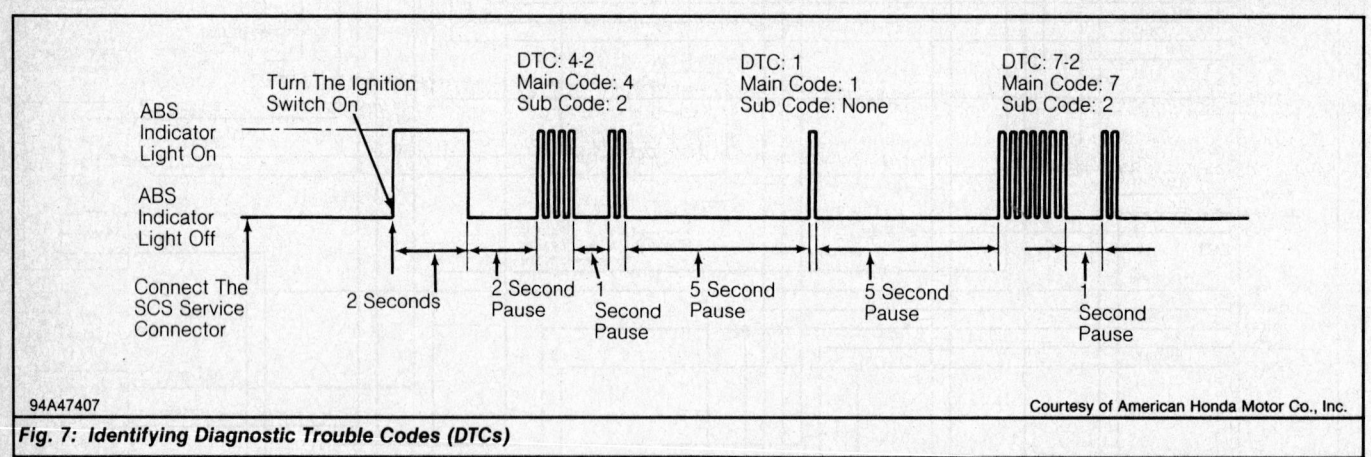

94A47407   Courtesy of American Honda Motor Co., Inc.

Fig. 7: Identifying Diagnostic Trouble Codes (DTCs)

DIAGNOSTIC TROUBLE CODE (DTC)		DIAGNOSIS/ SYMPTOM	DIAGNOSTIC PERIOD			PROBLEM LOCATION	PROBABLE CAUSE
MAIN CODE	SUB CODE		INITIAL DIAGNOSIS	INDIVIDUAL DIAGNOSIS	REGULAR DIAGNOSIS		
—		ABS indicator light does not come on when ignition switch is turned ON					• Blown BACK-UP LIGHTS/METER LIGHTS (10 A) fuse • Open circuit between the BACK-UP LIGHTS/METER LIGHTS (10 A) fuse and ABS indicator light • Blown ABS indicator light bulb • Open circuit between the ABS indicator light and ABS control unit • Open circuit between the ABS control unit and body ground • Poor body ground • Faulty ABS control unit
		ABS indicator light does not go off after engine is started					• Blown R/C MIRROR (7.5 A) fuse • Open circuit between the under-dash fuse/relay box and ABS control unit. • Open circuit between the battery and under-hood ABS fuse/relay box • Blown ABS B2 (15 A) fuse • Open circuit inside the under-hood ABS fuse/relay box • Open circuit between the under-hood ABS fuse/relay box and ABS control unit • Faulty alternator • Open circuit between the alternator and ABS control unit • Short to body ground in the WARN circuit between the ABS indicator light and ABS control unit • Faulty ABS control unit
①	—	ABS pump motor over-run	O	O			• Pressure switch stuck OFF • Open circuit between the pressure switch and ABS control unit • Open circuit in the P-SW circuit between the pressure switch and body ground, or a poor ground • Drop in pump discharge volume • Leaking outlet valve • Leaking relief valve • ABS brake fluid leakage • Faulty ABS control unit
	②	Pump motor	O		O		• Open circuit or short to body ground between the R/C MIRROR (7.5 A) fuse and under-hood ABS fuse/relay box • Open circuit or short to body ground in the PMR circuit inside the under-hood ABS fuse/relay box • Faulty pump motor relay • Open circuit or short to body ground in the PMR circuit between the under-hood ABS fuse/relay box and ABS control unit • Open circuit between the battery and under-hood ABS fuse/relay box • Blown ABS MOTOR (40 A) fuse • Blown ABS UNIT (10 A) fuse • Open circuit or short to body ground in the motor drive circuit and MCK circuit inside the under-hood ABS fuse/relay box • Open circuit or short to body ground in the MCK circuit between the under-hood ABS fuse/relay box and ABS control unit • Open circuit or short to body ground between the under-hood ABS fuse/relay box and pump motor • Faulty pump motor • Open circuit between the pump motor and body ground or poor ground • Faulty ABS control unit
	③	High pressure leakage			O		• Leaking outlet valve • Leaking relief valve • Poor contact in pressure switch circuit
	④	Pressure switch	O				• Short to body ground between the ABS control unit and pressure switch • Pressure switch stuck ON • Faulty ABS control unit
	⑧	High pressure system	O				• Accumulator gas leakage • Changed relief valve set pressure • Rear outlet solenoid valve late to close • Changed pressure switch set pressure
②	①	Parking brake			O		• Low fluid level in the master cylinder reservoir • Open circuit between the BACK-UP LIGHTS/METER LIGHTS (10 A) fuse and brake system light • Blown brake system light bulb • Open circuit or short to body ground between the brake system light and ABS control unit • Parking brake switch stuck ON • Short to body ground between the brake system light and parking brake switch • Brake fluid level switch stuck ON • Short to body ground between the brake system light and brake fluid level switch • Faulty ABS control unit

94H47388

Fig. 8: Self-Diagnostics & DTC Diagnosis Chart (1 Of 2)

DIAGNOSTIC TROUBLE CODE (DTC) MAIN CODE	SUB-CODE	DIAGNOSIS/ SYMPTOM	DIAGNOSTIC PERIOD INITIAL DIAGNOSIS	INDIVIDUAL DIAGNOSIS	REGULAR DIAGNOSIS	PROBLEM LOCATION	PROBABLE CAUSE
③	①	Pulser			O	Right-front	• Chipped pulser gear • Improperly installed wheel sensor
	②					Left-front	
	④					Right-rear	
	⑧					Left-rear	
	⑫	Different dia-meter tire			O		• Different diameter tire installed
④	①	Wheel sensor		O	O	Right-front	• Open circuit, internal short or short to body ground in the wheel sensor • Open circuit or short to body ground in the positive (+) wire between the wheel sensor and ABS control unit • Open circuit or short to body ground in the negative (−) wire between the wheel sensor and ABS control unit • Positive (+) wire shorted to the negative (−) wire between the wheel sensor and ABS control unit • Loose connector or poor contact of terminals • Improper wheel sensor air gap • Faulty ABS control unit • Missing pulser • Modulator does not decrease pressure properly
	②					Left-front	
	④					Right-rear	
	⑧					Left-rear	
⑤	—	Rear wheel lock			O	Right/Left	• Open circuit, internal short or short to body ground in the wheel sensor system • Rear brake drag • Modulator does not decrease pressure properly • Faulty ABS control unit
	④					Right	
	⑧					Left	
⑥	—	Fail-safe relay	O			Front/rear	• Short to power in the relay drive circuit between the fail-safe relay and ABS control unit • Faulty relay drive transistor (ON) in the ABS control unit • Fail-safe relay stuck ON • Short to power in the solenoid drive circuits between the fail-safe relay and ABS control unit
	①					Front	
	④					Rear	
⑦	①	Solenoid	O		O	Right-front	• Fail-safe relay stuck OFF • Open circuit in the solenoid drive circuit between the under-hood ABS fuse/relay box and ABS control unit • Short to body ground in the solenoid drive circuit between the solenoid and ABS control unit • Faulty solenoid drive transistor (ON) in the ABS control unit • Short to power in the solenoid drive circuit between the solenoid and ABS control unit • Faulty solenoid drive transistor (OFF) in the ABS control unit • Short to power in the drive circuit inside the solenoid • Short to the outlet circuit in the inlet circuit between the solenoid and ABS control unit
	②					Left-front	
	④					Rear	
⑧	①	ABS function			O		• Wheel sensor signal disappears at speeds of 6 mph (10 km/h) or less • Faulty ABS control unit
	②	CPU comparison	O		O		• Faulty ABS control unit
	④	IC [Integrated Circuit]	O		O		• Faulty ABS control unit

94I47389

Courtesy of American Honda Motor Co., Inc.

Fig. 9: Self-Diagnostics & DTC Diagnosis Chart (2 Of 2)

ABS SELF-DIAGNOSTIC FLOW CHARTS

NO DTC (1 OF 2)
ABS INDICATOR LIGHT DOES NOT COME ON

The ABS indicator light does not come on when the ignition switch is turned ON.

When the ignition switch is turned ON, the ABS indicator light drive transistor in the ABS control unit is activated by self-bias and turns the ABS indicator light on.

Possible causes for an ABS indicator light that does not come on:
- Blown BACK-UP LIGHTS/METER LIGHTS (10 A) fuse
- Open circuit between the BACK-UP LIGHTS/METER LIGHTS (10 A) fuse and ABS indicator light.
- Blown ABS indicator light bulb
- Open circuit between the ABS indicator light and ABS control unit
- Open circuit between the ABS control unit and body ground
- Poor body ground
- Faulty ABS control unit

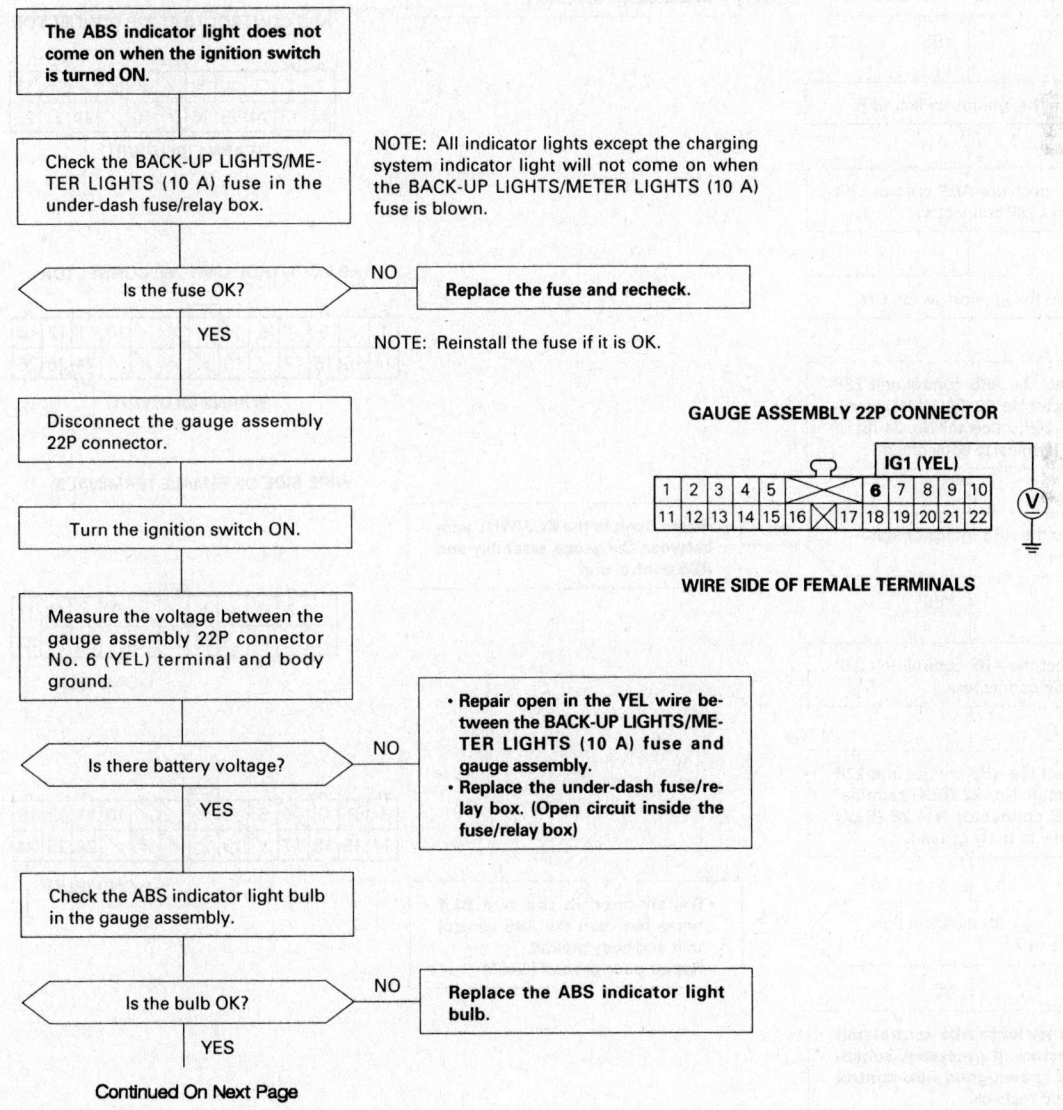

The ABS indicator light does not come on when the ignition switch is turned ON.

Check the BACK-UP LIGHTS/METER LIGHTS (10 A) fuse in the under-dash fuse/relay box.

NOTE: All indicator lights except the charging system indicator light will not come on when the BACK-UP LIGHTS/METER LIGHTS (10 A) fuse is blown.

Is the fuse OK? — NO → Replace the fuse and recheck.

YES

NOTE: Reinstall the fuse if it is OK.

Disconnect the gauge assembly 22P connector.

Turn the ignition switch ON.

Measure the voltage between the gauge assembly 22P connector No. 6 (YEL) terminal and body ground.

Is there battery voltage? — NO →
- Repair open in the YEL wire between the BACK-UP LIGHTS/METER LIGHTS (10 A) fuse and gauge assembly.
- Replace the under-dash fuse/relay box. (Open circuit inside the fuse/relay box)

YES

Check the ABS indicator light bulb in the gauge assembly.

Is the bulb OK? — NO → Replace the ABS indicator light bulb.

YES

Continued On Next Page

GAUGE ASSEMBLY 22P CONNECTOR

IG1 (YEL)

| 1 | 2 | 3 | 4 | 5 | | 6 | 7 | 8 | 9 | 10 |
| 11 | 12 | 13 | 14 | 15 | 16 | 17 | 18 | 19 | 20 | 21 | 22 |

WIRE SIDE OF FEMALE TERMINALS

1994 BRAKES
Anti-Lock – Accord (Cont.)

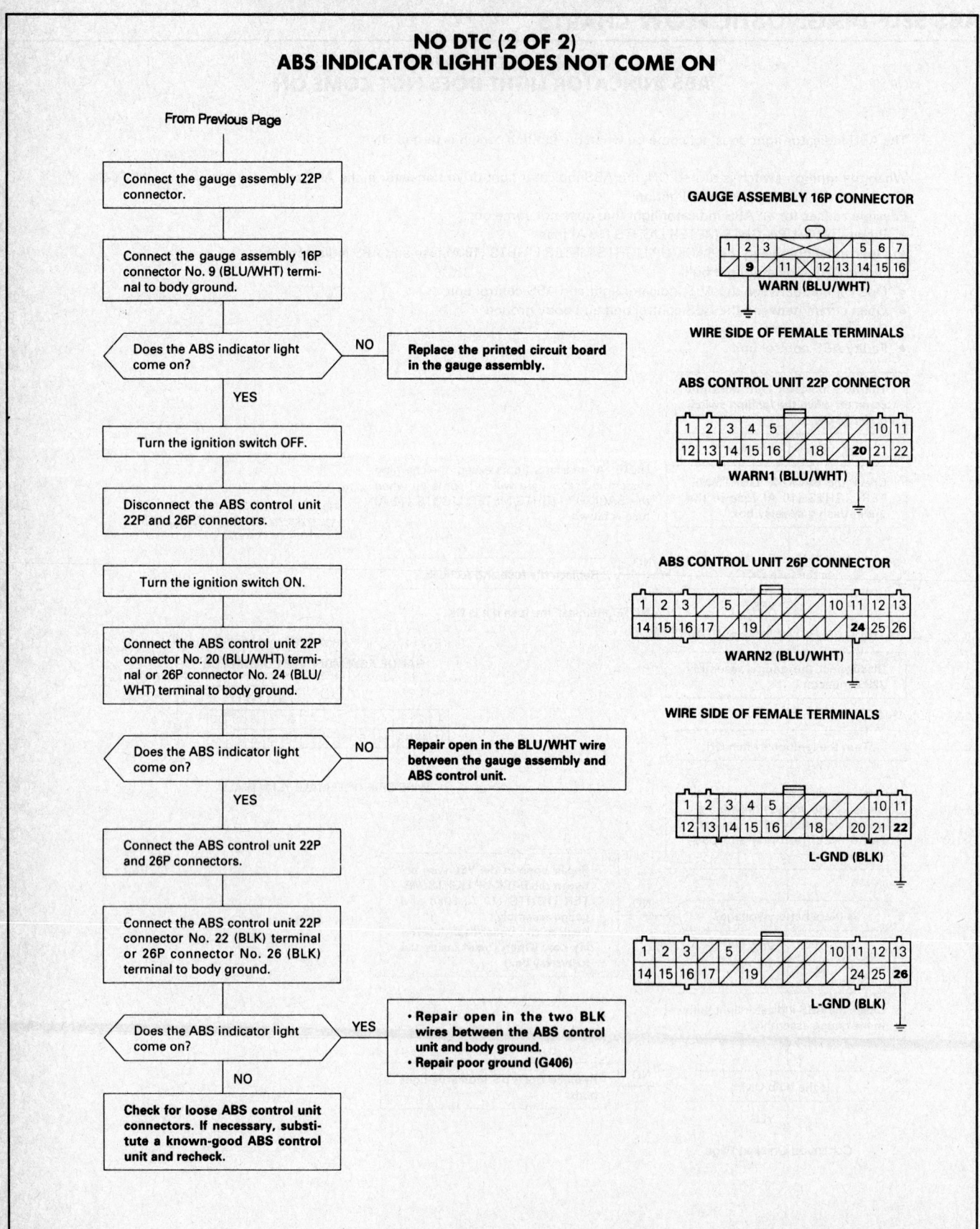

NO DTC (2 OF 2)
ABS INDICATOR LIGHT DOES NOT COME ON

From Previous Page

Connect the gauge assembly 22P connector.

Connect the gauge assembly 16P connector No. 9 (BLU/WHT) terminal to body ground.

Does the ABS indicator light come on? — NO → Replace the printed circuit board in the gauge assembly.

YES

Turn the ignition switch OFF.

Disconnect the ABS control unit 22P and 26P connectors.

Turn the ignition switch ON.

Connect the ABS control unit 22P connector No. 20 (BLU/WHT) terminal or 26P connector No. 24 (BLU/WHT) terminal to body ground.

Does the ABS indicator light come on? — NO → Repair open in the BLU/WHT wire between the gauge assembly and ABS control unit.

YES

Connect the ABS control unit 22P and 26P connectors.

Connect the ABS control unit 22P connector No. 22 (BLK) terminal or 26P connector No. 26 (BLK) terminal to body ground.

Does the ABS indicator light come on? — YES → • Repair open in the two BLK wires between the ABS control unit and body ground.
• Repair poor ground (G406)

NO

Check for loose ABS control unit connectors. If necessary, substitute a known-good ABS control unit and recheck.

GAUGE ASSEMBLY 16P CONNECTOR

| 1 | 2 | 3 | X | | 5 | 6 | 7 |
| 9 | | 11 | X | 12 | 13 | 14 | 15 | 16 |

WARN (BLU/WHT)

WIRE SIDE OF FEMALE TERMINALS

ABS CONTROL UNIT 22P CONNECTOR

| 1 | 2 | 3 | 4 | 5 | | | | 10 | 11 |
| 12 | 13 | 14 | 15 | 16 | | 18 | 20 | 21 | 22 |

WARN1 (BLU/WHT)

ABS CONTROL UNIT 26P CONNECTOR

| 1 | 2 | 3 | | 5 | | | | 10 | 11 | 12 | 13 |
| 14 | 15 | 16 | 17 | | 19 | | | 24 | 25 | 26 |

WARN2 (BLU/WHT)

WIRE SIDE OF FEMALE TERMINALS

| 1 | 2 | 3 | 4 | 5 | | | | 10 | 11 |
| 12 | 13 | 14 | 15 | 16 | | 18 | 20 | 21 | 22 |

L-GND (BLK)

| 1 | 2 | 3 | | 5 | | | | 10 | 11 | 12 | 13 |
| 14 | 15 | 16 | 17 | | 19 | | | 24 | 25 | 26 |

L-GND (BLK)

NO DTC (1 OF 3)
ABS INDICATOR LIGHT DOES NOT GO OFF

When no problem is found during the initial diagnosis, the ABS control unit turns the ABS indicator light drive transistor off to turn the ABS indicator light off.

Possible causes for an ABS indicator light that does not go off, but no Diagnostic Trouble Code (DTC) is indicated:

- Blown R/C MIRROR (7.5 A) fuse
- Open circuit between the under-dash fuse/relay box and ABS control unit
- Open circuit between the battery and under-hood ABS fuse/relay box
- Blown ABS B2 (15 A) fuse
- Open circuit inside the under-hood ABS fuse/relay box
- Open circuit between the under-hood ABS fuse/relay box and ABS control unit
- Faulty alternator
- Open circuit between the alternator and ABS control unit
- Short to body ground in the WARN circuit between the ABS indicator light and ABS control unit
- Faulty ABS control unit

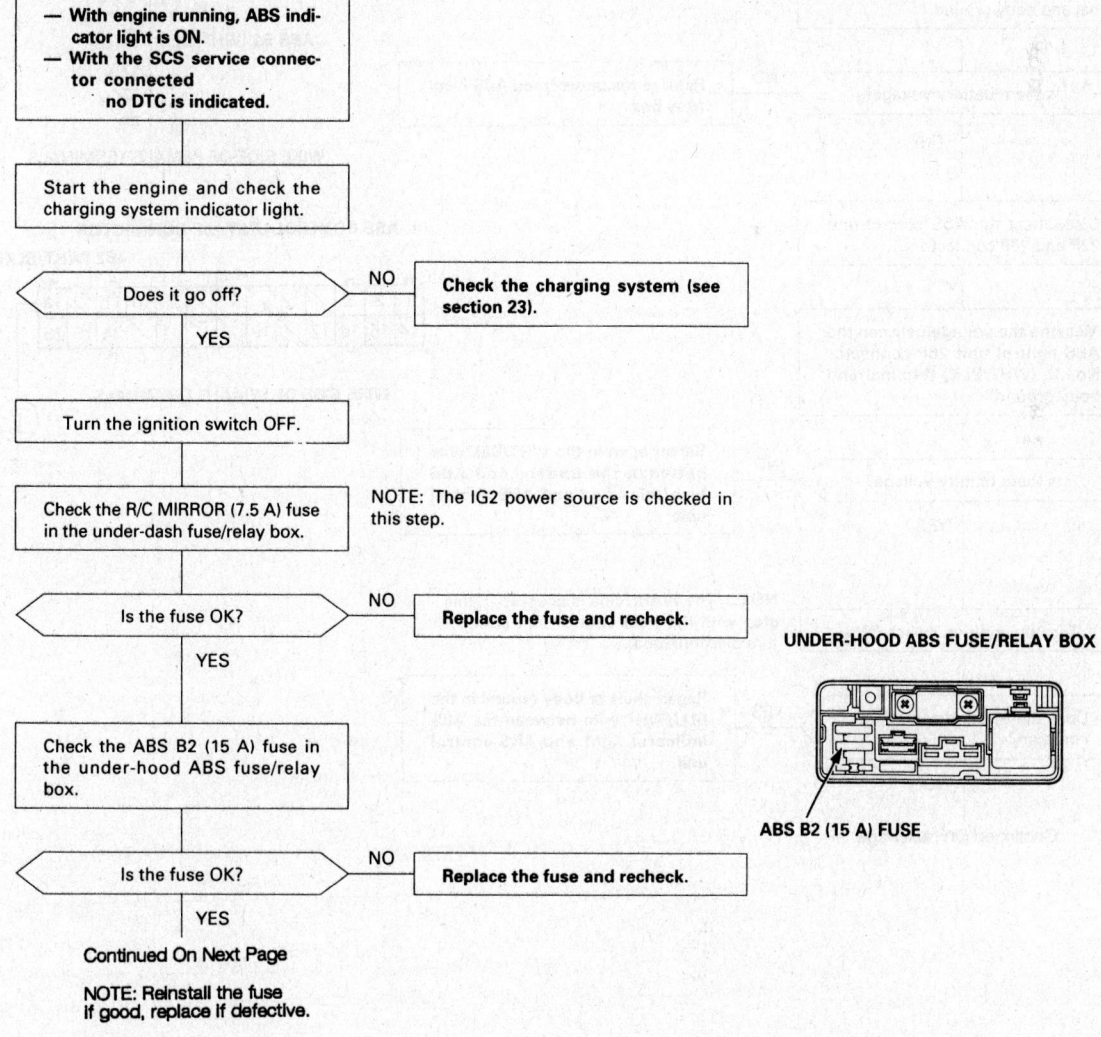

- With engine running, ABS indicator light is ON.
- With the SCS service connector connected no DTC is indicated.

Start the engine and check the charging system indicator light.

Does it go off? — NO — Check the charging system (see section 23).

YES

Turn the ignition switch OFF.

Check the R/C MIRROR (7.5 A) fuse in the under-dash fuse/relay box.

NOTE: The IG2 power source is checked in this step.

Is the fuse OK? — NO — Replace the fuse and recheck.

YES

Check the ABS B2 (15 A) fuse in the under-hood ABS fuse/relay box.

UNDER-HOOD ABS FUSE/RELAY BOX

ABS B2 (15 A) FUSE

Is the fuse OK? — NO — Replace the fuse and recheck.

YES

Continued On Next Page

NOTE: Reinstall the fuse if good, replace if defective.

NO DTC (2 OF 3)
ABS INDICATOR LIGHT DOES NOT GO OFF

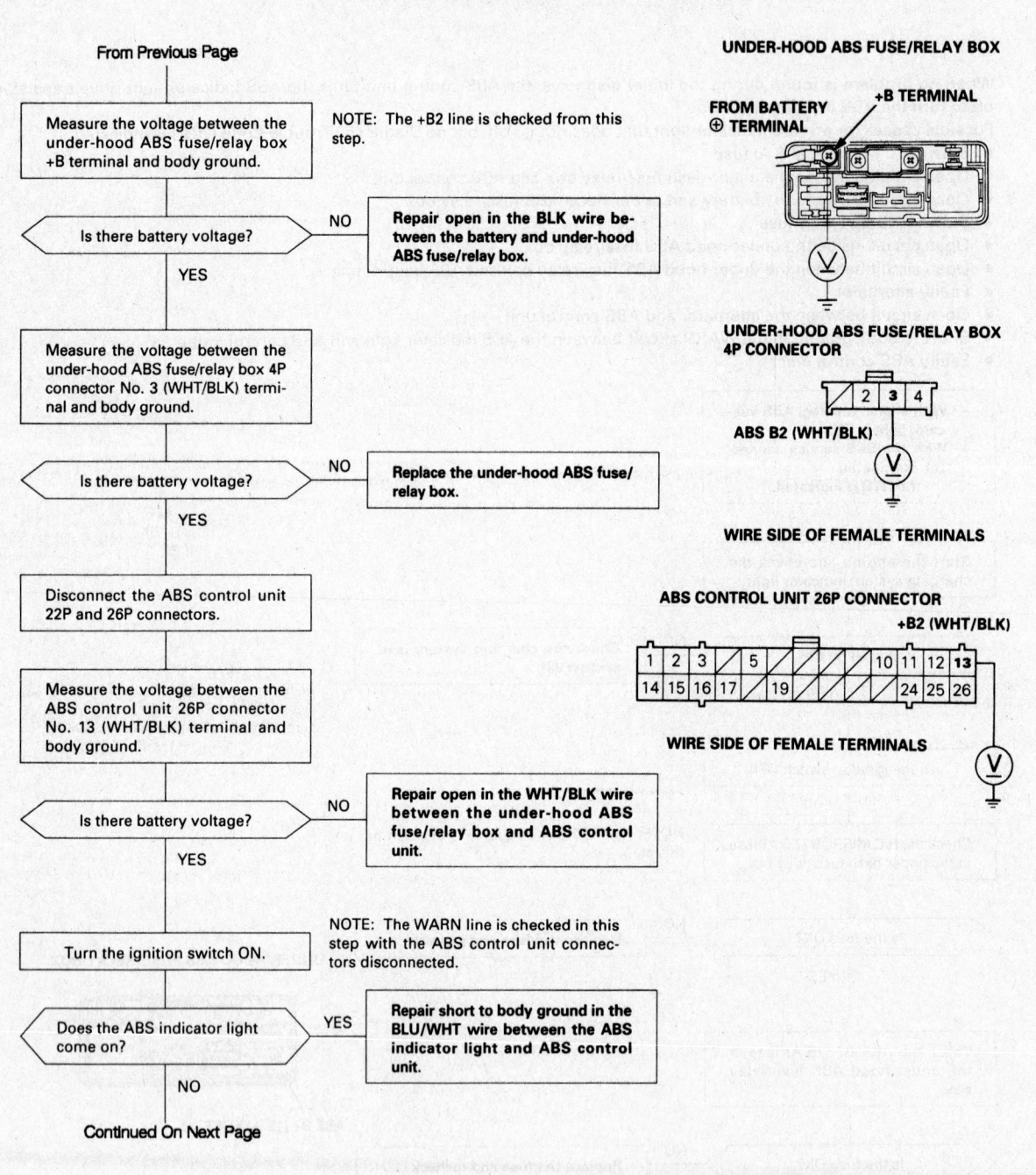

From Previous Page

Measure the voltage between the under-hood ABS fuse/relay box +B terminal and body ground.

NOTE: The +B2 line is checked from this step.

Is there battery voltage? — NO → Repair open in the BLK wire between the battery and under-hood ABS fuse/relay box.

YES

Measure the voltage between the under-hood ABS fuse/relay box 4P connector No. 3 (WHT/BLK) terminal and body ground.

Is there battery voltage? — NO → Replace the under-hood ABS fuse/relay box.

YES

Disconnect the ABS control unit 22P and 26P connectors.

Measure the voltage between the ABS control unit 26P connector No. 13 (WHT/BLK) terminal and body ground.

Is there battery voltage? — NO → Repair open in the WHT/BLK wire between the under-hood ABS fuse/relay box and ABS control unit.

YES

Turn the ignition switch ON.

NOTE: The WARN line is checked in this step with the ABS control unit connectors disconnected.

Does the ABS indicator light come on? — YES → Repair short to body ground in the BLU/WHT wire between the ABS indicator light and ABS control unit.

NO

Continued On Next Page

UNDER-HOOD ABS FUSE/RELAY BOX

FROM BATTERY ⊕ TERMINAL   +B TERMINAL

UNDER-HOOD ABS FUSE/RELAY BOX 4P CONNECTOR

2 3 4

ABS B2 (WHT/BLK)

WIRE SIDE OF FEMALE TERMINALS

ABS CONTROL UNIT 26P CONNECTOR
+B2 (WHT/BLK)

1 2 3   5   10 11 12 13
14 15 16 17   19   24 25 26

WIRE SIDE OF FEMALE TERMINALS

NO DTC (3 OF 3)
ABS INDICATOR LIGHT DOES NOT GO OFF

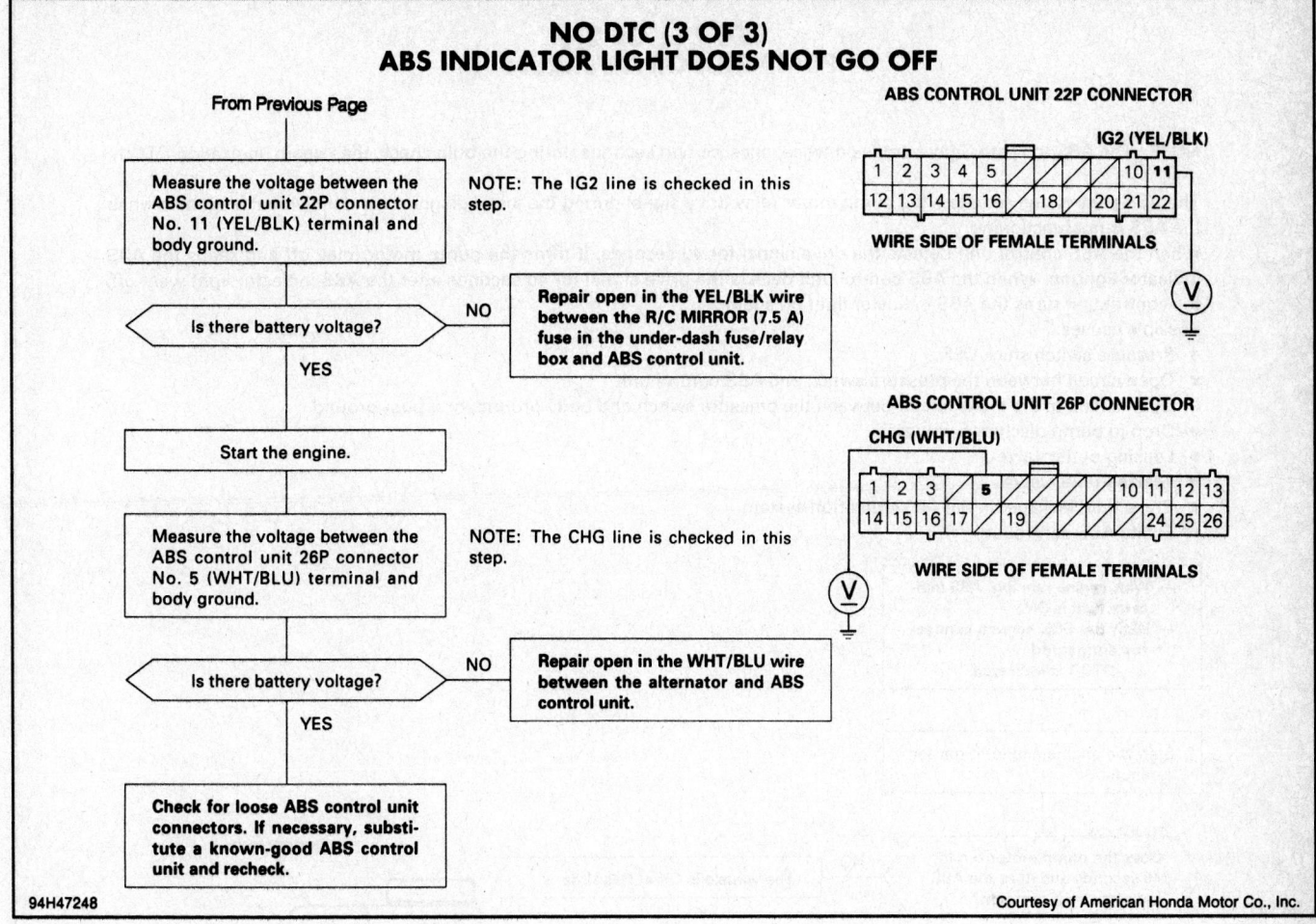

From Previous Page

Measure the voltage between the ABS control unit 22P connector No. 11 (YEL/BLK) terminal and body ground.

NOTE: The IG2 line is checked in this step.

Is there battery voltage?

NO → Repair open in the YEL/BLK wire between the R/C MIRROR (7.5 A) fuse in the under-dash fuse/relay box and ABS control unit.

YES

Start the engine.

Measure the voltage between the ABS control unit 26P connector No. 5 (WHT/BLU) terminal and body ground.

NOTE: The CHG line is checked in this step.

Is there battery voltage?

NO → Repair open in the WHT/BLU wire between the alternator and ABS control unit.

YES

Check for loose ABS control unit connectors. If necessary, substitute a known-good ABS control unit and recheck.

ABS CONTROL UNIT 22P CONNECTOR

IG2 (YEL/BLK)

| 1 | 2 | 3 | 4 | 5 | | | | 10 | 11 |
| 12 | 13 | 14 | 15 | 16 | | 18 | | 20 | 21 | 22 |

WIRE SIDE OF FEMALE TERMINALS

ABS CONTROL UNIT 26P CONNECTOR

CHG (WHT/BLU)

| 1 | 2 | 3 | | 5 | | | | 10 | 11 | 12 | 13 |
| 14 | 15 | 16 | 17 | | 19 | | | | 24 | 25 | 26 |

WIRE SIDE OF FEMALE TERMINALS

94H47248

DTC 1 (1 OF 2)
PUMP MOTOR OVERRUN

NOTE: The ABS indicator light comes on twice; once for two seconds during the bulb check, then again, indicating DTC 1.

The ABS control unit monitors the pump motor relay drive signal during the initial diagnosis and individual diagnosis when the ABS is not functioning.

When the ABS control unit detects the drive signal for 40 seconds, it turns the pump motor relay off and keeps the ABS indicator light on. When the ABS control unit detects the drive signal for 40 seconds after the ABS indicator light went off, the control unit turns the ABS indicator light on again.

Possible causes:
- Pressure switch stuck OFF
- Open circuit between the pressure switch and ABS control unit
- Open circuit in the P-SW circuit between the pressure switch and body ground, or a poor ground
- Drop in pump discharge volume
- Leaking outlet valve
- Leaking relief valve
- Brake fluid leakage on the ABS operation system
- Faulty ABS control unit

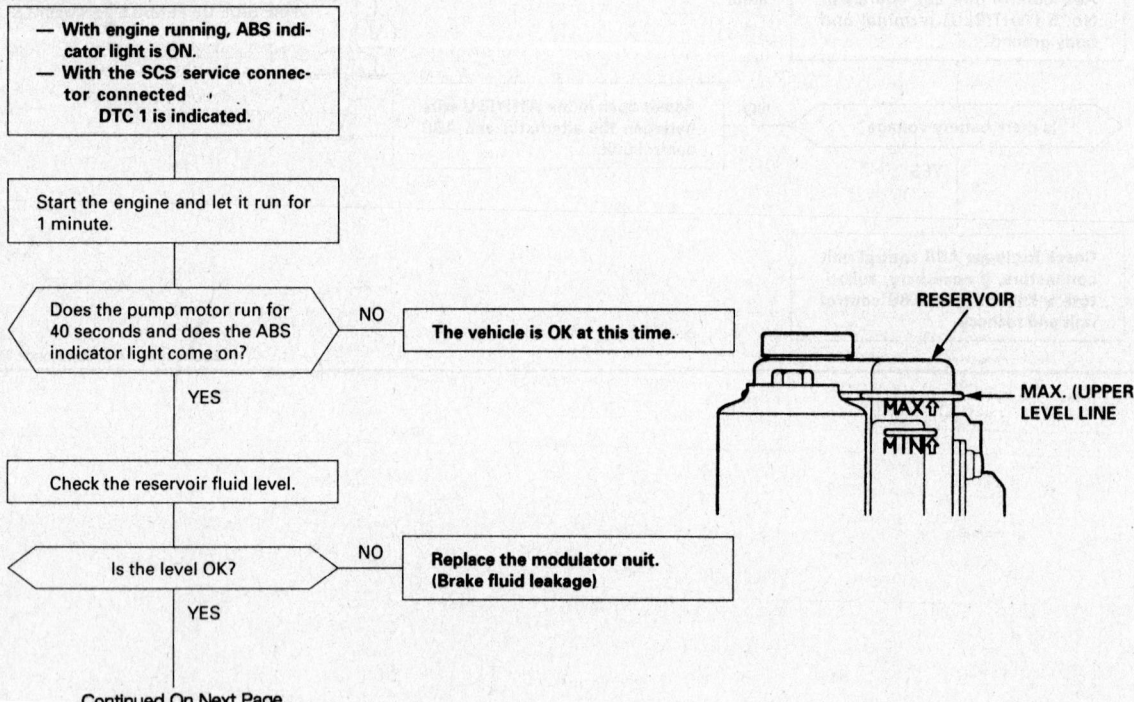

— With engine running, ABS indicator light is ON.
— With the SCS service connector connected
   DTC 1 is indicated.

Start the engine and let it run for 1 minute.

Does the pump motor run for 40 seconds and does the ABS indicator light come on? → NO → The vehicle is OK at this time.

YES

Check the reservoir fluid level.

Is the level OK? → NO → Replace the modulator nuit. (Brake fluid leakage)

YES

RESERVOIR

MAX⇧
MIN⇧

MAX. (UPPER) LEVEL LINE

Continued On Next Page

DTC 1 (2 OF 2)
PUMP MOTOR OVERRUN

From Previous Page

Turn the ignition switch OFF.

Disconnect the modulator unit 14P connector.

Check for continuity between the modulator unit 14P connector No. 4 (YEL) and No. 11 (BLK) terminals.

Is there continuity? — NO → Replace the modulator unit.
- Pressure switch stuck OFF
- Drop in pump discharge volume
- Leaking outlet valve
- Leaking releif valve

YES

Turn the ignition switch ON.

Measure the voltage between the modulator unit 14P connector No. 4 (YEL) terminal and body ground.

Is there battery voltage? — YES → Repair open in the BLK wire between the pressure switch and body ground, or poor ground.

NO

Measure the voltage between the ABS control unit 26P connector No. 19 (YEL) terminal and body ground.

Is there battery voltage? — YES → Repair open in YEL wire between the pressure switch and ABS control unit.

NO

Check for loose ABS control unit connectors. If necessary, substitute a known-good ABS control unit and recheck.

MODULATOR UNIT 14P CONNECTOR

P-SW (YEL)

1	2	3
4	5	6	7
8	9	10	11
12	13	14

GND (BLK)

Ω

WIRE SIDE OF FEMALE TERMINALS

MODULATOR UNIT 14P CONNECTOR

P-SW (YEL)

1	2	3
4	5	6	7
8	9	10	11
12	13	14

V

TERMINAL SIDE OF MALE TERMINALS

ABS CONTROL UNIT 26P CONNECTOR

| 1 | 2 | 3 | | 5 | | | | | 10 | 11 | 12 | 13 |
| 14 | 15 | 16 | 17 | | 19 | | | | 24 | 25 | 26 |

P-SW (YEL)

V

WIRE SIDE OF FEMALE TERMINALS

DTC 1-2 (1 OF 6)
PUMP MOTOR CIRCUIT

The ABS control unit checks the conditions at the pump motor relay drive (PMR) terminal and motor check (MCK) terminal during the initial diagnosis and regular diagnosis.
When the ABS control unit detects the following conditions during the diagnosis, it keeps the ABS indicator light on.
When the following conditions are detected after the ABS indicator light goes off, the ABS control unit turns the ABS indicator light on again.
- Battery voltage at the MCK terminal with an OFF signal at the PMR terminal
- 0 V at the MCK terminal with an ON signal at the PMR terminal

Possible causes:
- Open circuit or short to body ground between the R/C MIRROR (7.5 A) fuse and under-hood ABS fuse/relay box
- Open circuit or short to body ground in the PMR circuit inside the under-hood ABS fuse/relay box
- Faulty pump motor relay
- Open circuit or short to body ground in the PMR circuit between the under-hood ABS fuse/relay box and ABS control unit
- Open circuit between the battery and under-hood ABS fuse/relay box
- Blown ABS MOTOR (40 A) fuse
- Blown ABS UNIT (10 A) fuse
- Open circuit or short to body ground in the motor drive circuit and MCK circuit inside the under-hood ABS fuse/relay box
- Open circuit or short to body ground in the MCK circuit between the under-hood ABS fuse/relay box and ABS control unit
- Open circuit or short to body ground between the under-hood ABS fuse/relay box and pump motor
- Faulty pump motor
- Open circuit between the pump motor and body ground or poor ground
- Faulty ABS control unit

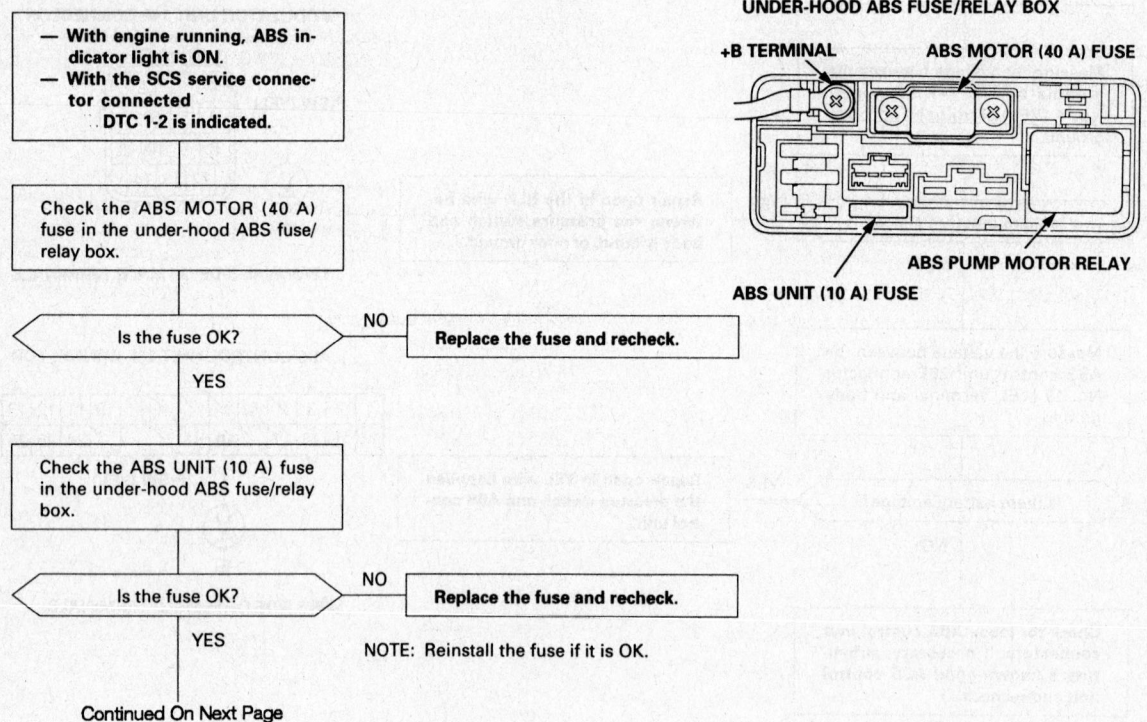

— With engine running, ABS indicator light is ON.
— With the SCS service connector connected DTC 1-2 is indicated.

Check the ABS MOTOR (40 A) fuse in the under-hood ABS fuse/relay box.

Is the fuse OK? → NO → **Replace the fuse and recheck.**

YES

Check the ABS UNIT (10 A) fuse in the under-hood ABS fuse/relay box.

Is the fuse OK? → NO → **Replace the fuse and recheck.**

YES

NOTE: Reinstall the fuse if it is OK.

Continued On Next Page

UNDER-HOOD ABS FUSE/RELAY BOX

+B TERMINAL   ABS MOTOR (40 A) FUSE

ABS PUMP MOTOR RELAY

ABS UNIT (10 A) FUSE

DTC 1-2 (2 OF 6)
PUMP MOTOR CIRCUIT

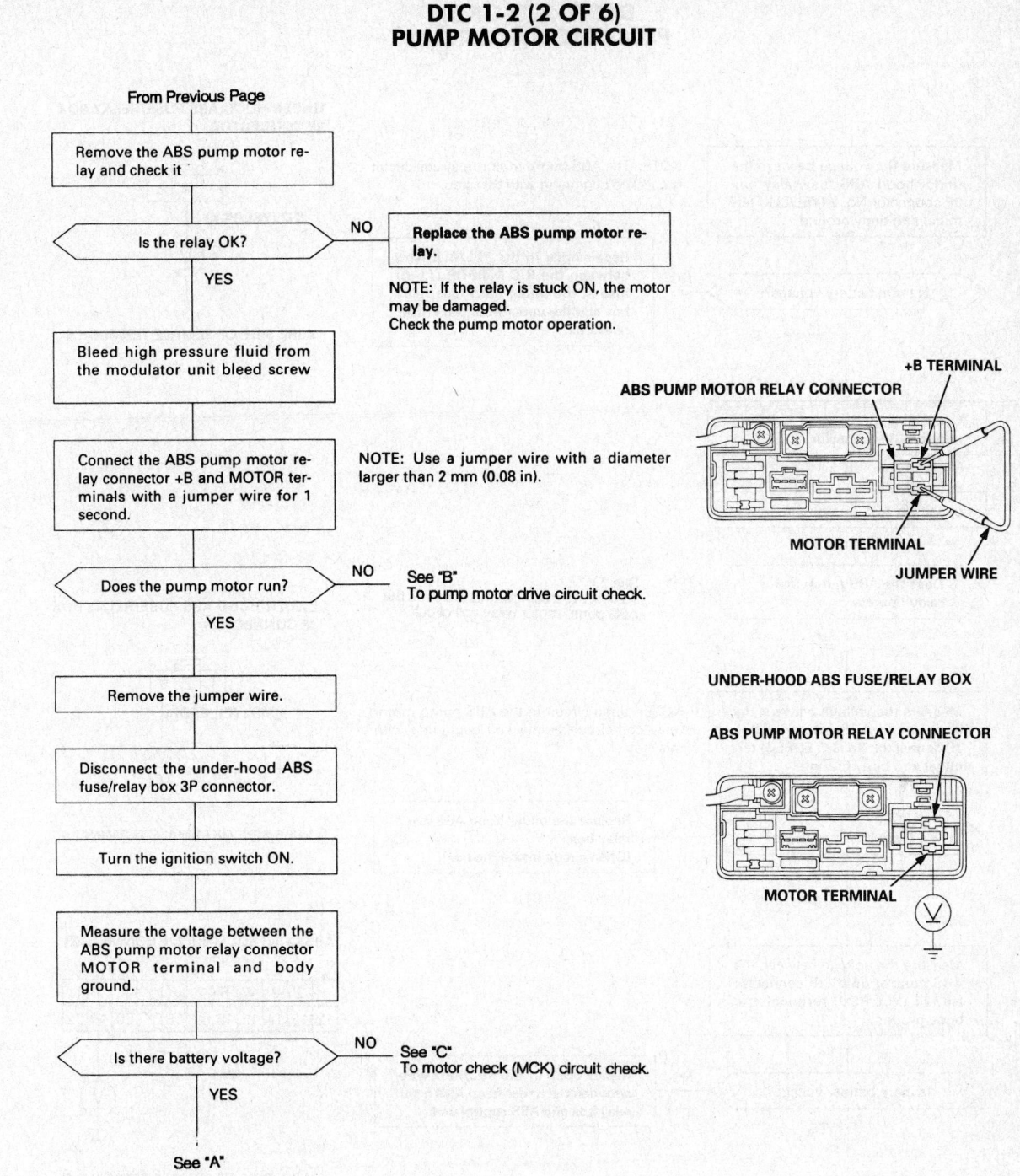

From Previous Page

Remove the ABS pump motor relay and check it

Is the relay OK? — NO → **Replace the ABS pump motor relay.**

NOTE: If the relay is stuck ON, the motor may be damaged.
Check the pump motor operation.

YES

Bleed high pressure fluid from the modulator unit bleed screw

Connect the ABS pump motor relay connector +B and MOTOR terminals with a jumper wire for 1 second.

NOTE: Use a jumper wire with a diameter larger than 2 mm (0.08 in).

+B TERMINAL

ABS PUMP MOTOR RELAY CONNECTOR

MOTOR TERMINAL

JUMPER WIRE

Does the pump motor run? — NO → See "B"
To pump motor drive circuit check.

YES

Remove the jumper wire.

Disconnect the under-hood ABS fuse/relay box 3P connector.

UNDER-HOOD ABS FUSE/RELAY BOX

ABS PUMP MOTOR RELAY CONNECTOR

Turn the ignition switch ON.

MOTOR TERMINAL

Measure the voltage between the ABS pump motor relay connector MOTOR terminal and body ground.

Is there battery voltage? — NO → See "C"
To motor check (MCK) circuit check.

YES

See "A"

DTC 1-2 (3 OF 6)
PUMP MOTOR CIRCUIT

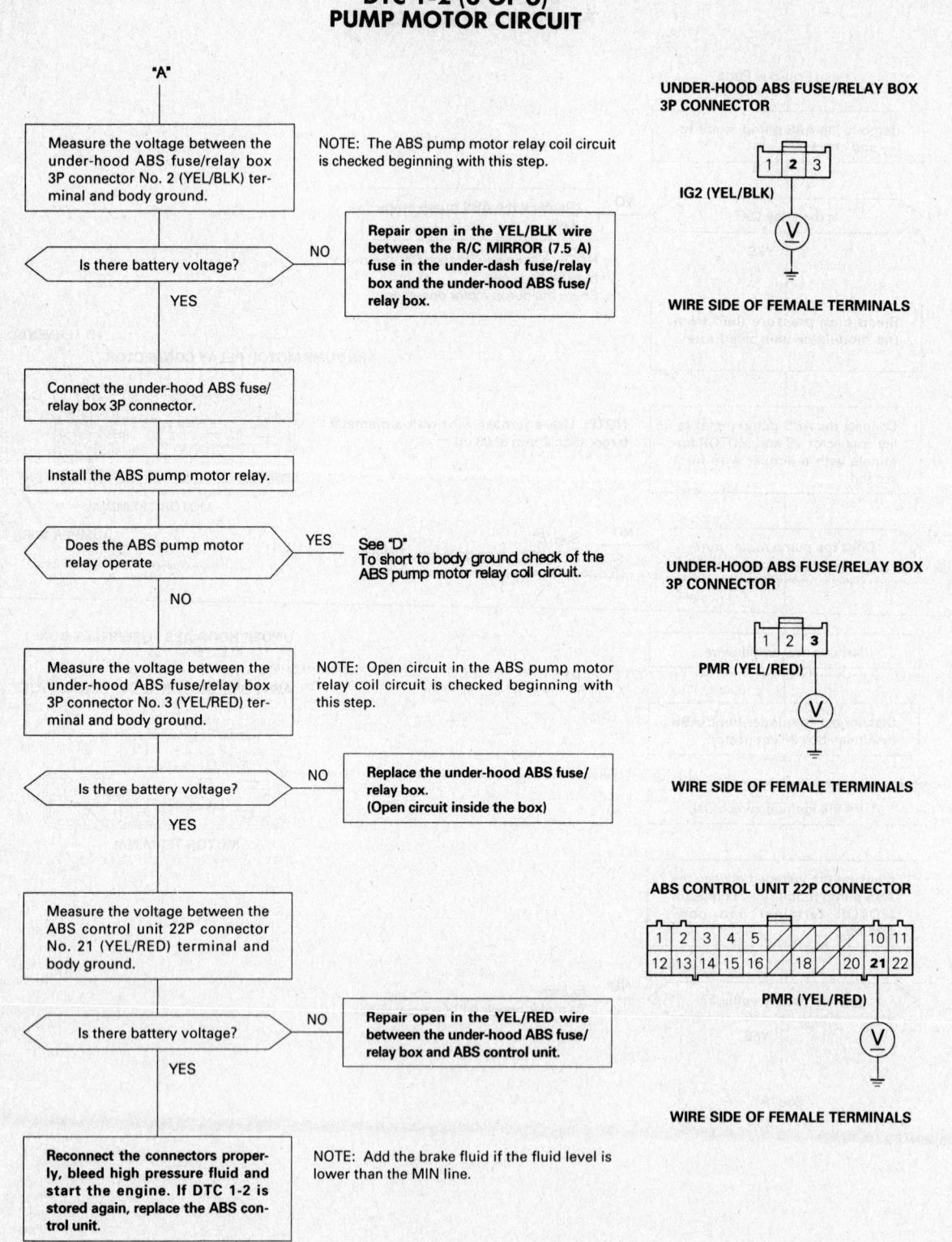

"A"

Measure the voltage between the under-hood ABS fuse/relay box 3P connector No. 2 (YEL/BLK) terminal and body ground.

NOTE: The ABS pump motor relay coil circuit is checked beginning with this step.

Is there battery voltage? — NO → Repair open in the YEL/BLK wire between the R/C MIRROR (7.5 A) fuse in the under-dash fuse/relay box and the under-hood ABS fuse/relay box.

YES

UNDER-HOOD ABS FUSE/RELAY BOX
3P CONNECTOR

| 1 | 2 | 3 |

IG2 (YEL/BLK)

WIRE SIDE OF FEMALE TERMINALS

Connect the under-hood ABS fuse/relay box 3P connector.

Install the ABS pump motor relay.

Does the ABS pump motor relay operate — YES → See "D"
To short to body ground check of the ABS pump motor relay coil circuit.

NO

Measure the voltage between the under-hood ABS fuse/relay box 3P connector No. 3 (YEL/RED) terminal and body ground.

NOTE: Open circuit in the ABS pump motor relay coil circuit is checked beginning with this step.

Is there battery voltage? — NO → Replace the under-hood ABS fuse/relay box.
(Open circuit inside the box)

YES

UNDER-HOOD ABS FUSE/RELAY BOX
3P CONNECTOR

| 1 | 2 | 3 |

PMR (YEL/RED)

WIRE SIDE OF FEMALE TERMINALS

Measure the voltage between the ABS control unit 22P connector No. 21 (YEL/RED) terminal and body ground.

Is there battery voltage? — NO → Repair open in the YEL/RED wire between the under-hood ABS fuse/relay box and ABS control unit.

YES

ABS CONTROL UNIT 22P CONNECTOR

| 1 | 2 | 3 | 4 | 5 | | | | 10 | 11 |
| 12 | 13 | 14 | 15 | 16 | | 18 | | 20 | 21 | 22 |

PMR (YEL/RED)

WIRE SIDE OF FEMALE TERMINALS

Reconnect the connectors properly, bleed high pressure fluid and start the engine. If DTC 1-2 is stored again, replace the ABS control unit.

NOTE: Add the brake fluid if the fluid level is lower than the MIN line.

DTC 1-2 (4 OF 6)
PUMP MOTOR CIRCUIT

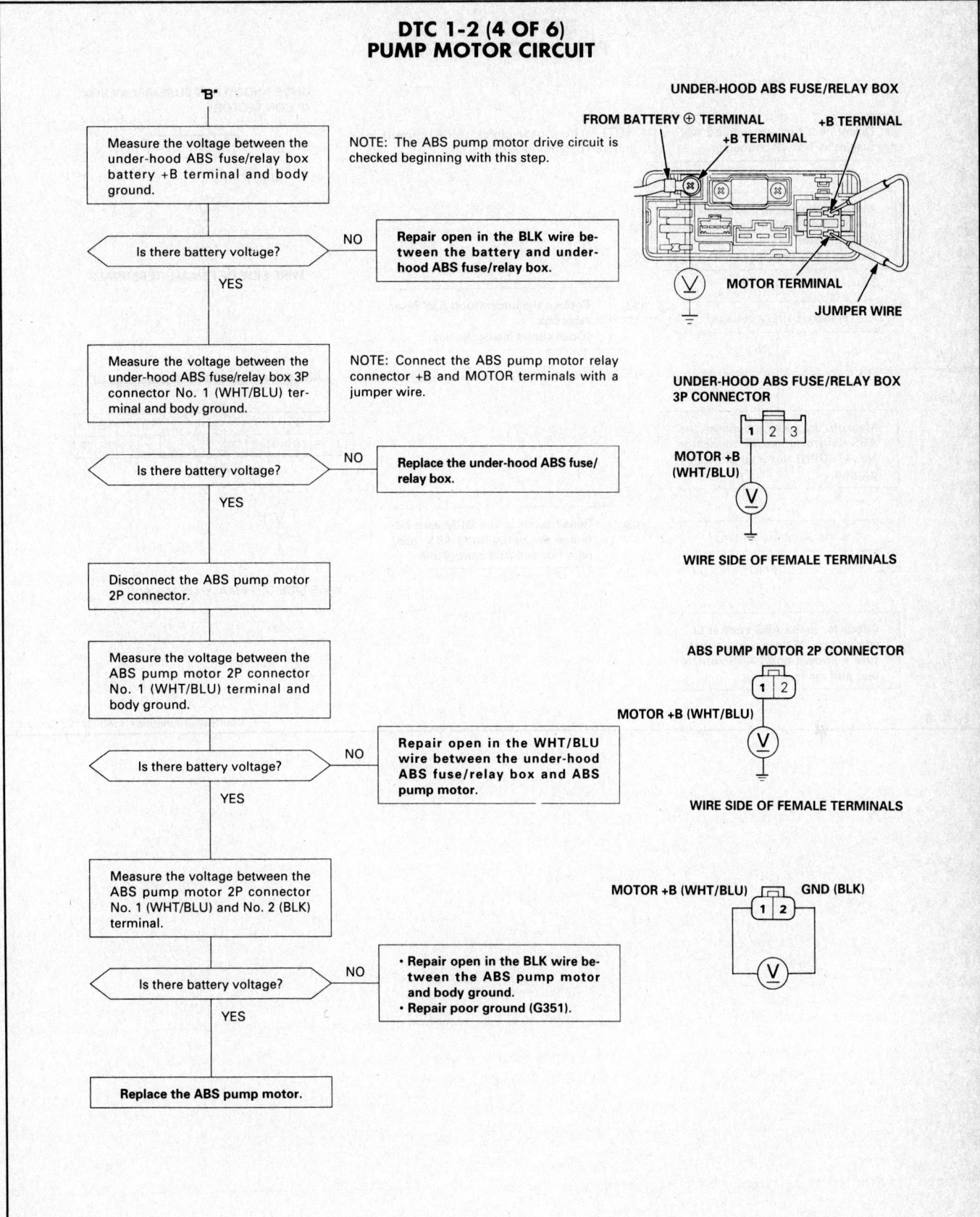

"B"

Measure the voltage between the under-hood ABS fuse/relay box battery +B terminal and body ground.

NOTE: The ABS pump motor drive circuit is checked beginning with this step.

Is there battery voltage? — NO → Repair open in the BLK wire between the battery and under-hood ABS fuse/relay box.

YES

UNDER-HOOD ABS FUSE/RELAY BOX

FROM BATTERY ⊕ TERMINAL   +B TERMINAL
+B TERMINAL
MOTOR TERMINAL
JUMPER WIRE

Measure the voltage between the under-hood ABS fuse/relay box 3P connector No. 1 (WHT/BLU) terminal and body ground.

NOTE: Connect the ABS pump motor relay connector +B and MOTOR terminals with a jumper wire.

Is there battery voltage? — NO → Replace the under-hood ABS fuse/relay box.

YES

UNDER-HOOD ABS FUSE/RELAY BOX 3P CONNECTOR

MOTOR +B (WHT/BLU)

WIRE SIDE OF FEMALE TERMINALS

Disconnect the ABS pump motor 2P connector.

Measure the voltage between the ABS pump motor 2P connector No. 1 (WHT/BLU) terminal and body ground.

Is there battery voltage? — NO → Repair open in the WHT/BLU wire between the under-hood ABS fuse/relay box and ABS pump motor.

YES

ABS PUMP MOTOR 2P CONNECTOR

MOTOR +B (WHT/BLU)

WIRE SIDE OF FEMALE TERMINALS

Measure the voltage between the ABS pump motor 2P connector No. 1 (WHT/BLU) and No. 2 (BLK) terminal.

Is there battery voltage? — NO → • Repair open in the BLK wire between the ABS pump motor and body ground.
• Repair poor ground (G351).

YES

MOTOR +B (WHT/BLU)   GND (BLK)

Replace the ABS pump motor.

94G47254

Courtesy of American Honda Motor Co., Inc.

DTC 1-2 (5 OF 6)
PUMP MOTOR CIRCUIT

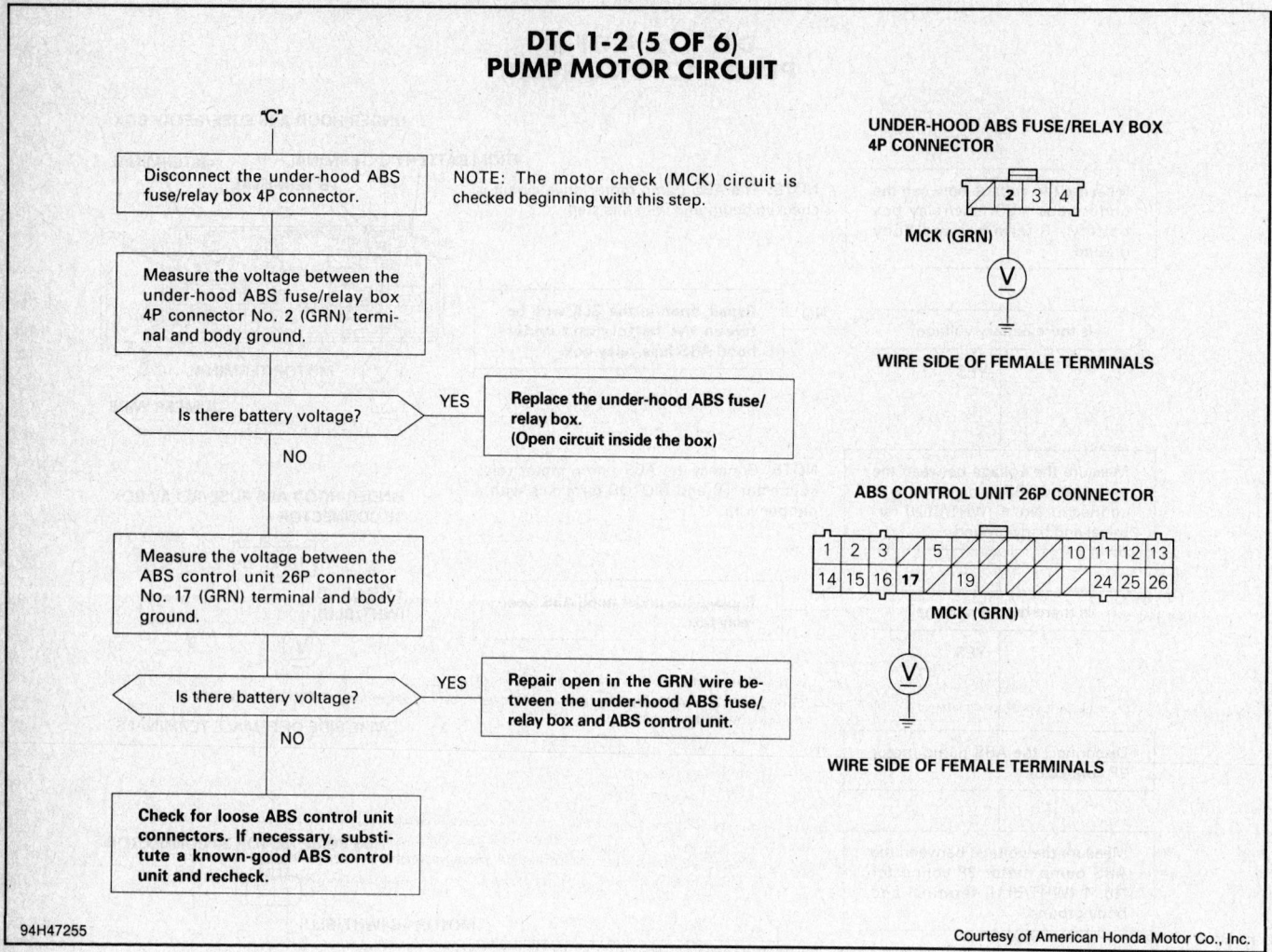

"C"

Disconnect the under-hood ABS fuse/relay box 4P connector.

Measure the voltage between the under-hood ABS fuse/relay box 4P connector No. 2 (GRN) terminal and body ground.

Is there battery voltage?

YES → Replace the under-hood ABS fuse/relay box. (Open circuit inside the box)

NO

Measure the voltage between the ABS control unit 26P connector No. 17 (GRN) terminal and body ground.

Is there battery voltage?

YES → Repair open in the GRN wire between the under-hood ABS fuse/relay box and ABS control unit.

NO

Check for loose ABS control unit connectors. If necessary, substitute a known-good ABS control unit and recheck.

NOTE: The motor check (MCK) circuit is checked beginning with this step.

UNDER-HOOD ABS FUSE/RELAY BOX
4P CONNECTOR

2 3 4

MCK (GRN)

WIRE SIDE OF FEMALE TERMINALS

ABS CONTROL UNIT 26P CONNECTOR

1 2 3   5   10 11 12 13
14 15 16 **17**   19   24 25 26

MCK (GRN)

WIRE SIDE OF FEMALE TERMINALS

94H47255

DTC 1-2 (6 OF 6)
PUMP MOTOR CIRCUIT

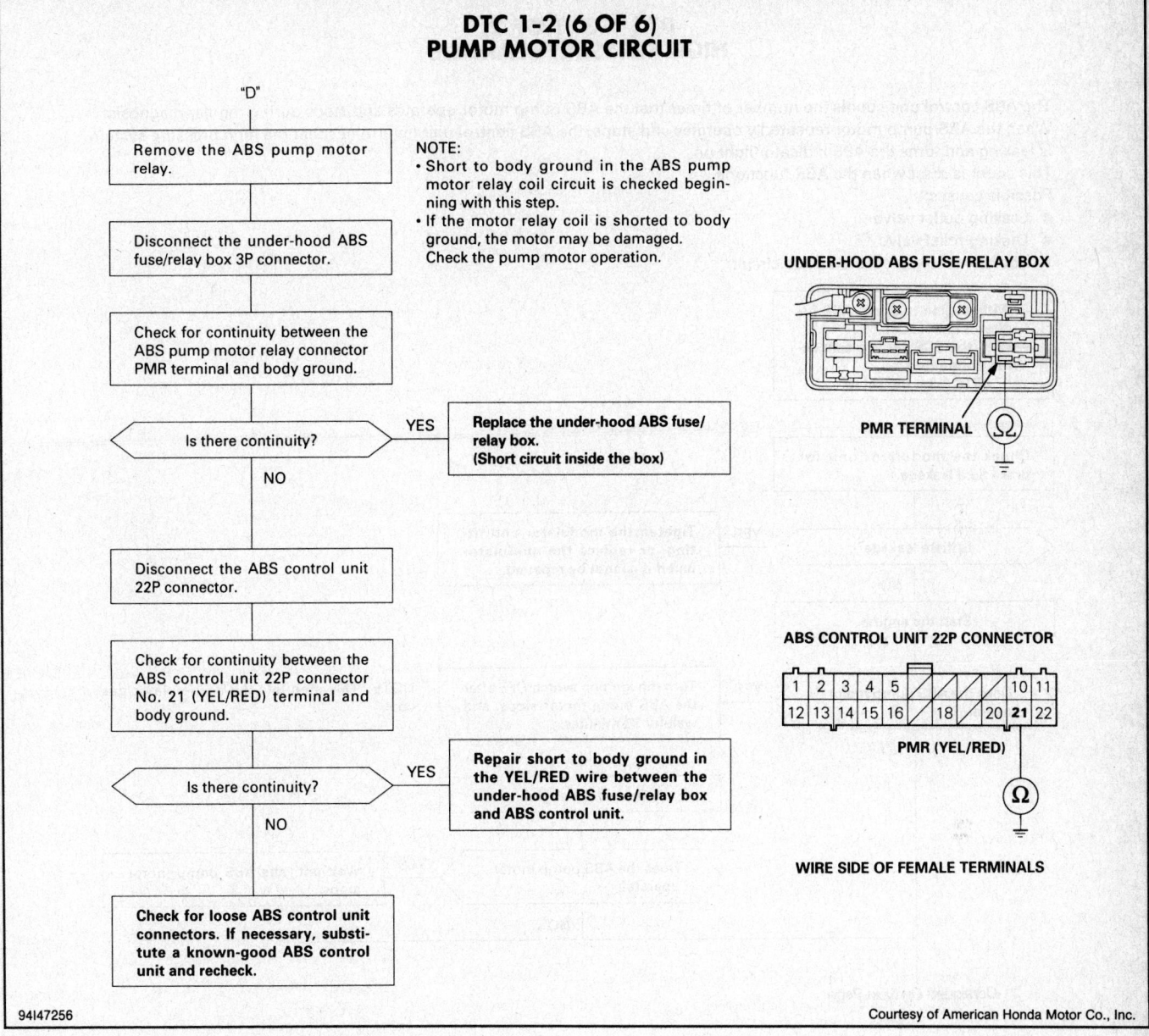

"D"

Remove the ABS pump motor relay.

Disconnect the under-hood ABS fuse/relay box 3P connector.

Check for continuity between the ABS pump motor relay connector PMR terminal and body ground.

Is there continuity? — YES → Replace the under-hood ABS fuse/relay box. (Short circuit inside the box)

NO

Disconnect the ABS control unit 22P connector.

Check for continuity between the ABS control unit 22P connector No. 21 (YEL/RED) terminal and body ground.

Is there continuity? — YES → Repair short to body ground in the YEL/RED wire between the under-hood ABS fuse/relay box and ABS control unit.

NO

Check for loose ABS control unit connectors. If necessary, substitute a known-good ABS control unit and recheck.

NOTE:
• Short to body ground in the ABS pump motor relay coil circuit is checked beginning with this step.
• If the motor relay coil is shorted to body ground, the motor may be damaged. Check the pump motor operation.

UNDER-HOOD ABS FUSE/RELAY BOX

PMR TERMINAL

ABS CONTROL UNIT 22P CONNECTOR

PMR (YEL/RED)

WIRE SIDE OF FEMALE TERMINALS

94147256

Courtesy of American Honda Motor Co., Inc.

DTC 1-3 (1 OF 2)
HIGH PRESSURE LEAKAGE

The ABS control unit counts the number of times that the ABS pump motor operates and stops during regular diagnosis. When the ABS pump motor repeatedly operates and stops, the ABS control unit determines that the high pressure system is leaking and turns the ABS indicator light on.

This count is reset when the ABS functions.

Possible causes:

- Leaking outlet valve
- Leaking relief valve
- Poor contact in pressure switch circuit

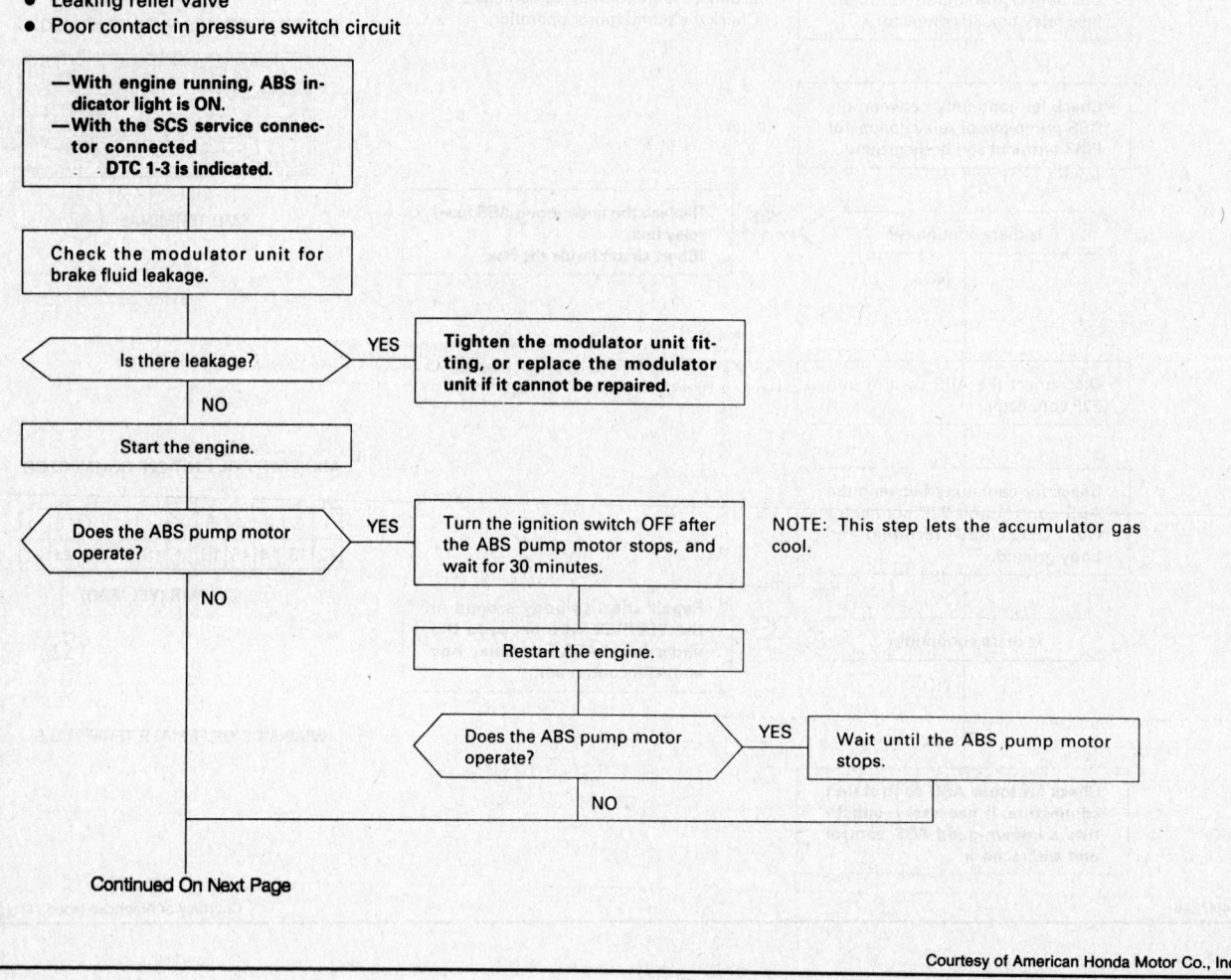

Continued On Next Page

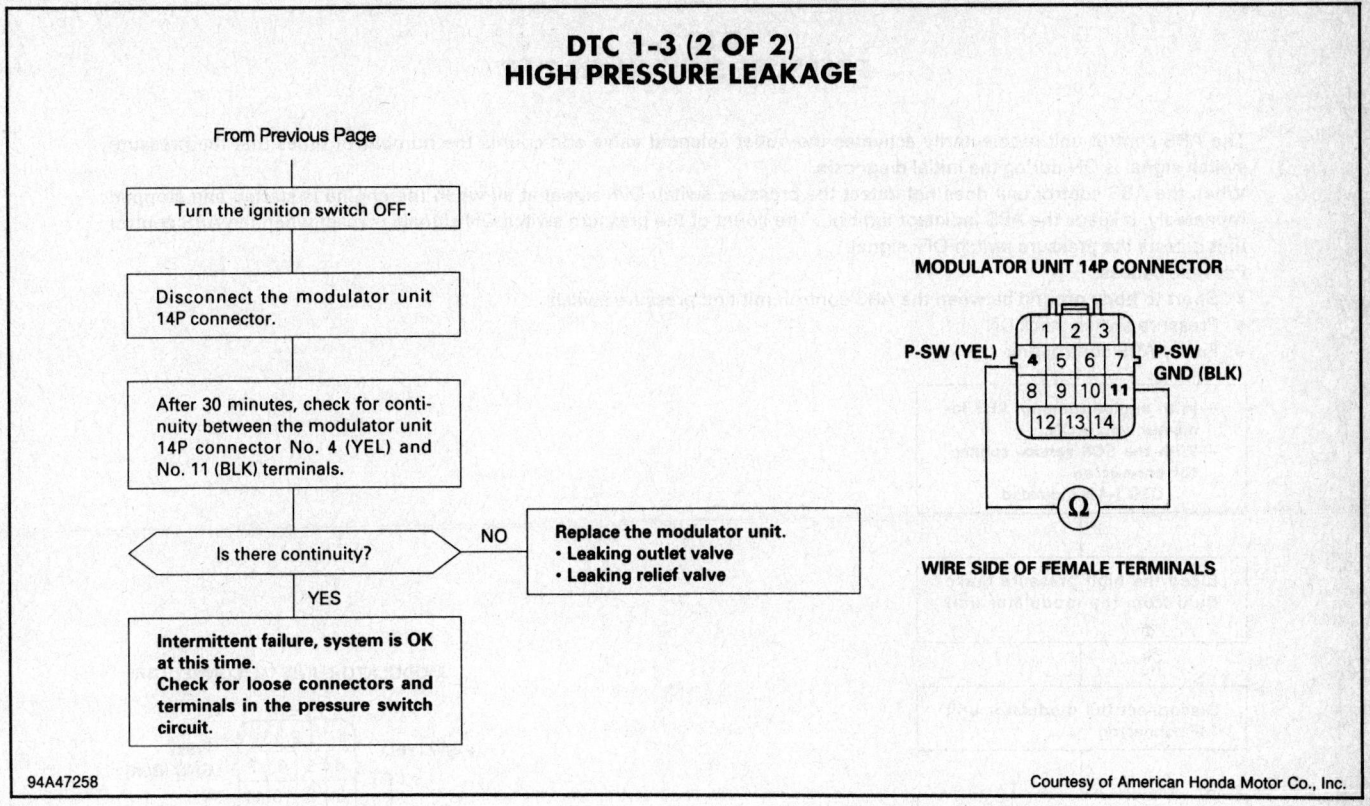

DTC 1-3 (2 OF 2)
HIGH PRESSURE LEAKAGE

From Previous Page

Turn the ignition switch OFF.

Disconnect the modulator unit 14P connector.

After 30 minutes, check for continuity between the modulator unit 14P connector No. 4 (YEL) and No. 11 (BLK) terminals.

Is there continuity? — NO → Replace the modulator unit.
• Leaking outlet valve
• Leaking relief valve

YES

Intermittent failure, system is OK at this time.
Check for loose connectors and terminals in the pressure switch circuit.

MODULATOR UNIT 14P CONNECTOR

P-SW (YEL)

P-SW GND (BLK)

1	2	3	
4	5	6	7
8	9	10	11
12	13	14	

WIRE SIDE OF FEMALE TERMINALS

94A47258

DTC 1-4
PRESSURE SWITCH CIRCUIT

The ABS control unit momentarily activates the outlet solenoid valve and counts the number of times that the pressure switch signal is ON during the initial diagnosis.

When the ABS control unit does not detect the pressure switch OFF signal at all when the engine is started and stopped repeatedly, it keeps the ABS indicator light on. The count of the pressure switch ON signals is reset when the ABS control unit detects the pressure switch OFF signal.

Possible causes:

- Short to body ground between the ABS control unit and pressure switch
- Pressure switch stuck ON
- Faulty ABS control unit

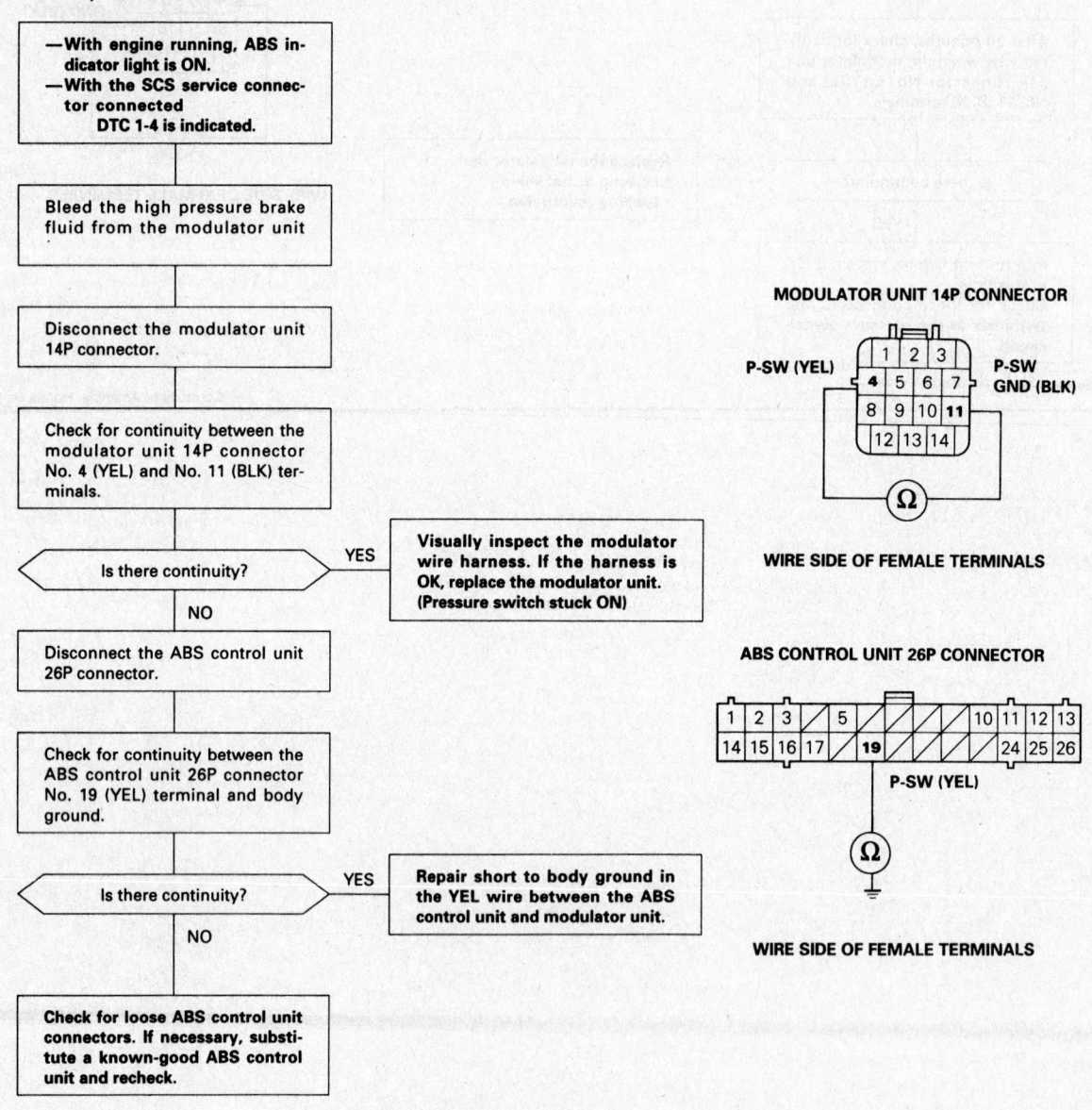

—With engine running, ABS indicator light is ON.
—With the SCS service connector connected
   DTC 1-4 is indicated.

Bleed the high pressure brake fluid from the modulator unit.

Disconnect the modulator unit 14P connector.

Check for continuity between the modulator unit 14P connector No. 4 (YEL) and No. 11 (BLK) terminals.

Is there continuity?

YES — Visually inspect the modulator wire harness. If the harness is OK, replace the modulator unit. (Pressure switch stuck ON)

NO

Disconnect the ABS control unit 26P connector.

Check for continuity between the ABS control unit 26P connector No. 19 (YEL) terminal and body ground.

Is there continuity?

YES — Repair short to body ground in the YEL wire between the ABS control unit and modulator unit.

NO

Check for loose ABS control unit connectors. If necessary, substitute a known-good ABS control unit and recheck.

MODULATOR UNIT 14P CONNECTOR

P-SW (YEL)   P-SW GND (BLK)

WIRE SIDE OF FEMALE TERMINALS

ABS CONTROL UNIT 26P CONNECTOR

P-SW (YEL)

WIRE SIDE OF FEMALE TERMINALS

DTC 1-8
ACCUMULATOR GAS LEAKAGE

When the ABS control unit detects the pressure switch OFF signal during the initial diagnosis, it drives the ABS pump motor until the pressure switch turns ON. Then, it momentarily activates the outlet solenoid valve and monitors the pressure switch signal.

The ABS control unit keeps the ABS indicator light on if it detects the pressure switch OFF signal at this time.

Possible causes:

- Accumulator gas leakage
- Changed relief valve set pressure
- Rear outlet solenoid valve late to close
- Changed pressure switch set pressure

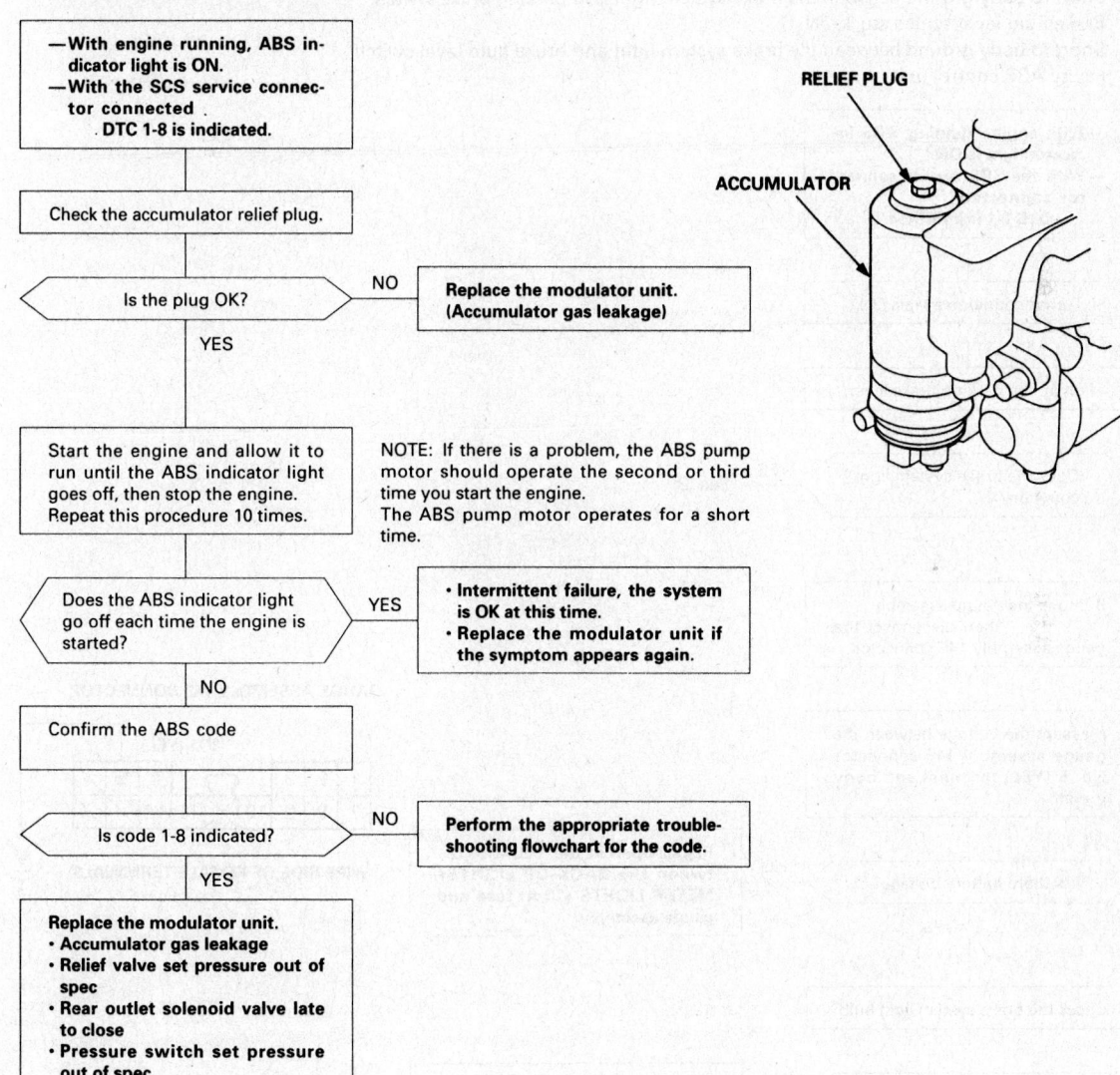

—With engine running, ABS indicator light is ON.
—With the SCS service connector connected
  DTC 1-8 is indicated.

Check the accumulator relief plug.

Is the plug OK? — NO → Replace the modulator unit. (Accumulator gas leakage)

YES

RELIEF PLUG

ACCUMULATOR

Start the engine and allow it to run until the ABS indicator light goes off, then stop the engine. Repeat this procedure 10 times.

NOTE: If there is a problem, the ABS pump motor should operate the second or third time you start the engine.
The ABS pump motor operates for a short time.

Does the ABS indicator light go off each time the engine is started? — YES →
- Intermittent failure, the system is OK at this time.
- Replace the modulator unit if the symptom appears again.

NO

Confirm the ABS code

Is code 1-8 indicated? — NO → Perform the appropriate troubleshooting flowchart for the code.

YES

Replace the modulator unit.
- Accumulator gas leakage
- Relief valve set pressure out of spec
- Rear outlet solenoid valve late to close
- Pressure switch set pressure out of spec

DTC 2-1 (1 OF 4)
PARKING BRAKE SWITCH & CIRCUIT

The ABS control unit monitors the parking brake signal during the regular diagnosis (during driving).
It turns the ABS indicator light on if it detects the parking brake ON signal for 30 seconds.
Possible causes:

- Driving with the parking brake applied
- Low fluid level in the master cylinder reservoir
- Open circuit between the BACK-UP LIGHTS/METER LIGHTS (10 A) fuse and brake system light
- Blown brake system light bulb
- Open circuit or short to body ground between the brake system light and ABS control unit
- Parking brake switch stuck ON
- Short to body ground between the brake system light and parking brake switch
- Brake fluid level switch stuck ON
- Short to body ground between the brake system light and brake fluid level switch
- Faulty ABS control unit

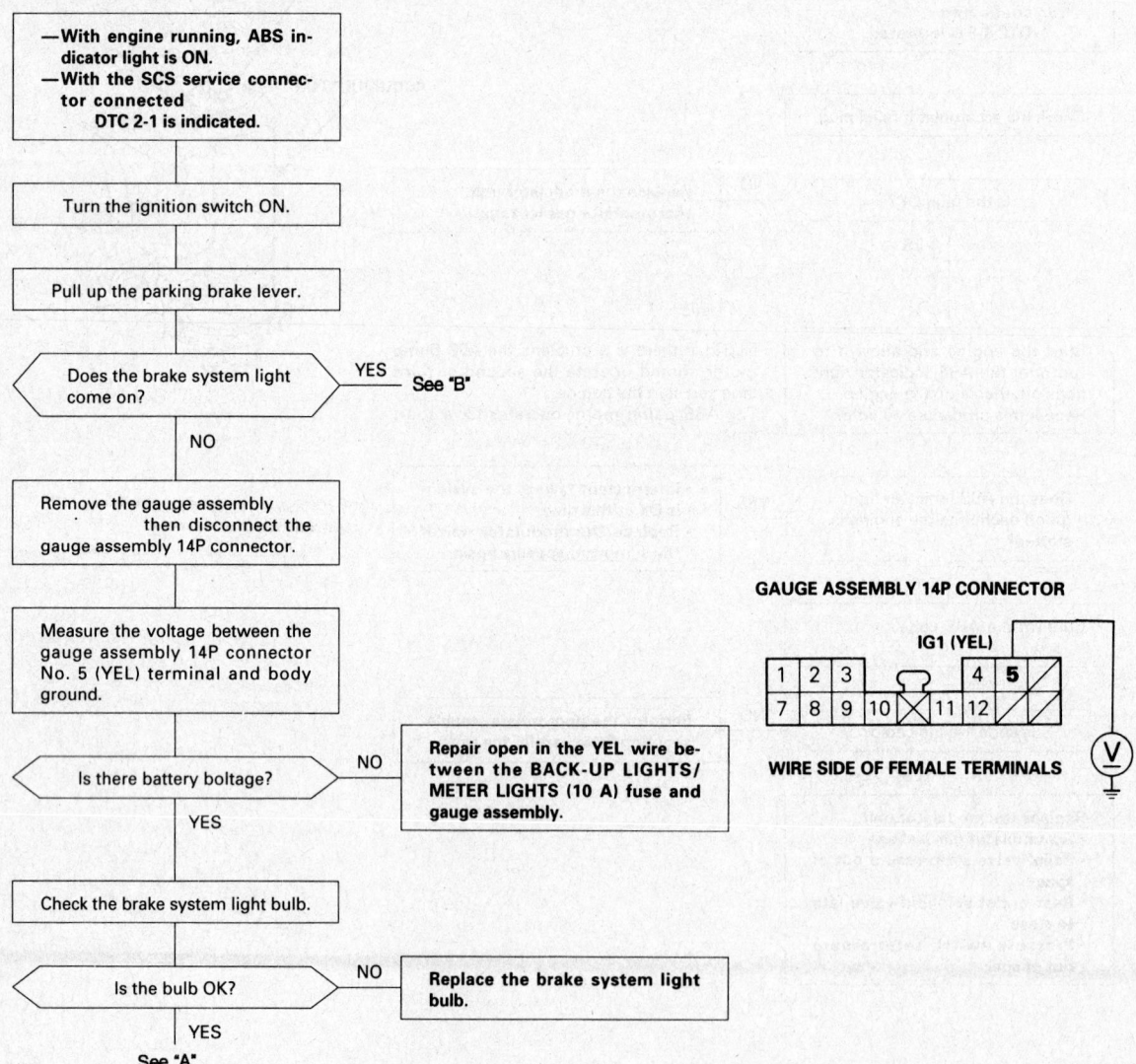

GAUGE ASSEMBLY 14P CONNECTOR

IG1 (YEL)

1	2	3			4	**5**
7	8	9	10	11	12	

WIRE SIDE OF FEMALE TERMINALS

DTC 2-1 (2 OF 4)
PARKING BRAKE SWITCH & CIRCUIT

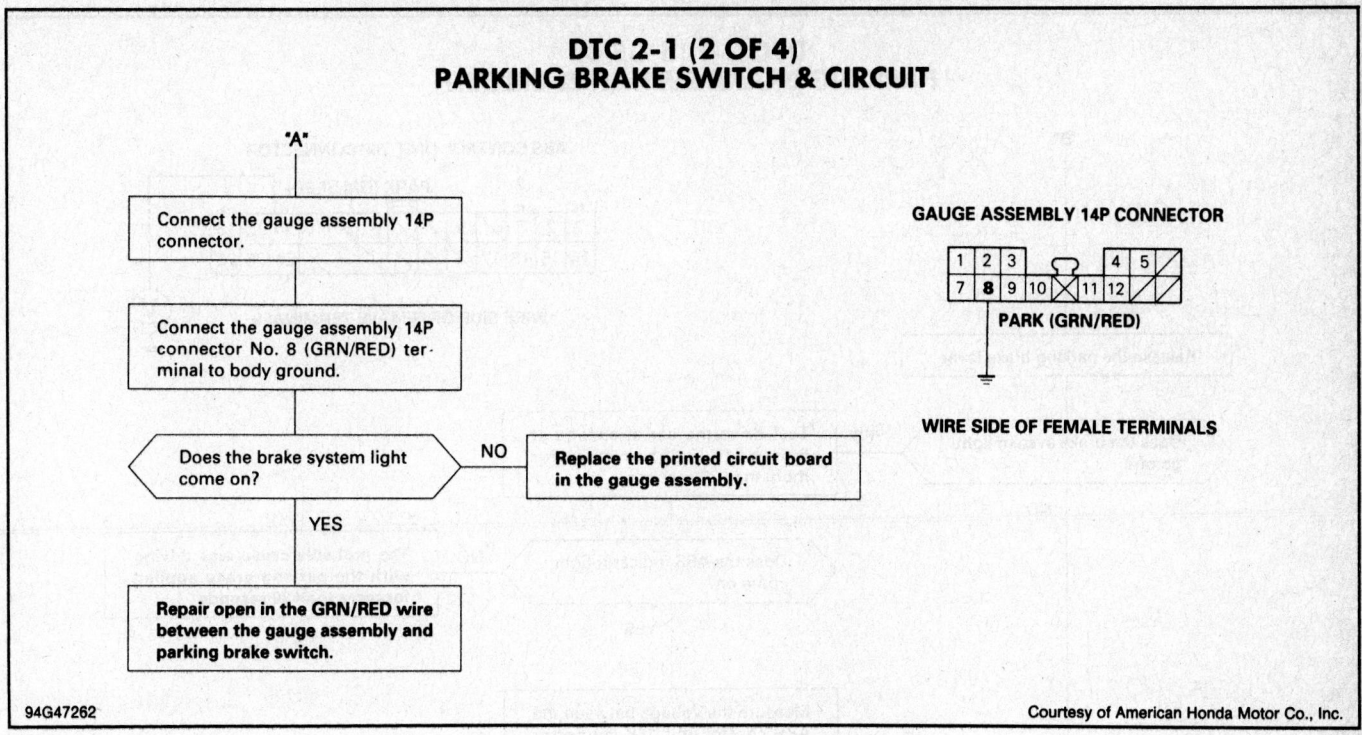

"A"

Connect the gauge assembly 14P connector.

Connect the gauge assembly 14P connector No. 8 (GRN/RED) terminal to body ground.

Does the brake system light come on? — NO → Replace the printed circuit board in the gauge assembly.

YES

Repair open in the GRN/RED wire between the gauge assembly and parking brake switch.

GAUGE ASSEMBLY 14P CONNECTOR

| 1 | 2 | 3 | | | 4 | 5 |
| 7 | **8** | 9 | 10 | | 11 | 12 |

PARK (GRN/RED)

WIRE SIDE OF FEMALE TERMINALS

94G47262

Courtesy of American Honda Motor Co., Inc.

DTC 2-1 (3 OF 4)
PARKING BRAKE SWITCH & CIRCUIT

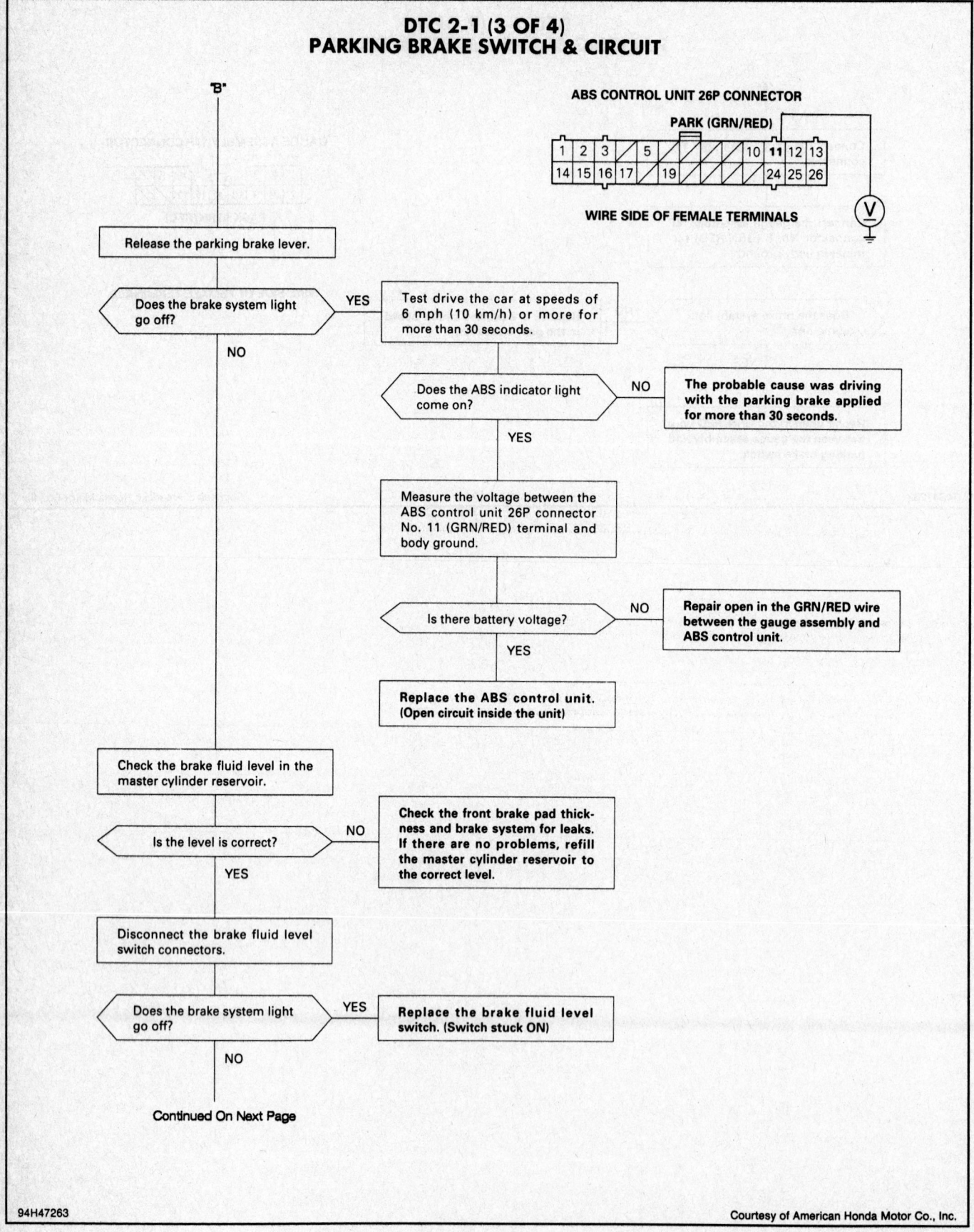

"B"

ABS CONTROL UNIT 26P CONNECTOR

PARK (GRN/RED)

| 1 | 2 | 3 | | 5 | | | 10 | **11** | 12 | 13 |
| 14 | 15 | 16 | 17 | | 19 | | | 24 | 25 | 26 |

WIRE SIDE OF FEMALE TERMINALS

Release the parking brake lever.

Does the brake system light go off? — YES → Test drive the car at speeds of 6 mph (10 km/h) or more for more than 30 seconds.

NO

Does the ABS indicator light come on? — NO → The probable cause was driving with the parking brake applied for more than 30 seconds.

YES

Measure the voltage between the ABS control unit 26P connector No. 11 (GRN/RED) terminal and body ground.

Is there battery voltage? — NO → Repair open in the GRN/RED wire between the gauge assembly and ABS control unit.

YES

Replace the ABS control unit. (Open circuit inside the unit)

Check the brake fluid level in the master cylinder reservoir.

Is the level is correct? — NO → Check the front brake pad thickness and brake system for leaks. If there are no problems, refill the master cylinder reservoir to the correct level.

YES

Disconnect the brake fluid level switch connectors.

Does the brake system light go off? — YES → Replace the brake fluid level switch. (Switch stuck ON)

NO

Continued On Next Page

DTC 2-1 (4 OF 4)
PARKING BRAKE SWITCH & CIRCUIT

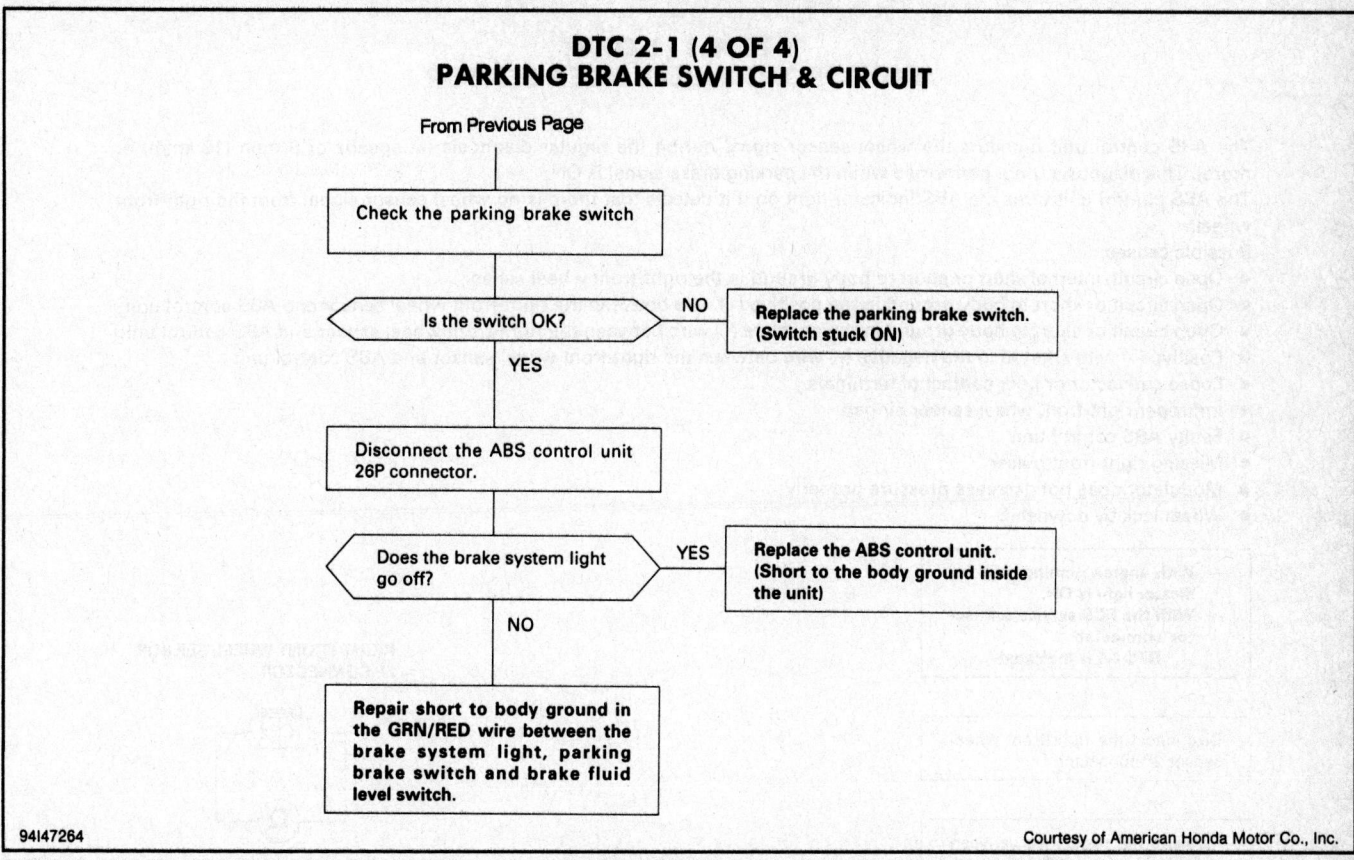

From Previous Page

Check the parking brake switch

Is the switch OK? — NO → **Replace the parking brake switch. (Switch stuck ON)**

YES

Disconnect the ABS control unit 26P connector.

Does the brake system light go off? — YES → **Replace the ABS control unit. (Short to the body ground inside the unit)**

NO

Repair short to body ground in the GRN/RED wire between the brake system light, parking brake switch and brake fluid level switch.

94I47264

Courtesy of American Honda Motor Co., Inc.

DTC 3-1 TO 3-8
PULSER DIAGNOSIS

The ABS control unit monitors the wheel sensor signals during the regular diagnosis (during driving).
It turns the ABS indicator light on if it detects a periodic change in the wheel sensor signal of each wheel caused by a chipped pulser gear, etc.
Possible causes:

- Chipped pulser gear
- Improperly installed wheel sensor

DTC		Pulser			
		Right-front	Left-front	Right-rear	Left-rear
3	1	○			
	2		○		
	4			○	
	8				○

94J47265

Courtesy of American Honda Motor Co., Inc.

DTC 3-12
DIFFERENT TIRE DIAMETER

The ABS control unit detects the wheel sensor signal speed during the regular diagnosis (during driving).
This diagnosis is not performed when the parking brake switch signal is ON.
The ABS control unit may turn the ABS indicator light on when one or more different diameter tires are installed.

94A47266

Courtesy of American Honda Motor Co., Inc.

DTC 4-1 (1 OF 3)
RIGHT FRONT WHEEL SPEED SENSOR

The ABS control unit monitors the wheel sensor signal during the regular diagnosis (at speeds of 6 mph (10 km/h) or more). This diagnosis is not performed when the parking brake signal is ON.

The ABS control unit turns the ABS indicator light on if it detects that there is no wheel sensor signal from the right-front wheel.

Possible causes:

- Open circuit, internal short or short to body ground in the right-front wheel sensor
- Open circuit or short to body ground in the positive (+) wire between the right-front wheel sensor and ABS control unit
- Open circuit or short to body ground in the negative (–) wire between the right-front wheel sensor and ABS control unit
- Positive (+) wire shorted to the negative (–) wire between the right-front wheel sensor and ABS control unit
- Loose connector or poor contact of terminals
- Improper right-front wheel sensor air gap
- Faulty ABS control unit
- Missing right-front pulser
- Modulator does not decrease pressure properly
- Wheel lock by downshift

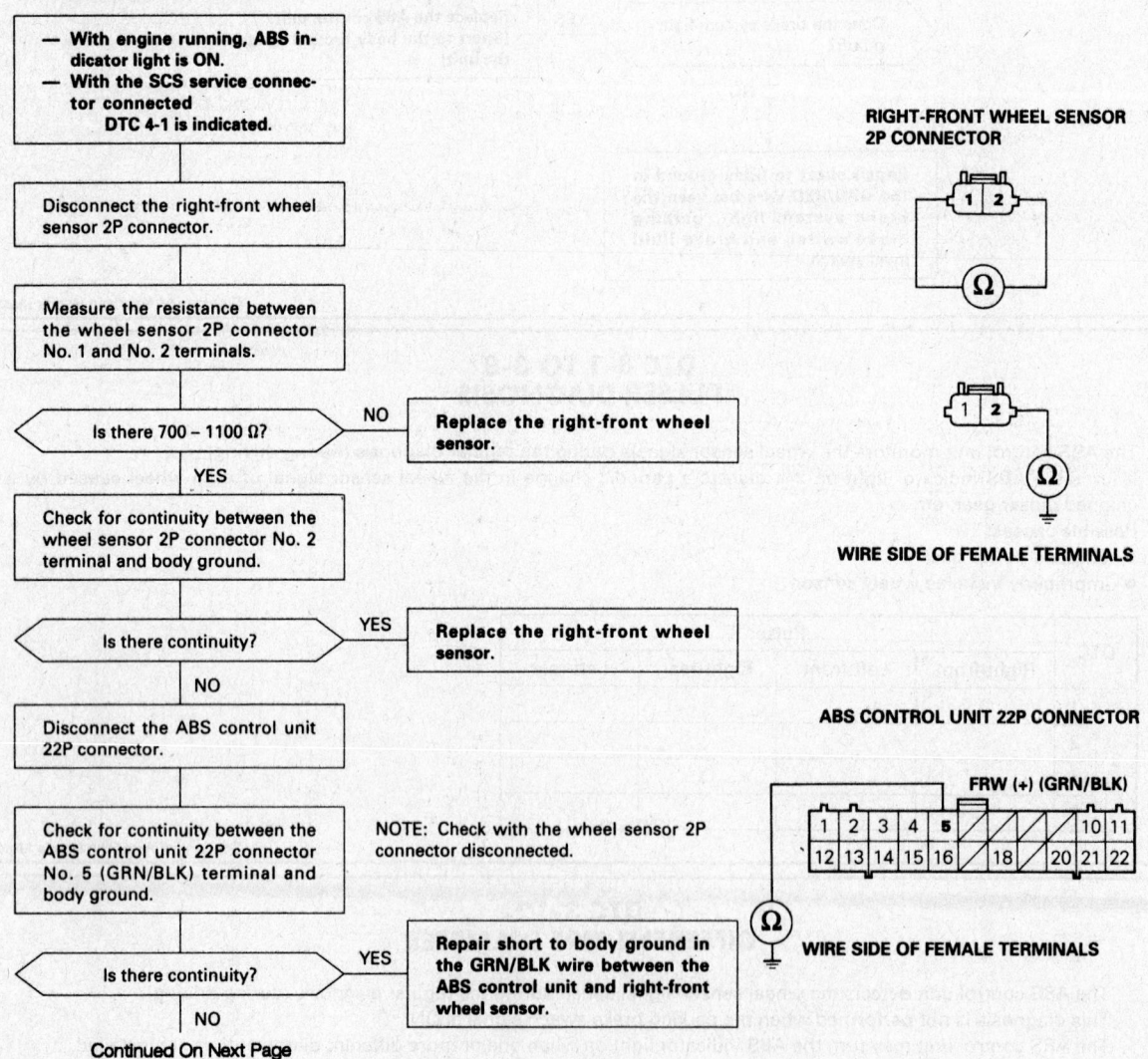

— With engine running, ABS indicator light is ON.
— With the SCS service connector connected
    DTC 4-1 is indicated.

Disconnect the right-front wheel sensor 2P connector.

Measure the resistance between the wheel sensor 2P connector No. 1 and No. 2 terminals.

Is there 700 – 1100 Ω? — NO → Replace the right-front wheel sensor.

YES

Check for continuity between the wheel sensor 2P connector No. 2 terminal and body ground.

Is there continuity? — YES → Replace the right-front wheel sensor.

NO

Disconnect the ABS control unit 22P connector.

Check for continuity between the ABS control unit 22P connector No. 5 (GRN/BLK) terminal and body ground.

NOTE: Check with the wheel sensor 2P connector disconnected.

Is there continuity? — YES → Repair short to body ground in the GRN/BLK wire between the ABS control unit and right-front wheel sensor.

NO

**RIGHT-FRONT WHEEL SENSOR
2P CONNECTOR**

1 2

Ω

1 2

Ω

WIRE SIDE OF FEMALE TERMINALS

ABS CONTROL UNIT 22P CONNECTOR

FRW (+) (GRN/BLK)

| 1 | 2 | 3 | 4 | 5 | | | 10 | 11 |
| 12 | 13 | 14 | 15 | 16 | | 18 | 20 | 21 | 22 |

Ω   **WIRE SIDE OF FEMALE TERMINALS**

Continued On Next Page

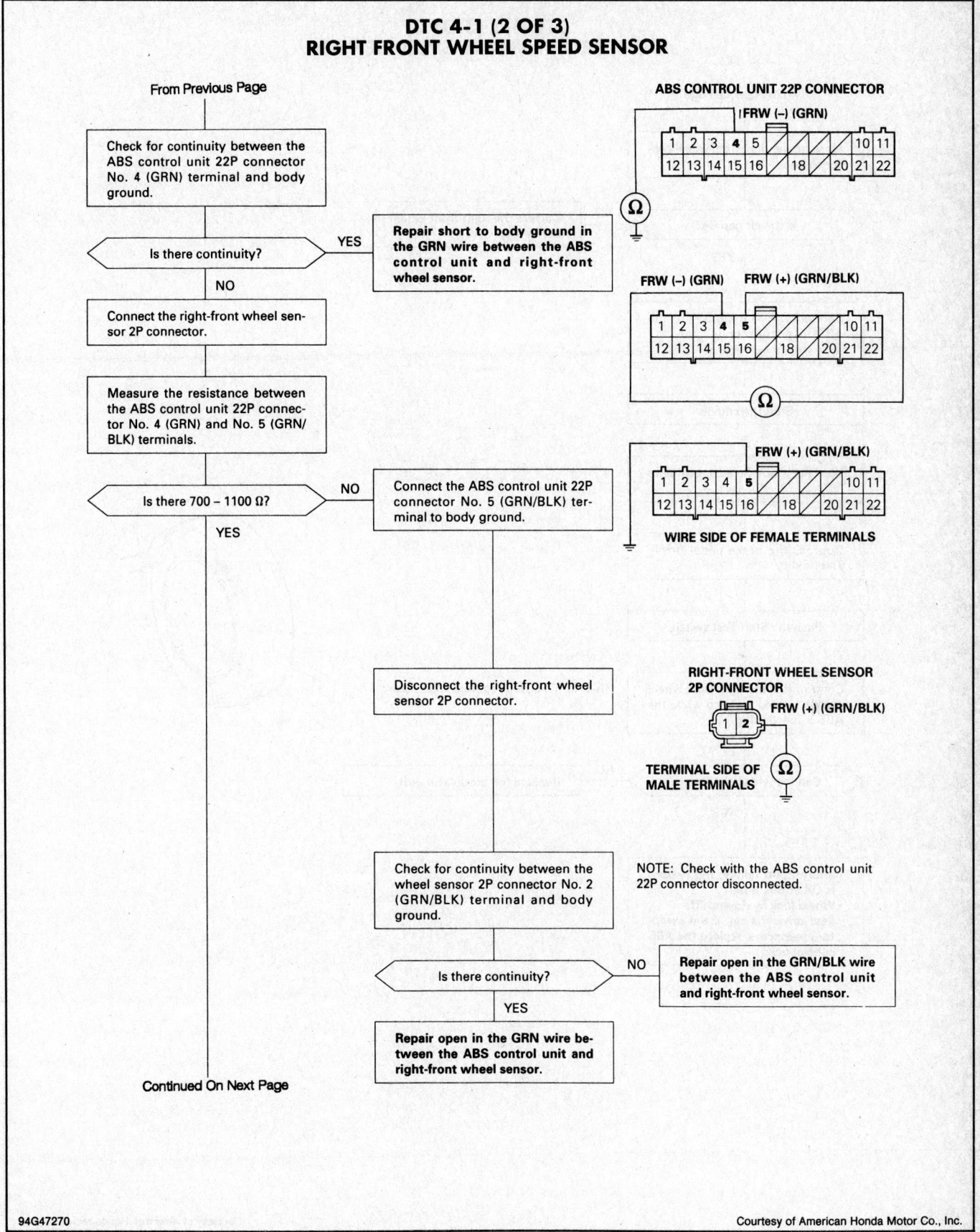

DTC 4-1 (2 OF 3)
RIGHT FRONT WHEEL SPEED SENSOR

From Previous Page

Check for continuity between the ABS control unit 22P connector No. 4 (GRN) terminal and body ground.

Is there continuity?

YES → Repair short to body ground in the GRN wire between the ABS control unit and right-front wheel sensor.

NO

Connect the right-front wheel sensor 2P connector.

Measure the resistance between the ABS control unit 22P connector No. 4 (GRN) and No. 5 (GRN/ BLK) terminals.

Is there 700 – 1100 Ω?

NO → Connect the ABS control unit 22P connector No. 5 (GRN/BLK) terminal to body ground.

YES

Disconnect the right-front wheel sensor 2P connector.

Check for continuity between the wheel sensor 2P connector No. 2 (GRN/BLK) terminal and body ground.

Is there continuity?

NO → Repair open in the GRN/BLK wire between the ABS control unit and right-front wheel sensor.

YES

Repair open in the GRN wire between the ABS control unit and right-front wheel sensor.

NOTE: Check with the ABS control unit 22P connector disconnected.

Continued On Next Page

ABS CONTROL UNIT 22P CONNECTOR

FRW (–) (GRN)

| 1 | 2 | 3 | 4 | 5 | | | | 10 | 11 |
| 12 | 13 | 14 | 15 | 16 | | 18 | | 20 | 21 | 22 |

FRW (–) (GRN)   FRW (+) (GRN/BLK)

| 1 | 2 | 3 | 4 | 5 | | | | 10 | 11 |
| 12 | 13 | 14 | 15 | 16 | | 18 | | 20 | 21 | 22 |

FRW (+) (GRN/BLK)

| 1 | 2 | 3 | 4 | 5 | | | | 10 | 11 |
| 12 | 13 | 14 | 15 | 16 | | 18 | | 20 | 21 | 22 |

WIRE SIDE OF FEMALE TERMINALS

RIGHT-FRONT WHEEL SENSOR 2P CONNECTOR

FRW (+) (GRN/BLK)

| 1 | 2 |

TERMINAL SIDE OF MALE TERMINALS

Courtesy of American Honda Motor Co., Inc.

1994 BRAKES
Anti-Lock – Accord (Cont.)

DTC 4-1 (3 OF 3)
RIGHT FRONT WHEEL SPEED SENSOR

From Previous Page

Measure the right-front wheel sensor air gap

Is the air gap OK? — NO → Correct the right-front wheel sensor air gap

YES

Connect the ALB checker to the ABS inspection connector

Start the engine.

Turn the Mode Selector switch to "5".

Depress the brake pedal firmly and hold it.

Push the Start Test switch.

Confirm that the right-front wheel can be rotated by hand while the ABS is functioning.

NOTE: This step requires an assistant.

Can the wheel be rotated? — NO → Replace the modulator unit.

YES

• Intermittent failure, the system is OK at this time.
• Wheel lock by downshift.
• Test drive the car. If the symptom reappears, replace the ABS control unit.

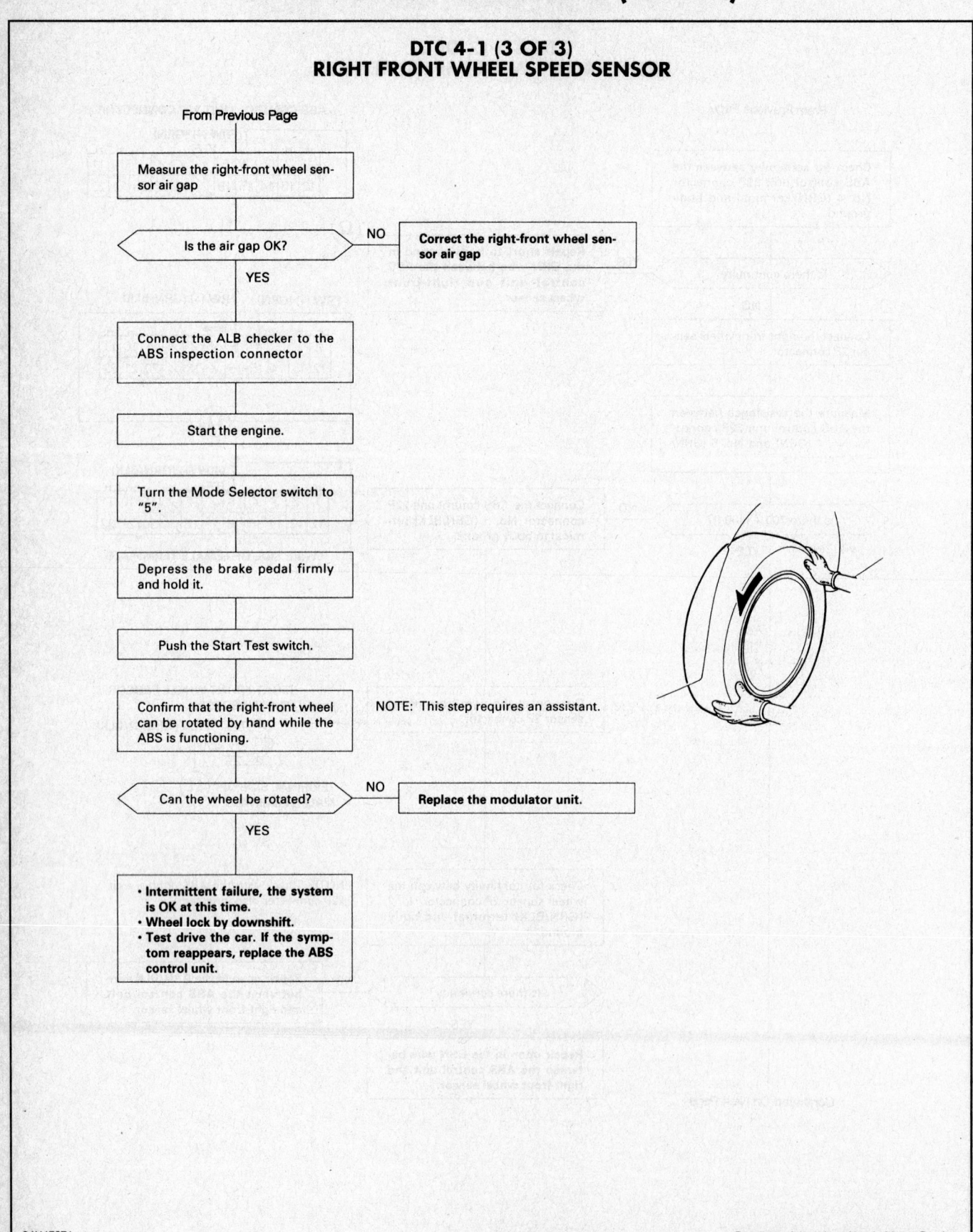

DTC 4-2 (1 OF 3)
LEFT FRONT WHEEL SPEED SENSOR

The ABS control unit monitors the wheel sensor signal during the regular diagnosis (at speeds of 6 mph (10 km/h) or more). This diagnosis is not performed when the parking brake signal is ON.

The ABS control unit turns the ABS indicator light on if it detects that there is no wheel sensor signal from the left-front wheel.

Possible causes:

- Open circuit, internal short or short to body ground in the left-front wheel sensor
- Open circuit or short to body ground in the positive (+) wire between the left-front wheel sensor and ABS control unit
- Open circuit or short to body ground in the negative (–) wire between the left-front wheel sensor and ABS control unit
- Positive (+) wire shorted to the negative (–) wire between the left-front wheel sensor and ABS control unit
- Loose connector or poor contact of terminals
- Improper left-front wheel sensor air gap
- Faulty ABS control unit
- Missing left-front pulser
- Modulator does not decrease pressure properly
- Wheel lock by downshift

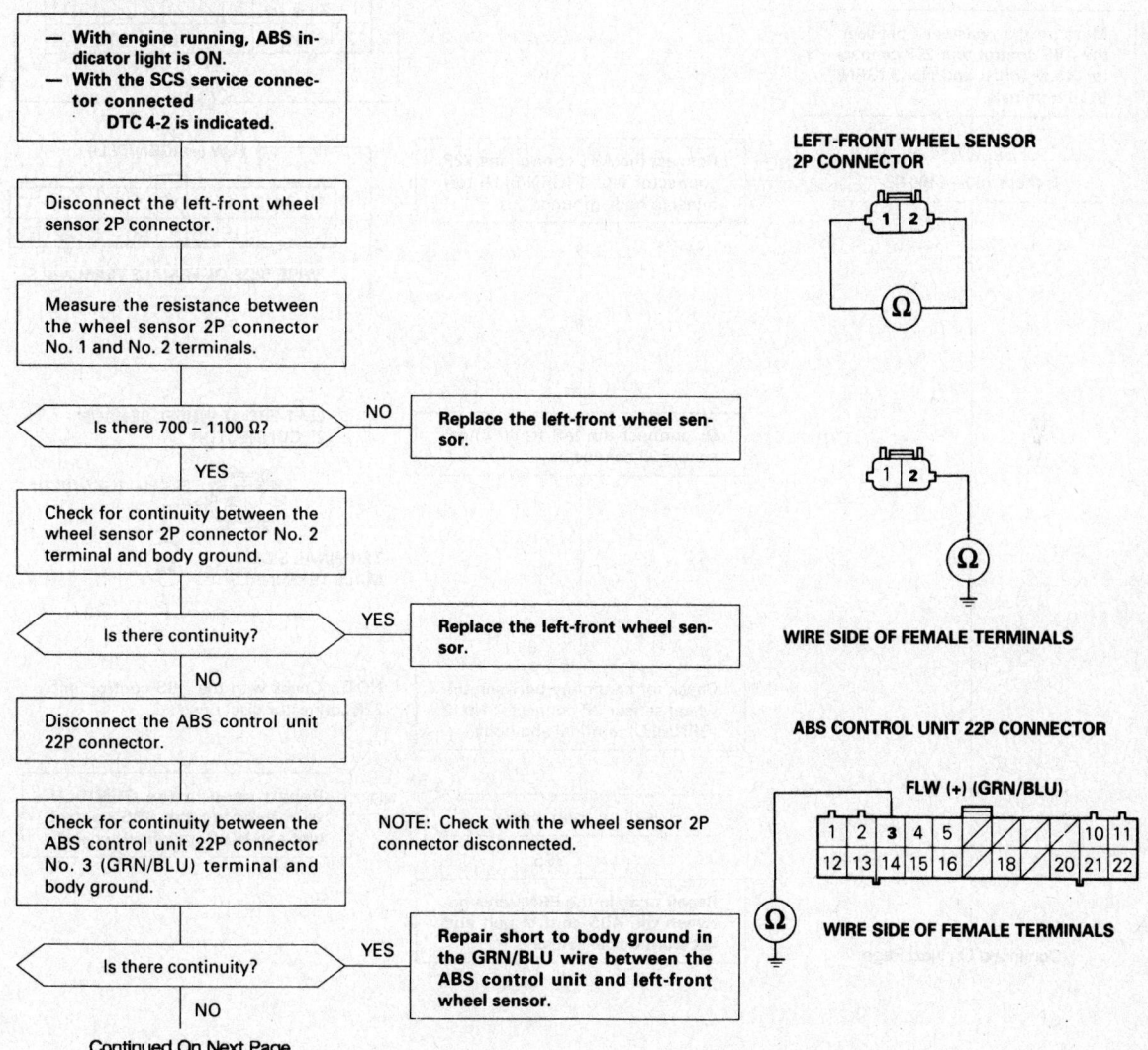

— With engine running, ABS indicator light is ON.
— With the SCS service connector connected
DTC 4-2 is indicated.

Disconnect the left-front wheel sensor 2P connector.

Measure the resistance between the wheel sensor 2P connector No. 1 and No. 2 terminals.

Is there 700 – 1100 Ω? — NO → **Replace the left-front wheel sensor.**

YES

Check for continuity between the wheel sensor 2P connector No. 2 terminal and body ground.

Is there continuity? — YES → **Replace the left-front wheel sensor.**

NO

Disconnect the ABS control unit 22P connector.

Check for continuity between the ABS control unit 22P connector No. 3 (GRN/BLU) terminal and body ground.

NOTE: Check with the wheel sensor 2P connector disconnected.

Is there continuity? — YES → **Repair short to body ground in the GRN/BLU wire between the ABS control unit and left-front wheel sensor.**

NO

Continued On Next Page

LEFT-FRONT WHEEL SENSOR 2P CONNECTOR

WIRE SIDE OF FEMALE TERMINALS

ABS CONTROL UNIT 22P CONNECTOR

FLW (+) (GRN/BLU)

| 1 | 2 | 3 | 4 | 5 | | | | 10 | 11 |
| 12 | 13 | 14 | 15 | 16 | | 18 | | 20 | 21 | 22 |

WIRE SIDE OF FEMALE TERMINALS

DTC 4-2 (2 OF 3)
LEFT FRONT WHEEL SPEED SENSOR

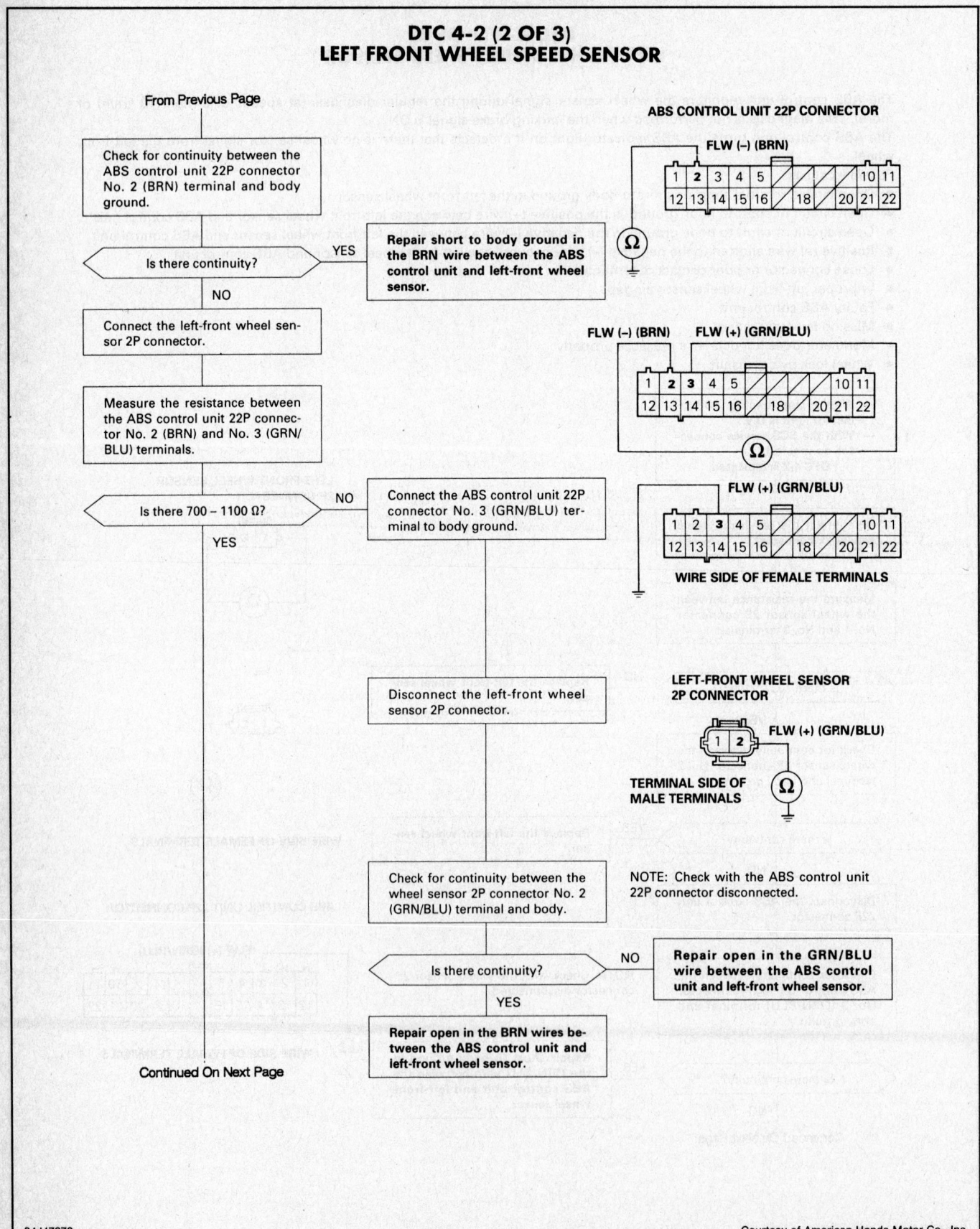

From Previous Page

Check for continuity between the ABS control unit 22P connector No. 2 (BRN) terminal and body ground.

Is there continuity? — YES → Repair short to body ground in the BRN wire between the ABS control unit and left-front wheel sensor.

NO

Connect the left-front wheel sensor 2P connector.

Measure the resistance between the ABS control unit 22P connector No. 2 (BRN) and No. 3 (GRN/BLU) terminals.

Is there 700 – 1100 Ω? — NO → Connect the ABS control unit 22P connector No. 3 (GRN/BLU) terminal to body ground.

YES

Disconnect the left-front wheel sensor 2P connector.

Check for continuity between the wheel sensor 2P connector No. 2 (GRN/BLU) terminal and body.

Is there continuity? — NO → Repair open in the GRN/BLU wire between the ABS control unit and left-front wheel sensor.

YES

Repair open in the BRN wires between the ABS control unit and left-front wheel sensor.

Continued On Next Page

ABS CONTROL UNIT 22P CONNECTOR

FLW (–) (BRN)

LEFT-FRONT WHEEL SENSOR 2P CONNECTOR

FLW (+) (GRN/BLU)

TERMINAL SIDE OF MALE TERMINALS

NOTE: Check with the ABS control unit 22P connector disconnected.

WIRE SIDE OF FEMALE TERMINALS

FLW (–) (BRN)   FLW (+) (GRN/BLU)

FLW (+) (GRN/BLU)

DTC 4-2 (3 OF 3)
LEFT FRONT WHEEL SPEED SENSOR

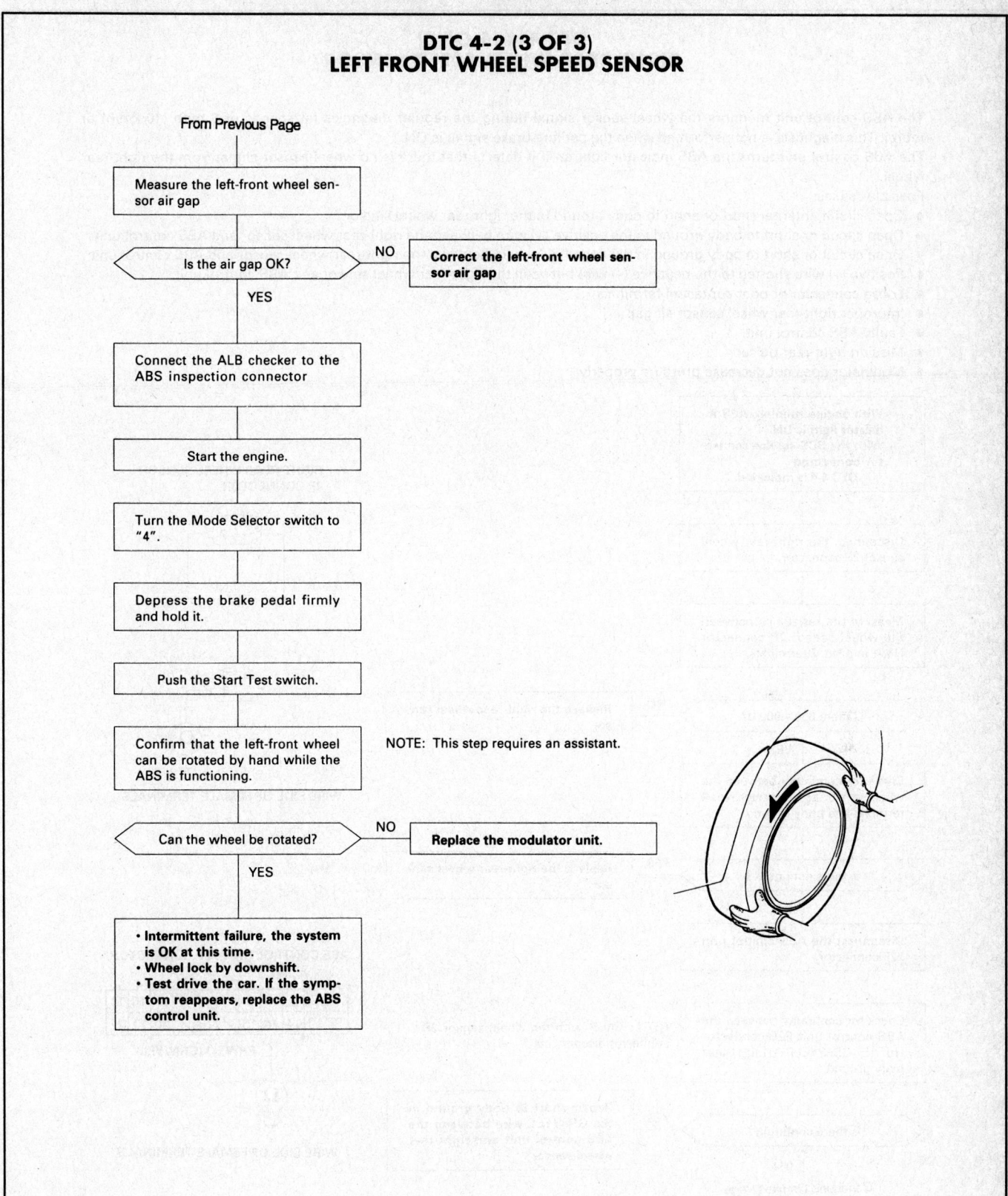

From Previous Page

Measure the left-front wheel sensor air gap

Is the air gap OK? — NO → Correct the left-front wheel sensor air gap

YES

Connect the ALB checker to the ABS inspection connector

Start the engine.

Turn the Mode Selector switch to "4".

Depress the brake pedal firmly and hold it.

Push the Start Test switch.

Confirm that the left-front wheel can be rotated by hand while the ABS is functioning.

NOTE: This step requires an assistant.

Can the wheel be rotated? — NO → Replace the modulator unit.

YES

• Intermittent failure, the system is OK at this time.
• Wheel lock by downshift.
• Test drive the car. If the symptom reappears, replace the ABS control unit.

DTC 4-4 (1 OF 3)
RIGHT REAR WHEEL SPEED SENSOR

The ABS control unit monitors the wheel sensor signal during the regular diagnosis (at speeds of 6 mph (10 km/h) or more). This diagnosis is not performed when the parking brake signal is ON.
The ABS control unit turns the ABS indicator light on if it detects that there is no wheel sensor signal from the right-rear wheel.
Possible causes:
● Open circuit, internal short or short to body ground in the right-rear wheel sensor
● Open circuit or short to body ground in the positive (+) wire between the right-rear wheel sensor and ABS control unit
● Open circuit or short to body ground in the negative (–) wire between the right-rear wheel sensor and ABS control unit
● Positive (+) wire shorted to the negative (–) wire between the right-rear wheel sensor and ABS control unit
● Loose connector or poor contact of terminals
● Improper right-rear wheel sensor air gap
● Faulty ABS control unit
● Missing right-rear pulser
● Modulator does not decrease pressure properly

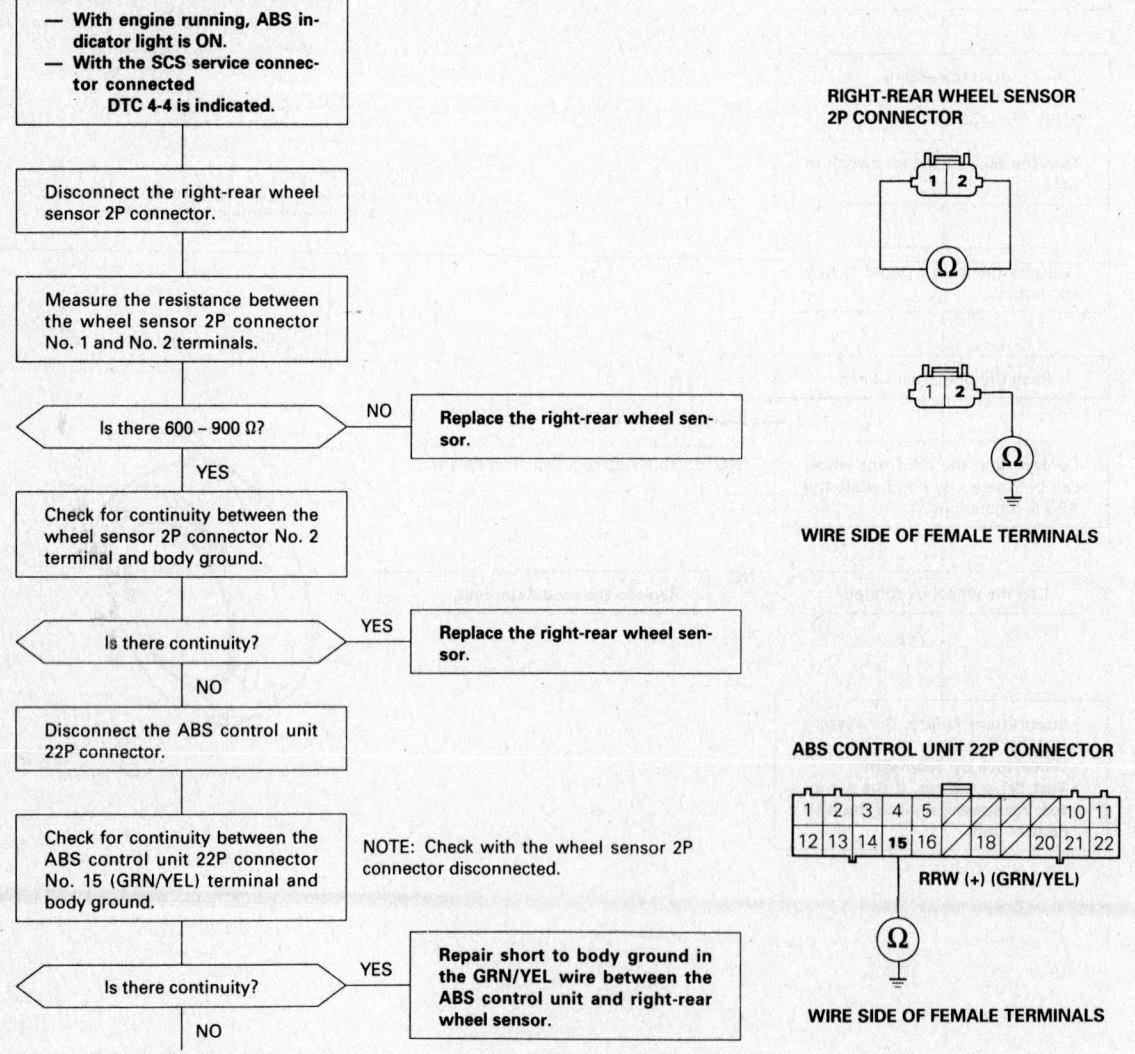

— With engine running, ABS indicator light is ON.
— With the SCS service connector connected
    DTC 4-4 is indicated.

Disconnect the right-rear wheel sensor 2P connector.

Measure the resistance between the wheel sensor 2P connector No. 1 and No. 2 terminals.

Is there 600 – 900 Ω?   NO → Replace the right-rear wheel sensor.

YES

Check for continuity between the wheel sensor 2P connector No. 2 terminal and body ground.

Is there continuity?   YES → Replace the right-rear wheel sensor.

NO

Disconnect the ABS control unit 22P connector.

Check for continuity between the ABS control unit 22P connector No. 15 (GRN/YEL) terminal and body ground.

NOTE: Check with the wheel sensor 2P connector disconnected.

Is there continuity?   YES → Repair short to body ground in the GRN/YEL wire between the ABS control unit and right-rear wheel sensor.

NO

Continued On Next Page

RIGHT-REAR WHEEL SENSOR
2P CONNECTOR

WIRE SIDE OF FEMALE TERMINALS

ABS CONTROL UNIT 22P CONNECTOR

RRW (+) (GRN/YEL)

WIRE SIDE OF FEMALE TERMINALS

DTC 4-4 (2 OF 3)
RIGHT REAR WHEEL SPEED SENSOR

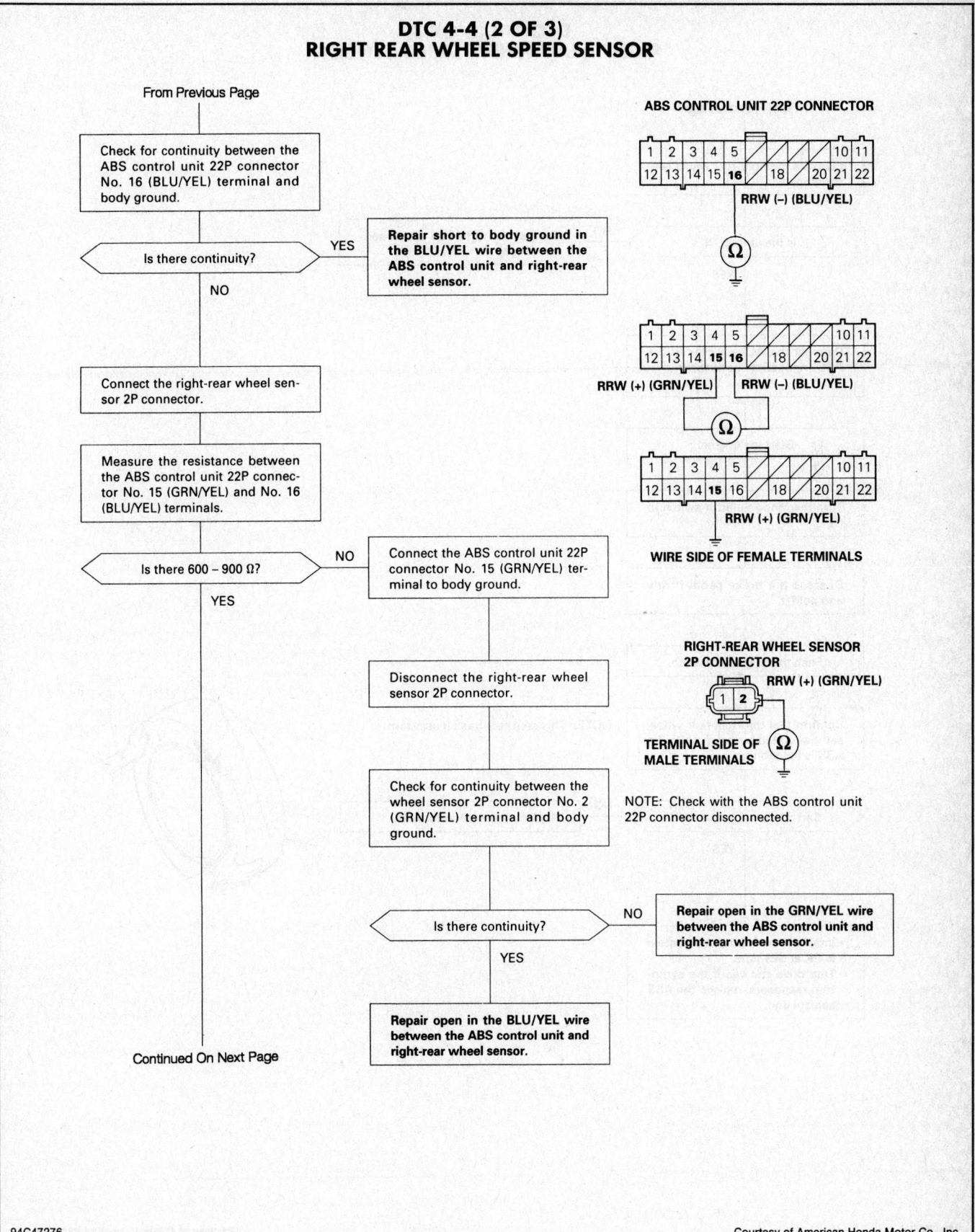

From Previous Page

Check for continuity between the ABS control unit 22P connector No. 16 (BLU/YEL) terminal and body ground.

Is there continuity? — YES → Repair short to body ground in the BLU/YEL wire between the ABS control unit and right-rear wheel sensor.

NO

Connect the right-rear wheel sensor 2P connector.

Measure the resistance between the ABS control unit 22P connector No. 15 (GRN/YEL) and No. 16 (BLU/YEL) terminals.

Is there 600 – 900 Ω? — NO → Connect the ABS control unit 22P connector No. 15 (GRN/YEL) terminal to body ground.

YES

Disconnect the right-rear wheel sensor 2P connector.

Check for continuity between the wheel sensor 2P connector No. 2 (GRN/YEL) terminal and body ground.

Is there continuity? — NO → Repair open in the GRN/YEL wire between the ABS control unit and right-rear wheel sensor.

YES

Repair open in the BLU/YEL wire between the ABS control unit and right-rear wheel sensor.

Continued On Next Page

ABS CONTROL UNIT 22P CONNECTOR

| 1 | 2 | 3 | 4 | 5 | | | | 10 | 11 |
| 12 | 13 | 14 | 15 | **16** | | 18 | | 20 | 21 | 22 |

RRW (–) (BLU/YEL)

Ω

RRW (+) (GRN/YEL)   RRW (–) (BLU/YEL)

Ω

RRW (+) (GRN/YEL)

WIRE SIDE OF FEMALE TERMINALS

RIGHT-REAR WHEEL SENSOR 2P CONNECTOR

1 | 2   RRW (+) (GRN/YEL)

TERMINAL SIDE OF MALE TERMINALS   Ω

NOTE: Check with the ABS control unit 22P connector disconnected.

DTC 4-4 (3 OF 3)
RIGHT REAR WHEEL SPEED SENSOR

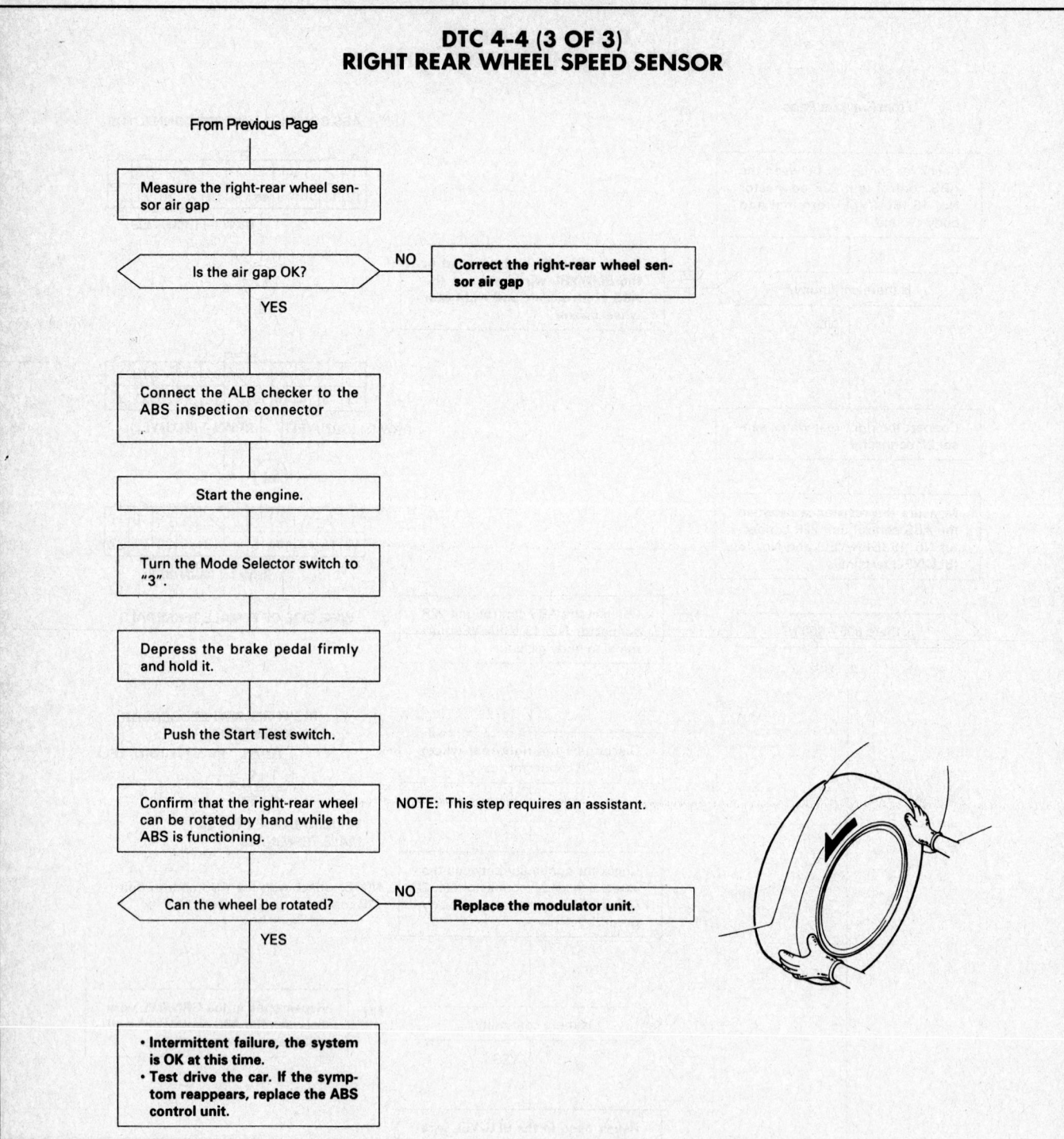

From Previous Page

Measure the right-rear wheel sensor air gap

Is the air gap OK? — NO → Correct the right-rear wheel sensor air gap

YES

Connect the ALB checker to the ABS inspection connector

Start the engine.

Turn the Mode Selector switch to "3".

Depress the brake pedal firmly and hold it.

Push the Start Test switch.

Confirm that the right-rear wheel can be rotated by hand while the ABS is functioning.

NOTE: This step requires an assistant.

Can the wheel be rotated? — NO → Replace the modulator unit.

YES

- Intermittent failure, the system is OK at this time.
- Test drive the car. If the symptom reappears, replace the ABS control unit.

DTC 4-8 (1 OF 3)
LEFT REAR WHEEL SPEED SENSOR

The ABS control unit monitors the wheel sensor signal during the regular diagnosis (at speeds of 6 mph (10 km/h) or more). This diagnosis is not performed when the parking brake signal is ON.

The ABS control unit turns the ABS indicator light on if it detects that there is no wheel sensor signal from the left-rear wheel.

Possible causes:

- Open circuit, internal short or short to body ground in the left-rear wheel sensor
- Open circuit or short to body ground in the positive (+) wire between the left-rear wheel sensor and ABS control unit
- Open circuit or short to body ground in the negative (–) wire between the left-rear wheel sensor and ABS control unit
- Positive (+) wire shorted to the negative (–) wire between the left-rear wheel sensor and ABS control unit
- Loose connector or poor contact of terminals
- Improper left-rear wheel sensor air gap
- Faulty ABS control unit
- Missing left-rear pulser
- Modulator does not decrease pressure properly
- Both front wheels spin (for example, when wheels are stuck)

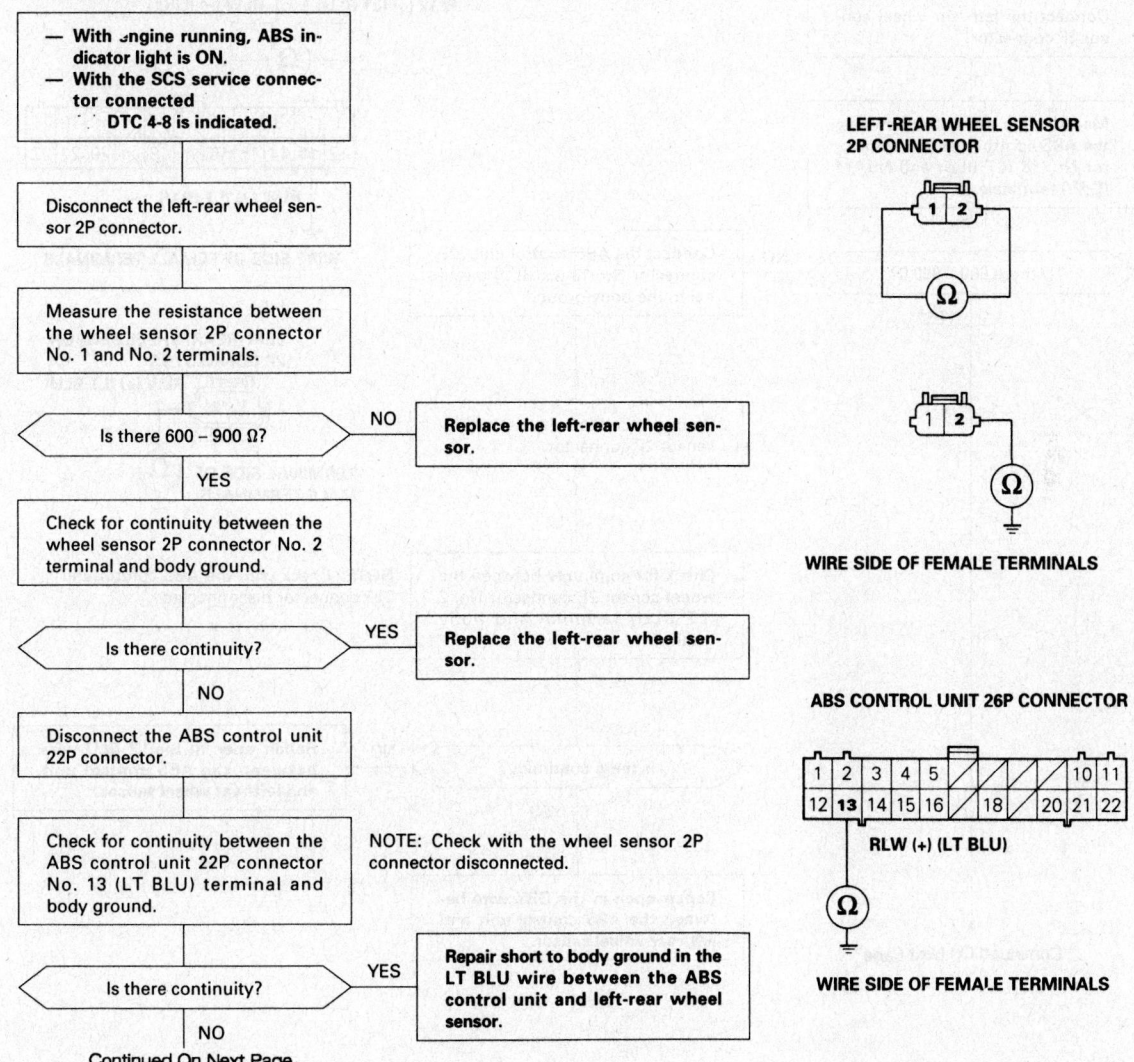

— With engine running, ABS indicator light is ON.
— With the SCS service connector connected
DTC 4-8 is indicated.

Disconnect the left-rear wheel sensor 2P connector.

Measure the resistance between the wheel sensor 2P connector No. 1 and No. 2 terminals.

Is there 600 – 900 Ω?

NO → Replace the left-rear wheel sensor.

YES

Check for continuity between the wheel sensor 2P connector No. 2 terminal and body ground.

Is there continuity?

YES → Replace the left-rear wheel sensor.

NO

Disconnect the ABS control unit 22P connector.

Check for continuity between the ABS control unit 22P connector No. 13 (LT BLU) terminal and body ground.

NOTE: Check with the wheel sensor 2P connector disconnected.

Is there continuity?

YES → Repair short to body ground in the LT BLU wire between the ABS control unit and left-rear wheel sensor.

NO

Continued On Next Page

LEFT-REAR WHEEL SENSOR 2P CONNECTOR

1 2

Ω

1 2

Ω

WIRE SIDE OF FEMALE TERMINALS

ABS CONTROL UNIT 26P CONNECTOR

1 2 3 4 5 | | 10 11
12 **13** 14 15 16 | 18 | 20 21 22

RLW (+) (LT BLU)

Ω

WIRE SIDE OF FEMALE TERMINALS

DTC 4-8 (2 OF 3)
LEFT REAR WHEEL SPEED SENSOR

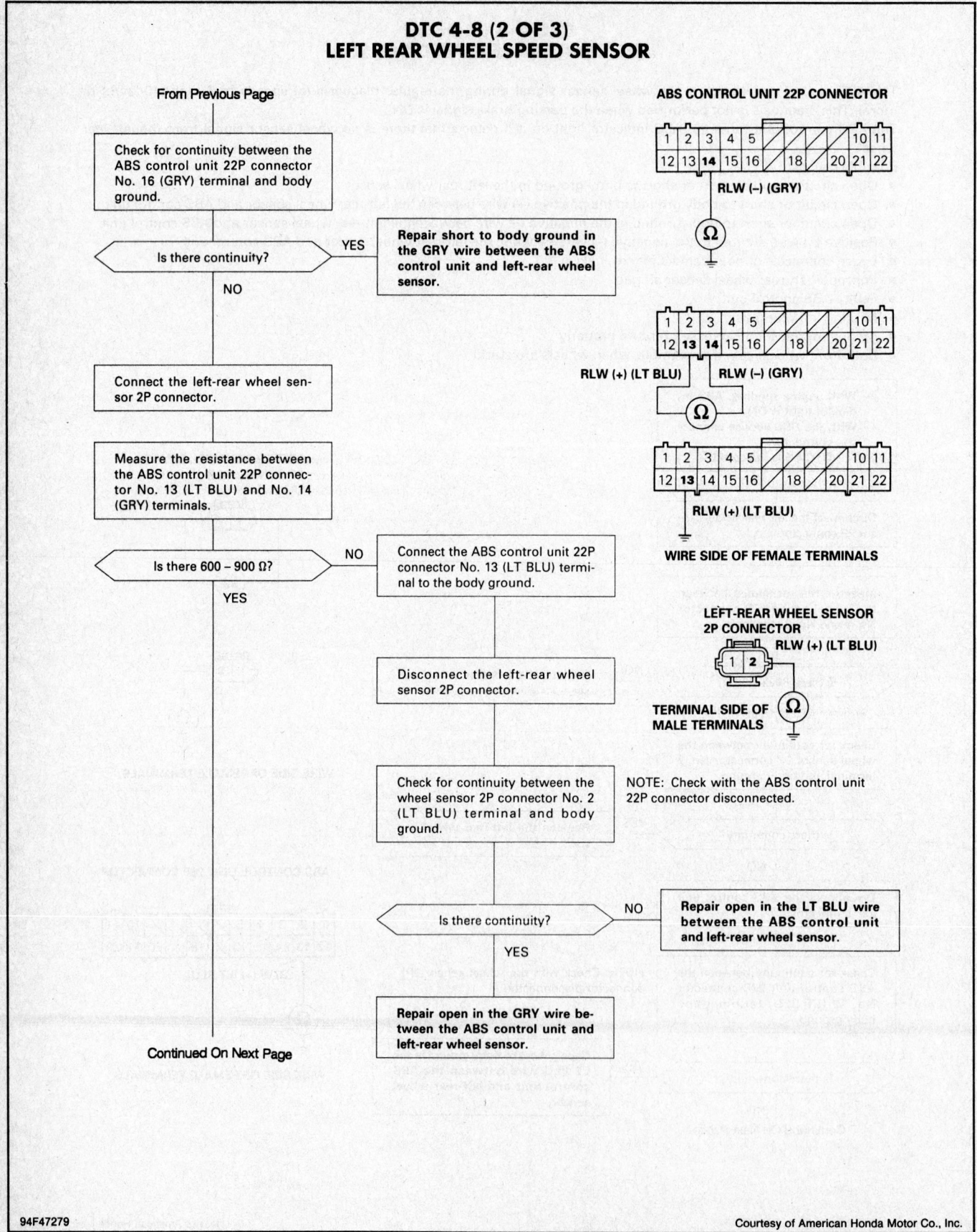

From Previous Page

Check for continuity between the ABS control unit 22P connector No. 16 (GRY) terminal and body ground.

Is there continuity? — YES → Repair short to body ground in the GRY wire between the ABS control unit and left-rear wheel sensor.

NO

Connect the left-rear wheel sensor 2P connector.

Measure the resistance between the ABS control unit 22P connector No. 13 (LT BLU) and No. 14 (GRY) terminals.

Is there 600 – 900 Ω? — NO → Connect the ABS control unit 22P connector No. 13 (LT BLU) terminal to the body ground.

YES

Disconnect the left-rear wheel sensor 2P connector.

Check for continuity between the wheel sensor 2P connector No. 2 (LT BLU) terminal and body ground.

Is there continuity? — NO → Repair open in the LT BLU wire between the ABS control unit and left-rear wheel sensor.

YES

Repair open in the GRY wire between the ABS control unit and left-rear wheel sensor.

Continued On Next Page

ABS CONTROL UNIT 22P CONNECTOR

RLW (–) (GRY)

RLW (+) (LT BLU)   RLW (–) (GRY)

RLW (+) (LT BLU)

WIRE SIDE OF FEMALE TERMINALS

LEFT-REAR WHEEL SENSOR 2P CONNECTOR

RLW (+) (LT BLU)

TERMINAL SIDE OF MALE TERMINALS

NOTE: Check with the ABS control unit 22P connector disconnected.

DTC 4-8 (3 OF 3)
LEFT REAR WHEEL SPEED SENSOR

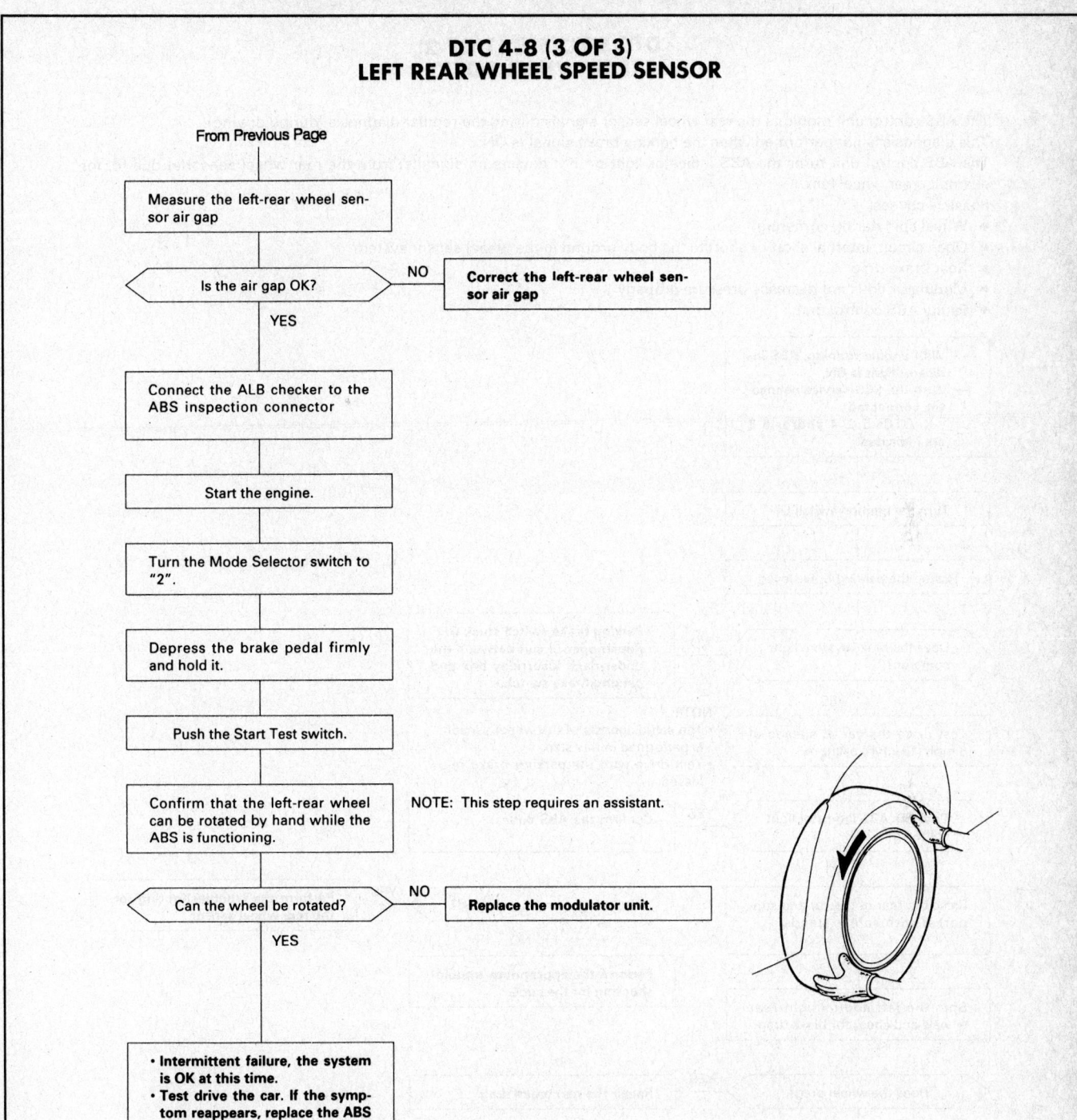

From Previous Page

Measure the left-rear wheel sensor air gap

Is the air gap OK? — NO → Correct the left-rear wheel sensor air gap

YES

Connect the ALB checker to the ABS inspection connector

Start the engine.

Turn the Mode Selector switch to "2".

Depress the brake pedal firmly and hold it.

Push the Start Test switch.

Confirm that the left-rear wheel can be rotated by hand while the ABS is functioning.

NOTE: This step requires an assistant.

Can the wheel be rotated? — NO → Replace the modulator unit.

YES

- **Intermittent failure, the system is OK at this time.**
- **Test drive the car. If the symptom reappears, replace the ABS control unit.**

DTC 5 TO 5-8 (1 OF 2)
REAR WHEEL LOCK

The ABS control unit monitors the rear wheel sensor signals during the regular diagnosis (during driving).
This diagnosis is not performed when the parking brake signal is ON.
The ABS control unit turns the ABS indicator light on if it detects no signal(s) from the rear wheel sensor(s) due to, for example, rear wheel lock.
Possible causes:
- Wheel spin during cornering
- Open circuit, internal short or short to the body ground in the wheel sensor system
- Rear brake drag
- Modulator does not decrease pressure properly
- Faulty ABS control unit

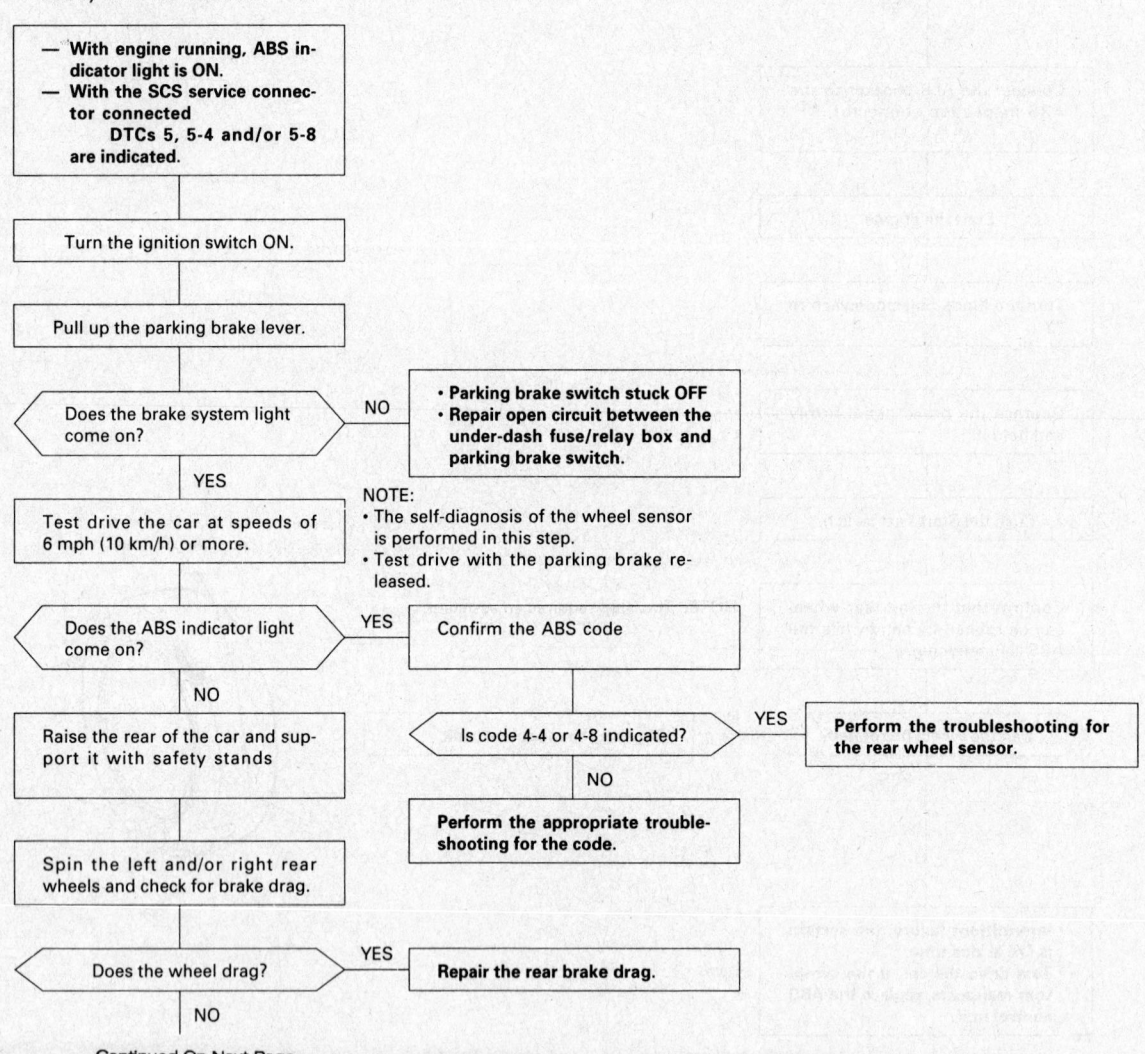

94J47315

DTC 5 TO 5-8 (2 OF 2)
REAR WHEEL LOCK

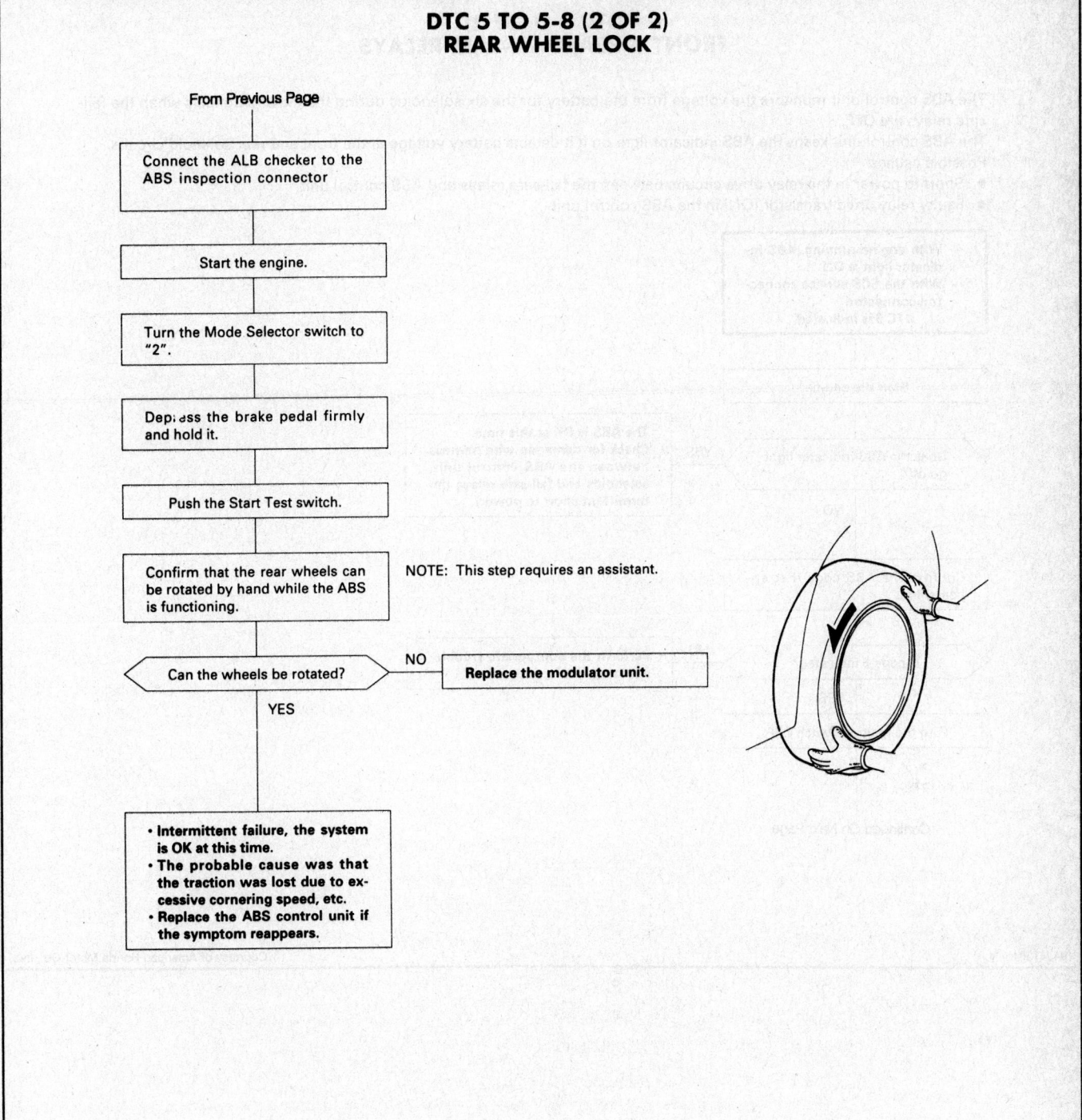

From Previous Page

Connect the ALB checker to the ABS inspection connector

Start the engine.

Turn the Mode Selector switch to "2".

Depress the brake pedal firmly and hold it.

Push the Start Test switch.

Confirm that the rear wheels can be rotated by hand while the ABS is functioning.

NOTE: This step requires an assistant.

Can the wheels be rotated?

NO → Replace the modulator unit.

YES

- Intermittent failure, the system is OK at this time.
- The probable cause was that the traction was lost due to excessive cornering speed, etc.
- Replace the ABS control unit if the symptom reappears.

94A47316

DTC 6 (1 OF 2)
FRONT & REAR FAIL-SAFE RELAYS

The ABS control unit monitors the voltage from the battery for the six solenoids during the initial diagnosis when the fail-safe relays are OFF.

The ABS control unit keeps the ABS indicator light on if it detects battery voltage at the front and rear solenoid circuits.

Possible causes:
- Short to power in the relay drive circuits between the fail-safe relays and ABS control unit
- Faulty relay drive transistor (ON) in the ABS control unit

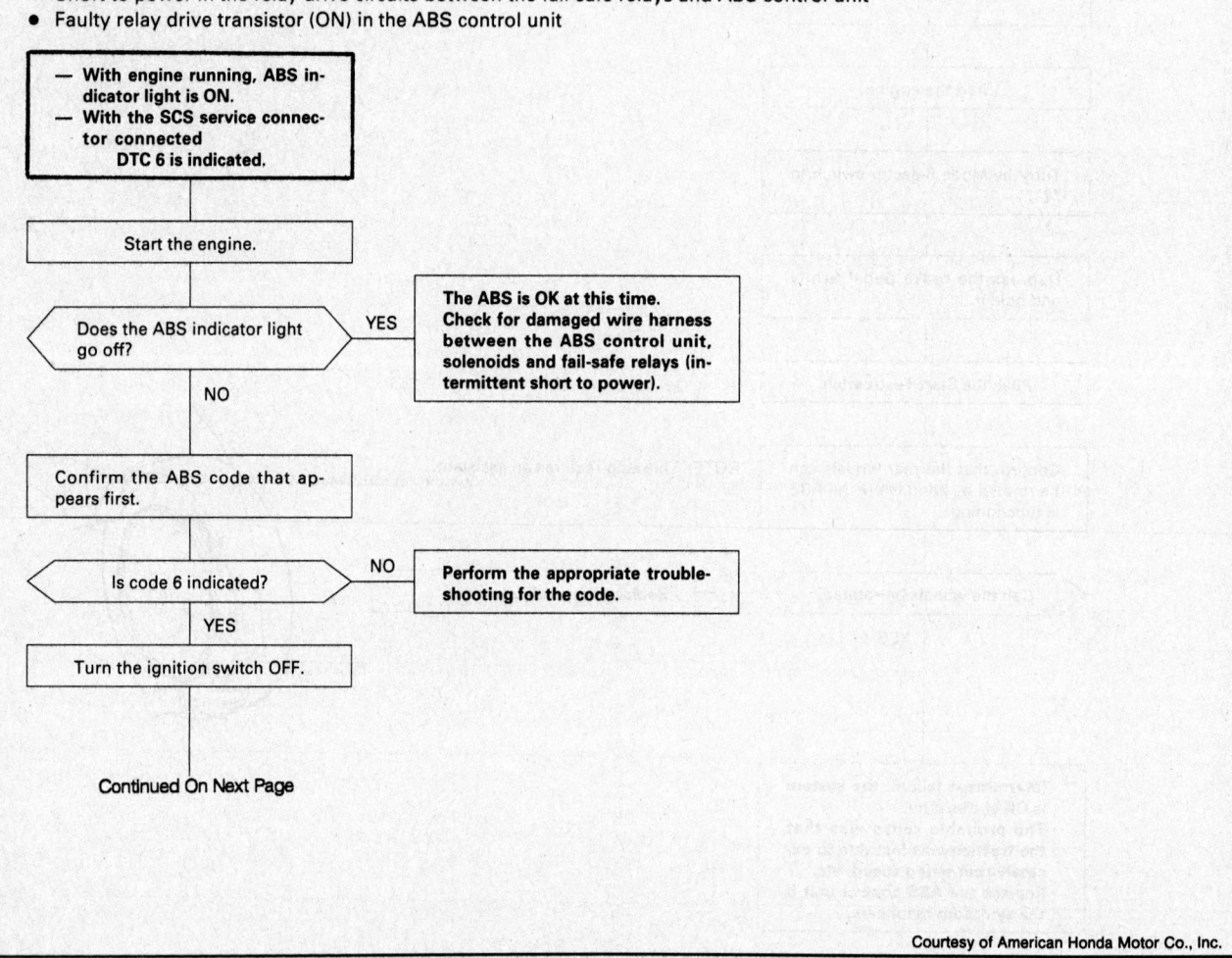

— With engine running, ABS indicator light is ON.
— With the SCS service connector connected
　　DTC 6 is indicated.

Start the engine.

Does the ABS indicator light go off? — YES → The ABS is OK at this time. Check for damaged wire harness between the ABS control unit, solenoids and fail-safe relays (intermittent short to power).

NO

Confirm the ABS code that appears first.

Is code 6 indicated? — NO → Perform the appropriate troubleshooting for the code.

YES

Turn the ignition switch OFF.

Continued On Next Page

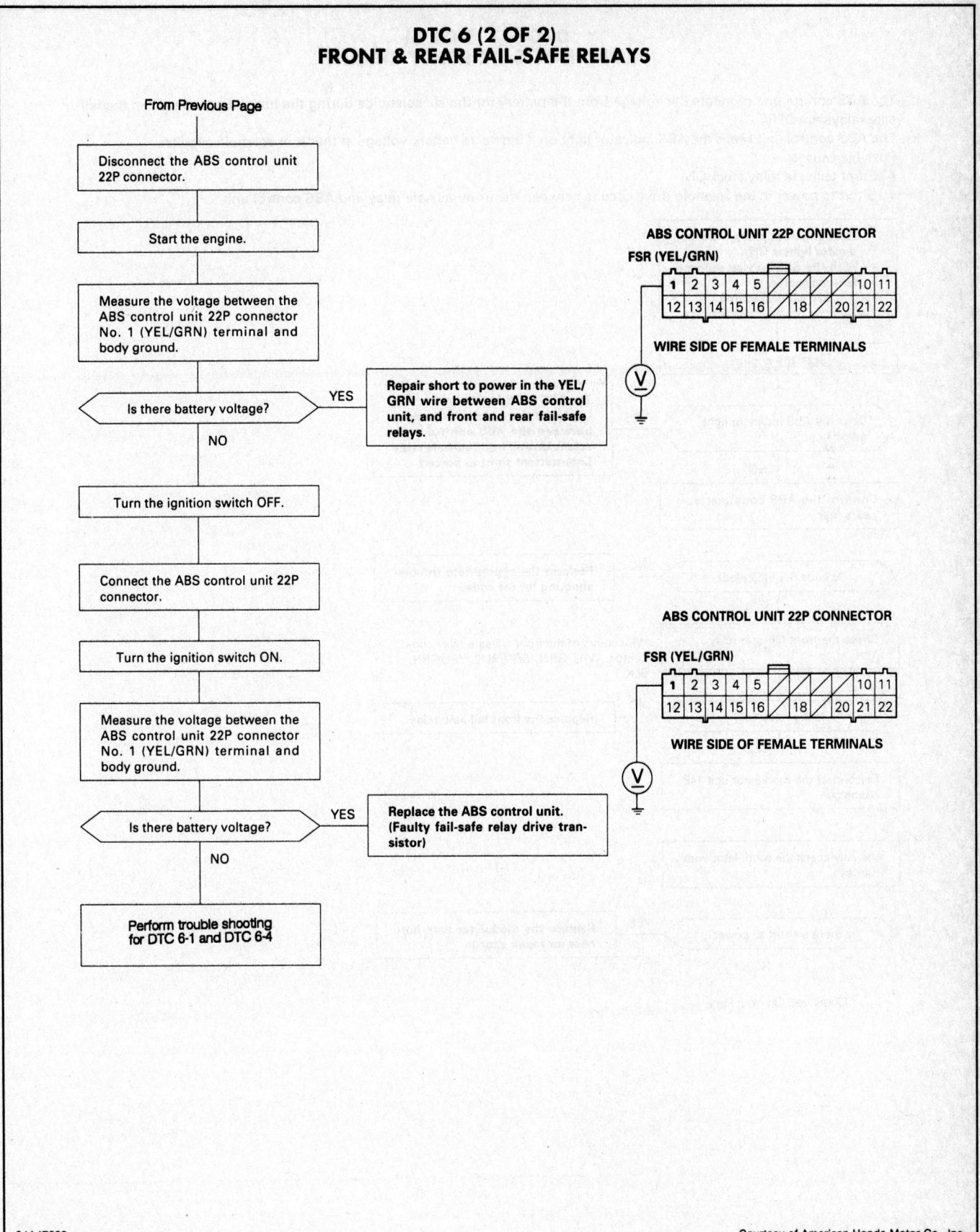

DTC 6 (2 OF 2)
FRONT & REAR FAIL-SAFE RELAYS

From Previous Page

Disconnect the ABS control unit 22P connector.

Start the engine.

Measure the voltage between the ABS control unit 22P connector No. 1 (YEL/GRN) terminal and body ground.

Is there battery voltage? — YES → Repair short to power in the YEL/GRN wire between ABS control unit, and front and rear fail-safe relays.

NO

Turn the ignition switch OFF.

Connect the ABS control unit 22P connector.

Turn the ignition switch ON.

Measure the voltage between the ABS control unit 22P connector No. 1 (YEL/GRN) terminal and body ground.

Is there battery voltage? — YES → Replace the ABS control unit. (Faulty fail-safe relay drive transistor)

NO

Perform trouble shooting for DTC 6-1 and DTC 6-4

ABS CONTROL UNIT 22P CONNECTOR

FSR (YEL/GRN)

| 1 | 2 | 3 | 4 | 5 | | | | 10 | 11 |
| 12 | 13 | 14 | 15 | 16 | | 18 | | 20 | 21 | 22 |

WIRE SIDE OF FEMALE TERMINALS

ABS CONTROL UNIT 22P CONNECTOR

FSR (YEL/GRN)

| 1 | 2 | 3 | 4 | 5 | | | | 10 | 11 |
| 12 | 13 | 14 | 15 | 16 | | 18 | | 20 | 21 | 22 |

WIRE SIDE OF FEMALE TERMINALS

DTC 6-1 (1 OF 3)
FRONT FAIL-SAFE RELAY CIRCUIT

The ABS control unit monitors the voltage from the battery for the six solenoids during the initial diagnosis when the fail-safe relays are OFF.

The ABS control unit keeps the ABS indicator light on if it detects battery voltage at the front solenoid circuits.

Possible causes:
- Front fail-safe relay stuck ON
- Short to power in the solenoid drive circuits between the front fail-safe relay and ABS control unit

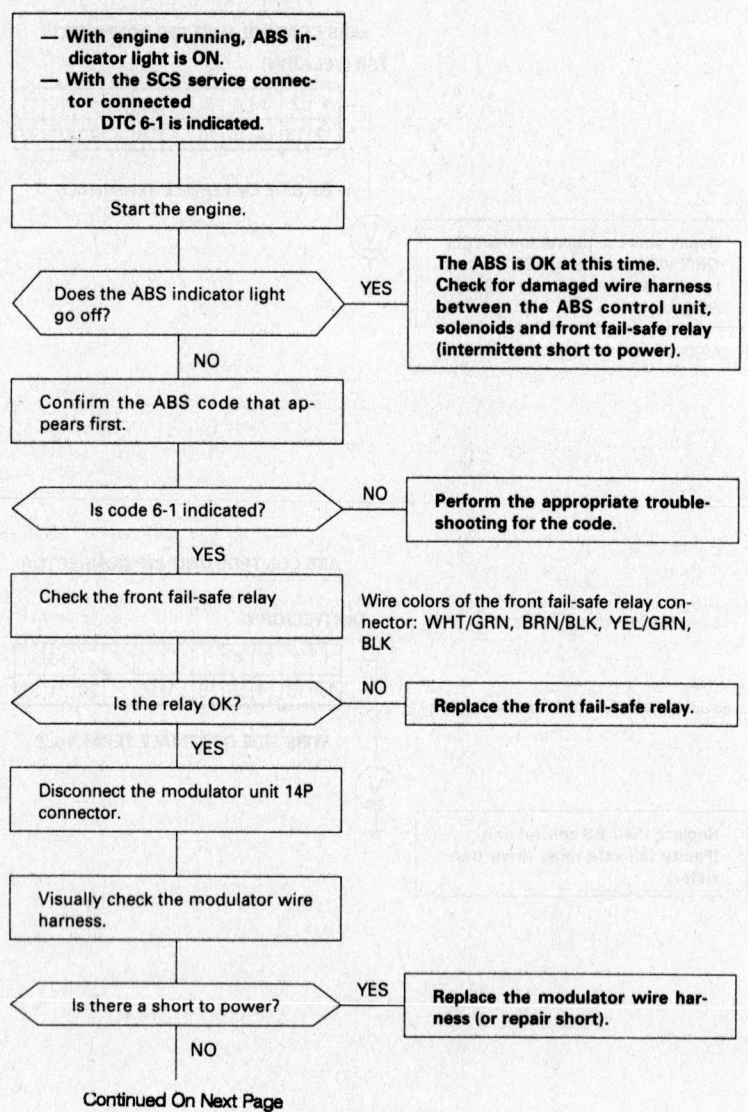

— With engine running, ABS indicator light is ON.
— With the SCS service connector connected
    DTC 6-1 is indicated.

Start the engine.

Does the ABS indicator light go off? — YES → The ABS is OK at this time. Check for damaged wire harness between the ABS control unit, solenoids and front fail-safe relay (intermittent short to power).

NO

Confirm the ABS code that appears first.

Is code 6-1 indicated? — NO → Perform the appropriate troubleshooting for the code.

YES

Check the front fail-safe relay — Wire colors of the front fail-safe relay connector: WHT/GRN, BRN/BLK, YEL/GRN, BLK

Is the relay OK? — NO → Replace the front fail-safe relay.

YES

Disconnect the modulator unit 14P connector.

Visually check the modulator wire harness.

Is there a short to power? — YES → Replace the modulator wire harness (or repair short).

NO

Continued On Next Page

DTC 6-1 (2 OF 3)
FRONT FAIL-SAFE RELAY CIRCUIT

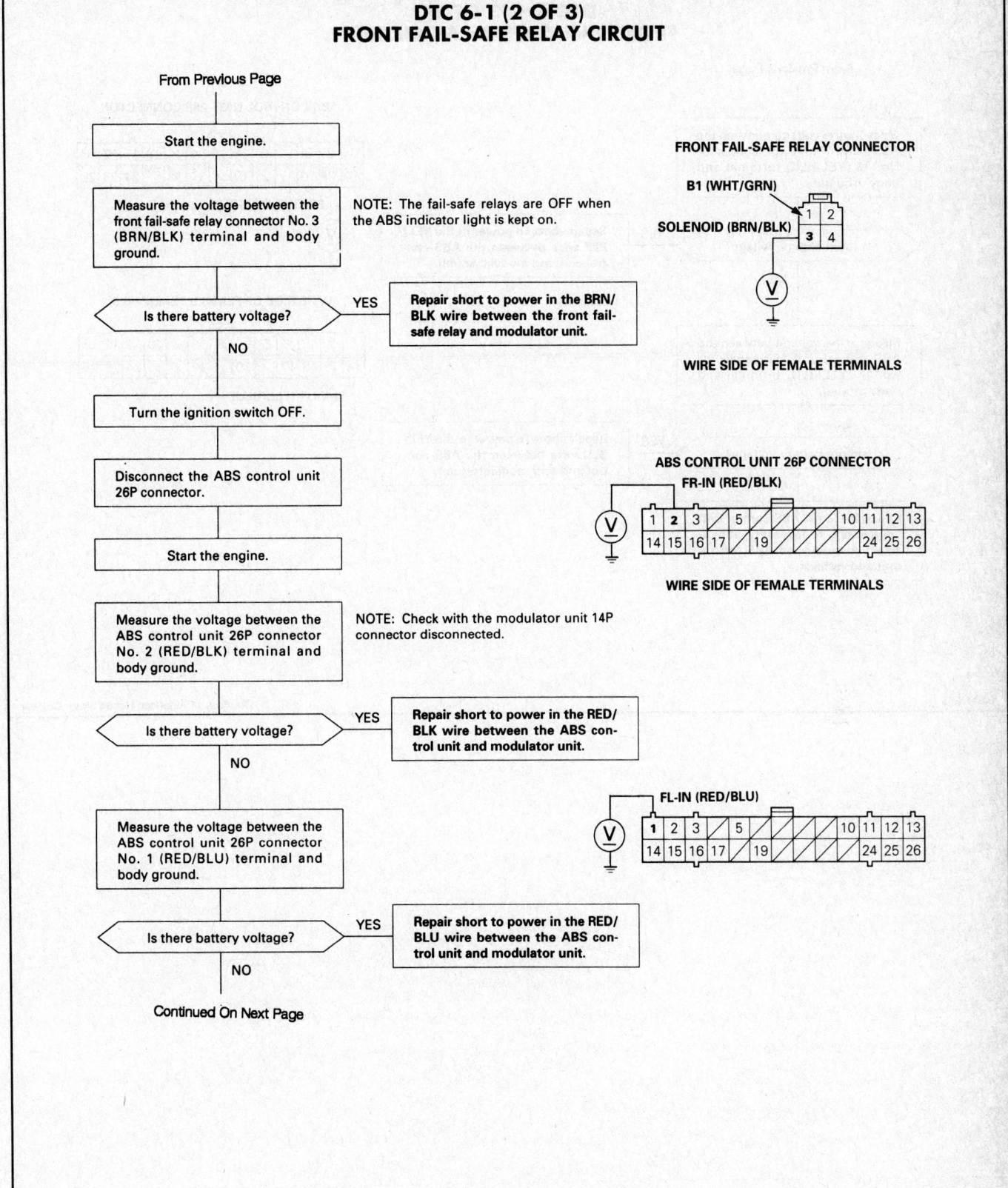

From Previous Page

Start the engine.

Measure the voltage between the front fail-safe relay connector No. 3 (BRN/BLK) terminal and body ground.

NOTE: The fail-safe relays are OFF when the ABS indicator light is kept on.

Is there battery voltage? — YES → Repair short to power in the BRN/BLK wire between the front fail-safe relay and modulator unit.

NO

Turn the ignition switch OFF.

Disconnect the ABS control unit 26P connector.

Start the engine.

Measure the voltage between the ABS control unit 26P connector No. 2 (RED/BLK) terminal and body ground.

NOTE: Check with the modulator unit 14P connector disconnected.

Is there battery voltage? — YES → Repair short to power in the RED/BLK wire between the ABS control unit and modulator unit.

NO

Measure the voltage between the ABS control unit 26P connector No. 1 (RED/BLU) terminal and body ground.

Is there battery voltage? — YES → Repair short to power in the RED/BLU wire between the ABS control unit and modulator unit.

NO

Continued On Next Page

FRONT FAIL-SAFE RELAY CONNECTOR

B1 (WHT/GRN)

SOLENOID (BRN/BLK)

WIRE SIDE OF FEMALE TERMINALS

ABS CONTROL UNIT 26P CONNECTOR
FR-IN (RED/BLK)

WIRE SIDE OF FEMALE TERMINALS

FL-IN (RED/BLU)

94C47284

Courtesy of American Honda Motor Co., Inc.

DTC 6-1 (3 OF 3)
FRONT FAIL-SAFE RELAY CIRCUIT

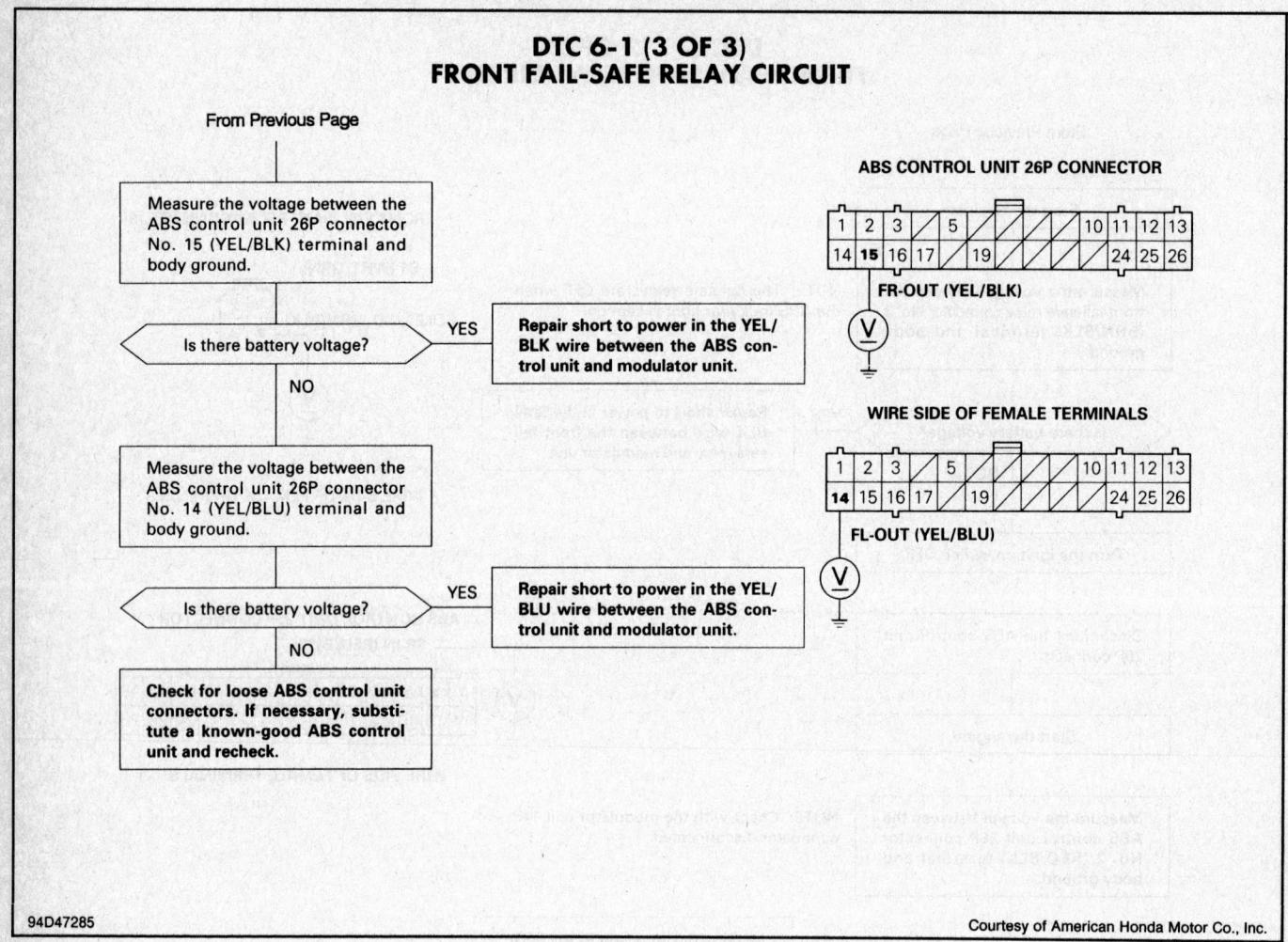

From Previous Page

Measure the voltage between the ABS control unit 26P connector No. 15 (YEL/BLK) terminal and body ground.

Is there battery voltage? — YES → Repair short to power in the YEL/BLK wire between the ABS control unit and modulator unit.

NO

Measure the voltage between the ABS control unit 26P connector No. 14 (YEL/BLU) terminal and body ground.

Is there battery voltage? — YES → Repair short to power in the YEL/BLU wire between the ABS control unit and modulator unit.

NO

Check for loose ABS control unit connectors. If necessary, substitute a known-good ABS control unit and recheck.

ABS CONTROL UNIT 26P CONNECTOR

FR-OUT (YEL/BLK)

WIRE SIDE OF FEMALE TERMINALS

FL-OUT (YEL/BLU)

94D47285

DTC 6-4 (1 OF 2)
REAR FAIL-SAFE RELAY CIRCUIT

The ABS control unit monitors the voltage from the battery for the six solenoids during the initial diagnosis when the fail-safe relays are OFF.
The ABS control unit keeps the ABS indicator light on if it detects the battery voltage at the two rear solenoid circuits.
Possible causes:
- Rear fail-safe relay stuck ON
- Short to power in the solenoid drive circuits between the rear fail-safe relay and ABS control unit

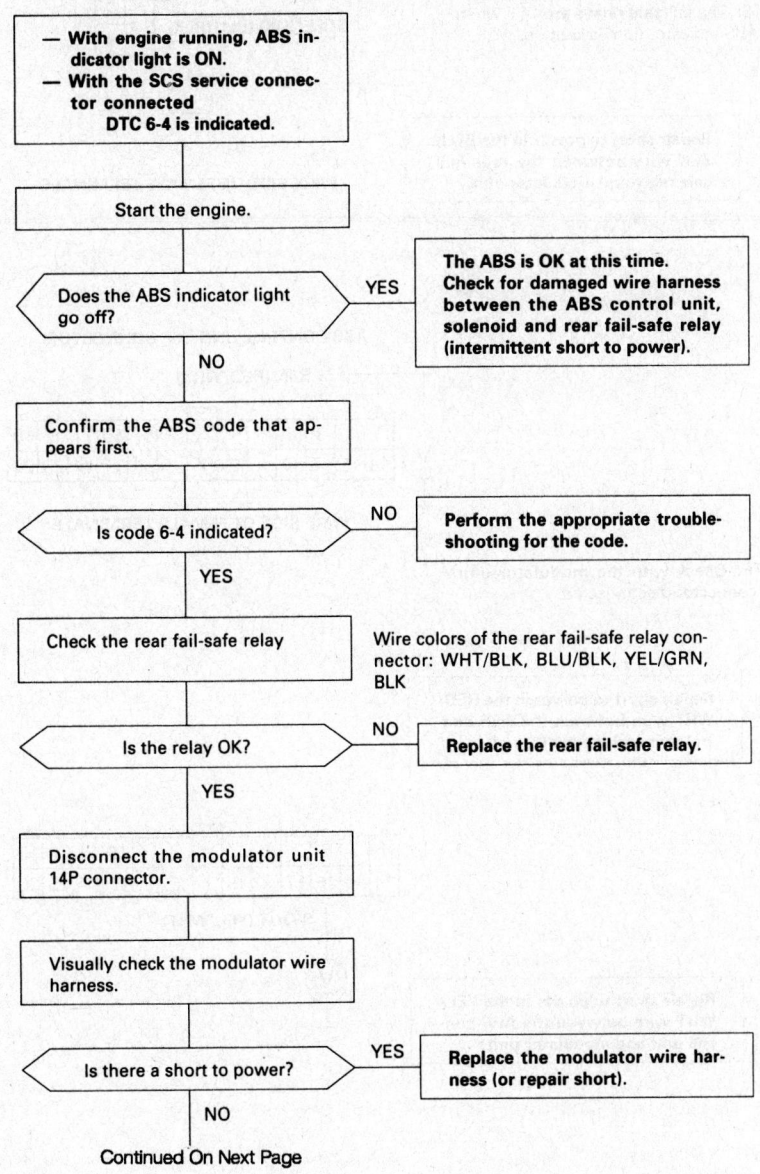

- With engine running, ABS indicator light is ON.
- With the SCS service connector connected
    DTC 6-4 is indicated.

Start the engine.

Does the ABS indicator light go off? — YES → The ABS is OK at this time. Check for damaged wire harness between the ABS control unit, solenoid and rear fail-safe relay (intermittent short to power).

NO

Confirm the ABS code that appears first.

Is code 6-4 indicated? — NO → Perform the appropriate troubleshooting for the code.

YES

Check the rear fail-safe relay

Wire colors of the rear fail-safe relay connector: WHT/BLK, BLU/BLK, YEL/GRN, BLK

Is the relay OK? — NO → Replace the rear fail-safe relay.

YES

Disconnect the modulator unit 14P connector.

Visually check the modulator wire harness.

Is there a short to power? — YES → Replace the modulator wire harness (or repair short).

NO

Continued On Next Page

94E47286

Courtesy of American Honda Motor Co., Inc.

DTC 6-4 (2 OF 2)
REAR FAIL-SAFE RELAY CIRCUIT

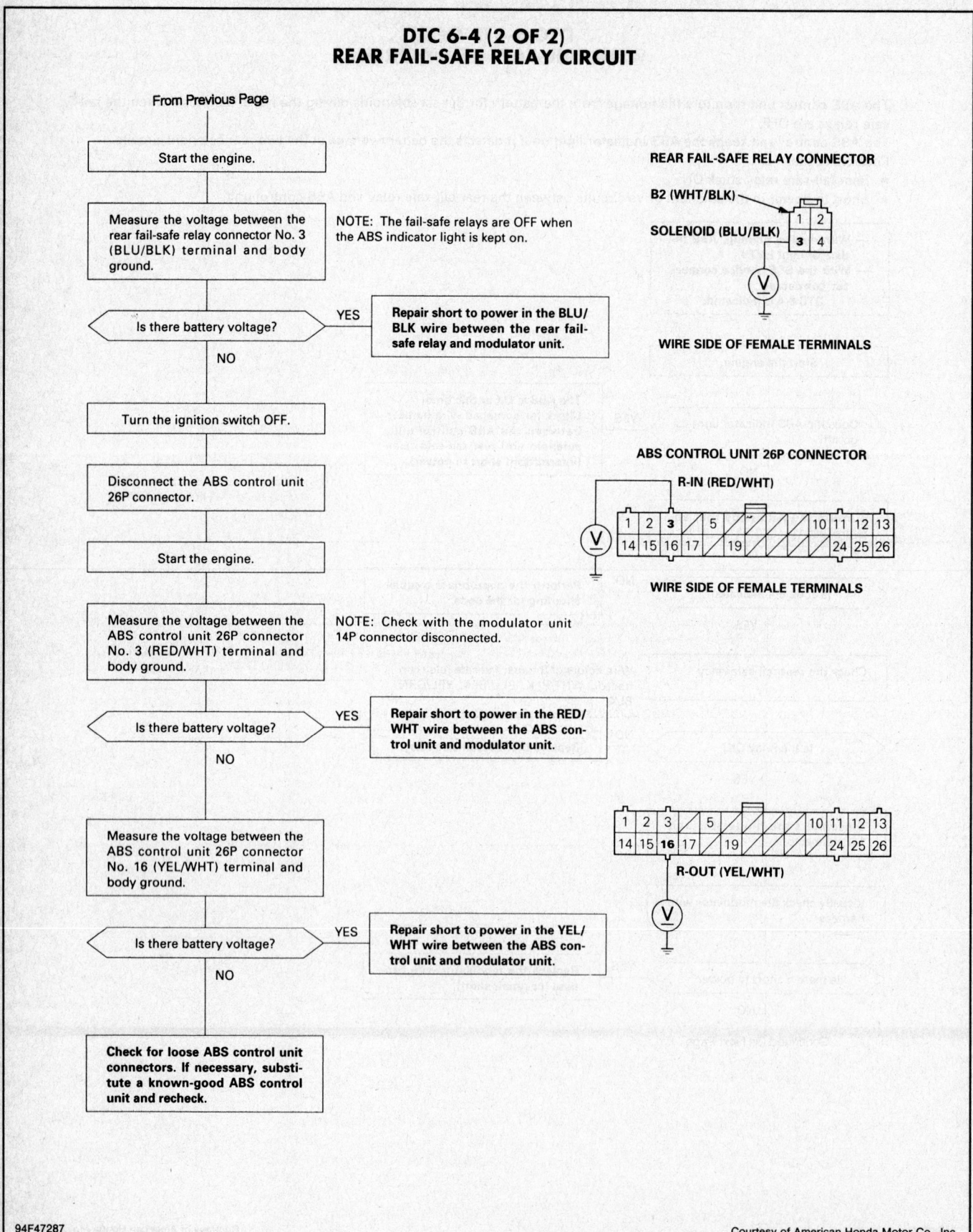

From Previous Page

Start the engine.

Measure the voltage between the rear fail-safe relay connector No. 3 (BLU/BLK) terminal and body ground.

NOTE: The fail-safe relays are OFF when the ABS indicator light is kept on.

Is there battery voltage?

YES — Repair short to power in the BLU/BLK wire between the rear fail-safe relay and modulator unit.

NO

Turn the ignition switch OFF.

Disconnect the ABS control unit 26P connector.

Start the engine.

Measure the voltage between the ABS control unit 26P connector No. 3 (RED/WHT) terminal and body ground.

NOTE: Check with the modulator unit 14P connector disconnected.

Is there battery voltage?

YES — Repair short to power in the RED/WHT wire between the ABS control unit and modulator unit.

NO

Measure the voltage between the ABS control unit 26P connector No. 16 (YEL/WHT) terminal and body ground.

Is there battery voltage?

YES — Repair short to power in the YEL/WHT wire between the ABS control unit and modulator unit.

NO

Check for loose ABS control unit connectors. If necessary, substitute a known-good ABS control unit and recheck.

REAR FAIL-SAFE RELAY CONNECTOR

B2 (WHT/BLK)

SOLENOID (BLU/BLK)

WIRE SIDE OF FEMALE TERMINALS

ABS CONTROL UNIT 26P CONNECTOR

R-IN (RED/WHT)

WIRE SIDE OF FEMALE TERMINALS

R-OUT (YEL/WHT)

94F47287

Courtesy of American Honda Motor Co., Inc.

DTC 7-1 (1 OF 4)
RIGHT FRONT SOLENOID

During the initial diagnosis, after the fail-safe relays are turned on, and during the regular diagnosis, the ABS control unit monitors the voltage from the battery for the six solenoids (when the ABS is not functioning).

If the detection circuit for the right-front solenoid detects 0 V, the ABS control unit keeps the ABS indicator light on after the engine is started. It turns the ABS indicator light on again if it detects 0 V after the light goes off.

Possible causes:

- Open circuit in the right-front solenoid drive circuits between the front fail-safe relay and ABS control unit
- Short circuit to body ground in the right-front solenoid drive circuits between the solenoids and ABS control unit
- Faulty right-front solenoid drive transistor (ON) in the ABS control unit

The ABS control unit momentarily outputs the ON signal to each solenoid (too momentary to turn the solenoid on) during the initial diagnosis, and each time the car is started, to check the voltage from the battery with the detection circuit.

If the detection circuit for the right-front solenoids detects battery voltage at this time, the ABS control unit keeps the ABS indicator light on. It turns the ABS indicator light on again if it detects battery voltage when the car is started.

Possible causes:

- Short circuit to power in the right-front solenoid drive circuits between the solenoids and ABS control unit
- Faulty right-front solenoid drive transistor (OFF) in the ABS control unit
- Short circuit to power in the right-front solenoid drive circuits in the modulator wire harness or solenoids
- Short circuit to the right-front solenoid outlet circuit in the inlet circuit between the solenoid and ABS control unit

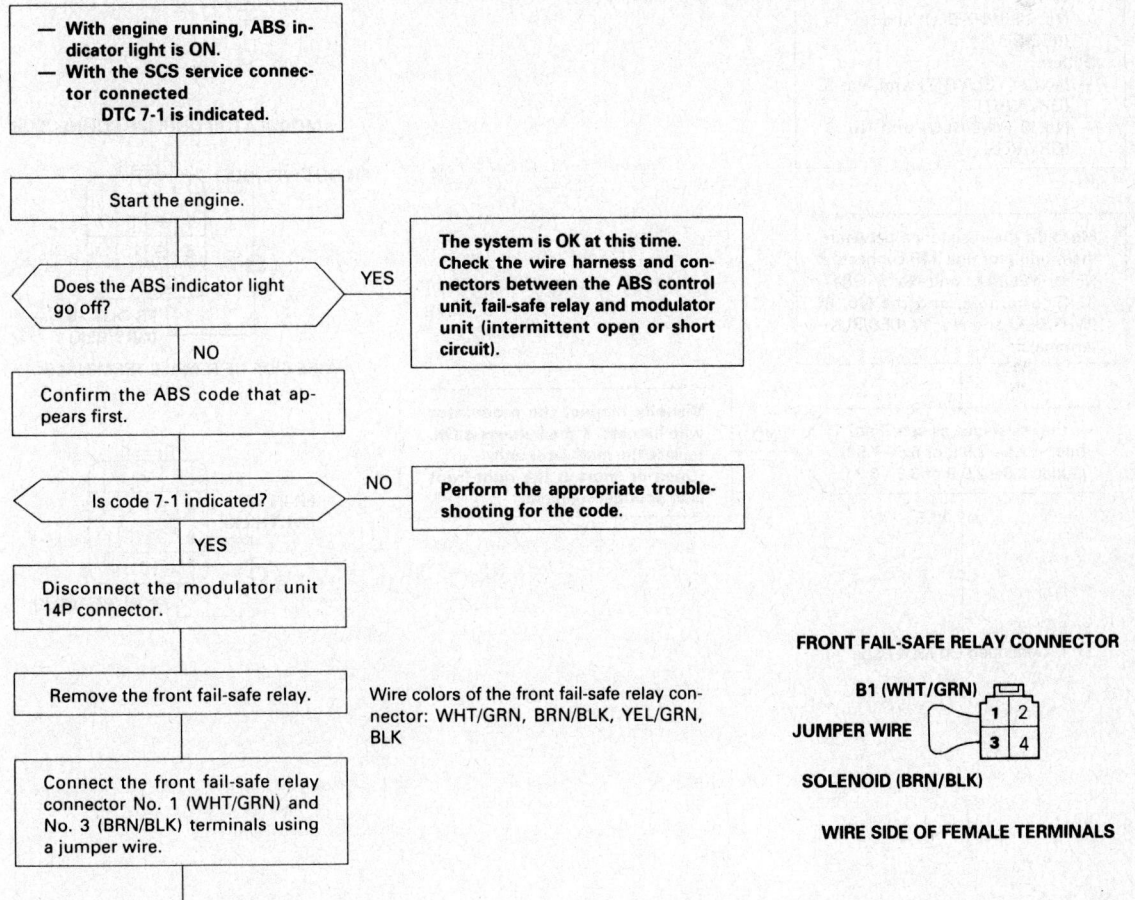

Continued On Next Page

1994 BRAKES
Anti-Lock – Accord (Cont.)

DTC 7-1 (2 OF 4)
RIGHT FRONT SOLENOID

From Previous Page

Measure the voltage between the modulator unit 14P connector No. 5 (BRN/BLK) and No. 8 (BRN/BLK) terminals and body ground.

Is there battery voltage?

NO → Repair open in the BRN/BLK wire(s) between the front fail-safe relay and modulator unit.

YES

Measure the resistance between the modulator unit 14P connector terminals to determine the solenoid standard resistance (A type or B type).
Inlet:
— No. 9 (WHT) and No. 13 (RED/WHT)
— No. 10 (WHT/BLU) and No. 14 (RED/BLU)
Outlet:
— No. 2 (YEL/WHT) and No. 6 (GRY/WHT)
— No. 3 (YEL/BLU) and No. 7 (GRY/BLU)

NOTE:

	STANDARD RESISTANCE	
	A TYPE	B TYPE
Inlet Solenoid	2.5 – 2.9 Ω	6.5 – 7.5 Ω
Outlet Solenoid	2.5 – 2.9 Ω	3.3 – 3.9 Ω

Measure the resistance between the modulator unit 14P connector No. 1 (YEL/BLK) and No. 5 (GRY/BLK) terminals, and the No. 8 (WHT/BLK) and No. 12 (RED/BLK) terminals.

Is the resistance as specified?
Inlet: 2.5 – 2.9 Ω or 6.5 – 7.5 Ω
Outlet: 2.5 – 2.9 Ω or 3.3 – 3.9 Ω

NO → Visually inspect the modulator wire harness. If the harness is OK, replace the modulator unit. (Open or short in the right-front inlet or outlet solenoid)

YES

Continued On Next Page

MODULATOR UNIT 14P CONNECTOR

FR-OUT +B (BRN/BLK)

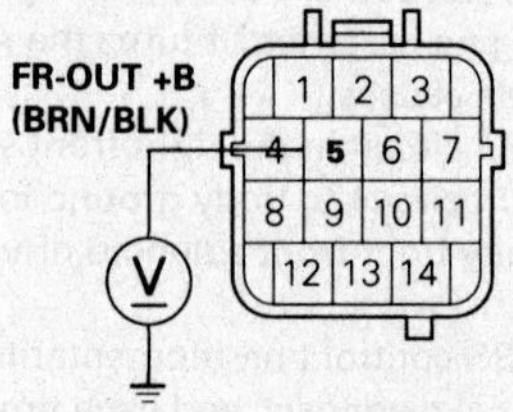

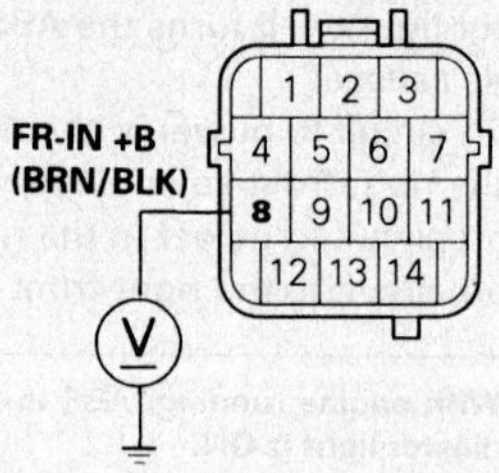

TERMINAL SIDE OF MALE TERMINALS

FR-IN +B (BRN/BLK)

MODULATOR UNIT 14P CONNECTOR

FR-OUT (YEL/BLK)

FR-OUT +B (GRY/BLK)

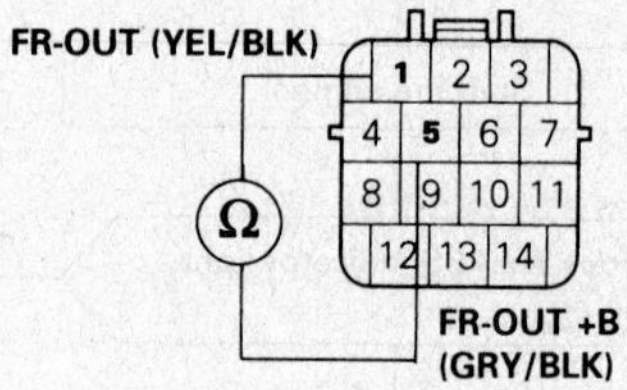

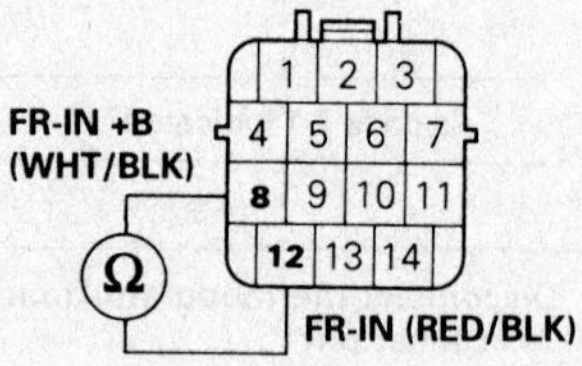

WIRE SIDE OF FEMALE TERMINALS

FR-IN +B (WHT/BLK)

FR-IN (RED/BLK)

DTC 7-1 (3 OF 4)
RIGHT FRONT SOLENOID

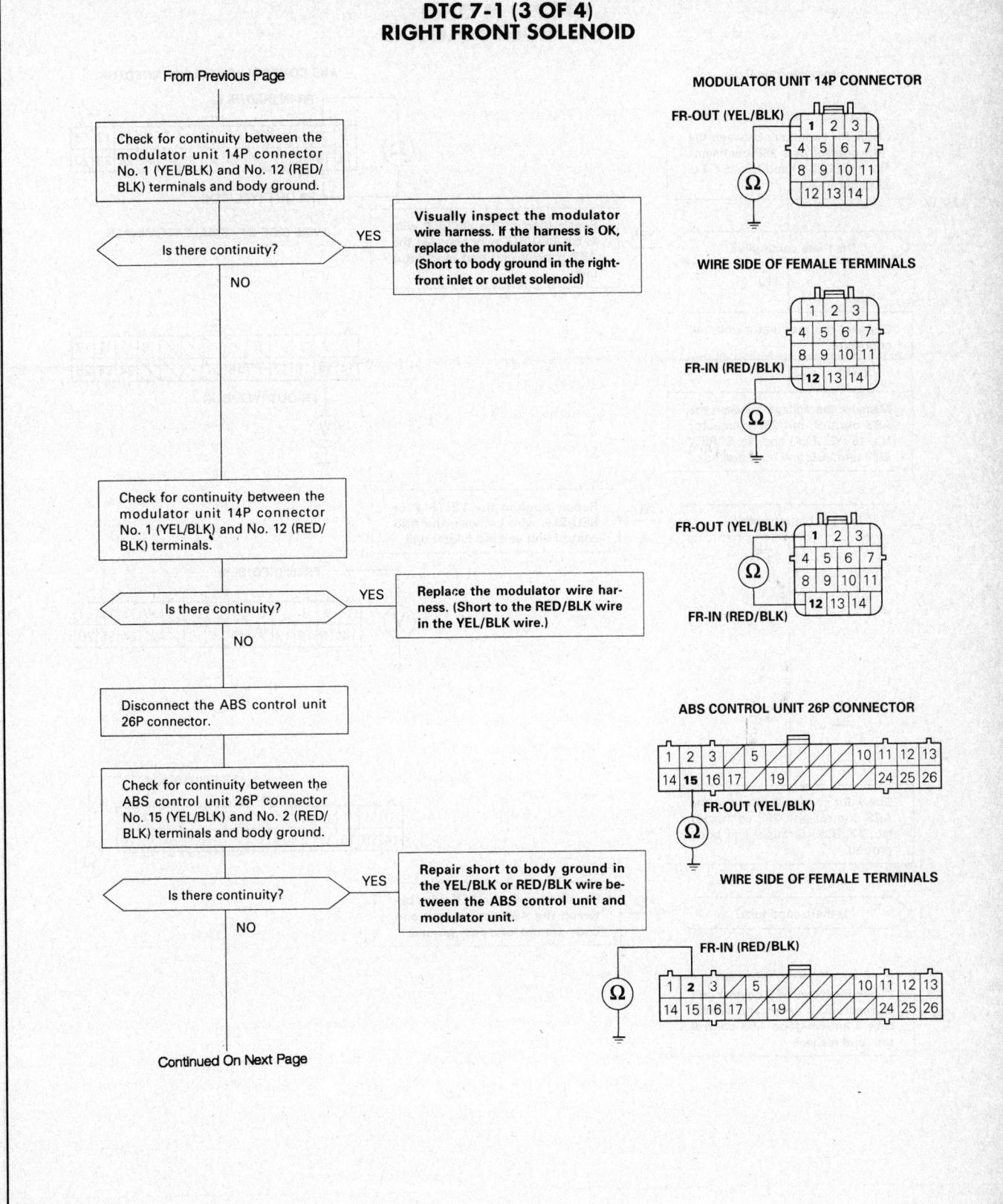

From Previous Page

Check for continuity between the modulator unit 14P connector No. 1 (YEL/BLK) and No. 12 (RED/BLK) terminals and body ground.

Is there continuity? — YES → Visually inspect the modulator wire harness. If the harness is OK, replace the modulator unit. (Short to body ground in the right-front inlet or outlet solenoid)

NO

Check for continuity between the modulator unit 14P connector No. 1 (YEL/BLK) and No. 12 (RED/BLK) terminals.

Is there continuity? — YES → Replace the modulator wire harness. (Short to the RED/BLK wire in the YEL/BLK wire.)

NO

Disconnect the ABS control unit 26P connector.

Check for continuity between the ABS control unit 26P connector No. 15 (YEL/BLK) and No. 2 (RED/BLK) terminals and body ground.

Is there continuity? — YES → Repair short to body ground in the YEL/BLK or RED/BLK wire between the ABS control unit and modulator unit.

NO

Continued On Next Page

MODULATOR UNIT 14P CONNECTOR

FR-OUT (YEL/BLK)

WIRE SIDE OF FEMALE TERMINALS

FR-IN (RED/BLK)

FR-OUT (YEL/BLK)

FR-IN (RED/BLK)

ABS CONTROL UNIT 26P CONNECTOR

FR-OUT (YEL/BLK)

WIRE SIDE OF FEMALE TERMINALS

FR-IN (RED/BLK)

94A47290

Courtesy of American Honda Motor Co., Inc.

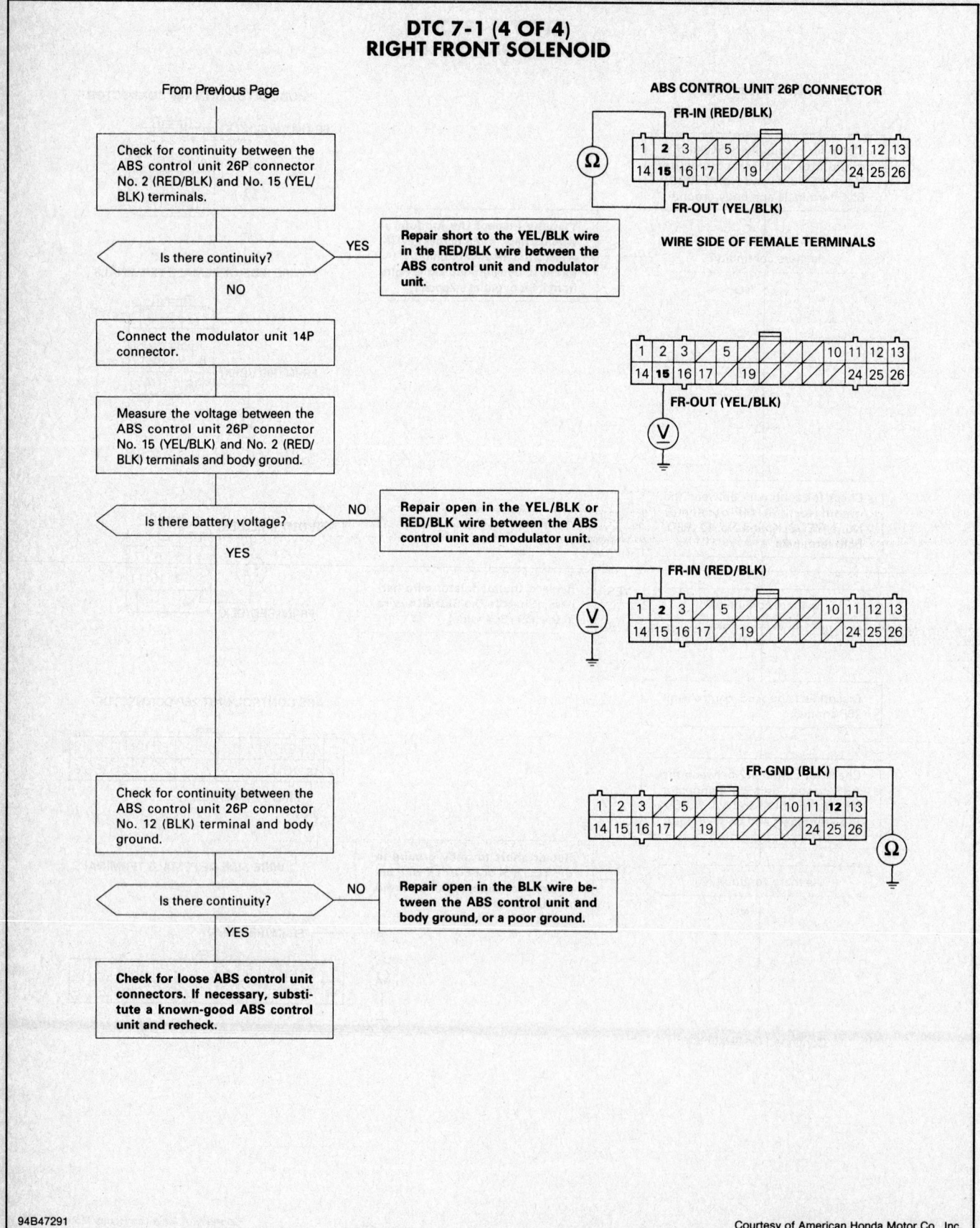

DTC 7-1 (4 OF 4)
RIGHT FRONT SOLENOID

DTC 7-2 (1 OF 7)
LEFT FRONT SOLENOID

During the initial diagnosis, after the fail-safe relays are turned on, and during the regular diagnosis, the ABS control unit monitors the voltage from the battery for the six solenoids (when the ABS is not functioning).

If the detection circuit for the left-front solenoid detects 0 V, the ABS control unit keeps the ABS indicator light on after the engine is started. It turns the ABS indicator light on again if it detects 0 V after the light goes off.

Possible causes:

- Front fail-safe relay stuck OFF
- Open circuit in the left-front solenoid drive circuits between the under-hood ABS fuse/relay box and ABS control unit
- Short circuit to body ground in the left-front solenoid drive circuits between the solenoids and ABS control unit
- Faulty left-front solenoid drive transistor (ON) in the ABS control unit

The ABS control unit momentarily outputs the ON signal to each solenoid (too momentary to turn the solenoid on) during the initial diagnosis, and each time the car is started, to check the voltage from the battery with the detection circuit.

If the detection circuit for the left-front solenoids detects battery voltage at this time, the ABS control unit keeps the ABS indicator light on. It turns the ABS indicator light on again if it detects the battery voltage when the car is started.

Possible causes:

- Short circuit to power in the left-front solenoid drive circuits between the solenoids and ABS control unit
- Faulty left front solenoid drive transistor (OFF) in the ABS control unit
- Short circuit to power in the left-front solenoid drive circuits in the modulator wire harness or solenoids
- Short circuit to the left-front solenoid outlet circuit in the inlet circuit between the solenoids and ABS control unit
- Short circuit to the right-front solenoid inlet or outlet circuit in the left-front solenoid inlet or outlet circuit between the solenoids and ABS control unit

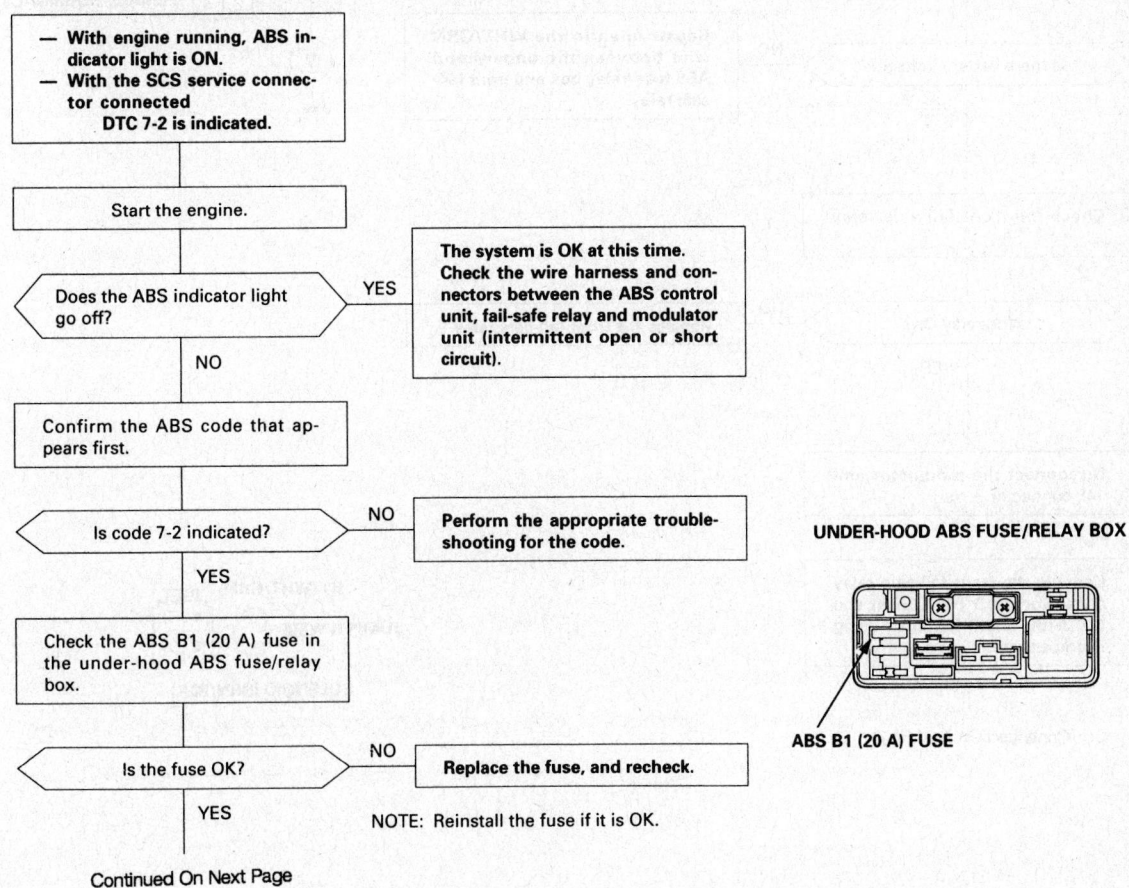

— With engine running, ABS indicator light is ON.
— With the SCS service connector connected
  DTC 7-2 is indicated.

Start the engine.

Does the ABS indicator light go off? — **YES** → The system is OK at this time. Check the wire harness and connectors between the ABS control unit, fail-safe relay and modulator unit (intermittent open or short circuit).

NO

Confirm the ABS code that appears first.

Is code 7-2 indicated? — **NO** → Perform the appropriate troubleshooting for the code.

YES

Check the ABS B1 (20 A) fuse in the under-hood ABS fuse/relay box.

Is the fuse OK? — **NO** → **Replace the fuse, and recheck.**

YES

NOTE: Reinstall the fuse if it is OK.

Continued On Next Page

UNDER-HOOD ABS FUSE/RELAY BOX

ABS B1 (20 A) FUSE

DTC 7-2 (2 OF 7)
LEFT FRONT SOLENOID

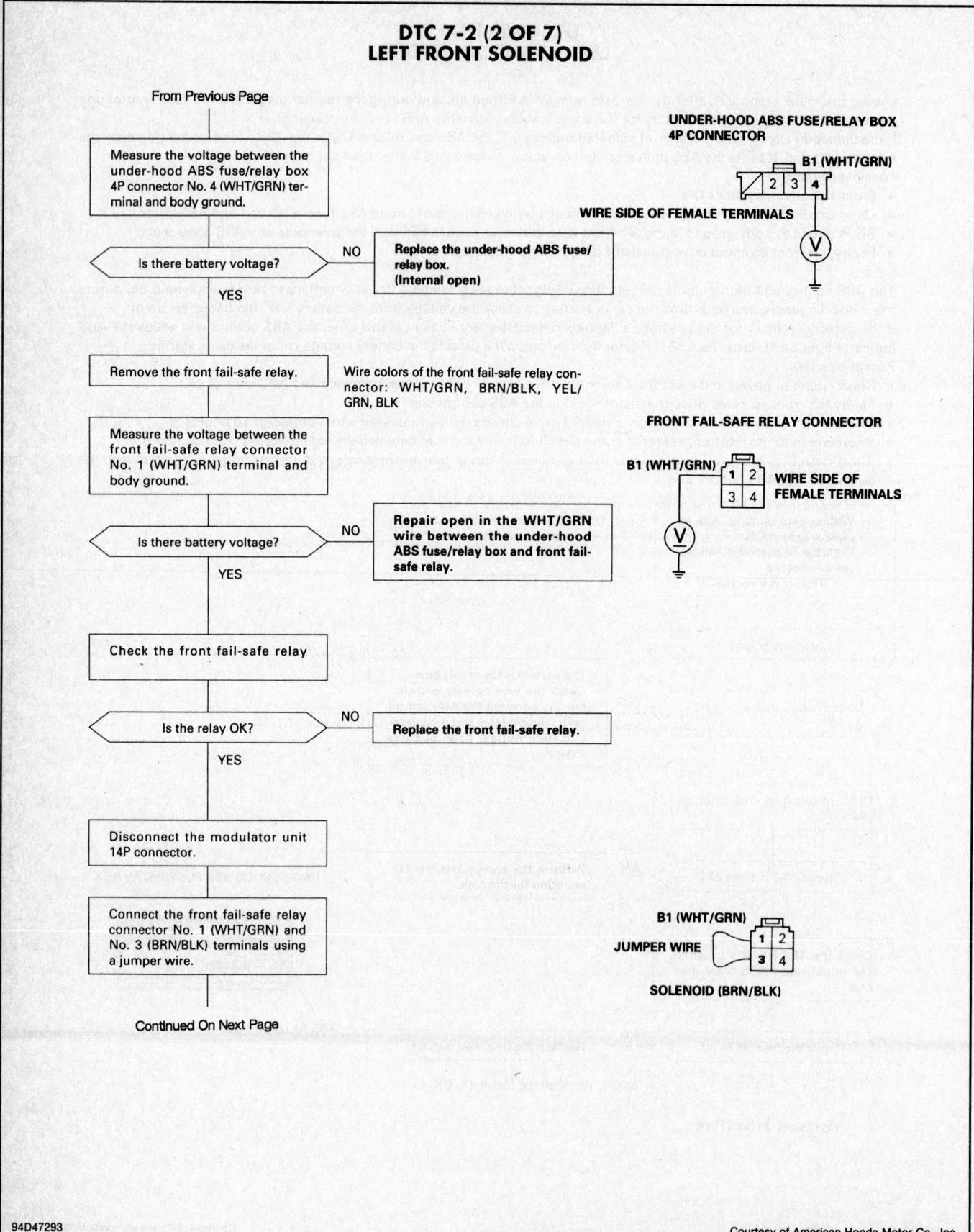

From Previous Page

Measure the voltage between the under-hood ABS fuse/relay box 4P connector No. 4 (WHT/GRN) terminal and body ground.

Is there battery voltage? — NO → Replace the under-hood ABS fuse/relay box. (Internal open)

YES

Remove the front fail-safe relay.

Wire colors of the front fail-safe relay connector: WHT/GRN, BRN/BLK, YEL/GRN, BLK

Measure the voltage between the front fail-safe relay connector No. 1 (WHT/GRN) terminal and body ground.

Is there battery voltage? — NO → Repair open in the WHT/GRN wire between the under-hood ABS fuse/relay box and front fail-safe relay.

YES

Check the front fail-safe relay

Is the relay OK? — NO → Replace the front fail-safe relay.

YES

Disconnect the modulator unit 14P connector.

Connect the front fail-safe relay connector No. 1 (WHT/GRN) and No. 3 (BRN/BLK) terminals using a jumper wire.

Continued On Next Page

UNDER-HOOD ABS FUSE/RELAY BOX
4P CONNECTOR

B1 (WHT/GRN)

WIRE SIDE OF FEMALE TERMINALS

FRONT FAIL-SAFE RELAY CONNECTOR

B1 (WHT/GRN)

WIRE SIDE OF FEMALE TERMINALS

B1 (WHT/GRN)

JUMPER WIRE

SOLENOID (BRN/BLK)

DTC 7-2 (3 OF 7)
LEFT FRONT SOLENOID

From Previous Page

Measure the voltage between the modulator unit 14P connector No. 7 (BRN/BLK) and No. 10 (BRN/BLK) terminals and body ground.

Is there battery voltage? — NO → Repair open in the BRN/BLK wire(s) between the front fail-safe relay and modulator unit.

YES

Measure the resistance between the modulator unit 14P connector terminals to determine the solenoid standard resistance (A type or B type).
Inlet:
— No. 8 (WHT/BLK) and No. 12 (RED/BLK)
— No. 9 (WHT) and No. 13 (RED/WHT)
Outlet:
— No. 1 (YEL/BLK) and No. 5 (GRY/BLK)
— No. 2 (YEL/WHT) and No. 6 (GRY/WHT)

NOTE:

	STANDARD RESISTANCE	
	A TYPE	B TYPE
Inlet Solenoid	2.5 – 2.9 Ω	6.5 – 7.5 Ω
Outlet Solenoid	2.5 – 2.9 Ω	3.3 – 3.9 Ω

Measure the resistance between the modulator unit 14P connector No. 3 (YEL/BLU) and No. 7 (GRY/BLU) terminals, and the No. 10 (WHT/BLU) and No. 14 (RED/BLU) terminals.

Is the resistance as specified?
Inlet: 2.5 – 2.9 Ω or 6.5 – 7.5 Ω
Outlet: 2.5 – 2.9 Ω or 3.3 – 3.9 Ω — NO → Visually inspect the modulator wire harness. If the wire harness is OK, replace the modulator unit. (Open or short in the left-front inlet or outlet solenoid)

YES

Continued On Next Page

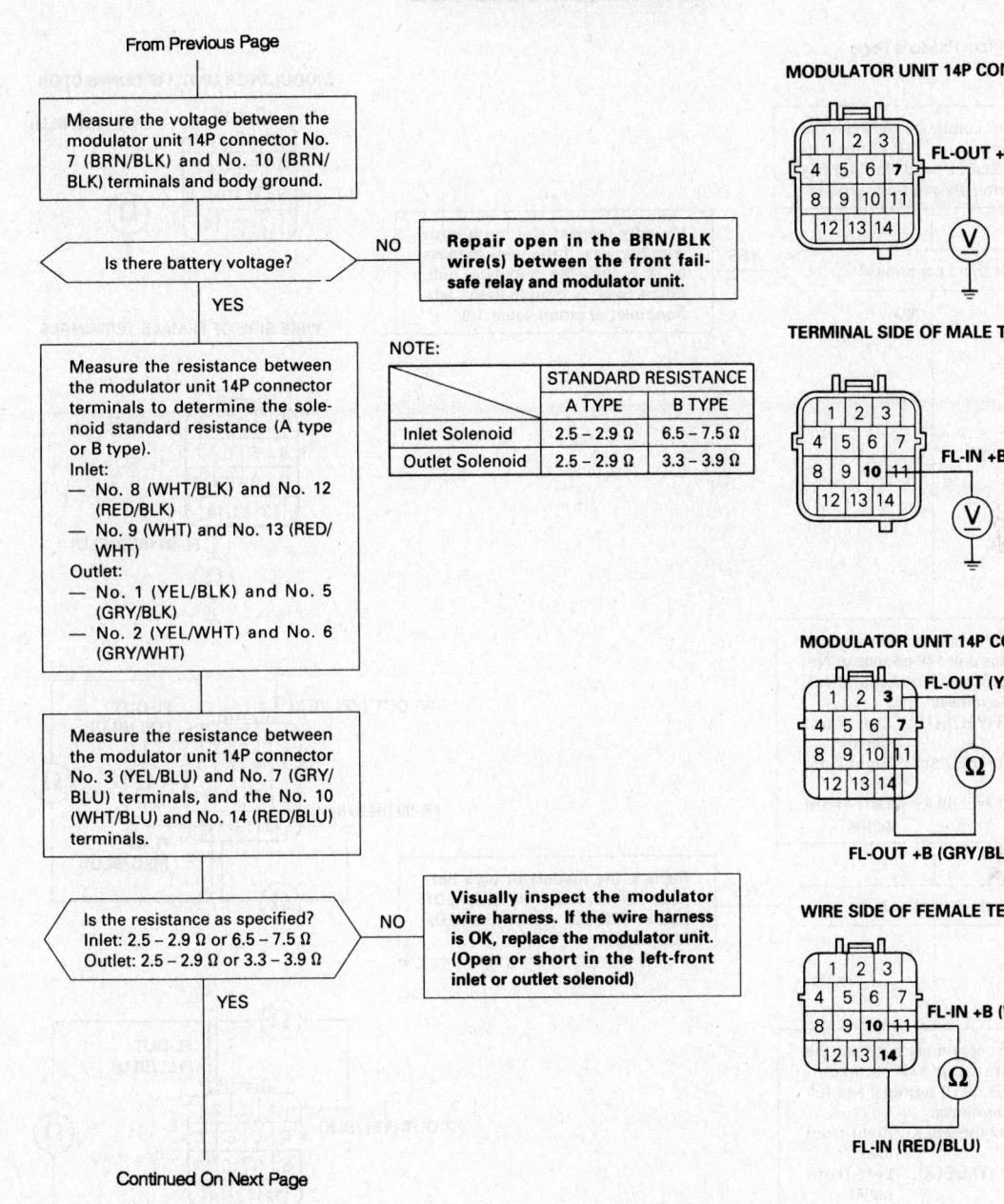

MODULATOR UNIT 14P CONNECTOR

FL-OUT +B (BRN/BLK)

TERMINAL SIDE OF MALE TERMINALS

FL-IN +B (BRN/BLK)

MODULATOR UNIT 14P CONNECTOR

FL-OUT (YEL/BLU)

FL-OUT +B (GRY/BLU)

WIRE SIDE OF FEMALE TERMINALS

FL-IN +B (WHT/BLU)

FL-IN (RED/BLU)

94E47294

Courtesy of American Honda Motor Co., Inc.

DTC 7-2 (4 OF 7)
LEFT FRONT SOLENOID

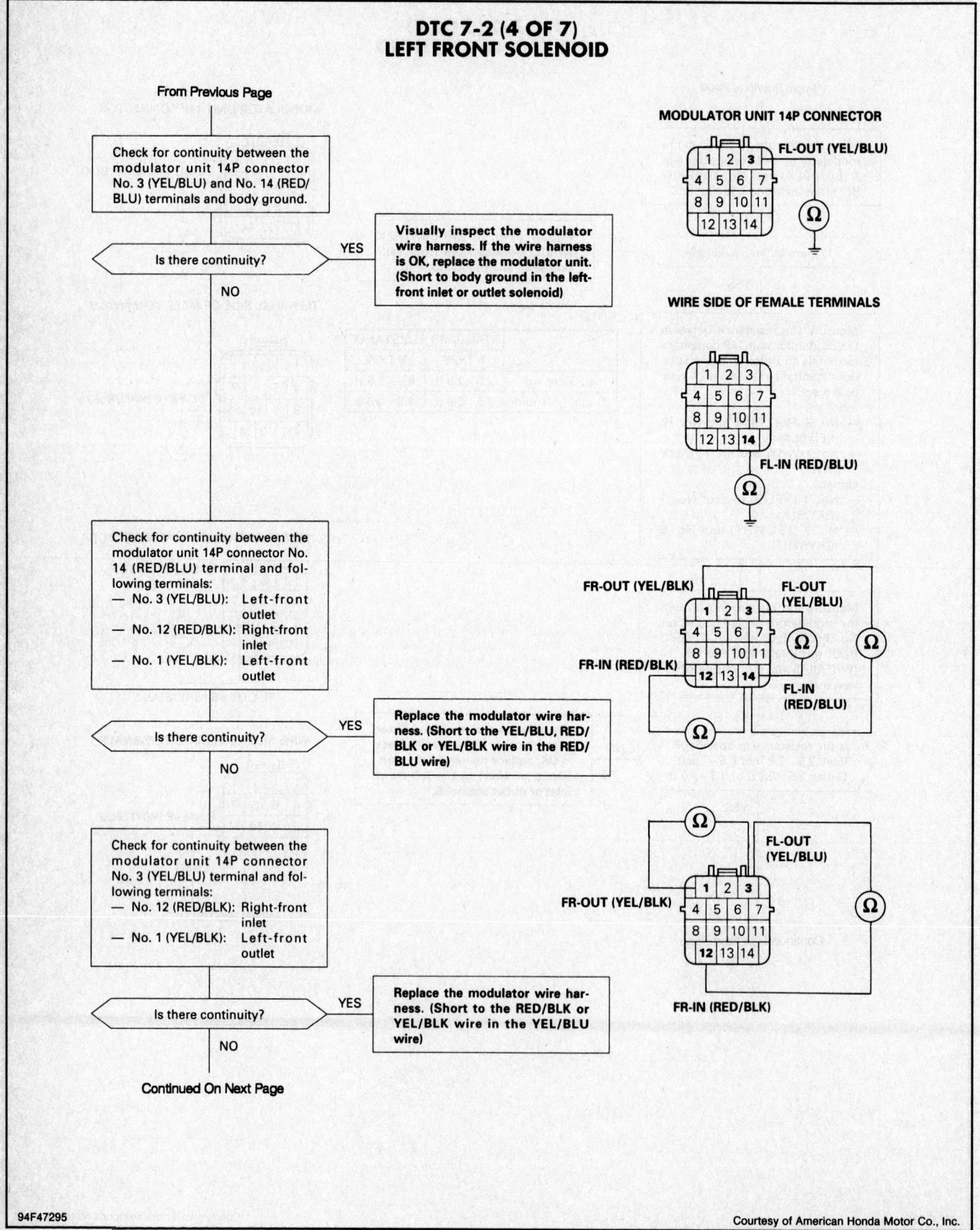

From Previous Page

Check for continuity between the modulator unit 14P connector No. 3 (YEL/BLU) and No. 14 (RED/BLU) terminals and body ground.

Is there continuity? — YES → Visually inspect the modulator wire harness. If the wire harness is OK, replace the modulator unit. (Short to body ground in the left-front inlet or outlet solenoid)

NO

MODULATOR UNIT 14P CONNECTOR
FL-OUT (YEL/BLU)

WIRE SIDE OF FEMALE TERMINALS

FL-IN (RED/BLU)

Check for continuity between the modulator unit 14P connector No. 14 (RED/BLU) terminal and following terminals:
— No. 3 (YEL/BLU): Left-front outlet
— No. 12 (RED/BLK): Right-front inlet
— No. 1 (YEL/BLK): Left-front outlet

Is there continuity? — YES → Replace the modulator wire harness. (Short to the YEL/BLU, RED/BLK or YEL/BLK wire in the RED/BLU wire)

NO

FR-OUT (YEL/BLK)   FL-OUT (YEL/BLU)

FR-IN (RED/BLK)   FL-IN (RED/BLU)

Check for continuity between the modulator unit 14P connector No. 3 (YEL/BLU) terminal and following terminals:
— No. 12 (RED/BLK): Right-front inlet
— No. 1 (YEL/BLK): Left-front outlet

Is there continuity? — YES → Replace the modulator wire harness. (Short to the RED/BLK or YEL/BLK wire in the YEL/BLU wire)

NO

FL-OUT (YEL/BLU)

FR-OUT (YEL/BLK)

FR-IN (RED/BLK)

Continued On Next Page

94F47295

DTC 7-2 (5 OF 7)
LEFT FRONT SOLENOID

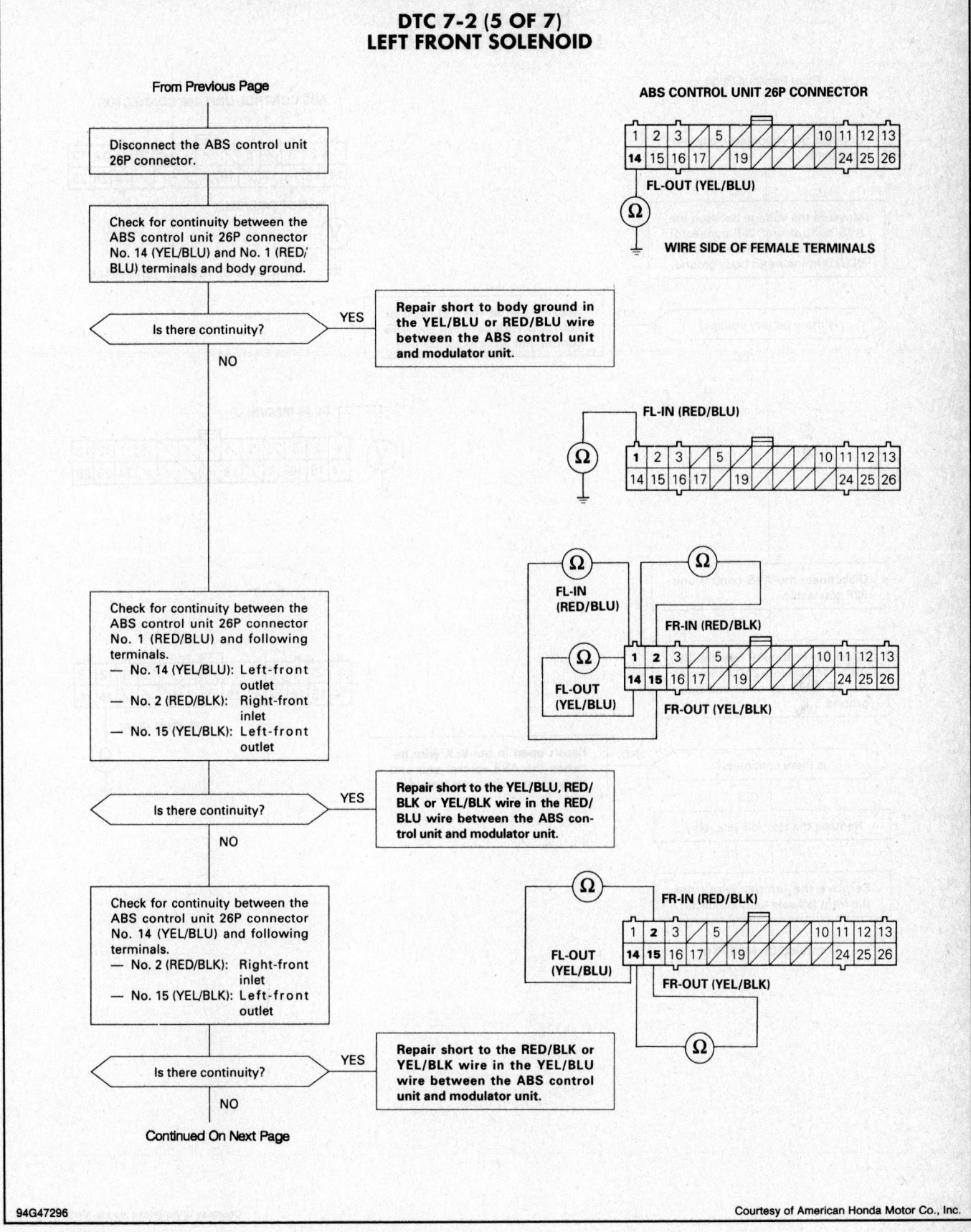

From Previous Page

Disconnect the ABS control unit 26P connector.

Check for continuity between the ABS control unit 26P connector No. 14 (YEL/BLU) and No. 1 (RED/BLU) terminals and body ground.

Is there continuity? — YES → Repair short to body ground in the YEL/BLU or RED/BLU wire between the ABS control unit and modulator unit.

NO

Check for continuity between the ABS control unit 26P connector No. 1 (RED/BLU) and following terminals.
— No. 14 (YEL/BLU): Left-front outlet
— No. 2 (RED/BLK): Right-front inlet
— No. 15 (YEL/BLK): Left-front outlet

Is there continuity? — YES → Repair short to the YEL/BLU, RED/BLK or YEL/BLK wire in the RED/BLU wire between the ABS control unit and modulator unit.

NO

Check for continuity between the ABS control unit 26P connector No. 14 (YEL/BLU) and following terminals.
— No. 2 (RED/BLK): Right-front inlet
— No. 15 (YEL/BLK): Left-front outlet

Is there continuity? — YES → Repair short to the RED/BLK or YEL/BLK wire in the YEL/BLU wire between the ABS control unit and modulator unit.

NO

Continued On Next Page

ABS CONTROL UNIT 26P CONNECTOR

FL-OUT (YEL/BLU)

WIRE SIDE OF FEMALE TERMINALS

FL-IN (RED/BLU)

FL-IN (RED/BLU)
FR-IN (RED/BLK)
FL-OUT (YEL/BLU)
FR-OUT (YEL/BLK)

FR-IN (RED/BLK)
FL-OUT (YEL/BLU)
FR-OUT (YEL/BLK)

DTC 7-2 (6 OF 7)
LEFT FRONT SOLENOID

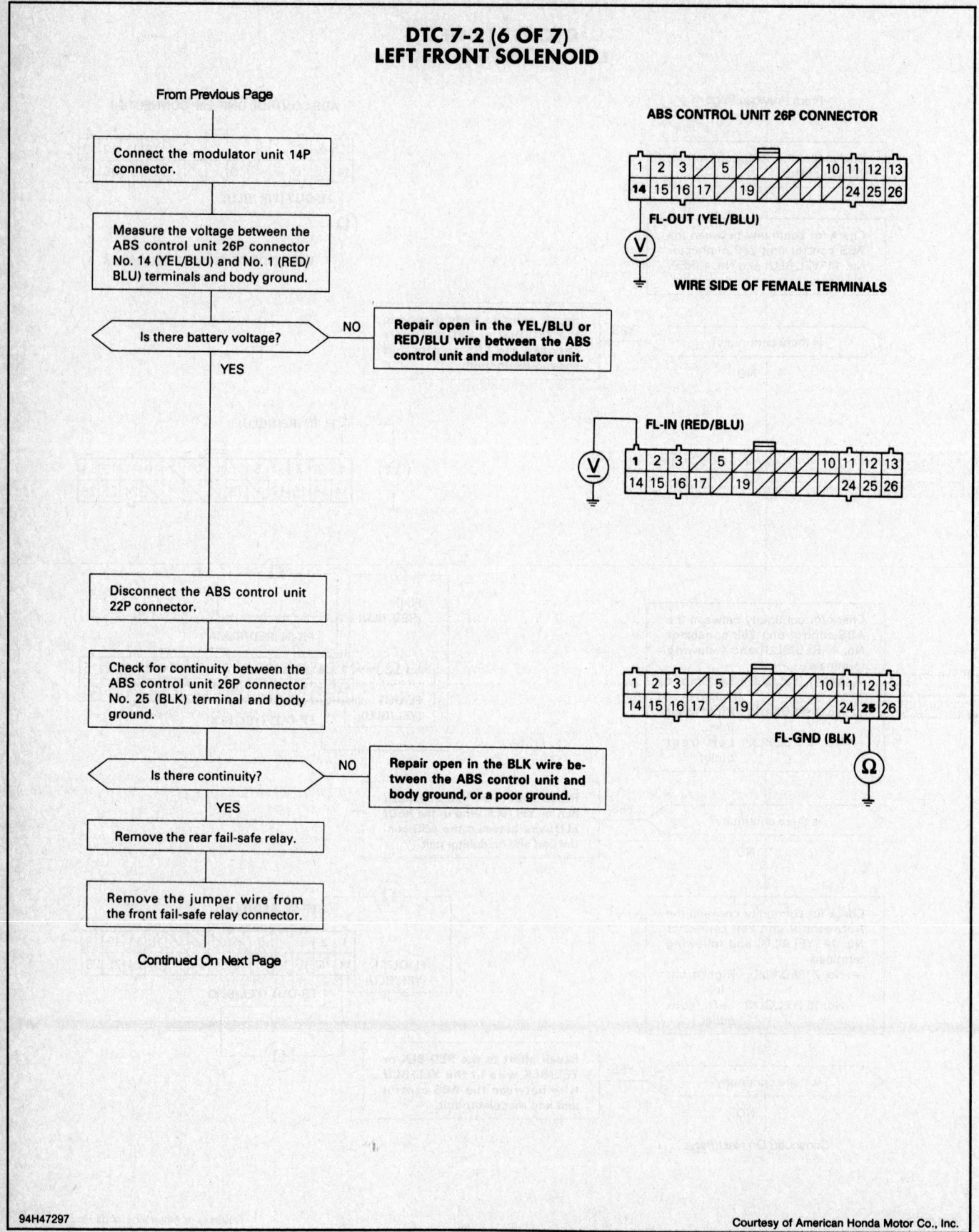

From Previous Page

Connect the modulator unit 14P connector.

Measure the voltage between the ABS control unit 26P connector No. 14 (YEL/BLU) and No. 1 (RED/BLU) terminals and body ground.

Is there battery voltage? — NO → Repair open in the YEL/BLU or RED/BLU wire between the ABS control unit and modulator unit.

YES

Disconnect the ABS control unit 22P connector.

Check for continuity between the ABS control unit 26P connector No. 25 (BLK) terminal and body ground.

Is there continuity? — NO → Repair open in the BLK wire between the ABS control unit and body ground, or a poor ground.

YES

Remove the rear fail-safe relay.

Remove the jumper wire from the front fail-safe relay connector.

Continued On Next Page

ABS CONTROL UNIT 26P CONNECTOR

FL-OUT (YEL/BLU)

WIRE SIDE OF FEMALE TERMINALS

FL-IN (RED/BLU)

FL-GND (BLK)

DTC 7-2 (7 OF 7)
LEFT FRONT SOLENOID

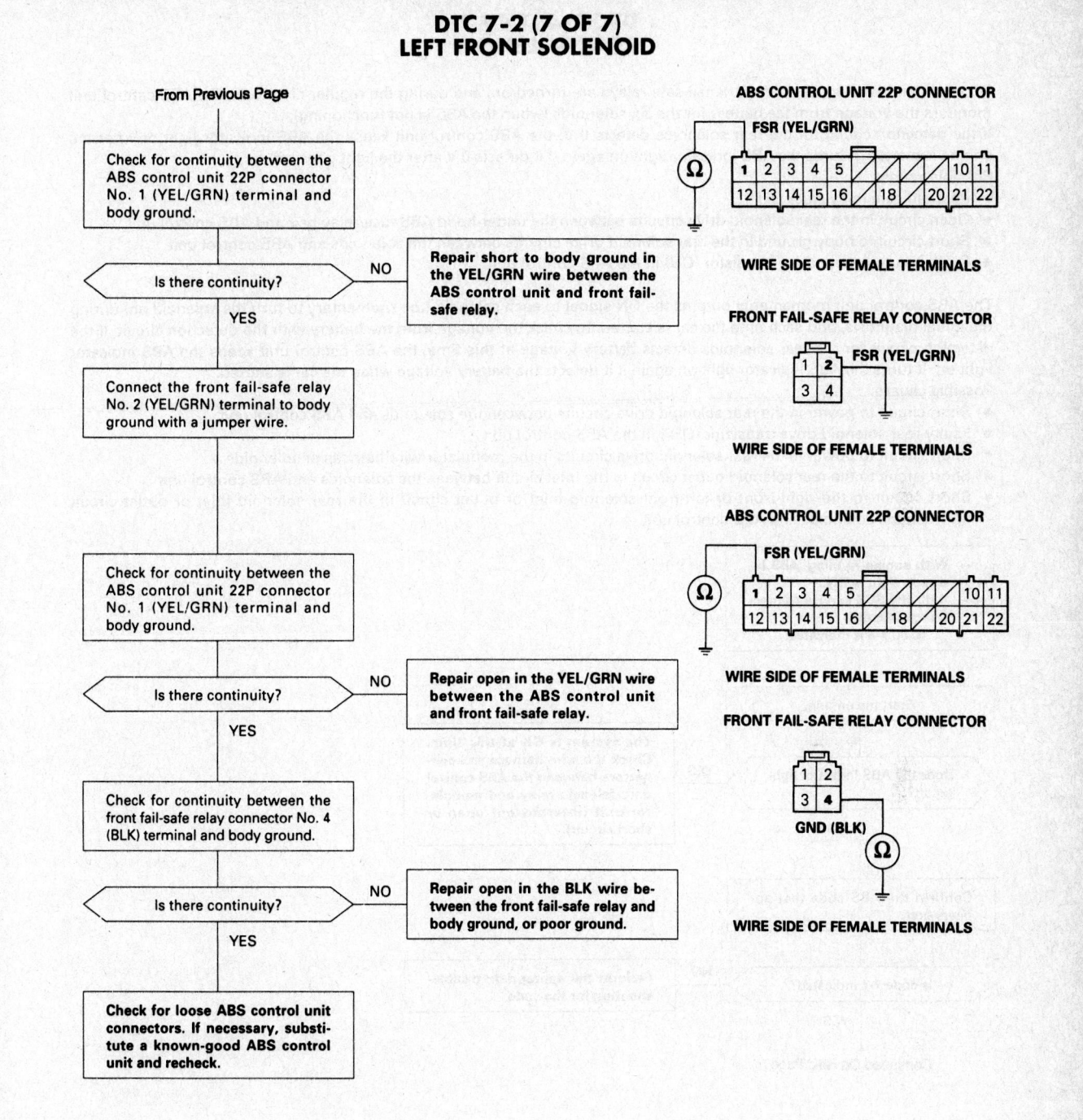

From Previous Page

Check for continuity between the ABS control unit 22P connector No. 1 (YEL/GRN) terminal and body ground.

Is there continuity? — NO → Repair short to body ground in the YEL/GRN wire between the ABS control unit and front fail-safe relay.

YES

Connect the front fail-safe relay No. 2 (YEL/GRN) terminal to body ground with a jumper wire.

Check for continuity between the ABS control unit 22P connector No. 1 (YEL/GRN) terminal and body ground.

Is there continuity? — NO → Repair open in the YEL/GRN wire between the ABS control unit and front fail-safe relay.

YES

Check for continuity between the front fail-safe relay connector No. 4 (BLK) terminal and body ground.

Is there continuity? — NO → Repair open in the BLK wire between the front fail-safe relay and body ground, or poor ground.

YES

Check for loose ABS control unit connectors. If necessary, substitute a known-good ABS control unit and recheck.

ABS CONTROL UNIT 22P CONNECTOR

FSR (YEL/GRN)

Ω

| 1 | 2 | 3 | 4 | 5 | | | | 10 | 11 |
| 12 | 13 | 14 | 15 | 16 | | 18 | | 20 | 21 | 22 |

WIRE SIDE OF FEMALE TERMINALS

FRONT FAIL-SAFE RELAY CONNECTOR

FSR (YEL/GRN)

| 1 | 2 |
| 3 | 4 |

WIRE SIDE OF FEMALE TERMINALS

ABS CONTROL UNIT 22P CONNECTOR

FSR (YEL/GRN)

Ω

| 1 | 2 | 3 | 4 | 5 | | | | 10 | 11 |
| 12 | 13 | 14 | 15 | 16 | | 18 | | 20 | 21 | 22 |

WIRE SIDE OF FEMALE TERMINALS

FRONT FAIL-SAFE RELAY CONNECTOR

| 1 | 2 |
| 3 | 4 |

GND (BLK)

Ω

WIRE SIDE OF FEMALE TERMINALS

DTC 7-4 (1 OF 7)
REAR SOLENOID

During the initial diagnosis, after the fail-safe relays are turned on, and during the regular diagnosis, the ABS control unit monitors the voltage from the battery for the six solenoids (when the ABS is not functioning).

If the detection circuit for the rear solenoids detects 0 V, the ABS control unit keeps the ABS indicator light on after the engine is started. It turns the ABS indicator light on again if it detects 0 V after the light goes off.

Possible causes:

- Rear fail-safe relay stuck OFF
- Open circuit in the rear solenoid drive circuits between the under-hood ABS fuse/relay box and ABS control unit
- Short circuit to body ground in the rear solenoid drive circuits between the solenoids and ABS control unit
- Faulty rear solenoid drive transistor (ON) in the ABS control unit

The ABS control unit momentarily outputs the ON signal to each solenoid (too momentary to turn the solenoid on) during the initial diagnosis, and each time the car is started, to check the voltage from the battery with the detection circuit. If the detection circuit for the rear solenoids detects battery voltage at this time, the ABS control unit keeps the ABS indicator light on. It turns the ABS indicator light on again if it detects the battery voltage when the car is started.

Possible causes:

- Short circuit to power in the rear solenoid drive circuits between the solenoids and ABS control unit
- Faulty rear solenoid drive transistor (OFF) in the ABS control unit
- Short circuit to power in the rear solenoid drive circuits in the modulator wire harness or solenoids
- Short circuit to the rear solenoid outlet circuit in the inlet circuit between the solenoids and ABS control unit
- Short circuit to the right-front or left-front solenoid inlet or outlet circuit in the rear solenoid inlet or outlet circuit between the solenoids and ABS control unit.

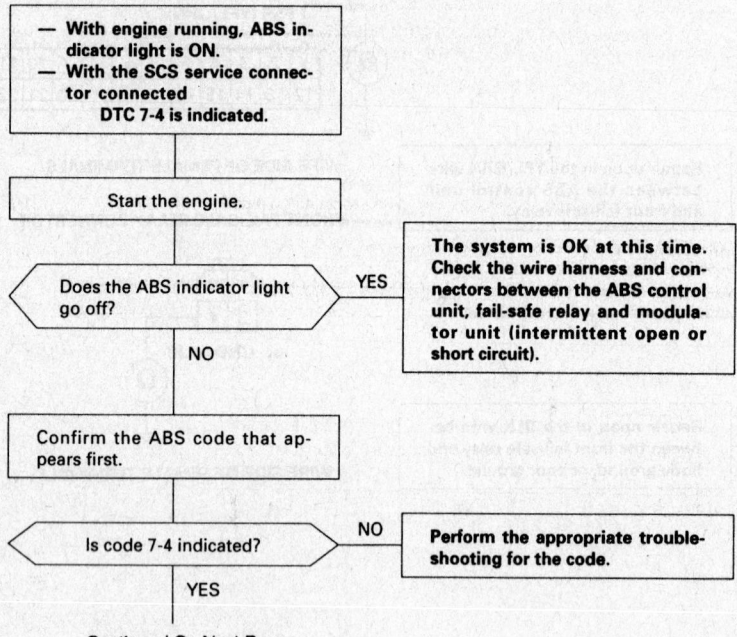

— With engine running, ABS indicator light is ON.
— With the SCS service connector connected
   DTC 7-4 is indicated.

Start the engine.

Does the ABS indicator light go off? — **YES** → The system is OK at this time. Check the wire harness and connectors between the ABS control unit, fail-safe relay and modulator unit (intermittent open or short circuit).

NO

Confirm the ABS code that appears first.

Is code 7-4 indicated? — **NO** → Perform the appropriate troubleshooting for the code.

YES

Continued On Next Page

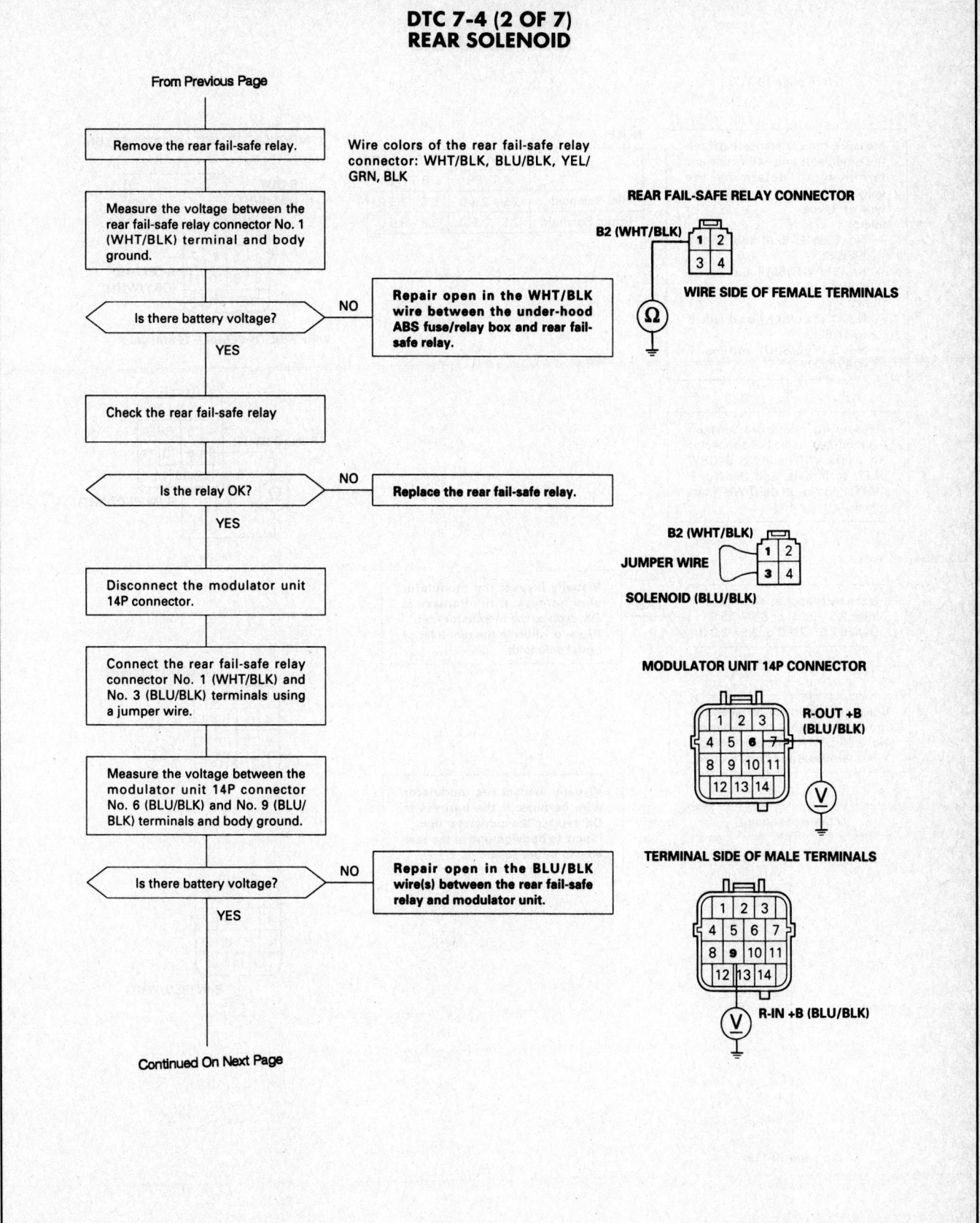

DTC 7-4 (2 OF 7)
REAR SOLENOID

From Previous Page

Remove the rear fail-safe relay.

Measure the voltage between the rear fail-safe relay connector No. 1 (WHT/BLK) terminal and body ground.

Is there battery voltage? — NO → Repair open in the WHT/BLK wire between the under-hood ABS fuse/relay box and rear fail-safe relay.

YES

Check the rear fail-safe relay

Is the relay OK? — NO → Replace the rear fail-safe relay.

YES

Disconnect the modulator unit 14P connector.

Connect the rear fail-safe relay connector No. 1 (WHT/BLK) and No. 3 (BLU/BLK) terminals using a jumper wire.

Measure the voltage between the modulator unit 14P connector No. 6 (BLU/BLK) and No. 9 (BLU/BLK) terminals and body ground.

Is there battery voltage? — NO → Repair open in the BLU/BLK wire(s) between the rear fail-safe relay and modulator unit.

YES

Continued On Next Page

Wire colors of the rear fail-safe relay connector: WHT/BLK, BLU/BLK, YEL/GRN, BLK

REAR FAIL-SAFE RELAY CONNECTOR

B2 (WHT/BLK)

WIRE SIDE OF FEMALE TERMINALS

B2 (WHT/BLK)
JUMPER WIRE
SOLENOID (BLU/BLK)

MODULATOR UNIT 14P CONNECTOR

R-OUT +B (BLU/BLK)

TERMINAL SIDE OF MALE TERMINALS

R-IN +B (BLU/BLK)

DTC 7-4 (3 OF 7)
REAR SOLENOID

(From page 19-117)

Measure the resistance between the modulator unit 14P connector terminals to determine the solenoid standard resistance (A type or B type).
Inlet:
— No. 8 (WHT/BLK) and No. 12 (RED/BLK)
— No. 10 (WHT/BLU) and No. 14 (RED/BLU)
Outlet:
— No. 1 (YEL/BLK) and No. 5 (GRY/BLK)
— No. 3 (YEL/BLU) and No. 7 (GRY/BLU)

NOTE:

	STANDARD RESISTANCE	
	A TYPE	B TYPE
Inlet Solenoid	2.5 – 2.9 Ω	6.5 – 7.5 Ω
Outlet Solenoid	2.5 – 2.9 Ω	3.3 – 3.9 Ω

MODULATOR UNIT 14P CONNECTOR

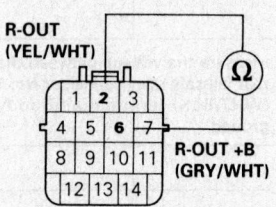

R-OUT (YEL/WHT)

R-OUT +B (GRY/WHT)

WIRE SIDE OF FEMALE TERMINALS

Measure the resistance between the modulator unit 14P connector No. 2 (YEL/WHT) and No. 6 (GRY/WHT) terminals, and the No. 9 (WHT) and No. 13 (RED/WHT) terminals.

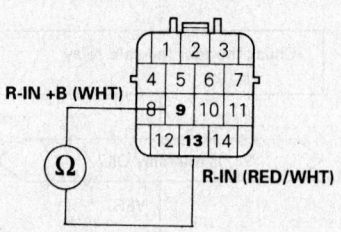

R-IN +B (WHT)

R-IN (RED/WHT)

Is the resistance as specified?
Inlet: 2.5 – 2.9 Ω or 6.5 – 7.5 Ω
Outlet: 2.5 – 2.9 Ω or 3.3 – 3.9 Ω

→ NO →

Visually inspect the modulator wire harness. If the harness is OK, replace the modulator unit. (Open or short in the rear inlet or outlet solenoid)

YES

Check for continuity between the modulator unit 14P connector No. 2 (YEL/WHT) and No. 13 (RED/WHT) terminals and body ground.

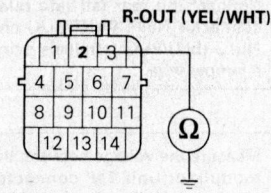

R-OUT (YEL/WHT)

Is there continuity?

→ YES →

Visually inspect the modulator wire harness. If the harness is OK, replace the modulator unit. (Short to body ground in the rear inlet or outlet solenoid)

NO

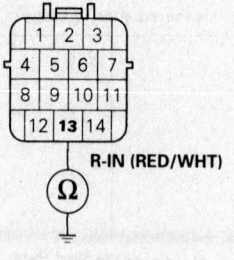

R-IN (RED/WHT)

(To page 19-119)

94D47301

DTC 7-4 (4 OF 7)
REAR SOLENOID

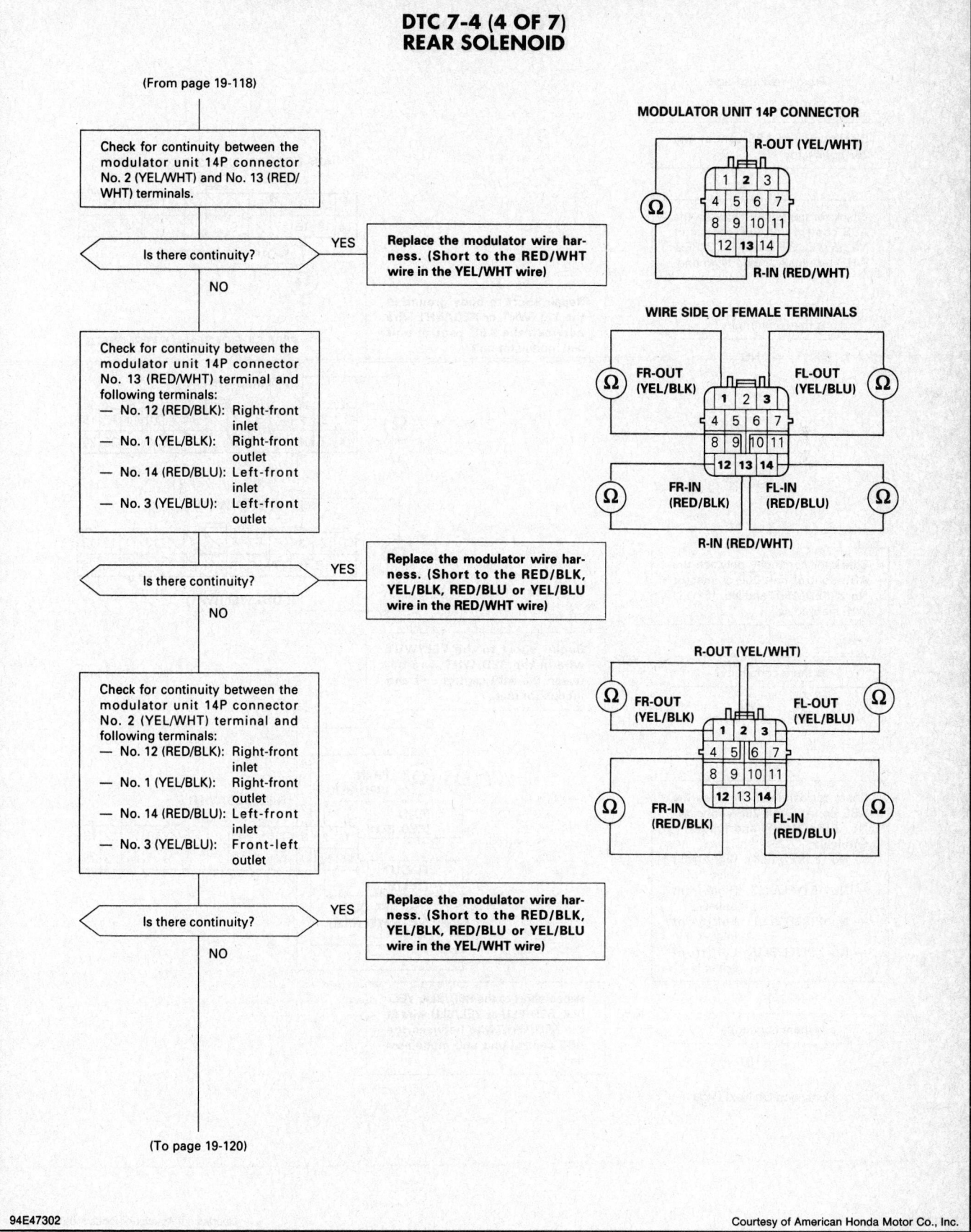

(From page 19-118)

Check for continuity between the modulator unit 14P connector No. 2 (YEL/WHT) and No. 13 (RED/WHT) terminals.

Is there continuity? — YES → Replace the modulator wire harness. (Short to the RED/WHT wire in the YEL/WHT wire)

NO

Check for continuity between the modulator unit 14P connector No. 13 (RED/WHT) terminal and following terminals:
— No. 12 (RED/BLK): Right-front inlet
— No. 1 (YEL/BLK): Right-front outlet
— No. 14 (RED/BLU): Left-front inlet
— No. 3 (YEL/BLU): Left-front outlet

Is there continuity? — YES → Replace the modulator wire harness. (Short to the RED/BLK, YEL/BLK, RED/BLU or YEL/BLU wire in the RED/WHT wire)

NO

Check for continuity between the modulator unit 14P connector No. 2 (YEL/WHT) terminal and following terminals:
— No. 12 (RED/BLK): Right-front inlet
— No. 1 (YEL/BLK): Right-front outlet
— No. 14 (RED/BLU): Left-front inlet
— No. 3 (YEL/BLU): Front-left outlet

Is there continuity? — YES → Replace the modulator wire harness. (Short to the RED/BLK, YEL/BLK, RED/BLU or YEL/BLU wire in the YEL/WHT wire)

NO

(To page 19-120)

MODULATOR UNIT 14P CONNECTOR

R-OUT (YEL/WHT)

R-IN (RED/WHT)

WIRE SIDE OF FEMALE TERMINALS

FR-OUT (YEL/BLK)   FL-OUT (YEL/BLU)

FR-IN (RED/BLK)   FL-IN (RED/BLU)

R-IN (RED/WHT)

R-OUT (YEL/WHT)

FR-OUT (YEL/BLK)   FL-OUT (YEL/BLU)

FR-IN (RED/BLK)   FL-IN (RED/BLU)

94E47302

DTC 7-4 (5 OF 7)
REAR SOLENOID

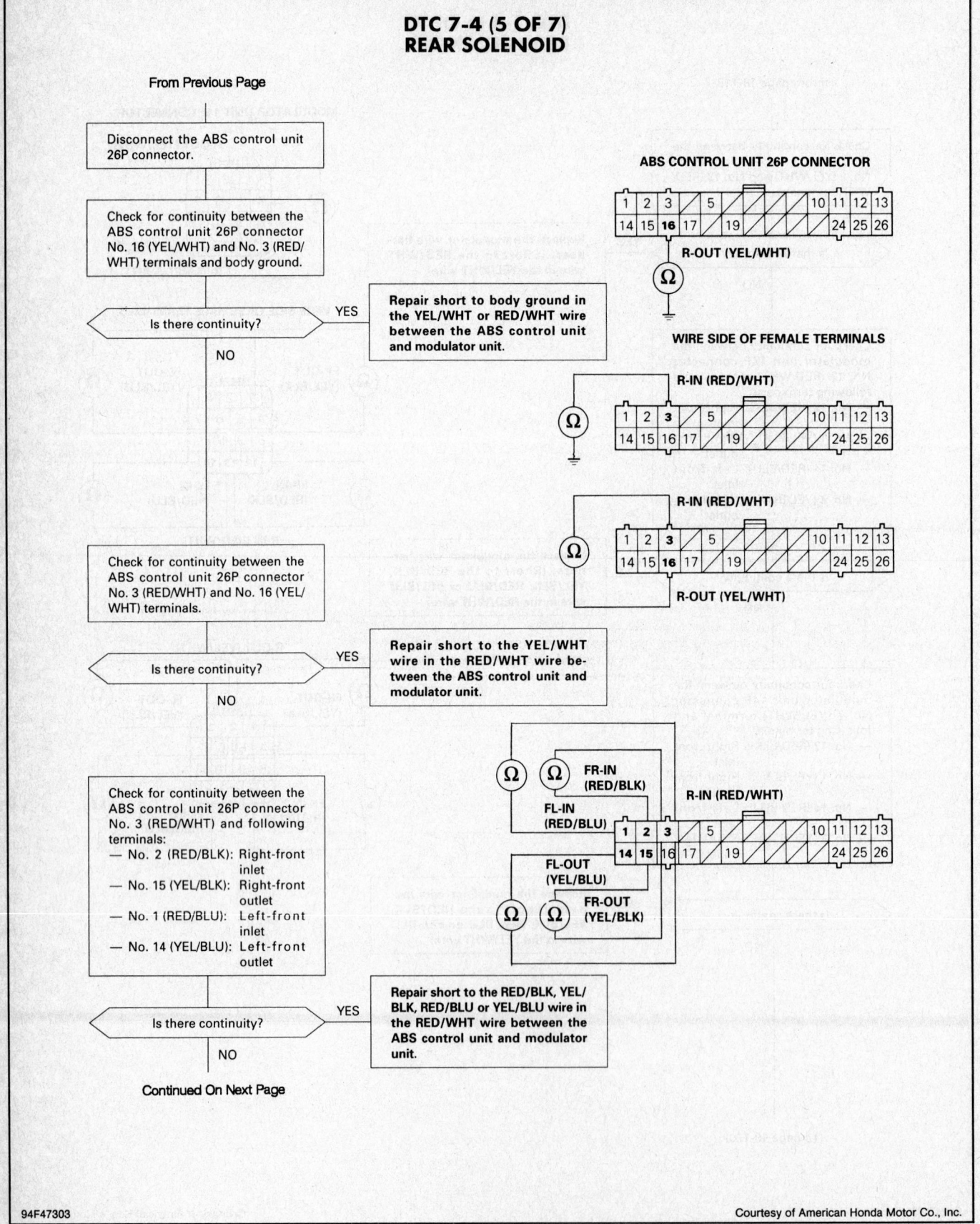

From Previous Page

Disconnect the ABS control unit 26P connector.

Check for continuity between the ABS control unit 26P connector No. 16 (YEL/WHT) and No. 3 (RED/WHT) terminals and body ground.

Is there continuity?

YES — Repair short to body ground in the YEL/WHT or RED/WHT wire between the ABS control unit and modulator unit.

NO

Check for continuity between the ABS control unit 26P connector No. 3 (RED/WHT) and No. 16 (YEL/WHT) terminals.

Is there continuity?

YES — Repair short to the YEL/WHT wire in the RED/WHT wire between the ABS control unit and modulator unit.

NO

Check for continuity between the ABS control unit 26P connector No. 3 (RED/WHT) and following terminals:
— No. 2 (RED/BLK): Right-front inlet
— No. 15 (YEL/BLK): Right-front outlet
— No. 1 (RED/BLU): Left-front inlet
— No. 14 (YEL/BLU): Left-front outlet

Is there continuity?

YES — Repair short to the RED/BLK, YEL/BLK, RED/BLU or YEL/BLU wire in the RED/WHT wire between the ABS control unit and modulator unit.

NO

Continued On Next Page

ABS CONTROL UNIT 26P CONNECTOR

R-OUT (YEL/WHT)

WIRE SIDE OF FEMALE TERMINALS

R-IN (RED/WHT)

R-IN (RED/WHT)

R-OUT (YEL/WHT)

FR-IN (RED/BLK)

FL-IN (RED/BLU)

R-IN (RED/WHT)

FL-OUT (YEL/BLU)

FR-OUT (YEL/BLK)

DTC 7-4 (6 OF 7)
REAR SOLENOID

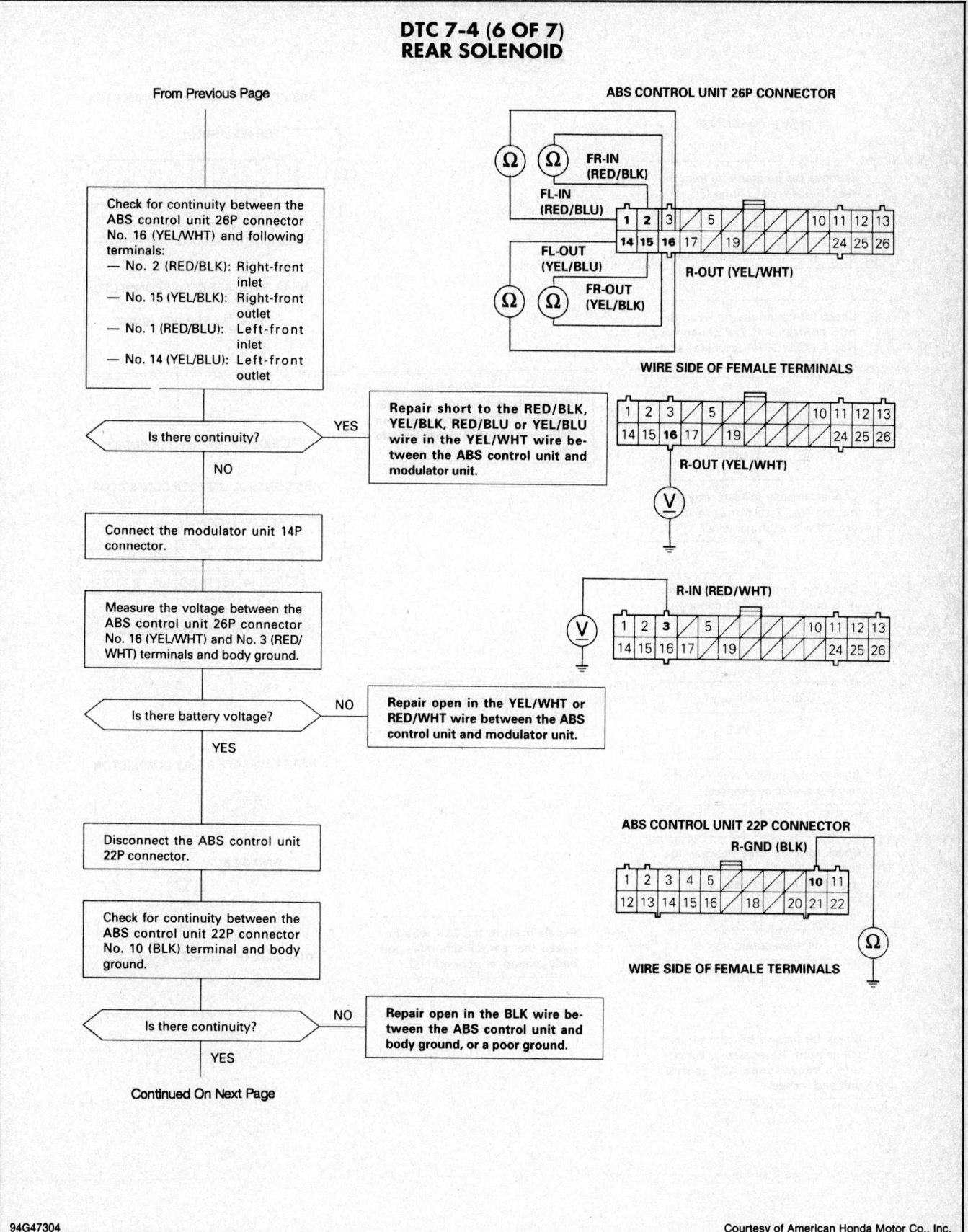

From Previous Page

Check for continuity between the ABS control unit 26P connector No. 16 (YEL/WHT) and following terminals:
— No. 2 (RED/BLK): Right-front inlet
— No. 15 (YEL/BLK): Right-front outlet
— No. 1 (RED/BLU): Left-front inlet
— No. 14 (YEL/BLU): Left-front outlet

Is there continuity?

YES → Repair short to the RED/BLK, YEL/BLK, RED/BLU or YEL/BLU wire in the YEL/WHT wire between the ABS control unit and modulator unit.

NO

Connect the modulator unit 14P connector.

Measure the voltage between the ABS control unit 26P connector No. 16 (YEL/WHT) and No. 3 (RED/WHT) terminals and body ground.

Is there battery voltage?

NO → Repair open in the YEL/WHT or RED/WHT wire between the ABS control unit and modulator unit.

YES

Disconnect the ABS control unit 22P connector.

Check for continuity between the ABS control unit 22P connector No. 10 (BLK) terminal and body ground.

Is there continuity?

NO → Repair open in the BLK wire between the ABS control unit and body ground, or a poor ground.

YES

Continued On Next Page

ABS CONTROL UNIT 26P CONNECTOR

FR-IN (RED/BLK)
FL-IN (RED/BLU)
FL-OUT (YEL/BLU)
FR-OUT (YEL/BLK)
R-OUT (YEL/WHT)

WIRE SIDE OF FEMALE TERMINALS

R-OUT (YEL/WHT)

R-IN (RED/WHT)

ABS CONTROL UNIT 22P CONNECTOR
R-GND (BLK)

WIRE SIDE OF FEMALE TERMINALS

DTC 7-4 (7 OF 7)
REAR SOLENOID

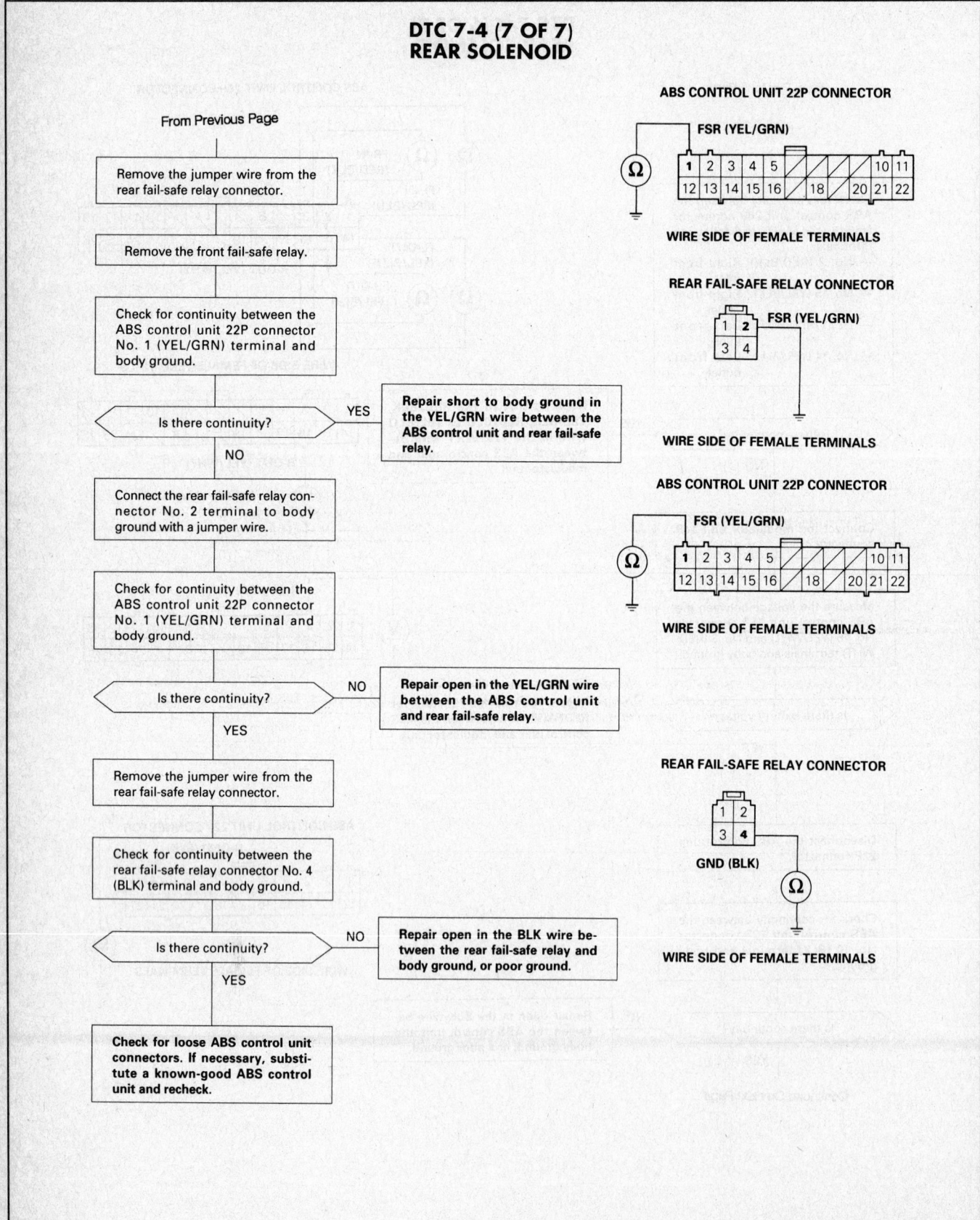

From Previous Page

Remove the jumper wire from the rear fail-safe relay connector.

Remove the front fail-safe relay.

Check for continuity between the ABS control unit 22P connector No. 1 (YEL/GRN) terminal and body ground.

Is there continuity? — YES → Repair short to body ground in the YEL/GRN wire between the ABS control unit and rear fail-safe relay.

NO

Connect the rear fail-safe relay connector No. 2 terminal to body ground with a jumper wire.

Check for continuity between the ABS control unit 22P connector No. 1 (YEL/GRN) terminal and body ground.

Is there continuity? — NO → Repair open in the YEL/GRN wire between the ABS control unit and rear fail-safe relay.

YES

Remove the jumper wire from the rear fail-safe relay connector.

Check for continuity between the rear fail-safe relay connector No. 4 (BLK) terminal and body ground.

Is there continuity? — NO → Repair open in the BLK wire between the rear fail-safe relay and body ground, or poor ground.

YES

Check for loose ABS control unit connectors. If necessary, substitute a known-good ABS control unit and recheck.

ABS CONTROL UNIT 22P CONNECTOR

FSR (YEL/GRN)

WIRE SIDE OF FEMALE TERMINALS

REAR FAIL-SAFE RELAY CONNECTOR

FSR (YEL/GRN)

WIRE SIDE OF FEMALE TERMINALS

ABS CONTROL UNIT 22P CONNECTOR

FSR (YEL/GRN)

WIRE SIDE OF FEMALE TERMINALS

REAR FAIL-SAFE RELAY CONNECTOR

GND (BLK)

WIRE SIDE OF FEMALE TERMINALS

DTC 8-1
ABS FUNCTION DIAGNOSIS

The ABS control unit monitors the ABS functioning time during regular diagnosis, and it turns the ABS indicator light on if the ABS is functioning for a prolonged time.

Possible causes:

- Wheel sensor signal disappears at speeds of 6 mph (10 km/h) or less
- Faulty ABS control unit

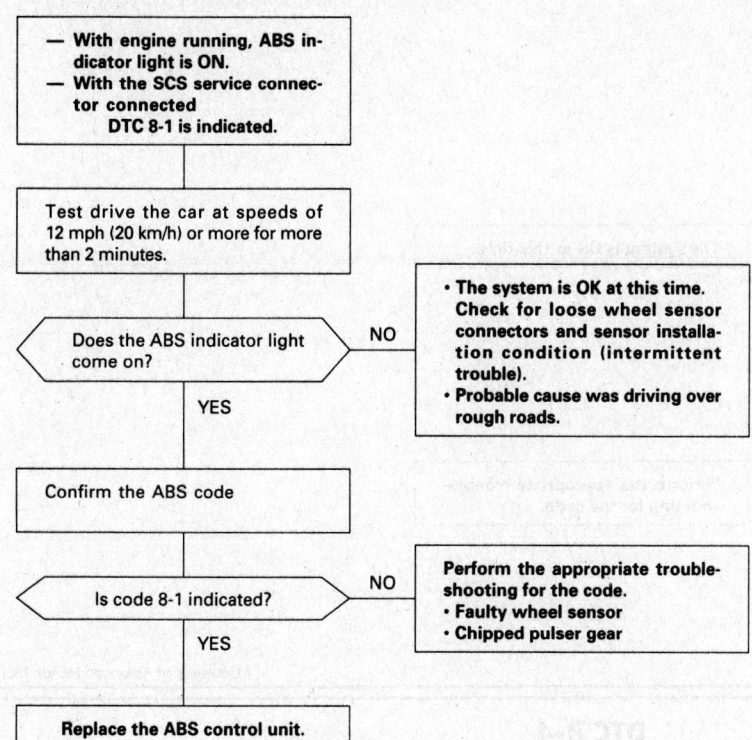

— With engine running, ABS indicator light is ON.
— With the SCS service connector connected
    DTC 8-1 is indicated.

Test drive the car at speeds of 12 mph (20 km/h) or more for more than 2 minutes.

Does the ABS indicator light come on?

NO →
- **The system is OK at this time. Check for loose wheel sensor connectors and sensor installation condition (intermittent trouble).**
- **Probable cause was driving over rough roads.**

YES

Confirm the ABS code

Is code 8-1 indicated?

NO →
Perform the appropriate trouble-shooting for the code.
- **Faulty wheel sensor**
- **Chipped pulser gear**

YES

Replace the ABS control unit.

94147306

Courtesy of American Honda Motor Co., Inc.

1994 BRAKES
Anti-Lock – Accord (Cont.)

DTC 8-2
ABS CONTROL UNIT (CPU COMPARISON)

The ABS control unit checks the data of the two CPUs by comparison, and it keeps the ABS indicator light on if there are any differences in the data between the CPUs. It turns the ABS indicator light on again if it detects any difference after the light goes off.

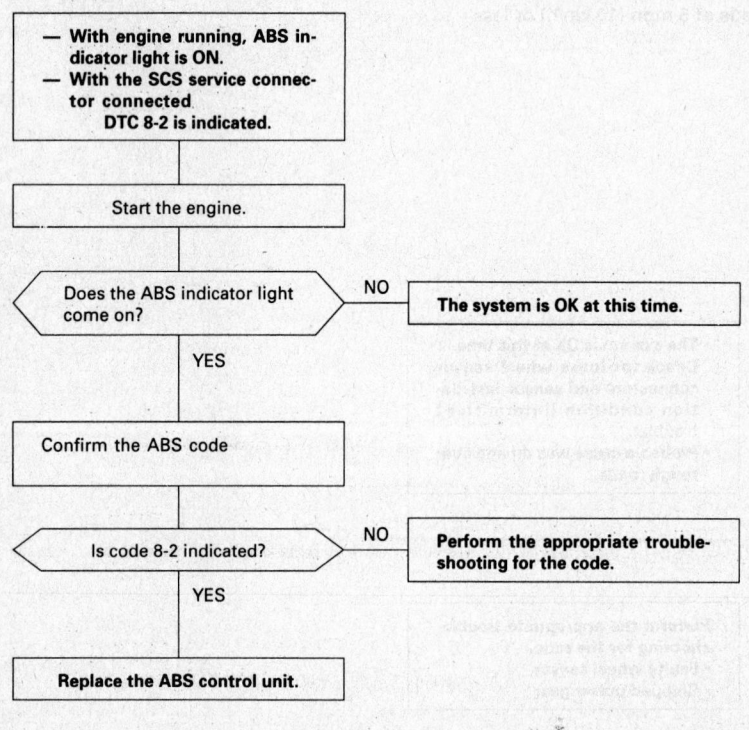

- **With engine running, ABS indicator light is ON.**
- **With the SCS service connector connected DTC 8-2 is indicated.**

Start the engine.

Does the ABS indicator light come on? — NO → **The system is OK at this time.**

YES

Confirm the ABS code

Is code 8-2 indicated? — NO → **Perform the appropriate troubleshooting for the code.**

YES

Replace the ABS control unit.

94J47307

DTC 8-4
INTEGRATED CIRCUIT (IC) DIAGNOSIS

The ABS control unit checks the internal ICs during the initial diagnosis and regular diagnosis, and it keeps the ABS indicator light on if it detects any abnormality. It turns the ABS indicator light on again if it detects any abnormality after the light goes off.

Replace the ABS control unit if DTC 8-4 is indicated with the SCS service connector connected

94A47308

NOTE: For information on Passport anti-lock brakes, refer to Rodeo in Isuzu BRAKES – REAR ANTI-LOCK article.

DESCRIPTION

The Anti-Lock Brake System (ABS) is designed to prevent wheel lock-up during hard braking, allowing driver to maintain vehicle control. System consists of control unit, accumulator, ABS pump (power unit), 4 speed sensors, modulator, warning light, master cylinder, power booster assembly and connecting wiring. *See Fig. 1.*

NOTE: For more information on brake system, see DISC & DRUM article in BRAKES.

OPERATION

ABS PUMP (POWER UNIT)

The power unit consists of an electric motor, filter, guide, piston rod and cylinder body. Guide is positioned off-set to the center of the motor shaft. Rotation of motor and cylinder body provides the reciprocating motion to the piston rod. This pressurizes brake fluid which is fed to relief valve, accumulator and modulator.

As the motor rotates and pressure in the accumulator exceeds a predetermined level, the pressure switch is turned on. Upon receiving this switching signal, the control unit stops motor relay operation. If accumulator pressure does not reach predetermined level after motor has run continuously for at least 2 minutes, the control unit stops motor operation and turns on ABS warning light in instrument panel.

ACCUMULATOR

The accumulator is a pneumatic, nitrogen-gas filled reservoir which accumulates high-pressure brake fluid. Accumulator feeds high-pressure brake fluid to modulator valve through inlet side of solenoid valve. Accumulator charging pressure is 1721 psi (121 kg/cm²). Maximum operating pressure is 3271 psi (230 kg/cm²).

CONTROL UNIT

The control unit has a main function, sub-function, self-diagnostic function and fail-safe function.
Main Function – Controls overall ABS system operation by interpreting speed sensor signals and activating solenoid valve in modulator unit.

Sub-Function – Controls pump motor and self-diagnostic function.
Self-Diagnostic Function – Monitors the main ABS system. When an abnormality is detected, ABS warning light comes on.
Fail-Safe Function – When an abnormality is detected in the main system, solenoid valve operation is turned off by fail-safe relay. Under these conditions, the ABS system operates as a conventional brake system. The fail-safe function comes on with ABS warning light.

MODULATOR

The modulator consists of 4 modulator pistons and 3 solenoid valves. Individual pistons and solenoids are used for the front wheels. Individual modulator pistons are used for each rear wheel, but are connected to a single solenoid valve used for both rear wheels. The modulator pistons for the rear brakes have proportioning control valves to prevent rear wheel lock-up if ABS system malfunctions.

PRESSURE SWITCH

The pressure switch monitors accumulator pump pressure. When pressure switch is turned off, the control unit activates pump motor relay to operate ABS pump motor. If accumulator pressure does not reach predetermined level, ABS warning light comes on.

SPEED SENSOR

The speed sensor detects wheel rotation speed. Speed sensor consists of a permanent magnet, coil and trigger wheel (pulser). As trigger wheel rotates, the magnetic flux around the coil in each speed sensor alternates, generating a voltage frequency proportional to wheel rotation speed. These pulses are sent to the control unit to determine wheel speed.

BLEEDING BRAKE SYSTEM

HYDRAULIC SYSTEM BLEEDING

CAUTION: DO NOT spill brake fluid on painted surfaces. To avoid paint damage, clean any spilled brake fluid with a clean cloth and clear water, immediately.

Fill master cylinder with clean brake fluid. Fluid should meet DOT 3 or DOT 4 specifications. Bleed master cylinder with bleeder valves (if equipped). Bleed wheel positions in sequence. See BRAKE LINE BLEEDING SEQUENCE table.

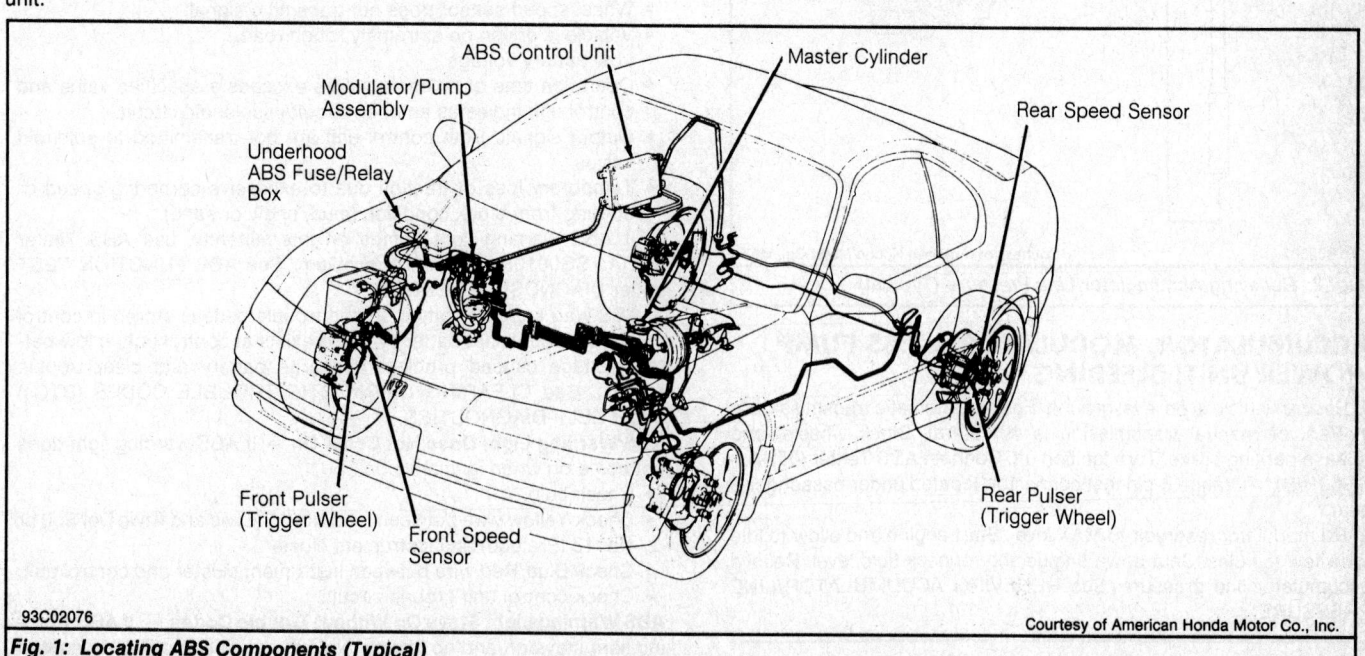

ABS Control Unit

Master Cylinder

Modulator/Pump Assembly

Rear Speed Sensor

Underhood ABS Fuse/Relay Box

Front Pulser (Trigger Wheel)

Front Speed Sensor

Rear Pulser (Trigger Wheel)

93C02076

Courtesy of American Honda Motor Co., Inc.

Fig. 1: Locating ABS Components (Typical)

HONDA
8-76

1994 BRAKES
Anti-Lock – Civic, Civic Del Sol & Prelude (Cont.)

BRAKE LINE BLEEDING SEQUENCE

Application	Sequence
All Models	RR, LF, LR, RF

RELIEVING ACCUMULATOR/LINE PRESSURE

Drain brake fluid from master cylinder and modulator reservoir. Remove Red cap from maintenance bleeder screw. *See Fig. 2.* Using ABS "T" Wrench (07HAA-SG00101), loosen maintenance bleeder screw. Turn "T" wrench 1/4 turn to relieve accumulator line pressure. Turn "T" wrench one complete turn to thoroughly drain pressure fluid. Tighten bleeder screw, and install Red cap.

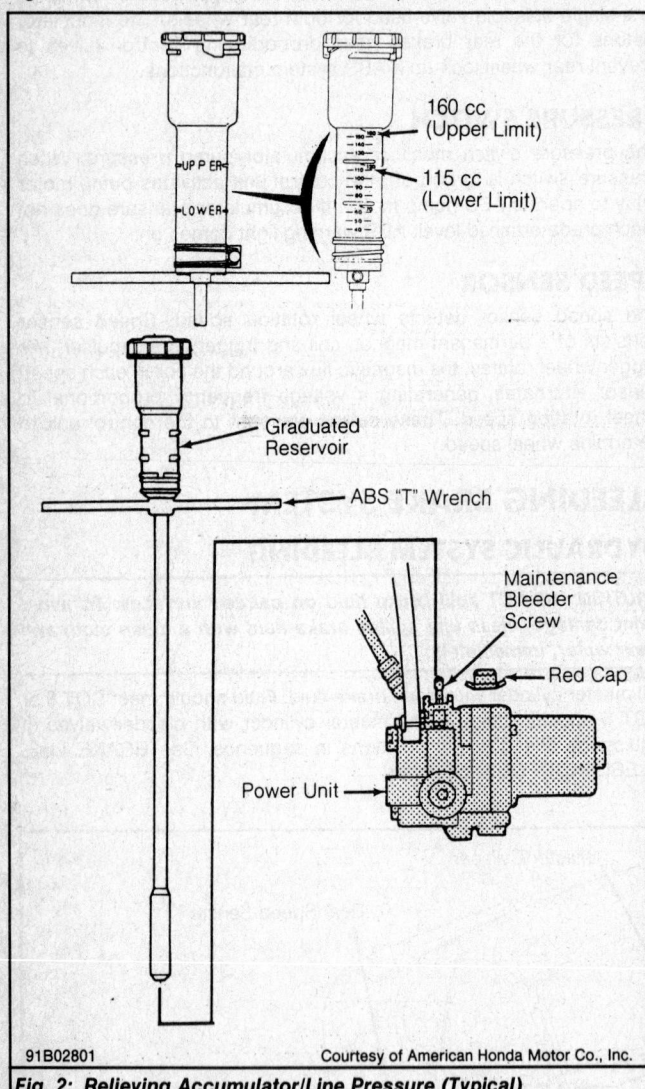

160 cc (Upper Limit)

115 cc (Lower Limit)

Graduated Reservoir

ABS "T" Wrench

Maintenance Bleeder Screw

Red Cap

Power Unit

91B02801   Courtesy of American Honda Motor Co., Inc.

Fig. 2: Relieving Accumulator/Line Pressure (Typical)

ACCUMULATOR, MODULATOR & ABS PUMP (POWER UNIT) BLEEDING

1) Ensure vehicle is on level ground. Ensure automatic transmission is in Park or manual transmission is in Neutral. Block wheels, and release parking brake. Turn ignition off. Connect ABS Tester (07HAJ-SG0010B) to Orange 6-pin test connector, located under passenger's seat.

2) Fill modulator reservoir to MAX level. Start engine and allow to idle for a few minutes. Shut down engine and recheck fluid level. Relieve accumulator line pressure. See RELIEVING ACCUMULATOR/LINE PRESSURE.

NOTE: Depress brake pedal firmly when operating ABS tester.

3) Start engine and allow to idle for a few minutes. Turn mode selector to "2" position. While depressing brake pedal firmly, press START TEST button to operate modulator/pump. *See Fig. 3.* There should be kickback on brake pedal. If there is no kickback or kickback is weak, repeat steps **2)** and **3)**.

4) Turn mode selector to "3", "4" and "5". Perform steps **2)** and **3)** in each mode. Refill reservoir to MAX level.

ADJUSTMENTS
PARKING BRAKE

NOTE: Before adjusting parking brake, loosen park brake equalizer adjusting nut. Start engine, and depress brake pedal several times to set self-adjusting brakes before adjusting parking brake.

1) With rear brakes adjusted, raise and support rear of vehicle. Loosen equalizer nut, and pull parking brake lever up one notch. Tighten equalizer adjusting nut until rear wheels drag slightly.

2) Release parking brake lever. Rear wheels should rotate freely. Rear wheels should lock when parking brake lever is pulled up 6-10 clicks.

BRAKE WARNING LIGHT

To adjust parking brake light operation, turn ignition on. Bend switch plate down until light comes on when parking brake lever is pulled one notch, and goes out when lever is released.

TROUBLE SHOOTING
ANTI-LOCK (ABS) WARNING LIGHT

NOTE: ABS system is okay if ABS warning light goes out after engine is started.

NOTE: Diagnostic Trouble Codes (DTCs) may also be referred to as problem codes.

Diagnostic Trouble Code (DTC) Recognition – 1) ABS control unit recognizes system related problems and causes ABS warning light to come on and stay on under any of following conditions:

* ABS pump runs longer than 2 minutes.
* Vehicle is driven with parking brake on longer than 30 seconds.
* One rear wheel is locked.
* Wheel speed sensor does not transmit a signal.
* Vehicle is driven on extremely rough road.
* Low battery voltage.
* Operation time of solenoid valves exceeds a specified value and control unit indicates an open circuit in solenoid circuit.
* Output signals from control unit are not transmitted to solenoid valves.
* Temporary loss of traction due to excessive cornering speed or starting from stuck condition (mud, snow or sand).

2) If ABS warning light comes on intermittently, use ABS Tester (07HAJ-SG0010B) to confirm problem. See ABS FUNCTION TEST under DIAGNOSIS & TESTING.

3) ABS warning light comes on and trouble code is stored in control unit when insufficient battery voltage exists at control unit. If low battery voltage caused problem, recharge battery and clear trouble code(s). See CLEARING DIAGNOSTIC TROUBLE CODES (DTCs) under SELF-DIAGNOSTICS.

ABS Warning Light Does Not Come On – If ABS warning light does not come on when ignition is on:

* Check bulb.
* Check Yellow wire between fuse No. 15 (Civic and Civic Del Sol) or No. 13 (Prelude) and instrument cluster.
* Check Blue/Red wire between instrument cluster and control unit.
* Check control unit ground circuit.

ABS Warning Light Stays On Without Trouble Codes – If ABS warning light stays on and no trouble code(s) have been stored in control unit, check for following items:

1994 BRAKES
Anti-Lock – Civic, Civic Del Sol & Prelude (Cont.)

HONDA
8-77

- Loose or poor control unit connector.
- Blown ABS fuse No. B2 in underhood fuse/relay box.
- Open circuit in White wire between ABS fuse No. B2 and control unit.
- Open circuit in Black/Yellow wire between fuse No. 13 (Civic and Civic Del Sol) or No. 9 (Prelude) and fail-safe relays.
- Short circuit in Blue/Red wire between instrument cluster and control unit.
- Open circuit in White/Blue wire between alternator and control unit.

If problem cannot be found, substitute a known good control unit, and retest.

ABS Warning Light Stays On With Trouble Codes – Turn ignition on. Ensure ABS warning light comes on. Start engine and observe ABS warning light. If ABS warning light stays on, retrieve and record trouble codes. See RETRIEVING TROUBLE CODES under SELF-DIAGNOSTICS. If ABS warning light goes out after engine starts, ABS system is okay.

DIAGNOSIS & TESTING

ABS FUNCTION TEST

WARNING: DO NOT drive vehicle with ABS tester connected to vehicle, or brake system failure may occur.

Preliminary Procedure – Confirm ABS warning light indicates system malfunction. See ANTI-LOCK (ABS) WARNING LIGHT under TROUBLE SHOOTING. Park vehicle on level surface. Block wheels, and put automatic transmission in Park or manual transmission in Neutral.

CAUTION: DO NOT move mode selector switch while TEST IN PROGRESS light is on.

Testing – 1) With ignition off, connect ABS Tester (07HAJ-SG0010B) to Orange 6-pin test connector, located under passenger's seat. Start engine. Release parking brake. Place mode selector to "1" position. Push START TEST button. See Fig. 3. TEST IN PROGRESS light should come on. Within 1-2 seconds, all 4 monitor lights should come on. If tester lights do not illuminate, ABS tester is faulty.

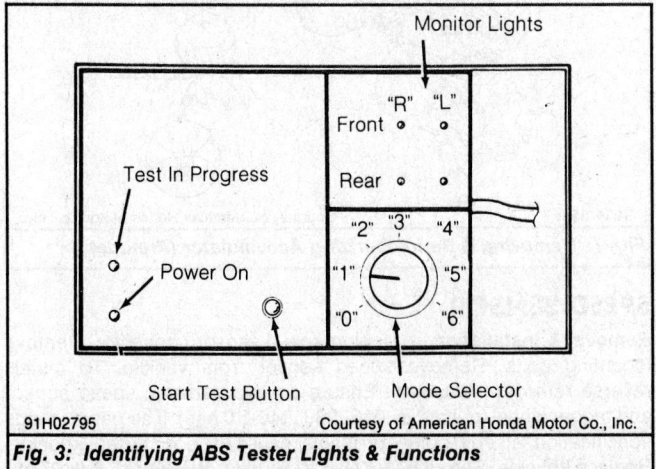

91H02795   Courtesy of American Honda Motor Co., Inc.
Fig. 3: Identifying ABS Tester Lights & Functions

2) If ABS warning light comes on, 6-pin connector or ABS tester harness is faulty. Turn mode selector to "2" position. Press brake pedal. Push START TEST button. ABS warning light should not come on and kickback should be felt on brake pedal.

3) If ABS warning light comes on or kickback is not felt, see ANTI-LOCK (ABS) WARNING LIGHT under TROUBLE SHOOTING. Place mode selector in "3", "4" and then "5" positions. Repeat step 2) for each test mode. Results should be same as in test mode "2". If results are not same as in test mode "2", see ANTI-LOCK (ABS) WARNING LIGHT under TROUBLE SHOOTING.

4) Breakdown of each test mode is as follows:

Mode 1 – Sends simulated driving signal of each wheel to control unit to check self-diagnostic circuit. No kickback should be felt in brake pedal.

Mode 2 – Sends driving signal of each wheel, and then sends lock signal of left rear wheel to control unit. A kickback should be felt in brake pedal.

Mode 3 – Sends driving signal of each wheel, and then sends lock signal of right rear wheel to control unit. A kickback should be felt in brake pedal.

Mode 4 – Sends driving signal of each wheel, and then sends lock signal of left front wheel to control unit. A kickback should be felt in brake pedal.

Mode 5 – Sends driving signal of each wheel, and then sends lock signal of right front wheel to control unit. A kickback should be felt in brake pedal.

Mode 6 – Not used on these models.

5) If brake pedal does not kickback in Modes 2-5 as indicated and ABS indicator light does not come on, repeat function test several times. If test results remain the same. check for air in high pressure line, restriction in high pressure line or faulty modulator unit.

SPEED SENSOR TEST

1) Turn ignition off, and connect ABS Tester (07HAJ-SG0010B) to Orange 6-pin test connector, located under passenger's seat. Turn ignition on. Place ABS tester mode selector to "0" position.

2) Raise and support vehicle so wheels can be turned. Place transmission in Neutral. Turn wheels by hand at one revolution per second. Appropriate monitor light should blink each time wheel is rotated.

3) In some instances, front wheels may not rotate fast enough to make tester light blink. If this happens, start engine. Slowly accelerate and decelerate front wheels. If light does not blink, check appropriate speed sensor, sensor air gap and wiring.

MODULATOR SOLENOID LEAK TEST

NOTE: If a solenoid leaks excessively, brake fluid level in modulator reservoir will rise when ABS pump motor is operated.

---

1) Connect an ohmmeter between the terminals (both wires are Yellow) of pressure switch connector. Using a fully charged 12 volt battery, connect jumper wire from positive terminal to Red/White wire at motor connector. Using another jumper wire, connect negative terminal to Green wire at motor connector with a switch between jumper and connector. See Fig. 4.

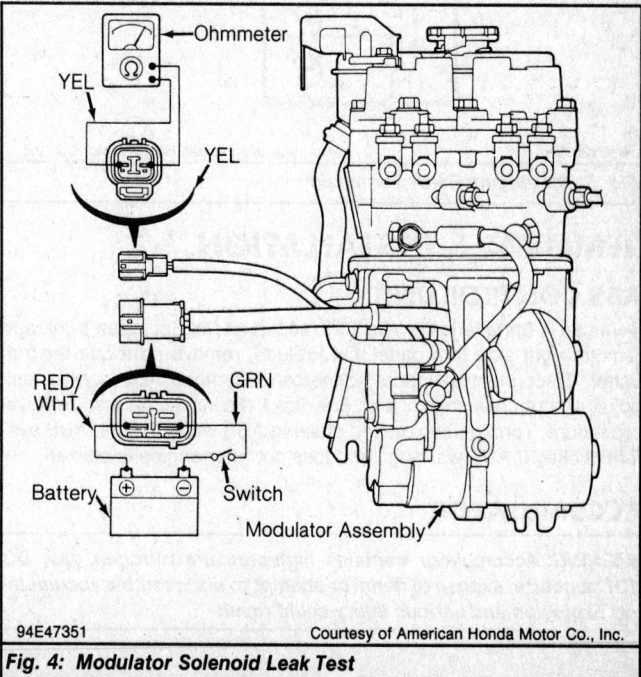

94E47351   Courtesy of American Honda Motor Co., Inc.
Fig. 4: Modulator Solenoid Leak Test

HONDA
8-78

1994 BRAKES
Anti-Lock – Civic, Civic Del Sol & Prelude (Cont.)

2) Turn switch on to allow pressure to build up in accumulator. Check for continuity at pressure switch terminals. If continuity exists, operate motor for 10 seconds more, then turn switch off. If continuity does not exist, check for open in Yellow wire(s). If wire(s) is good, replace pressure switch and repeat step **2)**.

3) If Solenoid hisses or squeaks, solenoid is leaking and must be replaced. Wait for 30 minutes and recheck pressure switch continuity. If no continuity exists, solenoid is faulty and must be replaced.

RELAY TEST

Check continuity between relay terminals "A" and "B". *See Fig. 5.* Continuity should not exist. Apply battery voltage across terminals "C" and "D". Continuity should exist between terminals "A" and "B". If continuity is not as indicated, replace relay.

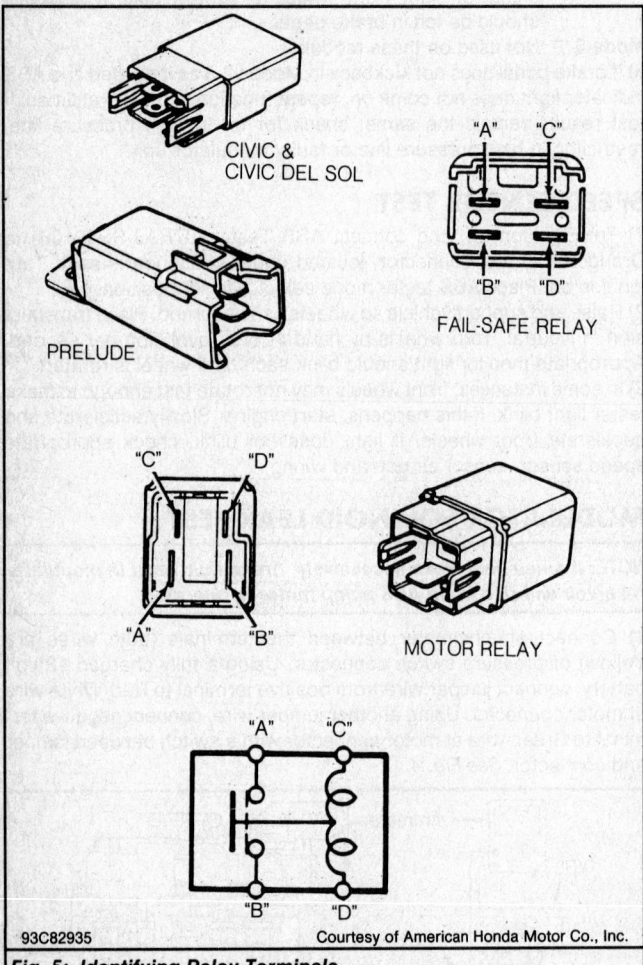

93C82935   Courtesy of American Honda Motor Co., Inc.
Fig. 5: Identifying Relay Terminals

REMOVAL & INSTALLATION

ABS CONTROL UNIT

Removal & Installation – On Civic and Civic Del Sol, open trunk and remove right side trim panel. On Prelude, remove right quarter trim panel. Disconnect electrical connectors. Remove ABS control unit bolts, and remove control unit. *See Fig. 1.* To install, reverse removal procedure. Turn ignition on and observe ABS warning light. ABS system is okay if ABS warning light goes out after engine is started.

ACCUMULATOR

WARNING: Accumulator contains high-pressure nitrogen gas. DO NOT puncture, expose to flame or attempt to disassemble accumulator. Explosion and serious injury could result.

Removal & Installation – **1)** Relieve accumulator line pressure. See RELIEVING ACCUMULATOR/LINE PRESSURE under BLEEDING BRAKE SYSTEM. Secure pump assembly in vise. On Civic and Civic Del Sol, remove accumulator pipe. Remove mounting bolts. Remove accumulator from bracket. On Prelude, using an open end wrench on accumulator mounting boss, unscrew and remove accumulator. *See Fig. 6 or 7.*

NOTE: Before disposal, accumulator pressure MUST be relieved. Failure to relieve accumulator pressure could result in explosion and serious injury.

---

2) To depressurize accumulator, secure accumulator in vise with relief plug pointing straight up. DO NOT tighten accumulator body in vise. SLOWLY turn relief plug 3 1/2 turns, and wait at least 3 minutes for all pressure to escape. Remove relief plug, and dispose of accumulator.
3) To install, reverse removal procedure. If necessary, bleed air from system. See ACCUMULATOR, MODULATOR and ABS PUMP (POWER UNIT) BLEEDING under BLEEDING BRAKE SYSTEM.

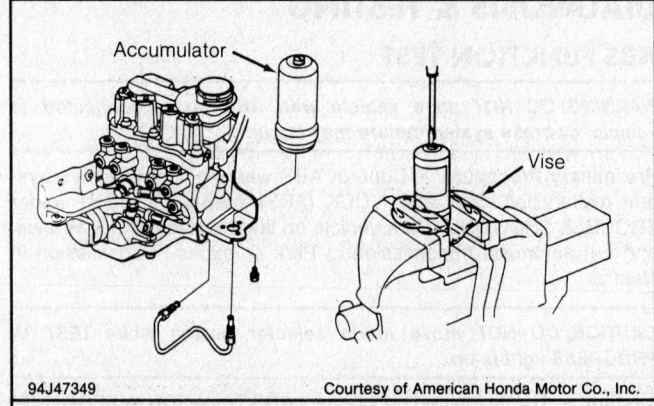

94J47349   Courtesy of American Honda Motor Co., Inc.
Fig. 6: Removing & Depressurizing Accumulator
            (Civic & Civic Del Sol)

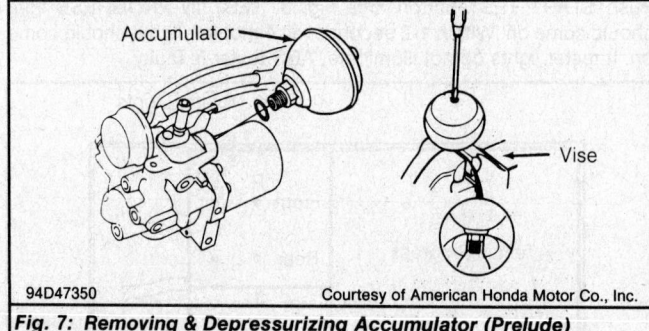

94D47350   Courtesy of American Honda Motor Co., Inc.
Fig. 7: Removing & Depressurizing Accumulator (Prelude)

SPEED SENSOR

Removal & Installation – Unplug speed sensor connector. Remove mounting bolts. Remove speed sensor from vehicle. To install, reverse removal procedure. Ensure air gap between speed sensor and trigger wheel (pulser) is .016-.039" (.40-1.0 mm). If air gap exceeds specification at any point, probable cause is a distorted knuckle. Replace knuckle. See HUB & KNUCKLE under REMOVAL & INSTALLATION in appropriate SUSPENSION article.

PULSER (TRIGGER WHEEL)

Removal and installation procedures not available from manufacturer.

MODULATOR/PUMP ASSEMBLY

Removal & Installation – **1)** On Civic and Civic Del Sol, remove battery and battery tray. On all models, relieve accumulator/line pressure. See RELIEVING ACCUMULATOR/LINE PRESSURE. Drain fluid from

1994 BRAKES
Anti-Lock – Civic, Civic Del Sol & Prelude (Cont.)

HONDA
8-79

modulator assembly. Remove intake air duct and emission control box. Disconnect solenoid, pump motor and pressure switch connectors.

2) Disconnect brake pipes from modulator. Disconnect brake hose from modulator reservoir. Remove clamp from modulator bracket. Remove mounting bolts. Remove modulator assembly. To install, reverse removal procedure. Bleed hydraulic system. See BLEEDING BRAKE SYSTEM.

PRESSURE SWITCH

Removal & Installation – Secure modulator/pump assembly in vise. Remove banjo bolt and sealing washers. Remove pressure switch. To install, reverse removal procedure, using NEW sealing washers.

TORQUE SPECIFICATIONS

TORQUE SPECIFICATIONS

Application	Ft. Lbs. (N.m)
Banjo Bolt Fittings	26 (35)
Brake Line Flare Nuts	14 (19)
Modulator Mounting Bolts	16 (22)
Speed Sensor Mounting Bolts (Accord & Prelude)	16 (22)
	INCH Lbs. (N.m)
ABS Control Unit Mounting Bolts	84 (9.5)
ABS Pump Mounting Bolts	89 (10)
Accumulator Mounting Bolts	89 (10)
Maintenance Bleeder Screw	80 (9)
Speed Sensor Lock Bolts (Civic & Civic Del Sol)	89 (10)

HONDA
8-80

1994 BRAKES
Anti-Lock – Civic, Civic Del Sol & Prelude (Cont.)

WIRING DIAGRAMS

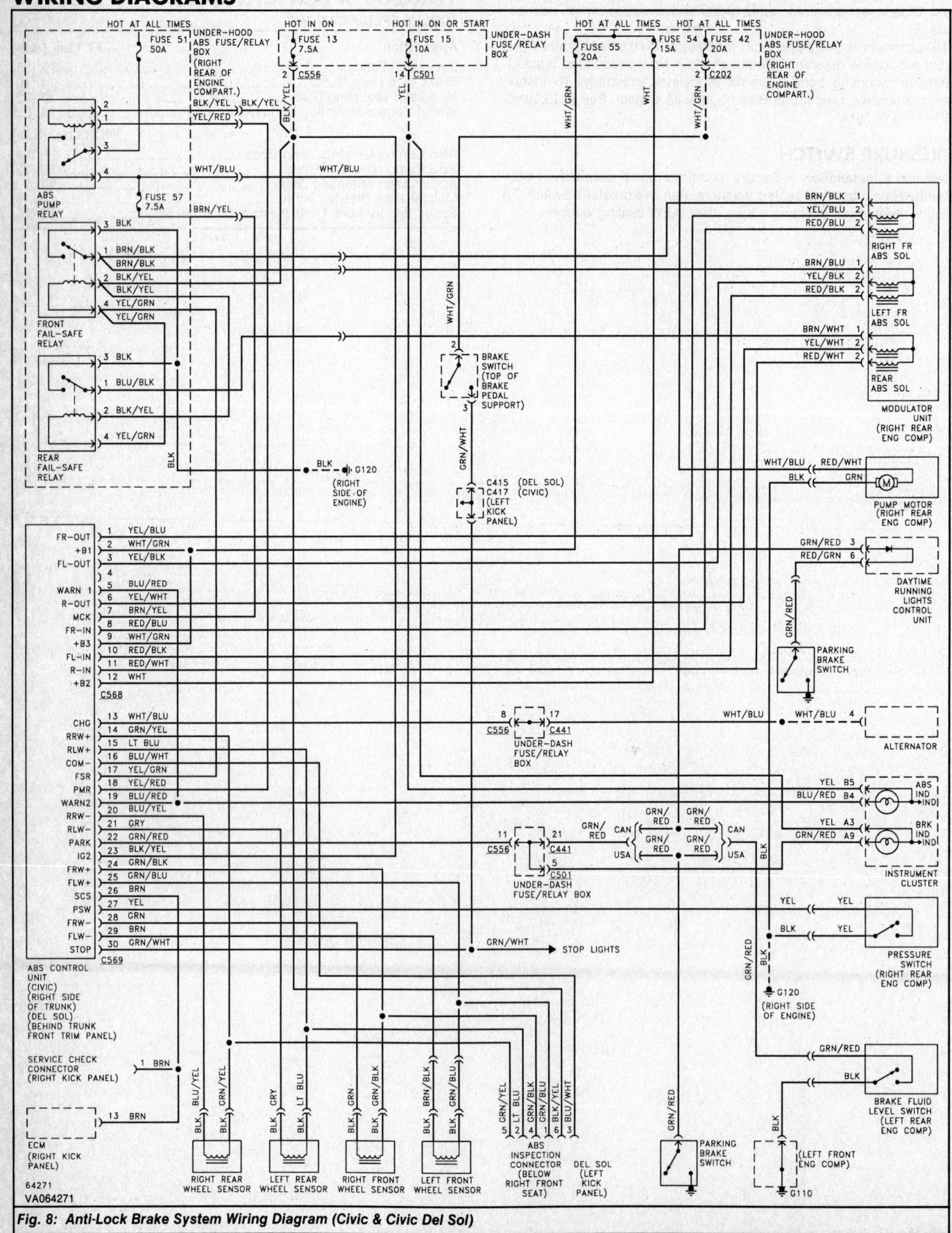

Fig. 8: Anti-Lock Brake System Wiring Diagram (Civic & Civic Del Sol)

1994 BRAKES
Anti-Lock – Civic, Civic Del Sol & Prelude (Cont.)

HONDA
8-81

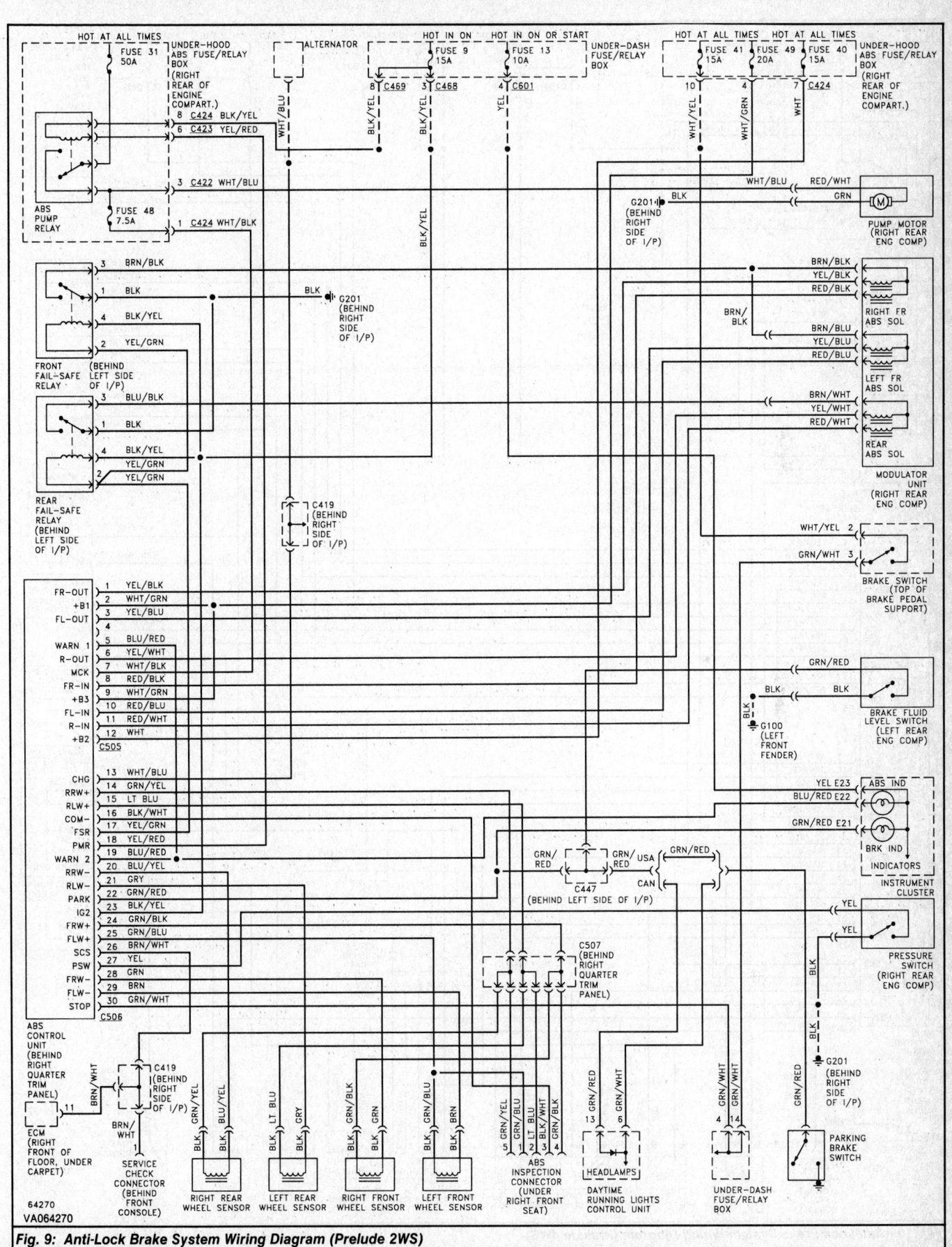

Fig. 9: Anti-Lock Brake System Wiring Diagram (Prelude 2WS)

HONDA
8-82

1994 BRAKES
Anti-Lock – Civic, Civic Del Sol & Prelude (Cont.)

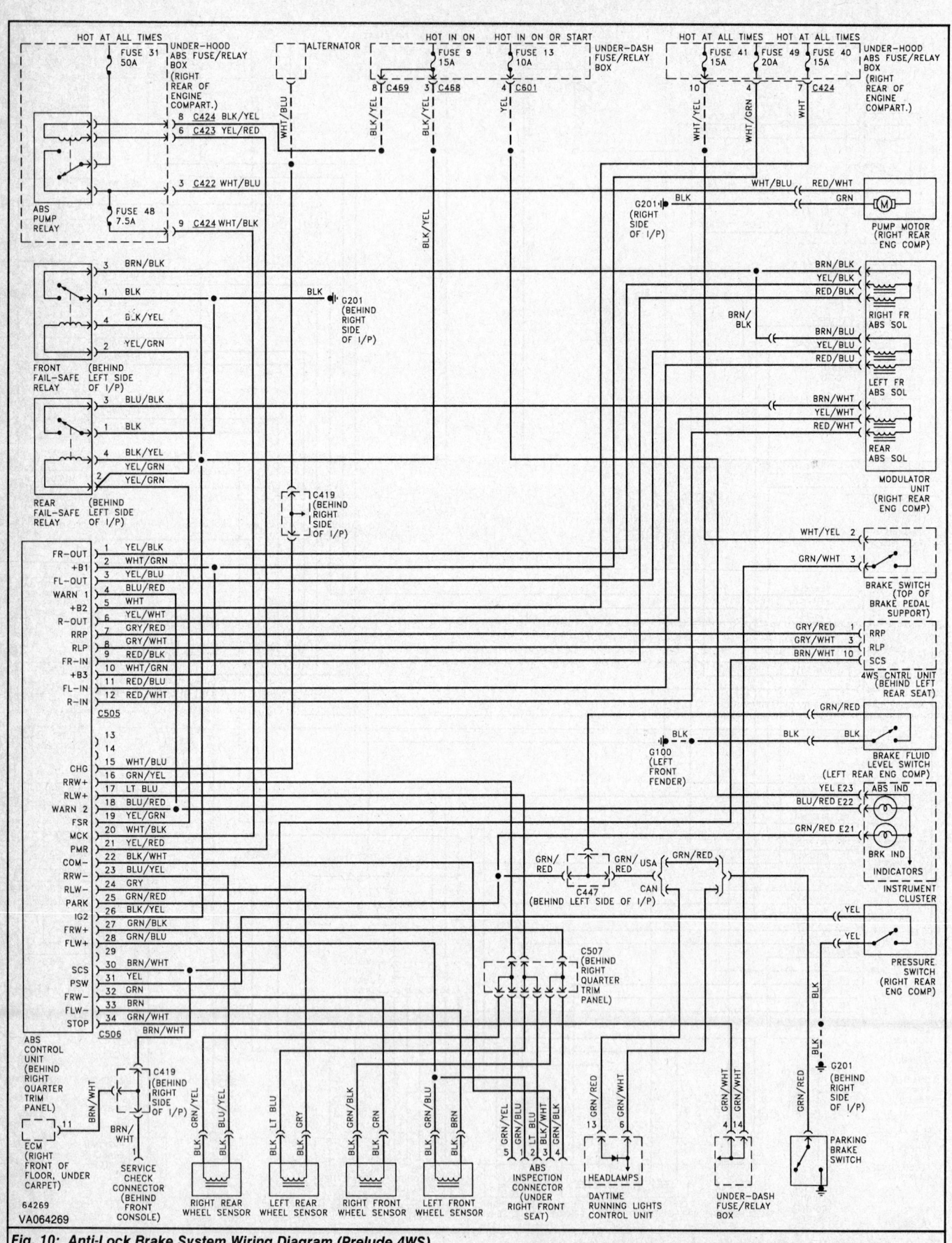

Fig. 10: Anti-Lock Brake System Wiring Diagram (Prelude 4WS)

64269
VA064269

1994 BRAKES
Anti-Lock – Civic, Civic Del Sol & Prelude (Cont.)

HONDA
8-83

SELF-DIAGNOSTICS

NOTE: Diagnostic Trouble Codes (DTCs) may also be referred to as problem codes.

RETRIEVING TROUBLE CODES

1) Turn ignition on (without engine running). Ensure ABS warning light comes on. Start engine, and observe ABS warning light. If warning light goes out, no trouble codes exist.

2) If ABS warning light stays on, turn ignition off. On Civic and Civic Del Sol, locate 2-pin test connector behind passenger-side kick panel. On Prelude, remove access cover on passenger-side of center console to locate 2-pin connector. On all models, install jumper wire between pins on 2-pin connector. *See Fig. 12 Or 13.* Turn ignition on (without engine running). Record blinking ABS warning light sequence.

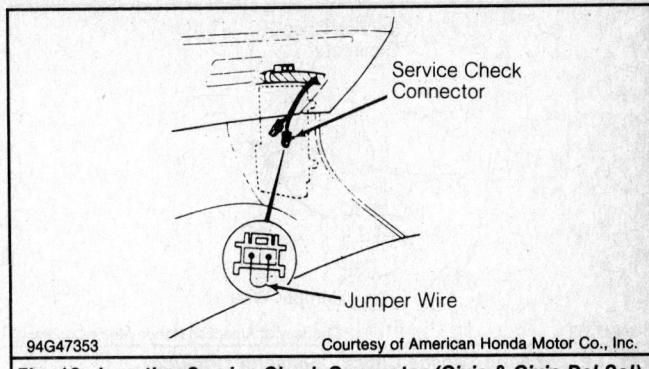

94G47353   Courtesy of American Honda Motor Co., Inc.

Fig. 12: Locating Service Check Connector (Civic & Civic Del Sol)

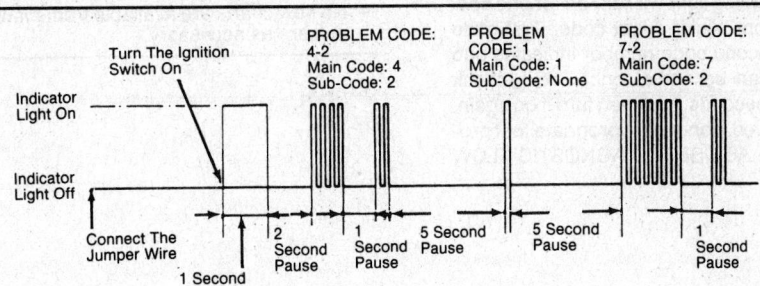

PROBLEM CODE		PROBLEMATIC COMPONENT/ SYSTEM	AFFECTED				OTHER COMPONENT
MAIN CODE	SUB-CODE		FRONT RIGHT	FRONT LEFT	REAR RIGHT	REAR LEFT	
①	—	Pump motor over-run	−	−	−	−	Pressure switch
	②	Pump motor circuit problem	−	−	−	−	Motor relay, Unit fuse, Motor fuse
	③	High pressure leakage	−	−	−	−	Solenoid
	④	Pressure switch	−	−	−	−	
	⑥	Accumulator gas leakage	−	−	−	−	
②	①	Parking brake switch-related problem	−	−	−	−	Brake fluid level switch BRAKE light
③	①	Pulser(s)	○				
	②			○			
	④				○	○	
④	①	Speed sensor	○				
	②			○			
	④				○		
	⑥					○	
⑤	—	Speed sensor(s)			○	○	Modulator
	④				○		
	⑥					○	
⑥	—	Fail-safe relay (Open, short)	−	−	−	−	Front or rear fail-safe relay
	①		−	−	−	−	Front fail-safe relay
	④		−	−	−	−	Rear fail-safe relay
⑦	①	Solenoid related problem (Open)	○				ABS B1 fuse
	②			○			Front fail-safe relay
	④				○	○	Rear fail-safe relay

94I47348   Courtesy of American Honda Motor Co., Inc.

Fig. 11: Self-Diagnostics & Trouble Code Diagnosis Chart

HONDA
8-84

1994 BRAKES
Anti-Lock – Civic, Civic Del Sol & Prelude (Cont.)

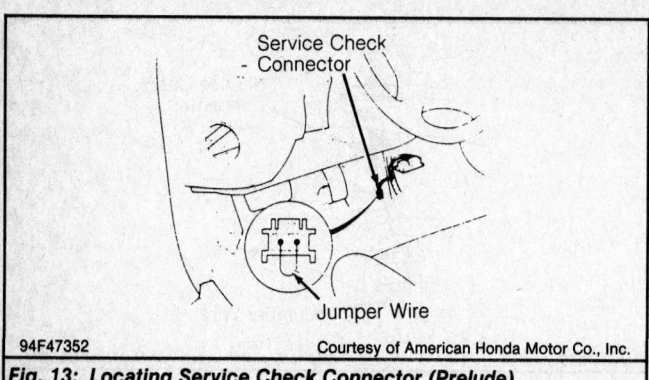

Service Check
- Connector

Jumper Wire

94F47352   Courtesy of American Honda Motor Co., Inc.

Fig. 13: Locating Service Check Connector (Prelude)

3) After ignition is turned on, ABS warning light will turn on for one second, then pause for 2 seconds before blinking first code. First code number indicates main code and second code number indicates sub code. *See Fig. 11*. Three codes can be set at once. To recheck sequence, turn ignition off for a few seconds, and then turn it on again. After trouble codes have been retrieved, conduct appropriate test procedures outlined in flow charts. See ABS SELF-DIAGNOSTIC FLOW CHARTS.

CLEARING TROUBLE CODES

With ignition off, remove ABS fuse No. B2 for at least 3 seconds. Install fuse, and turn ignition on. Observe ABS warning light. Codes are cleared if ABS warning light goes out after engine is started.

DIAGNOSTIC TROUBLE CODES (DTCs)
DIAGNOSTIC TROUBLE CODES (DTCs)

Code	System Affected
1 To 1-8	Hydraulically Controlled Components
2-1	Parking Brake Switch
3-1 To 3-4 [1]	Pulser(s)
4-1 To 4-8	Front & Rear Speed Sensor(s)
5 To 5-8	Rear Speed Sensor(s)
6 To 6-4	Front & Rear Fail-Safe Relay(s)
7-1 To 7-4	Front & Rear Solenoid(s)

[1] – No flow charts are available from manufacturer. Repair or replace pulsers as necessary.

1994 BRAKES
Anti-Lock – Civic, Civic Del Sol & Prelude (Cont.)

HONDA
8-85

ABS SELF-DIAGNOSTIC FLOW CHARTS

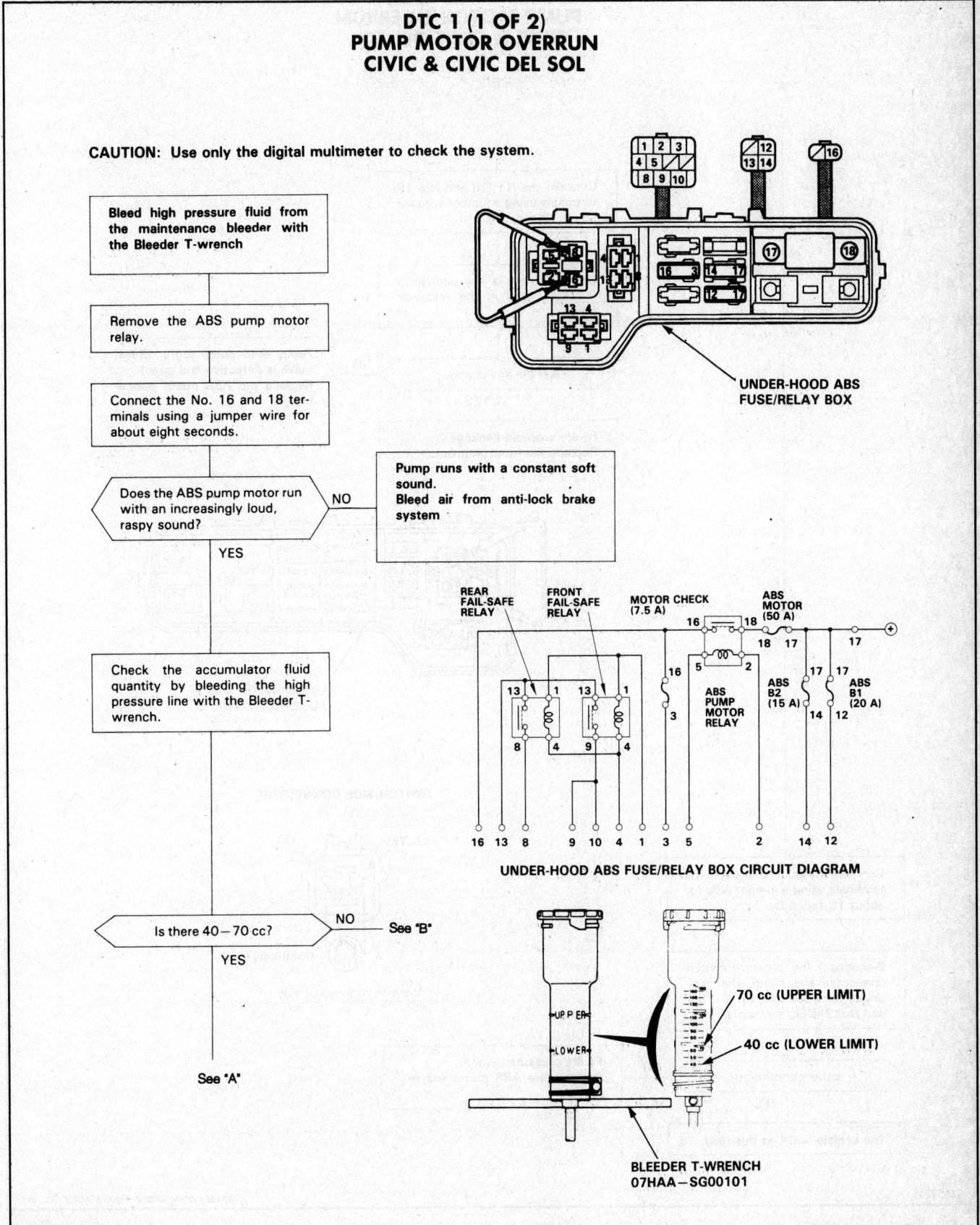

DTC 1 (1 OF 2)
PUMP MOTOR OVERRUN
CIVIC & CIVIC DEL SOL

CAUTION: Use only the digital multimeter to check the system.

Bleed high pressure fluid from the maintenance bleeder with the Bleeder T-wrench

Remove the ABS pump motor relay.

Connect the No. 16 and 18 terminals using a jumper wire for about eight seconds.

Does the ABS pump motor run with an increasingly loud, raspy sound? — NO → Pump runs with a constant soft sound. Bleed air from anti-lock brake system

YES

Check the accumulator fluid quantity by bleeding the high pressure line with the Bleeder T-wrench.

Is there 40—70 cc? — NO → See "B"

YES

See "A"

UNDER-HOOD ABS FUSE/RELAY BOX

REAR FAIL-SAFE RELAY
FRONT FAIL-SAFE RELAY
MOTOR CHECK (7.5 A)
ABS MOTOR (50 A)
ABS PUMP MOTOR RELAY
ABS B2 (15 A)
ABS B1 (20 A)

UNDER-HOOD ABS FUSE/RELAY BOX CIRCUIT DIAGRAM

70 cc (UPPER LIMIT)
40 cc (LOWER LIMIT)

BLEEDER T-WRENCH
07HAA—SG00101

HONDA
8-86

1994 BRAKES
Anti-Lock – Civic, Civic Del Sol & Prelude (Cont.)

DTC 1 (2 OF 2)
PUMP MOTOR OVERRUN
CIVIC & CIVIC DEL SOL

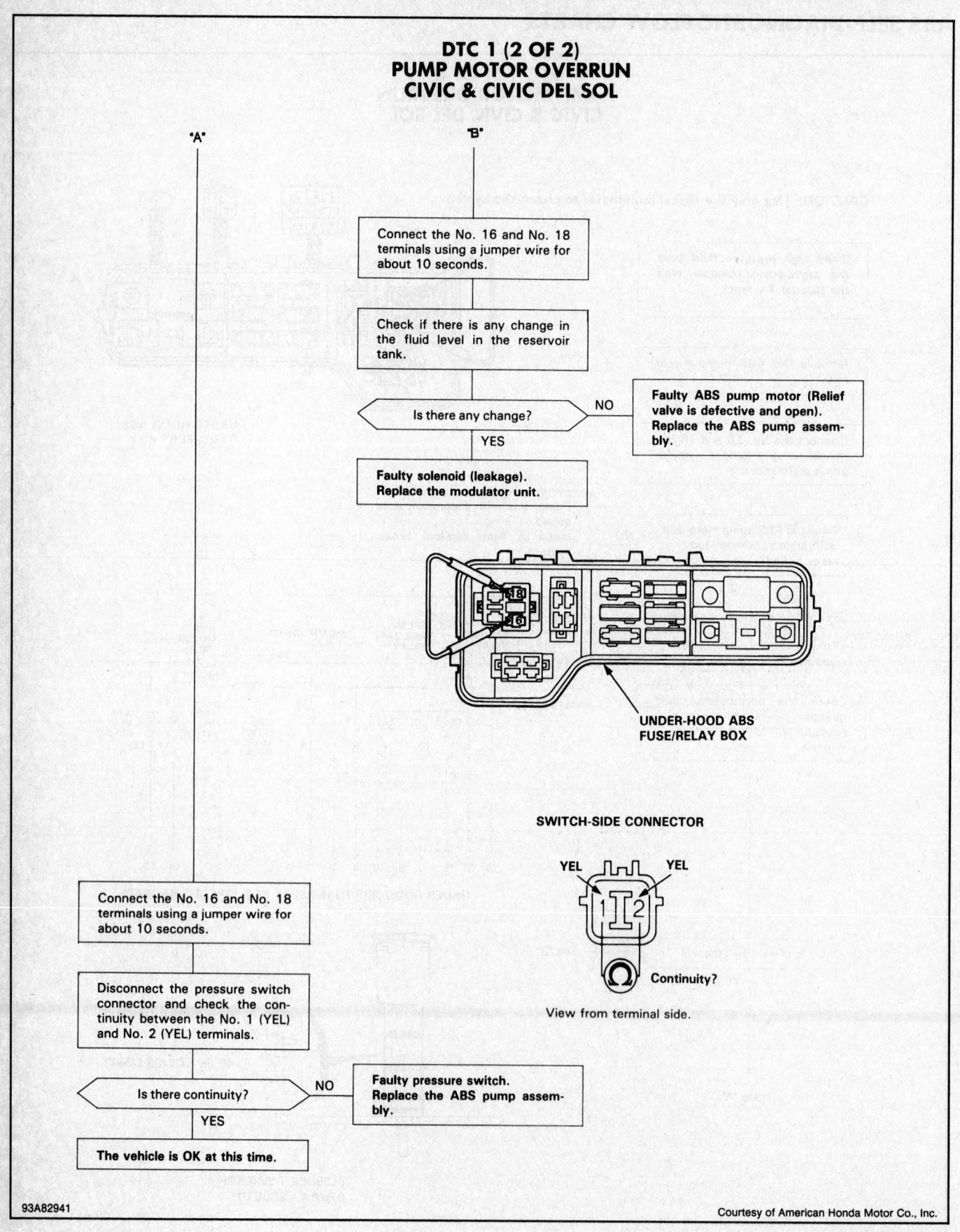

"A"

"B"

Connect the No. 16 and No. 18 terminals using a jumper wire for about 10 seconds.

Check if there is any change in the fluid level in the reservoir tank.

Is there any change? — NO → Faulty ABS pump motor (Relief valve is defective and open). Replace the ABS pump assembly.

YES

Faulty solenoid (leakage). Replace the modulator unit.

UNDER-HOOD ABS FUSE/RELAY BOX

SWITCH-SIDE CONNECTOR

YEL   YEL

Continuity?

View from terminal side.

Connect the No. 16 and No. 18 terminals using a jumper wire for about 10 seconds.

Disconnect the pressure switch connector and check the continuity between the No. 1 (YEL) and No. 2 (YEL) terminals.

Is there continuity? — NO → Faulty pressure switch. Replace the ABS pump assembly.

YES

The vehicle is OK at this time.

93A82941

1994 BRAKES
Anti-Lock – Civic, Civic Del Sol & Prelude (Cont.)

HONDA
8-87

DTC 1-2 (1 OF 3)
PUMP MOTOR CIRCUIT
CIVIC & CIVIC DEL SOL

CAUTION: Use only the digital multimeter to check the system.

NOTE: If a malfunction is detected, this code appears and the fail-safe function is activated. The ABS indicator light comes ON after restarting the engine until the DTC is erased (by disconnecting the ABS B2 (15A) fuse in the under-hood ABS fuse/relay box for three seconds).

Pre-test steps:
- Check ABS MOTOR (50 A) fuse in the under-hood ABS fuse/relay box.
- Check MOTOR CHECK (7.5 A) fuse in the under-hood ABS fuse/relay box.
- Check for loose under-hood ABS fuse/relay box connectors.

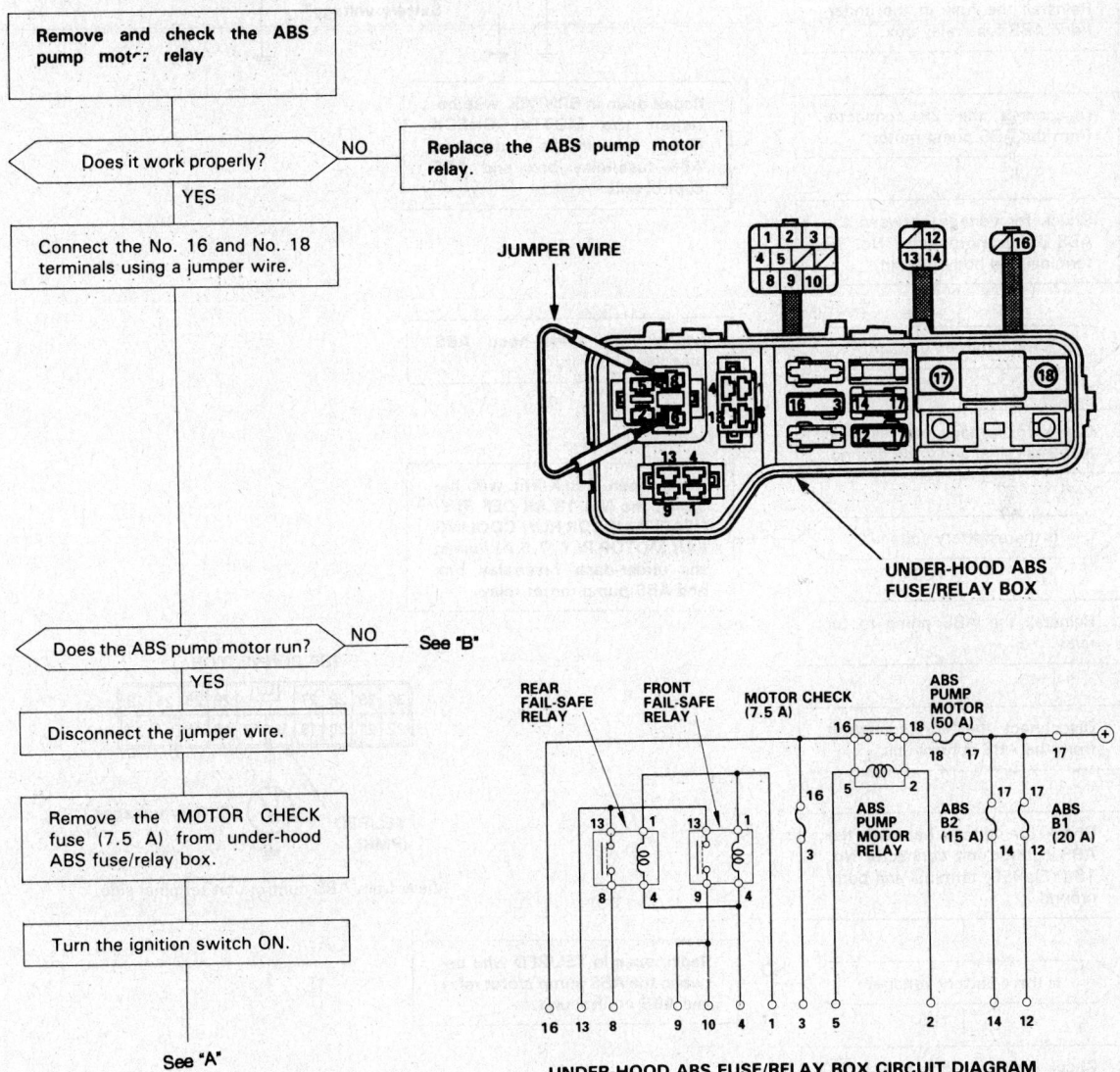

UNDER-HOOD ABS FUSE/RELAY BOX CIRCUIT DIAGRAM

Courtesy of American Honda Motor Co., Inc.

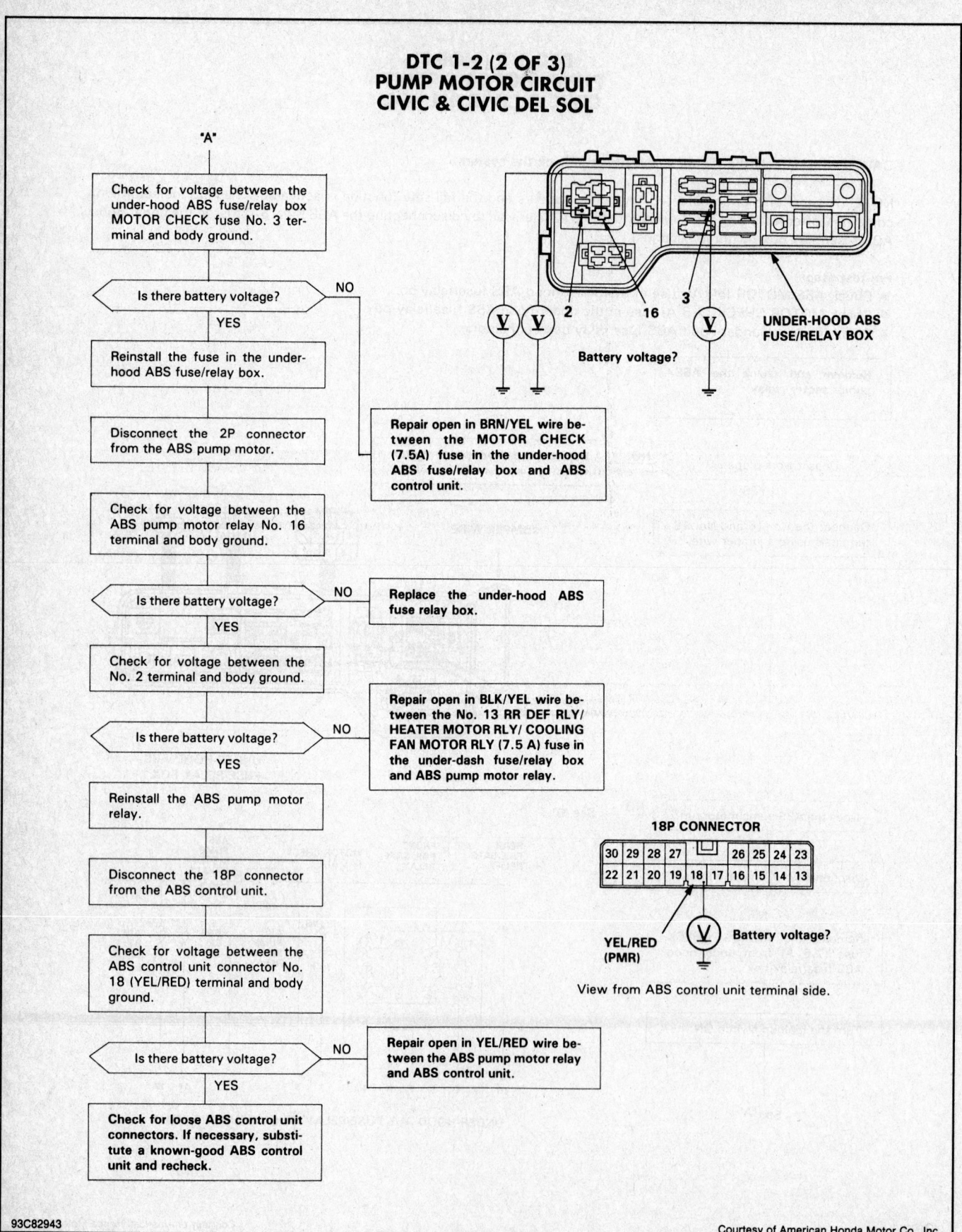

DTC 1-2 (2 OF 3)
PUMP MOTOR CIRCUIT
CIVIC & CIVIC DEL SOL

"A"

Check for voltage between the under-hood ABS fuse/relay box MOTOR CHECK fuse No. 3 terminal and body ground.

Is there battery voltage? — NO

YES

Reinstall the fuse in the under-hood ABS fuse/relay box.

Disconnect the 2P connector from the ABS pump motor.

Check for voltage between the ABS pump motor relay No. 16 terminal and body ground.

Is there battery voltage? — NO

YES

Check for voltage between the No. 2 terminal and body ground.

Is there battery voltage? — NO

YES

Reinstall the ABS pump motor relay.

Disconnect the 18P connector from the ABS control unit.

Check for voltage between the ABS control unit connector No. 18 (YEL/RED) terminal and body ground.

Is there battery voltage? — NO

YES

Check for loose ABS control unit connectors. If necessary, substitute a known-good ABS control unit and recheck.

Repair open in BRN/YEL wire between the MOTOR CHECK (7.5A) fuse in the under-hood ABS fuse/relay box and ABS control unit.

Replace the under-hood ABS fuse relay box.

Repair open in BLK/YEL wire between the No. 13 RR DEF RLY/ HEATER MOTOR RLY/ COOLING FAN MOTOR RLY (7.5 A) fuse in the under-dash fuse/relay box and ABS pump motor relay.

Repair open in YEL/RED wire between the ABS pump motor relay and ABS control unit.

2   16   3

Battery voltage?

UNDER-HOOD ABS FUSE/RELAY BOX

18P CONNECTOR

| 30 | 29 | 28 | 27 | | 26 | 25 | 24 | 23 |
| 22 | 21 | 20 | 19 | 18 | 17 | 16 | 15 | 14 | 13 |

YEL/RED (PMR)   V   Battery voltage?

View from ABS control unit terminal side.

1994 BRAKES
Anti-Lock – Civic, Civic Del Sol & Prelude (Cont.)

HONDA
8-89

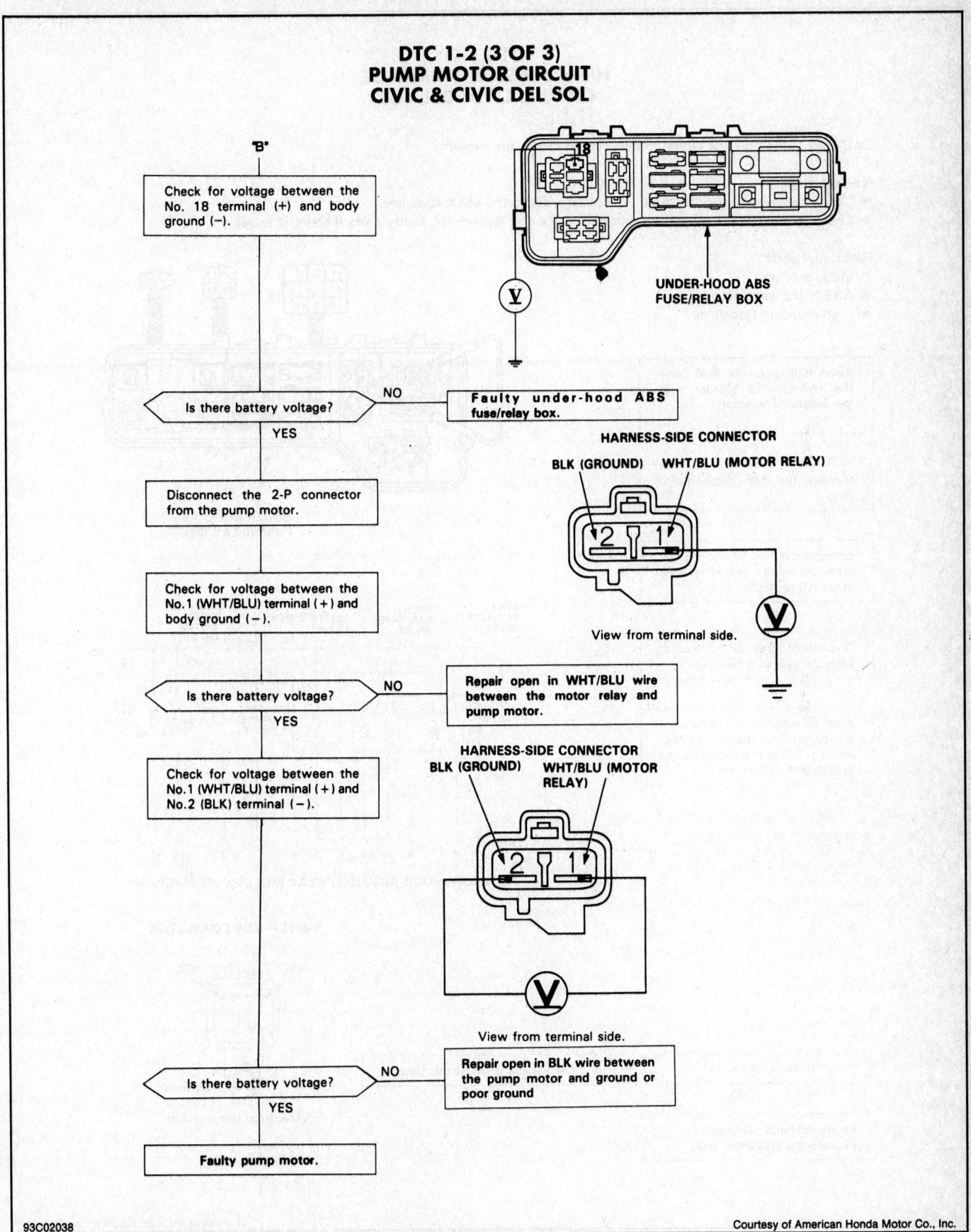

DTC 1-2 (3 OF 3)
PUMP MOTOR CIRCUIT
CIVIC & CIVIC DEL SOL

"B"

Check for voltage between the No. 18 terminal (+) and body ground (−).

18

UNDER-HOOD ABS FUSE/RELAY BOX

Is there battery voltage? — NO → Faulty under-hood ABS fuse/relay box.

YES

Disconnect the 2-P connector from the pump motor.

HARNESS-SIDE CONNECTOR
BLK (GROUND)   WHT/BLU (MOTOR RELAY)

2   1

Check for voltage between the No.1 (WHT/BLU) terminal (+) and body ground (−).

View from terminal side.

Is there battery voltage? — NO → Repair open in WHT/BLU wire between the motor relay and pump motor.

YES

HARNESS-SIDE CONNECTOR
BLK (GROUND)   WHT/BLU (MOTOR RELAY)

2   1

Check for voltage between the No.1 (WHT/BLU) terminal (+) and No.2 (BLK) terminal (−).

View from terminal side.

Is there battery voltage? — NO → Repair open in BLK wire between the pump motor and ground or poor ground

YES

Faulty pump motor.

HONDA
8-90

1994 BRAKES
Anti-Lock – Civic, Civic Del Sol & Prelude (Cont.)

DTC 1-3
HIGH PRESSURE LEAKAGE
CIVIC & CIVIC DEL SOL

CAUTION: Use only the digital multimeter to check the system.

Pre-test steps:
- Check reservoir fluid level, and if necessary, fill to the MAX level line.
- Check for fluid leaks from the functional parts and replace the faulty parts if there is a leak.

Functional parts:
- Modulator unit
- ABS Pump assembly
- High pressure hose/pipe

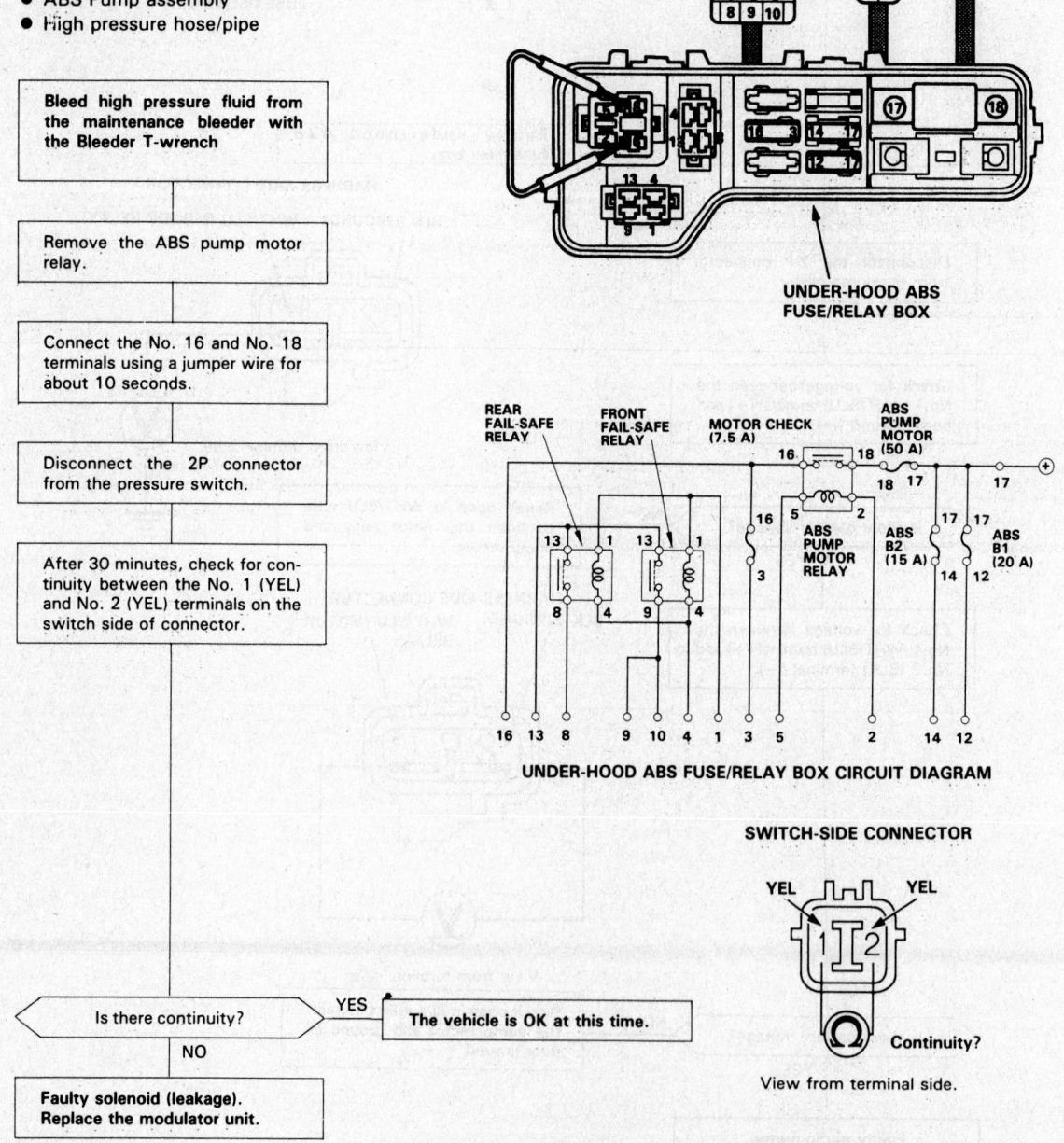

Bleed high pressure fluid from the maintenance bleeder with the Bleeder T-wrench	
Remove the ABS pump motor relay.	
Connect the No. 16 and No. 18 terminals using a jumper wire for about 10 seconds.	
Disconnect the 2P connector from the pressure switch.	
After 30 minutes, check for continuity between the No. 1 (YEL) and No. 2 (YEL) terminals on the switch side of connector.	

UNDER-HOOD ABS FUSE/RELAY BOX

UNDER-HOOD ABS FUSE/RELAY BOX CIRCUIT DIAGRAM

SWITCH-SIDE CONNECTOR

Is there continuity? — YES → The vehicle is OK at this time.

NO

Faulty solenoid (leakage). Replace the modulator unit.

Continuity?

View from terminal side.

1994 BRAKES
Anti-Lock – Civic, Civic Del Sol & Prelude (Cont.)

HONDA
8-91

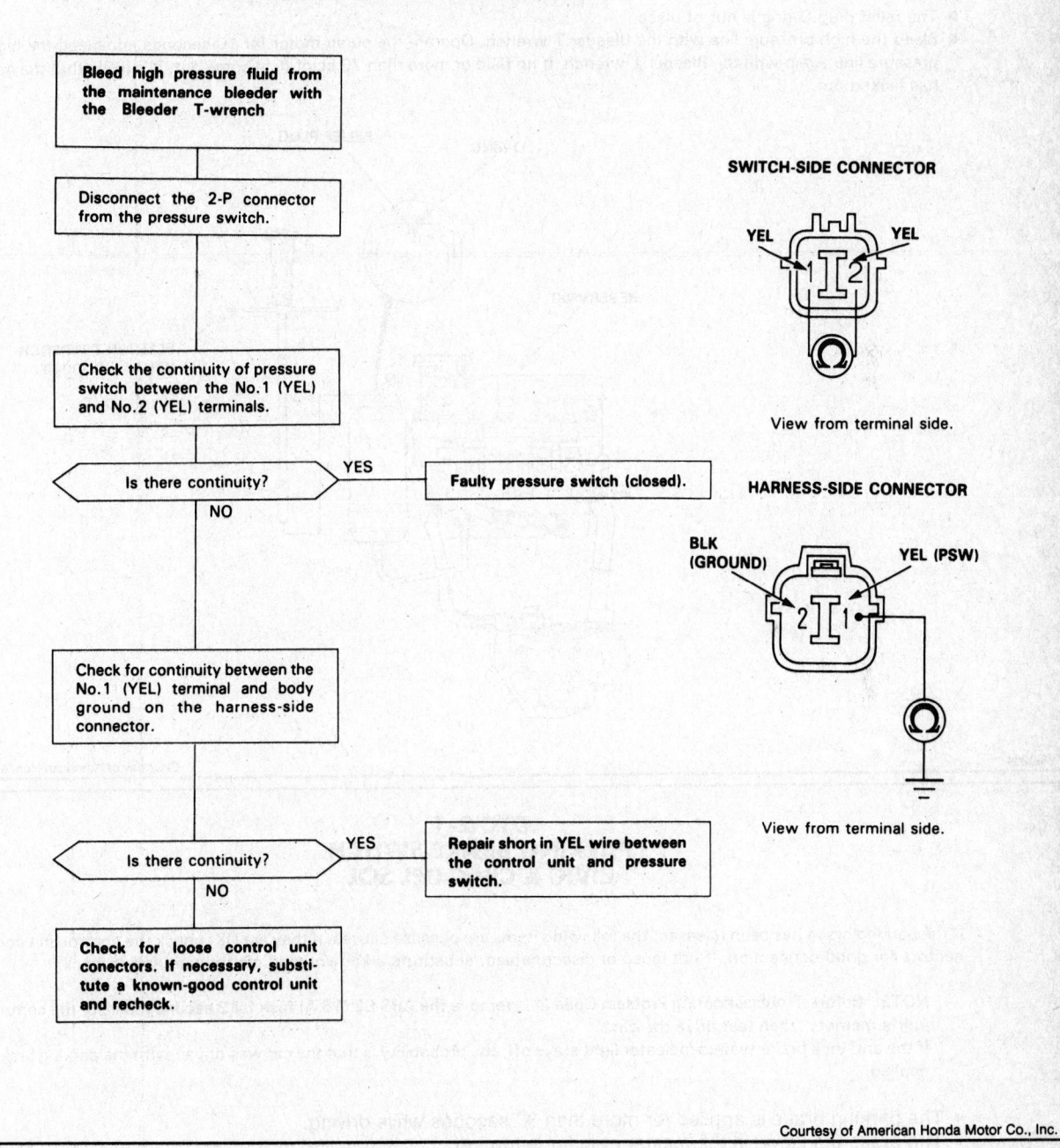

DTC 1-4
PRESSURE SWITCH CIRCUIT
CIVIC & CIVIC DEL SOL

CAUTION: Use only the digital multimeter to check the system.

Bleed high pressure fluid from the maintenance bleeder with the Bleeder T-wrench

Disconnect the 2-P connector from the pressure switch.

Check the continuity of pressure switch between the No.1 (YEL) and No.2 (YEL) terminals.

Is there continuity?

YES — Faulty pressure switch (closed).

NO

Check for continuity between the No.1 (YEL) terminal and body ground on the harness-side connector.

Is there continuity?

YES — Repair short in YEL wire between the control unit and pressure switch.

NO

Check for loose control unit conectors. If necessary, substitute a known-good control unit and recheck.

SWITCH-SIDE CONNECTOR

YEL   YEL

1 2

View from terminal side.

HARNESS-SIDE CONNECTOR

BLK (GROUND)   YEL (PSW)

2 1

View from terminal side.

93G02040

DTC 1-8
ACCUMULATOR GAS LEAKAGE
CIVIC & CIVIC DEL SOL

Check the following items:
- The relief plug is loose.
- The relief plug O-ring is out of place.
- Bleed the high pressure line with the Bleeder T-wrench. Operate the pump motor for 10 seconds and bleed the high pressure line again with the Bleeder T-wrench. If no fluid or more than 70 cc of fluid come out, it is likely that the gas has leaked out.

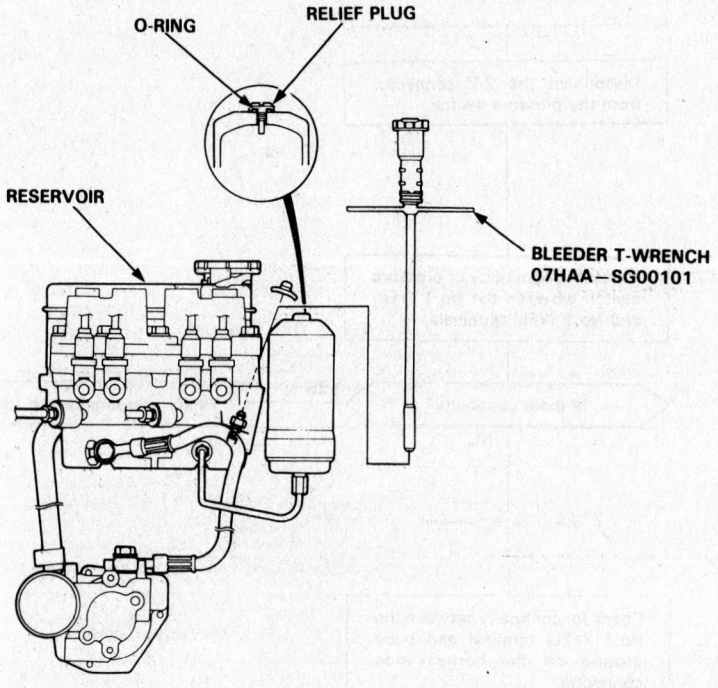

O-RING

RELIEF PLUG

RESERVOIR

BLEEDER T-WRENCH
07HAA−SG00101

93I02041

Courtesy of American Honda Motor Co., Inc.

DTC 2-1
PARKING BRAKE SWITCH
CIVIC & CIVIC DEL SOL

If the parking brake has been released, the following items are possible causes. If they are OK, check the control unit connectors for good connection. If not loose or disconnected, substitute a known-good control unit and recheck.

NOTE: Before Troubleshooting Problem Code 2-1, remove the ABS B2 (15 A) fuse for 3 seconds to clear the control unit's memory, then test drive the car.
If the anti-lock brake system indicator light stays off, the probability is that the car was driven with the parking brake applied.

- The parking brake is applied for more than 30 seconds while driving.
- The brake fluid level in the master cylinder is too low.
- GRN/RED wire is shorted between the BRAKE indicator light and parking brake switch.
- GRN/RED wire is shorted between the BRAKE indicator light and brake fluid level switch.
- The BRAKE indicator light is blown.
- GRN/RED wire has an open between the BRAKE indicator light and the control unit.

93E02242

Courtesy of American Honda Motor Co., Inc.

1994 BRAKES
Anti-Lock – Civic, Civic Del Sol & Prelude (Cont.)

HONDA
8-93

DTC 4-1 TO 4-8
SPEED SENSOR
CIVIC & CIVIC DEL SOL

CAUTION: Use only the digital multimeter to check the system.

NOTE: If a malfunction is detected, this code appears and the fail-safe function is activated. The indicator light may come ON after restarting the engine until the malfunction code is erased (by disconnecting the ABS B2 fuse for 3 seconds).

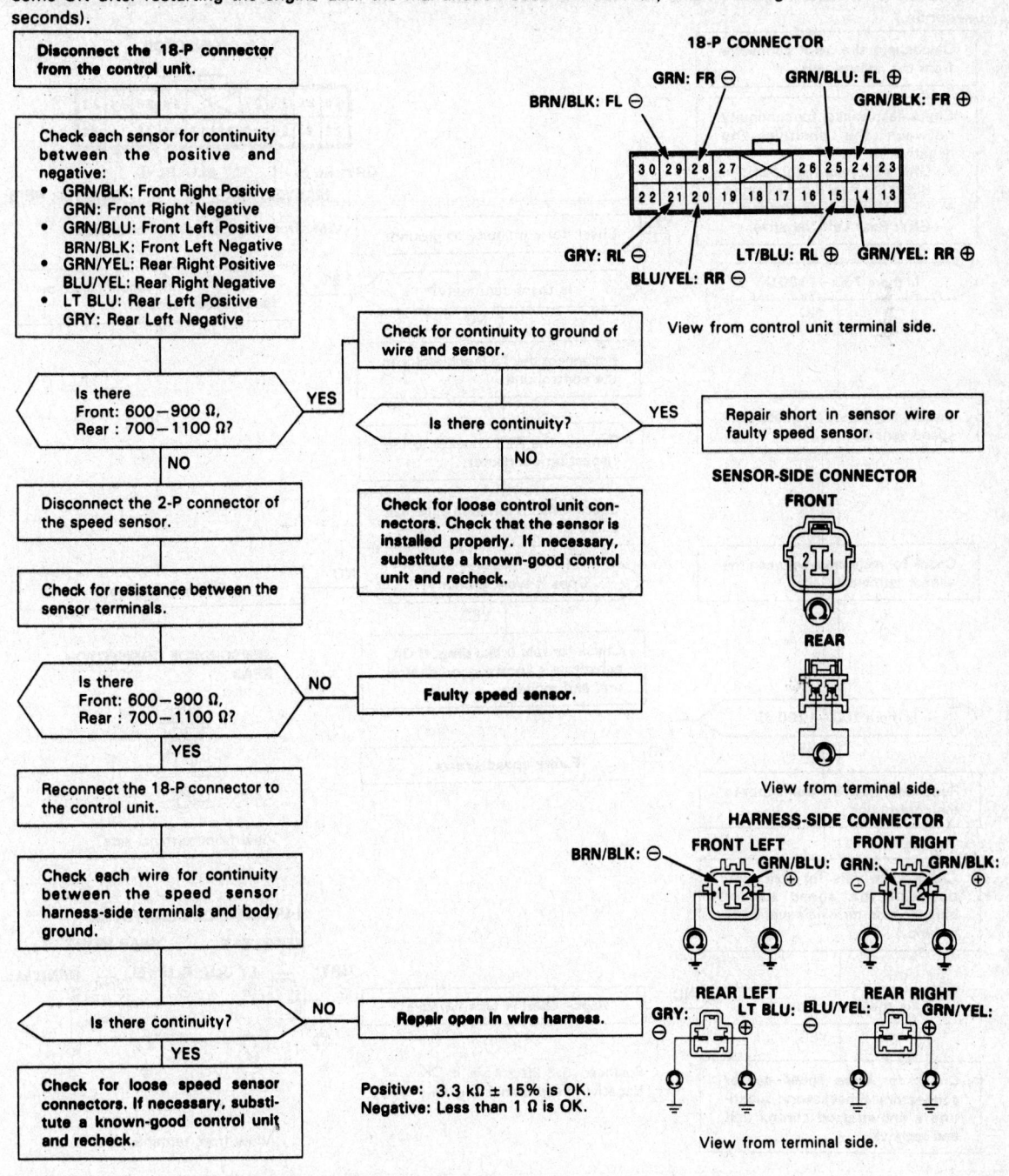

Disconnect the 18-P connector from the control unit.

Check each sensor for continuity between the positive and negative:
- GRN/BLK: Front Right Positive
  GRN: Front Right Negative
- GRN/BLU: Front Left Positive
  BRN/BLK: Front Left Negative
- GRN/YEL: Rear Right Positive
  BLU/YEL: Rear Right Negative
- LT BLU: Rear Left Positive
  GRY: Rear Left Negative

Is there Front: 600 – 900 Ω, Rear : 700 – 1100 Ω?

YES → Check for continuity to ground of wire and sensor.

Is there continuity?

YES → Repair short in sensor wire or faulty speed sensor.

NO → Check for loose control unit connectors. Check that the sensor is installed properly. If necessary, substitute a known-good control unit and recheck.

NO → Disconnect the 2-P connector of the speed sensor.

Check for resistance between the sensor terminals.

Is there Front: 600 – 900 Ω, Rear : 700 – 1100 Ω?

NO → Faulty speed sensor.

YES → Reconnect the 18-P connector to the control unit.

Check each wire for continuity between the speed sensor harness-side terminals and body ground.

Is there continuity?

NO → Repair open in wire harness.

YES → Check for loose speed sensor connectors. If necessary, substitute a known-good control unit and recheck.

Positive: 3.3 kΩ ± 15% is OK.
Negative: Less than 1 Ω is OK.

18-P CONNECTOR

BRN/BLK: FL ⊖   GRN: FR ⊖   GRN/BLU: FL ⊕   GRN/BLK: FR ⊕

| 30 | 29 | 28 | 27 | ✕ | 26 | 25 | 24 | 23 |
| 22 | 21 | 20 | 19 | 18 | 17 | 16 | 15 | 14 | 13 |

GRY: RL ⊖   BLU/YEL: RR ⊖   LT/BLU: RL ⊕   GRN/YEL: RR ⊕

View from control unit terminal side.

SENSOR-SIDE CONNECTOR

FRONT

REAR

View from terminal side.

HARNESS-SIDE CONNECTOR

FRONT LEFT   FRONT RIGHT
BRN/BLK: ⊖   GRN/BLU: ⊕   GRN: ⊖   GRN/BLK: ⊕

REAR LEFT   REAR RIGHT
GRY: ⊖   LT BLU: ⊕   BLU/YEL: ⊖   GRN/YEL: ⊕

View from terminal side.

HONDA
8-94

1994 BRAKES
Anti-Lock – Civic, Civic Del Sol & Prelude (Cont.)

DTC 5 TO 5-8
SPEED SENSOR(S)
CIVIC & CIVIC DEL SOL

CAUTION: Use only the digital multimeter to check the system.

NOTE: If a malfunction is detected, this code appears and the fail-safe function is activated. The indicator light may come ON after restarting the engine until the malfunction code is erased (by disconnecting the ABS B2 fuse for 3 seconds.)

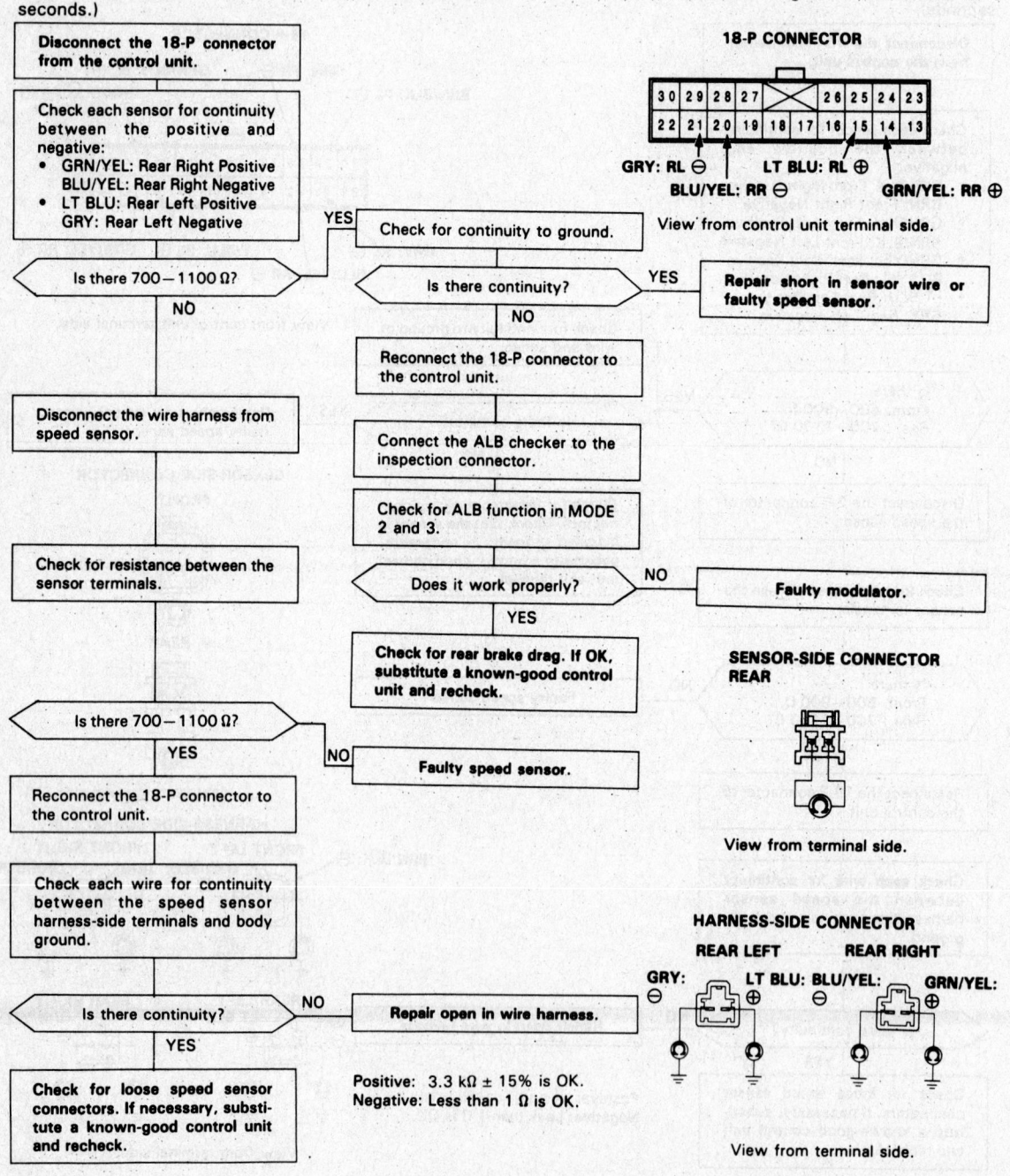

18-P CONNECTOR

| 30 | 29 | 28 | 27 | ✕ | 26 | 25 | 24 | 23 |
| 22 | 21 | 20 | 19 | 18 | 17 | 16 | 15 | 14 | 13 |

GRY: RL ⊖   LT BLU: RL ⊕
BLU/YEL: RR ⊖   GRN/YEL: RR ⊕

View from control unit terminal side.

Disconnect the 18-P connector from the control unit.

Check each sensor for continuity between the positive and negative:
• GRN/YEL: Rear Right Positive
  BLU/YEL: Rear Right Negative
• LT BLU: Rear Left Positive
  GRY: Rear Left Negative

Is there 700 – 1100 Ω? —YES→ Check for continuity to ground.

NO

Is there continuity? —YES→ Repair short in sensor wire or faulty speed sensor.

NO

Reconnect the 18-P connector to the control unit.

Connect the ALB checker to the inspection connector.

Check for ALB function in MODE 2 and 3.

Disconnect the wire harness from speed sensor.

Check for resistance between the sensor terminals.

Does it work properly? —NO→ Faulty modulator.

YES

Check for rear brake drag. If OK, substitute a known-good control unit and recheck.

SENSOR-SIDE CONNECTOR
REAR

View from terminal side.

Is there 700 – 1100 Ω? —NO→ Faulty speed sensor.

YES

Reconnect the 18-P connector to the control unit.

Check each wire for continuity between the speed sensor harness-side terminals and body ground.

HARNESS-SIDE CONNECTOR

REAR LEFT   **REAR RIGHT**

GRY: LT BLU: BLU/YEL: GRN/YEL:
⊖   ⊕   ⊖   ⊕

Is there continuity? —NO→ Repair open in wire harness.

YES

Check for loose speed sensor connectors. If necessary, substitute a known-good control unit and recheck.

Positive: 3.3 kΩ ± 15% is OK.
Negative: Less than 1 Ω is OK.

View from terminal side.

1994 BRAKES
Anti-Lock – Civic, Civic Del Sol & Prelude (Cont.)

HONDA
8-95

DTC 6-1 (1 OF 3)
FRONT FAIL-SAFE RELAY CIRCUIT
CIVIC & CIVIC DEL SOL

CAUTION: Use only the digital multimeter to check the system.

Pre-test steps:
- Check ABS B1 (20 A) fuse in the under-hood ABS fuse/relay box.
- Check for loose under-hood ABS fuse/relay box connectors.

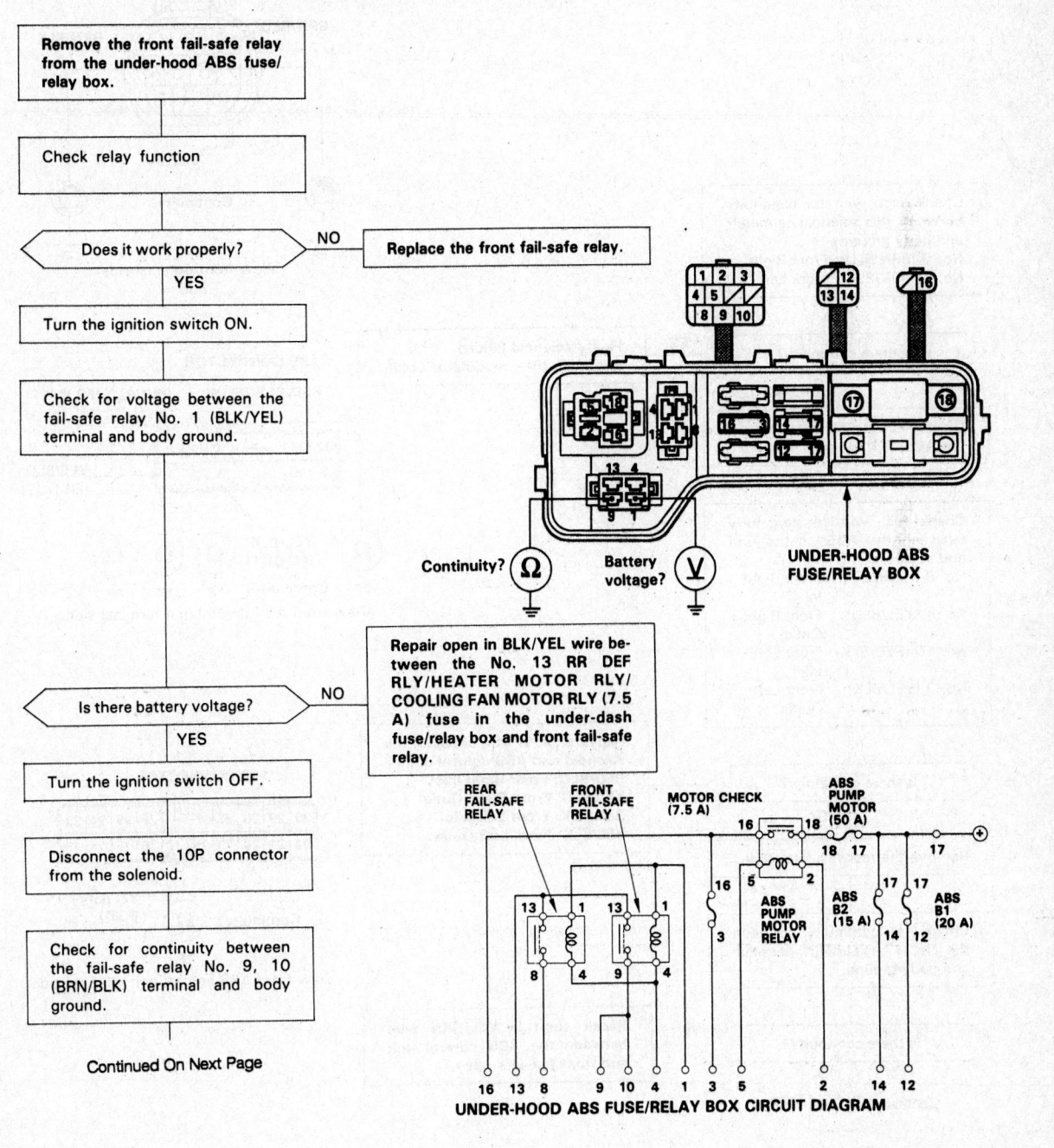

Remove the front fail-safe relay from the under-hood ABS fuse/relay box.

Check relay function

Does it work properly? — NO → Replace the front fail-safe relay.

YES

Turn the ignition switch ON.

Check for voltage between the fail-safe relay No. 1 (BLK/YEL) terminal and body ground.

Continuity? Ω

Battery voltage? V

UNDER-HOOD ABS FUSE/RELAY BOX

Is there battery voltage? — NO → Repair open in BLK/YEL wire between the No. 13 RR DEF RLY/HEATER MOTOR RLY/COOLING FAN MOTOR RLY (7.5 A) fuse in the under-dash fuse/relay box and front fail-safe relay.

YES

Turn the ignition switch OFF.

Disconnect the 10P connector from the solenoid.

Check for continuity between the fail-safe relay No. 9, 10 (BRN/BLK) terminal and body ground.

Continued On Next Page

REAR FAIL-SAFE RELAY
FRONT FAIL-SAFE RELAY
MOTOR CHECK (7.5 A)
ABS PUMP MOTOR (50 A)
ABS PUMP MOTOR RELAY
ABS B2 (15 A)
ABS B1 (20 A)

UNDER-HOOD ABS FUSE/RELAY BOX CIRCUIT DIAGRAM

HONDA
8-96

1994 BRAKES
Anti-Lock – Civic, Civic Del Sol & Prelude (Cont.)

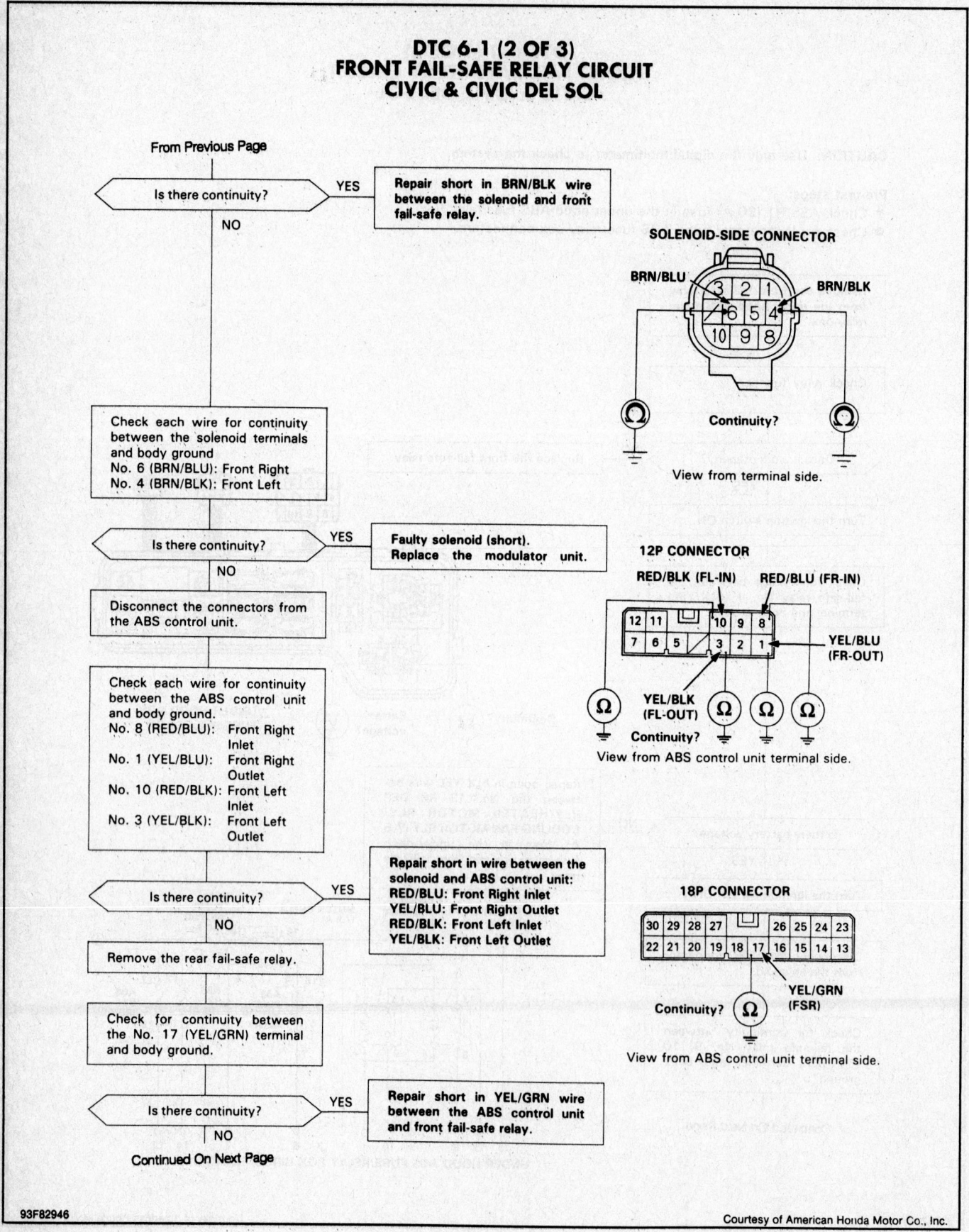

DTC 6-1 (2 OF 3)
FRONT FAIL-SAFE RELAY CIRCUIT
CIVIC & CIVIC DEL SOL

From Previous Page

Is there continuity? — YES → Repair short in BRN/BLK wire between the solenoid and front fail-safe relay.

NO

SOLENOID-SIDE CONNECTOR

BRN/BLU   BRN/BLK

3 2 1
6 5 4
10 9 8

Continuity?

View from terminal side.

Check each wire for continuity between the solenoid terminals and body ground
No. 6 (BRN/BLU): Front Right
No. 4 (BRN/BLK): Front Left

Is there continuity? — YES → Faulty solenoid (short). Replace the modulator unit.

NO

Disconnect the connectors from the ABS control unit.

12P CONNECTOR

RED/BLK (FL-IN)   RED/BLU (FR-IN)

12 11   10 9 8
7 6 5   3 2 1

YEL/BLU (FR-OUT)

YEL/BLK (FL-OUT)   Continuity?

View from ABS control unit terminal side.

Check each wire for continuity between the ABS control unit and body ground.
No. 8 (RED/BLU): Front Right Inlet
No. 1 (YEL/BLU): Front Right Outlet
No. 10 (RED/BLK): Front Left Inlet
No. 3 (YEL/BLK): Front Left Outlet

Is there continuity? — YES → Repair short in wire between the solenoid and ABS control unit:
RED/BLU: Front Right Inlet
YEL/BLU: Front Right Outlet
RED/BLK: Front Left Inlet
YEL/BLK: Front Left Outlet

NO

Remove the rear fail-safe relay.

18P CONNECTOR

30 29 28 27   26 25 24 23
22 21 20 19 18 17   16 15 14 13

YEL/GRN (FSR)

Continuity?

View from ABS control unit terminal side.

Check for continuity between the No. 17 (YEL/GRN) terminal and body ground.

Is there continuity? — YES → Repair short in YEL/GRN wire between the ABS control unit and front fail-safe relay.

NO

Continued On Next Page

93F82946

Courtesy of American Honda Motor Co., Inc.

1994 BRAKES
Anti-Lock – Civic, Civic Del Sol & Prelude (Cont.)

HONDA
8-97

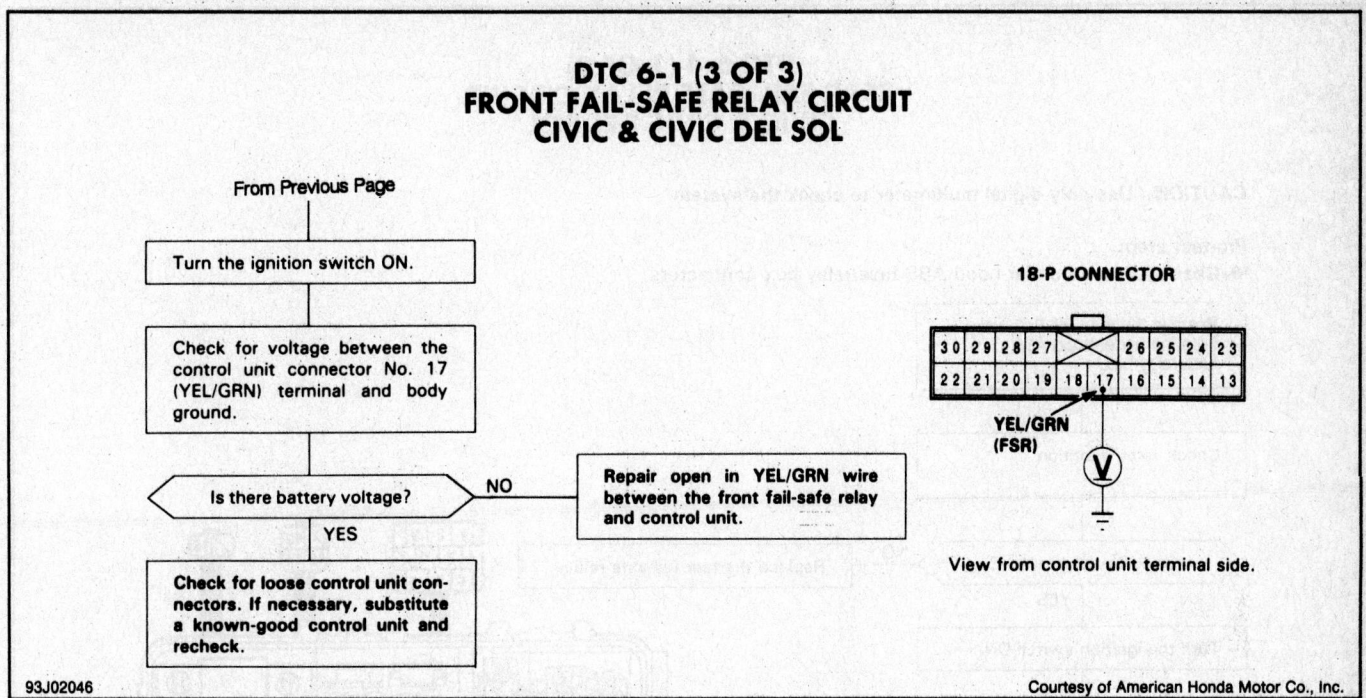

DTC 6-1 (3 OF 3)
FRONT FAIL-SAFE RELAY CIRCUIT
CIVIC & CIVIC DEL SOL

From Previous Page

Turn the ignition switch ON.

Check for voltage between the control unit connector No. 17 (YEL/GRN) terminal and body ground.

Is there battery voltage? — NO → Repair open in YEL/GRN wire between the front fail-safe relay and control unit.

YES

Check for loose control unit connectors. If necessary, substitute a known-good control unit and recheck.

18-P CONNECTOR

| 30 | 29 | 28 | 27 | | | 26 | 25 | 24 | 23 |
| 22 | 21 | 20 | 19 | 18 | 17 | 16 | 15 | 14 | 13 |

YEL/GRN
(FSR)

View from control unit terminal side.

93J02046

Courtesy of American Honda Motor Co., Inc.

HONDA
8-98

1994 BRAKES
Anti-Lock – Civic, Civic Del Sol & Prelude (Cont.)

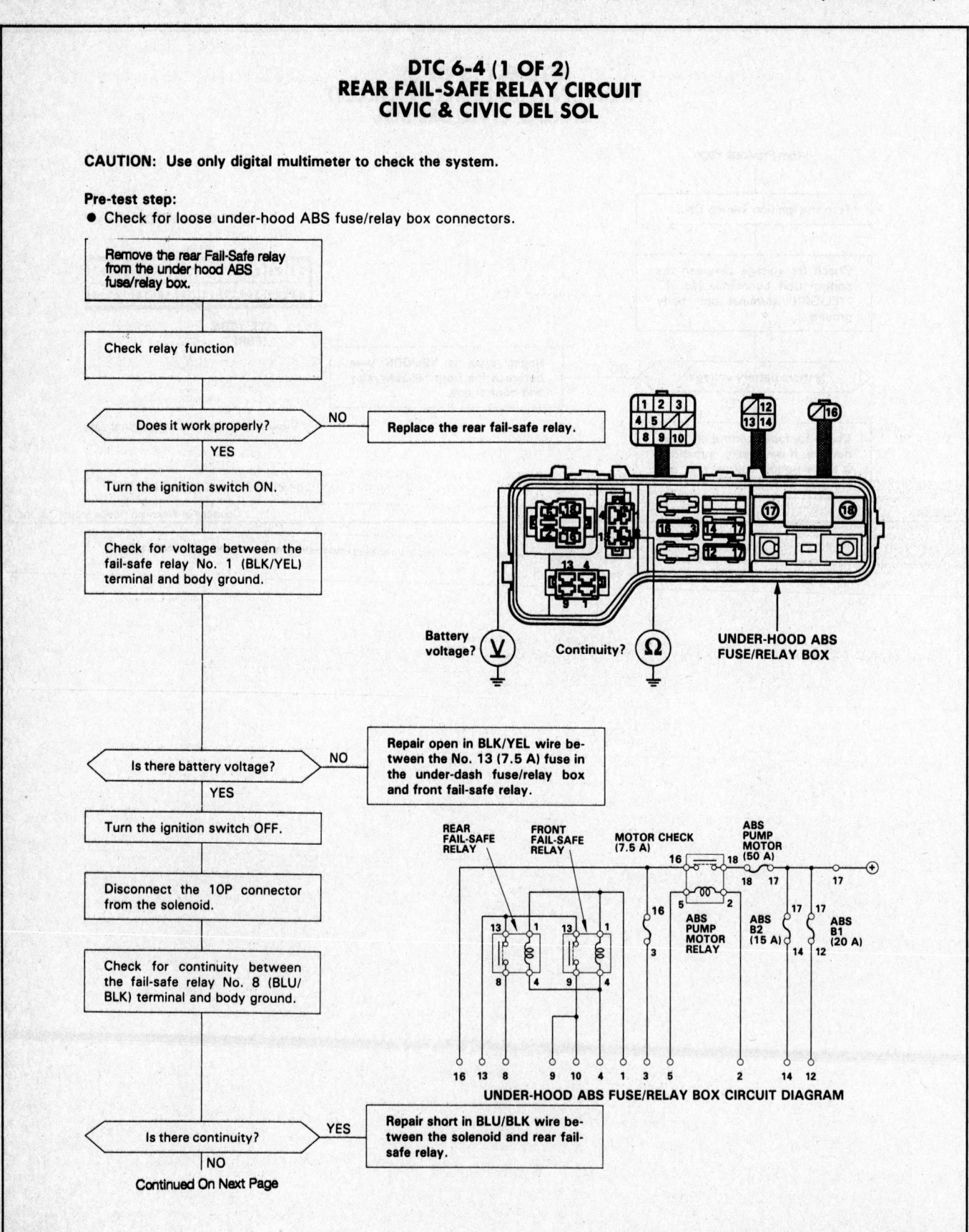

DTC 6-4 (1 OF 2)
REAR FAIL-SAFE RELAY CIRCUIT
CIVIC & CIVIC DEL SOL

CAUTION: Use only digital multimeter to check the system.

Pre-test step:
● Check for loose under-hood ABS fuse/relay box connectors.

Remove the rear Fail-Safe relay from the under hood ABS fuse/relay box.

Check relay function

Does it work properly? — NO → Replace the rear fail-safe relay.

YES

Turn the ignition switch ON.

Check for voltage between the fail-safe relay No. 1 (BLK/YEL) terminal and body ground.

Battery voltage? (V)   Continuity? (Ω)

UNDER-HOOD ABS FUSE/RELAY BOX

Is there battery voltage? — NO → Repair open in BLK/YEL wire between the No. 13 (7.5 A) fuse in the under-dash fuse/relay box and front fail-safe relay.

YES

Turn the ignition switch OFF.

Disconnect the 10P connector from the solenoid.

Check for continuity between the fail-safe relay No. 8 (BLU/BLK) terminal and body ground.

REAR FAIL-SAFE RELAY   FRONT FAIL-SAFE RELAY   MOTOR CHECK (7.5 A)   ABS PUMP MOTOR (50 A)

ABS PUMP MOTOR RELAY   ABS B2 (15 A)   ABS B1 (20 A)

UNDER-HOOD ABS FUSE/RELAY BOX CIRCUIT DIAGRAM

Is there continuity? — YES → Repair short in BLU/BLK wire between the solenoid and rear fail-safe relay.

NO

Continued On Next Page

Courtesy of American Honda Motor Co., Inc.

1994 BRAKES
Anti-Lock – Civic, Civic Del Sol & Prelude (Cont.)

HONDA
8-99

DTC 6-4 (2 OF 2)
REAR FAIL-SAFE RELAY CIRCUIT
CIVIC & CIVIC DEL SOL

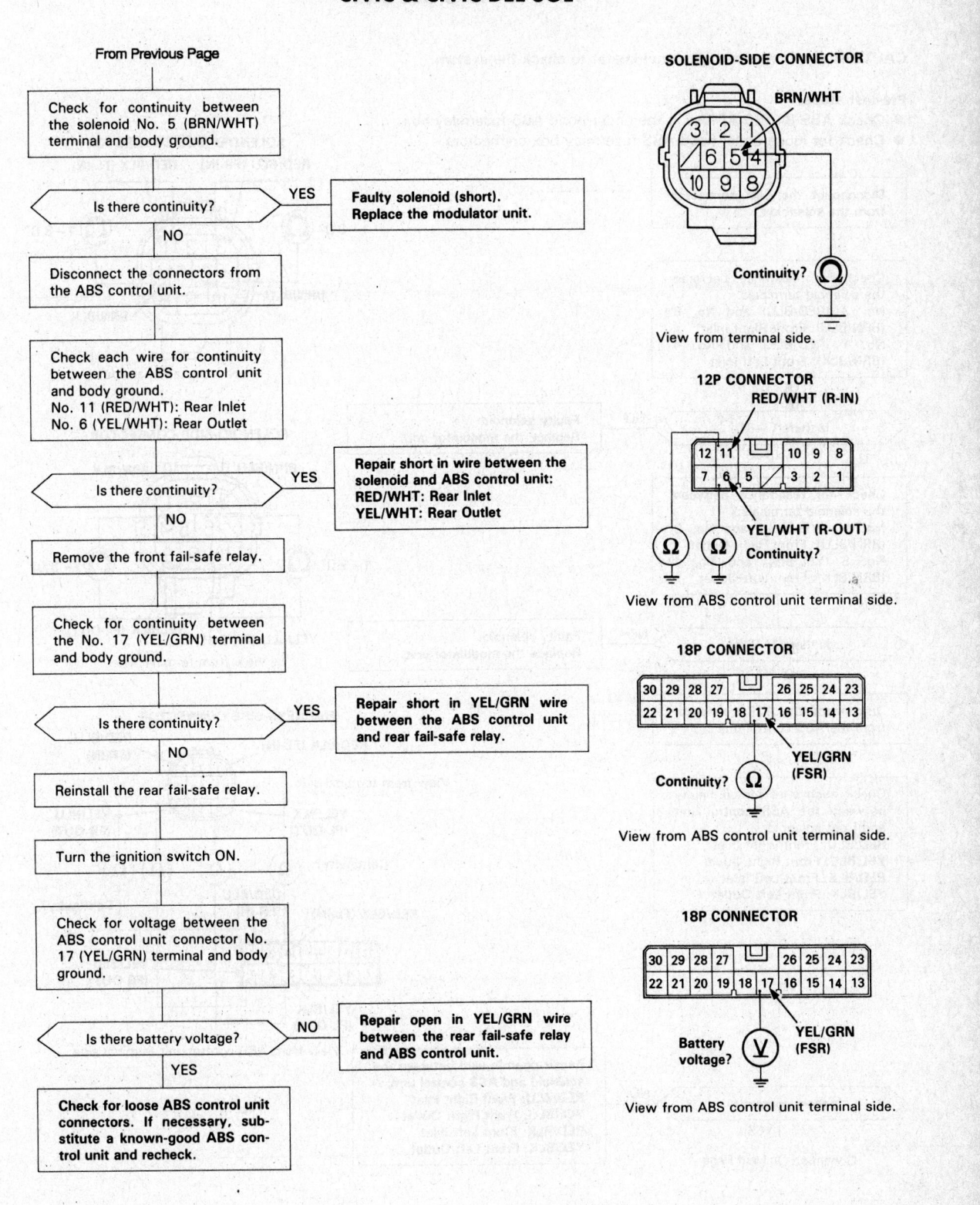

From Previous Page

Check for continuity between the solenoid No. 5 (BRN/WHT) terminal and body ground.

Is there continuity? — YES → Faulty solenoid (short). Replace the modulator unit.

NO

Disconnect the connectors from the ABS control unit.

Check each wire for continuity between the ABS control unit and body ground.
No. 11 (RED/WHT): Rear Inlet
No. 6 (YEL/WHT): Rear Outlet

Is there continuity? — YES → Repair short in wire between the solenoid and ABS control unit:
RED/WHT: Rear Inlet
YEL/WHT: Rear Outlet

NO

Remove the front fail-safe relay.

Check for continuity between the No. 17 (YEL/GRN) terminal and body ground.

Is there continuity? — YES → Repair short in YEL/GRN wire between the ABS control unit and rear fail-safe relay.

NO

Reinstall the rear fail-safe relay.

Turn the ignition switch ON.

Check for voltage between the ABS control unit connector No. 17 (YEL/GRN) terminal and body ground.

Is there battery voltage? — NO → Repair open in YEL/GRN wire between the rear fail-safe relay and ABS control unit.

YES

Check for loose ABS control unit connectors. If necessary, substitute a known-good ABS control unit and recheck.

SOLENOID-SIDE CONNECTOR

BRN/WHT

3 2 1
6 5 4
10 9 8

Continuity?

View from terminal side.

12P CONNECTOR
RED/WHT (R-IN)

12 11 | 10 9 8
7 6 5 / 3 2 1

YEL/WHT (R-OUT)
Continuity?

View from ABS control unit terminal side.

18P CONNECTOR

30 29 28 27 | 26 25 24 23
22 21 20 19 18 17 16 15 14 13

YEL/GRN (FSR)

Continuity?

View from ABS control unit terminal side.

18P CONNECTOR

30 29 28 27 | 26 25 24 23
22 21 20 19 18 17 16 15 14 13

Battery voltage?

YEL/GRN (FSR)

View from ABS control unit terminal side.

94J47216

Courtesy of American Honda Motor Co., Inc.

DTC 7-1 & 7-2 (1 OF 2)
FRONT SOLENOID
CIVIC & CIVIC DEL SOL

CAUTION: Use only the digital multimeter to check the system.

Pre-test steps:
- Check ABS B1 (20 A) fuse in the under-hood ABS fuse/relay box.
- Check for loose under-hood ABS fuse/relay box connectors.

Disconnect the 10P connector from the solenoids.

Check for resistance between the solenoid terminals:
No. 3 (RED/BLU) and No. 6 (BRN/BLU): Front Right Inlet
No. 1 (RED/BLK) and No. 4 (BRN/BLK): Front Left Inlet

Is there 1–3 Ω? — NO → Faulty solenoid. Replace the modulator unit.

YES

Check for resistance between the solenoid terminals:
No. 10 (YEL/BLU) and No. 6 (BRN/BLU): Front Right Outlet
No. 8 (YEL/BLK) and No. 4 (BRN/BLK): Front Left Outlet

Is there 1–3 Ω? — NO → Faulty solenoid. Replace the modulator unit.

YES

Disconnect the 12P connector from the ABS control unit.

Check each wire for continuity between the ABS control unit and front solenoid:
RED/BLU: Front Right Inlet
YEL/BLU: Front Right Outlet
RED/BLK: Front Left Inlet
YEL/BLK: Front Left Outlet

Is there continuity? — NO → Repair open in wire between the solenoid and ABS control unit:
RED/BLU: Front Right Inlet
YEL/BLU: Front Right Outlet
RED/BLK: Front Left Inlet
YEL/BLK: Front Left Outlet

YES

Continued On Next Page

SOLENOID-SIDE CONNECTOR

RED/BLU (FR-IN)   RED/BLK (FL-IN)

1–3 Ω?   1–3 Ω?

BRN/BLU   BRN/BLK

View from terminal side.

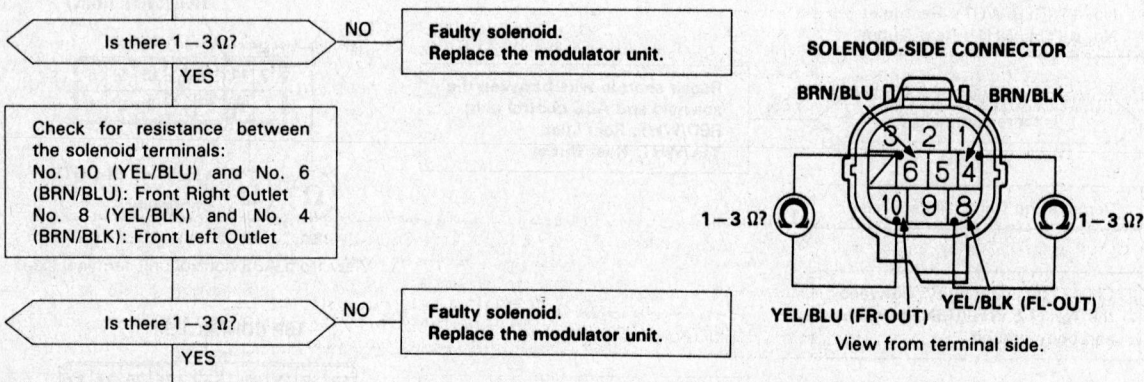

SOLENOID-SIDE CONNECTOR

BRN/BLU   BRN/BLK

1–3 Ω?   1–3 Ω?

YEL/BLU (FR-OUT)   YEL/BLK (FL-OUT)

View from terminal side.

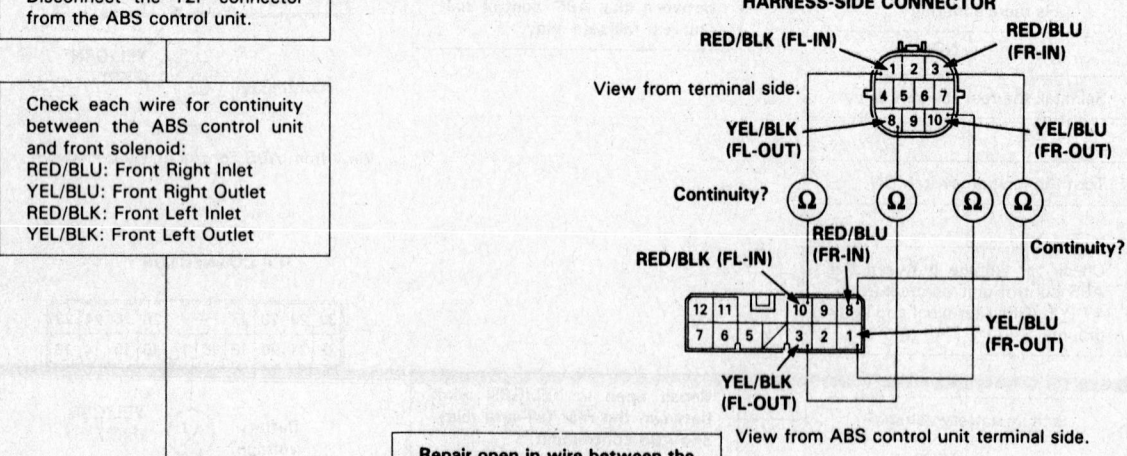

HARNESS-SIDE CONNECTOR

RED/BLK (FL-IN)   RED/BLU (FR-IN)

View from terminal side.

YEL/BLK (FL-OUT)   YEL/BLU (FR-OUT)

Continuity?   Continuity?

RED/BLK (FL-IN)   RED/BLU (FR-IN)

YEL/BLU (FR-OUT)

YEL/BLK (FL-OUT)

View from ABS control unit terminal side.

1994 BRAKES
Anti-Lock – Civic, Civic Del Sol & Prelude (Cont.)

HONDA
8-101

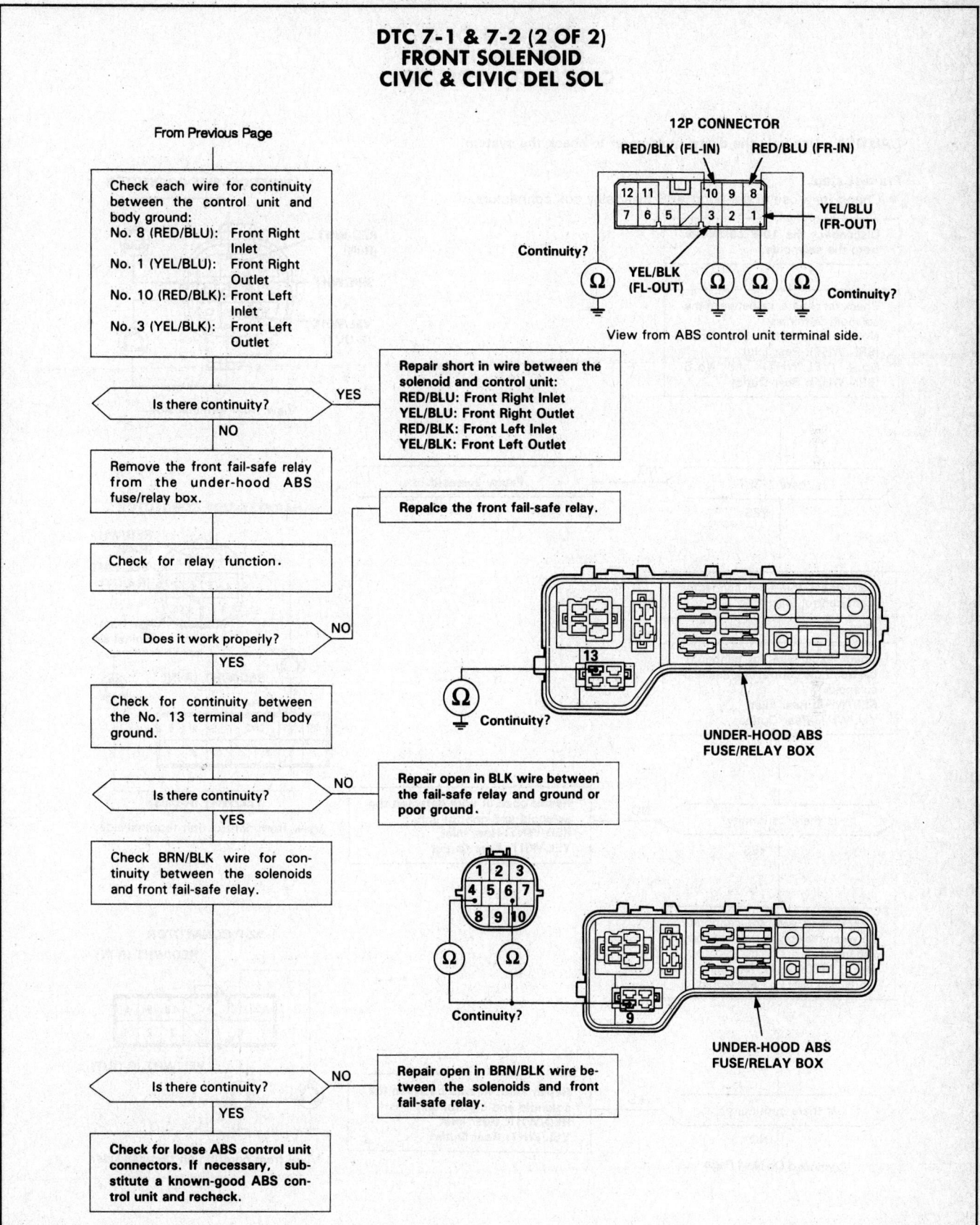

DTC 7-1 & 7-2 (2 OF 2)
FRONT SOLENOID
CIVIC & CIVIC DEL SOL

From Previous Page

Check each wire for continuity between the control unit and body ground:
No. 8 (RED/BLU): Front Right Inlet
No. 1 (YEL/BLU): Front Right Outlet
No. 10 (RED/BLK): Front Left Inlet
No. 3 (YEL/BLK): Front Left Outlet

Is there continuity? — YES → Repair short in wire between the solenoid and control unit:
RED/BLU: Front Right Inlet
YEL/BLU: Front Right Outlet
RED/BLK: Front Left Inlet
YEL/BLK: Front Left Outlet

NO

Remove the front fail-safe relay from the under-hood ABS fuse/relay box.

Check for relay function.

Does it work properly? — NO → Repalce the front fail-safe relay.

YES

Check for continuity between the No. 13 terminal and body ground.

Is there continuity? — NO → Repair open in BLK wire between the fail-safe relay and ground or poor ground.

YES

Check BRN/BLK wire for continuity between the solenoids and front fail-safe relay.

Is there continuity? — NO → Repair open in BRN/BLK wire between the solenoids and front fail-safe relay.

YES

Check for loose ABS control unit connectors. If necessary, substitute a known-good ABS control unit and recheck.

12P CONNECTOR
RED/BLK (FL-IN)   RED/BLU (FR-IN)
YEL/BLU (FR-OUT)
Continuity?
YEL/BLK (FL-OUT)
Continuity?
View from ABS control unit terminal side.

Continuity?
UNDER-HOOD ABS FUSE/RELAY BOX

Continuity?
UNDER-HOOD ABS FUSE/RELAY BOX

93182949

DTC 7-4 (1 OF 2)
REAR SOLENOID
CIVIC & CIVIC DEL SOL

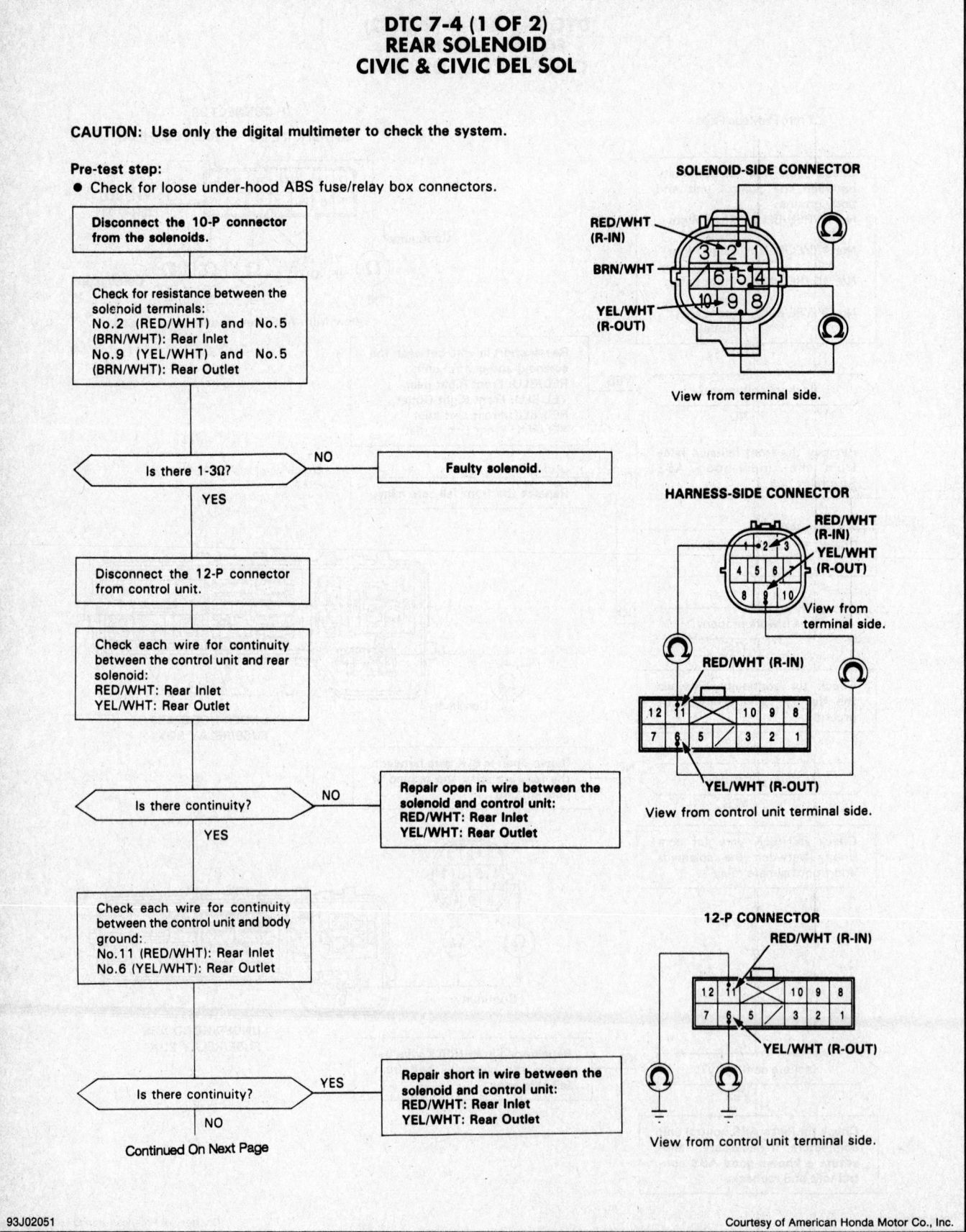

CAUTION: Use only the digital multimeter to check the system.

Pre-test step:
● Check for loose under-hood ABS fuse/relay box connectors.

Disconnect the 10-P connector from the solenoids.

Check for resistance between the solenoid terminals:
No.2 (RED/WHT) and No.5 (BRN/WHT): Rear Inlet
No.9 (YEL/WHT) and No.5 (BRN/WHT): Rear Outlet

Is there 1-3Ω? — NO → Faulty solenoid.

YES

Disconnect the 12-P connector from control unit.

Check each wire for continuity between the control unit and rear solenoid:
RED/WHT: Rear Inlet
YEL/WHT: Rear Outlet

Is there continuity? — NO → Repair open in wire between the solenoid and control unit:
RED/WHT: Rear Inlet
YEL/WHT: Rear Outlet

YES

Check each wire for continuity between the control unit and body ground:
No.11 (RED/WHT): Rear Inlet
No.6 (YEL/WHT): Rear Outlet

Is there continuity? — YES → Repair short in wire between the solenoid and control unit:
RED/WHT: Rear Inlet
YEL/WHT: Rear Outlet

NO

Continued On Next Page

SOLENOID-SIDE CONNECTOR

RED/WHT (R-IN)
BRN/WHT
YEL/WHT (R-OUT)

3 2 1
6 5 4
10 9 8

View from terminal side.

HARNESS-SIDE CONNECTOR

RED/WHT (R-IN)
YEL/WHT (R-OUT)

1 2 3
4 5 6
8 9 10

View from terminal side.

RED/WHT (R-IN)

12 11 10 9 8
7 6 5 3 2 1

YEL/WHT (R-OUT)

View from control unit terminal side.

12-P CONNECTOR

RED/WHT (R-IN)

12 11 10 9 8
7 6 5 3 2 1

YEL/WHT (R-OUT)

View from control unit terminal side.

1994 BRAKES
Anti-Lock – Civic, Civic Del Sol & Prelude (Cont.)

HONDA
8-103

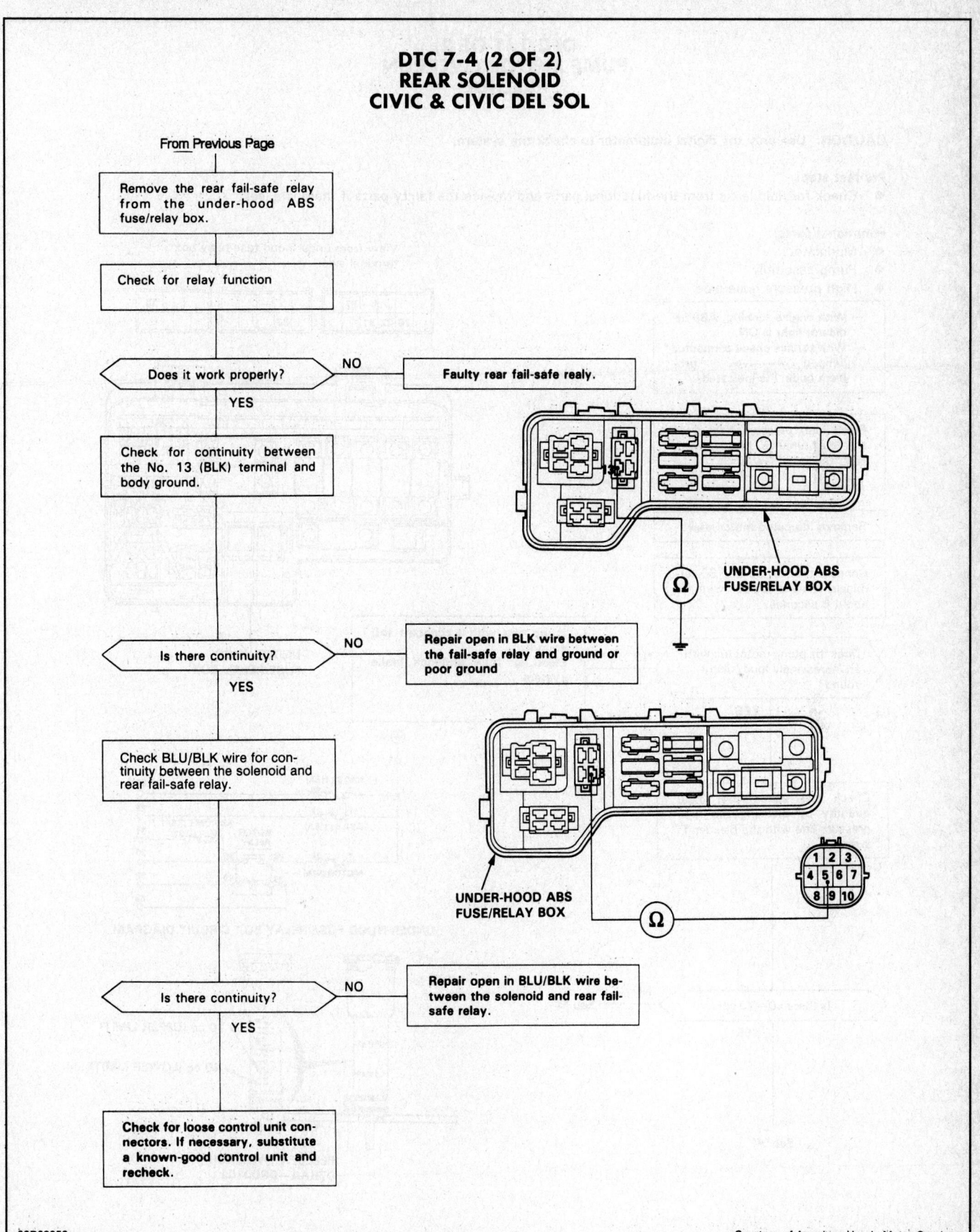

**DTC 7-4 (2 OF 2)
REAR SOLENOID
CIVIC & CIVIC DEL SOL**

From Previous Page

Remove the rear fail-safe relay from the under-hood ABS fuse/relay box.

Check for relay function

Does it work properly? — NO → Faulty rear fail-safe realy.

YES

Check for continuity between the No. 13 (BLK) terminal and body ground.

UNDER-HOOD ABS FUSE/RELAY BOX

Ω

Is there continuity? — NO → Repair open in BLK wire between the fail-safe relay and ground or poor ground

YES

Check BLU/BLK wire for continuity between the solenoid and rear fail-safe relay.

UNDER-HOOD ABS FUSE/RELAY BOX

1	2	3
4	5	6	7
8	9	10

Ω

Is there continuity? — NO → Repair open in BLU/BLK wire between the solenoid and rear fail-safe relay.

YES

Check for loose control unit connectors. If necessary, substitute a known-good control unit and recheck.

HONDA
8-104

1994 BRAKES
Anti-Lock – Civic, Civic Del Sol & Prelude (Cont.)

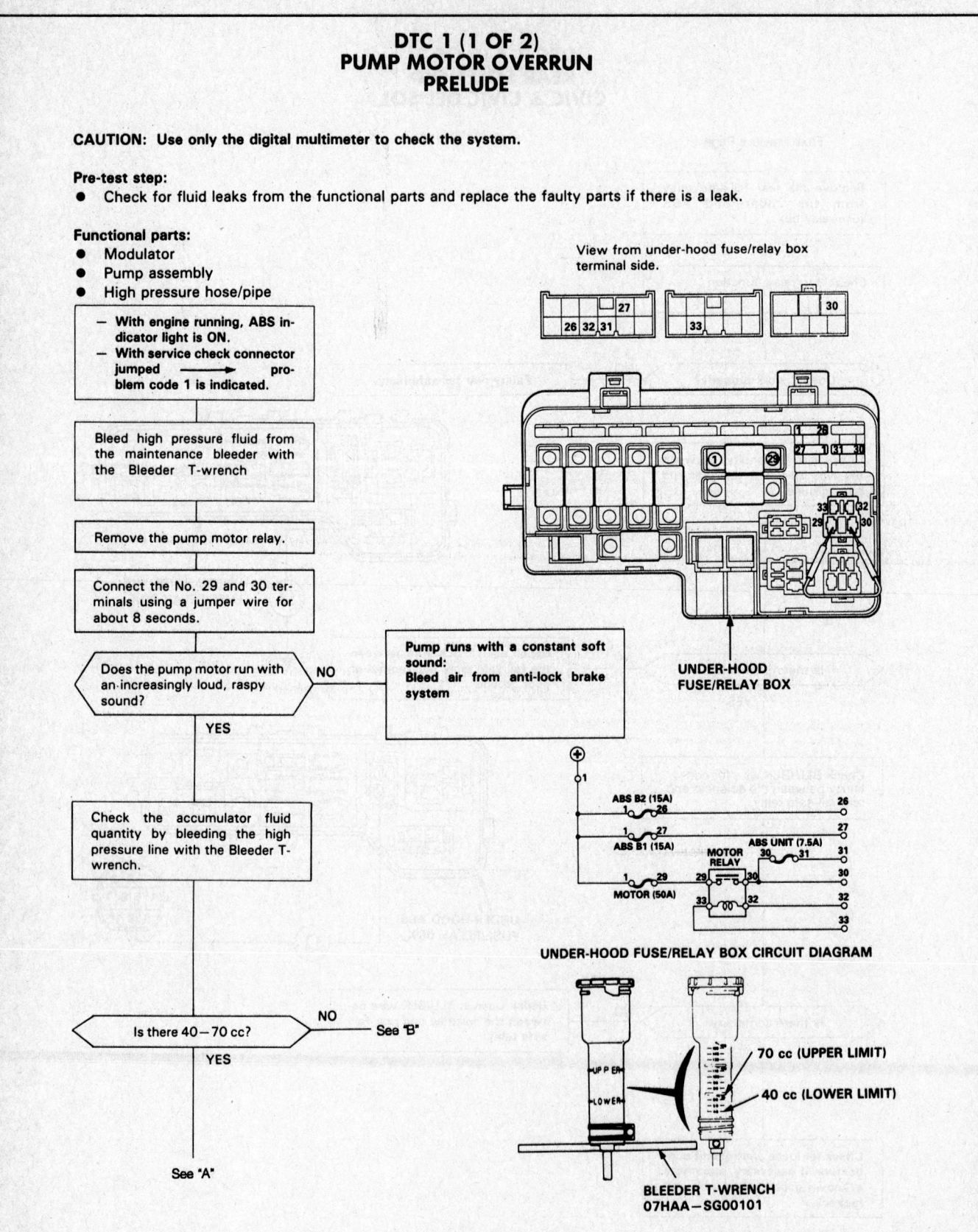

DTC 1 (1 OF 2)
PUMP MOTOR OVERRUN
PRELUDE

CAUTION: Use only the digital multimeter to check the system.

Pre-test step:
- Check for fluid leaks from the functional parts and replace the faulty parts if there is a leak.

Functional parts:
- Modulator
- Pump assembly
- High pressure hose/pipe

- With engine running, ABS indicator light is ON.
- With service check connector jumped ⟶ problem code 1 is indicated.

Bleed high pressure fluid from the maintenance bleeder with the Bleeder T-wrench

Remove the pump motor relay.

Connect the No. 29 and 30 terminals using a jumper wire for about 8 seconds.

Does the pump motor run with an increasingly loud, raspy sound? — NO → Pump runs with a constant soft sound:
Bleed air from anti-lock brake system

YES

Check the accumulator fluid quantity by bleeding the high pressure line with the Bleeder T-wrench.

Is there 40 – 70 cc? — NO → See "B"

YES

See "A"

View from under-hood fuse/relay box terminal side.

27
26 32 31   33   30

① ㉙

UNDER-HOOD FUSE/RELAY BOX

ABS B2 (15A)   26
ABS B1 (15A)   27
ABS UNIT (7.5A)   31
MOTOR RELAY   30
MOTOR (50A)   29   32
33   33

UNDER-HOOD FUSE/RELAY BOX CIRCUIT DIAGRAM

70 cc (UPPER LIMIT)
40 cc (LOWER LIMIT)

UPPER
LOWER

BLEEDER T-WRENCH
07HAA – SG00101

1994 BRAKES
Anti-Lock — Civic, Civic Del Sol & Prelude (Cont.)

HONDA
8-105

DTC 1 (2 OF 2)
PUMP MOTOR OVERRUN
PRELUDE

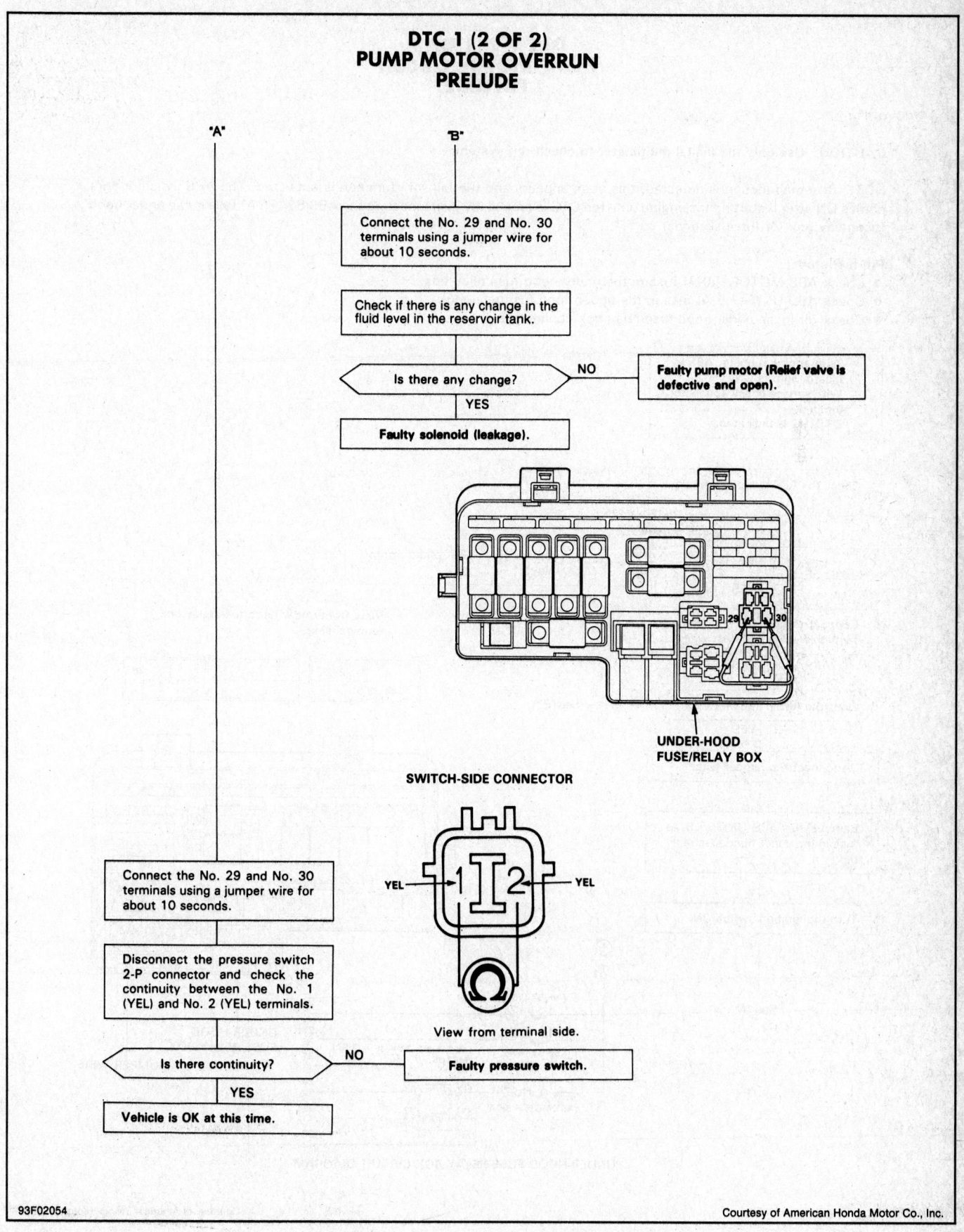

"A"

"B"

Connect the No. 29 and No. 30 terminals using a jumper wire for about 10 seconds.

Check if there is any change in the fluid level in the reservoir tank.

Is there any change? — NO → Faulty pump motor (Relief valve is defective and open).

YES

Faulty solenoid (leakage).

UNDER-HOOD FUSE/RELAY BOX

29   30

SWITCH-SIDE CONNECTOR

Connect the No. 29 and No. 30 terminals using a jumper wire for about 10 seconds.

Disconnect the pressure switch 2-P connector and check the continuity between the No. 1 (YEL) and No. 2 (YEL) terminals.

YEL ← 1 2 → YEL

View from terminal side.

Is there continuity? — NO → Faulty pressure switch.

YES

Vehicle is OK at this time.

93F02054

Courtesy of American Honda Motor Co., Inc.

HONDA
8-106

1994 BRAKES
Anti-Lock – Civic, Civic Del Sol & Prelude (Cont.)

DTC 1-2 (1 OF 3)
PUMP MOTOR CIRCUIT
PRELUDE

CAUTION: Use only the digital multimeter to check the system.

NOTE: If a malfunction is detected, this code appears and the fail-safe function is activated. The ABS indicator light comes ON after restarting the engine until the DTC is erased (by disconnecting the ABS B2 (15 A) fuse in the under-hood fuse/relay box for three seconds).

Pre-test steps:
- Check ABS MOTOR (50 A) fuse in the under-hood fuse/relay box.
- Check ABS UNIT (7.5 A) fuse in the under-hood fuse/relay box.
- Check for loose under-hood fuse/relay box connectors.

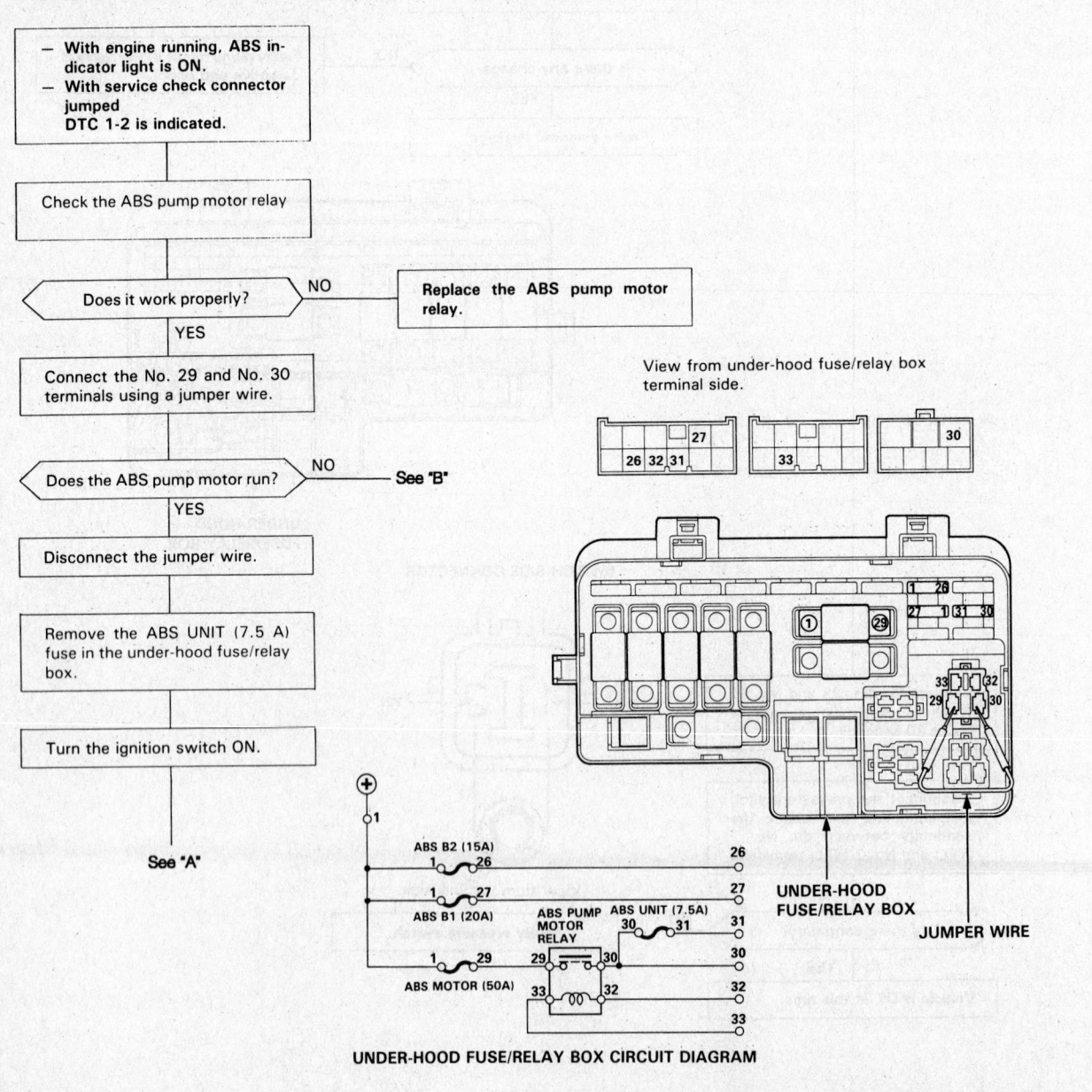

- With engine running, ABS indicator light is ON.
- With service check connector jumped DTC 1-2 is indicated.

Check the ABS pump motor relay

Does it work properly? — NO → Replace the ABS pump motor relay.

YES

Connect the No. 29 and No. 30 terminals using a jumper wire.

Does the ABS pump motor run? — NO → See "B"

YES

Disconnect the jumper wire.

Remove the ABS UNIT (7.5 A) fuse in the under-hood fuse/relay box.

Turn the ignition switch ON.

See "A"

View from under-hood fuse/relay box terminal side.

27
26 32 31
33
30

UNDER-HOOD
FUSE/RELAY BOX

JUMPER WIRE

ABS B2 (15A)
1 26   26
1 27   27
ABS B1 (20A)
ABS PUMP   ABS UNIT (7.5A)
MOTOR   30 31   31
RELAY
1 29   29   30   30
ABS MOTOR (50A) 33   32   32
                           33

UNDER-HOOD FUSE/RELAY BOX CIRCUIT DIAGRAM

1994 BRAKES
Anti-Lock – Civic, Civic Del Sol & Prelude (Cont.)

HONDA
8-107

DTC 1-2 (2 OF 3)
PUMP MOTOR CIRCUIT
PRELUDE

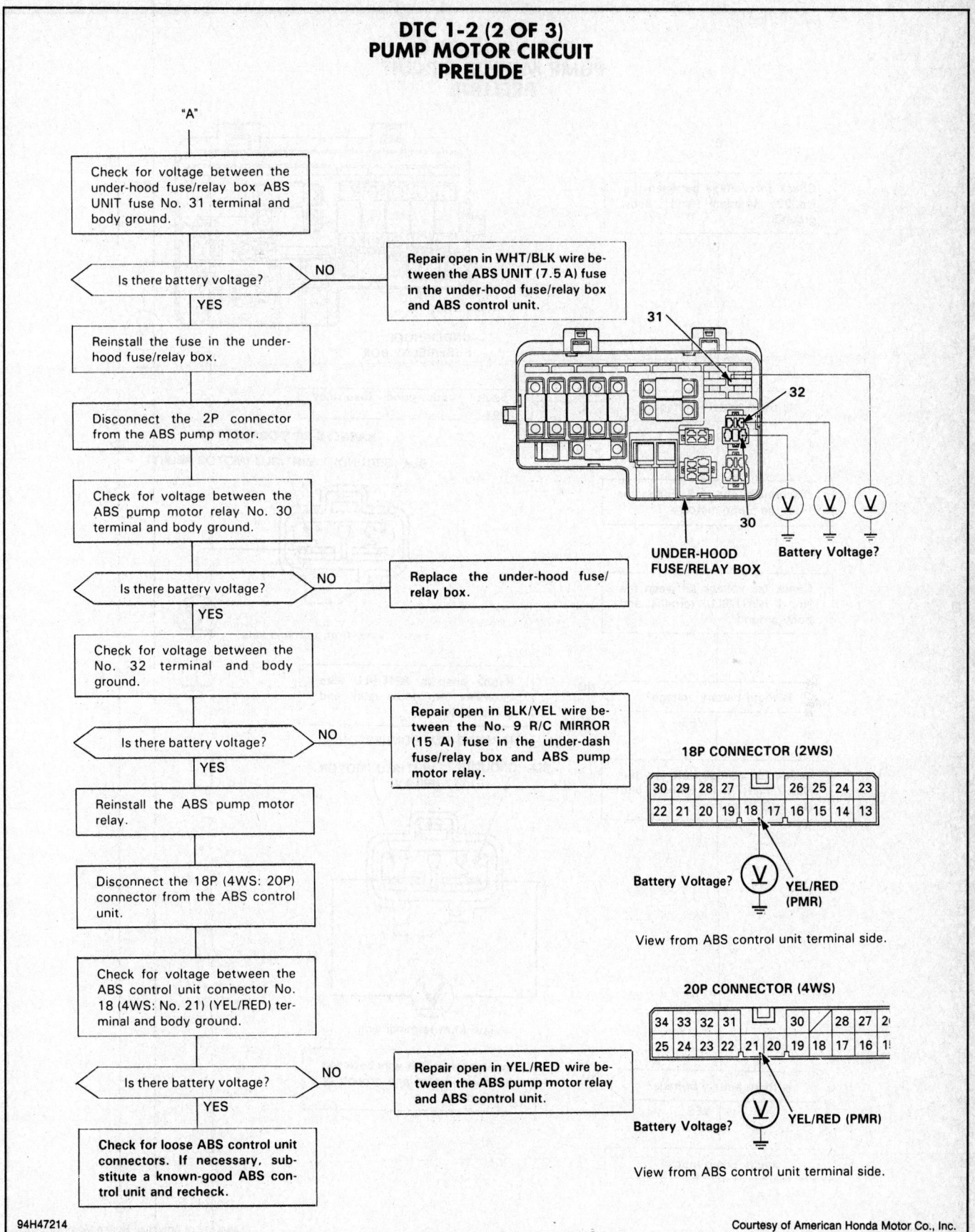

HONDA
8-108

1994 BRAKES
Anti-Lock – Civic, Civic Del Sol & Prelude (Cont.)

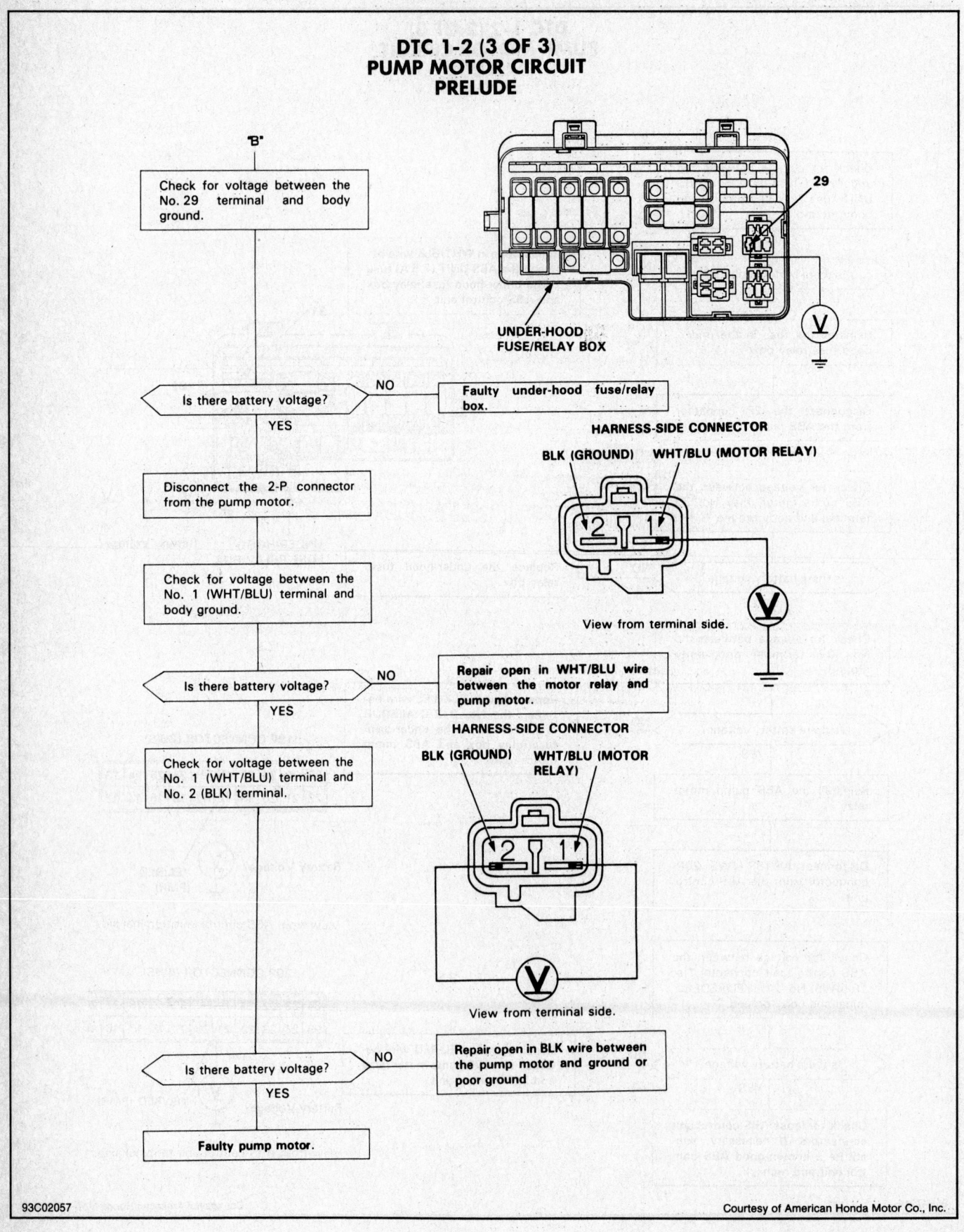

DTC 1-2 (3 OF 3)
PUMP MOTOR CIRCUIT
PRELUDE

"B"

Check for voltage between the
No. 29 terminal and body
ground.

UNDER-HOOD
FUSE/RELAY BOX

Is there battery voltage? — NO → Faulty under-hood fuse/relay box.

YES

Disconnect the 2-P connector
from the pump motor.

HARNESS-SIDE CONNECTOR

BLK (GROUND)   WHT/BLU (MOTOR RELAY)

Check for voltage between the
No. 1 (WHT/BLU) terminal and
body ground.

View from terminal side.

Is there battery voltage? — NO → Repair open in WHT/BLU wire between the motor relay and pump motor.

YES

HARNESS-SIDE CONNECTOR

BLK (GROUND)   WHT/BLU (MOTOR RELAY)

Check for voltage between the
No. 1 (WHT/BLU) terminal and
No. 2 (BLK) terminal.

View from terminal side.

Is there battery voltage? — NO → Repair open in BLK wire between the pump motor and ground or poor ground

YES

Faulty pump motor.

1994 BRAKES
Anti-Lock – Civic, Civic Del Sol & Prelude (Cont.)

HONDA
8-109

DTC 1-3
HIGH PRESSURE LEAKAGE
PRELUDE

CAUTION: Use only the digital multimeter to check the system.

Pre-test steps:
- Check reservoir fluid level, and if necessary, fill to the MAX level.
- Check for fluid leaks from the functional parts and replace the faulty parts if there is a leak.

Functional parts:
- Modulator
- Pump assembly
- High pressure hose/pipe

View from under-hood fuse/relay box terminal side.

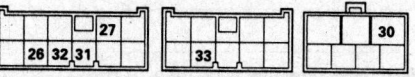

- With engine running, ABS indicator light is ON.
- With service check connector jumped ➔ problem code 1-3 is indicated.

Bleed high pressure fluid from the maintenance bleeder with the Bleeder T-wrench

Remove the pump motor relay.

Connect the No. 29 and No. 30 terminals using a jumper wire for about 10 seconds.

Disconnect the 2-P connector from the pressure switch.

After 30 minutes, check for continuity between the No.1 (YEL) and No.2 (YEL) terminals on the switch side of connector.

Is there continuity? — YES → Vehicle is OK at this time.

NO

Faulty solenoid (leakage).

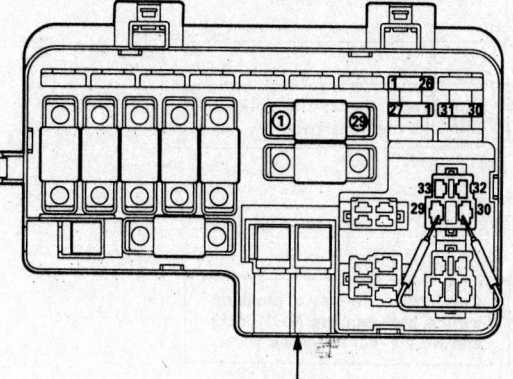

UNDER-HOOD FUSE/RELAY BOX

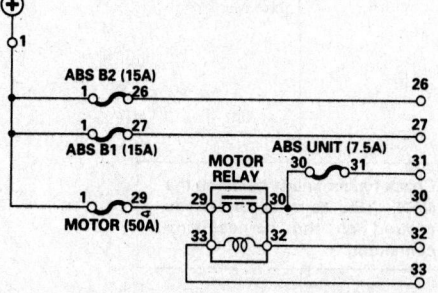

UNDER-HOOD FUSE/RELAY BOX CIRCUIT DIAGRAM

SWITCH-SIDE CONNECTOR

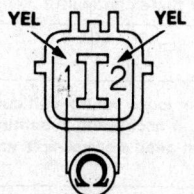

View from terminal side.

HONDA
8-110

1994 BRAKES
Anti-Lock – Civic, Civic Del Sol & Prelude (Cont.)

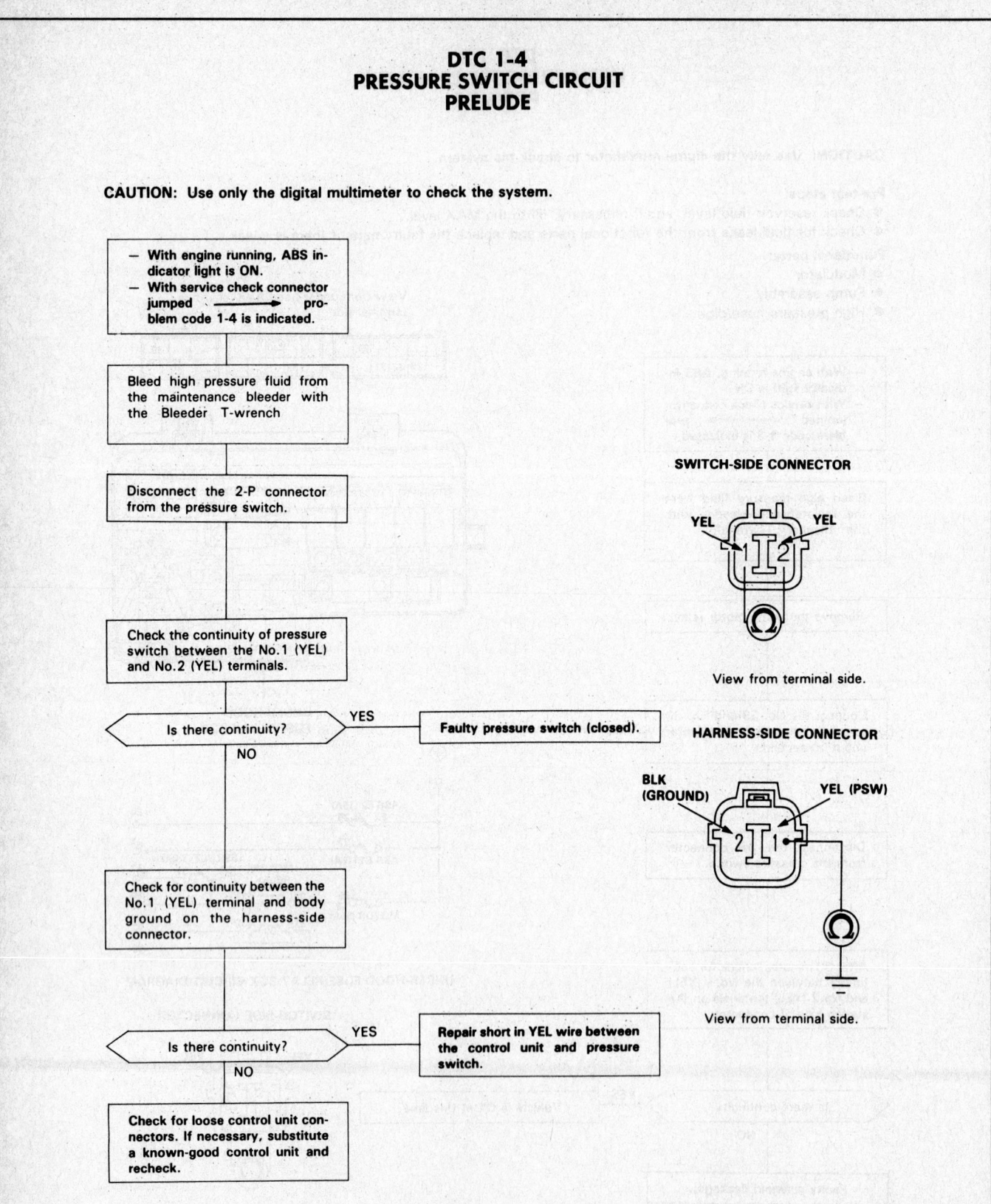

DTC 1-4
PRESSURE SWITCH CIRCUIT
PRELUDE

CAUTION: Use only the digital multimeter to check the system.

- With engine running, ABS indicator light is ON.
- With service check connector jumped ⟶ problem code 1-4 is indicated.

Bleed high pressure fluid from the maintenance bleeder with the Bleeder T-wrench

Disconnect the 2-P connector from the pressure switch.

Check the continuity of pressure switch between the No.1 (YEL) and No.2 (YEL) terminals.

Is there continuity? — YES — Faulty pressure switch (closed).

NO

Check for continuity between the No.1 (YEL) terminal and body ground on the harness-side connector.

Is there continuity? — YES — Repair short in YEL wire between the control unit and pressure switch.

NO

Check for loose control unit connectors. If necessary, substitute a known-good control unit and recheck.

SWITCH-SIDE CONNECTOR

YEL   YEL

View from terminal side.

HARNESS-SIDE CONNECTOR

BLK (GROUND)   YEL (PSW)

View from terminal side.

1994 BRAKES
Anti-Lock – Civic, Civic Del Sol & Prelude (Cont.)

HONDA
8-111

DTC 1-8
ACCUMULATOR GAS LEAKAGE
PRELUDE

Check the following items:
- The relief plug is loose.
- The relief plug O-ring is out of place.
- Bleed the high pressure line with the Bleeder T-wrench. Operate the pump motor for 10 seconds and bleed the high pressure line again with the Bleeder T-wrench. If no fluid or more than 70 cc of fluid come out, it is likely that the gas has leaked out.

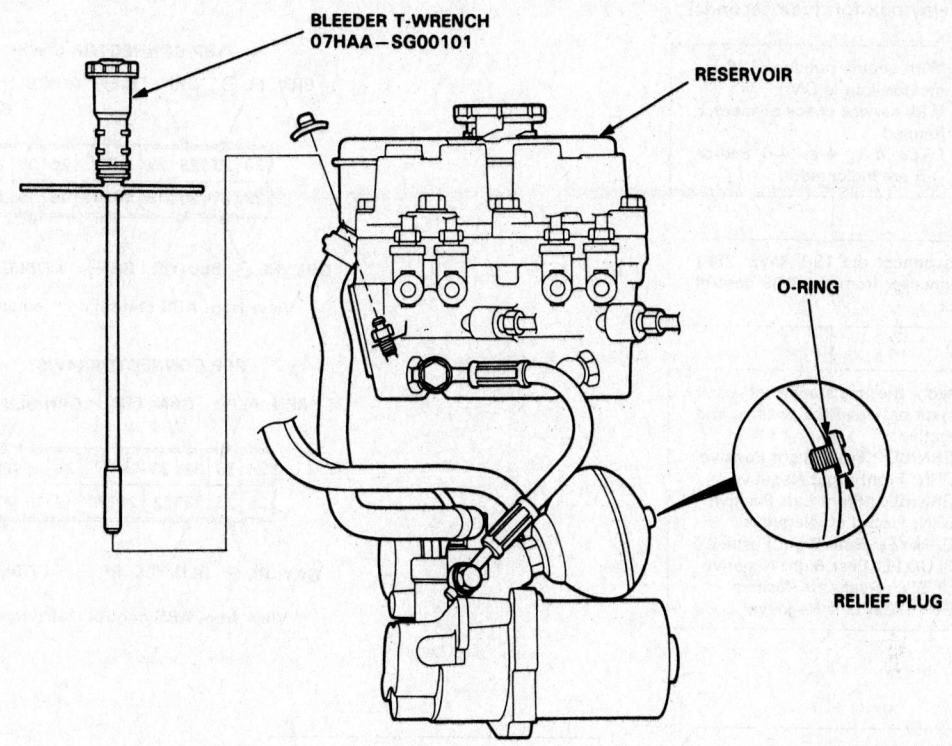

BLEEDER T-WRENCH
07HAA–SG00101

RESERVOIR

O-RING

RELIEF PLUG

93I02060

Courtesy of American Honda Motor Co., Inc.

DTC 2-1
PARKING BRAKE SWITCH
PRELUDE

If the parking brake has been released, the following items are possible causes. If they are OK, check the control unit connectors for good connection. If not loose or disconnected, substitute a known-good control unit and recheck.

NOTE: Before Troubleshooting Problem Code 2-1, remove the ABS B2 (15 A) fuse for 3 seconds to clear the control unit's memory, then test drive the car.
If the anti-lock brake system indicator light stays off, the probability is that the car was driven with the parking brake applied.

- The parking brake is applied for more than 30 seconds while driving.
- The brake fluid level in the master cylinder is too low.
- GRN/RED wire is shorted between the BRAKE indicator light and parking brake switch.
- GRN/RED wire is shorted between the BRAKE indicator light and brake fluid level switch.
- The BRAKE indicator light is blown.
- GRN/RED wire has an open between the BRAKE indicator light and the control unit.

93G02243

Courtesy of American Honda Motor Co., Inc.

HONDA
8-112

1994 BRAKES
Anti-Lock – Civic, Civic Del Sol & Prelude (Cont.)

DTC 4-1 TO 4-8 (1 OF 2)
SPEED SENSOR
PRELUDE

CAUTION: Use only the digital multimeter to check the system.

NOTE: If a malfunction is detected, this code appears and the fail-safe function is activated. The ABS indicator light may come ON after restarting the engine until the DTC is erased (by disconnecting the ABS B2 (15 A) fuse in the under-hood fuse/relay box for three seconds).

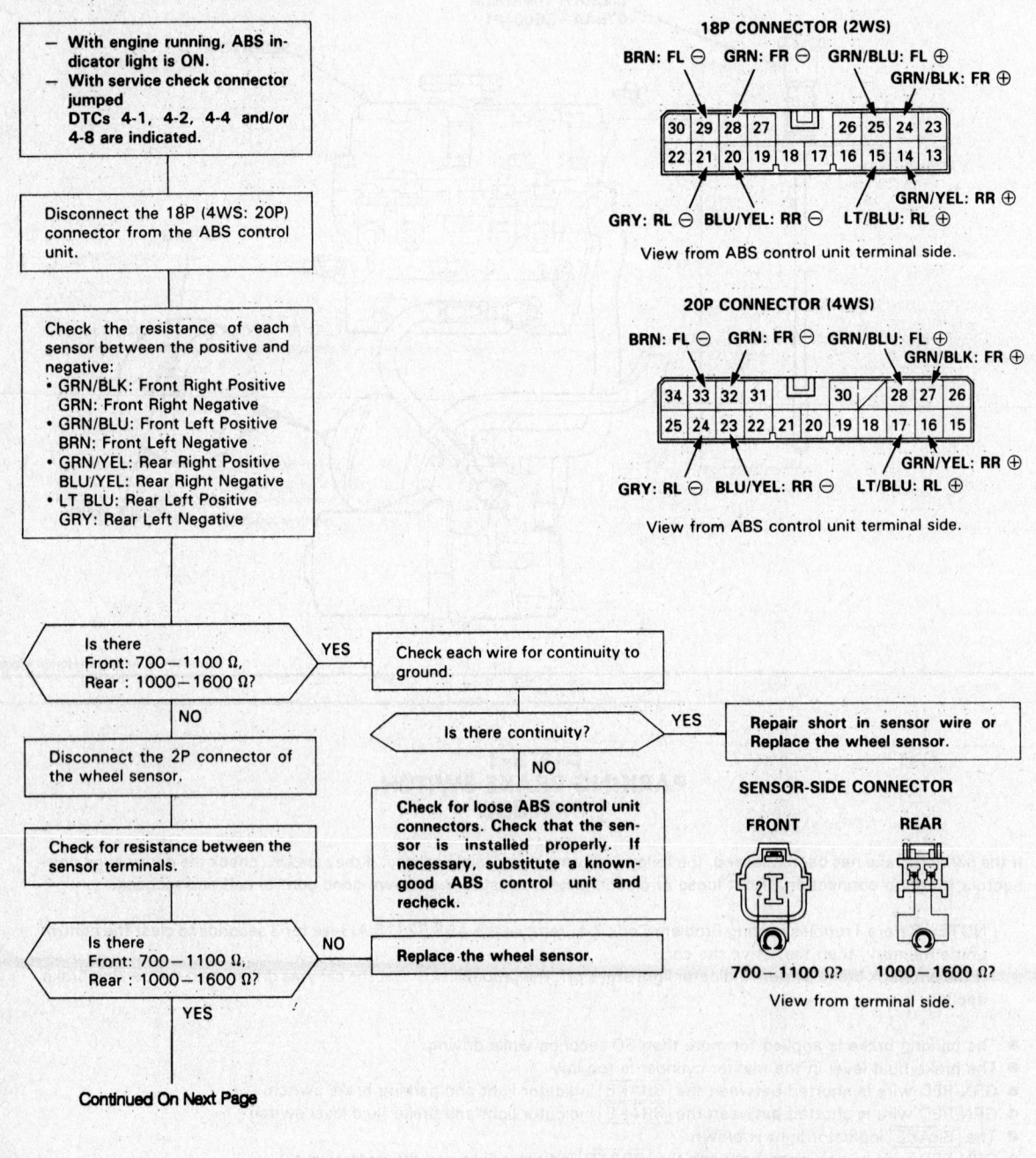

Continued On Next Page

1994 BRAKES
Anti-Lock – Civic, Civic Del Sol & Prelude (Cont.)

HONDA
8-113

DTC 4-1 TO 4-8 (2 OF 2)
SPEED SENSOR
PRELUDE

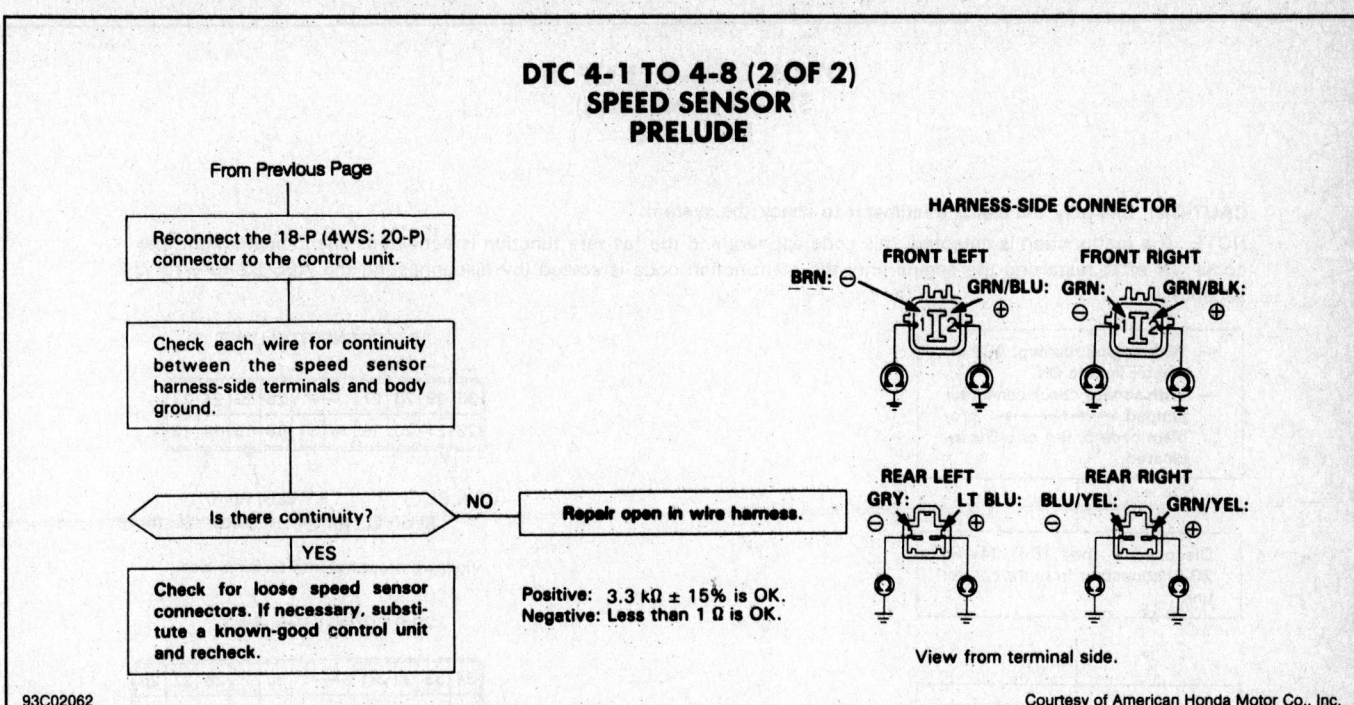

From Previous Page

Reconnect the 18-P (4WS: 20-P) connector to the control unit.

Check each wire for continuity between the speed sensor harness-side terminals and body ground.

Is there continuity? — NO → Repair open in wire harness.

YES

Check for loose speed sensor connectors. If necessary, substitute a known-good control unit and recheck.

Positive: 3.3 kΩ ± 15% is OK.
Negative: Less than 1 Ω is OK.

HARNESS-SIDE CONNECTOR

FRONT LEFT
BRN: ⊖   GRN/BLU: ⊕

FRONT RIGHT
GRN: ⊖   GRN/BLK: ⊕

REAR LEFT
GRY: ⊖   LT BLU: ⊕

REAR RIGHT
BLU/YEL: ⊖   GRN/YEL: ⊕

View from terminal side.

93C02062

Courtesy of American Honda Motor Co., Inc.

DTC 5 TO 5-8 (1 OF 2)
SPEED SENSOR(S)
PRELUDE

CAUTION: Use only the digital multimeter to check the system.

NOTE: If a malfunction is detected, this code appears and the fail-safe function is activated. The indicator light may come ON after restarting the engine until the malfunction code is erased (by disconnecting the ABS B2 fuse for 3 seconds.)

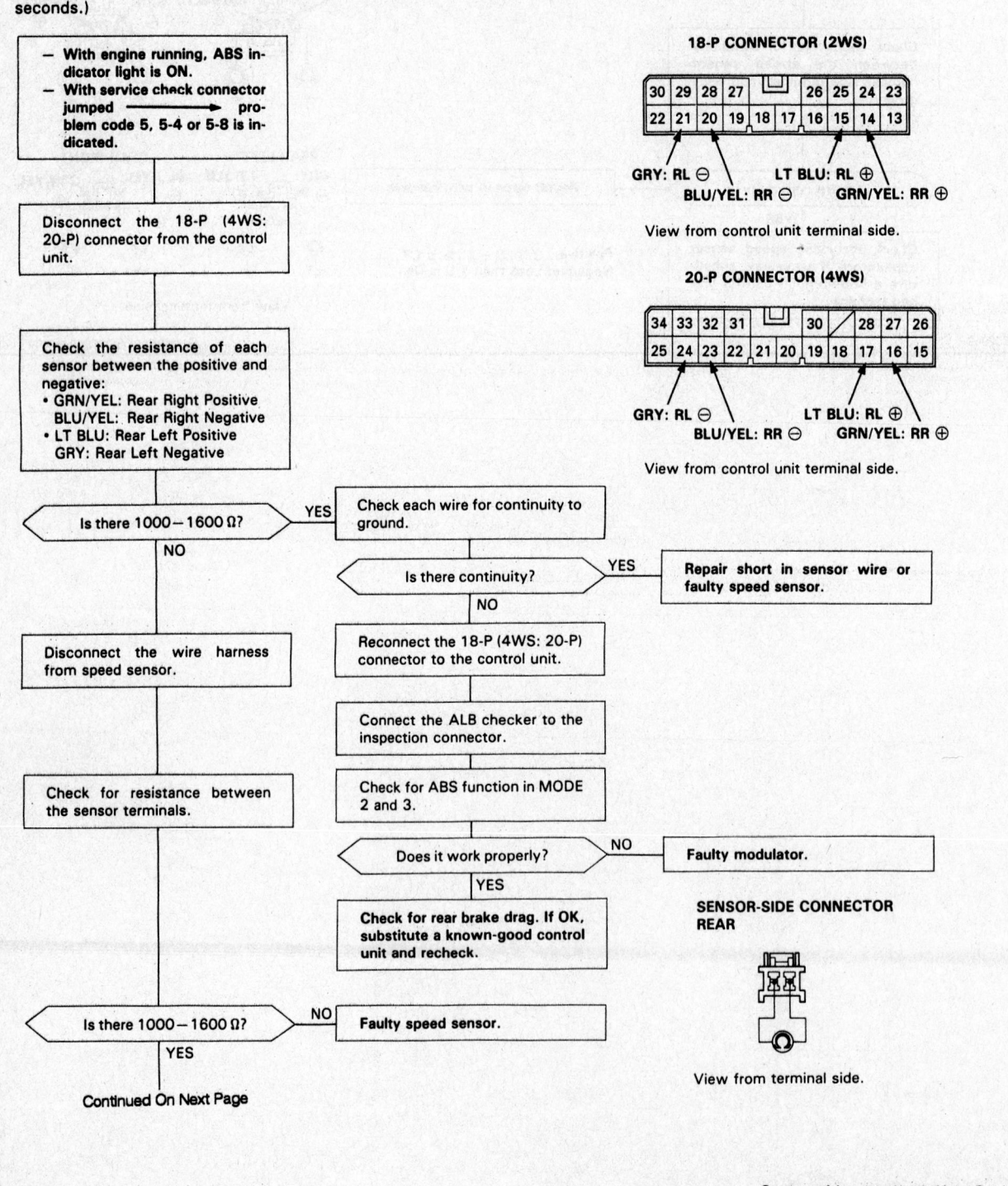

1994 BRAKES
Anti-Lock – Civic, Civic Del Sol & Prelude (Cont.)

HONDA
8-115

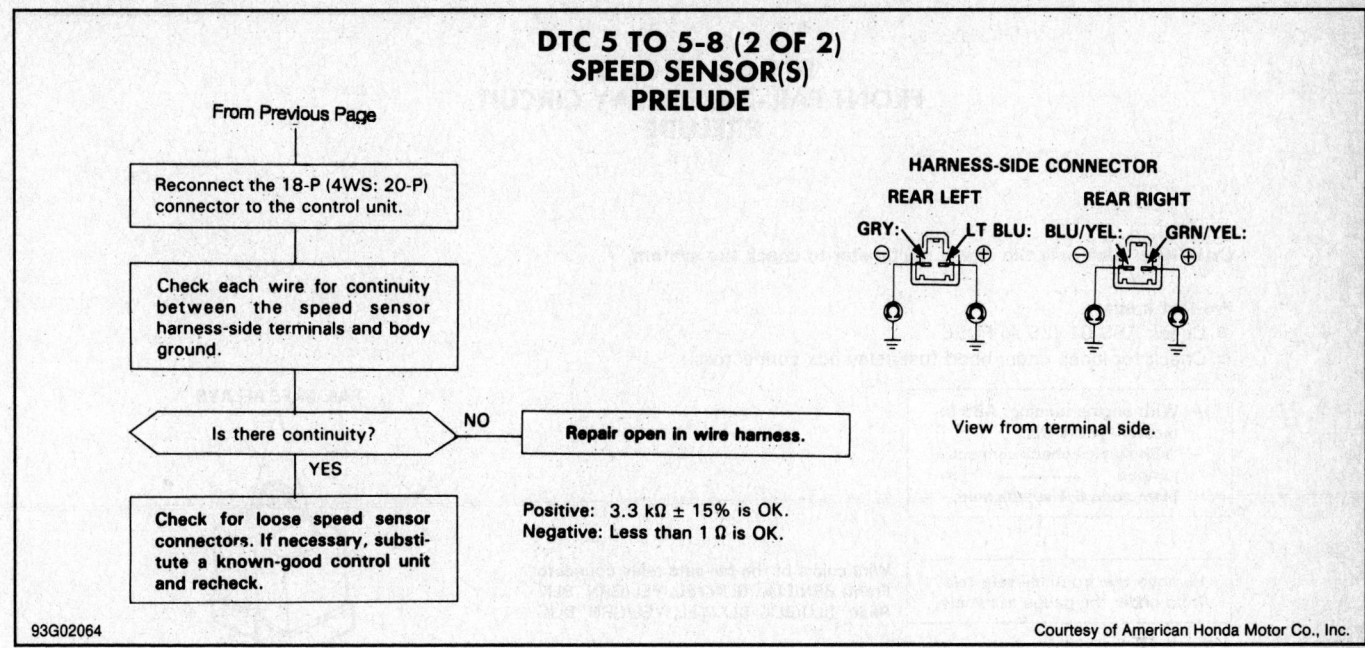

DTC 5 TO 5-8 (2 OF 2)
SPEED SENSOR(S)
PRELUDE

From Previous Page

Reconnect the 18-P (4WS: 20-P) connector to the control unit.

Check each wire for continuity between the speed sensor harness-side terminals and body ground.

Is there continuity? — NO → Repair open in wire harness.

YES

Check for loose speed sensor connectors. If necessary, substitute a known-good control unit and recheck.

HARNESS-SIDE CONNECTOR

REAR LEFT
GRY: LT BLU:

REAR RIGHT
BLU/YEL: GRN/YEL:

View from terminal side.

Positive: 3.3 kΩ ± 15% is OK.
Negative: Less than 1 Ω is OK.

93G02064

HONDA
8-116

1994 BRAKES
Anti-Lock – Civic, Civic Del Sol & Prelude (Cont.)

DTC 6-1 (1 OF 3)
FRONT FAIL-SAFE RELAY CIRCUIT
PRELUDE

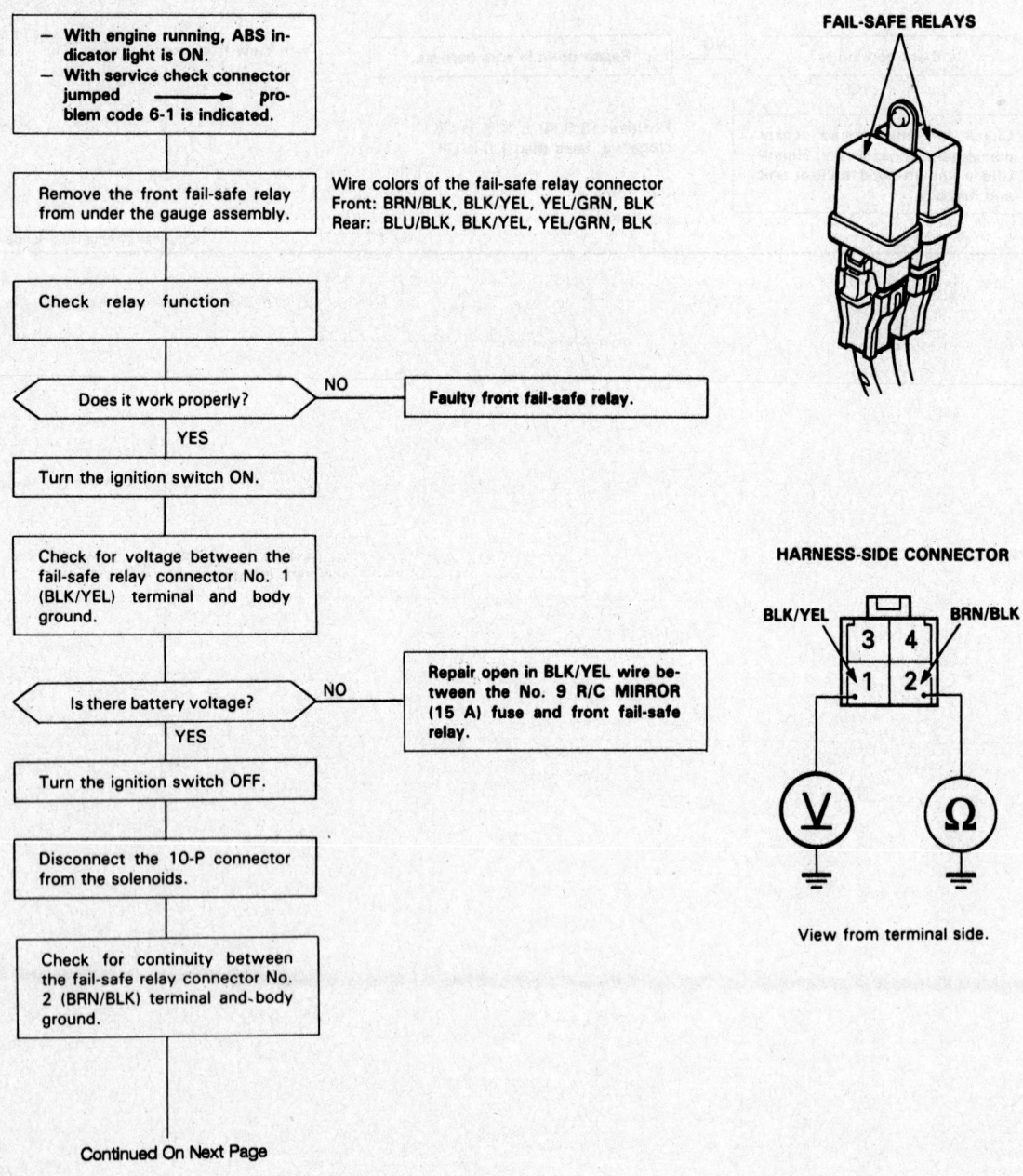

CAUTION: Use only the digital multimeter to check the system.

Pre-test steps:
- Check ABS B1 (20 A) FUSE
- Check for loose under-hood fuse/relay box connectors.

FAIL-SAFE RELAYS

- With engine running, ABS indicator light is ON.
- With service check connector
  jumped ⟶ pro-
  blem code 6-1 is indicated.

Remove the front fail-safe relay
from under the gauge assembly.

Wire colors of the fail-safe relay connector
Front: BRN/BLK, BLK/YEL, YEL/GRN, BLK
Rear: BLU/BLK, BLK/YEL, YEL/GRN, BLK

Check relay function

Does it work properly? ──NO──▶ **Faulty front fail-safe relay.**

YES

Turn the ignition switch ON.

HARNESS-SIDE CONNECTOR

Check for voltage between the
fail-safe relay connector No. 1
(BLK/YEL) terminal and body
ground.

BLK/YEL   BRN/BLK

| 3 | 4 |
| 1 | 2 |

Is there battery voltage? ──NO──▶ **Repair open in BLK/YEL wire between the No. 9 R/C MIRROR
(15 A) fuse and front fail-safe
relay.**

YES

Turn the ignition switch OFF.

Disconnect the 10-P connector
from the solenoids.

View from terminal side.

Check for continuity between
the fail-safe relay connector No.
2 (BRN/BLK) terminal and body
ground.

Continued On Next Page

1994 BRAKES
Anti-Lock – Civic, Civic Del Sol & Prelude (Cont.)

HONDA
8-117

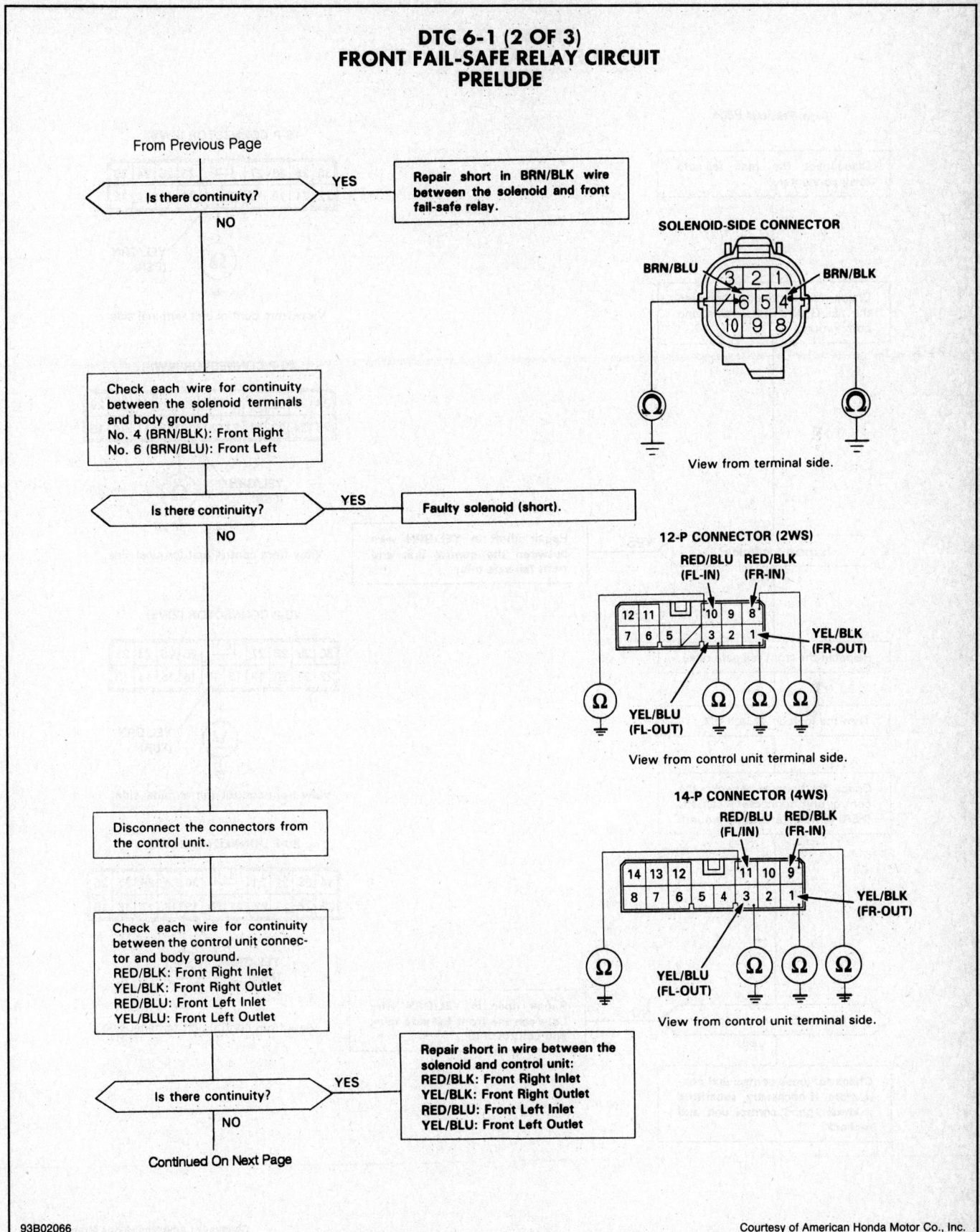

DTC 6-1 (2 OF 3)
FRONT FAIL-SAFE RELAY CIRCUIT
PRELUDE

HONDA
8-118

1994 BRAKES
Anti-Lock — Civic, Civic Del Sol & Prelude (Cont.)

DTC 6-1 (3 OF 3)
FRONT FAIL-SAFE RELAY CIRCUIT
PRELUDE

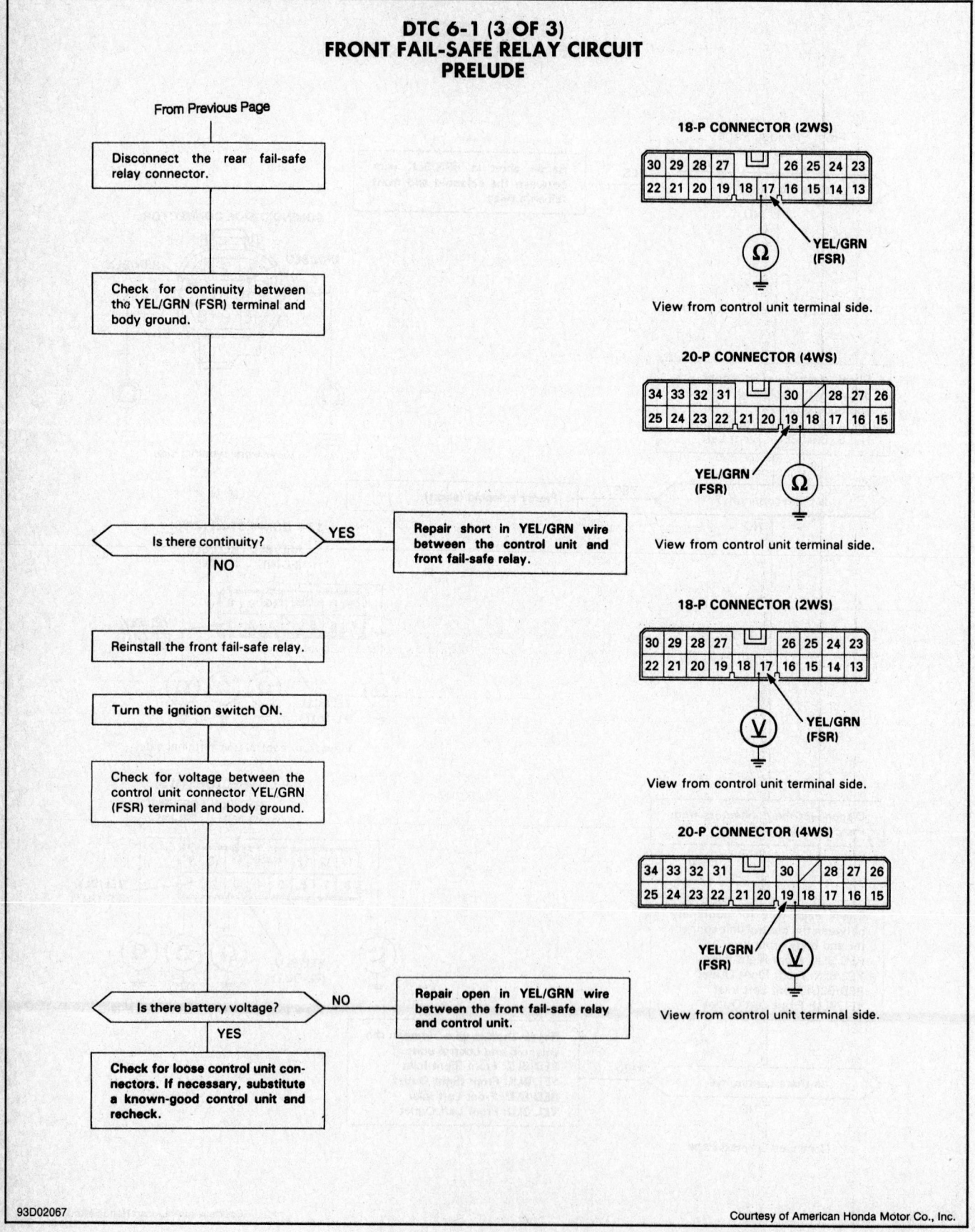

From Previous Page

Disconnect the rear fail-safe relay connector.

Check for continuity between the YEL/GRN (FSR) terminal and body ground.

Is there continuity? — YES — Repair short in YEL/GRN wire between the control unit and front fail-safe relay.

NO

Reinstall the front fail-safe relay.

Turn the ignition switch ON.

Check for voltage between the control unit connector YEL/GRN (FSR) terminal and body ground.

Is there battery voltage? — NO — Repair open in YEL/GRN wire between the front fail-safe relay and control unit.

YES

Check for loose control unit connectors. If necessary, substitute a known-good control unit and recheck.

18-P CONNECTOR (2WS)

30 29 28 27   26 25 24 23
22 21 20 19 18 17 16 15 14 13

YEL/GRN (FSR)

Ω

View from control unit terminal side.

20-P CONNECTOR (4WS)

34 33 32 31   30 / 28 27 26
25 24 23 22 21 20 19 18 17 16 15

YEL/GRN (FSR)

Ω

View from control unit terminal side.

18-P CONNECTOR (2WS)

30 29 28 27   26 25 24 23
22 21 20 19 18 17 16 15 14 13

YEL/GRN (FSR)

V

View from control unit terminal side.

20-P CONNECTOR (4WS)

34 33 32 31   30 / 28 27 26
25 24 23 22 21 20 19 18 17 16 15

YEL/GRN (FSR)

V

View from control unit terminal side.

1994 BRAKES
Anti-Lock – Civic, Civic Del Sol & Prelude (Cont.)

HONDA
8-119

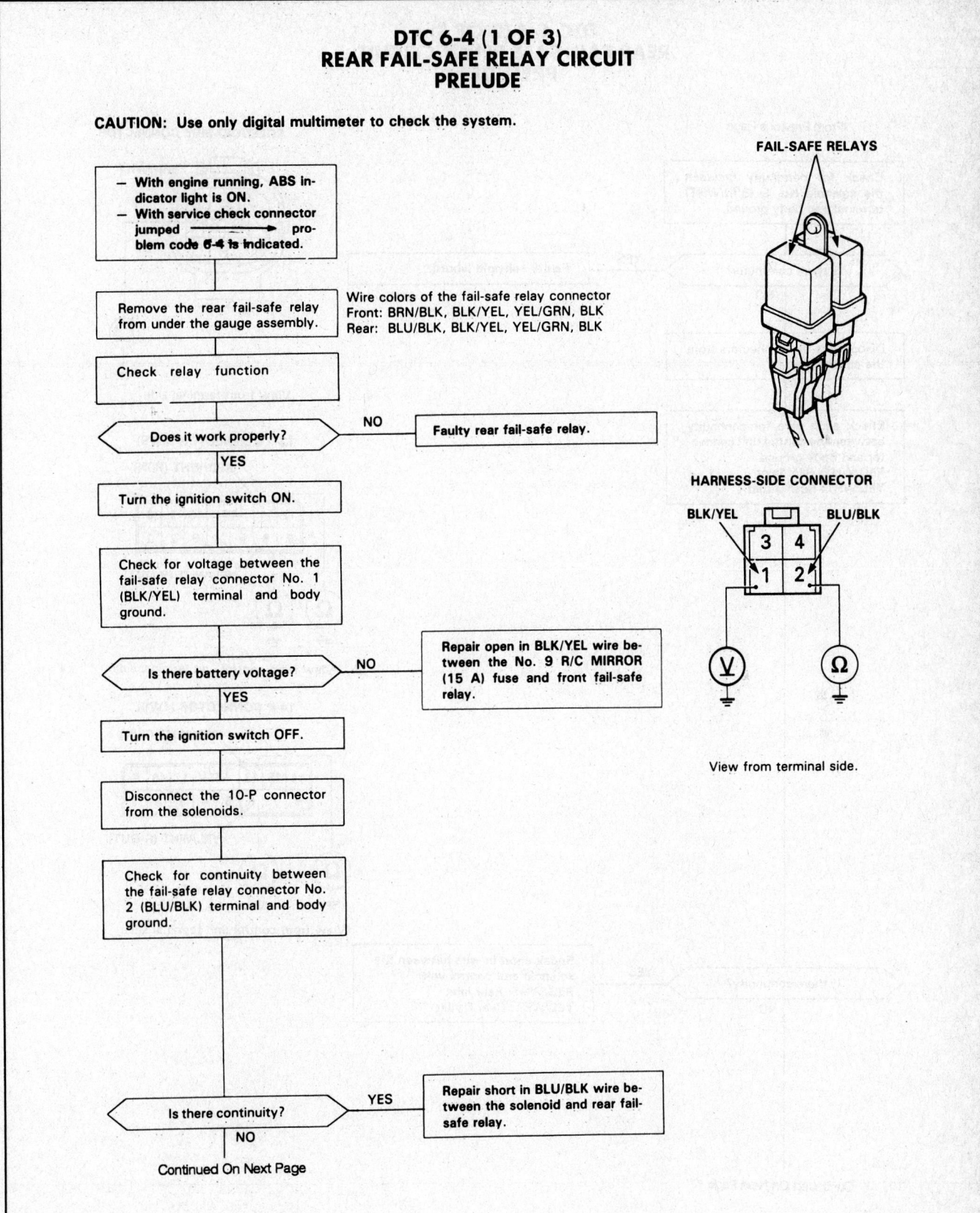

DTC 6-4 (1 OF 3)
REAR FAIL-SAFE RELAY CIRCUIT
PRELUDE

CAUTION: Use only digital multimeter to check the system.

— With engine running, ABS indicator light is ON.
— With service check connector
  jumped ⟶ pro-
  blem code 6-4 is indicated.

Remove the rear fail-safe relay
from under the gauge assembly.

Wire colors of the fail-safe relay connector
Front: BRN/BLK, BLK/YEL, YEL/GRN, BLK
Rear: BLU/BLK, BLK/YEL, YEL/GRN, BLK

Check relay function

Does it work properly? **NO** → Faulty rear fail-safe relay.

YES

Turn the ignition switch ON.

Check for voltage between the
fail-safe relay connector No. 1
(BLK/YEL) terminal and body
ground.

Is there battery voltage? **NO** → Repair open in BLK/YEL wire between the No. 9 R/C MIRROR
(15 A) fuse and front fail-safe
relay.

YES

Turn the ignition switch OFF.

Disconnect the 10-P connector
from the solenoids.

Check for continuity between
the fail-safe relay connector No.
2 (BLU/BLK) terminal and body
ground.

Is there continuity? **YES** → Repair short in BLU/BLK wire between the solenoid and rear fail-
safe relay.

NO

Continued On Next Page

FAIL-SAFE RELAYS

HARNESS-SIDE CONNECTOR

BLK/YEL   BLU/BLK

3 4
1 2

View from terminal side.

93F02068

Courtesy of American Honda Motor Co., Inc.

HONDA
8-120

1994 BRAKES
Anti-Lock – Civic, Civic Del Sol & Prelude (Cont.)

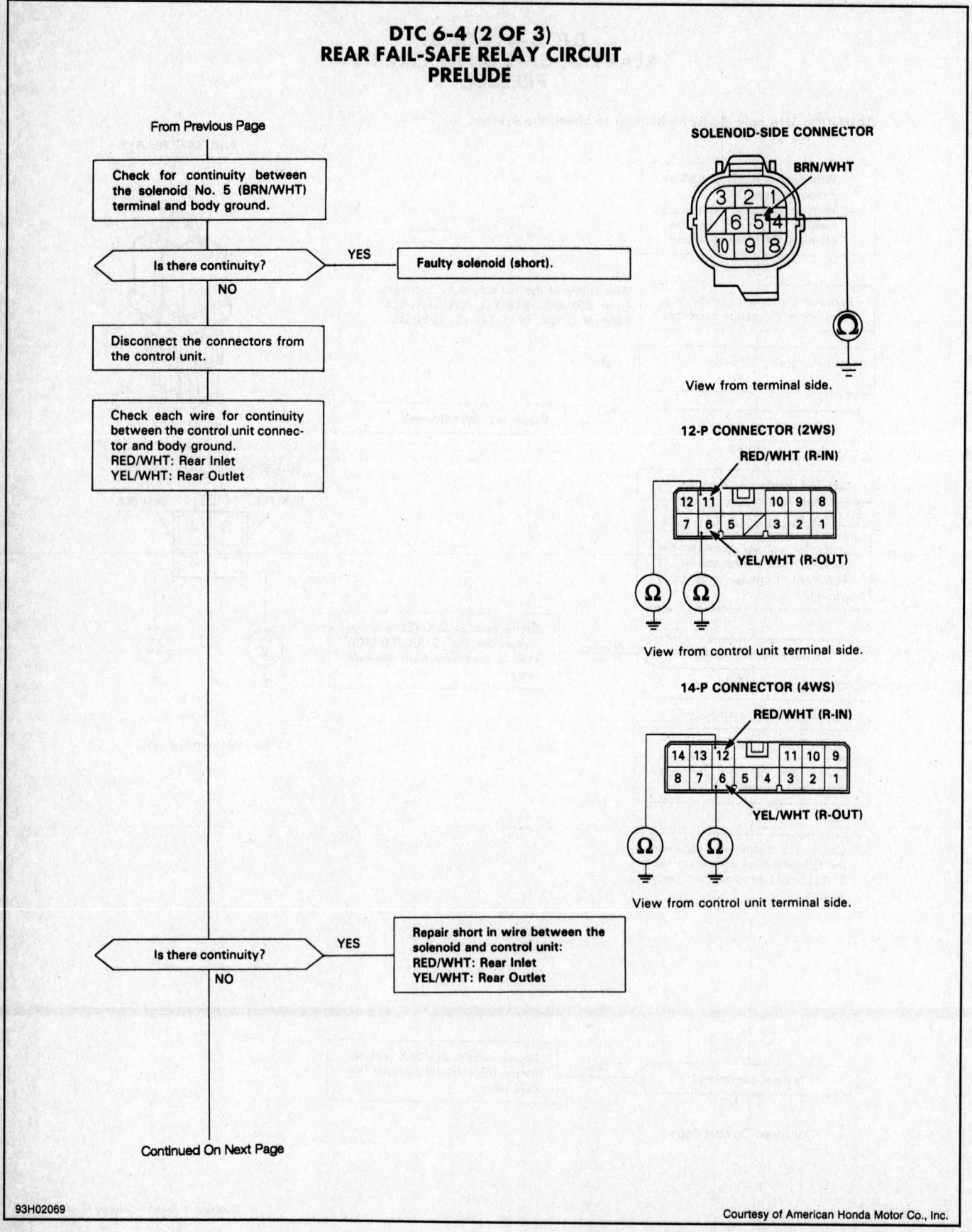

DTC 6-4 (2 OF 3)
REAR FAIL-SAFE RELAY CIRCUIT
PRELUDE

From Previous Page

Check for continuity between
the solenoid No. 5 (BRN/WHT)
terminal and body ground.

Is there continuity? — YES → Faulty solenoid (short).

NO

Disconnect the connectors from
the control unit.

Check each wire for continuity
between the control unit connector and body ground.
RED/WHT: Rear Inlet
YEL/WHT: Rear Outlet

SOLENOID-SIDE CONNECTOR

BRN/WHT

3 2 1
6 5 4
10 9 8

View from terminal side.

12-P CONNECTOR (2WS)

RED/WHT (R-IN)

12 11   10 9 8
7 6 5   3 2 1

YEL/WHT (R-OUT)

View from control unit terminal side.

14-P CONNECTOR (4WS)

RED/WHT (R-IN)

14 13 12   11 10 9
8 7 6 5 4 3 2 1

YEL/WHT (R-OUT)

View from control unit terminal side.

Is there continuity? — YES → Repair short in wire between the
solenoid and control unit:
RED/WHT: Rear Inlet
YEL/WHT: Rear Outlet

NO

Continued On Next Page

1994 BRAKES
Anti-Lock – Civic, Civic Del Sol & Prelude (Cont.)

HONDA
8-121

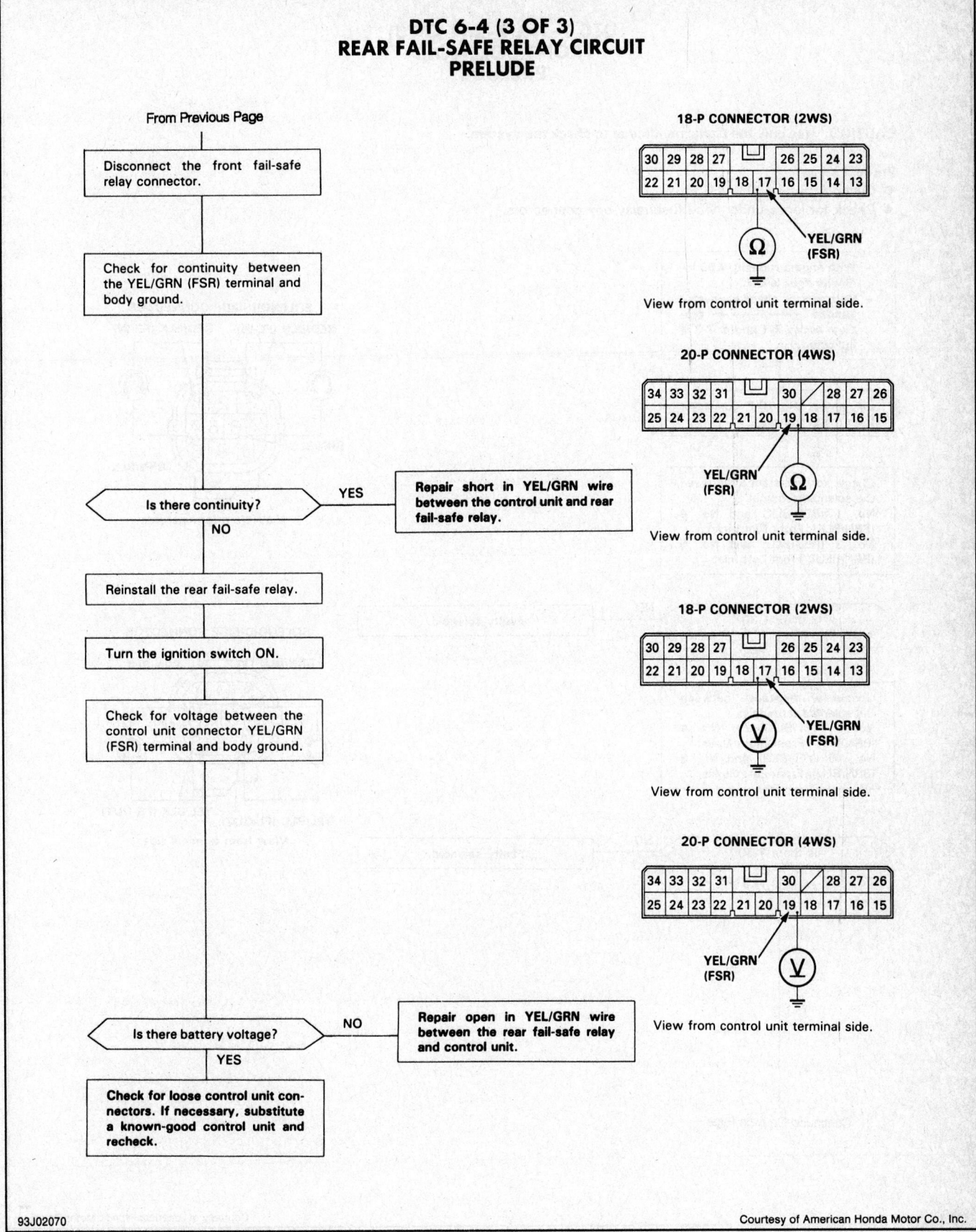

DTC 6-4 (3 OF 3)
REAR FAIL-SAFE RELAY CIRCUIT
PRELUDE

From Previous Page

Disconnect the front fail-safe relay connector.

Check for continuity between the YEL/GRN (FSR) terminal and body ground.

Is there continuity? — YES — Repair short in YEL/GRN wire between the control unit and rear fail-safe relay.

NO

Reinstall the rear fail-safe relay.

Turn the ignition switch ON.

Check for voltage between the control unit connector YEL/GRN (FSR) terminal and body ground.

Is there battery voltage? — NO — Repair open in YEL/GRN wire between the rear fail-safe relay and control unit.

YES

Check for loose control unit connectors. If necessary, substitute a known-good control unit and recheck.

18-P CONNECTOR (2WS)

| 30 | 29 | 28 | 27 | | 26 | 25 | 24 | 23 |
| 22 | 21 | 20 | 19 | 18 | 17 | 16 | 15 | 14 | 13 |

YEL/GRN (FSR)

View from control unit terminal side.

20-P CONNECTOR (4WS)

| 34 | 33 | 32 | 31 | | 30 | | 28 | 27 | 26 |
| 25 | 24 | 23 | 22 | 21 | 20 | 19 | 18 | 17 | 16 | 15 |

YEL/GRN (FSR)

View from control unit terminal side.

18-P CONNECTOR (2WS)

| 30 | 29 | 28 | 27 | | 26 | 25 | 24 | 23 |
| 22 | 21 | 20 | 19 | 18 | 17 | 16 | 15 | 14 | 13 |

YEL/GRN (FSR)

View from control unit terminal side.

20-P CONNECTOR (4WS)

| 34 | 33 | 32 | 31 | | 30 | | 28 | 27 | 26 |
| 25 | 24 | 23 | 22 | 21 | 20 | 19 | 18 | 17 | 16 | 15 |

YEL/GRN (FSR)

View from control unit terminal side.

93J02070

HONDA
8-122

1994 BRAKES
Anti-Lock – Civic, Civic Del Sol & Prelude (Cont.)

DTC 7-1 & 7-2 (1 OF 3)
FRONT SOLENOID
PRELUDE

CAUTION: Use only the digital multimeter to check the system.

Pre-test steps:
- Check ABS B1 (20 A) FUSE
- Check for loose under-hood fuse/relay box connectors.

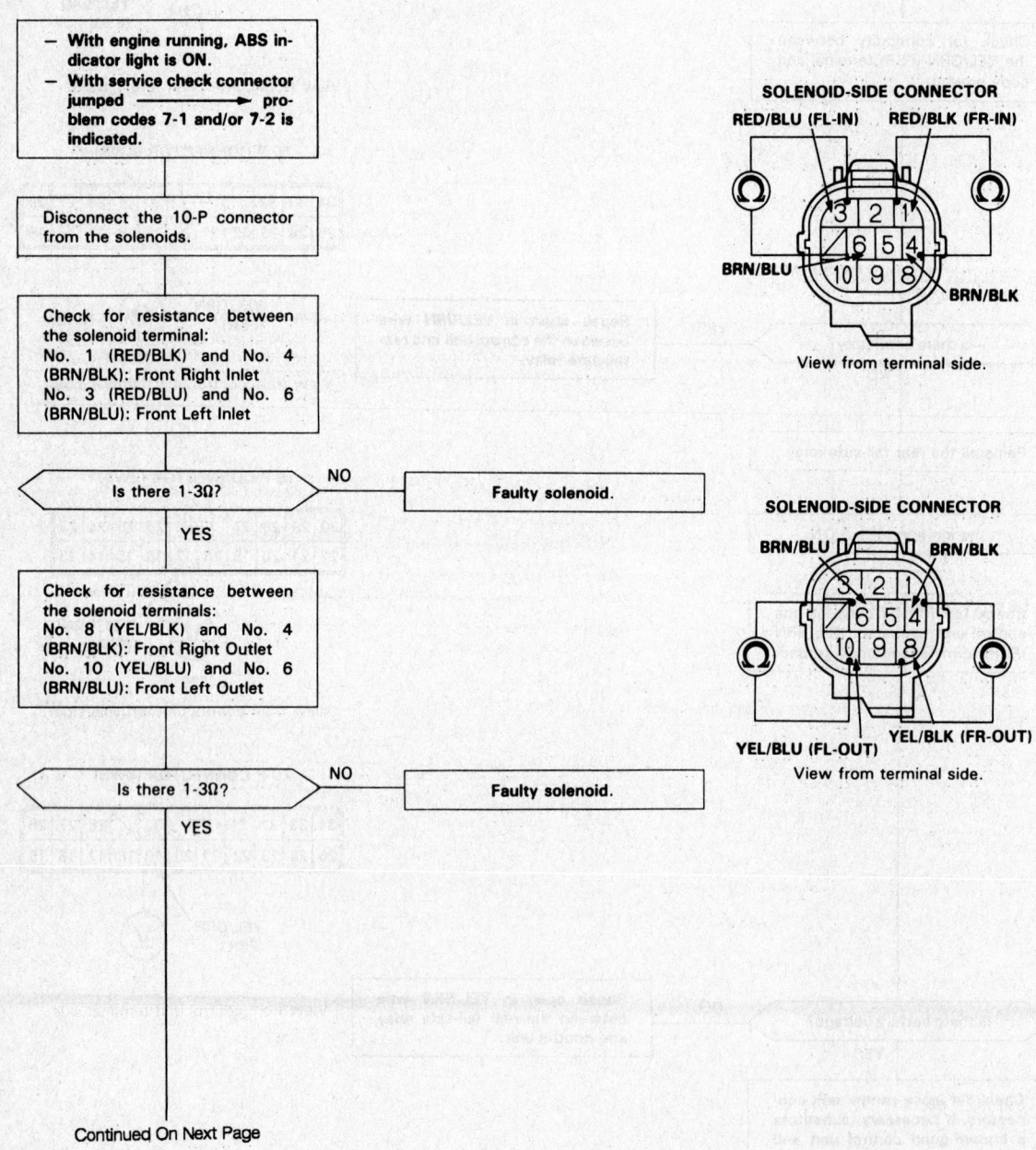

- With engine running, ABS indicator light is ON.
- With service check connector jumped ———► problem codes 7-1 and/or 7-2 is indicated.

Disconnect the 10-P connector from the solenoids.

Check for resistance between the solenoid terminal:
No. 1 (RED/BLK) and No. 4 (BRN/BLK): Front Right Inlet
No. 3 (RED/BLU) and No. 6 (BRN/BLU): Front Left Inlet

Is there 1-3Ω? — NO → Faulty solenoid.

YES

Check for resistance between the solenoid terminals:
No. 8 (YEL/BLK) and No. 4 (BRN/BLK): Front Right Outlet
No. 10 (YEL/BLU) and No. 6 (BRN/BLU): Front Left Outlet

Is there 1-3Ω? — NO → Faulty solenoid.

YES

SOLENOID-SIDE CONNECTOR
RED/BLU (FL-IN)   RED/BLK (FR-IN)

3 2 1
6 5 4
10 9 8

BRN/BLU   BRN/BLK

View from terminal side.

SOLENOID-SIDE CONNECTOR
BRN/BLU   BRN/BLK

3 2 1
6 5 4
10 9 8

YEL/BLU (FL-OUT)   YEL/BLK (FR-OUT)

View from terminal side.

Continued On Next Page

93B02071

1994 BRAKES
Anti-Lock – Civic, Civic Del Sol & Prelude (Cont.)

HONDA
8-123

DTC 7-1 & 7-2 (2 OF 3)
FRONT SOLENOID
PRELUDE

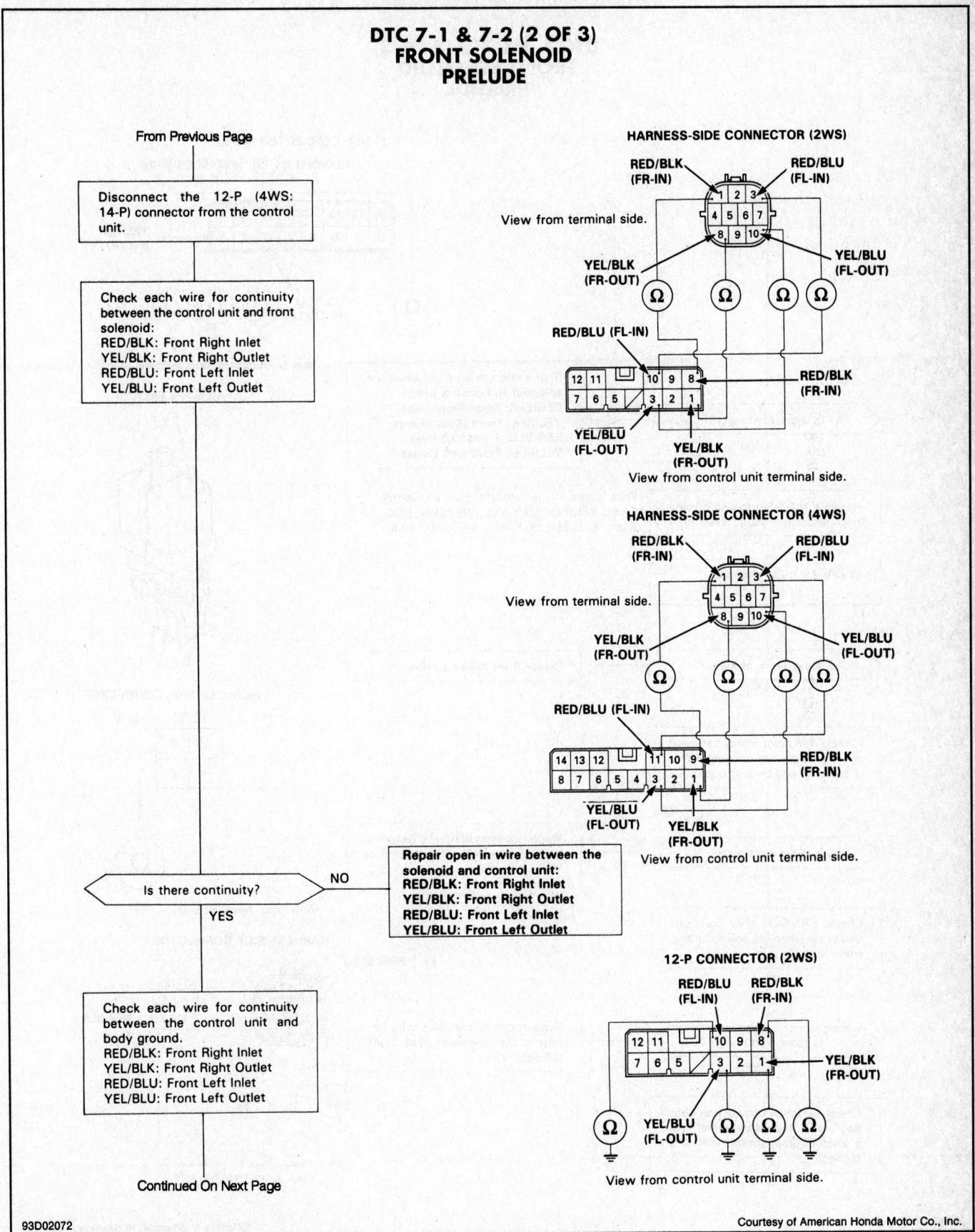

HONDA
8-124

1994 BRAKES
Anti-Lock – Civic, Civic Del Sol & Prelude (Cont.)

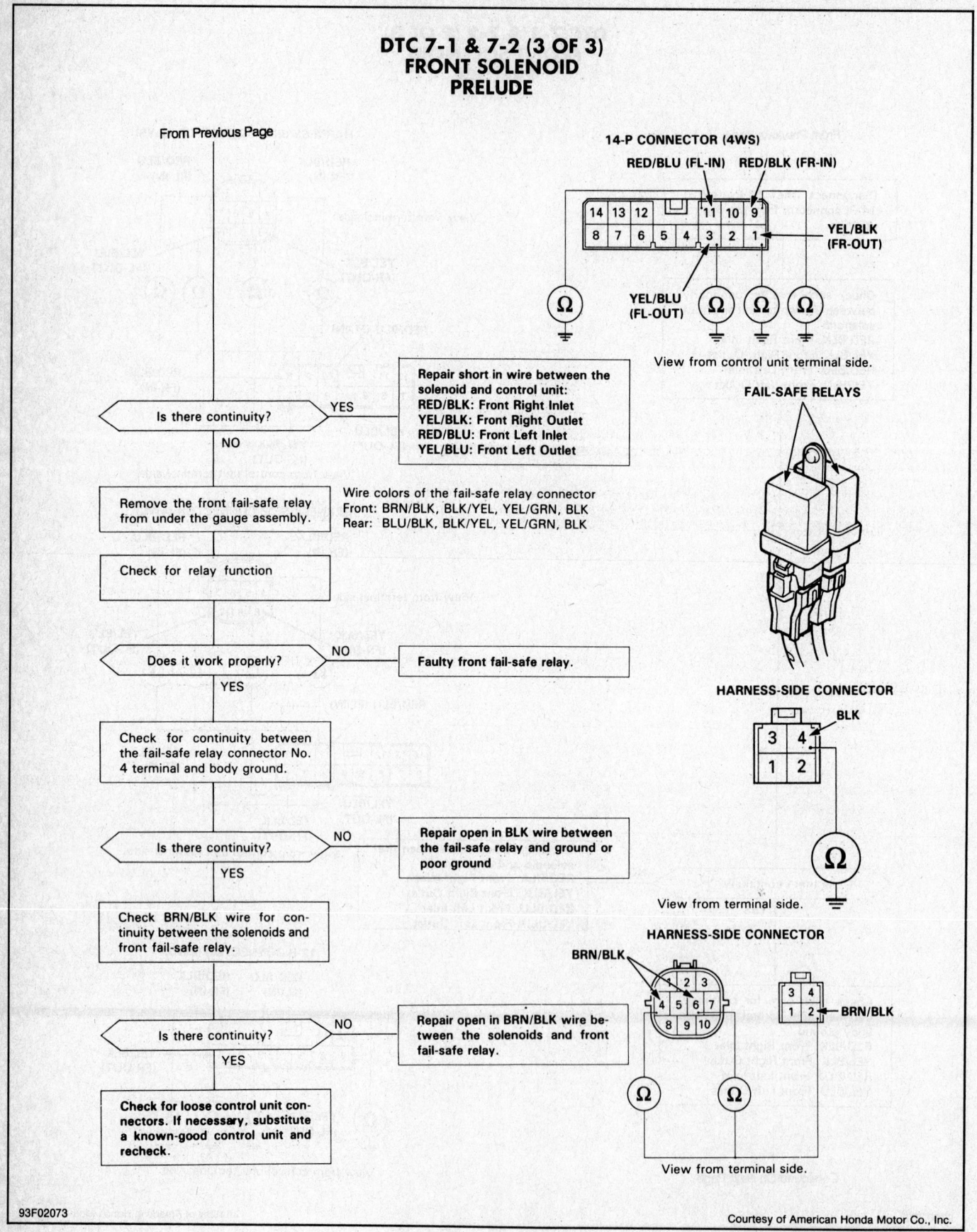

DTC 7-1 & 7-2 (3 OF 3)
FRONT SOLENOID
PRELUDE

From Previous Page

14-P CONNECTOR (4WS)

RED/BLU (FL-IN)   RED/BLK (FR-IN)

14	13	12		11	10	9
8	7	6	5	4	3	2	1

YEL/BLK (FR-OUT)

YEL/BLU (FL-OUT)

View from control unit terminal side.

Is there continuity? — YES →

Repair short in wire between the solenoid and control unit:
RED/BLK: Front Right Inlet
YEL/BLK: Front Right Outlet
RED/BLU: Front Left Inlet
YEL/BLU: Front Left Outlet

NO

Remove the front fail-safe relay from under the gauge assembly.

Wire colors of the fail-safe relay connector
Front: BRN/BLK, BLK/YEL, YEL/GRN, BLK
Rear: BLU/BLK, BLK/YEL, YEL/GRN, BLK

Check for relay function

FAIL-SAFE RELAYS

Does it work properly? — NO →

Faulty front fail-safe relay.

YES

Check for continuity between the fail-safe relay connector No. 4 terminal and body ground.

HARNESS-SIDE CONNECTOR

BLK

3	4
1	2

Is there continuity? — NO →

Repair open in BLK wire between the fail-safe relay and ground or poor ground

YES

View from terminal side.

Check BRN/BLK wire for continuity between the solenoids and front fail-safe relay.

HARNESS-SIDE CONNECTOR

BRN/BLK

1	2	3
4	5	6	7
8	9	10

3	4
1	2

BRN/BLK

Is there continuity? — NO →

Repair open in BRN/BLK wire between the solenoids and front fail-safe relay.

YES

Check for loose control unit connectors. If necessary, substitute a known-good control unit and recheck.

View from terminal side.

Courtesy of American Honda Motor Co., Inc.

1994 BRAKES
Anti-Lock – Civic, Civic Del Sol & Prelude (Cont.)

HONDA
8-125

DTC 7-4 (1 OF 2)
REAR SOLENOID
PRELUDE

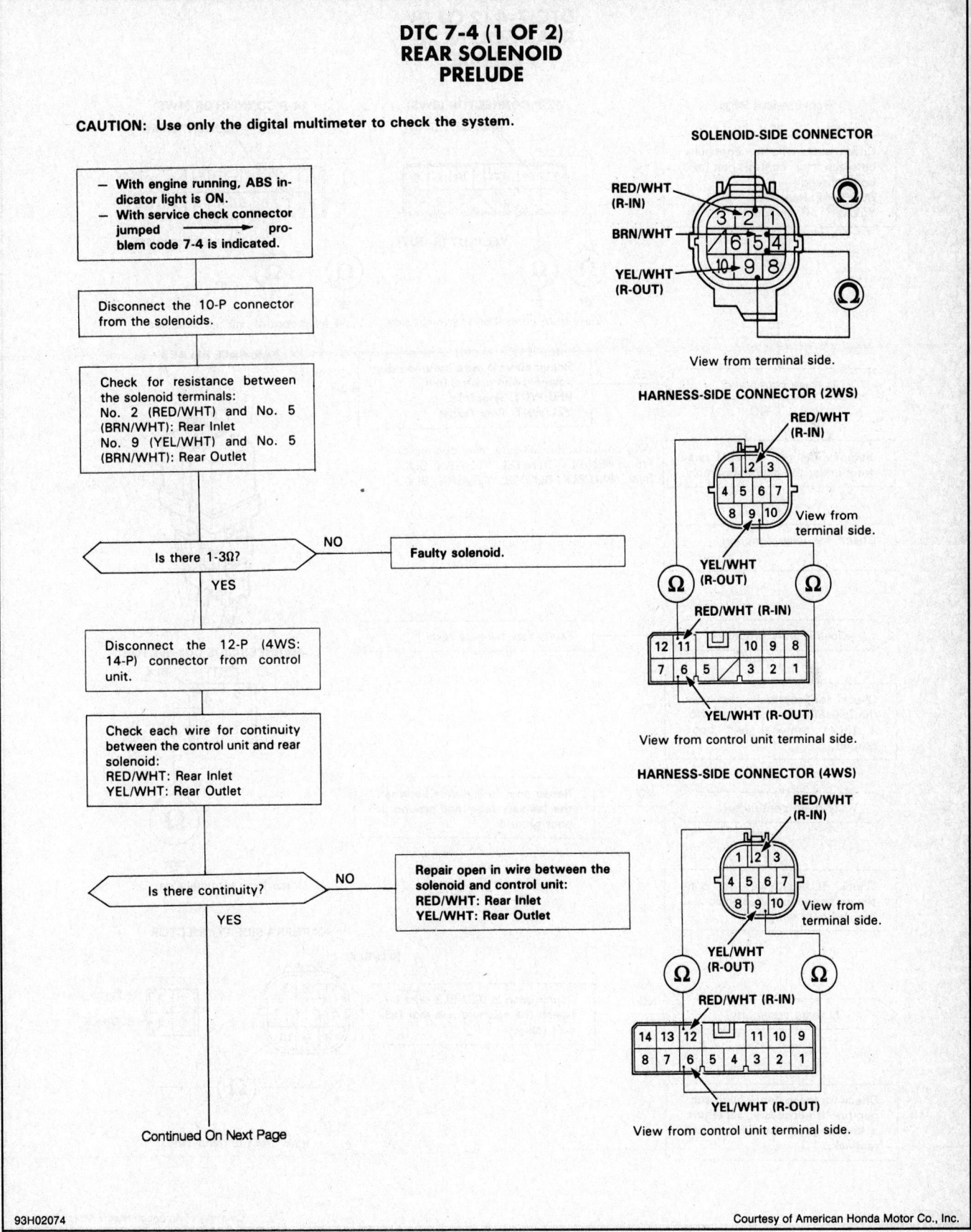

CAUTION: Use only the digital multimeter to check the system.

- With engine running, ABS indicator light is ON.
- With service check connector jumped ⟶ problem code 7-4 is indicated.

Disconnect the 10-P connector from the solenoids.

Check for resistance between the solenoid terminals:
No. 2 (RED/WHT) and No. 5 (BRN/WHT): Rear Inlet
No. 9 (YEL/WHT) and No. 5 (BRN/WHT): Rear Outlet

Is there 1-3Ω?

NO ⟶ Faulty solenoid.

YES

Disconnect the 12-P (4WS: 14-P) connector from control unit.

Check each wire for continuity between the control unit and rear solenoid:
RED/WHT: Rear Inlet
YEL/WHT: Rear Outlet

Is there continuity?

NO ⟶ Repair open in wire between the solenoid and control unit:
RED/WHT: Rear Inlet
YEL/WHT: Rear Outlet

YES

Continued On Next Page

SOLENOID-SIDE CONNECTOR

RED/WHT (R-IN)
BRN/WHT
YEL/WHT (R-OUT)

View from terminal side.

HARNESS-SIDE CONNECTOR (2WS)

RED/WHT (R-IN)

View from terminal side.

YEL/WHT (R-OUT)

RED/WHT (R-IN)

YEL/WHT (R-OUT)

View from control unit terminal side.

HARNESS-SIDE CONNECTOR (4WS)

RED/WHT (R-IN)

View from terminal side.

YEL/WHT (R-OUT)

RED/WHT (R-IN)

YEL/WHT (R-OUT)

View from control unit terminal side.

Courtesy of American Honda Motor Co., Inc.

HONDA
8-126

1994 BRAKES
Anti-Lock – Civic, Civic Del Sol & Prelude (Cont.)

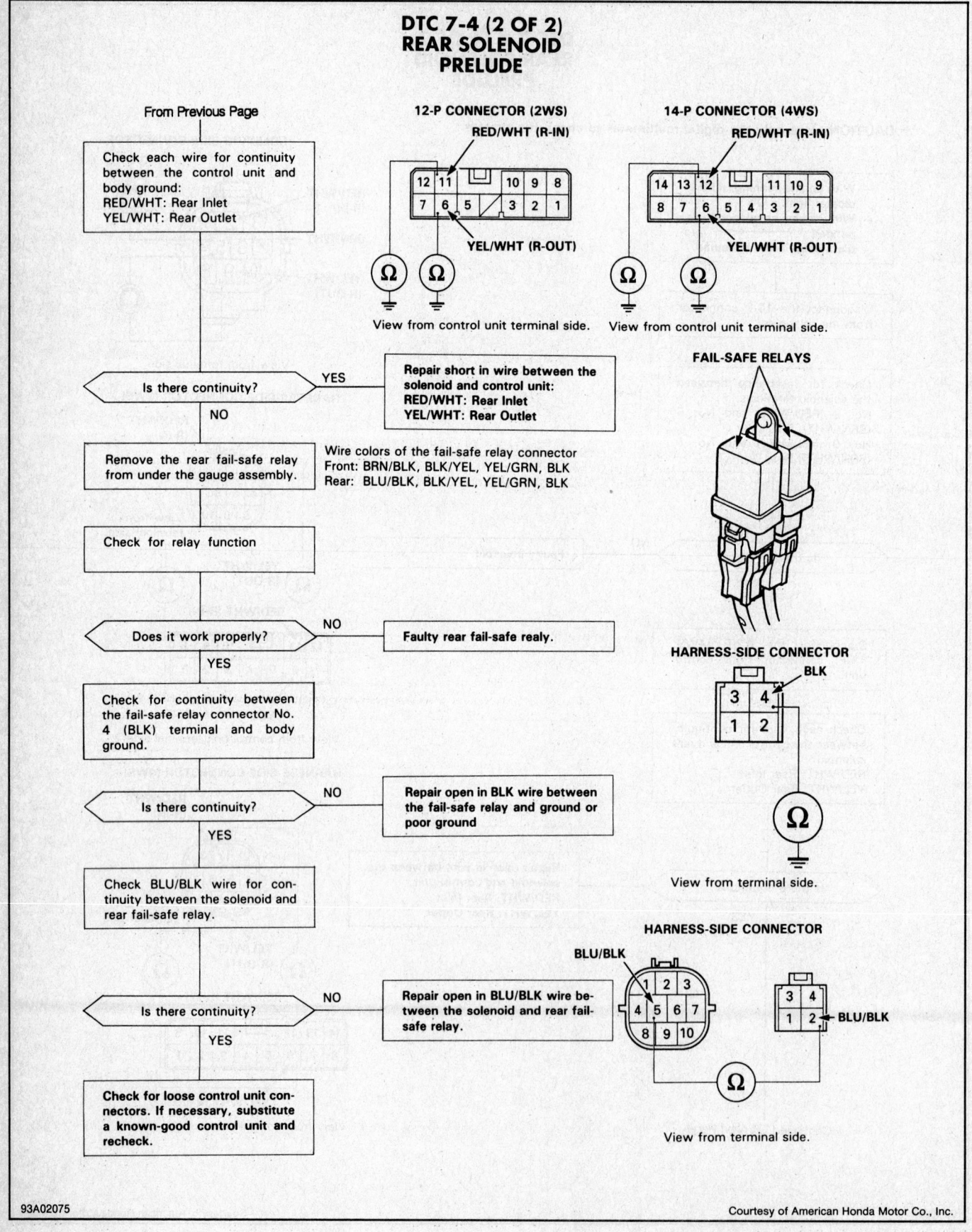

**DTC 7-4 (2 OF 2)
REAR SOLENOID
PRELUDE**

From Previous Page

Check each wire for continuity between the control unit and body ground:
RED/WHT: Rear Inlet
YEL/WHT: Rear Outlet

12-P CONNECTOR (2WS)
RED/WHT (R-IN)
YEL/WHT (R-OUT)
View from control unit terminal side.

14-P CONNECTOR (4WS)
RED/WHT (R-IN)
YEL/WHT (R-OUT)
View from control unit terminal side.

Is there continuity? YES →
Repair short in wire between the solenoid and control unit:
RED/WHT: Rear Inlet
YEL/WHT: Rear Outlet

NO

Remove the rear fail-safe relay from under the gauge assembly.

Wire colors of the fail-safe relay connector
Front: BRN/BLK, BLK/YEL, YEL/GRN, BLK
Rear: BLU/BLK, BLK/YEL, YEL/GRN, BLK

FAIL-SAFE RELAYS

Check for relay function

Does it work properly? NO → Faulty rear fail-safe realy.

YES

Check for continuity between the fail-safe relay connector No. 4 (BLK) terminal and body ground.

HARNESS-SIDE CONNECTOR
BLK
View from terminal side.

Is there continuity? NO →
Repair open in BLK wire between the fail-safe relay and ground or poor ground

YES

Check BLU/BLK wire for continuity between the solenoid and rear fail-safe relay.

HARNESS-SIDE CONNECTOR
BLU/BLK

Is there continuity? NO →
Repair open in BLU/BLK wire between the solenoid and rear fail-safe relay.

BLU/BLK
View from terminal side.

YES

Check for loose control unit connectors. If necessary, substitute a known-good control unit and recheck.

Accord, Civic, Civic Del Sol, Passport, Prelude

NOTE: For all wheel alignment adjustments and information on Passport, refer to Rodeo in Isuzu WHEEL ALIGNMENT Specifications & Procedures article.

NOTE: Prior to performing wheel alignment, perform preliminary visual and mechanical inspection of wheels, tires and suspension components. See PRE-ALIGNMENT INSTRUCTIONS in WHEEL ALIGNMENT THEORY & OPERATION article in GENERAL INFORMATION.

RIDING HEIGHT ADJUSTMENT

Before adjusting alignment, check riding height. Riding height must be checked with vehicle on level floor and tires properly inflated. Passenger and luggage compartments must be unloaded. Bounce vehicle several times, and allow suspension to settle. Visually inspect vehicle from front to rear and from side to side for signs of abnormal height.

Measure riding height. *See Fig. 1.* Riding height between left and right sides of vehicle should vary less than one inch (25.4 mm). If riding height is not within specification, check suspension components and repair or replace them as necessary.

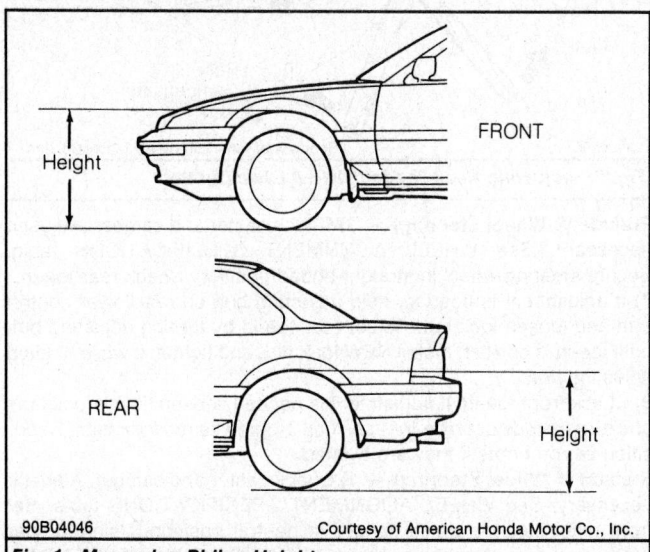

90B04046   Courtesy of American Honda Motor Co., Inc.

Fig. 1: Measuring Riding Height

JACKING & HOISTING

FLOOR JACK

1) Set parking brake. Block wheels that are not going to be lifted. When lifting rear of vehicle, place transmission in Reverse (M/T) or Park (A/T).
2) Place floor jack lift platform under lift bracket to raise vehicle. Front lift bracket is located under vehicle, on cross/center beam. Rear lift bracket is located under vehicle, near muffler. Place safety stands on reinforced support points of side body panels (between front and rear wheels).

EMERGENCY JACKING

Place manufacturer-supplied jack on reinforced support points of side body panels (between front and rear wheels).

HOIST

Place lift blocks on reinforced support points of side body panels (between front and rear wheels). These are same points as used with manufacturer-supplied jack.

WHEEL ALIGNMENT PROCEDURES

NOTE: On Prelude, wheel alignment should be checked and adjusted in following order: caster, front camber, rear camber, rear toe-in, front toe-in and steering wheel alignment.

CAMBER ADJUSTMENT

NOTE: Manufacturer recommends using commercially available computerized 4-wheel alignment equipment. Follow equipment manufacturer instructions to obtain current vehicle alignment settings. Use following procedures for necessary adjustments.

Accord, Civic & Civic Del Sol – Compare camber settings with vehicle manufacturer recommendations. See WHEEL ALIGNMENT SPECIFICATIONS table. If camber is incorrect, check for bent or damaged front suspension components. Replace faulty components. Recheck camber.
Prelude (Front) – Compare camber settings with vehicle manufacturer recommendations. See WHEEL ALIGNMENT SPECIFICATIONS table. If camber is incorrect, check for bent or damaged front suspension components. Replace faulty components. Recheck camber.
Prelude (Rear) – 1) On 4-wheel steering models, install Rear Steering Center Lock Pin (07NAJ-SS0020A) in rear steering gear assembly. *See Fig. 2.* On all models, compare camber settings with vehicle manufacturer recommendations. See WHEEL ALIGNMENT SPECIFICATIONS table. If camber is incorrect, adjust rear camber by loosening upper arm lock nuts and moving knuckle/hub assembly in or out.
2) On 4-wheel steering models, check static steering wheel alignment. If steering wheel alignment is off by more than 13/64" (5 mm) at steering wheel hub, remove steering wheel and reposition it on splines.
3) Remove rear steering center lock pin, and install rear steering gear assembly cap bolt. Turn steering wheel, centering it in straight-ahead position. Secure steering wheel in this position, and check toe-in.

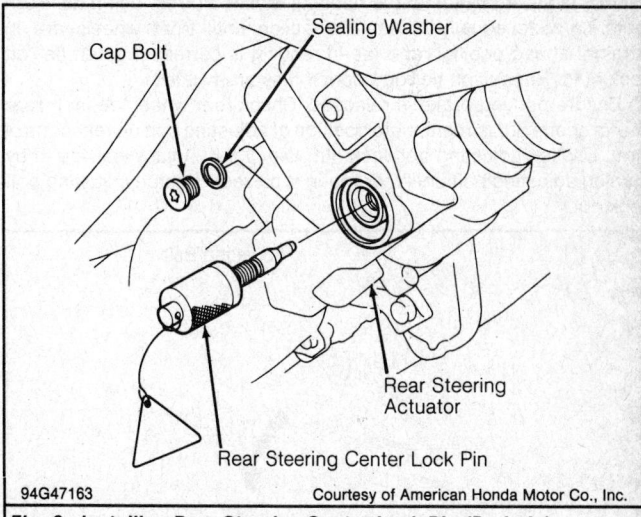

94G47163   Courtesy of American Honda Motor Co., Inc.

Fig. 2: Installing Rear Steering Center Lock Pin (Prelude)

CASTER ADJUSTMENT

NOTE: Manufacturer recommends using commercially available computerized 4-wheel alignment equipment. Follow equipment manufacturer instructions to obtain current vehicle alignment settings. Use following procedures for necessary adjustments.

NOTE: DO NOT use more than 2 shims. If more than 2 shims are required to adjust caster angle, check for bent or damaged suspension components.

Accord & Prelude – 1) If caster needs adjustment, raise front of vehicle and support it using safety stands. Remove lock nut on end of radius (strut) rod. *See Fig. 3.* Remove radius rod bolts and radius rod from lower control arm.

2) Adjust caster angle by increasing or decreasing adjusting shims. A 1/8" (3.2 mm) thick shim changes caster angle by 0.41 degree (25 minutes). Caster angle can be adjusted a maximum of 0.83 degree (50 minutes). Install and tighten radius rod bolts and lock nuts.

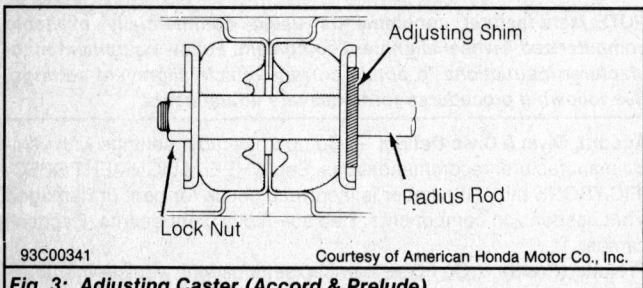

93C00341   Courtesy of American Honda Motor Co., Inc.

Fig. 3: Adjusting Caster (Accord & Prelude)

Civic & Civic Del Sol – Compare caster settings with vehicle manufacturer recommendations. See WHEEL ALIGNMENT SPECIFICATIONS table. If caster is incorrect, check for bent or damaged front suspension components. Replace faulty components. Recheck caster.

TOE-IN ADJUSTMENT

NOTE: Manufacturer recommends using commercially available computerized 4-wheel alignment equipment. Follow equipment manufacturer instructions to obtain current vehicle alignment settings. Use following procedures for necessary adjustments.

Accord – 1) Secure steering wheel in straight-ahead position. Measure front wheel toe-in. See WHEEL ALIGNMENT SPECIFICATIONS table. If adjustment is needed, loosen tie rod lock nuts. Turn both tie rods equally in same direction until front wheels are in straight-ahead position and toe-in reading is correct. Tighten tie rod lock nuts. Reposition tie rod boots if they are twisted.

2) Ensure parking brake is released. Check rear wheel toe-in. If rear toe-in needs adjustment, note position of adjusting bolt on rear control arm. Loosen adjusting bolt lock nut. *See Fig. 4.* Adjust rear toe-in by turning adjusting bolt until rear toe-in is correct. Tighten adjusting bolt lock nut.

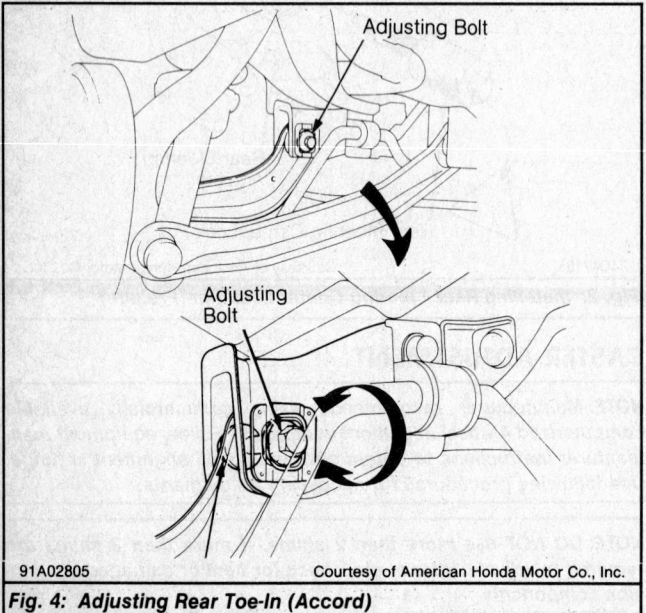

91A02805   Courtesy of American Honda Motor Co., Inc.

Fig. 4: Adjusting Rear Toe-In (Accord)

Civic & Civic Del Sol – 1) Secure steering wheel in straight-ahead position. Measure front wheel toe-in. See WHEEL ALIGNMENT SPECIFICATIONS table. If adjustment is needed, loosen tie rod lock nuts. Turn both tie rods equally in the same direction until front wheels are in straight-ahead position and toe-in reading is correct. Tighten tie rod lock nuts. Reposition tie rod boots if twisted.

2) Ensure parking brake is released. Check rear wheel toe-in. If adjustment is needed, hold adjusting bolt on rear compensator arm and loosen lock nut. *See Fig. 5.* Adjust rear toe-in by sliding rear control arm until rear toe-in is correct. Install NEW lock nut, and tighten it while holding adjusting bolt.

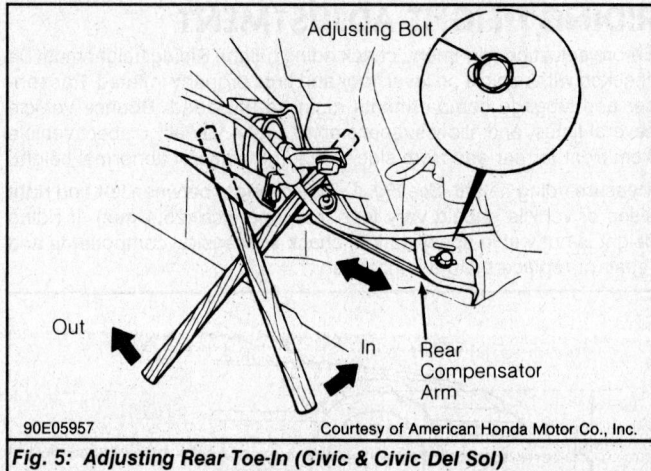

90E05957   Courtesy of American Honda Motor Co., Inc.

Fig. 5: Adjusting Rear Toe-In (Civic & Civic Del Sol)

Prelude (2-Wheel Steering) – 1) Check caster and camber. Adjust if necessary. See WHEEL ALIGNMENT SPECIFICATIONS table. Secure steering wheel in straight-ahead position. Check rear toe-in.

2) If adjustment is needed, hold adjusting bolt on rear lower control arm and loosen lock nut. Adjust rear toe-in by turning adjusting bolt until toe-in is correct. Install NEW lock nut, and tighten it while holding adjusting bolt.

3) Check front toe-in. If adjustment is needed, loosen tie rod lock nuts and turn tie rods until toe-in is correct. Tighten tie rod lock nuts. Reposition tie rod boots if they are twisted.

Prelude (4-Wheel Steering) – 1) Check caster and camber. Adjust if necessary. See WHEEL ALIGNMENT SPECIFICATIONS table. Set front main steering angle sensor in neutral position. Using jumper wire, jump service check connector to turn on 4WS indicator light in instrument cluster. See 4-WHEEL STEERING article in STEERING. Check front toe-in.

2) If adjustment is needed, loosen tie rod lock nuts and turn tie rods until toe-in is correct. After adjustment, tighten tie rod lock nuts. Reposition tie rod boots if they are twisted. Disconnect jumper wire.

3) Set rear main steering angle sensor in neutral position. Using jumper wire, jump service check connector to turn on 4WS indicator light in instrument cluster. See 4-WHEEL STEERING article. Check rear toe-in. If adjustment is needed, loosen tie rod lock nuts and turn tie rods until toe-in is correct. After adjustment, tighten tie rod lock nuts. Reposition tie rod boots if they are twisted. Disconnect jumper wire.

TORQUE SPECIFICATIONS

TORQUE SPECIFICATIONS

Application	Ft. Lbs (N.m)
Accord	
Radius Rod Lock Nut	32 (44)
Rear Control Arm Adjusting Bolt Lock Nuts	41 (55)
Spindle Nut	184 (250)
Tie Rod Lock Nut	33 (45)
Wheel Lug Nuts	81 (110)
Civic & Civic Del Sol	
Rear Control Arm Adjusting Bolt	48 (65)
Spindle Nut	136 (185)
Tie Rod Lock Nut	41 (55)
Wheel Lug Nuts	81 (110)
Prelude	
Radius Rod Lock Nut	41 (55)
Spindle Nut	184 (250)
Tie Rod Lock Nut	33 (45)
Upper Control Arm Nuts	48 (65)
Wheel Lug Nuts	81 (110)

WHEEL ALIGNMENT SPECIFICATIONS

WHEEL ALIGNMENT SPECIFICATIONS

Application	Preferred	Range
Accord		
Camber [1]		
Front	0	– 1 To 1
Rear	– 0.42	– 0.92 To 0.8
Caster [1]	3	2 To 4
Toe-In [2]		
Front	0 (0)	– 0.08 To 0.08 (– 2.0 To 2.0)
Rear	0.08 (2.0)	0 To 0.16 (0 To 4.0)
Toe-Out On Turns [1]		
Inner	39	.....
Outer	30	.....
Civic		
Camber [1]		
Front	0	– 1 To 1
Rear	– 0.33	– 1.33 To 0.67
Caster [1]	1.17	0.17 To 2.17
Toe-In [2]		
Front	0 (0)	– 0.08 To 0.08 (– 2.0 To 2.0)
Rear	0.08 (2.0)	0 To 0.16 (1.0 To 4.0)
Toe-Out On Turns [1]		
Inner	41.0	.....
Outer	33.5	.....
Civic Del Sol		
Camber [1]		
Front	0.25	– 0.75 To 1.25
Rear	– 0.5	– 1.5 To 1.0
Caster [1]	1.17	0.17 To 2.17

[1] – Measurement in degrees.
[2] – Measurement in inches (mm).

WHEEL ALIGNMENT SPECIFICATIONS (Cont.)

Application	Preferred	Range
Toe-In [2]		
Front	0 (0)	– 0.08 To 0.08 (– 2.0 To 2.0)
Rear	0.08 (2.0)	0 To 0.16 (1.0 To 4.0)
Toe-Out On Turns [1]		
Inner	40	.....
Outer	33	.....
Passport		
Camber [1]		
Front	0.5	– 0.5 To 1.5
Rear		
Caster [1]	2.33	1.58 To 3.08
Toe-In [2]		
Front	0.08 (2.0)	0 To 0.16 (0 To 4.0)
Rear		
Toe-Out On Turns [1]		
Inner	35	
Outer	33	
Prelude (2WS)		
Camber [1]		
Front	0	– 1 To 1
Rear	– 0.75	– 1.75 To 0.25
Caster [1]	2.67	1.67 To 3.67
Toe-In [2]		
Front	0 (0)	– 0.08 To 0.08 (– 2.0 To 2.0)
Rear	0.08 (2.0)	0 To 0.16 (0 To 4.0)
Toe-Out On Turns [1]		
Inner	36.33	.....
Outer	29.67	.....
Prelude (4WS)		
Camber [1]		
Front	0	– 1 To 1
Rear	– 0.75	– 1.70 To 0.30
Caster [1]	2.67	1.67 To 3.67
Toe-In [2]		
Front	0 (0)	– 0.08 To 0.08 (– 2.0 To 2.0)
Rear	0.08 (2.0)	0 To 0.16 (0 To 4.0)
Toe-Out On Turns [1]		
Inner		
Front	36.33	.....
Rear	6	.....
Outer		
Front	29.67	.....
Rear	6.33	.....

[1] – Measurement in degrees.
[2] – Measurement in inches (mm).

1994 SUSPENSION
Front

Accord, Civic, Civic Del Sol, Passport, Prelude

NOTE: For all data and information on Passport front suspension, refer to Rodeo in Isuzu SUSPENSION – Front article.

DESCRIPTION

All models use independent, double wish-bone, strut type suspension. The coil-over strut assembly is attached to the steering knuckle through the lower control arm. *See Fig. 1.* The steering knuckle is attached to upper and lower control arms by ball joints. A stabilizer bar and strut rod are attached to lower control arm.

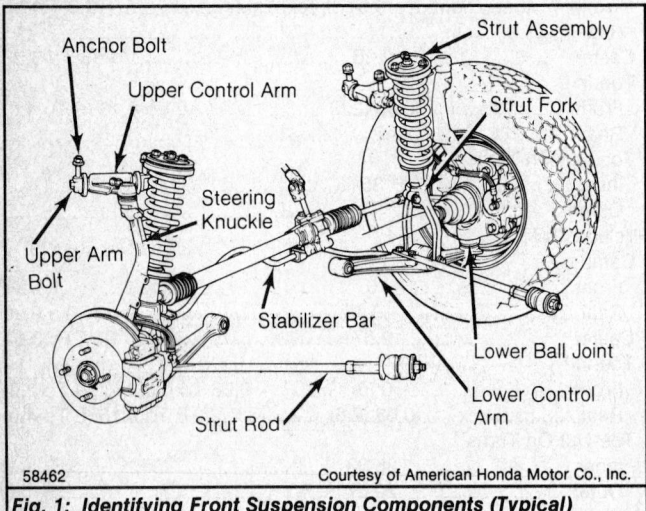

58462   Courtesy of American Honda Motor Co., Inc.

Fig. 1: Identifying Front Suspension Components (Typical)

ADJUSTMENTS & INSPECTION

WHEEL ALIGNMENT
SPECIFICATIONS & PROCEDURES

NOTE: See SPECIFICATIONS & PROCEDURES article in WHEEL ALIGNMENT.

WHEEL BEARING

Inspection – 1) Wheel bearings require no adjustment. Bearings should be checked for excessive movement. Support vehicle, and remove wheel.

2) Install dial indicator with stem positioned on front hub surface. Move hub assembly in and out. Note reading. Movement should be 0-.002" (0-.05 mm). If movement is not as specified, replace bearing. See WHEEL BEARING under REMOVAL & INSTALLATION.

REMOVAL & INSTALLATION

HUB & KNUCKLE ASSEMBLY

Removal (Accord) – **1)** Loosen lug nuts with vehicle weight on tires. Pry lock tab away from spindle nut, and loosen nut. Raise and support vehicle. Remove lug nuts and spindle nut. Remove wheel assembly. Remove caliper assembly, and support aside. DO NOT put weight on flexible brake line.

2) Remove cotter pin and nut from tie rod end. Using Ball Joint Remover (07MAC-SL00200), separate tie rod ball joint and lift tie rod end out of knuckle. Remove cotter pin from lower control arm ball joint, and loosen castle nut half length of joint threads. Using ball joint separator, separate lower ball joint from control arm. Remove nut. Remove hub/knuckle from control arm.

3) Remove upper ball joint shield. *See Fig. 2.* Remove cotter pin and nut from upper ball joint. Using ball joint remover, separate ball joint from upper control arm. Slide axle shaft from knuckle and hub assembly. Support axle shaft with wire. Remove hub/knuckle assembly.

Removal (Civic, Civic Del Sol & Prelude) – **1)** Loosen lug nuts with vehicle weight on tires. Pry lock tab away from spindle nut, and loosen nut. Raise and support vehicle. Remove lug nuts and spindle nut. Remove wheel assembly. Remove caliper assembly, and support aside. DO NOT put weight on flexible brake line.

2) Remove brake disc retaining screws. Install two 8 x 12-mm bolts in brake disc, and tighten bolts to force brake disc from hub. Alternate tightening of bolts to prevent brake disc from binding on hub. Remove cotter pin and nut from tie rod end.

3) Using Ball Joint Remover (07MAC-SL00200), separate tie rod ball joint and lift tie rod end out of knuckle. Remove cotter pin from lower control arm ball joint, and loosen castle nut half length of joint threads. Using ball joint separator, separate lower ball joint from control arm.

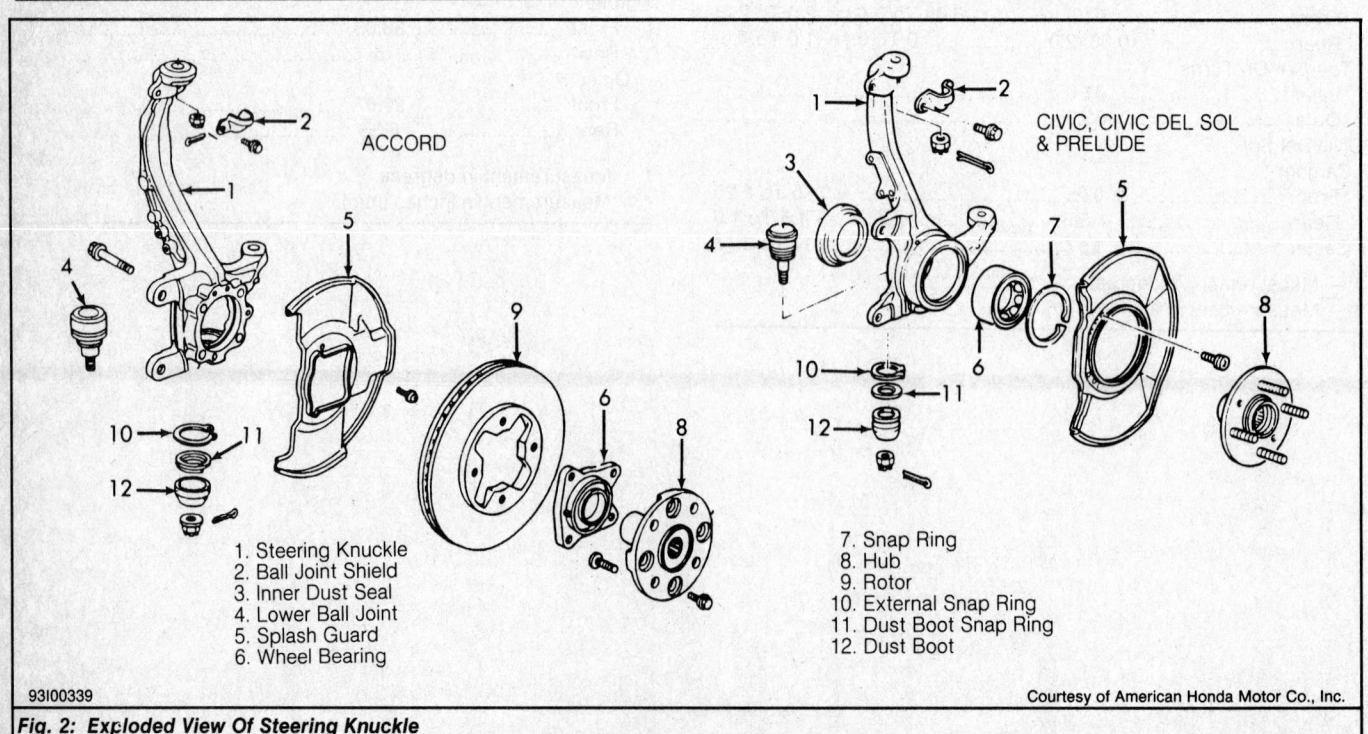

1. Steering Knuckle
2. Ball Joint Shield
3. Inner Dust Seal
4. Lower Ball Joint
5. Splash Guard
6. Wheel Bearing

7. Snap Ring
8. Hub
9. Rotor
10. External Snap Ring
11. Dust Boot Snap Ring
12. Dust Boot

93I00339   Courtesy of American Honda Motor Co., Inc.

Fig. 2: Exploded View Of Steering Knuckle

4) Remove upper ball joint shield. *See Fig. 2.* Remove cotter pin and upper ball joint stud nut. Using ball joint remover, separate ball joint from steering knuckle. Remove steering hub/knuckle assembly from axle shaft.

Installation – To install hub/knuckle, reverse removal procedure. Tighten bolts and nuts to specification. Use NEW spindle nut, and stake after tightening. See TORQUE SPECIFICATIONS.

LOWER CONTROL ARM & BALL JOINT

NOTE: Lower ball joint replacement procedure for Prelude is not available from manufacturer. Lower ball joint dust boot may be replaced in a separate procedure using same procedure and dust boot snap ring guide as Civic and Civic Del Sol.

Removal – **1)** Raise and support front of vehicle. Remove wheel assembly. Remove strut fork and strut rod (radius arm) bolts. Remove nut, bolt and bushings from stabilizer bar.

2) Remove cotter pin from lower control arm ball joint, and remove castle nut. Using puller, separate lower control arm from ball joint. Pull arm down until clear of lower ball joint stud. Remove lower control arm pivot bolt, and remove control arm.

3) Remove steering knuckle. See HUB & KNUCKLE ASSEMBLY. Remove dust boot snap ring, dust boot and external ball joint snap ring.

4) Install Ball Joint Remover/Installer (07HAF-SF10110 for Accord; 07965-SB00100 for Civic and Civic Del Sol) Place installer over ball joint stud with large diameter opening facing away from ball joint. Install stud nut.

5) Position Ball Joint Remover Base (07HAF-SF10130 for Accord; 07JAF-SH20200 for Civic and Civic Del Sol) with open end over ball joint flat surface. Place assembly in vise. Tighten vise and press ball joint from steering knuckle. *See Fig. 3.*

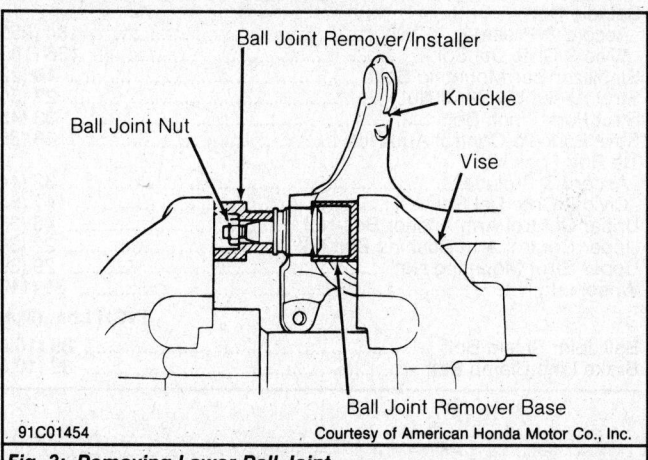

Fig. 3: Removing Lower Ball Joint

Installation – **1)** Position ball joint in steering knuckle. Install ball joint remover/installer on stud end of ball joint with large diameter opening facing ball joint. Position Ball Joint Installer Base (07HAF-SF10120 for Accord; 07965-SB00200 for Civic and Civic Del Sol) over end of ball joint. Using vise, press ball joint into knuckle.

2) Install ball joint snap ring and dust boot. Using Dust Boot Snap Ring Guide (07GAG-SD40700 for Accord; 07974-SA50700 for Civic and Civic Del Sol), install dust boot snap ring.

3) Reverse removal procedure to install control arm. Use a NEW lower control arm pivot bolt. Tighten bolt to specification.

UPPER BALL JOINT

Removal & Installation – Information is not available from manufacturer.

UPPER CONTROL ARM

Inspection – Raise and support front of vehicle. Remove wheel assembly. Rock upper ball joint front to back. On Accord and Prelude, upper control arm assembly must be replaced if play exists in bushings. On Civic and Civic Del Sol, replace upper control arm bushings if any play exists.

Removal – **1)** On all models, raise and support front of vehicle. Remove wheel assembly. Remove cotter pin and nut from upper ball joint stud.

2) Using ball joint remover, separate upper ball joint from steering knuckle. Remove upper control arm anchor bolts-to-body retaining nuts. *See Fig. 4.* Remove upper control arm. Clamp each upper arm anchor bolt in a vise. Remove upper arm bushings.

Bushing Replacement (Civic & Civic Del Sol) – Remove control arm bushing nuts and bolts. Clamp upper control arm anchor bolt in a soft-jawed vise. Drive out bushing. Grease and install NEW control arm bushing. Ensure bushing is centered in anchor bolt. Install bushing nuts and bolts, and tighten them to specification.

Installation – To install, reverse removal procedure. Tighten nuts and bolts to specification. Check camber, and adjust if necessary. See SPECIFICATIONS & PROCEDURES article in WHEEL ALIGNMENT.

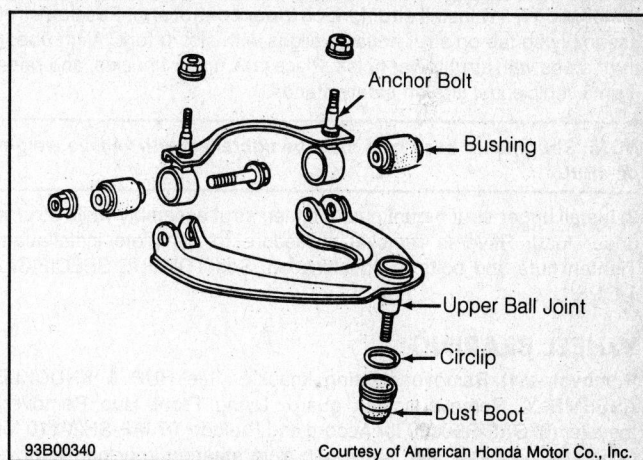

Fig. 4: Exploded View Of Upper Control Arm Assembly

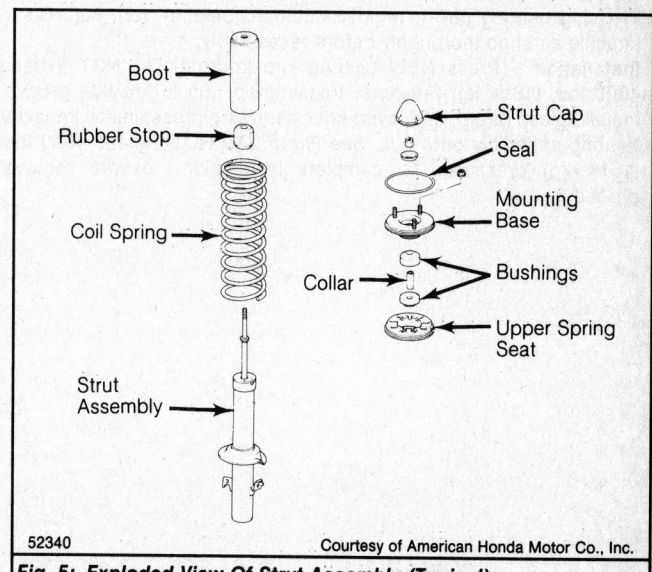

Fig. 5: Exploded View Of Strut Assembly (Typical)

STRUT ASSEMBLY

Removal – Raise and support front of vehicle. Remove wheel assembly and brake hose clamp from strut. Remove strut-to-fork self-locking pinch bolt and strut fork bolt. Remove strut fork assembly. Remove cap and nuts from top of strut. Remove strut assembly.

WARNING: Strut contains pressurized nitrogen gas. To dispose of properly, drill a 5/64" (2.0 mm) hole at base of strut. Always wear eye protection when drilling.

Disassembly – Using spring compressor, compress spring slightly to remove spring tension. Hold strut rod using an Allen wrench and remove nut retaining spring seat and mounting base. Slowly release spring compressor and lift spring off. Disassemble strut assembly, noting relative position of assembled parts. See Fig. 5.

Reassembly – Check parts for cracks, deterioration and damage. Check shock absorber for leaks and improper operation. Replace strut if resistance is weak, uneven or jerky when strut is compressed. Replace worn or damaged parts. Position mounting base with one stud aligned with tab on strut housing. To complete reassembly, reverse disassembly procedure.

Installation – 1) Install strut fork on lower control arm. Position strut assembly so tab on strut housing aligns with slot in fork. Align upper strut studs with strut tower holes. Place jack under knuckle, and raise it until vehicle just lifts off safety stands.

NOTE: Strut mount base nuts must be tightened with vehicle weight on strut.

---

2) Install upper strut mount nuts. Tighten strut assembly while strut is under load. Reverse removal procedure to complete installation. Tighten nuts and bolts to specification. See TORQUE SPECIFICATIONS.

WHEEL BEARING

Removal – 1) Remove steering knuckle. See HUB & KNUCKLE ASSEMBLY. Remove splash guard. Using Front Hub Remover/Installer (07GAF-SE0100 for Accord and Prelude; 07JAF-SH20110 for Civic and Civic Del Sol), press hub from steering knuckle. Remove bearing retaining snap ring and knuckle ring from knuckle. Press bearing out of knuckle.

2) Using bearing puller, remove outboard bearing from hub. Clean knuckle and hub thoroughly before reassembly.

Installation – Press NEW bearing into knuckle. DO NOT exceed 4000 lbs. (1814 kg) pressure. Install snap ring in knuckle groove. Install splash guard, and invert knuckle. Using press, install knuckle/bearing assembly onto hub. See Fig. 6. DO NOT exceed 4000 lbs. (1814 kg) pressure. To complete installation, reverse removal procedure.

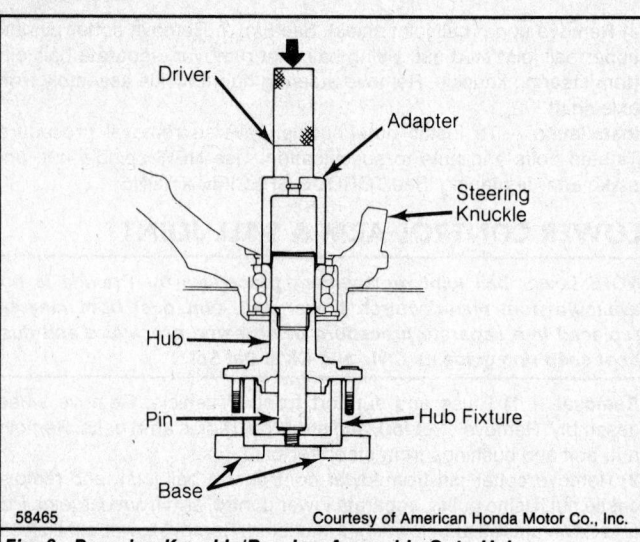

58465   Courtesy of American Honda Motor Co., Inc.

Fig. 6: Pressing Knuckle/Bearing Assembly Onto Hub

TORQUE SPECIFICATIONS
TORQUE SPECIFICATIONS

Application	Ft. Lbs. (N.m)
Ball Joint Nut	
Lower	37-44 (50-60)
Upper	30-35 (40-48)
Brake Caliper Mounting Bolt	81 (110)
Lower Control Arm Pivot Bolt	
Accord & Prelude	40 (54)
Civic & Civic Del Sol	47 (64)
Spindle Nut	
Accord & Prelude	184 (250)
Civic & Civic Del Sol	136 (185)
Stabilizer Bar Mounting Bolts	16 (22)
Strut Assembly Shaft Nut	22 (30)
Strut Fork Pinch Bolt	33 (45)
Strut Fork-To-Control Arm Nut	48 (65)
Tie Rod Lock Nut	
Accord & Prelude	32 (44)
Civic & Civic Del Sol	41 (55)
Upper Control Arm Anchor Bolt Nut	48 (65)
Upper Control Arm Bushing Bolt (2)	22 (30)
Upper Strut Mounting Nut	29 (39)
Wheel Lug Nut	81 (110)
	INCH Lbs. (N.m)
Ball Joint Shield Bolt	89 (10.0)
Brake Line Clamp Bolt	89 (10.0)

Accord, Civic, Civic Del Sol, Passport, Prelude

NOTE: For all data and information on Passport rear suspension, refer to Rodeo in Isuzu SUSPENSION – Rear article.

DESCRIPTION

Accord and Prelude use an independent strut type suspension. Suspension consists of a vertically-mounted strut, trailing arm, upper and lower control arms, knuckle, stabilizer bar and hub assembly. *See Figs. 1 and 2.*

Civic uses an independent strut and trailing control arm type rear suspension. Civic and Civic Del Sol rear suspension consists of a vertically-mounted strut inside of a coil spring, trailing control arm, upper and lower arms, compensator arm and hub assembly. *See Fig. 3.*

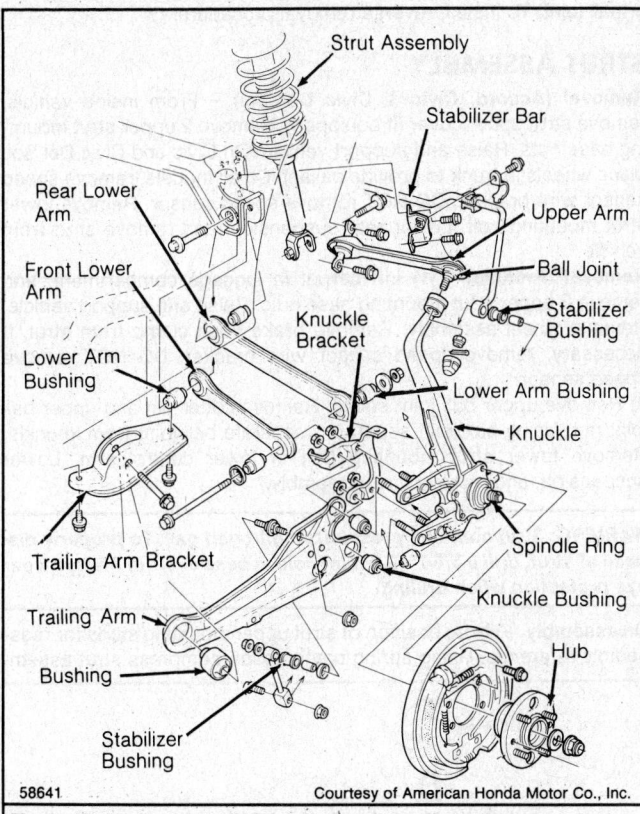

58641   Courtesy of American Honda Motor Co., Inc.

Fig. 1: Exploded View Of Rear Suspension (Accord)

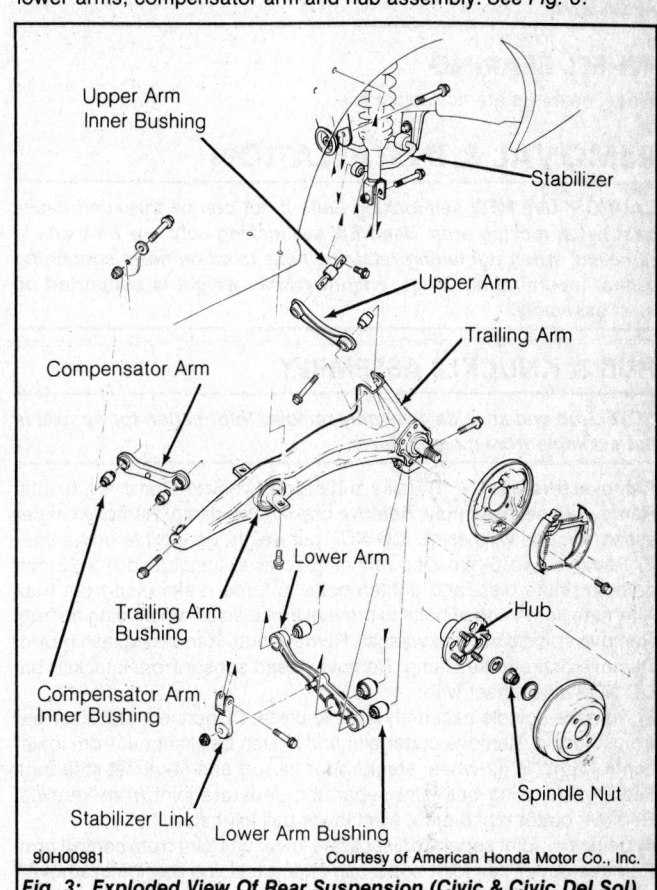

90H00981   Courtesy of American Honda Motor Co., Inc.

Fig. 3: Exploded View Of Rear Suspension (Civic & Civic Del Sol)

1. Upper Control Arm Assembly
2. Strut Assembly
3. Lower Control Arm "A"
4. Lower Control Arm "B" (2WS Only)
5. Trailing Arm
6. Trailing Arm Bracket
7. Stabilizer Bar
8. Stabilizer Link
9. Lower Ball Joint
10. Bushing
11. Stabilizer Bushing

93D00342   Courtesy of American Honda Motor Co., Inc.

Fig. 2: Exploded View Of Rear Suspension (Prelude)

ADJUSTMENTS & INSPECTION

WHEEL ALIGNMENT
SPECIFICATIONS & PROCEDURES

NOTE: See SPECIFICATIONS & PROCEDURES article in WHEEL ALIGNMENT.

WHEEL BEARING

Wheel bearings are not adjustable.

REMOVAL & INSTALLATION

CAUTION: Use NEW self-locking bolts if nut can be threaded easily past nylon locking area. Use NEW self-locking nuts any time one is removed. When tightening retaining bolts used on parts containing rubber mounting bushings, ensure vehicle weight is supported on strut assembly.

HUB & KNUCKLE ASSEMBLY

NOTE: Hub and knuckle assembly removal information for Accord is not available from manufacturer.

Removal (Prelude) – **1)** Raise and support vehicle. Remove lug nuts. Remove wheel assembly. Remove brake hose clamp. Remove caliper assembly, and wire aside. DO NOT put weight on flexible brake line.
2) Remove two 6-mm disc retaining screws. Install two 8 x 12-mm bolts in brake disc, and tighten bolts to force brake disc from hub. Alternate tightening of bolts to prevent brake disc from binding on hub. Remove spindle nut and washer. Remove hub. Remove splash guard. Remove brake hose clamp. Remove speed sensor from knuckle, but DO NOT disconnect wire.
3) Remove spindle assembly from knuckle. Disconnect stabilizer bar from knuckle. Remove cotter pin, and loosen ball joint nut from lower control arm "B" (2-wheel steering) or tie rod end (4-wheel steering). *See Fig. 4.* Using ball joint separator, separate joint from knuckle. Remove cotter pin and nut from lower ball joint stud.
4) Using ball joint separator, separate lower ball joint from control arm. Remove upper ball joint cotter pin and nut. Using ball joint remover, separate ball joint from knuckle. Remove knuckle from vehicle.
Installation – To install, reverse removal procedure. Tighten bolts to specification. See TORQUE SPECIFICATIONS (PRELUDE). Use NEW spindle nut, and stake after tightening to specification. Replace self-locking bolt if nut can be easily threaded past nylon lock area.

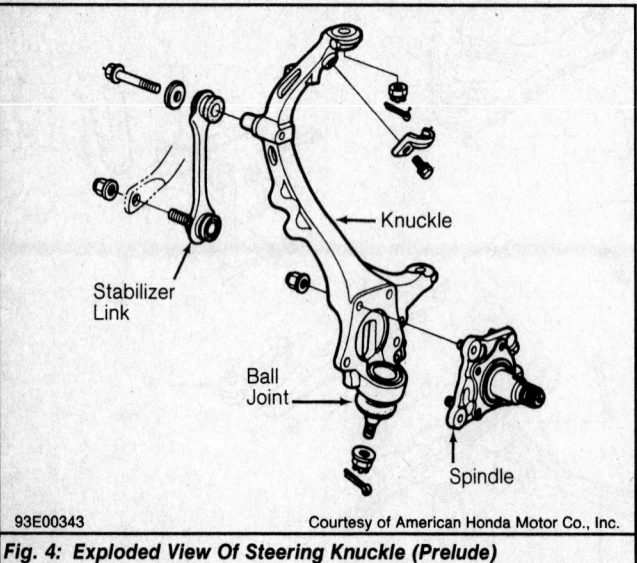

93E00343   Courtesy of American Honda Motor Co., Inc.

Fig. 4: Exploded View Of Steering Knuckle (Prelude)

LOWER BALL JOINT

NOTE: Lower ball joint removal information for Prelude (4WS) is not available from manufacturer.

Removal & Installation (Prelude 2WS) – Raise and support vehicle. Remove wheel assembly. Remove cotter pin and nut from lower ball joint. Using ball joint separator, separate ball joint from knuckle. Remove bolts securing ball joint to lower control arm "B". Remove lower ball joint. To install, reverse removal procedure.

STRUT ASSEMBLY

Removal (Accord, Civic & Civic Del Sol) – From inside vehicle, remove strut upper cover (if equipped). Remove 2 upper strut mounting base nuts. Raise and support vehicle. On Civic and Civic Del Sol, place wheels in trunk to provide ballast. On all models, remove speed sensor wire bracket. DO NOT remove speed sensor. Remove lower strut mounting bolt. Lower rear suspension, and remove strut from vehicle.
Removal (Prelude) – **1)** Lift carpet in luggage compartment, and remove 2 upper strut mounting base nuts. Raise and support vehicle. Remove wheel assembly. Remove brake hose clamp from strut. If necessary, remove speed sensor wire bracket. DO NOT remove speed sensor.
2) Remove upper ball joint shield. Remove cotter pin and upper ball joint nut. Using ball joint separator, separate ball joint from knuckle. Remove lower strut mounting bolt at lower control arm. Lower suspension, and remove strut assembly.

WARNING: Strut contains pressurized nitrogen gas. To properly dispose of strut, drill a 5/64" (2.0 mm) hole at base of strut. Always wear eye protection when drilling.

Disassembly – Note position of strut upper mounting studs for reassembly reference. Using spring compressor, compress strut assem-

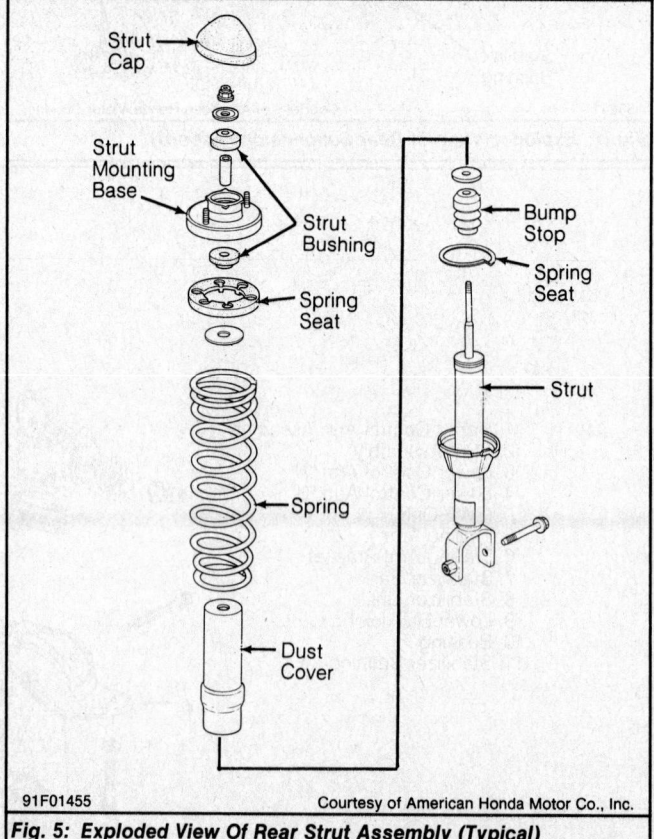

91F01455   Courtesy of American Honda Motor Co., Inc.

Fig. 5: Exploded View Of Rear Strut Assembly (Typical)

bly spring. DO NOT compress more than required to remove strut shaft nut. Remove strut shaft nut. Slowly release spring compressor. Disassemble strut assembly, noting location of components for reassembly reference. *See Fig. 5.*

Inspection & Reassembly – Check for weak spring tension. Inspect components for deterioration and damage. Strut assembly must be replaced if rod does not move smoothly through full travel or signs of oil leakage exist. Replace worn or damaged components. To assemble, reverse disassembly procedure. Install NEW strut shaft nut. Tighten nut to specification. See appropriate TORQUE SPECIFICATIONS.

Installation – **1)** Lower rear suspension, and place strut assembly in its original position. Loosely install lower strut mounting bolt. Loosely install upper strut mounting nuts.

2) Raise rear suspension so strut assembly supports vehicle weight. Loosely install strut mounting. Reverse removal procedure for remaining components. Raise rear suspension until weight of car is on strut. Tighten bolts to specification. Install strut cap (if equipped).

NOTE: Ensure vehicle weight is supported on strut assembly before tightening lower strut mounting bolt to specification.

UPPER BALL JOINT

NOTE: Upper ball joint removal information for Prelude is not available from manufacturer.

Removal & Installation (Accord) – Support knuckle using jack. Remove upper arm ball joint cap. Remove cotter pin and nut from ball joint stud. Using ball joint remover, separate knuckle from ball joint. Remove upper arm. Ball joint and upper arm are replaced as an assembly. To install, reverse removal procedure. Tighten bolts to specification. See TORQUE SPECIFICATIONS (ACCORD).

TRAILING ARM

NOTE: Center of gravity will be altered by trailing arm removal. Before removing trailing arms, add additional weight to trunk to ensure car does not tip forward.

Removal & Installation (Civic & Civic Del Sol) – **1)** Raise vehicle, and support using safety stands. Remove lug nuts, wheel and brake drum.

2) Remove parking brake cable from backing plate. Disconnect brake line from brake flexhose. Support lower arm using a floor jack. Remove trailing arm pivot bushing-to-body retaining bolts.

3) Remove compensator arm from trailing arm. Remove lower arm bolt at trailing arm. Remove trailing arm assembly.

4) To install, reverse removal procedure. Final tightening of nuts and bolts should be performed with vehicle on ground. Reconnect brake hose. Bleed hydraulic brake system. See BLEEDING BRAKE SYSTEM in DISC & DRUM article in BRAKES. Check rear toe-in adjustment. See SPECIFICATIONS & PROCEDURES article in WHEEL ALIGNMENT.

WHEEL BEARING

Removal & Installation – **1)** Raise and support vehicle. Remove wheel assembly and brake drum or rotor. See REAR BRAKE ROTOR or BRAKE DRUM under REMOVAL & INSTALLATION in DISC & DRUM article in BRAKES. Remove hub cap, nut, washer and hub bearing assembly. Replace hub and bearing assembly as a unit.

2) To install, reverse removal procedure using new hub retaining nut. Tighten nut to specification. See appropriate TORQUE SPECIFICATIONS table. Stake hub retaining nut against spindle.

TORQUE SPECIFICATIONS

TORQUE SPECIFICATIONS (ACCORD)

Application	Ft. Lbs. (N.m)
Ball Joint Nut	30-35 (40-48)
Knuckle-To-Lower Arm Bolt	48 (65)
Lower Arm-To-Body Bolt	
Front	41 (55)
Rear	48 (65)
Spindle Nut	136 (185)
Stabilizer Bar Mounting Bolts	16 (22)
Strut Assembly Lower Mounting Bolt	41 (55)
Strut Mount Base Nut (2)	29 (39)
Strut Shaft Nut	22 (30)
Trailing Arm Body Bracket	48 (65)
Trailing Arm-To-Body Bolt	48 (65)
Upper Arm-To-Body Bracket Bolts	28 (38)
Wheel Lug Nuts	81 (110)

TORQUE SPECIFICATIONS (CIVIC & CIVIC DEL SOL)

Application	Ft. Lbs. (N.m)
Backing Plate Nut	48 (65)
Compensator Arm Bolts	48 (65)
Lower Arm-To-Body Bolt	41 (55)
Lower Arm-To-Trailing Arm Bolt	41 (55)
Spindle Nut	136 (185)
Strut Assembly Lower Mounting Bolt	41 (55)
Strut Mount Base Nut (2)	29 (39)
Strut Shaft Nut	22 (30)
Trailing Arm Bushing Bracket Bolts	48 (65)
Upper Arm Bracket-To-Body Bolts	29 (39)
Upper Arm-To-Trailing Arm Bolt	41 (55)
Wheel Lug Nut	81 (110)

TORQUE SPECIFICATIONS (PRELUDE)

Application	Ft. Lbs. (N.m)
Brake Line Clamp Bolts	16 (22)
Lower Ball Joint Nut	37-44 (50-60)
Lower Control Arm Pivot Bolt	
2WS	61 (83)
4WS	48 (65)
Spindle Nut	136 (185)
Stabilizer Bar Mounting Bolts	16 (22)
Strut Assembly Lower Mounting Bolt	48 (65)
Strut Shaft Nut	22 (30)
Tie Rod Ball Joint Nut	37-44 (50-60)
Upper Control Arm Bracket	57 (77)
Wheel Lug Nuts	81 (110)

Accord, Civic, Civic Del Sol, Passport, Prelude

NOTE: For all data and information on Passport steering column, refer to Rodeo in Isuzu STEERING – Steering Columns article.

DESCRIPTION & OPERATION

A 2-piece safety steering column with slip-joint flange connection is used. The steering column is supported by a column tube and steering lock assembly. All models are equipped with standard driver's side air bag.

WARNING: Before performing ANY repairs on steering column or column components, Supplemental Restraint System (SRS) MUST be disabled. See DISABLING & ACTIVATING AIR BAG SYSTEM. Accidental air bag deployment could cause serious bodily injury.

DISABLING & ACTIVATING AIR BAG SYSTEM

NOTE: Some Accord and Prelude models are equipped with stereo theft protection system. Technician should obtain 5-digit security code before disconnecting battery cable.

DISABLING AIR BAG

Disconnect both battery cables. Remove maintenance lid from bottom rear of steering wheel. Remove Red short connector, located on inside of maintenance lid. Disconnect connector between air bag and cable reel. Connect Red short connector to air bag side of connector. *See Fig. 1.*

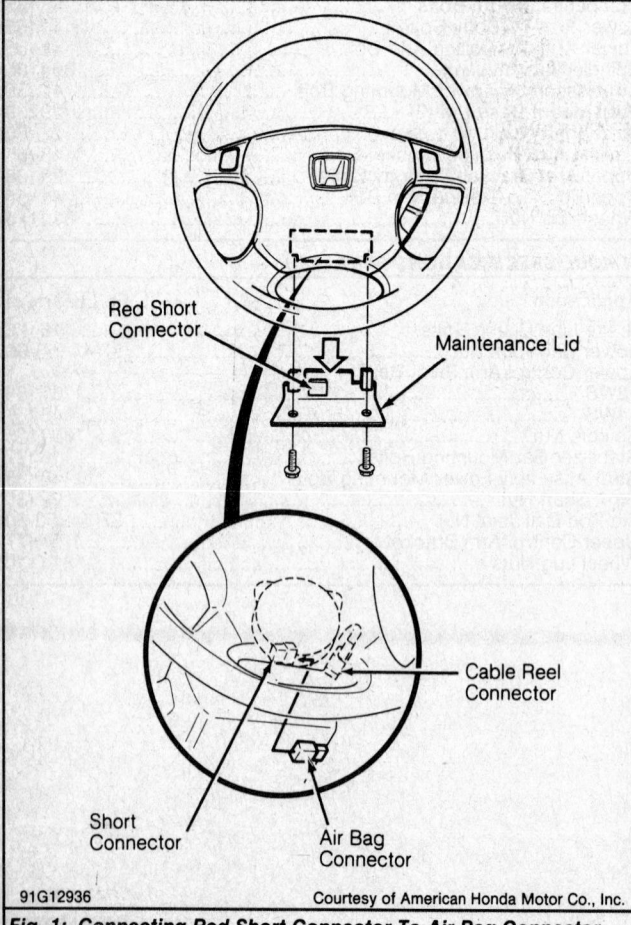

Red Short Connector

Maintenance Lid

Short Connector

Cable Reel Connector

Air Bag Connector

91G12936   Courtesy of American Honda Motor Co., Inc.

Fig. 1: Connecting Red Short Connector To Air Bag Connector

ACTIVATING AIR BAG

1) To activate SRS, remove Red short connector from air bag side of connector and reconnect connector between air bag and cable reel.
2) Return Red short connector to storage location on inside of maintenance lid. Install maintenance lid on back of steering wheel.
3) Reconnect battery cables. Check AIR BAG indicator light to ensure system is functioning properly.

REMOVAL & INSTALLATION

STEERING WHEEL & HORN PAD

Removal & Installation – 1) Disconnect negative battery cable. Disable air bag system. See DISABLING & ACTIVATING AIR BAG SYSTEM. To remove air bag assembly, remove 2 Torx bolts using a T30 bit.

WARNING: Place air bag assembly on workbench. Pad surface MUST face up. If air bag is stored face down, accidental deployment could propel assembly sufficiently to cause serious bodily injury.

2) Remove steering wheel nut. *See Fig. 2.* Using slight side-to-side motion, remove steering wheel assembly by pulling outward by hand. To install, reverse removal procedure.

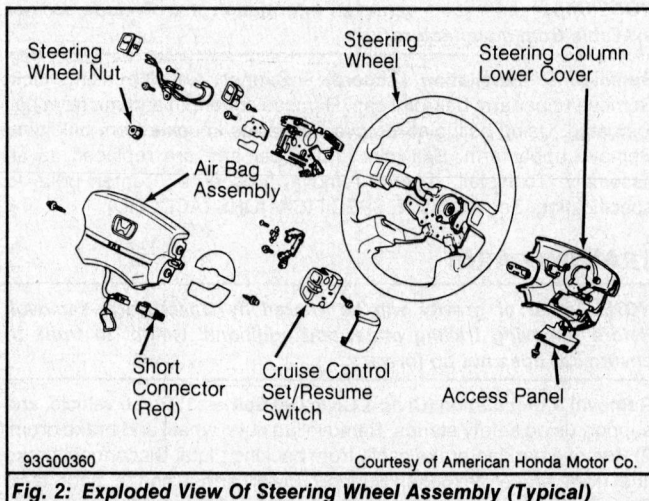

Steering Wheel Nut

Steering Wheel

Steering Column Lower Cover

Air Bag Assembly

Short Connector (Red)

Cruise Control Set/Resume Switch

Access Panel

93G00360   Courtesy of American Honda Motor Co.

Fig. 2: Exploded View Of Steering Wheel Assembly (Typical)

CAUTION: DO NOT install air bag assembly that is dented, cracked or shows signs of having been dropped.

COMBINATION SWITCH

WARNING: Before performing ANY repairs on steering column or column components, Supplemental Restraint System (SRS) MUST be disabled. See DISABLING & ACTIVATING AIR BAG SYSTEM. Accidental air bag deployment could cause serious bodily injury.

NOTE: Some Accord and Prelude models are equipped with stereo theft protection system. Technician should obtain 5-digit security code before disconnecting battery cable.

Removal & Installation – 1) Before proceeding, disable SRS. See DISABLING & ACTIVATING AIR BAG SYSTEM. Ensure front wheels are facing straight-ahead.
2) Cable reel is located under steering wheel, in upper steering column. *See Fig. 3.* Remove dashboard lower cover and knee bolster. On Prelude, remove air duct. On all models, disconnect cable reel connector from SRS main harness at base of steering column, then remove connector holder.

3) Remove air bag assembly from steering wheel. See STEERING WHEEL & HORN PAD. Disconnect connectors from horn and cruise control switches. Remove steering wheel nut. Mark steering wheel position to shaft and remove steering wheel. Remove upper and lower column covers. Disconnect combination switch connectors. Remove canceling sleeve, cable reel and combination switch. See Fig. 4.

4) To install, reverse removal procedure. Before installing steering wheel, center cable reel by rotating clockwise until it stops and then counterclockwise approximately 2 turns. Arrow mark should face up and Yellow gear tooth should be aligned with mark. See Fig. 3.

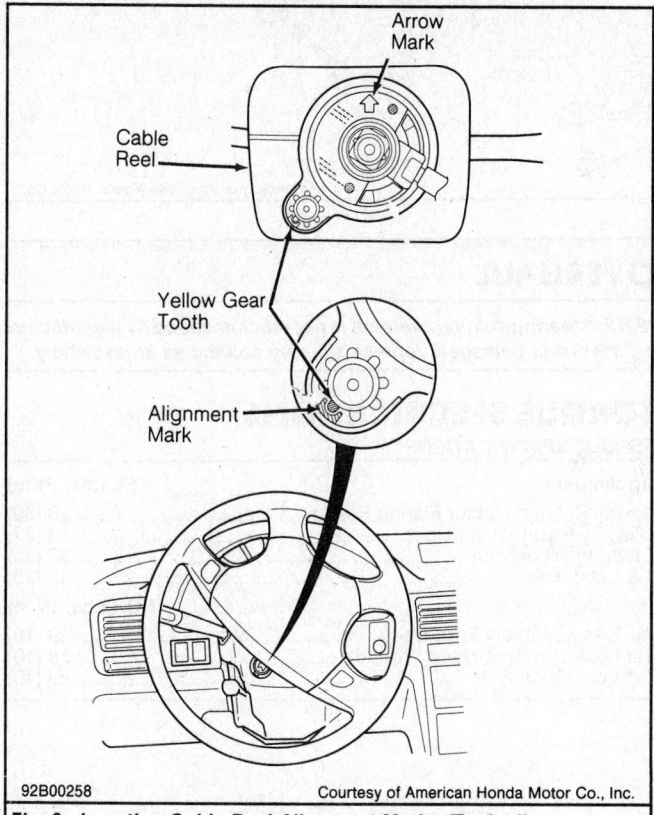

92B00258   Courtesy of American Honda Motor Co., Inc.

Fig. 3: Locating Cable Reel Alignment Marks (Typical)

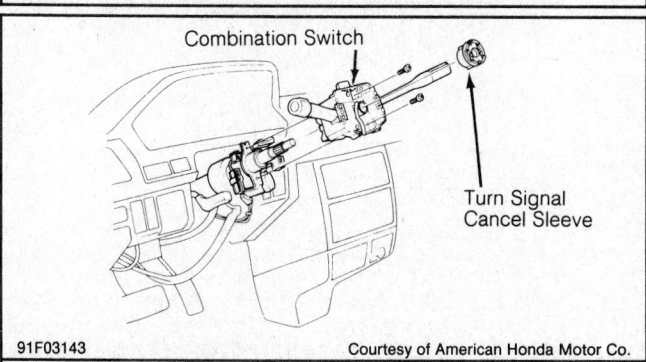

91F03143   Courtesy of American Honda Motor Co.

Fig. 4: Removing Turn Signal Cancel Sleeve & Combination Switch (Typical)

TURN SIGNAL SWITCH

See COMBINATION SWITCH.

IGNITION SWITCH

WARNING: Before performing ANY repairs on steering column or column components, Supplemental Restraint System (SRS) MUST be disabled. See DISABLING & ACTIVATING AIR BAG SYSTEM. Accidental air bag deployment could cause serious bodily injury.

Removal – Remove steering wheel and horn pad. See STEERING WHEEL & HORN PAD. Remove steering column covers. On Civic and Civic Del Sol, remove steering column holder flange bolts and lower steering column. On all models, disconnect ignition switch. Center punch 2 shear bolts and carefully drill heads off lock shear bolts. Remove bolts and switch.

Installation – 1) Install ignition switch. Use NEW shear bolts and tighten loosely. Ensure pin on ignition switch is aligned with hole in steering column.

2) Insert key and check for proper operation of ignition switch. If switch operates properly, tighten shear bolts until heads break off. To complete installation, reverse removal procedure.

STEERING COLUMN

WARNING: Before performing ANY repairs on steering column or column components, Supplemental Restraint System (SRS) MUST be disabled. See DISABLING & ACTIVATING AIR BAG SYSTEM. Accidental air bag deployment could cause serious bodily injury.

Removal – 1) Remove steering wheel and horn pad. See STEERING WHEEL & HORN PAD. Remove combination switch and set aside on vehicle floor. DO NOT disconnect combination switch connector. See COMBINATION SWITCH. If equipped with 4WS (Prelude only), remove main steering angle sensor over steering column. On all models, disconnect remaining wire connectors from left side fuse box, under dash.

2) Remove steering joint cover. Center tilt lock assembly. See Fig. 5. Remove steering joint bolts. Slide steering joint upward on column. Align steering joint upper bolt hole with groove around column. Loosely install upper bolt. See Fig. 6.

3) Loosen, but DO NOT REMOVE, column holder flange bolts. See Fig. 7. Remove upper and lower column covers. Remove holder flange bolts. Remove steering column assembly.

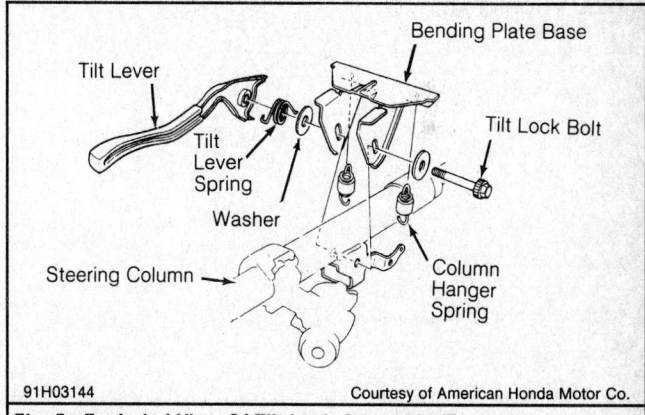

91H03144   Courtesy of American Honda Motor Co.

Fig. 5: Exploded View Of Tilt Lock Assembly (Typical)

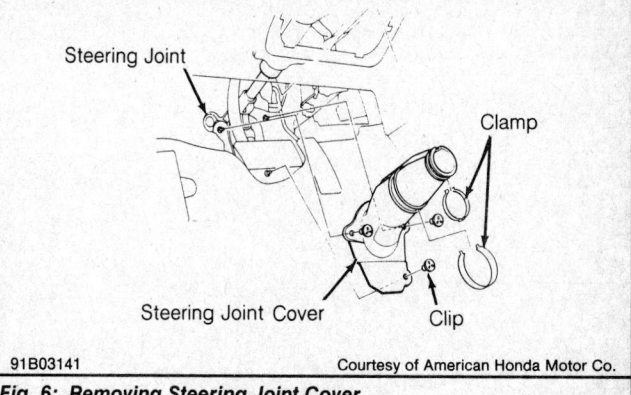

91B03141   Courtesy of American Honda Motor Co.

Fig. 6: Removing Steering Joint Cover

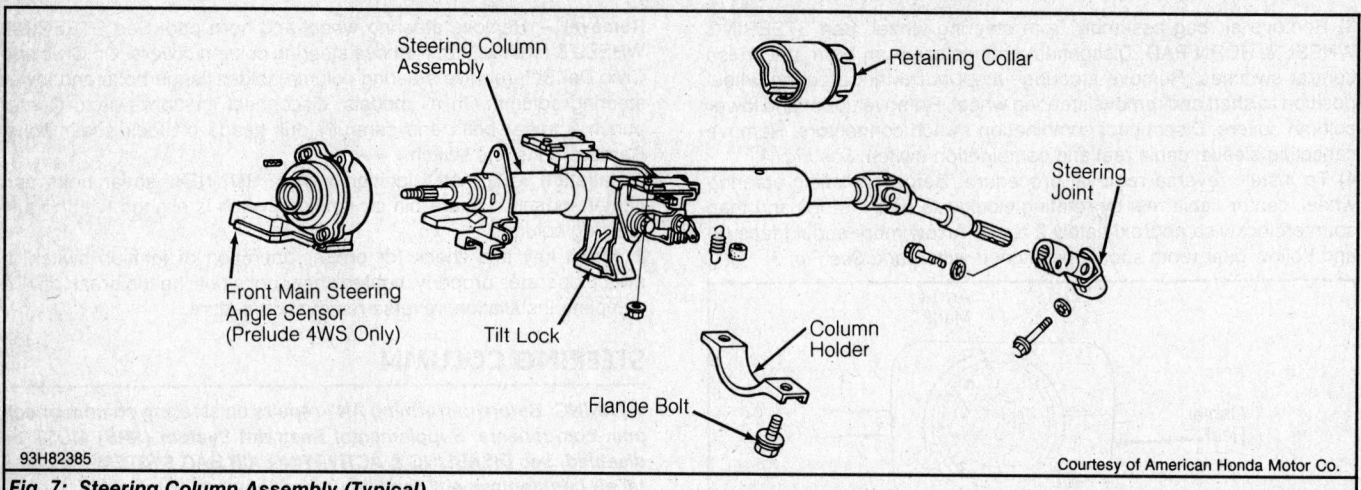

Fig. 7: Steering Column Assembly (Typical)

93H82385

Courtesy of American Honda Motor Co.

Installation – 1) Guide steering shaft through firewall. Align bolt hole in steering joint with slot in steering gear pinion shaft. Install steering joint on pinion shaft. Loosely install steering joint bolt. Install steering column and column holder flange bolts. Tighten bolts to specification. See TORQUE SPECIFICATIONS.

2) Connect ignition switch connector. Install steering joint cover. If equipped with 4WS (Prelude only), install main steering angle sensor over steering column. On all models, install combination switch, canceling sleeve and circlip. Install cable reel assembly, taking care to align slot in cancelling sleeve with projection on cable reel.

3) Install SRS wire harness on underside of column bracket with clip. Install upper and lower column covers. On Prelude, install air duct. On all models, install driver's side knee bolster and dashboard lower cover. Install steering wheel and air bag assembly. See STEERING WHEEL & HORN PAD.

OVERHAUL

NOTE: Steering column overhaul is not recommended by manufacturer. If worn or damaged, replace steering column as an assembly.

TORQUE SPECIFICATIONS
TORQUE SPECIFICATIONS

Application	Ft. Lbs. (N.m)
Lower Column Holder Flange Bolts	29 (39)
Lower Steering Joint Bolts	16 (22)
Steering Wheel Nut	37 (50)
Tilt Lock Bolt	15 (20)
	INCH Lbs. (N.m)
Air Bag Assembly Torx Bolts	89 (10)
Tilt Lock Nut (Left-Hand Thread)	89 (10)
Tilt Lock Plate Bolt	89 (10)

Civic, Civic Del Sol

DESCRIPTION & OPERATION

Steering gear housing mounts to crossmember with rubber bushings. Pinion shaft preload is adjustable. Pinion shaft connects to steering shaft by a "U" joint. Tie rods connect rack ends to steering knuckles.

ADJUSTMENTS

RACK PISTON ADJUSTMENT

1) Point wheels in straight-ahead position. Using Lock Nut Wrench (07916-SA500001), loosen lock nut. See Fig. 1. Tighten adjustment screw until it compresses spring and is lightly bottomed.
2) Back off screw 40-60 degrees. Tighten lock nut to specification. See TORQUE SPECIFICATIONS. Check steering wheel turning force. See STEERING WHEEL TURNING FORCE.

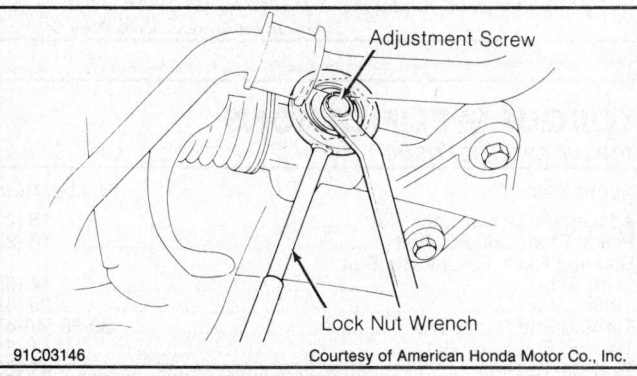

Fig. 1: Adjusting Steering Rack Piston

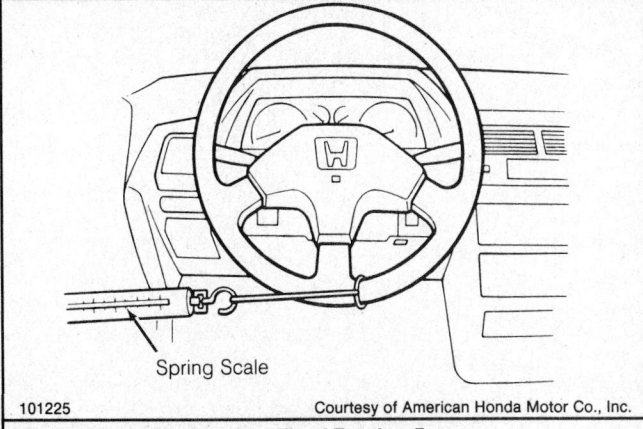

Fig. 2: Measuring Steering Wheel Turning Force

STEERING WHEEL TURNING FORCE

Raise and support vehicle. Attach spring gauge to spoke of steering wheel. Turn steering wheel and note reading on gauge. Steering wheel turning force should be 3.3 lbs. (1.5 kg). See Fig. 2. If turning force is not to specification, readjust rack piston. See RACK PISTON ADJUSTMENT.

REMOVAL & INSTALLATION

STEERING GEAR

Removal – 1) Remove lower steering column cover. Remove steering shaft lower "U" joint clamp bolt. Separate "U" joint from pinion shaft. Raise and support vehicle. Remove front wheels. Separate tie rod ends from steering knuckles. Remove left tie rod end.

2) On manual transmission models, disconnect shift lever torque rod from clutch housing. Remove pin retaining clip, and drive out spring pin. Disconnect shift rod. See Fig. 3.
3) On automatic transmission models, remove shift cable holder from transmission. Pull shift cable down by hand. On all models, remove catalytic converter.
4) To provide removal clearance, slide rack totally to right. Remove steering gear mounting brackets. Lower steering gear so pinion shaft end of gear clears bulkhead. Move steering gear to right until left end of rack clears bottom of rear chassis beam. Remove rack from left side.

Installation – To install, reverse removal procedure. On manual transmission models, slide retainer into place after driving in spring pin. Adjust steering gear. See RACK PISTON ADJUSTMENT under ADJUSTMENTS. Check steering gear for smooth operation.

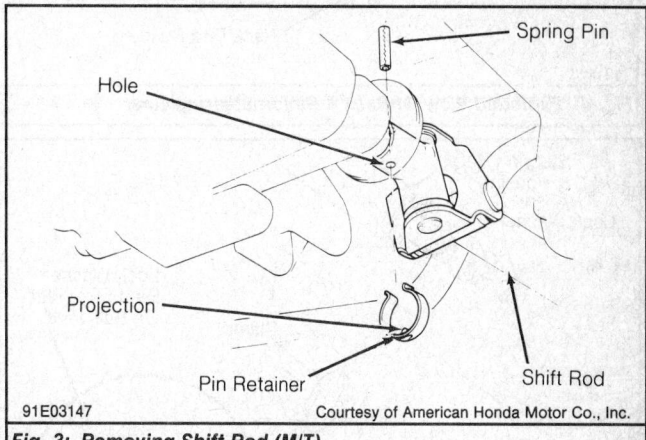

Fig. 3: Removing Shift Rod (M/T)

OVERHAUL

STEERING GEAR

Disassembly – 1) Place steering gear housing in soft-jawed vise. See Fig. 4. Loosen boot clamps. Pull dust boots away from steering gear. Unstake tie rod lock washers.
2) Hold rack with wrench and unscrew tie rods. Remove adjusting screw lock nut, adjusting screw, "O" ring, plunger spring and rack piston.
3) Remove outer dust seal, pinion dust seal and snap ring. Remove pinion from steering gear. Slide rack from steering gear.

Inspection – Clean parts with solvent and dry with compressed air. Check all parts for wear or damage. Replace parts as needed.
Rack End Bushing Replacement – Using puller, remove rack end bushing from housing. Apply grease to inside of NEW rack end bushing. DO NOT fill slots with grease. Align bushing round projections with holes in housing and install NEW bushing.
Reassembly – 1) Apply coat of grease to steering rack. Carefully install rack in rack housing. Ensure rack sliding surface is not damaged during reassembly. Install steering pinion in gear housing. Install pinion retaining snap ring (35 mm) in gear housing. Lubricate and install pinion seal.
2) Coat rack piston with grease. Install rack piston, spring, NEW "O" ring and adjusting screw. Tighten adjusting screw until it compresses spring and seats against rack piston. Adjust rack piston to specification. See RACK PISTON ADJUSTMENT under ADJUSTMENTS.
3) Align tie rod lock tabs, and install tie rods. Ensure stopper washers (if equipped) are installed with chamfered side facing out. Tighten tie rod to specification. Bend lock washer back against ball joint. See Fig. 5.
4) Grease tie rods. Install rack boots and NEW clamps. Ensure boots are not twisted or collapsed. Squeeze boots to remove excess air. Install tie rod ends on tie rods (if removed). Fill tie rod end boots with grease. Ensure clip is installed on tie rod end boot.

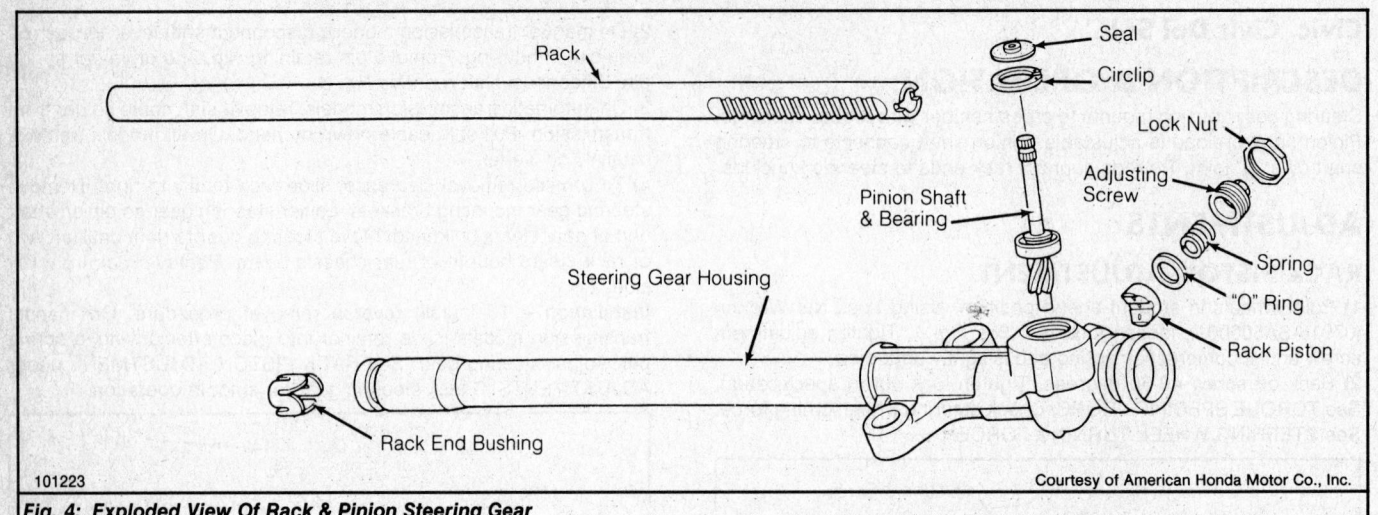

Fig. 4: Exploded View Of Rack & Pinion Steering Gear

101223

Courtesy of American Honda Motor Co., Inc.

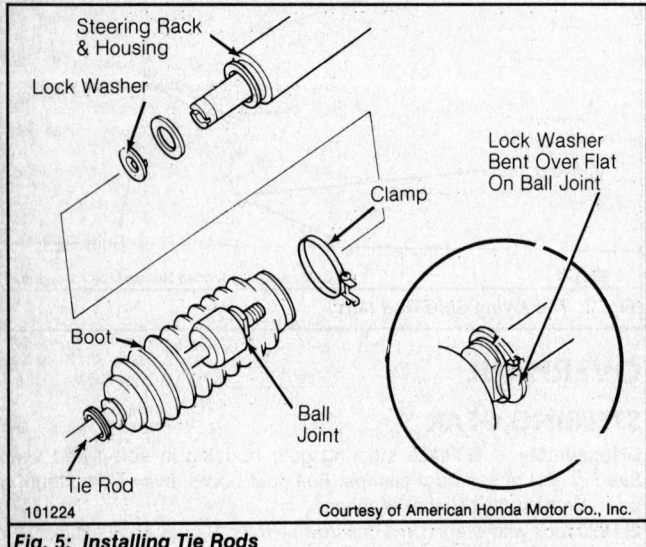

Fig. 5: Installing Tie Rods

101224

Courtesy of American Honda Motor Co., Inc.

TORQUE SPECIFICATIONS
TORQUE SPECIFICATIONS

Application	Ft. Lbs. (N.m)
Adjustment Screw Lock Nut	18 (25)
Pinion Shaft Coupler Bolt	16 (22)
Steering Rack-To-Chassis Bolt	
Left Side	44 (59)
Right Side	29 (39)
Tie Rod End Castle Nut	30-35 (40-48)
Tie Rod End Lock Nut	41 (55)
Tie Rod-To-Rack	41 (55)

Accord, Civic, Civic Del Sol, Passport, Prelude

DESCRIPTION & OPERATION

NOTE: For data and information on Passport manual and power recirculating ball steering, refer to Rodeo in Isuzu STEERING – Manual Recirculating Ball Steering and Power Recirculating Ball Steering articles.

The power steering system consists of a power rack and pinion steering gear, hydraulic pump, fluid reservoir, valve body unit, vehicle speed sensor and hoses. Power assist is proportional to vehicle speed and steering load. Assist is high when vehicle speed is low, and low as vehicle speed increases.

The vehicle speed sensor, used on Accord and Prelude, is a trochoid-rotor hydraulic pump, driven by a speedometer gear in the transmission. When vehicle is in motion, speed sensor pump relieves a portion of the hydraulic pressure, reducing power steering assist.

LUBRICATION

CAPACITY
POWER STEERING FLUID CAPACITIES

Application	Qts. (L)
Accord	1.2 (1.1)
Civic & Civic Del Sol	1.2 (1.1)
Prelude	1.8 (1.7)

FLUID TYPE

CAUTION: Using ATF or other then Honda (08208-311-61F) power steering fluid will damage system.

FLUID LEVEL CHECK

Check fluid when engine is cold and not running. Fluid level should be between upper and lower marks on fluid reservoir. If fluid level is excessively low, check for leaks. Add fluid (if needed) and recheck. DO NOT overfill.

HYDRAULIC SYSTEM BLEEDING

Fill reservoir to proper level. Start engine and run at fast idle. Turn steering wheel from lock-to-lock 2 or 3 times to bleed trapped air. Recheck fluid level.

ADJUSTMENTS

POWER STEERING PUMP BELT
BELT ADJUSTMENT SPECIFICATIONS [1]

Application	New	Used
Accord	.43-.49 (11.0-12.5)	.51-.63 (13-16)
Civic & Civic Del Sol	.24-.37 (6-9.5)	.31-.47 (8-12)
Prelude	.37-.45 (9.5-11.5)	.53-.65 (13.5-16.5)

[1] – Deflection measurement is In. (mm) with 22 lbs. (10 kg) pressure applied midway on longest belt run.

PINION ROTATING FORCE & RACK SLIDING FORCE

Using Lock Nut Wrench (07916-SA500001), loosen guide screw lock nut. *See Fig. 1, 2 or 3* for component location. Using a 14-mm wrench, tighten guide screw to 35 INCH lbs. (4 N.m). Loosen guide screw according to GUIDE SCREW ADJUSTMENT SPECIFICATIONS table. Holding rack guide screw in place, tighten lock nut.

GUIDE SCREW ADJUSTMENT SPECIFICATIONS

Application	[1] Counter-Rotation (Degrees)
Accord & Prelude	15-25
Civic & Civic Del Sol	40-60

[1] – After rack guide screw has been tightened to 35 INCH lbs. (4 N.m).

TESTING

HYDRAULIC SYSTEM PRESSURE TEST

1) Check fluid level and belt tension. Adjust as necessary. Disconnect outlet hose from pump. Install Pressure Gauge Set (07406-0010001). Fully open shutoff and pressure control valves.
2) Start and idle engine. Turn steering wheel from lock to lock several times to warm fluid to operating temperature. Completely close shut-off valve.

CAUTION: DO NOT close shutoff valve for more than 5 seconds or pump will be damaged.

3) Gradually close pressure control valve until pressure gauge needle stabilizes. Read pressure. Fully open shutoff valve. On Accord, pump pressure should be at least 934-1067 psi (65-75 kg/cm²). On Civic and Civic Del Sol, pump pressure should be at least 1138-1280 psi (80-90 kg/cm²). On Prelude, pump pressure should be 995-1138 psi (70-80 kg/cm²). Replace pump if pressure is too low.

STEERING WHEEL TURNING FORCE

Low Speed Assist (Accord & Prelude) – **1)** Check fluid level and belt tension. Start and idle engine. Turn steering wheel from lock to lock several times to warm fluid. Attach a spring-tension scale to outer end of steering wheel spoke.
2) Ensure vehicle is on a clean, dry surface. With engine idling, pull on spring-tension scale until tires move. Reading should be less than 6.6 lbs. (3.0 kg.). If reading is more than specified, stop engine and disconnect hose between control unit and speed sensor at sensor. *See Fig. 4.* Plug hose and sensor fitting.
3) Start and idle engine. Pull on spring-tension scale until tires move. If reading is less than specified, replace speed sensor. If reading is more than specified, check rack and pinion.
Simulated High Speed Assist (Accord & Prelude) – **1)** Check fluid level and belt tension. Start and idle engine. Turn steering wheel from lock to lock to warm fluid. Stop engine. Disconnect hoses at speed sensor.
2) Connect By-Pass Tube Connector (07406-0010101) to hoses at speed sensor. *See Fig. 5.* This connects cut-off valve and control unit to reservoir hose, simulating speed sensor operation at more than 30 MPH.
3) Attach spring-tension scale to outer end of steering wheel spoke. With vehicle on clean, dry floor, start and idle engine. Pull on spring-tension scale until tires move.
4) If turning force is less than 11 lbs. (5.0 kg), speed sensor is okay. If turning force is greater than specification, check for faulty speed sensor or sensor feed line restriction. Check power steering pump and steering gear for restrictions.
No Load Assist (Civic & Civic Del Sol) – **1)** Check fluid level and belt tension. Start and idle engine. Turn steering wheel from lock to lock several times to warm fluid. Attach a spring-tension scale to outer end of steering wheel spoke.
2) Raise and support front of vehicle. With engine idling, pull on spring-tension scale until tires move. Reading should be less than 3.3 lbs. (1.5 kg.). If reading is more than specified, stop engine and perform PINION ROTATING FORCE & RACK SLIDING FORCE adjustment. Recheck steering wheel turning force.

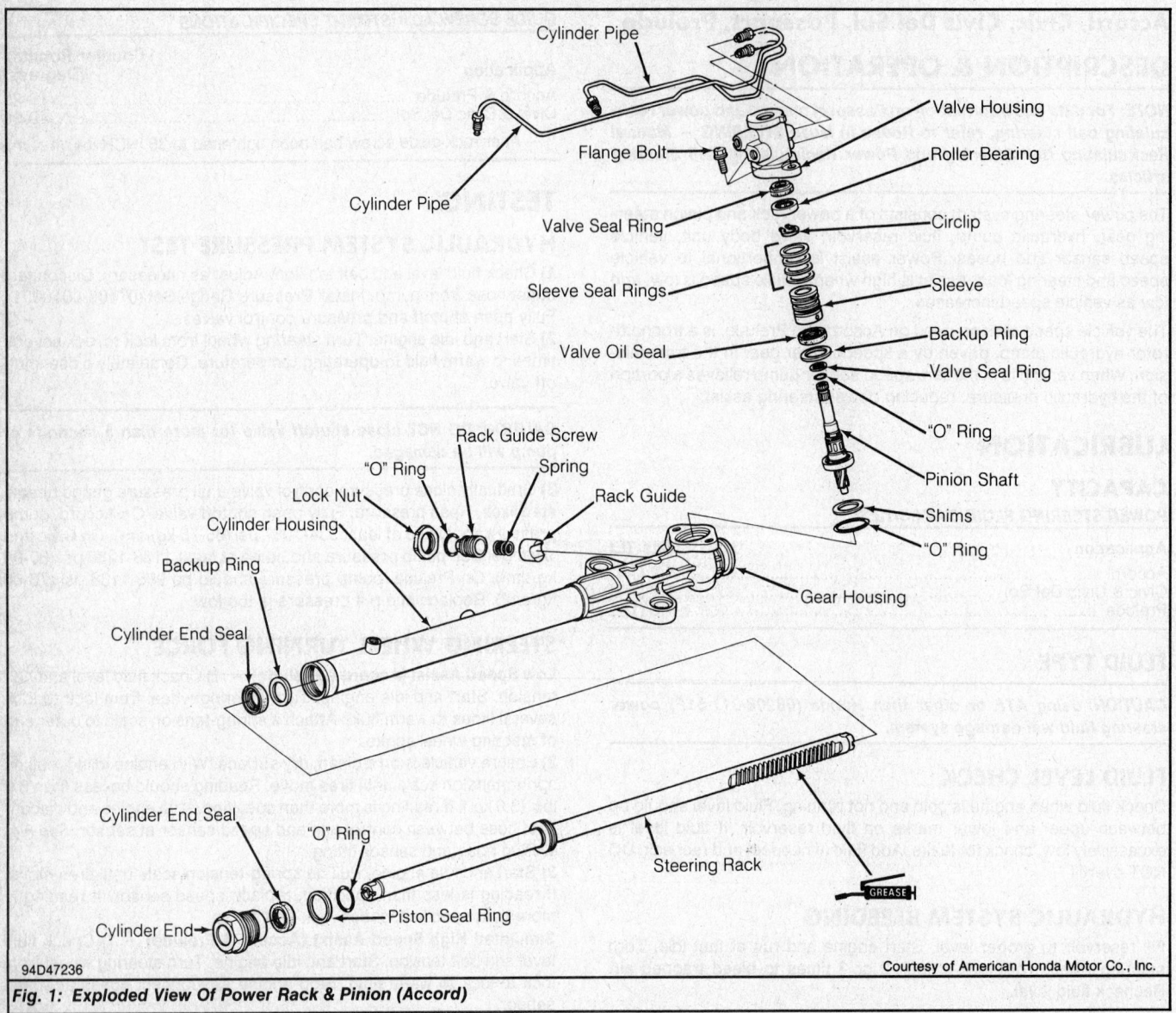

Fig. 1: Exploded View Of Power Rack & Pinion (Accord)

94D47236
Courtesy of American Honda Motor Co., Inc.

REMOVAL & INSTALLATION

POWER STEERING PUMP

Removal – Drain fluid. Disconnect inlet, outlet and return hoses at pump. Remove belt by loosening pump pivot and adjusting bolts. Remove pump retaining bolts and pump.

Installation – To install, reverse removal procedure. Adjust belt tension. Fill reservoir with NEW fluid. Bleed air from system. Check for leaks.

STEERING GEAR

Removal – **1)** Drain power steering fluid. Remove steering "U" joint from steering gear. Raise and support front of vehicle. Remove front wheels. Remove tie rod cotter pins. Partially loosen tie rod castle nuts. Using Ball Joint Remover (07941-6920002), disconnect tie rods from steering knuckles. Remove castle nuts and tie rods.

2) Remove center beam bolts and center beam. Disconnect oxygen sensor connector. Disconnect exhaust pipe at exhaust manifold. Remove steering gear splash guard. Clean steering gear and surrounding areas. Disconnect and plug fluid lines from control unit.

3) On A/T models, remove shift control cable from clamp. On all models, remove stabilizer bar. Disconnect left side tie rod end and slide tie rod completely to right. Slide unit to right until left tie rod clears frame. Lower unit and remove through left side wheel well.

Installation – To install, reverse removal procedure. Use NEW self-locking nuts if old nuts thread easily onto bolts. Use NEW exhaust pipe gaskets. Use NEW cotter pins when installing ball joints.

SPEED SENSOR

Removal – Remove speed sensor mounting bolts and pull speed sensor from transmission housing. Raise speedometer cable boot and remove retaining clip. Remove cable. Disconnect and plug speed sensor hoses and plug fittings.

Installation – To install, reverse removal procedure. After installing sensor, turn steering wheel from lock to lock several times with engine idling to bleed air from system. Check for leaks.

OVERHAUL

POWER STEERING PUMP FRONT SEAL

Disassembly – Remove pump from vehicle. See POWER STEERING PUMP under REMOVAL & INSTALLATION. Hold pulley using spanner wrench. Remove pulley nut and pulley. See Fig. 6. Loosen pump front cover bolts in a diagonal pattern. Remove cover. Using a screwdriver, pry out housing seal.

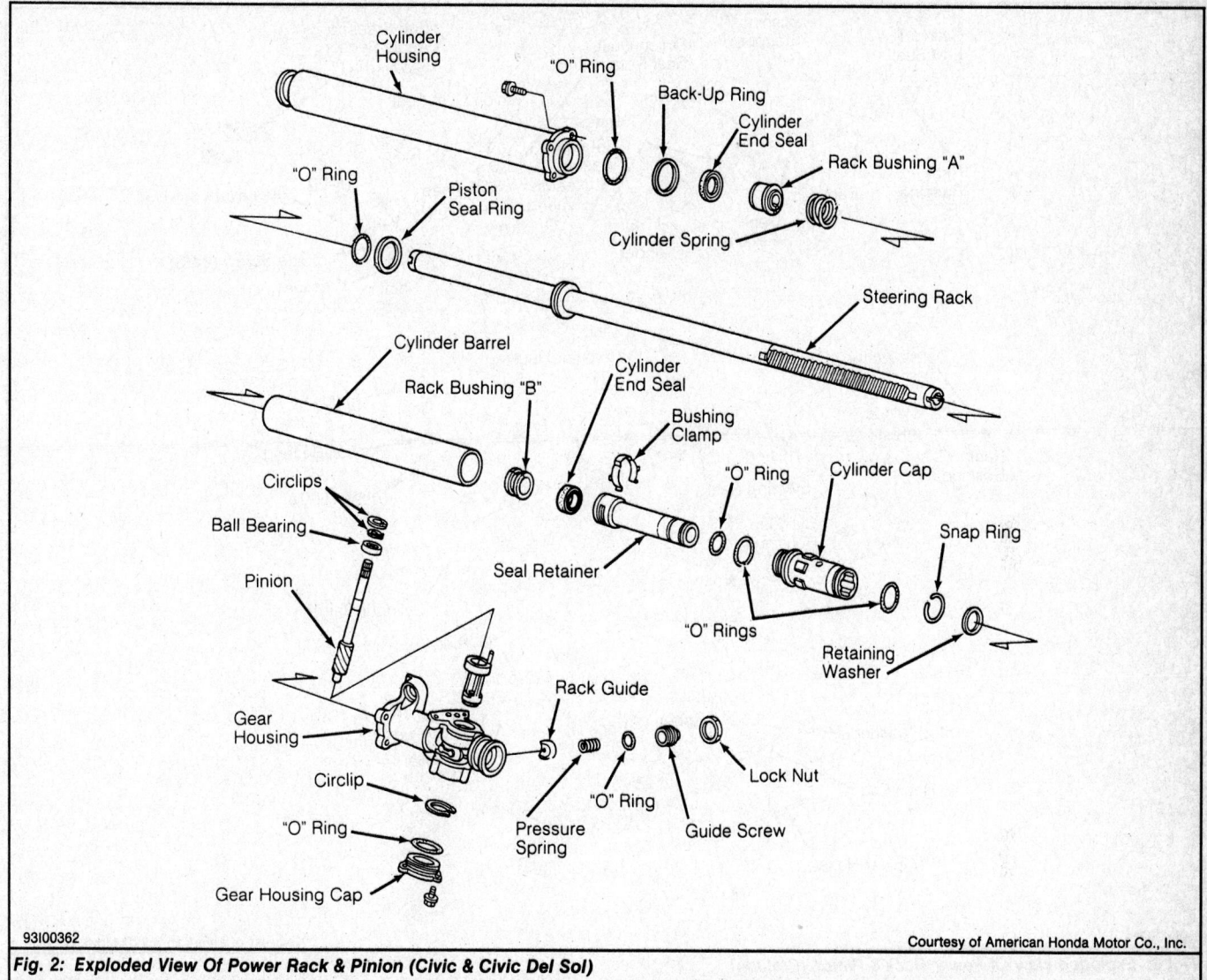

93100362

Courtesy of American Honda Motor Co., Inc.

Fig. 2: Exploded View Of Power Rack & Pinion (Civic & Civic Del Sol)

Reassembly – 1) Ensure oil passage in front cover is clear. Using a 19-mm socket, install NEW oil seal. Install front cover bolts. Tighten bolts diagonally to specification. See TORQUE SPECIFICATIONS. Install pulley. Tighten pulley bolt to specification. See TORQUE SPECIFICATIONS.

2) Turn pulley bolt using torque wrench to measure preload. Preload should be 71 INCH lbs. (8 N.m). Install and adjust belt. Add fluid. Bleed air from system. Check for leaks.

POWER STEERING PUMP

Disassembly – 1) Remove pump from vehicle. See POWER STEERING PUMP under REMOVAL & INSTALLATION. Mount pump in soft-jawed vise. Hold pulley using spanner wrench. Remove bolt. If pulley is damaged, separate pulley from hub. Loosen front cover (flange) bolts. *See Fig. 6.* Remove cover. Pry oil seal from front cover.

2) Remove flow control valve from pump housing. Remove inlet joint, pump cover and "O" ring. Remove pump cam ring from housing. Remove pump rotor and vanes. Remove 2 rollers from side plate. Remove side plate and preload springs. Remove pump hosing "O" rings, circlip and driveshaft. Remove seal spacer, seal and pump shaft bearing.

NOTE: Replace power steering pump as an assembly if damage or excessive wear exist on pump housing, side plate, rotor, vanes or pump cam ring,

Inspection – 1) Ensure oil passage in front cover is clear. Inspect control valve and filter. Check control valve for wear, burrs or damage to edges of groove. Slip control valve into bore and check for smooth movement. Replace valve (if necessary).

2) Pressure check control valve. Attach a hose to hexagonal side of control valve. Submerge valve in Honda power steering fluid. Using no more than 14.2 psi (1 kg/cm²), blow into hose and check for leakage.

3) If leak is found, disassemble and clean valve. Replace any shims found during disassembly. Retest for leakage. Replace valve if leak persists. Note if valve has an identification mark to determine correct replacement valve.

Reassembly – 1) To reassemble, reverse disassembly procedure. Lubricate all "O" rings and seals before installing.

2) Lubricate gears and shafts with power steering fluid. Install front cover. Tighten front cover bolts diagonally. Using a 19-mm socket, install seal into front cover.

STEERING GEAR

Disassembly (Accord) – 1) Remove air hose and clips between boots. Remove tie rod ends and lock nuts. Remove boot bands and tube clamps from boots. Pull boots away from ends of steering gearbox. *See Fig. 1.*

2) Unbend lock washer. Holding steering rack with one wrench, unscrew rack end with a second wrench.

Cylinder
End Seal

Bushing
Stopper
Ring

Pinion Dust
Seal Retainer

Sub Steering
Angle Sensor
(4WS Only)

Snap Ring

Pinion Dust Seal

Rack
Bushing
"B"

"O" Rings

"O" Ring

Back-Up
Ring

Retainer
Washer

"O" Ring

Lock Nut

Needle
Bearing

Snap
Ring

Seal
Retainer

Guide Screw (2WS)

Cylinder
Cap

Pressure
Spring

Rack
Guide

Port Orifices

"O" Ring

Gear Housing

Pinion

Cylinder
Spring

Rack
Bushing
"A"

Piston

Steering Rack

"O" Ring

Ball Bearing

Snap Ring

Cylinder
Housing

Cylinder Barrel

Stop Washer

Lock Washer

"O" Ring

Back-Up
Ring

Cylinder
End Seal

Rack End

Piston Seal

Transfer Hose

Clamp

93H00361

Courtesy of American Honda Motor Co., Inc.

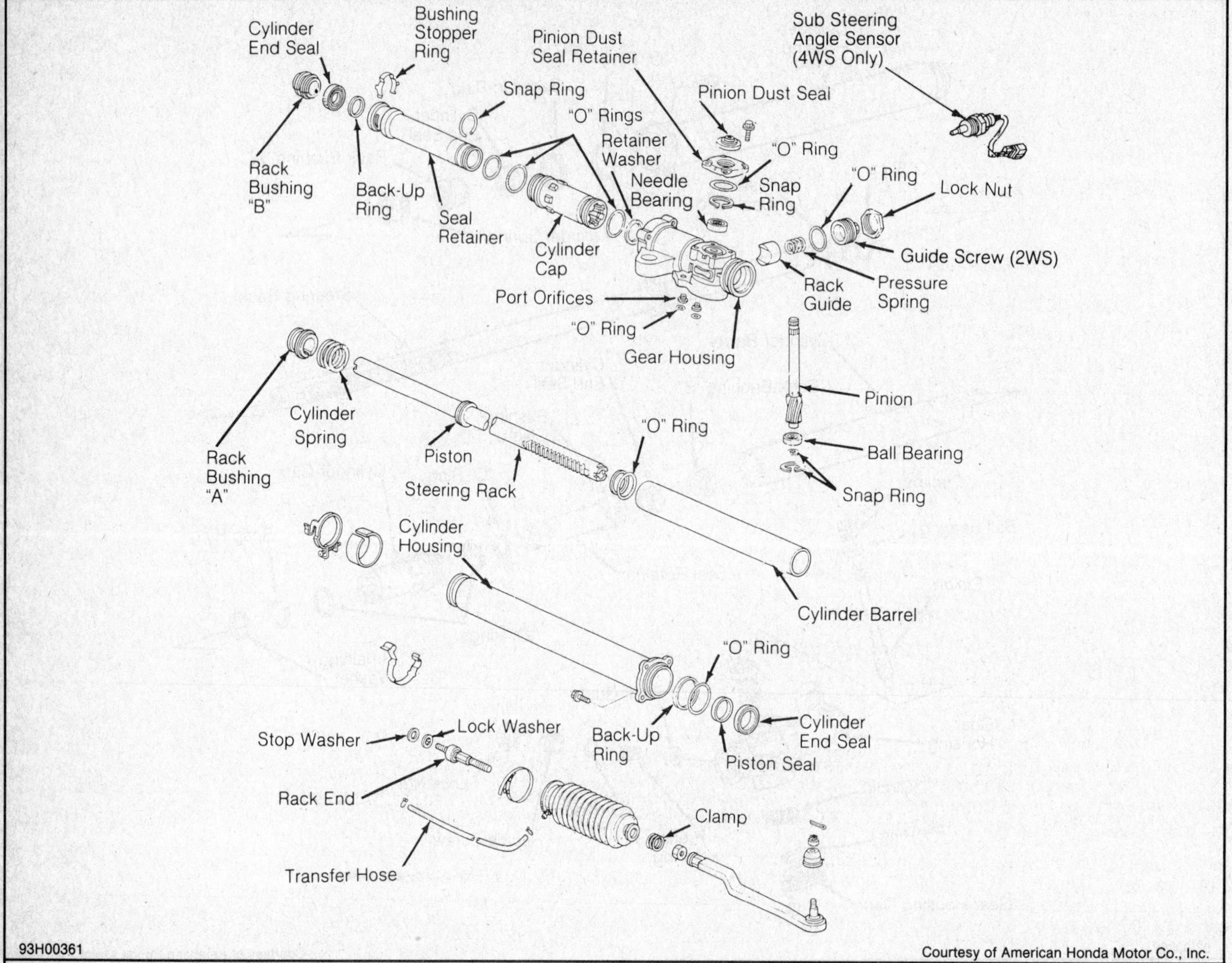

Fig. 3: Exploded View Of Power Rack & Pinion (Prelude)

CAUTION: Ensure wrench does not damage rack surface.

3) Loosen lock nut and remove rack guide screw. Remove spring and rack guide from gear housing. Remove cylinder pipes from gearbox. Drain fluid from cylinder fittings by slowly moving steering rack back and forth. Remove 2 flange bolts and remove valve body from gearbox.

4) Drill 0.12 in. (3mm) hole about 0.12 in. (3mm) deep in the staked point on cylinder end. Install a puller yoke to steering gearbox. (Snap-On® T/N CJ123-1, OTC® T/N 7372 or equivalent.) Clamp puller yoke in soft-jawed vise, then loosen and remove cylinder end.

CAUTION: DO NOT clamp cylinder housing. DO NOT allow metal shavings to enter cylinder housing. After removing cylinder end, remove any burrs at stake point.

5) Set gearbox in press with gear housing pointed up. Assemble a 12 x 1.25 mm flange nut onto a 12 x 170 mm grade 10 bolt.

NOTE: Wrap flange portion of bolt with vinyl tape to protect cylinder.

6) Install flange bolt into steering rack until it bottoms, then back out 1/4 turn. Hold flange bolt and tighten flange nut against rack by hand. Press cylinder end seal and steering rack out of gearbox. Remove bolt and nut from steering rack. Remove cylinder end seal from steering rack.

CAUTION: Hold steering rack to prevent falling when pressed clear. Be careful not to damage inner surface of cylinder housing with flange bolt.

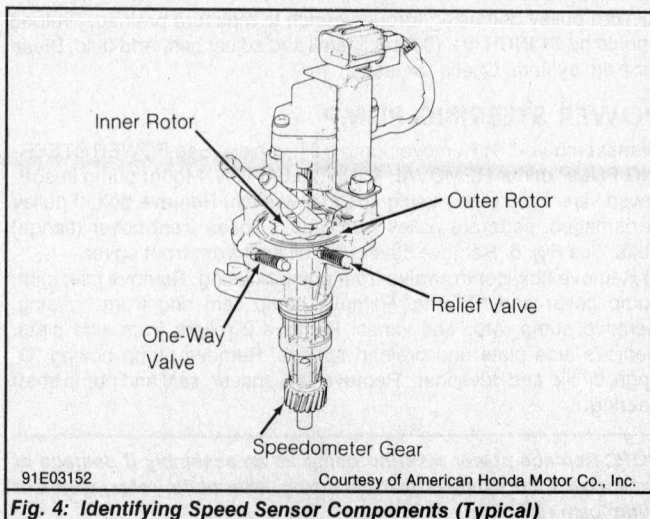

Inner Rotor

Outer Rotor

Relief Valve

One-Way
Valve

Speedometer Gear

91E03152

Courtesy of American Honda Motor Co., Inc.

Fig. 4: Identifying Speed Sensor Components (Typical)

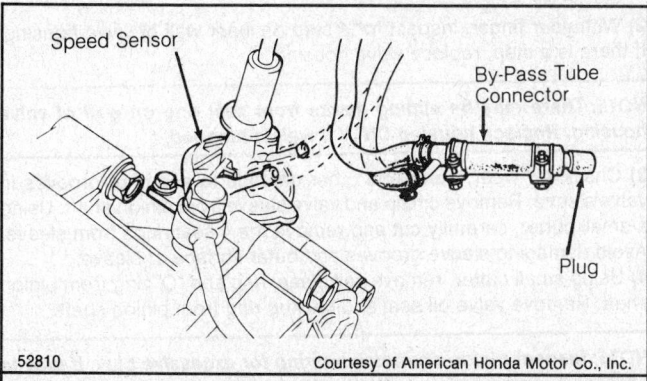

52810

Courtesy of American Honda Motor Co., Inc.

Fig. 5: Simulating High Speed Assist With By-Pass Tube Connector

7) Insert Seal Remover (07NAD-SR30300) and a 24" long 3/8" drive extension into cylinder from gearbox side. Press out cylinder end seal and backup ring from gearbox. Carefully pry piston seal ring and "O" ring off piston of the rack.

CAUTION: DO NOT damage inside of housing with tools. Keep extension straight to avoid contact with cylinder wall. Only use press to remove end seal. Use of a striking tool will break backup ring and leave seal in gearbox. DO NOT damage inside of seal ring groove and piston edges when removing seal ring.

Inspection – Check for leakage, scoring or other damage. Replace seals and "O" rings. If cylinder housing or gearbox is dented or scored, replace steering gear assembly.

Reassembly – 1) Coat piston seal ring guide with power steering fluid and slide onto rack, big end first. Position NEW "O" ring and NEW piston seal ring on Piston Seal Ring Guide (07HAG-SF10100) and slide them toward big end of guide.

NOTE: DO NOT over expand resin seal rings. Install resin seal rings with care to avoid damage. After installation, be sure to contract seal ring using Piston Seal Ring Sizer (07HAG-SF10200). Replace "O" ring and seal as a set.

2) Pull "O" ring off into piston groove, then pull piston seal ring off into piston groove on top of "O" ring. Coat piston seal ring and inside of sizer with power steering fluid. Carefully slide sizer onto rack and over seal ring. Move sizer back and forth several times forcing piston seal ring to fit in piston snugly.

3) Coat Cylinder End Seal Slider (07974-6890801) and NEW end seal with power steering fluid. Place seal on slider with grooved side away from slider. Apply thin coat of grease on inside of slider and install on steering rack. Separate end seal from slider and remove slider from steering rack.

CAUTION: Ensure rack teeth DO NOT face slot in slider. Confirm spring remains in cylinder end seal.

4) Install NEW backup ring on steering rack and slide cylinder end seal against piston. Grease steering rack teeth and insert steering rack into gear housing.

CAUTION: Ensure rack edges cause no damage to inner surface of cylinder housing.

5) Install flange bolt into steering rack until it bottoms, then back out 1/4 turn. Hold flange bolt and tighten flange nut against rack by hand. Install cylinder end seal into bottom of cylinder by pressing on bolt.

CAUTION: To prevent damage to cylinder end seal, DO NOT press bolt with excessive force.

6) Remove flange bolt and center steering rack. Install Cylinder End Seal Guide (07GAG-SD40400) on end of steering rack and coat with power steering fluid. Coat inside of NEW cylinder end seal with power steering fluid and install on steering rack with grooved side toward cylinder. Remove seal guide and push seal into cylinder with finger pressure.

CAUTION: DO NOT damage cylinder end seal with threads or burrs at staked position of cylinder. Confirm spring remains in cylinder end seal.

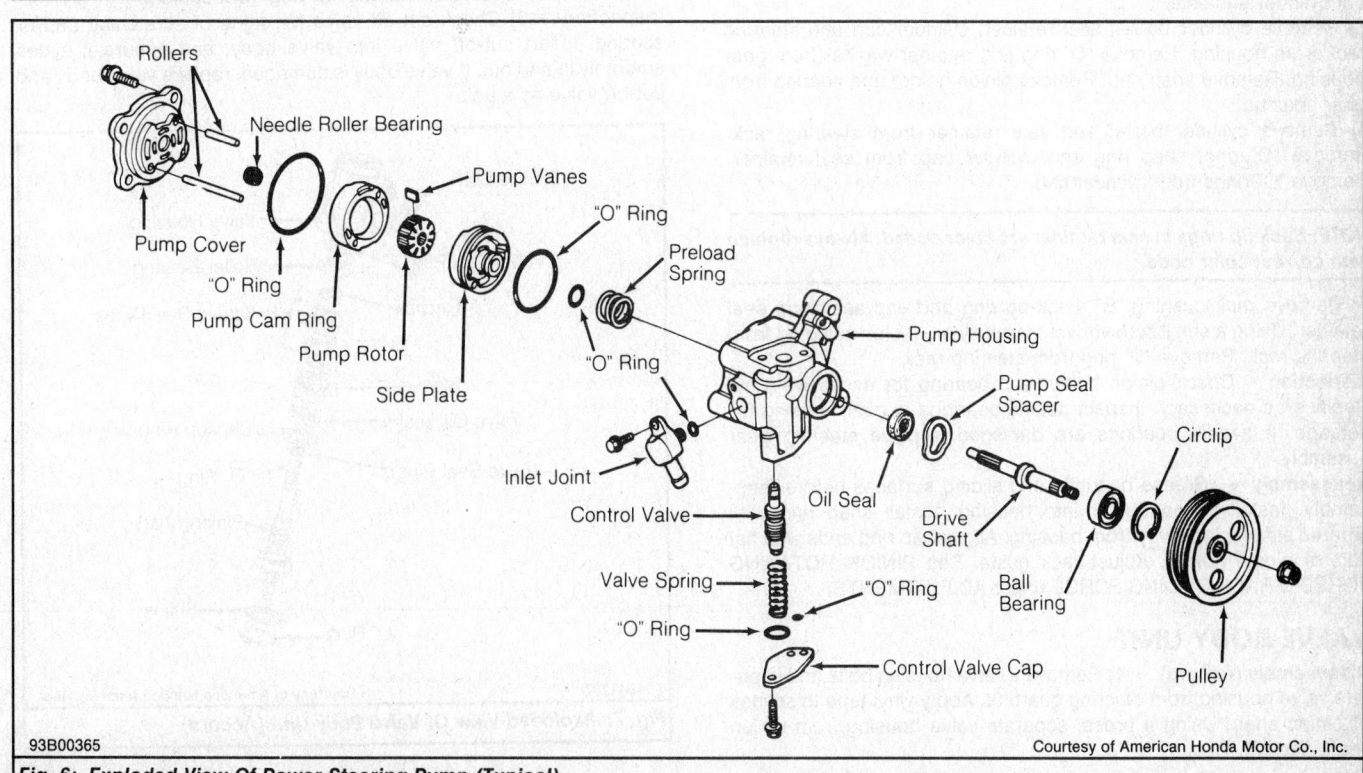

93B00365

Courtesy of American Honda Motor Co., Inc.

Fig. 6: Exploded View Of Power Steering Pump (Typical)

7) Install a puller yoke to steering gearbox. (Snap-On® T/N CJ123-1, OTC® T/N 7372 or equivalent.) Clamp puller yoke in soft jawed vise. DO NOT clamp cylinder housing. Grease inside surface of cylinder and screw cylinder end into housing. Tighten to 51 ft. lbs. (69 N.m) torque. Remove steering gearbox from vise and puller yoke. Stake cylinder in position opposite stake removed during disassembly.

8) If original valve housing and/or pinion shaft are reused, reinstall original 32 mm shims when steering gearbox is reassembled. If valve housing or pinion shaft are replaced, select new shims as follows.

- Place 4 shims on bearing surface of gearbox housing. Total thickness of shim pack should not exceed .028" (.70mm). Thickness of shims available is .10mm, .15mm, .20mm and .25mm, and are unmarked.
- Install valve body unit on gearbox and tighten flange bolts to 15 ft. lbs. (20 N.m). Using feeler gauge, measure clearance between gearbox and valve body at a point midway between mounting bolts.
- Determine required thickness of NEW shim pack by subtracting measured clearance from total thickness of installed shim pack. Select shims with total thickness close to but less than required thickness.

9) Place selected shim pack on bearing surface of gearbox housing. Coat NEW "O" ring with grease and carefully fit to valve housing. Apply grease to needle bearing in gearbox housing. Install valve body unit on gearbox housing and tighten flange bolts to 15 ft. lbs. (20 N.m). To complete reassembly, reverse disassembly procedure.

Disassembly (Civic, Civic Del Sol & Prelude) – 1) Remove valve body from gear housing. See Fig. 2 or 3. Loosen dust boot clamps. Pull dust boots away from cylinder barrel. Bend back tie rod lock washer tabs. Remove tie rod from rack.

2) Push rack into cylinder to protect rack from scratching. Loosen guide screw lock nut. Remove guide screw, spring and rack guide. Remove 4 inner dust seal cap bolts.

3) Remove pinion dust seal cap (gear housing cap). Remove 28-mm snap ring from bottom of housing. Working from top of pinion (shaft), use a drift and mallet and lightly tap pinion from housing.

4) Remove snap ring from pinion. Using a bearing puller, remove bearing from pinion. Remove 4 cylinder housing-to-gear housing bolts. Remove cylinder housing, rack bushing and spring from housing. Pry out cylinder end seal.

5) Remove cylinder barrel, seal retainer, cylinder cap and steering rack from housing. Remove "O" ring and retainer washer from gear housing. Remove snap ring. Remove pinion holder and bearing from gear housing.

6) Remove cylinder barrel and seal retainer from steering rack. Remove "O" ring, snap ring and cylinder cap from seal retainer. Remove "O" rings from cylinder cap.

NOTE: Back-up rings in seal retainer are color coded. Always replace with correct color code.

7) Remove rack bushing "B", back-up ring and end seal from seal retainer. Using a small screwdriver, carefully pry piston seal ring from steering rack. Remove "O" ring from steering rack.

Inspection – Check pinion holder and bearing for excessive play. Replace as necessary. Inspect needle bearings in gear housing for damage. If needle bearings are damaged, replace steering gear assembly.

Reassembly – Grease bearings and sliding surfaces before reassembly. Install pinion holder into housing. Install snap ring with tapered side facing away from housing. Align snap ring ends with flat part of pinion holder. Adjust rack guide. See PINION ROTATING FORCE & RACK SLIDING FORCE under ADJUSTMENTS.

VALVE BODY UNIT

Disassembly (Accord) – 1) Remove 2 valve housing bolts and separate valve housing from steering gearbox. Apply vinyl tape to splines of pinion shaft. Using a press, separate valve housing from pinion shaft. See Fig. 7.

2) With your finger, inspect for a step on inner wall of valve housing. If there is a step, replace valve housing.

NOTE: There may be sliding marks from seal ring on wall of valve housing. Replace housing ONLY if wall is stepped.

3) Check for wear, burrs and other damage to edges of grooves in valve sleeve. Remove circlip and valve sleeve from pinion shaft. Using a small cutter, carefully cut and remove the 4 seal rings from sleeve. Avoid damaging sleeve grooves and outer surface of sleeve.

4) Using small cutter, remove valve seal ring and "O" ring from pinion shaft. Remove valve oil seal and backup ring from pinion shaft.

NOTE: Inspect pinion shaft ball bearing for excessive play. If play is excessive, replace pinion shaft and valve sleeve as an assembly. DO NOT mix old and new pinion shafts and sleeves.

5) Using Pilot Collar (07GAF-PH70100), press valve oil seal and roller bearing out of valve housing.

Reassembly – For reassembly use NEW replacement parts and reverse disassembly procedure.

Disassembly (Civic, Civic Del Sol & Prelude) – 1) Remove 2 valve body-to-gear housing bolts. Remove "O" rings and port orifices from gear housing. Remove pinion shaft dust seal from valve body. See Figs. 8 and 9.

2) Remove 2 valve body cap flange bolts. Remove valve port and seal from side of valve body. Pull cut-off valve and spring from valve body. Remove valve body cap, cap seal and dowels from valve body.

3) Pushing reaction control valve to one side of valve body, remove roller from reaction control valve. Repeat procedure on other side of valve body to remove opposite roller. Remove control valve seal.

NOTE: Hold plungers with fingers to keep plungers from falling out when removing rollers.

4) On Prelude, remove sensor orifice and "O" ring from valve body. Using a 1/16" drill bit filed flat on shank end, pry orifice from valve body.

5) Using same drill bit used for orifice, insert bit through valve body and push out damping orifice and "O" ring from behind.

Inspection – 1) Check cut-off valve for signs of scratching and/or scoring. Insert cut-off valve into valve body, and ensure it slides smoothly in and out. If valve body is damaged, replace valve body and cut-off valve as a unit.

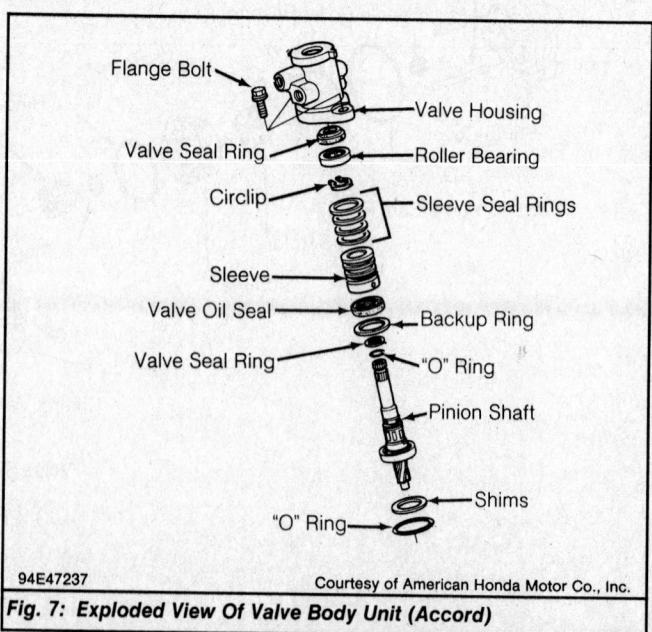

94E47237   Courtesy of American Honda Motor Co., Inc.

Fig. 7: Exploded View Of Valve Body Unit (Accord)

NOTE: *Cut-off valve, control valve and plungers are sized to fit valve body. If any of these need replacement, ensure NEW part has same identification letter.*

2) Inspect plungers for scoring or scratching. Insert plungers into valve body and check for smooth operation. Replace any damaged plunger. If valve body is damaged, replace valve body as a unit.
3) Check control valve for scoring or scratches. Insert reaction control valve into valve body and check for smooth operation. If valve body is damaged, replace valve body as a unit.
Reassembly – 1) Clean all parts before reassembly. Coat plungers, cut-off valve and control valve with Honda power steering fluid. Replace "O" rings and seals.
2) Grease cap seal and port seal grooves to hold seals in place during reassembly. Use grease to hold "O" rings in place during reassembly. To complete reassembly, reverse disassembly procedure.

TORQUE SPECIFICATIONS
TORQUE SPECIFICATIONS

Application	Ft. Lbs. (N.m)
Cylinder Rack-To-Gear Housing Bolt	16 (22)
Hydraulic Fittings	
14-mm	12 (17)
17-mm	22 (29)
Pump Pulley Nut	48 (65)
Pump-To-Bracket Bolt	33 (45)
Speed Sensor Mounting Bolts	13 (18)
Steering Gear Mounting Bolts	29 (39)
Tie Rod End Nuts	33 (45)
Tie Rod-To-Rack	41 (55)
	INCH Lbs. (N.m)
All 6-mm Bolts	
Accord & Prelude	89 (10)
Civic & Civic Del Sol	106 (12)
Hydraulic Fittings (12-mm)	106 (12)
Pump Front Cover Bolt	106 (12)

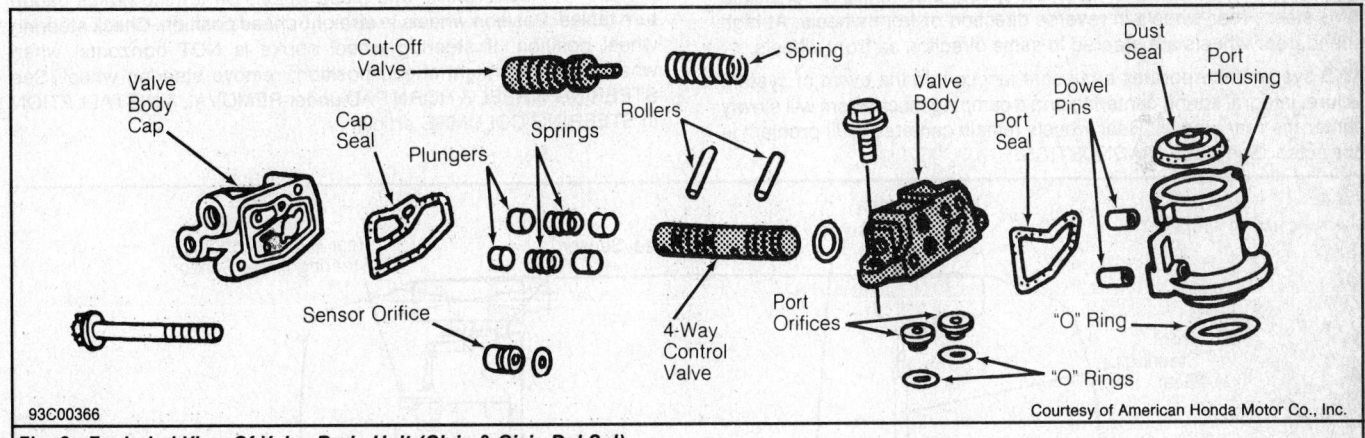

93C00366

Courtesy of American Honda Motor Co., Inc.

Fig. 8: Exploded View Of Valve Body Unit (Civic & Civic Del Sol)

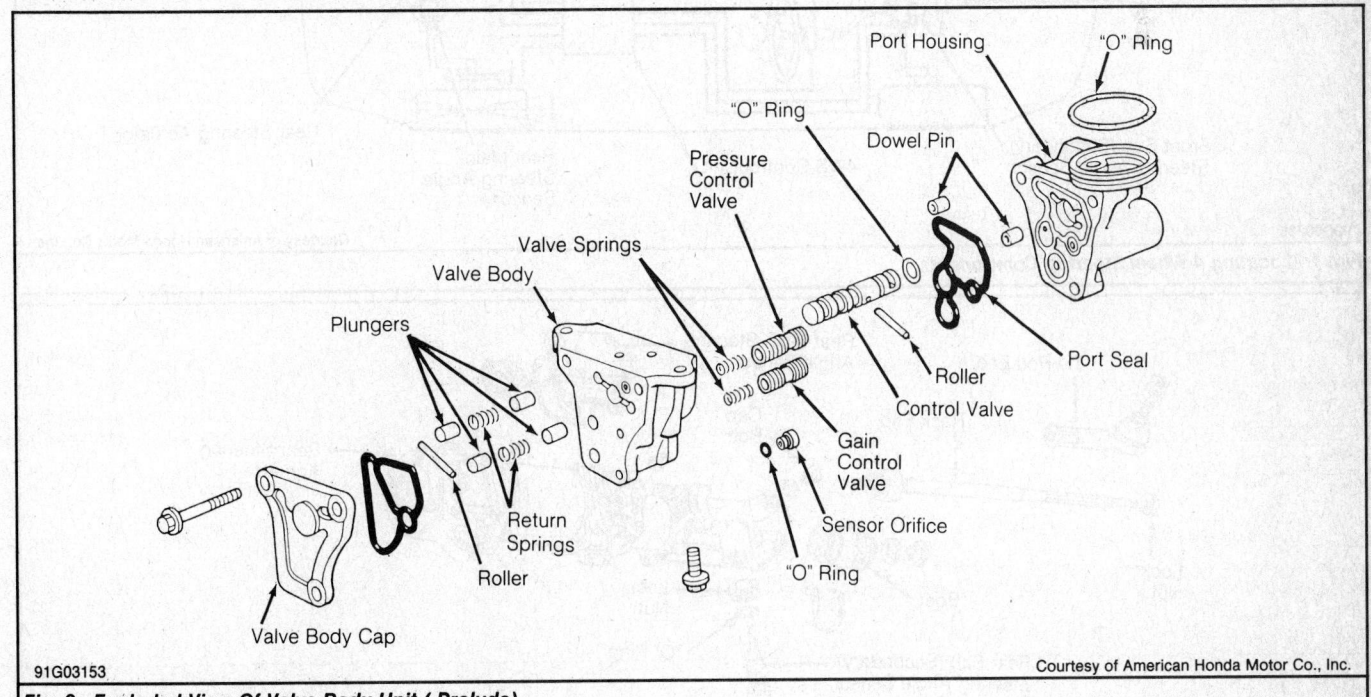

91G03153

Courtesy of American Honda Motor Co., Inc.

Fig. 9: Exploded View Of Valve Body Unit (Prelude)

1994 STEERING
4-Wheel Steering

Prelude

DESCRIPTION & OPERATION

The 4-Wheel Steering system consists of a rack and pinion steering gear at front and a steering actuator at rear. These units are linked electronically through 4WS control unit. Steering information is supplied to 4WS control unit by front main steering angle sensor, front sub (secondary) steering angle sensor and vehicle speed sensor. The control unit determines best angle to steer rear wheels. *See Figs. 1 and 2.*

The rear wheels are steered by an actuator motor which moves a rack connected to rear steering knuckles by tie rods. Rear wheel steering angle is determined by rear main steering angle sensor and rear secondary steering angle sensor. The control unit adjusts rear wheel steering angles according to differences of sensed steering angle and targeted steering angle.

Vehicle speed, determined by speed sensor mounted on transaxle, is supplied to 4WS control unit. At low speed, electronically controlled 4WS steers rear wheels in reverse direction of front wheels. At high speed, rear wheels are steered in same direction as front wheels.

4WS system incorporates a fail-safe function. In the event of system failure, integral spring centering and a damping mechanism will slowly center the rear wheels. Rear wheels remain centered until problem is corrected. See SELF DIAGNOSTICS.

ADJUSTMENTS

CAUTION: All models are equipped with Supplemental Restraint System (SRS). SRS wiring harness is routed close to instrument cluster, steering wheel and related components. All SRS wiring is covered by Yellow outer insulation. DO NOT use electrical test equipment on SRS circuits. Before working on steering column components, disable SRS system. See AIR BAG RESTRAINT SYSTEM article in ACCESSORIES & EQUIPMENT.

MAIN STEERING ANGLE SENSOR

NOTE: If power to 4WS control unit was shut down for battery replacement, 4WS control unit removal, or removal and/or replacement of No. 43 (10-amp) fuse from dash fuse box, 4WS control must be reset. To reset 4WS control unit, start engine and turn steering wheel to right lock then to left lock.

Front – 1) Raise vehicle and place wheels on turning radius gauge turn tables. Position wheels in straight-ahead position. Check steering wheel position. If steering wheel spoke is NOT horizontal when wheels are in straight-ahead position, remove steering wheel. See STEERING WHEEL & HORN PAD under REMOVAL & INSTALLATION in STEERING COLUMNS article.

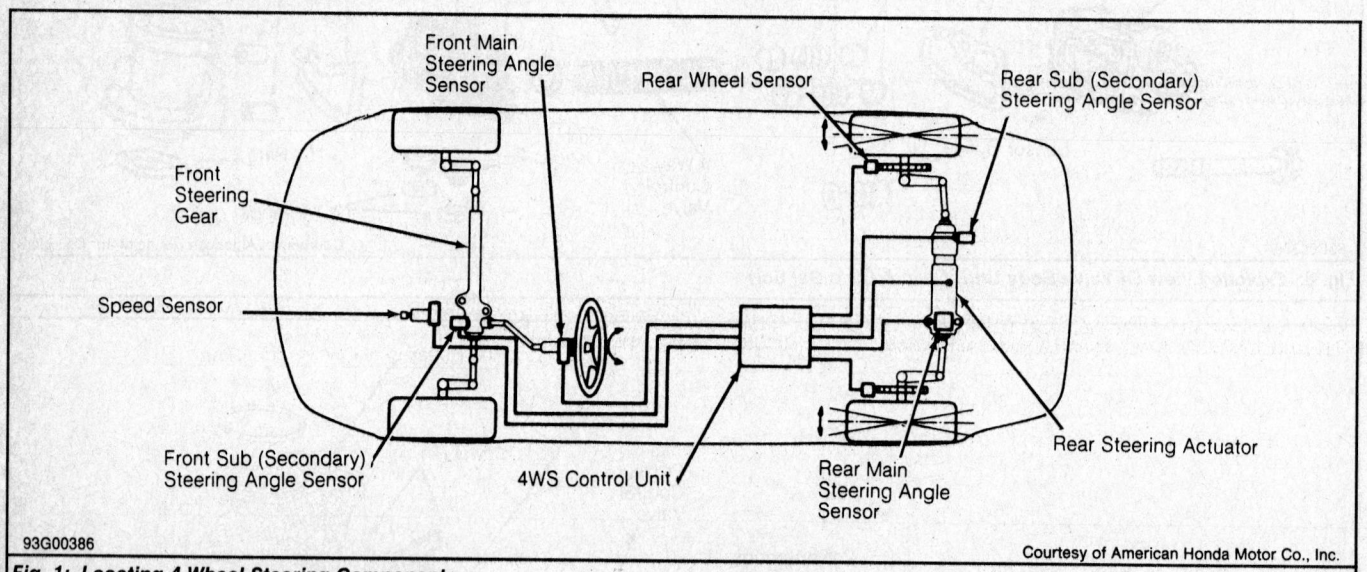

93G00386   Courtesy of American Honda Motor Co., Inc.

Fig. 1: Locating 4-Wheel Steering Components

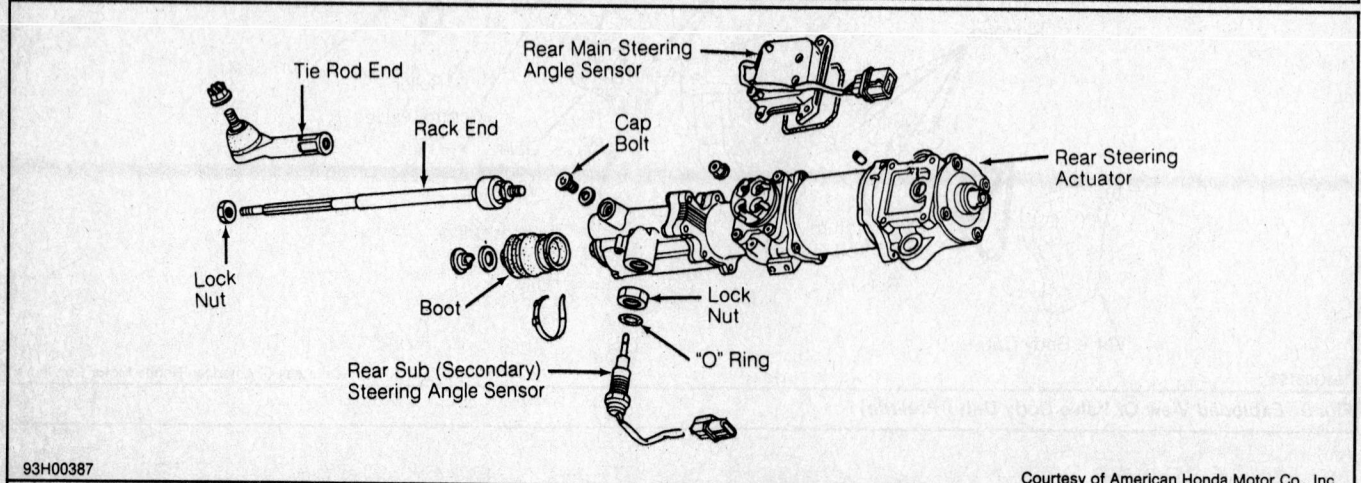

93H00387   Courtesy of American Honda Motor Co., Inc.

Fig. 2: Exploded View Of Rear Steering Actuator Assembly

2) Check yellow paint mark on front main steering angle sensor. Mark should be pointed down. *See Fig. 3*. This indicates sensor is in neutral position. If mark is not as specified, loosely install and turn steering wheel until yellow paint mark is pointed down. Install steering wheel with spoke as nearly horizontal as possible. Tighten steering wheel nut to specification. See TORQUE SPECIFICATIONS. Check front wheel alignment. Adjust alignment as necessary. See SPECIFICATIONS & PROCEDURES article in WHEEL ALIGNMENT.

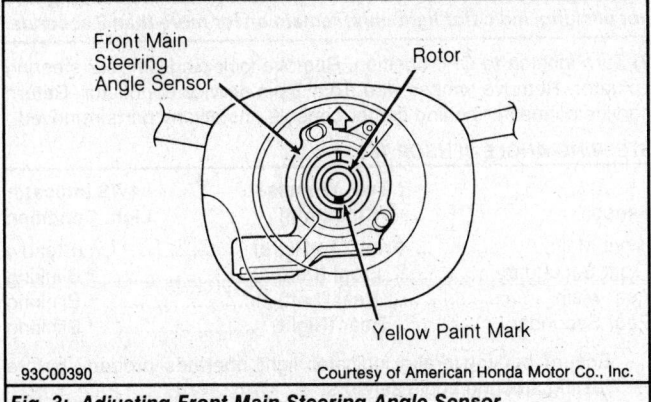

93C00390   Courtesy of American Honda Motor Co., Inc.

Fig. 3: *Adjusting Front Main Steering Angle Sensor*

Rear – Rear main steering angle sensor is not adjustable. If test results are not within specification, remove sensor and inspect for wear or damage. If defective, replace sensor as a unit. See MAIN STEERING ANGLE SENSOR CHECK (REAR) under ANGLE SENSOR NEUTRAL TEST in TESTING.

SUB (SECONDARY) STEERING ANGLE SENSOR

Front – 1) Ensure front main steering angle sensor is properly adjusted. See MAIN STEERING ANGLE SENSOR. Raise and support vehicle. Take 2-pin service connector (Blue wires) from behind center console. Connect terminals with jumper wire. *See Fig. 4*. 4WS indicator light will display Diagnostic Trouble Codes (DTC). Record and verify diagnostic DTCs before continuing with adjustments. See SELF DIAGNOSTICS.
2) Turn ignition switch to ON position. Apply parking brake. Ensure parking brake light functions. Turn ignition switch to OFF position.

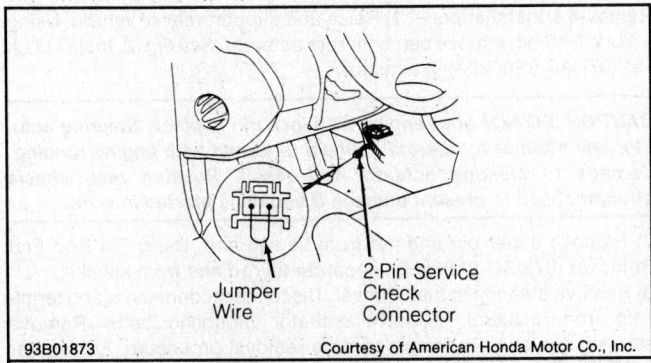

93B01873   Courtesy of American Honda Motor Co., Inc.

Fig. 4: *Locating Service Check Connector*

3) Secondary steering angle sensor is mounted on front steering gear. Remove cover from secondary steering angle sensor. Disconnect harness connector. Loosen sensor lock nut. Tighten sensor by hand, then back it off about 3/4 turn. Connect harness connector. Turn ignition switch to ON position. Ensure steering wheel is in straight-ahead position. If main steering angle sensor is properly adjusted, 4WS indicator light will blink.
4) Slowly rotate secondary sensor clockwise to determine point where indicator light starts blinking and where it stops. *See Fig. 5*. Position secondary sensor in center of range where indicator starts to blink and where it stops. Tighten secondary sensor lock nut to specification. See TORQUE SPECIFICATIONS. Ensure wire harness is not kinked. Install secondary sensor cover, and secure harness.

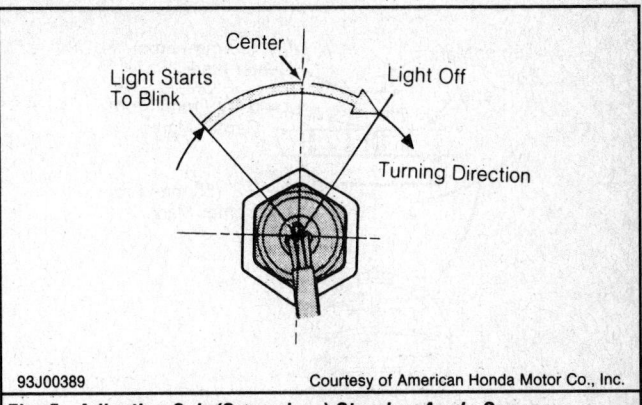

93J00389   Courtesy of American Honda Motor Co., Inc.

Fig. 5: *Adjusting Sub (Secondary) Steering Angle Sensor*

Rear – 1) Raise and support vehicle. Set steering wheel in straight-ahead position. Ensure front main steering angle sensor is properly adjusted. See MAIN STEERING ANGLE SENSOR.
2) Take 2-pin service connector (Blue wires) from behind center console. Connect terminals with jumper wire. *See Fig. 4*. 4WS indicator light will display DTCs. Record and verify DTCs before continuing with adjustments. See SELF-DIAGNOSTICS.
3) Release parking brake fully. Turn ignition switch to ON position. Ensure parking brake warning light is off. Turn ignition switch to OFF position.

CAUTION: DO NOT start engine with lock pin in place. Steering actuator will attempt to operate if wheel is turned with engine running. Damage to steering actuator will result. Position rear wheels straight-ahead to prevent damage if engine is started in error.

---

4) Remove rear actuator cover. Remove cap bolt and washer. Screw Locking Pin (07NAJ-SS00220A) into actuator as far as possible. Disconnect harness connector from rear secondary sensor. Loosen sensor lock nut. Tighten sensor fully by hand, then back it off about 1/2 turn. Connect harness connector.
5) Slowly rotate secondary angle sensor clockwise to determine point where indicator light starts blinking and where it stops. *See Fig. 5*. Position secondary angle sensor in center of range from where indicator starts to blink to where it stops. Tighten secondary angle sensor lock nut to specification. See TORQUE SPECIFICATIONS. Ensure wire harness is not kinked. Install secondary angle sensor cover and secure harness. Remove lock pin. Install cap bolt and washer. Remove jumper wire from service connector.

TESTING

ANGLE SENSOR NEUTRAL TEST

Preparation – 1) Raise vehicle. Set each wheel in center of turning radius gauge tables. Set wheels in straight-ahead position. Attach a piece of masking tape about 11.8" (300 mm) to top of steering wheel. Mark center line of steering wheel on tape. Add marks at appropriate measurement on both sides of center mark. *See Fig. 6*. Use heavy wire stock to make pointer. Using masking tape, attach pointer to dash aligned with center mark on steering wheel.
2) Take 2-pin service connector (Blue wires) from behind center console. Connect terminals with jumper wire. *See Fig. 4*. 4WS indicator light will display DTCs. Record and correct DTCs before continuing with neutral check. *See Figs. 7-10*.
3) Apply parking brake and turn ignition switch to ON position. This will turn parking brake indicator light on and set front sensors in inspection mode.
Main Steering Angle Sensor Check (Front) – 1) Turn ignition switch to ON position. Turn steering wheel slowly from center position to left, then to right past center mark. Align center mark on steering wheel with pointer. Turn steering wheel slowly to right, then to left past center mark. Repeat procedure several times until 4WS indicator light illumination point is positively identified. See STEERING ANGLE SENSOR TEST table.

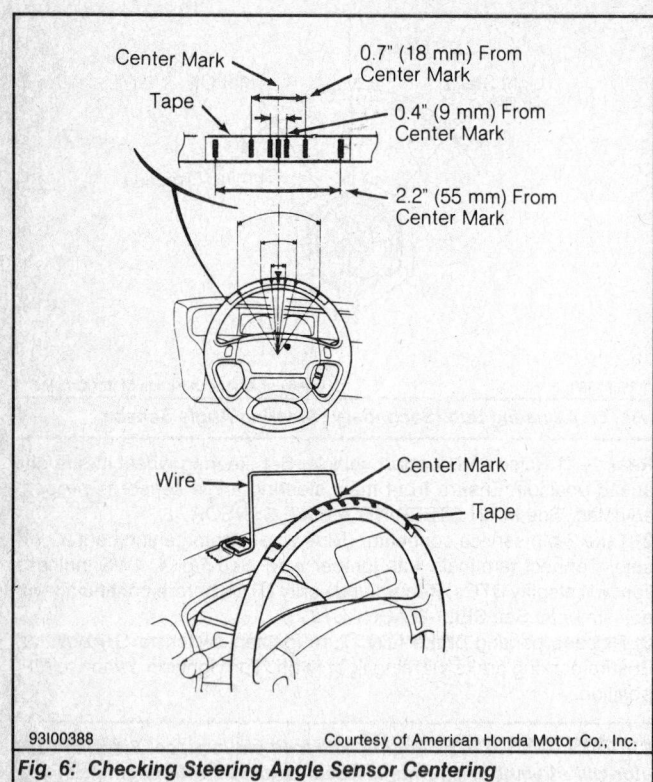

Fig. 6: Checking Steering Angle Sensor Centering
93100388   Courtesy of American Honda Motor Co., Inc.

NOTE: The 4WS indicator light may appear to blink near point at which light comes on. To determine point at which indicator light is not blinking, indicator light must remain on for more than 2 seconds.

2) The 4WS indicator light should come on within 0.4" (9 mm) on either side of center mark. If illumination point is not as specified, front main steering angle sensor must be adjusted. See MAIN STEERING ANGLE SENSOR under ADJUSTMENTS.

Sub (Secondary) Steering Angle Sensor Check (Front) – 1) Turn ignition switch to ON position (engine off). Turn steering wheel slowly from center position to right, then to left past center mark. Align center mark on steering wheel with pointer. Turn steering wheel slowly to left, then to right past center mark. Repeat procedure several times until center point of range where 4WS indicator light blinks is positively identified. See STEERING ANGLE SENSOR TEST table.

2) The 4WS indicator light should blink within 2.2" (55 mm) on either side of steering wheel center mark. If indicator light does not blink within range specified, adjust front main steering angle sensor. See MAIN STEERING ANGLE SENSOR under ADJUSTMENTS. After adjustment, center pointer should be within 0.7" (18 mm) on either side of steering wheel center mark.

Sub (Secondary) Steering Angle Sensor Check (Rear) – 1) Release parking brake fully to set rear sensors in inspection mode. Turn ignition switch to OFF position. Remove cap bolt and washer from rear steering actuator. Screw Lock Pin (07NAJ-SS0020A) into actuator as far as it will go.

CAUTION: DO NOT start engine with lock pin in place. Steering actuator will attempt to operate if wheel is turned with engine running. Damage to steering actuator will result. Position rear wheels straight-ahead to prevent damage if engine is started in error.

2) Turn ignition switch to ON position to check rear secondary steering angle sensor. Turn left rear wheel fully to right by hand, then slowly turn wheel fully to left. The 4WS indicator light should blink at intervals of 0.2 second when wheel is turned to left. If indicator light does not blink, adjust rear secondary steering sensor. See SUB (SECONDARY) STEERING ANGLE SENSOR under ADJUSTMENTS.

Main Steering Angle Sensor Check (Rear) – 1) Turn ignition switch to ON position to check rear main steering angle sensor. Turn left rear wheel fully to left by hand, then slowly turn wheel fully to right. The 4WS indicator light should illuminate when wheel is turned to right. If indicator light does not illuminate, remove rear main steering angle sensor and inspect for damage. If faulty, replace sensor.

NOTE: The 4WS indicator light may appear to blink near point at which light comes on. To determine point at which indicator light is not blinking, indicator light must remain on for more than 2 seconds.

2) Turn ignition to OFF position. Remove lock pin from rear steering actuator. Remove jumper wire from 2-pin service connector. Return service connector behind center console. Install any parts removed.

STEERING ANGLE SENSOR TEST

Sensor	Turn Wheels (Direction)	[1] 4WS Indicator Light Condition
Front Main	Front (To Right)	[2] On (Steady)
Front Secondary	Front (Left)	[3] Blinking
Rear Main	Rear (Left)	[4] Blinking
Rear Secondary	Rear (Right)	[4] Blinking

[1] – Ensure parking brake indicator light operates properly before testing steering angle sensors.
[2] – Pull up parking brake to set front sensors in inspection mode. The 4WS indicator light might appear to be blinking at a point near each end of turning range.
[3] – The 4WS indicator light should blink at 0.2 second intervals. When light is indicating front main sensor position, secondary steering angle sensor indicating condition is cancelled.
[4] – Release parking brake to set rear sensors in inspection mode. Turn rear wheels slowly BY HAND with lock pin set in rear actuator. Indicator light should blink at 0.2 second intervals.

SPEED SENSOR

See STEERING WHEEL TURNING FORCE under TESTING in POWER RACK & PINION article.

REMOVAL & INSTALLATION

REAR STEERING ACTUATOR

Removal & Installation – 1) Raise and support rear of vehicle. Using a Torx T-40 bit, remove cap bolt from actuator. *See Fig. 2.* Install Lock Pin (07NAJ-SS0020A) in actuator.

CAUTION: DO NOT start engine with lock pin in place. Steering actuator will attempt to operate if wheel is turned with engine running. Damage to steering actuator will result. Position rear wheels straight-ahead to prevent damage if engine is started in error.

2) Remove cotter pin and nut from tie rod end. Using Tie Rod End Remover (07MAC-SL00200), separate tie rod end from knuckle.
3) Remove steering actuator cover. Disconnect connectors and terminals from actuator. Remove actuator mounting bolts. Remove steering actuator. To install, reverse removal procedure. Adjust rear sub steering angle sensor. See SUB (SECONDARY) STEERING ANGLE SENSOR under ADJUSTMENTS.

4WS CONTROL UNIT

Removal & Installation – Ensure ignition switch is in OFF position. Remove rear seat back. Disconnect harness connectors. Loosen terminal nuts and disconnect wires from control unit. Remove mounting screws. Remove control unit. To install, reverse removal procedure.

MAIN STEERING ANGLE SENSOR

WARNING: Before performing ANY repairs on steering column or column components, Supplemental Restraint System (SRS) MUST be disabled. See DISABLING & ACTIVATING AIR BAG SYSTEM in STEERING COLUMNS article. Accidental air bag deployment could cause serious bodily injury.

Removal & Installation (Front) – Remove steering wheel and combination switch. See STEERING COLUMNS article. Remove harness connector from front main steering angle sensor. Slide sensor off steering shaft. To install, reverse removal procedure.

Removal & Installation (Rear) – Disconnect harness connector. Loosen terminal nuts and disconnect wires from sensor. Remove sensor retaining screws. Remove sensor. Cover sensor port to prevent contamination. Inspect sensor for dirt or rust contamination. Clean as necessary. Coat NEW "O" ring with grease and install in sensor "O" ring groove. To complete installation, reverse removal procedure.

SUB (SECONDARY) STEERING ANGLE SENSOR

Removal & Installation – Disconnect harness connector. Remove sensor cover screws and sensor cover. Loosen secondary sensor lock nut. Remove sensor and lock nut. To install, grease NEW "O" ring and install in sensor port. Screw lock nut on secondary sensor. Screw secondary sensor into sensor port. Adjust sensor as necessary. See SUB (SECONDARY) STEERING ANGLE SENSOR under ADJUSTMENTS.

SPEED SENSOR

Removal – Remove speed sensor mounting bracket stay. Unplug harness connector. Remove speed sensor mounting bolt, and pull speed sensor from transmission housing. Disconnect and plug speed sensor hoses and plug fittings.

Installation – To install, reverse removal procedure. After installing sensor, turn steering wheel from lock to lock several times with engine idling to bleed air from system. Check for leaks.

OVERHAUL

REAR STEERING ACTUATOR

NOTE: Overhaul procedure not available from manufacturer.

TORQUE SPECIFICATIONS

TORQUE SPECIFICATIONS

Application	Ft. Lbs. (N.m)
Actuator Rack End-To-Rack	41 (55)
Rear Steering Actuator Bracket Bolts	29 (39)
Rear Steering Actuator Cap Bolt	16 (22)
Rear Steering Actuator Mounting Bolts	32 (44)
Steering Angle Sub (Secondary) Sensor Lock Nut	18 (25)
Steering Wheel Nut	37 (50)
Tie Rod End Nuts	37-44 (50-60)
Tie Rod End Lock Nut	33 (45)
	INCH Lbs. (N.m)
Rear Main Angle Sensor Bolts	89 (10)
4WS Control Unit Wire Terminal Nuts	71 (8)

SELF-DIAGNOSTICS

NOTE: Fail-safe function will activate when failure is detected in 4WS system. Rear wheels will be slowly centered, and will remain centered until problem(s) is corrected and codes are cleared.

RETRIEVING DIAGNOSTIC TROUBLE CODES (DTC)

NOTE: The 4WS control unit may store 10 codes each in its main and secondary CPU. Codes from main CPU will be displayed first, followed by a 1.6 second pause and 3 seconds of rapid blinking. The codes stored in secondary CPU will then be displayed. The cycle will repeat until ignition is turned off.

The 4WS indicator light will illuminate whenever a fault is sensed in system. DTCs are stored in 4WS control unit even if condition is temporary. To retrieve DTCs, pull 2-pin service connector (Blue wires) from behind center console. Connect terminals with jumper wire. *See Fig. 4.* 4WS indicator light will display DTCs. Record codes and address them in numerical order. The 4WS indicator light will NOT come on when Code 71, 72 or 73 is set. Indicator light will flash these codes, if stored, when code retrieval function is activated. *See Figs. 7-10.*

CLEARING DIAGNOSTIC TROUBLE CODES

DTCs may be cleared from system memory by removing clock/radio fuse No. 43 (10-amp), disconnecting 4WS control unit harness connector or by disconnecting battery.

1994 STEERING
4-Wheel Steering (Cont.)

PROBLEM CODE	FAIL-SAFE (F/S) ITEM: SYSTEM	FAIL-SAFE (F/S) ITEM: POINT	FAIL-SAFE (F/S) ITEM: 4WS CONTROL UNIT TERMINAL NUMBER	AFFECTED: FRONT SUB STEERING ANGLE SENSOR	AFFECTED: REAR SUB STEERING ANGLE SENSOR	AFFECTED: FRONT MAIN STEERING ANGLE SENSOR	AFFECTED: REAR MAIN STEERING ANGLE SENSOR	AFFECTED: FRONT WHEEL SPEED SENSOR	AFFECTED: *REAR LEFT WHEEL SPEED SENSOR	AFFECTED: *REAR RIGHT WHEEL SPEED SENSOR	AFFECTED: ABS CONTROL UNIT	AFFECTED: 4WS CONTROL UNIT	AFFECTED: REAR ACTUATOR MOTOR	AFFECTED: POWER SYSTEM HARNESS	AFFECTED: ALTERNATOR	AFFECTED: PARKING BRAKE	AFFECTED: HARNESS CONNECTOR	ACTION
No code	–	——	7 + 23									O					O	1
No code	–	——	18 25 4 2 16 + 24									O			O		O	1
10	SUB STEERING ANGLE SENSOR	FRONT	22 26	O								O					O	1
11		REAR	29 17		O							O					O	1
12		FRONT	26 21	O								O					O	1
13		REAR	17 28		O							O					O	1
14		FRONT	——									O						Replace 4WS control unit
15		REAR	——									O						Replace 4WS control unit
16		FRONT	22 26 21	O								O					O	1
17		REAR	29 17 28		O							O					O	1
18		——	——									O						Replace 4WS control unit

1 – Go to SELF-DIAGNOSTIC FLOW CHARTS.

93D01874

Courtesy of American Honda Motor Co., Inc.

Fig. 7: Identifying 4WS Diagnostic Trouble Codes (1 Of 4)

PROBLEM CODE	SYSTEM	POINT	4WS CONTROL UNIT TERMINAL NUMBER	FRONT SUB STEERING ANGLE SENSOR	REAR SUB STEERING ANGLE SENSOR	FRONT MAIN STEERING ANGLE SENSOR	REAR MAIN STEERING ANGLE SENSOR	FRONT WHEEL SPEED SENSOR	*REAR LEFT WHEEL SPEED SENSOR	*REAR RIGHT WHEEL SPEED SENSOR	ABS CONTROL UNIT	4WS CONTROL UNIT	REAR ACTUATOR MOTOR	POWER SYSTEM HARNESS	ALTERNATOR	PARKING BRAKE	HARNESS CONNECTOR	ACTION
20		FRONT	8 15	○		○						○					○	1
21		REAR	6 13		○		○					○					○	1
22		FRONT	8 15	○		○						○					○	1
23	MAIN STEERING ANGLE SENSOR	REAR	6 13		○		○					○					○	1
24		FRONT	8 15	○		○						○					○	1
25		REAR	6 13		○		○					○					○	1
26		FRONT	—									○						Replace 4WS control unit
27		REAR	—									○						Replace 4WS control unit
28		FRONT	12	○		○						○					○	1
29		REAR	20		○		○					○					○	1
30	WHEEL SPEED	FRONT	19					○				○					○	1
31		REAR L	3						○		○	○					○	1
32		REAR R	1							○	○	○					○	1

¹ – Go to SELF-DIAGNOSTIC FLOW CHARTS.

93G01875

Fig. 8: Identifying 4WS Diagnostic Trouble Codes (2 Of 4)

1994 STEERING
4-Wheel Steering (Cont.)

PROBLEM CODE	SYSTEM	POINT	4WS CONTROL UNIT TERMINAL NUMBER	FRONT SUB STEERING ANGLE SENSOR	REAR SUB STEERING ANGLE SENSOR	FRONT MAIN STEERING ANGLE SENSOR	REAR MAIN STEERING ANGLE SENSOR	FRONT WHEEL SPEED SENSOR	*REAR LEFT WHEEL SPEED SENSOR	*REAR RIGHT WHEEL SPEED SENSOR	ABS CONTROL UNIT	4WS CONTROL UNIT	REAR ACTUATOR MOTOR	POWER SYSTEM HARNESS	ALTERNATOR	PARKING BRAKE	HARNESS CONNECTOR	ACTION
		FAIL-SAFE (F/S) ITEM						AFFECTED										
33		REAR R/L	3 1								○	○					○	1
34	WHEEL SPEED	FRONT	19					○				○					○	1
35		REAR L	3						○		○	○						1
36		REAR R	1							○	○	○					○	1
37		REAR L	—									○						Replace 4WS control unit
38		VEHICLE SPEED	—									○						Replace 4WS control unit
40	4WS CONTORL UNIT	4WS CONTROL UNIT	—									○						Replace 4WS control unit
41		4WS CONTROL UNIT	—									○						Replace 4WS control unit
42		4WS CONTROL UNIT	—									○						Replace 4WS control unit
43		4WS CONTROL UNIT	—									○						Replace 4WS control unit
44		4WS CONTROL UNIT	—									○						Replace 4WS control unit
45		4WS CONTROL UNIT	—									○						Replace 4WS control unit
46		4WS CONTROL UNIT	—									○						Replace 4WS control unit
50	CONTROL LOGIC	Motor lock	C + D −								○	○				○		1
51		Wheel caught in ditch; Motor mulfunction	C + D −								○	○					○	1

¹ – Go to SELF-DIAGNOSTIC FLOW CHARTS.

93I01876

Fig. 9: Identifying 4WS Diagnostic Trouble Codes (3 Of 4)

PROBLEM CODE	SYSTEM	FAIL-SAFE (F/S) ITEM POINT	4WS CONTROL UNIT TERMINAL NUMBER	FRONT SUB STEERING ANGLE SENSOR	REAR SUB STEERING ANGLE SENSOR	FRONT MAIN STEERING ANGLE SENSOR	REAR MAIN STEERING ANGLE SENSOR	FRONT WHEEL SPEED SENSOR	*REAR LEFT WHEEL SPEED SENSOR	*REAR RIGHT WHEEL SPEED SENSOR	ABS CONTROL UNIT	4WS CONTROL UNIT	REAR ACTUATOR MOTOR	POWER SYSTEM HARNESS	ALTERNATOR	PARKING BRAKE	HARNESS CONNECTOR	ACTION
60	POWER UNIT	MOTOR	C+•D− 33+•34−									○	○	○			○	1
61			C+•D−									○	○	○			○	1
62		Motor	33+•34−									○	○	○			○	1
63												○	○	○			○	1
64		4WS CONTROL UNIT	—									○						Replace 4WS control unit
65		4WS CONTROL UNIT	—									○						Replace 4WS control unit
70	TEMPORARY DRIVING CONDITIONS	—	25									○					○	Ask customer for symptoms, conditions
71		—										○						Ask customer for symptoms, conditions
72		—	4									○					○	Ask customer for symptoms, conditions
73		—										○			○			Ask customer for symptoms, conditions
74		—	14									○				○	○	Ask customer for symptoms, conditions

1 – Go to SELF-DIAGNOSTIC FLOW CHARTS.

93A01877

Fig. 10: Identifying 4WS Diagnostic Trouble Codes (4 Of 4)

1994 STEERING
4-Wheel Steering (Cont.)

PIN VOLTAGE CHARTS

4WS PIN VOLTAGE CHART

18P CONNECTOR (A)   12P CONNECTOR (B)   4P CONNECTOR (C)

POWER TERMINAL (D)

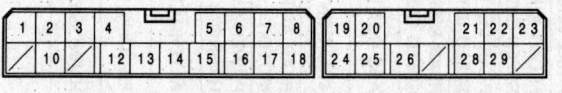

View from control unit terminal side

View from interior side

con-nector	con-nector No.	Wire color	Terminal name	Check		
				Measurement condition	Normal voltage	Measuremt termimals
A	1	GRY/RED	Rear right pulse	While the wheel is being rotated slowly	5 V↔0 V	1 — 24
	2	WHT/BLU	Charge	Engine ON	Battery voltage.	2 — 24
				Engine OFF	0 V	
	3	GRY/WHT	Rear left pulse	While the wheel is being rotated slowly	5 V↔0 V	3 — 24
	4	BLK/YEL	Ignition 2	IG SW ON	Battery voltage	4 — 24
				IG SW OFF, ACC, START	0 V	
	5	RED	Rear main steering angle sensor ground	IG SW ON	0 V	5 — ground
	6	WHT/GRN	Rear main steering angle sensor A phase	While actuator motor is running slowly	5 V↔0 V	6 — 24
	7	PNK	Warning 1	Light ON	0 V	7 — 24
				Light OFF	Battery voltage	
	8	GRN	Front main steering angle sensor A phase	While steering wheel is being rotated slowly	5 V↔0 V	8 — 24
	9	—	—	—	—	—
	10	BRN/WHT	Service check signal	Short	0 V	10 — 24
				Open	5 V (AT : 11 V)	
	11	—	—	—	—	—
	12	BLU	Front main steering angle sensor Z phase	While steering wheel is being rotated slowly	5 V↔0 V	12 — 24
	13	BLU/GRN	Rear main steering angle sensor B phase	While actuator motor is running slowly	5 V↔0 V	13 — 24
	14	GRN/RED	Parking brake	ON	0 V	14 — 24
				OFF	Battery voltage	
	15	YEL/RED	Front main steering angle sensor B phase	While steering wheel is being rotated slowly	5 V↔0 V	15 — 24
	16	BLK	Ground 2	IG SW ON	0 V	16 — ground
	17	GRY/YEL	Rear sub steering anble sensor center	Analog tester DC range	approx. 2.5 V	17 — 24
	18	WHT/YEL	Back up power source	At all times	Battery voltage	18 — 24

The normal voltage is the value when the system is working properly.
IG SW: Ignition switch, ACC: accessory (1 position).

94E47336

Courtesy of American Honda Motor Co., Inc.

Fig. 11: 4WS Pin Voltage Chart (1 Of 2)

4WS PIN VOLTAGE CHART (CONT.)

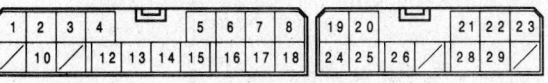  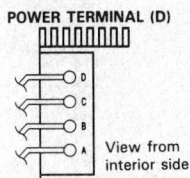

POWER TERMINAL (D)

18P CONNECTOR (A) 12P CONNECTOR (B) 4P CONNECTOR (C)

View from control unit terminal side

View from interior side

con-nector	con-nector No.	Wire color	Terminal name	Check			
				Measurement condition	Normal voltage		Measuremt terminals
B	19	ORN	Vehicle speed sensor	While front wheel is being rotated slowly	5 V↔0 V		19—24
	20	GRN	Rear main steering angle sensor Z phase	While actuator motor is running slowly	5 V↔0 V		20—24
	21	YEL/BLK	Front sub steering angle sensor left	Analog tester AC range	Left Center Right 3.0 V 2.5 V 2.0 V		21—26
	22	YEL/BLU	Front sub steering angle sensor right	Analog tester AC range	Left Center Right 2.0 V 2.5 V 3.0 V		22—26
	23	PNK	Warning 2	Light ON	0 V		23—24
				Light OFF	Battery voltage		
	24	BLK	Ground 1	IG SW ON	0 V		24—ground
	25	YEL/RED	Ignition 1	IG SW ON	Battery voltage		25—24
				IG SW OFF, ACC	0 V		
	26	YEL/GRN	Front sub steering angle sensor center	Analog tester DC range	approx. 2.5 V		26—24
	27	———	———	———	———		———
	28	GRY/BLK	Rear sub steering angle sensor left	Analog tester AC range	Left Center Right 2.0 V 2.5 V 3.0 V		28—17
	29	GRY	Rear sub steering angle sensor right	Analog tester AC range	Left Center Right 3.0 V 2.5 V 2.0 V		29—17
	30	———	———	———	———		———
C	31	———	———	———	———		———
	32	———	———	———	———		———
	33	YEL	Damper	Resistance range Disconnect 4P connector. Start the engine	Continuity ↓ Momentarily open, no continuity		33—34 control unit terminal
	34	BLU	Damper				
D	A	WHT	Motor power source	At all times	Battery voltage		A—ground
	B	BRN	power (motor) ground	IG SW ON	0 V		B—ground
	C	RED	Motor terminal	Start the engine	0 V ↓ Battery voltage		C—ground
	D	BLK	Motor terminal				D—ground

The normal voltage is the value when the system is working properly.
IG SW: Ignition switch, ACC: accessory (1 position).

Fig. 12: 4WS Pin Voltage Chart (2 Of 2)

WIRING DIAGRAM

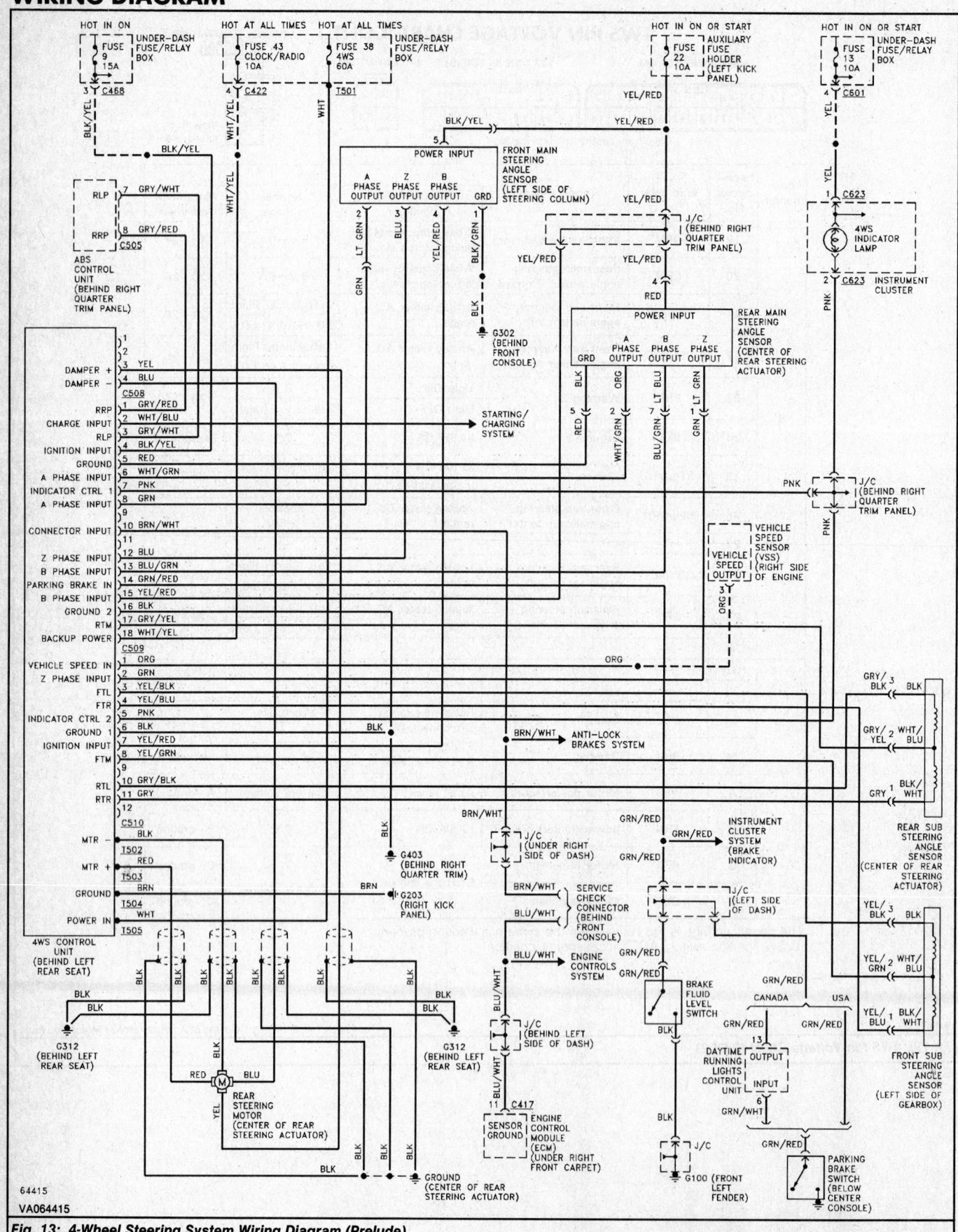

64415
VA064415

Fig. 13: 4-Wheel Steering System Wiring Diagram (Prelude)

SELF-DIAGNOSTIC FLOW CHARTS

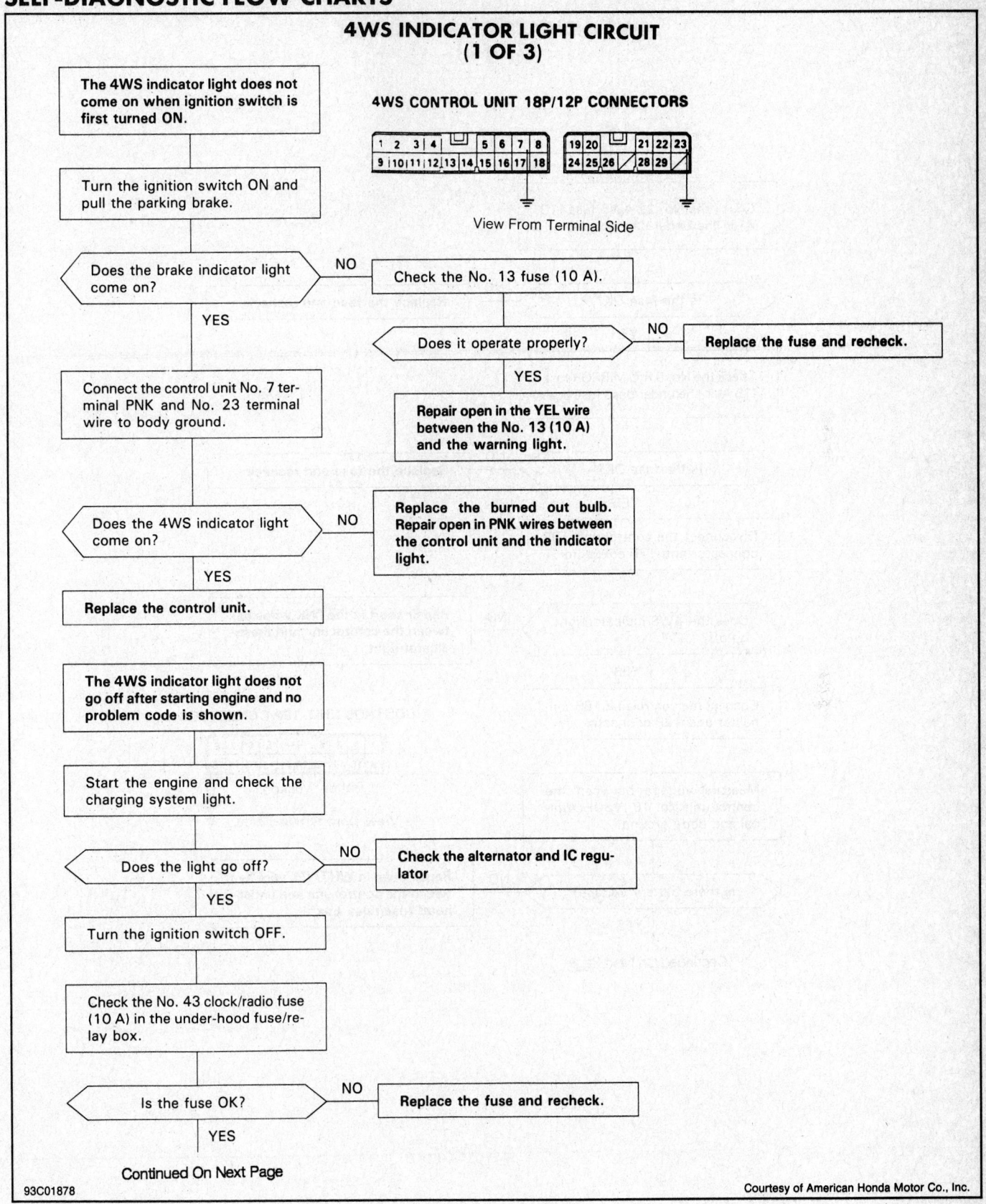

4WS INDICATOR LIGHT CIRCUIT
(1 OF 3)

The 4WS indicator light does not come on when ignition switch is first turned ON.

Turn the ignition switch ON and pull the parking brake.

Does the brake indicator light come on? — NO → Check the No. 13 fuse (10 A).

YES

Does it operate properly? — NO → Replace the fuse and recheck.

YES

Repair open in the YEL wire between the No. 13 (10 A) and the warning light.

Connect the control unit No. 7 terminal PNK and No. 23 terminal wire to body ground.

Does the 4WS indicator light come on? — NO → Replace the burned out bulb. Repair open in PNK wires between the control unit and the indicator light.

YES

Replace the control unit.

The 4WS indicator light does not go off after starting engine and no problem code is shown.

Start the engine and check the charging system light.

Does the light go off? — NO → Check the alternator and IC regulator

YES

Turn the ignition switch OFF.

Check the No. 43 clock/radio fuse (10 A) in the under-hood fuse/relay box.

Is the fuse OK? — NO → Replace the fuse and recheck.

YES

4WS CONTROL UNIT 18P/12P CONNECTORS

| 1 | 2 | 3 | 4 | | 5 | 6 | 7 | 8 |
| 9 | 10 | 11 | 12 | 13 | 14 | 15 | 16 | 17 | 18 |

| 19 | 20 | | 21 | 22 | 23 |
| 24 | 25 | 26 | | 28 | 29 |

View From Terminal Side

Continued On Next Page

93C01878

**4WS INDICATOR LIGHT CIRCUIT
(2 OF 3)**

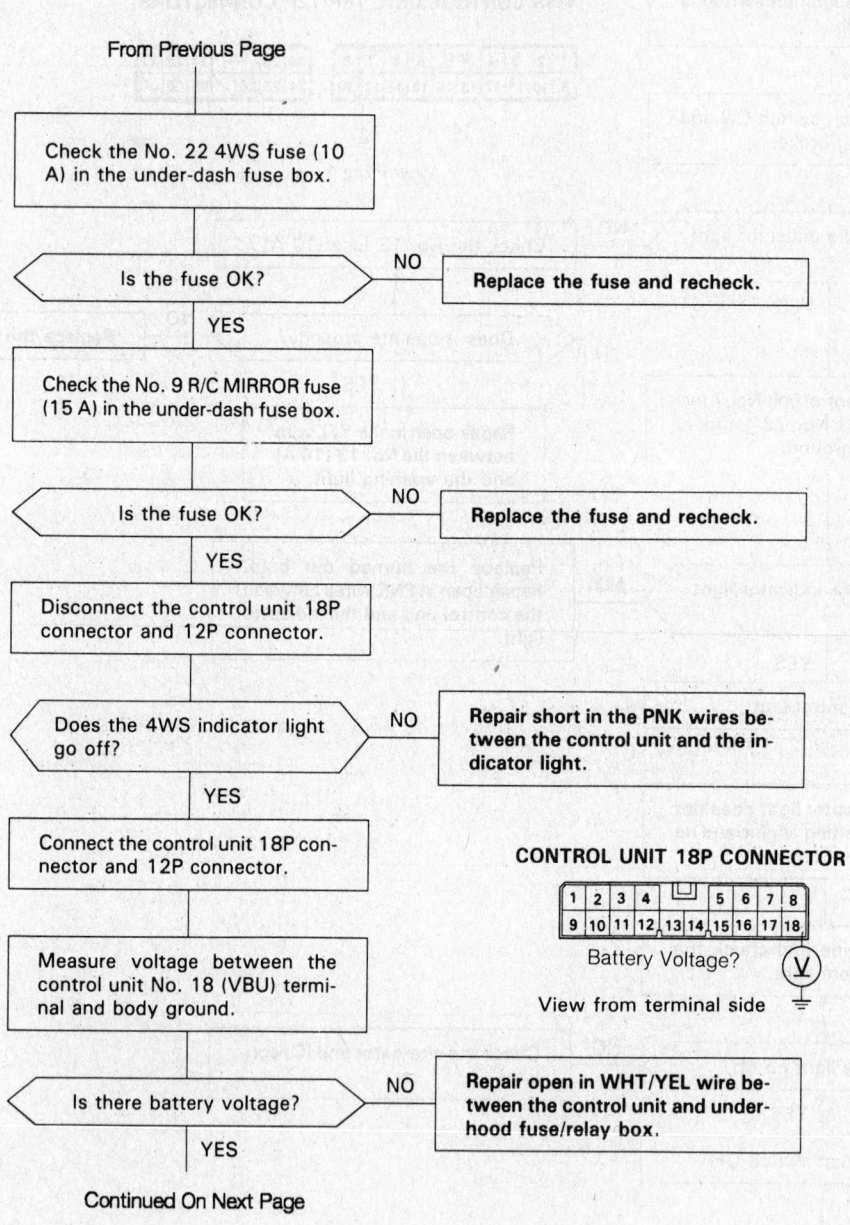

From Previous Page

Check the No. 22 4WS fuse (10 A) in the under-dash fuse box.

Is the fuse OK? — NO → **Replace the fuse and recheck.**

YES

Check the No. 9 R/C MIRROR fuse (15 A) in the under-dash fuse box.

Is the fuse OK? — NO → **Replace the fuse and recheck.**

YES

Disconnect the control unit 18P connector and 12P connector.

Does the 4WS indicator light go off? — NO → **Repair short in the PNK wires between the control unit and the indicator light.**

YES

Connect the control unit 18P connector and 12P connector.

Measure voltage between the control unit No. 18 (VBU) terminal and body ground.

Is there battery voltage? — NO → **Repair open in WHT/YEL wire between the control unit and under-hood fuse/relay box.**

YES

Continued On Next Page

CONTROL UNIT 18P CONNECTOR

| 1 | 2 | 3 | 4 | | 5 | 6 | 7 | 8 |
| 9 | 10 | 11 | 12 | 13 | 14 | 15 | 16 | 17 | 18 |

Battery Voltage?

View from terminal side

4WS INDICATOR LIGHT CIRCUIT
(3 OF 3)

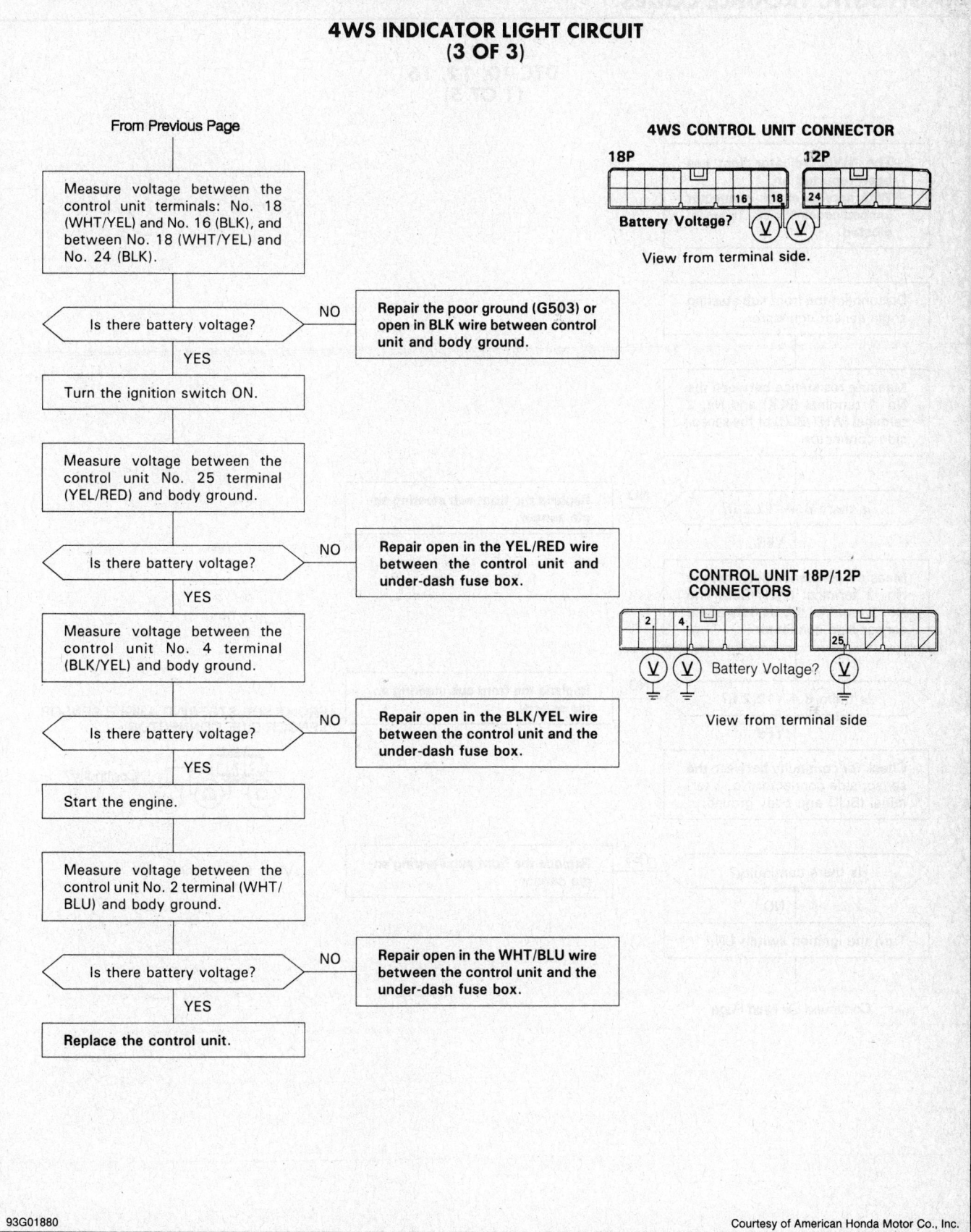

From Previous Page

Measure voltage between the control unit terminals: No. 18 (WHT/YEL) and No. 16 (BLK), and between No. 18 (WHT/YEL) and No. 24 (BLK).

Is there battery voltage? — NO → Repair the poor ground (G503) or open in BLK wire between control unit and body ground.

YES

Turn the ignition switch ON.

Measure voltage between the control unit No. 25 terminal (YEL/RED) and body ground.

Is there battery voltage? — NO → Repair open in the YEL/RED wire between the control unit and under-dash fuse box.

YES

Measure voltage between the control unit No. 4 terminal (BLK/YEL) and body ground.

Is there battery voltage? — NO → Repair open in the BLK/YEL wire between the control unit and the under-dash fuse box.

YES

Start the engine.

Measure voltage between the control unit No. 2 terminal (WHT/BLU) and body ground.

Is there battery voltage? — NO → Repair open in the WHT/BLU wire between the control unit and the under-dash fuse box.

YES

Replace the control unit.

4WS CONTROL UNIT CONNECTOR

18P   12P

16 18   24

Battery Voltage?

View from terminal side.

CONTROL UNIT 18P/12P CONNECTORS

2   4   25

Battery Voltage?

View from terminal side

93G01880

Courtesy of American Honda Motor Co., Inc.

DIAGNOSTIC TROUBLE CODES

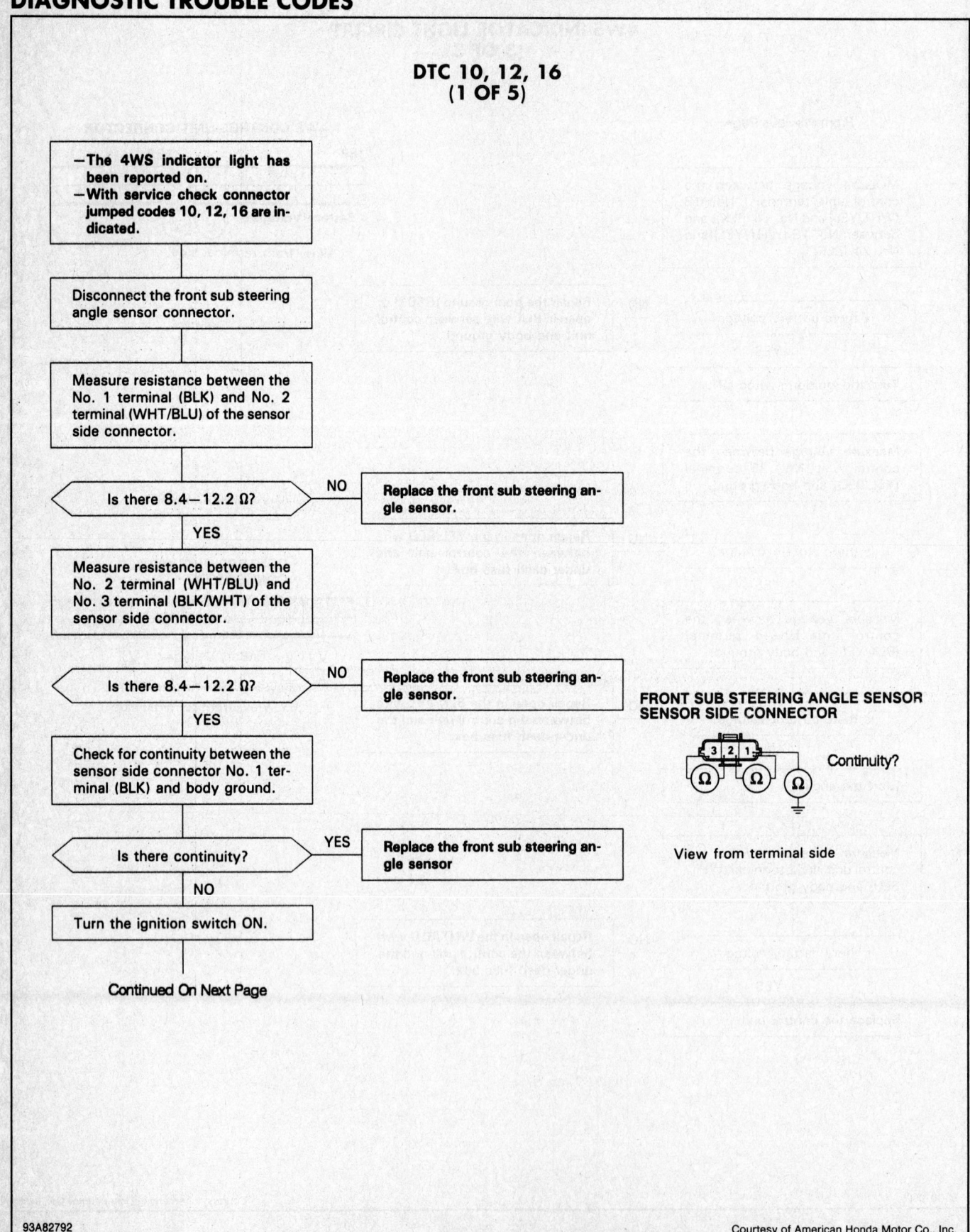

DTC 10, 12, 16
(1 OF 5)

—The 4WS indicator light has been reported on.
—With service check connector jumped codes 10, 12, 16 are indicated.

Disconnect the front sub steering angle sensor connector.

Measure resistance between the No. 1 terminal (BLK) and No. 2 terminal (WHT/BLU) of the sensor side connector.

Is there 8.4—12.2 Ω? — NO → Replace the front sub steering angle sensor.

YES

Measure resistance between the No. 2 terminal (WHT/BLU) and No. 3 terminal (BLK/WHT) of the sensor side connector.

Is there 8.4—12.2 Ω? — NO → Replace the front sub steering angle sensor.

YES

Check for continuity between the sensor side connector No. 1 terminal (BLK) and body ground.

Is there continuity? — YES → Replace the front sub steering angle sensor

NO

Turn the ignition switch ON.

Continued On Next Page

FRONT SUB STEERING ANGLE SENSOR
SENSOR SIDE CONNECTOR

Continuity?

View from terminal side

DTC 10, 12, 16
(2 OF 5)

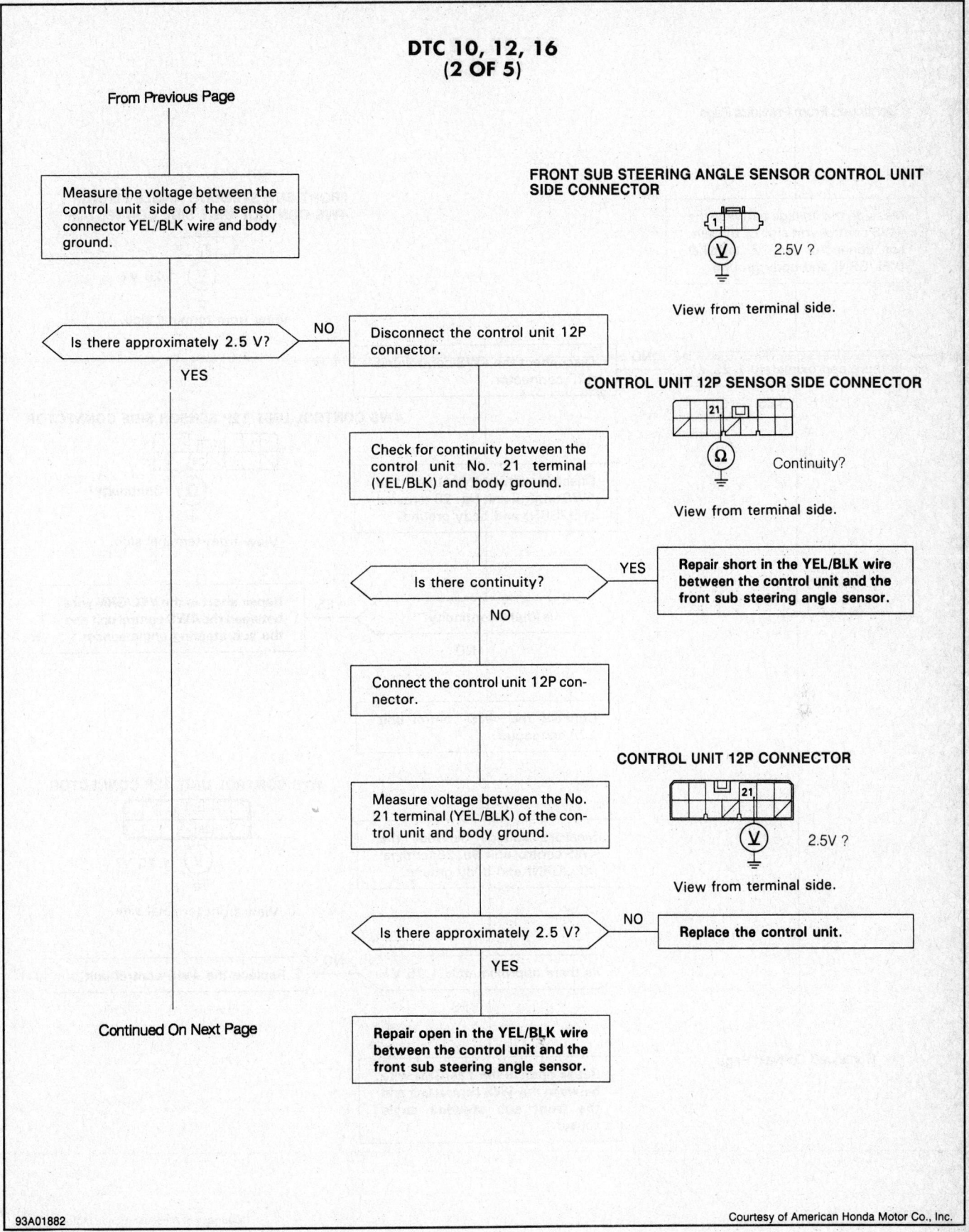

From Previous Page

Measure the voltage between the control unit side of the sensor connector YEL/BLK wire and body ground.

FRONT SUB STEERING ANGLE SENSOR CONTROL UNIT SIDE CONNECTOR

2.5V ?

View from terminal side.

Is there approximately 2.5 V? — NO → Disconnect the control unit 12P connector.

YES

CONTROL UNIT 12P SENSOR SIDE CONNECTOR

Continuity?

View from terminal side.

Check for continuity between the control unit No. 21 terminal (YEL/BLK) and body ground.

Is there continuity? — YES → Repair short in the YEL/BLK wire between the control unit and the front sub steering angle sensor.

NO

Connect the control unit 12P connector.

CONTROL UNIT 12P CONNECTOR

2.5V ?

View from terminal side.

Measure voltage between the No. 21 terminal (YEL/BLK) of the control unit and body ground.

Is there approximately 2.5 V? — NO → Replace the control unit.

YES

Continued On Next Page

Repair open in the YEL/BLK wire between the control unit and the front sub steering angle sensor.

DTC 10, 12, 16
(3 OF 5)

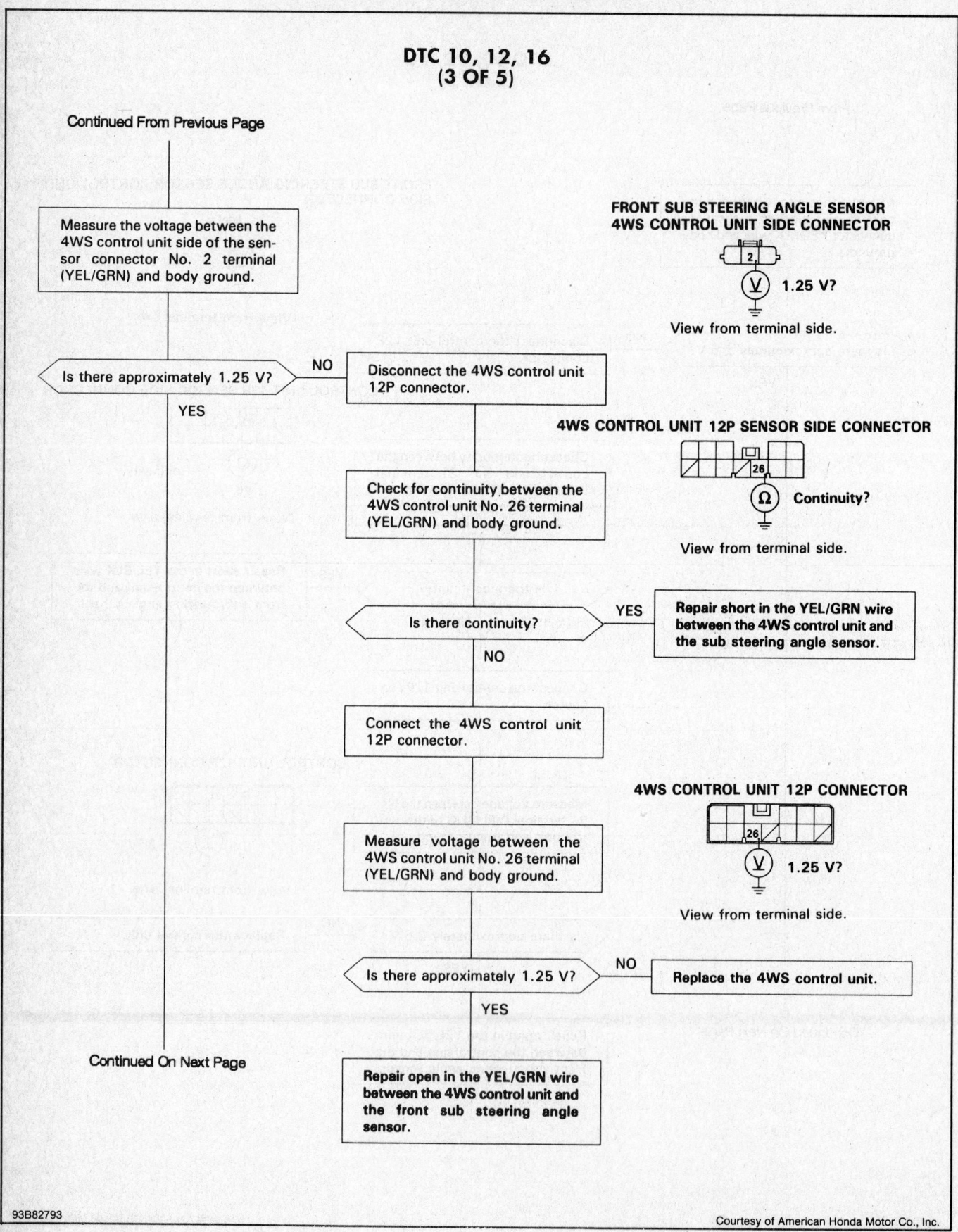

Continued From Previous Page

Measure the voltage between the 4WS control unit side of the sensor connector No. 2 terminal (YEL/GRN) and body ground.

FRONT SUB STEERING ANGLE SENSOR 4WS CONTROL UNIT SIDE CONNECTOR

1.25 V?

View from terminal side.

Is there approximately 1.25 V? — NO → Disconnect the 4WS control unit 12P connector.

YES

4WS CONTROL UNIT 12P SENSOR SIDE CONNECTOR

Continuity?

View from terminal side.

Check for continuity between the 4WS control unit No. 26 terminal (YEL/GRN) and body ground.

Is there continuity? — YES → Repair short in the YEL/GRN wire between the 4WS control unit and the sub steering angle sensor.

NO

Connect the 4WS control unit 12P connector.

4WS CONTROL UNIT 12P CONNECTOR

1.25 V?

View from terminal side.

Measure voltage between the 4WS control unit No. 26 terminal (YEL/GRN) and body ground.

Is there approximately 1.25 V? — NO → Replace the 4WS control unit.

YES

Continued On Next Page

Repair open in the YEL/GRN wire between the 4WS control unit and the front sub steering angle sensor.

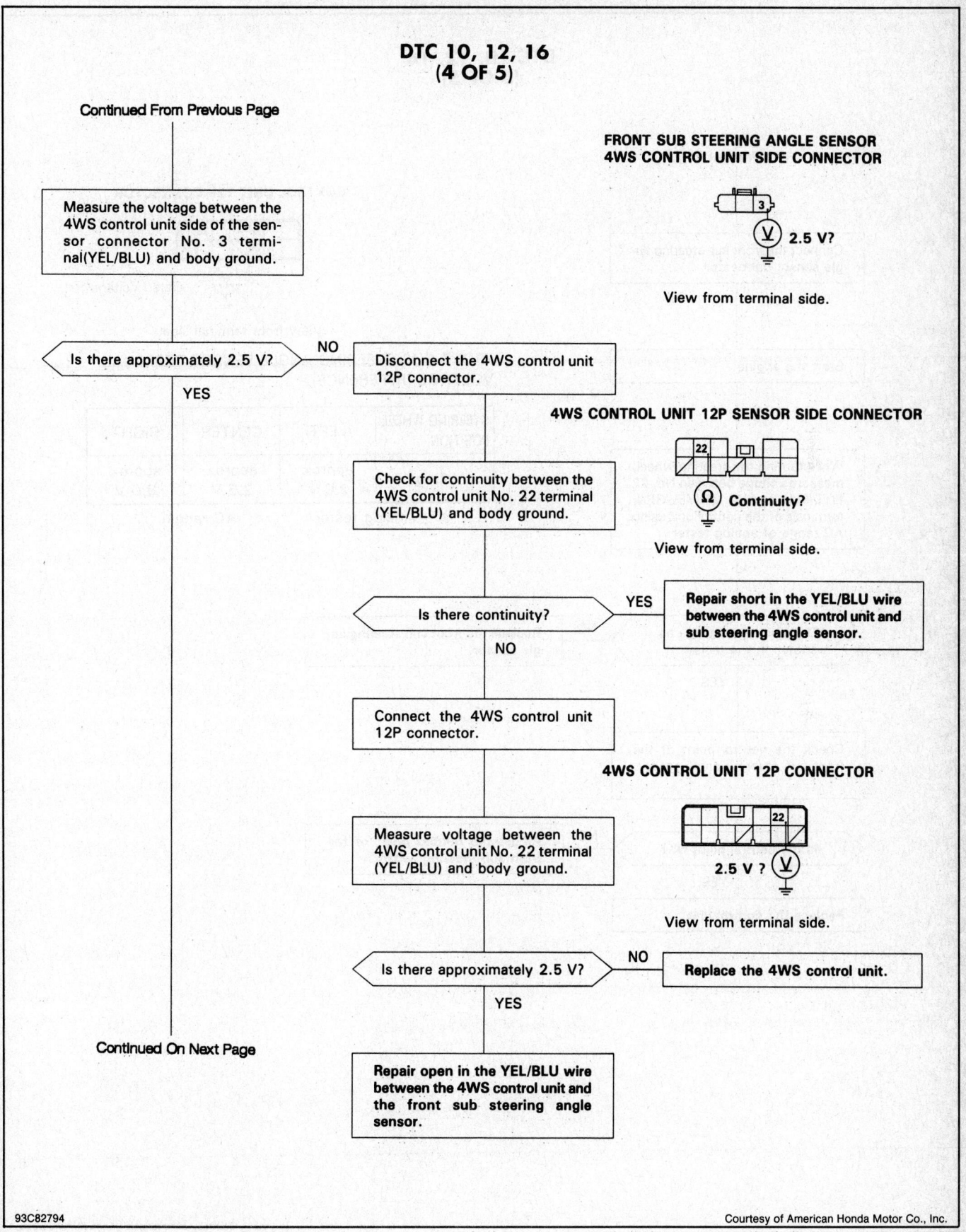

DTC 10, 12, 16
(4 OF 5)

Continued From Previous Page

Measure the voltage between the 4WS control unit side of the sensor connector No. 3 terminal(YEL/BLU) and body ground.

**FRONT SUB STEERING ANGLE SENSOR
4WS CONTROL UNIT SIDE CONNECTOR**

2.5 V?

View from terminal side.

Is there approximately 2.5 V? — NO → Disconnect the 4WS control unit 12P connector.

YES

4WS CONTROL UNIT 12P SENSOR SIDE CONNECTOR

Check for continuity between the 4WS control unit No. 22 terminal (YEL/BLU) and body ground.

Continuity?

View from terminal side.

Is there continuity? — YES → Repair short in the YEL/BLU wire between the 4WS control unit and sub steering angle sensor.

NO

Connect the 4WS control unit 12P connector.

4WS CONTROL UNIT 12P CONNECTOR

Measure voltage between the 4WS control unit No. 22 terminal (YEL/BLU) and body ground.

2.5 V ?

View from terminal side.

Is there approximately 2.5 V? — NO → Replace the 4WS control unit.

YES

Continued On Next Page

Repair open in the YEL/BLU wire between the 4WS control unit and the front sub steering angle sensor.

DTC 10, 12, 16
(5 OF 5)

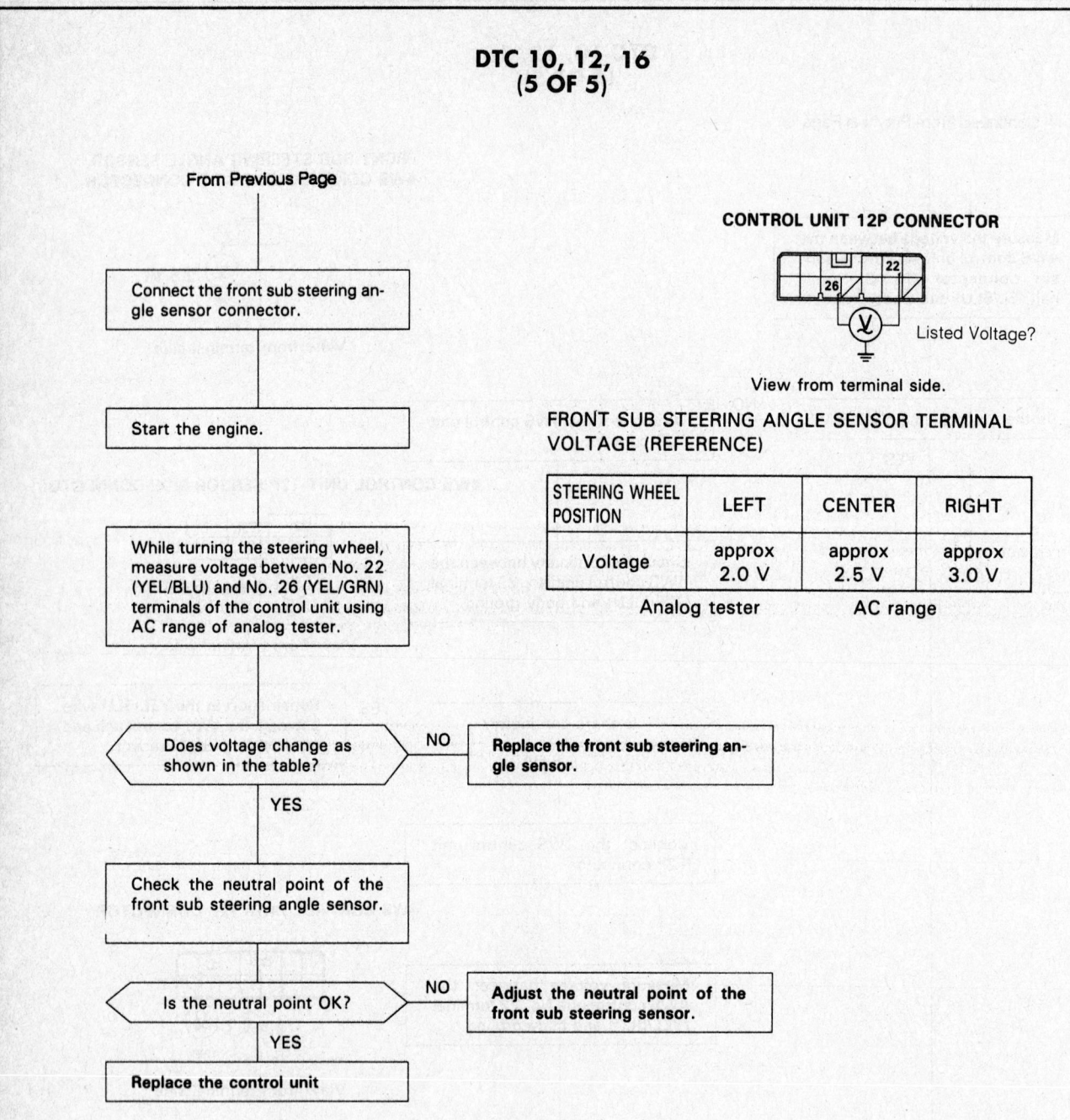

From Previous Page

Connect the front sub steering angle sensor connector.

Start the engine.

While turning the steering wheel, measure voltage between No. 22 (YEL/BLU) and No. 26 (YEL/GRN) terminals of the control unit using AC range of analog tester.

Does voltage change as shown in the table? —NO→ Replace the front sub steering angle sensor.

YES

Check the neutral point of the front sub steering angle sensor.

Is the neutral point OK? —NO→ Adjust the neutral point of the front sub steering sensor.

YES

Replace the control unit

CONTROL UNIT 12P CONNECTOR

22
26

Listed Voltage?

View from terminal side.

FRONT SUB STEERING ANGLE SENSOR TERMINAL VOLTAGE (REFERENCE)

STEERING WHEEL POSITION	LEFT	CENTER	RIGHT
Voltage	approx 2.0 V	approx 2.5 V	approx 3.0 V

Analog tester   AC range

DTC 11, 13, 17
(1 OF 5)

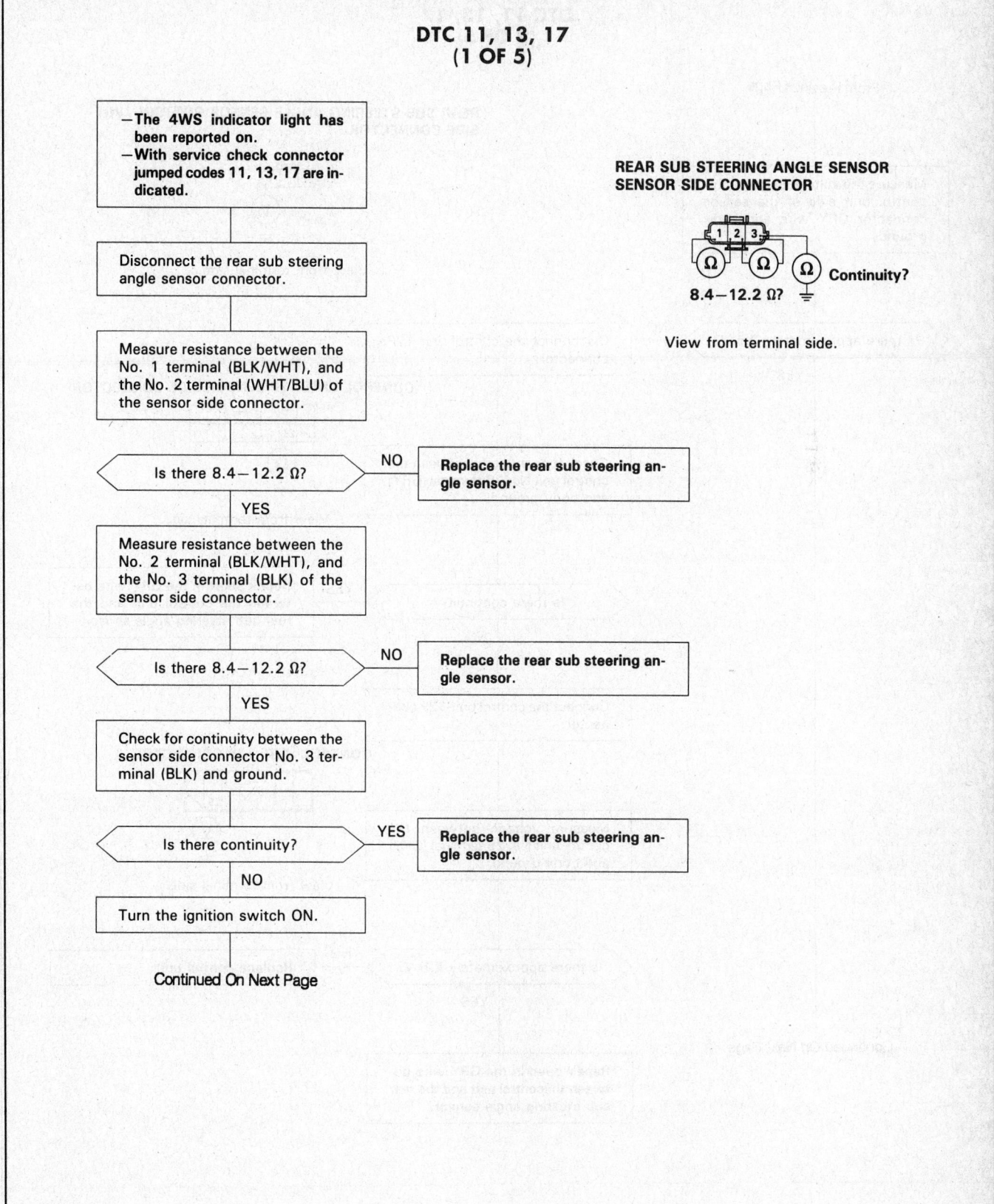

- The 4WS indicator light has been reported on.
- With service check connector jumped codes 11, 13, 17 are indicated.

Disconnect the rear sub steering angle sensor connector.

Measure resistance between the No. 1 terminal (BLK/WHT), and the No. 2 terminal (WHT/BLU) of the sensor side connector.

Is there 8.4—12.2 Ω? — NO → Replace the rear sub steering angle sensor.

YES

Measure resistance between the No. 2 terminal (BLK/WHT), and the No. 3 terminal (BLK) of the sensor side connector.

Is there 8.4—12.2 Ω? — NO → Replace the rear sub steering angle sensor.

YES

Check for continuity between the sensor side connector No. 3 terminal (BLK) and ground.

Is there continuity? — YES → Replace the rear sub steering angle sensor.

NO

Turn the ignition switch ON.

Continued On Next Page

REAR SUB STEERING ANGLE SENSOR SENSOR SIDE CONNECTOR

8.4—12.2 Ω?   Continuity?

View from terminal side.

Courtesy of American Honda Motor Co., Inc.

DTC 11, 13, 17
(2 OF 5)

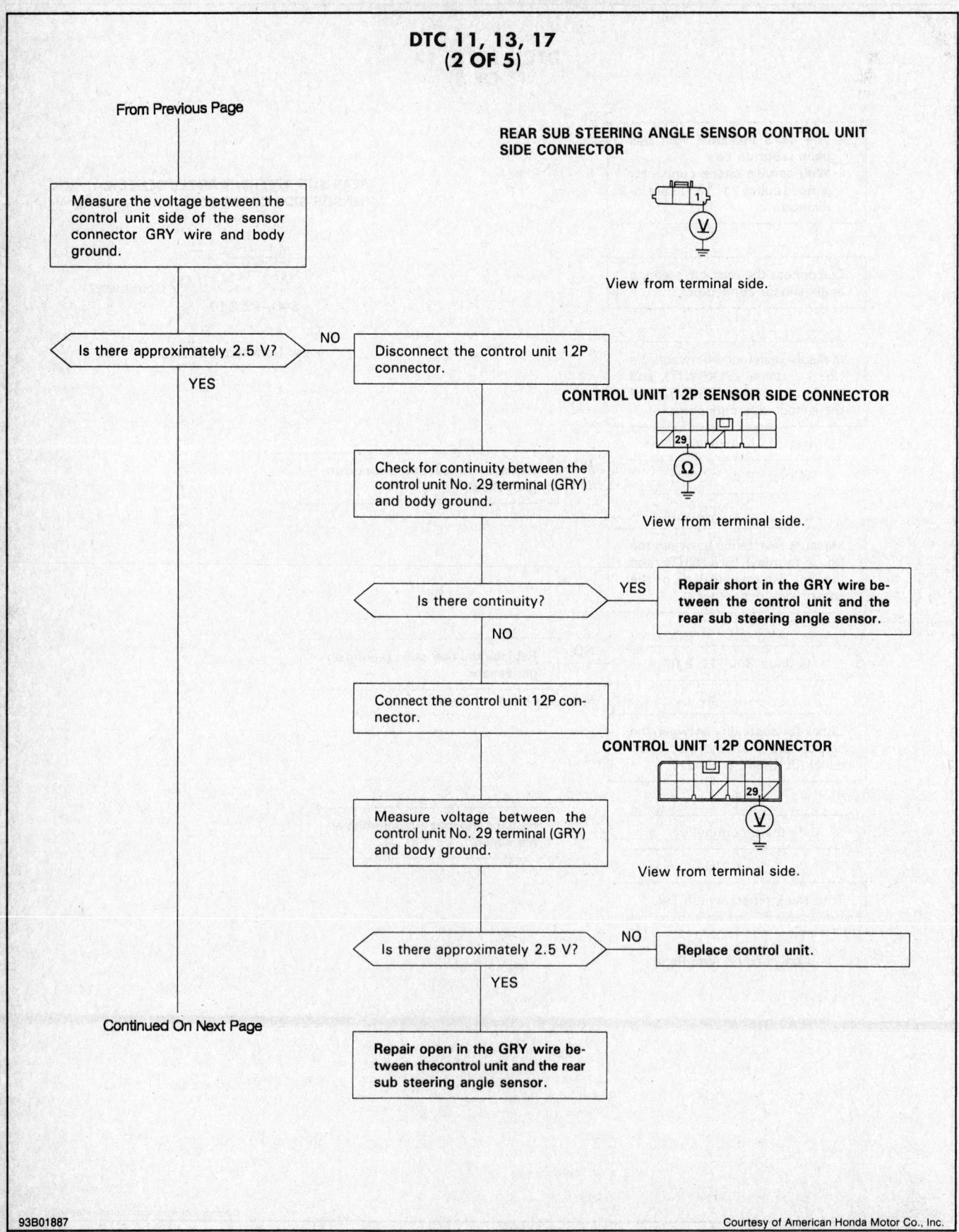

From Previous Page

Measure the voltage between the control unit side of the sensor connector GRY wire and body ground.

REAR SUB STEERING ANGLE SENSOR CONTROL UNIT SIDE CONNECTOR

View from terminal side.

Is there approximately 2.5 V? — NO → Disconnect the control unit 12P connector.

YES

CONTROL UNIT 12P SENSOR SIDE CONNECTOR

Check for continuity between the control unit No. 29 terminal (GRY) and body ground.

View from terminal side.

Is there continuity? — YES → Repair short in the GRY wire between the control unit and the rear sub steering angle sensor.

NO

Connect the control unit 12P connector.

CONTROL UNIT 12P CONNECTOR

Measure voltage between the control unit No. 29 terminal (GRY) and body ground.

View from terminal side.

Is there approximately 2.5 V? — NO → Replace control unit.

YES

Continued On Next Page

Repair open in the GRY wire between thecontrol unit and the rear sub steering angle sensor.

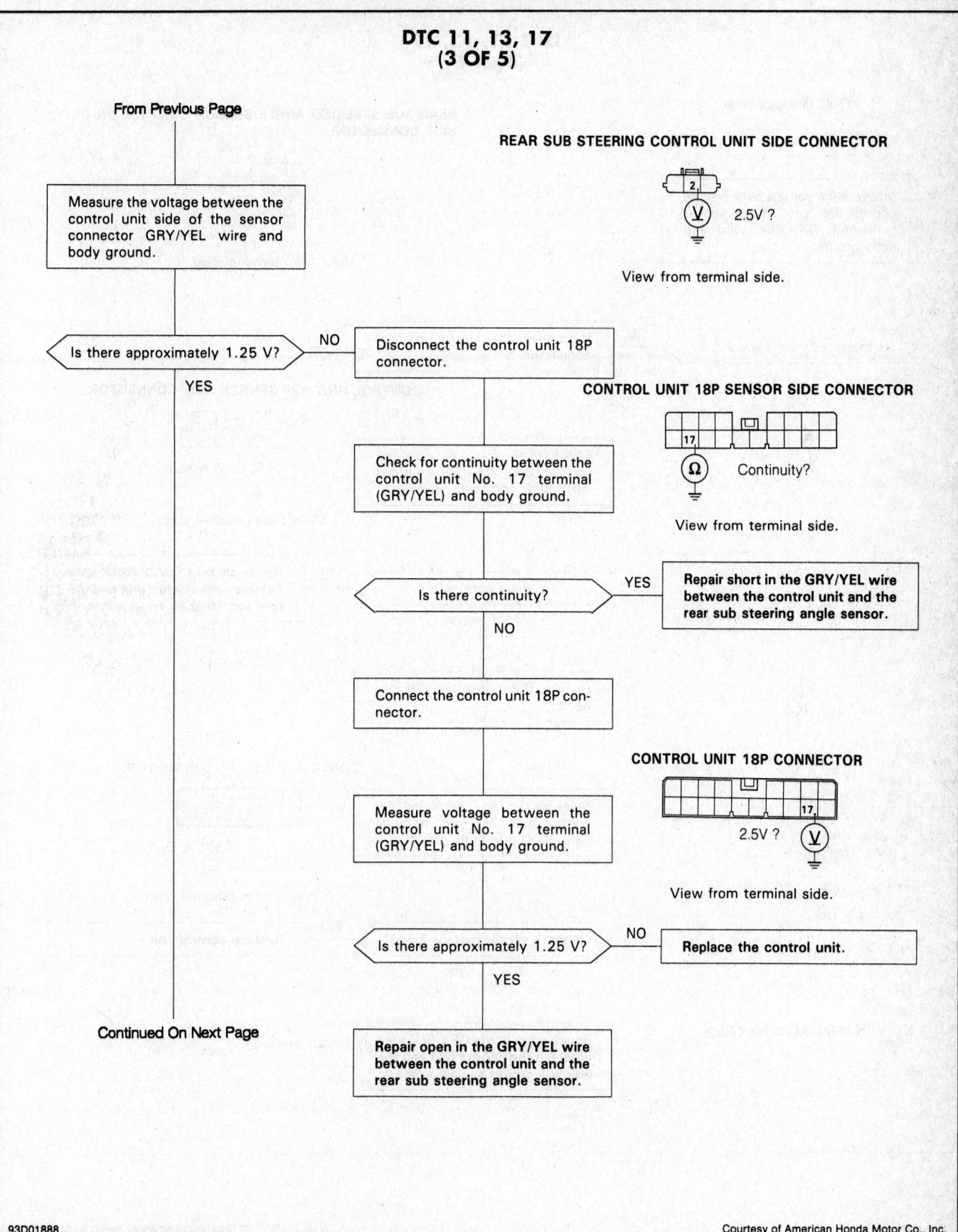

DTC 11, 13, 17
(3 OF 5)

From Previous Page

Measure the voltage between the control unit side of the sensor connector GRY/YEL wire and body ground.

REAR SUB STEERING CONTROL UNIT SIDE CONNECTOR

2.5V ?

View from terminal side.

Is there approximately 1.25 V? —NO→ Disconnect the control unit 18P connector.

YES

CONTROL UNIT 18P SENSOR SIDE CONNECTOR

Continuity?

View from terminal side.

Check for continuity between the control unit No. 17 terminal (GRY/YEL) and body ground.

Is there continuity? —YES→ **Repair short in the GRY/YEL wire between the control unit and the rear sub steering angle sensor.**

NO

Connect the control unit 18P connector.

CONTROL UNIT 18P CONNECTOR

2.5V ?

View from terminal side.

Measure voltage between the control unit No. 17 terminal (GRY/YEL) and body ground.

Is there approximately 1.25 V? —NO→ **Replace the control unit.**

YES

Continued On Next Page

Repair open in the GRY/YEL wire between the control unit and the rear sub steering angle sensor.

DTC 11, 13, 17
(4 OF 5)

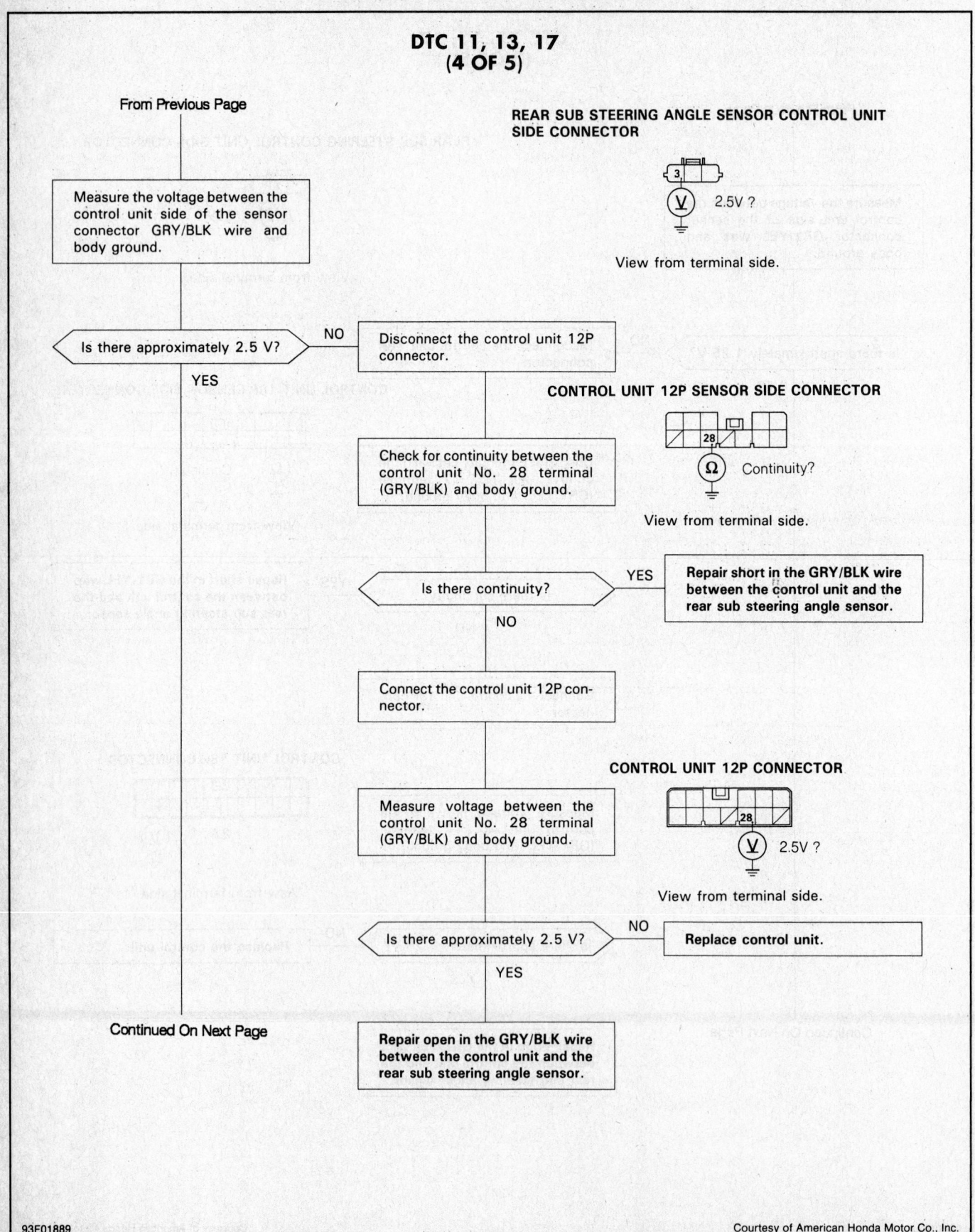

From Previous Page

REAR SUB STEERING ANGLE SENSOR CONTROL UNIT SIDE CONNECTOR

Measure the voltage between the control unit side of the sensor connector GRY/BLK wire and body ground.

2.5V ?

View from terminal side.

Is there approximately 2.5 V? — NO → Disconnect the control unit 12P connector.

YES

CONTROL UNIT 12P SENSOR SIDE CONNECTOR

Check for continuity between the control unit No. 28 terminal (GRY/BLK) and body ground.

28

Continuity?

View from terminal side.

Is there continuity? — YES → **Repair short in the GRY/BLK wire between the control unit and the rear sub steering angle sensor.**

NO

Connect the control unit 12P connector.

CONTROL UNIT 12P CONNECTOR

Measure voltage between the control unit No. 28 terminal (GRY/BLK) and body ground.

28

2.5V ?

View from terminal side.

Is there approximately 2.5 V? — NO → **Replace control unit.**

YES

Continued On Next Page

Repair open in the GRY/BLK wire between the control unit and the rear sub steering angle sensor.

DTC 11, 13, 17
(5 OF 5)

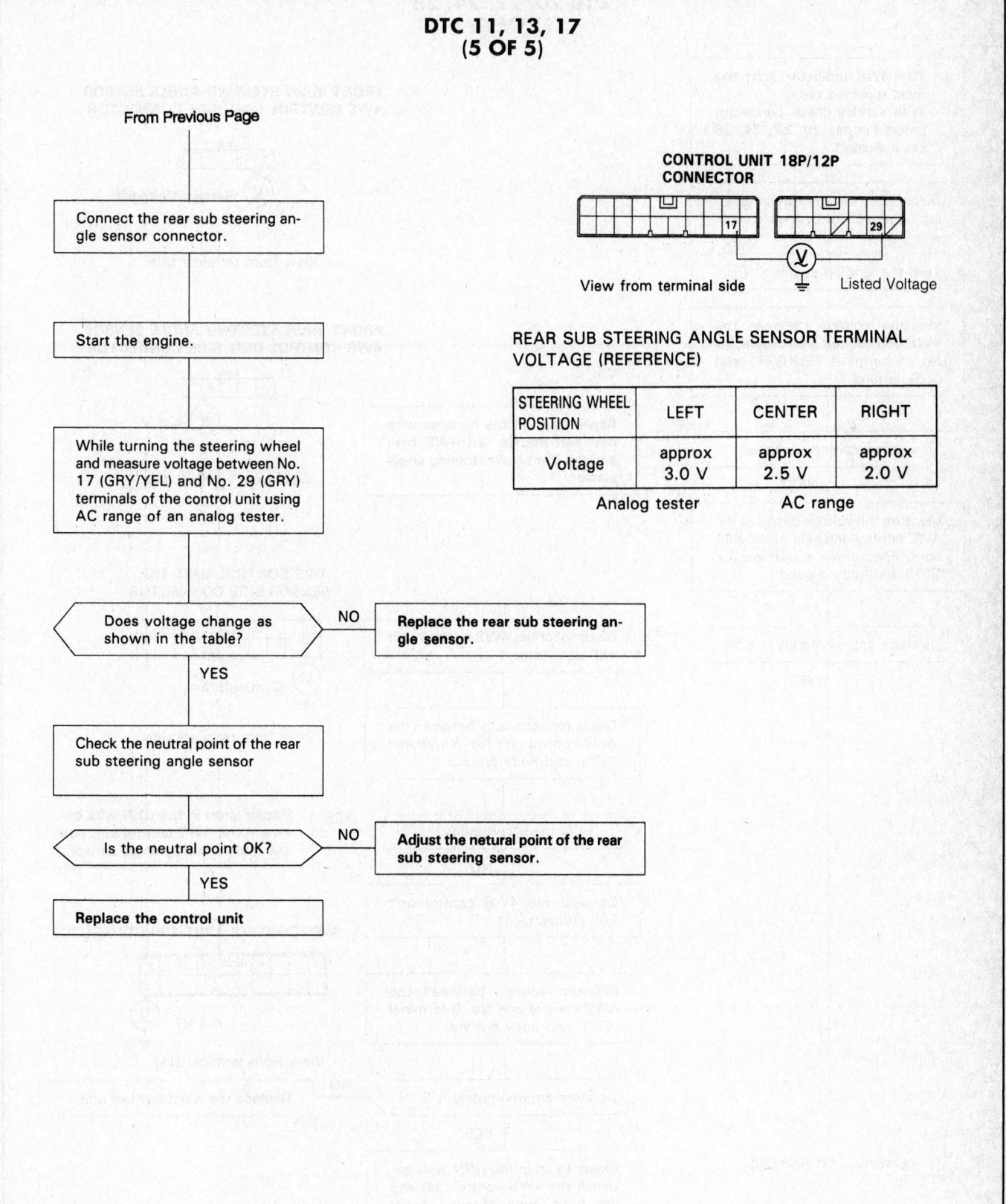

From Previous Page

Connect the rear sub steering angle sensor connector.

Start the engine.

While turning the steering wheel and measure voltage between No. 17 (GRY/YEL) and No. 29 (GRY) terminals of the control unit using AC range of an analog tester.

Does voltage change as shown in the table? —— NO —→ Replace the rear sub steering angle sensor.

YES

Check the neutral point of the rear sub steering angle sensor

Is the neutral point OK? —— NO —→ Adjust the netural point of the rear sub steering sensor.

YES

Replace the control unit

CONTROL UNIT 18P/12P CONNECTOR

17   29

View from terminal side   Listed Voltage

REAR SUB STEERING ANGLE SENSOR TERMINAL VOLTAGE (REFERENCE)

STEERING WHEEL POSITION	LEFT	CENTER	RIGHT
Voltage	approx 3.0 V	approx 2.5 V	approx 2.0 V

Analog tester   AC range

DTC 20, 22, 24, 28
(1 OF 4)

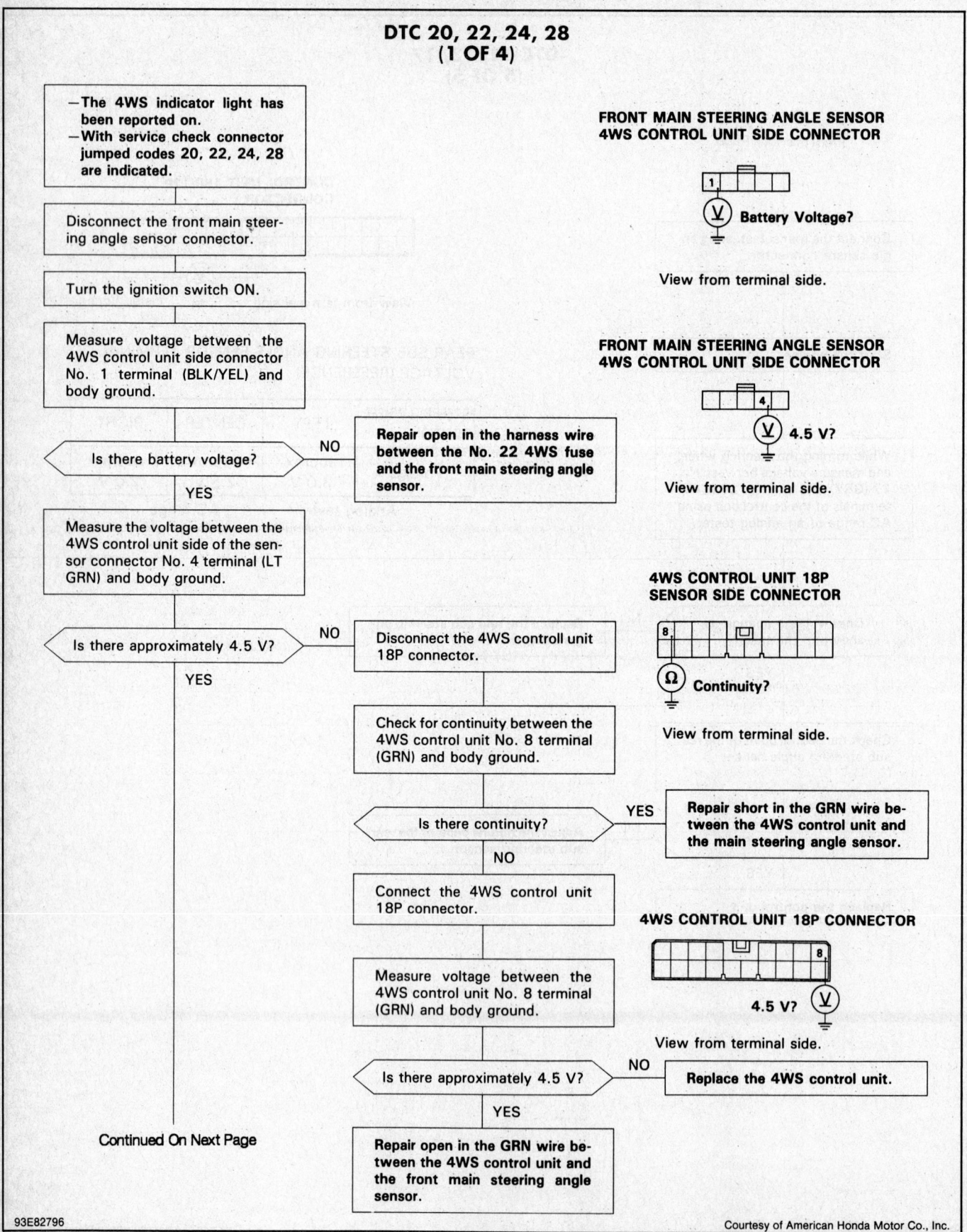

— The 4WS indicator light has been reported on.
— With service check connector jumped codes 20, 22, 24, 28 are indicated.

Disconnect the front main steering angle sensor connector.

Turn the ignition switch ON.

Measure voltage between the 4WS control unit side connector No. 1 terminal (BLK/YEL) and body ground.

Is there battery voltage? — NO → Repair open in the harness wire between the No. 22 4WS fuse and the front main steering angle sensor.

YES

Measure the voltage between the 4WS control unit side of the sensor connector No. 4 terminal (LT GRN) and body ground.

Is there approximately 4.5 V? — NO → Disconnect the 4WS control unit 18P connector.

YES

Check for continuity between the 4WS control unit No. 8 terminal (GRN) and body ground.

Is there continuity? — YES → Repair short in the GRN wire between the 4WS control unit and the main steering angle sensor.

NO

Connect the 4WS control unit 18P connector.

Measure voltage between the 4WS control unit No. 8 terminal (GRN) and body ground.

Is there approximately 4.5 V? — NO → Replace the 4WS control unit.

YES

Repair open in the GRN wire between the 4WS control unit and the front main steering angle sensor.

Continued On Next Page

FRONT MAIN STEERING ANGLE SENSOR 4WS CONTROL UNIT SIDE CONNECTOR

1 Battery Voltage?

View from terminal side.

FRONT MAIN STEERING ANGLE SENSOR 4WS CONTROL UNIT SIDE CONNECTOR

4 4.5 V?

View from terminal side.

4WS CONTROL UNIT 18P SENSOR SIDE CONNECTOR

8 Continuity?

View from terminal side.

4WS CONTROL UNIT 18P CONNECTOR

8 4.5 V?

View from terminal side.

DTC 20, 22, 24, 28
(2 OF 4)

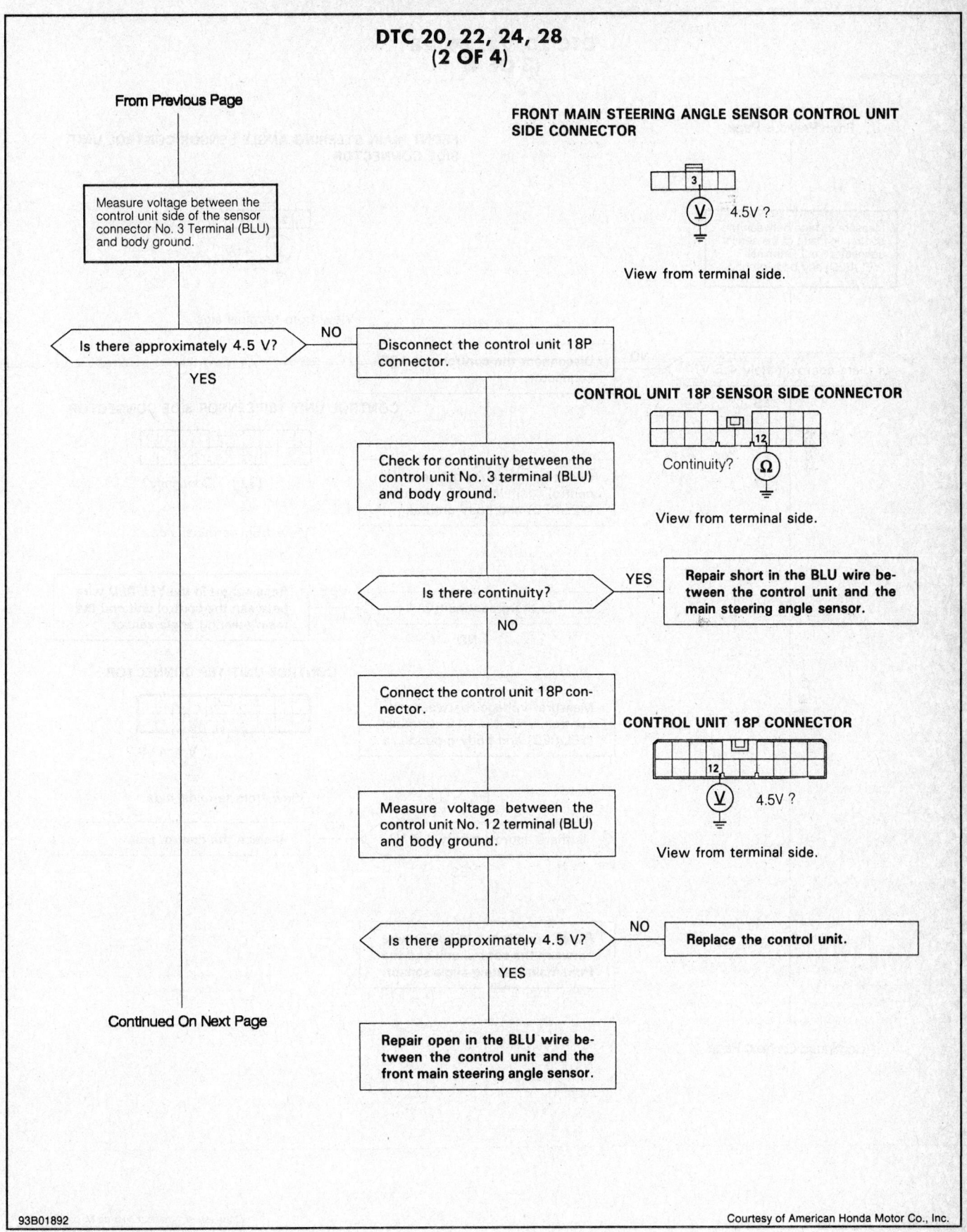

From Previous Page

Measure voltage between the control unit side of the sensor connector No. 3 Terminal (BLU) and body ground.

FRONT MAIN STEERING ANGLE SENSOR CONTROL UNIT SIDE CONNECTOR

3

V   4.5V ?

View from terminal side.

Is there approximately 4.5 V? — NO → Disconnect the control unit 18P connector.

YES

CONTROL UNIT 18P SENSOR SIDE CONNECTOR

12

Continuity?   Ω

View from terminal side.

Check for continuity between the control unit No. 3 terminal (BLU) and body ground.

Is there continuity? — YES → Repair short in the BLU wire between the control unit and the main steering angle sensor.

NO

Connect the control unit 18P connector.

CONTROL UNIT 18P CONNECTOR

12

V   4.5V ?

View from terminal side.

Measure voltage between the control unit No. 12 terminal (BLU) and body ground.

Is there approximately 4.5 V? — NO → Replace the control unit.

YES

Continued On Next Page

Repair open in the BLU wire between the control unit and the front main steering angle sensor.

DTC 20, 22, 24, 28
(3 OF 4)

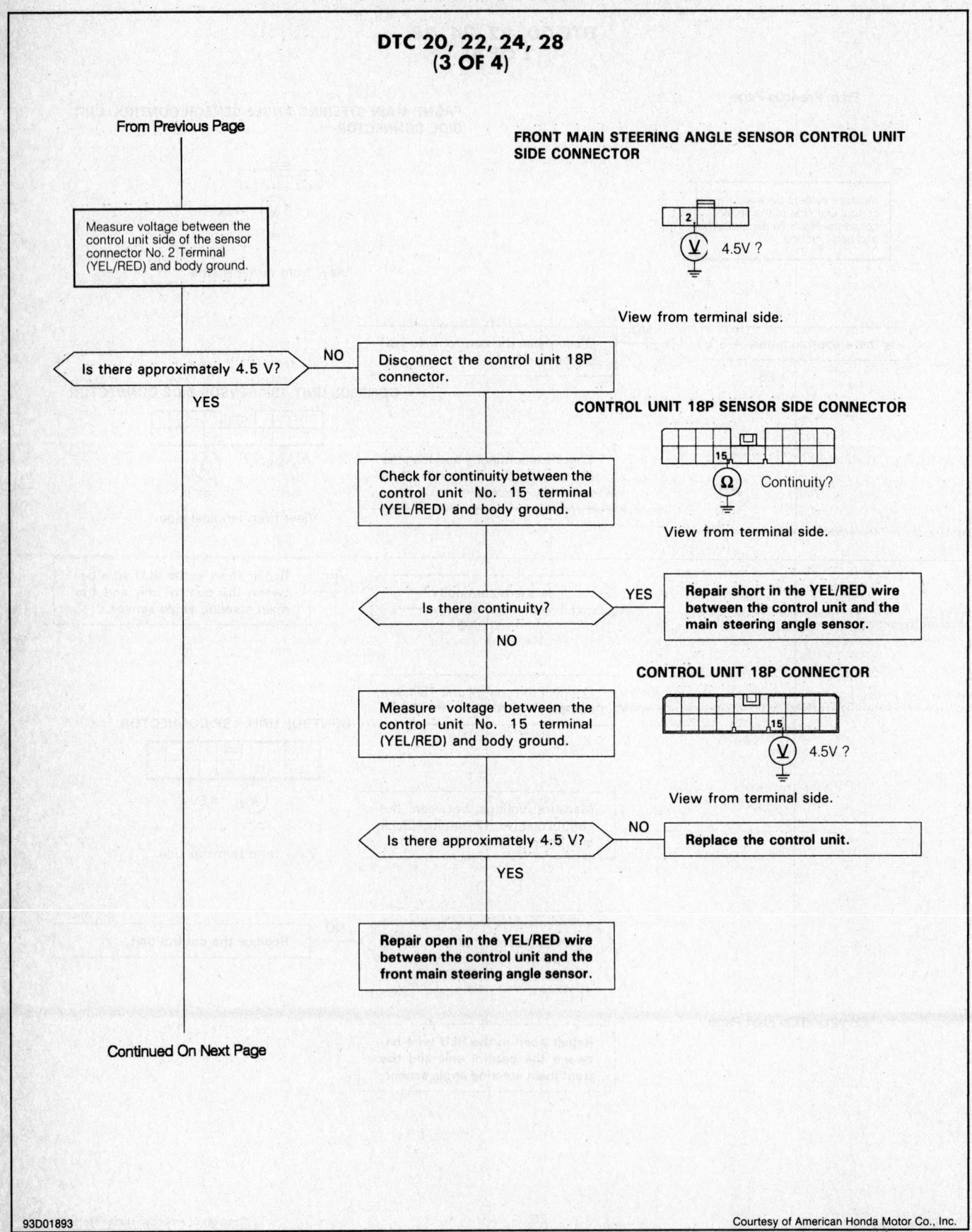

From Previous Page

Measure voltage between the control unit side of the sensor connector No. 2 Terminal (YEL/RED) and body ground.

FRONT MAIN STEERING ANGLE SENSOR CONTROL UNIT SIDE CONNECTOR

4.5V ?

View from terminal side.

Is there approximately 4.5 V? — **NO** → Disconnect the control unit 18P connector.

YES

CONTROL UNIT 18P SENSOR SIDE CONNECTOR

Continuity?

View from terminal side.

Check for continuity between the control unit No. 15 terminal (YEL/RED) and body ground.

Is there continuity? — **YES** → **Repair short in the YEL/RED wire between the control unit and the main steering angle sensor.**

NO

CONTROL UNIT 18P CONNECTOR

4.5V ?

View from terminal side.

Measure voltage between the control unit No. 15 terminal (YEL/RED) and body ground.

Is there approximately 4.5 V? — **NO** → **Replace the control unit.**

YES

Repair open in the YEL/RED wire between the control unit and the front main steering angle sensor.

Continued On Next Page

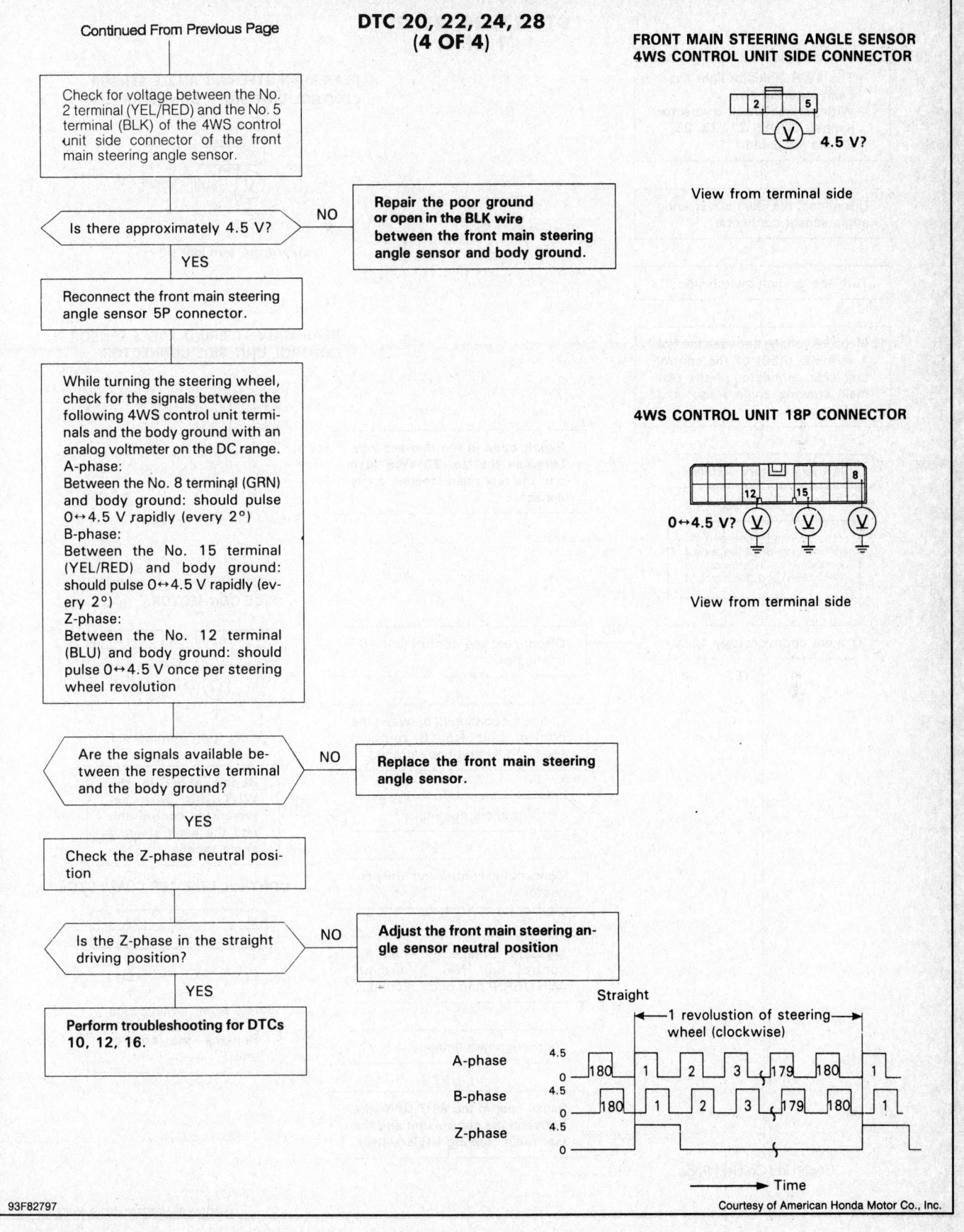

**DTC 20, 22, 24, 28
(4 OF 4)**

Continued From Previous Page

Check for voltage between the No. 2 terminal (YEL/RED) and the No. 5 terminal (BLK) of the 4WS control unit side connector of the front main steering angle sensor.

Is there approximately 4.5 V? — NO → Repair the poor ground or open in the BLK wire between the front main steering angle sensor and body ground.

YES

Reconnect the front main steering angle sensor 5P connector.

While turning the steering wheel, check for the signals between the following 4WS control unit terminals and the body ground with an analog voltmeter on the DC range.
A-phase:
Between the No. 8 terminal (GRN) and body ground: should pulse 0↔4.5 V rapidly (every 2°)
B-phase:
Between the No. 15 terminal (YEL/RED) and body ground: should pulse 0↔4.5 V rapidly (every 2°)
Z-phase:
Between the No. 12 terminal (BLU) and body ground: should pulse 0↔4.5 V once per steering wheel revolution

Are the signals available between the respective terminal and the body ground? — NO → Replace the front main steering angle sensor.

YES

Check the Z-phase neutral position

Is the Z-phase in the straight driving position? — NO → Adjust the front main steering angle sensor neutral position

YES

Perform troubleshooting for DTCs 10, 12, 16.

**FRONT MAIN STEERING ANGLE SENSOR
4WS CONTROL UNIT SIDE CONNECTOR**

2 5
4.5 V?

View from terminal side

4WS CONTROL UNIT 18P CONNECTOR

0↔4.5 V? 12 15 8

View from terminal side

Straight

1 revolution of steering wheel (clockwise)

A-phase 4.5 0 180 | 1 | 2 | 3 | 179 | 180 | 1
B-phase 4.5 0 180 | 1 | 2 | 3 | 179 | 180 | 1
Z-phase 4.5 0

Time

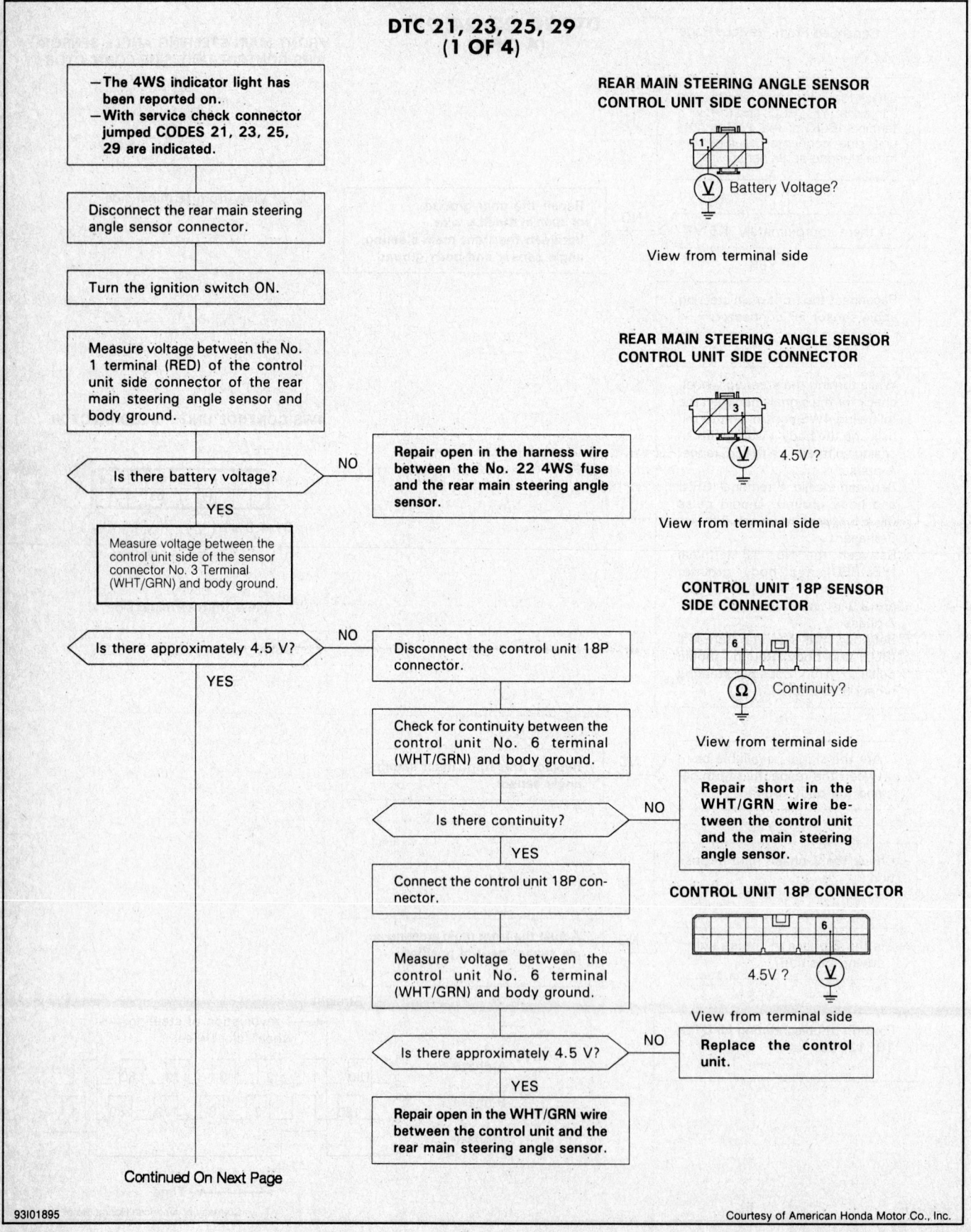

DTC 21, 23, 25, 29
(1 OF 4)

- The 4WS indicator light has been reported on.
- With service check connector jumped CODES 21, 23, 25, 29 are indicated.

Disconnect the rear main steering angle sensor connector.

Turn the ignition switch ON.

Measure voltage between the No. 1 terminal (RED) of the control unit side connector of the rear main steering angle sensor and body ground.

Is there battery voltage? — NO → Repair open in the harness wire between the No. 22 4WS fuse and the rear main steering angle sensor.

YES

Measure voltage between the control unit side of the sensor connector No. 3 Terminal (WHT/GRN) and body ground.

Is there approximately 4.5 V? — NO → Disconnect the control unit 18P connector.

YES

Check for continuity between the control unit No. 6 terminal (WHT/GRN) and body ground.

Is there continuity? — NO → Repair short in the WHT/GRN wire between the control unit and the main steering angle sensor.

YES

Connect the control unit 18P connector.

Measure voltage between the control unit No. 6 terminal (WHT/GRN) and body ground.

Is there approximately 4.5 V? — NO → Replace the control unit.

YES

Repair open in the WHT/GRN wire between the control unit and the rear main steering angle sensor.

REAR MAIN STEERING ANGLE SENSOR CONTROL UNIT SIDE CONNECTOR

Battery Voltage?

View from terminal side

REAR MAIN STEERING ANGLE SENSOR CONTROL UNIT SIDE CONNECTOR

4.5V ?

View from terminal side

CONTROL UNIT 18P SENSOR SIDE CONNECTOR

Continuity?

View from terminal side

CONTROL UNIT 18P CONNECTOR

4.5V ?

View from terminal side

Continued On Next Page

93I01895

DTC 21, 23, 25, 29
(2 OF 4)

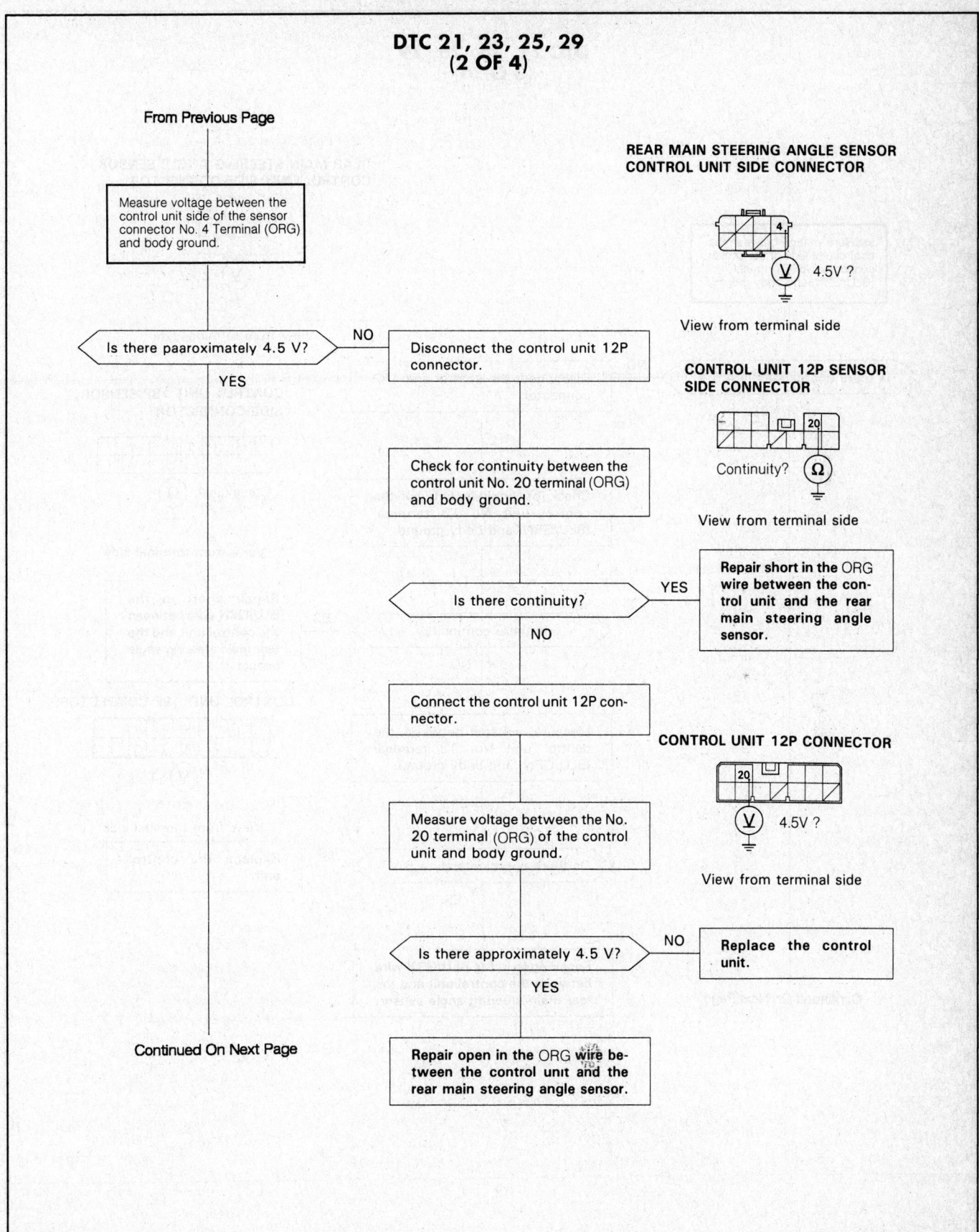

From Previous Page

Measure voltage between the control unit side of the sensor connector No. 4 Terminal (ORG) and body ground.

Is there paaroximately 4.5 V?

YES

NO

REAR MAIN STEERING ANGLE SENSOR CONTROL UNIT SIDE CONNECTOR

4.5V ?

View from terminal side

Disconnect the control unit 12P connector.

Check for continuity between the control unit No. 20 terminal (ORG) and body ground.

CONTROL UNIT 12P SENSOR SIDE CONNECTOR

Continuity?

View from terminal side

Is there continuity?

YES

NO

Repair short in the ORG wire between the control unit and the rear main steering angle sensor.

Connect the control unit 12P connector.

Measure voltage between the No. 20 terminal (ORG) of the control unit and body ground.

CONTROL UNIT 12P CONNECTOR

4.5V ?

View from terminal side

Is there approximately 4.5 V?

NO

YES

Replace the control unit.

Continued On Next Page

Repair open in the ORG wire between the control unit and the rear main steering angle sensor.

93A01896

Courtesy of American Honda Motor Co., Inc.

DTC 21, 23, 25, 29
(3 OF 4)

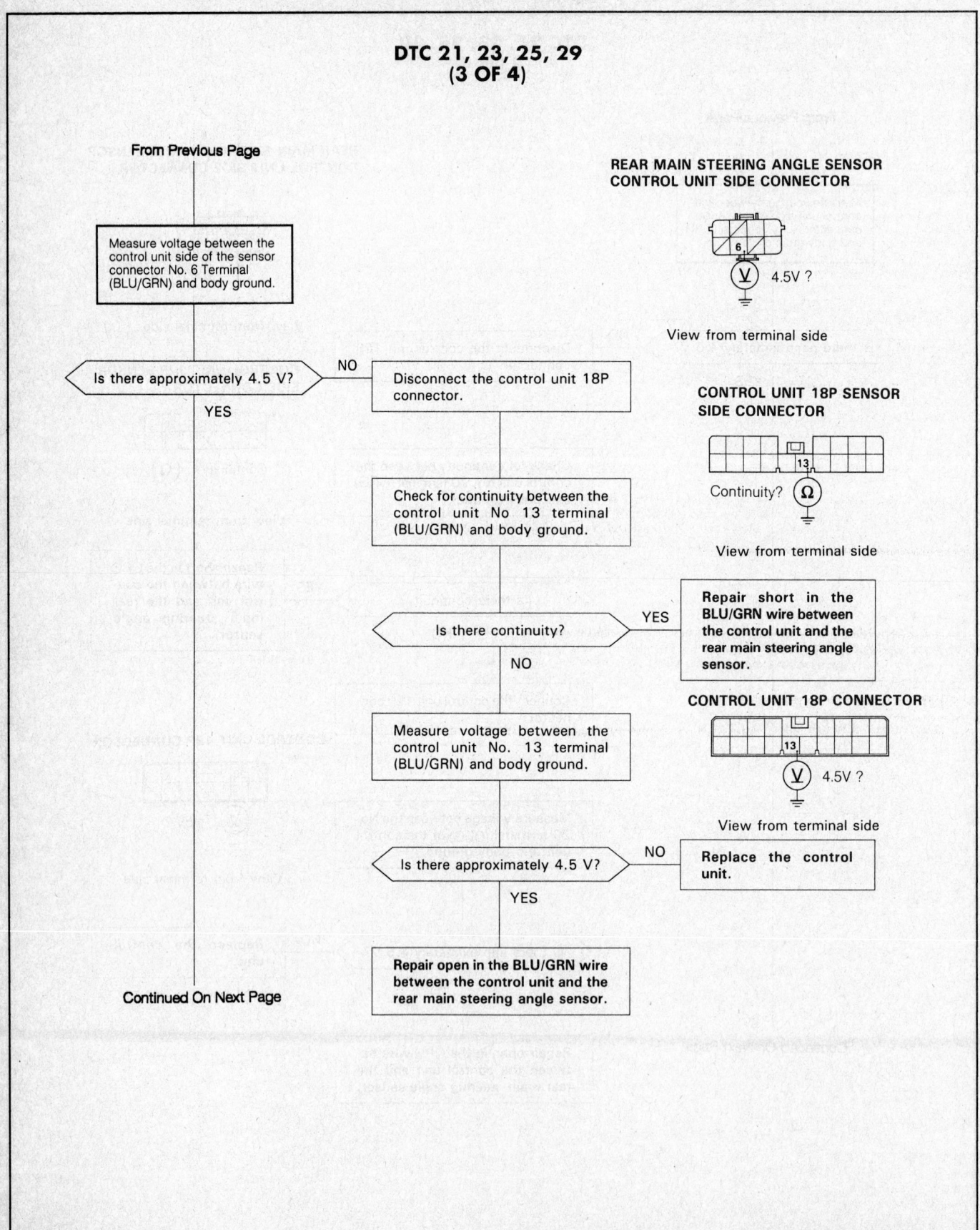

From Previous Page

Measure voltage between the control unit side of the sensor connector No. 6 Terminal (BLU/GRN) and body ground.

Is there approximately 4.5 V? — NO → Disconnect the control unit 18P connector.

YES

Check for continuity between the control unit No 13 terminal (BLU/GRN) and body ground.

Is there continuity? — YES → Repair short in the BLU/GRN wire between the control unit and the rear main steering angle sensor.

NO

Measure voltage between the control unit No. 13 terminal (BLU/GRN) and body ground.

Is there approximately 4.5 V? — NO → Replace the control unit.

YES

Repair open in the BLU/GRN wire between the control unit and the rear main steering angle sensor.

Continued On Next Page

REAR MAIN STEERING ANGLE SENSOR
CONTROL UNIT SIDE CONNECTOR

6

(V) 4.5V ?

View from terminal side

CONTROL UNIT 18P SENSOR
SIDE CONNECTOR

13

Continuity? (Ω)

View from terminal side

CONTROL UNIT 18P CONNECTOR

13

(V) 4.5V ?

View from terminal side

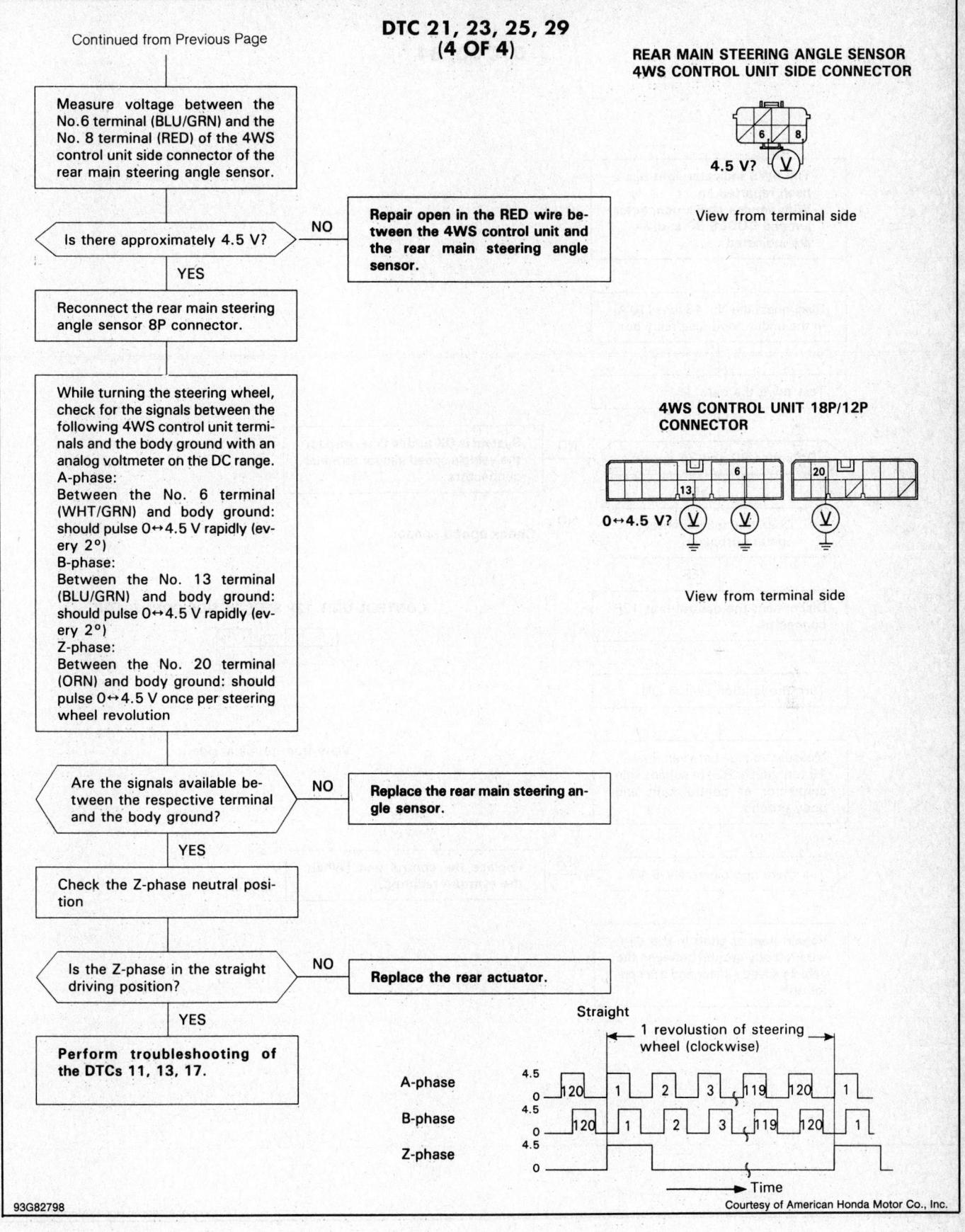

DTC 21, 23, 25, 29
(4 OF 4)

REAR MAIN STEERING ANGLE SENSOR
4WS CONTROL UNIT SIDE CONNECTOR

4.5 V?

View from terminal side

Measure voltage between the No. 6 terminal (BLU/GRN) and the No. 8 terminal (RED) of the 4WS control unit side connector of the rear main steering angle sensor.

Is there approximately 4.5 V? — NO → Repair open in the RED wire between the 4WS control unit and the rear main steering angle sensor.

YES

Reconnect the rear main steering angle sensor 8P connector.

4WS CONTROL UNIT 18P/12P CONNECTOR

0↔4.5 V?

View from terminal side

While turning the steering wheel, check for the signals between the following 4WS control unit terminals and the body ground with an analog voltmeter on the DC range.
A-phase:
Between the No. 6 terminal (WHT/GRN) and body ground: should pulse 0↔4.5 V rapidly (every 2°)
B-phase:
Between the No. 13 terminal (BLU/GRN) and body ground: should pulse 0↔4.5 V rapidly (every 2°)
Z-phase:
Between the No. 20 terminal (ORN) and body ground: should pulse 0↔4.5 V once per steering wheel revolution

Are the signals available between the respective terminal and the body ground? — NO → Replace the rear main steering angle sensor.

YES

Check the Z-phase neutral position

Is the Z-phase in the straight driving position? — NO → Replace the rear actuator.

YES

Perform troubleshooting of the DTCs 11, 13, 17.

Straight

1 revolution of steering wheel (clockwise)

A-phase   4.5 / 0   120 | 1 | 2 | 3 } 119 | 120 | 1
B-phase   4.5 / 0   120 | 1 | 2 | 3 } 119 | 120 | 1
Z-phase   4.5 / 0

Time

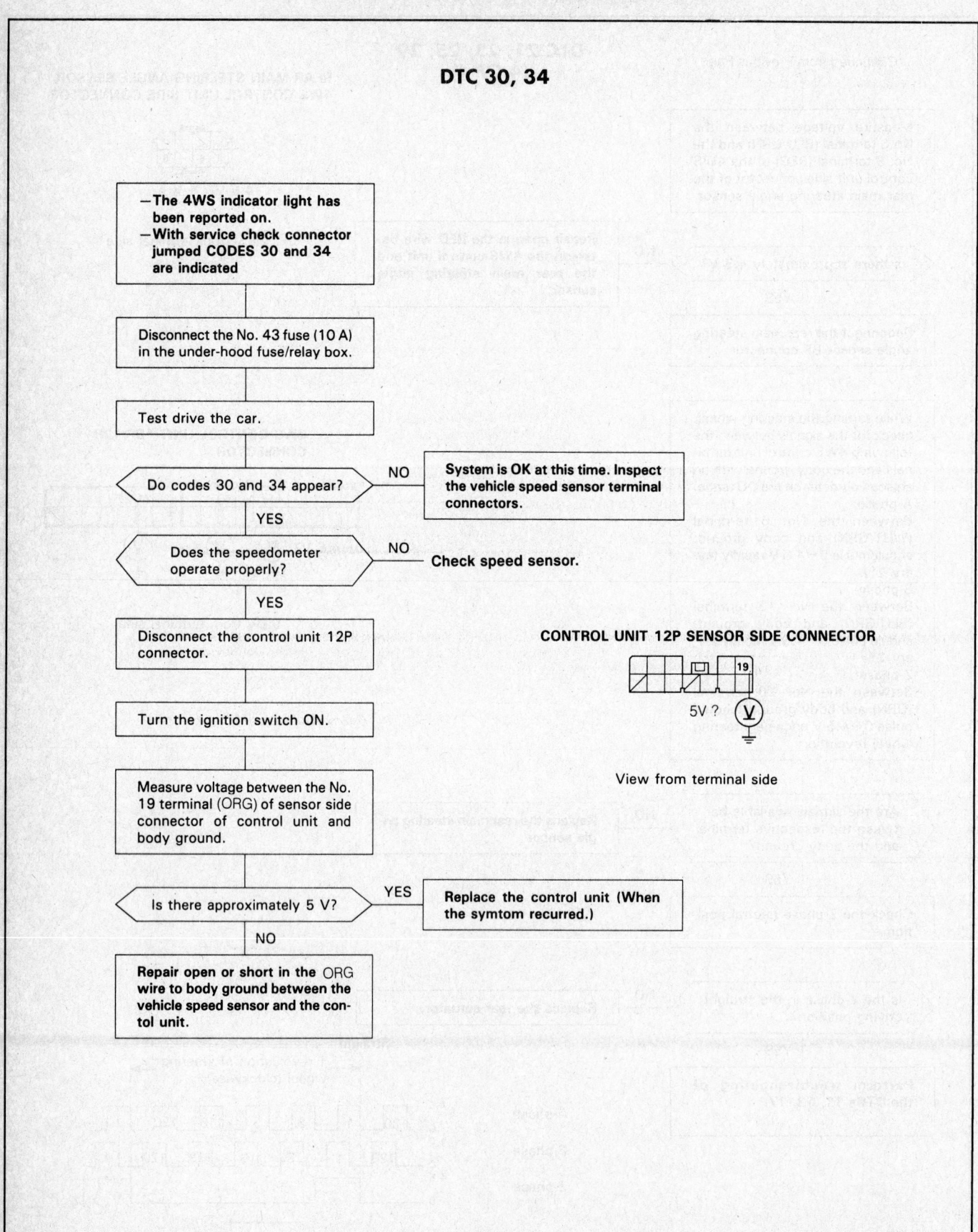

DTC 30, 34

- The 4WS indicator light has been reported on.
- With service check connector jumped CODES 30 and 34 are indicated

↓

Disconnect the No. 43 fuse (10 A) in the under-hood fuse/relay box.

↓

Test drive the car.

↓

Do codes 30 and 34 appear? — **NO** → System is OK at this time. Inspect the vehicle speed sensor terminal connectors.

YES

↓

Does the speedometer operate properly? — **NO** → Check speed sensor.

YES

↓

Disconnect the control unit 12P connector.

↓

Turn the ignition switch ON.

↓

Measure voltage between the No. 19 terminal (ORG) of sensor side connector of control unit and body ground.

↓

Is there approximately 5 V? — **YES** → Replace the control unit (When the symtom recurred.)

NO

↓

Repair open or short in the ORG wire to body ground between the vehicle speed sensor and the contol unit.

CONTROL UNIT 12P SENSOR SIDE CONNECTOR

5V ?

View from terminal side

DTC 31, 35
(1 OF 2)

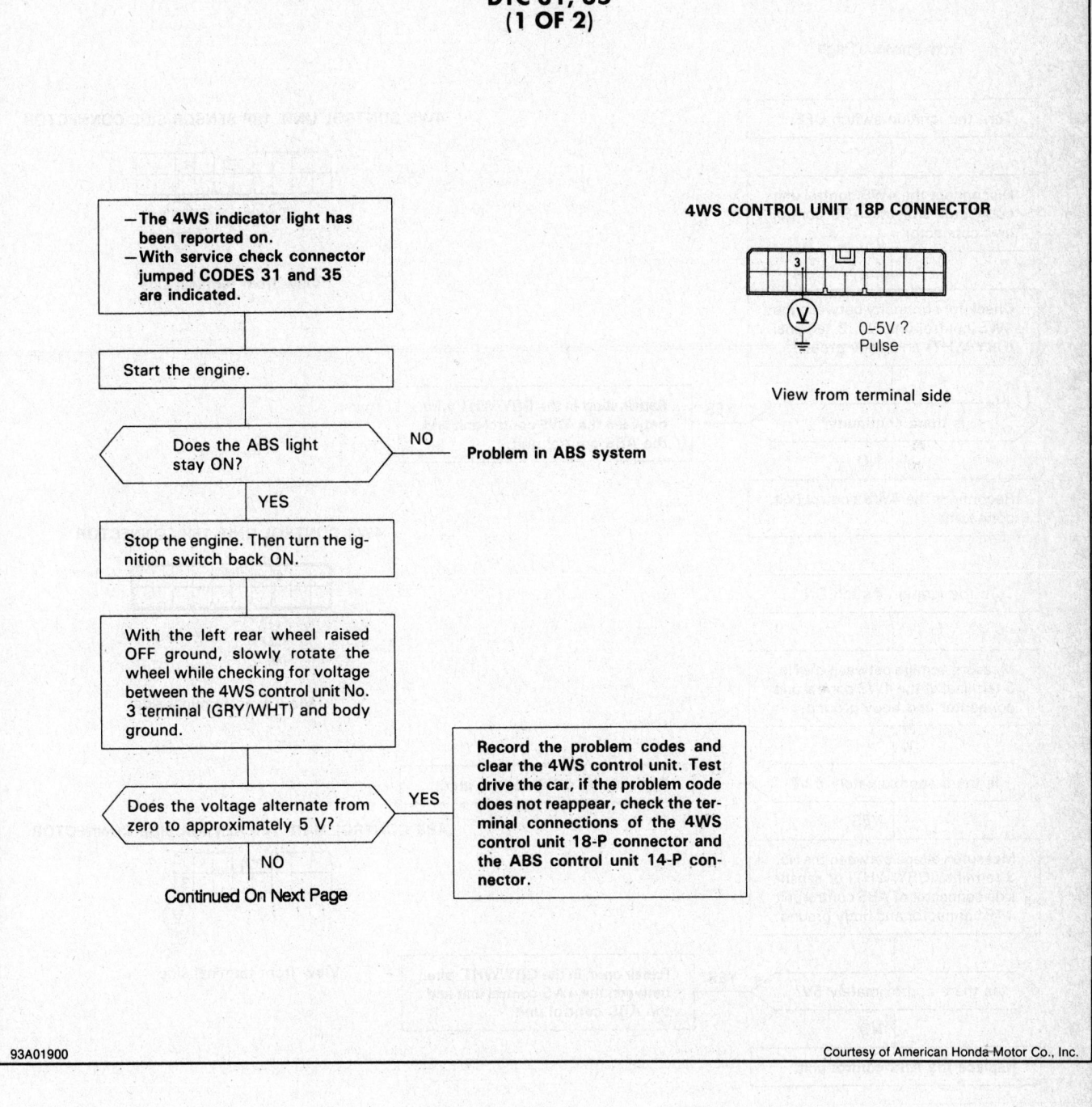

—The 4WS indicator light has been reported on.
—With service check connector jumped CODES 31 and 35 are indicated.

Start the engine.

Does the ABS light stay ON? → NO → **Problem in ABS system**

YES

Stop the engine. Then turn the ignition switch back ON.

With the left rear wheel raised OFF ground, slowly rotate the wheel while checking for voltage between the 4WS control unit No. 3 terminal (GRY/WHT) and body ground.

Does the voltage alternate from zero to approximately 5 V? → YES → Record the problem codes and clear the 4WS control unit. Test drive the car, if the problem code does not reappear, check the terminal connections of the 4WS control unit 18-P connector and the ABS control unit 14-P connector.

NO

Continued On Next Page

4WS CONTROL UNIT 18P CONNECTOR

0–5V ?
Pulse

View from terminal side

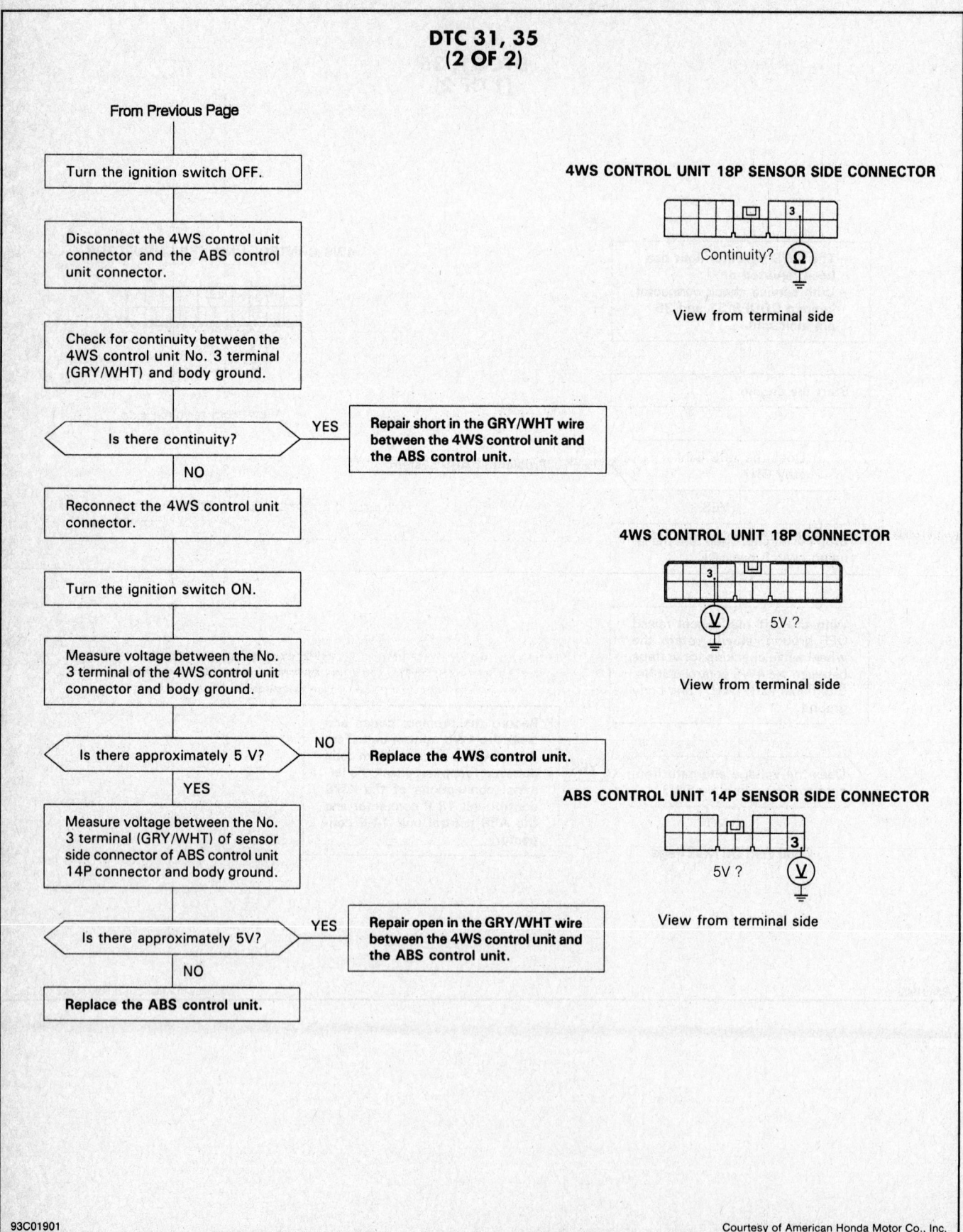

DTC 31, 35
(2 OF 2)

From Previous Page

Turn the ignition switch OFF.

Disconnect the 4WS control unit connector and the ABS control unit connector.

Check for continuity between the 4WS control unit No. 3 terminal (GRY/WHT) and body ground.

Is there continuity? — **YES** → Repair short in the GRY/WHT wire between the 4WS control unit and the ABS control unit.

NO

Reconnect the 4WS control unit connector.

Turn the ignition switch ON.

Measure voltage between the No. 3 terminal of the 4WS control unit connector and body ground.

Is there approximately 5 V? — **NO** → Replace the 4WS control unit.

YES

Measure voltage between the No. 3 terminal (GRY/WHT) of sensor side connector of ABS control unit 14P connector and body ground.

Is there approximately 5V? — **YES** → Repair open in the GRY/WHT wire between the 4WS control unit and the ABS control unit.

NO

Replace the ABS control unit.

4WS CONTROL UNIT 18P SENSOR SIDE CONNECTOR

3

Continuity? Ω

View from terminal side

4WS CONTROL UNIT 18P CONNECTOR

3

V 5V ?

View from terminal side

ABS CONTROL UNIT 14P SENSOR SIDE CONNECTOR

3

5V ? V

View from terminal side

DTC 32, 36
(1 OF 2)

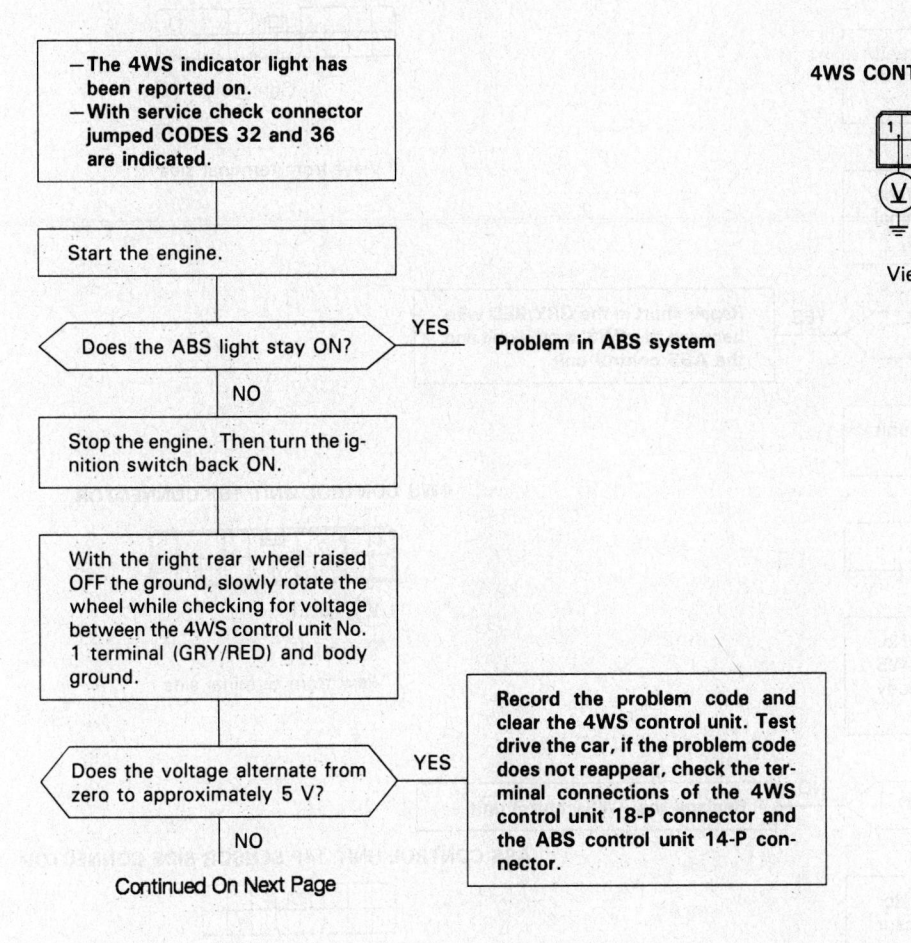

- The 4WS indicator light has been reported on.
- With service check connector jumped CODES 32 and 36 are indicated.

Start the engine.

Does the ABS light stay ON? — YES → **Problem in ABS system**

NO

Stop the engine. Then turn the ignition switch back ON.

With the right rear wheel raised OFF the ground, slowly rotate the wheel while checking for voltage between the 4WS control unit No. 1 terminal (GRY/RED) and body ground.

Does the voltage alternate from zero to approximately 5 V? — YES → Record the problem code and clear the 4WS control unit. Test drive the car, if the problem code does not reappear, check the terminal connections of the 4WS control unit 18-P connector and the ABS control unit 14-P connector.

NO

Continued On Next Page

4WS CONTROL UNIT 18P CONNECTOR

1

0–5V ?
Pulse

View from terminal side

DTC 32, 36
(2 OF 2)

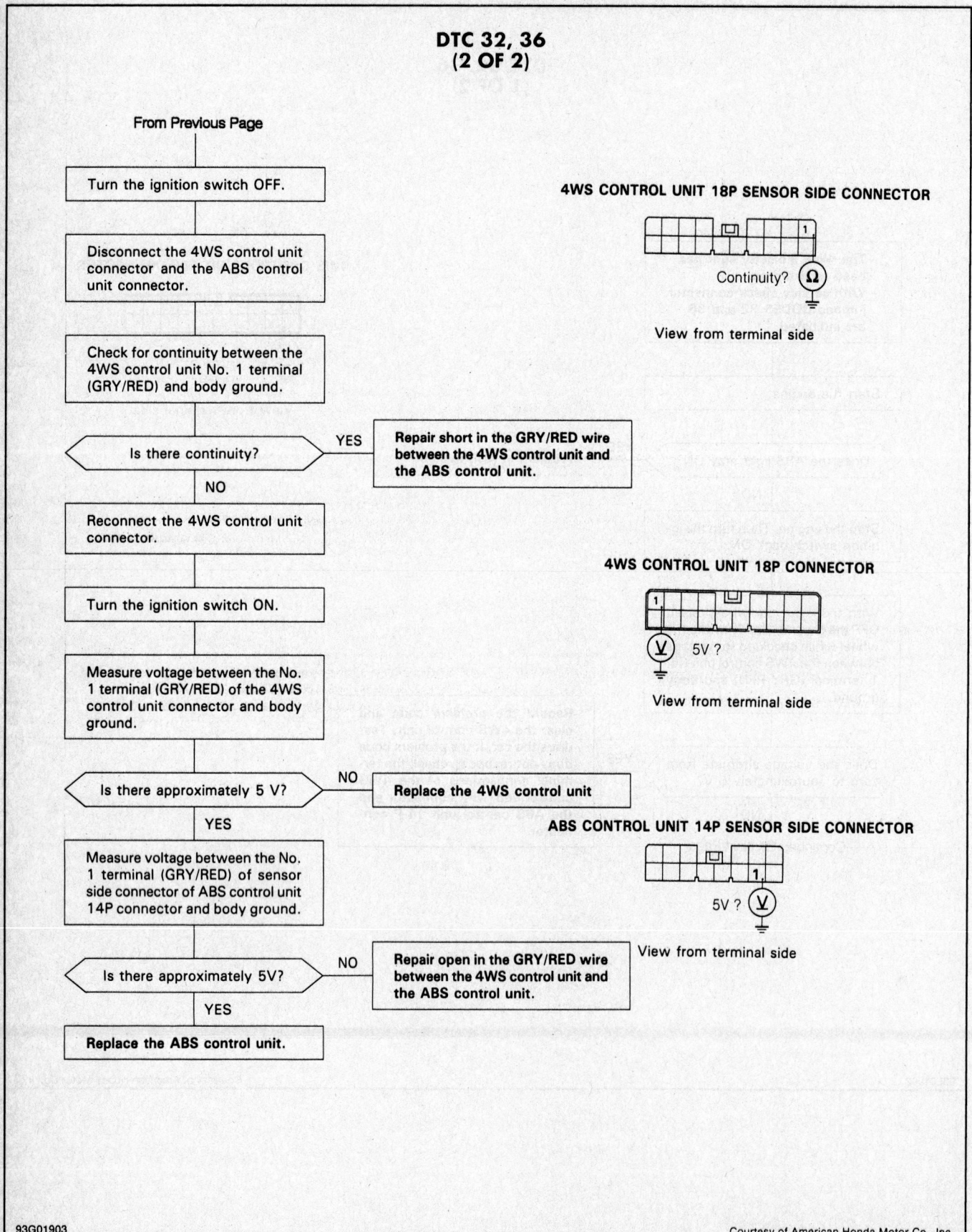

From Previous Page

Turn the ignition switch OFF.

Disconnect the 4WS control unit connector and the ABS control unit connector.

Check for continuity between the 4WS control unit No. 1 terminal (GRY/RED) and body ground.

Is there continuity? — YES → Repair short in the GRY/RED wire between the 4WS control unit and the ABS control unit.

NO

Reconnect the 4WS control unit connector.

Turn the ignition switch ON.

Measure voltage between the No. 1 terminal (GRY/RED) of the 4WS control unit connector and body ground.

Is there approximately 5 V? — NO → Replace the 4WS control unit

YES

Measure voltage between the No. 1 terminal (GRY/RED) of sensor side connector of ABS control unit 14P connector and body ground.

Is there approximately 5V? — NO → Repair open in the GRY/RED wire between the 4WS control unit and the ABS control unit.

YES

Replace the ABS control unit.

4WS CONTROL UNIT 18P SENSOR SIDE CONNECTOR

Continuity? Ω

View from terminal side

4WS CONTROL UNIT 18P CONNECTOR

5V ?

View from terminal side

ABS CONTROL UNIT 14P SENSOR SIDE CONNECTOR

5V ?

View from terminal side

DTC 33
(1 OF 3)

NOTE: Problem code 33 is memorized when the front wheels are turned at a speed of 30 km/h for 2 minutes with the front wheels raised off the ground and the rear wheels blocked. (Parking brake must be off to test this code.)

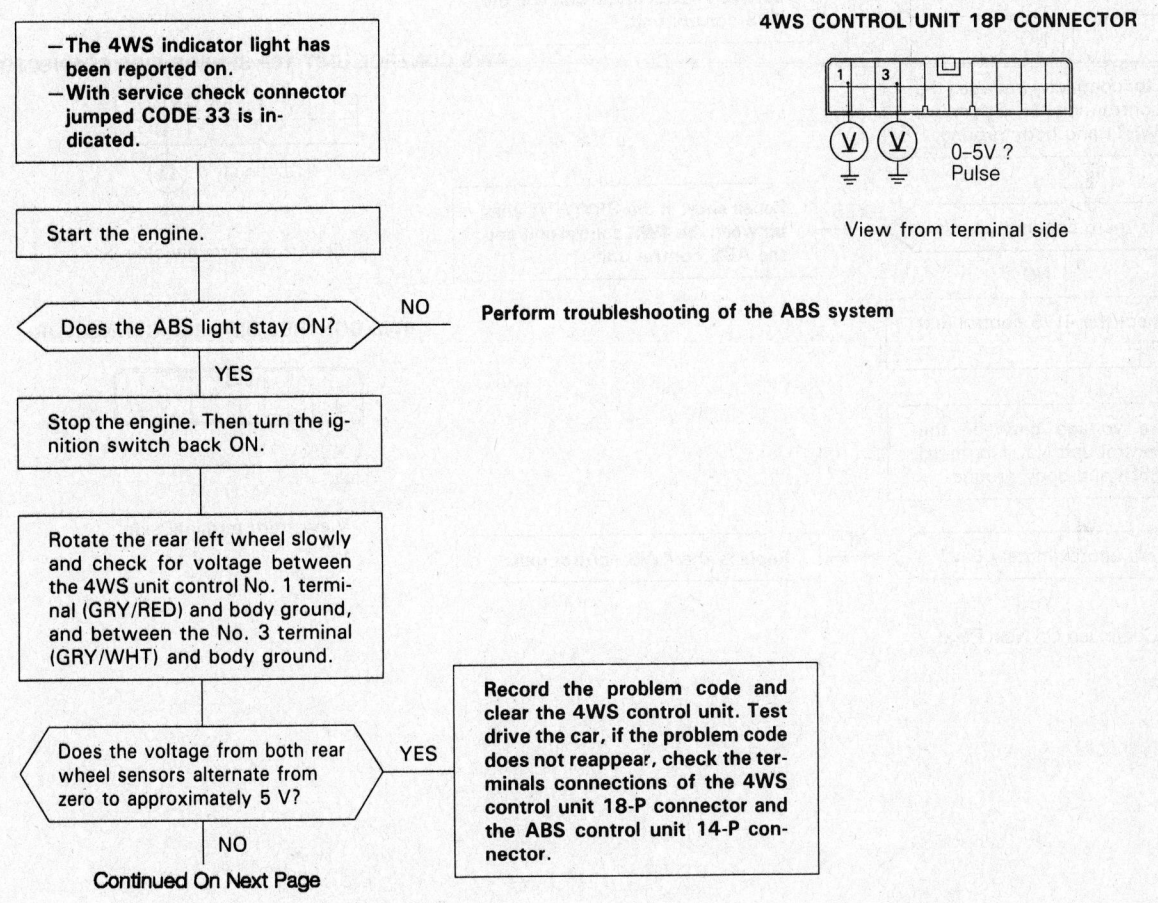

4WS CONTROL UNIT 18P CONNECTOR

0–5V ?
Pulse

View from terminal side

- The 4WS indicator light has been reported on.
- With service check connector jumped CODE 33 is indicated.

Start the engine.

Does the ABS light stay ON? — NO → **Perform troubleshooting of the ABS system**

YES

Stop the engine. Then turn the ignition switch back ON.

Rotate the rear left wheel slowly and check for voltage between the 4WS unit control No. 1 terminal (GRY/RED) and body ground, and between the No. 3 terminal (GRY/WHT) and body ground.

Does the voltage from both rear wheel sensors alternate from zero to approximately 5 V? — YES → Record the problem code and clear the 4WS control unit. Test drive the car, if the problem code does not reappear, check the terminals connections of the 4WS control unit 18-P connector and the ABS control unit 14-P connector.

NO

Continued On Next Page

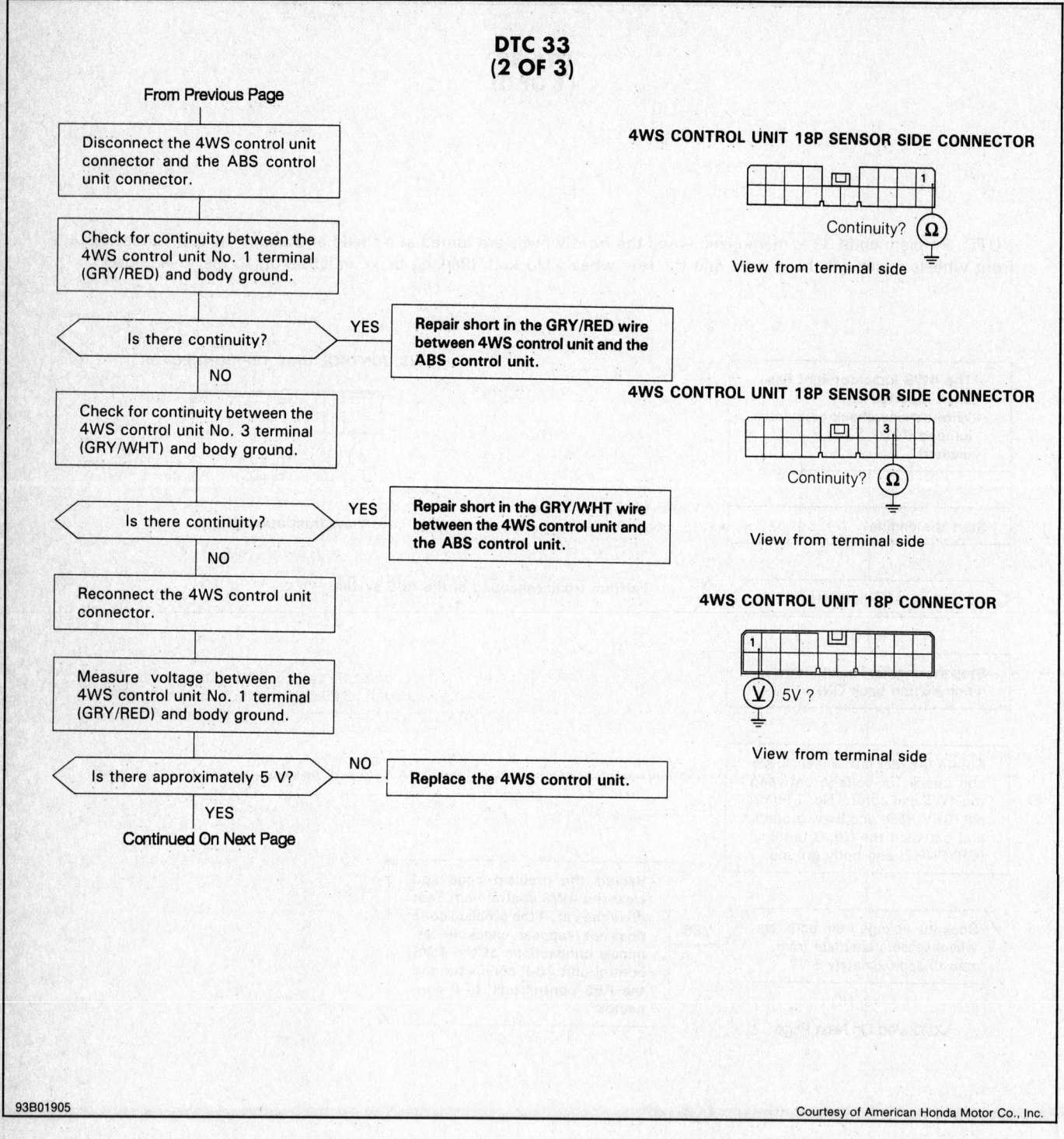

DTC 33
(2 OF 3)

From Previous Page

Disconnect the 4WS control unit connector and the ABS control unit connector.

Check for continuity between the 4WS control unit No. 1 terminal (GRY/RED) and body ground.

Is there continuity? — YES → Repair short in the GRY/RED wire between 4WS control unit and the ABS control unit.

NO

Check for continuity between the 4WS control unit No. 3 terminal (GRY/WHT) and body ground.

Is there continuity? — YES → Repair short in the GRY/WHT wire between the 4WS control unit and the ABS control unit.

NO

Reconnect the 4WS control unit connector.

Measure voltage between the 4WS control unit No. 1 terminal (GRY/RED) and body ground.

Is there approximately 5 V? — NO → Replace the 4WS control unit.

YES

Continued On Next Page

4WS CONTROL UNIT 18P SENSOR SIDE CONNECTOR

Continuity? Ω

View from terminal side

4WS CONTROL UNIT 18P SENSOR SIDE CONNECTOR

Continuity? Ω

View from terminal side

4WS CONTROL UNIT 18P CONNECTOR

V 5V ?

View from terminal side

93B01905

Courtesy of American Honda Motor Co., Inc.

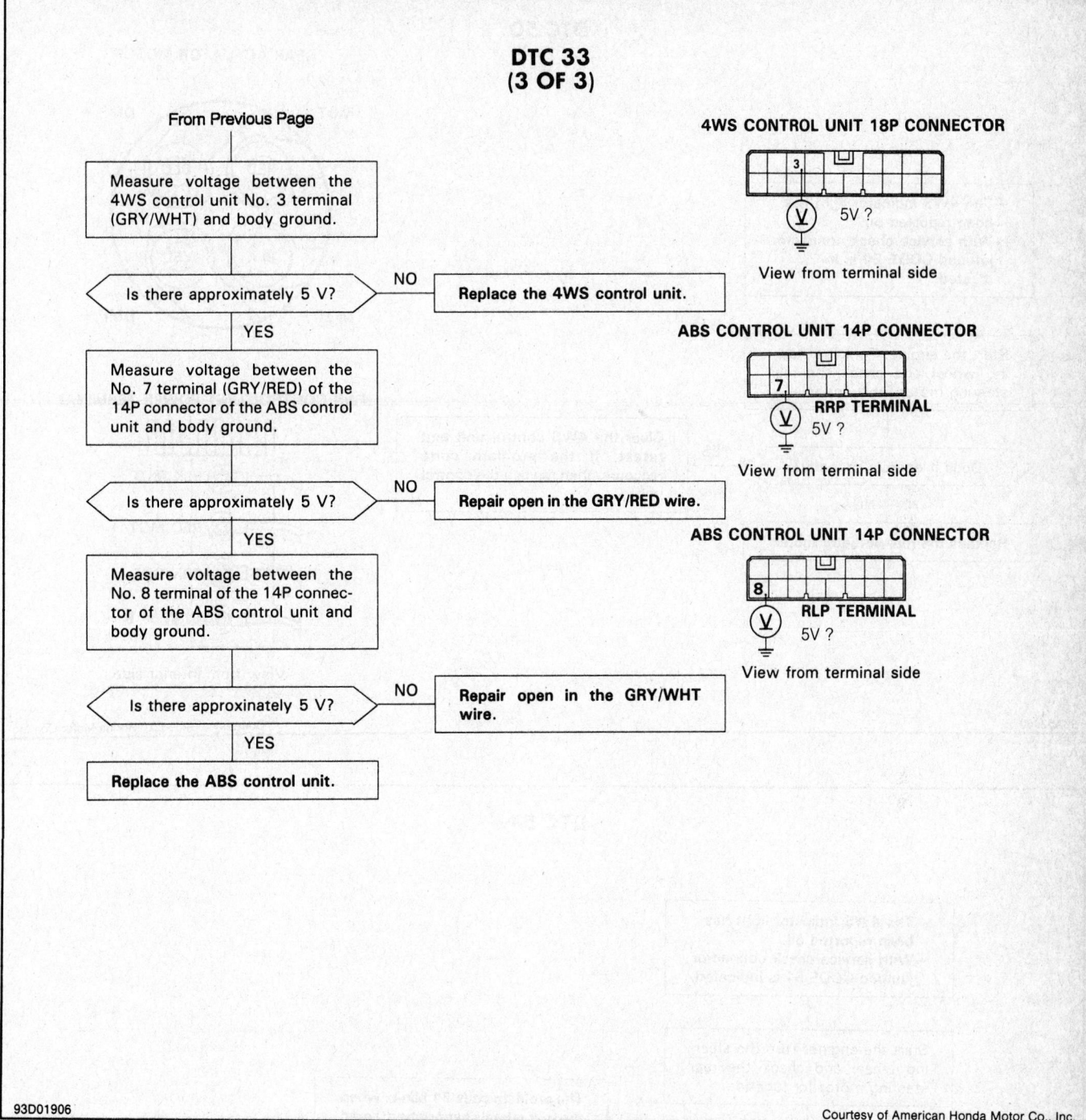

DTC 33
(3 OF 3)

From Previous Page

Measure voltage between the 4WS control unit No. 3 terminal (GRY/WHT) and body ground.

Is there approximately 5 V? — **NO** → Replace the 4WS control unit.

YES

Measure voltage between the No. 7 terminal (GRY/RED) of the 14P connector of the ABS control unit and body ground.

Is there approximately 5 V? — **NO** → Repair open in the GRY/RED wire.

YES

Measure voltage between the No. 8 terminal of the 14P connector of the ABS control unit and body ground.

Is there approximately 5 V? — **NO** → Repair open in the GRY/WHT wire.

YES

Replace the ABS control unit.

4WS CONTROL UNIT 18P CONNECTOR

3

5V ?

View from terminal side

ABS CONTROL UNIT 14P CONNECTOR

7 **RRP TERMINAL**

5V ?

View from terminal side

ABS CONTROL UNIT 14P CONNECTOR

8 **RLP TERMINAL**

5V ?

View from terminal side

1994 STEERING
4-Wheel Steering (Cont.)

DTC 50

REAR ACTUATOR MOTOR

MOT +
DMP –
RED
BLU
BLK
YEL
MOT –
DMP +

4WS CONTROL UNIT POWER TERMINAL

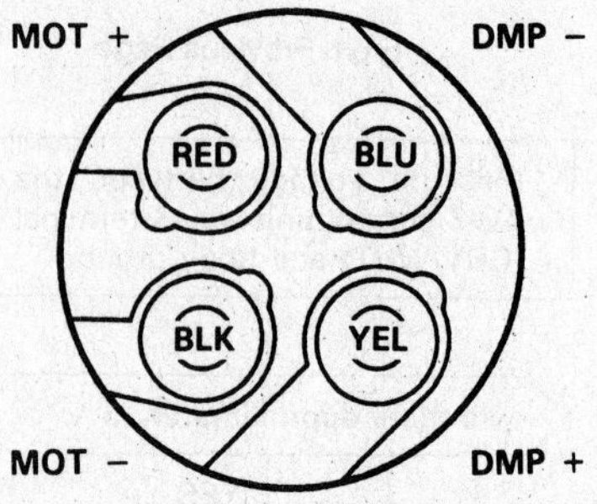

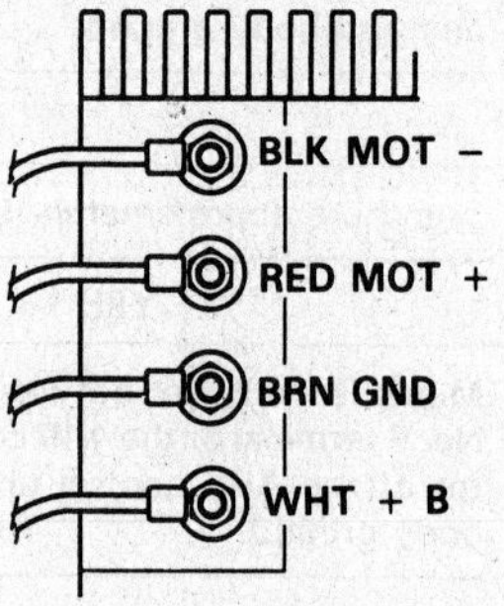

BLK MOT –
RED MOT +
BRN GND
WHT + B

View from interior side

- **–The 4WS indicator light has been reported on.**
- **–With service check connector jumped CODE 50 is indicated.**

Start the engine. Turn the steering wheel and check the rear steering motor for function.

Does it operate properly?

YES → **Clear the 4WS control unit and retest, if the problem code reccours, then replace the control unit.**

NO → **Replace the rear actuator motor.**

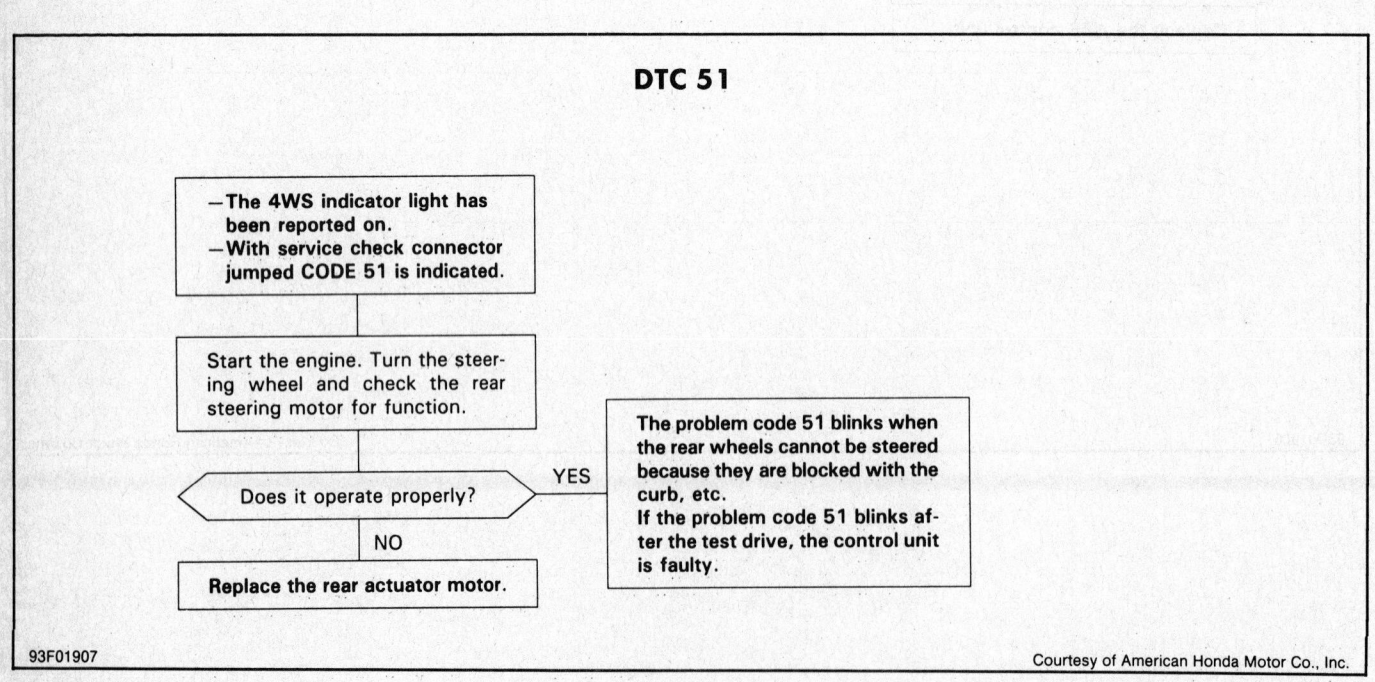

93A02080

Courtesy of American Honda Motor Co., Inc.

DTC 51

- **–The 4WS indicator light has been reported on.**
- **–With service check connector jumped CODE 51 is indicated.**

Start the engine. Turn the steering wheel and check the rear steering motor for function.

Does it operate properly?

YES → **The problem code 51 blinks when the rear wheels cannot be steered because they are blocked with the curb, etc.
If the problem code 51 blinks after the test drive, the control unit is faulty.**

NO → **Replace the rear actuator motor.**

93F01907

Courtesy of American Honda Motor Co., Inc.

DTC 60, 61, 62, 63
(1 OF 3)

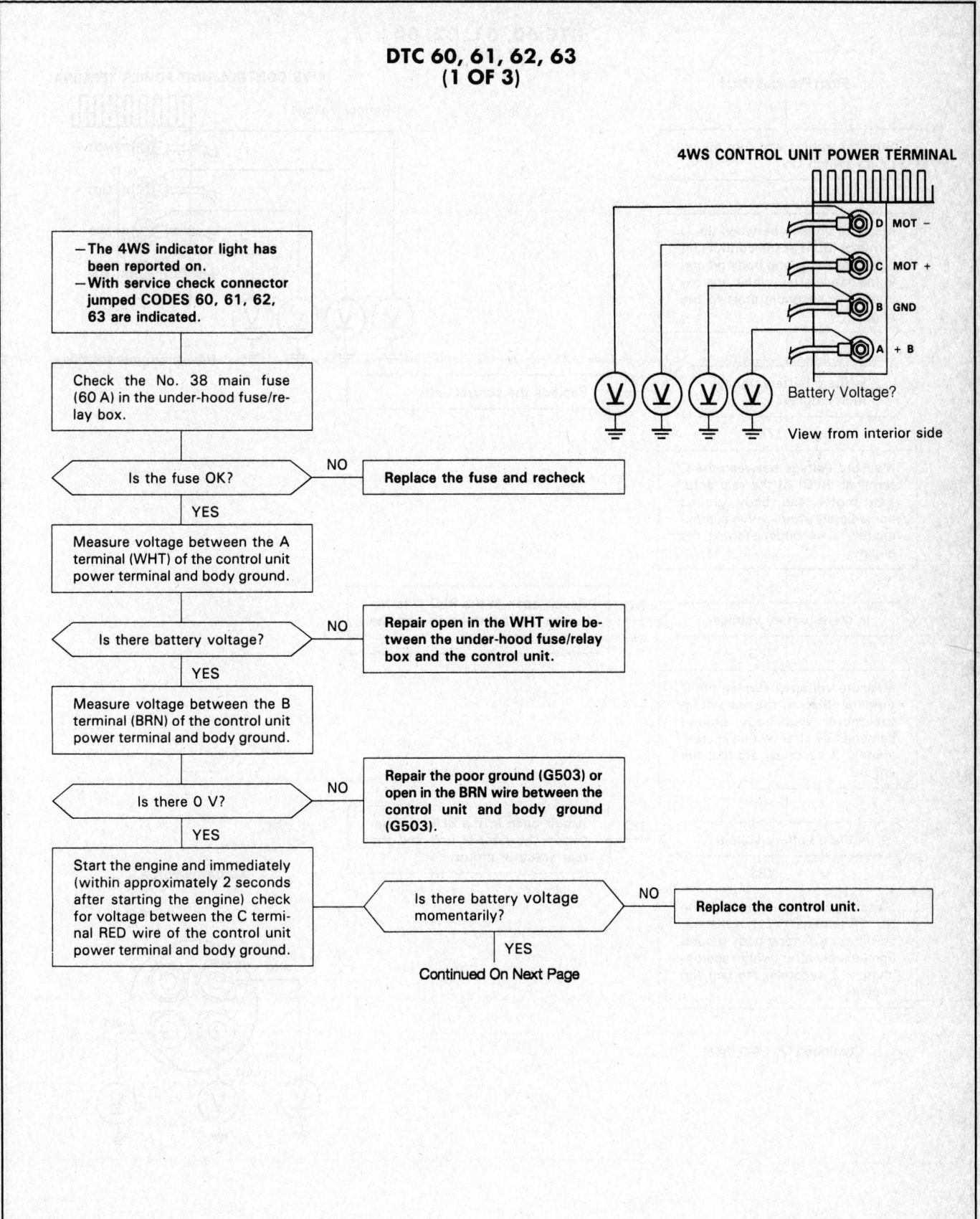

4WS CONTROL UNIT POWER TERMINAL

D MOT –
C MOT +
B GND
A + B

Battery Voltage?

View from interior side

—The 4WS indicator light has been reported on.
—With service check connector jumped CODES 60, 61, 62, 63 are indicated.

Check the No. 38 main fuse (60 A) in the under-hood fuse/relay box.

Is the fuse OK? — **NO** → **Replace the fuse and recheck**

YES

Measure voltage between the A terminal (WHT) of the control unit power terminal and body ground.

Is there battery voltage? — **NO** → **Repair open in the WHT wire between the under-hood fuse/relay box and the control unit.**

YES

Measure voltage between the B terminal (BRN) of the control unit power terminal and body ground.

Is there 0 V? — **NO** → **Repair the poor ground (G503) or open in the BRN wire between the control unit and body ground (G503).**

YES

Start the engine and immediately (within approximately 2 seconds after starting the engine) check for voltage between the C terminal RED wire of the control unit power terminal and body ground.

Is there battery voltage momentarily? — **NO** → **Replace the control unit.**

YES

Continued On Next Page

DTC 60, 61, 62, 63
(2 OF 3)

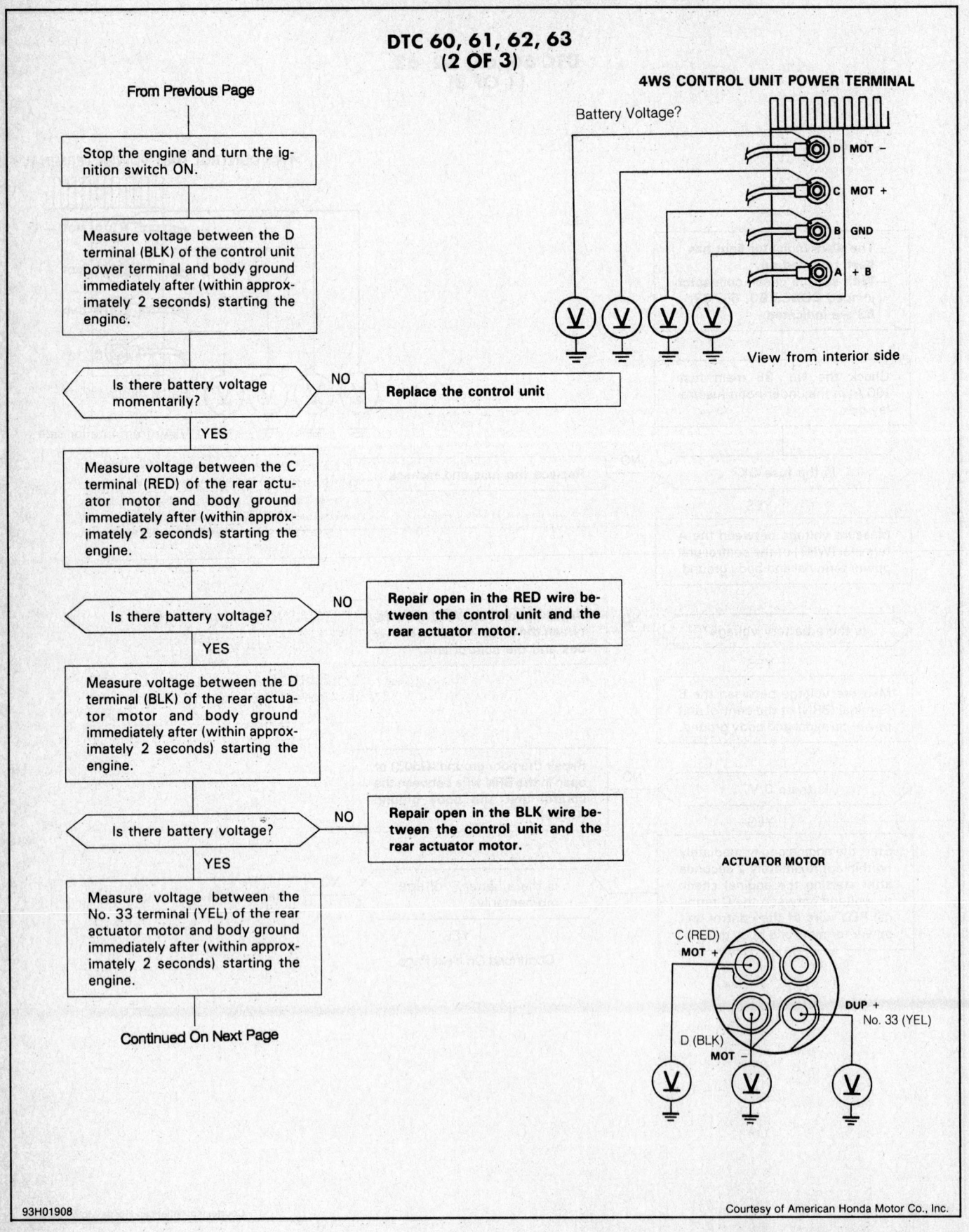

From Previous Page

Stop the engine and turn the ignition switch ON.

Measure voltage between the D terminal (BLK) of the control unit power terminal and body ground immediately after (within approximately 2 seconds) starting the engine.

Is there battery voltage momentarily? — NO → **Replace the control unit**

YES

Measure voltage between the C terminal (RED) of the rear actuator motor and body ground immediately after (within approximately 2 seconds) starting the engine.

Is there battery voltage? — NO → **Repair open in the RED wire between the control unit and the rear actuator motor.**

YES

Measure voltage between the D terminal (BLK) of the rear actuator motor and body ground immediately after (within approximately 2 seconds) starting the engine.

Is there battery voltage? — NO → **Repair open in the BLK wire between the control unit and the rear actuator motor.**

YES

Measure voltage between the No. 33 terminal (YEL) of the rear actuator motor and body ground immediately after (within approximately 2 seconds) starting the engine.

Continued On Next Page

4WS CONTROL UNIT POWER TERMINAL

Battery Voltage?

D MOT –
C MOT +
B GND
A + B

View from interior side

ACTUATOR MOTOR

C (RED)
MOT +

DUP +
No. 33 (YEL)

D (BLK)
MOT –

DTC 60, 61, 62, 63
(3 OF 3)

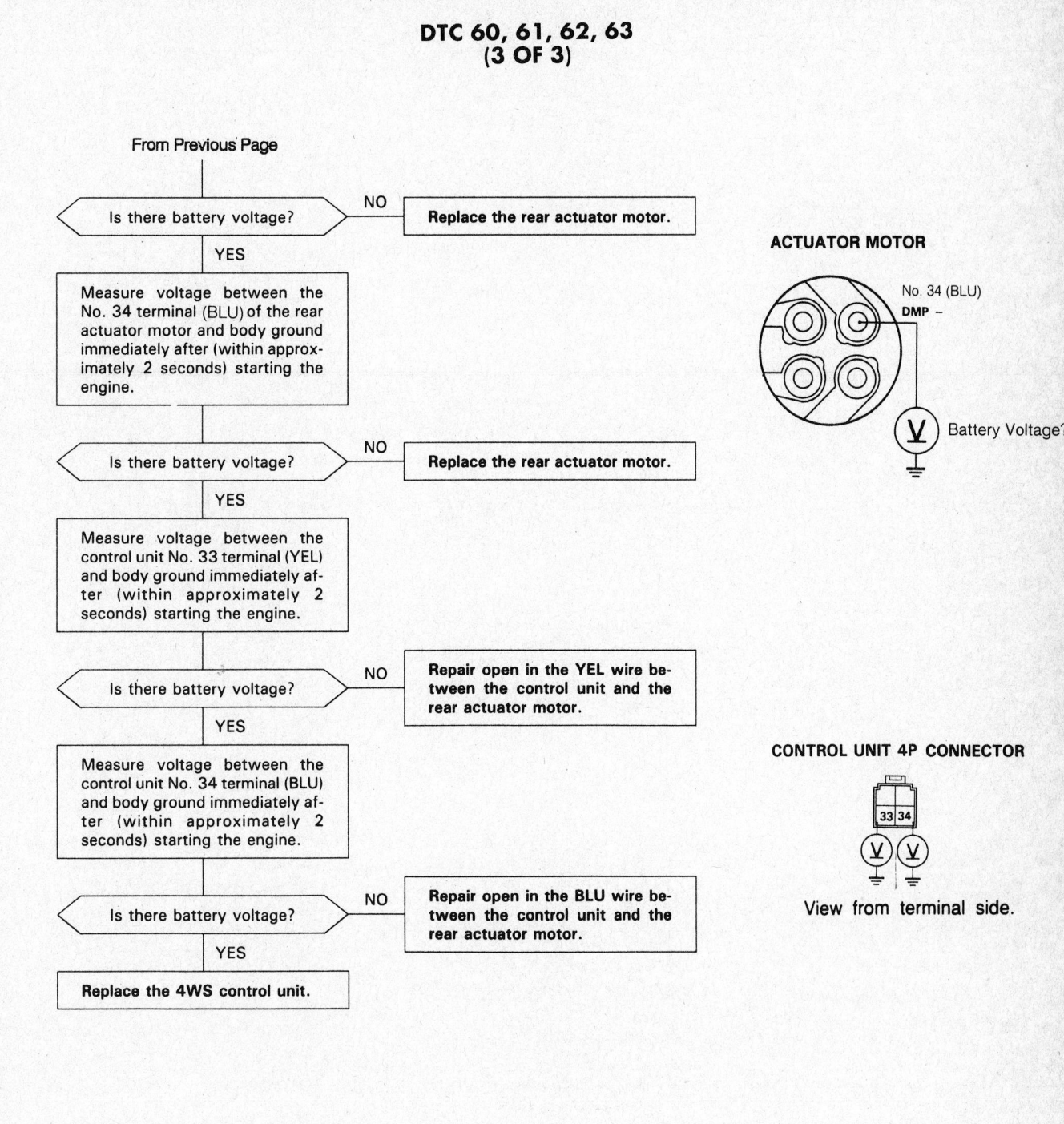

From Previous Page

Is there battery voltage? — **NO** → Replace the rear actuator motor.

YES

Measure voltage between the No. 34 terminal (BLU) of the rear actuator motor and body ground immediately after (within approximately 2 seconds) starting the engine.

Is there battery voltage? — **NO** → Replace the rear actuator motor.

YES

Measure voltage between the control unit No. 33 terminal (YEL) and body ground immediately after (within approximately 2 seconds) starting the engine.

Is there battery voltage? — **NO** → Repair open in the YEL wire between the control unit and the rear actuator motor.

YES

Measure voltage between the control unit No. 34 terminal (BLU) and body ground immediately after (within approximately 2 seconds) starting the engine.

Is there battery voltage? — **NO** → Repair open in the BLU wire between the control unit and the rear actuator motor.

YES

Replace the 4WS control unit.

ACTUATOR MOTOR

No. 34 (BLU)
DMP –

Battery Voltage?

CONTROL UNIT 4P CONNECTOR

33 | 34

View from terminal side.

Accord, Civic, Civic Del Sol, Prelude

NOTE: For information on Passport transmission servicing, refer to Rodeo in Isuzu TRANSMISSION SERVICING – AUTOMATIC TRANS-MISSION article.

IDENTIFICATION

Transaxles can be identified by identification tag located on bellhousing, near engine block, or on top of transaxle toward outer end.

AUTOMATIC TRANSAXLE APPLICATIONS

Model	Transaxle
Accord	MPOA
Civic & Civic Del Sol	M24A
Prelude	MP1A

LUBRICATION

SERVICE INTERVALS

Change fluid every 30,000 miles or 24 months under normal driving conditions. If driven under severe conditions, change fluid every 15,000 miles or 12 months. Filter replacement and band adjustment are not required.

CHECKING FLUID LEVEL

With vehicle on level floor and at normal operating temperature, stop engine. Within one minute after turning engine off, unscrew dipstick and wipe it clean. Insert dipstick into filler hole (without screwing in) and check fluid level. Fluid level should be between FULL and LOW marks on dipstick.

RECOMMENDED FLUID

Use Dexron-II ATF.

FLUID CAPACITIES

TRANSAXLE REFILL CAPACITIES

Application	Refill Qts. (L)	Dry Fill Qts. (L)
Accord & Prelude	2.5 (2.4)	6.3 (6.0)
Civic & Civic Del Sol	2.8 (2.7)	6.2 (5.9)

DRAINING & REFILLING

1) Ensure transaxle is at normal operating temperature (cooling fan comes on). Remove transaxle drain plug to drain fluid. Install NEW plug gasket. Tighten drain plug to specification. See DRAIN PLUG TORQUE SPECIFICATIONS table.

DRAIN PLUG TORQUE SPECIFICATIONS

Application	Ft. Lbs. (N.m)
Except Civic Del Sol	37 (50)
Civic Del Sol	[1]

[1] – Specification is not available from the manufacturer.

2) Add fluid through dipstick hole. Start engine. Move gear selector lever through all selector positions 3 times. Ensure each gear engages. With selector lever in Neutral or Park, let transmission fluid warm to normal operating temperature. Shut off engine. Check fluid level. Add enough fluid to bring level to upper mark on dipstick.

ADJUSTMENTS

SHIFT CONTROL CABLE

1) Start engine and move shift lever into Reverse. Verify transaxle engages in Reverse. With engine off, remove center console. Move shift lever into Neutral or Reverse. Remove lock pin from adjuster. Ensure adjuster and shift cable holes align perfectly. *See Fig. 1.*
2) Holes in end of adjuster are positioned to allow cable adjustments in 1/4 turn increments. Adjust shift cable if it is not perfectly aligned. Loosen lock nut and adjust cable as necessary. Tighten lock nut. Install lock pin into adjuster. *See Fig. 1.*
3) Lock pin should not bind during installation. Start engine and check shift lever in all gears. Vehicle should start only with shift lever in Park or Neutral. Adjust neutral safety switch (if necessary). Install center console.

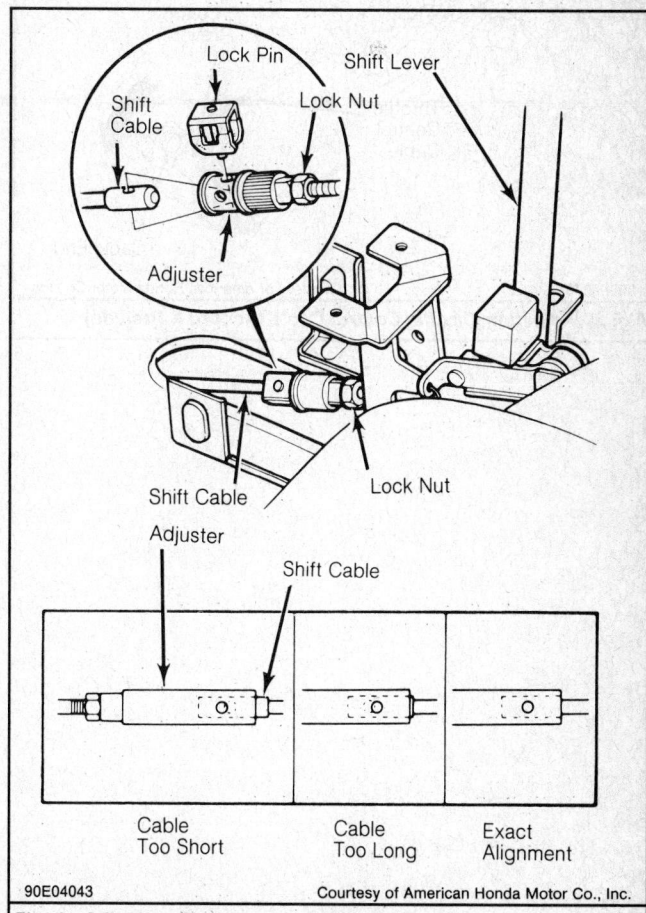

90E04043   Courtesy of American Honda Motor Co., Inc.

Fig. 1: Adjusting Shift Control Cable (Typical)

NEUTRAL SAFETY SWITCH

Neutral safety switch is located at bottom of shift lever, under center console. Ensure selector lever linkage is properly adjusted and vehicle starts only with shift lever in Park or Neutral. If vehicle starts in other gear positions, loosen 2 switch mounting screws and adjust switch.

THROTTLE CONTROL CABLE

NOTE: Before adjusting throttle control cable, ensure throttle cable connecting accelerator pedal to throttle body linkage has .39-.47" (10-12 mm) deflection with throttle closed. If deflection is not as specified, loosen lock nuts and adjust throttle cable.

1) With engine idling at normal operating temperature (cooling fan comes on), loosen throttle control cable adjustment lock nuts at transaxle control lever bracket. *See Fig. 2 or 3.*

2) Adjust lock nuts to synchronize movement of transaxle throttle control lever and throttle body throttle lever/linkage. Tighten adjustment lock nuts.

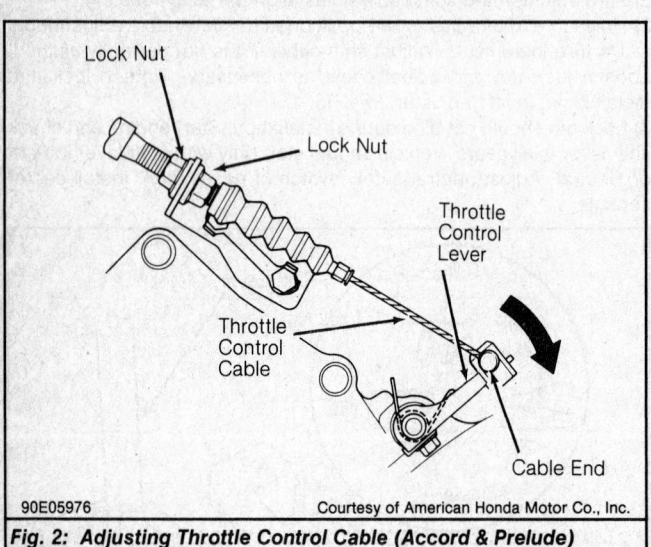

90E05976　　　　　Courtesy of American Honda Motor Co., Inc.

Fig. 2: Adjusting Throttle Control Cable (Accord & Prelude)

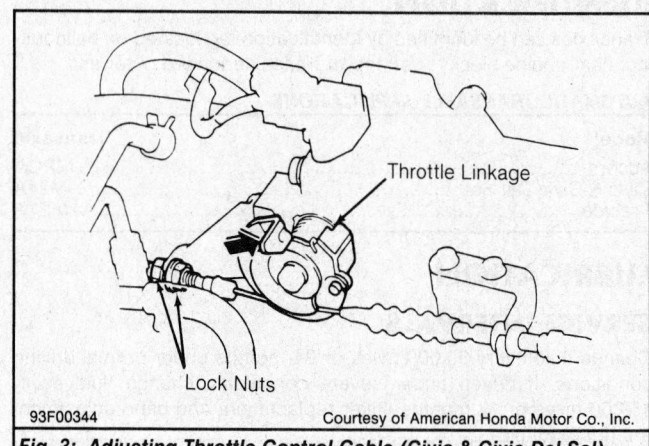

93F00344　　　　　Courtesy of American Honda Motor Co., Inc.

Fig. 3: Adjusting Throttle Control Cable (Civic & Civic Del Sol)

Accord, Civic, Civic Del Sol, Prelude

NOTE: For information on Passport manual transmission servicing, refer to Rodeo in Isuzu TRANSMISSION SERVICING – MANUAL TRANSMISSION article.

IDENTIFICATION
MANUAL TRANSAXLE APPLICATIONS

Model	Transaxle Code
Accord	H2UA
Civic & Civic Del Sol	
Except B16A3 Engine	S20
B16A3 Engine	Y21
Prelude	
F22A1 Engine	M2L5
H22A2 Engine (VTEC)	M2F4
H23A1 Engine	M2S4

LUBRICATION
SERVICE INTERVALS

Change lubricant every 30,000 miles or 24 months.

CHECKING FLUID LEVEL

Check fluid level with transaxle at operating temperature. Ensure engine is off and vehicle is level. Remove fill plug on side of transaxle case. Fluid level should be at bottom of fill hole. Tighten oil filler plug to 33 ft. lbs. (45 N.m) and oil drain plug to 30 ft. lbs. (40 N.m).

RECOMMENDED FLUID

Use SAE 10W-30 or 10W-40 with a rating of SF or SG.

FLUID CAPACITIES
TRANSAXLE REFILL CAPACITIES

Application	After Draining Qts. (L)	After Overhaul Qts. (L)
Accord & Prelude	2.0 (1.9)	2.1 (2.0)
Civic & Civic Del Sol		
Except B16A3 Engine	1.9 (1.8)	2.0 (1.9)
B16A3 Engine	2.3 (2.2)	2.4 (2.3)

ADJUSTMENTS

NOTE: External linkage adjustments are not required. Inspect gearshift linkage components for wear or damage. Replace components as required.

1994 TRANSMISSION SERVICING
Transaxle Removal & Installation

Accord, Civic, Civic Del Sol, Prelude

NOTE: For information on Passport transmission removal and installation, refer to Rodeo in Isuzu TRANSMISSION SERVICING – TRANSMISSION REMOVAL & INSTALLATION article.

MANUAL TRANSAXLE

NOTE: For manual transaxle removal and installation procedures, see appropriate article in CLUTCHES.

AUTOMATIC TRANSAXLE

Removal (Accord) – 1) Disconnect negative and then positive battery cables, and remove battery. Remove battery base and battery base support. Remove air filter assembly. Disconnect Intake Air Resonator (IAR) control solenoid valve connector. Remove vacuum hoses and IAR.
2) Disconnect throttle cable from control lever. Disconnect transaxle-to-chassis ground cable. Disconnect speed sensor connectors. Remove starter and all upper bellhousing bolts from transaxle. Attach an appropriate engine support fixture to engine hook hanger plate.
3) Raise and support vehicle. Disconnect lock-up control solenoid valve and shift control solenoid valve wire connectors. Remove front wheels. Drain transaxle, and install drain plug and NEW washer. Remove rear mounting bracket strut.
4) Remove power steering speed sensor and speedometer assembly without disconnecting hoses. Disconnect transaxle cooler hoses at coolant pipes. Plug openings to prevent contamination. Remove transaxle housing mounting bolts. Remove front engine mount bracket bolts. Remove transaxle mount. Remove center beam.
5) Remove O_2 sensor connector and front exhaust pipe. Remove splash shield. Remove ball joint pinch bolt from right lower control arm. Use a puller to separate ball joint from knuckle. Remove shock strut damper fork bolt.

CAUTION: When removing CV joints and drive axle assemblies from transaxle, DO NOT pull on drive axle or knuckle. Inboard CV joint may separate. Pull on inboard joint.

6) Pry drive axle inboard CV joints out 1/2" using 2 large screwdrivers, and then remove joints completely from transaxle. Protect ends of drive shafts and support them aside.
7) Remove control cable holder and torque converter cover plate. Remove shift control cable by removing cotter pin, control pin and control lever roller from control lever.
8) Ensure control cable is not bent. Manually turn crankshaft pulley clockwise to access and remove 8 torque converter mounting bolts from torque converter drive plate. Remove intake manifold bracket.
9) Remove engine housing bolts from transaxle, and remove rear engine mount. Using engine hoist, lift engine slightly. Remove remaining mounting bolts. Place transaxle jack under transaxle. Pull transaxle away from engine just enough to clear 14-mm engine dowel pins. Lower transaxle on jack away from chassis. Ensure torque converter remains with transaxle assembly.
Installation – 1) To install transaxle, reverse removal procedure. Inspect drive plate for cracks, elongated holes and warpage. Replace drive plate if necessary. Replace 26-mm spring clips on end of each inner CV joint splined shaft. Tighten bolts to specification. See TORQUE SPECIFICATIONS.
2) Ensure speedometer cable is completely installed. Check shift control cable and throttle control cable. Adjust cables as necessary. See AUTOMATIC TRANSAXLE article in TRANSMISSION SERVICING.

Removal (Civic & Civic Del Sol) – 1) Disconnect negative and then positive battery cables, and remove battery. Remove intake hose band bolt from throttle body. Remove complete air cleaner assembly with intake hose.
2) Remove transaxle ground cables. Disconnect wire connector from lock-up control solenoid valve. Disconnect speedometer sensor connector. Remove transaxle housing mounting bolts and rear engine mounting bolt.
3) Remove transaxle drain plug and drain fluid (remove fill plug to speed draining). Install drain plug and NEW washer. Tighten plug to specification. See TORQUE SPECIFICATIONS. Remove splash shields from bottom of engine and from right wheelwell.
4) Remove front exhaust header pipe and bracket. Remove cotter pin and remove lower control arm ball joint nut. Separate ball joint from lower control arm. Remove shock strut damper fork bolt and separate strut damper from fork. Remove right radius rod bolts and nut at opposite end of rod. Remove right radius rod.

CAUTION: When removing CV joint and drive axle assembly from transaxle, DO NOT pull on drive axle or knuckle. Inboard CV joint may separate. Pull on inboard joint.

5) Using 2 large screwdrivers, pry inboard CV joints from transaxle. Remove or support shafts aside. Protect inner CV joint spline from contamination by covering drive axle end by covering it with a plastic bag. Remove header pipe bracket, torque converter cover and shift control cable holder. Remove stopper mount. Disconnect cooler hoses at joint pipes. Using wire, support hoses aside. Remove shift control cable cover. Remove shift control cable end by removing cotter pin, control pin and control lever roller. Using wire, support cable aside.
6) Loosen lower throttle cable lock nut. Disconnect and remove throttle control cable from transaxle throttle lever. Remove front and rear engine stiffeners. Only Civic Del Sol with B16A3 engine uses a rear stiffener. Remove torque converter cover plate. Manually turn crankshaft pulley clockwise to access and remove 8 torque converter mounting bolts from torque converter drive plate.
7) Using engine hoist or an appropriate engine support fixture, relieve weight of engine from mounts. Support transaxle using transaxle jack and raise it slightly. Remove front and side mount bolts. Remove engine mounting bolts.
8) Remove all transaxle mounting bolts. Pull transaxle away from engine until it clears 14-mm guide pins on engine. Lower transaxle assembly from vehicle. Ensure torque converter remains with transaxle.
Installation – 1) To install transaxle, reverse removal procedure. Inspect drive plate for cracks, elongated holes and warpage. Replace drive plate if necessary. Replace distributor "O" ring.
2) Replace 26-mm spring clips on end of each inboard CV joint splined shaft. Check shift control cable and throttle control cable operation. Adjust cables as necessary. See AUTOMATIC TRANSAXLE article in TRANSMISSION SERVICING.
Removal (Prelude) – 1) Disconnect negative battery cable and ground strap at transaxle. Disconnect positive battery cable. Remove battery and battery base. Remove drain plug and drain transaxle fluid (remove fill plug to speed draining). Install drain plug with NEW washer and tighten plug to specification. See TORQUE SPECIFICATIONS.
2) Disconnect wiring for starter motor, transaxle lock-up control solenoid and shift control solenoid. Remove starter. Disconnect mainshaft and countershaft speed sensor connectors. Remove complete air cleaner case assembly. Disconnect and remove throttle control cable at transaxle bracket.

3) Disconnect oil cooler hoses at joint pipes. Plug and support hoses aside. Remove transaxle upper mount bracket and rear stiffener. Remove vehicle speed sensor from transaxle without removing power steering hoses. Remove 4 upper transaxle mounting bolts.

CAUTION: When removing CV joint and drive axle assembly from transaxle, DO NOT pull on drive axle or knuckle. Inboard CV joint may separate. Pull on inboard joint.

4) Raise and support vehicle and remove front wheels. Remove engine splash shield. Remove center crossmember bolts and remove crossmember. Remove shock strut damper fork bolts and separate strut damper from fork. Remove right radius rod from control arm and frame. While prying on inboard CV joints, remove both drive axles from transaxle. Remove or support shafts aside. Protect inner CV joint spline from contamination by covering drive axle end by covering it with a plastic bag. Remove left intermediate shaft.

5) Remove engine stiffener bracket from between lower transaxle and engine block. Remove torque converter cover plate. Manually turn crankshaft pulley clockwise to access and remove 8 torque converter mounting bolts from torque converter drive plate.

6) Remove shift control cable from transaxle. Using wire, hang cable aside. DO NOT bend cable. Support transaxle using transmission jack. Remove lower bolts from rear engine mount bracket. With jack in place, remove remaining transaxle mounting bolts.

7) Separate transaxle from engine block far enough to disengage both 14-mm dowel pins. Lower transaxle assembly.

Installation – 1) To install transaxle, reverse removal procedure. Inspect drive plate for cracks, elongated holes and warpage. Replace drive plate if necessary.

2) Replace 26-mm spring clips on end of each inner CV joint splined shaft. Check shift control cable and throttle control cable. Adjust cables as necessary. See AUTOMATIC TRANSAXLE article in TRANSMISSION SERVICING.

TORQUE SPECIFICATIONS
TORQUE SPECIFICATIONS

Application	Ft. Lbs. (N.m)
Ball Joint-To-Knuckle Bolt	40 (54)
Center Beam Stiffener Bolts	37 (50)
Control Cable Holder (Accord)	13 (18)
Drain Plug	
Except Civic Del Sol	37 (50)
Civic Del Sol	1
Drive Plate-To-Crankshaft Bolts	55 (74)
Engine Stiffener Mounting Bolts	33 (45)
Intake Manifold Bracket Bolts	16 (22)
Starter Mounting Bolts	32 (44)
Stopper Mount (Civic & Civic Del Sol)	
10-mm Bolts	29 (39)
12-mm Bolts	48 (65)
Strut Damper Fork Bolt Lock Nut	
Accord	41 (55)
Civic, Civic Del Sol & Prelude	48 (65)
Strut Damper Pinch Bolt	32 (44)
Transaxle-To-Engine Mounting Bolts	
Accord & Prelude	47 (64)
Civic & Civic Del Sol	44 (60)
Wheel Lug Nuts	81 (110)

	INCH Lbs. (N.m)
Torque Converter Cover Bolts	108 (12)
Torque Converter Mounting Bolts	108 (12)

¹ – Specification is not available from the manufacturer.

CONTENTS

C	**CONTENTS** Page HYUNDAI C-0
1	**ENGINE PERFORMANCE** Page HYUNDAI 1-1
2	**ELECTRICAL** Page HYUNDAI 2-1
3	**WIRING DIAGRAMS** Page HYUNDAI 3-1
4	**ACCESSORIES & EQUIPMENT** Page HYUNDAI 4-0
5	**ENGINES & ENGINE COOLING** Page HYUNDAI 5-0
6	**CLUTCHES** Page HYUNDAI 6-1
7	**DRIVE AXLES** Page HYUNDAI 7-1
8	**BRAKES** Page HYUNDAI 8-0
9	**WHEEL ALIGNMENT** Page HYUNDAI 9-1
10	**SUSPENSION** Page HYUNDAI 10-1
11	**STEERING** Page HYUNDAI 11-1
12	**TRANSMISSION SERVICING** Page HYUNDAI 12-1

ENGINE PERFORMANCE

ENGINE PERFORMANCE (Cont.)

1994 HYUNDAI CONTENTS (Cont.)

1993 MODEL COVERAGE

MODEL	BODY CODE [1]	ENGINE [2]	ENGINE ID	FUEL SYSTEM	IGNITION SYSTEM [3]
Elantra	JF	1.6L 4-Cyl.	R	MFI	DIS
	JF	1.8L 4-Cyl.	M	MFI	DIS
Excel	VD, VF	1.5L 4-Cyl.	J	MFI	Optical
Scoupe	VE	1.5L 4-Cyl.	N [4]	MFI	Optical
Sonata	BF	2.0L 4-Cyl.	F	MFI	DIS
	BF	3.0L V6	T	MFI	Optical

[1] – Body Code is Model Code and Body Type.
[2] – Engine code is located on front side at top of cylinder block.
[3] – Computer controlled.
[4] – Engine available in turbo and non-turbo.

VIN DEFINITION

K M H B F 3 2 T 8 P U 1 2 3 4 5 6
① ② ③ ④ ⑤ ⑥ ⑦ ⑧ ⑨ ⑩ ⑪ ⑫ ⑬ ⑭ ⑮ ⑯ ⑰

①②③ Indicates Manufacturer.
④ **Indicates Model.**
⑤ **Indicates Body Type.**
⑥ Indicates Model Version.
⑦ Indicates Restraint System (Front Seat).
⑧ **Indicates Engine ID.**
⑨ Indicates Check Digit.
⑩ **Indicates Model Year.**
⑪ Indicates Assembly Plant.
⑫ ⑬ ⑭ ⑮ ⑯ ⑰ Indicates Production Sequence.

MODEL YEAR VIN CODE APPLICATION

VIN Code	Model Year
N	1992
P	1993
R	1994

ENGINE CODE LOCATION

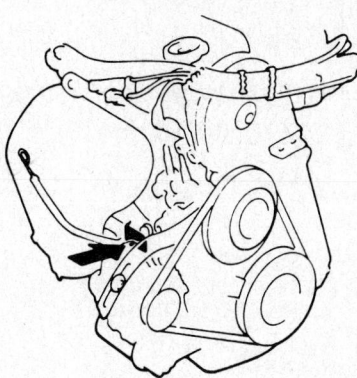

4-CYLINDER ENGINE

SONATA IS SHOWN;
ELANTRA, EXCEL
& SCOUPE
ARE SIMILAR

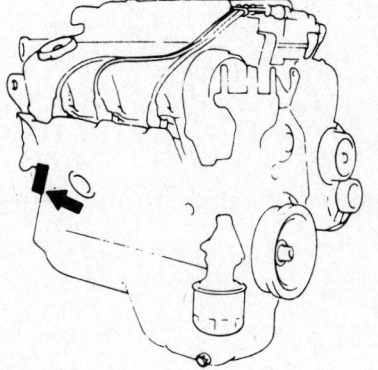

V6 ENGINE

92G24907 90F04816

Courtesy of Hyundai Motor Co.

1994 ENGINE PERFORMANCE
Emission Applications

1994 HYUNDAI

Model, Engine & Fuel System	Emission Control Systems & Devices
Elantra 1.6L & 1.8L, Excel 1.5L, Scoupe 1.5L & Sonata 2.0L & 3.0L MFI [1]	**PCV, EVAP, TWC, FR, EGR, SPK, O2S, CEC, MIL,** EVAP-VC, EVAP-CPCS, [2] EGR-CS, [3] EGR-TVV, [2] EGR-TS, SPK-CC

[1] – Airflow-Controlled Fuel Injection.
[2] – Except Federal Elantra.
[3] – Federal Elantra only.

NOTE: For quick reference, major emission control systems and devices are listed in bold type; components and other related devices are listed in light type.

CEC – Computerized Engine Controls	**EVAP** – Fuel Evaporative System	**MFI** – Multiport Fuel Injection
EGR – Exhaust Gas Recirculation	**EVAP-CPCS** – EVAP Canister Purge Control Solenoid	**O2S** – Oxygen Sensor
EGR-CS – EGR Control Solenoid		**PCV** – Positive Crankcase Ventilation
EGR-TS – EGR Temperature Sensor	**EVAP-VC** – EVAP Vapor Canister	**SPK** – Spark Controls
EGR-TVV – EGR Thermal Vacuum Valve	**FR** – Fill Pipe Restrictor	**SPK-CC** – SPK Computer Controlled
	MIL – Malfunction Indicator Light	**TWC** – Three-Way Catalyst

Elantra, Excel, Scoupe, Sonata

INTRODUCTION

Use this article to quickly find specifications related to servicing and on-vehicle adjustments. This is a quick reference article to use when you are familiar with an adjustment procedure and only need a specification.

CAPACITIES

BATTERY SPECIFICATIONS

Application	Group Size	CCA Rating
Sonata 3.0L	24	540
All Others	25	420

NOTE: *Refill capacities are approximate. Correct fluid level should be determined by mark on dipstick, if applicable.*

FLUID CAPACITIES

Application	Quantity
Automatic Transaxle (Dexron-II E)	
Elantra, Excel & Scoupe	6.4 Qts. (6.1L)
Sonata	
2.0L	6.4 Qts. (6.1L)
3.0L	6.1 Qts. (5.8L)
Cooling System (Includes Heater & Reserve Tank)	
Elantra	6.3 Qts. (6.0L)
Excel & Scoupe	5.6 Qts. (5.3L)
Sonata	
2.0L	7.7 Qts. (7.3L)
3.0L	9.0 Qts. (8.5L)
Crankcase (Includes Filter)	
Elantra	4.6 Qts. (4.4L)
Excel & Scoupe	3.6 Qts. (3.4L)
Sonata	
2.0L	3.9 Qts. (3.7L)
3.0L	4.2 Qts. (4.0L)
Manual Transaxle (SAE 75W-85/API GL-4)	
Elantra	
KM176	1.9 Qts. (1.8L)
Excel	
KM201	1.9 Qts. (1.8L)
Scoupe	2.3 Qts. (2.2L)
Sonata 2.0L	1.9 Qts. (1.8L)
Power Steering (Dexron-II)	1.0 Qt. (.9L)

QUICK-SERVICE

SERVICE INTERVALS & SPECIFICATIONS

REPLACEMENT INTERVALS

Component	Interval (Miles)
Air Filter	30,000
Automatic Transaxle Fluid	30,000
Brake Fluid	30,000
Coolant	30,000
Fuel Filter	52,500
Oil & Filter	7500
Spark Plugs	[1] 30,000
Timing Belt	[1] 60,000

[1] – Every 70,000 on Sonata 3.0L.

BELT ADJUSTMENT

Application	[1] Deflection New Belt – In. (mm)	[1] Deflection Used Belt – In. (mm)
Excel		
Alternator	.22-.28 (5.5-7.0)	.31 (8.0)
A/C	.34-.42 (8.6-10.6)	[2]
P/S	.28-.39 (7.0-10.0)	[2]
Elantra		
Alternator	.30-.35 (7.5-9.0)	.35-.41 (9.0-10.4)
A/C	.20-.22 (5.0-5.5)	.24-.28 (6.0-7.0)
P/S	.24-.35 (6.0-9.0)	[2]
Scoupe		
Alternator	.30-.35 (7.5-9.0)	.35-.41 (9.0-10.4)
A/C	.20-.22 (5.0-5.5)	.24-.28 (6.0-7.0)
P/S	.28-.39 (7.0-10.0)	[2]
Sonata		
2.0L		
Alternator	.30-.35 (7.5-9.0)	.39 (10.0)
A/C	.20-.22 (5.0-5.5)	.24-.28 (6.0-7.0)
P/S	.24-.35 (6.0-9.0)	[2]
3.0L		
Alternator & P/S	.16-.20 (4.0-5.0)	.28 (7.0)
A/C	.18-.22 (4.5-5.5)	[2]

[1] – Deflection with 22 lbs. (10 kg) pressure applied midway on belt run.

[2] – Information is not available from manufacturer.

MECHANICAL CHECKS

ENGINE COMPRESSION

COMPRESSION SPECIFICATIONS

Application	Specification
Compression Ratio	
1.5L	
Excel	9.4:1
Scoupe	
Non-Turbo	10.0:1
Turbo	7.5:1
1.6L	9.2:1
1.8L	9.2:1
2.0L	9.0:1
3.0L	8.9:1
Compression Pressure	
1.5L	
Excel	192 psi (13.5 kg/cm²)
Scoupe	
Non-Turbo	192 psi (13.5 kg/cm²)
Turbo	149 psi (10.5 kg/cm²)
1.6L	171 psi (12.0 kg/cm²)
1.8L	171 psi (12.0 kg/cm²)
2.0L	171 psi (12.0 kg/cm²)
3.0L	173 psi (12.2 kg/cm²)
Maximum Variation Between Cylinders	
All Models	14 psi (1.0 kg/cm²)

VALVE CLEARANCE

NOTE: *Elantra and Sonata are equipped with hydraulic lash adjusters; no adjustments are required.*

VALVE LIFTER APPLICATION

Application	Lifter Type
1.5L	Mechanical
1.6L	Hydraulic
1.8L	Hydraulic
2.0L	Hydraulic
3.0L	Hydraulic

VALVE CLEARANCE SPECIFICATIONS

Application	[1] In. (mm)
Excel	
Intake	.006 (.15)
Exhaust	.010 (.25)
Scoupe	
Intake	.010 (.25)
Exhaust	.012 (.30)

[1] – Adjust valves with engine at normal operating temperature.

IGNITION SYSTEM

IGNITION COIL

IGNITION COIL RESISTANCE – Ohms @ 68°F (20°C)

Application	Primary	Secondary
Elantra	.77-.95	10,300-13,900
Excel	.72-.88	10,300-13,900
Scoupe	.45-.55	10,300-13,900
Sonata		
2.0L	.77-.95	10,300-13,900
3.0L	.72-.88	10,300-13,900

HIGH TENSION WIRE RESISTANCE

HIGH TENSION WIRE RESISTANCE

Wire Application	Ohms
Excel	
No. 1	10,100
No. 2	11,800
No. 3	11,800
No. 4	14,200
Coil Wire	[1]
Elantra	
No. 1	5800
No. 2	8400
No. 3	10,600
No. 4	9700
Scoupe	
No. 1	4800
No. 2	10,000
No. 3	7300
No. 4	12,000
Coil Wire	[1]
Sonata	
2.0L	
No. 1	5800
No. 2	8400
No. 3	10,600
No. 4	9700
Coil Wire	[1]
3.0L	
No. 1	7400
No. 2	5400
No. 3	9100
No. 4	6900
No. 5	10,200
No. 6	8000
Coil Wire	5800

[1] – Information is not available from manufacturer.

SPARK PLUGS

SPARK PLUG TYPE

Application	Number
1.5L Excel, 1.6L, 1.8L & 2.0L	
NGK	BPR6ES-11/BUR6EA-11
Champion	RN9YC4
1.5L Scoupe	
Non-Turbo (NGK)	BKR5ES-11
Turbo (NGK)	BKR6ES
3.0L	
ND	P16PR-11
NGK	PGR5A-11

SPARK PLUG SPECIFICATIONS

Application	Gap In. (mm)	Torque Ft. Lbs. (N.m)
Scoupe Turbo	.031-.035 (.80-.90)	15-21 (20-28)
All Others	.039-.043 (1.0-1.1)	15-21 (20-28)

FIRING ORDER & TIMING MARKS

NOTE: For firing order, see Figs. 1-4.

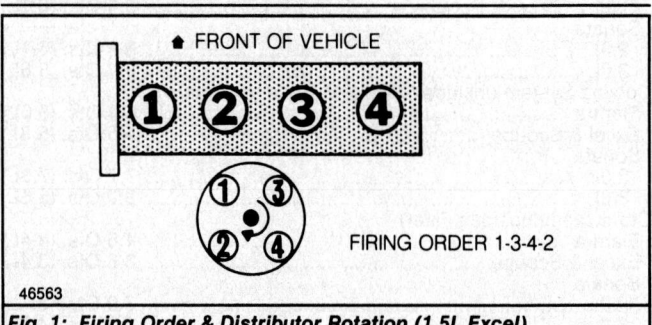

Fig. 1: Firing Order & Distributor Rotation (1.5L Excel)

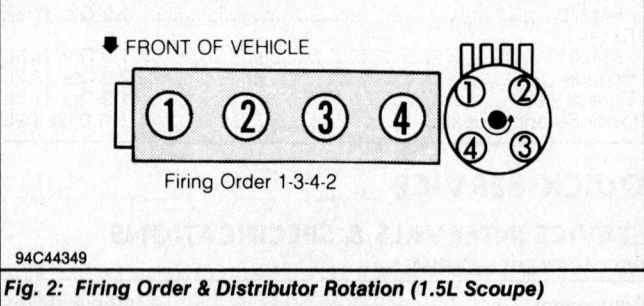

Fig. 2: Firing Order & Distributor Rotation (1.5L Scoupe)

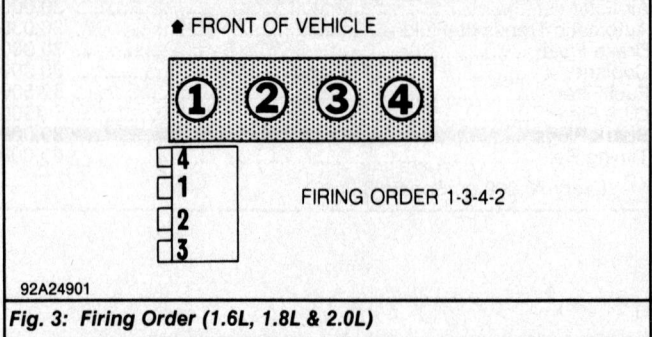

Fig. 3: Firing Order (1.6L, 1.8L & 2.0L)

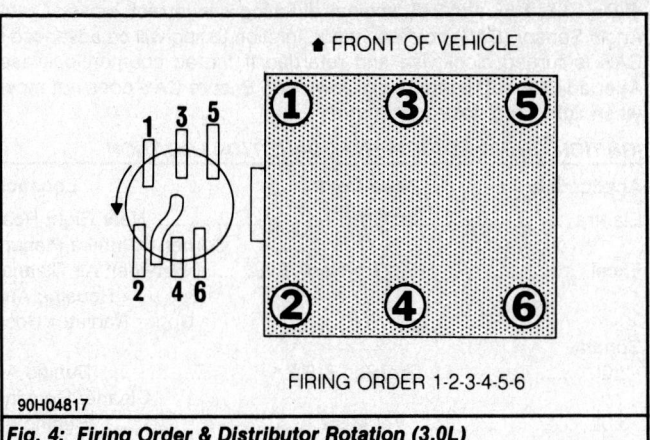

▲ FRONT OF VEHICLE

FIRING ORDER 1-2-3-4-5-6

Fig. 4: Firing Order & Distributor Rotation (3.0L)

90H04817

IGNITION TIMING

IGNITION TIMING (Degrees BTDC @ RPM)

Application	[1] Basic	[2] Actual
1.5L		
Excel	3-7 @ 725-925	10 @ 725-925
Scoupe	4-14 @ 700-900	[3]
1.6L	3-7 @ 650-850	8 @ 650-850
1.8L	3-7 @ 600-800	14 @ 600-800
2.0L	3-7 @ 650-850	8 @ 650-850
3.0L [4]	3-7 @ 600-800	15 @ 650-850

[1] – With ignition timing adjustment connector grounded.

[2] – With ignition timing adjustment connector ungrounded.

[3] – Information is not available from manufacturer.

[4] – DO NOT adjust basic timing with Multi-Use Tester (MUT) connected.

FUEL SYSTEM

FUEL PUMP

REGULATED FUEL PRESSURE

	At Idle	At Idle
	W/ Vacuum	W/O Vacuum
Application	psi (kg/cm²)	psi (kg/cm²)
Scoupe	37 (2.5)	44 (3.0)
All Others	39 (2.8)	46-49 (3.3-3.5)

INJECTOR RESISTANCE

INJECTOR RESISTANCE

Application	Ohms
Scoupe	15.5-16.2
All Others	13-16

IDLE SPEED & MIXTURE

NOTE: Idle speed and mixture are computer-controlled.

FAST IDLE SPEED

NOTE: Fast idle speed is computer-controlled.

THROTTLE POSITION SENSOR (TPS)

TPS VOLTAGE SPECIFICATIONS

Application	Volts At Idle
Scoupe	.25-.60
All Others	.48-.52

1994 ENGINE PERFORMANCE
On-Vehicle Adjustments

Elantra, Excel, Scoupe, Sonata

ENGINE MECHANICAL

Before performing any on-vehicle adjustments to fuel or ignition systems, ensure engine mechanical condition is okay.

VALVE CLEARANCE

NOTE: *Elantra and Sonata are equipped with hydraulic lash adjusters. No adjustments are required.*

CAUTION: *Never rotate crankshaft counterclockwise. Damage to timing belt can occur.*

Excel & Scoupe – 1) Ensure engine is at normal operating temperature. Remove all spark plugs and valve cover. Rotate crankshaft clockwise to position cylinder No. 1 on TDC of compression stroke. **2)** Adjust intake valves on cylinders No. 1 and 2, and exhaust valves on cylinders No. 1 and 3. See VALVE CLEARANCE SPECIFICATIONS table. Rotate crankshaft clockwise 360 degrees to position cylinder No. 4 on TDC of compression stroke. **3)** Adjust intake valves on cylinders No. 3 and 4, and exhaust valves on cylinders No. 2 and 4.

VALVE CLEARANCE SPECIFICATIONS

Application	In. (mm)
Excel [1]	
Intake	.006 (.15)
Exhaust	.010 (.25)
Scoupe [1]	
Intake	.010 (.25)
Exhaust	.012 (.30)

[1] – Adjust valves with engine at normal operating temperature.

CHECKING HYDRAULIC LASH ADJUSTERS

Elantra & Sonata – 1) Remove valve cover. Press area where rocker arm contacts lash adjuster. If adjuster feels hard, it is okay. If hydraulic lash adjuster moves easily downward, it is faulty and must be replaced. **2)** If hydraulic lash adjuster feels soft or spongy, air has probably entered hydraulic lash adjuster. If this occurs, check engine oil level. If engine oil level is okay, check oil screen and oil screen gasket for damage. **3)** After repairing cause of air leak, warm engine to operating temperature. If there is abnormal noise at idle, bleed hydraulic adjusters. **4)** To bleed hydraulic adjusters, slowly increase engine speed to 3000 RPM and back to idle over approximately 60 seconds. Repeat this several times. This will help remove air from hydraulic lash adjusters. If there is still abnormal noise, replace noisy hydraulic lash adjusters.

IGNITION TIMING

NOTE: *Manufacturer does not supply information for timing adjustment on Scoupe model.*

1) Ensure vehicle is at normal operating temperature, all accessories are off and transmission is in Park or Neutral. Ensure front wheels are in straight-ahead position and curb idle speed is set to specification. See CURB IDLE SPEED.
2) Ground ignition timing adjustment connector. See IGNITION TIMING ADJUSTMENT CONNECTOR LOCATION table. Check ignition basic timing. See IGNITION TIMING SPECIFICATIONS table. Disconnect ground wire on ignition timing adjustment connector. Check ignition actual timing.
3) On 1.5L and 3.0L engines, if timing is incorrect, loosen distributor hold-down nut and turn distributor until timing is correct. On 1.5L engine, ignition timing will be advanced if distributor is turned to left and retarded if turned to right. On 3.0L engine, ignition timing will be advanced if distributor is turned to right and retarded if turned to left. After adjustment, tighten hold-down nut. Ensure distributor does not move when tightening hold-down nut.

4) On 1.6L, 1.8L and 2.0L engines, if timing is incorrect, loosen Crank Angle Sensor (CAS) hold-down nut. Ignition timing will be advanced if CAS is turned clockwise and retarded if turned counterclockwise. After adjustment, tighten hold-down nut. Ensure CAS does not move when tightening hold-down nut.

IGNITION TIMING ADJUSTMENT CONNECTOR LOCATION

Application	Wire Color	Location
Elantra	Lt. Grn/Red	Near Right Rear Corner Of Intake Plenum
Excel	Lt. Grn/Red	Between Air Cleaner Housing And Upper Radiator Hose
Sonata		
2.0L	Lt. Grn/Red & Blk [1]	Behind Air Cleaner Housing
3.0L	Yel & Blk	Behind air Cleaner Housing

[1] – On Sonata with 2 wire connector, connect terminals with jumper wire.

IGNITION TIMING (Degrees BTDC @ RPM)

Application	[1] Basic	[2] Actual
1.5L		
Excel	3-7 @ 725-925	10 @ 725-925
Scoupe	4-14 @ 700-900	[3]
1.6L	3-7 @ 650-850	8 @ 650-850
1.8L	3-7 @ 600-800	14 @ 600-800
2.0L	3-7 @ 650-850	8 @ 650-850
3.0L [4]	3-7 @ 600-800	15 @ 650-850

[1] – With ignition timing adjustment connector grounded.
[2] – With ignition timing adjustment connector ungrounded.
[3] – Information is not available from manufacturer.
[4] – DO NOT adjust basic timing with Multi-Use Tester (MUT) connected.

IDLE SPEED & MIXTURE

CURB IDLE SPEED

Idle Speed Check – 1) Ensure coolant temperature is 176-203°F (80-95°C). Turn all accessories off. DO NOT check curb idle speed while cooling fan is operating. On power steering-equipped vehicles, ensure front wheels are in straight-ahead position.
2) Connect external tachometer to engine tachometer signal at noise filter. See NOISE FILTER LOCATION table. On all models except Scoupe, ground ignition timing adjustment connector. See IGNITION TIMING. Operate engine at curb idle speed for 2 minutes. On Elantra 1.6L and Sonata 2.0L, idle speed is 650-850 RPM. On Excel, idle speed is 725-925 RPM. On Scoupe, idle speed is 700-900 RPM. On Elantra 1.8L and Sonata 3.0L, idle speed is 600-800 RPM.
3) Disconnect ground wire from ignition timing adjuster connector (if connected in preceding step). Operate engine for at least 5 seconds at 2000-3000 RPM, then run engine at idle for 2 minutes. Check idle RPM. If RPM is not within specification, ensure timing is set to specification, and adjust Idle Speed Control (ISC) and Throttle Position Sensor (TPS). See IGNITION TIMING, IDLE SPEED CONTROL and THROTTLE POSITION SENSOR (TPS). Also see IDLE SWITCH for Sonata 3.0L.

NOISE FILTER LOCATION

Application	Wire Color [1]	Location
Elantra	Wht	Right Rear Corner Of Intake Plenum
Excel	Wht	Front Of Intake Plenum
Scoupe	Wht	Back Of Intake Plenum
Sonata		
2.0L	Wht	Front Of Intake Plenum
3.0L	Wht	Left Side Of Firewall

[1] – Backprobe noise filter connector.

IDLE SPEED CONTROL

NOTE: Manufacturer does not supply accelerator cable adjustment information.

NOTE: Manufacturer does not supply idle speed adjustment information for Scoupe model.

Excel – 1) Engine coolant temperature should be 176-203°F (80-95°C). Turn all accessories off. DO NOT check curb idle speed while cooling fan is operating. Place transmission in Neutral or Park. On power steering-equipped vehicles, ensure steering wheel and front wheels are in straight-ahead position.

2) Loosen accelerator cable. Connect tachometer. See CURB IDLE SPEED. Turn ignition switch to ON position for at least 15 seconds to retract ISC motor plunger. Turn ignition switch to OFF position. Disconnect ISC motor connector.

3) Open throttle valve by hand 2-3 times, allowing valve to snap closed each time. Loosen fixed Speed Adjusting Screw (SAS). *See Fig. 1.*

4) Start engine and run at idle. Check engine speed. Engine speed should be 725-925 RPM. If engine speed is not within specification, adjust idle speed with ISC adjusting screw. *See Fig. 1.*

5) Tighten fixed SAS until RPM increases. Loosen screw until RPM ceases to drop (touch point), then loosen screw an additional 1/2 turn. Check Throttle Position Sensor (TPS) adjustment. See THROTTLE POSITION SENSOR (TPS).

6) Turn ignition off and install accelerator cable. Connect ISC motor connector. Start engine and ensure idle speed is 600-800 RPM. Turn ignition off. Disconnect battery for 15 seconds to erase diagnostic memory. Connect battery.

Elantra & Sonata 2.0L – 1) Engine coolant temperature should be 176-203°F (80-95°C). Turn all accessories off. DO NOT check curb idle speed while cooling fan is operating. Place transmission in Neutral or Park. On power steering-equipped vehicles, ensure front wheels are in straight-ahead position.

2) Loosen accelerator cable. Connect a tachometer. See IGNITION TIMING. Ground self-diagnostic terminal. *See Fig. 2.* Ground ignition timing adjustment connector. See IGNITION TIMING. Start engine and check ignition timing. Adjust if necessary. See IGNITION TIMING.

3) Run engine at 2000-3000 RPM for at least 5 seconds. Allow engine to run at idle speed for 2 minutes. Engine speed on Elantra 1.6L and Sonata should be 650-850 RPM. Elantra 1.8L idle speed should be 600-800 RPM. If engine speed is not within specification, adjust speed using Speed Adjusting Screw (SAS). *See Fig. 1.*

4) If idle speed is greater than specification, even with speed adjusting screw fully closed, ensure fixed speed adjusting screw (idle switch) has not been moved from factory adjustment mark; adjust if necessary. See IDLE SWITCH. Check Throttle Position Sensor (TPS) adjustment. See THROTTLE POSITION SENSOR (TPS).

5) Turn ignition off. Remove ground from self-diagnostic check terminal. Disconnect tachometer. Disconnect battery for 15 seconds to erase diagnostic memory. Reconnect battery. Tighten accelerator cable. Start engine and run at idle for at least 5 minutes. Check engine idle speed.

Sonata 3.0L – 1) Engine coolant temperature should be 176-203°F (80-95°C). Turn all accessories off. DO NOT check curb idle speed while cooling fan is operating. Place transmission in Neutral or Park. On vehicles with power steering, ensure front wheels are in straight-ahead position.

2) Loosen accelerator cable. Connect a tachometer. Ground ignition timing adjustment connector. See IGNITION TIMING. Start engine and check ignition timing. Adjust if necessary.

3) Turn ignition switch to OFF position. Ground self-diagnostic check terminal. *See Fig. 2.* Operate engine at 2000-3000 RPM for at least 5 seconds. Allow engine to run at idle speed for 2 minutes. Engine speed should be 600-800 RPM. If engine speed is not within specification, adjust speed using speed adjusting screw, located on side of throttle body. *See Fig. 1.*

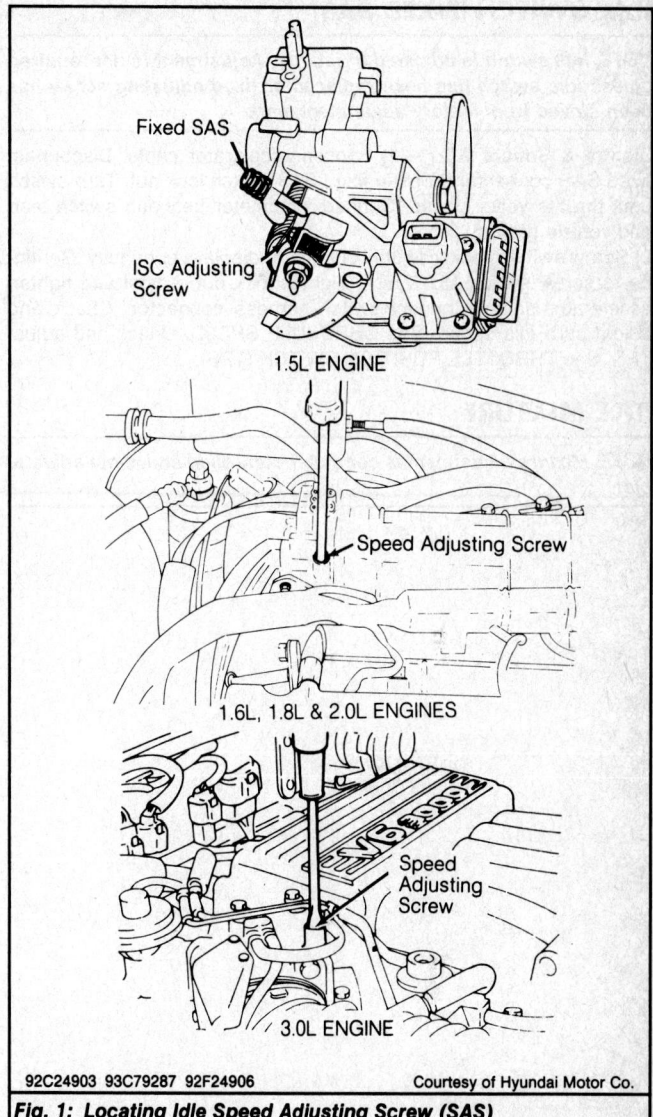

92C24903 93C79287 92F24906   Courtesy of Hyundai Motor Co.

Fig. 1: Locating Idle Speed Adjusting Screw (SAS)

4) If idle speed is greater than specification, even with speed adjusting screw fully closed, ensure fixed speed adjusting screw (idle switch) has not been moved from factory adjustment mark. Adjust if necessary. See IDLE SWITCH. Check Throttle Position Sensor (TPS) adjustment. See THROTTLE POSITION SENSOR (TPS).

5) Turn ignition off. Remove ground from self-diagnostic check terminal. Disconnect tachometer. Disconnect battery for 15 seconds to erase diagnostic memory. Reconnect battery. Tighten accelerator cable. Operate engine at idle for at least 5 minutes.

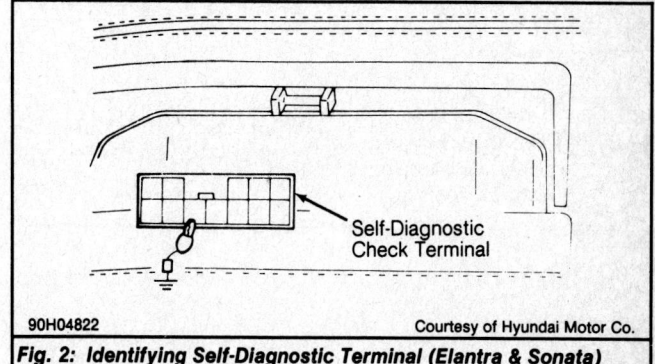

90H04822   Courtesy of Hyundai Motor Co.

Fig. 2: Identifying Self-Diagnostic Terminal (Elantra & Sonata)

1994 ENGINE PERFORMANCE
On-Vehicle Adjustments (Cont.)

IDLE SWITCH (FIXED SAS)

NOTE: Idle switch is adjusted at factory. Adjustment is not required unless idle switch has been replaced or fixed adjusting screw has been moved from factory adjustment mark.

Elantra & Sonata 2.0L – 1) Loosen accelerator cable. Disconnect fixed SAS connector. Loosen fixed SAS switch lock nut. Turn switch until throttle valve closes. Connect ohmmeter between switch lead and vehicle ground.
2) Screw switch clockwise until ohmmeter displays continuity. Continue to screw switch 15/16 turn. Tighten lock nut. Adjust and tighten accelerator cable. Connect switch harness connector. Check and adjust curb idle speed. See CURB IDLE SPEED. Check and adjust TPS. See THROTTLE POSITION SWITCH (TPS).

IDLE MIXTURE

NOTE: Mixture adjustment is computer-controlled and is not adjustable.

THROTTLE POSITION SENSOR (TPS)

NOTE: Manufacturer does not supply adjustment procedures for Scoupe TPS.

1) With ignition off, connect Test Harness (09351-33000) between TPS and harness connector. Connect a digital voltmeter between both terminals of test harness leads.
2) Turn ignition switch to ON position with engine off. Check TPS voltage. If reading is not .25-.60 volt on Scoupe, or .48-.52 volt on all others, loosen throttle cable. Loosen TPS mounting screws. Turn TPS clockwise (increase) or counterclockwise (decrease) until correct voltage is obtained.
3) After adjustment, on all models except Sonata 3.0L, tighten TPS screw to 13-22 INCH lbs. (1.5-2.5 N.m). On Sonata 3.0L, tighten TPS screw to 22-39 INCH lbs. (2.5-4.4 N.m).
4) Turn ignition off, and disconnect digital voltmeter. Tighten throttle cable. Disconnect vehicle battery for at least 15 seconds to erase diagnostic memory. Reconnect battery. Start engine and check idle speed.

Elantra, Excel, Scoupe, Sonata

INTRODUCTION

This article covers basic description and operation of engine performance-related systems and components. Read this article before diagnosing vehicles or systems with which you are not completely familiar.

TERMINOLOGY

Due to Federal government requirements, manufacturers may use names and acronyms for systems and components different than those used in previous years. The following table will help eliminate confusion when dealing with these components and systems. Only relevant components and systems whose names have been changed from previous Hyundai Motor Co. terminology have been listed. See REVISED TERMINOLOGY table.

REVISED TERMINOLOGY

1992 & Earlier	1994
CHECK ENGINE Light	Malfunction Indicator Light (MIL)
Crankshaft Angle Sensor	Crankshaft Position Sensor (CKP)
Electronic Control Unit (ECU)	Electronic Control Module (ECM)
Idle Speed Control (ISC)	Idle Air Control (IAC)
Inhibitor Switch	Transaxle Range Switch (TR)
Port Fuel Injection (PFI)	Multi-Point Fuel Injection (MFI)
Pulse Sensor	Camshaft Position Sensor (CMP)
Self-Diagnostic Connector	Data Link Connector (DLC)

AIR INDUCTION SYSTEM

NON-TURBOCHARGED ENGINES

All engines with Multi-Point Fuel Injection (MFI) use same basic air induction system. Remote air filter (with airflow sensor) is ducted to a plenum-mounted throttle body.

TURBOCHARGED ENGINES

In addition to basic air induction system used on all models, turbocharging system components include turbocharger, wastegate actuator, wastegate control solenoid valve and intake duct.

Wastegate Control Solenoid Valve – Engine Control Module (ECM) energizes solenoid valve, controlling leakage rate of turbocharger pressure to wastegate actuator.

COMPUTERIZED ENGINE CONTROLS

All models use a Multi-Point Fuel Injection (MFI) system. This is a computerized emission, fuel and ignition system. Electronic Control Module (ECM), determines at which point each injector supplies fuel. MFI system controls air/fuel ratio, ignition timing, Idle Air Control (IAC), fuel pressure and purge control.

ELECTRONIC CONTROL MODULE (ECM)

ECM receives and processes signals from data sensors and switches to control fuel delivery. ECM controls frequency and duration of injection (fuel delivery time). Fuel delivery time is modified for operating conditions such as cold starting, altitude, acceleration and deceleration.

NOTE: Components are grouped into 2 categories. First category is INPUT DEVICES, which are components that control or produce voltage signals monitored by ECM. Second category is OUTPUT SIGNALS, which are components controlled by ECM.

INPUT DEVICES

ECM determines control of various output devices based upon signals received from input devices. These devices include sensors, switches and simple monitored circuits such as a RPM reference signal from ignition coil. Vehicles are equipped with different combinations of input devices. Not all devices are used on all models. To determine input usage on a specific model, see WIRING DIAGRAMS article.

Available input signals include:

Air Conditioner Switch – When air conditioner is turned on, a signal is sent to ECM. ECM then adjusts Idle Air Control (IAC) servo to maintain optimum idle speed.

Airflow Sensor (Elantra, Excel & Sonata) – Karmen vortex-type AFS is mounted inside air cleaner assembly. AFS measures airflow rate through air cleaner and sends a proportionate electrical signal to ECM. ECM uses this signal to determine basic fuel injection duration.

Airflow Sensor (Scoupe) – On non-turbo models, hot film type sensor is mounted in intake hose between air cleaner and throttle body. Mass airflow rate is measured by amount of heat transfer from hot film probe. Change in temperature of probe controls resistance of circuit which ECM monitors.

On turbo models, AFS is mounted in intake hose. Operation of sensor is similar to non-turbo models. Instead of using hot film element, turbo AFS uses platinum wire sensor.

Atmospheric (Barometric) Pressure Sensor (Elantra, Excel & Sonata) – Pressure sensor, installed on airflow sensor, senses atmospheric pressure and converts it to voltage, which is sent to ECM. ECM computes altitude and corrects air/fuel ratio and ignition timing.

Coolant Temperature Sensor – Coolant temperature sensor is a thermal resistor. The resistance of thermistor decreases as coolant temperature increases. ECM uses coolant temperature information for controlling fuel enrichment when engine is cold.

Camshaft Position Sensor (Scoupe) – Assembly is located in distributor. It senses the TDC point of no. 1 cylinder in its compression stroke. Signal is sent to ECM to determine fuel injector firing sequence.

Crankshaft Position & TDC Sensor Assembly (Elantra, Excel & Sonata) – Assembly is located in distributor on SOHC and V6 engines. On DOHC engines, which use Direct (or Distributorless) Ignition System (DIS), assembly is a separate unit mounted in place of distributor. Assembly consists of triggering disc (mounted on shaft) and stationary optical sensing unit. Camshaft drives shaft, triggering optical sensing unit. ECM determines crankshaft position and TDC based on signals received from optical sensing unit.

Crankshaft Position Sensor (Scoupe) – Sensor is mounted to transaxle clutch housing. The reluctance-type sensor produces voltage signal to ECM as flywheel rotates. Signal monitored by ECM determines engine RPM and position of crankshaft.

EGR Temperature Sensor – Located on EGR valve, EGR temperature sensor is a thermistor that controls signal to ECM. When EGR malfunction occurs, EGR temperature decreases and ECM illuminates Malfunction Indicator Light (MIL).

Heated Oxygen Sensor (HO2S) – On single oxygen sensor equipped vehicles, sensor is located in exhaust system in front of catalytic converter. On dual oxygen sensor models, a second sensor is installed between converter and muffler.

Oxygen sensor monitors oxygen content of exhaust gases and produces voltage depending on concentration of oxygen. Voltage produced by sensor ranges from zero volts (lean) to about one volt (rich). ECM monitors sensor signal to control fuel delivery time.

Idle Air Control (IAC) Motor Position Sensor (Excel) – IAC motor position sensor is installed in IAC motor. It is a variable resistor-type sensor. The IAC motor position sensor monitors IAC motor plunger position and controls a signal to ECM. ECM then controls throttle valve opening and idle speed.

Idle Switch (Elantra, Excel & Sonata) – Idle switch is a contact-type switch. When throttle valve is closed, switch is activated. When throttle valve is in any other position, switch is deactivated. Switch is used by ECM for controlling fuel delivery time during deceleration and also as an idle speed adjusting device.

Ignition Timing Adjustment Terminal – Terminal is used for adjusting timing and basic idle speed. When terminal is grounded, ECM cancels ignition timing and idle speed control and then sets timing and idle speed control servos in adjustment mode.

Intake Air Temperature Sensor (Elantra, Excel & Sonata) – Air temperature sensor is located on airflow sensor. Thermistor-type sensor measures temperature of incoming air and controls signal to ECM. Sensor resistance decreases as temperature increases. ECM uses air temperature sensor information for controlling fuel delivery.

Knock Sensor (Turbo) – Sensor is attached to engine block and senses engine knock condition. A piezoelectric element produces electric signal from vibrational pressure. ECM retards timing based on signal received from sensor.

Power Steering Oil Pressure Switch – Power steering oil pressure switch activates with increase in power steering fluid pressure (load condition). With switch contact closed, circuit from ECM to vehicle ground is completed. ECM sends signal to IAC motor to adjust idle speed for increased engine load.

TDC Sensor – See CRANKSHAFT POSITION & TDC SENSOR ASSEMBLY.

Throttle Position Sensor – Throttle position sensor is a potentiometer connected to throttle valve shaft. As throttle opening changes, sensor varies voltage signal to ECM. ECM uses signal to determine fuel injection duration.

Transaxle Range Switch (A/T Models) – Transaxle Range switch is a multiple pole switch that controls battery voltage to ECM. When shift selector lever is in Neutral or Park position, switch inhibits ECM from voltage. Any other shifter selection supplies voltage to ECM. ECM determines automatic transmission load and signals Idle Air Control (IAC) servo to maintain optimum idle speed.

Vehicle Speed Sensor – Sensor, located in speedometer in instrument cluster, uses a reed switch to sense speedometer gear revolutions. VSS converts speedometer gear revolution (vehicle speed) into pulse signals which are input to ECM.

OUTPUT SIGNALS

NOTE: Vehicles are equipped with different combinations of computer-controlled components. Not all components listed below are used on every vehicle. For theory and operation on each output component, refer to system indicated after component.

ECM processes information from input sensors and sends appropriate voltage control signals to following engine controls:

A/C Clutch – See MISCELLANEOUS CONTROLS.

EGR Control Solenoid Valve – See EXHAUST GAS RECIRCULATION (EGR) CONTROL under EMISSION SYSTEMS.

Fuel Injectors – See FUEL CONTROL under FUEL SYSTEM.

Idle Air/Speed Control – See IDLE SPEED under FUEL SYSTEM.

MFI Control Relay – See FUEL DELIVERY under FUEL SYSTEM.

Malfunction Indicator Light (MIL) – See MALFUNCTION INDICATOR LIGHT under SELF-DIAGNOSTIC SYSTEM.

Power Transistor – See IGNITION SYSTEM.

Purge Control Solenoid – See EVAPORATIVE CONTROL under EMISSION SYSTEMS.

Self-Diagnostics – See SELF-DIAGNOSTIC SYSTEM.

FUEL SYSTEM

FUEL DELIVERY

Fuel is fed through in-tank filter by an electric fuel pump located in fuel tank. Passing through a second filter, fuel is maintained at a constant pressure at injectors by fuel pump and pressure regulator.

Fuel Pump – Located in fuel tank, fuel pump consists of an impeller driven by a DC motor. Pump has an internal check valve to maintain system pressure and a relief valve to protect fuel pressure circuit.

Fuel Pressure Regulator – Fuel pressure regulator, located on fuel delivery pipe, maintains a constant pressure at injectors during all engine operating conditions. Fuel flows from top of fuel injectors to pressure regulator. Regulator is a diaphragm-operated relief valve with pressure applied by intake manifold vacuum. If this pressure becomes less than fuel pressure, valve opens, causing excess fuel to return to fuel tank by return lines.

MFI Control Relay (Fuel Pump Relay) – Relay is located either at left side of driver-side console or right side of passenger-side console. This multipurpose relay switches power to the following vehicle sensors and actuators: airflow sensor, idle speed control, injectors and fuel pump. For specific system configuration, see WIRING DIAGRAMS article.

When ignition switch is turned to ON position, ECM energizes coils controlling injectors, airflow sensor and idle air/speed control. When ignition switch is turned to START position, ECM energizes coils (through inhibitor switch on automatic transmission) to supply power to fuel pump. Relay failure will cause a no-start condition.

FUEL CONTROL

Fuel Injectors – Fuel is supplied to engine through electronically pulsed (timed) injector valves located on fuel delivery pipe. ECM controls amount of fuel metered through injectors based on information received from input sensors.

IDLE SPEED

Idle Air Control (IAC) – During start mode, ECM controls throttle position in accordance with coolant temperature sensor input. After starting with idle switch activated (throttle closed), fast idle speed is controlled by coolant temperature input to ECM and engine RPM feedback to ECM. When idle switch is deactivated (throttle open), IAC motor moves to a preset position in accordance with coolant temperature sensor input.

Idle control increases idle speed when power steering oil pressure switch or A/C switch is activated or when transmission is shifted from Neutral to Drive (A/T). During deceleration, IAC motor delays closing of throttle valve to its normal idling position. On Excel, idle speed is controlled with a Idle Speed Control (ISC) motor. Motor plunger extends or retracts to control throttle valve opening. On Scoupe, idle speed is controlled with an idle speed actuator motor. Motor is installed in-line with air by-pass hose. ECM signal controls both idle control motors.

IGNITION SYSTEM

DIRECT IGNITION SYSTEM (DIS)

Elantra & Sonata 2.0L – DIS is a molded dual-coil system that supplies energy for ignition at high speeds. System does not use a distributor. Electronic Control Module (ECM) directly activates power transistor for ignition timing control.

When ignition is turned on, battery voltage is applied to ignition coil primary winding. As crankshaft position sensor shaft rotates, ignition signals are transmitted from ECM to power transistor. These signals activate power transistor, causing ignition coil primary winding current to either repeatedly flow from ignition coil negative terminal through power transistor to ground or to be interrupted. This action produces high voltage in secondary winding of ignition coil. From ignition coil, secondary winding current flows through spark plug to ground, creating ignition in appropriate cylinder.

ELECTRONIC IGNITION SYSTEM (EIS)

Excel, Scoupe & Sonata 3.0L – EIS consists of a distributor, spark plugs, ignition coil, power transistor, Electronic Control Module (ECM), high tension cables and wiring. ECM detects engine operating conditions from various sensor signals and regulates ignition timing based on these signals.

With ignition on, battery voltage is applied to ignition coil primary winding. As distributor shaft rotates, ignition signals are transmitted from ECM to power transistor. These signals activate power transistor, causing ignition coil primary winding current to either repeatedly flow from ignition coil negative terminal through power transistor to ground or to be interrupted. This action produces high voltage in secondary winding of ignition coil. From coil, secondary winding current flows through distributor and spark plug to ground, creating ignition in appropriate cylinder.

IGNITION TIMING CONTROL SYSTEM

Elantra & Sonata 2.0L – Ignition timing control system uses Electronic Control Module (ECM). ECM controls timing and firing of cylinders based on signals from various engine sensors. ECM activates power transistors so ignition occurs, taking operating conditions of engine into consideration. Optimum ignition timing control is determined by making preset corrections for engine coolant temperature, intake air temperature and other conditions of ignition advance angle, which are preset according to engine operating conditions.

Excel, Scoupe & Sonata 3.0L – Ignition timing control system is composed of various sensors, Electronic Control Module (ECM) and power transistor. Depending on engine operating conditions, ignition timing control system functions to regulate ignition timing and current flow time of primary current, ensuring good ignition performance. On-off switching of primary current flowing in ignition coil is performed by power transistor, which in turn is regulated by ECM.

EMISSION SYSTEMS

EXHAUST GAS RECIRCULATION (EGR) CONTROL

NOTE: Elantra models use a different EGR system between California and Federal models. All other models use a single EGR system.

Excel, Elantra California, Scoupe & Sonata Models – ECM controls EGR operation by activating EGR control solenoid valve according to engine load. When engine is cold, ECM signals EGR control solenoid valve to deactivate EGR. California models are equipped with an EGR temperature sensor. When EGR malfunction occurs, EGR temperature decreases and ECM illuminates Malfunction Indicator Light (MIL).

Elantra Federal Models – To lower oxides of nitrogen (NOx) emissions, a non-computer-controlled exhaust gas recirculation system is used. EGR operation is controlled by throttle body ported vacuum. Vacuum is routed through a thermovalve to prevent low temperature EGR operation. Spring pressure holds EGR closed during no/low vacuum conditions (engine idling or wide open throttle). When vacuum increases and overcomes spring pressure of EGR control valve, EGR pintle is lifted and allows exhaust gases to flow into intake manifold.

EGR Control Solenoid Valve (Except Federal Elantra Models) – Vacuum applied to EGR control valve is controlled by solenoid valve through control relay.

Thermovalve (Federal Elantra Models) – Thermovalve senses coolant temperature to prevent EGR operation at temperatures less than a preset level. At temperatures less than 140°F (60°C), thermovalve is open and vacuum is vented (no vacuum is supplied to EGR valve). At temperatures greater than 140°F (60°C), thermovalve closes (vacuum is supplied to EGR valve) and EGR operates.

EVAPORATIVE CONTROL

Fuel evaporation system prevents fuel vapor from entering atmosphere. System consists of a vacuum relief filler cap, overfill limiter (2-way valve), fuel check valve, charcoal canister, purge control valve and connecting lines and hoses.

Purge Control Solenoid – When ignition switch is in OFF position, fuel vapors are vented into charcoal canister. When engine is at normal operating temperature and engine speed is greater than idle, thermovalve will open and allow vacuum to open purge control valve. Canister vapors are then drawn into intake manifold for burning through purge control valve. Purge control valve is kept closed during idle and engine warm-up to reduce HC and CO emissions.

POSITIVE CRANKCASE VENTILATION (PCV) VALVE

PCV valve operates in closed crankcase ventilation system, which consists of PCV valve and ventilation hoses. PCV valve is a one-way check valve, located in valve cover. When engine is running, manifold vacuum pulls PCV valve open, allowing crankcase fumes to enter intake manifold. If engine backfires through intake manifold, PCV valve closes to prevent crankcase combustion.

SELF-DIAGNOSTIC SYSTEM

Self-diagnostic system monitors all input signals from each sensor. If an abnormal input signal occurs, that item is stored by ECM and given a code number. Codes can be read using a voltmeter or scan tester. Data Link Connector (DLC) is located in fuse box on left kick panel. ECM long term memory is not erased when ignition is turned off. ECM memory will erase if battery or ECM is disconnected.

MALFUNCTION INDICATOR LIGHT

NOTE: ECM diagnostic memory is kept alive by direct power supply from battery. Memory is not erased by turning ignition off. Memory will erase if battery or ECM is disconnected.

Malfunction Indicator Light (MIL) will glow when ignition switch is turned to ON position. It remains on for several seconds after engine has started. Self-diagnostic system monitors all input signals from each sensor. If an abnormal input signal occurs, MIL will glow and a code will be stored in ECM memory. For additional information, see SELF-DIAGNOSTICS article.

MISCELLANEOUS CONTROLS

NOTE: Although not considered true engine performance-related systems, controlled devices may affect driveability if they malfunction.

A/C CLUTCH

When A/C is turned on while engine is at idle, IAC servo is commanded to increase idle speed. To prevent A/C compressor clutch from switching on before idle speed has increased, ECM briefly opens A/C relay circuit.

1994 ENGINE PERFORMANCE
Basic Diagnostic Procedures

Elantra, Excel, Scoupe, Sonata

INTRODUCTION

The following diagnostic steps will help prevent overlooking a simple problem. This is also where to begin diagnosis for a no-start condition.

The first step in diagnosing any driveability problem is verifying the customer complaint with a test drive under the conditions the problem reportedly occurred.

Before entering self-diagnostics, perform a careful and complete visual inspection. Most engine control problems result from mechanical breakdowns, poor electrical connections or damaged/misrouted vacuum hoses. Before condemning the computerized system, perform each test listed in this article.

NOTE: Perform all voltage tests using a Digital Volt-Ohmmeter (DVOM) with a minimum 10-megohm input impedance, unless stated otherwise in test procedure.

PRELIMINARY INSPECTION & ADJUSTMENTS

VISUAL INSPECTION

Visually inspect all electrical wiring, looking for chafed, stretched, cut or pinched wiring. Ensure electrical connectors fit tightly and are not corroded. Ensure vacuum hoses are properly routed and are not pinched or cut. See VACUUM DIAGRAMS article to verify routing and connections (if necessary). Inspect air induction system for possible vacuum leaks.

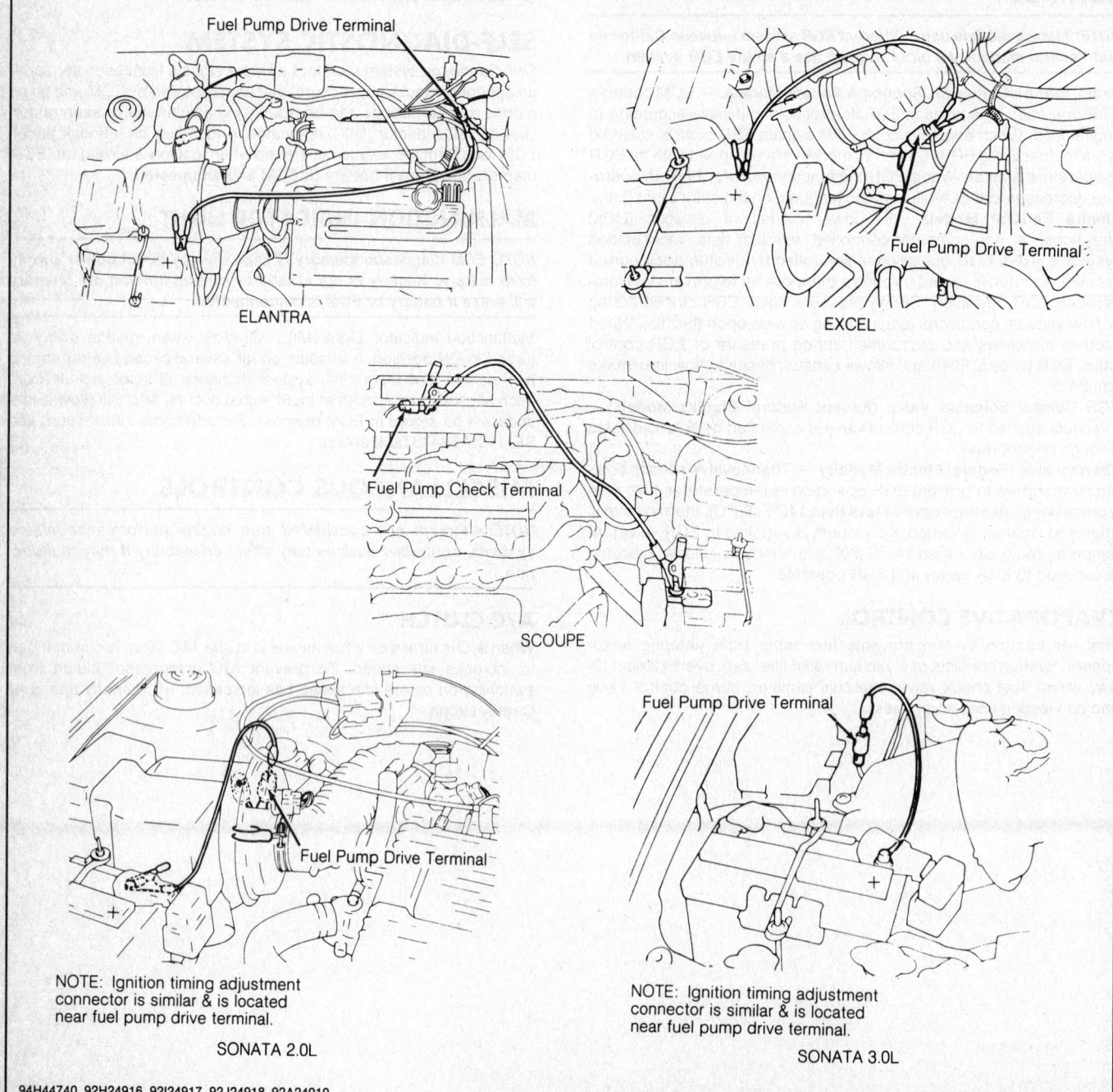

94H44740 92H24916 92I24917 92J24918 92A24919

Courtesy of Hyundai Motor Co.

Fig. 1: Jumping Fuel Pump Drive Connector

MECHANICAL INSPECTION

Compression – Check engine mechanical condition using a compression gauge, vacuum gauge or engine analyzer. See engine analyzer manual for specific instructions.

WARNING: DO NOT use ignition switch during compression tests on fuel injected vehicles. Use a remote starter to crank engine. Fuel injectors on many models are triggered by ignition switch during cranking mode, which can create a fire hazard or contaminate engine oiling system.

COMPRESSION SPECIFICATIONS

Application	Specification
Compression Ratio	
1.5L	
Excel	9.4:1
Scoupe	
Non-Turbo	10.0:1
Turbo	7.5:1
1.6L	9.2:1
1.8L	9.2:1
2.0L	9.0:1
3.0L	8.9:1
Compression Pressure	
1.5L	
Excel	192 psi (13.5 kg/cm²)
Scoupe	
Non-Turbo	192 psi (13.5 kg/cm²)
Turbo	149 psi (10.5 kg/cm²)
1.6L	171 psi (12.0 kg/cm²)
1.8L	171 psi (12.0 kg/cm²)
2.0L	171 psi (12.0 kg/cm²)
3.0L	173 psi (12.2 kg/cm²)
Maximum Variation Between Cylinders	
All Models	14 psi (1.0 kg/cm²)

Exhaust System Backpressure – Exhaust system can be checked with a vacuum or pressure gauge. If using a pressure gauge, remove HO2S sensor. Connect a 1-10 psi pressure gauge and run engine at 2500 RPM. If exhaust system backpressure is greater than 1 3/4 - 2 psi, exhaust system or catalytic converter is plugged.

If using a vacuum gauge, connect vacuum gauge hose to intake manifold vacuum port and start engine. Observe vacuum gauge. Open throttle part way and hold steady. If vacuum gauge reading slowly drops after stabilizing, check exhaust system for restrictions.

FUEL SYSTEM

WARNING: Always relieve fuel pressure before disconnecting any fuel injection-related component. DO NOT allow fuel to contact engine or electrical components.

FUEL PRESSURE RELEASE

Disconnect fuel pump harness connector at fuel tank rear side (under rear seat on Elantra and Sonata 2.0L). Start engine. After engine stalls, turn ignition off. Disconnect negative battery cable. Reconnect fuel pump harness connector.

FUEL PUMP TEST

Turn ignition off. Apply battery voltage to fuel pump drive terminal (Yellow wire on Elantra, Excel and Scoupe Turbo; Green/White wire on Scoupe Non-Turbo; Black/White wire on Sonata). *See Fig. 1.* Remove fuel tank cap and listen for fuel pump operation. Pinch fuel hoses by hand and ensure fuel pressure can be felt.

FUEL PRESSURE TEST

1) Release fuel pressure. See FUEL PRESSURE RELEASE. Disconnect high pressure fuel hose from top of fuel filter. Cover hose connection using rags to avoid spraying of fuel.
2) Using Fuel Pressure Gauge Adapter (09353-24200), install fuel pressure gauge to fuel filter. *See Fig. 2.* Tighten bolt to 18-25 ft. lbs. (25-34 N.m). Reinstall negative battery cable.

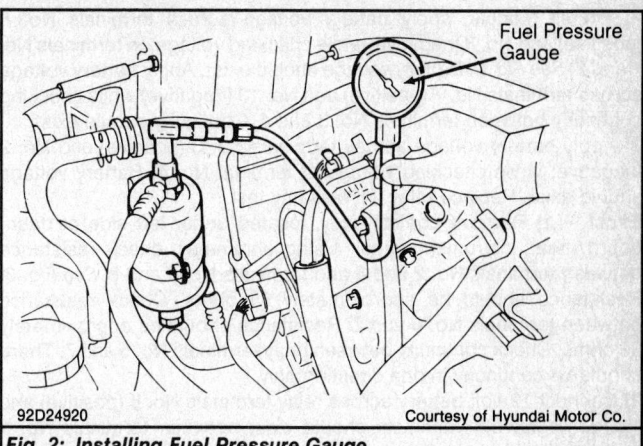

92D24920   Courtesy of Hyundai Motor Co.

Fig. 2: Installing Fuel Pressure Gauge

3) Start engine. Ensure no fuel leakage exists at pressure gauge or connection. Disconnect vacuum hose from fuel pressure regulator, and plug hose end.
4) Measure and record fuel pressure at idle. Reconnect vacuum hose, and again measure and record fuel pressure. See FUEL PUMP SPECIFICATIONS table. If measurements are not within specification, go to next step. If measurements are okay, go to step **8)**.

FUEL PUMP SPECIFICATIONS

Application	Pressure psi (kg/cm²)	Volume In One Min. Pts. (L)
Scoupe		
With Vacuum	37 (2.5)	[1]
Without Vacuum	44 (3.0)	[1]
Except Scoupe		
With Vacuum	39 (2.8)	[1]
Without Vacuum	46-49 (3.3-3.5)	[1]

[1] – Information is not available from manufacturer.

5) If fuel pressure is low, check for:
- Restricted fuel filter.
- Fuel leaking to return side. This can be caused by poor seating of valve in fuel pressure regulator.
- Low fuel pump discharge pressure.

6) If fuel pressure is too high, check for:
- Sticking valve in fuel pressure regulator.
- Restricted or bent fuel return hose or pipe.

7) If fuel pressure does not differ when regulator vacuum hose is connected or disconnected, check for:
- Restricted/damaged vacuum hose or fitting.
- Sticking or poor seating valve in fuel pressure regulator.

8) If measurements are okay in step **4)**, stop engine and ensure fuel pressure gauge reading does not drop. If fuel pressure drops slowly after engine is stopped, an injector is leaking. If fuel pressure drops immediately after engine is stopped, check valve inside fuel pump is not closed.
9) After testing is completed, release fuel pressure. See FUEL PRESSURE RELEASE. Disconnect fuel pressure gauge from adapter bolt. Ensure hose connection is covered by a shop towel to prevent fuel spray. Remove adapter bolt, install new "O" ring, and replace with original bolt. Apply battery voltage to fuel pump drive terminal. *See Fig. 1.* Check for leaks.

MFI CONTROL RELAY TEST

CAUTION: When applying direct battery voltage, ensure voltage is applied to correct terminal; otherwise, relay damage could result.

Elantra & Sonata – 1) Remove control relay. On Elantra, relay is located behind left side of driver's dashboard below instrument panel. On Sonata, relay is located under right side of dashboard, near blower motor housing.

2) On all models, apply battery voltage across terminals No. 6 (positive) and No. 8 (negative) while checking voltage on terminals No. 1 and 2. *See Fig. 3.* Battery voltage should exist. Apply battery voltage across terminals No. 7 (positive) and No. 10 (negative) while checking continuity between terminals No. 3 and 4. Continuity should exist.

3) Apply battery voltage across terminals No. 3 (positive) and No. 9 (negative) while checking voltage at terminal No. 4. Battery voltage should exist. Replace relay if it fails any test.

Excel – 1) Remove control relay, located under left side of dashboard, near instrument panel. Using ohmmeter, check resistance between terminals No. 2 and 8 and terminals No. 3 and 8. *See Fig. 3.* Resistance should be approximately 95 ohms. Check resistance between terminals No. 6 and 7. Resistance should be approximately 35 ohms. Check continuity between relay terminals No. 5 and 7. There should be continuity in one direction only.

2) Connect 12-volt battery across relay terminals No. 6 (positive) and No. 7 (negative). Continuity should exist between terminals No. 1 and 4 until voltage is disconnected.

3) Connect 12-volt battery across terminals No. 5 and 7, and check continuity between terminals No. 1 and 3. Continuity should exist between terminals No. 1 and 3 until voltage is disconnected. Replace control relay if it fails any test.

Scoupe – 1) Remove control relay, located under left side of dashboard, near instrument panel. Connect 12-volt battery across relay terminal No. 2 (negative) and terminal No. 4 (positive). *See Fig. 3.* Using ohmmeter, check continuity between terminals No. 1 and 5. Continuity should exist until voltage is disconnected.

2) Reconnect battery voltage between terminals No. 2 and 4. Check continuity between terminals No. 3 and 5. Continuity should exist until voltage is disconnected. Replace relay if it fails any test.

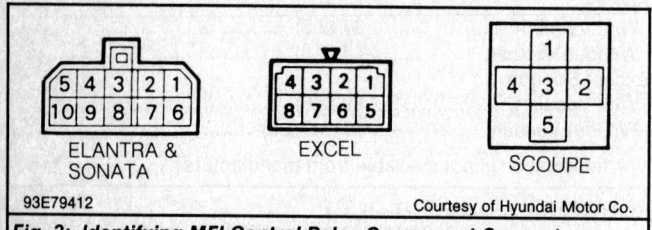

93E79412   Courtesy of Hyundai Motor Co.

Fig. 3: Identifying MFI Control Relay Component Connectors

IGNITION CHECKS

DIRECT IGNITION SYSTEM
(DIS – 1.6L, 1.8L & 2.0L)

Spark (Spark Plug) – Connect spark plug to a high tension cable. Ground outer electrode (main body of spark plug), and crank engine. Spark should occur in discharge gap between electrodes. Spark plug gap should be .039-.043" (1.0-1.1 mm).

Ignition Coil Power Source – Disconnect coil primary connector. Turn ignition on. Using voltmeter, check voltage between positive terminal and ground. Battery voltage should exist.

Ignition Coil Resistance – 1) Using an ohmmeter, measure primary coil resistance for cylinders No. 1 and 4 between coil connector terminals No. 1 and 3. Measure resistance for cylinders No. 2 and 3 between connector terminals No. 2 and 3. *See Fig. 4.* See DIS IGNITION COIL RESISTANCE table.

2) To measure secondary coil resistance, disconnect ignition coil connector. Measure resistance between coil towers No. 1 and 4 and between coil towers No. 2 and 3. See DIS IGNITION COIL RESISTANCE table. Replace coil if readings are not within specification.

DIS IGNITION COIL RESISTANCE – Ohms @ 68°F (20°C)

Application	Primary	Secondary
Elantra & Sonata 2.0L	.77-.95	10,300-13,900

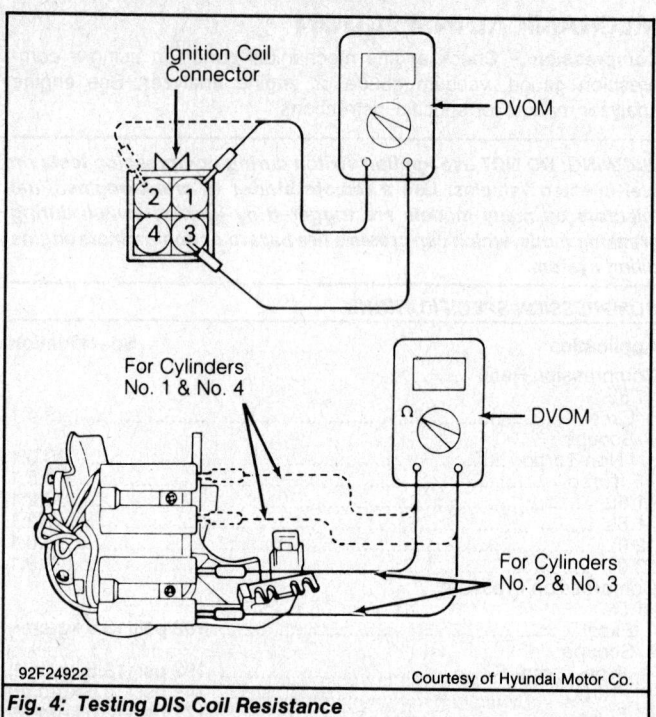

92F24922   Courtesy of Hyundai Motor Co.

Fig. 4: Testing DIS Coil Resistance

Power Transistor – 1) Disconnect connector from power transistor. To check power transistor for cylinders No. 1 and 4, apply 1.5 volts between power transistor terminals No. 3 (negative) and No. 4 (positive). *See Fig. 5.*

2) Using analog ohmmeter, check continuity between terminals No. 3 (positive lead) and No. 5 (negative lead). With voltage applied to terminal No. 4, continuity should exist. With voltage removed from terminal No. 4, continuity should not exist.

3) To check power transistor for cylinders No. 2 and 3, apply 1.5 volts between power transistor terminals No. 2 (positive) and No. 3 (negative). Using analog voltmeter, check for continuity between terminals No. 1 (negative lead) and No. 3 (positive lead). With voltage applied to terminal No. 2, continuity should exist. With voltage removed from terminal No. 2, continuity should not exist.

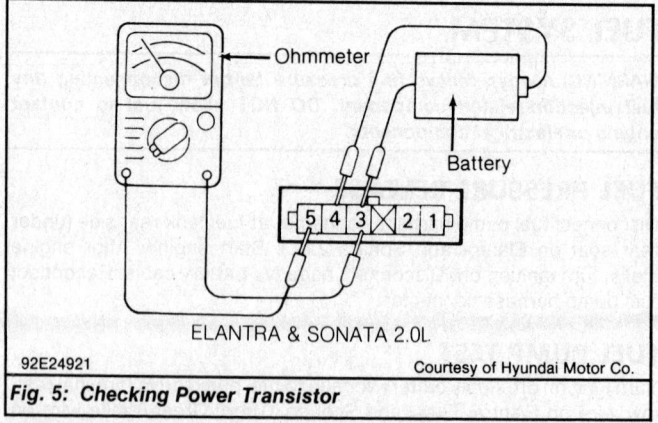

92E24921   Courtesy of Hyundai Motor Co.

Fig. 5: Checking Power Transistor

ELECTRONIC IGNITION SYSTEM
(EIS – 1.5L & 3.0L)

Spark (Coil) – Check for spark at coil wire. Hold wire about 1/4" from an engine ground, and crank engine. If spark is produced, coil is okay. If spark is not produced, use a voltmeter to check voltage at negative side of coil (tach signal) while cranking engine. If voltage does not exist, see IGNITION COIL POWER SOURCE. If voltage does not fluctuate, check coil wiring, power transistor, ECU and distributor assembly. If voltage fluctuates, check coil resistance, coil wire and connections.

Spark (Spark Plug) – Connect spark plug to a high tension cable. Ground outer electrode (main body of spark plug) and crank engine. Spark should occur in discharge gap between electrodes. Spark plug gap should be .039-.043" (1.0-1.1 mm).

Ignition Coil Power Source – Disconnect coil primary connector. Turn ignition on. Using voltmeter, check voltage between positive terminal and ground. Battery voltage should exist.

Ignition Coil Resistance – 1) Remove primary and secondary leads from ignition coil. Using an ohmmeter, check primary resistance between positive and negative terminals of coil. See EIS IGNITION COIL RESISTANCE table.

2) Check secondary resistance between ignition coil positive terminal (Black/White wire) and ignition coil tower. See EIS IGNITION COIL RESISTANCE table. Replace coil if readings are not within specification.

EIS IGNITION COIL RESISTANCE – Ohms @ 68°F (20°C)

Application	Primary	Secondary
Excel & Sonata 3.0L	.72-.88	10,300-13,900
Scoupe	.45-.55	10,300-13,900

Power Transistor (Excel) – 1) Disconnect connector from power transistor. Apply 3.0 volts between power transistor terminals No. 2 (negative) and No. 3 (positive). See Fig. 6.

2) Check continuity between terminals No. 1 and 2. With voltage applied to terminal No. 3, continuity should exist. With voltage removed from terminal No. 3, continuity should not exist. Replace power transistor if continuity is not as specified.

Power Transistor (Scoupe) – 1) Disconnect connector from power transistor. Apply 3.0 volts between power transistor terminals No. 1 (negative) and No. 4 (positive). See Fig. 6.

2) Check continuity between terminals No. 1 and 3. With voltage applied to terminal No. 4, continuity should exist. With voltage removed from terminal No. 4, continuity should not exist. Replace power transistor if continuity is not as specified.

Power Transistor (Sonata 3.0L) – 1) Disconnect connector from power transistor. Apply 3.0 volts between power transistor terminals No. 1 (positive) and No. 2 (negative). See Fig. 6.

2) Check continuity between terminals No. 2 and 3. With voltage applied to terminal No. 1, continuity should exist. With voltage removed from terminal No. 1, continuity should not exist. Replace power transistor if continuity is not as specified.

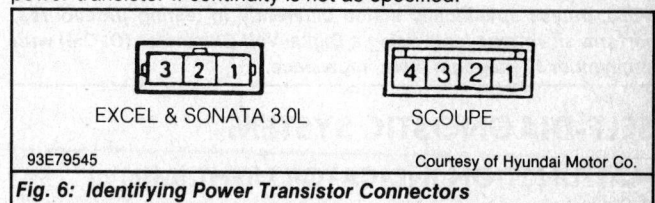

EXCEL & SONATA 3.0L   SCOUPE

93E79545   Courtesy of Hyundai Motor Co.

Fig. 6: Identifying Power Transistor Connectors

IDLE SPEED & IGNITION TIMING

Ensure idle speed and ignition timing are set to specification. For adjustment procedures, see ON-VEHICLE ADJUSTMENTS article.

SUMMARY

If no faults were found while performing BASIC DIAGNOSTIC PROCEDURES, proceed to SELF-DIAGNOSTICS article. If no hard codes are found in self-diagnostics, proceed to TROUBLE SHOOTING – NO CODES article for diagnosis by symptom (i.e., ROUGH IDLE, NO START, etc.) or intermittent diagnostic procedures.

1994 ENGINE PERFORMANCE
Self-Diagnostics – Elantra, Excel & Sonata

INTRODUCTION

Most engine control problems are the result of mechanical break-downs, poor electrical connections or damaged vacuum hoses. Before considering the computer system as a possible cause of problems, perform checks and inspections covered in BASIC DIAGNOSTIC PROCEDURES article. Failure to do so may result in lost diagnostic time.

If no faults were found while performing BASIC DIAGNOSTIC PROCEDURES, proceed with self-diagnostics. If no fault codes or only pass codes are present after entering self-diagnostics, proceed to TROUBLE SHOOTING – NO CODES article for diagnosis by symptom (i.e., ROUGH IDLE, NO START, etc.).

NOTE: Unless specifically stated differently in testing procedures, perform all voltage tests using a Digital Volt-Ohmmeter (DVOM) with a minimum 10-megohm input impedance.

SELF-DIAGNOSTIC SYSTEM

MALFUNCTION INDICATOR LIGHT (MIL)

Vehicles are equipped with a Malfunction Indicator Light (MIL). As a bulb check, light will illuminate for approximately 5 seconds when ignition is on. MIL will also illuminate when a system failure is detected; a corresponding trouble code will set in Electronic Control Module (ECM) memory.

ECM is equipped with a self-diagnostic system, which detects system failures or abnormalities. When a malfunction occurs, ECM will illuminate MIL (CHECK ENGINE light) on instrument panel. When malfunction is detected and light is turned on, a corresponding trouble code will be stored in ECM. To retrieve stored codes, see RETRIEVING CODES (NON-SCAN) or RETRIEVING CODES (SCAN TESTER). Malfunctions are recorded as hard failures or as intermittent failures.

Hard Failures – Hard failures cause Malfunction Indicator Light (MIL) to illuminate and remain on until problem is repaired. If light comes on and remains on during vehicle operation, retrieve code(s). See RETRIEVING CODES (NON-SCAN) table to determine cause of malfunction.

Intermittent Failures – Intermittent failures may cause malfunction light to flicker on and off after intermittent fault goes away. Corresponding trouble code will be retained in ECU memory. If related fault does not reoccur within a certain time frame, related trouble code may be erased from ECU memory. Intermittent failures may be caused by sensor, connector or wiring related problems. See INTERMITTENTS in TROUBLE SHOOTING – NO CODES article.

DIAGNOSTIC PROCEDURE

NOTE: Trouble codes will be recorded at various operating times. Some codes require operation of sensor or switch for 5 seconds; other components require operation for 5 minutes or longer at normal operating temperature, vehicle speed and load. Therefore, some codes may not set in a service bay operational mode and may require road testing vehicle in order to duplicate condition under which code will set.

Diagnosis of computerized engine control system should be performed in following order:

1) Ensure all engine systems other than computerized systems (i.e. compression, ignition, etc.) are operating properly. DO NOT proceed with testing unless all other problems have been repaired. If MIL light is illuminated, see RETRIEVING CODES (NON-SCAN) or RETRIEVING CODES (SCAN TESTER). For diagnosing hard codes, see FAULT CODES to determine cause of malfunction. See DIAGNOSTIC TESTS for test procedures corresponding to fault codes.

2) For diagnosing intermittent codes, proceed to INTERMITTENTS in TROUBLESHOOTING – NO CODES article. Inspect condition of system harness by conducting recommended voltage or continuity checks. See WIRING DIAGRAMS article for additional information on specific circuit configuration. Inspect condition of individual component. Repair or replace component as needed.

3) Recheck system operation after repair is made. If trouble code still is present, substitute ECM with known good unit. Verify that system is repaired. After repairs have been completed, clear trouble codes. See CLEARING TROUBLE CODES.

SERVICE PRECAUTIONS

Before proceeding with diagnosis, following precautions must be observed:

- Ensure vehicle has a fully charged battery and functional charging system.
- Visually inspect connectors and circuit wiring being worked on.
- DO NOT disconnect battery or ECM. This will erase any fault codes stored in ECM.
- DO NOT cause short circuits when performing electrical tests. This will set additional fault codes, making diagnosis of original problem more difficult.
- DO NOT use a test light in place of a voltmeter.
- When checking for spark, ensure coil wire is NOT more than 1/4" from ground. If coil wire is more than 1/4" from ground, damage to vehicle electronics and/or ECM may result.
- DO NOT prolong testing of fuel injectors. Engine may hydrostatically (liquid) lock.
- When a vehicle has multiple fault codes, always repair lowest number fault code first.

RETRIEVING CODES (NON-SCAN)

1) Before entering on-board diagnostics, refer to SERVICE PRECAUTIONS. Turn ignition switch to OFF position. Locate Data Link Connector (DLC), next to fuse block. Connect voltmeter positive lead to Data Link Connector (DLC) MFI diagnosis terminal and negative lead to ground terminal. *See Fig. 1.*

2) Turn ignition switch to ON position. Voltmeter (analog) will display trouble codes by 12-volt pulses of voltmeter needle. Trouble codes are retrieved in numerical order. A constant repetition of short 12-volt pulses indicates system is normal. If system is abnormal, voltmeter will pulse between zero and 12 volts.

3) Codes will appear on voltmeter as long and short 12-volt pulses. Long pulses represent tens; short pulses represent ones. For example: 4 long pulses and 3 short pulses indicate Code 43. After recording fault code(s), perform necessary repair(s) to indicated circuit(s). See FAULT CODES.

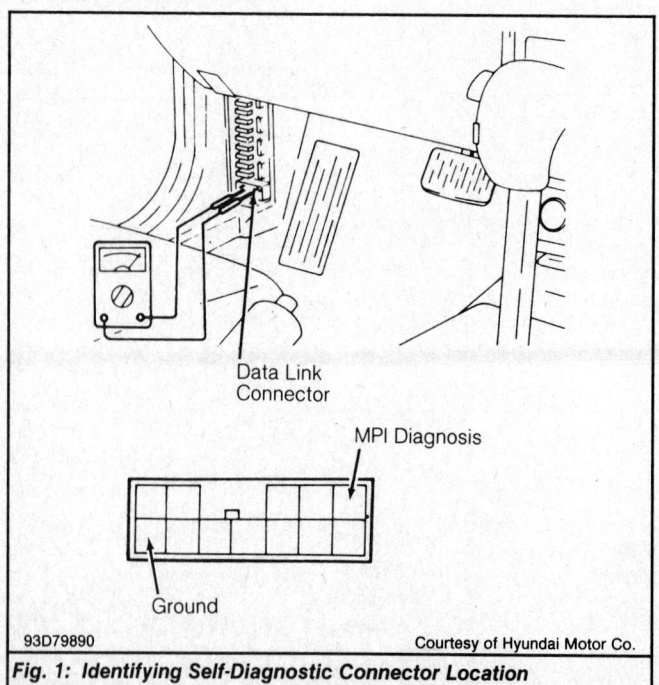

Data Link Connector

MPI Diagnosis

Ground

93D79890   Courtesy of Hyundai Motor Co.

Fig. 1: Identifying Self-Diagnostic Connector Location

RETRIEVING CODES (SCAN TESTER)

NOTE: If scan tester is needed to perform diagnostic test with key in START position, an auxiliary power source is needed to operate scan tester. Use optional Battery Harness (09391-33500).

NOTE: For specific operating procedures using scan tester, see instruction manual.

1) Before entering on-board diagnostics, refer to SERVICE PRECAUTIONS. Turn ignition switch to OFF position. Locate Data Link Connector (DLC), next to fuse block. Connect power source terminal of scan tester to cigarette lighter socket. *See Fig. 2.*
2) Connect scan tester to Data Link Connector (DLC). Turn ignition on. Read and record scan tester self-diagnostic output. Perform necessary repair(s). See FAULT CODES.

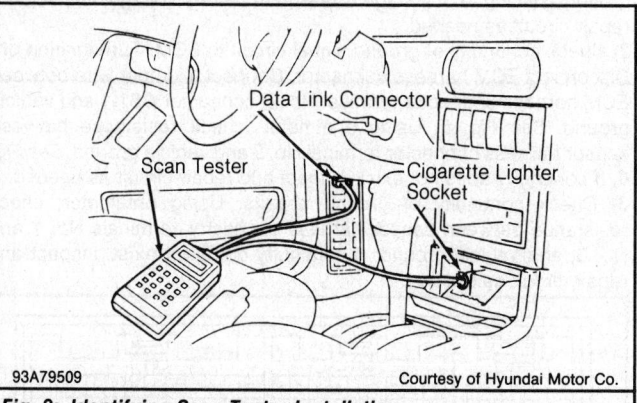

93A79509   Courtesy of Hyundai Motor Co.

Fig. 2: Identifying Scan Tester Installation

CLEARING CODES

After testing and repairs have been completed, disconnect negative battery cable for at least 15 seconds to clear codes.

ECM LOCATION

ECM is located behind driver's dash panel, behind hood release lever on Elantra and Excel. On Sonata, ECM is located behind right corner of passenger's dash panel.

ECM POWER & GROUND CIRCUITS

See SYSTEM & COMPONENT TESTING article.

FAULT CODES

NOTE: Codes listed in FAULT CODES are not used on all vehicles. For testing procedures, see DIAGNOSTIC TESTS.

MIL Stays On – ECM fault. Possible cause: faulty ECM.
Code 11 – Oxygen sensor (HO2S) fault. Possible causes: faulty HO2S, connector or harness, low or high fuel pressure, defective injector(s) or intake air leaks.
Code 12 – Airflow sensor fault. Possible causes: faulty airflow sensor, connector or harness.
Code 13 – Intake air temperature sensor fault. Possible causes: faulty intake air temperature sensor, connector or harness.
Code 14 – Throttle Position Sensor (TPS) fault. Possible causes: faulty TPS, connector or harness or closed throttle position switch.
Code 15 – Idle Speed Control (ISC) motor position sensor fault. Possible causes: faulty ISC motor position sensor or faulty throttle position sensor, connector or harness.
Code 21 – Coolant Temperature Sensor (CTS) fault. Possible causes: faulty coolant temperature sensor, connector or harness.
Code 22 – Crankshaft Position (CKP) sensor fault. Possible causes: faulty distributor assembly (if equipped) or faulty CKP sensor, connector or harness.

Code 23 – Top Dead Center (TDC) sensor fault. Possible causes: faulty distributor assembly (if equipped) or faulty TDC sensor, connector or harness.
Code 24 – Vehicle Speed Sensor (VSS) fault. Possible causes: faulty VSS, connector or harness.
Code 25 – Barometric (BARO) pressure sensor fault. Possible causes: faulty BARO pressure sensor, connector or harness.
Code 41 – Injector(s) fault. Possible causes: low or high injector coil resistance, connector or harness.
Code 42 – Fuel pump fault. Possible causes: faulty ECM or faulty MFI relay connector or harness.
Code 43 – EGR fault. Possible causes: faulty EGR valve, faulty EGR temperature sensor, faulty EGR solenoid or faulty EGR vacuum control connector or harness.
Code 44 – Ignition coil fault. Possible causes: faulty ignition coil or faulty ignition power transistor unit connector or harness.
Code 59 – Oxygen (HO2S) sensor fault. Possible causes: faulty HO2S, connector or harness, low or high fuel pressure, defective injector(s) or intake air leaks.

SUMMARY

If no hard fault codes (or only pass codes) are present, driveability symptoms exist, or intermittent codes exist, proceed to TROUBLE SHOOTING – NO CODES article for diagnosis by symptom (i.e., ROUGH IDLE, NO START, etc.) or intermittent diagnostic procedures.

DIAGNOSTIC TESTS

CAUTION: Ensure ignition switch is in OFF position when performing resistance tests.

NOTE: Perform all resistance and voltage tests using a Digital Volt-Ohmmeter (DVOM) with a minimum 10-megohm impedance, unless stated otherwise in test procedures.

Clear fault codes after each repair. See CLEARING CODES. Recheck for codes to confirm repair. See RETRIEVING CODES.

CODE 11 & 59 (HEATED OXYGEN SENSOR FAILURE)

NOTE: If after all testing procedures have been completed, system is still inoperative, substitute ECM with known good unit and retest.

System Inspection – Determine if vehicle is producing high emissions. High emissions can be caused by faulty HO2S, injector, coolant temperature sensor, vacuum leak and/or malfunctioning airflow sensor.
Scan Tester Procedure – Access scan tester service data item No. 11. Tester should display sensor voltage. Ensure engine is at normal operating temperature. See HO2S OPERATING VOLTAGE SPECIFICATIONS table.

HO2S OPERATING VOLTAGE SPECIFICATIONS

Engine RPM	Output (Volts)
750	.4 Or Less
2000	.6-1.0
4000 To 750 [1]	.2 Or Less
750 To 4000 [2]	.6-1.0

[1] – Sudden deceleration.
[2] – Sudden acceleration.

Harness Inspection (Elantra (Federal) & Sonata (4-Cylinder) – 1) Measure power supply voltage. Disconnect HO2S harness connector. Turn ignition on. Using DVOM, measure voltage between harness connector terminal No. 4 on Elantra (No. 3 on Sonata) and vehicle ground. *See Fig. 6.* If voltage is less than battery voltage, inspect and repair circuit as needed.
2) Check continuity of ground circuit to ECM. Turn ignition off. Disconnect ECM harness connector. Connect a jumper wire between ECM

harness connector terminal No. 9, connector C01-1 and vehicle ground. *See Fig. 3.* Using ohmmeter, measure resistance between HO2S sensor harness connector terminal No. 2 on Elantra (No. 4 on Sonata) and vehicle ground. If continuity does not exist, inspect and repair circuit as needed.

3) Check continuity of ground circuits. Using ohmmeter, check resistance between sensor harness connector terminal No. 3 on Elantra (No. 1 on Sonata) and vehicle ground. *See Fig. 6.* If continuity does not exist, inspect and repair circuit(s) as needed.

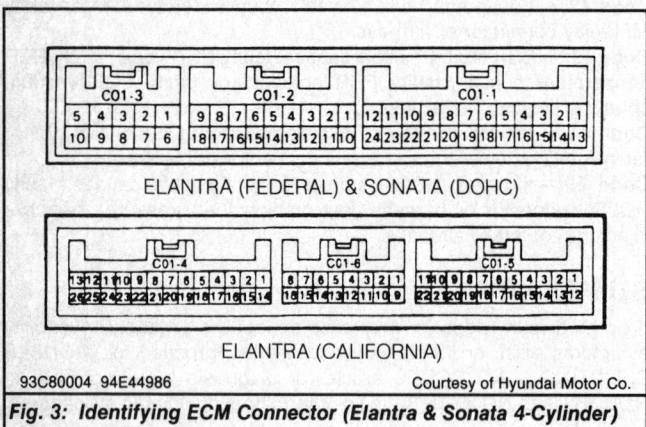

Fig. 3: Identifying ECM Connector (Elantra & Sonata 4-Cylinder)

NOTE: California Elantra models are equipped with front and rear heated oxygen sensors.

Harness Inspection (Elantra – California) – 1) Measure power supply voltage. Disconnect HO2S harness connector. Turn ignition on. Using DVOM, measure voltage between harness connector terminal No. 4 and vehicle ground. *See Fig. 6.* If voltage is less than battery voltage, inspect and repair circuit as needed.

2) Check continuity of ground circuit to ECM. Turn ignition off. Disconnect ECM harness connector. Connect a jumper wire between ECM harness connector terminal No. 6, connector C01-5 and vehicle ground. *See Fig. 3.* Using ohmmeter, measure resistance between front HO2S sensor harness connector terminal No. 1 and vehicle ground. If continuity does not exist, inspect and repair circuit as needed.

3) Move jumper wire to ECM harness connector terminal No. 7, connector C01-5 and vehicle ground. *See Fig. 3.* Using ohmmeter, measure resistance between rear HO2S sensor harness connector terminal No. 1 and vehicle ground. If continuity does not exist, inspect and repair circuit as needed.

4) Check continuity of ground circuits. Using ohmmeter, check resistance between sensor harness connector terminals No. 2 and No. 3, and vehicle ground. *See Fig. 6.* If continuity does not exist, inspect and repair circuit(s) between ECM and HO2S harness connectors as needed.

Excel – 1) Measure power supply voltage. Disconnect both HO2S harness connectors. Turn ignition on. Using DVOM, measure voltage between harness connector terminal No. 4 of front sensor and ground, and terminal No. 3 of rear sensor and ground. *See Fig. 6.* If voltage measured is less than battery voltage, inspect and repair circuit from MFI relay to HO2S sensors as needed.

2) Check continuity of ground circuit to ECM. Turn ignition off. Disconnect ECM harness connector. For front sensor, connect jumper wire between ECM harness connector terminal No. 6, connector No. C50-5 and vehicle ground. *See Fig. 4.* Check resistance between front sensor harness connector terminal No. 1 and vehicle ground. If continuity does not exist, inspect and repair circuit as needed.

3) Move jumper wire to ECM harness connector terminal No. 7, connector No. C50-5. *See Fig. 4.* Check resistance between rear sensor harness connector terminal No. 1 and vehicle ground. If continuity does not exist, inspect and repair circuit as needed.

4) Check continuity of sensor ground circuits. Using ohmmeter, check resistance between harness connector terminals No. 2 and 3 of front

sensor and ground, and terminals No. 2 and 4 of rear sensor and ground. If continuity does not exist, inspect and repair circuits as needed.

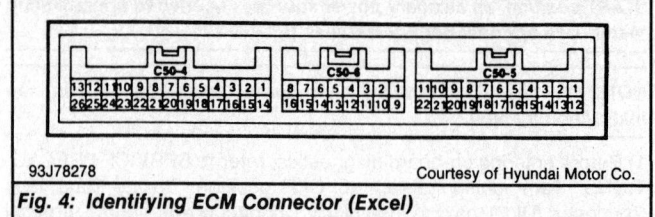

Fig. 4: Identifying ECM Connector (Excel)

Sonata V6 – 1) Measure HO2S power supply voltage. Disconnect HO2S harness connector. Turn ignition on. Using DVOM, measure voltage between harness connector terminal No. 4 and vehicle ground. *See Fig. 6.* If voltage is less than battery voltage, inspect and repair circuit as needed.

2) Check continuity of ground signal circuit to ECM. Turn ignition off. Disconnect ECM harness connector. Connect a jumper wire between ECM harness connector terminal No. 2, connector C81-1 and vehicle ground. *See Fig. 5.* Using ohmmeter, check resistance between sensor harness connector terminal No. 2 and vehicle ground. *See Fig. 6.* If continuity does not exist, inspect and repair circuit as needed.

3) Check continuity of ground circuits. Using ohmmeter, check resistance between sensor harness connector terminals No. 1 and No. 3, and vehicle ground. If continuity does not exist, inspect and repair circuit as needed.

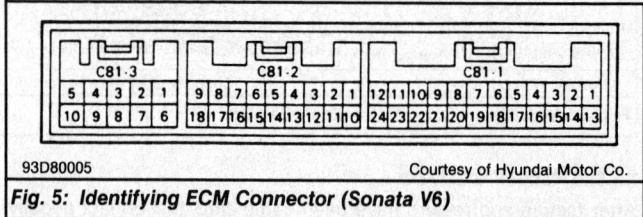

Fig. 5: Identifying ECM Connector (Sonata V6)

Heated Oxygen Sensor Inspection (Except Excel – Federal) – 1) Disconnect HO2S harness connector. Using ohmmeter, check resistance between sensor component connector terminals No. 3 and 4. *See Fig. 6.* Ensure engine is at normal operating temperature. Resistance should be 30 ohms or more. Replace HO2S if measurement is not within specification.

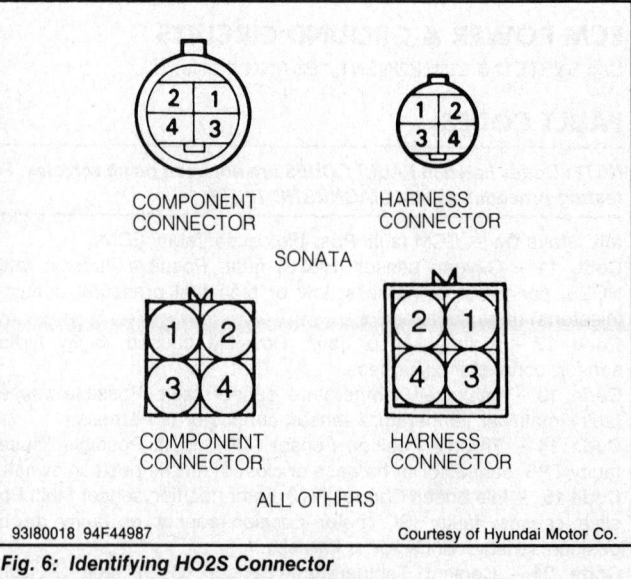

Fig. 6: Identifying HO2S Connector

2) Connect Test Harness (09392-33000) to HO2S. DO NOT connect harness connector to test harness. Connect 12-volt power source to test harness. Connect 12-volt power source positive lead to White test lead and negative to Black test lead. Connect DVOM positive lead to Yellow test lead and negative lead to Green test lead.

3) Start and run engine. Rapidly accelerate engine speed from 750 RPM to 4000 RPM and back to idle several times to enrich mixture. Disconnect HO2S sensor harness connector. Using DVOM, measure sensor output. Voltage from HO2S should be .6 volt minimum. Replace HO2S if it fails testing.

CODE 12
(AIRFLOW SENSOR FAILURE)

NOTE: If after all testing procedures have been completed, system is still inoperative, substitute ECM with known good unit and retest.

System Inspection – Inspect condition of Airflow Sensor (AFS) harness connector. A loose connection could cause intermittent stalling. Ensure there are no restrictions or clogs in air intake system.

Scan Tester Procedure – Access airflow sensor service data item No. 12. Tester should display sensor air volume measured in hertz (Hz). Ensure engine is at normal operating temperature with all accessories off. Transmission should be in Neutral or Park with steering straight ahead. Frequency should be 27-33 Hz at 750 RPM and 60-80 Hz at 2000 RPM.

Harness Inspection – 1) Check AFS power supply voltage. Disconnect harness connector. Turn ignition on. Using DVOM, measure voltage between harness connector terminal No. 2 (Red wire) and vehicle ground. If voltage is less than battery voltage, inspect and repair circuit as needed.

2) Check AFS signal circuit to ECM. Turn ignition on. Using DVOM, measure voltage between harness connector terminal No. 3 (Red/Green wire on Sonata V6, Green/White wire on all others) and vehicle ground. Voltage should be 4.8-5.2 volts. If voltage is not within specification, check continuity of circuit.

3) Turn ignition off. Disconnect ECM harness connector. Connect jumper wire between ECM connector terminal No. 15 on Sonata V6 (Red/Green wire, 24-pin connector), terminal No. 3 on Elantra (Calif.) and Excel models (Green/White wire, 22-pin connector) or terminal No. 3 on all other models (Green/White wire, 24-pin connector) and vehicle ground. *See Fig. 3, 4 and 5.*

4) Check AFS ground circuit. Using ohmmeter, check continuity between harness connector terminal No. 6 (Black) and vehicle ground. If continuity does not exist, inspect and repair circuit as needed.

Airflow Sensor Inspection – Manufacturer does not provide separate component testing procedures.

CODE 13
(INTAKE AIR TEMPERATURE SENSOR FAILURE)

NOTE: If after all testing procedures have been completed, system is still inoperative, substitute ECM with known good unit and retest.

System Inspection – Inspect condition of harness connector. Clean and repair as needed.

Scan Tester Procedure – Access intake air temperature sensor service data item No. 13. Scan tester should display sensor temperature. Start and run engine. Sensor temperature should match outside ambient temperature.

Harness Inspection – 1) Check sensor ground circuit to ECM. Disconnect sensor harness connector. Using ohmmeter, check resistance between terminal No. 6 (Black wire) and vehicle ground. If continuity does not exist, inspect and repair circuit.

2) Check sensor signal circuit to ECM. Turn ignition on. Using DVOM, measure voltage between harness connector terminal No. 4 (Green/Brown wire on Sonata 4-cylinder, Green/Black wire on Sonata V6, Green/Blue on Elantra and Excel, and ground. Voltage should be 4.5-4.9 volts. If voltage is not within specification, check continuity of circuit.

3) Turn ignition off. On all models except California Elantra and Excel, go to step **4)**. On California Elantra and Excel models, disconnect ECM harness connector. Connect jumper wire between ECM connector terminal No. 10 (Green/Blue wire, 22-pin connector) and vehicle ground. *See Figs. 3 and 4.* Using ohmmeter, check resistance between AFS harness connector terminal No. 4 (Green/Blue wire) and vehicle ground. If continuity does not exist, inspect and repair circuit as needed. If continuity does exist, substitute ECM with known good unit and retest.

4) On all models except California Elantra and Excel, disconnect ECM harness connector. Connect jumper wire between ECM connector terminal No. 3 (Green/Black wire, 24-pin connector) on Sonata V6 or terminal No. 5 (Green/Blue wire, 24-pin connector) on all others and vehicle ground. *See Fig. 3 and 5.* Using ohmmeter, check resistance between AFS harness connector terminal No. 4 (Green/Black wire on Sonata V6, Green/Blue wire on all others) and vehicle ground. If continuity does not exist, inspect and repair circuit as needed. If continuity does exist, substitute ECM with known good unit and retest.

Intake Air Temperature Sensor Inspection – Check resistance between component connector terminals No. 4 and 6. *See Fig. 7.* See INTAKE AIR TEMPERATURE SENSOR RESISTANCE table. Replace airflow sensor if temperature sensor is not within specifications.

INTAKE AIR TEMPERATURE SENSOR RESISTANCE

Air Temperature °F (°C)	Ohms
32 (0)	600
68 (20)	270
176 (80)	40

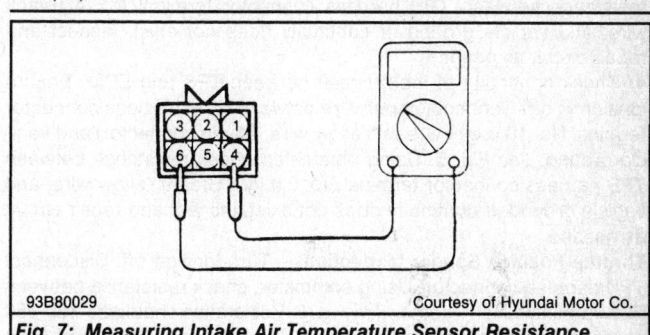

93B80029   Courtesy of Hyundai Motor Co.

Fig. 7: Measuring Intake Air Temperature Sensor Resistance

CODE 14
(THROTTLE POSITION SENSOR FAILURE)

NOTE: If after all testing procedures have been completed, system is still inoperative, substitute ECM with known good unit and retest.

System Inspection – Faulty Throttle Position Sensor (TPS) can cause abrupt automatic transmission shifting and poor performance.

Scan Tester Procedure – Access TPS service data item No. 14. Scan tester should display sensor voltage. Turn ignition on. At idle position, sensor voltage should be .45-.55 volt. Voltage should increase with throttle opening. Voltage at WOT should be 4.5-5.5 volts.

Harness Inspection (Except Sonata V6) – 1) Measure TPS power supply voltage. Disconnect TPS harness connector. Turn ignition on. Using DVOM, measure voltage between TPS harness connector terminal No. 4 (Green/Red wire) and vehicle ground. Voltage should be 4.8-5.2 volts.

2) If voltage is not within specification, turn ignition off. Disconnect ECM connector. On all models except Calif. Elantra and Excel, connect jumper wire between ECM harness connector terminal No. 14 (24-pin connector) and vehicle ground. *See Figs. 3 & 4.*

3) On Calif. Elantra and Excel, connect jumper wire between ECM harness connector terminal No. 1 (22-pin connector) and vehicle ground. Using ohmmeter, check resistance between TPS harness connector terminal No. 4 (Green/Red wire) and vehicle ground. If continuity does not exist, inspect and repair circuit as needed. If continuity exists, substitute ECM with known good unit and retest.

4) Check continuity of TPS ground circuit. Using ohmmeter, check resistance between TPS harness connector terminal No. 1 (Black wire) and vehicle ground. If continuity does not exist, inspect and repair circuit as needed.

5) Check continuity of output circuit between TPS and ECM. Ensure ignition is off. On all models except Calif. Elantra and Excel, connect jumper wire between ECM harness connector terminal No. 18 (Light Green/Yellow wire, 24-pin connector) and vehicle ground. See Figs. 3 and 4.

6) On Calif. Elantra and Excel, connect jumper wire between ECM harness connector terminal No. 20 (22-pin connector) and vehicle ground. Using ohmmeter, check resistance between TPS harness connector terminal No. 3 (Light Green/Yellow wire) and vehicle ground. If continuity does not exist, inspect and repair circuit as needed.

Harness Inspection (Sonata V6) – 1) Measure TPS power supply voltage. Disconnect TPS harness connector. Turn ignition on. Using DVOM, measure voltage between TPS harness connector terminal No. 1 (Green/Yellow wire) and vehicle ground. Voltage should be 4.8-5.2 volts.

2) If voltage is not within specification, turn ignition off. Disconnect ECM connector. Connect jumper wire between ECM harness connector terminal No. 16 (24-pin connector) and vehicle ground. See Fig. 5. Using ohmmeter, check resistance between TPS harness connector terminal No. 1 (Green/Yellow wire) and vehicle ground. If continuity does not exist, inspect and repair circuit as needed. If continuity exists, substitute ECM with known good unit and retest.

3) Check continuity of TPS ground circuit. Using ohmmeter, check resistance between TPS harness connector terminal No. 4 (Black wire) and vehicle ground. If continuity does not exist, inspect and repair circuit as needed.

4) Check continuity of input circuit between TPS and ECM. Ensure ignition is off. Connect jumper wire between ECM harness connector terminal No. 18 (Light Green/Yellow wire, 24-pin connector) and vehicle ground. See Fig. 5. Using ohmmeter, check resistance between TPS harness connector terminal No. 2 (Light Green/Yellow wire) and vehicle ground. If continuity does not exist, inspect and repair circuit as needed.

Throttle Position Sensor Inspection – Turn ignition off. Disconnect TPS harness connector. Using ohmmeter, check resistance between TPS terminals No. 1 and 4. See Fig. 8. Resistance should be 350-650 ohms. Connect ohmmeter between TPS terminals No. 1 and 2 on Sonata V6 or terminals No. 1 and 3 on all other models. Operate throttle from closed to WOT position. Monitor ohmmeter while opening throttle. Ohmmeter needle should move accordingly with throttle movement. Replace TPS if it fails any of above tests.

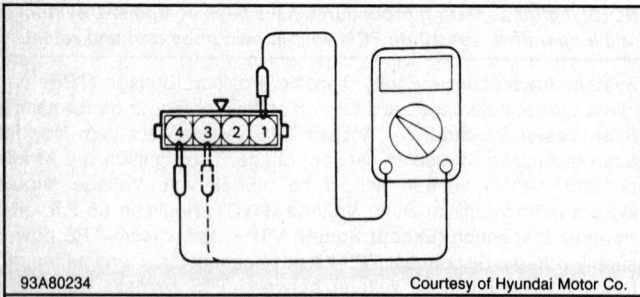

93A80234   Courtesy of Hyundai Motor Co.
Fig. 8: Measuring TPS Resistance (Except Sonata V6)

CODE 15
(IDLE SPEED CONTROL MOTOR POSITION SENSOR FAILURE)

NOTE: If after all testing procedures have been completed, system is still inoperative, substitute ECM with known good unit and retest.

System Inspection – Ensure idle speed is within specification. See ON-VEHICLE ADJUSTMENTS article. Poor ISC motor position sensor performance can be caused by dirty throttle valve, throttle valve-to-

plenum vacuum leak, miscellaneous vacuum leaks, EGR valve leak and/or poor engine performance caused by malfunctions of emission, fuel or ignition system.

Scan Tester Procedure – 1) Access ISC motor position sensor service data item No. 15. Tester should display sensor motor voltage. Ensure engine is at normal operating temperature with all accessories off. Transmission should be in Neutral or Park with steering straight ahead.

2) Voltage should be .5-1.3 volts with A/C off and .8-1.8 volts with A/C on. Continue with A/C on. Shift transmission into Drive. Ensure parking brake is set. Voltage should be .9-1.9 volts.

Harness Inspection – 1) Measure power supply voltage to sensor. Disconnect Motor Position Sensor (MPS) harness connector. Turn ignition on. Using DVOM, measure voltage between MPS harness connector terminals No. 1 and 5 (Green/Red wires) and vehicle ground. Voltage should be 4.8-5.2 volts. If voltage is not within specification, check continuity of circuit.

2) Turn ignition off. Disconnect ECM harness connector. Connect jumper wire between ECM harness connector terminal No. 1 (Green/Red wire, 22-pin connector) and vehicle ground. See Fig. 4. Using ohmmeter, check resistance between MPS harness connector terminals No. 1 and 5 (Green/Red and Green/Yellow wires) and vehicle ground. If continuity does not exist, inspect and repair circuit as needed. If continuity does exist, substitute ECM with known good unit and retest.

3) Check continuity of ground circuit. Using ohmmeter, check resistance between MPS harness connector terminal No. 4 (Black wire) and vehicle ground. If continuity does not exist, inspect and repair circuit as needed.

4) Check continuity of input circuit between MPS and ECM. Connect jumper between ECM harness connector terminal No. 22 (Light Green wire, 26-pin connector) and vehicle ground. Using ohmmeter, check resistance between MPS harness connector terminal No. 2 (Light Green wire) and vehicle ground. If continuity does not exist, inspect and repair wire as needed.

Idle Speed Control Motor Position Sensor Inspection – 1) Check resistance between MPS terminals No. 4 (Black wire) and No. 5 (Green/Red wire). Resistance should be 350-650 ohms. Connect 6-volt power source to ISC servo motor 2-pin connector. Monitor resistance between MPS terminals No. 2 (Light Green wire) and No. 4 (Black wire). As plunger extends or retracts, resistance should change accordingly. Erratic resistance changes indicate malfunction with sensor.

CODE 21
(COOLANT TEMPERATURE SENSOR FAILURE)

NOTE: If after all testing procedures have been completed, system is still inoperative, substitute ECM with known good unit and retest.

System Inspection – Inspect condition of connector. Clean and repair as needed. Faulty Coolant Temperature Sensor (CTS) can cause incorrect idle RPM during cold start-up condition and rich air/fuel mixture.

Scan Tester Procedure – Access Coolant Temperature Sensor (CTS) service data item No. 21. Scan tester should display sensor temperature with engine running. As engine temperature increases, monitor scan tester readings while measuring actual engine coolant temperature with thermometer. Scan tester readings should match thermometer readings.

Harness Inspection – 1) Measure sensor power supply voltage. Disconnect sensor harness connector. Turn ignition on. Using DVOM, measure voltage between vehicle ground and terminal No. 2 (Yellow/Green wire on Sonata V6, Yellow/Red wire on all other models). Voltage should be 4.5-4.9 volts. If voltage is within specification, go to step 3). If voltage is not within specification, go to step 2).

2) Turn ignition off. Disconnect ECM harness connector. Connect jumper wire between apropriate ECM harness connector terminal and vehicle ground. See CTS INPUT TERMINAL IDENTIFICATION table for ECM terminal number. Using ohmmeter, check continuity between

vehicle ground and sensor harness connector terminal No. 1 (Black wire). If continuity does not exist, inspect and repair circuit. If continuity exists, substitute ECM with known good unit and retest. Go to step **3**).

CTS INPUT TERMINAL IDENTIFICATION [1]

Application	ECM Terminal No.	Connector No.	Wire Color
Elantra (Calif.)	21	C01-5	Yellow/Red
Elantra (Fed.)	17	C01-1	Yellow/Red
Excel	21	C50-5	Yellow/Red
Sonata 4-Cylinder	17	C01-1	Yellow/Red
Sonata V6	17	C81-1	Yellow/Green

[1] – See Figs. 3, 4 and 5.

3) Check continuity of sensor to ECM ground circuit. Ensure ignition is off. Using ohmmeter, check resistance between sensor harness connector terminal No. 1 (Black wire) and vehicle ground. If continuity does not exist, inspect and repair circuit as needed.

Coolant Temperature Sensor Inspection – Remove sensor and immerse in water. Using ohmmeter, check resistance while increasing water temperature. See COOLANT TEMPERATURE RESISTANCE SPECIFICATIONS. Replace sensor if resistance measured is not within specification.

COOLANT TEMPERATURE RESISTANCE SPECIFICATIONS

Water Temperature °F (°C)	Ohms
32 (0)	5900
68 (20)	2500
104 (40)	1100
176 (80)	300

CODE 22
(CRANKSHAFT POSITION SENSOR FAILURE)

NOTE: If after all testing procedures have been completed, system is still inoperative, substitute ECM with known good unit and retest.

System Inspection – Inspect harness connector, clean and repair as needed. If tachometer is inoperative, Crankshaft Position Sensor (CKP) may be faulty. If it is determined that the CKP is out of specification but engine still runs, check for faulty coolant temperature sensor, idle air/speed control motor and/or incorrect idle speed adjustment.
Scan Tester Procedure – Access CKP service data item No. 22. Scan tester should display idle speed. See CKP IDLE SPEED SPECIFICATION table.

CKP IDLE SPEED SPECIFICATION

Coolant Temperature °F (°C)	Engine RPM
-4 (-20)	1500-1700
32 (0)	1350-1550
68 (20)	1200-1400
104 (40)	1000-1200
176 (80)	650-850

Harness Inspection (Elantra & Sonata 4-Cylinder) – **1**) Measure CKP power supply voltage. Disconnect sensor harness connector. Turn ignition on. Using DVOM, measure voltage between sensor harness connector terminal No. 2 (Red wire) and vehicle ground. If voltage is less than battery voltage, inspect and repair circuit as needed.
2) Check continuity of ground circuit. Turn ignition off. Using ohmmeter, check resistance between harness connector No. 1 (Black wire) and vehicle ground. If continuity does not exist, inspect and repair circuit as needed.
3) Check output voltage from ECM. Turn ignition on. Using DVOM, measure voltage between harness connector terminal No. 4 (Green wire on Elantra, Yellow wire on Sonata 4-Cylinder) and vehicle ground. Voltage should be 4.8-5.2 volts. If voltage is within specification, circuit is okay. If voltage is not within specification, go to step **4**).

4) Turn ignition off. Disconnect ECM harness connector. Connect jumper wire between ECM harness connector terminal No. 16 (Green wire, 24-pin connector) or No. 15 (22-pin connector) and vehicle ground. *See Fig. 3.* Using ohmmeter, check resistance between CKP harness connector terminal No. 4 (Green wire on Elantra, Yellow wire on Sonata 4-Cylinder) and vehicle ground. If continuity does not exist, inspect and repair circuit as needed. If continuity exists, substitute ECM with known good unit and retest.
Harness Inspection (Excel) – **1**) Measure CKP power supply voltage. Disconnect sensor harness connector. Turn ignition on. Using DVOM, measure voltage between sensor harness connector terminal No. 4 (Red wire) and vehicle ground. If voltage is less than battery voltage, inspect and repair circuit as needed.
2) Check continuity of ground circuit. Turn ignition off. Using ohmmeter, check resistance between harness connector No. 1 (Black wire) and vehicle ground. If continuity does not exist, inspect and repair circuit as needed.
3) Check output voltage from ECM. Turn ignition on. Using DVOM, measure voltage between harness connector terminal No. 2 (Yellow wire) and vehicle ground. Voltage should be 4.8-5.2 volts. If voltage is within specification, circuit is okay. If voltage is not within specification, go to step **4**).
4) Turn ignition off. Disconnect ECM harness connector. Connect jumper wire between ECM harness connector terminal No. 16 (Green wire, 24-pin connector) on Federal models, terminal No. 15 (Green wire, 22-pin connector) on California models and vehicle ground. *See Fig. 4.* Using ohmmeter, check resistance between CKP harness connector terminal No. 2 (Yellow wire) and vehicle ground. If continuity does not exist, inspect and repair circuit as needed. If continuity exists, substitute ECM with known good unit and retest.
Harness Inspection (Sonata V6) – **1**) Measure CKP power supply voltage. Disconnect sensor harness connector. Turn ignition on. Using DVOM, measure voltage between sensor harness connector terminal No. 3 (Red wire) and vehicle ground. If voltage is less than battery voltage, inspect and repair circuit as needed.
2) Check continuity of ground circuit. Turn ignition off. Using ohmmeter, check resistance between harness connector No. 2 (Black wire) and vehicle ground. If continuity does not exist, inspect and repair circuit as needed.
3) Check output voltage from ECM. Turn ignition on. Using DVOM, measure voltage between harness connector terminal No. 1 (Yellow wire) and vehicle ground. Voltage should be 4.8-5.2 volts. If voltage is within specification, circuit is okay. If voltage is not within specification, go to step **4**).
4) Turn ignition off. Disconnect ECM harness connector. Connect jumper wire between ECM harness connector terminal No. 22 (Green wire, 24-pin connector) and vehicle ground. *See Fig. 5.* Using ohmmeter, check resistance between CKP harness connector terminal No. 1 (Yellow wire) and vehicle ground. If continuity does not exist, inspect and repair circuit as needed. If continuity exists, substitute ECM with known good unit and retest.
CKP Sensor Inspection – Manufacturer does not provide component testing information.

CODE 23
(TOP DEAD CENTER SENSOR FAILURE)

NOTE: If after all testing procedures have been completed, system is still inoperative, substitute ECM with known good unit and retest.

System Inspection – Engine stalling, rough idle and/or poor acceleration could be caused by faulty Top Dead Center (TDC) sensor. Inspect harness connector, clean and repair as needed.
Scan Tester Procedure – Manufacturer does not provide testing information. See tester instruction manual for testing procedures.
Harness Inspection – **1**) Inspect TDC sensor power supply circuit. Disconnect TDC sensor harness connector. Turn ignition on. Using DVOM, measure voltage between sensor harness connector terminal No. 3 (Red wire) on Sonata V6, No. 2 (Red wire) on all other models and vehicle ground. Voltage should be battery voltage.

2) Check continuity of ground circuit. Turn ignition off. Using ohmmeter, check resistance between sensor harness connector terminal No. 2 (Black wire) on Sonata V6, No. 1 (Black wire) on all other models and vehicle ground. If continuity does not exist, inspect and repair circuit as needed.

3) Check sensor output voltage from ECM. Turn ignition on. Using DVOM, measure voltage between TDC sensor harness connector terminal No. 4 (White wire) on Sonata V6, No. 3 (Yellow wire) on all other models and vehicle ground. Voltage should be 4.8-5.2 volts. If voltage is within specification, circuit is okay. If voltage is not within specification, turn ignition off.

4) Disconnect ECM connector. Connect jumper wire between ECM harness connector terminal and vehicle ground. See TDC INPUT TERMINAL IDENTIFICATION for ECM terminal identification. Using ohmmeter, check resistance between TDC harness connector terminal No. 4 (White wire) on Sonata V6, No. 3 (Yellow wire) on all other models and vehicle ground. If continuity does not exist, inspect and repair circuit as needed. If continuity exists, substitute ECM with known good unit and retest.

Top Dead Center Sensor Inspection – Manufacturer does not provide individual component testing.

TDC INPUT TERMINAL IDENTIFICATION [1]

Application	ECM Terminal No.	Connector No.	Wire Color
Elantra (Calif.)	16	C01-5	Yellow
Elantra (Fed.)	15	C01-1	Yellow
Excel	16	C50-5	Yellow
Sonata 4-Cylinder	15	C01-1	Yellow
Sonata V6	23	C81-1	White/Red

[1] – See Figs. 3, 4 and 5.

CODE 24
(VEHICLE SPEED SENSOR FAILURE)

NOTE: If after all testing procedures have been completed, system is still inoperative, substitute ECM with known good unit and retest.

System Inspection – An open or short circuit in Vehicle Speed Sensor (VSS) signal circuit may cause engine to stall when vehicle is decelerating to a complete stop.

Scan Tester Procedure – Manufacturer does not provide testing information. See tester instruction manual for testing procedures.

Harness Inspection – 1) Check VSS power supply voltage from ECM. Disconnect VSS harness connector from back of instrument panel. Instrument panel removal may assist in accessing harness connector. Turn ignition on. Using DVOM, measure voltage between VSS harness connector terminal No. 2 (Yellow/White wire) and vehicle ground. Voltage should be 4.5-4.9 volts.

2) If voltage is within specification, circuit is okay. If voltage is not within specification, turn ignition off. Disconnect ECM harness connector. Connect jumper wire between ECM harness connector terminal No. 18 (Yellow wire, 22-pin connector) or terminal No. 19 (Yellow/White wire, 24-pin connector). See Figs. 3, 4 and 5. Using ohmmeter, check resistance between VSS harness connector terminal No. 2 (Yellow/White wire) and vehicle ground. If continuity does not exist, inspect and repair circuit as needed. If continuity exists, substitute ECM with known good unit and retest.

3) Check ground circuit of sensor. Using ohmmeter, check resistance between VSS harness connector terminal No. 1 (Black wire) and vehicle ground. If continuity does not exist, inspect and repair circuit as needed.

Vehicle Speed Sensor Inspection – Check output of VSS signal. Raise and support vehicle. Disconnect ECM harness connector. Using DVOM, measure voltage between ECM harness connector terminal No. 18 (Yellow wire, 22-pin connector) or terminal No. 19 (Yellow/White wire, 24-pin connector). See Figs. 3, 4 and 5. If DVOM does not display a pulse voltage, replace VSS and retest.

CODE 25
(BAROMETRIC PRESSURE SENSOR FAILURE)

NOTE: If after all testing procedures have been completed, system is still inoperative, substitute ECM with known good unit and retest.

System Inspection – Malfunctioning barometric pressure sensor can cause general poor engine performance. Ensure air filter is not clogged.

Scan Tester Procedure – Access scan tester service data item No. 25. With ignition on, scan tester should display 760 mm Hg at sea level. Other test specification readings are; 710 mm Hg at 1969 ft. (600 m), 660 mm Hg at 3937 ft. (1200 m) and 610 mm Hg at 5906 ft. (1800 m).

Harness Inspection (Elantra, Excel & Sonata 4-Cylinder) –
1) Check continuity of ground circuit. Ensure ignition is off. Disconnect airflow sensor connector. Using ohmmeter, check resistance between sensor harness connector No. 6 (Black wire) and vehicle ground. If continuity does not exist, inspect and repair circuit as needed.

2) Measure sensor power supply voltage. Turn ignition on. Using DVOM, measure voltage between sensor harness connector terminal No. 1 (Green/Red wire) and vehicle ground. Voltage should be 4.8-5.2 volts. If voltage is within specification, go to step 4).

3) If voltage is not within specification, turn ignition off. Disconnect ECM connector. Connect jumper wire between ECM harness connector terminal No. 14 (24-pin connector) or No. 1 (22-pin connector) and vehicle ground. See Figs. 3 and 4. Using ohmmeter, check resistance between sensor harness connector terminal No. 1 (Green/Red wire) and vehicle ground. If continuity does not exist, inspect and repair circuit as needed. If continuity exists, substitute ECM with known good unit and retest.

4) Check continuity of output circuit between barometric pressure sensor and ECM. Connect jumper wire between ECM harness connector terminal No. 21 (24-pin connector) or No. 19 (22-pin connector) and vehicle ground. Using ohmmeter, check resistance between sensor harness connector No. 5 (Brown wire) and vehicle ground. If continuity does not exist, check and repair circuit as needed.

Harness Inspection (Sonata V6) – **1)** Check continuity of ground circuit. Ensure ignition is off. Disconnect airflow sensor connector. Using ohmmeter, check resistance between sensor harness connector No. 6 (Black wire) and vehicle ground. If continuity does not exist, inspect and repair circuit as needed.

2) Measure sensor power supply voltage. Turn ignition on. Using DVOM, measure voltage between sensor harness connector terminal No. 1 (Green/Yellow wire) and vehicle ground. Voltage should be 4.8-5.2 volts. If voltage is within specification, go to step 4).

3) If voltage is not within specification, turn ignition off. Disconnect ECM connector. Connect jumper wire between ECM harness connector terminal No. 16 (Green/Yellow wire, 24-pin connector) and vehicle ground. See Fig. 5. Using ohmmeter, check resistance between sensor harness connector terminal No. 1 (Green/Yellow wire) and vehicle ground. If continuity does not exist, inspect and repair circuit as needed. If continuity exists, substitute ECM with known good unit and retest.

4) Check continuity of output circuit between barometric pressure sensor and ECM. Connect jumper wire between ECM harness connector terminal No. 24 (Blue/White wire, 24-pin connector) and vehicle ground. Using ohmmeter, check resistance between sensor harness connector No. 5 (Blue/White wire) and vehicle ground. If continuity does not exist, check and repair circuit as needed.

Barometric Pressure Sensor Inspection – Manufacturer does not provide individual component testing.

CODE 41
(FUEL INJECTOR FAILURE)

NOTE: Ensure engine compression is within specification. See SERVICE & ADJUSTMENT SPECIFICATIONS article. Ensure ignition system is operating properly. Low compression or ignition system breakdown can affect fuel injector performance.

NOTE: If after all testing procedures have been completed, fuel injection system is still inoperative, substitute ECM with known good unit and retest.

System Inspection – 1) Determine if vehicle is difficult to start when engine is hot. Check fuel pressure. See BASIC DIAGNOSTIC PROCEDURES article. Ensure there are no fuel leaks. Determine if all injectors are operating properly.
2) Inspect ECM power supply and ground circuits. Inspect MFI control relay. See SYSTEM & COMPONENT TESTING article. Inspect crankshaft position sensor and TDC sensor. See CODE 22 (CRANKSHAFT POSITION SENSOR) and CODE 23 (TOP DEAD CENTER SENSOR).
Scan Tester Procedure – 1) Access fuel injector service data item No. 41. Scan tester should display injector drive time. Ensure engine is at normal operating temperature. Turn all accessories off. Ensure shift selector is in Park or Neutral.
2) Inspect fuel injector drive times with engine cranking and running. See FUEL INJECTOR DRIVE TIME table.

FUEL INJECTOR DRIVE TIME

Coolant Temp. °F (°C)	Engine RPM	Drive Time (ms)
Engine Cranking		
32 (0)	Less than 250	18
68 (20)	Less than 250	34
176 (80)	Less than 250	6.1
Engine Running		
176 (80)	750	2.5-3.1
176 (80)	2000	2.2-2.8

3) Access injector actuator test. Select items 01 through 04 for injectors No. 1 through No. 4. Check decrease in engine idle speed when each injector is disabled to confirm injector operation.

FUEL INJECTOR GROUND CIRCUIT IDENTIFICATION

Injector No.	Wire Color	[1] Corresponding ECM Terminal No.
Elantra (Federal) & Sonata 4-Cylinder		
1	Yellow	9
2	Yellow/Black	8
3	Lt. Green	18
4	Lt. Green/White	17
Elantra (Calif.) & Excel		
1	Yellow	13
2	Yellow/Black	26
3	Lt. Green/Black	12
4	Lt. Green/White	25
Sonata V6		
1	Yellow/Green	4
2	Yellow/Black	5
3	Yellow/Blue	6
4	Yellow/Red	7
5	Yellow/White	8
6	Yellow	9

[1] – Use 18-pin connector on all models except Elantra (Calif.) and Excel. On Elantra (Calif.) and Excel use 26-pin connector. *See Figs. 3, 4 and 5 for terminal identification.*

Harness Inspection – 1) Measure injector power supply voltage. Disconnect injector harness connectors. Turn ignition on. Using DVOM, measure voltage at each injector harness connector terminal No. 1 (Black/Red wire) on Sonata V6, No. 2 (Red wire) on Sonata 4-Cylinder, No. 2 (Green/White wire) on all other models. If voltage measured is less than battery voltage, inspect and repair circuit(s) as needed.
2) Check continuity of injector ground circuit. Disconnect ECM harness connector. Ensure ignition is off. Connect a jumper wire between each injector ECM terminal and ground. Disconnect injector harness connectors. Using ohmmeter, check continuity between each injector terminal and vehicle ground. See FUEL INJECTOR GROUND CIRCUIT IDENTIFICATION table for ECM terminal numbers and wire colors.
Fuel Injector Inspection – 1) Check injector operation with engine running. Start engine and listen for injector operation (clicking sound). Ensure clicking sound of injector is not from adjacent injector with sound being transmitted through fuel delivery pipe. To check injector operating sound, use stethoscope or feel for vibration.
2) Check resistance between injector terminals. Disconnect injector harness connector. Using ohmmeter, check resistance. Resistance should be 13-16 ohms. Replace injector if measurement is not within specification.

CODE 42
(FUEL PUMP FAILURE)

NOTE: If after all testing procedures have been completed, system is still inoperative, substitute ECM with known good unit and retest.

System Inspection – Inspect all fuel hoses and electrical connectors. Clean and repair as needed.
Scan Tester Procedure – Access scan tester service data item No. 7. While cranking engine, check fuel return hose for pulsation, indicating fuel flow. Remove filler cap and listen for pump operating sound. Fuel pump is located inside fuel tank.
Harness Inspection – 1) Using a jumper wire, apply battery voltage to fuel pump check terminal. See BASIC DIAGNOSTIC PROCEDURES article for fuel pump check terminal location. If fuel pump does not operate, go to step **2)**. If fuel pump operates, go to step **4)**.
2) Disconnect fuel pump connector. Using DVOM, check continuity between chassis ground and fuel pump connector terminal No. 2 (Black wire). If continuity does not exist, inspect and repair circuit as needed.
3) Check continuity between fuel pump harness connector terminal No. 1 (White/Black wire on Sonata, Yellow wire on all other models) and fuel pump checking terminal. If continuity does not exist, inspect and repair circuit as needed.
4) Ensure ignition is off. Disconnect ECM control relay and ECM harness connectors. Move jumper wire connected to fuel pump checking terminal to vehicle ground. Using ohmmeter, check resistance between ECM control relay harness connector terminal and vehicle ground. See ECM CONTROL RELAY TERMINAL IDENTIFICATION table. If continuity does not exist, inspect and repair circuit as needed.

ECM CONTROL RELAY TERMINAL IDENTIFICATION

Application	Relay Terminal No.	Wire Color	Corresponding ECM Terminal No.
Elantra (Fed.)	4	Yellow	[1] 24
Elantra (Calif.) & Excel	4	Yellow	N/A
Sonata 4-Cyl.	4	White/Black	[1] 24
Sonata V6	4	Black/White	[2] 7

[1] – 24-pin connector.
[2] – 10-pin connector.

5) Check resistance between ECM harness connector terminal and vehicle ground. See ECM CONTROL RELAY TERMINAL IDENTIFICATION table. *See Figs. 3, 4 and 5.* If continuity does not exist, inspect and repair circuit as needed.

6) Turn ignition on. Using DVOM, measure voltage between ECM control relay harness connector terminal and vehicle ground. See ECM POWER SUPPLY TERMINAL IDENTIFICATION table. Voltage should be 8 volts or more. Turn ignition switch to START position. Measure voltage between ECM control relay connector terminal and vehicle ground. See ECM POWER SUPPLY TERMINAL IDENTIFICATION table. Voltage should be 8 volts or more. If voltage is not within specification, inspect and repair circuit(s) as needed.

ECM POWER SUPPLY TERMINAL IDENTIFICATION

Application	[1] Terminal No.	Wire Color
Ignition Switch		
ON Position		
Elantra	3	Black/White
Excel	1	White/Blue
Sonata 4-Cyl.	3	Black/White
Sonata V6	3	Blue
START Position		
Elantra	7	Black/Yellow
Excel	6	[2] Black/Green
Sonata 4-Cyl.	7	Black/Red
Sonata V6	7	Red/Green

[1] – See Figs. 3, 4 and 5.
[2] – Black/Yellow wire on manual transmission models.

7) Connect jumper wire between ECM harness connector terminal and vehicle ground. See ECM FUEL PUMP SIGNAL TERMINAL IDENTIFICATION table. Measure resistance between ECM control relay connector terminal and vehicle ground. See ECM FUEL PUMP SIGNAL TERMINAL IDENTIFICATION table. If continuity does not exist, inspect and repair circuit as needed.

8) Using ohmmeter, check resistance between chassis ground and ECM control relay harness connector terminal No. 7 (Black wire) on Excel, terminal No. 10 (Black wire) on all other models. If continuity does not exist, inspect and repair circuit as needed.

ECM FUEL PUMP SIGNAL TERMINAL IDENTIFICATION

Application	ECM Terminal No.	Wire Color	Relay Terminal No.
Elantra (Calif.) & Excel	[2] 6	White/Red	8
Elantra (Fed.)	[1] 4	White/Red	9
Sonata 4-Cyl.	[1] 4	White/Red	9
Sonata V6	[1] 13	White/Red	9

[1] – 18-pin connector.
[2] – 26-pin connector.

CODE 43
(EGR TEMPERATURE SENSOR FAILURE)

NOTE: If after all testing procedures have been completed, system is still inoperative, substitute ECM with known good unit and retest.

System Inspection – Ensure EGR system vacuum hoses and electrical connectors are secure and vacuum hoses are free from leaks and restrictions.
Scan Tester Procedure – Connect tachometer and scan tester to vehicle. Access EGR temperature sensor service data item No. 43. Tester should display sensor temperature. With engine at normal operating temperature and idling at 750 RPM for at least 2 minutes, check sensor temperature. Scan tester should display 158°F (70°C) or less. Accelerate engine to 3500 RPM. Scan tester should display 158°F (70°C) or more.
Harness Inspection – 1) Disconnect EGR temperature sensor harness connector. Turn ignition on. Using DVOM, measure voltage between EGR temperature sensor harness connector terminal No. 1 and vehicle ground. See EGR TEMPERATURE SENSOR TERMINAL IDENTIFICATION table. Voltage should be 4.3-4.7 volts. If voltage is within specification, circuit is okay. If voltage is not within specification, turn ignition off.

2) Disconnect ECM harness connector. Connect jumper wire between ECM harness connector terminal and vehicle ground. See EGR TEMPERATURE SENSOR TERMINAL IDENTIFICATION table.
3) Using ohmmeter, check resistance between EGR temperature sensor harness connector terminal No. 1 and vehicle ground. If continuity does not exist, inspect and repair circuit as needed. If continuity exists, substitute ECM with known good unit and retest.
4) Using ohmmeter, check resistance between EGR temperature sensor connector terminal No. 2 and vehicle ground. See EGR TEMPERATURE SENSOR TERMINAL IDENTIFICATION table. If continuity does not exist, inspect and repair circuit as needed.

EGR TEMPERATURE SENSOR TERMINAL IDENTIFICATION

Application	Wire Color	Corresponding ECM Terminal No.
Power Supply Circuit		
Terminal No. 1		
Elantra	Blue/White	[1] 9
Excel	Red	[1] 9
Sonata 4-Cyl.	Yellow/Black	[2] 22
Sonata V6	Green/Blue	[2] 14
Ground Circuit		
Terminal No. 2		
Elantra	Black	[1] 12
Excel	Black	[1] 12
Sonata 4-Cyl.	Black	[2] 13
Sonata V6	Black/White	[2] 13

[1] – 22-pin connector.
[2] – 24-pin connector.

EGR Temperature Sensor Inspection – Remove sensor and immerse in water. Using ohmmeter, check resistance while increasing water temperature. See EGR TEMPERATURE RESISTANCE SPECIFICATIONS table. Replace sensor if resistance measured is not within specification.

EGR TEMPERATURE RESISTANCE SPECIFICATIONS

Water Temperature °F (°C)	Ohms
122 (50)	6000-8300
212 (100)	1100-1400

CODE 44
(IGNITION COIL/POWER TRANSISTOR FAILURE)

NOTE: If after all testing procedures are completed, system is still inoperative, substitute ECM with known good unit and retest. Manufacturer does not provide scan tester test information.

System Inspection (Elantra & Sonata 4-Cylinder) – Connect timing light and tachometer. Ensure engine is at normal operating temperature. With engine at idle (750 RPM), check ignition timing. See ON-VEHICLE ADJUSTMENTS article for procedure to check and adjust timing.
Scan Tester Procedure – Manufacturer does not provide testing information. See tester instruction manual for testing procedures.
Harness Inspection – 1) Disconnect ignition coil harness connector. Turn ignition on. Using DVOM, measure voltage between ignition coil harness connector terminal No. 3 (Black/White wire) and vehicle ground. If battery voltage does not exist, inspect and repair circuit as needed.
2) Disconnect power transistor connector. Using ohmmeter, check resistance between ignition coil harness connector terminal No. 1 (Green/White wire on Elantra, White/Black wire on Sonata 4-Cylinder) and power transistor harness connector terminal No. 6. If continuity does not exist, inspect and repair circuit as needed.
3) Using ohmmeter, check resistance between ignition coil harness connector terminal No. 2 (Green/Blue wire on Elantra, White/Red wire on Sonata 4-Cylinder) and power transistor connector terminal No. 1. If continuity does not exist, inspect and repair circuit as needed.

4) Using ohmmeter, check resistance between power transistor harness connector terminal No. 3 (Black wire) and vehicle ground. If continuity does not exist, inspect and repair circuit as needed.

5) Turn ignition switch to START position. Using DVOM, measure voltage between power transistor harness connector terminal No. 5 (Brown wire on Elantra, Yellow/Black wire on Sonata 4-Cylinder) and vehicle ground. Voltage should be 0.5-4.0 volts. If voltage is within specification, circuit is okay.

6) If voltage is not within specification, turn ignition off. Disconnect ECM harness connector. Using ohmmeter, check resistance between power transistor harness connector terminal No. 5 (Brown wire on Elantra, Yellow/Black wire on Sonata 4-Cylinder) and ECM harness connector terminal No. 5 (18-pin connector) or No. 17 (26-pin connector). *See Fig. 3.* If continuity does not exist, inspect and repair circuit as needed. If continuity exists, substitute ECM with known good unit and retest.

7) Connect ECM harness connector. Turn ignition switch to START position. Using DVOM, measure voltage between power transistor harness connector terminal No. 2 (White/Black wire on Elantra, Yellow/Blue wire on Sonata 4-Cylinder) and vehicle ground. Voltage should be 0.5-4.0 volts. If voltage is within specification, circuit is okay.

8) If voltage is not within specification, turn ignition off. Disconnect ECM harness connector. Using ohmmeter, check resistance between power transistor harness connector terminal No. 2 (White/Black wire on Elantra, Yellow/Blue wire on Sonata 4-Cylinder) and ECM harness connector terminal No. 6 (18-pin connector) or No. 5 (26-pin connector). *See Fig. 3.* If continuity does not exist, inspect and repair circuit as needed. If continuity exists, substitute ECM with known good unit and retest.

9) Connect ECM harness connector. Turn ignition on. Using DVOM, measure voltage between timing adjustment terminal (Light Green/Red) and vehicle ground. Voltage should be 4.0-5.2 volts. If voltage is within specification, circuit is okay. If voltage is not within specification, turn ignition off.

10) Disconnect ECM harness connector. Using ohmmeter, check resistance between ECM harness connector terminal No. 1 (24-pin connector) or No. 5 (16-pin connector) and timing adjustment terminal. *See Fig. 3.* If continuity does not exist, inspect and repair circuit as needed. If continuity does exist, substitute ECM with known good unit and retest.

Ignition Coil and Power Transistor Inspection – See BASIC DIAGNOSTIC PROCEDURES article for specific circuit and component testing.

1994 ENGINE PERFORMANCE
Self-Diagnostics – Scoupe

INTRODUCTION

Most engine control problems are the result of mechanical breakdowns, poor electrical connections or damaged vacuum hoses. Before considering the computer system as a possible cause of problems, perform checks and inspections covered in BASIC DIAGNOSTIC PROCEDURES article. Failure to do so may result in lost diagnostic time.

If no faults were found while performing BASIC DIAGNOSTIC PROCEDURES, proceed with self-diagnostics. If no fault codes or only pass codes are present after entering self-diagnostics, proceed to TROUBLE SHOOTING – NO CODES article for diagnosis by symptom (i.e., ROUGH IDLE, NO START, etc.).

NOTE: *Unless specifically stated differently in testing procedures, perform all voltage tests using a Digital Volt-Ohmmeter (DVOM) with a minimum 10-megohm input impedance.*

SELF-DIAGNOSTIC SYSTEM

MALFUNCTION INDICATOR LIGHT (MIL)

Scoupe is equipped with a Malfunction Indicator Light (MIL). As a bulb check, light will illuminate for approximately 5 seconds when ignition is turned on. MIL will also illuminate when a system failure is detected; a corresponding trouble code will set in Electronic Control Module (ECM) memory.

ECM is equipped with a self-diagnostic system, which detects system failures or abnormalities. When a malfunction occurs, ECM will illuminate MIL (CHECK ENGINE light) on instrument panel. When malfunction is detected and light is turned on, a corresponding trouble code will be stored in ECM. To retrieve stored codes, see RETRIEVING CODES (NON-SCAN). Malfunctions are recorded as hard failures or as intermittent failures.

Hard Failures – Hard failures cause Malfunction Indicator Light (MIL) to illuminate and remain on until problem is repaired. If light comes on and remains on during vehicle operation, retrieve code(s). See RETRIEVING CODES (NON-SCAN). *See Figs. 3 and 4*, and DIAGNOSTIC CODES (MALFUNCTION INDICATOR LIGHT) table to determine cause of malfunction.

Intermittent Failures – Intermittent failures may cause malfunction light to flicker on and off after intermittent fault goes away. Corresponding trouble code will be retained in ECU memory. If related fault does not reoccur within a certain time frame, related trouble code may be erased from ECU memory. Intermittent failures may be caused by sensor, connector or wiring related problems. See INTERMITTENTS in TROUBLE SHOOTING – NO CODES article.

SERVICE PRECAUTIONS

Before proceeding with diagnosis, following precautions must be observed:

- Ensure vehicle has a fully charged battery and functional charging system.
- Visually inspect connectors and circuit wiring being worked on.
- DO NOT disconnect battery or ECM. This will erase any fault codes stored in ECM.
- DO NOT cause short circuits when performing electrical tests. This will set additional fault codes, making diagnosis of original problem more difficult.
- DO NOT use a test light in place of a voltmeter.
- When checking for spark, ensure coil wire is NOT more than 1/4" from ground. If coil wire is more than 1/4" from ground, damage to vehicle electronics and/or ECM may result.
- DO NOT prolong testing of fuel injectors. Engine may hydrostatically (liquid) lock.
- When a vehicle has multiple fault codes, always repair lowest number fault code first.

RETRIEVING CODES (MIL – NON-SCAN)

1) Ensure battery is fully charged before retrieving codes. ECM memory is erased when battery is disconnected. Turn ignition switch to ON position. Ground data link connector terminal No. 10 for at least 2.5 seconds, but not more than 4 seconds. *See Fig. 1.*
2) Malfunction indicator light (MIL) will flash first code stored or "no fault detected" Code (4444). MIL will continue to flash same code until terminal No. 10 is grounded again. Follow grounding procedure in step 1).
3) MIL will flash all codes stored with each terminal grounding until "end of output" (3333) is flashed. Retrieve trouble codes before conducting component or harness checks.

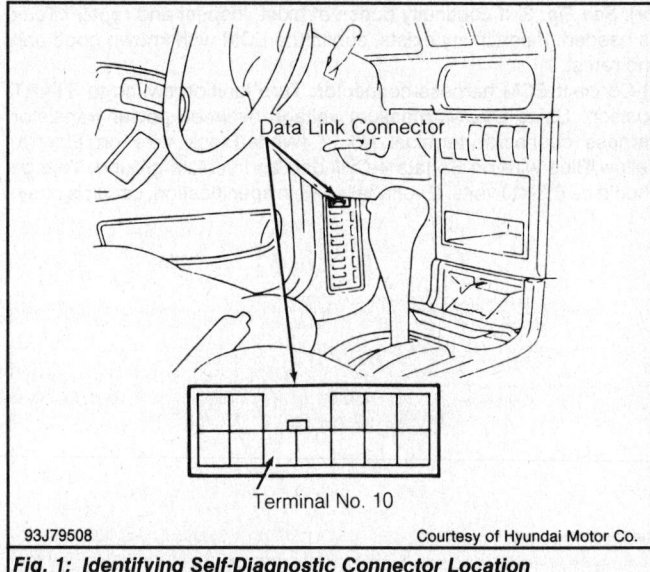

93J79508   Courtesy of Hyundai Motor Co.

Fig. 1: Identifying Self-Diagnostic Connector Location

RETRIEVING CODES (SCAN TESTER)

NOTE: *If scan tester is needed to perform diagnostic test with key in START position, an auxiliary power source is needed to operate scan tester. Use optional Battery Harness (09391-33500).*

NOTE: *For specific operating procedures using scan tester, see scan tester manual.*

1) Ensure ignition is off. Connect scan tester to diagnostic connector in fuse panel. *See Fig. 2.* Plug scan tester power cord into cigarette lighter. Turn ignition on. Check for trouble codes. *See Figs. 3 and 4.* Refer to appropriate diagnostic repair procedure.
2) Erase trouble codes after repair is done. Operate vehicle and verify no trouble codes are reset. Disconnect scan tester.

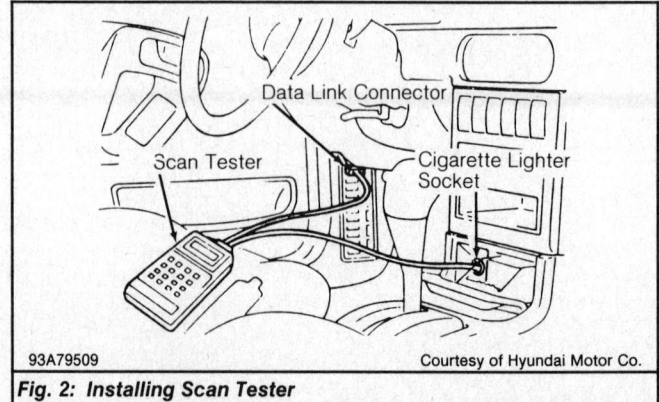

93A79509   Courtesy of Hyundai Motor Co.

Fig. 2: Installing Scan Tester

ACTUATOR CONTROL SEQUENCE PROCEDURE

1) Ensure ignition switch is in OFF position. Connect jumper wire to diagnostic connector terminal No. 10 and vehicle ground. *See Fig. 1.* Turn ignition switch to ON position. Disconnect ground wire in 2.5-4.0 seconds. Actuator test should start. See ACTUATOR TEST SEQUENCE table.

2) To proceed with next test, ground jumper wire for 2.5-4.0 seconds. If jumper wire is grounded longer than 4 seconds, test sequence will start from beginning. Continue to ground jumper wire until 3333 (end of output) is flashed.

ACTUATOR TEST SEQUENCE

Activated Component	Sequence No.	Flash Code
Injector No. 1	1	1312
Injector No. 3	2	1314
Injector No. 4	3	1313
Injector No. 2	4	1315
IAC Motor	5	1321
Purge Control Valve	6	1322

CLEARING CODES

After testing and repairs are completed, disconnect negative battery cable for at least 15 seconds to clear codes.

ECM LOCATION

ECM is located behind driver's dash panel, behind hood release lever.

ECM POWER & GROUND CIRCUITS

See SYSTEM & COMPONENT TESTING article.

DIAGNOSTIC PROCEDURE

NOTE: Trouble codes will be recorded at various operating times. Some codes require operation of sensor or switch for 5 seconds; other components require operation for 5 minutes or longer at normal operating temperature, vehicle speed and load. Therefore, some codes may not set in a service bay operational mode and may require road testing vehicle in order to duplicate condition under which code will set.

Diagnosis of computerized engine control system should be performed in following order:

1) Ensure all engine systems other than computerized systems (i.e., compression, ignition, etc.) are operating properly. DO NOT proceed with testing unless all other problems have been repaired. If MIL light is illuminated, see RETRIEVING CODES (NON-SCAN). For diagnosing hard codes, see TROUBLE CODE DEFINITION to determine cause of malfunction.

2) For diagnosing intermittent codes, proceed to INTERMITTENTS in TROUBLESHOOTING – NO CODES article. Inspect condition of system harness by conducting recommended voltage or continuity checks. See WIRING DIAGRAMS article for additional information on specific circuit configuration. Inspect condition of individual component. Repair or replace component as needed.

3) Recheck system operation after repair is made. If trouble code still is present, substitute ECM with known good unit. Verify if system is repaired. After repairs have been completed, clear trouble codes. See CLEARING CODES.

DIAGNOSTIC CODES (MALFUNCTION INDICATOR LIGHT)

Trouble Code	Fault Item	[1] Probable Cause
1122 [2]	ECM	ECM Failure – RAM/ROM
1233	ECM	ECM Failure – ROM
1234	ECM	ECM Failure – RAM
2121 [2]	Boost Sensor	Control Valve
3112	Injector	Injector No. 1
3114	IAC Motor	IAC Opening Failure
3116	Injector	Injector No. 3
3117	Airflow Sensor	Airflow Sensor
3121 [2]	Boost Sensor	Pressure Sensor Failure
3122	IAC Motor	IAC Closing Failure
3128	HO2S Sensor	HO2S Sensor
3135	Evaporative Purge Valve	Purge Control Solenoid Valve
3137	Battery	Alternator/Low Voltage
3145	Coolant Temperature Sensor	Coolant Temperature Sensor
3149	A/C Compressor	A/C Compressor
3152 [2]	Boost Sensor	Turbo Boost – Too High
3153	Throttle Position Sensor	Throttle Position Sensor
3211	Knock Sensor	Knock Sensor
3222	Phase Sensor	Phase Sensor
3224	ECM	Knock Evaluation Circuit
3232	Crankshaft Position Sensor	Crankshaft Position Sensor
3233 [2]	ECM	Knock Control Circuit
3234	Injector	Injector No. 2
3235	Injector	Injector No. 4
3241	ECM	Injector Or Purge Control Valve
3242	ECM	IAC Motor Or A/C Relay
4151	Air/Fuel Mixture	Air/Fuel Control
4152	Air/Fuel Mixture	Air/Fuel Adaptive Failure
4153	Air/Fuel Mixture	Air/Fuel Adaptive (Multiple) Failure
4154	Air/Fuel Mixture	Air/Fuel Adaptive (Additive) Failure
4155 [2]	ECM	A/C Relay, IAC Motor, Injector Or PCV
4156 [2]	Boost Sensor	Control Deviation Failure

[1] – Faulty components, harnesses and connectors are always a probable cause for setting a trouble code.

[2] – Turbo models only.

1993 ENGINE PERFORMANCE
Self-Diagnostics – Scoupe (Cont.)

TROUBLE CODE DEFINITION

Diagnosis item	Trouble code: M.U.T. Display	Trouble code: Check engine lamp	N/A: UL	N/A: L	T/C	Description
Electronic Control Unit	13.ECU-ROM	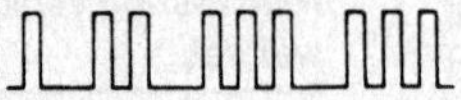	O	O	-	ECU Failure-ROM
	14. ECU-RAM	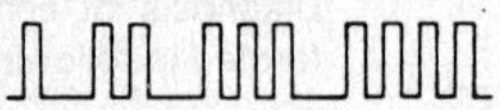	O	O	-	ECU Failure-RAM
	16.ECU-ROM/RAM	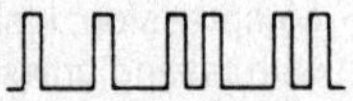	-	-	O	ECU Failure-ROM/RAM
	17. ECU-KNOCK EVA	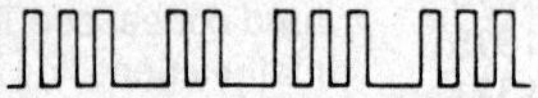	-	-	O	ECU Failure-Knock control
	19.ECU-KNOCK	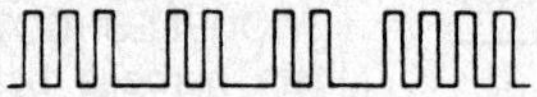	O	O	O	ECU Failure-Knock evaluation circuit
	61.INJ./PURGE V	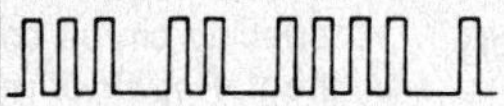	O	O	-	ECU Failure-injector or Purge control sol. valve
	62.ISA./AC RLY	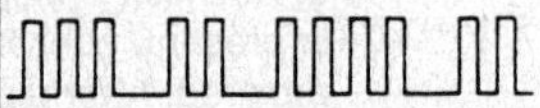	O	O	-	ECU Failure idle speed actuator or air con. relay
	63.ECU-DRIVE (A)		O	O	-	ECU Failure-Driving circuit (A)
	65.ACTUATORS	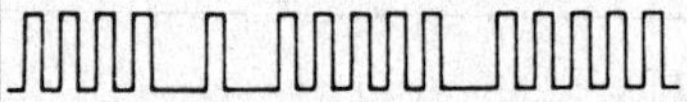	-	-	O	ECU-Failure inj. or PCV or ISA ro AC/relay
	69.ECU-DRIVE (B)		O	O	-	ECU Failure-Driving circuit (B)
Oxygen sensor	21.O2 sensor	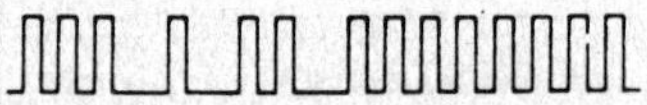	O	-	O	O2 sensor failure
Air flow sensor	22. AFS	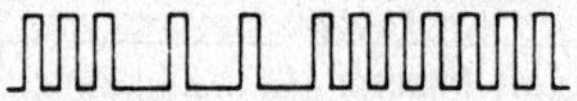	O	O	O	Air flow sensor failure
Coolant temperature sensor	23. WTS	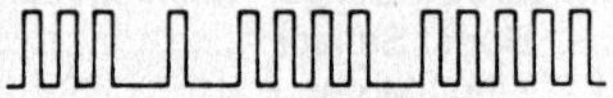	O	O	O	Coolant temperature sensor failure
Phase sensor	24.PHASE SENSOR	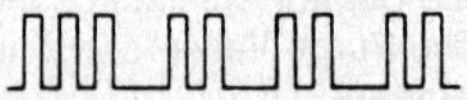	O	O	O	Phase sensor failure
Crankshaft position sensor	25. CRANK P.SNSR	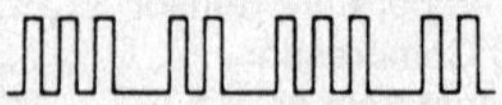	O	O	O	Crankshaft position sensor failure
Throttle position sensor	26.TPS	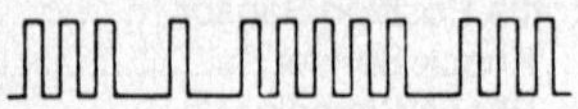	O	O	O	Throttle position sensor failure
Knock sensor	27.KNOCK SNSOR	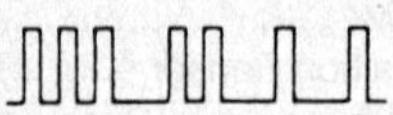	O	O	O	Knock sensor failure
Vehicle speed sensor	29. VEH. SPD. SNSR		O	O	O	Vehicle speed sensor failure
Battery	31.BATTERY	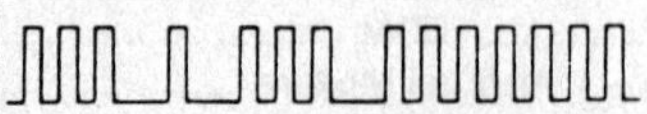	O	O	O	Battery voltage & alternator failure
Air conditioning compressor	33. A/C COMPRESR.	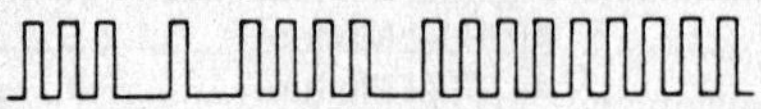	O	O	O	Air conditioning compressor failure

93C79592

Courtesy of Hyundai Motor Co.

Fig. 3: Self-Diagnostic Trouble Code Chart (1 Of 2)

Diagnosis item	Trouble code		Description
	M.U.T. Display	Check engine lamp	
Boost sensor	36. BOOST-HIGH		Turbo boost-too high failure
	37. BOOST-CNTL.		Turbo boost-control deviation failure
	38. BOOST-C. VLV.		Turbo boost-control valve failure
	39. BOOST-P. SNSR		Turbo boost-Pressure sensor failure
injector	41. NO.1 INJECTOR		No.1 Injector failure
	42. NO.2 INJECTOR		No.2 Injector failure
	43. NO.3 INJECTOR	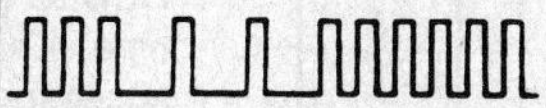	No.3 Injector failure
	44. NO.4 INJECTOR		No.4 Injector failure
Purge control solenoid	45. PURGE VALVE		Purge control solenoid valve failure
Idle speed actuator	47. ISA-OPEN'G		Idle speed actuator-opening failure
	48. ISA-CLOS'G		Idle speed actuator-closing failure
Fuel pump relay	53.FUEL PUMP RLY		Fuel pump relay failure
Air/Fuel ratio	81. A/F CTRL-INTG.		Air/Fuel control failure
	82.A/F ADAP.-MUL		Air/Fuel adaptive failure-multiplicative
	83.A/F ADAP.-A/N		Air/Fuel adaptive failure-A/N
	84. A/F ADAP.-ADD		Air/Fuel adaptive failure-additive

93D79593

Courtesy of Hyundai Motor Co.

Fig. 4: Self-Diagnostic Trouble Code Chart (2 Of 2)

DIAGNOSTIC TESTS

NO MALFUNCTION INDICATOR LIGHT (MIL)

1) Turn ignition switch to ON position. If MIL light on instrument panel does not illuminate, inspect bulb. Replace bulb if faulty. If bulb is okay, inspect ECM fuse (No. 16) and connector. Replace fuse if faulty. If light still will not illuminate, check power supply circuit.

2) Inspect fuse No. 13 and connector. Replace fuse if faulty. If fuse is okay, turn ignition off. Remove fuse No. 13 from fuse panel. Using ohmmeter, check continuity between Blue/Black wire of fuse No. 13 terminal and Blue/Red wire of MIL receptacle. If continuity does not exist, inspect and repair circuit as needed.

3) If MIL power supply circuit has continuity, inspect MIL ground circuit. Disconnect ECM harness connector. Using ohmmeter, check continuity between Black/Light Green wire of MIL receptacle and ECM harness connector terminal No. 2 (Turbo model) or terminal No. 21 (Non-turbo model). *See Fig. 5.* If continuity does not exist, inspect and repair circuit as needed.

4) If MIL ground circuit has continuity, substitute ECM with known good unit and retest system.

19	18	17	16	15	14	13	12	11	10	9	8	7	6	5	4	3	2	1
37	36	35	34	33	32	31	30	29	28	27	26	25	24	23	22	21	20	
55	54	53	52	51	50	49	48	47	46	45	44	43	42	41	40	39	38	

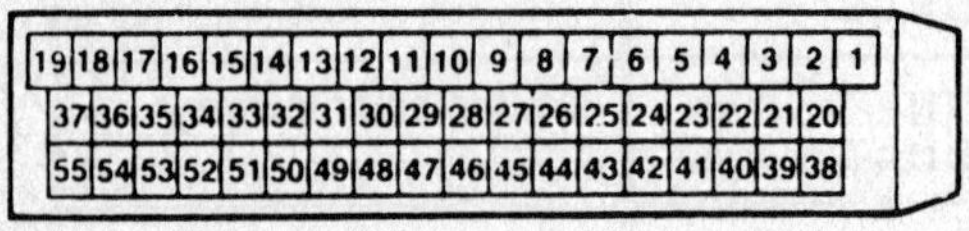

93E79511   Courtesy of Hyundai Motor Co.

Fig. 5: Identifying ECM Harness Connector

CODE 1122, 1233 OR 1234
(ECM RAM AND/OR ROM FAILURE)

Start engine and retrieve trouble codes. If Codes 1122, 1233 and/or 1234 are flashed by MIL light, substitute ECM with known good unit and retest system.

CODE 2121
(TURBO BOOST – CONTROL VALVE FAILURE)

NOTE: If after all testing procedures have been completed, system is still inoperative, substitute ECM with known good unit and retest.

System Inspection – Inspect control valve harness connection. Clean and repair as needed. Ensure vacuum hoses are in good condition.

Scan Tester Procedure – Manufacturer does not provide scan tester information. Refer to scan tester instruction manual for test procedures.

Harness Inspection – 1) Check circuit between ECM and control valve. Ensure ignition is off. Disconnect ECM connector. Connect jumper wire between ECM terminal No. 21 (Blue/Green wire) and vehicle ground. *See Fig. 5.*

2) Using ohmmeter, check continuity between control valve terminal No. 2 (Blue/Green wire) and vehicle ground. If continuity does not exist, inspect and repair circuit as needed.

3) If continuity exists, check for power supply voltage at control valve. Turn ignition on. Using DVOM, check for battery voltage at control valve harness connector terminal No. 1 (Green/White wire). If voltage does not exist, inspect and repair power supply circuit. See WIRING DIAGRAMS article.

Turbo Boost (Wastegate) Control Solenoid Valve Inspection – Using ohmmeter, check resistance between control valve terminals. Resistance should be approximately one megohm. Replace control valve if resistance measurement is not within specification. If control valve is okay, substitute ECM with known good unit and retest system.

CODE 3112, 3116, 3234 OR 3235
(FUEL INJECTOR FAILURE)

NOTE: Ensure engine compression is within specification. See SERVICE & ADJUSTMENT SPECIFICATIONS article. Ensure ignition system is operating properly. Poor compression or ignition system breakdown can affect fuel injector performance.

NOTE: If after all testing procedures have been completed, fuel injection system is still inoperative, substitute ECM with known good unit and retest.

System Inspection – 1) Determine if vehicle is difficult to start when engine is hot. Check fuel pressure. See BASIC DIAGNOSTIC PROCEDURES article. Ensure there are no fuel leaks. Determine if all injectors are operating properly. See FUEL INJECTOR INSPECTION.

2) Inspect ECM power supply and ground circuits. Inspect MPI control relay. See SYSTEM & COMPONENT TESTING article. Inspect crankshaft position sensor and phase sensor. See CODE 3232 (CRANKSHAFT POSITION SENSOR FAILURE) and CODE 3222 (PHASE SENSOR FAILURE).

Scan Tester Procedure – 1) Connect scan tester. See RETRIEVING CODES (SCAN TESTER). Using scan tester, read fuel injector drive time. Ensure engine is at normal operating temperature. Turn all accessories off. Ensure shift selector is in Park or Neutral.

2) Inspect fuel injector drive times at specified engine speeds. See FUEL INJECTOR DRIVE TIME table.

FUEL INJECTOR DRIVE TIME

Engine RPM	Drive Time (ms) Non-Turbo	Drive Time (ms) Turbo
800	4.0-4.5	2.5-3.0
2000	3.5-4.3	2.0-2.2
3000	3.5-4.2	2.0-2.2

Harness Inspection – 1) Measure injector power supply voltage. Disconnect injector harness connectors. Turn ignition on. Using DVOM, measure voltage at each injector harness connector terminal No. 1 (Green/White wire). If voltage measured is less than battery voltage, inspect and repair circuit. See WIRING DIAGRAMS article.

2) Check continuity of injector ground circuit. Disconnect ECM harness connector. Ensure ignition is off. Connect a jumper wire between each injector ECM terminal and ground. With injector harness connectors disconnected, use an ohmmeter to check continuity between terminal No. 2 and vehicle ground. See FUEL INJECTOR GROUND CIRCUIT IDENTIFICATION table for ECM terminal numbers and wire colors.

FUEL INJECTOR GROUND CIRCUIT IDENTIFICATION

Injector Number	Wire Color	Corresponding [1] ECM Terminal No.
1	Green/Yellow	17
2	Yellow/Blue	34
3	Lt. Green/Yellow	16
4	Lt. Green/White	35

[1] – See Fig. 5 for terminal identification.

Fuel Injector Inspection – 1) Check injector operation with engine running. Start engine and listen for injector operation (clicking sound). Ensure clicking sound of injector is not from adjacent injector with sound being transmitted through fuel delivery pipe. To check injector operating sound, use stethoscope or feel for vibration.

2) Measure resistance between injector terminals. Disconnect injector harness connector. Using ohmmeter, measure resistance. Resistance should be 15.5-16.0 ohms. Replace injector if measurement is not within specification.

CODE 3114 OR 3122 (IAC MOTOR FAILURE)

NOTE: If after all testing procedures have been completed, system is still inoperative, substitute ECM with known good unit and retest.

System Inspection – Inspect IAC motor harness connection. Clean and repair as needed. Ensure by-pass hoses are in good condition.

Scan Tester Procedure – Scan tester can be used to activate IAC motor. Refer to scan tester manual for procedure to activate motor. Connect scan tester. Turn ignition on. Access actuator test. Tester should display "05. ISCV". See ACTUATOR CONTROL SEQUENCE PROCEDURE for alternative procedure to activate IAC motor.

Harness Inspection – **1)** Measure power supply voltage of IAC motor. Disconnect harness connector. Turn ignition on. Using DVOM, measure voltage between middle terminal (Green/White wire) of harness connector and vehicle ground. If voltage is less than battery voltage, inspect and repair circuit as needed.

2) Check ground circuit between IAC motor and ECM. Turn ignition off. Ensure IAC harness connector is disconnected. Disconnect ECM connector. Connect jumper wire between ECM terminal No. 4 and vehicle ground. *See Fig. 5.* Using ohmmeter, measure resistance between IAC harness connector terminal No. 3 (White/Black wire) and vehicle ground.

3) If continuity does not exist, inspect and repair circuit as needed. Connect jumper wire between ECM terminal No. 22 and vehicle ground. Measure resistance between IAC harness connector No. 1 (Yellow/Black wire) and vehicle ground. If continuity does not exist, inspect and repair circuit as needed.

IAC Motor Inspection – Disconnect IAC connector. Measure resistance between terminals No. 1 and 2. *See Fig. 6.* Resistance should be 13 ohms. Measure resistance between terminals No. 2 and 3. Resistance should be 14 ohms. Replace motor if measurements are not within specification.

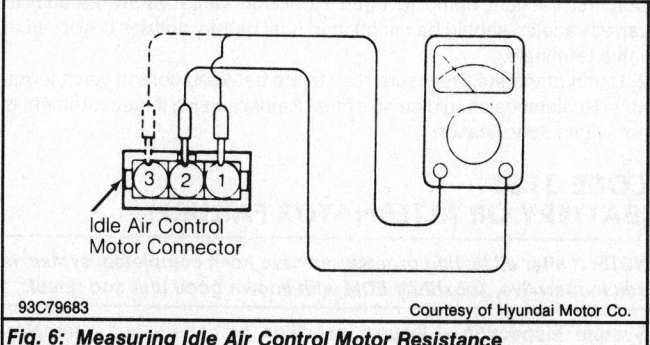

93C79683   Courtesy of Hyundai Motor Co.

Fig. 6: Measuring Idle Air Control Motor Resistance

CODE 3116

See CODE 3112, 3116, 3234 OR 3235 (FUEL INJECTOR FAILURE).

CODE 3117 OR 4151 (AIRFLOW SENSOR OR CONTROL FAILURE)

NOTE: If after all testing procedures have been completed, system is still inoperative, substitute ECM with known good unit and retest.

System Inspection – Inspect condition of Airflow Sensor (AFS) harness connector. A loose connection could cause intermittent stalling. Ensure there are no restrictions or clogs in air intake system.

NOTE: Refer to scan tester manual for specific test procedure instructions.

Scan Tester Procedure – **1)** Access service data item No. 35, 36 and 61. Scan tester should display readings (kg/h) of intake air quantity in fine steps. Ensure engine is at normal operating temperature.

2) All accessories should be off. Shift selector should be in Neutral or Park, and steering wheel should be in straight-ahead position. See appropriate INTAKE AIR QUANTITY SPECIFICATION table for scan tester readings.

INTAKE AIR QUANTITY SPECIFICATION (NON-TURBO)

Engine RPM	Air Quantity (kg/h)
Fine Step (No. 35)	
800	9-12
2000	21-27
3000	32-40
Coarse Step (No. 36)	
800	8.0-11.2
2000	20.8-25.6
3000	32.6-41.6
Idle Status (No. 61)	
800	9.6-10.8

INTAKE AIR QUANTITY SPECIFICATION (TURBO)

Engine RPM	Air Quantity (kg/h)
Fine Step (No. 35)	
800	9-12
2000	20-22
3000	29-32
Coarse Step (No. 36)	
800	8.0-11.2
2000	19.2-20.8
3000	28.9-32.0
Idle Status (No. 61)	
800	9.6-10.8

Harness Inspection (Non-Turbo) – **1)** Check AFS power supply voltage. Disconnect harness connector. Turn ignition on. Using DVOM, measure voltage between harness connector terminal No. 3 (Green/White wire) and vehicle ground. If voltage is less than battery voltage, inspect and repair circuit as needed.

2) Check AFS to ECM circuit. Turn ignition off. Disconnect ECM harness connector. Connect jumper wire between ECM connector terminal No. 7 and vehicle ground. *See Fig. 5.* Using ohmmeter, measure resistance between AFS harness connector terminal No. 4 (Green/Red wire) and vehicle ground. If continuity does not exist, inspect and repair circuit as needed.

3) Check AFS to ECM return circuit. Turn ignition off. Disconnect ECM harness connector. Connect jumper wire between ECM connector terminal No. 26 and vehicle ground. *See Fig. 5.* Using ohmmeter, measure resistance between AFS harness connector terminal No. 2 (Light Green/Black wire) and vehicle ground. If continuity does not exist, inspect and repair circuit as needed.

4) Check AFS ground circuit. Using ohmmeter, check continuity between harness connector terminal No. 1 (Black) and vehicle ground. If continuity does not exist, inspect and repair circuit as needed.

Harness Inspection (Turbo) – **1)** Check AFS power supply voltage. Disconnect harness connector. Turn ignition on. Using DVOM, measure voltage between harness connector terminal No. 5 (Green/White wire) and vehicle ground. If voltage is less than battery voltage, inspect and repair circuit as needed.

2) Check AFS to ECM circuit. Turn ignition off. Disconnect ECM harness connector. Connect jumper wire between ECM connector terminal No. 7 and vehicle ground. *See Fig. 5.* Using ohmmeter, measure resistance between AFS harness connector terminal No. 3 (Green/Red wire) and vehicle ground. If continuity does not exist, inspect and repair circuit as needed.

3) Check AFS to ECM clean burn circuit. Turn ignition off. Disconnect ECM harness connector. Connect jumper wire between ECM connector terminal No. 25 and vehicle ground. *See Fig. 5.* Using ohmmeter, measure resistance between AFS harness connector terminal No. 4 (Brown wire) and vehicle ground. If continuity does not exist, inspect and repair circuit as needed.

4) Check AFS to ECM return circuit. Turn ignition off. Disconnect ECM harness connector. Connect jumper wire between ECM connector terminal No. 26 and vehicle ground. *See Fig. 5.* Using ohmmeter, measure resistance between AFS harness connector terminal No. 2 (Light Green/Black wire) and vehicle ground. If continuity does not exist, inspect and repair circuit as needed.

5) Check AFS ground circuit. Using ohmmeter, check continuity between harness connector terminal No. 1 (Black) and vehicle ground. If continuity does not exist, inspect and repair circuit as needed.

Airflow Sensor Inspection (Non-Turbo) – Using DVOM, measure voltage output of AFS sensor. Ensure all harness connectors are connected. Voltage reading can be accessed at AFS connector terminal No. 3 (Green/Red wire) or ECM connector terminal No. 7 (Green/Red wire). Backprobe connector to measure voltage. Voltage measurements should be .94-.98 volt at 800 RPM and 1.76-1.79 volts at 3000 RPM. Replace AFS if measurements are not within specification.

Airflow Sensor Inspection (Turbo) – **1)** Using DVOM, measure voltage output of AFS sensor. Ensure all harness connectors are connected. Voltage reading can be accessed at AFS connector terminal No. 4 (Green/Red wire) or ECM connector terminal No. 7 (Green/Red wire). Backprobe connector to measure voltage. Voltage measurements should be 2.0-2.6 volts at 800 RPM and 2.6-3.3 volts at 3000 RPM.

2) Measure AFS clean burn output voltage. Backprobe connector to measure voltage. Voltage measurements should be 3-5 volts during clean burning state and 0-.5 volt during non-clean burning state. Replace AFS if measurements are not within specification.

CODE 3121
(TURBO BOOST – PRESSURE SENSOR FAILURE)

System Inspection – Inspect condition of vacuum hoses between intake manifold and ECM. Ensure there are no vacuum leaks. If vacuum hoses are okay, substitute ECM with known good unit and retest.

Scan Tester Procedure – Manufacturer does not provide scan tester inspection information. See tester manual for instructions.

Harness Inspection – Boost pressure sensor is integrated with ECM. Component is not serviceable.

CODE 3122

See CODE 3114 OR 3122 (IAC MOTOR FAILURE).

CODE 3128
(HEATED OXYGEN SENSOR FAILURE)

NOTE: If after all testing procedures have been completed, system is still inoperative, substitute ECM with known good unit and retest.

System Inspection – Determine if vehicle is producing high emissions. High emissions can be caused by faulty HO2S, injector, coolant temperature sensor, vacuum leak and/or malfunctioning airflow sensor.

Scan Tester Procedure – Manufacturer does not provide scan tester inspection information. See tester manual for instructions.

Harness Inspection – **1)** Check HO2S heater power supply voltage. Disconnect 2-pin harness connector. Turn ignition on. Using DVOM, measure voltage between Green/Yellow wire of harness connector and vehicle ground. If voltage is less than battery voltage, inspect and repair circuit as needed.

2) Check continuity of circuit between HO2S and ECM. Turn ignition off. Disconnect single pin harness connector and ECM harness connector. Connect jumper wire between ECM harness connector terminal No. 28 (Green wire) and vehicle ground.

3) Using ohmmeter, measure resistance between single pin harness connector terminal and vehicle ground. If continuity does not exist, inspect and repair circuit as needed.

4) Check HO2S heater ground circuit. Disconnect 2-pin harness connector. Using ohmmeter, measure resistance between Black wire of harness connector and vehicle ground. If continuity does not exist, inspect and repair circuit as needed.

Heated Oxygen Sensor Inspection – **1)** Measure HO2S output voltage. Ensure engine is at normal operating temperature. Using DVOM, backprobe ECM terminal No. 28. Voltage should be .1-.8 volt at 3000 RPM.

2) Disconnect HO2S 2-pin harness connector. Using ohmmeter, measure resistance between terminals of HO2S connector. Resistance should be 30 ohms or more. Ensure vehicle is at normal operating temperature. Replace sensor if measurements are not within specification.

CODE 3135, 4153 OR 4154
(PURGE CONTROL SOLENOID VALVE FAILURE)

NOTE: If after all testing procedures have been completed, system is still inoperative, substitute ECM with known good unit and retest.

System Inspection – Inspect purge control solenoid valve harness connection. Clean and repair as needed. Ensure hoses are in good condition.

Scan Tester Procedure – Scan tester can be used to activate control valve. Refer to scan tester manual for procedure to activate valve. Connect scan tester. Turn ignition on. Access actuator test. Tester should display "06. PURGE VALVE". See ACTUATOR CONTROL SEQUENCE PROCEDURE for alternative procedure to activate control valve.

Harness Inspection – **1)** Measure control valve power supply voltage. Disconnect valve harness connector. Turn ignition on. Using DVOM, measure voltage at harness connector terminal No. 2 (Green/White wire). If voltage is less than battery voltage, inspect and repair circuit as needed.

2) Check continuity of ground circuit to ECM. Turn ignition off. Disconnect ECM connector. Connect jumper wire between ECM terminal No. 5 and vehicle ground. *See Fig. 5.* Using ohmmeter, measure resistance between control valve harness connector terminal No. 1 (Red/Black wire) and vehicle ground. If continuity does not exist, inspect and repair circuit as needed.

Purge Control Solenoid Valve Inspection – **1)** Disconnect vacuum hose from intake plenum to valve. Disconnect harness connector. Connect vacuum pump to open nipple on valve. Apply vacuum to valve. Vacuum should be maintained until battery voltage is applied to valve terminals.

2) Using ohmmeter, measure resistance between control valve terminals. Resistance should be 45 ohms. Replace valve if measurement is not within specification.

CODE 3137
(BATTERY OR ALTERNATOR FAILURE)

NOTE: If after all testing procedures have been completed, system is still inoperative, substitute ECM with known good unit and retest.

System Inspection – Inspect condition of battery and alternator. Check battery and charging system. Replace battery and/or repair alternator as needed.

Scan Tester Procedure – Manufacturer does not provide scan tester information. Refer to scan tester manual for test procedures.

Harness Inspection – **1)** Inspect fuse No. 16 in fuse panel. Ensure fuse and connector are in good condition. Ensure ignition is off. Remove fuse No. 16. Disconnect ECM connector.

2) Connect jumper wire between ECM harness connector terminal No. 18 and vehicle ground. Measure resistance between Green/White wire terminal of fuse No. 16 receptacle and vehicle ground. If continuity does not exist, inspect and repair circuit as needed.

3) Connect jumper wire between ECM harness connector terminal No. 42 and vehicle ground. Measure resistance between Green/White wire terminal of fuse No. 16 receptacle and vehicle ground. If continuity does not exist, inspect and repair circuit as needed.

CODE 3145
(COOLANT TEMPERATURE SENSOR FAILURE)

System Inspection – Inspect condition of connector. Clean and repair as needed. Faulty coolant temperature sensor can cause incorrect idle RPM during cold start-up condition and rich air/fuel mixture.

Scan Tester Procedure – Access service data item No. 24. Scan tester should display sensor temperature with engine running. As engine temperature increases, monitor scan tester readings while measuring actual engine coolant temperature with thermometer. Scan tester readings should match thermometer readings.

Harness Inspection – **1)** Measure sensor power supply voltage. Disconnect sensor harness connector. Turn ignition on. Using DVOM, measure voltage at terminal No. 2 (Yellow/Red wire). Voltage should be 4.6-4.8 volts. If voltage is within specification, go to step **3)**. If voltage is not within specification, go to step **2)**.

2) Turn ignition off. Disconnect ECM harness connector. Connect jumper wire between ECM harness connector terminal No. 45 and vehicle ground. *See Fig. 5.* Using ohmmeter, check continuity between sensor harness connector terminal No. 2 (Yellow/Red wire) and vehicle ground. If continuity does not exist, inspect and repair circuit as needed. If continuity does exist, replace ECM and retest. Go to step **3)**.

3) Check continuity of sensor to ECM ground circuit. Ensure ignition is off. Using ohmmeter, check resistance between sensor harness connector terminal No. 1 (Black wire) and vehicle ground. If continuity does not exist, inspect and repair circuit as needed.

Coolant Temperature Sensor Inspection – Remove sensor and immerse in water. Using ohmmeter, measure resistance while increasing water temperature. See COOLANT TEMPERATURE SENSOR RESISTANCE SPECIFICATIONS. Replace sensor if resistance measured is not within specification.

COOLANT TEMPERATURE SENSOR RESISTANCE SPECIFICATIONS

Coolant Temperature °F (°C)	Ohms
-22 (-30)	22,220-31,780
14 (-10)	8160-10,740
32 (0)	5180-6600
68 (20)	2270-2730
104 (40)	1059-1281
140 (60)	538-650
176 (80)	290-354
194 (90)	217-269

CODE 3149
(AIR CONDITIONING SYSTEM FAILURE)

NOTE: If after all testing procedures have been completed, system is still inoperative, substitute ECM with known good unit and retest.

System Inspection – **1)** Inspect fuses No. 5 and 13. Replace faulty fuses as needed. Remove A/C relay. *See Fig. 7.* Turn ignition on. Using DVOM, measure voltage between relay receptacle terminal No. 4 (Red/Yellow wire) and vehicle ground. If voltage is less than battery voltage, inspect and repair circuit as needed.

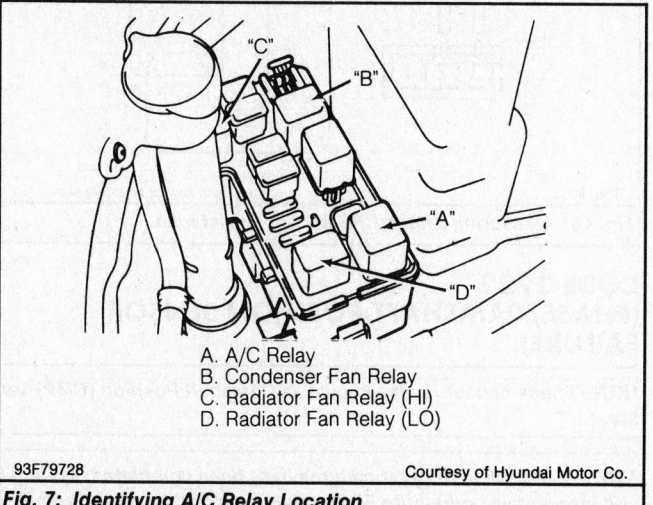

A. A/C Relay
B. Condenser Fan Relay
C. Radiator Fan Relay (HI)
D. Radiator Fan Relay (LO)

93F79728   Courtesy of Hyundai Motor Co.

Fig. 7: Identifying A/C Relay Location

2) Connect jumper wire between relay receptacle terminal No. 4 (Red/Yellow Wire) and terminal No. 2 (Black/White wire). Compressor clutch should engage. If clutch engages, go to step **4)**. If clutch does not engage, disconnect harness connector at compressor clutch. Using DVOM, measure voltage between clutch connector terminal No. 1 (Black/White wire) and vehicle ground.

3) If voltage is less than battery voltage, inspect and repair circuit between A/C clutch and relay receptacle as needed. If voltage is within specification, inspect and repair A/C compressor clutch as needed. See MITCHELL® AIR CONDITIONING & HEATING SERVICE & REPAIR manual.

4) Measure voltage between relay receptacle No. 1 (Black/Blue wire) and vehicle ground. If voltage is less than battery voltage, inspect and repair circuit as needed. Perform continuity check on A/C relay. *See Fig. 8.* Replace relay as needed.

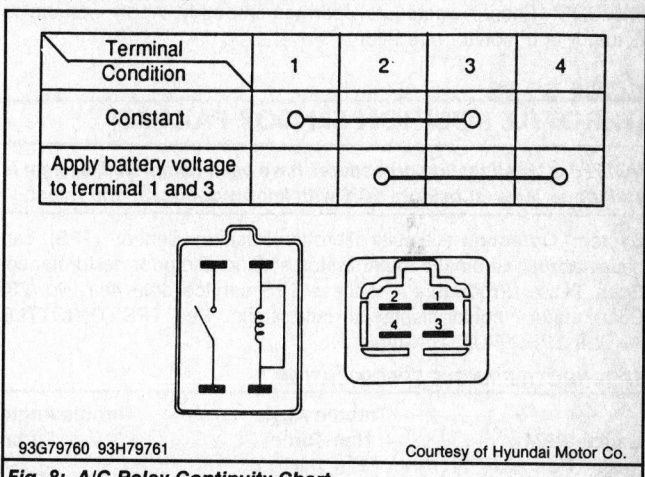

93G79760 93H79761   Courtesy of Hyundai Motor Co.

Fig. 8: A/C Relay Continuity Chart

5) Turn ignition off. Install A/C relay. Disconnect ECM harness connector. Connect jumper wire between ECM harness connector terminal No. 32 (Black/Red wire) and vehicle ground. *See Fig. 5.* Turn ignition on. If compressor does not engage, inspect and repair circuit as needed.

6) Turn on A/C and blower switch. Using DVOM, measure voltage between ECM harness connector terminal No. 40 (Black/White wire) and vehicle ground. *See Fig. 5.* If voltage is less than battery voltage, go to step **7)**. If battery voltage is present, substitute ECM with known good unit and retest system.

7) Turn ignition off. Connect ECM harness connector. Disconnect dual pressure switch harness connector. Turn on A/C and blower switch. Using DVOM, measure voltage between pressure switch harness connector terminal No. 2 (Black/Blue wire) and vehicle ground.

8) If voltage is less than battery voltage, go to step **10)**. If battery voltage is present, turn ignition off. Connect jumper wire between dual pressure switch terminals. Start engine. Turn on A/C and blower motor switches. If compressor does not operate, inspect and repair circuit between pressure switch and ECM terminal No. 40.

9) If compressor operates, remove jumper wire and connect pressure switch harness connector. If compressor fails to continue to operate, check A/C system refrigerant charge. See MITCHELL® AIR CONDITIONING & HEATING SERVICE & REPAIR manual. Ensure all safety procedures are followed. If refrigerant level is okay, replace dual pressure switch and recheck system.

10) Turn ignition off. Connect dual pressure switch harness connector. Disconnect thermostat switch harness connector. Connect jumper wire between thermostat switch terminals. Start engine. Turn on A/C and blower switches. If compressor does not operate, inspect and repair circuit between pressure switch and ECM terminal No. 40.

11) If compressor operates, remove jumper wire and connect thermostat switch harness connector. Retest system. Replace thermostat switch if compressor will not engage. If after all testing procedures have been completed, system is still inoperative, substitute ECM with known good unit and retest.

Scan Test Procedure – Access service date item No. 17. Scan tester should display switch position. With engine running, scan tester display should match A/C switch position. Access service date item No. 16. Scan tester should display A/C compressor. With engine running, scan tester display should match A/C switch position.

CODE 3152 OR 4156
(HIGH BOOST PRESSURE)

NOTE: If after all testing procedures have been completed, system is still inoperative, substitute ECM with known good unit and retest.

System Operation – 1) Inspect turbocharger system outlet tubes. Ensure there is no restriction or clog. Inspect condition of control valve. See CODE 2121 (TURBO BOOST – CONTROL VALVE FAILURE). Ensure wastegate operates smoothly. Apply vacuum to actuator and monitor operation.

CODE 3153
(THROTTLE POSITION SENSOR FAILURE)

NOTE: If after all testing procedures have been completed, system is still inoperative, substitute ECM with known good unit and retest.

System Operation – Faulty Throttle Position Sensor (TPS) can cause abrupt automatic transmission shifting and poor performance.
Scan Tester Procedure – Access TPS service data item No. 23. Scan tester should display throttle angle. See TPS THROTTLE ANGLE SPECIFICATION table.

TPS THROTTLE ANGLE SPECIFICATION

Engine RPM	Throttle Angle Non-Turbo	Throttle Angle Turbo
800	9-12°	9-12°
2000	16-18°	13-16°
3000	18-22°	16-18°
WOT	94-98°	94-98°

Harness Inspection – 1) Measure TPS power supply voltage. Disconnect TPS harness connector. Turn ignition on. Using DVOM, measure voltage between TPS harness connector terminal No. 2 (middle terminal) and vehicle ground. Voltage should be 4.8-5.2 volts.
2) If voltage is not within specification, turn ignition off. Disconnect ECM connector. Connect jumper wire between ECM harness connector terminal No. 12 and vehicle ground. *See Fig. 5.* Using ohmmeter, measure resistance between TPS harness connector terminal No. 2 (middle terminal) and vehicle ground. If continuity does not exist, inspect and repair circuit as needed. If continuity exists, substitute ECM with known good unit and retest.
3) Check continuity of TPS ground circuit. Using ohmmeter, check resistance between TPS harness connector terminal No. 1 (Yellow/Black wire on non-turbo, Black wire on turbo) and vehicle ground. If continuity does not exist, inspect and repair circuit as needed.
4) Check continuity of output circuit between TPS and ECM. Ensure ignition is off. Connect jumper wire between ECM harness connector terminal No. 53 (Green/Red wire) and vehicle ground. *See Fig. 5.* Using ohmmeter, check resistance between TPS harness connector terminal No. 3 (Green/Red wire) and vehicle ground. If continuity does not exist, inspect and repair circuit as needed.
Throttle Position Sensor Inspection – 1) Ensure all harness connectors are connected. Using DVOM, measure voltage between ECM harness connector No. 53 (Green/Red wire) and vehicle ground. Backprobe connector terminal. Voltage should be .25-.60 volt at 800 RPM and 4.25-4.60 volts at WOT.
2) Turn ignition off. Disconnect TPS harness connector. Using ohmmeter, measure resistance between TPS terminals No. 2 and 3. *See Fig. 9.* Resistance should be 1200-2800 ohms. Connect ohmmeter between TPS terminals No. 1 and 3. Operate throttle from closed to WOT position. Monitor ohmmeter while opening throttle. Ohmmeter needle should move accordingly with throttle movement. Replace TPS if it fails any of above tests.

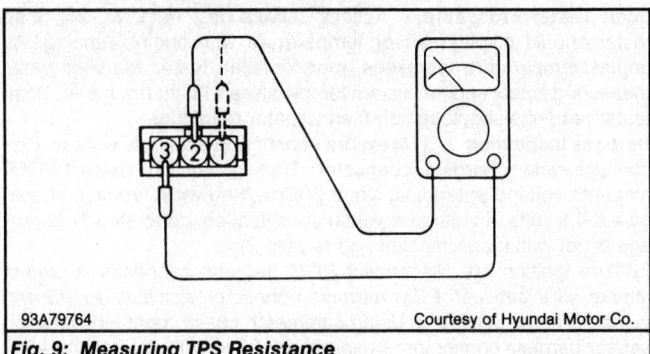
93A79764   Courtesy of Hyundai Motor Co.
Fig. 9: Measuring TPS Resistance

CODE 3211, 3224 OR 3233
(KNOCK SENSOR FAILURE)

NOTE: If after all testing procedures have been completed, system is still inoperative, substitute ECM with known good unit and retest.

System Inspection – Inspect sensor harness connection. Clean and repair as needed. Ensure sensor mounting bolt is tightened to 12-18 ft. lbs. (16-24 N.m).
Scan Tester Procedure – Manufacturer does not provide testing information. See scan tester manual for testing procedures.
Harness Inspection – 1) Inspect knock sensor voltage circuit. Ensure ignition is off. Disconnect knock sensor harness connector and ECM connector. Connect jumper wire between ECM harness connector terminal No. 11 (White/Yellow wire) and vehicle ground. *See Fig. 5.* Using ohmmeter, measure resistance between knock sensor harness connector terminal No. 2 (middle terminal) and vehicle ground. If continuity does not exist, inspect and repair circuit as needed.
2) Inspect knock sensor ground circuit. Ensure ignition is off. Connect jumper wire between ECM harness connector terminal No. 30 (Black/Yellow wire) and vehicle ground. Using ohmmeter, measure resistance between knock sensor harness connector terminal No. 3 (Black/Yellow wire) and vehicle ground. If continuity does not exist, inspect and repair circuit as needed.
Knock Sensor Inspection – Disconnect sensor connector. Measure resistance between terminals No. 2 and 3. *See Fig. 10.* Resistance should be 5 megohm (approximately). Replace sensor if measurement is not within specification.

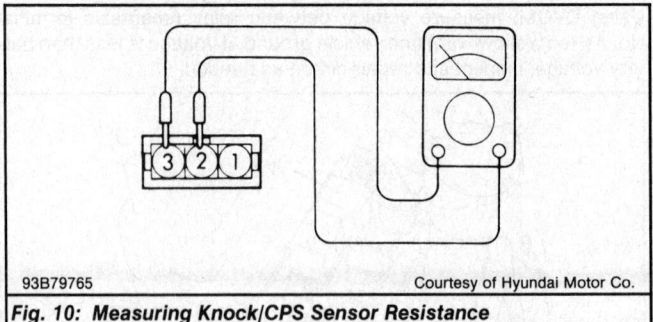
93B79765   Courtesy of Hyundai Motor Co.
Fig. 10: Measuring Knock/CPS Sensor Resistance

CODE 3222
(PHASE/CAMSHAFT POSITION SENSOR FAILURE)

NOTE: Phase sensor is also known as Camshaft Position (CMP) sensor.

NOTE: If after all testing procedures have been completed, system is still inoperative, substitute ECM with known good unit and retest.

System Inspection – Engine stalling, rough idle and/or poor acceleration could be caused by faulty phase sensor. Inspect harness connector, clean and repair as needed.

Scan Tester Procedure – Manufacturer does not provide testing information. See scan tester manual for testing procedures.

Harness Inspection – 1) Inspect phase sensor power supply circuit. Disconnect phase sensor harness connector. Turn ignition on. Using DVOM, measure voltage between sensor harness connector terminal No. 3 (White/Black wire) and vehicle ground. Voltage should be 4.8-5.2 volts. If voltage is okay, go to step 3).

2) If voltage is not within specification, turn ignition off. Disconnect ECM connector. Connect jumper wire between vehicle ground and ECM harness connector terminal No. 12. *See Fig. 5.* Using ohmmeter, measure resistance between phase harness connector terminal No. 3 (White/Black wire) and vehicle ground. If continuity does not exist, inspect and repair circuit as needed. If continuity exists, substitute ECM with known good unit and retest.

3) Check continuity of shield ground circuit. Using ohmmeter, check resistance between sensor harness connector terminal No. 1 (Black wire) and vehicle ground. If continuity does not exist, inspect and repair circuit as needed.

4) Check continuity of output circuit between phase sensor and ECM. Ensure ignition is off. Connect jumper wire between ECM harness connector terminal No. 8 (Orange/Black wire) and vehicle ground. *See Fig. 5.* Using ohmmeter, check resistance between sensor harness connector terminal No. 2 (Orange/Black wire) and vehicle ground. If continuity does not exist, inspect and repair circuit as needed.

Phase Sensor Inspection – Ensure all harness connectors are connected. Using DVOM, backprobe ECM harness connector terminal No. 8 (Orange/Black wire). Measure voltage between terminal No. 8 and vehicle ground. Voltage should be 0-5 volts with engine between idle and 3000 RPM. Replace sensor if measurement is not within specification.

CODE 3224

See CODE 3211, 3224 OR 3233 (KNOCK SENSOR FAILURE).

CODE 3232
(CRANKSHAFT POSITION SENSOR FAILURE)

NOTE: If after all testing procedures have been completed, system is still inoperative, substitute ECM with known good unit and retest.

System Inspection – Inspect harness connector. Clean and repair as needed. If tachometer is inoperative, Crankshaft Position Sensor (CKP) may be faulty. Remove CKP and inspect for damage or concentration of metal particles.

Scan Tester Procedure – Manufacturer does not provide testing information. See scan tester manual for testing procedures.

Harness Inspection – 1) Inspect CKP to ECM input circuit. Disconnect CKP sensor harness connector and ECM connector. Connect jumper wire between ECM harness connector terminal No. 48 and vehicle ground. *See Fig. 5.* Using ohmmeter, measure resistance between CKP harness connector terminal No. 2 (Black/Yellow wire) and vehicle ground. If continuity does not exist, inspect and repair circuit as needed.

2) Check continuity of shield ground circuit. Using ohmmeter, check resistance between sensor harness connector terminal No. 1 (Black wire) and vehicle ground. If continuity does not exist, inspect and repair circuit as needed.

3) Check continuity of output circuit between CKP sensor and ECM. Connect jumper wire between vehicle ground and ECM harness connector terminal No. 49 (White/Yellow wire) on non-turbo model or ter-

minal No. 47 (White/Yellow wire) on turbo model. *See Fig. 5.* Using ohmmeter, check resistance between CKP harness connector terminal No. 3 (White/Yellow wire) and vehicle ground. If continuity does not exist, inspect and repair circuit as needed.

CKP Sensor Inspection – Disconnect CKP harness connector. Using ohmmeter, measure resistance between terminals No. 2 and 3. *See Fig. 10.* Resistance should be 49-59 ohms. Replace sensor if measurement is not within specification. CKP clearance to sensor wheel should be .02-.06" (.5-1.5 mm).

CODE 3233

See CODE 3211, 3224 OR 3233 (KNOCK SENSOR FAILURE).

CODE 3234 OR 3235

See CODE 3112, 3116, 3234 OR 3235 (FUEL INJECTOR FAILURE).

CODE 3241, 3242 OR 4155
(MISCELLANEOUS COMPONENT FAILURE)

NOTE: If after all testing procedures have been completed, system is still inoperative, substitute ECM with known good unit and retest.

System Inspection – Code 3241, 3242 and 4155 trouble codes are set for various components. See TROUBLE CODE COMPONENT IDENTIFICATION table. Inspect suspected component harness connection. See appropriate trouble code diagnosis section.

TROUBLE CODE COMPONENT IDENTIFICATION

Trouble Code	Affected Components
3241	Fuel Injector, Purge Control Valve
3242	A/C Relay, IAC Motor
4155	A/C Relay, Fuel Injector, IAC Motor, Purge Control Valve

CODE 4151, 4152, 4153 OR 4154
(AIR/FUEL MIXTURE MALFUNCTION)

System Inspection – Numerous components can affect air/fuel mixture. Usually these trouble codes are set along with specific component trouble codes. A thorough inspection of emission, fuel and ignition systems is recommended. If after all testing procedures have been completed, system is still not functioning properly, substitute ECM with known good unit and retest.

Scan Tester Procedure – Manufacturer does not provide testing information. See scan tester manual for testing procedures.

CODE 4155

See CODE 3241, 3242 OR 4155 (MISCELLANEOUS COMPONENT FAILURE).

CODE 4156
(TURBOCHARGER – CONTROL DEVIATION FAILURE)

See CODE 3152 OR 4156 (HIGH BOOST PRESSURE).

SUMMARY

If no hard fault codes (or only pass codes) are present, driveability symptoms exist or intermittent codes exist, proceed to TROUBLE SHOOTING – NO CODES article for diagnosis by symptom (i.e., ROUGH IDLE, NO START, etc.) or intermittent diagnostic procedures.

1994 ENGINE PERFORMANCE
Trouble Shooting – No Codes

Elantra, Excel, Scoupe, Sonata

INTRODUCTION

Before diagnosing symptoms or intermittent faults, perform steps in BASIC DIAGNOSTIC PROCEDURES and SELF-DIAGNOSTICS articles. Use this article to diagnose driveability problems existing when a hard fault code is not present or vehicle is not equipped with a self-diagnostic system.

NOTE: Some driveability problems may have been corrected by manufacturer with a revised computer calibration chip or computer control unit. Check with manufacturer for latest chip or computer application.

Symptom checks can direct technician to malfunctioning component(s) for further diagnosis. A symptom should lead to a specific component, system test, or adjustment.

Use intermittent test procedures to locate driveability problems that DO NOT occur while vehicle is being tested. These test procedures should also be used if a soft (intermittent) trouble code was present, but no problem was found during self-diagnostic testing.

NOTE: For specific testing procedures, see SYSTEM & COMPONENT TESTING article. For specifications, see ON-VEHICLE ADJUSTMENTS or SERVICE & ADJUSTMENT SPECIFICATIONS article.

SYMPTOMS

SYMPTOM DIAGNOSIS

Symptom checks cannot be used properly unless problem occurs while vehicle is being tested. To reduce diagnostic time, ensure steps in BASIC DIAGNOSTIC PROCEDURES and SELF-DIAGNOSTICS articles were performed before diagnosing a symptom. Symptoms available for diagnosis include following:

- Will Not Start (Cranks Okay)
- Difficult To Start (Cranks Okay)
- Engine Surges
- Rough Or Unstable Idle
- Excessive Fast Idle
- Engine Stalls
- Engine Lacks Power
- Engine Misfires Or Hesitates
- Engine Runs Rough On Deceleration
- Afterburn In Exhaust System
- Poor Fuel Mileage
- Detonation Or Knocking
- Fails Emission Test.

WILL NOT START (CRANKS OKAY)

Spark Available

- Verify ignition fuse is not blown.
- Verify fusible link is not blown.
- Verify air intake system is not restricted.
- Ensure fuel system pressure and volume are correct.
- Check for poor quality or contaminated fuel.
- Check for use of fuel with high alcohol content.
- Check exhaust system for restriction.

No Spark Available

- Ensure secondary ignition system is in good condition.
- Ensure pick-up coil air gap is correct.
- Ensure ignition coil supply voltage is correct.
- Ensure ignition coil primary resistance is correct.
- Ensure ignition coil secondary resistance is correct.
- Ensure ignitor resistance is correct.
- Check ignitor primary leads for open or short circuit.
- Ensure ECU has correct voltage supply and is properly grounded.

DIFFICULT TO START (CRANKS OKAY)

- Ensure sufficient secondary spark is available.
- Check air intake system for restriction.
- Ensure vacuum hoses are not disconnected or damaged.
- Ensure fuel system pressure is correct.
- Ensure fuel injector operation is correct.
- Ensure EGR valve operation is correct.
- Ensure EGR valve closes completely.
- Check for cracks or poor connections at throttle body.
- Ensure ignition and valve timing are correct.
- Ensure distributor pick-up coil air gap is correct.
- Ensure distributor pick-up coil resistance is within specification.
- Ensure ignition coil resistance is within specification.
- Check coolant temperature sensor operation.
- Check control relay operation.
- Check power transistor operation.
- Check operation of air induction valve.
- Ensure electrical harness and connectors are not broken or loose.
- Ensure ECU has correct voltage supply and is properly grounded.
- Ensure engine has sufficient compression.

ENGINE SURGES

- Ensure there are no vacuum leaks.
- Ensure EGR valve operation is correct.
- Ensure EGR valve closes completely.
- Ensure fuel system pressure is correct and constant.
- Ensure ignition timing is correct.

ROUGH OR UNSTABLE IDLE

- Check IAC valve for malfunction.
- Ensure fuel system pressure is correct.
- Ensure idle speed is correct.
- Check air intake system for restrictions.
- Use stethoscope to verify operational noise coming from fuel injectors.
- Ensure sufficient secondary spark is available in all cylinders.
- Verify vacuum hose routing is correct and that there are no vacuum leaks.
- Ensure fuel system pressure and volume are correct.
- Check for EGR system malfunction.
- Check coolant temperature sensor operation.
- Check intake air temperature sensor operation.
- Verify throttle position sensor has correct adjustment and resistance value.
- Check air conditioner switch operation.
- Check inhibitor switch operation (automatic transmission).
- Check IAC servo drive signal and operation.
- Check airflow sensor voltage output.
- Check barometric pressure sensor voltage output.
- Check crank angle sensor operation.
- Check vehicle speed sensor operation.
- Check TDC sensor or cylinder No. 1 TDC sensor operation.
- Check electrical connections at fuel injectors.

EXCESSIVE FAST IDLE

- Check throttle cable adjustment.
- Verify vacuum hose routing is correct.
- Ensure there are no vacuum leaks.
- Ensure fuel system pressure and volume are correct.
- Check coolant temperature sensor operation.

ENGINE STALLS

- Ensure air intake system is not restricted.
- Ensure PCV system operation is correct.
- Check EGR system for correct operation.
- Check for cracks or poor connections at throttle body.
- Check coolant temperature sensor operation.
- Ensure fuel system pressure is correct. Use ohmmeter to verify correct fuel injector resistance.
- Verify correct throttle position sensor adjustment and resistance value.
- Check for poor quality or contaminated fuel. Check for use of fuel with high alcohol content.

ENGINE LACKS POWER

- Check throttle cable adjustment.
- Verify air intake system is not restricted.
- Check EGR system for correct operation.
- Ensure fuel system pressure is correct. Use ohmmeter to verify correct fuel injector resistance.
- Ensure base timing is correct and timing advance system is functional.
- Check purge control valve operation.
- Check vacuum switching valve operation.
- Check throttle position sensor operation.
- Check coolant temperature sensor operation.
- Verify throttle valve opens completely when accelerator pedal is fully applied.
- Check transmission for correct downshift (A/T).
- Check exhaust system for restriction.

ENGINE MISFIRES OR HESITATES

- Ensure vacuum hoses are not disconnected or damaged.
- Ensure electrical harness, connectors and wires are not broken or loose.
- Ensure fuel pressure is correct.
- Check air conditioner switch operation.
- Check air conditioner power relay operation.
- Check airflow sensor voltage output.
- Check barometric pressure sensor voltage output.
- Check crank angle sensor operation.
- Check coolant temperature sensor operation.
- Check idle position switch operation.
- Check ignition switch operation.
- Check inhibitor switch operation (A/T).
- Check intake air temperature sensor operation.
- Check IAC servo drive signal and operation.
- Check motor position sensor operation.
- Check oxygen (O_2) sensor voltage output.
- Check power steering oil pressure switch operation.
- Check throttle position sensor operation.
- Check TDC sensor or cylinder No. 1 TDC sensor operation.

ENGINE RUNS ROUGH ON DECELERATION

- Check IAC valve for malfunction.
- Ensure fuel system pressure is correct.

AFTERBURN IN EXHAUST SYSTEM

- Ensure there are no leaks in exhaust system.
- Ensure base timing is correct, and timing advance system is functional.
- Check throttle position sensor.
- Check coolant temperature sensor.
- Check IAC solenoid operation.
- Check A/C vacuum solenoid valve (if equipped).

POOR FUEL MILEAGE

- Ensure base timing is correct, and timing advance system is functional.
- Ensure fuel system pressure is correct.
- Check air conditioner switch operation.
- Check airflow sensor voltage output.
- Check barometric pressure sensor voltage output.
- Check engine coolant temperature sensor operation.
- Check idle position switch operation.
- Check ignition switch operation.
- Check inhibitor switch operation (A/T).
- Check injector operation.
- Check intake air temperature sensor operation.
- Check motor position sensor operation.
- Check oxygen (O_2) sensor operation.
- Check power steering oil pressure switch operation.
- Check throttle position sensor operation.
- Check TDC sensor or cylinder No. 1 TDC sensor operation.

DETONATION OR KNOCKING

- Check engine oil level.
- Check engine for overheating.
- Verify base timing is correct.
- Check for vacuum leaks.
- Check EGR system operation.
- Check for contaminated or poor quality fuel.
- Check for carbon build-up in combustion chamber.
- Ensure spark plug application is correct.
- Ensure ECM application is correct.

FAILS EMISSION TEST

- Ensure air intake system is not restricted.
- Ensure engine is at normal operating temperature.
- Ensure fuel system pressure is correct.
- Verify base timing is correct.
- Check for correct PCV valve operation.
- Check crankcase for gasoline contamination.
- Check IAC solenoid.
- Check EGR system for correct operation.
- Check purge control valve operation.
- Ensure throttle position sensor has correct adjustment and resistance value.
- Check operation of coolant temperature sensor.
- Ensure exhaust system is not restricted.

INTERMITTENTS

INTERMITTENT PROBLEM DIAGNOSIS

Intermittent fault testing requires duplicating circuit or component failure to identify problem. These procedures may lead to computer setting fault code which may help in diagnosis.

If problem vehicle does not produce fault codes, use a DVOM to pinpoint faults. Monitor voltage or resistance values using DVOM while attempting to reproduce conditions causing intermittent fault. Status change on DVOM indicates area of fault.

When monitoring voltage, ensure ignition switch is in ON position or vehicle is running. When monitoring circuit resistance, ensure ignition switch is in OFF position or negative battery cable is disconnected.

TEST PROCEDURES

Intermittent Simulation – To reproduce conditions creating intermittent fault, use following methods:
- Lightly vibrate component.
- Heat component.
- Wiggle or bend wiring harness.
- Spray component with water.
- Remove/apply vacuum source.

Monitor circuit/component voltage or resistance while simulating intermittent. If engine is running, monitor for self-diagnostic codes. Use test results to identify a faulty component or circuit.

Elantra, Excel, Scoupe, Sonata

INTRODUCTION

Before testing separate components or systems, perform procedures in BASIC DIAGNOSTIC PROCEDURES article. Since many computer-controlled and monitored components set a trouble code if they malfunction, also perform procedures in appropriate SELF-DIAGNOSTICS article.

NOTE: Testing individual components does not isolate shorts or opens. Perform all voltage tests using a Digital Volt-Ohmmeter (DVOM) with a minimum 10-megohm input impedance, unless stated otherwise in test procedure. Use ohmmeter to isolate wiring harness shorts or opens. For specific circuit diagrams to aid in diagnostic testing, see WIRING DIAGRAMS article.

AIR INDUCTION SYSTEMS

TURBOCHARGER

Wastegate Actuator – Actuator is mounted on turbocharger. Apply vacuum to wastegate actuator to ensure actuator rod moves. Ensure diaphragm holds vacuum. DO NOT apply excessive vacuum to wastegate actuator or attempt to adjust wastegate actuator rod.

Wastegate Control Solenoid Valve – **1)** Disconnect solenoid valve connector, located near air cleaner. Turn ignition on. Using DVOM, measure voltage at solenoid connector Green/White wire. If battery voltage exists, go to step **2)**. If battery voltage does not exist, check and repair circuit as necessary.

2) Disconnect ECM connector. Ground ECM connector terminal No. 21. *See Fig. 1.* Check for continuity between chassis ground and solenoid valve connector Blue/Green wire. If continuity exists, circuit is okay. Go to step **3)**. If continuity does not exist, check for open or short to ground between solenoid valve and ECM.

3) Disconnect solenoid valve connector. Using DVOM, check resistance between solenoid valve terminals. Resistance should be approximately one megohm at 68°F (20°C). If resistance is not within specification, replace solenoid valve.

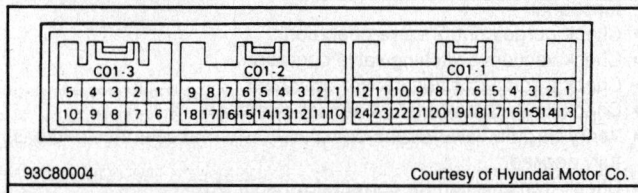

93E79511   Courtesy of Hyundai Motor Co.

Fig. 1: Identifying ECM Harness Connector (Scoupe)

COMPUTERIZED ENGINE CONTROLS

ELECTRONIC CONTROL MODULE (ECM)

Ground Circuits – **1)** Turn ignition off. Using an ohmmeter, check continuity between chassis ground and ECM ground terminals. See GROUND TERMINAL IDENTIFICATION table. Ohmmeter should indicate zero ohms. If resistance is not as specified, check and repair circuit between ECM and ground.

2) Connect voltmeter negative lead to chassis ground. Connect positive lead to ECM ground terminals. See GROUND TERMINAL IDENTIFICATION table. With engine running, voltmeter should indicate less than one volt. If voltmeter reading is greater than one volt, check for open, corrosion or loose connection in ground circuit.

Power Circuits – Turn ignition on. Check for battery voltage at ECM power terminals. See POWER TERMINAL IDENTIFICATION table. If battery voltage is not present, check operation of MFI control relay. See RELAYS.

GROUND TERMINAL IDENTIFICATION

Application	[1] ECM Terminal No.
Elantra (Fed.) & Sonata	[2] 5 & 10
Elantra (CA)	[3] 1 & 14
Excel	[3] 1 & 14
Scoupe	19

[1] – See Figs. 1-5.
[2] – 10-pin connector.
[3] – 26-pin connector.

POWER TERMINAL IDENTIFICATION

Application	[1] ECM Terminal No.
Elantra & Sonata 4-Cyl.	[2] 12 & 15
Excel	[3] 2 & 15
Scoupe	18 & [4] 42
Sonata V6	[5] 16 & 17

[1] – See Figs. 1-5.
[2] – 18-pin connector.
[3] – 16-pin connector.
[4] – Manual transmission only.
[5] – 10-pin connector.

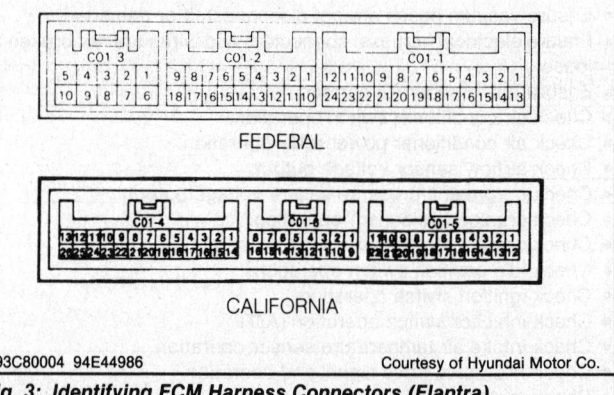

93C80004   Courtesy of Hyundai Motor Co.

Fig. 2: Identifying ECM Harness Connector (Sonata 4-Cylinder)

93C80004   94E44986   Courtesy of Hyundai Motor Co.

Fig. 3: Identifying ECM Harness Connectors (Elantra)

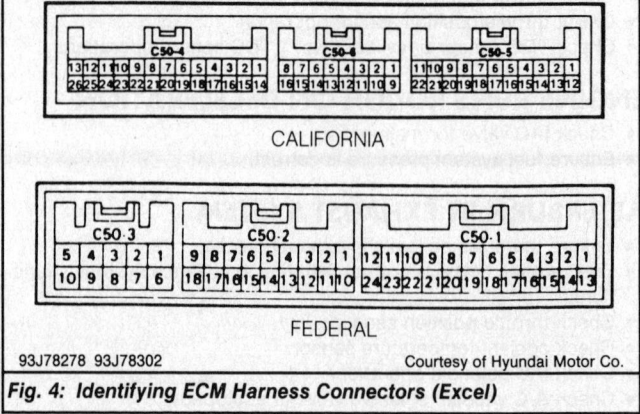

93J78278   93J78302   Courtesy of Hyundai Motor Co.

Fig. 4: Identifying ECM Harness Connectors (Excel)

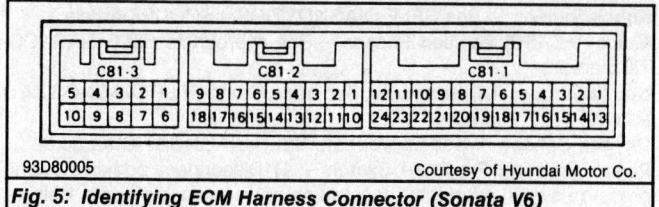

93D80005   Courtesy of Hyundai Motor Co.

Fig. 5: Identifying ECM Harness Connector (Sonata V6)

ENGINE SENSORS & SWITCHES

NOTE: For A/C switch testing information on Scoupe, see CODE 3149 (AIR CONDITIONING SYSTEM FAILURE) in SELF-DIAGNOSTICS – SCOUPE article.

A/C Switch (Elantra, Excel & Sonata) – Disconnect ECM connector. Turn ignition switch and A/C switch to ON position. Using a DVOM, measure voltage at ECM connector terminals No. 10 and 18 for Excel, terminals No. 6 and 13 on Sonata and terminals No. 6, 13 and 10 on Elantra. If battery voltage is present, circuit is okay. If battery voltage is not present, go to appropriate A/C SYSTEM INSPECTION procedure.

NOTE: If after all testing procedures have been completed, system is still inoperative, substitute ECM with known good unit and retest.

A/C System Inspection (Elantra & Sonata) – **1)** Inspect fuses No. 1, 12 and 18. Replace faulty fuses as needed. Remove A/C relay. Turn ignition on. Using DVOM, measure voltage between relay receptacle terminal No. 4 (Red/White wire) and vehicle ground. If voltage is less than battery voltage, inspect and repair circuit as needed.
2) Connect jumper wire between relay receptacle terminal No. 4 (Red/White Wire) and terminal No. 2 (Blue/Yellow wire). Compressor clutch should engage. If clutch engages, go to step **4)**. If clutch does not engage, disconnect harness connector at compressor clutch. Using DVOM, measure voltage between connector terminal No. 2 (Blue/Yellow wire) and vehicle ground.
3) If voltage is less than battery voltage, inspect and repair circuit as needed. If voltage is within specification, inspect and repair A/C compressor clutch as needed. See appropriate MITCHELL® AIR CONDITIONING & HEATING SERVICE & REPAIR MANUAL.
4) Measure voltage between relay receptacle No. 1 (Black/White wire) and vehicle ground. If voltage is less than battery voltage, inspect and repair circuit as needed. Perform continuity check on A/C relay. See appropriate MITCHELL® AIR CONDITIONING & HEATING SERVICE & REPAIR MANUAL. Replace relay as needed.
5) Turn on A/C and blower switch. Using DVOM, measure voltage between ECM harness connector terminal No. 6 on 4-cyl. (Black/White wire), or terminal No. 12 on V6 (Light/Green/Black wire) and vehicle ground. *See Figs. 2 and 3.* If voltage is less than battery voltage, go to step **6)**. If battery voltage is present, substitute ECM with known good unit and retest system.
6) Turn ignition off. Connect ECM harness connector. Disconnect low pressure switch harness connector. Turn on A/C and blower switch. Using DVOM, measure voltage between pressure switch harness connector terminal No. 2 (Black/Red wire) and vehicle ground.
7) If voltage is less than battery voltage, go to step **10)**. If battery voltage is present, turn ignition off. Connect jumper wire between low pressure switch terminals. Start engine. Turn on A/C and blower motor switches. If compressor does not operate, inspect and repair circuit between pressure switch and ECM terminal No. 6 on 4-cyl. or terminal No. 12 on V6.
8) If compressor operates, remove jumper wire and connect pressure switch harness connector. If compressor fails to continue to operate, check A/C system refrigerant charge. See appropriate MITCHELL® AIR CONDITIONING & HEATING SERVICE & REPAIR MANUAL. Ensure all safety procedures are followed. If refrigerant level is okay, replace low pressure switch and recheck system.

9) Turn ignition off. Connect low pressure switch harness connector. Disconnect thermostat switch harness connector. Connect jumper wire between thermostat switch terminals. Start engine. Turn on A/C and blower switches. If compressor does not operate, inspect and repair circuit between pressure switch and ECM terminal No. 6 or 12.
10) If compressor operates, remove jumper wire and connect thermostat switch harness connector. Retest system. Replace thermostat switch if compressor will not engage. If after all testing procedures have been completed, system is still inoperative, substitute ECM with known good unit and retest.

System Inspection (Excel) – **1)** Inspect fuses No. 1, 5 and 9. Replace faulty fuses as needed. Remove A/C relay. Turn ignition on. Using DVOM, measure voltage between relay receptacle terminal No. 4 (Red/Yellow wire) and vehicle ground. If voltage is less than battery voltage, inspect and repair circuit as needed.
2) Connect jumper wire between relay receptacle terminal No. 4 (Red/Yellow wire) and terminal No. 2 (Blue/Yellow wire). Compressor clutch should engage. If clutch engages, go to step **4)**. If clutch does not engage, disconnect harness connector at compressor clutch. Using DVOM, measure voltage between connector terminal No. 2 (Blue/Yellow wire) and vehicle ground.
3) If voltage is less than battery voltage, inspect and repair circuit as needed. If voltage is within specification, inspect and repair A/C compressor clutch as needed. See appropriate MITCHELL® AIR CONDITIONING & HEATING SERVICE & REPAIR MANUAL.
4) Measure voltage between relay receptacle No. 1 (Light Green/Black wire) and vehicle ground. If voltage is less than battery voltage, inspect and repair circuit as needed. Perform continuity check on A/C relay. See appropriate MITCHELL® AIR CONDITIONING & HEATING SERVICE & REPAIR MANUAL. Replace relay as needed.
5) Turn on A/C and blower switch. Using DVOM, measure voltage between ECM harness connector terminal No. 10 (16-pin connector Black/White wire) and vehicle ground. *See Fig. 4.* If voltage is less than battery voltage, go to step **6)**. If battery voltage is present, substitute ECM with known good unit and retest system.
6) Turn ignition off. Connect ECM harness connector. Disconnect low pressure switch harness connector. Turn on A/C and blower switch. Using DVOM, measure voltage between pressure switch harness connector terminal No. 2 (Black/Red wire) and vehicle ground.
7) If voltage is less than battery voltage, go to step **10)**. If battery voltage is present, turn ignition off. Connect jumper wire between low pressure switch terminals. Start engine. Turn on A/C and blower motor switches. If compressor does not operate, inspect and repair circuit between pressure switch and ECM terminal No. 10.
8) If compressor operates, remove jumper wire and connect pressure switch harness connector. If compressor fails to continue to operate, check A/C system refrigerant charge. See appropriate MITCHELL® AIR CONDITIONING & HEATING SERVICE & REPAIR MANUAL. Ensure all safety procedures are followed. If refrigerant level is okay, replace low pressure switch and recheck system.
9) Turn ignition off. Connect dual pressure switch harness connector. Disconnect thermostat switch harness connector. Connect jumper wire between thermostat switch terminals. Start engine. Turn on A/C and blower switches. If compressor does not operate, inspect and repair circuit between pressure switch and ECM terminal No. 10.
10) If compressor operates, remove jumper wire and connect thermostat switch harness connector. Retest system. Replace thermostat switch if compressor will not engage. If after all testing procedures have been completed, system is still inoperative, substitute ECM with known good unit and retest.
A/C System Scan Test Procedure – Access service data item No. 28. Scan tester should display switch position. With engine running, scan tester display should match A/C switch position. Access service date item No. 49. Scan tester should display A/C compressor. With engine running, scan tester display should match A/C switch position.
Airflow Sensor – See appropriate SELF-DIAGNOSTIC article.
Barometric Pressure Sensor – See appropriate SELF-DIAGNOSTICS article.

1994 ENGINE PERFORMANCE
System & Component Testing (Cont.)

Coolant Temperature Sensor – See appropriate SELF-DIAGNOSTICS article.

Crankshaft Position Sensor – See appropriate SELF-DIAGNOSTICS article.

EGR Temperature Sensor – See appropriate SELF-DIAGNOSTICS article.

Intake Air Temperature Sensor – See appropriate SELF-DIAGNOSTICS article.

Idle Switch (Excel) – 1) The idle switch is incorporated in the idle speed control position sensor. Ensure switch is adjusted correctly. See ON-VEHICLE ADJUSTMENTS article. Disconnect idle switch connector. Using ohmmeter, check continuity between terminal No. 3 (Yellow/Green wire) and ground. *See Fig. 6.*

2) With accelerator pedal depressed, continuity should not exist. With accelerator pedal released, continuity should exist. If continuity is not as specified, replace idle switch.

3) Measure power supply voltage from ECM to idle switch. Turn ignition on. Using DVOM, measure voltage between idle switch harness connector terminal No. 3 (Yellow/Green wire) and vehicle ground. Voltage should be 4 volts or more. If voltage is not within specification, turn ignition off.

4) Disconnect ECM harness connector. Connect jumper wire between vehicle ground and terminal No. 7 (24-pin connector) on Federal models, terminal No. 17 (22-pin connector) on California models. *See Fig. 4.* Using ohmmeter, check resistance between idle switch harness connector terminal No. 3 (Yellow/Green wire) and vehicle ground.

5) If continuity does not exist, inspect and repair circuit as needed. If continuity does exist, substitute ECM with known good unit and retest.

Idle Switch (Elantra & Sonata 4-Cylinder) – 1) Ensure switch is adjusted correctly. See ON-VEHICLE ADJUSTMENTS article. Disconnect idle switch connector. Check for continuity between terminal No. 1 (Yellow/Green wire on Elantra, Red/Black wire on Sonata) and ground. With accelerator pedal released, continuity should exist. With accelerator depressed, continuity should not exist. If continuity is not as specified, replace idle switch.

2) Measure power supply voltage from ECM to idle switch. Turn ignition on. Using DVOM, measure voltage between idle switch harness connector terminal No. 1 (Yellow/Green wire on Elantra, Red/Black wire on Sonata) and vehicle ground. Voltage should be 4 volts or more. If voltage is not within specification, turn ignition off. Inspect and repair circuit as needed.

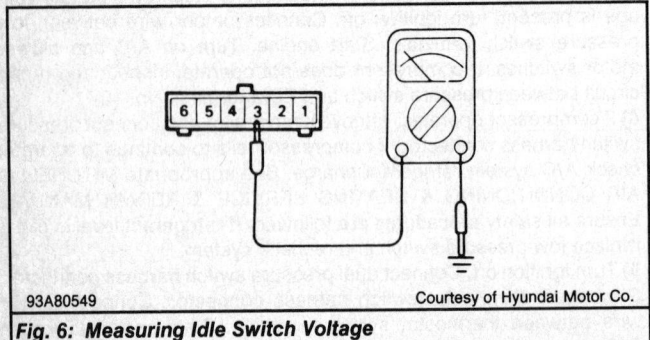

93A80549   Courtesy of Hyundai Motor Co.

Fig. 6: Measuring Idle Switch Voltage

Idle Switch (Sonata V6) – 1) Ensure switch is adjusted correctly. See ON-VEHICLE ADJUSTMENTS article. Disconnect idle switch connector. Check for continuity between terminal No. 2 (Yellow/Red wire) and ground. With accelerator pedal released, continuity should exist. With accelerator depressed, continuity should not exist. If continuity is not as specified, replace idle switch.

2) Measure power supply voltage from ECM to idle switch. Turn ignition on. Using DVOM, measure voltage between idle switch harness connector terminal No. 1 (Yellow/Red) and vehicle ground. Voltage should be 4 volts or more. If voltage is not within specification, turn ignition off.

3) Using ohmmeter, check resistance between idle switch harness connector terminal No. 2 (Yellow/Red wire) and vehicle ground.

4) If continuity does not exist, inspect and repair circuit as needed. If continuity does exist, substitute ECM with known good unit and retest.

Knock Sensor – See SELF-DIAGNOSTICS – SCOUPE article.

Motor (IAC/ISC) Position Sensor – See appropriate SELF-DIAGNOSTICS article.

No. 1 Cylinder TDC Sensor – See appropriate SELF-DIAGNOSTICS article.

Oxygen Sensor – See appropriate SELF-DIAGNOSTICS article.

Power Steering Pressure Switch – 1) Disconnect power steering pressure switch connector, located on power steering pump. Using a DVOM, check for continuity between switch and chassis ground. Continuity should not exist with wheels in straight-ahead position and engine idling. Continuity should exist when wheels are turned.

2) Using a DVOM, with ignition switch in ON position, check for battery voltage at sensor connector terminal. If battery voltage exists, circuit is okay. If battery voltage does not exist, check and repair circuit between switch connector and ECM connector terminal No. 8 (24-pin connector) on Elantra and Sonata (4-cylinder), terminal No. 2 (16-pin connector) on Excel or terminal No. 21 (24-pin connector) on Sonata V6.

Throttle Position Sensor – See appropriate SELF-DIAGNOSTICS article.

Transaxle Range Switch (A/T Models) – 1) Switch is mounted to automatic transaxle, near shift lever mechanism. Ensure switch is adjusted properly. Switch output can be affected by improper adjustment. Measure power supply voltage to switch. Disconnect ECM and inhibitor switch connectors. Turn ignition switch to START position.

2) Measure voltage between vehicle ground and inhibitor switch harness connector terminal No. 3 on Scoupe, terminal No. 11 on all other models. Inhibitor switch wire color is Black/White on Elantra and Sonata V6, Black/Yellow on Excel, Light Green/Black on Scoupe and Yellow/Red on Sonata 4-cylinder. Voltage measured should be battery voltage. If voltage is less than battery voltage, inspect and repair power supply circuit.

3) on all models except Scoupe, use DVOM and measure inhibitor switch terminal input voltage. Connect ECM connector. Ensure inhibitor switch connector is disconnected. Turn ignition switch to ON position. Measure voltage between vehicle ground and inhibitor switch harness connector terminal No. 3 on Scoupe, terminal No. 11 on all other models. Inhibitor switch wire color is Black/White on Elantra and Sonata V6, Black/Yellow on Excel and Yellow/Red on Sonata 4-cylinder. Voltage measured should be battery voltage. If voltage is less than battery voltage, inspect and repair input supply circuit.

4) On all models, use DVOM and measure input voltage of ECM. Turn ignition off. Disconnect ECM connector. Connect inhibitor switch connector. Ensure shift selector lever is in "P" position. Turn ignition switch to START position. Measure voltage between vehicle ground and ECM connector terminal. See ECM INHIBITOR SWITCH INPUT CIRCUIT IDENTIFICATION table. ECM input voltage should be 8 volts or greater. If voltage is within specification, circuit is okay. If voltage is less than 8 volts, inspect and repair circuit as necessary.

ECM TRANSAXLE RANGE SWITCH INPUT CIRCUIT IDENTIFICATION

Application	Wire Color	[1] ECM Terminal No.
Elantra (CA)	Black/Yellow	[2] 11
Elantra (Fed.)	Black/Yellow	[3] 8
Excel	[4] Black/Yellow	[2] 11
Scoupe	Green/White	42
Sonata 4-Cyl.	[5] Black/Red	[3] 8
Sonata V6	[6] Red/Green	[3] 8

[1] – See Figs. 1-5.
[2] – 22-pin connector.
[3] – 10-pin connector.
[4] – Wire color is Black/Green at switch harness connector.
[5] – 16-pin connector.
[6] – Wire color is Black/Yellow at switch harness connector.

Vehicle Speed Sensor – See appropriate SELF-DIAGNOSTICS article.

RELAYS

CAUTION: When applying direct battery voltage, ensure voltage is applied to correct terminal; otherwise, relay damage could result.

MFI Control Relay (Excel) – 1) Remove control relay, located behind glove box. Using an ohmmeter, check resistance between terminals No. 3 and 8 and then terminals No. 2 and 8. *See Fig. 7.* Resistance should be about 95 ohms. Check resistance between terminals No. 6 and 7. Resistance should be about 35 ohms. If resistance is not as specified, replace control relay. If resistance is as specified, go to next step.

2) Connect a 12-volt battery across relay terminals No. 6 (positive) and No. 7 (negative). *See Fig. 7.* Continuity should exist between terminals No. 1 and 4. Disconnect battery voltage from relay. Using an ohmmeter, check for continuity between terminals No. 1 and 3. Continuity should not exist. Connect 12-volt battery across terminals No. 5 and 7. Continuity should exist between terminals No. 1 and 3.

3) Disconnect battery voltage from relay. Check for continuity between terminals No. 7 and 5 and then reverse leads. Continuity should exist in one direction only. If results are not as specified, replace control relay.

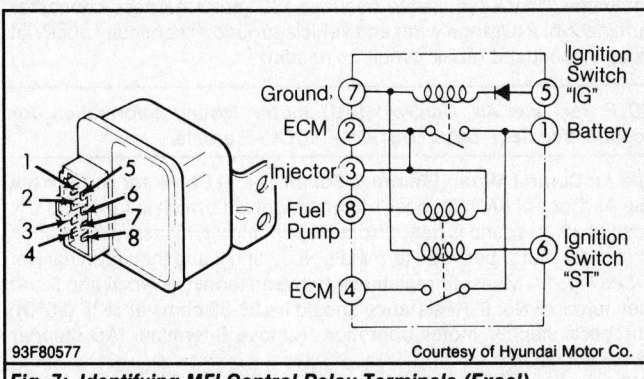

Ground (7) · ECM (2) · Injector (3) · Fuel Pump (8) · ECM (4) · Ignition Switch "IG" (5) · Battery (1) · Ignition Switch "ST" (6)

93F80577   Courtesy of Hyundai Motor Co.

Fig. 7: Identifying MFI Control Relay Terminals (Excel)

4) Check ignition switch supply voltage of control relay. Disconnect control relay connector. Turn ignition on. Using DVOM, measure voltage between terminal No. 5 (Black/White wire) of relay harness connector and vehicle ground. If voltage measured is not battery voltage, inspect and repair circuit between ignition switch and control relay.

5) Check continuity of control relay ground circuit. Turn ignition off. Using ohmmeter, check continuity between control relay harness connector terminal No. 7 (Black wire) and vehicle ground. If continuity does not exist, inspect and repair circuit between control relay and vehicle ground.

6) Check battery supply voltage of control relay. Using DVOM, measure voltage between terminal No. 1 (White/Blue wire) of relay harness connector and vehicle ground. If battery voltage is not present, inspect and repair circuit between battery and control relay.

7) Check continuity of circuit between control relay and ECM. Disconnect ECM connector. Check continuity between control relay harness connector terminal No. 2 (Red wire) and ECM terminals No. 2 and 15 of 26-pin connector. *See Fig. 4.*

8) If continuity exists, harness is okay. If continuity does not exist, inspect and repair circuits between control relay harness connector and ECM.

MFI Control Relay (Elantra & Sonata 4-Cylinder) – 1) Remove control relay, located under right side of dashboard, near blower motor housing on Sonata. Relay on Elantra is behind driver's dash panel next to hood release lever. Apply battery voltage across terminals No. 6 (positive) and No. 8 (negative) while checking voltage on terminals No. 1 and 2 for Sonata, or terminal No. 1 on Elantra. *See Fig. 8.* Replace relay if battery voltage does not exist.

2) Apply battery voltage across terminals No. 7 (positive) and No. 10 (negative) while checking continuity between terminals No. 3 and 4. Replace relay if continuity does not exist.

3) Apply battery voltage across terminals No. 3 (positive) and No. 9 (negative) while checking voltage on terminal No. 4. Replace relay if battery voltage does not exist.

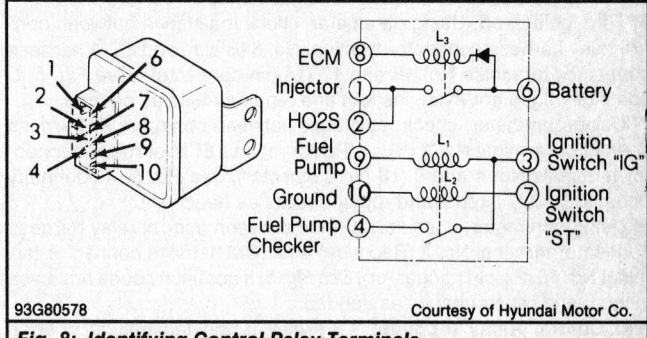

ECM (8) · Injector (1) · HO2S (2) · Fuel Pump (9) · Ground (10) · Fuel Pump Checker (4) · Battery (6) · Ignition Switch "IG" (3) · Ignition Switch "ST" (7)

93G80578   Courtesy of Hyundai Motor Co.

Fig. 8: Identifying Control Relay Terminals (Elantra & Sonata 4-Cylinder)

4) Disconnect ECM connector. Turn ignition on. Using DVOM, measure voltage between ECM harness connector terminal No. 6 (10-pin connector) (terminal No. 22 on Calif. Elantra – 22-pin connector), and vehicle ground. If voltage is less than battery voltage, inspect and repair circuit as needed.

5) Disconnect control relay harness connector. Using DVOM, measure voltage between control relay harness connector terminal No. 6 (White/Blue wire) and vehicle ground. If voltage is less than battery voltage, inspect and repair circuit as needed.

6) Turn ignition off. Using ohmmeter, check resistance between control relay harness connector terminal No. 8 (Brown/Red wire on Elantra, Black/White wire on Sonata V6, Brown/White on Sonata 4-cyl.) and ECM harness connector terminals No. 12 and 15 (18-pin connector), (terminal No. 1 on Calif. Elantra – 18-pin connector). *See Figs. 2 and 3.* If continuity does not exist, inspect and repair circuits as needed.

7) Using ohmmeter, check resistance between control relay harness connector terminal No. 1 (Red wire) and ECM harness connector terminals No. 4 and 9 (10-pin connector) (terminals No. 2 and 5 on Calif. Elantra – 26-pin connector). *See Figs. 2 and 3.* If continuity does not exist, inspect and repair circuits as needed.

MFI Control Relay (Sonata V6) – 1) Remove control relay, located under right side of dashboard, near blower motor housing. Apply battery voltage across terminals No. 6 (positive) and No. 8 (negative) while checking voltage on terminals No. 1 and 2. *See Fig. 9.* Replace relay if battery voltage does not exist.

2) Apply battery voltage across terminals No. 7 (positive) and No. 10 (negative) while checking continuity between terminals No. 3 and 4. Replace relay if continuity does not exist.

3) Apply battery voltage across terminals No. 3 (positive) and No. 9 (negative) while checking voltage on terminal No. 4. Replace relay if battery voltage does not exist.

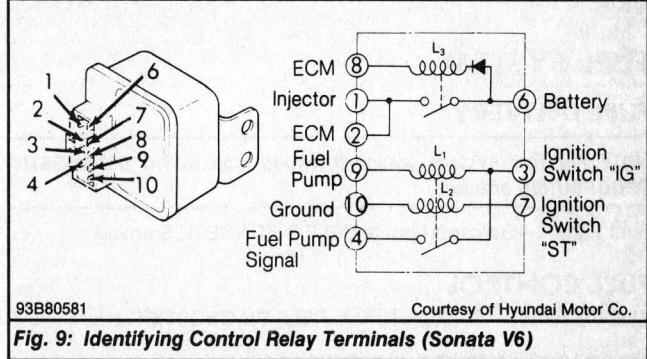

ECM (8) · Injector (1) · ECM (2) · Fuel Pump (9) · Ground (10) · Fuel Pump Signal (4) · Battery (6) · Ignition Switch "IG" (3) · Ignition Switch "ST" (7)

93B80581   Courtesy of Hyundai Motor Co.

Fig. 9: Identifying Control Relay Terminals (Sonata V6)

4) Disconnect ECM connector. Turn ignition on. Using DVOM, measure voltage between ECM harness connector terminal No. 6 (10-pin connector) and vehicle ground. If voltage is less than battery voltage, inspect and repair circuit as needed.

5) Disconnect control relay harness connector. Using DVOM, measure voltage between control relay harness connector terminal No. 6 (White/Blue wire) and vehicle ground. If voltage is less than battery voltage, inspect and repair circuit as needed.

6) Turn ignition off. Using ohmmeter, check resistance between control relay harness connector terminal No. 8 (Black) and ECM harness connector terminals No. 16 and 17 (18-pin connector). See Fig. 5. If continuity does not exist, inspect and repair circuits as needed.

7) Using ohmmeter, check resistance between control relay harness connector terminal No. 1 (Black/Red wire) and ECM harness connector terminals No. 4 and 9 (18-pin connector). See Fig. 5. If continuity does not exist, inspect and repair circuits as needed.

8) Using ohmmeter, check resistance between control relay harness connector terminal No. 2 (Red wire) and ECM harness connector terminal No. 10 (24-pin connector). See Fig. 5. If continuity does not exist, inspect and repair circuits as needed.

MPI Control Relay (Scoupe) – 1) Relay is located behind driver's dash panel, near ECM. Disconnect harness connector. Removal of relay may assist in testing. Apply battery voltage to terminal No. 4 (positive) and ground terminal No. 2 (negative). See Fig. 10.

2) Using a DVOM, check for continuity between terminal No. 1 and terminal No. 5. Continuity should exist. Check for continuity between terminal No. 5 and terminal No. 3. Replace relay if continuity does not exist.

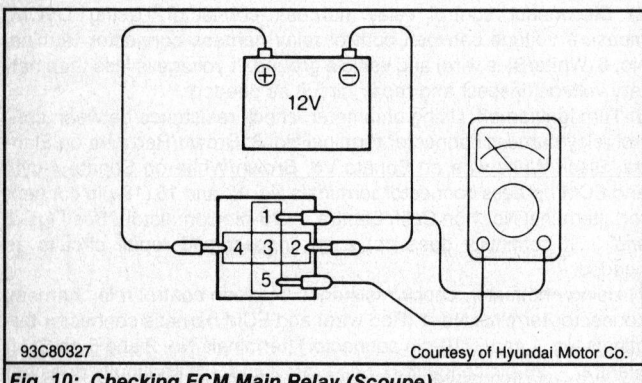

Fig. 10: Checking ECM Main Relay (Scoupe)

93C80327   Courtesy of Hyundai Motor Co.

3) Disconnect relay harness connector. Using DVOM, measure voltage between relay harness connector terminals No. 4 and 5 (White/Blue wires) and vehicle ground. If battery voltage is not present, inspect and repair circuit.

4) Ensure ignition is off. Disconnect ECM harness connector. Connect jumper wire between ECM harness connector terminal No. 36 and vehicle ground. See Fig. 1. Using ohmmeter, check resistance between relay harness connector terminal No. 2 (Black/Green wire) and vehicle ground. If continuity does not exist, inspect and repair circuit as needed.

Power Transistor – See BASIC DIAGNOSTIC PROCEDURES article.

FUEL SYSTEM

FUEL DELIVERY

NOTE: For fuel system pressure testing, see BASIC DIAGNOSTIC PROCEDURES article.

Fuel Pump – See appropriate SELF-DIAGNOSTICS article.

FUEL CONTROL

Fuel Injectors – See appropriate SELF-DIAGNOSTICS article.

IDLE CONTROL SYSTEM

CAUTION: Apply only 6 volts DC or less to ISC motor connector. Higher voltage could cause ISC motor gears to lock up.

NOTE: If after all testing procedures have been completed, system is still inoperative, substitute ECM with known good unit and retest.

Idle Speed Control Motor (Excel) – 1) Disconnect Idle Speed Control (ISC) motor connector. Check motor coil continuity between motor terminals. Resistance should be 5-70 ohms at 68°F (20°C). If resistance is not as specified, an open or short exists in motor coil. Replace ISC servo assembly.

2) Connect 6 volts DC (four 1.5-volt DC batteries) between ISC motor terminals to operate ISC motor. DO NOT apply more than 6 volts. If motor does not operate, replace ISC motor assembly.

ISC Motor Harness Inspection (Excel) – 1) Check continuity of circuits between ISC motor and ECM. Ensure ignition is off. Disconnect ECM harness connector. Connect jumper wire between ECM harness connector terminal No. 23 (Blue/Yellow wire, 26-pin connector) and vehicle ground. See Fig. 4.

2) Using ohmmeter, check resistance between ISC motor harness connector terminal No. 1 (Red wire) and vehicle ground. If continuity does not exist, inspect and repair circuit as needed.

3) Move jumper wire between ECM harness connector terminal No. 10 (Blue/White wire, 26-pin connector) and vehicle ground. Using ohmmeter, check resistance between ISC motor harness connector terminal No. 2 (Orange wire) and vehicle ground. If continuity does not exist, inspect and repair circuit as needed.

NOTE: For Idle Air Control (IAC) motor testing information for Scoupe, see SELF-DIAGNOSTICS – SCOUPE article.

Idle Air Control Motor (Elantra & Sonata) – 1) Check for sound from Idle Air Control (IAC) stepper motor as ignition switch is turned to ON position. If no sound is heard from stepper motor, measure resistance at stepper motor between terminals No. 2 and 3 and then terminal No. 1. See Fig. 11. Measure resistance between terminals No. 4 and 5 and then terminal No. 6. Resistance should be 28-33 ohms at 68°F (20°C). To check stepper motor operation, remove 6-terminal IAC stepper motor connector.

2) Connect positive lead of 6-volt battery to ISC motor connector terminals No. 2 and 5. Connect negative lead to terminals No. 1 and 4, terminals No. 3 and 4, terminals No. 3 and 6, terminals No. 1 and 6, and terminals No. 1 and 4. Repeat procedure in reverse sequence. If stepper motor moves as voltage is applied to each pair of terminals, stepper motor is operating correctly.

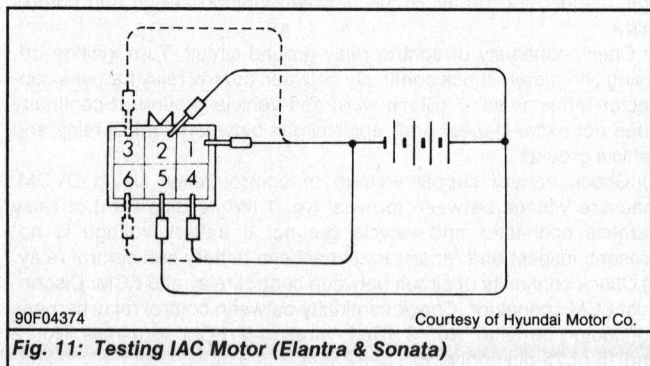

Fig. 11: Testing IAC Motor (Elantra & Sonata)

90F04374   Courtesy of Hyundai Motor Co.

IGNITION SYSTEM

NOTE: For basic ignition checks, see BASIC DIAGNOSTIC PROCEDURES article.

EMISSION SYSTEMS & SUB-SYSTEMS

EXHAUST GAS RECIRCULATION (EGR)

EGR Valve – Remove valve and inspect for carbon deposits. Ensure valve is not sticking. Apply vacuum to valve and check for leaking diaphragm. Check airflow through valve.

EGR Control Solenoid Valve (Exc. Elantra Federal) – **1)** Label and disconnect vacuum hoses and wiring harness from solenoid valve. Connect a hand-held vacuum pump to vacuum nipple where Red or Green-striped vacuum hose was connected, and apply vacuum.

2) While applying battery voltage to one terminal and grounding the other, ensure vacuum holds. Ensure vacuum is released when battery voltage is discontinued.

3) Using an ohmmeter, measure resistance between solenoid valve terminals. Resistance should be 36-44 ohms at 68°F (20°C). Replace solenoid if resistance is not within specification.

EGR Thermovalve (Elantra Federal) – Disconnect vacuum hoses from thermovalve, and connect a hand-held vacuum pump to thermovalve nipple. Vacuum should release at 122°F (50°C) or less. Vacuum should hold at 176°F (80°C) or more.

FUEL EVAPORATION

System Test – 1) Disconnect Red-striped vacuum hose between throttle body and purge control solenoid valve at throttle body. Connect a hand-held vacuum pump to disconnected vacuum hose. Plug nipple on throttle body where vacuum hose was removed.

2) With engine at idle and engine coolant temperature at 140°F (60°C) or less on 4-cylinder or 104°F (40°C) or less on V6, apply 7.3 in. Hg vacuum. Vacuum should hold. Raise engine speed to 3000 RPM, and again apply 7.3 in. Hg vacuum. Vacuum should hold.

3) With engine at idle and coolant temperature at 158°F (70°C) or more on 4-cylinder or 176°F (80°C) or more on V6, apply 7.3 in. Hg vacuum. Vacuum should hold. Turn engine off. Start engine, and apply vacuum, within 3 minutes of starting engine. Vacuum should bleed down.

4) With engine running for more than 3 minutes after starting, raise engine speed to 3000 RPM and apply 7.3 in. Hg. Vacuum should hold momentarily and then bleed down.

Purge Control Solenoid Valve – 1) Disconnect Red-striped vacuum hose from purge control solenoid valve and detach harness connector. Connect vacuum pump to nipple where Red-striped vacuum hose was removed. Apply vacuum and battery voltage to valve. With battery voltage applied, vacuum should release. With battery voltage disconnected, vacuum should hold.

2) Using an ohmmeter, measure resistance between solenoid valve terminals. At 68°F (20°C), resistance should be 45 ohms on Scoupe, or 36-44 ohms on all other models.

POSITIVE CRANKCASE VENTILATION (PCV)

PCV Valve – Remove PCV valve. Plunger should rattle freely when valve is shaken. Ensure air flows freely when blown through cylinder head side of PCV valve. Ensure air flows with difficulty when blown through intake manifold side of PCV valve.

1994 ENGINE PERFORMANCE
Sensor Operating Range Charts

Elantra, Excel, Scoupe, Sonata

INTRODUCTION

Sensor operating range information can help determine if a sensor is out of calibration. An out-of-calibration sensor may not set a trouble code, but it may cause driveability problems.

NOTE: Unless stated otherwise in test procedure, perform all tests using a Digital Volt-Ohmmeter (DVOM) with a minimum 10-megohm input impedance.

Airflow Sensor – Airflow sensor testing requires use of multi-use tester. See SELF-DIAGNOSTICS article.

Barometric Pressure Sensor – Barometric pressure sensor testing requires use of multi-use tester. See SELF-DIAGNOSTICS article.

COOLANT TEMPERATURE SENSOR RESISTANCE TEST [1]

Temperature °F (°C)	Ohms
Elantra, Excel & Sonata	
32 (0)	5900
68 (20)	2500
104 (40)	1100
176 (80)	300
Scoupe	
32 (0)	5180-6600
68 (20)	2270-2730
104 (40)	1059-1281
176 (80)	290-354
194 (90)	217-269

[1] – Measure resistance between sensor terminals.

INTAKE AIR TEMPERATURE SENSOR RESISTANCE TEST [1]

Temperature °F (C)	Ohms
32 (0)	6000
68 (20)	2700
176 (80)	400

[1] – Measure resistance between terminals No. 4 and 6. *See Fig. 1.*

THROTTLE POSITION SENSOR (TPS) TESTS

Throttle Position	Specification
Closed	
Scoupe	1200-2800 Ohms
Except Scoupe	3500-6500 Ohms
Idle Position To WOT	
Scoupe	250-600 To 4250-4600 mV
Except Scoupe	450-550 To 4500-5500 mV

TPS Testing Terminals [1]

Closed Throttle Resistance	
Elantra, Excel & Sonata	1 & 4
Scoupe	2 & 3
Closed to WOT Voltage	
Elantra, Excel, Scoupe & Sonata	1 & 3

[1] – See TPS TERMINAL IDENTIFICATION table. *See Fig. 2.*

TPS TERMINAL IDENTIFICATION

Application	Terminal No.	Wire Color
Elantra, Excel & Sonata 2.0L	1	Black
	3	Lt. Green/Yellow
	4	Green/Red
Scoupe		
Non-Turbo	1	Green/Red
	2	Yellow
	3	Black
Turbo	1	Black
	2	Black
	3	Green/Red
Sonata 3.0L	1	Green/Black
	3	Green/White
	4	Green/Red

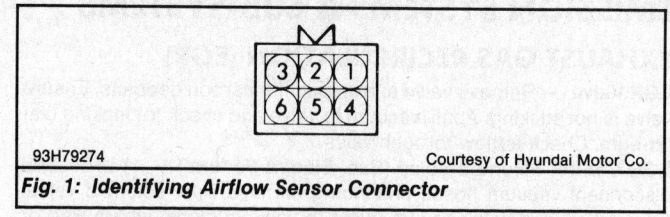

93H79274   Courtesy of Hyundai Motor Co.
Fig. 1: Identifying Airflow Sensor Connector

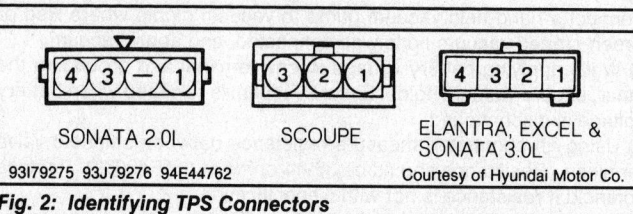

SONATA 2.0L   SCOUPE   ELANTRA, EXCEL & SONATA 3.0L
93I79275 93J79276 94E44762   Courtesy of Hyundai Motor Co.
Fig. 2: Identifying TPS Connectors

Crank Angle Sensor – Crank angle sensor testing requires use of multi-use tester. See SELF-DIAGNOSTICS article.

Top Dead Center (TDC) Sensor – Top dead center sensor testing requires use of multi-use tester. See SELF-DIAGNOSTICS article.

EGR Temperature Sensor – EGR temperature sensor testing requires use of multi-use tester. See SELF-DIAGNOSTICS article.

Vehicle Speed Sensor – Vehicle speed sensor testing requires use of multi-use tester. See SELF-DIAGNOSTICS article.

OXYGEN SENSOR (O2S) TEST

Condition	Specification
Race Engine	[1] 0.6 Volt Minimum
Sensor At 752°F (400°C)	[2] 30 Or More Ohms

[1] – On all models except Scoupe, measure voltage between sensor terminals No. 1 and 2. No information is available on Scoupe model. *See Fig. 4.*

[2] – On all models except Scoupe, measure between terminals No. 3 and 4. On Scoupe, measure between terminals No. 1 and 2.

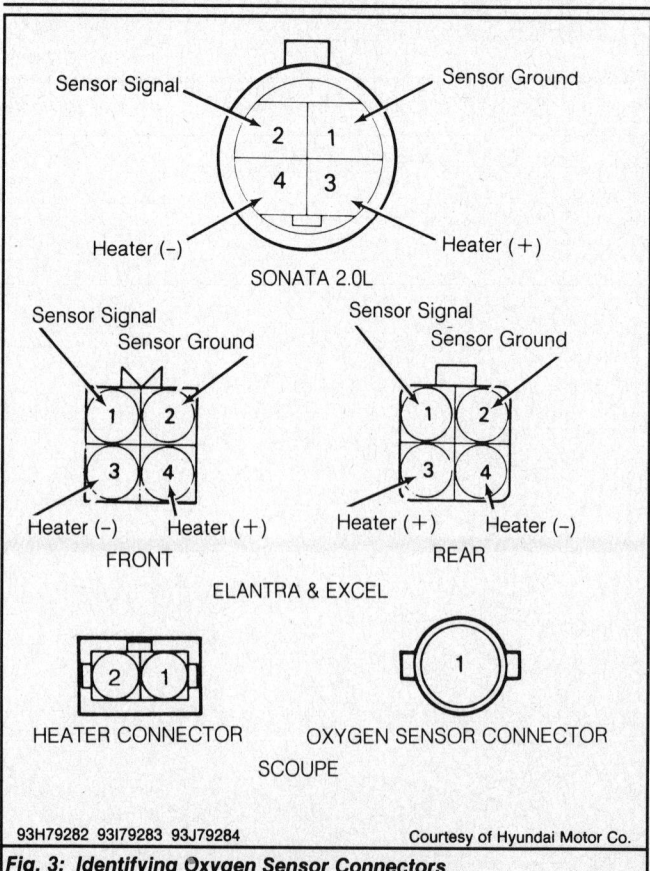

93H79282 93I79283 93J79284   Courtesy of Hyundai Motor Co.
Fig. 3: Identifying Oxygen Sensor Connectors

Elantra, Excel, Scoupe, Sonata

INTRODUCTION

NOTE: Manufacturer does not provide information for Scoupe.

This article contains underhood views or schematics of vacuum hose routing. Use these vacuum diagrams during the visual inspection in BASIC DIAGNOSTIC PROCEDURES article. This will assist in identifying improperly routed vacuum hoses which cause driveability and/or computer-indicated malfunctions.

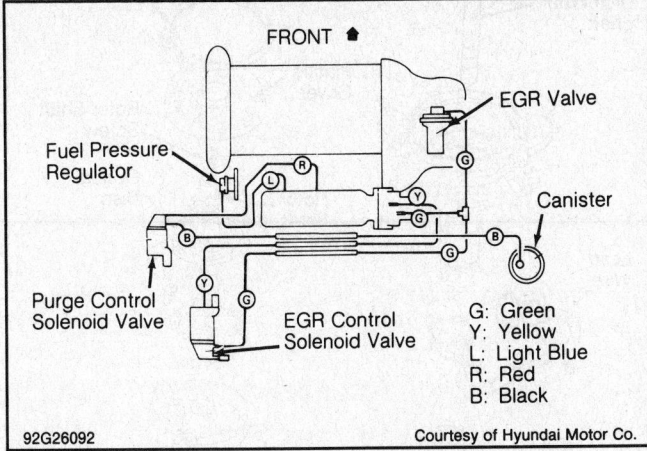

Fig. 1: Vacuum Diagram (Elantra – California)

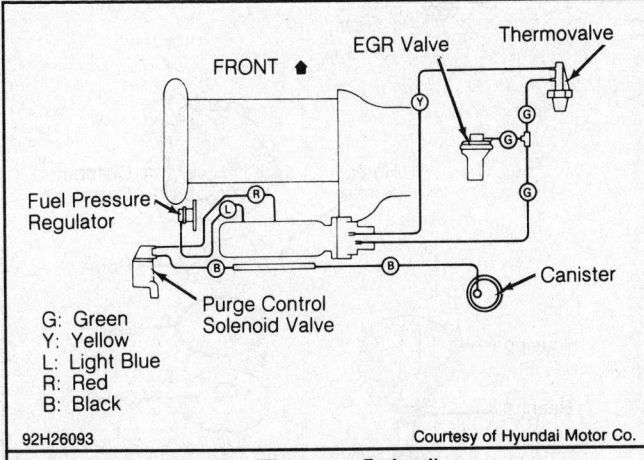

Fig. 2: Vacuum Diagram (Elantra – Federal)

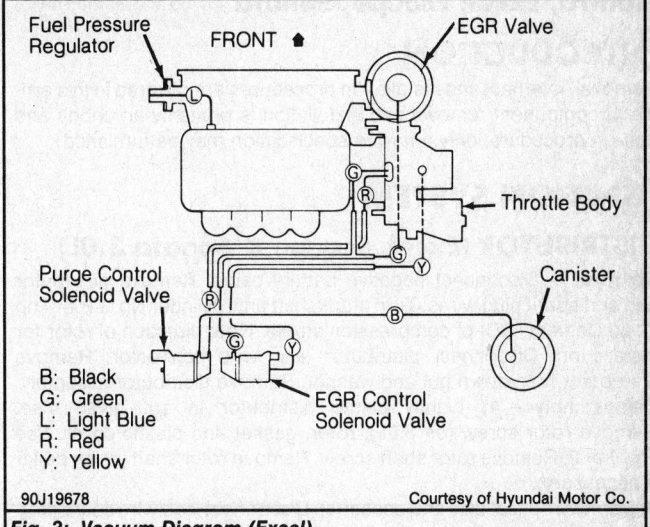

Fig. 3: Vacuum Diagram (Excel)

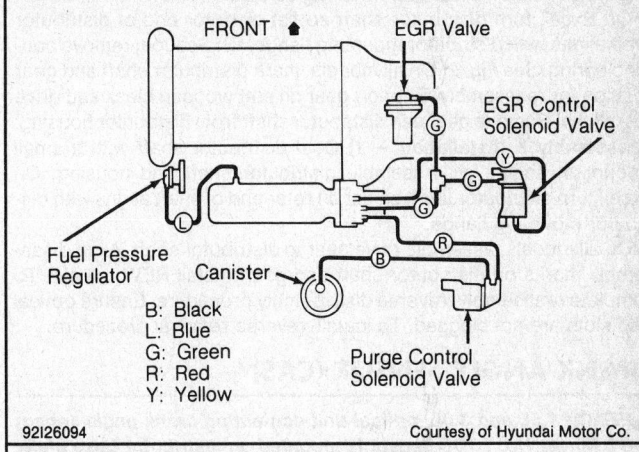

Fig. 4: Vacuum Diagram (Sonata 2.0L DOHC)

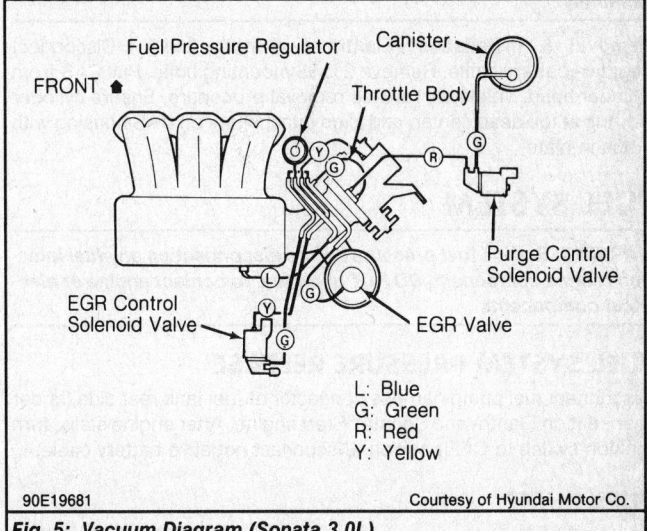

Fig. 5: Vacuum Diagram (Sonata 3.0L)

1994 ENGINE PERFORMANCE
Removal, Overhaul & Installation

Elantra, Excel, Scoupe, Sonata

INTRODUCTION

Removal, overhaul and installation procedures are covered in this article. If component removal and installation is primarily an unbolt and bolt-on procedure, only a torque specification may be furnished.

IGNITION SYSTEM

DISTRIBUTOR (Excel, Scoupe & Sonata 3.0L)

Removal – Disconnect negative battery cable. Remove distributor cap and spark plug wires. Turn crankshaft until cylinder No. 1 is at Top Dead Center (TDC) of compression stroke. Note direction of rotor for installation. Disconnect distributor lead wire connector. Remove distributor hold-down nut and washer. Remove distributor assembly.

Disassembly – 1) Lightly clamp distributor in soft-jawed vise. Remove rotor screw (on 3.0L), rotor, gasket and plastic cover. *See Fig. 1 or 2.* Remove rotor shaft screw. Remove rotor shaft (using puller if necessary).

2) Remove optical disc and spacer(s). Disconnect lead wire connector. Remove base plate mounting screws. Lift out base plate and optical unit. Remove distributor shaft bearing screws.

3) On Excel, turn distributor shaft so flat on rotor end of distributor shaft aligns with distributor mounting flange. On Scoupe, remove coupling spring. *See Fig. 2.* On all models, mark distributor shaft and gear position for reassembly. Support gear on soft wooden block and drive out roll pin. Remove gear and distributor shaft from distributor housing.

Reassembly & Installation – 1) Coat distributor shaft with a small amount of engine oil. Assemble distributor shaft and housing. On Excel, turn distributor shaft so flat on rotor end of shaft aligns with distributor mounting flange.

2) On all models, assemble drive gear to distributor shaft. Align disassembly marks on distributor shaft and gear. Install NEW roll pin. To complete reassembly, reverse disassembly procedure. Ensure optical disc slots are not clogged. To install, reverse removal procedure.

CRANK ANGLE SENSOR (CAS)

NOTE: On 1.5L and 3.0L, optical unit containing crank angle sensor and cylinder No. 1 TDC sensor is mounted on distributor base plate. Optical unit is removed and replaced with base plate as single assembly.

Removal & Installation (Elantra & Sonata 2.0L) – Disconnect negative battery cable. Remove 2 CAS mounting bolts. Pull CAS from cylinder head. To install, reverse removal procedure. Ensure cylinder No. 1 is at top dead center, and align punch mark on CAS housing with notch in plate.

FUEL SYSTEM

WARNING: Relieve fuel pressure before disconnecting any fuel injection-related component. DO NOT allow fuel to contact engine or electrical components.

FUEL SYSTEM PRESSURE RELEASE

Disconnect fuel pump harness connector at fuel tank rear side (under rear seat on Elantra and Sonata). Start engine. After engine stalls, turn ignition switch to OFF position. Disconnect negative battery cable.

FUEL PUMP

Removal – 1) Release fuel pressure. See FUEL SYSTEM PRESSURE RELEASE. Disconnect negative battery cable. Remove fuel tank cap. Remove drain plug and drain fuel from tank. Cover high pressure hose connection with shop towels to prevent fuel leakage. Disconnect high pressure hose at fuel tank. Disconnect vapor and return hoses, filler hose and fuel pump connector.

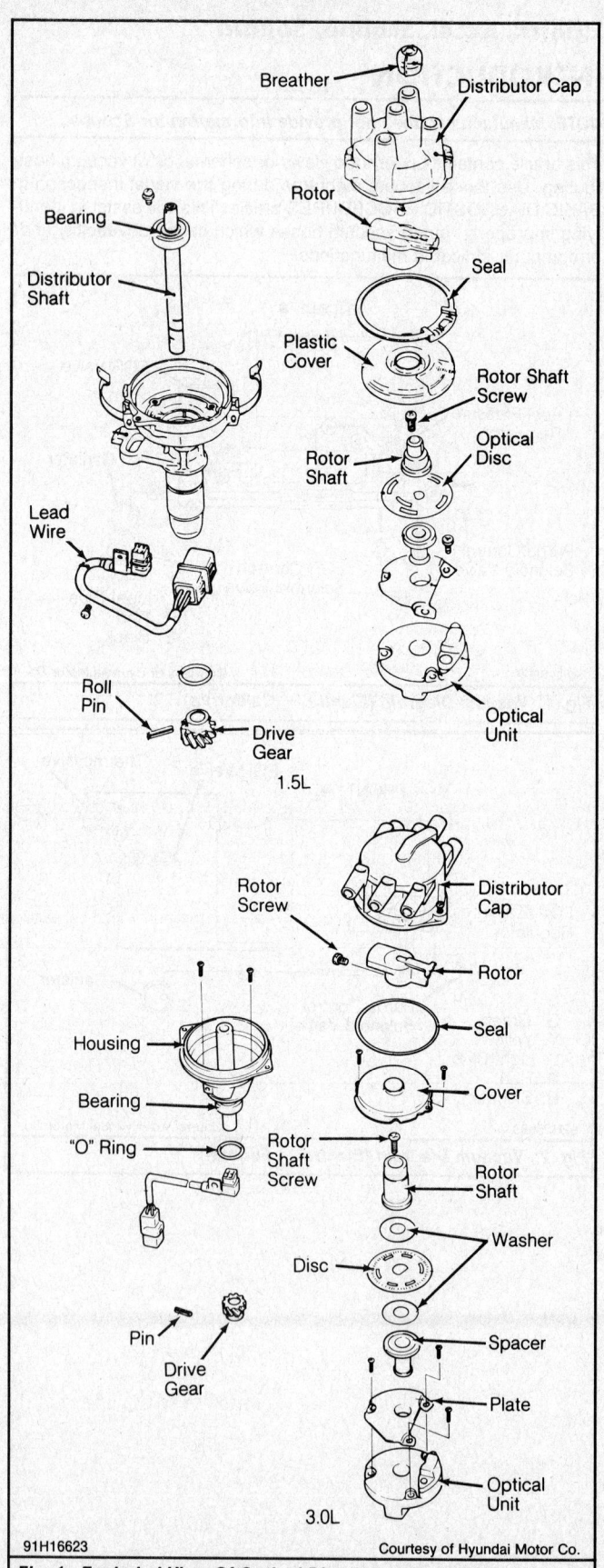

1.5L

3.0L

91H16623   Courtesy of Hyundai Motor Co.

Fig. 1: Exploded View Of Optical Distributor Assembly (Excel & Sonata 3.0L)

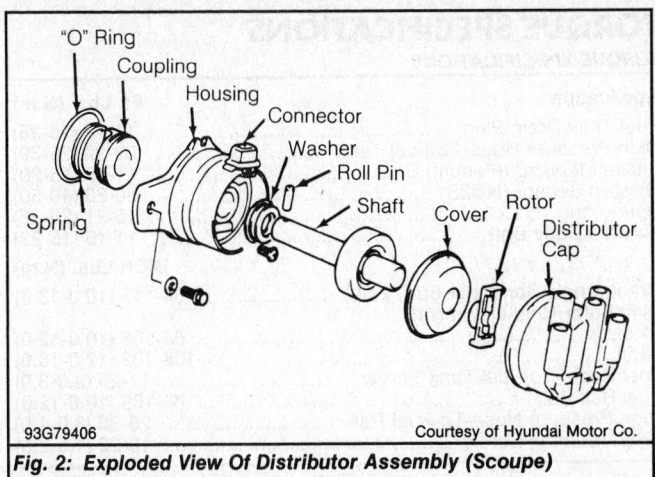

Fig. 2: Exploded View Of Distributor Assembly (Scoupe)

2) Support fuel tank with transmission jack, and remove tank support straps. Lower fuel tank, and remove fuel pump-to-fuel tank screws. Remove fuel pump support bolt on lower side of fuel tank. Remove fuel pump assembly from fuel tank.

Installation – Install fuel pump support bolt first. Use care not to pinch "O" ring. To complete installation, reverse removal procedure.

FUEL RAIL & INJECTORS

Removal – Release fuel pressure. See FUEL SYSTEM PRESSURE RELEASE. Reconnect fuel pump harness connector. On 3.0L, remove intake manifold (plenum). On all models, disconnect high pressure fuel hose while covering fitting using shop towel. Unplug fuel injector harness. Remove fuel rail attaching bolts. Remove fuel rail with fuel injectors and pressure regulator attached. Rotate injector while pulling outward to remove from fuel rail. *See Fig. 3 or 4.*

Installation – **1)** Lightly coat NEW injector "O" rings (fuel rail side) with fuel. Install NEW insulator in intake manifold. Rotate injector while pushing into fuel rail. If injector does not turn smoothly, remove injector and check "O" ring for binding.

2) Lightly coat NEW injector "O" rings (intake manifold side) with fuel. Position fuel rail assembly over insulators. Install injectors in intake manifold. Ensure injectors rotate smoothly. If injectors do not rotate smoothly, check "O" ring for binding.

3) Bolt fuel rail assembly to intake manifold. Connect high pressure fuel hose to fuel rail. With ignition on and engine off, check for fuel leaks before starting engine. To complete installation, reverse removal procedure. See TORQUE SPECIFICATIONS.

OXYGEN SENSOR (HO2S)

Removal & Installation – 1) On 1.5L Scoupe, 1.6L, 1.8L and 2.0L, HO2S sensor is mounted in exhaust manifold. On Excel models, front sensor is mounted in exhaust pipe in front of catalytic converter. Rear sensor is between converter and muffler. On 3.0L, HO2S sensor is mounted in exhaust pipe in front of catalytic converter. On all models, HO2S sensor has a permanent pigtail which must be protected from damage when removing sensor. Ensure sensor is free of contaminants. DO NOT use any cleaning solvents.

2) Ensure exhaust system is cool before removing HO2S sensor, or thread damage may occur. Disconnect negative battery cable and HO2S sensor connector. Remove HO2S sensor.

3) To install, reverse removal procedure. Apply anti-seize compound to HO2S sensor threads. Tighten to specification. See TORQUE SPECIFICATIONS. Install negative battery cable.

THROTTLE BODY

Removal – 1) Disconnect negative battery cable. Drain engine coolant so level is below throttle body. Disconnect accelerator cable from throttle valve lever and cable bracket.

2) Disconnect throttle position sensor connector. Label and disconnect all vacuum hoses from throttle body. Disconnect engine coolant hoses from throttle body. Remove throttle body from intake manifold.

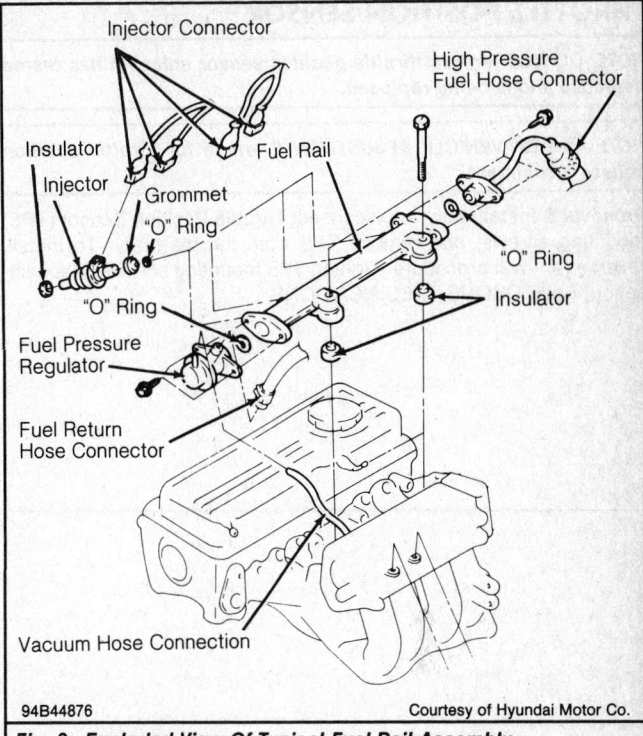

Fig. 3: Exploded View Of Typical Fuel Rail Assembly (4-Cylinder)

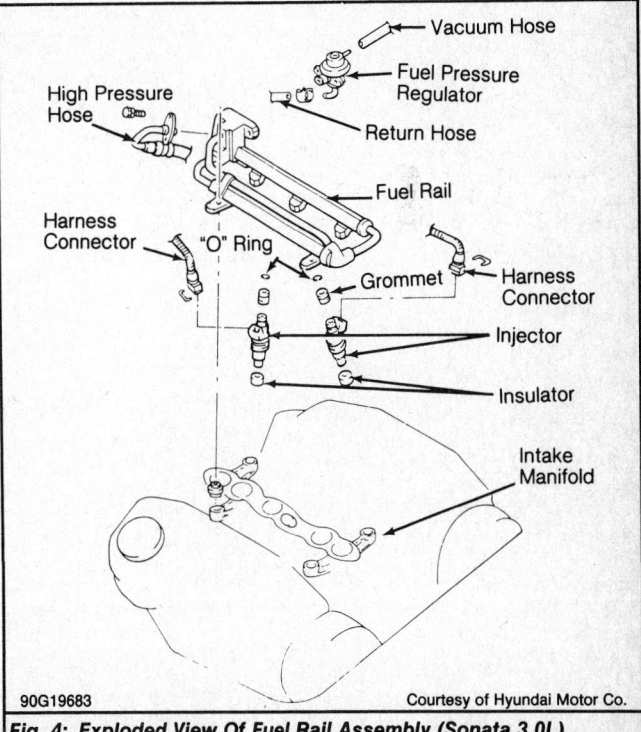

Fig. 4: Exploded View Of Fuel Rail Assembly (Sonata 3.0L)

Cleaning & Inspection – 1) Clean all components with solvent except throttle position sensor and IAC servo assembly.

2) Check for restrictions in vacuum ports and passages. Blow out using compressed air. DO NOT remove throttle valve.

Installation – Using new gasket, install throttle body on intake manifold (plenum). Tighten mounting bolts and nuts to specification. See TORQUE SPECIFICATIONS. After installing accelerator cable, hold exposed portion of cable at center and move cable up and down to ensure slight amount of play is available. Refill cooling system.

THROTTLE POSITION SENSOR

NOTE: DO NOT remove throttle position sensor unless it has tested defective and is being replaced.

NOTE: See ON-VEHICLE ADJUSTMENTS article for throttle position sensor adjustment.

Removal & Installation – Disconnect Throttle Position Sensor (TPS) mounting screws, and remove TPS from throttle body. To install, reverse removal procedure. Tighten TPS mounting screws to specification. See TORQUE SPECIFICATIONS.

TORQUE SPECIFICATIONS
TORQUE SPECIFICATIONS

Application	Ft. Lbs. (N.m)
Fuel Tank Drain Plug	11-18 (15-25)
High Pressure Hose-To-Fuel Tank	22-29 (29-39)
Intake Manifold (Plenum) Bolt	11-15 (15-20)
Oxygen Sensor (HO2S)	30-36 (40-50)
Spark Plug	15-21 (20-28)
Throttle Body Bolt	11-16 (15-22)
	INCH Lbs. (N.m)
Crank Angle Sensor (1.6L & 2.0L)	84-115 (10.0-13.0)
Distributor Hold-Down Nut	
1.5L	84-108 (10.0-12.0)
3.0L	108-192 (12.0-16.0)
Fuel Pump-To-Fuel Tank Screw	17-26 (2.0-3.0)
Fuel Rail Bolt	84-108 (10.0-12.0)
High Pressure Hose-To-Fuel Rail	26-36 (3.0-4.0)
TPS Mounting Screw	13-22 (1.5-2.5)

Elantra, Excel, Scoupe, Sonata

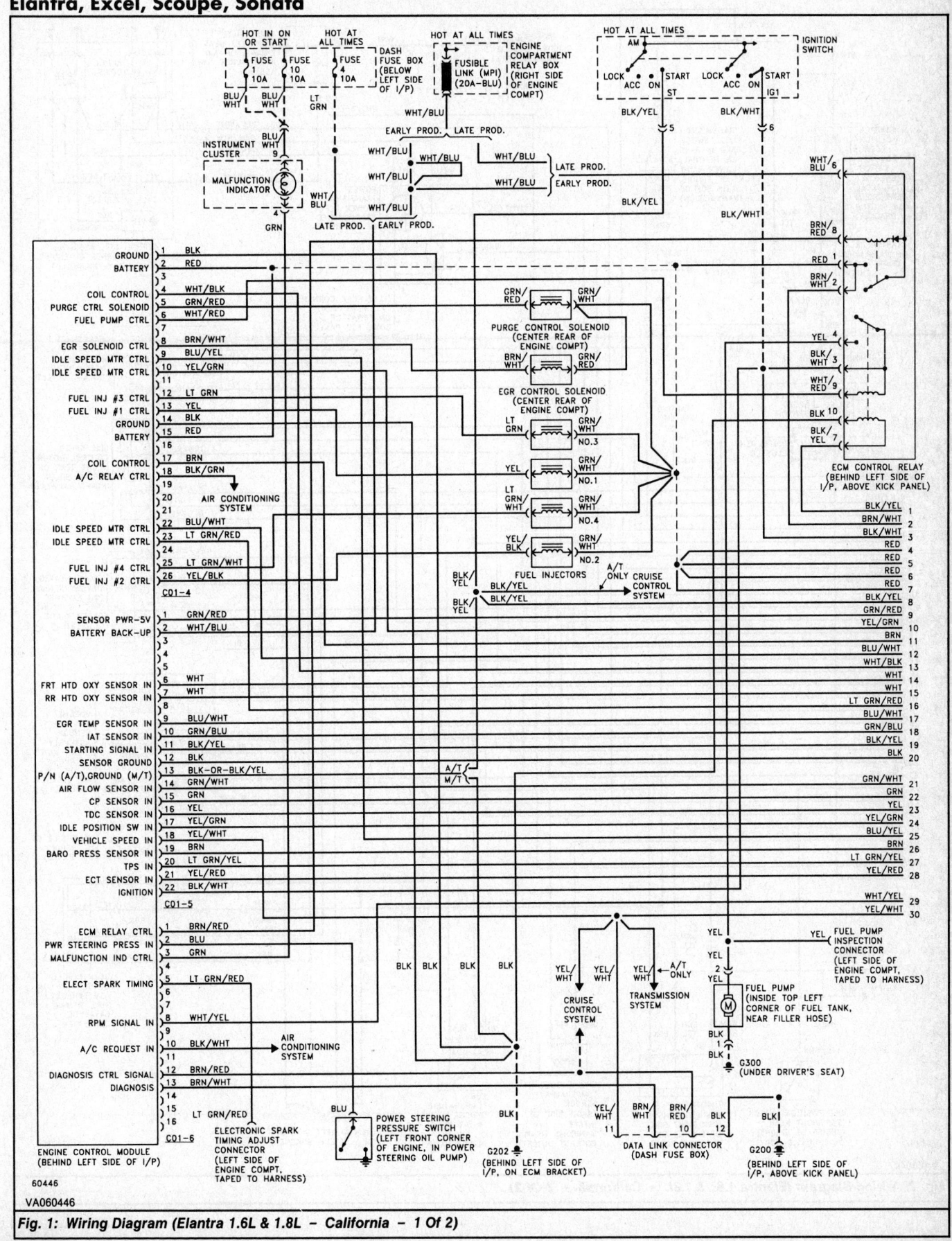

Fig. 1: Wiring Diagram (Elantra 1.6L & 1.8L – California – 1 Of 2)

60446

VA060446

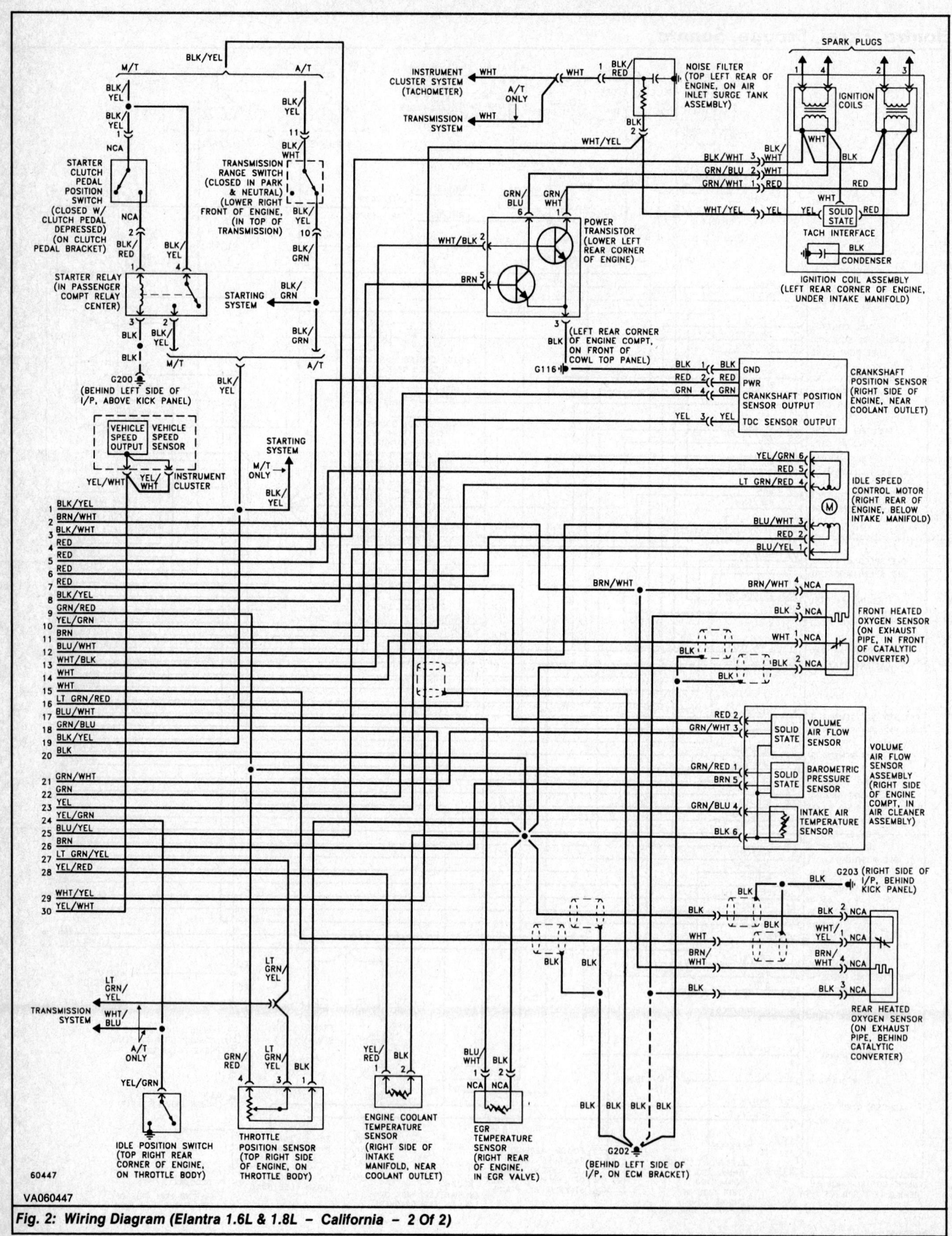

Fig. 2: Wiring Diagram (Elantra 1.6L & 1.8L – California – 2 Of 2)

VA060447

60447

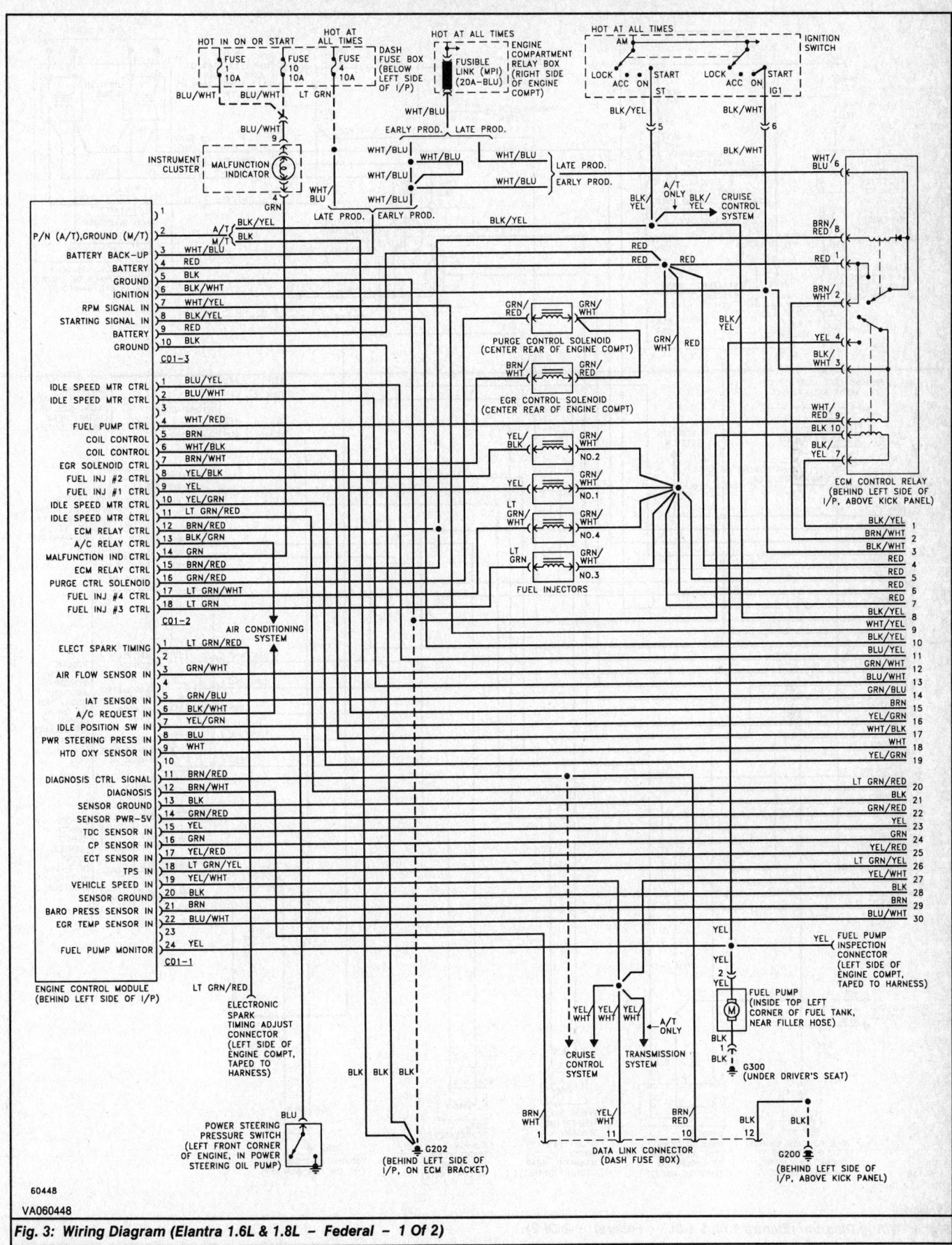

Fig. 3: Wiring Diagram (Elantra 1.6L & 1.8L – Federal – 1 Of 2)

60448

VA060448

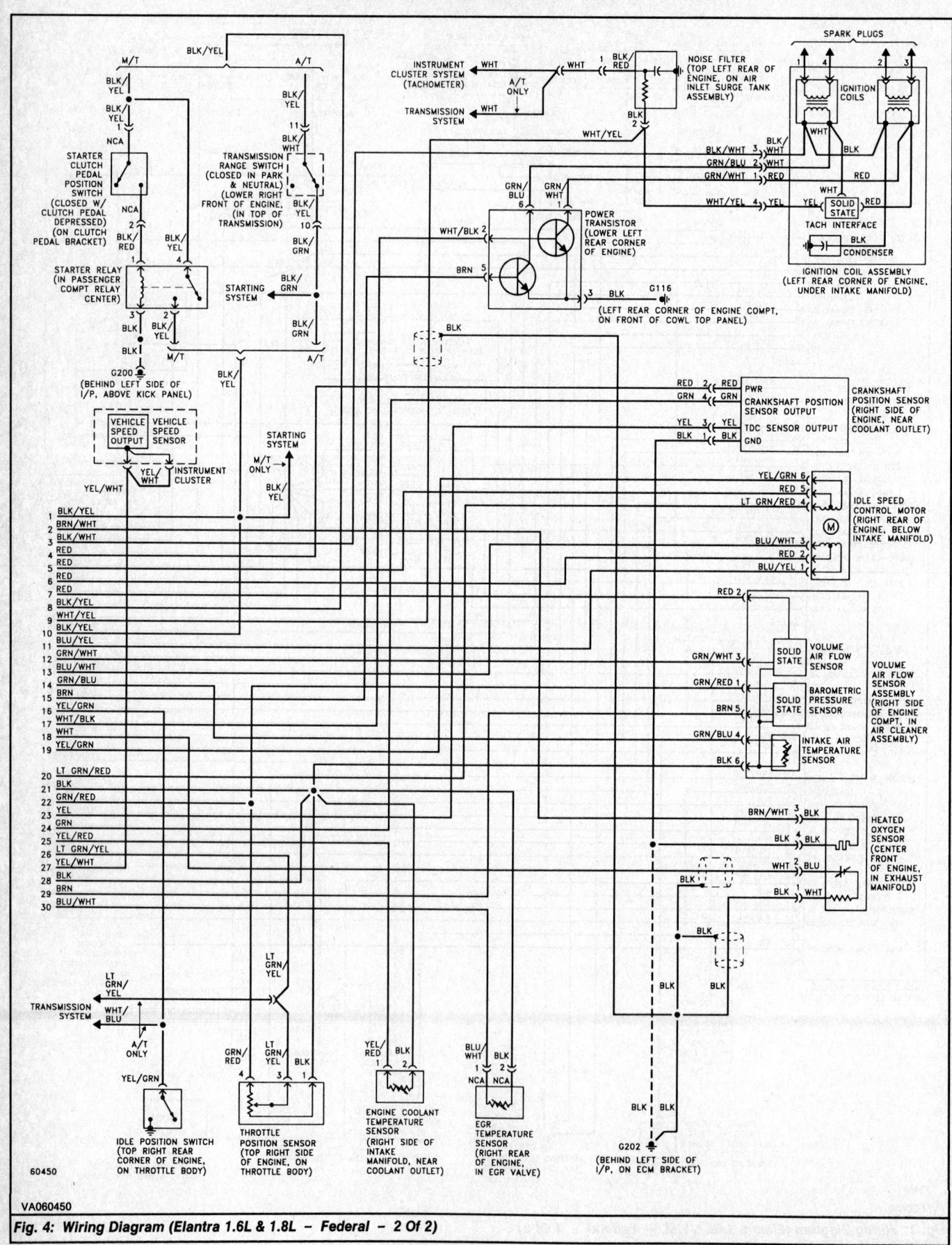

Fig. 4: Wiring Diagram (Elantra 1.6L & 1.8L - Federal - 2 Of 2)

60450

VA060450

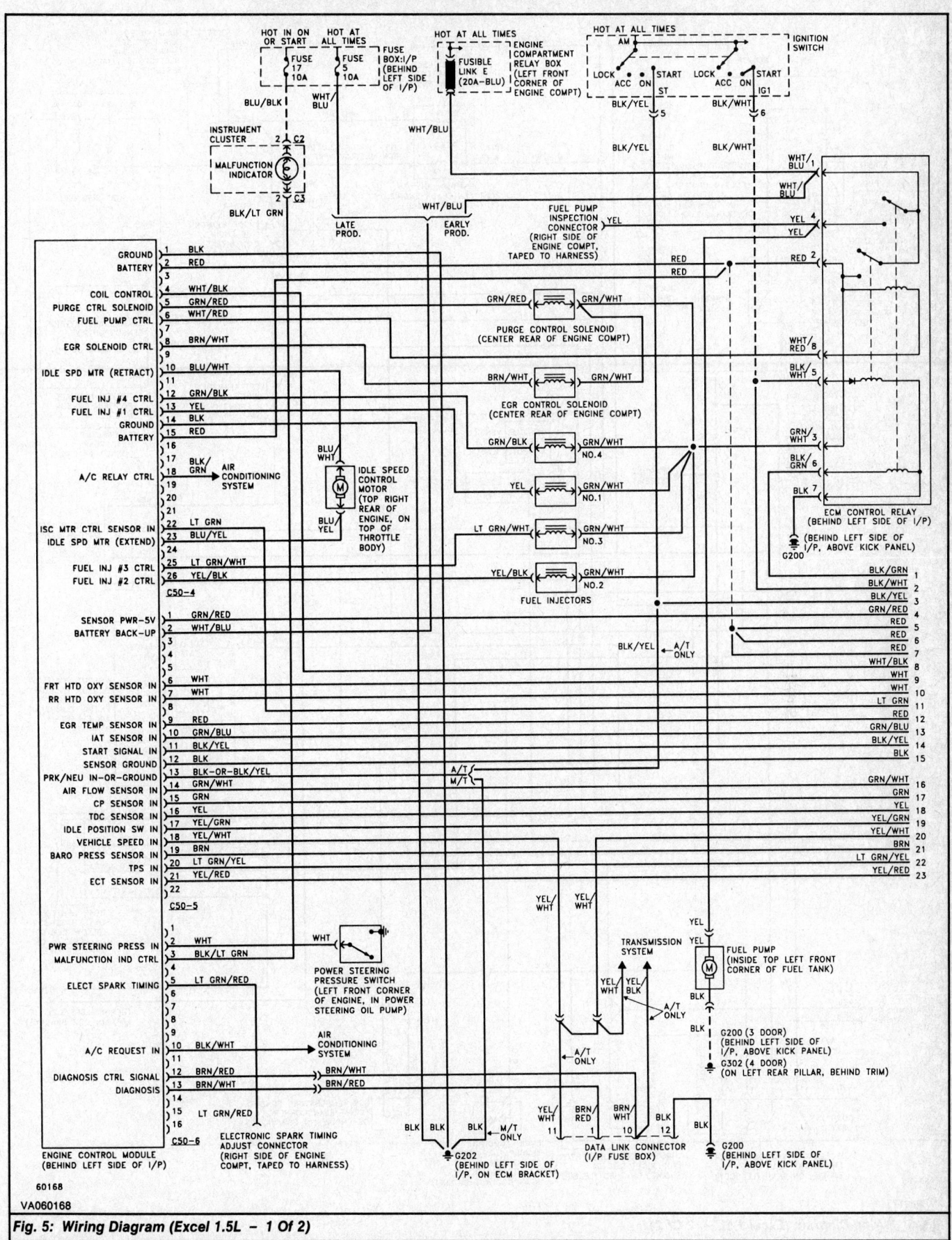

Fig. 5: Wiring Diagram (Excel 1.5L - 1 Of 2)

60168

VA060168

1994 ENGINE PERFORMANCE
Wiring Diagrams (Cont.)

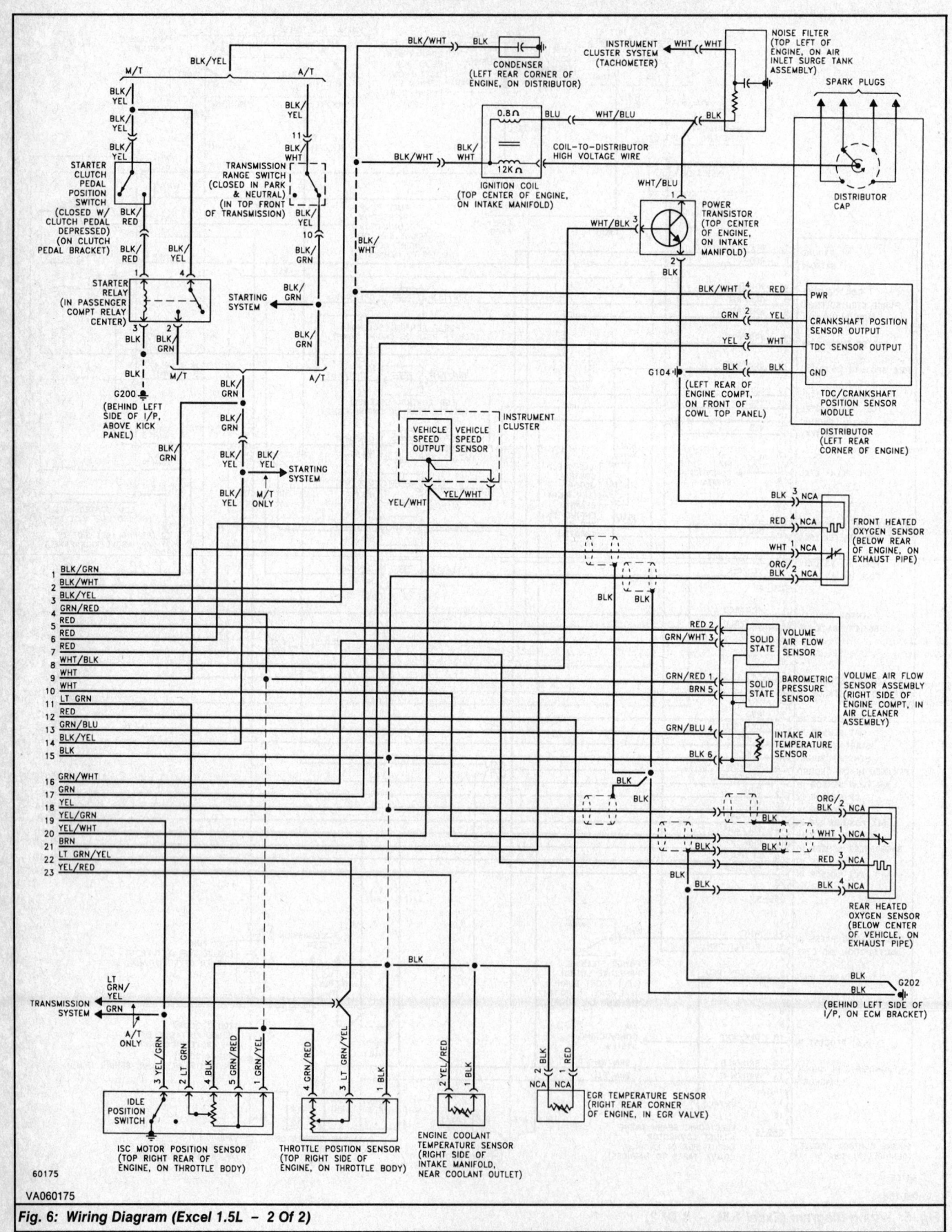

Fig. 6: *Wiring Diagram (Excel 1.5L – 2 Of 2)*

60175

VA060175

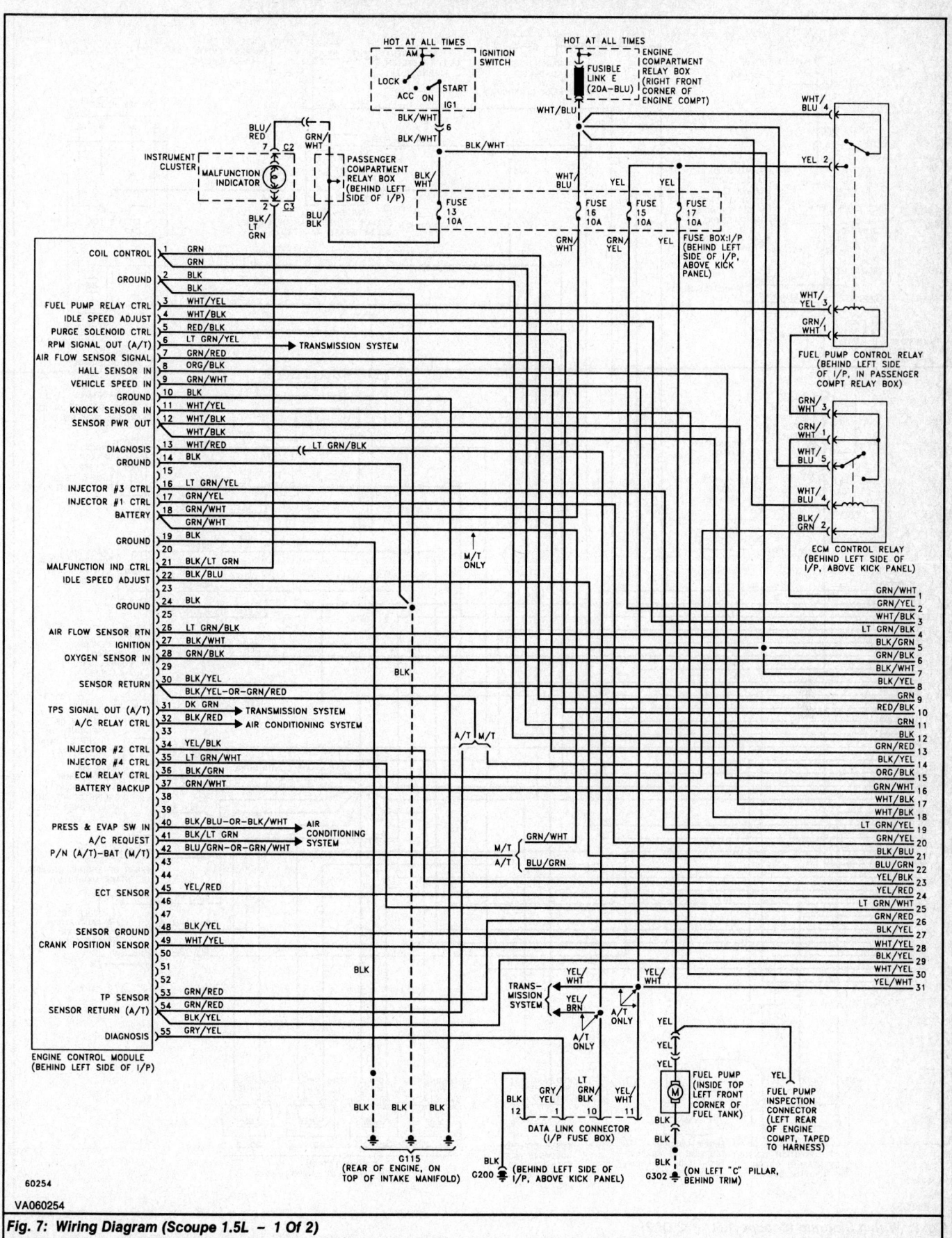

Fig. 7: Wiring Diagram (Scoupe 1.5L - 1 Of 2)

VA060254

60254

1994 ENGINE PERFORMANCE
Wiring Diagrams (Cont.)

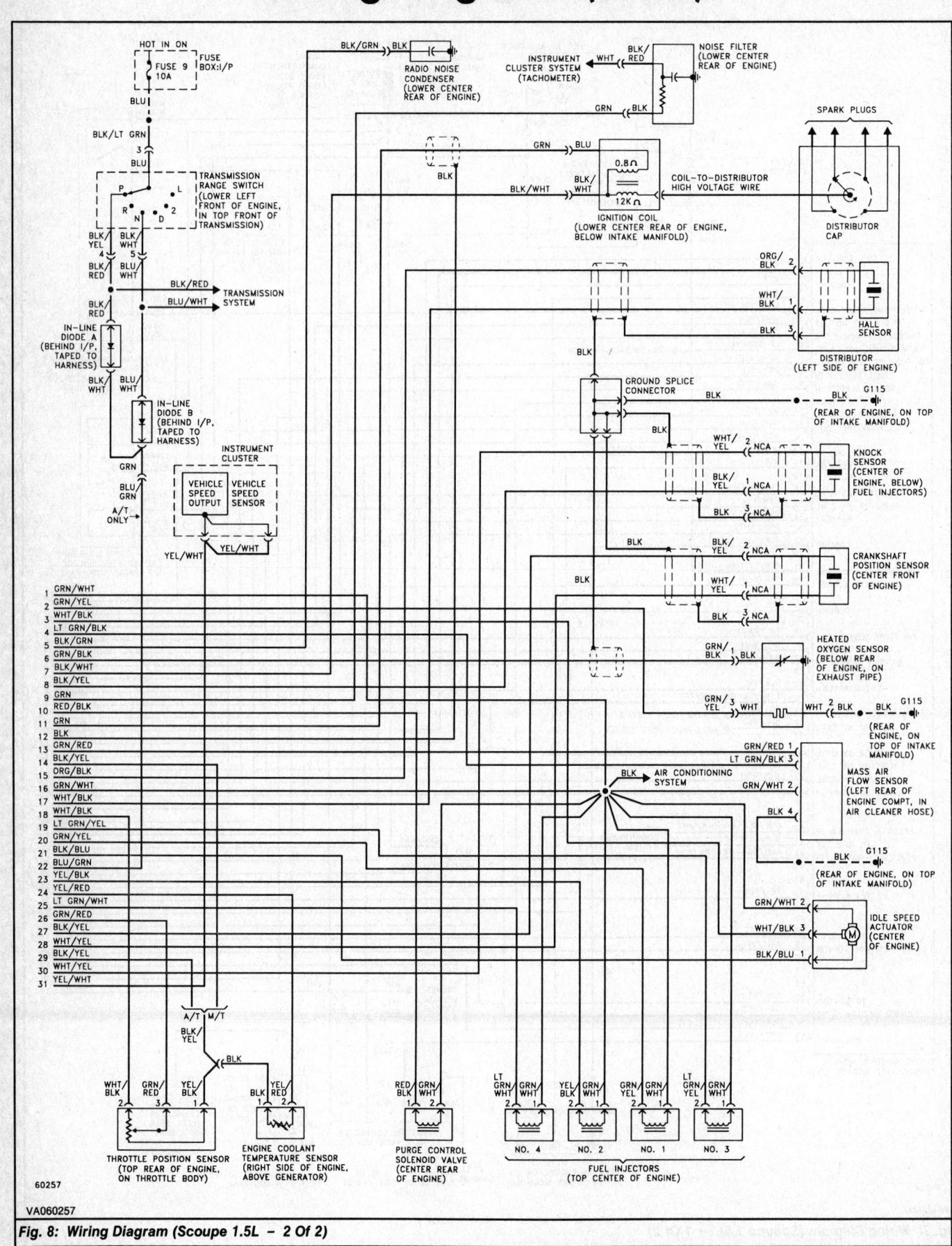

Fig. 8: Wiring Diagram (Scoupe 1.5L - 2 Of 2)

60257

VA060257

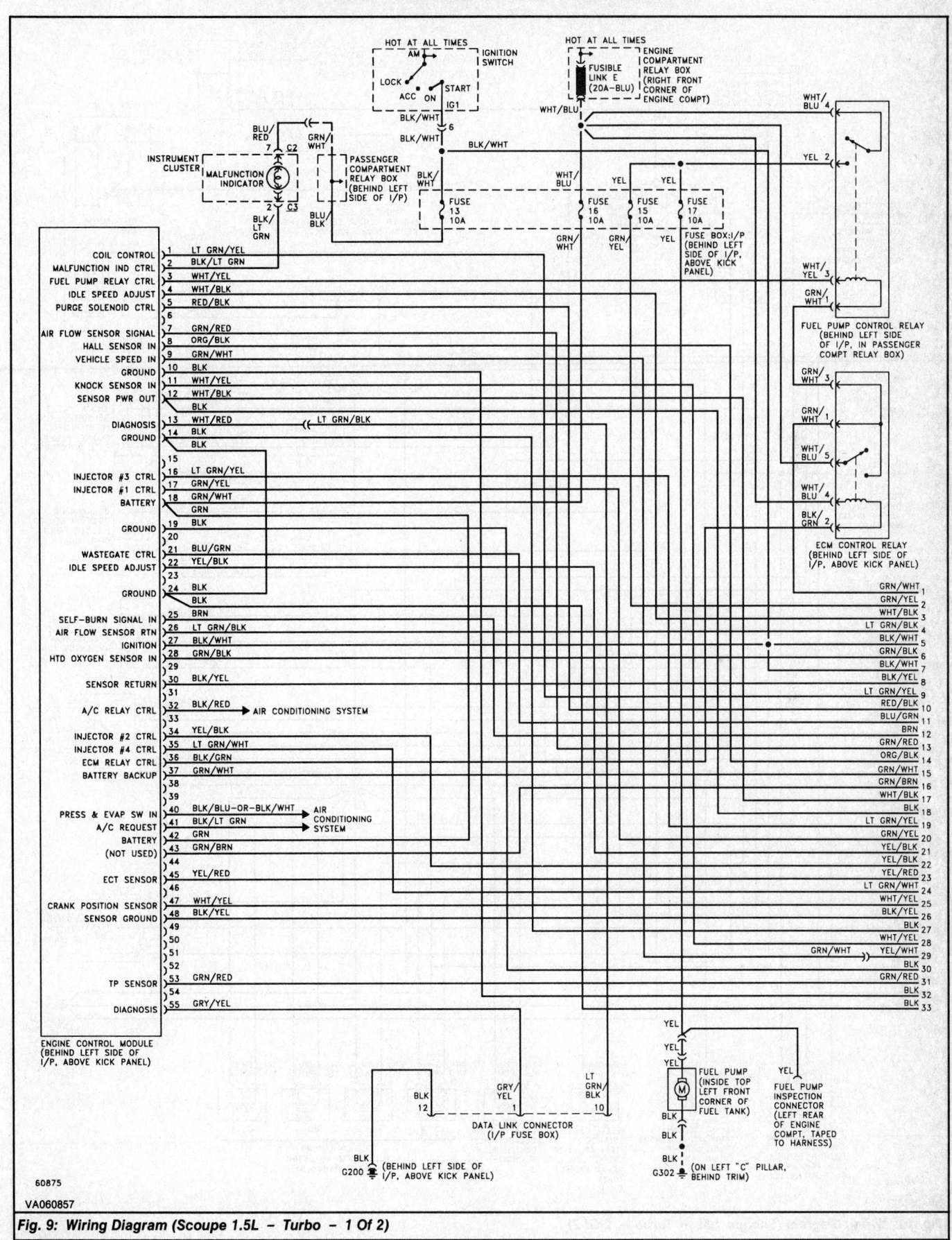

Fig. 9: *Wiring Diagram (Scoupe 1.5L - Turbo - 1 Of 2)*

60875

VA060857

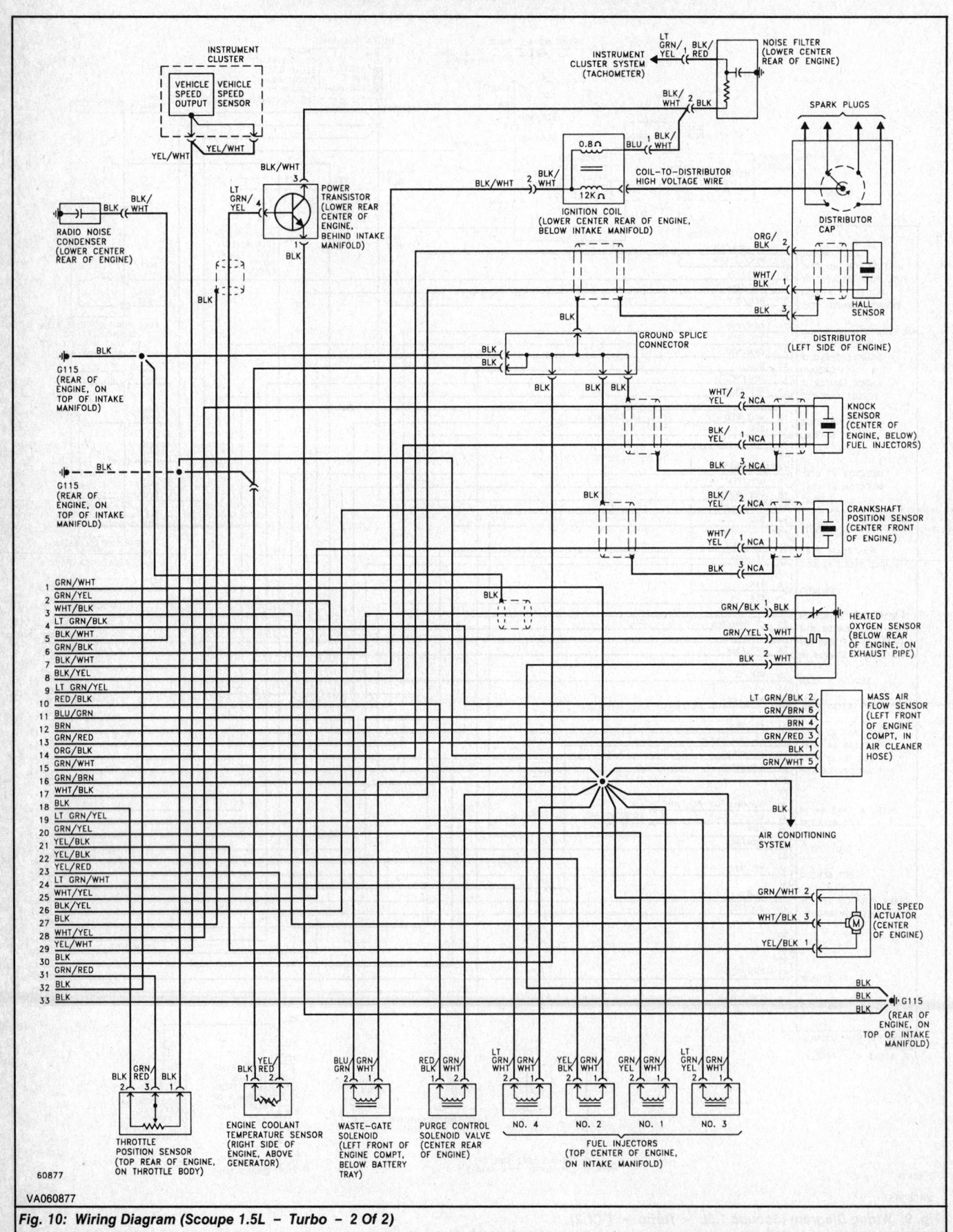

Fig. 10: Wiring Diagram (Scoupe 1.5L – Turbo – 2 Of 2)

60877

VA060877

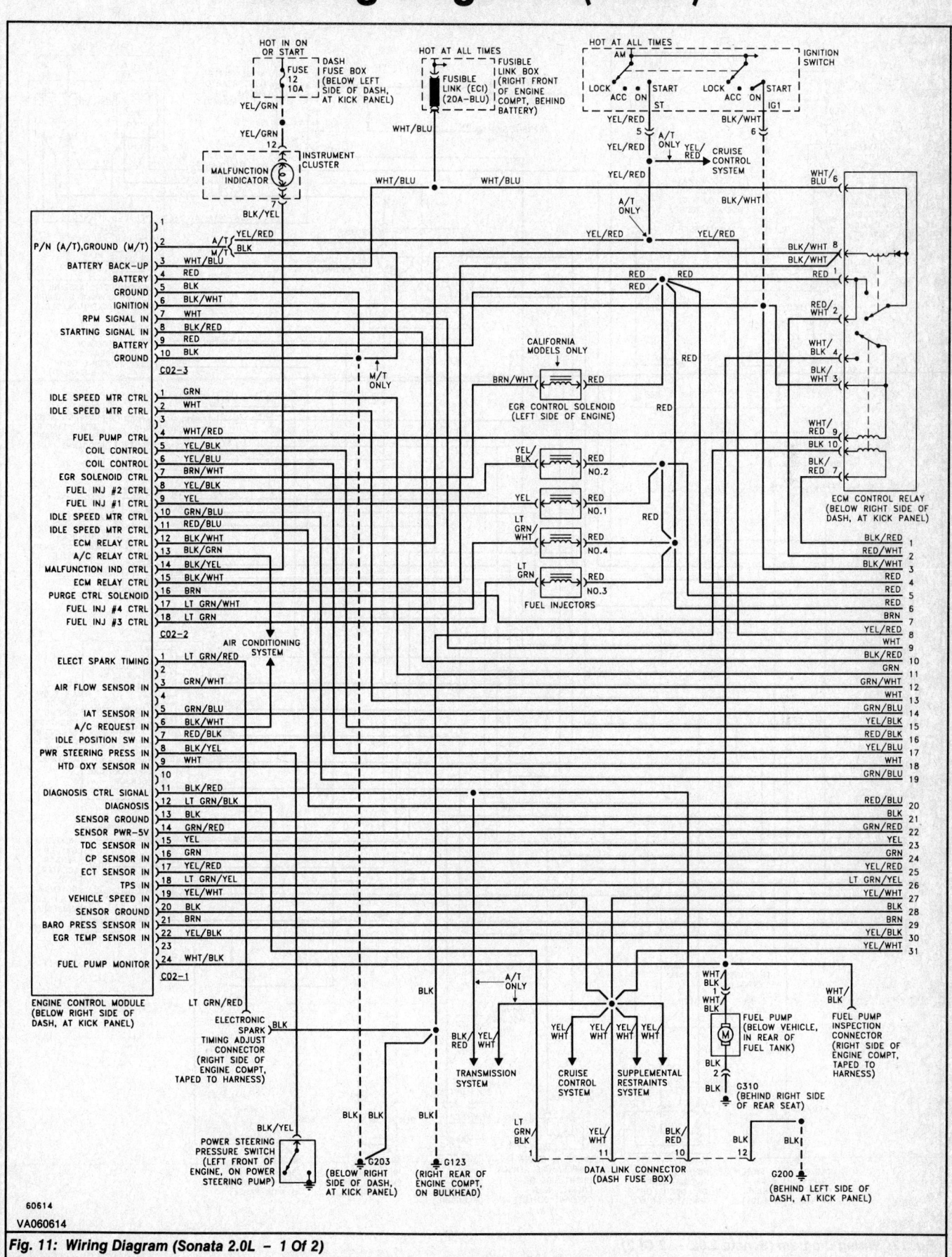

Fig. 11: Wiring Diagram (Sonata 2.0L – 1 Of 2)

VA060614

60614

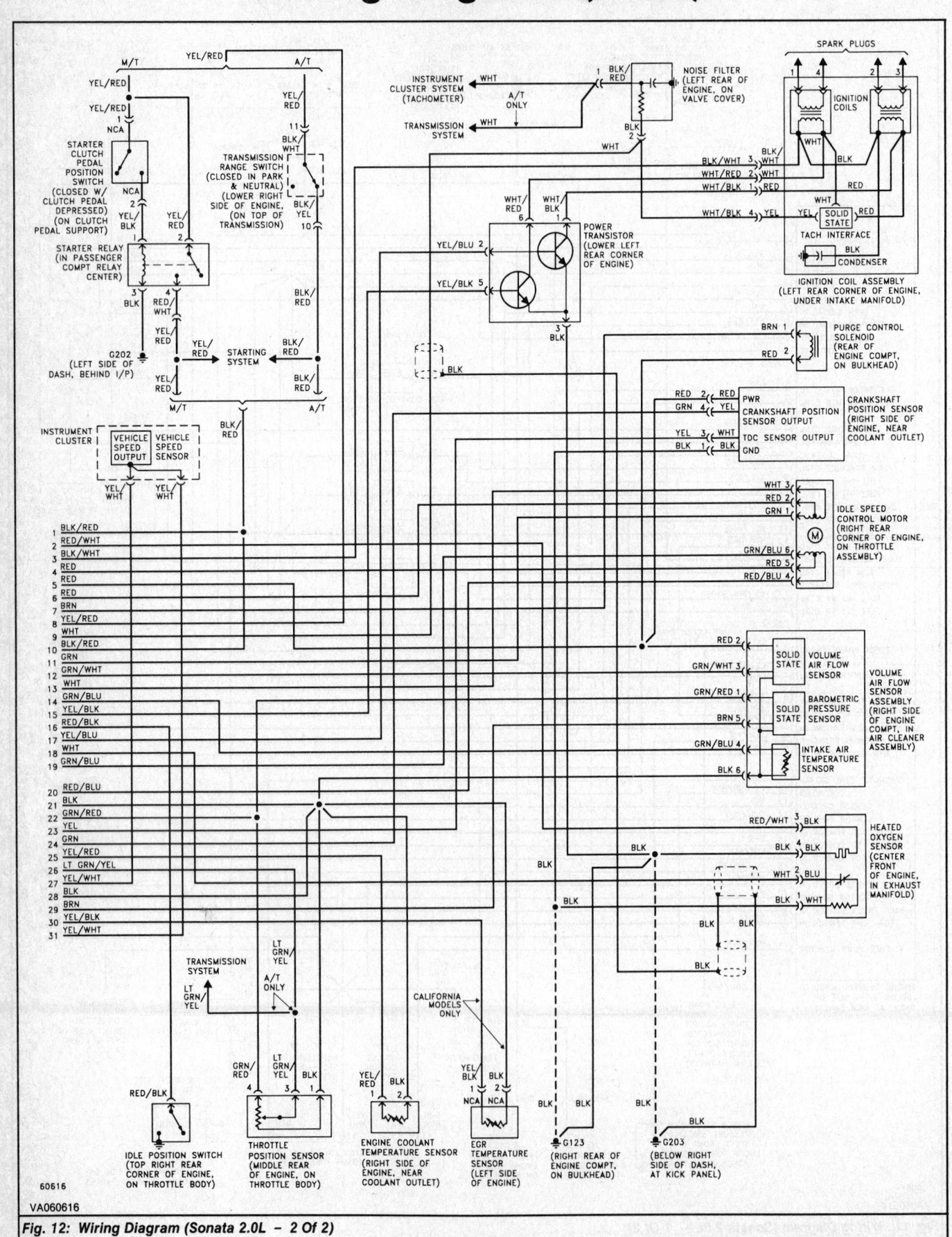

60616

VA060616

Fig. 12: Wiring Diagram (Sonata 2.0L – 2 Of 2)

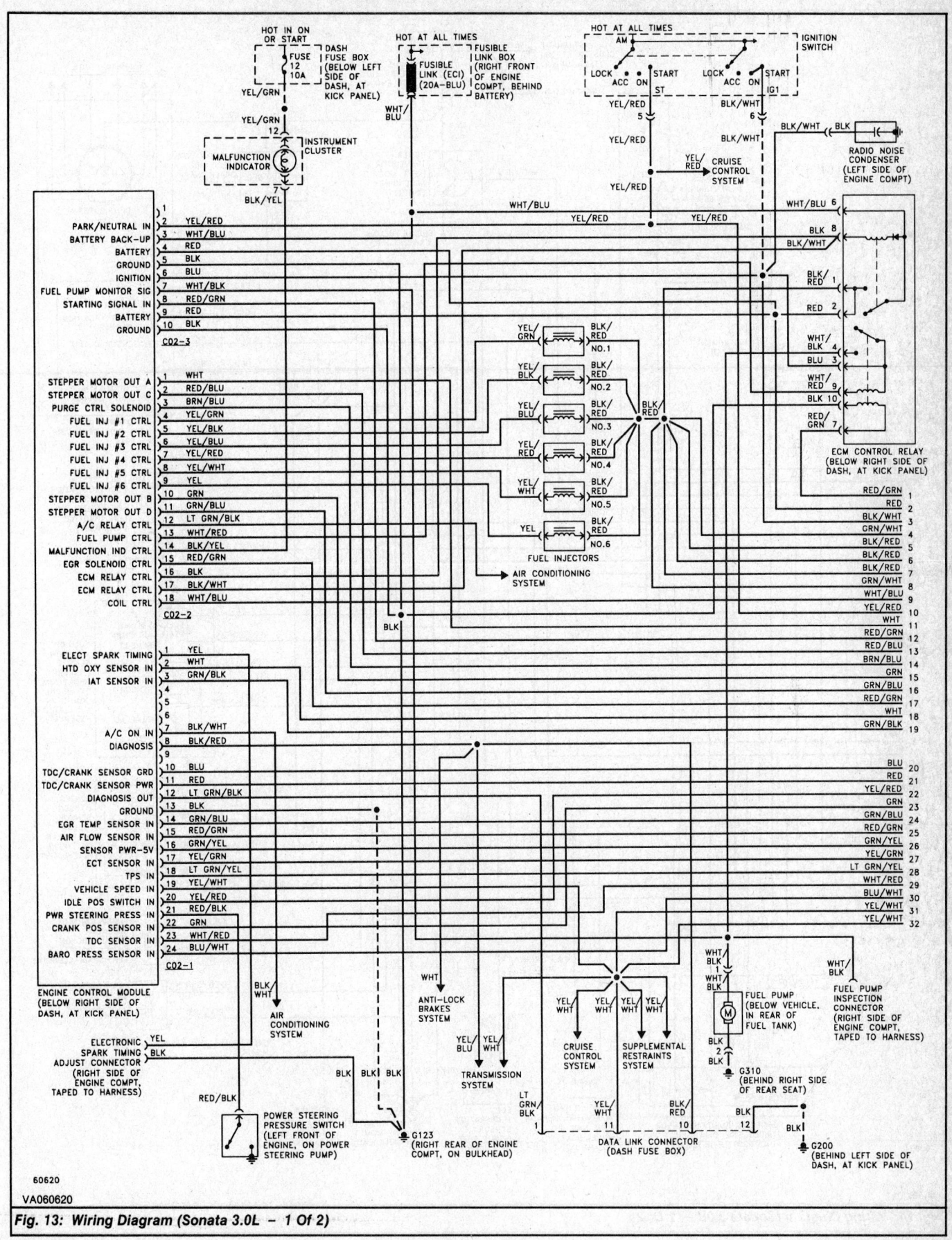

Fig. 13: Wiring Diagram (Sonata 3.0L - 1 Of 2)

60620
VA060620

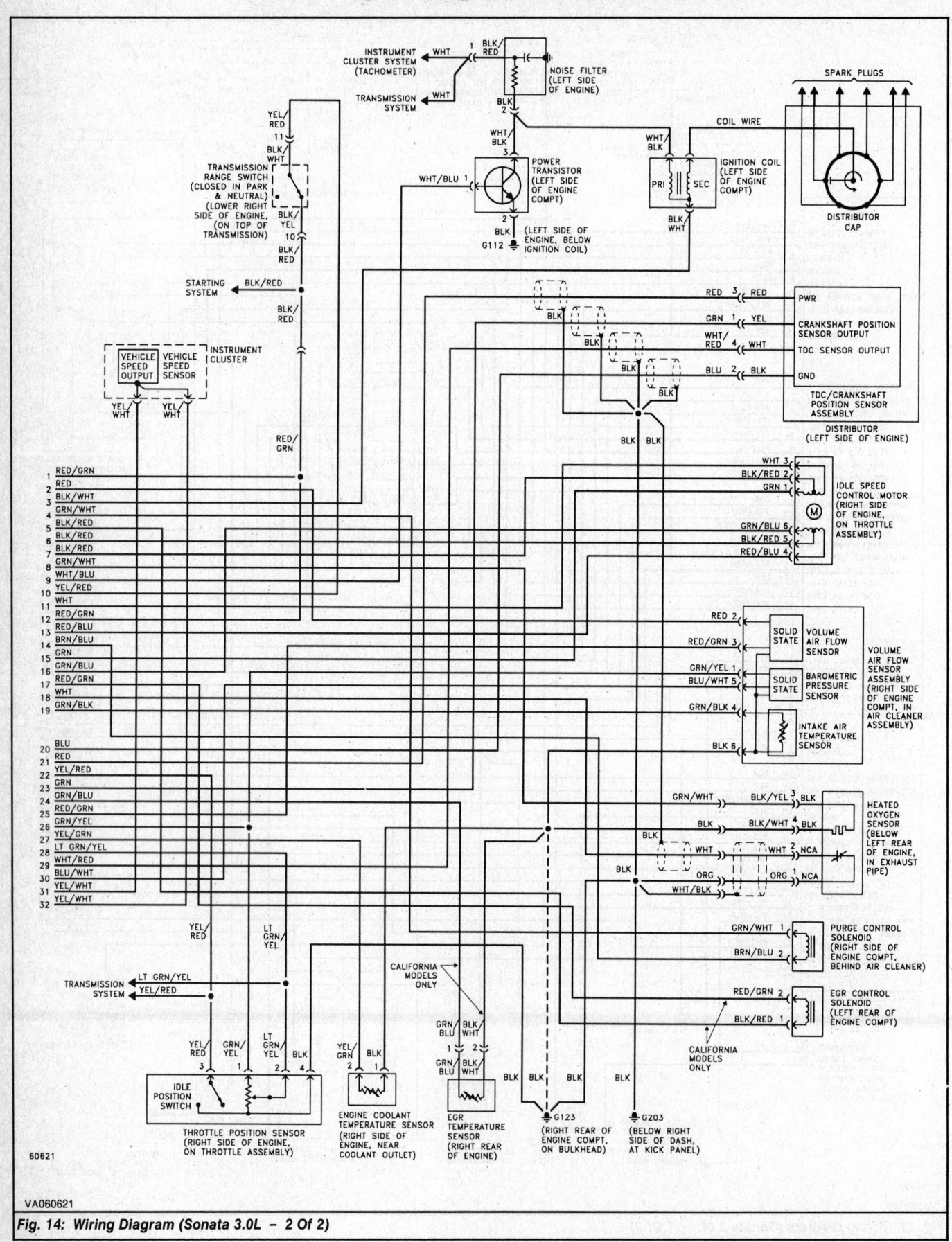

60621

VA060621

Fig. 14: Wiring Diagram (Sonata 3.0L - 2 Of 2)

Elantra, Excel, Scoupe, Sonata

DESCRIPTION

Mitsubishi alternators are conventional 3-phase, self-rectifying type units containing 6 diodes (3 positive and 3 negative), used to rectify current. All models utilize an Integrated Circuit (IC) regulator.

ADJUSTMENTS

BELT ADJUSTMENT

Application	[1] Deflection New Belt – In. (mm)	[1] Deflection Used Belt – In. (mm)
Excel	.22-.28 (5.5-7.0)	.28-.31 (7.0-8.0)
Elantra	.30-.35 (7.5-9.0)	.39 (10.0)
Scoupe	.30-.35 (7.5-9.0)	.35-.41 (9.0-10.4)
Sonata		
4-Cylinder	.30-.35 (7.5-9.0)	.39 (10.0)
V6	.16-.20 (4.0-5.0)	.28 (7.0)

[1] – Deflection with 22 lbs. (10 kg) pressure applied midway on belt run.

TROUBLE SHOOTING

NOTE: See TROUBLE SHOOTING article in GENERAL INFORMATION.

ON-VEHICLE TESTING

NOTE: Check alternator wiring harness connections and drive belt tension. Ensure battery is fully charged before beginning test. Wait at least 30 seconds after starting engine before measuring voltage.

ALTERNATOR OUTPUT TEST

1) Using a voltmeter, ensure battery voltage is present at terminal "B" of alternator. If battery voltage is not present, circuit from battery to alternator terminal "B" is open. Repair as required.

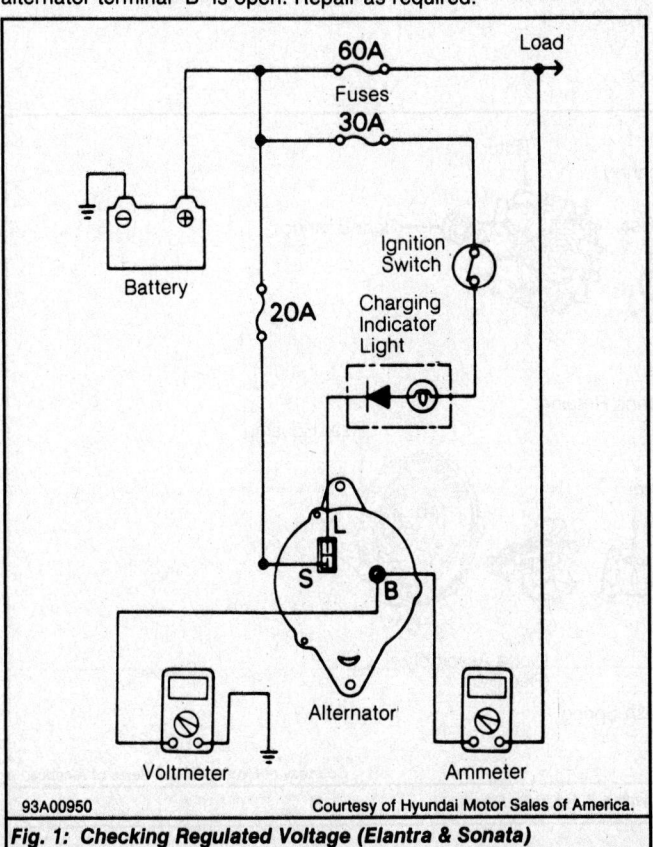

93A00950
Courtesy of Hyundai Motor Sales of America.

Fig. 1: Checking Regulated Voltage (Elantra & Sonata)

2) If battery voltage is present at terminal "B", connect an ammeter inductive pick-up around alternator's terminal "B" wire. See Fig. 1 or 2. Start engine, quickly turn lights and heater blower motor on high and run engine to 2500 RPM. Observe ammeter reading. See ALTERNATOR OUTPUT SPECIFICATIONS table. If alternator output is not within specification, remove and bench test alternator.

ALTERNATOR OUTPUT SPECIFICATIONS

Application	Output Amps
All Models Except Sonata V6	52.5
Sonata V6	53

REGULATED VOLTAGE TEST

1) Connect voltmeter and ammeter to alternator. See Fig. 1 or 2. Turn ignition on, engine off. If voltmeter reads zero volts, there is an open in circuit to terminal "S". Locate and repair.

2) Start engine. With all lights and accessories off, run engine at about 2500 RPM. When alternator output current drops to 10 amps (ammeter reading), ensure voltmeter reading is as specified. See REGULATOR VOLTAGE SPECIFICATIONS table. If voltage is not within specifications, test alternator and related wiring. If alternator and related wiring are okay, replace regulator.

REGULATOR VOLTAGE SPECIFICATIONS

Ambient Temperature	Voltage (75 & 90 Amp Alt.)
–4°F (–20°C)	14.2-15.4
68°F (20°C)	13.9-14.9
140°F (60°C)	13.4-14.6
176°F (80°C)	13.1-14.5

BENCH TESTING

BRUSHES

1) Replace brushes if worn to limit line. See Fig. 3. Replace all brush springs if any springs are damaged or corroded.
2) To remove brushes from holder, unsolder pigtail from terminal. To replace, install brush and spring so that brush projects .079-.118" (2-3 mm) from brush holder. Solder pigtail to terminal.

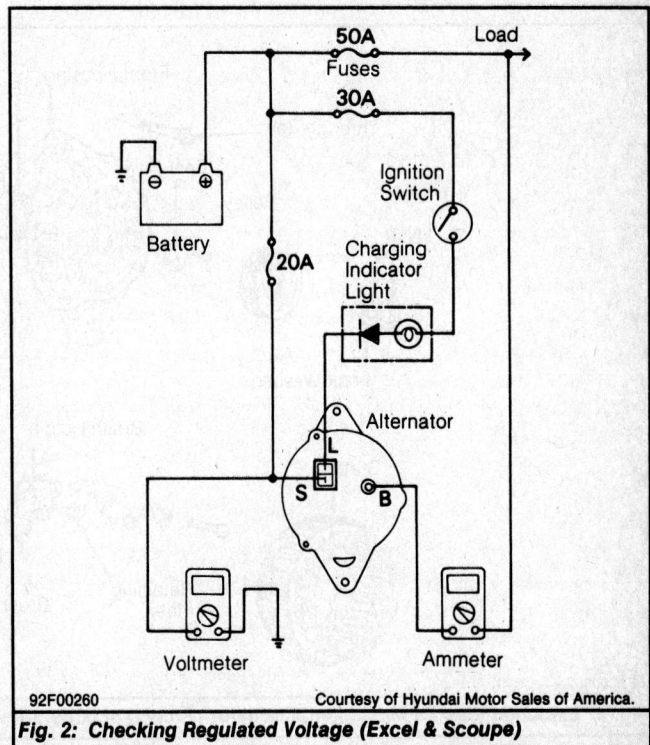

92F00260
Courtesy of Hyundai Motor Sales of America.

Fig. 2: Checking Regulated Voltage (Excel & Scoupe)

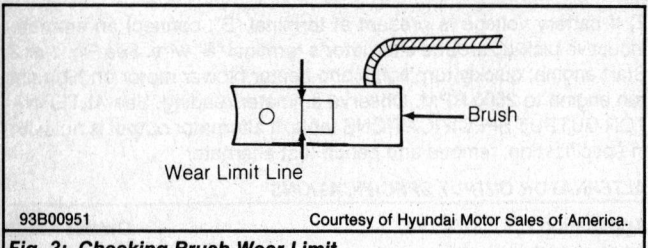

93B00951   Courtesy of Hyundai Motor Sales of America.

Fig. 3: Checking Brush Wear Limit

DIODE ASSEMBLY

1) Check each diode with ohmmeter in both directions as indicated in illustration. *See Fig. 4*. If diodes show high resistance in one direction and no resistance in the other direction, diodes are normal.

2) If diode shows low resistance in both directions, diode is shorted. If high resistance is shown in both directions, diode is open. If any diode is defective, replace complete rectifier assembly.

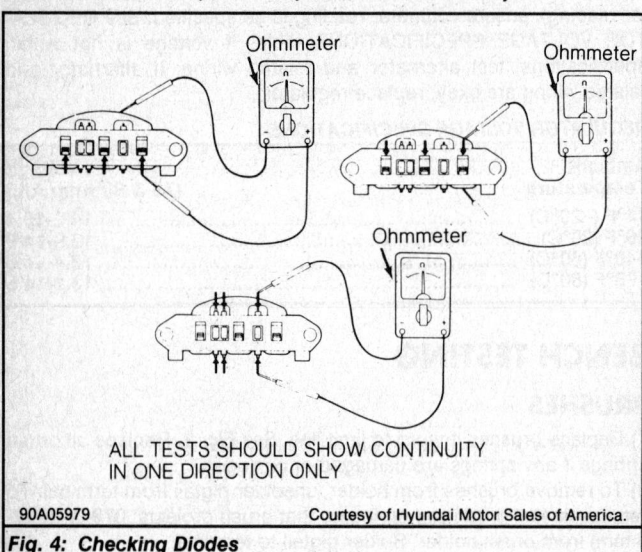

90A05979   Courtesy of Hyundai Motor Sales of America.

Fig. 4: Checking Diodes

ROTOR

Check resistance across rotor slip rings. Reading should be 3.1 ohms. If there is no continuity, replace rotor. Check continuity between each slip ring and rotor core/shaft (ground). If continuity exists, rotor coil or slip ring is grounded. Replace rotor assembly as necessary.

STATOR

Ensure continuity exists between all leads of stator coil. If continuity does not exist between all leads, replace stator. Ensure that continuity does not exist between any stator coil lead and stator core. If there is continuity, replace stator.

REMOVAL & INSTALLATION

Removal & Installation (Elantra & Sonata 4-Cylinder) – Disconnect negative battery cable. Remove radiator mount bolts. Disconnect coolant reservoir hose and fan motor connectors. Raise and support vehicle. Remove left side undercover. Disconnect oil pressure switch connector. Loosen alternator bolts and remove belt. Disconnect alternator "B" terminal. Remove alternator while lifting radiator as necessary for clearance. To install, reverse removal procedure. Tighten pivot bolt to 15-18 ft. lbs. (20-25 N.m), and tighten adjusting bolt to 9-11 ft. lbs. (12-15 N.m).

Removal & Installation (Excel & Scoupe) – Disconnect negative battery cable. Loosen belt tension and remove belt. Raise and support vehicle. Remove left side mud guard. Disconnect alternator battery "B+" terminal wire. Remove pivot bolt and remove alternator. To install, reverse removal procedure. On Excel, tighten pivot bolt to 15-18 ft. lbs. (20-25 N.m), and tighten adjusting bolt to 9-11 ft. lbs. (12-15 N.m). On Scoupe, tighten pivot bolt to 15-18 ft. lbs. (20-25 N.m), and tighten adjusting bolt to 9-11 ft. lbs. (12-15 N.m).

Removal & Installation (Sonata V6) – Disconnect negative battery cable. Remove distributor cap and power steering hose nut. Loosen belt tensioner and remove belt. Remove timing belt right side cover cap, and remove timing belt right side upper cover. Remove alternator. To install, reverse removal procedure. Tighten pivot bolt to 15-18 ft. lbs. (20-25 N.m), and tighten adjusting bolt to 11-16 ft. lbs. (15-22 N.m).

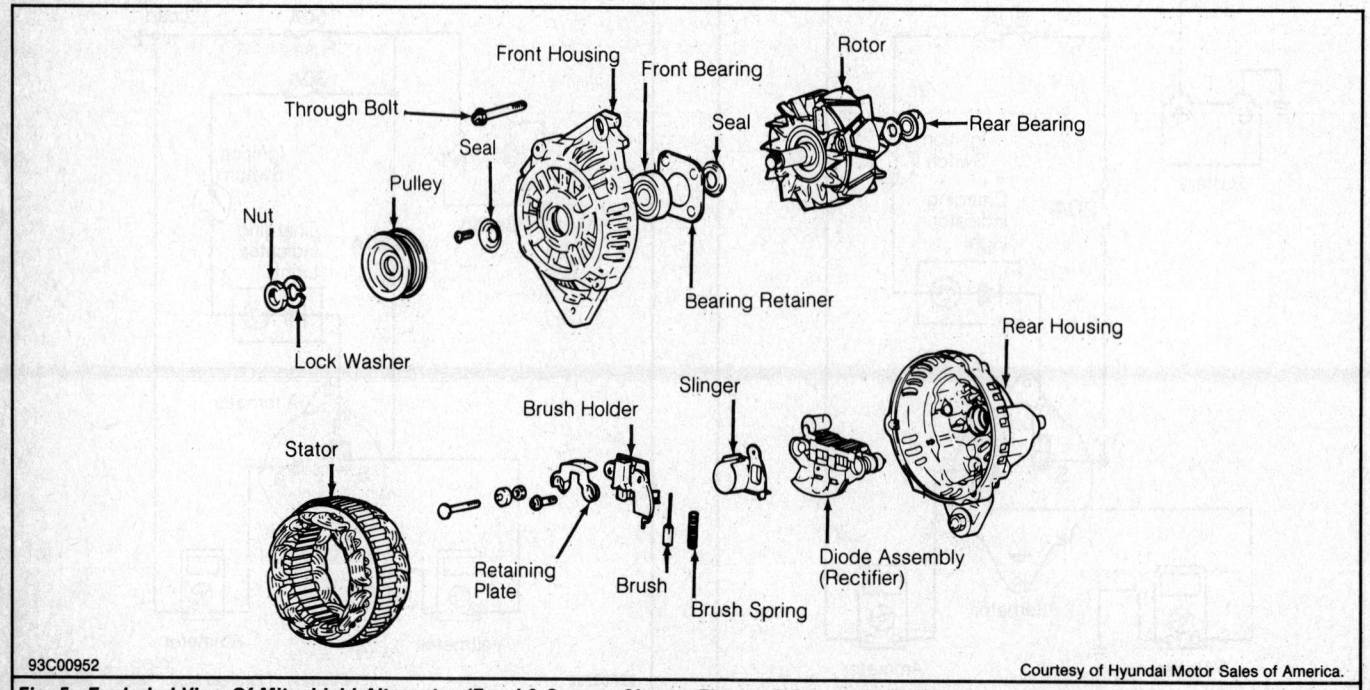

93C00952   Courtesy of Hyundai Motor Sales of America.

Fig. 5: Exploded View Of Mitsubishi Alternator (Excel & Scoupe Shown; Elantra & Sonata Similar)

OVERHAUL

NOTE: Use illustration for exploded view of Mitsubishi alternator. See Fig. 5.

WIRING DIAGRAMS

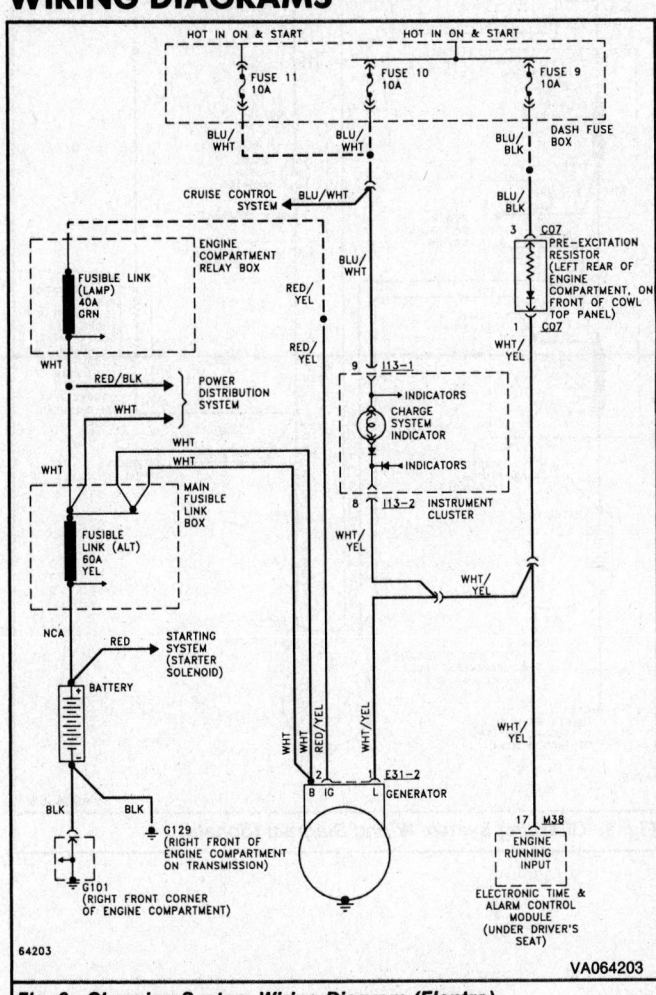

Fig. 6: Charging System Wiring Diagram (Elantra)

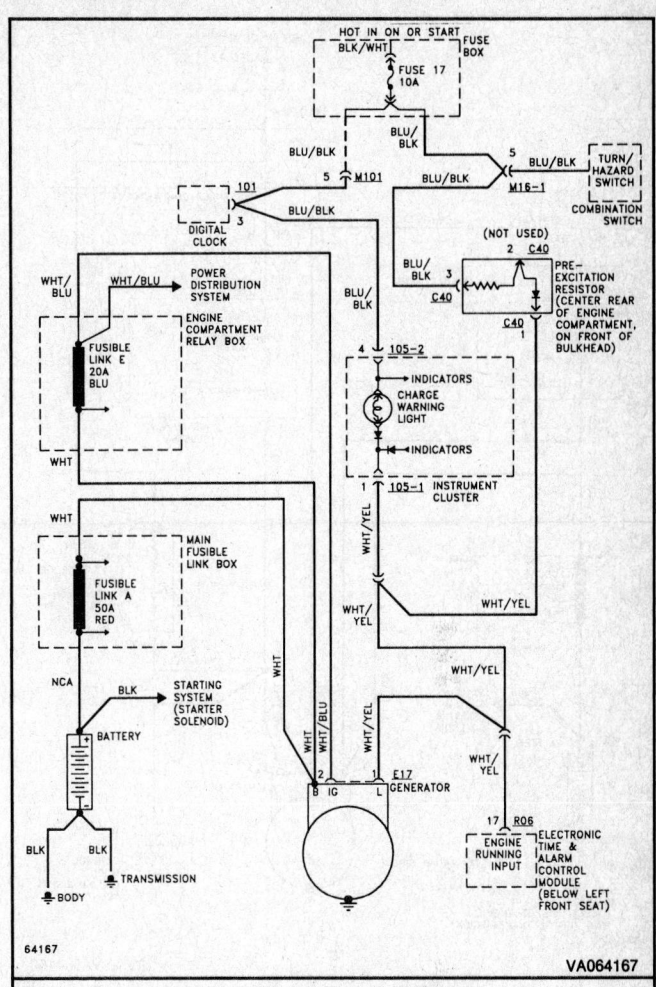

Fig. 7: Charging System Wiring Diagram (Excel)

1994 ELECTRICAL
Alternators & Regulators (Cont.)

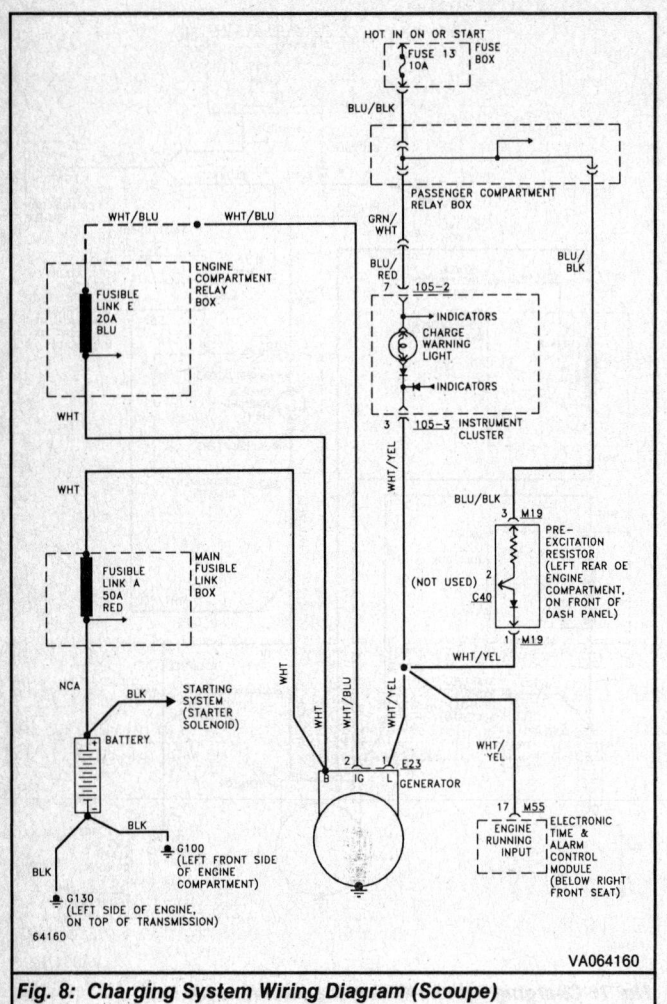

Fig. 8: Charging System Wiring Diagram (Scoupe)

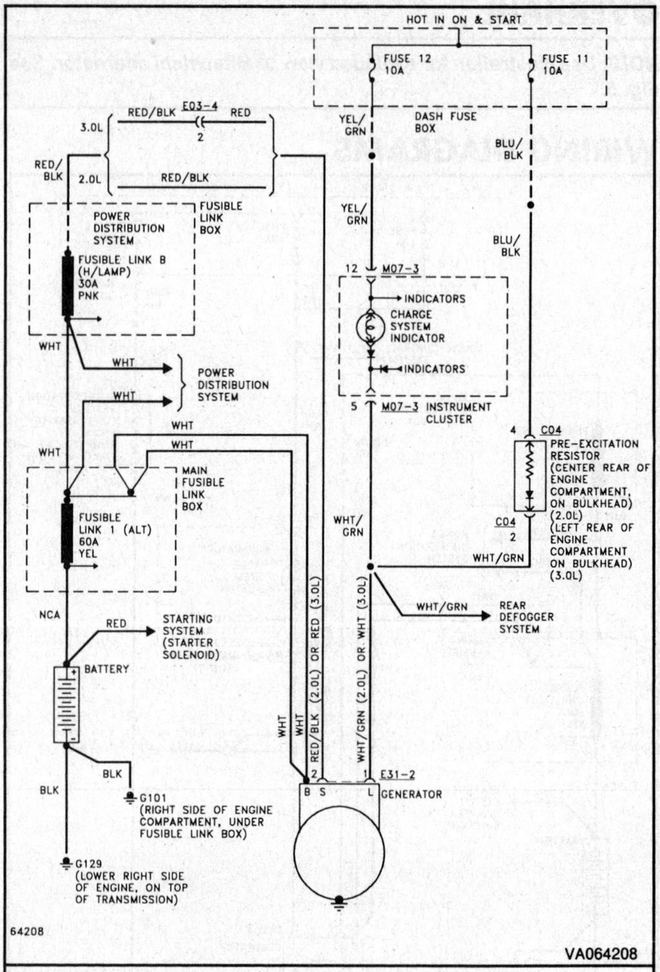

Fig. 9: Charging System Wiring Diagram (Sonata)

Elantra, Excel, Scoupe, Sonata

DESCRIPTION

Starters are conventional 12-volt, 4-pole brush-type motors. Excel and Scoupe starters are direct drive. Elantra and Sonata starters are reduction gear drive. The starter-mounted solenoid shifts overrunning clutch and pinion into flywheel when starter is energized.

TROUBLE SHOOTING

NOTE: See TROUBLE SHOOTING article in GENERAL INFORMATION.

ON-VEHICLE TESTING

STARTER RELAY TEST

Manual Transmission Models – 1) Starter relay is located in relay panel under left side of dash. Sonata starter relay is at lower left corner of relay panel. All others are at top left corner of relay panel. Remove relay. Check for continuity between terminals No. 1 and 3 of relay.

2) If continuity exists, apply 12 volts to terminals No. 1 and 3 (No. 3 is relay ground terminal) to energize relay. Continuity should exist between terminals No. 2 and 4. If relay does not perform as described, replace relay.

Automatic Transmission Models – Vehicles equipped with automatic transmissions do not utilize a starter relay. Transmission range switch completes ignition switch-to-starter circuit when transmission selector lever is in Neutral or Park. Testing information is not available from manufacturer. See WIRING DIAGRAMS.

IGNITION LOCK SWITCH TEST

Manual Transmission Models – Switch is mounted on bracket near top of clutch pedal. Disconnect switch harness connector. Using ohmmeter, ensure continuity exists between switch connector terminals when clutch pedal is depressed. If continuity does not exist, adjust or replace switch.

BENCH TESTING (ASSEMBLED)

CAUTION: Perform each solenoid test in less than 10 seconds to prevent solenoid coil damage.

NO-LOAD TEST

1) Install starter in soft-jawed vise. Connect starter in series with a fully charged 12-volt battery. *See Fig. 1.* Connect ammeter (100-amp scale) and carbon pile rheostat in series with positive battery terminal and starter motor terminal.

2) Install voltmeter across starter motor. *See Fig. 1.* Adjust carbon pile rheostat until voltmeter reads test voltage. See STARTER NO-LOAD SPECIFICATIONS table. Install jumper wire across solenoid terminals "B" and "S" (maximum 10 seconds).

3) Ensure maximum amperage draw is within specification and starter rotates smoothly. See STARTER NO-LOAD SPECIFICATIONS table. If starter is not within specification, overhaul or replace starter as required.

STARTER NO-LOAD SPECIFICATIONS

Application	Starter Type [1]	Test Voltage	Maximum Amps @ Minimum RPM
Excel & Scoupe	DD	11.5	60 @ 3000
Elantra & Sonata	GR	11	90 @ 3000

[1] – DD indicates direct drive and GR indicates gear reduction.

SOLENOID TESTS

CAUTION: Perform each solenoid test in less than 10 seconds to prevent solenoid coil damage.

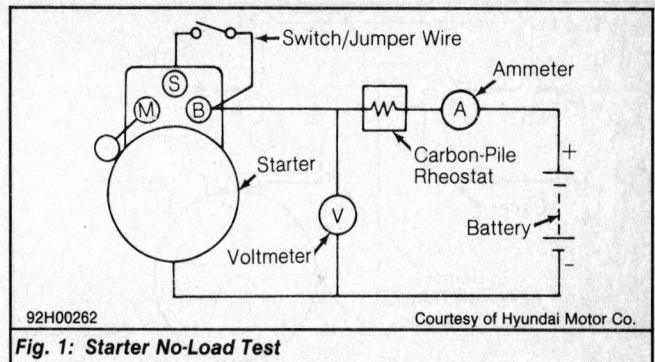

Fig. 1: Starter No-Load Test

Pull-In Test – Disconnect solenoid "M" terminal connector. Apply 12 volts to solenoid "S" terminal and ground solenoid "M" terminal connector to cause solenoid plunger to pull-in and extend pinion drive. *See Fig. 2.* If pinion drive moves outward, pull-in coil is good. If pinion does not move outward, replace solenoid.

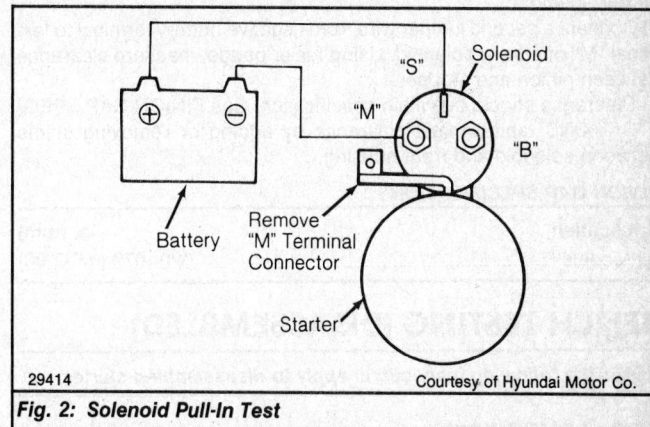

Fig. 2: Solenoid Pull-In Test

Hold-In Test – With solenoid "M" terminal connector still disconnected, apply 12 volts to solenoid "S" terminal and ground starter case to pull-in solenoid plunger. *See Fig. 3.* If pinion drive remains out when plunger is pulled in, hold-in circuit is good. If pinion drive moves in, hold-in circuit is open. Replace solenoid.

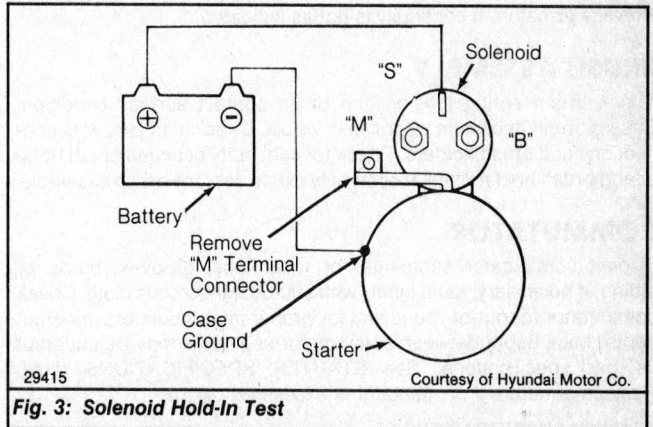

Fig. 3: Solenoid Hold-In Test

Return Test – Apply 12 volts to solenoid "M" terminal and ground starter case. Manually pull pinion drive out and then release it. *See Fig. 4.* Pinion drive should return quickly to original position. If pinion drive does not return to original position, replace solenoid.

PINION GAP

CAUTION: Perform pinion gap test in less than 10 seconds to prevent solenoid coil damage.

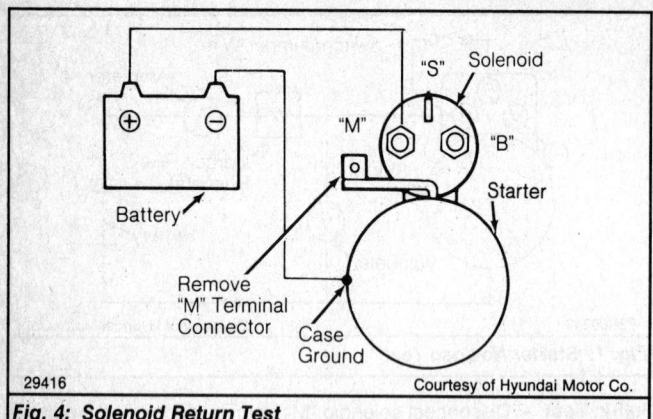

29416   Courtesy of Hyundai Motor Co.

Fig. 4: Solenoid Return Test

1) Disconnect field coil wire from starter solenoid "M" terminal. Connect jumper wire from positive battery terminal to terminal "S" of starter solenoid.
2) Connect a second jumper wire from negative battery terminal to terminal "M" of starter solenoid. Using feeler gauge, measure clearance between pinion and stopper.
3) Clearance should be within specification. See PINION GAP SPECIFICATIONS table. Adjust clearance by adding or removing shims between solenoid and front housing.

PINION GAP SPECIFICATIONS

Application	In. (mm)
All Models	.020-.079 (.50-2.00)

BENCH TESTING (DISASSEMBLED)

NOTE: The following inspections apply to disassembled starter.

ARMATURE TEST

Check external condition of armature for scoring or other damage. Measure shaft runout with dial indicator. Standard runout is .002" (.05 mm). Replace armature if shaft runout exceeds .004" (.10 mm). Ensure no continuity exists between armature core and commutator segments. Ensure continuity exists between commutator segments. Replace armature if continuity is not as indicated.

BRUSH ASSEMBLY

Check brush spring tension and brush contact surface condition. Ensure brush maximum wear line is visible. Check lead clip, wire connections and brush holders. Check for continuity between brush holder and brush holder plate. If continuity exists, replace brush assembly.

COMMUTATOR

Inspect commutator segments for roughness, grooves, burns or pitting. If necessary, sand lightly with 500-600 grit crocus cloth. Check commutator for out-of-round and for proper mica insulators undercut depth. Mica depth between commutator segments may be undercut as per specifications. See STARTER SPECIFICATIONS table. Replace armature if commutator is excessively worn.

STARTER SPECIFICATIONS [1]

Application	In. (mm)
Elantra & Sonata	
Commutator Standard Runout	.002 (.05)
Commutator Maximum Runout	.004 (.10)
Commutator Standard Diameter	1.157 (29.40)
Commutator Minimum Diameter	1.118 (28.40)
Commutator Undercut Depth	.020 (.50)

[1] – Information not available on Excel and Scoupe models.

FIELD COIL TEST

Excel & Scoupe – 1) Check field coil continuity by connecting ohmmeter probes to field coil positive terminal and to brush holder. If circuit is open (no continuity), replace field coil.
2) Check for grounded field coils by placing one ohmmeter probe on starter housing and other probe on field coil positive terminal. If continuity is present, field coil is grounded and must be replaced.

REMOVAL & INSTALLATION

STARTER

Removal & Installation (Excel) – Disconnect negative battery cable. Remove EGR valve (if equipped). Remove speedometer cable. Disconnect starter wires and remove starter mounting bolts. To install, reverse removal procedure. Tighten starter mounting bolts to 19-24 ft. lbs. (26-33 N.m). Tighten EGR valve mounting bolts to 7-11 ft. lbs. (10-15 N.m). See Fig. 5.
Removal & Installation (Scoupe) – Disconnect negative battery cable. Remove speedometer cable and shift cable. Disconnect high-tension cable from ignition coil to ignition coil module. Disconnect starter wires and remove starter mounting bolts. To install, reverse removal procedure. Tighten starter mounting bolts to 19-24 ft. lbs. (26-33 N.m). See Fig. 5.
Removal & Installation (Elantra & Sonata) – Disconnect negative battery cable. Disconnect starter wires and remove starter mounting bolts. To install, reverse removal procedure. Tighten starter mounting bolts to 19-24 ft. lbs. (26-33 N.m). See Fig. 6.

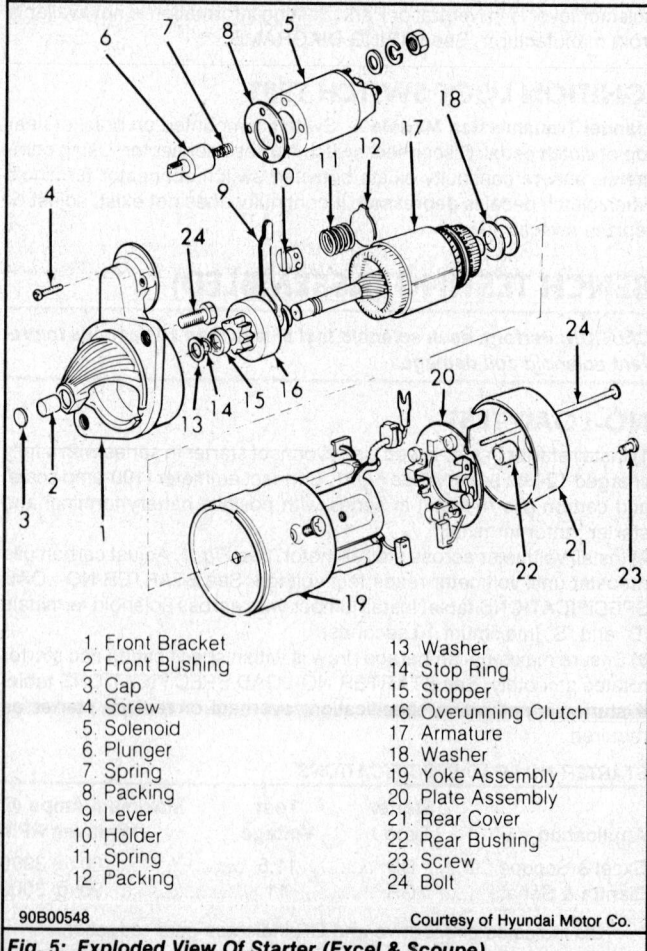

1. Front Bracket	13. Washer
2. Front Bushing	14. Stop Ring
3. Cap	15. Stopper
4. Screw	16. Overunning Clutch
5. Solenoid	17. Armature
6. Plunger	18. Washer
7. Spring	19. Yoke Assembly
8. Packing	20. Plate Assembly
9. Lever	21. Rear Cover
10. Holder	22. Rear Bushing
11. Spring	23. Screw
12. Packing	24. Bolt

90B00548   Courtesy of Hyundai Motor Co.

Fig. 5: Exploded View Of Starter (Excel & Scoupe)

OVERHAUL

NOTE: For exploded views of starters, see Fig. 5 or 6.

TORQUE SPECIFICATIONS

TORQUE SPECIFICATIONS

Application	Ft. Lbs (N.m)
Starter Mounting Bolts	19-24 (26-33)

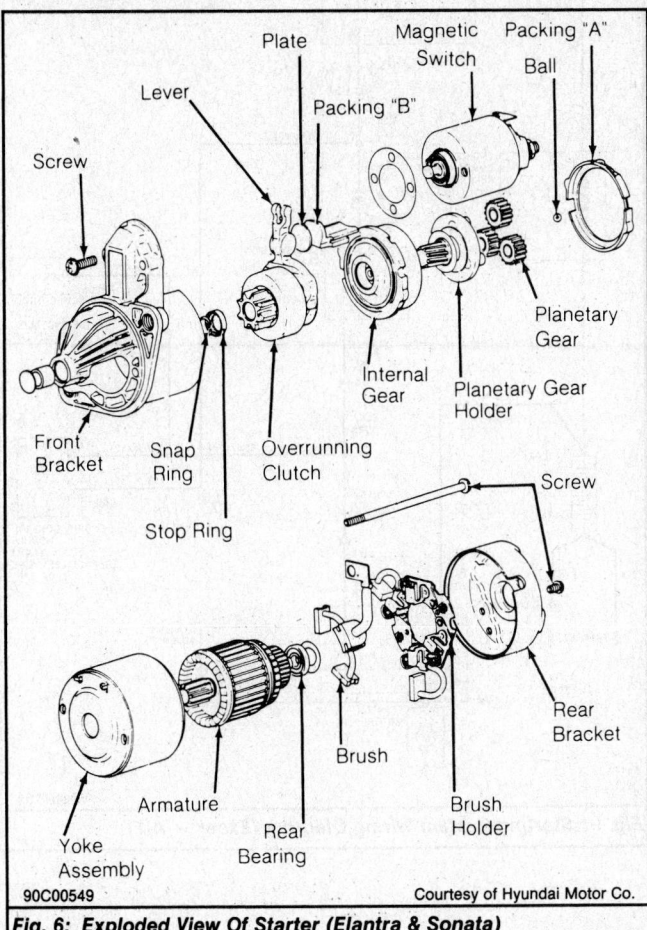

Fig. 6: Exploded View Of Starter (Elantra & Sonata)

90C00549   Courtesy of Hyundai Motor Co.

WIRING DIAGRAMS

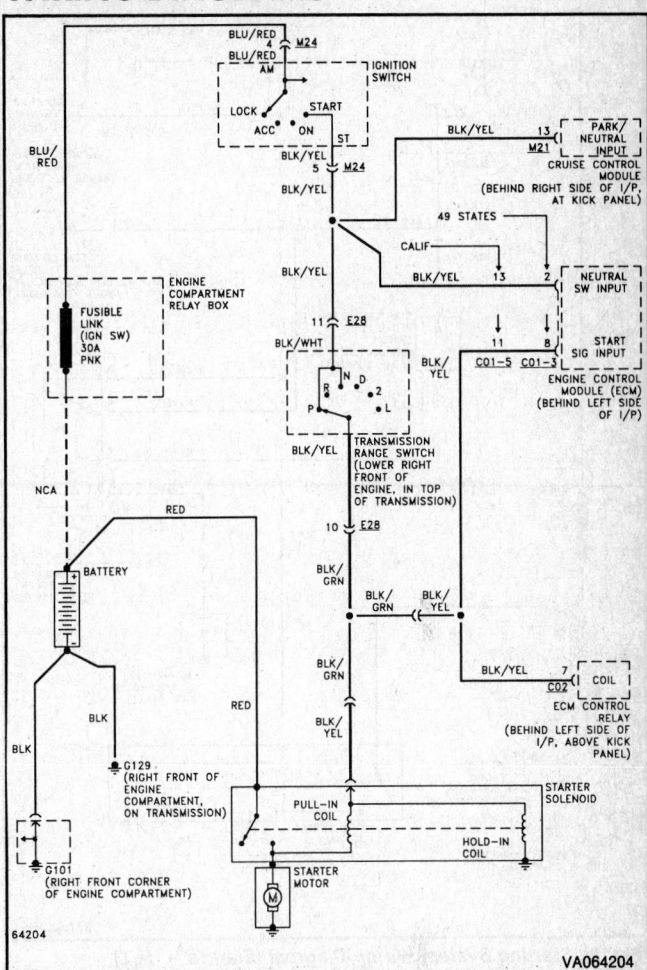

Fig. 7: Starting System Wiring Diagram (Elantra – A/T)

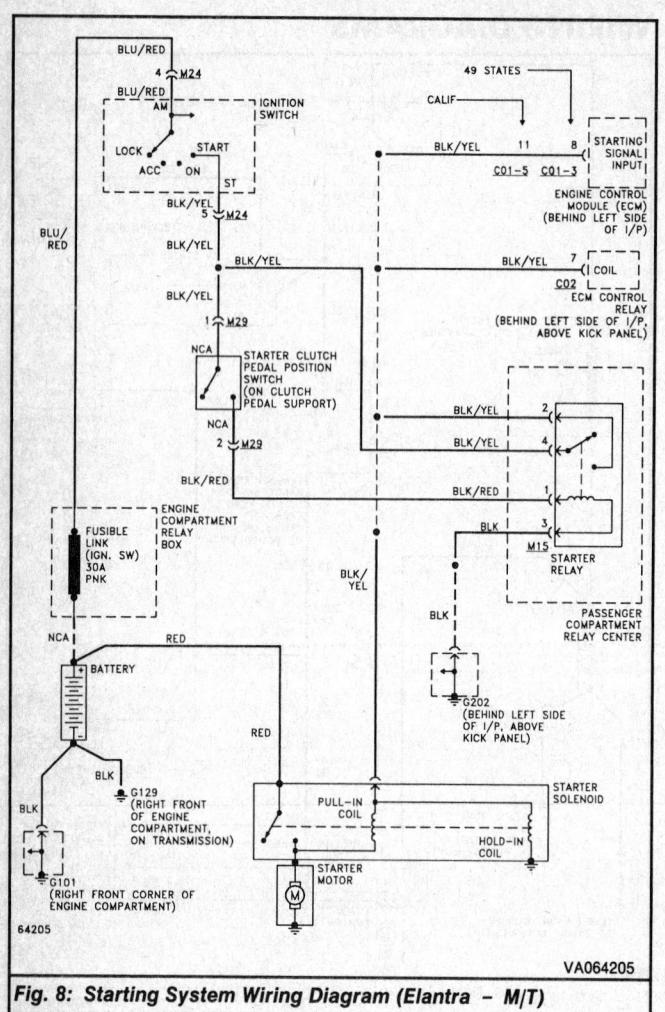

Fig. 8: Starting System Wiring Diagram (Elantra – M/T)

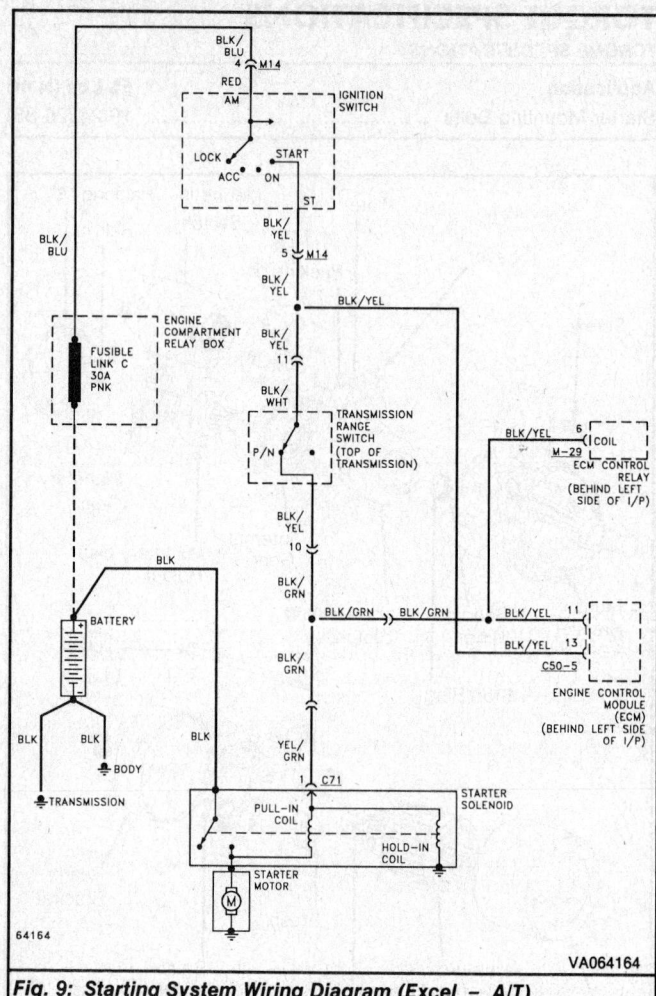

Fig. 9: Starting System Wiring Diagram (Excel – A/T)

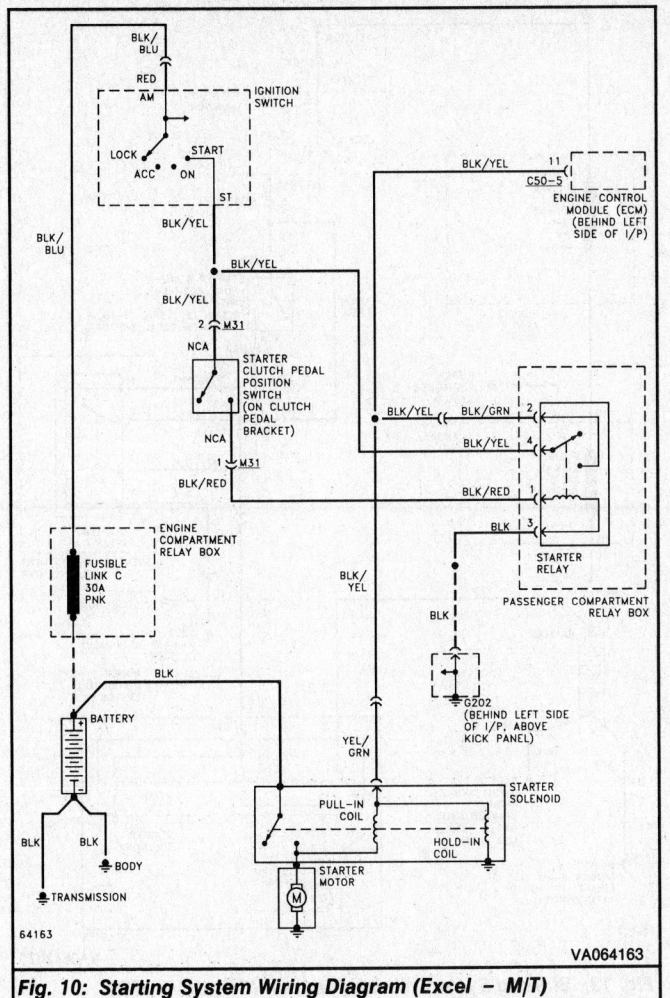

Fig. 10: Starting System Wiring Diagram (Excel – M/T)

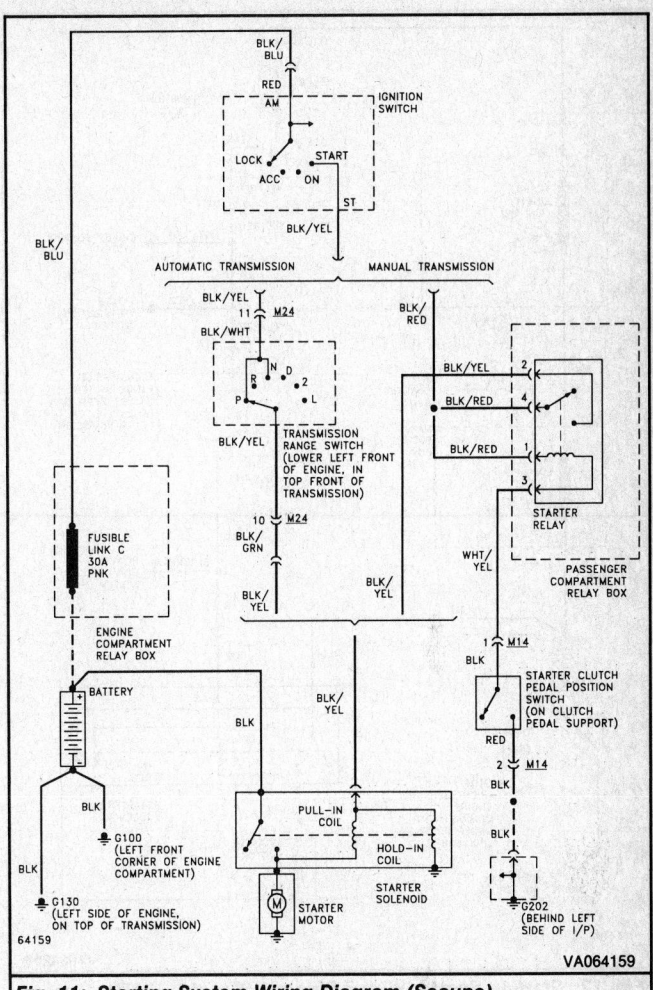

Fig. 11: Starting System Wiring Diagram (Scoupe)

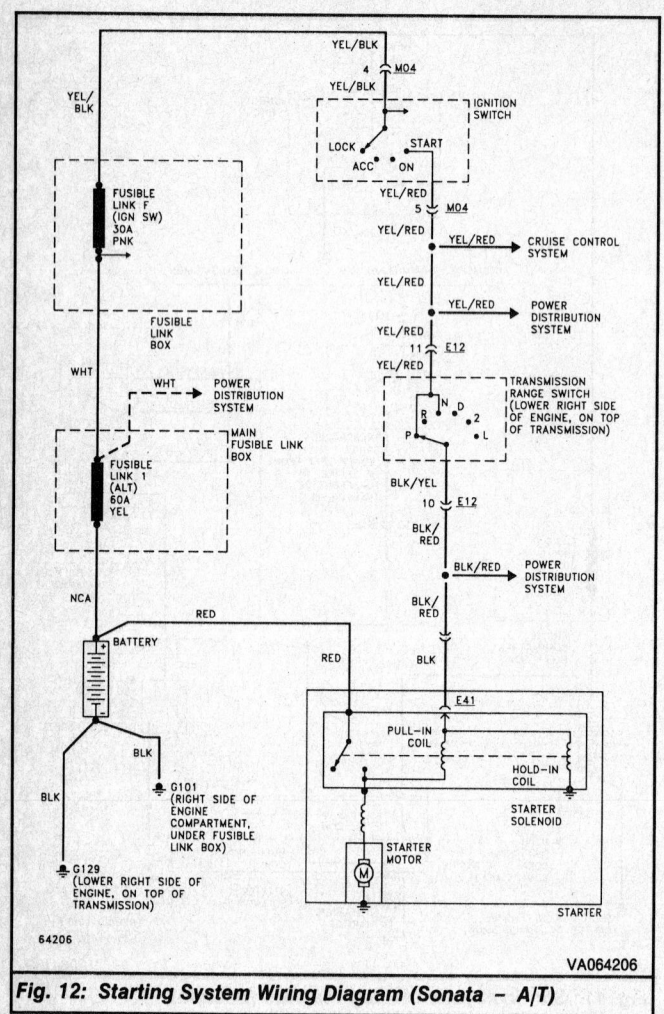

Fig. 12: Starting System Wiring Diagram (Sonata – A/T)

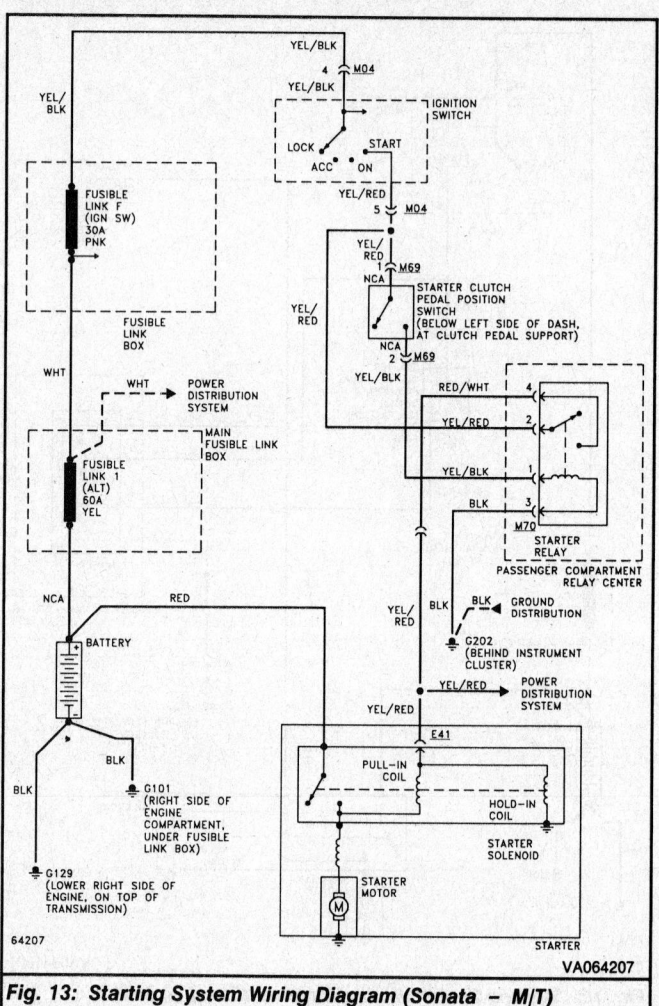

Fig. 13: Starting System Wiring Diagram (Sonata – M/T)

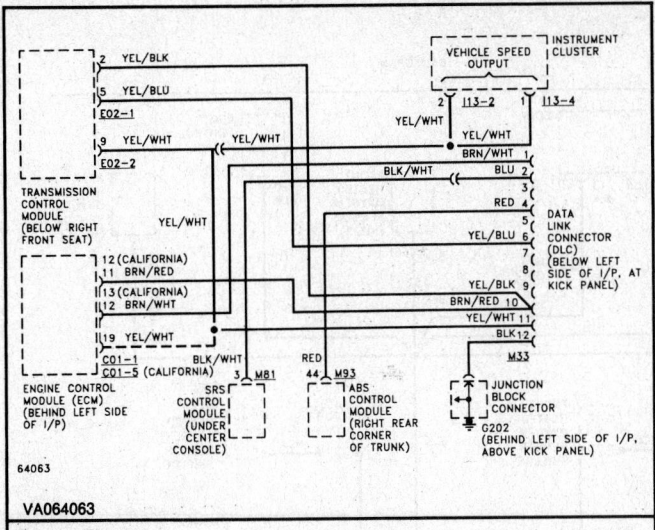

Fig. 1: Elantra

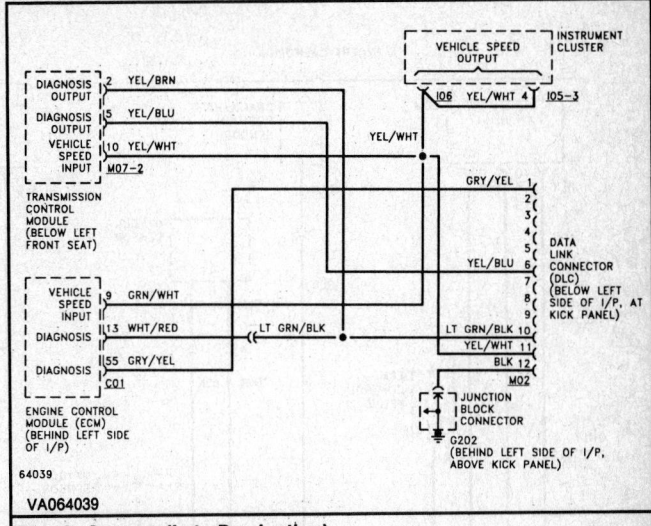

Fig. 4: Scoupe (Late Production)

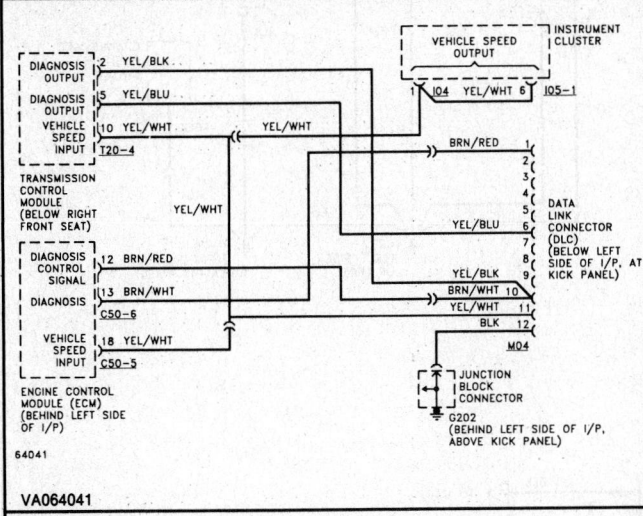

Fig. 2: Excel

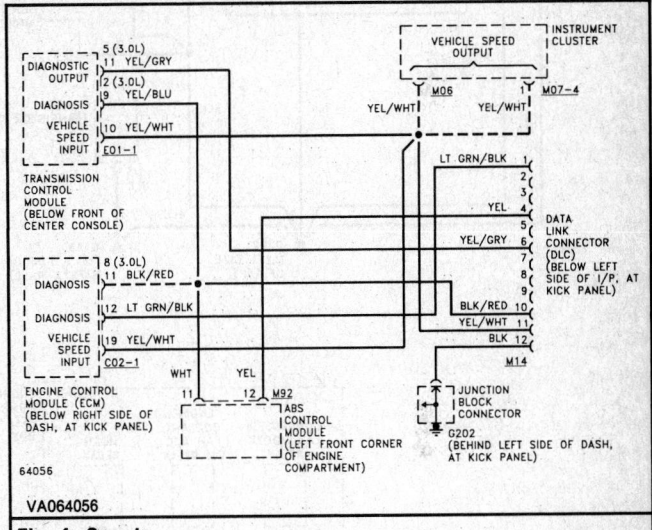

Fig. 4: Sonata

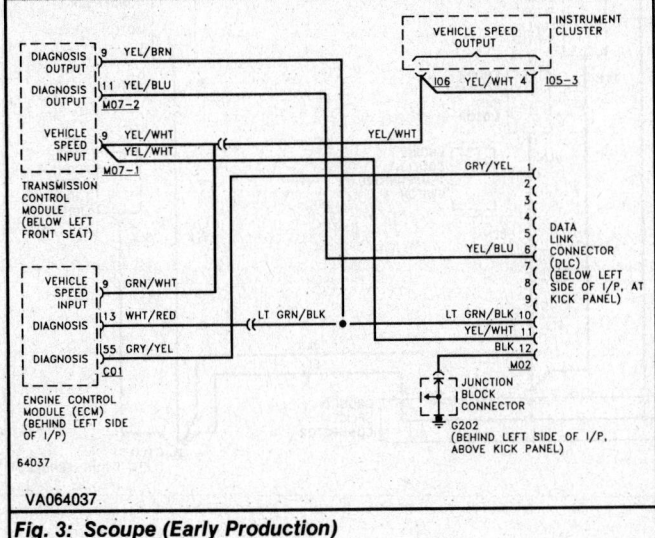

Fig. 3: Scoupe (Early Production)

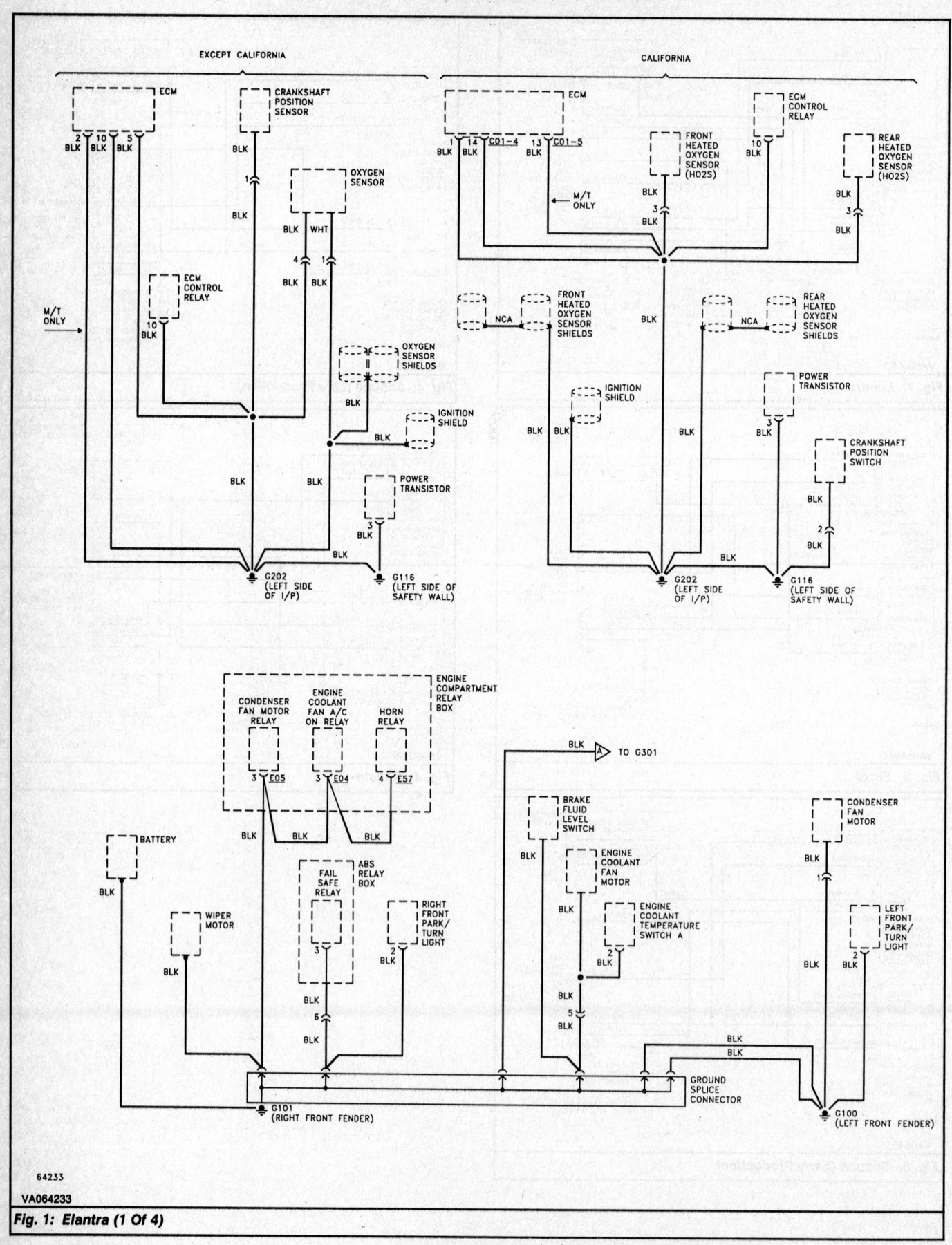

64233

VA064233

Fig. 1: Elantra (1 Of 4)

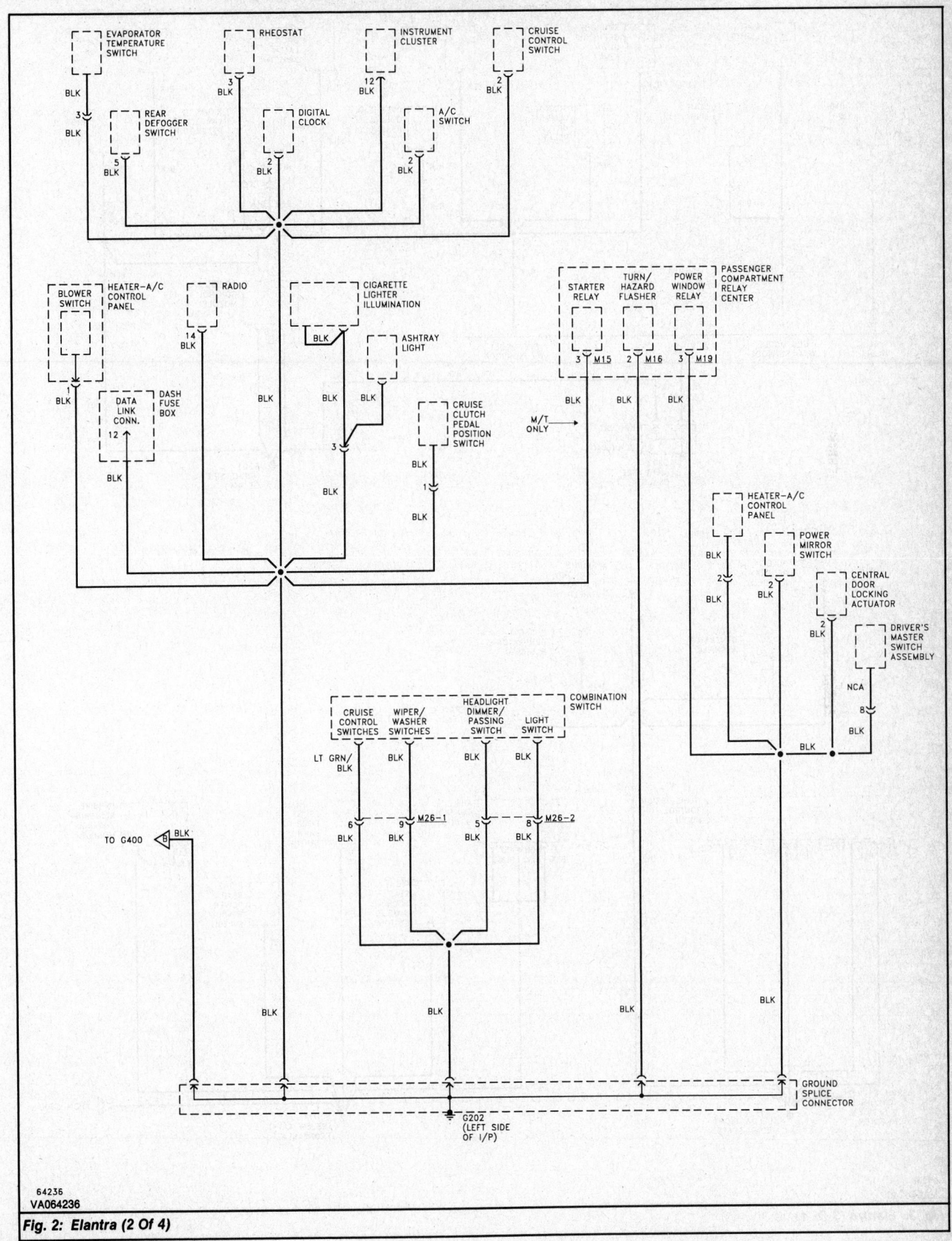

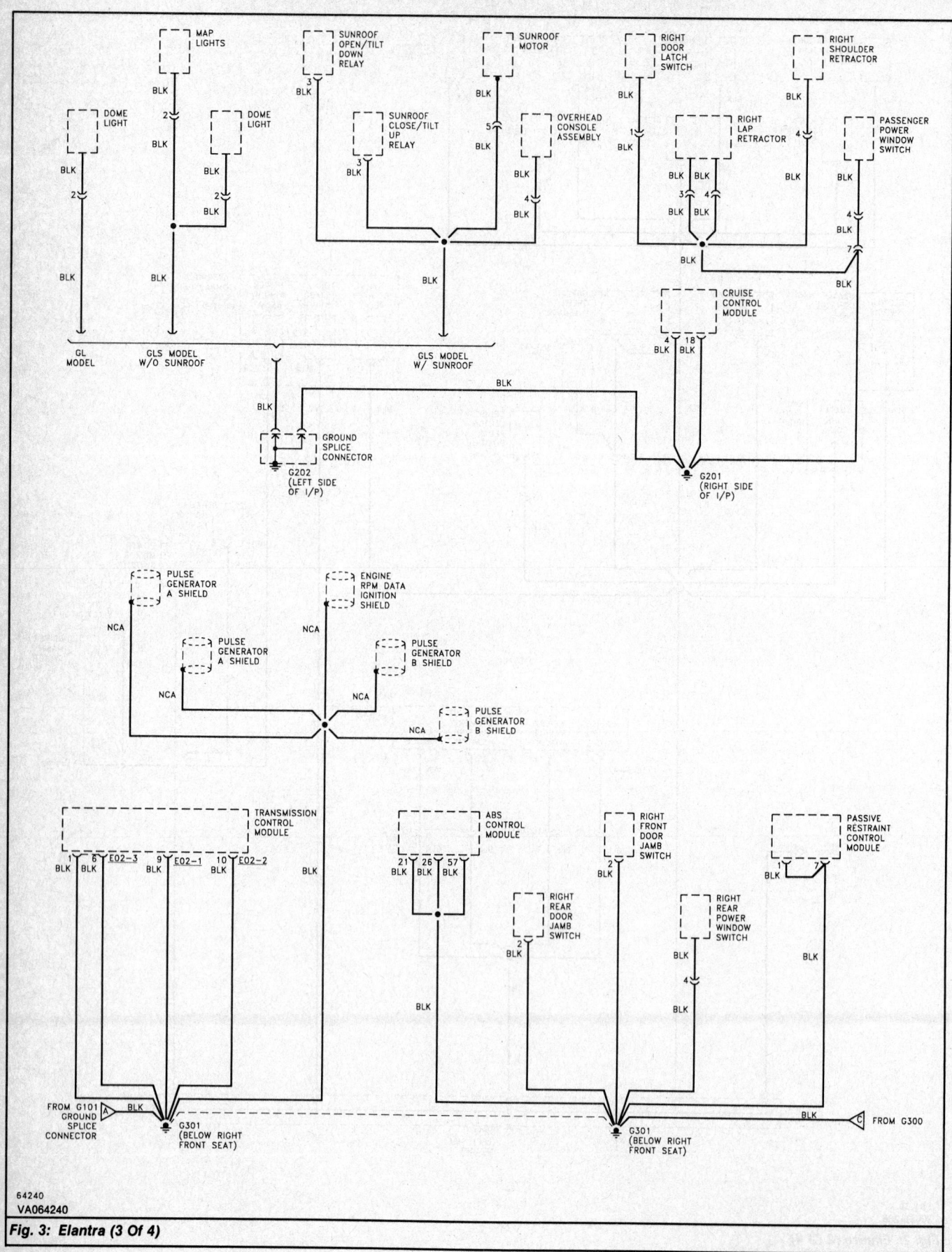

Fig. 3: Elantra (3 Of 4)

64240
VA064240

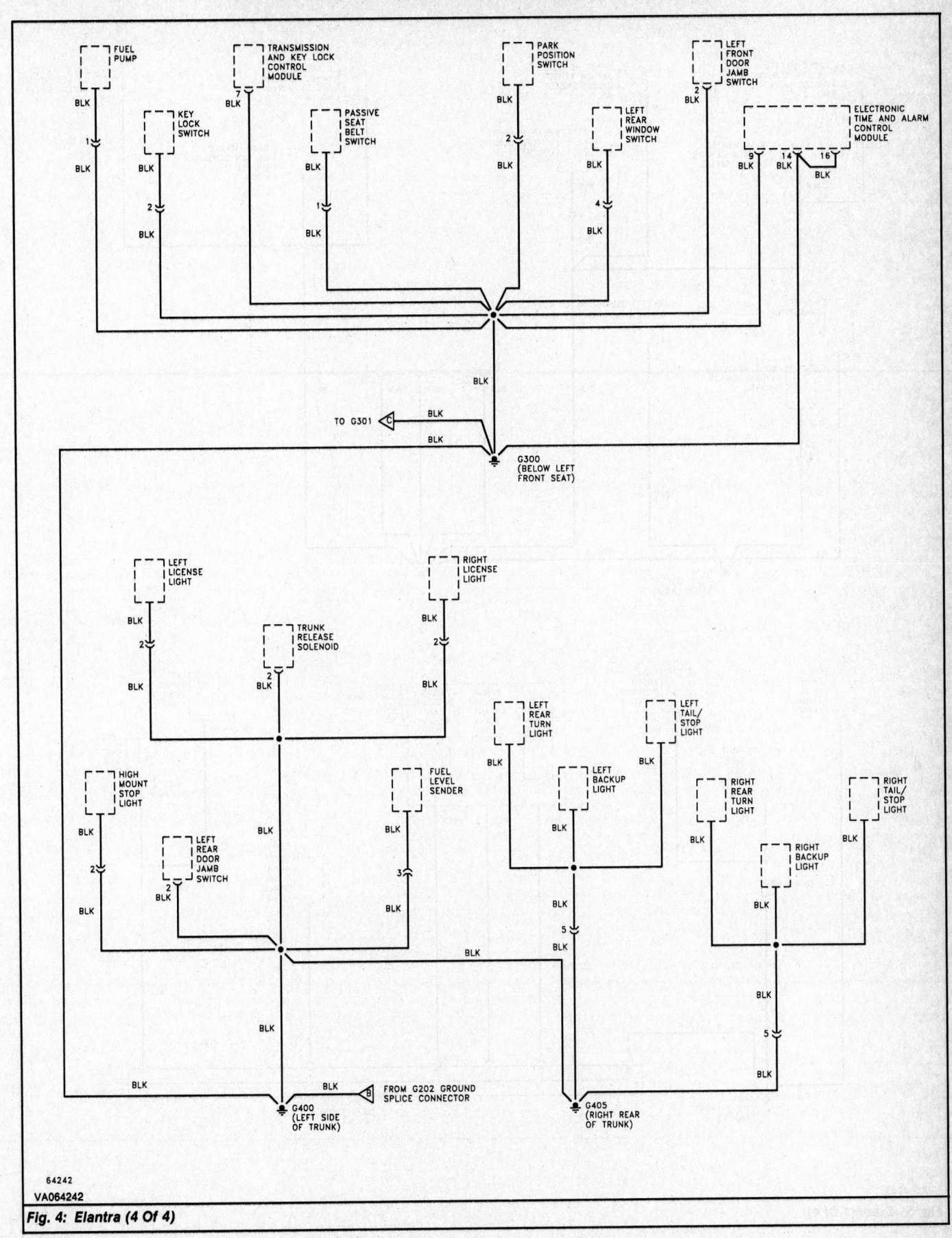

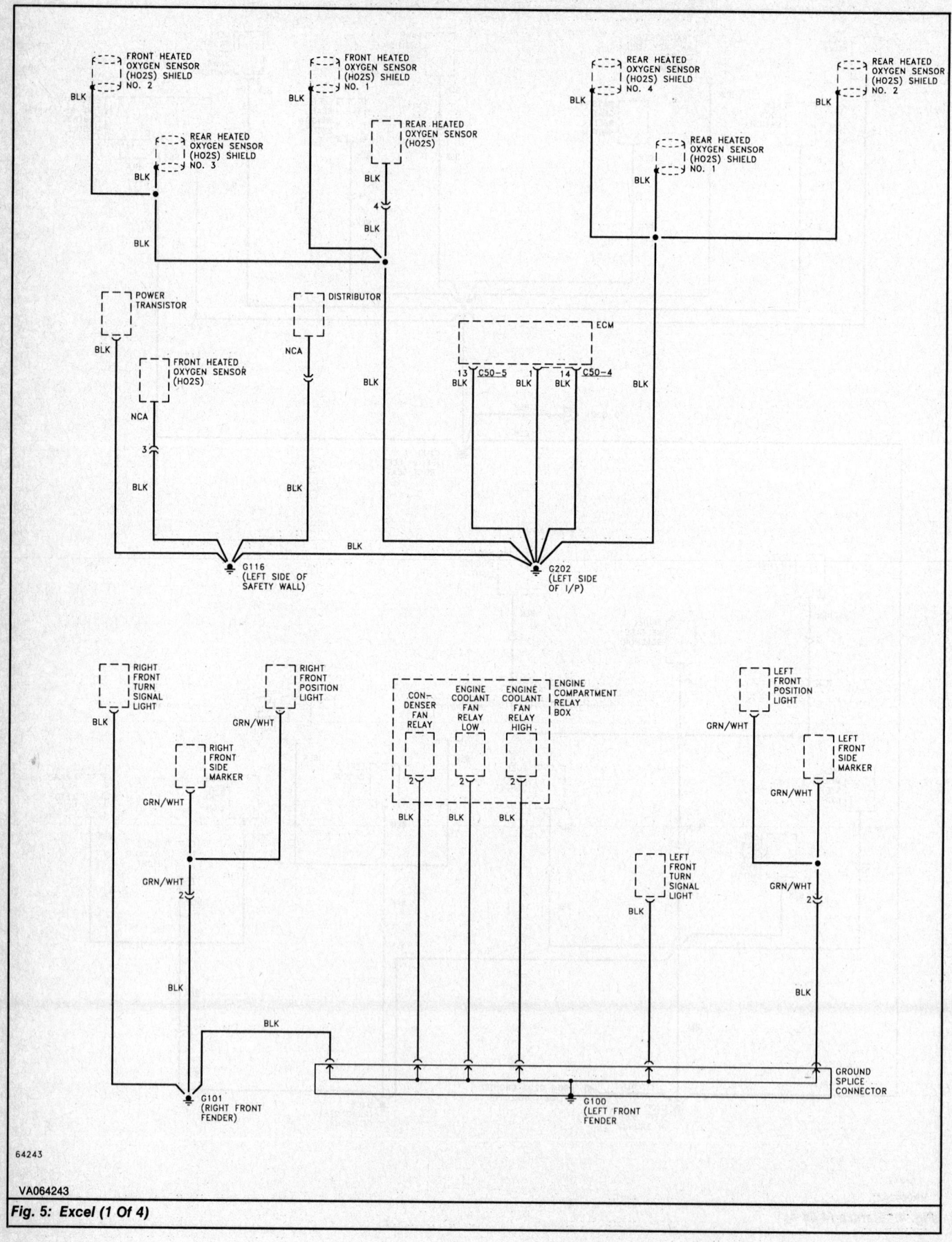

64243

VA064243

Fig. 5: Excel (1 Of 4)

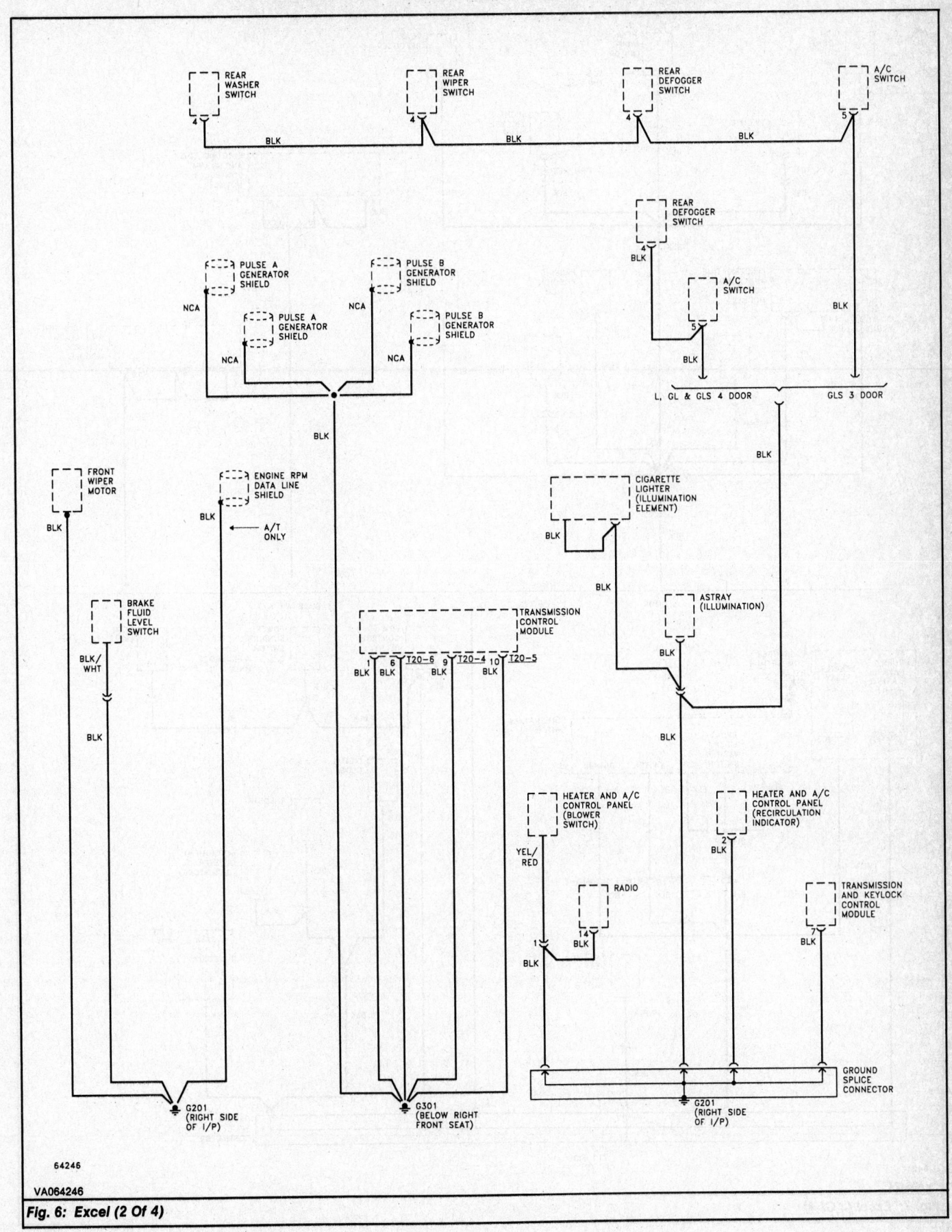

64246

VA064246

Fig. 6: Excel (2 Of 4)

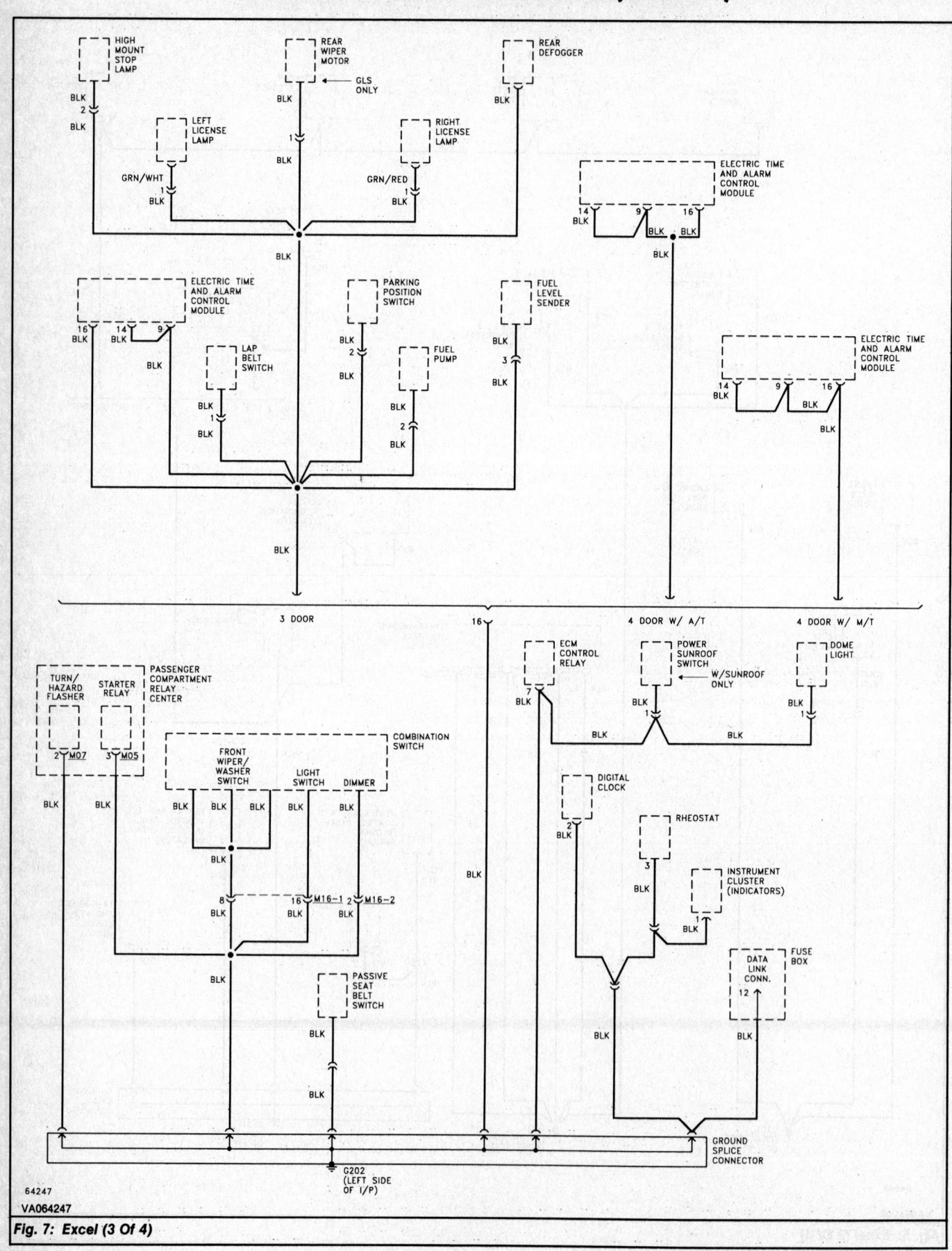

64247

VA064247

Fig. 7: Excel (3 Of 4)

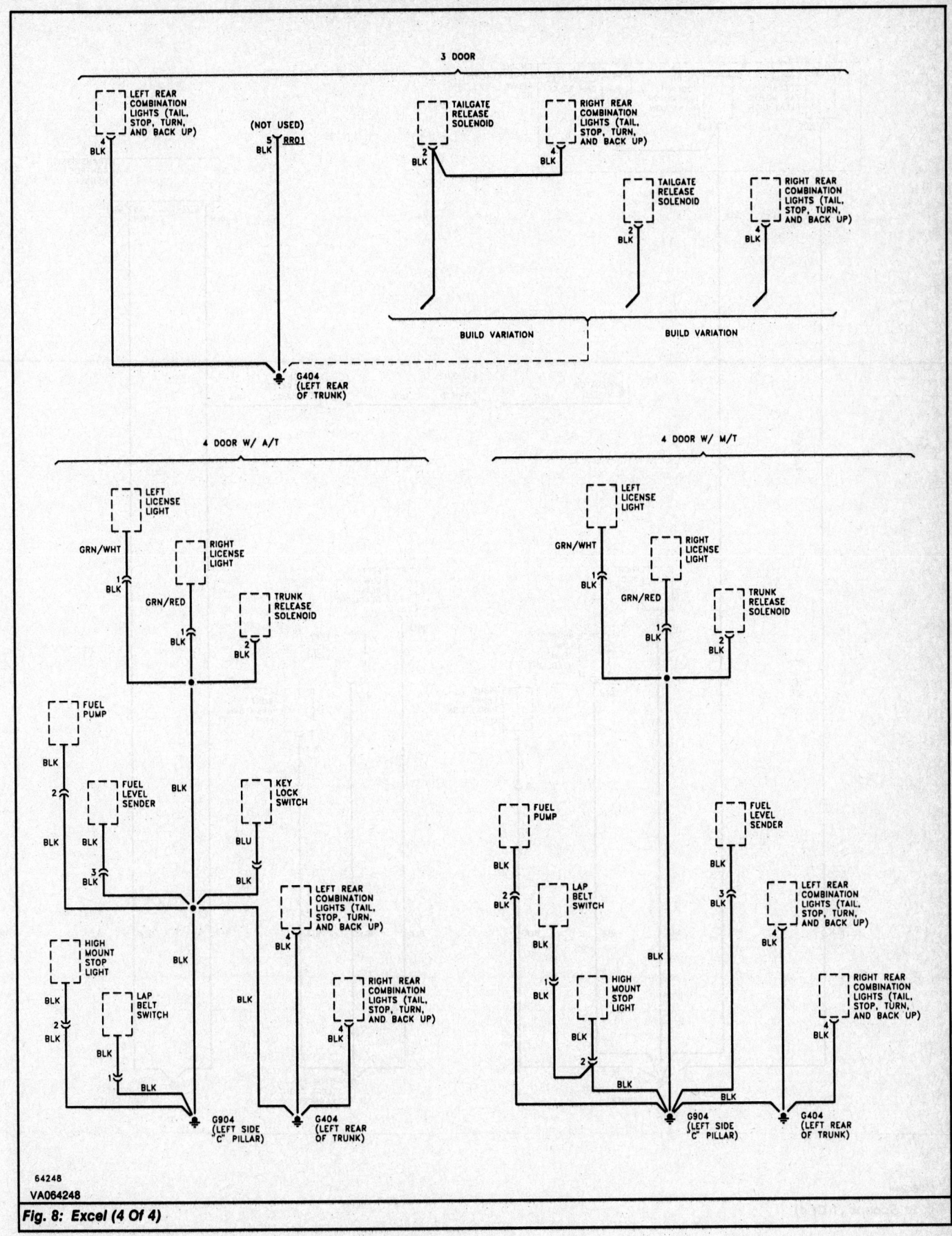

64248

VA064248

Fig. 8: Excel (4 Of 4)

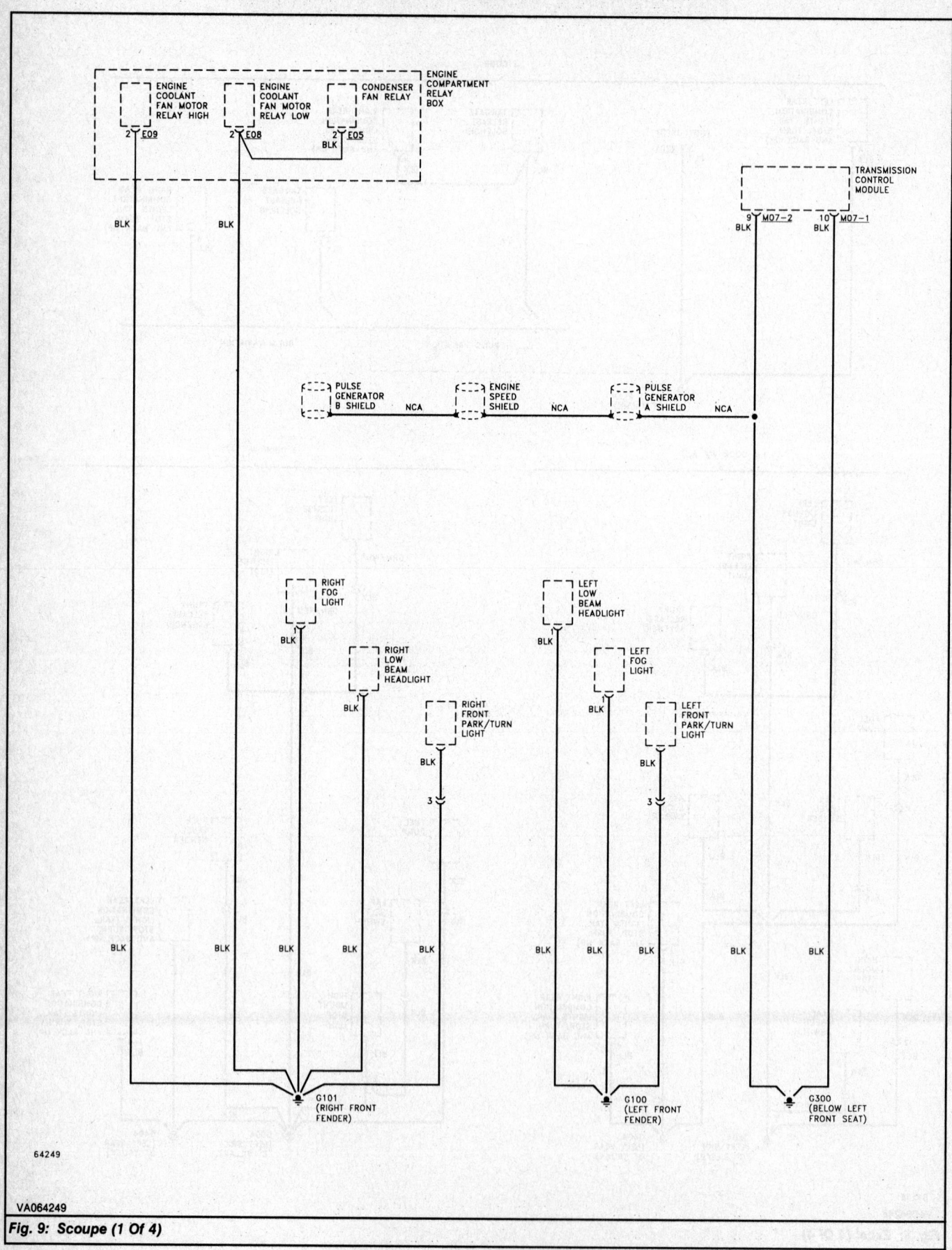

64249

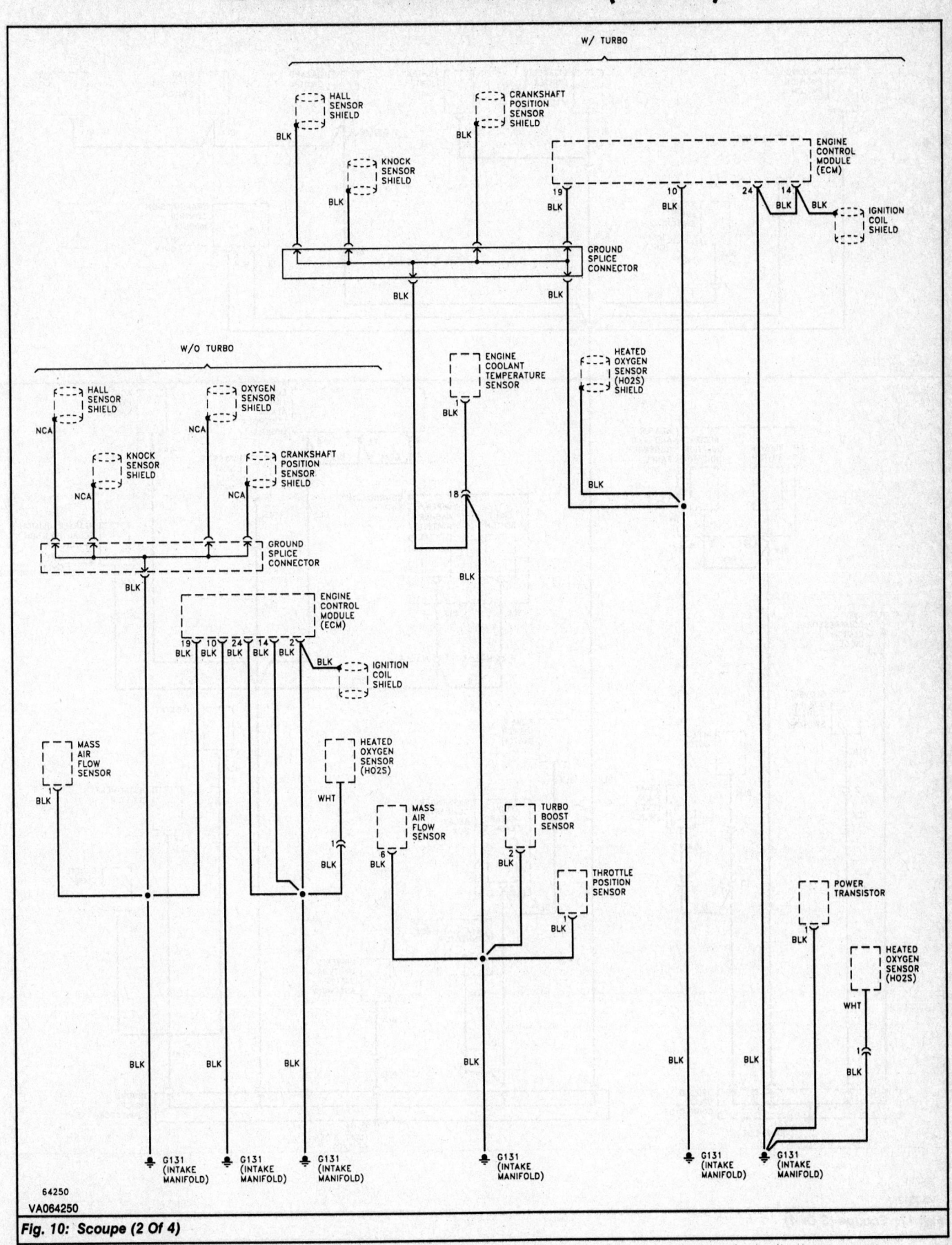

64250
VA064250

Fig. 10: Scoupe (2 Of 4)

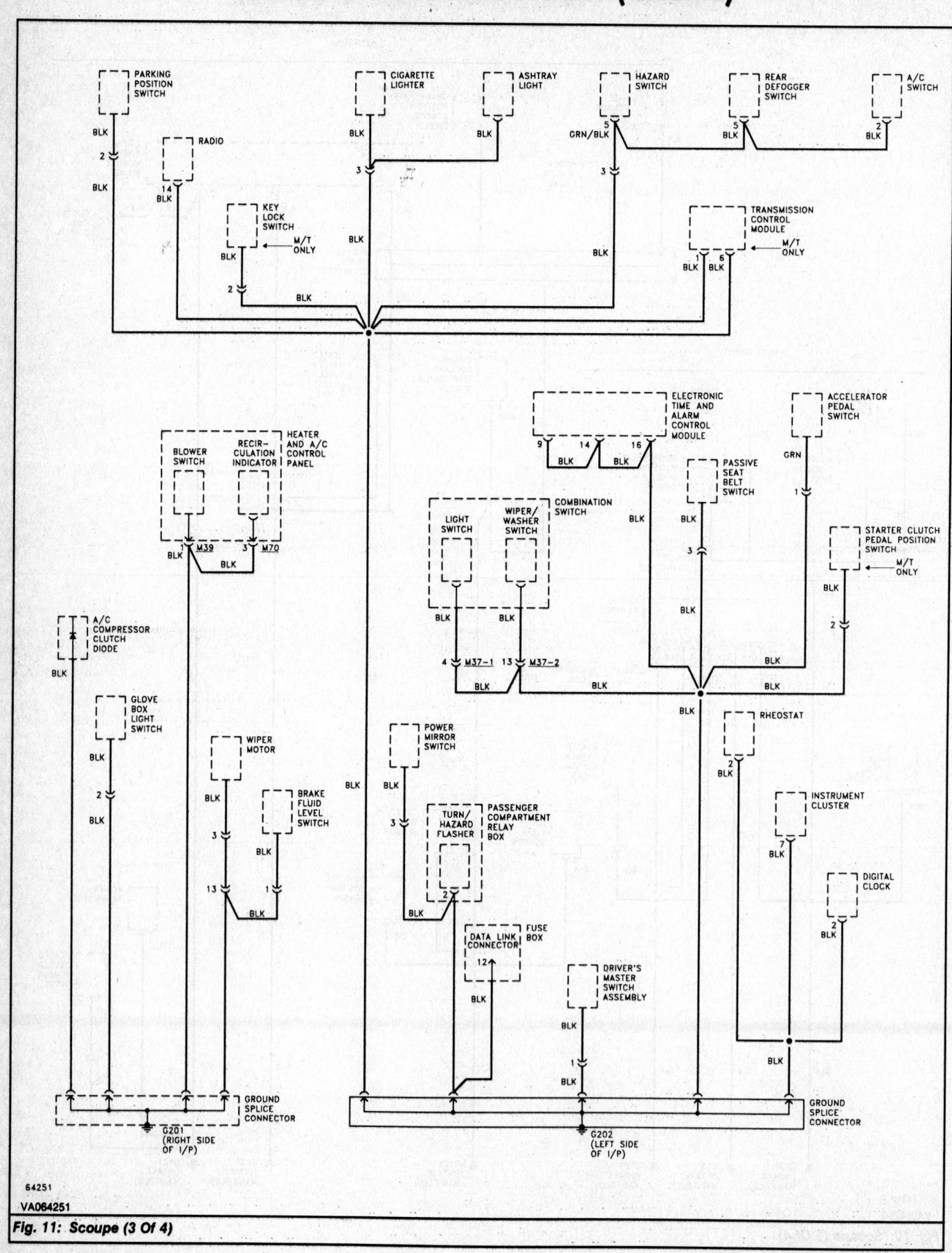

64251

VA064251

Fig. 11: Scoupe (3 Of 4)

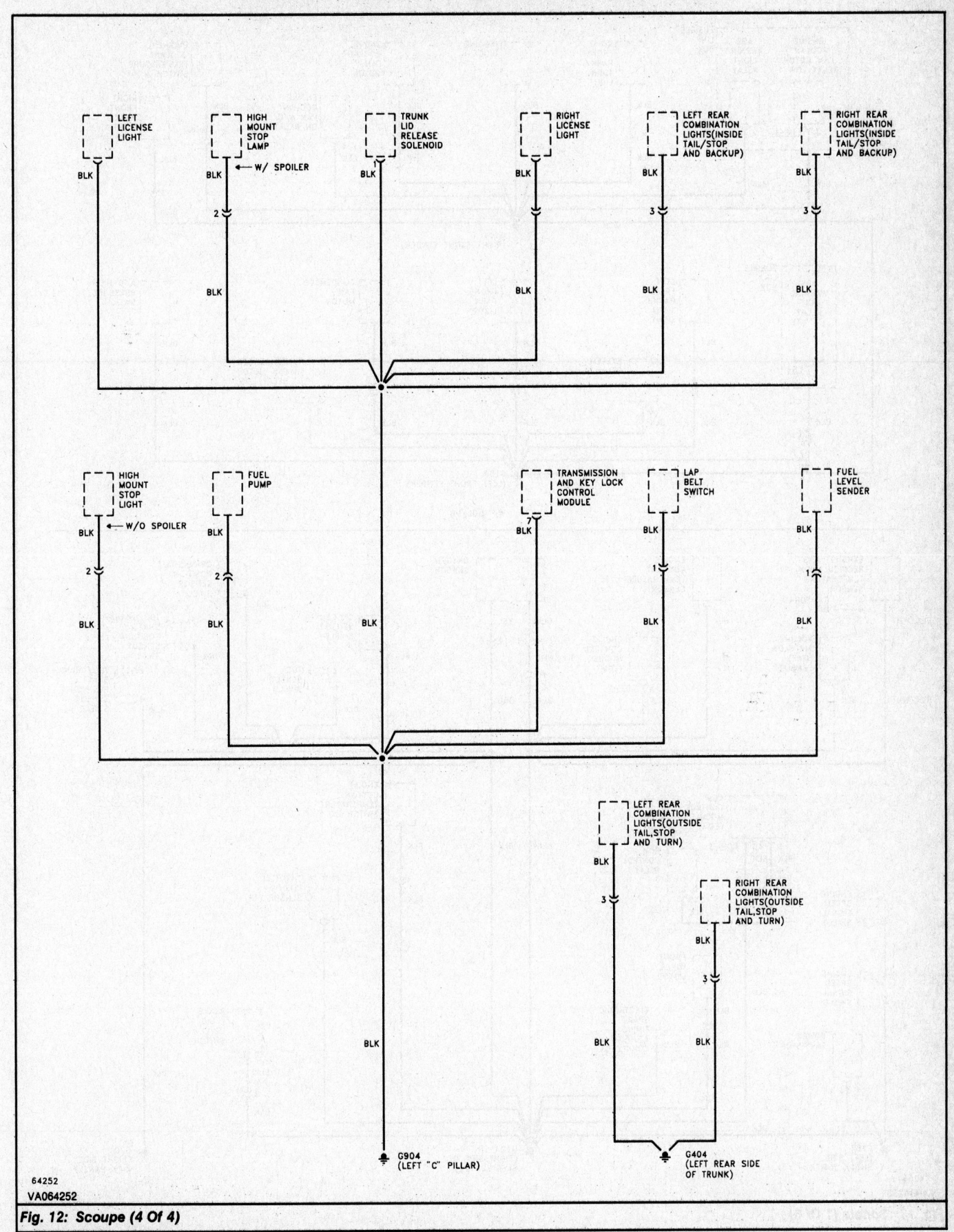

Fig. 12: Scoupe (4 Of 4)

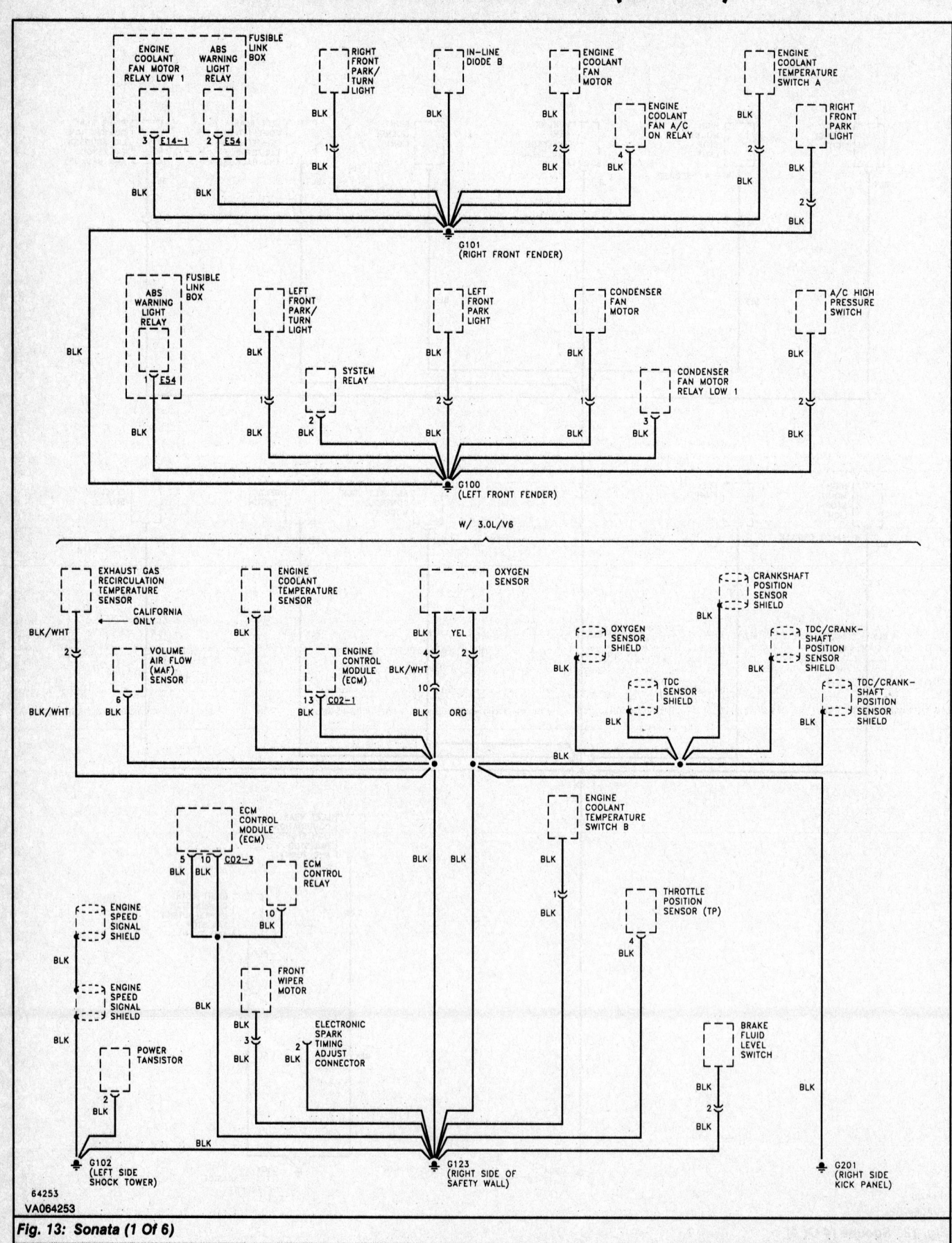

64253
VA064253

Fig. 13: Sonata (1 Of 6)

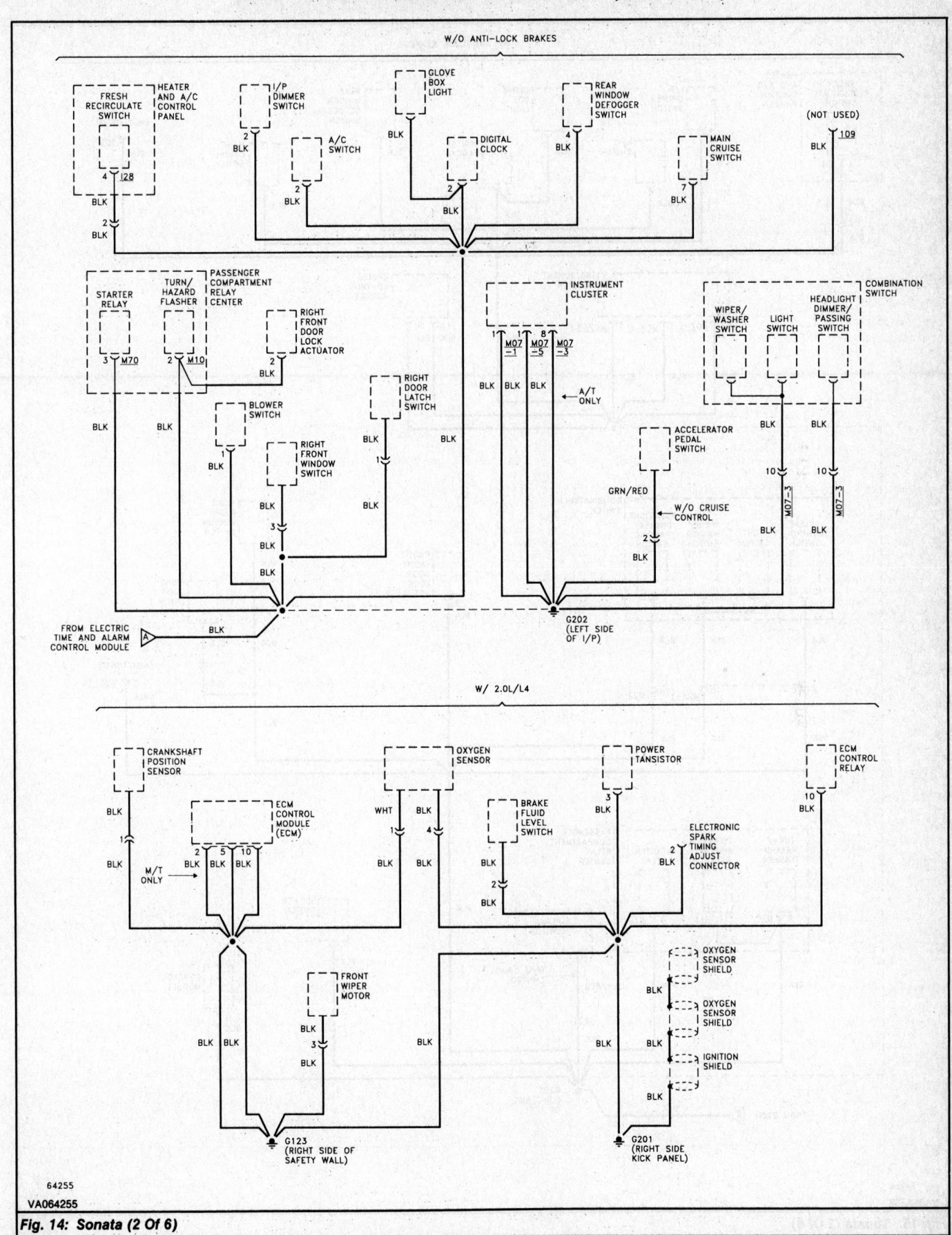

64255

VA064255

Fig. 14: Sonata (2 Of 6)

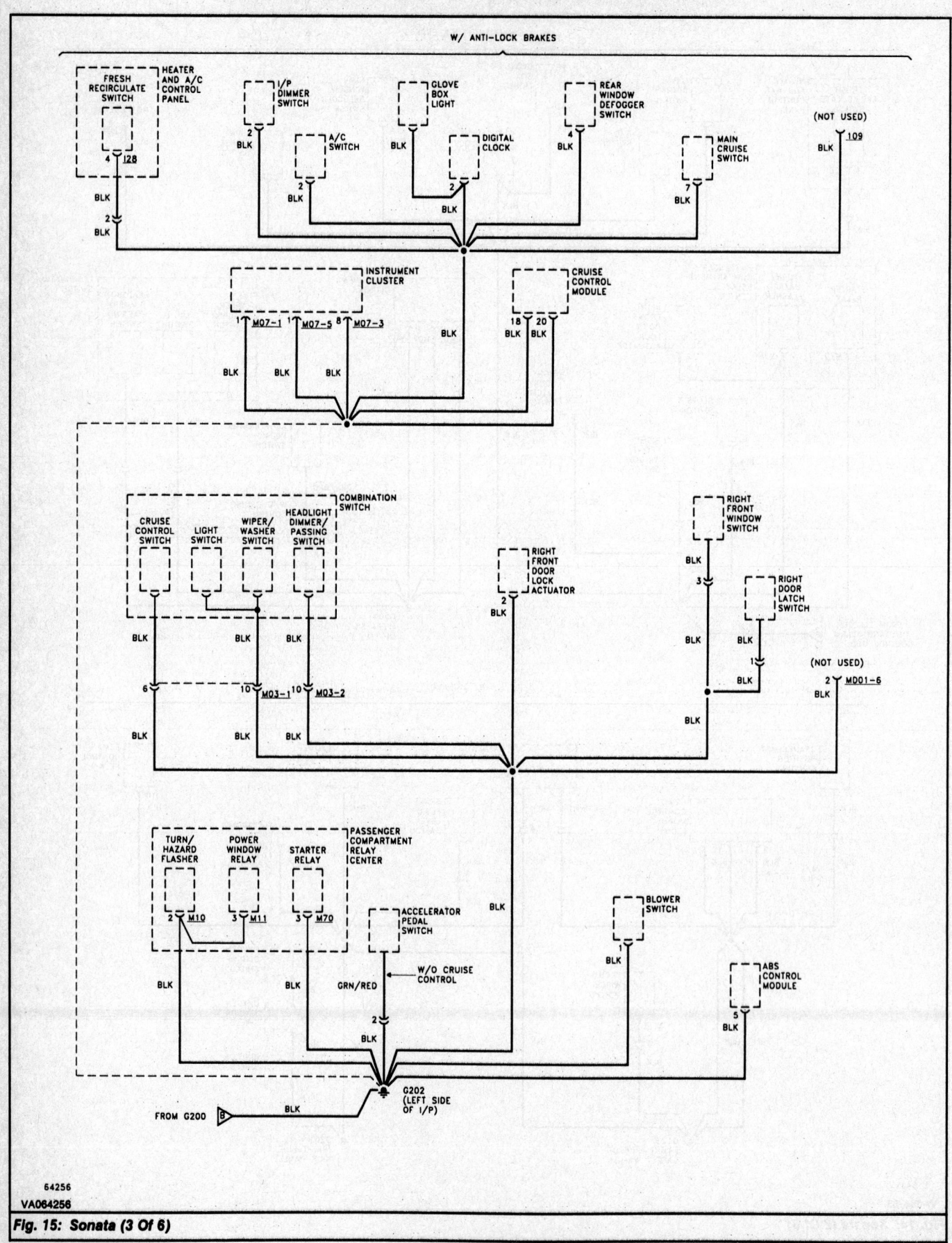

64256

VA064256

Fig. 15: Sonata (3 Of 6)

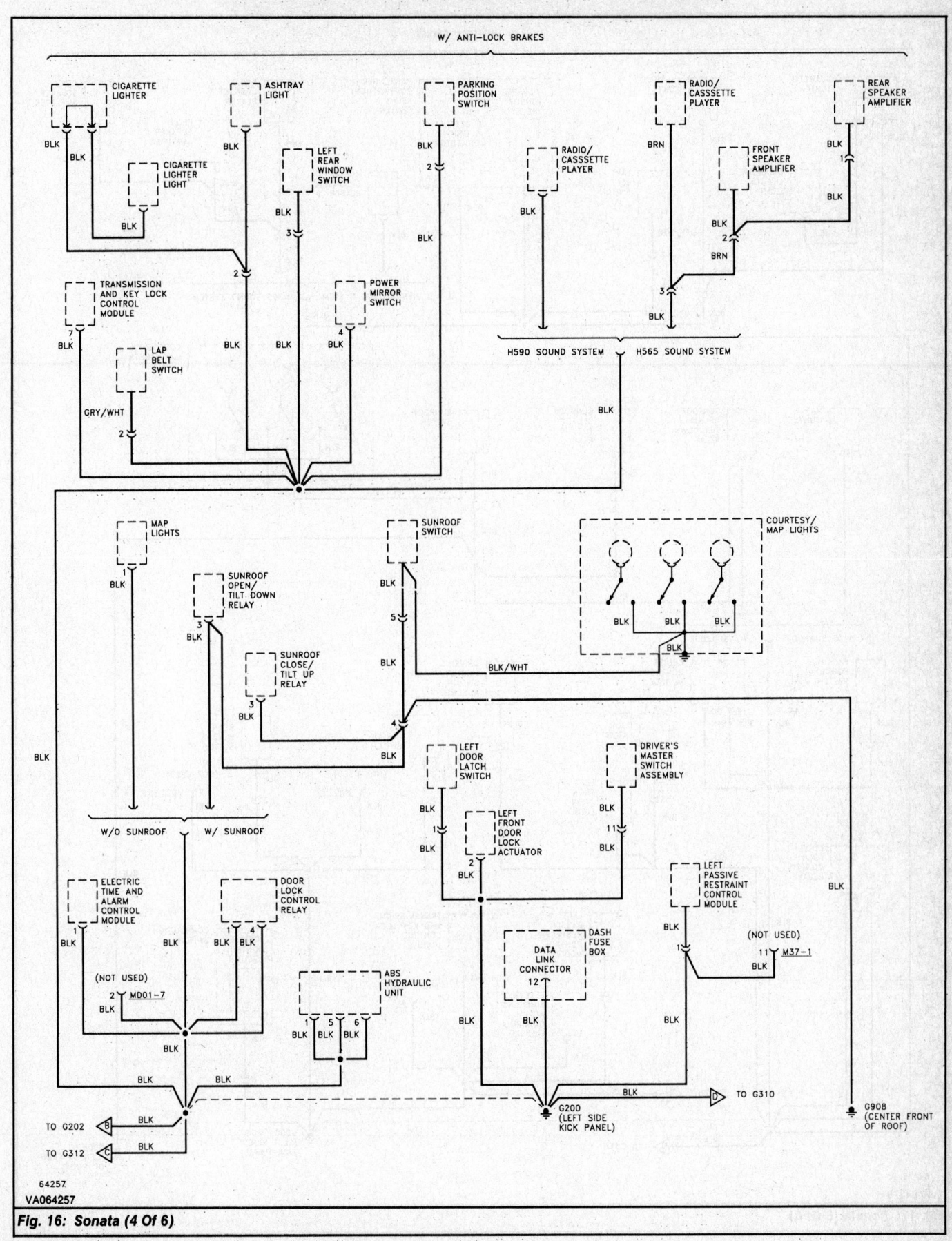

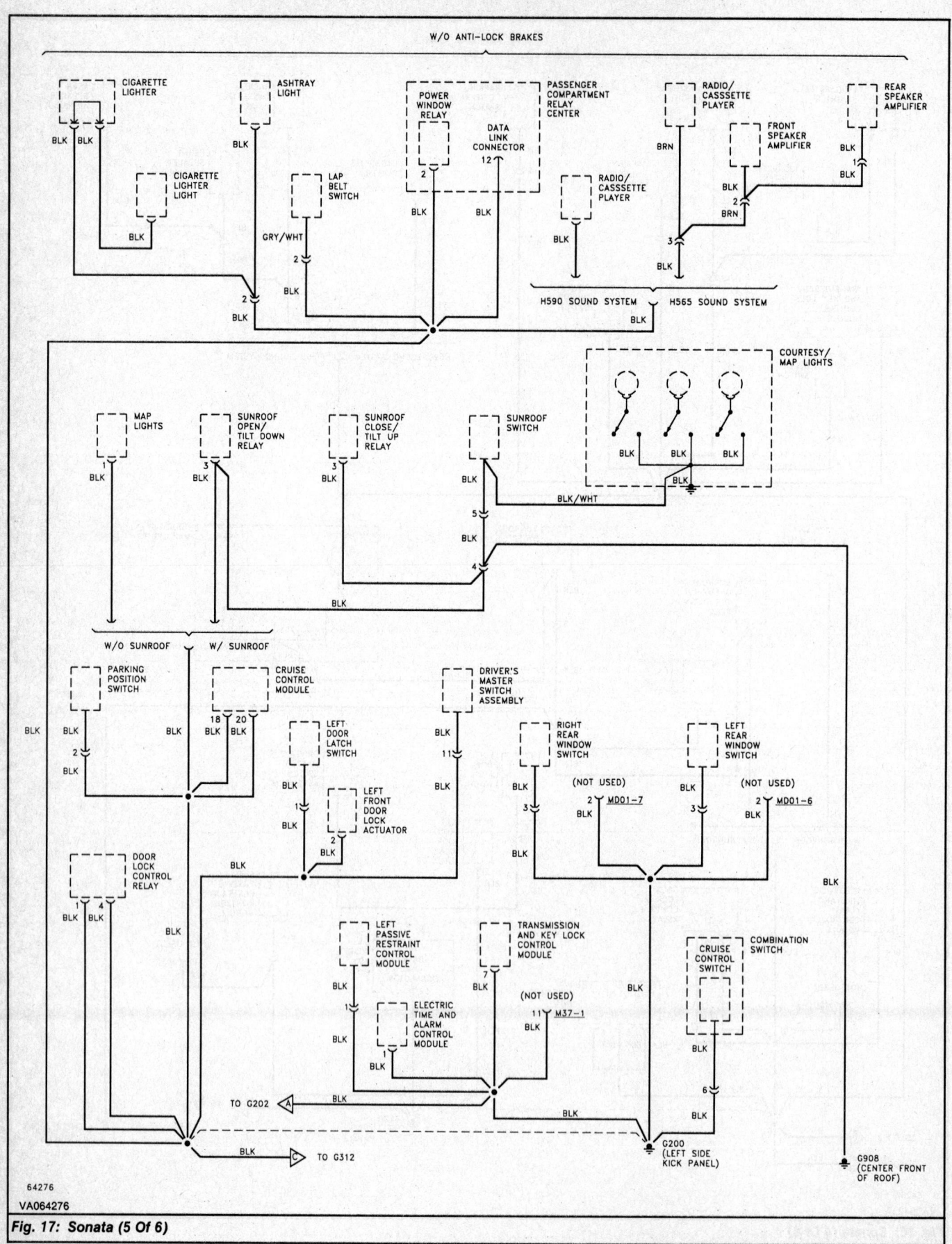

64276

VA064276

Fig. 17: Sonata (5 Of 6)

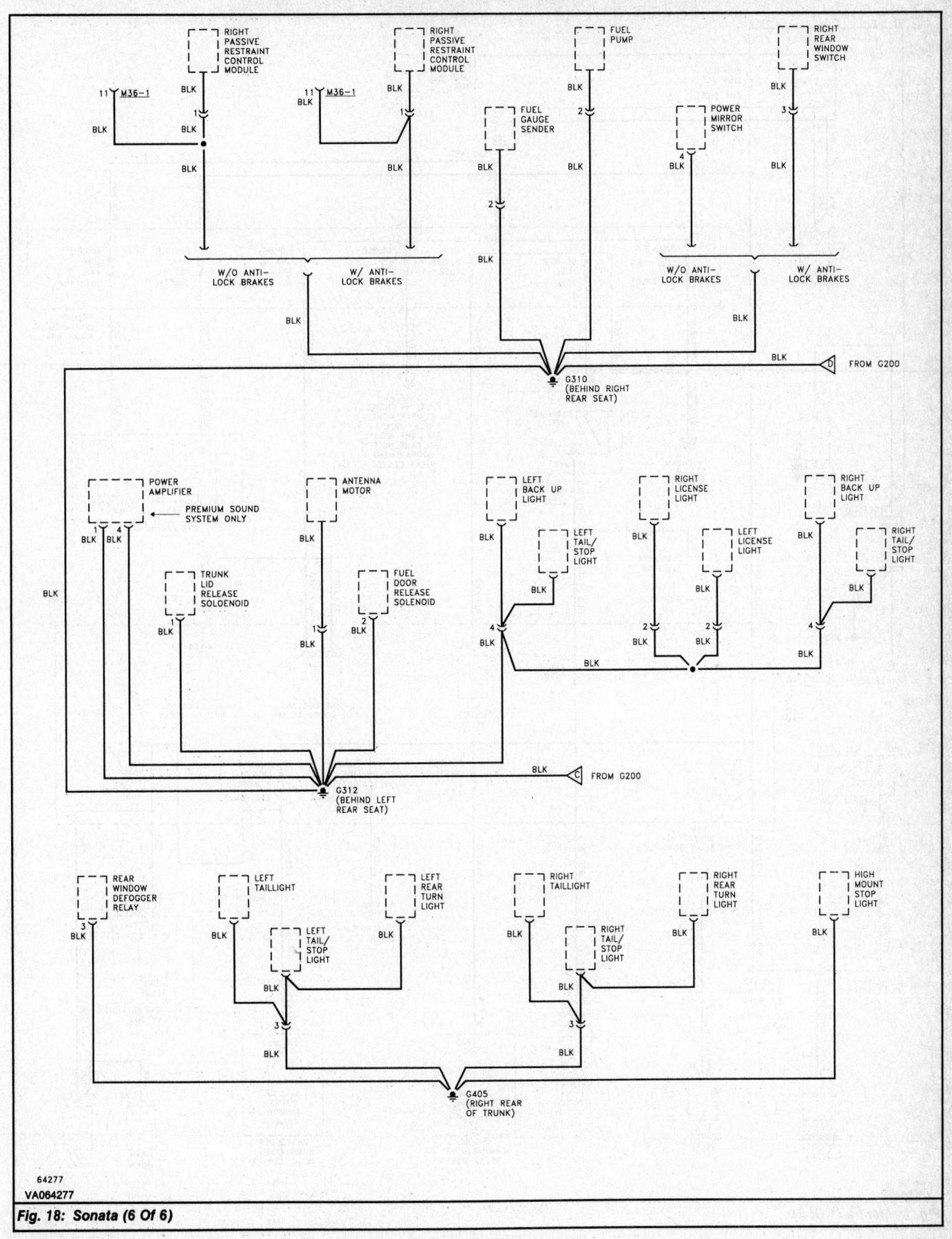

Fig. 18: Sonata (6 Of 6)

64277

VA064277

1994 WIRING DIAGRAMS
Power Distribution

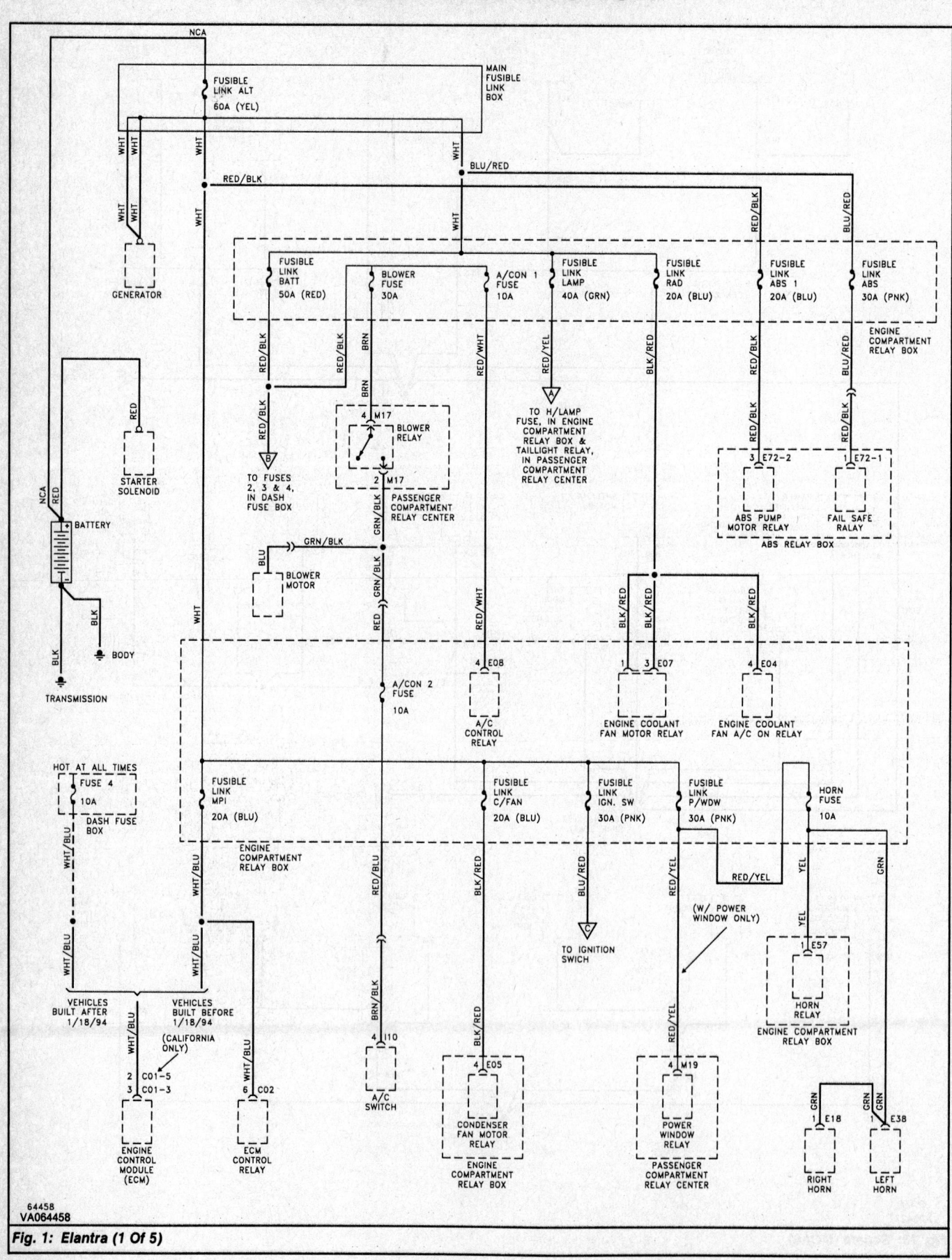

Fig. 1: Elantra (1 Of 5)

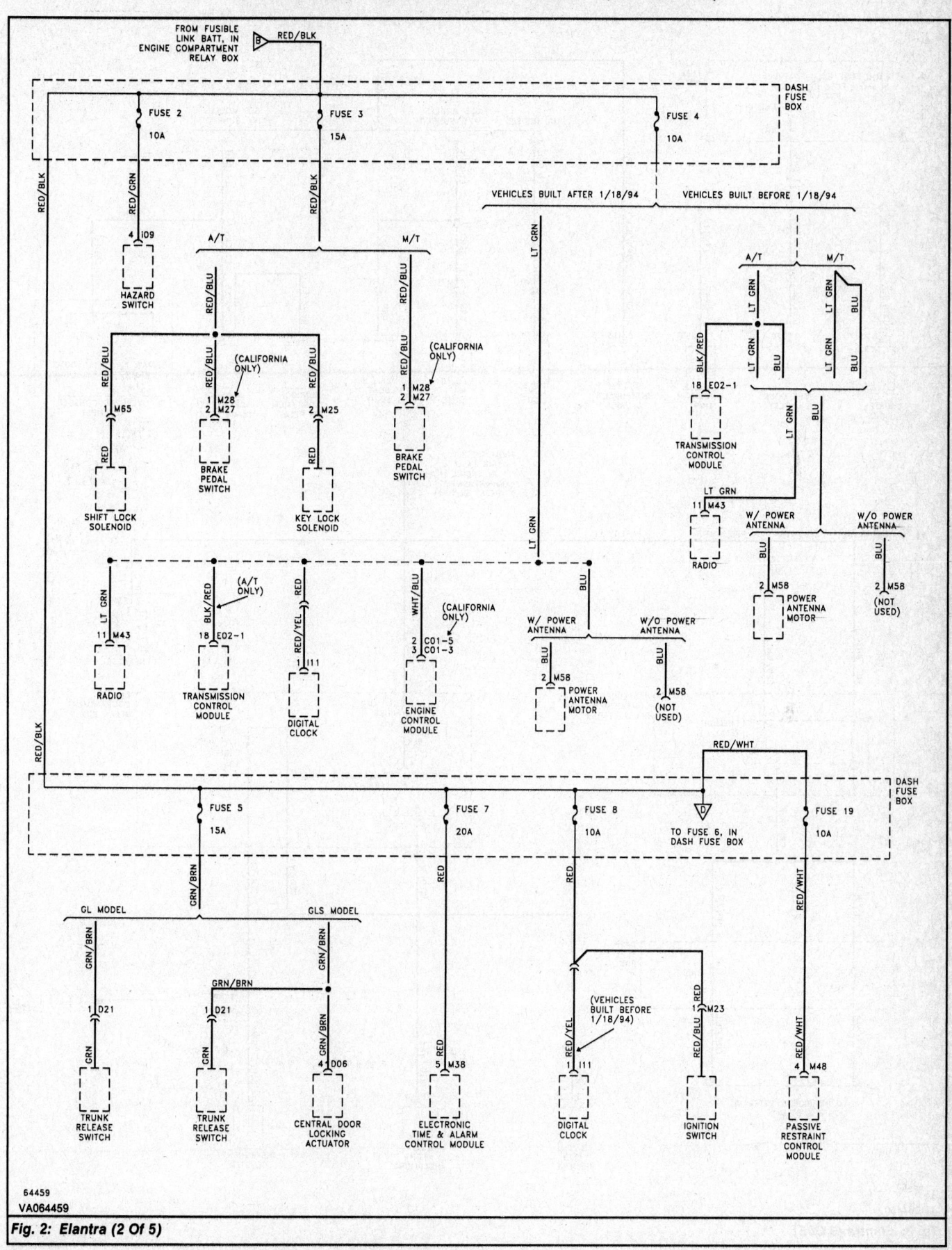

64459

VA064459

Fig. 2: Elantra (2 Of 5)

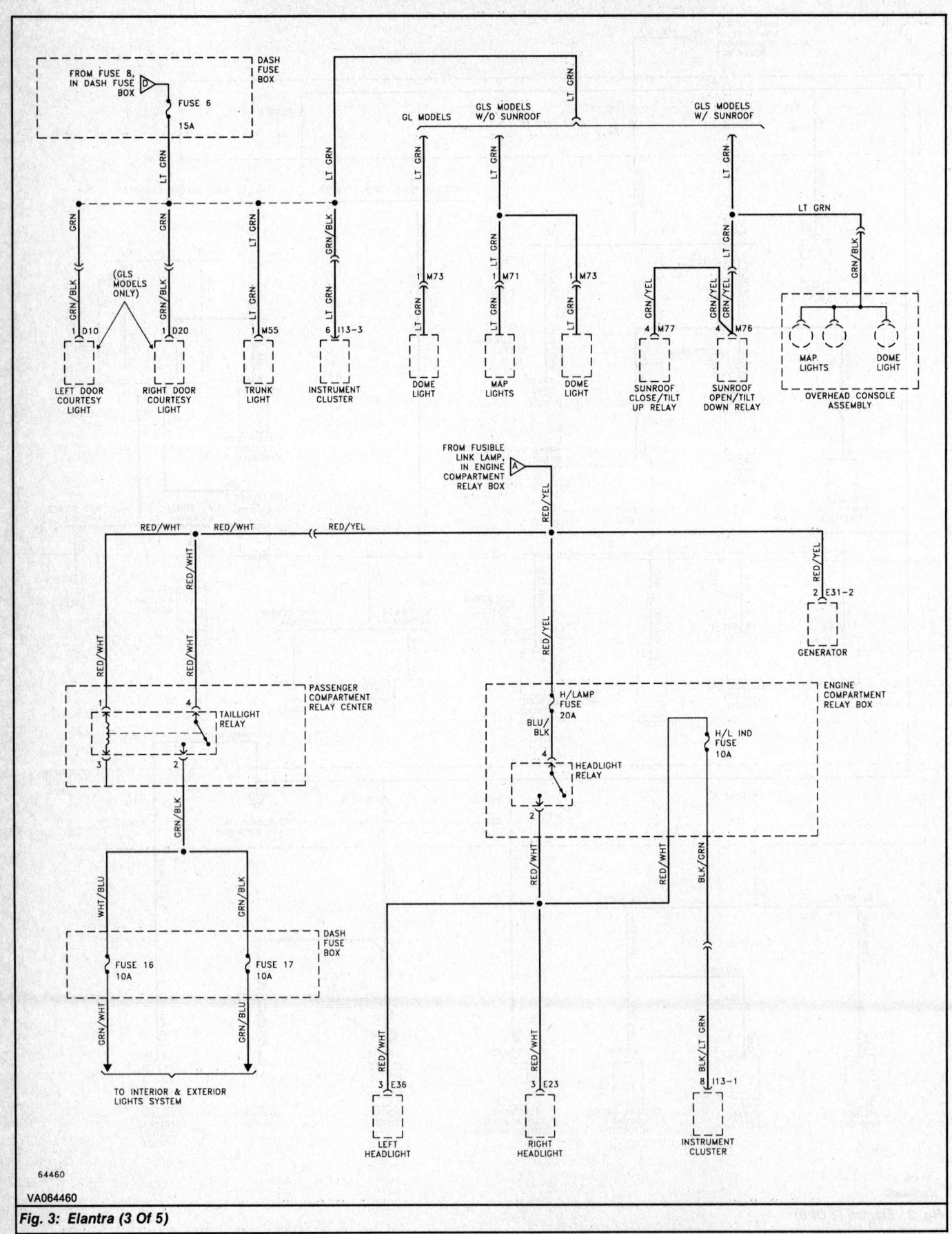

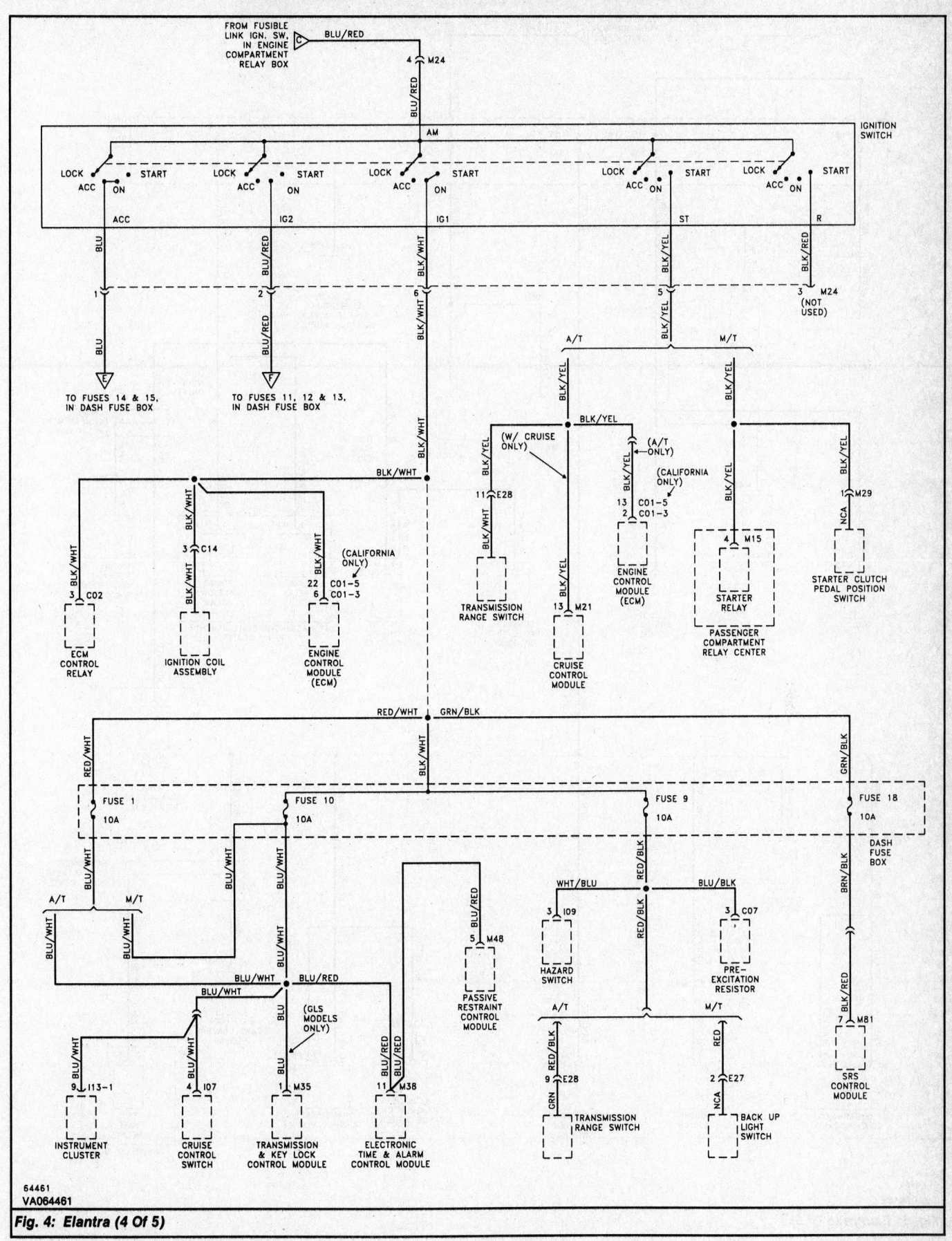

64461
VA064461

Fig. 4: Elantra (4 Of 5)

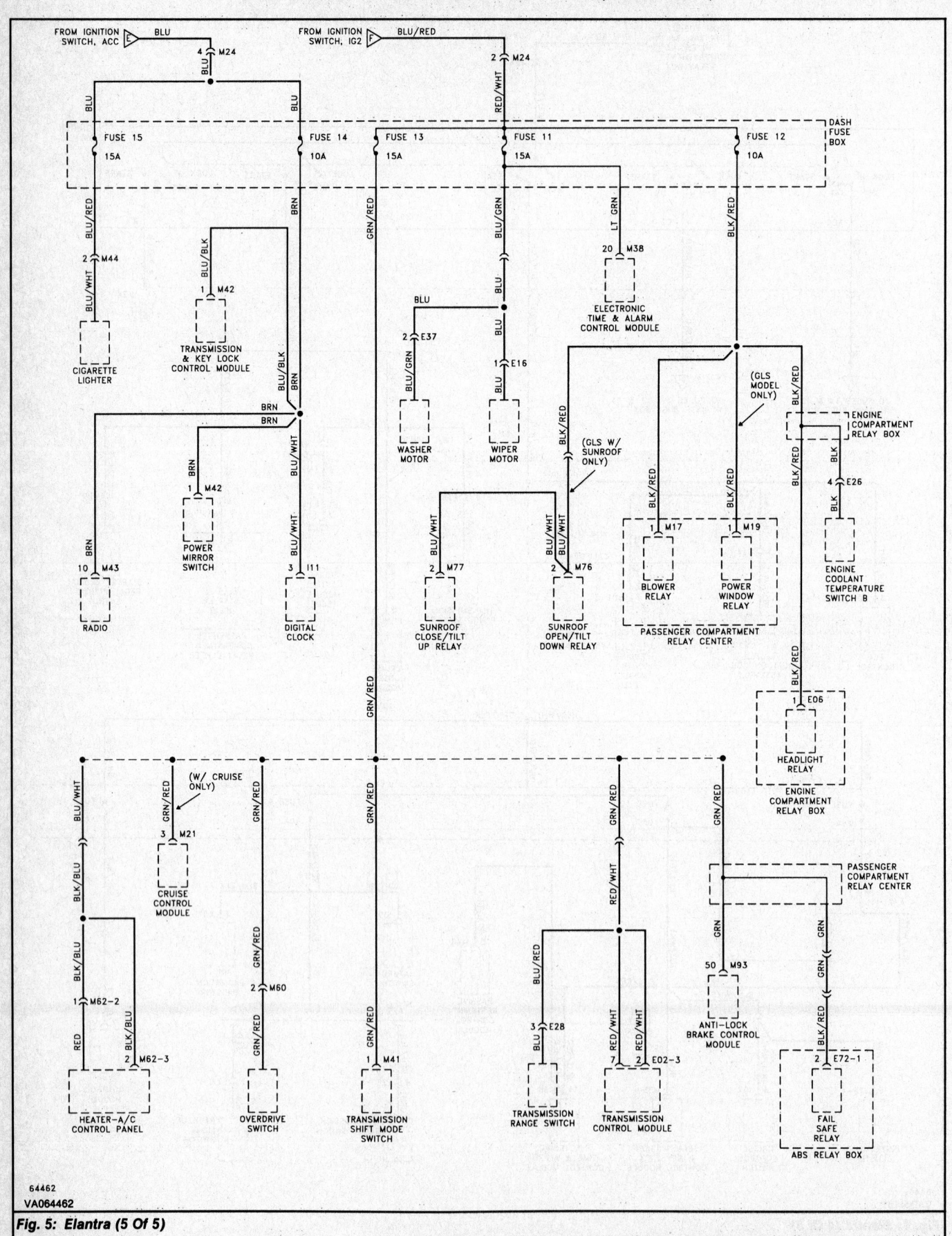

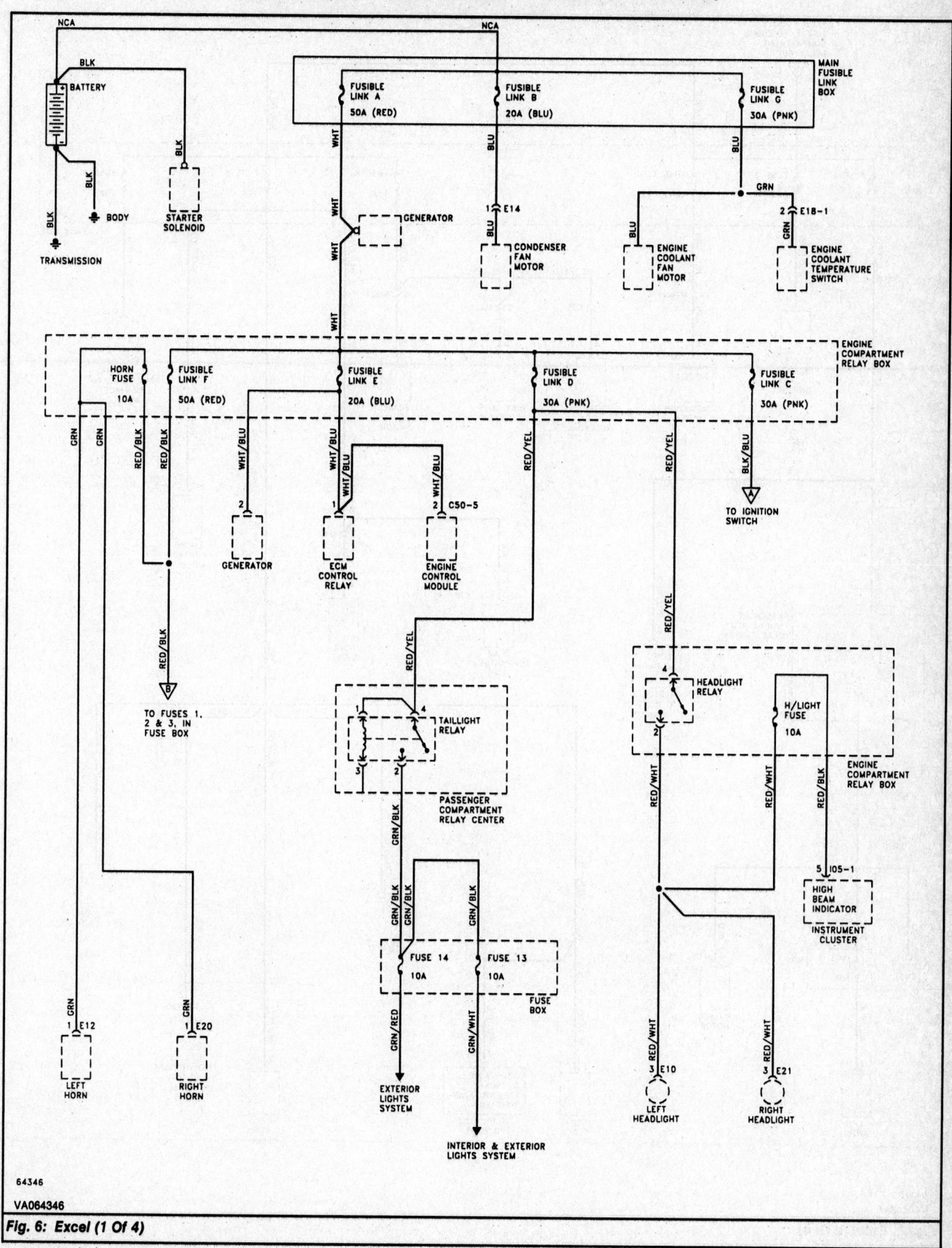

64346

VA064346

Fig. 6: Excel (1 Of 4)

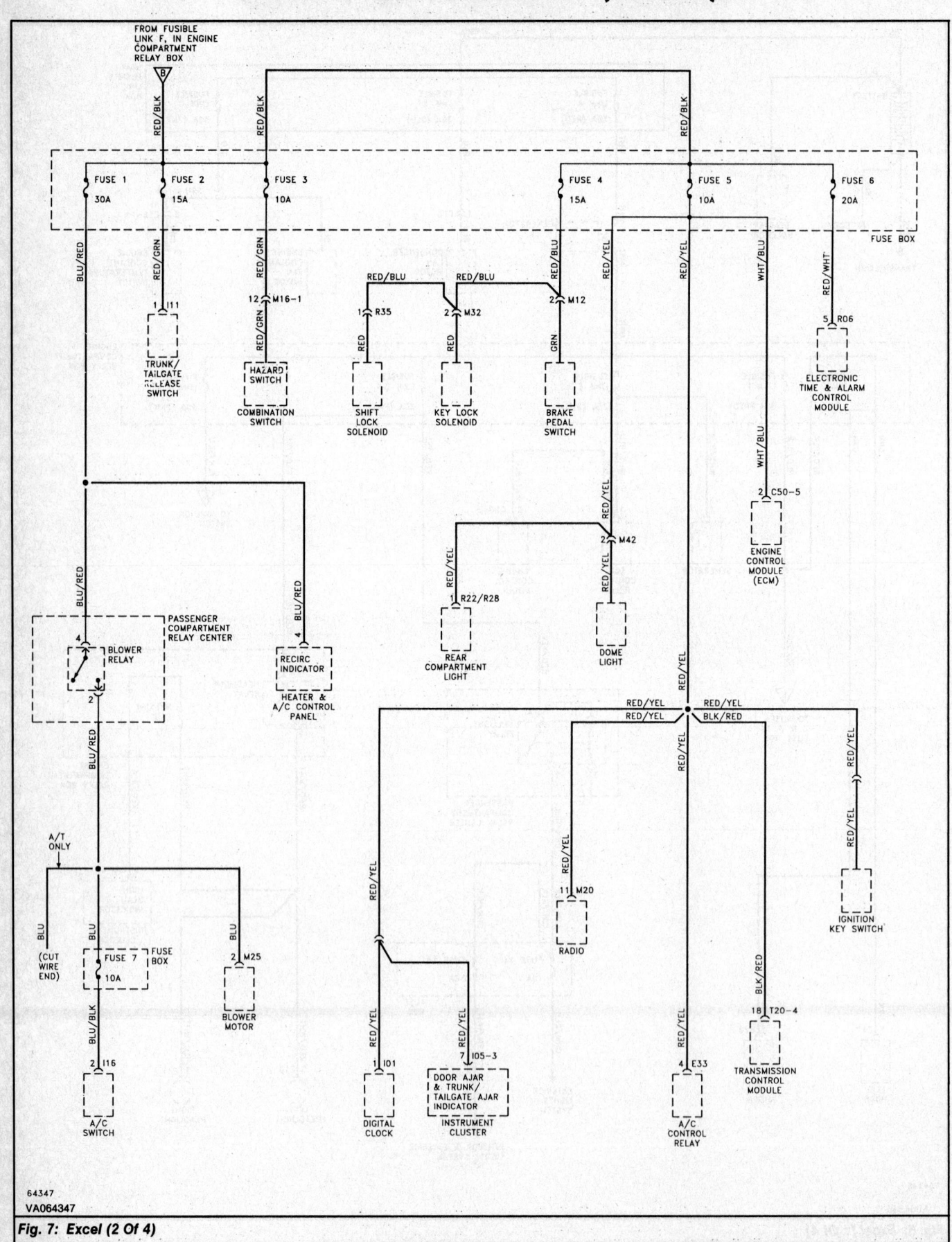

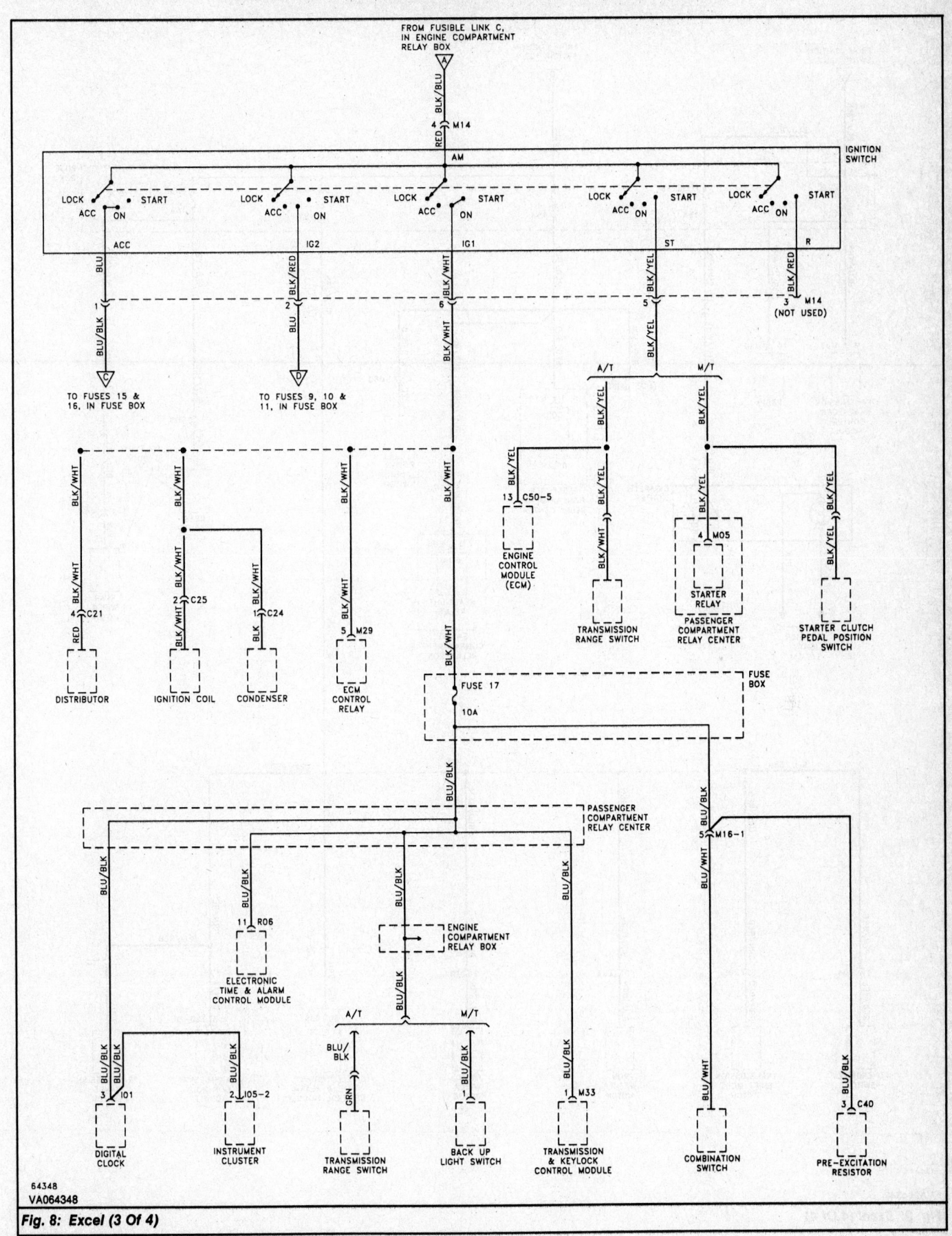

64348
VA064348

Fig. 8: Excel (3 Of 4)

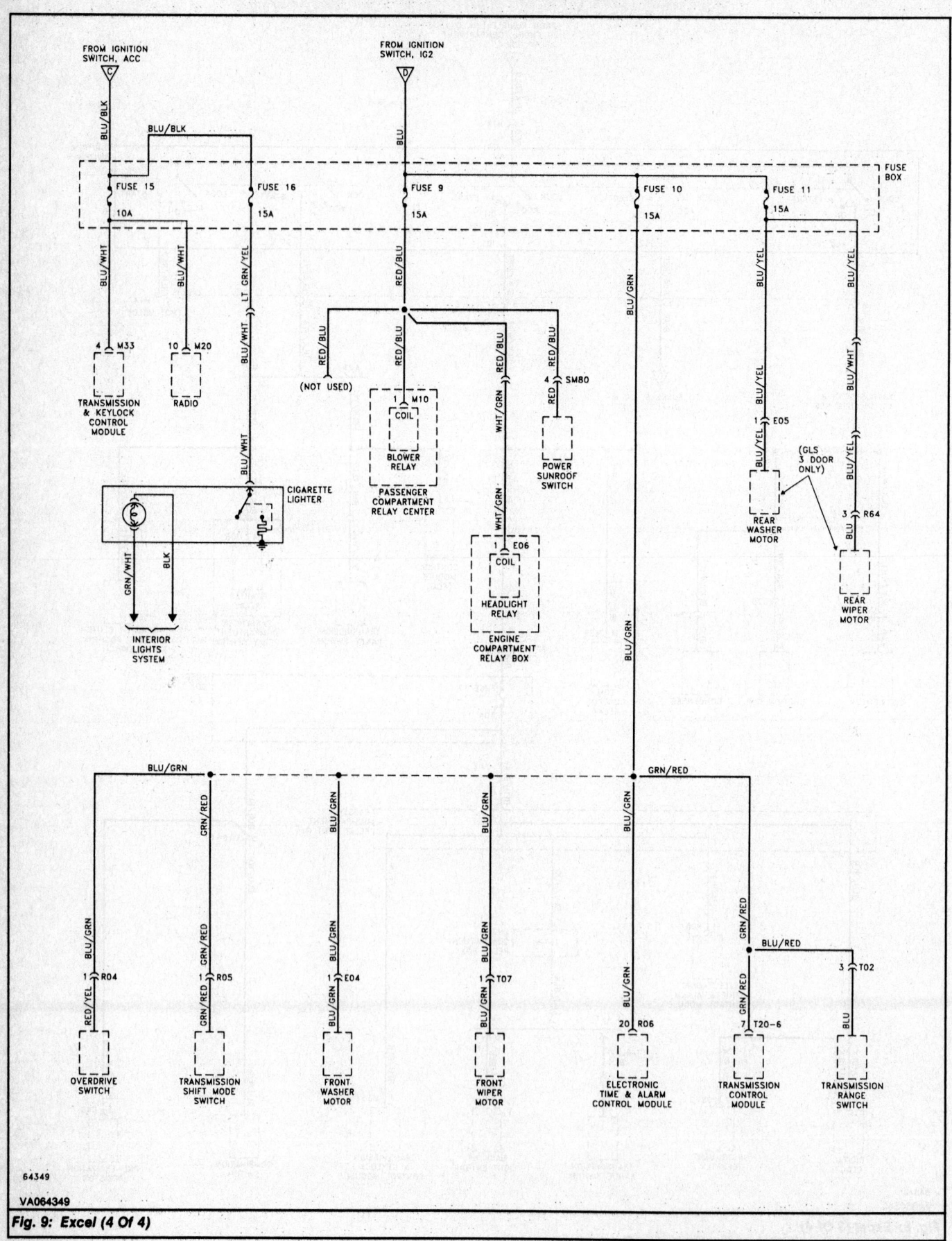

64349

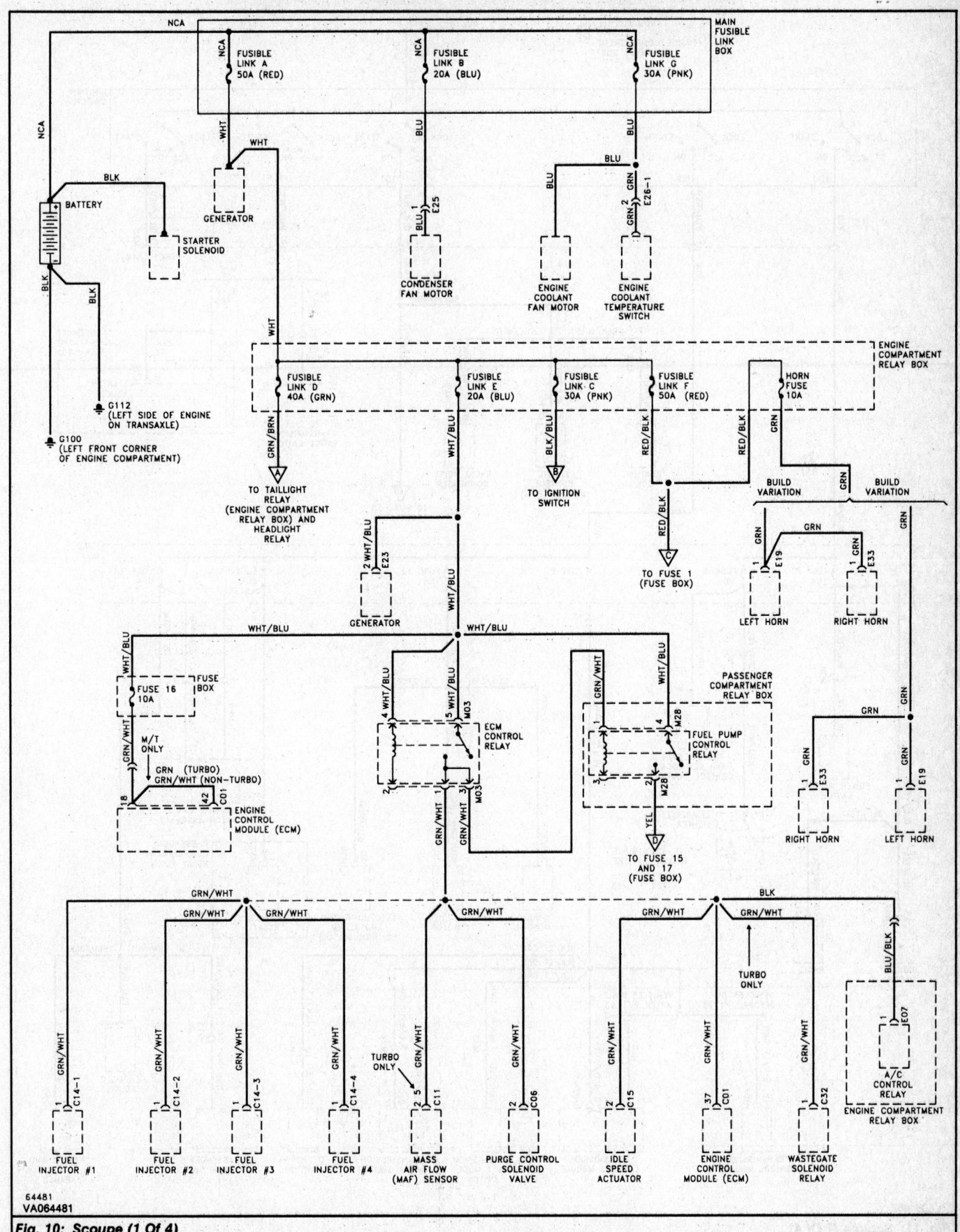

64481
VA064481

Fig. 10: Scoupe (1 Of 4)

1994 WIRING DIAGRAMS
Power Distribution (Cont.)

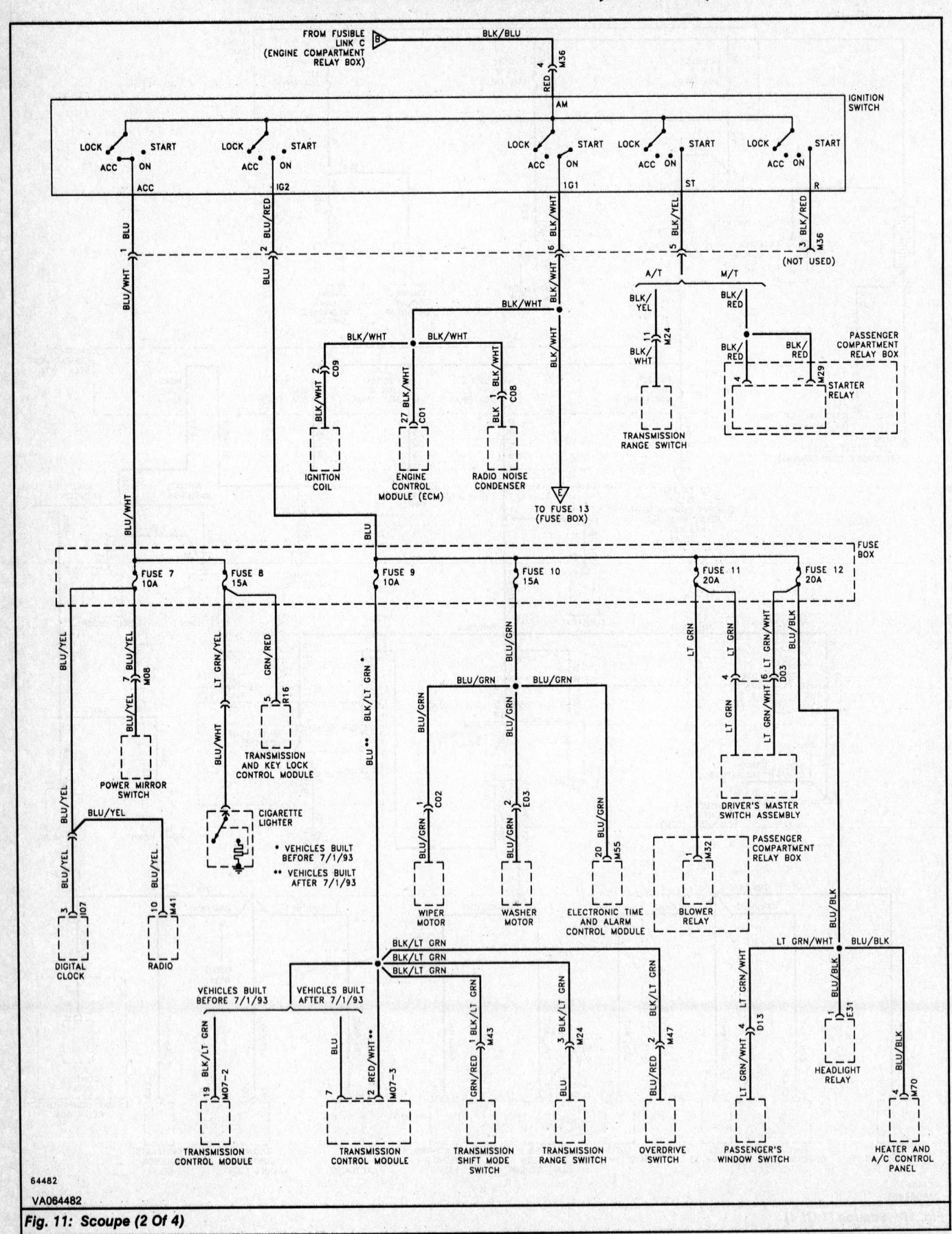

64482

VA064482

Fig. 11: Scoupe (2 Of 4)

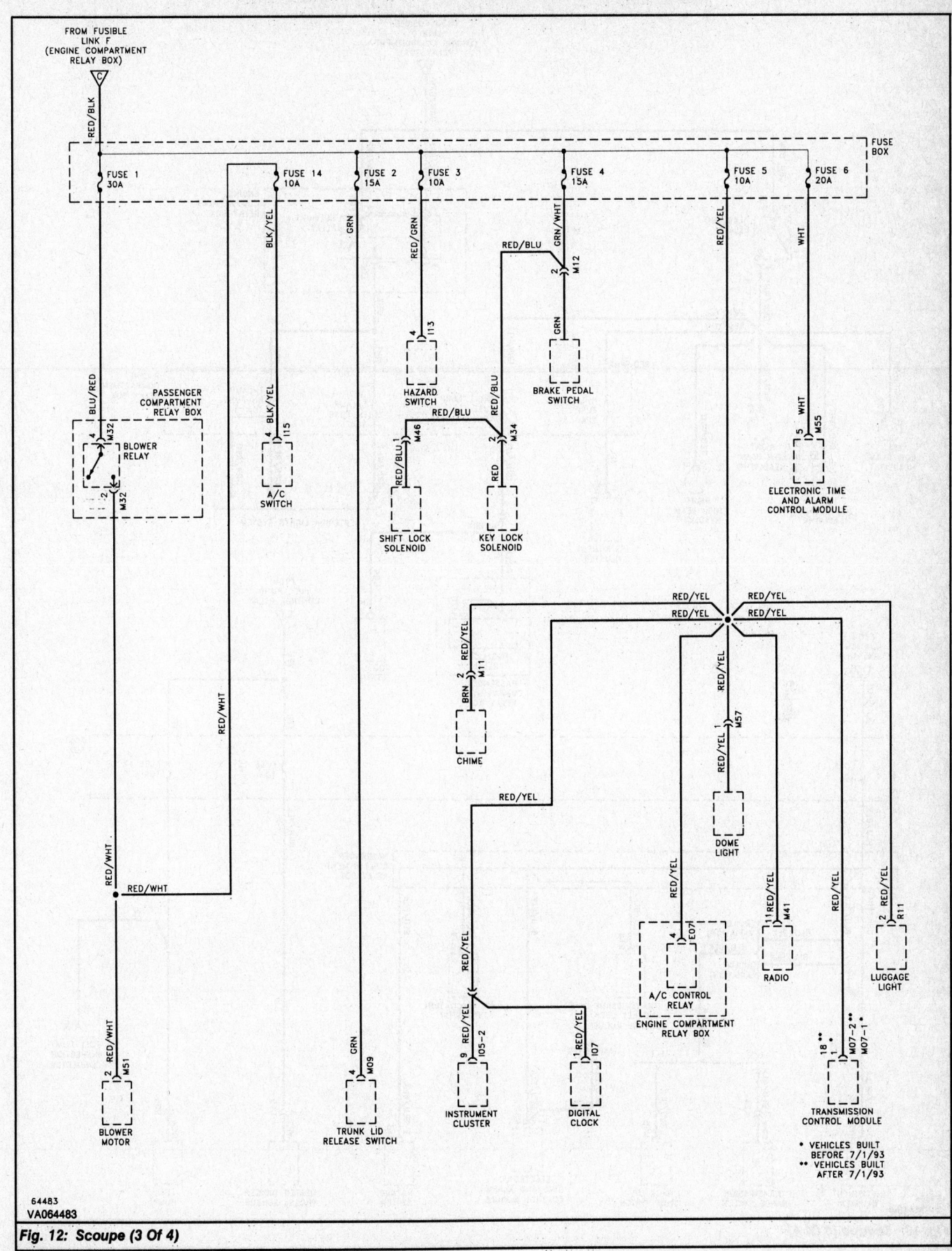

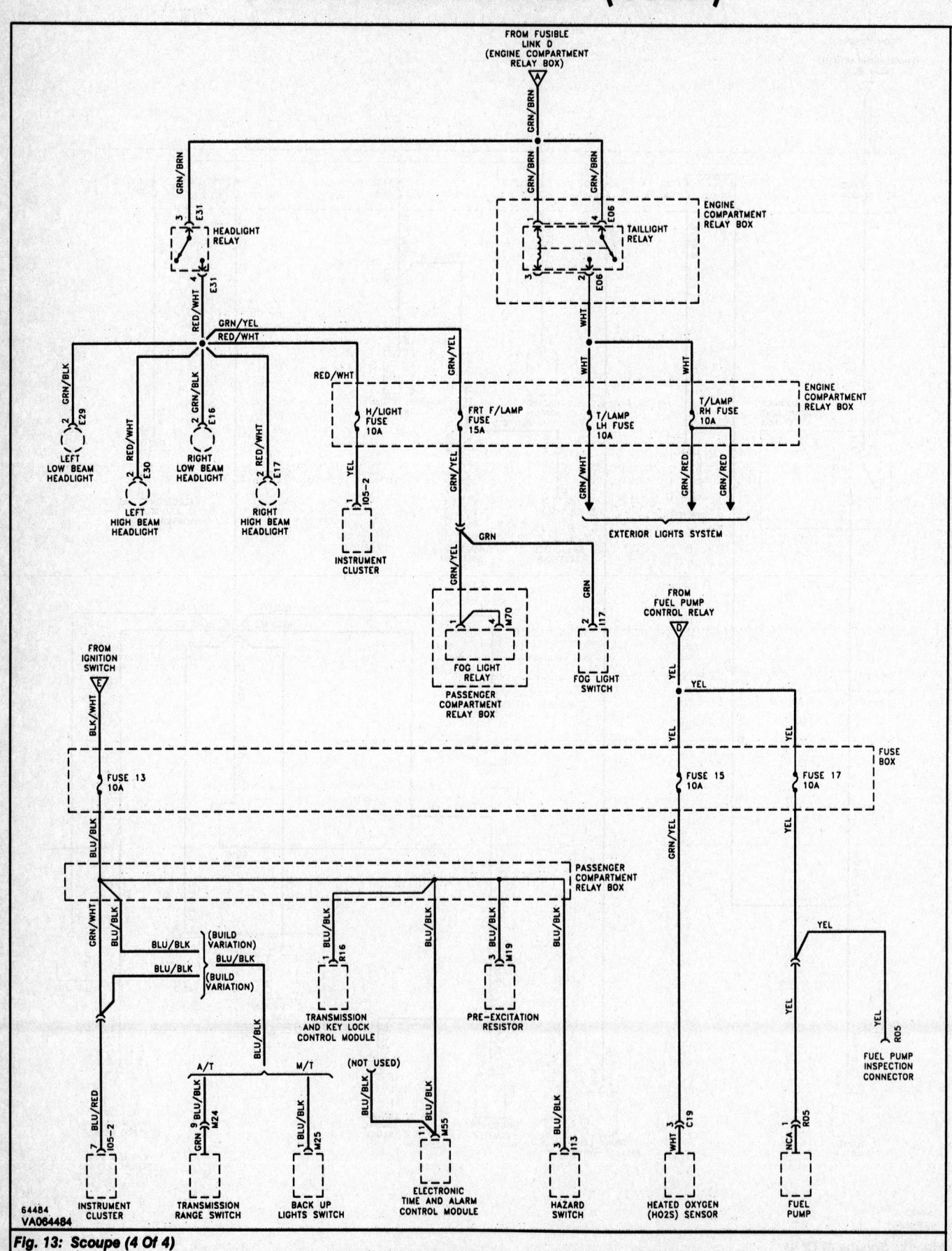

64484
VA064484
Fig. 13: Scoupe (4 Of 4)

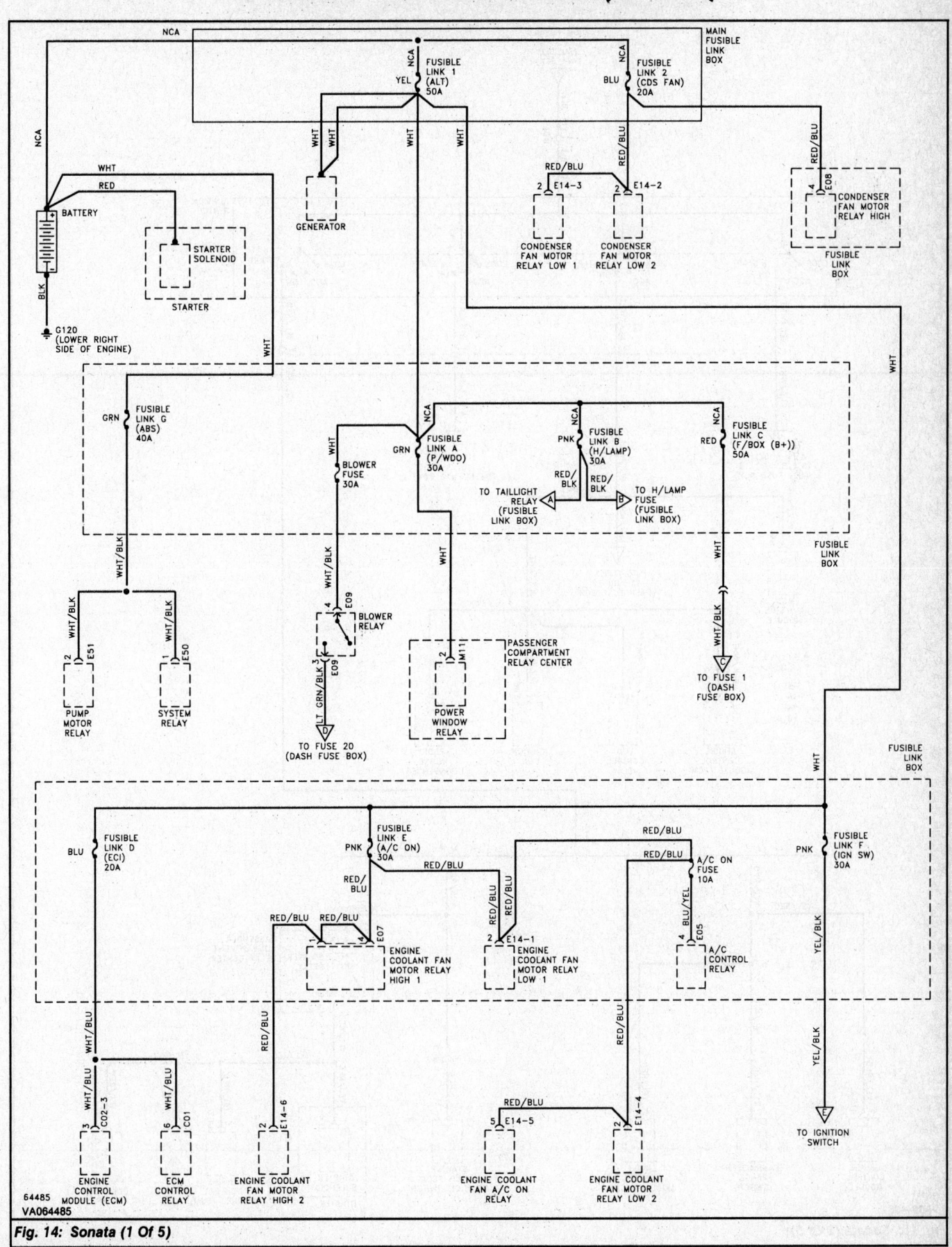

Fig. 14: Sonata (1 Of 5)

64485
VA064485

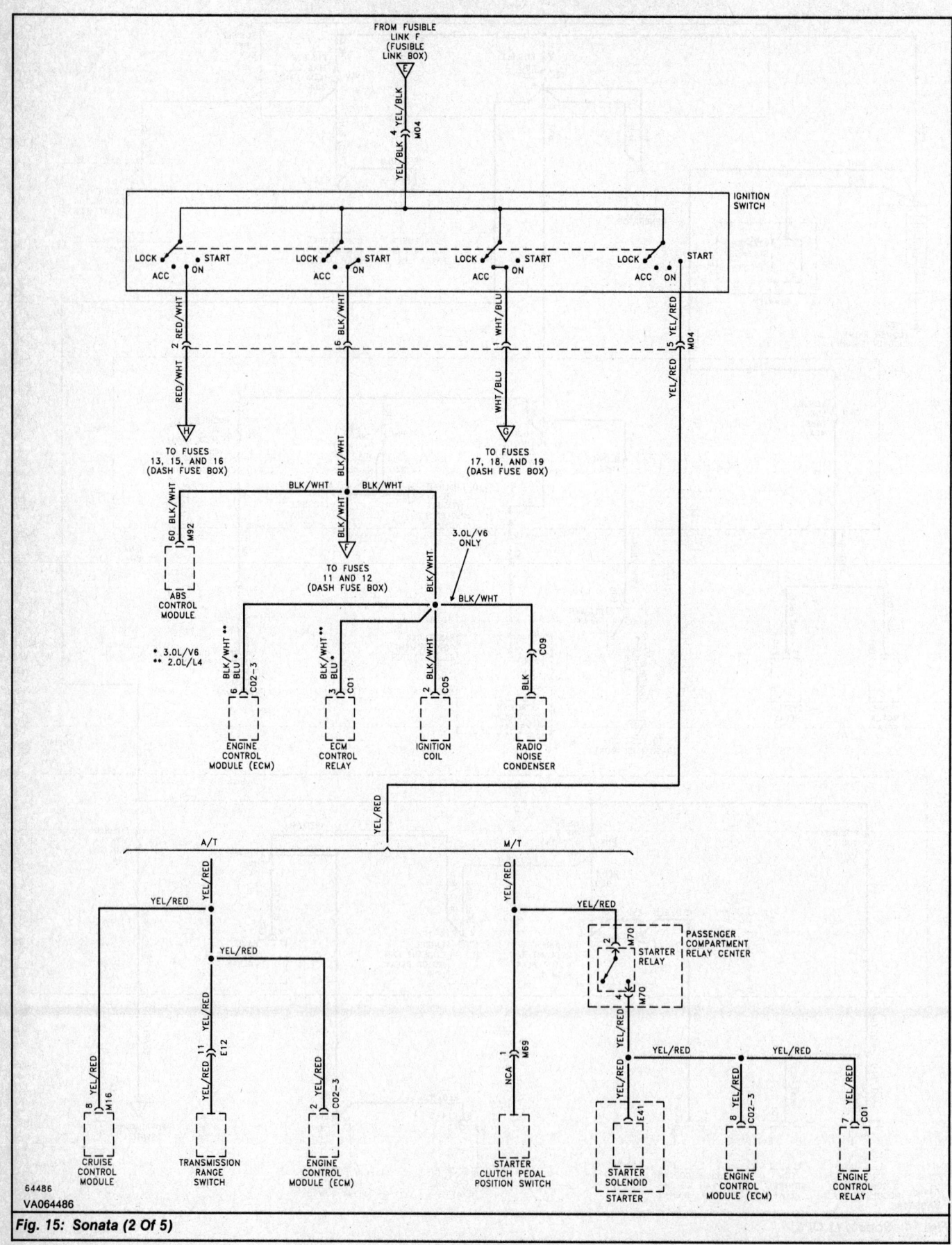

64486
HYU064486

Fig. 15: Sonata (2 Of 5)

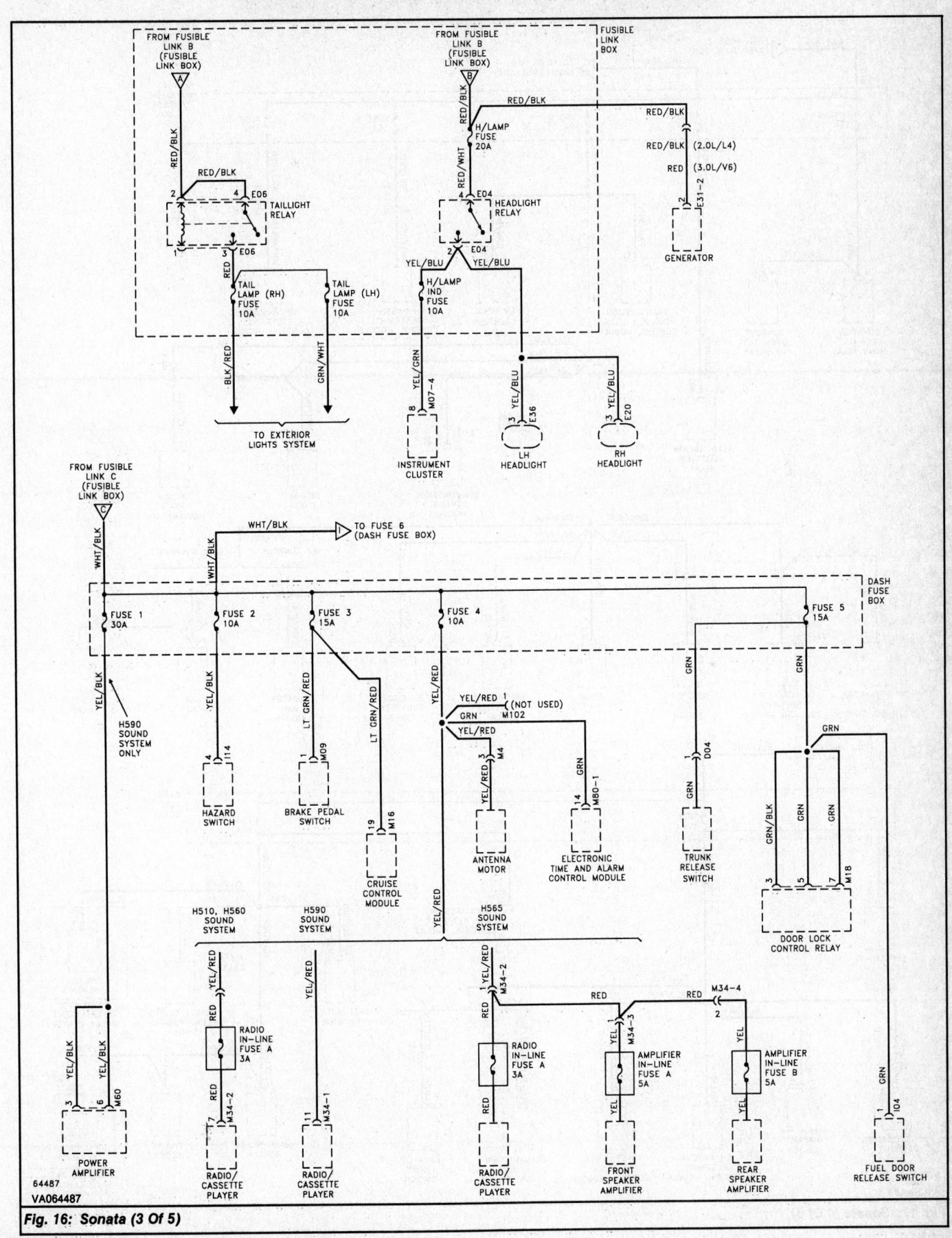

64487
VA064487

Fig. 16: Sonata (3 Of 5)

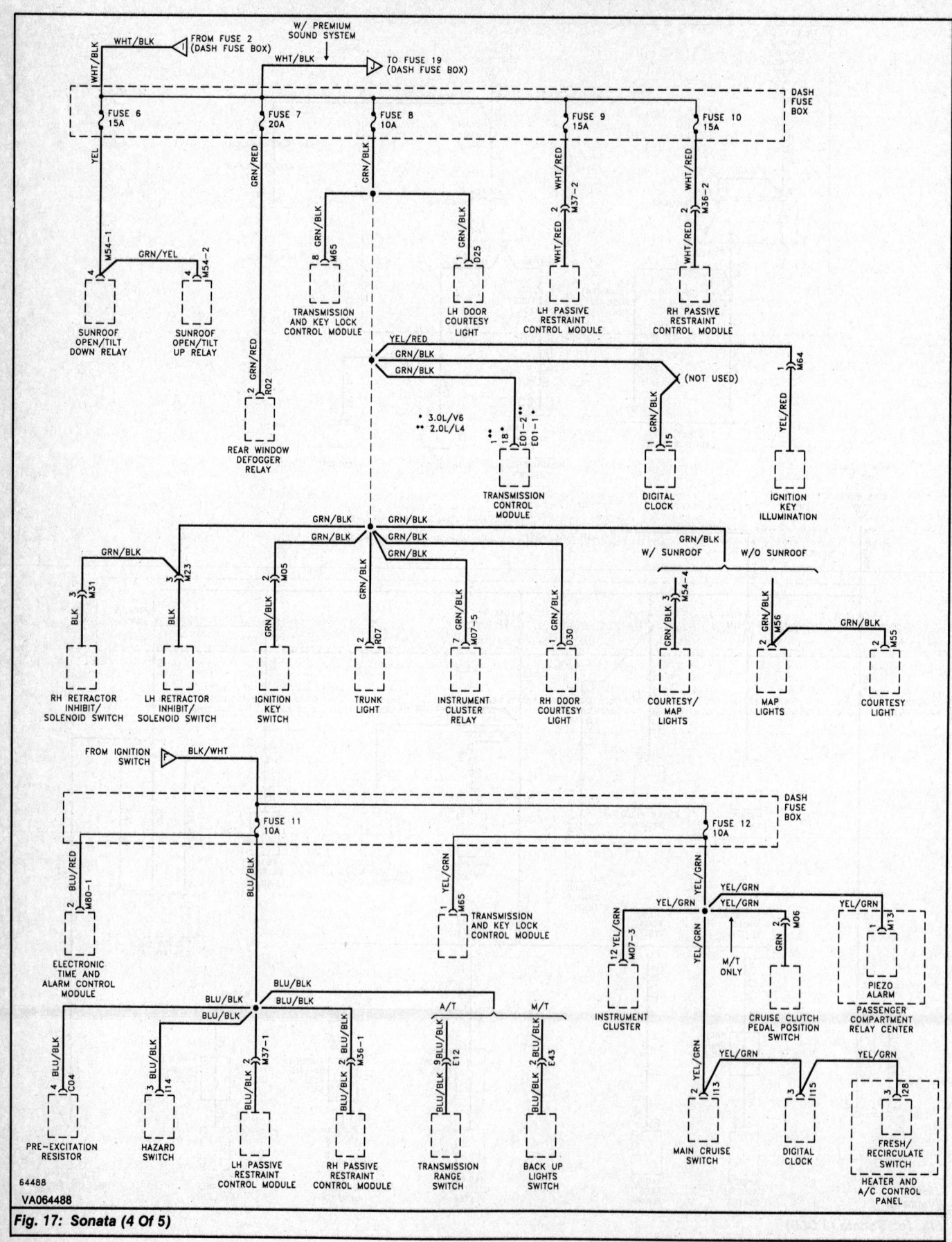

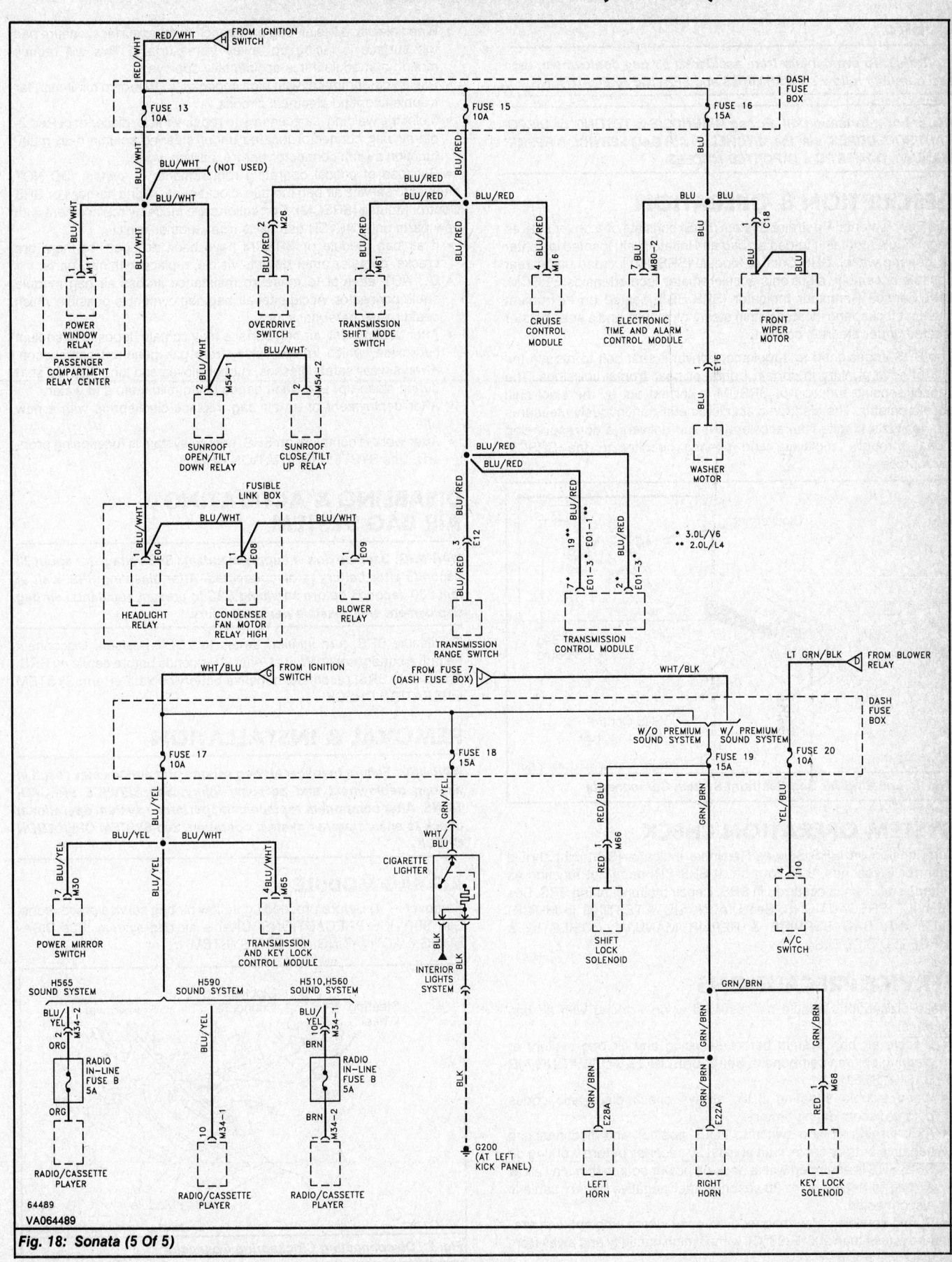

64489
VA064489

Fig. 18: Sonata (5 Of 5)

Elantra

WARNING: To avoid injury from accidental air bag deployment, read and carefully follow all WARNINGS and SERVICE PRECAUTIONS.

NOTE: For information on air bag DIAGNOSIS & TESTING or DISPOSAL PROCEDURES, see the MITCHELL® AIR BAG SERVICE & REPAIR MANUAL, DOMESTIC & IMPORTED MODELS.

DESCRIPTION & OPERATION

The Supplemental Restraint System (SRS) consists of a driver side air bag module (contains folded air bag and inflator unit) located in center of steering wheel, SRS Control Module (SRSCM) located under rear console assembly, electronic accelerometer located inside SRSCM, SRS Service Reminder Indicator (SRS SRI) located on instrument cluster, clockspring located within steering column, and a knee bolster located under steering column.

The SRS is designed to supplement driver's seat belt to reduce the risk of severe injury in certain frontal or near frontal collisions. The impact sensing function of SRSCM is carried out by the electronic accelerometer. The electronic accelerometer continuously measures the vehicle's longitudinal acceleration and delivers a corresponding signal through amplifying and filtering circuitry to the SRSCM microprocessor.

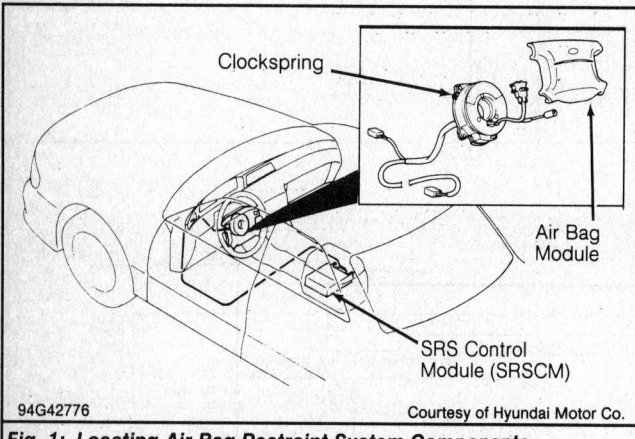

94G42776   Courtesy of Hyundai Motor Co.

Fig. 1: Locating Air Bag Restraint System Components

SYSTEM OPERATION CHECK

Turn ignition on. SRS Service Reminder Indicator (SRI) light should flash for 6 seconds, then turn off. If SRS SRI does not function as stated, a failure has occurred in SRS. Repair malfunctioning SRS. See SERVICE PRECAUTIONS. See DIAGNOSIS & TESTING in MITCHELL® AIR BAG SERVICE & REPAIR MANUAL, DOMESTIC & IMPORTED MODELS.

SERVICE PRECAUTIONS

These precautions should be observed when working with air bag systems:
- Disable air bag system before servicing any air bag system or steering column component. See DISABLING & ACTIVATING AIR BAG SYSTEM.
- When trouble shooting SRS, always check diagnostic codes before disconnecting battery.
- After turning ignition switch to LOCK position and disconnecting negative battery cable, wait at least 30 seconds before working on SRS. SRS is equipped with a back-up power source that may allow air bag to deploy up to 30 seconds after negative battery cable is disconnected.
- During servicing of air bag module, store where ambient temperature is less than 200°F (93°C), without high humidity and away from electrical noise.

- When placing a live air bag on a bench or other surface, ensure pad top surface is facing up, away from surface. This will reduce motion of module if it is accidentally deployed.
- Use a volt-ohmmeter with high impedance (10 k/ohm minimum) for trouble shooting electrical circuits.
- If electric welding is necessary to repair vehicle, disconnect Red 2-pin air bag connector located under steering column near multifunction switch connector before starting work.
- Because of critical operating requirements of system, DO NOT attempt to service air bag module, clockspring, wiring harness or SRS Control Module (SRSCM). Corrections are made by replacement with new parts only. NEVER use parts from another vehicle.
- If air bag module or SRSCM have been dropped, or there are cracks, dents or other defects visible, replace with new parts.
- DO NOT attempt to measure resistance across air bag module squib connector. Accidental air bag deployment is possible which could cause personal injury.
- After deployment, air bag surface may contain deposits of sodium hydroxide, which irritates skin, from gas generant combustion. Always wear safety glasses, rubber gloves and long-sleeved shirt during clean-up, and wash hands using mild soap and water.
- After deployment of an air bag, replace clockspring with a new one.
- After work is complete on SRS, ensure system is functioning properly. See SYSTEM OPERATION CHECK.

DISABLING & ACTIVATING AIR BAG SYSTEM

WARNING: Back-up power supply maintains SRS voltage for about 30 seconds after battery is disconnected. After disabling SRS, wait at least 30 seconds before servicing SRS to prevent accidental air bag deployment and possible personal injury.

To disable SRS, turn ignition switch to LOCK position. Disconnect negative battery cable. Wait at least 30 seconds before servicing SRS. To activate SRS, reconnect negative battery cable. Perform SYSTEM OPERATION CHECK.

REMOVAL & INSTALLATION

WARNING: Failure to follow air bag service precautions may result in air bag deployment and personal injury. See SERVICE PRECAUTIONS. After component replacement, perform a system operational check to ensure proper system operation. See SYSTEM OPERATION CHECK.

AIR BAG MODULE

Removal – 1) Before proceeding, follow air bag service precautions. See SERVICE PRECAUTIONS. Disable air bag system. See DISABLING & ACTIVATING AIR BAG SYSTEM.

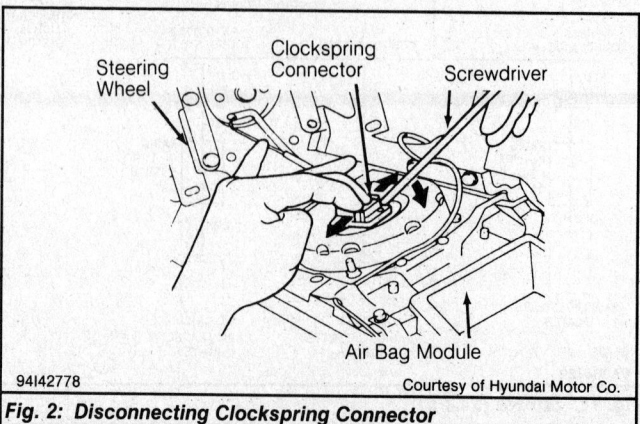

94I42778   Courtesy of Hyundai Motor Co.

Fig. 2: Disconnecting Clockspring Connector

2) Air bag module is located on steering wheel hub. Using a socket, remove 4 mounting nuts accessible from back side of air bag module. Tilt air bag module downward. Using a screwdriver, gently pry clockspring connector lock tabs outward to disconnect clockspring connector. *See Fig. 2.*

Installation – To install, reverse removal procedure. Reactivate air bag system. See DISABLING & ACTIVATING AIR BAG SYSTEM. Check AIR BAG indicator light to ensure system is functioning properly. See SYSTEM OPERATION CHECK.

CLOCKSPRING

Removal – **1)** Before proceeding, follow air bag service precautions. See SERVICE PRECAUTIONS. Disable air bag system. See DISABLING & ACTIVATING AIR BAG SYSTEM.

2) Place front wheels in straight ahead position. Remove air bag module. See AIR BAG MODULE under REMOVAL & INSTALLATION. Remove upper and lower horn plate. Disconnect horn button connector. Remove steering wheel lock nut. Make alignment marks on steering wheel and steering wheel shaft.

CAUTION: DO NOT hammer on steering wheel during removal. Damage may result to steering column.

---

3) Using a puller, remove steering wheel. Disconnect horn connector located behind steering wheel. Remove upper and lower steering column covers. Remove driver's knee bolster.

4) Disconnect clockspring connector and horn connector located near bottom of steering column. *See Fig. 3.* Remove clockspring mounting screws. Remove clockspring.

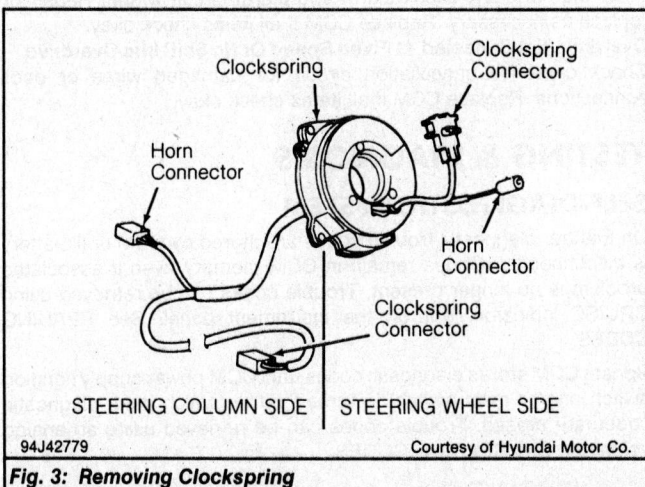

94J42779   Courtesy of Hyundai Motor Co.

Fig. 3: Removing Clockspring

Installation – **1)** Ensure front wheels are in straight ahead position. Align mating mark and NEUTRAL position indicator of clockspring. *See Fig. 4.* Install clockspring onto steering column. To complete installation, reverse removal procedure. Torque steering wheel nut to specification. See TORQUE SPECIFICATIONS.

2) Reactivate air bag system. See DISABLING & ACTIVATING AIR BAG SYSTEM. Check AIR BAG indicator light to ensure system is functioning properly. See SYSTEM OPERATION CHECK.

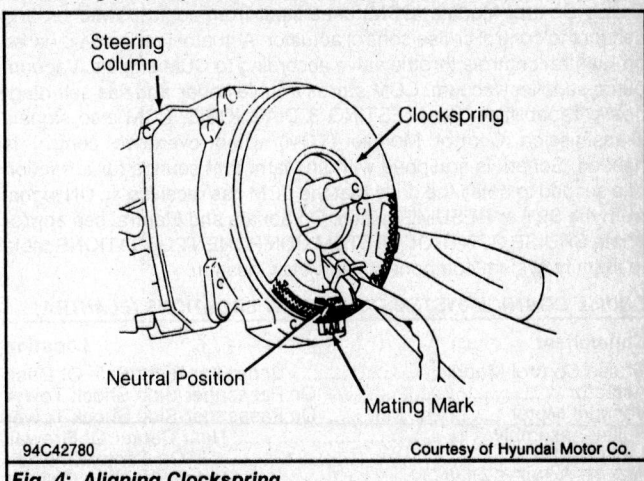

94C42780   Courtesy of Hyundai Motor Co.

Fig. 4: Aligning Clockspring

SRS CONTROL MODULE (SRSCM)

Removal – **1)** Before proceeding, follow air bag service precautions. See SERVICE PRECAUTIONS. Disable air bag system. See DISABLING & ACTIVATING AIR BAG SYSTEM.

2) Remove rear console assembly. Rear console assembly is located between driver and passenger seats. Disconnect SRS Control Module (SRSCM) connector. Remove SRSCM mounting bolts. Remove SRSCM.

Installation – To install, reverse removal procedure. Reactivate air bag system. See DISABLING & ACTIVATING AIR BAG SYSTEM. Check AIR BAG indicator light to ensure system is functioning properly. See SYSTEM OPERATION CHECK.

WIRE REPAIR

Manufacturer does not recommend repair on air bag system wiring or connectors. If wiring or connectors are found to be defective, replace with new components.

TORQUE SPECIFICATIONS

TORQUE SPECIFICATIONS [1]

Application	Ft. Lbs. (N.m)
Steering Wheel Bolt	26-33 (35-45)

[1] – Torque specifications are not available for air bag module, clockspring, and SRS Control Module (SRSCM).

WIRING DIAGRAM

NOTE: See ACCESSORIES & EQUIPMENT, Volume 5.

1994 ACCESSORIES & EQUIPMENT
Cruise Control Systems

Elantra, Sonata

DESCRIPTION & OPERATION

Cruise Control Module (CCM) uses input from control switches and sensors to control cruise control actuator. Actuator (vacuum-powered on Elantra) controls throttle valve according to CCM signals. Vacuum pump supplies vacuum. CCM stores trouble codes and has self-diagnostic capabilities. See TESTING & DIAGNOSIS. CCM also signals Transmission Control Module (TCM) when overdrive control is needed. Sonata is equipped with an alarm that sounds for a fraction of a second to notify the drive that the CCM has received an ON signal from the SET or RESUME switch. On Sonata and Elantra, see appropriate CRUISE CONTROL SYSTEM COMPONENT LOCATIONS table to identify system components and their location.

CRUISE CONTROL SYSTEM COMPONENT LOCATIONS (ELANTRA)

Component	Location
Cruise Control Module	Under Far Right Side Of Dash
Actuator	On Passenger-Side Shock Tower
Vacuum Motor	On Passenger-Side Shock Tower
Pulley Assembly	Near Center Of Firewall
Main Switch	On Center Of Dash
SET/RESUME Switch	Part Of Steering Column Combination Switch
Clutch Switch	On Clutch Pedal
Brakelight Switch	On Brake Pedal
Vehicle Speed Sensor (VSS)	In Instrument Cluster
CRUISE Indicator	On Instrument Cluster

CRUISE CONTROL SYSTEM COMPONENT LOCATIONS (SONATA)

Component	Location
Cruise Control Module	Under Left Side Of Dash
Actuator	Near Passenger-Side Shock Tower
Main Switch	On Dash Just Right Of Steering Column
SET/RESUME Switch	Part Of Steering Column Combination Switch
Accelerator Switch	On Bracket Above Accelerator Pedal
Clutch Switch	On Clutch Pedal
Brakelight Switch	On Brake Pedal
Vehicle Speed Sensor (VSS)	In Instrument Cluster

TROUBLE SHOOTING

System Cancels When Not Wanted Or Cannot Be Reset After An Automatic Cancellation – If system can be reset, try to duplicate symptom during test drive. If symptom reoccurs, check diagnostic codes. See TESTING & DIAGNOSIS. If symptom does not reoccur, check whether or not vehicle was driven on steep slope, or SET and RESUME switches were operated at the same time. If system cannot be reset, check diagnostic codes. See TESTING & DIAGNOSIS.

System Cannot Be Set (Sonata) – **1)** Check CCM power supply circuit and SET and RESUME switch function. If fault is found, repair affected area. If no fault is found, check SET switch ON function. Replace control switch if defective. Check for SET switch input wire short. Repair harness if necessary.

2) Check RESUME switch ON function and check input wire for short. Repair as necessary. Check each CANCEL circuit. Repair as necessary. Check vehicle speed sensor for malfunction. Repair or replace as necessary. Ensure actuator and circuit is functioning properly. If abnormal conditions are not found in actuator or actuator circuit, replace CCM.

Set Speed Varies (Hunting) – Check vehicle speed sensor, speedometer cable and speedometer drive gear. Repair or replace as necessary. Check actuator circuit connections for poor contact. Repair as necessary. Ensure actuator and vacuum pump are functioning properly. Replace CCM if all items check okay.

System Won't Cancel With Brake Pedal Application – Check for damaged wiring or disconnected brakelight switch. Repair harness or replace brakelight switch as necessary. Check actuator and vacuum pump (if equipped) drive circuit for short. Repair harness or replace actuator as necessary. Replace CCM if all items check okay.

System Won't Cancel With Clutch Pedal Application – Check for damaged wiring or disconnected clutch switch. Repair harness or replace brakelight switch as necessary. Check actuator and vacuum pump (if equipped) drive circuit for short. Repair harness or replace actuator as necessary. Replace CCM if all items check okay.

System Won't Cancel When Shifted Into Neutral But Will Cancel With Brake Pedal Application – Check for damaged wiring or disconnected neutral safety switch. Repair harness or replace switch as necessary. Check neutral safety switch for proper adjustment. Adjust as necessary. Replace CCM if all items check okay.

System Won't Decelerate (Coast) Using Set Switch – Check for intermittent operation of SET switch circuit or switch. Repair or replace as necessary. Check actuator circuit for poor contact and proper operation. Repair or replace as necessary. Replace CCM if all items check okay.

System Won't Accelerate Or Resume Speed – Check for damaged or disconnected wiring, or short circuit in RESUME switch circuit. Repair or replace as necessary. Check actuator circuit for poor contact and proper operation. Repair or replace as necessary. Replace CCM if all items check okay.

System Can Be Set At Less Than 25 MPH – Check vehicle speed sensor, speedometer cable and speedometer drive gear. Repair or replace as necessary. Check actuator circuit connections for poor contact. Ensure actuator is functioning properly. Repair as necessary. Replace CCM if all items check okay.

Main Indicator Light Off But System Works – Check for damaged or disconnected bulb of cruise control main switch. Check wiring for damage or disconnection. Repair or replace as necessary.

No Alarm When Set Or Resume Switch Is Used (Sonata) – If system functions normally, check alarm and alarm circuit wiring. Repair or replace as necessary. Replace CCM if all items check okay.

Overdrive Not Canceled At Fixed Speed Or No Shift Into Overdrive – Check overdrive cancellation circuit for damaged wires or poor connections. Replace CCM if all items check okay.

TESTING & DIAGNOSIS

SELF-DIAGNOSTIC SYSTEM

On Elantra, diagnostic trouble codes are stored by CCM until battery is disconnected. Codes remain in CCM memory even if associated problem is no longer present. Trouble codes can be retrieved using CRUISE indicator light on the instrument panel. See READING CODES.

Sonata CCM stores diagnostic codes until CCM power supply (ignition switch and/or main switch) is turned off, at which point diagnostic codes are erased. Trouble codes can be retrieved using an analog voltmeter. See READING CODES.

READING CODES

NOTE: *Multi-use testers CANNOT be used to retrieve cruise control diagnostic trouble codes.*

Using CRUISE Indicator Light (Elantra) – **1)** Cruise main switch and ignition switch must be in ON position. Ground data link connector terminal No. 5 for vehicles built before November, 1993, or terminal No. 10 for vehicles built after November, 1993. *See Fig. 1.* Data link connector is located in fuse panel under left side of dash.

2) Observe CRUISE indicator light on instrument cluster. Light flashes indicate trouble code. For example, if indicator light displays 2 quick flashes followed by a pause followed by 2 quick flashes, a code 2 is present. See TROUBLE CODE DEFINITION (ELANTRA) for code explanations.

Using Voltmeter (Sonata) – Connect voltmeter to data link connector terminals No. 5 and 12. *See Fig. 1.* Data link connector is located in fuse panel under left side of dash. Trouble codes are displayed on voltmeter as a series of voltages pulses. Display of trouble codes will start when vehicle speed decreases to 12 MPH, after cancellation of system and continue as long as main switch and ignition switch remain on. Example: Code 23 would be displayed as 2 long pulses followed by 3 short pulses followed by a 3 second pause. *See Fig. 2.* See TROUBLE CODE DEFINITION (SONATA) for code explanations.

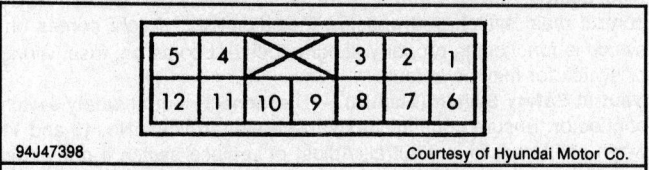

94J47398   Courtesy of Hyundai Motor Co.

Fig. 1: Identifying Data Link Connector Terminals

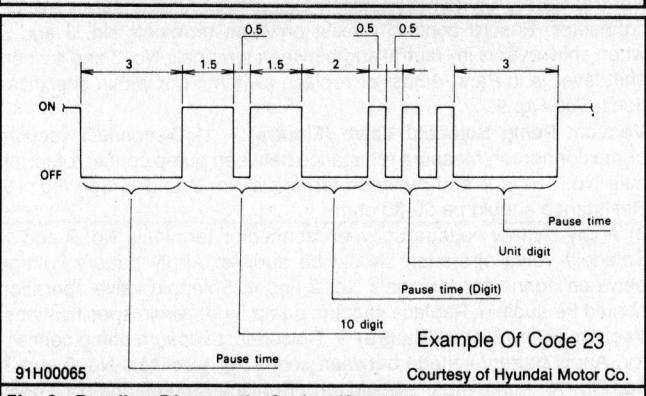

91H00065   Courtesy of Hyundai Motor Co.

Fig. 2: Reading Diagnostic Codes (Sonata)

TROUBLE CODE DEFINITION (ELANTRA)

Code 1 – Code indicates problem with vacuum pump drive system. Check vacuum pump assembly and related wiring and vacuum lines. Repair or replace as necessary. Replace CCM if all items check okay.

Code 2 – Code indicates problem with vehicle speed sensing system. Check vehicle speed sensor and related wiring.

Code 3 – Code is set when vehicle speed is less than 25 MPH (km/h) and attempts are made to engage cruise control system.

Code 4 – Code is set when vehicle speed drops below cruise set speed by about 10 MPH (15 km/h).

Code 5 – Code is set when CCM detects simultaneous SET and RESUME signals from cruise control switch.

Code 6 – Code indicates abnormal condition of CCM. Check for damaged or loose CCM connector. Replace CCM if connections are okay.

Code 7 – Code is set when CCM receives a continuous cancel signal from brakelight switch, clutch switch (M/T) of neutral safety switch (A/T). Inspect switches and related wiring. Repair as necessary.

TROUBLE CODE DEFINITION (SONATA)

Code 11 – Could be caused by an open transistor, open brake circuit, blown fuse, brakelight switch closed or brakelight circuit open.

Code 12 – Indicates that signal from vehicle speed sensor has not been received for more than one second.

Code 13 – Indicates low speed limiter activation. System is normal if it can be reset.

Code 14 – Indicates cancellation activated by reduction of vehicle speed. System is normal if it can be reset.

Code 15 – Indicates control switch malfunction (SET and RESUME switches ON simultaneously).

Code 16 – Could be caused by open fuse or circuit in brakelight switch, auto transaxle neutral safety switch ON (closed), open brakelight circuit, or brakelight switch ON.

NOTE: *On Sonata, codes 21-25 are accessed with main, set and resume switches in ON position. Any code remaining after related switch is turned OFF, indicates a failure in selected switch or circuit. Codes 24 and 25 are accessed with vehicle running.*

Code 21 – Set switch circuit normal.
Code 22 – Resume switch circuit normal.
Code 23 – Cancel switch circuits normal.
Code 24 – Greater than 25 MPH speed sensor circuit normal.
Code 25 – Less than 25 MPH speed sensor circuit normal.

COMPONENT TESTING

Actuator (Elantra) – Remove actuator. Using hand-held vacuum pump, apply vacuum to actuator. *See Fig. 3.* Actuator holder should protrude at least 1.38 in. (35 mm) and should remain protruded as long as vacuum is applied. Replace actuator if it does not test as specified.

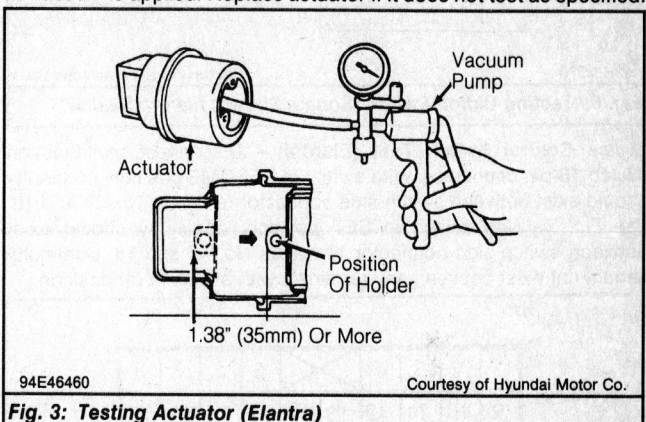

94E46460   Courtesy of Hyundai Motor Co.

Fig. 3: Testing Actuator (Elantra)

Actuator (Sonata) – Disconnect actuator connector. Measure resistance of clutch coil between terminals No. 3 and 4. Replace actuator if resistance is not about 55 ohms. *See Fig. 4.*

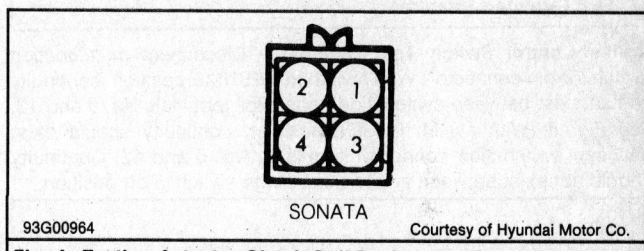

93G00964   Courtesy of Hyundai Motor Co.

Fig. 4: Testing Actuator Clutch Coil Resistance (Sonata)

Brakelight Switch – Check for continuity between terminal "C" and terminal "D" with switch plunger depressed. Check for continuity between terminal "A" and terminal "B" with switch plunger released. If continuity is not present in each case, replace switch. *See Fig. 5.*

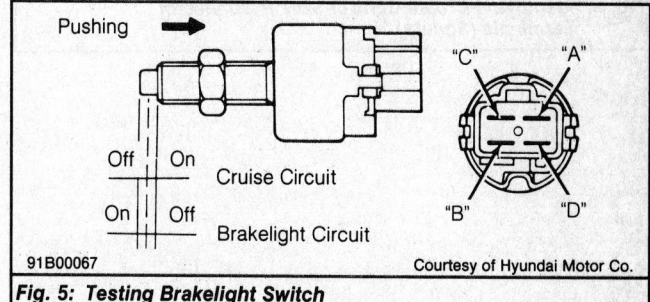

91B00067   Courtesy of Hyundai Motor Co.

Fig. 5: Testing Brakelight Switch

Clutch Switch – Ensure continuity exists when clutch switch plunger is depressed and no continuity exists when plunger is released. *See Fig. 6.*

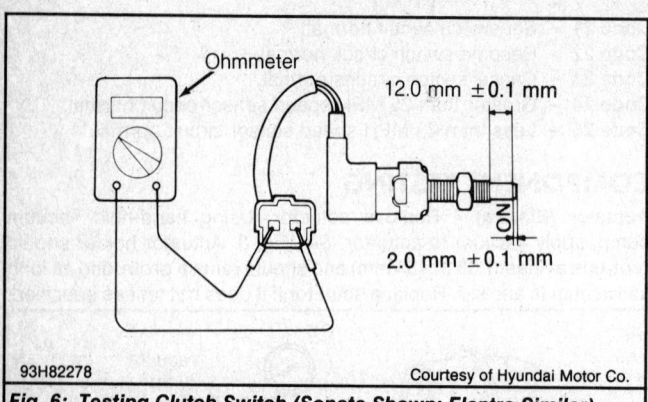

Fig. 6: Testing Clutch Switch (Sonata Shown; Elantra Similar)

Cruise Control Switch Test (Elantra) – Disconnect multifunction switch 18-pin connector. With switch in RESUME position, continuity should exist between switch-side connector terminals No. 16 and 18. See Fig. 7. With switch in SET position, continuity should exist between switch-side connector terminals No. 17 and 18. Continuity should not exist between any terminals with switch in off position.

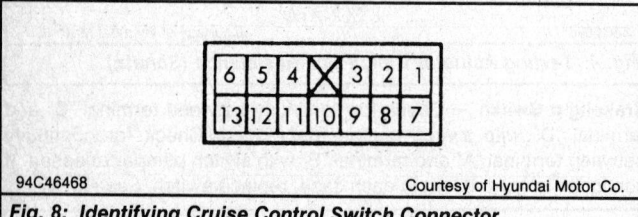

Fig. 7: Identifying Cruise Control Switch Connector Terminals (Elantra)

Cruise Control Switch Test (Sonata) – Disconnect multifunction switch 13-pin connector. With switch in RESUME position, continuity should exist between switch-side connector terminals No. 6 and 13. See Fig. 8. With switch in SET position, continuity should exist between switch-side connector terminals No. 6 and 12. Continuity should not exist between any terminals with switch in off position.

Fig. 8: Identifying Cruise Control Switch Connector Terminals (Sonata)

Main Switch Test (Elantra) – Manufacturer does not provide testing procedure. Use wiring diagram as a testing guide. See WIRING DIAGRAMS

Main Switch Test (Sonata) – Turn ignition switch on. Depress cruise control main switch and observe indicator light. If light comes on, switch is functioning properly. If light does not come on, fuse, wiring or switch for may be at fault.

Neutral Safety Switch (Elantra) – Disconnect neutral safety switch connector. Ensure continuity exist between terminals No. 10 and 11 when shift lever is in Neutral. Adjust or replace switch if not within specifications. See Fig. 9.

Neutral Safety Switch (Sonata) – Disconnect neutral safety switch connector. Ensure continuity exist between terminals No. 3 and 5 when shift lever is in Neutral and between terminals No. 3 and 4 when shift lever is in Park. Adjust or replace switch if not within specifications. See Fig. 9.

Vacuum Pump Solenoid Valve (Elantra) – 1) Disconnect vacuum pump connector. Measure resistance between pump connector terminals No. 1 and 2 and between terminals No. 2 and 4. See Fig. 10. Resistance should be 50-60 ohms.

2) Apply battery voltage between connector terminals No. 2 and 1. Solenoid valve operation should be audible. Apply battery voltage between connector terminals No. 2 and 4. Solenoid valve operation should be audible. Replace vacuum pump if not within specifications.

Vacuum Pump Motor (Elantra) – Disconnect vacuum pump connector. Apply battery voltage between connector terminals No. 2 and 3. See Fig. 10. Pump motor should turn. Replace vacuum pump if it does not test as specified.

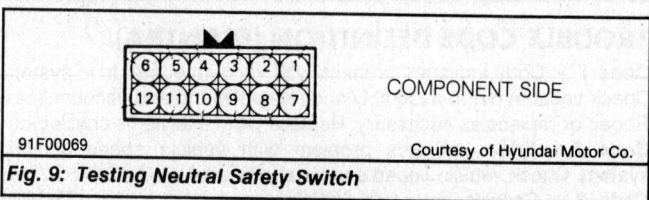

Fig. 9: Testing Neutral Safety Switch

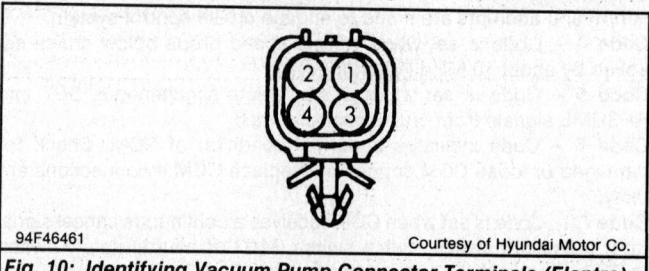

Fig. 10: Identifying Vacuum Pump Connector Terminals (Elantra)

WIRING DIAGRAMS

NOTE: See ACCESSORIES & EQUIPMENT, Volume 5.

Elantra, Excel, Scoupe, Sonata

DESCRIPTION

Rear window defogger system uses a heating filament grid, bonded to inside of rear window. On Elantra, Excel and Scoupe, heated rear window power is regulated by Time and Alarm Control Module (TACM). On Sonata, heated rear window power is regulated by Electronic Time and Alarm Control System (ETACS) module. All defogger systems have an instrument panel indicator light to show system is operating.

OPERATION

On Elantra, power is supplied by fuse panel fuse No. 7 to terminal No. 5 of TACM connector. On Excel and Scoupe, power is supplied by fuse panel fuse No. 6 to terminal No. 5 of TACM connector. Push button control switch is used as a ground switch by TACM to set internal timer, allowing power to rear window grid. TACM will power rear window grid for 7-10 minutes or until ignition switch is turned off.

On Sonata, power is supplied by fuse panel fuse No. 7 to defogger relay, then to rear window grid. Push button control switch is used as a ground switch by ETACS module to energize relay. ETACS module energizes relay for 10 minutes or until ignition is turned off.

TROUBLE SHOOTING

DEFOGGER DOES NOT WORK

Check for:
- Blown fuse
- Poor connection at window grid
- Defogger switch defective
- Poor harness connections
- Broken rear window grid wire
- Defective relay (if equipped)

INDICATOR LIGHT DOES NOT WORK

Check for:
- Burned out bulb
- Open wire
- Poor harness connections

TESTING

SYSTEM TESTING

Elantra, Excel & Scoupe – **1)** On Elantra, check fuse panel fuse No. 7 (20-amp). On Excel and Scoupe, check fuse panel fuse No. 6 (20-amp). On all models, turn ignition on. Push defogger control switch to ON position.
2) Use a test light or voltmeter to check for battery voltage at rear window grid feed wire connector. If battery voltage does not exist at grid connector, use a voltmeter to backprobe TACM harness connector terminal No. 5 for input voltage from fuse No. 6 (No. 7 on Elantra). See Fig. 1.

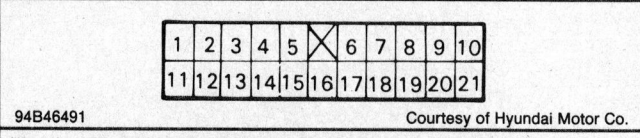

94B46491   Courtesy of Hyundai Motor Co.

Fig. 1: Identifying TACM Harness Connector Terminals (Elantra, Excel & Scoupe)

3) TACM is located under driver's seat on Excel and Scoupe and under center console on Elantra. On all models, if voltage exists at terminal No. 5, check terminal No. 6 for TACM voltage output to rear window.
4) If voltage exists, there is an open in circuit between TACM and rear window grid. If voltage does not exist at terminal No. 6, use a test light to backprobe TACM harness connector terminal No. 15 (defogger switch terminal) to ground.

5) Using voltmeter, recheck voltage at terminal No. 6. If voltage now exists and rear window grid has voltage, there is an open in circuit between TACM terminal No. 15 and ground (possibly faulty defogger switch). See WIRING DIAGRAMS.
6) If terminal No. 6 still does not have voltage after using test light to backprobe TACM terminal No. 15 (defogger switch terminal) to ground, replace TACM.
Sonata – **1)** Check fuse panel fuse No. 7 (20-amp). Turn ignition on. Push defogger control switch to ON position. Use a voltmeter or test light to check battery voltage at rear window grid feed wire connector.
2) If battery voltage does not exist at grid connector and indicator light is on, there is an open circuit between grid connector and defogger relay. Defogger relay is located in trunk, behind right side panel.

NOTE: Sonata ETACS module uses 2 14-pin connectors (M24-1 and M24-2). Use wire colors given in test procedure to identify connector terminals. Also see WIRING DIAGRAMS.

---

3) If battery voltage does not exist at grid connector and indicator light is NOT on, check defogger relay connector terminal No. 2 for input voltage from fuse. See Fig. 2. If voltage does not exist, repair open in circuit. If voltage does exist, use a test light to backprobe ETACS module 14-pin connector (M24-2) terminal No. 11 (Red/Black wire, defogger switch terminal) to ground. See Fig. 2. ETACS module is located behind left, lower instrument panel, on left side of steering column.
4) Using voltmeter, check rear window grid connector voltage. If voltage exists, replace control switch. If voltage does not exist at grid connector, use a voltmeter to check voltage at ETACS module 14-pin connector (M24-2) terminal No. 3 (Green/Black wire). See Fig. 2. If voltage does not exist, replace ETACS module. If voltage does exist, replace defogger relay.

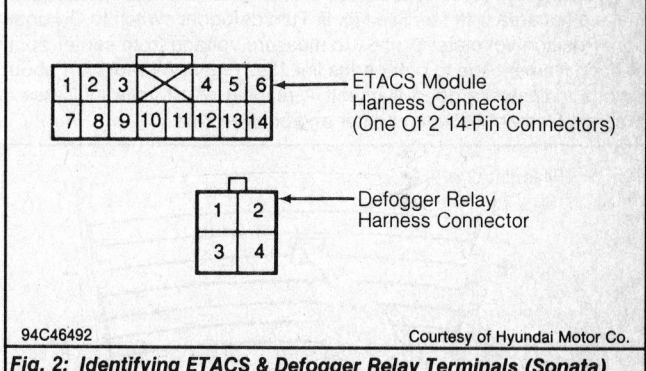

ETACS Module
Harness Connector
(One Of 2 14-Pin Connectors)

Defogger Relay
Harness Connector

94C46492   Courtesy of Hyundai Motor Co.

Fig. 2: Identifying ETACS & Defogger Relay Terminals (Sonata)

DEFOGGER SWITCH TEST

Elantra – Remove defogger switch by prying switch outward from center panel. Disconnect harness connector. Push switch to ON position. Using an ohmmeter, check for continuity between switch terminals No. 4 and 5 (ground wire), and between terminals No. 2 and 5. See Fig. 3. Continuity should exist in each case. Continuity should exist between terminals No. 1 and 3 at all time. Replace switch if it does not test as specified.
Excel – Remove defogger switch by prying switch outward from center panel. Disconnect harness connector. Push switch to ON position. Using an ohmmeter, check for continuity between switch terminals No. 2 and 4 (ground wire). See Fig. 3. If continuity does not exist, replace switch. Switch terminals should have no continuity in OFF position.
Scoupe – Remove defogger switch by prying outward from center panel. Disconnect harness connector. Push switch to ON position. Using an ohmmeter, check for continuity between switch terminals No. 5 and 4 (ground wire). See Fig. 3. If continuity does not exist, replace switch. Switch terminals should have no continuity in OFF position.

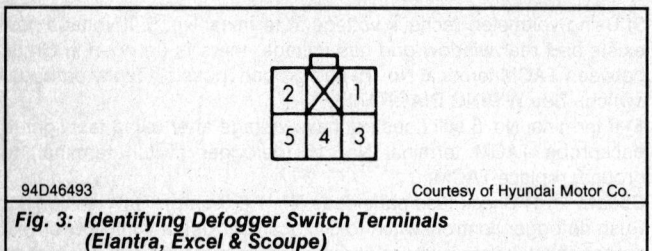

94D46493   Courtesy of Hyundai Motor Co.

Fig. 3: Identifying Defogger Switch Terminals (Elantra, Excel & Scoupe)

Sonata – Remove defogger switch by prying outward from instrument panel. Disconnect harness connector. Push switch to ON position. Using an ohmmeter, check for continuity between switch terminals No. 2 and 4 and between switch terminals No. 1 and 3. See Fig. 4. If continuity does not exist, replace switch. Switch terminals should have no continuity in OFF position.

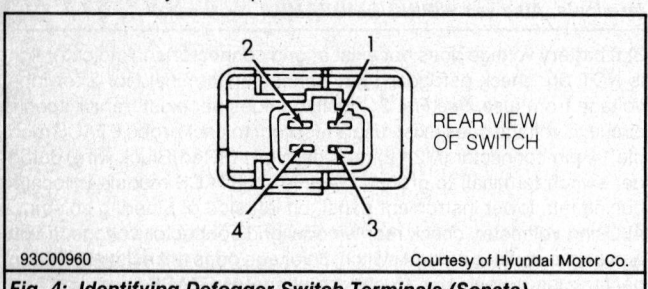

93C00960   Courtesy of Hyundai Motor Co.

Fig. 4: Identifying Defogger Switch Terminals (Sonata)

GRID FILAMENT TESTING

1) Wrap a small piece of aluminum foil around voltmeter probes and make a flat area with foil. See Fig. 5. Turn defogger switch to ON position. Position voltmeter probes to measure voltage from center point of each filament line to outer edge line. See Fig. 5. A reading of about 6 volts indicates a good filament. A reading of 12 volts indicates a break in filament between center and positive side.

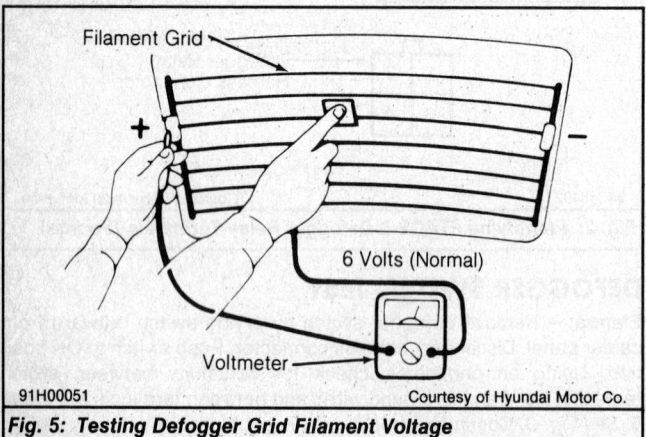

91H00051   Courtesy of Hyundai Motor Co.

Fig. 5: Testing Defogger Grid Filament Voltage

2) A reading of zero volts indicates a break in filament line between center point and negative side of line tested. To locate break, move probe along filament line until voltmeter needle moves abruptly. A broken filament may be repaired using conductive paint, after removing silicone covering. See GRID FILAMENT REPAIR under ON-VEHICLE SERVICE. See Fig. 6.

ON-VEHICLE SERVICE

GRID FILAMENT REPAIR

1) If repair is required, use silicone remover to remove small amount of silicone covering from damaged area, exposing grid line. Clean exposed broken grid line area with alcohol. Place masking tape along both sides of grid line area to be repaired. See Fig. 6.

2) Apply a small amount of conductive paint to grid line break area. Wait 15 minutes and then reapply paint. Repeat process a third time. After a few minutes drying time, carefully remove tape from line edges. DO NOT touch repaired area for 24 hours.

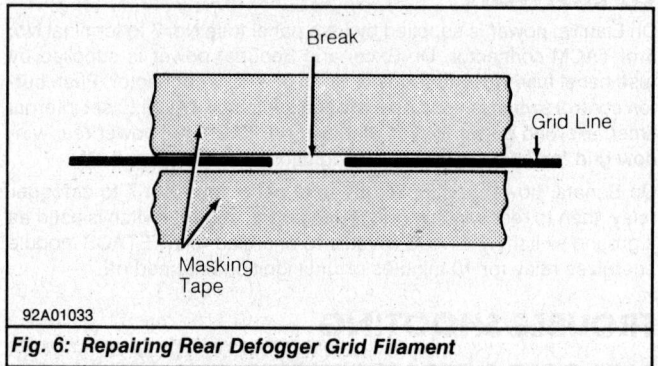

92A01033

Fig. 6: Repairing Rear Defogger Grid Filament

WIRING DIAGRAMS

NOTE: See ACCESSORIES & EQUIPMENT, Volume 5.

Elantra, Excel, Scoupe, Sonata

DESCRIPTION

Standard instrument cluster includes speedometer, tachometer, individual water temperature and fuel gauges, and warning indicator lights. Speedometer is cable-driven by transaxle gear. Oil pressure, brake fluid level, low fuel, door ajar, battery voltage, and seat belt warning indicators are represented in an illuminated light bar that uses light bulbs for backlighting. Illuminated light bar is located at bottom of instrument cluster.

TESTING

BRAKE WARNING LIGHTS

Brake Fluid Level Sensor (Elantra, Excel & Scoupe) – Unplug wiring connector to brake fluid reservoir switch. Using ohmmeter, ensure continuity exists between switch terminals while pushing down switch float inside reservoir. If continuity does not exist, replace brake fluid reservoir and switch assembly.

Brake Fluid Level Sensor (Sonata) – Unplug wiring connector to brake fluid reservoir switch. Using ohmmeter, ensure continuity exists between switch terminals when raising brake fluid reservoir cap from reservoir. If continuity does not exist, replace brake fluid reservoir cap and switch assembly.

Brake Fluid Level Warning Light – Chock wheels. Release parking brake lever. Start engine and let idle. Unplug harness connector at brake fluid reservoir switch. Jumper wiring harness connector terminals. Brake warning light should illuminate. If light does not illuminate, apply parking brake. If light still does not illuminate, wiring or bulb is defective. If light does illuminate after applying parking brake, locate and repair open in wiring from brake fluid reservoir switch to instrument cluster.

COOLANT TEMPERATURE GAUGE

1) Check if other gauges and indicator lights are inoperative. If these are also inoperative, check appropriate fuse in fuse panel. See GAUGES FUSE IDENTIFICATION table. Disconnect engine harness connector from temperature gauge sender on engine, near thermostat housing. Ground harness connector terminal, using a 12-volt test light (with a 3.4-watt light bulb installed).

GAUGES FUSE IDENTIFICATION [1]

Application	Fuse Number
Elantra	6 & 10
Excel	5 & 17
Scoupe	13
Sonata	12

[1] – Fuse(s) provides power supply for all instrument cluster gauges, speedometer, tachometer, low fuel indicator, oil pressure indicator, and low brake fluid indicator.

2) Turn ignition on. Test light should flash and gauge indicator should move. If test light does not flash, check power circuit from gauge to sending unit. If test light flashes and temperature gauge does not move, check gauge power feed and ground circuits. If circuits are good, replace gauge.

COOLANT TEMPERATURE SENDING UNIT

Unplug sending unit harness connector. Using an ohmmeter, connect probes to sending unit terminal and to ground on engine. Resistance readings should be as specified. See COOLANT TEMPERATURE SENDING UNIT RESISTANCE table.

FUEL GAUGE

Elantra – 1) Check if other gauges and indicator lights are inoperative. If these are also inoperative, check appropriate fuse in fuse panel. See GAUGES FUSE IDENTIFICATION table. Fuse panel is located vertically on left kick panel. If other gauges are operating and fuse is not blown, raise vehicle and disconnect fuel gauge harness connector at rear of tank.

COOLANT TEMPERATURE SENDING UNIT RESISTANCE

Application	Temperature – °F (°C)	Ohms
Elantra & Sonata	140 (60)	125
	185 (85)	48.4
	230 (110)	24
	257 (125)	15.2
Excel & Scoupe	112 (50)	230
	140 (60)	155
	158 (70)	90-118
	239 (115)	21-27
	248 (120)	21
	252 (122)	19.5

2) Connect a 12-volt test light (with a 3.4-watt light bulb installed) between harness connector terminal No. 2 and ground. See Fig. 1. Turn ignition on. Ensure test light is flashing and fuel gauge moves to "F" position.

3) If test light flashes but gauge DOES NOT move to "F" position, replace fuel gauge. If test light does not flash, first check for open in ground circuit. If open in wire is not found, remove instrument cluster.

4) Attach ohmmeter leads across fuel gauge test terminals on back of instrument cluster and measure gauge resistance. See Fig. 1. Resistance should be 55 ohms. If resistance is low, fuel gauge coil is shorted, replace gauge. If resistance is high, check for open wire to gauge coil. Repair as required or replace gauge.

Excel – 1) Check if other gauges and indicator lights are inoperative. If these are also inoperative, check appropriate fuse in fuse panel. See GAUGES FUSE IDENTIFICATION table. Fuse panel is located vertically on left kick panel. If other gauges are operating and fuse is not blown, raise vehicle and disconnect fuel gauge harness connector at left front of tank.

2) Connect a 12-volt test light (with a 3.4-watt light bulb installed) between harness connector terminal No. 2 and ground. See Fig. 2. Turn ignition on. Ensure test light is flashing and fuel gauge moves to "F" position.

3) If test light flashes but gauge DOES NOT move to "F" position, replace fuel gauge. If test light does not flash, first check for open in Black wire (ground circuit) from instrument cluster's 10-wire connector. Second, check for open in Green/Brown wire from instrument cluster's 10-wire connector to fuel sending unit harness connector terminal No. 2. If open in wire is not found, remove instrument cluster.

4) Attach ohmmeter leads across fuel gauge test terminals on back of instrument cluster and measure gauge resistance. See Fig. 2. Resistance should be 55 ohms. If resistance is low, fuel gauge coil is shorted, replace gauge. If resistance is high, check for open wire to gauge coil. Repair as required or replace gauge.

Scoupe – 1) Check if other gauges and indicator lights are inoperative. If these are also inoperative, check appropriate fuse in fuse panel. See GAUGES FUSE IDENTIFICATION table. Fuse panel is located vertically on left kick panel. If other gauges are operating and fuse is not blown, raise vehicle and disconnect fuel gauge harness connector at left front of tank. See Fig. 2.

2) Connect a 12-volt test light (with a 3.4-watt light bulb installed) between harness connector terminal No. 2 and ground. See Fig. 2. Turn ignition on. Ensure test light is flashing and fuel gauge pointer moves to "F" position.

3) If test light flashes but gauge DOES NOT move to "F" position, replace fuel gauge. If test light does not flash, first check for open in Black wire (ground circuit) from instrument cluster connector. Next, check for open in Green/Brown wire from instrument cluster connector, terminal No. 1 to fuel sending unit harness connector terminal No. 2. If open in wire is not found, remove instrument cluster.

4) Attach ohmmeter leads across fuel gauge test terminals on back of instrument cluster and measure gauge resistance. See Fig. 3. Resistance should be 55 ohms. If resistance is low, fuel gauge coil is shorted, replace gauge. If resistance is high, check for open wire to gauge coil. Repair as required or replace gauge.

REAR VIEW OF CLUSTER

Fuel Gauge Test
Terminals

Fuel Gauge
Sending Unit
Harness Connector
Terminals

IN VEHICLE

Fuel Gauge
Sending Unit
Connector
Terminals

OUT OF VEHICLE

93D00953 93E00954 93F00955

Courtesy of Hyundai Motor Co.

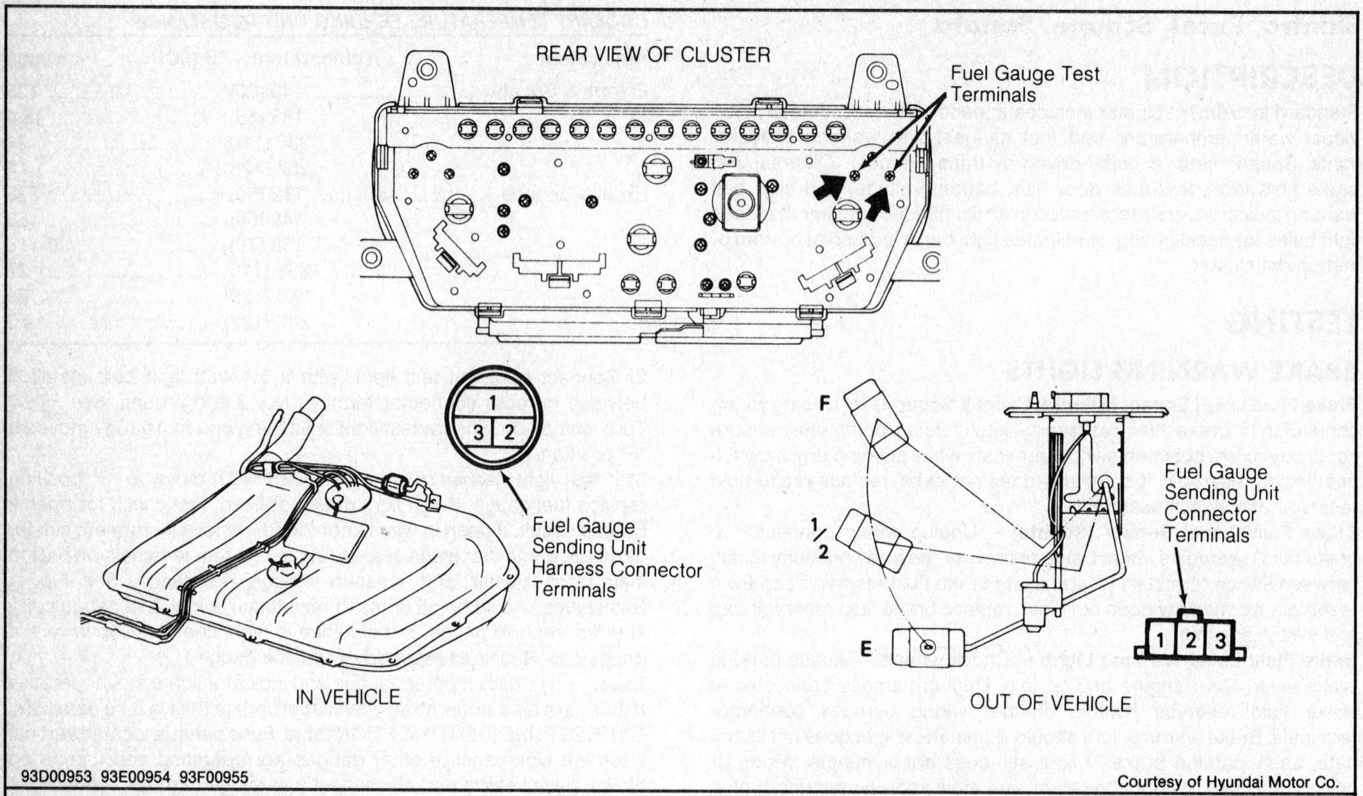

Fig. 1: Testing Fuel Gauge (Elantra)

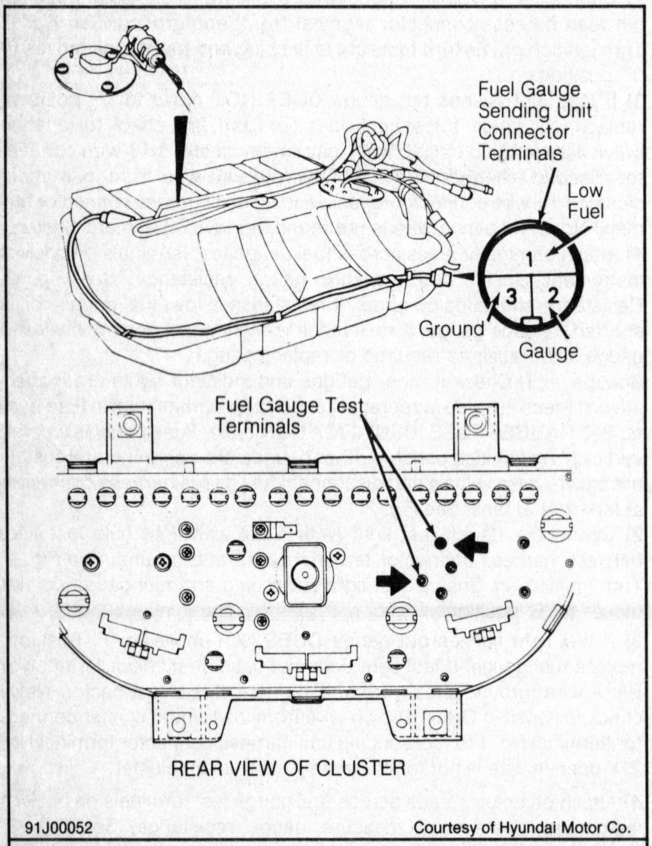

Fuel Gauge
Sending Unit
Connector
Terminals

Low
Fuel

Ground

Gauge

Fuel Gauge Test
Terminals

REAR VIEW OF CLUSTER

91J00052

Courtesy of Hyundai Motor Co.

Fig. 2: Testing Fuel Gauge (Excel Shown; Scoupe Is Similar)

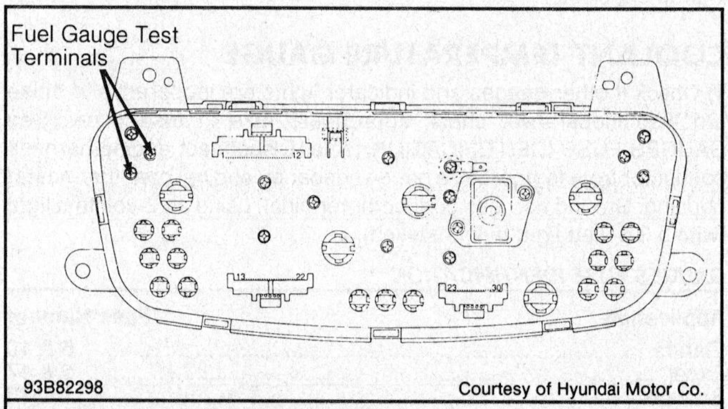

Fuel Gauge Test
Terminals

93B82298

Courtesy of Hyundai Motor Co.

Fig. 3: Testing Fuel Gauge (Scoupe)

Sonata – 1) Check if other gauges and indicator lights are inoperative. If these are also inoperative, check appropriate fuse in fuse panel. See GAUGES FUSE IDENTIFICATION table. Fuse panel is located on left kick panel. If other gauges are operating and fuse is not blown, raise vehicle and disconnect fuel gauge harness connector at left front of tank. See Fig. 4.

2) Connect a 12-volt test light (with a 3.4-watt light bulb installed) between harness connector terminals No. 3 and 2 (ground terminal). See Fig. 4. Turn ignition on. Ensure test light is flashing and note that fuel gauge pointer moves to "F" position.

3) If test light flashes but gauge DOES NOT move to "F" position, replace fuel gauge. If test light does not flash, first check for open in Black wire (ground circuit) from instrument cluster's 8-wire connector. Next, check for open in Light Green/Red wire from instrument cluster's 8-wire connector terminal No. 7 to fuel sending unit's harness connector terminal No. 3. If open in wire is not found, remove instrument cluster and replace fuel gauge.

FUEL GAUGE SENDING UNIT

To check operation of sending unit, remove sending unit from vehicle. Using ohmmeter, check resistance between terminals No. 2 and 3 in 3 float positions. *See Fig. 1, 2 or 4.* Results should be as follows.

Except Elantra – At "E" position, resistance should be 103-117 ohms. At 1/2 position, resistance should be 28-36 ohms. At "F" position, resistance should be 1-5 ohms.

Elantra – At "E" position, resistance should be 95 ohms. At 1/2 position, resistance should be 32-33 ohms. At "F" position, resistance should be 7 ohms.

LOW FUEL LEVEL LIGHT SENSOR

Elantra, Excel & Scoupe – 1) Remove sending unit from fuel tank. See FUEL GAUGE SENDING UNIT. Connect a 12-volt test light (with 3.4-watt bulb installed) between a 12-volt battery source and terminal No. 1 of fuel tank sending unit connector. *See Figs. 1 and 2.* Using jumper wire, ground connector terminal No. 3 to battery negative terminal.

2) Immerse sending unit in water. Test light should be off while sensor is beneath water and should illuminate when sensor and sending unit are taken out of water. If sensor/sending unit does not operate as specified, replace sending unit assembly.

Sonata – 1) Remove sending unit from fuel tank. Connect a 12-volt test light (with 3.4-watt bulb installed) between a 12-volt battery source and terminal No. 1 of fuel gauge sending unit connector. *See Fig. 4.* Using jumper wire, ground connector terminal No. 3 to battery negative terminal.

2) Immerse sending unit in water. Test light should be off while sensor is beneath water and should illuminate when sensor and sending unit is taken out of water. If sensor/sending unit does not operate as specified, replace sending unit assembly.

OIL PRESSURE GAUGE

Sonata – 1) Disconnect engine harness connector from oil gauge sending unit on engine. See OIL PRESSURE SWITCH/SENDING UNIT LOCATION table. Ground harness connector terminal using a 12-volt test light (with a 3.4-watt light bulb installed).

2) Turn ignition on. Test light should flash and gauge indicator should move. If test light does not flash, check for open circuit from gauge to sending unit. If test light flashes and gauge pointer does not move, check gauge ground circuit. If ground circuit is good, replace gauge.

OIL PRESSURE SWITCH/SENDING UNIT LOCATION

Application	Location
Elantra	Behind Alternator
Excel	Behind Alternator
Scoupe	Near Ignition Control Module
Sonata	Behind Alternator

OIL PRESSURE SENDING UNIT (GAUGE)

Sonata – 1) Unplug sending unit harness connector. See OIL PRESSURE SWITCH/SENDING UNIT LOCATION table. Using an ohmmeter, measure resistance between sending unit terminal and ground. High resistance indicates no oil pressure. Low resistance indicates oil pressure is present.

2) Check engine oil pressure with a known-good manual oil pressure tester gauge. Compare with instrument cluster oil gauge reading. If gauge does not register properly, replace sending unit.

OIL PRESSURE INDICATOR LIGHT

1) Check if other gauges and indicator lights are inoperative. If these are also inoperative, check appropriate fuse in fuse panel. See GAUGES FUSE IDENTIFICATION table. Disconnect engine harness connector from oil pressure switch on engine. See OIL PRESSURE SWITCH/SENDING UNIT LOCATION table.

2) Using jumper wire, ground harness connector terminal. Turn ignition on. Instrument cluster oil indicator light should be on. If indicator light is not on, check light bulb in instrument cluster, or check for open in circuit from cluster to switch. If light is on, replace defective oil pressure switch.

OIL PRESSURE SWITCH (INDICATOR LIGHT)

Disconnect engine harness connector from oil pressure switch on engine. See OIL PRESSURE SWITCH/SENDING UNIT LOCATION table. Using ohmmeter, measure resistance between switch terminal and engine (ground). There should be continuity with engine not running. There should NOT be continuity when engine is running and oil pressure is greater than 4-5 psi (.3-.4 kg/cm²). If switch does not react as described, replace switch.

TACHOMETER

Connect an external tachometer to engine. Start engine. Compare readings of external tachometer with tachometer gauge in instrument cluster. See TACHOMETER TEST table. If external tachometer RPM is not within cluster tachometer specification range, replace cluster tachometer.

CAUTION: When replacing tachometer, DO NOT reverse wiring connections or damage to tachometer's transistors and diodes will result.

TACHOMETER TEST [1]

External Tachometer RPM	Cluster Tachometer RPM
Elantra	
1000	900-1100
2000	1875-2125
3000	2850-3150
4000	3850-4150
5000	4850-5150
6000	5820-6180
7000	6790-7210
Excel	
750	650-850
2000	1900-2100
3000	2850-3150
4000	3800-4200
5000	4750-5250
6000	5700-6300
7000	6650-7350
Scoupe	
1000	900-1100
2000	1850-2150
3000	2800-3200
4000	3800-4200
5000	4800-5200
6000	5800-6200
7000	6700-7300
Sonata	
1000	900-1100
2000	1900-2100
3000	2850-3150
4000	3800-4200
5000	4750-5250
6000	5700-6300
7000	6650-7350

[1] – Tests performed at 77°F (25°C), with 13.5 volts at tachometer input power supply terminal.

VOLTMETER

Sonata – Connect external voltmeter in parallel with instrument cluster voltmeter. Instrument cluster voltmeter should be within .5 volt of external voltmeter. If voltage readings do not agree, replace instrument cluster voltmeter.

HAZARD WARNING SWITCH

Elantra – 1) Check for blown fuse (No. 2). Check flasher operation. Flasher is located in relay box, behind left dash. If okay, remove hazard switch from right side of instrument cluster trim panel. Unplug harness connector.

2) With switch in OFF position, use ohmmeter to ensure continuity exists between terminals No. 3 and 9, and terminals No. 1 and 5. *See Fig. 5.* With switch in ON position, continuity should exist between terminals No. 2, 6, 7, 8, and between terminals No. 4 and 9. Terminals No. 1 and 5 are for bulb illumination. Terminal No. 4 is fused input power supply to switch.

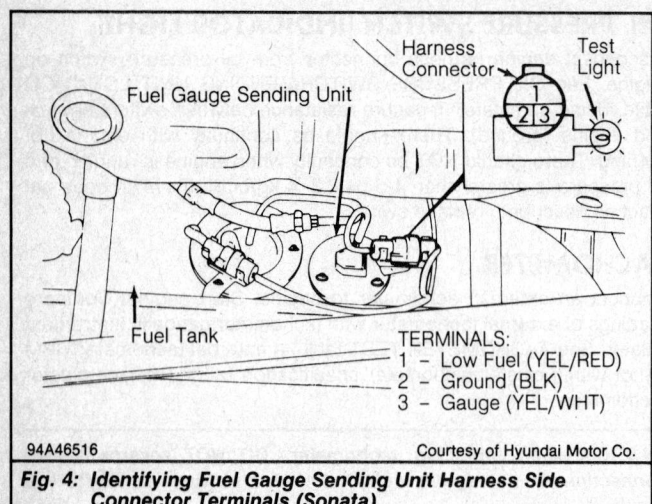

Fig. 4: Identifying Fuel Gauge Sending Unit Harness Side Connector Terminals (Sonata)

Excel – Excel has hazard switch mounted to top of steering column. See STEERING COLUMN SWITCHES article.

Scoupe – **1)** Check for blown fuse No. 13 and/or flasher. Flasher is located in relay box, behind left dash. Hazard switch is located to right of instrument cluster, in clock assembly bezel. Remove clock assembly by prying outward. Unplug harness connectors. Remove hazard switch retaining screws. Pry switch from panel.

2) With switch in OFF position, use ohmmeter to ensure continuity exists between terminals No. 3 and 9. *See Fig. 5.* With switch in ON position, continuity should exist between terminals No. 2, 6, 7, 8, and between terminals No. 4 and 9. Terminals No. 1 and 5 are for bulb illumination. Terminal No. 3 is fused input power supply to switch.

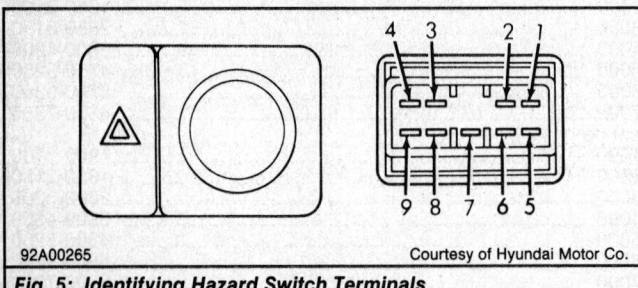

Fig. 5: Identifying Hazard Switch Terminals (Sonata Shown; Others Are Similar)

Sonata – **1)** Check for blown fuse No. 2 and/or flasher. Flasher is located in relay box, behind left dash. Remove hazard switch from right side of instrument cluster trim panel by prying switch outward. Unplug harness connector.

2) With switch in OFF position, use ohmmeter to ensure continuity exists between terminals No. 3, 4 and 9, and terminals No. 1 and 5. *See Fig. 5.* With switch in ON position, continuity should exist between terminals No. 2, 6, 7, 8, and between terminals No. 4 and 9. Terminals No. 1 and 5 are for bulb illumination. Terminal No. 4 is fused input power supply to switch.

WIPER SWITCH

For testing information on wiper switch, see WIPER/WASHER SYSTEMS or STEERING COLUMN SWITCHES article.

REMOVAL & INSTALLATION

INSTRUMENT CLUSTER

Removal & Installation (Elantra) – **1)** Disconnect negative battery cable. Remove coin box. Remove ash tray and center dash panel. Disconnect electrical connectors from center dash switches. Remove instrument panel face by removing 3 retaining screws. Remove 4 screws retaining instrument cluster. *See Figs. 6 and 7.*

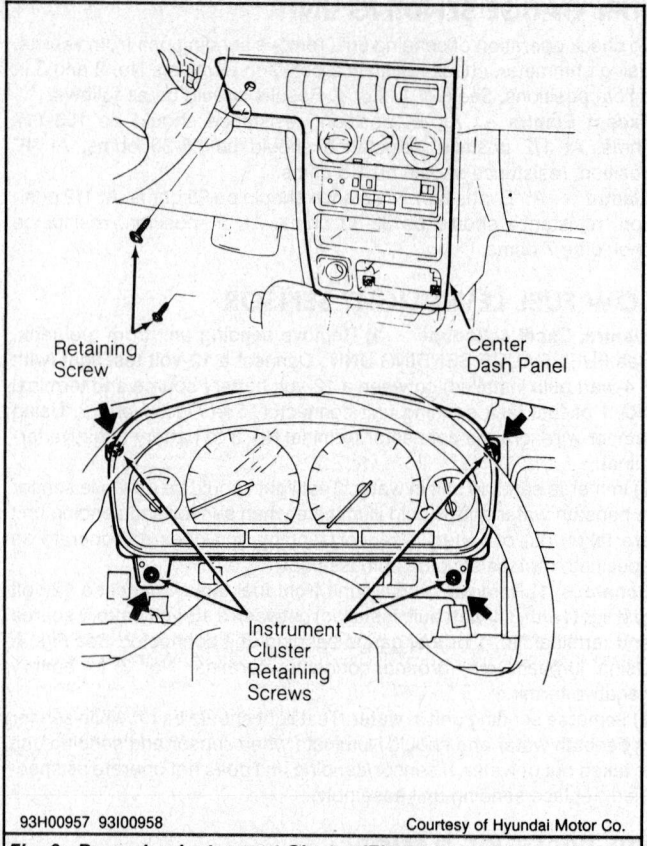

Fig. 6: Removing Instrument Cluster (Elantra)

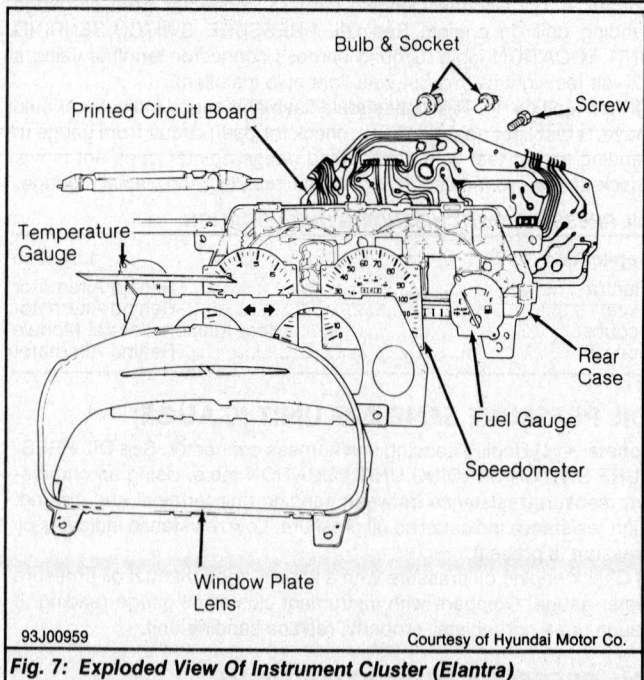

Fig. 7: Exploded View Of Instrument Cluster (Elantra)

2) Carefully pull cluster out enough to disengage speedometer cable and wiring connectors from printed circuit board. To install, reverse removal procedure.

Removal & Installation (Excel) – **1)** Disconnect negative battery cable. Remove instrument panel face by removing 3 retaining screws. Remove 4 screws retaining instrument cluster. *See Figs. 8 and 9.*

2) Carefully pull cluster out enough to disengage speedometer cable and wiring connectors from printed circuit board. To install, reverse removal procedure.

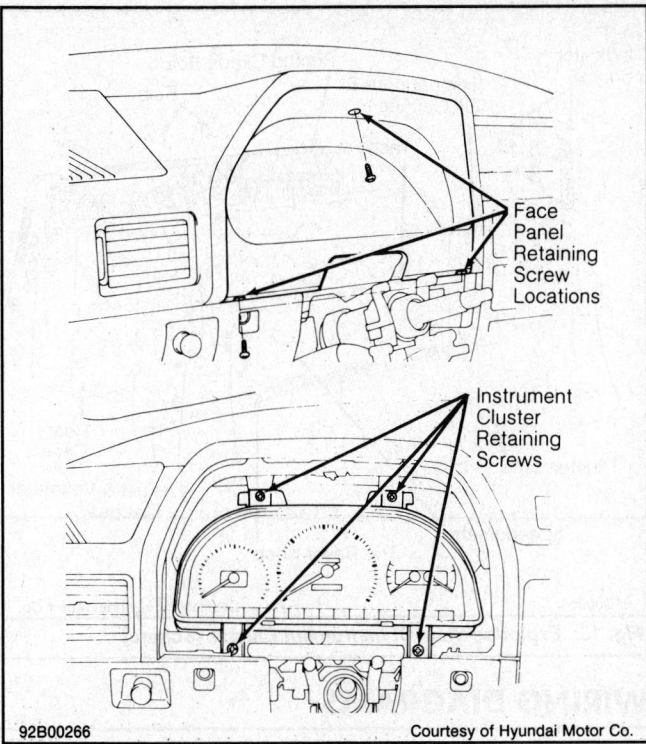

Face Panel Retaining Screw Locations

Instrument Cluster Retaining Screws

92B00266
Courtesy of Hyundai Motor Co.

Fig. 8: Removing Instrument Cluster (Excel)

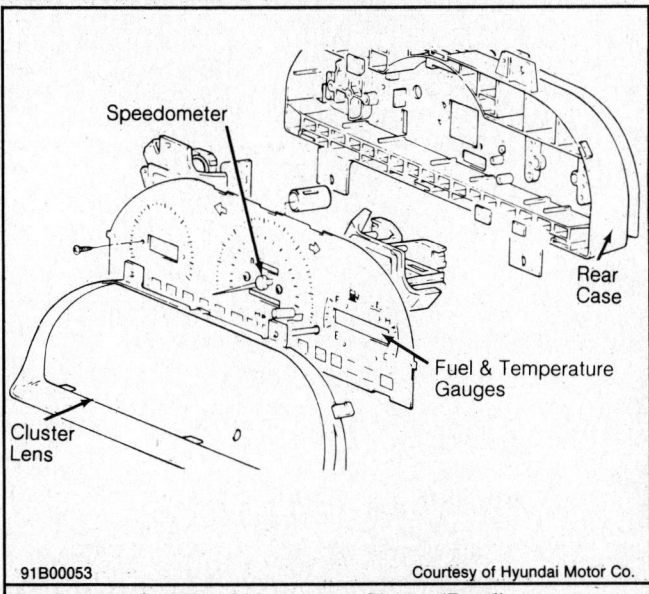

Speedometer

Rear Case

Fuel & Temperature Gauges

Cluster Lens

91B00053
Courtesy of Hyundai Motor Co.

Fig. 9: Exploded View Of Instrument Cluster (Excel)

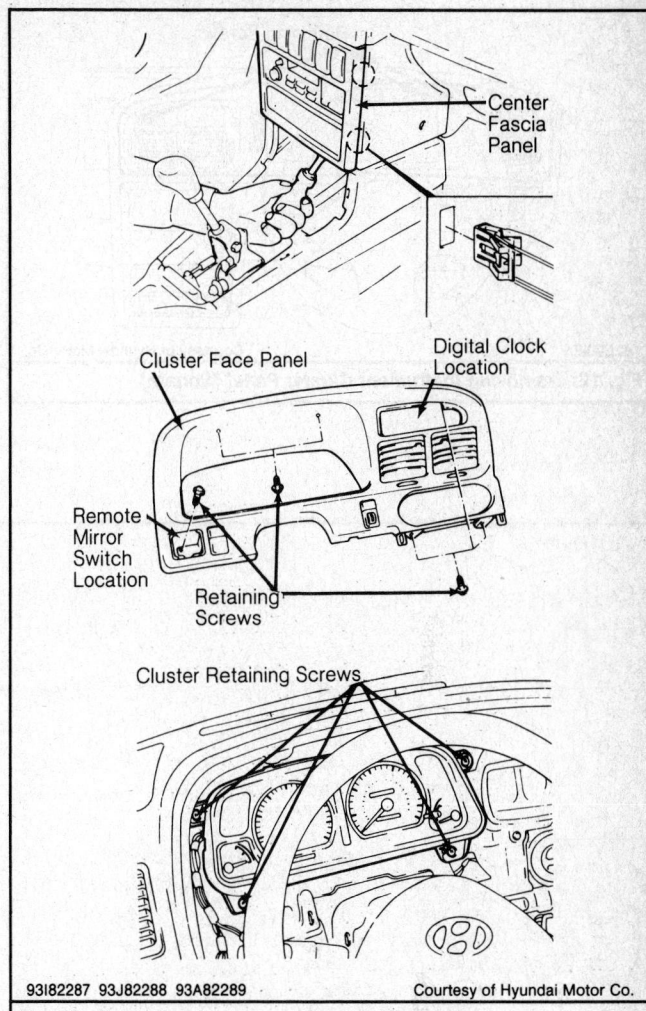

Center Fascia Panel

Cluster Face Panel

Digital Clock Location

Remote Mirror Switch Location

Retaining Screws

Cluster Retaining Screws

93I82287 93J82288 93A82289
Courtesy of Hyundai Motor Co.

Fig. 10: Removing Instrument Cluster (Scoupe)

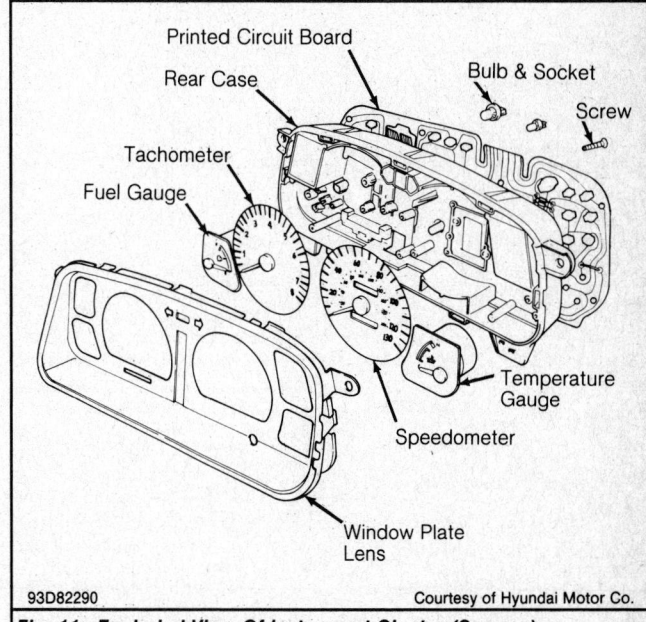

Printed Circuit Board

Rear Case

Bulb & Socket

Screw

Tachometer

Fuel Gauge

Temperature Gauge

Speedometer

Window Plate Lens

93D82290
Courtesy of Hyundai Motor Co.

Fig. 11: Exploded View Of Instrument Cluster (Scoupe)

Removal & Installation (Scoupe) – 1) Disconnect negative battery cable. Remove ashtray. Remove low crash pad center fascia panel. Remove digital clock assembly and remote mirror switch by prying units out from panel. See Figs. 10 and 11.
2) Remove screws at cluster fascia panel. Remove 4 screws retaining cluster and connections. To install, reverse removal procedure.
Removal & Installation (Sonata) – 1) Disconnect negative battery cable. Remove 4 retaining screws and pull instrument cluster panel outward. See Fig. 12. Disconnect wiring connectors and speedometer cable from rear of instrument cluster.
2) Remove instrument cluster from rear of panel by removing 4 cluster retaining screws. Remove cluster lens by unsnapping from rear case. See Fig. 13. To install, reverse removal procedure.

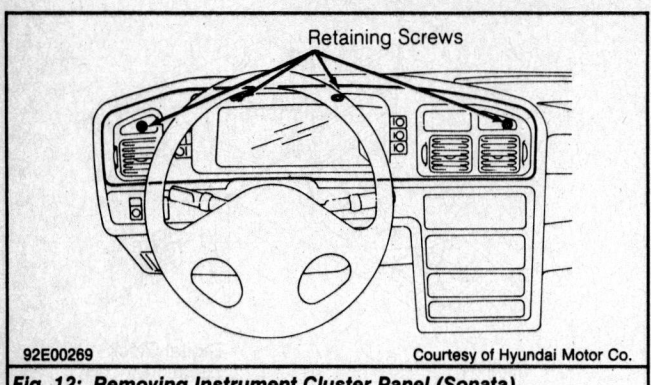

Retaining Screws

92E00269   Courtesy of Hyundai Motor Co.

Fig. 12: Removing Instrument Cluster Panel (Sonata)

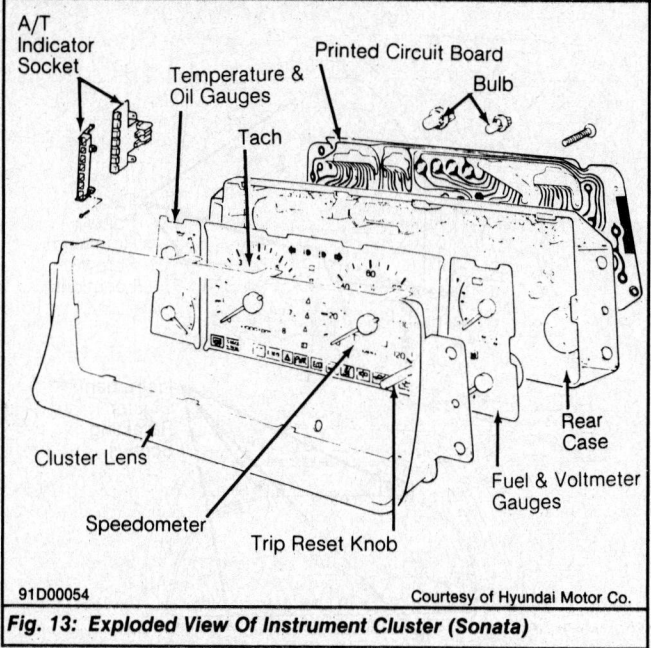

A/T Indicator Socket

Temperature & Oil Gauges

Printed Circuit Board

Bulb

Tach

Cluster Lens

Speedometer

Trip Reset Knob

Rear Case

Fuel & Voltmeter Gauges

91D00054   Courtesy of Hyundai Motor Co.

Fig. 13: Exploded View Of Instrument Cluster (Sonata)

WIRING DIAGRAMS

NOTE: See ACCESSORIES & EQUIPMENT, Volume 5.

Elantra, Excel, Scoupe, Sonata

DESCRIPTION & OPERATION

POWER DOOR LOCKS

Elantra – Battery voltage is supplied to central door locking actuator at all times from fuse No. 5. A metal rod links LH front door lock switch and central locking actuator. When LH front door lock switch is pushed to LOCK, the metal rod pushes actuator switches inside central door locking actuator to the lock position. The solid state circuit receives lock input and grounds the relay coil momentarily. Battery power is then supplied to all door lock actuators through relay contact and actuator switch.

Each motor is grounded through the diode and limit switch inside the appropriate door lock actuator and through the actuator switch inside the central door locking actuator. The solid state circuit de-energizes the relay coil when limit switches in the door lock actuators move to unlock positions. The door locks work similarly when LH front door lock switch is pushed to unlock, except that electrical current goes through each motor in the opposite direction. *See Fig 1.*

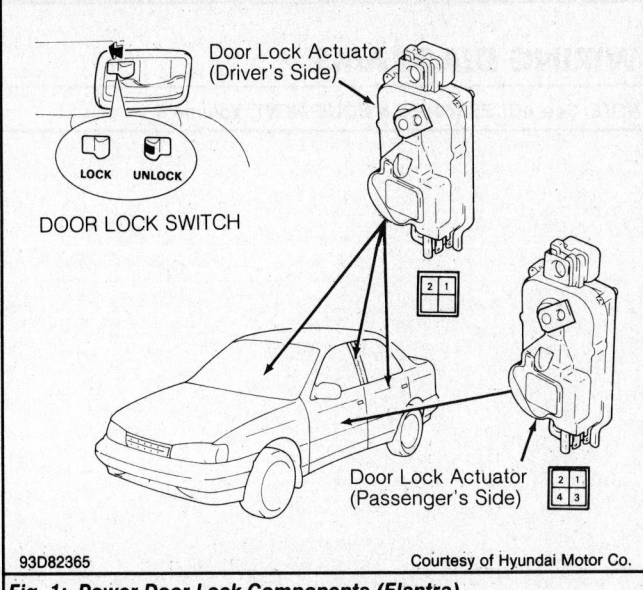

93D82365   Courtesy of Hyundai Motor Co.

Fig. 1: Power Door Lock Components (Elantra)

93E82366   Courtesy of Hyundai Motor Co.

Fig. 2: Power Door Lock Components (Sonata)

Sonata – Battery voltage is applied at all times to power door lock control unit. When locking vehicle by using driver's master switch assembly, switch assembly will provide a ground to the lock relay and the doors will lock. Locking the doors by using the vehicle key or pushing down lock knob, will send a signal to the Electronic Time and Alarm Control System (ETACS) module. The control unit will then ground the relay and the doors lock. The ETACS module also has an input from the ignition key switch. This input prevents doors from accidentally being locked when exiting vehicle with ignition off and key left in ignition switch.

When driver's master switch assembly is turned to UNLOCK position, a path to ground is supplied to control unit's unlock relay. Battery voltage is applied to door lock actuators. Polarity of voltage applied to actuators is now reversed and the doors unlock. *See Fig. 2.*

Excel & Scoupe – Power door locks are not available on Excel or Scoupe models.

TRUNK RELEASE

Battery voltage is applied at all times through fuse No. 5 (Elantra and Sonata) or fuse No. 2 (Excel and Scoupe) to the truck lid release switch. When the trunk lid release switch is depressed, battery voltage is applied to the trunk lid release solenoid. The solenoid energizes and the trunk lid opens. *See Figs. 3 and 4.*

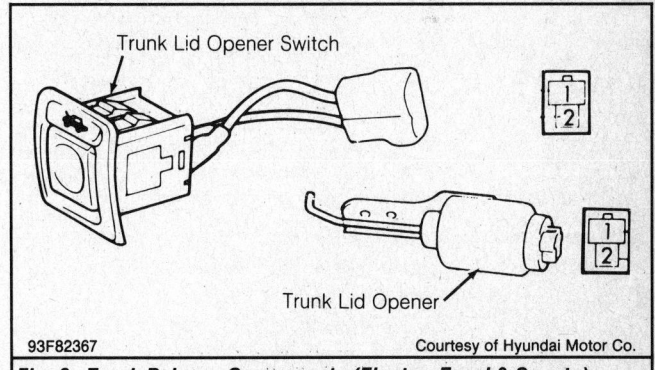

93F82367   Courtesy of Hyundai Motor Co.

Fig. 3: Trunk Release Components (Elantra, Excel & Sonata)

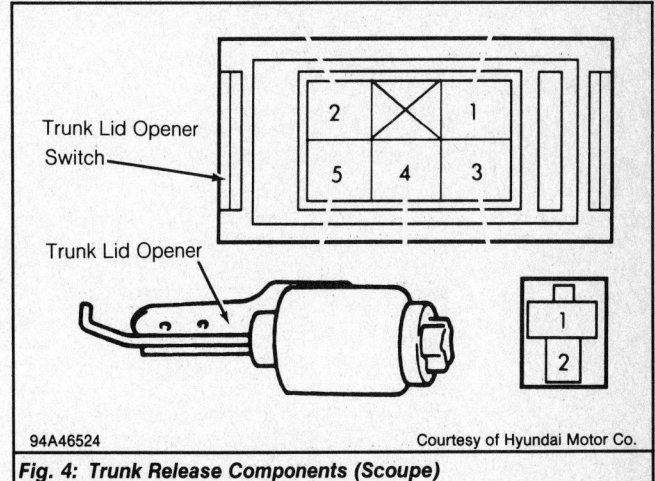

94A46524   Courtesy of Hyundai Motor Co.

Fig. 4: Trunk Release Components (Scoupe)

TROUBLE SHOOTING

Inspect all connectors for looseness or corrosion. Check all wires and harness lines for abrasion and/or cuts. Look for burned or overheated components.

TESTING

NOTE: Manufacturer provides only limited power door lock and trunk release testing procedures. Use wiring diagrams to help diagnose problems. See WIRING DIAGRAMS.

POWER DOOR LOCK ACTUATOR

Sonata – Disconnect actuator wiring harness. Use jumper wires to connect negative battery terminal to actuator terminal No. 2 and positive battery terminal to actuator terminal No. 1. *See Fig. 5.* Actuator should move toward unlock position. Reverse the jumper wires. Actuator should move toward lock position. Replace actuator if it does not test as specified.

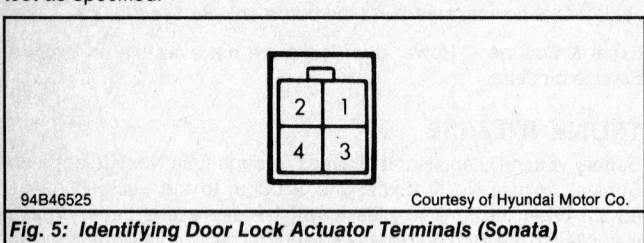

94B46525   Courtesy of Hyundai Motor Co.

Fig. 5: Identifying Door Lock Actuator Terminals (Sonata)

TRUNK LID OPENER SWITCH

Elantra, Excel & Sonata – Remove trunk lid opener switch and check continuity between terminals. There should be continuity when switch is in ON position, and no continuity when switch is in OFF position. *See Fig. 3.* Replace switch if it does not test as specified.

Scoupe – Remove trunk lid opener switch and check continuity between switch terminals No. 4 and 5. *See Fig. 4.* With switch in ON position, continuity should be present. With switch in OFF position, continuity should not be present. In either position, continuity should be present between switch terminals No. 1 and 3 (illumination circuit). Replace switch if it does not test as specified.

TRUNK LID OPENER

Remove trunk lid opener and check continuity between terminals. If there is no continuity, replace lid opener. *See Fig. 3 or 4.*

REMOVAL & INSTALLATION

NOTE: Manufacturer does not provide removal and installation procedures. Use illustrations as a guide. See Figs. 1-4.

WIRING DIAGRAMS

NOTE: See ACCESSORIES & EQUIPMENT, Volume 5.

Elantra, Scoupe, Sonata

DESCRIPTION & OPERATION

Power mirrors are controlled by a dual control switch located on driver-side door panel or instrument panel. The left/right switch directs current to desired mirror. The up/down and left/right switch directs current to one of 2 motors located in the mirror/motor assembly.

TROUBLE SHOOTING

All Mirrors Inoperative – Check for blown fuse or fusible link. Check power mirror switch ground. Check power mirror switch. Check for bad switch connections.
One Mirror Inoperative – Check power mirror switch. Check mirror motor. Check for open circuit between switch and mirror motors.

TESTING

POWER MIRROR SWITCH TEST

Remove power mirror switch. Disconnect harness connector and check for continuity at switch terminals with switch in indicated positions. See POWER MIRROR SWITCH CONTINUITY TEST table. *See Fig. 1*. Replace switch if it does not test as specified.

POWER MIRROR SWITCH CONTINUITY TEST

Application	Terminals No.
Elantra	
Left Mirror	
Up	1 & 7, 2 & 4
Down	1 & 4, 2 & 7
Off	No Continuity
Left	1 & 6, 2 & 4
Right	1 & 4, 2 & 6
Right Mirror	
Up	1 & 5, 2 & 4
Down	1 & 4, 2 & 5
Off	No Continuity
Left	1 & 3, 2 & 4
Right	1 & 4, 2 & 3
Scoupe	
Left Mirror	
Up	3 & 4, 5 & 7
Down	3 & 5, 4 & 7
Off	No Continuity
Left	2 & 7, 3 & 4
Right	2 & 3, 4 & 7
Right Mirror	
Up	3 & 4, 6 & 7
Down	3 & 6, 4 & 7
Off	No Continuity
Left	1 & 7, 3 & 4
Right	1 & 3, 4 & 7
Sonata	
Left Mirror	
Up	2 & 7, 4 & 5
Down	2 & 4, 5 & 7
Off	No Continuity
Left	3 & 7, 4 & 5
Right	3 & 4, 5 & 7
Right Mirror	
Up	1 & 7, 4 & 5
Down	1 & 4, 5 & 7
Off	No Continuity
Left	4 & 5, 6 & 7
Right	4 & 6, 5 & 7

POWER MIRROR MOTOR TEST

Access and disconnect power mirror motor connector. *See Fig. 2*. Apply battery voltage to connector as indicated in POWER MIRROR MOTOR TEST table. *See Figs. 3-5*. If motor does not operate as specified, replace it.

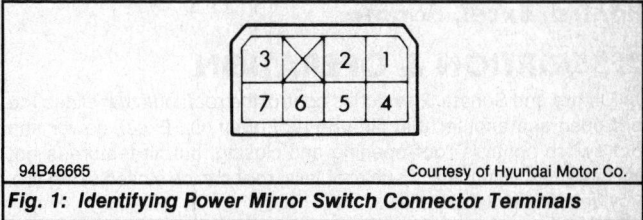

94B46665   Courtesy of Hyundai Motor Co.

Fig. 1: Identifying Power Mirror Switch Connector Terminals

POWER MIRROR MOTOR TEST

Apply 12 Volts To Pin No.	Ground Pin No.	Mirror Operation
1	2	Up
2	1	Down
3	2	Left
2	3	Right

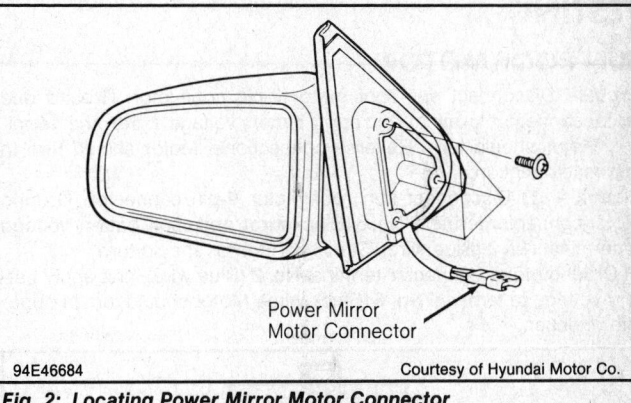

94E46684   Courtesy of Hyundai Motor Co.

Power Mirror Motor Connector

Fig. 2: Locating Power Mirror Motor Connector

94G46686   Courtesy of Hyundai Motor Co.

Fig. 3: Power Mirror Motor Connector Terminals (Elantra)

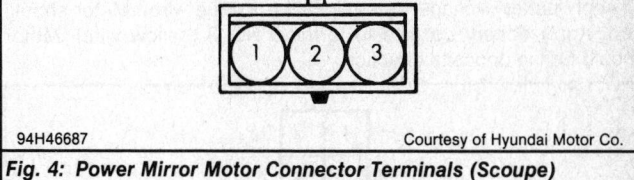

94H46687   Courtesy of Hyundai Motor Co.

Fig. 4: Power Mirror Motor Connector Terminals (Scoupe)

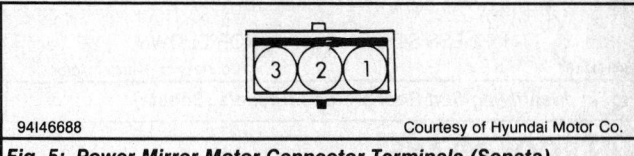

94I46688   Courtesy of Hyundai Motor Co.

Fig. 5: Power Mirror Motor Connector Terminals (Sonata)

REMOVAL & INSTALLATION

NOTE: Information is not available from manufacturer.

WIRING DIAGRAMS

NOTE: See ACCESSORIES & EQUIPMENT, Volume 5.

1994 ACCESSORIES & EQUIPMENT
Power Sun Roof

Elantra, Excel, Sonata

DESCRIPTION & OPERATION

On Elantra and Sonata, 2 switches control the roof: one that slides the roof open and another that tilts the roof open. On Excel, power sun roof switch controls roof opening and closing, but tilt feature is not available. On all models, if sun roof fails, roof can be closed using tool provided in vehicle's trunk.

On Elantra and Sonata, power is supplied to sun roof motor assembly through 2 sun roof relays: a close/tilt up relay and an open-tilt-down relay. On Excel, power is supplied to sun roof motor directly through power sun roof switch.

ADJUSTMENTS

NOTE: No adjustment procedures are furnished by manufacturer.

TESTING

SUN ROOF MOTOR

Excel – Disconnect sun roof motor 2-pin connector. Ground one motor connector terminal, and apply battery voltage to the other terminal. Motor should turn. Reverse connections. Motor should turn in opposite direction.

Elantra – 1) Disconnect sun roof motor 9-pin connector. Ground motor connector terminal No. 6 (Black wire), and apply battery voltage to terminal No. 2 (Blue wire). See Fig. 1. Motor should turn.

2) Ground motor connector terminal No. 2 (Blue wire), and apply battery voltage to terminal No. 6 (Black wire). Motor should turn in opposite direction.

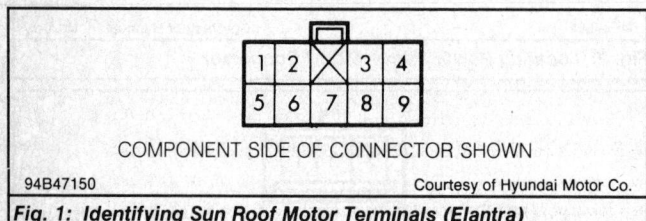

COMPONENT SIDE OF CONNECTOR SHOWN

94B47150   Courtesy of Hyundai Motor Co.

Fig. 1: Identifying Sun Roof Motor Terminals (Elantra)

Sonata – 1) Remove overhead console light. Disconnect sun roof motor 4-pin connector. Ground motor connector terminal No. 4 (Black wire). See Fig. 2.

2) Apply battery voltage to terminal No. 1 (Blue wire). Motor should turn. Apply battery positive to terminal No. 3 (Yellow wire). Motor should turn in opposite direction.

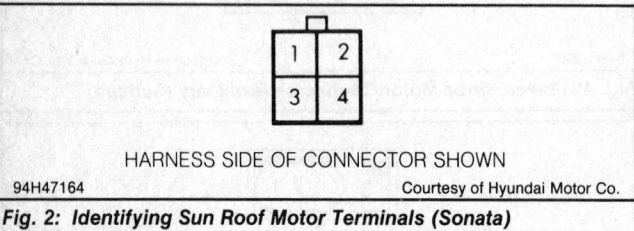

HARNESS SIDE OF CONNECTOR SHOWN

94H47164   Courtesy of Hyundai Motor Co.

Fig. 2: Identifying Sun Roof Motor Terminals (Sonata)

SUN ROOF RELAYS

Elantra & Sonata – 1) Remove overhead console. Remove relay(s), located on both sides of console and under headliner. Continuity should exist between terminals "C" and "F". See Fig. 3. Continuity should NOT exist between terminals "C" and "E".

2) Apply battery voltage between terminals "A" and "B". Continuity should now exist between terminals "C" and "E". Continuity should NOT exist between terminals "C" and "F".

SUN ROOF SWITCH

Elantra – 1) Remove sun roof switch. With switch in OFF position, continuity should not exist between terminals No. 1, 3, 4, 7, 8 and 9.

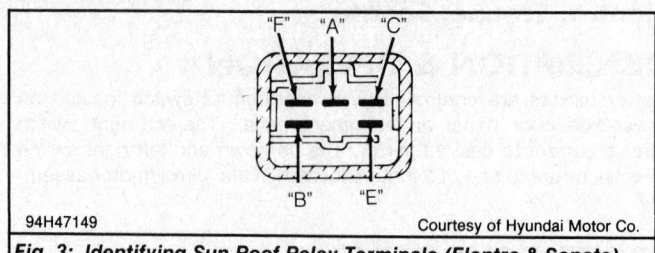

94H47149   Courtesy of Hyundai Motor Co.

Fig. 3: Identifying Sun Roof Relay Terminals (Elantra & Sonata)

With slide switch in OPEN position, continuity should exist between terminals No.1 (Blue wire) and 4 (Black wire), and between terminals No. 9 (Blue/Green wire) and 4 (Black wire). See Fig. 4. With slide switch in CLOSE position, continuity should exist between terminals No. 7 (Blue/White wire) and 4 (Black wire).

2) With tilt switch in OPEN position, continuity should exist between terminals No. 8 (Blue/Yellow wire) and 4 (Black wire). With tilt switch in CLOSE position, continuity should exist between terminals No. 3 (Blue wire) and 4 (Black wire).

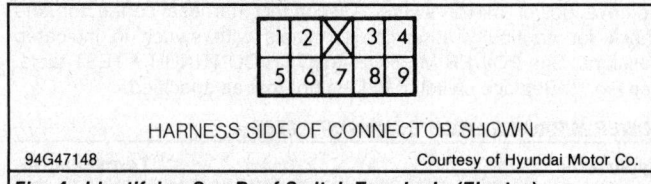

HARNESS SIDE OF CONNECTOR SHOWN

94G47148   Courtesy of Hyundai Motor Co.

Fig. 4: Identifying Sun Roof Switch Terminals (Elantra)

Excel – Disconnect 2 sun roof switch 2-pin connectors. See Fig. 5. With switch in OPEN position, continuity should exist between Blue wire terminal and Black wire terminal, and between Red/Blue wire terminal and Green wire terminal. With switch in CLOSE position, continuity should exist between Blue wire terminal and Red/Blue wire terminal, and between Black wire terminal and Green wire terminal.

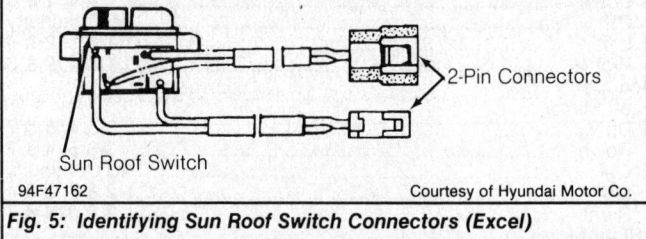

Sun Roof Switch

94F47162   Courtesy of Hyundai Motor Co.

Fig. 5: Identifying Sun Roof Switch Connectors (Excel)

Sonata – 1) Remove sun roof switch. With switch in OFF position, continuity should not exist between terminals No. 1-5. With slide switch in OPEN position, continuity should exist between terminals No. 4 (Blue wire) and 5 (Black wire). See Fig. 6. With slide switch in CLOSE position, continuity should exist between terminals No. 3 (Blue/White wire) and 5 (Black wire).

2) With tilt switch in OPEN position, continuity should exist between terminals No. 1 (Blue/Yellow wire) and 5 (Black wire). With tilt switch in CLOSE position, continuity should exist between terminals No. 2 (Blue/Green wire) and 5 (Black wire).

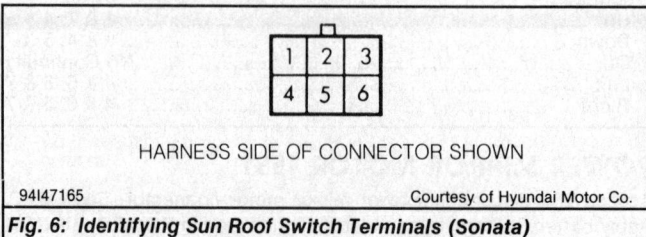

HARNESS SIDE OF CONNECTOR SHOWN

94I47165   Courtesy of Hyundai Motor Co.

Fig. 6: Identifying Sun Roof Switch Terminals (Sonata)

REMOVAL & INSTALLATION

SUN ROOF ASSEMBLY

NOTE: Manufacturer does not provide removal and installation procedure.

SUN ROOF MOTOR

Removal & Installation (Elantra & Sonata) – Ensure sun roof is fully closed before removing sun roof motor. Before installing new motor, ensure motor limit switches are at fully closed positions. Use sun roof wrench, located in vehicle's trunk, to manually rotate the motor. Manufacturer does not provide any additional procedures.

Removal & Installation (Excel) – Manufacturer does not provide removal and installation procedure.

WIRING DIAGRAMS

NOTE: See ACCESSORIES & EQUIPMENT, Volume 5.

1994 ACCESSORIES & EQUIPMENT
Power Windows

Elantra, Scoupe, Sonata

DESCRIPTION

A permanent magnet motor operates each of the power windows. The driver's master switch assembly controls all of the power window motors. Each window switch controls only one of the power window motors. If the lockout switch is depressed, rear power windows cannot be controlled by rear window switches, but they can still be controlled from driver's master switch assembly.

OPERATION

ELANTRA

Master Switch Assembly – When ignition switch is in ON position, battery voltage is applied to power window relay through fuse No. 12. When relay is energized, battery voltage is supplied to driver's master switch assembly by way of fusible link No. 30 (engine compartment relay box) through the closed relay contacts. When either switch in the master switch assembly is operated, battery voltage is applied to the power window motor. Power window motor is grounded through the opposite contact in the master switch assembly.

Window Switch – When ignition switch is in ON position, battery voltage is applied to power window relay through fuse No. 12 and the relay energizes. When relay is energized, battery voltage is supplied to driver's master switch assembly through closed relay contacts. When the passenger window switch is operated, battery voltage is applied to one terminal of the power window motor. The other terminal is grounded through the opposite contact in the window switch and master switch assembly.

SCOUPE

Master Switch Assembly – When ignition switch is in ON position, battery voltage is applied to master switch assembly through fuses No. 11 and 12. When either switch in the master switch assembly is operated, battery voltage is applied to the power window motor. The power window motor is grounded through the opposite contact in the master switch assembly.

Window Switch – When the ignition switch is in RUN position, battery voltage is applied to window switches through fuses No. 11 and 12. When the passenger window switch is operated, battery voltage is applied to one terminal of the power window motor. The other terminal is grounded through opposite contact in the window switch and master switch assembly.

SONATA

Master Switch Assembly – When ignition switch is in ON position, battery voltage is applied through fuse No. 13 to power window relay, which then allows power to flow to solid-state control unit through Pink 30-amp fusible link "A". All operation functions are controlled by solid-state control unit.

TROUBLE SHOOTING

TESTING

MOTOR TEST

Connect motor leads directly to battery terminals and ensure motor operates smoothly. Reverse polarity and ensure motor operates smoothly in opposite direction. If operation is abnormal, replace motor.

SWITCH TEST

Remove switch in question and perform continuity testing according to appropriate table. Main switch is driver's switch. Sub-switches are mounted at each passenger door.

CONTINUITY TESTING MAIN SWITCH (ELANTRA 2-DOOR) [1]

Position	Condition	[2] Terminals
Left	Up	No. 3 & 8, 1 & 7
Left	Off	No. 1, 3 & 8
Left	Down	No. 1 & 8, 3 & 7
Right	Up	No. 2 & 8, 7 & 9
Right	Off	No. 2, 7 & 9
Right	Down	No. 8 & 9, 2 & 7

[1] – Disconnect switch before testing. Check continuity between terminals. If continuity does not exist as shown, replace switch.

[2] – See Fig. 1.

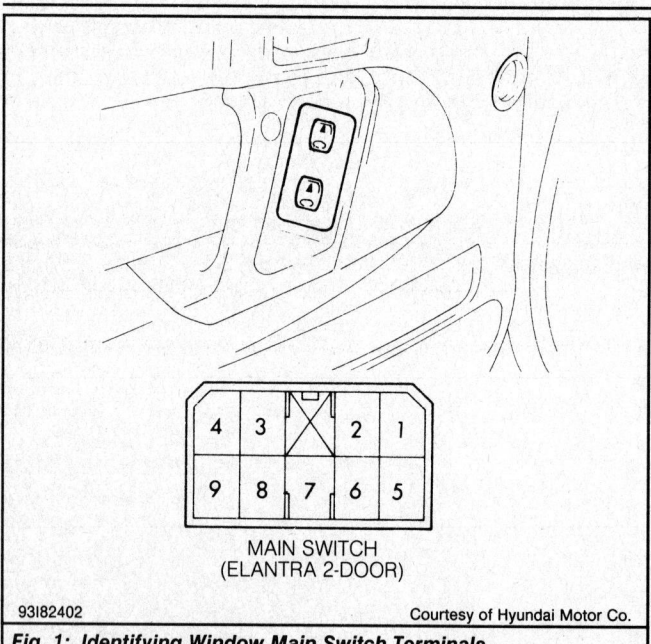

MAIN SWITCH
(ELANTRA 2-DOOR)

93182402   Courtesy of Hyundai Motor Co.

Fig. 1: Identifying Window Main Switch Terminals (Elantra 2-Door)

TROUBLE SHOOTING POWER WINDOWS (SCOUPE)

Symptom	Cause	Remedy
All Windows Do Not Operate	Sub-Fusible Link (IGN) Blown	Replace
	Fuse No. 12 (20-Amp) Blown	Check Circuit & Replace Fuse
	Poor Ground	Clean & Tighten Ground Terminal
	Defective Window Main Switch	Check Switch (Replace If Necessary)
	Open Wire(s), Loose Connector(s)	Repair Or Replace
Driver's Window Only Does Not Operate	Fuse No. 11 (20-Amp) Blown	Check Circuit & Replace Fuse
	Defective Window Main Switch	Check Switch (Replace If Necessary)
	Defective Motor Or Circuit Breaker	Repair Or Replace
	Open Wire(s), Loose Connector(s)	Repair Or Replace
Passenger's Window Only Does Not Operate	Defective Window Sub-Switch	Replace Switch
	Defective Motor Or Circuit Breaker	Repair Or Replace
	Open Wire(s), Loose Connector(s)	Repair Or Replace

CONTINUITY TESTING MAIN SWITCH (ELANTRA 4-DOOR) [1]

Position	Condition	[2] Terminals
Left Front	Up	No. 2 & 4; 8 & 11
Left Front	Off	No. 4, 8 & 11
Left Front	Down	No. 2 & 11; 4 & 8
Right Front	Up	No. 2 & 5; 8 & 12
Right Front	Off	No. 5, 8 & 12
Right Front	Down	No. 2 & 12; 5 & 8
Left Rear	Up	No. 2 & 6; 8 & 13
Left Rear	Off	No. 6, 8 & 13
Left Rear	Down	No. 2 & 13; 6 & 8
Right Rear	Up	No. 2 & 3; 8 & 9
Right Rear	Off	No. 3, 8 & 9
Right Rear	Down	No. 2 & 9; 3 & 8

[1] – Disconnect switch before testing. Check continuity between terminals. If continuity does not exist as shown, replace switch.
[2] – See Fig. 2.

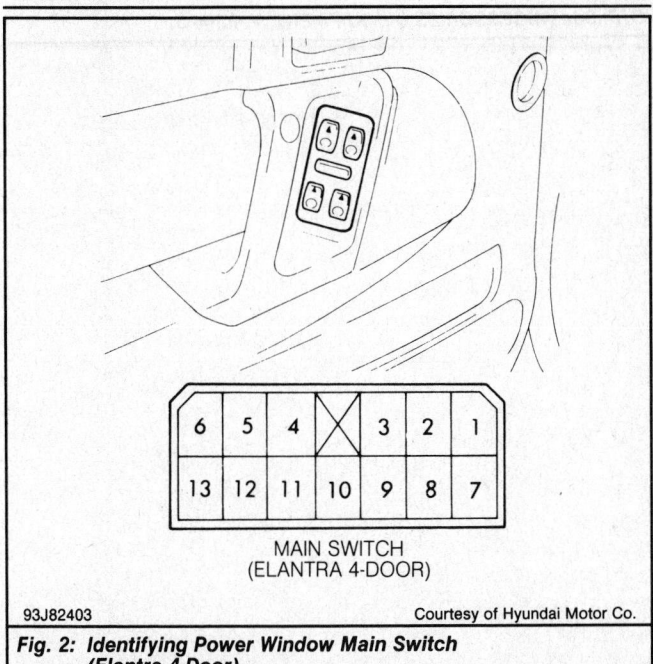

MAIN SWITCH
(ELANTRA 4-DOOR)

93J82403   Courtesy of Hyundai Motor Co.

Fig. 2: Identifying Power Window Main Switch (Elantra 4-Door)

CONTINUITY TESTING SUB-SWITCH (ELANTRA) [1] [2]

Position	[3] Terminals
Up	No. 3 & 6; 5 & 7
Off	No. 5 & 7; 2 & 6
Down	No. 3 & 5; 2 & 6

[1] – Disconnect switch before testing. Check continuity between terminals. If continuity does not exist as shown, replace switch.
[2] – With switch disconnected, there should be continuity between terminals No. 1 and 4 with positive lead on terminal No. 1. and No continuity with negative lead at terminal No. 1 (diode in circuit).
[3] – See Fig. 3.

CONTINUITY TESTING MAIN SWITCH (SCOUPE) [1]

Position	Condition	[2] Terminals
Left	Up	No. 1 & 3; 4 & 7
Left	Off	No. 1, 3 & 7
Left	Down	No. 1 & 7; 3 & 4
Right	Up	No. 1 & 2; 5 & 6
Right	Off	No. 1, 2 & 5
Right	Down	No.1 & 5; 2 & 6

[1] – Disconnect switch before testing. Check continuity between terminals. If continuity does not exist as shown, replace switch.
[2] – See Fig. 3.

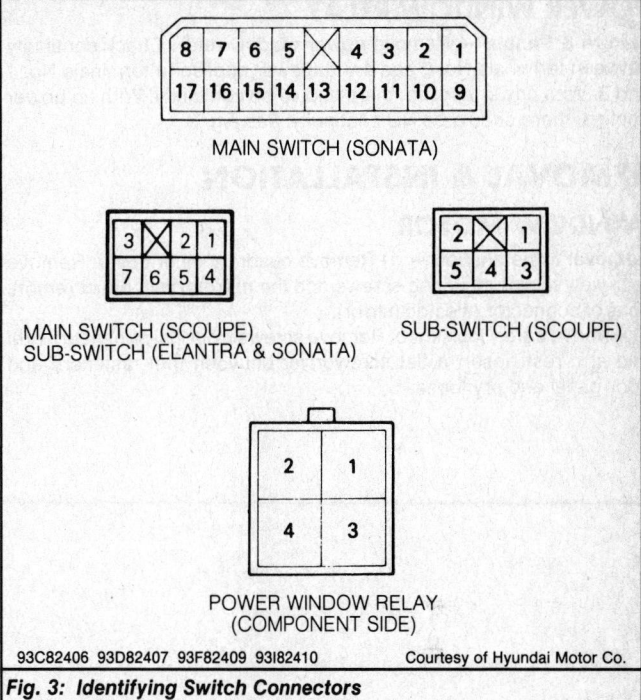

MAIN SWITCH (SONATA)

MAIN SWITCH (SCOUPE)
SUB-SWITCH (ELANTRA & SONATA)

SUB-SWITCH (SCOUPE)

POWER WINDOW RELAY
(COMPONENT SIDE)

93C82406 93D82407 93F82409 93I82410   Courtesy of Hyundai Motor Co.

Fig. 3: Identifying Switch Connectors

CONTINUITY TESTING SUB-SWITCH (SCOUPE) [1] [2]

Position	[3] Terminals
Up	No. 2 & 4; 3 & 5
Off	No. 1 & 2; 3 & 5
Down	No. 1 & 2; 4 & 5

[1] – Disconnect switch before testing. Check continuity between terminals. If continuity does not exist as shown, replace switch.
[2] – Continuity between terminals No. 1 and 4 with switch in ON position, and no continuity with switch in OFF position.
[3] – See Fig. 3.

CONTINUITY TESTING MAIN SWITCH (SONATA) [1]

Position	Condition	[2] Terminals
Left Front	Up	No. 3 & 5; 11 & 16
Left Front	Off	No. 5, 11 & 16
Left Front	Down	No. 3 & 16; 5 & 7
Right Front	Up	No. 3 & 6; 11 & 15
Right Front	Off	No. 6, 11 & 15
Right Front	Down	No. 3 & 15; 5 & 11
Left Rear	Up	No. 3 & 7; 11 & 14
Left Rear	Off	No. 7, 11 & 14
Left Rear	Down	No. 3 & 14; 7 & 11
Right Rear	Up	No. 3 & 4; 11 & 12
Right Rear	Off	No. 4, 11 & 12
Right Rear	Down	No. 3 & 12; 4 & 11

[1] – Disconnect switch before testing. Check continuity between terminals. If continuity does not exist as shown, replace switch.
[2] – See Fig. 3.

CONTINUITY TESTING SUB-SWITCH (SONATA) [1]

Position	[2] [3] Terminals
Up	No. 2 & 4; 5 & 6
Off	No. 1 & 2; 5 & 6
Down	No. 1 & 2; 4 & 5

[1] – Disconnect switch before testing. Check continuity between terminals. If continuity does not exist as shown, replace switch.
[2] – Continuity should exist between terminals No. 3 and 7 in one direction only.
[3] – See Fig. 3.

POWER WINDOW RELAY

Elantra & Sonata – Remove power window relay. Check continuity between terminals No. 2 and 4 with power applied to terminals No. 1 and 3. With power applied, there should be continuity. With no power applied, there should be NO continuity. *See Fig. 3.*

REMOVAL & INSTALLATION

WINDOW MOTOR

Removal & Installation – 1) Remove quadrant inner cover. Remove rear view mirror mounting screws and the mirror. Disconnect remote control connector (electric mirror).
2) Remove safety lock knob. Remove screws from inside handle bezel and arm rest. Insert a flat screwdriver between trim fasteners and door panel and pry loose.

3) Disconnect connectors at power window motor, power window main switch, door lock actuator, outside mirror and trunk lid opener Switch). Remove door trim seal.
4) Detach regulator assembly. Disconnect power window motor from regulator assembly. Installation is reverse of removal.

CAUTION: When loosening mounting screws of regulator and motor assembly, compressed force of regulator spring may cause regulator arm to spring up. When installing door trim seal, butyl tape should not be placed over door trim fastener mounting area.

WINDOW SWITCH

Removal & Installation – Manufacturer does not provide removal and installation procedures.

WIRING DIAGRAMS

NOTE: See ACCESSORIES & EQUIPMENT, Volume 5.

Elantra, Excel, Scoupe, Sonata

WARNING: Some Elantra models are equipped with air bags. To avoid injury from accidental air bag deployment, read and carefully follow all WARNINGS and SERVICE PRECAUTIONS in AIR BAG RESTRAINT SYSTEM article before working around steering column.

DESCRIPTION

MULTIFUNCTION SWITCH

Headlight, high beam, turn signal, cruise control and wiper switches are combined into one multifunction switch assembly mounted to top of steering column. On Excel, the hazard warning switch is also incorporated within this switch. For wiper washer and cruise control systems coverage, see WIPER/WASHER SYSTEMS or CRUISE CONTROL SYSTEMS article.

TESTING

WARNING: Some Elantra models are equipped with air bags. To avoid injury from accidental air bag deployment, read and carefully follow all WARNINGS and SERVICE PRECAUTIONS in AIR BAG RESTRAINT SYSTEM article before working around steering column.

HAZARD WARNING SWITCH TEST

NOTE: To test Elantra, Scoupe and Sonata hazard warning switches, see TESTING in INSTRUMENT PANELS article.

Excel – Ensure continuity exists between specified terminals. See HAZARD & TURN SIGNAL SWITCH CONTINUITY TEST (EXCEL) table. Check connector terminal identification. *See Fig. 3.*

HAZARD & TURN SIGNAL SWITCH CONTINUITY TEST (EXCEL)

Switch Position	Terminal Numbers	Continuity
Hazard Sw. Off		
Left	1 & 2; 5 & 11	Yes
Neutral	5 & 11	Yes
Right	1 & 3; 5 & 11	Yes
Hazard Sw. On		
Left, Neutral & Right	1, 2, 3 & 4; 11 & 12	Yes

HEADLIGHT SWITCH TESTS

With headlight switch in position indicated in table, ensure continuity exists between terminals listed. See LIGHTING SWITCH CONTINUITY TEST and DIMMER & PASSING SWITCH CONTINUITY TEST tables. Check connector and terminal identification. *See Figs. 1-5.*

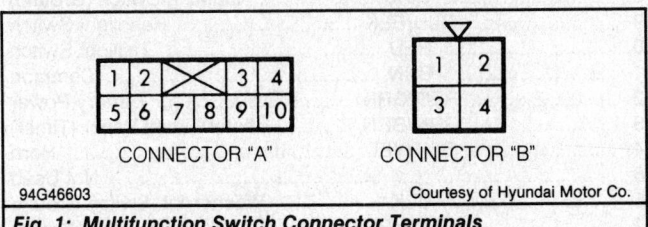

94G46603   Courtesy of Hyundai Motor Co.

Fig. 1: Multifunction Switch Connector Terminals (Elantra With Air Bag)

LIGHTING SWITCH CONTINUITY TEST

Switch Position	[1] Connector	Terminal Numbers	Continuity
Elantra			
With Air Bag			
Off	"A"	1, 2, 3 & 4	No
I	"A"	1 & 4	Yes
II	"A"	1, 2, 3 & 4	Yes
W/O Air Bag			
Off	"B"	1, 7, 8 & 9	No
I	"B"	1 & 8	Yes
II	"B"	1, 7, 8 & 9	Yes
Excel			
Off	"B"	7, 8, 9 & 10	No
I	"B"	7 & 10	Yes
II	"B"	7, 8, 9 & 10	Yes
Scoupe			
Off	"B"	4, 5, 10 & 11	No
I	"B"	4 & 11	Yes
II	"B"	4, 5, 10 & 11	Yes
Sonata			
Off	"A"	1, 2, 7 & 10 [2]	No
I	"A"	1, & 10 [2]	Yes
II	"A"	1, 2, 7 & 10 [2]	Yes

[1] – See Figs. 1-5.
[2] – Terminal No. 10 of connector "B".

DIMMER & PASSING SWITCH CONTINUITY TEST

Switch Position	[1] Connector	Terminal Numbers	Continuity
Elantra			
With Air Bag			
High Beam	"B"	1 & 4	Yes
Low Beam	"B"	1 & 2	Yes
Passing	"B"	1, 3 & 4	Yes
W/O Air Bag			
High Beam	"B"	3 & 5	Yes
Low Beam	"B"	4 & 5	Yes
Passing	"B"	2, 3 & 5	Yes
Excel			
High Beam	"A"	2 & 3	Yes
Low Beam	"A"	1 & 2	Yes
Passing	"A"	2, 3 & 4	Yes
Scoupe			
High Beam	"B"	8 & 9	Yes
Low Beam	"B"	7 & 9	Yes
Passing	"B"	6, 8 & 9	Yes
Sonata			
High Beam	"A"	9 & 10	Yes
Low Beam	"A"	3 & 10	Yes
Passing	"A"	8, 9 & 10	Yes

[1] – See Figs. 1-5.

93D00961   Courtesy of Hyundai Motor Co.

Fig. 2: Multifunction Switch Connector Terminals (Elantra Without Air Bag)

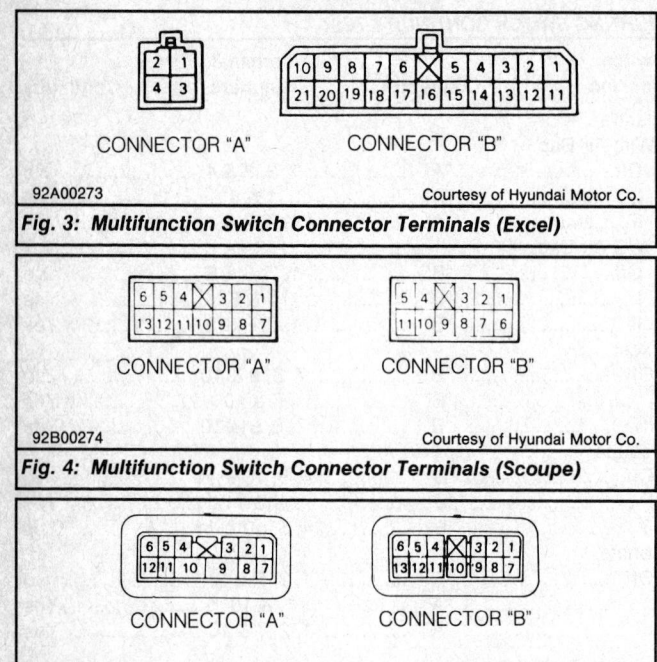

CONNECTOR "A"   **CONNECTOR "B"**

92A00273   Courtesy of Hyundai Motor Co.

Fig. 3: Multifunction Switch Connector Terminals (Excel)

CONNECTOR "A"   **CONNECTOR "B"**

92B00274   Courtesy of Hyundai Motor Co.

Fig. 4: Multifunction Switch Connector Terminals (Scoupe)

CONNECTOR "A"   **CONNECTOR "B"**

92C00275   Courtesy of Hyundai Motor Co.

Fig. 5: Multifunction Switch Connector Terminals (Sonata)

IGNITION SWITCH TEST

With ignition switch in position indicated in table, ensure continuity exists between appropriate terminals. See IGNITION SWITCH CONTINUITY TEST table. *See Fig. 6.*

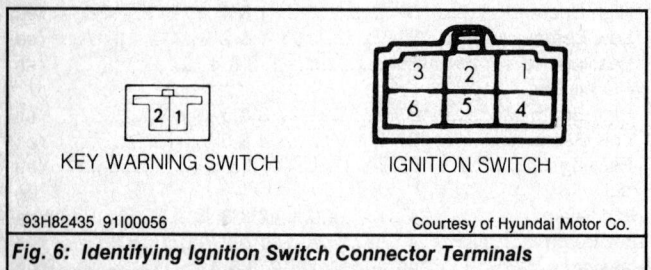

KEY WARNING SWITCH   IGNITION SWITCH

93H82435 91I00056   Courtesy of Hyundai Motor Co.

Fig. 6: Identifying Ignition Switch Connector Terminals

IGNITION SWITCH CONTINUITY TEST

Switch Position	Terminal Numbers	Continuity
Elantra, Excel & Scoupe [1]		
Lock	1, 2, 3, 4, 5 & 6	No
Accessory	1 & 4	Yes
On	1, 2, 4 & 6	Yes
Start	4, 5 & 6	Yes
Sonata [1]		
Lock	1, 2, 3, 4, 5 & 6	No
Accessory	1 & 4	Yes
On	1 & 2; 4 & 5	Yes
Start	3, 4, 5 & 6	Yes

[1] – Door warning switch terminals will have continuity when key is in ignition.

MULTIFUNCTION SWITCH CIRCUIT IDENTIFICATION

NOTE: Multifunction switch circuit identification for Elantra with air bag is not available from manufacturer.

MULTIFUNCTION SWITCH TERMINAL IDENTIFICATION (ELANTRA WITHOUT AIR BAG)

Terminal Number	Wire Color	Description
Connector "A" [1]		
1	... ...	Not Used
2	RED/BLU	Intermittent Wiper
3	RED/WHT	Wiper Park
4	RED/YEL	Wiper High Speed
5	YEL/BLK	Wiper Low Speed
6	...	Not Used
7	WHT/BLU	Washer Switch
8	GRN/BLK	Horn
9	BLK	Ground
10	GRN/WHT	Intermittent Wiper (Timer)
11	BLU	Cruise Speed Set
12	LT GRN/WHT	Cruise Resume/Accel
Connector "B" [1]		
1	YEL/RED	Taillight Switch
2	WHT/BLK	Headlight (Passing)
3	RED/GRN	Headlight (High Beam Power)
4	BRN	Headlight (Low Beam Power)
5	BLK	Dimmer & Passing Ground
6		Not Used
7	WHT/BLU	Headlight Switch
8	BLK	Lighting Switch Ground
9	GRN	Rear Foglight
10	RED/WHT	Flasher Power
11	RED/BLU	Left Turn Signal
12	RED/YEL	Right Turn Signal
13		Not Used

[1] – See Fig. 2.

MULTIFUNCTION SWITCH TERMINAL IDENTIFICATION (EXCEL)

Terminal Number	Wire Color	Description
Connector "A" [1]		
1	RED/YEL	Headlight (Low Beam Power)
2	BLK	Dimmer/Passing (Ground)
3	RED/BLU	Headlight (High Beam Power)
4	LT GRN/BLK	Headlight (Passing)
Connector "B" [1]		
1	GRN/WHT	Flasher Unit Power
2	GRN/BLU	Left Turn Signal
3	GRN/YEL	Right Turn Signal
4	BLU	Hazard Warning Indicator
5	BLK/WHT	Ignition Power
6	LT GRN/WHT	Rear Foglight
7		Not Used
8	BLK	Lighting Switch (Ground)
9	BLU/BLK	Headlight Switch
10	RED	Taillight Switch
11	BRN	Common
12	RED/GRN	Battery Power
13	GRN/BRN	Intermittent Wiper (Timer)
14	BLK/YEL	Horn
15		Not Used
16	BLK	Washer/Int. Switch Ground
17	BLU/YEL	Washer
18	GRN	Intermittent Wiper
19	GRN/BLK	Wiper Park
20	BLU/BLK	Wiper High Speed
21	BLU/WHT	Wiper Low Speed

[1] – See Fig. 3.

MULTIFUNCTION SWITCH TERMINAL IDENTIFICATION (SCOUPE)

Terminal Number	Wire Color	Description
Connector "A" [1]		
1	BLU/YEL	Washer
2	BLU/WHT	Wiper (Low Speed)
3	BLK/WHT	Horn
4	LT GRN/YEL	Cruise Resume/Accel
5	....	Not Used
6	....	Not Used
7	RED/BLK	Wiper (High Speed)
8	GRN/BLK	Wiper Park
9	GRN	Intermittent Wiper
10		Not Used
11	BLK/RED	Intermittent Wiper (Timer)
12	BLU	Cruise Set
13	BLK	Wiper Switch (Ground)
Connector "B" [1]		
1	GRN/YEL	Right Turn Signal
2	GRN/BLU	Left Turn Signal
3	GRN/RED	Flasher Unit Power
4	BLK	Lighting Switch Ground
5		Not Used
6	LT GRN/BLK	Headlight (Passing)
7	RED/YEL	Headlight (Low Beam Power)
8	RED/BLU	Headlight (High Beam Power)
9	BLK	Lighting Ground
10	BLU/WHT	Headlight Switch
11	RED	Taillight Switch

[1] – See Fig. 4.

MULTIFUNCTION SWITCH TERMINAL IDENTIFICATION (SONATA)

Terminal Number	Wire Color	Description
Connector "A" [1]		
1	YEL/RED	Taillight Switch
2	WHT/BLK	Headlight Switch
3	BRN	Headlight (Low Beam Power)
4	RED/BLK	Turn Signal Flasher Power
5	RED/BLU	Left Turn Signal
6	RED/YEL	Right Turn Signal
7	....	Not Identified By Manufacturer
8	WHT/BLK	Headlight Passing Switch
9	RED/GRN	Headlight Switch High Beam
10	BLK	Lighting Ground
11	....	Not Identified By Manufacturer
12	....	Not Identified By Manufacturer
Connector "B" [1]		
1	RED/WHT	Wiper Park Timer
2	RED/YEL	Wiper (High Speed)
3	YEL/BLK	Wiper (Low Speed)
4	....	Not Used
5	....	Not Used
6	....	Not Identified By Manufacturer
7	RED/BLU	Intermittent Wiper Switch
8	WHT/BLU	Washer Switch
9	GRN/WHT	Intermittent Wiper Timer
10	BLK	Ground
11	GRN/BLK	Horn
12	BLU	Cruise Set
13	LT GRN/WHT	Cruise Resume/Accel

[1] – See Fig. 5.

TURN SIGNAL SWITCH TEST

With turn signal switch in position indicated in table, ensure continuity exists between appropriate terminals. See TURN SIGNAL SWITCH CONTINUITY TEST table. *See Figs. 1-5.*

NOTE: *For Excel turn signal switch testing, see HAZARD WARNING SWITCH TEST under TESTING.*

TURN SIGNAL SWITCH CONTINUITY TEST [1]

Switch Position	Connector	Terminal Numbers	Continuity
Elantra [1]			
With Air Bag			
Left	"A"	9 & 10	Yes
Neutral	"A"	8, 9 & 10	No
Right	"A"	8 & 10	Yes
W/O Air Bag			
Left	"B"	10 & 11	Yes
Neutral	"B"	10, 11 & 12	No
Right	"B"	10 & 12	Yes
Scoupe [1]			
Left	"B"	2 & 3	Yes
Neutral	"B"	1, 2 & 3	No
Right	"B"	1 & 3	Yes
Sonata [1]			
Left	"A"	4 & 5	Yes
Neutral	"A"	4, 5 & 6	No
Right	"A"	4 & 6	Yes

[1] – Ensure hazard switch is in OFF position.

WIPER SWITCH TEST

For testing information on wiper/washer switch, see WIPER/WASHER SYSTEMS article.

REMOVAL & INSTALLATION

STEERING WHEEL & HORN PAD

WARNING: Some Elantra models are equipped with air bags. To avoid injury from accidental air bag deployment, read and carefully follow all WARNINGS and SERVICE PRECAUTIONS in AIR BAG RESTRAINT SYSTEM article before working around steering column.

Removal (Elantra) – On models equipped with air bag, see AIR BAG RESTRAINT SYSTEM article for air bag module removal procedures. On models without air bag, disconnect negative battery cable. Remove horn pad retaining screws on back of steering wheel. Lift out horn pad and disconnect horn switch wires. Remove steering wheel nut. Install suitable steering wheel puller and pull steering wheel from shaft.

Removal (Excel) – 1) Disconnect negative battery cable. Remove horn pad retaining screws on back of steering wheel. Remove horn pad. Remove upper and lower horn contact plates and disconnect horn button connector.

2) Remove lock nut and washer. Make alignment marks on steering shaft and steering wheel for installation reference. Install suitable steering wheel puller and pull steering wheel from shaft.

Removal (Scoupe) – 1) Disconnect negative battery cable. Remove horn pad by prying up horn cover. Remove upper and lower horn contact plates and disconnect horn button connector.

2) Remove lock nut and washer. Make alignment marks on steering shaft and steering wheel for installation reference. Install suitable steering wheel puller and pull steering wheel from shaft.

Removal (Sonata) – 1) Disconnect negative battery cable. Remove horn pad retaining screws on back of steering wheel. Lift out horn pad and disconnect horn contact wires. *See Fig. 7.*

2) Remove lock nut and washer. Remove dynamic damper. Make alignment marks on steering shaft and steering wheel for installation reference. Install suitable steering wheel puller and pull steering wheel from shaft.

Installation (All Models) – To install, align reference marks on steering shaft and steering wheel. Install washer and lock nut. Tighten nut to specification. See TORQUE SPECIFICATIONS. Reverse removal procedure to complete installation.

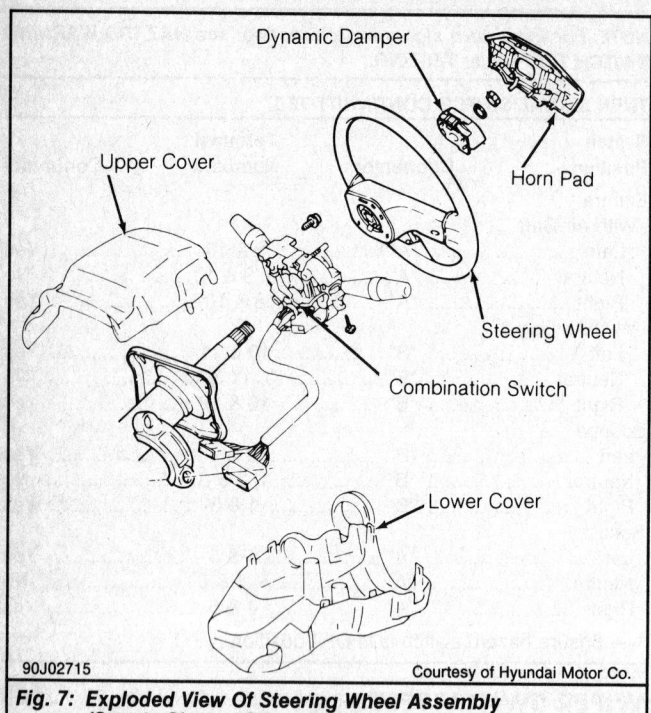

Fig. 7: Exploded View Of Steering Wheel Assembly (Sonata Shown; Others Similar)

90J02715   Courtesy of Hyundai Motor Co.

MULTIFUNCTION SWITCH

WARNING: Some Elantra models are equipped with air bags. To avoid injury from accidental air bag deployment, read and carefully follow all WARNINGS and SERVICE PRECAUTIONS in AIR BAG RESTRAINT SYSTEM article before working around steering column.

Removal & Installation – **1)** On Elantra models with air bag, see AIR BAG RESTRAINT SYSTEM article to remove air bag module and clockspring assembly. On all other models, disconnect negative battery cable. Remove steering wheel. Remove screws retaining lower instrument panel crash pad. *See Fig. 8.* On Scoupe, disconnect rheostat connector behind lower instrument panel crash pad.

2) Remove 3 screws retaining lower steering column covers and remove both covers. *See Fig. 8.* Disconnect multifunction switch connectors on lower steering column and remove harness retaining tie-straps.

3) Remove multifunction switch 4 retaining screws and pull multifunction switch off steering shaft. *See Fig. 9.* To install, reverse removal procedure.

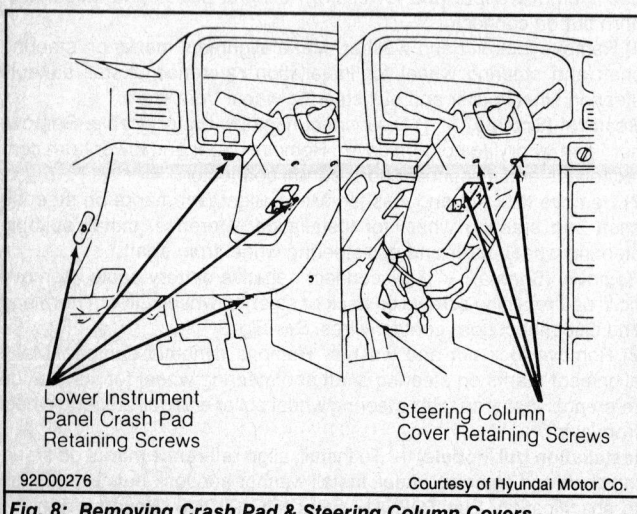

92D00276   Courtesy of Hyundai Motor Co.

Fig. 8: Removing Crash Pad & Steering Column Covers

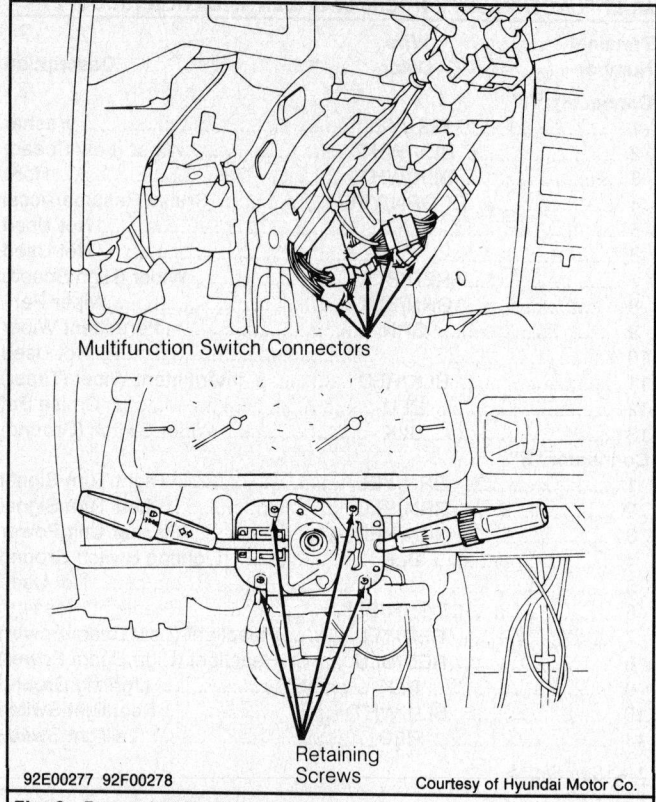

92E00277 92F00278   Courtesy of Hyundai Motor Co.

Fig. 9: Removing Multifunction Switch

IGNITION SWITCH & LOCK CYLINDER

WARNING: Some Elantra models are equipped with air bags. To avoid injury from accidental air bag deployment, read and carefully follow all WARNINGS and SERVICE PRECAUTIONS in AIR BAG RESTRAINT SYSTEM article before working around steering column.

Removal – **1)** Remove steering wheel, upper and lower steering column covers. If necessary, multifunction switch may also be removed to ease access to shear bolt heads. Disconnect ignition switch harness connectors strapped to lower steering column.

2) If shear bolt stud heads are accessible, use a hacksaw to cut a slot into the exposed stud heads. Using a blade screwdriver, remove studs.

3) If shear bolt stud heads are recessed or hard to reach with a hacksaw, center punch stud heads. Use a suitable drill bit and a screw extractor to remove studs. Remove steering lock and ignition switch assembly.

Installation – **1)** To install, reverse removal procedure. Install NEW shear bolts and temporarily make finger tight. Ensure proper operation of steering lock and ignition switch mechanism.

2) With ignition switch in lock position, tighten shear bolts until heads break off. Install multifunction switch, upper and lower steering column covers and steering wheel.

TORQUE SPECIFICATIONS
TORQUE SPECIFICATIONS

Application	Ft. Lbs. (N.m)
Steering Wheel Nut	
Elantra	28-33 (38-45)
Excel & Scoupe	26-33 (35-45)
Sonata	30-37 (40-50)

WIRING DIAGRAMS

NOTE: See ACCESSORIES & EQUIPMENT, Volume 5.

Elantra, Excel, Scoupe, Sonata

WARNING: Some Elantra models are equipped with air bags. To avoid injury from accidental air bag deployment, read and carefully follow all WARNINGS and SERVICE PRECAUTIONS in AIR BAG RESTRAINT SYSTEM article before working around steering column.

DESCRIPTION & OPERATION

The wiper/washer system uses a 2-speed wiper motor. Intermittent wiper cycle is standard equipment. Front washer systems are used on all models. Rear wiper/washer systems are available on Excel models. An electric washer pump is mounted under fluid reservoirs.

ADJUSTMENTS

WIPER ARM ADJUSTMENT

Mount wiper arm and blade assembly onto pivot shaft so the horizontal wiper blade is 1.2" (30 mm) above lower window trim molding in park position. On Elantra and Scoupe, the driver's side wiper blade should be 2.0" (50 mm) above lower window trim molding in park position.

TESTING

FRONT WIPER MOTOR TEST

Elantra – 1) Unplug wiper motor harness connector. Using 2 jumper wires, connect battery positive to wiper motor connector terminal No. 5 and connect battery negative to terminal No. 3. *See Fig. 1*. Wiper motor should run at low speed.

2) Connect battery positive to wiper motor connector terminal No. 6 and connect battery negative to terminal No. 3. Wiper motor should run at high speed.

3) To check wiper automatic parking, operate wiper motor at low speed as described in step **1)**. Stop motor operation at any point but park position by disconnecting battery positive wire at terminal No. 5. Using jumper wire, connect terminals No. 5 and 2. Connect positive wire to terminal No. 1. Wiper motor should run, then stop at park position.

4) If wiper motor fails any of these tests, replace wiper motor assembly. If wiper motor operates as described but does not operate from switch, check multifunction switch continuity and check wiring for open circuits. If switch and wiring are okay, replace Time and Alarm Control Module (TACM).

Excel – 1) Unplug wiper motor harness connector. Using 2 jumper wires, connect battery positive to wiper motor connector terminal No. 1 and connect battery negative to terminal No. 5. *See Fig. 2*. Wiper motor should run at low speed.

2) Connect battery positive to wiper motor connector terminal No. 1 and connect battery negative to terminal No. 2. Wiper motor should run at high speed.

3) To check wiper automatic parking, operate wiper motor at low speed as described in step **1)**. Stop motor operation at any point but park position by disconnecting battery negative wire at terminal No. 5, and then connect wire to terminal No. 3. Using another jumper wire, connect terminals No. 5 and 6. Wiper motor should run, then stop at park position.

4) If wiper motor fails any of these tests, replace wiper motor assembly. If wiper motor operates as described but does not operate from switch, check multifunction switch continuity and check wiring for open circuits. If switch and wiring are okay, replace Time and Alarm Control Module (TACM).

Scoupe & Sonata – 1) Unplug wiper motor harness connector. Using 2 jumper wires, connect battery positive to wiper motor connector terminal No. 1 and connect battery negative to terminal No. 5. *See Fig. 1*. Wiper motor should run at low speed.

2) Connect battery positive to wiper motor connector terminal No. 1 and connect battery negative to terminal No. 6. Wiper motor should run at high speed.

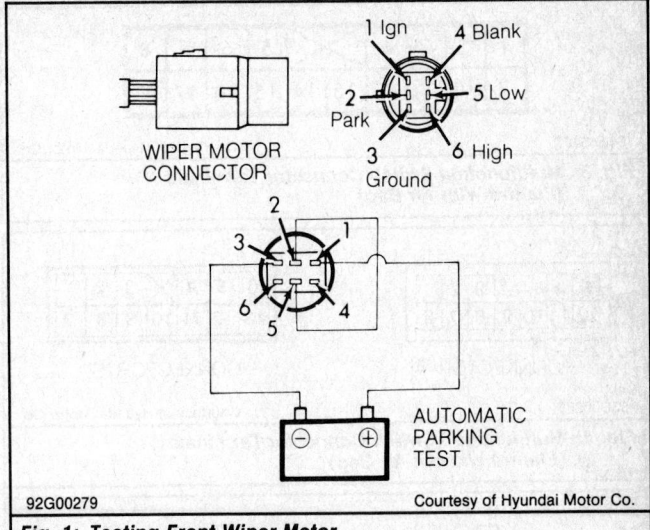

Fig. 1: Testing Front Wiper Motor
(Scoupe & Sonata Shown; Elantra Is Similar)

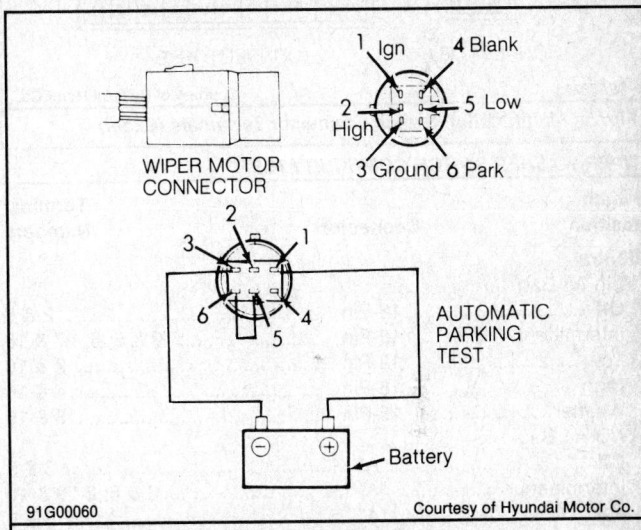

Fig. 2: Testing Front Wiper Motor (Excel)

3) To check wiper automatic parking, operate wiper motor at low speed as described in step **1)**. Stop motor operation at any point but park position by disconnecting battery negative wire at terminal No. 5, and then connect wire to terminal No. 3. Using another jumper wire, connect terminals No. 5 and 2. Wiper motor should run, then stop at park position.

4) If wiper motor fails any of these tests, replace wiper motor assembly. If wiper motor operates as described but does not operate from switch, check multifunction switch continuity and check wiring for open circuits. If switch and wiring are okay, replace Time and Alarm Control Module (TACM) on Scoupe, or Electronic Time and Alarm Control System (ETACS) module on Sonata.

FRONT WIPER/WASHER SWITCH TEST

WARNING: Some Elantra models are equipped with air bags. To avoid injury from accidental air bag deployment, read and carefully follow all WARNINGS and SERVICE PRECAUTIONS in AIR BAG RESTRAINT SYSTEM article before working around steering column.

Wiper/washer switch is incorporated within multifunction switch, mounted on steering column. Test continuity of wiper switch circuits with switch in position indicated in table. See WIPER/WASHER SWITCH CONTINUITY TEST table. *See Figs. 3-7* for terminal identification. For terminal descriptions, see STEERING COLUMN SWITCHES article.

1994 ACCESSORIES & EQUIPMENT
Wiper/Washer Systems (Cont.)

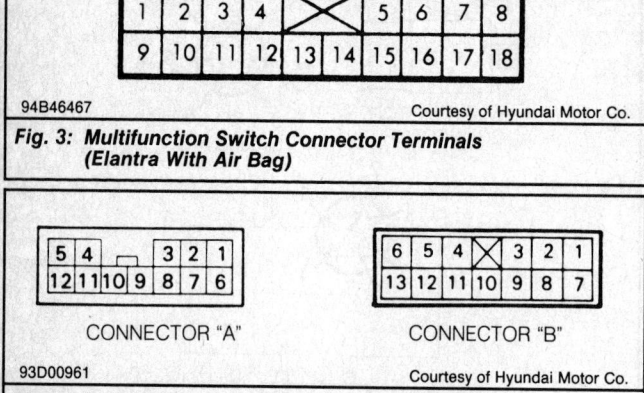

94B46467   Courtesy of Hyundai Motor Co.

Fig. 3: Multifunction Switch Connector Terminals (Elantra With Air Bag)

CONNECTOR "A"   CONNECTOR "B"

93D00961   Courtesy of Hyundai Motor Co.

Fig. 4: Multifunction Switch Connector Terminals (Elantra Without Air Bag)

CONNECTOR "A"   CONNECTOR "B"

92A00273   Courtesy of Hyundai Motor Co.

Fig. 5: Multifunction Switch Connector Terminals (Excel)

WIPER/WASHER SWITCH CONTINUITY TEST [1]

Switch Position	Connector	Terminal Numbers
Elantra		
With Air Bag		
Off	18-Pin	2 & 5
Intermittent [2]	18-Pin	2 & 5; 6, [2] 7 & 16
Low	18-Pin	2 & 16
High	18-Pin	4 & 16
Washer	18-Pin	8 & 16
W/O Air Bag		
Off	"A"	3 & 5
Intermittent [2]	"A"	3 & 5; 2 [2] 9 & 10
Low	"A"	5 & 9
High	"A"	4 & 9
Washer	"A"	7 & 9
Excel		
Off	"B"	19 & 21
Intermittent [2]	"B"	19 & 21; 18, [2] 16 & 13
Low	"B"	16 & 21
High	"B"	16 & 20
Washer	"B"	16 & 18
Scoupe		
Off	"A"	2 & 8
Intermittent [2]	"A"	2 & 8; [2] 9, 11 & 13
Low	"A"	2 & 13
High	"A"	7 & 13
Washer	"A"	1 & 13
Sonata		
Off	"B"	1 & 3
Intermittent [2]	"B"	1 & 3; 7, [2] 9 & 10
Low	"B"	3 & 10
High	"B"	2 & 10
Washer	"B"	8 & 10

[1] – Continuity should exist between terminals listed.

[2] – A resistor in circuit should fluctuate resistance between terminals No. 6, 7 and 16 (Elantra with air bag), terminals No. 2, 9 and 10 (Elantra without air bag), terminals No. 16 and 13 (Excel), terminals No. 9, 11 and 13 (Scoupe), or terminals No. 7, 9 and 10 (Sonata).

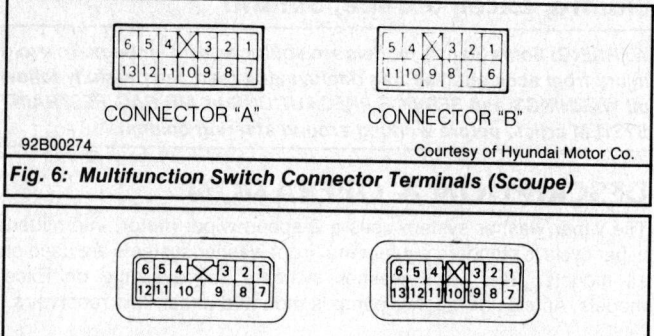

CONNECTOR "A"   CONNECTOR "B"

92B00274   Courtesy of Hyundai Motor Co.

Fig. 6: Multifunction Switch Connector Terminals (Scoupe)

CONNECTOR "A"   CONNECTOR "B"

92C00275   Courtesy of Hyundai Motor Co.

Fig. 7: Multifunction Switch Connector Terminals (Sonata)

WASHER PUMP MOTOR TEST

Disconnect harness connector and washer hose at pump. Ensure reservoir has clean water in it before running pump. Attach jumper leads from battery to washer motor connector terminals listed in WASHER PUMP MOTOR TEST CONNECTIONS table. Washer motor should operate. Replace as required. If washer pump does not operate, check for restriction in hose and/or nozzle, and/or check for open in wiring circuit.

WASHER PUMP MOTOR TEST CONNECTIONS

Battery Positive	Battery Negative
Elantra	
Blue Wire Terminal	White/Blue Wire Terminal
Excel	
Blue/Yellow Wire Terminal	Black/White Wire Terminal
Scoupe	
Blue/Green Wire Terminal	Blue/Yellow Wire Terminal
Sonata	
Blue Wire Terminal	White/Blue Wire Terminal

REAR WIPER MOTOR TEST

Remove connector from wiper motor. Attach jumper lead from battery positive to terminal No. 1 of wiper motor connector. *See Fig. 8.* Attach jumper from battery negative to terminal No. 4 of wiper motor connector. Wiper motor should operate. Replace as required.

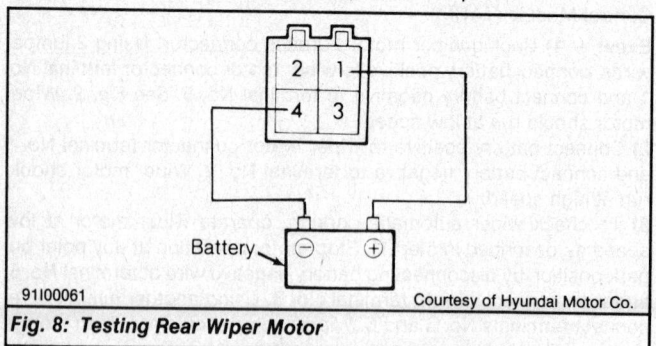

Battery

91I00061   Courtesy of Hyundai Motor Co.

Fig. 8: Testing Rear Wiper Motor

REAR WIPER SWITCH TEST

NOTE: Testing information for rear wiper switch is not available from manufacturer.

REMOVAL & INSTALLATION
FRONT WIPER MOTOR

Removal & Installation (Elantra, Excel & Scoupe) – 1) Remove wiper arm/blade assembly and retaining nut. Remove cowl top sealing cap by removing plastic retainers. Remove cowl top cover. Remove wiper motor harness connector.

2) Remove wiper motor mounting bolts. Make reassembly reference mark on wiper linkage and wiper motor crank arm. Disconnect wiper linkage from motor crank arm, and remove motor. To install, reverse removal procedure. Adjust wiper arm-to-windshield trim distance. See ADJUSTMENTS.

Removal & Installation (Sonata) – 1) Remove 6 screws attaching front deck panel to underside if hood, and remove panel. Remove wiper arm/blade assemblies and retaining nuts. Remove cowl top cover panel screws. Remove cowl top cover by prying upward. Remove air inlet covers by pressing side tabs. Remove wiper motor harness connector.

2) Remove wiper motor mounting bolts. Make reassembly reference mark on wiper linkage and wiper motor crank arm. Disconnect wiper linkage from motor crank arm, and remove motor. To install, reverse removal procedure. Adjust wiper arm-to-windshield trim distance. See ADJUSTMENTS.

FRONT WIPER/WASHER SWITCH

Wiper/washer switch is incorporated within multifunction switch, mounted on steering column. For removal and installation procedures, see STEERING COLUMN SWITCHES article.

REAR WIPER MOTOR

Removal & Installation – Note location of wiper arm. Remove rear wiper arm assembly and sealing washers. Remove rear door/tailgate inside trim panel. Disconnect harness connector. Remove rear wiper motor from tailgate mounting bracket. To install, reverse removal procedure. Tighten wiper arm nut to specification. See TORQUE SPECIFICATIONS.

REAR WIPER SWITCH

Removal & Installation – Use flat bladed screwdriver to pry rear wiper switch from center instrument panel. To install, push switch into dash opening with thumb pressure.

TORQUE SPECIFICATIONS

TORQUE SPECIFICATIONS

Application	INCH Lbs. (N.m)
Rear Wiper Arm Retaining Nut (Excel)	35-53 (4-6)
Rear Wiper Motor Retaining Bolts (Excel)	62-97 (7-11)
Wiper Arm Linkage Mounting Bolts	35-53 (4-6)
Wiper Arm Mounting Nuts	
Elantra & Sonata	160-194 (18-22)
Excel & Scoupe	35-53 (4-6)
Scoupe	62-97 (7-11)
Wiper Motor Mounting Bolts	62-97 (7-11)

WIRING DIAGRAMS

NOTE: See ACCESSORIES & EQUIPMENT, Volume 5.

1994 ENGINES
1.5L 4-Cylinder – Excel

NOTE: For repair procedures not covered in this article, see ENGINE OVERHAUL PROCEDURES article in GENERAL INFORMATION.

ENGINE IDENTIFICATION

The 8th character in Vehicle Identification Number (VIN) identifies engine type. Engine identification code is stamped at top right front side of cylinder block.

ENGINE IDENTIFICATION CODES

Application	Code	VIN
1.5L	[1] G4AJR	J

[1] – Third character may not be the same for all 1.5L engines.

ADJUSTMENTS

VALVE CLEARANCE ADJUSTMENT

1) Ensure head bolts are properly tightened before adjusting valves. Ensure engine is at normal operating temperature. Rotate crankshaft clockwise to position cylinder No. 1 on TDC of compression stroke.
2) Adjust intake valves on cylinders No. 1 and 2, and exhaust valves on cylinders No. 1 and 3. See VALVE CLEARANCE SPECIFICATIONS table. Rotate crankshaft clockwise 360 degrees to position cylinder No. 4 on TDC of compression stroke.
3) Adjust intake valves on cylinders No. 3 and 4, and exhaust valves on cylinders No. 2 and 4.

VALVE CLEARANCE SPECIFICATIONS

Application	[1] In. (mm)
1.5L	
Intake	.006 (.15)
Exhaust	.010 (.25)

[1] – Adjust valves with engine hot.

REMOVAL & INSTALLATION

NOTE: For reassembly reference, label all electrical connectors, vacuum hoses and fuel lines before removal. Also place mating marks on engine hood and other major assemblies before removal.

FUEL PRESSURE RELEASE

WARNING: ALWAYS relieve fuel pressure before disconnecting any fuel injection-related component. DO NOT allow fuel to contact engine or electrical components.

Disconnect fuel pump harness connector at fuel tank rear side. Start engine. After engine stalls, turn ignition switch to OFF position. Disconnect negative battery cable.

ENGINE

Removal – 1) Engine and transaxle can be removed as a unit. Drain transaxle oil and cooling system. Remove battery and air cleaner assembly.
2) Label and disconnect electrical connections and vacuum hoses from engine and transaxle. On A/T models, mark and disconnect transaxle cooler lines. Plug cooler lines.

NOTE: Mark transaxle cooler line location before removal. Install lines in original location.

3) Disconnect radiator and heater hoses, and remove radiator. Disconnect fuel hoses and accelerator cable. Disconnect A/C compressor and mounting bracket (if equipped).
4) Disconnect speedometer cable at transaxle. On M/T models, disconnect clutch cable, shift control rod and extension rod. On A/T models, disconnect shift control cable from transaxle.

5) On all models, raise and support vehicle. Disconnect exhaust pipe and support with wire. Remove underbody cover. Remove lower ball joint-to-lower control arm bolts.
6) Install pry bar between transaxle case and drive axle shaft. Pry drive axle shaft from transaxle. Pull drive axle shaft assembly from transaxle and support shaft assembly and lower control arm from body with wire. Plug shaft openings in transaxle.
7) Install engine hoist and raise engine slightly. Remove front engine support bar from engine. Disconnect rear engine support bar from crossmember. Remove front engine mounting bolts and mounting bracket.
8) Remove cover from inside right inner fender panel. Remove transaxle mounting bracket bolts located near right strut assembly. Remove left mount bolt. Remove engine/transaxle assembly from vehicle while pushing transaxle side downward during removal.

CAUTION: Replace drive axle shaft retainer rings whenever drive axle shafts are removed from transaxle.

Installation – To install, reverse removal procedure. With engine installed, loosely install front engine support bar bolts. Perform final tightening of mounting bolts and nuts with weight of engine on insulators. Replace all fluids, and adjust all control cables and linkages.

INTAKE MANIFOLD

CAUTION: Release fuel pressure before disconnecting fuel lines. See FUEL PRESSURE RELEASE.

Removal & Installation – Disconnect negative battery cable. Remove air cleaner, spark plug wires and distributor. Label and disconnect all wiring, hoses, cables and brackets interfering with intake manifold removal. Remove intake manifold-to-cylinder head attaching bolts and intake manifold. To install, reverse removal procedure.

EXHAUST MANIFOLD

Removal – Disconnect exhaust pipe from manifold. Remove exhaust manifold outer heat shield, oxygen sensor and engine hanger (if equipped). Remove manifold bolts, manifold, gasket and manifold inner heat shield.
Installation – To install, reverse removal procedure using NEW gaskets. Install NEW exhaust pipe-to-manifold nuts.

CYLINDER HEAD

Removal – 1) Drain coolant and remove upper radiator hose. Remove intake manifold. See INTAKE MANIFOLD. Remove exhaust manifold. See EXHAUST MANIFOLD.
2) Remove fan, spacer, water pump pulley and upper section of timing belt cover. Loosen timing belt tensioner, and move belt tensioner toward water pump. Temporarily tighten tensioner bolt.
3) Note location of timing belt on camshaft sprocket. Remove timing belt from camshaft sprocket.

CAUTION: DO NOT allow timing belt to come off crankshaft sprocket. DO NOT rotate engine with timing belt removed from camshaft. It may be necessary to remove timing belt. See TIMING BELT.

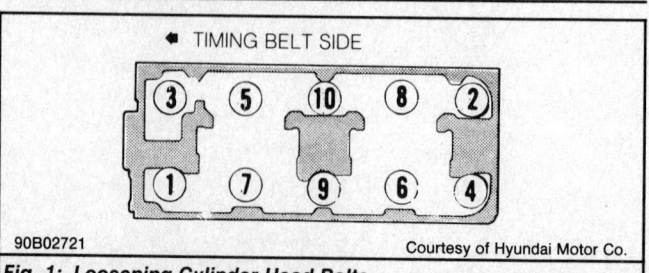

90B02721   Courtesy of Hyundai Motor Co.

Fig. 1: Loosening Cylinder Head Bolts

4) Remove rocker cover. Using Wrench (09221-11001), loosen cylinder head bolts in proper sequence. See Fig. 1. Remove cylinder head.

Installation – 1) Install cylinder head using NEW gasket. DO NOT apply sealant to head gasket. Tighten bolts to specification in proper sequence. See Fig. 2. See TORQUE SPECIFICATIONS table.

2) Install timing belt in original location on camshaft sprocket. Ensure all timing marks are aligned, and adjust timing belt. See TIMING BELT. To install remaining components, reverse removal procedure.

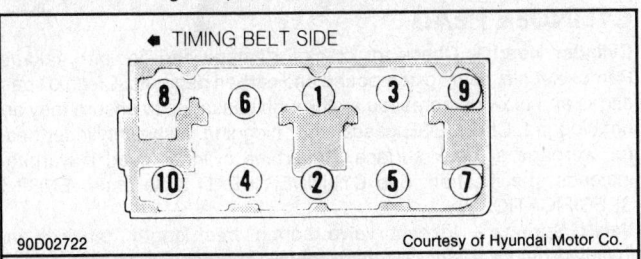

90D02722   Courtesy of Hyundai Motor Co.

Fig. 2: Tightening Cylinder Head Bolts

FRONT COVER OIL SEAL

Removal & Installation – Remove timing belt. See TIMING BELT. Remove oil pump and front case. See OIL PUMP under ENGINE OILING. Use seal remover to remove seal. To install, reverse removal procedure.

TIMING BELT

Removal – 1) Loosen water pump pulley bolts. Remove all drive belts and drive pulleys from crankshaft and water pump.

CAUTION: DO NOT rotate engine counterclockwise. If reusing timing belt, place reference mark on timing belt to indicate direction of rotation before removal.

2) Remove timing belt covers and gaskets, noting bolt length and location. Rotate engine clockwise to align timing mark on camshaft sprocket with mark on cylinder head. Ensure all timing marks are aligned. See Fig. 3.

3) Place mark on belt to indicate direction of belt rotation. Remove timing belt tensioner bolts. Move tensioner inward toward water pump, and temporarily tighten bolt in slotted side of tensioner. Remove timing belt from camshaft sprocket. Remove camshaft sprocket. Remove crankshaft pulley. Remove timing belt.

4) If crankshaft sprocket requires removal, remove sprocket bolt, sprocket and flange (located behind sprocket). Note flange position.

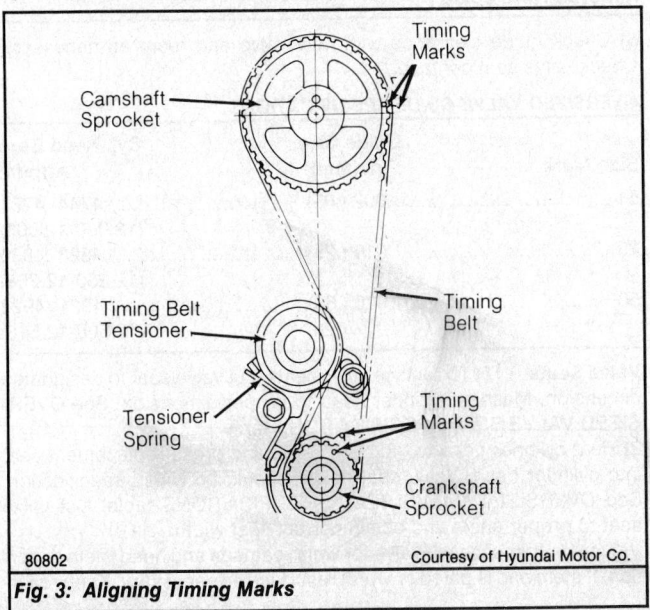

80802   Courtesy of Hyundai Motor Co.

Fig. 3: Aligning Timing Marks

Inspection – Check belt teeth for cracks, damage or oil contamination. Inspect all sprockets for damage. Check belt tensioner for signs of grease leakage or roughness in tensioner rotation. Replace components if damaged.

Installation – 1) Install flange on crankshaft with chamfered edge facing away from cylinder block (toward front of engine). Install camshaft sprocket and tighten bolt to specification. See TORQUE SPECIFICATIONS.

2) Install belt tensioner, tension spring and spacer. Ensure spring is properly engaged against front case. Rotate tensioner toward water pump, and temporarily tighten bolts. Rotate camshaft and crankshaft, and align all timing marks. See Fig. 3.

3) Install timing belt on crankshaft. Ensure belt is installed in original direction of rotation. Apply pressure on tension side of belt while installing belt on camshaft sprocket. See Fig. 4.

4) Apply counterclockwise force on camshaft sprocket to apply tension on tension side of belt. Ensure all timing marks are aligned. Temporarily install crankshaft pulley to retain timing belt.

5) Loosen timing belt tensioner bolts on belt tensioner to place tension on timing belt. See Fig. 4. Tighten timing belt tensioner bolts to specification. See TORQUE SPECIFICATIONS.

CAUTION: Slot-side timing belt tensioner bolt must be tightened before pivot-side to prevent belt tensioner from rotating, causing belt to be overtightened.

6) Rotate crankshaft clockwise at a constant speed for one full revolution. Loosen pivot-side bolt and then slot-side bolt. Tighten slot-side bolt, and then pivot-side bolt to specification.

7) To check belt tension, hold belt tensioner and timing belt together and apply slight thumb pressure at center point of belt tensioner. See Fig. 4. Ensure belt cog will reach half the width of timing belt tensioner bolt on slot-side of belt tensioner. To install remaining components, reverse removal procedure.

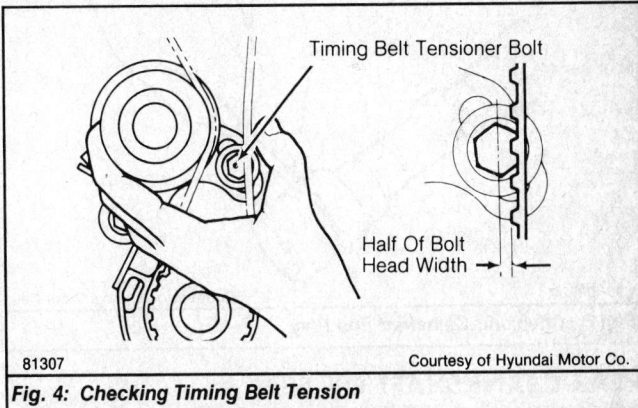

81307   Courtesy of Hyundai Motor Co.

Fig. 4: Checking Timing Belt Tension

ROCKER ARM SHAFT ASSEMBLY

Removal & Installation – 1) Remove breather, PCV hoses and rocker cover. It may be necessary to remove air cleaner. Loosen rocker arm shaft retaining bolts evenly in small increments, and remove shaft assemblies.

2) To install, reverse removal procedure. Tighten rocker arm shaft assembly retaining bolts to specification. See TORQUE SPECIFICATIONS table. Adjust valve clearance. See VALVE CLEARANCE ADJUSTMENT under ADJUSTMENTS.

CAMSHAFT

Removal – 1) Remove rocker arms and shafts. See ROCKER ARM SHAFT ASSEMBLY. Remove timing belt and camshaft sprocket. See TIMING BELT.

2) Remove camshaft thrust case retaining bolt. See Fig. 5. Remove cylinder head rear cover, gasket, thrust plate bolt, thrust plate, camshaft thrust case, camshaft and oil seal from cylinder head.

Inspection – 1) Inspect camshaft journal diameter and lobe height for signs of wear. Replace camshaft if not within specification. See CAMSHAFT table under ENGINE SPECIFICATIONS.

2) Install camshaft thrust case, thrust plate and bolt on camshaft. Tighten bolt. Using feeler gauge, measure end play clearance between thrust case and camshaft. See Fig. 6. Replace thrust case and recheck clearance if not within specification. See CAMSHAFT table. If end play is still not within specification, replace camshaft.

Installation – 1) To install, reverse removal procedure. Install camshaft thrust case with threaded hole facing upward, toward top of cylinder head and aligned with bolt opening of cylinder head. Install thrust case retaining bolt.

2) With camshaft installed, coat camshaft seal contact surface with engine oil. Using Seal Installer (09221-21000), install oil seal in cylinder head. To install remaining components, reverse removal procedure. Adjust valve clearance. See VALVE CLEARANCE ADJUSTMENT under ADJUSTMENTS.

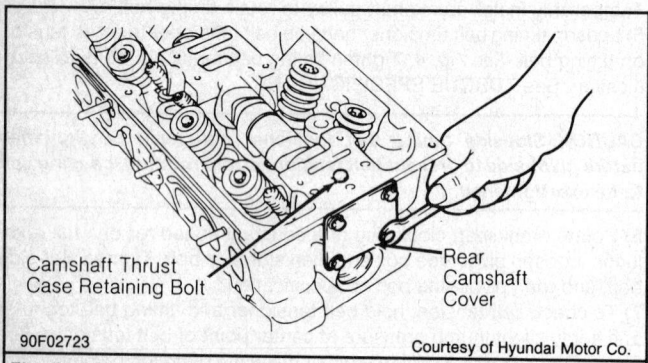

Fig. 5: Removing Camshaft

90F02723 — Courtesy of Hyundai Motor Co.

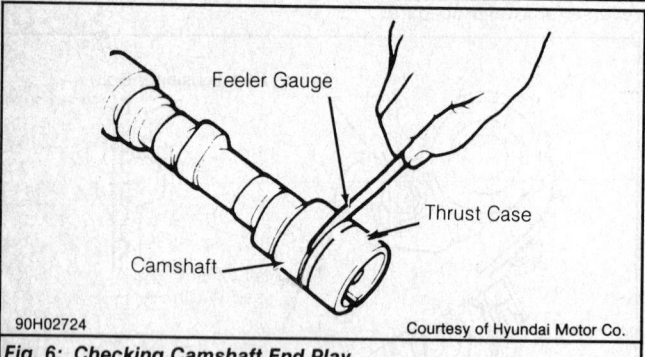

Fig. 6: Checking Camshaft End Play

90H02724 — Courtesy of Hyundai Motor Co.

REAR CRANKSHAFT OIL SEAL

Removal – Remove flywheel or drive plate. Remove oil seal case from rear of cylinder block. It may be necessary to remove oil pan. Remove oil seal from seal case.

Installation – Using Seal Installer (09231-11000), install oil seal. Install oil seal and case with NEW gasket. To install remaining components, reverse removal procedure.

WATER PUMP

CAUTION: Note bolt length and location during removal. Different length bolts are used and must be installed in original location.

Removal – Drain cooling system and disconnect battery. Remove necessary coolant hoses. Remove timing belt. See TIMING BELT. Remove pump mounting bolts. Note bolt length and location. Remove alternator brace and water pump.

Installation – To install, reverse removal procedure using NEW gasket and "O" ring. Install "O" ring on coolant pipe and then apply water to "O" ring. DO NOT apply grease or oil to "O" ring. Ensure bolts are installed in original location.

OIL PAN

Removal & Installation – Drain engine oil. Remove oil pan retaining bolts. Using gasket cutter, cut gasket along sealing surface of cylinder block. Remove oil pan and gasket. To install, reverse removal procedure. Apply a .16" (4.1 mm) bead of sealant to groove areas in oil pan sealing surfaces before installation.

OVERHAUL

CYLINDER HEAD

Cylinder Head – Check for cracks, damage and coolant leakage. Remove scale, sealing compound and carbon deposits. Clean oil passages and blow compressed air through passages to ensure they are not clogged. Check EGR passage for clogging. Inspect cylinder head for warpage at deck surface. Resurface cylinder head if warpage exceeds specification. See CYLINDER HEAD table under ENGINE SPECIFICATIONS.

Valve Springs – Inspect valve spring free length, tension and installed height. Using a square, check squareness of each spring. Replace if not within specification. See VALVES & VALVE SPRINGS table under ENGINE SPECIFICATIONS. Installed spring height is measured from spring seat to valve retainer. Install all valve springs with painted area toward rocker arm.

Valve Stem Oil Seals – Use Valve Seal Installer (09222-21100) for seal installation to provide proper positioning of oil seal.

Valve Guides – 1) Ensure valve stem diameter and clearance are within specifications. See VALVES & VALVE SPRINGS and CYLINDER HEAD tables under ENGINE SPECIFICATIONS.

2) If clearance exceeds service limits, valve guide can be replaced with an oversized valve guide. See OVERSIZED VALVE GUIDE SPECIFICATIONS table.

CAUTION: Measure valve guide installed height before removal. Intake valve guides are shorter than exhaust valve guides.

3) Use valve guide remover/installer to drive valve guide out toward cylinder block area of cylinder head. Machine cylinder head valve guide bore to specification for oversized valve guide. See OVERSIZED VALVE GUIDE SPECIFICATIONS table.

4) Using valve guide installer, press new guides into cylinder head from top. Install proper length valve guide to original height of .579-.602" (14.71-15.29 mm). Intake valve guides are shorter than exhaust valve guides.

CAUTION: DO NOT install valve guide with same outside diameter as removed valve guide.

5) Check guide clearance with new valve and ream as necessary. Check valve seat contact.

OVERSIZED VALVE GUIDE SPECIFICATIONS

Size Mark	Guide Size In. (mm)	Cyl. Head Bore In. (mm)
5	.002 (.05)	.4744-.4751 (12.050-12.068)
25	.010 (.25)	.4823-.4830 (12.250-12.268)
50	.020 (.50)	.4921-.4928 (12.500-12.518)

Valve Seats – 1) To replace valve seats, cut valve seat to designated dimension. Machine cylinder head to proper dimension. See OVERSIZED VALVE SEAT SPECIFICATIONS table.

2) Heat cylinder head to 482°F (250°C), and press replacement seat into cylinder head. Valve seat height should be within specification. See OVERSIZED VALVE SEAT SPECIFICATIONS table. Cut valve seat to proper angle and obtain correct seat width.

Valves – Inspect each valve for wear, damage and head/stem distortion. If stem end is pitted or worn, resurface as necessary. Keep resurfacing to a minimum. Resurface valve face. If valve margin has decreased to less than service limit, replace valve. See VALVES & VALVE SPRINGS table under ENGINE SPECIFICATIONS.

OVERSIZED VALVE SEAT SPECIFICATIONS

Size Mark	Seat Size In. (mm)	Cyl. Head Bore In. (mm)	Seat Height In. (mm)
Int. Valve			
30	.012	1.429-1.430	.276-.283
	(.30)	(36.30-36.33)	(7.00-7.20)
60	.024	1.441-1.442	.287-.295
	(.60)	(36.60-36.63)	(7.30-7.50)
Exh. Valve			
30	.012	1.272-1.273	.291-.299
	(.30)	(32.30-32.33)	(7.40-7.60)
60	.024	1.283-1.285	.303-.311
	(.60)	(32.60-32.63)	(7.70-7.90)

VALVE TRAIN

Rocker Arm Shaft Assembly – **1)** Note location of all components for reassembly. Remove bolts from shafts, and remove components. Note length of valve springs. Intake valve springs are longer than exhaust valve springs. Inspect components for wear or damage.
2) Install components in original location. Rocker arms are marked "1-3" for odd cylinders and "2-4" for even cylinders. *See Fig. 7.* Install short springs on exhaust valves and long springs on intake valves.

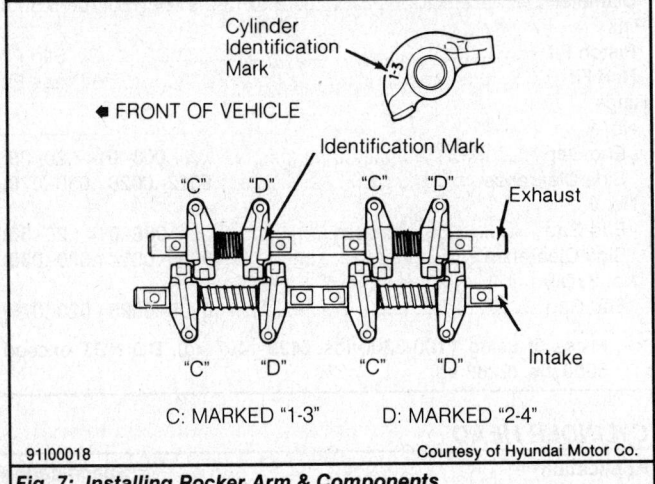

Fig. 7: Installing Rocker Arm & Components

CYLINDER BLOCK ASSEMBLY

Piston & Rod Assembly – Piston must be installed in cylinder block with front mark on top of piston toward timing belt side of engine. Note position of connecting rod on piston before removal.

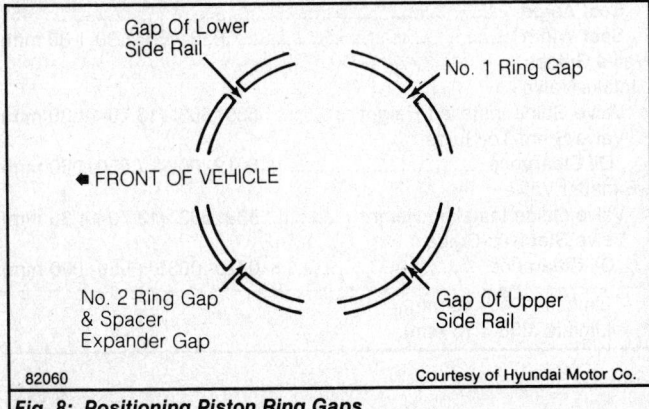

Fig. 8: Positioning Piston Ring Gaps

Fitting Pistons & Rings – Ensure ring end gap and side clearance are within specifications. See PISTONS, PINS & RINGS table under ENGINE SPECIFICATIONS. Properly position ring gaps before installation. *See Fig. 8.*
Piston Pin Replacement – Note piston location before removing piston from connecting rod. Fitting piston pin in connecting rod requires use of proper force during installation. See PISTONS, PINS & RINGS table under ENGINE SPECIFICATIONS.

Manufacturer recommends using Piston Pin Remover/Installer Kit (09234-33001) for piston pin removal and installation. See application chart in kit for selection of pin installation depth guides, etc.

CAUTION: DO NOT exceed 5000 lbs. (2268 kg.) of force at any time during removal or installation of piston pin.

Crankshaft & Main Bearings – Install main bearing caps with arrow on top of cap pointing toward crankshaft pulley side of engine and in numerical sequence according to cap number stamped near arrow. Tighten main bearing caps in 2 steps to specification, starting at center and working outward. See TORQUE SPECIFICATIONS.

ENGINE OILING

ENGINE LUBRICATION SYSTEM

A crankshaft-driven oil pump is mounted in timing cover.
Crankcase Capacity – Oil capacity with oil filter is 3.6 qts. (3.4L).
Oil Pressure – Normal oil pressure is at least 11 psi (.78 kg/cm²) at curb idle with oil temperature of 167-203°F (75-95°C).

OIL PUMP

Removal – Remove timing belt and crankshaft sprocket. See TIMING BELT under REMOVAL & INSTALLATION. Remove oil filter, oil pan and oil screen. Remove front cover and oil pump assembly.
Disassembly & Inspection – **1)** Remove rear cover. Note gear position, and mark direction of gear for reassembly reference.
2) Check outer gear-to-cover and outer gear tooth-to-crescent clearance. Check inner gear-to-crescent clearance. Place straight-edge across front cover housing, and measure gear end play clearance between each gear and straightedge.
3) Ensure pressure relief valve moves freely in bore, and check relief spring tension and free length. Replace components if not within specification. See OIL PUMP SPECIFICATIONS table.

OIL PUMP SPECIFICATIONS

Application	Specification
Gear End Play	.0016-.0039" (.040-.10 mm)
Inner Gear-To-Crescent	.0083-.0126" (.210-.320 mm)
Outer Gear-To-Cover	.0039-.0079" (.100-.200 mm)
Outer Gear Tooth-To-Crescent	.0087-.0134" (.220-.340 mm)
Relief Valve Spring	
Free Length	1.835" (46.60 mm)
Spring Tension	13.4 lbs @ 1.579" (6.1 kg @ 40.10 mm)

Reassembly & Installation – **1)** Install oil pump rear cover. Install oil pump and gasket assembly onto engine block. Coat outer surface of Seal Guide (9214-21100) with oil, and install seal guide over end of crankshaft.
2) Using Seal Installer (09214-21000), install seal into front cover. Install oil filter bracket. Install proper length bolts and tighten to specification. *See Fig. 9.* See TORQUE SPECIFICATIONS table.
3) Using plug cap wrench, install plug cap and tighten to specification. See TORQUE SPECIFICATIONS table. To install remaining components, reverse removal procedure.

PRESSURE RELIEF VALVE

NOTE: Pressure relief valve is nonadjustable and is located in front cover.

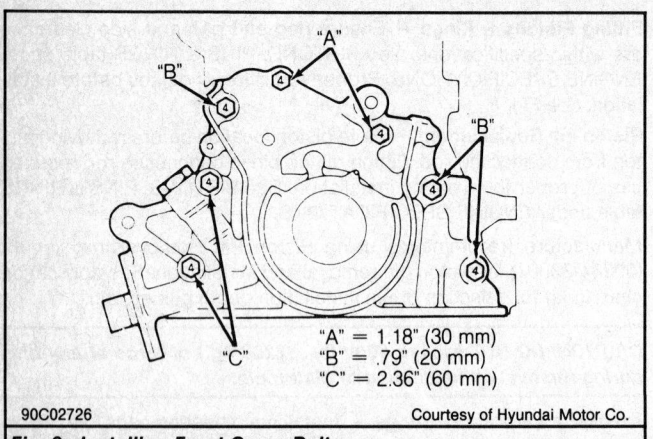

"A" = 1.18" (30 mm)
"B" = .79" (20 mm)
"C" = 2.36" (60 mm)

90C02726   Courtesy of Hyundai Motor Co.

Fig. 9: Installing Front Cover Bolts

TORQUE SPECIFICATIONS

TORQUE SPECIFICATIONS

Application	Ft. Lbs. (N.m)
Camshaft Sprocket Bolt	48-55 (65-75)
Connecting Rod Cap Bolt	24-26 (32-35)
Crankshaft Pulley-To-Sprocket Bolt	10-11 (14-15)
Crankshaft Sprocket Bolt	52-74 (70-100)
Cylinder Head Bolt [1]	
Cold Engine	51-55 (69-75)
Hot Engine	59-63 (80-85)
Drain Plug	26-33 (35-45)
Drive Plate-To-Crankshaft Bolt	96-103 (130-140)
Exhaust Manifold-To-Engine Bolt	11-15 (15-20)
Exhaust Pipe-To-Manifold Bolt	22-30 (30-40)
Flywheel-To-Crankshaft Bolt	96-103 (130-140)
Intake Manifold Bolt	11-15 (15-20)
Intake Manifold Brace Bolt	13-18 (18-25)
Main Bearing Cap Bolt	37-40 (50-54)
Oil Pressure Switch	11-16 (15-22)
Oil Pump Relief Valve Plug Cap	30-37 (40-50)
Oil Screen Bolt	11-16 (15-22)
Rocker Arm Adjusting Screw Lock Nut	9-13 (12-18)
Rocker Arm Shaft Assembly Retaining Bolt	15-20 (20-27)
Throttle Body-To-Intake Manifold Bolt	11-16 (15-22)
Timing Belt Tensioner Bolt	15-20 (20-27)
Torque Converter-To-Drive Plate Bolt	54-57 (73-77)
	INCH Lbs. (N.m)
Front Case Bolt	89-106 (10-12)
Oil Pan Bolt	53-71 (6-8)
Oil Pump Cover Bolt	106-133 (12-15)
Rocker Cover Bolt	13-18 (1.5-2.0)
Timing Belt Cover Bolt	89-106 (10-12)
Water Pump Pulley Bolt	71-89 (8-10)

[1] – Tighten in sequence. See Fig. 2.

ENGINE SPECIFICATIONS

GENERAL SPECIFICATIONS

Application	Specification
Displacement	89.6 Cu. In. (1.468L)
Bore	2.97" (75.5 mm)
Stroke	3.23" (82.0 mm)
Compression Ratio	9.4:1
Fuel System	PFI
Horsepower @ RPM	81 @ 5500
Torque Ft. Lbs. @ RPM	91 @ 3000

CRANKSHAFT, MAIN & CONNECTING ROD BEARINGS

Application	In. (mm)
Crankshaft	
End Play	.002-.007 (.05-.18)
Runout	.0012 (.030)
Main Bearings	
Journal Diameter	1.89 (48.0)
Journal Out-Of-Round	.0004 (.010)
Journal Taper	.0004 (.010)
Oil Clearance	.0008-.0028 (.020-.070)
Connecting Rod Bearings	
Journal Diameter	1.65 (42.0)
Journal Out-Of-Round	.0004 (.010)
Journal Taper	.0004 (.010)
Oil Clearance	.0006-.0017 (.014-.044)

CONNECTING RODS

Application	In. (mm)
Side Play	.0039-.0098 (.100-.250)

PISTONS, PINS & RINGS

Application	In. (mm)
Pistons	
Clearance	.0008-.0016 (.020-.040)
Diameter	2.9713-2.9724 (75.470-75.500)
Pins	
Piston Fit	Slip Fit
Rod Fit	[1] Press Fit
Rings	
No. 1	
End Gap	.008-.014 (.20-.35)
Side Clearance	.0012-.0028 (.030-.070)
No. 2	
End Gap	.008-.014 (.20-.36)
Side Clearance	.0008-.0024 (.020-.060)
No. 3 (Oil)	
End Gap	.0008-.0028 (.020-.070)

[1] – Press fit using 1100-3300 lbs. (499-1497 kg). DO NOT exceed 5000 lbs. (2268 kg).

CYLINDER HEAD

Application	Specification
Maximum Warpage	.004" (.10 mm)
Valve Seats	
Intake Valve	
Seat Angle	45°
Seat Width	.035-.051" (.90-1.30 mm)
Exhaust Valve	
Seat Angle	45°
Seat Width	.035-.051" (.90-1.30 mm)
Valve Guides	
Intake Valve	
Valve Guide Installed Height	.539-.563" (13.70-14.30 mm)
Valve Stem-To-Guide	
Oil Clearance	[1] .0012-.0024" (.030-.060 mm)
Exhaust Valve	
Valve Guide Installed Height	.539-.563" (13.70-14.30 mm)
Valve Stem-To-Guide	
Oil Clearance	[2] .0020-.0035" (.050-.090 mm)

[1] – Limit is .004" (.10 mm).
[2] – Limit is .006" (.15 mm).

CAMSHAFT

Application	In. (mm)
End Play	.002-.008 (.05-.20)
Lobe Height	
Intake	[1] 1.532 (38.91)
Exhaust	[2] 1.534 (38.97)

[1] - Wear limit is 1.512" (38.41 mm).
[2] - Wear limit is 1.514" (38.47 mm).

CYLINDER BLOCK

Application	In. (mm)
Cylinder Bore	
Standard Diameter	2.9724-2.9736 (75.500-75.530)
Maximum Taper	.0008 (.020)
Maximum Out-Of-Round	.0008 (.020)
Maximum Deck Warpage	.002 (.05)

VALVES & VALVE SPRINGS

Application	Specification
Intake Valves	
Face Angle	45°
Minimum Margin	.028" (.70 mm)
Stem Diameter	.260" (6.60 mm)
Exhaust Valves	
Face Angle	45°
Minimum Margin	.039" (1.00 mm)
Stem Diameter	.260" (6.60 mm)
Valve Springs	
Free Length	1.756" (44.60 mm)
Installed Height	1.417" (36.00 mm)
Out-Of-Square (Max)	3°

	Lbs. @ In. (kg @ mm)
Pressure	
Valve Closed	53 @ 1.075 (24 @ 27.30)

1994 ENGINES
1.5L 4-Cylinder – Scoupe

NOTE: For repair procedures not covered in this article, see ENGINE OVERHAUL PROCEDURES article in GENERAL INFORMATION.

ENGINE IDENTIFICATION

The 8th character in Vehicle Identification Number (VIN) identifies engine type. Engine identification code is stamped at top right front side of cylinder block.

ENGINE IDENTIFICATION CODES

Application	Code	VIN
1.5L	[1] G4AER	N

[1] – Third character may not be the same for all engines.

ADJUSTMENTS

VALVE CLEARANCE ADJUSTMENT

NOTE: On Federal models built after March 31, 1994, rocker arms were changed from contact type to roller type to reduce friction between camshaft and rocker arms. On models with roller type rocker arms, automatic valve lash adjusters are used and valve clearance is not adjustable.

1) Ensure head bolts are properly tightened before adjusting valves. Ensure engine is at normal operating temperature. Rotate crankshaft clockwise to position cylinder No. 1 on TDC of compression stroke.
2) Adjust valves on cylinder No. 1. See VALVE CLEARANCE SPECIFICATIONS table. Rotate crankshaft clockwise to position cylinder No. 3 on TDC of compression stroke.
3) Adjust valves on cylinder No. 3. Rotate crankshaft clockwise to position cylinder No. 4 on TDC of compression stroke.
4) Adjust valves on cylinder No. 4. Rotate crankshaft clockwise to position cylinder No. 2 on TDC of compression stroke. Adjust valves on cylinder No. 2.

VALVE CLEARANCE SPECIFICATIONS

Application	In. (mm)
Hot [1]	
Intake	.010 (.25)
Exhaust	.012 (.30)

[1] – 176-203° F (80-95° C) coolant temperature.

REMOVAL & INSTALLATION

NOTE: For reassembly reference, label all electrical connectors, vacuum hoses and fuel lines before removal. Also place mating marks on engine hood and other major assemblies before removal.

FUEL PRESSURE RELEASE

WARNING: Relieve fuel pressure before disconnecting any fuel injection-related component. DO NOT allow fuel to contact engine or electrical components.

Disconnect fuel pump harness connector at rear of fuel tank. Start engine. After engine stalls, turn ignition switch to OFF position. Disconnect negative battery cable.

ENGINE

Removal – 1) Engine and transaxle are removed as a unit. Drain transaxle oil and cooling system. Release fuel pump pressure. See FUEL PRESSURE RELEASE. Remove battery and air cleaner assembly.
2) Label and disconnect electrical connections and vacuum hoses from engine and transaxle. On A/T models, mark and disconnect transaxle cooler lines. Plug cooler lines.

NOTE: Mark transaxle cooler line location before removal. Install lines in original location.

3) Disconnect radiator and heater hoses and remove radiator. Disconnect fuel hoses and accelerator cable. Disconnect A/C compressor and mounting bracket (if equipped).
4) Disconnect speedometer cable at transaxle. On M/T models, disconnect clutch cable, shift control rod and extension rod. On A/T models, disconnect shift control cable from transaxle.
5) On all models, raise and support vehicle. Disconnect exhaust pipe and support with wire. Remove underbody cover. Remove lower ball joint-to-lower control arm bolts.
6) Insert pry bar between transaxle case and drive axle shaft. Pry drive axle shaft from transaxle. Pull drive axle shaft assembly from transaxle, and support shaft assembly from body with wire. Plug shaft openings in transaxle.
7) Install engine hoist and raise engine slightly. Remove front engine support bar from engine. Disconnect rear engine support bar from crossmember. Remove front engine mounting bolts and mounting bracket.
8) Remove caps from inside left fender shield and remove transmission mount strut bolts. Remove transaxle mounting bracket bolts located near right strut assembly. Remove engine/transaxle assembly from vehicle while pushing transaxle side downward during removal.

CAUTION: Replace drive axle shaft retainer rings whenever drive shafts are removed from transaxle.

Installation – To install, reverse removal procedure. With engine installed, loosely install front engine support bar bolts. Perform final tightening of mounting bolts and nuts with weight of engine on insulators. Replace all fluids, and adjust all control cables and linkages.

INTAKE MANIFOLD

CAUTION: Release fuel pressure before disconnecting fuel lines. See FUEL PRESSURE RELEASE.

Removal & Installation – 1) Remove idle speed actuator. Remove air intake hose connected to throttle body. (On turbo, remove intake pipe connected to turbocharger). Remove accelerator cable. Remove water hose and throttle body.

NOTE: Label all wiring, hoses, cables and brackets before removal.

2) Remove PCV hose and brake booster vacuum hoses. Disconnect vacuum hose connections. Disconnect high pressure fuel hose. Remove plenum stay. Remove plenum assembly and gasket. Disconnect fuel injector harness connector.

CAUTION: DO NOT drop injectors when removing delivery pipe.

3) Remove delivery pipe with fuel injectors and pressure regulator attached. Remove insulator from intake manifold, and disconnect heater hose. Remove intake manifold. To install, reverse removal procedure.

TURBOCHARGER

Removal & Installation – Remove air intake pipe and air intake hose. Remove water feed and return hose. Disconnect oil feed and oil drain connector hoses. Remove turbocharger discharge pipe and discharge pipe bracket. Remove turbocharger-to-exhaust manifold bolt. Remove turbocharger assembly. To install, reverse removal procedure.

EXHAUST MANIFOLD

Removal – Disconnect exhaust pipe from manifold. Remove exhaust manifold outer heat shield, oxygen sensor and engine hanger (if equipped). Remove manifold bolts, manifold, gasket and manifold inner heat shield.

Installation – To install, reverse removal procedure using NEW gaskets. Install NEW exhaust pipe-to-manifold nuts.

CYLINDER HEAD

Removal – 1) Drain coolant and remove upper radiator hose. Remove breather hose (between air cleaner and rocker cover). Remove air intake pipe (turbo) and air intake hose.

2) Remove vacuum hose, fuel hose and water hose. Remove cables from spark plugs. (Remove spark plug cables by pulling on boot.) Remove distributor. Remove intake plenum. Remove intake manifold.

3) Remove heat protector and exhaust manifold assembly. Remove water pump pulley and crankshaft pulley.

4) Remove timing belt cover. Move timing belt tensioner pulley toward water pump and temporarily secure it. Remove timing belt.

5) Remove rocker cover. Remove cylinder head bolts in proper sequence using Cylinder Head Bolt Wrench (09221-11001). *See Fig. 1.* Remove gasket pieces from cylinder block top surface and cylinder head bottom surface.

CAUTION: Ensure gasket pieces DO NOT fall into engine.

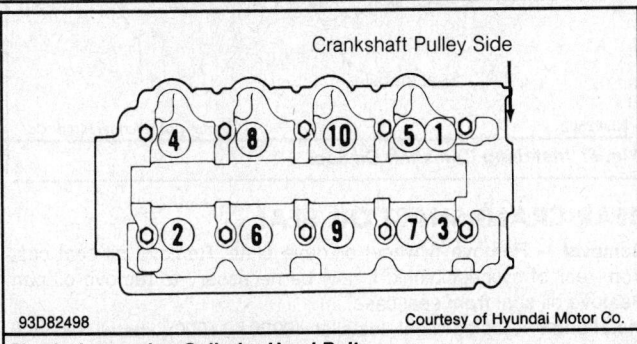

Crankshaft Pulley Side

93D82498   Courtesy of Hyundai Motor Co.

Fig. 1: Loosening Cylinder Head Bolts

Installation – 1) Install cylinder head using NEW gasket. DO NOT apply sealant to head gasket. Tighten bolts to specification in proper sequence. *See Fig. 2.* See TORQUE SPECIFICATIONS table.

2) Install timing belt in original location on camshaft sprocket. Ensure all timing marks are aligned, and adjust timing belt. See TIMING BELT. To install remaining components, reverse removal procedure.

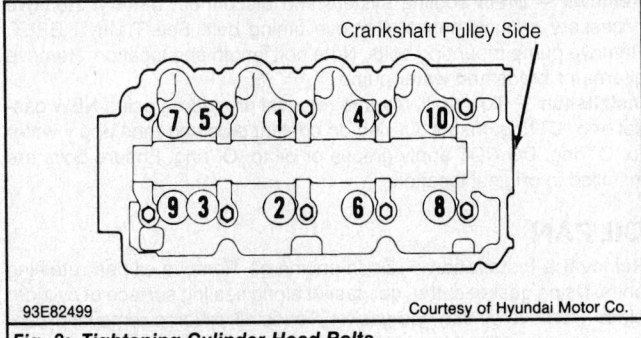

Crankshaft Pulley Side

93E82499   Courtesy of Hyundai Motor Co.

Fig. 2: Tightening Cylinder Head Bolts

FRONT COVER OIL SEAL

See OIL PUMP under ENGINE OILING.

TIMING BELT

Removal – 1) Loosen water pump pulley bolt. Loosen alternator bolt. Remove water pump pulley and belt. Remove crankshaft pulley. Remove timing belt cover.

2) Align timing marks. Move timing belt tensioner pulley toward water pump and temporarily secure. Remove timing belt from camshaft sprocket. Remove camshaft sprocket. Remove timing belt. *See Fig. 3.*

3) Remove crankshaft sprocket bolts. remove crankshaft sprocket and flange. Remove timing belt tensioner.

CAUTION: DO NOT rotate engine counterclockwise. If reusing timing belt, place reference mark on belt to indicate direction of rotation before removal.

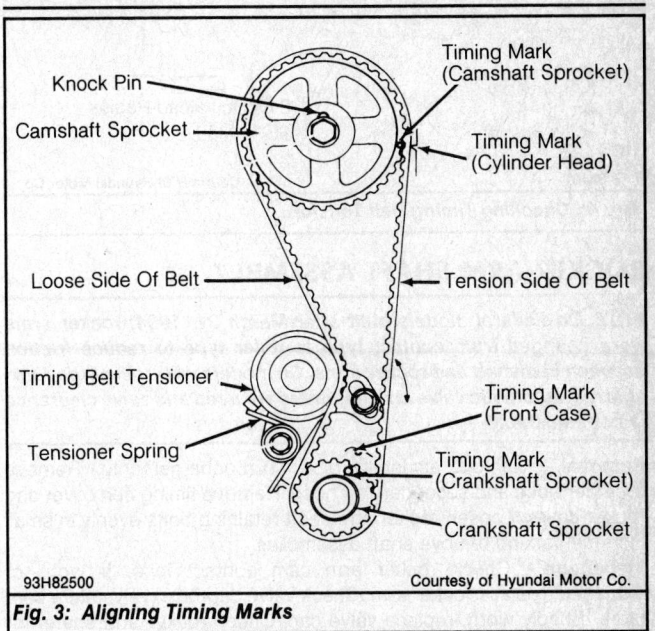

93H82500   Courtesy of Hyundai Motor Co.

Fig. 3: Aligning Timing Marks

Inspection – Check belt teeth for cracks, damage or oil contamination. Inspect all sprockets for damage. Check belt tensioner for signs of grease leakage or roughness in tensioner rotation. Replace components if damaged.

Installation – 1) Install flange on crankshaft with chamfered edge facing away from cylinder block (toward front of engine). Install camshaft sprocket and tighten bolt to specification. See TORQUE SPECIFICATIONS.

2) Align timing marks of camshaft sprocket and crankshaft sprocket, with piston No. 1 at TDC on compression stroke. *See Fig. 3.*

3) Install belt tensioner, tension spring and spacer. Ensure spring is properly engaged against front case. Rotate tensioner toward water pump, and temporarily tighten bolts. Rotate camshaft and crankshaft, and align all timing marks. *See Fig. 3.*

4) Install timing belt on crankshaft. Ensure belt is installed in original direction of rotation. Apply pressure on tension side of belt while installing belt on camshaft sprocket. *See Fig. 4.*

5) Apply counterclockwise force on camshaft sprocket to apply tension on tension side of belt. Ensure all timing marks are aligned. Temporarily install crankshaft pulley to retain timing belt.

6) Loosen timing belt tensioner bolts on belt tensioner to place tension on timing belt. *See Fig. 4.* Tighten timing belt tensioner bolts to specification. See TORQUE SPECIFICATIONS.

CAUTION: Slot-side timing belt tensioner bolt must be tightened before pivot-side to prevent belt tensioner from rotating, causing belt to be overtightened.

---

7) Rotate crankshaft clockwise at a constant speed for one full revolution. Loosen pivot-side bolt and then slot-side bolt. Tighten slot-side bolt, and then pivot-side bolt to specification.

8) To check belt tension, hold belt tensioner and timing belt together and apply slight thumb pressure at center point of belt tensioner. *See Fig. 4.* Ensure belt cog will reach half the width of timing belt tensioner bolt on slot-side of belt tensioner. To install remaining components, reverse removal procedure.

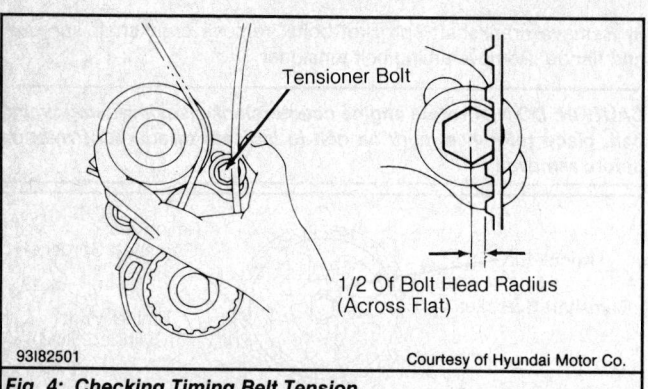

93I82501   Courtesy of Hyundai Motor Co.

Fig. 4: Checking Timing Belt Tension

ROCKER ARM SHAFT ASSEMBLY

NOTE: On Federal models built after March 31, 1994, rocker arms were changed from contact type to roller type to reduce friction between camshaft and rocker arms. On models with roller type rocker arms, automatic valve lash adjusters are used and valve clearance is not adjustable.

Removal – Remove air intake pipe. (Turbocharger only.) Remove breather hose and secondary air hose. Remove timing belt cover and rocker cover. Loosen rocker arm shaft retaining bolts evenly in small increments, and remove shaft assemblies.

Inspection – Check rocker arm cam contact face. If worn or damaged, replace rocker arm. Check valve cap face (valve stem contact). If badly worn, replace valve cap. Check rocker arm shafts for damage. Replace as necessary. *See Fig. 5.*

Installation – To install, reverse removal procedure. Tighten rocker arm shaft assembly retaining bolts to specification. See TORQUE SPECIFICATIONS. Adjust valve clearance. See VALVE CLEARANCE ADJUSTMENT under ADJUSTMENTS.

NOTE: When installing rocker arms, note exhaust side needs "A" type only and inlet side uses both "A" and "B" types. See Fig. 5.

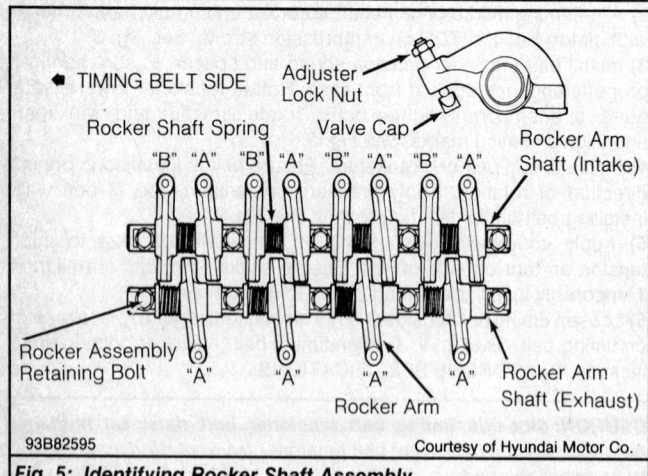

93B82595   Courtesy of Hyundai Motor Co.

Fig. 5: Identifying Rocker Shaft Assembly

CAMSHAFT

Removal – Remove rocker arms and shafts. See ROCKER ARM SHAFT ASSEMBLY. Remove timing belt and camshaft sprocket. See TIMING BELT. Remove distributor. Remove camshaft bearing caps. Remove camshaft.

Inspection – Inspect camshaft journal diameter and lobe height for signs of wear. Replace camshaft if not within specification. See CAMSHAFT table under ENGINE SPECIFICATIONS. Check bearing

surfaces and replace bearing caps or cylinder head as necessary. Check camshaft oil seal lips for wear and replace as necessary. Check oil seal contact surface on cam and replace cam if worn in stages.

Installation – **1)** To install, coat journals with engine oil and reverse removal procedure. With camshaft installed, coat camshaft seal contact surface with engine oil. Using Seal Installer (09222-22000), install camshaft oil seal. *See Fig. 6.*

2) To install remaining components, reverse removal procedure. Adjust valve clearance. See VALVE CLEARANCE ADJUSTMENT under ADJUSTMENTS. After warming engine to normal running temperature, adjust valve clearance. See VALVE CLEARANCE ADJUSTMENT under ADJUSTMENTS.

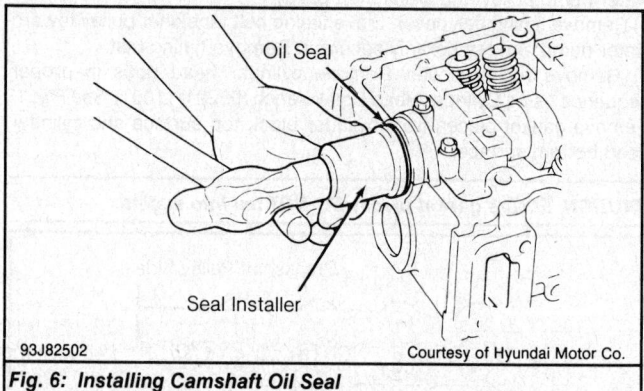

93J82502   Courtesy of Hyundai Motor Co.

Fig. 6: Installing Camshaft Oil Seal

REAR CRANKSHAFT OIL SEAL

Removal – Remove flywheel or drive plate. Remove oil seal case from rear of cylinder block. It may be necessary to remove oil pan. Remove oil seal from seal case.

Installation – Using Seal Installer (09231-11000), install oil seal. Install oil seal and case with NEW gasket. To install remaining components, reverse removal procedure.

WATER PUMP

CAUTION: Note bolt length and location during removal. Different length bolts are used and must be installed in original location.

Removal – Drain cooling system and disconnect battery. Remove necessary coolant hoses. Remove timing belt. See TIMING BELT. Remove pump mounting bolts. Note bolt length and location. Remove alternator brace and water pump.

Installation – To install, reverse removal procedure using NEW gasket and "O" ring. Install "O" ring on coolant pipe and then apply water to "O" ring. DO NOT apply grease or oil to "O" ring. Ensure bolts are installed in original location.

OIL PAN

Removal & Installation – Drain engine oil. Remove oil pan retaining bolts. Using gasket cutter, cut gasket along sealing surface of cylinder block. Remove oil pan and gasket. To install, reverse removal procedure. Apply a .16" (4.1 mm) bead of sealant to groove areas in oil pan sealing surfaces before installation.

OVERHAUL

CYLINDER HEAD

Cylinder Head – Check for cracks, damage and coolant leakage. Remove scale, sealing compound and carbon deposits. Clean oil passages and blow compressed air through passages to ensure they are not clogged. Check EGR passage for clogging. Inspect cylinder head for warpage at deck surface. Resurface cylinder head if warpage exceeds specification. See CYLINDER HEAD table under ENGINE SPECIFICATIONS.

Valve Springs – Inspect valve spring free length, tension and installed height. Using a square, check squareness of each spring. Replace if not within specification. See VALVES & VALVE SPRINGS table under ENGINE SPECIFICATIONS. Installed spring height is measured from spring seat to valve retainer. Install all valve springs with painted area toward rocker arm.

Valve Stem Oil Seals – Use Valve Seal Installer (09222-22000) for seal installation to provide proper positioning of oil seal.

Valve Guides – **1)** Ensure valve stem diameter and clearance are within specifications. See VALVES & VALVE SPRINGS and CYLINDER HEAD tables under ENGINE SPECIFICATIONS.

2) If clearance exceeds service limits, valve guide can be replaced with an oversized valve guide. See OVERSIZED VALVE GUIDE SPECIFICATIONS table.

CAUTION: Measure valve guide installed height before removal. Intake valve guides are shorter than exhaust valve guides.

---

3) Use valve guide remover/installer to drive valve guide out toward cylinder block area of cylinder head. Machine cylinder head valve guide bore to specification for oversized valve guide. See OVERSIZED VALVE GUIDE SPECIFICATIONS table.

4) Using valve guide installer, press new guides into cylinder head from top. Install proper length valve guide to original height of .3496-.3512" (8.88-8.92 mm). Intake valve guides are shorter than exhaust valve guides.

CAUTION: DO NOT install valve guide with same O.D. as removed guide.

---

5) Check guide clearance with new valve and ream as necessary. Check valve seat contact.

OVERSIZED VALVE GUIDE SPECIFICATIONS

Size Mark	Guide Size In. (mm)	Cyl. Head Bore In. (mm)
5	.002 (.05)	.4350-.4354 (11.050-11.058)
25	.010 (.25)	.4429-.4432 (11.250-11.258)
50	.020 (.50)	.4528-.4531 (11.500-11.508)

Valve Seats – **1)** To replace valve seats, cut valve seat to designated dimension. Machine cylinder head to proper dimension. See OVERSIZED VALVE SEAT SPECIFICATIONS table.

2) Heat cylinder head to 482°F (250°C), and press replacement seat into cylinder head. Valve seat height should be within specification. See OVERSIZED VALVE SEAT SPECIFICATIONS table. Cut valve seat to proper angle and obtain correct seat width.

OVERSIZED VALVE SEAT SPECIFICATIONS

Size Mark	Seat Size In. (mm)	Cyl. Head Bore In. (mm)	Seat Height In. (mm)
Int. Valve			
30	.012 (.30)	1.134-1.135 (28.80-28.82)	.201-.209 (5.1-5.3)
60	.024 (.60)	1.456-1.1465 (29.100-29.121)	.213-.220 (5.4-5.6)
Exh. Valve			
30	.012 (.30)	1.350-1.351 (34.3-34.325)	.232-.240 (5.9-6.1)
60	.024 (.60)	1.362-1.363 (34.6-34.625)	.244-252 (6.2-6.4)

Valves – Inspect each valve for wear, damage and head/stem distortion. If stem end is pitted or worn, resurface as necessary. Keep resurfacing to a minimum. Resurface valve face. If valve margin has decreased to less than service limit, replace valve. See VALVES & VALVE SPRINGS table under ENGINE SPECIFICATIONS.

VALVE TRAIN

Rocker Arm Shaft Assembly – **1)** Note location of components for reassembly. Remove rocker arm shaft assembly. See ROCKER ARM SHAFT ASSEMBLY under REMOVAL & INSTALLATION. Remove bolts, rocker arms and rocker arm shaft springs from rocker arm shaft.

2) Reverse removal procedure and install components in original location. See Fig. 5.

CYLINDER BLOCK ASSEMBLY

Piston & Rod Assembly – Piston must be installed in cylinder block with front mark on top of piston toward timing belt. Note position of connecting rod on piston before removal.

Fitting Pistons & Rings – Ensure ring end gap and side clearance are within specifications. See PISTONS, PINS & RINGS table under ENGINE SPECIFICATIONS. Properly position ring gaps before installation. See Fig. 7.

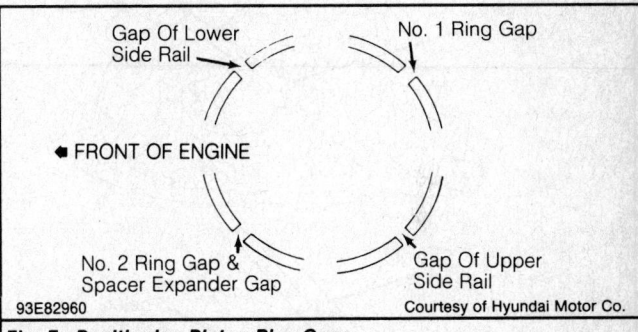

93E82960   Courtesy of Hyundai Motor Co.

Fig. 7: Positioning Piston Ring Gaps

Piston Pin Replacement – Note piston location before removing piston from connecting rod. Fitting piston pin in connecting rod requires use of proper force during installation. See PISTONS, PINS & RINGS table under ENGINE SPECIFICATIONS.

Manufacturer recommends using Piston Pin Remover/Installer Kit (09234-33001) for piston pin removal and installation. See application chart in kit for selection of pin installation depth guides, etc.

CAUTION: DO NOT exceed 5000 lbs. (2268 kg.) of force at any time during removal or installation of piston pin.

Crankshaft & Main Bearings – Install main bearing caps with arrow on top of cap pointing toward crankshaft pulley and in numerical sequence according to cap number stamped near arrow. Tighten main bearing caps in 2 steps to specification, starting at center and working outward. See TORQUE SPECIFICATIONS.

ENGINE OILING

ENGINE LUBRICATION SYSTEM

A crankshaft-driven oil pump is mounted in timing cover.

Crankcase Capacity – Oil capacity with oil filter is 3.48 qts. (3.3L).

Oil Pressure – Normal oil pressure is at least 21.33 psi (1.5 kg/cm²) at curb idle with oil temperature of 167-203°F (75-95°C).

OIL PUMP

Removal – Remove timing belt and crankshaft sprocket. See TIMING BELT under REMOVAL & INSTALLATION. Remove oil filter, oil pan and oil screen. Remove front cover and oil pump assembly.

Disassembly & Inspection – **1)** Remove rear cover. Note gear position, and mark direction of gear for reassembly reference.

2) Check outer gear-to-cover clearance. Check inner gear-to-outer gear clearance. Place straightedge across front cover housing and measure gear end play clearance between each gear and straightedge. See Fig. 8.

3) Ensure pressure relief valve moves freely in bore. Check relief spring tension and free length. Replace components if not within specification. See OIL PUMP SPECIFICATIONS table.

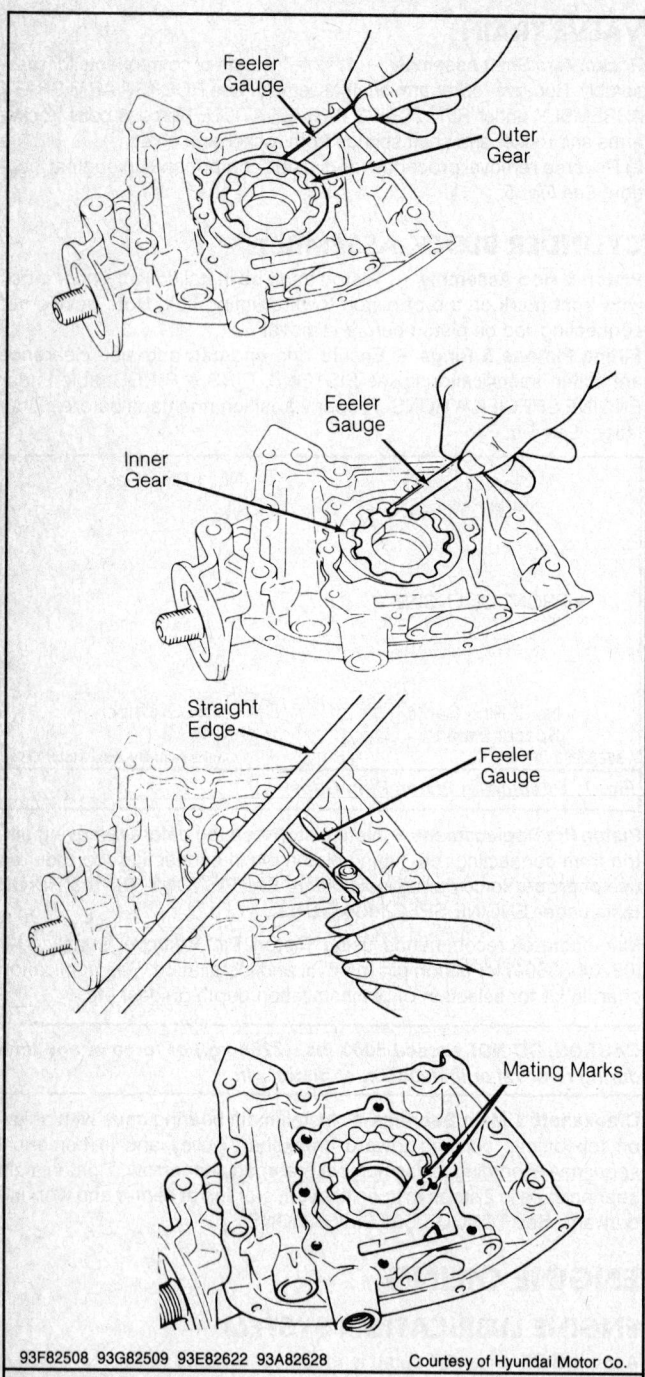

93F82508 93G82509 93E82622 93A82628   Courtesy of Hyundai Motor Co.

Fig. 8: Measuring Oil Pump

OIL PUMP SPECIFICATIONS

Application	Specification
Gear End Play	.0016-.0034" (.040-.087 mm)
Inner Gear-To-Outer Gear	.001-.003" (.25-.069 mm)
Outer Gear-To-Case	.005-.007" (.12-.18 mm)
Relief Valve Spring	
Free Length	1.835" (46.60 mm)
Spring Pressure	21.4 lbs. @ 1.4291" (9.7 kg @ 36.3 mm)

Reassembly & Installation – **1)** Install oil pump rear cover. Install oil pump and gasket assembly onto engine block. Coat outer surface of Seal Guide (9231-22100) with oil, and install seal guide over end of crankshaft.

2) Using Seal Installer (09231-22000), install seal into front cover. Install proper length bolts and tighten to specification. *See Fig. 9.* See TORQUE SPECIFICATIONS.

3) Using plug cap wrench, install plug cap and tighten to specification. See TORQUE SPECIFICATIONS. To install remaining components, reverse removal procedure.

PRESSURE RELIEF VALVE

NOTE: Pressure relief valve is nonadjustable and is located in front cover.

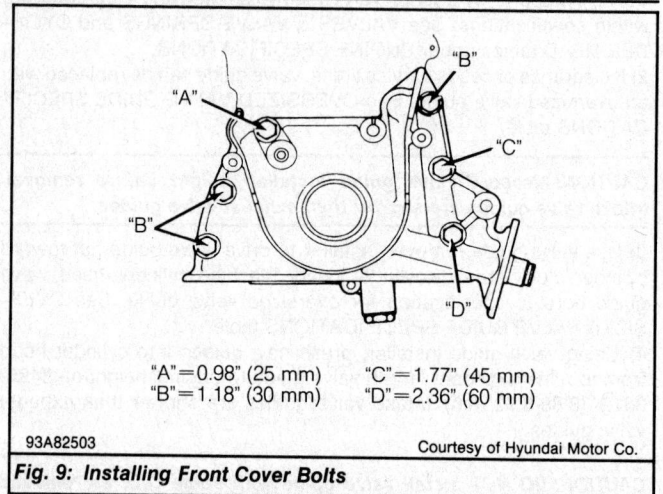

"A"=0.98" (25 mm)   "C"=1.77" (45 mm)
"B"=1.18" (30 mm)   "D"=2.36" (60 mm)

93A82503   Courtesy of Hyundai Motor Co.

Fig. 9: Installing Front Cover Bolts

TORQUE SPECIFICATIONS

TORQUE SPECIFICATIONS

Application	Ft. Lbs. (N.m)
Camshaft Sprocket Bolt	59-74 (80-100)
Connecting Rod Cap Nut	26-28 (35-38)
Crankshaft Pulley-To-Sprocket Bolt	9.6-10.3 (13-14)
Crankshaft Sprocket Bolt	140-148 (190-200)
Cylinder Head Bolt [1]	
Cold Engine	52-55 (70-75)
Hot Engine	59-63 (80-85)
Drain Plug	26-33 (35-45)
Drive Plate-To-Crankshaft Bolt	96-103 (130-140)
Exhaust Manifold-To-Engine Bolt	
Non-Turbo	11-15 (15-20)
Turbo	18-26 (25-35)
Exhaust Pipe-To-Manifold Bolt	22-30 (30-40)
Flywheel-To-Crankshaft Bolt	96-103 (130-140)
Front Cover Bolt	9-11 (12-15)
Intake Manifold Bolt	11-15 (15-20)
Intake Manifold Brace Bolt	13-18 (18-25)
Main Bearing Cap Bolt	41-44 (55-60)
Oil Pressure Switch	9.6-11 (13-15)
Oil Pump Cover Bolt	9-11 (12-15)
Oil Pump Relief Valve Plug Cap	30-37 (40-50)
Oil Screen Bolt	11-24 (15-33)
Rocker Arm Adjusting Screw Lock Nut	9-13 (12-18)
Rocker Arm Shaft Assembly Retaining Bolt	15-20 (20-27)
Sensor Wheel	9-11 (12-15)
Throttle Body-To-Intake Manifold Bolt	11-15 (15-20)
Timing Belt Tensioner Bolt	15-20 (20-27)
Torque Converter-To-Drive Plate Bolt	7-10 (9-14)
Water Pump Pulley Bolt	9-11 (12-15)
	INCH Lbs. (N.m)
Oil Pan Bolt	53-71 (6-8)
Rocker Cover Bolt	13-18 (1.5-2)
Timing Belt Cover Bolt	89-106 (10-12)

[1] – Tighten in sequence. *See Fig. 2.*

ENGINE SPECIFICATIONS

GENERAL SPECIFICATIONS

Application	Specification
Displacement	89.6 Cu. In. (1.495L)
Bore	2.97" (75.5 mm)
Stroke	3.29" (83.5 mm)
Compression Ratio	
Non-Turbo	10.0:1
Turbo	7.5:1
Fuel System	PFI
Turbo Unit	Garrett T15
Horsepower @ RPM	
Non-Turbo	92 @ 5500
Turbo	115 @ 5500
Torque Ft. Lbs. @ RPM	
Non-Turbo	97 @ 4500
Turbo	123 @ 4000

CRANKSHAFT, MAIN & CONNECTING ROD BEARINGS

Application	In. (mm)
Crankshaft	
End Play	.002-.007 (.05-.18)
Runout (Maximum)	.0012 (.030)
Main Bearings	
Journal Diameter	1.9685 (50.0)
Journal Out-Of-Round	.0004 (.010)
Journal Taper	.0004 (.010)
Oil Clearance	.0013-.0022 (.032-.056)
Connecting Rod Bearings	
Journal Diameter	1.7717 (45.0)
Journal Out-Of-Round	.0004 (.010)
Journal Taper	.0004 (.010)
Oil Clearance	.0010-.0022 (.026-.056)

CONNECTING RODS

Application	In. (mm)
Side Play	.004-.010 (.100-.250)

PISTONS, PINS & RINGS

Application	In. (mm)
Pistons	
Clearance	
Non-Turbo	.0008-.0016 (.020-.040)
Turbo	.0010-.0018 (.025-.045)
Diameter	2.9713-2.9724 (75.470-75.500)
Bowl Depth	
Non-Turbo	.012-.020 (0.3-0.5)
Turbo	.240-.248 (6.1-6.3)
Pins	
Piston Fit	Slip Fit
Rod Fit	[1] Press Fit
Rings	
No. 1	
End Gap	.012-.020 (.30-.50)
Side Clearance	.0016-.0031 (.040-.080)
No. 2	
End Gap	.012-.020 (.30-.50)
Side Clearance	.0016-.0031 (.040-.080)
No. 3 (Oil)	
End Gap	.010-.039 (0.25-1.00)

[1] - Press fit using 1100-3300 lbs. (499-1497 kg). DO NOT exceed 5000 lbs. (2268 kg).

CYLINDER BLOCK

Application	In. (mm)
Cylinder Bore	
Standard Diameter	2.9724-2.9736 (75.500-75.530)
Maximum Taper	.0004 (.010)
Maximum Out-Of-Round	.0004 (.010)
Maximum Deck Warpage	.002 (.05)

VALVES & VALVE SPRINGS

Application	Specification
Intake Valves	
Face Angle	45°
Minimum Margin	.043" (1.10 mm)
Stem Diameter	.236" (6.0 mm)
Exhaust Valves	
Face Angle	45°
Minimum Margin	.059" (1.50 mm)
Stem Diameter	.236" (6.0 mm)
Valve Springs	
Free Length	1.575" (40 mm)
Installed Height	1.2598" (32.00 mm)
Out-Of-Square (Max)	1.5°

	Lbs. @ In. (kg @ mm)
Pressure	
Valve Closed	44 @ 1.2598 (20 @ 32)

CYLINDER HEAD

Application	Specification
Maximum Warpage	.002" (.05 mm)
Valve Seats	
Intake Valve	
Seat Angle	45°
Seat Width	.059-.067" (1.50-1.70 mm)
Exhaust Valve	
Seat Angle	45°
Seat Width	.043-.059" (1.10-1.50 mm)
Valve Guides	
Intake Valve	
Valve Guide Length	1.68" (42.7 mm)
Valve Guide Installed Height	.3496-.3512" (8.88-8.92 mm)
Valve Stem-To-Guide	
Oil Clearance	[1] .0012-.0024" (.030-.060 mm)
Exhaust Valve	
Valve Guide Length	1.54" (39.1 mm)
Valve Guide Installed Height	.3496-.3512" (8.88-8.92 mm)
Valve Stem-To-Guide	
Oil Clearance	[2] .0020-.0031" (.050-.080 mm)

[1] - Limit is .004" (.10 mm).
[2] - Limit is .020" (.50 mm).

CAMSHAFT

Application	In. (mm)
End Play	Not Furnished By Manufacturer
Lobe Height	
Intake	
Non-Turbo	1.61746 (41.0837)
Turbo	1.62475 (41.2689)
Exhaust	1.62475 (41.2689)

1994 ENGINES
1.6L & 1.8L 4-Cylinder

Elantra

NOTE: For repair procedures not covered in this article, see ENGINE OVERHAUL PROCEDURES article in GENERAL INFORMATION.

ENGINE IDENTIFICATION

The 8th character in Vehicle Identification Number (VIN) identifies engine type. Engine identification code is stamped at top right front side of cylinder block.

ENGINE IDENTIFICATION CODE

Application	[1] Engine Code	VIN Code
1.6L G4DRR	.... R
1.8L G4DMR	.... M

[1] – Third character is a development order number and may not be the same for all engines.

ADJUSTMENTS

VALVE CLEARANCE ADJUSTMENTS

Intake & Exhaust Valves – Hydraulic valve lash adjusters are used, eliminating need for valve adjustment.

REMOVAL & INSTALLATION

NOTE: For reassembly reference, label all electrical connectors, vacuum hoses and fuel lines before removal. Also place mating marks on engine hood and other major assemblies before removal.

FUEL PRESSURE RELEASE

WARNING: ALWAYS relieve fuel pressure before disconnecting any fuel injection-related component. DO NOT allow fuel to contact engine or electrical components.

Disconnect fuel pump harness connector under rear seat. Start engine. After engine stalls, turn ignition switch to OFF position. Disconnect negative battery cable.

ENGINE

Removal – 1) Release fuel pressure. See FUEL PRESSURE RELEASE. Remove battery and air cleaner. Label and disconnect fuel lines and vapor hoses from engine. Drain cooling system, engine oil and transaxle oil.
2) Disconnect engine wiring harness and back-up light connector. On manual transaxle models, disconnect select control valve connector. On automatic transaxle models, disconnect oil cooler lines. On all models, disconnect alternator and oil pressure gauge wiring.
3) Disconnect radiator hoses and remove radiator. Disconnect ignition coil, engine ground and brake booster hose. Disconnect throttle cable, heater hoses and clutch cable on manual transaxles or shift control cable on automatic transaxles.
4) Disconnect speedometer cable from transaxle. Disconnect A/C compressor (with hoses attached), and secure with wire away from work area. Raise and support vehicle. Disconnect front exhaust pipe from manifold.
5) On manual transaxles, disconnect shift control and extension rods. On all models, disconnect lower ball joints and stabilizer bar from lower control arm. Remove axle shafts from transaxle. Plug axle shaft holes to prevent contamination.
6) Secure lower control arm aside and attach chain hoist to engine assembly. Raise engine slightly. Remove front roll stopper and disconnect rear roll stopper. Remove engine mounting bracket at front of timing cover.
7) Slowly raise engine and ensure all cables, wiring, hoses, etc. are disconnected. Remove right side fender shield and disconnect transaxle mount. Disconnect side left mount. While directing transaxle downward, lift and remove engine and transaxle from engine compartment.

CAUTION: Whenever axle shafts are removed from transaxle, replace axle shaft retainer rings.

Installation – To install, reverse removal procedure. Ensure throttle, transaxle cables and drive belts are properly adjusted. Tighten mounting bolts and nuts to specification with weight of engine on insulators. Replace all fluids, and check gauges for correct operation.

INTAKE MANIFOLD

CAUTION: Release fuel pressure before disconnecting fuel lines. See FUEL PRESSURE RELEASE.

Removal – 1) Release fuel pressure. Disconnect fuel supply hose. Carefully remove delivery pipe with fuel injectors and pressure regulator attached. DO NOT allow fuel injectors to fall from delivery pipe.
2) Label and disconnect all wiring, hoses, cables and brackets interfering with intake manifold removal. Remove intake manifold-to-cylinder head attaching bolts, and remove intake manifold assembly. Disassemble as necessary.
Installation – To install, reverse removal procedure using NEW gaskets. Tighten intake manifold bolts to specification. See TORQUE SPECIFICATIONS.

EXHAUST MANIFOLD

Removal – 1) Disconnect negative battery cable. Label and disconnect all wiring, hoses, cables and brackets interfering with exhaust manifold removal.
2) Remove exhaust manifold heat shield. Disconnect exhaust pipe from exhaust manifold. Remove exhaust manifold-to-cylinder head attaching bolts, and remove exhaust manifold.
Installation – To install, reverse removal procedure using NEW gaskets. Tighten exhaust manifold bolts to specification. See TORQUE SPECIFICATIONS.

CYLINDER HEAD

Removal – 1) Release residual fuel pressure. See FUEL PRESSURE RELEASE. Drain cooling system. Disconnect necessary hoses, electrical connections, cables and fuel lines. Remove center cover and spark plug wires.

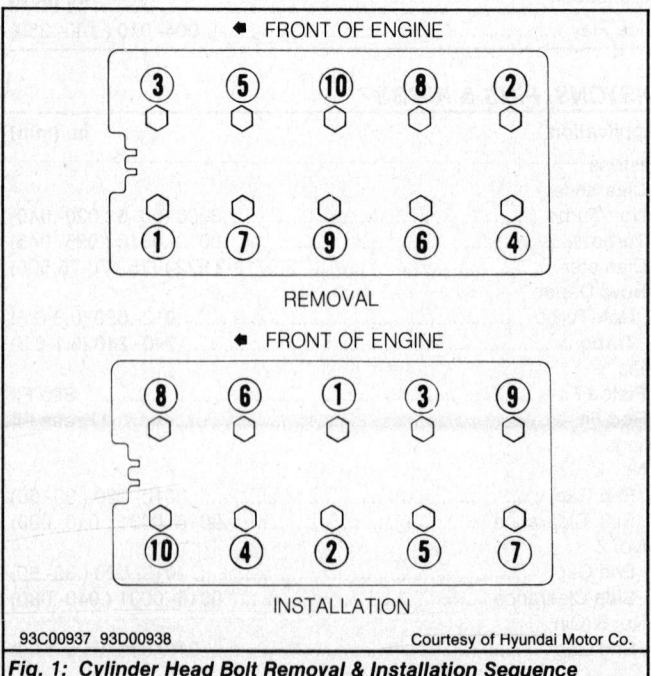

93C00937 93D00938   Courtesy of Hyundai Motor Co.

Fig. 1: Cylinder Head Bolt Removal & Installation Sequence

2) Remove crankshaft position sensor. Remove wiring harness. Remove timing belt. See TIMING BELT under REMOVAL & INSTALLATION. Remove rocker cover and semi-circular packing at rear of cover.

3) Disconnect exhaust pipe at manifold. Disconnect tension rod at rear of intake manifold. Using Wrench (09221-32001), loosen head bolts in proper sequence. *See Fig. 1.* Remove cylinder head with exhaust and intake manifolds attached. Remove exhaust and intake manifolds from cylinder head (if necessary).

Inspection – Inspect cylinder head for warpage at deck surface. Resurface cylinder head if warpage exceeds specification. See CYLINDER HEAD table under ENGINE SPECIFICATIONS.

Installation – **1)** Install cylinder head. Using NEW gasket, ensure identification mark on head gasket is toward timing belt side and faces up. *See Fig. 2.* DO NOT apply sealant to head gasket.

2) Install head bolts and tighten to specification in proper sequence. See TORQUE SPECIFICATIONS. *See Fig. 1.* To complete installation, reverse removal procedure.

3) Apply sealant to rocker cover sealing areas and proper areas of semi-circular packing. *See Fig. 3.* Apply gasoline to "O" ring on fuel line before installing fuel line in delivery pipe. Adjust all control cables.

FRONT COVER OIL SEAL

NOTE: "FRONT COVER" refers to cover at front of cylinder block. Cover contains oil pump, front cover oil seal (crankshaft front seal) and oil filter mount. Manufacturer lists oil seal removal procedure with front cover removed from engine. See OIL PUMP, FRONT COVER & BALANCE SHAFTS under ENGINE OILING.

TIMING BELT

Removal – **1)** Remove all drive belt and drive pulleys from crankshaft and water pump. Remove timing belt covers and gaskets, noting bolt lengths and locations.

CAUTION: DO NOT rotate engine counterclockwise (as viewed from timing belt end of engine). If reusing timing belt, place reference mark on timing belt to indicate direction of rotation before removing.

2) Rotate engine clockwise to align all timing marks so No. 1 cylinder is at TDC of compression stroke. *See Fig. 5.* Remove automatic tensioner.

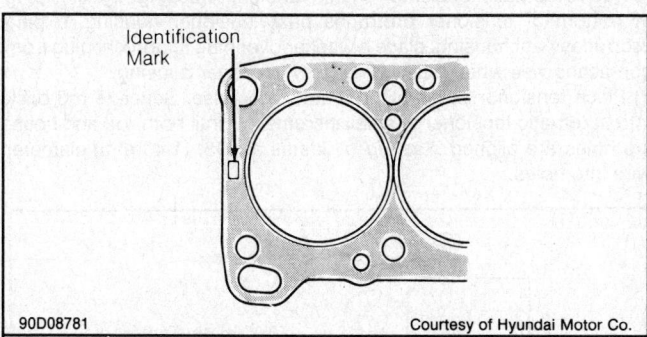

Identification Mark

90D08781   Courtesy of Hyundai Motor Co.

Fig. 2: Locating Cylinder Head Gasket Identification Mark

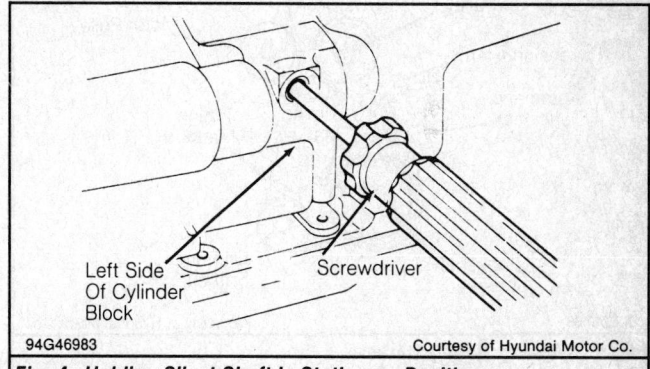

Left Side Of Cylinder Block

Screwdriver

94G46983   Courtesy of Hyundai Motor Co.

Fig. 4: Holding Silent Shaft In Stationary Position

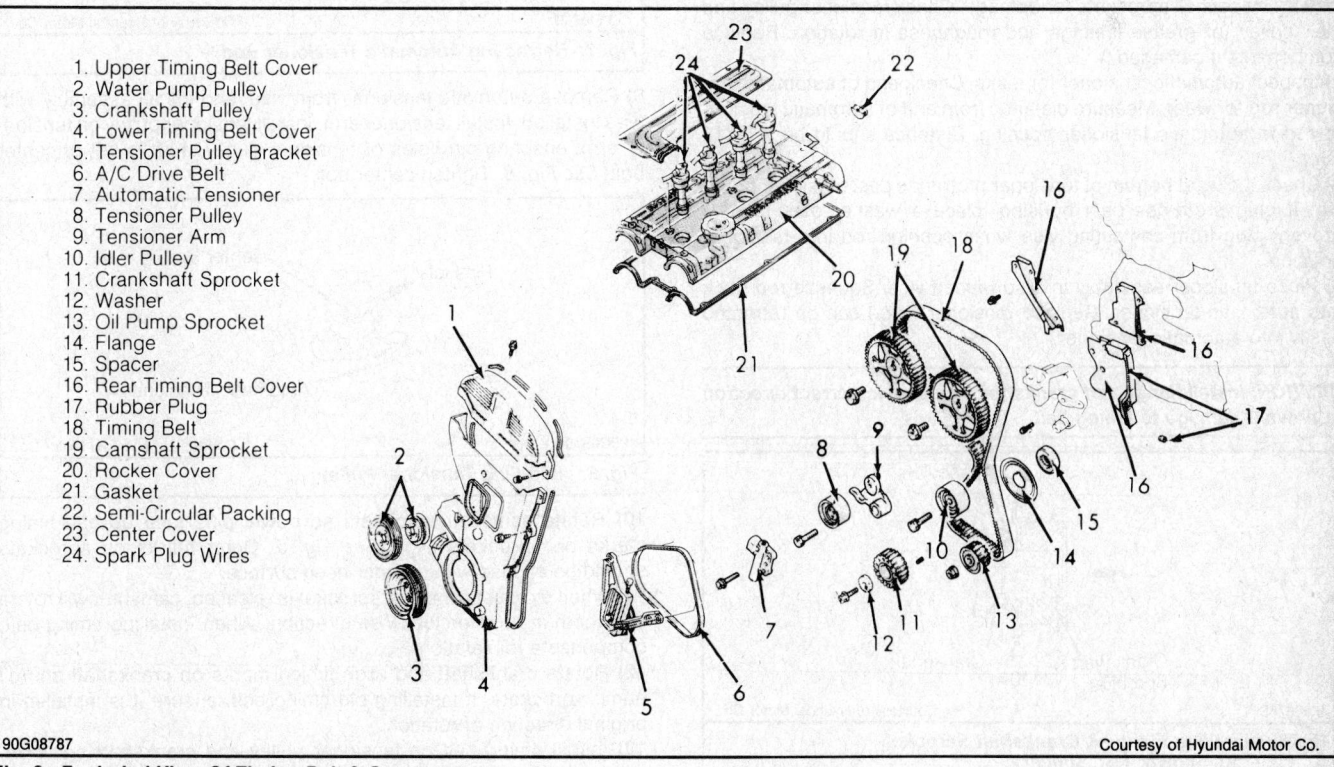

1. Upper Timing Belt Cover
2. Water Pump Pulley
3. Crankshaft Pulley
4. Lower Timing Belt Cover
5. Tensioner Pulley Bracket
6. A/C Drive Belt
7. Automatic Tensioner
8. Tensioner Pulley
9. Tensioner Arm
10. Idler Pulley
11. Crankshaft Sprocket
12. Washer
13. Oil Pump Sprocket
14. Flange
15. Spacer
16. Rear Timing Belt Cover
17. Rubber Plug
18. Timing Belt
19. Camshaft Sprocket
20. Rocker Cover
21. Gasket
22. Semi-Circular Packing
23. Center Cover
24. Spark Plug Wires

90G08787   Courtesy of Hyundai Motor Co.

Fig. 3: Exploded View Of Timing Belt & Components

3) Place mark on timing belt to indicate direction of belt rotation. Remove timing belt. Remove camshaft sprockets, carefully holding camshafts in place with an adjustable wrench.

4) On 1.6L engine, remove crankshaft sprocket. On 1.8L engines, remove plug at left side of cylinder block and insert screwdriver to hold left balance shaft in place. See Fig. 4. Remove oil pump sprocket.

5) Loosen right balance shaft sprocket bolt. Remove rear timing belt tensioner. Remove rear timing belt. Remove crankshaft sprocket.

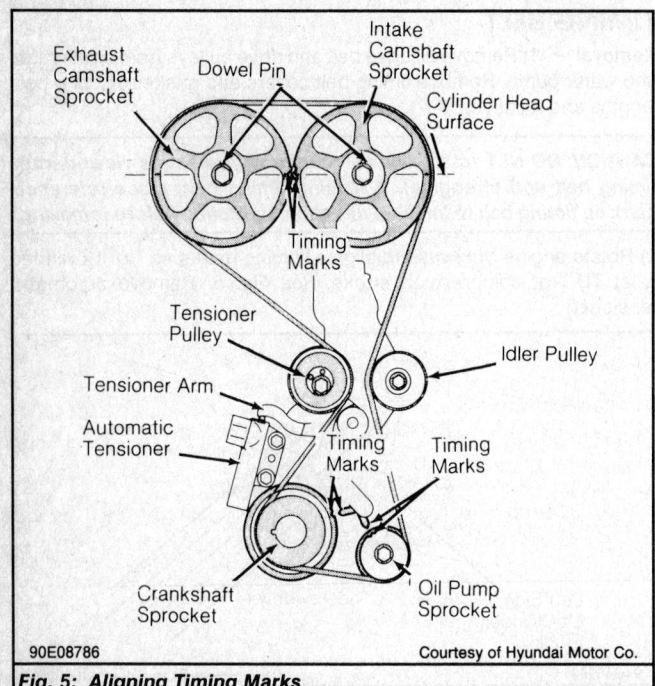

Exhaust Camshaft Sprocket — Dowel Pin — Intake Camshaft Sprocket — Cylinder Head Surface — Timing Marks — Tensioner Pulley — Idler Pulley — Tensioner Arm — Automatic Tensioner — Timing Marks — Timing Marks — Crankshaft Sprocket — Oil Pump Sprocket

90E08786   Courtesy of Hyundai Motor Co.

Fig. 5: Aligning Timing Marks

Inspection – 1) Check belt teeth for cracks, damage and oil contamination. Inspect all sprockets for damage. Check tensioner pulley and idler pulley for grease leakage and roughness in rotation. Replace components if damaged.

2) Inspect automatic tensioner for leaks. Check end of automatic tensioner rod for wear. Measure distance from end of automatic tensioner rod to automatic tensioner housing. Distance should be .47" (12 mm).

3) Check if plug at bottom of tensioner protrudes past tensioner housing. If plug protrudes past housing, place a washer over plug to prevent plug from contacting vise when pushing rod into tensioner housing.

4) Place tensioner assembly in a soft-faced vise. Squeeze rod back into automatic tensioner. Replace tensioner if rod can be retracted easily into automatic tensioner.

CAUTION: Install flange and crankshaft sprocket in correct direction to prevent damage to timing belt.

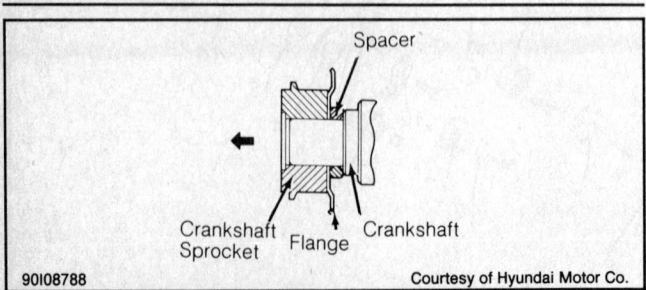

Spacer — Crankshaft Sprocket — Flange — Crankshaft

90I08788   Courtesy of Hyundai Motor Co.

Fig. 6: Installing Flange & Crankshaft Sprocket (1.8L Shown; 1.6L Similar)

Installation – 1) Install crankshaft sprocket, ensuring flange and crankshaft sprocket are installed in proper direction. Tighten sprocket bolt to specification. See TORQUE SPECIFICATIONS. *See Fig. 6.* On 1.6L, go to step **6)**. On 1.8L, go to next step.

2) Lightly apply engine oil to balance shaft sprocket spacer. Install spacer onto balance shaft with chamfered edge toward engine. Install balance shaft sprocket, tightening bolt finger tight.

3) Align timing marks on balance shaft and crankshaft sprockets with timing marks on front case. Install rear timing belt. No slack should be present in belt. Install rear timing belt tensioner. Tensioner bolt should be positioned below and to the right of tensioner center point.

4) Lift tensioner to tighten belt. While tightening tensioner bolt, ensure tensioner and sprockets do not rotate. Ensure timing marks are still aligned. Check belt tension by applying finger pressure to side of belt opposite tensioner. Deflection should be .20-.28" (5-7 mm).

5) Insert screwdriver through hole in left side of cylinder block to hold balance shaft in position. *See Fig. 4.* Install oil pump sprocket. Tighten nut to specification. See TORQUE SPECIFICATIONS.

6) Install camshaft sprockets. Tighten retaining bolts to specification while holding camshaft with adjustable wrench. See TORQUE SPECIFICATIONS.

7) Push automatic tensioner rod into tensioner housing. Check if plug at bottom of tensioner protrudes past tensioner housing. If plug protrudes past housing, place a washer over plug to prevent plug from contacting vise when pushing rod into tensioner housing.

8) Place tensioner assembly in a soft-faced vise. Squeeze rod back into automatic tensioner in small increments until both rod and housing holes are aligned. *See Fig. 7.* Install a .055" (1.40 mm) diameter wire into holes.

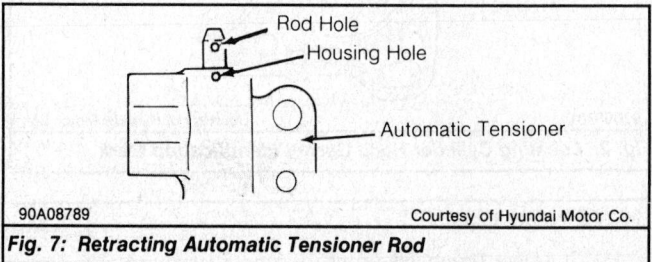

Rod Hole — Housing Hole — Automatic Tensioner

90A08789   Courtesy of Hyundai Motor Co.

Fig. 7: Retracting Automatic Tensioner Rod

9) Remove automatic tensioner from vise, and install assembly with wire installed. Install tensioner arm. Install tensioner pulley on tensioner arm, ensuring pin holes of tensioner pulley shaft is left of center bolt. *See Fig. 8.* Tighten center bolt.

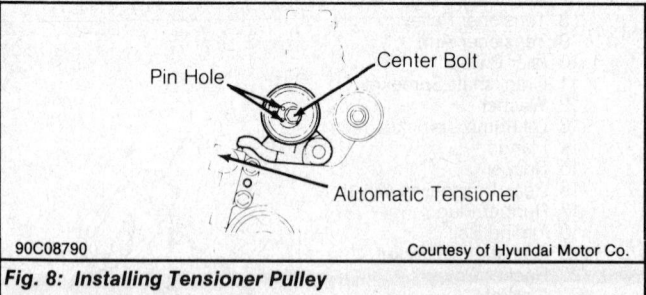

Pin Hole — Center Bolt — Automatic Tensioner

90C08790   Courtesy of Hyundai Motor Co.

Fig. 8: Installing Tensioner Pulley

10) Rotate camshaft sprockets so dowel pins face up and timing marks on sprockets align. *See Fig. 5.* Outer marks on sprockets should be aligned with cylinder head surface.

11) When exhaust camshaft sprocket is released, camshaft will rotate one tooth in counterclockwise direction. When installing timing belt, compensate for rotation.

12) Rotate crankshaft and align timing marks on crankshaft and oil pump sprockets. If installing old timing belt, ensure it is installed in original direction of rotation.

13) Install timing belt on tensioner pulley and crankshaft sprocket. Hold belt in place using left hand. Pull belt around oil pump sprocket using right hand. Pull belt around idler pulley.

14) Install timing belt around intake camshaft sprocket. Ensure exhaust timing mark on camshaft sprocket aligns with cylinder head surface. *See Fig. 5.* Using both hands, install timing belt around exhaust camshaft sprocket.

15) Rotate tensioner pulley in toward timing belt until belt does not sag. Temporarily tighten center bolt on tensioner pulley. Ensure all timing marks are aligned.

16) To adjust belt tension, rotate crankshaft 1/4 turn counterclockwise, and then rotate clockwise until No. 1 cylinder is at TDC. Loosen center bolt on tensioner pulley.

17) To rotate tensioner pulley, install Socket Wrench (09244-28100) into pin holes offset from center of pulley. Using INCH-lb. torque wrench and socket wrench, apply a torque of 23-24 INCH lbs. (2.6-2.7 N.m) on tensioner pulley. With torque applied to tensioner pulley, tighten tensioner pulley center bolt to 31-40 ft. lbs. (42-54 N.m).

NOTE: If engine is in vehicle, it may be necessary during tensioner pulley adjustment to jack up engine slightly for clearance.

---

18) Install Set Screw (09244-28000) in left engine support bracket until screw end contacts tensioner arm. *See Fig. 9.* Turn set screw further until wire can be removed from automatic tensioner. Remove set screw.

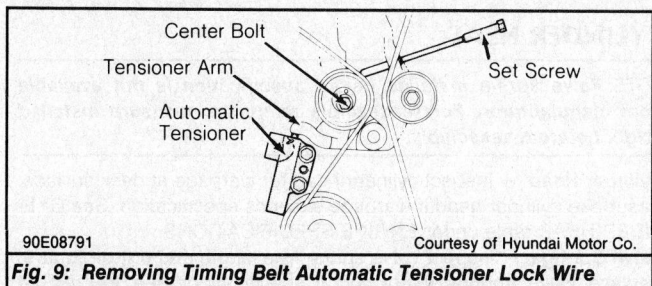

90E08791   Courtesy of Hyundai Motor Co.

Fig. 9: Removing Timing Belt Automatic Tensioner Lock Wire

19) Rotate crankshaft clockwise 2 complete revolutions, and leave it in this position for approximately 15 minutes. After 15 minutes, measure distance between tensioner arm and automatic tensioner body (automatic tensioner rod extension). Distance should be .15-.18" (3.8-4.5 mm). Repeat steps **16)** through **19)** until correct distance is obtained.

20) If distance is okay, go to step **22)**. If engine is in vehicle or distance cannot be measured due to lack of clearance, an alternate method can be used: Install Set Screw (09244-28000) until it contacts tensioner arm.

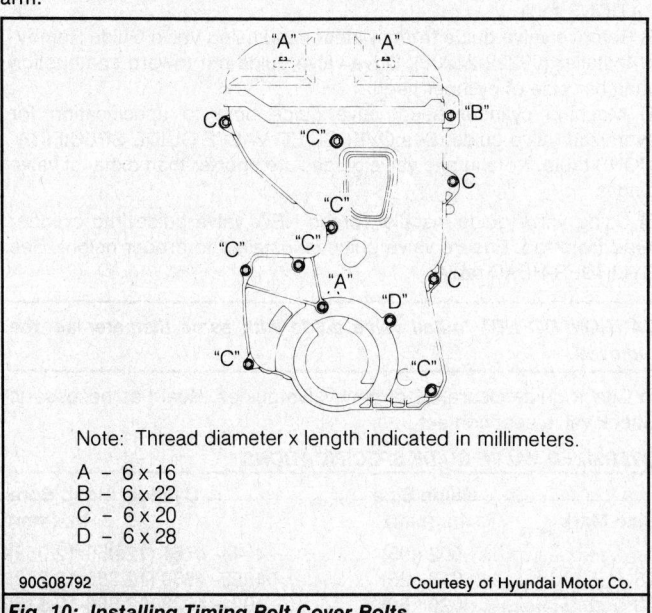

Note: Thread diameter x length indicated in millimeters.

A – 6 x 16
B – 6 x 22
C – 6 x 20
D – 6 x 28

90G08792   Courtesy of Hyundai Motor Co.

Fig. 10: Installing Timing Belt Cover Bolts

21) Turn set screw inward, counting number of turns until tensioner arm contacts automatic tensioner housing. Set screw should rotate 2 1/2 - 3 turns inward if belt tension is correct. Repeat steps **16)** through **21)** until correct number of turns is obtained. Remove set screw.

22) Install rubber plug in rear timing belt cover. To complete installation, reverse removal procedure. Ensure timing belt cover bolts are installed in proper location. *See Fig. 10.*

ROCKER ARM & VALVE LASH ADJUSTER

Removal & Installation – Remove camshafts. See CAMSHAFTS under REMOVAL & INSTALLATION. Remove rocker arm and lash adjuster. *See Fig. 11.* To install, reverse removal procedure.

CAMSHAFTS

Removal – **1)** Remove timing belt. See TIMING BELT under REMOVAL & INSTALLATION. Remove camshaft sprockets. Remove crankshaft position sensor from rear of intake camshaft.

CAUTION: Note location and direction of installed bearing cap before removing. Bearing caps are marked with "L" to indicate intake camshaft or "R" to indicate exhaust camshaft.

---

2) Remove front and rear bearing caps. Remove camshaft oil seals. *See Fig. 11.* Remove remaining bearing caps in sequence: No. 5, 2, 4 and 3. Remove camshafts.

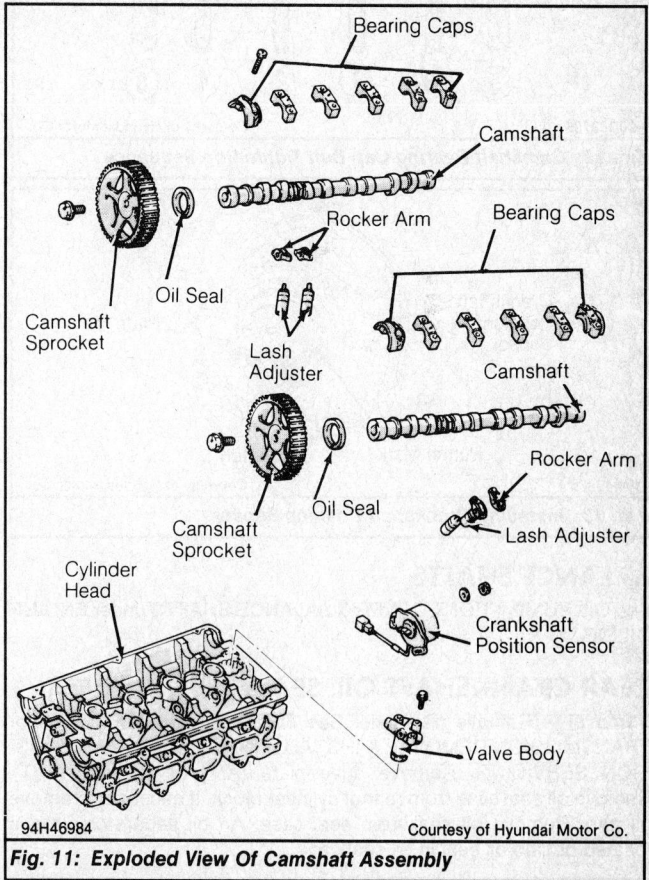

94H46984   Courtesy of Hyundai Motor Co.

Fig. 11: Exploded View Of Camshaft Assembly

Inspection – Inspect all components for damage. Inspect camshaft journal diameter and lobe height for wear. Replace camshaft if journal diameter and lobe height are not within specifications. See CAMSHAFT table under ENGINE SPECIFICATIONS. Ensure rocker arms do not show wear.

Installation – 1) Lubricate camshafts with engine oil. Note intake camshaft has a slit in rear to drive crankshaft position sensor. Install camshafts with dowel pin for camshaft sprockets at a 12 o'clock position.

2) Install bearing caps. Ensure rocker arm is mounted on lash adjuster and valve stem. Tighten bearing cap bolts in sequence to specification (in 2 steps). *See Fig. 12.*

3) Install Seal Guide (09221-21100) on camshaft. Coat oil seal with engine oil, and install on seal guide. Using Seal Installer (09221-21000), install seal into cylinder head.

4) Ensure dowel pin for intake camshaft sprocket is at 12 o'clock position. Align punch mark on crankshaft position sensor housing with notch in plate. *See Fig. 13.* Install crankshaft position sensor on cylinder head. To complete installation, reverse removal procedure.

CAUTION: Ensure crankshaft position sensor is installed with punch mark aligned with notch in plate. Otherwise, incorrect fuel injection and ignition timing will result.

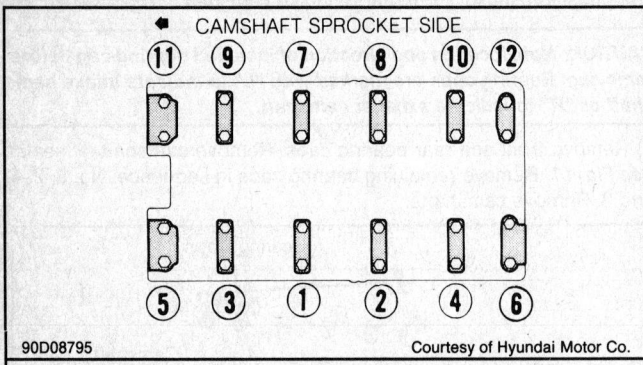

90D08795   Courtesy of Hyundai Motor Co.

Fig. 12: Camshaft Bearing Cap Bolt Tightening Sequence

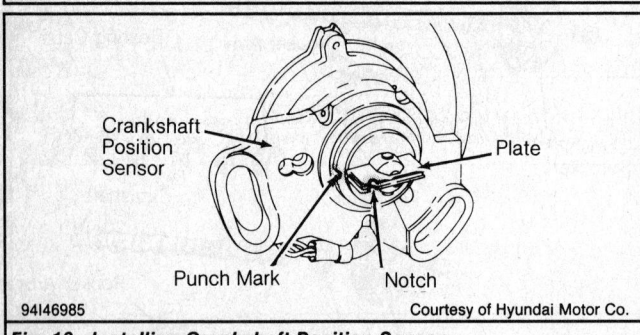

94I46985   Courtesy of Hyundai Motor Co.

Fig. 13: Installing Crankshaft Position Sensor

BALANCE SHAFTS

See OIL PUMP, FRONT COVER & BALANCE SHAFTS under ENGINE OILING.

REAR CRANKSHAFT OIL SEAL

Removal – Remove transaxle. See FWD article in CLUTCHES or TRANSMISSION REMOVAL & INSTALLATION article in TRANSMISSION SERVICING. Remove drive plate (A/T) or flywheel (M/T). Remove oil seal case from rear of cylinder block. If necessary, remove oil pan. Remove oil seal from seal case. An oil separator plate is located behind oil seal in oil seal case.

NOTE: Ensure oil separator plate is installed in oil seal case, with oil hole located toward oil pan sealing area, at bottom of oil seal case.

Installation – 1) Install oil separator plate in oil seal case. Ensure oil hole of oil separator plate is located at bottom of oil seal case (toward oil pan sealing surface).

2) Install seal in oil seal case until it bottoms using Seal Installer (09231-21000). Install oil seal case with NEW gasket. To complete installation, reverse removal procedure.

WATER PUMP

Removal – Drain cooling system, and disconnect battery. Remove necessary coolant hoses. Remove timing belt. See TIMING BELT under REMOVAL & INSTALLATION. Remove pump mounting bolts. Note bolt length and locations. Remove alternator brace and water pump.

Installation – To install, reverse removal procedure. Use NEW gasket and "O" ring. Install "O" ring on coolant pipe, and apply water to "O" ring. DO NOT apply grease or oil to "O" ring. Ensure bolts are installed in original location.

NOTE: For further information on cooling systems, see SPECIFICATIONS & ELECTRIC COOLING FANS article in ENGINE COOLING.

OIL PAN

Removal & Installation – Drain engine oil. Remove oil pan retaining bolts. Using a gasket cutter, cut gasket along sealing surface of cylinder block. Remove oil pan and gasket. To install, reverse removal procedure. Apply a .16" (4.0 mm) bead of sealant to groove areas in oil pan sealing surfaces before installing.

OVERHAUL

CYLINDER HEAD

NOTE: Valve spring installed height specification is not available from manufacturer. For reassembly reference, measure installed height before disassembly.

Cylinder Head – Inspect cylinder head for warpage at deck surface. Resurface cylinder head if warpage exceeds specification. See CYLINDER HEAD table under ENGINE SPECIFICATIONS.

Valve Springs – Inspect valve spring free length and out-of-square. Replace valve springs if not within specification. See VALVES & VALVE SPRINGS table under ENGINE SPECIFICATIONS. Install all valve springs with painted area toward rocker arm.

Valve Stem Oil Seals – Install seal using Valve Seal Installer (09222-28200) to properly position oil seal.

Valve Guides – 1) Ensure valve stem diameter is within specification. Check valve stem clearance. Ensure clearance is within specification. See CYLINDER HEAD and VALVES & VALVE SPRINGS tables under ENGINE SPECIFICATIONS at end of article.

2) If clearance exceeds service limits, valve guide can be replaced with an oversized valve guide. See OVERSIZED VALVE GUIDE SPECIFICATIONS table.

3) Remove valve guide from cylinder head using Valve Guide Remover/Installer (09222-21200). Drive valve guide out toward combustion chamber side of cylinder head.

4) Machine cylinder head valve guide bore to specification for oversized valve guide. See OVERSIZED VALVE GUIDE SPECIFICATIONS table. Note intake valve guides are shorter than exhaust valve guides.

5) Using valve guide installer, press NEW valve guide into cylinder head from top. Ensure valve guide is installed to proper height. See CYLINDER HEAD table.

CAUTION: DO NOT install valve guide with same diameter as one removed.

6) Check guide clearance of new valve guides. Ream as necessary. Check valve seat contact.

OVERSIZED VALVE GUIDE SPECIFICATIONS [1]

Size Mark	Guide Size In. (mm)	Cylinder Head Bore In. (mm)
5	.002 (.05)	.4744-.4751 (12.050-12.068)
25	.010 (.25)	.4823-.4830 (12.250-12.268)
50	.020 (.50)	.4921-.4928 (12.500-12.518)

[1] – For installed valve guide height, see CYLINDER HEAD table under ENGINE SPECIFICATIONS.

Valve Seats – **1)** To replace valve seats, cut valve seat to designated dimension. *See Fig. 14.* Remove valve seats. Machine cylinder head to proper dimension. See OVERSIZED VALVE SEAT SPECIFICATIONS table.

2) Heat cylinder head to 482°F (250°C) and press replacement seat into cylinder head. Ensure valve seat height is within specification. Cut valve seat to proper angle to obtain correct seat width.

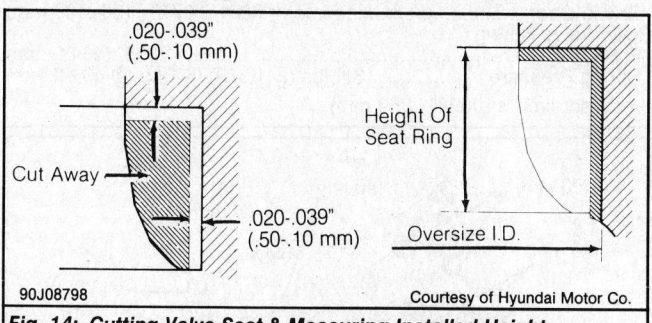

90J08798   Courtesy of Hyundai Motor Co.

Fig. 14: Cutting Valve Seat & Measuring Installed Height

OVERSIZED VALVE SEAT SPECIFICATIONS

Size Mark	Seat Size In. (mm)	Cyl. Head Bore In. (mm)	Seat Height In. (mm)
Intake			
30	.012	1.390-1.390	.311-.319
	(.30)	(35.30-35.33)	(7.90-8.10)
60	.024	1.402-1.403	.323-.331
	(.60)	(35.60-35.63)	(8.20-8.40)
Exhaust			
30	.012	1.311-1.312	.311-.319
	(.30)	(32.30-33.33)	(7.90-8.10)
60	.024	1.323-1.324	.323-.331
	(.60)	(33.60-33.63)	(8.20-8.40)

Valves – Ensure valve stem diameter and valve margin are within specifications. See VALVES & VALVE SPRINGS table under ENGINE SPECIFICATIONS. Replace valve if diameter and margin are not to specifications.

VALVE TRAIN

Ensure rocker arm and valve lifter are undamaged and not excessively worn. When hydraulic valve lifter is pressed down, lifter should resist and require some effort to move. No overhaul is possible. Replace as necessary.

CYLINDER BLOCK ASSEMBLY

Piston & Rod Assembly – Mark piston and rod assembly with corresponding cylinder number before removing. Install piston and rod assembly in cylinder block, with front mark on piston top toward timing belt side of engine.

Fitting Pistons – **1)** Measure piston skirt diameter .08" (2 mm) above bottom of piston skirt and at 90-degree angle to piston pin. If piston diameter is not within specification, replace piston. See PISTONS, PINS & RINGS table under ENGINE SPECIFICATIONS.

2) Measure cylinder bore diameter in 3 places: .47" (12 mm) from top of bore, .47" (12 mm) from bottom of bore and near center of bore. If cylinder bore diameter or taper is not within specification, machine cylinder bore. See CYLINDER BLOCK table under ENGINE SPECIFICATIONS.

3) If piston-to-cylinder bore clearance is not within specification, replace piston and/or machine cylinder bore. See PISTONS, PINS & RINGS table.

Piston Rings – Ensure ring end gap and side clearance are within specification. See PISTONS, PINS & RINGS table under ENGINE SPECIFICATIONS. DO NOT use ring expander to install oil ring side rails. Position ring end gaps around circumference of piston properly before installing. *See Fig. 15.*

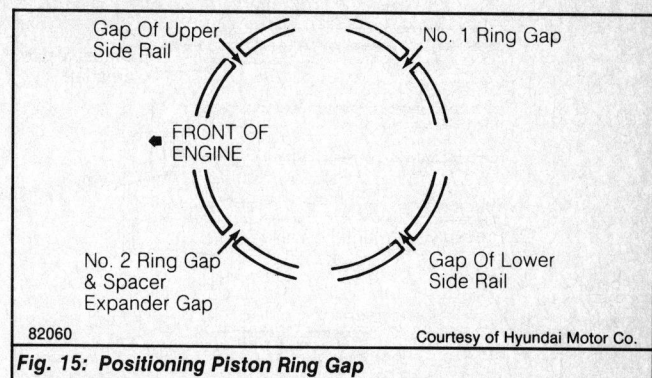

82060   Courtesy of Hyundai Motor Co.

Fig. 15: Positioning Piston Ring Gap

Rod Bearings – Note position of connecting rod in relation to bearing cap before removing. Ensure bearing oil clearance and side play are within specification. See CRANKSHAFT, MAIN & CONNECTING ROD BEARINGS and CONNECTING RODS tables under ENGINE SPECIFICATIONS.

Crankshaft & Main Bearings – **1)** Check diameters of main bearing journals and connecting rod bearing journals. Check journals for taper and out-of-round. Check crankshaft end play. See CRANKSHAFT, MAIN & CONNECTING ROD BEARINGS table under ENGINE SPECIFICATIONS.

2) Install main bearing caps with arrow on top of cap pointing toward timing belt end of engine. "F" stamped on top of cap (next to arrow) indicates front main bearing cap and "R" indicates rear main bearing cap.

Thrust Bearing – Replace thrust bearing if crankshaft end play is not within specification. See CRANKSHAFT, MAIN & CONNECTING ROD BEARINGS table under ENGINE SPECIFICATIONS.

Cylinder Block – **1)** Check cylinder block deck warpage. Ensure warpage does not exceed specification. See CYLINDER BLOCK table under ENGINE SPECIFICATIONS. If warpage exceeds specification, machine surface. DO NOT remove more than a combined total of .008" (0.20 mm) material from cylinder head or cylinder block gasket surfaces.

2) Check cylinder bore wear and taper. Measure cylinder bore diameter in 3 places: .47" (12 mm) from top of bore, .47" (12 mm) from bottom of bore and near center of bore. If cylinder bore diameter or taper is not within specification, machine cylinder bore. See CYLINDER BLOCK table.

ENGINE OILING

ENGINE LUBRICATION SYSTEM

The 1.6L engine uses a timing belt-driven oil pump mounted in front cover. *See Fig. 16.* Oil is delivered to hydraulic lifters from oil passage at rear of engine.

Pressure relief valve is nonadjustable and located in oil filter bracket. See OIL PUMP, FRONT COVER & BALANCE SHAFTS.

Crankcase Capacity – Fill capacity including oil filter is 4.6 qts. (4.4L).

Oil Pressure – At curb idle and with oil temperature 167-194°F (75-90°C), normal oil pressure should be at least 11 psi (.77 kg/cm²).

OIL PUMP, FRONT COVER & BALANCE SHAFTS

NOTE: *Only 1.8L engines use balance shafts(2).*

Removal – **1)** Remove timing belt and crankshaft sprocket. See TIMING BELT under REMOVAL & INSTALLATION. Remove oil filter. Using Oil Pressure Switch Remover (09260-32000), remove oil pressure switch. Remove oil pan, oil screen and oil filter bracket. Remove front cover and oil pump assembly. Using Plug Cap Wrench (09213-33000), remove plug cap located on front of front cover.

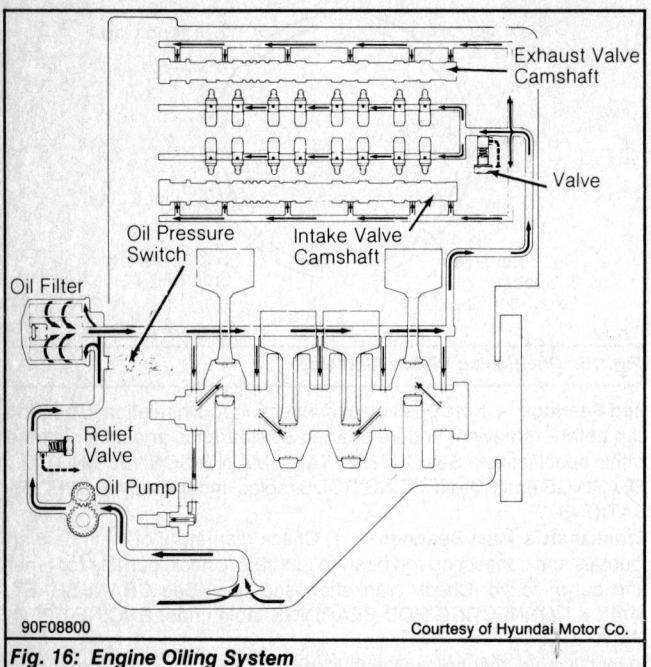

Fig. 16: Engine Oiling System

90F08800   Courtesy of Hyundai Motor Co.

OIL PUMP SPECIFICATIONS

Application	Specification
Gear End Play	
Drive Gear	[1] .0031-.0055" (.080-.140 mm)
Driven Gear	[1] .0024-.0047" (.060-.120 mm)
Gear Tip-To-Body Clearance	
Drive Gear	[1] .0063-.0083" (.160-.210 mm)
Driven Gear	[1] .0051-.0071" (.130-.180 mm)
Relief Valve Spring	
Free Length	1.835" (46.60 mm)
Spring Pressure	13.4 lbs @ 1.579" (6.1 kg @ 40.10 mm)

[1] – Wear limit is .0098" (.250 mm).

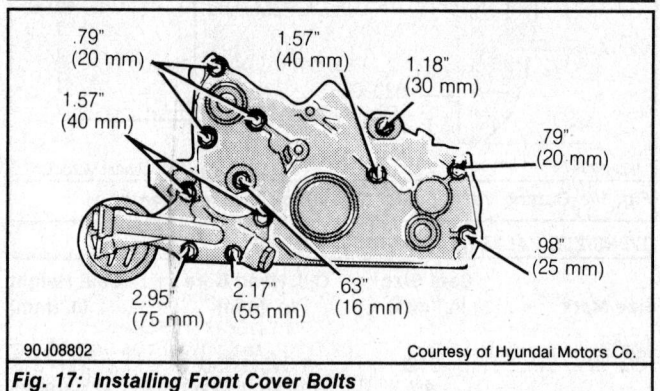

90J08802   Courtesy of Hyundai Motors Co.

Fig. 17: Installing Front Cover Bolts

2) On 1.6L, remove front case mounting bolts, and remove front case assembly and gasket. On 1.8L, remove plug on left side of cylinder block, and insert screwdriver into plug hole. *See Fig. 4.* Remove oil pump driven gear and left balance shaft retaining bolt.

3) Remove front case mounting bolts, and remove front case assembly and gasket. Remove both balance shafts from cylinder block.

4) On all models, remove oil pump cover from front case. Remove oil pump.

Disassembly & Inspection – 1) Check clearance between tip of gear teeth and front cover. Place straightedge across front cover housing. Measure gear end play clearance between each gear and straightedge.

2) Check pressure relief valve for freedom of movement in bore. Check spring tension and free length of relief valve spring. Replace components if not within specifications. See OIL PUMP SPECIFICATIONS table. Check oil pan for cracks and damage and oil screen for clogging.

3) On 1.8L, check balance shaft journals and bearings for wear or signs of seizure. Replace bearings as necessary. See BALANCE SHAFT BEARING REPLACEMENT.

Balance Shaft Bearing Replacement – 1) To remove either balance shaft front bearing, use Bearing/Seal Remover/Installer (09212-32000) to remove bearing from cylinder block. To remove right balance shaft rear bearing, use Bearing/Seal Remover/Installer (09212-32100) to remove bearing from cylinder block.

2) To remove left balance shaft rear bearing, use Bearing/Seal Remover/Installer (09212-32100) and Holder (09212-32300) to remove bearing from cylinder block. To install, reverse removal procedure. Apply engine oil to outer surface of bearing. Align bearing hole with oil hole in cylinder block.

Reassembly & Installation – 1) Ensure timing marks are aligned on gears. Install gear cover. Use Seal Installer (09214-32000) to install seal in front cover. Coat outer surface of Seal Guide (09214-32100) with oil, and install over end of crankshaft.

2) Install front cover with NEW gasket. Install oil filter bracket. Install proper length front cover bolts in appropriate locations. *See Fig. 17.* Tighten to specification. See TORQUE SPECIFICATIONS table.

3) Using plug cap wrench, install plug cap, and tighten to specification. To complete installation, reverse removal procedure.

TORQUE SPECIFICATIONS

TORQUE SPECIFICATIONS

Application	Ft. Lbs. (N.m)
Automatic Tensioner Bolt	14-20 (19-27)
Camshaft Bearing Cap Bolt [1]	14-15 (19-21)
Camshaft Sprocket Bolt	58-72 (80-100)
Connecting Rod Cap Bolt	36-38 (50-53)
Crankshaft Pulley-To-Sprocket Bolt	14-22 (19-30)
Crankshaft Sprocket Bolt	80-94 (110-130)
Cylinder Head Bolt [2]	76-83 (105-115)
Drive Plate-To-Crankshaft Bolt	94-101 (130-140)
Exhaust Manifold-To-Engine Nut	18-22 (25-30)
Exhaust Pipe-To-Manifold Nut	22-29 (30-40)
Flywheel-To-Crankshaft Bolt	94-101 (130-140)
Front Cover Bolt	
8 x 30-mm Bolt	20-26 (27-35)
Except 8 x 30-mm Bolt	14-20 (19-27)
Idler Pulley Bolt	22-30 (30-42)
Intake Manifold Bolts	11-14 (15-20)
Intake Manifold Stay Bolts	18-22 (25-30)
Main Bearing Cap Bolt	47-51 (65-70)
Oil Filter Bracket Bolt	11-16 (15-22)
Oil Pump Cover Bolt	11-13 (15-18)
Oil Pump Driven Gear Bolt	25-29 (34-40)
Oil Pump Relief Valve Plug	29-36 (40-50)
Oil Pump Sprocket Bolt	36-43 (50-60)
Oil Screen Bolt	11-16 (15-22)
Plug Cap	14-20 (19-27)
Tensioner Pulley Bracket Bolt	12-19 (17-26)
Tensioner Pulley Center Bolt	31-40 (43-55)
Throttle Body-To-Intake Manifold Bolt	11-16 (15-22)
Torque Converter-To-Drive Plate Bolt	53-55 (73-77)

TORQUE SPECIFICATIONS (Cont.)

Application	INCH Lbs. (N.m)
Oil Pan Bolt	44-71 (5-8)
Rear Oil Seal Case Bolt	89-106 (10-12)
Rocker Cover Bolt	22-31 (2.5-3.5)
Timing Belt Cover Bolt	
Left Lower Rear Cover Bolt	[3]
Except Left Lower Rear Cover Bolt	89-106 (10-12)

[1] – Tighten in sequence. *See Fig. 12.*
[2] – Tighten in sequence with engine cold. *See Fig. 1.*
[3] – Tighten to 22-30 ft. lbs. (30-42 N.m).

ENGINE SPECIFICATIONS

GENERAL SPECIFICATIONS

Application	Specification
Displacement	
1.6L	97 Cu. In. (1.6L)
1.8L	112 Cu. In. (1.8L)
Bore	
1.6L	3.24" (82.3 mm)
1.8L	3.21" (81.5 mm)
Stroke	
1.6L	2.95" (75.0 mm)
1.8L	3.46" (88 mm)
Compression Ratio	9.2:1
Fuel System	MFI
Horsepower @ RPM	
1.6L	113 @ 6000
1.8L	124 @ 6000
Torque Ft. Lbs. @ RPM	
1.6L	102 @ 5000
1.8L	116 @ 4500

CRANKSHAFT, MAIN & CONNECTING ROD BEARINGS

Application	In. (mm)
Crankshaft	
End Play	
Standard	.002-.007 (.05-.18)
Service Limit	.010 (.25)
Main Bearings	
Journal Diameter	2.2441 (57.000)
Journal Out-Of-Round	.0006 (.015)
Journal Taper	.0002 (.005)
Oil Clearance	
Standard	.0008-.0020 (.020-.050)
Service Limit	.004 (.10)
Connecting Rod Bearings	
Journal Diameter	1.7717 (45.000)
Journal Out-Of-Round	.0006 (.015)
Journal Taper	.0002 (.005)
Oil Clearance	
Standard	.0009-.0020 (.022-.050)
Service Limit	.004 (.10)

CONNECTING RODS

Application	In. (mm)
Maximum Bend	.002 (.05)
Maximum Twist	.004 (.10)
Side Play	
Standard	.004-.010 (.10-.25)
Service Limit	.016 (.40)

PISTONS, PINS [1] & RINGS

Application	In. (mm)
Pistons	
Clearance	.0008-.0016 (.020-.040)
Diameter [2]	
1.6L	3.2390-3.2402 (82.270-82.300)
1.8L	3.2075-3.2087 (81.470-81.500)
Rings	
No. 1	
End Gap	
Standard	.010-.016 (.25-.40)
Service Limit	.031 (.80)
Side Clearance	
Standard	.0012-.0028 (.030-.070)
Service Limit	.004 (.10)
No. 2	
End Gap	
Standard	
1.6L	.014-.020 (.35-.50)
1.8L	.0177-.0236 (.450-.600)
Service Limit	.031 (.80)
Side Clearance	
Standard	.0012-.0028 (.030-.070)
Service Limit	.004 (.10)
No. 3 (Oil)	
End Gap	
Standard	.008-.028 (.20-.70)
Service Limit	.040 (1.00)

[1] – Pin specifications are not available from manufacturer.
[2] – Diameter is measured at specified location and at 90° angle to piston pin. See CYLINDER BLOCK ASSEMBLY under OVERHAUL.

CYLINDER BLOCK

Application	In. (mm)
Cylinder Bore	
Standard Diameter	
1.6L	3.2402-3.2413 (82.300-82.330)
1.8L	3.2087-3.2098 (81.500-81.530)
Maximum Taper	.0004 (.010)
Maximum Out-Of-Round	.0004 (.010)
Maximum Deck Warpage	[1] .002 (.05)

[1] – If deck warpage exceeds specification, machine deck surface. DO NOT remove more than a combined total of .008" (.20 mm) material from original surfaces of cylinder head and cylinder block.

VALVES & VALVE SPRINGS

Application	Specification
Intake Valves	
Face Angle	45.5°
Minimum Margin	
Standard	.040" (1.00 mm)
Service Limit	.028" (.70 mm)
Stem Diameter	.2585-.2591" (6.565-6.580 mm)
Exhaust Valves	
Face Angle	45.5°
Minimum Margin	
Standard	.059" (1.50 mm)
Service Limit	.040" (1.00 mm)
Stem Diameter	.2571-.2579" (6.530-6.550 mm)
Valve Springs	
Free Length	
Standard	1.902" (48.3 mm)
Service Limit	1.862" (47.3 mm)

1994 ENGINES
1.6L & 1.8L 4-Cylinder (Cont.)

VALVES & VALVE SPRINGS (Cont.)

Application	Specification
Valve Springs (Cont.)	
Out-Of-Square	
Standard	1.5°
Service Limit	4.0°
	Lbs. @ In. (kg @ mm)
Pressure	
Valve Closed	66 @ 1.575 (30 @ 40)

CYLINDER HEAD

Application	Specification
Maximum Warpage	[1] .002" (.05 mm)
Valve Seats	
Intake Valve	
Seat Angle	44-44.5°
Seat Width	.035-.051" (.90-1.30 mm)
Exhaust Valve	
Seat Angle	44-44.5°
Seat Width	.035-.051" (.90-1.30 mm)
Valve Guides	
Valve Guide Installed Height	.768" (19.5 mm)
Intake Valve	
Valve Stem-To-Guide Oil Clearance	
Standard	.0008-.0019" (.020-.047 mm)
Service Limit	.004" (.10)
Exhaust Valve	
Valve Stem-To-Guide Oil Clearance	
Standard	.0020-.0033" (.050-.085 mm)
Service Limit	.0059" (.150 mm)

[1] – If deck warpage exceeds specification, machine deck surface. DO NOT remove more than a combined total of .008" (.20 mm) material from original surfaces of cylinder head and cylinder block.

CAMSHAFT

Application	In. (mm)
End Play	.004-.008 (.10-.20)
Journal Diameter	1.0236 (26.000)
Lobe Height	
Intake	
Standard	
1.6L	1.3858 (35.200)
1.8L	1.3974 (35.493)
Service Limit	
1.6L	1.3661 (34.700)
1.8L	1.3777 (34.993)
Exhaust	
Standard	
1.6L	1.3743 (34.907)
1.8L	1.3858 (35.200)
Service Limit	
1.6L	1.3546 (34.407)
1.8L	1.3661 (34.700)
Oil Clearance	.0020-.0035 (.050-.090)

Sonata

NOTE: For repair procedures not covered in this article, see ENGINE OVERHAUL PROCEDURES article in GENERAL INFORMATION.

ENGINE IDENTIFICATION

The 8th character in Vehicle Identification Number (VIN) identifies engine type. Engine identification code is stamped at top right front side of cylinder block, near dipstick tube.

ENGINE IDENTIFICATION CODE

Application	Engine Code	VIN Code
2.0L .... [1] G4APR .... F

[1] – Third character is a development order number and may not be the same for all engines.

ADJUSTMENTS

VALVE CLEARANCE ADJUSTMENT

Hydraulic lash adjusters are used. Valve adjustment is not required.

REMOVAL & INSTALLATION

NOTE: For reassembly reference, label all electrical connectors, vacuum hoses and fuel lines before removal. Also place mating marks on engine hood and other major assemblies before removal.

FUEL PRESSURE RELEASE

Disconnect fuel pump connector under rear seat. Start engine, and allow it to idle until it stalls. Turn ignition off. Reconnect fuel pump connector. Disconnect negative battery cable before disconnecting fuel lines.

ENGINE

CAUTION: To prevent fire hazard, release residual pressure in fuel system before disconnecting fuel lines.

Removal – **1)** Release fuel pressure. See FUEL PRESSURE RELEASE. Label and disconnect fuel lines and vapor hoses from engine. Remove battery and air cleaner. Drain cooling system, engine oil and transaxle oil.
2) Disconnect electrical connectors from oxygen sensor, A/C compressor, alternator and oil pressure switch. Disconnect throttle cables. Disconnect power steering pump, leaving hoses attached and secure with wire away from work area.
3) Label, disconnect and plug transaxle cooler lines (if equipped). Remove upper and lower radiator hoses from engine. Remove radiator assembly with hoses. Disconnect heater hoses at engine side. On A/T models, remove transaxle control cable. On M/T models, disconnect clutch cable and shift linkage.
4) On all models, raise and support vehicle. Remove oil pan shield. Disconnect front exhaust pipe at manifold and suspend pipe from bottom of vehicle with wire. Remove lower ball joint bolts and stabilizer bar where bar is mounted to lower control arm. Remove axle shafts from transaxle. Plug holes in transaxle to prevent entry of dirt or foreign material.

NOTE: Replace axle shaft retainer rings whenever axle shafts are removed from transaxle.

5) Attach engine hoist to engine, and raise engine just enough to relieve load on engine mounts. Remove front roll stopper, damper and rear roll stopper. Remove engine mount bolts. Remove bolts and nuts securing engine mount bracket to body. Raise engine a few inches.

NOTE: Ensure all cables, hoses, harnesses, connectors, etc. are disconnected from engine.

6) Remove blind plugs from inside right front fender apron. Remove transaxle mounting bracket bolts. Remove left mount insulator bolt. Direct transaxle side downward and lift assembly out of vehicle.
Installation – To install, reverse removal procedure. Ensure throttle, transaxle cables and drive belts are properly adjusted. Tighten mounting bolts and nuts to specification with weight of engine on mounts. See TORQUE SPECIFICATIONS. Replace all fluids and check gauges for correct operation.

INTAKE MANIFOLD

CAUTION: To prevent fire hazard, release residual pressure in fuel system before disconnecting fuel lines.

Removal – **1)** Release residual fuel pressure from fuel system. See FUEL PRESSURE RELEASE under REMOVAL & INSTALLATION.
2) Disconnect negative battery cable. Drain cooling system. Disconnect air intake hose from throttle body inlet. Remove air cleaner assembly (if necessary).

CAUTION: DO NOT allow fuel injectors to fall out when removing fuel delivery pipe.

3) Disconnect all necessary electrical connectors, vacuum hoses, coolant hoses, fuel hoses and cables from intake manifold, injectors and throttle body. Remove delivery pipe with fuel injectors and pressure regulator attached.
4) Remove support brace from below intake manifold. Remove lower intake manifold-to-cylinder head bolts. Remove lower intake manifold and gasket. If necessary, remove remaining components from intake manifold.
Installation – To install, reverse removal procedure using NEW gaskets, fuel injector insulators and "O" rings. Adjust all control cables, and fill cooling system.

EXHAUST MANIFOLD

Removal – On vehicles equipped with A/C, it may be necessary to remove condenser fan motor assembly. On all models, disconnect exhaust pipe and gasket from manifold. Remove outer heat shield from manifold. Disconnect oxygen sensor. Remove manifold.
Installation – To install, reverse removal procedure using NEW gaskets. Install NEW manifold nuts and exhaust pipe-to-manifold nuts.

CYLINDER HEAD

CAUTION: Release residual pressure in fuel system before disconnecting fuel lines. To compensate for removal of left engine mount, support oil pan to maintain level engine while working on engine.

Removal – **1)** Release residual fuel pressure from fuel system. See FUEL PRESSURE RELEASE under REMOVAL & INSTALLATION.
2) Drain cooling system. Remove air cleaner assembly. Disconnect all necessary electrical connectors, vacuum hoses, coolant hoses, fuel hoses and cables. Remove timing belt. See TIMING BELT under REMOVAL & INSTALLATION.
3) Remove rocker cover. Disconnect exhaust pipe from exhaust manifold. Loosen cylinder head bolts (in 2-3 steps) in proper sequence using Cylinder Head Bolt Wrench (09221-32001). *See Fig. 1.* Remove cylinder head and gasket.
Inspection – Inspect cylinder head for warpage at deck surface. Resurface cylinder head if warpage exceeds specification. See CYLINDER HEAD table under ENGINE SPECIFICATIONS.
Installation – **1)** Install cylinder head using NEW gasket. Ensure identification mark at timing belt end of gasket faces upward. DO NOT apply sealant to head gasket. Install and tighten cylinder head bolts (in 2-3 steps) to specification in proper sequence. *See Fig. 1.* See TORQUE SPECIFICATIONS.
2) To complete installation, reverse removal procedure. Apply sealant to contact surfaces of semi-circular packing. Apply gasoline to "O" ring on fuel line before installing fuel line in fuel delivery pipe. Adjust all control cables. Fill cooling system.

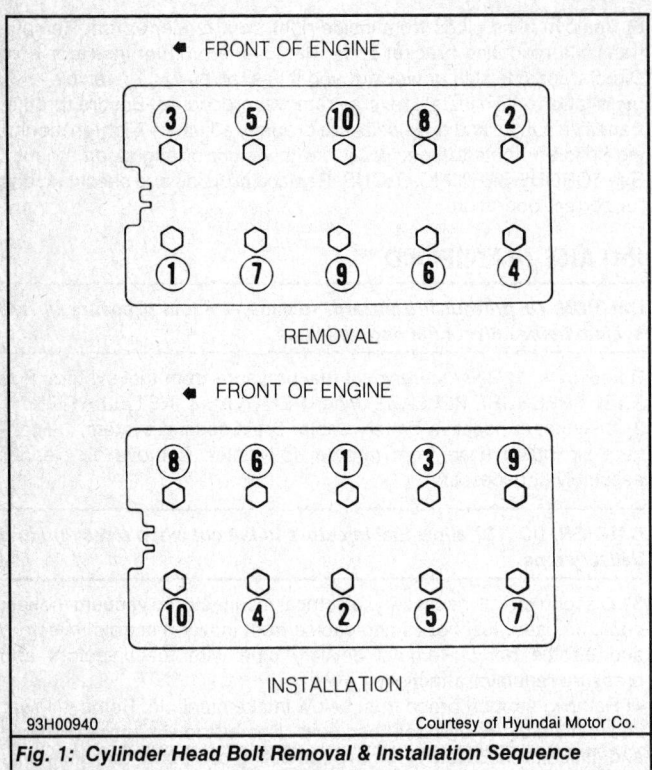

Fig. 1: **Cylinder Head Bolt Removal & Installation Sequence**

FRONT COVER OIL SEAL

NOTE: Front cover refers to cover at front of cylinder block. Cover contains oil pump and front cover oil seal (crankshaft front seal). Manufacturer lists oil seal removal procedure with front cover removed from engine. See OIL PUMP & FRONT COVER under ENGINE OILING.

TIMING BELT

Removal – 1) Remove all drive belts and drive pulleys from crankshaft and water pump. Remove upper and lower timing belt covers. Note bolt lengths and locations.

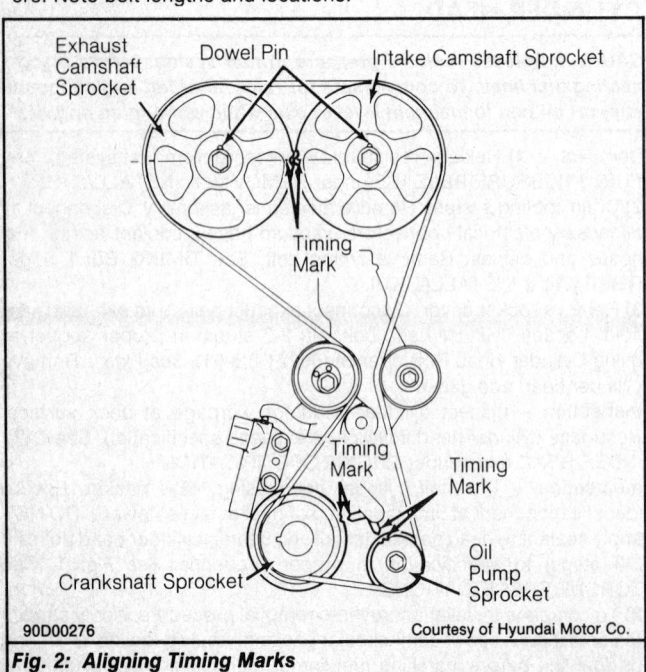

Fig. 2: **Aligning Timing Marks**

2) Turn crankshaft clockwise and align timing marks so No. 1 cylinder is at TDC. Timing marks on camshaft sprockets should be aligned at upper surface of cylinder head. *See Fig. 2*. Camshaft sprocket dowel pins should face upward.

CAUTION: DO NOT rotate crankshaft counterclockwise (as viewed from timing belt end of engine). If reusing timing belt, mark direction of belt rotation before removing.

3) Remove timing belt automatic tensioner. *See Fig. 3*. Mark timing belt to indicate original direction of rotation. Remove timing belt. Remove camshaft sprockets.

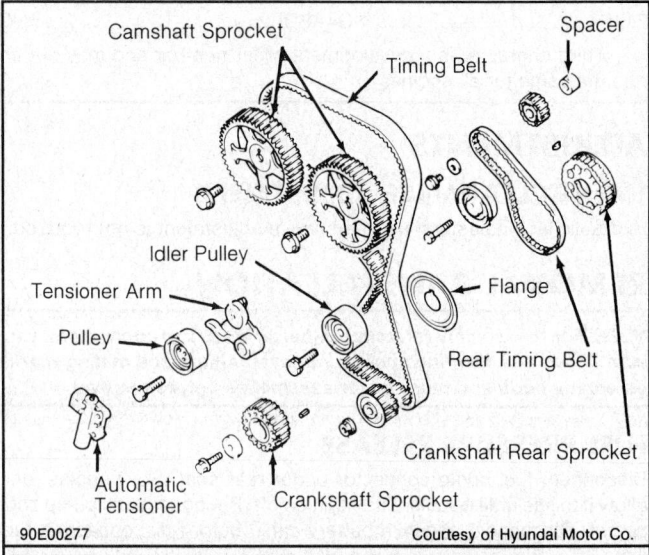

Fig. 3: **Exploded View Of Timing Belt & Related Components**

4) Remove silent shaft access plug from cylinder block. Insert Phillips screwdriver to block left silent shaft. *See Fig. 4*. Remove oil pump sprocket nut, and remove sprocket.

5) Loosen right silent shaft sprocket mounting bolt. Remove rear timing belt tensioner and remove rear timing belt. Remove crankshaft rear sprocket.

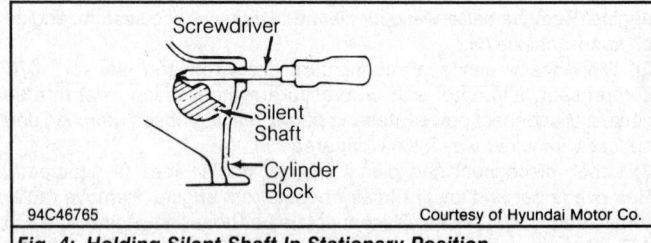

Fig. 4: **Holding Silent Shaft In Stationary Position**

Inspection – 1) Check belt teeth for damage and oil contamination. Inspect belt for glossy, hardened or non-elastic surface. Ensure belt is not cracked, separated or showing canvas fiber.
2) Inspect all sprockets for damage. Check tensioner pulley and idler pulley for grease leakage and roughness in rotation. Replace components if damaged.
3) Inspect automatic tensioner for leaks. Check rod end of automatic tensioner for wear. Measure distance from tensioner rod end to tensioner housing. Distance should be .47" (12 mm).

NOTE: If plug at bottom of tensioner protrudes past tensioner housing, place a washer over plug to prevent it from contacting vise when pushing rod into tensioner housing.

4) Retract rod into tensioner housing by placing automatic tensioner assembly in a soft-faced vise. Close vise to push rod back into tensioner. Replace automatic tensioner assembly if rod can be easily pushed into automatic tensioner.

Installation – 1) Install rear timing belt covers (if removed). Install rear crankshaft sprocket and flange. Ensure flange and crankshaft sprockets are installed correctly. *See Fig. 5.* Install idler pulley (if removed).

2) Install silent shaft sprocket and lubricated spacer. Ensure chamfered end of spacer is facing into seal. Align timing marks on silent shaft rear crankshaft sprockets with timing marks on engine case.

3) Install rear timing belt and tensioner. Hold tensioner tightly against belt while tightening bolts. To check tension, depress belt with finger midway between sprockets. Deflection should be between .20-.28" (5-7 mm).

4) Place crankshaft sprocket on shaft. Ensure flange is positioned correctly. *See Fig. 5.* Install washer and sprocket bolt, and tighten to specification. See TORQUE SPECIFICATIONS. Insert screwdriver through left side of cylinder block to hold silent shaft in place. Install oil pump and camshaft sprocket. Tighten sprocket bolts to specification while holding hexagonal area of camshaft. See TORQUE SPECIFICATIONS.

5) Retract automatic tensioner rod into tensioner housing by placing tensioner assembly in a soft-faced vise. Push rod back into automatic tensioner in small increments until both rod and housing holes are aligned. *See Fig. 6.* Install a .055" (1.40 mm) diameter wire into holes.

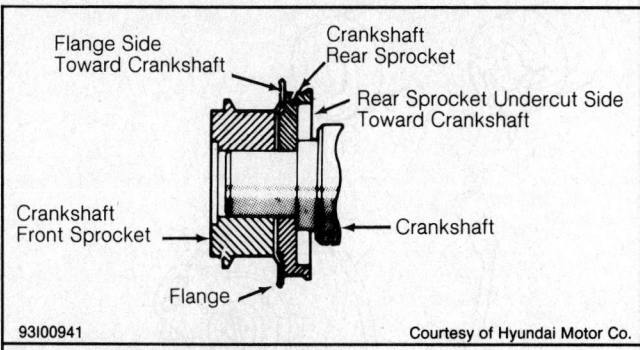

Fig. 5: *Installing Crankshaft Sprockets*

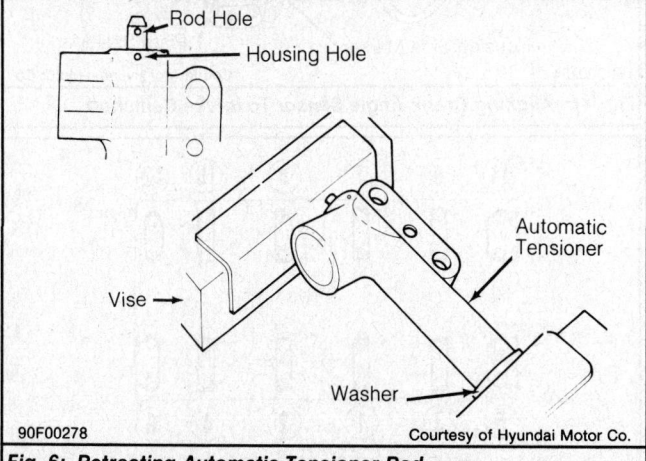

Fig. 6: *Retracting Automatic Tensioner Rod*

6) Remove automatic tensioner from vise with wire attached. Install tensioner and arm. Install tensioner pulley on tensioner arm. Ensure pin holes of tensioner pulley shaft are left of pulley center bolt. Tighten center bolt.

7) Rotate camshaft sprockets so dowel pins face upward and timing marks on sprockets align. *See Fig. 2.* Outer marks on sprockets should be aligned with cylinder head surface.

8) Align crankshaft sprocket timing marks and oil pump sprocket timing marks. *See Fig. 2.* Install timing belt around tensioner pulley and crankshaft sprocket. Hold timing belt on tensioner pulley using left hand. Pulling belt with right hand, install belt around oil pump sprocket.

9) Install belt around idler pulley. Align timing mark on exhaust camshaft sprocket with top of cylinder head. Pulling belt with both hands, install it around exhaust camshaft sprocket.

10) Gently raise tensioner pulley so belt does not sag, and temporarily tighten center bolt. *See Fig. 7.*

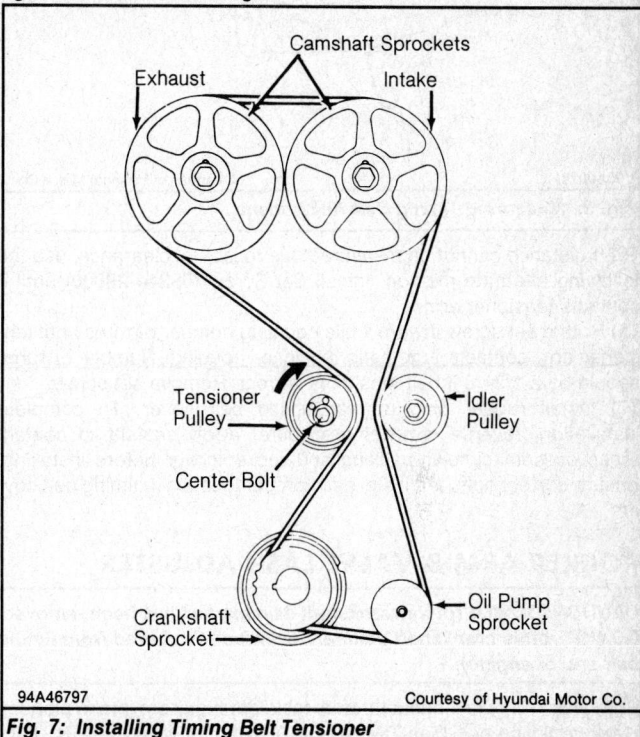

Fig. 7: *Installing Timing Belt Tensioner*

11) To adjust belt tension, rotate crankshaft 1/4 turn counterclockwise, and then rotate clockwise until No. 1 cylinder is at TDC. Ensure timing marks are aligned. Loosen center bolt on tensioner pulley. Note location of pin holes in tensioner pulley.

12) Using INCH-lb. torque wrench and Socket Wrench (09224-28100), apply a torque of 22-24 INCH lbs. (2.5-2.7 N.m) on tensioner pulley. *See Fig. 8.* With torque applied to tensioner pulley, tighten tensioner pulley center bolt to 31-40 ft. lbs. (42-54 N.m).

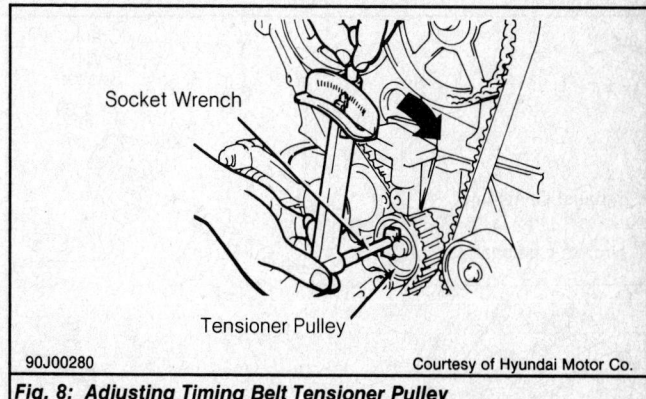

Fig. 8: *Adjusting Timing Belt Tensioner Pulley*

13) Install Set Screw (09244-28000) in left engine support bracket until set screw end contacts tensioner arm. Rotate set screw further until wire can be removed from automatic tensioner. *See Fig. 9.* Remove set screw.

14) Rotate crankshaft clockwise 2 complete revolutions, and allow to remain in this position for about 15 minutes. Measure distance between tensioner arm and automatic tensioner body. Distance should be .15-.18" (3.8-4.5 mm). If distance can be measured and is okay, go to step **17).**

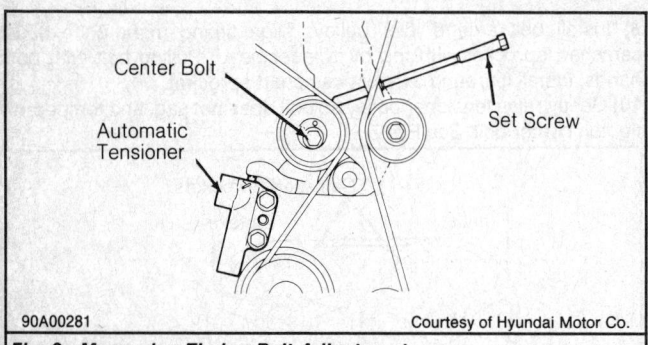

Fig. 9: Measuring Timing Belt Adjustment

15) If distance cannot be measured due to lack of clearance, use the following alternate method. Install Set Screw (09244-28000) until it contacts tensioner arm.

16) Rotate set screw inward while counting number of turns until tensioner arm contacts automatic tensioner housing. Number of turns should be 2 1/2 - 3 if belt tension is correct. Remove set screw.

17) Install rubber plug in rear timing belt cover. To complete installation, reverse removal procedure. Apply sealant to contact areas on semi-circular packing and rocker cover before installing. Ensure correct bolts are installed in proper location in timing belt covers.

ROCKER ARM & VALVE LASH ADJUSTER

CAUTION: DO NOT rotate crankshaft if timing belt has been removed. DO NOT rotate crankshaft counterclockwise (as viewed from timing belt end of engine).

Removal – **1)** Disconnect throttle cable bracket from intake plenum. Remove timing belt. See TIMING BELT under REMOVAL & INSTALLATION.

2) Remove crank angle sensor. *See Fig. 10*. Secure exhaust camshaft at hexagonal area using wrench, and remove sprocket bolt and sprocket. Repeat procedure for intake cam. Uniformly loosen front camshaft bearing cap bolts in 3 steps. Remove caps and seals.

3) Repeat procedure for remaining camshaft bearing cap bolts. Remove rear bearing caps last. Remove remaining camshaft bearing caps. Remove intake and exhaust camshafts. Remove rocker arms and lash adjusters from cylinder head.

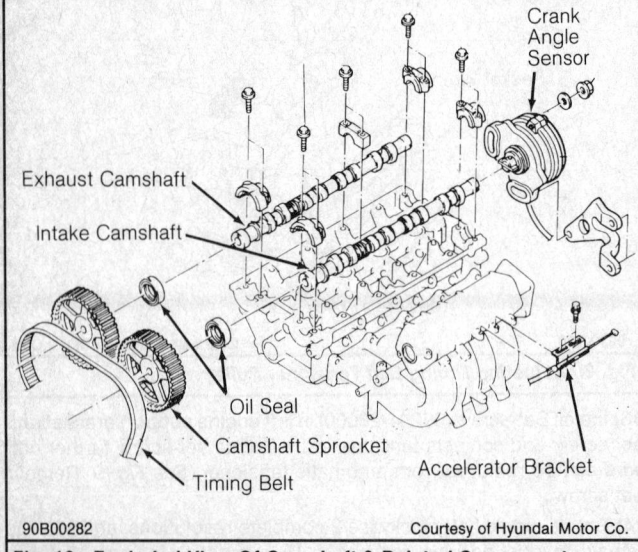

Fig. 10: Exploded View Of Camshaft & Related Components

Inspection – Check rocker arm friction surfaces for wear and damage. Check rocker arm rollers for smooth rotation. Check camshaft journal diameter and lobe height. Replace camshaft if journal diameter and lobe height are not within specification. See CAMSHAFT table under ENGINE SPECIFICATIONS.

Installation – **1)** If new camshafts are being installed, check for smooth rotation by installing camshaft in cylinder head without rocker arms. Lubricate journals, and install bearing caps. New camshafts should turn easily by hand. If camshafts are okay, remove bearing caps and camshafts.

2) Install lash adjusters and rocker arms on cylinder head. Lubricate camshaft lobes and bearing journals. Install camshafts in cylinder head with dowel pins at 12 o'clock position. Note intake camshaft is notched at rear. *See Fig. 11*.

3) Install camshaft bearing cap bolts in original location, and tighten in sequence in 2-3 steps. *See Fig. 12*. See TORQUE SPECIFICATIONS.

4) Lubricate inside diameter of camshaft oil seal. Using Seal Installer (09221-21000 and 09221-21100), install camshaft oil seal. To complete installation, reverse removal procedure.

CAUTION: Install crank angle sensor so mark on housing aligns with notch on plate; otherwise, incorrect fuel and ignition timing will result. See Fig. 11.

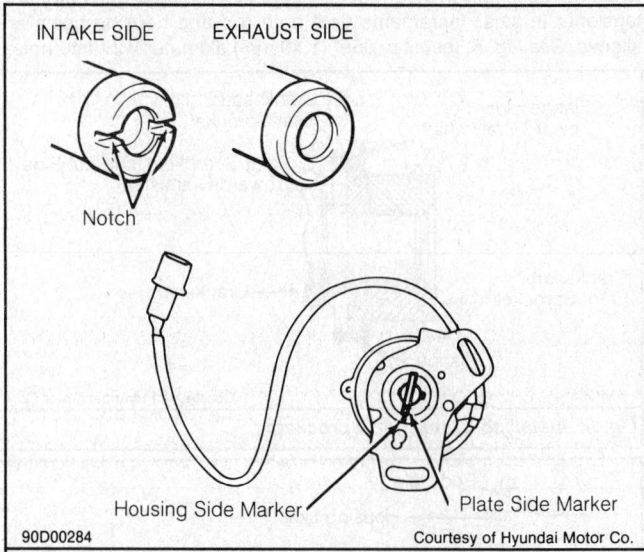

Fig. 11: Aligning Crank Angle Sensor To Intake Camshaft

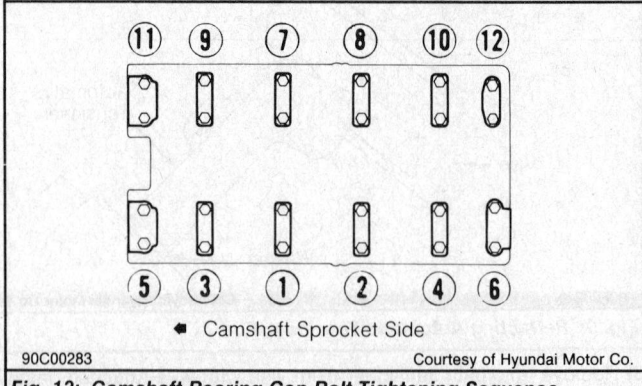

Fig. 12: Camshaft Bearing Cap Bolt Tightening Sequence

CAMSHAFT

NOTE: For removal and installation of camshaft, see ROCKER ARM & VALVE LASH ADJUSTER under REMOVAL & INSTALLATION.

SILENT SHAFTS & BEARINGS

Removal – Remove front cover and oil pump. See OIL PUMP & FRONT COVER under ENGINE OILING. Remove silent shafts from cylinder block.

NOTE: *Rear bearing(s) cannot be removed unless front bearings have been removed from block.*

Inspection – 1) Inspect silent shaft and bearings for damage. Ensure silent shaft journal O.D. (Outside Diameter) and oil clearance is within specification. See SILENT SHAFT SPECIFICATIONS table. Replace components if not within specification.

2) If bearings need replacing, use indicated puller. See SILENT SHAFT BEARING REMOVAL & INSTALLATION table.

NOTE: *Install rear bearings before installing front bearings.*

Installation – 1) Coat bearing outer area with engine oil before installing. Mount rear silent shaft bearing on indicated installer. See SILENT SHAFT BEARING REMOVAL & INSTALLATION table.

2) Ensure oil hole in bearing aligns with oil hole in cylinder block. Note left rear bearing does not have oil hole. Install rear bearings in cylinder block.

3) Repeat procedure for front bearings. Install balance shafts in original location. To complete installation, reverse removal procedure.

SILENT SHAFT SPECIFICATIONS

Application	In. (mm)
Left Silent Shaft	
Journal O.D.	
Front	.7270-.7276 (18.467-18.480)
Rear	1.6126-1.6132 (40.959-40.975)
Oil Clearance	
Front Journal	.0008-.0021 (.020-.054)
Rear Journal	.0017-.0033 (.042-.083)
Right Silent Shaft	
Journal O.D.	
Front	1.6519-1.6526 (41.959-41.975)
Rear	1.6122-1.6129 (40.951-40.967)
Oil Clearance	
Front Journal	.0008-.0024 (.020-.061)
Rear Journal	.0020-.0036 (.050-.091)

SILENT SHAFT BEARING REMOVAL & INSTALLATION

Application	Tool No.
Installation	
Installer	09212-32200
Left Rear Bearing Guide Plate	09212-32300
Removal	
Front Bearing Puller	09212-32000
Rear Bearing Puller	09212-32100
Left Rear Bearing Guide Plate	09212-32300

REAR CRANKSHAFT OIL SEAL

Removal – 1) Remove transaxle. For A/T vehicles, see TRANSMISSION REMOVAL & INSTALLATION article in TRANSMISSION SERVICING. For M/T vehicles, see appropriate article in CLUTCHES.

2) Remove flywheel or drive plate. Remove rear main oil seal case and gasket from rear of cylinder block. Remove oil separator and oil seal from seal case.

Installation – 1) To install, coat seal lip with oil. Using Seal Installer (09231-21000), install seal in seal case until it bottoms.

2) Install oil separator in seal case, with hole of separator at bottom of seal case (toward oil pan). Install seal case and gasket. Install flywheel or drive plate. To complete installation, reverse removal procedure.

WATER PUMP

CAUTION: *Note length and location of bolts during removal. Different length bolts are used and must be installed in original location.*

Removal – Drain cooling system. Remove necessary coolant hoses. Remove timing belt. See TIMING BELT under REMOVAL & INSTALLATION. Remove water pump mounting bolts. Note bolt length and location. Remove water pump.

Installation – To install, reverse removal procedure using NEW gasket and "O" ring. Install "O" ring on coolant pipe, and apply water to "O" ring. DO NOT apply grease or oil to "O" ring. Ensure bolts are installed in original location.

OIL PAN

Removal – Drain engine oil. Disconnect exhaust pipe at manifold (if necessary). Remove oil pan bolts. Using gasket cutter, cut gasket along sealing surface of cylinder block. Remove oil pan and gasket.

Installation – To install, apply sealant to oil pan flange at timing chain case and rear seal case areas. Install oil pan and gaskets. To complete installation, reverse removal procedure. Tighten bolts to specification. See TORQUE SPECIFICATIONS.

OVERHAUL

CYLINDER HEAD

Cylinder Head – Inspect cylinder head for warpage at deck surface. Resurface cylinder head if warpage exceeds specification. See CYLINDER HEAD table under ENGINE SPECIFICATIONS.

Valve Springs – Inspect valve spring free length. Also inspect valve spring for out-of-square and proper installed height. Replace valve spring if not within specification. See VALVES & VALVE SPRINGS table under ENGINE SPECIFICATIONS. Installed height of spring is measured between spring seat and valve retainer. Install all valve springs with painted area toward rocker arm.

Valve Stem Oil Seals – DO NOT reuse oil seals. Install valve spring seat before installing oil seals. To provide proper positioning of oil seal, install NEW oil seals using Valve Seal Installer (09222-28200).

Valve Guides – Ensure valve stem diameter is within specification. Check valve stem clearance. Clearance should be within specification. See VALVES & VALVE SPRINGS and CYLINDER HEAD tables under ENGINE SPECIFICATIONS. If clearance exceeds service limits, replace valve guide with an oversized valve guide.

Valves – Ensure valve stem diameter and margin are within specification. See VALVES & VALVE SPRINGS table under ENGINE SPECIFICATIONS.

VALVE TRAIN

Rocker Arms – For reassembly reference, note location and order of assembly for all components. Inspect components for wear and damage. Check rollers for smooth operation. Install components in original location when reassembling.

Lash Adjusters – Before installing lash adjuster, submerge lash adjuster in diesel fuel. Use a small wire to hold down internal check valve. Pump plunger up and down 4 or 5 times to bleed air from lash adjuster.

CYLINDER BLOCK ASSEMBLY

Piston & Rod Assembly – 1) Mark piston and rod assembly with corresponding cylinder number before removing. Center piston pin in piston. Measure and record piston pin installation depth. Use Piston Pin Removal & Installation Set (09234-33001) with hydraulic press to remove piston pin.

2) Piston pin should be easily pushed into piston. If looseness or resistance is encountered, replace piston and pin as a set. Check connecting rod for damage and excessive bend and twist. See CONNECTING RODS table under ENGINE SPECIFICATIONS.

3) Position piston, piston pin and rod on press. Ensure front mark on piston will face timing belt side of engine when installed. Using piston pin removal and installation set, install piston pin into piston and rod to depth recorded in step 1). Ensure piston pin is centered in rod and piston.

4) Press load should be 1653-3858 lbs. (750-1750 kg). DO NOT exceed 5000 lbs. (2268 kg). If press load exceeds specification, replace piston pin and/or connecting rod.

Fitting Pistons – 1) Measure piston skirt diameter at 90-degree angle to piston pin. If piston diameter is not within specification, replace piston. See PISTONS, PINS & RINGS table under ENGINE SPECIFICATIONS.

2) Measure cylinder bore diameter at 3 places: .47" (12 mm) from top of bore, .47" (12 mm) from bottom of bore and near center of bore. If cylinder bore diameter or taper is not within specification, machine cylinder bore.

3) If piston-to-cylinder bore clearance is not within specification, replace piston and/or machine cylinder bore.

Piston Rings – Ensure ring end gap and side clearance are within specification. See PISTONS, PINS & RINGS table under ENGINE SPECIFICATIONS. DO NOT use a ring expander to install oil ring side rails. Properly position ring end gaps around circumference of piston before installing. *See Fig. 13.*

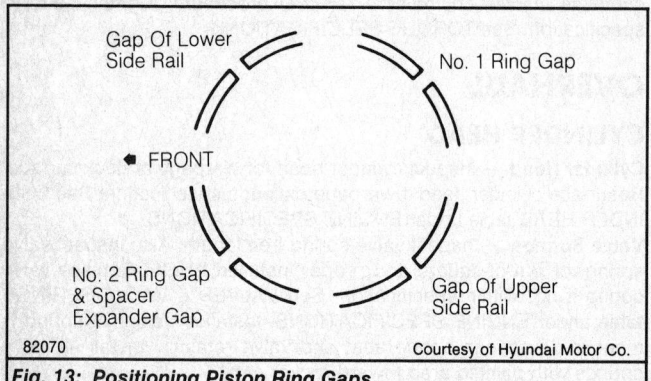

Fig. 13: Positioning Piston Ring Gaps

Rod Bearings – Note position of connecting rod in relation to bearing cap before removing. Ensure bearing oil clearance and side play are within specification. See CRANKSHAFT, MAIN & CONNECTING ROD BEARINGS and CONNECTING RODS tables under ENGINE SPECIFICATIONS.

Crankshaft & Main Bearings – **1)** Check diameter of crankshaft main bearing journals and connecting rod bearing journals. Check journals for taper and out-of-round. Check crankshaft end play. See CRANKSHAFT, MAIN & CONNECTING ROD BEARINGS table under ENGINE SPECIFICATIONS.

2) Tighten main bearing caps (in 2 steps) to specification, starting at center and working outward. See TORQUE SPECIFICATIONS.

Thrust Bearing – Replace thrust bearing if crankshaft end play is not within specification. See CRANKSHAFT, MAIN & CONNECTING ROD BEARINGS table under ENGINE SPECIFICATIONS.

Cylinder Block – **1)** Check cylinder block head surface warpage. If warpage exceeds specification, machine surface. See CYLINDER BLOCK table under ENGINE SPECIFICATIONS. DO NOT remove more than a combined total .008" (.20 mm) material from original surfaces of cylinder head or cylinder block.

2) Check cylinder bore wear and taper. Measure cylinder bore diameter at 3 places: .47" (12 mm) from top of bore, .47" (12 mm) from bottom of bore and near center of bore. If cylinder bore diameter or taper is not within specification, machine cylinder bore. See CYLINDER BLOCK table under ENGINE SPECIFICATIONS.

ENGINE OILING

ENGINE LUBRICATION SYSTEM

Oil pressure is provided by a timing belt-driven oil pump mounted in front cover. Pressure relief valve, located in oil filter bracket, is not adjustable. *See Fig. 14.*

Crankcase Oil Capacity – During oil change 3.25 qts. (3.7L) can be added (including oil filter).

Oil Pressure – Oil pressure should be at least 11.4 psi (.80 kg/cm²) at curb idle with an oil temperature of 167-194°F (75-90°C).

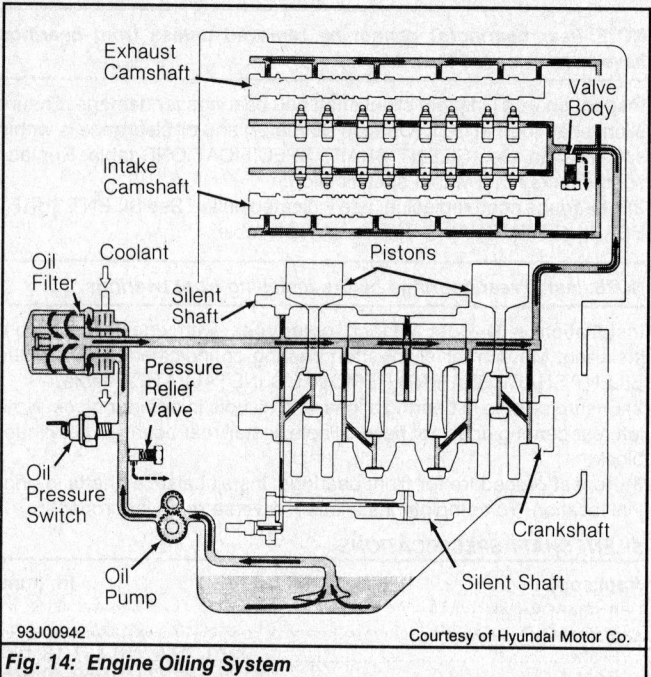

Fig. 14: Engine Oiling System

OIL PUMP & FRONT COVER

Removal – **1)** Remove timing belt and sprockets. See TIMING BELT under REMOVAL & INSTALLATION. Remove oil pan. See OIL PAN under REMOVAL & INSTALLATION. Remove oil filter. Using Socket (09260-32000), remove oil pressure switch.

2) Remove oil pressure gauge sending unit. Remove oil pick-up tube. Remove oil filter bracket and gasket.

3) Remove plug, gasket, spring and relief plunger. Using Plug Cap Wrench (09213-33000), remove plug cap and "O" ring from front cover.

4) Remove plug from side of cylinder block, and install a .31" (8.0 mm) diameter Phillips screwdriver to hold left silent shaft. *See Fig. 4.* Remove oil pump driven gear-to-silent shaft bolt.

5) Remove front cover and gasket from cylinder block. Remove silent shaft and crankshaft oil seals from front cover. Remove oil pump cover. Note timing marks on oil pump gears, and remove gears from front cover.

Inspection – **1)** Inspect components for damage. Install oil pump gears in front cover. Using feeler gauge, measure gear-to-front cover clearance between tips of teeth on each gear and front cover.

2) Place straightedge across front cover above oil pump gears. Using feeler gauge, check gear side clearance between straightedge and both oil pump gears. Check for ridge on oil pump cover in gear operating area.

3) Ensure relief plunger slides freely in bore. Check free length and spring pressure of relief plunger spring. Replace components if not within specification. See OIL PUMP SPECIFICATIONS table.

Installation – **1)** Lubricate oil pump gears with engine oil, and install. Ensure timing marks are aligned. Install oil pump cover, and tighten bolts to specification. See TORQUE SPECIFICATIONS.

2) If crankshaft oil seal was removed, use Seal Installer (0914-32000) to install seal in front cover. Use a socket of proper diameter to install silent shaft oil seals.

3) Position Oil Seal Guide (09214-32100) over front of crankshaft. Lubricate crankshaft oil seal and oil seal guide with engine oil. Install front cover with NEW gasket, and temporarily tighten bolts. Install oil filter bracket. Ensure bolts of appropriate length are installed.

4) To complete installation, reverse removal procedure. Install plug cap using NEW "O" ring, and tighten to specification. Apply thread sealant to oil pressure switch threads before installing. Tighten all bolts to specification. See TORQUE SPECIFICATIONS.

OIL PUMP SPECIFICATIONS

Application	Specification
Gear Side Clearance	
Drive Gear	
Standard	.0031-.0055" (.080-.140 mm)
Limit	.0098" (.250 mm)
Driven Gear	
Standard	.0024-.0047" (.060-.120 mm)
Limit	.0098" (.250 mm)
Gear-To-Front Cover Clearance	
Drive Gear	
Standard	.0063-.0083" (.160-.210 mm)
Limit	.0098" (.250 mm)
Driven Gear	
Standard	.0051-.0071" (.130-.180 mm)
Limit	.0098" (.250 mm)
Relief Plunger Spring	
Free Length	1.835" (46.60 mm)
Spring Pressure	13.4 lbs. @ 1.579" (6.1 kg @ 40.10 mm)

TORQUE SPECIFICATIONS
TORQUE SPECIFICATIONS

Application	Ft. Lbs. (N.m)
A/C Tensioner Pulley Bracket Bolt	17-20 (23-27)
Auto Tensioner Bolt	15-20 (20-27)
Camshaft Bearing Cap Bolt [1]	14-15 (19-20)
Camshaft Sprocket Bolt	59-74 (80-100)
Connecting Rod Nut	37-39 (50-53)
Crankshaft Pulley Bolt	15-22 (20-30)
Crankshaft Sprocket Bolt	81-96 (110-130)
Cylinder Head Bolt [2]	65-74 (90-100)
Engine Support Bracket Bolt	
Front	37-52 (50-70)
Left	22-31 (30-42)
Exhaust Manifold Nut	18-22 (25-30)
Exhaust Pipe-To-Manifold Nut	22-30 (30-40)
Flywheel/Drive Plate Bolt	96-103 (130-140)
Front Cover Bolt	11-13 (15-18)
Front Tensioner Pulley Bolt	32-41 (43-55)
Idler Pulley Bolt	25-31 (34-42)
Intake Manifold Bolt/Nut	
8-mm	11-15 (15-20)
10-mm	22-31 (30-42)
Intake Manifold Stay Bolt	18-22 (25-30)
Main Bearing Cap Bolt	48-52 (65-70)
Oil Filter Bracket Bolt	11-16 (15-22)
Oil Pump Cover Bolt	11-13 (15-18)
Oil Pump Driven Gear Bolt	25-30 (34-40)
Oil Pump Pick-Up Tube Bolt	11-16 (15-22)
Oil Pump Sprocket Nut	37-44 (50-60)
Oxygen Sensor	30-37 (40-50)
Plug Cap	15-20 (20-27)
Rear Tensioner Retaining Bolt	11-16 (15-22)
Rocker Arm Assembly Bolts	14-15 (19-20)
Silent Shaft Sprocket Bolt	32-36 (43-49)
Throttle Body Bolt	11-16 (15-22)
Timing Belt Rear Left Cover Bolt	22-30 (30-42)
Water Pump Mounting Bolt	
Except 8 x 65 mm	11 (15)
8 x 65 mm	15-20 (20-27)

[1] - Tighten bolts in sequence. See Fig. 12.
[2] - Tighten bolts in sequence. See Fig. 1.

TORQUE SPECIFICATIONS (Cont.)

Application	INCH Lbs. (N.m)
Crankshaft Position Sensor Nut	89-106 (10-12)
Distributor Nut	89-106 (10-12)
Fuel Rail Bolt	89-106 (10-12)
Oil Pan Bolt	53-71 (6-8)
Oil Pressure Switch	71-106 (8-12)
Rear Crankshaft Oil Seal Case Bolt	89-106 (10-12)
Timing Belt Cover Bolt	89-106 (10-12)
Valve Body Bolt	89-106 (10-12)
Valve Cover Bolt	22-31 (2.5-3.5)
Water Pump Pulley Bolt	71-89 (8-10)

[1] - Tighten bolts in sequence. See Fig. 12.
[2] - Tighten bolts in sequence. See Fig. 1.

ENGINE SPECIFICATIONS

GENERAL SPECIFICATIONS

Application	Specification
Displacement	122 Cu. In. (2.0L)
Bore	3.35" (85.0 mm)
Stroke	3.46" (88.0 mm)
Compression Ratio	9.0:1
Fuel System	MFI
Horsepower @ RPM	128 @ 6000
Torque Ft. Lbs. @ RPM	121 @ 5000

CRANKSHAFT, MAIN & CONNECTING ROD BEARINGS

Application	In. (mm)
Crankshaft End Play	
Standard	.002-.007 (.05-.18)
Wear Limit	.010 (.25)
Main Bearings	
Journal Diameter	2.2433-2.2439 (56.980-56.995)
Journal Out-Of-Round	.0006 (.015)
Journal Taper	.0002 (.005)
Oil Clearance	
Standard	.0008-.0020 (.020-.050)
Wear Limit	.004 (.10)
Connecting Rod Bearings	
Journal Diameter	1.7709-1.7715 (44.980-44.995)
Journal Out-Of-Round	.0006 (.015)
Journal Taper	.0002 (.005)
Oil Clearance	
Standard	.0008-.0020 (.020-.050)
Wear Limit	.004 (.10)

CONNECTING RODS

Application	In. (mm)
Maximum Bend	.002 Per 3.937 (.05 Per 100.00)
Maximum Twist	.004 Per 3.937 (.10 Per 100.00)
Side Play	
Standard	.004-.010 (.10-.25)
Wear Limit	.016 (.40)

PISTONS, PINS & RINGS

Application	In. (mm)
Pistons	
Clearance	.0004-.0012 (.010-.030)
Diameter	3.3453-3.3465 (84.97-85.00)
Pins	
Rod Fit	[1]
Rings	
No. 1	
End Gap	
Standard	.0098-.0177 (.250-.450)
Wear Limit	.031 (.80)
Side Clearance	
Standard	.0012-.0028 (.030-.070)
Wear Limit	.004 (.10)
No. 2	
End Gap	
Standard	.0138-.0197 (.350-.500)
Wear Limit	.031 (.80)
Side Clearance	
Standard	.0012-.0028 (.030-.070)
Wear Limit	.004 (.10)
No. 3 (Oil)	
End Gap	
Standard	.0079-.0276 (.200-.700)
Wear Limit	.040 (1.0)

[1] – Press fit with load of 1653-3858 lbs. (750-1750 kg).

CYLINDER BLOCK

Application	In. (mm)
Cylinder Bore	
Standard Diameter	3.3465-3.3476 (85.000-85.030)
Maximum Taper	.0004 (.010)
Maximum Out-Of-Round	.0004 (.010)
Deck Height	11.18 (284)
Maximum Deck Warpage	[1] .002 (.05)

[1] – Combined maximum total grind limit of cylinder head and cylinder block is .008" (.20 mm).

VALVES & VALVE SPRINGS

Application	Specification
Intake Valves	
Face Angle	45-45.5°
Margin	
Standard	.040" (1.00 mm)
Wear Limit	.028" (.70 mm)
Stem Diameter	.2585-.2591" (6.565-6.580 mm)
Valve Length	4.311" (109.50 mm)
Exhaust Valves	
Face Angle	45-45.5°
Margin	
Standard	.059" (1.50 mm)
Wear Limit	.040" (1.00 mm)
Stem Diameter	.2571-.2579" (6.53-6.55 mm)
Valve Length	4.319" (109.70 mm)
Valve Springs	
Free Length	1.862-1.902" (47.30-48.31 mm)
Out-Of-Square	
Standard	Less Than 1.5°
Wear Limit	4°

CYLINDER HEAD

Application	Specification
Maximum Warpage	[1] .0020" (.050 mm)
Valve Seats	
Intake Valve	
Seat Angle	45°
Seat Width	.035-.051" (.90-1.30 mm)
Exhaust Valve	
Seat Angle	45°
Seat Width	.035-.051" (.90-1.30 mm)
Valve Guides	
Intake Valve	
Guide Length	1.791" (45.50 mm)
Valve Stem-To-Guide Oil Clearance	
Standard	.0008-.0019" (.020-.047 mm)
Wear Limit	.004" (.10 mm)
Exhaust Valve	
Guide Length	1.988" (50.50 mm)
Valve Stem-To-Guide Oil Clearance	
Standard	.0020-.0033" (.050-.085 mm)
Wear Limit	.006" (.15 mm)

[1] – Combined maximum total grind limit of cylinder head and cylinder block is .008" (.20 mm).

CAMSHAFT

Application	In. (mm)
End Play	.004-.008 (.10-.20)
Journal Diameter	1.02 (26.0)
Lobe Height	
Intake	1.3974 (35.493)
Limit	1.3777 (34.993)
Exhaust	1.3858 (35.20)
Limit	1.3661 (34.7)
Oil Clearance	.0020-.0035 (.05-.09)

Sonata

NOTE: For repair procedures not covered in this article, see ENGINE OVERHAUL PROCEDURES article in GENERAL INFORMATION.

ENGINE IDENTIFICATION

The 8th character in Vehicle Identification Number (VIN) identifies engine type. Engine identification code is stamped at top right front side of cylinder block.

ENGINE IDENTIFICATION CODE

Application	Engine Code	VIN Code
3.0L	¹ G6ATR	T

¹ – Third character is a development order number and may not be the same for all engines.

ADJUSTMENTS

VALVE CLEARANCE ADJUSTMENT

Intake & Exhaust Valves – Hydraulic valve lash adjusters are used and valve adjustment is unnecessary.

REMOVAL & INSTALLATION

NOTE: For reassembly reference, label all electrical connectors, vacuum hoses and fuel lines before removal. Also place mating marks on engine hood and other major assemblies before removal.

FUEL PRESSURE RELEASE

WARNING: Always relieve fuel pressure before disconnecting any fuel injection-related component. DO NOT allow fuel to contact engine or electrical components.

Disconnect fuel pump harness connector at rear of fuel tank. Start engine. After engine stalls, turn ignition switch to OFF position. Disconnect negative battery cable.

ENGINE

Removal – **1)** Release fuel pressure. See FUEL PRESSURE RELEASE. Label and disconnect fuel lines and vapor hoses from engine. Drain cooling system, engine oil and transaxle oil.
2) Disconnect electrical connectors from oxygen sensor, A/C compressor, alternator and oil pressure switch. Disconnect throttle cables. Disconnect power steering pump, leaving hoses attached and secure with wire away from work area.
3) Label, disconnect and plug transaxle cooler lines. Remove upper and lower radiator hoses from engine. Remove radiator assembly with hoses. Disconnect heater hoses at engine side. Remove transaxle control cable.
4) Raise and support vehicle. Remove oil pan shield. Disconnect front exhaust pipe at manifold and suspend pipe from bottom of vehicle with wire. Remove lower ball joint bolts and stabilizer bar where bar is mounted to lower control arm. Remove axle shafts from transaxle. Plug holes in transaxle to prevent contamination.

NOTE: Replace axle shaft retainer rings whenever axle shafts are removed from transaxle.

5) Attach engine hoist to engine, and raise engine just enough to relieve load on engine mounts. Remove front roll stopper, damper and rear roll stopper. Remove engine mount bolts. Remove bolts and nuts securing engine mount bracket to body. Raise engine a few inches.

NOTE: Ensure all cables, hoses, harnesses, connectors, etc. are disconnected from engine.

6) Remove blind plugs from inside right front fender apron. Remove transaxle mounting bracket bolts. Remove left mount insulator bolt. Direct transaxle side downward and lift assembly out of vehicle.
Installation – To install, reverse removal procedure. Ensure throttle, transaxle cables and drive belts are properly adjusted. Tighten mounting bolts and nuts to specification with weight of engine on mounts. See TORQUE SPECIFICATIONS. Replace all fluids and check gauges for correct operation.

INTAKE MANIFOLD

CAUTION: Release fuel pressure before disconnecting fuel lines.

Removal & Installation – **1)** Release fuel pressure. See FUEL PRESSURE RELEASE. Drain cooling system. Label and disconnect all wiring, hoses, cables and brackets interfering with intake plenum and manifold removal.
2) Remove intake plenum. Remove fuel rail with injectors attached. Remove intake manifold-to-cylinder head attaching bolts and remove intake manifold. To install, reverse removal procedure using NEW gaskets.

EXHAUST MANIFOLD

Removal & Installation – **1)** Disconnect negative battery cable. Label and disconnect all wiring, hoses, cables and brackets interfering with exhaust manifold removal. Remove exhaust manifold heat shield.
2) Disconnect exhaust pipe from exhaust manifold. Remove exhaust manifold-to-cylinder head attaching bolts and exhaust manifold. To install, reverse removal procedure using NEW gaskets.

CYLINDER HEAD

CAUTION: Release fuel pressure before disconnecting fuel lines.

Removal – **1)** Drain cooling system. Release fuel pressure. See FUEL PRESSURE RELEASE. Remove timing belt cover.
2) Turn crankshaft to TDC of No. 1 cylinder compression stroke by aligning marks on upper inner cover with mark on camshaft sprockets. *See Fig. 4.* Mark timing belt at timing mark on camshaft sprockets for reassembly.
3) Remove camshaft sprocket retaining bolt. Slide camshaft sprocket (with belt attached) off camshaft. DO NOT turn crankshaft. Ensure belt remains engaged with crankshaft. Remove distributor cap. Reference mark rotor to distributor position. Reference mark distributor to adapter position. Remove distributor and adapter.
4) Remove rocker cover. Loosen rocker arm retaining bolts in 2 or 3 passes. Using Lash Adjuster Retainer (09246-32000), secure lash adjusters. *See Fig. 5.* Remove rocker arm assembly and camshaft. See ROCKER ARM SHAFT ASSEMBLY under REMOVAL & INSTALLATION.
5) Label and disconnect wiring, hoses, linkages, cables and brackets interfering with cylinder head removal. Disconnect exhaust pipe. Remove intake air plenum and manifold. Loosen cylinder head bolts in 2 stages using proper sequence. *See Fig. 1.*
6) Remove cylinder head bolts. Remove cylinder head with exhaust manifold attached. Remove exhaust manifold from cylinder head (if necessary).

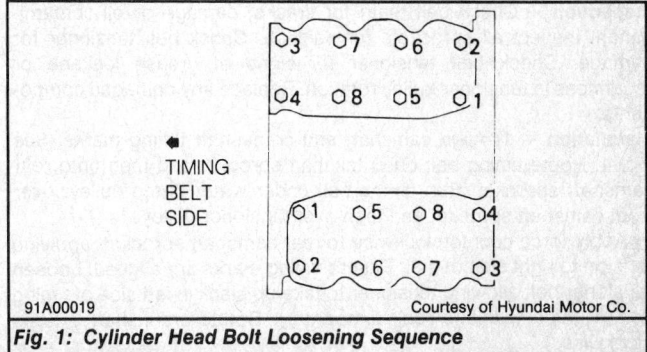

91A00019   Courtesy of Hyundai Motor Co.

Fig. 1: Cylinder Head Bolt Loosening Sequence

Installation – **1)** Install cylinder head using NEW gasket. Tighten cylinder head bolts in proper sequence. *See Fig. 2.*
2) Carefully remove Lash Adjuster Retainers (09246-32000). DO NOT allow lash adjusters to fall out. Tighten rocker shaft mounting bolts uniformly to 14-15 ft. lbs. (19-21 N.m). To complete installation, reverse removal procedure.

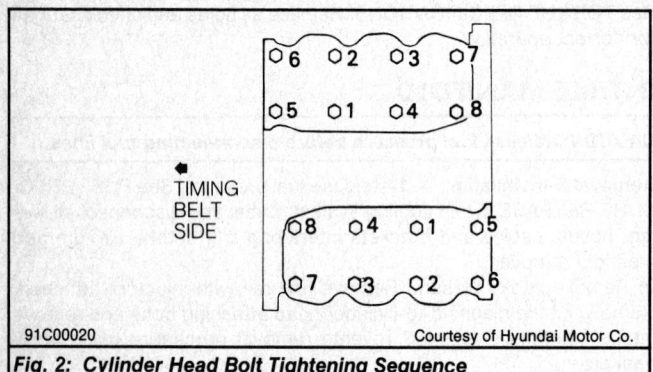

91C00020   Courtesy of Hyundai Motor Co.

Fig. 2: Cylinder Head Bolt Tightening Sequence

FRONT COVER OIL SEAL
See OIL PUMP under ENGINE OILING.

TIMING BELT

Removal – **1)** Remove all drive belts. Support oil pan with jack and block of wood. Remove power steering pump with hoses connected. Remove engine support bracket bolts in sequence. Slowly remove reamer bolt. *See Fig. 3.*

NOTE: Reamer bolt may sometimes become seized on engine support bracket. Remove reamer bolt carefully without damaging threads.

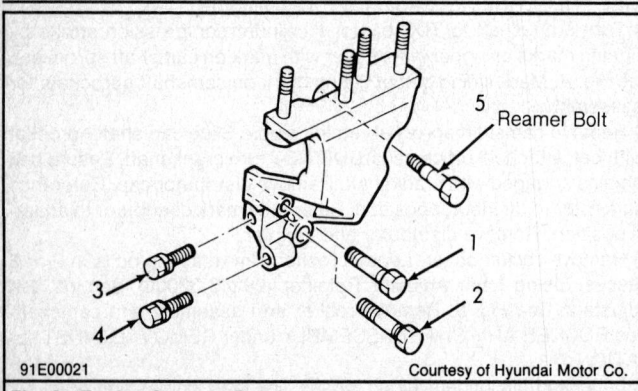

91E00021   Courtesy of Hyundai Motor Co.

Fig. 3: Engine Support Bolt Loosening & Tightening Sequence

2) Ensure engine is on No. 1 cylinder compression stroke and timing marks are aligned. Remove crankshaft pulley and timing belt covers. Loosen timing belt tensioner bolt and pivot tensioner counterclockwise; lock tensioner in retracted position. If reusing timing belt, mark direction of travel on belt. Remove timing belt.
Inspection – Check belt teeth for cracks, damage or oil contamination. Inspect all sprockets for damage. Check belt tensioner for damage. Check belt tensioner for signs of grease leakage or roughness in tensioner pulley rotation. Replace any damaged components.
Installation – **1)** Align camshaft and crankshaft timing marks. *See Fig. 4.* Route timing belt on crankshaft sprocket and then onto rear camshaft sprocket. Run timing belt under water pump pulley, over front camshaft sprocket and then over tensioner pulley.
2) Apply force counterclockwise to rear camshaft sprocket, applying tension to right side of belt. Ensure timing marks are aligned. Loosen tensioner bolt allowing tensioner to take up slack in left side of timing belt. Tighten tensioner bolt temporarily. Rotate crankshaft 2 turns clockwise.

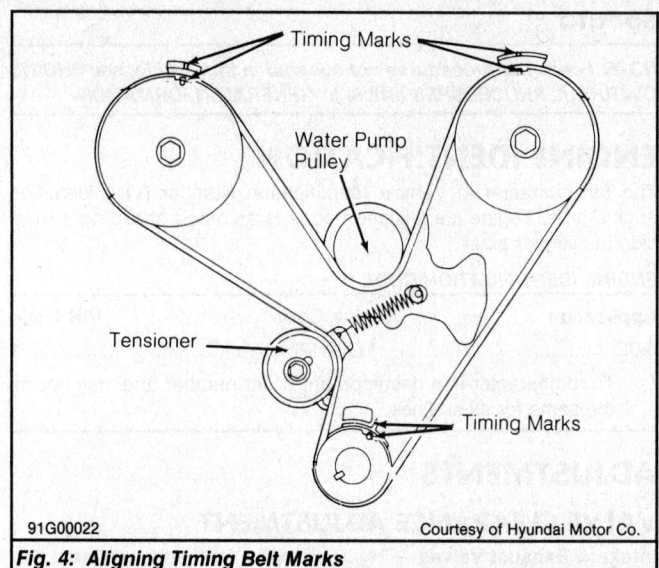

91G00022   Courtesy of Hyundai Motor Co.

Fig. 4: Aligning Timing Belt Marks

3) Realign timing marks. Loosen tensioner bolt, allowing tensioner to take up timing belt slack. Tighten tensioner bolt. Measure timing belt tension using belt tension gauge. For new belt, tension should be 57-84 lbs. (26-38 kg).
4) Install front timing belt cover. Install crankshaft pulley and tighten to specification. To complete installation, reverse removal procedure. Tighten nuts and bolts to specification. See TORQUE SPECIFICATIONS.

CAMSHAFT
See ROCKER ARM SHAFT ASSEMBLY.

ROCKER ARM SHAFT ASSEMBLY

Removal – **1)** Remove timing belt cover. Turn crankshaft so No. 1 piston is at TDC of compression stroke. Align timing marks on upper inner cover with mark on camshaft sprockets. *See Fig. 4.*
2) Make reassembly reference mark on timing belt in alignment with timing mark on camshaft sprockets. Remove camshaft sprocket retaining bolt. Slide camshaft sprocket (with belt attached) off camshaft. DO NOT turn crankshaft. Prevent belt from disengaging from crankshaft sprocket. Remove distributor cap. Reference mark rotor to distributor. Reference mark distributor to adapter. Remove distributor and adapter.
3) Remove rocker cover. Loosen rocker arm retaining bolts in 2 or 3 passes. Using Lash Adjuster Retainer (09246-32000), secure lash adjusters. *See Fig. 5.* Remove rocker arm assembly and camshaft.

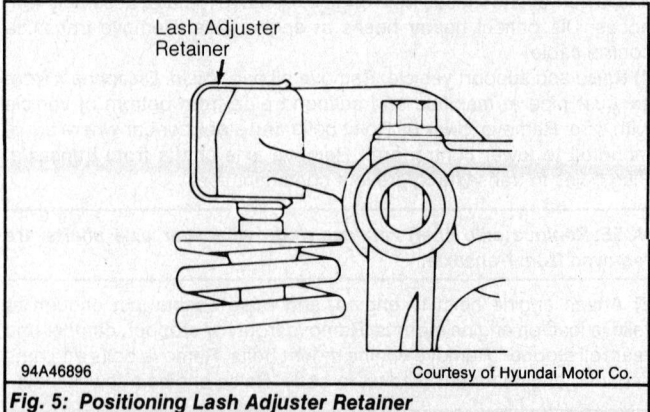

94A46896   Courtesy of Hyundai Motor Co.

Fig. 5: Positioning Lash Adjuster Retainer

Installation – **1)** Lubricate bearing journals and lobes of camshaft. Install camshaft into cylinder head. Insert lash adjusters into cam followers. Using Lash Adjuster Retainers (09246-32000), prevent adjusters from falling out during installation.

2) Apply a minimum amount of sealer to outside corners of front and rear camshaft bearing caps. Install rocker arm assembly to cylinder head so arrow mark on bearing caps face the same way as arrow mark on cylinder head. Tighten bearing cap bolts to 14-15 ft. lbs. (19-21 N.m). Remove Lash Adjuster Retainer (09246-32000) from lash adjuster. To complete installation, reverse removal procedure.

REAR CRANKSHAFT OIL SEAL

Removal – Remove flywheel or drive plate. Remove rear main oil seal case and gasket from rear of cylinder block. Remove oil separator and oil seal from seal case.
Installation – **1)** To install, coat seal lip with oil. Using Seal Installer (09231-33000), install seal in seal case until it bottoms.
2) Install oil separator in seal case with hole of separator at bottom of seal case. Install seal case and gasket. Tighten bolts to specification. See TORQUE SPECIFICATIONS. Install flywheel or drive plate. Tighten bolts to specification. To complete installation, reverse removal procedure.

WATER PUMP

Removal – Drain cooling system and disconnect battery. Remove necessary coolant hoses. Remove timing belt. See TIMING BELT under REMOVAL & INSTALLATION. Remove pump mounting bolts. Note bolt length and location for reassembly reference. Remove alternator brace and water pump.

NOTE: Note bolt length and location during removal. Different length bolts are used and must be installed in original location.

Installation – To install, reverse removal procedure using NEW gasket and "O" ring. Install "O" ring on coolant pipe, and then apply water to "O" ring. DO NOT apply grease or oil to "O" ring. Ensure bolts are installed in original location.

OIL PAN

Removal & Installation – Drain engine oil. Remove oil pan retaining bolts. Using gasket cutter, cut gasket along sealing surface of cylinder block. Remove oil pan and gasket. To install, clean gasket surfaces and apply sealant into groove of oil pan. To complete installation, reverse removal procedure.

OVERHAUL

CYLINDER HEAD

Cylinder Head – Check for cracks, damage and coolant leakage. Remove scales, sealing compound and carbon deposits. Clean oil passages, and blow compressed air through passages to ensure they are not clogged. Inspect cylinder head for warpage at deck surface. Resurface cylinder head if warpage exceeds specification. See CYLINDER HEAD table under ENGINE SPECIFICATIONS.
Valve Springs – Inspect valve spring free length, tension and installed height. Using a square, test squareness of each spring. Replace spring(s) if not within specification. See VALVES & VALVE SPRINGS table under ENGINE SPECIFICATIONS. Installed spring height is measured from spring seat to valve spring retainer. Install all valve springs with painted area toward rocker arm.
Valve Stem Oil Seals – Use Valve Seal Installer (09222-32100) for seal installation to properly position oil seal.
Valve Guides – **1)** Ensure valve stem diameter and valve stem clearance are within specification. See CYLINDER HEAD table under ENGINE SPECIFICATIONS.
2) If clearance exceeds service limits, replace valve guide. Remove valve guides toward bottom of cylinder head. Machine cylinder head valve guide bore to specification for oversized valve guide. See OVERSIZED VALVE GUIDE SPECIFICATIONS table.

OVERSIZED VALVE GUIDE SPECIFICATIONS

Size Mark	Guide Oversize In. (mm)	Cyl. Head Bore In. (mm)
5	.002 (.05)	.5140-.5145 (13.050-13.068)
25	.010 (.25)	.5217-.5224 (13.250-13.268)
50	.020 (.50)	.5315-.5322 (13.500-13.518)

3) Press NEW guides into cylinder head from top using Valve Guide Installer (09222-32200).
4) Intake valve guides are shorter than exhaust valve guides. DO NOT install valve guide with same diameter as guide removed. Check guide clearance with new valve and ream as necessary. Check valve seat contact.
Valve Seats – **1)** To replace valve seats, cut away old valve seat and remove. Machine cylinder head to proper dimension. See OVERSIZED VALVE SEAT SPECIFICATIONS table.

OVERSIZED VALVE SEAT SPECIFICATIONS

Size Mark	Seat Size In. (mm)	Cyl. Head Bore In. (mm)	Seat Height In. (mm)
Intake Valve			
30	.012 (.30)	1.7441-1.7451 (44.300-44.325)	.311-.319 (7.9-8.1)
60	.024 (.60)	1.7559-1.7569 (44.600-44.625)	.323-.331 (8.2-8.4)
Exhaust Valve			
30	.012 (.30)	1.5079-1.5089 (38.300-38.325)	.311-.319 (7.9-8.1)
60	.024 (.60)	1.5197-1.5207 (38.600-38.625)	.323-.331 (8.2-8.4)

2) Heat cylinder head to 482°F (250°C) and press replacement seat in cylinder head. Valve seat height should be within specification. Cut valve seat to proper angle and obtain correct seat width.
Valves – Inspect each valve for wear, damage and distortion of head and stem. If stem end is pitted or worn, resurface as necessary. This correction must be held to a minimum. Resurface valve face. If valve margin has decreased to less than service limit, replace valve. See VALVES & VALVE SPRINGS table under ENGINE SPECIFICATIONS.

VALVE TRAIN

Rocker Arm Shaft Assembly – **1)** Note location of all components for reassembly. Remove bolts from shaft assembly and remove components. Inspect components for wear or damage. Ensure oil passages are clear.
2) Install components in original position. See Fig. 6. Bearing caps No. 1 and 4 and caps No. 2 and 3 look alike. Check for proper stamped cap number. Ensure rocker arm shaft oil groove faces down and oil port faces up.

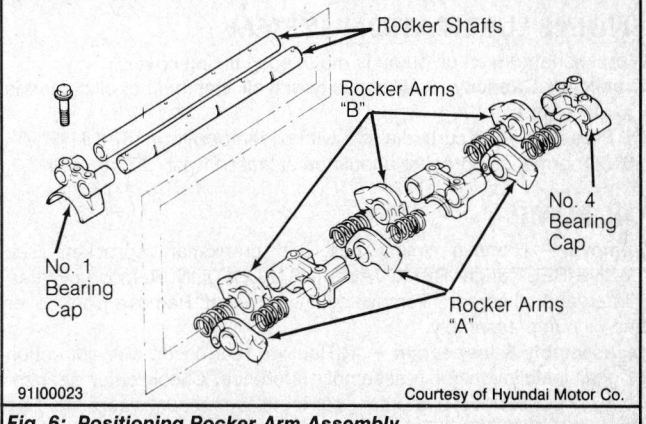

91I00023   Courtesy of Hyundai Motor Co.

Fig. 6: Positioning Rocker Arm Assembly

CYLINDER BLOCK ASSEMBLY

Piston & Rod Assembly – Piston should have factory mark to indicate front (timing belt side) of piston. If pistons are not marked, install piston according to valve cut-outs. Intake valve cut-outs are deeper than exhaust. Orient piston accordingly. Note direction of connecting rod installation on piston prior to removal.

Fitting Pistons & Rings – Ensure ring end gap and side clearance are within specifications. See PISTONS, PINS & RINGS table under ENGINE SPECIFICATIONS. Position ring gaps correctly prior to installation. *See Fig. 7.*

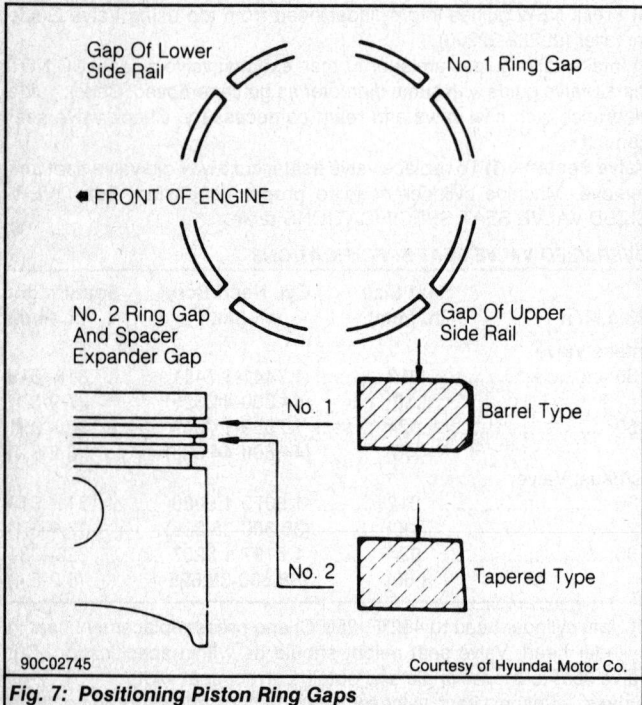

Fig. 7: Positioning Piston Ring Gaps

Piston Pin Replacement – Piston location must be noted before removing piston from connecting rod. Piston pin fit in connecting rod requires use of proper force during installation. See PISTONS, PINS & RINGS table under ENGINE SPECIFICATIONS.

Crankshaft & Main Bearings – Install main bearings with oil hole and groove on cylinder block side.

Thrust Bearing – Install thrust bearings in No. 3 main bearing cap with oil groove facing outward.

Cylinder Block – Visually inspect cylinder block for scores, rust and corrosion. Check for cracks or other defects. Repair or replace block if defective. Measure cylinder bore in 3 areas from top to bottom of bore, checking for taper and out-of-round.

ENGINE OILING

ENGINE LUBRICATION SYSTEM

A crankshaft driven oil pump is mounted in timing cover.

Crankcase Capacity – Oil capacity with oil filter (but not oil cooler) is 4.5 qts. (4.3L).

Oil Pressure – At curb idle and with oil temperature 167-194°F (75-90°C), normal oil pressure should be at least 11 psi (.77 kg/cm²).

OIL PUMP

Removal – Remove timing belt and crankshaft sprocket. See TIMING BELT under REMOVAL & INSTALLATION. Remove oil filter, oil pan and oil screen. Remove oil filter bracket. Remove front cover and oil pump assembly.

Disassembly & Inspection – **1)** Remove rear cover. Mark direction of gear installation for reassembly reference. Check outer gear-to-body (oil pump body) and outer gear tooth-to-crescent clearance. See OIL PUMP SPECIFICATIONS table.

2) Check inner gear-to-crescent clearance. Place straightedge across front cover housing and measure gear end play clearance between each gear and straightedge.

3) Check pressure relief valve for freedom of movement in bore and relief spring tension and free length. Replace components if not within specification.

OIL PUMP SPECIFICATIONS

Application	Specification
Gear-To-Crescent &	
Gear-To-Body Clearance	.0038-.0071" (.100-.181 mm)
End Play Clearance	.0016-.0037" (.040-.095 mm)
Relief Valve Spring	
Free Length	1.724" (43.80 mm)
Spring Pressure	8.2 lbs @ 1.579" (3.7 kg @ 40.10 mm)

Reassembly & Installation – **1)** Using Installer (09214-33000), install NEW seal into front cover. Install front cover using NEW gasket. Install oil filter bracket. Install proper length bolts and tighten to specification. See TORQUE SPECIFICATIONS. *See Fig. 8.*

2) Using plug cap wrench, install plug cap and tighten to specification. See TORQUE SPECIFICATIONS. To install remaining components, reverse removal procedure.

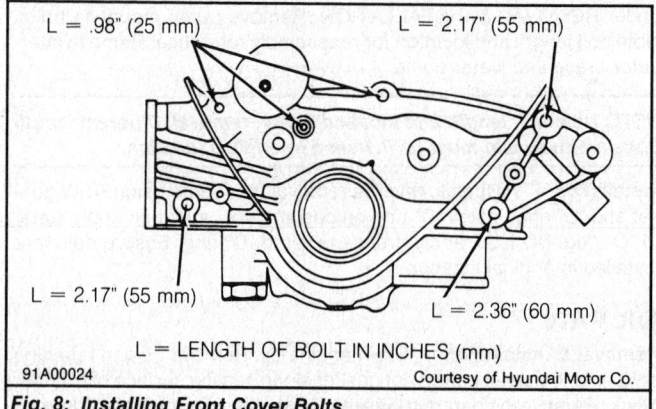

L = LENGTH OF BOLT IN INCHES (mm)

Fig. 8: Installing Front Cover Bolts

TORQUE SPECIFICATIONS

TORQUE SPECIFICATIONS

Application	Ft. Lbs. (N.m)
Automatic Tensioner Bolt	16-22 (22-30)
Camshaft Bearing Cap Bolts	14-15 (19-21)
Camshaft Sprocket Bolt	59-74 (80-100)
Connecting Rod Cap Nut	37-39 (50-53)
Crankshaft Sprocket Bolt	111-118 (150-160)
Cylinder Head Bolt (Cold)	77-85 (105-115)
Drive Plate-To-Crankshaft Bolt	54-57 (73-77)
Exhaust Manifold-To-Engine Bolt	11-16 (15-22)
Exhaust Pipe-To-Manifold Bolt	22-30 (30-40)
Front Case Bolt	9-11 (12-15)
Intake Manifold-To-Engine Bolt	11-15 (15-21)
Main Bearing Cap Bolt	55-63 (75-85)
Oil Pan Drain Plug	26-33 (35-45)
Oil Pump Relief Valve Plug	30-37 (40-50)
Oil Screen Bolt	11-15 (15-21)
Torque Converter-To-Drive Plate Bolt	34-39 (46-53)

	INCH Lbs. (N.m)
Delivery Pipe Bolt	89-106 (10-12)
Oil Pan Bolt	44-62 (5-7)
Oil Pressure Switch	71-106 (8-12)
Oil Pump Cover Screw	71-106 (8-12)
Rear Oil Seal Case Bolt	89-106 (10-12)
Rocker Cover Bolt	71-89 (8-10)
Timing Belt Cover Bolt	89-106 (10-12)

ENGINE SPECIFICATIONS

GENERAL SPECIFICATIONS

Application	Specification
Displacement	181 Cu. In. (3.0L)
Bore	3.587" (91.1 mm)
Stroke	2.992" (76.0 mm)
Compression Ratio	8.9:1
Fuel System	MFI
Horsepower @ RPM	142 @ 5000
Torque Ft. Lbs. @ RPM	168 @ 2500

CRANKSHAFT, MAIN & CONNECTING ROD BEARINGS

Application	In. (mm)
Crankshaft	
End Play	.002-.010 (.05-.25)
Main Bearings	
Journal Diameter	2.361-2.362 (59.98-60.00)
Journal Out-Of-Round	.0012 (.030)
Journal Taper	.0002 (.005)
Oil Clearance	.0008-.0019 (.020-.048)
Connecting Rod Bearings	
Journal Diameter	1.968-1.969 (49.98-50.00)
Journal Out-Of-Round	.0012 (.030)
Journal Taper	.0002 (.005)
Oil Clearance	.0006-.0018 (.016-.046)

CONNECTING RODS

Application	In. (mm)
Maximum Bend	.002 (.05)
Maximum Twist	.0039 (.10)
Side Play	.0039-.0098 (.10-.25)

PISTONS, PINS & RINGS

Application	In. (mm)
Pistons	
Clearance	.0008-.0016 (.03-.05)
Diameter	3.585-3.587 (91.07-91.10)
Pins	
Piston Fit	Slip Fit
Rod Fit	[1] Press Fit
Rings	
No. 1	
End Gap	.012-.018 (.30-.45)
Side Clearance	.0012-.0035 (.030-.090)
No. 2	
End Gap	.010-.016 (.25-.40)
Side Clearance	.0008-.0024 (.020-.060)
No. 3 (Oil)	
End Gap	.012-.035 (.30-.90)

[1] - Press fit in rod using 1686-3934 lbs. (765-1785 kg). DO NOT exceed 5000 lbs. (2268 kg) pressure.

CYLINDER BLOCK

Application	In. (mm)
Cylinder Bore	
Standard Diameter	3.587-3.588 (91.10-91.14)
Maximum Taper	.0008 (.020)
Maximum Out-Of-Round	.0008 (.020)
Maximum Deck Warpage	.002 (.05)

VALVES & VALVE SPRINGS

Application	Specification
Intake Valves	
Face Angle	45-45.5°
Minimum Margin	.028" (.70 mm)
Stem Diameter	.3143-.3148" (7.982-7.995 mm)
Exhaust Valves	
Face Angle	45-45.5°
Minimum Margin	.059" (1.5 mm)
Stem Diameter	.3126-.3134" (7.94-7.96 mm)
Valve Springs	
Free Length	1.988" (50.5 mm)
Installed Height	[1] 1.591" (40.4 mm)
Out-Of-Square	2-4°

	Lbs. @ In. (kg @ mm)
Pressure	
Valve Closed	74 @ 1.591 (32.9 @ 40.4)

[1] - Service limit is 1.630" (41.4 mm).

CYLINDER HEAD

Application	Specification
Maximum Warpage	.008" (.2 mm)
Valve Seats	
Intake Valve	
Seat Angle	45°
Seat Width	.035-.051" (.9-1.3 mm)
Exhaust Valve	
Seat Angle	45°
Seat Width	.035-.051" (.9-1.3 mm)
Valve Guides	
Intake Valve	
Valve Guide Installed Height	[1]
Valve Stem-To-Guide	
Oil Clearance	.0012-.0024" (.03-.06 mm)
Exhaust Valve	
Valve Guide Installed Height	[1]
Valve Stem-To-Guide	
Oil Clearance	.0020-.0035" (.05-.09 mm)

[1] - Valve Guide Installer (09222-32200) used to set guide height.

CAMSHAFT

Application	In. (mm)
End Play	.004-.008 (.10-.20)
Journal Diameter	1.336-1.337 (33.935-33.950)
Lobe Height	1.620-1.628 (41.15-41.35)
Oil Clearance	.0020-.0035 (.05-.09)

1994 ENGINE COOLING
Specifications & Electric Cooling Fans

Elantra, Excel, Scoupe, Sonata

SPECIFICATIONS

BELT ADJUSTMENT

Application	[1] Deflection New Belt – In. (mm)	[1] Deflection Used Belt – In. (mm)
Excel		
Alternator	.22-.28 (5.5-7.0)	.31 (8.0)
A/C	.34-.42 (8.6-10.6)	[2]
P/S	.28-.39 (7.0-10.0)	[2]
Elantra		
Alternator	.30-.35 (7.5-9.0)	.35-.41 (9.0-10.4)
A/C	.20-.22 (5.0-5.5)	.24-.28 (6.0-7.0)
P/S	.24-.35 (6.0-9.0)	[2]
Scoupe		
Alternator	.30-.35 (7.5-9.0)	.35-.41 (9.0-10.4)
A/C	.20-.22 (5.0-5.5)	.24-.28 (6.0-7.0)
P/S	.28-.39 (7.0-10.0)	[2]
Sonata		
2.0L		
Alternator	.30-.35 (7.5-9.0)	.39 (10.0)
A/C	.20-.22 (5.0-5.5)	.24-.28 (6.0-7.0)
P/S	.24-.35 (6.0-9.0)	[2]
3.0L		
Alternator & P/S	.16-.20 (4.0-5.0)	.28 (7.0)
A/C	.18-.22 (4.5-5.5)	[2]

[1] – Deflection with 22 lbs. (10 kg) pressure applied midway on belt run.

[2] – Information is not available from manufacturer.

COOLING SYSTEM SPECIFICATIONS

COOLING SYSTEM SPECIFICATIONS

Application	Specification
Coolant Replacement Interval	[1] 30,000 Miles
Coolant Capacity [2]	
Elantra	6.3 qts. (6.0L)
Excel & Scoupe	5.6 qts. (5.3L)
Sonata	
4-Cylinder	7.7 qts. (7.3L)
V6	9.0 qts. (8.5L)
Pressure Cap	11-15 psi
Thermostat Opens	190°F (88°C)

[1] – Or every 12 months.

[2] – Including heater core and reserve tank.

ELECTRIC COOLING FANS

COMPONENT TESTING

Radiator Fan Motor – Ensure fan motor rotates when battery voltage is applied between connector terminals. *See Figs. 1 and 2.* Ensure abnormal noises are not produced while motor is running.

NOTE: Testing of condenser fan motor is similar, but information is not available from manufacturer.

Condenser Fan Motor (Elantra) – Power for condenser fan motor is provided to thermoswitch and condenser fan relay through 10-amp fuse in dash panel. Ensure fan motor rotates when battery voltage is applied between motor connector terminals. Ensure abnormal noises are not produced while motor is running.

Condenser Fan Motor (Excel & Scoupe) – Power for condenser fan motor is provided through Blue 20-amp fusible link in power distribution center. Ground is provided by condenser fan relay. Ensure fan motor rotates when battery voltage is applied between connector terminals. Ensure abnormal noises are not produced while motor is running.

Condenser Fan Motor (Sonata) – Power source for condenser fan motor is Blue 20-amp fusible link and Blue 20-amp sub-fusible link in

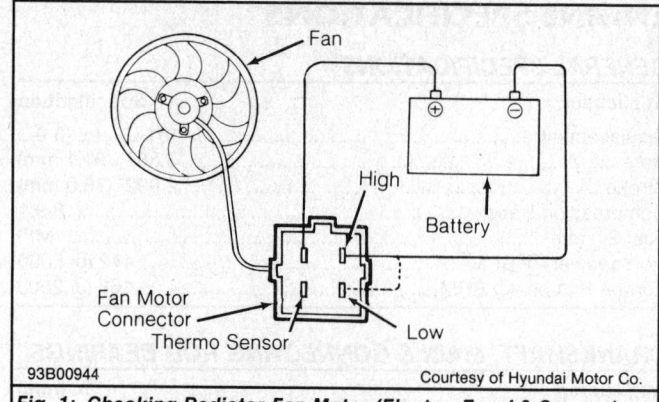
Fig. 1: Checking Radiator Fan Motor (Elantra, Excel & Scoupe)

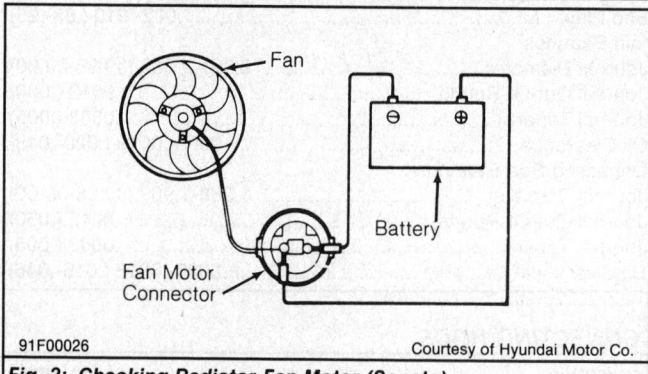
Fig. 2: Checking Radiator Fan Motor (Sonata)

the power distribution center and 10-amp fuse is dash panel. Power is distributed by one of three A/C relays. Ensure fan motor rotates when battery voltage is applied between connector terminals. Ensure abnormal noises are not produced while motor is running.

Condenser Fan & Radiator Fan Relay (Elantra) – Remove cover from relay box in engine compartment. Radiator fan relay is top right relay. Condenser fan relay is just below radiator fan relay. Remove relay. Continuity should exist between terminals No. 2 and 4 when battery power is applied between terminals No. 1 and 3. *See Fig. 3.*

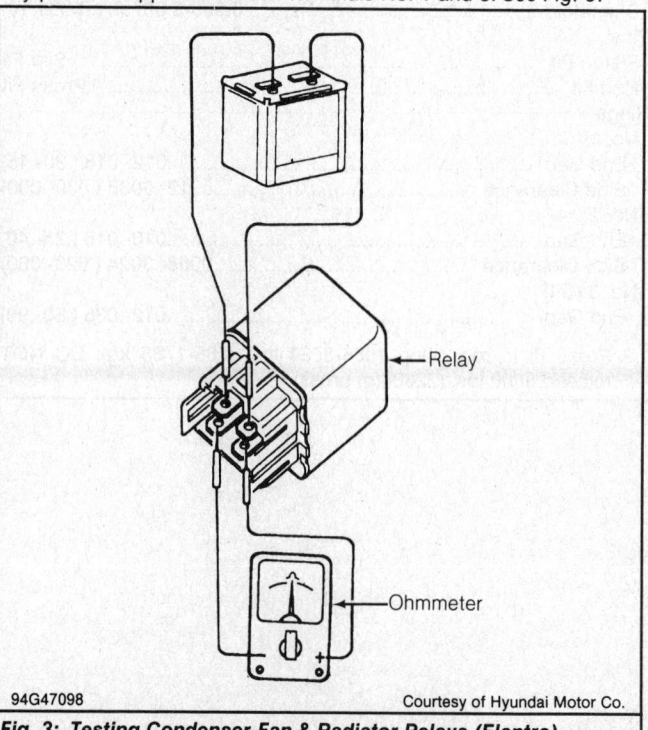
Fig. 3: Testing Condenser Fan & Radiator Relays (Elantra)

Condenser Fan Relay (Excel & Sonata) – On Sonata models, 2 condenser fan relays are used (high and low). On Excel and Sonata, ensure continuity is not present between relay terminals "L" and "B". If continuity is present, replace relay. When battery voltage and ground are applied to terminals "S₁" and "S₂", continuity should be present across terminals "L" and "B". *See Fig. 4.*

Condenser Fan Relay (Scoupe) – Ensure continuity is not present between relay terminals No. 2 and 3. *See Fig. 5.* If continuity is present, replace relay. When battery voltage and ground are applied to terminals No. 1 and 2, continuity should be present across terminals No. 2 and 3.

Condenser Fan Thermoswitch (Elantra) – A/C thermoswitch is located left of radiator fan thermoswitch and controls A/C condenser fan. Continuity should exist in A/C thermoswitch at 217-235°F (103-113°C). Continuity should not exist at any other temperature.

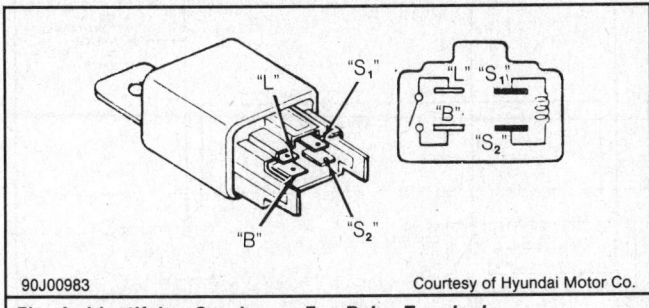

90J00983   Courtesy of Hyundai Motor Co.

Fig. 4: Identifying Condenser Fan Relay Terminals (Excel & Sonata)

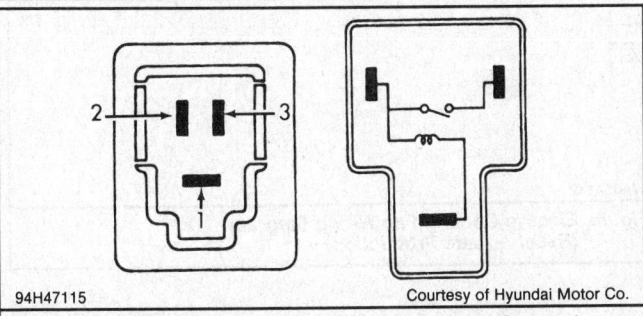

94H47115   Courtesy of Hyundai Motor Co.

Fig. 5: Identifying Condenser Fan Relay Terminals (Scoupe)

Engine Coolant Temperature (ECT) Sensor – Remove ECT sensor, located on thermostat housing. Place sensor in container of water. Resistance between sensor terminals should be as specified in ENGINE COOLANT TEMPERATURE SENSOR RESISTANCE table. If resistance at given temperatures is not as specified, replace sensor.

ENGINE COOLANT TEMPERATURE SENSOR RESISTANCE

Temperature – °F (°C)	Ohms
Elantra, Excel & Sonata	
68 (20)	2210-2690
176 (80)	264-328
Scoupe	
68 (20)	2270-2730
176 (80)	290-354

Radiator Fan Relay (Elantra) – See CONDENSER FAN & RADIATOR FAN RELAY (ELANTRA) under COMPONENT TESTING.

Radiator Fan Relay (Excel, Scoupe & Sonata) – Two radiator fan relays (high and low) are used in radiator fan circuit. Relays are located in engine compartment fuse/relay box. Testing information is not provided by manufacturer. See WIRING DIAGRAMS to identify internal circuits for testing.

Radiator Fan Thermoswitch (Elantra) – 1) System is equipped with 2 fan thermoswitches, located on lower right radiator tank near radiator hose. Thermoswitch "A" is closest to radiator hose. Thermoswitch "B" is to left of thermoswitch "A".

2) Use ohmmeter and container of oil or coolant to test switches. On 1.6L thermoswitch "A", continuity should exist in switch at 180-190°F (82-88°C) and no continuity should exist at 178°F (81°C) or below. On 1.8L thermoswitch "A", continuity should exist in switch at 189-195°F (87-93°C) and no continuity should exist at 181°F (83°C) or below.

3) On 1.6L and 1.8L thermoswitch "B", continuity should not exist in switch at 217°F (103°C). And continuity should exist at 225-235°F (107-113°C).

Radiator Fan Thermoswitch (Excel & Scoupe) – Use ohmmeter and container of oil or coolant to test switch, located on lower radiator tank. Continuity should exist between switch terminals at 180-190°F (82-88°C). No continuity should exist at 172°F (78°C) or lower. Replace switch if not within specification.

Radiator Fan Thermoswitch (Sonata) – 1) System is equipped with 2 fan thermoswitches. Use ohmmeter and container of oil or coolant to test switches. Radiator thermoswitch "A" is located on lower right radiator tank near radiator hose. Continuity should exist in radiator coolant temperature switch at 189-199°F (87-93°C) and no continuity should exist at 181°F (83°C) or below.

2) Radiator coolant temperature switch "B" is located to left of thermoswitch "A". Continuity should exist in radiator coolant temperature switch at 224-235°F (107-113°C). Continuity should not exist at 217°F (103°C) or below.

WIRING DIAGRAMS

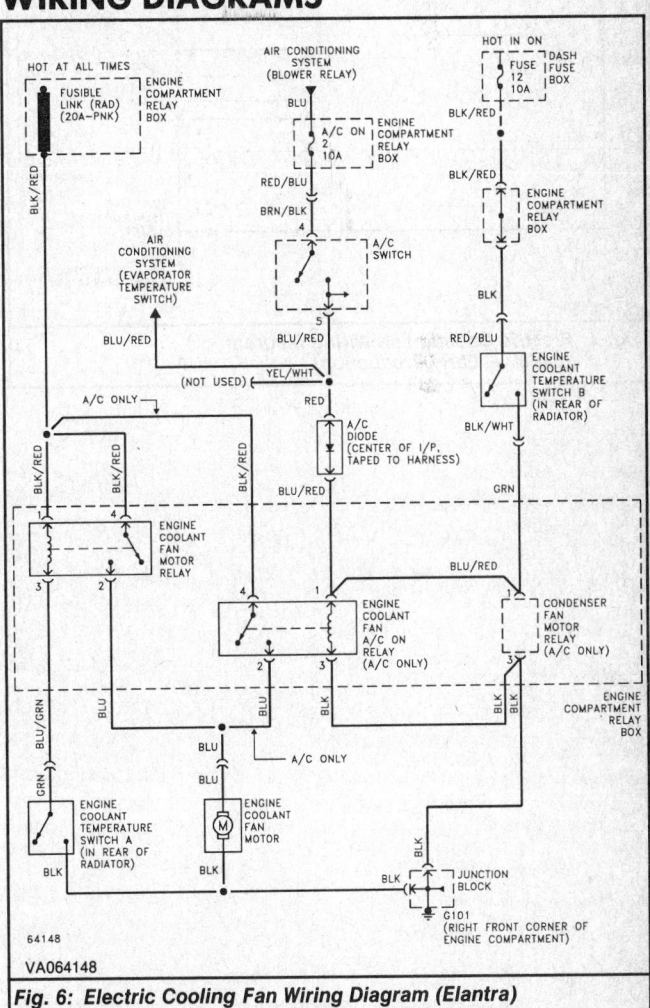

64148

VA064148

Fig. 6: Electric Cooling Fan Wiring Diagram (Elantra)

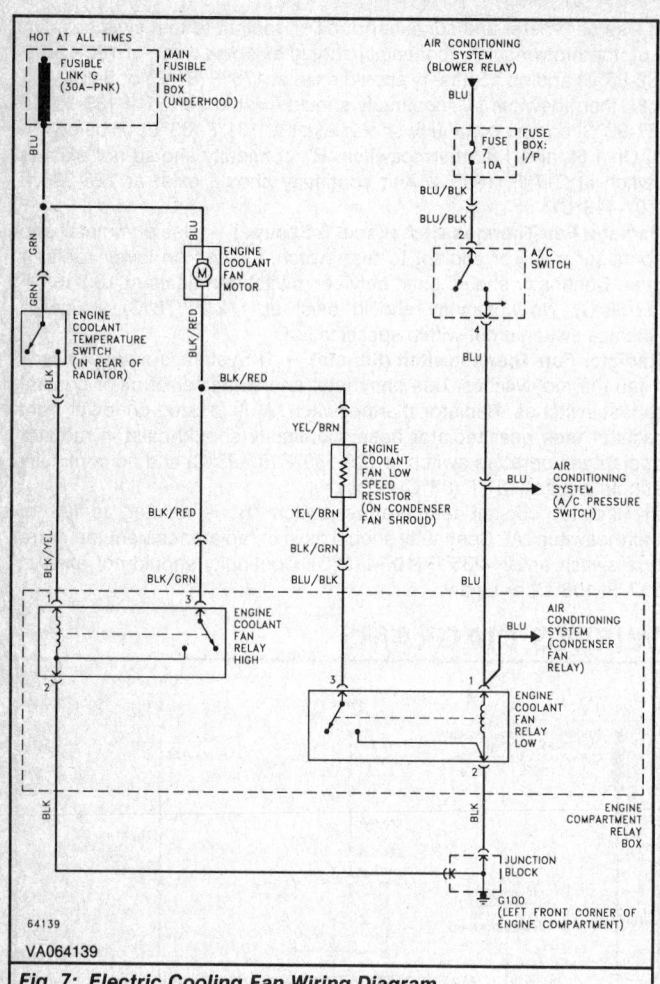

64139

VA064139

Fig. 7: Electric Cooling Fan Wiring Diagram (Excel – Early Production)

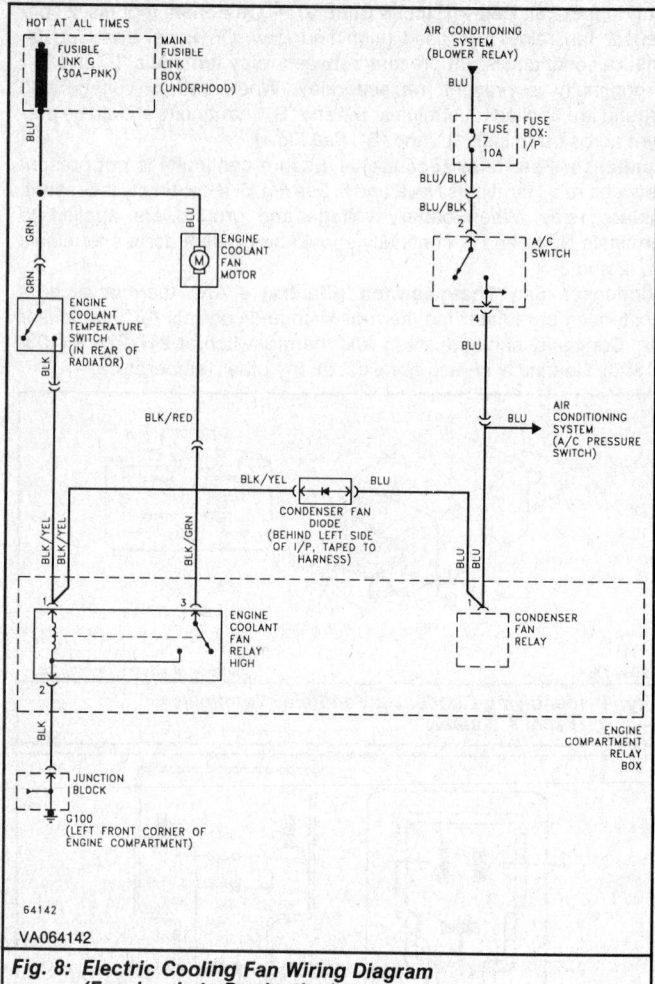

64142

VA064142

Fig. 8: Electric Cooling Fan Wiring Diagram (Excel – Late Production)

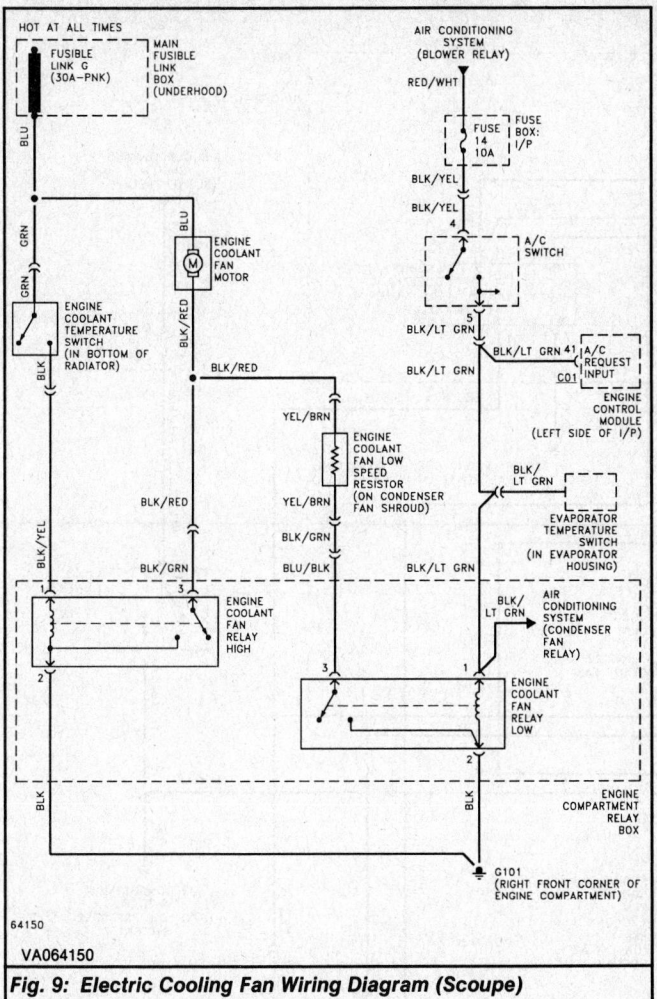

Fig. 9: Electric Cooling Fan Wiring Diagram (Scoupe)

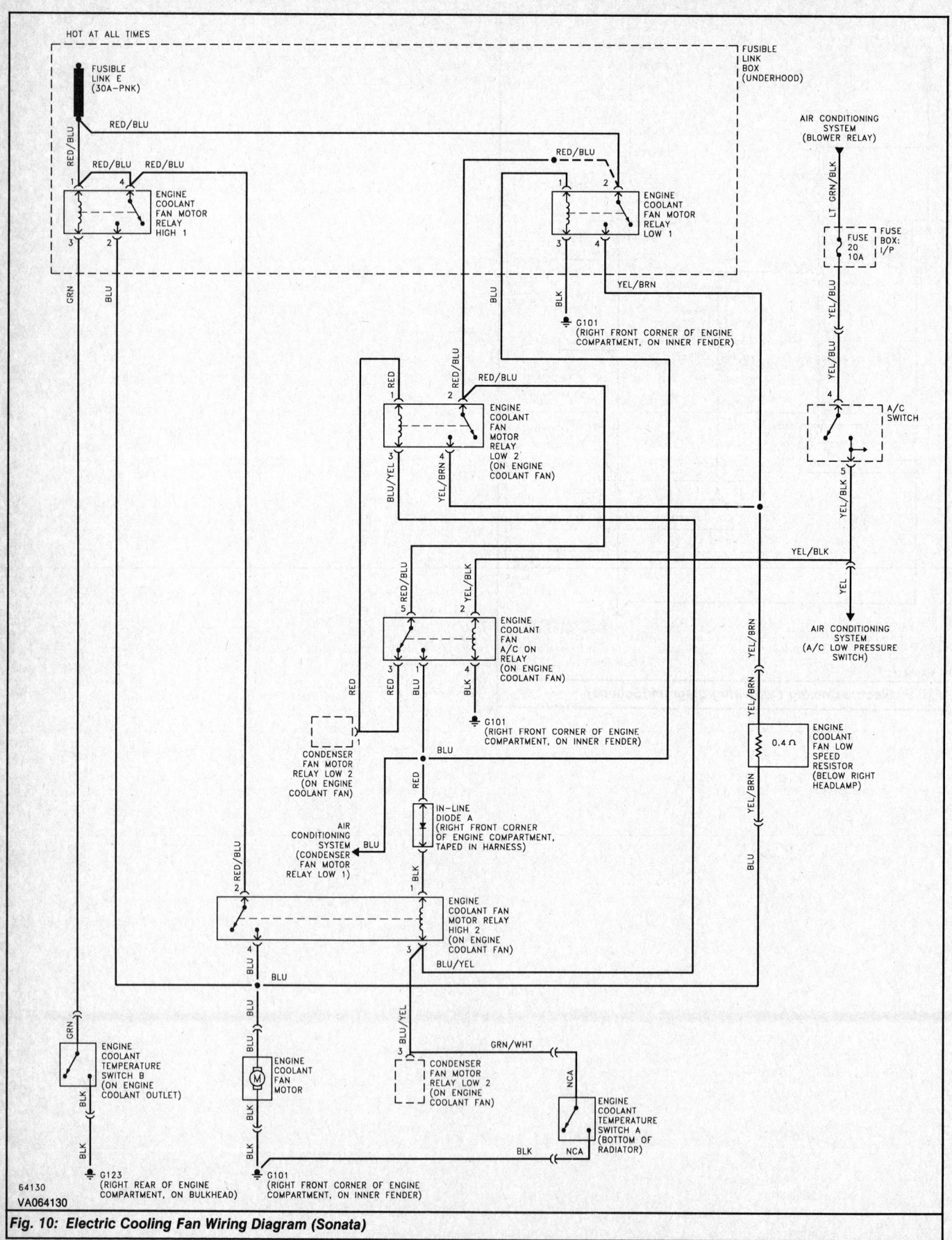

Fig. 10: Electric Cooling Fan Wiring Diagram (Sonata)

Elantra, Excel, Scoupe, Sonata

DESCRIPTION

The clutch is a single-plate type. Pressure plate assembly uses a diaphragm spring to engage the pressure plate. All models use a hydraulic release system, consisting of clutch cylinder, hydraulic tubing, slave cylinder, release fork and release bearing.

ADJUSTMENTS

CLUTCH PEDAL HEIGHT & FREE PLAY

1) Measure pedal height from top of pedal to floorboard. See CLUTCH PEDAL HEIGHT SPECIFICATIONS table. If pedal height is not to specification, loosen lock nut and turn clutch height adjusting bolt (vehicle without cruise control) or clutch pedal position switch (vehicles with cruise control) in or out to obtain proper height.

2) Check clutch pedal free play. See CLUTCH PEDAL FREE PLAY SPECIFICATIONS table. If free play is not to specification, adjust pedal free play by lengthening or shortening clutch cylinder rod at clutch pedal.

3) When clutch pedal is adjusted properly and clutch pedal is fully depressed, distance between top center of clutch pedal and floorboard should be 2.8" (70 mm). If pedal height is not as specified after adjustment, check for air in hydraulic system or faulty clutch or slave cylinder.

CLUTCH PEDAL HEIGHT SPECIFICATIONS

Application	In. (mm)
Elantra	
1.6L	7.2 (182)
1.8L	7.4 (189)
Excel	6.8 (172)
Scoupe	7.0 (178)
Sonata	7.0-7.2 (178-182)

CLUTCH PEDAL FREE PLAY SPECIFICATIONS

Application	In. (mm)
Elantra & Sonata	0.2-0.5 (6-13)
Excel & Scoupe	.04-.12 (1-3)

REMOVAL & INSTALLATION

CLUTCH ASSEMBLY

Removal – 1) Disconnect negative battery cable. Remove air cleaner assembly. Remove clutch release cylinder. Remove drain plug and drain transmission fluid. Remove speedometer cable. Remove backup light switch connector. Remove starter motor.

2) Remove stabilizer bar, tie rod end and lower ball joint. Remove splash shield. Remove axle shafts. See FWD AXLE SHAFTS article in DRIVE AXLES. Remove bellhousing cover. Remove transaxle-to-engine block mounting bolts.

3) Remove transaxle mount bracket and transaxle. Install clutch centering tool. Diagonally loosen bolts attaching pressure plate to flywheel 2 turns at a time.

4) On Excel, if removal of release fork assembly is necessary, use Spring Pin Remover (09414-24000) to remove spring pins. Hold fork assembly components and pull release fork shaft from bellhousing.

Inspection – 1) Check clutch cover diaphragm spring end for wear and uneven height. Replace clutch cover if height difference is greater than .02" (.5 mm). Check pressure plate surface for wear, cracks and color change. Check for loose rivets. If any defects are found, replace clutch cover.

2) Check disc facing for loose rivets, uneven contact, and oil or grease contamination. Rivet depth should be greater than .012" (.3 mm). Check torsion springs for damage. Ensure disc slides freely on transaxle input shaft. If any defects are found, replace clutch disc.

NOTE: On Excel, DO NOT reuse release fork spring pins.

Installation – 1) Apply multipurpose grease to contact surfaces of release fork, shaft and bearing. On Excel, reinstall release shaft (if removed). *See Fig. 1.* Install spacers, return spring and release fork. Align lock pin holes of release fork and release shaft.

2) Install 2 NEW spring pins. Ensure spring pin slots face release fork fingers. On all models, apply grease into groove of release bearing, and install release bearing on front bearing retainer of transaxle. On Elantra, Scoupe and Sonata, install release fork. *See Fig. 2.*

3) On all models, install return clip to release bearing and fork. Reverse removal procedure to complete installation. Fill transaxle with proper amount of oil.

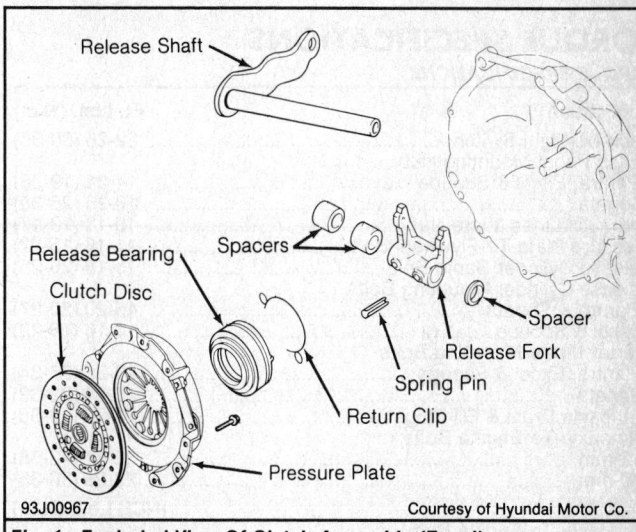

93J00967   Courtesy of Hyundai Motor Co.

Fig. 1: Exploded View Of Clutch Assembly (Excel)

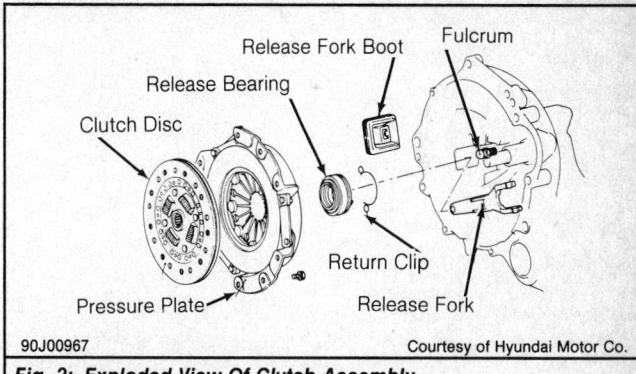

90J00967   Courtesy of Hyundai Motor Co.

Fig. 2: Exploded View Of Clutch Assembly (Elantra, Scoupe & Sonata)

CLUTCH MASTER CYLINDER

Removal & Installation – Drain clutch fluid through bleeder screw. From inside of vehicle, remove cotter pin, washer and clevis pin. From engine compartment, remove fluid line and master cylinder mounting bolts. Remove master cylinder. To install, reverse removal procedure. Bleed system.

CLUTCH RELEASE CYLINDER

Removal & Installation – Drain clutch fluid through bleeder screw. Remove fluid line. Remove release cylinder mounting bolts. Remove cylinder. To install, reverse removal procedure. Bleed system.

OVERHAUL

CLUTCH MASTER CYLINDER

Disassembly & Reassembly – 1) Disassemble as shown. *See Fig. 3.* Check cylinder bore and piston for rust or scars. Replace master cylinder assembly if cylinder-to-piston clearance exceeds .006" (.15 mm).

2) To reassemble, apply brake fluid to inner surfaces and piston assembly. Reverse disassembly procedure.

CLUTCH RELEASE CYLINDER

Disassembly & Reassembly – 1) Disassemble as shown. *See Fig. 4.* Check cylinder bore and piston for rust or scars. Replace clutch release cylinder assembly if cylinder-to-piston clearance exceeds .006" (.15 mm).

2) To reassemble, apply brake fluid to inner surfaces and piston assembly. Reverse disassembly procedure.

TORQUE SPECIFICATIONS

TORQUE SPECIFICATIONS

Application	Ft. Lbs. (N.m)
Back-Up Light Switch	22-26 (30-35)
Clutch Pedal Mounting Nut	
Elantra, Excel & Scoupe	14-21 (19-28)
Sonata	18-26 (25-35)
Hydraulic Lines (Flare Nut)	10-13 (13-17)
Pressure Plate-To-Flywheel Bolts	11-16 (15-22)
Release Cylinder Banjo Bolt	15-18 (20-25)
Release Cylinder Mounting Bolts	
Elantra & Sonata	15-20 (20-27)
Excel & Scoupe	11-16 (15-22)
Starter Motor Mounting Bolts	
Elantra, Excel & Scoupe	20-25 (27-34)
Sonata	16-24 (22-32)
Transaxle Drain & Fill Plugs	22-26 (30-35)
Transaxle-To-Engine Bolts	
12-mm	32-41 (43-55)
10-mm	22-26 (30-35)
	INCH Lbs. (N.m)
Transaxle-To-Engine Bolts	
8-mm	71-89 (8-10)

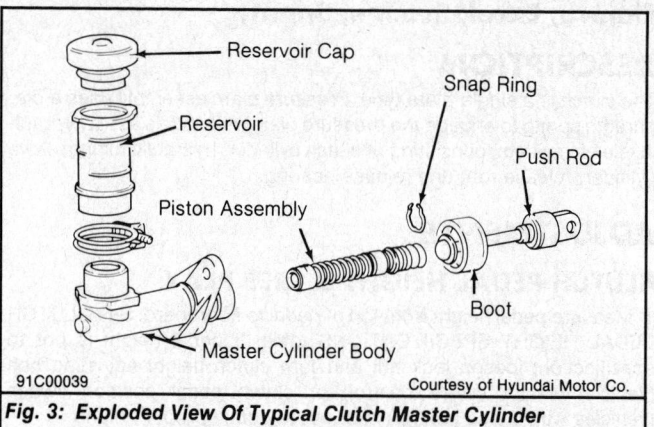

Fig. 3: Exploded View Of Typical Clutch Master Cylinder

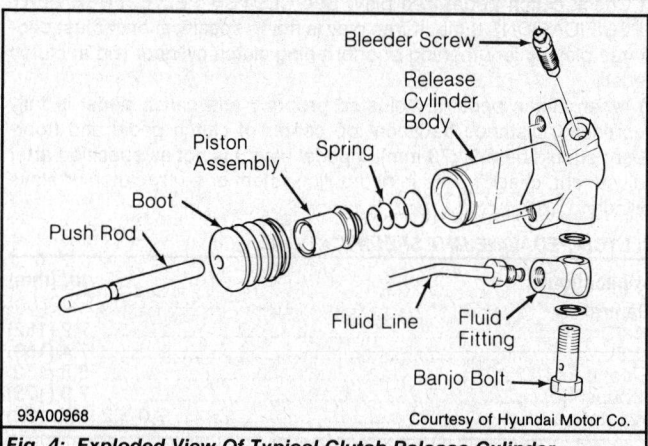

Fig. 4: Exploded View Of Typical Clutch Release Cylinder

Elantra, Excel, Scoupe, Sonata

DESCRIPTION & OPERATION

Axle shafts transfer power from transaxle to driving wheels. Axle shafts consist of a center shaft with a flexible Constant Velocity (CV) joint at each end. Inner CV joint is either a Double Offset Joint (DOJ) or a Tripod Joint (TJ) that is splined into transaxle. Outer CV joint is a Birfield Joint (BJ) that is splined into wheel hub assembly and secured by an axle nut.

CV joint boots protect CV joints by maintaining proper lubrication and preventing contaminants from entering joint. Boots must be replaced when signs of leakage or cracks are present, to prevent premature CV joint failure.

TROUBLE SHOOTING

NOTE: See TROUBLE SHOOTING article in GENERAL INFORMATION.

REMOVAL, DISASSEMBLY, REASSEMBLY & INSTALLATION

FWD AXLE SHAFTS

Removal (All Models) – **1)** Raise and support vehicle. Remove front wheel. Remove axle nut cotter pin, and loosen axle nut. Remove engine undercover (if equipped). Drain transaxle fluid.

2) Remove lower ball joint-to-lower control arm mounting bolts or separate lower ball joint from steering knuckle. Remove tie rod from steering knuckle. On Elantra, remove stabilizer bar self-locking nut.

3) Insert pry bar between transaxle case and inner CV joint housing. Pry axle shaft assembly from transaxle. *See Fig. 1.* Use care not to damage oil seal.

NOTE: On Scoupe Turbo and Sonata V6 left axle shaft, insert pry bar between center bearing bracket and CV joint housing. See Fig. 8.

4) Using a universal puller, press outer CV joint axle shaft through wheel hub. Prevent hub spacer from falling out when removing shaft.

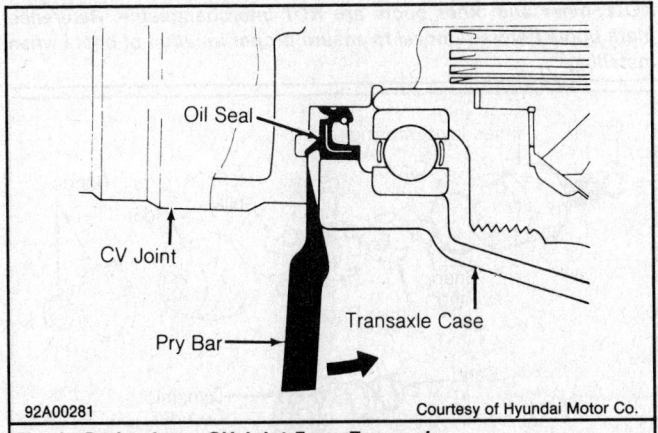

92A00281   Courtesy of Hyundai Motor Co.

Fig. 1: Prying Inner CV Joint From Transaxle

NOTE: Outer CV joint assembly is not repairable and should not be disassembled. Remove large boot band and check for foreign substances in grease. If necessary, clean assembly and repack with proper CV joint grease. Always install new boot bands.

Disassembly (Elantra With DOJ Type CV Joint & Sonata 4-Cylinder) – **1)** Measure distance between CV joint boot bands for reassembly reference. *See Fig. 2.* Remove CV joint boot bands and slide boots from joint assemblies.

2) Remove large circlip from inner joint housing. *See Fig. 3.* Remove axle shaft from joint assembly. Remove snap ring. Remove inner race, cage, and balls as an assembly. If reusing CV joint boots, wrap tape around axle shaft to protect boot. Remove CV joint boots.

NOTE: Inner and outer boots are NOT interchangeable. Reference mark boots before removal to ensure proper location of boots when installing.

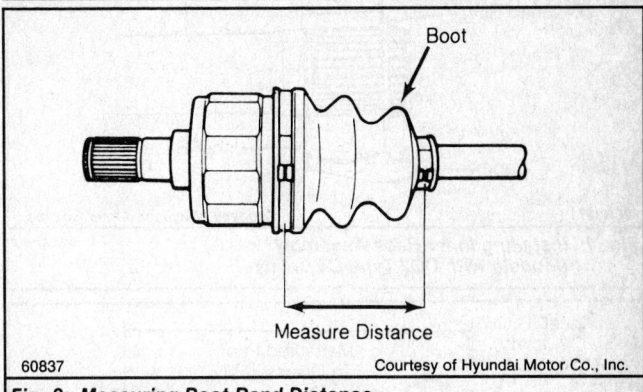

60837   Courtesy of Hyundai Motor Co., Inc.

Fig. 2: Measuring Boot Band Distance

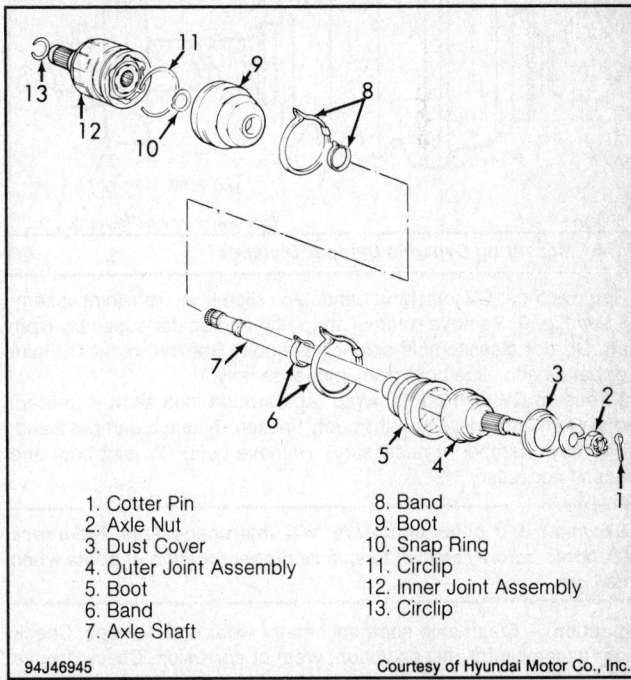

1. Cotter Pin	8. Band
2. Axle Nut	9. Boot
3. Dust Cover	10. Snap Ring
4. Outer Joint Assembly	11. Circlip
5. Boot	12. Inner Joint Assembly
6. Band	13. Circlip
7. Axle Shaft	

94J46945   Courtesy of Hyundai Motor Co., Inc.

Fig. 3: Exploded View Of Axle Shaft Assembly (Elantra With DOJ Type CV Joint & Sonata 4-Cylinder)

Inspection – Clean inner race, cage and balls without disassembling. Check for rusted or damaged DOJ outer race, inner race, cage and balls. Check for worn splines. Check for water, foreign material or rust in Birfield Joint boot. Replace components as necessary.

Reassembly – **1)** Wrap tape around shaft splines to protect boot during installation. Install boots and bands, but do not tighten bands. Pack outer joint assembly and boot with same amount of grease that was wiped away at time of inspection.

2) Pack joint inner race, cage and ball bearings with 2.0-2.1 ounces of grease. Install assembly on axle shaft with chamfered side (small end) of cage facing away from shaft end. *See Fig. 4.* Install snap ring.

3) Install large circlip into joint assembly. Apply 1.1-1.3 ounces of grease into inner CV joint boot. Position boot and boot band over joint housing. Ensure distance between bands is same as measurement made before disassembly. Tighten bands.

Disassembly (Elantra With Tripod Joint (TJ) Type CV Joint) – **1)** Measure distance between CV joint boot bands for reassembly reference. *See Fig. 2.* If dynamic damper is to be removed, mark location of damper on shaft to maintain distance from center of inner CV joint housing to center of dynamic damper. *See Fig. 5.*

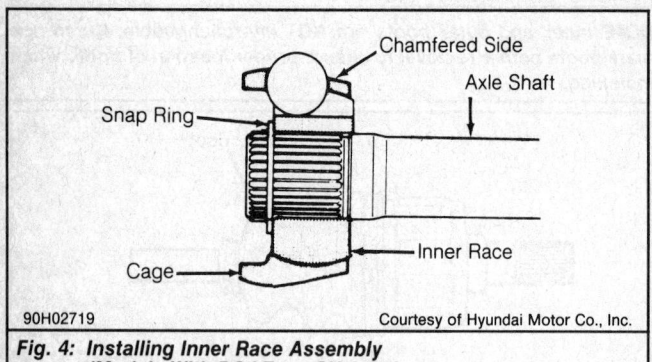

Fig. 4: Installing Inner Race Assembly (Models With DOJ Type CV Joint)

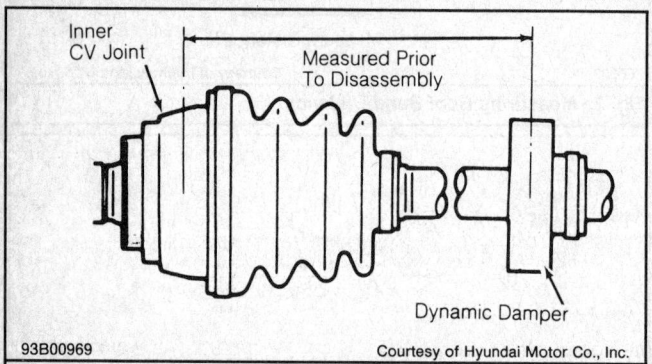

Fig. 5: Measuring Dynamic Damper Distance

2) Remove inner CV joint boot bands and slide boot from joint assembly. *See Fig. 6.* Remove remove snap ring and spider assembly from shaft. Do not disassemble spider assembly. Remove outer CV joint boot bands and slide boot from joint assembly.

3) If reusing CV joint boots, wrap tape around axle shaft to protect boots. Remove inner CV joint boot. Loosen dynamic damper band, and remove damper (if necessary). Remove outer CV joint boot and bands, if necessary.

NOTE: Inner and outer boots are NOT interchangeable. Reference mark boots before removal to ensure proper location of boots when installing.

Inspection – Clean axle shaft splines for wear and damage. Check spider assembly for roller rotation, wear or corrosion. Check groove inside TJ housing for wear or corrosion. Check dynamic damper for cracking or damage. Check for water, foreign material or rust in Birfield Joint boot. Replace components as necessary.

Reassembly – 1) Wrap tape around shaft splines to protect boot during installation. Install outer CV joint boot and bands, but do not tighten bands. Pack outer joint assembly and boot with same amount of grease that was wiped away at time of inspection.

2) Install dynamic damper, if removed. Ensure distance from center of inner CV joint housing to center of dynamic damper is same as measurement made before disassembly. Install inner CV joint boot and bands, but do not tighten bands. Pack inner CV joint boot with 1.3-1.5 ounces of grease.

3) Pack spider assembly with 2.2-2.4 ounces of grease. Install spider assembly onto axle shaft. Install snap ring. Position boot and boot band over joint housing. Ensure distance between bands is same as measurement made before disassembly. Tighten bands.

Disassembly (Excel, Scoupe & Sonata V6) – 1) Measure distance between CV joint boot bands for reassembly reference. *See Fig. 2.* On Excel and Scoupe Non-Turbo, if dynamic damper is to be removed, mark location of damper on shaft to maintain distance from center of inner CV joint housing to center of dynamic damper. *See Fig. 5.*

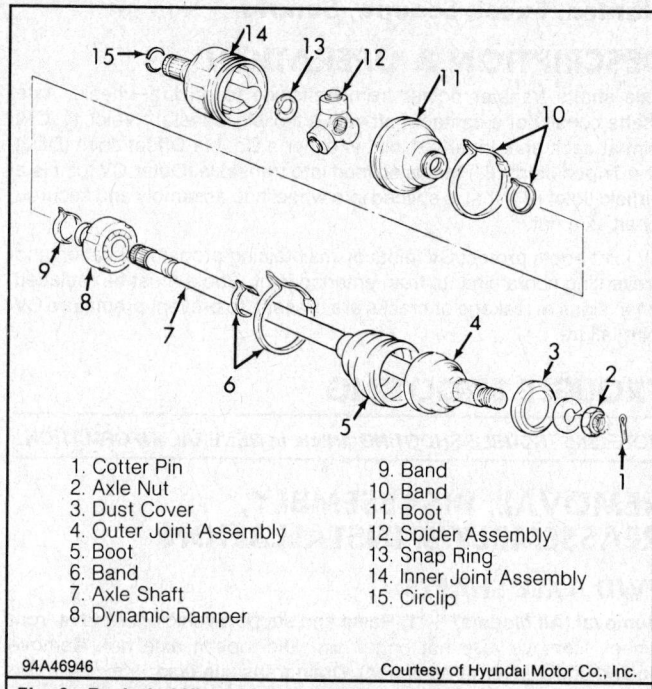

1. Cotter Pin
2. Axle Nut
3. Dust Cover
4. Outer Joint Assembly
5. Boot
6. Band
7. Axle Shaft
8. Dynamic Damper
9. Band
10. Band
11. Boot
12. Spider Assembly
13. Snap Ring
14. Inner Joint Assembly
15. Circlip

Fig. 6: Exploded View Of Axle Shaft Assembly (Elantra With Tripod Joint (TJ) Type CV Joint)

2) On all models, remove outer CV joint boot bands and slide boot from joint assembly. Remove large circlip from inner joint housing. *See Fig. 7 or 8.* Remove axle shaft from joint assembly. Remove snap ring. Remove inner race, cage and balls as an assembly.

3) If reusing CV joint boot, wrap tape around axle shaft to protect boot. Remove inner CV joint boot. On Excel and Scoupe Non-Turbo, loosen dynamic damper band and remove damper (if necessary). On all models, remove outer CV joint boot, if necessary.

NOTE: Inner and outer boots are NOT interchangeable. Reference mark boots before removal to ensure proper location of boots when installing.

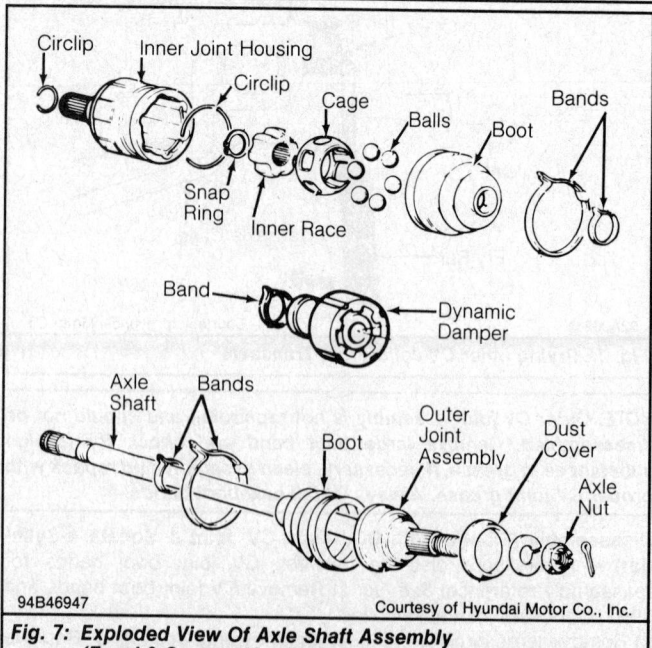

Fig. 7: Exploded View Of Axle Shaft Assembly (Excel & Scoupe Non-Turbo)

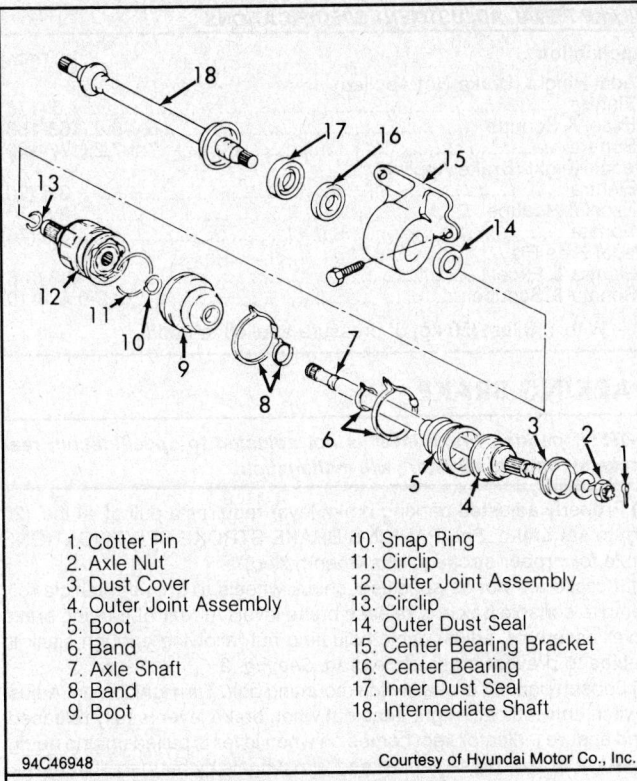

1. Cotter Pin
2. Axle Nut
3. Dust Cover
4. Outer Joint Assembly
5. Boot
6. Band
7. Axle Shaft
8. Band
9. Boot
10. Snap Ring
11. Circlip
12. Outer Joint Assembly
13. Circlip
14. Outer Dust Seal
15. Center Bearing Bracket
16. Center Bearing
17. Inner Dust Seal
18. Intermediate Shaft

94C46948   Courtesy of Hyundai Motor Co., Inc.

Fig. 8: Exploded View Of Axle Shaft Assembly (Scoupe Turbo Shown; Sonata V6 Is Similar)

Inspection – Clean inner race, cage and balls without disassembling. Check for rusted or damaged DOJ outer race, inner race, cage and balls. Check for worn splines. Check for water, foreign material or rust in Birfield Joint boot. Replace components as necessary.

Reassembly – 1) Wrap tape around shaft splines to protect boot during installation. Install outer CV joint boot and bands, but do not tighten bands. Pack outer joint assembly and boot with same amount of grease that was wiped away at time of inspection.

2) On Excel and Scoupe Non-Turbo, install dynamic damper, if removed. Ensure distance from center of inner CV joint housing-to-center of dynamic damper is same as measurement made before disassembly. On all models, install inner CV joint boot and bands, but do not tighten bands. Pack joint inner race, cage and ball bearings with 1.4-1.9 ounces of grease.

3) Install assembly on axle shaft with chamfered side (small end) of cage facing away from shaft end. *See Fig. 4.* Install snap ring. Install circlip into joint assembly. Apply 0.7-1.4 ounces of grease into inner CV joint boot. Position boot and boot band over joint housing. Ensure distance between bands is same as measurement made before disassembly. Tighten bands.

Installation (All Models) – To install, reverse removal procedure. Install NEW circlip (retainer ring) on inner CV joint splined shaft before installation. Install axle nut convex washer with outside beveled edge toward nut. Tighten nut to specification. See TORQUE SPECIFICATIONS. Fill transaxle with required amount of fluid. See appropriate article in TRANSMISSION SERVICING.

INTERMEDIATE SHAFT

Removal (Scoupe Turbo & Sonata V6) – **1)** Raise and support vehicle. Remove left wheel and loosen axle shaft nut. Remove engine undercover. Drain transaxle fluid. Disconnect tie rod and lower ball joint from steering knuckle.

2) Insert pry bar between center bearing bracket and axle shaft inner CV joint housing. Separate axle shaft from center bearing bracket. Using a puller, press outer CV joint axle shaft through wheel hub. Prevent inner spacer from falling out when removing axle shaft from hub.

3) Remove oxygen sensor connector from center bearing bracket. Remove center bearing bracket mounting bolts. Insert pry bar between intermediate shaft assembly and transaxle. *See Fig. 1.* Remove center bearing bracket and intermediate shaft assembly.

Disassembly – Using suitable puller, remove center bearing bracket from intermediate shaft. Remove outer dust seal from bracket. Press bearing from center bearing bracket.

NOTE: Center bracket bearing can only be removed and installed from one side of bracket.

Reassembly – Apply multipurpose grease to center bearing and to inside of bracket. Press center bearing into center bearing bracket. Apply grease to inside of seals, and install dust seals flush with edge of center bearing bracket.

Installation – To install, reverse removal procedure. Install axle nut convex washer with outside beveled edge toward nut. Tighten axle nut and bracket bolts to specifications. See TORQUE SPECIFICATIONS. Fill transaxle with required amount of fluid. See appropriate article in TRANSMISSION SERVICING.

TORQUE SPECIFICATIONS
TORQUE SPECIFICATIONS

Application	Ft. Lbs. (N.m)
Axle Nut	148-192 (200-260)
Ball Joint-To-Lower Arm Bolt	70-89 (95-120)
Brake Caliper Mounting Bolts	
Except Sonata	48-55 (65-75)
Sonata	51-63 (69-85)
Knuckle-To-Strut Bolts	
Elantra	81-96 (110-130)
Except Elantra	66-77 (90-105)
Lower Arm Ball Joint Nut	44-53 (60-72)
Tie Rod Nut	18-25 (24-34)

1994 BRAKES
Disc & Drum

Elantra, Excel, Scoupe, Sonata

DESCRIPTION & OPERATION

Disc/drum brake system is hydraulically operated, using a master cylinder with a single reservoir and 2 outlets. A vacuum assist power brake unit is used on all models. Proportioning valves are used to control anti-skid braking action. Mechanical parking brake system is self-adjusting. Sonata master cylinder cannot be rebuilt.

Disc brake pads have built-in wear indicator warning sensors. When brake pad lining is low, sensor will rub against rotor, causing a very notable squealing sound. Elantra and Sonata models have 4-wheel disc brakes as an option or as standard equipment with Anti-Lock Brake System (ABS).

BLEEDING BRAKE SYSTEM

BLEEDING PROCEDURES

1) Ensure master cylinder reservoir is full of brake fluid. Connect hose to wheel cylinder bleed screw and insert other end of hose in a clear container partly filled with brake fluid.
2) Slowly pump brake pedal several times. While depressing brake pedal, loosen bleed screw at right wheel cylinder until fluid starts to flow. Then close bleed screw.
3) Repeat operation until there are no bubbles in fluid. Tighten bleed screw to specification. See TORQUE SPECIFICATIONS. Repeat procedure for left front, left rear and right front wheel cylinder, in that order.

ADJUSTMENTS

PEDAL HEIGHT & FREE PLAY

Pedal Height (Brake Not Applied) – 1) Measure pedal height from surface of floor panel to top of brake pedal. *See Fig. 1*. See BRAKE PEDAL ADJUSTMENT SPECIFICATIONS table.
2) If pedal height is not to specification, back stoplight switch out until it does not contact pedal arm. Turn stoplight switch in until clearance between stoplight switch outer case and pedal arm is .02-.04" (.5-1.0 mm). Tighten lock nut. Recheck pedal height.
Pedal Height (Brake Applied) – Start engine. Apply brake pedal with 110 lbs. (50 kg) force. Measure clearance between floor board and top of brake pedal. See BRAKE PEDAL ADJUSTMENT SPECIFICATIONS table. If clearance is not to specification, check brake adjustment, then check for air in system.

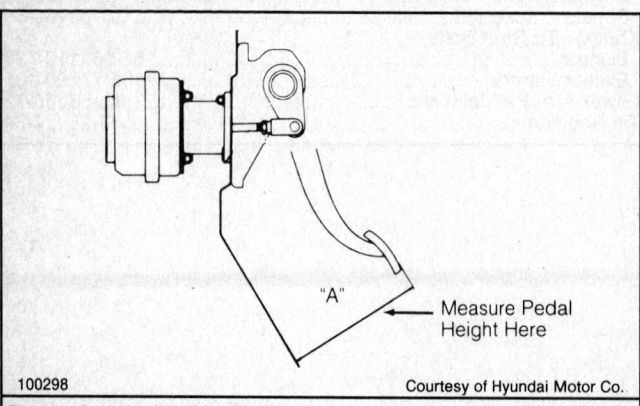

100298   Courtesy of Hyundai Motor Co.

Fig. 1: Checking Pedal Height

Pedal Free Play – Check brake pedal free play. If free play is not to specification, adjust brake pedal push rod until correct clearance is obtained. See BRAKE PEDAL ADJUSTMENT SPECIFICATIONS table.

BRAKE PEDAL ADJUSTMENT SPECIFICATIONS

Application	In. (mm)
Pedal Height (Brake Not Applied)	
Elantra	7.0 (178)
Excel & Scoupe	6.4-6.6 (163-168)
Sonata	7.0-7.2 (177-182)
Pedal Height (Brake Applied) [1]	
Elantra	3.5 (90)
Excel & Scoupe	2.8 (70)
Sonata	3.0 (75)
Pedal Free Play	
Elantra & Excel	0.1-0.3 (3-8)
Sonata & Scoupe	0.2-0.4 (4-10)

[1] – With 110 lbs. (50 kg) of pressure applied to pedal.

PARKING BRAKE

NOTE: If parking brake lever is not adjusted to specification, rear brake automatic adjusters will malfunction.

1) Properly adjusted parking brake lever requires a pull of 44 lbs. (20 kg) to set brake. See PARKING BRAKE STROKE SPECIFICATIONS table for proper stroke (clicks when pulled).
2) If clicks are not as specified, chock wheels to prevent vehicle roll, remove console box and release brake lever. At rear of parking brake lever assembly, adjust cable adjusting nut, allowing enough slack in cables to prevent brake shoe drag. *See Fig. 2*.
3) Loosen parking brake switch mounting bolt. Turn ignition on. Adjust switch until indicator light goes out when brake lever is fully released, and ensure indicator light comes on when lever is pulled up one notch. Release brake. Raise vehicle and turn wheels by hand to ensure rear brakes do not drag.

PARKING BRAKE STROKE SPECIFICATIONS

Application	Number Of Clicks
Elantra	7-8
Excel & Scoupe	6-7
Sonata	8-9

[1] – With 44 lbs. (20 kg) of pressure applied at lever.

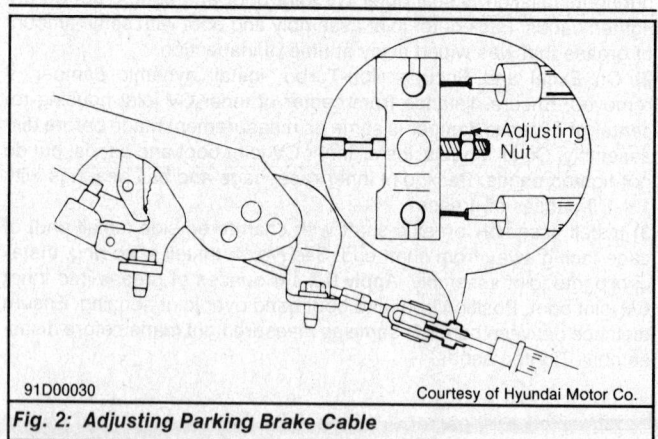

91D00030   Courtesy of Hyundai Motor Co.

Fig. 2: Adjusting Parking Brake Cable

TESTING

POWER BRAKE UNIT CHECK VALVE

1) Remove check valve, leaving engine vacuum hose attached to check valve. Place finger over check valve hole. Start engine. Vacuum should be felt. Leave finger on check valve hole and turn off engine.
2) Vacuum should be maintained after engine is turned off. If vacuum is not as described, check vacuum hose and its connections for leaks, and/or replace check valve.

POWER BRAKE UNIT

1) Run engine 2 minutes, then turn off. Depress brake pedal several times using normal foot pressure. Maximum travel should be obtained on first application and gradually raise after each following application. If okay, proceed to next step.

2) With engine stopped, depress brake pedal several times. Hold brake pedal down and start engine. If brake pedal goes down slightly, power brake unit is functioning properly.

3) With engine running, depress brake pedal and turn engine off. Hold pedal down for 30 seconds. If pedal height does not change, power brake unit is functioning properly. If all tests are okay, power brake unit is in good condition. If tests results are not as stated, check vacuum hose, vacuum supply and vacuum check valve before replacing power brake unit.

PROPORTIONING VALVE

NOTE: Manufacturer does not provide testing procedures for Scoupe proportioning valves.

1) Install 2 pressure gauges that will measure to at least 2000 psi (140.6 kg/cm²) to input and output sides of proportioning valve. *See Fig. 3.*

2) Measure both input and output pressure with brakes applied. *See Fig. 4.* If measured pressures are NOT within specification, replace proportioning valve. See PROPORTIONING VALVE TEST SPECIFICATIONS table. DO NOT disassemble proportioning valve.

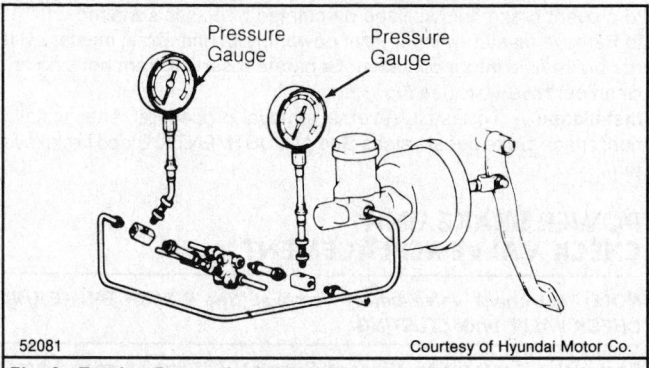

52081   Courtesy of Hyundai Motor Co.

Fig. 3: Testing Proportioning Valve

PROPORTIONING VALVE TEST SPECIFICATIONS

Application	Input Pressure psi (kg/cm²)	Output Pressure psi (kg/cm²)
Elantra	569 (40)	540-654 (38-46)
	1138 (80)	676-775 (47.5-54.5)
	1991 (140)	896-1010 (63-71)
Excel	569 (40)	498 (35)
	1138 (80)	640-740 (45-52)
	1991 (140)	868-981 (61-69)
Scoupe [1]	569 (40)	498 (35)
Sonata	290 (20.4)	300 (21.1)
	501 (35.2)	339-397 (23.8-27.9)
	2001 (140.7)	828-929 (58.2-65.3)

[1] – Complete information on Scoupe is not available from manufacturer.

REMOVAL & INSTALLATION

FRONT DISC BRAKE PADS

Removal – 1) Raise and support vehicle. Remove front wheel. Remove caliper lower guide bolt. Rotate caliper upward and wire in position. Remove disc pads, shims and springs; noting location and order of assembly for installation reference.

2) Check disc pad minimum thickness wear limit specification. See appropriate DISC BRAKE SPECIFICATIONS table.

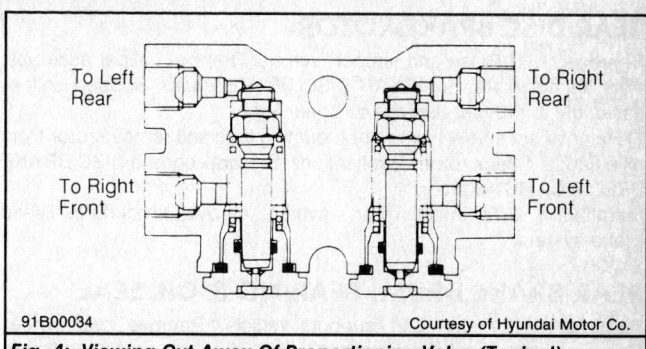

91B00034   Courtesy of Hyundai Motor Co.

Fig. 4: Viewing Cut-Away Of Proportioning Valve (Typical)

Installation – 1) To compress piston into caliper, install hose onto bleed screw and open bleed screw. Using hammer handle or similar, press piston back into caliper bore. Tighten bleed screw when piston is seated in caliper bore.

2) To complete installation, reverse removal procedure. Tighten caliper guide bolt to specification. See TORQUE SPECIFICATIONS. Bleed brake system.

FRONT DISC BRAKE CALIPER

Removal – Raise and support vehicle. Remove front wheel. Disconnect brake hose from caliper. Remove both caliper guide bolts. Rotate caliper upward and remove caliper. Note shims and springs for installation reference.

Installation – To install, reverse removal procedure. Tighten bolts to specification. See TORQUE SPECIFICATIONS. Bleed brake system.

FRONT DISC BRAKE ROTOR

Removal – 1) Raise and support vehicle. Remove front wheel. Remove caliper assembly torque plate-to-steering knuckle bolts. Remove caliper assembly and wire aside.

2) Remove axle shaft hub nut. Using Rotor Puller (09526-11001), press axle shaft out of hub. Remove rotor and hub. Check rotor specifications. See appropriate DISC BRAKE SPECIFICATIONS table.

Installation – To install rotor, reverse removal procedure. Tighten axle shaft hub nut and brake caliper torque plate bolts to specification. See TORQUE SPECIFICATIONS.

REAR DISC BRAKE PADS

Removal (Elantra) – Raise and support vehicle. Remove rear wheel. Remove caliper mounting bolts. Loosen parking cable adjusting nut. Remove parking cable. Remove brake fluid hose from caliper. Remove brake caliper. Remove brake pads.

Installation – Install hose to caliper bleed screw and open bleed screw. Using hammer handle or similar, press piston back into caliper bore. Tighten bleed screw when piston is seated in caliper bore. Install pads. To complete installation, reverse removal procedure. Bleed brake system.

Removal (Sonata) – Raise and support vehicle. Remove rear wheel. Remove bolt holding front support key to anchor plate. *See Fig. 11.* Move caliper rearward and slide support key outward to remove. Remove both caliper support pins. While holding caliper downward, swing front of caliper upward and remove caliper. Remove brake pads

Installation – Install hose to caliper bleed screw and open bleed screw. Using hammer handle or similar, press piston back into caliper bore. Tighten bleed screw when piston is seated in caliper bore. Install pads. To complete installation, reverse removal procedure. Bleed brake system.

REAR DISC BRAKE CALIPER

See REAR DISC BRAKE PADS.

REAR DISC BRAKE ROTOR

Removal – 1) Raise and support vehicle. Remove caliper assembly from anchor plate. See REAR DISC BRAKE PADS. Support caliper assembly to prevent damage to brake hose.

2) Remove set screw from rotor mounting face and remove rotor from axle flange. Check rotor specifications. See appropriate DISC BRAKE SPECIFICATIONS table.

Installation – To install rotor, reverse removal procedure. Bleed brake system.

REAR BRAKE DRUM, BEARING & OIL SEAL

Removal – 1) Raise and support vehicle. Remove rear wheel. Remove brake drum. If brake drum is difficult to remove, insert 2 suitable metric bolts into threaded holes in brake drum and, alternating from side to side, tighten bolts to remove drum. Drum may also be removed along with hub assembly as described in step **2)**.

2) Remove grease cap. Remove self-locking nut or remove cotter pin, lock nut, adjusting nut and washer. Remove outer wheel bearing. Remove brake drum and or hub assembly. Using a flat-bladed screwdriver, pry out oil seal. Remove inner wheel bearing. If necessary to remove wheel bearing races, drive out races from opposite side using a brass drift.

Installation – 1) To install, reverse removal procedure. Tighten axle self-locking nut to specification while rotating wheel. See TORQUE SPECIFICATIONS.

2) Check end play using dial indicator. Position indicator plunger tip on axle flange rim nearest spindle. With parking brake off, move drum/hub assembly in and out. Maximum limit of end play allowed is .008" (.20 mm) for Elantra or .004" (.10 mm) for all other models. If end play exceeds limit, replace wheel bearings.

3) Fill grease cap with grease and install cap. Apply and release parking brake lever several times. Depress and release brake pedal. This will automatically adjust shoe clearance.

REAR BRAKE SHOES

Removal – Raise and support vehicle. Remove brake drum. Remove automatic adjuster spring and automatic adjuster lever. *See Figs. 5 and 6.* Spread shoes and remove adjuster strut. Remove shoe-to-shoe spring and front shoe hold-down spring. Remove front shoe. Remove rear shoe hold-down spring and parking cable clip at shoe. Remove shoe.

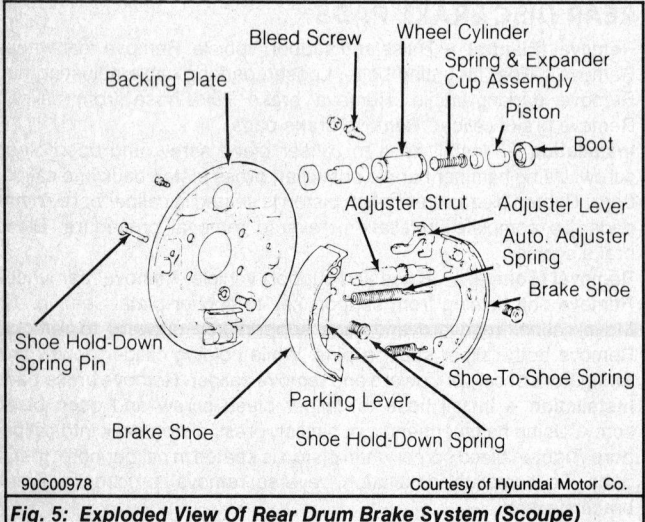

90C00978   Courtesy of Hyundai Motor Co.

Fig. 5: Exploded View Of Rear Drum Brake System (Scoupe)

NOTE: The adjuster strut is marked "R" or "L" for right or left side of vehicle.

Installation – 1) To install, reverse removal procedure. Apply Lubriplate to all shoe contact points, adjuster assembly and parking brake attachment. Retract adjuster strut all the way in.

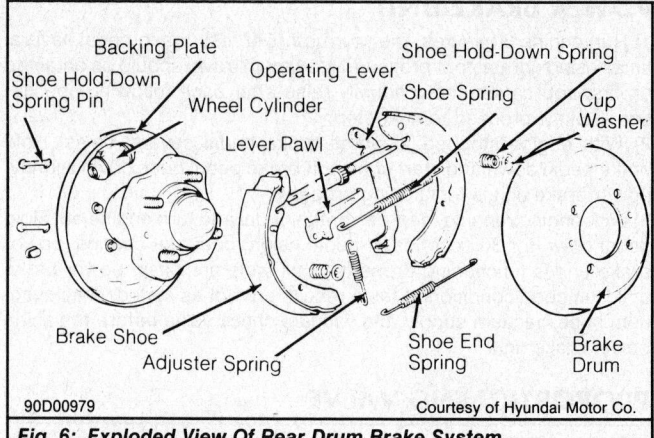

90D00979   Courtesy of Hyundai Motor Co.

Fig. 6: Exploded View Of Rear Drum Brake System (Except Scoupe)

2) To complete installation, reverse removal procedure. Apply and release parking brake lever. Depress and release brake pedal. This will automatically adjust shoe clearance.

MASTER CYLINDER

Removal – 1) Remove fluid level sensor harness connector. Remove brakelines from master cylinder. Plug fitting holes in master cylinder to prevent brake fluid spillage on painted or plastic surfaces.

2) Remove master cylinder from power brake unit. Drain master cylinder brake fluid into a container. Separate reservoir from housing and clean out reservoir. *See Fig. 12.*

Installation – To install, reverse removal procedure. After installation, check brake pedal height. See ADJUSTMENTS. Bleed brake system.

POWER BRAKE UNIT
CHECK VALVE REPLACEMENT

NOTE: Test check valve before removal. See POWER BRAKE UNIT CHECK VALVE under TESTING.

Removal & Installation (Except Sonata) – Remove hose clamps from both ends of check valve. Remove check valve. To install, coat both ends of check valve with non-hardening sealer. Install check valve in vacuum hose with arrow pointing toward intake manifold hose. *See Fig. 7.* Install check valve clamps.

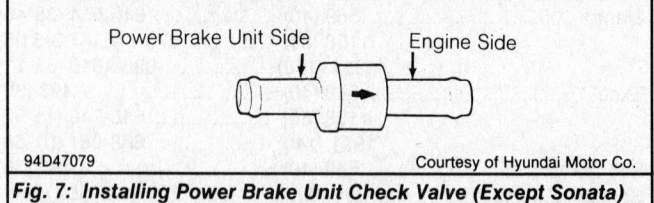

94D47079   Courtesy of Hyundai Motor Co.

Fig. 7: Installing Power Brake Unit Check Valve (Except Sonata)

Removal & Installation (Sonata) – Remove check valve from power brake unit. Remove vacuum hose clamp and remove valve from hose. Install NEW valve into vacuum hose and install clamp. Coat valve hose barb with non-hardening sealer and install into power brake unit.

POWER BRAKE UNIT

Removal – Remove brake master cylinder. See MASTER CYLINDER. Disconnect check valve/vacuum hose from power brake unit. From inside vehicle, disconnect power brake unit actuating rod at brake pedal. Remove 4 nuts attaching power brake unit to firewall. Remove power brake unit.

Installation – To install, reverse removal procedure. Bleed brake system. See BLEEDING BRAKE SYSTEM.

OVERHAUL

FRONT & REAR DISC BRAKE CALIPER

WARNING: DO NOT place fingers between piston and wooden block when removing piston. Wear appropriate eye protection.

Disassembly – **1)** Remove caliper piston boot. *See Fig. 8, 9, 10 or 11* Place a narrow wooden block between piston and caliper that will allow piston to clear its bore and not be damaged by caliper end when removed.

2) Using low pressure compressed air, apply air into caliper fitting hole to force piston out of caliper. Remove wood block and piston. Remove dust boot and piston seal (use small flat bladed screwdriver if necessary).

Cleaning & Inspection – **1)** Clean all parts with water first, then clean metal parts with alcohol. DO NOT expose rubber parts to alcohol or damage to parts will occur. Inspect caliper bore and piston for wear, damage or rust.

2) Light rust in caliper bore can be removed with crocus cloth or small wire wheel. Replace piston if rusty. DO NOT reuse caliper piston seal and/or dust boot. Replace any worn or defective parts.

Reassembly – **1)** Apply brake caliper lubricant to piston seal and install piston seal into caliper bore groove. Apply caliper lube to piston, cylinder bore and inside dust boot. Install dust boot onto piston.

2) Position piston with boot into caliper bore and install dust boot lip into cylinder groove. Press piston into caliper bore, ensuring boot remains in groove. Apply brake caliper lube or rubber grease to guide sleeve and inner portion of sleeve boots, and install caliper.

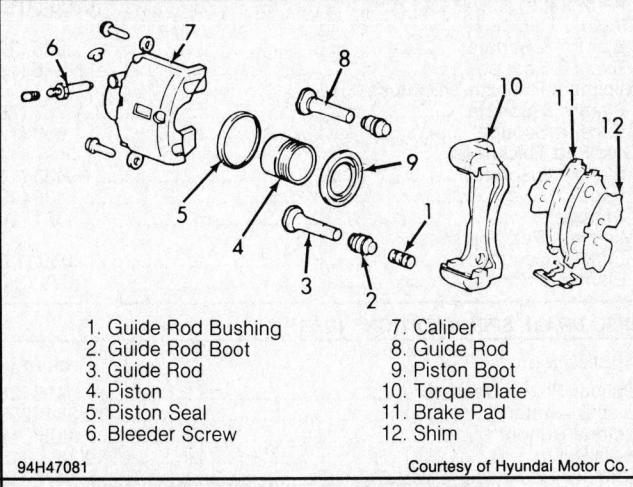

1. Guide Rod Bushing	7. Caliper
2. Guide Rod Boot	8. Guide Rod
3. Guide Rod	9. Piston Boot
4. Piston	10. Torque Plate
5. Piston Seal	11. Brake Pad
6. Bleeder Screw	12. Shim

94H47081   Courtesy of Hyundai Motor Co.

Fig. 8: Exploded View Of Front Disc Brake Caliper (Elantra Shown; Sonata Is Similar)

MASTER CYLINDER

NOTE: Master cylinder for Sonata models cannot be disassembled or overhauled and must be replaced if found defective.

Disassembly – Place cylinder mounting flange in a soft-jawed vise. Remove reservoir cap and drain brake fluid into a suitable container. Remove reservoir from master cylinder. While depressing piston, remove snap ring. *See Fig. 12.* Withdraw primary and secondary piston assemblies from master cylinder.

NOTE: DO NOT disassemble master cylinder piston assemblies.

Cleaning & Inspection – Check master cylinder bore for rust or scoring. Check primary and secondary pistons for rust, scoring, wear, damage or deterioration. If any parts are found to be worn or defective, replace part or replace master cylinder as complete assembly.

Reassembly – To reassemble, reverse disassembly procedure. Before reassembly, apply brake fluid to all parts.

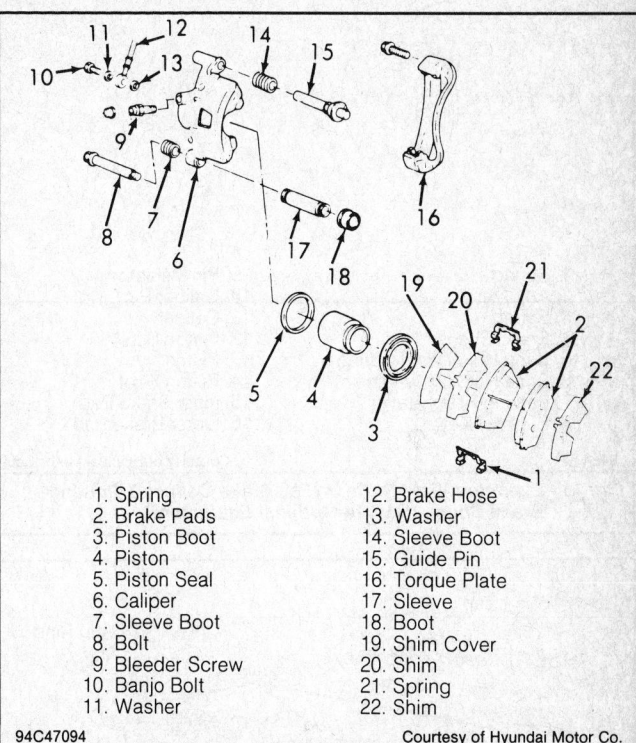

1. Spring	12. Brake Hose
2. Brake Pads	13. Washer
3. Piston Boot	14. Sleeve Boot
4. Piston	15. Guide Pin
5. Piston Seal	16. Torque Plate
6. Caliper	17. Sleeve
7. Sleeve Boot	18. Boot
8. Bolt	19. Shim Cover
9. Bleeder Screw	20. Shim
10. Banjo Bolt	21. Spring
11. Washer	22. Shim

94C47094   Courtesy of Hyundai Motor Co.

Fig. 9: Exploded View Of Front Disc Brake Caliper (Excel Shown; Scoupe Is Similar)

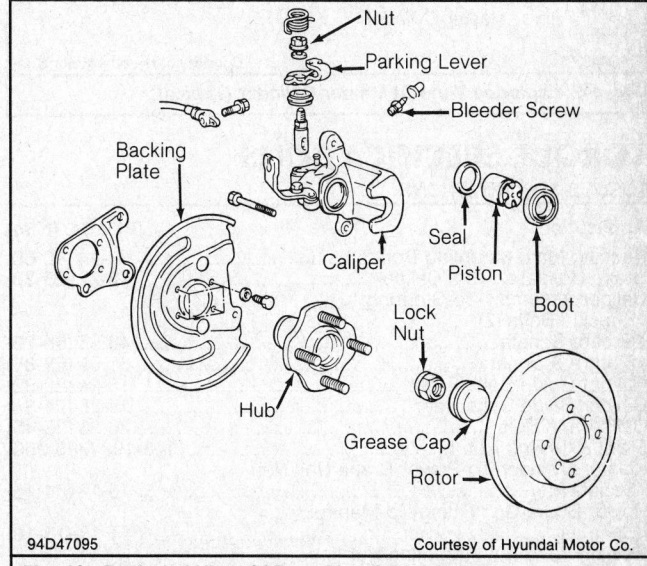

94D47095   Courtesy of Hyundai Motor Co.

Fig. 10: Exploded View Of Rear Disc Brake Caliper (Elantra Optional Equipment)

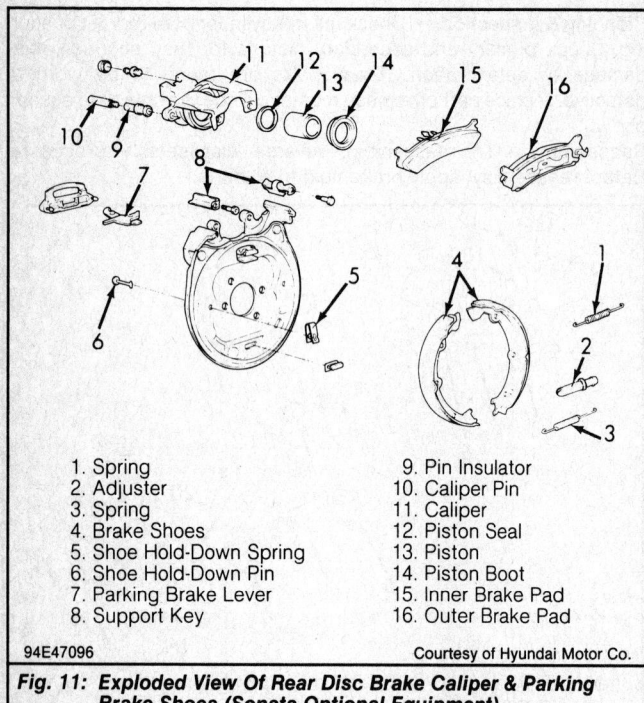

1. Spring
2. Adjuster
3. Spring
4. Brake Shoes
5. Shoe Hold-Down Spring
6. Shoe Hold-Down Pin
7. Parking Brake Lever
8. Support Key
9. Pin Insulator
10. Caliper Pin
11. Caliper
12. Piston Seal
13. Piston
14. Piston Boot
15. Inner Brake Pad
16. Outer Brake Pad

94E47096   Courtesy of Hyundai Motor Co.

Fig. 11: Exploded View Of Rear Disc Brake Caliper & Parking Brake Shoes (Sonata Optional Equipment)

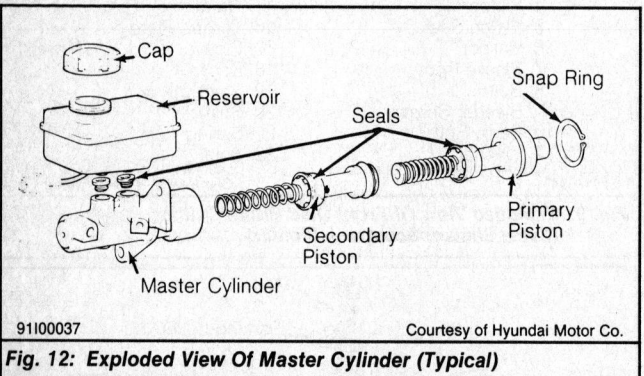

91I00037   Courtesy of Hyundai Motor Co.

Fig. 12: Exploded View Of Master Cylinder (Typical)

TORQUE SPECIFICATIONS
TORQUE SPECIFICATIONS

Application	Ft. Lbs. (N.m)
Backing Plate Mounting Bolt	37-44 (50-60)
Brake Hose-To-Front Caliper	18-22 (25-30)
Caliper Assembly-To-Steering Knuckle Bolts (2)	
Except Sonata	48-55 (65-75)
Elantra & Sonata	51-63 (69-85)
Caliper Guide Bolts Front	16-24 (22-32)
Caliper Guide Bolts Rear	18-25 (24-34)
Caliper Pin Bolt	26-33 (35-45)
Front Axle Hub Nut	148-192 (200-260)
Master Cylinder-To-Power Brake Unit Nut	
Sonata	10-12 (14-16)
Power Brake Unit Fitting-To-Manifold	
Sonata	11-13 (15-18)
Power Brake Unit Mounting Nut	
Sonata	10-21 (14-22)
Proportioning Valve-To-Master Cylinder	
Except Scoupe	10-16 (14-22)
Rear Axle Self-Locking Hub Nut	
Except Sonata	111-148 (150-200)
Sonata	177-221 (240-300)
Wheel Cylinder Mounting Bolt	
Except Excel	10-13 (14-18)
Wheel Lug Nuts	66-81 (90-110)

TORQUE SPECIFICATIONS (Cont.)

Application	INCH Lbs. (N.m)
Bleed Screw	
Elantra	62-115 (7-13)
Excel & Scoupe	
Front	62-115 (7-13)
Rear	62-80 (7-9)
Sonata	
Front	62-115 (7-13)
Rear	71-177 (8-20)
Power Brake Unit Mounting Nut	
Except Sonata	71-106 (8-12)
Master Cylinder-To-Power Brake Unit Nut	
Except Sonata	71-106 (8-12)
Proportioning Valve Mounting Nut	71-106 (8-12)
Proportioning Valve-To-Master Cylinder	
Scoupe	71-106 (8-12)

DISC BRAKE SPECIFICATIONS
DISC BRAKE SPECIFICATIONS (FRONT)

Application	In. (mm)
Caliper Piston Diameter	
Except Sonata	2.126 (54)
Sonata	2.252 (57.2)
Disc Diameter	
Elantra & Sonata	10.118 (257)
Excel & Scoupe	9.528 (242)
Lateral Runout	
Except Sonata	.006 (.15)
Sonata	.004 (.10)
Parallelism	
All Models	.0006 (.015)
Original Thickness	
Elantra & Sonata	.866 (22)
Excel & Scoupe	.75 (19)
Minimum Refinish Thickness	
Elantra & Sonata	.787 (20)
Excel & Scoupe	.669 (17)
Disc Pad Thickness	
Elantra & Sonata	.433 (11)
Excel	.354 (9)
Scoupe	.391 (10)
Minimum Pad Thickness	
Excel & Scoupe	.039 (1.0)
Elantra & Sonata	.079 (2.0)

DISC BRAKE SPECIFICATIONS (REAR)

Application	In. (mm)
Caliper Piston Diameter	1.496 (38)
Disc Diameter	10.354 (263)
Lateral Runout	.005 (.13)
Parallelism	.0006 (.015)
Original Thickness	.472 (12)
Minimum Refinish Thickness	.413 (10.5)
Disc Pad Thickness	.335 (8.5)
Minimum Pad Thickness	.03 (.8)
Parking Brake Drum (Inside Disc)	
Maximum Refinish Diameter	7.283 (185)

DRUM BRAKE SPECIFICATIONS
DRUM BRAKE SPECIFICATIONS

Application	In. (mm)
Drum Diameter	
Elantra	8.00 (203.2)
Excel & Scoupe	7.09 (180.0)
Sonata	9 (228.6)
Maximum Refinish Diameter	
Elantra	8.08 (205.2)
Excel & Scoupe	7.09 (180.0)
Sonata	8.94 (227.0)
Minimum Lining Thickness	
Elantra	.059 (1.50)
Excel	.039 (1.00)
Scoupe & Sonata	.031 (0.80)
Wheel Cylinder Diameter	
Elantra	.750 (19.05)
Excel, Scoupe & Sonata	.811 (20.62)

DESCRIPTION

The Anti-Lock Brake System (ABS) keeps wheels from locking up under extreme braking conditions. ABS prevents excessive wheel slip by pulsing modulation of brake pressure. The ABS Electronic Control Module (ECM) monitors wheel speed. If any wheel slows too quickly (approaches lock-up) during brake actuation, ECM will signal modulator assembly to reduce pressure to that wheel to prevent lock-up.

ABS system consists of Wheel Speed (W/S) sensors, sensor rotors (tone wheels), ABS warning light, ABS Electronic Control Module, ABS modulator and modulator sub-assemblies. See Fig. 1.

NOTE: For information on non-ABS brake components, see DISC & DRUM article.

OPERATION

In Anti-Lock Braking mode (wheel speed signals indicate a wheel is about to lock-up), ECM operates 4 independent control solenoids to increase or decrease pressure as necessary to prevent wheel lock-up. This function continues as long as necessary during braking.

The ABS system also has a Failure mode. When system detects a malfunction, the ECM disables anti-lock braking and allows normal braking only. System then stores Trouble Code(s) and illuminates ABS Warning Light (ABS Service Reminder Indicator). Trouble codes are retrieved for diagnosis through use of the Hyundai Multi-Use Tester (MUT).

SERVICING

CAUTION: See ANTI-LOCK BRAKE SAFETY PRECAUTIONS article in GENERAL INFORMATION.

BRAKE FLUID REPLACEMENT

Brake fluid replacement is recommended every 30 months or 30,000 miles, whichever comes first. Use DOT 3 or equivalent brake fluid.

BLEEDING BRAKE SYSTEM

BLEEDING PROCEDURE

NOTE: There is no special bleeding procedure for ABS system. ABS bleeding procedure is same for conventional brake system.

1) If master cylinder is new or reservoir is empty, bleed master cylinder first. Connect a plastic hose to right rear wheel bleeder screw. Place other end of hose in container partly filled with fresh brake fluid.
2) Press on pedal until no bubbles are seen in container. Bleed remaining wheels starting with left front, left rear and right front in that order. Refill brake fluid reservoir.

ADJUSTMENTS

NOTE: For information on adjustments, see DISC & DRUM article.

TROUBLE SHOOTING

PRETEST CHECKS

Battery Check – Before beginning DIAGNOSIS & TESTING, perform battery test and warning light operation check. Battery voltage must be between 9 and 16 volts. Charge or replace battery as necessary.
Warning Light Operation Check – Turn ignition switch to ON position. ABS warning light should illuminate for 6 seconds before going out. If light does not light, check fuse No. 10. If fuse is okay, check bulb and bulb circuit. If bulb and bulb circuit is okay, fail safe relay may be defective.

DIAGNOSIS & TESTING

RETRIEVING & CLEARING TROUBLE CODES

1) Turn ignition off. Connect Hyundai Multi-Use Tester (MUT) to diagnostic connector and to cigarette lighter socket. Diagnostic connector is located in fuse box on driver's side kick panel. See Fig. 2.
2) MUT unit performs a self-test and then displays model selection menu. Models are selected by pressing YES key to select or NO key to go to next model. After model selection is made, select system from system selection menu in the same way.
3) The function menu will appear. Select self-diagnostic function for ABS system. Codes and related components will be displayed until CLEAR key is pressed. If no codes are in memory, NORMAL will appear on screen. For trouble code descriptions, see TROUBLE CODES table. Identify code and perform appropriate test. See DIAGNOSTIC TESTS.

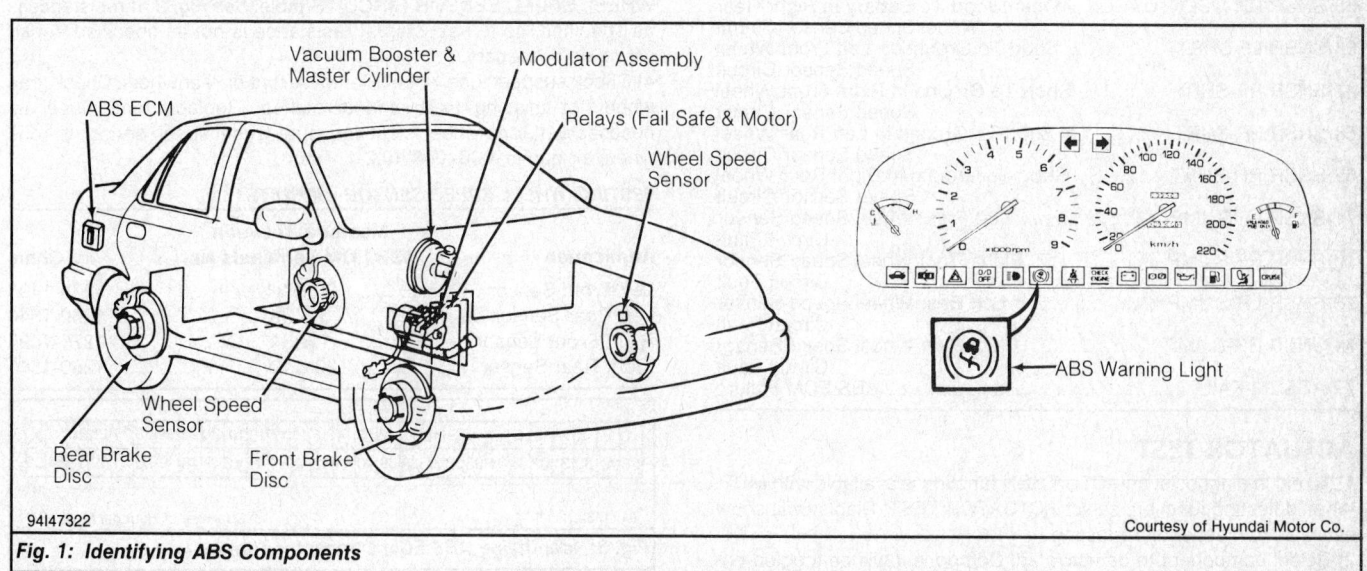

94I47322

Courtesy of Hyundai Motor Co.

Fig. 1: Identifying ABS Components

TROUBLE CODES

Code/MUT Display	Symptom
19/TONE WHEEL	Defective Tone Wheel
21/SOL LF-SHRT	Left Front Solenoid Shorted To Battery
22/SOL LF-OPEN	Left Front Solenoid Open/Short To Ground
23/SOL RF-SHRT	Right Front Solenoid Shorted To Battery
24/SOL RF-OPEN	Right Front Solenoid Open/Short To Ground
25/SOL LR-SHRT	Left Rear Solenoid Shorted To Battery
26/SOL LR-OPEN	Left Rear Solenoid Open/Short To Ground
27/SOL RR-SHRT	Right Rear Solenoid Shorted To Battery
28/SOL RR-OPEN	Right Rear Solenoid Open/Short To Ground
31/SNSR LF-GAP	Left Front Wheel Speed Sensor Air Gap Incorrect
32/SNSR RF-GAP	Right Front Wheel Speed Sensor Air Gap Incorrect
33/SNSR LR-GAP	Left Rear Wheel Speed Sensor Air Gap Incorrect
34/SNSR RR-GAP	Right Rear Wheel Speed Sensor Air Gap Incorrect
35/MOTOR PUMP	Defective Motor Pump
36/MP RLY-OPEN	Open/Short To Ground From Motor Pump Relay
37/MP RLY-SHRT	Open/Short To Battery From Motor Pump Relay
38/MP BATT-SHRT	Short To Battery From Motor Pump Relay
39/MP GND-SHRT	Short To Ground At Motor Pump Relay
41/FAIL RLY-SHRT	Defective Fail Safe Relay
42/FAIL RLY-OPEN	Defective Fail Safe Relay
43/FAIL COIL	Voltage Too High Or Low From Fail Safe Relay
44/ABS SRI-GND	Short To Ground In ABS Warning Light Circuit
45/ABS SRI-DIODE	Open Diode Circuit For ABS Warning Light
54/ABS SRI-BATT	Short To Battery In ABS Warning Light Circuit
55/ABS SRI-OPEN	Open In ABS Warning Light Circuit
56/BATT VOLT-LO	Low Battery Voltage
57/BATT VOLT-HI	High Battery Voltage
62/SNSR LF-OPEN	Open/Short To Battery In Left Front Wheel Speed Sensor Circuit
63/SNSR RF-OPEN	Open/Short To Battery In Right Front Wheel Speed Sensor Circuit
64/SNSR LR-OPEN	Open/Short To Battery In Left Rear Wheel Speed Sensor Circuit
65/SNSR RR-OPEN	Open/Short To Battery In Right Rear Wheel Speed Sensor Circuit
66/SNSR LF-SHRT	Short To Ground In Left Front Wheel Speed Sensor Circuit
67/SNSR RF-SHRT	Short To Ground In Right Front Wheel Speed Sensor Circuit
68/SNSR LR-SHRT	Short To Ground In Left Rear Wheel Speed Sensor Circuit
69/SNSR RR-SHRT	Short To Ground In Right Rear Wheel Speed Sensor Circuit
71/SNSR LF-S JMP	Left Front Wheel Speed Sensor Circuit Fault
72/SNSR RF-S JMP	Right Front Wheel Speed Sensor Circuit Fault
73/SNSR LR-S JMP	Left Rear Wheel Speed Sensor Circuit Fault
74/SNSR RR-S JMP	Right Rear Wheel Speed Sensor Circuit Fault
77/ABSCM-FAIL	ABS ECM Failure

ACTUATOR TEST

1) To aid in diagnosis, an ACTUATION function is available with MUT. When selecting function, select ACTUATOR TEST. Display will show available components for testing.

2) Select component to be activated. Component will be toggled on-off. Solenoids will be heard clicking when selected. Actuation time is limited to a maximum of 20-seconds.

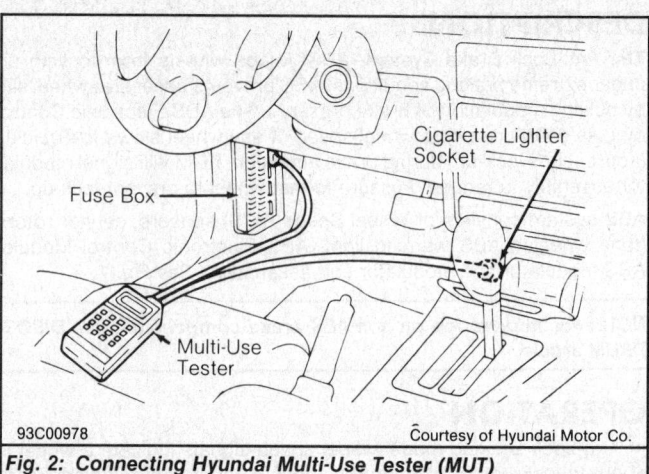

93C00978   Courtesy of Hyundai Motor Co.

Fig. 2: Connecting Hyundai Multi-Use Tester (MUT)

3) Any component that fails to operate as specified should be repaired or replaced. After replacing or repairing malfunctioning components, clear diagnostic codes using MUT erase function. Codes WILL NOT be erased if battery cable is disconnected.

DIAGNOSTIC TESTS

CODE 19, DEFECTIVE TONE WHEEL
CODE 71, LF WHEEL SPEED SENSOR CIRCUIT
CODE 72, RF WHEEL SPEED SENSOR CIRCUIT
CODE 73, LR WHEEL SPEED SENSOR CIRCUIT
CODE 74, RR WHEEL SPEED SENSOR CIRCUIT

1) Disconnect suspect wheel speed sensor connector. Using an ohmmeter, measure resistance between wheel speed sensor connector terminals. Resistance should be 1275-1495 ohms (front sensor) or 1260-1540 ohms (rear sensor). If resistance is not as specified, replace sensor. If resistance is as specified, go to next step.

2) Set voltmeter to AC scale. Connect a voltmeter between suspect wheel speed sensor connector terminals. Observe voltmeter and rotate wheel by hand. If voltage is indicated, go to next step. If no voltage is indicated, replace sensor.

3) Disconnect negative battery cable. Disconnect ABS ECM connector. ECM is located on right side of trunk, behind trim panel. Measure resistance between ABS ECM connector terminals. See TESTING WHEEL SPEED SENSOR CIRCUITS table. *See Fig. 3.* If resistance is as specified, go to next step. If resistance is not as specified, repair wiring as necessary.

4) Check suspect tone wheel. Remove front or rear wheel. Check tone wheel for missing teeth and scratches. Replace tone wheel as necessary. If tone wheel is okay, ensure wheel speed sensor-to-tone wheel air gap is .008-.043" (0.2-1.1 mm).

TESTING WHEEL SPEED SENSOR CIRCUITS

Application	Measure Between ABS ECM Terminals No.	Ohms
Left Front Sensor	32 & 34	1275-1495
Left Rear Sensor	3 & 29	1260-1540
Right Front Sensor	1 & 31	1275-1495
Right Rear Sensor	36 & 37	1260-1540

1	2	3	4	5	6	7	8	9	10	11	12	13	14	15	16	17	18	19	20	21	22	23	24	25	26	27	⊠
28	29	30	31	32	33	34	35	36	37	38	39	40	41	42	43	44	45	46	47	48	49	50	51	52	53	54	55

94J47323   Courtesy of Hyundai Motor Co.

Fig. 3: Identifying ABS ECM Connector Terminals

CODE 21, LF SOLENOID SHORTED TO BATTERY
CODE 23, RF SOLENOID SHORTED TO BATTERY
CODE 25, LR SOLENOID SHORTED TO BATTERY
CODE 27, RR SOLENOID SHORTED TO BATTERY

1) Disconnect negative battery cable. Disconnect ABS modulator and ABS ECM connectors. ABS ECM is located on right side of trunk, behind trim panel. Connect negative battery cable. Turn ignition on. Measure voltage between ground and specified terminal of modulator connector (wiring harness side). See MODULATOR CONNECTOR IDENTIFICATION (WIRING HARNESS SIDE) table. *See Fig. 4.* If no voltage is present, go to next step. If voltage is present, repair short to voltage in wiring harness.

MODULATOR CONNECTOR IDENTIFICATION (WIRING HARNESS SIDE)

Application	Modulator Terminal No.
Left Front Solenoid	8
Left Rear Solenoid	6
Right Front Solenoid	7
Right Rear Solenoid	5

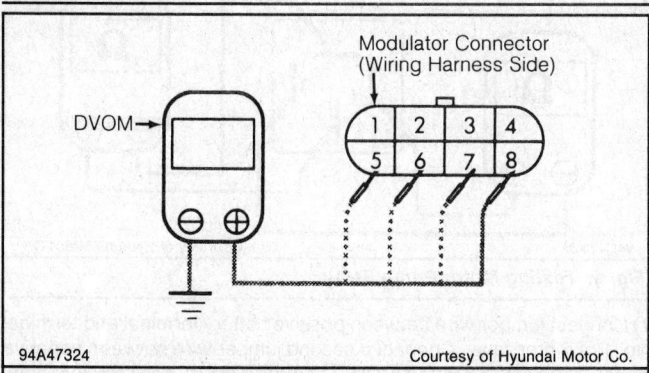

94A47324   Courtesy of Hyundai Motor Co.

Fig. 4: Identifying ABS Modulator Connector Terminals (Wiring Harness Side)

2) Turn ignition off. Ensure modulator connector is still disconnected. Measure resistance between indicated modulator terminals. See MODULATOR CONNECTOR IDENTIFICATION table. *See Fig. 5.* If resistance is 3.10-3.34 ohms, go to next step. If resistance is not 3.10-3.34 ohms, replace modulator.

MODULATOR CONNECTOR IDENTIFICATION

Application	Measure Between Modulator Terminals No.
Left Front Solenoid	4 & 8
Left Rear Solenoid	2 & 6
Right Front Solenoid	3 & 7
Right Rear Solenoid	1 & 5

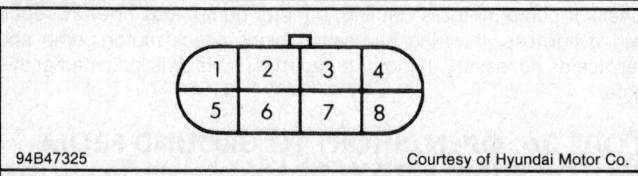

94B47325   Courtesy of Hyundai Motor Co.

Fig. 5: Identifying ABS Modulator Connector Terminals (Relay Box 8-Pin Connector Is Similar)

3) Disconnect negative battery cable. Disconnect ABS ECM connector. Connect negative battery cable. Turn ignition on. Measure voltage between terminal No. 27 (ground) and ABS ECM connector terminals. See CHECKING MODULATOR CIRCUITS table. *See Fig. 3.* If no voltage is present, no problem is indicated at this time. Fault may be intermittent. If battery voltage is present, repair short to battery in wiring harness.

CHECKING MODULATOR CIRCUITS

Application	ECM Terminal No.
Left Front Solenoid	54
Left Rear Solenoid	53
Right Front Solenoid	52
Right Rear Solenoid	25

CODE 22, LF SOLENOID OPEN/SHORT TO GROUND
CODE 24, RF SOLENOID OPEN/SHORT TO GROUND
CODE 26, LR SOLENOID OPEN/SHORT TO GROUND
CODE 28, RR SOLENOID OPEN/SHORT TO GROUND

1) Disconnect negative battery cable. Disconnect ABS modulator and ABS ECM connectors. ABS ECM is located on right side of trunk, behind trim panel. Check for continuity between ground and indicated modulator connector (wiring harness side) terminals. See MODULATOR CONNECTOR IDENTIFICATION (WIRING HARNESS SIDE) table. *See Fig. 4.* If continuity exists, go to next step. If continuity does not exist, repair wiring harness.

MODULATOR CONNECTOR IDENTIFICATION (WIRING HARNESS SIDE)

Application	Modulator Terminal No.
Left Front Solenoid	8
Left Rear Solenoid	6
Right Front Solenoid	7
Right Rear Solenoid	5

2) Using a jumper wire, ground terminal No. 28 (Yellow/Black wire) of ABS ECM connector. Connect negative battery cable. Turn ignition on. Measure voltage between ground and specified terminal of ABS ECM connector (wiring harness side). See MODULATOR CONNECTOR IDENTIFICATION (WIRING HARNESS SIDE) table. If voltage is 9-14 volts, go to next step. If voltage is not 9-14 volts, repair open in wiring harness.

3) Turn ignition off. Disconnect modulator connector. Measure resistance between indicated modulator terminals. See MODULATOR CONNECTOR IDENTIFICATION table. *See Fig. 5.* If resistance is 3.10-3.34 ohms, go to next step. If resistance is not 3.10-3.34 ohms, replace modulator.

MODULATOR CONNECTOR IDENTIFICATION

Application	Measure Between Modulator Terminals No.
Left Front Solenoid	4 & 8
Left Rear Solenoid	2 & 6
Right Front Solenoid	3 & 7
Right Rear Solenoid	1 & 5

4) Ensure ABS ECM and modulator connectors are disconnected. Measure resistance between indicated ABS ECM connector terminals. See IDENTIFYING ABS ECM CONNECTOR TERMINALS table. *See Fig. 3.* If resistance is 3.0-3.8 ohms, no fault is indicated at this time. Fault is intermittent or ABS ECM may be defective. If resistance is not 3.0-3.8 ohms, repair wiring harness.

IDENTIFYING ABS ECM CONNECTOR TERMINALS

Application	Measure Between ABS ECM Terminals No.
Left Front Solenoid	27 & 54
Left Rear Solenoid	27 & 53
Right Front Solenoid	27 & 52
Right Rear Solenoid	25 & 27

CODE 31, LF WHEEL SPEED SENSOR AIR GAP INCORRECT
CODE 32, RF WHEEL SPEED SENSOR AIR GAP INCORRECT
CODE 33, LR WHEEL SPEED SENSOR AIR GAP INCORRECT
CODE 34, RR WHEEL SPEED SENSOR AIR GAP INCORRECT

1) Remove front or rear wheel. Check suspect tone wheel for missing teeth and scratches. Replace tone wheel as necessary. If tone wheel is okay, check wheel speed sensor-to-tone wheel air gap. If air gap is .008-.043" (0.2-1.1 mm), go to next step. If air gap is not .008-.043" (0.2-1.1 mm), replace components as necessary.

2) Disconnect suspect wheel speed sensor connector. Using an ohmmeter, measure resistance between wheel speed sensor connector terminals. Resistance should be 1275-1495 ohms (front sensor) or 1260-1540 ohms (rear sensor). If resistance is not as specified, replace sensor. If resistance is as specified, go to next step.

3) Turn ignition off. Disconnect ABS ECM connector. ECM is located on right side of trunk, behind trim panel. Measure resistance between ABS ECM connector terminals. See TESTING WHEEL SPEED SENSOR CIRCUITS table. See Fig. 3. If resistance is as specified, go to next step. If resistance is not as specified, repair wiring as necessary.

4) Check for continuity between ABS ECM connector terminals. See CHECKING ABS ECM WIRING HARNESS table. If continuity exists, repair wiring harness as necessary. If continuity does not exist, fault is intermittent or ABS ECM may be defective.

TESTING WHEEL SPEED SENSOR CIRCUITS

Application	Measure Between ABS ECM Terminals No.	Ohms
Left Front Sensor	32 & 34	1275-1495
Left Rear Sensor	3 & 29	1260-1540
Right Front Sensor	1 & 31	1275-1495
Right Rear Sensor	36 & 37	1260-1540

CHECKING ABS ECM WIRING HARNESS

Application	Measure Between ABS ECM Terminals No.
Left Front Solenoid	27 & 32
Left Rear Solenoid	27 & 29
Right Front Solenoid	1 & 27
Right Rear Solenoid	27 & 36

CODE 35, DEFECTIVE MOTOR PUMP
CODE 37, OPEN/SHORT TO BATTERY FROM MOTOR PUMP RELAY
CODE 38, SHORT TO BATTERY FROM MOTOR PUMP RELAY

1) Turn ignition off. Disconnect relay box 2-pin connector. See Fig. 8. Measure voltage between ground and terminal No. 2 (Green wire) of relay box 2-pin connector (wiring harness side of connector). If voltage is 9-14 volts, go to next step. If voltage is not 9-14 volts, locate and repair open in wiring harness.

2) Disconnect motor pump 2-pin connector. Connect jumper wire between positive battery terminal and terminal No. 1 (Red wire) of motor pump 2-pin connector. Connect a second jumper wire between negative battery terminal and terminal No. 2 (Black wire) of motor pump 2-pin connector. DO NOT apply battery voltage to motor pump for more than 2 seconds. Check if pump motor is running. If motor pump runs, go to next step. If motor pump does not run, replace modulator assembly.

3) Ensure ignition is off. Disconnect relay box 8-pin connector. Check for continuity between terminals No. 4 (Red wire) and No. 5 (Green/White wire) of relay box 8-pin connector. See Fig. 5. If continuity exists, go to next step. If continuity does not exist, go to step 6).

4) Check for continuity between terminal No. 1 (Blue/Black wire) of relay box 8-pin connector and terminal No. 2 (Blue/Black wire) of relay box 2-pin connector. If continuity does not exist, go to next step. If continuity exists, go to step 6).

5) Connect jumper wire between positive battery terminal and terminal No. 4 (Red wire) of relay box 8-pin connector. Connect a second jumper wire between negative battery terminal and terminal No. 5 (Green/White wire) of relay box 8-pin connector. See Fig. 5. Check for continuity between terminal No. 1 (Blue/Black wire) of relay box 8-pin connector and terminal No. 2 (Blue/Black wire) of relay box 2-pin connector. If continuity does not exist, go to next step. If continuity exists, go to step 8).

6) Turn ignition off. Remove relay box cover. Remove motor relay. See Fig. 8. Check for continuity between terminals No. 1 and 4 of motor relay. Continuity should exist. See Fig. 6. Check for continuity between terminals No. 2 and 3 of motor relay. No continuity should exist. If continuity is as specified, go to next step. If continuity is not as specified, replace relay.

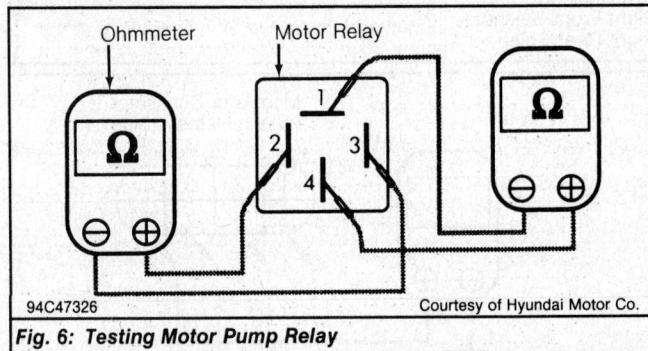
94C47326   Courtesy of Hyundai Motor Co.
Fig. 6: Testing Motor Pump Relay

7) Connect jumper wire between positive battery terminal and terminal No. 1 of motor relay. Connect a second jumper wire between negative battery terminal and terminal No. 4 of motor relay. Check for continuity between relay terminals No. 2 and 3. If continuity does not exist, replace relay. If continuity exists, no fault is indicated at this time. Fault may be intermittent.

8) Turn ignition off. Disconnect ABS ECM connector. ECM is located on right side of trunk, behind trim panel. Measure resistance between terminals No. 19 and 43. See Fig. 3. If resistance is 50-60 ohms, go to next step. If resistance is not 50-60 ohms, repair wiring harness.

9) Turn ignition on. Measure voltage between terminals No. 27 (ground) and No. 42. Also, measure voltage between terminals No. 19 and 27 (ground). If both voltage readings are zero volts, go to next step. If any voltage reading is more than zero volts, repair short to battery.

10) Turn ignition off. Using 2 jumper wires, ground terminals No. 19 and 28 of ABS ECM connector. Turn ignition on. DO NOT connect jumper wires to ground for more than 2 seconds with ignition on. Check if pump motor is running. If motor pump does not run, repair wiring harness. If wiring harness is okay, check motor pump and replace as necessary. If motor pump runs, no fault is indicated at this time.

CODE 36, OPEN/SHORT TO GROUND FROM MOTOR PUMP RELAY
CODE 39, SHORT TO GROUND AT MOTOR PUMP RELAY

1) Turn ignition off. Disconnect relay box 2-pin connector. Measure voltage between ground and terminal No. 2 (Green wire) of relay box 2-pin connector (wiring harness side). If voltage is 9-14 volts, go to next step. If voltage is not 9-14 volts, locate and repair open in wiring harness.

2) Ensure ignition is off. Disconnect relay box 8-pin connector. Check for continuity between terminals No. 4 (Red wire) and No. 5 (Green/White wire) of relay box 8-pin connector. See Fig. 5. If continuity exists, go to next step. If continuity does not exist, go to step 5).

3) Check for continuity between terminal No. 1 (Blue/Black wire) of relay box 8-pin connector and terminal No. 2 (Blue/Black wire) of relay box 2-pin connector. If continuity does not exist, go to next step. If continuity exists, go to step 5).

4) Connect jumper wire between positive battery terminal and terminal No. 4 (Red wire) of relay box 8-pin connector. Connect a second jumper wire between negative battery terminal and terminal No. 5 (Green/White wire) of relay box 8-pin connector. See Fig. 5. Check for continuity between terminal No. 1 (Blue/Black wire) of relay box 8-pin connector and terminal No. 2 Blue/Black wire) of relay box 2-pin connector. If continuity does not exist, go to next step. If continuity exists, reconnect connectors and go to step 7).

5) Turn ignition off. Remove relay box cover. Remove motor relay. See Fig. 8. Check for continuity between terminals No. 1 and 4 of motor relay. Continuity should exist. See Fig. 6. Check for continuity between terminals No. 2 and 3 of motor relay. No continuity should exist. If continuity is as specified, go to next step. If continuity is not as specified, replace relay.

6) Connect jumper wire between positive battery terminal and terminal No. 1 of motor relay. Connect a second jumper wire between negative battery terminal and terminal No. 4 of motor relay. Check for continuity between relay terminals No. 2 and 3. If continuity does not exist, replace relay. If continuity exists, no fault is indicated at this time. Fault may be intermittent.

7) Turn ignition off. Disconnect ABS ECM connector. ECM is located on right side of trunk, behind trim panel. Measure resistance between terminals No. 19 and 43. See Fig. 3. If resistance is 50-60 ohms, go to next step. If resistance is not 50-60 ohms, repair wiring harness.

8) Check for continuity between terminals No. 27 and 42 of ABS ECM connector. See Fig. 3. If resistance is 0.9 ohm or less, go to next step. If resistance is more than 0.9 ohm, repair wiring harness.

9) Using 2 jumper wires, ground terminals No. 19 and 28 of ABS ECM connector. Turn ignition on. DO NOT connect jumper wires to ground for more than 2 seconds with ignition on. Check if motor pump is running. If motor pump does not run, repair wiring harness. If wiring harness is okay, check motor pump and replace as necessary. If motor pump runs, no fault is indicated at this time.

CODE 41, DEFECTIVE FAIL SAFE RELAY
CODE 42, DEFECTIVE FAIL SAFE RELAY
CODE 43, VOLTAGE TOO HIGH OR LOW FROM FAIL SAFE RELAY

1) Turn ignition off. Disconnect relay box 2-pin connector and 8-pin connector. See Fig. 8. Connect negative lead of voltmeter to terminal No. 7 (Black wire) of relay box 8-pin connector (wiring harness side). Connect positive lead of voltmeter to terminal No. 2 (Blue/Black wire) of relay box 2-pin connector (wiring harness side). If voltage is 9-14 volts, go to next step. If voltage is not 9-14 volts, repair open in wiring harness.

2) Check for continuity between terminals No. 7 (Black wire) and No. 8 (Red wire) of relay box 8-pin connector. See Fig. 5. Also, check for continuity between terminals No. 3 (White/Red wire) and No. 6 (Black/Yellow wire) of relay box 8-pin connector. If both readings indicate continuity, go to next step. If one or more readings indicate no continuity, go to step 6).

3) Check for continuity between terminal No. 8 (Red wire) of relay box 8-pin connector and terminal No. 1 (Red/Black wire) of relay box 2-pin connector. If continuity exists, go to step 6). If continuity does not exist, go to next step.

4) Connect a jumper wire between positive battery terminal and terminal No. 3 (White/Red wire) of relay box 8-pin connector. Connect a second jumper wire between negative battery terminal and terminal No. 6 (Black/Yellow wire) of relay box 8-pin connector. DO NOT apply battery voltage for more than 2 seconds. Check for continuity between terminals No. 7 (Black wire) and No. 8 (Red wire) of relay box 8-pin connector. If continuity does not exist, go to next step. If continuity exists, go to step 6).

5) Check for continuity between terminals No. 8 (Red wire) of relay box 8-pin connector and No. 1 (Red/Black wire) of relay box 2-pin connec-

tor. If continuity exists, go to step 8). If continuity does not exist, go to next step.

6) Turn ignition off. Remove relay box cover. See Fig. 8. Remove fail safe relay. Check for continuity between relay terminals. See TESTING FAIL SAFE RELAY table. See Fig. 7. If continuity is not as specified, replace relay. If continuity is as specified, go to next step.

TESTING FAIL SAFE RELAY

Relay Terminals No.	Continuity
1 & 5	No
2 & 4	Yes
3 & 5	Yes

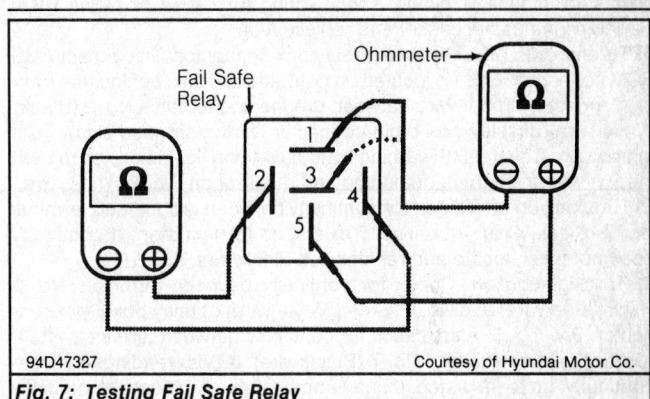

94D47327   Courtesy of Hyundai Motor Co.

Fig. 7: Testing Fail Safe Relay

7) Connect a jumper wire between positive battery terminal and terminal No. 2 of fail safe relay. Connect a second jumper wire between negative battery terminal and terminal No. 4 of fail safe relay. Check for continuity between relay terminals No. 1 and 5. Continuity should exist. Check for continuity between relay terminals No. 3 and 5. No continuity should exist. If continuity is not as specified, replace relay. If continuity is as specified, no fault is indicated at this time. Fault may be intermittent.

8) Reconnect relay box connectors. Turn ignition off. Disconnect ABS ECM connector. ECM is located on right side of trunk, behind trim panel. Measure resistance between terminals No. 27 (Black wire) and No. 43 (Red/Green wire) of ABS ECM connector. If resistance is one ohm or less, go to next step. If resistance is more than one ohm, repair wiring harness.

9) Measure resistance between terminals No. 28 (Yellow/Black wire) and No. 50 (Green/Red wire) of ABS ECM connector. If resistance is 20-28 ohms, go to next step. If resistance is not 20-28 ohms, repair wiring harness.

10) Connect a jumper wire between ground and terminal No. 28 (Yellow/Black wire) of ABS ECM connector. Turn ignition on. DO NOT connect jumper wire to ground for more than 2 seconds. Measure voltage between terminals No. 27 (Black wire) and No. 43 (Red/Green wire) of ABS ECM connector. If voltage is not 9-14 volts, repair wiring harness. If voltage is 9-14 volts, no fault is indicated at this time. Fault may intermittent.

CODE 44, SHORT TO GROUND IN ABS WARNING LIGHT CIRCUIT
CODE 45, OPEN DIODE CIRCUIT FOR ABS WARNING LIGHT
CODE 54, SHORT TO BATTERY IN ABS WARNING LIGHT CIRCUIT
CODE 55, OPEN IN ABS WARNING LIGHT CIRCUIT

1) If ABS warning light is off, go to step 4). If ABS warning light is on, turn ignition off. Disconnect negative battery cable. Disconnect ABS ECM connector. ECM is located on right side of trunk, behind trim panel. Disconnect relay box connector. See Fig. 8. Reconnect negative battery cable. Turn ignition on. Check ABS warning light. If light is off, go to next step. If light is on, go to step 7).

2) Check for continuity between ground and terminal No. 2 (Black/White wire) of relay box 8-pin connector (wiring harness side). If continuity exists, repair wiring harness. If continuity does not exist, go to next step.

3) Disconnect negative battery cable. Ensure ABS ECM connector is still disconnected. Check for continuity between ground and terminal No. 17 (Yellow/Black wire) of ABS ECM connector. See Fig. 3. If continuity exists, repair short to ground in wiring harness. If continuity does not exist, no fault is indicated at this time. Fault may be intermittent.

4) Check fuse No. 10 in instrument fuse panel. If fuse is okay, go to next step. If fuse is blown, check wiring for cause of blown fuse. Repair wiring as necessary and replace fuse.

5) Turn ignition off. Disconnect relay box connector. Disconnect ABS ECM connector. ECM is located on right side of trunk, behind trim panel. Connect a jumper wire between ground and terminal No. 2 (Black/White wire) of relay box 8-pin connector (wiring harness side). Turn ignition on. Check ABS warning light. If warning light is on, go to next step. If warning light is off, locate and repair open Black/White wire.

6) Turn ignition off. Check for continuity between ground and terminal No. 7 (Black wire). If continuity exists, go to next step. If continuity does not exist, locate and repair open Black wire.

7) Turn ignition off. Check for continuity between terminals No. 3 (White/Red wire) and No. 6 (Green/White wire) of relay box 8-pin connector. See Fig. 5. Also, check for continuity between terminals No. 2 (Green/Yellow wire) and No. 7 (Black wire). If both readings indicate continuity, go to next step. If one or both readings indicate no continuity, go to step 11).

8) Check for continuity between terminals No. 2 (Green/Yellow wire) of relay box 8-pin connector and No. 1 (Red/Black wire) of relay box 2-pin connector. If continuity does not exist, go to next step. If continuity exists, go to step 11).

9) Connect jumper wire between positive battery terminal and terminal No. 3 (White/Red wire) of relay box 8-pin connector. Connect a second jumper wire between negative battery terminal and terminal No. 6 (Black/Yellow wire) of relay box 8-pin connector. See Fig. 5. DO NOT apply battery voltage to connector for more than 2-seconds. Check for continuity between terminals No. 2 (Green/Yellow wire) and No. 7 (Black wire) of relay box 8-pin connector. If continuity exists, go to step 11). If continuity does not exist, go to next step.

10) Check for continuity between terminals No. 2 (Green/Yellow wire) of relay box 8-pin connector and No. 1 (Red/Black wire) of relay box 2-pin connector. If continuity does not exist, go to next step. If continuity exists, go to step 3).

11) Turn ignition off. Remove relay box cover. See Fig. 8. Remove fail safe relay. Check for continuity between relay terminals. See TESTING FAIL SAFE RELAY table. See Fig. 7. If continuity is not as specified, replace relay. If continuity is as specified, go to next step.

TESTING FAIL SAFE RELAY

Relay Terminals No.	Continuity
1 & 5	No
2 & 4	Yes
3 & 5	Yes

12) Connect jumper wire between positive battery terminal and terminal No. 2 of fail safe relay. Connect a second jumper wire between negative battery terminal and terminal No. 4 of fail safe relay. Check for continuity between relay terminals No. 1 and 5. Continuity should exist. Check for continuity between relay terminals No. 3 and 5. No continuity should exist. If continuity is not as specified, replace relay. If continuity is as specified, no fault is indicated at this time. Fault may be intermittent.

CODE 56, LOW BATTERY VOLTAGE
CODE 57, HIGH BATTERY VOLTAGE

1) Check fuse No. 13 in instrument panel fuse box. If fuse is okay, go to next step. If fuse is blown, check wiring harness for cause of blown fuse. Repair as necessary and replace fuse.

2) Disconnect negative battery cable. Disconnect ABS ECM connector. ECM is located on right side of trunk, behind trim panel. Reconnect negative battery cable. Turn ignition on. Measure voltage between terminals No. 27 (Black wire) and No. 50 (Green/Yellow wire). If voltage is not 9-14 volts, go to next step. If voltage is 9-14 volts, no fault is indicated at this time. Fault may be intermittent.

3) Turn ignition off. Measure resistance between ground and terminals No. 26 (Black wire), No. 27 (Black wire) and No. 51 of ABS ECM connector. If all readings are 0.5 ohm or less, locate and repair open circuit between fuse No. 13 and ABS ECM connector. If one or more readings is more than 0.5 ohm, located and repair open Black wire between ground and ABS ECM connector.

CODE 62, OPEN/SHORT TO BATTERY IN LF WHEEL SPEED SENSOR CIRCUIT
CODE 63, OPEN/SHORT TO BATTERY IN RF WHEEL SPEED SENSOR CIRCUIT
CODE 64, OPEN/SHORT TO BATTERY IN LR WHEEL SPEED SENSOR CIRCUIT
CODE 65, OPEN/SHORT TO BATTERY IN RR WHEEL SPEED SENSOR CIRCUIT

1) Turn ignition off. Disconnect suspect wheel speed sensor connector. Using an ohmmeter, measure resistance between wheel speed sensor connector terminals. Resistance should be 1275-1495 ohms (front sensor) or 1260-1540 ohms (rear sensor). If resistance is not as specified, replace sensor. If resistance is as specified, go to next step.

2) Measure voltage between ground and suspect wheel speed sensor connector terminals. If voltage is zero volts, go to next step. If voltage is more than zero volts, locate and repair short to battery in sensor wiring.

3) Turn ignition off. Disconnect ABS ECM connector. ECM is located on right side of trunk, behind trim panel. Measure resistance between ABS ECM connector terminals. See TESTING WHEEL SPEED SENSOR CIRCUITS table. See Fig. 3. If resistance is as specified, go to next step. If resistance is not as specified, repair wiring as necessary.

TESTING WHEEL SPEED SENSOR CIRCUITS

Application	Measure Between ABS ECM Terminals No.	Ohms
Left Front Sensor	32 & 34	1275-1495
Left Rear Sensor	3 & 29	1260-1540
Right Front Sensor	1 & 31	1275-1495
Right Rear Sensor	36 & 37	1260-1540

4) Measure voltage between ABS ECM connector terminals. See Checking ABS ECM VOLTAGE table. If all voltage readings are zero volts, no fault is indicated at this time. Fault may be intermittent. If one or more voltage readings is more than zero volts, locate and repair short to battery in wiring harness.

CHECKING ABS ECM VOLTAGE

Application	Measure Between ABS ECM Terminals No.
Left Front Sensor	27 & 32
Left Rear Sensor	27 & 29
Right Front Sensor	1 & 27
Right Rear Sensor	27 & 36

CODE 66, SHORT TO GROUND IN LF WHEEL SPEED SENSOR CIRCUIT
CODE 67, SHORT TO GROUND IN RF WHEEL SPEED SENSOR CIRCUIT
CODE 68, SHORT TO GROUND IN LR WHEEL SPEED SENSOR CIRCUIT
CODE 69, SHORT TO GROUND IN RR WHEEL SPEED SENSOR CIRCUIT

1) Turn ignition off. Disconnect suspect wheel speed sensor connector. Using an ohmmeter, measure resistance between wheel speed sensor connector terminals. Resistance should be 1275-1495 ohms (front sensor) or 1260-1540 ohms (rear sensor). If resistance is not as specified, replace sensor. If resistance is as specified, go to next step.
2) Check for continuity between ground and suspect wheel speed sensor connector terminals. If continuity does not exist, go to next step. If continuity exists, locate and repair short to ground in sensor wiring.
3) Disconnect negative battery cable. Disconnect ABS ECM connector. ECM is located on right side of trunk, behind trim panel. Measure resistance between ABS ECM connector terminals. See TESTING WHEEL SPEED SENSOR CIRCUITS table. *See Fig. 3.* If resistance is as specified, go to next step. If resistance is not as specified, repair wiring as necessary.

TESTING WHEEL SPEED SENSOR CIRCUITS

Application	Measure Between ABS ECM Terminals No.	Ohms
Left Front Sensor	32 & 34	1275-1495
Left Rear Sensor	3 & 29	1260-1540
Right Front Sensor	1 & 31	1275-1495
Right Rear Sensor	36 & 37	1260-1540

4) Check for continuity between ABS ECM connector terminals. See CHECKING ABS ECM CONTINUITY table. If all readings indicate no continuity, no fault is indicated at this time. Fault may be intermittent. If one or more readings indicate continuity, locate and repair short to ground in wiring harness.

CHECKING ABS ECM CONTINUITY

Application	Measure Between ABS ECM Terminals No.
Left Front Sensor	27 & 32
Left Rear Sensor	27 & 29
Right Front Sensor	1 & 27
Right Rear Sensor	27 & 36

CODE 77, ABS ECM FAILURE

If Code 77 is present, replace ABS ECM. ECM is located on right side of trunk, behind trim panel.

REMOVAL & INSTALLATION

ABS ECM

Removal & Installation – 1) Turn ignition off. Disconnect negative battery cable. ABS ECM in located in right rear of trunk. *See Fig. 1.* Remove right side trim panel from trunk. Disconnect ABS ECM connector.
2) Remove ABS ECM mounting bolts and washers. Remove ABS ECM from vehicle. To install, reverse removal procedure. Tighten bolts to specification. See TORQUE SPECIFICATIONS.

MODULATOR

NOTE: DO NOT attempt to disassemble ABS modulator. If ABS modulator is defective, modulator must be replaced as an assembly.

Removal & Installation – 1) Turn ignition off. Open brake caliper bleed screws and drain master cylinder. Use syringe to remove any remaining fluid in fluid reservoir. Remove air cleaner assembly.
2) Disconnect wiring harness connectors as necessary. See Fig. 8. Disconnect brakelines from modulator assembly. Remove relay box from modulator mounting bracket. Remove modulator mounting bracket. Remove modulator.
3) To install, reverse removal procedure. Tighten nuts and bolts to specification. See TORQUE SPECIFICATIONS. Bleed brake system. See BLEEDING BRAKE SYSTEM.

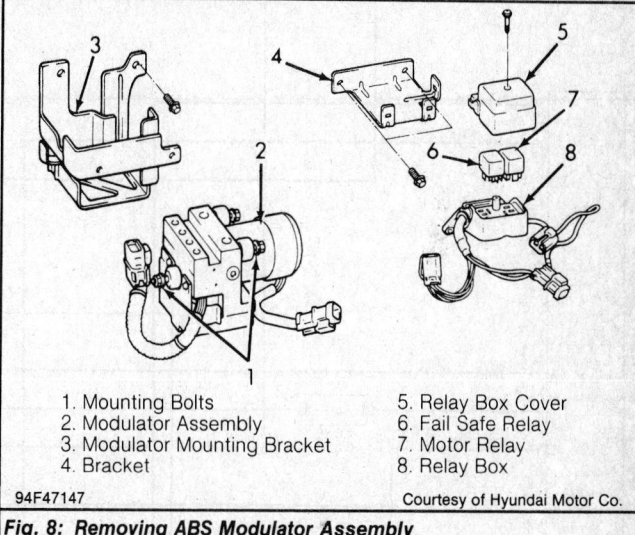

1. Mounting Bolts
2. Modulator Assembly
3. Modulator Mounting Bracket
4. Bracket
5. Relay Box Cover
6. Fail Safe Relay
7. Motor Relay
8. Relay Box

94F47147   Courtesy of Hyundai Motor Co.

Fig. 8: Removing ABS Modulator Assembly

WHEEL SPEED SENSORS

Removal & Installation – 1) Loosen wheel lug nuts. Raise and support front of vehicle. Remove wheel. Remove bolts for sensor and cable. Disconnect wheel speed sensor connector.
2) Remove wheel speed sensor from vehicle. To install, reverse removal procedure. Tighten wheel speed sensor and cable bolts to specification. See TORQUE SPECIFICATIONS.

OVERHAUL

DO NOT overhaul or disassemble modulator assembly. If modulator is defective, replace modulator as an assembly.

TORQUE SPECIFICATIONS

TORQUE SPECIFICATIONS

Application	Ft. Lbs. (N.m)
Brakelines	10-12 (14-16)
Modulator Bracket Bolt	12-19 (16-26)
Modulator Mount Bolt	12-19 (16-26)
Wheel Speed Sensor & Cable Bolts	12-19 (16-26)

	INCH Lbs. (N.m)
Caliper Bleed Screws	
Front	62-115 (7-13)
Rear	71-177 (8-20)

WIRING DIAGRAM

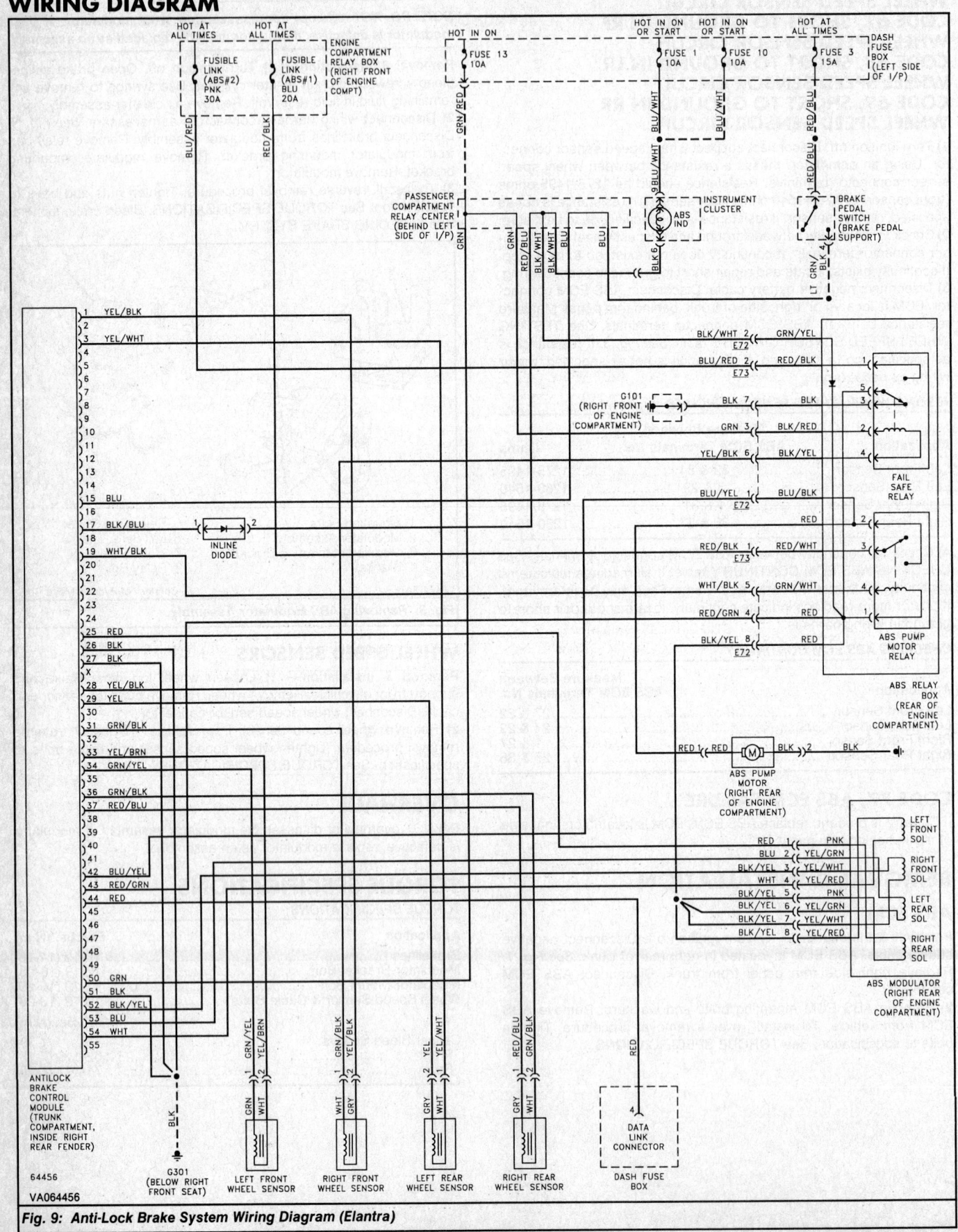

Fig. 9: Anti-Lock Brake System Wiring Diagram (Elantra)

64456
VA064456

DESCRIPTION

The Anti-Lock Brake System (ABS) keeps wheels from locking up under extreme braking conditions. ABS prevents excessive wheel slip by pulsing modulation of brake pressure. The ABS Electronic Control Unit (ECU) monitors wheel speed. If any wheel slows too quickly (approaches lock-up) during brake actuation, ECU will signal hydraulic unit to reduce pressure to that wheel to prevent lock-up.

ABS system consists of Wheel Speed (W/S) sensors, sensor rotors, ABS warning light, ABS Electronic Control Unit, ABS modulator and modulator sub-assemblies. *See Fig. 1.*

NOTE: For information on non-ABS brake components, see DISC & DRUM article.

OPERATION

There are 3 normal modes of system operation. In No Braking mode (when vehicle is first started), the ignition switch is in RUN position. ECU performs a self-check, an external circuit check and begins operation. When brake pedal is fully released and vehicle speed reaches 3 MPH, ECU performs an electrical and hydraulic check of pump and solenoid functions.

In Normal Braking mode (driver applies brakes), the ECU does not affect either front or rear brake hydraulic functions. The ECU monitors each of the 4 wheel speed signals in preparation for possible initiation of anti-lock control.

In Anti-Lock Braking mode (wheel speed signals indicate a wheel is about to lock-up), ECU operates 4 independent control solenoids to increase or decrease pressure as necessary to prevent wheel lock-up. This function continues as long as necessary during braking.

The ABS system also has a Failure mode. When system detects a malfunction, the ECU disables anti-lock braking and allows normal braking only. System then stores Trouble Code(s) and illuminates ABS Warning Light. Trouble codes are later retrieved for diagnosis through use of the Hyundai Multi-Use Tester (MUT).

SERVICING

CAUTION: See ANTI-LOCK BRAKE SAFETY PRECAUTIONS article in GENERAL INFORMATION.

BRAKE FLUID REPLACEMENT

Brake fluid replacement is recommended every 30 months or 30,000 miles, whichever comes first. Use DOT 3 or equivalent brake fluid.

BLEEDING BRAKE SYSTEM

BASIC BLEEDING PROCEDURE

1) If master cylinder is new or reservoir is empty, bleed master cylinder first. Connect a plastic hose to right rear wheel bleeder screw. Place other end of hose in container partly filled with fresh brake fluid.
2) Press on pedal until no bubbles are seen in container. Bleed remaining wheels starting with left front, left rear and right front in that order. Proceed to ABS BLEEDING PROCEDURE.

ABS BLEEDING PROCEDURE

1) Connect Hyundai Multi-Use Tester (MUT) to diagnostic connector and to cigarette lighter socket. Diagnostic connector is located in fuse box on driver's side kick panel. *See Fig. 2.*

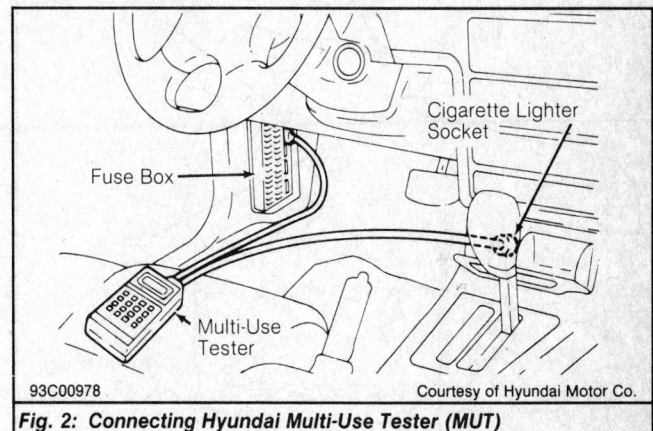

93C00978   Courtesy of Hyundai Motor Co.
Fig. 2: Connecting Hyundai Multi-Use Tester (MUT)

2) Turn ignition switch to ON position. MUT should be activated. Place clear plastic tube onto modulator assembly bleed screw No. 1. *See Fig. 3.* Place other end of plastic tube into container partly filled with fresh brake fluid.

CAUTION: Fluid is under high pressure. DO NOT bleed without hose attached.

3) Apply a constant light pressure on brake pedal. Use MUT to actuate Right Front Build/Decay valves (RF B/D) and Left Rear Build/Decay valves (LR B/D). See ABS MODULATOR ASSEMBLY BLEEDING table. This will bleed right front and left rear fluid sump.
4) Open bleed screw. As valve cycles, fluid and air will emerge and the pedal will fall slightly. Observe fluid flow. Flow is cycled on and off with MUT. When pedal drops and if it is necessary to reapply pedal, close bleed screw before releasing pedal.

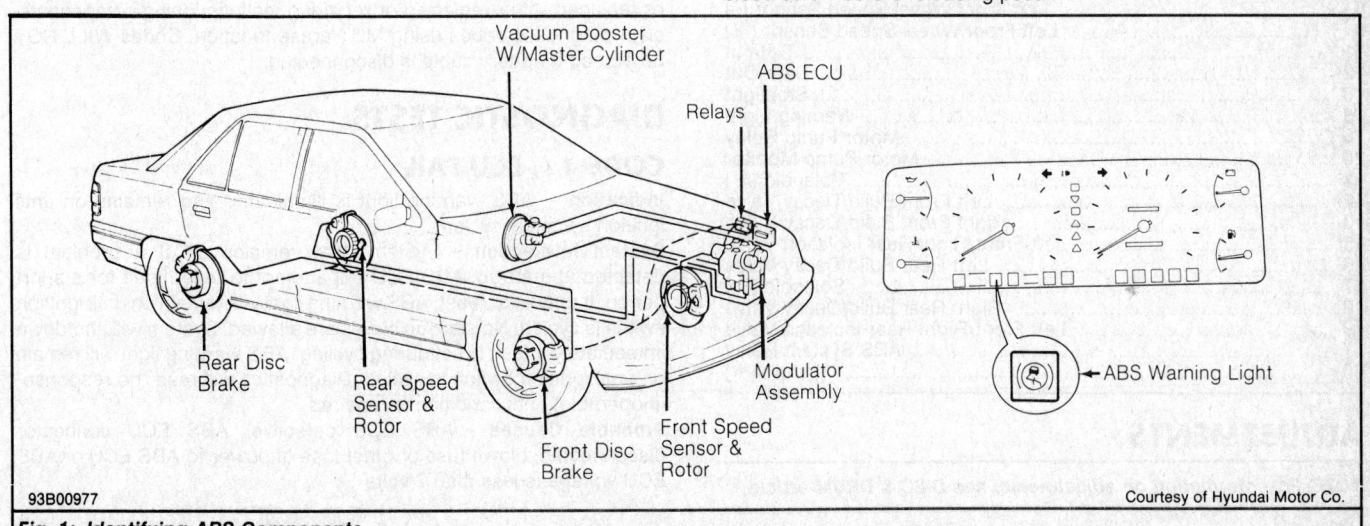

93B00977   Courtesy of Hyundai Motor Co.
Fig. 1: Identifying ABS Components

5) When fluid flows with no air bubbles, close bleed screw and tighten to specification. See TORQUE SPECIFICATIONS. Proceed with No. 2 bleed screw and components (left front sump and right rear sump).

6) When No. 2 bleeding is complete, continue with No. 3 and 4 using MUT to cycle appropriate Isolation (ISO) valve or Build/Decay (B/D) valve. Tighten all bleed screws to specification.

ABS MODULATOR ASSEMBLY BLEEDING

Order	ABS Component	Valves To Cycle
1	RF & LR Sump	RF B/D & LR B/D
2	LF & RR Sump	LF B/D & RR B/D
3	RF & LR Accumulator	RF/LR ISO Valve & RF B/D
4	LF & RR Accumulator	LF/RR ISO Valve & LF B/D

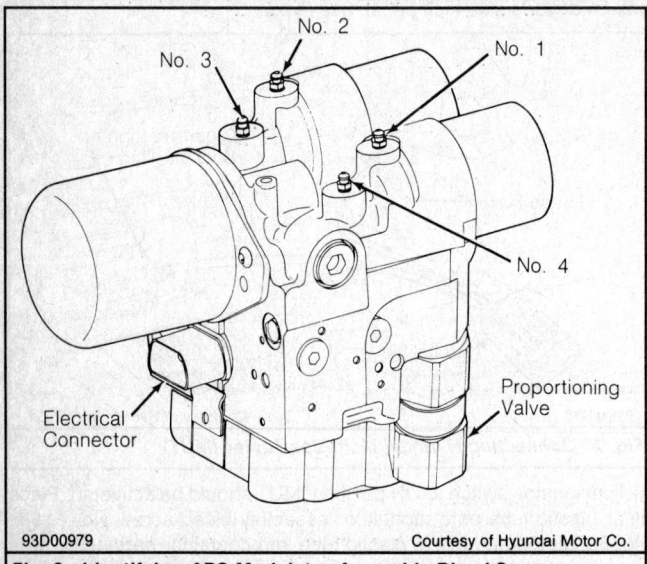

No. 2
No. 3
No. 1
No. 4
Electrical Connector
Proportioning Valve

93D00979   Courtesy of Hyundai Motor Co.

Fig. 3: Identifying ABS Modulator Assembly Bleed Screws

NOTE: Not all cavities are used.

ABS WIRING HARNESS PIN IDENTIFICATION

Cavity No.	Function
1	Right Rear Wheel Speed Sensor (−)
2	Right Rear Wheel Speed Sensor (+)
3	Left Rear Wheel Speed Sensor (−)
4	Left Rear Wheel Speed Sensor (+)
5	Ground
6	Right Front Wheel Speed Sensor (−)
7	Right Front Wheel Speed Sensor (+)
8	Left Front Wheel Speed Sensor (−)
9	Left Front Wheel Speed Sensor (+)
11	Data In
12	Data Out
13	Stoplight
15	Warning Light
16	Motor Pump Relay
20	Motor Pump Monitor
41	Solenoid (+)
42	Left Front Build/Decay Valve
43	Right Front Build/Decay Valve
45	Left Front/Right Rear Isolation Valve
46	Left Rear Build/Decay Valve
47	Solenoid (+)
48	Right Rear Build/Decay Valve
49	Left Front/Right Rear Isolation Valve
57	ABS System Relay
60	Ignition (+)

ADJUSTMENTS

NOTE: For information on adjustments, see DISC & DRUM article.

TROUBLE SHOOTING

PRETEST CHECKS

Battery Check – Before beginning DIAGNOSIS & TESTING, perform battery test and warning light operation check. Battery voltage must be between 9 and 16 volts. Charge or replace battery as necessary.

Warning Light Operation Check – Turn ignition switch to ON position. ABS warning light should illuminate for one second before going out. If light does not light, check fuse No. 12. If fuse is okay, use ohmmeter to check bulb and bulb circuit. See ABS WIRING HARNESS PIN IDENTIFICATION table. See Fig. 4.

ABS ECU Pin Voltage/Resistance Check – **1)** Performing ABS ECU pin voltage/resistance check can help determine if ABS ECU is receiving proper voltage/resistance signals. Performing this check can also help determine if ABS ECU wiring harness has shorts or opens.

2) Disconnect ABS ECU connector. ECU is located on left side of engine compartment. Perform checks at wiring harness side of ABS ECU connector. See Fig. 4.

DIAGNOSIS & TESTING

RETRIEVING & CLEARING TROUBLE CODES

1) Ensure battery voltage is 12 volts. Turn ignition on. ABS warning light should illuminate for one second. If warning light does not illuminate, check fuse, bulb and wiring harness.

2) Turn ignition switch to OFF position. Connect Hyundai Multi-Use Tester (MUT) to diagnostic connector and to cigarette lighter socket. Diagnostic connector is located in fuse box on driver's side kick panel. See Fig. 2.

3) MUT unit performs a self-test and then displays model selection menu. Models are selected by pressing YES key to select or NO key to go to next model. After model selection is made, select system from system selection menu in the same way.

4) The function menu will appear. Select self-diagnostic function for ABS. Codes and related components will be displayed until CLEAR key is pressed. Perform appropriate code test. See DIAGNOSTIC TESTS. If no codes are in memory, NORMAL will appear on screen.

ACTUATOR TEST

1) To aid in diagnosis, an ACTUATION function is available with MUT. When selecting function, select ACTUATOR TEST. Display will show available components for testing.

2) Select component to be activated. Component will be toggled on-off every 1.6 seconds. If warning light was selected, it will flash on and off. If motor pump is selected, it will operate. Solenoids will be heard clicking when selected. Actuation test lasts 400 seconds.

3) Any component that fails to operate as specified should be repaired or replaced. After replacing or repairing malfunctioning components, clear diagnostic codes using MUT erase function. Codes WILL NOT be erased if battery cable is disconnected.

DIAGNOSTIC TESTS

CODE 11, ECU FAIL

Indication – ABS warning light is illuminated and remains on until ignition switch is cycled.

System Interaction – System relay remains off if a problem is detected at start-up. ABS ECU will attempt to reset itself for a short period. If unable to reset, ABS warning light will remain on until ignition switch is cycled. No start-up cycles are allowed. System will shutdown immediately if fault is set during cycling. ABS warning light will remain on until ignition switch is cycled. Diagnostics will read "no response" (inoperable) until condition is repaired.

Probable Causes – ABS ECU defective, ABS ECU connector disconnected, blown fuse or other loss of power to ABS ECU or ABS ECU voltage is less than 7 volts.

CODE 12, MODULATOR

Indication – ABS warning light comes on immediately after detection occurs. During normal operation a 15-second delay occurs before a failure is detected.

System Interaction – If a failure is present and vehicle is not cycling, system relay is disabled. If a failure is detected during cycling, a sequenced shutdown is initiated followed by disabling of the system relay. The failure is sensed by an ABS ECU test that is run once every 15 seconds during normal operation and once every 400 milliseconds during cycling. Start-up cycle is included.

Probable Causes – Loose ABS ECU connector, loose modulator 10-pin connector, short or open solenoid coil or excessive modulator wiring voltage drop.

CODE 13, EXCESS DECAY

Indication – ABS warning light is illuminated if 2 channels call for decay for more than 2 seconds while cycling.

System interaction – When the failure occurs, front channels go through a sequenced shutdown. Rear channels continue to cycle to maintain vehicle stability. ABS warning light will remain on until decay timers on vehicle come to a complete stop.

Probable Causes – Hydroplaning, incompatible tone wheel count between vehicle and ABS ECU, brakelines not connected to modulator correctly, miswired modulator or miswired ABS ECU or associated connector.

CODE 22, WARNING LIGHT

Indication – None

System Interaction – Test is conducted at start-up. Fault is stored when drive-off occurs or 3 minutes elapses after vehicle is started.

Probable Causes – Blown fuse, open circuit, burned out warning light bulb, ABS warning light relay defective or system relay defective.

CODE 23, WARNING LIGHT RELAY

Indication – None

System Interaction – Test is conducted at start-up. Fault is stored when drive-off occurs or 3 minutes elapses after vehicle is started.

Probable Causes – Faulty ground for ABS warning light relay contacts or ABS warning light relay stuck in energized position.

CODE 24, SYSTEM RELAY

Indication – ABS warning light comes on when fault is set and remains on until ignition switch is cycled.

System Interaction – This condition is detected at start-up. ABS warning light remains on and fault is stored in ABS ECU memory. Motor pump runs for 250 milliseconds and no solenoid start-up cycles are allowed (no power to solenoids). If failure occurs during cycling, a shutdown is executed. ABS warning light will remain on until ignition switch is cycled.

Probable Cause – System relay stuck on.

CODE 25, SOLENOID LOW VOLTAGE

Indication – ABS warning light is illuminated about 300 milliseconds after ABS ECU senses less than 9 volts at modulator. ABS warning light is turned off and system is enabled when condition goes away.

System Interaction – If system is cycling, a sequenced shutdown is initiated. After shutdown sequence is completed, system relay is disabled until condition subsides. If condition is present upon ignition, warning light is not illuminated and fault is not set until start-up cycle is completed.

Probable Causes – Open system relay, excessive system load on battery or electrical system, long stop in cold weather, loose wiring harness connector, or a short or open 12-volt wire.

CODE 28, MOTOR PUMP

Indication – ABS warning light is illuminated until ignition switch is cycled.

System Interaction – Before drive-off occurs and anytime while not cycling, motor pump voltage is tested every 3 seconds. Upon any ABS ECU requested initial turn on, voltage is checked after a 250 millisecond delay. While cycling, motor pump voltage is again tested every 3 seconds. This is run continuously. A failure results in disabling of the system relay (maximum 3 second delay) and ABS warning light. No shutdown sequence is executed.

Probable Causes – Motor pump relay stuck on, no/low voltage at motor pump or open motor circuit.

CODE 85, LEFT FRONT SENSOR
CODE 86, RIGHT FRONT SENSOR
CODE 87, LEFT REAR SENSOR
CODE 88, RIGHT REAR SENSOR

Interaction – ABS warning light is illuminated until ignition switch is cycled.

System Interaction – Vehicle speed sensor faults are set in one or more of 3 sensor fail-safe modes. Each sets the respective fault code and turns on ABS warning light until ignition switch is cycled.

Intermittent Sensor Failure – Sensor fault is set and ABS warning light comes on when ABS ECU senses a high frequency of wheel "G" forces when vehicle is accelerating or is at a steady speed and is not cycling.

Probable Causes – Excessive sensor gap, traveling over bumpy terrain, wheel spin on loose or bumpy terrain, weak sensor output or excessive axle runout.

Missing Speed Signal – This functions when one or 2 wheel speed signals are missing. ABS warning light comes on when there is an absence of wheel speed signal for 3 seconds on any channel and the second highest wheel speed has exceeded 15 MPH, or when vehicle speed exceeds 8 MPH. If ABS has been initiated and fault is set (3 seconds after loss of signal) system goes to rear only cycling mode to maintain stability and front channels go through shutdown sequence. If both rear wheel speed sensor signals are lost, a complete sequenced shutdown is initiated.

Special logic is included to prevent a failure from being set in the event 2 drive wheels are spinning when vehicle is stuck. If both rear wheel speeds are less than 0.5 MPH and vehicle velocity is less than 3 MPH, then fault setting is delayed for 20 seconds.

NOTE: A sensor fault cannot be set if a sensor fault has been stored previously. Only one sensor fault can be stored at a time.

Probable Causes – Loose sensor connector, excessive sensor gap or weak or no sensor output.

CODE 95, LEFT FRONT SENSOR CONTINUITY
CODE 96, RIGHT FRONT SENSOR CONTINUITY
CODE 97, LEFT REAR SENSOR CONTINUITY
CODE 98, RIGHT REAR SENSOR CONTINUITY

Indication – ABS warning light is illuminated until ignition switch is cycled.

System Interaction – Sensor continuity test is run only when vehicle velocity is zero MPH and at least 2 of the 4 channels have no signal for 5 seconds. A fault is set when ABS ECU detects a lack of continuity in any wheel speed sensor circuit. ABS warning light comes on immediately.

Probable Causes – One broken, cracked or short circuited (to ground) sensor wire, loose sensor connector or excessive external environment noise.

REMOVAL & INSTALLATION

ABS ECU

Removal & Installation – **1)** Ensure ignition is off. Disconnect negative battery cable. Locate ABS ECU in left side of engine compartment. Disconnect ABS ECU connector.

2) Remove ABS ECU mounting bolts and washers. Remove ABS ECU from vehicle. To install, reverse removal procedure. Tighten bolts to specification. See TORQUE SPECIFICATIONS.

ABS CIRCUIT PIN VOLTAGE/RESISTANCE

Test connection (connector pin NO)	Check Item	Vehicle condition	Specification	Trouble part
60—5 (ground)	Voltage	Ignition switch ON	Battery vol.	Power
5—Batt. (—)	Countinuity	Ignition switch OFF	Continuity	Ground
13—5 (ground)	Voltage	Ignition switch OFF and brake pedal depressed	Battery vol.	Stop lamp SW
60—15	Voltage	Ignition switch OFF Ignition switch ON	OV Battery vol.	Warning light lamp
57—5 (ground)	Resistance	Ignition switch OFF		System relay
41—5 (ground) (47)	Resistance	Ignition switch OFF		Warning light relay
41—16 (47)	Resistance	Ignition switch OFF		Motor pump relay
20—5 (ground)	Resistance	Ignition switch OFF		Motor
45—5 (ground)	Resistance	Ignition switch OFF	2.5 ± 0.1 ohm	LF/RR ISO valve
42—5 (ground)	Resistance	Ignition switch OFF	2.5 ± 0.1 ohm	LF B/D valve
46—5 (ground)	Resistance	Ignition switch OFF	2.5 ± 0.1 ohm	LR B/D valve
49—5 (ground)	Resistance	Ignition switch OFF	2.5 ± 0.1 ohm	RF/LR ISO valve
43—5 (ground)	Resistance	Ignition switch OFF	2.5 ± 0.1 ohm	RF B/D valve
48—5 (ground)	Resistance	Ignition switch OFF	2.5 ± 0.1 ohm	RR B/D valve
8—9	Resistance	Ignition switch OFF	2.5 ± 0.25 Kohm	LF sensor
6—7	Resistance	Ignition switch OFF	2.5 ± 0.25 Kohm	RF sensor
3—4	Resistance	Ignition switch OFF	2.5 ± 0.25 Kohm	LR sensor
1—2	Resistance	Ignition switch OFF	2.5 ± 0.25 Kohm	RR sensor

ABS ECU WIRING HARNESS CONNECTOR, DISCONNECTED

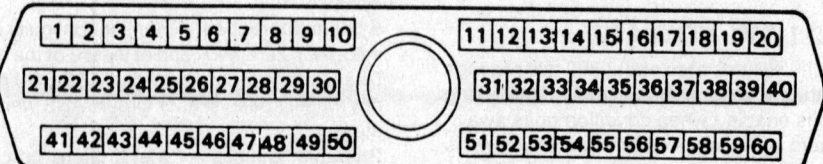

93G00980   Courtesy of Hyundai Motor Co.

Fig. 4: ABS ECU Harness Pin Voltage/Resistance Chart

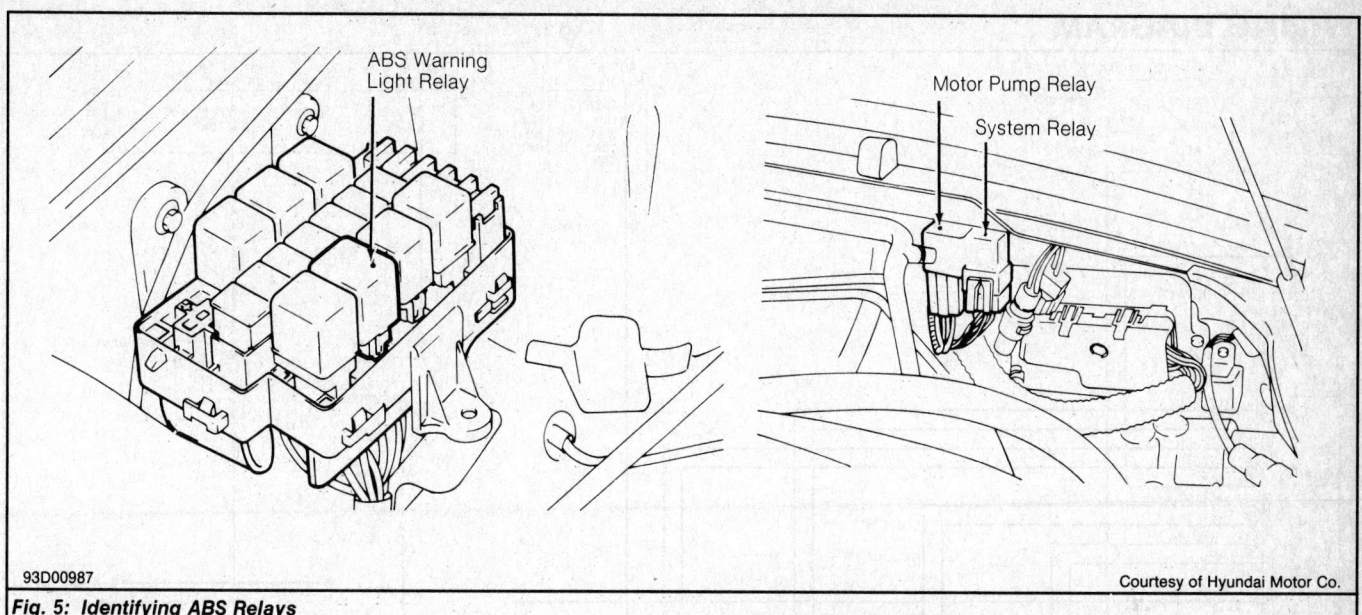

93D00987

Courtesy of Hyundai Motor Co.

Fig. 5: Identifying ABS Relays

MODULATOR

WARNING: Use caution when opening system, as hydraulic system may be under high pressure.

Removal & Installation – 1) Turn ignition off. Open caliper bleed screws and drain master cylinder. Use syringe to remove any remaining fluid. Disconnect electrical connector.

2) Disconnect 6 brakelines from modulator. Remove mounting bolts and washers. Remove 3 modulator brackets. Inspect rubber grommets and replace as necessary.

3) To install, reverse removal procedure. Tighten nuts and bolts to specification. See TORQUE SPECIFICATIONS. Bleed brake system. See BLEEDING BRAKE SYSTEM.

PROPORTIONING VALVES

Removal & Installation – 1) Remove right rear and left rear brakelines from modulator. Remove right and left side proportioning valves from modulator. *See Fig. 3.* Inspect "O" rings and replace as necessary.

2) To install, reverse removal procedure. Tighten proportioning valve and brakelines to specification. See TORQUE SPECIFICATIONS. Bleed brake system. See BLEEDING BRAKE SYSTEM.

RELAYS

Removal & Installation – 1) To remove motor pump relay or systems relay, remove harness connector from relay. *See Fig. 5.*

2) Remove mounting bolts and relay assembly. To remove ABS warning lamp relay, remove relay from relay box. *See Fig. 5.* To install, reverse removal procedure.

WHEEL SPEED SENSORS

Removal & Installation – 1) Loosen wheel lug nuts. Raise and support front of vehicle. Remove wheel. Remove bolts for sensor and cable. Disconnect wheel speed sensor connector.

2) Remove wheel speed sensor from vehicle. To install, reverse removal procedure. Tighten wheel speed sensor and cable bolts to specification. See TORQUE SPECIFICATIONS.

OVERHAUL

DO NOT overhaul or disassemble modulator assembly. If modulator is defective, replace modulator as an assembly.

TORQUE SPECIFICATIONS

TORQUE SPECIFICATIONS

Application	Ft. Lbs. (N.m)
Modulator Bracket Bolt	17-19 (23-26)
Modulator Mount Bolt	10-12 (13-16)
Proportioning Valve	10-16 (13-22)
Primary & Secondary Brakeline Bolt	20-23 (27-31)
Wheel Brakeline Nut	13-17 (18-23)
Wheel Lug Nut	66-81 (90-110)
	INCH Lbs. (N.m)
Bleed Screws	44-53 (5.0-6.0)
ECU Mount Bolt	31-44 (3.5-5.0)
Wheel Speed Sensor & Cable Bolts	110 (12.4)

1994 BRAKES
Anti-Lock – Sonata (Cont.)

WIRING DIAGRAM

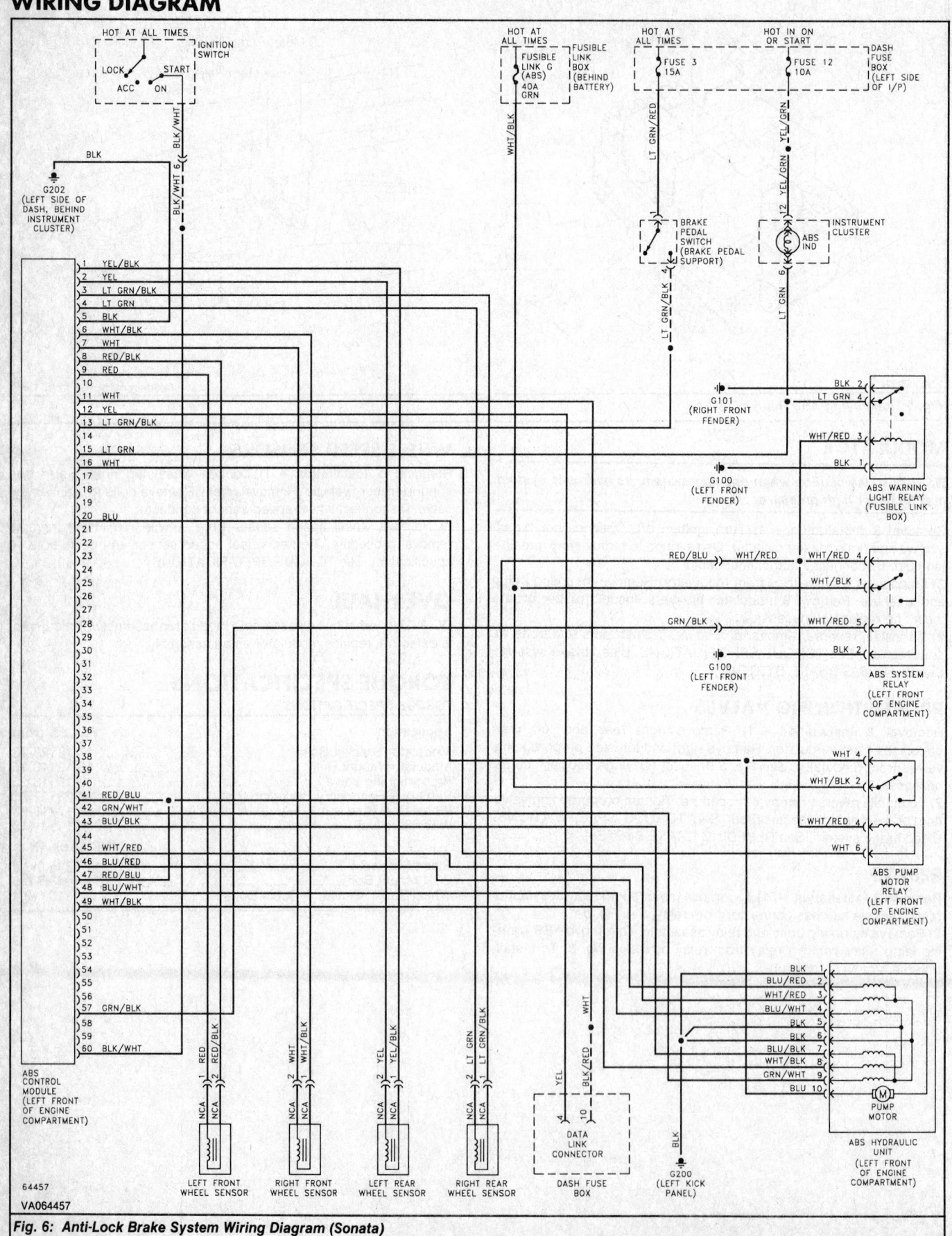

64457
VA064457

Fig. 6: Anti-Lock Brake System Wiring Diagram (Sonata)

Elantra, Excel, Scoupe, Sonata

RIDING HEIGHT ADJUSTMENT

NOTE: Riding height specifications are not provided by manufacturer. However, riding height between left and right side of vehicle should vary less than 1" (25.4 mm).

JACKING & HOISTING

FLOOR JACK

Front of vehicle may be raised with floor jack by placing jack under center crossmember lifting pad. Rear of vehicle may be raised by placing jack under lifting pad to rear of fuel tank . *See Figs. 1 and 2.*

BUMPER JACK

DO NOT raise vehicle by the bumper at any time.

HOIST

CAUTION: Follow hoist manufacturer's instructions. DO NOT allow hoist or adapters to contact suspension, exhaust or steering components.

Adapters must be placed at 4 contact points. *See Figs. 1 and 2.* Position adapters so they are centered on contact area. All 4 contact points must contact adapters.

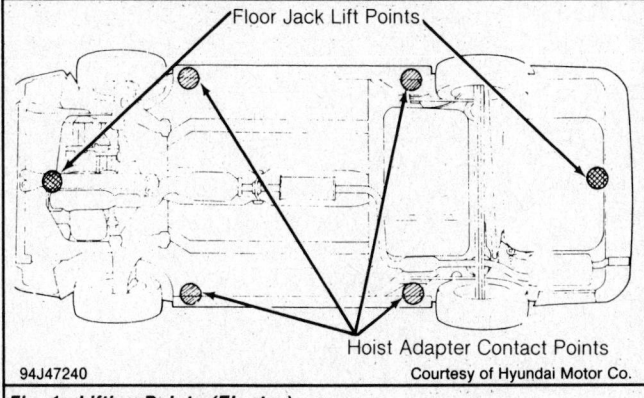

94J47240   Courtesy of Hyundai Motor Co.

Fig. 1: Lifting Points (Elantra)

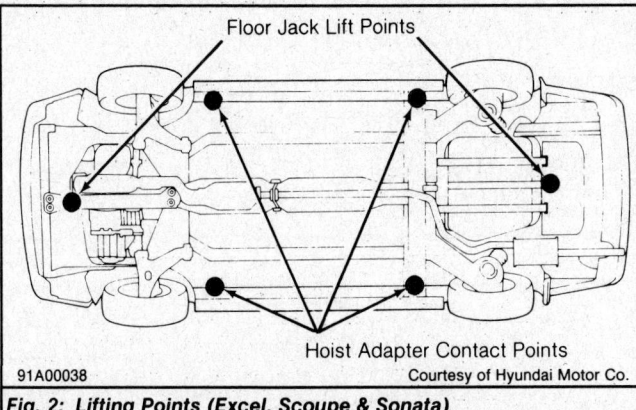

91A00038   Courtesy of Hyundai Motor Co.

Fig. 2: Lifting Points (Excel, Scoupe & Sonata)

WHEEL ALIGNMENT PROCEDURES

CAMBER ADJUSTMENT

Camber is pre-adjusted at the factory and requires no adjustment.

CASTER ADJUSTMENT

Caster is pre-adjusted at the factory and requires no adjustment, although it can be adjusted slightly by moving the strut bar.

TOE-IN ADJUSTMENT

Toe-in is adjusted by loosening tie rod end lock nut and turning tie rod. Toe-in change is achieved by turning the tie rods for right and left wheels in equal amounts.

WHEEL ALIGNMENT SPECIFICATIONS

WHEEL ALIGNMENT SPECIFICATIONS

Application	Preferred	Range
Elantra		
Camber [1]		
Front	0	– 0.5 to 0.5
Rear	– 0.67	– 1.17 to 0.25
Caster [1]	2.57	2.07 to 3.07
Toe-In [1]		
Front	0	– 0.124 to 0.12
Rear	0	– 0.12 to 0.12
Toe-In [2]		
Front	0	– 0.12 to 0.12 (– 3 to 3)
Rear	0	– 0.12 to 0.12 (– 3 to 3)
Steering Axis		
Inclination (SAI) [1]	13.05	
Excel		
Camber [1]		
Front	0	– 0.5 to 0.5
Rear	– 0.67	– 1 to – 0.17
Caster [1]		
Manual Steering		
Front [3]	1.03	0.53 to 1.53
Power Steering		
Front	1.67	1.17 to 2.17
Toe-In [1]		
Front	0.08	– 0.16 to 0.32
Rear	0.12	– 0.24 to 0.46
Toe-In [2]		
Front	0.04 (1)	– 0.08 to 0.16 (– 2 to 4)
Rear	0.06 (1.5)	– 0.12 to 0.23 (– 3 to 6)
Toe-Out On Turns [1]		
Front [3]		
Inner	37.4	
Outer	31.52	
Steering Axis		
Inclination (SAI) [1]	12.98	
Scoupe		
Camber [1]		
Front	– 0.17	– 0.67 to 0.33
Rear	– 0.67	– 1.17 to – 0.33
Caster [1]		
Manual Steering		
Front [3]	1.08	0.58 to 1.58
Power Steering		
Front	1.73	1.23 to 2.23
Toe-In [1]		
Front	0.08	– 0.16 to 0.32
Rear	0.12	– 0.24 to 0.46
Toe-In [2]		
Front	0.04 (1)	– 0.08 to 0.16 (– 2 to 4)
Rear	0.06 (1.5)	– 0.12 to 0.23 (– 3 to 6)
Toe-Out On Turns [1]		
Front [3]		
Inner	37.4	
Outer	31.52	
Steering Axis		
Inclination (SAI) [1]	13.23	

[1] – Measurement in degrees.
[2] – Measurement in inches (mm).
[3] – Specifications for rear angles not available from manufacturer.

WHEEL ALIGNMENT SPECIFICATIONS (Cont.)

Application	Preferred	Range
Sonata		
Camber [1]		
Front	0.5	0 to 1
Rear	0	– 0.5 to 0.5
Caster [1]	2	1.5 to 2.5
Toe-In [1]		
Front	0	– 0.24 to 0.24
Rear	0	– 0.24 to 0.24
Toe-In [2]		
Front	0	– 0.12 to 0.12 (– 3 to 3)
Rear	0	– 0.12 to 0.12 (– 3 to 3)
Toe-Out On Turns [1]		
Front [3]		
Inner	37.12	
Outer	30.18	
Steering Axis		
Inclination (SAI) [1]	13.42	

[1] – Measurement in degrees.
[2] – Measurement in inches (mm).
[3] – Specifications for rear angles not available from manufacturer.

TORQUE SPECIFICATIONS
TORQUE SPECIFICATIONS

Application	Ft. Lbs. (N.m)
Ball Joint Nut	44-53 (60-72)
Centermember Bolts	
Except Sonata	44-59 (60-80)
Sonata	59-74 (80-100)
Front Axle Hub Nut	148-192 (200-260)
Lower Control Arm Front Mounting Nut	
Elantra	69-87 (95-120)
Lower Control Arm Rear Mounting Nut	
Elantra	44-59 (60-80)
Lower Control Arm Clamp Bolt	
Excel & Scoupe	44-59 (60-80)
Sonata	59-74 (80-100)
Lower Control Arm Clamp Nut	
Except Elantra	26-35 (35-47)
Stabilizer Bar Bracket Bolt	
Except Sonata	13-19 (17-26)
Sonata	22-31 (30-42)
Strut Assembly-To-Steering Knuckle Nut	
Except Elantra	66-77 (90-105)
Elantra	81-96 (110-130)
Strut Assembly-To-Body Nut	
Elantra	26-33 (35-45)
Excel & Scoupe	18-26 (25-35)
Sonata	11-15 (15-20)
Tie Rod End-To-Knuckle	
Except Sonata	11-25 (15-34)
Sonata	18-26 (25-35)
Wheel Lug Nut	66-81 (90-110)

Elantra, Excel, Scoupe, Sonata

DESCRIPTION

Independent front suspension uses a MacPherson strut with coil spring, attached to a steering knuckle. Knuckle is mounted on control arm by a ball joint. Front suspension consists of a strut assembly, steering knuckle, control arm and stabilizer bar. *See Fig. 1.*

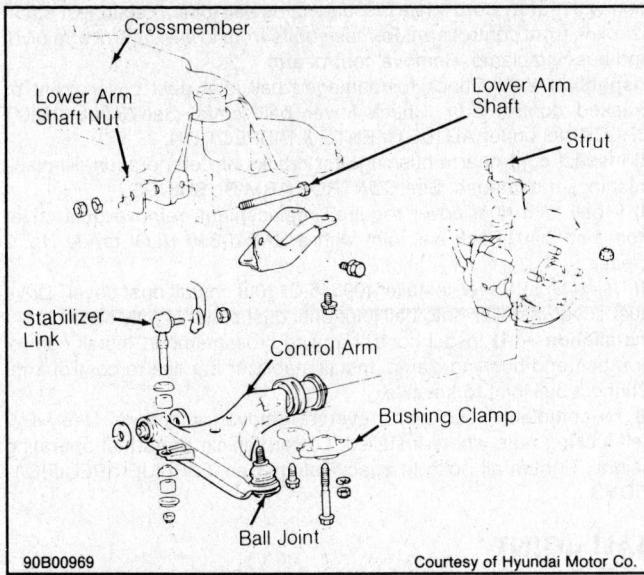

90B00969   Courtesy of Hyundai Motor Co.

Fig. 1: Exploded View Of Front Suspension (Sonata Shown; Others Are Similar)

ADJUSTMENTS & INSPECTION

WHEEL ALIGNMENT SPECIFICATIONS & PROCEDURES

NOTE: See SPECIFICATIONS & PROCEDURES article in WHEEL ALIGNMENT.

WHEEL BEARING

1) Front wheel bearings are nonadjustable. Raise and support vehicle. Remove wheel assembly. Remove caliper. Attach dial indicator at right angle to hub.
2) Move hub in and out and measure axial play. Check bearings or installation procedure if movement exceeds specifications. See WHEEL BEARING AXIAL PLAY SPECIFICATIONS table.

WHEEL BEARING AXIAL PLAY SPECIFICATIONS

Application	In. (mm)
Except Sonata	.0043 (.11)
Sonata	.0040 (.10)

BALL JOINT CHECKING

1) With ball joint disconnected from steering knuckle, install nut on ball joint stud. Move stud from side to side several times.
2) Using INCH-lb. torque wrench, rotate ball joint stud approximately 2 revolutions per minute and note starting torque. See BALL JOINT ROTATING TORQUE table.
3) Replace ball joint if starting torque exceeds specification. If starting torque is less than specification, ball joint may be used if no vertical play, roughness or lack of lubrication exists.

BALL JOINT ROTATING TORQUE

Application	Starting INCH Lbs. (N.m)	Rotating INCH Lbs. (N.m)
Elantra	18-84 (2.0-9.5)	18-49 (2.0-5.5)
Excel & Scoupe	27-89 (3.0-10.0)	27-53 (3.0-6.0)
Sonata	18-89 (2.0-10.0)	[1]

[1] – Information is not available from manufacturer.

REMOVAL & INSTALLATION

STEERING KNUCKLE

Removal – 1) Remove hub cap. Remove drive axle nut and washer. Note direction of nut and washer installation. Raise and support vehicle. Remove wheel assembly. Remove caliper. Disconnect stabilizer bar from control arm.
2) Support control arm. Using Ball Joint Separator (09568-31000), disconnect lower ball joint and tie rod end from steering knuckle. Install Hub Puller (09526-11001) on hub. Tighten puller and separate drive axle from hub.
3) Disconnect steering knuckle from strut. Remove knuckle/hub assembly from vehicle. Separate hub from steering knuckle. See WHEEL BEARINGS.
Installation – To install, reverse removal procedure. Install washer on drive axle with chamfer toward axle shaft nut. Tighten bolts to specification. See TORQUE SPECIFICATIONS. Tighten drive axle nut and knuckle-to-lower arm ball joint nut with vehicle at normal operating height.

WHEEL BEARINGS

CAUTION: Use special hub remover/installer and puller to separate hub from steering knuckle. Bearing damage will result if hub is removed using a hammer.

Removal – 1) Remove steering knuckle and hub assembly. See STEERING KNUCKLE. Install Hub Remover/Installer (09517-21500) and Puller (09517-21600) on steering knuckle. *See Fig. 2.*

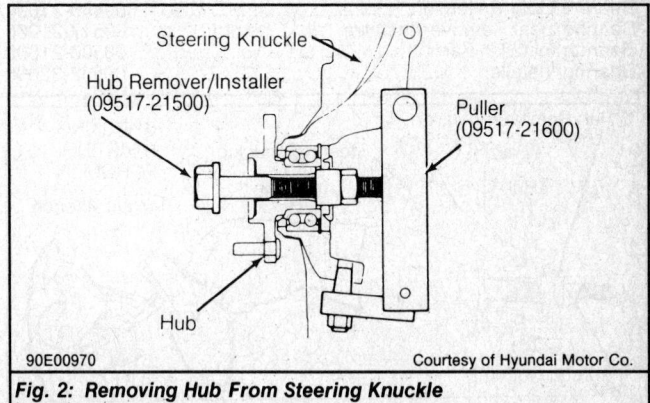

90E00970   Courtesy of Hyundai Motor Co.

Fig. 2: Removing Hub From Steering Knuckle

2) Separate hub from steering knuckle. Remove brake disc from hub. Using bearing puller, remove outer bearing inner race from hub.
3) Remove seal and inner bearing inner race from steering knuckle. *See Fig. 3.* Sonata models have a snap ring that must be removed before inner bearing can be removed. Also a special base is used to hold knuckle in position while bearings are being removed. See WHEEL BEARING REMOVAL & INSTALLATION EQUIPMENT table.
4) On all models, use drift and hammer to remove outer races from steering knuckle. If either race requires replacement, replace as a set.

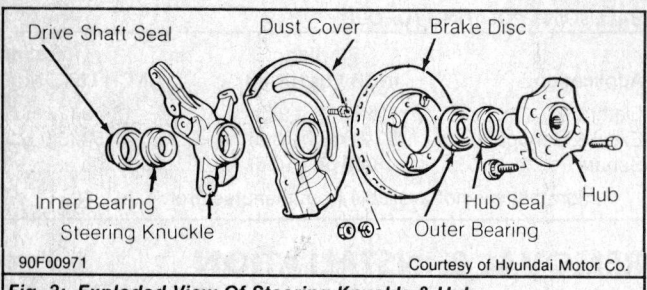

Fig. 3: Exploded View Of Steering Knuckle & Hub

Installation – 1) Use handle with correct race installer and base to install bearing races. See WHEEL BEARING REMOVAL & INSTALLATION EQUIPMENT table. Ensure races are fully seated.

2) Install brake disc on hub. Pack wheel bearings with grease. Install outer bearing into knuckle. Apply grease to seal lip and hub contact surface.

3) Using correct seal installer and handle, install outer seal until seal is even with steering knuckle end surface. See WHEEL BEARING REMOVAL & INSTALLATION EQUIPMENT table. Install inner bearing into steering knuckle.

4) Using hub remover/installer, mount hub on steering knuckle. See Fig. 4. Tighten hub-to-knuckle nut to specification. See TORQUE SPECIFICATIONS.

WHEEL BEARING REMOVAL & INSTALLATION EQUIPMENT

Application	Part No.
Elantra, Excel & Scoupe	
Hub Remover/Installer	09517-21500
Puller	09517-21600
Wheel Bearing Puller	09532-11000
Puller Cup	09532-11301
Hub Bearing Remover	09517-21100
Bearing Installer Bar	09517-21000
Seal Installer	09517-21000
Front Axle Base	09517-21200
Sonata	
Hub Remover/Installer	09517-21500
Puller	09517-21600
Bearing/Gear Puller	09455-21000
Bearing/Seal Remover/Installer	09517-21000
Bearing Installer Bar	09500-21000
Bearing Installer	09532-32000

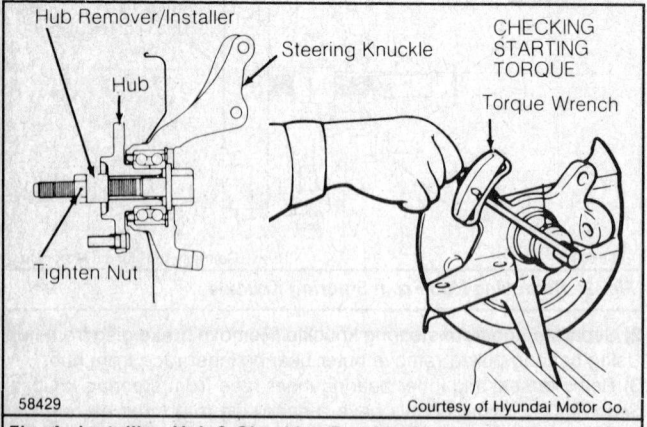

Fig. 4: Installing Hub & Checking Bearing Starting Torque

5) Rotate hub to seat bearing. Using an INCH-lb. torque wrench, measure hub starting torque. Starting torque should be 12 INCH lbs. (1.3 N.m) or less on all models except Sonata. Sonata should be 16 INCH lbs. (1.8 N.m) or less. See Fig. 4.

6) Using dial indicator, move hub in and out and measure axial play. Check assembly procedure if movement exceeds specification. See WHEEL BEARING under ADJUSTMENTS & INSPECTION. Remove hub remover/installer.

7) Using seal installer and handle, install inner seal until seal contacts bearing outer race. Coat inner seal lip with grease. To complete installation, reverse removal procedure.

LOWER CONTROL ARM

Removal – Use Ball Joint Separator (09568-3100) to disconnect ball joint from lower control arm. Ensure separator is secured to suspension with safety cord while disconnecting ball joint. Disconnect stabilizer link from control arm. Remove bolts from lower control arm pivot and bushing clamp. Remove control arm.

Inspection – 1) Check for damaged ball joint dust cover, bent or cracked control arm. Check lower ball joints. See BALL JOINT CHECKING under ADJUSTMENTS & INSPECTION.

2) Inspect control arm bushings for cracks or deterioration. Replace bushings if damaged. See CONTROL ARM BUSHINGS.

3) If ball joint dust cover requires replacement, remove dust cover from ball joint. Pack ball joint with a SAE J-310 NLGI grade No. 2 grease.

4) Using Dust Cover Installer (09545-21100), install dust cover. Drive dust cover installer onto ball joint until dust cover is fully seated.

Installation – 1) Install control arm to crossmember. Install control arm bolt and bushing clamp. Install stabilizer bar link to control arm. Connect ball joint to knuckle.

2) To complete installation, reverse removal procedure. Use NEW self-locking nuts where installed. Lower vehicle to normal operating height. Tighten all bolts to specification. See TORQUE SPECIFICATIONS.

BALL JOINT

Removal & Installation (Elantra, Excel & Scoupe) – Disconnect ball joint from steering knuckle. Remove control arm-to-ball joint retaining bolts. Remove ball joint. To install, reverse removal procedure.

Removal & Installation (Sonata) – 1) Remove control arm. Using a screwdriver, remove dust cover from ball joint. Remove snap ring. Press ball joint from control arm using Base (09545-11000-B) and Adapters (09221-21000 and 09545-11000-A).

2) Using Base (09545-11000-B) and Adapter (09545-11000-A), press ball joint into control arm. Install snap ring. Reinstall control arm.

CONTROL ARM BUSHINGS

NOTE: Information on Sonata not available from manufacturer.

Removal (Elantra) – Remove control arm from vehicle. See LOWER CONTROL ARM. Install Control Arm Bushing Remover/Installer Arbor (09545-28000) and Base (09545-28100). See Fig. 5. Apply soapy water solution to control arm shaft, bushing and tools. Remove Bushing.

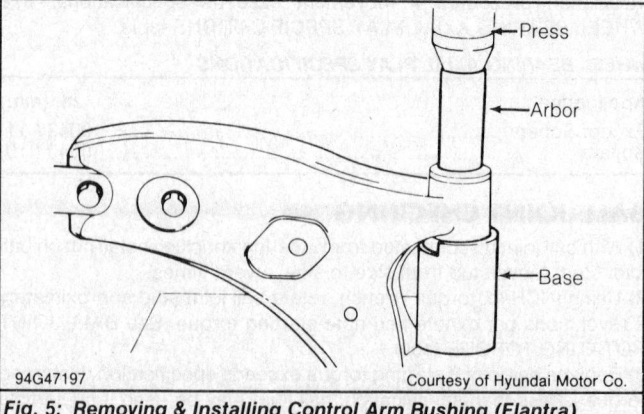

Fig. 5: Removing & Installing Control Arm Bushing (Elantra)

Installation – Press bushing into control arm, using same tools as in removal. See Fig. 5. Ensure bushing is centered. Press fit control arm mounting shaft, and tighten control arm shaft nut to specification. See TORQUE SPECIFICATIONS.

Removal (Excel & Scoupe) – Remove control arm from vehicle. See LOWER CONTROL ARM. Install Control Arm Bushing Remover/Installer Arbor (09432-21500), Ring (09545-24000) and Base (09545-24100). *See Fig. 6.* Apply soapy water solution to control arm shaft, bushing and tools. Remove Bushing.

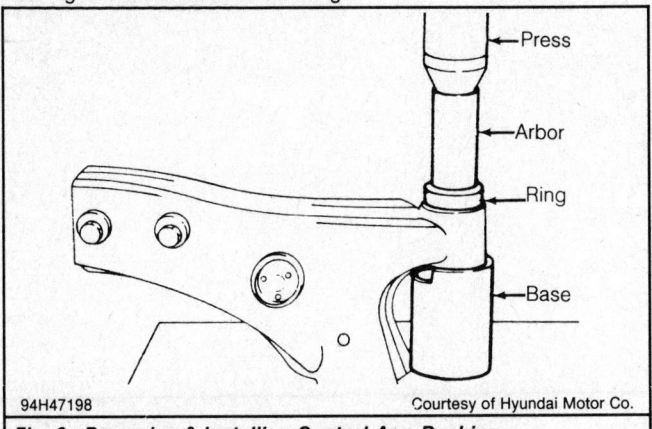

94H47198   Courtesy of Hyundai Motor Co.

Fig. 6: Removing & Installing Control Arm Bushing (Excel & Scoupe)

Installation – Press bushing into control arm, using same tools as in removal. *See Fig. 5.* Ensure bushing is centered. Press fit control arm mounting shaft, and tighten control arm shaft nut to specification. See TORQUE SPECIFICATIONS. Clearance between control arm mounting shaft and bushing should be .06-.10" (1.5-2.5 mm).

STRUT ASSEMBLY

Removal – 1) Raise and support vehicle. Remove wheel assembly. Disconnect brake line bracket from strut assembly. Support control arm. Remove strut-to-steering knuckle bolts. Separate strut from steering knuckle.

2) Remove dust cap from top of strut. *See Fig. 7.* Remove strut-to-body nuts. Remove strut assembly from vehicle. If no mark is present, mark bottom edge of coil spring for reassembly reference.

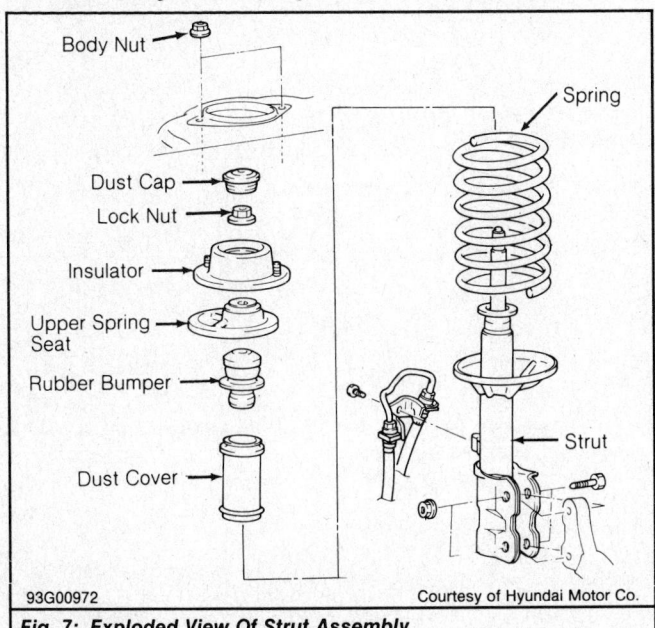

93G00972   Courtesy of Hyundai Motor Co.

Fig. 7: Exploded View Of Strut Assembly (Elantra Shown; Others Are Similar)

Disassembly – Mount strut assembly in vise. Compress coil spring using coil spring compressor. Remove self-locking bearing nut while holding upper spring seat with Spanner Wrench (09546-33000) for Sonata or (09546-21000) for all others. Remove insulator and spring

seat. Remove rubber bumper and dust cover. *See Fig. 7.* Slowly release coil spring compressor tension. Remove coil spring.

Inspection – Check parts for deterioration or damage. Check strut assembly for leaks and proper operation. Replace strut if fluid leakage exists. Replace worn or damaged parts.

Reassembly – 1) Reverse disassembly procedure for reassembly. Place coil spring identification mark toward knuckle. Ensure "D"-shaped upper seat hole is aligned with notch in piston rod. Align coil spring ends in spring seat grooves.

2) Pack insulator bearing with grease and install dust cap. Avoid getting grease on insulators. Compress coil spring. Install rubber bumper and dust cover, spring seat and insulator. Using spanner wrench, tighten piston shaft lock nut to specification. See TORQUE SPECIFICATIONS.

Installation – To install, reverse removal procedure. Ensure strut assembly and steering knuckle mating surfaces are clean. Tighten fasteners to specification. Check front end alignment. See SPECIFICATIONS & PROCEDURES article in WHEEL ALIGNMENT.

STABILIZER BAR

Removal (Except Sonata) – 1) Raise and support vehicle. Disconnect tie rod ends from steering knuckle. On Excel and Scoupe, remove rear roll stopper mount and bracket bolts and pivot roll stopper aside. DO NOT disconnect center crossmember.

2) On all models, disconnect stabilizer bar from control arms. Note location of bushings. Remove stabilizer bar brackets or mounts from body or frame. Remove stabilizer bar through access hole.

3) Remove brackets and bushings from stabilizer bar. Check for bent or damaged bolts. Inspect all bushings for wear and deterioration. Replace damaged parts as necessary.

Installation – To install, reverse removal procedure. Install stabilizer bar brackets as marked on right or left side. Tighten bolts and nuts to specification. See TORQUE SPECIFICATIONS.

Removal (Sonata) – 1) Raise and support vehicle. Disconnect stabilizer bar bracket from crossmember. Disconnect stabilizer bar links from stabilizer bar.

2) Lower rear portion of crossmember and remove stabilizer bar. Remove stabilizer bar links from control arms.

Inspection – 1) Check for bent or damaged components. Inspect all bushings for wear and deterioration. Replace damaged parts as necessary.

2) Install nut on stabilizer bar link ball joint stud. Move stud from side to side several times. Using INCH-lb. torque wrench, rotate ball joint stud approximately 2 revolutions per minute and note starting torque. Starting torque should be 15-28 INCH lbs. (1.7-3.2 N.m).

3) Replace link and ball joint if starting torque exceeds specification. If starting torque is less than specification, link ball joint may be used if no vertical play, roughness or lack of lubrication exists.

Installation – 1) To install, reverse removal procedure. Install stabilizer bar with marked side facing downward. Install stabilizer link onto stabilizer bar and lower control arm.

2) Bottom of link should project through control arm, bushings and lock nut. Threaded portion projecting from lock nut should measure 0.2-0.3" (5-7 mm). Tighten bolts and nuts to specification. See TORQUE SPECIFICATIONS.

TORQUE SPECIFICATIONS

TORQUE SPECIFICATIONS

Application	Ft. Lbs. (N.m)
Ball Joint Nut	44-53 (60-72)
Caliper Assembly-To-Knuckle Bolt	
Except Sonata	48-55 (65-75)
Sonata	51-63 (69-85)
Center Member-To-Body Bolt	
Except Sonata	44-59 (60-80)
Sonata	59-74 (80-100)
Front Axle Hub Nut	148-192 (200-260)
Hub-To-Knuckle Nut	170 (230)
Lower Arm-To-Shaft Nut	70-89 (95-120)
Lower Control Arm Clamp Bolt	59-74 (80-100)
Lower Control Arm Clamp Nut	26-35 (35-47)
Lower Control Arm Mounting Bolt	69-87 (95-120)
Lower Control Arm Mounting Shaft Bolt	69-87 (95-120)
Stabilizer Bar Bracket Bolt	
Except Sonata	13-19 (17-26)
Sonata	22-31 (30-42)
Stabilizer Bar Link Ball Joint Nut	44-52 (60-70)
Strut Assembly-To-Steering Knuckle Nut	
Elantra	81-96 (110-130)
Except Elantra	66-77 (90-105)
Strut Assembly-To-Body Nut	
Elantra	26-33 (35-45)
Excel & Scoupe	11-15 (15-20)
Sonata	18-26 (25-35)
Strut Piston Assembly Lock Nut	
Elantra & Sonata	44-52 (60-70)
Excel & Scoupe	30-37 (40-50)
Tie Rod End-To-Knuckle	
Except Sonata	11-25 (15-34)
Sonata	18-25 (25-34)
Wheel Lug Nuts	66-81 (90-110)

Elantra, Excel, Scoupe, Sonata

DESCRIPTION

Excel and Scoupe use an independent-type suspension, consisting of an integral axle, suspension arms, shock absorbers, coil springs and stabilizer bar. Elantra and Sonata use a 3-link, independent-type suspension, consisting of torsion axle, trailing arms, lateral rod and strut type rear spring/shock assembly.

ADJUSTMENTS & INSPECTION

WHEEL ALIGNMENT
SPECIFICATIONS & PROCEDURES

NOTE: See SPECIFICATIONS & PROCEDURES article in WHEEL ALIGNMENT.

WHEEL BEARING END PLAY

1) Raise and support vehicle. Release parking brake. Remove wheel and wheel bearing dust cap. Remove caliper and disc (if equipped). Set dial indicator against edge of axle (Sonata) or brake drum center flange.

2) Push and pull on axle hub or brake drum. Note bearing end play. See REAR WHEEL BEARING MAXIMUM END PLAY table.

3) If end play exceeds specification, retighten wheel bearing nut. See TORQUE SPECIFICATIONS. Recheck end play. If end play is still beyond limit, replace wheel bearings.

REAR WHEEL BEARING MAXIMUM END PLAY

Application	In. (mm)
Elantra, Excel & Scoupe	1
Sonata	.0040 (.10)

¹ – No end play should exist

WHEEL BEARING STARTING FORCE

1) Raise and support vehicle. Remove wheel. Release parking brake. On models with disc brakes, remove caliper and brake rotor. On all models, turn hub several times by hand. Attach a spring scale to hub bolt at a 90° angle to hub. Measure force needed to turn hub.

2) If force needed to turn hub exceeds limit, loosen wheel bearing nut and retighten it. See WHEEL BEARING STARTING FORCE table. Recheck starting force. Replace wheel bearing as necessary.

WHEEL BEARING STARTING FORCE

Application	Lbs. (N)
Elantra, Excel & Scoupe	4.9 (22)
Sonata	7.0 (31)

REMOVAL & INSTALLATION

WHEEL BEARING

Removal – 1) Raise and support vehicle. Release parking brake. Remove wheel assembly. Remove dust cap and wheel bearing nut. Remove brake drum and outer bearing (except models with disc brakes).

2) On models with disc brakes, remove wheel bearing nut and washer (if equipped). Remove caliper and disc. Remove hub and bearing assembly.

3) On models with drum brakes, pry grease seal from brake drum. Remove inner bearing. If outer bearing races require removal, use a brass drift and hammer to remove bearing races from brake drum.

Inspection – Inspect dust cover and brake drum for wear or damage. Check oil seal for damage. Inspect spindle for signs of bearing movement. Inspect bearings for roughness or damage. If Sonata bearings need to be replaced, replace bearing hub assembly as a unit.

Installation – 1) Install outer bearing races in brake drum. Ensure races are fully seated. Pack wheel bearings and center of brake drum with grease. Install inner bearing and grease seal. Apply grease to seal lip.

2) On models with drum brakes, install brake drum, outer bearing, washer (if equipped) and nut. On models with disc brakes, reverse removal procedure. Crimp wheel bearing nut into axle groove after tightening to specification.

REAR SUSPENSION ASSEMBLY

Removal (Elantra & Sonata) – 1) Raise and support frame rails of vehicle with jack stands. Disconnect lateral rod from vehicle and wire to torsion axle. *See Fig. 1.* Remove wheel assemblies. Remove brake drums or calipers and discs.

2) Disconnect brakelines and parking brake cable. Raise suspension slightly with floor jack. Disconnect shock absorbers and trailing arm mounts from vehicle. Lower suspension and remove as an assembly.

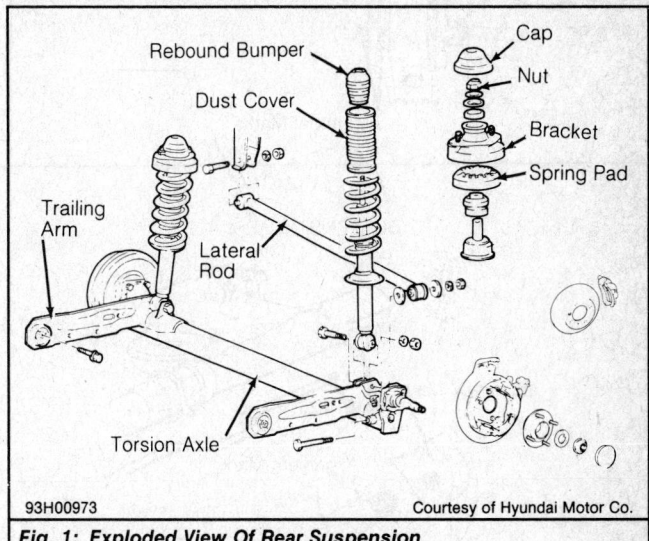

93H00973   Courtesy of Hyundai Motor Co.

Fig. 1: Exploded View Of Rear Suspension (Sonata Shown; Elantra Is Similar)

Inspection – Check for bent or damaged suspension arm and axle. Check for worn or damaged rubber stopper and bushings. Replace as necessary. Check lateral rod for damage.

Installation – 1) To install, reverse removal procedure. Check upper and lower spring seats for proper installation. Tighten bolts.

2) Tighten suspension arm nuts and shock absorber bolts to specification with vehicle at normal operating height and with no load. See TORQUE SPECIFICATIONS. Bleed and adjust brakes.

Removal (Excel & Scoupe) – 1) Raise and support frame rail of vehicle with jack stands. Remove wheel assemblies. Remove brake drums and wheel bearings. Disconnect brakelines and parking brake cable. Remove brake assembly. Remove muffler and pipe.

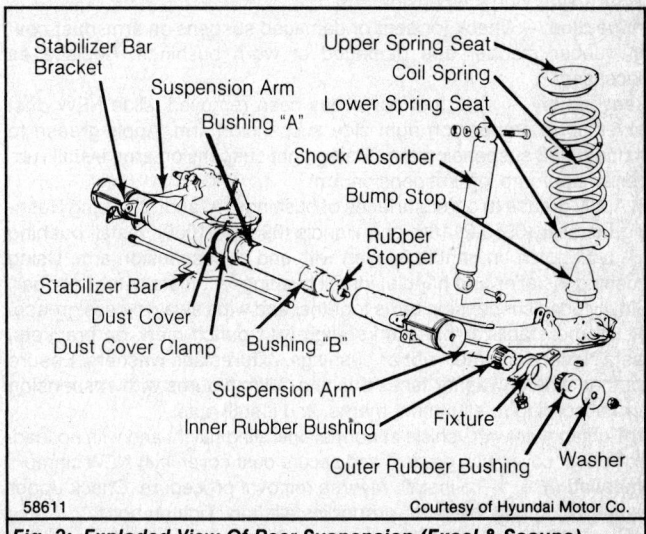

58611   Courtesy of Hyundai Motor Co.

Fig. 2: Exploded View Of Rear Suspension (Excel & Scoupe)

2) Raise suspension slightly with floor jack. Disconnect shock absorbers from suspension arms. Lower suspension enough to remove coil springs. Remove fixture-to-body bolts. *See Fig. 2.* Remove suspension assembly.

Disassembly – 1) Scribe or punch alignment marks on fixture-to-suspension arm position for reassembly reference. Scribe or punch alignment mark on stabilizer bar in alignment with punch mark on stabilizer bar bracket for reassembly reference. *See Fig. 3.*

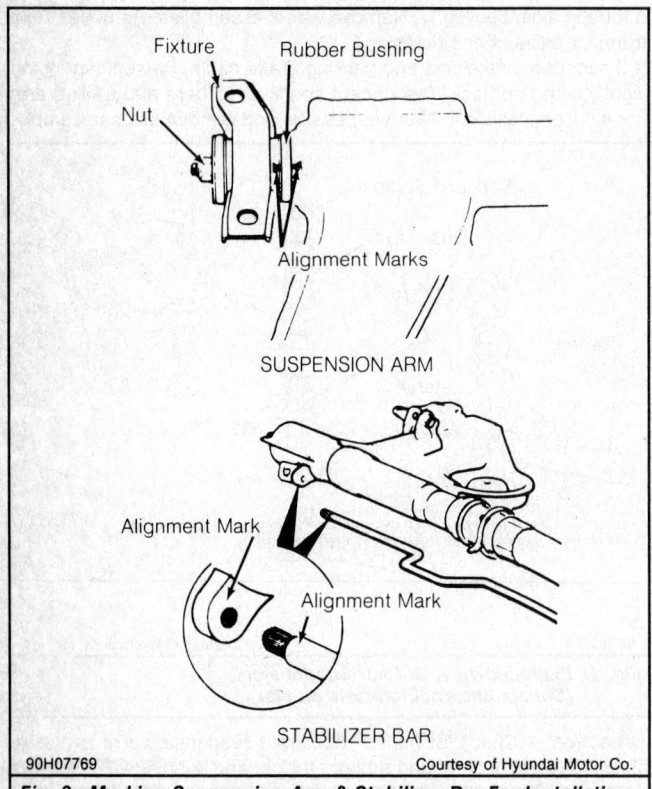

Fig. 3: Marking Suspension Arm & Stabilizer Bar For Installation Reference (Excel & Scoupe)

2) Remove fixture retaining nuts at both ends of suspension arm. Remove fixtures and rubber bushings. Note position of rubber bushings. Remove dust cover clamp, and slide dust cover toward right side suspension arm. DO NOT damage dust cover.

3) Separate suspension into right and left arms. Remove stabilizer bar. Remove rubber stoppers. Using a screwdriver and hammer, drive bushing "A" from left side suspension arm. *See Fig. 2.* Drive bushing "B" from left side suspension arm.

Inspection – Check for bent or damaged suspension arm, dust cover, rubber stopper and damaged or worn bushings. Replace as necessary.

Reassembly – 1) If dust cover has been removed, slide NEW dust cover up to stopper on right side suspension arm. Apply grease to inside of left suspension arm. Using right suspension arm, install rubber stopper into left suspension arm.

2) Apply grease to outer surfaces of bushings "A" and "B". Using Bushing Installer (0955-21100) and Handle (09555-21000), install bushing "B" until notch on handle is even with end of suspension arm. Using bushing installer and handle, install bushing "A". Install stabilizer bar. Slowly push suspension arms together and wipe away excess grease.

3) Ensure stabilizer bar marks align with punch mark on brackets. Install inner and outer rubber bushings, fixtures and washers. Ensure toothed side of washer faces bushing. Align fixtures with suspension arm according to alignment marks, and install nuts.

4) Tighten nuts with vehicle at normal operating height and with no load. Pack dust cover with grease, and secure dust cover with NEW clamp.

Installation – 1) To install, reverse removal procedure. Check upper and lower spring seats for proper installation. Tighten bolts.

2) Tighten suspension arm nuts and shock absorber bolts to specification with vehicle at normal operating height and with no load. Bleed and adjust brakes.

COIL SPRINGS

Removal & Installation (Elantra & Sonata) – 1) Raise and support frame rail of vehicle with jack stands. Disconnect or remove components as necessary to obtain clearance for shock absorber assembly removal.

2) From inside vehicle, remove cap from upper strut tower. Remove strut retaining nuts. Remove lower shock bolt. Lower axle assembly just enough to withdraw shock and spring assembly.

3) Using spring compressor, compress spring. Remove shock piston nut. Remove washer, upper bushing, bracket and spring pad. Remove spring. To install, reverse removal procedure. Ensure both rear springs have same color identification mark.

Removal & Installation (Excel & Scoupe) – Raise and support frame rails of vehicle with jack stands. Remove wheel assemblies. Remove brake drums and wheel bearings. Raise suspension slightly with floor jack. Disconnect shock absorbers from suspension arms. Lower suspension enough to remove coil springs. To install, reverse removal procedure. Tighten bolts to specification.

LATERAL ROD BUSHING

Removal & Installation (Elantra & Sonata) – Remove lateral rod from vehicle. Press out old bushing with Arbor (09545-21400), Adapter (09556-31000) and Base (09216-21100). Install NEW bushing using same tools.

TRAILING ARM BUSHING

Removal & Installation (Elantra & Sonata) – Remove rear suspension assembly. Press out old bushing using correct tools. See TRAILING ARM BUSHING REMOVAL & INSTALLATION EQUIPMENT table. Install new bushing into beveled side of arm. Ensure holes in bushing are pointing directly to front and rear as viewed from side of arm.

TRAILING ARM BUSHING REMOVAL & INSTALLATION EQUIPMENT

Application	Part No.
Elantra	
Adapter	09556-31000
Base	09216-21100
Bushing Remover/Installer	09545-21400
Sonata	
Adapter	09552-33000
Base	09624-31000
Bushing Remover/Installer	09552-33100

TORQUE SPECIFICATIONS
TORQUE SPECIFICATIONS

Application	Ft. Lbs. (N.m)
Elantra & Sonata	
Backing Plate-To-Arm Bolt	37-44 (50-60)
Brakeline Nut	10-13 (13-17)
Lateral Rod Mounting Nut	
Except Sonata Axle Side	59-74 (80-100)
Sonata Axle Side	74-89 (100-120)
Shock Absorber Lower Nut	59-74 (80-100)
Shock Absorber Upper Nut	18-26 (25-35)
Trailing Arm Mounting Nut	74-89 (100-120)
Wheel Bearing Self-Locking Nut	
Elantra	111-148 (150-200)
Sonata	177-221 (240-300)
Excel & Scoupe	
Backing Plate-To-Arm Bolt	37-44 (50-60)
Brakeline Nut	10-13 (13-17)
Bump Stop-To-Suspension Arm Nut	13-18 (18-25)
Shock Absorber Bolt	48-59 (65-80)
Suspension Arm End Nut	96-111 (130-150)
Suspension Fixture-To-Body Bolt	65-80 (88-108)
Wheel Bearing Self-Locking Nut	111-148 (150-200)

Elantra, Excel, Scoupe, Sonata

WARNING: Some Elantra models are equipped with air bags. To avoid injury from accidental air bag deployment, read and carefully follow all WARNINGS and AIR BAG SERVICE PRECAUTIONS.

NOTE: For information on air bag DIAGNOSIS & TESTING or DISPOSAL PROCEDURES, see the MITCHELL® AIR BAG SERVICE & REPAIR MANUAL, DOMESTIC & IMPORTED MODELS.

DESCRIPTION & OPERATION

The collapsible steering system consists of an upper and lower shaft joined by a collapsible (bellows type) section. The bellows section compresses under impact, without affecting turning motion.

AIR BAG SYSTEM OPERATION CHECK

Turn ignition on. SRS Service Reminder Indicator (SRI) light should flash for 6 seconds, then turn off. If SRS SRI does not function as stated, a failure has occurred in SRS. Repair malfunctioning SRS. See AIR BAG SERVICE PRECAUTIONS. See DIAGNOSIS & TESTING in MITCHELL® AIR BAG SERVICE & REPAIR MANUAL, DOMESTIC & IMPORTED MODELS.

AIR BAG SERVICE PRECAUTIONS

These precautions should be observed when working with air bag systems:

* Disable air bag system before servicing any air bag system or steering column component. See DISABLING & ACTIVATING AIR BAG SYSTEM.
* After turning ignition switch to LOCK position and disconnecting negative battery cable, wait at least 30 seconds before working on SRS. SRS is equipped with a back-up power source that may allow air bag to deploy up to 30 seconds after negative battery cable is disconnected.
* During servicing of air bag module, store where ambient temperature is less than 200°F (93°C), without high humidity and away from electrical noise.
* When placing a live air bag on a bench or other surface, ensure pad top surface is facing up, away from surface. This will reduce motion of module if it is accidentally deployed.
* Because of critical operating requirements of system, DO NOT attempt to service air bag module, clockspring, wiring harness or SRS Control Module (SRSCM). Corrections are made by replacement with new parts only. NEVER use parts from another vehicle.
* If air bag module or SRSCM have been dropped, or there are cracks, dents or other defects visible, replace with new parts.
* After work is complete on SRS, ensure system is functioning properly. See AIR BAG SYSTEM OPERATION CHECK.

DISABLING & ACTIVATING AIR BAG SYSTEM

WARNING: Back-up power supply maintains SRS voltage for about 30 seconds after battery is disconnected. After disabling SRS, wait at least 30 seconds before servicing SRS to prevent accidental air bag deployment and possible personal injury.

To disable SRS, turn ignition switch to LOCK position. Disconnect negative battery cable. Wait at least 30 seconds before servicing SRS. To activate SRS, reconnect negative battery cable. Perform AIR BAG SYSTEM OPERATION CHECK.

REMOVAL & INSTALLATION

STEERING WHEEL & HORN PAD

WARNING: Some Elantra models are equipped with air bags. To avoid injury from accidental air bag deployment, read and carefully follow all WARNINGS and AIR BAG SERVICE PRECAUTIONS before working around steering column.

Removal (Elantra) – On models with air bag, remove air bag module and clockspring assembly. See AIR BAG MODULE and CLOCKSPRING. On models without air bag, disconnect negative battery cable. Remove horn pad retaining screws on back of steering wheel. Lift out horn pad and disconnect horn switch wires. Remove steering wheel nut. Install suitable steering wheel puller and pull steering wheel from shaft.

Removal (Excel) – 1) Disconnect negative battery cable. Remove horn pad retaining screws on back of steering wheel. Remove horn pad. Remove upper and lower horn contact plates and disconnect horn button connector.

2) Remove lock nut and washer. Make alignment marks on steering shaft and steering wheel for installation reference. Install suitable steering wheel puller and pull steering wheel from shaft.

Removal (Scoupe) – 1) Disconnect negative battery cable. Remove horn pad by prying up horn cover. Remove upper and lower horn contact plates and disconnect horn button connector.

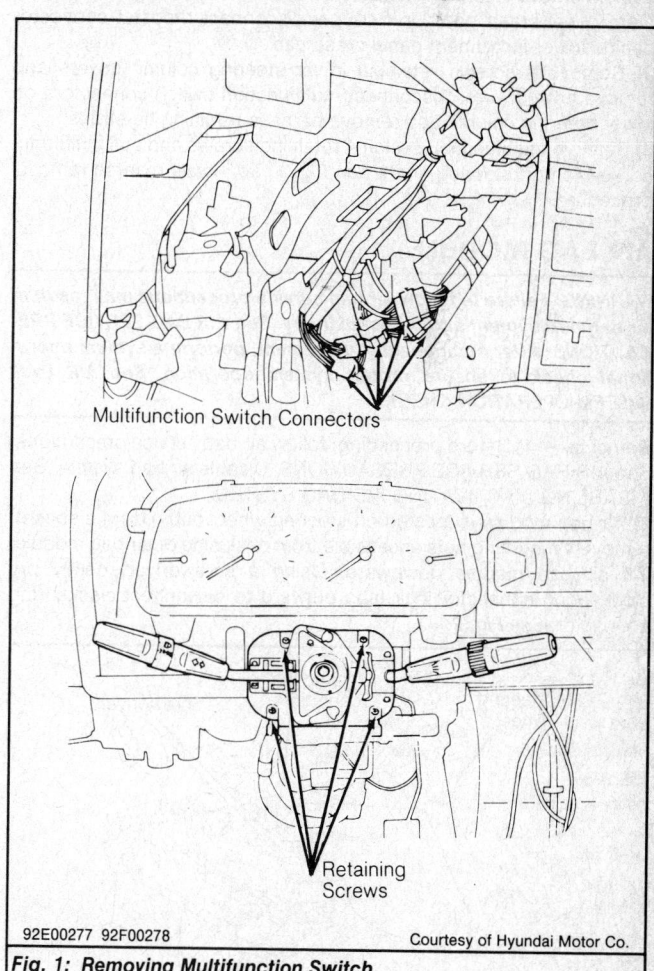

Multifunction Switch Connectors

Retaining Screws

92E00277 92F00278   Courtesy of Hyundai Motor Co.

Fig. 1: Removing Multifunction Switch

2) Remove lock nut and washer. Make alignment marks on steering shaft and steering wheel for installation reference. Install suitable steering wheel puller and pull steering wheel from shaft.

Removal (Sonata) – 1) Disconnect negative battery cable. Remove horn pad retaining screws on back of steering wheel. Lift out horn pad and disconnect horn contact wires.

2) Remove lock nut and washer. Remove dynamic damper. Make alignment marks on steering shaft and steering wheel for installation reference. Install suitable steering wheel puller and pull steering wheel from shaft.

Installation (All Models) – To install, align reference marks on steering shaft and steering wheel. Install washer and lock nut. Tighten nut to specification. See TORQUE SPECIFICATIONS. Reverse removal procedure to complete installation.

MULTIFUNCTION SWITCH

WARNING: Some Elantra models are equipped with air bags. To avoid injury from accidental air bag deployment, read and carefully follow all WARNINGS and AIR BAG SERVICE PRECAUTIONS before working around steering column.

Removal & Installation – 1) On Elantra models with air bag, remove air bag module and clockspring assembly. See AIR BAG MODULE and CLOCKSPRING. On all other models, disconnect negative battery cable. Remove steering wheel. Remove screws retaining lower instrument panel crash pad. On Scoupe, disconnect rheostat connector behind lower instrument panel crash pad.

2) Remove 3 screws retaining lower steering column covers and remove both covers. Disconnect multifunction switch connectors on lower steering column and remove harness retaining tie-straps.

3) Remove multifunction switch 4 retaining screws and pull multifunction switch off steering shaft. See Fig. 1. To install, reverse removal procedure.

AIR BAG MODULE

WARNING: Failure to follow air bag service precautions may result in air bag deployment and personal injury. See AIR BAG SERVICE PRECAUTIONS. After component replacement, perform a system operational check to ensure proper system operation. See AIR BAG SYSTEM OPERATION CHECK.

Removal – 1) Before proceeding, follow air bag service precautions. See AIR BAG SERVICE PRECAUTIONS. Disable air bag system. See DISABLING & ACTIVATING AIR BAG SYSTEM.

2) Air bag module is located on steering wheel hub. Using a socket, remove 4 mounting nuts accessible from back side of air bag module. Tilt air bag module downward. Using a screwdriver, gently pry clockspring connector lock tabs outward to disconnect clockspring connector. See Fig. 2.

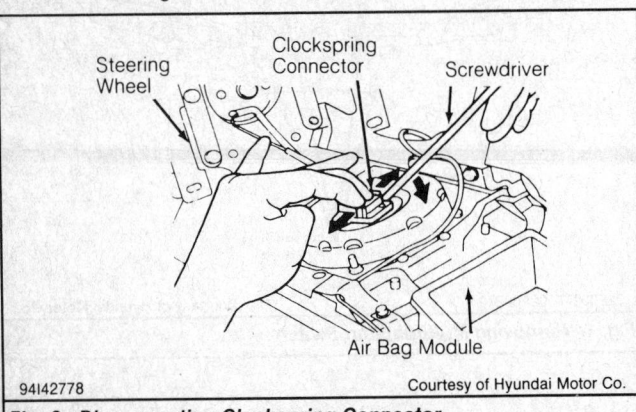

94I42778   Courtesy of Hyundai Motor Co.
Fig. 2: Disconnecting Clockspring Connector

Installation – To install, reverse removal procedure. Reactivate air bag system. See DISABLING & ACTIVATING AIR BAG SYSTEM. Check AIR BAG indicator light to ensure system is functioning properly. See AIR BAG SYSTEM OPERATION CHECK.

CLOCKSPRING

Removal – 1) Before proceeding, follow air bag service precautions. See AIR BAG SERVICE PRECAUTIONS. Disable air bag system. See DISABLING & ACTIVATING AIR BAG SYSTEM.

2) Place front wheels in straight ahead position. Remove air bag module. See AIR BAG MODULE under REMOVAL & INSTALLATION. Remove upper and lower horn plate. Disconnect horn button connector. Remove steering wheel lock nut. Make alignment marks on steering wheel and steering wheel shaft.

CAUTION: DO NOT hammer on steering wheel during removal. Damage may result to steering column.

3) Using a puller, remove steering wheel. Disconnect horn connector located behind steering wheel. Remove upper and lower steering column covers. Remove driver's knee bolster.

4) Disconnect clockspring connector and horn connector located near bottom of steering column. See Fig. 3. Remove clockspring mounting screws. Remove clockspring.

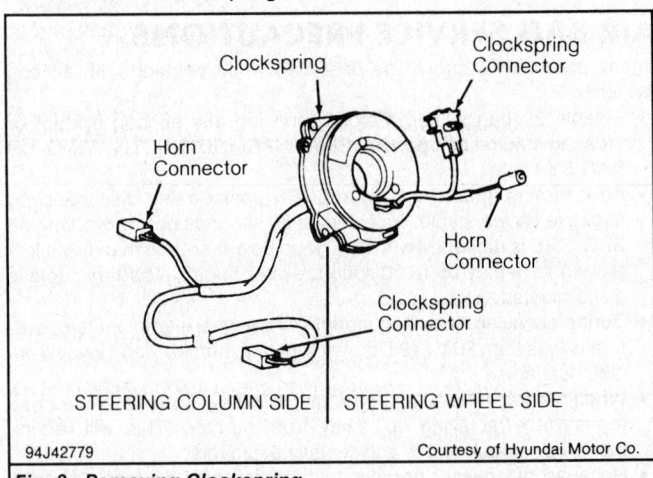

94J42779   Courtesy of Hyundai Motor Co.
Fig. 3: Removing Clockspring

Installation – 1) Ensure front wheels are in straight ahead position. Align mating mark and NEUTRAL position indicator of clockspring. See Fig. 4. Install clockspring onto steering column. To complete installation, reverse removal procedure. Torque steering wheel nut to specification. See TORQUE SPECIFICATIONS.

2) Reactivate air bag system. See DISABLING & ACTIVATING AIR BAG SYSTEM. Check AIR BAG indicator light to ensure system is functioning properly. See AIR BAG SYSTEM OPERATION CHECK.

STEERING COLUMN

WARNING: Some Elantra models are equipped with air bags. To avoid injury from accidental air bag deployment, read and carefully follow all WARNINGS and AIR BAG SERVICE PRECAUTIONS before working around steering column.

Removal & Installation (Elantra) – 1) Remove steering wheel. See STEERING WHEEL & HORN PAD. Remove lower crash pad and steering column upper and lower covers. Disconnect combination switch connectors and rheostat connector. Remove combination switch. See Fig. 5.

2) Remove 4 steering column mounting bolts. Lift dust cover and remove universal joint coupling bolt (at steering gear box). Pull coupling and "U" joint from steering gear box. Remove steering column assembly from vehicle. To install, reverse removal procedure.

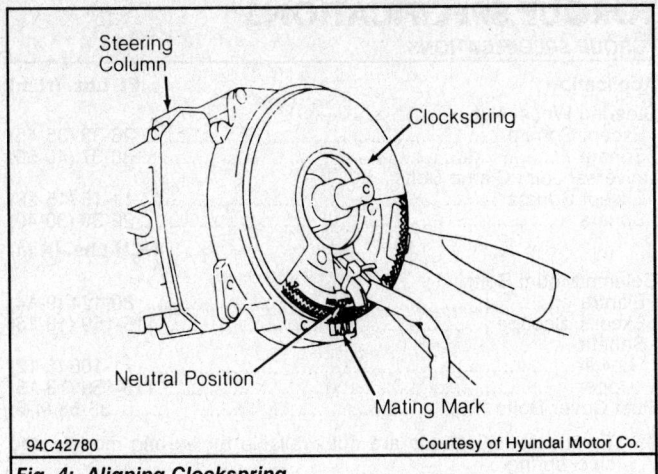

Steering
Column

Clockspring

Neutral Position

Mating Mark

94C42780

Courtesy of Hyundai Motor Co.

Fig. 4: Aligning Clockspring

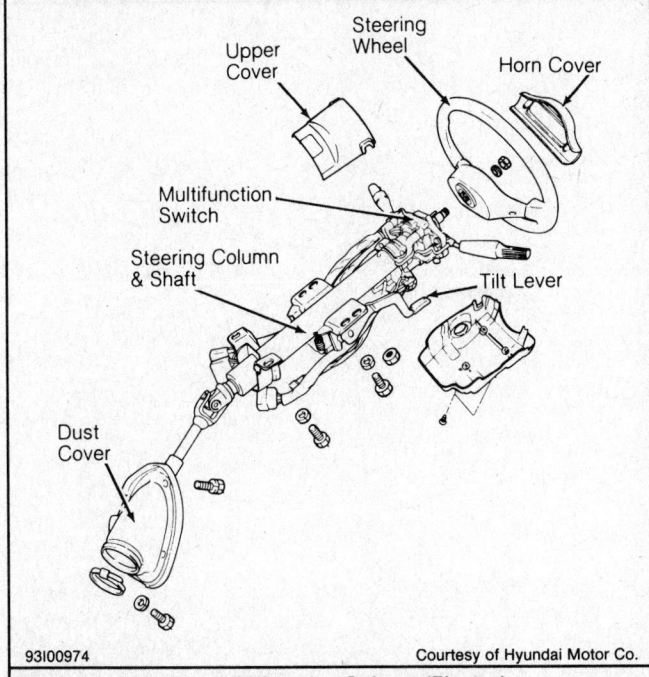

Upper
Cover

Steering
Wheel

Horn Cover

Multifunction
Switch

Steering Column
& Shaft

Tilt Lever

Dust
Cover

93I00974

Courtesy of Hyundai Motor Co.

Fig. 5: Exploded View Of Steering Column (Elantra)

3) On vehicles with tilt steering, lower steering column assembly toward floor by removing lower bracket and tilt bracket bolts. Remove "U" joint-to-steering shaft retaining bolt. Remove steering column assembly.

4) On all models, remove intermediate shaft lower coupling bolt at steering gear. Remove dust cover bolts. Remove intermediate shaft, with dust cover, toward inside of vehicle.

Installation – Install intermediate shaft to column shaft. Ensure intermediate shaft is installed correctly. See Fig. 7. Align intermediate shaft to steering gear pinion and temporarily tighten. Install steering column to frame. Tighten intermediate shaft coupling bolts. Reverse removal procedure to complete installation.

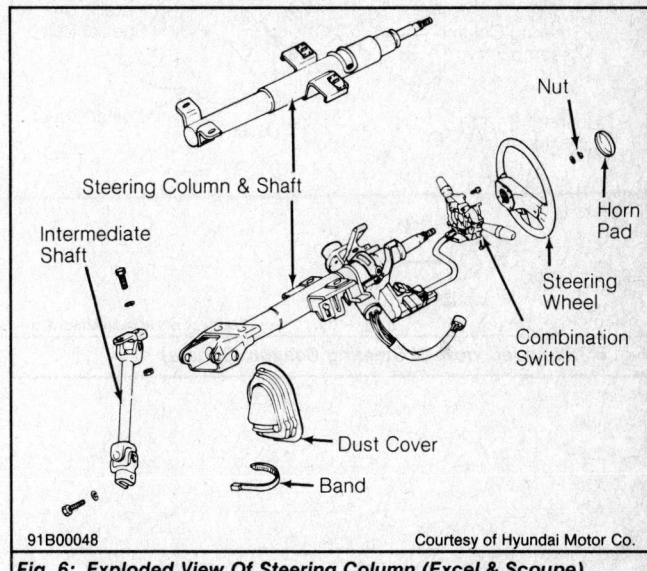

Steering Column & Shaft

Intermediate
Shaft

Nut

Horn
Pad

Steering
Wheel

Combination
Switch

Dust Cover

Band

91B00048

Courtesy of Hyundai Motor Co.

Fig. 6: Exploded View Of Steering Column (Excel & Scoupe)

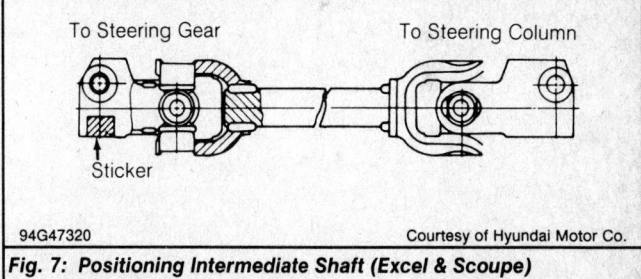

To Steering Gear

To Steering Column

Sticker

94G47320

Courtesy of Hyundai Motor Co.

Fig. 7: Positioning Intermediate Shaft (Excel & Scoupe)

Removal (Excel & Scoupe) – 1) Remove steering wheel. See STEERING WHEEL & HORN PAD. See Fig. 6. Remove 4 screws and lower crash pad. Remove 3 screws and steering column cover. Disconnect combination switch and rheostat connectors. Remove 4 screws and combination switch.

2) On vehicles without tilt steering, remove steering shaft upper coupling bolt. Remove steering column bracket-to-frame bolts. Disconnect steering shaft from coupling inside vehicle. Remove steering column assembly.

Removal & Installation (Sonata) – Remove steering wheel. See STEERING WHEEL & HORN PAD. See Fig. 8. Remove lower crash pad and steering column upper and lower covers. Disconnect combination switch connectors. Remove 4 steering column mounting bolts. Remove intermediate shaft coupling bolts. Pull coupling and "U" joint from steering gear box. Remove dust cover bolts. Remove steering column, intermediate shaft and dust cover together. To install, reverse removal procedure.

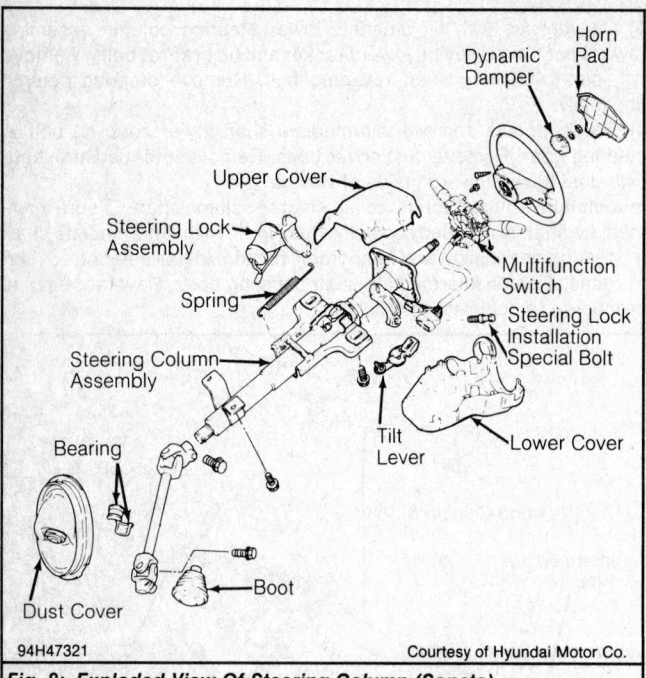

94H47321   Courtesy of Hyundai Motor Co.

Fig. 8: Exploded View Of Steering Column (Sonata)

TORQUE SPECIFICATIONS
TORQUE SPECIFICATIONS

Application [1]	Ft. Lbs. (N.m)
Steering Wheel Nut	
Except Sonata	26-33 (35-45)
Sonata	30-37 (40-50)
Universal Joint Clamp Bolts	
Except Sonata	11-15 (15-20)
Sonata	22-30 (30-40)
	INCH Lbs. (N.m)
Column Mount Bolts	
Elantra	80-124 (9-14)
Excel & Scoupe	115-159 (13-18)
Sonata	
Lower	71-106 (8-12)
Upper	115-159 (13-18)
Dust Cover Bolts	35-53 (4-6)

[1] – Torque specifications are not available for air bag module and clockspring.

Excel, Scoupe

DESCRIPTION

Rack and pinion type steering gears are connected to steering knuckles by tie rods. A flexible coupling connects steering gear assembly to steering column.

ADJUSTMENTS

Necessary adjustments are made during reassembly procedure. See OVERHAUL.

REMOVAL & INSTALLATION

STEERING GEAR

Removal – 1) Disconnect battery ground cable. Raise and support vehicle. Remove both front wheels. Remove "U" joint-to-pinion shaft clamp bolt. Remove tie rod end cotter pins and castle nuts.
2) Using a tie rod end puller, separate tie rods from steering knuckles. Remove steering gear mounting bolts. Remove steering gear. DO NOT damage rubber boots.
Installation – To install, reverse removal procedure. Check and adjust toe-in. See SPECIFICATIONS & PROCEDURES article in WHEEL ALIGNMENT.

OVERHAUL

STEERING GEAR

Disassembly – 1) Mount steering gear in a soft-jawed vise. Remove tie rod assemblies. Remove adjusting plug lock nut. Remove adjusting plug, plunger spring, rubber cushion and rack support from housing.
2) Pry pinion shaft oil seal from housing. Remove pinion bearing snap ring from housing. Remove pinion bearing with pinion shaft.
3) Remove bearing snap ring retainer from pinion shaft. *See Fig. 1.* Using an appropriate sized sleeve and press, remove bearing from pinion shaft. Remove boot retaining clamps. Remove boots.

4) Using appropriate chisel point punch, unstake right side (opposite pinion shaft) rack end tab washer. Move rack all the way toward pinion shaft side housing. Place exposed end of rack in soft-jawed vise.
5) Loosen tie rod ball joint. Remove tie rod from rack. Pulling toward side of pinion shaft, remove rack from housing. *See Fig. 2.*

Inspection – 1) Check steering housing rubber mounts for deterioration or cracking. Inspect rack bushing for excessive play. Check for damage to rack teeth, pinion shaft teeth and pinion shaft splines.
2) Inspect bushing and seal mating surfaces for scratching or scoring. Check housing for cracks or dents. Inspect all rotating surfaces for wear. Replace components as necessary.
Reassembly – 1) Clean all components in solvent. Use NEW seals. Using an appropriate size sleeve and press, install pinion shaft bearing onto pinion shaft.
2) Install bearing snap ring to pinion shaft. Grease rack, pinion shaft, bushing, needle bearing and other sliding surfaces.

NOTE: When lubricating components with grease, DO NOT cover air passages in housing bushing.

---

3) Install rack into housing from pinion shaft side of housing. Install pinion shaft into housing while meshing pinion shaft with rack teeth.
4) Ensure rack is properly centered. Measure travel of rack at each end of housing. If travel is not equal, remove pinion shaft. Recenter rack and reinstall pinion shaft. Select and install snap ring to minimize pinion shaft axial play. See SNAP RING THICKNESS table.

SNAP RING THICKNESS

Color Code	In. (mm)
Blue	.063 (1.59)
White	.065 (1.66)
Yellow	.069 (1.74)

5) Grease oil seal lip and oil seal-to-housing mating surface. Install oil seal into housing. Grease rack support. Install rack support, rubber cushion, plunger spring and adjusting plug into housing. Center rack.

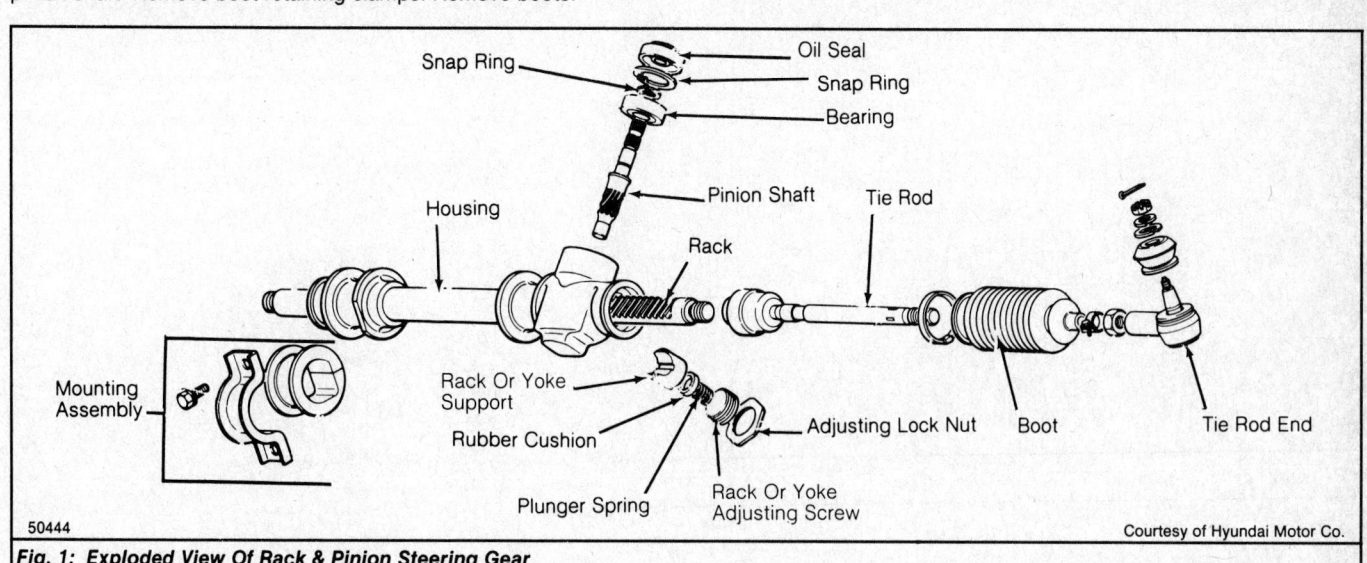

50444

Fig. 1: Exploded View Of Rack & Pinion Steering Gear

Courtesy of Hyundai Motor Co.

6) Tighten adjusting plug to 97 INCH lbs. (11 N.m). Back off adjusting plug 30-60 degrees. Apply sealer to adjusting plug lock nut threads. Tighten adjusting plug lock nut to 37-52 ft. lbs. (50-70 N.m).

7) Install tie rod assemblies with NEW tab washers. Stake tie rod-to-rack end nuts. Install boots and boot clamps. Using a socket and torque wrench, measure pinion preload and rack starting force.

8) Pinion preload should be 4-10 INCH lbs. (.4-1.1 N.m). Rack starting force should be 11-66 lbs. (5-30 kg). If not within specifications, replace plunger spring and rubber cushion. Recheck rack starting force and pinion preload.

TIE ROD ASSEMBLY

Disassembly – 1) Mount steering gear in a soft-jawed vise. Remove boot clamps. Remove boots. Using appropriate chisel point punch, unstake left tie rod. Move tie rod all the way to right. Place rack in soft-jawed vise. Loosen tie rod end nut. *See Fig. 1.*

2) Remove tie rod from rack. Repeat step **1)** for right side tie rod, moving rack to left side and loosen end nut.

Inspection – 1) Inspect ball joints for pitting or wear. Check for damaged or deformed tie rod. Check boots for cracks or cuts.

2) Check ball stud starting torque. Starting torque should be 4-22 INCH lbs. (0.5-2.5 N.m). If not, replace tie rod end.

3) Check tie rod rotating torque. Rotating torque should be 17-43 INCH lbs (2-5 N.m). Check tie rod length. Measure between boot and tie rod end lock nut. Distance should be 6.98-7.22" (177.3-183.3 mm) on Excel, 7.06-7.14" (174.3-176.3 mm) on Scoupe. Adjust as needed.

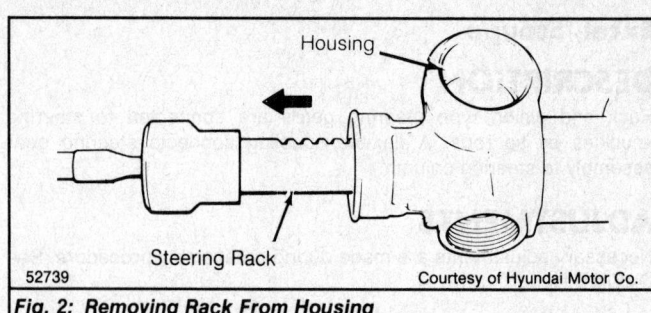

52739   Courtesy of Hyundai Motor Co.

Fig. 2: Removing Rack From Housing

Reassembly – Install tie rod to rack. Install boots and boot clamps. Check and adjust toe-in. See SPECIFICATIONS & PROCEDURES article in WHEEL ALIGNMENT.

TORQUE SPECIFICATIONS
TORQUE SPECIFICATIONS

Application	Ft. Lbs. (N.m)
Inner Tie Rod End Lock Nut	37-41 (50-55)
Rack Mount Bolt	44-59 (60-80)
Tie Rod-To-Knuckle Nut	11-25 (15-34)
Tie Rod-To-Rack	59-74 (80-100)
Universal Joint Clamp Bolt	11-15 (15-20)
Yoke Plug Lock Nut	37-52 (50-70)

Elantra, Excel, Scoupe, Sonata

DESCRIPTION & OPERATION

Power-assisted rack and pinion steering system consists of a vane pump, flow control valve and an oil reservoir. The belt-driven vane pump supplies fluid through hoses to a flow control valve. The flow control valve supplies fluid to the rack and pinion steering gear.

LUBRICATION

CAPACITY

Fluid capacity is approximately .95 qt. (.9L).

FLUID TYPE

Fluid type is Dexron-II.

FLUID LEVEL CHECK

1) Place vehicle on level ground. Start engine. Allow engine to idle. Turn steering wheel lock-to-lock several times to bring steering fluid to normal operating temperature.

2) Turn steering wheel lock-to-lock left and right several times while checking fluid for foaming or bubbling. Fluid level should be between MIN and MAX marks on dipstick attached to filler cap. Fill with Dexron-II to MAX mark.

3) Fluid level should vary by .2" (5 mm) after engine is tuned off. Bleed system if fluid level varies beyond specification.

CAUTION: DO NOT hold steering wheel at full lock left or right for more than 10 seconds.

HYDRAULIC SYSTEM BLEEDING

1) Jack up front of vehicle. Turn oil pump pulley several times by hand. Turn steering wheel from left to right 5-6 times. Disconnect coil high tension wire. Crank engine intermittently for 15-20 seconds, while turning steering wheel left and right. Connect coil high tension wire. Start engine and let it idle. Turn steering wheel left and right until there are no air bubbles in the oil reservoir.

2) Check fluid level and ensure fluid is not milky. Turn steering wheel left and right, and ensure fluid level does not change. If fluid level changes more than .2" (5 mm) or if noise is heard from pump and control valve, fill with fluid to MAX mark on dipstick.

3) Repeat step **2)** until air bubbles are no longer present in fluid and fluid level ceases to fluctuate more than .2" (5 mm).

CAUTION: DO NOT hold steering wheel at full lock left or right for more than 10 seconds.

ADJUSTMENTS

POWER STEERING PUMP BELT

BELT ADJUSTMENT

Application	[1] New Belt Deflection – In. (mm)
All Models	.28-.39 (7-10)

[1] – Deflection measured with 22 lbs. (10 kg) pressure applied midway on longest belt run.

PINION PRELOAD

NOTE: Manufacturer does not provide pinion load checking procedures for Sonata TRW-type. Pinion preload specification for TRW-type is 5-13 INCH lbs. (.6-1.5 N.m).

Elantra, Excel & Scoupe – Using INCH-lb. torque wrench and Adapter (09565-11100), measure preload while turning pinion gear through one rotation. If preload is not 5-12 INCH lbs. (.6-1.3 N.m), adjust rack support cover. Check preload again. Tighten rack support cover lock nut.

Sonata (Mando-Type) – Center rack. Tighten rack support cover to 15-18 ft. lbs. (20-25 N.m). Loosen rack support cover about 10 degrees until preload is 5-12 INCH lbs. (.6-1.3 N.m).

TESTING

STEERING PUMP PRESSURE TEST

1) Disconnect pressure hose from oil pump. Install pressure tester between pump and pressure hose, using Gauge (09572-21000), Adapter (09572-21200) and Adapter (09572-33100). *See Fig. 1.*

2) Bleed air from system. Start engine and allow it to idle. Turn steering wheel lock-to-lock several times until fluid temperature reaches 122°F (50°C). Set engine idle speed to 1000 RPM.

3) Close and open shutoff valve to measure fluid pressure. Relief pressure should be at or near specification. See RELIEF PRESSURE SPECIFICATIONS table. If relief pressure is not as specified, replace pump. Install pressure hose. Bleed system.

CAUTION: DO NOT leave shutoff valve on pressure gauge closed more than 10 seconds, or damage to oil pump will result.

RELIEF PRESSURE SPECIFICATIONS

Application	psi (kg/cm²)
Elantra	782-882 (55-62)
Excel & Scoupe	924 (65)
Sonata	1138 (80)

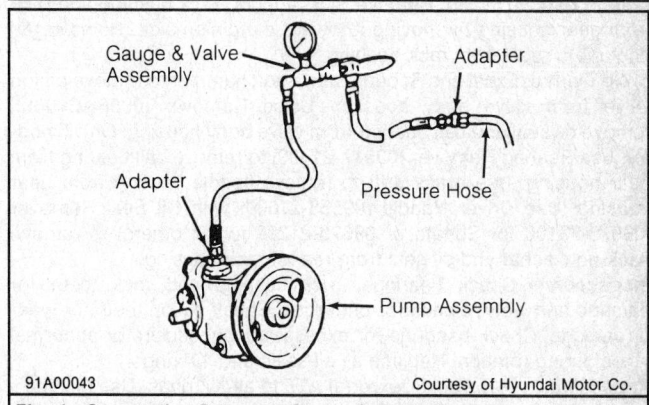

91A00043   Courtesy of Hyundai Motor Co.

Fig. 1: Connecting Pressure Gauge & Shutoff Valve

REMOVAL & INSTALLATION

STEERING GEAR

Removal – **1)** Raise and support front of vehicle. Using Puller (09568-31000), separate tie rod ends from steering knuckles. Remove coupling bolt from pinion shaft joint inside passenger compartment.

2) Disconnect hydraulic lines from steering gear. Drain fluid. On Sonata 4-cylinder, remove center crossmember and stabilizer bar. On Sonata V6, temporarily disconnect muffler, remove left lower control arm and remove stabilizer bar.

3) On all models, remove steering gear mounting bolts. On Elantra, Excel and Scoupe, carefully remove steering gear from right side. On Sonata, move steering gear completely to right, and remove steering gear to left of crossmember. Avoid damaging rubber boots.

Installation – To install steering gear, reverse removal procedure. Tighten nuts and bolts to specification. See TORQUE SPECIFICATIONS. Fill and bleed system. Ensure steering wheel rotates smoothly and check toe-in. See SPECIFICATIONS & PROCEDURES article in WHEEL ALIGNMENT.

POWER STEERING PUMP

Removal – Disconnect pressure and return hoses from pump. Drain fluid into container. Disconnect pressure switch connector. Remove oil pump mounting bolts, belt and oil pump. If necessary for repair or replacement, remove reservoir retaining bolts and reservoir.

Installation – To install, reverse removal procedure. Tighten nuts and bolts to specification. See TORQUE SPECIFICATIONS. Fill and bleed system.

OVERHAUL

STEERING GEAR

NOTE: Power steering gear box used on some Sonata models produced by TRW must be replaced as a complete assembly. Manufacturer does not recommend disassembly or repair.

Disassembly – 1) With rack and pinion assembly mounted in soft-jawed vise, remove tie rod ends, boot clamps and rubber boots. Remove hydraulic feed tubes. While moving the rack slowly, drain fluid from gear housing. Remove end plug, and turn pinion fully clockwise and remove self-locking nut.

2) Using a chisel-point punch, unstake tie rod tab washer. Remove tie rod assemblies. Remove rack support cover locking nut. Using Remover (09565-21100 for Elantra, Excel and Scoupe, or 09565-31300 on Sonata), remove rack support cover.

3) Remove rack support spring, rack support and rack support bushing. Remove 2 pinion valve body housing bolts and pinion valve body (Elantra, Excel and Scoupe). On Sonata, remove pinion dust seal and snap ring and withdraw pinion assembly. On all models, turn rack stopper clockwise to align circlip with slot in gear housing for removal.

4) When circlip comes out of housing, turn rack stopper counterclockwise to remove circlip. Remove rack stopper, rack bushing and rack from gear housing by moving it toward the pinion side. Remove "O" ring and oil seal from rack bushing.

5) On Elantra, Excel and Scoupe, use a soft hammer to remove pinion valve from valve body housing. Using Remover (09565-21000), remove oil seal and ball bearing from valve body housing. On all models, use Bearing Remover (09517-21400) to remove ball bearing from gear housing. Use brass drift to remove needle bearing from gear housing. Use Driver Handle (09555-21000) with Oil Seal Remover (09573-33100 for Sonata or 09573-21200 for all others) to remove back-up washer and oil seal from rear of rack housing.

Inspection – Check bearings, rack bushing and rack teeth for damage and wear. Check for bent rack. Check pinion teeth for wear or damage. Check bearings for excessive play, seizure or abnormal noise during rotation. Replace all oil seals and "O" rings.

Reassembly – 1) Apply Dexron-II ATF to all "O" rings. Use multipurpose grease to lubricate rack teeth, bearings and teeth on pinion valve assembly. Reassemble in reverse order of disassembly.

2) Using Driver Handle (09555-21000) and appropriate guide and installer, seat back-up washer and oil seal in gear housing. See POWER STEERING GEAR ASSEMBLY EQUIPMENT table. *See Fig. 2.* Using correct bearing installer, seat NEW bearings (needle, taper or ball) in gear housing.

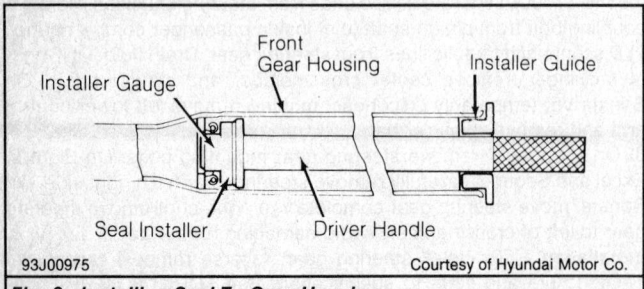

93J00975   Courtesy of Hyundai Motor Co.
Fig. 2: Installing Seal To Gear Housing

3) Using correct seal installer, seat rack bushing seal. Install NEW "O" ring onto rack bushing. Install lubricated rack into gear housing. DO NOT cover rack vent hole with grease.

4) Install rack bushing and rack stopper. Push in rack stopper until snap ring groove of rack stopper is aligned with slotted hole in rack housing. Install circlip while turning rack stopper. When installed, end of circlip should not be visible through slotted hole in rack housing. *See Fig. 3.*

POWER STEERING GEAR ASSEMBLY EQUIPMENT

Application	Part No.
Elantra, Excel & Scoupe	
Gear Housing Tapered Bearing Installer	09432-21600
Gear Housing Ball Bearing Installer	09222-21100
Rack Bushing Oil Seal Installer	09434-14200
Rack Oil Seal Installer Gauge	09573-21000
Rack Oil Seal Installer	09573-21100
Rack Oil Seal Installer Guide	09573-21200
Rack Support Cover Socket	09565-21100
Valve Body Oil Seal Installer	09434-14200
Sonata (Mando-Type)	
Gear Housing Ball Bearing Installer	09222-21100
Gear Housing Needle Bearing Installer	09222-21100
Gear Housing Seal Installer	09431-11000
Rack Bushing Oil Seal Installer	09431-11000
Rack Oil Seal Installer	09573-33000
Rack Oil Seal Installer Gauge	09573-21000
Rack Oil Seal Installer Guide	09573-33100
Valve Housing Oil Seal Installer	09432-21601

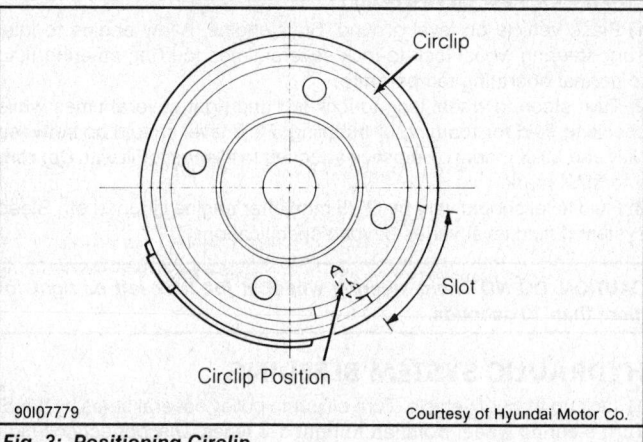

90I07779   Courtesy of Hyundai Motor Co.
Fig. 3: Positioning Circlip

5) On Elantra, Excel and Scoupe, use Installer (09432-21600) to seat oil seal and ball bearing into valve body. On Elantra, install sealing rings onto pinion valve assembly. On all models, apply multipurpose grease to pinion valve assembly gears and Dexron-II fluid to valving areas. *See Fig. 4.* Install pinion valve into gear housing.

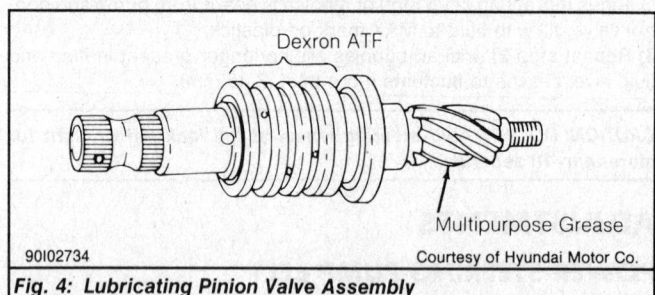

90I02734   Courtesy of Hyundai Motor Co.
Fig. 4: Lubricating Pinion Valve Assembly

6) On Elantra, Excel and Scoupe, use Seal Installer (09434-14200) to seat seal and bearing into valve body housing. *See Figs. 5 and 6.* On Sonata, use Bearing Installer (09222-21100) and Seal Installer (09432-21601) to seat bearing and seal into valve housing. *See Figs. 7 and 8.* Install snap ring.

7) On Elantra, Excel and Scoupe, install NEW gear housing-to-gear box oil seal and install gear box to rack housing. On all models, install tab washer and then tie rod. Align tab washer tabs with grooves in rack. Stake tab washer into place.

8) With pinion shaft turned fully clockwise, tighten a NEW self-locking nut to specification. Tighten end plug to specification. Using a punch, stake plug in 2 locations on its circumference.

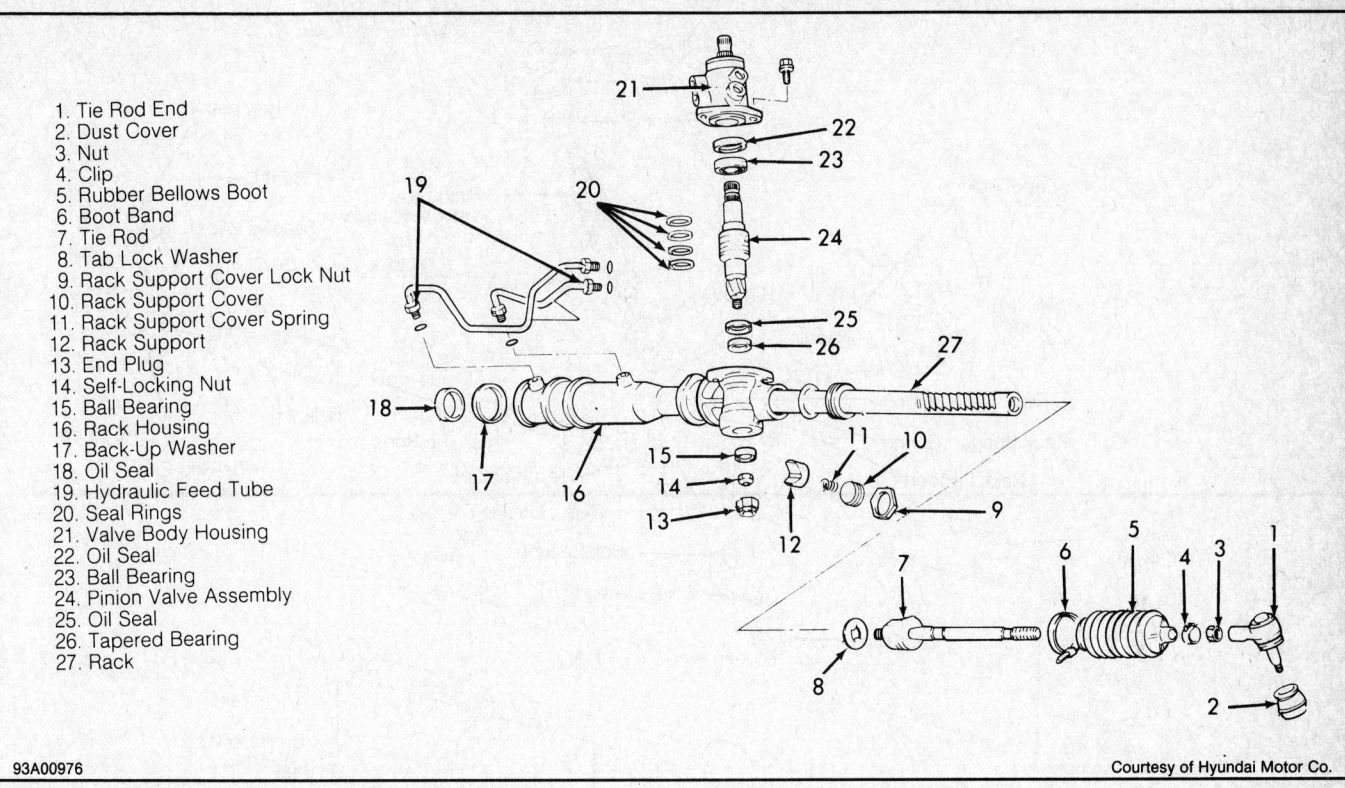

1. Tie Rod End
2. Dust Cover
3. Nut
4. Clip
5. Rubber Bellows Boot
6. Boot Band
7. Tie Rod
8. Tab Lock Washer
9. Rack Support Cover Lock Nut
10. Rack Support Cover
11. Rack Support Cover Spring
12. Rack Support
13. End Plug
14. Self-Locking Nut
15. Ball Bearing
16. Rack Housing
17. Back-Up Washer
18. Oil Seal
19. Hydraulic Feed Tube
20. Seal Rings
21. Valve Body Housing
22. Oil Seal
23. Ball Bearing
24. Pinion Valve Assembly
25. Oil Seal
26. Tapered Bearing
27. Rack

93A00976

Courtesy of Hyundai Motor Co.

Fig. 5: Exploded View Of Power Steering Gear (Elantra)

1. Tie Rod End
2. Dust Cover
3. Dust Cover Clip
4. Tie Rod End Lock Nut
5. Boot Retaining Clip
6. Rubber Bellows Boot
7. Boot Band
8. Tie Rod
9. Tab Lock Washer
10. Rack Support Cover Lock Nut
11. Rack Support Cover
12. Rack Support Cover Spring
13. Rack Support
14. Rack Support Bushing
15. End Plug
16. Self-Locking Nut
17. Ball Bearing
18. Gear Housing
19. Snap Ring
20. Rack Stopper
21. Rack Bushing & "O" Ring
22. Back-Up Washer
23. Oil Seal
24. Hydraulic Feed Tube
25. Oil Seal
26. Ball Bearing
27. Pinion Valve Assembly
28. Oil Seal
29. Valve Body Housing
30. Seal Ring
31. Needle Bearing
32. Rack

90H00973

Courtesy of Hyundai Motor Co.

Fig. 6: Exploded View Of Power Steering Gear (Excel & Scoupe)

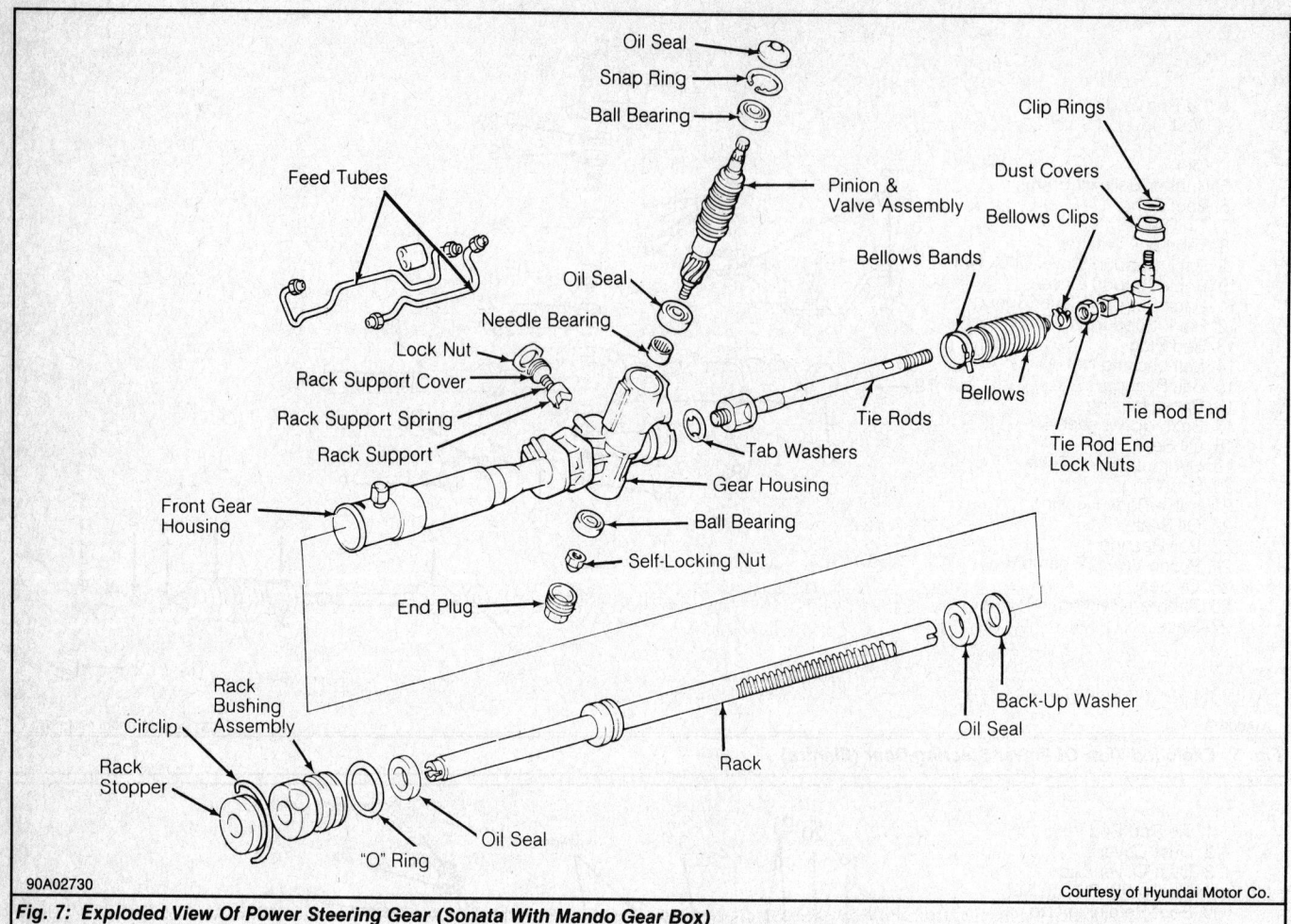

Fig. 7: Exploded View Of Power Steering Gear (Sonata With Mando Gear Box)

90A02730

Courtesy of Hyundai Motor Co.

9) Install rack support bushing, rack support and rack support spring into rack. Center rack in housing. Install rack support cover. Move rack to center position. Tighten rack support cover to 11 ft. lbs. (15 N.m) for Elantra or 8 ft. lbs. (11 N.m) for all others.

10) Loosen cover approximately 30-60 degrees on Sonata and approximately 10 degrees on all others. Install lock nut and tighten to specification. See TORQUE SPECIFICATIONS.

11) On all models, install hydraulic feed tubes. Lubricate boot attaching groove in tie rod with multipurpose grease. Slide NEW rubber boot attaching band onto tie rod.

12) Carefully install boot in position. DO NOT twist boot. Install attaching band onto boot. Fill tie rod end with multipurpose grease, and install NEW dust cover with clip ring.

13) Install tie rod ends. Adjust length of each tie rod. Measure from outer edge of clamped boot to outer edge of tie rod lock nut. See TIE ROD INSTALLED LENGTH table. Check and adjust pinion preload as necessary. See PINION PRELOAD under ADJUSTMENTS.

TIE ROD INSTALLED LENGTH

Application	In. (mm)
Elantra	7.1 (181)
Excel	6.51-7.30 (165.3-185.3)
Scoupe	6.86-6.94 (174.3-176.3)
Sonata	
Mando-Type	7.38 (187.4)
TRW-Type	6.93 (176.1)

POWER STEERING PUMP

Disassembly – **1)** Remove suction connector and suction connector "O" ring. Remove oil pump cover, cam case and ring. Remove "O" ring from cam case. Remove vanes from rotor. Remove snap ring from shaft, and separate rotor from shaft.

2) Tap rotor side of shaft lightly with a plastic hammer. Remove shaft assembly. Remove oil seal from pump body. See Fig. 9. Remove connector from pump body, and remove flow control valve and spring. DO NOT disassemble flow control valve. Remove oil pressure switch, spring and spool.

Inspection & Reassembly – Check pulley assembly and shaft, cam ring, rotor and vanes for wear. Check pump cover and pump body for abrasion. Check flow control valve for clogging. Apply Dexron-II ATF to "O" rings and vanes. Using NEW seals and "O" rings, reassemble pump in reverse order of disassembly. Install vanes into rotor in correct direction. See Fig. 10.

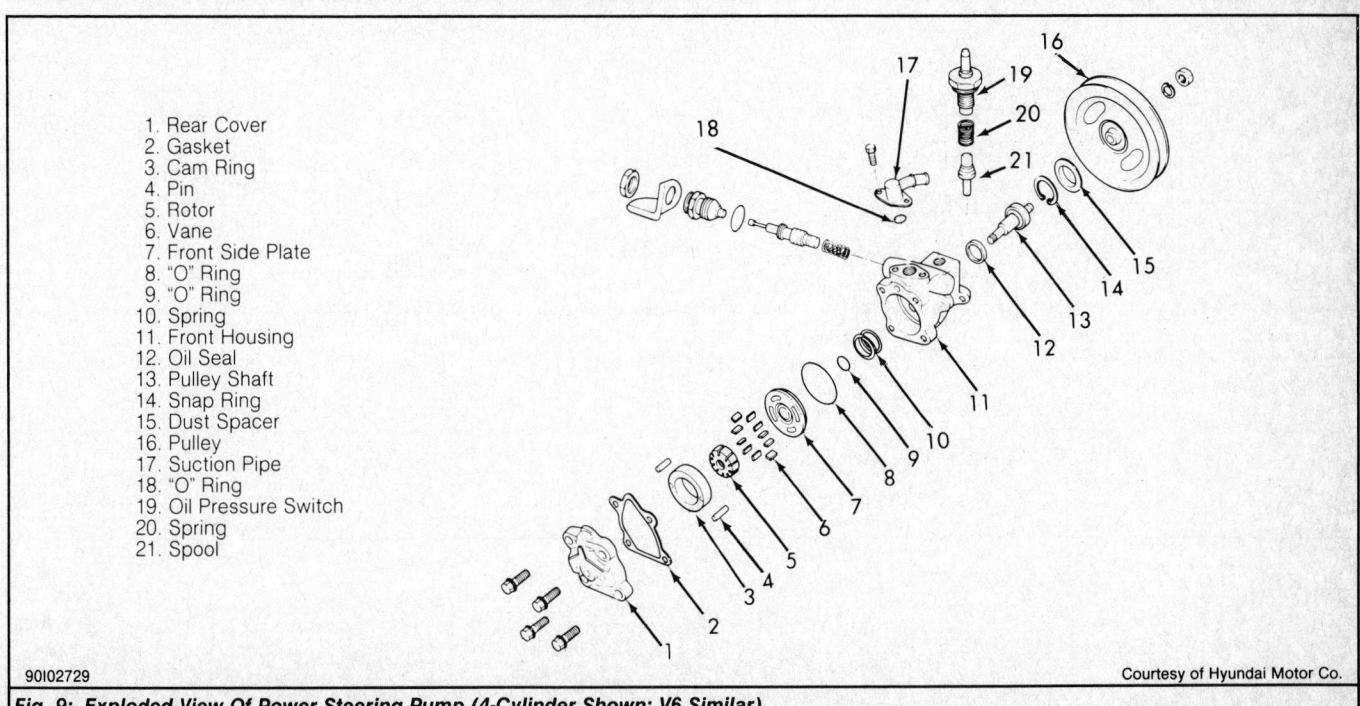

1994 STEERING
Power Rack & Pinion (Cont.)

Feed Tubes
Oil Seal
Snap Ring
Ball Bearing
Pinion &
Valve Assembly
Clip Ring
Dust Cover
Oil Seal
Rack Support Cover
Lock Nut
Rack Support Spring
Rack Support
Bellows Clip
Bellows Band
Tie Rod End
Tie Rod
Bellows
Tie Rod End
Lock Nut
Gear Housing
Ball Bearing
Self-Locking Nut
End Plug
Back-Up Washer
Oil Seal
Rack
Circlip
Oil Seal
Rack
Stopper
Rack Bushing Assembly
"O" Ring
91C00044
Courtesy of Hyundai Motor Co.

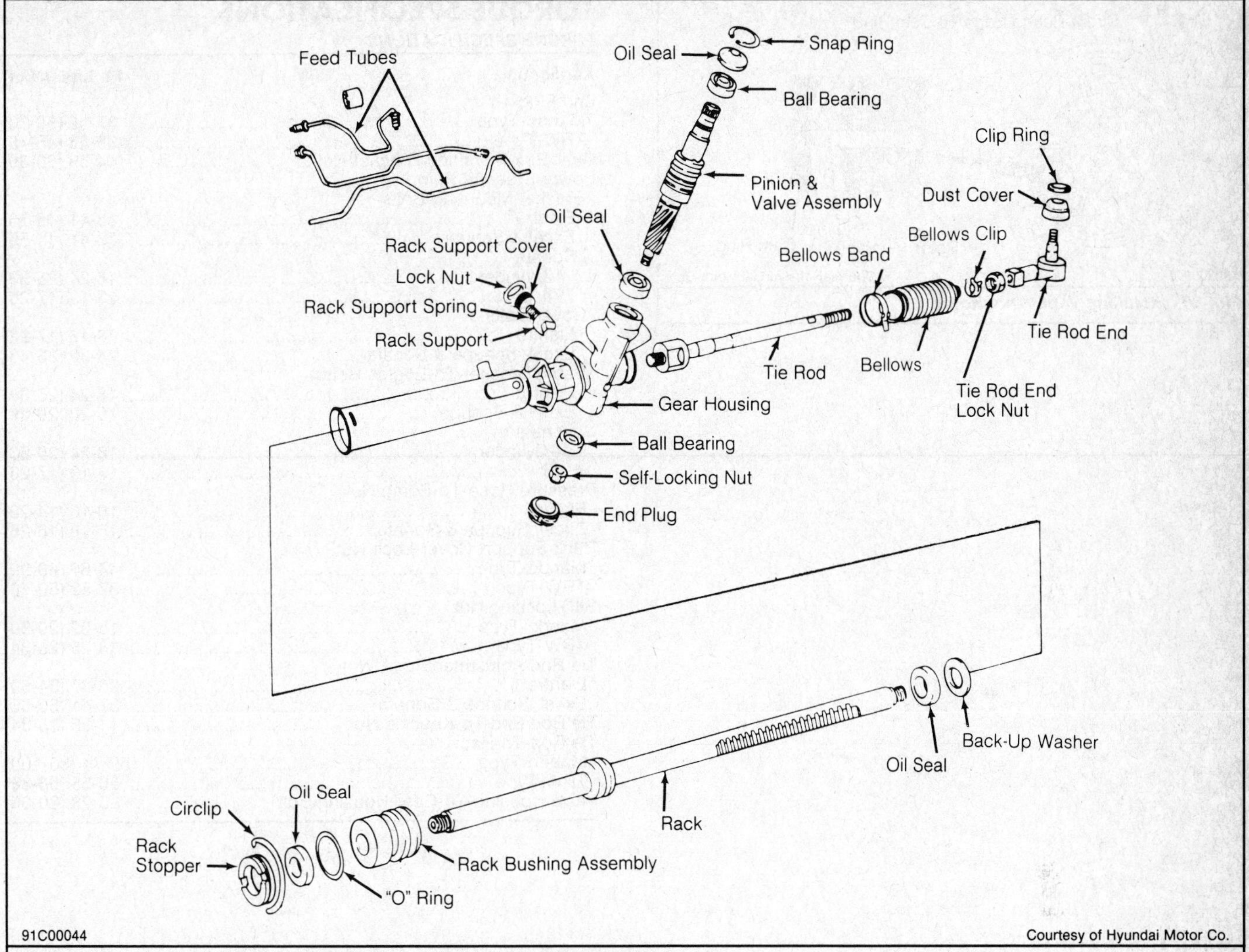

Fig. 8: Exploded View Of Power Steering Gear (Sonata With TRW Gear Box)

1. Rear Cover
2. Gasket
3. Cam Ring
4. Pin
5. Rotor
6. Vane
7. Front Side Plate
8. "O" Ring
9. "O" Ring
10. Spring
11. Front Housing
12. Oil Seal
13. Pulley Shaft
14. Snap Ring
15. Dust Spacer
16. Pulley
17. Suction Pipe
18. "O" Ring
19. Oil Pressure Switch
20. Spring
21. Spool
90I02729
Courtesy of Hyundai Motor Co.

Fig. 9: Exploded View Of Power Steering Pump (4-Cylinder Shown; V6 Similar)

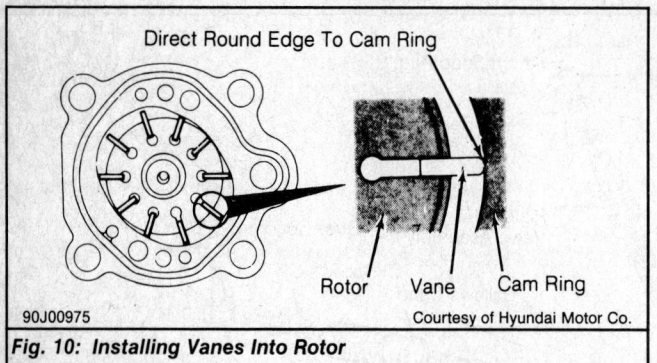

Direct Round Edge To Cam Ring

Rotor   Vane   Cam Ring

90J00975   Courtesy of Hyundai Motor Co.

Fig. 10: Installing Vanes Into Rotor

TORQUE SPECIFICATIONS
TORQUE SPECIFICATIONS

Application	Ft. Lbs. (N.m)
End Plug	
Mando-Type	37-52 (50-70)
TRW-Type	35-56 (48-76)
Gear Box Mounting Bracket	44-59 (60-80)
Power Steering Pump	
Bracket Mounting Bolts	
Elantra	33-41 (45-55)
Excel & Scoupe	33-41 (45-55)
Sonata	
4-Cylinder	18-24 (25-33)
V6	13-19 (17-26)
Cover Bolts	
Elantra	13-16 (17-22)
Excel, Scoupe & Sonata	24-32 (33-43)
Pump Bracket-To-Engine Bolts	
Elantra	18-24 (25-33)
Excel & Scoupe	15-20 (20-27)
Sonata	
4-Cylinder	18-24 (25-33)
V6	13-19 (17-26)
Pressure Hose-To-Pump Nut	
Elantra	10-15 (14-20)
Excel, Scoupe & Sonata	12-18 (16-25)
Rack Support Cover Lock Nut	
Mando-Type	44-66 (60-90)
TRW-Type	37-52 (50-70)
Self-Locking Nut	
Mando-Type	15-22 (20-30)
TRW-Type	18-25 (25-34)
Tie Rod Adjustment Lock Nut	
Elantra	25-37 (34-50)
Excel, Scoupe & Sonata	37-41 (50-55)
Tie Rod End-To-Knuckle Nut	11-25 (15-34)
Tie Rod-To-Rack	
Mando-Type	59-74 (80-100)
TRW-Type	50-65 (68-88)
Valve Housing-To-Gear Housing Bolt	15-22 (20-30)

Elantra, Excel, Scoupe, Sonata

IDENTIFICATION
AUTOMATIC TRANSAXLE APPLICATIONS

Model	Transaxle Model
Elantra	KM175
Excel	KM171 Or KM176
Scoupe	A4AF1
Sonata	
4-Cylinder	KM175
V6	KM177

LUBRICATION

SERVICE INTERVALS

Check fluid at every engine oil change. Under normal conditions, replace fluid and oil screen every 30,000 miles. Under severe conditions, change oil and screen at 15,000 mile intervals.

CHECKING FLUID LEVEL

Vehicle must be level, with engine at normal operating temperature. Ensure gearshift lever is in "P" position. Add enough ATF to bring fluid level to lower mark on dipstick. With engine idling (in "P" position) fluid level should be full, between upper and middle marks of dipstick (HOT range). See Fig. 1. Insert dipstick fully into tube to prevent dirt from entering transaxle.

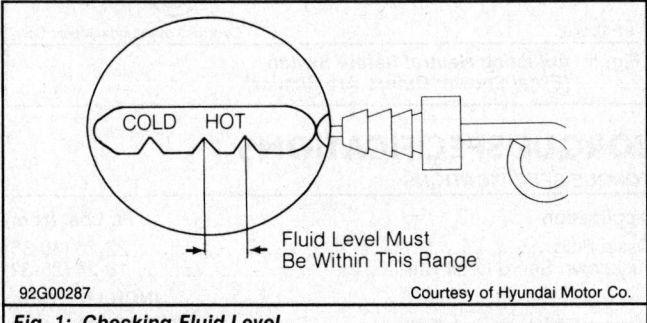

Fluid Level Must
Be Within This Range

92G00287   Courtesy of Hyundai Motor Co.

**Fig. 1: Checking Fluid Level
(Sonata KM177 Shown; Other Models Are Similar)**

RECOMMENDED FLUID

Manufacturer recommends Mopar ATF PLUS Type 7176.

FLUID CAPACITIES
TRANSMISSION REFILL CAPACITIES

Application	Refill Qts. (L)	Dry Fill Qts. (L)
Elantra, Excel & Scoupe	4.8 (4.5)	6.4 (6.1)
Sonata		
KM175	4.8 (4.5)	6.4 (6.1)
KM177	4.8 (4.5)	6.1 (5.8)

DRAINING & REFILLING

1) Remove drain plug from transaxle oil pan. Drain fluid. Remove oil pan bolts and tap pan to break it loose. Remove oil pan. Clean or replace oil filter/screen. Tighten filter bolts to specification. See TORQUE SPECIFICATIONS.
2) Clean gasket surfaces of transaxle case and oil pan. Install oil pan with NEW gasket and tighten oil pan bolts to specification. Using a NEW gasket, install and tighten drain plug to specification.
3) Pour 4.2 qts. (4.0L) of ATF into case through dipstick hole. Unless torque converter was drained, dry fill amount is not necessary. Start engine and allow to idle for at least 2 minutes. With parking brake on, move gearshift lever slowly to each position and back to Park. Recheck fluid level on dipstick.

4) Add sufficient ATF to bring fluid level to lower mark. Recheck fluid level after transaxle is at normal operating temperature. Fluid level should be between marks of dipstick HOT range. See Fig. 1. Insert dipstick fully into tube to prevent dirt from entering transaxle.

ADJUSTMENTS

GEARSHIFT LEVER SLEEVE

1) If control cable has been replaced, or gearshift lever does not properly lock into each position, cable sleeve must be readjusted.
2) Set parking brake. Place gearshift lever Neutral. Remove set screws and lift off gearshift lever handle. Turn sleeve so that clearance between gearshift lever end and sleeve is .598-.625" (15.2-15.9 mm). See Fig. 2.
3) Apply grease to push button contact area and to slope of sleeve before reassembly. Ensure angled side faces push button side of handle when reassembled.

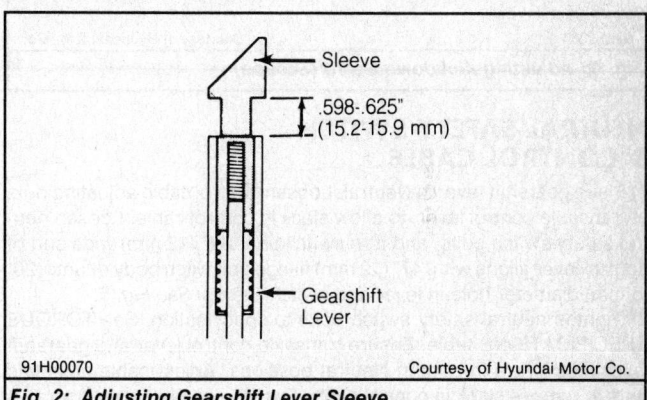

Sleeve

.598-.625"
(15.2-15.9 mm)

Gearshift
Lever

91H00070   Courtesy of Hyundai Motor Co.

Fig. 2: Adjusting Gearshift Lever Sleeve

KICKDOWN SERVO

Except Scoupe – 1) Clean dirt and other contaminants from servo switch and cover. Remove snap ring. Remove kickdown servo switch. Prevent servo piston from turning by using Holder (09454-33101A). See Fig. 3. Loosen adjusting screw lock nut.

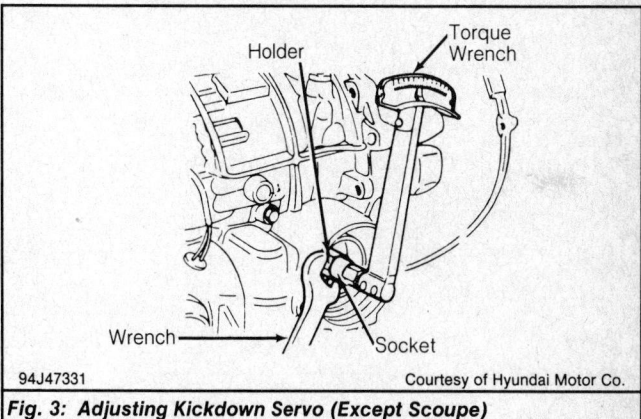

Holder

Torque
Wrench

Wrench

Socket

94J47331   Courtesy of Hyundai Motor Co.

Fig. 3: Adjusting Kickdown Servo (Except Scoupe)

2) Using Socket (09454-33101B) and INCH-lb. torque wrench, tighten adjustment screw 89 INCH lbs. (10 N.m). Loosen adjustment screw and tighten screw 2 turns. Tighten adjustment screw to 44 INCH lbs. (5 N.m). Finally, loosen adjustment screw 2-2 1/4 turns.
3) Hold adjustment screw at that setting, and tighten lock nut 18-24 ft. lbs. (25-32 N.m). Install "O" ring in groove and lightly lubricate with ATF. Install servo cover to case and install snap ring. Install kickdown switch to cover.
Scoupe – 1) Clean dirt and other contaminants from servo switch and cover. Loosen adjusting screw lock nut. See Fig. 4.
2) Loosen and tighten adjusting screw twice with a torque of 44 INCH lbs. (5 N.m). After tightening screw the second time, loosen 3-3 1/3 turns. Tighten lock nut to 11-18 ft. lbs. (15-25 N.m).

NOTE: *Before assembly, apply sealant to center portion of the adjusting screw.*

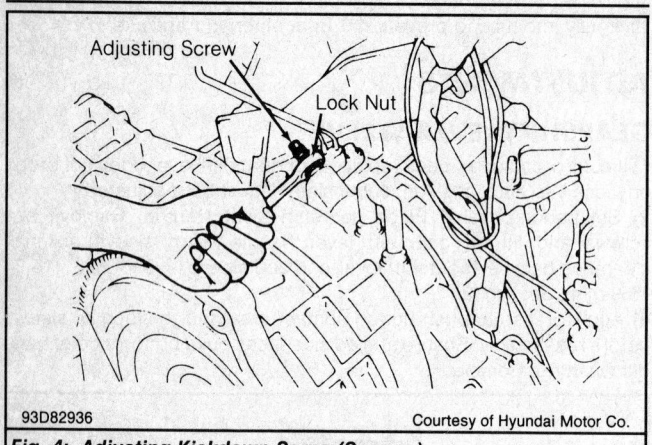

93D82936   Courtesy of Hyundai Motor Co.

Fig. 4: *Adjusting Kickdown Servo (Scoupe)*

NEUTRAL SAFETY SWITCH & CONTROL CABLE

1) Place gearshift lever in Neutral. Loosen control cable adjusting nuts at transaxle control lever, to allow slack in control cable. Loosen neutral safety switch bolts, and turn switch until .47" (12 mm) wide end of control lever aligns with .47" (12 mm) flange on switch body or until .20" (5 mm) diameter hole in lever and switch line up. *See Fig. 5.*

2) Tighten neutral safety switch bolts to specification. See TORQUE SPECIFICATIONS table. Ensure transaxle control lever and gearshift lever handle are in both in Neutral positions. Adjust cable adjusting nuts to remove slack in control cable. Ensure gearshift lever operates smoothly. Drive vehicle to ensure transaxle shifts into each position selected.

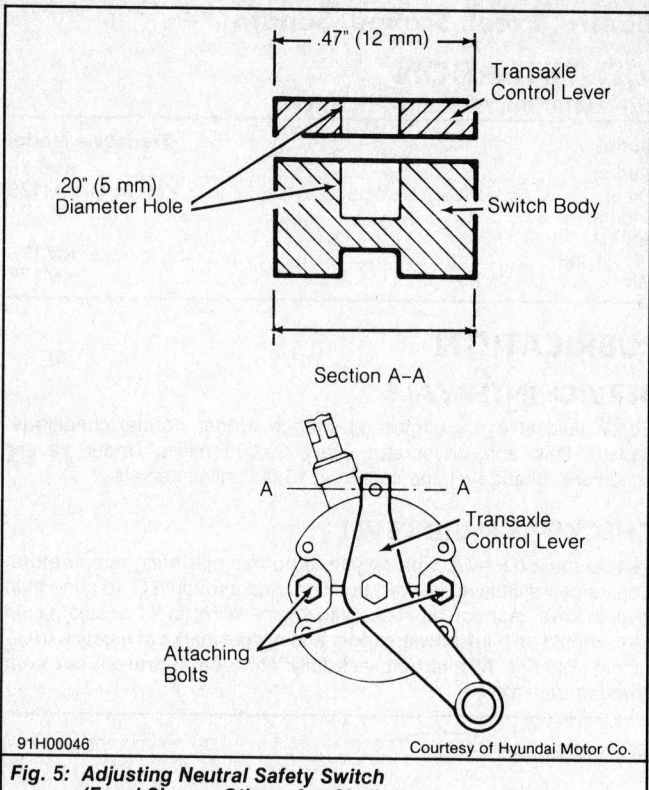

91H00046   Courtesy of Hyundai Motor Co.

Fig. 5: *Adjusting Neutral Safety Switch (Excel Shown; Others Are Similar)*

TORQUE SPECIFICATIONS
TORQUE SPECIFICATIONS

Application	Ft. Lbs. (N.m)
Drain Plug	22-26 (30-35)
Kickdown Servo Lock Nut	18-24 (25-32)

	INCH Lbs. (N.m)
Neutral Safety Switch Bolts	89-106 (10-12)
Oil Pan Bolts	89-106 (10-12)
Oil Filter/Screen Bolts	44-62 (5-7)

Elantra, Excel, Scoupe, Sonata

IDENTIFICATION

MANUAL TRANSAXLE APPLICATIONS

Model	Transaxle
Elantra & Sonata [1]	
5-Speed	KM202
Excel	
4-Speed	KM200
5-Speed	KM201
Scoupe	
5-Speed	M5AF

[1] – Sonata V6 is only available with automatic transaxle.

LUBRICATION

SERVICE INTERVALS

Check oil level at every engine oil change. Under normal conditions, replace oil every 30,000 miles. Under severe conditions, change oil at 15,000 mile intervals.

CHECKING FLUID LEVEL

Remove filler plug and ensure oil level is even with bottom of filler hole. Oil level should not be lower than .31" (8 mm) below bottom of filler hole.

RECOMMENDED FLUID

Manufacturer recommends SAE 75W-85W (API GL-4).

FLUID CAPACITY

TRANSAXLE REFILL CAPACITIES

Application	Qts. (L)
KM200	1.8 (1.7)
KM201	1.9 (1.8)
KM202	1.9 (1.8)
Scoupe	2.3 (2.2)

DRAINING & REFILLING

With vehicle on level surface, remove drain plug, draining transaxle oil into suitable container. Replace drain plug. Fill transaxle with recommended type and amount of oil. Ensure oil level is even with bottom of fill plug hole.

ADJUSTMENTS

LINKAGE

No external adjustments are necessary.

1994 TRANSMISSION SERVICING
Transmission Removal & Installation

Elantra, Excel, Scoupe, Sonata

MANUAL

NOTE: For manual transaxle removal and installation procedures, see FWD article in CLUTCHES.

AUTOMATIC

SONATA V6

Removal – 1) Remove drain plug and drain transmission fluid. Remove air cleaner assembly. Remove battery. Disconnect fluid cooler hoses at top of transaxle and plug fittings and lines.
2) Remove control cable and speedometer cable. Remove top transaxle-to-engine mounting bolts "C". *See Fig. 1.* Remove transaxle top mounting bracket.
3) Disconnect all harness connectors from transaxle case. Remove starter. Raise vehicle. Remove engine undercover panel. Remove both axle shaft assemblies, and intermediate shaft and bearing bracket assembly. See FWD AXLE SHAFTS article in DRIVE AXLES.
4) Support transaxle with appropriate type jack. Remove transaxle lower brace behind starter. Remove lower bellhousing cover to access torque converter bolts. Ensure transaxle is in Neutral and remove torque converter special bolts. Push torque converter into transaxle bellhousing, away from flywheel. Remove lower transaxle-to-engine mounting bolts. Remove transaxle from vehicle.
Installation – 1) To install, reverse removal procedure. Before installing transaxle to engine, install torque converter into transaxle first, aligning torque converter to transaxle pump drive.
2) Install transaxle-to-engine mounting bolts in correct locations. *See Fig. 1.* Tighten mounting bolts to specification. See TRANSAXLE MOUNTING BOLT TORQUE SPECIFICATIONS table.

TRANSAXLE MOUNTING BOLT TORQUE SPECIFICATIONS

Location	Bolt Size (mm)	Ft. Lbs. (N.m)
Elantra		
"A"	10 x 40	32-41 (43-55)
"B"	10 x 65	32-41 (43-55)
"C"	10 x 55	20-25 (27-34)
"D"	8 x 60	22-26 (30-35)
"E"	6 x 12	7-9 (10-12)
"F"	8 x 12	22-26 (30-35)
"G"	[1]	34-39 (46-53)
Excel & Sonata 4-Cyl.		
"A"	10 x 40	32-41 (43-55)
"B"	10 x 65	32-41 (43-55)
"C"	10 x 55	16-24 (22-32)
"D"	10 x 60	22-26 (30-35)
"E"	8 x 14	7-9 (10-12)
"F" [2]	8 x 20	11-16 (15-22)
"G"		
Excel	[1]	26-31 (35-42)
Sonata 4-Cyl.	[1]	34-39 (46-53)
Scoupe		
"A"	12 x 40	32-41 (43-55)
"B"	10 x 70	32-41 (43-55)
"C"	10 x 55	20-25 (27-34)
"D"	8 x 60	22-26 (30-35)
"E"	6 x 12	6-7 (8-10)
"F"	[1]	17-20 (24-27)
Sonata V6		
"A"	10 x 55	22-31 (30-42)
"B"	10 x 55	20-25 (27-34)
"C"	12 x 40	48-61 (65-85)
"D"	12 x 55	59-74 (80-100)
"E"	[1]	34-39 (46-53)

[1] – These short shank bolts are special torque tronverter bolts.
[2] – Sonata 4-cylinder has 2 "F" bolts between "B" and "E" locations. See Fig. 2.

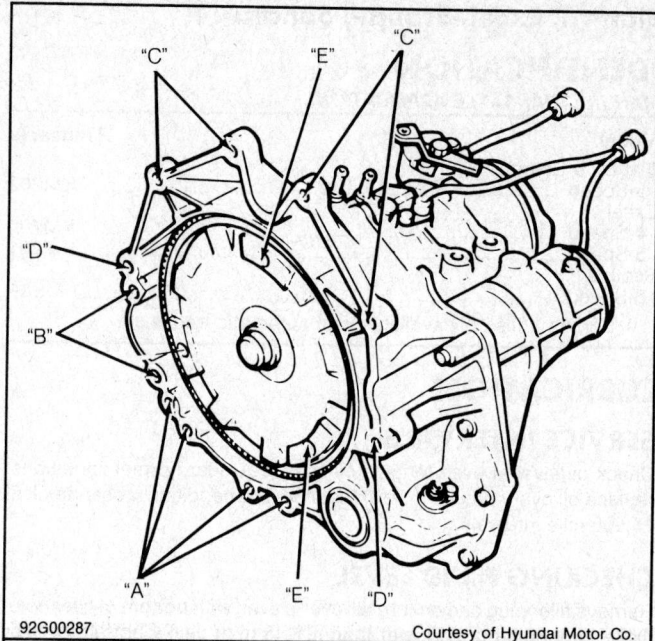

Fig. 1: Locating Transaxle-To-Engine Mounting Bolts (Sonata V6)

92G00287   Courtesy of Hyundai Motor Co.

3) Tighten all other bolts to specification. See TORQUE SPECIFICATIONS. Refill transaxle fluid to specified level on dipstick. Adjust control cable.
4) Check neutral safety switch adjustment. See ADJUSTMENTS in AUTOMATIC TRANSMISSION article. Recheck fluid level after engine is at operating temperature and before driving vehicle.

EXCEPT SONATA V6

Removal – 1) Remove drain plug and drain transmission fluid into appropriate container. Remove air cleaner assembly. Disconnect fluid cooler hoses on top of transaxle and plug all fittings and lines.
2) Remove control cable and speedometer cable. Disconnect all harness connectors from transaxle case. Remove starter. Remove top transaxle-to-engine mounting bolts "A". *See Fig. 2 or 3.*

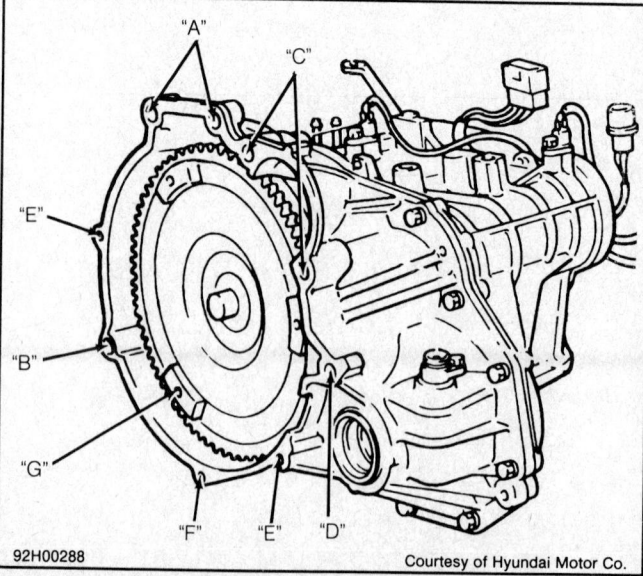

Fig. 2: Locating Transaxle-To-Engine Mounting Bolts (Elantra & Excel Shown; Sonata 4-Cylinder Similar)

92H00288   Courtesy of Hyundai Motor Co.

3) On Elantra, Excel and Scoupe, remove transaxle top mounting bracket. *See Fig. 4.* On Sonata, remove bolt hole rubber covers inside fenderwell, and remove transaxle mounting bracket bolts. *See Fig. 5.* Ensure transaxle is in Neutral.

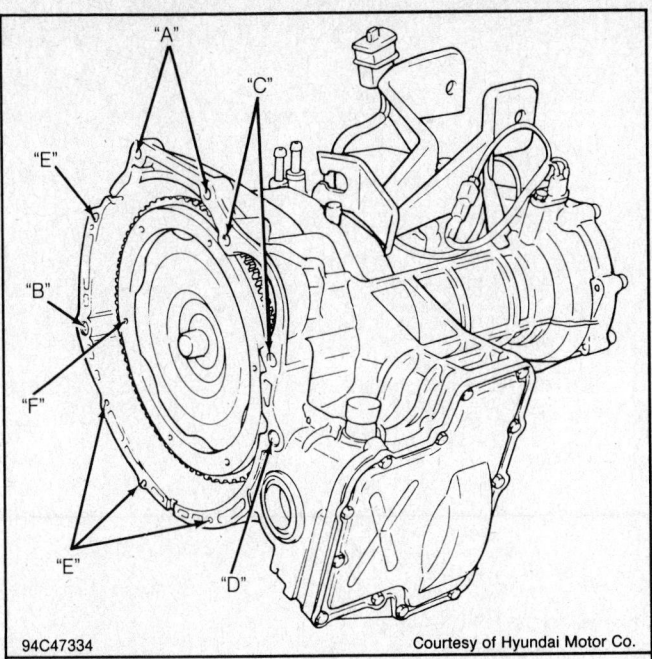

Fig. 3: Locating Transaxle-To-Engine Mounting Bolts (Scoupe)

94C47334 — Courtesy of Hyundai Motor Co.

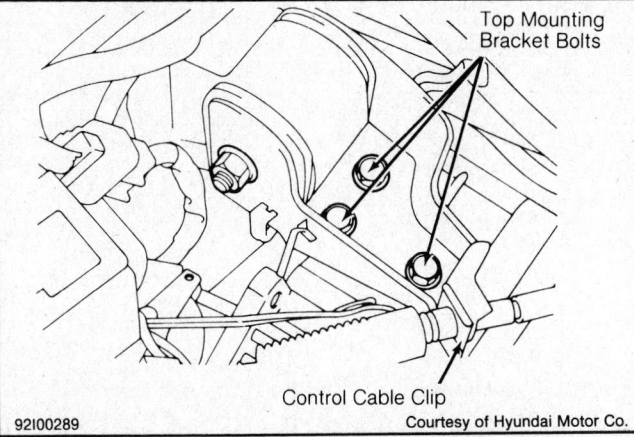

Top Mounting Bracket Bolts

Control Cable Clip

92I00289 — Courtesy of Hyundai Motor Co.

Fig. 4: Locating Transaxle Top Mounting Bracket Bolts (Excel Shown; Elantra & Scoupe Are Similar)

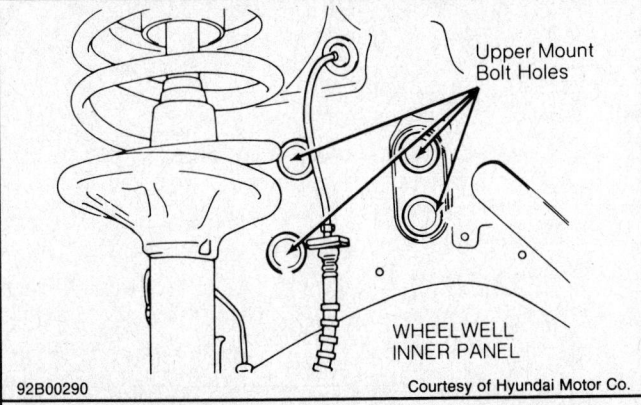

Upper Mount Bolt Holes

WHEELWELL INNER PANEL

92B00290 — Courtesy of Hyundai Motor Co.

Fig. 5: Locating Transaxle Top Mounting Bracket Bolt Holes (Sonata 4-Cylinder)

4) On all models, support engine from top, or by suitable jack from bottom, using care not to damage engine oil pan. Remove centermember support under engine. See Fig. 6. Remove lower bellhousing cover to access torque converter bolts.

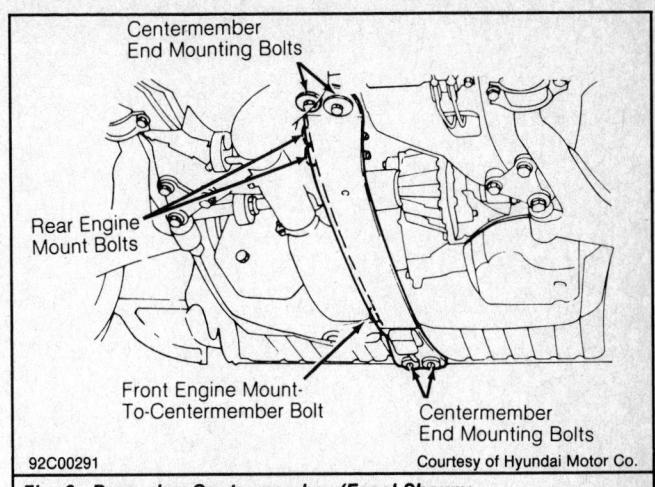

Centermember End Mounting Bolts

Rear Engine Mount Bolts

Front Engine Mount-To-Centermember Bolt

Centermember End Mounting Bolts

92C00291 — Courtesy of Hyundai Motor Co.

Fig. 6: Removing Centermember (Excel Shown; Elantra & Scoupe Are Similar)

5) Index mark torque converter to flywheel/drive plate and remove special torque converter bolts. Push torque converter away from engine into transaxle. Reinstall centermember support under engine, but only snug tighten bolts.

6) Remove undercover panel(s). Remove both axle shaft assemblies. See FWD AXLE SHAFTS article in DRIVE AXLES. Support transaxle with appropriate type jack. Remove lower transaxle-to-engine mounting bolts. Remove transaxle from vehicle.

Installation – 1) To install, reverse removal procedure. Before installing transaxle to engine, be sure to install torque converter into transaxle first, aligning torque converter to transaxle pump drive.

2) Install transaxle-to-engine mounting bolts in correct locations. See Fig. 2 or 3. Tighten to proper specification. See TRANSAXLE MOUNTING BOLT TORQUE SPECIFICATIONS table.

3) Tighten all bolts to specification. See TORQUE SPECIFICATIONS. Refill transaxle fluid to correct level on dipstick. Adjust control cable. Check neutral safety switch adjustment. See ADJUSTMENTS in AUTOMATIC TRANSMISSION article. Recheck fluid level after engine is brought to operating temperature before driving vehicle.

TORQUE SPECIFICATIONS

TORQUE SPECIFICATIONS

Application	Ft. Lbs. (N.m)
Bellhousing Lower Cover Bolt (Sonata 4-Cylinder)	11-16 (15-22)
Centermember End Mounting Bolt	44-59 (60-80)
Centermember-To-Front Engine Mount Bolt	22-30 (30-40)
Centermember-To-Rear Engine Mount Bolt	33-44 (45-60)
Drain Plug	22-26 (30-35)
Lower Control Arm/Ball Joint	
Mounting Bolts (Excel & Scoupe)	70-89 (95-120)
Lower Ball Joint Nut	44-53 (60-72)
Starter Bolt	
Except Sonata 4-Cylinder	20-25 (27-34)
Sonata 4-Cylinder	16-24 (22-32)
Strut Bar Nut	55-66 (75-90)
Tie Rod End Nut	18-26 (24-35)
Torque Converter-To-Drive	
Plate Special Bolt	34-39 (46-53)
Transaxle Top Mounting	
Bracket-To-Transaxle Bolt	44-59 (60-80)
Bracket-To-Body Sidemember Bolt	22-30 (30-40)
Bracket Long Through Bolt	66-80 (90-108)
Transaxle Lower Brace (Sonata V6) [1]	
Engine Side Bolt	48-63 (65-85)
Transaxle Side Bolt	22-31 (30-42)

	INCH Lbs. (N.m)
Air Cleaner Mounting Bolt	71-89 (8-10)
Bellhousing Lower Cover Bolt	89-106 (10-12)
Neutral Safety Switch Bolts	89-106 (10-12)
Oil Pan Bolts	89-106 (10-12)
Speedometer Sleeve Locking Bolt	27-44 (3-5)

[1] – Brace is located behind starter.

NOTE: LATEST CHANGES & CORRECTIONS represents a collection of last minute information and relevant technical service bulletins. Read this section and make notations in appropriate manuals for easy reference later.

ACURA

ACCESSORIES & EQUIPMENT

1 *1993 LEGEND & VIGOR: REVISED ANTI-THEFT SYSTEM TESTING PROCEDURE* – Please note that procedures listed under FRONT PASSENGER'S DOOR LOCK KNOB SWITCH have been revised as follows:

Remove passenger's door panel. Disconnect door latch assembly 8-pin connector. Check continuity between terminals listed in FRONT PASSENGER'S DOOR LOCK KNOB SWITCH TEST table. If continuity is not as specified in table, replace door latch assembly.

FRONT PASSENGER'S DOOR LOCK KNOB SWITCH TEST

Position	Terminals	Continuity
Lock	4 & 5	No
Unlock	4 & 5	Yes

This revision applies to the following publications:
IMPORTED CARS, LIGHT TRUCKS & VANS, SERVICE & REPAIR manual and IMPORTED CARS, LIGHT TRUCKS & VANS, ELECTRICAL SERVICE & REPAIR supplement.
- 1993 – Page ACURA 4-12

2 *1993 LEGEND & VIGOR: REVISED ANTI-THEFT SYSTEM TESTING PROCEDURE* – Please note that procedures listed under REAR DOOR LOCK KNOB SWITCH been revised as follows:

Remove rear door panel. Disconnect door latch assembly 4-pin connector. Check continuity between terminals listed in REAR DOOR LOCK KNOB SWITCH TEST table. If continuity is not as specified in table, replace door latch assembly.

REAR DOOR LOCK KNOB SWITCH TEST

Position	Terminals	Continuity
Lock	1 & 2	No
Unlock	1 & 2	Yes

This revision applies to the following publications:
IMPORTED CARS, LIGHT TRUCKS & VANS, SERVICE & REPAIR manual and IMPORTED CARS, LIGHT TRUCKS & VANS, ELECTRICAL SERVICE & REPAIR supplement.
- 1993 – Page ACURA 4-15

3 *1993 LEGEND: REVISED POWER MIRROR TESTING PROCEDURE* – Please note that procedure listed under BOTH MIRRORS INOPERATIVE, have been revised as follows:

Both Mirrors Inoperative – 1) Check fuse No. 19 in underdash fuse panel. Replace as necessary. Remove power mirror switch. See POWER MIRROR SWITCH under REMOVAL & INSTALLATION.
2) Turn ignition on. Check for voltage between Black/Yellow² wire and ground. If battery voltage exists, go to next step. If battery voltage does not exist, repair open Black/Yellow² wire between mirror switch and fuse box.
3) Check for continuity between Black wire and ground. If continuity does not exist, repair open circuit in Black wire or poor ground connection. If wiring is okay, substitute known good switch and retest.
This revision applies to the following publications:
IMPORTED CARS, LIGHT TRUCKS & VANS, SERVICE & REPAIR manual and IMPORTED CARS, LIGHT TRUCKS & VANS, ELECTRICAL SERVICE & REPAIR supplement.
- 1993 – Page ACURA 4-40

4 *1993 LEGEND: REVISED POWER MIRROR TESTING PROCEDURE* – Please note that procedure listed under RIGHT MIRROR INOPERATIVE, have been revised as follows:

Right Mirror Inoperative – 1) Remove power mirror switch. See POWER MIRROR SWITCH under REMOVAL & INSTALLATION. Using jumper wires, connect Black/Yellow² wire to Yellow/Red wire, and either the Blue/White or Yellow/Black wire to ground. Turn ignition on for 2 seconds, then off.
2) If mirror does not tilt down (or swing left), check for open in Blue/White or Yellow/Black wire between mirror switch and mirror. If mirror doesn't move at all, check Yellow/Red wire. If wiring is okay, test mirror motor. See POWER MIRROR MOTOR TEST. If mirror operates correctly, test switch. See POWER MIRROR SWITCH TEST.
This revision applies to the following publications:
IMPORTED CARS, LIGHT TRUCKS & VANS, SERVICE & REPAIR manual and IMPORTED CARS, LIGHT TRUCKS & VANS, ELECTRICAL SERVICE & REPAIR supplement.
- 1993 – Page ACURA 4-40

ENGINES

5 *1993 VIGOR 2.5L: REVISED VALVE CLEARANCE SPECIFICATIONS* – Please note that valve clearance specifications have been revised as follows:

VALVE CLEARANCE SPECIFICATIONS

Application	In. (mm)
Exhaust	0.011-0.013 (0.28-0.32)
Intake	0.009-0.011 (0.24-0.28)

This revision applies to the following publications:
IMPORTED CARS, LIGHT TRUCKS & VANS, ENGINE, CLUTCH & DRIVE AXLE SERVICE & REPAIR supplement and the IMPORTED CARS, LIGHT TRUCKS & VANS, SERVICE & REPAIR manual.
- 1993 – Page ACURA 5-22

6 *1993 VIGOR 2.5L: REVISED ILLUSTRATION* – Please note that Fig. 9 has been revised. For revised illustration, see the 1994 publication.
This revision applies to the following publications:
IMPORTED CARS, LIGHT TRUCKS & VANS, ENGINE, CLUTCH & DRIVE AXLE SERVICE & REPAIR supplement and the IMPORTED CARS, LIGHT TRUCKS & VANS, SERVICE & REPAIR manual.
- 1993 – Page ACURA 5-26

CHRYSLER/MITSUBISHI

ENGINE PERFORMANCE

7 *ALL 1993 MODELS: REVISED ILLUSTRATION* – Please note that Fig. 5 has been revised. For revised illustration, see the 1994 publication.
This revision applies to the following publications:
IMPORTED CARS, LIGHT TRUCKS & VANS, ENGINE PERFORMANCE supplement and the IMPORTED CARS, LIGHT TRUCKS & VANS, SERVICE & REPAIR manual.
- 1993 – Page CHRYSLER/MITSU. 1-23

8 ▷ *ALL 1993 MODELS: REVISED AFS TO ECM WIRING HARNESS TERMINAL IDENTIFICATION* – Please note that AFS to ECM wiring harness terminal identification has been revised as follows:

AFS-TO-ECM WIRING HARNESS TERMINAL IDENTIFICATION

Application	AFS Terminal No.	ECM Terminal No.
Montero 3.0L	3	10
	7	57
All Other Models	3	70
	7	19

This revision applies to the following publications:
IMPORTED CARS, LIGHT TRUCKS & VANS, ENGINE PERFORMANCE supplement and the IMPORTED CARS, LIGHT TRUCKS & VANS, SERVICE & REPAIR manual.
* 1993 – Page CHRYSLER/MITSU. 1-25

9 ▷ *ALL 1993 MODELS: REVISED VSS OUTPUT CIRCUIT IDENTIFICATION* – Please note that VSS output circuit identification has been revised as follows:

VSS OUTPUT CIRCUIT IDENTIFICATION

Application	Terminal No.
Eclipse, Montero SOHC & Pickup	18
All Other Models	66

This revision applies to the following publications:
IMPORTED CARS, LIGHT TRUCKS & VANS, ENGINE PERFORMANCE supplement and the IMPORTED CARS, LIGHT TRUCKS & VANS, SERVICE & REPAIR manual.
* 1993 – Page CHRYSLER/MITSU. 1-31

10 ▷ *ALL 1993 MODELS: REVISED ILLUSTRATION* – Please note that Fig. 1 has been revised. For revised illustration, see the 1994 publication.
This revision applies to the following publications:
IMPORTED CARS, LIGHT TRUCKS & VANS, ENGINE PERFORMANCE supplement and the IMPORTED CARS, LIGHT TRUCKS & VANS, SERVICE & REPAIR manual.
* 1993 – Page CHRYSLER/MITSU. 1-50

GEO

DRIVE AXLES

11 ▷ *1992-93 TRACKER: REVISED OVERHAUL PROCEDURES* – Please note that step **12)**, under FRONT & REAR DIFFERENTIAL ASSEMBLIES has been revised as follows:
12) Set dial indicator to zero. On front differentials, slowly rotate arbor on 97-mm step of gauge plate to determine point of greatest deflection, and reset dial indicator to zero. *See Fig. 5.*
This revision applies to the following publications:
IMPORTED CARS, LIGHT TRUCKS & VANS, CHASSIS SERVICE & REPAIR supplement and the IMPORTED CARS, LIGHT TRUCKS & VANS, SERVICE & REPAIR manual.
* 1992 – Page GEO 7-6
* 1993 – Page GEO 7-6

BRAKES

12 ▷ *1992 PRIZM: REVISED ABS TESTING PROCEDURE* – Please note that ABS test procedure listed under DTC A087, has been revised. For revised procedure, see the 1994 publication
This revision applies to the following publications:
IMPORTED CARS, LIGHT TRUCKS & VANS, SERVICE & REPAIR manual and IMPORTED CARS, LIGHT TRUCKS & VANS, CHASSIS SERVICE & REPAIR supplement.
* 1993 – Page GEO 8-59

NOTES

NOTES

NOTES

NOTES

NOTES

NOTES

NOTES

NOTES

NOTES

NOTES

NOTES

NOTES

NOTES

NOTES

COMMENTS AND SUGGESTIONS

Please let us know if you have any comments or recommended changes to this book. Mail this postage-paid card today. We'd like to hear from you!

☐ Domestic Cars ☐ Imported Cars & Trucks ☐ Domestic Light Trucks ☐ Medium & Heavy Duty Trucks
☐ Engine Performance ☐ Electrical ☐ Engine ☐ Chassis ☐ Transmission
☐ Air Conditioning ☐ Electrical Component Locators ☐ Other _____

Section No. _____ Page No. _____ Vehicle Model & Year _____

Comments: _____
_____
_____
_____

Name _____ Company _____
Address _____ City _____ State _____ Zip _____
Phone ( ) _____ Date _____ THANK YOU

ADIA 94

Be sure to fill out this form completely.

COMMENTS AND SUGGESTIONS

Please let us know if you have any comments or recommended changes to this book. Mail this postage-paid card today. We'd like to hear from you!

☐ Domestic Cars ☐ Imported Cars & Trucks ☐ Domestic Light Trucks ☐ Medium & Heavy Duty Trucks
☐ Engine Performance ☐ Electrical ☐ Engine ☐ Chassis ☐ Transmission
☐ Air Conditioning ☐ Electrical Component Locators ☐ Other _____

Section No. _____ Page No. _____ Vehicle Model & Year _____

Comments: _____
_____
_____
_____

Name _____ Company _____
Address _____ City _____ State _____ Zip _____
Phone ( ) _____ Date _____ THANK YOU

ADIA 94

Be sure to fill out this form completely.

COMMENTS AND SUGGESTIONS

Please let us know if you have any comments or recommended changes to this book. Mail this postage-paid card today. We'd like to hear from you!

☐ Domestic Cars ☐ Imported Cars & Trucks ☐ Domestic Light Trucks ☐ Medium & Heavy Duty Trucks
☐ Engine Performance ☐ Electrical ☐ Engine ☐ Chassis ☐ Transmission
☐ Air Conditioning ☐ Electrical Component Locators ☐ Other _____

Section No. _____ Page No. _____ Vehicle Model & Year _____

Comments: _____
_____
_____

Name _____ Company _____
Address _____ City _____ State _____ Zip _____
Phone ( ) _____ Date _____ THANK YOU

ADIA 94

Be sure to fill out this form completely.